# WORLD RADIO TV

# WRTH

## THE DIRECTORY OF GLOBAL BROADCASTING

# 2019

# VOLUME 73 – 2019

**Publisher**
Nicholas Hardyman

**International Editor**
Sean Gilbert

**'A' Schedule & Web Updates Editor**
Mauno Ritola

**Television Editor**
Bernd Trutenau

**Technical Editor**
John Nelson


**Contributing Editors**
George Jacobs *Editor Emeritus*
Bengt Ericson *Editor Emeritus*
Dave Kenny
Mauno Ritola
Bernd Trutenau
Torgeir Woxen


**Cover Design**
Richard Boxall Design Associates

**WRTH Publications Limited**
PO Box 290
Oxford OX2 7FT
United Kingdom
Tel: +44 (0) 1865 339355
Fax: +44 (0) 1865 339301
Email: wrth@wrth.com
Web: www.wrth.com
ISBN 978-1-9998300-1-4

Printed and bound in the UK by CPI William Clowes, Beccles NR34 7TL

# WORLD RADIO TV HANDBOOK

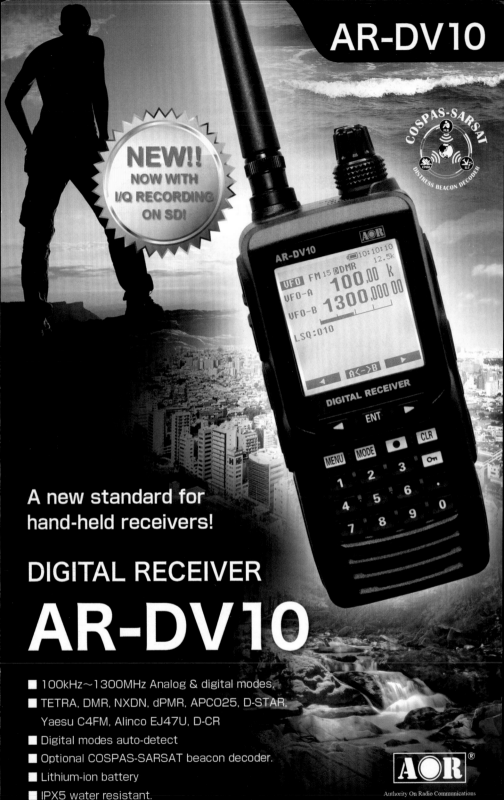

# AR-DV10

**NEW!!**
NOW WITH
I/Q RECORDING
ON SD!

COSPAS-SARSAT
DISTRESS BEACON DECODER

## A new standard for hand-held receivers!

## DIGITAL RECEIVER

# AR-DV10

- 100kHz~1300MHz Analog & digital modes.
- TETRA, DMR, NXDN, dPMR, APCO25, D-STAR, Yaesu C4FM, Alinco EJ47U, D-CR
- Digital modes auto-detect
- Optional COSPAS-SARSAT beacon decoder.
- Lithium-ion battery
- IPX5 water resistant.
- Record I/Q on SD, playback with SDR# on PC.

**AOR®**
Authority On Radio Communications

www.aorja.com

# CONTENTS

## Section Contents

## Features & Reviews

**EDITORIAL** .............................. 7
**CONTRIBUTORS** .................... 8

**REVIEWS**
WinRadio Excalibur Sigma ....... 10
SDRPlay RSPDuo ................... 13
Airspy HF+ ............................. 14
Reuter RDR51 'Pocket' ............ 16
XHDATA D-808 ........................ 19
Icom IC-R30 ............................ 20
WRTH Receiver Guide 2019 .... 22

**FEATURES**
HF Curtain Arrays ................... 24
Broadcasting for Peace ............ 28
V7AB Radio Marshall Islands ... 32
TWR Bonaire .......................... 36
Digital Update .......................... 40
HF Conditions 2019 ................. 44

**INFORMATION**
Most Suitable Frequencies ....... 45
How to use WRTH ................... 46
World Maps ............................. 50
World Time Zone Map ............. 62
World Time Table .................... 63

National Radio

International Radio

Frequency Lists

National Television

Reference

# Editorial

## NEW WAVES

We are very pleased to welcome you to the 73rd edition of *WRTH*, which is also the 21st edition produced by us. Once again we provide the most comprehensive and up-to-date information on global broadcasting available anywhere in the world. This book is the result of the hard work and dedication of our team of editors and contributors without whom the compilation of such a large volume of data would not be possible.

We were sorry recently to 'accept the resignation' of Bengt Ericson as a contributing editor with responsibility for Sweden, a post he has held for more than 21 years. In that time he has also provided invaluable help with other matters relating to the production of the book. We wish him well in his 'retirement'. Bengt joins George Jacobs as an Editor Emeritus of *WRTH*

This year has been notable for the very high quality of the receivers we have reviewed. The Excalibur *Sigma* from WinRadio is so good that we have given it the award, without qualification, of 'Best Receiver'. As we do not give awards each year, this means it is the best receiver we have ever tested. The Airspy HF+ lived up to its reputation as a particularly effective HF receiver, especially considering its price. The Reuter RDR51 'Pocket' is a truly impressive piece of mechanical and software engineering and produces results, particularly on FM, that most other SDRs or conventional receivers can only hope to emulate. That all this excellence in contained in a pocket-sized handheld unit is even more remarkable. It has been a fascinating review season for our Technical Editor.

Unfortunately we were once again unable to obtain a sample of the Gospell GR-216 DRM receiver from China and we are forced, in our *Digital Update,* to lament the effective passing of the consumer DRM receiver and by association the standard itself.

## RADIO SAVES LIVES

This year we have read of two fascinating examples of the power of radio to save lives, not only in the aftermath of a natural disaster but as a potentially on-going process.

The first was a study by Development Media International (DMI) in rural Burkina Faso to see if radio could be used to improve health. DMI produced 150 radio messages giving the symptoms of diseases that are the biggest killers of children under five in the country. The messages were broadcast across seven local radio stations for three years. The results showed that radio is the most effective way to provide this information and that many lives were saved as a result.

We cover the second, where both shortwave and FM radio is being used to help bring peace to one of the most troubled regions of the Sahel, in our article *Broadcasting for Peace*. In areas of the world without access to modern digital information sources, analogue broadcasts which can be received on inexpensive radios are still the most effective medium of communication.

## *WRTH* FREQUENCY BARGRAPH

The bargraph frequency CDs proved once again to be very popular, and we will be producing them for the B18 and A19 seasons. There will also be the facility to download a file containing all the data on the CD. The CDs and downloads will again only be available from our website.

## WEBSITE UPDATES

We will as usual be uploading free pdf updates to our website. Updates to the B18 season will be available in February 2019. The full schedules for the A19 season will be posted in May 2019 with an update in July 2019. We will also continue to provide updates to the National Radio section on the *WRTHmonitor* page on our website.

## PRIZE DRAW RESULTS

These winners were again drawn by members of the British DX Club. The Reader's Questionnaire this year will be on an online form which can be accessed from a link on the website. Please do fill in the form. We greatly value your feedback and you will also be entered into a Prize Draw with the chance to win a copy of *WRTH* 2020.

---

### RESULTS OF THE
### *WRTH* 2018 PRIZE DRAW

**5 WINNERS will receive a copy of *WRTH* 2019**
P. H. Sørensen, Denmark
D. Hockley, Australia
H. Meerman, The Netherlands
M. Herbert, UK
J. Gray, USA

---

I hope you will enjoy reading and using this new edition of *WRTH*

## Nicholas Hardyman
**Publisher**

# *WRTH* Contributors 2019

**WRTH** contributors & editors come from all walks of life, yet share a common fascination with all aspects of global broadcasting. Each year we profile one of the people whose dedicated enthusiasm makes possible the enormous task of updating *WRTH* each year. This year it is the turn of Kai Ludwig to give us an insight into what makes a *WRTH* Contributor.

Kai Ludwig

Getting involved in broadcasting can happen in the least likely of ways. In my case it started with Rundfunk der DDR at Berlin-Oberschöneweide, in what was known as 'East Germany', which ran not only Radio Berlin International but also an extensive domestic service. One of its programmes evolved from a large youth event called Deutschlandtreffen held in 1964. This event led to the creation of a programme block called Jugendstudio DT64 which was broadcast on MW and FM. In 1986 this became a separate FM network.

The programme was created to avoid losing young audiences to what were known as 'other stations' that is, stations from West Germany. This opened new market areas which were used with success: A loyal audience could be developed of listeners who did not know what to make of the polished pop stations from the other side of the Iron Curtain, talking about things that had little to do with the lives of the young in the DDR.

The success of this station became obvious in 1990, a few weeks before the German Democratic Republic ceased to exist as a result of the reunification of Germany. Rundfunk der DDR and Rundfunk im Amerikanischen Sektor in Berlin (RIAS) agreed that RIAS would be relayed on all DT64 frequencies outside Berlin and its Brandenburg surroundings. Presumably RIAS expected a warm welcome, but they found themselves booed off the stage. Confronted with protests from the DT64 audience, including spontaneous demonstrations, the deal was reversed after only 24 hours.

As 31 December 1991 approached, when the whole broadcasting organization, now called *Einrichtung nach Artikel 36 des Einigungsvertrags*, was scheduled to be dissolved and replaced by new institutions, this outcome was remembered. Again the DT64 audience did not accept that their favourite station, their companion through massive changes in their lives, would disappear. Again the protest was too massive to ignore it. The political non-solution was a reprieve of six months, a decision that could be easily made because the commercial stations, which would now take over the DT64 frequencies, were not ready yet.

Meanwhile Mitteldeutscher Rundfunk was established and they, too, did not want to lose such a valuable station. But what to do with a radio station that was losing all its FM frequencies to the competition? At that time there was one option: transfer the network to mediumwave. This duly happened and, re-named MDR Sputnik, the network ran for a while before being transferred to satellite.

The result for me was contact with the world beyond FM. At this time, in the 1990s, there was still a lot of interesting programming in German to be discovered on the AM band. And of course also many other interesting things: I felt I had the whole world with me, during shifts as a signalmen, on the radio I illegally brought to the signal tower. And that is the rig I still use to tune into something when not using the digital equipment available for exploring todays media landscape.

Many of the German services, and indeed the stations, that I used to listen to have disappeared. It is not a matter of the old medium of linear radio being replaced; many of the editorial departments would still have interesting things to say, whatever the distribution platform would be.

One thing, however, has remained. When DT64 was on mediumwave it launched a series of broadcasts with tips for dealing with that band. This became a kind of a DX programme and finally a full-scale broadcast about media politics. This programme is now on the Radio Eins station of Rundfunk Berlin-Brandenburg, and still deals with news about international and AM broadcasting.

*Kai Ludwig*

**Official *WRTH* Contributor for Germany**

**A large project such as *WRTH* could not be produced without the help of many people from all over the world. The following organisations and publications give invaluable help:**

Asian Broadcasting Institute, Australian Radio DX Club, BC-DX Top News, British DX Club, DX-Listening Digest, DX Re Mix News, Grupo Radioescucha Argentino, International Radio Club of America, National Radio Club Inc (USA listings), Radio Heritage Foundation, World SW Radio Association

**our Country Contributors provide us with updated entries for the countries for which they are responsible:**

Herman Boel, Luís Carvalho, Swopan Chakroborty, Bryan Clark, Svetomir Cuckovic, Alan Davies, Alok Dasgupta, Stuart Forsyth, David Foster, Christian Ghibaudo, Martin Hadlow, Stig Hartvig Nielsen, Kevin Hand, István Hegedüs, Karel Honzík, Richard Jary, Jose Jacob, Dave Kenny, Tetsuya Kondo, Vashek Korinek, Kai Ludwig, Dario Monferini, Paul Rawdon, Andy Reid, David Ricquish, Mauno Ritola, Francisco Rubio Cubo, Roberto Scaglione, Mike Smith, Bernd Trutenau, Max van Arnhem, Thierry Vignaud, Tore B Vik, Torgeir Woxen

**they and we are greatly aided by our other major contributors:**

Ian Baxter, Erich Bergmann, Hansjörg Biener, Dino Bloise, Héctor García Bojorge, Mustafa Cancurt, Alfredo Cañote, Julio Pineda Cordón, Marcelo Cornachioni, Fredrik Dourén, Amine Ferhane, Santiago San Gil, Dan Goldfarb, Victor Goonetilleke, Noel Green, Chris Greenway, Rudolf Walter Grimm, Wolf Harranth, Glenn Hauser, Tetsuya Hirahara, Dave Kernick, Henrik Klemetz, Anatoly Klepov, Miller Liu, William López, James MacDonell, Humberto Molina, Adán Mur, Michael Nevradakis, Horacio Nigro, Victor Osorio, Samuel Ouma, Anker Petersen, Mieczyslaw Pietruski, Julio Pineda, Arnulf Piontek, Rimantas Pleikys, Patrick Robic, Rafael Rodríguez, Victor Rutkovsky, Jari Savolainen, Zhang ShiFeng, David Stanley, Luis Toranzo, Tarek Zeidan

**We thank them, and also all our readers who have written or emailed us with useful ideas and information. Please keep sending your thoughts and updates to:**

# wrth@wrth.com

**or write to:**
**WRTH Publications Limited, PO Box 290, Oxford OX2 7FT, UK**

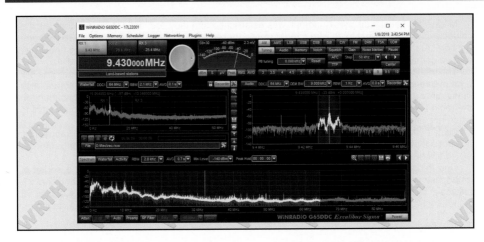

# WinRadio Excalibur Sigma

### US$8500   £6200   €6950

## OVERVIEW

Several years ago we reviewed the WinRadio WR-G33DDC *Excalibur Pro* and said that in our view it represented a new benchmark in the development of the software-defined receiver. In fact we were so impressed with it that we retained it on a loan basis as our 'gold standard' reference receiver against which everything else was judged. It has subsequently proved a formidably good performer and in many salient respects it has remained one of the best receivers we have ever encountered. We subsequently tested the *Excalibur Ultra*, which differed from the Pro in that it was not a stand-alone device but was intended for mounting internally within a PC. It also differed in one other remarkable respect.

Before we describe the difference we should perhaps provide a brief recapitulation for readers who may not be familiar with some of the terminology. The Excalibur family are members of a class of receivers known as software-defined and generally referred to in the literature as 'SDRs'. In a software-defined receiver the RF and mixer stages of a conventional superheterodyne give way to what is referred to as direct down-conversion (DDC). In effect the fixed IF generated by the RF and mixer stage is replaced by a technique in which the entire radio spectrum of interest is digitised as a whole. If you happened to have massive computing power at your disposal, you might well be able to process all the resulting signals simultaneously in real time. For those of us not so favourably endowed the SDR designer arranges for a smaller portion of the spectrum to be selected by a process known as decimation. The result can then be sent to a PC which will carry out filtering and demodulation functions using digital processing techniques implemented in software.

One obvious advantage of this technique is that if enough hard-drive storage is available it is easily possible to record and replay the decimated part of the spectrum and subject it to whatever analysis and processing is required. Early software-defined receivers could record and replay segments a few hundred kilohertz wide. Later iterations of receivers such as the Perseus offered 400, then 800 and 1600kHz which was enough to cater for the MF and several HF broadcast and amateur bands. Our reference Excalibur Pro can handle 4MHz segments which at the time of its introduction was extremely impressive, but the Ultra offered a maximum selectable real-time recording and processing bandwidth of 32MHz. To put that into perspective, it amounts to the entire LF, MF and HF spectrum. You may wish to re-read that sentence and consider it carefully before continuing. In essence, it means that the entire contents of the LW, MW and SW broadcast bands together with everything in between can be recorded and replayed at leisure.

## FEATURES

The newest product from WinRadio, the WR-G65DDCe *Excalibur Sigma*, takes this to yet another level. In fact it doubles it. The Sigma offers "…up to 64MHz wide instantaneous bandwidth available for recording, demodulation and further digital processing". So not only can it potentially record and replay the entire AM broadcast spectrum but can in addition handle another 32MHz on top, which is well into the VHF area. We know of no other commercially available SDR which offers anything resembling this bandwidth.

The ability to handle such an enormous amount of spectrum immediately raises the issue of the amount of storage required to take full advantage of it. The calculation is a little approximate but in round numbers about 10TB would be needed for six hours or so of storage at the full 64MHz bandwidth. Modern hard-disk drives capable of storing anything up to 14TB are readily available but their cost begin to rise fairly steeply in sizes over about 2TB. It is probably just as well that the DDC bandwidth is selectable and we imagine that the majority of us will not approach anything like the capability limit of the Sigma in this area. Despite intensive use for receiver comparison and a variety of laboratory purposes, we have very seldom used the full 4MHz bandwidth of the Pro during our time with it. Equally, it should not be forgotten that one would need a fairly exotic antenna system to deliver consistently good performance over the entire spectrum covered by this receiver. A wide-band HF antenna such as a Wellbrook loop will work well for the HF portion of the spectrum but antennas additionally capable of coping with an extra octave above that are few and far between. In practice one will need multiple antennas, and presumably the hard-core user willing to invest a large sum in such a capable receiver will also be willing to invest time, thought, money and space in the best available.

Such a user will also have to invest in a very high-grade PC. The WinRadio specification calls for a 2GHz or faster quad-core CPU with a free USB 3.0 or Ethernet socket and running Windows 7, 8 or 10. On paper that is not too demanding a specification but in practice the processor requirement is a bare minimum. For our testing we were able to borrow a Dell OptiPlex with quad-core i7-8700 2.6GHz processor, 8GB of RAM, an HDD array amounting to 5TB and a very fast nVidia GeForce graphics card. Our impression over the review period was that this was just about enough to cater for the Sigma but there were still occasional 'stutters'.

Visually resembling other Excalibur receivers with the addition of a large heatsink with a small integral fan for further cooling, the Sigma measures 166 x 98 x 60mm and weighs a little over 800g. It is actually two almost entirely independent receivers in one enclosure although only one can be used at a time. The HF portion of its coverage is 1kHz to 88MHz and the VHF portion is 118-190MHz. As such it excludes the FM broadcast band. It can also be considered as a very capable spectrum analyser offering 88 and 72MHz width respectively at HF and VHF. There are two separate SMA sockets for the antenna inputs and the interface with the PC can be via either a USB 3.0 port or a 1GB Ethernet LAN port with PoE (Power over Ethernet) functionality. Incidentally it is worth noting that the full 64MHz bandwidth is only available via USB and that a 'mere' 16MHz limit applies to the Ethernet port due to limitations in the latter's throughput. There is also a coaxial power supply input socket and out sample had a suitable mains supply providing 12V at 2A. The Sigma consumes a not inconsiderable 12W in normal operation and its associated PSU must have an appropriate power rating.

For the HF range the signal chain begins at the antenna input and its associated protective and impedance matching circuitry, followed by a preselector and switchable attenuator. The preselector contains a bank of 18 user-configurable filters which can be used to filter out strong frequencies in the vicinity of the received signal. The attenuator is adjustable from zero to 21dB in 3dB increments and is used to reduce signal levels if required. It can either be operated either manually or left to the receiver to determine its optimum level automatically to avoid overloading.

The signal then passes through a switchable low-noise low-distortion amplifier with about 10dB gain, followed by an anti-aliasing filter. For the VHF range the antenna input circuitry is followed by a 118MHz high pass anti-alias filter, switchable 10dB preamplifier and attenuator. In this range the anti-aliasing LPF is at 190MHz. The signals from both ranges are automatically switched according to the tuned frequency and sampled by a 16-bit ADC operating at 210 megasamples/s to produce data for the DDC. This is passed to the associated PC via one of the output ports. The software supplied with our sample was v1.01 and it is visually and operationally very like that used in conjunction with other Excalibur receivers. As usual it provides all the additional processing, filtering, demodulation and signal-strength measurement together with squelch, noise blanking, notch filtering, audio filtering and other functions. Like the Ultra, three independent 'receivers' can be placed within the DDC spectrum, each of which is capable of independently demodulating signals of different modulation types and different bandwidths. These can be separately recorded and then played back

## PERFORMANCE

The Sigma's specification is comprehensive and very impressive. The supported modes are AM, synchronous AM, LSB, USB, DSB, ISB, CW, narrow FM, a 'user-defined' mode and optionally DRM. In the HF range the claimed SFDR is 111dB with the preamp off, which is the same as that of the Ultra and a very good figure for any receiver. The close-in phase noise was beyond our measurement capability, implying that it at least -140dBc, and the claimed $IPI_3$ with preamp off is +38dBm, which is phenomenally high for an SDR. Measurements in accordance with our normal protocol for this parameter gave a still impressive +35dBm. The stated noise figure is 16dB with preamp off and 9dB with it on and both figures suggest that external noise will usually be the limiting factor. At 29MHz with preamp off we actually measured 12.5dB. In general the performance figures on the VHF range are similar although both the SFDR and $IPI_3$ are slightly worse. Sensitivity is certainly not an issue on either range. In the HF band the Sigma's sensitivity is broadly comparable with that of both the Pro and the Ultra with MDS figures of between -128 and -131dBm in a selected 2.8kHz SSB bandwidth depending on the tuned frequency and whether or not the preamp was switched into circuit. This is entirely on a par with what would be expected with a high-grade conventional receiver. The quoted MDS for the VHF range is -138dBm at 150MHz in a 500Hz bandwidth, which as with the Airspy HF+ is a slightly disingenuous claim since very few signals in the VHF region require such small bandwidths. CW signals are not common at 150MHz. Our sample turned in a still very useful -135dBm at this frequency in a 3kHz bandwidth. The tuning resolution throughout both bands is 1Hz and the tuning steps are whatever you want them to be. The demodulator filter is variable between 1Hz and 64kHz and is continuously variable in 1Hz steps. All in all, we imagine that quite a lot of the Sigma's internal circuitry is similar to that in the Ultra given that some specification points and numbers are virtually identical.

WinRadio went to a good deal of trouble to get a sample of the Sigma to us in time for our deadline. Some delays at Customs and in delivery meant that we were not able to spend quite as much time as we had hoped in testing and evaluating the unit. However, in the course of several lengthy comparative trials against such illustrious receivers as a Racal RA3791, a Harris RF590 and the Excalibur Pro, it became clear that the Sigma was in certain respects better than all of them. Few receivers come close to an RF590 (albeit with preselector) in terms of strong-signal handling and overall dynamic range but the Sigma was definitely better in both areas. No conventional DSP receiver we are aware of has filters which approach the performance of those in the RA3791 but here again the Sigma had the edge when taking very weak signals adjacent to very strong ones. In fact the conclusion after a good deal of work was that the Sigma is generally quite similar to the Ultra and performs to the same overall level whilst doubling the bandwidth of the latter and adding the separate VHF receiver. Selectivity is superb and strong-signal handling is excellent; it is at least as good as the Ultra and definitely even better than that of the Pro. Some tests in various portions of the VHF range suggested that the Sigma was an extremely good

performer in that region as well. Unfortunately the FM broadcast band is not included.

At this level of achievement it is very difficult indeed to make accurate and repeatable comparative RF measurements. A great deal of care needs to be taken with issues such as cable and connector quality, grounding and shielding. What is abundantly clear is that the performance of the Sigma is on a par with that of any of the high-grade conventional 'professional' receivers we have measured and assessed over the years. Certainly the Sigma was not troubled at any time by anything our various antennas could throw at it despite the fact that we went to considerable lengths to provoke it with some extremely strong local signals.

EXCALIBUR SIGMA
BEST
RECEIVER

## CONCLUSION

The final verdict is that the WinRadio Excalibur Sigma is the best and most capable SDR we have used. In certain respects this makes it the best receiver we have ever used. It is undoubtedly the case that the average reader of *WRTH* will not have a requirement for anything approaching such a level of capability. Equally, it must be said that very nearly €7000 is not a negligible amount of money. But for those who must have the best at any price – and the ability to deploy what amounts to three separate high-grade receivers within an overall 64MHz slice of spectrum is exceedingly impressive – there will be no argument. WinRadio has again produced an outstandingly good receiver and one which must be regarded as one of the best in the world.

### Rating table for Excalibur Sigma

| | |
|---|---|
| Constructional quality | ★★★★★ |
| Sensitivity | ★★★★★ |
| Dynamic range | ★★★★★ |
| RF intermodulation | ★★★★★ |
| Versatility | ★★★★★ |
| VFM | ★★★★ |

**Overall rating**  ★★★★★

**Key:**
★ = Poor   ★★ = Fair   ★★★ = Average
★★★★ = Very Good   ★★★★★ = Excellent
VFM = Value for money

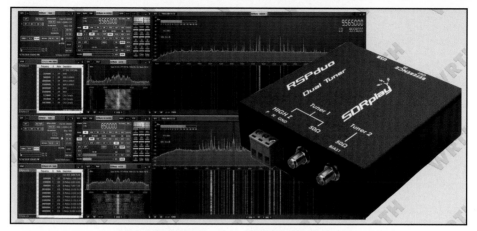

# SDRPlay RSPDuo

### $330  £240  €270

We reviewed the original SDRplay receiver and its later incarnation as the 'RSP' some time ago and also looked at the 'RSP2' in last years' edition with a view to evaluating its new software called 'SDRuno'. We were consequently very interested in examining a variation on the theme in the shape of the 'RSPduo'. Externally this unit resembles other receivers in the RSP product line but internally there are some salient differences. In effect it is a dual-tuner 14-bit SDR covering 1kHz-2GHz and allowing two separate 2MHz segments anywhere within that range to be monitored. The manufacturer indicates a number of scenarios in which this function might be useful including simultaneous operation with two antennas to enable direction-finding, diversity, and noise-reduction applications. Others might well be of great interest to transmitting amateurs and those interested in aircraft tracking and ATC reception.

The RSPduo is housed in a metal box measuring 95 x 90 x 30mm rather than the plastic enclosures used by other RSP receivers and is beautifully made and finished. There are three antenna inputs overall. 'Tuner 1' has a high-impedance input presumably intended for non-resonant wire antennas and a 50ohm SMA input. 'Tuner 2' has a single SMA input which also provides a 4.7V Bias-T feed for a masthead preamplifier or other external device. On the other side of the box are MCX input and output sockets for an external 24MHz reference (in our opinion the ability to use a 10MHz reference would be more useful) and a USB Type B port. Internally the RSPduo embodies no less than ten selectable low-pass filters, a 1GHz high-pass filter and eight selectable notch filters including – very unusually – two for the DAB frequency range.

Presumably continuing to use the Mirics chipset from the RSP2, the rearranged front-end

of the RSPduo appears to have improved the already impressive dynamic range of the former although unfortunately we were not in a position to make a direct comparison. A newer version of the SDRuno software can be downloaded from the SDRplay web site and this seems to us to be a little easier to use than the first version. In fact it could almost be described as plug-and-play although there remains a mildly daunting number of options and settings available; indeed the software almost deserves a review of its own. There is currently no facility in SDRuno to enable diversity reception although we understand that a version which will offer this facility is under development. Our view is that diversity reception can be a very effective way of addressing persistent problems of local noise via cancellation and it was (and is) much used professionally for this and other purposes. If SDRuno could be made to provide such a facility in the context of a high-grade software-defined receiver, the result could be a step change in the quality of MF and HF reception for enthusiasts and listeners.

Our listening tests in conjunction with a variety of antennas suggested that the RSPduo has few peers in its price class. Despite our best efforts we found very few problems of overloading. The 'Hi-Z' input seemed to be slightly noisier than the SMA in the HF region when used with long wires, which was to be expected, but gave noticeably better reception results on weak medium-wave broadcast outlets and NDBs. A look at VHF and UHF performance showed that the RSPduo was performed well in this portion of the spectrum.

We very much like the RSPduo and we find it remarkable that so much functionality can be made available for what is in effect an astonishingly low price. For those wanting a wideband SDR, it would represent an excellent choice.

# Airspy HF+

### US$320   £230   €260

## OVERVIEW

The origins of Airspy lie with the appearance some years ago of low-cost software-defined 'dongles' intended for digital television reception. With some creative modifications these could be made to receive a much wider frequency range than that used for DTV although their strong-signal performance could be best described as poor. One of the most popular programs used to control them was (and remains) 'SDR#' commonly referred to as 'SDR Sharp' and written chiefly by Youssef Touil. As well as being a skilled software designer, Touil was a hardware engineer who was well aware of the limitations of the simple dongle. In 2014 he designed the first of the 'Airspy' range of SDRs which was an immediate success. Today there are four receivers in the Airspy range of which the HF+ is the subject of this review. It was jointly developed by Airspy, the Shenzhen-based iTead Studio and ST Microelectronics with the intention of producing a high-grade SDR for broadcast reception.

## FEATURES

The Airspy HF+ coverage is 1kHz-31MHz and 60-260MHz with a maximum bandwidth of 768kHz. In fact 48, 96, 192, 384 & 768kHz are all available, with the caveat that 660kHz is the maximum alias-free bandwidth. There are of course a number of SDRs which offer larger bandwidths than this but Airspy's literature suggests that one of the main intentions of the design was the achievement of very good strong-signal handling in conjunction with a sensitivity figure appropriate to the coverage. We have discussed this area of receiver design on several occasions in the pages of *WRTH* but in essence the issue is one of dynamic range – essentially the 'window'

between the weakest signal the receiver can resolve and the strongest it can handle without some form of overload setting in. So the designer of an SDR (or for that matter any other receiver) has to consider two parameters carefully. One is the overall amount of dynamic range available. The other is where the 'window' should be placed. A wideband receiver can make use of high sensitivity at higher frequencies because these are not noise-limited in the same way that frequencies in the AM broadcast spectrum tend to be. What matters at lower frequencies is the ability to handle strong signals without overloading. Lack of absolute sensitivity is not likely to be an issue.

The HF+ is not a direct-sampling receiver; it adopts the arrangement of a bandpass filter followed by a tuner and a 16-bit sigma-delta ADC. This is followed by a decimating 18-bit DDC. Airspy does not give details but the front end apparently uses "polyphase harmonic rejection" architecture. The web site explains that "…essentially this means that harmonics produced in the mixing stages are naturally rejected, making the front-end filtering requirements much more relaxed. So unlike the tuners used in other SDRs, this one is extremely unlikely [to] overload in the mixing stage." On this basis Airspy claims a "best in class" strong-signal performance.

Realised as a very well finished metal box 90 x 55 x 10mm in size, the HF+ uses two SMA inputs for the antenna connections and a standard USB socket. Being familiar with SDR# we used this on our admittedly elderly office PC running a fully patched version of Windows 10. Apart from the limitations introduced by the computer we had no difficulty with this arrangement during the review period. We gather that in addition the Airspy HF+ can be used with 'SDR-Console' for

Windows and GQRX for the MacOS and Linux. Most listening tests were conducted with the resident Wellbrook loop with various other wire antennas used as required. The main receiver used for comparison was a Racal RA3791.

## PERFORMANCE

Airspy makes some very impressive specification claims for the HF+ and we were able to substantiate almost all of them. These include typical MDS of -141.0dBm (0.02 µV/50 ohms) in a 500Hz bandwidth at HF (we measured -139dB which was almost at our reliable measurement limit) and -141.5dBm MDS at 500Hz bandwidth at 60-108MHz. The latter is rather a meaningless claim since the number of occasions on which you would want to receive a signal in that frequency range with such a small bandwidth must be exceedingly limited. However, it is correct to within a dB or so. The claimed $IPI_3$ at maximum gain on HF is +26dBm although the frequency spacing is not stated. We tend to think that the classical $IPI_3$ measurement is not particularly useful when assessing an SDR but the Airspy HF+ certainly appears to have very good odd-order intermodulation performance and had no difficulty with some extremely strong 6/7MHz broadcast signals at night. Interestingly it also did very well with low-power aeronautical non-diectional beacons (NDBs) in the LF and MF range and managed to produce copy when even the RA3791 with its excellent DSP filters was struggling to do so. We imagine the Airspy HF+ is capable of producing very good results on MW DX if used with a suitable antenna.

Some brief tests with the 'other' antenna input suggested that the performance in the VHF spectrum was very good. FM broadcasts were well received using a four-element outdoor antenna; since the review period included a spell of tropospheric enhancement, it was no great surprise to receive French and Dutch FM stations at good strength and fully quieting. Aircraft-band reception via the resident Icom discone was also very effective with two or three VOLMET stations not normally heard at the test site easily audible. In passing we noted that the frequency setting and stability of the HF+ were both excellent.

Interestingly Airspy claims a blocking dynamic range (BDR) of 110dB at HF. This is the first time we have seen an explicit specification claim for BDR by the manufacturer of an SDR although it is an important measurement in conventional receivers. "Blocking" is the degree to which a receiver's sensitivity is reduced by the presence of high-power signals adjacent to the frequency to which it is currently tuned. The BDR is usually defined as the difference in dB between the level of an incoming signal which will cause 1dB of gain compression to the wanted signal and the level of the receiver noise floor. It is sometimes referred to as the "1dB compression point". A typical high-grade conventional HF receiver would be expected to exhibit a BDR of somewhere in the region of 110-120dB; for example, our RA3791 is about 118dB at 10MHz and slightly better than that at higher frequencies. It is a remarkably difficult parameter to measure with accuracy and very capable test equipment is required but the claimed BDR for the Airspy HF+ is certainly around the 110dB mark at 10MHz and we would estimate an

### AIRSPY HF+
### BEST VALUE
### HF SDR

uncertainty of perhaps 2dB either way in that figure. In comparison the BDR of most SDRs we have measured would be expected to be considerably less. Most simple 'dongle' SDRs would probably be 30-40dB worse and possibly worse than that in some cases.

In practical terms this implies that the Airspy HF+ can be expected to give a very good account of itself when used with relatively large antennas and also when operating in frequency bands where very strong signals are adjacent. Our listening tests suggested that it did both these things with aplomb. We carried out some tests on the amateur 7MHz band when a major contest was in progress and some extremely strong local signals were encountered. Using a full-size 7MHz three-element Yagi antenna at 30m (90ft) we expected major problems of overloading and spurious responses but found none whatsoever apart from very occasional and small increases in the local noise floor when an extremely strong local CW signal was encountered. This was a remarkable performance for any receiver, let alone a low-cost SDR, and one which many high-grade professional receivers from an earlier era would have found difficult to emulate. Another interesting point to emerge from the listening tests is that the Airspy sounds remarkably 'quiet' and unfatiguing in use, unlike many SDRs in its overall price class. This is presumably the result of careful design of the DDC and audio system.

## CONCLUSION

We were very impressed by the Airspy HF+. As with many SDRs, the unimpressive metal box contains some state-of-the-art and very effective electronics which in conjunction with 'SDR#' provides a highly capable receiving system. It would appear that the price point for SDRs at which the law of diminishing returns sets in is becoming lower every year, which can of course only benefit us all in the long run.

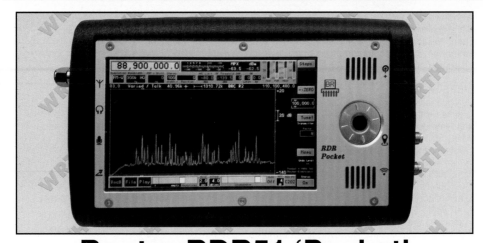

# Reuter RDR51 'Pocket'

**US$1200-2350   £880-1700   €990-1900**

## OVERVIEW

We have reviewed two receivers from Reuter Elektronik – the RDR54C and the RDR55D – and been very impressed by both. In comparison with some other companies active in the software-defined receiver market, Reuter is not perhaps one of the best-known but its high-end products have achieved a considerable measure of popularity amongst discerning listeners. The newest addition to the range is the RDR51 'Pocket' and Burkhardt Reuter was kind enough to supply a sample for review. This is a very unusual device in that it is not only a high-grade receiver but is also portable and embodies innovatory features which as far as we know are unique. We might observe that it is also beautifully made.

There are in fact four basic variants of the RDR51 notated by suffix. The B1 covers frequency ranges of 0-30MHz and 50-71MHz and uses 2 x 14-bit ADCs. The C1 covers the same frequency range but uses 2 x 16-bit ADCs. Both these provide for an 8GB flash recorder. The B2 and C2 are similar to the B1 and C1 respectively but include 87-110 and 130-156MHz. A fifth variant, the C4, adds the 174-240MHz band for DAB reception and – as if all this was not enough – a transmitter for 11 amateur-radio bands between 1.8 and 50MHz with about 5W PEP output on SSB and CW. The transmitter circuitry is very interesting and unusual, and it was only with considerable difficulty that we refrained from discussing it at length in this review! The B1 costs €999 and the B2 is €1350. The C1 is €1250 and the C2 €1550. The C4 costs €1900. Various accessories are available at additional cost including 'high-end FM' filters and a 'wideband spectrum' option extending the displayable spectrum width to a maximum of 52.6MHz. We were supplied with the C4 for our review.

## FEATURES

The RDR51 measures 160 x 112 x 32mm and weighs 720g. It is finished in a lustrous pearlescent grey and comes in a carrying case which also holds a PDA stylus, a GPS antenna with a 3m cable, a charging and PSU cable and an SMA-BNC adaptor. A CD-ROM containing software and a well-written and comprehensive 72-page operating manual is provided, the latter repaying careful study. The upper front panel of the receiver is taken up with a very bright touch-screen TFT display with a 4.3in (109 mm) diagonal and WVGA (800 x 480) 256-colour resolution. The display area proper measures 95 x 57mm and with this resolution some of the display icons and legends may appear a little on the small side for older users. The screen of a modern smartphone is of a similar size to that of the RDR51 and is likely to exhibit a 'Full HD' 1920 x 1080 resolution or better. Those used to such devices may find the RDR51's display rather hard going. However, the available viewing angles are very wide in both lateral and vertical orientations and the backlighting is excellent with no 'hot spots'. The small icons make finger-tip operation a little uncertain but the PDA stylus solves this problem and its use is highly recommended.

Next to the display is a tiny stepless rotary encoder with an on-off power button at its centre. Above and below it are two speakers. The encoder runs freely and is just the right size for finger-tip operation. On the right-hand side of the unit is a LEMO charging and power socket and SMA sockets for the GPS antenna and an optional WLAN antenna. This latter allows easy connection to a PC via a Wi-Fi-enabled router and enables future firmware updates and screenshots. The GPS antenna can be used if extreme frequency stability is required or position data is to be displayed but its use is not mandatory. On the left-hand side is an SMA socket for the antenna and 3.5mm jacks for headphones, a microphone and a Morse key.

Most of the display screen is given over to a conventional 'waterfall' display of the selected band. Above it is a small sub-display indicating frequency and signal strength, the latter calibrated in both S-units and dBm. Below this are smaller windows in which modulation type, bandwidth, passband tuning and shift and some other parameters can be set by selection with the stylus and subsequent adjustment with the rotary encoder. The demodulation window allows for selection of synchronous AM, DSB, LSB, USB and CW, in what the manual refers to as 'spectrum-based' modes. In so-called 'time-based' modes it offers AM envelope detection, narrow and wide FM, USBQ, LSBQ and some digital modes. Some functions are not available in these modes, notably the excellent noise blanker, the remarkably good notch filter and passband tuning. A total of 15 DSP filters is provided and work well.

As with the RDR55D, the reference to 'spectrum-based' modes offers a clue to a most interesting element of the RDR51s architecture. A lengthy technical description in the manual states that the receiver:

> …operates on a completely new principle, Spectrum-Based Signal Processing (SBSP). It allows for an extremely selective filtering and low-noise demodulation with finely tenable parameters without the use of internal or external computers. The basic concept of the Pocket is based on fully digital signal processing. The amplified and filtered antenna signal is digitized directly (DSR: Direct Sampling Receiver). There is no preceding frequency transformation ("mixing"), no adjustable frequency processing (PLL, VCO, DDS or similar) and no conventional filters (Quartz, Piezo, LC or similar). This results in an extremely linear phase response without additional phase noise or mixing interference, a prerequisite for clean, trouble-free and low-distortion demodulation.

> The Pocket's frequency selection ("tuning") is purely computational without any change of frequencies within the device. There is only one free running very low-noise fixed frequency oscillator. A GPS-based measurement system determines all frequency deviations to within 1Hz and corrects them without interfering with frequency generation. The digitized received signals are not processed by a processor or by software. The Pocket does not have a DSP, built-in PC or similar high-speed CPUs. PCs or PC accessories (monitor, keyboard, mouse) cannot be connected to the Pocket. All signal processing occurs internally with a maximum of 167 MHz clock frequency in dedicated, parallel-working hardware ("FPGA").

The specification is extensive. The audio bandwidth is continuously adjustable between 10Hz and 20kHz in 40Hz steps. The tuning step size is adjustable between 0.5Hz and 999.999.5KHz with direct selection of pre-programmed step sizes. The spectrum width is adjustable between 6.2kHz and 52MHz. There are no less than eight FM filter settings (38, 50, 80, 120, 240 and 300kHz) with the latter four offering either steep (S) or flatter (HQ) slopes for what the manual describes as "optimum listening pleasure". Judging by the performance of his receivers we rather suspect that Burkhardt Reuter is particularly interested in this mode.

## PERFORMANCE

We said of the RDR55D that it was "one of the most capable and impressive FM broadcast receivers we have ever measured or encountered professionally" and the RDR51 is fractionally better still. The signal/noise ratio of the RDR51 on FM is within 1dB of the theoretical CCIR maximum and it exhibits phenomenally low audio distortion. In the context of a stereo FM broadcast we would regard our test equipment of being reliably capable of measuring down to about 0.008% THD. All we can say for certain is that the RDR51 with the 240kHz HQ filter selected is almost certainly better than that and consequently better than most FM broadcasts. The RDS implementation is simply the best we have ever encountered. It is blazingly fast and extremely effective even on weak and fading signals. Most RDS-capable receivers require a minimum RF input of about -70dBm to produce a PS name. The RDR51 is quite happy to do so with about -90dBm and display the errored blocks as it does so!

The DAB+ implementation is also remarkable. Selecting 'DAB Discover' causes the receiver to spend a minute or two searching for every multiplex (ensemble) and outlet it can find. It then lists them in order together with the programme type, bit rate, sample rate and RSSI ('receiver signal strength indication', a numerical measure often used in IEEE 802 wireless applications) and the required programme can be selected by scrolling with the rotary encoder and tapping with the stylus. We found an occasional firmware 'glitch' in this mode whereby the encoder would try to change one of the windowed parameters instead of scrolling but switching off and on again resolved it. Clicking on the required programme with the stylus immediately produces audio; unfortunately we were unable to make formal distortion measurements in DAB mode but the result sounded very good. The sensitivity is again remarkably good. We compared the RDR51 with two other high-grade DAB+ receivers at our elevated test site in east Wales using an Icom discone as the test antenna. The RDR51 brought in perfect audio from one multiplex not detected by the other units, at an RSSI of about 55.

As with the RDR55D we noticed that the latency of the RDR51 was unusually low for an SDR. Typically there is a distinct audible delay between the output of an SDR (or indeed a digital radio) and an FM receiver due to the latency inevitable in digital signal processing. Listeners may be aware of the phenomenon when listening to both types of receiver tuned to the same outlet. One tiresome complication is that radio time signals such as the famous Greenwich Time Signal can be delayed by a second or two. Latency is not easy to measure precisely but in Band II at least the RDR51 exhibits about 80mS, which from memory is the lowest we have ever come across.

The internal architecture of the device is not described in detail but we imagine it to be similar to that in other Reuter receivers. From the strong-signal performance test results we guess that switched narrowband (possibly half-octave) filters are provided early in the signal path and that a very high-speed custom FPGA is at the heart of the unit. At 7dB the measured noise figure of the RDR51 was about the same as that of the RDR55D, implying that HF reception will always be limited by the local noise floor rather than any shortcoming in the receiver. Unfortunately we ran into considerable difficulty when trying to measure the reciprocal-mixing performance, simply because the RDR51 was better in this respect than our test equipment could reliably measure. The close-in phase noise is certainly in excess of -140dBm at ±1kHz which is the sort of figure one usually associates only with a very carefully designed crystal oscillator. The measured sensitivity is very similar to that of the RDR55D at about -119dBm for a 10dB s/n in a 5kHz bandwidth for 50% AM modulation at 1kHz. This again is a very good result and one which in conjunction with the excellent strong-signal performance implies a very well designed front end. In fact the RDR51 is an addition to a very select list. This consists of the receivers (currently four) which can produce demodulated audio from the lowest RF output level available from our IFR 2025 RF generator in a normal AM bandwidth at 80% sine-wave modulation at 1kHz.

We compared the RDR51 with a variety of high-grade receivers during the review period, including the excellent Excalibur Pro. This is still our main reference SDR although it has been supplanted by some newer WinRadio products since its inception. Test antennas were chiefly a seven-element tri-band Yagi, several resonant dipoles and a Wellbrook loop. The results were most impressive and suggest that the superb performance of the RDR55D has been essentially replicated in a pocket-sized receiver. Assuming the built-in attenuator (0-36dB in 1dB steps) was used as required to bring signals from the larger antennas down to a level manageable by the ADC – overload being indicated by the frequency display background turning red – there was no trace whatsoever of second-order intermodulation in the 6/7MHz band. Some very large signals from local amateurs were encountered on several HF bands in the course of a major contest taking place during the review period. This proved interesting insofar as it demonstrated the effectiveness of the DSP filters. With a little practice it proved possible to copy very weak CW signals separated by perhaps 200Hz from signals strong enough to overload the ADC without introducing attenuation as required. Few SDRs can emulate this sort of performance. Weak and fading 28MHz amateur-band beacons and LF/MF aeronautical non-directional beacons (NDBs) can also form very valuable comparison sources and we spent some considerable time exploring the RDR51's capabilities in this area. It can be very difficult on occasions to be absolutely sure of what one is hearing, and listening fatigue can set in very easily. But a great deal of careful comparative listening suggested that the RDR51 was fractionally better than the Excalibur Pro in its ability to produce audible copy from very weak NDBs. Quite why this was the case is difficult to state with certainty. At these frequencies the receiver's noise figure will be irrelevant because its internal noise will be swamped by other noise sources and one must therefore assume that it is a subtle function of the DSP techniques used.

## CONCLUSION

The RDR51 'Pocket' is a remarkable device in many respects. It packs an enormous amount of functionality into a very small size and in consequence its ergonomics are not its best feature. But our impression is that its designers were strongly focused on achieving the best possible RF performance and have coupled that with what appears to have been an almost fanatical attention to detail. Our guess is that for those who can afford one and wish to have an extremely high-performance portable receiver, the RDR51 will be a 'must-have'. Reuter Elektronik should again be congratulated for creating a very fine radio and we shall be extremely sorry to return our sample.

## Rating table for RDR-Pocket

| | |
|---|---|
| Constructional quality | ★★★★★ |
| Sensitivity | ★★★★★ |
| Dynamic range | ★★★★★ |
| RF intermodulation | ★★★★★ |
| Ergonomics | ★★★★ |
| Versatility | ★★★★★ |
| VFM | ★★★★★ |

### Overall rating          ★★★★★

**Key:**
★ = Poor    ★★ = Fair    ★★★ = Average
★★★★ = Good    ★★★★★ = Excellent
VFM = Value for money

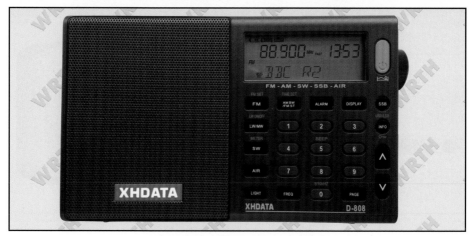

# XHDATA D-808

**US$95   £70   €80**

The XHDATA D-808 is a new member of the class of receivers sometimes referred to as 'ultra-portable' in that it is very small and light. Measuring 158 x 95 x 33mm and turning the scales at about 300g, it would certainly fit the average jacket pocket or handbag with no difficulty. The D-808 offers coverage of 150-450kHz, 522-1620kHz (in 9kHz steps) or 520-1710kHz (10kHz steps), 1711kHz-29.999MHz and 87.5-108MHz. In addition it covers the 118-137MHz aircraft band although unfortunately in 25kHz and 1kHz steps rather than the mandated 8.33kHz channels in which allocations in this band are now made. The lack of a squelch facility in this band would make lengthy reception periods rather hard on the ears.

Visually very reminiscent of the C.Crane 'Skywave SSB' and according to the excellent *SWLing Post* blog (www.swling.com) manufactured in the same part of China by C.Crane's Redsun partner, it seems a reasonable presumption that the D-808 can be considered a "development" of the latter. Finished in an attractive charcoal grey, the left-hand half of the front panel is taken up with the speaker grille. An external wire antenna is supplied. At the top of the right-hand side is a rotary tuning control with another marked 'fine tune' beneath it. This latter is similar to the volume control in that it is edge-operated whereas the main tuning knob works in a fore-and-aft sense. The main control tunes in 9kHz steps on LW and MW, 5kHz on SW and 100kHz steps on FM. The second tunes in 1kHz steps on LW, MW and SW and 10kHz steps on FM.

The telescopic antenna is swivel-mounted on the upper panel and most of the listening tests were carried out with this since almost any external antenna proved too much for the front-end circuitry of the D-808 and led to a variety of inter-modulation and noise issues. The manual refers to bandwidths of 500Hz and 1, 1.2, 2.2, 3 and 4kHz as being available for AM reception but in fact these are the bandwidths for SSB and (in the case of the 500Hz filter at least) potentially CW. The displayed bandwidths on AM are 1, 1.8, 2, 2.5, 3, 4 and 6kHz. Selectivity is very good for a small portable and the chosen filter bandwidths are quite useful in practice.

## PERFORMANCE

Reception quality on FM was very good and the built-in speaker gave reasonable results although the radio sounded rather better on headphones, when of course stereo reception was available. The RDS sub-system appears to be quite well implemented and reliably provides the PS name and programme type (PTY). It could not be persuaded to supply radiotext and the display persistently indicated 'No RT' even when the tuned station was known to be radiating it. It did use the CT data to set the radio clock, which was a nice touch. Curiously there is no mention at all of RDS in the supplied user manual.

Overall the HF performance could be characterised as very good for a small portable receiver. Strong stations gave quite respectable audio and the AGC coped fairly well with fading although its attack time was a little too long for good results with utility and amateur SSB and CW stations. There is no synchronous detector and the SSB performance was not such as to be very usable for exalted-carrier reception. However, strong local SSB and CW stations were copied easily and with pleasant if rather noisy audio.

With that said, if you are in the market for a low-cost small and light ultraportable which covers most of the AM and FM broadcast spectrum, the XHDATA D-808 is well worth consideration.

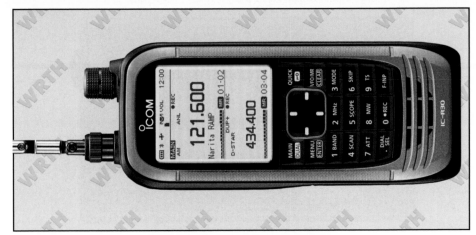

# Icom IC-R30

### US$800　£570　€630

Wideband hand-held so-called 'scanners' (more formally scanning receivers) were very popular some years ago, and we have reviewed several of them in *WRTH*. Offering coverage of the entire AM broadcast spectrum together with assorted VHF and UHF bands, they were of rather limited use for HF broadcast reception. The main reasons were poor strong-signal performance – which made them difficult to use with large antennas – and IF filtering which was not optimised for the purpose although there were other factors (e.g. noisy synthesizes) in addition.

A few such receivers remain available although others such as the Yupiteru range disappeared with the introduction of the *Restriction of Hazardous Substances* (RoHS) legislation in 2006. This precluded the use of lead in electronic products destined for sale in Europe and amongst other things mandated the introduction and use of lead-free solder. Since this required manufacturers to make very expensive changes to production methods, some smaller companies elected not to comply and simply withdrew from the market entirely. Rather ironically the change to lead-free solder caused major issues of unreliability for a period and also proved to be at least as bad for the environment as the leaded variety.

## OVERVIEW

The Icom IC-R30 is a successor to the R-20 which was not reviewed in *WRTH* but seems to have been quite highly regarded. It is a hand-held receiver in the classic 'scanner' mould and covers an exceedingly wide frequency range of 100kHz to 3.305GHz. Dimensionally it measures 143 x 58 x 31mm and weighs about 200g; visually it resembles a hand-held mobile telephone of the pre-smartphone era. As usual with Icom products it is very well made and finished in contrasting

shades of grey. Interestingly there are in effect two receivers, the 'main' covering the full range and a 'sub' receiver catering for 108-520MHz. This gives useful dual-watch functionality and is evidently intended chiefly for listeners to the 118-137MHz aeronautical allocation. The manual states that the main receiver is a down-converting triple superheterodyne with intermediate frequencies of 266MHz, 58.05MHz (10.7 MHz for wideband FM) and 450kHz. The sub-receiver's IFs are 46.35MHz and 450kHz. There are assorted references to digital systems and techniques in the manual but it does not appear that the receiver uses DSP except for processing digital modes. As if all this RF technology was not enough, the IC-R30 embodies a GPS receiver. This can display position in terms of latitude and longitude and also the 'Maidenhead' locator grid square, the latter being of interest to radio amateurs. It also computes and displays time and altitude together with speed and approximate course if the receiver is moving.

## FEATURES

The available modes are wide, normal and narrow FM, normal and narrow AM, USB and LSB, wide and narrow CW, D-STAR, P25, dPMR, NXDN-VN, NXDN-N and DCR. Many of these will not be of interest to broadcast listeners who will perhaps regret the omission of digital modes such as DAB or even DRM. The receiver is tunable in selectable steps of 0.01, 0.1, 1, 3.125, 5, 6.25, 8.33, 9, 10, 12.5, 15, 20, 25, 30, 50, 100, 125 and 200kHz. The 8.33kHz step is available in the 118-137MHz band only but unfortunately does not display the frequencies in the correct channelized format appropriate to this spectrum. There are 2000 memory channels arranged in 100 groups together with a further 400 which set the start and end of scannable bands as required.

The IC-R30 is supplied with a telescopic antenna with an SMA connector, the latter being more mechanically reliable than the usual BNC although making connection of an external antenna slightly more difficult unless the appropriate adaptor is available. Adjacent to the antenna connector on the top surface of the receiver is the VFO knob (actually a rotary encoder) which runs in light detents and has a very pleasant feel. Below is the large backlit LCD and a numeric keypad and function keys. These have almost ideally weighted characteristics for their size with an exemplary combination of travel and tactile feedback. A small speaker is located beneath the keypad. Power and squelch buttons and up/down keys are on the left-hand side together with a slot for a microSD card. A 3.5mm jack and USB socket are on the right, and an integral Bluetooth function allows cordless use with a suitable headset. This is the first time we have seen such a feature in a receiver and we found it very useful on occasions. We even managed to 'pair' the IC-R30 with the audio system in our car, which was perhaps an exercise of limited utility but proved interesting nonetheless. There is an integral 3.7V 3.28A-h lithium-ion battery back and a drop-in charger requiring a 12V 1A DC input is supplied. A suitable AC mains adaptor is also provided although our sample ran marginally too hot for comfort. Interestingly the battery can also be charged via the USB port. About 6h are required to reach full charge in this mode as opposed to a couple of hours via the charging base. A fully charged battery gives about 16-18 hours of operation.

The receiver is supplied with what Icom calls a 'basic' manual. A more advanced manual is available as a PDF download from the Icom web site and is considerably more comprehensive; it covers several topics in a good deal of detail and is well worth careful study.

## PERFORMANCE

The IC-R30 was tested with a variety of external antennas including the resident Wellbrook loop. With a claimed sensitivity in the HF region of 1.4µV for a 10dB signal/noise ratio and what is presumably a simple wideband front-end, it is perhaps not surprising that the receiver was not very happy with any external antenna despite its integral three-step RF attenuator and 10-stage RF gain facility. The test site is not particularly close to any high-power broadcast transmitters but in daylight it proved quite easy to induce intermodulation and other overload effects in the MF and HF bands. Probably the best results were achieved with the Wellbrook loop and an external 12dB attenuator, with the Icom's RF gain and attenuation subsequently set by experimentation for best results. At night it was found that an external adjustable high-pass filter worked quite well to keep strong broadcast 6/7MHz signals

from repeating themselves elsewhere in the HF bands and also removed most of the spurious MW breakthrough which became evident in those bands without it. That said, some good usable results were achieved with the IC-R30's own telescopic antenna and also with an elderly Icom AH-7000 discone normally used for VHF and UHF reception at the test site. For some reason this latter seemed to allow the IC-R30 to attain its best balance between sensitivity and strong-signal performance. In fact we ended up using it for most of the listening tests during the review although in principle it should not have worked very well at AM broadcast frequencies.

Some brief trials on VHF and UHF suggested that the IC-R30 gave a very convincing performance in this portion of the spectrum. The squelch action in particular was superb (which is seldom the case even in expensive receivers) and the audio quality from the small speaker was very good indeed. In fact the overall audio from the receiver belied its small size and FM broadcasts sounded particularly pleasant. Here again the IC-R30 did not much care for external antennas in the FM broadcast band and there was a noticeable increase in the noise floor – presumably from complex high-order intermodulation – when a three-element Yagi was connected. However, in most circumstances the receiver will not be used in conjunction with an external Band II antenna and its own telescopic 'whip' should give perfectly good FM reception in most situations. The SSB performance was surprisingly good and gave excellent results with local and semi-local amateur stations. It could also be used for exalted-carrier reception and the IF filters seemed reasonably well adapted to this task.

## CONCLUSION

Clearly the IC-R30 is not principally intended for broadcast reception. As with almost all receivers of this general type, its usable dynamic range is not very wide in the first place and it is biased towards sensitivity rather than strong-signal handling. This allows the receiver to perform generally well with its integral antenna but does not allow very much latitude for connection of external antennas because of the relative ease with which its front-end will be overloaded by strong signals – a shortcoming of wideband scanning radios. With that limitation in mind, however, the Icom IC-R30 is a useful hand-held receiver which will give good results if used with care. There is much to admire in its mechanical design and several features of its user interface make it pleasantly easy to use. It should be said, however, that careful study of the manuals is required to make use of all the functionality built into the receiver.

All in all, if you are in the market for a high-grade wideband hand-held scanning receiver the Icom IC-R30 should be a very strong contender for your consideration.

# WRTH HF Receiver Guide 2019

## Hand-held, Portables & Budget

| Maker | Model | Size | SEL | DR | OV | US$ | £ | € |
|---|---|---|---|---|---|---|---|---|
| AOR | AR8200D | H | *** | *** | *** | 1000 | 665 | 730 |
| Icom | IC-R30 | H | **** | *** | **** | 800 | 570 | 630 |
| Reuter Elektronik | RDR51 'Pocket' | H | ***** | ***** | ***** | †1775 | 1290 | 1445 |
| C. Crane | CC Skywave | S | **** | **** | **** | 90 | 65 | 75 |
| Degen (Kaito) | DE-1103 | S | *** | *** | ** | 70 | 50 | 60 |
| Sangean | ATS-909X | S | **** | **** | **** | 205 | 225 | 250 |
| Tecsun | PL-380 | S | **** | **** | ***** | 46 | 45 | 50 |
| Tecsun | PL-600 | S | **** | *** | **** | 95 | 90 | 80 |
| Tecsun | PL-660 | S | *** | **** | **** | 130 | 118 | 120 |
| Tecsun | PL-680 | S | *** | *** | *** | 140 | 100 | 115 |
| Tecsun | PL-880 | S | *** | **** | **** | 160 | 190 | 230 |
| Tecsun | S-8800 | S | *** | *** | *** | 375 | 280 | 375 |
| XHDATA | D-808 | S | *** | *** | *** | 95 | 70 | 80 |

† prices quoted are the middle of the variant price spread

## SDRs, Serious Shortwave & Semi-pro Receivers

| Maker | Model | Size | SEL | DR | OV | US$ | £ | € |
|---|---|---|---|---|---|---|---|---|
| Afedri | SDR-Net | C | *** | *** | *** | 250 | 300 | 355 |
| Airspy | HF+ | C | ***** | ***** | ***** | 320 | 230 | 260 |
| Alinco | DX-R8E | M | **** | **** | **** | 430 | 470 | 530 |
| AOR | AR5001D | M | ***** | **** | **** | 4450 | 2670 | 3200 |
| AOR | AR6000 | L | **** | ***** | **** | 6600 | 5000 | 5600 |
| AOR | AR8600 | L | ** | *** | *** | 990 | 600 | 700 |
| AOR | AR-DV1 | M | **** | **** | **** | 1220 | 1290 | 1430 |
| Apache Labs | ANAN-10 | M | ***** | **** | **** | 2000 | 1500 | 1700 |
| Cross Country | SDR-4+ | C | **** | **** | **** | 280 | 180 | 210 |
| Expert Electronics | ColibriNano | C | **** | **** | **** | 300 | 250 | 270 |
| FlexRadio | FLEX-1500 | C | **** | **** | *** | 1000 | 750 | 825 |
| FunCube Dongle | Pro+ | C | **** | *** | **** | 190 | 150 | 165 |
| Icom | IC-718 | L | *** | **** | **** | 650 | 580 | 650 |
| Icom | IC-7300 | L | **** | **** | **** | 1050 | 1200 | 1345 |
| Icom | IC-7600 | L | ***** | **** | **** | 2700 | 2300 | 2500 |
| Icom | IC-8600 | L | ***** | **** | **** | 2400 | 2500 | 2750 |
| Icom | IC-R9500 | L | ***** | ***** | ***** | 12800 | 11000 | 12100 |
| Microtelecom | Perseus | C | ***** | ***** | ***** | 900 | 750 | 750 |
| Palstar | R30 | M | ***** | ***** | **** | 895 | 1250 | 1400 |
| Reuter Elektronik | RDR55D | L | ***** | ***** | ***** | 5500 | 4000 | 4500 |
| SDRplay | SDRplay RSP2 | C | **** | **** | **** | 170 | 155 | 170 |
| SDRplay | SDRplay RSPDuo | C | ***** | ***** | ***** | 330 | 240 | 270 |
| Ten-Tec | RX340 | L | ***** | ***** | ***** | 4950 | 4500 | 5000 |
| WinRadio | G31 Excalibur | C | ***** | **** | ***** | 970 | 700 | 795 |
| WinRadio | G33 Excalibur Pro | C | ***** | ***** | ***** | 1900 | 1600 | 1800 |
| WinRadio | G35 Excalibur Ultra | C | ***** | ***** | ***** | 5000 | 3800 | 4200 |
| WinRadio | G65 Excalibur Sigma | C | ***** | ***** | ***** | 8500 | 6200 | 6950 |
| WinRadio | G313i | C | ***** | **** | ***** | 1200 | 925 | 1000 |
| WinRadio | G313e | C | ***** | ***** | ***** | 1200 | 925 | 1000 |

**KEY:** SEL = Selectivity, DR = Dynamic Range, OV = Overall Value. C = SDR, H = Hand-held, L = Large, table top use, M = Medium, suitcase size, S = Small, easily portable.   * = Avoid ** = Poor *** = Fair **** = Very Good ***** = Outstanding.
**NOTE:** Prices vary due to exchange rate fluctuations. Some models may be unavailable in certain markets.

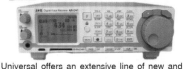

# HF Curtain Arrays

*Former BBC Senior Transmitter Engineer* **Dave Porter G4OYX** *outlines the history and development of a classic HF broadcast antenna.*

A curtain array at Ascension used on the west beam for South America and east beam for North Africa

The first thing you are likely to notice when approaching a large HF broadcast transmitter site is the array of masts or towers and the many wire antennas strung between them. The story of how these beautiful arrays of wire and steel evolved and came to be built is a fascinating one, and what follows can only be a brief introduction to a lengthy and intriguing story.

By the late 1920s engineers were experimenting with various techniques for transmitting radio signals over long distances. It was clear that using a vertical dipole to radiate the signal from a transmitter was effective for non-directional broadcasting but they wanted to add directionality in order to target specific areas. They found that an omni-directional signal could be made stronger in one direction at the expense of others by placing a reflector at the rear of the dipole. This also increased signal strength and hence produced gain. This arrangement is the foundation of what later became known as a Yagi array and can be considered the basis of the curtain array. These can take various forms (the 'Bruce' and the 'Sterba curtain' being amongst the earliest, both dating from 1929) but in essence a num-ber of dipoles and reflectors are placed on top of each other and side by side, created from lengths of wire strung from tall masts.

Initial tests at Daventry in the UK took place with masts only 80ft (24m) high, but results were not impressive so more tests were conducted and by 1934 the support towers had reached a height of up to 350ft (106m). This increased the field strength of the signal by a factor of about 10 and allowed tests to be made on 12MHz with both vertical and horizontal dipoles. The conclusions reached by 1935 were that horizontal polarisation was better than vertical; it was unnecessary to have more than four horizontal dipoles stacked vertically at intervals of half a wavelength ($\lambda/2$); and that the lowest element should be not more than one wavelength ($1\lambda$) above the ground. The towers could then be sited so that the antennas 'beamed' in specific directions. A bearing of 80° from the UK, for example, allowed broadcasts to be beamed to Malaysia, India and Sri Lanka. For other bearings more masts were erected to support more curtain arrays, thus creating an HF system with the capability to direct broadcasts to any region in the world.

## THE CLASSIC SINGLE-BAND END-FED CURTAIN MULTI-DIPOLE ARRAY

The single-band end-fed curtain multi-dipole array, in which the stack of dipoles was fed with power from the bottom of the stack upwards, was ideally suited to this task. The arrangement of such an array is shown below. Incidentally, the diagram also illustrates the 1960s development of a wire-mesh (aperiodic) reflector screen.

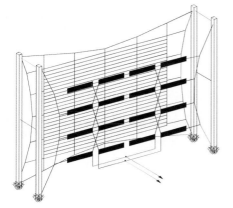

*Fig. 1 End-fed dipole array with aperiodic screen (from ITU-R BS.705-1, courtesy of the ITU)*

Originally another set of identical dipoles was placed to act as the reflector. By manually switching the transmitter feed from the front set of dipoles to the rear set, it was possible to use the reverse bearing of the antenna. In the example given above, the reverse bearing of the 80°

antenna – 260° – could be used to send signals to the West Indies, Central America, and on the long path to Australia. This was the classic **HRR 4/4/1** array. This means that the array is **H**orizontally polarised, it has a **R**eflector, it can be **R**eversed, it is **four** full-wave dipoles wide, **four** dipoles high and the lowest dipole is **1λ** above the ground. This produces a concentrated beam with a take-off angle (TOA) of 7-8° and was a DX array which produced the best coverage at long distances.

If a very large area, such as a continent, needed to be covered then only half the array (one stack of four dipoles) could be powered and the beam significantly widened at the expense of slightly lower signal strength. This technology advanced to the extent that by the mid-1960s it was possible to produce an effective radiated power (erp) of just over 30MW from a single 250kW transmitter. By using two 250kW transmitters and two side-by-side identical arrays, 500kW of transmitter power produced 60MW of erp.

## CURTAIN ANTENNA DEVELOPMENTS

To broadcast to nearer countries the standard HRR 4/4/1 array was still used but with two important alterations. By reducing the distance from the ground of the lowest dipole from 1λ to λ/2, the TOA was altered to be much steeper, often up to 20-30°. This meant, for example, that broadcasts to the Baltic states from the UK during World War II could be covered directly by one short hop. In addition, by altering the input power feed point from the usual centre fed position between the vertical stacks to an off-set position, a change in the bearing, or *slew*, of up to ±12° could be

The array at Saipan used by Radio Free Asia

Some arrays and groundworks at the now dismantled Sackville site (Thomas Witherspoon)

effected. This meant that it was possible to target multiple countries as well as regions, and the same array could be used to broadcast to, say, Morocco, Algeria and Libya. The designation then became HRRS 4/4/1 with the **S** indicating that the array was slewable.

### DUAL-BAND CURTAIN ARRAYS

The antennas we have been discussing were typically manufactured by the broadcasters but the advent of the Cold War led to the need for many more transmitters, with specialist antenna manufacturers offering their own antenna versions. The

Cold War also led to an increase in the number of HF stations which did not always have access to the large areas of land needed for single-band arrays. By the early 1960s this led the development of dual-band curtain arrays which by employing sets of dipoles in a fan-arrangement gave a broader bandwidth to cover two adjacent bands. The dipoles themselves were 'fattened up'; that is, they were made of multi-wire (*sausage*) elements rather than just a couple of wires as for the single band types. Instead of end-feeding two stacks of dipoles, the energy was brought in to a central point half way up the array

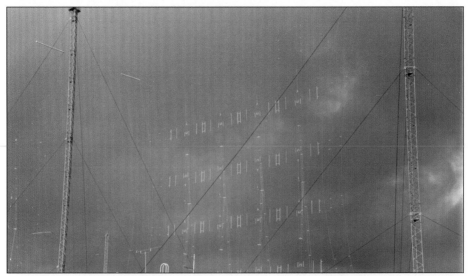

A TCI Type 611 array at the BBC/VOA site at Woofferton for 9, 11, 13, 15 and 17MHz (Jeff Cant)

and split to the upper and lower pair of the four and then again to each individual dipole, this is called *branch feeding*. Those designs operating on the popular 41 and 49 metre bands were some of the most sought-after, as many Western Countries were broadcasting to the Soviet Bloc via one hop. A classic example of this was Playa de Pals in Spain for Radio Free Europe and Radio Liberty to the Soviet Union for the peak-time breakfast and evening programmes.

## MULTI-BAND CURTAIN ANTENNAS

With the introduction of computer-aided design in the mid-1970s it was possible to design multi-band arrays. Typical models covered a 2:1 frequency ratio with, for example, a low frequency of 6MHz and a high frequency of 12MHz. Common designs were for 6, 7, 9 and 11MHz; 9, 11, 13, 15 and 17MHz; and 13, 15, 17, 21 and 26MHz. The US company TCI pioneered the development of these antennas with its famous Type 611 design, followed by Marconi Antennas and Thomcast.

Folded dipoles are employed in these designs rather than the earlier regular or fan dipoles. A folded dipole is a λ/2 dipole with an additional wire connecting its two ends. If the additional wire has the same diameter and cross-section as the dipole, two nearly identical radiating currents are generated. The folded dipole has a wider bandwidth than a single dipole as again like the fan dipole there is more metal in its construction, so it is a broad, radiating element.

Figure 2 shows how this was accomplished. This typical design has 16 folded dipoles. Because the RF feed to each of the four stacks of centre-fed folded dipoles can be controlled at the

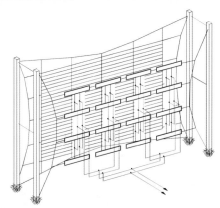

Fig. 2 Multi-band array with centre-fed dipoles and aperiodic screen (from ITU-R BS.705-1 with permission)

near ground level feeder runs by the addition of switches that add a length of feeder into the circuit, slewing is achieved by advancing the relative phase to each stack in equal pre-determined steps as the extra lengths of groundwork feeder are switched progressively into or out of circuit. By this method slews of up to ±30° are possible before unwanted sidelobes are produced. For even more versatility intermediate slews of ±15° are possible. Now, from the UK for example, St Petersburg on 45°, Moscow on 75° and the Balkans on 105° could be targeted over four or five bands on one array making this a cost effective solution for international broadcasting.

Further modifications took place over the years but curtain arrays had now evolved into effective and versatile HF transmitting antennas.

Some of the spectacular arrays at the Edward R Murrow site at Greenville, North Carolina (Thomas Witherspoon)

# Broadcasting for Peace

**Hans Johnson** *explores the origins and development of two stations which were founded with the aim of using radio to help bring peace to a troubled region*

A village in the Lake Chad region

Imagine finding yourself in the midst of a conflict in which you have no say. Messages are either intimidating or in someone else's native tongue.

The nine million Kanuri people of Africa's Lake Chad basin found themselves in exactly this situation several years ago as they suffered attacks from so-called Boko Haram, a jihadist extremist group active in the region, especially in Borno state of northeastern Nigeria. Local Nigerian stations had limited FM coverage and their programming was primarily in Hausa and English. No one was speaking to the Kanuri in their own language.

A new station, known as Dandal Kura Radio International (DKRI), stepped into this information vacuum in January 2015. Meaning 'meeting place' in Kanuri, Dandal Kura became "the first Kanuri-language radio station in the world", according to David Smith, the founder of DKRI and previously founder of Radio Okapi in the Democratic Republic of the Congo.

Boko Haram controlled sections of Borno state at the time, so DKRI's first studio and production facility was at the private station Freedom Radio in Kano. "They're not getting information from anyone. Nobody comes to them

to hear their side of the story. But now they have a new sense of belonging, a sense that society cares", Umar Tudunwada, Freedom's General Manager, told *The Globe and Mail* at the time.

The national and regional state broadcasters broadcast mainly in Hausa and mostly on FM which reached the towns but not the immense rural area. Some Kanuri were poor and others were displaced, but shortwave receivers costing just a few dollars were available in the shops, and those who do not own a radio usually have access to one. So DKRI initially purchased one hour a day via Babcock's Ascension Island site. Shortwave provided coverage of the large rural areas where many Kanuri live.

The purchase included the rather clever selection of a frequency close to the one used by BBC's morning Hausa service at 9440kHz. This is a service Kanuris tune into as quite a few of them also understand Hausa. By December 2015, DKRI was on shortwave six hours a day using Ascension Island and some of Babcock's other shortwave sites.

DKRI aimed to give Kanuris a voice, to help dissuade them from joining Boko Haram, and to protect them from violence, such as what to do in

RNI's roving ambassador Kachalla Kolo and Maiduguri studio manager Maude Gwadabe

a suicide-bomber attack. "These basic tips have helped save lives of people in the theatre of violence", Tudunwada told AFP in 2016. As the security situation improved in early 2016, and needing a presence in the area in order to produce better programmes in Kanuri, DKRI moved its studios to Maiduguri, capital of Borno state.

Measures of success came in many forms. The Kanuri heard people like them talking about the issues they faced in a language they could understand. The station was receiving about 120 responses a week. A Boko Haram commander called in to complain about the reporting of one of their attacks and, says Smith, some commanders have laid down their arms after hearing the broadcasts. Boko Haram is said to have started an FM station of its own on the border of Nigeria and Cameroon, and has referred to DKRI in its

One of the HF curtain arrays on Ascension Island set to the east beam for West Africa

Construction of the new studio from shipping containers at N'Djamena

video reports. David Smith was summoned to the Shehu (or King) of Borno's palace where the king told him, "I wanted to meet the person who gave dignity to our language".

There was growing recognition that Boko Haram was not just a Nigerian problem but also a regional one. This led Smith to establish, with funds from the Dutch Foreign Ministry, a regional studio and FM transmitter at the African Union mandated Multinational Joint Task Force base in the Chadian capital of N'Djamena. This new station started broadcasting on FM in August 2017. Programming is in the Chadian language of Kanembu, a close relative of Kanuri, with local speakers being trained as broadcasters.

This studio became a new regional service, Radio Ndarason International (RNI), in early 2018. This resulted in some initial confusion as both RNI and DKRI were on the same shortwave frequency at times. However, things were soon sorted out and the broadcasts were separated.

Ndarason, which means 'wherever you go' in Kanembu, is now carried on shortwave for six hours a day, morning and evening via Encompass transmitter sites. Encompass recently acquired Babcock's Media Services business. RNI is also disseminating programming from its FM service to relay transmitters in the region. There are plans to begin broadcasting in Buduma, a language spoken on the islands of Lake Chad which are fertile recruiting grounds for Boko Haram.

DKRI is now on via Media Broadcast's shortwave transmitter sites in Issoudun and Nauen, for four hours a day, and has recently recieved Nigerian government approval to operate two FM stations in Abuja and Maiduguri.

RNI maintains its regional focus and has established its own studio in Maiduguri. Programmes in Kanuri are sent to N'Djamena for uploading to Encompass. It also has plans to expand within the Lake Chad region to better serve the Kanuri living in neighbouring Niger and Cameroon. The French Development Agency is exploring ways to make this possible.

Smith believes that the solution to solving the Boko Haram conflict resides with local people. Call-in programmes and dramas are used to explore the issues. "Everyone speaks and that is the best path for peace", Smith adds.

The Kanuri and others now have a voice. Now that all can speak, one can only hope that enough listening and reconciliation will take place to bring peace to this troubled region.

David Smith with new reporters at Maiduguri

# V7AB Radio Marshall Islands

*YLE journalist and radio enthusiast **Mika Mäkeläinen** travelled to the exotic Marshall Islands and visited the national broadcaster which beams a powerful AM signal at sea level*

Coconut palms in the Marshall Islands

Finding the AM radio station in Majuro, the capital of the Marshall Islands in the middle of the Pacific Ocean, isn't very difficult even without a proper address. Majuro is built on such a narrow speck of land, 30 miles (48km) long and often no more than 200 yards (m) wide, that almost everything is located along a single road running the length of the crescent-shaped island.

We had arrived in Majuro to report on the nuclear legacy of the Marshall Islands for the Finnish Broadcasting Company YLE, where I work as foreign news journalist. We were getting ready to travel across the vast nation by sea to reach the remote Enewetak Atoll, where some of the most destructive nuclear tests were conducted until 1958. Some residents of Enewetak and the better known Bikini Atoll ended up on Majuro. However, before embarking on a four-day catamaran trip, I decide to say 'hello' to broadcasting colleagues, with whom I have had a special connection for over a decade.

The national broadcaster V7AB Radio Marshall Islands broadcasts on 1098kHz in the AM band, and has a surprisingly powerful signal which reaches far beyond the Pacific Ocean. The Pacific is the most coveted area for AM broadcast band DXers like me, hunting for distant signals. With 25kW of power V7AB is usually, at least in Northern Europe, the most powerful AM station from all of the Pacific islands. There used to be another AM station in the Marshall Islands, namely American Forces Network on Kwajalein Atoll which hosts a US military base, but this was closed in 2015.

I picked up V7AB for the first time in 2005 and since then it has been an annual pleasure to listen to island rhythms in my DX shack in Lapland, with a 1,000-meter-long Beverage antenna pointing at the Marshall Islands.

Few radio stations are haunted by an environmental hazard such as that facing V7AB. When I step out of the car to head into the modest roadside building which hosts the station, I am sternly warned to watch out for stray dogs. Packs of dogs tend to be particularly aggressive in this part of the island and a day earlier my cameraman was injured when he was chased by dogs in the same neighbourhood.

Radio Marshall Islands transmitter location and MW mast

Once safely inside V7AB's offices, I start looking for a familiar face, but Station Manager Antari Elbon is unfortunately out of the office and the only person inside is busy hosting a live programme. I don't understand any of the announcements, as all locally produced programming is in the native Marshallese language, although most Marshallese also speak good English as well.

After surviving an exciting visit by sea to Enewetak, I returned a couple of weeks later to Majuro and went to V7AB. Elbon, who had kindly confirmed my reception report back in 2006, was in the office. He told me that William Ring, whose voice I had heard in 2005, was also still working at the station. Employee turnover is small as job opportunities in Majuro are very limited.

The latest development at V7AB is a new website at www.v7abradio.info. Streaming audio is planned for the future so as to allow the sizable Marshallese community in the United States to listen to their home country's transmissions. Up to a third of all Marshallese have emigrated to the US in search of better-paying jobs and a majority has settled in Arkansas, lured there by the local meat industry.

V7AB's antenna is located on a separate

V7AB Station Manager Antari Elbon

BNJ Church, Majuro, home to Eagle Christian Radio's studio

small island just north of the capital. Like all the Marshall Islands it is barely two meters above the sea and even a modest rise in sea level is an existential risk to V7AB and its audience.

Financially the future of V7AB looks stable as it is a government station and operates under the Ministry of Culture and Internal Affairs. It airs public and community programmes and benefits from some commercial income.

Alongside the V7AB powerhouse, there may be hope of resurrecting another AM station in the Marshall Islands in the near future. A station called Eagle Christian Radio used to broadcast on 1170kHz but, due to a lack of spare parts, it has been off the air since November 2016, and its

Eagle Christian Radio Technician Thomas Jennet

FM transmitter on 99.9MHz is also no longer operational. Eagle Christian Radio has a 25kW AM transmitter, which could only be used at 5kW, and is located on the western end of the Majuro atoll, in a rural district called Laura.

Just before heading back to Europe, I decided to visit Eagle Christian Radio's studio which is located on the top floor of the BNJ Church in downtown Majuro. BNJ stands for 'Bukot Nan Jesus', or 'Look for Jesus' and is a Pentecostal church which occupies one of the tallest buildings in the country.

There was nobody at the church and the doors were locked, so I gave a call to technician Thomas Jennet, who kindly promised to come over and show me the premises. Jennet arrived, but as the lock had been changed we couldn't actually visit the studio. However, we had a nice chat at the steps of the church.

The station used to transmit up to 18 hours a day, and also had educational programming in addition to Christian teaching. The station's tecnician Thomas Jennet hopes to get the station back on air as soon as the technical problems have been overcome. Importing technical equipment is both difficult and expensive: living on a remote paradise island doesn't come cheap.

After I left the island I received news that an agreement had been reached between V7AB and KMWR 98.9 FM in Springdale, Arkansas. The two stations will share material to broadcast in the US and Majuro. As part of the deal V7AB's programmes will air in Springdale and within the online KMWR app. In return, V7AB will receive new Marshallese songs produced in the US.

# CLAIM YOUR FREE ISSUE

## Try Practical Wireless or RadioUser for FREE

Get your free copy by calling
## 01778 395161 or online at...

Practical Wireless: bit.ly/freepracticalwireless
RadioUser: bit.ly/freeradiouser

# TWR Bonaire

*TWR Broadcast Engineer,* **Dave Pedersen**, *outlines the reasons for, and operational complexities of, installing a new MW transmitter at TWR's Bonaire faciity*

TWR Bonaire towers at night (Brad Swanson)

The voice of hope across the Caribbean and South America got a lot louder in January 2018 as TWR inaugurated the most powerful radio station in the Western Hemisphere. Known as 'Shine 800AM', the station broadcasts Bible-based Gospel programs on 800kHz from its new 440kW transmitter. The station has a potential audience of more than 100 million listeners from Cuba south to Venezuela and Brazil, as well as from the Yucatan Peninsula east across the Caribbean. TWR president Lauren Libby describes the station as "a big voice for Jesus".

TWR began broadcasting from Bonaire in 1964. Initial broadcasts were on medium wave to the Caribbean and South America and on shortwave to many other regions of the world, supplementing TWR's other transmission facility at the time in Monaco. The shortwave transmissions from Bonaire ceased in 1999 as TWR broadcasting facilities grew around the world, with regional studios and transmitters serving their regions

more directly. TWR now broadcasts over a global network of transmitters owned by TWR as well as facilities owned by many partners worldwide.

Since its inception in 1952, TWR has grown to become one of the world's largest multinational Christian media outlets. Its radio transmissions now speak hope to the world in more than 230 languages and 160 countries. Known for several decades as Trans World Radio, the ministry's branding identity was changed to TWR in 2009 to reflect the organization's growing use of other communications media. TWR has, however, also continued to increase its radio ministry.

TWR Bonaire began medium wave broadcasts in 1964 with 500kW, operating a variety of tube-based transmitters until 1999. The facility initially operated its own power generators because the power demand was more than the local infrastructure could provide. The island's power grid and generation capacity have expanded, and adequate power is now provided commercially.

Storm behind the salt flats and towers (Brad Swanson)

Unfortunately though, the high cost of electricity on the island led to a reduction of transmitter power to 100kW in 1999. Since then many listeners have reported they could hear the signals from Bonaire only poorly or not at all, a situation made worse by the increasing noise floor in urban areas. It became clear by the end of 2010 that a return to high power was needed.

Because the station retained its 500kW licensing, TWR was able to start the Bonaire 'Power Up' project in 2011, bringing back superpower broadcasting to the Caribbean with the 2018 inauguration of a new Nautel NX400 transmitter. This was chosen for its cost, reliability, and high efficiency: it typically operates at greater than 92 percent total efficiency and is an entirely solid-state transmitter. TWR Bonaire also uses modulation dependent carrier level control (MDCL) that reduces carrier power on modulation peaks, lowering electrical costs by another 30 per cent. After visiting the Nautel factory in Canada for training on installing and operating the new transmitter, TWR staff members performed the transmitter installation themselves.

A broadcast station is a system, much more than the transmitter alone. More RF output power requires more of everything else. New electrical transformers were installed by the local power company. The hall that housed the old 500kW tube in the 1990s needed renovation; one quarter of the hall is now dedicated to the Nautel NX400 and the rest houses the new phasor array from Kintronic Labs. New 30-ton air-conditioners were installed to cool the transmitter and hall, new

feedlines had to be run, and the four-tower array was modified to handle the higher power. The layout of the antenna array is rectangular, with two towers being driven and the other two acting as reflectors when beaming northwest towards Cuba or southeast towards Venezuela and Brazil. A single tower is employed for the modified non-directional Caribbean pattern.

The southern part of the island of Bonaire, where the TWR transmitter is located, is very low-lying. The radial system is less than 60 centimeters above the limestone layer that is permeated with ocean water, and very close to the seashore and salt ponds. The ground conductivity in this layer is extremely good, further enhancing the antenna effectiveness and lowering the radiation pattern. The negative side of this location is that the salt-laden trade winds lead to a continuing battle with corrosion. The towers must be scraped and cleaned every two years.

Most of the installation work was performed by dedicated volunteers assisting TWR staff over the course of a five-year period. They helped with building renovation; electrical system and air-conditioner installation; construction of the new antenna tuning unit houses (which have no nails or screws in the roofs to avoid the risk of corona discharge starting a fire in the high-RF field); painting; and phasor and ATU assembly. Hundreds of people used their vacation times to be part of the project. The entire power upgrade was funded by donations, with work proceeding as funding was received.

In addition to daily broadcasts of inspirational

TWR Rigger Kevin Baker performs tower modifications above the salt flats (Jonas Fischer)

gospel messages, Shine 800AM serves the Caribbean during and after natural disasters. Its high power transmissions can effectively reach any island or country in the region. Ground wave signals travel very well over the ocean even in broad daylight. The station broadcast special programing during and after hurricanes Irma and Maria in 2017, as well as after the Haiti earthquake in 2010. Bonaire is located south of the hurricane belt and is therefore usually unaffected by the passing storms, so the station is in a good position to assist others.

Shine 800AM broadcasts overnight on 800kHz from 2130 to 1230UTC. The direction and power of the broadcasts change throughout the broadcasting period based on distances and propagation to the intended audiences. The current broadcast schedule can be downloaded at www.twrbonaire.com/broadcast_schedule/
More information on TWR Bonaire can be found at www.twrbonaire.com
More information on TWR's work worldwide is available at www.twr.org

Nautel NX400 Transmitter (Brad Swanson)

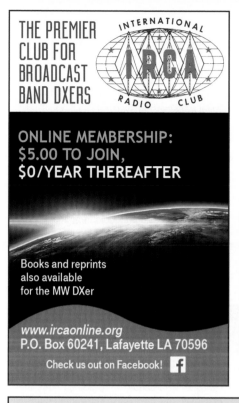
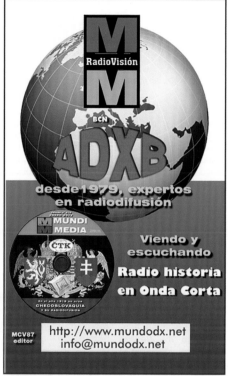

# Digital Update

*Our regular round-up of digital broadcasting, looking in particular this year at the distinctive characteristics of analogue and digital transmission systems*

We have been running our 'Digital Update' feature in *WRTH* for some years, with a view to keeping readers informed about the dramatic changes in broadcasting technology that have taken place since digital techniques began to be introduced. Indeed it is sometimes argued that in the long term all broadcasting – and indeed practically all uses of the electromagnetic spectrum – will involve digital systems of one sort or another. One of our correspondents observed recently that perhaps we should now regard analogue broadcasting as an "endangered species" and re-cast our feature as a diary of its final demise.

The world has not quite reached that stage but it is perhaps worth reminding ourselves why digital methods have supplanted analogue to the degree they have. Reduced to its lowest terms the answer lies in two words – *bandwidth* and *reliability*. The radio-frequency spectrum is a finite

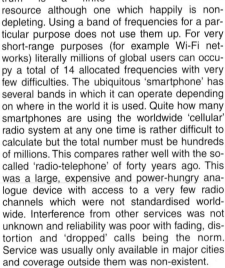

resource although one which happily is non-depleting. Using a band of frequencies for a particular purpose does not use them up. For very short-range purposes (for example Wi-Fi networks) literally millions of global users can occupy a total of 14 allocated frequencies with very few difficulties. The ubiquitous 'smartphone' has several bands in which it can operate depending on where in the world it is used. Quite how many smartphones are using the worldwide 'cellular' radio system at any one time is rather difficult to calculate but the total number must be hundreds of millions. This compares rather well with the so-called 'radio-telephone' of forty years ago. This was a large, expensive and power-hungry analogue device with access to a very few radio channels which were not standardised world-wide. Interference from other services was not unknown and reliability was poor with fading, distortion and 'dropped' calls being the norm. Service was usually only available in major cities and coverage outside them was non-existent.

It is of course accepted that technology has given today's smartphone easy access to very high radio frequencies that were not readily usable by consumer technology forty years ago

and where more bandwidth is available. But the main difference between analogue and digital systems is how efficiently they use the available bandwidth. A radio-frequency 'carrier' is not intrinsically very useful as a communications system unless perhaps it is switched on and off by a Morse key. It is the process of *modulation* – in effect the impressing of audio frequencies on the carrier – which transforms it into a useful method of broadcasting. There were (and are) two main analogue modulation techniques used by broadcasters. One is so-called *amplitude* modulation (AM) in which a set of sidebands derived from the audio are in effect added either side of the carrier,  transmitted along with it and turned back into audio at the receiver. The other is so-called *frequency* modulation (FM) which in formal terms is almost identical in that it involves the generation and addition of sidebands. In passing, both these techniques have been habitually mis-described over the years, chiefly to keep the explanations intelligible but at the expense of accuracy. The amplitude of the carrier in an AM broadcast transmitter does not vary at all; the modulation is carried exclusively in the sidebands. The frequency of the carrier in an FM broadcast does not vary either although paradoxically its amplitude does. Here again the modulation resides entirely in the sidebands which extend either side of the carrier by an amount formally referred to as *deviation*.

Both these systems work tolerably well but by modern standards they are exceedingly inefficient in terms of the bandwidth they use. Consider a medium-wave AM broadcast on a nominal frequency of 800kHz and assume that the frequency range of the audio being sent to it from the studio is 30Hz-15kHz, the latter being a reasonable approximation to the highest frequency audible to the human ear. Because the sidebands fall both above and below the carrier, the total bandwidth occupied by this broadcast would be (800-15) to (800+15) or 30kHz. If the MW band is taken to be 520-1710kHz, the result is that only 40 stations could fit within it. Given the range of MW transmissions, particularly at night, the consequence would be massive interference. Readers will of course know that the MW and

SW bands are channelized at either 9 or 10kHz and that the upper frequency limit of the modulation has to be severely restricted to make this possible. This is why MW and SW broadcasts with their upper limit of about 4kHz sound very muffled. For the record, suppressing one set of sidebands in the transmitter and not radiating them effectively halves the bandwidth of the transmitted signal. So-called *single sideband* (SSB) transmissions are often used for communications purposes but for various reasons are not generally suited to broadcasting. FM broadcasts sound considerably better than their AM equivalents, chiefly because the upper limit of the modulating frequency is about 15kHz. In addition FM systems in general are nowhere near as susceptible to noise and impulse interference. However the deviation in an FM system is ±75kHz and hence the transmission requires a bandwidth of 150kHz. In most countries the FM broadcast band is channelized at 200kHz intervals to avoid interference from other stations.

Armed with this information we can now consider how a digital system could make use of such channel bandwidths. There are three basic techniques of digital modulation – for interested readers wishing to investigate further they are ASK, FSK and PSK – and different sub-types which combine elements of each. The essence of all of them is that the instantaneous amplitude of the audio is encoded as a stream of digital 'bits' (that is to say ones or zeros) and the intention is to maximise the amount of data in a given portion of spectrum. One way to think about spectrum efficiency in digital broadcasting systems is "programmes per MHz" and an excellent numerical analysis of DAB versus FM in a 2005 BBC paper used this for comparison purposes. It stated that with 200kHz channel spacing, conventional FM broadcasting required 0.2 MHz per programme. The "frequency re-use factor" in most countries is approximately 15 for stereo FM broadcasts, implying that only one in every 15 transmitter sites can use the same frequencies without causing problems of co-channel interference. FM broadcasting takes place in the 87.5-108MHz band and a total of 102 channels with a bandwidth of 0.2MHz can be fitted into it. Consequently an average of 102/15 = 6.8 radio channels are feasible on each transmitter site. This gives a system spectral efficiency of (1/15/0.2) or 0.3 programmes per transmitter per MHz. In comparison, DAB with a 192kbit/s codec requires (1.536 MHz x 192 kbit/s /1,136 kbit/s) or 0.26MHz per audio programme. The frequency re-use factor for local programmes and multi-fre-

quency broadcasting networks (MFN) can be taken as 4 which gives (1/4/0.26) or 0.96 programmes per transmitter per MHz. Hence DAB can be said to be 3.2 times as efficient as FM for local stations. For national DAB transmissions using a single-frequency network (SFN) the channel re-use factor is 1. This gives (1/1/0.25) or 3.85 programmes per transmitter per MHz, making it 12.7 times more efficient than FM for national and regional networks. Lower bit rates than 192kbit/s are commonly used nowadays and give even better efficiency, and DAB+ adds a further level of improvement. Generally speaking DAB+ as currently used is about twenty times more spectrum-efficient than FM.

A similar analysis can be performed for television transmissions. In the days of analogue TV broadcasting, the required channel width was somewhere between 4 and 6MHz depending on the system used. In very approximate terms it can be said that somewhere between 12 and 20 digital television channels can fit into the space taken up by one analogue channel.

The other major issue to consider is reliability, by which is meant the ability of the broadcast radio link to resist corruption of various types. Readers will be only too familiar with the audible effects of selective fading, interference and other forms of noise on MW and SW broadcasts, and low-level multipath distortion is not uncommon during FM reception. Those who have DAB receivers in their cars will have noticed that the audio is consistently 'cleaner' than that from FM which for several reasons is not at all well suited to mobile operation. Whereas FM is adversely affected by multipath, the modulation system (OFDM) used for DAB actually benefits from it.

Considerable engineering efforts were made in the past to find ways of introducing error correction into analogue radio systems to try to deal with the consequences of transmission paths which were less than perfect. Unfortunately it is not at all easy to do so. In contrast, digital systems can very easily be engineered to embody very powerful and effective error correction and the signal processing in modern receivers can handle it with ease. One slight drawback is that digital reception tends either to be perfect or (when the system runs out of error correction due to weak signals or chronic interference) hopelessly garbled or non-existent. If you ever used an analogue cellular telephone you will be well aware of the fading and interruptions that took place all too often during your conversations. Modern smartphones usually either give consistently good results for the duration of the call or drop the connection entirely. As usual with digital systems, there is no half-way house.

One final attribute of digital modulation systems worth mentioning is that they can give very effective results even when signals are extremely weak. Satellite navigation systems using GPS are a case in point. If you tune a receiver to 1575.42MHz (the frequency on which the so-called C/A code used in civilian GPS applications is transmitted) you will hear nothing whatsoever. The signal from a GPS satellite is about 26dB below the noise floor even at a very electrically quiet location on earth. However, a GPS receiver has about 40dB of what is sometimes called processing gain and can quite easily recover the required information from the signal. Informally one could say that it 'knows' what to look for before it starts looking. The ability of a digital receiver to work with very low levels of signal in this way is one reason why the transmitters in digital systems can be far less powerful than their analogue equivalents whilst giving similar performance. This is one feature of the admittedly moribund DRM system, where quite low-power transmitters can give reliable coverage of quite large areas. Or at least they could if someone had a suitable receiver which happened to be tuned to a DRM broadcast.

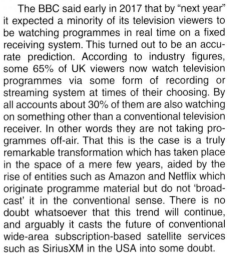

On the subject of DRM we have little to add to our remarks last year. The continuing lack of availability of any retail DRM-capable receivers at prices remotely approaching those of conventional radios suggests that the mode is somewhere between dormant and defunct. In the last edition of *WRTH* we mentioned that a new DRM receiver, the Gospell GR-216, had appeared in early 2017. This was billed as being available directly from the Chinese manufacturer for $240 plus shipping. We did our best to obtain a sample of the GR-216 for review last year but no response to our emails was received – and despite several promises to the contrary this year, no sample was forthcoming. However it is clear that at this price point there is no chance whatsoever of the Gospell or any other DRM receiver being a contender for a mass market. It is a discretionary purchase for the enthusiast. What was always required was a $10 DRM radio that can run off batteries for a week or two (or be rechargeable) and fit in a shirt pocket. But for the same reason that digital portables in general are relatively rare – the requirement for considerable processing power in the receiver is inimical to battery life – the low-cost portable DRM receiver will almost certainly remain in the realms of what might have been. And sadly we are forced to the conclusion that no new mass-market DRM receivers will now be destined to see the light of day.

The BBC said early in 2017 that by "next year" it expected a minority of its television viewers to be watching programmes in real time on a fixed receiving system. This turned out to be an accurate prediction. According to industry figures, some 65% of UK viewers now watch television programmes via some form of recording or streaming system at times of their choosing. By all accounts about 30% of them are also watching on something other than a conventional television receiver. In other words they are not taking programmes off-air. That this is the case is a truly remarkable transformation which has taken place in the space of a mere few years, aided by the rise of entities such as Amazon and Netflix which originate programme material but do not 'broadcast' it in the conventional sense. There is no doubt whatsoever that this trend will continue, and arguably it casts the future of conventional wide-area subscription-based satellite services such as SiriusXM in the USA into some doubt.

As we said last year, it is abundantly clear that 'broadcasting' as it used to be understood is slowly and quietly giving way to something else – and that its future is bound up with digital methods and systems to a degree which would have seemed wildly improbable forty years ago. Quite what the future holds for AM and FM services is anyone's guess although very few countries have so far opted for the wholesale replacement of FM broadcasting by some form of digital service. One of the major obstacles is lack of standardisation. In very general terms one might say that in a good deal of ITU Region 1 – that is to say Europe – digital radio broadcasting has more or less settled on DAB+ as its standard. This is the case even in France where the early adoption of DMB-R as a national digital broadcasting system has largely given way in the marketplace to DAB+. By contrast, neither North nor South America has anything resembling a digital standard. Nominally the USA has adopted HD Radio (also referred to as IBOC) but take-up has been very limited and sporadic and the technology involved is obsolescent. Elsewhere in the world DAB+ seems to be slowly gaining ground but there remain a plethora of other standards, most of which we have discussed at some length in these pages over the years.

By contrast, FM and AM broadcasts continue to be made in every country in the world and a low-cost low-technology receiver purchased anywhere can receive them all without difficulty. In the process it consumes very little power and can operate from cheap and readily available batteries. It is this simple fact which will postpone the replacement of analogue broadcasting by digital techniques for some years yet.

# HF BROADCASTING RECEPTION CONDITIONS EXPECTED DURING 2019

*Likely listening conditions in the coming year by* **Ulf-Peter Hoppe**

## SUNSPOT MINIMUM IN 2019

We will likely reach solar minimum in 2019. We can expect very quiet and very stable conditions in the ionosphere in the coming year.

The sunspot cycle that is now closing is the 24th observed since 1756. Fig. 1 provided by Dr David Hathaway shows the courses of Cycles 22 and 23, and the expected course of Cycle 24.

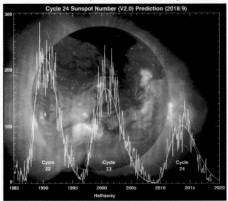

*Fig. 1 Sunspot Cycles 22, 23 and 24 (Hathaway)*

Solar scientists estimate that the smoothed sunspot number will steadily decrease from about 4 in Jan-Apr 2019 to only about 2 in May-Aug and rise to about 3 in Sept-Dec. These numbers have been used for the prediction of most suitable frequencies opposite. Predicting the behaviour of a sunspot cycle is fairly reliable once the cycle is well underway, even if little is known about the actual solar process. One reliable technique uses measurements of perturbations to the Earth's magnetic field at and before sunspot minimum. Another studies the magnetic polarity of sunspot pairs on the solar surface. This prediction was created using a combination of techniques.

Solar ultraviolet radiation creates the ionosphere, the ionized fraction of the earth's atmosphere. The F-region of the ionosphere starts about 93 miles (150 km) above the ground and constitutes the most important refractive medium for HF radio waves. The E-region at 62 to 74 miles (100 to 120 km) is weaker, but sometimes also plays a role in HF radio communication. The flux of ultraviolet light from the sun is greatest when the solar cycle is near its maximum, and decreases as the sunspot number decreases. The electron density in the ionosphere will remain relatively small during the course of 2019. The actual number of sunspots will vary in a similar way to previous Cycles, reaching 20 or 30 on

### TABLE 1

| MHz | m. | % | Reception Characteristics |
|---|---|---|---|
| 26 | 11 | * | No significant HF broadcasting |
| 21/19 | 13 | 9 | Day: long distance, all seasons |
| 17 | 16 | 9 | Day: mid and long distance, all seasons |
| 15 | 19 | 15 | Day: mid and long distance, all seasons |
| 13 | 22 | 12 | Day: mid and long distance, all seasons |
| | | | Eve: mid and long distance, not local winter |
| 11 | 25 | 13 | Day: short and mid distance, all seasons |
| | | | Eve: mid and long distance, not winter |
| 9 | 31 | 14 | Day: short and mid distance, all seasons |
| | | | Eve: mid and long distance, all seasons |
| | | | Night: mid and long distance, all seasons |
| 7 | 41 | 14 | Day: short and mid distance, all seasons |
| | | | Night: mid and long distance, all seasons |
| 6/5 | 49 | 12 | Day: short and mid distance, all seasons |
| | | | Night: mid and long distance, all seasons |
| 4/3 | 75 | 2 | Day: short distance, all seasons |
| | | | Night: short and mid distance, all seasons |

**m. = Metre Bands % = % of total band usage**
**\* = used for local digital broadcasting in Europe**
**Short-distance**: up to *c.* 1200 miles (2000 km)
**Mid-distance**: c. 1000-2400 miles (1600-4000 km)
**Long-distance**: over 2400 miles (4000 km)

some individual days. We also expect long periods without sunspots, as we have already experienced several times during 2018. Therefore the best reception conditions on a given day can occur in a shortwave band neighboring the ones given in the prediction table.

The ionospheric conditions at the reflection point halfway along the great circle from transmitter to receiver have the greatest influence on the best frequency to use, except for the rarer two-hop circuits and the even rarer circuits taking the opposite direction, along the longest part of the great circle. When the reflection point is in daylight, the 17, 19, and 21 MHz bands often give the most stable reception conditions. When the reflection point is on the night side, the 11, 9, 7, 6, and 5 MHz bands give the best results.

Compared to other years with more sunspots, we will often use the next lower frequency band, or even two frequency bands lower, than in the more active years. This choice is already taken care of in the frequency predictions on the next page. Reception conditions will be at least as good as in other years, but the changes will be smaller from day to day.

We still observe little interference between stations, so we can expect a good year of reception on the HF broadcasting bands.

### ABOUT THE AUTHOR

Ulf-Peter Hoppe is an adjunct professor of physics at the Arctic University of Norway.

# Most Suitable Frequencies
# 2019

Prepared by Prof. Dr. rer. nat. Ulf-Peter Hoppe, Chief Scientist
E-mail: ulf-peter.hoppe@tveco.net
Web: http://tinyurl.com/pg46arx

## TRANSMITTING STATION LOCATION

| LISTENER'S AREA | LOCAL TIME | APPROX. UTC TIME | JAN/FEB & NOV/DEC | | | | | | | | MAR/APR & SEPT/OCT | | | | | | | | MAY-AUGUST | | | | | | | |
|---|---|---|---|---|---|---|---|---|---|---|---|---|---|---|---|---|---|---|---|---|---|---|---|---|---|---|
| | | | EUR/NAF | N.AM(E) | N.AM(W) | C/S.AM | C/S.AF | ME/S.AS | E.AS | AUS/NZ | EUR/NAF | N.AM(E) | N.AM(W) | C/S.AM | C/S.AF | ME/S.AS | E.AS | AUS/NZ | EUR/NAF | N.AM(E) | N.AM(W) | C/S.AM | C/S.AF | ME/S.AS | E.AS | AUS/NZ |
| EUROPE AND NORTH AFRICA | 00:00-04:00 | 23:00-03:00 | 6 | 7 | 9 | 9 | 7 | 7 | 9 | - | 6 | 9 | 9 | 9 | 9 | 9 | 9 | - | 7 | 9 | 11 | 9 | 7 | 9 | 9 | - |
| | 04:00-08:00 | 03:00-07:00 | 6 | 7 | 7 | 9 | 13 | 13 | - | | 7 | 7 | 9 | 9 | 11 | 15 | 17 | 17 | 9 | 7 | 11 | 9 | 9 | 15 | 15 | 15 |
| | 08:00-12:00 | 07:00-11:00 | 13 | 7 | 9 | 9 | 17 | 17 | 15 | 21 | 15 | 9 | 9 | 11 | 17 | 17 | 17 | 21 | 11 | 11 | 11 | 11 | 13 | 15 | 17 | 17 |
| | 12:00-16:00 | 11:00-15:00 | 13 | 15 | 9 | 15 | 21 | 13 | 11 | 17 | 17 | 13 | 9 | 17 | 21 | 17 | 17 | 13 | 17 | 13 | 11 | 17 | 15 | 17 | 15 | - |
| | 16:00-20:00 | 15:00-19:00 | 9 | 15 | 13 | 17 | 13 | 7 | 9 | 11 | 9 | 17 | 13 | 21 | 13 | 9 | 11 | 13 | 15 | 13 | 13 | 17 | 15 | 11 | 11 | 13 |
| | 20:00-00:00 | 19:00-23:00 | 6 | 9 | 9 | 11 | 9 | 7 | 9 | 11 | 7 | 11 | 15 | 13 | 11 | 9 | 9 | 13 | 9 | 13 | 15 | 11 | 9 | 9 | 9 | 11 |
| NORTH AMERICA (EAST) | 22:00-02:00 | 03:00-07:00 | 7 | 7 | 6 | 7 | 9 | - | - | | 7 | 6 | 6 | 7 | 9 | - | - | | 7 | 6 | 9 | 7 | 9 | - | - | 13 |
| | 02:00-06:00 | 07:00-11:00 | 7 | 7 | 6 | 7 | - | - | 7 | 11 | 9 | 6 | 6 | 6 | - | - | 9 | 9 | 11 | 6 | 7 | 7 | - | - | 7 | 9 |
| | 06:00-10:00 | 11:00-15:00 | 11 | 9 | 7 | 13 | 17 | 13 | 9 | 11 | 13 | 11 | 7 | 11 | 17 | 13 | 13 | 13 | 13 | 11 | 9 | 13 | 17 | 15 | 13 | 13 |
| | 10:00-14:00 | 15:00-19:00 | 13 | 13 | 11 | 21 | 17 | - | 11 | - | 15 | 13 | 13 | 15 | 17 | 15 | - | - | 15 | 15 | 17 | 17 | 17 | 17 | - | - |
| | 14:00-18:00 | 19:00-23:00 | 9 | 13 | 13 | 13 | 15 | 11 | 9 | 21 | 11 | 11 | 11 | 15 | 17 | 13 | 13 | - | 11 | 11 | 13 | 13 | 13 | 15 | 15 | 17 |
| | 18:00-22:00 | 23:00-03:00 | 6 | 7 | 9 | 9 | 9 | 11 | - | | 6 | 9 | 9 | 7 | 13 | 13 | 13 | - | 9 | 11 | 11 | 11 | 9 | 15 | 15 | 17 |
| NORTH AMERICA (WEST) | 00:00-04:00 | 08:00-12:00 | 9 | 7 | 6 | 9 | - | 9 | 9 | 9 | 9 | 7 | 9 | - | - | 9 | 11 | | 11 | 7 | 7 | 9 | - | - | 9 | 9 |
| | 04:00-08:00 | 12:00-16:00 | 13 | 11 | 6 | 13 | 15 | 9 | 9 | 9 | 13 | 11 | 7 | 13 | 15 | 11 | 11 | 11 | 13 | 13 | 7 | 13 | 13 | 13 | 11 | 11 |
| | 08:00-12:00 | 16:00-20:00 | 13 | 15 | 9 | 17 | 21 | 11 | 11 | 13 | 15 | 13 | 11 | 17 | 15 | 15 | 11 | - | 13 | 17 | 17 | 17 | 17 | 15 | 13 | - |
| | 12:00-16:00 | 20:00-00:00 | 7 | 15 | 13 | 15 | 17 | 11 | 13 | 21 | 11 | 15 | 11 | 17 | 17 | - | 15 | 21 | 13 | 13 | 11 | 17 | - | 15 | 15 | 17 |
| | 16:00-20:00 | 00:00-04:00 | 7 | 7 | 9 | 9 | 11 | 13 | 13 | - | 7 | 9 | 9 | 11 | 15 | 15 | 21 | | 9 | 11 | 9 | 11 | 9 | 15 | 15 | 17 |
| | 20:00-00:00 | 04:00-08:00 | 6 | 7 | 6 | 9 | 9 | - | - | 11 | 9 | 7 | 6 | 7 | - | - | 13 | 11 | 9 | 7 | 9 | 9 | 11 | - | 15 | 13 |
| CENTRAL AND SOUTH AMERICA | 00:00-04:00 | 04:00-08:00 | 7 | 7 | 9 | 9 | 11 | - | 15 | 15 | 9 | 7 | 9 | 9 | 11 | - | - | 17 | 9 | 7 | 11 | 9 | 9 | - | - | 11 |
| | 04:00-08:00 | 08:00-12:00 | 13 | 7 | 9 | 9 | 17 | 17 | 13 | 9 | 13 | 7 | 9 | 7 | 17 | 13 | 9 | | 15 | 7 | 9 | - | 17 | 17 | 13 | 7 |
| | 08:00-12:00 | 12:00-16:00 | 17 | 15 | 11 | 17 | 21 | 21 | - | - | 17 | 15 | 13 | 17 | 21 | 25 | - | - | 17 | 11 | 15 | 17 | 21 | 17 | - | |
| | 12:00-16:00 | 16:00-20:00 | 15 | 17 | 21 | 21 | 25 | - | - | - | 17 | 17 | 15 | 21 | 25 | - | - | - | 15 | 15 | 17 | 21 | 15 | 17 | - | - |
| | 16:00-20:00 | 20:00-00:00 | 9 | 13 | 15 | 17 | 21 | 11 | 9 | 17 | 9 | 13 | 15 | 17 | 13 | 11 | 13 | 17 | 9 | 15 | 15 | 15 | 13 | 11 | 15 | 17 |
| | 20:00-00:00 | 00:00-04:00 | 9 | 6 | 9 | 9 | 13 | 11 | - | 21 | 9 | 7 | 13 | 11 | 15 | 15 | 17 | 21 | 9 | 9 | 13 | 9 | 13 | 17 | 15 | |
| CENTRAL AND SOUTH AFRICA | 00:00-04:00 | 22:00-02:00 | 9 | 11 | 15 | 11 | 7 | 9 | 11 | | 9 | 15 | 15 | 11 | 7 | 9 | 15 | - | 7 | 9 | - | 7 | 7 | 7 | 11 | - |
| | 04:00-08:00 | 02:00-06:00 | 7 | 7 | - | 9 | 6 | 13 | 15 | - | 7 | 9 | 11 | 9 | 6 | 15 | 17 | - | 7 | 7 | 9 | 7 | 6 | 13 | 17 | - |
| | 08:00-12:00 | 06:00-10:00 | 17 | - | - | 17 | 17 | 17 | 17 | | 17 | - | - | 17 | 21 | 25 | 21 | | - | - | - | 13 | 21 | 25 | 17 | |
| | 12:00-16:00 | 10:00-14:00 | 17 | 21 | - | 25 | 17 | 21 | 17 | 17 | 21 | 17 | - | 25 | 17 | 21 | 25 | | 21 | 17 | - | 13 | 17 | 21 | - | |
| | 16:00-20:00 | 14:00-18:00 | 15 | 21 | 13 | 25 | 13 | 13 | 11 | 11 | 17 | 21 | 13 | 21 | 17 | 11 | 11 | 11 | 17 | 17 | 15 | 17 | 11 | 9 | 13 | 9 |
| | 20:00-00:00 | 18:00-22:00 | 9 | 15 | 15 | 17 | 9 | 9 | 11 | 11 | 9 | 17 | - | 15 | 7 | 9 | 11 | 9 | 9 | 15 | 15 | 17 | 7 | 7 | 11 | 9 |
| MIDDLE EAST AND SOUTH ASIA | 00:00-04:00 | 21:00-01:00 | 7 | 11 | 11 | 11 | 7 | 7 | 7 | - | 7 | 11 | 13 | 13 | 9 | 7 | 7 | - | 7 | 11 | - | 11 | 6 | 9 | 11 | - |
| | 04:00-08:00 | 01:00-05:00 | 7 | 9 | 13 | 9 | 7 | 11 | 15 | 21 | 7 | 9 | 15 | 13 | 7 | 15 | 15 | 21 | 9 | 11 | 13 | 13 | 7 | 15 | 17 | 21 |
| | 08:00-12:00 | 05:00-09:00 | 15 | - | - | - | 17 | 15 | 17 | 25 | 15 | - | - | - | 17 | 25 | 21 | 25 | 13 | - | 15 | - | 11 | 17 | 17 | 21 |
| | 12:00-16:00 | 09:00-13:00 | 15 | - | 9 | - | 17 | 15 | 11 | 17 | 15 | - | - | 21 | 17 | 25 | 17 | 15 | 15 | 15 | - | 17 | 15 | 17 | 17 | 13 |
| | 16:00-20:00 | 13:00-17:00 | 11 | 15 | 9 | 21 | 15 | 11 | 7 | 15 | 13 | 17 | 11 | 25 | 17 | 11 | 11 | 11 | 13 | 17 | 11 | 21 | 15 | 11 | 15 | 11 |
| | 20:00-00:00 | 17:00-21:00 | 7 | - | 9 | - | 11 | 9 | 7 | 11 | 9 | 17 | 13 | - | 11 | 11 | 9 | 11 | 11 | 17 | 15 | 17 | 7 | 9 | 11 | 9 |
| EAST ASIA AND FAR EAST | 00:00-04:00 | 16:00-20:00 | 9 | - | 7 | - | 11 | 7 | 6 | 6 | 9 | - | - | 13 | 9 | 7 | 6 | | 11 | - | 9 | - | 13 | 11 | 11 | 7 |
| | 04:00-08:00 | 20:00-00:00 | 9 | 15 | 13 | 17 | 9 | 6 | 6 | 11 | 7 | 15 | 15 | 11 | 13 | 7 | 9 | 13 | 11 | 13 | 15 | 13 | 9 | 9 | 9 | 11 |
| | 08:00-12:00 | 00:00-04:00 | 9 | - | 13 | - | 17 | 15 | 17 | 21 | 9 | 15 | - | - | 15 | 17 | 21 | | 11 | 11 | 13 | 17 | - | 17 | 15 | 11 |
| | 12:00-16:00 | 04:00-08:00 | 13 | 9 | 9 | 11 | 21 | 17 | 15 | 21 | 13 | - | 11 | 15 | 25 | 21 | 21 | 17 | 15 | 11 | 13 | - | 21 | 17 | 17 | 15 |
| | 16:00-20:00 | 08:00-12:00 | 13 | 9 | 6 | 9 | 17 | 11 | 7 | 11 | 15 | 7 | 9 | 25 | 17 | 13 | 9 | | 15 | 9 | 7 | 11 | 21 | 17 | 11 | 9 |
| | 20:00-00:00 | 12:00-16:00 | 9 | 9 | 6 | - | 11 | 7 | 6 | 7 | 15 | 11 | 6 | - | 17 | 9 | 7 | 9 | 15 | 13 | 7 | - | 17 | 13 | 11 | 9 |
| AUSTRALIA AND NEW ZEALAND | 00:00-04:00 | 14:00-18:00 | 13 | 15 | 9 | - | 11 | 13 | 9 | 6 | 13 | - | 11 | - | 11 | 9 | 7 | 6 | 11 | - | 9 | - | 9 | 11 | 7 | 6 |
| | 04:00-08:00 | 18:00-22:00 | 9 | 17 | 15 | 17 | 11 | 11 | 6 | 6 | 11 | 21 | 15 | - | 9 | 11 | 7 | 6 | 11 | - | 15 | - | 9 | 7 | 7 | 6 |
| | 08:00-12:00 | 22:00-02:00 | - | 21 | 21 | 17 | - | 13 | 17 | 7 | - | 21 | 17 | 21 | 13 | 15 | 15 | 7 | - | 17 | 17 | 15 | - | 13 | 15 | 7 |
| | 12:00-16:00 | 02:00-06:00 | - | - | 15 | 21 | 17 | 21 | 25 | 11 | 17 | - | 21 | 17 | 21 | 21 | 11 | | 17 | 15 | 17 | 15 | - | 17 | 21 | 7 |
| | 16:00-20:00 | 06:00-10:00 | 21 | 13 | 9 | 11 | 15 | 17 | 17 | 11 | 21 | 9 | 9 | 11 | 21 | 17 | 17 | 11 | 17 | 9 | 13 | 9 | - | 17 | 13 | 7 |
| | 20:00-00:00 | 10:00-14:00 | 15 | 9 | 9 | 13 | 17 | 15 | - | 6 | 17 | 11 | 9 | 11 | - | 13 | 9 | 6 | - | 11 | 9 | 9 | - | 9 | 9 | 6 |

**Band selections have been made according to predicted propagation conditions. Also check neighbouring bands of the most suitable bands shown here. A '-' means there is no reliable propagation in any frequency band.**

# How to use *WRTH*

## ORGANISATION OF THE BOOK

The book consists of three main areas: **Features**, consisting of equipment reviews, broadcasting predictions and informative radio-related articles; **Directory**, which is further divided into *National Radio, International Radio* (including Clandestine and Other Target Broadcasts), *Frequency Lists* (which includes Mediumwave lists by region, Shortwave Stations of the World, International Broadcasts in selected languages and International DRM broadcasts), and *Terrestrial Television*; and finally **Reference** where a full country index, abbreviations used in WRTH and transmitter site location tables, as well as other useful information related to the world of radio broadcasting can be found.

Each section is identified by a unique 'side-bar', which can be found both on the main contents page and on each individual page throughout the book. Each section starts with an alphabetical country listing.

In the Directory, countries are listed alphabetically within each section so that they may be easily located by flicking forward to the relevant location. Alternatively, the index in the Reference section may be used to find the exact page number for a specific country of interest.

Under each country in the National Radio section, state broadcasters are listed first followed by major networks and then other stations. Armed forces stations and local relays of international stations are at the end of the entry. For all stations, mediumwave is listed first, followed by shortwave and finally FM. Many stations now only broadcast on FM. Details are given of digital radio multiplexes where appropriate.

## OPERATING TECHNIQUES

When operating their receivers, the majority of listeners tend to operate in one of two main modes, switching between them as and when they seem appropriate. One method is to 'target' a given station or country by monitoring known frequencies and the other is simply to 'cruise' a specific band and identify each station as they occur (known as 'band scanning'). We have designed WRTH in such a way that either of these methods can be accommodated.

When operating in the targeting mode there are two ways to find a particular country. The first option is to go to the main contents page and use the section 'side-bars' to direct you to the right area of the book. Once there, you then only have to flick forward a few pages to locate the country of interest. Alternatively you can use the country index at the back of the book, which will tell you the

precise page number. As you develop a 'feel' for the book and get used to the alphabetical layout, you will probably find that the side-bar method is simpler and quicker than using the country index.

Should you prefer to use band-scanning, there are listings of both medium wave and international short-wave broadcasts available in the Frequency Listings. These can also be useful for casual listening, but in either case can help to identify a station by frequency – whereupon further details can be obtained using the country entry to identify alternative frequencies for the station of interest.

## UTC

UTC (Coordinated Universal Time) is the current time standard used throughout the world by broadcasters and many other organisations. UTC replaced Greenwich Mean Time, GMT, as the world time standard some years ago. UTC, like its predecessor, is based on the Greenwich meridian at 0 degrees longitude (in London, England). To find out how many hours ahead or behind UTC your location is, refer to the World Time Table elsewhere in this section. If your location is ahead of UTC (indicated by a '+' sign in the table), you will need to add that number of hours to the time shown in the schedules. Likewise, if your location is behind UTC (indicated by '-'), you will need to subtract that many hours from the time shown in the schedules in order to find out at what time the broadcast can be heard at your location.

## RECEPTION REPORTS

When requesting a verification of the reception report you sent (commonly referred to as a QSL-card), it is important that you include details of the programming heard (over a period of time, usually at least 15 minutes wherever possible); The date and time, in UTC (as explained above); how well you heard the broadcast and what receiver/antenna you were using. Where possible, try to use the language of the broadcast, rather than English, as there may be no English speakers available at the station. Be polite and do not demand a QSL card – stations on a tight budget may not have the resources to print QSL cards, but may send you promotional items and a verification letter instead.

It is courteous to enclose return postage when writing to small domestic broadcasters. This can be in the form of an International Reply Coupon (IRC) available from post offices. In all cases, when writing to radio stations you must write clearly. Remember, if the station cannot read your address, then you cannot expect to receive a reply!

---

**Local Time, with respect to UTC** ·····→

**Population**

**Country**

## ANGOLA

**Principal Language(s)**

**L.T:** UTC +1h — **Pop:** 10 million — **Pr.L:** Portuguese + ethnic — **E.C:**
50Hz, 220V — **ITU:** AGL

**Country Code** ·····→

**Electricity supply (Electric Current)**

### RÁDIO NACIONAL DE ANGOLA (RNA)

**Address** ·····→ ☞ Rua Rainha Jinga, CP. 1329, Luanda ☎ +244 2 323172/321258 ·····→
🖷 +244 2 324647/391234 **W:** www.rna.ao **E:** dgeral@rna.ao **LP:** DG:
Filipe Diatezua. PD: Júlio Mendonça. TD: Candido R. Pinto.

**Telephone & Fax**

**Mediumwave Stations** ·····→ **MW:**

**Leading Personnel**

| Location | kHz | kW | Prgr. | H. of tr. |
|----------|-----|-----|-------|-----------|
| Mulenvos | 1088 | 25 | A | 24h |

**SW Stations** ·····→ **SW:**

**Web & email**

**Frequency in kiloHertz** ·····→

| Location | kHz | kW | Prgr. | H. of tr. |
|----------|-----|-----|-------|-----------|
| Mulenvos | 4950 | 25 | A | 24h |
| Mulenvos | 7217v | 15 | N/A | 24h |

**Hours of Transmission**

**FM Stations** ·····→ **FM** (MHz): Luanda (4kW): 93.5 (A), 94.5 (5), 96.5MHz (FME), 99.9 (RL), 101.4MHz (N).

**Power in kiloWatts**

**Announcement** ·····→ **Ann:** "Rádio Nacional de Angola". **F.PI:** new 100kW tx on MW.

**Prgrs: A=Canal A in Portuguese** (general coverage): 24h. **N:** on the
**Programme decode** ·····→ h. **N=Rádio N'Gola Yetu** (ethnic): 0000-2000. **N:** rel. Canal A.
**FME=Rádio FM Estéreo** (music): 1000-2400. **RL=Rádio Luanda**
(capital channel): 24h. **5=Rádio 5** (sports): 0500-2300.

**Programme**

**Future Plans (F.PI)**

---

**NB:** Not all entries are in the same format, example above is given for guidance and should cover most entries. If a country observes Daylight Savings Time/Summer Time, the effective dates are shown after the local time (**L.T**).

# THE SPECTRUM MONITOR

From the writers and editors of Monitoring Times comes a new, monthly electronic magazine. The Spectrum Monitor delivers full-spectrum coverage of amateur, short-wave, scanning, AM/FM/TV, satellite, WiFi, vintage radio and more. TSM's expert columnists bring readers an in-depth look at every segment of the radio frequency spectrum. Our feature writers offer long-form articles on every radio subject from spark gap to space.

TSM readers get the latest frequencies from longwave to super high frequency; reviews of the latest receivers, antennas, software and accessories you need to explore the spectrum. There are tips for beginner and advanced hobbyists alike. Be the first to read about advances in telecommunications on the analog/digital and amateur/commercial radio front.

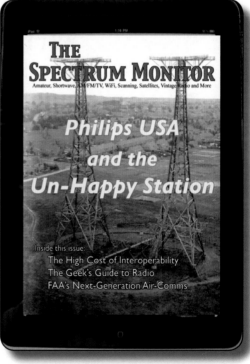

The Spectrum Monitor is an electronic magazine available in PDF format that can be read on any desktop, laptop, iPad, Kindle Fire, or other device capable of opening a PDF file. Subscription information is available at:

## www.thespectrummonitor.com

# WRTH
# Bargraph Frequency Guide

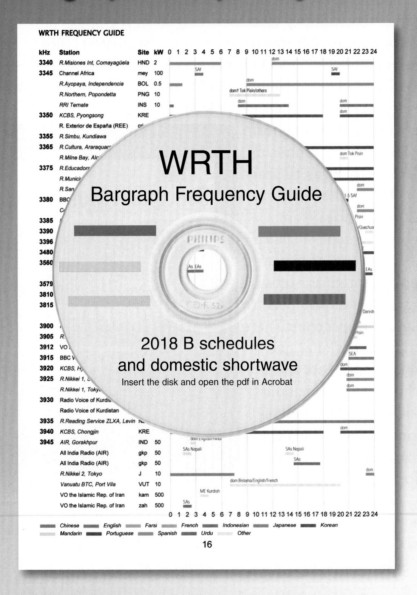

The B18 Bargraph Frequency Guide on CD and
download will be available from December 2018
exclusively from www.wrth.com

# DX Kiwi-Style!

New Zealanders are well known for their innovation, friendly attitude and southern spirit.

That's what you'll find when you join the **New Zealand Radio DX League**, along with a monthly magazine (now available in PDF format for US$15 p.a., free sample available on our website), free yourname@ radiodx.com e-mail address, a warm welcome and the hottest DX from the South Pacific.

Write to us now: NZRDXL, P.O. Box 178, Mangawhai 0540, New Zealand or visit www.radiodx.com/join-us

## The National Radio Club

### The World's Oldest and Largest Medium Wave DX Club proudly announces E-DXN!

Now joining our **DX News Magazine** in keeping hobbyists informed: *E-DXN*, available by subscription via the Internet for US$15.00 anywhere in the world.

*E-DXN* includes all the news printed in *DX News* – at a fraction of the cost for those wishing to subscribe from overseas, an *E-DXN* subscription includes full membership in the NRC. You can pay by credit card, too!

Visit the **E-DXN** website at:
http://www.e-dxn.com
for more details!

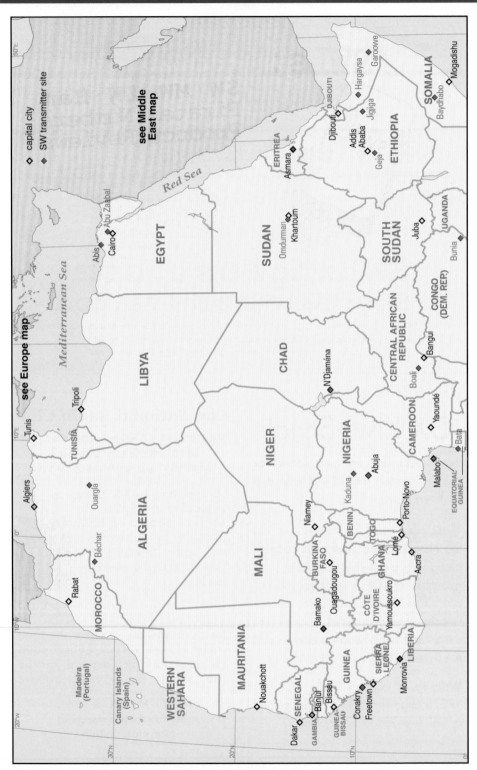

**Africa map**

Legend:
- ◇ capital city
- ◆ SW transmitter site

see Middle East map

see Europe map

Mediterranean Sea

Red Sea

**MOROCCO** — Rabat, Béchar

**ALGERIA** — Algiers, Ouargla

**TUNISIA** — Tunis, Tripoli

**LIBYA**

**EGYPT** — Cairo, Abu Zaabal, Abis

**WESTERN SAHARA**

**MAURITANIA** — Nouakchott

**MALI** — Bamako

**NIGER** — Niamey

**SUDAN** — Khartoum, Omdurman

**CHAD** — N'Djaména

**ERITREA** — Asmara

**DJIBOUTI** — Djibouti

**SOMALIA** — Mogadishu, Baydhabo, Garoowe

**ETHIOPIA** — Addis Ababa, Geja, Jigjiga, Hargeysa

**SOUTH SUDAN** — Juba

**UGANDA**

**CONGO (DEM. REP.)** — Bunia

**CENTRAL AFRICAN REPUBLIC** — Bangui, Boali

**CAMEROON** — Yaoundé

**NIGERIA** — Abuja, Kaduna

**BENIN** — Porto-Novo

**TOGO** — Lomé

**GHANA** — Accra

**CÔTE D'IVOIRE** — Yamoussoukro

**BURKINA FASO** — Ouagadougou

**SENEGAL** — Dakar

**GAMBIA** — Banjul

**GUINEA-BISSAU** — Bissau

**GUINEA** — Conakry

**SIERRA LEONE** — Freetown

**LIBERIA** — Monrovia

**EQUATORIAL GUINEA** — Malabo, Bata

Madeira (Portugal)

Canary Islands (Spain)

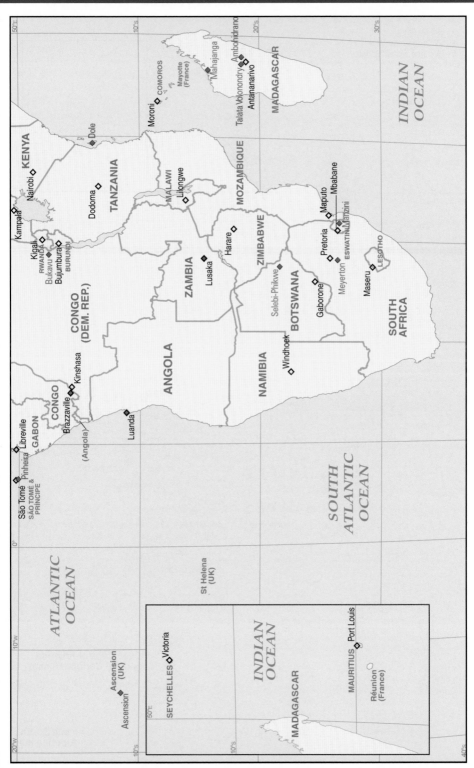

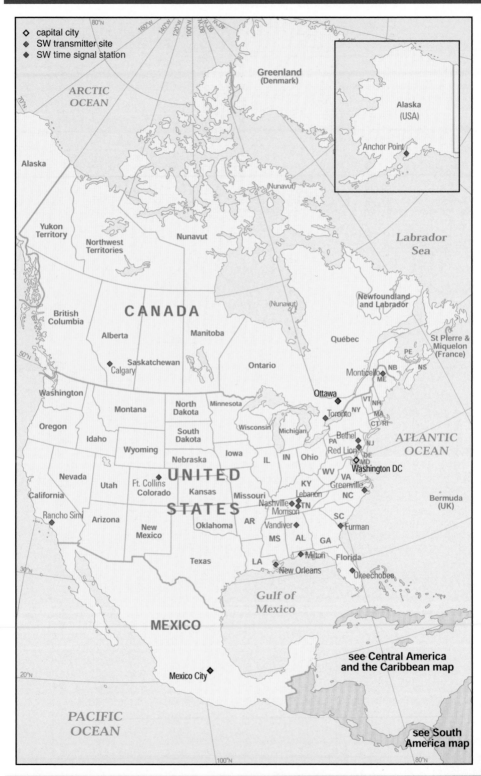

- ◇ capital city
- ◆ SW transmitter site
- ◆ SW time signal station

ARCTIC OCEAN

Greenland (Denmark)

Alaska (USA)

Anchor Point

Alaska

Yukon Territory

Northwest Territories

Nunavut

Labrador Sea

British Columbia

CANADA

Alberta

Saskatchewan

Manitoba

Ontario

Calgary

Newfoundland and Labrador

Québec

St Pierre & Miquelon (France)

PE

NB

NS

Washington

Montana

North Dakota

Minnesota

Monticello

ME

Ottawa

VT

NH

Oregon

Idaho

Wyoming

South Dakota

Wisconsin

Michigan

Toronto

NY

MA

CT RI

Nevada

Utah

Nebraska

Iowa

IL

IN

Ohio

Bethel

Red Lion

PA

NJ

DE

ATLANTIC OCEAN

Ft. Collins

Colorado

Kansas

Missouri

WV

MD

Washington DC

VA

Greenville

California

Rancho Simi

Arizona

New Mexico

Oklahoma

AR

KY

Lebanon

Nashville

Morrison

TN

NC

SC

Bermuda (UK)

Texas

MS

AL

Vandiver

Furman

GA

LA

Milton

Florida

New Orleans

Okeechobee

Gulf of Mexico

MEXICO

see Central America and the Caribbean map

Mexico City

PACIFIC OCEAN

see South America map

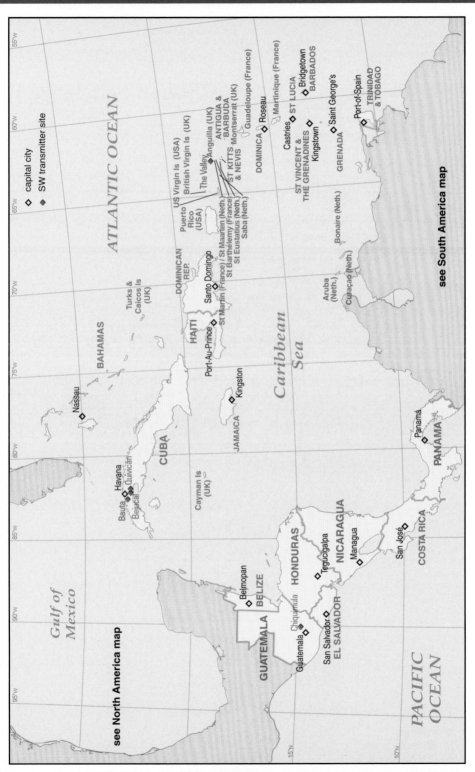

see Central America and the Caribbean map

see Central America and the Caribbean map

Caracas

VENEZUELA

COLOMBIA

Bogotá

Puerto Lleras

GUYANA

Georgetown
Paramaribo

SURINAME

French Guiana

NORTH ATLANTIC OCEAN

Boa Vista

São Gabriel da Cachoeira

Quito

ECUADOR

Iquitos

Tefé

Manaus

Parintins

Belém

B R A Z I L

Huancabamba

Chachapoyas
Bolívar
Santiago de Chuco
Huaraz

Cruzeiro do Sul

PERU

Atalaya
Tarma

Rio Branco

Porto Velho

Araguaína

Chilca
Lima
Huancavelica

Quillabamba
Cusco
Urubamba
Huanta

Riberalta

Puerto Maldonado

Reyes

Santa Ana del Yacuma

Cuiabá

La Paz

BOLIVIA
Cochabamba

Brasília

Jacobo Hunter

Santa Cruz

Yura
Siglo Veinte

S. José de Chiquitos

Goiânia

Campo Grande

Ibitinga

Congonhas
São Gonçalo
Rio de Janeiro

SOUTH PACIFIC OCEAN

PARAGUAY

Araraquara

Asunción

Foz do Iguaçu

Londrina
Limeira

Aparecida
São Paulo

CHILE

Curitiba

Camboriú

Porto Alegre

Santiago

General Pacheco

URUGUAY

Buenos Aires

Montevideo

ARGENTINA

SOUTH ATLANTIC OCEAN

Falkland Is. (UK)

◇ capital city
◆ SW transmitter site
◆ SW time signal station

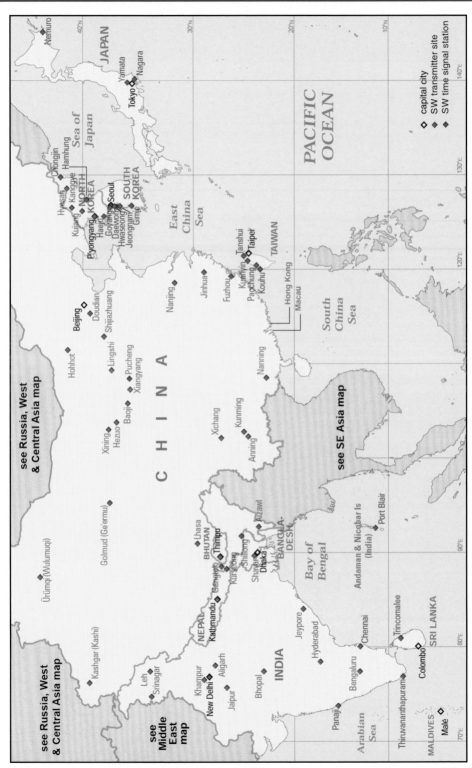

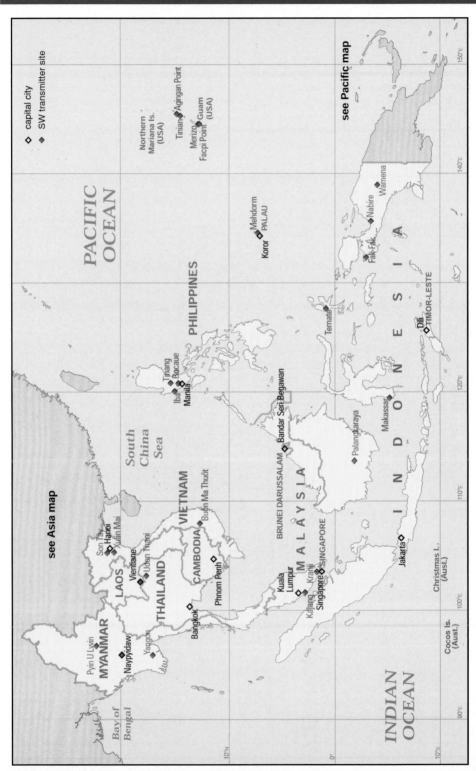

capital city
SW transmitter site

PACIFIC OCEAN

Northern Mariana Is. (USA)
Tinian Aginган Point
Merizo Guam (USA)
Facpi Point

see Pacific map

Wamena
Nabire
Fak-Fak

Mehdorm
Koror PALAU

PHILIPPINES

Ternate

TIMOR-LESTE
Dili

Tinang Bocaue
Iba Manila

South China Sea

Bandar Seri Begawan
BRUNEI DARUSSALAM

I N D O N E S I A

Makassar
Palangkaraya

see Asia map

VIETNAM
Son Tay Hanoi
Xuan Mai
Buôn Ma Thuôt

LAOS
Vientiane
Udon Thani

M A L A Y S I A

CAMBODIA
Phnom Penh

THAILAND
Bangkok

Kuala Lumpur
Kranji
Kajang SINGAPORE

Jakarta

Christmas I. (Aust.)

Pyin U Lwin MYANMAR
Naypyidaw
Yangon

Cocos Is. (Aust.)

Bay of Bengal

INDIAN OCEAN

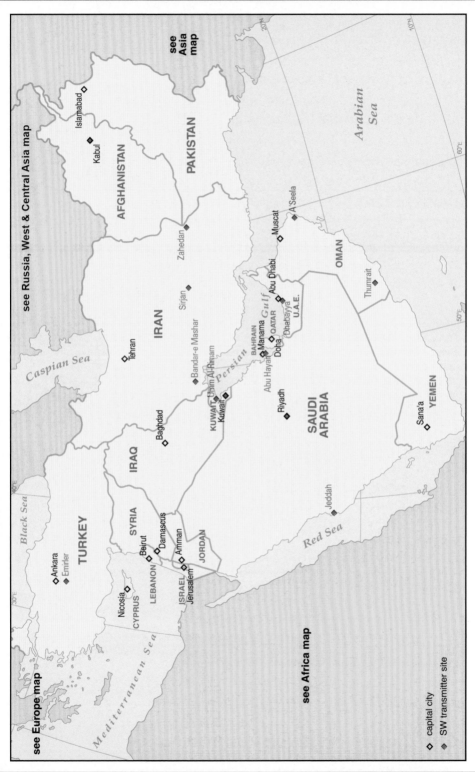

see Asia map

see Russia, West & Central Asia map

Islamabad ◇

Kabul ◆

AFGHANISTAN

PAKISTAN

Zahedan ◆

Arabian Sea

A'Seela ◆

Muscat ◆

OMAN

Abu Dhabi ◆

U.A.E.

Thumrait ◆

Sirjan ◆

IRAN

Dhabayya ◆

BAHRAIN
Manama *Gulf*
QATAR
Doha ◆
Abu Hayat

Bandar-e Mashar ◆

Tehran ◆

Umm Al Rmam

*Persian*

KUWAIT
Kuwait ◆

Riyadh ◆

SAUDI ARABIA

YEMEN

Caspian Sea

Baghdad ◆

IRAQ

Sana'a ◇

Jeddah ◆

Red Sea

Black Sea

TURKEY

SYRIA

Beirut ◆
Damascus ◆

Amman ◆

JORDAN

Ankara ◇
Emirler ◆

Nicosia ◇

CYPRUS

LEBANON

ISRAEL
Jerusalem ◇

*Mediterranean Sea*

see Europe map

see Africa map

◇ capital city
◆ SW transmitter site

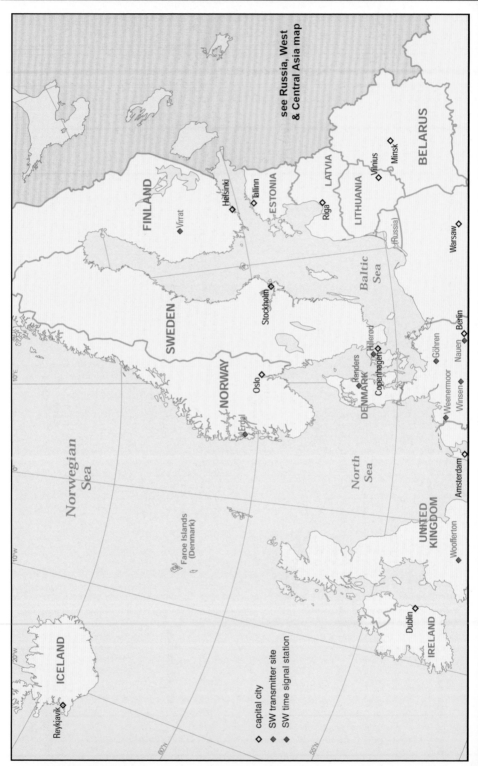

see Russia, West & Central Asia map

BELARUS

◇ Minsk

◇ Vilnius

LITHUANIA

LATVIA

◇ Riga

ESTONIA

◇ Tallinn

(Russia)

◇ Warsaw

FINLAND

◆ Virrat

Helsinki ◇

Baltic Sea

SWEDEN

Stockholm ◆

◆ Göhren

◇ Berlin

Nauen ◆

Weenermoor ◆

Winsen ◆

NORWAY

Oslo ◇

Randers ◆

Hillerød ◆

Copenhagen ◇

DENMARK

Ergil ◆

North Sea

Amsterdam ◆

Norwegian Sea

Faroe Islands (Denmark)

UNITED KINGDOM

Woofferton ◆

Dublin ◇

IRELAND

ICELAND

Reykjavik ◇

◇   capital city
◆   SW transmitter site
◆   SW time signal station

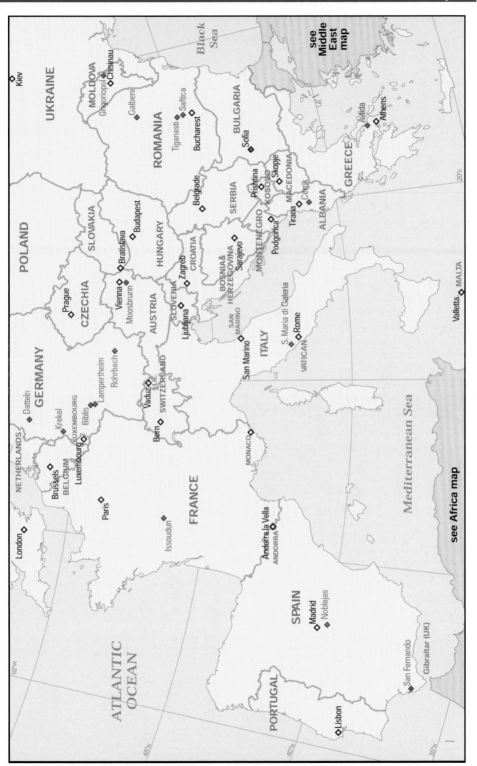

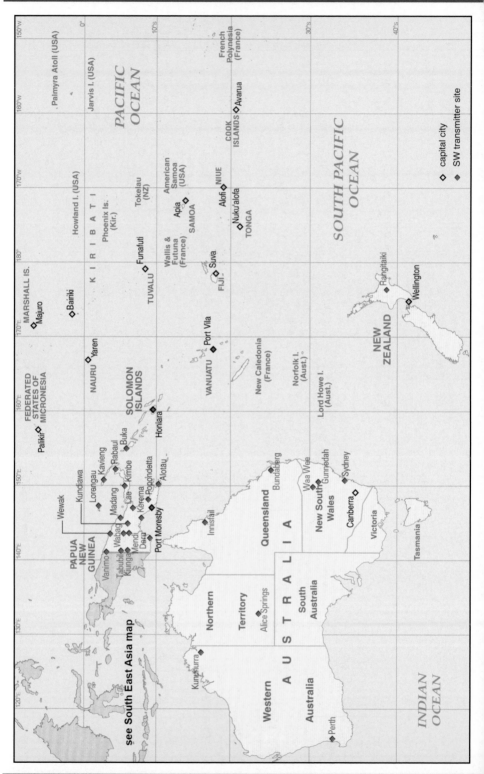

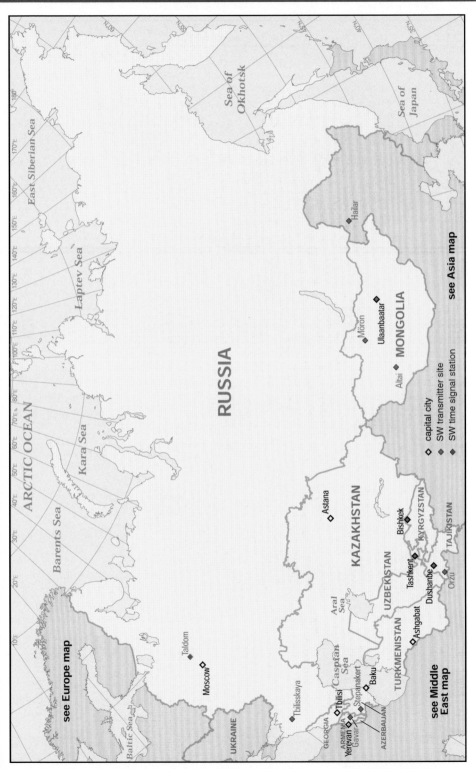

ARCTIC OCEAN

East Siberian Sea

Laptev Sea

Kara Sea

Barents Sea

Baltic Sea

Sea of Okhotsk

Sea of Japan

see Asia map

RUSSIA

MONGOLIA

Hailar

Mörön

Ulaanbaatar

Altai

◇ capital city
◆ SW transmitter site
◈ SW time signal station

KAZAKHSTAN

Astana

Bishkek

KYRGYZSTAN

TAJIKISTAN

Tashkent

Dushanbe

Orzu

UZBEKISTAN

Aral Sea

Ashgabat

TURKMENISTAN

Taldom

Moscow

Tbilisskaya

Caspian Sea

Baku

Tbilisi

Stepanakert

AZERBAIJAN

GEORGIA

ARMENIA

Yerevan

Gavar

UKRAINE

see Europe map

see Middle East map

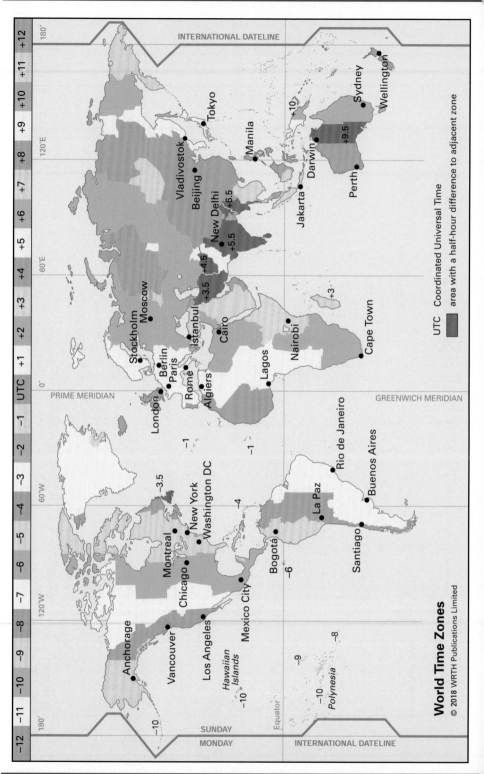

**World Time Zones**

© 2018 WRTH Publications Limited

UTC   Coordinated Universal Time

   area with a half-hour difference to adjacent zone

# WORLD TIME TABLE

Differences marked + or - show the number of hours ahead, or behind, UTC. Variations from Standard Time for part of the year (referred to as DST or Summer Time) are shown below; see the various country sections for the dates of operation.
**N**=Normal (Standard) Time; **D**=Daylight Saving Time (DST) [1] in parts of the territory [2] for other regions, see country section

| | N | D |
|---|---|---|
| Afghanistan | +4½ | +4½ |
| Alaska | −9 | −8 |
|   Aleutian Is | −10 | −9 |
| Albania | +1 | +2 |
| Algeria | +1 | +1 |
| American Samoa | −11 | −11 |
| Andorra | +1 | +2 |
| Angola | +1 | +1 |
| Anguilla | −4 | −4 |
| Antarctica | | |
|   (Argentine) | −3 | −3 |
|   (Chilean) | −4 | −3 |
|   (McMurdo) | +12 | +13 |
| Antigua | −4 | −4 |
| Argentina | −3 | −3 |
| Armenia | +4 | +4 |
| Aruba | −4 | −4 |
| Ascension I. | UTC | UTC |
| Australia | | |
|   We. Australia | +8 | +8 |
|   No. Territory | +9½ | +9½ |
|   So. Australia | +9½ | +10½ |
|   Queensland | +10 | +10 |
|   VIC, NSW, TAS | +10 | +11 |
| Austria | +1 | +2 |
| Azerbaijan | +4 | +4 |
| Azores | −1 | UTC |
| Bahamas | −5 | −4 |
| Bahrain | +3 | +3 |
| Bangladesh | +6 | +6 |
| Barbados | −4 | −4 |
| Belarus | +3 | +3 |
| Belgium | +1 | +2 |
| Belize | −6 | −6 |
| Benin | +1 | +1 |
| Bermuda | −4 | −3 |
| Bhutan | +6 | +6 |
| Bolivia | −4 | −4 |
| Bonaire | −4 | −4 |
| Bosnia & Herzegovina | +1 | +2 |
| Botswana | +2 | +2 |
| Brazil (Brasília)[2] | −3 | −2 |
| British Ind. Oc. Terr. | +6 | +6 |
| British Virgin Is | −4 | −4 |
| Brunei | +8 | +8 |
| Bulgaria | +2 | +3 |
| Burkina Faso | UTC | UTC |
| Burundi | +2 | +2 |
| Cabo Verde | −1 | −1 |
| Cabo Verde | −1 | −1 |
| Cambodia | +7 | +7 |
| Cameroon | +1 | +1 |
| Canada | | |
|   NL (SE Labr. & Is) | −3½ | −2½ |
|   NL[1], NB, NS, PE, QC[1] | −4 | −3 |
|   QC[1] | −4 | −4 |
|   NT[1], NU[1], ON[1], QC[1] | −5 | −4 |
|   NU[1] | −5 | −5 |
|   MB, NU[1], ON[1] | −6 | −5 |
|   SK[1] | −6 | −6 |
|   AB, BC[1], NT, NU[1], SK[1] | −7 | −6 |
|   BC[1] | −7 | −7 |
|   BC[1], YT | −8 | −7 |
| Canary Is | UTC | +1 |
| Cayman Is | −5 | −5 |
| Ce. African Rep. | +1 | +1 |
| Chad | +1 | +1 |
| Chile | −4 | −3 |
| China (P.R.) | +8 | +8 |
| Christmas Is | +7 | +7 |
| Cocos (Keeling) Is | +6½ | +6½ |
| Colombia | −5 | −5 |
| Comoros | +3 | +3 |

| | N | D |
|---|---|---|
| Congo (Kinshasa)[2] | +1 | +1 |
| Congo (Rep.) | +1 | +1 |
| Cook Is | −10 | −10 |
| Costa Rica | −6 | −6 |
| Côte d'Ivoire | UTC | UTC |
| Croatia | +1 | +2 |
| Cuba | −5 | −4 |
| Curaçao | −4 | −4 |
| Cyprus | +2 | +3 |
|   Akrotiri & Dhekelia | +2 | +3 |
|   Northern | +3 | +3 |
| Czechia | +1 | +2 |
| Denmark | +1 | +2 |
| Djibouti | +3 | +3 |
| Dominica | −4 | −4 |
| Dominican Rep. | −4 | −4 |
| Easter I. | −5 | −4 |
| Ecuador | −5 | −5 |
| Egypt | +2 | +2 |
| El Salvador | −6 | −6 |
| Equatorial Guinea | +1 | +1 |
| Eritrea | +3 | +3 |
| Estonia | +2 | +3 |
| Eswatini | +2 | +2 |
| Ethiopia | +3 | +3 |
| Falkland Is | −3 | −3 |
| Faroe Is | UTC | +1 |
| Fiji | +12 | +13 |
| Finland | +2 | +3 |
| France | +1 | +2 |
| French Guiana | −3 | −3 |
| French Poly.(Tahiti)[2] | −10 | −10 |
| French So.& Ant. L. | +5 | +5 |
| Gabon | +1 | +1 |
| Galapagos Is | −6 | −6 |
| Gambia | UTC | UTC |
| Georgia | +4 | +4 |
| Germany | +1 | +2 |
| Ghana | UTC | UTC |
| Gibraltar | +1 | +2 |
| Greece | +2 | +3 |
| Greenland (Nuuk)[2] | −3 | −2 |
| Grenada | −4 | −4 |
| Guadeloupe | −4 | −4 |
| Guam | +10 | +10 |
| Guatemala | −6 | −6 |
| Guinea | UTC | UTC |
| Guinea-Bissau | UTC | UTC |
| Guyana | −4 | −4 |
| Haiti | −5 | −4 |
| Hawaii | −10 | −10 |
| Honduras | −6 | −6 |
| Hong Kong | +8 | +8 |
| Hungary | +1 | +2 |
| Iceland | UTC | UTC |
| India | +5½ | +5½ |
| Indonesia (Jakarta)[2] | +7 | +7 |
| Iran | +3½ | +4½ |
| Iraq | +3 | +3 |
| Ireland | UTC | +1 |
| Israel | +2 | +3 |
|   West Bank & Gaza | +2 | +3 |
| Italy | +1 | +2 |
| Jamaica | −5 | −5 |
| Japan | +9 | +9 |
| Jordan | +2 | +3 |
| Kazakhstan (Astana)[2] | +6 | +6 |
| Kenya | +3 | +3 |
| Kiribati (Tarawa)[2] | +12 | +12 |
| Korea, North | +9 | +9 |
| Korea, South | +9 | +9 |
| Kosovo | +1 | +2 |
| Kuwait | +3 | +3 |

| | N | D |
|---|---|---|
| Kyrgyzstan | +6 | +6 |
| Laos | +7 | +7 |
| Latvia | +2 | +3 |
| Lebanon | +2 | +3 |
| Lesotho | +2 | +2 |
| Liberia | UTC | UTC |
| Libya | +2 | +2 |
| Liechtenstein | +1 | +2 |
| Lithuania | +2 | +3 |
| Lord Howe I. | +10½ | +11 |
| Luxembourg | +1 | +2 |
| Macau | +8 | +8 |
| Macedonia | +1 | +2 |
| Madagascar | +3 | +3 |
| Madeira | UTC | +1 |
| Malawi | +2 | +2 |
| Malaysia | +8 | +8 |
| Maldives | +5 | +5 |
| Mali | UTC | UTC |
| Malta | +1 | +2 |
| Marshall Is | +12 | +12 |
| Martinique | −4 | −4 |
| Mauritania | UTC | UTC |
| Mauritius | +4 | +4 |
| Mayotte | +3 | +3 |
| Mexico (Mexico City)[2] | −6 | −5 |
| Micronesia | | |
|   Chuuk, Yap | +10 | +10 |
|   Kosrae, Pohnpei | +11 | +11 |
| Moldova | +2 | +3 |
| Monaco | +1 | +2 |
| Mongolia (U-baataar)[2] | +8 | +8 |
| Montenegro | +1 | +2 |
| Montserrat | −4 | −4 |
| Morocco | UTC | +1 |
| Mozambique | +2 | +2 |
| Myanmar | +6½ | +6½ |
| Namibia | +2 | +2 |
| Nauru | +12 | +12 |
| Nepal | +5¾ | +5¾ |
| Netherlands | +1 | +2 |
| New Caledonia | +11 | +11 |
| New Zealand | +12 | +13 |
| Nicaragua | −6 | −6 |
| Niger | +1 | +1 |
| Nigeria | +1 | +1 |
| Niue | −11 | −11 |
| Norfolk I. | +11 | +11 |
| No. Mariana Is | +10 | +10 |
| Norway | +1 | +2 |
| Oman | +4 | +4 |
| Pakistan | +5 | +5 |
| Palau | +9 | +9 |
| Panama | −5 | −5 |
| Papua New Guinea | +10 | +10 |
| Paraguay | −4 | −3 |
| Peru | −5 | −5 |
| Philippines | +8 | +8 |
| Pitcairn Is | −8 | −8 |
| Poland | +1 | +2 |
| Portugal | UTC | +1 |
| Puerto Rico | −4 | −4 |
| Qatar | +3 | +3 |
| Réunion | +4 | +4 |
| Romania | +2 | +3 |
| Russia (Moscow)[2] | +3 | +3 |
| Rwanda | +2 | +2 |
| Saba | −4 | −4 |
| Samoa | +13 | +14 |
| San Marino | +1 | +2 |
| São Tomé & Prínc. | +1 | +1 |
| Saudi Arabia | +3 | +3 |

| | N | D |
|---|---|---|
| Senegal | UTC | UTC |
| Serbia | +1 | +2 |
| Seychelles | +4 | +4 |
| Sierra Leone | UTC | UTC |
| Singapore | +8 | +8 |
| Slovakia | +1 | +2 |
| Slovenia | +1 | +2 |
| Solomon Is | +11 | +11 |
| Somalia | +3 | +3 |
| South Africa | +2 | +2 |
| South Sudan | +3 | +3 |
| Spain | +1 | +2 |
| Sri Lanka | +5½ | +5½ |
| St. Barthélemy | −4 | −4 |
| St. Eustatius | −4 | −4 |
| St. Helena | UTC | UTC |
| St. Kitts & Nevis | −4 | −4 |
| St. Lucia | −4 | −4 |
| St. Martin | −4 | −4 |
| St. Pierre & Miq. | −3 | −2 |
| St. Vincent & Gren. | −4 | −4 |
| Sudan | +2 | +2 |
| Suriname | −3 | −3 |
| Sweden | +1 | +2 |
| Switzerland | +1 | +2 |
| Syria | +2 | +3 |
| Taiwan | +8 | +8 |
| Tajikistan | +5 | +5 |
| Tanzania | +3 | +3 |
| Thailand | +7 | +7 |
| Timor-Leste | +9 | +9 |
| Togo | UTC | UTC |
| Tokelau | +13 | +13 |
| Tonga | +13 | +13 |
| Trinidad | −4 | −4 |
| Tristan da Cunha | UTC | UTC |
| Tunisia | +1 | +1 |
| Turkey | +3 | +3 |
| Turkmenistan | +5 | +5 |
| Turks & Caicos Is | −4 | −4 |
| Tuvalu | +12 | +12 |
| Uganda | +3 | +3 |
| Ukraine | +2 | +3 |
| United Arab Em. | +4 | +4 |
| United Kingdom | UTC | +1 |
| Uruguay | −3 | −3 |
| USA | | |
|   Eastern Time (CT, DE, FL, | | |
|   GA, IN[1], KY, MA, MD, | | |
|   ME, MI, NC, NH, NJ, | | |
|   NY, OH, PA, RI, SC, | | |
|   VA, VT, WV) | −5 | −4 |
|   Central Time (AL, AR, IA, | | |
|   IL, IN[1], KS, LA, MN, MO, | | |
|   MS, ND, NE, OK, | | |
|   SD, TN, TX, WI) | −6 | −5 |
|   Mountain Time[a] (N-E AZ, | | |
|   CO, ID, MT, NM, | | |
|   UT, WY) | −7 | −6 |
|   [a]) exc. most of AZ | −7 | −7 |
|   Pacific Time (CA, NV, | | |
|   OR, WA) | −8 | −7 |
| Uzbekistan | +5 | +5 |
| Vanuatu | +11 | +11 |
| Vatican City State | +1 | +2 |
| Venezuela | −4 | −4 |
| Vietnam | +7 | +7 |
| Virgin Is | −4 | −4 |
| Wake I. | +12 | +12 |
| Wallis & Futuna | +12 | +12 |
| Yemen | +3 | +3 |
| Zambia | +2 | +2 |
| Zimbabwe | +2 | +2 |

# NATIONAL RADIO

## Section Contents

Initial entries for each letter,
see Main Index for full details

Afghanistan.................. 66
Bahamas..................... 93
Cabo Verde.................. 137
Denmark..................... 186
Easter Island............... 189
Falkland Islands............ 196
Gabon....................... 208
Haiti....................... 230
Iceland..................... 236
Jamaica..................... 254
Kazakhstan.................. 259
Laos........................ 268
Macau....................... 273
Namibia..................... 292
Oman........................ 307
Pakistan.................... 307
Qatar....................... 334
Réunion..................... 334
Saba........................ 354
Taiwan...................... 383
USA......................... 407
Vanuatu..................... 449
Wake Island................. 453
Yemen....................... 453
Zambia...................... 454

Features & Reviews

National Radio

International Radio

Frequency Lists

National Television

Reference

## AFGHANISTAN

**L.T:** UTC +4½h — **Pop:** 34 million — **Pr.L:** Dari, Pashto, Turkmen, Uzbek — **E.C:** 50Hz, 230V — **ITU:** AFG

### AFGHANISTAN TELECOM REGULATORY AUTHORITY (ARTA) ✉ Moh. Jaan Khan Watt 10th floor MoCIT Building, Kabul ☎+93 20 2105361 **W:** atra.gov.af

### RADIO TELEVISION AFGHANISTAN (RTA, Gov.)
✉ PO Box 544, Street No. 13, near Wazir Mohammad Akbar Khan Hospital, Kabul ☎+93 20 2102487 **W:** rta.org.af **E:** info@rta.org.af **L.P:** DG: Zarin Anzor. DG Radio: Abdul Ghaney Mudaqiq.
**MW:** Kabul (Pol-e-Charkhi) 1107kHz 400kW.
**FM:** Kabul 93.0 1kW, 105.2MHz 30W.
**D.Prgr:** 0030-1930 on 1107kHz and 105.2MHz. 93.0MHz carries R. Kabul local sce 0130-1530 and Ext. Sce 1530-1730. Main **N:** Pashto 1430, Dari 1530. **Ann:** "Radyo Afghanistan, Kabul".

**EXTERNAL SERVICE:** see International Radio section.

### PROVINCIAL STATIONS
**R. Badakhshan,** Faizabad: 105.1MHz 30W – **R. Badghis,** Qalay-e Naw: 91.4MHz 250W – **R. Baghlan,** Pol-e-Khomri 103.0MHz, Baghlan: 106.6MHz 250W – **R. Balkh,** Mazar-e-Sharif: 105.1MHz 0.1kW. – **R. Bamyan:** 88.0MHz – **R. Day Kundi:** Nili 103.2MHz 30W, Qalat 99.0MHz 0.5kW – **R. Farah,** Farah: 88.5MHz 1kW – **R. Faryab,** Maimana: 104.3MHz 30W – **R. Ghazni:** 92.4MHz 30W – **R. Ghor,** Chaghcharan: 93.4MHz – **R. Helmand,** Lashkar Ga: 96.1MHz 1kW – **R. Herat:** 95.5MHz 250W – **R. Jowzjan,** Sheberghan 106.6MHz 250W – **R. Kandahar:** 1305kHz 10kW, 90.6MHz 1kW. 0230-1430 **W:** kandahartv-gov.com – **R. Kapisa,** Mahmud-e-Raqi: 101.1MHz 600W – **R. Khost:** 91.2MHz 1kW – **R. Kunar,** Asadabad: 100.5MHz 1kW – **R. Kunduz:** 94.4MHz 250W – **R. Laghman,** Mehtarlam: 88.2MHz‡ 0.5kW – **R. Logar,** Pol-e-Alam: 92.7MHz – **R. Nangarhar,** Jalalabad: 93.5MHz 250W – **R. Nimroz,** Zaranj: 90.0MHz 1kW – **R. Nuristan,** Nuristan: 88.5MHz 300W – **R. Paktia,** Gardez: 104.2MHz 0.5kW – **R. Paktika,** Zareh Sharan: 93.2MHz – **R. Panjshir,** Bazarak: 88.0MHz 0.1kW – **R. Parwan,** Charikar: 88.9MHz – **R. Samangan,** Aybak: 90.4MHz 150W – **R. Sar-e-Pol:** 89.9MHz – **R. Takhar,** Taloqan: 91.2MHz 30W – **R. Uruzgan,** Tarin Kowt: 93.0MHz 50W – **R. Wardak,** Meydan Shahr: 88.9MHz – **R. Zabul,** 88.7MHz.

### BBG–R. FREE AFGHANISTAN / R. MASHAAL / VOA ASHNA & DEEWA R. (US Gov.)
**R. Free Afghanistan & VOA Ashna R:**
**MW:** Kabul (Pol-e-Charkhi) 1296kHz 400kW 0030-1730. **FM:** Ghazni/ Herat/Jalalabad/Kabul/Kandahar//Lashkar Gah/Mazar-e-Sharif/ Mehtar Lam/Nuristan/Pil-Alam/Qalat/Sharan 100.5MHz. 24h in Dari/ Pashto/English.
**R. Mashal & VOA Deewa R: MW:** Khost 621kHz 0100-1900.
**FM:** Asadabad/Gardez/Khost 100.5MHz.
For SW broadcasts & more details see International R. section (USA).

**Independent commercial stations:**
**Radio Talwasa** ✉ Daud Khan Sqaure, Ahmad Shak Baba, District 12 Kabul / Sherana, Paktika **W:** talwasa.com **E:** talwasa@talwasa.af **L.P:** Dir: Sulaiman Faisal **MW:** Sharana 945kHz 10/2.5kW **FM:** Sharana 87.9MHz 6kW. **D.Prgr:** 0130-1730.
**Arman FM** ✉ P.O. Box 1045, Central PO, Kabul **W:** arman.fm **E:** info@arman.fm **L.P:** Dir: Saad Mohseni. **FM:** 98.1MHz in Kabul (2kW)/ Ghazni/Herat/Jalalabad/Kandahar/Konduz/Lashkar Ga/ Mazar-e-Sharif – **Ariana R.** ✉ Darlaman St. (near Ministry of Trade), Kabul ☎+93 70 151515 **W:** arianatelevision.com **E:** marketing@arianatelevision. com **L.P:** Dir: Ahmad Zubair. **FM:** Kabul 93.5MHz – **R. City** ✉ Karte 3, District 6, Street 3, House no. 96, Kabul ☎+93 20 2100995/77 7955955 **W:** citymedia.af **E:** info@citymedia.af **L.P:** Saleem Totakh-il, CEO. **FM:** Kabul/Mazar-i-Sharif: 95.5MHz 3.5/1kW – **R. Killid** ✉ The Killid Group, House No. 442, Street No. 6, Chardehi Watt, Near to Uzbekha Mosque, Karta-e-sea, Kabul 442 ☎+93 77 1088888 **W:** tkg. af **E:** info@killid.com **L.P:** Dir: Najiba Ayubi. **FM:** Kabul 88.0MHz 4kW, Herat 88.0MHz 2kW, Khost 88.2MHz. **Kabul Rock R:** 108.0MHz – **R. Maiwand,** Kabul: 92.7MHz 1.5kW – **Nawa R. W:** sabacent.org **L.P:** Dir: Mohammad Waqfi. **FM:** Kabul/Ghazni/Herat/Jalalabad/Kandahar/Konduz/Mazar e-Sharif/Paktia: 103.1MHz – **Sheba Radio:** Kabul 99.9MHz 8kW, Herat/Jalalabad/Kandahar/Mazar-e Sharif 104.3MHz 1kW. **F.PI:** coverage of smaller cities.

**Other Stations** (powers 50-600W if not stated otherwise, frqs in MHz)**:** **Ayna R,** Shahrak-e Shirpoor: 88.0 – **Badlon 1,** Kunduz: 99.0 1kW – **Enikas,** Jalalabad: 97.1 – **ERTV R,** (UNESCO), Kabul: 96.8 – **Gorbat**

---

**FM,** Kabul: 91.8 – **Khoshi FM,** Baghlani Jadid: 89.2 – **Police FM,** Kabul: 96.5 – **R. Abasin,** Jalalabad: 93.7 **W:** moi.gov.af/en/page/pfm – **R. Adib,** Shahr-e Jadid: 89.7 – **R. Aliksiz,** Kabul: 90.0 – **R. Alina,** Nurgaram: 89.6 – **R. Amo,** Faizabad: 87.6 – **R. Amozgar,** Kabul: 101.3 – **R. Arghawan,** Ada-e Kabul: 90.1 – **R. Arkozia,** Charahi: 90.3 – **R. Armaghan,** Sheberghan: 89.9 – **R. Arya,** Kabul: 100.2 – **R. Arzu,** Mazar-e-Sharif: 91.8 – **R. Arzu ha FM,** Jada-e Sahat: 88.1 – **R. Awkhtoon,** Gardez: 88.8 – **R. Aye Khanum,** Shahr-e Taliqan: 88.9 – **R. Azad Afgan,** Kandahar: 88.1 – **R. Azad Paktia Ghagh,** Gardez: 94.2 – **R. Badlon,** Asadabad: 88.0 1kW – **R. Baharistan,** Baharak: 89.7 – **R. Bakhtar,** Kabul: 99.2 – **R. Banoo,** Sar-e Pol: 87.6 – **R. Baran,** Herat: 98.4 1kW – **R. Biltoon,** Kabul: 104.9 – **R. Bustan,** Shibirghan: 87.7 – **R. Charchino,** Uruzgan prov: 88.1 – **R. Cheragh,** Kunduz: 88.7 – **R. Dahwat,** Kabul: 102.5 – **R. Daikundi,** Shahr-e Nili: 88.9 – **R. Darman,** Aqcha: 89.5 – **R. Dehkada,** Shahr-e Naw: 91.6 – **R. Dehrawod,** Dehrawod: 87.5 – **R. Dunya-e-Naweei,** Parwan: 87.9 – **R. Ejtima,** Logar: 88.5 – **R. Ertibat,** Malistan: 88.3 – **R. Farhat,** Dushi: 83.1 – **R. Faryad,** Farh: 88.3 – **R. Ghazal,** Shibirghan: 99.9 1kW – **R. Ghaznawiyan,** Ghazni: 89.3 1kW – **R. Hamasa,** Shibirghan: 91.7 – **R. Hamdard,** Ghazni prov: 94.9 – **R. Hamisha Bahar,** Nangarhar: 90.6 – **R. Hanzala,** Qalay-e Naw: 91.4 – **R. Helo Karwan,** Khost: 90.6 1kW – **R. Humsada,** Takhar: 89.6 – **R. Istiqlal,** Baraki-Barak: 89.6 – **R. Jaghori,** Jaghori: 90.0 – **R. Jaihoon,** Imam Shahib: 88.0 – **R. Javan,** Ghazni: 96.6 – **R. Jawanan,** Kabul: 97.5 – **R. Jurm,** Jurm: 87.9 – **R. Kaihan,** Kunduz: 87.7 – **R. Kalagush,** Nuristan prov: 90.0 – **R. Kawoon ,** Mehtarlam: 89.3 – **R. Kishim,** Kishm: 90.3 – **R. Khorasan,** Rokha: 89.3 – **R. Khushi,** Baghlan prov: 89.2 – **R. Kokcha,** Badakshan: 96.0 – **R. Meena,** Jalalabad: 92.7 – **R. Meher,** Dasht-e Shor: 99.3 – **R. Milli e-Paygham,** Mohammad Agha: 94.0 – **R. Milma,** Urgun: 88.3 – **R. Mirman,** Kandahar: 92.0 – **R. Mowj,** Kabul: 105.5 1kW – **R. Mumtaz,** Maymana: 89.9 – **R. Muram,** Nangarhar: 97.8 – **R. Muzdah,** Herat: 91.5MHz – **R. Najrab,** Najrab: 96.0 – **R. Nargis,** Jalalabad: 88.6 – **R. Nan:** Ghani Khel: 89.1 – **R. Naw-e-Bahar,** Balkh: 89.9 – **R. Nedaye Afghan,** Kabul: 99.6 – **R. Nedaye Solh,** Ghoreyan: 90.4 – **R. Nedaye Subh,** Ghoryan: 90.4 – **R. Nehad,** Mazar-e Sharif: 90.4MHz – **R. Nida,** Kabul: 97.2 – **R. Nin,** Khost: 89.1 – **R. Omid-e Jawan,** Ghazni: 96.9 – **R. Paiwastoon,** Terinkot: 89.9 – **R. Paktika Voice,** Zareh Sharan: 92.9 – **R. Payman,** Baghlan: 90.0 – **R. Pashtun Voice,** Sharan: 89.4 – **R. Payam,** Faizabad: 94.7 – **R. Qarabagh,** Qarabagh: 94.7 – **R. Qoyash,** Maimana: 89.0 – **R. Rabia Balkhi,** Mazar-e Sharif: 89.7 – **R. Rah-e Farda,** Kabul: 92.0 – **R. Raihan,** Taloqan: 87.9 – **R. Roshani,** Kunduz: 89.0 – **R. Rustam,** Aibak: 88.1 – **R. Sabawoon,** Lashkar Ga: 88.0 2kW – **R. Sadat,** Ghazni: 90.9 – **R. Safa,** Jalalabad: 89.7 1.5kW – **R. Sahar,** Herat: 88.8 – **R. Samun,** Lashkar Ga: 88.6 – **R. Sana,** Pol-e Khumri: 87.7 – **R. Sanga,** Kandahar: 92.3 1kW – **R. Setara,** Kabul: 87.2 – **R. Setara-e Sahar,** Balkh: 91.3 – **R. Shahr,** Kabul: 95.5 – **R. Shahrwand,** Aybak: 87.8 – **R. Sharq,** Jalalabad: 91.3 – **R. Solh-e Paygham,** Khost: 88.8 – **R. Sor Ghar,** Shahjoy: 89.5 – **R. Sorobi,** Sorobi: 100.4 – **R. Spin Ghar,** Ghani Khel: 89.4 – **R. Tahlim ul-Salaam,** Kandahar: 94.6 – **R. Tajala,** Maydan Shahr: 87.8 – **R. Takharistan,** Taloqan: 87.5 – **R. Tamana,** Maymana: 89.6 1kW – **R. Tanin,** Shindand: 89.7 – **R. Tiraj Mir,** Pol-e Khumri: 89.4 – **R. Tolina,** Sharan: 88.0 – **R. Turkistan,** Andkhoy: 89.9 1kW – **R. Waranga,** Kandahar: 95.2 – **R. Watan,** Kabul: 100.8 – **R. Watandar,** Herat/Kabul 87.5 0.5/1kW – **R. Vo Adalat,** Chaghcharan: 88.5 – **R. Vo Doost,** Zaranj: 87.9 – **R. Vo Haqiqat,** Aibaq: 90.9 – **R. Vo Islam,** Kabul: 104.3 – **R. Vo Jawan,** Herat University: 92.3 – **R. Vo Peace,** Naray: 94.6 – **R. Vo Peace,** Jabal Saraj: 96.7 – **R. VO Jawan,** Herat University: 92.3 – **R. Vo Samkani,** Chamkanay: 101.0 – **R. Yawaly Voice,** Sayedabad: 94.4 – **R. Zafar,** Paghman: 96.5 – **R. Zala Kunar,** Asadabad: 89.2 – **R. Zalah,** Kunduz prov.: 106.6 0.6kW – **R. Zhwandoon,** Kabul: 107.0 – **R. Zohra,** Kunduz: 89.9 1kW – **R. Zrak,** Logar prov: 97.2 – **R. Zuhal,** Herat prov: 90.0 – **Rana FM,** Kandahar: 88.5. **W:** ranafm.org – **Salam Watandar,** Kabul: 98.9 1kW. **W:** salamwatandar.com – **Saraish FM,** Sheberghan: 91.1 1kW **W:** facebook.com/Saraishfm – **Shamshad FM,** Ghanikhel: 92.1/92.6/103.5 **W:** shamshadfm.com – **Spogmai R,** Kabul: 102.2 – **University R.** (UNESCO), Kabul: 106.7 1.2kW, Herat 92.3 – **VO Afghan Women** (UNESCO), Kabul 96.3 10kW, Herat 88.7 – **Zala FM,** Naray: 89.2 600W – **Zawon Voice R,** Khost: 99.7 – **Zenat R,** Pol-e Alam: 105.7.

**NB:** many stations are Internews affiliates and relay their news prgr: "Salam Watandar". **W:** internews.org

**Relays of international stations:**
**BBC World Sce:** in English/Pashto/Dari/Uzbek/Farsi: Kunar 87.5, Gardez 87.9, Imam Sahib/Konduz 88.1, Ghazni/Taloqan 88.3, Fayzabad 88.4, Bamian/Farah/Jalalabad/Kabul/Mazar-e-Sharif/Qalat/Rustaq/ Uruzgan/Zareh Sharan 89.0, Jabal Saraj/Sar-e Pul 89.1, Chaghcharan/ Herat/Lashkar-Ga/Shindand 89.2, Kandahar 90.0, Khost 90.1, Maidan Shahr 90.2, Shebergan 91.0, Maimana 92.1, Pul-e Khomri 99.6, Kabul 101.6 (English), Pul-e Alam 105.7MHz.

**R. France Int:** Kabul 89.5 0.2kW.
**BFBS Radio: FM:** HKIA, HQRS & Qargha: R. 2 105.8MHz, R. Gurkha 107.5MHz **W:** forces.net/radio

## ALASKA (USA)

**L.T:** UTC -9h (10 Mar-3 Nov -8h) Aleutian Is. UTC -10h (10 Mar-3 Nov -9h) — **Pop:** 735,000 — **Pr.L:** English — **E.C:** 60Hz, 120/240V — **ITU:** ALS

**FEDERAL COMMUNICATIONS COMMISSION (FCC)** see USA for details

### ALASKA BROADCASTERS ASSOCIATION
700 W 41st Ave, Anchorage 99503 ☎ +1 907 258 2424 ▤ +1 907 258 2414 **W:** alaskabroadcasters.org

| | kHz | Call | kW | N | Location |
|---|---|---|---|---|---|
| 2) | 550 | KTZN | 3.1/5 | | Anchorage |
| 3) | 560 | KVOK | 1 | | Kodiak |
| 5) | 590 | KHAR | 5 | | Anchorage |
| 6) | 620 | KGTL | 5 | | Homer |
| 7) | 630 | KJNO | 5/1 | | Juneau |
| 8) | 630 | KIAM | 10/3.1 | | Nenana |
| 9) | 640 | KYUK | 10 | | Bethal |
| 10) | 650 | KENI | 50 | | Anchorage |
| 11) | 660 | KFAR | 10 | | Fairbanks |
| 12) | 670 | KDLG | 10 | | Dillingham |
| 13) | 680 | KBRW | 10 | | Barrow |
| 14) | 700 | KBYR | 10 | | Anchorage |
| 15) | 720 | KOTZ | 10 | | Kotzebue |
| 16) | 750 | KFQD | 50 | | Anchorage |
| 17) | 770 | KCHU | 9.7 | | Valdez |
| 18) | 780 | KNOM | 25/14 | | Nome |
| 19) | 790 | KCAM | 5 | | Glennallen |
| 20) | 800 | KINY | 10/7.6 | | Juneau |
| 21) | 820 | KCBF | 10 | | Fairbanks |
| 22) | 830 | KSDP | 1 | | Sand Point |
| 24) | 850 | KICY | 50 | * | Nome |
| 26) | 890 | KBBI | 10 | | Homer |
| 27) | 900 | KZPA | 5 | r | Fort Yukon |
| 28) | 910 | KIYU | 5 | | Galena |
| 29) | 920 | KSRM | 5 | | Soldotna |
| 30) | 930 | KTKN | 5/1 | | Ketchikan |
| 12) | 930 | KNSA | 4.2 | r | Unalakleet |
| 33) | 970 | KFBX | 10 | | Fairbanks |
| 34) | 1020 | KVNT | 10 | d | Eagle River |
| 36) | 1080 | KOAN | 10 | | Anchorage |
| 35) | 1110 | KAGV | 10 | | Big Lake |
| 29) | 1140 | KSLD | 10 | | Soldotna |
| 37) | 1170 | KJNP | 50/21 | | North Pole |
| 38) | 1230 | KIFW | 1 | | Sitka |
| 39) | 1230 | KVAK | 1 | | Valdez |
| 20) | 1330 | KXXJ | 10/3 | | Juneau |
| 41) | 1430 | KVHZ | 1 | | Soldotna |
| 42) | 1450 | KLAM | 0.25 | | Cordova |

d=directional *=directional 0800-1200 (Summer -1h) r=relay

| FM Call | MHz | kW | Location | FM Call | MHz | kW | Location |
|---|---|---|---|---|---|---|---|
| KAKL | 88.5 | 11 | Anchorage | KDJF | 93.5 | 20.5 | Ester |
| KATB | 89.3 | 4.9 | Anchorage | KZVV | 88.3 | 3.2 | Fairbanks |
| KNBA | 90.3 | 100 | Anchorage | KRFF | 89.1 | 10 | Fairbanks |
| KSKA | 91.1 | 100 | Anchorage | KUAC | 89.9 | 38 | Fairbanks |
| KFAT | 92.9 | 10 | Anchorage | KSUA | 91.5 | 3 | Fairbanks |
| KAFC | 93.7 | 27 | Anchorage | KQHE | 92.7 | 2 | Fairbanks |
| KEAG | 97.3 | 55 | Anchorage | KWDD | 94.3 | 28 | Fairbanks |
| KLEF | 98.1 | 25 | Anchorage | KXLR | 95.9 | 28 | Fairbanks |
| 2) KYMG | 98.9 | 100 | Anchorage | KYSC | 96.9 | 5.8 | Fairbanks |
| 2) KBFX | 100.5 | 25 | Anchorage | KWLF | 98.1 | 25 | Fairbanks |
| 2) KGOT | 101.3 | 26 | Anchorage | 33) KAKQ-FM | 101.1 | 50 | Fairbanks |
| KTMB | 102.1 | 23 | Anchorage | 33) KIAK-FM | 102.5 | 100 | Fairbanks |
| KMXS | 103.1 | 100 | Anchorage | 33) KKED | 104.7 | 50 | Fairbanks |
| 5) KBRJ | 104.1 | 55 | Anchorage | KEUL | 88.9 | 1.4 | Girdwood |
| 34) KMVN | 105.7 | 51 | Anchorage | 19) KCAM-FM | 88.7 | 1.7 | Glennallen |
| 5) KWHL | 106.5 | 100 | Anchorage | 17) KXGA | 90.5 | 3.2 | Glennallen |
| 2) KASH-FM | 107.5 | 100 | Anchorage | KHNS | 102.3 | 3 | Haines |
| KJNR | 91.9 | 3 | Bethel | 6) KWVV-FM | 103.5 | 25 | Homer |
| 8) KYKD | 100.1 | 12 | Bethel | KBBO-FM | 92.1 | 10 | Houston |
| KCUK | 88.1 | 6 | Chevak | 34) KZND-FM | 94.7 | 15 | Houston |
| KTDZ | 103.9 | 28 | College | KXLW | 96.3 | 10 | Houston |
| 42) KCDV | 100.9 | 1.2 | Cordova | KAKI | 88.1 | 1.7 | Juneau |
| KRUP | 99.1 | 6 | Dillingham | KLSF | 89.7 | 1.7 | Juneau |

| FM Call | MHz | kW | Location | FM Call | MHz | kW | Location |
|---|---|---|---|---|---|---|---|
| KXLL | 100.7 | 6 | Juneau | 37) KJNP-FM | 100.3 | 25 | North Pole |
| KRNN | 102.7 | 6 | Juneau | KNLT | 95.5 | 64 | Palmer |
| KTOO | 104.3 | 1.4 | Juneau | KFSK | 100.9 | 2 | Petersburg |
| 20) KTKU | 105.1 | 3.8 | Juneau | KIBH-FM | 91.7 | 1 | Seward |
| KSUP | 106.3 | 10 | Juneau | KSBZ | 103.1 | 3.1 | Sitka |
| KWJG | 91.5 | 1 | Kasilof | KCAW | 104.7 | 3.6 | Sitka |
| 29) KFSE | 106.9 | 8 | Kasilof | 29) KKIS-FM | 96.5 | 10 | Soldotna |
| KOGJ | 88.1 | 1.1 | Kenai | 6) KPEN-FM | 101.7 | 25 | Soldotna |
| KDLL | 91.9 | 4.9 | Kenai | KUHB-FM | 91.9 | 15 | St. Paul |
| 9) KWHQ-FM | 100.1 | 25 | Kenai | KKNI-FM | 105.3 | 25 | Sterling |
| KRBD | 105.3 | 3.4 | Ketchikan | KTNA | 88.9 | 7.2 | Talkeetna |
| KRXX | 101.1 | 3.1 | Kodiak | K220AD | 91.9 | 1.1 | Valdez |
| KYKA | 104.9 | 19 | Meadow Lk | 39) KVAK-FM | 93.3 | 1.2 | Valdez |
| KAKN | 100.9 | 3 | Naknek | KMBQ-FM | 99.7 | 51 | Wasilla |
| KXBA | 93.3 | 50 | Nikiski | KAYO | 100.9 | 50 | Wasilla |
| 18) KNOM-FM | 96.1 | 1 | Nome | KSTK | 101.7 | 3 | Wrangell |
| 24) KICY-FM | 100.3 | 1 | Nome | | | | |

**NB:** Txs 1kW and higher. FM reference numbers for addr only

**Addresses & other information** (add AK before zip code):
**2)** 800 E Dimond Blvd, Suite #3-370, Anchorage 99515-2058 **W:** 550thezone.com – **3)** Box 708, Kodiak 99615-0708 **W:** kvok.com – **5)** 301 Arctic Slope Ave #200, Anchorage 99518-3035 **W:** khar590.com – **6)** Box 109, Homer 99603-0109 – **7)** as 20) – **8)** Box 474, Nenana 99760-0474 **W:** vfcm.org – **9)** Box 468, Bethel 99559-0468 **W:** kyuk. org – **10)** as 2) **W:** 650keni.com – **11)** 529 5th Ave Suite 200, Fairbanks 99701 **W:** kfar660.com – **12)** Box 670, Dillingham 99576-0670 **W:** kdlg.org – **13)** Box 109, Barrow 99723-0109 **W:** kbrw.org – **14)** 833 Gambell St, Anchorage 99501-3756 **W:** kbyr.com – **15)** Box 78, Kotzebue 99752-0078 **W:** kotz.org – **16)** as 5) **W:** kfqd.com – **17)** Box 467, Valdez 99686-0467 **W:** kchu.org – **18)** Box 988, Nome 99762-0988 **W:** knom.org – **19)** Box 249, Glennallen 99588-0249 **W:** kcam. org – **20)** 3161 Channel Dr Suite 2, Juneau 99801-7815 **W:** kinyradio. com – **21)** as 11) **W:** 820sports.com – **22)** Box 328, Sand Point 99661 **W:** apradio.org – **24)** Box 820, Nome 99762-0820 **W:** kicy.org. Russian 0800-1200 (Summer -1h) – **26)** 3913 Kachemak Way, Homer 99603-7618 **W:** kbbi.org – **27)** Box 50, Fort Yukon 99740-0050 **W:** kzparadio. com – **28)** Box 165, Galena 99741-0165 **W:** kiyu.com – **29)** 40960 Kalifornsky Beach Rd, Kenai 99611-6445 **W:** radiokenai.us – **30)** 526 Stedman St, Ketchikan 99901-6629 **W:** ketchikanradio.com – **33)** 546 9th Ave, Fairbanks 99701-4902 **W:** 970kfbx.com – **34)** 4700 Business Park Blvd #E-44A, Anchorage 99503-7176 **W:** 1020kvnt. com – **35)** 4723 King David St, Houston 99694-0096 **W:** as 8) – **36)** as 34) **W:** koanfm.com – **37)** Box 56359, North Pole 99705-1359 **W:** mosquitonet.com/~kjnp – **38)** 611 Lake St, Sitka 99835-7402 **W:** sitkaradio.com – **39)** Box 367, Valdez 99686-0367 **W:** kvakradio.com – **41)** Box 4307, Soldotna 99669-4307 **W:** 1430hometownradio.com – **42)** Box 60, Cordova 99574-0060 **W:** cordovaradio.com

**EXTERNAL SERVICE: Radio Station KNLS**
See International Broadcasting section.

## ALBANIA

**L.T:** UTC +1h (31 Mar-27 Oct: +2h) — **Pop:** 2.9 million — **Pr.L:** Albanian — **E.C:** 230V/50Hz — **ITU:** ALB

### AUTORITETI I MEDIAVE AUDIOVIZIVE (AMA)
**(Audiovisual Media Authority)**
Rr. Papa Gjon Pali II nr. 15, 1010 Tiranë ☎ + 355 42226288 **E:** info@ ama.gov.al **W:** ama.gov.al **L.P:** Chmn: Gentian Sala

### RADIO TELEVIZIONI SHQIPTAR (RTSH) (Pub)
Rr. Ismail Qemali nr. 11, 1001 Tiranë ☎ +355 42230842 **E:** marketing@rtsh.al **W:** rtsh.al **L.P:** DG: Thoma Gëllçi

| FM (MHz) | 1 | 2 | 3 | kW | FM | 1 | 2 | 3 | kW |
|---|---|---|---|---|---|---|---|---|---|
| Delvinë | 107.0 | - | - | 1 | Pogradec | 99.1 | - | - | 3 |
| Elbasan | 95.4 | - | - | 1 | Shkodër | 91.0 | - | - | 1.3 |
| Gllavë | 97.0 | - | - | 1.6 | Tiranë | 99.5 | 95.8 | 101.2 | 25/2.3/38 |
| Llogarë | 88.3 | - | - | 1.6 | Vlorë | 99.8 | - | - | 3 |
| Midë | 96.0 | - | - | 5 | | | | | |

+ sites with only txs below 1kW.
**D.Prgr: Prgr 1 (R. Tirana):** 24h. – **Prgr 2 (R. Tirana 2):** 24h. – **Prgr 3 (R. Tirana Klasik):** 24h.

### RTSH Regional Stations
**Radio Televizioni Gjirokastra (RTGJ):** 6001-2 Gjirokastër. On 102.5MHz (0.3kW). Incl. prgrs in Greek, Macedonian. – **Radio Televizioni Korça (RTK):** Rr. Don Gjon Buzuku, 7001-4 Korçë. On

89.5MHz (0.9kW). Incl. prgrs in Macedonian, Montenegrin, Romany, Vlakh – **R. Kukësi:** Rr. Gjalica nr. 13, 8501-3 Kukësi. On 100.4MHz (0.9kW) – **R. Shkodra:** Sheshi Demokracia, 4001 Shkodër. On 92.0MHz (1.6kW).

## OTHER STATIONS

| FM | MHz | kW | Location | Station |
|---|---|---|---|---|
| 32) | 88.1 | 1 | Shkodër | R. Dimension |
| 24) | 88.5 | 6 | Tiranë | R. Ngjallja |
| 21) | 89.3 | 1.6 | Tiranë | R. Kontakt |
| 9) | 89.5 | 1 | Shkodër | R. 1 |
| 5) | 89.6 | 1 | Fier | R. Klan |
| 6) | 89.8 | 60 | Tiranë | Best R. |
| 1) | 90.3 | 4 | Pogradec | R. +2 |
| 2B) | 90.3 | 1 | Fier | R. Top Gold |
| 4) | 90.7 | 1.6 | Tiranë | Love R. |
| 9) | 92.2 | 5 | Midë | R. 1 |
| 2A) | 93.0 | 1.6 | Gjirokastër | Top Albania R. |
| 9) | 93.2 | 5 | Tiranë | R. 1 |
| 2A) | 94.1 | 3 | Shkodër | Top Albania R. |
| 33) | 94.3 | 1 | Elbasan | R. Hit FM |
| 1) | 94.3 | 5.6 | Midë | R. +2 |
| 18) | 94.4 | 1.6 | Tiranë | R. EuroStar |
| 2) | 95.0 | 3 | Cardhak | Top Albania R. |
| 23) | 95.2 | 4 | Tiranë | R. Maria |
| 17) | 95.7 | 4 | Korçë | R. Emanuel |
| 2A) | 96.0 | 31 | Gllavë | Top Albania R. |
| 16) | 96.1 | 3 | Tiranë | R. DJ 96.1 |
| 28) | 96.4 | 1.6 | Tiranë | R. Spektrum |
| 25) | 96.7 | 1 | Tiranë | R. Ora News |
| 27) | 97.0 | 3 | Tiranë | R. Rash |
| 8) | 97.3 | 3 | Tiranë | My Music R. |
| 11) | 97.5 | 1 | Shkodër | R. 7 |
| 34) | 97.5 | 1 | Vlorë | R. Albania News |
| 1) | 97.6 | 3 | Gllavë | R. +2 |
| 11) | 97.7 | 6 | Tiranë | R. 7 |
| 20) | 98.1 | 2 | Tiranë | R. Sot |
| 2A) | 98.5 | 5 | Pogradec | Top Albania R. |
| 13) | 98.7 | 1.6 | Tiranë | Super Star R. |
| 2A) | 99.0 | 1.6 | Durrës | Top Albania R. |
| 2B) | 99.3 | 1 | Shkodër | R. Top Gold |
| 2A) | 100.0 | 50 | Tiranë | Top Albania R. |
| 12) | 100.1 | 2 | Korçë | R. ABC |
| 15) | 100.4 | 12.5 | Tiranë | R. Club FM |
| 2A) | 100.6 | 28 | Sarandë | Top Albania R. |
| 2B) | 100.8 | 56 | Tiranë | R. Top Gold |
| 2A) | 101.3 | 22.4 | Midë | Top Albania R. |
| 1) | 101.6 | 9 | Tiranë | R. +2 |
| C) | 102.0 | 1 | Tiranë | RFI relay |
| C) | 102.0 | 1 | Korçë | RFI relay |
| 2A) | 102.2 | 3 | Vlorë | Top Albania R. |
| 3) | 102.6 | 6.3 | Tiranë | Alfa dhe Omega R. |
| 14) | 103.1 | 3 | Tiranë | MCN R. |
| 26) | 103.3 | 2 | Vlorë | R. Val'e Kaltër |
| 2A) | 103.5 | 3 | Fier | Top Albania R. |
| 1) | 103.6 | 3 | Sarandë | R. +2 |
| A) | 103.9 | 2 | Tiranë | BBCWS relay |
| 2A) | 104.0 | 14 | Delvinë | Top Albania R. |
| 2A) | 104.3 | 7 | Prezë | Top Albania R. |
| 31) | 104.6 | 25 | Tiranë | R. Travel |
| 35) | 105.0 | 1 | Tiranë | ABC News R. |
| 30) | 105.5 | 1.6 | Fier | R. Star |
| 7) | 105.7 | 1 | Tiranë | IN R. 105.7 |
| B) | 106.0 | 2 | Tiranë | R. Ejani (CRI relay) |
| 36) | 106.3 | 1 | Tiranë | Alsion R. |
| 10) | 106.6 | 1.6 | Tiranë | NRG |
| 22) | 107.0 | 3.5 | Korçë | R. Magic Star |
| 1) | 107.4 | 3 | Delvinë | R. +2 |
| 19) | 108.0 | 10 | Tiranë | R. Scan |

+ txs below 1kW.

### Addresses & other information:

**1)** Rr. Aleksandër Moisiu nr. 76, 1001 Tiranë **E:** enkeledapura2@gmail. com – **2A,B)** Rr. 5 Dëshmorët nr. 20, Mëzez, 1050 Tiranë **E:** 2A) contact@ topalbaniaradio.com; 2B) financa@topgold.al – **3)** Rr. Vaso Pasha, 1000 Tiranë **E:** info@alfaeomegaradio.com – **4)** Rr. Abdyl Frashëri, EGT Tower, 1000 Tiranë **E:** info@loveradio.al – **5)** Rr. Aleksandër Moisiu nr. 97, 1007 Tiranë **E:** radioklan@hotmail.com – **6)** Asim Vokshi, pranë Arkivit të Shtetit, 1000 Tiranë **E:** bestradio.al@gmail.com – **7)** Rr. Dhaskal Tod'hri nr. 26, Kashar, 1051 Tiranë **E:** info@intv.al – **8)** Bvd. Dëshmorët e Kombit, Qendra Ndërkombëtare e Kulturëse "Arbnori", 1000 Tiranë – **9)** Rr. Kashar, Mëzes, pranë shkollës "Kasem Shima", 1050 Tiranë **E:** info@ radio1.al – **10)** Rr. Faik Konica nr. 1, 1010 Tiranë **E:** info@radionrg.net

**– 11)** Rr. Sefer Kondi nr. 35, 1000 Tiranë **E:** info@radio-7.net – **12)** Bvd. Shën Gjergji, Qendra Baze, 7000 Korçë **E:** radioabckorce@live.com – **13)** Rr. Naim Frashëri, 1001 Tiranë **E:** superstaralbania@gmail.com – **14)** Rr. Ismail Qemali nr. 11, 1001 Tiranë **E:** marketing@mcnradio.al – **15)** Rogner Hotel, Bvd. Dëshmorët e Kombit, 1000 Tiranë **E:** info@clubfm. al – **16)** Rr. Abdyl Frashëri, EGT Tower, 1000 Tiranë **E:** info@radiodj. al – **17)** Rr. Thimi Mitko nr. 13, 7000 Korçë **E:** radioemanuel@gmail. com – **18)** Rr. Hamdi Pepa, Qyteti i Nxënësve, 1000 Tiranë **E:** info@radio-oeurostar.net – **19)** Rr. Aleksandër Moisiu, 1001 Tiranë **E:** info@scan-tv. com – **20)** 1000 Tiranë – **21)** Rr. Fadil Rada, pranë ATSH, 1000 Tiranë **E:** media@radiokontakt.al – **22)** Rr. e Xhamisë së Re, 7000 Korçë – **23)** Rr. Papa Gjon Pali II nr. 4, 1047 Fushë e Kërçikëve **E:** administration.alb@ radiomaria.org. In Italian. Rel. R. Maria (Italy). – **24)** Rr. Dritan Hoxha, Pallati Komfort, 1000 Tiranë **E:** orthchal@orthodoxalbania.org – **25)** Rr. Aleksandër Moisiu nr. 76, 1001 Tiranë **E:** info@oranews.tv – **26)** Lagjia 24 Maji, 9400 Vlorë **E:** radio.valekalter@yahoo.com – **27)** Rr. Ali Demi, Ish Kombinati i Autotraktorëve, Zyrat e Administratës, 1000 Tiranë **E:** marketing.news24@yahoo.com – **28)** Rr. Jordan Misja, Kompleksi Usluga, 1000 Tiranë **E:** radiospektrum96.4@gmail.com – **29)** Rr. 5 Dëshmorët nr. 20, Mëzez, 1050 Tiranë – **30)** Lagjja "Apolonia", 9300 Fier **E:** star.tv@live.com – **31)** Rr. Ibrahim Rugova nr. 28, 1000 Tiranë **E:** info@radiotravel.al – **32)** 4000 Shkodër – **33)** L. "Vullnetari", Pll. 648/1, Kati 4, 3000 Elbasan **E:** beharstrumi@gmail.com – **34)** Bvd. Dëshmorët e Kombit, Kullat Binjake, Kati 12, Hyrja 1, 1000 Tiranë **E:** bmulaj@gmail. com – **35)** Rr. Aleksandër Moisiu, 1001 Tiranë – **36)** Lagjja "Hekurudha", Rr. Syrja Dylgjeri, 3000 Elbasan – **A)** Rel. BBCWS (UK) – **B)** Rel. CRI (P.R. China) **E:** crialb@163.com – **C)** Rel. RFI (France)

## ALGERIA

**L.T:** UTC +1h — **Pop:** 41 million — **Pr.L:** Arabic, French, Tamazight — **E.C:** 50Hz, 230V — **ITU:** ALG

### TÉLÉDIFFUSION D'ALGERIE (TDA)

Direction Générale, B.P. 50, Bouzaréah, Route de Baïnam, 16340 Algér **☎**+213 21 901717 ▤ +213 21 902424 **W:** tda.dz **E:** contact@ tda.dz

### RADIO ALGÉRIENNE (RA, Pub.)

21 Boulevard des Martyrs, El Mouradia, Algér (Jil FM: DCRR, 12 Rue Shakespeare, El Mouradia, Algér) **☎**+213 21 230805 ▤ +213 21 694620 **W:** radioalgerie.dz **E:** radionet@radioalgerie.dz

| LW/MW | kHz | kW | Pr. | Hrs. |
|---|---|---|---|---|
| Béchar | ‡153 | | 1 | 24h |
| Ouargla | ‡198 | | 1 | 24h |
| Tipaza | 252 | *1500 | 3 | 24h |
| F'Kirina | 531 | 600 | J | 24h |
| Sidi Hamadouche | 549 | 600 | J | 24h |
| 20) Touggourt | 558 | 10 | 1/L | 24h |
| 4) Béchar | 576 | *400 | L | 24h |
| 30) Tindouf | 666 | 10 | 1/L | 24h |
| Aboudid (Ain el H.) | ‡693 | 5 | 2 | 24h |
| 1) Reggane | 693 | 10 | 1/L | 24h |
| 14) Laghouat | 702 | 25 | 3/L | 24h |
| 12) In Amenas | 738 | 5 | 1/L | 24h |
| 12) Djanet | 783 | 10 | 1/L | 24h |
| 24) El Oued | 783 | 10 | 1/L | 24h |
| Béchar | ‡837 | 5 | 3 | 24h |
| 10) Ghardaïa | 873 | 10 | 1/L | 24h |
| Ouled Fayet (Algér) | ‡891 | *600 | 1 | 24h |
| Tamanrasset | 909 | 10 | 1 | 24h |
| 1) Timimoun | 927 | 10 | 1/L | 24h |
| Ouled Fayet (Algér) | 981 | 100 | 2 | 24h |
| 20) Hassi Messaoud | 1026 | 10 | 1/L | 24h |
| Illizi | 1071 | 5 | 1 | 24h |
| 1) Adrar | 1089 | 10 | 1/L | 24h |
| 27) In Salah | 1161 | 5 | 1/L | 24h |
| Ouled Fayet | 1422 | 50 | M | 24h |

*) half-power 1900-0600.

| FM (MHz) | 1 | 2 | 3 | I | M | J | kW(TRP) |
|---|---|---|---|---|---|---|---|
| Abadla | 90.8 | 100.8 | 94.0 | 97.3 | - | 104.9 | |
| Adrar | - | - | 98.0 | 105.0 | - | 90.0 | 2.5 |
| Aflou | 90.7 | 93.9 | 97.2 | - | - | - | 10 |
| Aïn N'Sour | 94.0 | 100.8 | 97.3 | 104.4 | - | - | 10 |
| Aïn Oussera | 89.8 | 92.9 | 99.4 | - | - | - | 1 |
| Aïn Tagourait | 99.0 | - | - | - | - | - | 0.1 |
| Akfadou | 101.8 | 91.8 | 105.4 | 95.0 | 98.3 | - | 10 |
| Béchar | 92.4 | - | 98.8 | 90.5 | - | 103.5 | 5 |
| Bordj El Bahri | 91.0 | 104.2 | 89.2 | - | 100.5 | - | 2.5 |
| Bordj Omar Driss | 101.6 | 105.2 | - | - | - | - | 0.1 |
| Bouachoui | 102.4 | - | - | - | - | - | 0.1 |

| FM (MHz) | 1 | 2 | 3 | I | M | J | kW(TRP) |
|---|---|---|---|---|---|---|---|
| Bouzaréah | - | 100.0 | - | 95.6 | - | - | 0.1 |
| Bouzizi | 89.7 | 102.8 | 92.8 | - | - | - | 0.1 |
| Chréa | 98.0 | - | 88.4 | 101.5 | 105.1 | 94.7 | 10 |
| Debdeb | 103.5 | 90.4 | 93.5 | - | - | - | 0.1 |
| Dellys | 102.9 | 106.5 | - | - | - | - | |
| Dirah | 90.2 | 96.5 | - | - | - | - | 2.5 |
| Djelfa | 88.0 | - | - | 95.9 | - | - | |
| Doukhane | 94.2 | 97.5 | 91.0 | - | - | - | 2.5 |
| El Bayadh | - | - | - | 102.1 | 105.7 | - | 2.5 |
| El Hadjira | 88.7 | 95.0 | 98.3 | 105.4 | 101.8 | - | 10 |
| El Oued | - | - | - | - | 102.8 | 94.7 | 0.1 |
| Filfila | 96.1 | 98.1 | 101.6 | - | - | - | 2.5 |
| Gara Djebilet | 98.0 | - | - | - | - | - | 0.1 |
| Ghardaïa | 93.2 | 96.4 | - | - | - | 94.7 | 2.5 |
| Illizi | 95.9 | 89.6 | 99.2 | - | - | 94.7 | 0.1 |
| In Amenas | 91.7 | 94.9 | 98.2 | - | - | - | |
| In Guezzam | 92.6 | - | 89.5 | - | 95.8 | - | |
| Kef El Akhal | 90.7 | 97.2 | 87.6 | 104.3 | 100.7 | - | 10 |
| Kerzaz | 92.0 | 95.2 | 98.9 | 105.3 | - | 107.9 | 0.1 |
| Khar | 107.2 | - | - | - | - | - | 2.5 |
| Laghouat | - | - | 92.0 | - | 106.0 | 101.1 | |
| Mahouna | 94.3 | - | 91.1 | - | - | - | 2.5 |
| M'Cid | 91.9 | 101.9 | 105.5 | 98.4 | - | - | 10 |
| Mécheria | 87.8 | 100.9 | 97.4 | 94.1 | 104.5 | - | 10 |
| Meghriss | 93.5 | 96.7 | 100.0 | 107.1 | 103.5 | - | 10 |
| Metlili | 94.4 | 101.2 | 97.7 | - | 104.8 | - | 10 |
| Mihoub | 104.6 | - | - | - | - | - | 0.1 |
| Nador | 98.0 | 88.4 | 91.5 | 101.5 | 105.1 | - | 10 |
| Ouargla | 98.6 | 95.3 | 105.7 | - | 98.0 | 94.7 | 0.2 |
| Oum Ali | 97.9 | - | 91.4 | - | - | - | 2.5 |
| Puits des Zouaves | 98.9 | 96.1 | 102.4 | - | - | 92.4 | 0.1 |
| Regheiss | 98.9 | - | - | - | - | - | 0.5 |
| Riyad el Fath | - | - | - | - | 93.6 | - | |
| Sidi Abdelkrim | 97.8 | 88.2 | 91.3 | - | - | - | 2.5 |
| Tamanrasset | 92.6 | - | 89.5 | - | 95.8 | 94.7 | 2.5 |
| Tessala | 102.7 | 89.6 | 106.3 | - | - | - | 2.5 |
| Thar | 93.0 | 96.2 | 99.5 | - | - | - | 2.5 |
| Tiaret | 89.4 | - | - | - | - | - | 2.5 |
| Timimoun | 90.9 | - | - | 101.0 | - | 102.0 | |
| Tindouf | - | - | - | 101.4 | - | 102.9 | |
| Tinzaouten | 92.9 | - | - | 96.1 | - | - | 0.1 |
| Tizi Ouzou | - | 88.0 | - | - | - | - | 0.1 |
| Zarga | 95.3 | - | - | - | - | - | 2.5 |
| Zouggara | - | - | 93.7 | - | 96.9 | 103.7 | 2.5 |

**Regional Stations:**

| FM | Station, location | MHz | kW(TRP) |
|---|---|---|---|
| 14) | R. Laghouat, Aflou | 87.6 | 10 |
| 4) | R. Béchar, Abadla | 87.7 | |
| 5) | R. Chlef, Ain N'sour | 87.7 | 10 |
| 1) | R. Adrar, Timimoun | 87.8 | |
| 28) | R. Tébessa, Doukhane | 87.9 | 2.5 |
| 3) | R. Batna, Metlili | 88.1 | 10 |
| 11) | R. El Tarf, Oum Ali | 88.3 | 2.5 |
| 26) | R. Soummam, Akfadou | 88.7 | 10 |
| 2) | R. Annaba, M'Cid | 88.8 | 10 |
| 3) | R. Batna, Regheiss | 89.3 | 0.5 |
| 4) | R. Béchar | 89.3 | 5 |
| 39) | R. Tipaza | 89.9 | |
| 9) | R. Setif, Meghriss | 90.4 | 10 |
| 19) | R. Oran, Khar | 90.5 | 2.5 |
| 39) | R. Tipaza, Chrea | 90.6 | |
| 21) | R. Rélizane, Ain N'sour | 90.8 | 10 |
| 18) | R. Naama, Mecheria | 90.9 | 10 |
| 16) | R. Djelfa, Sbaa Mokrane | 91.1 | 2.5 |
| 32) | R. Biskra, Metlili | 91.2 | 10 |
| 7) | R. El Bahdja, Chréa | 91.5 | 10 |
| 20) | R. Ouargla | 91.8 | |
| 1) | R. Adrar | 91.9 | 2.5 |
| 20) | R. Ouargla | 92.1 | 2.5 |
| 29) | R. Tiaret | 92.5 | 2.5 |
| 35) | R. Khenchela, Regheiss | 92.4 | 0.5 |
| 19) | R. Oran, Tessala | 92.7 | 10 |
| 44) | R. Tizi Ouzou, Belloua | 93.0 | 0.25 |
| 40) | R. Médéa, Dirah | 93.3 | 2.5 |
| 12) | R. Illizi | 93.5 | 0.1 |
| 6) | R. Constantine, Kef El Akhal | 93.9 | 10 |
| 7) | R. El Bahdja, Bordj el Bahri | 94.2 | 2 |
| 41) | R. Saïda, Sidi Abdelkrim | 94.5 | 2 |
| 32) | R. Tlemcen, Nador | 94.7 | 10 |
| 23) | R. Skikda, Filfila | 94.8 | 2 |
| 25) | R. Souk Ahras, M'cid | 95.1 | 10 |

| FM | Station, location | MHz | kW(TRP) |
|---|---|---|---|
| 43) | R. Aïn Defla, Anneb | 95.2 | 0.25 |
| 45) | R. Oum El Bouaghi, Regheiss | 95.6 | 0.5 |
| 36) | R. Aïn Témouchent, Tessala | 95.9 | 10 |
| 45) | R. Oum El Bouaghi, Chettaia | 96.4 | 2.5 |
| 12) | R. Illizi, Debdeb | 96.7 | 0.1 |
| 17) | R. Mostanagem, Mostanagem | 96.8 | 0.1 |
| 46) | R. Blida, Bordj el Bahri | 97.5 | 2.5 |
| 20) | R. Ouargla, El Borma | 98.0 | 0.1 |
| 12) | R. Illizi, Bordj Omar Driss | 98.1 | 0.1 |
| 47) | R. Guelma, Mahouna | 97.6 | 2.5 |
| 10) | R. Ghardaïa, El Golea | 98.0 | 2.5 |
| 14) | R. Laghouat, Hassi R'Mel | 98.0 | 2.5 |
| 24) | R. El Oued, 3 locations | 98.0 | |
| 27) | R. Tamanrasset, 2 locations | 98.0 | 1 |
| 30) | R. Tindouf | 98.0 | 0.1 |
| 4) | R. Béchar, Kerzaz | 98.5 | 0.1 |
| 15) | R. Mascara, Chareb Rih | 98.5 | 2.5 |
| 37) | R. Bordj Bou Arreridj, Tafartas | 98.7 | 2.5 |
| 27) | R.Tamanrasset, In Guezzam/Taman. | 99.1 | 0.2 |
| 27) | R. Tamanrasset, Tinzaouten | 99.4 | 0.1 |
| 22) | R. Sidi Bel Abbés, Tessala | 99.2 | 10 |
| 34) | R. Bouira, Dirah | 99.8 | 0.5 |
| 8) | R. El Bayadh | 100.1 | 0.1 |
| 40) | R. Médéa, Médéa | 100.7 | 0.1 |
| 46) | R. Blida, Chréa/Dirah | 100.9 | 0.2 |
| 41) | R. Saïda, Saïda | 101.3 | 0.1 |
| 42) | R. Boumerdes | 102.6 | 0.1 |
| 38) | R. Mila, Kef Bouderga | 102.7 | 2.5 |
| 13) | R. Jijel, Kern | 103.0 | 2.5 |
| 33) | R. Tissemsilt | 103.2 | 0.1 |
| 17) | R. Mostaganem | 104.0 | 2.5 |
| 48) | R. M'Sila | 104.5 | 1.5 |
| 35) | R. Khenchela, Chettaia | 105.7 | 2.5 |
| 7) | R. El Badhja, Puits des Zouaves | 106.0 | 2.5 |

+tens of more low power transmitters.

**DAB:** Algér channel 5B 176.64MHz 600W: Chaîne 1-3, Jil FM.
**D.Prgr:** 1=Chaîne 1 in Arabic: 24h. 2=Chaîne 2 in Tamazight: 24h.
3=Chaîne 3 in French: 24h. **Int=R. Algérie Internationale** in Arabic, French, English & Spanish: 24h. **M= Radio Multichaine** consists of **R. Culture** in Arabic: 1400-2300 & **R. Quran** 2300-1400. 1422kHz carries also Radio UFC 1200-1600 and may carry Ch. 2 in the evening. **J: Jil FM:** youth channel in Algerian Arabic: 24h.

**L=Local stations:** times of local prgrs vary slightly by stn, but mostly between 0800-1900 (R. Bahdja and R. Oran 24h). Most local stns transmit Chaîne 1/2, Culture or R. Algérie Int. after 1900. At 2300 many stations switch to relaying R. Quran. Most local stns carry news from Chaîne 1 at 0600, 1200, 1630 & 1830.

**Addresses & other information:**
Audio feeds for local stations: **W:** radioalgerie.dz/player/fr
**1)** B.P. 309, Adrar – **2)** 7, Boulevard Radji Mokhtar, Quartier Annasr, Annaba – **3)** B.P. 453, Batna **W:** radio-batna.dz – **4)** Cité Badr, B.P. 330, Béchar **W:** radiobechar.com – **5)** Ain N'sour – **6)** B.P. 28B El Koudia, Constantine **W:** radio-constantine.dz – **7) W:** facebook.com/pages/Radio-El-Bahdja-FM/239397829331 – **8)** B.P. 195, El Bayadh – **9)** B.P. 54, Ain Tbinet, Sétif **W:** radio-setif.com – **10)** B.P. 17, Ghardaïa – **11)** El Tarf **W:** radio-eltarf.com – **12)** Route de l'aéroport, B.P. 230, Illizi **W:** facebook.com/radioillizi.dz – **13)** B.P. 48, Jijel – **14)** B.P. 1410, Bd. de l'Indépendance Mamourah, El Maqam, Laghouat **W:** radiolagh.voila.net – **15)** Place Mostfa Ben Touhami, Mascara – **16)** Djelfa – **17)** Place El Matemar, B.P. 1014, Mostaganem 027000 **W:** radiomostaganem.net – **18)** Av. du 1 Novembre, BP 223, Naama **W:** radionaamafm.com – **19)** 4 place Aïssa Messaoudi, Oran – **20)** Ruissat, B.P. 83, Ouargla – **21)** 15 Rue Ismail Mustapha, Maison de Culture, Rélizane **W:** radiorelizane.net – **22)** Ex Gare de l'État, Sidi Bel Abbés 022000 – **23)** Porte des Aurès, B.P. 55, Skikda **W:** facebook.com/pages/Radio-skikda/1625659967647250 – **24)** Cité Reml El Oued, B.P. 172, El Oued – **25)** Blvd. Messous Hamid, Souk Ahras – **26)** Boulevard Youcef Bouchebah, Béjaia – **27)** B.P. 1080, Tamanrasset – **28)** Unité de Tébéssa, Parc des Loisirs, Tébessa – **29)** Rue des Fréres Saim Tiaret, B.P. 671, Tiaret **W:** radiotiaret.dz – **30)** B.P. 213, Agence Enasr, Tindouf – **31)** B.P. 44K, Tlemcen – **32)** Av. Idriss Mohamed, Biskra **W:** radiobiskra.com – **33)** Tissemsilt – **34)** Bouira – **35)** Khenchela – **36)** Aïn Témouchent **W:** radioaintemouchent.com – **37)** Bordj Bou Arreridj **W:** facebook.com/radio.bordj – **38)** Mila – **39)** Tipaza – **40)** Médéa – **41)** Saïda – **42)** Boumerdes – **43)** Aïn Defla – **44)** Tizi Ouzou – **45)** Boulevard Houari Boumédiène, 0400 Oum el Bouaghi **W:** facebook.com/radio.oeb – **46)** Blida – **47)** Guelma **W:** facebook.com/radio.guelma.fm – **48)** M'Sila

**Ann:** Chaîne 1: "Al Kanet al Oula min Idha'at al-Djazairiyah.", 2: "Radio Isnath", 3: "Algérie Chaîne trois", C: "Idha'atul-Thaqafiyah", K:"Idha'atul-Koran al Karim".

## ANDORRA

**L.T:** UTC + 1h (31 Mar-27 Oct: + 2h) — **Pop:** 73.100 — **Pr.L:** Catalan, French, Spanish — **E.C:** 50Hz, 230V — **ITU:** AND

### ANDORRA TELECOM (Gov)
◻ Mn. Lluís Pujol 8-14, AD500 Santa Coloma (Admin.) ◻Prat de la Creu 2, AD500 Andorra la Vella (Comm.) ☎+376 875000 🖷 +376 821414 **E:** comunicacio@andorratelecom.ad **W:** andorratelecom.ad **L.P:** Admin Dir: Jordi Nadal Bentadé

### RNA RÀDIO NACIONAL D'ANDORRA (Pub)
◻ RTVA Ràdio i Televisió d'Andorra S.A., Baixada del Molí 24, AD500 Andorra la Vella ☎+376 873777 🖷 +376 863242 **E:** web@rtva.ad **W:** andorradifusio.ad **L.P:** DG: Xavier Mujal Closa

### CADENA PIRENAICA DE RÀDIO I TELEVISIÓ (Comm.)
◻ Cadena Pirenaica de Ràdio i Televisió, SA, Av. Príncep Benlloch 24, AD200 Encamp ☎+376 732000 🖷 +376 834831 - Av. Pau Claris 8, ES-25700 Seu d'Urgell, Spain **E:** info@cadenapirenaica.com **W:** cadenapirenaica.com

### GRUP FLAIX ANDORRA (Comm.)
◻ Ràdio i Televisió de les Valls S.A., (GRUP FLAIX ANDORRA), Av. del Fener 11-13, 1r 3a - Edifici Eland-Unió, AD500 Andorra la Vella ☎+376 862288 **W:** andorra1.fm **W:** flaixfmandorra.com **E:** publicitat@andorra1.fm

### COPE- AD RÀDIO (Comm.)
◻ Avda. Bonaventura Riberaygua, 39, 5è Pis, Edifici Alexandre, AD500 Andorra la Vella ☎+376 877477 **W:** diariandorra.ad **E:** laradio@adradio.ad

### SER PRINCIPAT D'ANDORRA (Comm.)
◻ C. Prat de la Creu, 32, AD500 Andorra la Vella ☎+376 808300 🖷 +376 828301 **E:** msfuentes@prisaradio.com **W:** cadenaser.ad

| FM | MHz | kW | Location | Station |
|----|-----|-----|----------|---------|
| 2) | 87.8 | 0.3 | La Comella | Gestiona R. |
| 1) | 88.1 | 0.3 | Pic de Carroi | Cadena Dial |
| 2) | 89.0 | 0.3 | Pic de Carroi | R7P - RAC1 |
| 2) | 89.5 | 0.3 | Pic de Carroi | Europa FM |
| 2) | 90.1 | 0.3 | Valls Valira | R. Tele Taxi |
| 7) | 90.7 | 0.1 | Pas de la Casa | Pyrénées FM |
| 8) | 90.9 | 0.1 | Valls Valira | iCat |
| 6) | 91.4 | 0.1 | Pic de Maià | R. Nacional d'Andorra |
| 1) | 92.1 | 1 | Pic de Carroi | Maxima FM Andorra |
| 1) | 92.6 | 1 | Pic de Carroi | M80 R. |
| 2) | 93.3 | 0.3 | Pic de Carroi | R. Valira - Onda Cero |
| 10) | 93.8 | 0.3 | Pic de Carroi/Pic de Maià | Flaix FM Andorra |
| 6) | 94.2 | 1 | Pic de Carroi/Pic de Maià | R. Nacional d'Andorra |
| 2) | 94.6 | 0.3 | Encamp | Pròxima FM |
| 2) | 95.0 | 0.3 | Pic de Carroi | Pròxima FM |
| 8) | 95.6 | 0.1 | Valls Valira | Catalunya Informació |
| 10) | 96.0 | 1 | Pic de Carroi/Pic de Maià | R. Flaixbac |
| 8) | 96.5 | 0.1 | Valls Valira | Catalunya Música |
| 6) | 97.0 | 1 | Pic de Carroi/Pic de Maià | Andorra Música |
| 3) | 97.7 | 0.1 | Sant Julià de Lòria | R. Festa Major |
| 2) | 98.1 | 0.1 | Valls Valira | RAC 105 |
| 2) | 98.5 | 0.1 | La Comella | Qué! R. |
| 2) | 98.9 | 1 | Pic de Carroi | Kiss FM |
| 2) | 100.2 | 0.1 | Valls Valira | RAC 105 |
| 4) | 100.6 | 0.3 | Pic de Carroi | NRJ |
| 9) | 101.5 | 1 | Pic de Carroi/Pic de Maià | COPE - AD R. |
| 4) | 101.8 | 1 | Pic de Carroi/Pic de Maià | France Inter |
| 1) | 102.3 | 1 | Pic de Carroi/Pic de Maià | R. SER Principat d'Andorra |
| 4) | 102.6 | 1 | Pic de Carroi/Pic de Maià | France Musique |
| 1) | 103.3 | 1 | Pic de Carroi/Pic de Maià | Los 40 Andorra |
| 4) | 104.0 | 1 | Pic de Carroi/Pic de Maià | France Culture |
| 8) | 104.6 | 1 | Pic de Carroi/Pic de Maià | Catalunya R. |
| 4) | 106.0 | 1.2 | Pic de Carroi/Pic de Maià | RNE R. 4 |
| 4) | 106.8 | 1.2 | Pic de Carroi/Pic de Maià | RNE R. 1 |
| 5) | 107.5 | 1.2 | Valls Valira | R. Principat - Ràdio Estel |
| 4) | 107.9 | 1.2 | Pic de Carroi/Pic de Maià | RNE R. 3 |

**Addresses & other information:**
**1)** SER Principat d'Andorra ◻ C. Prat de la Creu, 32, AD500 Andorra la Vella ☎+376 808300 🖷 +376 828301 **E:** informatiusserandorra@prisaradio.com **W:** cadenaser.ad – **2)** Cadena Pirenaica de Ràdio i Televisió, SA, ◻ Av. Príncep Benlloch 24, AD200 Encamp

☎+376 732000 🖷 +376 834831 **E:** info@cadenapirenaica.com **W:** cadenapirenaica.com – **3)** R. Festa Major, ◻ Plaça Major, 3, AD600 Sant Julià de Lòria ☎+376 842601 (temporary stn only last week of July) – **4)** Andorra Telecom ◻ Mn. Lluís Pujol 8-14, AD500 Santa Coloma (Admin.) ☎+376 875000 🖷 +376 821414 **E:** comunicacio@andorratelecom.ad **W:** andorratelecom.ad – **5)** R. Principat - R. Estel ◻ Comtes de Bell-lloc, 67-69 ES-08014 Barcelona, Spain. ☎+973 354400 **E:**radioestel@radioestel.cat – **6)** RTVA Ràdio i Televisió d'Andorra S.A., ◻ Baixada del Molí 24, AD500 Andorra la Vella **W:** andorradifusio.ad – Broadcast in French every Wednesday 1730 UTC "Le rendez-vous de l'Aliança". **7)** Pyrénées FM ◻ Le Barry d'en Fort 09110 Montaillou Cedex - 99 Route d'Espagne, F-31100 Toulouse, France **W:** pyreneesfm.com – **8)** CCMA ◻ Av. Diagonal 614-616, ES-08021 Barcelona, Spain ☎+34 933069200 **W:** catradio.cat – **9)** COPE - AD RÀDIO ◻ Avda. Bonaventura Riberaygua, 39, 5 Pis, Edifici Alexandre, AD500 Andorra la Vella ☎+376 877477 **W:** diariandorra.ad **E:** laradio@adradio.ad – **10)** GRUP FLAIX ANDORRA ◻ Av. del Fener, 11-13, 1r 3a - Edifici Eland-Unió, AD500 Andorra la Vella ☎ +376 862288 **E:** publicitat@andorra1.fm **W:** andorra1.fm **W:** flaixfmandorra.com

## ANGOLA

**L.T:** UTC +1h — **Pop:** 27 million — **Pr.L:** Portuguese + ethnic — **E.C:** 50Hz, 220V — **ITU:** AGL

### MINISTÉRIO DA COMUNICAÇÃO SOCIAL (MCS)
◻ Av. Comandante Valódia 1°& 2° amdar , CP. 2608, Luanda ☎+244 22 2443495 🖷 +244 22 2392649 **W:** mcs.gov.ao **L.P:** Min: Carolina Cerqueiro.

### RÁDIO NACIONAL DE ANGOLA (RNA, Pub.)
◻ Av. Comandante Gika, CP. 1329, Luanda ☎+244 22 2323172 🖷 +244 22 2324647 **W:** rna.ao **L.P:** CEO: Pedro Cabral. PD: Júlio Mendonça. TD: Cândido R. Pinto.

| MW | kHz | kW | Prgr. | H of tr |
|----|-----|-----|-------|---------|
| Mulenvos | 945 | 25 | N/E | 24h |
| Mulenvos | 1134 | 10 | A | |
| SW | kHz | kW | Prgr. | H of tr. |
| Mulenvos | 4950 | 25 | A | 24h |

**Ann:** "Rádio Nacional de Angola".
**Prgrs: A=Canal A in Portuguese** (general coverage): 24h. **N:** on the h.
**N=Rádio N'Gola Yetu** (ethnic languages): 24h. **N:** rel. Canal A.
**E=External service:** relayed on Rádio N'Gola Yetu's fqs 2000-2400 in Lingala, French, English and Portuguese.
**RFM=Rádio FM Estéreo** (music): 1000-2400.
**5=Rádio 5** (sports): 0500-2300.
**P=Emissora Provincial:** 0400-2300, rel. A at night.

**Provincial MW transmitters:**

| MW | | kHz | kW | Pr | MW | | kHz | kW | Pr |
|----|----|-----|----|----|----|----|-----|----|----|
| 18) | Soyo | v1290 | 5 | P | 15) | Luena | v1458 | 10 | P |

| FM.Location | | A | N | 5 | RFM | P | kW |
|-------------|----|------|-------|------|------|----------|----|
| 1) | Luanda | 93.5 | 101.4 | 94.5 | 96.5 | 99.9 | 4 |
| 1) | Viana | 90.0 | 101.0 | 94.2 | - | 92.8/101.0 | |
| 2) | Caxito | 91.5 | - | 88.2 | - | 87.9 | 4 |
| 3) | Lobito | 93.5 | 104.9 | 101.0 | 98.5 | 89.1 | 1 |
| 3) | Benguela | 91.5 | 90.4 | - | 92.3 | 92.9 | 2 |
| 3) | Bocoio | 93.3 | - | - | - | 98.3 | |
| 3) | Ganda | 90.0 | - | 93.1 | - | 95.1 | |
| 3) | Cubal | 91.3 | - | 88.2 | - | 94.4 | |
| 3) | Canjala | 100.0 | - | - | - | 98.0 | |
| 3) | Caimbambo | 88.1 | - | - | - | 99.1 | |
| 3) | Balombo | 95.3 | - | - | - | 93.1 | |
| 3) | Dombe Grande | 88.5 | - | 98.0 | - | - | |
| 4) | Kuito | 92.0 | 91.0 | 94.5 | - | 106.7 | 4 |
| 4) | Chinguar | 101.8 | - | 88.9 | - | 98.5 | |
| 5) | Cabinda | - | 98.8 | 95.0 | - | 88.2/91.3 | 4 |
| 5) | Malembo | 97.7 | - | - | - | 90.8 | |
| 5) | Belize | 102.5 | - | - | - | 100.0 | |
| 6) | Ondjiva | 92.2 | 101.0 | 91.8 | - | 88.7 | 5 |
| 6) | Xangongo | 98.9 | - | - | - | 94.7 | |
| 6) | Huambo | 99.2 | 89.0 | 91.6 | - | 88.5/98.7 | 4 |
| 7) | Bailundo | 95.9 | - | - | - | 99.2 | |
| 7) | Caála | - | - | - | - | 94.8 | |
| 8) | Lubango | 95.8 | 90.2 | 99.1 | 92.8 | 96.6 | 4 |
| 9) | Menongue | 91.4 | 92.0 | 94.6 | 96.5 | 88.3 | |
| 9) | Kuito Kuanavale | 91.1 | - | 88.0 | - | - | |
| 10) | N'dalatando | 95.5 | 90.5 | 91.8 | - | 92.3/98.8 | 1 |
| 10) | Dondo | 92.7 | - | - | - | 88.2 | |

| Prov. | Location | A | N | 5 | RFM | P | kW |
|---|---|---|---|---|---|---|---|
| 10) | Golungo Alto | 97.2 | - | 105.4 | - | - | |
| 10) | Camabatela | 100.0 | - | 98.0 | - | - | |
| 11) | Sumbe | 101.1 | 104.7 | 91.7 | - | 97.6 | 4 |
| 11) | Waco Cungo | 100.7 | - | 97.2 | - | - | |
| 11) | Gabela | 95.7 | - | - | - | 100.7 | |
| 11) | Porto Ambuim | 90.0 | - | - | - | 93.3 | |
| 11) | Libolo | 92.7 | - | 90.2 | - | - | |
| 11) | Kibala | 94.7 | - | 91.7 | - | - | |
| 12) | Dundo | 94.4 | - | 93.3 | - | 90.3/97.7 | 4 |
| 12) | Lucapa | 88.7 | - | - | - | 91.7 | |
| 12) | Cafunfo | 90.2 | - | 99.9 | - | - | |
| 13) | Saurimo | 103.7 | 106.2 | 90.3 | - | 100.2 | |
| 14) | Malanje | 92.0 | 93.7 | 90.9 | 94.8 | 100.7 | 4 |
| 15) | Luena | 90.7 | 107.3 | 103.7 | - | 97.2 | 2 |
| 15) | Cazombo | 87.9 | - | 90.3 | - | - | |
| 15) | Luau | 90.2 | - | 93.3 | - | - | |
| 16) | Namibe | 88.5 | 92.5 | 91.6 | 97.7 | 95.2 | 4 |
| 16) | Bibala | 88.5 | - | 92.6 | - | - | |
| 16) | Camucuio | 90.3 | - | 93.4 | - | - | |
| 16) | Tômbwa | 87.7 | - | - | - | 95.9 | |
| 17) | Uíge | 99.8 | 106.3 | 92.5 | - | 89.6/91.0 | 4 |
| 17) | Negage | 94.4 | - | 88.0 | - | 103.0 | |
| 17) | Quitexi | 99.3 | - | - | - | 92.4 | |
| 17) | Bungo | - | - | - | - | 97.3 | |
| 18) | Mbanza Congo | 101.9 | 97.1 | 92.7 | - | 95.1 | 2 |
| 18) | Soyo | 103.7 | - | 88.7 | - | 92.3 | |

+50 more low power transmitters.

**Provincial & local stations:**
**1)** R. Luanda, R. Cacuaco 105.0MHz, R. Cazenga 102.1MHz – **2)** R. Bengo, Caxito – **3)** R. Benguela, R. Lobito. R. Ganda & R. Kubal are carried together on R. 5 fqs. – **4)** R. Bié, Kuito – **5)** R. Cabinda – **6)** R. Cunene, Ondjiva & R. Xangongo – **7)** R. Huambo & R. Caála – **8)** R. Huíla, Lubango – **9)** R. Cuando Cubango, Menongue – **10)** Cuanza Norte: R. N'dalatando & R. Dondo – **11)** Cuanza Sul: R. Sumbe – **12)** R. Lunda Norte, Lucapa – **13)** Lunda Sul: R. Saurimo – **14)** R. Malanje – **15)** R. Moxico, Luena – **16)** R. Namibe, R. Tombwa – **17)** R. Uíge, R. Negage, R. Quitexi, R. Bungo – **18)** R. Zaire, Mbanza Congo & R. Soyo. Affiliated community stations on FM in Buco Zau, Camabatela, Golungo Alto, Tombwa, Viana and Virei.

**EXTERNAL SERVICE: Angolan National Radio**
see International Radio section.

**Other stations:**
**A Voz da Esperança**, Luanda: 89.2MHz. **W:** insjcm-tokoistas.org
**Luanda Antena Comercial**, Luanda: 95.5MHz 5kW. **W:** lacluanda.
com **E:** lac@lacluanda.com
**Rádio Ecclesia** (Rlg.), Rua Comandante Bula 118, São Paulo, CP. 3579, Luanda. **FM:** 97.5MHz 5kW. **W:** radioecclesia.org)

## ANGUILLA (UK)

**L.T:** UTC -4h — **Pop:** 15,000 — **Pr.L:** English — **E.C:** 60Hz, 110V — **ITU:** AIA

**RADIO ANGUILLA (Gov. Comm.)**
✉ PO Box 60, AI-2640 The Valley AI-2640 ☎ +1 264 497 2218 🖷 +1 264 497 5432 **E:** radioaxa@anguillanet.com **W:** radioaxa.com **L.P:** Dir.: Farrah Banks. PM: Keithstone Greaves. Eng.: Lester Richardson
**FM:** 95.5MHz, Crocus Hill.

**THE CARIBBEAN BEACON (Rlg.)**
✉ PO Box 690, AI-2640 The Valley ☎+1 264 497 4348 🖷 +1 264 497 4311
**MW:** 1610kHz 50kW **SW:** 6090/11775kHz 100kW (irr.)
**FM:** 100.1MHz 20kW
**D.Prgr:** University Network, 24h. No local programming.
Owned by University Network (see under USA for SW schedule)

**PRIVATE FM STATIONS (FM in MHz):**
**KLASS FM,** Wilmot Estate Rock Farm, PO Box 339, AI-2640 The Valley ☎ +1 264 497 3791 **W:** klass929.com **FM:** 92.9 – **KOOL FM,** North Side, AI-2640 The Valley ☎ +1 264 497 0103 **W:** koolfm103.com **FM:** 103.3. Format: Urban Compilation – **PULSE FM,** Sachasses, Sugar Hill, The Valley ☎ +1 264 497 1075 **FM:** 107.5 – **UP BEAT RADIO,** Cedar Av., Rey Hill, PO Box 5045, AI-2640 The Valley ☎ +1 264 498 3354 🖷 +1 264 497 5995 **W:** hbr1075.com **FM:** 97.7 – **VOICE OF CREATION RADIO,** Sachasses, AI-2640 The Valley ☎ +1 264 497 0106 **FM:** 106.7 Format: Gospel – **ZRON PYRATE RADIO,** 398 East Dania Beach Blvd. Ste. 220, Dania Beach, FL 33004, USA ☎ +1 305 459 1559 **W:** pyrateradio.com **FM:** 105.1

## ANTARCTICA

**L.T:** Antártida Argentina: UTC -3h; Antártida Chilena: UTC -4h (12 Aug 18-7 Apr 19, 8 Sep 19-5 Apr 20: -3h; dates subject to confirmation); Ross Dependency (NZL)/South Pole Station: UTC +12h (30 Sep 18-7 Apr 19, 29 Sep 19-5 Apr 20: +13h) — **Pop:** 5,000 (Su), 1,000 (Wi) — **ITU:** ATA

**RADIO NACIONAL ARCANGEL SAN GABRIEL**
✉ LRA36 Radio Nacional Arcangel San Gabriel, Base de Ejercito Esperanza, CP 9411-Antártida Argentina, Argentina. ☎+54 2974 44 5304, 810 222 0776 (from Argentina) **E:** esperanzaantar@infovia. com.ar, lra36esperanza@yahoo.com.ar **L.P:** Dir: Guillermo Bolger, Op.: Pablo González
**SW:** see international section. **FM:** 97.6MHz 24h.

**SOBERANIA FM,** Villa Las Estrellas, Antartica Chilena, Chile. **FM:** 90.5MHz 0.1kW.
**ICE FM,** McMurdo Station, Ross Dependency. **FM:** 104.5MHz 0.05kW. Rel AFRTS exc. some local prgrs
**KOLD,** South Pole Station, Ross Dependency. **FM:** 87.5MHz
**88.7 FM,** McMurdo Station, Ross Dependency. **FM:** 88.7MHz
**SCOTT BASE R.,** Scott Base, Ross Dependency. **FM:** 97.0MHz
**AMERICAN FORCES ANTARCTIC NETWORK,** AFAN McMurdo, US Naval Support Force Antarctica, 651 Lyons Str, Port Hueneme, CA 93043-4345, USA. **FM:** 93.9MHz 0.03kW. **D.Prgr:** 24h.

## ANTIGUA & BARBUDA

**L.T:** UTC -4h — **Pop:** 103,000 — **Pr.L:** English — **E.C:** 60Hz, 230V — **ITU:** ATG

**ANTIGUA & BARBUDA BROADCASTING SERVICE (Gov. Comm.)**
✉ Cecil Charles Bldg, Cross Street, St. John's ☎ +1 268 462 1233 **W:** abstvradio.com **L.P:** PM: Blondell Anthony. CEN: Denis Leandro
**FM:** 90.5/101.5MHz **D.Prgr: ABS Radio** 24h

**CARIBBEAN RADIO LIGHTHOUSE (Rlg.)**
✉ Jolly Hill, PO Box 1057, St. John's ☎ +1 268 462 1454 VOiP: +423 468 9225 **E:** lighthouseBIMI@gmail.com **W:** radiolighthouse.org **L.P:** SM & CE: Nathan Owens. Owned by Baptist Int. Missions Inc.
**MW:** 1160kHz 10kW **FM:** 92.3MHz 1kW **D.Prgr:** MW & FM: 24h

**GRENVILLE RADIO LTD. (Comm.)**
✉ Bird Rd, PO Box 1100, St. John's ☎ +1 268 462 1116 🖷 +1 268 462 1101 **E:** mail@radiozdk.com & info@jump268.com **W:** radiozdk.com & jump268.com **L.P:** PD: Ivor Bird
**FM: Liberty Radio ZDK** 97.1MHz 1kW 24h – **Jump 100FM:** 100.1MHz 2.5kW 24h

**OBSERVER MEDIA GROUP (Comm.)**
✉ Ryans Place, High Street, PO Box 1318, St. John's ☎ +1 268 481 9100 **W:** antiguaobserver.com
**FM: Observer Radio** 91.1MHz (News/talk) – **Hitz 91.9:** 91.9MHz

**OTHER FM STATIONS (FM in MHz):**
**ABUNDANT LIFE RADIO,** Codrington Village, Barbuda ☎ +1 268 562 4821 🖷 +1 268 562 6813 **E:** lifefm1031@gmail.com **W:** abundantliferadioag.com **L.P:** MD: Clifton Francois **FM:** Barbuda: 103.1 (1kW) & Antigua 103.9 (1kW). Format: Gospel – **BBC,** Caribbean Relay Co. Ltd., PO Box 1203, St. John's ☎ +1 268 462 0994. **FM** 89.1 – **CATHOLIC RADIO,** Michaels Mount, PO Box 836, St. John's ☎ +1 268 562 6868 **E:** catholicradio@candw.ag **W:** s212802169.onlinehome.us **FM** 89.7 – **CRUSADOR RADIO,** Newgate/Popesheard St, St. John's ☎ +1 268 562 1075 **FM** 107.3 – **GOD FIRST RADIO,** 68 Newgade St, St. John's **E:** godfirstradioag@gmail.com **W:** godfirstradio.com **L.P.:** William Dorset. **FM** 102.9. Format: Gospel – **HEALTHY CHOICE FM,** Ramco Bldg, Independence Ave, PO Box 1296, St. John's ☎ +1 268 462 2273 🖷 +1 268 462 2275 **W:** healtychoicefm.com **L.P:** CEO: Lester Storm. **FM** 94.9 – **NICE FM,** All Saints Rd, Clarkes Hill ☎ +1 268 462 4343 **W:** nicefmradio.com **FM** 104.3 – **POINTE FM,** The Point ☎ +1 268 562 3989 **E:** info@pointefmradio.com **W:** pointefmradio.com **FM** 99.1 – **RED HOT RADIO,** Carlisle Estate, St. John's ☎ +1 268 701 1581 **E:** redhotfm@hotmail.com **W:** redhotflames.com **FM** 98.5 – **ROGERS RADIO CARIBBEAN,** Rogers Media House, PO Box W1481, Scotts Hill, St. John's ☎ +1 268 736 2255 **W:** rogersradiocaribbean.com **L.P.** MD Julian E. Rogers, CCO Denise Francis. **FM** 94.1. Format: News/talk/entertainment – **SECOND ADVENT RADIO,** America Rd, PO Box 109, St. John's ☎ +1 268 562 1015 **L.P.:** SM Necole Caleb. **W:**

secondadventradio.org **FM** 101.5. Format: Rlg. – **VIBZ FM - FAMILY RADIO NETWORK**, Belmont School of Business, All Saints Rd, St. John's ☎ +1 268 560 7578/9 **FM** 92.9 – **ZOOM RADIO**, Blackburn St. 5, Villa, St. John's ☎ +1 268 734 0485 **W:** zoomradiofm.com **FM** 95.7 Format: Classic soul and jazz.

## ARGENTINA

**L.T:** UTC -3h; exc. SC: -4h — **Pop:** 44 million — **Pr.L:** Spanish — **E.C.:** 50Hz, 220V — **ITU:** ARG — **Int. dialling code:** +54

### SISTEMA FEDERAL DE MEDIOS Y CONTENIDOS PÚBLICOS (SFMCP)
▣ Balcarce 50, (C1064AAB)CA Buenos Aires ☎ 11 4344 3600 **W:** argentina.gob.ar/comunicacionpublica **L.P:** Jorge Grecco (Secretario de Comunicación Pública

### ENTE NACIONAL DE COMUNICACIONES (ENaCom)
▣ Perú 103, (C1067AAC)CA Buenos Aires ☎ 11 4347 9850 **W:** enacom.gob.ar **E:** contacto@enacom.gob.ar **L.P.:** Silvana Myriam Guidici (Presidente)

° = on-air stn name not confirmed, ‡ = inactive, ± = varying freq.

| MW | Call | kHz | kW | Station, location and h of tr |
|---|---|---|---|---|
| CF34) | | 530 | 1/0.25 | Somos Radio 530, Buenos Aires: 24h |
| CF53) | | 540 | | R.Pasión, Buenos Aires |
| BA119) | | 540 | | R. Italia, Villa Martelli (nf 1620) |
| SF01) | LRA14 | 540 | 25/1 | R. Nacional, Santa Fé |
| SA01) | LRA25 | 540 | 10 | R. Nacional,Tartagal: 0900-0300 |
| CB04) | LU17 | 540 | 5 | R. Golfo Nuevo, Pto. Madryn: 24h |
| TF03) | ‡540 | 20/5 | | Ushuaia (F.PI) |
| NE11) | LRG206 | 550 | 5/0.5 | AM 550 La Primera, Neuquen: 24h |
| CB01) | LRA9 | 560 | 25/1 | R. Nacional, Esquel: 24h |
| BA01) | LRA13 | 560 | 25/5 | R. Nacional, Bahia Blanca: 24h |
| ER01) | LT15 | 560 | 10/3 | R. del Litoral, Concordia |
| SJ01) | LV1 | 560 | 25/5 | R. Colón, San Juan: 24h |
| JU01) | LRA16 | 560 | 25/1 | R. Nacional, La Quiaca: 24h |
| CF30) | | 570 | 5 | R. Argentina, Buenos Aires: 24h |
| CB02) | LU20 | 580 | 20 | R. Chubut, Trelew: 24h |
| CO01) | LW1 | 580 | 25/5 | R. Univ. Nal. de Córdoba, Córdoba |
| ME12) | | 580 | 3 | R. Andina, San Rafael |
| CF01) | LS4 | 590 | 50 | R. Continental, Buenos Aires: 24h |
| RN01) | LRA30 | 590 | 25/5 | R. Nacional, San Carlos de Bariloche: 24h |
| TU01) | LV12 | 590 | 5 | R. Independencia, San Miguel de Tucumán: 24h |
| NE04) | LU5 | 600 | 25/1 | R. Neuquén, Neuquén: 24h |
| SE03) | LRK201 | 610 | 2 | R. Solidaridad, Añatuya |
| BA91) | | 610 | 5 | R. General San Martin - "La Buena" San Martin: 24h |
| ME07) | LV4 | 620 | 25/5 | R. Nacional, San Rafael: 1000-0400 |
| LR01) | LRA28 | 620 | 25/5 | R. Nacional, La Rioja |
| SC01) | LRA18 | 620 | 25/5 | R. Nacional, Río Turbio: 24h |
| MS01) | LT17 | 620 | 25/5 | R. Provincia de Misiones, Posadas: 24h |
| CH03) | LRA26 | 620 | 25 | R. Nacional Resistencia: 24h |
| CF02) | LS5 | 630 | 50 | R. Rivadavia, Buenos Aires: 24h |
| JU03) | LW8 | 630 | 25/5 | R. San Salvador de Jujuy: 0900-0500 |
| CB05) | LRF201 | 630 | 10/5 | R. Nacional Patagonia, Comodoro Rivadavia: 24h |
| TF01) | LRA24 | 640 | 25/5 | R. Nacional, Río Grande: 24h |
| RN02) | LU18 | 640 | 10 | R. El Valle, General Roca: 24h |
| SL01) | LV15 | 640 | 10/5 | R. Villa Mercedes |
| CF38) | | 650 | 3 | Belgrano AM 650, Buenos Aires: 24h |
| ER04) | LT41 | 660 | 1/0.5 | R. LV del Sur Entrerriano, Gualeguaychú: 0830-0030 Sat: 0900-0000(Sun: -0400) |
| BA36) | | 660 | 1 | Amplitud 660, Ciudad Evita: 24h |
| BA172) | | 670 | 4 | R. Republica, Ciudad Evita |
| CB03) | LRA11 | 670 | 25/5 | R. Nacional, Comodoro Rivadavia: 24h |
| LR04) | | ‡670 | 5/1 | R. Universidad, La Rioja (F.pl) |
| NE01) | LRA52 | 670 | 10 | R. Nacional, Chos Malal: 24h |
| MS02) | LT4 | 670 | 1 | R. LT4 Digital, Posadas: 0800-0200 |
| BA02) | LRI209 | 670 | 25/5 | R. Mar del Plata, Mar del Plata: 24h |
| BA68) | | 680 | 1 | R. Popular, Claypole (nf 660) |
| BA173) | | 680 | 2 | R. Magna, Villa Martelli |
| SF07) | LT3 | 680 | 5 | R. Cerealista, Rosario: 24h |
| SC02) | LU12 | 680 | 25/5 | R. Río Gallegos, Río Gallegos |
| ME01) | LV6 | 680 | 15 | R. Nihuil, Mendoza: 24h |
| CF45) | | 690 | 2 | K-24 en R., Virrey del Pino |
| SA02) | LRA4 | 690 | 25/5 | R. Nacional. Salta: 24h |
| RN03) | LU19 | 690 | 10/5 | R. LV de Comahue, Cipolletti: 0900-0500 |
| CO05) | LV3 | 700 | 5 | Cadena 3 - R. Córdoba: 24h |
| NE02) | LRA17 | 710 | 25/1 | R. Nacional, Zapala: 0900-0300 |
| MS03) | LRA19 | 710 | 25/5 | R. Nacional, Pto. Iguazú: 0900-0300 |
| CF13) | LRL202 | 710 | 50 | R. Diez, Buenos Aires: 24h |

| MW | Call | kHz | kW | Station, location and h of tr |
|---|---|---|---|---|
| SC03) | LRA59 | 720 | 1 | R. Nal., Gobernador Gregores: 1100-2300 |
| ME02) | LV10 | 720 | 50/5 | LV Diez, Mendoza: 24h |
| LP01) | LRA3 | 730 | 20/5 | R. Nacional, Santa Rosa: 0900-0300 |
| SC04) | LU23 | 730 | 25/1 | R. Lago Argentino – R.Nal., El Calafate: 1000-0300 |
| CA01) | LRA27 | 730 | 25/5 | R. Nacional, Catamarca: 24h |
| CF27) | | 730 | 10/5 | R. Concepto (BBN-R.), Gonzáles Catán 24h |
| CB07) | LRA55 | 740 | 1 | R. Nacional, Alto Río Senguer: 0900-0300 |
| CF48) | | 740 | | R. Rebelde, Buenos Aires:1000-0200 (Sat: -0300) Sun: 1400-0100 |
| SC05) | LRI200 | 740 | 10/1 | R. Municipal, Puerto Deseado: 24h |
| CH05) | LRH251 | 740 | 25/5 | R. Provincia del Chaco, Resistencia |
| RN13) | | 740 | 10 | AM 740 La Carretera, Allen |
| CF51) | LRL203 | 750 | 1/0.25 | R. AM 7-50, Lomas de Zamora |
| CO02) | LRA7 | 750 | 100/10 | R. Nacional, Córdoba: 0900-0500 |
| BA09) | LU6 | 760 | 18/4 | Emisora Atlántica, Mar del Plata: 24h |
| CF21) | | 770 | 5/1 | R. Cooperativa, Valentín Alsina: 24h |
| TF02) | LRA10 | 780 | 25/5 | R. Nacionall, Ushuaia: 24h |
| CS01) | LRA12 | 780 | 25/5 | R. Nacional, Santo Tomé |
| ME03) | LV8 | 780 | 25/5 | R. Libertador (R.Nacional), Mendoza: 24h |
| CB06) | LRF210 | 780 | 10/5 | R. Tres "Cadene Patagoni", Trelew: 24h |
| ME06) | LV19 | 790 | 10 | R. Malargüe: 1100-0400 |
| CF04) | LR6 | 790 | 25/5 | R. Mitre "AM 80," Buenos Aires: 24h |
| JU02) | LRA22 | 790 | 25/5 | R. Nacional, San Salvador de Jujuy |
| RN04) | LU15 | 800 | 25/2 | R. Viedma: 24h |
| ME04) | LV23 | 800 | 1/0.25 | R. Andina General Alvear:1000-0400 |
| CH01) | LT43 | 800 | 5 | R. Mocoví, Charata: 0900-0300 |
| CF52) | | 810 | | R. Federal, CF Buenos Aires |
| CO16) | | 810 | 10/1 | R. Mitre AM 810, Córdoba: 24h |
| F001) | LRA8 | 820 | 25/5 | R. Nacional, Formosa: 0855-0400 |
| BA04) | LU24 | 820 | 5/1 | R. Tres Arroyos : 0900-0400 |
| BA33) | LRI208 | 820 | 2/0.5 | Estacion 820, Lomas de Zamora : 24h |
| CF24) | | 830 | 5 | R. Del Pueblo, Villa Forito: 24h |
| SF02) | LT8 | 830 | 10/5 | R. Rosario "La Ocho", Rosario: 24h |
| ME08) | LV18 | 830 | 25/5 | R. Municipal, San Rafael: 1030-0230 |
| SC06) | LU14 | 830 | 25 | R. Provincia de Santa Cruz,Río Gallegos: 0900-0500 |
| CS05) | LT21 | 830 | 1/0.5 | R. Municipal, Alvear |
| CS02) | LT12 | 840 | 10/5 | R. General Madariaga, Paso de los Libres: 0900-0300 |
| BA05) | LU2 | 840 | 25/5 | R. Bahía Blanca, Bahía Blanca: 24h |
| SA03) | LV9 | 840 | 25/5 | R. Salta AM 840, Salta: 1000-0500 |
| CF18) | | 840 | 5 | R. General Belgrano, Buenos Aires |
| BA182) | | 850 | 1 | R. La Gauchita, Morón: 24h |
| BA139) | | 860 | 0.5 | R. Digital, Lanus: 24h |
| SC07) | LRA56 | 860 | 1 | R. Nacional, Perito Moreno: 0955-0300 |
| CF05) | LRA1 | 870 | 100 | R. Nacional, Buenos Aires: 24h |
| BA260) | | 880 | | R. Democracia, Longchamps |
| RN12) | | ‡880 | 1/0.25 | R. Provincial de Sierra Colorada, Sierra Colorada (F.PI: move from 1580) |
| SC06) | LU14 | 880 | 5/3 | R. Provincia de Santa Cruz, Las Heras (//LU14 830): 1000-0300 |
| BA183) | | 890 | 10 | R. Libre, Villa Caraza: 1000-0400 |
| LP02) | LU33 | 890 | 25/1 | Emisora Pampeana, Santa Rosa: 24h |
| SE01) | LV11 | 890 | 25/5 | Em. Santiago del Estero, Santiago del Estero: 24h |
| CS03) | LT7 | 900 | 25/2.5 | R. Provincia de Corrientes, Corrientes: 0900-0300 |
| LP05) | | 900 | 1 | R. Municipal, 25 de Mayo |
| SJ02) | LRA23 | 910 | 25/5 | R. Nacional,San Juan: 0855-0400 |
| CF06) | LR5 | 910 | 150 | R. La Red, Ituzaingó: 24h |
| TU02) | LV7 | 930 | 25/5 | R. Tucumán, San Miguel de Tucumán: 24h |
| CO09) | LV28 | 930 | 5/0.5 | R. Villa María, Villa María: 24h |
| BA138) | | 930 | 5 | R. Nativa, Ciudad Evita |
| BA56) | | 940 | 1.5 | R. Excelsior, Monte Grande |
| SL03) | LRJ241 | 940 | 20/5 | R. Dimensión, San Luís: 0900-0300 |
| ER07) | LRH200 | 940 | 3/5 | R. Chajarí, Chajarí: 24h |
| CF07) | LR3 | 950 | 25/5 | R. Belgrano, Buenos Aires: 24h |
| CH04) | LT16 | 950 | 25/5 | RSP - R. Sáenz Peña , Roque Saénz Peña: 0900-0300 |
| ME05) | LRA6 | 960 | 25/5 | R. Nacionall, Guaymallén: 24h |
| BA06) | LU13 | 960 | 10/1 | R. Necochea, Necochea: 0900-0400 |
| CF35) | | 970 | 3 | R. Génesis, Valentin Alsina |
| CS07) | LT25 | 970 | 1/0.25 | R. Guaraní, Curuzú Cuatiá:0900-0300 |
| NE12) | LRA43 | ‡970 | 25 | R. Nacional, Neuquén (F.PI) |
| LP03) | LU37 | 980 | 3/1 | R. General Pico "Radio37": 0900-0300 |
| ER06) | LT39 | 980 | 5 | R. Victoria, Victoria: 0900-0400 |
| JU06) | | ‡980 | 5/1 | San Salvador de Jujuy (F.PI.) |
| RN11) | | 980 | 1 | R. Luján, Valcheta |
| SC08) | | ‡980 | 25/5 | Rio Gallegos (F.PI. |
| CF12) | LR4 | 990 | 25/5 | La 990 Radio, Buenos Aires: 24h |
| SJ03) | LRJ201 | 990 | 1 | R. Calingasta, Tamberías: 1000-0500 |

| MW | Call | kHz | kW | Station, location and h of tr |
|---|---|---|---|---|
| FO03) | LRH203 | 990 | 25/5 | R. AM 990, Formosa: 24h |
| BA120) | | 1000 | 1 | R. Sintonia, José C.Paz: 24h |
| LR03) | | ‡1000 | 10/1 | La Rioja (FPI.) |
| RN05) | LU16 | 1000 | 3 | R. Río Negro, Villa Regina: 0900-0300 |
| CS06) | LT42 | 1000 | 5 | R. Del Iberá, Mercedes: 0900-0300 |
| CH09) | | ‡1000 | 51 | Comodoro Rivadavia (FPI.) |
| CO04) | LV16 | 1010 | 20/10 | R. Rio Cuarto, Rio Cuarto: 0830-0500 |
| SA05) | LW2 | ‡1010 | 0.25 | R. Emis. Tartagal: 1000-0300 |
| CF15) | | 1010 | 4 | R. Onda Latina, Valentin Alsina: 24h |
| SJ07) | LRJ214 | 1020 | 25/2.5 | AM Mil 20, San Juan |
| SF03) | LT10 | 1020 | 10/5 | R. Univ. Nal. del Litoral, Santa Fé: 0800-0430 |
| CH02) | LRA58 | 1020 | 5 | R. Nacional, Río Mayo: 1100-2300 |
| CF08) | LS10 | 1030 | 25/5 | R. del Plata, Buenos Aires: 24h |
| BA249) | | 1040 | | R. Revolution, Luján |
| LP06) | LRG203 | 1040 | 10/1 | R. Capital "Antena 10", Santa Rosa |
| CF50) | | 1050 | 1.3 | R. General Güemes, Villa Lynch |
| CO08) | LV27 | 1050 | 10 | R. San Francisco, San Francisco |
| BA232) | | 1060 | | R. La Más Santiagueña, Gregorio de Laferrere: 0900-0300 |
| CB11) | | ‡1070 | 25/1 | Paseo de Indios (FPI) |
| CF09) | LR1 | 1070 | 25/5 | R. El Mundo, Buenos Aires: 24h |
| BA08) | LU3 | 1080 | 25/5 | Ondas del Sur, Bahía Blanca: 0900-0400 |
| CO21) | | ‡1080 | 10/1 | Paso de los Libres (FPI) |
| SA06) | LW4 | 1080 | 0.25 | R. Orán/R.Maria, Argentina: 24h |
| BA141) | | 1090 | 3 | R. Décadas, José León Suárez |
| BA79) | | ‡1090 | 2 | R. Popular, Valentín Alsina |
| SF17) | | 1090 | 1 | Libertad AM 1100, Rosario: 24h |
| BA66) | | 1100 | 1 | R. Estilo, Glew: 24h |
| CO17) | | 1100 | 10/0.5 | R. Mitre, Corrientes |
| LP08) | | 1100 | 1 | Red Pampeana, General Pico |
| CF03) | LS1 | 1110 | 25/5 | R. de la Ciudad, Dique Luján: 24h: |
| BA184) | | 1120 | 1 | R. Sudamericana, San Martin: 24h |
| BA198) | | 1120 | 1 | Em. Santiago y Copla, Ciudad Evita: 24h |
| CF33) | | ‡1120 | 2 | AM Tango "Nacional y Popular", Villa Dominico: 24h |
| SJ04) | LV5 | 1120 | 25/5 | R. Sarmiento, San Juan: 0900-0400 |
| TU04) | LRK204 | 1120 | 1/0.5 | R. 21, Yerba Buena: 24h |
| BA229) | | 1130 | 5 | R. Show, Francisco Alvarez |
| SE02) | LRA21 | 1130 | 25/5 | R. Nal., Santiago del Estero: 0900-0400 |
| BA12) | LU22 | 1140 | 10/1 | R. Tandil, Tandil: 0830-0300 |
| BA208) | | 1140 | 1 | R. La Luna, El Palomar |
| RN06) | LRA2 | 1150 | 25 | R. Nacional, Viedma: 0900-0400 |
| SJ05) | LRA51 | 1150 | 5 | R. Nacional, Jáchal: 1030-0300 |
| SF04) | LT9 | 1150 | 10/1 | R. Brigadier López, Santa Fé: 24h |
| MS07) | LRH202 | 1150 | 50 | R. Tupá Mbaé, Posadas: 0900-0300 |
| BA154) | | 1150 | 0.1 | R. Sagrada Familia (R.Maria), Ciudad Madero |
| RN07) | LRA57 | 1160 | 5/1 | R. Nacional, El Bolsón: 0900-0300 |
| MS04) | LRH253 | 1160 | 5/0.5 | R. Cataratas, Pto. Iguazú: 24h |
| BA10) | LU32 | 1160 | 10/2.5 | R. Coronel Olavarría, Olavarría: 0900-0300 |
| BA185) | | 1160 | 1 | R. Independencia, Remedios de Escalada |
| SA07) | | ‡1160 | 5/1 | Salta. (FPI.) |
| SL02) | LRA29 | 1170 | 10 | R. Nacional, San Luis: 1000-0500 |
| BA51) | | 1170 | 1 | R. Luz del Mundo, Rafael Calzada (nf 1610) |
| BA77) | | 1170 | 5 | R. Mi País, Hurlingham: 24h |
| BA155) | LRI230 | 1180 | 1/0.5 | R. de la Sierra, Tandil (R.Maria) |
| BA253) | | 1180 | 0.25 | AM San Ponciano, Abasto |
| TU03) | LRA15 | 1190 | 25 | R. Nacional., San Miguel de Tucumán: 24h |
| CF10) | LR9 | ‡1190 | 100/10 | Buenos Aires (FPI) |
| BA250) | | 1200 | | AM 1200 La Radio del Chamamé, Morón |
| CB09) | LRF203 | 1200 | 10/1 | R. 3 AndinA "Cad. Patagonia", Ejido: 24h |
| CS04) | LT6 | 1200 | 1 | R. Goya, Goya: 0900-0300 |
| TF04) | | ‡1200 | 25/5 | Rio Grande (F.PI) |
| BA29) | LRI229 | 1210 | 1/0.5 | R. Las Flores, Las Flores: 24h |
| BA200) | | 1210 | 1.5 | R. Mailin, Gregorio de Laferrere (nf 1330 |
| BA233) | | 1210 | | R. del Promesero, José C. Paz |
| BA83) | LRI224 | 1220 | 10/5 | R. Onda Marina, Mar del Plata (Cad. Eco) |
| CF16) | | 1220 | 5/1 | Eco R. AM 1210, Buenos Aires: 24h |
| CH06) | | ‡1220 | 1 | LRC R. "La Radio de Chaco", Pres. Roque Sanez Peña: 24h |
| SF05) | LT2 | 1230 | 25/5 | R. Gen. San Martín "R.Dos", Rosario: 24h |
| JU05) | LW5 | 1230 | 5/1 | R. Libertador, General San Martin |
| BA89) | | 1230 | 1 | R. Litoral, Isidro Casanova |
| CF44) | | 1230 | 1 | R. Creativa, Lanus: 24h |
| BA127) | | 1230 | | R. Claridad, Monte Grande: 24h (nf 1080) |
| BA230) | LRI218 | 1240 | 1 | R. Universidad Nal. del Sur, Bahia Blanca |
| CF31) | | 1240 | 1 | R. Cadena Uno, Paso del Rey: 24h |
| BA31) | | 1250 | 10 | R. Estirpe Nacional., San Justo: 24h |
| CB10) | | ‡1250 | 25/5 | Puerto Madryn (F.PL) |
| BA131) | | 1260 | 2 | R. Amor, Villa Tesel: 24h |
| CF36) | | ‡1260 | 9 | R. Oliva "Unicon del Cielo", General Rodriguez |
| ER02) | LT14 | 1260 | 10/5 | R. General Urquiza, Paraná: 24h |

| MW | Call | kHz | kW | Station, location and h of tr |
|---|---|---|---|---|
| NE10) | | ‡1260 | | R. y Television del Neuquén, Neuquén (F.PI) |
| FO02) | LRA20 | 1270 | 25/5 | R. Nacional, Las Lomitas: 0900-0300 |
| BA11) | LS11 | 1270 | 100 | R. Provincia de Buenos Aires, La Plata: 24h |
| BA15) | LU11 | 1280 | 10/5 | R. Trenque Lauquén, Tr. Lauquén: 0900-0300 |
| CF17) | | 1280 | 6 | R. Cad. Eco, CA Buenos Aires: 24h (nf 1530) |
| BA72) | | 1280 | 1 | R. Provinciana, San Miguel (nf 1290) |
| BA244) | | 1280 | | AM 1280 El Sonido de la Gente, Gregorio de Laferrere |
| SF11) | LRI371 | 1290 | 1/0.5 | R. Amanecer, Reconquista: 0800-0400 |
| BA53) | | 1290 | 1 | R. Interactiva, Ciudad Madero |
| ME10) | LRJ212 | 1290 | 5/1 | R. Murialdo, Villa Nueva de Guaymallén |
| SF06) | LRA5 | 1300 | 10/1 | R. Nacional, Rosario: 0853-0303 |
| CF26) | | 1300 | 2 | R. La Salada - RLS, Buenos Aires: 24h |
| BA199) | | 1310 | 0.25 | Gesell Radio, Villa Gesell |
| BA205) | | 1310 | 0.8 | AM Renacer, Moreno |
| ER03) | LRA42 | 1310 | 10 | R. Nacional, Gualeguaychú: 24h |
| NE06) | | 1310 | 0.5 | R. Dr. Gregorio Alvarez (Cadena Eco) Piedra del Aguila: 24h |
| CF29) | | ‡1310 | 1 | R.dif. Antártida Argentina, Buenos Aires |
| BA13) | LU10 | 1320 | 10 | R. Azul, Azul: 0900-0300 |
| BA63) | | 1320 | | Plus Radio, Lanús: 1100-0300 |
| BA187) | | 1320 | 1 | R. Máster, Luján (nf 1310) |
| BA209) | | 1320 | | R. Area Uno, Caseros |
| ME09) | LV24 | 1320 | 0.25 | R. Andina, Tunuyán: 1000-0600 |
| SF19) | | 1330 | 1/0.25 | AM Rosario, Rosario |
| BA225) | | 1340 | | R.Tradicional Conurbano Norte, Florida (†) |
| BA90) | | 1340 | | R. Imagen, Castelar: 0900-0100 |
| CS08) | | ‡1340 | 1/0.25 | Goya (F.PI.) |
| ER13) | | 1340 | 1 | R. Mediterránea, Rosario del Tala |
| CF11) | LS6 | 1350 | 10/5 | R. Buenos Aires, Burzaco:24h |
| CH07) | | ‡1350 | 1/0.25 | Juan José Castelli, Chaco (F.PI.) |
| CO13) | LRJ747 | 1350 | 5/1 | R. Sucesos, Villa Carlos Paz |
| BA38) | | 1360 | 0.4 | R. Itatí, Morón |
| ER15) | | 1360 | 1 | AM 1360 R.Cooperativa Estirpe Entrerriana, Maria Grande: 0930-2300 |
| RN08) | LRA54 | 1370 | 10 | R. Nal., Ingeniero Jacobacci: 0900-0300 |
| BA76) | | 1370 | 3 | AM Trece-70, González Catan: 24h |
| BA226) | | ‡1370 | | Junin (F.PI.) |
| SF20) | | 1370 | 1/0.25 | AM Pilar - Aire de Santa Fe, Potencia |
| BA144) | | 1380 | 2 | R. Buenas Nuevas, Merlo |
| BA179) | | 1380 | 0.5 | R. AM Súper Sport, Temperley |
| BA190) | LRI231 | 1380 | 1 | LV del Sudeste, Necochea |
| BA14) | LR11 | 1390 | 10 | R. Univ. Nacional, La Plata: 24h |
| BA216) | | 1390 | 1 | R. General Paz, José C. Paz |
| BA254) | | 1390 | | La Rocha Azul AM 1390, Libertad |
| BA255) | | 1400 | | AM 1400, Luján |
| BA266) | | 1400 | | R. Carandá, Gregorio de Laferrerè |
| NE07) | LRG202 | 1400 | 5/1 | R. Cumbre, Neuquén: 24h |
| CH08) | LRH207 | 1400 | 1/0.25 | AM del NEA, Charata |
| SF23) | | ‡1400 | 0.25 | Red 24, Rosario |
| BA42) | | 1410 | 5/1 | R. Folclorismo, Moreno: 0900-0200 |
| BA214) | | 1410 | 0.5 | R. Fundacion, Rafael Calzada |
| BA218) | | 1410 | 1 | La Mil 410, Chivilcoy |
| ME14) | | ‡1410 | 1 | R. Lider, Mendoza |
| ME15) | | ‡1410 | 1 | Godoy Cruz – (F.PI) |
| SL04) | | 1410 | 0.5 | R. María de La Paz, Villa Mercedes |
| BA108) | | 1420 | 1 | R. Génesis 2000, General Conesa |
| CF28) | LRI220 | 1420 | 1/0.25 | R. Dime, Villa Martelli |
| JU04) | LRK221 | 1420 | 1/0.25 | R. Ciudad Perico, Perico: 1000-0400 |
| BA16) | LT24 | 1430 | 1/0.25 | R. San Nicolas, San Nicolás |
| CA02) | | 1430 | | San Fernando del Valle (F.PI) |
| CO06) | LV26 | 1430 | 1/0.25 | R. Rio Terceo, Río Tercero: 24h |
| BA17) | LRI235 | 1430 | 0.25 | R. Balcarce, Balcarce: 0900-0300 |
| BA212) | | 1430 | 1 | R. Cunumi Guazú, Rafael Castillo: 24h |
| BA146) | | 1440 | 0.25 | R. Cristo Viene, Mar del Plata |
| BA257) | | 1440 | | AM 1440 Radio FEDETUR, Mar de Ajó |
| NE03) | LRA53 | 1440 | 5 | R. Nal, San Martín de los Andes: 0900-0500 |
| BA18) | LU36 | 1440 | 5 | R. Coronel Suárez, Coronel Suárez: 1000-0300 |
| CO07) | LV20 | 1440 | 1/0.25 | R. Laboulaye, Laboulaye |
| BA52) | | 1440 | 2 | R. Impacto, Ciudad Madero: 24h |
| BA234) | | ‡1440 | 0.25 | Villa Gesell (F.PI) |
| SE04) | | 1440 | 5/1 | Santiago del Estero (F.PI) |
| SF12) | LRI221 | 1440 | 5/1 | R. General Obligado, Avellaneda: 0830(SS 1000)-0300 |
| BA235) | | 1450 | 5 | R. Banderas, Moreno |
| CF37) | LRI213 | 1450 | 1.32 | R. El Sol, Porción Quilmes |
| CS09) | | ‡1450 | 5/1 | R. Epoca, Corrientes (F.PI) |
| LP09) | | 1450 | 1/0.5 | General Acha (F.PI) |
| SJ06) | LRI211 | 1450 | 5 | R. Las 40, Villa Aberastain |
| SF08) | LT29 | 1460 | 1/0.25 | R. Venado Tuerto, Venado Tuerto: 24h |
| BA19) | LU30 | 1460 | 0.25 | R. Maipú (Cad. Eco), Maipú: 0900-0100 (Sat/Sun -2300) |

| MW | Call | kHz | kW | Station, location and h of tr |
|---|---|---|---|---|
| BA20) | LU34 | 1460 | 0.1 | R. Pigüé, Pigüé: 24h |
| BA41) | | 1460 | 1 | R. Contacto, San Antonio de Padua: 1100-0300 |
| BA191) | | 1460 | 0,25 | R. Jerusalén, Monte Grande |
| BA21) | LT20 | ±1470 | 1/0.25 | R. Junín, Junín |
| BA22) | LU26 | 1470 | 0.25 | La Dorrego AM 1470, Coronel Dorrego: 24h (r. 1468) |
| BA174) | | 1470 | | R. Lider, Mariano Acosta |
| BA84) | | 1470 | 0.7 | Cadena 1470, Remedios de Escalada: 1000-0200 |
| ER05) | LT26 | 1470 | 1/0.25 | R. Nuevo Mundo, Colón: 0900-0300 |
| RN09) | | 1470 | 1 | R. Municipal, Luis Beltrán: 1200-0100 |
| SF09) | LT28 | 1470 | 1/0.25 | R. Rafaela, Rafaela: 0900-0300 |
| BA147) | | 1480 | 1 | R. Sensaciones, Tapiales: 1000-0200 |
| CO15) | LV22 | 1490 | 1/0.25 | R. Huinca Renancó, Huinca Renancó: |
| BA67) | | ‡1490 | | R. Vida, Mar del Plata |
| BA69) | | 1490 | 1.5 | R. Gama, Lanús: 1000-0300 |
| BA169) | | 1490 | | R. Dif. Emanuel, Partido de Ezieza (nf 1600) |
| BA246) | | 1490 | | R. Ciudad de Caá Cati, José C. Paz |
| CO18) | | 1490 | | R. Vida, Córdoba |
| SJ08) | | ‡1490 | 1/0.25 | Rivadavia (F.PI.) |
| BA07) | LRI214 | 1500 | 2 | R. Bonaerense, Lavallol |
| BA23) | LT34 | ±1500 | 0.25 | R. Nuclear, Zárate |
| BA178) | | 1500 | 0.25 | R. Olivera, General Rodriguez (nf 1590) |
| BA237) | | 1500 | | AM Entre Mares, San Clemente del Tuyú |
| CO20) | | 1500 | | R. Vida, Río Cuarto |
| ME16) | | 1500 | 5/1 | Mendoza (F.PI) |
| BA34) | | 1510 | | LV del Oeste,Libertad: 24h |
| BA220) | | 1510 | 1 | R. RBN "Radio de las Buenas Nuevas", Banfield Oeste |
| CF23) | | 1510 | 2 | R. Nueva Bolivia, Ciudad Madero (Rel: R. Patria y Nueva, La Paz) (nf 1260) |
| BA74) | | 1510 | 5/1 | R. Alabanza, Guernica |
| CH11) | | ‡1510 | | Villa Angela (F.PI) |
| SF14) | LRI253 | 1510 | 1/0.25 | R. Belgrano, Suardi: 0900-0400 |
| ER08) | LT38 | 1520 | 0.25 | R. Gualeguay, Gualeguay: 0900-0300 |
| BA40) | | ‡1520 | 1 | R. Metropolitana "R.Metro", Ciudadela |
| BA47) | | 1520 | 3 | R. Cielo Nuevo, Isidro Casanova (nf 1490) |
| BA92) | | 1520 | 5/1 | R. Chascomus – LVRegional, Chascomús |
| BA145) | | 1520 | 2 | R. Norteña, Los Polvorines: 0900-0100 |
| BA258) | | 1520 | 2 | LV del Sur, Luis Guillón |
| BA192) | | 1530 | 1.5 | R. Esencia "LV del Litoral", San Miguel Oeste |
| BA238) | | 1530 | 5 | LV del Futuro, Merlo |
| BA262) | | 1530 | | Am. Siloé, Gregorio de Laferrere |
| CO12) | LRJ200 | 1530 | 0.25 | R. Centro Morteros, Morteros: 0900-0300 |
| BA25) | LT35 | 1540 | 0.25 | R. Mon, Pergamino: 0900-0400 |
| BA26) | LU28 | 1540 | 0.25 | R. Tuyú:1000-0300 |
| BA100) | | 1540 | 1 | AM Lider, Benavidez |
| BA148) | | ‡1540 | | Cadena D, Monte Chingolo |
| BA231) | | 1540 | | R. Zorobabel, 9 de Abril |
| SC09) | | 1540 | | Rio Gallegos (F.PI) |
| BA251) | | 1550 | | Estacion Quince Cincuenta, Villa Florito |
| SF10) | LT23 | 1550 | 5/0.25 | R. Regional, San Jenaro Norte: 0900-0300 |
| BA27) | LT32 | 1550 | 0.25 | R. Chivilcoy, Chivilcoy: 1000-0400 |
| ER09) | LT40 | 1550 | 1 | R. LV de la Paz, La Paz: 0900-0100 |
| BA175) | | 1550 | | R. Popular, José León Suárez |
| BA213) | | ‡1550 | | R. Esperanza, Gregorio de Laferrere |
| BA259) | | 1550 | | R. La Amistad, José C. Paz |
| ER10) | LT11 | 1560 | 2.5/1.5 | R. Gral. Francisco Ramírez, Concepción del Uruguay (La R. Publica): 0900-0300 |
| BA28) | LT33 | 1560 | 0.25 | Cadena Nueve, 9 de Julio: 0900-0300 |
| BA44) | | 1560 | 1.5 | R. Castañares, Ituzaingó |
| BA99) | | ‡1560 | | R. Restauración, Llavollol |
| BA194) | | 1560 | 0.5/0.25 | AM 1560 "La R. de la Gente", Tandil |
| BA196) | | ‡1560 | 1 | R. Antena, Lobos: 24h |
| ME13) | | ‡1560 | 1/0.25 | Mendoza (F.PI) |
| BA55) | | 1570 | 2.5 | R. Melody, Remedios de Escalada: 1200-0300 |
| BA71) | | 1570 | 1 | R. AM Rocha, Tolosa: 24h |
| BA163) | | 1570 | | R. La Morena de Itati, Grand Bourg |
| BA267) | | 1570 | 0.5 | R. Eben-Ezer, Ezeiza |
| BA264) | LRI223 | ‡1570 | 5/1 | Lomas de Zamora (FPI) |
| SF22) | | 1570 | | R. Alegría Regional, Luis Palacio: 24h |
| ER11) | LT27 | 1580 | 1 | R. LV del Montiel, Villaguay: 0900-0300 |
| BA48) | | 1580 | 2 | R. Tradición, San Martín |
| BA135) | | 1580 | | R. 26. de Julio, Longchamps: 0900-0100 |
| BA176) | LT36 | 1580 | 0.25 | R. Chacabuco, Chacabuco |
| BA247) | | 1580 | | R. Cóndor, Moreno |
| CH10) | | 1580 | | Charata (F.PI) |
| MS08) | | 1580 | 1 | R. La Cueva, 25 de Mayo |
| RN12) | | 1580 | | R. Provincial de Sierra Colorada, Sierra Colorada (F.pl. move to 880) |
| BA124) | | 1590 | 1 | R. Guabiyú, Gregorio de Laferrere:24h (nf 1610) |
| BA223) | | 1590 | 1 | R. Dolores, Dolores: 24h |

| MW | Call | kHz | kW | Station, location and h of tr |
|---|---|---|---|---|
| BA240) | | ‡1590 | 1 | R. Sin Fronteras, Merlo |
| CF49) | | ‡1590 | | R. Stentor, Buenos Aires |
| SF24) | | 1590 | | R. Serodino, Serodino |
| BA37) | | 1600 | 1 | R. Armonia, Caseros: 24h |
| SF21) | | 1600 | 0.25 | R. EME Centro, Montes de Oca: 24h |
| BA261) | | 1610 | 0.5 | R. Santa Fe, Canning |
| CO14) | | ‡1610 | 0.5 | R. Comunitaria Regional, Laboulaye |
| BA45) | | 1620 | 2 | R. Vida, Monte Grande: 24h |
| BA180) | | 1620 | 10/1 | AM 16-20 La Radio, Mar del Plata |
| BA224) | | 1620 | | R. Sentires,Merlo: 1100-0100 |
| SF25) | | 1620 | | R. Mitre, Cañada de Gómez //790 (F.PI) |
| BA134) | | 1630 | 1 | R. Restauración, Hurlingham |
| BA219) | | 1630 | 1 | R. Unidad, Alejandro Korn |
| ER12) | | 1630 | 1/0.25 | R. America, San José: 24h |
| BA177) | | 1640 | 1 | R. Hosanna 1640, Isidro Casanova |
| BA268) | | ‡1640 | | General Madariaga (F.PI) |
| BA239) | | 1650 | | R. Estrellas, Longchamps |
| BA181) | LRI227 | ‡1650 | 1/0.5 | Antares AM 1650 |
| BA245) | | 1650 | | R. El Mensajero, Rafael Castillo |
| BA156) | | 1660 | 1 | R. Revivir, Gregorio de la Ferrere |
| BA265) | | ‡1660 | | Junin (F.PI) |
| ER14) | LRI232 | 1660 | 5/0.25 | R. Ciudad de Nogoyá Nogoyá |
| CO19) | | ‡1660 | 1/0.25 | Paso de los Libres (F.PI.) |
| BA167) | | 1680 | | R. Bethel, Banfield |
| BA107) | | ‡1690 | 1 | R. Cristo la Solucuión, San Justo: 24h |
| CF47) | LRI236 | ‡1700 | 5/1 | R. Fantastico, Tigre |
| BA241) | | 1700 | | R. Juventud, Florencia Varela (nf 1200) |
| BA263) | | 1710 | | AM Selva, Paretido de La Matanza |

## ASOCIACION DE RADIODIFUSORAS PRIVADAS ARGENTINAS (ARPA)

✉ Tte. Gral. Juan D. Perón 1561, Piso 3, (C1037ACB) Buenos Aires ☎11 4371 5999 📠11 4382 4483 **W:** arpa.org.ar **E:** arpaorg@arpa.org.ar **LP:** Edmundo Omar RéboraARPA is an association of privately owned commercial stns.

## ASOCIACION DE RADIODIFUSORES CATOLICOS ARGENTINOS (ARCA)

✉ Tucumán 1993, (C1050AAM) CA Buenos Aires ☎11 4375 0376 **W:** radiocatolicasarca.or.ar **E:** arcato@sminter.com.ar **LP:** Presidente: Osvaldo Bufarini

**Addresses & other information:**
**BA00) BUENOS AIRES (PROV.):**
**BA01)** Moreno 30, 1° Piso, (B8000FWB) Bahía Blanca ☎ 291 453 2700 **W:** radionacional.com.ar **E:** administracionlra13@radionacional.gov.ar - **FM:** 95.1 MHz – **BA02)** Hipólito Yrigoyen 2641, (B7600DPG) Mar del Plata 📠223 494 1039 📠223 492 2020 **W:** lu9mardelplata.com.ar **E:** lu9-adm@lacapitalnet.com.ar – **FM:** 103.3MHz FM 103 Universo – **BA04)** Av. Belgrano 457, (B7500EBE) Tres Arroyos ☎2983 42 3504 📠2983 42 7000 **W:** lu24.com.ar **E:** noticias@lu24.com.ar – **FM:** 95.3MHz FM Ilusiones – **BA05)** Rodriguez 55 (B8000HSA) Bahía Blanca ☎291 459 0002 📠291 455 5556 **W:** lu2.com.ar **E:** radio@lu2.com.ar – **FM:** 94.7MHz FM Ciudad – **BA06)** Calle 64 N° 2946, Gran Galería Central, EP, (B7630CIR) Necochea ☎2262 42 0100 **W:** radionecochea.com.ar **E:** administracion@lu13radionecochea.com.ar – **FM:** 88.1MHz FM Oceánica – **BA07)** Doyhenard 316, (B1836EVH) Lavallol ☎11 4231 3225 **W:** am1500.com.ar **E:** radiobonarense@gmail.com – **BA08)** Av. Lamadrid 116, (B8000FKD) Bahía Blanca ☎291 452 0382 **W:** lu3amondasfm.wixsite.com/lu3amfm **E:** radiolu3@yahoo.com.ar – **FM:** 94.3MHz FM Ondas – **BA09)** Córdoba 1865, (B7600DVM) Mar del Plata ☎223 491 7047 📠223 491 2355 **W:** lu6.com.ar **E:** radioa@lu6.com.ar - **FM:** 93.3MHz – **BA10)** Alsina 3377, (B7400COW) Olavarría ☎2284 41 0911 **W:** lu32.com.ar **E:** administracion@lu32.com.ar - **FM:** 98.7MHz FM Cristal – **BA11)** Calle 53 N°. 810, (B1900BBQ) La Plata ☎221 424 9713 **W:** provinciaradio.com.ar **E:** secretaria@amprovincia.com.ar – **FM:** 97.1MHz FM Provincia – **BA12)** Gral. Rodriguez 762, PA, (B7000AOP) Tandil ☎249 442 7493 **W:**radiotandil.com **E:** contacto@radiotandil.com – **FM:** 97.1MHz Galática FM – **BA13)** Av. Bartolomé Mitre 819, (B7300IKQ) Azul ☎2281 42 5628 **W:** lu10radioazul.com **E:** lu10radioazul@hotmail.com – **FM:** 89.5MHz FM Más Rock – **BA14)** Plaza Rocha 133, 2°Piso, (B1900DVA) La Plata ☎221 422 0330 📠221 422 4165 **W:** radiouniversidad.unlp.edu.ar/am-1390 **E:** administracion@radiouniversidad.unlp.edu.ar – **FM:** 107.5MHz – **BA15)** Av. Pedro García Salinas 1815, (B6400EIF) Trenque Lauquen ☎2392 42 5454 **W:** radiotrenquelauquen.com.ar **E:** radiolu11@speedy.com.ar – **FM:** 88.5MHz FM Proyección – **BA16)** Av. Moreno 124, (B2900GPO) San Nicolás ☎336 442 5222 📠336 442 4479 **W:** diario24.com.ar **E:** lt24@cablenet.com.ar – **FM:** 88.3MHz FM 88 – **BA17)** Av. San Martin 2700, (B7620) Balcarce ☎2266 43 0780 **W:** //radiobalcarce.blogspot.com **E:** radiobalcarce@telefax.com.ar - **FM:** 89.7MHz FM Balcarce – **BA18)**

Garibaldi 71, (B7540DQA) Coronel Suárez ☎2926 43 2706 **W:** radiocoronelsuarez.com.ar **E:** lu35am1440@speedy.com.ar - **FM:** 100.5MHz "Frecuencia 36" – **BA19)** Lavalle Sud 312, (B7160BAH) Maipú ☎2268 42 1774 **W:** lu3radiomaipu.com.ar **E:** lu30rm@yahoo.com.ar - **FM:** 104.1 FM Cristal – **BA20)** Lavalle 210, (B8170CHF) Pigüé ☎2923 47 2205 **W:** radiopigue.com.ar **E:** radiolu34@s8.coopenet.com.ar - **FM:** 96.3MHz FM Serrana – **BA21)** Roque Sáenz Peña 167, (B6000DDB) Junín ☎236 446 3310 **W:** radiojunin.com **E:** mensajes.radio@grupolaverdad.com - **FM:** 89.1MHz Nova Retro – **BA22)** Uslenghi 592, 1° Piso, (B8150EGD) Coronel Dorrego ☎2921 40 6576 **W:** ladorrego.com.ar **E:** ladorrego@yahoo.com.ar – **BA23)** Independencia 501, (B2800JIG) Zárate ☎3487 42 3116 🖷3487 43 9500 **W:** radionuclear.com.ar **E:** audioradionuclear@yahoo.com.ar - **FM:** 90.1MHz FM Top – **BA25)** Dr. Alem 340, (B2700LHH) Pergamino ☎2477 42 4022 **W:** lt35radiomon.com.ar **E:** lt35radiomon@speedy.com.ar - **FM:** 90.3MHz FM Mágica – **BA26)** Av. San Martín 366, (B7163EGQ) General Madariaga ☎ 2267 55 1540 **W:** radiotuyu.blogspot.com **E:** radiotuyu@telpin.com.ar - **FM:** 92.5MHz FMTuy – **BA27)** Av. Mitre 924. (B6620BMW) Chivilcoy ☎2346 43 0690 **W:** facebook.com/radiochivilcoy **E:** radiochivilcoy@speedy.com - **FM:** 101.1MHz FM Sónica – **BA28)** Pte. Hipólito Yrigoyen 969, (B6500DJQ) 9 de Julio ☎2317 52 1333 **W:** cadenanueve.com **E:** lt33@cadenanueva.com - **FM:** 89.9MHz Maxima FM – **BA29)** Av. Avellaneda 773, (B7200AOH) Las Flores ☎2244 45 2320 **W:** radio.orange.com/es/radios/radio_las_flores_am_1210 **E:** am1210@s2coopnet.com.ar - **FM:** 89.7MHz FM Condor – **BA31)** Juan Florio 3573, (B1754AJK) San Justo ☎11 4441 1400 **W:** estirpe1250.com.ar **E:** estirpe1250@yahoo.com.ar – **BA33)** Antonio Sáenz 572, 2° piso, (B1832HUL) Lomas de Zamora ☎11 4243 7891 🖷11 4292 5559 **W:** radioestacion820.com.ar **E:** administracion@estacion820.com.ar – **BA34)** Isla Soledad 2510, (B1716NXB) Libertad ☎220 497 4623 **W:** lavozdeloesteam1510.com.ar **E:** lavozdeloesteam1510@hotmail.com – **BA36)** Dr. Ignacio Arieta 3950 (B1754AQT) San Justo ☎11 4651 0193 **W:** am660.com.ar **E:** am660khz@gmail.com – **BA37)** Wenceslao Paunero 2915, (B1678DSG) Caseros ☎11 4716 2279 **W:** am1600armonia.com **E:** armoniaam1600@gmail.com – **BA38)** San Luís 991, (B1708JUE) Morón ☎11 4627 7439 **W:** radioitati.com.ar – **BA40)** Julio A. Roca 3414, (B1702BCL) Ciudadela ☎11 4488 3644. 🖷11 4657 4098 **E:** amradiometro@yahoo.com.ar – **BA41)** Agustin Zárate 154, (B1718BPD) San Antonio de Padua ☎220 482 4526 **W:** amcontacto.blogspot.com.ar **E:** contacto1460@gmail.com – **BA42)** Lacroze 1871 –(Ex 7277)-, (B1655LVS) José León Suárez ☎11 4720 2688 **W:** radiofolclorisimo.com.ar **E:** folclorísimo@hotmail.com – **BA44)** Treinta y Tres 1033, Villa Ariza, (B1714NOS) Ituzaingó ☎11 4623 7773 **W:** //emisoraam1560.com.ar – **BA45)** Vidam Alegre 23, (B1842FSA) Monte Grande ☎11 4281 4094 **E:** radiovidaam1620@gmail.com – **BA47)** Juan Jofré 4243, (B1765MOY) Isidro Casanova ☎11 4694 8131 **W:** emisoracielonuevo.weebly.com **E:** radiocielonuevo@hotmail.com – **BA48)** Pueyrredón 3846, (B1650CVP) San Martín ☎11 4754 8784 **W:** amtradicion.com **E:** amtradicion@gmail.com – **BA51)** Catamarca 2560, (B1847CXH) Rafael Calzada ☎11 4219 1150 **E:** radioluzdelmundo@hotmail.com – **BA52)** Juncal 12, 1° Piso, Of. "3", (B1770AOB) Tapiales ☎11 4442 6333 **W:** am-1440.com.ar **E:** impactoam@hotmail.com – **BA53)** Mariquita Sánches de Thompson 1850, (B1768BDP) Ciudad Madero ☎11 4622 1570 **W:** radiointeractiva1290.com.ar **E:** radiointeractiva1290@hotmail.com – **BA55)** Las Piedras 2447, (B1826DJO) Remedios de Escalada ☎11 4249 6047 **W:** radiomelody1570.com.ar **E:** melody1570@hotmail.es – **BA56)** Andrés Berasain 659, (B1842AMM) Monte Grande ☎11 4281 3740 **W:** amexcelsior.com.ar **E:** amexcelsior@gmail.com – **FM:** 91.7MHz FM Malvinas – **BA63)** Eva Perón 1169, (B1824IBI) Lanús ☎11 4247 3106 **W:** amplusradio.com **E:** plusradio1300@hotmail.com – **BA66)** Florencio Sánchez 119, Bo Los Alamos, (B1856FXE) Glew ☎11 4233 1323 **W:** am1100estilo.blogspot.com **E:** amestilo@hotmail.com – **BA67)** Gascón 6343, (B7604BGA) Mar del Plata ☎223 478 2947 **W:** radioamvida.com **E:** info@radioamvida.com – **BA68)** Potrerillos 1246, (B1849DVX) Claypole ☎11 4219 3850 **W:** am660popular.com.ar **E:** info@am660popular.com.ar - **FM:** 89.1MHz FM Popular – **BA69)** Choele Choel 1233, (B1822DPY) Valentín Alsina ☎11 4218 5333 **W:** radiogamaeninternet.com **E:** radiogama@hotmail.com – **BA71)** Calle 39 N° 256 (B1902APL) La Plata ☎221 427 3360 **W:** radiorocha.com **E:** rocha1570@gmail.com – **BA72)** Domingo F.Sarmiento 2220, (B1663GFX) San Miguel ☎11 4667 4460 **W:** radioprovinciana.com **E:** radioprovincianaam1290@hotmail.com – **BA74)** Santiago del Estero 73, (B1862SCA) Guernica ☎2224 47 6963 **W:** radioalabanzas.net **E:** radioalabanzas@hotmail.com – **BA76)**Av. Cristianía 3747, (B1765HOK) Isidro Casanova ☎11 4694 8499 **W:**la1370.com.ar- **FM:** 92.1MHz R. Cosmos – **BA77)** Jauretche 1052, 1° Piso "B", (B1686FCD) Hurlingham ☎11 4662 5016 **W:** laradiodeimpais.com.ar **E:** info@laradiodeimpais.com.ar – **BA79)** Santander 892, 1° Piso, (C1424CSL) CA Buenos Aires ☎11 4296 1623 **W:**radio1090.com.ar **E:** mensajes@radio1090.com.ar – **BA83)** Av. Pedro Luro 2237, 16° Piso "A", (B7600GTO) Mar del Plata

☎11 4325 2020 **W:** ondamarinaam1220.com.ar **E:** radio@ondamarinaam1220.com.ar - **FM:** 89.1MHz – **BA84)** Carlos Gardel 1133. (B1824NTW) Lanús ☎11 4225 7304 **W:** cadenaam1470.com **E:** info@cadenaam1470.com – **BA89)** Francisco Beazley 1209 (B1755CLY) Rafael Castillo ☎11 4697 7333 **W:** am1230radiolitoral.com **E:** litoral1230@gmail.com – **BA90)** Madrid 3987, Barrio San Juan, (B1712NMO) Castelar ☎11 4692 4412 **W:** amimagen.com.ar **E:** amimagen@hotmail.com – **BA91)** Av. General Paz 3755, (B1672AMA) Villa Lynch ☎11 4755 9061 **W:** radioam610.com.ar **E:** radioam610@gmail.com – **BA92)** Juárez 250, (B7130CWF) Chascomús ☎2241 42 5367 **W:** lavozregional.com - **FM:** 90.9MHz – **BA99)** Av. Alte. Francisco Seguí 1059, (B1836BYK) Llavallol ☎11 4293 9904 **W:** FB **E:** restaurandote@hotmail.com – **BA100)** Pte Hipólito Yrigoyen 51, Oficina 303, (B1640HEA) Martinez ☎11 4793 7471 **W:** amlider.com.ar **E:** info@amlider.com.ar - **FM:** 99.3MHz – **BA107)** Av. Brig. Gral. Juan Manuel de Rosas 4357, (B1754FVB) San Justo ☎11 4484 4517 **W:** Facebook **E:** contacto@cristolasolucion.com– **FM:** 91.1MHz – **BA108)** Manuel Dorrego 292, (B7101) General Conesa ☎2245 49 2140 **W:** am1420.com **E:**am1420radioconesa@hotmail.com – **BA119)** Gral. Martín Miguel de Güemez 5025, (B1603CUE) Villa Martelli ☎11 4709 1172 **W:** amitalia.com.ar **E:** radioitalia.am@gmail.com – **BA120)** Domingo F.Sarmiento 4154, (B1665KON) José C.Paz ☎2320 42 3306 **W:** sintonia1000.com.ar **E:** sintonia1000@yahoo.com.ar – **BA124)** Soberanía Nacional 2945, (B1757KHY) Gregorio de Lafferrere ☎11 4457 3674 **W:** guabiyu1610.com.ar **E:** oyentes@guabiyu1600.com.ar – **BA127)** Vicente López 235 2° Piso, (B1842AUE) Monte Grande ☎11 4284 3186 **W:** radioclaridad.com.ar **E:** radioclaridad@hotmail.com.ar – **BA131)** Cnl. Brandsen 1175, (B1646ABW) San Fernando ☎11 4746 6856 **W:** radiooasis92.com **E:** angelbonarrico@yahoo.com.ar – **FM:** 92.5MHz FM Sencacion – **BA134)** Cuzco 2821, (B1681CGU) William C. Morris, Hurlingham ☎11 4662 8800 **W:** amrestauracion.blogspot.no/ **E:** restauracionam@hotmail.com – **BA135)** San Martin 513 (B1854FEM) Longchamps ☎11 4233 5560 **W:** radio26.com.ar **E:** radio26dejulio@gmail.com – **BA138)** Juan Florio 3573, (B1754AJK), San Justo ☎11 4484 0808 **W:**amnativa.com.ar – **BA139)** Fray Mamerto Esquiú 1161, (B1824BFQ) Lanús ☎11 4225 2256 **W:** digital860.blogspot.com **E:** digital860@hotmail.com – **BA141)** Jauretche 1052, 1° Piso "C", (B1686FCD) Hurlingham ☎11 4452 8688 **W: radio**decadas.com.ar **E:** info@radiodecadas.com.ar – **BA144)** Santa Fe 2540, (B1722BGZ) Merlo ☎220 485 6696 **W:** buenasnuevasradio.com.ar **E:** radiobuenasnuevasam1380@yahoo.com.ar - **FM:** 92.5MHz – **BA145)** Ex. Combatientes de Malvinas 2053, (B1613ECO) Los Polvorines ☎2320 44 7711 **W:** radionorteña.com.ar **E:** radionortena@hotmail.com – **BA146)** Av Dr. Juan Héctor Jara 2075, (B7604EOE) Mar del Plata ☎223 506 3266 **W:** creedcristoviene.com - **FM:** 91.1MHz – **BA147)** Donovan 1433, (B1770AHK) Tapiales ☎11 4426 0185 **W:** am1480.com.ar **E:** sensacionesam@gmail.com – **BA148)** Victor Hugo 647, (B1825FBI) Monte Chingolo ☎11 4220 6822 **W:** cadenad.com **E:** director@cadenad.com – **BA154)** Salta 2641, (B1754iQS) San Justo ☎11 4441 8196 - **FM:** 104.5MHz FM Sintonia – **BA155)** Gral. Belgrano 531, (B7000GEK) Tandil ☎249 444 6383 **W:** am1180.com.ar **E:** contacto@am1180.com.ar - **FM:** 99.5MHz – **BA156)** Av Bdr. Juan Manuel de Rosas N° 10840, (B1757EPS) Gregorio de Laferrere ☎11 4640 1021 **W:** radiorevivir.net **E:** radiorevivir@gmail.com – **FM:** 89.7MHz – **BA163)** Juan F.Segui 895, (B1615MNA) Grand Bourg ☎2320 68 6565 **W:** lamorenadeitati – **BA167)** Benito Pérez Galdós 688, Villa Centenario, (B1821EON) Banfield ☎11 4276 5194 **E:** bethel1670@hotmail.com – **BA169)** Yatay 628,Bo Lamadrid, (B1804CMH) Ezeiza ☎11 4232 7070 **W:** radiodifusoraemanuel.jimdo.com **E:** radiodifusoraemanuel@hotmail.com – **BA172)** Juan Florio 3573, (B1754AJK) San Justo ☎11 4441 8200 **W:** radiorepublica670.com.ar – **BA173)** Belgrano 4033, (B1650CCS) San Martin ☎11 4713 8808 **W:**am680.com.ar – **BA174)** Heredia 920, Augstín Ferrari, (B1724EOT) Mariano Acosta ☎220 498 1498 **W:** radiolider1470.blogspot.com **E:** laradiolider@hotmail.com – **BA175)** Av. Brigadier Juan Manuel de Rosa 2468, (B1655MSS) José León Suárez ☎11 4729 1545 **W:** popular1550blogspot.com **E:** radio1550popular@hotmail.com – **BA176)** Remedios de Escalada San Martin 76, (B6740ELB) Chacabuco ☎2352 42 6156 **W:**lt36radiochacabuco.com.ar **E:** lt36radio_chacabuco@yahoo.com - **FM:** 91.7 MHz FM Universal – **BA177)** Zufriategui 871, (B1765CKQ) Isidro Casanova ☎11 4467 2468 **W:** radiohosannaam1640.com.ar - **E:** hosannaam1640@hotmail.com – **BA178)** Pedro Laurenz 237, Las Malvinas (B1748), General Rodríguez ☎11 3268 0057 **W:** radioolivera.es.tl **E:** radioolivera@yahoo.com – **BA179)** Bombero Ariño 1150, (B1834IAX) Temperley ☎11 2098 8508 **W:**lasupersport.com **E:** lasuper@lasupersport.com – **BA180)** Hipólito. Yrigoyen 2629, (B7600DPG) Mar del Plata ☎223 494 1428 **E:** am1620@yahoo.com.ar – **BA181)** Cjal. Manuel Martitegui 598, Fátima, (B1629JGL) Pilar ☎ 230 437 3150 **W:** am1650antares.com.ar **E:** info@1650antares.com.ar – **BA182)** Salta 138, 2° Piso "C", (B1708JOD) Morón ☎11 4489 2024 **W:** am850.com.ar **E:** lagauchita810@hotmail.

com – **BA183)** Av Cnl Ramón L. Falcón 6219 (C14085DRQ) CA Buenos Aires ☎11 4641 2821 **W:** am890.com.ar **E:** administracion@am890.com.ar – **BA184)** Santa Rosalía (Diagonal 78) 1465 (B1651CXE) San Andrés ☎11 4839 8145 **W:** sudamericana1120.com.ar **E:** info@sudamericana1120.com.ar – **BA185)** Fray Mamerto Esquiú 2855, (B1826GBO) Remedios de Escalada ☎11 4225 3198 **W:** radioindependencia.com.ar **E:** radioindependencia@hotmail.com – **FM:** 99.3MHz R. G – **BA187)** Las Heras 1478, (B6700AUO) Luján ☎2323 42 9595 **W:**masterradiolujan.com.ar **E:** master1310@ciudad.com.ar – **BA190)** Avenida 59 N° 2465, PA, (B7630GYJ) Necochea ☎2262 52 0003 **W:** am1380.com.ar **E:** contacto@am1380.com.ar – **FM:** 103.9MHz – **BA191)** Florentino Ameginho 34, 1° Piso, Oficino 6, (B1842CAB) Monte Grande ☎11 4296 3890 **W:** jerusalenradio.com **E:** info@jerusalenradio.com – **BA192)** Paula Albarracin 3957, Barrio Sarmiento (B1663CPE) San Miguel Oeste ☎2320 46 0649 **W:** amesencia.com.ar **E:** radioesencia@live.com.ar – **BA194)** Av. Aristóbulo del Valle 1202 (B7000HLN) Tandil ☎249 444 8008 **W:**lavozdetandil.com.ar **E:** 1560@lavozdetandil.com.ar – **BA196)** Aristóbulo del Valle 23, (B7240IXA) Lobos ☎2227 42 1211 **W:** amradioantena.com.ar **E:** amradioantena@hotmail.com.ar – **BA198)** Luis Vernet 6654, (B1757MOB) Gregorio de Laferrere ☎11 4467 4224 **W:** la1120.com.ar **E:** santiagoycopla@hotmail.com – **BA199)** Av. Buenos Aires 735, Galeria Pinar, Local 11, (B7165JCH) Villa Gesell ☎2255 47 6749 **W:** am1310gesell.com.ar **E:** am1310gesell@hotmail.com – **FM:** 89.9MHz – **BA200)** Calle Carabobo 5493, Villa Luzuraga, Partido de La Matanza ☎11 4457 7204 **W:** radioiofmailin.com.ar **E:** radiomailinam1330@gmail.com – **BA205)**Dr Eugenio Asconape 371, (B1744FIG) Moreno ☎237 460 0878 **W:**amrenacer.com.ar **E:** radiorenaceram1340@hotmail.com – **BA208)** Ramón L.Falcón 2193, (B1685BDY) El Palomar ☎11 4443 7424 **W:** radiolaluna.com.ar **E:** loscoloresdelanoche@gmail.com – **FM:** 90.5MHz – **BA209)** Dr.Rebizzo- (Calle 626) – N° 3917 (B1678BCC) Caseros ☎11 4578 5130 **E:** radioarea1@gmail.com – **BA212)** Marcelo T.de Alvear 548 (B1755JML) Rafael Castillo ☎11 4697 4919 **W:** cunumiguasu.com.ar **E:** cunumiquasu@hotmail.com – **BA213)** Mñor. López May 3372, (B1757DHJ) Gregorio de Laferre ☎11 4467 3600 **W:** radioesperanzaamyfm.com.ar **E:** radioesperanza@gmail.com – **FM:** 88.3MHz **BA214)** General Lavalle 2307, (B1847BQW) Rafael Calzada ☎11 4219 1903 **W:** radiofundacion.org.ar **E:** contacto@radiofundacion.org.ar – **BA216)** Andrés Blanqui 4233, (B1666CZS) José C. Paz ☎2320 59 9321 **W:** radiogeneralpaz.com **E:** generalpazam1390@hotmail.com – **BA218)** General Pinto 230,(CB6620KUF) Chivilcoy ☎2346 42 4532 **W: E:** cope1410@gmail.com – **FM:** 101.5 MHz – **BA219)** Juan Manuel de Rosas 1053, (B1864HZN), Alejandro Korn ☎2225 42 6063 **W:** radiounidadam1630.com **E:** radiounidad941@yahoo.com.ar – **FM:** 94.1MHz – **BA220)** Ejército de los Andes 5, Villa Florito, (B1821BWA) Banfield Oeste ☎11 4276 2423 **W:** rbn1510am.com.ar **E:** rbn_am1510@hotmail.com – **BA223)** Faustino Brughetti 1392, (B7100) Dolores ☎2245 44 3131 **W:** radiodolores.com.ar **E:** radiodolores@hotmail.com – **FM:** 94.9MHz – Red 94 – **BA224)** Mozart 1015, (B1721EUS) Parque San Martin, Merlo ☎220 470 4265 **W:** amsentires.com.ar **E:** sentires1620@hotmail.com – **BA225)** Av Maipú 18, L-28, (B1602AAN) Florida ☎11 4797 0687 **W:** amradiotradicional.jimdo.com. **E:**amradiotradicional@yahoo.com.ar – **BA226)** Remedios de Escalada de San Martin 65, PB "1", (B6000CZA) Junin ☎236 444 4450 – **FM:** 96.5MHz – **BA229)** Lavalle 1625. P.B., Oficina 4 (C1048AAM) CA Buenos Aires ☎11 4372 1548 **W:** am1130.com.ar **E:** am1130radio@gmail.com – **BA230)** San Andrés 800, Barrio Altos de Palihue, (B8000FTN) Bahia Blanca ☎291 459 5190 **W:** radio.uns.edu.ar **E:** radio@uns.edu.ar – **BA231)** Carmen de Areco 406 (B1841HHJ9 Monte Grande ☎11 4263 4108 – **BA232)** Hilario Ascasubi 4446 (B1757AZB) Gregorio de Laferrere ☎11 4457 1466 **E:** radiolamas@live.com – **BA233)** Dr. Carlos Saavedra Lamas 3636, (B1666MDV) José C. Paz ☎2320 45 3200 **W:** promesero.radiofm.com.ar **E:** laradiodelpromesero-2016@hotmail.com – **FM:** 91.3MHz – **BA235)** Autopista Acceso Oeste –Colectora Lado Norte- N° 6589 (B1743NVD) Moreno ☎237 468 7766 **W:** ambanderas.com.ar **E:** banderas@gmail.com – **BA236)** José Miró1453, (B1738BIC) La Reja ☎237 487 1145 - **FM:** 90.7 MHz – **BA237)** Calle 51 N° 559, (B7105BJK) San Clemente del Tuyó ☎2252 42 1228 **W:** amentremares.com.ar **E:** amentremares@hotmail.com – **FM:** 101.7 MHz Cadena Virtual – **BA238)** Patricias Argentinas 456, Parque San Martin, (B1721BTD) Merlo ☎220 480 2134 **W:** am1530.com.ar **E:** info@am1530.com.ar – **BA239)** Carlos Diehl 2196, (B1854CGN) Longchamps ☎11 2119 9094 **E:**radio@radiolasestrellassd.com.ar Av Hipólito Yrigoyen 1700, Dpto. 1, (B1722JMP) Merlo ☎220 486 5767 **W:** radiosinfronterasam1590. blogspot.com.ar **E:** chamamesinfronteras@hotmail.com – **BA241)** Cjal. José Dans Rey –Calle 26- N° 742 (B1888ELF) Florencio Varela ☎11 4255 0739 **W:** siemprechamame.com.ar **E:** info@siemprechamame.com.ar - **FM:** 90.1MHz –**BA244)** Soberania Nacional 2945, (B1757KHY) Gregorio de Laferrere ☎11 4457 3674 **W:** elsonidodelagente.com.ar – **BA245)** Cayetano Cazón 2338, (B1755HDH) Rafael Castillo ☎11

4698 3163 **E:** radioelmensajero@hotmail.com **BA246)** Chaco 67 (B1620EOA) Maquinista Savio ☎3484 483825 **W:** radioam1490caacati.com **E:**radioam1490caacati@gmail.com – **BA247)** Sófocles 4825, (B1743FFA) Moreno ☎237 468 7195 **W:** radioam1580.com.ar **E:** radiocondoram1580@hotmail.com – **BA249)** Dr José Manuel Galvez 950, Bo Juan XXIII, (B6702COV) Luján ☎2323 15 642763 **W:** Facebook **E:** radiorevolution1040@gmail.com – **BA250)** Salta 138, 2° piso "C", (B1708JOD) Morón ☎11 4628 3348 **W:** laradiodelchamame.com.ar – **BA251)** Oliden 2872, Villa Caraza, Lanus ☎11 4218 0549 **W:** am1550.com.ar **E:** estacion1550@gmail.com – **BA253)** Call 515 s/n, e /Calles 203 y 204, (B1903) Abasto ☎221 491 6476 **W:** fmsanponciano.com.ar **E:**fmsanponciamo@yahoo.com.ar – **FM:** 99.7MHz–**BA254)** Aconquija 1053 (B1716BNG) Libertad ☎220 494 2303 **W:** larocaazulradioam.com.ar **E:** dijitalradio@hotmail.com.ar – **BA255)** 25 de Mayo 579, (B6700ALK) Luján ☎2323 44 2020 **E:** am1400lujan@yahoo.com.ar – **FM:** 91.9 MHz FM Fantástica – **BA257)** Azopardo 186, (B7109AHD) Mar de Ajó ☎2257 60 4540 **W:** radioam1440.com.ar **E:** radiofedetur@gmail.com –**BA258)** Robertson 1249, 1° Piso, (B1838AIE) Luis Guillón ☎11 4290 2892 **W:** lavozdelsur.com.ar **E:** amlavozdelsur@gmail.com – **BA259)** General Arenales 2154, (B1666AEB)José C. Paz **W:** radiolaamistad.com **E:** radiolaamistad@hotmail.com–**BA261)** Alvarez de Toledo 3150, (B1847GDR), Canning ☎11 4235 1510 **W:** // fmsintonia977.blogspot.com.ar **E:** fmsintonia977@hotmail.com – **FM:** 95.7 MHz –**BA262)** Isidro Casanova ☎11 2069 2380 **W:** facebook.com/Siloe1530– **BA263)** Villegas 2157, (BA1714PAK) Ituazingó ☎11 2082 3860 **W:** amselva1710.wixsite.com/envivo **E:** amselva1710@gmail.com – **BA264)** Laprida 1166, (B1832HOX) Lomasde Zamora – **BA265)** Junin – **BA266)** Calle Soberania Nacional 2945,(B1757KHY) Gregorio de Laferrere ☎11 4457 8712 – **BA267)** Catamarca 445, Villa Golf, (B1803DYI) La Union-Ezeiza, Buenos Aires ☎11 4687 8352 **W:** radiodediosebenezer.com.ar **E:** radio@radiodediosebenezer.org.ar – **BA268)** General Madariaga

**CA00) CATAMARCA:**

**CA01)** Chacabuco 762, (K4700BTP) S.F. del Valle de Catamarca ☎3833 42 4223 **W:** radionacional.com.ar **W:** nacionalcatamarca.com.ar **E:** catamarca@radionacional.gov.ar - **FM:** 103.3MHz – **CA02)** San Fernando del Valle, Catamtca

**CB00) CHUBUT:**

**CB01)** Av. Alvear 1180, (U9200AXY) Esquel ☎2945 45 1900 **W:** radionacional.com.ar **E:** esquel@radionacional.gov.ar - **FM:** 88.7MHz – **CB02)** Av. Hipólito Yrigoyen 1735, (U9102BGM) Trelew ☎280 443 0580 📠280 442 5457 **W:** radiochubut.com **E:** info@radiochubut.com - **FM:** 95.7MHz Galaxia – **CB03)** 25 de Mayo 453, (U9000CXC) Comodoro Rivadavia ☎297 447 2125 **W:** radionacional.com.ar **E:** nacionalcomodoro@hotmail.com - **FM:** 94.7MHz – **CB04)** Estivariz 226, (U9120KEF) Puerto Madryn ☎280 445 9200 **W:** lu17.com.ar **E:** lu17@lu17.com - **FM:** 94.1MHz Paraiso FM – **CB05)** Av. Rivadavia 198, (U9000AKP) Comodoro Rivadavia ☎297 447 6561 **W:** lu4radio.com.ar **E:** direccion@lu4radio.com - **FM:** 101.7MHz FM Alfa – **CB06)** 25 de Mayo 740, (U9100BRP) Trelew ☎280 443 5221 **W:** radio3cadenapatagonia.com **E:** radio3trelew@gmail.com – **CB07)** Av. Comandante Fontana y Dr. Mariano Moreno, (U9033) Alto Rio Senguer ☎2945 49 7050 **W:** radionacional.com.ar **E:** lra_55@radionacional.gov.ar - **FM:** 93.5MHz – **CB09)** 25 de Mayo 740 (U9100BRP) Trelew ☎280 113 5221 **W:** radio3cadenapatagonia.com **E:** radiotres@speedy.com.ar – **CB10)** Puerto Madryn – **CB11)** Paseo de Indioas

**CF00) CIUDAD AUTÓNOMA DE BUENOS AIRES (BUENOS AIRES):**

**CF01)** Rivadavia 835, (C1002AAG) CA Buenos Aires 📠11 4338 4250 **W:** continental.com.ar **E:** info@continental.com.ar – **CF02)** Arenales 2467, (C1124AAM) CA Buenos Aires ☎11 5219 4744 📠11 5219 4760 **W:** rivadavia.com.ar **E:** info@rivadavia.com.ar – **CF03)** Sarmiento 1551, 8° Piso, (C1042ABC) CA Buenos Aires ☎11 5371 4646 📠11 5371 4613 **W:** buenosaires.gob.ar/radiociudad **E:** laoncediez@gmail.com – **CF04)** Gral. Mansilla 2668, 1° piso (C1425BPD) CA Buenos Aires ☎11 5777 1500 📠11 5777 1504 **W:** radiomitre.com.ar **E:** info@radiomitre.com.ar – **CF05)** Maipú 555, (C1006ACE) CA Buenos Aires ☎11 4327 3021 📠11 4325 9433 **W:** radionacional.com.ar **E:** buenosaires@radionacional.gov.ar - **External Sce:** see Int. Broadc. section – **CF06)** Angel Justiano Carranza 1441 (C1414CHX) CA Buenos Aires ☎11 4535 2011 **W:** lared.com.ar **E:** info@radiolared.com.ar – **CF07)** Cap. Gral. Ramón Freire 932 (C1426AVT) CA Buenos Aires ☎11 4010 7145 **W:** am950belgrano.com **E:** info@am950belgrano.com – **CF08)** José Ignacio Gottiti 5963, (C1414BKK) CA Buenos Aires ☎11 4556 9200 📠11 4556 9056 **W:** amdelplata.com **E:** prensa@amdelplata.com F.P.I.: 100 kW – **CF09)** Gorriti 5995, (C1414BKK) CA Buenos Aires ☎4535 2525 **W:** facebook.com/ElMundoAM1070/ **E:** info@radioelmundo.com – **CF10)** CA Buenos Aires – **CF11)** Av. Entre Ríos 1931, (C1133AAH) CA Buenos Aires ☎11 4307 2200 **W:** radiobuenosaires.com.ar **E:** am1350@radiobuenosaires.com – **CF12)** Conde 935, (C1426AYS) Ciudad de Buenos Aires ☎11 3961 7600 **W:** la990.com.ar **E:** contacto@la990.com – **CF13)** Nicaragua 4994, (C1414BVN) CA Buenos Aires ☎11 4535

4000 **W:** minutouno.com/radio10 **E:** radio10@inradios.com.ar – **CF15)** Sarmiento 1586, 6° Piso "E", 2° Cuerpo, (C1042ABD) CA Buenos Aires ☎11 4372 2841 **W:** am1010ondalatina.com.ar **E:** contactoam1010@yahoo.com.ar – **CF16)** Lavalle 900, 9° Piso B, (C1047AAR) CA Buenos Aires ☎11 4325 2020 **W:** ecomedios.com **E:** radio@cadenaeco.com. ar– **CF17)** Av. Rivadavia 10561, 3° Piso, (C1408AAF) CA Buenos Aires ☎11 5631 1000 ▤11 5631 1001 **W:** cadenaderadioeco.com.ar **E:** am1530@cadenaderadioeco.com.ar – **CF18)** Traful 3834, (C1437HML) CA Buenos Aires ☎11 4912 0497 **W:** am840generalbelgrano.com **E:** am840generalbelgrano@hotmail.com – **CF21)** Cerrito 242, PB "B", (C1010AAF) CA Buenos Aires ☎11 5275 0770 **W:** radiocooperativa. com.ar **E:** contacto@radiocooperativa.com.ar – **CF23)** Av. Larrazábal 4300, Casa 32, (C1439EDR) CA Buenos Aires ☎11 4638 7644 – **CF24)** Lavalle 1625, P.B., Oficina 4, (C1048AAMI) CA Buenos Aires ☎11 4371 2597 **W:** radiodelpueblo.com.ar **E:** gerencia@radiodelpueblo. com.ar – **CF26)** Bonpland 1114, (C1414CMJ) CA Buenos Aires ☎11 4856 8819 **W:** am1300lasalada.com.ar **E:** info@am1300lasalada. com.ar – **CF27)** Maipu 267 7° Piso, (C1084ABE) CA Buenos Aires ☎11 4136 1050 **W:** conceptoam.com.ar **E:** radio@conceptoam.com. ar – **CF28)** Humboldt 1477, (C1414CKT) CA Buenos Aires ☎11 4778 8200 **W:** la1420.com.ar **E:** contacto@radiodime.com.ar – **CF29)** Santander 892, 1° Piso (C1424CSL) CA Buenos Aires ☎11 4926 0177 **W:** am1310.com.ar **E:** radioam1310@gmail.com – **CF30)** San Martin 569 2° Piso "7", (C1004AAK) CA Buenos Aires ☎11 4893 1701 **W:** am570radioargentina.com.ar **E:** info@am570radioargentina.com. ar – **CF31)** Manzanares 4006, (C1430AEN) CA Buenos Aires ☎11 4541 0303 **W:** cadenauno1240.com.ar **E:** cadenaunoradio@gmail. com – **CF33)** Tacuari 1594, (C1139AAH) CA Buenos Aires ☎11 4307 1835 **W:** amtango.com.ar **E:** amtango@amtango.com.ar – **CF34)** Pte. Luis Sàenz Peña 210 (C1110AAF) CA Buenos Aires ☎11 4382 9327 **W:** somosradioam530.com**E:** radio530somos@gmail.com – **CF35)** Santander 892, 1° Piso (C1424CSL) CA Buenos Aires ☎11 4926 1622 **W:** radiogenesis970.com.ar **E:** administracion@radiogenesis970.com. ar – **CF36)** Fonrouge 76, (C1408HFB) CA Buenos Aires ☎11 3979 5663 **W:** radiooliva.com **E:** radiooliva2006@hotmail.com – **CF37)** Alicia Moreau de Justo 2050, 1°P, Of. "132", (C1107AFP) CA Buenos Aires ☎11 4893 7555 **W:** radioelsol.com.ar **E:** radio@radioelsol.com.ar – **CF38)** San Martín 569, 2° Piso "6", (C1004AAK) CA Buenos Aires ☎11 4313 8575 **W:** belgrano650.com.ar **E:** info@belgrano650.com.ar – **CF44)** Av. Callao 449, 5° Piso "C", (C1022AAE) CA Buenos Aires ☎11 4372 5863 **W:** am1230creativa.wix.com **E:** am1230creativa@yahoo. com.ar – **CF45)** Ulrico Schmidt 6057, 4° Piso, (C1440CFS) CA Buenos Aires ☎11 4642 5533 **W:** am690.com.ar **E:** radioam690@yahoo. com.ar – **CF47)** Pje. Gibson 3999 (C1255AAA) CA Buenos Aires ☎11 4921 9999 **W:** radiofantastico.com.ar **E:** interior@radiofantastico.com. ar – **CF48)** Av.Pueyrrdeón 19, 2° Piso, (C1032ABA) CA Buenos Aires ☎11 4864 2230 **W:** radiorebelde.com.ar **E:** amrebelde@hotmail. com – **CF49)** Libertad 434, 1° Subsuelo, Of. 5, (C1012AAJ) CA Buenos Aires ☎11 4381 4305 **W:** am1590.com.ar – **CF50)** Av.Pte. Roque Sáenz Peñ 1124, 2° Piso "B" (C1035AAT) Buenos Aires ☎11 4381 2569 **W:** guemesam.com.ar **E:** guemes1050am@gmail.com – **CF51)** Venezuela 370, 2° piso, (C1095AAH) CA Buenos Aires ☎11 5354 6651 **W:** radioam750.com.ar **E:** web@radioam750.com.ar – **FM:** 89.1 R.Malena – **CF52)** Av Colonel Ramón L Falcón 6219 (C1408DRQ) CA Buenos Aires ☎11 4641 3920 **W:** 810am.com.ar **E** administracion@810am.com. ar – **CF53)** Ca Ulrico Schmidt 6057, 4° Piso, (C1440CFS)CA Buenos Aires ☎11 4642 5315 **W:** am540.com.ar **E:** radioam540@yahoo.com

## CH00) CHACO:
**CH01)** Av. General Güemes 1103, (H3730AML) Charata ☎3731 42 0150 ▤ 3731 42 0735 **W:** mocovi.com.ar **E:** am800@mocovi.com. ar - **FM:** 95.7MHz FM Lider – **CH02)** Acceso Ruta Nacional N° 40 s/n, Bo Gendarmería, (U9030) Río Mayo ☎2903 42 0099 **W:** radionacional. com.ar **E:** direccionlrg58@radionacional.gov.ar - **FM:** 88.1MHz – **CH03)** Av. Sarmiento 1202, (H3502COE) Resistencia ☎362 443 2920 - **W:** radionacional.com.ar **E:** resistencia@radionacional.gov.ar Guaraní: Sat. 1800 - **FM:** 96.7MHz – **CH04)** Hermana Hortensia - Calle 19 - N° 151, (H3700ASC) Presidencia Roque Sáenz Peña ☎364 442 8047 **W:** radiorsp.com.ar **E:** lt16am950@yahoo.com.ar - **FM:** 93.3MHz FM Sentimientos – **CH05)** Casa de las Culturas,Marcelo T. de Alvear 90, 4° Piso,(H3500ABC) Resistencia ☎362 441 9319 **W:** chaco.tv/radiochaco - **FM:** 101.5MHz – **CH06)** Av. 25 de Mayo 775, (H3700AKQ) Presidencia Roque Sáenz Peña ☎364 442 6520 – **CH07)** Juan José Castelli – **CH08)** Maipú 550 (H3730DPL) Charata ☎3731 42 1569 **W:** amdelnea.com.ar **E:** nuevaeracharate@gmail.com – **FM:** 92.1 MHz – **CH09)** Comodoro Rivadavia – **CH10)** Charata – **CH11)** Villa Angela

## CO00) CORDOBA:
**CO01)** Fray Miguel de Mojica 1600, Bo Marquez de Sobremonte, (X5008CCN) Córdoba ☎351 410 5000 **W:** cba24n.com.ar **E:** am580@srt.com - **FM:** 102.3MHz Nuestra Radio – **CO02)** Santa Rosa 241, (X5000ESE) Córdoba ☎351 422 5664 ▤351 422 5665 **W:** radionacional.com.ar **E:** direccionlr7@radionacional.gov.ar - **FM:**

100.1 MHz –**CO04)** Constitución 399, (X5800BBB) Río Cuarto ☎358 463 8255 **W:** lv16.com **E:** lv16@lv16.com - **FM:** 93.9, 106.9MHz – **CO05)** Alvear 139, (X5000ILC) Córdoba ☎351 526 0597 ▤351 526 0584 **W:** cadena3.com **E:** info@cadena3.com.ar - **FM:** 92.3, 100.5, 106.9MHz –**CO06)** Libertad 455 2° Piso, (X5850KNI) Río Tercero ☎3571 42 1019 **W:** lv26.com.ar **E:** lv26@itc.com.ar - **FM:** 101.9 - 94.5MHz FM Libra – **CO07)** Av. Independencia 77, 1° Piso, (X6120ESA) Laboulaye ☎3385 42 6259 ▤3385 42 5848 **W:** radiolv20.com **E:** info@radiolv20.com – **FM:** 89.9MHz Stereo Atlántica – **CO08)** Córdoba 50,"Edifico Reggio II", (X2400PQA) San Francisco ☎3564 42 2186 **W:** radiosanfrancisco.com.ar **E:** am1050radio@gmail.com - **FM:** 88.7MHz FM Galaxia – **CO09)** Santa Fe 1490, (X5900DTJ) Villa María ☎353 452 2699 **W:** radiovillamaria.com **E:** contame.radiovillsmaria@gmail. com - **FM:** 98.5MHz FM Record – **CO12)** Blvd. 25 de Mayo 133, PB, (X2421ABB) Morteros ☎3562 42 2148 **W:** radiomorteros.com.ar **E:** info@diomorteros.com.ar - **FM:** 90.3MHz FM Selección – **CO13)** Av. Concepción Arenal 1174, (X5004AAY) Córdoba ☎351 460 1010 **W:** radiosucesos.com **E:** radiosucesos@gmail.com – **FM:** 104.7MHz – **CO14)** Pte.Gral. Julia A.Roca 36, (X6120CGB) Laboulaye ☎3385 42 5199 **W:** radio.luis@hotmail.com – **CO15)** Santa Fé 804, (X6270CWR) Huinca Renancó ☎2336 44 2007 **W:** lv22. com.ar **E:** lv22_1490@yahoo.com.ar – **CO16)** Av. Fernando Fader 3469, Bo Cerro de Las Rosas, (X5009ABB) Córdoba ☎351 526 1300 **W:** radiomitrecordoba.com.ar **E:** comercial@radiomitre.com - **FM:** 97.9MHz – **CO17)** La Rioja 995. , (X3400BZK) Corrientes ☎379 442 6600 **W:** mitrecorrientes.com **E:** radio@mitrecorrientes.com – **FM:** 92.9MHz R.Ciudad – **CO18)** Tolosa 2379, Bo Maipú, (X5014JSE) Córdoba ☎351 4119190 **W:** facebook.com/radioamvida1490 **E:** info@radioamvida.com.ar – **CO19)** Paso de los Libres – **CO20)** Florencio Sánches 450, (X5804HIH) Río Cuarto ☎358 4628179 **W:** radiovida. tumbir.com **E:** lausassa@gmail.com – **FM:** 89.3 MHz – **CO21) Colón 1030,**(W3230AAT) Paso delos Libres ☎3772 12 3456 – **FM:** Radio 3 93.3 MHz

## CS00) CORRIENTES:
**CS01)** Chacra 46, Km 3, La Tablada, (W3340) Santo Tomé ☎3756 42 0090 **W:** radionacional.com.ar **E:** santotome@radionacional.gov.ar – **FM:** 100.5MHz –**CS02)** Juan Sitja Nin 941, (W3230GEQ) Paso de los Libres ☎3772 42 4332 **W:** radiolt12.com.ar **E:** contacto@radiolt12.com. ar - **FM:** 92.7MHz FM Confluencia –**CS03)** La Rioja 743, (W3400BZG) Corrientes ☎379 442 3560 **W:** radiolt7.com **E:** contacto@radiolt7.com - **FM:** 95.3MHz FM Capital – **CS04)** Mariano I. Loza 231, (W3450BXE) Goya ☎3777 42 2653 **W:** facebook.com/lt6am1200radiogoya/ **E:** lt6radiogoya@hotmail.com.ar - **FM:** 98.3MHz FM Splendida – **CS05)** General Paz 903, (W3344AYQ) Alvear ☎3772 47 0699 **W:** radiolt21. blogspot.com.ar **E:** radiomunicipalalvear@hotmail.com – **CS06)** Av. Atanaico Aguirre Km 2, (W3470EHA) Mercedes ☎3773 42 0087 **W:** radiodelibera.com.ar **E:** radiodelibra@gmail.com – **FM:** 93.5MHz – **CS07)** San Martín 1380, (W3461AKA) Curuzú Cuatiá ☎3774 42 2634 **W:** lt25.com.ar **E:** am970administracion@hotmail.com - **FM:** FM Guarani 107.1MHz – **CS08)** Goya – **CS09)** Hipólito Yrigoyen 835, (W3400ASQ)Corrientes ☎379 443 4333

## ER00) ENTRE RIOS:
**ER01)** San Martín 371, (E3202FUG) Concordia ☎345 421 5506 **W:** lt15concordia.com.ar **E:** gerencia@lt15concordia.com.ar – **FM:** 89.3MHz – **ER02)** Almeda de la Federacion 126, (E3100GNO) Paraná ☎343 423 0101 **W:** radionacional.com.ar **E:** lt14web@gmail.com - **FM:** 93.1MHz Baxada del Paraná – **ER03)** Justo José de Urquiza al oeste esq. Parada 12 N° 4200, (E2820) Gualeguaychú ☎3446 42 6159 **W:** radionacional.com.ar **E:** gualeguaychu@radionacional.gov. ar – **FM:** 98.7MHz – **ER04)** Montiel 29, (E2820FBA) Gualeguaychú ☎3446 43 1471 **W:** radiolt41.com.ar **E:** info@radiolt41.com.ar – **FM:** 90.3 / 97.9MHz – **ER05)** Av. Pte. Juan D. Perón 117, (E3280CBS) Colón ☎3447 42 1067 **W:** nuevomundodigital.com.ar **E:** radionmundo@colonred.com.ar - **FM:** 93.7MHz FM Palmares – **ER06)** Blvd Eva Peron - Ex Sarmiento - 474, (E3153EZH) Victoria ☎3436 42 1285 **W:** lt39noticias.com.ar **E:** gerencia@lt39am980.com.ar - **FM:**90.3MHz FM Victoria – **ER07)** Pablo Stampa 2430, (E3228FDD) Chajarí ☎3456 42 0002 **W:** chajarialdia.com **E:** info@multimedioschajari.com - **FM** 107.7MHz – **ER08)** Chacabuco 38, 1° Piso, (E2840BFB) Gualeguay ☎3444 42 4915 **W:** radiogualeguay.com **E:** info@radiogualeguay.com. ar - **FM:** 104.9MHz – **ER09)** Roque Sáenz Peña 1082, (E3190FZJ) La Paz ☎3437 42 1568 **W:** lt40.com.ar **E:** info@lt40.com.ar - **FM:** 91.3MHz FM La Paz – **ER10)** Onésimo Leguizamón 269, (E3260FQE) Concepción del Uruguay ☎3442 42 5661 **W:** radionacional.com.ar **E:** lt11@live. com.ar - **FM:** 92.9MHz FM Arena – **ER11)** Av. Vélez Sársfield 1111, (E3240AUL) Villaguay ☎3455 42 1717 **W:** lt27lavozdelmontiel.com.ar **E:** lt27lavozdelmontiel@gmail.com - **FM:** 88.7MHz - R.Urbans – **ER12)** Chacabuco 1514, (E3283AWB) San José ☎3447 47 0998 **W:** 10tv.com. ar **E:** danycanal@hotmail.com - **FM:** 105.3 MHz R.Melody – **ER13)** Dr. Rozados 533, (E3174BEK) Rosario del Tala ☎344 542 3009 **W:** radiomediterranea.com.ar **E:** frecuenciamediterranea@gmail.com -

**FM:** 102.5MHz – **ER14)** Ca.Urquiza 1115, Nogoya ☎3435 42-2524 **W:** FB **E:** radioam1660@gmail.com – **FM:** 96.1 MHz – **ER15)** Av.libertador Gral. San Martin 359, (E3133CXG) Maria Grande ☎343 494 0486 **E:** comercialam1360@hotmail.com.ar

## F000) FORMOSA:
**F001)** Junín 655, (P3600IDM) Formosa ☎3717 42 6197 **W:** radionacional.com.ar **E:** radionacionalformosa@yahoo.com.ar - **FM:** 94.1MHz – **F002)** Ruta Nacional 81 y Ruta Provincial 32, (F3630) Las Lomitas ☎3715 43 2167 **W:** radionacional.com.ar **E:** laslomitas@radionacional.gov.ar - **FM:** 93.5MHz – **F003)** Av. 9 de Julio 165, (P3600BCB) Formosa ☎370 442 2590 **W:** am990formosa.com **E:** info@produccionesyprogramas.com - **FM:** 98.9MHz FM Unica

## JU00) JUJUY:
**JU01)** Av. España (Sur) 700, (Y4650ALN) La Quiaca ☎3885 42 2356 **E:** radionacional.com.ar **E:** lra16radionacionallaquiaca@gmail. **com** - **FM:** 92.5MHz – **JU02)** Rio Bermejo y Olavarria, (Y4600) San Salvador de Jujuy ☎388 422 2781 **W:** radionacional.com.ar **E:** jujuy@radionacional.com.ar - **FM:** 94.1MHz – **JU03)** Dr. Horacio Guzmán 496, (Y4600) San Salvador de Jujuy ☎388 423 0035 **W:** radiovisionjujuy.com.ar **E:** info@radiovisionjujuy.com.ar - **FM:** 97.7MHz FM Tropico – **JU04)** Av. Chile – Ex Villafane y Guatemala, (Y4608) Perico ☎388 491 1465 **W:** radiovisionjujuy.com.ar **E:** radiociudadperico@gmail.com – **JU05)** Jujuy 470, (Y4512DRJ) Libertador General San Martin ☎3886 42 6440 **W:** radiovisionjujuy.com.ar **E:** gerencia@grupovisionjujuy.com. ar - **FM:** 104.5MHz – **JU06)** San Salvador de Jujuy - **FM:** 92.1 MHz

## LP00) LA PAMPA:
**LP01)** Av. Dr.Alfredo Palacios 955, (L6304ACC) Santa Rosa ☎2954 41 3600 **W:** radionacional.com.ar **E:** santarosa@radionacional.gov. ar - **FM:** 95.9MHz – **LP02)** Lisandro de la Torre 474, (L6300BQJ) Santa Rosa ☎2954 41 4015 **W:** lu33pampeana.com **E:** lu33lp. marcelomonsalvo@gmail.com - **FM:** 103.7MHz FM Power – **LP03)** Calle 40 No 1250, (L6360EVZ) General Pico ☎2302 43 0055 **W:** radiolu37.com.ar **E:** radiolu37@radiolu37.com.ar - **FM:** 88.9MHz Melodías FM – **LP05)** General Pico 610, (L8201BIL) 25 de Mayo ☎299 494 8086 **W:** am900.com.ar **E:** radiomunicipal25@gmail.com - **FM:** 91.1MHz FM Rio – **LP06)** Pasaje Rabinad 545, (L6304BJA) Santa Rosa ☎2954 42 7545 **W:** lu100.com.ar **E:** radioantena10@gmail.com - **FM:** 102.5MHz R.10 – **LP08)** Ca 105 Bis (Oeste) Nº 546, (L6360FLL) General Pico ☎2302 43 2331 **W:** laredpampeana.com.ar **E** contacto@laredpampeana.com.ar - **FM:** 89.7 MHz – **LP09)** General Acha

## LR00) LA RIOJA:
**LR01)** Hipólito Yrigoyen 318, (F5300DIH) La Rioja ☎380 442 5396 **W:** radionacional.com.ar **E:** larijo@radionacional.gov.ar – **FM:** 102.5MHz – **LR03)** La Rioja – **LR04)** Av Dr. Luis Maria de la Fuente y Av Laprida, 9° Piso (5300) La Rioja ☎380 445 7038 **W:** radiounlar.com.ar **E:** unlarfm@gmail.com - **FM:** 90.9 MHz

## ME00) MENDOZA:
**ME01)** Manuel A.Sáez 2421, (M5539HSW) Las Heras ☎261 430 1600 **W:** radionihuil.com.ar **E:** radionihuil@radionihuil.com.ar - **FM:** 98.9MHz – **ME02)** Rioja 1093, (M5500ALU) Mendoza ☎261 521 5100 📠261 521 5121 **W:** lvdiez.com.ar **E:** eleve10@infovia.com.ar or info@lvdiez.com. ar - **FM:** 104.1MHz – **ME03)** Rioja 1484, (M5500AMD) Mendoza ☎261 4238872 **W:** radionacional.com.ar **E:** direccionlv8@radionacional.gov. ar - **FM:** 92.7MHz – **ME04)** Bernado de Irigoyen 17, PA (M5620BDA) General Alvear ☎2625 42 6566 **W:** radioandina.com.ar **E:** admlv23@yahoo.com.ar - **FM:** 88.9MHz FM Paraiso – **ME05)** Emilio Civit 460, (M5502GVR) Mendoza ☎261 438 0596 **W:** radionacional.com.ar **E:** mendoza@radionacional.gov.ar - **FM:** 97.1MHz – **ME06)** Esquivel Aldao 350, (M5613AEH) Malargüe ☎260 447 1160 📠260 447 0658 **W:** radionacional.com.ar **E:** radiomalargue@radionacional.com.ar - **FM:** 88.1MHz – **ME07)** Av. Hipólito Yrigoyen 223, (M5602HBC) San Rafael ☎260 443 0055 **W:** radionacional.com.ar **E:** lv4@radiosanrafael.com.ar - **FM:** 97.3MHz – **ME08)** Comandante. Salas 150 1° Piso Of. 6, (M5600DJD) San Rafael ☎260 442 6057 **W:** lv18radio.com.ar **E:** lv18@sanrafael. gov.ar - **FM:** 101.5MHz – **ME09)** Av. Pellegrini 692, (M5560EMT) Tunuyán ☎2622 42 5588 **W:** radioandina.com.ar **E:** lv24am1320@yahoo.com - **FM:** 104.5MHz – **ME10)** Av. Bandera de los Andes 4420, (M5521AXL) Villa Nueva de Guaymallén ☎261 421 3992 **W:** radiomurialdo.com.ar **E:** mensajes@radiomurialdo.com.ar - **FM:** 90.5MHz FM Familia –**ME12)** Comandante Salas 200, (M5602AVD) San Rafael ☎260 442 6265 **W:**radioandina.com.ar **E:** andinasr@gmail. com - **FM:** 104.5 FM Andina – **ME13)** Mendoza – **ME14)** General Gregorio Paz 25, 6° Piso (M5500GNA) Mendoza ☎261 637 2700 **W:** amlider.jimdo.com **E:** cumbre1410@gmail.com - **FM:** Godoy Cruz – **ME16)**Mendoza

## MS00) MISIONES:
**MS01)** Cristóbal Colón 1452, (N3300LXF) Posadas ☎376 443 8727 **W:** radiolt17.com.ar **E:** info@radiolt17.com.ar - **FM:** 107.3MHz FM Provincia – **MS02)** CI 93 No 2289, (N3300JRZ) Posadas ☎376 446 1603 **W:** lt4digital.com - **FM:** 104.5MHz – **MS03)** Av. Victoria Aguirre Sur 809, (N3370AYI) Puerto Iguazú ☎3757 420099 **W:** radionacional.

com.ar **E:** direccionlra19@radionacional.gov.ar- **FM:** 99.1MHz – **MS04)** Av. Las Calandrias y Las Golondrinas, Bo IPRODHA, (N3370) Puerto Iguazú ☎3757 42 0060 **W:** radiocataratas.com **E:** info@radiocataratas.com - **FM:** 94.7MHz – **MS07)** Domingo F.Sarmiento 1847, 7° Piso, (N3300HUM) Posadas ☎376 42 0203 📠376 42 2758 **W:** radiotupambae.com.ar **E:** administracion@radiotupambae.com.ar - **FM:** 105.9MHz – **MS08)** Calle Manantial s/n (N3363) 25 de Mayo ☎3755 58 0030 **W:** radiolacueva1580.com **E:** radiolacueva.sinai@gmail.com - **FM:** 106.5 MHz R.Sinaí

## NE00) NEUQUÉN:
**NE01)** Gral. Paz 536, (Q8353CGL) Chos Malal ☎2948 42 1198 **W:** radionacional.com.ar **E:** chosmalal@radionacional.gov.ar - **FM:** 92.3MHz – **NE02)** Av. San Martín 324, (Q8340EYQ) Zapala ☎2942 42 2960 **W:** radionacional.com.ar **E:** direccionlra17@radionacional. gov.ar - **FM:** 93.9MHz – **NE03)** Gral. Villegas 1375, (Q8370ELB) San Martín de los Andes ☎2972 42 7766 **E:** radionacional.com.ar **E:** lra53@smandes.com.ar - **FM:** 92.5MHz – **NE04)** Fotheringham 445, (Q8302HBI) Neuquén ☎299 449 0485 **W:** lu5am.com.ar **E:** info@lu5am.com.ar - **FM:** 88.7 MHz FM Ciudad – **NE06)** Las Rosas 81, Bo Jardín, (Q8315AYA) Piedra del Aguila ☎2942 49 3216 **W:** radiogregorioalvarez.net **E:** contactorga@gmail.com - **FM:** 99.5MHz – **NE07)** Pte. Bernardino Rivadavia 609, (Q8300HDM) Neuquén ☎299 443 0249 **W:** amcumbre.com - **FM:** 89.9MHz FM Cumbre – **NE10)** Santa Cruz 679, (Q8300BNI) Neuquén ☎299 449 5109 📠299 442 1568 **W:** rtnweb.gob.ar **E:** rtnweb@neuquen.gov.ar – **FM:** 104.9MHz – **NE11)** Montevideo 605 (Q8300LTM) Neuquen ☎299 443 4472 **W:** am550laprimera.com **E:** info@am550laprimera.com - **FM:** 90.7MHz – **NE12)** Maestro Thames Alderete 560, (Q8300HWL) Neuquén ☎299 448 5788 **W:** radionacional.com.ar **E:**nacionalneuquen@gmail.com – **FM:** 103.3MHz

## RN00) RIO NEGRO:
**RN01)** Av. 12 de Octubre 2421, (R8403AOH) San Carlos de Bariloche ☎294 443 1856 **W:** radionacona.com.ar **E:** administracionlra30@radionacional.com.ar - **FM:** 95.5MHz – **RN02)** Tucumán 1074, (R8332HQV) General Roca ☎298 442 4715 **W:** radioelvalle.com **E:** buzon@radioelvalle.com - **FM:** 99.3MHz FM Color – **RN03)** Gral. Roca 365, 2° piso, (R8324BPG) Cipolletti ☎299 477 6333 📠299 477 6800 **W:** lu19.com.ar **E:** publicidadradiolu19@yahoo.com.ar - **FM:** 102.9MHz FM Comanhue – **RN04)** Av. Alvaro Barros 1148, (R8500FFX) Viedma ☎2920 42 7700 **W:** lu15am.com.ar **E:** radiolu15@speedy. com - **Italian:** Sat 1500-1600. - **FM:** 94.3MHz FM Rio – **RN05)** Remedios de Escalada 52, (R8336FED) Villa Regina ☎298 446 1102 📠298 446 2620 **W:** lu16radiorn.com.ar **E:** administracion@lu16radio.com.ar - **FM:** 92.7MHz FM Rio Negro – **RN06)** Gral. Manuel Belgrano 710, (R8500FAP) Viedma ☎2920 43 1697 **W:** radionacional.com.ar **E:** viedma@radionacional.gov.ar - **FM:** 93.5MHz – **RN07)** Av. San Martín y Salta, (R8430) El Bolsón ☎2944 49 2350 **W:** radionacional. com.ar **E:** elbolson@radionacional.gov.ar - **FM:** 92.3MHz – **RN08)** José Hernández 326, (R8418) Ingeniero Jacobacci ☎2940 43 2032 **W:** radionacional.com.ar **E:** ingenierojacobacci@radionacional.gov. ar - **FM:** 93.5MHz – **RN09)** Casa de Tucumán 481, (R8361BKO) Luis Beltrán ☎2946 41 3090 **W:** municipalam1470.com.ar **E:** contacto@municipalam1470.com.ar - **FM:** 96.5 MHz – **RN11)** Hipólito Yrigoyen y Remedios de Escalada, (R8536BBE) Valcheta ☎2934 49 3283 **E:** aznarezmarco@hotmail.com - **FM:** 105.3MHz FM Luján – **RN12)** Hipólito Yrigoyen 402, (R8534) Sierra Colorada ☎2940 49 5176 **W:** Facebook: R.Provincial **E:** am_provincia@hotmail.com – **RN13)** Ruta Nacional Nº 22, Km 1200 y Acceso Martin Fierro, (R8328) Allen ☎298 445 4000 **W:** radioam740.com.ar **E:** radioam740@gmail.com

## SA00) SALTA:
**SA01)** Ruta Nal. 34, Km. 1433, (A4560CJA) Tartagal ☎3875 421600 **W:** radionacional.com.ar **E:** tartagal@radionacional.gov.ar - **FM:** 92.3MHz – **SA02)** Dr.Carlos Pellegrini 715, 1° piso, (A4402FYO) Salta ☎387 426 0243 📠387 426 0109 **W:** radionacional.com.ar **E:** saltalra4@radionacional.gov.ar - **FM:** 102.7MHz – **SA03)** Av Ex Combatientes de Malvinas 3890, (A4412BYA) Salta ☎387 424 6234 📠378 431 1140 **W:** radiosalta.com **E:** info@radiosalta.com - **FM:** 96.9MHz FM Genesis –**SA05)** Gorriti 524, (A4560BRL) Tartagal ☎3873 42 4141 **E:** lw2@fullnet.com.ar - **FM:** 96.1 FM Tartagal – **SA06)** 9 de Julio 163, (A4530XBF) San Ramón de la Nueva Orán ☎3878 42 1026 **W:** radiomaria.org.ar **E:** oranradio@yahoo.com - **FM:** 90.9MHz FM Orán –**SA07)** Salta

## SC00) SANTA CRUZ:
**SC01)** Comodoro Py 342, Casa 16, Dept. 1, Bo Las Lengas (Z9407BFH) Río Turbio ☎2902 421131 **W:** radionacional.com.ar **E:** rioturbio@radionacional.gov.ar - **FM:** 90.3MHz – **SC02)** Zapiola 25, (Z9400BCA) Río Gallegos ☎2966 42 0023 📠2966 42 2608 **W:** lu12.com.ar **E:** lu12_am680@speedy.com.ar - **FM:** 92.9MHz FM Laser – **SC03)** Av. San Martín 1114, (Z9311AVY) Gobernador Gregores ☎2962 49 1044 **W.** radionacional.com.ar **E:** direccionlra59@radionacional.gov. ar - **FM:** 99.9MHz – **SC04)** Hermanos Vidal 127, (Z9405) El Calafate

**W:** radionacional.com.ar **E:** cotecal.com.ar ☎2902 49 5696. - **FM:** 88.1MHz, Glaciar FM – **SC05)** Ramón Lista 36, (Z9050DLB) Puerto Deseado ☎297 487 1211 **E:** lri200@deseado.gov.ar – **FM:** 99.3 MHz – **SC06)** Av. Néstor Kirchner Ex Roca - 823, 1°piso, (Z9400BAH) Río Gallegos **W:** lu14.com.ar **E:** oyenteslu14@gmail.com ☎2966 42 2315 📠2966 42 3510 - **FM:** 96.3MHz FM Provincia – **SC07)** Saavedra 1318, (Z9040BQN) Perito Moreno ☎2963 43 2233 **W:** radionacional.com.ar **E:** administracionlra56@radionacional.gov.ar – **FM:** 93.5MHz – **SC08)** Río Gallegos – **SC09)** Río Gallegos

### SE00) SANTIAGO DEL ESTERO:
**SE01)** 9 de Julio 390, (G4200DEH) Santiago del Estero ☎385 421 3230 **W:** radiolv11.com.ar **E:** contacto@radiolv11.com.ar – **FM:** 88.1, 89.5MHz FM Total – **SE02)** Urquiza 332, 1° Piso, (G4300DHH) Santiago del Estero ☎385 421 2565 **W:** radionacional.com.ar **E:** nacionalsantiago@hotmail.com **FM:** 98.5MHz – **SE03)** Av. 25 de Mayo sur 69, (G3760AEA) Añatuya ☎3844 42 1661 **W:** amradiosolidaridad.com.ar **E:** amsolidaridad@yahoo.com.ar – **SE04)** Santiago del Estero

### SF00) SANTA FE:
**SF01)** Juan de Gary 2960, (S3000CRL) Santa Fé ☎342 483 5327 **W:** radionacional.com.ar **E:** administracionlra14@radionacional.gov.ar - **FM:** 102.9MHz – **SF02)** Sarmiento 763, (S2000CMK) Rosario ☎341 422 9500 **W:** lt8.com.ar **E:** info@lt8.com.ar – **FM:** 99.5MHz – **SF03)** 9 de Julio 3560, (S3002EXB) Santa Fé ☎342 452 0187 **W:** lt10.com.ar **E:** info@lt10digital.com.ar – **FM:** 103.5MHz FM X – **SF04)** 4 de Enero 2153, (S3000FHY) Santa Fé ☎342 410 9999 **W:** lt9.com.ar **E:** info@lt9.com.ar – **FM:** 92.5MHz – **SF05)** Av. Pte. Juan Domingo Perón 8101, (S2010ACF) Rosario ☎341 457 7000 **W:** rosario3.com **E:** radio2@rosario3.com – **FM:** 90.1MHz – **SF06)** Córdoba 1331, 1° Piso, (S2000AWS) Rosario ☎341 440 2490 **W:** radionacional.com.ar **E:** rosario@radionacional.gov.ar – **FM:** 104.5MHz – **SF07)** Balcarce 840, (S2000DNR) Rosario ☎341 528 2680 **W:** lt3.com.ar **E:** digital@lt3.com.ar – **FM:** 102.7MHz – **SF08)** Av. Casey 642, (S2600FJN) Venado Tuerto ☎346 242 0777 **W:** radiovenadotuerto.com **E:** lt29@radiovenadotuerto.com - **FM:** 88.9MHz – **SF09)** Cornelia Saavedra 52, 1° piso, (S2300KJB) Rafaela ☎3492 45 0300 **W:** radiorafaela.com **E:** lt28radiorafaela@gmail.com – **FM:** 96.5MHz – **SF10)** Juan Chavarri 458, (S2147AUH) San Jenaro Norte ☎3401 49 3069 **W:** lt23.com.ar **E:** gerencialt23@co19set.com.ar - **FM:** 92.1MHz FM Concierto – **SF11)** Lucas Funes 1258, (S3560ETZ) Reconquista ☎3482 42 8945 **W:** radioamanecer.com.ar **E:** radioamanecer@radioamanecer.com.ar - **FM:** 92.7MHz FM Amanecer – **SF12)** Calle 107 N° 55, (S3561AIA) Avellaneda ☎3482 48 2716 **W:** am1440.com.ar **E:** am1440rqta@yahoo.com.ar - **FM:** 95.7MHz – **SF14)** Belgrano 470, (S2349AJJ) Suardi ☎3562 47 7612 **W:** radiobelgranosuardi.com.ar **E:** belgrano@suardi.com.ar - **FM:** 104.9MHz – **SF17)** San Luis 935, Oficina 7, (S2000BBK) Rosario ☎341 558 1090 **W:** amlibertad.com **E:** contacto@amlibertad.com.ar – **FM:** FM Latina 94.5MHz – **SF19)** Av Carlos Pellegrini 168, (S2000BTO) Rosario ☎341 424 5259 **W:** am1330rosario.com.ar **E:** am1330rosario@gmail.com - **FM:** 106.1 MHz – **SF20)** 25 de Mayo 3255, (S3000FUI) Santa Fe ☎342 410 1917 **W:** airedesantafe.com.ar **E:** info@airedesantafe.com.ar - **FM:** 91.1MHz – **SF21)** De Lisandro De La Torre 547, (S2521AKK) Montes de Oca ☎3471 49 5143 **W:** radioemecentro.com.ar **E:** am1600@am1600.com.ar - **FM:** 102.7MHz FM La Red – **SF22)** Av.San Martín 710, (S3142XAC) Luis Palacios ☎3476 49 9249 **W:** radioalegria.supersitio.net **E:** radioalegriaregional@hotmail.com.ar - **FM:** 95.9MHz – **SF23)** Casilda 5670, (S2007CKN) Rosario ☎341 437 3431 **E:** amred24@hotmail.com – **FM:** 89.7 MHz Cadena Solidaria – **SF24)** Las Heras 608, (S2216ANL) Serodino 3476 ☎55 4036 **W:** radioserodino.com.ar **E:** contacto@radioserodino.com.ar - **FM:** 104.3MHz – **SF25)** Ruta Nacional N° 9, Cañada de Gómez **W:** facebook.com/RadioMitreAm1620

### SJ00) SAN JUAN:
**SJ01)** Sargento Cabral 1186 Oeste, (J5402CNJ) San Juan ☎264 427-6867 **W:** radiocolon.com.ar **E:** prensa@radiocolon.com.ar - **FM:** 105.7MHz – **SJ02)** Av. Ignacio de la Roza 293 Este, 2° Piso, (J5402DBC) San Juan ☎264 421 4149 **W:** radionacional.com.ar **E:** sanjuan@radionacional.gov.ar - **FM:** 101.9MHz – **SJ03)** General Soler s/n, (J5405AAA) Barreal ☎2648 44 1260 **E:** radiocalingasta@gmail.com - **FM:** FM Nuestra 103.5MHz – **SJ04)** Mendoza 452 Sur, (J5402GUJ) San Juan ☎264 420 4028 **W:** lv5sarmiento.com.ar **E:** contacto@lv5sarmiento.com.ar – **FM:** 102.3, 103.7, 104.3, 104.7MHz Sarmiento FM – **SJ05)** General Paz 631, (J5460BBM) San José de Jáchal ☎2647 42 0028. **W:** radionacional.com.ar **E:** jachal@radionacional.gov.ar - **FM:** 102.7MHz – **SJ06)** Mitre 11 este, (J5402CWA) San Juan ☎264 427 2740 **E:** amlas40@yahoo.com.ar - **FM:** 105.1 – **SJ07)** Santa Fe 668 oeste, (J5402ACN) San Juan ☎264 420 3424 **W:** am1020.com.ar **E:** info@am1020sj.com.ar – **FM:** 96.3 – **SJ08)** Rivadavia

### SL00) SAN LUIS:
**SL01)** Lavalle 291, PA, (D5732AEE) Villa Mercedes ☎📠2657 42 4400 **W:** radiolv15.com.ar **E:** lv15@speedy.com.ar - **FM:** 95.5MHz FM Unica – **SL02)** Av. Lafinur 488, (D5700DCR) San Luís ☎266 443 1318

**W:** radionacional.com.ar **E:** administracionlra29@radionacional.gov.ar - **FM:** 96.7MHz – **SL03)** Belgrano 927, 1° piso, (D5700ISS) San Luís ☎266 442 7300 **W:** cadenadimension.com.ar **E:** dimensionsl@yahoo.com.ar - **FM:** 94.7MHz – **SL04)** General Paz 1078, (D5732AGJ) Villa Mercedes ☎2657 43 7734 **W:** radiomariadelapaz.com.ar **E:** contacto@radiomariadelapaz.com.ar - **FM:** 105.3 MHz

### TU00) TUCUMAN:
**TU01)** Lapride 530, (T4000IFL) San Miguel de Tucmán ☎381 484 5100 **W:** lv12.com.ar **E:** contacto@v12.com.ar - **FM:** 105.1 MHz FM Independencia – **TU02)** Mendoza 273, (T4000DAE) San Miguel de Tucumán ☎381 497 5080 **W:** lv7.com.ar **E:** lv7@radio21tucuman.com.ar - **FM:** 102.7MHz – **TU03)** San Martín 251, 4° Piso, (T4000CVE) San Miguel de Tucumán ☎381 431 0131 **W:** radionacional.com.ar **E:** tucuman@radionacional.gov.ar - **FM:** 98.7MHz – **TU04)** Av Belgrano 50, (T4107DUN) Yerba Buena ☎381 411 1247 **W:** radio21tucuman.com.ar **E:** radio21tucuman@yahoo.com.ar

### TF00) TIERREA DEL FUEGO:
**TF01)** Leonardo Rosales 490, (V9420CMJ) Río Grande ☎2964 42 2176 **W:** radionacional.com.ar **E:** direccionlra24@radionacional.gov.ar - **FM:** 88.1MHz – **TF02)** Av. San Martín 331, (V9410BFD) Ushuaía ☎2901 42 1670 **W:** radionacional.com.ar **E:** ushuaia@radionacional.gov.ar - **FM:** 92.1MHz – **TF03)** Ushuaia – **TF04)** Río Grande

**Capital Federal: CF16)** – **FM:** 90.3 MHz Delta FM – **CF05)** 93.7 R.Pop Nac – 96.7 FM Clásica Nacional – 98.7 Folclórica FM – **CF22)** 89.1 – **CF28)** 89.9 FM Con Vos – **CF16)** 90.3 Eco Radio, 91.1 R.Abierta, 92.1 Mambo, 92.3 La Radio – **CF03)** 92.7 La Ciudad – **CF37)** 93.1 R.Late – 93.7, FM Federal – **CF09)** 94.3 Disney **CF23) 94.3** R.Nueva Bolivia 94.7 FM Palermo – **CF08)** 95.1 La Metro – **CF12)** 95.9 Rock & Pop, 96.3 R.Jai – **CF05)** 96.7 Clásica, 97.1 FM Europa, 97.3 Contacto FM, 97.9 R.Cultura – **CF13)** 98.3 Mega – **CF05)** 98.7 FM Folklorica, 99.1 Cadena 3 Argentina – **CF04)** 99.9 Cadena 100, 100.3 FM Cultural Musical – **CF07)** 100.7 Blue FM, 101.1 La Ciento Uno – **CF06)** 101.5 Pop Radio – **CF10)** 102.3 Aspen Classic – **CF02)** 103.1 R. Uno, 103.7 Amadadeus FM – **CF01)** 104.3 – **CF01)** 105.5 FM Hit – **CF11)** 106.3 R.Aleluya, 106.7 X4, 107.3 Milenium, 107.9 Kabul Rock.
In the city area there are over 150 unlicensed LP FM stns; about 900 in the rest of the country.

## ARMENIA

**L.T:** UTC +4h — **Pop:** 3 million — **Pr.L:** Armenian — **E.C:** 230V/50Hz — **ITU:** ARM

### HERUSTATESUTYAN YEV RADIOYI AZGAYIN HANDZNAZHOGHOV (HRAH)
**(National Commission on Radio & TV)**
✉ Isahakyan St. 28, 0009 Yerevan ☎+374 10 528370 **E:** nctr@tvradio.am **W:** tvradio.am **L.P:** Chmn: Gagik Buniatyan

### HAYASTANI HANRAYIN RADIOYNKERUTYUN PBY (Pub) (Public R. Company of Armenia CJSC)
✉ A.Manoogian St. 5, 0025 Yerevan ☎ +374 10 551143 **E:** info@armradio.am **W:** armradio.am
**L.P:** CEO: Mark Grigoryan

| MW | kHz | kW | Prgr | SW | | kHz | kW | Prgr |
|---|---|---|---|---|---|---|---|---|
| Gavar | 1314 | 500 | M, F | Gavar | | 4810 | 100 | M, F |
| **FM** | **1** | **2** | **kW** | **FM** | | **1** | **2** | **kW** |
| Jermuk | 100.3 | - | 1 | Vanadzor | | 103.7 | - | 1 |
| Noyemberyan | 101.7 | - | 5 | Yerevan | | 107.7 | 103.8 | 1 |
| Pushkini Lernantsk | 101.1 | - | 5 | Zovashen | | 104.0 | - | 1 |

+ sites with only txs below 1kW. F=Intern. service

**D.Prgr: Prgr 1 (Arajin tsragir):** 24h. – **Prgr 2 (Im R.):** 24h. – **Prgrs for ethnic minorities (M):** 1530-1700 on 1314/4810kHz (1530 Assyrian, 1545 Greek, 1600 Kurmanji, 1630 Kurmanji for the Yezidi ethnic community).
**International Service (Public R. of Armenia):** see Int. Radio section.

### OTHER STATIONS

| FM | MHz | kW | Location | Station |
|---|---|---|---|---|
| 14) | 88.3 | 4 | Yerevan | Kiss FM |
| 2B) | 89.7 | 4 | Yerevan | Autoradio |
| 4) | 90.1 | 1 | Yerevan | R. Shanson |
| 5) | 90.7 | 1 | Yerevan | R. Jan |
| 13) | 91.1 | 1 | Yerevan | R. Vem |
| 1A) | 100.2 | 2 | Dilijan | R. Hay |
| 1A) | 100.4 | 5 | Armavir | R. Hay |
| 8) | 100.6 | 1 | Yerevan | R. Aurora |
| 11) | 101.1 | 2 | Amasia | R. Shirak |
| 2A) | 101.9 | 2 | Yerevan | R. Yerevan |
| 9) | 102.4 | 1 | Yerevan | RFI Relay |

| FM | MHz | kW | Location | Station |
|----|-----|----|---------|---------|
| 3) | 103.5 | 1 | Yerevan | R. Marshal |
| 1A) | 103.6 | 2 | Noyemberyan | R. Hay |
| 1A) | 104.1 | 1 | Yerevan | R. Hay |
| 12) | 104.1 | 1 | Gyumri | R. Shant |
| 2A) | 104.4 | 1 | Charentsavan | R. Yerevan |
| 2A) | 104.6 | 1 | Vedi | R. Yerevan |
| 7) | 104.9 | 1 | Yerevan | Russkoye R. |
| 2A) | 105.4 | 5 | Pushkini Lernantsk | R. Yerevan |
| 2A) | 105.2 | 1 | Talin | R. Yerevan |
| 1B) | 105.5 | 1 | Yerevan | FM 105.5 |
| 10) | 106.0 | 1 | Yerevan | R. Sputnik Relay |
| 2A) | 106.1 | 2 | Noyemberyan | R. Yerevan |
| 2) | 106.8 | 1 | Zovashen | R. Yerevan |
| 6) | 106.9 | 1 | Yerevan | Lav R. 106.9 |
| 2A) | 107.2 | 1 | Vanadzor | R. Yerevan |
| 2A) | 107.3 | 1 | Jermuk | R. Yerevan |

+ txs below 1kW

**Addresses & other information:**
**1A,B)** Pavstos Buzandi St. 1/3, 0010 Yerevan – **2A,B)** A.Manoogian St. 5, 0025 Yerevan – **3)** Armeniak Armenakyan St. 250, 0047 Yerevan – **4)** A.Manoogian St. 5, 0025 Yerevan. Rel. R. Shanson (Russia) – **5)** Acharyan St. 42, 0040 Yerevan – **6)** Hyusisain Ave. 1, 0001 Yerevan. Rel. R. Sputnik (Russia) – **7)** Khandjyan St. 13a, 0010 Yerevan. Rel. Russkoye R. (Russia) – **8)** Nairi Zaryan St. 22, 0051 Yerevan – **9)** Ovsepyan St. 95, 0047 Yerevan. Rel. RFI (France) – **10)** Yerevan – **11)** Abovyan St. 248, 3104 Gyumri – **12)** Kievyan St. 16, 0028 Yerevan – **13)** Pavstos Buzandi St. 1/3, 0010 Yerevan – **14)** Nairi Zaryan St. 22a, 0051 Yerevan.

**Int. relays on MW:** (Upon demand) Gavar 864/1350/1377kHz 1000kW, 1395kHz 500kW. See International Radio section.

## ARUBA (Netherlands)

**L.T:** UTC -4h — **Pop:** 115,000 — **Pr.L:** Dutch (official), Papiamentu, English, Spanish — **E.C:** 60Hz, 127V — **ITU:** ABW

### DIRECTIE TELECOMMUNICATIE ZAKEN
☞ Rumbastraat 19, Oranjestad ☎ +297-582-6069 🖷 +297-582-5307 **E:** dirtelza@setarnet.aw **W:** dtz.aw

| FM | MHz | kW | Station, location |
|----|-----|----|------------------|
| 12) | 88.1 | 1 | Mega 88FM, Ponton |
| 11) | 88.9 | 0.1 | Bo Guia, Jaburibari |
| 3) | 89.9 | 0.25 | Canal 90FM, Nobenta Superstation Ponton |
| 14) | 90.7 | 0.45 | Caliente FM, Hooiberg |
| 7) | 91.5 | 0.125 | R Coneccion Sobre Natural, Hooiberg |
| 10) | 92.3 | 0.1 | Latina Tu FM, Hooiberg |
| 1) | 93.1 | 0.66 | R. Victoria, Hooiberg (Rlg.) |
| 12) | 94.1 | 1 | Hit 94 FM, Ponton |
| 7) | 95.1 | 0.325 | Top 95 FM, Hooiberg |
| 8) | 96.5 | 0.2 | Magic 96.5 FM, Hooiberg |
| 6) | 97.9 | 0.2 | Easy FM ,Hooiberg |
| 13) | 98.9 | 0.75 | Cool FM 98.9, Hooiberg |
| 9) | 99.9 | 0.5 | GFM Galactica 99.9 , Urataka |
| 16) | 100.9 | 0.85 | Hits 100, Balashi |
| 17) | 101.7 | 0.7 | Power 101.7 FM, Jaburibari |
| 18) | 104.3 | 0.6 | Fresh FM |
| 15) | 105.3 | 0.5 | Vision FM, Urataka |
| 19) | 106.7 | 0.6 | I love Aruba FM, Oranjestad |
| 2) | 107.5 | 0.2 | Blue FM 107.5 |

**Addresses & other information:**
**1)** Washington 23 Noord, Oranjestad ☎ +297 587 3444 Mngr: Nico J. Arts. Rlg: 24h in English, Spanish, Papiamentu, Dutch, Creole, Tagalog and Cantonese **W:** srv931fm.org **E:** radiovictoria@setarnet. aw – **2)** Rotonde di Paradera, Oranjestad ☎ +297 588 2488 🖷 +297 588 2438 – **3)** Van Leeuwenhoekstraat 26, PO Box 219, Oranjestad ☎+297 582 8952 and 297-582-1601 🖷 +297 583 7340 Dir: Mrs Leoncita Arends Programs: 24h in English, Papiamentu, Dutch and Spanish **W:** canal90fm.aw **E:** canal90fm@gmail.com –**6)** Sabana Basora 31-D, Oranjestad ☎+297 593 3637 🖷 +297 585 2639 GM: Wouter Gesterkamp 24h easy listening modern hits in English, Papiamentu, Spanish and Dutch **E:** info@easyfm.aw **W:** easyfm.aw – **7)** Santa Cruz 110, Oranjestad ☎+297 585 9500 🖷+297 583 0551 24h in Papiamentu on Top 95 FM and 24 h Christian Radio on R Coneccion Sobre Natural **W:** top95fm.aw **E:** solodipueblo@gmail.com Dir. Edmond Croes – **8)** South Beach Centre, Palm Beach ☎+297 586 0965 🖷 +297 586 5350 24h **E:** magicarubapromo@gmail.com **W:** magic96-5. com – **9)** Macapruimstraat 1-J, Oranjestad +297 588 2536 Man. Dir: Richard A. Arends Stn Man.: Maikel Oduber 24h in Papiamentu, English and Dutch **E:** gfmgalactica@gmail.com and awecugalactica@hotmail.

com – **10)** Tanki Leendert 8 ☎ +297 5942700 🖷 +297 583 3101 Pop Latino **E:** radio.latinaaruba@gmail.com– **11)** Tanki Flip 26B ☎+297 587 7889 🖷 +297 587 5889 Dir. Francisco Rosel **W:** boguiafm.com **E:** radio.boguia@gmail.com ; 24 h in Papiamentu, Christian Gospel and cultural programmes – **12)** Caya Ernesto Petronia 68-A, Oranjestad. Mega 88 FM ☎ +297 582 6888 🖷 +297 582 0494 **W:** mega88fm. com **E:** mail@mega88fm.com 24h in Papiamentu, Spanish and English: Latin Caribbean R **W:** hit94.com **E:** hit94fm@gmail.com – **12)** +297 582 0694 and +297 583 9494 🖷 +297 582 0494 24h in Papiamentu, Spanish and English. Dir: John A. Habibe – **13)** Caya G.F.(Betico) Croes 23 ☎ + 297 583 3111 and +297 588 1495 🖷+ 297 583 3101 Dir. Alexander Ponson 24 prgr in Papiamentu, and English **W:** coolaruba.com **E:** info@ coolaruba.com – **14)** Windstraat 29, Oranjestad ☎+ 297 582 2339 and +297 588 9077 🖷+ 297 583 1515 **W:** calientefmaruba.com **E:** info@ calientefmaruba.com – **15)** Cumana 20, Oranjestad ☎+297 583 5656 🖷+ 297 582 5477 Rlg prgr – **16)** Kolibristraat 2, Oranjestad, +297 594 2400 **W:** hits100fm@gmail.com – **17)** news.hits100fm@gmail.com – **17)** Piedra Plat 44 C-D, Lok 12, Paradera, Oranjestad ☎+297 585 2021 **W:** powerfmaruba.com and powerfm1017.com **E:** info@powerfm1017. com and power101fm@gmail.com – **18)** Caya G.F. (Betico) Croes 19-23, Oranjestad ☎ +297 583 2220; Dir. Alexander Ponson 24 prgr in Dutch, **E:** info@fresharuba.com **W:** fresharuba.com – **19)** Pos Aboa 45, Oranjestad ☎ +297 5889096 **E:** llovearubafm.com

## ASCENSION ISLAND (UK)

**L.T:** UTC — **Pop:** 800 — **Pr.L:** English — **E.C:** 50Hz, 220V — **ITU:** ASC

### VOLCANO RADIO (USAF)
☞ Ascension Radio Station, Ascension AAF, P.O. Box 4235, Patrick AFB, FL 32925-0235, USA.
**FM:** AFN, 98.7MHz 0.4kW 24h.
**NB:** MW service ZD8VR on 1602kHz currently inactive ‡

### BBC ATLANTIC RELAY STATION
☞ English Bay, Ascension Island, So. Atlantic.
**Local Sce: FM:** 93.2MHz 15W (24h relay of BBCWS in English plus occ. local prgrs). See International section for details of SW relays.

**BRITISH FORCES BROADC. SCE: W:** forces.net/radio **FM**(MHz): Travellers Hill: BFBS 1 100.9 BFBS 2 97.3, Green Mt: BFBS 1 107.3 BFBS 2 105.3.

**SAINT FM:** Jamestown, 91.4 & 95.5MHz 25W

## AUSTRALIA

**L.T:** See World Time Table. DST (where applicable): 7 Oct 18-7 Apr 19, 6 Oct 19-5 Apr 20 — **Pop:** 24 million — **Pr.L:** English — **E.C:** 50Hz, 230V — **ITU:** AUS

### DEPT. OF COMMUNICATIONS AND THE ARTS (DoCA)
☞ 38 Sydney Ave, Forrest ACT 2603 (☞ GPO Box 2154, Canberra ACT 2601) ☎+61 2 6271 1000 🖷 +61 2 6271 1901 **W:** communications. gov.au **E:** communications.gov.au/who-we-are/contact-us/form The Australian Government's lead advisor on Communications and the Arts. Works to promote innovative cultural and communications sectors through policy advice, prgr. implementation and sce delivery to the benefit of all Australians. Regulates radio, television, internet, phone, post and spectrum.

### AUSTRALIAN COMMUNICATIONS AND MEDIA AUTHORITY (ACMA)
☞ Level 5 The Bay Centre, 65 Pirrama Road, Pyrmont NSW 2009 (☞ PO Box Q500, Queen Victoria Building NSW 1230) ☎+61 2 9334 7700 🖷 +61 2 9334 7799 **W:** acma.gov.au **E:** info@acma.gov. au Government agency responsible for regulation of broadcasting, the internet, radiocommunications and telecommunications.

### COMMERCIAL RADIO AUSTRALIA (CRA)
☞ Lvl 5, 88 Foveaux St, Surry Hills NSW 2010 ☎+61 2 9281 6577 🖷 +61 2 9281 6599 **W:** commercialradio.com.au **E:** commercialradio. com.au/contact-us Peak body representing most commercial radio services.

### COMMUNITY BROADCASTING ASSOCIATION OF AUSTRALIA (CBAA)
☞ Suite One, Level Three, 44-54 Botany Rd. Alexandria, NSW 2015 (☞ POB 564, Alexandria, NSW 1435) ☎+61 2 9310 2999 🖷 +61 2 9319 4545 **W:** cbaa.org.au **E:** office@cbaa.org.au Peak body representing most community radio services.

## AUSTRALIAN NARROWCAST RADIO ASSOCIATION (ANRA)

🖂 34 Torres Cct, Shell Cove NSW 2529 ☎+61 2 4295 6740 **W**: anra.org.au **E**: secretary@anra.org.au Peak body representing most High Power Open Narrowcast and Low Power Open Narrowcast services.

## INDIGENOUS REMOTE COMMUNICATIONS ASSOCIATION (IRCA)

🖂 2/70 Elder St, Alice Springs NT 0870 (🖂 PO Box 2731, Alice Springs NT 0871) ☎+61 8 8952 6465 🖷 +61 8 8992 9669 **W**: irca.net.au **E**: info@irca.net.au Peak body representing remote indigenous media organisations.

## AUSTRALIAN BROADCASTING CORP. (ABC) (Pub)

**HQ**: Ultimo Centre, 700 Harris Str, Ultimo, NSW 2007(🖂 GPO Box 9994, Sydney NSW 2001) ☎+61 2 9333 1500 🖷 +61 2 9333 5305.
**LP**: Act. MD: David Anderson
**Networks**: N=Radio National, L=Local Radio, FM=Classic FM, JJJ=Triple J Network (alternative), PNN=Parliamentary/News R
**Digital-only Networks**: Double J (AC Music), ABC Country, ABC Jazz, ABC Grandstand (sport), ABC Extra (special events), Triple J Unearthed (independent music)
**Callsigns** typically N = xRN, xABCRN, L = xABCRR,, FM = xABCFM, JJJ = xJJJ, PNN = xPB, xPNN - some are localised. **Call letters:** 1 = A.C.T., 2 = NSW (some A.C.T.), 3 = Victoria, 4 = Queensland, 5 = So. Australia, 6 = We. Australia, 7 = Tasmania, 8 = Northern Territory, 9 = External Territories

| MW | Call | kHz | kW | Netw | Location |
|---|---|---|---|---|---|
| 46) | 6DL | 531 | 10 | L | Dalwallinu |
| 29) | 4QL | 540 | 50 | L | Longreach |
| 11) | 2CR | 549 | 50 | L | Orange (Cumnock) |
| 44) | 6WA | 558 | 50 | L | Wagin |
| 25) | 4JK | 567 | 10(d) | L | Julia Creek |
| 47) | 6MN | 567 | 0.1 | L | Newman |
| 47) | 6PN | 567 | 0.1 | L | Pannawonica |
| 47) | 6PU | 567 | 0.1 | L | Paraburdoo |
| 47) | 6TP | 567 | 0.1 | L | Tom Price |
| 2) | 2RN | 576 | 50 | N | Sydney |
| 6) | 6PB | 585 | 10 | P | Perth |
| 7) | 7RN | 585 | 10 | N | Hobart |
| 42) | 3WV | 594 | 50 | L | Horsham |
| 2) | 2RN | 603 | 10 | N | Nowra |
| 26) | 4CH | 603 | 10(d) | L | Charleville |
| 47) | 6PH | 603 | 2 | L | Port Hedland |
| 4) | 4QR | 612 | 50 | L | Brisbane |
| 6) | 6RN | 612 | 10 | N | Dalwallinu |
| 3) | 3RN | 621 | 50 | N | Melbourne |
| 2) | 2PB | 630 | 10 | P | Sydney |
| 24) | 4QN | 630 | 50 | L | Townsville (Brandon) |
| 48) | 6AL | 630 | 5 | L | Albany |
| 7) | 7RN | 630 | 0.4 | N | Queenstown |
| 23) | 4MS | 639 | 1 | L | Mossman |
| 31) | 5CK | 639 | 10 | L | Port Pirie (Crystal Brook) |
| 8) | 8RN | 639 | 2 | N | Katherine |
| 14) | 2NU | 648 | 10 | L | Tamworth (Manilla) |
| 43) | 6GF | 648 | 2 | L | Kalgoorlie |
| 19) | 2BY | 657 | 10(d) | L | Byrock |
| 8) | 8RN | 657 | 2 | N | Darwin |
| 1) | 2CN | 666 | 5 | L | Canberra ACT |
| 2) | 2CO | 675 | 10 | L | Albury (Corowa) |
| 45) | 6BE | 675 | 5 | L | Broome |
| 13) | 2KP | 684 | 10 | L | Kempsey (Smithtown) |
| 49) | 6BS | 684 | 5 | L | Busselton |
| 8) | 8RN | 684 | 1 | N | Tennant Creek |
| 34) | 5SY | 693 | 2(d) | L | Streaky Bay |
| 2) | 2BL | 702 | 50 | L | Sydney |
| 47) | 6KP | 702 | 10 | L | Karratha |
| 26) | 4QW | 711 | 10(d) | L | Roma/St.George |
| 16) | 2ML | 720 | 0.4 | L | Murwillumbah |
| 2) | 2RN | 720 | 0.05 | N | Armidale |
| 38) | 3MT | 720 | 2(d) | L | Omeo |
| 23) | 4AT | 720 | 4 | L | Atherton |
| 6) | 6WF | 720 | 50 | L | Perth |
| 5) | 5RN | 729 | 50 | N | Adelaide |
| 16) | 2NR | 738 | 50 | L | Grafton |
| 49) | 6MJ | 738 | 5(d) | L | Manjimup |
| 26) | 4QS | 747 | 10 | L | Toowoomba (Dalby) |
| 7) | 7PB | 747 | 3.5 | P | Hobart |
| 8) | 8JB | 747 | 0.2 | L | Jabiru |
| 13) | 2TR | 756 | 2(d) | L | Taree |
| 3) | 3RN | 756 | 10(d) | N | Wangaratta |
| 3) | 3LO | 774 | 50 | L | Melbourne |
| 20) | 8AL | 783 | 2 | L | Alice Springs |
| 4) | 4RN | 792 | 25 | N | Brisbane |
| 23) | 4QY | 801 | 2 | L | Cairns |
| 17) | 2BA | 810 | 10 | L | Bega |
| 6) | 6RN | 810 | 20 | N | Perth |
| 14) | 2GL | 819 | 10 | L | Glen Innes |
| 45) | 6KW | 819 | 5 | L | Kununurra |
| 38) | 3GI | 828 | 10 | L | Sale (Longford) |
| 46) | 6GN | 828 | 10 | L | Geraldton |
| 21) | 4RK | 837 | 10 | L | Rockhampton (Gracemere) |
| 43) | 6ED | 837 | 1 | L | Esperance |
| 1) | 2RN | 846 | 10 | N | Canberra |
| 47) | 6CA | 846 | 2.5 | L | Carnarvon |
| 30) | 4QB | 855 | 10(d) | L | Pialba |
| 30) | 4QO | 855 | 10 | L | Eidsvold |
| 45) | 6DB | 873 | 2 | L | Derby |
| 5) | 5AN | 891 | 50 | L | Adelaide |
| 4) | 4PB | 936 | 10 | P | Brisbane |
| 7) | 7ZR | 936 | 10(d) | L | Hobart |
| 5) | 5PB | 972 | 2 | P | Adelaide |
| 3) | 3RN | 990 | 0.5 | N | Albury-Wodonga |
| 8) | 8GO | 990 | 0.5 | L | Nhulunbuy (Gove) |
| 10) | 2NB | 999 | 2(d) | L | Broken Hill |
| 45) | 6WH | 1017 | 0.5 | L | Wyndham |
| 3) | 3PB | 1026 | 14.5 | P | Melbourne |
| 18) | 2UH | 1044 | 2(d) | L | Muswellbrook |
| 23) | 4WP | 1044 | 0.5 | L | Weipa |
| 49) | 6BR | 1044 | 1 | L | Bridgetown |
| 23) | 4TI | 1062 | 2 | L | Thursday Island |
| 32) | 5MV | 1062 | 2 | L | Renmark/Loxton |
| 2) | 2RN | 1098 | 0.2 | N | Goulburn |
| 6) | 6PB | 1152 | 10(d) | P | Busselton |
| 33) | 5PA | 1161 | 10(d) | L | Naracoorte |
| 35) | 7FG | 1161 | 1(d) | L | Fingal |
| 47) | 6XM | 1188 | 2 | L | Exmouth |
| 46) | 6NM | 1215 | 0.5 | L | Northam |
| 15) | 2NC | 1233 | 10 | L | Newcastle |
| 6) | 6RN | 1269 | 5 | N | Busselton |
| 6) | 6RN | 1296 | 10 | N | Wagin |
| 5) | 5RN | 1305 | 2 | N | Renmark/Loxton |
| 11) | 2LG | 1395 | 0.2 | L | Lithgow |
| 2) | 2RN | 1431 | 2 | L | Wollongong |
| 2) | 2PB | 1458 | 2 | P | Newcastle |
| 33) | 5MG | 1476 | 1 | L | Mt. Gambier |
| 2) | 2RN | 1485 | 0.1 | N | Wilcannia |
| 24) | 4HU | 1485 | 0.05 | L | Hughenden |
| 34) | 5LN | 1485 | 0.2 | L | Port Lincoln |
| 2) | 2RN | 1512 | 10 | N | Newcastle |
| 21) | 4QD | 1548 | 50 | L | Emerald |
| 30) | 4GM | 1566 | 0.2 | L | Gympie |
| 10) | 2WA | 1584 | 0.1 | L | Wilcannia |
| 31) | 5WM | 1584 | 0.05 | L | Woomera |
| 7) | 7SH | 1584 | 0.1 | L | St. Helens |
| 17) | 2CP | 1602 | 0.4 | L | Cooma |
| 41) | 3WL | 1602 | 0.25 | L | Warrnambool |
| 31) | 5LC | 1602 | 0.2 | L | Leigh Creek South |

| | FM Area | State | N | L | FM | JJJ |
|---|---|---|---|---|---|---|
| 5) | Adelaide | SA | - | - | 103.9 | 105.5 |
| 5) | Adel. Foothills | SA | - | - | 97.5 | 95.9 |
| 39) | Alexandra | VIC | 104.5 | 102.9 | - | - |
| 14) | Armidale | NSW | - | 101.9 | 103.5 | 101.1 |
| 3) | Bairnsdale | VIC | 106.3 | - | - | - |
| 36) | Ballarat | VIC | - | 107.9 | 105.5 | 107.1 |
| 17) | Batemans Bay | NSW | 105.1 | 103.5 | 101.9 | - |
| 2) | Bega/Cooma | NSW | 100.9 | - | 99.3 | 100.1 |
| 37) | Bendigo | VIC | - | 91.1 | 92.7 | 90.3 |
| 17) | Bombala | NSW | - | 94.1 | - | - |
| 2) | Bourke | NSW | 101.1 | - | - | - |
| 4) | Brisbane | QLD | - | - | 106.1 | 107.7 |
| 5) | Broken Hill | NSW | 102.9 | - | 103.7 | 102.1 |
| 6) | Broome | WA | 107.7 | - | - | - |
| 6) | Bunbury | WA | - | - | 93.3 | 94.1 |
| 35) | Burnie | TAS | - | 102.5 | - | - |
| 23) | Cairns | QLD | 105.1 | 106.7 | 105.9 | 107.5 |
| 23) | Cairns North | QLD | 93.9 | 95.5 | 94.7 | 97.1 |
| 6) | Camballin | WA | - | 102.1 | - | - |
| 1) | Canberra | ACT | - | - | 102.3 | 101.5 |
| 6) | Cen.Agricult | WA | - | - | 98.9 | 98.1 |
| 2) | Cen.Table'nds | NSW | 104.3 | - | 102.7 | 101.9 |
| 11) | Cen. West. Sl. | NSW | 107.9 | 107.1 | 105.5 | 102.3 |
| 4) | Darling Downs | QLD | 105.7 | - | 107.3 | 104.1 |
| 8) | Darwin | NT | - | 105.7 | 107.3 | 103.3 |
| 2) | Deniliquin | NSW | 99.3 | - | - | - |
| 19) | Dubbo (City) | NSW | - | 95.9 | - | - |
| 35) | E. Devonport | TAS | - | 100.5 | - | - |
| 4) | Emerald | QLD | 93.9 | - | 90.7 | - |
| 6) | Esperance | WA | 106.3 | - | 104.7 | - |

| FM | Area | State | N | L | FM | JJJ |
|---|---|---|---|---|---|---|
| 6) | Geraldton | WA | 99.7 | - | 94.9 | 98.9 |
| 2) | Glen Innes | NSW | 105.1 | - | - | - |
| 22) | Gold Coast | QLD | 90.1 | 91.7 | 88.5 | 97.7 |
| 39) | Goulburn V. | VIC | - | 97.7 | 96.1 | 94.5 |
| 13) | Grafton/Kemp. | NSW | 99.5 | 92.3 | 97.9 | 91.5 |
| 30) | Gympie | QLD | 96.9 | 95.3 | 93.7 | - |
| 9) | Hay | NSW | 88.9 | 88.1 | - | - |
| 7) | Hobart | TAS | - | - | 93.9 | 92.9 |
| 12) | Illawarra | NSW | - | 97.3 | 95.7 | 98.9 |
| 2) | Jerilderie | NSW | 94.1 | - | - | - |
| 6) | Kalgoorlie | WA | 97.1 | - | 95.5 | 98.7 |
| 50) | Katherine | NT | - | 106.1 | - | - |
| 5) | Keith | SA | 96.9 | - | - | - |
| 35) | King Island | TAS | - | 88.5 | - | - |
| 38) | Latrobe Valley | VIC | - | 100.7 | 101.5 | 96.7 |
| 35) | Lileah | TAS | 89.7 | 91.3 | - | - |
| 16) | Lismore | NSW | 96.9 | 94.5 | 95.3 | 96.1 |
| 4) | Longreach | QLD | 99.1 | - | - | - |
| 28) | Mackay | QLD | 102.7 | 101.1 | 97.9 | 99.5 |
| 13) | Manning River | NSW | 97.1 | 95.5 | 98.7 | 96.3 |
| 35) | Maydena | TAS | - | 89.7 | - | - |
| 4) | Meandarra | QLD | 104.3 | - | - | - |
| 3) | Melbourne | VIC | - | - | 105.9 | 107.5 |
| 40) | Mildura | VIC | 105.9 | 104.3 | 102.7 | 101.1 |
| 23) | Mission Beach | QLD | 90.9 | 89.3 | - | - |
| 4) | Monto | QLD | 101.9 | - | - | - |
| 28) | Moranbah | QLD | 106.5 | 104.9 | - | - |
| 4) | Mossman | QLD | 90.1 | - | - | - |
| 5) | Mount Gambier | SA | 103.3 | - | 104.1 | 102.5 |
| 25) | Mount Isa | QLD | 107.3 | 106.5 | 101.7 | 104.1 |
| 39) | Murray Valley | VIC | - | 102.1 | 103.7 | 105.3 |
| 9) | Murrumbidgee | NSW | 98.9 | 100.5 | 97.3 | 96.5 |
| 18) | Muswellbrook | NSW | - | 105.7 | - | - |
| 27) | Nambour | QLD | - | 90.3 | 88.7 | 89.5 |
| 6) | Narrogin | WA | - | - | 92.5 | - |
| 35) | NE Tas. | TAS | 94.1 | 91.7 | 93.3 | 90.9 |
| 2) | Newcastle | NSW | - | - | 106.1 | 102.1 |
| 3) | Nhill | VIC | 95.7 | - | - | - |
| 6) | Perth | WA | - | - | 97.7 | 99.3 |
| 6) | Port Hedland | WA | 95.7 | - | - | - |
| 41) | Portland | VIC | 98.5 | 96.9 | - | - |
| 5) | Renmark | SA | - | - | 105.1 | 101.9 |
| 4) | Rockhampton | QLD | 103.1 | - | 106.3 | 104.7 |
| 4) | Roebourne | WA | 107.5 | - | - | - |
| 4) | Rolleston Mine | QLD | - | - | - | 98.5 |
| 26) | Roma | QLD | 107.3 | 105.7 | 97.7 | - |
| 31) | Roxby Downs | SA | 101.9 | 102.7 | 103.5 | - |
| 34) | Salmon Gums | WA | 100.7 | - | - | - |
| 46) | S. Agricultural | WA | 96.9 | - | 94.5 | 92.9 |
| 46) | South'n Cross | WA | 107.9 | 106.3 | - | - |
| 26) | South'n Downs | QLD | 106.5 | 104.9 | 101.7 | 103.3 |
| 5) | Spencer Gulf N | SA | 106.7 | - | 104.3 | 103.5 |
| 5) | Streaky Bay | SA | 100.9 | - | - | 103.3 |
| 9) | SW Slopes | NSW | 89.1 | 89.9 | 88.3 | 90.7 |
| 3) | Sydney | NSW | - | - | 92.9 | 105.7 |
| 2) | Tamworth | NSW | 93.9 | - | 103.1 | 94.7 |
| 2) | Townsville | QLD | 104.7 | - | 101.5 | 105.5 |
| 5) | Tumby Bay | SA | 101.9 | - | - | - |
| 39) | Upper Murray | VIC | - | 106.5 | 104.1 | 103.3 |
| 14) | Upper Namoi | NSW | 100.7 | 99.1 | 96.7 | 99.9 |
| 3) | Warrnambool | VIC | 101.7 | - | 92.1 | 89.7 |
| 42) | Western Vic. | VIC | 92.5 | 94.1 | 93.3 | 94.9 |
| 30) | Wide Bay | QLD | 100.9 | 100.1 | 98.5 | 99.3 |
| 4) | Winton | QLD | 107.9 | - | - | - |
| 5) | Wirrulla | SA | 107.3 | - | - | - |
| 5) | Wudinna | SA | 107.7 | - | - | 105.3 |
| 6) | Wyndham | WA | - | - | - | 98.9 |

**NB:** Txs 1kW and higher

**Parliamentary/News Radio Network (MHz):** 89.1 Emerald QLD (8d), 89.3 Horsham VIC (20), 89.5 Bendigo VIC (10), 89.7 Bega/Cooma NSW (112d), 90.5 Burnie TAS (1d), 90.7 Grafton/Kempsey NSW (20d), 90.9 Illawarra NSW (150d), 91.3 Warrnambool VIC (3.2d), 91.5 SW Slopes/E Riverina NSW (80), 91.5 Tumby Bay SA (2), 91.7 Tamworth NSW (10), 91.7 Western Victoria (80d), 91.9 Central Tablelands NSW (5d), 92.1 Southern Agricultural WA (80), 92.5 NE Tasmania (192d), 93.5 Inverell NSW (10), 93.9 Renmark SA (150d), 94.3 Ballarat VIC (5d), 94.3 Townsville QLD (92d), 94.5 Gympie QLD (20d), 94.5 Nambour QLD (20d), 94.7 Manning River NSW (5), 94.9 Port Hedland WA (2), 95.1 Latrobe Valley VIC (200d), 95.7 Gold Coast (26d), 95.9 Murray Valley VIC (20), 96.3 Cairns North QLD (10d), 96.3 Warwick QLD (2), 96.3 Wagin WA (5), 96.7 Toowoomba QLD (2.5d), 97.7 Portland VIC (2.6d), 97.7 Wide Bay QLD (10d), 98.1 Murrumbidgee I.A. NSW (100), 98.5 Lismore NSW (100d), 99.7 Central Agricultural WA (80), 100.3 Mildura VIC (150d), 100.3 Kalgoorlie WA (6), 100.5 Batemans Bay NSW (40d),

100.9 Deniliquin NSW (2d), 100.9 Upper Murray VIC (2), 101.1 Cairns QLD (100), 101.3 Geraldton WA (10), 101.5 Upper Namoi NSW (20d), 102.1 E.. Devonport TAS (1.2), 102.5 Darwin (32d), 102.7 Armidale NSW (4), 102.7 Spencer Gulf North SA (70), 103.1 Esperance WA (5), 103.9 Canberra ACT (80), 104.1 Alice Springs NT (1), 104.3 Mackay QLD (100d), 104.5 Broken Hill NSW (4), 104.7 Colac VIC (10d), 104.9 Muswellbrook NSW (16), 104.9 Mount Isa QLD (1), 105.3 Katherine NT (1), 105.5 Rockhampton QLD (80), 105.7 Mt Gambier SA (240d), 106.3 Central West. Slopes NSW (220d), 106.9 Broome WA (2), 107.7 Goulburn Valley VIC (5d), 107.9 Bairnsdale VIC (2d)

**Digital Radio**

| DAB+ | Call | Ch | MHz | kW |
|---|---|---|---|---|
| 1) Canberra ACT | DAB10B | 10B | 211.648 | 3(d) |
| 1) Sydney NSW | DAB9C | 9C | 206.352 | 50 |
| 2) Melbourne VIC | DAB9C | 9C | 206.352 | 50(d) |
| 1) Brisbane QLD | DAB9C | 9C | 206.352 | 50 |
| 1) Adelaide SA | DAB9C | 9C | 206.352 | 50 |
| 1) Perth WA | DAB9C | 9C | 206.352 | 50(d) |
| 1) Darwin ACT | DAB10B | 10B | 211.648 | 5(d) |

All permanent digital multiplexes shared with SBS and carry all ABC radio networks. Several digital on-channel repeaters provide in-fill coverage (ERP 300-500W). Canberra and Darwin are trials, shared with Commercials & have more limited content. All programming at **W:** digitalradioplus.com.au/listen. Reports to originating stns.

**ABC addresses:**

**NB:** Reports for R. National, Parliament/News, ABC-FM, Triple J and DAB+ only channels should go to the capital city ABC office in that state (Addresses 1-8).

**1)** ABC Canberra, GPO Box 9994, Canberra ACT 2601 – **2)** ABC Sydney, GPO Box 9994, Sydney NSW 2001 – **3)** ABC Melbourne, GPO Box 9994, Melbourne VIC 3001 – **4)** ABC Brisbane, GPO Box 9994, Brisbane QLD 4001 – **5)** ABC Adelaide, GPO Box 9994, Adelaide SA 5001 – **6)** ABC Perth, GPO Box 9994, Perth WA 6848 – **7)** ABC Hobart, GPO Box 9994, Hobart TAS 7001 – **8)** ABC Darwin, PO Box 9994, Darwin NT 0801 – **9)** ABC Riverina, 100 Fitzmaurice St, Wagga Wagga NSW 2650 – **10)** ABC Broken Hill, PO Box 315, Broken Hill NSW 2880 – **11)** ABC Central West, PO Box 8549, East Orange NSW 2800 – **12)** ABC Illawarra, PO Box 973, Wollongong NSW 2520 – **13)** ABC Mid North Coast, PO Box 42, Port Macquarie NSW 2444 – **14)** ABC New England / North West, PO Box 558, Tamworth NSW 2340 – **15)** ABC Newcastle, PO Box 2205, Dangar NSW 2309 – **16)** ABC North Coast, PO Box 908, Lismore NSW 2480 – **17)** ABC South East NSW, PO Box 336, Bega NSW 2550 – **18)** ABC Upper Hunter, PO Box 400, Muswellbrook NSW 2333 – **19)** ABC Western Plains, PO Box 985, Mudgee NSW 2830 – **20)** ABC Alice Springs, PO Box 1144, Alice Springs NT 0871 – **21)** ABC Capricornia, GPO Box 911, Rockhampton QLD 4700 - **22)** ABC Gold Coast, PO Box 217, Mermaid Beach QLD 4218 – **23)** ABC Far North, PO Box 932, Cairns QLD 4810 – **24)** ABC North Queensland, PO Box 694, Townsville QLD 4810 – **25)** ABC North West Queensland, 114 Camooweal St, Mount Isa QLD 4825 – **26)** ABC Southern Queensland, PO Box 358, Toowoomba QLD 4350 – **27)** ABC Sunshine Coast, PO Box 1212, Maroochydore QLD 4558 – **28)** ABC Tropical Queensland, PO Box 127, Mackay QLD 4740 – **29)** ABC Western Queensland, PO Box 318, Longreach QLD 4730 – **30)** ABC Wide Bay, PPO Box 1152, Bundaberg QLD 4670 – **31)** ABC North and West South Australia, PO Box 289, Port Pirie SA 5540 – **32)** ABC Riverland, PO Box 20, Renmark SA 5341 – **33)** ABC Southeast, PO Box 1448, Mount Gambier SA 5290 – **34)** ABC Eyre Peninsula, PO Box 679, Port Lincoln SA 5606 – **35)** ABC Northern Tasmania, PO Box 201, Launceston TAS 7250 – **36)** ABC Ballarat, PO Box 7, Ballarat VIC 3353 – **37)** ABC Central Victoria, PO Box 637, Bendigo VIC 3550 – **38)** ABC Gippsland, PO Box 330, Sale VIC 3850 – **39)** ABC Goulburn Murray, PO Box 1063, Wodonga VIC 3690 – **40)** ABC Mildura / Swan Hill, PO Box 10083, Mildura VIC 3502 – **41)** ABC South West Victoria, PO Box 310, Warrnambool VIC 3280 – **42)** ABC Western Victoria, PO Box 506, Horsham VIC 3402 – **43)** ABC Goldfields / Esperance, PO Box 125, Kalgoorlie WA 6430 – **44)** ABC Great Southern, 58 Tudhoe St, Wagin WA 6315 – **45)** ABC Kimberley, PO Box 217, Broome WA 6725 – **46)** ABC Mid West & Wheatbelt, PO Box 211, Geraldton WA 6530 – **47)** ABC North West, PO Box 994, Karratha WA 6714 – **48)** ABC South Coast, 2 St Emilie Way, Albany WA 6330 – **49)** ABC South West, PO Box 242, Bunbury WA 6231 – **50)** PO Box 1240, Katherine NT 0851

**EXTERNAL SERVICE: Radio Australia**
No shortwave broadcasts. Available via satellite, internet, and some local retransmissions.

**SPECIAL BROADCASTING SERVICE (SBS)**
HQ: 14 Herbert St, Artarmon, NSW 2064 Locked Bag 028, Crows Nest, NSW 1585 +61 (02) 9430 2828 +61 (02) 9430 3700 Networks: Radio 1 (Syd/Mlb AM), Radio 2 (Syd/Mlb FM), National

Radio Network (NRN, mix of Radio 1 & 2 for regional areas), Radio 3 (digital only), Radio 4 (BBS WS & special events, digital only), Arabic24 (digital only), Chill (digital only), PopAsia (digital only), PopDesi (digital only). Non-music networks time-shifted to accord local time in each State.
**NB:** (t) translator stn licensed to SBS. (rt) retransmission sce licensed to self-help groups such as local councils.

| MW | Call | kHz | kW | Service |
|---|---|---|---|---|
| 1) Wollongong | 2EA(t) | 1035 | 2 | Radio 2 |
| 1) Sydney | 2EA | 1107 | 5 | Radio 1 |
| 2) Melbourne | 3EA | 1224 | 5(d) | Radio 1 |
| 1) Newcastle | 2EA(t) | 1413 | 5(d) | NRN |
| 1) Canberra | 1EA(t) | 1440 | 2 | Radio 1 |
| 1) Wollongong | 2EA(t) | 1485 | 0.15 | Radio 1 |

| FM | Call | MHz | kW | Service |
|---|---|---|---|---|
| 1) Cairns | 4SBSFM(rt) | 90.5 | 1(d) | NRN |
| 1) Griffith | 2SBSFM(rt) | 92.7 | 1 | NRN |
| 1) Melbourne | 3SBSFM | 93.1 | 100 | Radio 2 |
| 1) Brisbane | 4SBSFM | 93.3 | 100(d) | NRN |
| 1) Adel. Hills | 5SBSFM(t) | 95.1 | 2(d) | NRN |
| 1) Ballarat | 3SBSFM(rt) | 95.9 | 1 | NRN |
| 1) Perth | 6SBSFM | 96.9 | 100 | NRN |
| 1) Sydney | 2SBSFM | 97.7 | 150(d) | Radio 2 |
| 1) Lismore | 2SBSFM(rt) | 98.9 | 1 | NRN |
| 1) Wondai | 4SBS(rt) | 98.9 | 2 | NRN |
| 1) Darwin | 8SBSFM | 100.9 | 18(d) | NRN |
| 1) Sapphire | 4SBS(rt) | 103.5 | 1 | NRN |
| 1) Canberra | 2SBS | 105.5 | 80 | Radio 2 |
| 1) Hobart | 7SBS | 105.7 | 56 | NRN |
| 1) Adelaide | 5SBS | 106.3 | 32 | NRN |

| DAB+ | Call | Ch | MHz | kW |
|---|---|---|---|---|
| 1) Canberra | DAB9C | 9C | 206.352 | 5 |
| 1) Sydney | DAB9C | 9C | 206.352 | 50(d) |
| 2) Melbourne | DAB9C | 9C | 206.352 | 50(d) |
| 1) Brisbane | DAB9C | 9C | 206.352 | 50(d) |
| 1) Adelaide | DAB9C | 9C | 206.352 | 50(d) |
| 1) Perth | DAB9C | 9C | 206.352 | 50(d) |
| 1) Hobart | DAB9C | 9C | 206.352 | 50(d) |

**NB:** Txs 1kW and higher
All permanent digital multiplexes shared with ABC and carry all SBS radio networks excepting NRN. Several digital on-channel repeaters provide infill coverage (ERP 300-500W). All prgr at **W:** digitalradioplus.com.au/listen
**Addresses: 1)** Locked Bag 028, Crows Nest, NSW 158 – **2)** PO Box 294, South Melbourne, Vic 3205

## COMMERCIAL RADIO SERVICES

**NB:** (t) is a designated translator stn which may carry local content.
**News:** Additional newscasts are often carried during breakfast and drive times.

| MW | Call | kHz | kW | Location |
|---|---|---|---|---|
| 1) | 2PM | 531 | 5(d) | Kempsey |
| 2) | 3GG | 531 | 5(d) | Warragul |
| 3) | 4KZ | 531 | 5 | Innisfail |
| 4) | 7SD | 540 | 5(d) | Scottsdale |
| 5) | 4AM | 558 | 5(d) | Atherton |
| 6) | 4GY | 558 | 5(d) | Gympie |
| 7) | 7BU | 558 | 2 | Burnie (F.PI FM) |
| 8) | 2BH | 567 | 0.5 | Broken Hill |
| 164) | 6EL | 621 | 2 | Bunbury |
| 133) | 2HC | 639 | 5(d) | Coffs Harbour |
| 33) | 4CC(t) | 666 | 2(d) | Biloela |
| 103) | 4LM | 666 | 2 | Mount Isa |
| 160) | 6LN | 666 | 1 | Carnarvon (F.PI FM) |
| 105) | 3AW | 693 | 5(d) | Melbourne |
| 9) | 4KQ | 693 | 10/5(d) | Brisbane |
| 3) | 4KZ(t) | 693 | 0.5 | Tully |
| 103) | 4LM(t) | 693 | 1 | Cloncurry |
| 131) | 6SE | 747 | 5(d) | Esperance (F.PI FM) |
| 166) | 6TZ | 756 | 2 | Margaret River |
| 10) | 2EC | 765 | 5(d) | Bega |
| 73) | 4GC(t) | 765 | 0.5 | Hughenden |
| 134) | 5CC | 765 | 5(d) | Port Lincoln |
| 147) | 8HOT(t) | 765 | 0.5 | Katherine |
| 13) | 6VA | 783 | 2 | Albany (F.PI FM) |
| 14) | 5RM | 801 | 2 | Berri |
| 73) | 4GC | 828 | 1 | Charters Towers |
| 17) | 4EL | 846 | 5(d) | Cairns |
| 18) | 4GR | 864 | 2 | Toowoomba |
| 19) | 6AM | 864 | 2 | Northam |
| 21) | 2GB | 873 | 6 | Sydney |
| 24) | 4BH | 882 | 5(d) | Brisbane |
| 23) | 6PR | 882 | 10 | Perth |

| MW | Call | kHz | kW | Location |
|---|---|---|---|---|
| 25) | 2LM | 900 | 5(d) | Lismore (F.PI FM) |
| 107) | 2LT | 900 | 5(d) | Lithgow (F.PI FM) |
| 58) | 6BY | 900 | 2 | Bridgetown |
| 27) | 7AD | 900 | 2 | Devonport (F.PI FM) |
| 28) | 8HA | 900 | 2 | Alice Springs |
| 29) | 2XL | 918 | 2 | Cooma (F.PI FM) |
| 153) | 4VL | 918 | 2/2.5 | Charleville |
| 164) | 6NA | 918 | 2 | Narrogin |
| 32) | 3UZ | 927 | 5 | Melbourne |
| 33) | 4CC | 927 | 5(d) | Gladstone |
| 69) | 4HI(t) | 945 | 1(d) | Dysart |
| 36) | 2UE | 954 | 5 | Sydney |
| 17) | 4EL(t) | 954 | 0.35 | Gordonvale |
| 38) | 2RG | 963 | 5(d) | Griffith |
| 37) | 4WK | 963 | 5(d) | Warwick |
| 93) | 5SE | 963 | 5(d) | Mt. Gambier |
| 164) | 6TZ | 963 | 2 | Bunbury |
| 86) | 2DU(t) | 972 | 0.3 | Cobar |
| 39) | 2MW | 972 | 5(d) | Murwillumbah |
| 112) | 2NM | 981 | 5(d) | Muswellbrook |
| 41) | 3HA | 981 | 2 | Hamilton |
| 42) | 6KG | 981 | 2 | Kalgoorlie |
| 43) | 4RO | 990 | 5(d) | Rockhampton |
| 45) | 2ST | 999 | 5(d) | Nowra |
| 46) | 4TAB | 1008 | 10(d) | Brisbane |
| 49) | 2KY | 1017 | 5 | Sydney |
| 139) | 4AA | 1026 | 5(d) | Mackay |
| 53) | 5AU(t) | 1044 | 2 | Port Pirie |
| 54) | 2CA | 1053 | 5(d) | Canberra |
| 55) | 3EL | 1071 | 2 | Maryborough |
| 56) | 4SB | 1071 | 2 | Kingaroy |
| 151) | 6WB | 1071 | 2 | Katanning |
| 57) | 2MO | 1080 | 2 | Gunnedah |
| 167) | 6IX | 1080 | 2 | Perth |
| 59) | 2EL | 1089 | 5(d) | Orange |
| 60) | 3WM | 1089 | 5(d) | Horsham |
| 61) | 4LG | 1098 | 2 | Longreach |
| 62) | 6MD | 1098 | 2 | Merredin |
| 156) | 3AK | 1116 | 5(d) | Melbourne |
| 65) | 4BC | 1116 | 6.3/17(d) | Brisbane |
| 135) | 6MM | 1116 | 2 | Mandurah (F.PI FM) |
| 113) | 5MU | 1125 | 5(d) | Murray Bridge |
| 66) | 2AD | 1134 | 2(d) | Armidale (F.PI FM) |
| 67) | 3CS | 1134 | 5(d) | Colac |
| 164) | 6TZ(t) | 1134 | 2 | Collie |
| 68) | 2HD | 1143 | 2 | Newcastle |
| 69) | 4HI | 1143 | 5(d) | Emerald |
| 70) | 2WG | 1152 | 2 | Wagga Wagga |
| 30) | 4FC | 1161 | 2 | Maryborough |
| 72) | 2CH | 1170 | 5 | Sydney |
| 75) | 2NZ | 1188 | 2 | Inverell |
| 80) | 2CC | 1206 | 5/5(d) | Canberra |
| 78) | 2GF | 1206 | 5(d) | Grafton |
| 69) | 4HI(t) | 1215 | 0.25 | Moranbah |
| 82) | 3GV | 1242 | 5(d) | Sale |
| 85) | 4AK | 1242 | 2 | Toowoomba |
| 84) | 5AU | 1242 | 2(d) | Port Augusta |
| 86) | 2DU | 1251 | 2 | Dubbo |
| 32) | 3SR | 1260 | 2 | Shepparton |
| 89) | 2SM | 1269 | 5 | Sydney |
| 90) | 3EE | 1278 | 5 | Melbourne |
| 91) | 2TM | 1287 | 2 | Tamworth (F.PI FM) |
| 32) | 3BT | 1314 | 5(d) | Ballarat |
| 40) | 5DN | 1323 | 3.3 | Adelaide |
| 98) | 3SH | 1332 | 2 | Swan Hill |
| 99) | 4BU | 1332 | 5(d) | Bundaberg |
| 102) | 2LF | 1350 | 5(d) | Young |
| 104) | 2GN | 1368 | 2 | Goulburn (F.PI FM) |
| 105) | 3MP | 1377 | 5(d) | Melbourne |
| 106) | 5AA | 1395 | 5(d) | Adelaide |
| 108) | 2PK | 1404 | 2 | Parkes/Forbes |
| 5) | 4AM(t) | 1422 | 1(d) | Port Douglas |
| 111) | 2MG | 1449 | 5(d) | Mudgee |
| 32) | 3ML | 1467 | 2 | Mildura |
| 115) | 4ZR | 1476 | 2 | Roma |
| 116) | 2AY | 1494 | 2 | Albury |
| 117) | 2BS | 1503 | 0.111/5 | Bathurst (F.PI FM) |
| 142) | 6BAY(t) | 1512 | 5 | Morawa |
| 119) | 2QN | 1521 | 2 | Deniliquin |
| 120) | 2VM | 1530 | 2 | Moree |
| 121) | 2RE | 1557 | 2 | Taree |
| 122) | 3NE | 1566 | 5(d) | Wangaratta |
| 10) | 2EC(t) | 1584 | 0.2 | Narooma |
| 33) | 4CC(t) | 1584 | 0.5 | Rockhampton |
| 153) | 4VL(t) | 1584 | 0.2 | Cunnamulla |

| FM | Call | MHz | kW | Location | FM | Call | MHz | kW | Location |
|---|---|---|---|---|---|---|---|---|---|
| 117) | 2BS(t) | 88.1 | 2(d) | Burraga NSW | 151) | 6BUN | 95.7 | 55(d) | Bunbury WA |
| 3) | 4KZ(t) | 88.5 | 1(d) | Mission Beach QLD | 73) | 4CHT | 95.9 | 1.5 | Charters Towers QLD |
| 165) | 4RGC | 88.5 | 1 | Mossman QLD | 12) | 2ONE | 96.1 | 5 | Katoomba NSW |
| 170) | 8SAT | 88.7 | 4(d) | Urana NSW | 6) | 4NNN | 96.1 | 5(d) | Gympie QLD |
| 170) | 8SAT | 88.7 | 1 | Hawker SA | 150) | 4RBL | 96.1 | 1 | Weipa QLD |
| 41) | 3HFM | 88.9 | 20(d) | Hamilton VIC | 93) | 5SEF | 96.1 | 20 | Mount Gambier SA |
| 56) | 4KRY | 89.1 | 15 | Kingaroy QLD | 125) | 6NOW | 96.1 | 40(d) | Perth WA |
| 117) | 2BS(t) | 89.3 | 1(d) | Blayney NS | 29) | 2XL(t) | 96.3 | 2(d) | Jindabyne NSW |
| 63) | 7LAA | 89.3 | 5(d) | Launceston TAS | 8) | 2HIL | 96.5 | 4 | Broken Hill NSW |
| 46) | 4TAB | 89.7 | 5(d) | Beaudesert QLD | 95) | 2UUL | 96.5 | 40(d) | Wollongong NSW |
| 71) | 5CCC | 89.9 | 6(d) | Port Lincoln SA | 142) | 6GGG | 96.5 | 30(d) | Geraldton WA |
| 48) | 7EXX | 90.1 | 5(d) | Launceston TAS | 19) | 6NAM | 96.5 | 10 | Northam WA |
| 69) | 4HIT(t) | 90.3 | 1 | Blackwater QLD | 170) | 8SAT | 96.5 | 4(d) | Pinnaroo SA |
| 130) | 5SSA (t) | 90.3 | 2(d) | Adelaide Foothills SA | 40) | 5ADD(t) | 96.7 | 2(d) | Adelaide Foothills SA |
| 154) | 4SEA | 90.9 | 25(d) | Gold Coast QLD | 161) | 2SYD | 96.9 | 150(d) | Sydney NSW |
| 170) | 8SAT | 90.9 | 4(d) | Maitland SA | 118) | 3SUN | 96.9 | 100(d) | Shepparton VIC |
| 168) | 4MCY | 91.1 | 10(d) | Nambour QLD | 170) | 8SAT | 96.9 | 5 | Meringur VIC |
| 123) | 2MAC | 91.3 | 1 | Campbelltown NSW | 14) | 5RIV | 97.1 | 2.5(d) | Morgan SA |
| 120) | 2NOW(t) | 91.3 | 1 | Lightning Ridge NSW | 159) | 4BFM | 97.3 | 12 | Brisbane QLD |
| 96) | 4HIT | 91.3 | 5 | Moranbah QLD | 135) | 6CST | 97.3 | 5(d) | Mandurah WA |
| 148) | 3PTV | 91.5 | 56(d) | Melbourne VIC | 57) | 2GGG | 97.5 | 20(d) | Gunnedah NSW |
| 29) | 2SKI(t) | 91.7 | 1 | Bombala NSW | 29) | 2SKI | 97.7 | 50(d) | Cooma NSW |
| 45) | 2ST(t) | 91.7 | 1(d) | St Georges Basin NSW | 170) | 8SAT | 97.7 | 3(d) | Coonalpyn SA |
| 17) | 4HOT(t) | 91.7 | 1 | Mossman QLD | 136) | 3RMR | 97.9 | 12(d) | Mildura VIC |
| 52) | 6HED | 91.7 | 5(d) | Port Hedland WA | 5) | 4AMM | 97.9 | 5(d) | Atherton QLD |
| 135) | 6MM | 91.7 | 5(d) | Mandurah WA | 42) | 6KAR | 97.9 | 4(d) | Kalgoorlie WA |
| 55) | 3BDG | 91.9 | 120(d) | Bendigo VIC | 170) | 8SAT | 97.9 | 1.3(d) | Roxby Downs SA |
| 18) | 4RGD | 91.9 | 2 | Warwick QLD | 112) | 2VLY | 98.1 | 20(d) | Muswellbrook NSW |
| 15) | 4SEE | 91.9 | 10(d) | Nambour QLD | 123) | 2WIN | 98.1 | 40(d) | Wollongong NSW |
| 169) | 5ADL | 91.9 | 20(d) | Adelaide SA | 142) | 6BAY | 98.1 | 30(d) | Geraldton WA |
| 16) | 7AUS | 92.1 | 2(d) | Queenstown/Zeehan TAS | 120) | 2NOW | 98.3 | 100(d) | Moree NSW |
| 11) | 4TOO(t) | 92.3 | 1 | Ayr/Home Hill QLD | 82) | 3GV | 98.3 | 5(d) | Bainsdale VIC |
| 29) | 2XL(t) | 92.5 | 1 | Bombala NSW | 11) | 4TOO | 98.3 | 2(d) | Bowen QLD |
| 96) | 4CCA(t) | 92.5 | 1 | Mossman QLD | 3) | 4ZKZ | 98.3 | 20(d) | Innisfail QLD |
| 155) | 4GLD | 92.5 | 25(d) | Gold Coast QLD | 77) | 5MMM(t) | 98.3 | 2(d) | Adelaide Foothills SA |
| 86) | 2ZOO | 92.7 | 10 | Dubbo NSW | 60) | 3WWM(t) | 98.5 | 1(d) | Ararat VIC |
| 15) | 4SSS | 92.7 | 10(d) | Nambour QLD | 98) | 3SHI(t) | 98.7 | 1(d) | Kerang VIC |
| 29) | 2SKI(t) | 92.9 | 1 | Thredbo NSW | 158) | 4RGM | 98.7 | 100(d) | Mackay QLD |
| 91) | 2TTT | 92.9 | 20(d) | Tamworth NSW | 113) | 5EZY | 98.7 | 20(d) | Murray Bridge SA |
| 120) | 2VM(t) | 92.9 | 1 | Lightning Ridge NSW | 170) | 8SAT | 98.9 | 10(d) | Minlaton SA |
| 41) | 3HA/t | 92.9 | 1(d) | Portland VIC | 169) | 5ADL(t) | 99.1 | 2(d) | Adelaide Foothills SA |
| 44) | 6PPM | 92.9 | 40(d) | Perth WA | 117) | 2BXS | 99.3 | 10 | Bathurst NSW |
| 143) | 2GEE | 93.1 | 10 | Mudgee NSW | 170) | 8SAT | 99.3 | 4 | Streaky Bay SA |
| 70) | 2WZD | 93.1 | 80 | Wagga Wagga NSW | 150) | 4RBL | 99.4 | 2(d) | Mt. Tamborine QLD |
| 150) | 4BRZ | 93.1 | 1 | Bulahdelah NSW | 107) | 2ICE | 99.5 | 1(d) | Katoomba NSW |
| 154) | 4RGB | 93.1 | 3(d) | Bundaberg QLD | 114) | 3MDA | 99.5 | 20(d) | Mildura VIC |
| 14) | 5RIV | 93.1 | 10(d) | Renmark/Loxton SA | 82) | 3TFM | 99.5 | 20(d) | Sale VIC |
| 163) | 2DBO | 93.5 | 10 | Dubbo NSW | 157) | 4RGC | 99.5 | 10(d) | Cairns QLD |
| 1) | 2PM(t) | 93.5 | 3(d) | Port Macquarie NSW | 170) | 8SAT | 99.5 | 1(d) | Kapunda SA |
| 104) | 2SNO | 93.5 | 40 | Goulburn NSW | 38) | 2RGF | 99.7 | 50 | Griffith NSW |
| 35) | 3BBO | 93.5 | 120(d) | Bendigo VIC | 113) | 5EZY | 99.7 | 1 | Victor Harbour SA |
| 43) | 4ROK | 93.5 | 1(d) | Gladstone QLD | 132) | 6CAR | 99.7 | 5 | Carnarvon WA |
| 41) | 3HFM(t) | 93.7 | 2(d) | Portland VIC | 154) | 7RGS | 99.7 | 5(d) | Scottsdale TAS |
| 87) | 3SUN(t) | 93.7 | 1(d) | Alexandra/Eildon VIC | 82) | 3TFM(t) | 99.9 | 5(d) | Bairnsdale VIC |
| 87) | 3SUN(t) | 93.7 | 1(d) | Yea VIC | 69) | 4HI(t) | 100.1 | 1(d) | Rolleston Mine QLD |
| 150) | 4RBL | 93.7 | 4 | Tenterfield NSW | 147) | 8HOT | 100.1 | 17(d) | Darwin NT |
| 47) | 6PER | 93.7 | 40(d) | Perth WA | 66) | 2NEB | 100.3 | 10 | Armidale NSW |
| 102) | 2LFF | 93.9 | 40 | Young NSW | 121) | 2RE(t) | 100.3 | 1.6 | Forster NSW |
| 101) | 3BAY | 93.9 | 56(d) | Geelong VIC | 172) | 3MEL | 100.3 | 56(d) | Melbourne VIC |
| 99) | 4RUM | 93.9 | 3.2(d) | Bundaberg QLD | 51) | 4MKY | 100.3 | 100(d) | Mackay QLD |
| 170) | 8SAT | 93.9 | 3 | Bunnaloo NSW | 113) | 5EZY(t) | 100.3 | 1 | Mount Barker SA |
| 150) | 4RBL | 94.1 | 1(d) | Bulahdelah NSW | 170) | 8SAT | 100.3 | 5(d) | Padthaway East SA |
| 83) | 2BDR | 94.1 | 1(d) | Falls Creek VIC | 116) | 2AAY(t) | 100.5 | 1(d) | Falls Creek VIC |
| 52) | 6NW | 94.1 | 5(d) | Port Hedland WA | 88) | 6BET | 100.5 | 5 | Bridgetown WA |
| 2) | 3SEA(t) | 94.3 | 7(d) | Warragul VIIC | 164) | 6NAN | 100.5 | 5 | Narrogin WA |
| 60) | 3WWM(t) | 94.5 | 2 | Nhill/Lawloit VIC | 150) | 4BRZ | 100.6 | 2(d) | Mt. Tamborine QLD |
| 22) | 3YB | 94.5 | 20(d) | Warrnambool VIC | 1) | 2PQQ | 100.7 | 20(d) | Port Macquarie NSW |
| 79) | 6MIX | 94.5 | 40(d) | Perth WA | 18) | 4RGD | 100.7 | 10(d) | Toowoomba QLD |
| 29) | 2SKI(t) | 94.7 | 2 | Jindabyne NSW | 11) | 4RGR | 100.7 | 100(d) | Townsville QLD |
| 69) | 4HIT | 94.7 | 5 | Emerald QLD | 25) | 2ZZZ | 100.9 | 32(d) | Lismore NSW |
| 45) | 2WSK | 94.9 | 50(d) | Nowra NSW | 144) | 7TTT | 100.9 | 36 | Hobart TAS |
| 141) | 4MIX | 94.9 | 50(d) | Ipswich QLD | 107) | 2LT/t | 101.1 | 1(d) | Katoomba NSW |
| 88) | 6KAN | 94.9 | 5 | Katanning WA | 50) | 3TTT | 101.1 | 56(d) | Melbourne VIC |
| 75) | 2GEM | 95.1 | 10 | Inverell NSW | 140) | 2CFM | 101.3 | 16 | Gosford NSW |
| 43) | 4RGK | 95.1 | 1(d) | Gladstone QLD | 60) | 3WWM | 101.3 | 20(d) | Horsham VIC |
| 115) | 4ROM | 95.1 | 1 | Roma QLD | 52) | 6HED | 101.3 | 2 | Broome WA |
| 145) | 2PTV | 95.3 | 150(d) | Sydney NSW | 170) | 8SAT | 101.5 | 5(d) | Lake Cargellico NSW |
| 32) | 3SRR | 95.3 | 100(d) | Shepparton VIC | 43) | 4RGK | 101.5 | 10 | Rockhampton QLD |
| 162) | 3YFM | 95.3 | 20(d) | Warrnambool VIC | 81) | 2UUS | 101.7 | 150(d) | Sydney NSW |
| 13) | 6AAY | 95.3 | 50(d) | Albany WA | 33) | 4CCC | 101.7 | 2 | Charleville QLD |
| 170) | 8SAT | 95.3 | 5 | Speed VIC | 20) | 7HHO | 101.7 | 36 | Hobart TAS |
| 170) | 8SAT | 95.3 | 2(d) | Karoonda SA | 27) | 7SEA(t) | 101.7 | 20(d) | Burnie TAS |
| 108) | 2ROK | 95.5 | 10 | Parkes/Forbes NSW | 120) | 2NOW(t) | 101.9 | 1 | Collarenebri NSW |
| 101) | 3CAT | 95.5 | 56(d) | Geelong VIC | 126) | 3FOX | 101.9 | 56(d) | Melbourne VIC |
| 170) | 8SAT | 95.5 | 3(d) | Kingscote SA | 149) | 4CEE | 101.9 | 10(d) | Maryborough QLD |

| FM | Call | MHz | kW | Location |
|----|------|-----|-----|----------|
| 139) | 4MMK | 101.9 | 100(d) | Mackay QLD |
| 122) | 3NNN | 102.1 | 25(d) | Wangaratta VIC |
| 1) | 2ROX | 102.3 | 20 | Port Macquarie NSW |
| 94) | 3RBA | 102.3 | 20(d) | Ballarat VIC |
| 11) | 4TOO | 102.3 | 100(d) | Townsville QLD |
| 40) | 5ADD | 102.3 | 20(d) | Adelaide SA |
| 131) | 6SEA | 102.3 | 2.5(d) | Esperance WA |
| 10) | 2EEE | 102.5 | 5 | Bega NSW |
| 119) | 2MOR | 102.5 | 50 | Deniliquin NSW |
| 150) | 4BRZ | 102.5 | 4 | Tenterfield NSW |
| 150) | 4BRZ | 102.5 | 1 | Childers QLD |
| 88) | 6KA | 102.5 | 1(d) | Karratha WA |
| 170) | 8SAT | 102.5 | 3 | Bourke NSW |
| 96) | 4CCA | 102.7 | 10(d) | Cairns QLD |
| 75) | 2GEM | 102.9 | 2 | Warialda NSW |
| 109) | 2KKO | 102.9 | 8(d) | Newcastle NSW |
| 45) | 2ST | 102.9 | 2 | Bowral NSW |
| 76) | 4HTB | 102.9 | 25(d) | Gold Coast QLD |
| 52) | 6NW | 102.9 | 2(d) | Broome WA |
| 94) | 3BBA | 103.1 | 20(d) | Ballarat VIC |
| 34) | 4RAM | 103.1 | 100(d) | Townsville QLD |
| 120) | 2VM(t) | 103.5 | 1 | Collarenebri NSW |
| 96) | 4HOT | 103.5 | 10(d) | Cairns QLD |
| 149) | 4MBB | 103.5 | 10(d) | Maryborough QLD |
| 78) | 2GF(t) | 103.9 | 5(d) | Maclean NSW |
| 128) | 2DAY | 104.1 | 150(d) | Sydney NSW |
| 39) | 2MW(t) | 104.1 | 1(d) | Gold Coast QLD |
| 10) | 2EEE | 104.3 | 20(d) | Batemans Bay/Moruya NSW |
| 25) | 2LM(t) | 104.3 | 1(d) | Kyogle NSW |
| 74) | 3KKZ | 104.3 | 56(d) | Melbourne VIC |
| 171) | 2GOS | 104.5 | 16 | Gosford NSW |
| 61) | 4LRE | 104.5 | 1(d) | Longreach QLD |
| 127) | 4MMM | 104.5 | 12 | Brisbane QLD |
| 78) | 2CLR | 104.7 | 20(d) | Grafton NSW |
| 138) | 2ROC | 104.7 | 20 | Canberra ACT |
| 77) | 5MMM | 104.7 | 20(d) | Adelaide SA |
| 116) | 2AAY | 104.9 | 100(d) | Albury NSW |
| 129) | 2MMM | 104.9 | 150(d) | Sydney NSW |
| 150) | 4RBL | 104.9 | 3 | Bourke NSW |
| 146) | 8MIX | 104.9 | 17(d) | Darwin NT |
| 120) | 2NOW(t) | 105.1 | 1(d) | Walgett NSW |
| 59) | 2OAG | 105.1 | 5 | Orange NSW |
| 1) | 2ROX | 105.1 | 10(d) | Kempsey NSW |
| 124) | 3MMM | 105.1 | 56(d) | Melbourne VIC |
| 62) | 6MER | 105.1 | 6(d) | Merredin WA |
| 139) | 2NEW | 105.3 | 20(d) | Newcastle NSW |
| 92) | 4BBB | 105.3 | 12 | Brisbane QLD |
| 133) | 2CSF | 105.5 | 15 | Coffs Harbour NSW |
| 10) | 2EC(t) | 105.5 | 1 | Eden NSW |
| 120) | 2VM(t) | 105.5 | 1 | Mungindi NSW |
| 83) | 2BDR | 105.7 | 100(d) | Albury NSW |
| 167) | 6IX(t) | 105.7 | 4(d) | Wanneroo WA |
| 10) | 2EC(t) | 105.9 | 20(d) | Batemans Bay/Moruya NSW |
| 59) | 2GZF | 105.9 | 5 | Orange NSW |
| 84) | 5AUU | 105.9 | 20 | Spencer Gulf North SA |
| 170) | 8SAT | 106.1 | 3 | Ceduna/Smoky Bay SA |
| 133) | 1CBR | 106.3 | 20 | Canberra ACT |
| 133) | 2CFS | 106.3 | 15(d) | Coffs Harbour NSW |
| 67) | 3CCS | 106.3 | 10(d) | Colac VIC |
| 11) | 4RGT | 106.3 | 100(d) | Townsville QLD |
| 64) | 2WFM | 106.5 | 150(d) | Sydney NSW |
| 170) | 8SAT | 106.5 | 5(d) | Birchip VIC |
| 88) | 6RED | 106.5 | 1(d) | Karratha WA |
| 1) | 2PQQ | 106.7 | 10(d) | Kempsey NSW |
| 45) | 2ST(t) | 106.7 | 1.6 | Ulladulla NSW |
| 120) | 2VM(t) | 106.7 | 1 | Walgett NSW |
| 150) | 4RBL | 106.7 | 1 | Childers QLD |
| 100) | 2XXX | 106.9 | 20(d) | Newcastle NSW |
| 26) | 4BNE | 106.9 | 12 | Brisbane QLD |
| 170) | 8SAT | 106.9 | 2 | Minnipa SA |
| 146) | 8MIX | 106.9 | 1 | Katherine NT |
| 120) | 2NOW(t) | 107.1 | 1 | Mungindi NSW |
| 130) | 5SSA | 107.1 | 20(d) | Adelaide SA |
| 121) | 2MVB | 107.3 | 10(d) | Taree NSW |
| 150) | 4BRZ | 107.3 | 1 | Bourke NSW |
| 152) | 7XXX | 107.3 | 36 | Hobart TAS |
| 170) | 8SAT | 107.3 | 2(d) | Kingston SE SA |
| 97) | 2GGO | 107.7 | 10(d) | Gosford NSW |
| 98) | 3SHI | 107.7 | 10 | Swan Hill VIC |
| 27) | 7DDD | 107.7 | 7(d) | Devonport TAS |
| 107) | 2ICE | 107.7 | 10 | Lithgow NSW |
| 43) | 4ROK | 107.9 | 10 | Rockhampton QLD |
| 34) | 4TSV(t) | 107.9 | 2(d) | Bowen QLD |

**NB:** Txs 1kW and higher

## Digital Services

| DAB+ | Call | Ch | MHz | kW |
|------|------|-----|-----|-----|
| Canberra | DAB9A | 9A | 201.072 | 5 |
| Canberra | DAB10B | 10B | 211.648 | 3 |
| Sydney | DAB9A | 9A | 202.928 | 50(d) |
| Sydney | DAB9B | 9B | 204.64 | 50(d) |
| Melbourne | DAB9A | 9A | 202.928 | 50(d) |
| Melbourne | DAB9B | 9B | 204.64 | 50(d) |
| Brisbane | DAB9A | 9A | 202.928 | 50(d) |
| Brisbane | DAB9B | 9B | 204.64 | 50(d) |
| Adelaide | DAB9B | 9B | 204.64 | 50(d) |
| Perth | DAB9B | 9B | 204.64 | 50(d) |
| Darwin | DAB10B | 10B | 211.648 | 5(d) |

All permanent digital multiplexes carry simulcasts of all local wide-coverage commercial services, are shared with Community services, and carry additional digital only content. Several digital on-channel repeaters provide infill coverage (ERP 300-500W). Canberra is a trial shared with ABC & SBS. Darwin is a trial shared with ABC. Both trials have more limited content. All prgr at **W:** digitalradioplus.com.au

## Commercial addresses & other information:

**NB:** ARN=Australian Radio Network The term midnight-to-dawn refers to local time. Exact hrs vary from stn to stn

**1)** PO Box 1161, Port Macquarie NSW 2444 (DMG). Supplementary stn. on 102.3MHz and 105.1MHz – **2)** PO Box 253, Warragul Vic. 3820. (N-2) – **3)** PO Box 19, Innisfail, Qld. 4860 **E:** zedamfm@4kz.com.au (N-1): Translators: Tully 693kHz 0.5kW, Dunk Island 88.5MHz 0.5kW – **4)** PO Box 189, Scottsdale, TAS. 7254 (N-1).Part of TASmanian Broadcasting Network – **5)** PO Box 177, Mareeba, QLD 4880 (N-1) Translators: Port Douglas 1422kHz, Weipa 97.7MHz – **6)** PO Box 42, Gympie QLD 4370 (N-1) – **7)** PO Box 120, Burnie, TAS. 7320 (N-1) – **8)** 25 Garnet St, Broken Hill, NSW 2880 (N-3). Supplementary stn on 106.9MHz – **9)** PO Box 693, Newstead, QLD 4006 (N-1) – **10)** PO Box 471, Bega, NSW 2550. Translators: 1584=Narooma, 105.9MHz = Batemans Bay – **11)** PO Box 986, Townsville, QLD 4810 **E:** fourto@ultra.net.au **W:** ozemail.com. au/~aschter (N-1:) – **12)** PO Box 145, Penrith, NSW 2750 (N-1) – **13)** PO Box 293, Albany, WA 6330. (N-1) – **14)** PO Box 321, Berri SA 5343 **E:** fiverm@riverland.net. au **W:** riverland.net.au /~fiverm/ (N-1) – **15)** PO Box 828, Nambour, QLD 4560 (N-1) – **16)** PO Box 315, Queenstown, TAS 7467 (N-3). Translators at Strahan 105.1MHz 25w & Rosebery 107.1MHz 0.3kW – **17)** PO Box 6110, Cairns, QLD 4870. (N-1:Sky Radio) – **18)** PO Box 111, Toowoomba, QLD 4350 (N-1) – **19)** PO Box 256 Northam, WA 6401 – **20)** GPO Box 542F, Hobart, TAS 7001 (N-3) – **21)** GPO Box 4290, Sydney 2001 (N-3) – **22)** PO Box 485, Warrnambool, Vic. 3280 – **23)** GPO Box 6072, Perth, W.A. 6000 (N-1) – **24)** GPO Box 906, Brisbane, QLD 4001 (N-1) – **25)** PO Box 44, Lismore, NSW 2480. (N-1) – **26)** Locked Bag 1069, Fortitude Value BC, QLD 4006 – **27)** PO Box 635, Launceston TAS 7310 – **28)** PO Box 2106, Alice Springs 0871 (N-1). Translator at Yulara on 100.5MHz with 100w. Supplementary st. 8SUN on 96.9MHz with 300w at Alice Springs – **29)** PO Box 651, Cooma, NSW 2630 (N-1) Relays 2UE 9:00-10:00 and AUSTEREO 18:00-18:00. Translators: Thredbo 92.1MHz 1kW, Jindabyne 96.3MHz 2kW and Perisher 98.7MHz 1kW – **30)** 625 Wyndham St, Shepparton, VIC 3630 – **31)** PO Box 665, Carnarvon WA 6701 – **32)** 3UZ Pty Ltd, PO Box 927, Carlton, VIC 3053 (N-1) ID's as "Sport 927" – **33)** PO Box 420, Gladstone, QLD 4680. (N-1). Translator at Rockhampton on 1584 with 500w and at Biloela on 666kHz with 2.5 kw – **34)** PO Box 986, Townsville, QLD 4810 (FM **E:** hotfm@ultra.net.au) (N-1). 4RR: Racing format, prgrs 8.00-24.00, also relays 4TAB 1008. 4RAM: Translator at Mt Stuart 107.9MHz 1kW, ID's as "103.1 Hot FM" – **35)** PO Box 108, Golden Square, Vic. 3555 (N-1) – **36)** PO Box 950, North Sydney, NSW 2059 (N-3) – **37)** PO Box 195, Warwick, QLD 4370 (N-1) Rel 2TM 1287 7:00pm to 6:00am. Translator: Toowoomba 1359kHz 0.3kW – **38)** PO Box 493, Griffith, NSW 2680 (N-10) – **39)** PO Box 97, Coolangatta, QLD 4225 (N-1). Ids as "Radio 97" – **40)** 201 Tynte St, Nth Adelaide SA 5006. **W:** 5dn.com.au (N-1) – **41)** PO Box 981, Hamilton, VIC 3300 (N-1) – **42)** PO Box 440, Kalgoorlie, WA 6430 (N-1) – **43)** PO Box 159, Rockhampton, QLD 4700 (N-1) – **44)** PO Box 157, Subiaco, WA 6008 (N-1) – **45)** PO Box 540, Nowra 2540 (N-1). Translators: Uladulla 106.7MHz. Supplementary St. on 94.9MHz. (N-1) – **46)** Radio 4TAB, PO Box 275, Albion, QLD 4010. Racing format – **47)** Level 1, 464 Hay St, Subiaco, WA 6008 – **48)** G.PO Box 572F, Hobart, TAS 7001 on 1008kHz & 1080kHz, 87.6MHz 1W narrowcast throughout Queenstown, Strahan, Zeehan, Roseberry, Tullah, Stanley& Smithton (N-1:Sky Radio). Racing format. Rel 2UE M-F – **49)** 79 Frenchs Forest Rd., Frenchs Forest NSW 2086 (N-3: Sky Sports) Provides relays to over 100 NSW stns carrying racing: – **50)** Private Bag 1011, Richmond Vic. 3121 (N-1) – **51)** PO Box 183, Mackay, QLD 4740 (N-1). Airlie Beach on 94.7MHz. Bowen on 107.9MHz – **52)** PO Box 2216, South Hedland, WA 6722 – **53)** PO Box 481, Pt. Pirie, SA 5540 (N-1) – **54)** PO Box 163, Canberra City, ACT 2601 **W:** 2ca.village.com.au (N-3) – **55)** PO Box 178, Bendigo VIC 3550 – **56)** PO Box 305, Kingaroy, QLD 4610 (N-1) ID's as "1071AM" and "Classic Gold" – **57)** PO Box 62,

Gunnedah 2380 – **58)** 3 Gommes Lane, Yornup WA 6256 – **59)** PO Box 88, Orange, NSW 2800. (N-1:Sky Radio) – **60)** PO Box 606, Horsham, VIC 3400. (N-1) – **61)** PO Box 20, Longreach, QLD 4730 – **62)** PO Box 264, Merredin, WA 6415. (N-1) – **63)** PO Box 835G, Launceston, TAS 7250 (N-3) – **64)** PO Box 1107, Neutral Bay NSW 2089 (N-1). ID's as "Mix 106.5 FM" – **65)** G.PO Box 95, Brisbane, QLD 4001 (N-1) – **66)** PO Box 270, Armidale, NSW 2350. **E:** 2AD@mpx.com.au (N-1 – **67)** PO Box 63, Colac, Vic. 3250 (N-1) – **68)** PO Box 19, Mayfield, NSW 2304 (N-3) – **69)** PO Box 267, Emerald, QLD 4720. (N-1). Translators: 945kHz 1kW, 1215kHz 0.1kW, 88.1MHz 30W, 92.5MHz 10W, 98.2MHz 0.1kW, 102.1MHz 0.25kW. Rel 4AM 558kHz, 4ZR 1476kHz, 4CC 927kHz – **70)** PO Box 480, Wagga Wagga, NSW 2650. (N-1). Translator at Tumut on 107.9MHz with 10w. Supplementary St. on 93.1MHz. Both stns – **71)** PO Box 143, Maryborough, QLD 4650. (N-1) – **72)** GPO Box 2516, Nth Sydney, NSW 2001 (N-1) – **73)** PO Box 381, Charters Towers, QLD 4820 Translator: Hughenden 765kHz 0.5kW – **74)** Private Bag 1043, Richmond Vic. 3121 (N-1) as "Gold FM" – **75)** PO Box 770, Inverell, NSW 2360. (N-3) – **76)** PO Box 10290, Southport BC, QLD 4215 – **77)** PO Box 1047, Unley, SA 5061 (N-1) Translator in Adelaide city on 98.3MHz 0.5kW – **78)** PO Box 276, Grafton, NSW 2460. (N-1) – **79)** PO Box 945, Subiaco, WA 6008 (N-1: BBC) – **80)** PO Box 1499, Canberra City, ACT 2601 (N-1) – **81)** PO Box 234, Seven Hills, NSW 2147 (N-1 – **82)** PO Box 160, Sale, Vic. 3850 (N-1) – **83)** 490 David Street, Albury NSW 2640 – **84)** PO Box 496, Port Augusta, SA 5700 (N-1) – **85)** PO Box 783, Toowoomba, QLD 4350 (N-1) – **86)** PO Box 1221, Dubbo, NSW 2830 **E:** 2du@lisp.com.au. (N-1) FM station "ZOO FM" Dubbo 92.7MHz, Cobar 103.7MHz – **88)** PO Box 153, Karratha, WA 6714. (N-1) – **89)** 8 Jones Bay Road, Pyrmont NSW 2009 **E:** contact@kick-am.com.au. **W:** kick-am.com.au/ (N-1) ID's as "Kick AM" – **90)** GPO Box 369F, Melbourne 3001 **W:** 3aw.com.au/ – **91)** PO Box 497, Tamworth, NSW 2340 (N-1). Supplementary stn. on 92.9MHz – **92)** PO Box 105, Albion, QLD 4010 (N-1) ID's as "B105" – **93)** PO Box 500, Mt. Gambier, SA 5290 (N-1) – **94)** PO Box 360, Ballarat, VIC 3350. (N-1) – **95)** PO Box 1234, Wollongong, NSW 2500 **E:** mike@w151.aone.net.au (N-1) – **96)** 68 Abbott St Cairns QLD 4870 – **97)** PO Box 564, Gosford, NSW 2250 (N-1) – **98)** PO Box 504, Swan Hill, VIC 3585 (N-1) – **99)** PO Box 1059, Bundaberg, QLD 4670 (N-1) – **100)** PO Box 97, Charlestown, NSW 2290 (N-1) – **101)** PO Box 9550, Geelong, VIC 3220 **E:** krock@slanreach.com.au (N-1). ID's as "K-Rock" – **102)** PO Box 31, Young, NSW 2594 (N-1) – **103)** PO Box 780, Mount Isa, QLD 4825 (N-1). Relays to 4GC 828. Translator: Cloncurry 693kHz. Supplementary FM license at Mt. Isa. (N-1) – **04)** PO Box 115, Goulburn, NSW 2580 (N-1: Sky Radio) – **105)** PO Box 75, Frankston, Vic. 3199 **E:** magic@magic.com.au (N-1). 3EE ID's as "Magic" – **106)** GPO Box 5AA, Adelaide SA 5001 (N-1) – **107)** Mailbag 90, Wangaratta VIC 3799 **E:** 2lt@tisp.com.au. (N-1) (for QSL'ing purposes) c/o John Wright, 15 Olive Cres, Peakhurst NSW 2210 – **108)** PO Box 295, Parkes, NSW 2870. (N-1) – **109)** PO Box 606, Charlestown, NSW 2290. (N-1) – **111)** PO Box 17, Mudgee, NSW 2850 – **112)** PO Box 600, Muswellbrook, NSW 2333 (N-1) 2VLY 98.1 ID's as "Power FM" – **113)** PO Box 470, Murray Bridge, SA 5253 (N-1). Serves Murray Bridge, The Coorong and Meningie – **114)** PO Box 539, Mildura, VIC 3500 (N-1). 3MA 99.5 ID's as "Today's Music 99.5FM" – **115)** PO Box 22, Roma, QLD 4455. (N-1:Sky Radio) – **116)** PO Box 670, Albury, NSW 2640 **W:** albury.net.au/radio.albury.wodonga/2ay.html (N-1). Supplementary stn. on FM – **117)** PO Box 310, Bathurst, NSW 2795 **E:** stereo@2bs.ix.net.au or 2bs@csu.edu.au **W:** 2bs.ix.net.au (N-1) FM service on 99.3MHz – **118)** PO Box 195, Shepparton, Vic. 3630 – **119)** PO Box 312, Deniliquin, NSW 2710. (N-1) 2MOR 102.5 ID's as "Classic Rock 102.5" – **120)** PO Box 389, Moree, NSW 2400. (N-1). Supplementary license on 98.3MHz. Translator on 88.7MHz with 250w r. (N-1) – **121)** PO Box 275, Taree, NSW 2430 (N-1). Translator: Gloucester 100.1MHz and Forster on 100.3MHz (N-1) – **122)** PO Box 606, Wangaratta, VIC 3677 (N-1). 3NE Translators: Mt. Hotham 89.3MHz 0.02kW, Mt. Buffalo 105.3MHz 0.2kW, Mt. Beauty 90.3MHz 10w. 3NNN ID's as "Edge FM" – **123)** Locked Bag 6198 Sth Coast Mail Centre NSW 2521 (N-1) ID's as "98FM" – **124)** GPO Box 105, Melbourne, VIC (N-1) – **125)** 111 Wellington Str, East Perth, WA 6004. (N-1) – **126)** PO Box 1019, St. Kilda, Vic. 3182 (N-1) – **127)** GPO Box 1041, Brisbane, QLD 4001. (N-1) – **128)** Level 15, 50 Goulburn Street, Sydney, NSW 2000 **W:** 2dayfm.com.au (N-1) – **129)** Level 14, 50 Goulburn Street, Sydney, NSW 2000 (N-1). **W:** triplem.com.au – **130)** PO Box 1071, Unley, SA 5061.24h (N-1) Translator South Tce, Adelaide on 91.1MHz 1kW. ID's as "SAFM" – **131)** PO Box 527, Esperance, WA 6450. N-1. Rel. 6PPM-FM 1000-2200 – **132)** PO Box 665, Carnarvon, WA 6701. 2200-1500 (N-1). Translator: Exmouth – **133)** PO Box 1950, Coffs Harbour, NSW 2450 (N-1). Rp – **134)** PO Box 483, Port Lincoln, SA 5606. (N-1) – **135)** 141 Mandurah Tce, Mandurah, WA 6210 (N-1) – **136)** GPO Box 163, Canberra, ACT 2601. Belongs to 5AU. **F.PI:** translator for Tuggeranong area – **137)** PO Box 106, Dickson, ACT 2602. (N-1) ID's as "Mix 106.3" – **138)** GPO Box 163, Canberra, A.C.T. 2601 (N-1) – **139)** PO Box 185, Mackay QLD 4740 – **140)** PO Box 2101, Gosford, NSW 2250 (N-1) – **141)** PO Box 7, Ipswich, QLD 4305 (N-1) ID's as "Mix 106.9 QFM"

– **142)** PO Box 128 Geraldton, WA 6530. 24h (N-1) – **143)** 15 Puttabucca Rd, Mudgee NSW 2850 – **144)** G.PO Box 1800, Hobart, TAS. 7001 (N-1) – **145)** Locked Bag 5000, Broadway NSW 2007 – **146)** GPO Box 2510, Darwin NT 0801 – **147)** 4 Peary St., Darwin, NT 0800 (N-1) Translators: Katherine 765kHz 0.5kW – **148)** 678 Victoria St, Richmond VIC 3121 – **149)** 403 The Esplanade, Torquay QLD 4655 – **150)** PO Box 332, Beaudesert QLD 4285 – **151)** PO Box 148, Bunbury WA 6231 – **152)** GPO Box 1345, Hobart TAS 7001 – **153)** PO Box 84, Charleville, QLD 4470 (N-1) ID's as "Outback Radio". Translator: Cunnamulla 1584kHz 0.2kW – **154)** PO Box 5910 Gold Coast Mail Centre Bundall QLD 4217 r. (N-1) – **155)** Private Bag 925 Gold Coast Mail Centre QLD 4215. (N-1) – **156)** Paul Taylor, 41 Allards Crt., Clifton Springs VIC 3222 – **157)** Sea FM, 320 Sheridan St Cairns QLD 4870 – **158)** Sea FM, Suncorp/Metway Building Suite 3, Level 3, 123 Victoria St, Mackay QLD 4740 – **159)** 444 Logan Rd, Stones Corner QLD 4120 – **160)** PO Box 665 Carnarvon WA 6701 – **161)** 33 Saunders Road, Pyrmont NSW 2009 – **162)** Regional Communications Pty Ltd, PO Box 7515, St Kilda Road VIC 3004 – **163)** 47 Wingewarra St Dubbo NSW 2830 – **164)** DMG Regional Radio, Locked Bag 5000, Broadway NSW 2007 – **165)** 68 Aboott St, Cairns QLD 4870 – **166)** PO Box 112, Bunbury WA 6230 – **167)** PO Box 33, Tuart Hill WA 6060 – **168)** cnr Plaza Pde & Carnaby St, Maroochydore QLD 4558 – **169)** Locked Bag 919, Adelaide SA 5001 – **170)** PO Box 579, Lilydale VIC 3140 – **171)** PO Box 3535, Erina NSW 2250 – **172)** Level 2, 678 Victoria Street, Richmond, Vic, 3121

## COMMUNITY RADIO SERVICES

| MW | Call | Location | kHz | kW |
|---|---|---|---|---|
| 1) | 2WEB | Bourke | 585 | 10(d) |
| 2) | 6WR | Kununurra | 693 | 5 |
| 3) | 3CR | Melbourne | 855 | 2(d) |
| 4) | 7RPH | Hobart | 864 | 2 |
| 9) | 3RPH | Warrnambool | 882 | 2 |
| 15) | 6FX | Fitzroy Crossing | 936 | 5 |
| 220) | 6RPH | Perth (inactive?) | 990 | 5 |
| 7) | 1RPH | Canberra | 1125 | 2(d) |
| 9) | 3RPH | Melbourne | 1179 | 5 |
| 8) | 4YB | Brisbane | 1197 | 0.5 |
| 10) | 5RPH | Adelaide | 1197 | 2 |
| 11) | 2RPH | Sydney | 1224 | 5(d) |
| 6) | 4MW | Thursday Is. | 1260 | 2 |
| 18) | 4RPH | Brisbane | 1296 | 5(d) |
| 193) | 3KND | Melbourne | 1503 | 5(d) |

| FM | Call | MHz | kW | Location |
|---|---|---|---|---|
| 151) | 3MFM | 88.1 | 2(d) | Leongatha |
| 9) | 3BPH | 88.7 | 6.6 | Bendigo |
| 176) | 3RUM | 88.7 | 1 | Walwa/Jingellic |
| 13) | 2RBR | 88.9 | 1(d) | Coraki |
| 14) | 2YOU | 88.9 | 1 | Tamworth |
| 217) | 4CCR | 89.1 | 2(d) | Cairns |
| 148) | 5BBB | 89.1 | 1 | Barossa Valley |
| 239) | 5UMA | 89.1 | 4(d) | Port Augusta |
| 17) | 4CRB | 89.3 | 25(d) | Gold Coast |
| 16) | 4SDB | 89.3 | 2 | Warwick |
| 149) | 5EFM | 89.3 | 1 | Victor Harbour |
| 150) | 5GFM | 89.3 | 5(d) | Arthurton |
| 3) | 3MFM | 89.5 | 1(d) | Foster |
| 218) | 2HIM | 89.7 | 1 | Tamworth |
| 19) | 2TEN | 89.7 | 4 | Tenterfield |
| 147) | 5TCB(t) | 89.7 | 1.5 | Naracoorte |
| 158) | 6TCR | 89.7 | 2(d) | Wanneroo |
| 238) | 3TSC | 89.9 | 56(d) | Melbourne |
| 20) | 4DDD | 89.9 | 2 | Dalby |
| 152) | 5GSFM | 90.1 | 1 | Victor Harbour |
| 153) | 3SYN | 90.7 | 35(d) | Melbourne |
| 21) | 4CSB | 90.7 | 5(d) | Wondai |
| 22) | 5KIX | 90.7 | 3(d) | Kangaroo Island |
| 23) | 1CMS | 91.1 | 20 | Canberra |
| 24) | 2CBD | 91.1 | 5 | Deepwater |
| 1) | 2WEB(t) | 91.1 | 1(d) | Coonamble |
| 25) | 2MAX | 91.3 | 10(d) | Narrabri |
| 102) | 4BRR | 91.5 | 1 | Gayndah |
| 26) | 4GCR | 91.5 | 1 | Gympie |
| 27) | 1WAY | 91.9 | 20 | Canberra |
| 198) | 2STA | 91.9 | 1(d) | Inverell |
| 28) | 4RGL | 91.9 | 1 | Gladstone |
| 37) | 2ARM | 92.1 | 2 | Armidale |
| 30) | 2MFM | 92.1 | 15(d) | Sydney |
| 31) | 6RTR | 92.1 | 16(d) | Perth |
| 33) | 2MCE | 92.3 | 1 | Bathurst |
| 34) | 3ZZZ | 92.3 | 56(d) | Melbourne |
| 35) | 1ART | 92.7 | 20 | Canberra |
| 155) | 5FBI | 92.7 | 20(d) | Adelaide |
| 36) | 2NCR | 92.9 | 6 | Lismore |
| 147) | 5TCB | 92.9 | 2 | Kingston SE |

| FM | Call | MHz | kW | Location | FM | Call | MHz | kW | Location |
|---|---|---|---|---|---|---|---|---|---|
| 38) | 2BBB | 93.3 | 3.2 | Dorrigo | 177) | 2PAR | 101.9 | 1 | Ballina |
| 156) | 2MNO | 93.3 | 2 | Monaro | 86) | 4ZZZ | 102.1 | 12 | Brisbane |
| 157) | 2SNR | 93.3 | 2(d) | Gosford | 87) | 6WR | 102.1 | 1 | Wyndham |
| 9) | 3RPH | 93.5 | 1 | Warragul | 88) | 2NIM | 102.3 | 1 | Nimbin |
| 39) | 2BAR | 93.7 | 1(d) | Bega | 89) | 2MBS | 102.5 | 50(d) | Sydney |
| 212) | 2LND | 93.7 | 50(d) | Sydney | 90) | 3RRR | 102.7 | 56(d) | Melbourne |
| 40) | 5DDD | 93.7 | 6.3 | Adelaide | 91) | 2CVC | 103.1 | 1(d) | Grafton |
| 226) | 2CCM | 94.1 | 2(d) | Gosford | 92) | 2WET | 103.1 | 1 | Kempsey |
| 41) | 2LIV | 94.1 | 4(d) | Wollongong/Nowra | 210) | 3BBR | 103.1 | 1 | Warragul |
| 43) | 2DCB | 94.3 | 2 | Dubbo | 93) | 5EBI | 103.1 | 20(d) | Adelaide |
| 213) | 2FBI | 94.5 | 150(d) | Sydney | 94) | 2CBA | 103.2 | 50(d) | Sydney |
| 9) | 3RPH | 94.5 | 5(d) | Warrnambool | 95) | 2TLP | 103.3 | 3(d) | Taree |
| 45) | 8KNB | 94.5 | 15 | Darwin | 97) | 2CCB | 103.5 | 5 | Orange |
| 33) | 2MCE | 94.7 | 1 | Orange | 98) | 3MBR | 103.5 | 4.8 | Murrayville |
| 228) | 3PLS | 94.7 | 56(d) | Geelong | 99) | 3MBS | 103.5 | 56(d) | Melbourne |
| 47) | 4BCR | 94.7 | 3(d) | Bundaberg | 100) | 2NUR | 103.7 | 10(d) | Newcastle |
| 194) | 2GCB | 94.9 | 2 | Gosford | 53) | 3WAY | 103.7 | 5 | Warrnambool |
| 160) | 2MIA | 95.1 | 3.5 | Griffith | 101) | 4MBS | 103.7 | 12 | Brisbane |
| 229) | 2TRR | 95.3 | 2 | Coolah | 179) | 7LTN | 103.7 | 2(d) | Launceston |
| 161) | 6EBA | 95.3 | 16(d) | Perth | 103) | 2WAY | 103.9 | 3 | Port Macquarie |
| 229) | 2TRR | 96.1 | 1 | Dunedoo | 104) | 3BGR | 103.9 | 3 | Ballarat |
| 11) | 7RPH | 96.1 | 3.2 | Devonport | 209) | 3GCB | 103.9 | 10(d) | Latrobe Valley |
| 32) | 7THE | 96.1 | 3(d) | Hobart | 105) | 4TTT | 103.9 | 20 | Townsville |
| 48) | 2CCC | 96.3 | 2(d) | Gosford | 106) | 6ESP | 103.9 | 5 | Esperance |
| 49) | 3GGR | 96.3 | 56(d) | Geelong | 107) | 2CHY | 104.1 | 5 | Coffs Harbour |
| 137) | 6PAC | 96.3 | 6 | Kalgoorlie | 44) | 8TFM | 104.1 | 15 | Darwin |
| 50) | 2CHR | 96.5 | 2(d) | Cessnock/Maitland | 69) | 2UUU | 104.5 | 2(d) | Nowra |
| 51) | 3EON | 96.5 | 1(d) | Bendigo | 147) | 5TCB | 104.5 | 1.6 | Keith |
| 52) | 4FRB | 96.5 | 12 | Brisbane | 109) | 2BOB | 104.7 | 5 | Taree |
| 46) | 4RFM | 96.9 | 4 | Moranbah | 110) | 3GCR | 104.7 | 4 | Latrobe Valley |
| 159) | 2OLD | 97.3 | 1 | Lake Macquarie | 111) | 3GRR | 104.7 | 5(d) | Echuca |
| 54) | 3HCR | 97.3 | 1 | Omeo | 112) | 7DBS | 104.7 | 2 | Devonport |
| 165) | 7TAS | 97.7 | 1 | Tasman Peninsula | 181) | 4SFM | 104.9 | 3 | Nambour |
| 55) | 8GGG | 97.7 | 15 | Darwin | 182) | 5RCB | 104.9 | 20(d) | Mt. Gambier |
| 56) | 2LVR | 97.9 | 4.2(d) | Parkes/Forbes | 113) | 4WBR | 105.1 | 10(d) | Maryborough |
| 57) | 6DBY | 97.9 | 2 | Derby | 201) | 5TRX | 105.1 | 5 | Port Pirie |
| 58) | 4EB | 98.1 | 12 | Brisbane | 114) | 7WAY | 105.3 | 3.2 | Launceston |
| 59) | 1XXR | 98.3 | 20 | Canberra | 115) | 4MET | 105.7 | 10(d) | Gold Coast |
| 60) | 6MKA | 98.3 | 1 | Meekatharra | 24) | 2CBD | 105.9 | 3 | Glen Innes |
| 61) | 2OOO | 98.5 | 25(d) | Sydney | 116) | 2NVR | 105.9 | 2(d) | Nambucca Heads |
| 62) | 3ONE | 98.5 | 10(d) | Shepparton | 175) | 4MUR | 105.9 | 1 | Mackay |
| 167) | 4YOU | 98.5 | 1 | Rockhampton | 147) | 5TCB | 106.1 | 1.6 | Bordertown |
| 63) | 6SON | 98.5 | 16(d) | Perth | 112) | 7DBS | 106.1 | 10(d) | Wynyard |
| 64) | 2KRR | 98.7 | 1 | Kandos | 117) | 2CUZ | 106.5 | 10 | Bourke |
| 65) | 4CIM | 98.7 | 10(d) | Cairns | 183) | 4CLG | 106.5 | 2(d) | Nambour |
| 66) | 4AAA | 98.9 | 12 | Brisbane | 96) | 7HFC | 106.5 | 18 | Hobart |
| 29) | 3SFM | 99.1 | 1 | Swan Hill | 227) | 3HOT | 106.7 | 1 | Mildura |
| 67) | 3RPC | 99.3 | 2(d) | Portland | 118) | 3PBS | 106.7 | 56(d) | Melbourne |
| 168) | 7EDG | 99.3 | 1 | Hobart South | 119) | 2VOX | 106.9 | 2(d) | Wollongong |
| 68) | 2RFM | 99.7 | 10(d) | Newcastle | 120) | 3UGE | 106.9 | 1 | Alexandra/Eildon |
| 70) | 3MCR | 99.7 | 1 | Mansfield | 4) | 7RPH | 106.9 | 3.2 | Launceston |
| 215) | 4ACR | 99.7 | 1 | Woorabinda | 121) | 4KIG | 107.1 | 16 | Townsville |
| 169) | 4RED | 99.7 | 2(d) | Redcliffe | 122) | 2REM | 107.3 | 2 | Albury |
| 71) | 6GME | 99.7 | 2 | Broome | 123) | 2SER | 107.3 | 14 | Sydney |
| 170) | 2BAY | 99.9 | 3 | Byron Bay | 124) | 4CAB | 107.3 | 10(d) | Gold Coast |
| 72) | 2PMQ | 99.9 | 1(d) | Port Macquarie | 125) | 2EAR | 107.5 | 1.6(d) | Moruya |
| 73) | 3BBB | 99.9 | 3 | Ballarat | 173) | 2OCB | 107.5 | 5 | Orange |
| 74) | 4TCB | 99.9 | 20(d) | Townsville | 9) | 3MPH | 107.5 | 1 | Mildura |
| 171) | 5MBS | 99.9 | 2.5 | Adelaide Foothills | 126) | 4CRM | 107.5 | 1 | Mackay |
| 75) | 2BCB | 100.1 | 10 | Bathurst | 176) | 3RUM | 107.7 | 1 | Tumbarumba |
| 9) | 3SPH | 100.1 | 10(d) | Shepparton | 127) | 2AIR | 107.9 | 1(d) | Coffs Harbour |
| 172) | 4RIM | 100.1 | 1 | Boonah | 128) | 2COW | 107.9 | 1 | Casino |
| 214) | 5GTR | 100.1 | 1 | Mt. Gambier | 129) | 5RAM | 107.9 | 20(d) | Adelaide |
| 5) | 6NR | 100.1 | 6.5(d) | Perth | 130) | 6CCR | 107.9 | 1(d) | Fremantle |
| 216) | 2YAS | 100.3 | 2 | Yass | | | | | |
| 77) | 4BAY | 100.3 | 3(d) | Wynnum/Redlands | | | | | |

**NB:** Txs 1kW and higher

| 11) | 2RPH(t) | 100.5 | 4 | Newcastle |
| 11) | 2RPH(t) | 100.5 | 1(d) | Sydney Eastern Suburbs |
| 1) | 2WEB | 100.7 | 1(d) | Nyngan |
| 78) | 3CH | 100.7 | 1(d) | Kyneton |
| 79) | 4US | 100.7 | 1 | Rockhampton |
| 76) | 5LFM | 100.7 | 5(d) | Renmark |
| 211) | 2PSR | 100.9 | 1(d) | Port Stephens |
| 80) | 6CRA | 100.9 | 8(d) | Albany |
| 166) | 6NME | 100.9 | 16(d) | Perth |
| 81) | 4CBL | 101.1 | 4(d) | Logan |
| 82) | 3WPR | 101.3 | 1 | Wangaratta |
| 85) | 8KTR | 101.3 | 1 | Katherine |
| 83) | 2GLA | 101.5 | 10(d) | Forster |
| 230) | 3BBS | 101.5 | 1 | Bendigo |
| 174) | 4BSR | 101.5 | 1 | Beaudesert |
| 84) | 4OUR | 101.5 | 3(d) | Caboolture |
| 185) | 5UV | 101.5 | 20(d) | Adelaide |
| 9) | 2APH | 101.7 | 2 | Albury |
| 231) | 6SEN | 101.7 | 8(d) | Perth |

### Digital Community Radio

| DAB+ | Call | Ch | MHz | kW |
|---|---|---|---|---|
| Sydney | DAB9A | 9A | 202.928 | 50(d) |
| Sydney | DAB9B | 9B | 204.64 | 50(d) |
| Melbourne | DAB9A | 9A | 202.928 | 50(d) |
| Melbourne | DAB9B | 9B | 204.64 | 50(d) |
| Brisbane | DAB9A | 9A | 202.928 | 50(d) |
| Brisbane | DAB9B | 9B | 204.64 | 50(d) |
| Adelaide | DAB9B | 9B | 204.64 | 50(d) |
| Perth | DAB9B | 9B | 204.64 | 50(d) |

Digital multiplexes carry simulcasts of many local wide coverage community services.

### HIGH POWER OPEN NARROWCAST SERVICES (HPON)

**NB**: These stns are licenced in the usual MW & FM broadcast bands. Programming is narrowcast. Official callsigns are issued but not used on-air, actual on-air identifiers may resemble normal callsigns. Many stns not using full licensed tx power/ERP.

| MW | Station | kHz | kW | Location |
|---|---|---|---|---|
| 188) | R. Italiana 531 | 531 | 0.5 | Adelaide SA |
| 141) | Niche R. Network | 657 | 2 | Perth WA |
| 141) | Niche R. Network | 801 | 5(d) | Gosford NSW |
| 189) | 4AY | 873 | 2 | Innisfail QLD |
| 138) | R. TAB | 891 | 5(d) | Townsville QLD |
| 146) | RSN | 945 | 2 | Bendigo VIC |
| 139) | Sky Sports R. | 1008 | 0.3 | Canberra ACT |
| 132) | TAB R. (WA) | 1008 | 2 | Geraldton WA |
| 138) | R. TAB | 1008 | 5(d) | Launceston TAS |
| 164) | Vision Christian R. | 1017 | 1 | Bunbury WA |
| 140) | R. Rhythm | 1053 | 0.5 | Brisbane QLD |
| 138) | R. TAB | 1080 | 5(d) | Hobart TAS |
| 132) | TAB R. (WA) | 1206 | 2 | Perth WA |
| 138) | R. TAB | 1242 | 2 | Darwin NT |
| 139) | Sky Sports R. | 1314 | 5(d) | Wollongong NSW |
| 144) | Star AM | 1323 | 0.4(d) | Canberra ACT |
| 139) | Sky Sports R. | 1341 | 5(d) | Newcastle NSW |
| 192) | 3CW 1341 | 1341 | 5(d) | Geelong VIC |
| 146) | RSN | 1359 | 0.2 | Mildura VIC |
| 132) | TAB R. (WA) | 1404 | 4 | Busselton WA |
| 164) | Vision Christian R. | 1413 | 0.5(d) | Shepparton VIC |
| 195) | 3XY R. Hellas | 1422 | 5 | Melbourne VIC |
| 200) | R. Great Southern | 1422 | 2 | Wagin WA |
| 164) | Vision Christian R. | 1431 | 2 | Kalgoorlie WA |
| 132) | TAB R. (WA) | 1449 | 2 | Mandurah WA |
| 141) | Niche R. Network | 1539 | 1 | Sydney NSW |
| 138) | R. TAB | 1539 | 5(d) | Adelaide SA |
| 136) | KIX Country | 1557 | 0.5(d) | Renmark/Loxton SA |
| 141) | Niche R. Network | 1575 | 5(d) | Wollongong NSW |
| 139) | Sky Sports R. | 1593 | 0.2 | Murwillumbah NSW |
| 141) | Niche R. Network | 1593 | 5(d) | Melbourne VIC |

| FM | Station | MHz | kW | Location |
|---|---|---|---|---|
| 197) | KIK FM | 88.7 | 2(d) | Atherton QLD |
| 132) | TAB R. (WA) | 89.5 | 1.2 | Esperance WA |
| 141) | Niche R. Network | 90.3 | 1 | Griffith NSW |
| 136) | KIX Country | 90.5 | 1(d) | Barossa Valley SA |
| 139) | Sky Sports Radio | 90.5 | 1(d) | Tamworth NSW |
| | | ‡90.9 | 1 | Mossman QLD ‡ |
| 139) | Sky Sports Radio | 90.9 | 1 | Mudgee NSW |
| 135) | The Range | 91.5 | 1 | Toowoomba QLD |
| 135) | The Range | 91.9 | 1(d) | Latrobe Valley VIC |
| 136) | KIX Country | 92.3 | 10(d) | Maryborough QLD |
| 139) | Sky Sports Radio | 92.7 | 1 | Inverell NSW |
| 139) | Sky Sports Radio | 92.7 | 3(d) | Port Macquarie NSW |
| 164) | Vision Christian R. | 93.7 | 5 | Albany WA |
| 139) | Sky Sports Radio | 94.3 | 1 | Goulburn NSW |
| 164) | Vision Christian R. | 94.9 | 4 | Broken Hill NSW |
| 139) | Sky Sports Radio | 95.5 | 10(d) | Wagga Wagga NSW |
| 138) | Radio TAB | 95.5 | 3(d) | Bundaberg QLD |
| 138) | Radio TAB | 95.5 | 4.5(d) | Emerald QLD |
| 138) | Radio TAB | 95.5 | 5(d) | Renmark/Loxton SA |
| 139) | Sky Sports Radio | 95.9 | 20(d) | Gunnedah NSW |
| 138) | Radio TAB | 95.9 | 1 | Alice Springs NT |
| 139) | Sky Sports Radio | 96.9 | 1(d) | Cooma NSW |
| 164) | Vision Christian R. | 97.5 | 2(d) | Bairnsdale VIC |
| 138) | Radio TAB | 97.5 | 1 | Blackwater QLD |
| 138) | Radio TAB | 97.7 | 1(d) | Burnie TAS |
| 136) | KIX Country | 98.1 | 1 | Inglewood QLD |
| 184) | Tourist Gold 98.7 FM | 98.7 | 1 | Alice Springs NT |
| 141) | Niche R. Network | 99.1 | 2(d) | Atherton QLD |
| 139) | Sky Sports Radio | 99.9 | 10 | Parkes/Forbes NSW |
| 138) | Radio TAB | 99.9 | 1 | Rockhampton QLD |
| 139) | Sky Sports Radio | 100.5 | 4 | Broken Hill NSW |
| 132) | TAB R. (WA) | 100.5 | 1 | Wyndham WA |
| 139) | Sky Sports Radio | 100.9 | 10 | Bathurst NSW |
| 136) | KIX Country | 101.1 | 10(d) | Nowra NSW |
| 138) | Radio TAB | 101.3 | 2 | Devonport TAS |
| 139) | Sky Sports Radio | 101.5 | 1 | Grafton NSW |
| 139) | Sky Sports Radio | 101.5 | 1 | Kempsey NSW |
| 132) | TAB R. (WA) | 101.7 | 1 | Karratha WA |
| 164) | Vision Christian R. | 102.1 | 1 | Hamilton VIC |
| 139) | Sky Sports Radio | 102.7 | 2(d) | Jindabyne NSW |
| 164) | Vision Christian R. | 102.9 | 2 | Horsham VIC |
| 139) | Sky Sports Radio | 103.3 | 1 | Muswellbrook NSW |
| 138) | Radio TAB | 103.5 | 100(d) | Mackay QLD |
| 139) | Sky Sports Radio | 103.7 | 1 | Moree NSW |
| 139) | Sky Sports Radio | 103.7 | 2(d) | Nowra NSW |
| 138) | Radio TAB | 103.7 | 1 | Katherine NT |
| 139) | Sky Sports Radio | 104.3 | 10 | Armidale NSW |
| 138) | Radio TAB | 104.3 | 10(d) | Cairns QLD |
| 164) | Vision Christian R. | 105.3 | 1 | Portland VIC |
| 136) | KIX Country | 105.3 | 2(d) | Wollongong NSW |
| 139) | Sky Sports Radio | 105.7 | 5 | Taree NSW |
| 136) | KIX Country | 106.1 | 1 | Deniliquin NSW |
| 139) | Sky Sports Radio | 106.7 | 5 | Orange NSW |

| FM | Station | MHz | kW | Location |
|---|---|---|---|---|
| 146) | RSN | 106.9 | 10 | Swan Hill VIC |
| 139) | Sky Sports Radio | 107.1 | 1 | Eden NSW |
| 139) | Sky Sports Radio | 107.5 | 3 | Glen Innes NSW |

**NB**: Txs 1kW and higher

## MEDIUM FREQUENCY-NARROWBAND AREA SERVICES (MF-NAS)

**NB**: These stns are licenced to channels 1611-1701kHz. Programming is narrowcast except for earlier services which may be commercial format. Official callsigns are issued but not used on-air, on-air identifiers may resemble normal callsigns. Many stns are licensed but not operational. Many stns not using full licensed tx power of 400W.

| MW | Station | kHz | kW | Location |
|---|---|---|---|---|
| 164) | Vision Christian R. | 1611 | 0.4 | Grafton NSW |
| 164) | Vision Christian R. | 1611 | 0.4 | Sydney [West] NSW |
| 164) | Vision Christian R. | 1611 | 0.4 | Tamworth NSW |
| 199) | Old Gold 1611AM | 1611 | 0.4 | Mildura VIC |
| 164) | Vision Christian R. | 1611 | 0.4 | Chiltern VIC |
| 164) | Vision Christian R. | 1611 | 0.4 | Melbourne [West] VIC |
| 197) | KIK FM | 1611 | 0.05 | Croydon QLD |
| 189) | 4KZ | 1611 | 0.4 | Karumba QLD |
| 145) | Hot Country (4EM) | 1611 | 0.4 | Emerald QLD |
| 145) | Hot Country | 1611 | 0.4 | Goondiwindi QLD |
| 141) | Niche R. Netw. | 1611 | 0.4 | Mackay QLD |
| 141) | Niche R. Netw. | 1611 | 0.4 | Rockhampton QLD |
| 145) | Hot Country | 1611 | 0.4 | Roma QLD |
| 145) | Hot Country | 1611 | 0.4 | St George QLD |
| 164) | Vision Christian R. | 1611 | 0.4 | Adelaide SA |
| 164) | Vision Christian R. | 1611 | 0.4 | Margaret River WA |
| 200) | Easy Listening 1611 | 1611 | 0.4 | Wagin WA |
| 237) | Gold MX | 1611 | 0.4 | Albany WA |
| 141) | Niche R. Netw. | 1611 | 0.4 | Esperance WA |
| 141) | Niche R. Netw. | 1611 | 0.4 | Kalgoorlie WA |
| 141) | Niche R. Netw. | 1611 | 0.4 | Devonport TAS |
| 141) | Niche R. Netw. | 1611 | 0.4 | Hobart TAS |
| 141) | Niche R. Netw. | 1611 | 0.4 | Launceston TAS |
| 141) | Niche R. Netw. | 1611 | 0.4 | Darwin NT |
| 236) | Canberra Chinese R. | 1620 | 0.4 | Canberra ACT |
| 190) | R. 2MORO | 1620 | 0.4 | Sydney NSW |
| 192) | 3CW 1620 | 1620 | 0.4 | Melbourne VIC |
| 141) | Niche R. Netw. | 1620 | 0.4 | Wangaratta VIC |
| 141) | Niche R. Netw. | 1620 | 0.4 | Brisbane QLD |
| 141) | Niche R. Netw. | 1620 | 0.4 | Gladstone QLD |
| 141) | Niche R. Netw. | 1620 | 0.4 | Gold Coast QLD |
| 141) | Niche R. Netw. | 1620 | 0.4 | Sunshine Coast QLD |
| 189) | 4KZ | 1620 | 0.4 | Taylors Beach QLD |
| 141) | Niche R. Netw. | 1620 | 0.4 | Toowoomba QLD |
| 203) | Unforgettable 1629 | 1629 | 0.1 | Newcastle NSW |
| 164) | Vision Christian R. | 1629 | 0.4 | Bathurst NSW (‡) |
| 164) | Vision Christian R. | 1629 | 0.4 | Dubbo NSW |
| 202) | ACR Huaxia | 1629 | 0.4 | Melbourne VIC |
| 141) | Niche R. Netw. | 1629 | 0.4 | Shepparton VIC |
| 145) | Hot Country (4DB) | 1629 | 0.4 | Dalby QLD |
| 154) | R. Italia Uno | 1629 | 0.4 | Adelaide SA |
| 141) | Niche R. Netw. | 1629 | 0.4 | Mount Gambier SA |
| 234) | 3ABN | 1629 | 0.4 | Busselton WA |
| 141) | Niche R. Netw. | 1629 | 0.4 | Albany WA |
| 222) | 2ME | 1638 | 0.4 | Sydney NSW |
| 222) | 2ME | 1638 | 0.4 | Melbourne VIC |
| 164) | Vision Christian R. | 1647 | 0.4 | Mackay QLD |
| 140) | R. Rhythm | 1656 | 0.4 | Melbourne VIC |
| 223) | VAC Chinese R. | 1656 | 0.4 | Brisbane QLD |
| 204) | 2MM | 1656 | 0.4 | Darwin NT |
| 204) | 2MM | 1665 | 0.4 | Sydney NSW |
| 225) | R. Haanji | 1674 | 0.4 | Melbourne VIC |
| 207) | R. Club AM | 1683 | 0.4 | Sydney NSW |
| 207) | R. Club AM | 1683 | 0.4 | Melbourne VIC |
| 133) | Radio Symban | 1692 | 0.4 | Campbelltown NSW |
| 140) | R. Rhythm (F.PI) | 1692 | 0.4 | Cairns QLD |
| 164) | Vision Christian R. | 1692 | 0.06 | Nanango QLD |
| 140) | R. Rhythm (F.PI) | 1692 | 0.4 | Adelaide SA |
| 140) | R. Rhythm | 1692 | 0.4 | Perth WA |
| 235) | Voice of Purity | 1701 | 0.4 | Sydney NSW |
| 224) | Islamic Voice R. | 1701 | 0.4 | Somerton VIC |
| 208) | R. Brisvaani | 1701 | 0.1 | Brisbane QLD |
| 192) | 3CW-1620 | 1701 | 0.4 | Adelaide SA |

**Community, HPON & MF-NAS addresses & other information**
**1)** Western Region Educational Broadc. Co. Ltd, PO Box 426, Bourke NSW 2840. Plus 5 FM translators. — **2)** Radio Station 6WR., PO Box 162 Kununurra WA 6743. (N-1:CBAA) Aboriginal prgrs from National Indigenous Radio Service — **3)** Community R. Federation Ltd, PO Box 277, Collingwood VIC 3066. Various foreign languages — **4)** Radio 7RPH Broadcasting Services for Handicapped Inc., 136 Davey St, Hobart TAS.

7000. Information and reading service format. Relays BBCWS 11:00pm to 10:00am Mon-Sat, Sunday – **5)** Curtin Univ of Technology, GPO Box U1987, Perth WA 6001. Rel. CBAA Network at times and BBCWS overnight – **6)** PO Box 385, Thursday Island QLD 4875 – **7)** Print-Handicapped Radio of ACT Inc, Barton Highway, Gungahlin, ACT 2912 – relays BBCWS Mon-Fri 1:00pm to 6:00pm SA noon to Su 9:30am – **8)** Brisbane Youth Radio, PO Box 5130, West End QLD, 4101 – **9)** Vision Australia, 454 Glenferrie Rd, Kooyong 3144. Relays BBCWS overnight – **10)** Radio 5RPH, 231 Morphett St. Adelaide SA 5000. Relays BBCWS overnight – **11)** R. for the Print-Handicapped (NSW) Co-op Ltd, 7/184 Glebe Point Rd, Glebe NSW 2037 – **12)** PO Box 148, Toogoolawah QLD 4313 – **13)** 50 Houghwood Rd, Bora Ridge NSW 2471 – **14)** PO Box 998, Tamworth NSW 2340 – **15)** PO Box 52, Fitzroy Crossing WA 6765 – **16)** Rainbow FM, PO Box 473, Warwick QLD 4370 – **17)** PO Box 86, Burleigh Heads QLD 4220 – **18)** Unit 3/17 Henry Street, Spring Hill QLD 4000 – **19)** PO Box 93, Tenterfield NSW 2372 – **20)** PO Box 483, Dalby QLD 4405 – **21)** Crow FM, PO Box 171, Emerald QLD 4606 – **22)** PO Box 90, Kingscote SA 5223 – **23)** PO Box 3882, Weston ACT 2611 (Ethnic) – **24)** Gough St, Deepwater NSW 2371 – **25)** PO Box 94, Narrabri NSW 2390 – **26)** The Positive Alternative, PO Box 774, Gympie QLD 4570 (Christian) – **27)** Canberra Christian Radio, PO Box 927, Fyshwick ACT 2609 (Christian) – **28)** 257 Goondoon St Warwick QLD 4680 (Christian) – **29)** PO Box 998, Swan Hill VIC 3585 – **30)** Muslim Community Radio, PO Box 969, Bankstown NSW 1885 (Ethnic) – **31)** Arts Radio, PO Box 949, Nedlands WA 6009 – **32)** GPO Box 1324, Hobart TAS 7001 – **33)** Charles Sturt University, Locked Bag 30, Bathurst NSW 2795 – **34)** PO Box 1106, Collingwood VIC 3066 (Ethnic) – **35)** Artsound, PO Box 87, Curtin ACT 2605 – **36)** PO Box 5123, East Lismore NSW 2480 – **37)** PO Box 707, Armidale NSW 2350 – **38)** PO Box 304, Dorrigo NSW 2454 – **39)** Edge FM, PO Box 771, Bega NSW 2550 – **40)** 48 Nelson St, Stepney SA 5069 – **41)** Living Sound Broadcasters, PO Box 7, Coniston NSW 2500 (Christian) – **42)** Radio Hope Island, PO Box 16, Sanctuary Cove QLD 4212 – **43)** Radio Rhema, PO Box 1502, Dubbo NSW 2830 (Christian) – **44)** 1041 Territory FM, Charles Darwin University NT 0909 – **45)** Radio Larrakia, Shop 2, Alawa Shops, Alawa NT 0810 (Aboriginal) – **46)** PO Box 597, Moranbah QLD 4744 – **47)** PO Box 2678, Bundaberg QLD 4670 – **48)** PO Box 19, Gosford NSW 2250 – **49)** Rhema FM, PO Box 886, Belmont VIC 3216 (Christian) – **50)** PO Box 421, Cessnock NSW 2325 – **51)** Radio KLFM, PO Box 2997, Bendigo Delivery Centre VIC 3554 – **52)** Family Radio, PO Box 1700, Milton QLD 4064 – **53)** PO Box 752, Warrnambool VIC 3280 – **54)** PO Box 86, Murwon VIC 3898 – **55)** Darwin Christian Broadcasters, PO Box 43146, Casaurina NT 0810 (Christian) – **56)** Parkes Road, Forbes NSW 2871 – **57)** PO Box 655, Derby WA 6728 – **58)** 140 Main St, Kangaroo Point QLD 4169 – **59)** 2XX, GPO Box 812, Canberra ACT 2601 – **60)** PO Box 259, Meekatharra WA 6642 – **61)** Radio 2000, 2/25 Belmore Rd, Burwood NSW 2134 (Ethnic) – **62)** PO Box 6824, Shepparton VIC 3630 – **63)** Sonshine FM, PO Box 6340, Morley WA 6062 (Christian) – **64)** PO Box 99, Kandos NSW 2848 – **65)** PO Box 1856, Cairns QLD 4870 (Aboriginal) – **66)** Box 6229, Fairfield Gardens QLD 4103 (Aboriginal) – **67)** PO Box 450, Portland VIC 3305 – **68)** Rhema FM, PO Box 2000, Dangar NSW 2309 (Christian) – **69)** PO Box 884, Nowra NSW 2541 – **70)** PO Box 667, Mansfield VIC 3724 – **71)** PMB Turkey Creek, via Kununurra WA 6743 (Aboriginal) – **72)** Radio Rhema, PO Box 1537, Port Macquarie NSW 2444 (Christian) – **73)** Voice FM, PO Box 149, Ballarat VIC 3350 – **74)** Live FM, PO Box 332, Aitkenvale QLD 4814 (Christian) – **75)** Radio Rhema, PO Box 615, Bathurst NSW 2795 (Christian) – **76)** PO Box 1680, Loxton SA 5333 – **77)** PO Box 1003, Cleveland QLD 4163 – **78)** Central Highlands Broadc. Inc, PO Box 966, Woodend VIC 3442 – **79)** PO Box 663, Rockhampton QLD 4700 (Aboriginal) – **80)** 211-217 North Road, Albany WA 6330 – **81)** PO Box 2101, Logan City DC QLD 4114 – **82)** PO Box 605, Wangaratta VIC 3676 – **83)** PO Box 1015, Tuncurry NSW 2428 – **84)** PO Box 418, Caboolture QLD 4510 – **85)** PO Box 889, Katherine NT 0851 – **86)** PO Box 509, Fortitude Valley QLD 4006 – **87)** PO Box 815, Kununurra WA 6743 (Aboriginal) – **88)** PO Box 523, Nimbin NSW 2480 – **89)** 76 Chandos St, St Leonards NSW 2065 – **90)** PO Box 304, Fitzroy VIC 3065 – **91)** PO Box 115, Grafton NSW 2460 (Christian) – **92)** PO Box 200, West Kempsey NSW 2440 – **93)** 10 Byron Pl, Adelaide SA 5000 (Ethnic) – **94)** PO Box 54, Five Dock NSW 2046 – **95)** Ngarralinyi, The Listening Place, PO Box 657, Taree NSW 2430 (Aboriginal) – **96)** PO Box 1033, New Town TAS 7008 – **97)** Radio Rhema, PO Box 974, Orange NSW 2800 – **98)** PO Box 139, Murrayville VIC 3512 – **99)** 146 Cotham Road, Kew VIC 3101 – **100)** University Dr, Callaghan NSW 2308 – **101)** 384 Old Cleveland Rd, Coorparoo QLD 4151 – **102)** PO Box 915, Gayndah QLD 4625 – **103)** PO Box 603, Port Macquarie 2446 – **104)** Good News Radio, PO Box 312, Ballarat VIC 3350 – **105)** PO Box 1033, Townsville QLD 4810 – **106)** PO Box 2154, Esperance WA 6450 – **107)** PO Box J233, Coffs Harbour NSW 2450 – **108)** PO Box 40146, Casaurina NT 0810 – **109)** PO Box 400, Taree NSW 2430 – **110)** PO Box 579, Morwell VIC 3840 – **111)** 1/15 Matong Rd, Echuca VIC 3564 – **112)** PO Box 333, Wynyard TAS 7325 – **113)** Rhema FM, PO Box 384, Hervey Bay

QLD 4655 (Christian) – **114)** 93 Reatta Rd, Trevallyn TAS 7250 (Christian) – **115)** Radio Metro, PO Box 6530, GCMC QLD 9726 – **116)** PO Box 69, Bowraville NSW 2449 – **117)** PO Box 363, Bourke NSW 2840 (Aboriginal) – **118)** PO Box 2917, Fitzroy VIC 3065 – **119)** PO Box 1663, Wollongong NSW 2500 – **120)** PO Box 270, Alexandra VIC 3714 – **121)** PO Box 5483, Townsville QLD 4810 (Aboriginal) – **122)** Garland Ave, North Albury NSW 2640 – **123)** PO Box 123, Broadway NSW 2007 – **124)** Life FM, PO Box 948, Southport QLD 4125 (Christian) – **125)** PO Box 86, Moruya NSW 2537 – **126)** PO Box 1075, Mackay QLD 4740 – **127)** PO Box 2028, Coffs Harbour NSW 2450 – **128)** PO Box 1149, Casino NSW 2470 – **129)** Radio Alta Mira, PO Box 1079, North Adelaide SA 5006 (Christian) – **130)** Unit 4, 153 Rockingham Rd, Hamilton Hill WA 6163 – **131)** Aboriginal Resource and Development Services, 64 Winnellie Rd, Winnellie NT 0820 – **132)** TAB WA, 14 Hasler Rd, Osborne Park WA 6017 – **133)** 867 New Canterbury Rd, Hurlstone Park NSW 2193 – **133)** 867 New Canterbury Rd, Hurlstone Park NSW 2193 – **134)** PO Box 403, Murgon QLD 4605 – **135)** PO Box 111, Toowoomba QLD 4350 – **136)** Program Manager, KIX Country, PO Box 1059, Bundaberg QLD 4670 – **137)** PO Box 1049, Kalgoorlie WA 6433 – **138)** Radio TAB, PO Box 275, Albion QLD 4010 – **139)** 79 Frenchs Forest Rd, Frenchs Forest NSW 2086 – **140)** 2/110 Logan Rd, Wooloongabba QLD 4102 – **141)** PO Box 250, Brunswick West VIC 3068. Broadcasts the Rete Italia program until 1500LT then Asian language programs until 2200LT – **142)** Ambersky, PO Box 540, Nowra NSW 2541 – **143)** PO Box 5109, GCMC, Bundall QLD 9726 – **144)** Suite 14, 3 Jamison Centre, Macquarie ACT 2614 – **145)** PO Box 1172, Kingaroy QLD 4610 – **146)** PO Box 927, Carlton VIC 3053 – **147)** PO Box 526, Bordertown SA 5268 – **148)** PO Box 654, Tanunda SA 5352 – **149)** PO Box 591 Victor Harbour SA 5211 – **150)** PO Box 390, Kadina SA 5554 – **151)** PO Box 144, Inverloch VIC 3996 – **152)** PO Box 999, Victor Harbour SA 5211 – **153)** PO Box 12013, A'Beckett St, Melbourne VIC 8006 – **154)** 7/60 West Terrace, Adelaide SA 5000 – **155)** Level 2, 230-232 Angas St, Adelaide SA 5000 – **156)** PO Box 28, Nimmitabel NSW 2631 – **157)** PO Box 2050, Gosford NSW 2250 – **158)** PO Box 281, Wanneroo WA 6946 – **159)** PO Box 205, Budgewoi NSW 2262 – **160)** PO Box 2122, Griffith NSW 2680 – **161)** PO Box 1005, Subiaco WA 6904 – **162)** c/- PO, Gordon St, Poatina TAS 7302 – **163)** PO Box 79, Earlwood NSW 2206 – **164)** Locked Bag 3, Springwood QLD 4127 (Christian) – **165)** GPO Box 1345, Hobart TAS 7001 – **166)** PO Box 105, Bentley WA 6102 – **167)** PO Box 5035, North Rockhampton MC QLD 4701 – **168)** GPO Box 252-44, Hobart TAS 7001 – **169)** PO Box 139, Redcliffe QLD 4020 – **170)** PO Box 440, Byron Bay NSW 2481 – **171)** PO Box 7016, Hutt St, Adelaide SA 5000 – **172)** PO Box 243, Boonah QLD 4310 – **173)** PO Box 1031, Orange NSW 2800 – **174)** PO Box 235, Beaudesert QLD 4285 – **175)** PO Box 5337, Mackay MC QLD 4741 – **176)** 55 Main St, Walwa VIC 3709 – **177)** PO Box 612, Ballina NSW 2478 – **178)** PO Box 400, Toowoomba QLD 4350 – **179)** 43 Tamar St, Launceston TAS 7250 – **180)** CAAMA, PO Box 2608, Alice Springs NT 0871 – **181)** 5 Desiree Cl, Buderim QLD 4556 – **182)** Radio Rhema, PO Box 1465, Mt. Gambier SA 5290 – **183)** Radio Rhema, PO Box 200, Woombye QLD 4559 – **184)** PO Box 2106, Alice Springs NT 0871 – **185)** 3 Cinema Pl, Adelaide SA 5000 – **186)** 8/12 Mulloon St, Queanbeyan East NSW 2620 – **187)** C/-John Wright, 71 Hilton Avenue, Roselands NSW 2196 **E:** dxer1234@gmail.com – **188)** GPO Box 1329, Adelaide SA 5001 (Italian) – **189)** PO Box 19, Innisfail QLD 4860 – **190)** 2MORO, Suite 1B, 9 Burwood Rd, Burwood NSW 2134 – **191)** GPO Box 572F, Hobart TAS 7001 – **192)** Suite 3, 15-29 Bank St, South Melbourne VIC 3205 – **193)** 48 Mary Street, Preston VIC 3072 – **194)** Radio Rhema, Suite 4, 162 The Entrance Road, Erina NSW 2250 – **195)** Level 2, 280 William St, Melbourne VIC 3000 – **196)** 5 Phoenix St, Castle Hill NSW 2154 – **197)** 175A Byrnes St, Mareeba QLD 4880 – **198)** PO Box 866, Inverell NSW 2360 – **199)** PO Box 2181, Mildura VIC 3501 – **200)** PO Box 280, Wagin WA 6315 – **201)** PO Box 887, Port Pirie SA 5540 – **202)** E3, 350 Ingles St, Port Melbourne VIC 3207 – **203)** 70 Dawson St, Cooks Hill NSW 2300 – **204)** PO Box 163, Dulwich Hill NSW 2203 – **205)** 1 Woodley Close, Kariong NSW 2250 – **206)** Locked Bag 888, St. Peters NSW 2044 – **207)** 1546A Canterbury Rd, Punchbowl NSW 2196 – **208)** PO Box 1187, Oxley QLD 4075 – **209)** PO Box 124, Sale VIC 3853 – **210)** PO Box 995, Drouin VIC 3818 – **211)** PO Box 22 Salamander Bay NSW 2317 – **212)** PO Box 966, Strawberry Hills NSW 2012 – **213)** PO Box 1962, Strawberry Hills NSW 2012 – **214)** PO Box 2161, Mt Gambier SA 5290 – **215)** Rankin St, Woorabinda QLD 4702 – **216)** PO Box 51, Yass NSW 2582 – **217)** PO Box 891, Manunda QLD 4870 – **218)** PO Box 1527, Tamworth NSW – **219)** PO Box 866, Inverell NSW 2360 – **220)** Vision Australia, 454 Glenferrie Rd, Kooyong VIC 3144 – **221)** 12 Pickering Close, Hoppers Crossing VIC 3029 – **222)** 5 Macquarie St, Parramatta NSW 2150 – **223)** Level 5, 189 Gray St, South Brisbane QLD 4101 – **224)** 44 Kyabram St, Coolaroo VIC 3048 – **225)** 1/203 William Street, St Albans VIC 3021 – **226)** PO Box 1042, Gosford NSW 2250 (country format) – **227)** PO Box 1067, Mildura VIC 3502 – **228)** 68-70 Little Ryrie Street, Geelong VIC 3220 – **229)** PO Box 1000, Dunedoo NSW 2844 – **230)** PO Box 1206,

Bendigo Central VIC 3552 – **231)** PO Box 1388, Booragoon WA 6954 – **232)** 395 William St, Perth WA 6000 – **233)** PO Box 1921, Southport BC QLD 4125 – **234)** PO Box 752, Morrisset NSW 2264 – **235)** 22 Frank St, Mt. Druitt NSW 2770 – **236)** Level 2, 31-33 London Circuit, Canberra City ACT 2601 – **237)** 36 Stead Road, Albany WA 6330 – **238)** Locked Bag 899, Mitcham VIC 3132 – **239)** PO Box 2192, Port Augusta SA 5700.

## HF DOMESTIC SHORTWAVE

### 4KZ / COASTAL BROADCASTERS P/L
✉ PO Box 19, Innisfail QLD 4860 **W**: 4kz.com.au **E**: reception@4kz.com.au **SW**: Innisfail QLD 5055kHz 1kW **F.PI**: 2018

### OZY RADIO
✉ 5 Riviera Pl, Glenmore Park NSW 2745 **W**: ozyradio.com **E**: 3210kHz@gmail.com **SW**: Sydney (Razorback Range) NSW 4835kHz 0.5kW, F.PI Alice Springs NT 2310 & 2350kHz 5kW DRM & 5045kHz 1kW **(F.PI)**

### STATION X
✉ PO Box 223, Wee Waa NSW 2388 ☎+61 415 112 645 **W**: stationx.com.au **E**: admin@stationx.com.au **SW**: Wee Waa NSW **2325**, 3230kHz & 5035kHz 1kW **(F.PI)**

## AUSTRIA

**L.T:** UTC +1h (31 Mar-27 Oct: +2h) — **Pop:** 8.5 million — **Pr.L:** German — **E.C:** 230V/50Hz, — **ITU:** AUT

### RUNDFUNK UND TELEKOM REGULIERUNGS-GMBH
✉ Mariahilfer Str. 77-79, 1060 Wien ☎ +43 1 580580 🖷 +43 1 580589191 **E:** rtr@rtr.at **W:** www.rtr.at **L.P:** Chmn: Michael Ogris

### ORF - ÖSTERREICHISCHER RUNDFUNK (Pub)
✉ ORF-Funkhaus, Argentinierstr. 30A, 1040 Wien ☎+43 1 50101 18699 🖷 +43 1 50101 82500 **W:** orf.at
**L.P:** DG: Dr. Alexander Wrabetz MD: Monika Eigensperger Tech. Dir.: Michael Götzhaber

| FM (MHz) | Ö-1 | Ö-Reg | Ö-3 | FM4 | kW |
|---|---|---|---|---|---|
| Bad Gleichen | - | 94.9a | - | - | 6 |
| Bludenz | 87.6 | 96.0h | 98.8 | - | 4 |
| Bregenz | 93.3 | 98.2h | 89.6 | 102.1 | 50 |
| Bruck/Mur | 87.6 | 93.2f | 98.7 | 102.1 | 20 |
| Graz | 91.2 | 95.4f | 89.2 | 101.7 | 67 |
| Innsbruck | 92.5 | 96.4g | 88.5 | 101.4 | 45 |
| Klagenfurt | 92.8 | 97.8b | 90.4 | 102.9 | 100 |
| Kufstein | 97.5 | 95.4g | 103.9 | 99.9 | 5 |
| Lienz | 89.3 | 93.8b | 99.3 | 101.0 | 2.6 |
| | - | 95.9g | - | - | 2.6 |
| Linz | 97.5 | 95.2d | 88.8 | 104.0 | 100 |
| | - | 90.1c | - | - | 10 |
| Mattersburg | 89.0 | 96.2a | 100.9 | - | 0.6/3/0.6 |
| Rechnitz | 90.6 | 93.5a | 87.9 | 97.4 | 6 |
| | - | 100.1f | - | - | 2 |
| Salzburg | 90.9 | 94.8e | 99.0 | 104.6 | 100 |
| | - | 101.2d | - | - | 7 |
| St. Pölten | 97.0 | 91.5c | 89.4 | 98.8 | 100 |
| Schärding | 92.5 | 99.5d | 88.2 | - | 3/4/3 |
| Schladming | 94.3 | 96.3f | 101.3 | 103.3 | 3 |
| Semmering | 90.3 | 95.8c | 88.2 | 92.4 | 9 |
| Spittal/Drau | 91.6 | 100.4b | 87.9 | 103.6 | 3 |
| Weitra | 92.7 | 95.7c | 98.1 | 101.4 | 2 |
| Wolfsberg | 96.7 | 94.5b | 99.5 | 102.3 | 1.5 |
| Wien | 92.0 | 89.9i | 99.9 | 103.8 | 100 |
| | - | 97.9c | - | - | 100 |
| Wien | - | 94.7a | - | - | 2.4 |

+ more than 500 low power txs
**Österreich-1 (Ö1):** 24h **N:** on the h
**Österreich 2 (Ö2): Regional services**
**a)** Burgenland – Buchgraben 51, 7001 Eisenstadt **W:** burgenland.orf.at **b)** Kärnten – Sponheimerstr. 13, 9010 Klagenfurt **W:** kaernten.orf.at **c)** Niederösterreich – Radioplatz 1, 3100 St. Pölten **W:** noe.orf.at **d)** Oberösterreich – Europaplatz 3, 4010 Linz **W:** ooe.orf.at **e)** Salzburg – Nonntaler-Haupstr. 49d, 5020 Salzburg **W:** salzburg.orf.at **f)** Steiermark – Marburgerstr. 20, 8042 Graz **W:** steiermark.orf.at **g)** Tirol – Rennweg 14, 6010 Innsbruck **W:** tirol.orf.at **h)** Vorarlberg – Höchsterstrasse 38, 6851 Dornbirn **W:** vorarlberg.orf.at **i)** Wien – Argentinierstr. 30a, 1040 Wien **W:** wien.orf.at
**Österreich 3 (Ö3):** 24h **N:** on the h
**FM4:** Prgrs in English (0000-1300), otherwise in German **W:** fm4.orf.at
**Ann:** "Österreich 1", "Ö2 (Wien, Niederösterreich, Tirol )", "Ö3"

**IS:** Österreich 1: composition by Werner Pirchner. Ö2: Composition by Bert Breit. Ö3: Electronic Music
**F.PI:** Permission to use the following freq for commercial radio (kHz): 585, 630, 774, 891, 963, 1026, 1125, 1143, 1314, 1458, 1485, 1548 & 1602

**EXTERNAL SERVICES: Relay of Ö1 on SW:** see international radio section

### PRIVATE STATIONS:
**KRONEHIT**
Nationwide network with regional news windows.
✉ Daumegasse 1, A-1100 Wien **W:** kronehit.at

| FM | MHz | kW | FM | MHz | kW |
|---|---|---|---|---|---|
| Weitra | 90.2 | 3 | Schärding | 104.9 | 8 |
| Linz | 92.6 | 14 | St. Pölten | 105.3 | 100 |
| Semmering | 102.9 | 8 | Schladming | 105.6 | 2 |
| Bad Gleichenberg | 103.2 | 1.5 | Wien | 105.8 | 100 |
| Mattersburg | 103.4 | 1 | Innsbruck | 106.5 | 32 |
| Klagenfurt | 103.7 | 2 | Lienz | 107.1 | 1 |
| Rechnitz | 104.1 | 6 | Graz | 107.5 | 1 |
| + 40 txs below 1kW | | | | | |

**Other Private Stations by Area - FM (MHz):**
**BURGENLAND: 88.6 Radio Live Stream**, 106.3 Mattersburg, 1kW; 105.5 Rechnitz, 2.5kW + 1rly
**KÄRNTEN (Carinthia): Antenne Kärnten**, 104.9 Klagenfurt, 100kW; 107.4 Spittal a.d.Drau, 3kW; 104.3 Wolfsberg, 2kW + 4rly – **R. Dva (ORF)-Agora**, (German/Slovenian progr), 105.5 Klagenfurt, 10kW; 106.8 Wolfsberg, 1kW + 7rly – **Welle 1 Kärnten**, 95.2 Klagenfurt, 2kW + 4rly – **R. Maria**, 99.3 Spittal a.d. Drau, 0.2kW – **Lokalradio Spittal a.d.Drau**, 101.6 Spittal a.d.Drau, 1kW (F.PI).
**NIEDERÖSTERREICH (Lower Austria): 88.6 Radio Live Stream**, 104.9 Weitra/Nebelstein, 3kW; 103.3 Melk, 3kW; 100.8 St. Pölten, 2kW; 106.7 Hornstein, 1kW; 101.6 Horn 1kW; 96.0 Oed 1kW + 9rly – **Campus & City R. St. Pölten**, 94.4 St. Pölten, 0.4kW – **R. Ypsilon Live**, 94.5 Hollabrunn, 0.1kW; 93.7 Mistelbach, 0.3kW + 2rly – **R. Maria**, 95.5 St. Pölten, 0.2kW; 104.7 Waidhofen a.d.Ybbs, 0.5kW; 93.4 Baden-Tattendorf, 0.4kW – **R. Arabella NOE (Tulln)**, 99.4 Tulln-Judenau, 0.3kW + 1rly – **R. Arabella NOE (Mostviertel)**, 96.5 Ybbs a.d. Donau, 2kW + 2rly – **R. Ö24**, 96.3 St.Pölten, 1kW
**OBERÖSTERREICH (Upper Austria): Life R.**, 100.5 Linz, 100kW; 102.6 Schärding, 3kW; 100.2 Bad Ischl, 0.4kW + 7rly – **Welle 1 Linz**, 91.8 Linz, 0.3kW – **Welle 1 Steyr**, 102.6 Steyr, 1.4kW; 107.5 Kirchdorf b. Krems, 0.3kW + 3 rly – **R. Arabella Oö Live**, 96.7 Linz, 4kW – **R. FRO Stream**, 105.0 Linz, 0.3kW – **LoungeFM OOE**, 102.0 Linz, 2kW; 95.8 Ried im Innkreis, 1kW (F.PI.); 95.8 Schärding, 1kW (F.PI.) + 2rly – **Freies R. Salzkammergut**, 100.2 Bad Ischl, 1kW; 107.3 Gmunden, 0.1kW + 4rly – **FRF Freies R. Freistadt**, 107.1 Freistadt, 0.6kW + 1rly
**SALZBURG: Antenne Salzburg**, 101.8 Salzburg/Gaisberg, 10kW; 105.9 Zell am See, 1kW; 102.5 St. Michael i. Lungau, 0.5kW + 15rly – **Welle 1 Salzburg**, 106.2 Salzburg/Gaisberg, 2kW; 107.1 Zell am See, 0.3kW; 107.5 St. Johann Pongau, 0.2kW – **Radiofabrik Livestream**, 107.5 Salzburg/Hochgitzen, 0.5kW – **Klassik R. - Live**, 102.5 Salzburg/Högl (D), 0.3kW – **Energy Salzburg**, 94.0 Salzburg/Gaisberg, 0.3kW – **LoungeFM Salzburg**, 106.6 Salzburg/Hochgitzen, 0.5kW
**STEIERMARK (Styria): Antenne Steiermark**, 99.1 Graz/Schöckl, 80kW; 105.7 Bruck a.d. Mur, 20kW; 92.0 Schladming, 2kW; 106.1 Rechnitz, 3kW + 17rly – **Soundportal**, 89.6 Bruck a.d. Mur 8kW, 97.9 Graz, 2kW; 100.4 Bad Gleichenberg 1.3kW + 5rly – **R. Helsinki**, 92.6 Graz, 1kW – **R. Grün-Weiss**, 106.3 Schladming 2kW, 106.6 Bruck a.d.Mur 2.5kW + 3rly – **R. Freequenns**, 100.8 Liezen/Salberg, 0.6kW – **Welle 1 Graz**, 104.6 Graz, 0.5kW – **LoungeFM Steiermark**, 89.6 Graz 1kW – **R. Klassik Stephansdom**, 94.2 Graz, 0.5kW
**TIROL (Tyrol): Life R. Tirol**, 103.4 Inzing 8kW; 101.8 Innsbruck 1kW; 104.4 Lienz 1kW; 105.4 Haiming 1kW; 106.0 Landeck 1kW; 106.8 Kufstein 1kW + 8rly – **Antenne Tirol**, 100.8 Zirog (Italy) 1kW; 105.1 Innsbruck 0.2kW; 106.4 Lienz 0.5kW; 104.6 Jenbach 0.2kW; + 4rly – **Welle 1 Innsbruck**, 92.9 Innsbruck 0.3kW; 104.3 Inzing 0.4kW; 103.9 Haiming (Telfs) 0.5kW; 107.1 Landeck 0.4kW; 104.0 Reutte 0.3kW + 2rly – **R. U1 Tirol**, 97.0 Innsbruck 1kW; 89.2 Jenbach 0.4kW; 101.6 Landeck 0.5kW; 106.8 Haiming 0.5kW + 8rly – **FREIRAD - Freies R. Innsbruck**, 105.9 Innsbruck 1kW – **R. Osttirol**, 101.7 Matrei-Hopfgarten 1kW; 107.8 Lienz 0.4kW; + 6rly – **Energy Innsbruck**, 99.9 Innsbruck 0.3kW – **Klassik R. - Live**, 95.5 Innsbruck 0.3kW – **R. Maria**, 91.1 Innsbruck 0.4kW; 107.9 Jenbach 0.2kW; 90.6 Mayrhofen 0.2kW – **LoungeFM Tirol**, 92.1 Innsbruck 0.4kW – **T-ROCK**, 103.8 Inzing 0.5kW
**VORARLBERG: Antenne Vorarlberg**, 106.5 Bregenz/Pfänder, 50kW; 101.1 Bludenz, 0.5kW; 105.1 Feldkirch 0.2kW + 2rly – **R. Proton**, 104.6 Bludenz, 0.5kW; 95.9 Bregenz, 0.3kW; 104.3 Feldkirch 0.2kW – **LokalR. Bregenz**, 103.2 Bregenz/Pfänder, 1kW (F.PI.)

**WIEN (Vienna): 88.6 Radio Live Stream**, 88.6 Wien/Kahlenberg, 10kW – **R. O24**, 102.5 Wien/Kahlenberg, 20kW – **R. Arabella Wien Live**, 92.9 Wien-Donauturm, 3kW – **Energy Wien**, 104.2 Wien/RiFu-Arsenal, 1kW – **R. Klassik Stephansdom**, 107.3 Wien-Donauturm, 2kW – **R. Orange 94.0**, 94.0 Wien/Donauturm, 0.4kW; **98.3 Superfly**, 98.3 Wien/Donauturm, 1.4kW – **Mein Kinderradio**, 103.2 Wien – Reiffeisenhaus 0.3kW

### DIGITAL RADIO (DAB+)
DAB+ Wien in Vienna on Block 11C (12.6kW) with 15 private stns.

## AZERBAIJAN

**L.T:** UTC +4h — **Pop:** 10 million — **Pr.L:** Azeri, Armenian — **E.C:** 230V/50Hz — **ITU:** AZE

### MILLI TELEVIZIYA VÄ RADIO SURASI (MTRS)
**(National TV & Radio Council)**
Nizami küç. 145, AZ 1000 Baki ☎ +994 12 5983659 🖷 +994 12 4987668 **E:** office@ntrc.gov.az **W:** www.ntrc.gov.az
**L.P:** Chmn: Nusirävan Mähärrämov

### AZÄRBAYCAN TELEVIZIYA VÄ RADIO VERILISLÄRI QSC (Gov) (Azerbaijan TV and Radio Broadcasting CJSC)
Mehdi Hüseyn küç. 1, AZ 1011 Baki ☎ +994 12 4923807 **E:** info@aztv.az **W:** aztv.az **L.P:** Chmn: Arif Alisanov

| MW | kHz | kW | Prgr | MW | kHz | kW | Prgr |
|---|---|---|---|---|---|---|---|
| Gäncä (a)° | 612 | 7 | Resp. | Haciqabul (b)° | 1296 | 125 | M, F |
| Haciqabul (b)° | 801 | 150 | Resp. | Sixli° | 1476 | 1 | Resp. |
| Baki° | 891 | 30 | Resp. | (a) Göygöl (b) Pirsaat | | | |

Resp.=Respublika Radiosu F=International Service °) Status uncertain

| FM (Resp.) | MHz | kW | FM (Resp.) | MHz | kW |
|---|---|---|---|---|---|
| Gülüstan | 88.0 | 5 | Danaçi | 103.0 | 2 |
| Astara | 90.0 | 1 | Ordubad* | 103.0 | 1 |
| Poylu | 90.0 | 5 | Säki | 104.0 | 1 |
| Daskäsän | 101.5 | 2 | Babäk* | 104.5 | 1.5 |
| Lerik | 101.5 | 2 | Särur* | 105.0 | 1 |
| Yergüc | 101.5 | 2 | Baki | 105.0 | 5 |

+ sites with only txs below 1kW. *) situated in Naxçivan (autonomous republic)
**D.Prgr: Respublika Radiosu** 24h. For ethnic minorities: (N. in Russian) 1100-1105 (W) – **Prgrs for ethnic minorities (M)** on 1296kHz (status uncertain): 0725-0740 (Mon/Wed) Lezgi, 0730-0745 (Tue/Thu) Talysh, 0745-0800 (Tue/Thu) Kurdish (Kurmanji), 1300-1400 Azeri/Armenian (for listeners in Mountainous Karabagh), 1800-1830 Russian.

### ASAN RADIO (Gov)
Akademik Häsän Äliyev küç. 36, AZ 1078 Baki ☎ +994 12 4474448 🖷 +994 12 5417663 **E:** info@asan.gov.az **W:** asanradio.az
**L.P:** Dir: Emin Musävidir
**FM:** So. Azerbaijan 92.7, No. Azerbaijan 96.5, Baki 100.0MHz (5kW)
**D.Prgr: ASAN R.** 24h.

### ICTIMAI TELEVIZIYA VÄ RADIO YAYIMLARI SIRKÄTI (Pub) (Public TV and Radio Broadcasting Co.)
Särifzadä küç. 241, AZ 1012 Baki ☎ +994 12 4313968 🖷 +994 12 4302958 **E:** info@itv.az **W:** itv.az **L.P:** DG: Balakisi Qasimov

| FM | MHz | kW | FM | MHz | kW |
|---|---|---|---|---|---|
| Daskäsän | 88.3 | 1 | Danaçi | 100.6 | 1 |
| Lerik | 88.3 | 1 | Gülüstan | 102.5 | 5 |
| Yergüc | 88.3 | 1 | Poylu | 103.0 | 5 |
| Baki | 90.0 | 5 | Babäk* | 103.0 | 1 |
| Säki | 91.6 | 1 | | | |

+ txs below 1kW. *) situated in Naxçivan (autonomous republic)
**D.Prgr: Ictimai R.** 24h.

#### OTHER STATIONS
| FM | MHz | kW | Location | Station |
|---|---|---|---|---|
| 1) | 88.6 | 1 | Danaçi | R. 105 FM |
| 7) | 89.0 | 1 | Gäncä | Xäzär FM |
| 7) | 89.0 | 1 | Lerik | Xäzär FM |
| 7) | 89.6 | 5 | Gülüstan | Xäzär FM |
| 1) | 91.0 | 1 | Gülüstan | R. 105 FM |
| 2) | 100.0 | 1 | Poylu | R. Antenn |
| 2) | 100.0 | 1 | Lerik | R. Antenn |
| 1) | 100.7 | 1 | Quba | R. 105 FM |
| 2) | 101.0 | 1 | Baki | R. Antenn |
| 2) | 101.2 | 1 | Gülüstan | R. Antenn |
| 3) | 102.7 | 1 | Poylu | Käpäz FM |
| 1) | 102.8 | 1 | Lerik | R. 105 FM |
| 7) | 103.0 | 2 | Baki | Xäzär FM |

| FM | MHz | kW | Location | Station |
|---|---|---|---|---|
| 10) | 103.3 | 4 | Baki | Araz FM |
| 4) | 104.0 | 2 | Baki | R. Space |
| 6) | 105.0 | 1 | Gäncä | Lider Jazz R. |
| 2) | 105.3 | 2 | Daskäsän | R. Antenn |
| 8) | 105.5 | 2.5 | Baki | Media FM |
| 5) | 106.3 | 2 | Baki | 106.3 FM |
| 6) | 107.0 | 1 | Baki | Lider Jazz R. |
| 6) | 107.0 | 1 | Imisli | Lider Jazz R. |
| 9) | 107.7 | 1 | Baki | Avto FM |

+ txs below 1kW
**Addresses & other information:**
**1)** Atatürk pr. 28, AZ 1069 Baki – **2)** Azadliq pr. 189, AZ 1130 Baki **E:** info@antenn.az – **3)** C.Räfibäyi küç. 66, AZ 2003 Gäncä **E:** admin@kepezfm.az – **4)** C.Cabbarli küç. 33, AZ 1009 Baki **E:** radio@spacetv.az – **5)** A.Abbaszadä küç. 8, AZ 1001 Baki **E:** info@atv.az – **6)** S. Mehdiyev küç. 83/23, AZ 1141 Baki **E:** radiolider107fm@gmail.com – **7)** Atatürk pr. 28, AZ 1069 Baki. **E:** info@xazar.tv – **8)** Teymur Äliyev küç. 25A, AZ 1130 Baki **E:** mediafm@mediafm.az – **9)** Närimanov Mämmäd Araz küç. 43, AZ 1106 Baki – **10)** Mätbuat pr. 23M, AZ 1100 Baki. **E:** info@arazfm.az. Incl. rel. R. Sputnik (Russia).

### NAKHCHIVAN
(Autonomous republic)

### NAXÇIVAN MUXTAR RESPUBLIKASI DÖVLÄT TELEVIYIZA VÄ RADIO VERILISLÄRI KOMITÄSI (State TV-Radio Committee of the Autonomous Republic of Nakhchivan)
Istiqlaliyyät küç, 82, AZ 7000 Naxçivan ☎ +994 136 440711 **E:** ntv@nakhchivan.az **W:** ntv.nakhchivan.az
**L.P:** Chmn: Sahil Tahirli
**FM:** Naxçivan 104.0MHz. **D.Prgr: Naxçivan Dövlät Radiosu** 24h.

#### OTHER STATIONS
| FM | MHz | kW | Location | Station |
|---|---|---|---|---|
| 11) | 96.0 | 1 | Sädäräk | Naxçivanin säsi |
| 11) | 100.6 | 1 | Naxçivan | Naxçivanin säsi |
| 11) | 106.0 | 1 | Babäk | Naxçivanin säsi |
| 11) | 106.0 | 1 | Ordubad | Naxçivanin säsi |

+ txs below 1kW.
**Addresses & other information:**
**11)** Çänlibel mähälläsi 11, AZ 7000 Naxçivan.

### MOUNTAINOUS KARABAGH
(Self-proclaimed "Nagorno-Karabakh Republic")

### LERNAYIN GHARABAGH HANRAYIN HERUSTARADIOYIN KERUTYUN (Pub*) (Public Radio & TV Co. of Mountainous Karabagh)
(* Run by the administration of the "Nagorno-Karabakh Republic")
Tigran Mets St. 23a, 375000 Stepanakert, Mountainous Karabagh (mail: via Armenia) ☎ +374 47 945261
**L.P:** Chmn: Norek A. Gasparyan
**FM:** Stepanakert 102.3MHz. **D.Prgr:** in Armenian.

#### OTHER STATIONS
| SW | kHz | kW | Location | Station |
|---|---|---|---|---|
| 1) | °9677± | 5 | Stepanakert | Tolisstoni Sädo |

| FM | MHz | kW | Location | Station |
|---|---|---|---|---|
| 6) | 101.8 | - | Stepanakert | Ekho Moskvy |
| 4) | 103.0 | - | Stepanakert | Star FM |
| 3) | 104.3 | - | Stepanakert | R. Pace |
| 5) | 105.0 | - | Stepanakert | Mix FM |
| 2) | 105.5 | - | Stepanakert | R. Hay |
| B) | 106.0 | - | Stepanakert | R. Sputnik relay |
| A) | 106.3 | - | Stepanakert | Armenian Public R. relay |
| 8) | 106.6 | - | Stepanakert | R. Smile |
| 7) | 107.5 | - | Stepanakert | R. Sevan |

°) The freq is jammed with an FM signal (F3E mode) carrying Ictimai R., from an unknown location outside of Mountainous Karabagh.
**Addresses & other information:**
**1)** c/o Modus Vivendi Center, Agatangeghos St. 2, 0010 Yerevan, Armenia **E:** tolishstonisado@gmail.com; info@modusvivendi-center.org. İn Talysh, Azeri – **2)** Azatamartikneri St. 18a, 375000 Stepanakert. Rel. Hay FM (Armenia) – **3)** Vazgen Sarkisyan St. 25, 375000 Stepanakert – **4)** A.Akopyan St. 30, 375000 Stepanakert. In Russian – **5)** Azatamartikneri St. 18a, 375000 Stepanakert – **6)** 375000 Stepanakert. Rel. Ekho Moskvy (Russia) – **7)** 375000 Stepanakert. Rel. R. Sevan (Lebanon) – **8)** 375000 Stepanakert – **A)** Rel. Armenian Public R. (Armenia) – **B)** Rel. R. Sputnik (Russia)

## AZORES (Portugal)

**L.T:** UTC -1h (31 Mar-27 Oct: UTC) — **Pop:** 245,000 — **Pr.L:** Portuguese — **E.C:** 50Hz, 230V — **ITU:** AZR

**ANACOM-Autoridade Nacional de Comunicações, Delegação dos Açores**
✉ Rua dos Valados 18, 9500-652 Relva (São Miguel)
☎+351 296 30 20 40 📠 +351 296 30 20 41

**RÁDIO E TELEVISÃO DE PORTUGAL, S.A. (RTP) (Pub) - Centro Regional da RDP-Açores**
✉ Rua de Castelo Branco, 9500-062 Ponta Delgada ☎+351 296 201100 📠 +351 296 201120 **E:** rdp.acores@rtp.pt, rtpa@rtp.pt **W:** rtp.pt **L.P:** Lorina Bernardo

**RDP Antena 1 Açores**

| MW | kHz | kW | Island | |
|---|---|---|---|---|
| Monte das Cruzes | 828 | 1 | Flores | |
| **FM (MHz)** | **Ant. 1** | **Ant. 2** | **Ant. 3** | **kW** |
| Arrife | 94.5 | 97.5 | - | 0.3 |
| Cabeço Gordo | 88.9 | 105.8 | - | 9.1 |
| Cabeço Verde | 98.1 | 92.9 | - | 1 |
| Cascalho Negro | 92.2 | 103.3 | 104.2 | 1 |
| Espalamaca | 93.8 | 101.4 | 102.7 | 0.03/0.5/1 |
| Fajãzinha | 100.4 | 103.7 | - | 1 |
| Furnas | 93.6 | - | - | 0.5 |
| Lajes das Flores | 102.6 | 97.0 | - | 0.2/0.5 |
| Lajes do Pico | 96.5 | 93.5 | 98.6 | 1 |
| Macela | 87.6 | 93.2 | - | 1 |
| Monte das Cruzes | 99.8 | 97.4 | 102.0 | 1 |
| Morro Alto | 93.5 | 91.9 | 95.6 | 1 |
| Mosteiros | 95.5 | 105.2 | 107.0 | 0.1 |
| Nordeste | 104.6 | - | - | 0.1 |
| Nordestinho | 103.7 | 91.8 | - | 1 |
| Pico Alto Santa Maria | 96.7 | - | - | 10 |
| Pico Bartolomeu | 92.7 | 89.9 | 99.1 | 0.5/1 |
| Pico da Barrosa | 97.9 | 101.7 | 87.7 | 33/33/30 |
| Pico das Éguas | 89.5 | - | - | 10 |
| Pico do Geraldo | 103.7 | 107.5 | - | 1 |
| Pico do Jardim | 97.0 | - | - | 0.9 |
| Pico São Mateus | 103.4 | - | - | 0.1 |
| Ponta Delgada | 94.1 | 100.8 | - | 0.3/1.3 |
| Ponta Ruiva | 87.6 | - | - | 1 |
| Povoação | 102.8 | 97.2 | 94.2 | 0.5 |
| Santa Bárbara | 90.5 | 98.9 | 103.0 | 35/35/30 |
| Serra do Cume | 99.7 | 89.2 | 103.9 | 0.9 |

**D.Prgrs:** all networks 24h
**V:** by QSL card via RTP in Lisboa
**Prgr:** Antena 1 Açores carries its own prgrs M-F 0630-0200, Sat. 0700-0200, Sun. 0800-0200 LT; Antena 2 & Antena 3 relay Lisboa 24h

**DAB:** RTP halted T-DAB broadcasts in June 2011. There are no current plans to reactivate this service but it may be restored in future.

### COMMERCIAL STATIONS:
**RÁDIO RENASCENÇA – Emissora Católica Portuguesa (Rlg/Comm)**
✉ (see Portugal) - **FM:** Pico da Barrosa 95.2MHz 50kW (RR), 100.0MHz 50kW (RFM)

### Private stations
**RÁDIO CLUBE DE ANGRA – "A VOZ DA TERCEIRA" (Comm.)**
✉ Av. Tenente Coronel José Agostinho, 4, Apartado 12, 9700-108 Angra do Heroísmo ☎+351 295 213101 📠 +351 295 213102 **E:** direccao@rcangra.pt **W:** rcangra.pt
**FM:** Santa Bárbara 101.1MHz 0.4kW, Serra do Cume 94.7MHz 0.05kW & Pico Matias Simão 89.6 MHz 0.05 kW (all in Terceira island)

**ESTAÇÃO EMISSORA DO CLUBE ASAS DO ATLÂNTICO (Comm.)**
✉ Aeroporto de Santa Maria, Apartado 545, 9580-908 Vila do Porto ☎+351 296 820720/1/2 📠+351 296 820725 **E:** geral@asasdoatlantico.pt radio@asasdoatlantico.pt nformacao@asasdoatlantico.pt **W:** asasdoatlantico.pt
**FM:** Pico Alto, 103.2MHz, 2kW **D.Prgr:** 24h
**NB:** R. Clube de Angra & R. Clube Asas do Atlântico own also MW licenses although they have been broadcasting only on VHF-FM.

### Private stations owning only FM licences:
**CANAL FM (Comm.)**
✉Rua Manuel Augusto Amaral, 1-D 2-Direito, 9500-222 Ponta Delgada ☎+351 296 307470 📠+351 296 307479 **E:** radio@canal.fm, info@canal.fm **W:** canal.fm
**FM:** S. Miguel island: 91.0 MHz 0.5 kW Pico da Barrosa, 91.5, 94.5

& 95.8 Povoação (all 0.05 kW); S. Jorge island: 100.5 MHz 0.5 kW Calheta (Macelinha); Pico island: 92.7 MHz 0.05 kW Madalena; Flores Island: 104.5 MHz 0.5 kW Santa Cruz das Flores
**Local FM stn relaying prgrs from Canal FM: R. Graciosa** 107.9 MHz 0.5 kW Santa Cruz da Graciosa (Graciosa Island - see below)

**MY TOP FM (Comm.)**
✉ Rua Serpa Pinto, 66, 9760-438 Praia da Vitória ☎295 701657 **E:** geral@mytop.fm **W:** mytop.fm
**FM:** S. Miguel island: tx at Pico da Barrosa (Ponta Delgada) 102.4 MHz 0.5 kW & 98.4 MHz 0.050 kW Sete Cidades (Ponta Delgada); Terceira island: Santa Bárbara (Praia da Vitória) 106.6 MHz 1 kW, Serra do Cume (Praia da Vitória) 92.4 MHz 0.050 kW & Quatro Ribeiras (Praia da Vitória) 96.6 MHz 0.050 kW

**RÁDIO HORIZONTE AÇORES (Comm.)**
✉Caminho do Meio, n° 51, S. Carlos, 9700 Angra do Heroísmo ☎295 332 161 & 962 296 789 📠295 216 015 **E:** gerencia@horizonteacores.com comercial@horizonteacores.com **W:** horizonteacores.com
**FM:** Terceira island: 104.4 MHz 1 kW Serra de Stª Bárbara (Angra do Heroísmo) & 98.1 MHz 0.05 kW Serra do Cume (Praia da Vitória); São Miguel Island: 107.2 MHz 1 kW Pico da Barrosa (Ponta Delgada)

### OTHER STATIONS:

| | FM Island | MHz | kW | Station, location |
|---|---|---|---|---|
| 5) | São Miguel | 88.5 | 3 | R. Atlântida, Ponta Delgada |
| 4) | São Miguel | 90.2 | 0.5 | R80 R., Nordeste |
| 1) | Faial | 91.3 | 0.5 | Antena Nove, Horta |
| 6) | São Miguel | 99.4 | 3 | TSF - Rádio Açores, Ponta Delgada |
| 3) | Pico | 100.2 | 0.5 | R. Pico, Madalena do Pico |
| 2) | Pico | 104.7 | 0.5 | R. Clube das Lajes do Pico, "A Voz da Montanha", Lajes do Pico |
| 11) | São Miguel | 105.0 | 0.5 | 105 FM, Pico da Barrosa |
| 7) | São Miguel | 105.5 | 2 | R. Nova Cidade,Ribeira Grande |
| 9) | Pico | 106.1 | 0.5 | R. Cais, São Roque do Pico |
| 10) | São Jorge | 107.1 | 0.5 | R. Lumena, Pico de Santo Amaro (Velas) |
| 8) | Graciosa | 107.9 | 0.5 | R. Graciosa, Serra Branca |

+ 13 relays of 50W used by 7 stns
**Addresses & other information** (add +351 to tel/fax nos):
**1)** Rua de São João, 38-B, 9900-129 Horta ☎292-29 33 90, 📠 292-39 16 02 **W:** antenanove.com – **2)** R. S. Pedro, 9, 9930-129 Lajes do Pico ☎292-672299 📠292 - 672950 **E:** radiomontanha@gmail.com **W:** radiomontanha.com – **3)** Avenida Machado Serpa n° 57, 9950-321 Madalena do Pico ☎292- 622 727 📠292- 622 874 **E:** geral@radiopico.com, radiopico@sapo.pt **W:** radiopico.com – **4)** Rua Bento José Morais, 23 - 5° Esq°, 9500-772 Ponta Delgada ☎296- 201 919 **E:** r80.superonda@gmail.com **W:** r80.pt – **5)** Rua Bento José Morais 23 - 5° Sul, 9500-772 Ponta Delgada ☎296 201 910 📠296 629 856 **E:** geral@radioatlantida.net, director@radioatlantida.net **W:** radioatlantida.net – **6)** (relays TSF Lisboa) Rua Dr. Bruno Tavares Carreiro, 34-2.°, 9500-055 Ponta Delgada ☎ 296 202 800 📠 296 202 825 **E:** radioacores@acorianooriental.pt **W:** acorianooriental.pt/pagina/acores-tsf – **7)** R. Adolfo Coutinho de Medeiros, 24 / Apartado 007, 9600-516 Ribeira Grande ☎296 472738/296, 914 067 271 & 962 048 094 📠296 472654 **E:** radionovacidade@gmail.com **W:** radionovacidade.pt – **8)** R. do Corpo Santo, 37, 9880-368 Santa Cruz da Graciosa ☎295-732536 & 919 204 526 📠295 712768 **E:** radiograciosa@sapo.pt **W:** radiograciosa.com– **9)** (Relays R. Atlântida 88.5) Pct. dos Baleeiros, Cais do Pico, 9940-301 São Roque do Pico ☎292642930 📠 292 642 934 **E:** radiocais@sapo.pt – **10)** Rua Cunha da Silveira, 25, Apartado 8, 9800-531 Velas ☎295 412575/295 412819 📠295 412810 **E:** radiolumena@iol.pt, radiolumena@radiolumena.com **W:** radiolumena.com – **11)** Solmar Avenida Center, Av. Infante D. Henrique, 71 - 1° Piso, Loja 129, 9504-529 Ponta Delgada ☎296 654 112 /277 **E:** geral@105fm.pt **W:** 105fm.pt

### Military Stations:
**RADIO LAJES – A VOZ DA FAP-FORÇA AÉREA PORTUGUESA (The Voice of the Portuguese Air Force)**
✉ Comando da Zona Aérea dos Açores, 9760-290 Lajes, Terceira ☎+351 295 540891/2/3 📠+351 295 540791 **E:** fap.radiolajes@emfa.pt **W:** radiolajes.pt **LP:** Dir.: Major Paulo Roda
**FM** 93.5MHz 150W **F.PI.:** 500W 24h
**N.B.** R. Lajes owns also a MW licence, although the stn. has been broadcasting only on FM. There are plans to reactivate the MW service on the new freq. of 1530kHz (ex-648) 1kW
**UNITED STATES AFRTS**
✉ Lajes, Terceira, 9760 Praia da Vitoria ☎+351 295 57 34 97 **W:** lajes.af.mil
**MW** 1503kHz 100W (1kW nominal). **FM** 96.1MHz 150W
**D.Prgr:** Locally produced & relays of AFRTS

## BAHAMAS

**L.T:** UTC -5h (10 Mar–3 Nov: -4h) — **Pop:** 400,000 — **Pr.L:** English — **E.C:** 60Hz, 120V — **ITU:** BAH

### UTILITIES REGULATION & COMPETITION AUTHORITY (URCA)
✉ Frederick House, Frederick St., Nassau ☎ +1 242 3930234 🖷 +1 242 3930153
**E:** info@urcabahamas.bs **W:** www.urcabahamas.bs
**L.P:** Chmn: Randol Dorsett

### ZNS – THE BROADCASTING CORPORATION OF THE BAHAMAS (Comm., Gov.)
✉ Harcourt 'Rusty' Bethel Drive, Third Terrace, Centreville, PO Box N-1347, Nassau
☎ +1 242 502 3800 🖷 +1 242 322 6598 **W:** znsbahamas.com **E:** info@znsbahamas.com
**L.P:** GM: Kayleaser Deveaux-Isaacs. CEN: Keith Gomez.
**MW: ZNS-1 National Voice of Bahamas**: Nassau: 1540kHz 50kW
**ZNS-3 Gospel**: Freeport 810kHz 10kW
**FM: ZNS-1 National Voice of Bahamas**: Nassau: 104.5MHz 5kW
**ZNS-2**: Alice Town 107.1MHz 0.3kW & Nassau 107.9MHz 10kW
**ZNS-Power FM**: Freeport 104.5MHz 10kW. All four channels are on the air 24h.

### TRIBUNE MEDIA GROUP (Comm.)
✉ Radio House, Shirley St- & School Lane, PO Box N-3207, Nassau & Media House, Yellow Pine Street, PO Box F-40773, Freeport ☎ +1 242 328 0950 **W:** 100jamz.com **L.P:** COO: Ollie Ferguson
**Stations: 100 JAMZ:** FM: Nassau 100.3 & Freeport 100.3. Format: Urban Contemporary — **KISS FM:** FM: Freeport 96.1MHz. Format: Urban AC — **Y98.7:** FM: Nassau 98.7MHz. Format: AC — **JOY FM,** Dowdeswell St., PO Box N-3207, Nassau ☎ +1 242 356 5112 FM: Nassau 101.9MHz. Format: All gospel and inspirational — **CLASSICAL 98.1:** FM: Nassau 98.1MHz. Format: Easy listening

### THE NASSAU GUARDIAN (Comm.)
✉ 7 Carter St, PO Box N-3011, Nassau ☎ +1 242 302 2300/328 6868 🖷 +1 242 328 5311 **W:** guardiantalkradio.com / hot917fm.com / star106fm.com
**Stations: GUARDIAN RADIO:** FM 96.9MHz – **HOT 91.7:** FM 91.7MHz – **STAR 106.5:** FM 106.5MHz

### OTHER STATIONS (FM IN MHZ):
**BAHAMIAN OR NUTTIN**, Rum Cay Media Group, PO Box SP-64038, Nassau **W:** bahamianornuttin.com **FM:** Nassau: 92.5 – **BREEZE FM,** Farmers Hill Settlement, PO Box EE-17095, Exuma ☎ +1 242 358 7201 **W:** exumabreezefm.com **L.P:** CEO Dwight Hart. FM: 98.3 – **DOVE 103,** PO Box F-44008, Freeport, Grand Bahama ☎ +1 242 351 3683 **W:** dove103fm.com **FM:** Freeport 103.7 – **GEMS R.,** Mt. Rose Ave, Sears Hill, PO Box SS-6094, Nassau ☎ +1 242 326 4381 🖷 +1 242 326 4371 **W:** gemsradio105.9.com **FM:** Nassau: 105.9 – **GLOBAL 99.5 FM,** Union Court, Pent House, Shirley St/Elisabeth Ave, Nassau ☎ +1 242 326 0270 **W:** globalradio995.com **FM:** Nassau: 99.5 – **GLORY FM,** Carmichael Rd, PO Box N-10538, Nassau ☎ +1 242 677 8165 **FM:** Nassau 93.9 (†) – **INFOLIGHT 90.1,** Bahamas National Library, PO Box N-3913, Nassau. **FM:** Nassau 90.1 – **ISLAND FM,** Center Marketing, Edmark House, Dowdeswell St, PO Box N-1807, Nassau ☎ +1 242 332 8826 **W:** islandfmonline.com **FM:** Nassau 102.9 – **LOVE-97 FM,** East St North, PO Box N-3909, Nassau ☎ +1 242 356 4960 🖷 +1 242 356 7256. **FM:** Nassau 97.5 – **MIX 102.1,** RND Plaza West Suite 2, PO Box F-44008, Freeport ☎ +1 242 374 1021 🖷 +1 242 373 2271 **L.P:** GM: Don Martin. **FM:** Freeport 102.1 (5kW) – **MORE 94 FM,** Carmichael Rd, PO Box CR54245, Nassau ☎ +1 242 361 2447 **W:** more94fm.com **FM:** Nassau 94.9 – **PEACE 107,** McKinney Broadcasting Network, Gibbs Lane 6, Fort Charlotte, PO Box N-1220, Nassau ☎ +1 242 325 0235 **W:** peace107.5.com **FM:** Nassau 107.5 – **PRAISE FM 88.5,** Cathedral of Olive, Morgan's Bluff Drive, Andros ☎ +1 242 329 7524 **FM:** Andros: 88.5 – **RADIO ABACO,** Mars Harbour, PO Box 20418, Abaco ☎ +1 242 367 2935/4935 **FM:** 91.1/93.5 (†) – **SPLASH FM SPIRIT GOSPEL,** #12 St., PO Box EL-27495, Spanish Wells, Eleuthera ☎ +1 242 333 4638 🖷 +1 242 333 4693. **W:** splash899fm.com **L.P:** Chris Forsythe. **FM:** Eleuthera: 89.9, Abaco 95.5, South Eleuthera 98.5 – **TURNING POINT RADIO (BBN),** PO Box N-8993 Nassau ☎ +1 242 322 6273 **W:** tprb1023fm.com **FM:** Nassau: 102.3 – **WORD SBS 88.3 FM,** South Bahamas Conference of Seven-day Adventists, Tonique Williams-Darling Highway, PO Box N-356, Nassau. **W:** soencouragement.com **FM:** 88.3 (1.4kW)

## BAHRAIN

**L.T:** UTC +3h — **Pop:** 1.4 million — **Pr.L:** Arabic — **E.C:** 50Hz, 230V (60Hz/110V at Awala) — **ITU:** BHR

### MINISTRY OF INFORMATION AFFAIRS (MIA)
✉ P.O. Box 33766, Al Esteglal Highway, Manama ☎ +973 17 684222 🖷 +973 17 781400 **W:** mia.gov.bh **E:** info@mia.gov.bh **L.P:** Dir. Tech Affairs: Abdulla Ahmed Al-Balooshi.

### BAHRAIN RADIO & TV CORPORATION (BRTC, Gov.)
✉ P.O.Box 33766, Manama ☎ +973 17 686000 🖷 +973 17 687567 **W:** radiobahrain.fm **E:** btw@brtc.gov.bh **L.P:** CEO: Ahmed Najim. Dir. of Bc: Hamad Al-Manai. Dir. of Eng: Ebrahim Al-Murbati.
**General Prgr. in Arabic**: 24h **MW:** 801kHz 100kW. **FM:** 102.3MHz 5kW – **Quran Prgr:** 24h on **MW:** 612kHz 100kW. **FM:** 106.1MHz 5kW – **Bahrain TV audio:** MW: 1521kHz 10kW, FM: 89.8MHz 5kW – **English Sce (R. Bahrain):** 0300-2100 on **MW:** 1584kHz 1kW, **FM:** 96.5MHz 10kW. 1600-2100 on 99.5MHz 0.5kW – **Bahrain FM in Arabic** : 24h 93.3MHz 10kW – **Shabab FM**(Youth prgr.): 98.4MHz 4kW – **Traditional channel:** 95.0MHz 5kW – **Classical music channel:** 96.9MHz 5kW – **Indian prgr:** 104.2MHz 5kW
**Ann:** A: "Idha'atul-Bahrain". E: "Radio Bahrain".
**IS:** Local composition on guitar and violin.
**Relay for abroad on shortwave:** see International Radio section.

### OTHER STATIONS:
**Sowt al-Khaleej,** Manama: 100.8MHz. See Qatar for main entry.
**Sawt el-Ghad,** Manama: 94.8MHz. **W:** sawtelghad.com
**Emarat FM,** Manama: 92.3MHz 5kW. See main entry under UAE.
**Panorama FM,** Manama: 103.0MHz. See main entry under UAE.
**AFN,** Manama: 106.3MHz 250W.
**BBC World Sce:** English 101.0MHz 2kW, Arabic 103.8MHz 2kW.
**Monte Carlo Doualiya,** Manama: 90.9MHz 1kW.
**R. Sawa,** Manama: 89.3MHz
**F.PI: BFBS Radio** on FM, currently via wifi only.

## BANGLADESH

**L.T:** UTC +6h — **Pop:** 164 million — **Pr.L:** Bengali — **E.C:** 50Hz, 220V — **ITU:** BGD

### BANGLADESH TELECOMMUNICATIONS REGULATORY COMMISSION
✉ IEB Bhaban, Ramna, Dhaka-1000 ☎ +880 2 9611111 🖷 +880 2 9556677 **E:** btrc@btrc.gov.bd **W:** www.btrc.gov.bd
**L.P:** Chmn: Shahjahan Mahmood

### BANGLADESH BETAR (Gov.)
✉ National Broadcasting Authority, NBA House, 121 Kazi Nazrul Islam Ave, Dhaka-1000 ☎ +880 2 ,8625538 8625904 🖷 +880 2 8612021 **E:** rrc@dhaka.net **W:** betar.gov.bd
**L.P:** DG: Narayan Chandra Shil DDG (News): Hosne Ara Talukdar : Chief Engr: Ahmed Kamruzzaman Sr. Engr.: Sattar Sarkar Sr. Engr (Research): Zia Hassan Dy. Stn. Engr.: Zakir Uddin Asst. Radio Engr:Nusrat Ruma

| MW | kHz | kW | Times |
|---|---|---|---|
| Khulna | 558 | 100 | 0030-0400, 0600-1710 |
| Dhaka-B | 630 | 100 | 0000-0145, 0300-1710, 1800-2100 |
| Dhaka-A | 693 | 1000 | 0030-0610, 0830-1730 |
| Rajshahi | 846 | 100 | 0030-0400, 0600-1710 |
| Chittagong | 873 | 100 | 0030-0400, 0600-1710 |
| Dhaka | 819 | 100 | Test trs |
| Sylhet | 963 | 20 | 0030-0400, 0800-1710 |
| Thakurgaon | 999 | 10 | 0950-1710 |
| Rangpur | 1053 | 10 | 0030-0400, 0800-1710 |
| Rajshahi | 1080 | 10 | 0030-0400 0600-1710 |
| Rangamati | 1161 | 10 | 0530-1030 |
| Dhaka-C | 1170 | 20 | 0900-1100 |
| Barishal | 1287 | 10 | 0030-0510, 1030-1710 |
| Cox's Bazar | 1314 | 10 | 0545-1045 |
| Comilla | 1413 | 10 | 1000-1710 |
| Bandorban | 1431 | 10 | 0530-1030 |
| **SW** | **kHz** | **kW** | **Times** |
| Shavar | 4750 | 100 | 0600-1715 |

**NB:** Rel. Dhaka A prog. Sign on/off varies due to special prgr rel.

| FM | MHz | kW | Rel | Times |
|---|---|---|---|---|
| Chittagong | 105.4 | 5 | c | Test trs |
| Chittagong | 88.8 | 10 | j, b | 0030-0400 0500-1710 |
| Chittagong | 90.0 | 5 | c | 0000-1800 |
| Comilla | 101.2 | 2 | j | 1500-1545 |
| Comilla | 103.6 | 10 | b | 0030-0200 1200-1710 |

| FM | MHz | kW | Rel | Times |
|---|---|---|---|---|
| Dhaka | 97.6 | 5 | | 0030-0600 0800-1730 |
| Dhaka | 104.0 | 10 | j | 1500-1545 |
| Dhaka | 90.0 | 5 | a | 0100-0400, 1230-2000 |
| Dhaka | 103.2 | 5 | | 1330-1600 |
| Dhaka | 102.0 | 10 | c | 0000-1830 |
| Dhaka | 100.0 | 3 | b | 0000-0600, 0700-0900 1100-1700 |
| Dhaka | 106.0 | 10 | | 0300-0600 1200-1730 |
| Khulna | 102.0 | 1 | | 0000-0400, 0830-1715 |
| Khulna | 88.8 | 10 | j, b | 0030-0700 1300-1715 |
| Khulna | 90.0 | 5 | | 0415-0515 1330-1700 |
| Rajshahi | 104.0 | 5 | | 0030-0400 0600-1710 |
| Rajshahi | 88.8 | 10 | j, b | 0030-0400 1000-1710 |
| Rajshahi | 90.0 | 5 | | 0400-0500 1330-1700 |
| Rajshahi | 105.0 | 1 | | Test trs |
| Rangpur | 104.6 | 1 | j | 1110-1235 1500-1545 |
| Rangpur | 88.8 | 10 | b | 0030-0300 0800-1710 1300-1600 |
| Rangpur | 90.0 | 5 | | 0330-0420 |
| Sylhet | 105.0 | 1 | j | 0030-0400 1300-1700 |
| Sylhet | 88.8 | 10 | b | 0030-0400 0500-1710 |
| Sylhet | 90.0 | 5 | | 1330-1700 |
| Thakurgaon | 92.0 | 5 | b | 0030-0200 1330-1700 |
| Traffic Channel | 88.8 | 10 | | 0100-1500 |
| Barisal | 105.2 | 10 | b | 0030-0200 0445-1115 1330-1700 |
| Coxsbazar | 100.8 | 10 | b | 0030-0200 0545-1045 1330-1700 |
| Rangamati | 103.2 | 5 | | 0530-1030 |
| Bandorban | 104.0 | 10 | | 0530-1030 |
| Jessore | 100.8 | 10 | | Test trs |

a) Rel. Ext. Sce 12:30-20:00 b) Rel. BBC World Service Dhaka 100 MHz 0000-0600, 1100-1700, other cities 0030-0100 0130-0200, 1330-1400, 1630-1700 c) China R Int. 1300-1400 j) Radio Japan 1500-1545
**N. in English:** 0200, 1100, 1530, 1805. **N. in Bengali:** 0100, 0300, 0400, 0500, 0600, , 0900, 1000, 1200, 1430, 1600, 1700 **SAARC N. in Bengali:** 1235 **SAARC N. in English:** 1250 Every Mon
**F.PI:** Inauguration of new 10 kW FM stns located in Gopalganj & Mymensingh, 100kW tx at Chittagong to be replaced. Replacement of 100kW tx at Dhaka B. One standby 100kW tx for Dhaka B. Digitisation and modernisation of transmitters, Modernisation and shifting of Shahbag office to Agargaon

**EXTERNAL SERVICE: BANGLADESH BETAR**
See International Radio section.

**OTHER STATIONS:**
**RADIO TODAY** ⊡ Radio Broadcasting FM (Bangladesh) Co. Ltd Awal Centre (13th & 19th floors), Kamal Atraturk Avenue, Banani, Dhaka 1213 ☎ +880 2 982 0370-4 🖷 +880 2 9821486 **E:** wm@radiotodaybd. fm **W:** radiotodaybd.fm **FM:** 89.6MHz 10kW Dhaka Khulna Chittagong Coxsbazar Sylhet Rajshahi Barishal Mymensingh
**RADIO FOORTI** ⊡ Radio Foorti Limited Landmark (8th floor), 12-14 Gulshan-2 North C/A, Dhaka 1212 ☎ +880 2 8835747 8835748 **E:** info@radiofoorti.fm **W:** radiofoorti.fm **FM:** 88.0MHz 20kW Dhaka Chittagong, Sylhet, Mymensingh, Rajshahi, Barishal, Khulna, Cox's Bazar
**UNIWAVE BROADCASTING COMPANY LTD** ⊡ Uniwave Broadcasting Company Limited, Silver Tower (12th floor), 52, Gulshan Avenue, Gulshan- 1, Dhaka- 1212 ☎ +880 2 9886800, 9861133, 8832989 **E:** info@radioaamar.com **W:** radioaamar.com **LP:** CEO: Zulfiker Ahmed **FM:** Radio Aamar 24h 88.4 MHz Dhaka
**AYENA BROADCASTING CORPORATION** ⊡ Dhaka Trade Centre, 99 Kazi Nazrul Islam Avenue, Kawran Bazar, Dhaka 1215 ☎ +880 2 8142038 8189307 🖷 +880 2 9128141 **E:** program@abcradiobd.com **W:** abcradiobd.fm **LP:** Man. Dir.: Matiur Rahman Choudhury. **FM:** 89.2MHz 24h in Dhaka Chittagong Coxsbazar
**DHAKA FM** ⊡ Navana Tower (15th floor), 45, Gulshan South, Circle-1 Dhaka-1212 ☎ +880 2 8811720-21 🖷 +880 2 8811722 **E:** admin90.4@dhakafm904.com **W:** dhakafm904.com **FM:** 90.4MHz 10kW 24h Dhaka Rajshahi Bogra Barishal Chittagong Coxsbazar Sylhet Khulna Rangpur Mymensingh
**PEOPLES RADIO** ⊡ 41, Samsuddin Mashon, 5th floor, Gulshan-2 Dhaka 1212 ☎ +880 2 9890952-3 🖷 +880 2 9570757 **E:** hello@peoplesradio.com **W:** peoplesradio.fm **FM:** Dhaka 91.6MHz
**RADIO SHADHIN** ⊡ Asiatic Centre, House 63, Block H, Road 7B, Banani, Dhaka 1213 ☎+880 9666924924 **E:** sales@radioshadhin.fm **W:** radioshadhin.fm - **FM** Dhaka 92.4 MHz
**RADIO BHUMI** ⊡ 40, Shahid Tajuddin Ahmed Sarani Tejgaon, Dhaka – 1208 ☎ +880 1191928928 **E:** info@radiobhumi.fm **W:** radiobhumi.fm - **FM** Dhaka 92.8 MHz 24h
**CITY FM** ⊡ Hasan Holdings Building, 14th floor, New Eskaton Road, Banglamotor, Dhaka -1000,☎ +880 2 9341828-9, **W:** cityfm.com - **FM:** Dhaka, 96 MHz 24h 5kW
**ASIAN RADIO** ⊡ Ka-34 Chowdhury Bari, South Badda Gulshan,

Dhaka -1212 ☎ +880 2 9854475-78 **E:** info@asianradiofm.com **W:** asianradiofm.com **LP:** Chrmn.: Alhaj Harun Ur Rashid **FM:** Dhaka 90.8 MHz 24h
**COLOURS FM** ⊡ 67/4, Pioneer Road, Kakrail, Dhaka-1000, Dhaka, Bangladesh **W:** colours.fm - **FM:** Dhaka 101.6MHz 24h
**JAGO FM** ⊡ Pran RFL Centre, 105 Middle Badda, Dhaka 1212 ☎ +880 2 9881792 **E:** info@jago.fm **W:** jago.fm - **FM:** Dhaka 94.4MHz
**RADIO EDGE** ⊡ 7th Floor, 84 Skylark Mark, Road-11, Dhaka 1213 ☎ +880 2 9820971 **E:** info@radioedge.rocks **W:** radioedge.rocks - **FM:** Dhaka 95.6MHz
**RADIO CAPITAL** ⊡ 371/A, Block-D, Bashundhara R/A, 1229 Dhaka ☎ +880 2 8402047 **E:** info@radiocapital.fm **W:** radiocapital.fm - **FM:** Dhaka 94.8MHz
**RADIO AAMAR** ⊡ Water Front (1st floor) House #28 , Road#130, Gulsan-1 Dhaka-1212 **W:** radioaamar.com - **FM:** Dhaka 88.4MHz
**RADIO DHONI** ⊡ 80/A, Siddheswari Circular Road, Hazrat Shahjalal Tower (15th floor), Dhaka ☎ +880 2 9361430 **E:** info@radiodhoni.fm **W:** radiodhoni.fm - **FM:** Dhaka 91.2 MHz
**RADIO NEXT** ⊡ 17 Bir Uttam AK Khandakar Rd, Mohakhali, Dhaka ☎ +8809636100932 **W:** radionext.fm - **FM:** Dhaka 93.2 MHz
**RADIO DIN RAAT E:** radiodinraat93.6@gmail.com **W:** radiodinraat. fm **FM:** Dhaka 93.6 MHz
**RADIO DHOL** ⊡ LK Tower -2 (Level 16) 59 & 61 Gulshan South Avenue Gulshan-1, Dhaka- 1212 ☎ +880 2 9889494 **E:** info@radiodhol.fm **W:** radiodhol.fm **FM:** Dhaka 94.0 MHz
**BANGLA RADIO** ⊡ Shwadesh Tower 16th floor 41/6 Box Culvert Road, Purana Paltan, Dhaka-1000 ☎ +880 2 9513765-67 **E:** info@banglaradio.fm **W:** banglaradio.fm - **FM:** Dhaka 95.2 MHz
**SPICE FM** ⊡ Radio Masala Limited, MG Tower,13th floor, 389/B West Rampura, Dhaka-1219 ☎ +880 2 58315184-85 1841964000 **E:** info@spicefmbd.com **W:** spicefmbd.com - **FM:** Dhaka 96.4 MHz

**Community Stations**
**R. Chilmari**, Kurigram - **FM:** 99.2MHz – **R. Mukti**, Bogra - **FM:** 99.2MHz – **Barendra R.**, Naogaon - **FM:** 99.2MHz – **R. Mahananda**, Chapai Nawabganj - **FM:** 98.8MHz – **R. Padma**, Rajshahi - **FM:** 99.2MHz – **R. Jhenuk**, Jhenidah - **FM:** 99.2MHz – **R. Nalta**, Satkhira - **FM:** 99.2MHz – **R. Sundarban**, Khulna - **FM:** 98.8MHz – **Loko Betar**, Barguna - **FM:** 99.2MHz – **Krishi R.**, Barguna - **FM:** 98.8MHz – **R. Naf**, Cox's Bazar - **FM:** 99.2MHz – **R. Sagor Giri**, Chittagong - **FM:** 99.2MHz – **R. Bikrampur**, Munsiganj - **FM:** 99.2MHz – **R. Pallikantho**, Moulavi Bazar - **FM:** 99.2MHz
**F.PI:** Licence to be issued for one community stn in each district.

## BARBADOS

**L.T:** UTC -4h — **Pop:** 290,000 — **Pr.L:** English — **E.C:** 50Hz 115V — **ITU:** BRB

**FAIR TRADING COMMISSION**
⊡ Good Hope, Green Hill. St. Michael ☎ +1 246 4240260 Ext 222 🖷 +1 246 4240300 **E:** info@ftc.gov.bb **W:** www.ftc.gov.bb
**L.P:** CEO: Sandra Sealy

**CARIBBEAN BROADCASTING CORP. (Gov. Comm.)**
⊡ The Pine, Wildey, St.Michael ☎ +1 246 467 5400 🖷 +1 246 429 4795 **W:** cbc.bb, 947fm.bb, theone.bb & qfm.bb **LP:** Chrmn: Peter Earle. GM: Doug Hoyte. Head of R.: Pearson Bowen
**MW:** FM 94.7: 900kHz 5kW: 24h (// 94.7)
**FM:** FM 94.7: 94.7MHz 5kW: 24h — **98.1 FM The One:** 98.1MHz 5kW: 24h — **Quality/Q FM 100.7** 100.7MHz 5kW – **Government Emergency Broadcast Station:** 91.1MHz 1kW

**BARBADOS BROADCASTING SERVICE (Comm.)**
⊡ Astoria, St George ☎ +1 246 437 9550 🖷 +1 246 437 9203
**L.P:** MD: Anthony T. Brian. GM: Shery Anne Padmore
**FM: BBS-FM** 90.7MHz 5kW: 24h – **Faith FM** (Rlg.) 102.1MHz 1kW: 24h

**STARCOM NETWORK INC. (Comm.)**
⊡ River Road, PO Box 1267, Bridgetown ☎ +1 246 430 7300 🖷 +1 246 426 5377 **W:** starcomnetwork.net, life975, vob929.com, hott953. com & thebeat104.com **LP:** CEO: Victor Fernandez
**FM:** Life 97.5: 97.5MHz 1kW – **VOB Voice of Barbados:** 92.9MHz 5kW – **Hott 95.3 FM:** 95.3MHz 3kW – **The Beat 104.1 FM:** 104.1MHz 3kW

**HABMAR INVESTMENTS INC. (Comm.)**
⊡ Haggatt Hall, Bridgetown ☎ +1 246 434 1011 🖷 +1 246 437 7526
**W:** slam101fm.com & y103fm.com
**FM: Slam** 101.1MHz 5kW – **Y103:** 103.3MHz 5kW

**OTHER STATIONS (FM in MHz):**
**BBC:** Bridgetown 92.1 5kW. 24h relay of BBC World Service –

**CAPITAL MEDIA HD** ☐ The Loft, Lifestyle Centre, St. James ☎ +1 246 629 0991 FM 99.3 – **CHRIST IS THE ANSWER RADIO** (Rlg.): ☐ Bishop's Court Hill, BB46307, St. Michael ☎ +1 246 430 3599 **W:** citaradio.com. FM 90.1 (5kW) – **MIX 96.9** (Comm./rlg.) ☐ Garden House, Upper Bay St., St. Michael ☎ +1 246 228 4183 ▤ +1 246 228 3550 L.P: MD: Scott Weatherhead. FM 96.9 (4kW) – **NBG RADIO** (Rlg.): ☐ Building #6, Harbour Rd, St. Michael ☎ +1 246 228 1509 **W:** nbglive.com. FM 104.7 – **RADIO GED** (Educ.) ☐ Barbados Community College, General Education Dept., Eyrie Howells Cross Road, St. Michael ☎ +1 246 426 3312 ▤ +1 246 429 5935 **W:** bcc.edu.bb/Divisions/GEDRadio/ FM 106.1 (lp). D.Prgr: 1500-1900MF during school terms only

## BELARUS

**L.T:** UTC +3h — **Pop:** 9.5 million — **Pr.L:** Belarusian, Russian — **E.C:** 230V/50Hz — **ITU:** BLR

### MINISTERSTVA KULTURY (Ministry of Culture)
☐ pr. Peramožcau 11, 220004 Minsk ☎ +375 17 2037574 **E:** minister-stvo@kultura.by **W:** kultura.gov.by **L.P:** Minister: Jurij Bondar
**NB:** The Ministry of Culture is issuing broadcasting licenses.

### NACYJANALNAJA DZIARŽAUNAJA TELERADYJO-KAMPANIJA RESPUBLIKI BELARUS (Gov)
☐ vul. Makaionka 9, 220807 Minsk ☎ +375 17 3896352 **E:** pr@tvr.by **W:** tvr.by
▤ **Radio studios:** vul. Cyrvonaja 4, 220807 Minsk; exc. **Radyus FM:** vul. Cyhunacnaja 27/2, 220014 Minsk.
**L.P:** Chmn: Ivan Ejsmant

| FM (MHz) | 1 | 2 | 3 | 4 | °1 | °2 | kW |
|---|---|---|---|---|---|---|---|
| Asipovicy | 91.0 | 107.7 | 72.47 | 104.9 | 67.46 | 71.69 | 1/3x2/2x4 |
| Asveja | 103.5 | 106.0 | - | - | | | |
| Babrujsk | 101.6 | 106.0 | 73.01 | 104.1 | 71.45 | 68.96 | 2x2/4/2/2x4 |
| Berazino | 94.7 | 107.4 | 67.07 | 100.7 | 70.79 | - | 1/0.25/3x1 |
| Brahin | 103.3 | 105.8 | 69.11 | 100.8 | 67.37 | 68.30 | 2/2x4/2/2x4 |
| Braslau | 105.7 | 107.7 | 73.49 | 102.3 | 69.08 | 71.99 | 2/2x4/2/2x4 |
| Brest | 100.0 | 88.5 | 72.47 | 103.7 | 70.91 | 71.69 | 2x1/4x4 |
| Drahicyn | 101.8 | - | 69.80 | 102.4 | 72.14 | - | 0.5/1/0.5/1 |
| Heraniony | 105.8 | 102.2 | 69.26 | 103.2 | 72.32 | 68.39 | 2/1/4/2/2x4 |
| Homiel | 105.1 | 91.5 | 66.20 | 100.1 | 67.76 | 69.26 | 2x1/2/1/2x2 |
| Hrodna | 103.0 | 95.0 | 68.90 | 100.5 | 66.98 | 66.20 | 4/1/4/2/2x4 |
| Kapyl | 102.3 | 101.6 | 73.22 | 103.9 | - | 70.97 | 4/0.5/3x0.1 |
| Kasciukovicy | 104.7 | 107.2 | 69.38 | 102.2 | 66.47 | 68.03 | 2/1/4/2/2x4 |
| Krupki | 103.8 | 106.3 | - | - | - | - | 4 |
| Luki | 90.6 | 94.7 | - | 104.3 | - | - | 1 |
| Mahiliou | 105.9 | 99.1 | 71.18 | 100.9 | 72.74 | 71.96 | 2/1/4/1/2x4 |
| Miadziel | 106.4 | 104.9 | 66.86 | 103.8 | 68.69 | 70.31 | 2x2/4x4 |
| Minsk | 106.2 | 102.9 | 105.1 | 103.7 | 71.33 | 70.43 | 2/1/1/3x4 |
| Minsk | - | - | 72.89 | 72.11 | - | - | 4 |
| Mscislaul | 106.7 | 101.7 | 73.73 | 102.9 | 66.89 | - | 1/0.25/3x1 |
| Pinsk | 104.5 | 106.8 | 67.88 | 102.0 | 66.32 | 67.10 | 2/5x4 |
| Salihorsk | 100.3 | 106.7 | 68.57 | 102.8 | 70.22 | 72.23 | 4/2/1/4/2x1 |
| Slonim | 106.5 | 97.3 | - | 104.0 | 66.56 | 67.34 | 4/1/3x4 |
| Smarhon | 103.6 | - | 66.38 | 101.4 | 67.97 | 70.13 | 3x1/2x2 |
| Smiatanicy | 106.3 | 104.6 | 70.28 | 103.8 | 67.22 | 68.00 | 4 |
| Staryja Darohi | 100.6 | 103.1 | - | - | - | - | 1 |
| Svislac | 105.9 | 98.9 | 68.72 | 96.7 | - | 66.08 | 0.5/4/0.1/2x4 |
| Trokeniki | 104.5 | - | - | - | - | 70.76 | 1/0.5 |
| Ušacy | 106.7 | 101.7 | 70.94 | 102.7 | 72.65 | 66.74 | 4/1/4x4 |
| Vasilievicy | 102.0 | 106.5 | 73.19 | - | - | - | 1 |
| Viciebsk | 100.5 | 99.3 | 72.26 | 105.5 | 70.67 | 69.92 | 2x2/4x4 |
| Vorša | 107.0 | 105.0 | 73.82 | 100.2 | 67.85 | 69.14 | 3x1/2x2/4 |
| Žlobin | 105.5 | 101.0 | 71.81 | 100.5 | 69.68 | 71.03 | 2/1/4x2 |

+ sites with only txs below 1kW. °) Prgr 1+2 freqs in the OIRT FM band, to be phased out

**D.Prgr: Prgr 1 (Peršy nacyjanalny kanal):** 24h in Belarusian, Russian. – **Prgr 2 (Kanal Kultura):** 24h in Belarusian, Russian. – **Prgr 3 (Radyjo Stalica):** 24h in Belarusian. – **Prgr 4 (Radyus FM):** 24h in Russian. – **Prgr 5 (R. Belarus):** 24h in Belarusian, Polish, Russian on Brest 96.4 (0.5kW), Hrodna 96.9 (1kW), Heraniony 99.9 (1kW), Svislac 100.8 (1kW), Miadziel 102.0 (4kW), Braslau 106.6 (1kW).

### Belteleradyjokampanija Regional Stations
**D.Prgr:** all stns 24h in Belarusian, Russian. **TRK "Brest",** vul. Kujbyšava 64, 224030 Brest. **E:** radiobrestgosti@tut.by. Prgr 1 ("R. Brest") on (MHz) 69.08 (Pinsk 4kW), 69.44 (Slonim 4kW), 69.68 (Brest 4kW), 94.6 (Pinsk 1kW), 101.1 (Baranavicy 0.5kW), 102.5 (Stolin 0.5kW), 104.2 (Drahicyn 2kW), 104.8 (Brest 2kW), 105.6 (Pruzany 0.1kW); Prgr 2 ("Horod FM") on 97.7MHz (Brest 0.1kW). – **TRK "Homiel",** vul. Puškina 8, 246050 Homiel. **E:** radio@tvrgomel.by.

Prgr 1 ("Homiel FM") on (MHz) 66.44 (Smiatanicy 4kW), 66.98 (Homiel 2kW), 68.45 (Žlobin 2kW), 69.92 (Brahin 4kW), 101.3 (Homiel 1kW), 103.0 (Žlobin 2kW), 103.3 (Smiatanicy 2kW), 105.3 (Brahin 1kW), 105.4 (Mazyr 0.5kW), 107.8 (Vasilievicy 1kW); Prgr 2 ("Homiel Plus"): on Homiel 103.7MHz (0.5kW). – **TRK "Hrodna",** vul. Horkaha 85, 230015 Hrodna. **E:** radio@tvr.grodno.by. "R. Hrodna" on (MHz) 67.76 (Hrodna 4kW), 68.12 (Slonim 4kW), 68.48 (Masty 0.5kW), 71.54 (Heraniony 4kW), 72.80 (Trokeniki 0.5kW), 101.2 (Hrodna 1kW), 101.8 (Luki 1kW), 102.5 (Slonim 1kW), 102.8 (Smarhon 1kW), 104.4 (Svislac 4kW), 107.8 (Heraniony 1kW). – **TRK "Mahiliou",** vul. Peršamajskaja 83, 212030 Mahiliou. **E:** radiomogilev@tut.by. "R. Mahiliou" on (MHz) 66.02 (Babrujsk 4kW), 67.25 (Kasciukovicy 4kW), 70.10 (Mahiliou 4kW), 70.91 (Asipovicy 2kW), 96.4 (Mahiliou 1kW), 99.4 (Kasciukovicy 1kW), 100.0 (Krycau 0.5kW), 100.4 (Mscislaul 0.25kW), 102.3 (Asipovicy 1kW), 102.7 (Slavharad 0.25kW), 106.6 (Babrujsk 1kW), 106.8 (Ciachcin 0.25kW). – **TRK "Viciebsk",** vul. Kamunistycnaja 8, 210602 Viciebsk. **E:** info@radio.vitebsk.by. "R. Viciebsk" on (MHz) 67.64 (Miadziel 4kW), 68.30 (Ušacy 4kW), 71.48 (Viciebsk 4kW), 91.2 (Viciebsk 2kW), 100.6 (Hara 1kW), 102.0 (Asveja 1kW), 102.4 (Vorša 2kW), 104.0 (Bycycha 0.5kW), 104.6 (Braslau 1kW), 105.2 (Sianno 1kW), 107.8 (Ušacy 4kW).

### OTHER STATIONS

| FM | MHz | kW | Location | Station |
|---|---|---|---|---|
| 20) | 87.5 | 2 | Brest | Yumor FM |
| 9B) | 87.5 | 1 | Hrodna | Narodnoye R. |
| 20A) | 87.5 | 1 | Minsk | Relax FM |
| 18) | 88.2 | 1 | Hrodna | Dushevnoye R. |
| 20B) | 89.9 | 1 | Hrodna | Yumor FM |
| 6) | 90.0 | 1 | Mahiliou | R. Unistar |
| 6) | 90.2 | 1 | Babrujsk | R. Unistar |
| 1A) | 91.0 | 1 | Homiel | R. BA |
| 20) | 91.9 | 1 | Mahiliou | Yumor FM |
| 5) | 92.2 | 1 | Viciebsk | Pilot FM |
| 15) | 92.4 | 2 | Minsk | R. Minsk |
| 5) | 93.2 | 1 | Mahiliou | Pilot FM |
| 20) | 93.7 | 2 | Minsk | Yumor FM |
| 22) | 94.1 | 1 | Minsk | Legendy FM |
| 1A) | 95.7 | 1 | Hrodna | R. BA |
| 1B) | 96.2 | 1 | Minsk | Melodii veka |
| 20) | 97.0 | 1 | Baranavicy | Yumor FM |
| 20) | 97.0 | 1 | Slonim | Yumor FM |
| 21) | 97.4 | 2 | Minsk | MV-Radyjo |
| 7) | 97.8 | 1 | Viciebsk | Evropa plus Vitebsk |
| 9) | 98.4 | 1 | Minsk | Novoye R. |
| 11) | 98.6 | 1 | Mahiliou | Russkoye R. Mahiliou |
| 9A) | 98.7 | 1 | Viciebsk | Novoye R. |
| 3) | 98.9 | 2 | Minsk | Russkoye R. |
| 6) | 99.5 | 2 | Minsk | R. Unistar |
| 6) | 99.8 | 1 | Homiel | R. Unistar |
| 19) | 100.0 | 1 | Baranavicy | Baranavicy FM |
| 13) | 100.4 | 1.5 | Minsk | Hit R. |
| 4) | 100.8 | 2 | Brest | Alfa-Radio |
| 2) | 101.2 | 1 | Brest | R. ROKS |
| 5) | 101.2 | 2 | Minsk | Pilot FM |
| 1A) | 101.5 | 1 | Slonim | R. BA |
| 14) | 101.7 | 2 | Minsk | R. ONT |
| 8) | 101.8 | 1 | Viciebsk | R. Mir Belarus |
| 5) | 102.1 | 1 | Hrodna | Pilot FM |
| 2) | 102.1 | 1 | Minsk | R. ROKS |
| 6) | 102.3 | 1 | Brest | R. Unistar |
| 21) | 102.4 | 1 | Miadziel | MV-Radyjo |
| 9B) | 102.5 | 1 | Minsk | Narodnoye R. |
| 2) | 102.6 | 1 | Homiel | R. ROKS |
| 5) | 102.9 | 2 | Brest | Pilot FM |
| 2) | 103.0 | 1 | Viciebsk | R. ROKS |
| 2) | 103.4 | 1 | Mahiliou | R. ROKS |
| 8) | 103.6 | 1 | Babrujsk | R. Mir Belarus |
| 8) | 104.3 | 2 | Salihorsk | R. Mir Belarus |
| 1A) | 104.5 | 1 | Mahiliou | R. BA |
| 1A) | 104.6 | 4 | Minsk | R. BA |
| 12) | 104.6 | 1 | Viciebsk | Retro FM |
| 12) | 104.7 | 1 | Palack | Retro FM |
| 21) | 104.8 | 1 | Kapyl | MV-Radyjo |
| 16) | 105.0 | 1 | Hrodna | MFM |
| 21) | 105.3 | 1 | Salihorsk | MV-Radyjo |
| 21) | 105.5 | 1 | Berazino | MV-Radyjo |
| 21) | 105.6 | 1 | St. Darohi | MV-Radyjo |
| 18) | 105.7 | 2 | Minsk | Dushevnoye R. |
| 18) | 106.0 | 1 | Homiel | Dushevnoye R. |
| 10) | 106.1 | 1 | Pinsk | Svaje R. |
| 1A) | 106.2 | 4 | Brest | R. BA |

| FM | MHz | kW | Location | Station |
|----|-----|----|----------|---------|
| 15) | 106.4 | 1 | Viciebsk | R. Minsk |
| 8) | 106.6 | 1 | Brest | R. Mir Belarus |
| 9A) | 106.7 | 1 | Homiel | Novoye R. |
| 2) | 106.9 | 1 | Hrodna | R. ROKS |
| 8) | 107.1 | 4 | Minsk | R. Mir Belarus |
| 17) | 107.4 | 1 | Homiel | R. 107.4 FM |
| 21) | 107.4 | 2 | Maladzecna | MV-Radyjo |
| 4) | 107.6 | 1 | Viciebsk | Alfa-Radio |
| 17) | 107.6 | 1 | Žlobin | R. 107.4 FM |
| 8) | 107.8 | 1 | Mahiliou | R. Mir Belarus |
| 4) | 107.9 | 2 | Minsk | Alfa-Radio |

+ txs below 1kW.

**Addresses & other information:**
**1A,B)** vul. Surhanova 26, 220010 Minsk – **2)** vul. Starazouskaja 8a, 220002 Minsk. In Russian. – **3)** vul. Starazouskaja 8a, 220002 Minsk. In Russian. – **4)** pr. Nezaleznasci 181, 220125 Minsk. In Russian. – **5)** vul. K.Marksa 40, 220030 Minsk – **6)** pr. Nezaleznasci 4, 220050 Minsk. In Russian. – **7)** Maskauski pr. 10, 210015 Viciebsk. In Russian. – **8)** vul. Kamunistycny 17, 220029 Minsk. In Russian. – **9A.B)** pr. Puškina 39, 220092 Minsk. In Russian. – **10)** vul. Karasiova 6, 225710 Pinsk. In Russian. – **11)** vul. Caljuskincau 105, 212003 Mahiliou. Rel. Russkoye R. (Russia) – **12)** vul. Hoholia 11, 210601 Viciebsk. Rel. Retro FM (Russia) –**13)** vul. Kamunistycny 6a, 220029 Minsk. Rel. Hit FM (Russia) – **14)** vul. Kamunistycny 6, 220029 Minsk – **15)** zav. Kaliningradski 20a, 220012 Minsk. In Russian. – **16)** pl. Saveckaja 6, 230025 Hrodna – **17)** vul. Šasiejnaja 41 , 246004 Homiel. In Russian. – **18)** vul. K.Marksa 40, 220030 Minsk. In Russian. – **19)** vul. Haharina 40, 225409 Baranavicy. In Russian. – **20A,B)** vul. Uschodnjaja 131, 220113 Minsk. 20A) in Russian. – **21)** vul. Ckalova 5, 220039 Minsk – **22)** Minsk.

**Radio via DTT:** see National TV section

## BELGIUM

**LT:** UTC +1h (31 Mar-27 Oct: +2h) — **Pop:** 11.35 million — **Pr.L:** Flemish, French, German — **E.C:** 50Hz, 230V — **ITU:** BEL

**FLANDERS Pop:** 6.5 million (+1.2 million in Brussels) — **Pr.L:** Flemish

### VLAAMSE REGULATOR VOOR MEDIA (VRM)
Koning Albert II-laan 20, 1000 Brussel ☎ +32 2 5534504 ▤ +32 2 5534506 **E:** vrm@vlaanderen.be **W:** www.vlaamseregulatormedia.be
**L.P:** Chmn: Matthias Stormer

### VLAAMSE RADIO EN TELEVISIEOMROEP (VRT)
**(Pub) Flemish (Dutch) Language Network**
Public Sce grants by Flemish government.
VRT, August Reyerslaan 52, B-1043 Brussels ☎+32 2 741 3111 ▤ +32 2 734 9351 **W:** vrt.be **E:** info@vrt.be **L.P:** General Director Media: Peter Claes; Radiomanager: Els Van de Sijpe
**Regional Centres Radio 2:**
**Antwerpen:** Jan Van Rijswijcklaan 157, 2018 Antwerpen ☎+32 3 2479111▤ +32 3 2378282 **E:** redactieantwerpen@radio2.be
**Vlaams-Brabant:** Dikke Lindelaan 2, 1020 Brussels ☎+32 2 7414111 ▤ +32 2 4780800 **E:** redactievlaamsbrabant@radio2.be
**Oost-Vlaanderen:** Martelaarslaan 232, 9000 Gent ☎+32 9 2247256 ▤ +32 9 2254903 **E:** redactieoostvlaanderen@radio2.be
**West-Vlaanderen:** Doorniksesteenweg 241B, 8500 Kortrijk ☎+32 56 247311 ▤ +32 56 221358 **E:** redactiewestvlaanderen@radio2.be
**Limburg:** Via Media 2, 3500 Hasselt ☎+32 11 249611 ▤ +32 11 242436 **E:** redactielimburg@radio2.be

| FM (MHz) | R1 | R2 | RK | SB | M | kW |
|----------|-----|-----|------|------|------|------|
| Antwerpen | - | - | 92.0 | - | - | 1 |
| Brussegem | - | 90.7 | - | - | - | 2 |
| Brussels | - | - | - | - | 88.3 | 1 |
| Diest | - | 92.4 | - | - | - | 1 |
| Egem O.+W.-VI. | 95.7 | - | 90.4 | 102.1 | 101.5 | 50/50/50/40 |
| Egem O.-VI | - | 98.6 | - | - | - | 50 |
| Egem W.-VI. | - | - | - | 100.1 | - | 50 |
| Genk | 99.9 | 97.9 | 89.9 | 101.4 | 102.0 | 20/20/20/40/40 |
| | - | - | - | - | 93.0 | 3 |
| Gent | - | - | 94.5 | - | 0.5 |
| Leuven | - | - | 88.0 | - | 0.5/0.5 |
| N'kerken Waas | - | 89.8 | - | - | 1 |
| Schoten | 94.2 | 97.5 | 96.4 | 100.9 | 89.0 | 20/20/3/40/20 |
| St-Pieters-Leeuw | 91.7 | 93.7 | 89.5 | 100.6 | 97.0 | 50/50/50/2 |
| Veltem | - | 88.7 | - | - | 94.8 | 1/1 |

+3 txs under 1kW
**R1**=Radio Een (information and music), **R2**=Radio Twee (light &

popular music), **RK**=Radio Klara (classical music), **SB**=Studio Brussel (youth stn), **M**=MNM (hit music stn)
**Radio 2 Regional prgrs:** 0500-0700 (M-F), 1100-1200 (M-F), 1500-1700 (daily) on FM
**Sporza:** replaces normal R.1 prgrs during sports events **W:** sporza.be
**D.Prgr:** Night prgr on all frequencies.
**DAB:** 223.936 MHz all services plus all regional Radio 2 outlets, Sporza, MNM hits, Klara continuo, and VRT NWS (news repeat).
**Ann:** R1:"Radio Een", R2: "Radio Twee", RK: "Klara", SB: "Studio Brussel", M: "MNM"

### COMMERCIAL NETWORKS:
**NB:** For up-to-date information on all radio stns in Flanders visit **W:** radioinvlaanderen.be

| FM | Mhz | kW | Location | Station |
|----|-----|----|----------|---------|
| 1) | 87.6 | 5 | Oostende | Nostalgie |
| 1) | 88.0 | 8 | Kortrijk | Nostalgie |
| 1) | 88.1 | 1 | Brugge | Nostalgie |
| 2) | 88.3 | 1 | Oost-Vleteren | QMusic |
| 2) | 88.6 | 3 | Gent | Qmusic |
| 3) | 88.8 | 1 | Lummen | Joe |
| 6) | 88.9 | 1 | Diksmuide | VBRO |
| 3) | 89.1 | 3 | Tongeren | Joe |
| 3) | 89.2 | 1 | Sint-Truiden | Joe |
| 6) | 89.6 | 2 | Brugge | VBRO |
| 3) | 90.6 | 5 | Turnhout | Joe |
| 3) | 90.9 | 4 | Herzele | Joe |
| 5) | 91.3 | 3 | Brugge | NRJ |
| 3) | 92.2 | 3 | Dendermonde | Joe |
| 2) | 92.2 | 2 | Herentals | Qmusic |
| 7) | 92.7 | 2 | Kortrijk | TOP R. |
| 3) | 92.8 | 1 | Gent | Joe |
| 1) | 92.8 | 1.5 | Beringen | Nostalgie |
| 3) | 93.5 | 2 | Sint-Niklaas | Joe |
| 3) | 93.5 | 2.5 | Meeuwen | Joe |
| 3) | 93.5 | 2 | Westerlo | Joe |
| 8) | 93.6 | 20 | Ardooie | Stadsradio Vlaanderen |
| 7) | 94.0 | 6 | Ardooie | TOP R. |
| 1) | 94.7 | 1 | Genk | Nostalgie |
| 3) | 94.8 | 1 | Tongeren | Joe |
| 5) | 95.1 | 1 | Turnhout | NRJ |
| 3) | 95.5 | 1 | StPietersLeeuw | Joe |
| 3) | 95.6 | 1 | Brussegem | Joe |
| 2) | 95.8 | 1 | Veltem | Qmusic |
| 6) | 96.3 | 2 | Gent | VBRO |
| 1) | 96.5 | 1.2 | Hamont-Achel | Nostalgie |
| 3) | 96.7 | 2 | Mechelen | Joe |
| 1) | 96.9 | 1 | Sint-Truiden | Nostalgie |
| 9) | 98.0 | 1 | Antwerpen | R. Minerva |
| 1) | 98.1 | 4 | Brussel | Nostalgie |
| 1) | 98.2 | 15 | Egem | Nostalgie |
| 4) | 98.8 | 3 | Brussel | Bruzz |
| 1) | 98.2 | 1 | Scherpenheuvel | Nostalgie |
| 6) | 99.0 | 1 | Mechelen | VBRO |
| 2) | 99.2 | 10 | Antwerpen | Qmusic |
| 10) | 99.3 | 1 | Bree | FM Goud Noordoost-Limburg |
| 5) | 99.4 | 3 | Gent | NRJ |
| 2) | 100.0 | 1 | Wuustwezel | Qmusic |
| 6) | 100.2 | 2 | Antwerpen | VBRO |
| 1) | 101.0 | 20 | Ieper | Nostalgie |
| 2) | 102.5 | 1 | Brussel | QMusic |
| 2) | 102.5 | 50 | Genk | Qmusic |
| 7) | 102.6 | 2 | Leuven | TOP R. |
| 11) | 102.6 | 1 | Eeklo | R. Tamboer |
| 7) | 102.7 | 2 | Aalst | TOP R. |
| 12) | 102.7 | 3 | Brugge | R. Brugs Ommeland |
| 7) | 102.8 | 1 | Brussel | TOP R. |
| 1) | 102.9 | 100 | Schoten | Nostalgie |
| 2) | 103.0 | 20 | Egem | Qmusic |
| 1) | 103.0 | 2 | Bree | Nostalgie |
| 2) | 103.1 | 50 | StPietersLeeuw | Qmusic |
| 3) | 103.3 | 1 | Diest | Joe |
| 2) | 103.3 | 1 | Brugge | Qmusic |
| 3) | 103.4 | 31 | Brussel | Joe |
| 3) | 103.4 | 5 | Antwerpen | Joe |
| 3) | 103.4 | 20 | Genk | Joe |
| 1) | 103.5 | 20 | Gent | Nostalgie |
| 5) | 103.6 | 1 | Oostende | VBRO |
| 3) | 103.7 | 2 | Wuustwezel | Joe |
| 3) | 103.7 | 2 | Lommel | Joe |
| 1) | 103.7 | 2 | Sint-Niklaas | Nostalgie |
| 1) | 103.8 | 3 | Leuven | Nostalgie |
| 8) | 103.8 | 2 | Gent | Stadsradio Vlaanderen |

| FM | Mhz | kW | Location | Station |
|---|---|---|---|---|
| 5) | 103.8 | 1 | Geel | NRJ |
| 5) | 103.8 | 1 | Hasselt | VBRO |
| 3) | 104.1 | 50 | Egem | Joe |
| 5) | 104.1 | 2 | Hasselt | NRJ |
| 5) | 104.2 | 3 | Leuven | NRJ |
| 3) | 104.2 | 1 | Aalst | Joe |
| 7) | 104.2 | 2 | Antwerpen | TOP R. |
| 13) | 104.5 | 1 | Gent | Zen FM |
| 8) | 104.5 | 1 | Oostende | Stadsradio Vlaanderen |
| 5) | 104.5 | 1 | Poperinge | NRJ |
| 1) | 104.5 | 1 | Mechelen | Nostalgie |
| 1) | 104.5 | 1 | Oud-Turnhout | Nostalgie |
| 1) | 104.6 | 2 | Geel | Nostalgie |
| 5) | 104.6 | 2 | Antwerpen | NRJ |
| 8) | 104.7 | 1 | Hasselt | Stadsradio Vlaanderen |
| 1) | 104.8 | 3 | Aalst | Nostalgie |

+ many stns below 1kW

**Addresses & other information:**
**1)** Katwilgweg 2, 2050 Antwerpen **W:** nostalgie.eu – **2)** Medialaan 1, 1800 Vilvoorde **W:** qmusic.be – **3)** Medialaan 1, 1800 Vilvoorde **W:** joe.be – **4)** Eugène Flageyplein 18 bus 18, 1050 Elsene **W:** bruzz.be – **6)** Vlamingstraat 35, 8000 Brugge **W:** vbro.be – **7)** Nekkerputstraat 150, 9000 Gent **W:** topradio.be – **8)** P. Cuyperstraat 3, 1040 Brussel **W:** stadsradiovlaanderen.be – **9)** Wandeldijk 20, 2050 Antwerpen **W:** minerva.be – **10)** Peerderbaan 84, 3990 Peer **W:** fmgoud.be – **13)** Overpoortstraat 70, 9000 Gent **W:** zenfm.be

**DAB+:** Operator Norkring on 216.928 MHz: TOPradio, VBRO Radio, Radio Maria, Family Radio, Roxx, VBRO Evergreen, BBC World Service, Joe, and QMusic – to be added in the last quarter of 2018: Radio Nostalgie, NRJ, Stadsradio Vlaanderen

**WALLONIA Pop:** 3.6 million (+1.2 million in Brussels)
— **Pr.L:** French, German

## CONSEIL SUPERIEUR DE L'AUDIOVISUEL (CSA)
✉ Rue Royale 89, 1000 Bruxelles ☎ +32 2 3495880 ▤ +32 2 3495897 **E:** info@csa.be **W:** www.csa.be **L.P:** DG: Bernardo Herman

## MEDIENRAT DER DEUTSCHSPRACHIGEN GEMEINSCHAFT BELGIENS
✉ Gospertstr. 42 4700, Eupen ☎ +32 87 596300 ▤ +32 87 552891 **E:** info@medienrat.be **W:** www.medienrat.be **L.P:** Pres: Oswald Weber

## RADIO-TÉLÉVISION BELGE DE LA COMMUNAUTÉ FRANÇAISE (R.T.B.F.) (Pub.)
**French Language Network**
Public sce. Grants by French Parliament.
✉ Cité de la Radio-Television, B-1044 Brussels ☎ +32 2 737 2111 ▤ +32 2 737 4357 **W:** rtbf.be
**L.P:** Admin. Gen: Jean-Paul Philippot. Dir. Radio: Francis Goffin
**Regional & Local Centres: Bruxelles:** Reyerslaan 52, 1044 Brussel **Charleroi:** Passage de la Bourse, 6000 Charleroi **Liège:** Palais des congrès, 4020 Liège **Hainaut:** Rue du gouvernement 15, 7000 Mons **Namur-Brabant-Wallon:** Av. Golenvaux 8, 5000 Namur **Verviers:** Rue de Verviers 203, 4821 Andrimont **Luxembourg:** Parc des Expositions, 6700 Arlon

| MW | kHz | kW | Prgr | MW | kHz | kW | Prgr |
|---|---|---|---|---|---|---|---|
| Wavre | 621 | 300 | La 1ère Houdeng | 1125 | | 9 | Vivacité |

**NB:** Both 621 & 1125 kHz may be closed at the end of 2018; still broadcasting at time of publishing

| FM (MHz) | 1 | 2 | 3 | 4 | 5 | kW |
|---|---|---|---|---|---|---|
| Anderlues | 93.4 | 92.3 | - | 99.1 | 96.6 | 0.6/40/40/40 |
| Bruxelles | - | 99.3 | 91.2 | 93.2 | 88.8 | 3/40/1/0.5 |
| Léglise | 96.4 | 91.5 | 94.1 | 87.6 | - | 10/10/10/10 |
| Liège | 96.4 | 90.5 | 99.5 | 95.6 | 92.5 | 5/40/40/13/0.1 |
| Malmédy | 89.2 | 91.6 | - | - | - | 1/0.1 |
| Marche | 93.3 | 95.2 | - | - | - | 0.5/4 |
| Profondeville | 102.7 | - | 92.8 | 90.8 | | 25/10/10 |
| Tournai | 106.0 | 101.8 | 102.6 | 104.6 | 90.6 | 25/30/30/30/? |
| Verviers | 91.3 | 103.0 | - | - | 87.9 | 1/3/0.1 |
| Wavre | 96.1 | 97.3 | - | - | 101.1 | 10/35/50 |

+ many txs under 1kW

**Network 1** (Première – information & musique)
**Network 2** (Vivacité – light music)
**Reg. Prgrs:** W 0530-0800, 1200-1300, 1600-1800; Fri 1800-2100 – R. Hainaut (Mons) on 92.3/101.8MHz – R. Liège 90.5/103.0/94.6/89.1/89.4MHz – R. Namur on 97.3/92.8/89.3/91.5/89.4/90.2MHz – R. Bruxelles on 93.2MHz
**Local Prgrs:** R. Verviers (Radiolène) on 103.0MHz

**Network 3** (Musique 3 – classical music)
**Network 4** (Classic 21 – oldies & rock classics)
**Network 5** (Pure FM – youth stn)
**DAB:** 225.648MHz - all services plus Tarmac (Belgian hip hop) and BRF 1 & 2
**Ann:** "Vous écoutez La Première, Vivacité, Musique trois, Radio 21, Pure FM, Classic 21"

### EXTERNAL SERVICE: RTBFi
See International Broadcasting section

## BELGISCHES RUNDFUNK-UND FERNSEHZENTRUM DER DEUTSCHSPRACHIGEN GEMEINSCHAFT (BRF)
**German Language Network (Pub)**
Grants by RDG-Rat (German speaking community council)
✉ Kehrweg 11, B-4700 Eupen ☎ +32 87 59 1111 ▤ +32 87 591199 **W:** brf.be **E:** info@brf.be
**Regional:** ✉ Blvd. Reyers 52, B-1044 Brussels – Malmedyer Str. 25, B-4780 St. Vith **L.P:** Dir.: Toni Wimmer

| FM | MHz | kW | Ch. | FM | MHz | kW | Ch. |
|---|---|---|---|---|---|---|---|
| Lüttich | 88.5 | 50 | 1 | Eupen | 94.9 | 0.05 | 1 |
| Lüttich | 91.0 | 0.5 | 1 | Brussel* | 95.2 | 2 | 1 |
| Auel | 92.2 | 0.16 | 1 | Eupen | 98.4 | 1 | 2 |
| Lontzen | 93.2 | 5 | 2 | Recht | 104.1 | 20 | 2 |
| Recht | 94.9 | 5 | 1 | Raeren | 105.9 | 0.1 | 2 |

*: broadcasts joined prgrs of Deutschlandfunk and BRF
**Ann:** "Hier ist der Belgischer Rundfunk"

## COMMERCIAL NETWORKS:

| FM | Mhz | kW | Location | Station |
|---|---|---|---|---|
| 14) | 87.6 | 1 | Ath | Sud R. |
| 14) | 88.2 | 1 | Charleroi | Sud R. |
| 11) | 88.7 | 1 | Sambreville | NRJ |
| 1) | 88.9 | 1 | Ronquières | Bel RTL |
| 14) | 90.0 | 1 | Tournai | Sud R |
| 10) | 90.2 | 2 | Bruxelles | R. Judaica |
| 11) | 91.9 | 1 | Charleroi | NRJ |
| 10) | 92.3 | 1 | Verviers | R. Nostalgie |
| 11) | 92.7 | 1 | Malmédy | NRJ |
| 7) | 92.9 | 1 | Bastogne | Fun R. |
| 3) | 94.1 | 1 | Louvain-la-Neuve | R. Antipode |
| 2) | 94.4 | 1 | Bütgenbach | 100.5 Das Hitradio |
| 9) | 94.7 | 5 | Bouillon | Must FM |
| 10) | 95.0 | 1 | Liège | R. Nostalgie |
| 10) | 95.6 | 1 | Houdeng | DH R. |
| 8) | 97.1 | 1 | Liège | Maximum FM |
| 7) | 97.4 | 1 | Mont-St-Aubert | Fun R. |
| 14) | 97.6 | 1 | Braine-le-cte | Sud R. |
| 18) | 97.8 | 1.2 | Bruxelles | R. Kif |
| 8) | 98.6 | 1 | Esneux | Maximum FM |
| 12) | 98.8 | 1 | Ciney | R. Contact |
| 1) | 99.0 | 2.5 | Bouillon | Bel RTL |
| 7) | 99.0 | 1 | Liège | Fun R. |
| 16) | 99.9 | 1 | Quevaucamps | Beloeil FM |
| 10) | 100.0 | 5 | Brussel | R. Nostalgie |
| 4) | 100.1 | 1 | Liège | Equinoxe FM |
| 10) | 100.2 | 1 | Limal | Bel RTL |
| 10) | 100.2 | 4 | Saint-Hubert | R. Nostalgie |
| 10) | 100.4 | 4 | Namur | R. Nostalgie |
| 2) | 100.5 | 20 | Eupen | 100.5 Das Hitradio |
| 10) | 100.5 | 2 | Couvin | R. Nostalgie |
| 10) | 100.6 | 5 | Bouillon | R. Nostalgie |
| 10) | 100.7 | 1 | Dinant | R. Nostalgie |
| 8) | 100.9 | 2 | Liège | Maximum FM |
| 15) | 101.4 | 1 | Bruxelles | DH R. |
| 1) | 101.6 | 5 | Marche-en-F | Bel RTL |
| 12) | 101.6 | 1 | Verviers | R. Contact |
| 1) | 101.7 | 2 | Namur | Bel RTL |
| 1) | 101.7 | 1 | Couvin | Bel RTL |
| 12) | 101.8 | 1 | Meix-le-Tige | R. Contact |
| 14) | 102.0 | 2 | Mons | Sud R |
| 12) | 102.2 | 10 | Brussel | R. Contact |
| 12) | 102.2 | 5 | Charleroi | R. Contact |
| 12) | 102.2 | 2 | Liège | R. Contact |
| 12) | 102.3 | 2 | Mons | R. Contact |
| 10) | 102.4 | 1 | Arlon | R. Nostalgie |
| 12) | 102.5 | 1 | Houffalize | R. Contact |
| 12) | 103.2 | 10 | Vlessart | NRJ |
| 15) | 103.2 | 2 | Liège | DH R. |
| 1) | 103.4 | 5 | Mons | Bel RTL |
| 1) | 103.6 | 5 | Liège | Bel RTL |
| 11) | 103.7 | 5 | Brussel | NRJ |

| FM | Mhz | kW | Location | Station |
|---|---|---|---|---|
| 1) | 104.0 | 15 | Brussel | Bel RTL |
| 1) | 104.0 | 2 | Charleroi | Bel RTL |
| 6) | 104.3 | 1 | Brussel | BXFM |
| 11) | 104.5 | 5 | Liège | NRJ |
| 12) | 104.5 | 1 | Bièrges | R. Contact |
| 12) | 104.6 | 1 | Marche | R. Contact |
| 7) | 104.7 | 5 | Brussel | Fun R. |
| 12) | 104.7 | 1 | Malmédy | R. Contact |
| 12) | 104.7 | 5 | Namur | R. Contact |
| 2) | 104.8 | 3 | Sankt Vith | 100.5 Das Hitradio |
| 12) | 104.8 | 2 | Virton | R. Contact |
| 12) | 105.1 | 1 | Ath | R. Contact |
| 7) | 105.5 | 1 | Wavre | Fun R. |
| 8) | 106.0 | 1 | Verviers | Maximum FM |
| 12) | 106.2 | 1 | Florzé | R. Ourthe Amblève |
| 3) | 106.3 | 2 | Tubize | R. Antipode |
| 5) | 106.8 | 1 | Malmédy | Impact FM |
| 10) | 100.2 | 50 | Saint-Hubert | R. Nostalgie |
| 11) | 104.5 | 5 | Liège | NRJ |
| 12) | 107.0 | 1 | Eupen | R. Contact (DE) |
| 19) | 107.2 | 1.5 | Bruxelles | Vibration FM |
| 7) | 107.5 | 1 | Arlon | Fun R. |
| 2) | 107.6 | 1 | Honsfeld | 100.5 Das Hitradio |
| 11) | 107.6 | 1 | Mons-St-Aubert | NRJ |
| 12) | 107.8 | 1 | Libramont | R. Contact |

+ many stns below 1kW

**Addresses & other information:**
**1)** Avenue Georgin 2, 1030 Bruxelles +32 2 3376911 **W:** belrtl.be – **2)** Kehrweg 11, B-4700 Eupen +32 87 591259 ▤ +32 87 591249 **W:** hitradioworld.fm – **3)** Boîte postale 2, 1348 Louvain-La-Neuve ☎ +32 10 451110 ▤ +32 10 451717 **W:** antipode.be – **4)** Rue Montagne St Walburge, 261, 4000 Liège **W:** equinoxfm.be – **5)** Malmédy **W:** impact-fm.be – **6)** **W:** bxfm.be – **7)** Av. Telemaque 33, 1190 Bruxelles ☎ +32 2 3457575 **W:** funradio.be – **8)** 22 Rue de la Chaudronnerie, 4030 Grivegnée **W:** maximumfm.be – **9)** BP20, 1360 Perwez ☎ +32 81 655469 **W:** mustfm.be – **10)** Quai au Foin 55, 1010 Bruxelles ☎ +32 2 2270450 ▤ 02-2231455 **W:** nostalgie.eu – **11)** Chaussèe de Louvain 467, 1030 Bruxelles ☎ +32 2 5137575 ▤ +32 2 5114859 **W:** nrj.be – **12)** Avenue des Croix de Guerre 94, 1120 Bruxelles ☎ +32 2 2442711 ▤ +32 2 2442710 **W:** radiocontact.be and derbestemix.be (DE) – **13)** Rue Armand Binet 35B, 4140 Rouvreux (Sprimont) – **14)** 42, rue de la chaussée de Mons, 7000 Mons ☎ +32 65 401010 ▤ +32 65 401011 **W:** sudradio.net – **15)** Rue des Francs, 79, 1040 Bruxelles **W:** dhnet.be/medias/dh-radio – **16)** **W:** beloeil-fm.be – **17)** **W:** radiojudaica.be – **18)** **W:** radiokif.be – **19)** **W:** vibration.fm

**Military Stations:**
**AMERICAN FORCES NETWORK, SHAPE**
✉ Box 7, 7010 SHAPE. (APO AE 09700) ☎ +32 65 44 41 21
**L.P:** Officer-in-charge: Cpt. G. Martel. Broadc. Superv: SFC C. Kubicek. Chief Eng: René Libre
**Stations:** Kleine Brogel 106.2MHz 0.1kW, Brussels 101.7MHz 0.9kW, SHAPE 104.2/106.5MHz 4kW, Florennes 107.7MHz 0.1kW, Chievres 107.9MHz 0.1kW
**D.Prgr:** 24h on 101.7/104.2/107.7MHz. Own prgrs Mon-Fri 0500-0800, 1400-1700; Sat 0800-1200. Other times rel. AFN Europe.
**AFN-2:** 24h easy listening stereo prgr on 106.5MHz

**BRITISH FORCES BROADCASTING SERVICE**
**Stations:** BFBS 1 Casteau 107.6MHz 0.04kW
✉ Wentworth B., Listnstr., D-32049 Herford, Germany **W:** forces.net/radio **D.Prgr:** rel. BFBS Germany

## BELIZE

**L.T:** UTC -6h — **Pop:** 375,000 — **Pr.L:** English, Spanish — **E.C:** 110//60Hz, 220V/60Hz — **ITU:** BLZ

**PUBLIC UTILITIES COMMISSION (PUC)**
✉ PO Box 300, 41 Gabourel Lane, Belize City ☎ +501 2234938 ▤ +501 2236818 **W:** puc.bz **E:** info@puc.bz

| FM | MHz | kW | Name and loc. |
|---|---|---|---|
| 5) | 88.1 | 4 | Love FM, Punta Gorda |
| 5) | 88.9 | 4 | Love FM, Ladyville |
| 1) | 90.5 | 0.25 | Positive Vibes R, Belize City |
| 6) | 91.1 | 13 | Krem FM, Ladyville |
| 2) | 92.3 | 1 | Reef R, San Pedro |
| 8) | 93.7 | 1 | My Refuge Christian R, Roaring Creek |
| 11) | 94.1 | 1 | Faith FM, Pine Ridge |
| 5) | 95.1 | 1 | Love FM, Belize City |
| 17) | 95.5 | | Power FM, Orange Walk |
| 5) | 95.9 | 1 | Estéreo Amor, Belmopan |
| 15) | 96.3 | | BFBS R. 2, Belize |
| 6) | 96.5 | 6 | Krem FM, Belize/Carmelita/Cattle Landing |
| 7) | 97.1 | 1 | Integrity R, Belize City |
| 4) | 97.5 | | Estéreo Amor, Belize City |
| 5) | 98.1 | | Love FM, 4 sites |
| 15) | 98.3 | | BFBS R. Gurkha, Belize |
| 17) | 98.9 | | Power FM, Belize City |
| 16) | 99.5 | 1 | More FM, Belize City |
| 14) | 99.7 | 1 | R. Bahia, Corozal |
| 2) | 100.5 | 0.2 | My Refuge Christian R, Belize City |
| 6) | 101.1 | 1 | Krem FM, Dangriga |
| 9) | 101.3 | | Lighthouse Christian R, San Pedro |
| 1) | 102.9 | | Positive Vibes R, Belmopan |
| 10) | 103.1 | 1 | Sugar City R. Station, Orange Walk |
| 11) | 104.5 | | Faith FM, Punta Gorda |
| 13) | 106.7 | | Fiesta FM, Orange Walk |
| 16) | 107.1 | | More FM, Belmopan |

**NB: H of Tr:** usually 24h
**Addresses & other information:**
**1) W:** facebook.com/vibesradiobz – **2) W:** facebook.com/Reef-Radio-100202586796704 – **4)** 5 more txs **W:** estereoamor.com – **5)** 3 more txs **W:** lovefm.com – **6) W:** krembz.com – **7) W:** facebook.com/IntegrityRadio97.1FM – **8) W:** myrefugebelize.com – **9) W:** lighthouseradio.org – **10) W:** scrs.bz – **11) W:** faithfmbelize.com – **13) W:** fiestafmbz.com – **14) W:** facebook.com/rabahia99.7 – **15) W:** forces.net/radio – **16) W:** facebook.com/morefm – **17) W:** powerfm955belize.com

## BENIN

**L.T:** UTC +1h — **Pop:** 12 million — **Pr.L:** French + 18 ethnic — **E.C:** 220V/50Hz — **ITU:** BEN

**HAUTE AUTORITÉ DE L'AUDIOVISUEL ET DE LA COMMUNICATION (HAAC)**
✉ BP 3567, Ave. de la Marina, Face Hôtel du Port, 01 Cotonou ☎ +229 21311743 ▤ +229 21311742 **W:** haacbenin.org

**OFFICE DE RADIODIFFUSION ET TÉLÉVISION DU BENIN (ORTB, Gov.)**
✉ 01 B.P. 366, Cotonou ☎ +229 21360047 **W:** ortb.bj **E:** ortb@intnet.bj **L.P:** DG: Hamado Ouangraoua. Chief Tech. Sces: Anastase Adjoko.
**Regional** ✉ B.P. 128, Parakou ☎ +229 23611096
**FM:** Cotonou 94.7 10kW, Parakou 89.4/92.5MHz 2kW.
**Radio Nationale:** from Cotonou in French/ethnic.
**N. in French:** 0615MF, 0800SS, 1200SS, 1215MF, 1930, 2115.
**R. Regionale Parakou:** in French/ethnic.
(Cotonou & Parakou carry the same programme between 1900-2000).
**Atlantic FM,** Cotonou: 0700-2300 on 92.2MHz.
**Ann:** "Ici R. Bénin, Office de Radiodiffusion et Télévision du Bénin, émettant de Cotonou". "Ici Parakou, Office de Radiodiffusion et Télévision du Bénin, station regionale" **IS:** Bénin Tam-Tam

**Other stations:**
**R. Adja Ouèrè FM,** Cotonou: 92.6/100/100.6/107.6MHz – **R. Afrique Espoir,** Porto-Novo: 99.1MHz – **Benin Culture,** Porto-Novo: 93.4MHz – **CAPP FM,** Cotonou: 99.6MHz – **R. Carrefour,** Cotonou: 90.4MHz – **Cité Savalou Culture FM,** Cotonou: 87.8MHz – **Deeman R,** Parakou: 90.2MHz – **FM Ahémé,** Possotome: 99.6MHz – **FM Alakétou,** Ketou: 95.8MHz – **FM Monts Kouffé,** Bassila: 103MHz – **FM Noon Sina,** Bembereke: 90.8MHz – **FM Oré Ofé,** Tchetti: 102.1MHz – **Gerddes FM,** Cotonou: 89.5 MHz – **Golfe FM,** Cotonou: 105.7MHz **W:** eit.to/golfefm.htm – **La Voix de la Lama,** Porto-Novo: 103.8MHz – **La Voix de l'Islam,** Cotonou: 91.2MHz – **R. Immaculee Conception** (Rlg.): Djougou 89.1MHz, Natitingou 93.1MHz, Parakou 93.3MHz, Cotonou 98.7MHz, Bembèrèkè 100.8MHz, Bohicon 100.9MHz, Allada 101.3MHz, Dassa-Zoumey 107.3MHz – **R. Liéma,** Cotonou: 104MHz – **R. Planète,** Cotonou: 95.7MHz – **R. Maranatha,** Cotonou: 103.1MHz **W:** eit.to/RadioMaranatha.htm – **R. Allodalome,** Cotonou: 97.4MHz – **R. Star,** Cotonou: 94.3/96.3MHz – **R. Tokpa,** Cotonou: 104.3MHz – **R. Tonassé,** Cové: 107.6MHz – **R. Wekê,** Cotonou: 107MHz – **R. Rurale** stns in Tanguiéta 90, Ouessè 97.7, Dogbo 100, Ouaké 101 & Banikoara 104.2MHz
**BBC African Service:** Cotonou 101.7MHz.
**RFI Afrique:** Cotonou 90.0MHz, Parakou 106.1MHz.
**Trans World R,** Parakou (Serarou): 1566kHz 100kW 0315-0545, 1725-2230. **F.PI:** second MW tx of 200 kW, probably on 1476kHz. (For details see International Radio section)

## BERMUDA (UK)

**L.T:** UTC -4h (10 Mar-3 Nov: -3h) — **Pop:** 61,000 — **Pr.L:** English — **E.C:** 120//60Hz, 230V/60Hz — **ITU:** BER

### BERMUDA BROADCASTING CO. LTD. (Comm.)
✉ 4 Fort Hill Road, Prospect, Devonshire DV 02, PO Box HM 452, Hamilton HM BX ☎ +1 441 295 2828 **W:** bbcbda.com **L.P:** Owner: Chris Perry. CEO: Patrick Singleton, News Dir.: Gary Moreno, CEN: Earlston Chapman
**FM: Ocean 89:** 89.1MHz 1kW — **Power 95 FM:** 94.9MHz 2kW — **Inspire 105** (Rlg.): 105.1MHz 2kW

### DEPARTMENT OF EMERGENCY MEASURES ORGANIZATION
✉ Global House, 43 Church Street, Hamilton HM 12 ☎ +1 441 295 5151 **L.P:** Steve Cosham **Gov. Emergency Broadc. Stn:** Prospect, Devonshire 100.1MHz 1kW

### INTER-ISLAND COMMUNICATIONS (Comm.)
✉ 49 Union Square Mall, Hamilton ☎ +1 441 297 1076 ▤ +1 441 296 7680 **E:** feedback@hott1075bermuda.bm **L.P:** CEO: Glenn A. Blakeney.
**FM: Magic 102.7:** 102.7MHz – **Hott 107.5** 107.5MHz

### LTT BROADCASTING LTD. (Comm.)
✉ P.O. Box 1564 HMGX, Hamilton HMEX ☎ +1 441 700 9810 ▤ +1 441 292 9492 **E:** iriebermuda@gmail.com **W:** irie.bm **L.P:** Leo Trott
**FM: Irie FM:** 98.3MHz

### HARPER DIGITAL ENTERTAINMENT LTD. (Comm.)
✉ 12 Whale Bay Rd, Southhampton SB03 ☎ +1 441 232 0699 **E:** info@vibe103.com **W:** vibe103.com **L.P:** Zarah Harper **FM: Vibe 103**
**FM:** 103.3MHz

## BHUTAN

**L.T:** UTC +6h — **Pop:** 2 million — **Pr.L:** Dzongha, Sharchhop, Lhotsam (Nepali), English — **E.C:** 230V/50Hz — **ITU:** BTN

### BHUTAN INFOCOMM AND MEDIA AUTHORITY
✉ Olakha, Expressway Road, Thimphu ☎ +975 2 321506 ▤ +975 2 326909 **E:** bicma@bicma.bt **W:** www.bicma.gov.bt
**L.P:** Chmn: Dasho Karma W. Penjore

### BHUTAN BROADCASTING SERVICE (Gov)
✉ P.O. Box 101, Thimphu ☎ +975 2 322866/322533/323071 ▤ +975 2 323073 **W:** bbs.bt **E:** request@bbs.com.bt
**L.P:** Exec. Dir: Sonam Tshong.Tech. MD: Pema Choden, Dir: Dorji Wangchuk. Prgr. Dir: Tashi Dhendup. News Dir: Thinley Tobgye

| SW(kHz) | kW | Location |
|---|---|---|
| 6035 | †100 | Thimpu (r. irr. and running at 30kW) |

| FM(MHz) | Main | R.Dz | FM(MHz) | Main | R.Dz |
|---|---|---|---|---|---|
| Bangtar | 90.0 | 96.0 | Samtse-Saurani | 98.0 | 96.0 |
| Bumthang | 90.0 | 92.0 | Samtse-Tendu | 93.0 | 90.0 |
| Chukha-Dala | 98.0 | 96.0 | Sarpang | 98.0 | 96.0 |
| Chukha-Pachu | 90.0 | 93.0 | Thimphu | 88.1 | 90.0 |
| Dagana | 90.0 | 88.1 | Thimphu | 96.0 | 98.0 |
| Haa | 98.0 | 90.0 | Thonphu | 96.0 | 98.0 |
| Lamsorong | 90.0 | 93.0 | Trashigang | 90.0 | 88.1 |
| Mongar | 90.0 | 88.1 | Trongsa | 93.0 | 96.0 |
| Ngalamdung | 98.0 | 93.0 | Tsirang | 92.0 | 88.1 |
| Panbang | 90.0 | 93.0 | Wangdue | 98.0 | 96.0 |
| Paro | 92.0 | 93.0 | Zhemgang | 88.1 | 90.0 |
| Phuentsholing | 92.0 | - | Zorchen Tranhiyangtse | 98.0 | 96.0 |

**NB: R.Dz =** R. Dzongkha 24h on FM only.

**Main D.Prgr: on SW:** 0000-1300(s/on & s/off varies), **on FM** 24h **English:** Daily 0800-1200. 1800-2100 English Music/Repeat broadcast **N:** Daily: 0800,1100; **English Request Show:**Sun 0910; **UN Radio Prgr:** Thurs 0815; **Live Call In** Mon-Sat 0900 ; **NHK Prog** Mon 1015; **Bhutan This week** Fri 1015; **Sharchhop:** 0000-0400,1200-1400 (N:0100,0200,0300,1200,1300), 2100-2400 Music/ Repeat broadcast; **Lhotsam** (Nepali): Daily 0400-0800, 1400-1600 (N:0400,0700,1400,1500), 1600-1800 Music/Repeat broadcast.
**V.** by QSL card. 15 min prgr details req. Rp. (2 IRCs)

**Other FM Stations**
**Kuzoo FM,** ✉ P.O. Box 419, Thimphu **W:** kuzoo.net **DPrgr:** 24h in English on 105.0MHz and Dzongkha on 104.0MHz – **Radio Valley,** ✉ P.O. Box 224/225, Thimphu **W:** radiovalley.bt **DPrgr:** 0200-1630 in

E on 99.9MHz – **Sherubtse FM** 94.7MHz (including College Campus at 1300-1500)– **Centennial Radio** Thimphu 101.0 MHz – **Radio High** Thimphu 92.7 MHz (alliance with India's Big FM netw.) – **Radio Waves** Thimpu 88.8 MHz (Music Stn) – **Yiga Radio** Thimphu 94.7 MHz 0000-1600 in English and Dzongkha

## BOLIVIA

**L.T:** UTC -4h — **Pop:** 11 million — **Pr.L:** Spanish, Quechua, Aymara — **E.C:** 50Hz, La Paz 115/220V, Santa Cruz 220V — **ITU:** BOL — **Int. dialling code:** +591

### AUTORIDAD DE FISCALIZACIÓN Y CONTROL SOCIAL DE TELECOMUNICACIONES Y TRANSPORTES (ATT)
Dirección Oficina Central: ✉Calle 13 Calacote No. 8260 La Paz ☎2 2772266 ▤2 2772299 **E:** informacions@att.gov.bo **W:**att.gob.bo **L.P:** Superintendente: Lic. Jóse Antonio Morales. Office in Santa Cruz: Calle Prolongación No 29, Edifico Bicentenario Tercer Piso, Santa Cruz de la Sierra ☎3 120587 ▤3 1220978. Office in Cochabamba: Av. Ayacucho No 460, enter Calama y Jordan, edifico Santa Isabel Piso 3, Cochabamba ☎4 458182. Office in Tarija: Calle General Trigo No 474, Edifico Colonial Center Piso 1, Of. 7-8-9, Tarija ☎4 4666484

**NB:** ‡ = inactive, ± = varying freq., † = irregular, RPO – Radioemisoras de los Pueblos Originarios

| MW | kHz | kW | Station, location, h of tr |
|---|---|---|---|
| LP77) | 540 | | Radiodifusora Victoria, La Paz |
| LP03) | 560 | 15 | R. El Mundo, La Paz |
| LP01) | 580 | 10 | R. Panamericana, La Paz: 1000-0300 (Sun 1100-0100) |
| CH01) | 600 | 10 | R. ACLO, Sucre: 0800-0200 |
| LP35) | 600 | 1 | Radioemisoras del Recobro, La Paz |
| SC55) | 600 | | R. Familiar, Santa Cruz |
| LP02) | 620 | 10 | R. San Gabriel, El Alto |
| TA12) | 640 | | R. ACLO, Tarija: 0850-0130 |
| LP11) | 650 | 15 | R. Dif. Integración, El Alto: 0930-0200 |
| LP150) | 660 | | R. Taller de Historia Oral Andina, La Paz |
| SC10) | 660 | 1 | R. ABC, Santa Cruz: 0900-0100 |
| LP147) | 670 | | R. Comunitaria Cadena Provincial, Jihuacuta |
| PO28) | 680 | | R. ACLO, Potosi: 0850-0130 |
| LP27) | 680 | 5 | R. Andina, La Paz: 0900-0300 |
| LP155) | 680 | 10 | R. Jallalla Coca, Chulumani |
| LP116) | 700 | | R. Pacha Kamasa, El Alto (RPO): 0955-0100 (Sat -1805, Sun -1615) |
| PO40) | 710 | | R. Pío XII, Siglo Veinte: 0830-0230 |
| LP06) | 720 | 10 | R. La Cruz del Sur, La Paz: Sat 1300(Sun 1200)-2100 |
| LP05) | 730 | 2.5 | R. Yungas, Chulumani: 0900-1700, 2000-0100 |
| LP151) | 740 | | R. Pueblo de Dios, La Paz |
| LP07) | 760 | 50 | R. Fides, La Paz: 1045-0100 |
| CO02) | 770 | 5 | R. Cosmos, Cochabamba: 1100-0300 |
| LP08) | 800 | 5 | R. Play, La Paz |
| LP10) | 820 | 10 | R. Altiplano Advenir, La Paz: 24h |
| LP75) | 840 | 3 | R. Atipiri, El Alto: 1045-0030 (Sun: 2300) |
| SC03) | 850 | 5 | R. María, Montero: 0900-0100 |
| LP12) | 860 | 10 | R. Nueva America, La Paz |
| CO86) | 860 | | R. FM Colores, Cochabamba |
| LP42) | 880 | | R. Inca, El Alto: -0200 |
| SC39) | 880 | | Rdif. Oriente, Santa Cruz |
| CH31) | 900 | | R. Tomina la Frontera, Villa Tomina |
| TA01) | 900 | 0.25 | R. LV Nacional, Tarija: 0100-2300 |
| LP36) | 900 | 5/0.1 | La Popular, La Paz: 1000-0100 |
| PO39) | 900 | | R. Dios es Amor Universal, Potosi |
| CO33) | †900 | 1 | R. Central Misionera, Cochabamba:1100-0100 |
| CO85) | 920 | | R. Dios es Amor Universal, Cochabamba |
| CH11) | 920 | 3 | R. Encuentro, Sucre: 0900-0100, Sat: 2300-0200, Sun: 1000-2200 |
| LP65) | 920 | 1 | R. San Andres de Topohoco, Topohoco: 0900-0330 |
| LP88) | 920 | | R. Bartolina Sisa, El Alto |
| CH13) | 940 | 1 | R. Chquisaca XXI, Sucre |
| LP13) | 940 | | R. Metropolitana, La Paz: 0930-0430, Sat: 1100-0530 Sun: 1000-0400 |
| SC53) | 940 | | R. Pan de de Vida, Santa Cruz |
| PO02) | 960 | 1 | R. Kollasuyo, Potosí: 1000-0400(Sun -0200) |
| SC04) | 960 | 10 | R. Fe y Alegria, Santa Cruz |
| LP43) | 960 | 1 | R. Huayna Potosí, Milluni |
| CO04) | 980 | 3 | R. Esperanza, Aiquile: 0900-0100(Fri -0400), Sat 1000-0300(Sun -2230) |
| LP14) | 980 | 2.5 | R. Mar, La Paz: 1000-0200 |
| OR41) | 980 | | R.dif. Concordia, Oruro |
| CH26) | 980 | | R. La Bohemia, Sucre |
| PO30) | 990 | | R. Municipal de Colcha "K" |
| CO84) | 1000 | | FM Unica, Cochabamba |

| MW | kHz | kW | Station, location, h of tr |
|---|---|---|---|
| SC33) | 1000 | 1 | Rdif. del Oriente, Santa Cruz: 0930-0400, Sat: 0900-0330, Sun: 1130-0430 |
| LP115) | 1000 | | R. LV del Arrebatamiento, Guaqui |
| LP44) | 1000 | 1 | R. Taypi, La Paz: 1000-0400 |
| OR03) | 1010 | 10 | R. Bahá'í de Bolivia, Oruro |
| LP15) | 1020 | 10 | R. Illimani - R. Patria Nueva, La Paz: 0900-0400 |
| CO57) | 1020 | | R. Illimani - R. Patria Nueva, Cochabamba |
| CO59) | 1020 | | R. Illimani - R. Patria Nueva, Valle Alto |
| CO60) | 1020 | | R. Illimani - R. Patria Nueva. Tarata |
| CO61) | 1020 | | R. Illimani - R. Patria Nueva, Chapare |
| CO70) | 1020 | | R. Illimani - R. Patria Nueva, Colomi |
| CO87) | 1020 | | R. Illimani - R. Patria Nueva, Tiraque |
| BE21) | 1020 | | R. Illimani - R. Patria Nueva, Trinidad |
| BE22) | 1020 | | R. Illimani - R. Patria Nueva, San Borja |
| BE24) | 1020 | | R. Illimani - R. Patria Nueva, Riberalta |
| PA10) | 1020 | | R. Illimani - R. Patria Nueva, Cobija |
| PO07) | 1020 | | R. Illimani - R. Patria Nueva, Potosi |
| PO08 | 1020 | | R. Illimani - R. Patria Nueva, Catavi |
| PO32) | 1020 | | R. Illimani - R. Patria Nueva, Unica |
| PO33) | 1020 | | R. Illimani - R. Patria Nueva, Villazon |
| PO34) | 1020 | | R. Illimani - R. Patria Nueva, Llica |
| PO35) | 1020 | | R. Illimani - R. Patria Nueva, Tupiza |
| PO35) | 1020 | | R. Illimani - R. Patria Nueva, Uyuni |
| SC40) | 1020 | | R. Illimani - R. Patria Nueva, Santa Cruz |
| SC41) | 1020 | | R. Illimani - R. Patria Nueva, Vallegrande |
| SC42) | 1020 | | R. Illimani - R. Patria Nueva, Camiri |
| SC43) | 1020 | | R. Illimani - R. Patria Nueva, Yapacani |
| SC56 | 1020 | | R. Illimani - R. Patria Nueva, Puerto Quijarro |
| CO62) | 1020 | | R. Illimani - R. Patria Nueva, Kami |
| CO68) | 1020 | | R. Illimani - R. Patria Nueva, Independencia |
| CH21) | 1020 | | R. Illimani - R. Patria Nueva, Sucre |
| CH32) | 1020 | | R. Illimani - R. Patria Nueva, Sopachuy |
| CH35) | 1020 | | R. Illimani - R. Patria Nueva, Azurduy |
| CH36) | 1020 | | R. Illimani - R. Patria Nueva, Machareti |
| TA13) | 1020 | | R. Illimani - R. Patria Nueva, Tarija |
| TA14) | 1020 | | R. Illimani - R. Patria Nueva, Bermejo |
| TA16) | 1020 | | R. Illimani - R. Patria Nueva, Villamontes |
| TA18) | 1020 | | R. Illimani - R. Patria Nueva, Yacuiba |
| TA19) | 1020 | | R. Illimani - R. Patria Nueva, Entre Rios |
| OR29) | 1020 | | R. Illimani - R. Patria Nueva, Oruro |
| OR36) | 1020 | | R. Illimani - R. Patria Nueva, Caracolla |
| OR37) | 1020 | | R. Illimani - R. Patria Nueva, Huanuni |
| OR44) | 1020 | | R. Illimani - R. Patria Nueva, Challapata |
| LP89) | 1020 | | R. Illimani - R. Patria Nueva, Ichoca-Quime |
| LP90) | 1020 | | R. Illimani - R. Patria Nueva, Pucarani |
| LP91) | 1020 | | R. Illimani - R. Patria Nueva, Copacabana |
| LP92) | 1020 | | R. Illimani - R. Patria Nueva, Caranavi |
| LP93) | 1020 | | R. Illimani - R. Patria Nueva, Chulumani |
| LP94) | 1020 | | R. Illimani - R. Patria Nueva, Guaqui |
| LP126) | 1020 | | R. Illimani - R. Patria Nueva, Topohoco |
| LP127) | 1020 | | R. Illimani - R. Patria Nueva, Vilaque |
| LP128) | 1020 | | R. Illimani - R. Patria Nueva, Taraco |
| LP129) | 1020 | | R. Illimani - R. Patria Nueva, Tapichullo |
| LP130) | 1020 | | R. Illimani - R. Patria Nueva, Tiawanaku |
| LP132) | 1020 | | R. Illimani - R. Patria Nueva, Qhurpa |
| LP133) | 1020 | | R. Illimani - R. Patria Nueva, La Asunta |
| LP135) | 1020 | | R. Illimani - R. Patria Nueva, Escoma |
| LP136) | 1020 | | R. Illimani - R. Patria Nueva, Desaguadero |
| LP140) | 1020 | | R. Illimani - R. Patria Nueva, Coro Coro |
| CH19) | 1030 | | R. Mojocoya AM (RPO), Mojocoya:1000-0200 |
| LP156) | 1030 | | R. Illimani - R. Patria Nueva, Coripata |
| LP157) | 1030 | | R. Illimani - R. Patria Nueva, Coroico |
| OR26) | 1030 | 3 | R. de los Pueblos Originarios (RPO) , Orinaca |
| PO)41 | 1030 | | R. Illimani - R. Patria Nueva, San Pablo de Lipez |
| CO48) | 1030 | 3 | R. Independencia (RPO), Independencia |
| CO51) | 1030 | | R. 24 de Junio (RPO) Totora |
| BE20) | 1030 | 3 | R. Comunitaria Riberalte (RPO), Riberalta |
| CH41) | 1030 | | R. Illimani – R.Patria Nueva, Camargo |
| CH18 | 1040 | | R. 12 de Marzo (RPO), Tarabuco |
| SC38) | 1040 | | R. San Julián (RPO), San Julián |
| LP45) | 1040 | 1 | R. Bolivianíssima, La Paz |
| OR14) | 1040 | 0.25 | R. Atlántida, La Paz: 1100-2400 |
| CH33) | 1050 | | R. Comunitaria, Huacaya |
| OR27) | 1050 | 3 | R. Sabaya (RPO) Sabaya |
| PO26) | 1050 | | R. Caiza D (RPO), Caiza D |
| LP95) | 1060 | | R. Qhana Amazonía, Caranavi |
| OR01) | 1060 | 1.5 | R. Noticias, Oruro: 1000-2200, 0200-0600 |
| CH02) | 1060 | 1 | R. Dif. Colosal, Sucre: 0900-0300 |
| CH30) | 1080 | | R. Comunitaria, Sopachuy |
| CH34) | 1080 | | R. Comunitaria, Juana Azurduy |
| CH40) | 1080 | | R. Comunitaria Carama, Sucre |
| LP158) | 1080 | | R. Comunitario Carama, Machareti |

| MW | kHz | kW | Station, location, h of tr |
|---|---|---|---|
| LP159) | 1080 | | R. Espiritu Santo, La Paz |
| LP110) | 1090 | | R. Comunitaria Pachakuti, Achocalla |
| OR06) | 1100 | 1 | R. Universidad de Oruro: 1100(Sun 1200)-2300 |
| LP29) | 1100 | | R. Chaka, Pucarani: 0900-1300, 2030-0130 |
| LP153) | 1100 | | Universal R. Concienia, El Alto |
| CO76) | 1110 | | R. Raqaypampa (RPO), Raqaypampa |
| CO53) | 1120 | | R. El Porvenir, Tiquipaya |
| LP96) | 1120 | | R. Celestial el Milagro, El Alto |
| LP97) | 1120 | | R. Wiñay Khantatt, Tiawuanaku |
| LP124) | 1120 | | R. Illimani - R. Patria Nueva, Huarina |
| SC57) | 1130 | | R. Illimani - R. Patria Nueva, Montero |
| CO69) | 1140 | | R. San Isidro, Colomi |
| LP23) | 1140 | | R. Sol Poder de Dios, La Paz: 0930-0300 |
| LP23) | 1140 | | R. Sol Poder de Dios, Huancane: 0930-0300 |
| LP50) | 1150 | 0.3 | R. Guaqui, Puerto de Guaqui |
| SC11) | 1160 | 5 | R. Centenario "La Nueva", Sta. Cruz |
| CO08) | 1160 | 3/1 | R. RTC Deportiva, Cochabamba: 10454-2330 |
| CH03) | 1160 | 1 | R. Nuevo Mundo, Sucre: 1000-0300 |
| LP33) | 1160 | 10 | R. Continental, La Paz: 0930-2400 |
| LP18) | 1180 | 1 | R. Ingavi, Viacha: 1000-0200 (Sun 1100-2400) |
| OR40) | 1180 | | R. Sajama Estero, Oruro |
| LP122) | 1190 | | R. Comunitaria, Guaqui |
| LP100) | 1200 | | Cuarzo Comunicaciones, La Paz |
| SC12) | 1200 | 5 | R. Oriental, Santa Cruz |
| CO10) | 1200 | 0.25 | R. 24 de Noviembre, Valle Alto |
| OR31) | 1200 | | R. Capital, Oruro |
| CO80) | 1220 | | R. Progreso La Luz del Alba, Cochabamba |
| LP19) | 1220 | 1 | R. Nueva Splendid, La Paz: 0800-0200 |
| LP134) | 1220 | | R. La Asunta, Asunta |
| LP143) | 1220 | | R. La Voz Cristiana, Achacachi |
| OR09) | 1220 | 1 | R. Batallión Topátar, Oruro 1055-0100 |
| TA03) | 1240 | 2 | R. Los Andes, Tarija: 1000-2200 |
| LP131) | 1240 | | R. Nueva Generación, Qhurpa |
| LP154) | 1240 | | R. Lider Zaráte Willka, La Paz |
| CH04) | 1250 | 2.5 | R. La Plata, Sucre: 1430-2400 |
| LP51) | 1250 | | Rdif. Achocalla, Achocalla |
| LP146) | 1250 | | R. Comunitaria Compi, Capilaya |
| PO29) | 1250 | | R. Indoamerica, Potosi |
| SC52) | 1250 | | R. Amboro, Santa Cruz |
| SC54) | 1250 | | R. Sararenda, Camiri |
| CO54) | 1260 | | R. LV de la Esperanza, Quillacollo |
| LP137) | 1260 | | R. SERVIR, Caranavi |
| LP160) | 1260 | | Red de Com. Nueva Imagen Para Bolivia |
| OR20) | 1260 | 10 | R. Nacional de Huanuni, Hunanuni: 0930-0200, Sat 1100-1800(Sun -1600) |
| TA21) | 1280 | | R. Dios es Amor Universal, Tarija |
| CO65) | 1280 | | R. Comunitaria del Sur, Cochabamba |
| LP68) | 1280 | | R. Comunitaria Ondas del Titicaca, Huarina |
| LP142) | 1280 | | R. Altar de Dios, Achacachi |
| TA17) | 1280 | | R. Fronera, Yacuiba |
| LP148) | 1290 | | R. Comunitaria Alaxpacha, Canaviri |
| OR12) | 1290 | 1 | Radiodifusoras Minería, Oruro |
| PO31) | 1290 | | R. Tomas Katari de America, Ocuri |
| CH05) | 1300 | 2.5 | R. Loyola, Sucre: 1000-2400, Sun 1015-0200 |
| CO72) | 1300 | | R. San Simón, Cochabamba |
| SC16) | 1300 | 1 | R. Fuerzas Armadas, Sta. Cruz |
| LP23) | 1300 | 15/6 | R. Sol Poder de Diós, El Alto: 0930-0300 |
| BE18) | 1300 | 5 | R. Bandera Beniana, Trinidad |
| OR39) | 1300 | | Sistem de Comuncacion "Perez", Oruro |
| CO14) | 1320 | 10 | R. San Rafael, Cochabamba: 0900-0200 |
| CH25) | 1320 | | R. Sucre, Sucre |
| LP53) | 1320 | | R. Comunitaria Tawantinsuyo, Taraco |
| LP111) | 1320 | | R. Em. Septima Voz, Achocalla |
| LP121) | 1320 | 3 | R. Comunitaria La Lumbrera, La Paz |
| CO79) | 1340 | | TV Sist. de Comunicacione Mundial, Cochabama |
| LP39) | 1340 | 0.5 | R. Copacabana, Copacabana: 1000(Sun 1100)-0200 |
| LP40) | 1340 | 0.5 | R. Comunitaria Jach'a Suyu, Corocoro: 1000-1630, 2000-0100 |
| LP145) | 1340 | | R. Comunitaria La Voz de Valle, Sococoni |
| LP152) | 1340 | | R. La Mision, La Paz |
| CH06) | 1350 | | R. America, Sucre: 1000-0400 |
| LP113) | 1350 | | R. Comunitario Inti, Contorno/Viacha |
| LP123) | 1350 | | R. Llacxa, Achocalla |
| SC49) | 1350 | | R. TV Salesiana, Yapacani |
| CO15) | ±1355 | 0.25 | R. Armonía, La Paz (n.f.: 1350) |
| CO05) | 1360 | 2.5 | R. Cochabamba "CBA", Cochabamba: 1030-0200 |
| PO37) | 1360 | | R. La Cruz del Sur, Potosi |
| SC47) | 1360 | | R. 24 de Septiembre, Santa Cruz |
| CO16) | 1370 | 0.15 | R. Libertad, Cliza |
| OR32) | 1370 | | R. Coral, Oruro |
| CH22) | 1380 | | R. Global, Sucre |
| LP104) | 1380 | | R. Maria, La Paz |

| MW | kHz | kW | Station, location, h of tr |
|---|---|---|---|
| LP141) | 1380 | | R. TV Minera Matilde, Carabuco |
| LP161) | 1380 | | R. Em. Tunupa, Tianawaku |
| LP162) | 1380 | | LV del Espiritu Santo, El Alto |
| SC51) | 1380 | | R. Maria, Santa Cruz |
| CO34) | 1380 | 1.5 | R. Bandera Tricolor, Cochabamba: 1100-0300 |
| OR33) | 1380 | | R. Horizontes, Huanuni |
| TA06) | 1380 | 0.5 | R. Luis de Fuentes, Tarija: 0930-0400 |
| CO50) | 1390 | | R. Andina (RPO), Pongo Khasa |
| CH20) | 1400 | | R. Antena 2000, Sucre |
| LP25) | ‡1400 | 5 | R. Nacional de Bolivia, La Paz: 0900-0200 |
| OR38) | 1410 | 0.25 | R. Atlantida, Oruro |
| LP105) | 1420 | | R. Omasuyos Andina, Achacachi |
| LP114) | 1420 | | R. Creo en Milagros, Murillo |
| TA05) | 1420 | 1.5 | R. Guadalquivir, Tarija: 0900-0100 |
| CO18) | 1420 | 1 | R. Centro, Cochabamba: 1030-2300 (Sun 1100-0000) |
| CH15) | 1420 | 1 | R. Real Audiencia, Sucre: 0900-0200 |
| SC50) | 1420 | | R. Comunitaria, José Ballivian |
| SC58) | ‡1420 | | R. Luz del Mundo, Santa Cruz (F.Pl.) |
| CH39) | 1440 | | Sistema de Comunicaciones Horizontes, Sucre |
| LP26) | 1440 | | R. Batallón Colorados, La Paz: 1000-0400(Sun 1100-) |
| LP39) | 1440 | | R. Comunitaria Eco Saywani, Carabuco |
| SC21) | 1440 | 2/1 | R. Yaguary, Vallegrande: 1000- 0200 |
| CO42) | ‡1440 | 0.25 | R. Bolivia, Cochabamba |
| CO74) | 1440 | | LV de Junio (RPO), Tiraque |
| BE02) | 1440 | | R. Dif. Tropico, Trinidad |
| CO39) | 1450 | 0.5 | R. Magnal, Capinota |
| OR13) | 1450 | 1 | R. Em. Bolivia, Oruro |
| LP106) | 1460 | | R. Plenitud de Vida, El Alto |
| LP138) | 1460 | | R. Jiwasa, Carabuco |
| CO78) | 1460 | | R. Canal de Television Quillacollo |
| CH29) | 1470 | 1 | R. Integración, Padilla |
| LP109) | 1470 | | R. Em. Ayni, Corapata |
| CH24) | 1480 | | R. Charcas-Mundial, Sucre |
| LP108) | 1480 | | LV de los Andes, Carabuco |
| PO12) | 1480 | 0.1 | R. Cadena Sur, Potosi |
| CO32) | 1480 | 1/0.8 | R. Chiwalakii, Vacas: 0900-1400, 2100-0100 |
| CO40) | 1480 | | R. Domingo Savio, Independencia |
| CO66) | 1480 | | R. Bendita Trinidad y Espiritu Santo, Cochabamba |
| PA09) | 1480 | | R. Bendita Trinidad y Espiritu Santo, Cobija |
| SC48) | 1480 | | R. Bendita Trinidad y Espiritu Santo, Santa Cruz |
| LP58) | 1480 | | R. Amor de Diós, El Alto |
| LP107) | 1480 | | R. Comunitaria Waley, Desaguadero |
| OR15) | 1490 | 1 | R. San José, San José, Oruro |
| CO77) | 1500 | | R. Litoral, Cochabamba |
| LP101) | 1500 | 2 | R. Comunitaria Tawantinsuyo, Laja: 0800-0100 |
| SC25) | 1500 | 1 | R. Sagrado Corazón, Mineros |
| TA15) | 1500 | | R. Universidad Juan Misael Saracho, Villamontes |
| LP144) | 1510 | | R. Wiñay Jatha, El Alto |
| CH38) | 1520 | | R. Universidad Juan Misael Saracho, Sucre |
| CO64) | 1520 | 1 | R. la Chiwana, Cochabamba |
| CO73) | 1520 | | R. Rural, Tarata |
| LP59) | 1520 | | R. La Luz del Tiempo, El Alto |
| LP120) | 1520 | | R. San Pedro, Tiawuanaku |
| CO67) | 1530 | | R. Salesiana, Kami |
| PO10) | 1530 | 0.25 | R. Litoral, Llica |
| CH37) | 1540 | | R. Comunitaria Rio Chico, Sucre |
| LP34) | 1540 | 0.8 | R. Sariri, Escoma: 1000-1300, 2200-0200 |
| LP112) | 1540 | | R. Comunitario Tutuka, Vilaque |
| LP67) | 1540 | | R. Bendita Trinidad y Espiritu Santo, El Alto |
| LP28) | 1550 | 10 | R. Caranavi, Caranavi: 0930-1800, 2200-0200 |
| LP149) | 1560 | 15 | R. Luz del Mundo, La Paz |
| OR19) | 1560 | 1 | R. Occidental, Oruro |
| CO27) | 1560 | 0.5 | R. Urkupiña, Quillacollo: 1000-2400 |
| BE23) | 1570 | | R. Pedro Ignacio Muiba |
| CH28) | 1580 | | R. Contacto, Sucre: 0830-2300, Sat/Sun.: 1800 |
| CO75) | 1580 | | LV del Valle, Valle Alto |
| OR35) | 1580 | | R. Comunitaria Jacinto Rodrìguez, Caracolla |
| SC29) | 1580 | 1 | R. Adonai, Santa Cruz: 1000-0300 |
| LP62) | 1580 | | R. El Fuego del Espíritu Santo, El Alto: 1000-2400 |
| TA07) | 1580 | 3 | R. Bermejo, Bermejo |
| TA20) | 1580 | | R. Magazine Tarija, Tarija |
| CO24) | 1590 | 1 | R. Wayana Songo, Pongo K´asa |
| LP61) | 1590 | | R. Kollasuyo Marka, Tiawanaku |
| CO28) | 1600 | 0.5 | R. P.C.A., Valle Alto |
| CO88) | 1600 | | LV del Campesino, Cochabamba |

| SW | kHz | kW | Station, location, h of tr |
|---|---|---|---|
| CO29) | 3310 | 10 | R. Mosoj Chaski, Cochabamba: 0900-1300, 2100-0100 |
| SC30) | †5580 | 10 | R. San José, San José de Chiquitos: 1100-1700, 2100-0200± |
| PO15) | 5935 | | R. Yura, Yura |
| PO40) | ±5952 | 5 | R. Pío XII, Siglo Veinte: (n. 5955) |

| SW | kHz | kW | Station, location, h of tr |
|---|---|---|---|
| LP15) | 6025 | 10 | Red Patria Nueva, La Paz: 0930-0300 |
| LP01) | ±6105 | 10 | R. Panamericana, La Paz |
| SC04) | 6135 | 10 | R. Santa Cruz, Santa Cruz: 1100-0200 |

**Addresses and other information:**

**NB:** Whenever listed, Casilla addresses should preferably be used for mailing purposes.

**ERBOL** (Educación Radiofónica de Bolivia), Calle Ballivián 1323, 4° piso (Cas. 5946), La Paz ☎ 2 2324606, 232 4768 📠 2 2391985 **W:** erbol. combo – Pte.: Jorge Trias S.J. Secr. Ejecutivo: Jorge Aliaga Murillo

**UNESBO** (Unión de Emisoras Sindicales de Bolivia), Yanacocha 689, La Paz ☎1 2341881 Pte: Jorge Bustillo Burgos

**BE00 (BENI)**

**BE02)** Avenida Panamericana Carretera a Santa Crtuz km 2½ - EPARU, Trinidad ☎3 4635300 **W:** Facebook: Radio Tropico **E:** radiodifusorastropico@yahoo.com - **FM:** 92.2 MHz – **BE06)** Sucre 320, Guayaramerín – **BE09)** Av Selim Majuli ( Correo Central), San Borja, Pcia BalliviáN – **BE12)** Calle Nicanor Gonzalo Salvatierra 249, Riberalta - **FM:** 91.1MHz – **BE13)** Ballivián s/n, San Ignacio de Moxos – **BE14)** Cas 395, Guayaramerín – **BE15)** Calle Beni s/n, Guayaramerín – **BE16)** Plaza Fr Martín Baltasar de Espinosa, Santa Ana del Yacuma – **BE18)** Calle Santa Cruz esq Mamoré s/n, Trinidad – **BE19)** Avenida Primero de Mayo esquina Loreto, Guayaramerin **E:** ninafelima@hotmail.com – **BE20)** Riberalta, Prov Vaca Diez – **BE21)** Trinidad – **BE22)** San Borja – **BE23)** Calle Isiboro esquina Machupo, Trinidad **W:** apcbolivia.org/Medios/muiba.aspx - **FM:** 89.5 MHz – **BE24)** Riberalta

**CH00 (CHUQUISACA)**

**CH01)** Guillermo Loayza N° 274 esq Vicente Donso (Zona Mercado Campesino, (Cas 538), Sucre ☎4 6441665 Prgrs in **Quechua** except **Spanish** 1330-2030 0900-0200 **W:** aclo.org.bo **E:** aclochuquisaca@aclo.org.bo – **FM:** 101.5 MHz – **CH02)** Calle San Alberto N° 19 (Cas 335), Sucre ☎4 6442888 📠4 6444433 **W:** colosal.com.bo **E:** fundacionradiotv@colosal.com.bo - **FM:** 90.7MHz – **CH03)** Junin N° 841 (Cas 25), Sucre **W:** radiolaplata.com.bo/ **E:** info@laplata.com. bo- **FM:** 99.7MHz – **CH05)** Calle Ayacucho 161, Sucre ☎4 6453677 📠4 6442555 **E:** loyola@radiofides.com - **FM:** 98.3MHz "Onda Joven" – **CH06)** Calle Guillermo Loayza 377, Mercado Campesino, Sucre ☎4 46446574 📠4 46444445 – **W:** radioamericatk.com.bo **E:** info@radioamericatk.com.bo – **FM:** 97.5 MHz – **CH09)** Alcaldía Municipal, Padilla **CH11)** Calle Loa No 41, Sucre ☎6 441300 **W:** encuentroradio. com – **FM:** 95.9MHz – **CH13)** Calle Kantuta 3 Ed. Canal 15, Barrio Ferroviario, Zona San Matias, Sucre ☎6 461157 📠6 458321 **E:** pulsartv@bolivia.com– **CH15)** Calle Avarioa 537, Sucre – **CH16)** Sucre – **CH17)** Sucre – **CH18)** Comunidad de Tarabco, Prov Yamparáez – **CH19)** Comunida de Mojocoya, Prov Zudáñez – **CH20)** Calle Lima Pampa 72, Esq. Elidora Ayllón, Sucre ☎6 440 606 **E:** contacto@radioantena2000.com - **FM:** 89.1 MHz – **CH21)** Sucre – **CH22)** Barrio Petrolero, Sucre ☎6 442900 **W:** radioglobalbolivia.com - **FM:** 106.7 MHz – **CH23)** Calle Eduardo Berdecio 568, Sucre. **W:** radiohorizonte. boliviastreaming.com - **FM:** 91.1 MHz – **CH24)** Calle Eduardo Berdecio N° 522, Sucre ☎6 461 112 **W:** facebook.com - Radio Charcas-Mundial **E:** radiocharcasam1480@hotmail.com - **FM:** 96.4 MHz – **CH25)** Sucre **W:** radiosucre1320.com – **FM:** 105.9 MHz – **CH26)** Sucre – **CH28)** Calle Bustillos N° 322, Sucre ☎4 6435205 **W:** radiocontactosucre.com **E:** direccion@radiocontactosucre.com - **FM:** 98.5 MHz – **CH29)** Sucre – **CH30)** Sopachuy – **CH31)** Villa Tomina – **CH32)** Sopachuy – **CO33)** Huacaya – **CH34)** Azurduy – **CH35)** Azurduy – **CH36)** Machareti – **CH37)** Sucre – **CH39)** Sucre – **CH40)** Sucre – **CH41)** Camargo

**CO00 (COCHABAMBA)**

**CO02)** Av Heroinas O-0467, Centro Nor Oeste, (Cas 1092), Cochabamba ☎4 4250422 📠4 4251173 **Quechua:** 0930-1030, 0000-0200 1100-0300 - **FM:** 95.1MHz "Fides" – **CO04)** Calle Loa Final s/n, Ivirganzama, (Cas 5716), Cochabamba. ☎4 4343044 **W:** Facebook: R.Esperanza **E:** radioesperanza.aiquile@gmail.com **Quechua:** 8 hours daily - **FM:** 100.3MHz – **CO05)** Calle 25 de Mayo 230 entre Bolívar y Sucre (Cas 5500), Cochabamba ☎4 4251504 📠4 4251561 **E:** ragarobol@yahoo. es - **FM:** 104.3MHz "Gaviota" – **CO07)** Cochabamba – **CO08)** Lanza esq Ecuador N-0261 (Cas 846), Cochabamba ☎4 4257289 📠4 4241414 **W:** web.supernet.com.bo/radiortc **E:** radiortc@yahoo.com – **CO10)** Valle Alto – **CO14)** Calle Calama E-0315 (Cas 546), Cochabamba ☎4 4256563 📠4 250 522 **Quechua/Aymara:** 0900-0200 - **FM:** 92.1MHz – **CO15)** Calle 6 de Agosto 11, Cliza – **CO16)** Calle Santa Cruz 4, Cliza – **CO18)** Calle Ecuador casi Avenida Ayacucho No 115 (Cas 839), Cochabamba ☎4 4251434 **W:** grupocentro.com.bo **E:** contactos@grupocentro.com.bo - **FM:** 96.3 & 106.7 MHz – **CO24)** Cas 1151, Cochabamba 📠4 8119295 **W:** sdb.bo **E:** japaricio@sdb.bo – **CO27)** A. Suarez Miranda final s/n, Zona Norte, Cochabamba ☎4 260 661 **E:** radioam1560@hotmail.com – **CO28)** Ayacucho 138, Punata – **CO29)** Calle Abaroa S-0254 (Cas 4493), Cochabamba **E:** rmchaski@bo.net ☎4 4220651 📠4 4251041 – **CO32)** Misuk'ani (Cas 80), Vacas ☎4

223089 ▤4 255390 **E:** chiwalak@entelnet.bo Prgrs mainly in **Quechua** 0900-1400, 2100-0100 – **CO33)** Av Petrolera Km 0.5, Cochabamba – **CO34)** Av. Oquendo No 560 entre Paccieri y Federeico Blanco (Cas 3655), Zona Muyurina, Cochabamba ☎4 520202 **E:** latripple999@ yahoo.com **Quechua:** 1000-1200 – FM: 99.9MHz "La Triple" – **CO39)** Augusto Larrain, Capinota. – **CO40)** Independencia, Prov. Ayopaya (Av. Papa Paulo No 0982, Muyurina, Cochabamba) **W:** radiosavio. galeon.com **E:** radiosavio@hotmail.com - **FM:** 98.1 MHz – **CO42)** Calle Calama 0-0135, Cochabamba – **CO43)** Calle Junín 309, Tiraque, Prov Arani – **CO48)** Independencia – **CO50)** Calle Tumusla esquina Ecuador No 310, Plazuela Cobija, area Oeste (Cas. 1986) Cochabamba ☎4 589366 ▤4 589377 **W:** ceprabolivia.org **E:** cepra@supernet.com. bo - **FM:** 101.1 MHz – **CO51)** Totora, Prov Carrasco – **CO53)** Calle Pablo Jaimes 188, Tiquipaya, Prov Quillacollo - **FM:** 90.5MHz – **CO54)** Calle Montenegro N° 234 Zona: Villa Paraiso, Cochabamba ☎4 448647– **CO57)** Cochabamba – **CO59)** Valle Alto – **CO60)** Tarata – **CO61)** Chapare – **CO62)** Kami – **CO64)** Junin casi Aroma, Edif. De la Federacion de Campesinos - 5° piso, Cochabamba ☎4 4584389 **W:** radiolachiwana.org **E:** radiolachiwana@gmail.com - **FM:** 107.9 MHz – **CO65)** Heroinas esquina 16 de Julio, Cochabamba ☎4 661203 **W:** http//radiocomunitariadelsur.com **E:** info@radiocomunitariadelsur. com – **CO66)** Av. Circunbalacion, Calle Atahuallpa, Cochabamba ☎7 9361282 **FB:** - Radio Bendita Trinidad Bolivia – **CO67)** Kami – **CO68)** Independencia – **CO69)** Colomi – **CO70)** Colomi – **CO72)** Campus Universitaria, Prolongaión Jordán s/n, Cochabamba - **FM:** 104.7 MHz – **CO73)** Tarata – **CO74)** Tiraque – **CO75)** Valle Alto – **CO76)** Raqay Pampa – **CO77)** Cochabamba – **CO78)** Cochabamba – **CO79)** Cochabamba – **CO80)** Cochabamba – **CO84)** Cochabamba – **CO85)** Cochabamba – **CO86)** Cochabamba – **CO87)** Tiraque – **CO88)** Cochabamba

## LP00 (LA PAZ)

**LP01)** Edificio 16 de Julio, P.9, Of 902, El Prado, La Paz **W:** panamericana-bolivia.com **E:** pana@panamericana.bo ☎2 2334271 **N:** «El Panamericano» relayed by many stns – **LP02)** Pza de la Cruz N° 100 – Av.Bolivia, Comunidad Charapaqui Colpani Villa Adela, (C.P. 4792) El Alto ☎2 2832544 **W:** radiosangabriel.org.bo **E:** info@radiosangabriel. org.bo Prgrs in **Aymara** exc Sp & Quechua 1400-1430, Sat 2100-2130 – **LP03)** Av. La Bandera No 1462, V.Pabón, La Paz – **LP05)** Calle Nuñez del Prado s/n esquina Calle Santa Cruz, Chulumani (Cas 4535, La Paz) ☎2 896031 **W:** radioyungas.com **E:** radio.yungas@hotmail.com - **FM:** 92.1MHz – **LP06)** Calle Nicaragua 1759(Cas 1408), La Paz ☎2 220541 ▤2 243337 **W:** radiocruzdelsur.com **E:** contactos@ radiocruzdelsur.com – **LP07)** Calle Jenaro Sanjinés 799, Centro (Cas 9143), La Paz ☎2 406363 ▤2 406332 **W:** radiofides.com **E:** sistemas@ radiofides.com – **N:** «La hora del país», relayed by many stns, at 1100, 1630, 2230, 0130 – **LP08)** Calle 24 de Calacoto, Edif. TorreCesur, Piso 4 Of 402,La Paz ☎2 790743 ▤2 770292 **W:** radioplaybolivia.com **E:** info@radioplaybolivia.com – **LP10)** Calle Abdon Saavedra N° 2110 casi esquina Fernando Guachalla, (Cas 8631), Sopocachi) La Paz ☎2 426742 redadvenir.org/proyectos/radio-altiplano – **LP11)** Calle 2 No 95 P.3 entre Av. 6 de Marzo y Jorge Carrasco, Ceja, El Alto (Cas. 312472, La Paz) ☎2 810048 ▤2 810048 **W:** radiointegracion.com **E:** integracionam@yahoo.es **Aymara:** 0830-1200 0900-0130 – **LP12)** Calle Abdón Saavedra 1990 (or Cas 2431), La Paz ☎2 2356622 – **LP13)** Juan de la Riva 1527 (Cas 8704), Zona Central, La Paz ☎2 203339 **W:** rtpbolivia.com.bo **E:** contactosrtp@rtpbolivia.com.bo – **LP14)** Calle Jenaro Sanjinés 799 esqquina Calle Sucre, Centro, La Paz ☎2 406 590 ▤2 406740 **E:** editor@radiofides.com – **LP15)** Av Camacho 1485, Edificio Ministerio Informaciones P 6, La Paz ☎2 2200282 ▤2 200390 **W:** patrianueva.bo – **LP18)** Calle General Lanza 93, Viacha, Provincia Ingavi – **LP19)** Calle Máx paredes, Zona Garita de Lima N° 408. 1er Piso, La Paz. ☎2 2452422 Prgr. in Aymara 0800-0200 **W:** cercacomunicaciones.com **E:** radiosplendid@ cercacomunicaciones. com – **LP23)** Calle Calama s/n entre Humahuca y Montenegro, Zona Norte, La Paz ☎2 286983 - **FM:** 90.1 MHz – **LP25)** Av. Tumusla No 639, 2° piso (or Cas 2532), Zona 14 de Septiembre, La Paz. ☎2 453945 ▤2 454 211 **W:** lafolklorisima1035.com.ar - **FM:** 103.5/107.7 MHz – **LP26)** Av. Saavedra del Ejército, Zona Miraflores, La Paz ☎2 149439 **Aymara:** 1100-1200 **W:** radiobatalloncolorados.com – **LP27)** Calle Francisco de Chirino No 1080, Miraflores (Cas. 12413), La Paz– **LP28)** Liga de Oración en Misión Mundial, Av Civica S/n, Caranavi, (Cas. 296, La Paz) ☎2 ▤2 823 2239 **W:** Facebook: Radio Television Caranavi **E:** rtc@hotmail.com - **FM:** 92.1 MHz – **LP29)** Casilla 204, Colegio Don Bosco, Pucarani Prgrs mainly in **Aymara**, but also in Spanish 0900-1300, 2030-0130 **W:** Facebook – **LP33)** Av República 870 Esq. Quintanilla Zuazo, Zona Pura Pura, La Paz ☎2 463470 – **LP34)** Colegio Don Bosco, Parroquia Escoma, Escoma ( Cas 204, La Paz) **E:** escoma@ caoba.entelnet.bo ☎▤2 135336 - **FM:** 104.7MHz – **LP35)** Calle Murillo 1379, La Paz ☎2 350588 – **LP36)** Calle Panama N° 1153 Shopping Miraflores Pido 4 Oficina 1, Zona Miraflores sobre la Plaza Uyuni, La Paz ☎2 222368 **W:** radiogentebolivia.com **E:**

sistemapopular@hotmail.com - **FM:** 88.9 MHz – **LP39)** Ca Gral. Hugo Ballivián No 11 Copacabana, Prov. Manco Capac ☎2 341920 **W:** apcbolivia.org/Medios/copacabana.aspx - **FM:** 95.7 MHz – **LP40)** Plaza 15 de Agosto, Corocoro, Prov Pacajes **E:** tricolor-jachasuyu@hotmail. com ☎2 830192 Prgr In **Aymara & Sp** 1000-1630, 2000-0100 – **LP42)** Av. Patriótica # 3048 entre c.Topáter y Héroes del Acre Z. Bolívar Municipal P.1, El Alto ☎▤2 821675 – **LP43)** Avenida del Ejercito No 30, Viacha ☎2 800208 – **FM:** 101.9 MHz – **LP44)** Ca Policarpio Eyzaguirre N° 1156 entre Padre L. Bertonio y Calatayod, Zona Callampaya (Cementerio), La Paz ☎2 2461224 ▤2455319 **W:** radiotaypi.com **E:** radio-taypi@hotmail.com – **LP45)** Calle Viacha # 360 e/ Avenida Manco Kapac y Av. América, Barrio Churubamba, La Paz– **LP46)** Comunidad Contorno Letania, Camino a Collana 30, Letania, Prov Ingavi – **LP47)** Av Manco Kapac 50, Tiawanaku, Prov Ingavi – **LP50)** Calle Costa Rica No 1229, Miraflores, La Paz ☎2 220401 – **LP51)** Av. Franco Valle No 87, Achocalla, Prov. de Murillo – **LP53)** Plaza 16 de Julio s/n, Cantón Taraco, Taraco ☎8 114157 - **FM:** 105.3 MHz – **LP54)** Calle Noel Kempf 140, El Alto, La Paz – **LP55)** Tiawanaku, Prov Ingavi – **LP56)** Calle Yanacocha 70, Achacachi – **LP57)** Plaza 4 de Octubre, Rosario, Corapata, Prov Los Andes – **LP58)** Calle Noaviri 2105, Zona Amor de Dios, El Alto ☎2 223916 – **LP59)** Raúl Salmón 92 entre Calle 4 y 5, Zona Ceja, El Alto ( Cas. 8631, Murillo, La Paz) ☎2 2825169 **E:** radiomisionglobal@yahoo.es– **LP60)** Plaza Principal, Cantón Villa Iquiaca, Vilaque, Prov Los Andes – **LP61)** Tihuanaco Provincia Ingavi S/N, Comunidad Achaca, Tiahuanacu ☎2 822470 – **LP62)** Avenida Panoramica No. 5018, Zona Faro Murillo , El Alto ☎2 2813504 **W:** cesi. pastoralcl – **LP64)** Calle Topater 830, La Paz – **LP65)** Plaza Principal, Topohoco, Prov. Pacajes – **LP66)** Ca Jotan Save 3132 entre Bluniel, Zona 16 de Julio, La Paz – **LP67)** Calle Pascoe N° 2614-B, Zona 16 de Julio, El Alto ☎77444761 **FB:** Radio Bendita Trinidad Bolivia **E:** radio_bendita_trinidad_bolivia@hotmail.com – **LP68)** Ca Batalla de Huarina No 255, Huarina ☎71977644 – **LP74)** Tumupasa, Prov de Iturralde – **LP75)** Av. Grigota N° 1514, Urb. Atipiris 8 Sector Ex-Tranca Senkata, La Paz – El Alto ☎2 2882066 **FB:** Radio-Atipiri-Oficial **E:** radioatipiri@gmail.com – **LP77)** Calle 18 de Calacote No 7837, La Paz. – **LP88)** Calle S.Rodriguez No 1155, Zona 16 de Febrero, Distrito 4 Carretera a Laja antes del Puente Seke, Zona 16 de Febrero ☎73700079 **E:** bartolinasisa920am@gmail.com – **LP89)** Ichoca-Quime – **LP90)** Pucarani – **LP91)** Copacabana – **LP92)** Caranavi – **LP93)** Chulumani – **LP94)** Guaqui – **LP95)** Av Ciivica frente Estadio Orlando Quiroga, Caranavi ☎2 8243810 **W:** qhana.org.bo **E:** rqamazonia@qhana.org.bo – **LP96)** Pza. Ballivian No 525, 16 de Julio, El Alto ☎2 844344 – **LP97)** Av.Manco Kapaca No 50, Tiawanacu ☎2 597 357 – **LP98)** Calle Calama s/n entre Humahuca y Montenegro, Zona Norte, La Paz ☎2 286983 – **LP99)** Calle Calama s/n entre Humahuca y Montenegro, Zona Norte, La Paz ☎2 286983 – **LP100)** Calle Topáter # 830, Zona Norte, La Paz – **LP101)** Laja, Calle Carrasco No 16, entre Hermani y Av. La Paz, El Alto ☎2 847197 **W:** facebook.com/red.tawantinsuyo **E:** redtawantinsuyo@hotmail.com – **LP104)** Lanza N° 844, Cochabamba ☎4 520313 **W:** radiomaria.org.bo **E:** info.bol@radiomaria.org – **LP105)** Calle Bolivar No 249, Achacachi – **LP106)** Av. Chacaltaya, calle Tiquina N° 6580 Alto Lima primera sección (Cas.8628), El Alto ☎▤2 2842492 **W:** plenituddevida.net **E:** info@plenituddevida.net – **LP107)** Ave. Cornelio Saavedra No 2875 esq. Kantuta, Desaguadero ☎2 730 628 – **LP108)** Batallas, ☎71580034 – **LP109)** Corapata, Prov. De Los Andes – **LP110)** Letania, Prov. de Ingavi – **LP111)** Achocalla, Prov. de Murillo – **LP112)** Villa Iquiaca, Prov. de Los Andes – **LP113)** Contorno/ Viacha, Prov. de Ingavi – **LP114)** Av.Eduardo 1168, Zona Los Andes, Murillo ☎2 2458567 **E:** jorgetito@redcotel.bo – **LP116)** Plaza Avaroa N° 105, Carr. Viacha, El Alto. ☎2 825504 ▤2 821007 **E:** pachaqamasa700@yahoo.es – **LP120)** Unidad Académica Campesina de Tiahuanacu, Tiawuanaku ☎2 898542 – **LP121)** Diócesis de El Alto, Zona Ferropetrol, Plaza Boris Banzer, El Alto 2 ☎28444264 – **LP122)** Ca Cochabamba N° 102, Puerto de Guaqui ☎77592170 **W:** http//1190radioguaqui.blogspot.no **E:** radio1190guaqui@hotmail.com – **LP123)** Achocalla – **LP124)** Huarina – **LP126)** Topohoco – **LP127)** Vilaque – **LP128)** Taraco – **LP129)** Tapichullo – **LP130)** Tiawanaku – **LP131)** Qhurpa – **LP132)** Qhurpa – **LP133)** Asunta – **LP134)** Asunta – **LP135)** Escoma – **LP136)** Desaguadero – **LP137)** Caranavi – **LP138)** Carabuco – **LP139)** Corocoro – **LP140)** Carabuco – **LP141)** Carabuco – **LP142)** Achacachi – **LP143)** Achacachi – **LP144)** El Alto – **LP145)** Sococoni – **LP146)** Capilaya – **LP147)** Jihuacuta – **LP148)** Canaviri – **LP149)** Calle Jorge Carrasco N°12 entre calle 1 y calle 2 - Zona 12 de Octubre, El Alto ☎2 821473 **W:** radioluzdelmundobolivia.com **E:** luzdelmundo.bolivia@hotmail.com – **LP150)** León M. Loza No. 1199, Esquina Ascencio Padilla Alto San Pedro, La Paz ☎2-483395 – **LP151)** Ca 140 N° 140, Zona Villa Avaros, El Alto ☎2 115472 – **LP152)** La Paz – **LP153)** 3er piso, Edifico Las Delicias, frente a la linea roja del Teleférico, Av. Panorámica, El Alto – **LP154)** La Paz – **LP155)** Chulumani **W:** radiojallallacoca.com - **FM:** 100.1MHz – **LP156)** Coripata – **LP157)** Coroico – **LP158)** Machareti – **LP159)** La Paz –

**LP160)** La Paz – **LP161)** Tianawaku – **LP162)** Cl 6#777 esq. Moscoso, Zona Villa Dolores **W:** radiolavozdelespiritusantobolivia.com **E:** jorgenriveros.bo@gmail.com

**OR00 (ORURO)**
**OR01)** Calle Ayacucho 785 (Alto) (Cas 670), Oruro ☎2 5253500 ⓑ2 5252500 **E:** cpi@coteor.net.bo **Aymara & Quechua:** 1000-2200, 0200-0600 – **OR03)** Cas 1019, Oruro ☎2 5112259 **W:** bahai.org. bo **E:** servicio@bahai.org.bo **Aymara & Quechua:** 11 hours daily – **OR05)** Oruro – **OR06)** Calle Cochabamba esquiina 6 de Octubre (Cas 49), Oruro ☎2 525 0004 ⓑ2 524 2215 – **OR09)** Calle Junín y 6 de Agosto, Oruro ☎2 5260200 **W:** radiobatallontopater.com **Aymara & Quechua:** 1000-1100 - **FM:** 98.2MHz – **OR12)** San Felipe 493 entre Tarapacá y Tejerina (Cas 247), Oruro **Aymara:** 2200-2400 - **FM:** 107.7MHz – **OR13)** Av. Velasco Galvarro entre León y Rodriguez 1551, Oruro - **FM:** 105.1 MHz – **OR14)** Linares 1160 entre Cochabamba y Caro, Oruro – **OR15)** Caro 235 entre Pagador y Av Velasco Galvarro, Oruro – **OR19)** Av Bakovic 1027 entre Caro y Montecinos, (Cas 326), Oruro **Aymara & Quechua:** 0930-1030 - **FM:** 93.1MHz – **OR20)** Calle Sucre, Huanuni ( Cas 681), Oruro ☎2 5520421 **W:** nacionaldehuanuni. com **E:** nacionaldehuanuni@gmail.com – **OR24)** Calle Adolfo Mier 1231, Oruro – **OR26)** Orinoca, Prov Sud Carangas – **OR27)** Sabaya, Prov Sabaya – **OR29)** Oruro – **OR31)** Calle 6 de Octubre # 6160, Oruro ☎5 275344 **E:** radiocapitaloruro@hotmail.com – **FM:** 102.7 MHz – **OR32)** Avenida 6 de Octubre y Montecinos 1042, Oruro ☎5 25143 ⓑ5 276 645 - **FM:** 97.1 MHz **E:** Davidglg@hotmail. com – **OR33)** Centro de Apoyo a la Educación Popular (CAEP), Huanuni – **OR34)** Oruro – **OR35)** Caracollo – **OR36)** Caracolla – **OR37)** Huanuni – **OR38)** Oruro – **OR39)** Oruro – **OR40)** Oruro – **OR41)** Oruro - **FM:** 98.7 MHz – **OR44)** Challapata

**PA00 (PANDO)**
**PA09)** Barrio Paraiso, Calle Margarita, Esquina Jazmin, Cobija **W:** FB.com – Radio Bendita Trinidad Bolivia ☎76510837 – **PA10)** Cobija

**P000 (POTOSI)**
**PO02)** Calle Cobija 15, Zona Central, Potosí ☎6 222680 ⓑ6 226210 **W:** radiokollasuyo.net - **FM:** 105.1MHz – **P007)** Potosi – **PO08)** Catavi – **PO10)** Llica, Pcia Daniel Campos – **P012)** Potosi - **FM:** 107.5 MHz – **P014)** Campamento Minero Tazna, Pcia Nor Chichas – **P015)** Cas 326, Yura, Prov Antonio Quijarro **E:** radioyura@hotmail.com – **P016)** Dtto Minero de Animas – **P019)** Calle Final Uruguay s/n ( Cas 16), Uyuni, Prov Antonio Quijarro ☎2 693 2145 **E:** max_nelson_t@ hotmail.com – **P026)** Comunidad de Caiza, Prov Chayanta – **P028)** Av. Cívica 739 (Cas. 538), Potosi. ☎2 62236660 **W:** aclo.org.bo/bolivia **E:** aclopotosi@aclo.org.bo - **FM:** 106.7 MHz – **P029)** Calle Matos No 107 (Cas.472), Potosi. ☎6 223 936 **W:** indoamericafm.com **E:** info@ indoamericafm.com – **P030)** Colcha "K" – **P031)** Ocuri – **P032)** Unica – **P033)** Villazon – **P034)** Llica – **P035)** Tupiza – **PU36)** Uyuni – **P037)** Potosi **W:** radiocruzdelsur.com **E:** contactos@radiocruzdelsur.com – **P039)** Potosi – **P040)** Campamento Siglo XX, Llallagua (or Cas 434, Oruro) **W:** radiopio12.com.bo **E:** rpiodoce@entelnet.bo ☎2 5820250 ⓑ 2 5820554 **Aymara & Quechua** 6 hrs daily - **FM:** 99.9MHz – **P041)** San Pablo de Lipez

**SC00 (SANTA CRUZ)**
**SC02)** Plaza 31 de Julio, San Ignacio de Velasco ☎3 962 2188 **W:** sanignacio-diocesis.com/ **E:** radiojuan@hotmail.com - **FM:** 100.3MHz – **SC03)** Calle Potosí s/n entre calles German Bush y Rafael Terrazas, Barrio la Floresta (or Cas 38), Montero ☎3 9220237 **W:** radiomariaauxiliadora.sdb.bo **E:** ramacon@cotas.com.br - **FM:** 105.5MHz "Concierto" – **SC04)** Calle Mariano Saucedo Sevilla esquina Güendá No 20, Santa Cruz **W:** irfabolivia.org **E:** radiosantacruzbolivia@ gmail.com ☎3 3531817 **Guaraní:** 1830-1900 - **FM:** 92.2MHz – **SC10)** Warnes 334 (Cas 629), Santa Cruz ☎3 3363990 ⓑ3 3363992 - **FM:** 92.7MHz – **SC11)** Av. Grigota s/n, B.Matpetrol (2Cdra. Antes del 4to Anillo) Cas 818), Santa Cruz ☎3 3529265 ⓑ3 3524747 **E:** mision. eplabol@scbbs-bo.com **Quechua & Guarani:** 0900-0945 - **FM:** 90.7MHz "R Super Color" – **SC12)** Independencia 372 (Cas 186), Santa Cruz ☎3 3337194 ⓑ3 3335778 - **FM:** 96.3MHz – **SC16)** Av Charcas 1051 lado octava División del Ejército, Santa Cruz ☎3 3360447 ⓑ3 3372242 - **FM:** 98.1MHz – **SC21)** Florida esq Montes Claros 143, Vallegrande ☎3 9422033 – **SC25)** Cas 507, Santa Cruz - **FM:** 89.5MHz. Prgrs also in **Quechua** – **SC29)** Calle España 572, 2°piso, Santa Cruz - **FM:** 97.9MHz – **SC33)** Cas 1766, Santa Cruz **W:** difusorasdeloriente. galeon.com **E:** verdeyblanco5@hotmail.com – **SC35)** Calle Quijarro 74 esq Av Uruguay, Santa Cruz - **FM:** 105.5MHz – **SC38)** Comunidad de San Julián, Prov Nuflo de Chávez – **SC39)** Santa Cruz – **SC40)** Santa Cruz – **SC41)** Vallegrande – **SC42)** Camiri – **SC43)** Yapacani – **SC45)** Calle Lanza No 84 entre La Paz y Oruro, Santa Cruz ☎4 4526100 ⓑ4 4681178 **W:** radiomaria.org.bo **E:** info.bol@radiomaria.org – **SC47)** Santa Cruz – **SC48)** Zona Plan 3000 Av. Paurito Frente al Mercado Guapurú, Santa Cruz ☎3 3318829 **W:** facebook.com/Radio.Bendita. Trinidad.Bolivia.OFFICIAL – **SC49)** Yapacani – **SC50)** José Ballivian – **SC51)** Calle Lanza 844 (entre C La Paz y C Oruro) Santa Cruz **W:**

radiomaria.org.bo **E:** web@radiomaria.org.bo - **FM:** 97.5 MHz – **SC52)** Santa Cruz ☎3 33346299 **W:** facebook.com- Radio Amboro - **FM:** 98.5 MHz – **SC53)** Santa Cruz – **SC54)** Camiri – **SC55)** Tercer Anillo Externo Av. Radial13 y Av. Santos Dumont, Lado FELCC, Santa Cruz ☎3353 4400 **W:** Facebook: RadioFamiliar925FmY600KhzAm - **FM:** 92.5 MHz – **SC56)** Puerto Quijarro – **SC57)** Montero – **SC58)** Santa Cruz

**TA00 (TARIJA) TA01)**
Calle Virginio Lema 788 (Cas 404), Tarija ☎4 6643890 – **TA03)** Av Las Américas 9630, Edif Radiofónico Los Andes (Cas 344), Tarija ☎6 642800 - **FM:** 103.1MHz – **TA05)** Calle Bolivar esq. Méndez Nº 327 piso 1 Tarija ☎4 6634444 ⓑ4 6635555 **W:** facebook.com – Radio Guadalquivir **E:** radioguadalquivir@entelnet.com.bo - **FM:** 91.5MHz – **TA06)** Bolívar 376, Edificio Borda (Cas 125), Tarija - **FM:** 93.1MHz – **TA07)** Av Barrientos esq Ameller, Bermejo ☎ⓑ4 6961584 - **FM:** 99.1MHz – **TA10)** Av Bolívar 608, Bermejo – **TA12)** Calle Oruro E-1458 Esq. España (Cas. 1003), Tarija ☎4 6643425 **W:** aclo.org.bo/bolivia **E:** aclotarija@aclo.org.bo - **FM:** 101.5 MHz – **TA13)** Tarija – **TA14)** Bermejo – **TA15)** Villamontes – **TA16)** Villamontes – **TA17)** Yacuiba – **TA18)** Ycuiba – **TA19)** Entre Rios – **TA20)** Ca Cochabamba Nº 1403, Tarija ☎4 6664141 - **FM:** 101.5 MHz – **TA21)** Tarija

**FM in La Paz (MHz):** 87.7 87.7FM – 88.5 Doble 8 Latina – 88.9 Gente – 89.3 Sistema Cristiano de Comunicaciones – 89.7 Salesiana – **LP23)** 90.1 R.Sol Poder de Dios – 90.5 Panamericana Classica – 90.9 PCM – 91.3 Ciudad – 91.7 El Comercio – 92.1 Estudio 92 FM – 92.5 Estelar – 92.9 Galáctica – 93.3 Melodía – 93.7 Chacaltaya – 94.1 R La Voz de Bolivia – 94.5 Red Nuevo Tiempo – 94.9 Gigante – **LP06)** 95.3 – 95.7 Digital Sur – 96.1 – 96.5 R.Panamericana – 96.9 Diferente – 97.3 Stereo 97 – 97.7 – 98.1 Láser – 98.5 Andina – 98.9 Restauración – 99.3 Melodía – 99.7 Cristo Viene – 100.1 FM Cien – 100.5 Constelación – 100.9 R. Color – **LP07)** 101.3 – 101.7 Graffitti – 102.1 RRB – 102.5 Sintonia – 102.9 Cristal – 103.3 R. Deseo – **LP25)** 103.5 - 103.7 San Francisco de Asis – 104.1 Cadena CNT – 104.5 RCN – **LP26)** 104,8 - 104.9 Fantástica – 105.3 Nuevo Amanacer – 105.7 Majestad – 106.1 Pachamama – 106.5 – 106.9 Paris-La Paz – 107.3 Nueva Cosmos – **LP08)** 107.5 R.Play – 107.7 Central FM

## BONAIRE (Netherlands)

**L.T:** UTC -4h – **Pop:** 19,400 – **Pr.L:** Dutch (official), Papiamentu, English – **E.C:** 50Hz, 230V – **ITU:** BES

**AGENTSCHAP TELECOM Bonaire, Sint Eustatius, Saba**
✉ Kaya Grandi 69, P.O. Box 791, Bonaire ☎ + 599 717 3140 ⓑ +599 717 3554 **W:** agentschaptelecom.nl **E:** bes@agentschaptelecom.nl

| MW | Call | kHz | kW | Station, location |
|---|---|---|---|---|
| 1) | PJB | 800 | 440 | Trans World R., Kralendijk |
| **FM** | **MHz** | **kW** | **Station, location** | |
| 1) | 89.5 | 0.5 | Trans World R., Kralendijk | |
| 9) | 91.1 | | R. Atventista Boneiru 91.1FM | |
| 2) | 93.1 | 0.5 | Alpha FM 93.1, Kralendijk | |
| 2) | 94.7 | 0.5 | Voz di Bonaire, Kralendijk | |
| 5) | 96.1 | 0.5 | R. Energia 96.1 FM, Kralendijk | |
| 3) | 97.1 | | Play FM, Kralendijk | |
| 4) | 97.5 | 0.5 | Dolfijn FM, Kralendijk | |
| 8) | 99.9 | | Live 99.9 FM, Kralendijk | |
| 2) | 101.1 | 0.5 | Mega Hit FM, Kralendijk | |
| 6) | 102.7 | | Bon FM, Kralendijk | |
| 7) | 107.7 | | Rumbera Network, Kralendijk | |

**Addresses & other information:**
**1)** Kaya Gobernador N. Debrot 64, Kralendijk, Bonaire ☎ +599 717 8800 ⓑ +599 717 8808 ; 800khz: 00:00-08:00 Spanish; 00:00-03:00 440kW North pattern; 03:00-05:00 225kW Caribbean pat.;05:00-08:00 100kW Caribbean pat. - 08:00-10:00 Portuguese; 08:00-10:00 440kW South pattern - 10:00-12:30 Spanish; 10:00-11:00 225kW Caribbean pat.; 11:00-12:00 100kW Caribbean pat.; 12:00-12:30 50kW Caribbean pat.- 21:30-23:00 Spanish; 21:30-23:00 50kW Caribbean pattern ;23:00-00:00 English; 23:00-00:00 225kW Caribbean pattern 89.5MHz The Voice of Hope 24h mostly music with English news and occasional Bible based prgrs in English, Spanish, Dutch and Papiamentu **W:** twrbonaire.org **E:** 800am@twr.org and bonaire@twr.org ,**2)** Radiodifucion Boneriano NV, Kaya Gobernador N. Debrot 2, Kralendijk, ☎ +599 717 5947 ⓑ +599 717 8820, Dir: Feliciano da Silva Piloto **W:** vozdibonaire.com **E:** vozdibonaire@ gmail.com – **2) Voz di Bonaire:** Papiamentu and Dutch, music and information 24h **Mega Hit FM:** Dutch and English, music and information 24h **Alpha FM:**Spanish, music and information 24h – **3) Kaya Grandi 8,** Kralendijk ☎ +599 701 3303 **E:**playfmbonaire.com **E: info@playfmbonaire.com** – **4)** Kaya Amsterdam 27, Kralendijk

☎ +599 9 465 9975 🖷 +599 9 461 9975 Station Manager: Egon Sybrandy **DPrgr.** 24h in Dutch **E:** info@dolfijnfm.com **W:** dolfijnfm. com – **5)** Kaya Frater Odulfinus 17, Kralendijk Dir. Esmeralda C. Huerta ☎ +599 717 9171 and +599 717 2210 **E:** energia96.1@ hotmail.com; 24h prgrs in Papiamentu and Dutch – **6)** Kaya Irlandia 11, Kralendijk ☎ +599 717 2102 🖷 +599 717 2002 GM: Carmo R. Cecilia. 24h in Papiamentu **W:** bonfm.com **E:** bonfm@hotmail. com – **7)** Caracasbaaiweg 194, Willemstad, Cuaraco ☎ +599 9 465 9580 🖷 +599 9 461 5028 **W:** rumberacuracao.com **E:** contacto@ rumberanetwork.com.ve – **8)** Kaya Atom 33, Kralendijk ☎+599 717 0999 **W:** live99fm.com **E:** info@live99fm.com – **9)** Kaya Pos di Amor #1 ☎+599 796 0911 **W:** rabonaire.interamerica.org **E:** bonaire@awr. org GM : Ashley Thomas, Prgrs: 24 hrs in Papiamentu (main language), Spanish, Dutch and English

**TRANS WORLD RADIO (Rlg. Cult. Educ. )**
see International Broadcasting section

## BOSNIA & HERZEGOVINA

**L.T:** UTC +1h (31 Mar-27 Oct: +2h) — **Pop:** 3.8 million — **Pr.L:** Bosnian, Croatian, Serbian — **E.C:** 230V/50Hz — **ITU:** BIH

**REGULATORNA AGENCIJA ZA KOMUNIKACIJE BIH (RAK) (Communications Regulatory Agency BH)**
🖳 Mehmeda Spahe 1, 71000 Sarajevo ☎ +387 33 250600 🖷 +387 33 713080 **E:** info@rak.ba **W:** rak.ba **L.P:** DG: Predrag Kovac

**RADIO-TELEVIZIJA BOSNE I HERCEGOVINE (BHRT)(Pub)**
🖳 Bulevar Meše Selimovica 12, 71000 Sarajevo ☎ +387 33 461101 **E:** pitajte@bhrt.ba **W:** bhrt.ba **L.P:** DG: Belmin Karamehmedovic

| FM | MHz | kW | FM | MHz | kW |
|---|---|---|---|---|---|
| Tušnica | 88.1 | 30 | Vlašic | 97.0 | 100 |
| V. Gomila | 88.8 | 30 | Lisin | 100.3 | 30 |
| Lipik | 93.7 | 30 | Hum | 100.7 | 10 |
| Leotar | 94.1 | 30 | Kozara | 103.1 | 30 |
| Drvar | 94.7 | 5 | Trebevic | 103.7 | 10 |

+ txs below 1kW.
**D.Prgr: BHR1** in Bosnian, Croatian, Serbian: 24h.

### FEDERACIJA BOSNE I HERCEGOVINE

**RADIO-TELEVIZIJA FEDERACIJE BOSNE I HERCEGOVINE (RTV FBiH) (Pub)**
🖳 Bulevar Meše Selimovica 12, 71000 Sarajevo ☎ +387 33 461539 🖷 +387 33 461539 **E:** press@rtvfbih.ba **W:** rtvfbih.ba
**L.P:** DG: Džemal Šabic

| FM | MHz | kW | FM | MHz | kW |
|---|---|---|---|---|---|
| Tuzla | 88.5 | 10 | V. Gomila | 95.7 | 30 |
| Capljina | 89.1 | 1 | Hum | 95.7 | 10 |
| Vlašic | 89.3 | 100 | Lipik | 98.9 | 30 |
| Fortica | 91.7 | 5 | Hadžica Brdo | 99.5 | 5 |
| Tušnica | 92.5 | 30 | Gradacac | 103.5 | 5 |
| Lisin | 94.5 | 30 | + txs below 1kW. | | |

**D.Prgr: Radio FBiH** in Bosnian, Croatian: 24h.

### OTHER STATIONS

| MW | kHz | kW | Location | Station |
|---|---|---|---|---|
| 44) | ‡ 792 | 1 | Banovici | R. Banovici |
| 45) | 1503 | 1 | Zavidovici | R. 1503 Zavidovici |

‡) Stn has licenses for MW+FM, but currently only uses FM

| FM | MHz | kW | Location | Station |
|---|---|---|---|---|
| 12) | 88.1 | 1 | Mostar | R. Mostarska Panorama |
| 4) | 88.6 | 1 | Mostar | R. Gradska Mreža |
| 15) | 88.7 | 1 | Tešanj | R. Antena |
| 26) | 88.8 | 1 | Makljen | R. Rama |
| 33) | 89.5 | 2 | Drvar | R. Drvar |
| 37) | 89.9 | 1 | Cazin | R. Cazin |
| 22) | 90.0 | 2 | Mostar | R. Kalman |
| 23) | 90.3 | 1 | Radovan | R. Plus |
| 27) | 90.5 | 1 | Kupres | Kupreški Radio |
| 14) | 90.5 | 1 | Sarajevo | R. Mix |
| 38) | 90.9 | 5 | Mostar | R. Grude |
| 5) | 90.9 | 1 | Sarajevo | Antena Sarajevo |
| 22) | 91.2 | 2 | Lisin | R. Kalman |
| 39) | 91.3 | 1 | Capljina | R. Postaja Capljina |
| 22) | 91.5 | 1 | Sarajevo | R. Kalman |
| 7) | 91.5 | 1 | Livno | R. Livno |
| 7) | 91.5 | 5 | Bos. Grahovo | R. Livno |
| 34) | 91.6 | 1 | Velika Kladuša | Trend R. |

| FM | MHz | kW | Location | Station |
|---|---|---|---|---|
| 41) | 91.8 | 3 | Srebrenik | R. TK |
| 2) | 93.1 | 5 | Grude | R. Široki Brijeg |
| 19) | 94.3 | 2.5 | Majevica | Obiteljski R. Valentino |
| 18) | 94.7 | 1 | Bihac | R. Bihac |
| 36) | 94.7 | 1 | Jablanica | R. Jablanica |
| 25) | 94.8 | 1 | Brcko** | R. Brcko |
| 35) | 95.0 | 1 | Lisin | R. Konjic |
| 30) | 95.1 | 2 | Tomisvlagrad | R. Tomislavgrad |
| 3) | 95.2 | 1 | Sarajevo | R. Miljacka |
| 38) | 95.5 | 5 | Grude | R. Grude |
| 6) | 95.6 | 5 | Gradacac | R. Kameleon |
| 30) | 95.9 | 1 | Duvno | R. Tomislavgrad |
| 11) | 96.2 | 1 | Mostar | R. Dobre Vibracija |
| 20) | 96.5 | 5 | Sarajevo | R. BIR |
| 32) | 96.9 | 3.5 | Posušje | R. Herceg-Bosne |
| 13) | 97.5 | 5 | Zenica | RSG R. |
| 28) | 97.6 | 1 | Livno | R. Studio N |
| 9) | 97.9 | 5 | Mostar | R. Mostar |
| 32) | 98.1 | 30 | Fojnica | R. Herceg-Bosne |
| 8) | 98.7 | 1 | Trebevic* | R. M |
| 40) | 99.1 | 1 | Kljuc | R. Kljuc |
| 1) | 99.5 | 1.5 | Sanski Most | R. USK |
| 42) | 99.9 | 1 | Gradacac | R. Bet Fratello |
| 20) | 100.1 | 1 | Bugojno | R. BIR |
| 7) | 100.9 | 1 | Livno | R. Livno |
| 6) | 101.2 | 1 | Sarajevo | R. Kameleon |
| 16) | 101.5 | 1.2 | Goražde | R. BPK |
| 17) | 101.5 | 5 | Biokovo | R. Mir Medjugorje |
| 17) | 101.8 | 1 | Bugojno | R. Mir Medjugorje |
| A) | 102.0 | 1 | Sarajevo | BFBS R. (UK) relay |
| 24) | 102.9 | 1 | Radovan | R. Posušje |
| 29) | 103.4 | 5 | Mostar | R. Oscar - C |
| 10) | 103.7 | 2 | Lokveni Vrh* | R. Sana |
| 32) | 103.9 | 5 | Hrgud* | R. Herceg-Bosne |
| 8) | 104.2 | 1 | Banja Luka* | R. M |
| 13) | 104.3 | 16 | Lisin | RSG R. |
| 13) | 104.3 | 1 | Capljina | RSG R. |
| 17) | 104.7 | 1 | Makljen | R. Mir Medjugorje |
| 1) | 105.1 | 30 | Velika Gomila | R. USK |
| 43) | 105.2 | 1 | Tuzla | R. Glas Drine |
| 32) | 106.0 | 5 | Motajica* | R. Herceg-Bosne |
| 21) | 106.6 | 10 | Lisac | R. Zenica |
| 17) | 106.7 | 3 | Kozara* | R. Mir Medjugorje |
| A) | 106.9 | 1 | Sarajevo | BFBS R.2 (UK) relay |
| 31) | 107.0 | 5 | Pecigrad | R. Velkaton |
| 17) | 107.8 | 50 | Licka Plješivica*** | R. Mir Medjugorje |
| 22) | 107.8 | 1 | Bugojno | R. Kalman |
| 22) | 107.8 | 1 | Zenica | R. Kalman |
| 22) | 107.8 | 2 | Trebacko Brdo | R. Kalman |
| 22) | 107.8 | 1 | Tuzla | R. Kalman |

+ txs below 1kW. *) Located in Republika Srpska **) Located in Brcko district ***) Located in Croatia

**Addresses & other information:**
**1)** Kulturni centar bb, 77000 Bihac – **2)** Trg Gojka Šuška 5c, 88220 Široki Brijeg – **3)** Kujundžija 6, 71000 Sarajevo – **4)** Rade Bitange 13, 88104 Mostar – **5)** Urijan Dedina 7, 71000 Sarajevo – **6)** Dr. Milana Jovanovica 6, 75000 Tuzla – **7)** Kneza Mutimira 29, 80101 Livno – **8)** Fra Andjela Zvizdovica 1, 71000 Sarajevo – **9)** Lacina bb, 88000 Mostar – **10)** Banjalucka 2, 75260 Sanski Most – **11)** Kralja Petra Kresimira IV bb, 88000 Mostar – **12)** Trg hrvatskih velikana bb, 88000 Mostar – **13)** Urijan Dedina 7, 71000 Sarajevo – **14)** Urijan Dedina 7, 71000 Sarajevo – **15)** Titova bb, 74264 Jelah – **16)** Marka Oreškovica 42, 80260 Drvar – **17)** Gospin Trg 1, 88266 Medjugorje – **18)** Krupska bb, 77000 Bihac – **19)** Kolodvorska 108a, 76204 Bijela – **20)** Reisa Džemaludina Cauševica 2, 71000 Sarajevo – **21)** Bulevar Kralja Tvrtka I bb, 72000 Zenica – **22)** Varaždinska 18, 71000 Sarajevo – **23)** Fra Grge Martica bb, 88240 Posušje – **24)** Kraljice Jelene 2, 88240 Posušje – **25)** Klosterska br. 20, 76100 Brcko – **26)** Kralja Tomislava bb, 88440 Prozor-Rama – **27)** Mate Bobana 1, 80320 Kupres – **28)** Splitska bb, 80101 Livno – **29)** Smrcenjaci bb, 88000 Mostar – **30)** Mijata Tomica bb, 80240 Tomislavgrad – **31)** Kulište 4, 77230 Velika Kladuša – **32)** Kralja Petra Krešimira IV. b.b, 88000 Mostar – **33)** Marka Oreškovica 42, 80260 Drvar – **34)** Fadila Šerica bb, 77230 Velika Kladuša – **35)** Trg Državnosti - Alija Izetbegovic 1, 88400 Konjic – **36)** Trg oslobodjenja bb., 88420 Jablanica – **37)** Cazinskih brigada 12, 77200 Cazin – **38)** Viteza Ranka Bobana, 88340 Grude – **39)** Rudjera Boškovica 4, 88340 Capljina – **40)** Branilaca BiH bb., 79280 Kljuc – **41)** Mije Keroševica 20, 75000 Tuzla – **42)** 1. maja 1, 76 250 Gradacac – **43)** Srebrenickog odreda bb, 75430 Srebrenica – **44)** 7. novembra 4, 75290 Banovici

**E:** radiobanovici@yahoo.com — **45)** Maršala Tita 3, 72220 Zavidovici
**E:** dadozavi@zona.ba. Incl. rel. BHR1 & R. FBiH at times — **A)** Butmir Camp, Sarajevo. Rel. BFBS R. (UK).

### REPUBLIKA SRPSKA

## RADIO TELEVIZIJA REPUBLIKE SRPSKE (RTRS) (Pub)
☐ Trg Republike Srpske 9, 78000 Banja Luka ☎ +387 51 339900 **E:** radiodesk@rtrs.tv **W:** rtrs.tv **L.P:** DG: Draško Milinovic

| FM | MHz | kW | FM | MHz | kW |
|---|---|---|---|---|---|
| Kmur | 87.8 | 1 | Duge Njive | 90.7 | 10 |
| Trebevic | 88.7 | 10 | Kozara | 92.7 | 30 |
| Udrigovo | 89.9 | 30 | Leotar | 92.8 | 30 |
| Veliki Zep | 92.3 | 30 | | | |

+ txs below 1kW. *) Located in Federacija Bosne i Hercegovine.
**D.Prgr: Radio RS** in Serbian: 24h.

### OTHER STATIONS
| | FM | MHz | kW | Location | Station |
|---|---|---|---|---|---|
| 9) | 87.7 | 5 | Hum* | Nes R. |
| 5) | 88.4 | 6 | Silos | R. Slobomir |
| 9) | 88.4 | 1 | Banja Luka | Nes R. |
| 11) | 88.9 | 1 | Kmur | Bobar R. |
| 7) | 88.9 | 1 | Prnjavor | R. Ljubic |
| 17) | 89.6 | 1 | Udrigovo | R. HIT |
| 6) | 89.6 | 1 | Kostreš | Vikom R. |
| 13) | 89.9 | 2.2 | Kozara | R. Kozara |
| 6) | 89.9 | 2 | Gig | Vikom R. |
| 16) | 90.0 | 1 | Gacko | R. Gacko |
| 12B) | 91.5 | 1 | Banja Luka | BIG R. 2 |
| 21) | 92.0 | 2 | Lipovac | R. Džungla |
| 4) | 92.0 | 1.4 | Trebevic | BN R. |
| 8) | 92.5 | 1 | Kmur | R. Foca |
| 4) | 93.1 | 1 | Busija | BN R. |
| 12B) | 93.2 | 1 | Trebevic | BIG R. 2 |
| 12A) | 93.6 | 1 | Banja Luka | BIG R. 1 |
| 3) | 94.7 | 2 | Bosanska Dubica | R. Feniks |
| 4) | 95.3 | 1 | Bileca | BN R. |
| 11) | 95.3 | 23 | Kozara | Bobar R. |
| 1) | 95.9 | 1 | Banja Luka | R. Gradski FM |
| 10) | 95.9 | 1 | Leotar | R. Trebinje |
| 2) | 96.3 | 2 | Doboj | R. Doboj |
| 12C) | 96.5 | 1 | Banja Luka | BIG R. 3 |
| 15) | 96.5 | 1 | Kozarska Dubica | Dub R. |
| 14) | 97.6 | 1 | Banja Luka | Pop FM |
| 9) | 99.3 | 2 | Velika Kladuša* | Nes R. |
| 4) | 99.9 | 9 | Banja Luka | BN R. |
| 23) | 100.7 | 2 | Lipovac | R. Studio M |
| 11) | 100.9 | 10 | Busija | Bobar R. |
| 4) | 102.4 | 30 | Vlašic* | BN R. |
| 18) | 102.7 | 2.2 | Banja Luka | Hard Rock R. |
| 11) | 102.8 | 8 | Trebevic | Bobar R. |
| 19) | 104.0 | 1 | Višegrad | R. Višegrad |
| 4) | 104.1 | 2 | Modrica | BN R. |
| 11) | 104.7 | 30 | Vlašic* | Bobar R. |
| 24) | 105.0 | 1 | Kmur | R. Istocno Sarajevo |
| 20) | 105.3 | 3 | Banja Luka | Plavi R. |
| 4) | 105.4 | 1 | Livno | BN R. |
| 11) | 105.5 | 22 | Leotar | Bobar R. |
| 24) | 105.6 | 1 | Trebevic | R. Istocno Sarajevo |
| 11) | 105.9 | 40 | Hrgud | Bobar R. |
| 9) | 106.4 | 22.5 | Kozara | Nes R. |
| 22) | 107.5 | 1 | Banja Luka | R. Uno |

+ txs below 1kW. *) Located in Federacija Bosne i Hercegovine.

**Addresses & other information:**
**1)** Lazarica 2, 78000 Banja Luka – **2)** Kneza Lazara 8, 74000 Doboj – **3)** Svetosavska bb, 79240 Kozarska Dubica – **4)** Laze Kostica 146, 76320 Bijeljina – **5)** Trzni centar bb, 76300 Bijeljina – **6)** Srpska 2/ II, 78000 Banja Luka – **7)** Trg Srpskih Boraca bb, 78430 Prnjavor – **8)** Njegoševa 1, 73300 Foca – **9)** Brace Pišteljic 1, 78000 Banja Luka – **10)** Svetosavska 21, 79240 Kozarska Dubica – **11)** Filipa Višnjica 211, 76320 Bijeljina – **12A-C)** Vuka Karadzica 6, 78000 Banja Luka – **13)** Vidovdanska 2, 78400 Gradiška – **14)** Brace Pišteljica 1, 78000 Banja Luka – **15)** Svetosavska 21, 79240 Kozarska Dubica – **16)** Solunskih Dobrovoljaca 2, 89240 Gacko – **17)** Miroslava Krleze 48, 76100 Brcko – **18)** 78000 Banja Luka – **19)** Vuka Karadzica bb, 73240 Višegrad – **20)** Branka Popovica 92a, 78000 Banja Luka – **21)** Nikole Pašica bb, 74000 Doboj – **22)** Veselina Masleše br. 1/12, 78000 Banja Luka – **23)** Stevana Mokranjca 10, 74270 Teslic – **24)** Stefana Nemanje 8, 71123 Istocno Sarajevo

---

**L.T:** UTC +2h — **Pop:** 2 million — **Pr.L:** Setswana, English — **E.C:** 50Hz, 230V — **ITU:** BOT

## NATIONAL BROADCASTING BOARD (NBB)
☐ 206/207 Independence Ave, Private Bag 00495, Gaborone ☎ +267 3957755 ☐ +267 3957976 **W:** bta.org.bw/nbb.htm **E:** info@bta.org.bw
**L.P:** Chairman: Dr. Masego Mpotokwane.

## RADIO BOTSWANA (Pub, Comm.)
☐ Private Bag 0060, Gaborone ☎ +267 3653000 **W:** radiobotswana. gov.bw dib.gov.bw **E:** Rbeng@info.bw **L.P:** Dir. Broadc. Sces: Habuji Sosome. Chief Broadc. Officer: Mrs Banyana Segwe. CE: Kingsley Reetsang. Mgr RB: Margaret Modise.

| MW | kHz | kW | MW | kHz | kW |
|---|---|---|---|---|---|
| Maun | 531 | 50 | Mmathethe | †945 | 25 |
| Muchenje | †558 | 50 | Takotokwane | 972 | |
| Selebi-Phikwe | 621 | 100 | Jwaneng | †1071 | 25 |
| Mopipi | 648 | 50 | Mahalapye | †1215 | 50 |
| Shakawe | 693 | 25 | Tshabong | 1350 | 50 |
| Gantsi | 873 | 50 | †=irregular | | |

| FM(MHz) | RB1 | RB2 | kW | FM(MHz) | RB1 | RB2 | kW |
|---|---|---|---|---|---|---|---|
| Bobonong | 95.9 | 102.7 | 0.5 | Mabule | 92.3 | 105.9 | |
| Charleshill | 93.5 | 103.5 | | Mabutsane | 94.2 | 104.6 | |
| Francistown | 103.6 | 90.5 | 3 | Mahalapye | 96.6 | 107.0 | 2.5 |
| Gaborone | 89.9 | 103.0 | 5 | Maun | 94.2 | 104.6 | 0.5 |
| Gantsi | 94.0 | 100.8 | 0.1 | Olifant's Drift | 88.0 | 104.7 | |
| Good Hope | 94.6 | 101.6 | 0.5 | Orapa | 89.9 | 98.6 | 0.1 |
| Hukuntsi | 95.9 | 96.2 | 0.5 | Palapye | 92.1 | 101.5 | 0.5 |
| Jwaneng | 99.2 | 106.3 | 0.5 | Sekakangwe Hill | 91.9 | 101.9 | 2 |
| Kanye | 89.0 | 95.3 | 0.5 | Selebi-Phikwe | 94.2 | 104.6 | 0.1 |
| Kang | 89.3 | 98.9 | | Serowe | 99.4 | 92.9 | 1 |
| Kasane | 94.4 | 104.8 | 0.5 | Sojwe | 87.7 | 90.7 | |
| Lobatse | 98.6 | 105.7 | 1 | Tsabong | 96.6 | 107.0 | 0.5 |

**National Sce (RB1)** in Setswana/English on MW/FM: 24h.
**N. in English:** on the hour exc. **in Setswana:** 1100, 1600, 1900.
**Commercial Sce (RB2):** 24h. **N:** rel. RB1.
**Ann:** E: "This is R. Botswana broadcasting from Gaborone", "RB", "RB1", "RB2". Setswana: "Se Ke Seromamowa Sa Botswana mo Gaborone".
**IS:** RB1: Bird chirps and first bars of the National Anthem.

**Other stations** (all MHz):
**Duma FM:** Gaborone 93.0, Francistown 93.6 – **Gabz FM,** Private Bag BO 319, 2nd Floor, Beta House, Plot 17954, Old Lobatse Rd, Gaborone. **W:** gabzfm.com **FM:** Maun/Selebi-Phikwe 91.0, Mahalapye 93.4, Lobatse 94.1, Palapye 94.7, Serowe 96.1, Gaborone 96.2, Francistown 96.8 – **Yarona FM:** Francistown 100.1, Gaborone: 106.6. **W:** yaron-afm.co.bw
**Voice of America relay station (MW):**
Selebi-Phikwe, Moepeng Hill: 909kHz 600kW 0300-0700 ,1600-2200 & SW. For further details see International Radio section (USA)

---

**L.T:** PE (Fernando de Noronha only): UTC -2h. AL, AP, BA, CE, DF*, ES*, GO*, MA, MG*, PA, PB, PE, PI, PR*, RJ*, RN, RS*, SC*, SP*, TO: UTC -3h (*=DST: -2h). AC, AM, MS*, MT*, RO, RR: UTC -4h (*=DST: -3h). *) DST: 4 Nov 18-17 Feb 19, 3 Nov 19-16 Feb 20 — **Pop:** 211 million — **Pr.L:** Portuguese — **E.C:** 60Hz, 110V and 220V — **ITU:** B — **Int. dialling code:** +55

## AGÊNCIA NACIONAL DE COMUNICAÇÕES (ANATEL)
☐ SAS Quadra 06 Bloco H, Ed. Ministro Sérgio Motta, 2° andar, 70313-900 Brasília, DF **W:** anatel.gov.br
**L.P:** Dir. Gen. Dr. Rubens Bussacos. Dir. of Radio: Roberto Blois Montes de Souza. Dir. Dept. of Authorizations: Domingo Poty Chabalgoity

## ASSOCIAÇÃO BRASILEIRA DE EMISSORAS DE RADIO E TELEVISÃO (ABERT)
☐ SCN Quadra 4 Bloco B-100, sala 501, Centro Empresarial Varig, 70714-900 Brasília, DF (C.P. 08780, 70312-970)
☎ 61 2104 4600 ☐ 61 2104 4626 **W:** abert.org.br
**L.P:** Pres.: Paulo Machado de Carvalho Neto. Exec. Dir: Antonio Abelin

**Callsign** For the full callsign add ZY to the front of the calls shown. The letters preceding the stn number indicate the state or territory.
‡ = inactive ± = varying freq † = irregular * stn may **migrate to FM during 2019**
**N.B:** all stns carry «A Voz do Brasil» (official prgr). Main tr. M-F 2200-2300 but stns may also transmit at other times during the day.

| MW | Call | kHz | kW | Station, location, h. of tr. |
|---|---|---|---|---|
| BA01) | H481 | *540 | 1/0.25 | R. Regional, Irecê: 24h |
| CE01) | H610 | 540 | 1/0.25 | R. Jornal, Canindé |
| GO01) | H755 | 540 | 10/1 | R. Riviera, Goiânia |
| MA01) | H894 | 540 | 1/0.25 | R. Guajajara, Barra do Corda |
| MG151) | L331 | 540 | 1/0.5 | R. Ipanema, Ipanema |
| PI31) | I914 | 540 | 1/0.25 | R. Primeiro de Julho, Agua Branca |
| PR110) | J322 | 540 | 1/0.25 | R. Nova Era, Borrazópolis |
| RJ01) | J450 | 540 | 10/2.5 | R. Fluminense, Niterói |
| RS01) | K226 | 540 | 1/0.5 | R. Real, Canoas: 0900-0200 |
| RS02) | K322 | 540 | 10/1 | R. Sepé, Santo Ângelo: 24h |
| SC01) | J778 | 540 | 10/1 | R. Mirador, Rio do Sul: 0800-0300 |
| SE01) | J924 | 540 | 10/2.5 | R. Jornal AM, Aracaju: 24h |
| SP01) | K697 | 540 | 1/0.25 | R. Globo, Biriguí |
| SP02) | K734 | 540 | 1/0.25 | R. Nova Sumaré, Sumaré: 24h |
| CE59) | H644 | 550 | 1/0.25 | R. Vale do Quincoê, Acopiara: 1400-2100 Sun 1600-2100 |
| MG01) | L225 | 550 | 5/0.5 | R. Cataguases, Cataguases |
| MG02) | L263 | 550 | 20/5 | Super Rede Boa Vontade |
| MT29) | I429 | 550 | 10/5 | R. Mais, Sinop |
| PE01) | I796 | 550 | 5/1 | R. Meridional, Garanhuns |
| PI01) | I902 | 550 | 1/0.25 | R. Serra da Capivara, São Raimundo Nonato |
| PI22) | I907 | 550 | 10/0.5 | R. Globo, Parnaíba: 24h |
| PR139) | J331 | 550 | 10/0.5 | R. Banda B, Curitiba: 24h |
| RS03) | K287 | 550 | 2.5/0.25 | R. Sta. Cruz do Sul, Sta. Cruz do Sul: 0800-0230 |
| SP03) | K578 | 550 | 5/0.5 | R. Mantiqueira, Cruzeiro: 0800-0300 |
| SP04) | K700 | 550 | 5/0.5 | Super Rede Boa Vontade, Sertãozinho: 24h |
| AM09) | H289 | 560 | 1/0.25 | R. Coari, Coari |
| BA02) | H456 | 560 | 5/1 | R. Jornal, Itabuna: 0700-0100 (SS-2200) |
| CE41) | H604 | 560 | 1/0.25 | R. Educ. Jaguaribana, Limoeiro do Nte. |
| GO25) | H769 | 560 | 5/0.25 | R. Sul Goiana, Quirinópolis: 24h |
| MA02) | H887 | 560 | 25/5 | R. Educadora do Maranhão, São Luís: 0800-0300 (SS 24h) |
| MG05) | L277 | *560 | 5/0.25 | R. Dif., Patrocínio |
| MT01) | I395 | 560 | 10/2.5 | R. Aruanã, Pontal do Aragua |
| MT24) | I419 | 560 | 10/1 | R. Pioneira, Tangará da Serra |
| PB16) | I695 | 560 | 1/0.25 | R. Maná, Mamanguape |
| PR01) | J214 | 560 | 1/0.5 | R. Londrina Londrina |
| PR02) | J281 | *560 | 25/0.25 | R. Cultura, Guarapuava: 24h |
| RJ02) | J496 | 560 | 5/0.25 | R. Costa do Sol, Araruama:24h |
| RS04) | K231 | 560 | 5/1 | R. São Francisco Sat, Caxias do Sul: 24h |
| SP213) | K761 | 560 | 35/1 | R. Paulista, Santa Isabel: 24h |
| AL01) | H244 | *570 | 5/1 | R. Novo Nordeste, Arapiraca: 24h |
| CE02) | H613 | 570 | 5/0.25 | R. Verde Vale, Juazeiro do Norte |
| CE03) | H614 | 570 | 1/0.25 | R. Uirapuru, Itapipoca: 0800-0100 |
| GO02) | H750 | *570 | 2.5/0.5 | R. Cultura, Catalão |
| MA42) | H898 | *570 | 10/2.5 | R. Timon, Timon |
| MG03) | L261 | 570 | 25/5 | R. Capital, Belo Horizonte: 24h |
| MT30) | N407 | 570 | 1/0.25 | R. Jornal, São José dos Quatro Marcos: 0900-0000 |
| PR146) | J349 | 570 | 1/0.5 | R. Continental, Palotina |
| RS05) | K267 | 570 | 1/0.5 | R. Dilário da Manhã, Passo Fundo: 24h |
| SC02) | J735 | 570 | 5/0.5 | R. Eldorado, Criciúma: 24h |
| SC99) | J794 | 570 | 1/0.25 | R. Fronteira, Dionísio Cerqueira: 0800-0100, Sun 1000-0000 |
| SP05) | K595 | *570 | 1/0.25 | R. Clube Gospel, Itapeva |
| SP06) | K672 | 570 | 5/1 | R. Dif., Taubaté |
| SP195) | K698 | 570 | 1/0.25 | R. Jornal, Nhandeara |
| SP150) | K717 | 570 | 10/2.5 | Bariri R. Clube, Bariri |
| BA03) | H477 | *580 | 1/0.25 | R. Dif., Teixeira de Freitas: 0630-0300 |
| GO44) | H799 | 580 | 1/0.25 | R. Serra Azul, Caiapônia |
| MG04) | L328 | 580 | 7/0.5 | R. América, Uberlândia: 24h |
| MS01) | I387 | 580 | 25/1 | R. Imaculada Conceicao, Campo Grande: 24h |
| PE02) | I776 | 580 | 20/10 | R. Rede Brasil, Recife: 24h |
| PI12) | I905 | *580 | 5/1 | R. Itamaraty, Piripiri |
| PR105) | J327 | 580 | 2/0.25 | R. Pitanga, Pitanga: 24h |
| PR03) | J330 | 580 | 2.5/0.25 | R. Grande Lago, Santa Helena |
| RJ03) | J465 | 580 | 50/5 | R. Relogio, Sao Gonçalo: 24h |
| RS06) | K299 | 580 | 2/0.5 | R. São Gabriel, São Gabriel: 0900-0300 |
| RS07) | K318 | *580 | 10/5 | R. Fátima, Vacaria: 24h |
| SP07) | K540 | 580 | 1/0.25 | R. Você, Americana |
| SP08) | K724 | 580 | 1/0.25 | R. Regional, Palmital: 0800-0200 |
| TO01) | H785 | *580 | 10/2 | R. Tocantins, Porto Nacional |
| BA04) | H445 | 590 | 10/5 | R. Cruzeiro da Bahia, Salvador: 24h |
| CE04) | H627 | 590 | 5/1 | R. Poty, Crateús: 0730(SS 0800)-0300 |
| ES01) | I213 | 590 | 5/0.5 | R. Tribuna, Vitória |
| GO03) | H798 | 590 | 10/1 | R. Manchester, Anápolis |
| MG93) | L249 | 590 | 10/0.5 | R. Cultura, João Monlevade |

| MW | Call | kHz | kW | Station, location, h. of tr. |
|---|---|---|---|---|
| PB25) | I692 | 590 | 5/0.25 | R. Serrana, Araruna: 0800-0100 |
| PR04) | J234 | 590 | 10/5 | R. Difusora AM 590, Curitiba: 24h |
| PR38) | J240 | 590 | 2.7/0.75 | R. Dif. Regional, Cruzeiro do Oeste |
| RR01) | O700 | 590 | 10 | R. Dif. de Roraima, Boa Vista: 0800-0300 (SS 0900-0230) |
| RS08) | K210 | 590 | 5/0.5 | R. Alegrete, Alegrete: 0830-0230 |
| SC03) | J901 | 590 | 2/1 | R. Progresso, Descanso: 24h |
| SP09) | K534 | 590 | 10/1 | R. Atlântica, Santos: 24h |
| SP10) | K612 | 590 | 1/0.25 | R. Clube, Mirandópolis: 0800-2300 Sat -1530 Sun 0900-1200 |
| SP11) | K643 | 590 | 5/1 | R. 79, Ribeirão Preto |
| AM02) | H287 | 600 | 10 | R. Municipal, São Gabriel da Cachoeira: 24h |
| BA05) | H486 | 600 | 10/1 | R. Vale do Rio Grande, Barreiras: 1100-000 Sun 1500-1500 |
| BA64) | H... | 600 | 1/0.25 | R. Dif.de Rio Real, Rio Real: 0900-0100 Sat -2200 Sun -0000 |
| CE38) | H627 | 600 | 1/0.25 | R. Cultura, Aracati |
| MA38) | H920 | 600 | 10/1 | R. Mirante, São Luís: 24h |
| PE03) | I789 | 600 | 1/0.25 | R. Cardeal Arcoverde, Arcoverde |
| RS09) | K278 | 600 | 100 | R. Gaúcha, Porto Alegre:24h |
| AL10) | H249 | 610 | 10/2 | R. Imperial, Marechal Deodoro |
| AM18) | H321 | 610 | 10 | Super Rede Boa Vontade, Manaus: 24h |
| GO10) | H786 | 610 | 25/0.5 | R. Mega, Luziânia |
| MG06) | L268 | 610 | 100/25 | R. Itatiaia, Belo Horizonte: 24h |
| PB01) | I678 | 610 | 1/0.25 | R. Progresso, Sousa |
| PI02) | I899 | ‡*610 | 10/1 | R. Poty, Teresina |
| SC04) | J746 | 610 | 10/0.5 | R. Super Condá, Chapecó |
| SP12) | K532 | ‡610 | 1/0.25 | CBN, Mogi Mirim |
| SP13) | K577 | *610 | 1/0.25 | R. Globo, Catanduva: 24h |
| SP14) | K589 | *610 | 1/0.25 | Super R. Piratininga, Guaratinguetá |
| SP15) | K726 | *610 | 1/0.25 | R. Paranapanema, Piraju: 0800-0100 |
| SP113) | K502 | *610 | 1/0.25 | R. Presidente Venceslau, Pres. Venceslau: 0900-0200 (Sun silent) |
| CE05) | H590 | 620 | 10 | R. Assunção CearenseFortaleza: 24h |
| PR05) | J332 | 620 | 2.5/0.25 | R. Jandaia, Jandaia do Sul: 0800(Sun 1030)-0100 |
| RS10) | K270 | 620 | 10/1 | R. Pelotense, Pelotas: 24h |
| RS11) | K315 | 620 | 1/0.25 | R. Municipal, Tenente Portela |
| SC05) | J779 | 620 | 5/0.25 | Super-R. Dif., Rio do Sul: 24h |
| SP16) | K521 | 620 | 50/10 | R. Jovem Pan, São Paulo: 24h |
| AP01) | H422 | *630 | 25/10 | R. Dif. de Macapá, Macapá: 24h |
| CE58) | H636 | 630 | 1/0.5 | R. Cidade, Campos Sales: 24h |
| GO04) | H777 | *630 | 1/0.25 | R. Gospel 630 AM, Pires do Rio |
| MA16) | H924 | 630 | 10/0.5 | R. Macaru, Viana |
| MG07) | L299 | *630 | 1/0.5 | R. Jornal da Manhã - R.JM, Uberaba |
| MS32) | N603 | 630 | 10/1 | R. Novo Tempo, Campo Grande: 24h |
| MT05) | I384 | 630 | 10/5 | R. Dif. Bom Jesús, Cuiabá |
| PI03) | I904 | 630 | 1/0.5 | R. Dif., Barras |
| PR06) | J284 | 630 | 10/0.5 | R. Educativa, Curitiba: 24h |
| PR07) | J300 | 630 | 5/0.25 | R. Educadora, Marechal Cândido Rondón |
| RJ04) | J466 | 630 | 25/10 | R. Roquete Pinto, Rio de Janeiro: 24h |
| RS12) | K259 | *630 | 1/0.25 | R. Cacique, Lagoa Vermelha: 24h |
| RS13) | K289 | 630 | 1/0.25 | R. Santamariense, Santa Maria |
| SC06) | J800 | 630 | 1/0.25 | R. Doze de Maio, São Lourenço d'Oeste: 0800-0200 |
| SE02) | J920 | 630 | 10/5 | R. Aperipe, Aracaju: 24h |
| SP17) | K613 | *630 | 1/0.25 | R. Dif. Mirassol: 0800-0300, Sun 1000-2330 |
| SP18) | K635 | ‡630 | 5/0.25 | R. Cidade, Presidente Prudente |
| BA12) | H458 | 640 | 10/0.5 | R. Dif. Sul da Bahia, Itabuna: 0700-0300 |
| ES02) | I204 | 640 | 10/0.5 | R. Vitória, Vitória: 24h |
| GO05) | H757 | 640 | 50/5 | R. Dif. Goiânia, Goiânia |
| MG08) | L308 | *640 | 3/0.25 | R. Santa Cruz, Pará de Minas: 24h |
| MG125) | L320 | 640 | 10/0.25 | R. Educadora, Porteirinha: 24h |
| MT06) | I406 | *640 | 10/5 | R. Progresso, Alta Floresta: 0800-0200, (Sun 0900-0100) |
| MT18) | I424 | 640 | 10/1 | R. Tangará, Tangará da Serra |
| PI28) | I924 | 640 | 1/0.25 | R. Cruzeiro, Pedro II: 0800-0000, (SS 0900-2300) |
| PR08) | J262 | 640 | 20/1 | Super R. Deus é Amor, Londrina: 24h |
| RJ05) | J489 | 640 | 5/1 | R. Agulhas Negras, Resende |
| RN01) | J590 | 640 | 10/5 | R. Globo, Natal: 24h |
| RS14) | K277 | 640 | 50/10 | R. Bandeirantes, Porto Alegre: 24h |
| SP19) | K547 | 640 | 5/1 | R. Morada do Sol, Araraquara: 24h |
| BA06) | H462 | 650 | 5/0.5 | R. Clube, Valença: 24h |
| GO06) | H790 | 650 | 1/0.25 | R. Kompleta, Jussara |
| MG09) | L200 | 650 | 10/0.5 | R. Vitoriosa, Lagoa Formosa |
| MG85) | L309 | 650 | 5/0.5 | R. Globo, Unaí: 24h |
| MG142) | L372 | 650 | 10/1 | R. Itatiaia AM Vale do Aço, Timóteo |
| MT19) | I414 | *650 | 5 | R. Educadora, Colider: 0800-0300 |
| PA20) | I540 | 650 | 10/1 | R. Tropical, Santarém |

| MW | Call | kHz | kW | Station, location, h. of tr. |
|---|---|---|---|---|
| PB02) | I672 | 650 | 5/0.5 | R. Alto Piranhas, Cajazeiras |
| PI26) | I925 | 650 | 1/0.25 | R. Tapuio, Miguel Alves |
| PR09) | J202 | 650 | 1/0.5 | R. Banda B Norte Pioneiro, Cambará: 24h |
| PR91) | J250 | 650 | 8/1 | R. Colméia, Cascavel: 24h |
| RS15) | K238 | 650 | 5/0.5 | R. Dif. Sul Riograndense, Erechim |
| SP20) | K508 | 650 | 1/0.25 | R. Andradina, Andradina |
| SP22) | K518 | 650 | 5/1 | R. da Cidade, Santos |
| SP21) | K524 | 650 | 5/0.8 | R. Dif., Piracicaba: 24h |
| BA07) | H465 | 660 | 5/0.25 | R. Nova Jornal, Itapetinga: 0800-2300 |
| BA36) | H480 | 660 | 10/0.25 | R. Bom Jesus, Bom Jesus da Lapa: 0800-0300(Sun -0000) |
| BA65) | H518 | 660 | 1/0.25 | R. Planalto, Euclides da Cunha |
| CE06) | H619 | 660 | 1/0.25 | R. Rio das Garças, Itarema (Acaraú) |
| GO07) | H778 | *660 | 5/0.25 | R. Primavera, Itapuranga: 0800-0300 |
| GO51) | H794 | *660 | 1/0.25 | R. Alvorada, Quirinópolis |
| MG11) | L206 | 660 | 10/0.25 | R. Clube, Curvelo:24h Sun 1000-0300 |
| MT07) | I401 | 660 | 10/0.5 | R. Amorim Juventude, Rondonópolis |
| PA21) | I552 | 660 | 1/0.25 | R. Xinguara, Xinguara: 0800(SS 0900) -0100 |
| PE04) | I787 | 660 | 5/1 | R. Jornal, Limoeiro |
| PE05) | I795 | *660 | 1/0.25 | R. Grande Serra, Araripina |
| PI34) | I925 | 660 | 1/0.25 | R. Tacarijus, São Miguel do Tapuio |
| RJ06) | J472 | 660 | 5/1 | R. Friburgo, Nova Friburgo: 24h |
| R001) | J673 | 660 | 10/5 | R. Boas Novas AM, Porto Velho |
| RS16) | K286 | 660 | 1/0.25 | R. Marajá, Rosário do Sul: 0815-0255, Sat 0830-0200, Sun 0900-0255 |
| RS17) | K319 | 660 | 1/0.25 | R. Esmeralda, Vacaria: 24h |
| SP23) | K639 | 660 | 10/0.5 | R. Clube, Ribeirão Preto |
| SP112) | K777 | 660 | 20/0.5 | R. Mundial, São Paulo |
| AC11) | H208 | 670 | 0.25 | R. Dif., Sena Madureira: 0900-0400 |
| AM04) | H288 | 670 | 1 | R. Nac. do Alto Solimões, Tabatinga: 24h |
| AM03) | H297 | 670 | 1/0.25 | R. Vale do Rio Madeira R-VRM, Humaitá: 0900-0200, Sun 1000-2100 |
| AP02) | H420 | 670 | 10/1 | R. Globo - Equatorial, Macapá: 24h |
| CE07) | H606 | *670 | 1/0.25 | R. Cultura, Várzea Alegre: 0800-0100 |
| GO08) | H747 | *670 | 10/1 | R. São Francisco, Anápolis |
| MG12) | L310 | 670 | 10/2.5 | R. Educadora, Montes Claros: 0800-0300 |
| MG126) | L347 | 670 | 1/0.25 | R. Montanhera, Ponte Nova: 24h |
| MG123) | L361 | 670 | 5/0.25 | R. Vitoriosa, Uberaba |
| MG135) | N202 | 670 | 1/0.25 | R. Cidade, Bambuí: 0800-0300(Sat -0000) |
| MS28) | N600 | *670 | 10 | Super R. Fronteira, Ponta Porã |
| MT16) | I422 | 670 | 6/1 | R. Transpantaneira, Poconé |
| PA02) | I537 | 670 | 1/0.25 | R. Rural, Altamira: 0730-0100 |
| PA22) | I539 | 670 | 5/0.25 | R. Atalaia, Óbidos |
| PA27) | I546 | 670 | 1/0.25 | R. Tropical, Paragominas* |
| PI32) | I927 | 670 | 1/0.25 | R. Livramento, José de Freitas |
| PR10) | J231 | 670 | 3/0.25 | R. Canção Nova Esperança, Nova Esperança: 24h |
| PR11) | J248 | 670 | 10/2 | R. Globo, Curitiba:24h |
| RS18) | K296 | 670 | 2.5/0.25 | R. Cult. Jaguarão, Santa. Vitória do Palmar |
| RS19) | K370 | 670 | 10/0.5 | R. Gazeta, Carazinho: 24h |
| SE03) | J921 | 670 | 10/5 | R. Cultura de Sergipe, Aracaju: 24h |
| SP24) | K574 | 670 | 1/0.5 | R. Oceânica, Caraguatatuba: 0900-2200 (SS silent) |
| SP25) | K585 | 670 | 1/0.25 | R. Centro Oeste, Garça |
| SP26) | K598 | 670 | 1/0.5 | R. Convenção, Itu: 24h |
| BA08) | H471 | *680 | 10/2 | R. Clube, Sto. Antônio de Jesús: 24h |
| GO09) | H765 | 680 | 10/0.5 | R. Difusora, Jataí |
| GO49) | H787 | *680 | 5/1 | R. Mantiqueira, Niquelândia: 0800-0100, (Sat -2200, Sun 1100-) |
| MA03) | H885 | 680 | 20 | R. Dif. do Maranhão, São Luís: 24h |
| MG173) | L270 | *680 | 2/0.25 | R. Difusora, Ouro Fino: 24h |
| MG13) | L326 | 680 | 1/0.25 | R. União, João Pinheiro |
| MG71) | L296 | 680 | 5/0.25 | R. Novo Tempo, Governador Valadares |
| MG196) | L348 | *680 | 10/1 | R. Futura, Ibiá |
| MS02) | I389 | *680 | 10/1 | R. Cultura, Campo Grande: 0830-0500, Sun 1000-0400 |
| PB26) | I683 | *680 | 2.5/0.25 | R. Integração do Brejo, Bananeiras: 24h |
| PE06) | I793 | 680 | 10/1 | R. Grande Rio, Petrolina |
| PR155) | J362 | 680 | 5/0.25 | R. Poema, Pitanga: 24h |
| RJ07) | J452 | 680 | 20/5 | R. Copacabana, Rio de Janeiro |
| RS69) | K275 | 680 | 50 | R. Farroupilha, Porto Alegre: 24h |
| SP27) | K576 | *680 | 1/0.25 | R. Dif.680 AM, Catanduva |
| SP28) | K628 | *680 | 2/0.25 | R. Piratininga, Piraju |
| BA96) | H453 | 690 | 10/1 | R. Cultura, Ilhéus: 24h |
| CE08) | H587 | 690 | 25/10 | R. Shalom, Fortaleza: 24h |
| ES10) | I201 | 690 | 10/1 | R. America, Vitoria: 24h, SS 1000-2200 |
| GO48) | H780 | 690 | 50/1 | R. Sociedade Ceres, Ceres |
| MG14) | L228 | 690 | 50/5 | R. Mineira, Belo Horizonte: 1200-0245 |
| MS03) | I402 | 690 | 5/0.25 | R. Cultura, Naviraí: 0800-0300, Sun 1100-0100 |
| MT31) | I451 | *690 | 5/1 | R. Parecis, Diamantino |

| MW | Call | kHz | kW | Station, location, h. of tr. |
|---|---|---|---|---|
| PA03) | I532 | 690 | 20/5 | R. Clube do Pará, Belém: 24h |
| PR13) | J229 | 690 | 5/1 | R. Dif. de Londrina, Londrina |
| PR143) | J360 | 690 | 5/0.25 | R. Voz do Sudoeste, Coronel Vivida: 24h |
| RS21) | K252 | 690 | 5/0.5 | R. Progresso, Ijuí: 0800-0400 SS -0300 |
| SC07) | J772 | *690 | 5/1 | R. Clube, Lages: 24h |
| SP29) | K561 | *690 | 1/0.25 | R. Bebedouro, Bebedouro: 0800-0100 |
| SP30) | K588 | 690 | 1/0.25 | R. Clube, Guaratinguetá |
| SP31) | K625 | 690 | 1/0.25 | R. Cidade, Pereira Barreto: 0800-2300 |
| SP220) | K646 | 690 | 1/0.25 | R. Brasil, Santa Bárbara d'Oeste: 24h |
| TO12) | N661 | 690 | 25/1.5 | R. Liberdade, Palmas: 24h |
| BA10) | H500 | 700 | 25/1 | R. Cultura, Feira de Santana: 24h |
| GO47) | H801 | 700 | 25/0.5 | R. Pouso Alto, Piracanjuba |
| MT21) | I428 | *700 | 20/1 | R. Sorriso, Sorriso |
| PI04) | I890 | 700 | 10/5 | R. Globo, Teresina: 24h |
| PR92) | J225 | *700 | 10/0.25 | R. Capital do Papel, Telêmaco Borba |
| RJ56) | J507 | 700 | 5/0.4 | R. Aliança, Itálva |
| RS123) | K247 | *700 | 1/0.25 | R. Sideral, Getúlio Vargas: 24h |
| RS22) | K356 | 700 | 1/0.25 | R. Batovi, São Gabriel |
| SP32) | K686 | 700 | 50 | Nossa Radio, São Paulo |
| AL02) | H240 | 710 | 5/1 | R. Jornal, Maceió |
| BA46) | H490 | 710 | 10/0.25 | R. 21 News, Eunápolis |
| CE09) | H628 | *710 | 1/0.25 | R. Asa Branca, Boa Viagem: 0800-2300 |
| DF07) | H710 | 710 | 10/2.5 | R. Aliança, Brasília: 24h |
| MA12) | H891 | *710 | 1 | R. Verdes Campos, Pinheiro: 0800-0100 |
| MA27) | H910 | 710 | 1/0.5 | R. Verdes Vales, Grajaú |
| MG79) | L219 | 710 | 10/0.5 | R. Cancella, Ituiutaba: 0800-0200 |
| MG15) | L258 | 710 | 20/0.5 | R. Manhuaçu, Manhuaçu: 24h |
| MG80) | L319 | 710 | 2/0.25 | R. Planeta, Carmo do Paranaíba: 24h |
| MG16) | L333 | 710 | 2/0.25 | R. Dif., Pouso Alegre: 24h |
| MT08) | I386 | 710 | 5/0.5 | R. Cultura, Cuiabá* |
| MT23) | I436 | *710 | 5/1 | R. Nova Xavantina, Nova Xavantina |
| PA04) | I534 | 710 | 25/5 | R. Rural, Santarém: 0700-0300 |
| PB03) | I685 | 710 | 1/0.25 | R. Educadora, Conceição: 24h |
| PI19) | I901 | +710 | 1/0.25 | R. Alvorada do Sertão, São João do Piauí |
| PI23) | I933 | 710 | 1/0.5 | R. Clube, Barras |
| PR141) | J328 | 710 | 1/0.25 | R. Alternativa, Cândido de Abreu: 0800-0100(Sun -1000) |
| RJ09) | J451 | 710 | 10 | R. Sucesso AM, Rio de Janeiro:24h |
| SC08) | J793 | *710 | 1/0.25 | R. Fraiburgo, Fraiburgo: 0800-0300 |
| SP33) | K559 | 710 | 10/0.25 | R. 710, Bauru |
| ACO1) | H202 | 720 | 10 | R. Integração, Cruzeiro do Sul: 0900-0300 |
| AM05) | H281 | 720 | 1/0.25 | CBN, Itacoatiara: 24h |
| MG28) | L330 | *720 | 2.5/0.5 | R. Divinópolis, Divinópolis: 24h |
| MS04) | I390 | 720 | 5/1 | R. Clube, Dourados |
| MT20) | I411 | 720 | 5/1 | R. Difusora, Barra do Garças |
| PE07) | I770 | 720 | 100 | R. CI de Pernambuco, Recife: 24h |
| RS23) | K276 | 720 | 100 | R. Guaíba, Porto Alegre: 24h |
| SP34) | K575 | 720 | 1/0.25 | R. Difusora, Casa Branca |
| SP35) | K701 | 720 | 1/0.25 | R. Sentinela, Ourinhos: 24h |
| SP36) | K718 | 720 | 1/0.25 | R. RC Vale, Cruzeiro |
| SP37) | K722 | 720 | 1/0.25 | R. Espaço Livre, Olímpia: 24h |
| CE45) | H498 | *720 | 1/0.5 | R. Sinal, Aracati |
| ES16) | I217 | 730 | 10/0.5 | R. Novo Tempo, Vitória |
| GO31) | H759 | 730 | 50/5 | R. Sagres 730 AM, Goiânia |
| MA04) | H896 | 730 | 1/0.25 | R. Eldorado, Codó |
| MG17) | L287 | 730 | 5/1 | R. JM 730, Uberaba |
| MG18) | L297 | 730 | 10/1 | R. Manchester, Juiz de Fora |
| MS38) | I452 | *730 | 1/0.5 | R. Princesa do Vale, Camapuã |
| MT09) | I410 | 730 | 10/2.5 | R. Jornal, Cáceres |
| PE08) | I780 | 730 | 10/5 | Em. Rural, A Voz do São Francisco, Petrolina |
| PR15) | J208 | 730 | 7/0.6 | R. Marumby, Curitiba |
| PR16) | J323 | 730 | 1/0.25 | R. Objetiva, Campo Mourão |
| PR147) | J353 | 730 | 5/0.25 | R. Integração Metropolitana, Corbélia |
| RS24) | K268 | 730 | 5/1 | R. Planalto, Passo Fundo: 24h |
| SC09) | J787 | 730 | 5/1 | R. Tubá: 0800-0100 |
| SP38) | K523 | 730 | 10/0.25 | R. Cidade, Jundiaí |
| SP39) | K610 | 730 | 10/1 | R. Dirceu, Marília |
| ACO2) | H206 | *740 | 20/10 | CBN Amazonia, Rio Branco:24h |
| BA11) | H446 | 740 | 100 | R. Soc. da Bahia, Salvador: 24h |
| PR17) | J259 | *740 | 1/0.25 | R. Goioerê, Goioerê: 0800-0100(Sun -2100) |
| PR135) | J354 | *740 | 1/0.25 | R. Placar, Ortigueira: 1000-2100(Sun -1800) |
| RS25) | K265 | 740 | 2.5/0.25 | R. Palmeira, Palmeira das Missões: 0900-0300 |
| RS26) | K283 | 740 | 1/0.25 | R. Cultura Riograndina, Rio Grande: 24h |
| SC10) | J753 | 740 | 10/1 | CBN, Florianópolis: 24h |
| SP40) | K553 | 740 | 1/0.25 | R. Cultura, Bariri: 0730-0200(Sat-0100), Sun 1000-2300 |
| SP41) | K650 | 740 | 25/0.5 | R. Trianon, São Paulo |
| DF01) | H709 | 750 | 50/25 | R. Jovem Pan, Brasília: 24h |
| MG19) | L213 | 750 | 100/5 | R. América, Belo Horizonte |
| PA28) | I541 | 750 | 1/0.25 | R. Ximango, Alenquer |

| MW | Call | kHz | kW | Station, location, h. of tr. |
|---|---|---|---|---|
| PB04) | I682 | *750 | 1/0.25 | R. Panati, Patos |
| PI05) | I897 | 750 | 1/0.25 | R. Liberdade, Campo Maior |
| RS27) | K264 | *750 | 5/0.25 | R. Osório, Osório: 0900-0200 Sun -2300 |
| SC11) | J815 | 750 | 5/0.25 | R. Aliança, Concórdia: 0730-0300 |
| SE04) | J927 | *750 | 10/0.25 | R. Progresso, Lagarto: 0800-0300 |
| SP42) | K516 | 750 | 1/0.25 | R. Clube, Osvaldo Cruz: 1000-2200, (Sat 1200-1800, Sun 0900-1700) |
| SP43) | K642 | 750 | 12/0.5 | R. CMN, Ribeirão Preto |
| SP44) | K661 | 750 | 1.5/0.25 | R. Super Piratininga, São José dos Campos |
| SP283 | K684 | 750 | 5/0.5 | R. Atual, Registro |
| TO03) | H792 | 750 | 1/0.25 | R. Tocantins, Tocantinópolis |
| AL12) | H252 | 760 | 1/0.25 | R. Delmiro, Delmiro Gouveia: 0900-2400 |
| AP03) | H424 | 760 | 5 | Rede Amapaense de Rdif., Macapá |
| BA44) | H461 | 760 | 5/0.5 | R. Cidade, Vitória da Conquista (F.Pl. 1550) |
| CE10) | H588 | 760 | 25/10 | R. Uirapuru, Fortaleza |
| GO43) | H775 | 760 | 5/0.5 | R. Rio Claro, Iporã: 0800-2300 |
| GO11) | H783 | *760 | 10/0.5 | R. Pousada do Rio Quente, Caldas Novas: 0800-0300 SS -2200 |
| MG83) | L257 | 760 | 2.5/0.25 | R. Difusora, Machado |
| MG137) | L360 | 760 | 10/0.5 | R. Terra, Monte Claros |
| MT32) | N408 | 760 | 10/5 | R. Natureza, Chapada dos Guimarães: 24h |
| PR12) | J343 | *760 | 10/0.25 | R. Cacique, Guarapuava |
| RJ11) | J478 | 760 | 25/1 | R. Manchete AM, Niterói: 24h |
| RS29) | K351 | 760 | 2.5/0.25 | R. Ametista, Planalto: 0800-0200 |
| SC12) | J742 | 760 | 25/2 | R. Nereu Ramos, Blumenau: 0730-0100 |
| SP149) | K541 | 760 | 1/0.25 | R. Urubupungá, Andradina |
| SP45) | K560 | *760 | 1/0.25 | R. Auri-Verde, Bauru |
| BA51) | H491 | *770 | 1/0.25 | R. Rio Corrente, Santa Maria da Vitória |
| CE11) | H609 | *770 | 10/0.25 | R. Vale do Salgado, Lavras da Mangabeira: 0800-2300, SS 0900-2200 |
| ES03) | I211 | *770 | 5/0.25 | R. Globo AM, Cachoeiro de Itapemirim |
| GO12) | H745 | 770 | 5/1 | R. A Voz do Coração Imaculado, Anápolis: 24h |
| MA28) | H922 | 770 | 5/0.25 | R. Vitória, Coelho Neto |
| MA41) | H902 | *770 | 10 | R. Boa Noticia, Balsas |
| MG20) | L209 | 770 | 2.5/0.25 | R. Cultura d'Oeste, Lavras: 0800-0200 |
| MG21) | L302 | *770 | 10/0.5 | R. Clube de Patos, Patos de Minas: 0700-0200(SS. 0900-0300) |
| MG108) | L315 | *770 | 5/0.5 | R. Pontal, Ituruma |
| MG22) | L337 | 770 | 1/0.25 | R. Itabira, Itabira |
| MS11) | I412 | 770 | 5/0.5 | R. Caiuás, Dourados |
| MT28) | N404 | *770 | 1 | R. Cidade de Matupá, Matupá: 0900-0300 |
| MT45) | I434 | 770 | 5/1 | R. Xavantes, Jaciara: 0900-0030, (Sun 1000-2200) |
| PA29) | I560 | 770 | 10/0.25 | R. Clube, Marabá |
| PR131) | J344 | 770 | 5/0.25 | R. Cidade, Cambé |
| SP46) | K506 | 770 | 5/0.5 | R. Mix, Limeira: 0700-0000 SS -0100 |
| GO13) | H789 | 780 | 10/1 | R. Soc. Vera Cruz, Goianésia: 0700-2300 |
| MA24) | H919 | 780 | 10/5 | R. Alvorada, Zé Doca |
| MG23) | L246 | *780 | 1 | R. Educadora Jovem Pan, Uberlândia |
| MG103) | L259 | 780 | 10/1 | R. Manhumirim, Manhumirim: 0800-0100(Sat -0300, Sun -0000) |
| PE09) | I771 | 780 | 30/10 | R. Jornal do Comércio, Recife: 24h |
| PR18) | J247 | 780 | 1/0.25 | R. Porta Voz, Cianorte: 24h |
| PR19) | J305 | *780 | 5/0.25 | R. Chopinzinho, Chopinzinho: 24h |
| RS30) | K229 | 780 | 5/2 | R. Diário da Manhã, Carazinho:24h |
| RS31) | K279 | 780 | 25 | R. Caicara, Porto Alegre: 24h |
| SC13) | J788 | *780 | 2.5 | R. Marconi, Urussanga: 0900-0200, Sun 1000-2230 |
| SP161) | K619 | *780 | 1/0.25 | R. Dif Aparecida, Monte Aprazível: 0800-0100 |
| BA13) | H484 | 790 | 10/1 | R. Barreiras "RB 790", Barreiras: 0800-0500(SS -0300) |
| BA14) | H505 | 790 | 1/0.25 | R. Regional, Serrinha |
| CE12) | H629 | 790 | 1/0.25 | R. Jornal Centro Sul, Iguatu |
| GO28) | H761 | 790 | 5/0.5 | R. Xavantes, Ipameri |
| GO14) | H771 | *790 | 1/0.5 | R. Eldorado, Mineiros |
| MA29) | H904 | *790 | 1/0.25 | R. Rio Turiaçu, Santa Helena |
| MA20) | H915 | *790 | 1/0.25 | R. Cultura, Açailândia |
| MA30) | H899 | 790 | 1/0.25 | R. Rio Flores,Tuntum: 24h |
| MG24) | L279 | 790 | 1/0.25 | R. Soc. Ponte Nova, Ponte Nova: 0800-0200 |
| MG25) | L311 | *790 | 1/0.25 | R. Treze de Junho, Mantena |
| MG26) | L314 | 790 | 5/1 | R. Tropical, Lagoa da Prata: 24h |
| MT22) | I456 | 790 | 1 | R. Regional, Nortelândia |
| PB05) | I679 | *790 | 2.5/1 | R. Cultura 790, Guarabira: 0700-0300 |
| PI36) | I931 | 790 | 1/0.25 | R. Mafrense, Simplício Mendes |
| PR130) | J316 | 790 | 2.5/0.25 | R. Clube, Faxinal |
| PR20) | J337 | 790 | 10/0.25 | R. RCC, Curitiba: 24h |
| RS32) | K285 | *790 | 1/0.25 | R. Rio Pardo, Rio Pardo |
| SC14) | J789 | 790 | 1/0.5 | R. Videira, Videira: 0830-0300 |
| SP48) | K538 | *790 | 1/0.25 | R. Brasil, Adamantina: 24h |
| SP49) | K546 | 790 | 5/0.5 | R. Cultura, Araraquara: 24h |
| SP162) | K674 | 790 | 5/0.25 | R. Cultura, Taubaté |
| AL17) | H256 | 800 | 10 | R. Palmares, Maceió |
| DF02) | H705 | 800 | 10/1 | R. MEC, Brasília: 24h |
| PI08) | I921 | 800 | 10 | R. Antares, Teresina: 0930-0100 |
| RJ12) | J457 | 800 | 100 | R. MEC, Rio de Janeiro: 24h |
| RS33) | K292 | 800 | 10 | R. Universidade, Santa Maria: 24h |
| BA54) | H528 | 810 | 10/0.25 | R. Nossa Senhora de Guadalupe, Riacho de Santana |
| CE13) | H589 | 810 | 50/5 | R. Verdes Mares, Fortaleza: 24h |
| GO15) | H767 | 810 | 5/0.5 | R. Alvorada, Rialma: 0830-0100 |
| MG27) | L202 | 810 | 1 | R. Aimorés, Aimorés |
| MG92) | L252 | 810 | 1/0.25 | R. Educadora, Ubá: 24h |
| MG76) | L266 | *810 | 2/0.25 | R. Clube, Nepomuceno |
| MG138) | L354 | 810 | 1/0.25 | R. Cidade, Capinópolis |
| MG156) | L366 | 810 | 5/0.5 | R. Rainha de Paz, Patrocínio: 24h |
| MT33) | N402 | *810 | 1/0.25 | R. Floresta, São José do Rio Claro: 0900-0200 |
| MT34) | N406 | *810 | 1/0.25 | R. Floresta AM, Alta Floresta: 0900-0200 |
| PR49) | J261 | 810 | 2/0.25 | Rede Terra Nativa, Cornélio Procópio |
| PR111) | J336 | 810 | 5/0.5 | R. Esperança, Prudentópolis |
| RS136) | K324 | 810 | 1.9/0.25 | R. Cinderela, Campo Bom |
| SP50) | K604 | 810 | 5/0.25 | R. Dif. Jundiaiense, Jundiaí |
| SP89) | K655 | 810 | 1/0.5 | R. Universal, Santos |
| SP51) | K732 | 810 | 5/0.5 | R. Cancao Nova São José do Rio Preto |
| AC03) | H... | 820 | 1/0.25 | R. Educ. 6 de Agosto, Xapuri: 1000-0100 |
| AC12) | H207 | 820 | 0.25 | R. Dif. de Tarauacá, Tarauacá |
| AM06) | H294 | *820 | 1/0.25 | R. Princesa, Manacapuru: 24h |
| BA15) | H534 | 820 | 20/1 | R. Cultura, Utinga: 0830-0100 |
| CE14) | H624 | 820 | 1/0.25 | R. União, Camocim |
| CE60) | H655 | ‡*820 | 1/0.25 | R. Sul Cearense, Brejo Santo |
| ES04) | I212 | 820 | 10/2.5 | R. Gazeta, Vitória |
| GO16) | H752 | 820 | 50/5 | R. Bandeirantes, Goiânia |
| MG29) | L255 | *820 | 5/0.25 | R. Globo, Barbacena: 24h |
| MG167) | L373 | *820 | 3/0.25 | R. Bom Sucesso, Minas Movas |
| MG30) | L291 | 820 | 1/0.25 | R. da Familia, São Sebastião do Paraíso: 24h |
| MT10) | I400 | *820 | 10/1 | R. Dif., Cáceres: 0800-0130 |
| PA05) | I543 | *820 | 1 | R. Regional, Conceição do Araguaia: 0900-2300 |
| PE10) | I775 | 820 | 5/1 | R. Universitária, Recife |
| PI06) | I912 | 820 | 5/0.25 | R. Cacique Bruenque, Regeneração |
| PR21) | J238 | 820 | 10/5 | R. Cultura, Foz do Iguaçu |
| PR150) | J357 | 820 | 5/0.25 | R. Princesa, Roncador: 0830-0030 |
| RJ13) | J477 | 820 | 5/0.25 | R. Globo, Macaé: 24h |
| RS34) | K241 | 820 | 5/1 | R. do Vale, Estrela: 0900-0200 |
| SC15) | J738 | 820 | 10/5 | R. Globo, Vale do Itajaí: 24h |
| SP53) | K602 | 820 | 10/5 | R. Jauense, Jaú: 0700-0300, Sun 0800-2200 |
| SP54) | K622 | 820 | 0.5/0.25 | R. Clube, Ourinhos |
| SP55) | K624 | *820 | 1/0.25 | R. Difusora, Penápolis |
| BA67) | H506 | 830 | 1/0.25 | R. Extremo Sul da Bahia, Itamaraju: 0700-0100 Sun: -0000 |
| CE65) | H659 | 830 | 1/0.25 | R. Pioneira, Forquilha: 0800-0230, Sat 1000(Sun 0800)-0100 |
| GO50) | H805 | *830 | 1/0.25 | R. Sempre, Goiatuba: 24h |
| MA26) | H905 | 830 | 10/1 | R. Mirante do Maranhão, Imperatriz |
| MA21) | H925 | 830 | 10/1 | R. Boa Esperança, Esperantinópolis |
| MG31) | L244 | 830 | 15/5 | R. Gerais, Belo Horizonte |
| MS07) | I396 | *830 | 5/0.5 | R. Cidade Maracaju, Maracaju: 0900-2300 |
| MT26) | N401 | *830 | 10/1 | R. Educadora, Juina |
| PA24) | I556 | 830 | 10/1 | R. Guarany de Marajó, Soure |
| PI07) | I906 | 830 | 1/0.25 | R. Primeira Capital, Oeiras |
| PI37) | I934 | 830 | 1/0.25 | R. União, União |
| PR22) | J224 | 830 | 7.5/0.75 | R. Iguassu, Araucária: 24h |
| PR24) | J266 | 830 | 10/0.5 | CBN, Londrina: 24h |
| PR23) | J311 | 830 | 1/0.25 | R. Progresso, Clevelândia |
| RJ39) | J488 | 830 | 10/0.5 | R. Tropical Solimões, Rio de Janeiro: 24h |
| RN02) | J595 | 830 | 1/0.5 | R. Rural do Caicó, Caicó |
| RS35) | K332 | 830 | 5/0.25 | R. Independente, Cruz Alta |
| RS232) | K346 | 830 | 5/0.6 | R. Cassino, Rio Grande: M-F 0900-2300 |
| RS200) | K346 | 830 | 5 | R. Cassino, Rio Grande: 0900-2300 |
| SC16) | J773 | *830 | 1/0.25 | R. Cruz de Malta, Lauro Müller |
| SE06) | J926 | 830 | 20/1 | R. Princesa da Serra, Itabaiana: 24h |
| SP56) | K681 | *830 | 10/1 | R. Lider, Votuporanga: 24h |
| SP227) | K746 | 830 | 5/1 | R. Novo Tempo, Nova Odessa: 24h |
| AL13) | H253 | 840 | 10/0.25 | R. Canavieiro, União dos Palmares |
| AM07) | H298 | 840 | 1/0.25 | R. Rio Madeira, Manicoré |
| BA16) | H447 | 840 | 25/5 | R. Excelsior da Bahia, Salvador: 24h |
| CE51) | H648 | 840 | 1/0.5 | R. Campo Maior, Quixeramobim: 0800-2000 Sat -2200 Sun -2300 |

| MW | Call | kHz | kW | Station, location, h. of tr. |
|---|---|---|---|---|
| PI38) | I930 | 840 | 1/0.25 | R. Ribeirão, Demerval Lobão |
| PI39) | J937 | ‡840 | 1/0.25 | R. Vitória, Batalha |
| PR75) | J320 | 840 | 10/1.2 | R. Inconfidência, Umuarama: 24h |
| RS36) | K248 | 840 | 10 | R. Capital, Porto Alegre |
| SC17) | J750 | 840 | 10/1 | R. Rural, Concórdia: 24h |
| SP57) | K687 | 840 | 100/50 | R. Bandeirantes, São Paulo: 24h |
| BA17) | H474 | 850 | 5/0.25 | R. Caraíba, Senhor do Bonfim |
| CE15) | H599 | *850 | 1 | R. Iracema, Juazeiro do Nte |
| GO17) | H776 | *850 | 5/1 | R. Tropical, Porangatu: 0900-0300 |
| MA31) | H923 | *850 | 10/0.5 | R. Cidade, Vitória do Mearim: 0900-0200 |
| MG32) | L233 | *850 | 1/0.25 | R. Difusora Formiguense, Formiga |
| MG34) | L295 | *850 | 5/0.25 | R. Tupaciguara, Tupaciguara: 0900-0300 |
| MS30) | I438 | *850 | 1/0.25 | R. Difusora Nor'estado, São Gabriel |
| MT02) | I416 | *850 | 10/2 | R. Sulmatogrossense, Poxoréo: 24h, (Sat -1900), Sun 0800-1700 |
| PA17) | I538 | *850 | 10/1 | R. Itacaiúnas, Marabá |
| PA06) | I555 | 850 | 1/0.25 | R. Tocantins, Cametá |
| PA18) | I557 | 850 | 5/1 | R. Itaituba, Itaituba |
| PB22) | I693 | 850 | 5/1 | R. Rural, Guarabira |
| PI30) | I909 | 850 | 1/0.25 | R. Grande Picos, Picos |
| PR50) | J254 | 850 | 5/0.25 | R. Dif. Colméia, Campo Mourão |
| PR86) | J291 | *850 | 2/0.25 | R. Alvorada do Sul, Rebouças |
| RJ31) | J470 | 850 | 10/0.5 | R. Campos Dif., Campos dos Goytacazes: 24h |
| RO03) | J675 | ‡850 | 5/1 | R. Ariquemes, Ariquemes |
| SC20) | J808 | 850 | 2.5/0.25 | R. Cidade, Brusque |
| SC102) | J807 | 850 | 1/0.25 | R. Atalaia, Campo Erê |
| SP59) | K563 | *850 | 2.5/0.5 | R. Nova Clube, Birigui |
| SP58) | K644 | 850 | 2.5/0.25 | R. Jornal, Rio Claro |
| CE16) | H592 | 860 | 25/10 | R. Cidade de Fortaleza, Maracanaú |
| RS37) | K288 | 860 | 10/1 | R. Guarathan, Santa Maria: 0800-0300 |
| AL03) | H245 | *870 | 5/1 | R. Educ. Sampaio, Palmeira dos Indios: 0800-0300 |
| AM19) | H322 | 870 | 1/0.25 | R. Cidade, Manacapuru: 1000-0200 |
| BA18) | H457 | 870 | 12/0.25 | R. Nacional, Itabuna |
| BA84) | H499 | 870 | 5/1 | R. Cidade, Juazeiro: 24h, Sun 1000-2200 |
| CE17) | H591 | 870 | 1/0.25 | R. Liberdade, Iguatu |
| CE66) | H658 | *870 | 1/0.25 | R. Tabajara, São Benedito |
| ES20) | I213 | *870 | 5/0.25 | R. Globo. Linhares: 24h |
| GO18) | H749 | 870 | 5/0.5 | R. Lago Dourado, Uruaçu |
| GO32) | H754 | 870 | 10/0.5 | R. Universitária, Goiânia:24h |
| MA05) | H906 | 870 | 10/0.5 | R. Mirante, Codó: 24h |
| MG78) | L304 | *870 | 10/0.5 | R. Juriti, Paracatu |
| MG38) | L318 | 870 | 1/0.5 | R. Cultura, Diamantina |
| MG66) | L324 | *870 | 5/0.25 | R. Sacramento, Sacramento: 0800-2300, Sat 1200-2200) |
| MG128) | L349 | 870 | 5/0.25 | R. Atividade Muriaé |
| MT35) | N409 | 870 | 1/0.5 | R. Garça Branca, Guiratinga |
| PA11) | I547 | 870 | 1/0.25 | R. Marajó, Breves |
| PR25) | J243 | 870 | 5/0.25 | R. Nova Ingá, Maringá: 0100-0100 |
| SC96) | J784 | 870 | 12/0.25 | R. São Francisco, São Francisco do Sul: 24h |
| SP60) | K620 | 870 | 1/0.25 | R. Novo Horizonte, Novo Horizonte |
| SP61) | K705 | 870 | 5/1 | R. Central, Campinas: 24h |
| T004) | H762 | *870 | 1/0.25 | R. Anhanguera, Araguaína |
| MG35) | L275 | 880 | 100 | R. Inconfidência, Belo Horizonte: 24h |
| PB18) | I680 | 880 | 1/0.25 | R. Maringá, Pombal |
| RS38) | K249 | 880 | 25/2.5 | R. Itaí, Porto Alegre: 24h |
| SP87) | K317 | 880 | 2.5/0.25 | R. São Miguel, Uruguaiana |
| RS20) | K363 | 880 | 8/0.25 | R. Seberi, Seberi: 24h |
| CE46) | H642 | 890 | 1/0.25 | R. Itatiaia, Santa Quitéria: 0800-0100 (Sun 0900-) |
| DF03) | H706 | 890 | 50/2.5 | R. Planalto, Brasília: 24h |
| MG36) | L250 | 890 | 10/1 | R. Santa Cruz, Almenara: 0900-2300(Sun -1500) |
| MG154) | L370 | 890 | 5/0.25 | R. Clube, Inhapim |
| MS33) | I453 | 890 | 10/0.5 | R. Guaicurus, Fátima do Sul: 1000-0000 (Sat -1900), Sun 0800-1700 |
| PA13) | I536 | 890 | 5/1 | R. Ponta Negra, Santarém |
| PE11) | I772 | 890 | 20/10 | R. Tamandaré, Olinda: 24h |
| PR117) | J287 | 890 | 2.5/0.25 | R. Ubá, Ivaiporã: 0800-0100 |
| PR26) | J338 | 890 | 5/0.25 | R. Itapuã, Pato Branco24h |
| RJ59) | J499 | 890 | 10/0.5 | R. Musical, Cantagalo |
| RS39) | K215 | 890 | 5/0.25 | R. Difusora, Bento Gonçalves |
| RS40) | K290 | 890 | 5/0.5 | R. Noroeste, Santa Rosa |
| SC18) | J755 | 890 | 5/1 | R. Santa Catarina, Florianópolis |
| SP62) | K690 | 890 | 50/10 | R. Gazeta, São Paulo |
| SP178) | K562 | 890 | 1/0.25 | R. Imaculada Conceicao, Bilac |
| BA19) | H488 | 900 | 1 | R. Sisal, Conceição do Coité: 0800-0100(SS -2300) |
| GO41) | H768 | *900 | 10/1 | R. Rio Verde AM, Rio Verde |
| MG148) | L311 | 900 | 2.5/0.25 | Rede Gerais, Carangola: 24h |
| MG124) | L338 | 900 | 1/0.25 | R. Vinícola, Andradas |
| MT36) | I455 | 900 | 10/2.5 | R. Dif. Arco-Iris, Araputanga: 0900-0030 |
| MT41) | I431 | *900 | 5/1 | R. Integração, Primavera do Leste |
| PA10) | I533 | 900 | 25/5 | R. Liberal, Belém: 24h |
| PR28) | J295 | 900 | 1/0.25 | R. União, Toledo: 0800-0300, Sun 0900-2300 |
| RJ15) | J454 | 900 | 50/10 | R. Tamoio, Rio de Janeiro: 24h |
| RN03) | J591 | 900 | 10 | R. Nordeste Evangélica, Natal: 24h |
| RO04) | J672 | 900 | 5/1 | R. Alvorada de Rondônia, Ji-Paraná: 0800-0400 |
| RS41) | K211 | 900 | 2.5/0.5 | R. Aratiba, Aratiba: 24h |
| RS179) | K263 | 900 | 5/0.5 | R. ABC 900, Nôvo Hamburgo: 24h |
| RS164) | K301 | 900 | 1/0.25 | R. Municipal, São Pedro do Sul: 24h |
| SP63) | K511 | 900 | 1/0.25 | R. Difusora, Presidente Prudente |
| SP64) | K664 | 900 | 10/0.8 | R. Jovem Pan, São José do Rio Preto |
| SP65) | K742 | 900 | 1/0.25 | R. Globo, Itapetininga |
| GO20) | H763 | 910 | 5/0.25 | R. Paranaíba, Itumbiara: 0800-0300 |
| GO23) | H804 | 910 | 10/0.5 | R. Cidade, Jaraguá: 0800-0300 |
| MG37) | L292 | 910 | 1/0.25 | R. Teófilo Otoni, Teófilo Otoni: 24h |
| MG132) | L346 | *910 | 1/0.25 | R. Gospel CRN, Nova Serrana |
| MG149) | N206 | 910 | 5/1 | R. Globo, Juiz de Fora: 24h |
| PE12) | I785 | 910 | 5/1 | R. Super Liberdade, Caruaru: 24h |
| PI41) | I935 | *910 | 10/1 | CBN, Teresina: 24h |
| PR29) | J207 | 910 | 1/0.25 | R. Nova AM, Apucarana: 0800-0000 |
| RS43) | K320 | 910 | 5/0.5 | R. Venâncio Aires, Venâncio Aires: |
| SC19) | J811 | 910 | 4/0.5 | R. Difusora, Içara: 24h |
| SC90) | J824 | *910 | 1/0.25 | R. Rainha das Quedas, Abelardo Luz |
| SP66) | K536 | 910 | 7.5/0.25 | R. Onda Livre, Piracicaba: 24h |
| SP228) | K763 | *910 | 1/0.25 | R. Princesa, Monte Azul Paulista |
| BA42) | H476 | 920 | 1/0.25 | R. Educ. Santana de Caetité, Caetité: 24h |
| BA57) | H519 | 920 | 25/2 | R. Novo Tempo, Salvador |
| ES05) | I207 | 920 | 10/5 | R. Cultura, Linhares |
| GO33) | H788 | 920 | 5/1 | R. Vale da Serra, São Luís de Monte Belos: 0800-2300 |
| MG39) | L271 | 920 | 5/0.5 | R. Cultura, Visconde do Rio Branco: 0800-0200, Sun 0900-2100 |
| PB31) | I697 | ‡920 | 5/0.5 | R. CBN, João Pessoa |
| PI09) | I895 | 920 | 1/0.25 | R. Dif. Grande, Picos |
| PI11) | I893 | 920 | 10/0.5 | R. Educadora, Parnaíba |
| RJ41) | J494 | *920 | 1/0.5 | R. Sociedade, Volta Redonda |
| RN04) | J600 | 920 | 1/0.25 | R. Currais Novos, Currais Novos |
| RS44) | K348 | 920 | 20/2 | R.Tramandaí, Tramandaí |
| SP67) | K584 | 920 | 10/0.25 | R. Imperador, Franca |
| SP222) | K769 | *920 | 1/0.25 | R. Bandeirantes, Penápolis: 24h |
| SP221) | K775 | 920 | 40/1 | R. Nacional Gospel, Cotia |
| AM16) | H296 | *930 | 10 | R. Boas Novas, Manaus: 24h |
| CE18) | H605 | *930 | 1/0.25 | R. Verde Mares, Barbalha |
| CE52) | H646 | 930 | 7/0.25 | R. Metropolitana, Caucaia |
| MG41) | L220 | *930 | 2.5/0.25 | R. Clube, Campo Belo: 0900-0100 (SS -2100) |
| MG42) | L229 | 930 | 10/5 | R. Vitoriosa, Araguari |
| MS05) | L454 | *930 | 10/0.25 | R. Capital, Campo Grande |
| MT12) | I423 | 930 | 10/0.5 | R. Clube, Rondonópolis: 0900-0200 (Sat -2200, Sun -0000) |
| MT37) | N400 | *930 | 10/0.25 | R. Jornal, Pontes e Lacerda: 0900-0100 |
| PR30) | J227 | 930 | 1/0.25 | R. Cultura, Rolândia |
| PR31) | J232 | 930 | 10/1 | R. Cultura, Curitiba |
| PR69) | J235 | 930 | 10/1 | R. Princesa, Francisco Beltrão: 0845-0200, Sun 0955-0100 |
| RS45) | K230 | 930 | 20/2.5 | R. Caxias, Caxias do Sul:24h |
| RS46) | K298 | 930 | 10/0.5 | R. Santo Ângelo, Santo Ângelo: 0800-0300 |
| SE07) | J923 | 930 | 20/5 | R. 930AM - Liberdade AM, Aracaju |
| SP71) | K500 | *930 | 1/0.25 | R. Dinâmica, Santa Fé do Sul: 0900-0100 (Sun -0000) |
| SP68) | K503 | 930 | 1/0.25 | R. Clube, Itapira |
| SP69) | K652 | 930 | 10/1 | R. Cultura, Santos: 24h |
| SP70) | K713 | 930 | 5/1 | R. Canção Nova, Agudos |
| SP214) | K747 | *930 | 1/0.25 | R. Jóia, Adamantina: 0900-0100 |
| AC04) | H204 | *940 | 10/1 | R. Verdes Florestas, Cruzeiro do Sul: 0930-0200 Sun 1000-0040 |
| PI25) | I911 | *940 | 10/0.25 | R. AM 7 Cidades, Piracuruca |
| RJ16) | J453 | 940 | 100 | Super Rede Boa Vontade, Rio de Janeiro |
| BA50) | H489 | *950 | 1/0.25 | R. Bahia Noroeste, Paulo Afonso |
| CE19) | H593 | 950 | 10/1 | R. Educadora do Nordeste, Sobral: 0800-0130 |
| GO21) | H764 | *950 | 5/0.25 | R. Dif., Itumbiara: 0800-0300(Sun-1000) |
| MA17) | H916 | 950 | 10/0.25 | R. Dif. Karajás, João Lisboa |
| MG43) | L212 | 950 | 25/10 | R. Atalaia, Belo Horizonte |
| MG44) | L281 | 950 | 10/0.25 | R. Indy, Bueno Brandão: 0800-2200 |
| MT17) | I439 | 950 | 5/1 | R. Tucunaré, Juara: 24h |
| PB17) | I681 | 950 | 1/0.25 | R. Jornal, Sousa |
| PE13) | I782 | 950 | 25/5 | R. Planalto, Carpina: 24h |

| MW | Call | kHz | kW | Station, location, h. of tr. |
|---|---|---|---|---|
| PI20) | I932 | 950 | 10/0.25 | R. São José dos Altos, Altos |
| PI42) | I923 | 950 | 1/0.25 | R. Boa Esperança, Padre Marcos |
| RS47) | K260 | 950 | 10/0.25 | R. Independente, Lajeado: 24h |
| SC21) | J736 | 950 | 1/0.25 | R. Vale, Tijucas: 24h |
| SP72) | K510 | 950 | 5/0.25 | R. 950, Vera Cruz |
| AL04) | H241 | 960 | 10 | R. Difusora de Alagôas, Maceió: 24h |
| CE37) | H618 | 960 | 1/0.25 | R. Cultura dos Inhamuns, Tauá |
| ES15) | I216 | *960 | 25/0.25 | R. Diocesana, Cachoeiro de Itapemirim: 24h, Sat 0700-1510 |
| GO45) | H802 | 960 | 50/1 | R. Caraíba, Aparecida de Goiânia: 0500-0100 |
| MS61) | N609 | *960 | 5 | R. Fronteira, Corumbá |
| PA26) | I551 | 960 | 1/0.25 | R. Clube, Itaituba |
| PR32) | J257 | 960 | 1/0.25 | R. Globo, Maringá: 24h |
| SC22) | J733 | 960 | 5/0.25 | R. Guarujá, Orleans: 0800-0100(Sun -0000) |
| SC23) | J813 | 960 | 8/0.25 | R. Super Difusora, Xanxerê |
| SP73) | K689 | 960 | 50/10 | R. São Paulo, São Paulo |
| TO09) | H793 | *960 | 25/5 | R. Jovem Palmas, Palmas |
| BA20) | H451 | *970 | 10/5 | R. Sociedade, Feira de Santana: 0700-0100 |
| CE20) | H612 | 970 | 5/0.25 | R. Monólitos, Quixadá |
| MG45) | L243 | 970 | 5/0.25 | R. Caratinga, Caratinga |
| MG46) | L285 | *970 | 2.5/0.25 | R. São João Del Rey, São João DR: 24h |
| MS18) | I399 | *970 | 5/0.5 | R. Vale do Taquari, Coxim: 1000-0500, Sun 24h |
| PB06) | I684 | *970 | 1/0.25 | R. Princesa Isabel, Princesa Isabel: 0830-2300 |
| PI43) | I910 | *970 | 3/0.5 | R. Vale do Parnaíba, Luzilândia: 0940-2100 (Sat 1500-2100, Sun 1430-1700) |
| PR33) | J260 | 970 | 7.5/1 | R. Alvorada, Londrina |
| PR34) | J277 | 970 | 10/0.25 | R. Difusora do Paraná, Marechal Cândido Rondón: 0800-0300 |
| RS49) | K201 | 970 | 50/10 | R. Liberdade, Porto Alegre: 24h |
| RS50) | K349 | *970 | 1/0.5 | R. Alto Uruguai, Humaitá: 0800-0200 (Sat -2200), Sun 0900-0100 |
| SC24) | J730 | 970 | 5/0.25 | R. Araguaia, Brusque: 24h |
| SP74) | K505 | 970 | 5/0.25 | R. Super Dif., Itapetininga: 24h, Sun 1400-0300 |
| SP75) | K529 | 970 | 1/0.25 | R. Piratininga, São João da Boa Vista |
| SP76) | K684 | 970 | 5/0.25 | R. Hertz, Franca: 24h |
| DF04) | H707 | 980 | 50/300 | R. Nacional, Brasília: 24h |
| AM23) | H299 | 990 | 1 | R. Independência, Maués: 0900-0200 |
| BA21) | H483 | 990 | 1/0.25 | R. Alvorada Gospel, Teixeira de Freitas |
| PI44) | I922 | 990 | 1/0.25 | R. Vale do Canindé, Oeiras |
| PR121) | J321 | *990 | 5/0.25 | R. Capital, Cianorte: 24h |
| RJ53) | J461 | 990 | 100/10 | R. Record, Rio de Janeiro: 24h |
| RN05) | J596 | 990 | 10/1 | R. Rural, Mossoró: 24h |
| RS51) | K314 | 990 | 2/0.5 | R. Tupa, Tupaneireta: 24h |
| RS52) | K335 | *990 | 2.5/0.25 | R. Sananduva, Sananduva: 0900-0100 |
| RS154) | K360 | 990 | 5/0.25 | R. Clube, Pedro Osório |
| SC25) | J763 | 990 | 2/0.25 | R. Itapiranga, Itapiranga: 0800-0300 |
| SP239) | K579 | 990 | 10/0.25 | R. Cultura Regional, Dois Córregos |
| PB30) | I698 | 1000 | 2.5/0.5 | R. Oeste da Paraíba, Cajazeiras |
| PE14) | I791 | 1000 | 1/0.25 | R. Princesa Serrana, Timbaúba: 0800-0100(SS -2230) |
| SP77) | K522 | 1000 | 200 | R. Record, São Paulo: 24h |
| BA22) | H448 | 1010 | 25/5 | R. Bahia, Salvador |
| CE21) | H625 | 1010 | 12.5/2.5 | R. O'Povo, Fortaleza |
| GO39) | H772 | 1010 | 10/0.5 | R. Santelenense, Sta. Helena de Goiás |
| MG50) | L230 | 1010 | 10/1 | R. Educadora, Coronel Fabriciano |
| MG48) | L264 | 1010 | 5/0.5 | CBN, Juiz de Fora: 24h |
| MG49) | L325 | *1010 | 5/0.5 | R. Estância, Jacutinga: 0800-2300 (SS -0230) |
| MT13) | I421 | 1010 | 5/1 | R. Dif., Mirassol d'Oeste: 0900-0200 |
| PR35) | J263 | 1010 | 25/5 | R. Celinauta, Pato Branco |
| RS53) | K232 | 1010 | 7.0/75 | R. 1010, Caxias do Sul: 24h |
| RS54) | K344 | 1010 | 3/1 | R. Missioneira, São Luíz Gonzaga: 0800(Sun 0900)-0200 |
| SC71) | J764 | 1010 | 10/0.3 | R. Jaraguá, Jaraguá do Sul: 24h |
| SC75) | J758 | *1010 | 10/0.25 | R. Bandeirantes, Imbituba |
| SP151) | K507 | 1010 | 5/0.5 | R. Dif., Lençóis Paulista: 0700-0300 |
| SP78) | K556 | *1010 | 1/0.5 | R. Independente, Barretos |
| SP79) | K611 | 1010 | 5/0.25 | R. Diario, Martinópolis |
| AL05) | H247 | 1020 | 25/1 | R. Jovem Pan, Rio Largo |
| AP04) | H423 | *1020 | 1/0.25 | R. Porto, Santana |
| CE22) | H600 | 1020 | 5/1 | R. Educadora Cariri, Crato: 24h |
| CE79) | H664 | 1020 | 1/0.25 | R. Macambira, Ipueiras: 0800-0000 (Sat -2230), Sun 0700-2130 |
| ES06) | I205 | 1020 | 10/0.4 | R. Difusora, Colatina: 0800-0300 |
| GO52) | H781 | 1020 | 10/0.5 | R. Boas Novas, Firminópolis |
| MG55) | L224 | 1020 | 10/1 | R. Congonhas, Congonhas: 0800-0100 |
| MG51) | L260 | *1020 | 10/0.25 | R. Globo, Uberlândia |
| MS06) | I381 | *1020 | 10/0.25 | R. Independente, Aquidauana |
| PB19) | I686 | *1020 | 1/0.25 | R. Cenecista, Picuí: 0800(SS 1000)-2300 |
| PR36) | J244 | 1020 | 10/0.25 | R. Super Colombo, Curitiba:24h |
| PR37) | J307 | 1020 | 1/0.25 | R. Independência, Medianeira: 0800-0100 |
| PR142) | J359 | *1020 | 1/0.25 | R. Campo Aberto, Laranjeiras do Sul: 0800-0000 |
| RJ42) | J484 | 1020 | 5/0.25 | R. Canção Nova, Campos dos Goytacazes: 24h |
| RO02) | J680 | 1020 | 5/1 | R. Educadora, Rolim de Moura |
| RR04) | J702 | 1020 | 10/5 | R. Folha, Boa Vista: 0800-0200(Sun -2300) |
| RS49) | K202 | 1020 | 25/5 | R. Eldorado, Porto Alegre: 24h |
| SC27) | J805 | 1020 | 2.5/0.25 | R. Continental, Coronel Freitas: 0500-0100, SS silent |
| SP80) | K513 | 1020 | 10/0.25 | R. Canção Nova, Cachoeira Paulista |
| SP81) | K515 | 1020 | 5/0.25 | R. Cultura, Assis |
| SP82) | K531 | 1020 | 2.5/0.5 | R. Educadora, Limeira:24h |
| SP83) | K600 | *1020 | 1.6/0.25 | R. Cultura, Jales |
| BA40) | H475 | 1030 | 10/1 | R. Bahiana, Itaberaba |
| GO22) | H746 | *1030 | 10/1 | R. Imprensa, Anápolis: 0800-0300 |
| MA07) | H892 | 1030 | 10/1 | R. Jainara, Bacabal |
| PE15) | I777 | 1030 | 20/5 | R. Olinda, Olinda: 24h |
| PR39) | J271 | 1030 | 5/0.25 | R. Atalaia, Londrina |
| PR120) | J312 | 1030 | 2.5/0.25 | R. Clube, Realeza: 0830-0300 |
| PR40) | J329 | *1030 | 1/0.25 | R. Dif. do Xisto, São Mateus do Sul: 0800-0300 |
| RJ18) | J467 | 1030 | 100/5 | R. Capital, Rio de Janeiro: 24h |
| RN31) | J612 | *1030 | 1/0.25 | R. Vale do Apodi, Apodi: 0800-0200 |
| RO10) | J683 | 1030 | 5/1 | R. Rondônia, Ariquemes |
| RS129) | K224 | 1030 | 1/0.25 | R. Cultura, Canguçu: 0900-0000 |
| RS55) | K253 | 1030 | 10/0.5 | R. Repórter, Ijuí |
| SC28) | J771 | 1030 | 2/0.5 | R. Princesa, Lages |
| SP84) | K525 | 1030 | 5/0.25 | R. Difusora, Franca |
| SP85) | K554 | 1030 | 1/0.25 | R. Emissora da Barra, Barra Bonita |
| SP86) | K606 | *1030 | 1/0.25 | Lins Rádio Clube, Lins |
| TO05) | H791 | 1030 | 1/0.25 | R. Colinas, Colinas do Tocantins |
| SP87) | K537 | 1040 | 200/100 | R. Capital, São Paulo: 24h |
| BA47) | H494 | 1050 | 25/0.75 | R. Noticias, Camaçari: 24h |
| CE54) | H647 | *1050 | 10/0.5 | R. Primeira Capital, Aquiraz |
| ES07) | I203 | 1050 | 100/1 | R. Capixaba, Vitória |
| GO40) | H760 | *1050 | 1/0.25 | R. Jornal, Inhumas |
| MG52) | L236 | 1050 | 1/0.25 | R. Rural, Tupaciguara: 0900-2200, Sun 0800-1900* |
| MS20) | I391 | *1050 | 10/0.5 | R. Dif. Paranaibense, Paranaíba: 24h |
| PB07) | I676 | *1050 | 5/1 | R. Caturité, Campina Grande: 24h |
| PR66) | J226 | *1050 | 1/0.25 | R. Dif. Platinense, Sto. Antônio da Platine |
| PR99) | J286 | *1050 | 5/0.25 | R. Cl. AM, Palmas: 24h |
| RJ19) | J497 | 1050 | 10/0.5 | R. Angra, Angra dos Reis |
| SP160) | K601 | 1050 | 10/0.5 | R. Show Jardinópolis |
| BA23) | H460 | 1050 | 5/1 | R. Cl. de Conquista, Vitória da Conquista |
| BA68) | H520 | 1060 | 2.5/0.25 | R. Cl., Itapicuru: 0800-0200 |
| GO54) | H807 | 1060 | 5 | R. Serra Dourada, Minacu: 24h |
| MG53) | L278 | 1060 | 25 | R. 880, Belo Horizonte |
| MG54) | L306 | 1060 | 1/0.25 | R. Itajubá, Itajubá: 24h |
| MS39) | N604 | 1060 | 5/1 | R. Imaculada Conceição, Dourados: 24h |
| PR42) | J246 | 1060 | 10/0.5 | R. Evangelizar, Curitiba: 24h |
| PR44) | J306 | 1060 | 10/0.5 | R. Educadora, Francisco Beltrão |
| RJ20) | J495 | 1060 | 30/1 | R. Canção Nova, Nova Iguaçu |
| RN06) | J597 | 1060 | 5 | R. Tapuyo, Mossoró (RPC) |
| RS56) | K220 | 1060 | 5/0.25 | R. Camaqüense, Camaquã |
| RS57) | K302 | 1060 | 2/0.25 | R. São Luís, São Luís Gonzaga: 24h |
| RS81) | K307 | *1060 | 2/0.5 | R. Cristal, Soledade: 24h |
| SC103) | J830 | 1060 | 2/0.4 | R. Mais Alegria, Florianópolis |
| SP88) | K533 | 1060 | 5/0.25 | R. Educadora, Piracicaba: 24h |
| SP229) | K765 | 1060 | 5/0.5 | R. Universitária, Garça |
| BA48) | H492 | *1070 | 5/0.5 | R. Rural "R. Tropical, Ipiaú |
| MG56) | L316 | 1070 | 1/0.25 | R. do Povo, Muzambinho |
| MG150) | L355 | *1070 | 10/0.25 | Super Radio Patos, Patos de Minas |
| MT14) | I427 | 1070 | 10/2.5 | R. Industrial, Várzea Grande: 24h |
| PB08) | I673 | 1070 | 20/2.5 | R. Dif. Cajazeiras, Cajazeiras: 0730-0300 |
| PR45) | J203 | *1070 | 5/0.25 | R. Dif. União, União da Vitória |
| PR46) | J319 | *1070 | 1/0.25 | Super RG, Guaraniaçu: 0830-0300, Sun 1000-0200 |
| RJ21) | J483 | 1070 | 10/0.25 | R. Cultura Fluminense, Campos dos Goitacazes |
| RS58) | K218 | 1070 | 5/0.25 | R. Caçapava, Caçapava do Sul |
| RS59) | K343 | 1070 | 1/0.25 | R. Metrópole, Crissiumal: 0830-0200, Sun 0900-0000 |
| RS60) | K357 | 1070 | 2/0.25 | R. Viva, Bento Gonçalves |
| SC91) | J747 | *1070 | 1/0.25 | R. Gralha Azul, Urubici: 0930(Sat 1100)-0200, Sun 1300-1440 |
| SP91) | K603 | *1070 | 10/0.25 | R. Nova Piratininga, Jaú: 24h |
| SP145) | K615 | 1070 | 10/0.25 | R. Metropolitana, Mogi das Cruzes: 24h |

| MW | Call | kHz | kW | Station, location, h. of tr. |
|---|---|---|---|---|
| SP92) | K633 | 1070 | 10/1 | R. Presidente Prudente, P. Prudente: 24h |
| SP212) | K758 | 1070 | 1/0.25 | R. Jornal, Barretos: 24h |
| BA24) | H470 | 1080 | 10/0.5 | R. Subaé, Feira de Santana:24h |
| BA25) | H485 | 1080 | 1/0.25 | R. Fascinação, Itapetinga: 0800-0230 |
| CE82) | H670 | *1080 | 2.5/0.25 | R. Cultura, Quixadá: 0800-2300(SS-0030) |
| DF05) | H708 | 1080 | 25/5 | R. Capital, Brasília |
| MG109) | L232 | 1080 | 2.5/0.5 | R. Cultura, Dores do Indaiá |
| MG57) | L251 | 1080 | 25/0.7 | R. Capital, Juiz de Fora |
| MT27) | I437 | *1080 | 1/0.25 | R. Difusora, Itiquira: 24h |
| PA32) | I540 | 1080 | 15/5 | R. Novo Tempo, Belém: 24h |
| PE16) | I784 | 1080 | 10/0.5 | R. Jornal do Comercio, Caruaru: 24h |
| PE33) | I824 | *1080 | 1/0.25 | R. Voluntários da Pátria, Ouricuri |
| PR48) | J245 | *1080 | 1/0.25 | R. Cultura do Norte, Paranavaí: 24h |
| RS61) | K254 | 1080 | 3/0.25 | R. Marabá, Iraí: 0830-0130 |
| RS62) | K280 | 1080 | 10 | R. da Universidade, Porto Alegre: 24h |
| SC29) | J759 | *1080 | 2/1 | R. Clube, Indaial: 0400-000 |
| SP94) | K557 | 1080 | 5/1 | R. Difusora, Batatais: 24h |
| SP95) | K607 | *1080 | 1/0.25 | R. Alvorada, Lins |
| SP96) | K669 | 1080 | 10/1 | R. Boa Nova, Sorocaba |
| SP97) | K704 | 1080 | 1/0.25 | R. Monumental, Aparecida: 24h |
| SP190) | K710 | *1080 | 1/0.25 | R. Alvorada, Cardoso: 0900-0100 |
| AL15) | H254 | 1080 | 5/0.5 | R. Gazeta, Pão de Açúcar |
| BA26) | H455 | 1090 | 1/0.25 | R. Santa Cruz, Ilhéus: 24h |
| GO24) | H758 | 1090 | 25/1 | R. 1090, Aparecida de Goiânia: 24h |
| MA08) | H893 | 1090 | 10 | R. Rio Balsas, Balsas |
| MG145) | L357 | 1090 | 5/0.25 | R. Catuaí, Manhuaçu |
| PR51) | J283 | 1090 | 2.5/0.25 | R. Vicente Palotti, Coronel Vivida: 0800-0200(SS -0100) |
| PR171) | J345 | 1090 | 1/0.25 | R. Banda 1, Sarandi: 0800-0330 |
| RJ22) | J468 | 1090 | 50/5 | R. Metropolitana, Rio de Janeiro: 24h |
| RN07) | J592 | *1090 | 10/5 | R. Rural, Natal |
| RS63) | K216 | *1090 | 5/0.25 | R. Cachoeira, Cachoeira do Sul |
| RS64) | K262 | 1090 | 1/0.25 | R. Salette, Marcelino Ramos: 0900-0100 |
| RS65) | K341 | 1090 | 1/0.25 | R. Giruá, Giruá: 0800-0300 |
| SC30) | J732 | 1090 | 1/0.25 | R. Colón, Joinville |
| SC31) | J786 | 1090 | 5/0.5 | R. Bandeirantes, Tubarão |
| SP98) | K609 | 1090 | 3/0.5 | R. Clube, Marília: 24h |
| SP99) | K618 | 1090 | 3/0.25 | R. Cultura, Monte Alto: 0830-0100 |
| SP233) | K768 | 1090 | 1/0.25 | R. Canção Nova, Paulina |
| CE67) | H638 | 1100 | 1/0.25 | R. Dif. dos Inhamuns, Tauá: 0730 (Sun 0800)-0030 |
| CE73) | H668 | 1100 | 1/0.25 | R. Difusora do Vale Acaraú, Acaraú |
| RN18) | J607 | *1100 | 1/0.25 | R. Seridó, Caicó |
| SP100) | K694 | 1100 | 150/50 | R. Globo, São Paulo: 24h |
| BA100) | ZYH464 | 1110 | 1 | R.Vox, Muritiba |
| CE32) | H620 | 1110 | 5/0.25 | R. Litoral, Cascavel: Tu 0800-2100, Sat 0800-2300, Sun 0900-0300 |
| GO46) | H782 | 1110 | 25/2 | R. Redentor, Sto. Antônio do Descoberto: 24h |
| MG58) | L205 | 1110 | 1/0.25 | R. Planalto, Araguari: 24h |
| MG59) | L267 | 1110 | 1 | R. Aurilândia, Nova Lima |
| MS08) | I392 | 1110 | 1 | R. Transamérica, Ponta Porã |
| PB09) | I689 | 1110 | 20/10 | R. Tabajara, João Pessoa |
| PR52) | J241 | 1110 | 10/1 | R. Paiquerê, Londrina: 24h, Sat 0900-0300 |
| PR151) | J356 | *1110 | 1/0.5 | R. Clube, Ubiratã |
| RJ23) | J471 | 1110 | 50/5 | R. Record, Campos dos Goitacazes: 24h |
| RS66) | K257 | 1110 | 2.5/0.25 | R. Cultura Jaguarão, Jaguarão: 24h |
| RS67) | K306 | 1110 | 2/0,25 | R. Sobradinho, Sobradinho |
| RS68) | K325 | 1110 | 2.5/0.25 | R. Cruzeiro do Sul, Itaqui: 0830-0200 |
| RS152) | K364 | *1110 | 1/0.25 | R. Solaris, Antônio Prado: 24h |
| SC74) | J743 | 1110 | 1/0.25 | R. Caçanjure, Caçador: 0900-0300 |
| SC32) | J752 | 1110 | 1/0.5 | R. Cultura, Florianópolis: 24h |
| SC33) | J812 | *1110 | 2.5 | R. São Carlos, São Carlos |
| SP101) | K544 | 1110 | 1/0.25 | R. Jovem Luz, Araçatuba: 1000-0000 |
| SP102) | K592 | *1110 | 3/0.25 | R. Ibitinga, Ibitinga |
| SP103) | K617 | 1110 | 1/0.25 | Transamerica Hits, Mogi Mirim |
| BA72) | H513 | 1120 | 5/0.5 | R. Belo Campo, Belo Campo |
| BA79) | H511 | 1120 | 0.3 | R. Jornal, Souto Soares: 0830-2200, Sun 0800-2100 |
| BA98) | H257 | 1120 | 10 | R. Estrela, Valenta: 0900-2200(Sun -1500) |
| CE23) | H598 | 1120 | 5/1 | R. Tupinambá, Sobral |
| ES14) | I215 | 1120 | 10/1 | R. Cricare, São Mateus |
| MG10) | L272 | *1120 | 10/0.5 | R. Itatiaia, Ouro Preto |
| MG61) | L332 | *1120 | 1/0.25 | R. Serra AM, Boa Esperança: 24h |
| MS40) | N606 | *1120 | 25/1 | R. Concordia, Campo Grande |
| PE17) | I778 | 1120 | 5/1 | R. Relógio, Paulista: 24h |
| PR53) | J253 | 1120 | 25/1 | R. Mais, São José dos Pinhais: 24h |
| PR85) | J285 | *1120 | 5/0.5 | R. Educadora, Laranjeiras do Sul: 0800-0200(Sun -0100) |
| RS191) | K274 | 1120 | 50 | R. Rural, Porto Alegre |
| RS156) | K367 | 1120 | 10/0.6 | R. Querência, Santo Augusto: 0800-0300 |
| SP104) | K631 | *1120 | 1/0.25 | R. Nova Porto, Porto Feliz: 24h |
| SP105) | K660 | 1120 | 10/1 | R. Cidade, São José dos Campos: 24h |
| SP106) | K671 | 1120 | 1/0.25 | R. Clube Imperial, Taquaritinga: 24h |
| CE72) | H667 | 1130 | 10/0.25 | R. Patu, Senador Pompeu: 1700-2200 (Sun -1800) |
| PA08) | I531 | 1130 | 10 | R. Marajoara, Belém: 24h |
| PE18) | I783 | 1130 | 5/1 | R. Cultura do Nordeste, Caruaru: 24h |
| PR55) | J220 | *1130 | 1/0.25 | R. Castro, Castro: 24h |
| PR54) | J333 | 1130 | 5/0.25 | R. Ingamar, Marialva |
| RJ17) | J460 | 1130 | 100/50 | R. Nacional, Rio de Janeiro: 24h |
| RO06) | J677 | *1130 | 5/0.25 | R. Ji-Parana, Ji-Paraná |
| RS70) | K290 | *1130 | 5/1 | R. Medianeira, Santa Maria |
| SC34) | J790 | 1130 | 5/1 | R. Princesa d'Oeste, Xanxerê: 24h |
| BA81) | H449 | 1140 | 10 | R. Cultura da Bahia, Salvador: 24h |
| CE24) | H607 | 1140 | 10/1 | R. Progresso, Russas |
| GO26) | H751 | *1140 | 5/0.25 | R. Formosa, Formosa: 0800-2300, Sat 1200-2200, Sun silent |
| MG62) | L204 | 1140 | 5/0.25 | R. Minas, Divinópolis |
| MG63) | L248 | 1140 | 1/0.25 | R. Doicesana, Campanha: 1100-0300, SS 24h |
| MG64) | L253 | 1140 | 8/0.5 | R. Muriaé, Muriaé: 0800-0300 |
| MG129) | L362 | *1140 | 10/0.5 | R. Clube, Bocaiuva: 0800-0300 |
| MS22) | I398 | 1140 | 10/0.5 | R. Globo, Fátima do Sul: 24h |
| PR144) | J352 | 1140 | 1/0.25 | R. Dif. America, Chopinzinho: 24h |
| RS71) | K228 | 1140 | 2/0.25 | R. Cruz Alta, Cruz Alta |
| RS72) | K316 | 1140 | 5/0.7 | R. Charrua, Uruguaiana: 0900-2200 |
| RS73) | K330 | 1140 | 2/0.5 | R. Jornal Sobral, Butiá: 1000-2200 |
| SP108) | K550 | 1140 | 10/0.5 | R. Difusora, Assis |
| SP109) | K555 | *1140 | 2/0.5 | R. Barretos, Barretos |
| SP110) | K645 | 1140 | 1/0.25 | R. Educação e Cultura, Rio Claro |
| SP111) | K709 | 1140 | 5/0.25 | R. Costa Azul, Ubatuba |
| SP273) | K708 | 1140 | 1/0.25 | R. Nova Regional, Registro: 24h |
| AL11) | H250 | 1150 | 20/1 | R. Cultura, Arapiraca |
| CE47) | H643 | *1150 | 5/0.5 | R. Cult. - Rede Imaculada, Paracuru: 24h |
| PI10) | I891 | 1150 | 10/5 | R. Pioneira, Teresina: 24h |
| RJ24) | J456 | 1150 | 10/0.5 | R. Três Rios, Três Rios |
| RN25) | J617 | 1150 | 5/0.5 | R. Cabugi do Seridó, Jardim do Seridó: 0800-0100, Sat 1700-0000 |
| SP232) | K656 | 1150 | 100/50 | Super Radio, São Paulo: 24h |
| AM24) | H323 | 1160 | 1/0.25 | R. Soc. TV Manauara, Boca do Acre |
| BA94) | H... | *1160 | 5/0.25 | R. Interativa, Itabuna |
| CE62) | H652 | 1160 | 1/0.25 | R. Vale do Coreaú, Granja |
| CE80) | H660 | 1160 | 1/0.25 | R. Montevideo, Cedro: 0800-0100 (Sun -2330) |
| DF09) | H714 | 1160 | 30/0.5 | R. Globo, Brasilia: 24h |
| ES08) | I202 | 1160 | 50/10 | R. Espírito Santo, Vitória |
| MT15) | I385 | 1160 | 10/5 | R. A. Voz d'Oeste, Cuiabá |
| PA30) | I558 | 1160 | 5/1 | R. Guamá, São Miguel do Guamá: 0800-0300 |
| PR56) | J258 | 1160 | 10/1 | R. Globo, Londrina: 24h |
| RS74) | K242 | 1160 | 9/1 | R. Miriam, Farroupilha: 0830-2100 |
| RS75) | K245 | 1160 | 5/1 | R. Luz e Alegria, Frederico Westphalen |
| RS76) | K256 | *1160 | 2.5/0.5 | R. Jaguari, Jaguari |
| RS77) | K273 | 1160 | 2.5/1 | R. Universidade Católica, Pelotas: |
| SC36) | J741 | 1160 | 9/0.7 | R. Itaberá, Blumenau: 24h |
| SP114) | K517 | 1160 | 5/0.5 | R. Cacique, Sorocaba |
| SP124) | K558 | 1160 | 2.5/1 | R. Bandeirantes, Bauru: 24h |
| SP115) | K582 | 1160 | 5/0.25 | R. Difusora, Fernandópolis |
| SP237) | K673 | 1160 | 4/0.25 | R. Cacique, Taubaté |
| SP116) | K685 | 1160 | 10/0.25 | R. Boa Nova, Mococa: 24h |
| AC15) | H205 | 1170 | 1/0.25 | R. Dif. de Feijó, Feijó |
| AM08) | H284 | 1170 | 5/2.5 | R. Guaranópolis, Maués |
| BA27) | H473 | 1170 | 5/0.25 | R. Jornal, Eunápolis |
| MG152) | L234 | *1170 | 1/0.25 | R. Clube Fronteira |
| MG104) | L269 | 1170 | 5/0.25 | R. Sociedade, Oliveira |
| MG75) | L327 | *1170 | 10/0.25 | R. Vanguarda, Ipatinga |
| MG67) | L336 | 1170 | 5/0.25 | R. Cidade, Araxá: 0800-0000* |
| PR57) | J273 | 1170 | 20/10 | R. Atalaia, Curitiba |
| PR90) | J334 | 1170 | 2.5/0.45 | R. Entre Rios, Sto. Antônio do Sudoeste: 0800-020000 SS -2200 |
| PR154) | J363 | *1170 | 8/1 | R. Colméia, Mandaguaçu: 24h |
| RJ49) | J498 | 1170 | 5/0.25 | R. Bom Jesus, Bom Jesus de Itabapoana: 24h |
| RN08) | J598 | 1170 | 10/1 | R. Difusora, Mossoró |
| RS78) | K207 | 1170 | 1/0.25 | R. Itapuí, Santo Antônio da Patrulha: 0900-0300 |
| RS79) | K213 | *1170 | 5/1 | R. Difusora, Bagé: 0900-0230 |
| RS80) | K359 | 1170 | 5/0.6 | R. Uirapuru, Passo Fundo: 24h |
| RS155) | K380 | 1170 | 1.5 | R. Pitangueira, Itaqui:24h |
| SP117) | K569 | 1170 | 10/5 | R. Bandeirantes, Campinas: 24h |
| AL06) | H248 | 1170 | 1/0.25 | R. Correio do Sertão, Santana do Ipanema |
| MA09) | H889 | 1170 | 10/5 | R. Capital, São Luís |
| MG118) | L203 | 1180 | 10/0.25 | R. Cultura, Alfenas: 24h |

| MW | Call | kHz | kW | Station, location, h. of tr. |
|---|---|---|---|---|
| MT38) | N405 | *1180 | 1/0.25 | R. Enauan, Guarantã do Norte |
| PB20) | I690 | *1180 | 1/0.25 | R. Bonsucesso, Pombal: 0830-0100 SS -2100 |
| PE19) | I797 | 1180 | 1/0.25 | R. Jornal, Vitória de Sto. Antão |
| PR126) | J223 | *1180 | 2.5/0.5 | R. Atalaia, Guarapuava |
| PR58) | J237 | 1180 | 10/0.5 | R. Guaçu, Toledo: 0800-0000 |
| PR81) | J314 | 1180 | 2.5/0.25 | R. Educadora, São João do Ivaí: 24h |
| RJ25) | J463 | 1180 | 50/10 | R. Mundial, Rio de Janeiro: 24h |
| RS128) | K340 | 1180 | 10/0.5 | R. Gazeta, Santa Cruz do Sul: 24h |
| SC39) | J737 | 1180 | 5/0.25 | R. Integração d'Oeste, São José do Cedro: 0830-0100 |
| SC72) | J770 | *1180 | 1/0.5 | R. Guri, Lages |
| SP260) | K567 | 1180 | 5/0.25 | R. Brotense, Brotas:24h |
| SP179) | K647 | *1180 | 2/0.5 | R. Super Nova Difusora, Santa Cruz do Rio Pardo: 0800-0100 |
| SP217) | K749 | 1180 | 5/0.25 | R. Nova, Bebedouro |
| BA28) | H459 | 1190 | 10/1 | R. Juazeiro, Juazeiro: 0800-2300 (Sat -1930, Sun -1800) |
| CE68) | H663 | *1190 | 1/0.25 | R. Guaraciaba, Guaraciaba do Norte: 24h |
| MG68) | L221 | 1190 | 50/1 | R. Guarani, Belo Horizonte |
| MG40) | L276 | 1190 | 10/0.25 | R. Mineira do Sul, Passa Quatro: 0800-0100, SS 24h |
| PR136) | J355 | *1190 | 5/0.4 | R. Cidade, Palmital: 0830-0100 |
| RS82) | K234 | 1190 | 5/0.5 | R. Cerro Azul, Cerro Largo |
| RS102) | K301 | 1190 | 2.5/0.25 | R. São Lourenço, São Lourenço do Sul: 0900-0300, Sun 1000-0200 |
| RS83) | K354 | 1190 | 2.5/1 | R. Rosário, Serafina Corrêa |
| SC40) | J783 | 1190 | 5/1 | R. Clube, São João Batista: 24h |
| SC87) | J817 | *1190 | 1/0.25 | R. Planalto, Major Vieira: 24h |
| SC41) | J820 | 1190 | 2.5/0.25 | R. Clube, São Domingos |
| SP199) | K512 | 1190 | 2.5/0.25 | R. Marconi, Paraguaçu Paulista: 0800-0100 |
| SP118) | K700 | *1190 | 5/0.25 | R. Cidade, Votuporanga: 0800-0100 |
| SP119) | K729 | 1190 | 10/0.25 | R. 31 de Março, Sta. Cruz das Palmeiras |
| SP120) | K741 | 1190 | 1/0.5 | R. Regional, Taquarituba: 0800-0200, (Sun Silent) |
| AL14) | H251 | 1200 | 50/1 | R. Correio, Pilar |
| BA29) | H482 | 1200 | 10/0.5 | R. Clube Rio do Ouro, Jacobina: 24h |
| CE26) | H585 | 1200 | 10 | R. Clube, Fortaleza: 24h |
| RS84) | K239 | 1200 | 5/1 | R. Erechim, Erechim: 0800(SS 0900)-0300 |
| RS85) | K342 | 1200 | 1/0.5 | R. Fundação Cotrisel, São Sepé: 0800-0200(SS -0100) |
| SP121) | K520 | 1200 | 100/20 | R. Cultura Brasil, São Paulo |
| BA30) | H452 | 1210 | 10/1 | R. Povo, Feira de Santana |
| BA58) | H498 | 1210 | 10/0.25 | R. Canção Nova, Vitória da Conquista |
| CE50) | H637 | 1210 | 5/0.25 | R. Príncipe Imperial, Crateús |
| CE48) | H641 | *1210 | 5/0.25 | R. Boa Esperança, Barro |
| DF08) | H711 | 1210 | 50/2.5 | Super Rede Boa Vontade (RBV), Brasília: 24h |
| ES09) | I200 | *1210 | 25/1 | R. Sim Cachoeiro, Cachoeiro de Itapemirim: 24h |
| MG69) | L238 | 1210 | 10/0.5 | R. Clube, Varginha: 24h |
| PE20) | I786 | 1210 | 10/1 | R. Jornal, Garanhuns: 24h |
| PR60) | J219 | 1210 | 25/5 | Super Rádio Deus é Amor, Curitiba: 24h |
| PR140) | J325 | 1210 | 1/0.5 | R. Brotense, Porecatu: 24h |
| RN29) | J620 | 1210 | 5/0.5 | R. Potengi, São Paulo do Potengi: 0800-0300, Sun 1000-1500 |
| RS86) | K240 | 1210 | 10/5 | R. Catedral, Porto Alegre |
| RS88) | K353 | 1210 | 1/0.5 | R. Blau Nunes, Santa Bárbara do Sul |
| SC42) | J785 | 1210 | 10/0.5 | R. Super Santa, Tubarão: 0800-0200 (Sun -2300) |
| SP122) | K509 | 1210 | 10/1 | R. Vida Nova, Jaboticabal |
| SP125) | K668 | 1210 | 5/0.25 | R. Vanguarda, Sorocaba: 24h |
| BA59) | H532 | 1230 | 1/0.25 | R. Povo, Ubatã |
| GO27) | H756 | 1230 | 10/2.5 | R. Daqui, Goiânia |
| MA23) | H.... | 1230 |  | R. Veneza, Caxias |
| MG105) | L208 | 1230 | 5/0.25 | R. Correio da Serra, Barbacena |
| MG102) | L216 | 1230 | 2.5/0.25 | R. Passos, Passos:24h |
| MG176) | N203 | 1230 | 10/0.7 | R. Estrela de Ibiúna, Campina Verde |
| PB12) | I670 | 1230 | 10/1 | R. Correio Jovem Pan, João Pessoa |
| PR170) | J350 | *1230 | 1/0.25 | R. Nova Mensagem, Telêmaco Borba: 1200(Sat 1000)-0300, Sun 1300-1900 |
| RS89) | K326 | 1230 | 2/0.25 | R. Clube Nonoai, Nonoai |
| RS90) | K333 | 1230 | 2.3/0.35 | R. Prata, Nova Prata: 0800-0100 SS -2200 |
| RS91) | K352 | 1230 | 1/0.25 | R. Encruzilhadense, Encruzilhada do Sul |
| SC38) | J776 | 1230 | 5/0.65 | R. Dif. Colméia, Porto União: 0800(Sun 0900)-0300 |
| SC88) | J816 | *1230 | 10/1 | R. Guararema, São José: 24h |
| SP126) | K573 | 1230 | 10/1 | R. Cacique, Capão Bonito: 24h |
| SP258) | K637 | 1230 | 10/0.25 | R. Difusora, Rancharia |
| SP128) | K716 | 1230 | 5/0.5 | R. Jequitibá, Campinas |
| SP266) | R699 | 1230 | 50/10 | Super Rede Boa Vontade, São Paulo |
| BA31) | H463 | *1240 | 10/0.5 | R. Nova AM 1240, Alagoinhas: 0900-0200(Sat-1900), Sun 1000-2200 |
| CE49) | H654 | 1240 | 1/0.25 | R. São Francisco, Canindé |
| MG97) | L294 | 1240 | 5/0.25 | R. Três Pontas, Três Pontas |
| MG84) | L298 | 1240 | 1/0.25 | R. Ubaense, Ubá: 24h |
| MG72) | L303 | 1240 | 10/0.35 | R. Globo, Ituiutaba: 24h |
| MG116) | L317 | 1240 | 5/0.25 | R. Pirapora AM, Pirapora: 24h |
| MS09) | I388 | *1240 | 5/1 | R. Dif. Pantanal, Campo Grande: 24h |
| PE21) | I774 | 1240 | 5 | R. Capibaribe, Recife: 0900-0300 |
| PR112) | J215 | 1240 | 1/0.25 | R. Arapongas, Arapongas: 24h |
| PR61) | J280 | 1240 | 2/0.25 | R. Matelândia, Matelândia: 0800-0100 |
| RS92) | K200 | 1240 | 1/0.25 | R. Aparados da Serra, Bom Jesus: 0830-0300 Sat 1030-0230 Sun 1000-0300 |
| RS93) | K251 | 1240 | 1/0.25 | R. Ibirubá, Ibirubá: 0800-0100(SS -2300) |
| RS94) | K355 | 1240 | 1/0.25 | R. São Jerônimo, São Jerônimo |
| SC43) | J774 | *1240 | 5/0.5 | R. São José, Mafra: 24h |
| SC44) | J810 | 1240 | 2.2 | R. Iracema, Cunhae Porã |
| SP129) | K565 | 1240 | 10/0.25 | R. Municipalista, Botucatu |
| SP130) | K621 | 1240 | 5/0.25 | Orlândia R. Clube, Orlândia: 24h |
| SP131) | K653 | 1240 | 10/2.5 | R. Clube, Santos |
| SP132) | K711 | *1240 | 1/0.25 | R. Vale do Tietê, José Bonifácio: 24h |
| CE27) | H594 | 1250 | 1 | R. Educadora, Crateús |
| CE69) | H669 | 1250 | 1/0.25 | R. Liberdade, Itarema |
| ES18) | I218 | 1250 | 10/1 | R. Nova Estação, Vitória |
| GO29) | H748 | 1250 | 1/0.25 | R. Coração Fiel, Ceres |
| MG153) | L367 | 1250 | 50 | R. Metropolitana, Vespasiano |
| MS10) | I394 | 1250 | 1/0.25 | R. Difusora, Três Lagoas: 0900-0300, Sun 1000-0200 |
| MS11) | I412 | 1250 | 5/0.5 | R. Caiuás, Dourados |
| PB27) | I701 | 1250 | 1/0.25 | R. Sociedade de Soledade, Soledade |
| PI47) | I915 | 1250 | 1/0.25 | R. João de Paiva, Altos |
| PR64) | J313 | 1250 | 2.5/0.25 | R. Danúbio Azul, Sta. Isabel do Oeste: 24h |
| RJ50) | J500 | 1250 | 15/0.5 | R. Litoral, Casimiro de Abreu |
| RS95) | K233 | 1250 | 15/0.5 | R. Dif. Caxiense, Caxias do Sul |
| RS96) | K272 | 1250 | 1 | R. Tupanci, Pelotas: 0800-0200, Sun 0900-0000 |
| RS142) | K361 | 1250 | 5/0.6 | R. Aguas Claras, Catuípe: 0800-0200 (Sat -0100), Sun 1000-2200 |
| SC45) | J766 | 1250 | 5/0.25 | R. Cultura, Joinville: 24h |
| SE08) | J925 | *1250 | 10/1 | R. Esperança, Estância |
| SP133) | K702 | 1250 | 5/0.5 | R. Canção Nova, Caçapava |
| AL07) | H242 | 1260 | 50/5 | R. Gazeta de Alagoas, Maceió: 24h |
| CE28) | H596 | *1260 | 1/0.25 | R. Vale do Jaguaribe, Limoeiro do Nte 0730-0100 |
| RO09) | J670 | *1260 | 5 | R. Educação, Guajará Mirim: 0900-0300 |
| RS97) | K204 | 1260 | 5/0.25 | R. Cultura, São Borja: 0500-2400 |
| RS98) | K327 | 1260 | 5/0.25 | R. Fandango, Cachoeira do Sul: 0830-0100 |
| RS99) | K345 | *1260 | 1/0.25 | R. Gaurama, Gaurama |
| SC46) | J740 | 1260 | 10/0.5 | R. Arca da Aliança, Blumenau |
| SP257) | K629 | 1260 | 1/0.25 | Pirajuí R. Clube, Pirajuí: 24h |
| SP134) | K688 | 1260 | 100/40 | R. Morada do Sol, São Paulo: 24h |
| AM10) | H271 | *1270 | 5 | R. Educação Rural, Tefé: 1000-0200 |
| GO30) | H753 | 1270 | 100/10 | R. Brasil Central, Goiânia |
| MG74) | L227 | *1270 | 5/1 | R. Carijós, Conselheiro Lafaiete |
| MG107) | L300 | 1270 | 2.5/0.5 | R. Estância, São Lourenço |
| MG155) | L240 | *1270 | 5/1 | R. Globo, Ipatinga: 24h |
| PA09) | I530 | 1270 | 10/2.5 | R. Boas Novas, Belém: 24h |
| PB28) | I696 | *1270 | 5/0.25 | R. Cidade, Sumé: 1100-0300 |
| PR65) | J222 | 1270 | 5/0.5 | R. Guairacá, Mandaguari: 0800-0100, SS 0800-0000 |
| PR67) | J236 | 1270 | 10/1 | R. Continental, Curitiba: 24h |
| PR68) | J289 | 1270 | 10/0.5 | R. Globo, Cascavel: 24h |
| RJ26) | J474 | 1270 | 5/0.5 | R. Continental, Campos dos Goitacazes: 0800-0230 |
| RN10) | J593 | 1270 | 5/0.5 | R. Clube AM 1270, Natal: 24h |
| RS131) | K206 | 1270 | 5/0.5 | R. América, Montenegro: 24h |
| RS101) | K250 | 1270 | 5/0.5 | R. Vera Cruz, Horizontina: 0800-0300 |
| SC47) | J765 | *1270 | 12/0.25 | R. Catarinense, Joaçaba |
| SC48) | J768 | *1270 | 1/0.25 | R. Garibaldi, Laguna: 09000-0200, Sun 1045-2200 |
| SP136) | K678 | 1270 | 5/0.5 | R. Brasil, Campinas: 24h |
| SP274) | K640 | 1270 | 2/0.5 | R. Bandeirantes, Ribeirao Preto |
| PB21) | I688 | 1280 | 10/5 | R. Sanhauá, Bayeux: 0800-0300(SS -2300) |
| RJ27) | J455 | 1280 | 100 | R. Tupi, Rio de Janeiro |
| AM11) | H286 | *1290 | 10/2.5 | R. Rio Mar, Manaus: 0900-0300 |
| BA32) | H450 | 1290 | 10/1 | R. Metropole, Salvador |
| ES24) |  | 1290 | 1 | R. Sim, Vila Velha |
| MA10) | H888 | 1290 | 10/5 | R. Timbira, São Luís: 0800(Sun 1000)-0300 |
| MG77) | L273 | 1290 | 10/5 | R. Uberlandia, Uberlandia |
| PR73) | J310 | 1290 | 25/0.5 | R. Brasil Sul, Londrina: 24h |
| RN26) | J619 | *1290 | 5/0.5 | R. Caicó, Caicó |
| RS103) | K331 | 1290 | 5/2 | R. Planetário, Espumoso: 0800-0100 |

| MW | Call | kHz | kW | Station, location, h. of tr. |
|---|---|---|---|---|
| | | | | (Sun -2300) |
| SC81) | J734 | 1290 | 5/1 | R. Araranguá, Araranguá: 0800-0100 (Sun -0900) |
| SC49) | J804 | 1290 | 5/1 | R. Camboriú, Balneário Camboriú |
| SP240) | K662 | 1290 | 5/0.5 | R. Difusora, São José do Rio Pardo |
| SP137) | K663 | 1290 | 5/1 | R. Novo Tempo, São José do Rio Preto:24h |
| SP216) | K745 | 1290 | 1/0.5 | R. Estadão, São José dos Campos: 24h |
| CE29) | H586 | 1300 | 10 | R. Iracema, Fortaleza:24h |
| ES11) | I210 | 1300 | 5/0,25 | R. Novo Tempo, Afonso Cláudio |
| MG143) | L339 | 1300 | 5/1 | R. Eldorado, Sete Lagoas: 24h |
| PE22) | I799 | 1300 | 1/0.25 | R. Guarany, Camaragibe |
| PR71) | J278 | *1300 | 1/0.25 | CBN, Ponta Grossa: 24h |
| PR127) | K288 | 1300 | 5/0.25 | R. Educadora, Dois Vizinhos: 0800-0300 |
| RS104) | K203 | 1300 | 80/13 | Super Rede Boa Vontade, Porto Alegre: 24h |
| RS105) | K337 | 1300 | 1/0.25 | R. Regional, Santo Cristo |
| RS106) | K347 | *1300 | 5/0.5 | R. Maratan, Santana do Livramento: 24h |
| SC89) | J819 | *1300 | 5/1 | R. Alvorada, Santa Cecília |
| SP138) | K535 | 1300 | 50/1 | R. Universo, São Paulo: 24h |
| SP252) | K649 | 1300 | 30/0,25 | R. Onda Viva, Santo Anastácio |
| SP226) | K762 | 1300 | 2/0.25 | R. Realidade, São Carlos |
| AP05) | H422 | 1310 | 1/0.25 | R. Nova Mazagão, Mazagão |
| BA33) | H454 | 1310 | 1/0.25 | R. Bahiana, Ilhéus: 0800-0300 |
| CE30) | H602 | *1310 | 1 | R. Progresso de Juazeiro, Juazeiro do Nte. |
| CE63) | H656 | 1310 | 1/0.25 | R. Liberdade, Boa Viagem: 0800-2300 |
| MG144) | L359 | *1310 | 1/0.25 | R. Montanheza, Vazante |
| MG168) | L351 | 1310 | 10/0.25 | R. Difusora, Salinas |
| MS31) | I426 | *1310 | 5/1 | R. Pindorama, Sidrolândia |
| PB23) | I691 | 1310 | 10/0.5 | R. Cidade Esperança, Esperança |
| PR70) | J274 | 1310 | 10/0.5 | R. Atalaia, Maringá |
| RJ28) | J504 | 1310 | 1/0.25 | R. Coroados, São Fidélis: 0800-0100 (SS -2100) |
| RO17) | J684 | 1310 | 10/5 | CBN, Porto Velho: 24h |
| RS107) | K305 | 1310 | 10/1 | R. Sarandi, Sarandi: 24h |
| RS124) | K329 | 1310 | 5/0.45 | R. Integração, Restinga Seca: 0830-0200 (Sat -2300), Sun 0900-2300 |
| RS160) | K371 | 1310 | 5/0.5 | R. Horizonte, Capão da Canoa |
| SC85) | J801 | *1310 | 10/0.25 | R. Sintonia, Ituporanga |
| SP141) | K566 | 1310 | 5/0.25 | R. Bragança, Bragança Paulista |
| SP139) | K566 | 1310 | 2/1 | R. Difusora, Itápolis |
| AL08) | H243 | *1320 | 10/0.25 | R. Imaculada Conceição, Maceió: 24h |
| BA69) | H503 | 1320 | 5/0.5 | R. Regional, Cícero Dantas: 0900-2300 |
| CE31) | H597 | ‡1320 | 1 | R. Regional, Sobral |
| CE70) | H672 | *1320 | 1/0.5 | R. Moriá, Aracati |
| MG136) | L322 | 1320 | 5/0.25 | R. Mucuri, Teófilo Otoni: 24h, Sun silent |
| PE31) | I823 | 1320 | 1/0.25 | R. Cultura, São José do Egito |
| PR72) | J255 | 1320 | 12/0.5 | R. Tropical, Curitiba: 24h |
| PR145) | J351 | 1320 | 5/0.5 | CBN, Foz do Iguaçu: 24h |
| RJ29) | J475 | 1320 | 50/5 | R. Boas Novas, Petrópolis: 24h |
| RS108) | K223 | 1320 | 1/0.25 | R. Clube, Canela |
| RS109) | K266 | 1320 | 3/0.25 | R. Sulbrasileira, Panambi |
| RS110) | K271 | 1320 | 5/1 | R. Cultura, Pelotas: 24h |
| SC68) | J762 | 1320 | 9 | R. Litoral, Imaruí: 24h |
| SC104) | | 1320 | 5/0.45 | R. Vitória, Videira |
| SP140) | K630 | 1320 | 1/0.25 | R. Difusora, Pirassununga: 24h |
| SP241) | K675 | *1320 | 0.5 | R. Clube, Tupã |
| BA34) | K468 | 1330 | 1 | R. Continental, Serrinha |
| MS54) | N610 | *1330 | 1/0,25 | R. Pantanal, Coxim |
| PA07) | I600 | †1330 | 5/1 | R. Liberal, Castanhal |
| PR74) | J264 | 1330 | 10/0.5 | R. Jaguariaíva, Jaguariaíva |
| RN27) | J621 | 1330 | 10/0.5 | R. Eldorado, Natal |
| RS111) | K236 | 1330 | 1/0.25 | R. Upacaraí, Dom Pedrito: 0900-0200 |
| RS112) | K323 | *1330 | 2.5/0.5 | R. Diplomata, São Marcos: 0800-0200 Sun 0800-0100 |
| SC50) | J739 | 1330 | 10/0.5 | R. Clube, Blumenau: 0800(Sun 0900)-0100 |
| SC51) | J749 | 1330 | 5/1 | R. Chapecó, Chapecó |
| SP142) | K638 | 1330 | 30/0.25 | R. Paulista, Regente Feijó |
| SP143) | K641 | 1330 | 5/1 | R. Cultura, Ribeirão Preto |
| SP187) | K736 | 1330 | 50/10 | R. Terra, Osasco: 24h |
| CE71) | H661 | 1340 | 2.5/0.25 | R. Pitaguary, Maracanaú: 0800-0300 (Sun -1900) |
| MA11) | H886 | 1340 | 10/2 | R. São Luís, São Luís: 24h |
| MG81) | L241 | 1340 | 10/5 | R. Cultura, Itabirito: 24h |
| MG139) | L352 | 1340 | 5/0.5 | R. Jovem Pan, Passos: 24h |
| MS12) | I380 | *1340 | 3/0.25 | R. Dif. 1340, Aquidauana: 0900-0300 (SS -0020) |
| PB13) | I671 | 1340 | 5/1 | R. Correio, João Pessoa |
| PR76) | J205 | 1340 | 2.5/0.25 | R. Difusora, Rio Negro |
| PR77) | J249 | 1340 | 5/0.25 | R. Cultura, Arapongas |
| PR41) | J368 | 1340 | 20/0.25 | CBN, Cascavel: 24h |
| RJ40) | J490 | 1340 | 5/0.5 | R. 1340, Rio Bonito |
| RS113) | K227 | 1340 | 25/4 | CBN, Porto Alegre: 24h |
| RS173) | K374 | 1340 | 10/4 | R. Journal da Manhã, Ijuí: 24h |
| SP144) | K543 | *1340 | 5/1 | R. Cultura, Araçatuba |
| SP203) | K571 | 1340 | 5/0.25 | R. Em. Campos do Jordão, Campos do Jordão: 24h |
| SP146) | K738 | 1340 | 1/0.25 | R. Nova Canoa Grande, Igaraçu do Tietê |
| AC05) | H201 | 1350 | 50/5 | R. Capital (RBV), Rio Branco |
| BA70) | H520 | 1350 | 50/10 | Super Rede Voa Vontade, Salvador: 24h |
| CE56) | H662 | 1350 | 1/0.25 | R. Liberal Jagoaribana, Morada Nova |
| PB14) | I675 | *1350 | 5/0.5 | R. Clube AM 1350, Campina Grande: 24h |
| RS114) | K205 | 1350 | 2.5/0.25 | R. Aurora, Guaporé |
| RS115) | K313 | 1350 | 5/1 | R. Difusora, Três Passos |
| RS116) | K336 | *1350 | 2.5/0.25 | R. Agudo, Agudo |
| SC53) | J760 | 1350 | 5/1 | R. Bandeirantes, Itajaí |
| SP265) | K692 | 1350 | 50/0.25 | R. Excelsior, Ibiúna: 24h |
| BA35) | H469 | 1360 | 10/1 | R. Cultura, Paulo Afonso: 24h |
| CE57) | H650 | 1360 | 5/0.25 | R. Iracema, Ipu: 0900-0200, SS 0800-2100 |
| MS64) | I383 | *1360 | 2 | R. Difusora, Corumbá |
| PR165) | J265 | 1360 | 10/0.25 | R. Cidade, Pato Branco: 24h |
| PR78) | J268 | 1360 | 1/0.25 | Rede Terra Nativa, Assaí: 24h |
| RJ30) | J464 | 1360 | 50/10 | R. Bandeirantes, Rio de Janeiro: 24h |
| RN11) | J605 | *1360 | 1/0.5 | R. Ouro Branco, Currais Novos |
| RS117) | K261 | *1360 | 5/0.5 | R. Alvorada, Marau: 24h |
| RS151) | K281 | 1360 | 3/0.25 | R. Navegantes, Porto Lucena: 0800-0300 |
| SC69) | J757 | *1360 | 25/0.4 | R. Belos Vales, Ibirama: 0800-0100 |
| SP148) | K739 | 1360 | 1/0.25 | R. Regional, Dracena: 24h |
| SP235) | K759 | 1360 | 1/0.25 | R. Luzes da Ribalta, Santa Bárbara d'Oeste |
| BA82) | H555 | 1370 | 0.25 | R. Jornal Grande, Monte Santo: 0800-0300 |
| CE81) | H628 | 1370 | 1/0.25 | R. Vanguarda, Caridade |
| PE34) | I800 | 1370 | 1/0.25 | R. Vale do Capibaribe, Sta. Cruz do Capibaribe |
| PI13) | I892 | 1370 | 2.5 | R. Difusora, Teresina |
| PR80) | J267 | 1370 | 50/7 | R. Canção Nova, Curitiba: 1000-0200 |
| RN28) | J618 | 1370 | 2.5/0.25 | R. Dif.,São Miguel: 0930-2100, Sun silent |
| RS118) | K243 | 1370 | 25/0.5 | R. Mãe de Deus, Flores da Cunha: 24h |
| RS119) | K334 | 1370 | 1/0.25 | R. Gazeta, Alegrete: 0900-0200 (Sun -0000) |
| SC55) | J782 | 1370 | 10/0.5 | R. Peperí AM, São Miguel do Oeste: 0800-0300 |
| SE09) | J929 | *1370 | 5/0.5 | R. Capital do Agreste, Itabaiana: 0700(Sun 0800)-0300 |
| SP223) | K766 | 1370 | 100/20 | R. Da Cidade, São Paulo: 24h |
| AM12) | H283 | 1380 | 5/1 | R. Alvorada, Parintins: 0900-0200 |
| BA83) | H495 | ‡1380 | 5/0.25 | R. União, Gandu |
| ES21) | I… | 1380 | 10/1 | R. Itaí de Rio Claro, Iúna |
| MA40) | H909 | 1380 | 1/0.25 | R. Tropical, Caixas |
| MG172) | L218 | 1380 | 1/0.25 | Rede Gerais, Brasópolis |
| MG120) | L284 | *1380 | 5/0.25 | R. Paranaíba, Rio Paranaíba |
| MG130) | L323 | 1380 | 1/0.25 | R. Gorutubana, Janaúba |
| PE23) | I773 | 1380 | 10/5 | R. Novas de Paz, Recife |
| PR122) | J276 | 1380 | 2/0.25 | R. Bom Jesus, Siqueira Campos: 24h |
| PR152) | J367 | 1380 | 1/0.25 | R. Integração, Toledo: 0800-0300 |
| RS120) | K293 | 1380 | 1/0.25 | R. Cultura, Santana do Livramento |
| RS121) | K350 | 1380 | 6/0.25 | R. Cultura, Tapera: 0830-0100(SS -2300) |
| RS165) | K372 | 1380 | 6/0.25 | R. Chiru, Itaqui: 24h SS Silent |
| SC56) | J821 | *1380 | 6/0.25 | R. Cidade, Itaiópolis: 0900(Sun 1200)-0100 |
| SC93) | J827 | 1380 | 6/0.25 | R. Barriga Verde, Capinzal: 0830-2000 |
| SC105) | J831 | 1380 | 6/0.25 | R. Freguencia, Garopaba |
| SP152) | K616 | 1380 | 1/0.5 | R. Difusora, Mogi Guaçu |
| SP247) | K623 | *1380 | 5/0.25 | R. Cultura, Pederneiras: 24h |
| SP224) | K751 | 1380 | 5/0.25 | R. Globo, Presidente Prudente: 24h |
| SP234) | K772 | 1380 | 1/0.25 | R. República, Morro agudo: 24h |
| ES13) | I209 | *1380 | 5/0.25 | R. Educadora, Afonso Cláudio: 0700-0100 |
| MG157) | L358 | 1390 | 2.5/0.25 | R. Ouro Verde, São Sebastião do Paraíso: 0800-0300 |
| MG178) | L305 | 1390 | 10/0.5 | R. Vitoriosa, Uberlândia |
| PA12) | I535 | 1390 | 10/1 | R. Educadora, Bragança: 0830-0100 |
| PE24) | I788 | 1390 | 5/1 | R. Jornal, Pesqueira |
| PR82) | J242 | 1390 | 10/1 | R. Cultura, Maringá |
| PR83) | J335 | 1390 | 1/0.25 | R. Independência, Salto do Lontra: 0830-0005(SS -0100) |
| RJ32) | J473 | 1390 | 5/0.5 | R. Sul Fluminense, Barra Mansa |
| RN32) | J599 | 1390 | 5/0.25 | R. Farol, Touros: 1000-2200 |
| RO18) | J687 | ±*1390 | 5/1 | R. Planalto, Ji-Paraná |
| RR02) | 0701 | 1390 | 10/5 | R. Roraima, Caracaraí |
| RS122) | K209 | 1390 | 25 | R. Esperança, Porto Alegre: 24h |
| RS166) | K368 | 1390 | 8/0.25 | R. Atlântica, Constantina: 0900-0100 |
| SP153) | K570 | 1390 | 25 | R. Globo, Campinas: 24h |
| SP154) | K636 | 1390 | 1/0.25 | R. Cultura, Promissão |
| SP2859) | K594 | 1390 | 2.5 | R. Anchieta, Itanhaém |
| AC06) | H200 | 1400 | 10/1 | R. Dif. Acreana, Rio Branco: 0900-0400 |

| MW | Call | kHz | kW | Station, location, h. of tr. |
|---|---|---|---|---|
| BA71) | H529 | *1400 | 1/0.25 | R. Vale do Vaza Barris, Jeremoabo |
| PB15) | I677 | 1400 | 5/1 | R. Espinharas, Patos |
| PI27) | I926 | 1400 | 1/0.25 | R. Cantagalo, Jaicós |
| PR84) | J256 | 1400 | 5/0.25 | R. Globo, Londrina: 24h |
| PR119) | J339 | 1400 | 10/1 | R. Ágape, Balsa Nova: 0800-0100 |
| PR148) | J346 | 1400 | 2/0.45 | R. Jornal São Miguel, São Miguel do Iguaçu: 0900-0200 |
| RJ33) | J462 | 1400 | 50/5 | R. Rio de Janeiro, Rio de Janeiro: 24h |
| RS192) | K376 | 1400 | 1/0.4 | R. Educadora, São João da Urtiga: 0800-0130 SS 0900-0100 |
| SC58) | J775 | 1400 | 5/0.35 | R. Entre Rios, Palmitos: 0000-0200 |
| SP155) | K527 | 1400 | 1/0.25 | R. Difusora, Lucélia |
| SP156) | K658 | 1400 | 5/0.25 | R. Cl., São Carlos: 0900(Sun 1100)-0300 |
| SP157) | K682 | 1400 | 5/0.25 | R. Metrópole, São José do Rio Preto |
| TO08) | N660 | 1400 | 1 | Radiodifusão Guaraí, Guaraí |
| BA37) | H467 | 1400 | 10/0.5 | R. Planeta, São Gonçalo dos Campos: 0800-2000 SS -0000 |
| CE25) | H639 | 1410 | 10/1 | R. Boa Nova, Pacajus |
| GO19) | H803 | 1410 | 30/0.85 | R. JK AM, Santo Antônio do Descoberto |
| MS14) | I382 | 1410 | 5/1 | Nova R. Clube, Corumbá: 0700-2200 (Sat -0100), Sun Silent |
| RJ34) | J486 | *1410 | 10/0.5 | R. Itaperuna, Itaperuna: 0800-0300 |
| RN21) | J614 | 1410 | 5/0.5 | R. Santa Cruz, Santa Cruz: 0800-0200, Sun 0900-0100 |
| RS137) | K246 | 1410 | 5/1 | R. Garibaldi, Garibaldi: 24h |
| RS125) | K284 | 1410 | 1/0.25 | R. Minuano, Rio Grande: 24h |
| RS126) | K294 | 1410 | 5 | R. Santa Rosa, Santa Rosa |
| SC84) | J818 | *1410 | 5/0.25 | R. Pomerode, Pomerode |
| SP158) | K691 | 1410 | 50/25 | R. América, São Paulo: 24h |
| SP264 | K683 | 1410 | 1/0.25 | R. Excelsior, Rio Claro |
| BA60) | H504 | *1420 | 1/0.25 | R. Cidade, Irecê: 24h |
| MG89) | L288 | 1420 | 5/1 | R. Cultura, Sete Lagoas |
| MG90) | L313 | 1420 | 1/0.25 | R. Montanhês Botelhos, Botelhos |
| MS16) | I397 | *1420 | 1/0.25 | R. Difusora Cacique, Nova Andradina |
| PR88) | J269 | 1420 | 5/0.25 | R. Cult., Umuarama: 0900-2105(Sun -1000) |
| PR89) | J282 | *1420 | 1/0.25 | R. Educadora, Jacarezinho: 24h |
| RN12) | J609 | 1420 | 1/0.25 | R. Farol, Alexandria |
| RS149) | K258 | *1420 | 5/0.25 | R. 14 de Julho, Júlio de Castilhos |
| RS171) | K308 | 1420 | 3 | R. Tapense, Tapes: 0900-0130(Sun -2300) |
| SC59) | J754 | 1420 | 10/2.5 | R. Guarujá, Florianópolis |
| SP159) | K597 | 1420 | 2.5/0.5 | C.R.N., Itatiba: 24h |
| SP163) | K733 | 1420 | 1/0.25 | R. Nova São Manuel, São Manuel: 0800-0300 |
| MG158) | L371 | 1430 | 2.5/0.25 | R. Globo, Perdizes |
| PE32) | I826 | 1430 | 1/0.25 | R. Independência, Goiana |
| PR42) | J200 | 1430 | 50/10 | R. Evangelizar, Curitiba: 24h |
| RN13) | J604 | 1430 | 10/0.5 | R. Libertadora, Mossoró |
| RO11) | J671 | *1430 | 10 | R. Caiari, Porto Velho: 24h |
| RS167) | K366 | 1430 | 1/0.25 | R. Guarita, Coronel Bicaco: 0900-0100 |
| RS198) | K379 | 1430 | 1 | R. AM 1430, Portão: 0900-0130 |
| SP164) | K666 | 1430 | 1/0.25 | R. Serra Negra, Serra Negra |
| SP275) | K707 | 1430 | 25/0.25 | R. Imaculada Conceição, São Roque |
| BA38) | H466 | 1440 | 50/1 | R. Independência, Santo Amaro |
| CE33) | H603 | *1440 | 10/1 | R. Canaã Araripe, Crato |
| MG159) | L365 | 1440 | 1/0.25 | R. Som 2000, Santa Vitória: 0900-0200 |
| MS41) | I407 | 1440 | 1/0.25 | R. Bela Vista, Bela Vista: 24h |
| RJ35) | J469 | 1440 | 20/5 | R. Livre, Rio de Janeiro: 24h |
| RS168) | K221 | 1440 | 2.5/0.5 | R. Ceres, Naõ Me Toque: 24h |
| RS130) | K328 | 1440 | 5/0.3 | R. Excelsior, Gramado: 0900-0300 |
| RS153) | K362 | *1440 | 2.5/0.25 | R. Caibaté, Caibaté: 0830-0200 |
| SC61) | J792 | *1440 | 2.5/0.25 | R. Difusora, Maravilha: 24h |
| SE11) | J930 | *1440 | 5/0.25 | R. Educadora, Frei Paulo: 0700-0300 |
| SP253) | K568 | 1440 | 1/0.25 | R. Eldorado Centro Norte Paulista, Cajuru |
| SP165) | K634 | 1440 | 10/0,25 | R. Comercial, Presidente Prudente: 24h |
| SP218) | K752 | 1440 | 1/0.25 | R. Azul Celeste, Americana: 24h |
| SP284) | | 1440 | 2.5/0.5 | R. Clarim de Palmas, Itai |
| BA73) | H531 | 1450 | 1/0.25 | R. Ipirá, Ipirá |
| CE34) | H601 | 1450 | 1/0.25 | R. Difusora Cristal, Quixeramobim |
| CE35) | H623 | 1450 | 1/0.25 | R. Pinto Martins, Camocim |
| CE99) | | *1450 | | R. Carinhosa, Acopiara: 0800-0100 (SS -2300) |
| ES12) | I208 | *1450 | 1/0.5 | R. Sim, Guarapari |
| MA32) | H900 | 1450 | 1/0.25 | R. Boa Esperança, São João dos Patos |
| MA13) | H901 | 1450 | 1/0.25 | R. Cultura, Pedreiras |
| MG94) | L312 | 1450 | 3/0.25 | R. Diamante, Coromandel |
| MS13) | I417 | *1450 | 1/0.25 | R. Difusora, Rio Brilhante: 0900-0200 |
| MS63) | | 1450 | 1 | R. Portal, Bataguassu: 24h, Sun Silent |
| PA33) | I559 | 1450 | 1/0.25 | R. Juruá, São Felix do Xingu |
| PA56) | I56I | *1450 | 1 | R. Paraense, Castanhal |
| PB29) | I699 | 1450 | 1/0.25 | R. Certao, Patos: 0700-0300 |
| PE25) | I794 | 1450 | 1/0.25 | R. Cultura, Palmares: 24h |
| PI21) | I908 | 1450 | 1/0.25 | R. Cultura do Gurguéia, Bom Jesus |

| MW | Call | kHz | kW | Station, location, h. of tr. |
|---|---|---|---|---|
| PI35) | I917 | 1450 | 1/0.25 | R. Confederação Valenciana, Valença do Piauí |
| PR93) | J279 | *1450 | 1/0.25 | R. Cabiúna, Bandeirantes |
| PR95) | J317 | 1450 | 1/0.25 | R. Rainha de Altônia, Altônia: 24h |
| PR179) | J301 | 1450 | 1/0.25 | R. Dif. Ubiratanense, Ubiratã: 0800-2300 |
| PR188) | J279 | *1450 | 1 | R. Cabiúna, Bandeirantes: 0800-0200 |
| RJ36) | J480 | 1450 | 5/0.25 | R. Comércio, Barra Mansa: 24h |
| RJ37) | J503 | *1450 | 1/0.25 | R. Feliz, Santo Antônio de Pádua: 0800-0100 |
| RO12) | J674 | 1450 | 1/0.25 | R. Vilhena, Vilhena: 0800-0400(SS -2000) |
| RR03) | O701 | 1450 | 1/0.25 | R. Transamérca Hits, Alto Alegre |
| RS177) | K338 | 1450 | 1/0.25 | R. Cultura, Arvorezinha |
| SC62) | J802 | *1450 | 1/0.25 | R. São Bento, São Bento do Sul: 0800-0200 |
| SC63) | J822 | 1450 | 10/0.25 | R. Hulha Negra, Criciúma: 24h |
| SC97) | J828 | *1450 | 2.5/0.25 | R. Belos Montes, Seara: 0800-0300 |
| SP238) | K526 | 1450 | 2.5/0.25 | R. Cultura, Ituverava: 24h |
| SP167) | K591 | 1450 | 50/5 | R. Boa Nova, Guarulhos: 24h |
| SP168) | K657 | 1450 | 1/0.25 | R. São Carlos, São Carlos do Pinhal: 24h |
| AM17) | H300 | 1460 | 5 | R. Clube, Parintins |
| BA39) | H472 | *1460 | 1 | R. Povo, Jequié |
| BA85) | H523 | 1460 | 1/0.25 | R. Ferro Doido, Morro do Chapéu |
| BA74) | H536 | *1460 | 1/0.25 | R. Excelsior, Cruz das Almas |
| CE53) | H595 | 1460 | 1/0.25 | R. Ressurreição, Massapé |
| CE36) | H616 | 1460 | 1/0.25 | R. Uirapuru, Morada Nova |
| GO34) | H766 | *1460 | 1/0.25 | R. Morrinhos, Morrinhos |
| MA33) | H917 | 1460 | 1/0.25 | R. Vanguarda, Santa Luzia |
| MG95) | L201 | 1460 | 1/0.25 | R. Cul. do Porto Novo, Além Paraíba |
| MG161) | L356 | *1460 | 1/0.25 | R. Buritis, Buritis |
| MG131) | L363 | 1460 | 1/0.25 | R. Gerais AM, Raul Soares: 24h |
| MS56) | I.... | 1460 | 1/0.25 | R. Globo, Costa Rica |
| PI14) | I903 | 1460 | 1/0.25 | R. Cultura, Amarante |
| PR96) | J204 | *1460 | 2/0.25 | R. Difusora, Paranaguá |
| PR97) | J228 | *1460 | 1/0.25 | R. Central do Paraná, Ponta Grossa: 24h |
| PR100) | J297 | *1460 | 1/0.25 | R. Guaíra, Guaíra: 24h |
| PR101) | J308 | 1460 | 5/0.25 | R. Ampere, Ampere: 0830-0100 |
| PR102) | J318 | *1460 | 1/0.25 | R. Guadalupe AM, Loanda: 24h |
| RN20) | J615 | 1460 | 10/0,25 | R. Agreste, Santo Antônio |
| RS133) | K214 | 1460 | 1/0.25 | R. Cultura, Bagé |
| RS135) | K312 | *1460 | 1/0.25 | R. Colonial, Três de Maio: 0800-0300 |
| RS175) | K373 | 1460 | 1/0.25 | R. Campinas, Campinas do Sul |
| RS176) | K378 | 1460 | 0.25 | R. Mostardas, Mostardas: 24h |
| RS199) | K382 | 1460 | 1 | R. Litoral, Imbé: 24h |
| SC64) | J756 | 1460 | 2.5 | R. Sentinela do Vale, Gaspar |
| SE12) | J932 | 1460 | 10/0.5 | R. Abais, Estância: 0900-2300(SS -1700) |
| SP242) | K548 | 1460 | 5/0.5 | R. Clube Ararense, Araras: 24h |
| SP170) | K608 | 1460 | 1/0.25 | R. Cultura, Lorena: 24h |
| TO02) | H774 | 1460 | 1/0.25 | R. Independência do Tocantins, Paraíso do Tocantins |
| BA86) | H509 | 1470 | 0.25 | R. Morro Verde, Mairi |
| CE64) | H665 | 1470 | 1/0.25 | R. Guanancés de Itapajé, Itapajé: |
| ES17) | I214 | *1470 | 1/0.25 | R. Globo, Barra de São Francisco: 24h |
| GO36) | H773 | 1470 | 10/0.25 | R. Dif. Serra dos Cristais, Cristalina |
| GO37) | H779 | 1470 | 1/0.25 | R. Cidade, Goiás |
| MA34) | H908 | 1470 | 1/0.25 | R. Paranoá, Presidente Dutra |
| MA39) | H901 | 1470 | 1/0.25 | R. Urbano Santos,Urbano Santos |
| MA43) | | 1470 | 1 | R. Cidade, Turiaçu |
| MG96) | L247 | 1470 | 1/0.25 | R. Dif., Ituiutaba: 24h |
| MS29) | I413 | 1470 | 1/0.25 | R. Alvorada, Itaporã |
| PA25) | I548 | 1470 | 1/0.25 | R. Moreno Braga, Vigia |
| PE35) | I822 | 1470 | 1/0.25 | R. Educadora, Belém de São Francisco: 0900-0300, Sat 1100-0100, Sun 1700-2000 |
| PE37) | I827 | *1470 | 1/0.25 | R. Papacaça, Bom Conselho: 0700-0300, Sun 0800-0100 |
| PI15) | I900 | 1470 | 1/0.25 | R. Difusora Vale do Uruçuí, Uruçuí |
| PI24) | I913 | 1470 | 1/0.25 | R. Ingazeira, Paulistana |
| PI33) | I928 | 1470 | 1/0.25 | R. Cidade, Castelo do Piauí |
| PR103) | J294 | *1470 | 1/0.25 | R. Educadora, Ibaiti: 24h |
| PR104) | J304 | *1470 | 5/0.25 | R. Jornal, Assis Chateaubriand |
| PR173) | J... | 1470 | 3/0.25 | R. Tradição, Rio Branco do Sul: 24h |
| RJ08) | J476 | 1470 | 1/0.25 | R. Absoluta, Campos dos Goytacazes |
| RJ38) | J481 | *1470 | 1/0.25 | R. Barra do Pirai, Barra do Pirai: 0900-0300 |
| RN23) | J616 | 1470 | 1/0.25 | R. Rural de Parelhas, Parelhas |
| RO05) | J676 | 1470 | 1/0.25 | R. Rondônia, Cacoal |
| RS169) | K219 | 1470 | 0.25 | R. Cultura, Cacequi |
| SC65) | J781‡ | *1470 | 10/1 | R. Jornal A Verdad, São José |
| SC66) | J798 | 1470 | 3/0.25 | R. Nova Líder, Herval d'Oeste |
| SP172) | K586 | 1470 | 1/0.25 | R. Cultura, Guaíra |
| SP173) | K599 | 1470 | 5/0.25 | R. Mensagem, Jacareí: 24h |
| SP174) | K632 | 1470 | 1/0.25 | R. Primavera, Porto Ferreira |
| SP175) | K712 | 1470 | 1/0.25 | R. Jornal, Indaiatuba: 24h |
| SP243) | K771 | 1470 | 1/0.25 | R. Bastos AM, Bastos |

| MW | Call | kHz | kW | Station, location, h. of tr. |
|---|---|---|---|---|
| BA66) | H510 | 1480 | 1/0.25 | R. Tribuna do Vale do São Francisco, Xique-Xique |
| BA75) | H524 | 1480 | 1/0.25 | R. Santana, Santana |
| CE74) | H671 | 1480 | 1/0.25 | R. Princesa do Norte, Morrinhos. 0800-2000, Sat 1400-1500 |
| MA14) | H897 | 1480 | 10 | R. Itapecuru, Colinas |
| MG98) | L235 | 1480 | 1/0.25 | R. Nova Frutal AM, Frutal |
| MG99) | L265 | 1480 | 5/0.25 | R. Difusora, Nanuque |
| MG100) | L307 | 1480 | 2.5/0.25 | R. Emboabas, Tiradentes: 24h |
| MS17) | I393 | *1480 | 1/0.25 | R. Caçula, Três Lagoas: 24h |
| MT66) | | *1480 | | R. Continental, Campo Verde |
| PE26) | I790 | *1480 | 1/0.25 | R. A Voz do Sertão, Serra Talhada: 0900-0100, Sat 0800-2200 |
| PE36) | I825 | 1480 | 5/0.25 | R. Canção Nova, Gravatá: 24h |
| PI29) | I929 | 1480 | 1/0.25 | R. Vale do Coroatá, Elesbão Veloso |
| PR79) | J302 | *1480 | 1/0.25 | R. Cultura, Iporã |
| PR106) | J230 | 1480 | 1/0.25 | R. Astorga, Astorga |
| PR174) | J370 | 1480 | 1/0.25 | R. Pérola, Pérola d'Oeste |
| RJ55) | J485 | 1480 | 10/0.5 | R. Popular, Duque de Caxias |
| RN14) | J601 | *1480 | 1/0.25 | R. Princesa do Vale, Açu: 0700-2333, Sat 0915-1500 Sun 1100-0100 |
| RO15) | J681 | 1480 | 1/0.25 | R. Rondônia, Pimenta Bueno |
| RS178) | K255 | *1480 | 0.5/0.25 | R. Guaramano, Guarani das Missões: 0800-0200(Sun -0100) |
| SC67) | J731 | 1480 | 1/0.25 | R. Arca da Aliança, Joinville |
| SC94) | J826 | 1480 | 2.5/0.25 | R. Caibi, Caibi* |
| SE10) | J928 | *1480 | 1/0.25 | R. Nova Cidade, Simão Dias: 24h |
| SP176) | K539 | *1480 | 1/0.25 | R. Cult. Regional, Altinópolis: 0900-2110 (Sun -0100) |
| SP177) | K551 | 1480 | 1/0.25 | R. Atibaia, Atibaia |
| SP255) | K767 | 1480 | 0.5 | R. Boituva, Boituva |
| T006) | H795 | 1480 | 1/0.25 | R. Cultura, Miracema do Tocantins: 24h |
| AL09) | H246 | 1490 | 5/1 | Em. Rio São Francisco, Penedo |
| BA41) | H478 | 1490 | 1/0.25 | R. Educadora, Ipiaú: 0800-0300 |
| BA77) | H507 | 1490 | 1/0.25 | R. Rio São Francisco, Bom Jesus da Lapa |
| BA87) | H512 | 1490 | 0.25 | R. Planalto d'Oeste, Correntina: 0800-0100 |
| MG162) | L231 | 1490 | 0.25 | R. Onda Viva, Araguari |
| MG163) | L274 | 1490 | 1/0.25 | R. Paraisópolis, Paraisópolis |
| MG165) | L353 | 1490 | 1/0.25 | R. Pirapetinga, Pirapetinga: 0800-0100(Sun -2300) |
| MS19) | I404 | *1490 | 1/0.25 | R. Nova Paiaguás, Glória de Dourados |
| PR108) | J210 | 1490 | 1/0.25 | R. Cornélio, Cornélio Procópio |
| PR149) | J347 | 1490 | 1/0.25 | R. Dif., São Jorge do Oeste: 0900-0100 |
| RS138) | K208 | 1490 | 25/0.25 | R. Assisense, São Francisco de Assis |
| RS140) | K309 | 1490 | 3/0.25 | R. Taquara, Taquara: 0830-0200 |
| SC70) | J791 | 1490 | 2.5/0.25 | R. Cultura, Xaxim |
| SP180) | K530 | 1490 | 1/0.25 | R. Difusora, Olímpia: 24h |
| SP181) | K580 | *1490 | 1/0.25 | R. Globo, Dracena: 24h |
| SP182) | K583 | 1490 | 1/0.25 | R. Educadora, Fernandópolis: 24h |
| SP244) | K680 | 1490 | 1/0.25 | R. Cult., Vargem Grande do Sul: 0900-0100 |
| SP183) | K764 | 1490 | 25/0.5 | R. Imaculada Conceição, Mauá |
| BA49) | H487 | 1500 | 0.5 | R. Jacuípe, Riachão do Jacuípe |
| CE39) | H615 | *1500 | 2.5/0.25 | R. Macico, Baturité |
| MG140) | L340 | 1500 | 1/0.25 | R. Aparecida do Sul, Ilicínea: 0900-2200 |
| PA19) | I542 | *1500 | 1/0.25 | R. Floresta, Tucuruí |
| PE27) | I779 | 1500 | 1/0.25 | R. Pajeu, Afogados da Ingazeira: 0700(SS 0800)-0300 |
| PI46) | I919 | 1500 | 1/0.25 | R. Voz do Longa, Esperantina |
| PR163) | J366 | 1500 | 2.5/0.25 | R. Aracauria, Mangueirinha |
| RS139) | K225 | 1500 | 4/0.25 | R. Liberdade, Canguçu: 0900-0100 |
| RS161) | K365 | 1500 | 3/0.25 | R. Simpatia, Chapada: 0900-0100 |
| SC106) | J...... | *1500 | 1/0.25 | R. Catolica, Balneário Camboriú |
| SP184) | K549 | 1500 | 2.5/0.25 | R. Fraternidade, Araras |
| SP185) | K626 | *1500 | 1/0.25 | R. Difusora, Pindamonhangaba |
| SP186) | K706 | 1500 | 1/0.25 | R. Vale do Rio Grande, Miguelópolis |
| SP211) | K773 | 1500 | 1/0.25 | R. Cumbica, Guarulhos: 24h |
| SP236) | K776 | 1500 | 1/0.25 | R. Cidade, Apiaí: 24h |
| BA52) | H493 | 1510 | 5/0.5 | R. Dif. do Descobrimento, Porto Seguro |
| CE40) | H608 | 1510 | 1/0.25 | R. Planalto, São Benedito: 24h |
| CE84) | H630 | 1510 | 0.25 | R. Trapiá, Pedra Branca: W |
| ES25) | | 1510 | | R. Cidade, Nova Venecia* |
| GO38) | H770 | 1510 | 1/0.25 | R. Goiatuba, Goiatuba |
| MS62) | N613 | *1510 | 1/0.25 | R. Maria, Mundo Novo |
| PA01) | I544 | 1510 | 10/0.25 | R. Oriente de Redenção, Redenção |
| PI16) | I894 | *1510 | 1/0.25 | R. Difusora, Floriano |
| PI17) | I896 | ‡1510 | 1/0.25 | R. Progresso, Corrente |
| PI49) | I936 | 1510 | 1/0.25 | R. Nordeste, Picos |
| PR115) | J326 | 1510 | 1/0.25 | R. União, Céu Azul |
| RJ43) | J492 | 1510 | 1/0.25 | R. Teresópolis, Teresópolis: 0900-0300 |
| RN15) | J602 | 1510 | 1/0.25 | R. Centenário, Caraúbas: 0700-0100 (SS -2300) |
| RO24) | | 1510 | 0.25 | R. Central, Jaru |
| SC73) | J795 | *1510 | 1/0.25 | R. Centro Oeste, Pinhalzinho: 0800-0200 (Sun -0100) |
| SP188) | K654 | 1510 | 10/1 | R. Cacique, Santos |
| SP189) | K665 | 1510 | 1/0.25 | R. Cl. Regional, São Manuel: 0700-2300 |
| SP256) | K770 | 1510 | 0.5/0.25 | R. Vale do Tietê, Salto |
| SP230) | K.... | 1510 | 1/0.25 | R. Rural, Rinópolis |
| SP269) | K719 | 1510 | 1/0.25 | R. Athenas Paulista, Jaboticabal |
| BA78) | H530 | 1520 | 5/1 | R. Povo, Poções |
| CE75) | H635 | 1520 | 1/0.25 | R. Regional, Ipu: 0800-0300 |
| CE83) | H653 | 1520 | 1/0.25 | R. Cachoeira, Solonópole |
| GO53) | H806 | 1520 | 1/0.25 | R. Nova RCB, Campos Belos: 24h |
| MA15) | H899 | 1520 | 1/0.25 | R. Mirante, Pindaré-Mirim |
| MA35) | H928 | 1520 | 1/0.25 | R. Mirante AM, Chapadinha |
| MG174) | L223 | 1520 | 0.25 | R. Cultura, Cássia |
| MG106) | L245 | 1520 | 2.5/0.25 | R. Clube, Itaúna |
| MS21) | I405 | *1520 | 1/0.25 | R. Globo, Amambaí: 24h |
| MS42) | N605 | 1520 | 1/0.25 | R. Campo Alegre, Rio Verde de Mato Grosso |
| PE28) | I801 | 1520 | 1/0.25 | R. Surubim, Surubim: 0800-0100 (Sat -1700), Sun silent |
| PR116) | J218 | 1520 | 2.5/0.25 | R. Serra do Mar, Antonina: 24h |
| PR118) | J292 | 1520 | 1/0.25 | R. Nova Cultura, Palotina |
| PR132) | J340 | *1520 | 1/0.25 | R. Cidade, Quedas do Iguaçu: 0830-0100, SS: 0900-0000 |
| RJ44) | J491 | 1520 | 10/0.5 | R. Continental, São João do Meriti: 24h |
| RN22) | J610 | 1520 | 1/0.25 | R. Salinas, Macau* |
| RS141) | K217 | *1520 | 1/0.25 | R. Vale do Jacui, Cachoeira do Sul: 0830-0100 |
| SC76) | J806 | *1520 | 2.5/0.25 | R. Cultura, Timbó |
| SE13) | J931 | 1520 | 10/0.5 | R. Ilha AM, Tobias Barreto |
| SP191) | K614 | 1520 | 10/1 | R. da Cidada., Mogi das Cruzes: 24h |
| SP192) | K627 | 1520 | 1/0.25 | Pinhal R. Cl., Espírito Sto. do Pinhal |
| SP225) | K760 | 1520 | 1/0.25 | R. Manchester, Sorocaba |
| SP270) | K.... | *1520 | 1/0.25 | Dif. Torre Forte, Buritama |
| SP286) | K.... | 1520 | 0.25 | R. Legal, Viradouro: 24h |
| TO07) | H797 | 1520 | 1/0.25 | R. Cristal, Cristalândia |
| BA99) | H533 | 1530 | 0.25 | R. Progresso, Capim Grosso |
| CE76) | H666 | 1530 | 1/0.25 | R. Tres Fronteiras, Campos Sales: 0800-2300 |
| MG175) | L262 | 1530 | 0.25 | R. Progresso, Monte Santo de Minas |
| MG110) | L280 | 1530 | 1/0.25 | R. Clube, Pouso Alegre |
| MT42) | I432 | *1530 | 1/0.25 | R. Continental, Peixoto de Azevedo |
| MT64) | | *1530 | 1/0.25 | R. Parecis. Campo Novo de Parecis |
| PE29) | I781 | *1530 | 1/0.25 | R. Bitury, Belo Jardim |
| PR157) | J348 | *1530 | 2.5/0.25 | R. Vale do Iguaçu, Verê: 0800-0100 |
| RJ57) | J482 | *1530 | 1/0.25 | R. Búzios, Cabo Frio |
| RJ45) | J502 | *1530 | 1/0.25 | R. Princesinha do Norte, Miracema: 0800-0100(Sat -2030, Sun -1700) |
| RN16) | J603 | *1530 | 1/0.25 | R. Curimataú, Nova Cruz |
| RO16) | J685 | *1530 | 5/1 | R. Planalto, Vilhena: 0900-0330 |
| RS143) | K235 | 1530 | 1/0.25 | R. Sulina, Dom Pedrito: 0800-0030 |
| RS144) | K300 | 1530 | 5/0.25 | R. Progresso, São Leopoldo: 1000-0100 |
| RS145) | K304 | *1530 | 4/0.25 | R. Tapejara, Tapejara: 24h |
| SC77) | J761 | 1530 | 1/0.25 | R. Dif., Itajaí: 0800-0300, Sun 1000-0200 |
| SC78) | J780 | *1530 | 2.5/0.25 | R. Difusora, São Joaquim: 0900-0200 |
| SC79) | J796 | 1530 | 2.5 | R. Porto Feliz, Mondaí |
| SP193) | K677 | 1530 | 1/0.25 | R. Difusora Digital, Tupi Paulista |
| SP194) | K714 | 1530 | 1/0.25 | R. Noticias, Tatuí: 24h |
| SP231) | K755 | 1530 | 1/0.25 | R. Universal, Teodoro Sampaio |
| BA89) | H.... | 1540 | 0.25 | R. Sociedade, Itiruçu |
| CE42) | H611 | *1540 | 1/0.5 | R. Sant'Ana, Tianguá: 0830-0100, SS 0900-2300 |
| CE77) | H631 | *1540 | 1/0.25 | R. Sertões, Mombaça |
| MA36) | H921 | *1540 | 1/0.25 | R. Santa Maura, Lago da Pedra |
| MG111) | L217 | 1540 | 1/0.25 | R. Bomdespachense, Bom Despacho |
| MG113) | L293 | 1540 | 2.0/0.25 | R. Tropical, Três Corações: 24h |
| MS35) | N601 | *1540 | 1/0.5 | R. Nova Piravevê, Ivinhema |
| MT65) | I442 | *1540 | 1/0.25 | R. Ativa, Barra do Burges: 0830-0200 Sun: silent |
| PA14) | I545 | 1540 | 1/0.25 | R. Boa Vista, São Sebastião da Boa Vista |
| PB24) | I694 | 1540 | 1/0.5 | R. Santa Maria, Monteiro |
| PR168) | J206 | *1540 | 1/0.25 | R. Litorânea, Guaratuba: 24h |
| RJ54) | J508 | 1540 | 1/0.25 | R. Clube, Paraíba do Sul: 0900-0300 |
| RN30) | J611 | ‡1540 | 1/0.25 | R. Baixa Verde, João Câmara: 0900-0000 |
| RS157) | K282 | 1540 | 1/0.25 | R. Quaraí, Quaraí |
| SC80) | J803 | 1540 | 5/0.25 | R. Capinzal, Capinzal: 0800-0200 Sun 24h |
| SP245) | K514 | 1540 | 1/0.25 | R. Cultura, Leme |
| SP196) | K564 | 1540 | 2/0.5 | R. Em. Botucatu, Botucatu: 0800-0300 |
| SP197) | K723 | 1540 | 50/1 | R. Nova Difusora, Osasco: 0900-0100 |
| SP246) | K737 | 1540 | 0.5/0.25 | R. Central, Pompéia |
| SP288) | | 1540 | | R. Novo Milenio, Ribeirao Preto (IPDA) |

| MW | Call | kHz | kW | Station, location, h. of tr. |
|---|---|---|---|---|
| BA80) | H518 | 1550 | 5/0.25 | R. Independencia do São Francisco, Juazeiro |
| MA37) | H926 | 1550 | 10/1 | Sist. Janaina de Rdif, Vargem Grande |
| MG114) | L211 | 1550 | 1/0.25 | R. Cultura, Monte Carmelo: 24h |
| MG169) | L222 | 1550 | 1/0.25 | R. Difusora, Carmo do Rio Claro |
| MG115) | L289 | *1550 | 1/0.25 | R. Difusora Santarritense, Santa Rita do Sapucaí: 0800-0200 |
| MG195) | N211 | 1550 | 1/0.25 | R. Cidade, Guanhães: 24h |
| PA34) | I550 | 1550 | 1/0.25 | R. Cabano, Maracanã |
| PB32) | I700 | 1550 | 10/0.25 | R. Jardim da Borborema, Areia: 0800-0200 |
| PR133) | J213 | 1550 | 1/0.25 | R. Ipiranga, Palmeira |
| PR123) | J303 | 1550 | 1/0.25 | R. Pioneira, Formosa do Oeste: 1000-2200, Sun silent |
| PR124) | J315 | 1550 | 2.5/0.25 | R. Cristal, Marmeleiro: 24h |
| PR169) | J217 | 1550 | 1/0.25 | R. Itay, Lapa: 0900-2200 |
| PR185) | J371 | *1550 | 1 | R. Globo, Jacarezinho: 24h |
| RJ46) | J479 | 1550 | 1/0.25 | R. Imperial, Petrópolis: 0900-0300 |
| RN19) | J606 | 1550 | 1/0.25 | R. Ivipanin, Areia Branca (RPC) |
| RO23) | J... | 1550 | 0.25 | R. Suprema, Cacoal: 24h |
| RS162) | K377 | 1550 | 1/0.25 | R. Opinião Gospel, Capão do Leão |
| RS159) | K375 | 1550 | 1/0.25 | R. Soledad, Soledade: 0800(Sun 0900)-0300 |
| SC92) | J814 | *1550 | 5/0.25 | R. Imigrantes, Turvo: 0800-0100 |
| SP198) | K501 | 1550 | 1/0.25 | R. Clube, Itararé |
| SP259) | K528 | *1550 | 1/0.25 | R. Tambaú, Tambaú: 0900-0300 |
| SP200) | K572 | 1550 | 1/0.25 | R. Cacique, Capivari |
| SP201) | K590 | 1550 | 10/1 | R. Guarujá AM, Guarujá: 24h |
| SP202) | K659 | *1550 | 1/0.5 | R. São Joaquim, São Joaquim da Barra |
| SP219) | K740 | 1550 | 1/0.25 | R. Nova Difusora, Auriflama |
| AL16) | H257 | 1560 | 1/0.25 | R. Princesa das Matas, Viçosa: 0830-0200, SS 24h |
| BA90) | H526 | *1560 | 0.25 | R. Povo Pombal, Ribeira do Pombal |
| CE43) | H622 | 1560 | 1/0.25 | R. Difusora Vale de Curu, Pentecoste |
| MA18) | H903 | 1560 | 1/0.25 | R. Agua Branca, Vitorino Freire |
| MG117) | L256 | 1560 | 1/0.25 | R. Jornal, Leopoldina: 0800-0500 |
| MT56) | I... | 1560 | 1/0.25 | R. Paranaita. Paranaita |
| PR125) | J275 | *1560 | 1/0.25 | R. Capanema, Capanema: 24h |
| PR161) | J361 | 1560 | 0.25 | R. Cultura Serpin, Ribeirão do Pinhal: 0800-0200(Sun -2100) |
| PR184) | | 1560 | 10/0.25 | R. Barigui, Almirante Tamandaré: 24h |
| PR162) | J364 | 1560 | 1/0.25 | R. Clube, Mallet |
| RJ47) | J501 | 1560 | 5/0.25 | R. Grande Rio, Itaguaí: 24h |
| RN17) | J608 | *1560 | 1/0.25 | R. Cultura do Oeste, Pau dos Ferros: 0800-0100 |
| RS158) | K310 | 1560 | 2.5/0.25 | R. Açoriana, Taquari: 1000-0100 (Sun -2200) |
| SC95) | J825 | 1560 | 1/0.25 | R. Cidade, São Miguel d'Oeste |
| SP261) | K593 | 1560 | 1/0.25 | R. Show, Igarapava: 24h |
| SP249) | K725 | ‡1560 | 0.25 | R. Cidade, Pedreira |
| SP250) | K778 | 1560 | 1/0.25 | R. Vale do Rio Paraná, Presidente Epitácio |
| BA56) | H496 | *1570 | 1/0.25 | R. Povo, Jaguaquara |
| CE44) | H621 | 1570 | 1/0.25 | R. Sertão Central, Senador Pompeu |
| MA22) | H907 | 1570 | 10/0.5 | R. Cultura do Rio Jordão, Coroatá |
| MG146) | L242 | 1570 | 0.25 | R. Unifei, Itajubá |
| MG141) | L344 | 1570 | 1/0.25 | R. Cidade, Corinto |
| MG170) | L364 | 1570 | 10/0.25 | R. Difusora, Piranga |
| MS24) | I409 | *1570 | 1/0.25 | R. Nova Difusora, Caarapó |
| MS55) | I418 | *1570 | 1/0.25 | R. Cidade, Aparecida do Taboado |
| PE30) | I798 | 1570 | 5/1 | R. Asa Branca, Salgueiro |
| PR158) | J324 | *1570 | 0.25 | R. Nova Brasileira, Bela Vista do Paraíso |
| PR137) | J341 | *1570 | 1/0.25 | R. Clube, Nova Aurora: 24h |
| PR159) | J365 | *1570 | 1/0.25 | R. Clube, Arapoti |
| PR166) | J209 | *1570 | 0.25 | R. Terra Nativa, Paranaguá |
| RJ48) | J493 | 1570 | 1/0.25 | R. Cultura, Valença: 24h |
| RO19) | J678 | *1570 | 5/0.25 | R. Soc. Espigão, Espigão d'Oeste |
| RS147) | K358 | 1570 | 1/0.25 | R. Metrópole, Gravataí: 24h |
| SC83) | J777 | *1570 | 1/0.25 | R. Rio Negrinho, Rio Negrinho |
| SC98) | J829 | *1570 | 1/0.25 | R. Modelo, Modelo: 0800(SS 0900)-0100 |
| SC107) | J... | 1570 | 1/0.25 | R. Tangrá, Tangará |
| SP204) | K552 | 1570 | 1/0.25 | R. Avaré, Avaré |
| SP205) | K605 | 1570 | 1/0.25 | R. Junqueirópolis, Junqueirópolis: 0900-2300 |
| SP262) | K648 | 1570 | 1/0.25 | R. Zequinha de Abreu, Santa Rita do Passa Quatro: 0800-2300 |
| SP206) | K651 | 1570 | 10/0.25 | R. ABC, Santo André: 24h |
| SP207) | K667 | 1570 | 1/0.25 | R. Socorro, Socorro |
| SP208) | K670 | *1570 | 1/0.25 | R. Clube, Tanabi: 24h |
| TO10) | N665 | 1570 | 1/0.25 | R. Nossa R., Gurupi: 0900-0300 Sat -2100 Sun 1100-1500 |
| BA53) | H497 | 1580 | 2.5/0.25 | R. Barra de Mendes, Barra do Mendes |
| BA62) | H502 | 1580 | 1/0.25 | R. Atalaia, Canavieiras |
| MG119) | L210 | 1580 | 1/0.25 | R. Liberdade, Itapecirica |
| MG121) | L290 | 1580 | 1/0.25 | R. Cultura, Santos Dumont |
| MG122) | L329 | 1580 | 1/0.25 | R. Educadora, Espinosa |
| MG133) | L335 | 1580 | 1/0.25 | R. Nova Guaranésia, Guaranésia |
| MS25) | I415 | 1580 | 1/0.25 | R. Laguna, Jardim: 0900-0200 |
| MS43) | N611 | 1580 | 1/0.25 | R. Difusora, Ivinhema |
| PI18) | I898 | 1580 | 1/0.25 | R. Santa Clara, Floriano: 0800-0030, Sun 1000-1500 |
| PR164) | J342 | 1580 | 2.5/0.25 | R. São João do Sudoeste, São João: 24h |
| PR186) | | *1580 | 0.25 | R. Terra Nativa, Cambé |
| RJ51) | J487 | 1580 | 1/0.5 | R. Popular Fluminense, Conceição de Macabu: 24h |
| RJ52) | J506 | 1580 | 5/0.25 | R. Resende AM, Resende: 0800-0100, (SS 1000-0100) |
| RJ58) | J505 | 1580 | 0.25 | R. Geração 2000, Teresópolis |
| RN24) | J613 | 1580 | 1/0.25 | R. Novos Tempos, Ceará Mirim |
| RS148) | K237 | 1580 | 9/0.25 | R. Encantado AM, Encantado |
| RS150) | K339 | *1580 | 0.25 | R. Dif. Fronteira, Arroio Grande: 24h |
| SP251) | K504 | 1580 | 1/0.25 | R. Difusora, Amparo: 24h |
| SP209) | K743 | 1580 | 0.25 | R. Pedra Bonita, Itaporanga |
| SP289) | | 1580 | 0.25 | R. Grande Vale, Paraibuna |
| BA55) | H... | 1590 | 0.3 | R. Vale do Jiquiriçá, Jiquiriça |
| CE100) | H... | 1590 | 1 | R. Veneza, Eusébio |
| ES22) | I... | *1590 | 1/0.25 | R. Sim Tupi, Cachoeiro de Itapemirim |
| MG171) | L368 | 1590 | 1/0.25 | R. Cidade Carinho, Ubá |
| MG134) | L369 | 1590 | 10/1 | R. Guaicuí, Várzea da Palma |
| MG193) | N207 | 1590 | 0.25 | R. Globo, Lambari |
| MS26) | I403 | 1590 | 1/0.25 | R. Independência, Eldorado |
| PB34) | I703 | 1590 | 1/0.25 | R. Correio do Vale, Itaporanga |
| PE41) | ZYI802 | 1590 | 1 | R. Restauração, Bezerros:24h |
| PR129) | J290 | 1590 | 1/0.25 | R. Super Cultura, Andirá |
| PR160) | J296 | 1590 | 1/0.25 | R. Hawaí, Capitão Leônidas Marques |
| RS174) | K212 | *1590 | 0.25 | R. Clube, Bagé: 0900-0300 |
| SC101) | J823 | 1590 | 10/0.5 | R. Clube, Joinville |
| SP254) | K771 | 1590 | 10/0.5 | R. Japi, Cabreúva |
| BA45) | H464 | 1600 | 10/1 | R. Nova Voz, Muritiba |
| SP263) | K779 | 1600 | 100/20 | R. Nove de Julho, São Paulo: 24h |

| SW | Call | kHz | kW | Station, location, h. of tr. |
|---|---|---|---|---|
| SP49) | G855 | 3365 | 1 | R. Cultura, Araraquara |
| AM02) | F276 | 3375 | 1 | R. Municipal, São Gabriel da Cachoeira |
| MG55) | G274 | 4775 | 1 | R. Congonhas, Congonhas: 0800-0100 |
| AM20) | F273 | 4805 | 10/5 | R. Dif. do Amazonas, Manaus |
| SP287) | G869 | 4845 | 1 | R. Meteorologia Paulista, Ibitinga: (rel. R. Ternura FM) |
| AM14) | F278 | 4845 | 10 | R. Cultura, Manaus: 1000-0200 |
| PR33) | G641 | 4865 | 5 | R. Alvorada, Londrina |
| RR01) | G810 | 4875 | 10 | R. Roraima, Boa Vista: 0800-0300 |
| AC06) | F201 | 4885 | 5 | R. Dif. Acreana, Rio Branco: 0900-0400 |
| PA03) | G362 | 4885 | 10 | R. Clube do Pará, Belém: 24h |
| MS32) | R200 | 4895 | 5 | R. Novo Tempo, Campo Grande |
| RJ03) | G683 | 4905 | 5 | R. Relogio Federal, São Gonçalo |
| GO27) | F691 | 4915 | 10 | R. Daqui, Goiânia |
| AM10) | F282 | 4925 | 5 | R. Educação Rural, Tefé: 1000-1600, 2000-0200 |
| AM12) | ZYF275 | 4965 | 5 | R. Alvorada, Parintins: 2200- 0200 |
| GO30) | F690 | 4985 | 10 | R. Brasil Central, Goiânia |
| AM09) | F272 | ‡5035 | 5 | R. Educação Rural, Coari |
| SC86) | | 5940 | 10 | R. Voz Missionária, Camboriú |
| MG06) | E523 | ‡5970 | 10 | R. Itatiaia, Belo Horizonte |
| MG35) | E521 | 6010 | 5 | R. Inconfidência, Belo Horizonte |
| PR42) | E275 | 6040 | 7.5 | R. Evangelizar, Curitiba |
| PR60) | E726 | 6060 | 10 | Super Rádio Deus é Amor, Curitiba |
| PR15) | E726 | 6080 | 10 | R. Marumby, Curitiba |
| PR138) | E728 | 6105 | 10 | R. Cultura Filadélfia, Foz do Iguaçu: 24h |
| PR60) | E968 | 6120 | 10 | Super Rádio Deus é Amor, São Paulo |
| RS104) | E864 | 6160 | 1 | Super Rede Boa Vontade, Porto Alegre |
| DF06) | E365 | 6180 | 250 | R. Nal. da Amazônia, Brasília: 0900-0400 |
| PR15) | E726 | 9515 | 10 | R. Marumby, Curitiba |
| RS104) | E855 | 9550 | 10 | Super Rede Boa Vontade, Porto Alegre |
| PR60) | E727 | 9565 | 20 | Super Rádio Deus é Amor, Curitiba (r) |
| SC86) | E890 | 9665 | 10 | R. Voz Missionária, Camboriú |
| SP80) | E971 | 9675 | 10 | R. Canção Nova, Cachoeira Paulista |
| PR42) | E725 | 9725 | 7.5 | R. Evangelizar, Curitiba |
| SP263) | E971 | 9820 | 10 | R. Nove de Julho, São Paulo: 24h |
| PR60) | E726 | 11765 | 20 | Super Rádio Deus é Amor, Curitiba |
| DF06) | E365 | 11780 | 250 | R. Nal. da Amazônia, Brasília |
| GO30) | E440 | 11815 | 7.5 | R. Brasil Central, Goiânia |
| RS104) | E856 | 11895 | 10 | Super Rede Boa Vontade, Porto Alegre |
| RS09) | E851 | 11915 | 10 | R. Gaucha, Porto Alegre |
| PR42) | E725 | 11935 | 7.5 | R. Evangelizar, Curitiba |
| MG35) | E521 | 15190 | 5 | R. Inconfidência, Belo Horizonte |

## RADIO NETWORKS

There are several radio networks. Below are listed just some of them. The affiliated outlets are often subject to alteration.

**CENTRAL BRASILEIRA DE NOTÍCIAS – CBN: W:** radioclick.globo.com/cbn
**EMPRESA BRASIL DE COMUNIÇÃO – EBC: W:** facebook.com/ebcnarede/info
**IGREJA PENTECOSTAL DEUS È AMOR: W:** ipda.com.br
**IGREJA UNIVERSAL DO REINO DE DEUS: W:** igrejauniversal.org.br
**Rede JOVEM PAN** ⬛ Av. Paulista 807, 24° andar, 01311-915 São Paulo, SP **W:** jovempan.uol.com.br
**RADIO BANDEIRANTES: W:** radiobandeirantes com.br
**RADIO GLOBO: W:** radioclick.globo.com
**REDE BOA VONTADE - LBV** ⬛ Legião da Boa Vontade, Rua Doraci 90, Bairro Bom Retiro, 01134-020 São Paulo, SP **W:** redeboavontada.com
**REDE BOAS NOVAS – RBN: W:** rbn.org.br
**REDE CANÇÃO NOVA DE RÁDIO** ⬛ Rua João Paulo II s/, Alto da Bela Vista, 12630-030 Cachoeira Paulista, SP **W:** cancaonova.com **E:** radio@cancaonova.com
**REDE CATÓLICA DE RÁDIO - RCR:** ⬛ União de Radiodifusão Católica, Rua Vergueiro 3086, Conj. 91, Vila Mariana, 04102-001 São Paulo, SP **W:** rcrunda.com.br **E:** rcr@rcrunda.com.br
**REDE DO ESTADO DE SÃO PAULO: W:** redecbs.com.br
**REDE GAÚCHA SAT** ⬛ Av. Erico Veríssimo 400, Edifício Maurício Sirotsky Sobrinho, 90169-900 Porto Alegre, RS **W:** rbs.clicrbs.com.br
**REDE ESPERANCA: W:** redeesperança.com
**REDE ITATIAIA: W:** itatiaia.com.br/rede
**REDE MILICIA SAT: W:** milicia.org.br
**REDE MINERIA DE RADIO; W:** redemineiraderadio.com.br
**REDE NOVO TEMPO: W:** novotempo.org.br
**REDE PAULUS SAT:** ⬛ Rua Doutor Pinto Ferraz 183, Vila Mariana, 04117-900 São Paulo, SP **W:** radioamericasp.com.br/paulussat.htm
**REDE POTGUAR DE COMUNICAÇÃO (RPC): W:** redepotiguar.com
**REDE SUL DE RÁDIO: W:** saofrancisco.am.br
**REDE TRANSAMÉRICA DE RÁDIO: W:** transanet.uol.com.br
**SISTEMA GLOBO DE RÁDIO: W:** radioclick.globo.com/globobrasil
**SISTEMA GUAÍBA SAT:** ⬛ Rua Caldas Jr. 219, 2° andar, 90019-900 Porto Alegre, RS **W:** guaiba.com.br
**REDE SOMZOOM SAT:** ⬛ Av. Herois do Acre 590, Passaré, 60743-760 Fortaleza, CE **W:** somzoom.com.br **E:** somzoomsat@somzoom.com.br

### AC00) ACRE

**AC01)** Rua de Alagoas, 270, Colégio, 69980-000 Cruzeiro do Sul ☎68 3322 4637 **W:** radioetvintegracao.com.br **E:** radiointegracao@hotmail.com - **FM:** 99.9MHz – **AC02)** Rua Marechal Deodoro, 197 sala 210/211, 69900-066 Rio Branco ☎68 3223 2239 **W:** cbnamazonia.com.br/riobranco – **AC03)** Rua Coronel Brandão, 1665, Bairro Aeroporto, 69930-000 Xapuri ☎68 3542 2830 **E:** raimari.cardoso@gmail.com – **AC04)** Travessa Mário Lobão 81, 69980-000 Cruzeiro do Sul ☎68 3322 3309 ▤68 3322 2634 **W:** verdesflorestas.com.br **E:** verdesflorestas@yahoo.com.br – **AC05)** Rua Epaminondas Jacome, 3121, Base, 69900-280 Rio Branco ☎68 3224 0505 – **AC06)** Rua Benjamin Constant 1232, 69900-161 Rio Branco ☎68 3223 9696 **W:** difusora.ac.gov.br **E:** comercial.difusora@ac.gov.br – **AC11)** Rua Maria Glória Farias, 1 qd 3 c 4, Cannisio Brasil, 69940-000 Sena Madureira ☎68 3612 3733 **E:** rivaldosevero@hotmail.com - **FM:** 105.9MHz – **AC12)** Rua Nilo Freire de Albuquerqe, s/n, Novo, 69970-000 Tarauacá ☎68 3462 1416 **E:** railtonrodrigues@ac.gov.br – **AC15)** Travasse Posto, 168, Cidade Novo, 69960-000 Feijo ☎68 3463 3310 **E:** jocivaldogomes@bol.com.br

### AL00) ALAGOAS

**AL01)** Av. Deputada Cecj Cunha, 6, Brásilia, 57313-085 Arapiraca ☎82 3522 085 **W:** novonordeste.com **E:** am@novonordeste.com.br – **AL02)** Av Siqueira 494, Prado, 57010-000 Maceió ☎82 3223 1710 **W:** Facebook: Rádio-Jornal **E:** comercial@jornalam710.com.br – **AL03)** Rua José e Maria Passos 25, 57600-030 Palmeiras dos Indios ☎82 3421 2289 **W:** radiosampaio.com.br **E:** estudio@radiosampaio.com.br - **FM:** 92.5MHz – **AL04)** Av Fernandes Lima,1047, Farol, 57050-000 Maceió ☎82 3315 9927 **W:** izp.al.gov.br **E:** ascom@izp.al.gov.ar – **AL05)** Rua Miguel Palmeira 1513, 7° andar, Farol, 57055-330 Maceió ☎82 3241 2284 **W:** jovempanam1020.com.br – **AL06)** Praça Senador Eneas Araújo 61, 57500-000 Santana do Ipanema **W:** radiocorreiodosertao.com.br – **AL07)** Av Aristeu Andrade, 355, Farol, 57051-090 Maceió ☎82 3336 1260 **W:** gazetaweb.globo.com - **FM:** 94.1MHz – **AL08)** Rua Vila Kennedy, 45, Ponta Grosse, 57014-630 Maceió ☎82 3362 1320 **W:** miliciaimaculada.rcr.org.br **E:** 1320am@miliciadaimaculada.org.br – **AL09)** Cj São José s/n, gdC, Dom Constantino, 57200-000 Penedo ☎82 3551 2215 – **AL10)** Loteamento Cidade Imperia,l 4 lt 3,

Pedras, 57160-000 Taperagua ☎82 3263 7298 **W:** jovempanam1020.com.br/afiliadas.html – **AL11)** Rua Miguel Palmeira, 1513 7° andar, Farol, 57055-330 Maceió **W:** jovempanam1020.com.br/afiliadas.html – **AL12)** Praça Manoel Monteiro 72, 57480-000 Delmiro Gouveia ☎82 3641 2007 ▤82 3641 4047 **W:** radiodelmiro.com.br **E:** radiodelmiro@gclnet.com.br - **FM:** 89.9MHz– **AL13)** BR-104 Km 36, Roberto Correia de Arajuó, 57800-000 União dos Palmares – **AL14)** Rua Pedro Oliverio Rocha 784, 3 AND SL 01, Farol, 57075-560 Maceió ☎82 4009 0009 **W:** radiocorreio.com.br - **FM:** 91.7 MHz – **AL15)** Rua Aristeu de Andrade, 355, Farol, 57021-050 Maceió ☎82 3624 1157 – **AL16)** Rua Frederico Maia s/n, 57700-000 Viçosa ☎82 3283 1842 **W:** princesadasmatas.com **E:** contato@princesadasmatas.com – **AL17)** Rua Coronel Francisco Silva, 97, Pitanguinha, 57052-190 Maceió ☎82 3356 8019 **W:** Facebook: PalmaresAM

### AM00) AMAZONAS

**AM02)** Av Alvaro Maia s/n, 69750-000 São Gabriel da Cachoeira ☎97 3471 1109 – **AM03)** Rua Júlio de Oliveira, 1323, São Pedro, 69800-000 Humaitá ☎97 3373 3946 **W:** radiovrm.com.br **E:** radiovrm@bol.com.br – **AM04)** A/C Prefeitura Municipal de Tabatinga (✉C.P 31), 69640-000 Tabatinga ☎97 3412 2829 **W:** radios.ebc.com.br/nacionalaltosolimo **E:** altossolimoes@ebc.com.br - **FM:** 96.1 MHz – **AM05)** Rua Solimões 809, 69100-000 Itacoatiara ☎92 3521 1635 **W:** facebook.com/cbnitacoatiara **E:** radiodifusora_ita@hotmail.com - **FM:** 94.5MHz –**AM06)** Rua Joana D'Angelo, s/n, Biri Biri, 69400-000 Manacapuru ☎92 3361 2042– **AM07)** Av Major Santana 2502, 69280-000 Manicoré – **AM08)** Rua Guaranápolis 533, 69190-000 Maués ☎92 3542 1254 **E:** radioguaranopolis@hotmail.com – **AM09)** Praça São Sebastião 263, 69460-000 Coari ☎97 3561 2383 **W:** radiocoariamot.blogspot.no **E:** radiocoari@hotmail.com – **AM10)** Praça Santa Tereza, 283 (✉ C.P. 21), 69470-000 Tefé ☎97 3343 3017 **W:** radioruraltefe.com.br **E:** radioruralam1270@hotmail.com – **AM11)** Rua José Clemente 500, 69010-070 Manaus ☎92 3633 2295 **W:** rederiomar.com.br **E:** contato@rederiomar.com - **FM:** 103.3 MHz – **AM12)** Rua Governador Leopoldo Neves (✉ C.P. 004)503, 69151-460 Parintins ☎92 3533 3097 **W:** alvoradaparintins.com.br **E:** carlosalexandre.alvorada@gmail.com - **FM:** 100.1MHz – **AM14)** Rua Barcelos, s/n, Praça 14, 69020-200 Manaus ☎92 3215 4743 ▤92 3215 4759 **W:** tvcultura.am.gov.br **E:** radiocultura@tvcultura.am.gov.br or radiocultura@hotmail.com – **AM16)** Av General Rodrigo Jordão Ramos, 1655 Anexo 3, Japiim, 69077-000 Manaus ☎92 3614 0007 **W:** ipda.com.br/radio/amazonas/index.htmk - **FM:** 107.9 MHz – **AM17)** Estrada Odvaldo Novo, s/n Km 1, Parintins/AM, 69152-470 Parintins ☎92 3533 1564 **W:** radioclubeparintinsam.com.br **E:** contato@radioclubeparintinsam.com.br – **AM18)** Rodovia Manoel Urbano, km 2, 69405-000 Iranduba **W:** boavontade.com/radio – **AM19)** Boulevard Pedro Rate, 176, São José, 69400-000 Manacapuru. ☎ 92 3361 2192 ▤ 92 3361 2453 – **AM20)** Av Eduardo Ribeiro 639, 69010-001 Manaus ☎92 3633 1009 **W:** difusora24h.com **E:** comercial@difusora24h.com - **FM:** 93.7MHz – **AM23)** Rua Coronel Jorge Vercosa, 47 - Centro, 69190-000 Maués ☎92 3542 1897 **W:** facebook.com Rádio-Independência – **AM24)** Av Eduardo Ribeiro 520, 2 andar sala 201/215, 69010-690 Manaus ☎92 3633 2345

### AP00) AMAPÁ

**AP01)** Av. Padre Júlio Maria Lombeard, 1614, Santa Rita, 68901-283 Macapá ☎96 3312 1000 **W:** difusora.ap.gov.br **E:** rdm@rdm.ap.gov.br – **AP02)** Rua Eliezer Levy 684, 68900-140 Macapá ☎96 3222 3111 **W:** zsistemaequatorial.com – **AP03)** Av Nações Unidas 256, 68906-100 Macapá – **AP04)** Av. Rio Branco 3748, Fonte Nova, 68925-000 Santana ☎96 3281 5649 **W:** radioporto.xpg.com.br – **AP05)** Rua Hildemar Maia 1000, 68940-000 Mazagão ☎96 3271 1227 **W:** facebook.com/radionova.mazagao

### BA00) BAHIA

**BA01)** Praça Mario Dourado 78-A, 44900-000 Irecê ☎74 3641 3717 **W:** regionalam.com.br **E:** comercial@redecaraibes.com.br – **BA02)** Av. Itajunpe, 1789, Santo Antonio, 45602-380 Itabuna. ☎73 3211 2385 **W:** radiojornaldeitabuna.br **E:** radiojornaldeitabuna@hotmail.com – **BA03)** Praça da Independência 244, 45995-000 Teixeira de Freitas **W:** radiodifusoraam580.com.br **E:** Rua Lord Cochrane, 66, Barra, 40140-070 Salvador ☎71 3264 1244 **W:** sistemacruzeiro.com.br **E:** cruzeiro@veloxmail.com.br – **BA05)** Rua Dom Pedro II, 306 2° andar, Primavera, 47804-510 Barreiras ☎77 3611 3570 **W:** radiovale@radiovale.com.br **E:** radiovale@radiovale.com.br – **BA06)** R Jorge Antonio Menezes Silva, 220, Dezedeiros, 45400-000 Valença ☎75 3641 0660 **W:** radioclubedevalenca.com.br – **BA07)** Alameada Rui Barbosa 42, 45700-000 Itapetinga ☎77 3261 1010 **W:** novajornal.net – **BA08)** Rua Monsenhor Francisco Manoel da Silva 46, 44571-022 Santo Antônio de Jesus ☎75 3631 5680 **W:** radioclube680.com.br **E:** clubeam@hotmail.com – **BA10)** Rua Castro Alves 868, 44001-592 Feira de Santana ☎75 3223 0700 **W:** radioculturafeiradesantana.com.br **E:** radioculturadefeiradesantana@hotmail.com – **BA11)** Rua Jardim Federacão, 81, Federacão, 40231-901 Salvador ☎71 3486 3201 ▤71

3486 3214 **W:** radiosociedadeam.com.br **E:** comercial@radiosociedadeam.com.br – **BA12)** Av. Cinquenteário 1429, 45600-006 Itabuna ☎73 3215 2271 **W:** difusorabahia.com.br – **BA13)** Rua Guadaljara, 389, Vila Dulca, 47800-000 Barreiras ☎77 3611 4545 **W:** rb.am.br **E:** comercialfmrb@hotmail.com – **BA14)** Praça Luiz Nogueira 385, 48700-000 Serrinha **W:** grupoolmos.com.br **E:** grupolomes@grupolomes.com.br– **BA15)** Rua Antonio Neto 27, 46810-000 Utinga ☎75 3337 1011 **W:** radiocultura820.com.br **E:** comercial@radiocultura820.com.br – **BA16)** Fundação Dom Avelar Brandão, Rua Martin Afonso de Souza, 270, Garcia, 40100-050 Salvador ☎71 3114 5088 📠71 3114 3319 **W:** am840.com.br **E:** excelsiorcomercial@gmail.com – **BA17)** Av Visconde do Rio Branco 68, 48970-000 Senhor do Bonfim ☎74 3541 4617 **W:** radiocaraiba.com.br – **BA18)** Travessa da Catedral s/n, 45600-000 Itabuna ☎73 3215 0909 – **BA19)** Rua Wercelêncio da Mota 81, 48730-000 Conceição do Coité ☎75 3262 1010 **W:** radiosisal.com **E:** comercial@radiosisal.com – **BA20)** Rua Frei Hermenegildo, 300, Capuchinos (C.P. 1525), 44050-000 Feira de Santana ☎75 2101 9700 **W:** sociedadedefeiraam.com.br **E:** comercialsociedade@princesafm.com.br - **FM:** 96.9MHz – **BA21)** Gleba Fazenda Ouro Verde, 45900-000 Caravelas ☎73 3011 1299 **W:** Facebook, R.Alvorado Gospel – **BA22)** Rua Gabriel Soares, 23, Ladeira dos Aflitos, 40060-040 Salvador – **BA23)** Praça Barão do Rio Branco 42, 45100-000 Vitória da Conquista **W:** radioclubeconquista.com.br – **BA24)** Av Maria Quitéria, 223, Serraria Brasil, 44062-630 Feira de Santana ☎75 3623 8927 📠75 3623 2851 **W:** radiosubaeam.com.br - **FM:** 95.3MHz Nordeste FM – **BA25)** Rua José Bonifacio, 17 2° andar, 45700-000 Itapetinga ☎77 3261 2610 **W:** radiofascinacao.com.br **E:** comercial@radiofascinacao.com.br – **BA26)** Rua Marquês de Paranagua, 259 - Centro 45660-000 ☎73 3231 3612 **W:** santacruzam.com.br – **BA27)** Av. Dq de Caxias, 491 S 301(C.P 29), 45820-000 Eunápolis ☎73 3281 5370 – **BA28)** Rua Cel. Aprigio Duarte N 05, 48903-410 Juazeiro ☎76 3611 7211 **W:** radiojuazeiro.com.br **E:** contato@radiojuazeiro.com.br – **BA29)** Rua Senador Pedro Lago 54, 44700-000 Jacobina ☎74 3621 3636 **W:** radiocluberiodoouro.com.br **E:** radio@radiocluberiodoouro.com.br – **BA30)** Rua Monte Castelo,45, Sobradinha, 44018-210 Feira de Santana ☎75 3623 0717 **W:** radiopovo.com.br– **BA31)** Rua Dom Pedro II 98, 48100-000 Alagoinhas ☎75 3423 4366 **W:** novaam1240.com.br – **BA32)** Rua Conde Pereire Carneiro, 226 -Pernambues, 41100-010 Salvador ☎71 3460 8500 **W:** radiometropole.com.br - **FM:** 101.3MHz – **BA33)** Av. Itabuna , 45653-160 Ilhéus ☎73 3231 5462 **W:** radionovabahianaam1310.blogspot.com.br **E:** clinton.alves@hotmail.com – **BA34)** Praça Luiz Nogueira 99 1° andar, 48700-000 Serrinha **W:** continentalam.com.br – **BA35)** Rua São Francisco 159-163A, 48601-070 Paulo Afonso ☎75 3281 5588 **W:** redecultura.com.br **E:** redecultura@redecultura.com.br - **FM:** 92.7MHz – **BA36)** Praça da Bandeira, s/n , 47600-000 Bom Jesus da Lapa ☎77 3481 4329 **W:** radiobomjesusam.com.br – **BA37)** Av Getúlio Vargas 394 44330-000 São Gonçalo dos Campos ☎77 3481 6161 **W:**planeta1410.com.br – **BA38)** Av Barros Reis 295, 40353-100 Salvador ☎71 3383 5283 **W:** radioindependenciabahia.com.br – **BA39)** Rua 1 Lotm Jardim Amaralina s/n 45204-010, 45204-010 Jequié ☎73 3527 4114 **W:** radiopovo.com.br/jequie **E:** radiopovojequie@gmail.com– **BA40)** Rodovia BR 242, s/n km 98, Zona Rural , 46880-000 Itaberaba ☎75 3252 1184 - **FM:** 95.5 MHz – **BA41)** Praça Virgilio Damasio, 140b 1° andar - Centro, 45570-000 Ipiaú ☎73 3531 3441 📠73 3531 3419 **W:** radioeducadoradeipiau.com.br – **BA42)** Av. Dom Manuel Raimundo de Mello, 607, São José, 46400-000 Caetité ☎77 3454 1819 **W:** educadorasantana.com.br **E:** educadora920@yahoo.com.br – **BA44)** Av Ascendino Melo 297, 267, Sis 106/107, Shopping Itatiaia, Recreio, 45020-908 Vitória da Conquista ☎77 3472 0760 **W:** clubenet.com.br **E:** radiocidade@clubenet.com.br – **BA45)** Tv Virgillo Gonzalves Pereira 196, 44340-000 Muritiba ☎73 3424 2048 – **BA46)** Av Porto Seguro, 718 1° andar, 45820-006 Eunápolis. ☎73 3281 5594 **W:** facebook.com/radio21news – **BA47)** Rua da Bandeira 27, 42800-000 Camaçari – **BA49)** Rua Padre Argemiro Guimarães 32, 44640-000 Riachão do Jacuípe ☎75 3264 2189 **W:** radiojacuipe.com.br – **BA50)** Av Getúlio Vargas 43, 48601-000 Paulo Afonso ☎75 3281 3009 **W:** radiobahianordeste.com.br – **BA51)** Rua Rio Corrente s/n, 47000-000 Santa Maria da Vitória – **BA52)** Rua Saldanha Marinho, 30 Sala 23/24, Mesmo, 45810-000 Porto Seguro ☎73 3288 2136 **E:** radioguadalupeam@yahoo.com.br – **BA53)** Rua Alvaro Campos 83, 44990-000 Barra do Mendes **W:** facebook.com: Radio Barra do Mendes– **BA54)** Av Dom Avelar Brandão Vilella, s/n, Sítio São Félix, 46470-970 Riacho de Santana ☎77 3457 2104 **E:** radioguadalupeam@yahoo.com.br – **BA55)** Rua Coronel Vicente s/n, 45470-000 Jiquiriça – **BA56)** Loteamento Nova Jaguaquara s/n, Casca, 45345-000 Jaguaquara ☎73 3534 1422 **W:** radiopovo.com.br/povojaguaquara **E:** educadoraam1570@hotmail.com – **BA57)** Rua Gamboa de Cima 18, Campo Grande, 40060-008 Salvador ☎71 3337 3216 **W:** novotemposalvador.com.br – **BA58)** Av Regis Pacheco 534, 45100-000 Vitória da Conquista **W:** blog.cancaonova/conquista **E:**

radioconquista@cancaonova.com – **BA59)** Rua Lauro de Freitas, 1176, Alto da Bela Vista, 45550-000 Ubatã ☎73 3245 1233 **W:** radiopovo.com.br **E:** admpovoubata@gmail.com – **BA60)** Rua Antônio Otaviano Dourado 91, 44900-000 Irecê ☎74 3641 3111 **W:** programacao10cidade.com.br – **BA62)** Rua Virgilio Brasil, 175, Cidade Nova, 45860-000 Canavieiras ☎73 9823 0453 **W:** atalaiaamba.webnode.pt **E:** radioatalaia_am@hotmail.com – **BA64)** Rua Farias Goes 164, 48330-000 Rio Real **W:** radiodifusora600.com.br – **BA65)** Rua Manoel Conselho Campos 135, 48500-000 Euclides da Cunha ☎75 3271 1652 – **BA66)** Rua Rui Barbosa 119, 47400-000 Xique-Xique – **BA67)** Rua Jose de Anchita, 128 2° andar, 45836-000 Itamaraju. ☎73 3294 5455 **W:** extremosulam.com.br – **BA68)** Av José Candido dos Santos, 20 - Centro, Lagos Redonda, 49300-000 Itapicuru ☎79 3541 1067 **W:** radioclube1060.combr **E:** radioclube.ba@bol.com.br – **BA69)** Rua Frei Apolônio de Tody 10, 48410-000 Cícero Dantas ☎75 3278 2298 📠75 3278 2252 **W:** radioregionalam.com.br **E:** radioregional@tadioregionalam.com.br – **BA70)** Terreiro de Jesus 13 - Centro Histórico, Pelourino, 40025-010 Salvador ☎71 3421 6300 📠71 3231 9324 **W:** radio.boavontade **E:** radiocristal@uol.com.br – **BA71)** Rua Vicente Paula Costa 16, 48540-000 Jeremoabo ☎75 3203 2358 – **BA72)** Rua 2 de Julho s/n, 45160-000 Belo Campo ☎77 3437 2122 – **BA73)** Praça São José 279, 44600-000 Ipirá – **BA74)** Rua Desidério Brandão 15, 44380-000 Cruz das Almas ☎ 75 3621 2716 **W:** radioalvoradaam1460.com.br **E:** alvoradaamcomercial@hotmail.com – **BA75)** Rua Teixeira de Freitas s/n, 47700-000 Santana – **BA77)** Rua Barão do Rio Branco s/n, 47600-000 Bom Jesus da Lapa – **BA78)** Rua Dulce Pazzi, 6, Alto da Bela Vista, 45260-000 Poções ☎77 3431 1135 **W:** radiopovo.com.br **E:** povopocoes@hotmail.com – **BA79)** Av Luis Eduardo Magalhães, s/n - Centro, 46990-000 Souto Soares ☎75 3339 2328 **W:** radiojornal1120.com.br **E:** radiojornal@bol.com.br – **BA80)** Rua Jvencio Alves, 01, 1 andar - Centro, 48930-480 Juazeiro – **BA81)** Rua Carlos Gomes 980, 40285-280 Salvador ☎71 3329 7463 – **BA82)** Rua Élcio Cardoso de Matos s/n, 48800-000 Monte Santo ☎75 3275 1212 – **BA83)** Praça Simões Filho 54, 45450-000 Gandu – **BA84)** Praça Sta Terezinha, 3, Piranga, 48900-130 Juazeiro ☎74 3611 5533 **W:** radiocidadeam870.com.br **E:** cidade870@yahoo.com.br – **BA85)** Rua Coronel Dias Coelho 249, 44850-000 Morro do Chapéu – **BA86)** Travessa Juracy Magalhães 4, 2° andar, 44630-000 Mairi – **BA87)** Praça Raimundo Sales, 94 - Centro, 1° andar, 47650-000 Correntina ☎77 3488 2827 **W:** radioplanaltodooeste.com.br **E:** radioplanaltoba@yahoo.com.br – **BA90)** Rua: Ferreira Brito 26, 48400-000 Ribeira do Pombal ☎75 3276 1164 **W:** radiopovo.br/povopombal **E:** educadorapombalgerencia@hotmail.com – **BA94)** Rua Dr Gil Nunes Maia 373, 45600-000 Itabuna ☎73 3043 6026 **W:** interativa93.com.br – **BA96)** Rua Juana Angélica, 125, Conquista, 45650-023 Iléhus ☎73 3634 7020 **W:** radioculturadeilheus.com.br **E:** radiocultura@radioculturadeilheus.com.br - **FM:** 97.9 MHz – **BA98)** Rua Padroeira de Brasil 100, 48890-970 Valente ☎71 8727 8216 **W:** radioestreladovale.com **E:** radioestreladoval@hotmail.com – **BA99)** Av. ACM 229, 44695-000 Campim Gross ☎74 3651 0800 **W:** grupolomesderadidifusao.com.br – **BA100)** Travessa Virigilio Pereira 196, 44340 Muritiba **W:** radiovoxbahia.com/

**CE00) CEARA**
**CE01)** Rua Romeu Martins - Centro S/N, Ed 29 de Julho, 62700-000 Canindé ☎85 3343 2233 **W:** radiojornal540.com **E:** radiojornal540@hotmail.com – **CE02)** Rua Monsenhor Lima, 227, Lagoa Seca, 63050-020 Juazeiro do Norte ☎88 3512 5557 **W:** radioverdevale570.com.br **E:** contato@radioverdevale570.com.br – **CE03)** Av Monsenhor Tabosa, 2514 - Centro, 60500-000 Itapipoca ☎88 3631 2173 **W:** radiouirapurudeitapipoca.com.br **E:** ribamar.p@bol.com.br – **CE04)** Rodovia BR 226, s/n, Zona Rural, 63700-000 Crateús ☎88 3691 0355 **W:** radiopoty.com.br **E:** radiopoty@bol.com.br – **CE05)** Av.Rui Barbosa, 1901, Aldeota, 60115-221 Fortaleza ☎88 3264 5500 **W:** 620am.com.br – **CE06)** Praça da Matriz s/n, 62590-000 Itarema – **CE07)** Rua Dep. Luiz Otacílio Correia 221, 63540-000 Várzea Alegre ☎88 3541 1055 **W:** radiocultura670.com.br **E:** culturaam670@hotmail.com – **CE08)** Shalom da Paz, Rua Maria Tomásia, 72, Aldeota, 60150-170 Fortaleza ☎85 3261 4444 **W:** shalom690.com.br **E:** benfeitordapaz@comshalom.org **FM:** 89.1 MHz – **CE09)** Praca Monsenhor José Cândido, 91 - Centro, 63870-000 Boa Viagem ☎88 3427 1104 **W:** radioasabranca.com.br – **CE10)** Rua Uirapuru, 500, Jardim Cearence, 60711-790 Fortaleza ☎88 3298 2655 Facebook: Rádio Uirapuru de Fortaleza – **CE11)** Rua Hilda Augusto 201, 63300-000 Lavras da Mangabeira ☎88 3536 1257 **W:** radiovaledosalgado.com.br **E:** radiovaledosalgado@gmail.com – **CE12)** Rua Deoclesiano Bezerra 649, 63500-000 Iguatu ☎88 3581 1403 📠88 3581 0828 **W:** jornalam.com.br **E:** contato@jornalam.com.br – **CE13)** Av. Desembargador Moreira, 2430, Dionísio Torres, 60170-002 Fortaleza ☎85 3261 2323 **W:** verdinha.com.br **E:** radios@verdesmares.com.br – **CE14)** Rua Dr João Thomé 16, 62400-000 Camocim ☎88 3621 0370 **W:** radiouniaodecamocim.blogspot.no – **CE15)** Rua Padre Cicero 1045, Salesiano, 63010-020 Juazeiro do Norte ☎88 3512 3581

– **CE16)** Av Desembargo Moreira, 2565, Dionísio Torres, 60170-002 Fortaleza ☎85 3261 7000 **W:** cidadeam860.com.br **E:** comercial860@yahoo.com.br – **CE17)** Rua Floriano Peixoto 358, 63500-000 Iguatu **W:** radioliberdadeam.com – **CE18)** Rua Totonho Figueiras 244, 63180-000 Barbalha ☎88 3532 3020 **W:** radiocetama.com.br – **CE19)** Praça Quirino Rodrigues 76/3, 62011-260 Sobral ☎88 3611 2496 ▤88 3611 1550 **W:** radioeducadora950.com.br **E:** radioeducadora@gmail.com – **CE20)** Rua Tabelião Enéas 495 2° Andar, (✉ C.P 87, 63901-970) 63900-000 Quixadá ☎88 3414 5970 ▤88 3412 0554 **W:** sistemamonolitos.com.br/radiomonolitosam **E:** contato@sistemamonolitos.com.br - **FM:** 105.9 MHz – **CE21)** Av. Aguanambi, 282, José Bonifácio, 60060-200 Fortaleza ☎85 3066 4000 **W:** radios.opovo.com.br/opovocbn - **FM:** 95.5 MHz CBN – **CE22)** Rua Coronel Antônio Luiz, 1068, Pimenta, 63100-000 Crato ☎88 3523 3198 **W:** radioeducadora1020.com.br **E:** comercial@radioeducadora1020.com.br – **CE23)** Travessa Crateús 46, 62010-560 Sobral ☎88 3614 8282 **W:** radiotupinamba.com **E:** radiotupinambaam@bol.com.br – **CE24)** Av Francisco R Oliveira 643, Alto Bela Vista, 62900-000 Russas ☎88 3411 0320 **W:** radioprogresso1140.com.br – **CE25)** Rodovia BR 116 s/n km 54/ Fazende Guarani, Zona Rural 62870-000 Pacajús ☎85 3348 0725 **W:** comshalom.org/radio **E:** radioboanova1410@hotmail.com – **CE26)** Av Senador Virgilio Távora, 2279, Dionisio Torres, 60170-251 Fortaleza.☎85 3264 2944 **W:** radioclubece.com.br **E:** fransilveira@gmail.com – **CE27)** Rua Coronel Zezé 1158, 63700-000 Crateús – **CE28)** Rua Luis Vicente Ferreira Lima 222, José Brito, 62930-000 Limoeiro do Norte ☎▤88 3423 2400 **W:** radiovaledojaguaribeam.com.br/siteE: radiovale1260@gmail.com – **CE29)** Av General Osóri Paiva, 7235, Canindezinho, 60731-335 Fortaleza ☎ 85 3498 4796 **W:** ipda.com.br/nova/vozlibertacao/nr/iracema.html – **CE30)** Rua Sáo Francisco 374, 63010-210 Juazeiro do Norte ☎88 3511 2404 **W:** radioprossoam.com.br – **CE31)** Rua Cel Joaquim Ribeiro 405 sala 04, 62011-020 Sobral ☎88 3611 7888 – **CE32)** Av Dr Pedro de Queiroz Ferreira 2129, 62850-000 Cascavel **W:** litoralam.com – **CE33)** Rua São Francisco, 139, Villa Lobo, 63100-000 Crato **W:** rcnesportes.com.br – **CE34)** Rua Monsenhor Salviano Pinto 71, 63800-000 Quixeramobim ☎88 3441 1516 **W:** difusoracristal.com.br **E:** contato@difusoracristal.com.br – **CE35)** Praça Pinto Martins 260, 62400-000 Camocim – **CE36)** Av Manoel Castro 815, 62940-000 Morada Nova ☎88 3422 1198 – **CE37)** Av. Moacir Pereira Gondim, 333, Planalto dos Colibris, 63660-000 Tauá ☎▤88 3437 1345 **W:** cultura960am.com.br **E:** cultura960am@hotmail.com – **CE38)** Travessa São Pedro, 62800-000 Aracati ☎88 3421 1805 – **CE39)** Rua Hildo Furtado, s/n - Centro, 62760-000 Baturité ☎88 3347 1117 – **CE40)** Rua Italiano Júlio Filisola, 512, 62370-000 São Benedito ☎88 3626 2142 – **CE41)** Rua Coronel Antônio Joaquim 2143, 62930-000 Limoeiro do Norte ☎88 3423 4225 **W:** radioeducadora.com.br **E:** educadora560@yahoo.com.br – **CE42)** Av. Pref. Jaques Nunes 648, 62320-000 Tianguá ☎88 3671 1322 **W:** santana1540.com.br – **CE43)** Rua João Verçosa s/n, 62640-000 Pentecoste ☎85 3352 2554 **W:** difusoravaledocuru.com.br – **CE44)** Av Francisco Franca 414, 63600-000 Senador Pompeu ☎88 3449 0206 **W:** radiosertaocentralam.com.br **E:** radiosertaocentral@hotmail.com – **CE45)** Praça Adolfo Caminha 247, 62800-000 Aracati ☎88 3421 4567 – **CE46)** Rua Doutor Otávio Lobo, 198, Santa Quitéria, 62280-000 Santa Quitéria ☎88 3628 0033 **W:** itataia890.com.br – **CE47)** Rua Coronel Austragésilo s/n, 62680-000 Paracuru ☎85 3344 1111 **W:** redeimaculada.org.br **E:** pr.francisco.oliveira@hotmail.com – **CE48)** Rua Justino Alves Ferreira, 364 - Centro, 63380-000 Barro ☎88 3554 1166 – **CE49)** Rua Simão Barbosa,1209, São Mateus, 62700-000 Canindé ☎ 85 3343 1597 **W:** sistemadecomunicacao.net – **CE50)** Rua Coronel Lucio 489, 63700-000 Crateús ☎88 3691 5155 – **CE51)** Rua Monsenhor Salviano Pinto 57, 63800-000 Quixeramobim ☎88 3441 0263 ▤88 3441 1209 **W:** sistemamaior.com.br/radio_campomaior **E:** contatomaior@sistemamaior.com.br – **CE52)** Rua Engenheiro Aljandro Alfredo, 1554 - Centro, 61600-050 Caucaia ☎85 3342 3677 – **CE53)** Av da Ressurreiçao, 926, Pe Ibiapina, 62000-000 Sobral ☎88 3111 3121 **W:** radioressurreicao.com.br – **CE54)** Rua Tibúrcio Targino 155, 61700-000 Aquiraz ☎85 3361 1285 – **CE56)** Rua Raimundo Nonato 81, 62940-000 Morada Nova ☎88 3422 2561 – **CE57)** Rua Dr Chagas Pinto 351, 62250-000 Ipu ☎88 3683 2186 **W:** radioiracemadeipu.com.br **E:** recados1360@hotmail.com – **CE58)** Rua Francisco Gomes de Souza 198, 63150-000 Campos Sales. ☎88 3533 1188 **W:** cidadeam630.com. br –**CE59)** Av Cazuzinha Marques 87, 63560-000 Acopiara ☎88 3565 0063 **W:** radiovaleacopiara.am.br **E:** radiovaleacopiara@gmail.com – **CE60)** Rua Manoel Inacio de Lucena 249 an 2, 63260-000 Brejo Santo ☎88 3531 1093 **W:** radiosulcearense.com.br – **CE62)** Av. Senador Esmerino Arruda s/n, 62430-000 Granja ☎88 3624 1106 **W:** Facebook:Rádio Vale do Coreaú Am **E:** radiovaleam@hotmail.com – **CE63)** Rua Antônio Queiroz 343, 63870-000 Boa Viagem ☎88 3427 1064 **W:** radioamliberdade.blogspot.no**E:** deadator@gmail.com – **CE64)** Rua Major Barreto 3000, 62600-000 Itapajé ☎85 9104 5447 **W:** radioguanaces.com.br **E:** kekpubli@hotmail.com – **CE65)** Rua Padre

Fialho 265, 62010-970 Sobral ☎88 3613 2749 **W:** pioneiraam830.com.br **E:** gerardoneto@pioneiraam830.com.br – **CE66)** Rua Capitão Carapeba 67, 62370-000 São Benedito ☎88 3626 2266 **W:** tabajara.am.br **E:** radiotabajara1@hotmail.com – **CE67)** Rua Monsenhor Jovinano Baretto 22 2° andar, 63660-000 Tauá ☎88 3437 1509 **W:** difusorataua.com.br **E:** contato@difusorataua.com.br – **CE68)** Rua Monsenhor Furtado 149, 62380-000 Guaraciaba do Norte ☎88 3652 2112 **W:** somzoom.com.br/guaraciaba-am-1190 **E:** somzoom@hotmail.com – **CE69)** Rua Mangel Sales Pereira 273, 62590-000 Itarema ☎88 3667 1212 **W:** Facebook: R.Liberdade de Itarema AM 1250 – **CE70)** Av Coronel Alexanzito 369, 62800-000 Aracati ☎88 3421 3033 **W:** Facebook: R.Moria – **CE71)** Av.7 N 260 Altos Conj. Jereissati, Maracanau, 61900-320 Maracanaú ☎85 3382 2222 **W:** radiopitaguaryam.com **E:** radiopitaguary@ibest.com.br – **CE72)** Rodovia BR-226 km 20, Distrito de Bonfim, 63600-000 Senador Pompeu **W:** facebook.com/AMPATU1130 – **CE73)** Avenida José Júlio Lousada 312 , 62580-000 Acaraú ☎88 36611280 **W:** difusoraacarau.com **E:** rdifusoraacarau@hotmail.com – **CE74)** Avenida Alcides Rocha, s/n, São Luis, 62550-000 Morrinhos ☎88 3665 1422 **W:** princesaam.com **E:** princesaam@outlook.com – **CE75)** Rua Cel. José Lourenço, 97, Altos, (C.P. 063) 62250-000 Ipu ☎88 3683 1204 **W:** radioregionaldeipu.com.br **E:** radioregional1520am@hotmail.com – **CE76)** Rua Joaquim Távora 333, 63150-000 Campos Sales ☎88 3533 1530 **W:** tresfronteirasam.com.br **E:** tresfrontelrasam@gmail.com – **CE77)** Rua Manoel Alencar 35, 63610-000 Mombaça ☎88 3685 1368 **W:** radiomacambira.com.br – **CE80)** Rua Raimundo Guedes Martins 25, 63400-000 Cedro ☎88 3564 1075 **W:** radiomontevideoam.com.br – **CE81)** Ro BR 020, s/n, Zona Rural, 62730-000 Caridade ☎85 3324 1292 – **CE82)** Rua Francisco Brasileiro 213, 63900-000 Quixadá ☎88 3412 3047 **W:** am1080.com.br **E:** radioculturaquixada@gmail.com – **CE83)** Av. Rabelo, s/n, Alto Vistoso, 63620- 000 Solonópole ☎88 3518 1520 **W:** radiocachoeiraam.com.br MSN: radio.cachoeira.am@hotmail.com – **CE84)** Rua Augusto Vieira 32, 63630-000 Pedro Branca ☎88 3515 2121 **W:** amtrapia1510.com.br **E:** contato@amtrapia1510.com.br – **CE99)** Rua Afonso Pena 109, 63560-000 Acopiara ☎88 3565 0214 **W:** carinhosaam.com.br **E:** contato@carinohsaam.com.br – **CE100)** Rua Mário Perdigão 130, 61760-000 Eusébio ☎85 3361 2755

## DF00) DISTRITO FEDERAL

**DF01)** SRTS, Qd 701, Ed Assis Chateaubriand, Bl 2, salas 701 a 716, 70340-906 Brasília ☎61 3039 8771 **W:** brasilia.jovempanfm.virgula.uol.com.br **E:** jovempan@jovempadf.com.br - **FM:** 107.9 MHz –**DF02)** SCS Q 08, Bloco B-60, 1° Subsolo, Ed. Venâncio, 70333-900 Brasília ☎61 3799 5700 **W:** radiomec.com.br – **DF03)** Sig Quadra.02 Lt 340 Bl.02, 1° andar,(✉ C.P. 8042, 70673-1080) 70610-901 Brasília ☎61 3342 1080 **W:** radioplanalto.com.br **E:** contato@clube.fm – **DF04)** SCRN 702/03, B1 «B», Edifício Radiobrás, (CP 259) 70710-750 Brasília ☎61 3799 5474 **W:** radios.ebc.com.br/nacionalbrasiliaam **E:** centraldoouvinte@ebc.com.br – **DF05)** SRTV/Sul, Q-701, bloco E, Térreo, 70340-000 Brasília – **DF06)** C.P 259, 70710-750 Brasília **W:** radios.ebc.com.br/nacionalamazonia **E:** amazoniabrasileira@ebc.com.br – **DF07)** SGAS 601 Módulos 3/4, Av L2 Sul, 70340-902 Brasília ☎61 2103 0710 **W:** novaalianca.org.br **E:** contato@novaalianca.org.br - **FM:** 103.3MHz –**DF08)** SGAS 915 lt 75, 70390-150 Asa Sul ☎61 3114 1010 **W:** redeboavontade.com.br **E:** superrbv@boavontade.com –**DF09)** C-01, Lotes 1/12, Ed. Taguatinga Trade Center, Sala 1025, 72010-010 Taguatinga ☎61 3451 3700 – **DF10)** Senado Federal, Praça dos Tres Poderes, Anexo II, Bloco B, Térreo, 70165-900 Brasília ☎61 3303 4691 **W:** senado.gov.br/radio **E:** radio@senado.gov.br

## ES00) ESPÍRITO SANTO

**ES01)** Rua Joaquim Plácido da Silva, 225, Ihla de Santa Maria, 29051-070 Vitória ☎27 3331 9000 **W:** redetribuna.com.br/radio/am **E:** diretoriatvradios@redetribuna.com.br - **FM:** 99.1MHz –**ES02)** Av. Presidente Florentino Avidos, 350, 29018-190 Vitória ☎27 3322 0640 **W:** radiovitoriaes.com.br **E:** janandaCS@radiovitoriaes.com.br – **ES03)** Praça Hilda Calazans dos Santos, 4, Gilberto Machada, 29303-275 Cacheiro de Itapemirim ☎28 3511 0770 – **ES04)** Rua Chafic Murad, 902, Ilha de Monte Belo, 29050-901 Vitória **W:** Facebook: R.Gazeta AM - **FM:** 92.5MHz «Antena Um», 102.3MHz «Litoral FM» – **ES05)** Av. Prefeito Samuel Batista Cruz 4530, 29904-000 Linhares ☎27 3373 2000 **W:** radioculturadelinhares.com.br **E:** contato@radioculturadelinhares.com.br - **FM:** 98.7MHz – **ES06)** Rua Geraldo Pereira 194, 29700-971 Colatina ☎27 3721 1506 **W:** difusoracolatina.com.br **E:** difusoracolatina.com.br – **ES07)** Av Santo Antônio, 366 al Caratoira, 29025-645 Vitória ☎27 3222 4376 ▤27 3222 7747 **W:** radiocapixaba.com.br – **ES08)** Av NS da Penha, 2141, Santa Luiza, 29045-403 Vitória ☎27 3137 2900 **W:** rtv.es.gov.br – **ES09)** Rua Walter de Oliveira, 05, Gilbertao Mchado, 29303-292 Cachoeiro de Itapemirim ☎28 3521 6640 **W:** simnoticias.com.br **E:** sbcachoeiro@gmail.com - **FM:** 107.7 MHz – **ES10)** Rua Alberto de Oliveira Santos 42, Edifico Ames 19° andar, salas 1916-1920 - Centro,

29010-901 Vitória ☎27 3198 0850 🖳27 3222 4960 **W:** redeamericaes.com.br - **FM:** 101.5MHz "Cidade" – **ES11)** Rua José Cupertino 120, 29600-000 Afonso Cláudio **W:** novotempo.com/radio **E:** contatornt@novotempo.org.br – **ES12)** Rua da Matriz 85, 29200-000 Guarapari **W:** simnoticias.com.br – **ES13)** Av Presidente Vargas 449, 29600-000 Afonso Cláudio ☎27 3735 1120 **W:** educadoraafonsoclaudio.com.br – **ES14)** Rua Doutor Ademar Oliveira Neves, 826, Sernamby, 29930-670 São Mateus ☎27 3773 3604 – **ES15)** Rua Costa Pereira 37, 29300-090 Cachoeiro de Itapemirim ☎28 3521 1960, **W:** radiodiocesana.com.br **E:** radio@radiodiocesana.com.br – **ES16)** Rua Graciano Neves 250, 29156-050 Cariacica ☎27 3331 8300 **W:** novotemponet.com.br **E:** recepcaonovotempo@gmail.com – **FM:** 95.9 MHz – **ES17)** Rua Astrogildo Romão dos Anjos 277, 29800-000 Barra de São Francisco ☎27 3765 2779 **W:** radiosaofranciscoam.com.br **E:** couvinte@gmail.com – **ES18)** Av Marechal Campos, 310 pa 2, Horto29050-135 Vitória ☎27 3322 1250 – **ES20)** Rua Governador Avidos, 33, Conceição, 29900-490 Linhares ☎22 3372 3100 **W:** globolinhares.com.br **E:** diretoria@globolinhares.com.br – **ES21)** Rodovia Mickel Chequer, s/n, Zona Rural, 293900-000 Iúna ☎28 3545 1205 – **ES22)** 29300-000 Cachoeiro de Itapemirim **W:** Facebook: R.Tupi AM 1590 Cachoeiro – **ES24)** Rua Dr Moacir Veloso, 63, Gloria, 29122-610 Vila Velha ☎27 3434 5700 **W:** simnoticias.com.br – **ES25)** Nova Venecia

**GO00) GOIÁS**

**GO01)** Av. Goiás Q 10 1449, 74010-010 Goiânia ☎62 3212 0735 **W:** radioriviera.webnode.com **E:** radioam.riviera@gmail.com – **GO02)** Av. João XXIII 381, S Central, 75703-902 Catalão ☎64 3441 3206 **W:** radioculturaonline.com.br – **GO03)** Rua Rui Barbosa, 420, Central, 75025-060 Anápolis **W:** radiomanchester.com.br **E:** fm@radiomanchester.com.br - **FM:** 93.3 MHZ – **GO04)** Av Egídio Francisco Rodrigues 54, 75200-000 Pires do Rio ☎64 3461 7346 **W:** Facebook: Gospel AM 630 kHz **E:** am630gospel@hotmail.com – **GO05)** Av 24 de Outubro, 1854, Campinas, 74505-011 Goiânia ☎62 3233 4000 **W:** difusoragoiania.com.br **E:** difusora@netgo.com.br – **GO06)** Av Marechal Rondón, 1088, 76270-000 Jussara ☎62 3373 1739 **W:** kompletafm.net **E:** komletafm@gmail.com **FM:** 96.7 MHz – **GO07)** Rua 48, 1254, Joaquim da Silva Moreira, 76680-000 Itapuranga ☎62 3312 1546 **W:** radioprimaveraam.com.br **E:** comercial@radioprimaveraam.com.br – **GO08)** Av 1° de Maio 30 75020 050 Anápolis ☎62 3315 6927 **W:** radiosaochico.com.br - **FM:** 96.3MHz – **GO09)** Rua José de Carvalho 542, 75800-447 Jataí ☎64 3631 1245 **W:** difusoraonline.com.br **E:** contato@difusoraonline.com.br – **GO10)** Rua Evangelino Meireles 26, 72800-680 Luziânia ☎61 3621 4700 - **FM:** 90.9 MHz – **GO11)** Rua Coronel Gonzaga 540, 75690-000 Caldas Novas ☎64 3435 1100 **W:** radiopousada.com.br – **GO12)** Chacara Miranapolis br 153 km 1209 (C.P. 354) 75024-970 Anápolis ☎62 3098 3977 **W:** radiovozdocoracaoimaculado.com **E:** radiovozdocoracaoimaculado@gmail.com – **GO13)** Rua 29, 234, Carrilho, 76380-000 Goianésia ☎62 3353 3355 **W:** rvc780.com.br – **GO14)** Praca Carrijo 30, 75830-000 Mineiros ☎62 3661 1353 **W:** eldorado790.com.br **E:** radioeldorado@gmail.com – **GO15)** Rua José Pedro Rêgio 45, 76310-000 Rialma ☎62 3397 1181 **W:** radioalvorada810.com.br – **GO16)** Rua Teixeira de Freitas Qd. 04 Lt 26, Setor Serrinha 74463-300 Goiânia ☎62 3945 3820 **W:** 820am.com.br – **GO17)** Av Belém Brasilia Q5 10 lt 4, S Central, 76550-000 Porangatu ☎62 3362 4085 **W:** radiotropical850am.com.br – **GO18)** Av Tocantins N° 65 1° andar, 76400-000 Uruaçu ☎62 3357 6626 **W:** radiolagodourado.com.br **E:** contato@radiolagodourado.com.br – **GO19)** SBS Qd 2, s/n Bl Q lt 03 Ed João Carlos Saad. Asa Sul, 70070-120 Brasilia ☎61 3325 1499 – **GO20)** Rua Minas Gerais, 135, Central ☎64 3431 8888 **W:** radioparanaiba.com.br - **FM:** 92.3MHz – **GO21)** Rua Uberaba 9, 75510-140 Itumbiara ☎64 3431 7400 **W:** difusoraitumbiara.com.br – **GO22)** Av. Tiradentes, 1.402 Sl. 04, 75040-010 Anápolis ☎66 3327 0000 **W:** radioimprensa.am.br **E:** diretoria@radioimprensa.am.br – **GO23)** Rua Diógenes de Castro Ribeirao, 223, Central, 76330-000 Jaraguá ☎62 3326 4020 **W:** portal910.com.br – **GO24)** Rua F-52 Qd. 164 Lt 5/18 No 120, Faiçalville IV, 74350-450 Goiânia ☎62 8401 0508 **W:** redefonte.com **E:** portalredefonte@gmail.com – **GO25)** Rua Freio João Batista 76, 75860-000 Quirinópolis. ☎64 3651 1452 **W:** sulgoiana.com.br **E:** quirinopolis@hotmail.com – **GO26)** Praça Rui Barbosa 276, 73800-000 Formosa ☎61 3642 1140 **W:** radioformosaam.com.br – **GO27)** Rua Thomaz Edson Qd 07, St. Serrinha, 74835-130 Goiânia ☎62 3250 1455 **W:** facebook.com Radio Daqui **E:** jornaldaqui@jdaqui.com.br – **GO28)** Av. Br. Rio Branco, 1, S. Central, (✉C.P 34, 75781-970) 75780-000 Ipameri ☎64 3491 1314 **W:** xavantes.net **E:** radio_xavantes@hotmail.com – **GO29)** Rua Coração Fiel 50, Rialma II,76310-000 Rialma ☎62 3397 2175 **W:** coracaofiel.com **E:** radio@coracaofiel.com.br – **GO30)** Agencia Goiania de Comunicao, Rua SC-01, 299, Parque Santa Cruz, 74860-270 Goiânia ☎62 3201 7600 **W:** radiobrasilcentral.com.br **E:** rbc@agecom.go.gov.br – **GO31)** Rua Monsenhor Celso, Quadra Área, Lote 2, s/n, Vila Santa, 74912-590 Aparecidsa de Goiania, ☎62 3216 0730 **W:** sagresonline.com.br **E:** jornalismo@radio730.com.br – **GO32)** Alameda

das Rosas, 2.200, Setor Oeste, 74126-010 Goiânia ☎62 3521 0600 **W:** radio.ufg.br **E:** radioufg870@gmail.com – **GO33)** Av Amazonas, 356, Central, 76100-000 São Luís de Montes Belos ☎64 3671 1621 **W:.** redediocesanaderadio.com **E:** radiovaleamfm@hotmail.com – **GO34)** Rua Barão Rio Branco Qd 40, 989 lt 7, Central, 75650-000 Morrinhos ☎64 3416 2416 Facebook: R.Morrinhos **E:** 1460am@morrinhosam.com.br – **GO36)** Rua Tapajós, 137, St Oeste, 73850-000 Cristalina ☎61 3612 2929 **W:** radioserradoscristais.com.br – **GO37)** Rua 15 Novembro Q ,1 36 lt 1, 76600-000 Goiás ☎62 3371 1575 – **GO38)** Rua Sao Paulo 557, 75600-000 Goiatuba☎64 3495 1802 – **GO39)** Praça Pres Médici, s/n, Central, 75920-000 Santa Helena de Goiás ☎63 3641 1555 **W:** radiosantelenense.com.br **E:** radiosantelenense@globo.com – **GO40)** Rua Dr Antonio Balduino 1260, 75400-000 Inhumas ☎62 3511 2040 **W:** radiojornaldeinhumas.com.br**E:** rjiamcom@gmail.com – **GO41)** Av. Pauzanes Carvalho Q 25,s/n lt 7/9, S.Pauzanes (✉ C.P 131, 75901-970) 75930-000 Rio Verde ☎64 3621 4433 **W:** rioverdeam.com.br – **GO43)** Av Pará, 541, 76200-000 Iporá ☎64 3674 1153 **W:** redediocesanaderadio.com – **GO44)** Rua 23 Q 1 s/n lt 3, Andrade, 75850-000 Caiapônia ☎64 3363 1219 – **GO45)** Rua Lazer Q82, s/n lt 2, Res Village Garavelo, 74900-000 Aparecida de Goiânia ☎62 3283 1040 **W:** radiocaraiba.com.br **E.** caraiba@radiocaraiba.com.br – **GO46)** QS 03 lotes 3,5,7 e 9 salas 1513/1515, Ed. Pátio Capital. Aguas Claros, 71953-000 Brasilia DF (C.P 06-799, 71701-970 Brasília, DF) ☎61 3039 1162 **W:** radioredentor.com.br **E:** contato@radioredentor.com.br – **GO47)** Rua 22, 150, St.Aeroporto, 75640-000 Piracanjuba ☎64 3405 1919 **W:** radiopousoalto.com.br – **GO48)** Rua 49, Q 53 218, Nova Vila, 76300-000 Ceres ☎62 3307 3042 – **GO49)** Praça Silva Junior 184,76420-000 Niquelândia ☎🖳62 3354 1430 **W:** radiomantiqueiraam.com.br **E:** radiomantiqueira@uol.com.br – **GO50)** Rua Maranhão 1355, 75600-000 Goiatuba ☎64 3495 7556 **W:** radiosempre.com.br **E:** contato@radiosempre.com.br – **GO51)** Rua Francisco Corra Neves, 100, 2° andar , 75860-000 Quirinópolis ☎🖳 64 3651 2106 **W:** radioalvoradaam.com.br **E:** radioalvorada@cultura.com.br – **GO52)** Av Joaquim David Ferreira 1390, 76105-000 Firminópolis ☎64 3681 1217 **W:** radioboasnovas1020am.com.br – **GO53)** Av Santana, Qd 55, lote 01, Sector Vila Baiana, 73840-000 Campas Belos ☎62 3451 1209 **W:** novarcbam.websom.net – **GO54)** Rua 73, 349-Bloco A Térreo, Jardim Goiás, 74810-370 Minacu ☎62 8401 0530 **W:** reedeserradourada.br/emissora/minacu

**MA00) MARANHÃO**

**MA01)** Av Eliézer Moreira s/n, 65950-000 Barra do Corda – **MA02)** Rua Frei Querubim, 57, Apicum Centro, 65025-420 São Luís ☎98 3878 5709 **W:** educadora560.com.br – **MA03)** Av Camboa do Mato, 120, Camboa, 65020-260 São Luís ☎98 3214 3094 **W:** difusora94fm.com - **FM:** 94.3MHz – **MA04)** Pc Pallmeiro Cantanhede 1524, 65400-000 Codó ☎99 3661 1944 **W:** eldoradoam.com.br **E:** radioeldoradoam@hotmail.com – **MA05)** Av São Benedito, 1075, Bairro São Benedito, 65400-000 Codó – **MA07)** Rua Manoel Alves de Abreu 373, 65700-000 Bacabal ☎99 3621 1510 **W:** Facebook: R.Jainari – **MA08)** Av Coronel Fonseca 200, 65800-000 Balsas ☎99 3541 2458 – **MA09)** Av Cel Colares Moreira, 1000 sala 12- Marcus Center, Sao francisco, 65075-440 São Luís ☎98 3235 7676 **W:** http//radio.capital118+.com.brt **E:** radio@capital1180.com.br – **MA10)** Rua Beira Mar 276, 65010-400 Sao Luis ☎98 2108 6329 **W:** ma.gov.br/timbira **E:** timbira@secom.ma.gov.br – **MA11)** Av President Media, 77, Areinha, 65032-075 São Luís ☎98 2109 7777 **W:** grupozildenifalcao.com.br **E:** edjandejesus@yahoo.com.br – **MA12)** Rua 18 de Março 627, 65200-000 Pinheiro ☎98 3381 3215 **W:** sistemapericuma.com.br – **MA13)** Av Rio Branco, 670, 65725-000 Pedreiras – **MA14)** Av Kennedy 353, 65690-000 Colinas ☎99 3552 1411 – **MA15)** Av. Ana Jansen 200, 65076-902 São Luis ☎98 3235 3013 – **MA16)** Rua Antônio Lopes 971, 65215-000 Viana ☎98 3351 1353 – **MA17)** Rua Guarani, s/n QD 03 LOTE 09, Caicara, 65922-000 João Lisboa – **MA18)** Rua João Castelo s/n, 65320-000 Vitorino Freire ☎98 3655 1240 **W:** sistemaaguabranca.com – **MA20)** Rua Piauí 895, 65930-000 Açailândia – **MA21)** Rua Cláudio Carneiro 177, 65750-000 Esperantinópolis ☎99 3645 1403 – **MA22)** Alexandre Trovao 338, 65415-000 Coroatá ☎99 3641 0931 – **MA23)** Rua Aarão Reis, 1963, Morro Alecrim, 65604-060 Caxias ☎93 3521 0047 – **MA24)** Rua Tiradente 134, 65365-000 Zê Doca ☎98 3655 3972 – **MA26)** Rua Alagoas 497, 65900-450 Imperatriz ☎99 3524 6611 **W:** imirante.globo.com**E:** imirante@mirante.com.br - **FM:** 96.1 MHz – **MA27)** Av Amaral Raposo s/n, 65940-000 Grajaú ☎99 3532 6165 – **MA28)** Rua Rui Barbosa s/n, 65620-000 Coelho Neto – **MA29)** Rua Dr Paulo Ramos 495, 65208-000 Santa Helena ☎98 3382 1196 **W:** radiorioturiacuam.com.br **E:** contato@radiorioturiacuam.com.br – **MA30)** Rua Frederico Coelho esquina com Av Frei Aniceto, 65763-000 Tuntum **W:** imirante.globo.com **E:** imirante@mirante.com.br – **MA31)** Praca Rio Branco 5, 65350-000 Vitória do Mearim ☎98 3352 1108 **W:** radiocidadedevitoria.com.br – **MA32)** Parque da Bandeira, 222, Edificio Ariana, 65665-000 São João dos Patos ☎95 3551 2418 – **MA33)** Praça do Guarim s/n, 65390-000 Santa Luzia – **MA34)** Rua Terra esquina com Rua Jupiter s/n, 65760-0000 Presidente Dutra – **MA35)** Praça Coronel Luis Vieira 26, 65500-000 Chapadinha ☎98 3471 1337 **W:** imirante.globo.com **E:** imirante@mirante.com.br – **MA36)** Rua Senador Vitorino Freira 85, 65715-000 Lago da Pedra ☎99 3644 1220 **W:** radiosantamaura.com.br – **MA37)** Rua Hemeterio Leitão 103, 65430-00 Vargem Grande – **MA38)** Av Ana Jansen 200, 65076-902 São Luís ☎98 3230 3013 **W:** imirante.globo.com – **MA39)** Rua Monsenhor Gentil s/n, 65530-000 Urbano Santos – **MA40)** Rua Bela Vista 1894, Castelo Branco, 65604-160 Caxias ☎99 3521 033 – **MA41)** Praça Roosevelt Moreira s/n, 65800-000 Balsas ☎99 3541 2999 ▤99 3541 7308 **W:** radioboanoticia.com.br **E:**radio@radioboanoticia.com. br – **MA42)** Belo Horizonte, s/n, Formosa, 65634-080 Timon ☎89 2107 3000 – **MA43)** Rua Principal, Turiaçu

**MG00) MINAS GERAIS**

**MG01)** Rua Rabelo Horta 39, 36770-064 Cataguases ☎32 3422 1724 **W:** radiocataguases.com **E:** contato@radiocataguases.com- **FM:** 89.5MHz – **MG02)** Rua General Carneiro 10, Edificio Milinardo s 200 à 305, 39400-095 Montes Claros – **MG03)** Rua Serrinha, 1200, Vale do Jacobá, 30668-250 Belo Horizonte ☎31 3322 1945 – **MG04)** Praça Nossa Senhora Aparecida, 134, Aparecida, 38400-726 Uberlândia ☎34 3292 0401 **W:** radioamerica.com.br **E:** america@radioamerica. com.br – **MG05)** Av Padre Matias, 1089, Marciano Pires, 38740-000 Patrocínio ☎34 3839 9880 **W:** sistemadifusoraderadio.com.br - **FM:** 98.9MHz – **MG06)** Rua Itatiaia, 117, Bonfim, 31210-170 Belo Horizonte ☎31 2105 3588 ▤31 2105 3613 **W:** www itatiaia.com.br **E:** itatiaia@ itatiaia.com.br - **FM:** 95.7MHz – **MG07)** Av. Dr. Fidélis Reis 820, 38010-030 Uberaba ☎34 3331 7900 ▤34 3321 8200 **W:** jmonline.com.br **E:** jmonlin@emonline.com.br – **MG08)** Av Presidente Vargas 372, 35661-000 Pará de Minas ☎37 3232 1588 **W:** santacruzam.com.br **E:** comercial@santacruzam.com - **FM:** 101.7 MHz – **MG09)** Rua Euripides Ribeiro 739, 38720-000 Lagoa Formosa ☎34 3824 9980 **W:** radiovitoriosa.com.br – **MG10)** Rua Xavier de Veiga 85, 35400-000 Ouro Preto ☎31 3551 2166 **W:** itatiaia.com.br/ouropreto/ **E:** ouropreto@itatiaia.com.br – **MG11)** Avenida Juscelino Kubitschek, 30, Passaginha, 35790-000 Curvelo ☎38 3721 2300 **W:** radioclubecurvelo. com.br - **FM:** 95.5 MHz – **MG12)** Rua Lincoln Alves Santos, 20, Distrito Industrial Montes Claros ☎38 3216 6045 **W:** educadoraam670.com.br **E:** contatoradioouvinte@gmail.com – **MG13)** Rua Geraldo Rios 98, 38770-000 João Pinheiro ☎38 3561 1381 – **MG14)** Rua Entre Rios, 33, Carlos Prates, 30710-080 Belo Horizonte ☎31 8406 0673 **W:** radiomineiro.com **E:** radiomineiro@radiominerio.com – **MG15)** Praça 15 de Novembro 339 5° andar, 36900-000 Manhuaçu ☎33 3332 4080 **W:** radiomanhuacu.com.br **E:** contato@radiomanhuacu.com.br - **FM:** 88 MHz – **MG16)** Rua Cel. José Inácio 96, 37550-000 Pouso Alegre ☎35 3423 1488 **W:** difusora710am.com.br **E:** difusora@difusora710am.com. br – **MG17)** Av Dr Fidélis Reis 810, 38010-030 Uberaba ☎34 3331 7999 **W:** radiojm730.com.br – **MG18)** Av Barão do Rio Branco 3231 Sl 1004 , 36010-012 Juiz de Fora ☎32 3231 1388 – **MG19)** Av Itaú, 515 Sl 1013, Dom Bosco, 30850-035 Belo Horizonte **W:** americabh.com.br **E:** radioamerica-diretoria@pucminas.br ☎31 3336 2600 – **MG20)** Praça Leonardo Venerando Pereira 200, 37200-000 Lavras ☎35 3822 5000 **W:** radiocultura770.com.br – **MG21)** Avenida Getúlio Vargas 142, 38700 128 Patos de Minas ☎38 3418 1770 **W:** clubeam.com **E:** clubeam@clubeam.com – **MG22)** Rua dos Cravos, 467, Bairro São Pedro, 35900-125 Itabira ☎31 3831 2928 **W:** radioitabira.com.br **E:** euclideseder@yahoo.com.br – **MG23)** Av Prof José Ignácio de Souza 2710, Umuarama, 38405-330 Uberlândia ☎34 3222 0780 **W:** educadorajp.com.br – **MG24)** Rua Reporter Luiz Quirino 100, 35430-017 Ponte Nova ☎31 3817 1025 **W:** radiopontenova.com.br **E:**diretoria@ radiopontenova.com.br – **MG25)** Rua Margarida Monteiro 125, 35290-000 Mantena ☎33 3241 3000 **W:** radio13dejunho.com.br **E:** radio13dejunho@ralnet.com.br – **MG26)** Rua Luiz, 235 -Américo Silva, (CP 34) 35590-000 Lagoa da Prata ☎▤37 3261 4500 **W:** tropical790. com **E:** tropical@tropical790.com – **MG27)** Rua Profesora Esposalina Leal 141, 35200-000 Aimorés ☎33 3267 1021 **W:** radioam810.org.br – **MG28)** Rua Maranhao 400, 35500-066 Divinópolis ☎37 3222 7070 **W:**divinopolisam.com.br **E:** contato@divinopolisam.com.br - **FM:**100.5MHz – **MG29)** Praça Dom Pedro Teixeira, 49, 5° andar, 36200-001 Barbacena ☎32 3331 8788 **E:** radioglobo@barbacena.com.br – **MG30)** Rua Dos Antunes 1175 Ed São Sebastião, 37950-000 São Sebastião do Paraíso ☎35 3531 2396 **W:** radiodafamilia.com.br **E:** contato@radiofamilia.com.br **MG31)** Rua Rio Mantiqueira, 769, Novo Riacho, 30130-003 Contagem ☎31 3565 6289 **W:** redegeraisderadio. com.br/am830.php **E:** contato@redegeraisradio.com.br – **MG32)** Rua Barão de Piunhi 247, 35570-000 Formiga ☎37 3322 2565 **W:** difusoraformiga.com.br - **FM.** 93 MHz – **MG34)** Rua José Bueno Azerdo, 89 sl 1, Tiradentes, 38430-000 Tupaciguara ☎34 3281 4050 **W:** radiotupaciguara.com.br – **MG35)** Av Raja Gabáglia, 1666, Gutierrez, 30441-194 Belo Horizonte ☎31 3298 3401 ▤31 3298 3400 **W:** inconfidencia.com.br **E:** inconfidencia@inconfidencia.com.br - **FM:** 100.9 MHz – **MG36)** Rua Dr Olinto Martins 207, 39960-000

Jequitinhonha ☎33 3741 1521 **W:** santacruz890.com.br – **MG37)** Av Getúlio Vargas 420, 39800-015 Teófilo Otoni ☎33 3522 3635 **W:** radioteofilotoni.com.br **E:** vanessa@radioteofilotoni.com.br – **MG38)** Largo Dom João 122, 39100-000 Diamantina ☎38 3531 1408 – **MG39)** Praça 28 de Setembro, 95 - Centro, 36520-000 Visconde do Rio Branco ☎32 3551 1877 **W:** radioculturariobranco.com.br **E:** radioculturavrb@ gmail.com or radiocultura920@hotmail.com – **MG40)** Rua Brandão Carneiro, 33 - Centro, 37460-000 Passa Quatro ☎35 3371 3301 **W:** mineiradosul.com.br **E:** radio@mineiradosul.com.br – **MG41)** Av Afonso Pena, 795 2° andar - Centro, (CP 586) 37270-000 Campo Belo ☎35 3832 2700 **W:** radioclubecampobelo.com. br **E:** radioclube10@ gmail.com – **MG42)** Av Minas Gerais 3399, Bosque, 38440-000 Araguari ☎34 3512 0291 **W:** radiovitoriosa.com.br – **MG43)** Rua Santa Catarina, 610 3° andar, Lourdes, 30170-081 Belo Horizonte ☎31 3349 7308 **W:** radioatalaiabh.com.br – **MG44)** Av Bom Jesus, 330 - Centro, (CP 10) 37578-000 Bueno Brandão ☎35 3463 1006 **W:** radioindy.com.br **E:** indyamcomercial@gmail.com – **MG45)** Rua Radialista Hamilton Macedo, 204, Limoeiro, 35300-121 Caratinga ☎33 3321 2800 – **MG46)** Rua Santa Teresa 97 - Centro, 36300-114 São João del Rei ☎32 3371 7777 **W:** radiosaojoaodelrei.am.br **E:** radiosaojoaodelrei@hotmail.com – **MG48)** Rua Espírito Santo, 95, Poco Rico, 36020-000 Juiz de Fora ☎32 3215 2120 **W:** radiosolaram. com.br **E:** comercial@radiosolar.com.br – **MG49)** Rua Afonso Pena, 340 - Centro, 37590-000 Jacutinga ☎35 3443 2121 **W:** radiojacutinga.com. br **E:** radioestanciajacutinga@hotmail.com – **MG50)** Rua Manoel Joaquim Pires 63, 35170-082 Coronel Fabriciano ☎31 3842 1400 **W:** educadoramg.com.br - **FM:** 107.1MHz – **MG51)** Rua Rio Grande do Norte, 1096, Umuarama, 38402-016 Uberlândia ☎34 3291 5566 **W:** culturaam.net - **FM:** 95.1MHz – **MG52)** Rua Duque de Caixas 258, Primavera, 38430-000 Tupaciguara ☎34 3281 5800 **W:** rural1050.com – **MG53)** Av. Alvares Cabral, 1030 s 206, Lourdes, 30170.001 Belo Horizonte ☎31 3453 3989 **W:** ipda.com.br – **MG54)** Rua Olegário Maciel, 200, Avenida, 37500-000 Itajubá ☎35 3623 2471 **W:** radioitajuba-.com.br – **MG55)** Praça da Basílica, 130, Barrio Basilica, (✉CP 05) 36415-000 Congonhas ☎31 3731 8308 ▤31 3731 8313 **W:** radiocongonhas.com.br **E:** gerencia@radiocongonhas.com.br – **MG56)** Av Dr Américo Luz, 153, Sala 105 - Centro, 37890-000 Muzambinho ☎35 3571 1145 **W:** radiodopovo.com.br **E:** radiodopovoam@yahoo. com.br – **MG57)** Rua Halfeld 744 Sl 401,36010-003 Juiz de Fora ☎32 3215 4477 – **MG58)** Av Bahia 720, 38440-000 Araguari ☎34 3241 3131 **W:** radioplanaltoaraguari.com **E:** ouvintes@radioplanaltoaraguari. com – **MG59)** Rua Areião do Matadouro, 1281, Matadouro, 34000-000 Nova Lima ☎31 3541 1823 – **MG61)** Rua Governador Valadares, 80, Sala 112 Ed. José Mateiro, 37170-000 Boa Esperança ☎35 3851 1000 ▤35 3851 1475 **W:** radioserraam.com.br **E:** radioserra@yahoo.com. br – **MG62)** Av Antonio Olímpio de Morais 545, 35500-005 Divinópolis ☎37 3222 0001 **W:** radiominasam.com.br ☎37 3222 0001 - **FM:** 99.3 MHz – **MG63)** Rua João Bressane 1, 37400-000 Campanha ☎35 3261 1229 **W:** radiodiocesanaam.com.br **E:** radiocesana@yahoo.com.br – **MG64)** Av Constantino Pinto 90, 36880-000 Muriaé ☎32 3729 2929 **W:** radiomuriae.com.br **E:** diretoria@radiomuriae.com.br – **MG66)** Rua do Rádio, 60, Pepétuo Socorro, 38190-000 Sacramento ☎34 3351 1735 **W:** radiosacramento.net **E:** contato@radiosacramento.net – **MG67)** Rua Cassiano Lemos 87, 38183-036 Araxá ☎34 3612 3000 **W:** cidadeamfm.com.br **E:** cidade@radiocidadedearaxa.com.br - **FM:** 94.5 MHz – **MG68)** Av Assis Chateaubriand, 499, Floresta, 30150-101 Belo Horizonte ☎31 3237 6000 **W:** guarani.com.br **E:** guarani@guarani.com - **FM:** 96.5 MHz **MG69)** Praça Cleber de Holanda, 111, Alton Sion, 37048-370 Varginha ☎35 3222 8288 **W:** sistemaclube.com **E:** sac@ sistemaclube.com.br - **FM:** 99.3MHz – **MG71)** Rua Afonso Pena 3402, 35010-001 Governador Valadares ☎33 3271 4002 **W:** novotempo.com/ gv/ **E:** radio@novotempo.com – **MG72)** Av. Treze, 658 6° andar, Edifico Ituiutaba - Centro, 38300-140 Ituiutaba ☎34 3271 7400 **W:** radioglobotuiutaba.com - **FM:** 97.3 MHz – **MG74)** Pc. Getúlio Vargas 81, 36400-000 Conselheiro Lafaiete ☎31 3763 1470 **W:** radiocarijos. com.br - **FM:** 89.9MHz **MG75)** Rua Itajubá 62, 35160-035 Ipatinga ☎31 3801 4300 **W:** vanguardaam.com.br **E:** comercial@radio95fm. com.br - **FM:** 95 MHz – **MG76)** Rua Ernane Vilela Lima Apart 114-A 1° andar, 37250-000 Nepomuceno ☎35 3861 1278 **W:** radioam810. com.br **E:** radionep@hotmail.com – **MG77)** Rua Duque de Caxias, 450, 16° andar, Edifício Chams, Erlan, 38400-066 Uberlândia ☎34 3219 4707 – **MG78)** Rua Alexandre Silva 295, 38600-000 Paracatu ☎38 3671 3047 **W:** radiojuriti.com.br **E:** contato@radiojuriti.com.br – **MG79)** Av Treze, 658, 6° andar, Edifício Ituiutaba 6° andar, 38300-140 Ituiutaba ☎34 3271 7400 **W:** cancelaam.com - **FM:** 97.3MHz **MG80)** Av Costa Junior 467, 38840-000 Carmo do Paranaíba ☎34 3851 2066 **W:** sistemaplaneta.net **E:** rplaneta@sistemaplaneta.net – **MG81)** Rua Mariana, 178 -Monte Sinai, 35450-000 Itabirito ☎31 3561 3499 **W:** redegeraisderadio.com.br/am1340.php **E:** rgr1340amitabirito@ redegeraisderadio.com.br – **MG83)** Rua Col José Paulino, 261 - Centro, 37750-000 Machado ☎35 3295 1361 **W:** difusoramachado.com.br **E:**

gilson0408@gmail.com – **MG84)** Peixito Filho 112 s 310, 36500-000 Ubá ☎32 3532 2934 **W:** ubaensam.com.br **E:** gleidsonetkd@gmail.com – **MG85)** Rua Calixto Martins de Melo391, 38610-000 Unaí ☎38 3676 1490 **W:** radioveredas.com.br **E:** contato@radioveredas.com.br – **FM:** 98.0MHz – **MG89)** Rua Niquel, 457, Industrial, 35701-107 Sete Lagoas ☎31 3773 3694 **W:** culturasl.com.br – **FM:** 92.1MHz «Musirama» – **MG90)** Av Major Antônio Alberto Fernandes 178, 37720-000 Botelhos ☎35 3741 1277 – **MG92)** Rua XV de Novembro 62, 36500-000 Ubá ☎32 3531 1830 **W:** educadora.com.br – **FM:** 94.5MHz – **MG93)** Praça Minas Gerais, 50, Satélite, 35930-259 João Monlevade ☎31 3851 6001 **W:** cultura590.com.br – **MG94)** Av Governador Israel Pinheiro 651, 38550-000 Coromandel ☎34 8855 2288 **W:** Facebook: R.Diamante **E:** locutoresdiamanteam@gmail.com – **MG95)** Rua Juliano Marques Duarte, 110, Iha Gama Cerqueira, 36660-000 Além Paraíba ☎32 3462 7400 **W:** Facebook: R.Cultura de Porto Novo **E:** sistemahf@gmail.com – **MG96)** Av 15 895, 10° andar Sala 1002 e 1005, Edifico Executivo, 38300-000 Ituiutaba ☎34 3261 7118 **W:** difusoraituiutaba.com.br **E:** administracao@difusoraituiutaba.com.br – **MG97)** Av. Iparanga, 198 - Centro, 37190-000 Três Pontas ☎35 3265 2252 – **MG98)** Rua Bias Fortes 597, 38200-000 Frutal ☎34 3421 7075 – **MG99)** Av Belo Horizonte 108, 39860-000 Nanuque – **MG100)** Praça Dr. Antônio das Chaqas Viegas, 130 2° andar, 36300-060 São João del Rei ☎32 3371 8025 **W:** emboabasfm.com.br **E:** administrativo@emboabas.com – **FM:** 96.9 MHz – **MG102)** Rua Doutor Bernardino Vieira, 41 an 2 sl 7, 37090-060 Passos ☎35 3521 7416 **W:** radiopassos.com.br **E:** radiopassos@passos.com.br – **MG103)** Rua Nunes Roas 70, 36970-000 Manhumirim ☎33 3341 1491 **W:** radiomanhumirim.com **E:** radiomanhumirimfinanceiro@gmail.com – **MG104)** Rua Dr Coelho de Moura 158, 35540-000 Oliveira ☎37 3331 1170 **W:** radiosociedade.com.br **E:** geral@radiosociedade.com.br – **MG105)** Rua João Ribeiro Navarro 285, 36200-000 Barbacena ☎32 3331 7988 **W:** correiosat.com.br – **FM:** 100.3 MHZ – **MG106)** Praça Dr Augusto Gonçalves, 146, salas 411/412, 35680-054 Itaúna ☎37 3242 1910 **W:** clubeamfm.com.br **E:** comercial@clubeamfm.com.br – **FM:** 93.5 MHz – **MG107)** Alameda Monteiro Lobato, Solar dos Lagos, 37470-000 São Lourenço ☎35 3332 4333 **W:** radioestancia.com.br **E:** estancia@radioestancia.com.br – **FM:** 94.3MHz – **MG108)** Av Juscelino Kubtschek, 1016, Boa Vista, 38280-000 Iturama ☎34 3411 0055 **W:** centralcomunicacao.com.br **E:** pontalam@yahoo.com.br – **MG109)** Av Magalhães Pinto, 829, São Sebastião, 35610-000 Dores do Indaiá ☎37 3551 1402 – **MG110)** Rua Cel Otávio Meyer 150 s 507, 37550-000 Pouso Alegre ☎35 3423 6566 **W:** radioclubepousoalegre.com.br **E:** radioclube@tcnet.com.br – **MG111)** Rua Dr José Gonçalves 17 sl 17, 35600-000 Bom Despacho ☎37 3522 4111 – **MG113)** Rua Casemiro Avelar Filho 143, 37410-000 Três Corações ☎35 231 1000 **W:** radiotropical.net - **FM:** 95.7MHz – **MG114)** Praça Nossa Senhora do Carmo 224, 38500-000 Monte Carmelo ☎34 3842 1361 **W:** // radioculturaammontecarmelomg.blogspot.com – **MG115)** Rua Sancho Vilela, 19, Radio, 37540-000 Santa Rita do Sapucaí ☎35 3473 4400 **W:** difusora1550.com.br **E:** comercial@difusora1550.com.br - **FM:** 95.3MHz – **MG116)** Av Brasil 508, 39270-000 Pirapora ☎38 3741 1400 **W:** facebook.com/radiopirapora **E:** radiopirapora@hotmail.com – **MG117)** Praça João XXIII 15, Sala 15, 36700-000 Leopoldina ☎32 3441 4260 **W:** radiojornalleopoldina@gmail.com – **MG118)** Rua Bias Fortes 191, 37130-000 Alfenas ☎35 3299 3886 **W:** radioculturaalfenas.com.br **E:** radiocultura@unifenas.br – **MG119)** Av JK 108, 35500-000 Itapecerica ☎37 3341 8533 **FM:** 101.3MHz – **MG120)** Rua Anastácio José Gonçalves 139, 38810-000 Rio Paranaíba ☎34 3855 1433 **W:** paranaibamaximus.com.br **E:** contato@paranaibamaximus.com.br - **FM:** 101.5 MHz – **MG121)** Rua Sérgio Neves, 63/Sala 103, 36240-000 Santos Dumont ☎32 3251 6534 **W:** radioculturasd.com.br – **MG122)** Av Minas Gerais 584, 39510-000 Espinosa ☎38 3812 1299 – **MG123)** Rua Pepino Laterza, 920, Independência, 38304-216 Uberaba ☎34 3269 0255 ▤34 3269 0244 **W:** redevitoriosa.com.br **E:** comercial@redevitoriosa.com.br – **MG124)** Av Hermenegildo Donatti, 199, Jd. Nova Andradas, 37795-000 Andradas ☎35 3731 2291 **W:** radiovinicola.com.br **E:** vinicola@andradas-net.com.br - **FM:** 94.9MHz – **MG125)** Praça Coronel Odilon Coelho 123, 39520-000 Porteirinha ☎38 3831 1228 **W:** educadoraam640.com.br – **MG126)** Av. Dr. Otávo Soares 108, Palmeiras, 35330-229 Ponte Nova ☎31 3881 6700 **W:** montanhesa.am.br/pontenova/ **E:** montanhesapontenova@montanhesa.am.br – **MG128)** Rua Benedito Valadares 433, Barra, 36880-000 Muriaé ☎32 3729 4800 **W:** redeatividade.com/radioam - **FM:** 94.7MHz – **MG129)** Rua Padre Pedro, 53, Bonfim, 39390-000 Bocaiúva ☎38 3251 1995 **W:** radioclubebocaiuva.com.br – **MG130)** Rua José Teotônio 87-b., 39440-000 Janaúba ☎38 3821 2000 ▤38 3821 2263 **W:** radiogorutubanaam.com **E:** radiogorutubanaam@gmail.com – **MG131)** Av Afonso Pena, 726, Conj. 1000 10° andar, 30130-003 Belo Horizonte **W:** redegeraisderadio.com.br/am1460.php **E:** contato@redegeraisderadio.com.br – **MG132)** Rua Eli Correie de Lacerda, Apt. 119, São Marcos,

35519-000 Nova Serrana ☎37 9199 4681 **W:** radioclickgospel.blogspot.no **E:** dercysat@hotmail.com – **MG133)** Av. Deputada Humborta de Almeida, 60 - Centro, 37810-000 Guaranésia ☎35 3555 1350 **W:** radioam1580guaranesia.com.br **E:** radioam1580@guaranesia.com.br – **MG134)** BR-496 Km 33, 39260-000 Várzea da Palma – **MG135)** Rua Expedicionário, 68 an 2, 38900-000 Bambuí ☎37 3431 3290 **W:** cidadeambambui.com – **MG136)** Rua Jair Werneck, 330, Cidade Alta, 39800-000 Teófilo Otoni ☎33 3522 2000 **W:** radiomucuri.com.br – **MG137)** Rua Major Honor Sarmento, 393, São João, 39400-533 Montes Claros ☎38 3223 5666 ▤38 3221 5590 **W:** radioterraam.com.br – **MG138)** Av 119 N° 122, Brasilia, 38360-000 Capinópolis ☎34 3263 1095 – **MG139)** Avenida Dr. Breno Soares Maia 493, 37900-110 Passos ☎35 3521 4070– **MG140)** Rua Tiradentes, 784, Nova Horizonte, 37175-000 Ilicínea ☎35 3854 1342 **W:** radioaparecidadosulam.com **E:** apdosulam@gmail.com – **MG141)** Rua Astor Goulart de Moura, 51, Vila Virgilio, 39200-000 Corinto ☎38 3751 1858 **W:** radiocidadecorinto.com.br **E:** radiocidadadecorinto@futuretec.com.br – **MG142)** Rodovia, BR-381 Km 195, Cachoeira, 35180-001 Timóteo ☎31 3849 4000 **W:** classificadositatiaiavale.com.br **E:** contato@classificadositatiaiavale.com.br - **FM:** 95.7MHz – **MG143)** Rua Dr Pena 35, 35700-032 Sete Lagoas ☎31 3772 0244 **W:** eldorado1300.com.br **E:** contato@eldorado1300.com.br – **MG144)** Av Paracatu 778, 38780-000 Vazante ☎34 3813 1113 **W:** montanheza.com.br **E:** radio@montanheza.com.br – **MG145)** Pc Cordovil Pinto Coelho, 165, Sala 1003, 36900-000 Manhuaçu – **MG146)** Av BPS, 1303, Pinheirinho, 37500-000 Itajubá ☎35 3622 1008 **W:** unifei.edu.br/radio **E:** radiounifei@unifei.edu.br – **MG148)** Praça Getúlio Vargas 108, 36800-000 Carangola ☎32 3741 1770 **W:** redegeraisderadio.com.br/am900.php br **E:** rgr900amcarangola@redegeraisderadio.com.br – **FM:** 102.7MHz «Caparaó» – **MG149)** Rua Oscar Vidal 416, 36016-290 Juiz de Fora ☎32 2102 9500 **W:** radioglobojf.com.br **E:** atendimento@radioglobojf.com.br – **MG150)** Rua Ceara, 833, Cristo Redentor, 38700-208 Patos de Minas ☎34 3823 1070 **W:** radiopatos.com.br **E:** radiopatos@radiopatos.com.br – **MG151)** Av 7 de Setembro 55-A, 36950-000 Ipanema **W:** radioipanemaam.com.br – **MG152)** Rua Julio Cosi 5, 38230-000 Fronteira ☎34 3428 2099 – **MG153)** Av Francisco Epifâno Fagundes,161, Fagundes, 33200-000 Vespasiano ☎31 3621 3811 – **MG154)** Rua Padre Vigilato 230, 35330-000 Inhapim ☎33 3315 1299 **W:** Facebook: Radio Clube de Inhapim – **MG155)** Rua Buritis, 105, Horto, 35160-300 Ipatinga ☎31 3824 7700 **W:** radiogloboipatinga.com.br – **MG156)** Rua Nonato Matias 524, Mathina, 38740-000 Patrocínio ☎34 3831 7244 **W:** radiorainhadapaz.com.br **E:** contato@radiorainhadapaz.com.br – **MG157)** Av. Zezé Amaral, 180, Cristo Rei, 37950-000 São Sebastião do Paraiso ☎35 3531 7461 **W:** facebook.com/ouroverdeam – **MG158)** Praça Governador Valadares, 255, Perdizes, 38170-000 Perdizes ☎34 3663 1309 **W:** planaltoam.com.br – **MG159)** Av Joaquim Ribeiro de Gouveia 1651, 38320-000 Santa Vitória ☎34 3251 2000 **W:** radiosom2000.com.br – **MG161)** Rua Ceara 677, 38660-000 Buritis ☎38 3662 1492 **W:** Fcebook: R.Buritis **E:** radioburitis@hotmail.com – **MG162)** Rua Silvino Brandão, 164, Aeroporto, 38440-170 Araguari ☎34 3246 0103 **W:** ondavivaaraguari.com.br **E:** comercialmaisfm@yahoo.com.br - **FM:** 93.5 MHz – **MG163)** Travessa Cônego Benedito Profício, 95, 37660-000 Paraisópolis ☎35 3651 1119 **W:** paraisopolisam.com.br – **MG165)** Rua Antônio Ribeiro da Costa Junior 16, 36730-000 Pirapetinga ☎32 3465 1233 **W:** radiopirapetinga.com.br – **MG167)** Praça Dr Badaró, 112, 39650-000 Minas Novas ☎33 3764 1185 **W:** radiobomsucesso.com.br – **MG168)** Rua Marcos Vinícius Ferreira, 226, São Miguel, 39560-000 Salinas ☎38 341 1060 **W:** radiodifusoradesalinas.com.br **E:** programacao@radiodifusoradesalinas.com.br – **MG169)** Av Rondón Pacheco, 450, Santo Antônio, 37150-000 Carmo do Rio Claro ☎35 3561 1967 – **MG170)** Rua Vereador Maria Anselmo, 33 - Centro, 36480-000 Piranga ☎31 3746 1322 – **MG171)** Rua Coronel Carlos Brandão 98, sala 07/08, 36500-000 Ubá ☎32 3532 3122 – **MG172)** Av Dr Pedro Rosa s/n, 37530-000 Brasópolis ☎35 3641 1317 **W:** redegeraisderadio.com.br/am1380.php **E:** contato@redegeaisderadio.com.br – **MG173)** Rua Silviano Brandão 795, (✉ C.P 100) 37570-000 Ouro Fino ☎35 3441 1433 **W:** difusoraourofino.com.br **E:** radio@difusoraourofino.com.br – **MG174)** Praça Vital Brasil 56, 37980-000 Cássia ☎35 3541 5100 **W:** cassia.mg.gov./radio_cultura_am.php **E:** radiocultura@cassia.mg.gov.br – **MG175)** Praça Coronel Silverio de Melo 172, 37958-000 Monte Santo de Minas **W:** radioprogresoam.zip.net – **MG176)** Rua 18, 1974, Industrial, 38270-000 Campina Verde ☎34 3412 1504 – **MG178)** Av Bernardo Guimarães - Centro, 38440-198 Uberlândia ☎34 3293 1300 **W:** radiovitoriosa.com.br **E:** comercial@redevitoriosa.com.br – **MG193)** Rua Coronel Ferraz 135, 37470-000 São Loureço ☎35 3332 6092 **W:** radioglobolambari.blogspot.com.br – **MG195)** Av. Gov. Milton Campos, 2232 sl 201 - Centro, 39740 000 Guanhães ☎33 3421 3503 **W:** cidadeam.com.br **E:** cidadeam@hotmail.com – **MG196)** Rua 20, 2080, Santa Cruz,38950-000 Ibiá ☎34 9981 7016 **W:** maximafm.com.br **E:**

futura@ibiamg.com.br - **FM:** 87.9 MHz
**MS00) MATO GROSSO DO SUL**
**MS01)** Av Mato Grosso 530, 79002-233 Campo Grande **W:** miliciadaimaculada.org.br/v2/Rural580.asp **E:** 580am@miliciadaimaculada.org.br — **MS02)** Av Senador Felinto Müller 59, 79004-383 Campo Grande ☎67 3323 6500 **W:** culturaam680.com. br — **MS03)** Rua Jamil Selem 27(⬛C.P 104 79951-970) 79950-000 Naviraí **W:** cultura690.com.br **E:** culturanav@terra.com.br — **MS04)** Rua Ciro Melo 2045, 79805-000 Dourados ☎67 3421 1540 — **MS05)** Rua Anchieta, 871, Parati, 79081-180 Campo Grande ☎67 3346 2686 **W:** amcapital.com.br — **MS06)** Rua 15 de Agosto, 98, Alto, 79200-000 Aquidauana ☎67 3241 2902 **W:** pantanalnews. com.br/radioindependente — **MS07)** Rua Melanio Garcia Barbosa 749, 79150-000 Maracaju ☎67 3454 1181 **W:** rcmdigital.com.br **E:** rcmdigital@terra.com.br — **MS08)** Rua Jorge Roberto Salomão, 1301, Vila Industrial, 79904-170 Ponta Porã — **MS09)** Rua Marrey Junior, 448, Tiradentes, 79042-150 Campo Grande ☎67 3341 1240 **W:** difusorapantanal.com.br **E:** contato@difusorapantanal.com.br — **MS10)** Rua Tiburcia Queiroz Monteiro, 850, Jardim das Oliveiras 79630-212 Três Lagoas ☎67 3524 2129 **W:** radiodifusora1250.com. br **E:** contato@radiodifusora1250.com.br — **MS11)** Av Marcelino Pires 1404, 79801-002 Dourados ☎67 3423 0498 — **MS12)** Rua Marechal Deodoro, 504, Guanandy, 79200-000 Aquidauana ☎67 3241 3957 **W:** difusora1340.com.br **E:** difusora@difusora1340.com. br — **MS13)** Rua Antônio Lino Barbosa 961, 79130-970 Rio Brilhante ☎67 3452 7451 **W:** difusorarb.com.br — **MS14)** Rua Dom Pedro II, 26, Previsul, 79300-000 Corumbá ☎67 3231 7397 **W:** novaclubeam. com **E:** novaclube1410am@gmail.com — **MS16)** Av Ivinhema. 1493, Vila Operária, 79750-000 Nova Andradina ☎67 3441 1420 **W:** radiocacique.com **E:** radiocacique@hotmail.com — **MS17)** Av Aldair Rosa de Oliveira 1045, Circular da Lagoa, 79640-100 Três Lagoas ☎67 3521 2305 **E:** radiocacula.com.br — **MS18)** Rua Ferreira, 69 B, Cidade Piracema, 79400-000 Coxim ☎67 3291 1124 **W:** radiovaledotaquari. com.br — **MS19)** Rua Angélica 455, 79730-000 Glória de Dourados ☎63 3466 1128 **W:** paiaguas.grupofeitosa.com.br — **MS20)** Rua Visconde de Taunay 895, 79500-000 Paranaíba ☎67 3668 2080 **W:** radiodifusoraam.com.br **E:** radiodifusoraparanaibenseltda@yahoo.com.br — **MS21)** Rua General Câmara 888 1° andar, 79990-000 Amambaí ☎67 3481 1391 **W:** radiogloboamambai.com.br **E:** radiojornaldeamambai@gmail.com - **FM:** 102.5MHz — **MS22)** Rua Severino Araújo 1375, 79700-000 Fátima do Sul ☎67 3467 1833 — **MS24)** Av Presidente Vargas 669, 79940-000 Caarapó ☎67 3453 1810 — **MS25)** Rua/Av.Ra 7 de Setembro 704, 79240-000 Jardim ☎67 3251 1531 **W:** radiolaguna. com.br — **MS26)** Rua Ponta Porã, s/n, Jardim das Grevileas, 79970-000 Eldorado ☎67 3473 2022 — **MS28)** Rua 7 de Setembre 915, 79900-00 Ponta Porã — **MS29)** Pedro Celestino C Costa 687, 79890-000 Itapora ☎67 3421 1104 **W:** radioalvorada1470.com.br — **MS30)** Rua São Paulo 1359, 79490-000 São Gabriel d'Oeste ☎67 3295 1816 **W:** difusora850.com.br — **MS31)** Rua Thomás Cáceres, 349, São Bento, 79170-000 Sidrolândia ☎67 3272 1543 — **MS32)** 135 Rua Amando do Oliveira, 135, Amambai, 79005-370 Campo Grande ☎67 3383 6300 **W:** novotempo.com/campogrande **E:** radio@novotempo.com — **MS33)** Rua Severino de Araujo Ferreira, 1375, Marta Rocha, 79700-000 Fátima do Sul ☎67 3467 1833 **W:** radioguaicurus.com.br — **MS35)** Rua Joao Ferreira Borges, 369, Piravevé, 79740-000 Ivinhema ☎67 3442 4052 — **MS38)** Rua Candido Severino 462, 79420-000 Camapuã ☎67 3286 1366 — **MS39)** Rua Ipiranga, 556, Jardim Itaipu, 79824-190 Douradas ☎67 3426 9261 **W:** miliciadaimaculada.org.br **E:** 1060am@miliciadaimaculada.org.br — **MS40)** Av Aracruz, 21, Parque dos Novas Estados, 79034-450 Campo Grande ☎67 3354 2222 **W:** ipda.com. br — **MS41)** Rua Antônio Maria Coelho 480, 79260-000 Bela Vista ☎67 3439 1243 **W:** radiobelavista.com.br **E:** contato@radiobelavista. com.br — **MS42)** Rua Santos Dumont 880, 79480-000 Rio Verde de Mato Grosso ☎67 3292 1561 **W:** radiocampoalegre.com.br **E:** rcams@brturbo.com.br — **MS43)** Rua Reinaldo Massi 2144, 79740-000 Ivinhema — **MS54)** Rua Viriato Bandeira, 79400-000 Coxim ☎67 3291 4455 — **MS55)** Av.Joao Pedro Pedrossian 4058, 79570-000 Aperecida do Taboado 67 3565 1075 — **MS56)** Av José Ferreira da Costa, 771, 79550-000 Costa Rica ☎67 3247 1090 **W:** radiocostarica.com.br **E:** contato@radiocostarica.com.br — **MS61)** Rua 15 de Novembro, 564, Sala 2, 79300-000 Corumbá ☎67 3232 8080 **W:** radiofronteiraam960. com **E:** radiofronteira@terra.com.br — **MS62)** QE 13 Conjunto C casa 02, Guará II, 71050-030 Brasilia **W:** radiomaria.net.br **E:** imprensa@radiomaria.org.br — **MS63)** Rua Ribas de Rio Pardo 263, 79780-000 Bataguassu ☎67 3541 1630 **W:**radioortal.omegasistemas.com.br — **MS64)** Rua 15 de Novembro 564, 79330-000 Corumbá ☎67 3231 1059
**MT00) MATO GROSSO**
**MT01)** Rua Borórus 673, 78600-000 Barra do Garças ☎66 3401 1345 **W:** radioaruana.com.br **E:** radioaruana@gmail.com — **MT02)** Av Brasil 55 , 78600-000 Poxoréo ☎66 3436 1080 **W:** rsm850.com.br/novo/ — **MT05)** Praça do Seminário 239, 78015-140 Cuiabá ☎65 3046

7900 **W:** blog.cancaonova.com/radiodifusora/sobre **E:** radiocuiaba@cancaonova.com — **MT06)** Av Ludovico de Riva Netto 3224, 78580-000 Alta Floresta ☎66 3521 3501 **W:** radioprogresso640.com.br **E:** ouvinte@radioprogresso640.com.br — **MT07)** Rua Joao Pessao 453(C.P 401, 78700-970) 78700-082 Rondonópolis ☎66 3423 1226 — **MT08)** Rua Joaquim Murtinho,1456 - Centro Sul, Porto, 78025-000 Cuiabá ☎65 3321 6198 **W:** radioculturadecuiaba.com.br — **MT09)** Rua São Pedro 806, 78200-000 Cáceres — **MT10)** Rua Tiradentes 979, 78200-000 Cáceres ☎65 3223 3830 **W:** difusoracaceres.com.br **E:** difusora102@difusoracaceres.com.br - **FM:** 102.3MHz — **MT12)** Av Cuiabá 829, Edifício Mikerinos, 12° andar, 78700-090 Rondonópolis ☎66 3425 1070 **W:** radioclubemt.com.br — **MT13)** Rua 28 de Outubro 3391, 78280-000 Mirassol d'Oeste ☎65 3241 1288 **W:** difusoramirassol. com.br **E:** contato@difusoramirassol.com.br — **MT14)** Av. Governador Júlio Campos, 3111, Jardim Glória, 78140-400 Várzea Grande ☎65 3682 2525 **W:** industrial1070.com.br **E:** radioindustrial@industrial1070. com.br — **MT15)** Rua Zulmira Canavarros 285, 78005-390 Cuiabá — **MT16)** Rua 2 No 32, 78175-000 Poconé — **MT17)** Rua aracuai 1105, 78575-000 Juara ☎66 3556 1316 **W:** radiotucunare.com.br **E:** contato@radiotucunare.com.br — **MT18** Rua João do Padro Arantes 95S, 78300-000 Tangará da Serra ☎65 3326 2080 **W:** radiotangara. com.br — **MT19)** Av T Neves 1682, 78500-000 Colíder ☎66 3541 1233 **W:** radioeducadoracolider.com.br **E:** educadoralider@hotmail. com — **MT20)** Travessa Pref Alexandrina Gomes 87, 78600-000 Barra do Garças ☎65 3401 6155 **W:** difusora720.com.br — **MT21)** Rua Criciúma 165, 78890-000 Sorriso ☎66 3544 2595 **W:** radiosorriso. com.br **E:** radiosorriso@radiosorriso.com.br — **MT22)** Praça Edgar de Araujo, (⬛ CP40) 78430-000 Nortelândia ☎65 3346 1729 — **MT23)** Av Mato Grosso 133, 78690-000 Nova Xavantina ☎65 3438 1218 **W:** Facebook: R.Nova Xavantina — **MT24)** Rua 6 No, Manoel D Sobrino 498, 78300-000 Tangará da Serra ☎65 3326 3131 **W:** radiopioneira. com.br — **MT27)** Av Mario Correa 350, 78790-000 Itiquira ☎65 3491 1070 **W:** radiodifusora1080.com.br **E:** contato@radiodifusora1080.com. br — **MT28)** Rua 01, 600, Bairro ZH3-00|, 78525-000 Matupá ☎66 3595 1144 **W:** cidade770.com.br **E:** radiocidade@vsp.com.br — **MT29)** Rua das Gravioeas 52, (⬛ C.P. 509) 78550-116 Sinop ☎66 3517 3550 **W:** rtvmais.com.br — **MT30)** Avenida Luiz Barbosa esq. c/ Sete de Setembro No 477, 78285-000 São José dos Quatro Marcos ☎65 3251 1062 **W:** radiojornalam570.com.br — **MT31)** Rua 6, s/n, Jardim Eldorado, 78400-000 Diamantino ☎65 3366 1000 **W:** radioparecis690am.com. br **E:** contato@radioparecis690am.com.br — **MT32)** Rua Cipriano Curvo s/n, (⬛ CP 29) 78195-000 Chapada dos Guimarães ☎65 3301 2525 **W:** naturezaam.com.br **E:** contato@naturezaam.com.br — **MT33)** Av Roberto Valdecir Brinante 99, 78435-000 São José do Rio Claro ☎66 3386 2216 **W:** sj.radiofloresta.com.br **E:** contato@radiofloresta.com. br — **MT34)** Rua U-2, s/n, Canteiro Central, 78580-000 Alta Floresta **W:** af.radiofloresta.com.br **E:** contato@radiofloresta.com.br — **MT35)** Rua Jovino Lopes, 1292, 2° andar, Santa Maria Bertila, 78760-000 Guiratinga ☎66 3431 2002 **W:** radiorgbam.com — **MT36)** Rua Joaquim Nabuco 450, 78260-000 Araputanga ☎65 3261 1460 **W:** radioarcoiris. com.br **E:** arcoir@terra.com.br — **MT37)** Av São Paulo 1440, 78250-000 Pontes e Lacerda ☎65 3266 1809 **W:** radiojornal930.com.br — **MT38)** Rua do Burtis s/n, 78520-000 Guarantã do Norte ☎66 3552 1114 **W:** Facebook: Radio Enauan — **MT41)** Rua do Comercio, 1155, Castelândia, 78850-000 Primavera do Leste ☎66 3496 1414 — **MT42)** Rotary Internacional 26, 78530-000 Peixoto de Azeveda ☎66 3575 2842 **W:** continental1530.com.br **E:** radiocontinental1530@gmail.com — **MT45)** Rua Potiguaras, 809 - Centro Edifico Santa Fé, 2° andar, (⬛ C.P. 227), 78800-000 Jaciara ☎66 3461 1966 **W:** radioxavantes.com.br **E:** radioxavantes@gmail.com — **MT64)** Campo Novo de Parecis **W:** radioparecisam.com.br — **MT65)** Av Catselo Branco 341, 78390-000 Barra do Bugres ☎65 9978 5368 **W:** radioativaam.com **E:** ativaam@gmail.com — **MT66)** Rua Santos 1724, 78840-000 Campo Verde ☎66 5566 3419 — **W:** continental96fm.com.br - **FM:** 96.3 MHz
**PA00) PARÁ**
**PA01)** Av Araguaia 247, 68551-000 Redenção — **PA02)** Manoel Umbuzeiro, 1456 -Altos Centro, 68371-180 Altamira ☎93 9171 0908 **W:** radiorruralaltamira.no.comunidades.net **E:** radiorruralaltamira@hotmail.com — **PA03)** Av Almirante Barroso, 2190 3° andar, Marco, 66095-000 Belém 📠91 3084 0112 **W:** radioclubedopara.com.br **E:** timaocampeao@radioclubedopara.com.br — **PA04)** Av São Sebastião 622-A Bloco A, 68005-090 Santarém ☎93 3523 1066 📠93 3523 2685 **W:** radiorruraldesantarem.com.br **E:** edilrural@gmail.com — **PA05)** Av. Juscalino Kubitschek Oliveira 3975, 68540-000 Conceição do Araguaia ☎94 3421 1576 **W:** radioregionaldoaraguaia.com.br — **PA06)** Praça dos Notáveis 1006, 68400-000 Cametá ☎91 3781 1495 — **PA07)** Rodovia BR-316 Km 58, 68742-190 Castanhal Grande — **PA08)** Travessa Campos Sales 370, 68600-280 Belém ☎91 4005 4400 **W:** supermarajoara. com.br **E:** contato@supermarajoara.com.br - **FM:** 100.9MHz — **PA09)** Travessa Vileta 2193, 66093-380 Belém ☎91 3344 4718 **W:** boasnovas. net **E:** marketing@boasnovas.net — **PA10)** Av Brás de Aguiar, 351,

Nazaré, 66035-395 Belém ☎91 3213 1540 **W:** radioliberal.com.br – **PA11)** Tv. Cap 75, 68801-970 Breves ☎91 3783 1269 – **PA12)** Rua 13 de Mayo s/n, 68600-000 Bragança ☎91 3425 1774 **W:** fundacaoeducadora.com.br – **FM:** 106.7MHz –**PA13)** Av Mendonça Furtado, 1481, Santa Clara, 68005-100 Santarém **W:** rtvpontanegra.com.br **E:** am890@rtvpontanegra.com.br ☎93 3523 3348 – **PA14)** Av Coronel Monfredo 42, 68820-000 São Sebastião da Boa Vista **(PA16)** Av Almirante Barroso 735, 66093-020 Belém ☎91 4005 7700 **W:** portalcultura.com.br - **FM:** 93.7MHz – **PA17)** Rod. Transamazonica Km, 4 Rua das TV´s, Folha Industrial Qd. 05 Lt 06, 68507-765 Marabá ☎94 3322 2200 – **PA18)** Rodovia Transamazonica Km 01, 68180-010 Itaituba – **PA19)** Rua Lauro Sodré 730, 68456-000 Tucuruí ☎94 3787 1288 **W:** sistemafloresta.com.br – **PA20)** Av Afonso Pena, 25, Aeroporto Velho, 68005-390 Santarém ☎93 3523 5114 **E:** tvsantarem@hotmail.com – **PA21)** Av Xingu s/n, 68555-010 Xinguara ☎94 3426 1008 **W:** radioxinguaraam.com.br **E:** radioxinguara@hotmail.com – **PA22)** Travessa Dom Floriano 330, 68250-000 Óbidos ☎93 3547 1966 – **PA24)** Travessa 18 No 1863, entre 4 e 5 ruas, 68870-000 Soure ☎91 3741 1248 **W:** Facebook: R.Guarany do Marajó – **PA25)** Av Marcionilo Alves 537, 68780-000 Vigia ☎91 3731 1015 **W:** radiomorenobraga.com.br – **PA26)** Av.Fernando Guilhon, 358 Bela Vista, 68180-000 Itaituba ☎93 3518 4169 **W:** radioclubedeitaituba.com.br **E:** radioclube@hotmail.com – **PA27)** Rua Rui Barbosa 153, 68625-000 Paragominas ☎91 3729 3333 – **PA28)** Travessa sete de setembro com a Rua Visconde do Rio Branco, 68200-000 Alenquer ☎93 9175 6458 **W:** radioximango.com.br **E:** radioximango@hotmail.com – **PA29)** Rodovia Transamazônica s/n Km 04, 68502-290 Marabá ☎94 3322 4838 **W:** radioclubemaraba.com.br – **PA30)** Rodovia BR-010 Km 1409, Industrial, 68660-000 São Miguel do Guamá ☎91 8022 0000 **W:** http//radioguama.com **E:** direcao.radioguama@gmail.com – **PA32)** Rodovia BR-316 KM 11 3528, São João, 67200-000 Marituba ☎91 3323 3059 **W:** novotempobelem.org.br **E:** belemnovotempo@hotmail.com – **PA33)** Av Antonio Marques Ribeiro 242, 68380-000 São Felix do Xingu ☎91 4351 1243 – **PA34)** Av Bertoldo Costa, 68710-000 Maracanã – **PA56)** Rua do Contorno s/n, 68746-475 Castanhal ☎91 3711 0053 **W:** radioparanaense.com.br **E:** contato@radioparaense.com.br

**PB00) PARAÍBA**
**PB01)** Rua Pres. João Pessoa 07,Centro, 58800-000 Sousa ☎83 3521 2197 **W:** portalprogresso.com – **PB02)** Rua Justino Bezerra 41, 58900-000 Cajazeiras ☎83 3531 1236 **W:** radioaltopiranhas.com.br **E:** altopiranhas@uol.com.br – **PB03)** Rua Padre Manoel Otaviano 340, 58970-000 Conceição ☎83 3453 2656 **W:** radioeducadoradeconceicao.com **E:** radioeducadoradeconceicao@hotmail.com – **PB04)** Rua Presidente Epitácio Pessoa 242, 58700-020 Patos ☎83 3421 3884 **W:** radiopanati.com.br - **FM:** 93.9 MHz – **PB05)** Rod PB 075 s/n km 1,25, Zona Rural 58200-000 Guarabira **W:** Facebook: R.Cultra AM 790 – **PB06)** Praça Pres Epitácio Pessoa 167, 58755-000 Princesa Isabel ☎83 3457 2183 **W:** radioprincesa970.com **E:** radioprincesaisabel@bol.com.br – **PB07)** Rua Joao Pessoa 313 1° andar, Campina Grande ☎83 3349 2101🖳83 3341 3613 **W:** radiocaturite.com.br **E:** radiocaturite@radiocaturite.com.br – **PB08)** Rua Coronel Juvêncio Cameiro 160, (CP 20) 58900-000 Cajazeiras ☎83 3531 4530 **W:** radioscajazeiras.com.br **E:** radiocajazeiras@hotmail.com - **FM:** 94.5 MHz – **PB09)** Av D.Pedro II s/n, Torre, (C.P 1089, 58001-970) 58040-440 João Pessoa ☎83 3218 7900 **W:** radiotabajara.pb.gov.br **E:** redacaotabajara@gmail.com – **PB12)** Av Pedro II 523,, 58013-420 João Pessoa ☎83 3216 5044 **W:** correiosat.com.br – **PB13)** Rua das Trincheiras 198, 58011-000 João Pessoa ☎83 3216 5015 – **PB14)** Rua Venâncio Neiva 287, 58400-090 Campina Grande ☎83 3349 2910 – **PB15)** Rua Rui Barbosa 5358700-060 Patos ☎83 3421 3791 **W:** radioespinharas.com.br **E:**radioespinhares@uol.com.br – **PB16)** Rua Antônio Fernandes 25, Mamanguape ☎83 3292 2645 **W:** http//manaam560.blogspot.no **E:** blogradiomana@gmail.com – **PB17)** Rua Dr Carlos Pires 17, São José, 58804-200 Sousa ☎83 3522 1796 **W:** Facebook: R.Jornal 950 AM Sousa **E:** – **PB18)** Rua Monsenhor Valeriano s/n, 58840-000 Pombal ☎83 3431 2277 **W:** maringa98fm.com.br **E:** maringa98fm@hotmail.com - **FM:** 98.7 MHz – **PB19)** Rua Antônio Firmino 344 - Centro, 58187-000 Picuí ☎83 3371 2217 **W:** radiocenecistapicui.com.br – **PB20)** Rua Coronel Jose Fernandes - Centro, 58840-000 Pombal ☎83 3431 3558 **W:** bonsucessoam.com.br **E:** contactos@bonsucessoam.com.br – **PB21)** Rua Conselheiro Henrique 17, 58000-000 João Pessoa ☎83 3249 2020 **W:** portalsanhaua.com.br **E:** radioshanua@hotmail.com – **PB22)** Rua Epitácio Pessoa 8, 58200-000 Guarabira ☎83 3271 1000 **W:** radioruralam850.com.br **E:** contato@radioruralam850.com.br – **PB23)** Rua Monsenhor Palmeira 471, 58135-000 Esperança ☎83 3361 2452**W:** redeesperanca.com.br – **PB24)** Rua Getúlio Vargas 129, 58500-000 Monteiro ☎83 3351 2612 **W:** correiosat.com.br/?radio=9 **E:** elson@sistemacorreio.com.br – **PB25)** Rua Coronel Pedro Targino s/n, 58233-000 Araruna ☎83 3373 1102 **W:** radioserranadeararuna.com.br/ **E:**radioserrana@gmail.com or radioserranaam@hotmail.com – **PB26)** Rod. PB 105, km 33, Anel do Brejo, 58220-000 Bananeiras ☎83 3363

2488 **W:**radiointegracaodobrejo.com.br **E:**radioinetgracao@hotmail.com – **PB27)** Rua Gouveia Nobrega 34, 58155-000 Soledade ☎83 3383 1229 – **PB28)** Rua João Sabiá 56, 58540-000 Sumé ☎83 3372 1089 **W:** radiocidadesume.com **E:** contato@radiocidadedesume.com.br - **FM:** 89 MHz – **PB29)** Praça Frei Martinho s/n, 1° andar, 58700-100 Patos ☎83 3421 3704 **W:** radiosertaoam.com.br **E:** marketing@radiosertaoam.com.br - **FM:** 102.9MHz – **PB30)** Rua Cel Guimarães 56, 58900-000 Cajazeiras ☎83 3531 3715 **W:** oeste1000.com.br **E:** radiooesteam@hotmail.com – **PB31)** Joao Pessoa – **PB32)** Rua Epitácio Pessoa 184, 58397-000 Areia ☎63 3362 2423 **W:** Facebook: Radio Jardim Da Borborema Am **E:** germanosoaresbrasil@hotmail.com – **PB34)** Av Ananias Conserva 18, 58780-000 Itaporanga ☎83 3451 3879 **W:** correiosat.com.br

**PE00) PERNAMBUCO**
**PE01)** Lotm Bela Vista, s/n, Heliopolis, ☎87 3762 2211 55290-000 Garanhuns – **PE02)** Rua Caramuru, 72, Santo Amaro, 81 3221-000 Recife ☎81 3221 6767 **W:** am.redebrasiloficial.com.br**E:**onlineredebrasil@gmail.com – **PE03)** Av Joaquim Nabuco, 322, São Crístovão,56503-150 Árcoverde ☎87 3821 0664 **MSN:** cardealam@hotmail.com – **PE04)** Rua Vigário Joaquim Pinto 721 al 12, 55700-000 Limoeiro ☎81 3628 9733 **W:** radiojornal.com.br **E:** programacao@radiojornal.com.br – **PE05)** Vila Conceição BR 317km 21.7, 56280-000 Araripina ☎87 3873 1366 **W:** radiograndeserra.com.br/am/ - **FM:** 87.9 & 94MHz – **PE06)** Av Sete de Setembro, s/n, Km 02, 56302-060 Petrolina ☎87 3861 4744 **W:** granderioam.com.br **E:** granderioam@uol.com.br – **PE07)** Rua do Veiga, 600, Santo Amaro, 50040-915 Recife ☎81 3412 4432 **W:** radioclubepe.com.br – **PE08)** Praça Maria Auxiliadora 205, 56302-335 Petrolina ☎87 3862 1522 **W:** am730.com.br – **PE09)** Rua Capitão Lima, 250, Santo Amaro, 50040-080 Recife ☎81 3413 6110 **W:** radiojornal.com.br **E:** programacao@radiojornal.com.br – **PE10)** Av.Norte, 68, Santo Amaro, 50040-200 Recife ☎81 3423 4000 🖳81 3423 8533 **W:** tvu.ufpe.br – **PE11)** Av Pres Kennedy, 3092, Peixinhos, 53260-640 Olinda ☎81 3423 0033 **W:** radiotamandare.com.br **E:** pastores@radiotamandares.com.br – **PE12)** Rua da Conceição, 16/22 2° andar, 55000-000 Caruaru ☎81 2103 1170 **W:** liberdade.com.br **E:** programacaoam@liberdade.com.br – **PE13)** Av Padre Rocha s/n, 55810-000 Carpina – **PE14)** Av Maria Emília Cavalcanti, 570, Bairro, 55870-000 Timbaúba ☎81 3631 2229 **W:** princesaserrana.com.br **E:** contato@princesaserrana.com.br – **PE15)** Rua Duarte Coelho, 240, Santa Tereza, 53010-010 Olinda ☎81 3444 7855 **W:** radioolindaam.com.br **E:** comercial@radioolindaam.com.br – **PE16)** C.P 88, 55001-970 Caruaru **W:** radiojornal.com.br **E:** programacao@radiojornal.com.br – **PE17)** Av Presidente Kennedy, 3092, Peixinhos, 53260-640 Olinda ☎81 3444 9499 **W:** radiorelogio1120am.com.br **E:** contato@radiorelogio1120am.com.br – **PE18)** Rua Rádio Cultura Nordeste. 1130, Indianópolis, 55026-690 Caruaru ☎81 37211130 **W:** radiocultura1130.com.br **E:** jornalismo@radiocultura1130.com.br – **PE19)** Rua Prefeito José Joaquim Silva, 50 an 2, Luminária, 55602-150 Vitória de Santo Antão ☎81 3523 2003 – **PE20)** Av. Rui Barbosa, 1236, Heliopólis 55293-300 Garanhuns ☎87 3762 7244 **W:** radiojornal.ne10.uol.com.br – **PE21)** Rua Coronel Urbano Ribeiro de Sena, 956, Água Fria, 52221-000 Recife ☎55 3444 2562 **W:** radiocapibaribe.com.br **E:** contato@radiocapibaribe.com.br – **PE22)** Rua Radio Guarany, Nova Tiúma, 54727-160 Sao Lourenço da Mata ☎81 3485 1322 **W:** radioguarany.com.br **E:** falecom@radioguarany.com.br – **PE23)** Rua Pajussara, 225, Tejipio, 50920-120 Recife ☎81 3252 5868 **W:** radionovasdepaz.com.br/novasdepaz – **PE24)** Av F Pessoa de Queiróz s/n, 55200-000 Pesqueira **W:** radiojornal.com.br – **PE25)** Rodovia BR101 Sul, s/n km 117, Newton Carneiro, 55540-000 Palmares ☎81 3662 1288 **W:**rcpalmares.com.br **E:** rcpalmares@yahoo.com.br – **PE26)** Rua Inocôncio Gomes Andrade, 619, Nossa Sra de Penha, 56912 440 Serra Talhada ☎87 3831 1700 **W:** radioavozdosertao.com.br – **PE27)** Rua 3 de Maio, s/n - Centro, 56800-000 Afogada da Ingazeira ☎87 3838 1213 **W:** radiopajeu.com.br **E:** radiopajeu@radiopajeu.com.br – **PE28)** Rua Agamenom Magalhães 271, 55750-000 Surubim ☎81 3634 1448 **W:** radiosurubimam.com.br – **PE29)** Rua Siquira Campos 1 2° andar, 55150-000 Belo Jardim ☎81 3726 1489 **W:** bituryam.com **E:** bituryam@hotmail.com – **PE30)** Rua Antônio F Soares, s/n, Nossa Sra de Fátima 56000-000 Salgueiro ☎87 3871 0471 **W:** asabrancaam.com – **PE31)** Tv José Paulo 16, 56700-999 São José do Egito ☎87 3844 1081 **W:** radiocultura1320.com.br**E;** radiocultura1320@yahoo.com.br – **PE32)** Praça Duque de Caxias 818, 55900-000 Goiana – **PE33)** Av Fernando Bezerra 1123, 56200-000 Ouricuri ☎87 3874 1559 **W:** voluntariosdapatriaam.com.br – **PE34)** Rua Maria Santina, 200, Bela Vista, 55190-000 Santa Cruz do Capibaribe ☎81 3731 4033 **W:** radiovaleam.br **E:** radio.vale.am@hotmail.com – **PE35)** Av Coronel Trapia s/n, 56440-000 Belém de São Francisco ☎87 3876 1105 **W:** radioeducadoradebelem.br **E:** educadoradebelem@yahoo.com.br – **PE36)** Rd Luis Gonzaga km 81 s/n, 55640-000 Gravatá (C.P 64, 55641-970) ☎81 3533 4709 **W:** cancaonova.com or blog.cancaonova.com/gravata **E:** radiogravata@cancaonova.com –

**PE37)** Rodovia PE 218 km 46, 654, Lagoa do Jacu, 55330-000 Bom Conselho ☎87 3771 1231 📠87 3771 1262 **W:** radiopapacaca.com.br **E:** atendimentopapacaca@gmail.com – **PE41)** Comunidade Restauração Casa-Mae, 55000-000 Caruaru ☎81 3728 8255 **W:** comunidadecr. blogspot.no **E:** radiorestauracao_am1590@hotmail.com

**PI00) PIAUÍ**
**PI01)** Av Professor João Menezea, 64770-000 São Raimundo Nonato ☎89 3582 1497 📠89 3582 1649 **W:** radioserradacapivara.com.br **E:** capivara550@yahoo.com.br – **PI02)** Rua Alvaro Mendes 972, 64000-060 Teresina – **PI03)** Rua Taumaturgo de Azevedo 995, 64100-000 Barras – **PI04)** Av Valter Alencar, 2120, Monte Castelo, 64076-410 Teresina ☎86 2107 6640 – **PI07)** Praça Coronel Orlando Carvalho 400, 64500-000 Oeiras 89 3462 1200 – **PI08)** Av Valter Alencar, 2021, Monte Castelo, 64019-625 Teresina ☎86 3216 5056 **W:** fundacaoantares. org **E:** antres@fundacaoantares.org – **PI09)** Rua Coronel Joaquim Balduino, 40, Bomba, 64600-000 Picos ☎89 3422 1989 – **PI10)** Rua 24 de Janeiro Sul 150, 64001-230 Teresina ☎86 2107 8121 **W:** radiopioneira.am.br **E:** jornalismopioneira@gmail.com – **PI12)** Rua Profesor Bem 712, 64260-000 Piripiri ☎86 3276 1734 **W:** itamaratyam. com.br– **PI13)** Rua Professor Magalhães, 4190, Recanto das Palmares, 64045-750 Teresina ☎86 3232 5411 **W:** portaldifusora.com – **PI14)** Av Mathias Olimpico s/n, 64400-000 Amarante ☎86 3292 1129 – **PI15)** Rua Barão Rio Branco 314, 64860-000 Uruçuí ☎89 3544 1328 – **PI16)** Rua Clementino Ribeiro 56 2° andar, 64800-000 Floriano ☎89 3522 1207 **W:**difusorafloriano.com.br – **PI17)** Av Des Amaral. 2616, 64980-000 Corrente – **PI18)** Rua Clementino Ribeiro, 187, Sambaida Veklha, 64800-000 Floriano ☎89 3522 1504 **W:** radiosantaclara. com.br **E:** radiosantaclara@veloxmail.com.br – **PI19)** Rua Sabino Paulo 696, 64760-000 São João do Piauí ☎89 3483 1317 – **PI20)** Pc Independencia 1, 64290-000 Altos ☎86 3262 1212 – **PI21)** Rua Arcenio Santos 555, 64900-000 Bom Jesus ☎89 3562 1525 – **PI22)** Praca Sto. Antônio, 1019, ap 101, Centero, 64200-361 Parnaíba ☎86 3322 3550 **W:** Facebook: R. Globo Parnaiba AM 550 – **PI23)** Rua Leonidas Melo 867, 64100-000 Barras ☎86 3242 1590 – **PI24)** Pc Presidente Castelo Branco 161, 64750-000 Paulistana ☎89 3487 1373 **W:** http//radioingazeira.com.br – **PI25)** Av. São Vicente Paula s/n, 64240-000 Piracuruca ☎86 3343 1107 **W:** amsetecidades940. blogspot.no – **PI26)** Av José de Deus Lacerda 584, 64130-000 Miguel Alves – **PI27)** Tv Benedito da C Alencar, 78 - Centro, 64575-000 Jaicós ☎89 3457 1610 – **PI28)** Rua Corinto Andrade 460, 64255-000 Pedro II ☎86 3271 1186 **W:** radiocruzeiroam.com.br **E:** radiocruzeiroam@ hotmail.com – **PI29)** Praça da Independência 69, 64325-000 Elesbão Veloso ☎86 3285 1276 – **PI30)** Rua Joaquim Baldoíno, 48, Bomba, 64600-000 Picos ☎89 3422 2512 – **PI31)** Av João Ferreira 199, 64460-000 Agua Branca ☎86 3282 1344 **W:** radio1dejulho.blogspot.com. br **E:** radio1dejulho@hotmail.com – **PI32)** Rua Hugo Napoleão 940, 64110-000 José de Freitas ☎86 3264 1407 – **PI33)** Av Antonio Freire 606, 64340-000 Castelo do Piauí ☎86 3274 1106 – **PI34)** Rua Pedro II, 249, 64330-000 São Miguel do Tapuio ☎86 3249 1101 – **PI35)** Rua Coronel Anibal Martins 481, 64300-000 Valença do Piauí ☎89 3465 1244 – **PI36)** Rua Matias Gomes 510, 64700-000 Simplício Mendes ☎89 3482 1105 – **PI37)** Rua Coronel Narciso 728, 64120-000 União ☎86 3265 1411 – **PI38)** Av Padre Joaquim Nonato 517, 64390-000 Demerval Lobão ☎86 3260 1158 – **PI39)** Rua Coronel Messeas Melo 430, 64190-000 Batalha ☎86 3347 1314 – **PI41)** Av Deputado Paulo Ferraz, 1940 2° andar, Beira Rio, 64075-535 Teresina ☎86 3194 3034 **W:** cbnteresina.com.br **E:** redacao@cbnteresina.com.br – **PI42)** Rua Joaquim Rodrigues Macedo 245, 64680-000 Padre Marcos ☎89 3431 1137 – **PI43)** Rua Sete de Setembro 471, 64160-000 Luzilândia ☎86 3393 1429 **W:** radiovaledoparnaiba.com **E:** radiorvpam@hotmail.com – **PI44)** Praça da Bandeira 91, 64500-000 Oeiras ☎89 3462 1482 – **PI46)** Rua Coronel José Fortes 549, 64180-000 Esperantina ☎86 3383 1245 – **PI47)** Rodovia BR-343 s/n, 64290-000 Altos ☎86 3262 1234 – **PI49)** Rua Padre Madeira 191,64600-000 Picos ☎89 3422 1900

**PR00) PARANÁ**
**PR01)** Rua Quintino Bocaiuva 41, 86020-100 Londrina ☎43 3344 2038 **W:** radiolondrina.com.br **E:** radiolondrina@onda.com – **PR02)** Rua XV do Novembro 7466, 85010-000 Guarapuava ☎42 3623 6423 📠42 3723 7269 **W:** centralcultura.com.br - **FM:** 93.7MHz – **PR03)** Av Brasil, 1720(✉C.P 10, 85892-970), 85892-000 Santa Helena ☎45 3268 1212 **W:** radiograndelago.com.br **E:** grandelago@rgl.com.br – **PR04)** Rua Humberto de Alencar Castelo Branco, 590, Cristo Rei, 82530-195 Curitiba ☎41 3268 6550 **W:** difusoraam590.com.br – **PR05)** Praça de Café N° 1100, 86900-000 Jandaia do Sul ☎43 3432 9797 **W:** radiojandaia.com.br **FM:** 103.3MHz – **PR06)** Rua Julio Perneta, 695, Mercês, 80810-110 Curitiba ☎41 3331 7400 **W:** e-parana.pr.gov.br - **FM:** 97.1 MHz – **PR07)** Rua 7 de Setembro 520, 85960-000 Marechal Cândido Rondón ☎45 3284 1212 **W:** radioeducadora.com.br **E:** educadora@rondonet.com.br – **PR08)** Rod João Carlos Strass, s/n, Heimtal, 86084-610 Londrina ☎43 3339 6244 **W:** superradioeuseamor. com.br – **PR09)** Rua António Costa, 529, Bela Vista Alegre, 80820-020

☎41 3240 7500 **W:** radiobandab.com.br **E:** portal@radiobandab.com. br – **PR10)** Rua Lord Lovat 497, 87600-000 Nova Esperança ☎44 3252 4533 **W:** cancaonova.com **E:** rede@cancaonova.com – **PR11)** Rua Oyapock, 649, Cristo Rei, 80050-450 Curitiba ☎41 3218 5800 **W:** radioglobocuritiba.com.br **E:** contato@radioglobocuritiba.com.br – **PR12)** Rua Saldanha Marinho, 1581 Apto B, Ventro, 85010-290 Guarapuava ☎42 3035 7010 **W:** radiocaciqueam.com **E:** contat@ radiocaciqueam.com – **PR13)** Rua Sergipe, 843, sala 05, 86010-360 Londrina ☎43 3306 1105 **W:** radiodifusoradelondrina.com.br **E:** contato@radiodifusoralondrina.com.br – **PR15)** Av Paraná, 1885, Boa Vista, 82510-000 Curitiba ☎41 3251 2410 **W:**radioevangelismo.com.br **E:** marumby@terra.com.br – **PR16)** Av. Capitão Indio Bandeira, 1400 5° Andar - Centro Empresarial Antares, 87300-005 Campo Mourão ☎44 3017 0013 **W:** Facebook: R.Objetiva – **PR17)** Av 19 de Agosto 522 1° andar, 87360-000 Goioerê ☎44 3522 7777 📠44 3522 1162 **W:** radiogoioere.com.br **E:** rgam@goioere.com.br – **PR18)** Av. Maranahão 62, Shopping Urbano 2° Andar, Sala 21, 87200-000 Cianorte ☎📠44 3629 1514 **W:** radioportavoz.com.br **E:** radioportavoz@irapida.com.br – **PR19)** Rua Frei Everaldo 3835, 85560-000 Chopinzinho ☎46 3242 1495 **W:** radiochopinzinho.com.br **E:** radio@radiochopinzino.com.br – **PR20)** Av D.Pedro I, 1596, Jardim São Silvestre, 86300-000 Cornélia Procópio ☎43 3524 1266 **W:** redecartario.com.br – **PR21)** Rua Francisco Rosa e Silva, 28, Parque Presidente, 85852-250 Foz do Iguaçu ☎45 3026 8020 **W:** radioculturafoz.com.br **E:** jornalismocultura@foz. net – **PR22)** Rodovia do Xisto BR 476 Km 20 No 2018, 83700-000 Araucária ☎41 3642 1010 **W:** radioiguassu.com.br **E:** radioiguassu@ radioiguassu.com.br – **PR23)** Rua Coronel Manoel Ferreira Bello 64, 85530-000 Clevelândia ☎46 3252 1286 **W:** rdprogresso.com.br **E:** redacao@rdprogreso.com.br – **PR24)** Rua Mchado de Assis, 25, Jd. Shangri-lá, 86070-620 Londrina ☎43 3032 1500 **W:** cbnlondrina.com. br **E:** cbnlondrina@cbnlondrina.com.br - **FM:** 93.5MHz – **PR25)** Av. Euclides Cunha 455, Zona 04, 87015-180 Maringá ☎44 3225 8050 **W:**novainga.com.br **E:**comercial@pingafogo.com.br – **PR27)** Praça Marechal Floriano Peixoto 581, 3° andar, (C.P 090 84001-970) 84010-910 Ponta Grossa ☎42 3028 0042 📠42 3222 3566 **W:** radiosantana. com.br **E:** comercial@radiosantana.com.br – **PR28)** Av Largo São Vicente de Paulo 1085, 85900-215 Toledo ☎45 3055 2841 **W:** radiouniaodetoledo.com.br **E:** contato@radiouniaodetoledo.com.br – **PR29)** Rua Sao Paulo 910, 86808-070 Apucarana ☎43 3423 1100 **W:** novaam.com.br **E:** novaam@uol.com.br – **PR30)** Av Aylton Rodrigues Alves 1189, 86600-000 43 3255 2276 Rolândia **W:** Facebook: R.Cultura de Rolândia **E:** radioculturaderolandia@gmail – **PR31)** Rua Robero Vichinheski, 242, Pilarzinh, 82530-130 Curitiba ☎41 3013 3280 **W:** Facebook: R.Cultura AM 930 – **PR32)** Av XV de Novembro, 462, Sala 05, Zona 01, 87013-230 Maringá ☎44 3041 4960 **W:** radioglobomaringa. com.br **E:** radioglobo@radioglobomaringa.com.br – **PR33)** Rua Dom Bosco, 145, Jd Dom Bosco, 86060-340 Londrina **W:** facebook.com/ radioalvoradalondrina/ **E:** radioalvoradalondrina@gmail.com ☎43 3347 0303 – **PR34)** Rua Santa Catarina 970, 85960-000 Marechal Cândido Rondón ☎45 3284 8080 **W:** radiodifusora.com.br **E:** comercial@radiodifusora.net – **FM:** 95.1 MHz – **PR35)** Rua Araribóia, 1909, Parque Santa Clara,(CP 540) 85505-030 Pato Branco ☎46 2101 2244 **W:** radiocelinauta.com.br **E:** comercial@redecelinauta.com.br – **PR36)** Praça Generoso Marques 90, Galeria Andrade, Ed Claudia 1° andar, 80020-230 Curitiba ☎41 3322 8483 **W:** radiocolombo.com.br **E:** comercial@radiocolombo.com.br – **PR37)** Av Pedro Soccol 542, 85884-000 Medianeira ☎45 3264 1713 **W:** independenciaam.com.br – **PR38)** Rua Paraná 650, 874-000 Cruzeiro do Oeste ☎44 3676 1184 **W:** difusoraregional.com.br – **PR39)** Rua Visconde de Mauá, 123, Jardim Shangrilá, 86070-540 Londrina ☎43 3328 1030 – **PR40)** Rua Ulisses Faria 1077, 83900-000 São Mateus do Sul ☎42 3532 1644 **W:** difusoradoxisto.com.br – **PR41)** Rua Maranhão, 2955, Alto Alegre, 85805-220 Cascavel ☎45 3321 7000 📠45 3226 5565 **W:** cbncascavel. com.br **E:** cantini@cbncascavel.com.br – **PR42)** Praça Senador Corrêa 128 (✉ CP 20548, 81810-980 Curitiba), 80230-130 Curitiba ☎41 3221 6070 **W:** padrereginaldomanzotti.org.br **E:** sas@evangelizarepreciso. com.br - **FM:** 90.9 & 99.5 MHz – **PR44)** Rua Porto Alegre 21, Edifico Scala 1° andar, 85601-480 Francisco Beltrão ☎46 3055 2255**W:** radioeducadorafb.com.br **E:** contato@radioeducadorefb.com.br – **PR45)** Rua Dario Antônio Bordin 313, 84600-000 União da Vitória ☎42 3521 2050 **W:** wale.com.br/radiouniaoam/ **E:** gerente@radiouniaoam. com.br – **PR46)** Av Ivan Ferreira do Amaral 331,85400-000 Guaraniaçu ☎45 3232 1129 **W:** superrg.com.br **E:** comercial@superrg.com.br – **PR48)** Rua Edson Martins, 1935 Esquina c/Avenida Parigot de Souza, 87703-420 Paranavaí ☎44 3423 6565 **W:** culturaparanavai.com.br **E:** am@culturaparanavai.com.br – **PR49)** Rua João Carlos Farias 85, 86300-000 Cornélio Procópio ☎43 3524 2333 **W:** terranativaam.com. br – **PR50)** Av Capitão Índio Bandeira 1400 s 509, 87300-005 Campo Mourão ☎44 3525 1413 **W:** radiocolmeiaam.com.br – **PR51)** Rua das Américas 255, 85550-000 Coronel Vivida ☎46 3232 1142 **W:** portalrvp. com.br **E:** atendimento@radiovicentepallotti.com.br – **PR52)** Av

Higienópolis 2100, 86015-905 Londrina ☎43 3325 2555 **W:** paiquere. com.br **E:** paiquere@paiquere.com.br – **PR53)** Rua Quince de Novembro 2175, 8° andar, 83005-000 São José dos Pinhais ☎40 3058 7404 **W:** radiomais.am.br **E:opec@gruporadiomais.com.br** – **PR54)** Av Cristóvão Colombo 1055, 86990-000 Marialva ☎44 3232 1115 – **PR55)** Praça Manoel Ribas 112, 84165-510 Castro ☎42 3232 0556 **W:** radiocastro.com.br – **PR56)** Rua Machado de Assis 25 , 86070-620 Londrina ☎43 3032 1500 **E:** radiogloblondrina.com.br - **FM:** 90.1 MHz – **PR57)** Av. Sete de Setembro, 3341, Cristo Rei, 80050-315 Curitiba ☎41 3025 5770 **W:** radioatalaiacuritiba.com.br – **PR58)** Rua Raimundo Leonardi 1301, 85900-110 Toledo ☎45 3378 3161 **W:** radioguacu.com. br **E:** radioguacu@uol.com.br – **PR60)** Rua João Negrão 595, 80010-200 Curitiba ☎41 3324 3849 **W:** superradiodeuseamor.com.br – **PR61)** Av Paraná 596, 85887-000 Matelândia ☎45 3262 1140 **W:** radiomatelandia.com.br **E:** radiomatelandia@matelnet.com.br – **PR64)** Rua Cedro 418, 85650-000 Santa Isabel do Oeste ☎46 3542 1239 **W:** radiodanubioazul.com.br **E:** contato@radiodanubioazul.com.br – **PR65)** Rua José Ferreira "Nhô Belo" 262, 86975-000 Mandaguari ☎44 3233 1180 **W:** radioguairaca.com.br **E:** guairaca@bwnet.com.br – **PR66)** Rua Marchal Deodora 1272, 86430-000 Santo Antônio da Platina ☎43 3534 4321 **W:** radioguacaba.com.br **E:** radiofmvaledosol@bol. com.br - **FM:**- 100.5MHz –**PR67)** Rua Pedro Eloy de Souza, 51, Alto, 82820-130 Curitiba ☎41 3367 3663 **W:** grpcom.com.br/continental – **PR68)** Rua Rio Grande do Sul 1110, 85806-010 Cascavel ☎45 3224 2717 **W:** radioglobocascavel.com.br **E:** radiocidade@certto.com.br – **PR69)** Rua Ponta Grossa 1682 1° Andar (✉ C.P. 71), 85601-600 Francisco Beltrão ☎46 3524 2676 **W:** seleski.com.br **E:** seleski@ seleski.com.br – **PR70)** Av Pedro Taques, 1864, Jd Alvorada 87033-000 Maringá ☎44 3267 3000 **W:** radioatalaia.com.br **E:** radioatalaiamaringa@hotmail.com – **PR71)** Rua XV de Novembro 591, 84010-020 Ponta Grossa ☎42 3028 1300 **W:** cbnpg.com.br **E:** cbnpg@ cbnpg.com.br – **PR72)** Rua Ana Berta Rosekamp, 940, Jardim Rosekamp, 81530-250 Curitiba ☎41 3266 1320 **W:** radiotropicalgospel. com.br – **PR73)** Rua Ébio Ferraz de Carvalho, 699, Jardim Montecatine, 86031-720 Londrina ☎43 3378 2100 **W:** radiobrasilsul.com.br **E:** comercial@radiobrasilsul.com.br – **PR74)** Rua TV Silvério Carneiro, 3 - Centro, 84220-000 Cidade Sengés ☎43 3535 1144 – **PR75)** Rua Doutor Camargo 5152, 87502-010 Umuarama ☎44 3622 5033 **W:** radioinconfidenciaam.com.br **E:**nova@radioinconfidenciaam.com.br – **PR76)** Rua Exp Adir Jorge 511, 83880-000 Rio Negro ☎47 3642 3969 – **PR77)** Rua Flamingos 357, 86701-390 Arapongas ☎42 3252 0570 **W:** cultura1340.com.br– **PR78)** Av Paul Harris, 50, Conjunto Paraiso, 86220-000 Assaí ☎43 3262 1367 **W:** redeterranativa.com.br **E:** radioliderm@hotmail.com.br – **PR79)** Rua Pedro Alvares Cabral 1574, 87560-000 Iporã ☎44 3652 1582 – **PR80)** Av. Marechal Floriano Peixa, 4809, Vila Hauer, 81610-150 Curitiba ☎41 3091 1370 **W:** blog. cancaonova.com/curitiba **E:** radiocuritiba@cancaonova.com – **PR81)** Rua Paraiba 168, 86930-000 São João do Ivaí ☎43 3477 1117 **E:** radioeducadora1180@gmail.com – **PR82)** Av.Mauá, 1988, Vila Operária, 87050-020 Maringa ☎44 3220 8061 - **FM:** 102.5MHz – **PR83)** Av Bertino Warmling 1110 sala 02, 85670-000 Salto do Lontra ☎46 3538 1320 **W:** rinet.com.br **E:** ricliente@slnet.com.br – **PR84)** Rua Pref Hugo Cabral 192 , 86020-110 Londrina ☎43 3373 5500 **W:** radioglobolondrina.com.br **E:** radioglobolondrina@radioglobolondrina. com.br – **PR85)** Av Dep Ivan Ferreira do Amaral Filho 86, 85301-070 Laranjeiras do Sul ☎42 3635 1120 **W:** radioeducadora1120.com.br **E:** comercial@radioeducadora1120.com.br – **PR86)** Rua Simão Domingues 26, 84550-000 Rebouças ☎42 3457 1150 **W:** alvoradanoar. com.br **E:** comercial@alvoradanoar.com.br – **PR88)** Rua Nicanor do Santos Silva 4465, 87501-120 Umuarama ☎44 3624 4664 **W:** culturaumuarama.com.br – **PR89)** Rua Antônio Lemos 807, 86400-000 Jacarezinho ☎43 3525 0773 **W:** educadora1420.com.br **E:** radio1420@ uol.com.br – **PR90)** Rua Dom Pedro I 420, 85710-000 Santo Antônio do Sudoeste ☎46 3563 1541 **W:** radioentrerios1170.com.br **E:** contato@ radioentrerios1170.com.br – **PR91)** Rua Mato Grosso 2229, 85812-020 Cascavel ☎45 3220 1717 **W:** radiocolmeia.com.br **E:** radiocolmeia@ brturbo.com – **PR92)** Rua V Pref V Pref Reginaldo G Nocera 335, 84261-020 Telêmaco Borba ☎42 3272 9000 **W:** radiocapitaldopapel.com.br – **PR93)** Rua Vicente Inácio Filho 241, 86360-000 Bandeirantes ☎43 3542 3233 **W:** radiocabiuna.com.br – **PR95)** Rua Mal Deodoro da Fonseca 717, 85650-000 Altônia ☎44 3659 3444 **W:** radiorainha.com. br – **PR96)** Rua Prof Cleto 281, 83203-070 Paranaguá ☎41 3423 4322 **W:** difusoraam1460.com.br **E:** administracao@difusoraam1460.com.br – **PR97)** Rua Coronel Dulcido 1101, 84010-908 Ponta Grossa ☎42 3225 2144 ▤3222 7115 **W:** centraldoparana.com.br **E:** central@ centraldoparana.com.br – **PR99)** Rua Jesuino Alves da Rocha Loures 1764, 85555-000 Palmas ☎46 3263 9000 **W:** radioclubeamfm.com.br **E:** comercial@radioclubeamfm.com.br – **PR100)** Rua Acácio Nunes 1065, 85980-000 Guaíra ☎44 3642 2068 **W:** radioguaira.com.br **E:** radioguaíra@gmail.com – **PR101)** Rua dos Andradas 249, 85640-000 Ampére ☎46 3547 1236 **W:** radioampere.com.br **E:** radioampere@

ampernet.com.br – **PR102)** Av. Belo Horizonte 497, 87900-00 Loanda ☎44 3425 5252 **W:** guadalupeam.com.br **E:** guadelupeam@ guadelupeam.com.br – **PR103)** Rua Nilo Sampaio 531, 84900-000 Ibaiti ☎43 3546 1291 **W:** radioeducadora1470.com **E:** contato@ radioeducadora1470.com – **PR104)** Praça Nossa Senhora do Carmo 99, 85935-000 Assis Chateaubriand ☎44 3528 4477 **W:** radiojornalam. com.br **E:** atendimento@radiojornalam.com.br – **PR105)** Rua Ebano Pereira 157, 85200-000 Pitanga ☎43 3641 1739 **W:** radiopitanga.com. br **E:** radiopitanga@radiopitanga.com.br – **PR106)** Av. Interventor Mnoel Ribas 115, 86730-000 Astorga ☎44 3234 3211 **W:** fmturquesa. com.br - **FM:** 93.9 MHz – **PR108)** Rua João Carlos Farias 85, 86300-000 Cornélio Procópio ☎43 3524 2333 **W:** rc1490.com/ **E:** radiocornelio@ uol.com.br – **PR110)** Avenida Paraná,540, 86925-000 Borrazópolis ☎43 3425 1233 **W:** radionovaera.com.br – **PR111)** Av, São João No. 1952 (✉C.P 121, 84400-970) 84400-000 Prudentópolis ☎42 3446 1547 **W:** radioesperancaam.com.br **E:** radioesperanca810@hotmail. yahoo.com.br – **PR112)** Rua Rouxinol 752, 86703-150 Arapongas ☎43 3055 2133 **W:** radioarapongas.com.br **E:** radioarapongas@uol.com.br – **PR115)** Rua Florianópolis 1636, 85840-000 Céu Azul ☎45 3266 1489 **W:** uniaoam.com.br – **PR116)** Praça Cel. Macado, 10 - Centro, (✉ C.P 55) 83370-000 Antonina ☎41 3432 1362 **W:** serradomaram1520.com **E:** radioserradomar@yahoo.com.br – **PR117)** Av Souza Naves 890, 86870-000 Ivaiporã ☎43 3472 4366 **W:** radiouba.com.br – **PR118)** Rua 1° DE Maio 694, 85950-000 Palotina ☎44 3694 5266 **W:** vivaoeste. com.br **E:** vivaoeste@novaradiocultura.co.br – **PR119)** Rua Dom Pedro II, 1889, Vila Dom Pedro II, 834608-380 Campo Largo ☎41 3392 1111 **W:**radioagapeam.com.br **E:**radioagapeam@brturbo.com.br – **PR120)** Rua Mauá 2518, 85770-000 Realeza ☎46 3543 1030 **W:** radiocluberza. com **E:** radioclube@wln.com.br – **PR121)** Rua Florianópolis, 1813, Zona 02, 87200-000 Cianorte ☎44 3629 1317 **W:** radiocapital990.com.br **E:** radiocapitalam@hotmail.com – **PR122)** Praça Alfredo João Lazzarotto 100, 89490-000 Siqueira Campos ☎43 3571 1588 **W:** radiobomjesus. com.br **E:** bomjesus@hotmail.com – **PR123)** Av. Redife, 434, 85830-970 Formosa do Oeste ☎41 3243 0950 **W:** pioneiraam.com.br **E:** radio@ pioneiraam.com.br – **PR124)** Av Dambros e Piva, 946 85615-000 Marmeleiro ☎46 3525 1183 **W:** cristal.seleski.com.br **E:** radiocristal@ wln.com.br – **PR125)** Av Brasil 502, 85760-000 Capanema ☎46 3552 1584 ▤46 3552 1336 **W:** radiocapanema.com.br **E.** radio@ radiocapanema.com.br – **PR126)** Rua Senador Pinheiro Machado 1536, 85010-100 Guarapuava ☎42 3035 8000 **E:** atalaia@mattosleao.com.br – **PR127)** Rua do Comércio 654, 85660-000 Dois Vizinhos ☎46 3536 3131 **W:** educadoradv.com.br **E:** radio@educadoradv.com.br – **PR129)** Rua Sao Paulo 180, 86380-000 Andirá ☎43 3538 3522 **W:** culturaandira.com.br **E:** comercial@culturaandira.com.br – **PR130)** Rua São Paulo 489, 86840-000 Faxinal ☎43 3461 1291 **W:** radioclubdefaxinal.com.br – **PR131)** Rua Noruega 98, 86182-000 Cambé ☎43 3154 1772 **W:** cidadem770.com.br – **PR132)** Rua Jacaranda 498, 85460-000 Quedas do Iguaçu ☎46 3532 1416 **W:** facebook.com/radiocidadequedas – **PR133)** Praça Marechal Floriano Peixito 108, 84130-000 Palmeira ☎42 3252 3669 **W:** radioipiranga. com.br **E:** radioipiranga@br10.com.br – **PR135)** Av Brasi 740, 84350-000 Ortigueira ☎42 3277 1366 **W:** radioplacar.com.br – **PR136)** Av Maximiliano Vicentin 240, 85270-000 Palmital ☎42 3657 1442 **W:** radiocidadepalmital.com.br **E:** radiopalmital@bol.com.br – **PR137)** Rua Melissa 520, 85410-000 Nova Aurora ☎45 3243 1233 **W:** clubamnovaaurora.com.br **E:** comercial@clubamnovaaurora.com.br – **PR138)** Avenida Brasil 531, 85851-000 Foz do Iguaçu ☎45 3572 2410 **W:** radiofiladelfia.com.br **E:** radioculturamorenafiladelfia@gmail.com – **PR139)** Rua Antônio Costa, 529, Vista Alegere das Mercês, 80820-020 Curitiba ☎41 3240 7000 **W:** radiobandab.com.br **E:** bandabad@ radiobandab.com.br – **PR140)** Rua Urbano Lunardelli 875, 86160-000 Porecatu ☎43 3623 1050 **W:** radiobrotense.com.br **E:** ouvinte@ radiobrotense.com.br – **PR141)** Av Paraná, 220 - Centro, 84470-000 Cândido de Abreu ▤43 3476 1244 **W:** alternativa710.com.br **E:** ralternativa@onda.com.br – **PR142)** Av Santos Dumont 2505, 85301-040 Laranjeiras do Sul ☎42 3635 1755 **W:** radiocampoaberto.com.br **E:** rca@radiocampoaberto.com.br – **PR143)** Av Genoroso Marques 599, 2° andar, 85550-000 Coronel Vivida ☎46 3232 1564 **W:** radiovozdosudoeste.com.br/2011 – **PR144)** Rua Cet San Tiago Dantas 159 , 85560-000 Chopinzinho ☎46 3242 1435 **W:** radiodifusoraamerica. com.br – **PR145)** Av Paraná, 201, Jardim Itajubá, 85857-970 Foz do Iguaçu ☎45 3523 2211 **W:** cbnfoz.com.br **E:** administrativo@cbnfoz. com.br – **PR146)** Av Presidente Kennedy, 170, Norte, 85950-000 Palotina ☎44 3649 0570 **W:** Facebook: R.Continental Palotina **E:** radiocontinentalam@hotmail.com – **PR147)** Av. Minas Gerais 31, 85420-000 Corbélia ☎45 3242 1799 **W:** radiointegracao.net – **PR148)** Rua Farroupilha 80, 2° andar, 85877-000 São Miguel do Iguaçu ☎43 3565 1033 **W:** radiojornalsaomiguel.com.br **E:** rjcomercial@brturbo. com.br – **PR149)** Av Iguaçu 288, 85575-000 São Jorge d'Oeste ☎46 3534 1184 **W:** difusorasaojorge.com.br **E:** radiodifusora1490@hotmail. com – **PR150)** Av Sao Paulo 440, 87320-000 Roncador ☎44 3575 1341

**W:** princesa820.com.br - **FM:** 87.9 MHz – **PR151)** Av Nilza de Oliveira Pipino 4444, 87350-000 Ubiratã ☎44 3543 1133 – **PR152)** Rua Dom Pedro II 1581, 85901-270 Toledo. ☎45 3055 2240 **W:** radiointegracaoam.com.br **E:** radiointegracao@uol.com.br – **PR154)** Rua Sao Vicente, 83, Alto da Gloria, (C.P 20) 87160-000 Mandaguaçu ☎44 3245 3265 **W:** colmeia1170am.com.br **E:** radio@colmeia1170am.com – **PR155)** Rua Rosalvo Petrechem 551, 85200-000 Pitanga ☎42 3646 3366.**W:** radiopoema.com.br **E:** radiopoema@radiopoema.com.br – **PR157)** Av Iguaçu 858, Ed Fabiane, 85585-000 Verê **W:** radiovaledoiguacu.com.br – **PR158)** Av Paraná s/n, 86130-000 Bela Vista do Paraíso ☎43 3242 1818 **W:** nrbr.com.br **E:** br1570@hotmail.com – **PR159)** Rua Telêmaco Carneiro 1060 Ed. Moreira I, sala 4, 84990-000 Arapoti ☎43 3557 2055 **W:** radioarapotiam.com.br **E:** radioarapoti@yahoo.com.br – **PR160)** Av Iguaçu 366, 85790-000 Capitão Leônidas Marques ☎43 3286 1314 **W:** radiohawai.com.br – **PR161)** Rua Antonio Rosa 1170, 86490-000 Ribeirão do Pinhal ☎43 3551 1438 **W:** culturapinhal.com **E:** contat@culturapinhal.com – **PR162)** Rua Vicente Machado, 84570-000 Mallet ☎42 3542 2004 – **PR163)** Rua Marechal Deodoro, 22 - Centro, 85540-000 Mangueirinha ☎46 3243 1541 **W:** radioaraucaria.com.br – **PR164)** Rua São Miguel 577 , 85570-000 São João ☎46 3533 1474 **W:** radiosaojoao.com.br **E:** radiosj@sudonet.com.br – **PR165)** Rua Guarani 829 , 85501-050 Pato Branco ☎46 3225 4000 **W:** radiopatobranco.com.br **E:** ouvinte@radiopatobranco.com.br – **PR166)** Rua Pres Getúlio Vargas 807, Raia, 83206-020 Paranaguá ☎41 3424 2408 **W:** terranativasul.com.br **E:** falecom@terranativasul.com.br – **PR168)** Rua Octaviano Henrique de Carvalho, 2920, Chopar, 83280-000 Guaratuba ☎41 3472 3275 ☎41 3472 3019 **W:** radiolitoranea.com.br **E:** radiolitoranea@gmail.com – **PR169)** Rua Ana Beje, 84300-000 Tibagi ☎42 3275 3247 **W:** radioitay.com.br **E:** radioitay@radioitay.com.br – **PR170)** Av Vice-Prefeito Reginaldo Guedes Nocera, 84260-000 Telêmaco Borba ☎42 3910 1230 **W:** radionovamensagem.com.br – **PR171)** Av Londrina 523, 87111-220 Sarandi ☎44 3042 1090 **W:** banda1am.com.br – **PR173)** Rua Paraná 21, 83540-000 Rio Branco do Sul ☎41 3652 7070 **W:** radiotradicaoam.com.br **E:** comercial@radiotradicaoam.com.br – **PR174)** Rua Parigot de Souza 47, 86740 Pérola d'Oeste ☎46 3556 1048 **W:** radioperola.com.br – **PR179)** Rua Pedro de Oliveira 938, 85440-000 Ubiratã ☎44 3543 1717 **W:** radiodifusoraubirata.com.br **E:** rdifusora@gmail.com – **PR184)** Rua José Carlos Colodel, 306 cj 5, Vila Santa Terezina, 83501-140 Almirante Tamandaré ☎41 3699 6622 **W:** radiobarigui.com.br – **PR185)** Rua Santos Dumont 268, 86400-000 Jacarezinho/ PR ☎43 3525 0877 **W:** radioglobo1550.com.br **E:** contato@radioglobo1550.com.br – **PR186)** Rua Esado Unidas 1768-A, 86181-100 Cambé ☎43 3154 1580 **W:** terranativacambe.com.br **E:** radioterranativacambe@gmail.com – **PR188)** Rua Vicente Inácio Filho, 241, Altos da Vila Maria, (✉ CP 111) 86360-000 Bandeirantes ☎43 3542 3233 ☎43 3542 4730 **W:** radiocabiuna.com.br

**RJ00) RIO DE JANEIRO**

**RJ01)** Rua Visconde Itaboraí, 184, Guaratiba, 23032-500 Niterói ☎21 2556 8131 **W:** ofluminense.com.br – **RJ02)** Rua Costa Rica, 151, Parque Hotel, 28970-000 Araruama ☎22 2665 4119 **W:** radiocostadosol.com.br **E:** contato@radiocostadosol.com.br – **RJ03)** Estrada dos Bandeirantes, 1000, Taquara, 22710-112 Rio de Janeiro ☎21 3412 1175 **W:** radiorelogiofederal.blogspot.no **E:** nossaradiorio@gmail.com – **RJ04)** Av.Erasmo Brage, 118, 11°andar,20020-000 Rio de Janeiro ☎21 2333 2094 **E:** faleconosco@94fm.rj.gov.br - **FM:** 94.1 MHz – **RJ05)** Av. Dr Jefferson Geraldo Bruno, s/n, Paraiso, 27365-015 Resende ☎24 3358 1600 **W:** radioagulhasnegras.com – **RJ06)** Praça Demerval Barbosa Moreira 28, 28610-160 Nova Friburgo ☎22 2523 3034 **W:** radiofriburgoam.com.br **E:** contato@novafriburgoam.com.br – **RJ07)** Rua General Gustavo Cordeiro de Farias, 84, Benfica, 20910-220 Rio de Janeiro ☎21 2567 2000 – **RJ08)** Rua Vinte e Um de Abril, 272 An 4 Sl 413, 28010-170 Campos dos Goytacazes ☎22 2723 8080 **W:** radioabsoluta.com.br – **RJ09)** Rua México 111 slj, 20031-145 Rio de Janeiro ☎21 2220 3656 **W:** redesucesso.com – **RJ11)** Rua de Assembléia, 10/3401, 20011-001 Rio de Janeiro ☎21 3572 0760 ☎21 3572 0770 **W:** radiomanchete.com.br **E:** comercial@radiomanchete.com.br – **RJ12)** Rua da Relação, 18, 12° andar, 20231-110 Rio de Janeiro ☎21 2117-6202 ☎21 2117 6235 **W:** radios.ebc.com.br – **RJ13)** Av Rui Barbosa, 749 3°andar, 27910-361 Macaé ☎22 3311 3145 **W:** radioglobomacae.com.br **E:** comercial@radioglobomacae.com.br – **RJ15)** Rua Prof Eurico Rabelo, s/n, Maracanã¨, 20271-150 Rio de Janeiro ☎21 4002 4190 **W:** radiotamoio.com.br – **RJ16)** Av. Marchal Floriano 114, 20080-002 Rio de Janeiro **W:** boavontade.com.br **E:** superrbv@boavontade.com – **RJ17)** Rua de Relação, 18, 12° andar, 20231 110 Rio de Janeiro ☎21 2117 6202 **W:** radios.ebc.com.br/nacionalrioam – **RJ18)** Rua Senador Pompeu, 27, 20008-010 Rio de Janeiro ☎21 2263 7521 **W:** radiocapitalrio.com.br – **RJ19)** Travessa Santa Luiza 91, 23900-900 Angra dos Reis ☎24 3365 1352 – **RJ20)** Rua Buenos Aires, 68, 19° andar, 20070-020 Rio de Janeiro ☎21 3171 1060 **W:** blog.cancaonova.com/riodejaneiro **E:** radioespiritosanto@cancaonova.com – **RJ21)** Av Deputada Alair Ferreira, 201, Parque Turf Club, 28024-600 Campos dos Goitacazes ☎22 2723 8989 – **RJ22)** Estrada Adhemar Bebiano (ex-Estr. Velha da Pavuna), 3517, Inhaúma, 20765-170 Rio de Janeiro ☎21 2176 8276 **W:** metropolitana1090.com.br **E:** contato@metropolitana1090.com.br – **RJ23)** Av Alair Ferreira, 201, Turf-Club, 28015-020 Campos dos Goitacazes ☎22 2728 1110 **W:** radiorecord1110.weebly.com **E:** producaoradiorecordcampos@gmail.com **RJ24)** Rua Presidente Vargas, 541 - Centro, 25802-220 Três Rios ☎24 2252 0720 **W:** Facebook: Radio 3 Rios **E:** rtr@radiotresrios.com.br - **FM:** 89.7MHz **RJ25)** Rua da Assembléia, 10, Sala 1201,20011-901 Rio de Janeiro ☎21 3799 1180 **W:** mundial1180.com.br – **RJ26)** Rua dos Andrades, 109, 3°andar, 28010-300 Campos dos Goitacazes ☎22 2733 1270 **W:** radiocontinentalam.com.br **E:** continental1270@yahoo.com.br – **RJ27)** Rua do Livramento, 189 8°andar, Gamboa, 20221-194 Rio de Janeiro ☎21 2126 2421 **W:** tupi.am - **FM:** 96.5 MHz – **RJ28)** Rua Alberto Torres, 410 an3°, 28400-000 São Fidelis ☎22 2758 1275 **W:** radiocoroadosam.com **E:** radiocoroadosam1310@hotmail.com – **RJ29)** Av 28 de Setembro, 258, Loja 01, Vila Isabel, 20551-031 Rio de Janeiro ☎21 2576 9737 **W:** radioboasnovas.com.br **E:** comercial@radioboasnovas.com.br – **RJ30)** Rua Alvaro Ramos, 350, Botafogo, 22280-110 Rio de Janeiro ☎21 2543 1360 – **RJ31)** Rua Carlos de Lacerda, 52, an 2°, 28010-242 Campos de Goytacazes ☎22 3055 0091 **W:** radiocamposdifusora.com.br **E:** angeladifusora@yahoo.com.br – **RJ32)** Rua Joaquim Leite, 465, ap 101, 27345-391 Barra Mansa ☎24 3323 3300 ☎24 3323 1152 **W:** sulfluminense.com.br **E:** comrcial@sulfluminense.com.br - **FM:** 96.1MHz – **RJ33)** Estrada do Dendê, 659-Tauá, Ilha do Governador, 21920-000 Rio de Janeiro ☎21 3386 1400 **W:** radioriodejaneiro.am.br **E:** marketing@radioriodejaneiro.am.br – **RJ34)** Av Cardoso Moreira, 422-Sobrado - Centro, 28300-000 Itaperuna ☎24 3824 1410 **W:** radioitaperuna1410.blogspot.no **E:** radioitaperunaam@gmail.com – **RJ35)** Rua do Mercado, 34-Sala 802, 20010-120 Rio de Janeiro ☎21 2233 8822 **W:** radiolivream.com.br **E:** falecom@radiolivream.com.br – **RJ36)** Av Joaquim Leite, 279 - Centro, 27330-042 Barra Mansa **W:** radiodocomercio.com.br **E:** atendimento@radiodocomercio.com.br ☎24 3323 3848 – **RJ37)** Rua Dr Temistocles de Almeida, 97, 28470-000 Santo Antônio de Pádua ☎22 3853 3173 **W:** radiofeliz.com.br – **RJ38)** Rua Ana Nery, 120 9° andar, 27123-150 Barra do Piraí ☎24 2443 1470 ☎24 2401 8367 **W:** gruporbp.com.br **E:** radiobpfm@gmail.com - **FM:** 89.9MHz – **RJ39)** Rua Senador Dantas 117, cob 02, Nova Iguaçú ☎21 2767 3333 **W:** tropical830am.com.br **E:** tropical@tropical830am.com.br – **RJ40)** Av Sete de Maio, 702 sala 301, 28800-000 Rio Bonito ☎21 2734 1693 **W:** radio1340.com.br – **RJ41)** Rua Lúcio Bittencourt, 107 an 2, Vila Santa Ccilia, 27260-119 Volta Redonda ☎24 3348 9533 **W:** Facebook: R.Soc. de Volta Redonda, **FM:** 101.5 MHz – **RJ42)** Rua Cardoso 357, 28013-460 Campos dos Goytacazes ☎22 2733 9072 **W:** cancaonova.com/campos – **RJ43)** Rua Rui Barbosa, 184 loja1, Várzea, 25963-090 Teresópolis ☎21 2643 5555 **W:** radioteresopolis.com.br **E:** radioteresopolisam@gmail.com – **RJ44)** Rua Carvalho de Souza, 20 an 3°, Madureira, 21350-180 Rio de Janeiro ☎21 3390 1422 **W:** continental1520.com.br **E:** contato@continental1520.com.br – **RJ45)** Rua Paulino Padilha 80, 28460-000 Miracema ☎22 3852 0899 **W:** princesinhaam.com.br **E:** radioprincesinha@yahoo.com.br – **RJ46)** Rua Marechal Deodoro, 46 an 9°salas 905, 25620-150 Petrópolis ☎24 2237 6161 ☎24 2237 6161 **W:** http//radioimperiala.com **E:** imperialam@compuland.com.br – **RJ47)** Rua Francisco Belisário, 439, Santa Cruz, 23570-510 Rio de Janeiro ☎21 3395 1560 **W:** granderioam.com **E:** dmxrio@yahoo.com.br – **RJ48)** Rua Carneiro de Mendonça. 29-A, 27600-000 Valença ☎24 2453 4418 **W:** radioculturadovale.com.br – **RJ49)** Rua Tenente José Teixeira, 147-an 1°, 28360-000 Bom Jesus do Itabapoana ☎22 3831 1570 **W:** bomjesusam.com.br – **RJ50)** Rodovia Barão 101, s/n Km 206, 28860-000 Casimiro de Abreu ☎22 2778 5101 – **RJ51)** Rua Frei Valerio 58, 28740-00 Conceição de Macabu ☎22 2779 2100 **W:** popularfluminens.com **E:** frpfluminense@yahoo.com.br – **RJ52)** Av Nilo Peçanha, 320 an 3°, Campos Eliseos, 27542-210 Resende ☎24 3354 7532 **W:** rlr2.com.br **FM:** 90.5 MHz – **RJ53)** Rua Gal.Gustavo C.Farias, 84, Benfica, 20910-220 Rio de Janeiro ☎21 2582 0990 **W:** radiorecordrj.com.br **E:** aovivo@radiorecordrj.com – **RJ54)** Rua Barão Piabanha, 107 Anexo 1 Mini Shopping, 25850-000 Paraíba do Sul ☎24 2263 2343 **W:** radioclube1540.com.br **E:** radioclube1540@hotmail.com – **RJ55)** Rua Gal Dionísio, 327, Guaratiba, 23025-330 Duque de Caxias ☎21 3652 1480 – **RJ56)** Rua Berlindo Figueiras de Barros 100, 28250-000 Italva ☎22 2783 1777 **W:** aliancaam.com.br **E:** superaliancaam@yahoo.com.br – **RJ57)** Praça Porto Rocha, 56, Apt 102, 28905-250 Cabo Frio ☎22 2645 4000 **W:** radiocabofrio.com.br **E:** contato@radiocabofrio.com.br – **RJ58)** Rua Coronel Santiago, 250, Agriões, 25963-220 Teresópolis ☎21 2642 2000 **W:** radiogeracao2000.com.br – **RJ59)** Av.Djalma Beda Combe 719, 28500-000 Cantagalo ☎22 2555 4455

**RN00) RIO GRANDE DO NORTE**

**RN01)** Av Duque de Caxias, 106, Ribeira, 59010-200 Natal ☎84 4006

6100 **W:** radioglobonatal.com.br **E:** comercial@radioglobonatal.com.br – **RN02)** Praça Dom José Delgado, s/n , 59300-000 Caicó ☎84 3471 2401 **W:** radiorural.com **E:** comercial@radiorural.com – **FM:** 95.0 MHz – **RN03)** Rua Luiz XV, 10, Nordeste, 59042-070 Natal ☎84 3653 3780 **W:** nordesteevangelica.com.br – **RN04)** Rua João Pessoa, 22 1° andar, 59380-000 Currais Novos ☎84 3431 1720 **W:** radiocurraisnovosam.com **E:** radiocurraisnovosam@hotmail.com – **RN05)** Praça Vigário Antonio Joaquim 39, 59600-520 Mossoró ☎84 8723 7993 **W:** ruraldemossoro.com.br **E:** gerencial@ruraldemossoro.com.br – **RN06)** Rua Augusto da Escossia Nogueira Neto, 2141, 59625-750 Mossoró ☎84 3312 4618 **W:** redepotiguar.com.br – **RN07)** Rua Açú, 335, Tirol, 59020-110 Natal ☎84 3201 1690 **W:** blog.cancaonova.com/natal **E:** radionatal@cancaonova.com – **RN08)** Av Dr Cunha Mota, s/n, Pereiros, 59600-160 Mossoró ☎🖥84 3317 6167 **W:** portaldifusoramossoro.com**E:** difusora@difusoramossore.com.br – **RN10)** Av Deodoro, 245, 59012-600 Natal **W:** redeclubebrasil.blogspot.no – **RN11)** Praça Desembargador Tomáz Salustino 42, 59380-000 Currais Novos ☎84 3431 1266 – **RN12)** Rua Francisca Delfina 30, 59860-620 Alexandria ☎84 3381 2321 **W:** redepotiguar.com.br **E:** comercial@rederpc.com.br – **RN13)** Pc Bento Praxedes 104, 59600-182 Mossoró ☎84 3321 3133 **W:** libertadoraevangelica.com.br **E:** radio.libertadora@gmail.com – **RN14)** Rua Otávio Amorim 643, 59650-000 Açu ☎84 3331 1223 **W:** radioprincesadovale.com.br **E;** contato@radioprincesadovale.com.br – **RN15)** Rua Nero Nazareno Fernandes, 250, Alto de Liberdade, 59780-0100 Caraúbas ☎84 3337 2297 **W:** rpccentenario.com.br/ **E:** rpccentenario@hotmail.com – **RN16)** Rua Frei Alberto Cabral 08, 59215-000 Nova Cruz ☎ 84 3281 2123 – **RN17)** Rua Getúlio Vargas 1296, 59900-000 Pau dos Ferros ☎🖥84 3351 2388 **W:** culturadooeste.com.br – **RN18)** Rua Major Lula, 59300-000 Caicó ☎84 3421 2500 **W:** radiocaico.com **E:** daguisoares @hotmail.com – **RN19)** Rua Avinida Rio Branco 173, 59655-000 Areia Branca ☎🖥84 3312 4618 **W:** redepotiguar.com **E:** comecial@rederpc.com.br – **RN20)** Rua Ana de Pontes, 419, 59255-000 Santo Antônio ☎84 3282 2347 – **RN21)** Rua Odorico Férreira de Souza, 70, Bairro DNER, 59200-000 Santa Cruz ☎84 3291 2300 **W:** radiosantacruzam.com.br **E:** radiosantacruzam@yahoo.com.br – **RN22)** Rua Experidião Coimbra, 22, 59500-000 Macau ☎84 3521 1765 **W:** redetropical.com.br – **RN23)** Rua Cícero Tomáz de Azevedo, 1052, Cruz do Monte, 59360-000 Parelhas ☎84 3471 2401 **W:** ruralam.com.br **E:** ruraldeparelhas@hotmail.com – **RN24)** Rua Heráclito Vilar, 59570-000 Ceará Mirim ☎84 3274 2794 – **RN25)** Rua Sebastião Guilherme Caldas, s/n, Baixa da Belexa, 59343-000 Jardim do Seridó ☎🖥84 3472 2587 **W:** radiocabugidoserido.com.br **E:** cabugidoserido@yahoo.com.br– **RN26)** A. Cel Martiniano, 1077, 59300-000 Caicó ☎84 3421 4181 **W:** radiocaico.com.br **E:** gizeldaa@hotmail.com – **RN27)** Rua Presidente Quaresma, 708, Alecrim, 59031-150 Natal ☎84 3213 8911 – **RN28)** Rua Deputado Hésiquio Fernandes, 59930-000 São Miguel ☎84 3353 2112 **W:** radiodifusoradesaomiguel.blogspot.com.br – **RN29)** Av Ouro Branco, 430, 59460-000 São Paulo do Potengi 84 3251 2381**W:** radiopotengi.com.br – **RN30)** Av 21 de Abril 460, BR-460, 59550-000 João Câmara ☎🖥84 3262 2189 – **RN31)** Rua Joel do Amaral Gurgel, 2512, Cohab, 59700-000 Apodi ☎84 3333 2512 **W:** radiovaledoapodi.com.br – **RN32)** Rua do Chafariz 1390, Bairro Novo Horizonte, 59584-000 Touros ☎84 3263 2121 **W:** R.Farol AM 1390 **E:** radiofarolgerencia@hotmail.com

**RO00) RONDÔNIA**
**RO01)** Rua José Bonifácio, 787, Olaria, 78902-280 Porto Velho ☎69 3224 1887 **W:** rbn-pvh.com.br – **RO02)** Av Dr Miguel Vieira Pereira, 5927, Cidade Alta, 78987-000 Rolim de Moura ☎69 3442 1122 – **RO03)** Av Jamari 4218, 78932-000 Ariquemes ☎69 3536 3385 **W:** radioariquemes.com **E:** amauri@ariquemes.com.br – **RO04)** Rua Capitão Silvio 145, 76900-117 Ji-Paraná ☎69 3421 5233 **W:** radialvoradajp.com.br **E:** contato@radioalvorada.com.br – **RO05)** Rua Rui Barbosa 3375, Floresta, 76965-736 Cacoal ☎69 3441 2122 **W:** portalradiorondonia.com.br – **RO06)** Rua Feijo, 2930, Cafézinho, 76913-152 Ji-Paraná ☎🖥69 3424 0432 **W:** radiojiparana.com.br – **RO09)** Praça Mário Correa 90, Cristo Rei, 76850-000 Guajará Mirim ☎69 3541 2670 **W:** radioeducadoraam.com.br – **RO10)** Rua Dourados 4, Setor Industriales, 78930-000 Ariquemes ☎69 3535 3000 **W:** portalradiorondonia.com.br – **RO11)** Av. Nações Unidas 605, Nossa Senhora das Graças, 76804-175 Porto Velho ☎69 3210 3621 **W:** radiocaiari.com **E:** radiocaiari@gmail.com – **RO12)** Rua Princesa Isabel, 128, 78995-000 Vilhena ☎69 3321 3309 **W:** radiovilhena.com.br **E:** radiovilhena@brturbo.com.br – **RO15)** Rua Carlos Doneje 1304, Ctg, 78984-000 Pimenta Bueno ☎69 3222 5308 **W:** radiorondonia.com **E:** comercialpb@radiorondonia.com.br – **RO16)** Rua 1005, 1522, Setor Pioneira (✉ C.P. 105), 76980-000 Vilhena ☎69 3322 2589 **W:** plansol.com.br **E:** plansol@hotmail.com – **RO17)** Av. Calama esquina com Rafael Vaz e Silva, 2666, Liberdade, 76803-884 Porto Velho ☎69 2182 0300 **W:** radiogloboro.com.br **E:** radiogloboro@hotmail.com – **RO18)** Rua 6 de Maio,1811, Casa Preta (✉ C.P. 163),

76980-000 Ji-Paraná ☎69 3421 1390 **W:** plansol.com.br – **RO19)** Rua Sergipe, 1766, Morada do Sol, 78983-000 Espigão d'Oeste ☎69 3481 3348 **W:** radiosociedadeespigao.com.br **E:** contate@radiosociedadeespigao.com.br – **RO23)** Rua Anel Viario, 1782, Parque Brizon, 78975-000 Cacoal ☎69 3443 2928 **W:** radiosuprema.com.br **E:** estudio@radiosuprema.com.br – **RO24)** Rua Jorge Texteira No 2005 Setor 07, 78940-000 Jaru ☎69 3521 4320 **W:** radiocentraljaru.com.br **E:** contato@radiocentraljaru.com.br

**RR00) RORAIMA**
**RR01)** Av Capitão Ene Garcez, 888, São Francisco, 69304-000 Boa Vista ☎95 3224 1651 **W:** radiororaima.com.br – **RR02)** Rua Sebastião Diniz, 363 - Centro, 69360-000 Caracaraí – **RR03)** 69350-000 Alto Alegre – **RR04)** Rua Lobo D´Almada, 43, Sao Francisco, 69035-050 Boa Vista ☎95 3623 8801 🖥95 3623 8801 **W:** folhabv.com **E:** radiofolha@folhabv.com.br

**RS00) RIO GRANDE DO SUL**
**RS01)** Av Victor Barreto 3056 Conj 207, 92010-000 Canoas ☎51 3059 5677 **W:** radiorealam.com.br **E:** bruno@radiorealam.com.br – **RS02)** Rua Antunes Ribas, 1535-an 3°, 98801-630 Santo Angelo ☎55 3313 3666 **W:** radiosepe.com.br **E:** contato@radiosepe.com.br – **RS03)** Rua Marechal Deodoro 1157, 96810-110 Santa Cruz ☎51 3715 5958 **W:** radiosantacruz.com.br **E:** gerencia@radiosantacruz.com.br – **RS04)** Rua General Sampaio, 161, Rio Branco, 95097-000 Caxias do Sul ☎54 3220 9400 🖥54 2101 5236 **W:** redesul.am.br/Sao-Francisco **E:** redsul@saofrancisco.am.br - **FM:** 98.5MHz – **RS05)** Av. Sete de Setembro 509, 99010-121 Passo Fundo ☎54 3316 4800 **W:** diarioam570.com.br **E:** diretoria@diariodamanha.net - **FM:** 98.7 MHz – **RS06)** Av Mascarenhas de Morães 586, 97300-000 São Gabriel ☎55 3232 6336 **W:** redetche.com.br – **RS07)** Avenida Moreira Paz, 726 (✉ C.P. 67), 95200-000 Vacaria ☎54 3231 7500 **W:** redesul.am.br/Fatima-AM **E:** gerente@fatima.am.br **RS08)** Praça Oswaldo Aranha 39, 97541-540 Alegrete ☎55 3422 1600 **W:** redetche.com.br/alegrete **E:** joaoulisses@radioalegrete.com.br – **RS09)** Av Ipiranga, 1075-an3°, Azenha, 90160-093 Porto Alegre ☎51 3218 6600 **W:** clicrbs.com.br **E:** gaucha@rdgaucha.com.br - **FM:** 93.7 MHz – **RS10)** Rua Andrade Neves, 2316-Centro 96020-080 Pelotas ☎🖥53 3222 7407 **W:** radiopelotense.com.br **E:** radiopelot@terra.com – **RS11)** Rua Suécia 255, 98500-000 Tenente Portela ☎55 3551 1395 **W:** radiomunicipalam.com **E:** sec@radiomunicipalam.com – **RS12)** Rua 14 de Julho 588, 95300-000 Lagoa Vermelha ☎🖥54 3358 6900 **W:** redesul.am.br/Cacique-AM **E:** cacique@cacique.am.br – **RS13)** Rua Paul Harris 02, 97015-480 Santa Maria ☎55 3220 2131 **W:** radiosantamariense.com.br **E:** radiosantamariense@terra.com.br – **RS14)** Rua Delfino Riet, 183, Santo Antonio, 90660-120 Porto Alegre ☎51 3218 2100 **W:** band.com.br/rs – **RS15)** Av Mauricio Cardoso, 88 1° andar, 99700-000 Erechim ☎54 3321 2243 **W:** radiodifusoasul.com.br - **FM:** 94.9 MHz – **RS16)** Rua Voluntários da Patria 1432 , 97590-000 Rosário do Sul ☎55 3231 2533 **W:** radiomaraja.com **E:** contacto@radiomaraja.com – **RS17)** Rua Farroupilha 110, 95200-000 Vacaria ☎54 3231 2828 **W:** radioesmeralda.com.br **E:** comercial@radioesmeralda.com.br - **FM:** 93.1MHz – **RS18)** Rua Neita Ramos 217, 96230-000 Santa Vitória do Palmar ☎53 3263 1660 **W:** redemeridional.com/sta.html **E:** culturasantavitoria@redemeridional.com – **RS19)** Rua Domingos Secchi 35, Boa Vista, 99500-000 Carazinho **W:** gazeta670.com.br **E:** comercial@gazeta670.com.br ☎54 3330 3143 – **RS20)** Travessa 4 de Junho 84, 98380-000 Seberi ☎55 3746 1040 🖥55 3746 1033 **W:** seberiam.com.br **E:** diretor@seberiam.com.br – **RS21)** Rua 15 de Novembro, 275, 9° andar, 98700-000 Ijuí ☎55 3332 9999 **W:** radioprogresso.com.br **E:** contato@radioprogresso.com.br – **RS22)** Rua Mascarenhas de Morães 298, 97300-000 São Gabriel ☎55 3232 2244 **W:** radiobatovi.com.br **E:** radiobatovi@terra.com.br – **RS23)** Rua Caldas Jr. 219, 90019-900 Porto Alegre ☎51 3215 6320 **W:** radioguaiba.com.br **E:** guaibeiro@radioguaiba.com.br - **FM:** 101.3MHz – **RS24)** Rua Coronel Chicuta, 436 5° andar, 99100-051 Passo Fundo ☎54 3045 3088 **W:** rdplanalto.com.br **E:** am@rdplanalto.com - **FM:** 105.9MHz – **RS25)** Av Júlio de Castilhos, 435, Vila Vista Alegre, 98300-000 Palmeira das Missões **W:** radiopalmeira.com **E:** am740@radiopalmeira.com.br ☎55 3742 2255 - **FM:** 101.7MHz – **RS26)** República do Libano 240, 96200-340 Rio Grande ☎53 3232 2303 **W:** radioculturariogr.com.br **E:** radiocultrariogrodina@vetorial.net – **RS27)** Av Marechal Floriano 920-Sala 301, 95520-000 Osório ☎51 3663 3435 **W:** radioosorio.com.br **E:** radioosori@hotmail.com – **RS29)** Av Gal Daltro Filho 1000, 98470-000 Planalto ☎55 3794 1025 **W:** radioametista.com.br **E:** contato@radioametista.com.br – **RS30)** Rua Pedro Vargas 846, 99500-000 Carazinho ☎54 3331 5250 **W:** diarioam780.com.br **E:** radio2@dariodamanha.net – **RS31)** Rua Orfanatrófio, 711, Alto Teresópolis, 90840-440 Porto Alegre ☎51 3218 2620 **W:** pampa.com.br/caicara **E:** ouvintrcaicara@pampa.com.br – **RS32)** Rua Senhor dos Passos, 34, 96640-000 Rio Pardo ☎51 3731 3790 **W:** Facebook: R.Rio Pardo AM **E:** radioriopardo@hotmaul.com – **RS33)** Av Roraima, 1000-Cidade Universitária, Camboi, 97105-900

Santa Maria ☎51 3220 8550 **W:** coral.ufsm.br/radio/ **E:** radio800am@ufsn.br – **RS34)** Rua Max Henrique Erichsen, 38 sala 101, Oriental, 95880-000 Estrela ☎51 3712 1259 **W:** 820dovale.com.br **E:** ouvinte@820dovale.com.br – **RS35)** Av Presidente Vargas 892, 98005-160 Cruz Alta ☎55 3322 1803 **W:** radioindependente.am.br – **RS36)** Av Julio de Castilhos, 607 - Centro Historico, 90030-131 Porto Alegre ☎51 3284 0772 **W:** radiocapital.net **E:** contato@radiocapital.net – **RS37)** Caladão Salvador Isaia, 1330, 3° andar, 97010-902 Santa Maria ☎55 3025 5757 **W:** guarathan.com.br **E:** guarathan@terra.com.br – **RS38)** Rua Álvaro Guaspari, 80, Marcilio Dias, 90035-020 Porto Alegre ☎51 3024 7421 **W:** radioitai.com.br **E:** radioitairs@gmail.com – **RS39)** Rua Osvaldo Aranha, 808 Sala 102B, Juventud, 95700-000 Bento Gonçalves ☎54 3452 7777 **W:** difusora890.com.br **E:** contato@difusora890.com.br – **RS40)** Praça da Bandeira 36, 98900-000 Santa Rosa ☎55 3512 5757 **W:** jornalnoroeste.com **E:** faleconosco@jornalnoroeste.com.br - **FM:** 97.7 Guaira – **RS41)** Rua XV de Novembro 336, 99770-000 Aratiba ☎54 3376 1138 **W:** radioaratiba.com.br **E:** am.900@hotmail.com – **RS43)** Rua 7 de Setembro, 1441 - Centro, 95800-000 Venâncio Aires ☎51 3741 2000 **W:** radiovenancioaires.com.br **E:** rva@radiovenancioaires.com.br – **RS44)** Av.Fernandes Bastos, 1683, Sobreloja, 95590-000 Tramandai ☎51 3661 5657 **W:** Facebook: Radio Tramandaí AM 920 **E:** radiotramandai@hotmail.com **FM:** 97.1 MHz – **RS45)** Rua Garibaldi, 789-21° andar, Ed. Estrela, 95084-900 Caxias do Sul ☎54 3289 3000 **W:** radiocaxias.am.br - **FM:** 93.5 MHz – **RS46)** Av. Brasil 523, 98801-590 Santo Ângelo ☎55 3313 2440 **W:** radiosantoangelo.com.br **E:** radiosan@radiosantoangelo.com.br – **RS47)** Av Alberto Müller, 242, Alto do Parque, 95900-000 Lajeado ☎51 3710 4900 **W:** independente.com.br **E:** recepcao@independente.com.br – **RS49)** Rua Orfanatrófio, 711, Alto Teresópolis, 90840-440 Canoas ☎51 3215 2525 **W:** redepampa.com.br/eldorado/ **E:** pampa@pampa.com.br – **RS50)** Av Getúlio Vargas 412, 98670-670 Humaitá ☎55 3525 1212 **W:** radioaltouruguai.com.br **E:** 970am@radioaltouruguai.com.br - **FM:** 92.5 MHz – **RS51)** Rua Tupancíretã de Azevedao, 9170-970 Tupaneiretã **W:** tupa.am.br **E:** contato@tupa.am.br – **RS52)** Rua Fiorentino Bachi, 791 - Centro, 99840-000 Sananduva ☎54 3343 1438 **W:** radiosananduva.com.br **E:** contato@radiosananduva.com.br - **FM:** 97.7MHz – **RS53)** Rua Garibaldi, 789 21° andar, 95084-900 Caxias do Sul ☎54 3289 3000 **W:** radio1010.am.br – **RS54)** Rua Julio de Castilhos, 2236, 97800-000 São Luís Gonzaga ☎55 3352 4141 **W:** radiomissioneira.com **E:** atendimento@radiomissioneira.com – **RS55)** Av David José Martins 1206, 98700-000 Ijuí ☎55 3332 8000 **W:** radioreporter.com.br **E:** atendimento@grupooreporter.com.br - **FM:** 101.5MHz «Iguatemi» – **RS56)** Rua General Zeca Netto 1396, 96180-000 Camaquã. ☎51 3671 0962 **W:** redemeridional.com **E:** radiocamaquense@redemeridional.com – **RS57)** Rua São João, 1894, 97800-000 São Luís Gonzaga ☎55 3352 4444 **W:** radiosaoluiz.com.br **E:** redacao@radiosaoluiz.com.br – **RS58)** Rua General Osório 625, 96570-000 Caçapava do Sul ☎55 3281 1495 **W:** redemeridional.com/cacapava.html **E:** radiocacapava@redemeridional.com – **RS59)** Rua Tucunduva 758, 98640-000 Crissiumal ☎55 3524 1212 **W:** metropole1070.com.br – **RS60)** Rua Marechal Deodoro, 101 7° andar, 95700-000 Bento Gonçalves **W:** radioviva.com.br **E:** geral1070@radioviva.com.br ☎54 3455 3999 – **RS61)** Rua João Carlos Machado 645, 98460-000 Iraí ☎55 3745 1444 **W:** radiomaraba.com.br **E:** maraba@speedrs.com.br – **RS62)** Rua Sarmento Leite, 426 - Centro, 90046-900 Porto Alegre ☎51 3316 3435 ▤51 3308 3017 **W:** ufrgs.br/radio **E:** radiodir@ufrgs.br – **RS63)** Rua Ramiro Barcelos, 2092, Augusta, 96508-070 Cachoeira do Sul ☎51 3722 4022 **W:** radiocachoeira.com.br **E:** radiocachoeira@radiocachoeira.com.br – **RS64)** Praça Padre Basso, 95, 99800-000 Marcelino Ramos ☎54 3372 1389 **W:** radiosalette.com.br **E:** radiosalette@terra.com.br – **RS65)** Av Bento Gonçalves, 733 - Centro, 98870-000 Giruá ☎55 3361 2020 **W:** radiogirua.com **E:** radiogirua@terra.com.br – **RS66)** Av Odilo Gonçalves 633, 96300-000 Jaguarão ☎53 3261 2933 **W:** redemeridional.com/jaguarao.html **E:** culturajaguarao@redemeridional.com – **RS67)** Rua Padre Oswaldo Stracke 56, 96900-000 Sobradinho ☎51 3742 1089 **W:** radiosobradinho.com.br **E:** recepcao@radiosobradinho.com.br - **FM:** 97.3MHz "R.Jacuí" – **RS68)** Rua Borges do Canto, 1056, 97650-000 Itaqui ☎55 3433 8181 **W:** radiocruzeirodosul.com **E:** radiocruzeirodosul@terra.com.br – **RS69)** Rua Corrêa Lima, 1960, Morro Santa Tereza, 90850-250 Porto Alegre ☎51 3218 5781 ▤51 3218 5789 **W:** radiofarroupilha.com.br **E:** farroupilha@rdfarroupilha.com.br – **RS70)** Av Rio Branco 809, 97010-423 Santa Maria ☎55 3222 9500 ▤55 3228 9500 **W:** radiomedianeiraam.com.br **E:** radiomed@terra.com.br – **RS71)** Rua Gel. João Manoel 341, 98005-170 Cruz Alta ☎55 3322 7222 **W:** radiocruzalta.com.br **E:** eduardo@radiocruzalta.com.br - **FM:** 105.1MHz – **RS72)** Rua Domingos de Almeida 2194, 97501-690 Uruguaiana ☎55 3412 1731 **W:** radiocharruaamfm.com.br **E:** amfm@radiocharrua.com.br - **FM:** 97.7MHz – **RS73)** Travess Victor Hugo Demaman Tomé 02, 96750-000 Butiá, **W:** radiojornalsobral.com **E:** radiosob@terra.com.br ☎51 3652 1140 – **RS74)** Rua Rui Barbosa

96, 95180-000 Farroupilha ☎54 3261 2121 **W:** radiomiriam.com.br **E:** radiomiriam@radiomiriam.com.br– **RS75)** Rua Tenente Lira 950 (C.P. 74), 98400-000 Frederico Westphalen ☎55 3744 3500 **W:** luzealegria.com.br **E:** direcao@luzealegria.com.br - **FM:** 95.9MHz – **RS76)** Rua General Osório 1160, 97760-000 Jaguari ☎55 3255 1474 **W:** radiojaguari.com.br **E:** radiojaguari@brturbo.com.br – **RS77)** Rua Félix da Cunha, 412, 96010-000 Pelotas ☎53 3225 1160 **W:** radiouniversidadeam.com.br – **RS78)** Av Coronel Victor Villa Verde, 491, Pitangueiras, 95500-000 Santo Antônio da Patrulha ☎51 3662 1255 **W:** radioitapui.com.br **E:** itapui@radioitapui.com.br – **RS79)** Av 7 de Setembro, 1115, 96400-000 Bagé ▤53 3242 5211 **W:** difusorabage.com.br **E:** difusora@difusorabage.com.br - **FM:** 99.7 FM Delta – **RS80)** Av 7 de Setembro, 160, Integração,99034-297 Passo Fundo ☎54 2104 1600 ▤54 2104 1612 **W:** radiouirapuru.com.br **E:** uirapuru@rduirapuru.com.br - **FM:** 90.1 MHz – **RS81)** Av Maurício Cardoso, 697, 99300-000 Soledade ☎54 3381 9100 **W:** redesul.am.br/index.php?emissora=24**E:** gerente@cristal.am.br – **RS82)** Rua Anunciação, 480, Morro do Convento, 97900-000 Cerro Largo ☎55 3359 2022 **W:** radiocerroazul.com.br **E:** radiocerroazul@via-rs.net - **FM:** 105.9MHz «Shamballa» – **RS83)** Plaza San Marco s/n, 99250-000 Serafina Corrêa ☎54 3444 1212 **W:** redesul.am.br/Rosario-AM**E:** rdrosario@net11.com.br –**RS84)** Av Cmdt Kraemer, 96 2° andar, 99700-000 Erechim ☎54 3522 1389 **W:** redetche.com.br **E:** administracao@radioerechim.com.br – **RS85)** BR 392, Km 232(▨ C.P. 130), 97340-000 São Sepé ☎55 3233 1113 ▤55 3233 1163 **W:** radiocotrisel.com.br **E:** radiocotrisel@radiocotrisel.com.br – **RS86)** Av Júlio de Castilho 607, 90030-131 Porto Alegre ☎51 3284 0778 **W:** radiotranscontinental.net **E:** radiorec@terra.com.br – **RS87)** Rua General Canabarro, 1450, Francisca Tarragaô, 97503-384 Uruguaiana ☎55 3412 1217 **W:** radiosaomiguel.com.br **E:** contato@radiosaomiguel.com.br – **RS88)** Rua Coronel Vitor Dumoncel 1756, 98240-000 Santa Bárbara do Sul ☎55 3372 2503 **W:** radioblaununes.com.br **E:** radioblaununes@radioblaununes.com.br – **RS89)** Rua Rui Barbosa 373, 99600-000 Nonoai ☎54 3362 1384 **W:** cluberadio.com.br - **FM:** 89.7 MHz – **RS90)** Av Adolfo Schneider,85 2° andar, 95320-000 Nova Prata ☎54 3242 1648 **W:** radioprata.com.br **E:** radioprata@radioprata.com.br – **RS91)** Praça Silvestre Corréa 77, 96610-000 Encruzilhada do Sul ☎51 3733 1157**W:** radioencruzilhadense.com.br – **RS92)** Rua Júlio de Castilhos 605 2° andar, 95290-000 Bom Jesus ☎54 3237 1247 **W:** bomjesus.rs.gov.br/radio_aparados.php **E:** radioaparados@bomjesus.rs.gov.br – **RS93)** Rua General Osório 1134, 98200-000 Ibirubá ☎54 3324 1758 **W:** sistemaepu.com.br **E:** atendimento@sistemaepu.com.br - **FM:** 96.6MHz – **RS94)** Rua Ponciano Ramos 74, 96700-000 São Jerônimo ☎51 3651 1113 **W:** radiosaojeronimo.com.br **E:** am.1240@hotmail.com – **RS95)** Av Júlio de Castilhos, 1511-8° andar, salas 81/84, 95010-003 Caxias do Sul ☎54 3221 7653 **W:** radiodifusoracaxiense.com.br **E:** radio@radiodifusoracaxiense.com.br – **RS96)** Rua 15 de Novembro 717, 96015-000 Pelotas **W:** radiotupanci.com.br **E:** tupanci@terra.com.br ☎53 3222 7263 – **RS97)** Rua Riachuelo 928, 97670-000 São Borja ☎55 3431 2244 **W:** radiocultura.am1260.com.br **E:** radio@gpsnet.com.br – **RS98)** Rua 15 de Noviembre, 884 Ed Cecilia Germano, 96508-750 Cachoeira do Sul ☎51 3722 3033 ▤51 3722 3622 **W:** radiofandango.com.br **E:** radiofandango@radiofandango.com.br – **RS99)** Rua José Sponchiado 418, 99830-000 Gaurama ▤54 3391 1134 **E:** radiogaurama@awo.com.br – **RS101)** Rua Baldulno Schneider 254, 98920-000 Horizontina ☎55 3537 1212 **W:** radioveracruz.com.br **E:** recepcao@radioveracruz.com.br – **RS102)** Rua Dr Pio Ferreira 453, 96170-000 São Lourenço do Sul ☎53 3251 1303 **W:** radiosaolourenco.com.br **E:** radio.sls@vetorial.net – **RS103)** Av Angelo Macalós, 246, 99400-000 Espumoso ☎54 3383 3600 **W:** radioplanetario.com **E:** contato@radioplanetario.com - **FM:** 95.3MHz – **RS104)** Av São Paulo, 722, 3° andar, São Geraldo, 90230-160 Porto Alegre **W:** boavontade.com/radio/ **E:** superrbv@bosvontade.com ☎51 3325 7000 – **RS105)** Rua 25 de Julho 39, 98960-000 Santo Cristo ☎55 3541 1188 **W:** radioregional1300.com.br – **RS106)** Rua dos Andrades 663, 97573-000 Santana do Livramento ☎55 3244 2444 **W:** facebook.com, Radio Maratan Am **E:** radiomaratan1300@gmail.com – **RS107)** Av Duque de Caxias 1320, 99560-000 Sarandi ☎54 3361 5656 **W:** redesul.am.br/sarandi-am **E:** midia1310@gmail.com – **RS108)** Av Júlio de Castilhos 232, 95680-000 Canela ☎54 3282 8822 **W:** radioclubedecanela.com.br **E:** radioclube@pdh.com.br - **FM:** 88.5MHz – **RS109)** Rua General Osório, 1276, 98280-000 Panambi ☎55 3375 8200 **W:** grupopilau.com.br **E:** panambi@grupopilau.com.br – **RS110)** Av Bento Goncalves 3361, 96015-145 Pelotas ☎53 3027 2175 **W:** radioculturapelotas.com.br **E:** estudio@radioculturapelotas.com.br – **RS111)** Av Rio Branco 401, 96450-000 Dom Pedrito ☎53 3243 4000 **W:** radioupacarai.com.br **E:** comercial.upacarai@hotmail.com – **RS112)** Rua Pe Feijó 833 Sala 42, 95190-000 São Marcos ☎54 3291 2422 **W:** radiodiplomata.am.br **E:** diplomata@radiodiplomata.am.br - **FM:** 99.7 – **RS113)** Av. Ipiranga, 1075, Azena, 90160-093 Porto Alegre ☎51 3218 6754 **W:** cbn.com.br **E:** cbn@rbsradios.com.br – **RS114)** Av Scalabrini, 777, 99200-000

Guaporé ☎54 3443 4488 **W:** redesul.am.br/Aurora-AM **E:** radioaurora@tl.com.br – **RS115)** Av Santos Dumont 240, 98600-000 Três Passos ☎55 3522 1011 **W:** rd3.net.br **E:** radiodifusoratrespassos@yahoo.com – **RS116)** Av Concordia 1480, 96540-970 Agudo ☎55 3265 1112 **W:** radioagudo.com.br **E:** radioagudo@terra.com.br – **RS117)** Rua Lauro R.Bortolo 402 - Centro, 99150-970 Marau ☎54 3342 3300 **W:** redesul.am.br/Alvorada-AM **E:** gerencia@alvorada.am.br – **RS118)** Rua John Kennedy 2220 sala 18, 95270-000 Flores da Cunha ☎54 3028 3888 **W:** http://comunidadeoasis.org.br **E:** oasis@comunidadeoasis.org.br - **FM:** 107.9 MHz – **RS119)** Rua Gaspar Martins 55-3° andar, 97542-000 Alegrete ☎55 3422 1236 **W:** gazetadealegrete.com.br **E:** rgta@ig.com.br – **RS120)** Rua Conde de Porto Alegre 521, 97573-581 Sant´Ana do Livramento ☎55 3242 5021 **W:** culturalivramento.com.br **E:** culturalivramento@brturbo.com.br – **RS121)** Rua Presidente Getúlio Vargas 153 , 99490-000 Tapera ☎54 3385 1166 **W:** sistemaepu.com.br **E:** cultura@sistemaepu.com.br – **RS122)** Rua Chaves Barcellos, 36, conj 1205 - Centro Historico, 90030-120 Porto Alegre ☎51 3228-903 **W:** radioesperanca.com.br **E:** adm@radioesperanca.com.br – **RS123)** Rua Pedro Toniollo 529, 99900-000 Getúlio Vargas **W:** radiosideral.com.br **E:** sideral@radiosideral.com.br ☎54 3341 1555 - **FM:** 98.1 MHz – **RS124)** Rua Augusto Rossi 316, 97200-970 Restinga Sêca **W:** radiojornalintegracao.com.br **E:** radio@integracao-rs.com.br ☎55 3261 1030 – **RS125)** Rua Marechal Floriano, 373, Cassino, 96205-190 Rio Grande ☎53 3035 3141 **W:** radiominuano.com **E:** minuano@radiominuano.com.br – **RS126)** Rua São Francisco 246, 98900-970 Santa Rosa ☎55 3312 4060 **W:** radiosantarosa.com.br – **RS128)** Rua Ramiro Barcelos 1206, 96810-900 Santa Cruz do Sul ☎51 3715 7831 **W:** grupogaz.com.br/radioam1180 **E:** radio@gazetaam.com.br - **FM:** 101.7MHz – **RS129)** Rua Teófilo Conrado de Matos 135, 96600-000 Canguçu br ☎53 3252 1144 **W:** radiocultura1030am.com.br **E:** cultura1030@brturbo.com.br – **RS130)** Av das Hortencias 78, 95670-000 Gramado ☎54 3286 2323 **W:** radioexcelsior.com.br **E:** excelsioram@serragaucha.com.br – **RS131)** Rua São João 1637, 95780-000 Montenegro ☎51 3632 1799 **W:** radioamerica1270.radiosom2.com.br/portal – **RS132)** Rua Republica de Líbano 135, 96200-360 Rio Grande ☎53 3035 3060 **W:** radiocassino.com.br **E:** diretor@radiocassino.com.br – **RS133)** Av Sete de Setembro 672, 96400-003 Bagé ☎53 3242 1471 **W:** radioculturabage.com.br **E:** radioculturabage@hotmail.com – **RS135)** Rua Dr Bruno Dockhorn 18 , 98910-000 Três de Maio ☎☐55 3535 1022 **W:** radiocolonial.com.br **E:** colonialam@gmail.com – **RS136)** Rua Santos Inacio de Loiola 253, sl 203, 93700-000 Campo Bom ☎51 3585 1470 **E:** radiocinderela@gmail.com.br – **RS137)** Rua Julio de Castilhos 325, 95720-000 Garibaldi ☎54 3464 7500 **W:** redesul.am.br/Garibaldi-AM/ **E:** jornalismo@garibaldi.am.br – **RS138)** Rua Gabriel Machado, 1590, 3° andar, 97610-000 São Francisco de Assis **E:** radiodifusao@terra.com.br ☎55 3252 1166 – **RS139)** Rua General Osorio 943, 96600-000 Canguçu ☎☐53 3252 1515 **W:** radioliberdadeam.com.br **E:** atendimento@radioliberdadeam.com.br – **RS140)** Rua Rio Branco 1006, 95600-000 Taquara **W:** jornalpanorama.com.br **E:** radiotaquara@faccat.br ☎51 3542 2288 – **RS141)** Rua São Vicente, 345, Gonçalves, 96501-180 Cachoeira do Sul ☎51 3723 6151 **W:** radiovale1520am.blogspot.no **E:** radiovaledopjacui@gmail.com – **RS142)** Av Rio Branco 616, 98770-000 Catuípe ☎55 3336 1328 **W:** radioaguasclaras.com.br **E:** contato@radioaguasclaras.com.br – **RS143)** Rua José Bonafácio 1128, (☒ C.P. 144) 96450-970 Dom Pedrito ☎53 3243 1434 **W:** modulosite.tecnologia.ws/modulo-am/SULINA **E:** **radio**sulina@hotmail.com – **RS144)** Rua Quitino Bocaiuva 100, 93135-030 São Leopoldo ☎51 3554 2894 **W:** redetche.com.br – **RS145)** Rua Cel Amâncio Cardoso, 596, 99950-000 Tapejara ☎54 3344 1185 **W:** radiotapejara.com.br **E:** contato@radiotapejara.com.br – **RS147)** Av Flores da Cunha 4283, 949150-004 Cachoeirinha ☎51 3421 1922 **W:** radiometropoleam.com.br **E:** radiometropoleam@terra.com.br – **RS148)** Rua 7 de Setembro 792, 95960-970 Encantado ☎51 3751 1580 **W:** rdencantado.com.br **E:** radio@encantoam.com.br - **FM:** 97.7 MHz – **RS149)** Av Assis Brasil 263, 98130-970 Júlio de Castilhos ☎55 3271 1414 **W:** radio14dejulho.com.br **E:** comercial@radio14dejulho.com.br – **RS150)** Rua José Bonifácio 41, 96330-970 Arroio Grande ☎53 3262 1008 **W:** difusora1580.com.br **E:** radiodifusoraam@terra.com.br – **RS151)** Rua Paraguai 42, 98980-000 Porto Lucena **W:** radionavegantes.com.br **E:** radionavegantes@san.psi.br ☎55 3565 1200 – **RS152)** Av Valdomiro Bocchese 872, 95250-970 Antônio Prado ☎54 3293 1110 ☎54 3293 1733 **W:** radiosolaris.com.br **E:** radiosolaris@radiosolaris.com.br - **FM:** 97.3 MHz – **RS153)** Av Santa Lúcia 1401, 97930-000 Caibaté **W:** radiocaibate.com.br **E:** radiocaibate@radiocaibate.com.br ☎55 3355 1335 – **RS154)** Rua Tiradentes 2839 Sala 5, 96360-970 Pedro Osório ☎53 3254 1239 **W:** radioclube990.com.br **E:** comercial@radioclube990.com.br – **RS155)** Av Borges de Medeiros, 1462, Chacara, 97650-000 Itaqui ☎56 3433 2301 **W:** radiopitangueira.com.br **E:** radio@pintagueira.com.br - **FM:** 94.5 MHz – **RS156)** Rua. Padre Roque Gonzáles 08, 98590-000 Santo Augusto ☎55 3781 1255 **W:**

radioquerenciaonline.com **E:** radio@querenciaonline.com – **RS157)** Rua Baltazar Brum, 343, 97560-000 Quaraí ☎55 3423 1065 –**RS158)** Rua Sete de Setembro, 1835 - Centro, 95860-000 Taquará ☎51 3653 4033 **W:** jornaloacoriano.com **E:** contato@jornaloacoriano.com– **RS159)** Av Maurício Cardoso 761, 99300-000 Soledade ☎54 3381 1550 **W:** radiosoledadeam.com.br **E:** radiosoledade@terra.com.br – **RS160)** Rua Dom Luiz Guanella 2313, 95555-970 Capão da Canoa ☎51 3625 2300 **W:** radiohorizonte.com.br **E:** radiohorizonte@radiohorizonte.com.br – **RS161)** Rua da República 220, 99530-000 Chapada ☎54 3333 1338 **W:** radiosimpatia.com.br **E:** simpatia@radiosimpatia.com.br – **RS162)** Av. Narciso Silva 1791, 96160-000 Capão do Leão ☎53 3227 4252 **W:** opiniaogospel.com.br **E:** opiniaogosplel1550@hotmail.com – **RS164)** Rua Floriano Peixoto 222, 97400-000 São Pedro do Sul ☎55 3276 1311 **W:** radiomunicipalsaopedrense.com.br **E:** contato@radiomunicipalsaopedrense.com.br – **RS165)** Rua Duque de Caxias 375, Sala 302, 98430-000 Palmitinho ☎55 3791 1175 **W:** radiochiru.com.br **E:** radiochiru@radiochiru.com.br - **FM:** 107.9 MHz – **RS166)** Rua João Mallheisen 10, 99680-000 Constantina ☎54 3363 1330 **W:** radioatlantica.net.br **E:** radio.atlantica@hotmail.com – **RS167)** Rua Francisco Gobbi 545, 98580-970 Coronel Bicaco ☎55 3557 1195 ☐55 3557 1220 **W:** radioguarita.com.br **E:** radioguarita@yahoo.com.br – **RS168)** Av Alto Jacuí, 435, 99470-000 Não Me Toque ☎54 3332 1488 **W:** radioceres.com.br **E:** radioceres@radioceres.com.br – **RS169)** Rua Brasil 806, 97450-000 Cacequi ☎55 3254 1366 **E:** radioculturacacequi@yahoo.com.br – **RS171)** Rua Luiz Vieira 525, 96760-970 Tapes ☎51 3672 1031 **W:** radiotapense.com **E:** rt@conectsul.com.br – **RS173)** Rua Albino Brendler, 122 - Centro, 98700-000 Ijuí ☎55 3332 7090 **W:** jmijui.com.br **E:** radiojmijui@gmail.com – **RS174)** Rua Consórcio s/n Conj 09, 96400-097 Bagé ☎53 3242 4668 **W:** radioclubebage.com.br **E:** radioclubebage@radioclubebage.com.br – **RS175)** Rua Pedro Alvares Cabral 164, 99660-000 Campinas do Sul ☎51 3366 1266 **W:** radiocampinasdosul.com.br **E:** radiocampinas@tolrs.com.br – **RS176)** Rua 15 de Novembro 690, 96270-000 Mostardas ☎51 3673 2062 **W:** radiomostardas.com.br **E:** radiomostardas@hotmail.com – **RS177)** Av Barão do Triunfo 584 2° andar, 95995-000 Arvorezinha ☎51 3772 2443 **W:** redeculturaderadio.com.br **E:** admcultura@msbnet.com.br - **FM:** 92.3MHz – **RS178)** Av. Castelo Branco 1053, 97950-000 Guarani das Missões **W:** grupoguaramano.com.br **E:** radioguaramano@brturbo.com.br ☎55 3353 1721 - **FM:** 91.1 – **RS179)** Rua Jornal NH, 99, Ideal, 93334-350 Novo Hamburgo ☎51 3593 9000 **W:** radioabc900.com.br **E:** diretorabc@gruposinos.com.br – **RS191)** Rua Correia Lima, 1960, Santa Tereza, 90850-250 Porto Alegre ☎51 3218 5693 **W:** clickrbs.com.br **E:** radiorural.am1120@rdrural.com.br – **RS192)** Rua Sanandua 178, 99855-970 São João da Urtiga ☎54 3532 1247 **W:** radioeducadorurtiga.com.br **E:** rdeducadora@brturbo.com.br – **RS198)** Av. Brasil, 385 sala 202, 93180-000 Portão ☎55 3562 6161 **W:** estacaoportao.com.br – **RS199)** Av. Paraguassu, 180/05, 95625-000 Imbé ☎51 3627 1988 **W:** radiolitoraljp.com.br **E:** contato@radiolitoraljp.com.br – **RS201)** Rua Orfanotrófio, 711, Santa Tereza, 90840-440 Porto Alegre ☎51 3218 2525 **W:** redepampa.com.br/rdgenral **E:** grenal@rdgrenal.com.br - **FM:** 95.9 MHz

**SC00) SANTA CATARINA**
**SC01)** Almeda Aristiliano Ramos 36 , 89160-149 Rio do Sul **W:** radiomirador.com.br **E:** am540@radiomirador.com.br ☎47 3531 2100 ☐47 3531 2102 – **SC02)** Av Centenario, 6050, Próspera, 88815-000 Criciúma ☎48 3461 5700 **W:** radioeldorado.net **E:** eldoradoam@radioeldorado.net - **FM:** 89.5 MHz – **SC03)** Av Martin Piaseski 25, 89910-970 Descanso. ☎49 3623 0307 **W:**progresso.am.br **E:** comerical@progresso.am.br – **SC04)** Rua Benjamin Constant, 286-D 3 e 4 andares, 89801-970 Chapecó ☎49 3323 5177 ☐49 3323 0526 **W:** superconda.com.br **E:** jornalismoconda@zipway.com.br – **SC05)** Rua Carlos Gomes 12, 89160-051 Rio do Sul ☎47 3521 1155 **W:** superdifusora.am.br/?pg=2Vale **E:** difusora@superdifusora.am.br - **FM:** 94.9 «Amanda FM» – **SC06)** Rua João Beux Sobredinho 350, 89990-000 São Lourenço d'Oeste **W:** radiodoze.com.br **E:** contato@radiodoze.com.br ☎49 3344 1544 – **SC07)** Rua Carlos Jofre do Amaral 67, 88501-015 Lages ☎49 3221 3147 **W:** radioclubedelages.com.br – **SC08)** Av Sete de Setembro 109, 89580-000 Fraiburgo ☎49 3246 2507 **W:** radiofraiburgo.am.br **E:** comercial@radiofraiburgo.am.br – **SC09)** Rua Gustavo Richard 90, 88701-220 Tubarão ☎48 3626 4633 **W:** radiotuba.com.br **E:** radiotuba@radiotuba.com - **SC10)** Rua General Vieira da Rosa 1570, 88020-420 Florianópolis ☎48 3216 2540 **W:** cbndiario.com.br **E:** cbndiario@rbsradios.com.br – **SC11)** Rua Guilherme Helmut Arent 277, 89700-970 Concórdia ☎49 3441 2800 **W:** radioalianca.com.br – **SC12)** Rua Buenos Aires, 145, Ponta Agude, 89051-050 Blumenau ☎47 3222 9004 **W:** radionereuramos.com.br – **SC13)** Rua da Criança 75, 88840-970 Urussanga ☎48 3465 1055 **W:** radiomarconi.net **E:** gerencia@radiomarconi.net – **SC14)** Rua Veneriano dos Passos 385, 89560-000 Videira 49 3533 4000 **W:** radiovideira.com.br – **SC15)** Rua Ângelo Dias 207, Cj 61/62/63, 89010-020 Blumenau ☎47 3041 9699 – **SC16)** Rua Alexandre Doneda 215, 88880-970 Lauro Müller ☎48

3464 3762 **W:** radiocruzdemalta.com.br **E:** radiocruzdemalta@netlm. com.br – **SC17)** Rua João Suzin Marini 64, 89700-000 Concórdia ☎49 3441 3838 **W:** radiorural.com.br – **SC18)** Av do Adão 1784, Morro da Cruz, 88025-150 Florianópolis **W:** ipda.com.br/radio/santacatarina/ index.html – **SC19)** Rua Rodovia SC 445 km3, 88820-000 Içara ☎48 3461 0700 ▤48 3461 0711 **W:** difusora910.com.br **E:** atendimento@ difusora910.com.br – **SC20)** Rua Conselheiro Rui Barbosa, 50 1° andar, 88350-320 Brusque ☎47 3351 4611 **W:** radiocidadeam.com.br **E:** diretoria@radiocidadeam.com.br – **SC21)** Rua Santa Catarina 93 Sala 2, 88200-000 Tijucas ☎48 3263 0303 **W:** radiovaletj.com.br **E:** contato@radiovaletj.com.br – **SC22)** Rua João Ramiro Machado, 321 Edifício Cidade das Colinas, 88870-000 Orleãs ☎48 3466 0533 **W:** guarujaam.com.br **E:** guarujadirecao@terra.com.br – **SC23)** Av Brasil, 260 Centro Comercial Tiradentes-3° andar, 89820-970 Xanxerê ☎49 3433 0171 **W:** superdifusora.com.br **E:** difusora@superdifusora.com.br – **SC24)** Centro Comercial Geschäfthaus, sala 20/21, 88353-120 Brusque ☎47 3351 1744 **W:** araguaia970.com.br **E:** fale@ araguaia970am.com.br – **SC25)** Rua São Bonifacio 280, 89896-000 Itapiranga ☎49 3677 0362 **W:** peperi.com.br – **SC27)** Rua Pernambuco 72, 89840-000 Coronel Freitas ☎49 3347 0131 **W:** continentalam1020. com.br – **SC28)** Rua Otacilio Vieira da Costa 40, 88501-050 Lages ☎49 3222 3011 **W:** radioprincesalages.com – **SC29)** Rua Manoel Simão, 177-Salas 24 e 25, Nações, 89130-970 Indaial ☎47 3333 0499 **W:** radioclubeindaial.com.br **E:** falecom@radioclubeindaial.com.br – **SC30)** Alameda Rolf Colin, 80, America, 89204-070 Joinville ☎47 3422 2325 **W:**radiocolon.com.br – **SC31)** Rua Vidal Ramos 519, 88701-160 Tubarão ☎48 3632 9009 **W:** bandeirantes1090.com.br – **SC32)** Rua Pe. Schrader, 01, Agronômica, 88025-090 Florianópolis ☎48 3224 6470 **W:** radioculturafloripa.blogspot.no **E** radio@radiocultura1110am. com.br – **SC33)** Av Santa Catarina 828, Edifico Dona Olivia-2° andar, 89885-000 São Carlos ☎49 3325 4355 ▤49 3325 4483 **W:** radiosaocarlos.com.br – **SC34)** Travessa João Winkler 15, 89820-000 Xanxerê ☎49 3433 1110 **W:** redeprincesa.com.br **E:** ademir@ redeprincesa.com.br - **FM:** 101.3 MHz – **SC36)** Rua 15 de Novembro, 600-sala 401, Edifício Visconde de Mauá, 89010-000 Blumenau ☎47 3322 9773 **W:** radioitabera.com **E:** contato@radioitabera.com – **SC38)** Rua Siqueira Campos 33, 89400-970 Porto União ☎42 3522 2245 **W:** colmeia.com.br **E:** colmeia@colmeia.am.br – **SC39)** Rua Padre Aurélio 240, 89930-970 São José do Cedro ☎49 3643 0211 **W:** radiointegracaoam1180.com.br **E:** comercial@radiointegracaoam1180. com.br – **SC40)** Rua Otavianpo Dadam 355, 88240-000 São João Batista ☎48 3265 0222 **W:** http//clubei.com.br **E:** redacao@rclubei.com – **SC41)** Rua São Cristóvão 393 (C.P 59, 89835-970), 89835-000 São Domingos ☎49 3443 6190 **W:** clubesd.com.br **E:** contato@clubesd. com.br – **SC42)** Bruno Pedro dal Bó, 3073 Humaitá de Cima, 88708-197 Tubarão ☎48 3628 0658 ▤48 3628 1356 **W:** radiosc.com.br **E:** radiosc@radiosc.com.br – **SC43)** Rua Tenente Ary Rauen 1361, 89300-970 Mafra ☎47 3642 3955 **W:** saojoseam.com.br **E:** radionovaera@ netuno.com.br - **FM:** 104.5MHz «Nova Era» – **SC44)** Av Canal 130, 89890-000 Cunha Porã ☎49 3646 0157 **W:** http//iracema.radio.br – **SC45)** Rua Nove de Março, 737-Ed.Turim 8° andar, 89201-400 Joinville ☎47 3026 1000 **W:** http//radioculturajoinville.blogspot.com **E:** jornalismo@jovempanjoinville.com.br - **FM:** 91.1 MHz – **SC46)** Rua Dr. Amadeu da Luz 31-sala 03 , 89010-160 Bluemau ☎47 3340 1260 **W:** arcadaalianca.com.br **E:** fale@radioblumenau.com.br – **SC47)** Av XV de Novembro 608, 89600-000 Joaçaba **W:** radiocatarinense.com.br **E:** radiocatarinense@radiocatarinense.com.br ☎49 3551 2424 ▤49 3551 2426 - **FM:** 97.3MHz – **SC48)** Rua Osvaldo Cabral 68-1° andar, 88790-000 Laguna, ☎48 3646 0337. **W:** garibaldilaguna.com.br **E:** radiogaribaldi@brturbo.com.br – **SC49)** Av Alvin Bauer 585, 88330-643 Balneário Camboriú ☎47 3405 1644 ▤47 3405 1609 **W:** radiocamboriu. com.br **E:** radiocamboriu@radiocamboriu.com.br – **SC50)** Rua Buenos Aires, 145, Ponta Aguda, 89051-050 Blumenau ☎47 3222 9070 **W:** radioclubeblumenau.com.br – **SC51)** Rua Marechal Floriano Peixoto 161, 89802-010 Chapecó ☎49 3322 0688 **W:** radiochapeco.com.br **E:** comercial@radiochapeco.com.br - **FM:** 107.1MHz – **SC53)** Rua Imbituba, 190, Dom Bosco, 88303-570 Itajaí ☎47 3241 0092 **W:** bandamitajai.com.br**E:** contato@bandamitajai.com.br – **SC55)** Rua Duque de Caxias 1302-2° andar, 89900-970 São Miguel do Oeste ☎49 peperi.com.br **E:** rede@peperi.com.br – **SC56)** Rua José Gonçalves 333, 89340-970 Itaiópolis ☎ ▤47 3652 2279 **W:** cidade1380.am.br **E:** comercial@cidade1380.am.br – **SC58)** Rua Visconde do Rio Branco 1028, 89887-000 Palmitos ☎49 3647 0292 **W:** radioentrerios.com.br **E:** entrerios@futurasc.net – **SC59)** Rua Nunes Machado 94, Edifico Tiradentes-10° andar, 88010-460 Florianópolis ☎ ▤48 2108 5555 **W:**radioguaruja.com.br - **FM:** 92.1 MHz – **SC61)** Rua 7 de Setembro 341, 89874-000 Maravilha ☎49 3664 0029 **W:** difusoramaravilha.com.br **E:** atendimento@difusoramaravilha.com.br – **SC62)** Rua Carlos Fürst 37, Serra Alta, 89291-697 São Bento do Sul ☎47 3633 0572 **W:** radiosaobento.com.br **E:** programacao@ radiosaobento.com.br – **SC63)** Av Centenario, 6050, Santa Barbara,

88804-972 Criciúma ☎48 3431 5190 **W:** hulhanet.com.br – **SC64)** Rua São Pedro 245, 89110-000 Gaspar ☎47 3332 0783 **W:** sentineladovale. com.br **E:** radiosentinela@terra.com.br – **SC65)** Av do Antão, 1762, Morro da Cruz, 88025-163 Florianopolis ☎49 3251 1470 – **SC66)** Rua Santos Dumont 204, 89610-000 Herval d'Oeste ☎49 3527 9013 **W:** radiolider.am.br **E:** gerencia@radiolider.am.br – **SC67)** Av Coronel Procópio Gomes, 1155, Bucarein, 89202-300 Joinville ☎47 3026 1480 **W:** arcadaalianca.com.br **E:** contato@radioarcadaalianca.com.br – **SC68)** Rua Antônio Bittencourt Capanama 260, 88770-000 Imaruí ☎48 3643 0000 **W:** litoralam.com.br – **SC69)** Rua Tiradentes, 283- Edifico D.Martha sala 21, 89140-000 Ibirama ☎47 3357 2236 **W:** belosvales. com.br – **SC70)** Av Plínio Arlindo de Nes 476, 89825-000 Xaxim ☎49 3353 2425 **W:** radioculturaxaxim.com.br **E:** cultura@radioculturaxaxim. com.br – **SC71)** Rua Max Wilhelm, 373, Baependi, 89256-000 Jaraguá do Sul ☎47 3371 1010 **W:** jaraguaam.com.br **E:** jaraguaam@ jaraguaam.com.br – **SC72)** Av Luis de Camões, 1370, Coral, 88523-000 Lages ☎43 3222 8222 **W:** radioguri.com.br **E:**comercial@radioguri. com.br– **SC73)** Av Belém 500, 89870-000 Pinhalzinho ☎49 3366 1111 **W:** rco.com.br **E:** rco@rco.com.br – **SC74)** Rua Altamiro Guimarães 480, 89500-000 Caçador ☎49 3536 2211 **W:** am1110.com.br – **SC75)** Av. Dr. João Rinsa 1002, 88780-000 Imbituba ☎48 3255 3787 **W:** bandeirantes1010.com.br – **SC76)** Rua Equador 245, 89120-970 Timbó ☎47 3382 3888 **W:** radioculturaam.com.br **E:** radioculturaam@ radiocuituraam.com.br – **SC77)** Rua Manoel Vieira Garcao 3-Edif. Catarinense 15 andar, 88301-425 Itajaí ☎47 3348 2992 **W:** difusoraitajai.com.br – **SC78)** Rua Boanerges Pereira de Medeiros, 205-Ed. Santa Rosa 2° e 3° andares, 88600-000 São Joaquim ☎49 3233 0021 **W:** difusora1530.com **E:** difusora@iscc.com.br – **SC79)** Av Porto Feliz 151, 89893-000 Mondaí ☎49 3674 0122 **W:** portofeliz. am.br **E:** jornalismo2@portofeliz.am.br – **SC80)** Rua Carmello Zocolli 205, 89600-000 Capinzal ☎49 3555 1333 ▤49 3555 1333 **W:** radiocapinzal.am.br **E:** contato@radiocapinzal.am.br – **SC81)** Av Getúlio Vargas 429, 88900-000 Araranguá ☎48 3524 0137 **W:** radioararangua.com.br **E:** radioararangua @radioararangua.com.br - **FM:** 92.5MHz – **SC83)** Rua Carlos Weber 228, 89295-000 Rio Negrinho ☎47 3644 2900 – **SC84)** Av 21 de Janeiro 1470, 89107-000 Pomerode ☎47 3395 1410 **W:** radiopomerode.com.br **E:** atendimento@ radiopomerode.com.br – **SC85)** Rua João Steffens 260, (C.P 100) 88400-000 Ituporanga ☎47 3533 8310 **W:** sintonia.am.br **E:** radio@ sintonia.am.br – **SC86)** Rua Joaquim Nuns 244, (C.P. 2008) 888340-000 Camboriú ☎47 3404 8700 **W:** gideoes.com.br **E:** contato@gideos.com. br – **SC87)** Rua João Florentino de Souza 700, 89480-000 Major Vieira ☎47 3655 1177 **W:** radioplanaltodemajorvieira.com.br – **SC88)** Rua Renato Ramos da Silva, 239, Barreiros, 88110-015 São José ☎48 3381 3500 **W:** radioguararema.com.br - **FM:** 103.5/107.7MHz – **SC89)** Rua Sargento Juvenil 476, 89540-000 Santa Cecília ☎49 3244 2188 **W:** radioalvorada1300.com – **SC90)** Av Getúlio Vargas 860, 89830-000 Abelardo Luz ☎49 3445 4297 **W:**rainhadasquedas.com.br – **SC91)** Rua Ricardo Kruger 140-sala 02, 88650-970 Urubici ☎49 3278 5095 **W:** radiogralhaazul.com.br – **SC92)** Rua Rui Barbosa 1321, 88930-000 Turvo ☎48 3525 0321 **W:** radioimigrantes.com.br **E:** imigrantes@ radioimigrantes.com.br – **SC93)** Rua AV XV de Novembro 6-sala 2, 89665-000 Capinzal ☎49 3555 1799 **W:** radiobarrigaverde.am.br – **SC94)** Av Progresso 569, 89888-000 Caibi ☎49 3648 0233 **W:** nossaradio.net.br/caibi – **SC95)** Rua Duque de Caxias, 1302-2° andar, 89900-000 São Miguel d'Oeste **W:** peperi.com.br ☎49 3622 1717 – **SC96)** Rua Rafael Pardinho 249, 89240-000 São Francisco do Sul ☎47 3444 2733 ▤47 3444 0450 **W:** radiosaofranciscosc.com.br **E:** ouvintes@ radiosaofranciscosc.com.br – **SC97)** Rua do Comercio 215, 89770-000 Seara ☎49 3452 8500 **W:** radiobelosmontes.com.br **E:** contato@ seara.psi.br – **SC98)** Rua do Comércio, 89872-000 Modelo ☎49 3365 3294 **W:** Facebook: Radio Modelo **E:** radiomodelo@mhnet.com.br – **SC99)** Rua 7 de Setembro 496, 89950-000 Dionísio Cerqueira ☎49 3644 1042 **W:** radiofronteira.com.br - **FM:** 94.3 – **SC101)** Av Dr Albano Schultz, 925 2° andar, 89201-220 Joinville ☎47 3481 3030 **W:** radioclubejoinville.com.br **E:** jornalismo@radioclubejoinville.com.br - **FM:** 103.1MHz – **SC102)** Rua Maranhão 700, sala 02, 89980-000 Campo Erê **W:** peperi.com.br – **SC103)** Rua Pref.Dib Cherem 3440 Salas 02/03, Capoeiras, 88090-001 Florianopolis ☎48 3028 1240 **W:** radiomaisalegria.com.br - **FM:** 106.5 MHz – **SC104)** Rua XV de Novembro 495, 89560-000 Videira ☎49 3650 2500 **W:** vitorioaam.com. br **E:** adm@vitoriaam.com.br – **SC105)** Rua João Lino da Silva Neto 621, 88495-000 Garopaba ☎48 3254 3055 **W:** radiofrequencia.net **E:** frequencia@radiofrequencia.net – **SC106)** 88330-000 Balneário Cambouri ☎47 3360 2344 **W:** radiocatolica1500am.blogspot.no.br **E:** radiocatolica am1500@gmail.com – **SC107)** 89642-000

## SE00) SERGIPE

**SE01)** Rua Claudio Batista, 334, Santo Antônio, 49060-100 Aracaju ☎79 3234 3232 **W:** radiojornal540.com.br **E:** jornal@radiojornal540. com.br – **SE02)** Rua Laranjeiras, 1837, Getúlio Vargas, 49055-380 Aracaju ☎79 3198 2700 **W:** aperipe.com.br - **FM:** 104.9MHz –

**SE03)** Rua Simão Dias 643, 49010-430 Aracaju ☎79 3226 8710 **W:** cultura670.com.br **E:** cultura@cultura670.com.br – **SE04)** Rua São José, s/n - Cidade Nova, 49400-000 Lagarto ☎79 3631 1866 **W:** radioprogressoam.com **E:** recepcao.aparecidafm@hotmail.com - **FM:** 87.5 MHz – **SE06)** Rua 13 de Maio 119, 49500-000 Itabaiana ☎79 3431 1762 **W:** radioprincesadaserra.com.br ☎79 3431 5036 – **SE07)** Rua Pacatuba 254, 49010-150 Aracaju ☎79 3213 1174 **W:** 930am.com.br **E:** jornalismo@930am.com.br – **SE08)** Praça Coronel Gonçalo Prado s/n, 49200-000 Estância ☎79 3522 1411**W.** radioesperancaestancia.com.br **E:** radioesperancaestancia@gmail.com – **SE09)** Av Dr Luíz Magalhães 346, 49500-970 Itabaiana ☎☎79 3431 1117 **W:** capitaldoagreste.com.br **E:** comercial@capitaldoagreste. com.br – **SE10)** Rodovia Lourival Batista 2153, 49480-000 Simão Dias ☎79 3611 1488 **W:** novacidadeam.com.br **E:** novacidadeam@ hotmail.com – **SE11)** Av. Napoleão Emifio Costa 1052, 49514-000 Frei Paulo ☎79 3447 1745 **W:** radioeducadoradefreipaulo.com.br **E:** radioeducadorafreipaulo@yahoo.com.br – **SE12)** Av Raimundo Silveira, 3996-01 Andar Sala 02, Alagoas, 49200-000 Estância ☎79 3522 4804 **W:** radioabaisam.com.br **E:** radioabaisamcomercial@hotmail.com – **SE13)** Travessa Santa Luzia, 69 - Centro, 49300-000 Tobias Barreto ☎79 3541 1548 **W:** redeilha.com.br **E:** am1520@redeilha.com

**SP00) SÃO PAULO**

**SP01)** Av Nove de Julho 2875, 16204-050 Biriguí ☎18 3642 3500 **W:** radiogloboirigui.com.br – **SP02)** Rua Antônio do Vale Mello, 807, 13170-011 Sumaré ☎19 3873 2972 **W:** radionovasumare.com.br **E:** rns@rns.com.br – **SP03)** Rua Dom Bosco, 573, 12700-000 Cruzeiro ☎12 3144 1364 **W:** radiomantiqueira.com **E:** atendimento@ mantiqueira.com - **FM:** 100.7MHz – **SP04)** Rua José Bonini, 1415, 14160-000 Sertãozinho **W:** boavontade.com/radio/?cdgEms=6 **E:** superrbv@boavontade.com – **SP05)** Prefeito João Benedito Barbosa,161, Vila Nova, 18400-000 Itapeva ☎15 3522 2000 **W:** radioclubegospel.com.br - **FM:** 93.5MHz «Cristal» – **SP06)** Rua Dr Sousa Alves 960, 12020-030 Taubaté ☎12 3632 8122 **W:** rededifusora. com.br **E:** mkt@rededifusora.com.br – **SP07)** Rua Tamoio, 875, Vila Santa Catarina, 13465-250 Americana ☎19 3475 8801 **W:** radiovoce. com.br **E:** radiovoce@radiovoce.com.br – **SP08)** Av Rotary 85, 19970-000 Palmital ☎18 3351 2601 **W:** radioregionalpalmital.com.br – **SP09)** Rua Pedro Lessa 1640, sala 809, Embaré, 11025-002 Santos ☎13 3273 6900 **W:** radioatlantica.com.br **E:** radioatlantica@radioatlantica.com.br – **SP10)** Rua das Nações Unidas 127, 16800-000 Mirandópolis ☎18 3701 4084 **W:** clubeam590.com.br – **SP11)** Av Maurilio Biagi, 2103, Ribeirânia, 14096-170 Ribeirão Preto ☎16 3968 7000 **W:** radio79.com. br **E:** natocampos@thathi.com.br – **SP12)** Mogi Mirim – **SP13)** Rua Pará 147, 15800-040 Catanduva ☎17 3531 1000 **W:** amglobo.com.br **E:** minhaglobo@globonoroestepaulista.com.br – **SP14)** Praça Conselheiro Rodrigues Alves, 104-3° andar, 12560-020 Guaratinguetá ☎12 3122 3155 **W:**superradiopiratininga.com.br **E:** jornalismo@ superradiopiratininga.com.br **SP15)** Av. Dr. Domingos Teodoro Galla 528 , 18800-000 Piraju ☎☎14 3351 1066 **W:** paranapanema.com.br **E:** atendimento610@paranapanema.com.br – **SP16)** Av Paulista, 807-24° andar, Bela Vista, 01311-941 São Paulo ☎11 2870 9700 **E:** info@ jovempam.com.br **W:** jovempam.com.br **E:** jovempanonline@jovempan. com.br – **SP17)** Rua Capitão Neves 1840, 15130-000 Mirassol ☎17 3242 2101 **W:** wwwdifusora630.com.br **E:** comercial@difusora630.com – **SP18)** Rua Casemiro Dias, 785, Vila Ocidental, 19015-250 Presidente Prudente – **SP19)** Av. Bento de Abreu 889, Jardim Mirmavera 14802-386 Araraquara ☎16 3303 3622 **W:** radiomorada.com.br **E:** radiomorada@uol.com.br - **FM:** 98.1MHz **SP20)** Rua Homero Rodrigues Silva 1072, 16901-025 Andradina ☎18 3722 2352 – **SP21)** Praça José Bonifácio 815, 13400-340 Piracicaba ☎19 2105 6622 **W:** portaldifusora.com.br **E:** atendimento@portaldifusora.com.br - **FM:** 102.3MHz – **SP22)** Rua Tolentino Figueiras, 119 7° andar, cj 71/72, Gonzaga, 11060-471 Santos ☎13 3289 4727 **W:** radiodacidadeam. com.br - **FM:** 105.5MHz – **SP23)** Av Nove de Julho, 600, Jardim Sumaré, 14025-000 Ribeirão Preto ☎16 2101 3500 **W:** clubeam.com. br - **FM:** 100.5MHz – **SP24)** Rua Teotonio Tibiriçá Pimenta 380, 11660-230 Caraguatatuba ☎12 3882 5000 **W:** radiooceanicaam.com.br – **SP25)** Rua Prefeito Salviano 20, 17400-000 Garça ☎14 3471 2241 **W:** 670am.com.br **E:** estudio@670am.com.br – **SP26)** Rua Quintino Bocaiúva 37, 13300-135 Itu.- ☎11 4023 2363 **W:** radioconvencao. com.br **E:** radioconvencao@hotmail.com – **SP27)** Rua 13 de Maio 720, 15800-010 Catanduva ☎17 3522 2228 **W:** difusora680.com.br – **SP28)** Av Vereador Eduardo Cassanho 317, 18800-970 Piraju ☎14 3351 1680 **W:** piratiningapiraju.com.br **E:** contato@piratiningapiraju.com.br – **SP29)** Rua Prudente Moraes 325 sl 2, 14700-000 Bebedouro ☎17 3342 2484 **W:** radiobebedouro.com.br **E:** gerencia.rb@mdbrasil.com.br – **SP30)** Praça Conselheiro Rodrigues Alves 170, 12500-020 Guaratinguetá ☎12 9138 1622 **W:** clubeam690.com.br **E:** cesarcornetti@ hotmail.com - **FM:** 97.1MHz – **SP31)** Av Humberto Liedtke 1936, 15370-970 Pereira Barreto ☎18 3704 2121 **W:** radiocidadeam690.com. br **E:** contato@radiocidadeam690.com.br **MSN:** radiocidadeampb@

hotmail.com – **SP32)** Av.Eng Caetano Alvares, 55, Limão, 02598-900 Sao Paulo ☎11 2108 6700 **W:** radio.estado.com.br - **FM:** 92.9MHz – **SP33)** Rua 1 de Agosto 927, 17010-011 Bauru – **SP34)** Rua dos Pelegrinis 11, Desterro, 13700-000 Casa Branca ☎19 3671 2101 **W:** radiodifusoracasabranca.com.br **E:** contato@radiodifusoracasabranca. com.br – **SP35)** Rua Antonio Carlos Mori 288, 19900 080 Ourinhos ☎14 3322 5758 **W:** sentinelaam.com.br – **SP36)** Rua Dr Carlos Varela 104, Cruzeiro ☎12 3143 6894 **W:** rcvale.com.br – **SP37)** Rua Washington Luis 576, 15400-000 Olímpia ☎17 3281 3044 **W:** espaciolivream.com.br **E:** adm@espaciolivream.com.br – **SP38)** Rua Siqueira de Morães, 578 10° andar, 13201-803 Jundiaí ☎11 4586 0969 ▤11 4586 4188 **W:** cidadeam.com.br **E:** radio@cidadeam.com – **SP39)** Rua Coronel Galdino de Almeida 55, 17500-100 Marília ☎14 3402 5128 **W:** dirceu.am.br – **SP40)** Av. João Lemos 578, 17250-970 Bariri ☎14 3662 1276 **W:** radioculturadebariri.com.br – **SP41)** Av Paulista, 900, Bela Vista, 01310-100 São Paulo ☎11 3289 3755 ▤11 3280 3768 **W:** new.radiotrianon.com.br **E:** contato@radiotrianon.com.br – **SP42)** Rua Itapura 6, 17700-970 Osvaldo Cruz ☎18 3528 1089 **W:** radioosvaldocruz.com.br **E:** contato@radioosvaldocruz.com.br - **FM:** 97.3MHz «California FM» – **SP43)** Rua Ramos de Azevedo, 622, Jardim Paulista, 14090-180 Ribeirão Preto ☎16 3624 2622 **W:** radiocmn.com. br – **SP44)** Rua Euclides Miragaia 394, 18° andar, 12245-820 São José dos Campos ☎12 3909 8000 **W:** radiopiratininga.com.br **E:** jornalismo@radiopiratininga.com.br - **FM:** 99.7MHz – **SP45)** Rua Virgilio Malta 6-78, 17015-220 Bauru ☎14 3104 0760 **W:** auriverde. am.br **E:** jornalismo@auriverde.am.br – **SP46)** Av Dr Lauro Correa da Silva, 3230, Jardim do Lago, 13480-041 Limeira ☎19 3404 4000 **W:** mixam.com.br **E:** manoelmixregional@gmail.com – **SP48)** Alameda Dr Armando de Salles Oliveira 575, 17800-000 Adamantina ☎18 3521 1242 **W:** radiobrasilam.com.br **E:** contato@radiobrasilam.com.br – **SP49)** Av Bento de Abreu, 889, Jardim Primavera, 14802-3986 Araraquara ☎16 3303 3622 **W:** radiocultura.net **E:** comercial@ radiocultura.net- **FM:** 97.3MHz – **SP50)** Rua Barão de Jundiaí 1041-9° andar, 13201-906 Jundiaí ☎11 4586 2020 **W:** radiodifusorajundiai. com.br **E:** radio@radiodifusorajundiai.com.br – **SP51)** Rua Quince de Novembro 3131, 15015-110 São José do Rio Preto ☎17 3233 4600**W:** blog.cancaonova.com/riopreto **E:** radioriopreto@cancaonova.com – **SP53)** Rua Tenente Lopes 191, (C.P.3) 17201-460 Jaú ☎14 3622 2800 ▤14 3622 4376 **W:** radiojauense.com.br **E:** radiojauense@netsite.com. br - **FM:** 101.1MHz – **SP54)** Rua José Galvão, 359, Vila Moraes, (C.P 94) 19900-260 Ourinhos ☎14 3322 2997 ▤14 3322 6255 **W:** radioclube820.com.br – **SP55)** Av.Antonieta Vilela Ferreira 900, Vilage, 16300-000 Penápolis ☎18 3654 2250 **W:** difusoradepenapolis.com.br **E:** difusora@difusoradepenapolis.com.br – **SP56)** Rua Pernambuco, 4006, Jardim Eldorado, 15500-006 Votuporanga ☎17 3422 3301 **W:** lider830.com.br – **SP57)** Rua Radiantes, 13, Jardim Leonor, 05614-900 São Paulo **W:** radiobandeirantes.band.uol.com.br **E:** rbnoar@band.com. br - **FM:** 90.9MHz – **SP58)** Avenida 2, 1420, Jardim Claret, 13502-240 Rio Claro ☎19 3533 2307 **W:** radioclubeam.am.br **E:** comercial@ radioclubefm.fm.br - **FM:** 94.3 MHz – **SP59)** Av Nove de Julho, 2875, Novo Jardim Stábile, 16204-050 Birigui ☎18 3642 2240 **W:** tropicalbirigui.com.br **E:** clubeam@tropicalbirigui.com – **SP60)** Rua Prudente de Morães 418, 14960-000 Novo Horizonte **W:** radio870.com. br – **SP61)** Rua Romualdo Andreazzi, 16, Jd Leonor, 13041-030 Campinas ☎19 3772 1750 ▤19 3772 1766 **W:** radiocentral.com.br **E:** radiocentral@radiocentral.com.br – **SP62)** Av.Paulista, 900 4° andar, Bela Vista, 01310-940 Sao Paulo ☎11 3170 5757 ▤11 3170 5630 **W:** gazetaam.com **E:** hrocha@radiogazeta.com.br - **FM:** 88.1 MHz – **SP63)** Rua Rui Barbosa 723, 19015-000 Presidente Prudente ☎18 222 2500 – **SP64)** Rua Siqueira Campos 3223, 15010-040 São José do Rio Preto - **FM:** 102.1MHz «R Onda Nova FM» – **SP65)** Rua Miguel Janez, 19, Vila Arlindo Luz, 18212-480 Itapetininga ☎15 3373 7301 **E:** radioglobo900@bol.com.br – **SP66)** Av Limeira, 222, Vila Areão,, 13414-018 Piracicaba ☎19 3436 6300 **W:** ondalivream.com.br **E:** comercial@ondalivre.com.br - **FM:** 105.3 – **SP67)** Rua Monsenhor Rosa 1561, 14400-670 Franca ☎16 3713 3977 **W:** radioimperador.com. br **E:** contato@radioimperador.com.br – **SP68)** Av Brasil, 31, Parque de Felicidade, 13973-255 Itapira ☎19 3863 0138 **W:** radioclubeitapira. com.br **E:** radioclube@dglnet.com.br – **SP69)** Av Ana Costa 532, 5° andar, Gonzaga, 11060-002 Santos ☎13 3289 5757 **W:** radiocultura. com.br **E:** cultura@radiocultura.com.br - **FM:** 106.7MHz – **SP70)** rRua Rio Branco 9-70, 17015-310 Bauru ☎14 3243 4104 **W:** cancaonova. com **E:** davibauru@cancaonova.com – **SP71)** Rua Doce 303, 15775-000 Santa Fé do Sul ☎17 3631 4859 **W:** radiosantafe.com.br **E:** comercial@ radiosantafe.com - **FM:** 104.7MHz – **SP72)** Av Sampaio Vidal, 185, Barbosa, 17500-441 Marília ☎14 3301 4341 **W:** radio950.com.br – **SP73)** Av João Dias, 1860, Santo Amaro, 04724-002 São Paulo ☎11 3442 2660 – **SP74)** Rua Quintino Bocaiuva 330 18200-014 Itapetininga 15 3271 2000 **W:** radiosuperdifusora.com.br – **SP75)** Rua Floriano Peixoto 64, 13870-060 São João da Boa Vista ☎19 3631 5853 **W:** piratininga970am.com.br **E:** radio970@dglnet.com.br – **SP76)** Rua Luis

Pires, 250, Jardim Redentor, 14409-283 Franca ☎16 3704 7733 **W:** radiohertz.com.br - **FM:** 96.5MHz – **SP77)** Rua da Várzea, 240, Várzea da Brra Funda, 01140-080 São Paulo ☎11 3661 6727 **W:** radiosetvs. com/radiorecord_sp **E:** radiorecordamsp@r7.com – **SP78)** Av. Zero Nove 1, 14781-574 Barretos ☎17 3321 7070 **W:** odiarioonline.com.br – **SP79)** Rua Kametaro Morishita, 95, 3°andar, Cidade Universitaria, 19050-700 Presidente Prudente – **SP80)** Rua João Paulo II s/n, (C.P 57), 12630-000 Cachoeira Paulista ☎12 3186 2600 **W:**radio.cancaonova. com/am-cachoeira-paulista/ **E:** radio@cancaonova.com – **SP81)** Rua Benjamin Constant 33 10° andar, 19806-130 Assis ☎18 3322 8811 **W:** culturadeassis.com.br **E:** cultura@culturadeassis.com.br – **SP82)** Rua Profa Aparecida M.Faveri, 988, Parque Egisto Ragazzo, 13485-316 Limeira ☎19 3441 3760 **W:** educadoraam.com.br **E:** radio@ educadoraam.com.br – **SP83)** Rua 24 2442 , 15700-000 Jales ☎17 3622 5508 **W:** radioculturadejales.com.br – **SP84)** Av Eliz Verzola Gosuen, 3103, Jardim Angela Rosa, , 14403-605 Franca ☎16 3713 8899 **W:** difusora.com.br **E:** difusora@gcn.net.br – **SP85)** Av Industrial José E Ortigosa, 570 an 1, Dis Industrial 1 - Centro, 17340-970 Barra Bonita ☎14 3641 0131 – **SP86)** Rua Luiz Gama 378 an 8, 16400-080 Lins 14 3532 7000 – **SP87)** Praça Rodrigues de Abreu, 228, Paraiso, 04040-080 São Paulo ☎11 3053 1040 **W:** radiocapital-1040.com.br **E:** faleconosco@radiocapital.am.br – **SP88)** Rua Boa Morte 1122, 13400-140 Piracicaba ☎19 3422 1060 **W:** educadora1060.com.br **E:** ouvinte@ educadora1060.com.br – **SP89)** Av Rangel Pestana, 147, Vila Matias, 11031-551 Santos ☎13 3224 3098 – **SP91)** Rua Marechal Bitencourt 346, 17201-430 Jaú **W:** radiopiratiningajau.com **E:** contato@ radiopiratiningajau.com – **SP92)** Av Washington Luiz 1250, 19015-150 Presidente Prudente ☎81 3916 1578 **W:** prudente.am.br - **FM** 101.1MHz – **SP94)** Rua Santos Dumont 239, 14300-000 Batatais **W:** difusoraam.com.br **E:** diretoria@difusoraam.com.br ☎16 3761 3600 – **SP95)** Rua Olavo Bilac 693, 16400-000 Lins ☎14 3522 4644 **W:** radioalvoradadelins.com.br **E:** alvorada@superig.com.br – **SP96)** Av André Luiz, 723, Picanco, 07082-050 Sorocaba ☎11 2457 7000 **W:** radioboanova.com.br **E:** rede@radioboanova.com.br – **SP97)** Av Zezé Valadão 359, 12570-970 Aparecida ☎12 3105 0754 **W:** radiomonumental.com.br **E:** radio_monumental@hotmail.com – **SP98)** Av Carlos Artêncio 117, 17519-255 Marília ☎14 3402 3077 **W:** radioclubemarilia.com.br **E:** clubeam@terra.com.br – **SP99)** Av 15 de Maio 455, 15910-970 Monte Alto ☎16 3242 5231 **W:** radioculturamontealto.com.br **E:** contato@radioculturamontealto.com. br –**SP100)** Rua das Palmeiras 315, 01221-010 São Paulo **W:**radioglobo. com.br **E:** midiassociais@radioglobo.com.br – **SP101)** Rua Marechal Deodoro da Fonseca 675, 16011-000 Araçatuba ☎18 3305 9852 **E:** radioluz@terra.com.br – **SP102)** Rua Gabriel Hadad 283,14940-970 Ibatinga ☎16 3341 9900 **W:** radioibitinga.com.br **E:** radio.ibatinga@ ibinet.com.br - **FM:** 99.3MHz «Ternura FM»– **SP103)** Av Luíz Gonzaga de Amoêdo Campos, 28, Vila Áurea, 13480-908 Mogi Mirim ☎19 3814 1234 **W:** hitstransamerica.com.br - **FM:** 91.1MHz – **SP104)** Rua Bandeirantes, 104 18540-970 Porto Feliz ☎15 3261 5003 **W:** radionovaporto.com.br **E:** jornalismo@radionovaporto.com.br – **SP105)** Rua Euclides Miragaia, 548 12245-820 São José dos Campos ☎12 3941 4108 **W:** cidadeam1120.com.br **E:** radio@cidadeam1120.com.br – **SP106)** Rua Duque de Caxias, 260 cj 22 an 2, 15900-970 Tanquaritinga ☎16 3252 2999 **W:** radioimperial.com.br – **SP108)** Rua Gonçalves Dias 208, 19800-110 Assis ☎18 3322 3833 **W:** difusoraassis.com.br **E:** difusora@difusoraassis.com.br – **SP109)** Praça Joel Waldo Dal Moro 1 , 14781-574 Barretos ☎17 3321 7070 **W:** odiarioonline.com.br **E:** contato@grupomonteirasdebarros.com.br – **SP110)** Av. 2, 1420, Jardim Claret, 13503-240 Rio Claro ☎19 3534 0555 – **SP111)** Rua Dr. Esteves da Silva 100, 11680-000 Ubatuba ☎12 3832 2993 **W:** radiocostaazul.com.br **E:** comercial@radiocostaazul.com.br – **SP112)** Av Paulista, 2200Cerquira Cesar, 01310-300, Sao Paulo ☎11 3036 5999 **W:** radiomundial.com.br - **FM:** 95.7MHz – **SP113)** Rua Almirante Barroso 456, 19400-970 Presidente Venceslau ☎18 3271 1386 **W:** www venceslaam.com.br **E:** contato@venceslauam.com.br - **FM:** 95.1MHz «R Jovem Som» – **SP114)** Rua Saldanha de Gama 184, 18035-040 Sorocaba ☎15 3232 3207 **W:** radiocacique.com.br **E:** contato@radiocacique.com.br - **FM:** 96.5MHz – **SP115)** Av. Manoel Marques Rosa, 1075-Ed. Atlântis, 15600-000 Fernandópolis ☎17 3442 2666 **W:** radiodifusorafernandopolis.com.br - **FM:** 99.0MHz – **SP116)** Rua Barão de Monte Santo 1211-3° andar, 13730-060 Mococa ☎19 3656 6534 **W:** radioboanova.com.br **E:** rede@radioboanova.com.br – **SP117)** Av Eng Antonio Francisco de Paula Souz, 2799, Vila Georgina, 13044-370 Campinas ☎19 3779 7500 **W:** senhorbomjesusdemonte. com.br/radio-difusora-aparecida **E:** jornalcps@band.com.br – **SP118)** Rua Barão do Rio Branco, 4454, Vila Paes, 15500-055 Votuporanga ☎17 3421 2113 **W:** radiocidade1190.com.br **E:** contato@ radiocidade1190.com.br – **SP119)** Av XV de Novembro 715, 13650-000 Santa Cruz das Palmeiras ☎19 3672 6976 – **SP120)** Rodovia Taquarituba Avare, s/n km 384, 18740-000 Taquarituba ☎14 3762 1487 **W:** radioregional1190.com.br **E:** regionalam@yahoo.com.br –

**SP121)** Rua Vladimir Herzog, 75, Agua Branca, 05036-900 São Paulo **W:** culturabrasil.com.br ☎11 2182 3080 – **SP122)** Rua Rui Barbosa 546-4° andar, 14870-300 Jaboticabal ☎16 3202 0266 **W:** radiovidanova.com.br **E:** falecom@dioviodanovaam.com.br **SP124)** Av Dr Nunu de Assis 5050, Jardim Bela Vista, 17010-120 Bauru ☎14 3232 3571 **W:** radiobandeirantesbauru.com.br – **SP125)** Av. Roberto Simonsen, 280, Jd. Santa Rosalia,18090-000 Sorocaba ☎15 3224 5300 **W:** radiovanguarda.com.br **E:** comercial@radiovanguardia.com.br - **FM:** 94.9MHz – **SP126)** Rua Rafael Machado Neto, 101, Vila Nova Capão Bonita, 18304-130 Capão Bonito ☎15 3542 1593 **W:** siteadministravel.com.br – **SP128)** Rua Dr Miguel Penteado 585, Jardim Chapadão, 13073-180 Santos – **SP129)** Praça Emilio Peduti 28, 18600-410 Botucatu ☎14 3882 0236 **W:** radiomunicipalista.com.br – **SP130)** Rua 8 472, 14620-000 Orlândia ☎16 3826 3000 📠16 3826 3006 **W:** orc.com.br **E:** orc@orc.com.br – **SP131)** Rua Julia Conceição,510, Encruzilhada 11055-320 Santos **W:** Facebook: Rádio Clube de Santos 1240AM – **SP132)** Av Nove de Julho 265, 15200-000 José Bonifácio ☎17 3245 1621 **W:** radiovaledotiete.com.br **E:** contato@radiovaledotiete.com.br – **SP133)** Rua Vilaa 195-Sala 23, 12210-000 São Jose dos Campos ☎12 3923 7000 **W:** blog.cancaonova. com/saojosedoscampos **E:** radiosjc@cancaonova.com – **SP134)** Av Bento Abreu 889, 1408-396 Araraquara ☎16 3303 3622 **W:** radiomorada.com.br **E:** radiomorada@uol.com.br – **SP136)** Rua Irmã Serafina, 88, Bosque, 13026-066 Campinas ☎19 3231 7860 **W:** brasilcampinas.com.br **E:** radio@brasilcampinas.com.br – **SP137)** Rua dos Radialistas Riopretense, 895, Nova Redentora, 15090-070 São José do Rio Preto ☎17 3233 3322 **W:** novotempoam.com.br **E:**comercial@novotempoam.com.br – **SP138)** Av do Estado, 4568, Cambuchi, 01516-901 Sao Paulo **W:** ipda.com.br **E:** webmaster@ipda. com.br – **SP139)** Rua Barao do Rio Branco 559, 14900-000 Itápolis ☎16 3262 3063 – **SP140)** Rua Antônio Gambagote, 27-esquina com Av. Newton Prado, 13631-096 Pirassununga ☎19 3561 2200 **W:** difusorapirassununga.com.br **E:** difusora@radiobraganca.com.br – **SP141)** Rua Coronel Osório 84, 12900-150 Bragança Paulista ☎11 4034 0442 **W:** radiobraganca.com.br **E:** radiobraganca@radiobraganca.com.br – **SP142)** Rua Siqueira Campos 633, 19010-061 Presidente Prudente ☎18 3222 6021 **W:** radiopaulista1330.com.br **E:** contato@radiopaulista1330.com.br – **SP143)** Rua Batatais, 36-Jardim Paulista, 14090-160 Ribeirão Preto ☎16 3967 6002 –**SP144)** Rua Osvaldo Cruz 67, 16010-040 Araçatuba. ☎18 3623 8726 **W:** culturaam1340.com - **FM:** 95.5MHz – **SP145)** Rua Barão de Jaceguai 468, 08710-905 Mogi das Cruzes ☎11 4799 2888 **W:** redemetropolitana.com.br – **SP146)** Rua Hipólito Lopes , 17350-000 Igaraçu do Tietê ☎14 3644 1122 **W:** novacanoa.com.br – **SP148)** Av Orlando Fruchi, 97, Distrito Industrial, 17900-000 Dracena ☎18 3821 2593 **W:** radioregionaljp.com.br **E:** contato@radioregionaljp. com – **SP149)** Rua Cuiabá 361, 16901-200 Andradina ☎18 3722 2729 – **SP150)** Av João Lemos 578, 17250-000 Bariri ☎14 3662 4000 **W:** baririradioclube.com.br **E:** contato@baririradioclube.com.br – **SP151)** Rua Pedro Natalia Lorenzetti 172, 18680-110 Lençóis Paulista ☎14 3264 8100 **W:** difusora1010.com.br **E:** administracao@difusora1010. com.br – **SP152)** Rua Vereador Eugênio Mazon, Jardim Centenário, 13845-197 Mogi Guaçu ☎19 3861 0098 – **SP153)** Av. Benjamin Constant 1214-3° andar, 13010-141 Campinas ☎19 3731 5100 **W:** globocampinas.com.br **E:** contato@globocampinas.com.br – **SP154)** Rua Dr Erico de Abreu Sodré 542, 16370-000 Promissão ☎14 3541 0508 **W:** radioculturaapromissao.com **E:** radiocultura@yahoo.com.br – **SP155)** Av Brasil, 1119, Zana Sul, 17780-000 Lucélia ☎18 3551 1831 – **SP156)** Rua Salomao Shevs, 670, Jardim Cruzeiro do Sul, 13572-083 São Carlos ☎16 3375 3046 **W:** clube.com.br **E:::** info@clube.com.br - **FM:** 104.7MHz **SP157)** Rua Voluntários de Sao Paulo. 3066-10 andar conjunto 1003, 15015-200 São José do Rio Preto ☎17 3212 7012 **W:** radiometropole1400am.blogspot.com.br **E:** metropoleam@terra.com.br – **SP158)** Av Brigadeiro Luiz Antonio, 3175, Jardim Paulista , 01401-001 São Paulo ☎11 2039 1410 **W:** blog.america.cancaonova **E:** americaweb.com.br **E:** americaweb@gmail.com – **SP159)** Ladeira Prof Irineu Lopes de Lima 418, 13250-241 Itatiba ☎11 4524 0003 **W:** crnitatiba.com.br **E:** crnitatiba@terra.com.br – **SP160)** Rua Cerqueira Cesar 481, 14010-130 Ribeirão Preto – **SP161)** Rua Mato Grosso, 37, Vila Aparecida, 15150-000 Monte Aprazível ☎17 3275 1772 **W:** difusoraaparecida.com.br **E:** difusoraaparecida@bol.com.br – **SP162)** Praça Barão do Rio Branco 30, 12010-090 Taubaté ☎12 3622 1866 **W:** dt7.com.br/radio **E:** contato@ radiocultura790.com.br – **SP163)** Av Doutor Júlio Faria, 828 - Centro , 18650-970 São Manuel ☎14 3841 3590 **W:** novasaomanuel.com.br – **SP164)** Rua Juca Cintra 85, 13930-000 Serra Negra ☎19 389 1125 **W:** Facebook: Rádio Serra Negra AM 1430 **E:** radio.serranegra@terra.com. br – **SP165)** Av Manoel Goulart, 291 1° andar, 19010-270 Presidente Prudente ☎18 3221 2900 **W:** comercialam.com.br – **SP167)** Av André Luís, 723, Picanço, 07082-050 Guarulhos. ☎11 2457 7000 **W:** radioboanova.com.br **E:** rede@radioboanova.com.br – **SP168)** Rua 9 de Julho 1801, 13560-042 Sao Carlos do Pinhal ☎16 3371 3724 **W:** saocarlosam.com.br **E:** comercial@saocarlosam.com.br – **SP170)** Rua

Duque de Caixas 53 2° andar, 12600-040 Lorena ☎☎12 3157 7032 **W:** radiocultura1460.com.br **E:** radiocultura@provale.com.br – **SP172)** Av 15 225, 14790-000 Guaíra 17 3331 1177 **W:** radioculturaguaira.com.br - **FM:** 90.1 MHz – **SP173)** Av Rui Barbosa 229, 12308-520 Jacareí ☎12 3954 3000 📠12 3954 3009 **W:** radiomensagem.am **E:** mensagem@ radiomensagem.am.br – **SP174)** Rua Sao Sebastiao 33, 13660-000 Porto Ferreira ☎19 3581 1552 – **SP175)** Rua 13 de Maio, 2680, Vila Georgina, 13333-080 Indaiatuba ☎19 3875 9141 **W:** radiojornalindaiatuba.com.br **E:** contato@radiojornalindaiatuba.com.br – **SP176)** Rua Renato Jardim 511, 14350-970 Altinópolis **W:** clubregionalam.com.br – **SP177)** Av Brigadeiro José Vicente Faria Lima 54, 12940-284 Atibaia ☎11 4411 8773 – **SP178)** Rua Conceiçao 596, 16210-000 Bilac ☎18 3659 1854 **W:** miliciadaimaculada.org.br **E:** 890am@miliciadaimaculada.org.br – **SP179)** Rua Conselheiro Dantas 30, 18900-000 Santa Cruz do Rio Pardo ☎14 3372 1763 **W:** difusorasantacruz.com.br **E:** contato@difusorasantacruz.com.br – **SP180)** Av Governador Ademar Pereira de Barros, 134, Lotamente Canterville, 15400-000 Olímpia ☎17 3281 1097 **W:** difusoraolimpia. com.br – **SP181)** Rua Monte Castelo 941, 17900-000 Dracena ☎18 3821 8132 **W:** radioglobodracena.com.br – **SP182)** Av Brasil, 1712, 15600-970Fernandópolis ☎📠1734621112**W:**educadorafernandopolis. com.br **E:** ouvinteeducadora@terra.com.br – **SP183)** Rua Padre Moro Grande, 870, Dos Finco, 09831-250 São Bernardo do Campo ☎11 4397 6500 **W:** miliciadaimaculada.org.br **E:** sam@miliciadaimaculada.org.br – **SP184)** Av Guerino Turatti, 200, DistritoIndustrial III, 13602-900 Araras ☎☎19 3543 7990 **W:** fraternidade.com.br **E:** contato@ fraternidadefm.com.br - **FM:** 97.9MHz – **SP185)** Rua Rubião Júnior 192, 12400-450 Pindamonhangaba ☎12 3643 1566 **W:** rededifusora. com.br/am1500/index.htm **E:** mkt@rededifusora.com.br – **SP186)** Av Leopoldo Carlos de Oliveira 1038, 14530-000 Miguelópolis ☎16 3835 1500 **W:** radiofmvale.com.br - **FM:** 87.9 MHz – **SP187)** Av.Paulista, 2200 13° andar, Cerqueira Cesar, 01310-300 Osasco ☎11 3266 6880 **W:** radioterra.am.br – **SP188)** Rua Silva Jardim, 480, Macuco, 11015-020 Santos ☎13 3221 9500 📠13 3327 7643 **W:** radiocacique1510. com.br **E:** radio.cacique@hotmail.com – **SP189)** Rua Coronel Rodrigues Simôs 69 , 18650-000 São Manuel ☎14 3841 2555 **W:** cluberegional. com.br **E:** jornalismo@cluberegional.com.br – **SP190)** Av Romeu Viana Romaneli 1510, 15570-970 Cardoso ☎☎17 3453 1376 **W:** radioalvoradacardoso.com **E:** radioalvoradacardoso@gmail.com – **SP191)** Rua Princesa Isabel de Braganca 235, 08710-460 Mogi das Cruzes ☎11 4796 1478 **W:** radiodacidadeam.com.br – **SP192)** Rua Vereador Rosas 171, 13990-000 Espírito Santo do Pinhal ☎19 3651 1755 **W:** pinhalradioclube.com.br **E:** radiopinhal@dglnet.com.br - **FM:** 102.7MHz – **SP193)** Rua Marchal Deodora 519, 17930-970 Tupi Paulista – **SP194)** Rua Capitão Lisboa 1080, 18270-000 Tatuí ☎15 3251 3840 **W:** radionoticias.com.br – **SP195)** Rua Benedito Carlos dos Reis 700, 15190-970 Nhandeara ☎17 3472 1668 – **SP196)** Rua Marechal Deodoro 320, 18600-320 Botucatu ☎14 3882 1535 **W:** radiof8.com.br **E:** gravadorf8@hotmail.com – **SP197)** Av Diogo Antonio Feijo, 1184, Jardim das Flores , 06114-029 Osasco ☎11 3681 1134 **W:** novadifusora.com.br **E:** faleconcoso@novadifusora.com.br – **SP198)** Rua Dom José Carlos Aguirre 567, 18460-000 Itararé ☎15 3532 4055 **W:** radioclube.cjb.net **E:** falecom@radioclubeam.net – **SP199)** Rua Pedro de Toledo 205, 19700-000 Paraguaçu Paulista ☎18 3361 1203 📠18 3362 2306 **W:** radiomarconi.com.br **E:** marconi@radiomarconi. com.br – **SP200)** Rua Lino Dorelli 120, 13360-000 Capivari ☎19 3492 1550 **W:** caciqueam.com.br **E:** matheus@caciqueam.com.br – **SP201)** Rua José Vaz de Porto, 175, Vila Santa Rosa, 11431-190 Guarujá ☎13 3269 1010 **W:** radioguarujaam.com.br **E:** radioguarujaam@ radioguarujaam.com.br - **FM:** 104.5MHz – **SP202)** Rua Minas Gerais 1225 , 124600-970 São Joaquim da Barra ☎16 3818 1324 **W:** radiosaojoaquim.com.br – **SP203)** Av Dr Januario Miraglia. 650, Vila Abernessia, 12460-970 Campos do Jordão ☎12 3662 1906 **W:** hcamposdojordao1340.com.br **E:** emisora1340am@hotmail.com – **SP204)** Rua Rio Grande do Sul, 2165, Braz I 18701-190 Avaré ☎14 3732 1564 **W:** radioavare.com.br **E:** radioavare@yahoo.com.br – **SP205)** Rua Belo Horizonte Nº930 17890-000 Junqueirópolis ☎18 3841 1465 **W:** radiojunqueiropolis.com.br **E:** contato@radiojunqueiropolis. com – **SP206)** Av Pereira Barreto, 1200, Vila Gilda, 09190-210 Santo André ☎11 4435 9000 📠11 4435 9001 **W:** radioabc.com.br **E:** faleconosco@radioabc.com.br – **SP207)** Rua Dr Vicente D´Anna 473, 13960-970 Socorro ☎19 3895 1444 **W:** radiosocorro.com.br **E:** comercial@radiosocrro.com.br – **SP208)** Rodovia Dep. Bady Bassit, km 15, Jardim Covizzi, 15170-000 Tanabi ☎17 3272 2967 **W:** radioclubetanabi.com.br **E:** contato@radioclubetanabi.com.br – **SP209)** Rua Dr Felipe Vita 1616, 18480-000 Itaporanga ☎15 9753 6358 – **SP211)** Rua Joaquim Moreira, 12, Parque São Miguel, 07260-220 Guarulhos ☎11 2496 1542 **W:** radiocumbica.com.br moacyrcustodio@radiocumbica.com.br – **SP212)** Av 17 560, 14780-000 Barretos ☎17 3324 1000 **W:** radiojornaldebarretos.com.br **E:** radiojornal@jornalbarretos.com.br - **FM:** 101.1 MHz – **SP213)** Av

Paulista 2202, 8° andar, Conj 81/82, 01310-300 São Paulo ☎11 5543 0762 – **SP214)** Av Capitão José Antônio de Oliveira 544, 17800-000 Adamantina ☎18 3521 3547 **W:** radiojoia.com.br **E:** contato@ radiojoia.com.br - **FM:** 93.7MHz «Antena 1» – **SP216)** Rua Rubião Junior, 84 sl.89, Shopping Centro, 12210-180 São José dos Campos ☎12 33221290 **W:** am1290.com.br – **SP217)** Rua Coronel João Manoel 604 sl, 14700-000 Bebedouro ☎17 3343 6528 **W:** radionovaamaovivo.com.br – **SP218)** Rua Antônio Lobo 237 1° andar, 13465-005 Americana ☎19 3462 3992 **W:** azulceleste.com.br **E:** azulceleste@azulceleste.com.br – **SP219)** Rua João Pacheco de Lima 56-89, 15350-000 Auriflama ☎17 3482 2068 **W:** radioauriflama.com. br **E:** radioauriflama@hotmail.com – **SP220)** A Monte Castelo 225, 13450-285 Santa Bárbara d'Oeste ☎19 3463 5255 **W:** radiobrasilsbo. com.br **E:** radiobrasil@radibrasilsbo.com.br – **SP221)** Rua Maximo Ribeiro Nunes, 75, Jardim Peri Peri, 05535-000 Sao Paulo ☎11 3723 7575 **W:** nacionalgospel.com.br **E:** radio@nacionalgospel.com.br - **FM:** 100.5 MHz – **SP222)** Av Antonieta Vilela Ferreira, 900, Vilage, 16300-000 Penápolis ☎18 3654 2250 **W:** banddepenapolis.com.br **E:** bandpenapolis@banddepenapolis.com.br – **SP223)** Av Paulista, 2200-10°andar, Cerqueira Cesar, 01310-300 São Paulo ☎11 3016 5999 **W:** radiodacidadeam.com.br – **SP224)** Rua Kametaro Morishita, 95, Cidade Universitária, 19050-700 Presidente Prudente ☎18 3299 0300 **W:** radioglobopp.com.br - **FM:** 106.7MHz – **SP225)** Rua Imperatriz Leopoldina, 41, Vila Delgado Romano, 18044-010 Sorocaba ☎15 3222 5740 – **SP226)** Rua Bento Carlos 61, 13560-660 São Carlos ☎16 3362 3322 **W:** portalrealidade.com.br – **SP227)** Rua Duque de Caxais 33, 13460-000 Nova Odessa ☎19 3466 5026 **W:** novotempocampinas.com.br **E:** comercial@novotempocampinas.com. br – **SP228)** Rua Américo Vespúcio 20, 14730-000 Monte Azul Paulista ☎17 3361 2215 **W:** radioprincesaam.com.br – **SP229)** Av Dr radioprincesamonteazulpaulista@hotmail.com.br – **SP229)** Av Dr Labiano da Costa Machado, 1735, Hilmar Machado, 17400-000 Garça ☎14 3471 0700 **W:** unimidianet.com.br – **SP231)** Francisco Troani 1211, 19280-000 Teodoro Sampaio ☎18 3282 1534 – **SP232)** Av Paulista, 2200-17 andar, Bela Vista, 01310-300 São Paulo ☎11 5081 579 **W: superradio1150.com.br – SP233)** Av 9 de Julho, 304, Nova Paulina, 13150-000 Paulínia ☎19 3844 8300 **W:** blog.cancaonova. com/paulinia **E:** cnpaulinia@cancaonova.com – **SP234)** Rua Carlos Gomes 534, 14640-000 Morro Agudo ☎16 3851 2414 **W:** radiorepublica.com.br **E:** republica@com4.com.br – **SP235)** Rua Joaquim de Oliveira 586, 13450-038 Santa Bárbara d'Oeste ☎19 3464 1300 **W:** radioluzes.com.br **E:** radioluzes@uol.com.br – **SP236)** Av Izodoro Alpheu Santiago 126, Santa Bárbara,18320-970 Apiaí ☎15 3552 4088 **W:** radiocidadeapiai.com.br – **SP237)** Rua Marechal Rondon, 170, Alto São Pedro, 12082-420 Taubaté ☎12 3632 0555 – **SP238)** Av Dr Soares de Oliveira 2070, 14500-970 Ituverava ☎16 3839 7739 **W:** radiocultura1450.com.br **E:** radiocultura@netsite.com. br – **SP239)** Av Frederico Ozanan, 554, 17300-000 Dois Córregos ☎14 3652 2949 **W:** radioculturaregional.com.br – **SP240)** Av Olinda Ralston 411B, 13720-000 São José do Rio Pardo **W** amdifusora.com. br – **SP241)** Rua Tocantins, 425, Vila Espanha, 17607-070 Tupã ☎14 3496 1756 – **SP242)** Av Washington Luíz 214, 13600-720 Araras ☎19 3541 3714 **W:** radioclube.com.br **E:** radioclube@radioclube.com.br – **SP243)** Rua Dom Pedro I 65, 17690-970 Bastos ☎14 3478 2525 – **SP244)** Rua Santana 440, 13880-000 Vargem Grande do Sul ☎19 3641 5646 **W:** http//radioculturaam.com **E:** r.cultura@itelefonica.com. br – **SP245)** R. Rafael de Barros 126, 13610-120 Lemé ☎19 3571 4288 **W:** radioculturadeleme.com.br **E:** ouvinte@radioculturadeleme. com.br – **SP246)** Rua Francisco Geraldino 71, 17580-970 Pompéia ☎14 3452 3900 **W:** radiojovemcentral.com.br – **SP247)** Rua 7 de Setembro 73, 17280-000 Pederneiras 14 3248 1989 **W:** amcultura.net - **FM:** 88.3MHz – **SP249)** Rua 15 de Novembro 52, 13920-000 Pedreira – **SP250)** Av Presidente Vargas 244, 19470-000 Presidente Epitácio ☎18 3281 2577 **W:** facebook.rádio.vela.do.rio.paraná – **SP251)** Rua Comendador Guimarães 25 sl 402, 13900-470 Amparo ☎19 3807 2237 **W:** difusoradeamparo.com.br **E:** radio@difusoradeamparo.com. br – **SP252)** Rua Padre João Goetz, 370, Jardim Esplanada, 19061-460 Presidete Prudente ☎18 3918 5300 **W:** ondaviva.com.br **E:** radioondaviva@stetnet.com.br – **SP253)** Rua 7 de Setembro 911, 14240-000 Cajuru – **SP254)** Av São Paulo, 100, Jacaré, 13318-000 Cabreúva **W:** radiojapi.radio.br – **SP255)** Alameda dos Lírios 111, 18550-000 Boituva ☎15 3363 7352 **W:** rboituva.com.br – **SP256)** Rua José Revel 477, 13320-020 Salto ☎11 4029 0198 **W:** radiovaledotiete. com.br – **SP257)** Rua 9 de Julho 666, 16600-000 Piraju ☎14 3357 1352 **W:** pirajuiradioclube.net **E:** contato@pirajuiradioclube.net.br – **SP258)** Rua dos Operários, 1441, Vila Rigueti, 19600-000 Rancharia ☎18 3265 1528 – **SP259)** Rua Antônio João de Carvalho 39 1° andar, 13710-000 Tambaú ☎19 3673 1729 **W:** radiotambauam.com.br **E:** leandro@radiotambauam.com.br – **SP260)** Av. Professor Jesuíno 352, 17380-000 Brotas ☎14 3653 1306 **W:** radiobrotense.com.br **E:** ouvinte@radiobrotense.com.br – **SP261)** Rua Nicalau Nassif, 523,

Jardim Imperial, 14540-000 Igarapava ☎16 3172 2570 **W:** radioshowam.blogspot.no/ **E:** radioshowigarapava@gmail.com – **SP262)** Rua Inácio Ribeiro 592, 13670-000 Santa Rita do Passa Quatro ☎19 3582 1278 **W:** radiozequinhadeabreu.com.br **E:** contato@radiozequinhadeabreu.com.br – **SP263)** Rua Manoel de Arzão, 85, Vila Albertina, 02730-030 São Paulo ☎11 3932 3393 **W:** radio9dejulho.com.br **E:** radio@radio9dejulho.com.br – **SP264)** Av 04 882, 13500-030 Rio Claro ☎19 3526 1055 **W:** jornalcidade.net **E:** radio@jcrioclaro.com.br – **SP265)** Av São Sebastião 162 3° piso sala 1, 18150-000 Ibiúna ☎15 3241 5679 **W:** radioexcelsiorad.com.br **E:**radioad1350@hotmail.com – **SP266)** Legião da Boa Vontade (LBV), Rua Doraci, 90, Bom Retiro, 01134-050 Sao Paulo **W:** redeboavontade. com.br **E:** superrbv@boavontade.com – **SP269)** Rua 24 de Maio, 690, 14870-350 Jaboticabal ☎16 3203 5355 **W:** radioathenas.com.br **E:** adm@radioathenas.com.br – **SP270)** Rua Dos Pereiras 1197, 15290-970 Buritama ☎18 3691 3279 **W:** torreforteam.radioamiga.com.br**E:** torreforteam@uol.com.br – **SP273)** Av Clara Gianotti de Souza 1124, 11900-970 Registro ☎13 3821 1606 **W:** radionovaregionalam. blogspot.com.br **E:** radionovaregionalam1140@gmail.com – **SP274)** Rdv. Anel Viário Contorno Sul, 99, City, 14021-800 Ribeirao Preto ☎16 3621 2337 **W:** radiobandeirantes.com.br – **SP275)** Rua Honório Mendes de Moraes, 23, Esplanada Mendes Moares, 18130-760 São Roque ☎11 4712 4976 **W:** miliciadaimaculada.org.br **E:** 1430am@ miliciadaiimaculada.org.bra – **SP280)** Rua Épiró, 110, Vila Alexandria, (C.P 80761, 04646-970) 04635-030 São Paulo **W:** transmundial.org.br **E:** rtm@transmundial.org.br Rec. Rpts to: qsl@transmundial.com.br – **SP283)** Praca Osvaldo Cruz, 124, Conjuto 116, 11900-000 Registro – **SP284)** Rua Aristides Pires 1397, 18370-970 Itai ☎14 3761 2753 – **SP285)** Rua Luiza Bechelli, 284, Jardim Sabaúna, 11740-000 Itanhaém ☎13 3422 1177 **W:** Facebook: Rádio Anchiete AM 1390 kHz – **SP286)** Rua Tiradentes 31,14740-000 Viradouro ☎17 3392 3008 **W:** cliqueradiolegal.com **E:** contato@ cliqueradiolegal.com – **SP287)** Rua Gabriel Hadad 283,14940-970 Ibatinga ☎16 3341 9900 **W:** radioibitinga.com.br **E:** radio.ibatinga@ibinet.com.br - **FM:** 99.3MHz «Ternura FM» – **SP288)** IPDA, Rua Saldanha Marinho 740, Ribeirao Preto ☎16 3636 6111 – **SP289)** Rua Coronel Nabor Nogueira Santos 258, 3° andar, 12260-000 Paraibuna **W:** radiograndevale.com.br **E:** ouvinte@radiograndevale.com.br

**T000) TOCANTINS**
**T001)** Av Joaquim Aires 2393, 77500-000 Porto Nacional ☎63 3363 1608 – **T002)** Praça Jose Tôrres 3, 77600-000 Paraíso do Tocantins ☎63 3602 1135 – **T003)** Av Nossa Senhora de Fátima 894, 77900-000 Tocantinópolis ☎63 3471 1572 – **T004)** BR-157 Km 1103, Zona Rural, 77804-970 Araguaína - **FM:** 99.7MHz «Araguaia» – **T005)** Rua Raul do Espírito Santo 1334,77760-000 Colinas do Tocantins ☎63 3476 1180 – **T006)** Rua Justianio Borpa, Q.3, Setor Santa Filomena, 77650-000 Miracema do Tocantins ☎63 3366 1264 **W:** radioojornal. com.br **E:** radiocultura1480@hotmail.com – **T007)** Almeda João Pires Querido 827, 77490-000 Cristalândia ☎63 3354 1600 – **T008)** Av Bernardo Sayão 2201, 77700-000 Guaraí **W:** Facebook: Rádio Guaraí Am 1400 kHz **E:** gersonnk@hotmail.com – **T009)** Rua Ns B Q Cj2, 0-Lt2, Acsu Ne 10, 77000-000 Palmas – **T010)** Av Piaui entre Ruas 3 e 4, 77402-970 Gurupi **W:** nossaradioto.com.br **E:** nossaradioto@outlook.com – **T012)** 306 Sul Almeda 2, Plano Diretor Sul, 77021-048 Palmas ☎63 3218 8585 **W:** liberdadeam.com.br **E:** financeiro@liberdadeam.com.br

## BRITISH INDIAN OCEAN TERRITORY

**L.T:** UTC + 6h — **Pr.L:** English — **Pop:** variable (US & British military personnel). Original population of c. 3000 was removed to Mauritius — **E.C:** 60Hz, 110/220V — **ITU:** BIO **Diego Garcia ITU:** DGA

### ARMED FORCES RADIO AND TELEVISION SCE (U.S. Mil.)
▣ Naval Media Center Detachment-Diego Garcia, PSC 466 Box 14, FPO, AP 96595-0014. ☎+246 370 3680/3685 ▤+246 370 3681 **E:** dgar@mediacen.navy.mil
**FM: Power 99,** 99.1MHz 0.25kW, weekdays 0600-1400, rock & roll, live DJ. **Island Variety,** 101.9MHz 250W, mixture of rock, alternative, urban & country. **D.Prgr:** 24h **V.** by letter.

### BRITISH FORCES BROADCASTING SERVICE
**W:** forces.net/radio **FM:** Diego Garcia 90.7MHz

## BRUNEI DARUSSALAM

**L.T:** UTC +8h — **Pop:** 435,000 — **Pr.L:** Malay, English, Chinese, Nepali (Gurkha) — **E.C:** 50Hz, 240V — **ITU:** BRU

### AUTHORITY FOR INFO-COMMUNICATIONS TECHNOLOGY INDUSTRY OF BRUNEI DARUSSALAM

**- AITI (Regulatory Body)**
▣ Block B14, Simpang 32-5, Kampung Anggerek Desa, Jalan Berakas BB3713 ☎ +673 2323232 ▤ +673 2382447 **E:** info@aiti.gov.bn **W:** aiti.gov.bn **LP:** Chmn: Yang Mulia Dato Seri Paduka Awang Haji Matsatejo Bin Sokiaw

### RADIO TELEVISION BRUNEI - RTB (Gov.)
▣ Jalan Elizabeth II, Bandar Seri Begawan BS8610 ☎ +673 2243111 ▤ +673 2241882 **E:** rtbipro@brunet.bn **W:** rtb.gov.bn
**LP:** Dir: Awang Haji Muhammad Suffian Bin Haji Bungsu. Dep. Dir: Development: Hajah Zalinar Binti Haji Abdullah. Dep. Dir. Operation: Madam Lim Soh Kwang Head R. Prgrs: Haji Hasnan bin Suhaili

| FM (MHz) | RN | RPi | RPe | RH | NI | kW |
|---|---|---|---|---|---|---|
| 1) Andulau | 93.8 | 96.9 | 91.0 | 97.7 | 94.9 | 5 |
| 2) Bukit Subok | 92.3 | 95.9 | 91.4 | 94.1 | 93.3 | 5/0.5 |

**DAB:** on 225.648MHz
**1)** Kuala Belait & Tutong area. **2)** Bandar Seri Begawan (BSB) area. RN = Rangkaian Nasional FM in Malay: 24h RPi = R. Pilihan. English: 0300-0800 (Sat 0300-0700), 1200-0100. Chinese: 0100-0300, 0800-1100. Gurkha: daily 1100-1200, Sat 0700-0800. RPe = Rangkaian Pelangi (Pelangi FM, prgrs for young people): 24h Additional FM freqs: 88.5MHz in BSB area, 96.3MHz in Kuala Belait area. RH = Rangkaian Harmoni (music sce.): 24h NI = Rangkaian Nur Islam (rlg. talk channel): 24h Ann: (RN in Malay) Nasional FM, R. Brunei

### KRISTAL MEDIA SDN. BHD. (subsidiary of DST Group, DataStream Technology Sdn Bhd) (Comm.)
▣ Unit 1-345, 1st Fl., Gadong Properties Centre, Gadong BE 4119 11 ☎ +673 2456828 ▤ +673 2420682 **W:** kristal.fm **E:** kristalfm@dst-group.com

| FM (MHz) | KFM | RQ | FM (MHz) | KFM | RQ |
|---|---|---|---|---|---|
| Andulau | 98.7 | 99.7 | Bukit Subok | 90.7 | 89.1 |

KFM=Kristal FM. RQ=Recital of Al-Quran.
**D.Prgr:** Kristal FM: 24h in English/Malay. RQ: 24h in Arabic **N:** (Kristal FM) rel. RTB (0500, 0930, 1200, 1300, 2300) and BBC WS (0600, 1100)

### BRITISH FORCES BROADCASTING SERVICE
▣ BFBS Brunei, BFPO 11 ☎ +673 3223424 ▤ +673 3224113 **E:** bfbsbrunei@bfbs.com **W:** www.forces.net/radio/stations/bfbs-brunei **Prgr.:** 24h in English on 101.7MHz 0.25kW, in Nepali (Gurkha) on 89.5MHz 0.25kW. Location: Brunei Garrison HQ, Tuker Lines, Seria, Belait District

## BULGARIA

**L.T:** UTC +2h (31 Mar-27 Oct: +3h) — **Pop:** 7 million — **Pr.L:** Bulgarian, Turkish — **E.C:** 230V/50Hz — **ITU:** BUL

### SAVET ZA ELEKTRONNI MEDII
**(Council for Electronic Media)**
▣ bul. Shipchenski prohod 69, 1574 Sofia ☎ +359 29708810 ▤+359 29733769 **E:** office@cem.bg **W:** cem.bg **LP:** Chair: Sofia Vladimirova

### BALGARSKO NATSIONALNO RADIO (BNR) (Pub)
▣ bul. Dragan Tsankov 4, 1040 Sofia ☎ +359 29336330 **E:** bnr@bnr. bg **W:** bnr.bg **LP:** DG/Chmn: Aleksandar Velev

| MW | kHz | kW | Prgr |
|---|---|---|---|
| Vidin | 576 | 200 | 1 |

| FM | 1 | 2 | kW | FM | 1 | 2 | kW |
|---|---|---|---|---|---|---|---|
| Babyak | 87.6 | - | 1 | Oryahovo | 99.8 | 101.7 | 1 |
| Belogradchik | 102.3 | 88.2 | 10/1 | Pleven | 102.7 | 100.2 | 1 |
| Berkovitsa | 101.4 | 99.5 | 10/7 | Plovdiv | 88.1 | 91.7 | 1 |
| Bistritsa | 91.8 | - | 1 | Popovo | 103.5 | 95.7 | 0.5/1 |
| Botev vrah | 100.9 | 92.2 | 10 | Provadiya | 88.9 | 102.9 | 3 |
| Burgas | 90.2 | 96.1 | 1 | Razgrad | 103.5 | 99.4 | 1 |
| Dobrich | 104.3 | 102.3 | 3/1 | Roman | 94.7 | - | 1 |
| Dupnitsa | 104.1 | 87.8 | 1 | Ruse | 103.0 | 95.7 | 10/1 |
| Dzhebel | 102.1 | 88.4 | 1 | Shumen | 102.0 | - | 10 |
| G.Delchev | 100.3 | 98.5 | 10/1 | Shumen (a) | *90.1 | - | 1 |
| Gabrovo | 103.2 | 95.4 | 1 | Shumen (a) | 94.5 | 100.4 | 0.25/1 |
| Ivailovgrad | 91.6 | 96.4 | 0.1/1 | Silistra | 103.3 | 107.2 | 3/1 |
| Karnobat | 103.2 | 95.0 | 1 | Sliven | 87.8 | 98.7 | 1 |
| Kavarna | 88.1 | 90.1 | 1 | Smolyan | 101.6 | 96.0 | 5/1 |
| Kresna | 88.8 | 89.7 | 1 | Sofia | 103.0 | 92.9 | 10 |
| Kyustendil | 102.1 | 99.3 | 10 | St.Zagora | - | 98.3 | 1 |
| M.Tarnovo | 90.2 | 106.1 | 1 | Svilengrad | 99.7 | 94.9 | 3 |
| Momchilgrad | 105.0 | 99.2 | 10/1 | Targovishte | 92.8 | 95.4 | 1/0.5 |
| Montana | 100.4 | - | 1 | Tran | 97.6 | 90.0 | 1 |
| Nesebar | 102.5 | 99.3 | 10 | Tsarevo | 102.2 | 90.8 | 1 |
| Nikopol | 96.4 | 98.2 | 0.1/1 | V. Tarnovo | 96.0 | 99.6 | 1 |

| FM | 1 | 2 | kW | FM | 1 | 2 | kW |
|---|---|---|---|---|---|---|---|
| Varna | 100.9 | 104.8 | 5/1 | Yablanitsa | 89.2 | | 95.0 1 |
| Vratsa | 103.4 | 97.8 | 1/0.45 | a) Shumen City | | | |

+ sites with only txs below 1kW. *) incl. T

**D.Prgr: Prgr 1 (Horizont):** 24h – **Prgr 2 (Hristo Botev):** 24h – **Service for Turkish ethnic minority (T):** 0600-0700, 1300-1400, 1830-1930 in Turkish.

## BNR Regional Stations

**D.Prgr:** all stns: 24h. – **BNR R. Blagoevgrad:** ul. Ivan Mihaylov 56, 2700 Blagoevgrad **E:** koordinacia.blg@bnr.bg. On (MHz) 90.9 (Yakoruda 0.1kW), 102.3 (Gotse Delchev 1kW), 103.2 (Blagoevgrad 0.25kW), 105.2 (Kresna 1kW), 106.6 (Kyustendil 1kW). – **BNR R. Burgas:** ul. Filip Kutev 2, 8000 Burgas **E:** radioburgas@bnr.bg. On (MHz) 90.2 (M.Tarnovo 1kW), 91.7 (Tsarevo 1kW), 91.9 (Yambol 1kW), 92.5 (Burgas 1kW), 106.0 (Elhovo 0.5kW): own prgrs 0400-1900; rel. BNR Prgr 1 (Horizont) at other times. – **BNR R. Kardzhali:** bul. Balgariya 74, 6600 Kardzhali. On 90.0MHz (Momchilgrad 1kW): own prgrs 0700-1000; rel. BNR Prgr 1 (Horizont) & BNR Service for the Turkish ethnic minority at other times. – **BNR R. Plovdiv:** ul. Dondukov korsakov 2, 4000 Plovdiv **E:** director@radioplovdiv.bg. On (MHz) 88.3 (Panagyurishte 0.25kW), 94.0 (Plovdiv 1kW), 100.1 (Velingrad 0.1kW), 100.6 (Dospat 0.2kW), 103.1 (Smolyan 1kW). – **BNR R. Sofia:** bul. Dragan Tsankov 4, 1040 Sofia **E:** sofia@bnr.bg. On (MHz) 90.4 (Svoge 0.15kW), 94.5 (Sofia 1kW), 100.0 (Samokov 0.2kW), 104.6 (Ihtiman 0.3kW). – **BNR R. Stara Zagora:** ul. Knyaz Boris 75, 6000 Stara Zagora **E:** rsz@radio-sz.net. On (MHz) 88.3 (Stara Zagora 1kW), 97.2 (Sliven 1kW), 107.8 (Svilengrad 1kW). – **BNR R. Shumen:** ul. Dobro Voynikov 7, 9700 Shumen **E:** admin@radioshumen.net. On (MHz) 87.6 (Shumen 10kW), 90.3 (Silistra 3kW), 93.4 (Shumen/City 1kW), 94.0 (Targovishte 0.5kW), 97.0 (Razgrad 0.5kW), 98.6 (Ruse 1kW). – **BNR R. Varna:** bul. Primorski 22, 9000 Varna **E:** bnr@radiovarna.com. On (MHz) 88.5 (Nesebar 1kW), 88.7 (Dobrich 1kW), 98.2 (Kavarna 0.5kW), 103.4 (Varna 1kW), 105.3 (Provadiya 1kW). – **BNR R. Vidin:** ul. Gradinska 1, 3700 Vidin **E:** office@radiovidin.com. On (MHz) 94.4 (Vratsa 0.3kW), 97.1 (Vidin 0.25kW), 103.9 (Berkovitsa 1.5kW), 106.8 (Belogradchik 1kW).

## OTHER STATIONS

| FM | MHz | kW | Location | Station |
|---|---|---|---|---|
| 2B) | 87.6 | 1 | Nesebar | Start FM |
| 1) | 87.9 | 1 | Sandanski | Darik R. |
| 5C) | 88.2 | 1 | Smolyan | The Voice |
| 7) | 89.5 | 1 | Varna | R. Fokus |
| 1) | 89.7 | 2 | Samokov | Darik R. |
| 10) | 90.2 | 1 | Petrich | R. Bella |
| 4) | 90.6 | 1 | Belogradchik | R. NRJ |
| 5B) | 90.9 | 1 | Smolyan | R. Vitosha |
| 1) | 91.0 | 1 | Belogradchik | Darik R. |
| 8) | 91.1 | 1 | Burgas | Power FM |
| 1) | 91.5 | 1 | Shumen | Darik R. |
| 3A) | 91.9 | 1 | Petrich | R. Vega+ |
| 1) | 93.2 | 1 | Momchilgrad | Darik R. |
| 7) | 93.4 | 1 | Primorsko | R. Fokus |
| 2B) | 94.1 | 1 | Burgas | R. Fresh |
| 5A) | 94.3 | 1 | Smolyan | R. Veselina |
| 5A) | 94.8 | 1 | Burgas | R. Veselina |
| 4) | 95.5 | 1 | Kozloduy | R. NRJ |
| 9) | 95.7 | 1 | Burgas | BG R. |
| 6) | 96.0 | 1 | Tutrakan | R. N-Joy |
| 1) | 96.7 | 1 | Yablanitsa | Darik R. |
| 5B) | 96.7 | 1 | Burgas | R. Vitosha |
| 11) | 97.3 | 1 | Sandanski | R. Gea |
| 12) | 98.3 | 1 | Burgas | Glast na Burgas (bTV R.) |
| 1) | 99.3 | 1 | Varna | Darik R. |
| 7) | 99.7 | 1 | Ruse | R. Fokus |
| 4) | 99.9 | 1 | Burgas | R. NRJ |
| 1) | 100.6 | 1 | Kyustendil | Darik R. |
| 2B) | 100.6 | 1 | Primorsko | R. Fresh |
| 1) | 100.7 | 1 | Silistra | Darik R. |
| 4) | 101.1 | 1 | Primorsko | R. NRJ |
| 1) | 101.2 | 1 | Sliven | Darik R. |
| 13) | 101.3 | 1 | Momchilgrad | R. Nova News |
| 6) | 101.8 | 1 | Burgas | R. N-Joy |
| 7) | 102.8 | 1 | Momchilgrad | R. Fokus |
| 5A) | 103.2 | 1 | Vidin | R. Veselina |
| 3B) | 103.4 | 1 | Sandanski | R. Ultra |
| 1) | 104.0 | 1 | Svilengrad | Darik R. |
| 4) | 104.5 | 2 | Burgas | R. NRJ |
| 7) | 104.5 | 1 | Tutrakan | R. Fokus |
| 1) | 105.0 | 2 | Sofia | Darik R. |
| 1) | 105.4 | 3 | Plovdiv | Darik R. |

| FM | MHz | kW | Location | Station |
|---|---|---|---|---|
| 5A) | 105.7 | 1 | Sandanski | R. Veselina |
| 1) | 106.2 | 1 | Gotse Delchev | Darik R. |
| 1) | 106.6 | 1 | V.Tarnovo | Darik R. |
| 1) | 106.8 | 1 | Kavarna | Darik R. |
| 1) | 107.0 | 1 | Smolyan | Darik R. |
| 1) | 107.2 | 1 | Blageovgrad | Darik R. |
| 7) | 107.5 | 1 | Nesebar | R. Fokus |
| 1) | 107.7 | 1 | Dobrich | Darik R. |
| 7) | 107.7 | 1 | Vidin | R. Fokus |

+ txs below 1kW.

**Addresses & other information:**
**1)** bul. Knyaz A.Dondukov 82, 1504 Sofia – **2A,B)** ul. Yerusalim 51, 1784 Sofia – **3A,B)** ul. Todor Aleksandrov 3, 2700 Blagoevgrad – **4)** bul. Tsar Boris III 23, 1612 Sofia – **5A-C)** ul. Srebarna 21, 1407 Sofia – **6)** ul. Panayot Volov 3, 1504 Sofia – **7)** ul. Filip Stanislavov 6, 1505 Sofia – **8)** ul. A.Bogoridi 16, 8000 Burgas – **9)** ul. Sofiyski geroy 3a, 1612 Sofia – **10)** pl. Makedonia10, 2850 Petrich – **11)** bul. Svoboda 13, 2800 Sandanski – **12)** ul. Aleksandrovska 26, 8000 Burgas. Rel. bTV R. at times – **13)** bul. Hristov Kolumb 41, 1592 Sofia

## BURKINA FASO

**L.T:** UTC — **Pop:** 19 million — **Pr.L:** French + 16 ethnic — **E.C:** 50Hz, 220V — **ITU:** BFA

### CONSEIL SUPÉRIEUR DE LA COMMUNICATION (CSC)
📠 01 BP 6437, Ouagadougou ☎+226 50301124 📠 +226 50301133 **W:** csc.bf **E:** infos@csc.bf **L.P:** Dir: Luc Adolphe Diao.

### RADIODIFFUSION TÉLÉVISION DU BURKINA (Gov.)
📠 BP 7029, Ouagadougou 01 ☎+226 50324302 📠 +226 50310441 **W:** rtb.bf **E:** radio@rtb.bf **L.P:** MD: Marcel Toe. Head of Tr. Centre: Marcel Teho. Prgr.Dir: Pascal Goba.
**FM:** 88.5/92.0/99.9MHz 0.02kW
**D.Prgr in French/Ethnic:** 24h. **N. in French:** 0630MF, 1000SS + Thurs, 1245 (regional), 1300, 1900, 2200. **N. in English:** W1920 (approx). **Ann:** "RTV Burkina", "RTB". **IS:** Balafon.
**Canal Arc-en-Ciel**, 03 BP 7045, Ouagadougou. **L.P:** Alphousseini Bassolet. **FM:** Ouagadougou 96.6MHz, Bobo-Dioulasso 89.8MHz.

### REGIONAL STATIONS:
**Radio Bobo**, BP 392, Bobo-Dioulasso. **FM:** 92.0MHz 0.02kW. **D.Prgr:** MF 0600-0800, 1200-1400, 1600-2400, SS 0800-2400 – **R. Gaoua**, Gaoua. **FM:** 90.1MHz – **R. Rurale:** FM txs in Diapaga, Djibasso, Gassan, Kongoussi, Orodara & Poura.

**Other Stations** (all MHz):
**Al Houda FM,** Ouagadougou: 98.5 – **Bankuy FM**, Dédougou: 107.7 – **Hit R**, Ouagadougou 87.7, Dori 104.6 **W:** hitradio.ma – **Horizon FM:** Tenkodogo 97.6, Banfora 98, Koudougou 98.7, Ouayigouya 100.4, Dédougou 102.7, Ouagadougou 104.4, Dori 104.6 – **Ouaga FM:** Bobo-Dioulasso 101.1, Ouagadougou 105.2 **W:** ouagafm-bf. com – **R. Ahmadiya**, Dori: 104.6 – **R. de l'Alliance Chrétienne**, Bobo-Dioulasso, Bobo-Dioulasso: 102.7 – **R. Balafon**, Bobo-Dioulasso: 102.7 – **R. Buayaba**, Diapaga 96.2MHz – **R. FM Boulgou**, Garango: 101.1 – **R. Cascade**, Banfora: 98 – **R. Catholique Teriya**, Banfora 94.7 – **R. Djawoampo**, Bogandé 98.0 – **R. Djongo**, Pô: 106.4 – **Echo des Cotonniers**, Solenzo: 95.1 – **R. Djibasso:** 94.6 – **R. Energie:** Kaya 92.2, Yako 94.9, Fada N'Gourma 98.8 – **R. de l'Espoir**, Réo: 102.8 – **R. Évangile Développement:** Ouagadougou 93.4, Houndé 95.5, Léo 97.8, Koudougou 101.0, Ouahigouya 104.0, Yako 105.3, Bobo-Dioulasso 106.3. **W:** red-burkina.org – **R. Evangile du Sud-Ouest**, Gaoua: 99.7 – **R. Eveil**, Bogandé 101.0 – **R. Fréquence Espoir:** Dédougou 96.8 1kW, Tougan 101.4 0.1kW – **R. Frontière**, Tenkodogo: 97.6 – **R. Gambidi**, Ouagadougou: 97.7 – **R. Gassan:** 105.5 – **R. Gayeri:** 91.8 – **R. Goulou**, Po 99.5 – **R. du Grand Nord**, Dori: 97.5 – **R. Kadoadb**, Ziniare: 107.7 – **R. Kantigya**, Nouna 88.8 – **R. Kongoussi:** 93.2 – **R. Kouritta**, Koupela: 93.7 – **R. La Voix des Bales**, Boromo 103.6 – **R. La Voix du Soum**, Djibo 92.1 – **R. Lotamu**, Solenzo 101.9 – **R. LCD**, Djibo 98.6 – **R. Loudon**, Sapouy 104.9 – **R. Lumière:** Ouagadougou: 98.1 – **R. Manegda**, Kaya: 99.4 – **R. Maria:** Ouagadougou 98.2 – **R. Nemaro**, Cassou 94.2 – **R. Natigmeb Zanga**, Kaya: 98.2 – **R. Naboswende**, Pouytenga: 103.7 – **R. Nerwaya**, Kongoussi 99.7 – **R. Notre Dame de la Réconciliation**, Koudougou 105.8 – **R. Nostalgie**, Ouagadougou, 94.4 – **R. Notre Dame:** Kaya 102.9, Kouhougou 105.8, Ouahigouya 102.6 – **R. Omega:** Ouagadougou 103.9, Bobo-Dioulasso 104.7 **W:** omegabf. net – **R. Paglayiri**, Zabré 94.3 – **R. Palabre**, B.P. 196, Kougougou:

92.2 – **R. Pog-Neere**, Pouytenga 100.2MHz – **R. Poura**: 98.2 – **R. Pulsar**, Ouagadougou: 94.8 0.4kW – **R. Salaki**, Dedougou 101.1 – **R. Salankoloto**, Ouagadougou: 97.3 – **R. Sanmentenga**, Kaya: 96.1 – **R. Tin-Taani**, Kantchari 100.0 – **La Voix du Sud-Ouest**, Diébougou: 101.5 – **R. Taanba**, Fada N'Gourma: 98.8 1kW **W:** radioafricanetwork. org.za/RadioTaanba.html – **R. Tapao**, Diapaga: 95.8 – **R. Unitas**, Diébougou: 94.7 – **R. Vive le Paysan**, Saponé: 107.0 – **R. la Voix du Passoré**, Yako: 105.3 – **R. la Voix du Paysan**, Ouahigouya: 97.0 – **R. La Voix du Verger**, Orodara: 91.2 – **R. Zoodo**, Ouahigouya: 100.4 **R. Savane**, Ouagadougou: 103.4 **W:** savanefm.bf
**BBC African Sce**: Ouagadougou 99.2 4kW.
**RFI Afrique**: Banfora 91.5, Koudougou 93.0, Ouagadougou 94.0, Ouahigouya 94.3, Bobo-Dioulasso 99.4.
**Voice of America**: Ouagadougou 102.4MHz

## BURUNDI

**L.T:** UTC +2h — **Pop:** 12 million — **Pr.L:** Kirundi, Swahili, French, English — **E.C:** 50Hz, 220V — **ITU:** BDI

**CONSEIL NATIONAL DE LA COMMUNICATION (CNC)**
☎+257 22223742 ⊟ +257 22226547 **W:** burundi.gov.bi
**L.P:** Chairman: Vestine Nahimana.

**RADIO-TÉLÉVISION NATIONALE DU BURUNDI (RTNB, Gov.)**
⊟ B.P. 1900, Bujumbura ☎+257 22223742 ⊟ +257 22226547
**W:** rtnbdi.bi **E:** rtnb@cbinf.com **LP:** D.G.: Innocent Muhozi

| FM(MHz) | RTNB1 | RTNB2 | FM(MHz) | RTNB1 | RTNB2 |
|---------|-------|-------|---------|-------|-------|
| Birime | 94.2 | 98.9 | Kaberenge | 94.7 | 98.0 |
| Bujumbura | 102.9 | 92.9 | Manga | 95.6 | 98.9 |
| Nanzerwe | 88.4 | 91.4 | Mutumba | 88.8 | 91.9 |

**D.Prgr:** W 0300-0700 & 0900-2100, Sun 0300-2100. (RTNB1 in Kirundi, RTNB2 in French/Swahili/English). **N.** in French: 0530, 1200, 1500, 1900. **N.** in Swahili: 0630, 1245, 1800. **N.** in Kirundi: 0500, 0700, 1130, 1800, 2000. **N.** in English: 0445, 1230, 1600, 1845.
**Ann:** "Ici Bujumbura, Radio-Télévision Nationale du Burundi". **IS:** Drums.

**Other stations** (FM MHz):
**R. Publique Africaine:** Bugesera 89.4, Birime 92.6, Bujumbura 93.7, Manga 107.1 **W:** rpa.bi . For relays on shortwave see International Radio section.
**Hit R**, Bujumbura 91.4 **W:** hitradio.ma – **R. CCIB FM,** Bujumbura: 99.4, nationwide 102.4 – **R. Culture**, Bujumbura: 88.2/99.9 – **R. Isanganiro:** Bujumbura 89.7, Bururi 93.3/95.1, Kirundo 90.6, Ruyigi 90.7, Manga 101.0. **W:** web-africa.org/isanganiro – **R. Ivyizigiro**, Bujumbura: 90.9/104.8 – **R. Renaissance**, Bujumbura 101.4 – **R. Scolaire Nderagakura**, Bujumbura 87.9 – **Rema FM**, Bujumbura: 88.6/103.6/107.5. **W:** remafm. com
**BBC African Sce**: Bujumbura 90.2, Mount Manga 105.6MHz.
**RFI Afrique**: Bujumbura 96.1, Mutemba 99.5, Mt. Manga 103.7MHz.
**VOA African Sce:** Bujumbura 94.9, Mount Manga 95.2MHz

## CABO VERDE

**L.T:** UTC -1h — **Pop:** 540,000 — **Pr.L:** Portuguese, Crioulo — **E.C:** 50Hz, 220V — **ITU:** CPV.

**AGENCIA NACIONAL DAS COMUNICAÇÕES (ANAC)**
⊟ C.P. 892, Edifício MIT, Ponta Belém, Praia ☎+238 2604400 ⊟ +238 2613069 **W:** anac.cv **E:** info.anac@anac.cv

**RÁDIOTELEVISÃO DE CABO VERDE (RCV, Gov.)**
⊟ Rua 13 de Janeiro 1-A, Achada de Santo António, Praia ⊟C.P. 29, Av. Marginal, Mindelo, São Vicente ⊟ C.P. 40, Espargos, Ilha do Sal ☎⊟+238 2411444 **W:** rtc.cv **E:** rtc@cvtelecom.cv
**L.P:** Dir: Marcos Oliveira. PD: Giordano Custodio. Dir. Inf: Mario Almeida. Dir. Tec: Francisco Lopes Monteiro.
**FM:** Monte Verde 87.6MHz 1kW, Morro Curral 89.7MHz 0.25kW, Monte Tchota 91.6MHz 1kW, Mindelo 95.6MHz 0.5kW, Praia 98.1MHz 0.1kW + 12 relays below 0.1kW. **D.Prgr:** 24h.

**Other stations (FM** MHz):
**R. Nova** (Rlg.): Pinhão 91.8, Monte Vermelho 94.1, Cachaço 95.1, Sal Rei 97.0, Monte Tropetona 99.1, Pedra Rachada 99.9, M. Tchota 101.6 0.25kW, Mindelo 102.3, M. Verde 104.3 0.5kW, Morro do Curral 106.4 **W:** radionova.cv – **R. Comercial**: Santiago 92.9 1kW, Ponta Rachada 96.1MHz, Praia/M. Verde 99.9 **W:** facebook.com/radiocomercial. cv – **R. Crioula:** M. Tchota, M. Barro/M. Verde 89.6, Praia 94.9,

Morro Curral 98.9 **W:** crioulafm.cv – **R. Educativa:** Monte Verde 101.5, M. Tchota 102.3, Praia & 4 sites 103.1 **W:** radioeducativa. cv – **Mosteiros FM:** M. Chota 96.1, São Filipe/Mosteiros 97.3 **W:** radiomosteirosfm.com

**RDP África**: Monte Verde 93.9MHz 3kW, Monte Tchota/Pedra Rachada 105.2MHz 3/1kW, Pedra Rachada 105.2MHz 1kW + 4 trs under 1kW.
**RFI Afrique**: Praia 99.3MHz 1kW, Mindelo 100.7MHz 0.25kW in French and Portuguese

## CAMBODIA

**L.T:** UTC +7h — **Pop:** 16 million — **Pr.L:** Khmer (Cambodian) — **E.C:** 50Hz, 230V — **ITU:** CBG

**MINISTRY OF INFORMATION**
⊟ 62, Preah Monivong, Phnom Penh ☎ +855 23 430514 ⊟ +855 23 430514 **W:** www.info.gov.kh **LP:** Minister: Khieu Kanharith

**NATIONAL RADIO OF KAMPUCHEA (RNK) (Gov)**
⊟ No 6 Street 19 (Corner Street 102), Sangkat Wat Phnom, Khan Daun Penh, Phnom Penh 12202 ☎ +855 23 725522 ⊟ +855 23 427319 **W:** rnk.gov.kh
**L.P:** Dir. Gen: HE Tun Sarath.
**AM 918:** Phnom Penh (Kandal Steung) 918kHz 600kW: 2200-1700
**Wat Phnom FM:** Phnom Penh 105.7MHz 10kW
**N.** in English & French: 0600-0620 & 1100-1120 on 918kHz & 105.7MHz.
**FM-96 (comm.):** ⊟ Steung Meanchey, Phnom Penh 12352 **FM:** 96.0MHz 20kW
**Cambodia-China Friendship Radio** (joint service with China Radio International)**:** 2300-1700 in Chaozhou, English, Khmer and Mandarin **FM:** Phnom Penh 96.5MHz 10kW, Siem Reap 105.0MHz
**Provincial sces:** ⊟ via the Information Department of the relevant provincial govt. Banteay Meanchey (Sisophon) 94.0MHz 5kW, Battambang (R. Chamka Chek) 92.7MHz 2kW, Kampong Cham 92.5MHz 2kW, Kampong Chhnang 92.3MHz, Kampong Speu (R. Kirirom, Chbar Mon) 89.3MHz, Kampot (R. 9 Makhara) 99.7MHz 2kW, Kampong Thom 98.3MHz, Kep (R. Chhner Kep) 99.0MHz, Kratie 98.5MHz 2kW, Mondulkiri (Sen Monorom) 97.0MHz, Oddar Meanchey (R. Prasat Ta Mean, Samraong) 91.5MHz, Pailin 90.5MHz 2kW, Pursat 98.5MHz 2kW, Preah Vihear (R. Phnom Tbeng) 97.0MHz, Prey Veng (R. Baray Andet) 97.3MHz, Ratanakiri (Ban Lung) 89.5MHz 2kW, Siem Reap (R. Nokor Phnom) 103.0MHz, Sihanoukville 93.0MHz 2kW, Stung Treng (R. Sekong) 99.0MHz, Svay Rieng 98.7MHz 2kW, Takeo (R. Kork Thlok) 92.5MHz 2kW, Tbong Khmum (Ponhea Kraek) 88.1MHz.
**Ann:** (Khmer): 'Thini Sathani Vithyu Cheat Kampuchea'

**PHNOM PENH MUNICIPAL RADIO STATION**
⊟ No 29, Street 335 / 1005 National Road 2, Phnom Penh 12312 ☎ +855 23 982265
**Sweet FM:** Phnom Penh 88.0MHz 10kW. **Sweet FM stations in provinces:** Banteay Meanchey (Sisophon) 103.5MHz 2.5kW Battambang 103.3MHz 1kW, Kampong Cham 100.5MHz 1kW, Kampong Chhnang 104.7MHz, Kampong Thom 103.5MHz 1kW, Kampot 93.3MHz, Koh Kong 103.5MHz, Kratie 103.5MHz, Preah Vihear (Chamksan) 99.5MHz, Prey Veng 99.0MHz, Pursat 100.5MHz 1kW, Siem Reap 100.5MHz 2kW, Sihanoukville 100.5MHz 1kW,, Stung Treng 100.5MHz, Svay Rieng 103.75MHz 10kW, Takeo 100.5MHz
**Love FM:** Phnom Penh 97.5MHz 1kW, Siem Reap 97.5MHz 1kW in English and Khmer
**Municipality R.:** Phnom Penh 103.0MHz, 10kW

**RADIO BAYON FM**
⊟ Russei Sros Village, Sangkat Niroth, Khan Meanchey, Phnom Penh 12410 ☎ +855 23 333795
**FM:** Kandal (Phnom Penh area) 95.0MHz 24kW. Rel. stns: Banteay Meanchay (Mongkol Borey) 97.5MHz 5kW, Battambang 104.0MHz 2kW, Kampong Cham 91.5MHz 10kW, Kampong Thom 91.0MHz 2kW, Kampot 91.0MHz 2kW, Koh Kong 95.5MHz 2kW, Kratie (Chhloung) 91.0MHz 2kW, Mondulkiri (Sen Monorom) 93.0MHz 2kW, Oddar Meanchey 94.0MHz 2kW, Preah Vihear (Chamksan) 95.0MHz 2.5kW, Pursat 91.5MHz 2kW, Ratanakiri (Ban Lung) 94.0MHz 1kW, Siem Reap 93.0MHz 10kW, Sihanoukville 92.0MHz 3kW, Stung Treng 92.0MHz 2kW, Svay Rieng 95.5MHz 2kW

**Other Stations**

| FM Location | MHz | kW | Station |
|-------------|-----|-----|---------|
| 1) Battambang | 87.5 | | PSN R. |
| 2) Phnom Penh | 87.5 | | Daun Penh EFM |

| FM | Location | MHz | kW | Station |
|---|---|---|---|---|
| 1) | Suong (t) | 87.5 | | PSN R. |
| 2) | Kampong Cham | 87.7 | 1 | Daun Penh EFM |
| 3) | Sen Monorom (m) | 87.7 | | Sok San Monorom |
| 4) | Phnom Penh | 87.7 | | Fresh FM |
| 2) | Siem Reap | 87.7 | 1 | Daun Penh EFM |
| 5) | Siem Reap | 88.0 | | Vayo FM |
| 6) | Stoung (kt) | 88.0 | | V. of Buddhism of Cambodia |
| 1) | Sihanoukville | 88.0 | | PSN R. |
| 7) | Kampong Chhnang | 88.3 | | KC FM |
| 8) | Phnom Penh | 88.3 | | R. Meanchey FM |
| 9) | Pursat | 88.3 | | Angel FM |
| 10) | Siem Reap | 88.3 | 2 | R. Mahanakor Khemara |
| 11) | Sisophon (m) | 88.3 | | Stung Khiev Thmey (Samleng Ek) |
| 12) | Battambang | 88.5 | | Kolyanmet R. |
| 13) | Kampong Thom | 88.5 | 1 | Steung Sen R. |
| 9) | Takeo | 88.5 | | Angel FM |
| 3) | Ban Lung (r) | 88.5 | | Sok San Monorom |
| 14) | Kampong Cham | 88.7 | 10 | Mongkulsavann FM |
| 15) | Kratie | 88.7 | | Vithyu Mekong |
| 16) | Phnom Penh | 88.7 | | R. Kong Meas |
| 17) | Siem Reap | 88.7 | | Friends FM |
| 18) | Sisophon (m) | 88.7 | | Cam TV |
| 19) | Sihanoukville | 88.8 | | V. of People with Disabilities (VOD, Samleng Chun Pikear) |
| 16) | Prey Veng | 89.0 | | R. Kong Meas |
| 16) | Pursat | 89.0 | | R. Kong Meas |
| 20) | Battambang | 89.0 | | NRG 89 FM |
| 20) | Kampong Thom | 89.0 | | NRG 89 FM |
| 20) | Phnom Penh | 89.0 | | NRG 89 FM |
| 20) | Siem Reap | 89.0 | | NRG 89 FM |
| 20) | Sihanoukville | 89.0 | | NRG 89 FM |
| 21) | Battambang | 89.3 | | Nature FM (Thommocheat) |
| 22) | Kampong Chhnang | 89.3 | | Samleng Kolbot Khmai (Voice of Khmer Youth) |
| 23) | Phnom Penh | 89.3 | | FM 89.25 |
| 24) | Takeo | 89.3 | | Sokha FM |
| 25) | Battambang | 89.5 | | ABC R. |
| 26) | Kratie | 89.5 | | Voice of Women (Samleng Strey) |
| 27) | Phnom Penh | 89.5 | 10 | VO New Life R. (Samleng Chivit Thmey) |
| 28) | Siem Reap | 89.5 | | ABC Cambodia R. (R. Krong Angkor) |
| 29) | Banteay Meanchey | 89.7 | | Wellness FM (Vithyu Pha Sokhpheap) |
| 29) | Phnom Penh | 89.7 | | Wellness FM (Vithyu Pha Sokhpheap) |
| 29) | Siem Reap | 89.7 | | Wellness FM (Vithyu Pha Sokhpheap) |
| 29) | Suong (t) | 89.7 | | Wellness FM (Vithyu Pha Sokhpheap) |
| 30) | Battambang | 89.8 | | Voice of Health |
| 14) | Kampong Thom | 90.0 | | R. Mongkulsovann |
| 31) | Phnom Penh | 90.0 | 10 | R. Khlaing Meoung (FM90) |
| 32) | Poipet (m) | 90.0 | | My FM |
| 31) | Battambang | 90.3 | 1 | R. Khlaing Meoung |
| 33) | Kampong Chhnang | 90.3 | | R, Sovannara |
| 34) | Siem Reap | 90.3 | | Voice of Entrak Tevy (PSN R.) |
| 19) | Svay Rieng | 90.3 | | V. of People with Disabilities (VOD, Samleng Chun Pikear) |
| 35) | Koh Kong | 90.7 | | South East Asia FM |
| 36) | Phnom Penh | 90.7 | | FM 90.75 |
| 35) | Pursat | 90.7 | | South East Asia FM |
| 35) | Sisophon (m) | 90.7 | | South East Asia FM |
| 37) | Battambang | 91.0 | 5 | R. FM Khemara |
| 38) | Phnom Penh | 91.0 | | People R. (Pracheachon) |
| 39) | Pursat | 91.0 | | Metta R. |
| 40) | Siem Reap | 91.0 | | Vithyu Changrit Meas (CMD FM, Golden Cricket) |
| 41) | Kampong Cham | 91.1 | | One FM |
| 42) | Kampong Chhnang | 91.3 | | Ratanak Kampong Chhnang |
| 43) | Phnom Penh | 91.3 | | Star FM |
| 44) | Pursat | 91.3 | | R. Sompov Meas |
| 45) | Phnom Penh | 91.5 | | VOY FM (Voice of Youth) |
| 46) | Stung Treng | 91.5 | | Stung Treng FM |
| 47) | Phnom Penh | 91.7 | | FM 91.7 |
| 47) | Siem Reap | 91.7 | | FM 91.7 |
| 48) | Sispohon (m) | 91.7 | | Solika FM |
| 14) | Sispohon (m) | 91.9 | | R. Mongkulsavann |
| 45) | Kampong Thom | 92.0 | | VOY FM (Voice of Youth) |
| 45) | Suong (t) | 92.0 | | VOY FM (Voice of Youth) |
| 45) | Battambang | 92.1 | | VOY FM (Voice of Youth) |
| 14) | Kampot | 92.3 | | R. Mongkulsavann |
| 49) | Phnom Penh | 92.3 | 5 | Top FM |
| 19) | Siem Reap | 92.3 | | V. of People with Disabilities (VOD, Samleng Chun Pikear) |
| 37) | Battambang | 92.5 | | People R. (Pracheachon) |
| 50) | Phnom Penh | 92.5 | | V. of Dharma, Vat Chbar Ampouv |
| 9) | Sihanoukville | 92.5 | | Angel FM |
| 25) | Kampong Cham | 92.7 | | R. ABC |
| 25) | Kampong Thom | 92.7 | | R. ABC |
| 51) | Pursat | 92.7 | | R. Sophal |
| 38) | Kampong Cham | 93.1 | | Metta R. |
| 32) | Battambang | 93.2 | | My FM |
| 27) | Kampong Chhnang | 93.2 | | VO New Life R. (Samlang Chivit Thmey) |
| 17) | Phnom Penh | 93.3 | | Friends FM – News R. |
| 52) | Poipet (m) | 93.3 | | Seven FM |
| 53) | Suong (t) | 93.3 | | Peanichakam FM |
| 14) | Batttambang | 93.5 | | R. Mongkulsavann |
| 54) | Siem Reap | 93.5 | | R. Sela Angkor |
| 55) | Stung Treng | 93.5 | | Stung Treng FM |
| 56) | Memot (t) | 93.7 | | ORM TV |
| 57) | Phnom Penh | 93.7 | | Vithyu Ekreach (Independent R.) |
| 9) | Sisophon (m) | 93.7 | | Angel FM |
| 58) | Siem Reap | 93.8 | | R. Ratanak Angkor |
| 59) | Kampong Cham | 94.0 | | R. Kontreum Asean |
| 45) | Kampot | 94.0 | | VOY FM (Voice of Youth) |
| 60) | Phnom Penh | 94.0 | | Phnom Penh R. |
| 45) | Siem Reap | 94.1 | | VOY FM (Voice of Youth) |
| 45) | Sihanoukville | 94.0 | | VOY FM (Voice of Youth) |
| 61) | Kampong Chhnang | 94.3 | | DP FM |
| 61) | Phnom Penh | 94.3 | | DP FM |
| 9) | Siem Reap | 94.3 | | Angel FM |
| 62) | Takeo | 94.3 | | Bayong FM |
| 63) | Kampong Thom | 94.5 | | Metrey R. |
| 64) | Koh Kong | 94.5 | | Sako Koh Kong |
| 65) | Phnom Penh | 94.5 | | Vibe R. Cambodia. |
| 66) | Svay Rieng | 94.5 | | R. Mohachun |
| 67) | Mongkol Borey (m) | 94.7 | | Luong FM |
| 50) | Phnom Penh | 94.7 | | V. of Dharma Buddhist R. |
| 50) | Svay Rieng | 94.7 | | V. of Dharma Buddhist R. |
| 68) | Battambang | 95.0 | | R. Bopha |
| 69) | Battambang | 95.3 | | R. Dewey FM |
| 70) | Kampong Cham | 95.3 | | Voice of the Blind (VOB, Samleng Chun Pikear Phnek) |
| 66) | Phnom Penh | 95.3 | | R. Mohachun |
| 57) | Kampong Chhnang | 95.5 | | Vithyu Ekreach (Independent R.) |
| 57) | Kampot | 95.5 | | Vithyu Ekreach (Independent R.) |
| 57) | Phnom Penh | 95.5 | | Vithyu Ekreach (Independent R.) |
| 71) | Poipet (m) | 95.5 | | Music FM (Dontreay) |
| 72) | Siem Reap | 95.5 | 10 | R. Angkor Ratha |
| 73) | Battambang | 95.7 | | Town FM |
| 74) | Memot (t) | 95.7 | | Sopheak Mongkul |
| 75) | Phnom Penh | 95.7 | 5 | Reasmey Hang Meas FM |
| 76) | Kampong Cham | 96.3 | | R. Nakor Bachey |
| 77) | Kampong Thom | 96.3 | | Phnom Santuk R. |
| 66) | Siem Reap | 96.3 | | R. Mohachun |
| 66) | Stung Treng | 96.5 | | R. Mohachun |
| 78) | Sisopohon (m) | 96.5 | 10 | Banteay Meanchey Provincial R. |
| 16) | Kampong Cham | 96.7 | | Kong Meas |
| 38) | Kampong Thom | 96.7 | | Metta R. |
| 38) | Phnom Penh | 96.7 | | Metta R. |
| 68) | Pursat | 96.7 | | R. Bopha |
| 38) | Sihanoukville | 96.7 | | Metta R. |
| 79) | Phnom Penh | 97.0 | 10 | R Apsara |
| 80) | Kompong Cham | 97.1 | | New Style |
| 70) | Banteay Meanchey | 97.3 | | Voice of the Blind (VOB, Samleng Chun Pikear Phnek) |
| 16) | Kampong Chhnang | 97.3 | | Kong Meas |
| 81) | Kampong Speu | 97.3 | | Rithy Sen |
| 9) | Kampot | 97.3 | | Angel FM |
| 82) | Phnom Penh | 97.3 | | Khemony Panya |
| 83) | Takeo | 97.3 | | R. Ponletrayroth |
| 68) | Ban Lung (r) | 97.5 | | Vithyu Khmer Isan |
| 46) | Kampong Cham | 97.5 | | DP FM |
| 16) | Kampong Thom | 97.5 | | Kong Meas |
| 84) | Pailin | 97.5 | | R O Torng Pailin |
| 68) | Ratanakiri | 97.5 | | R. Bopha |
| 85) | Svay Rieng | 97.8 | | Mohasal FM |
| 79) | Svay Rieng | 97.8 | | R. Apsara |
| 86) | Battambang | 97.8 | | Koltoteng R. |
| 86) | Phnom Penh | 97.8 | | Koltoteng R. |
| 86) | Siem Reap | 97.8 | | Koltoteng R. |
| 57) | Kampong Cham | 98.0 | | Vithyu Ekreach (Independent R.) |
| 87) | Phnom Penh | 98.0 | 10 | FM98 (Armed Forces R., Khemark Phomin) |
| 88) | Battambang | 98.1 | | R. Ratanak |
| 89) | Kampot | 98.3 | | Soren Mountain Top FM |
| 90) | Phnom Penh | 98.3 | | R. Ponleu Thom Preaphut |
| 91) | Poipet (m) | 98.3 | | FM98.3 |

| FM | Location | MHz | kW | Station |
|----|----------|-----|----|---------|
| 92) | Siem Reap | 98.3 | | Tourist R. (Tesachar) |
| 57) | Sihanoukville | 98.3 | | Vithyu Ekreach (Independent R.) |
| 93) | Kampong Thom | 98.5 | | R. Kong San |
| 57) | Phnom Penh | 98.5 | | Vithyu Ekreach (Independent R.) |
| 94) | Siem Reap | 98.5 | | Sovann Angkor FM |
| 25) | Sisophon (m) | 98.5 | | ABC Cambodia R. |
| 86) | Svay Rieng | 98.5 | | Koltoteng R. |
| 95) | Battambang | 98.7 | | R. Steung Khiev (VSK) |
| 96) | Kampong Cham | 98.7 | | Tonle Om |
| 32) | Kampong Chhnang | 98.7 | | My FM |
| 35) | Kampong Thom | 98.7 | | South East Asia FM |
| 25) | Phnom Penh | 98.7 | | R. ABC |
| 32) | Siem Reap | 98.8 | | Preah Neareay R. |
| 66) | Kampong Chhnang | 99.0 | | R. Mohachun |
| 98) | Phnom Penh | 99.0 | 10 | FM99 |
| 68) | Pursat | 99.0 | | Vithyu Khmer Isan |
| 99) | Siem Reap | 99.0 | 0.5 | Kiss FM |
| 8) | Sisophon (m) | 99.0 | 2 | Meanchey FM |
| 100) | Phnom Penh | 99.3 | | Vithyu Somaleu |
| 85) | Prey Veng | 99.3 | | Mohasal FM |
| 83) | Suong (t) | 99.3 | | R. Ponletrayroth |
| 32) | Kampong Cham | 99.5 | | My FM |
| 32) | Oddar Meanchey | 99.5 | | My FM |
| 101) | Phnom Penh | 99.5 | 10 | KRUSA FM (FEBC/Family FM) |
| 32) | Pursat | 99.5 | 1 | My FM |
| 32) | Sisophon (m) | 99.5 | 1 | My FM |
| 102) | Kampong Cham | 99.7 | | Kampong Cham R. Station |
| 81) | Kampong Chhnang | 99.7 | | Rithy Sen |
| 46) | Phnom Penh | 99.7 | | DP FM |
| 103) | Takeo | 99.7 | | Angkor Sunly FM |
| 101) | Kampong Thom | 99.8 | 0.5 | KRUSA FM (FEBC/Family FM) |
| 33) | Battambang | 100.0 | | VO Dombang Kronhoung |
| 106) | Ponhea Kraek (t) | 100.1 | | Neak Poun |
| 107) | Prey Veng | 100.1 | | Vithyu Kdei Sangkhum (Hope R.) |
| 33) | Battambang | 100.3 | | Sovannara |
| 108) | Kampong Chhnang | 100.3 | | Nokor Chum |
| 1) | Phnom Penh | 100.3 | 5 | PSN R. |
| 57) | Siem Reap | 100.3 | | Vithyu Ekreach (Independent R.) |
| 109) | Phnom Penh | 100.5 | | Lotus R. (Phka Chhouk) |
| 110) | Poipet (m) | 100.5 | | Vithyu Chokchai |
| 103) | Kampong Chhnang | 100.7 | | Angkor Sunly FM |
| 111) | Kampot | 100.7 | | Vithyu Yuvochon (Youth R.) |
| 112) | Phnom Penh | 100.7 | | Cool FM |
| 46) | Siem Reap | 101.7 | | DP FM |
| 113) | Phnom Penh | 101.3 | | EVO FM |
| 114) | Srey Santhor (kc) | 101.5 | | Mongkol Panha |
| 63) | Takeo | 101.5 | | Metrey R. |
| 115) | Ban Lung (r) | 101.7 | | Wildflower R. (Phka Prei) |
| 46) | Battambang | 101.7 | | DP FM |
| 106) | Kampong Cham | 101.7 | | Neak Poun |
| 46) | Phnom Penh | 101.7 | | DP FM |
| 14) | Pursat | 101.7 | | Mongkulsavann FM |
| 89) | Siem Reap | 101.7 | | Soren Mountain Top FM |
| 116) | Kampong Cham | 102.0 | | R. WMC |
| 116) | Kampong Thom | 102.0 | 1 | R. WMC |
| 116) | Kratie | 102.0 | 1 | R. WMC (Kratie FM) |
| 116) | Moung Roussei (b) | 102.0 | | R. WMC (Strey FM) |
| 116) | Phnom Penh | 102.0 | 10 | R. WMC |
| 116) | Svay Rieng | 102.0 | 1 | R. WMC |
| 9) | Battambang | 102.3 | | Angel FM |
| 46) | Kampong Thom | 102.3 | | DP FM |
| 73) | Phnom Penh | 102.3 | 5 | Town FM |
| 59) | Siem Reap | 102.3 | | Kontreum Siem Reap |
| 17) | Kampong Cham | 102.5 | | R. Tonle FM (River FM) |
| 17) | Phnom Penh | 102.5 | 2 | R. Tonle FM (River FM) |
| 117) | Siem Reap | 102.5 | 1 | Sathani Vithyu Krom Siem Reap (Siem Reap City R. Stn) |
| 5) | Sihanoukville | 102.5 | | Vayo FM |
| 50) | Battambang | 102.7 | | V. of Dharma Buddhist R. |
| 50) | Kampong Thom | 102.7 | | V. of Dharma Buddhist R. |
| 50) | Pursat | 102.7 | | V. of Dharma Buddhist R. |
| 50) | Phnom Penh | 102.8 | | V. of Dharma Buddhist R., Vat Than |
| 50) | Siem Reap | 102.8 | | V. of Dharma Buddhist R. |
| 50) | Sihanoukville | 102.8 | | V. of Dharma Buddhist R. |
| 50) | Kampong Cham | 102.9 | | V. of Dharma Buddhist R. |
| 63) | Phnom Penh | 103.3 | | Metrey R. |
| 118) | Phnom Penh | 103.5 | | VO Education (VOE, Samleng Abrom) |
| 119) | Battambang | 103.7 | | R. Phnom Sampov |
| 120) | Kampong Chhnang | 103.7 | | R. Chhnang Meas |
| 121) | Phnom Penh | 103.7 | | R. One |
| 130) | Takeo | 103.7 | | R. Phnom Borey |
| 90) | Sihanoukville | 103.7 | | Ponleu Thom Preaphut |
| 131) | Phnom Penh | 104.0 | 10 | R. Sovann Phum |
| 132) | Sihanoukville | 104.0 | 2 | Sung Meas FM |
| 133) | Phnom Penh | 104.3 | | R. Solida (Soft FM) |
| 85) | Battambang | 104.5 | | Mohasal FM (Sangke FM) |
| 134) | Phnom Penh | 104.5 | 5 | R. Hang Meas FM |
| 135) | Preah Vihear | 104.5 | | Krong Preah Vihear |
| 136) | Kampong Cham | 104.7 | | Kizuna FM |
| 90) | Kampot | 104.7 | | Ponleu Thom Preaphut |
| 137) | Phnom Penh | 104.7 | | FM 104.7 |
| 138) | Takeo | 104.7 | | FM 104.7 |
| 9) | Battambang | 105.0 | | R. Steung Khiev Thmey |
| 68) | Kratie | 105.0 | | R. Bopha |
| 139) | Phnom Penh | 105.0 | 5 | Sombok Ka Mum (R. Beehive) |
| 106) | Ban Lung (mk) | 105.1 | | Neak Poun |
| 18) | Kampong Cham | 105.1 | | Cam TV |
| 71) | Kampong Thom | 105.3 | | Music FM (Dontreay) |
| 96) | Memot (t) | 105.3 | | Tonle Om |
| 57) | Pursat | 105.3 | | Vithyu Ekreach (Independent R.) |
| 140) | Samraong (om) | 105.3 | | Vat Reach Boun Oddar Meanchey |
| 73) | Siem Reap | 105.3 | | Town FM |
| 88) | Sisophon (m) | 105.3 | | R. Ratanak |
| 5) | Phnom Penh | 105.5 | | Vayo FM |
| 14) | Siem Reap | 105.5 | | Mongkulsovann FM |
| 14) | Sihanoukville | 105.5 | | Mongkulsovann FM |
| 97) | Battambang | 105.7 | | Preah Neareay R. (PNR FM) |
| 94) | Battambang | 106.0 | | Sovann Angkor FM |
| 35) | Phnom Penh | 106.0 | 10 | South East Asia FM |
| 83) | Sihanoukville | 106.0 | | R. Ponletrayroth |
| 141) | Phnom Penh | 106.3 | | Vong Kamha Slek Meas |
| 142) | Siem Reap | 106.3 | 5 | National V. of Buddhism |
| 143) | Sisophon (m) | 106.5 | 1 | U FM |
| 66) | Battambang | 106.7 | | R. Mohachun |
| 59) | Kampong Cham | 106.7 | | Kontreum Kampong Cham |
| 144) | Kampong Chhnang | 106.7 | | Mean Leap |
| 145) | Phnom Penh | 106.7 | | Vithyu Dai Thom Bir |
| 146) | Siem Reap | 106.7 | | Mekea |
| 147) | Battambang | 107.0 | | Lotus Flower R. (Phka Chhouk) |
| 148) | Phnom Penh | 107.0 | 10 | FM107 (Smile R.) |
| 70) | Battambang | 107.3 | | Voice of the Blind (VOB, Samleng Chun Pikear Phnek) |
| 25) | Kampong Cham | 107.3 | | ABC Cambodia R. |
| 25) | Ban Lung (mk) | 107.5 | | ABC Cambodia R. |
| 25) | Battambang | 107.5 | | ABC Cambodia R. |
| 25) | Kampong Chhnang | 107.5 | | ABC Cambodia R. |
| 25) | Kampong Thom | 107.5 | | ABC Cambodia R. |
| 25) | Kampot | 107.5 | | ABC Cambodia R. |
| 25) | Koh Kong | 107.5 | | ABC Cambodia R. |
| 25) | Kratie | 107.5 | | ABC Cambodia R. |
| 25) | Phnom Penh | 107.5 | 5 | ABC Cambodia R. |
| 25) | Pailin | 107.5 | | ABC Cambodia R. |
| 25) | Pursat | 107.5 | | ABC Cambodia R. |
| 25) | Ratanakiri | 107.5 | | ABC Cambodia R. |
| 149) | Siem Reap | 107.5 | | Krong Kampuchea |
| 25) | Sihanoukville | 107.5 | | ABC Cambodia R. |
| 25) | Stung Treng | 107.5 | | ABC Cambodia R. |
| 150) | Kampong Cham | 107.7 | | Samleng Yeung (Our Voice) |
| 4) | Takeo | 107.7 | | Fresh FM |
| 151) | Phnom Penh | 107.7 | 5 | Sky R. |
| 141) | Siem Reap | 107.7 | 5 | Vong Kamha Slek Meas |
| 133) | Battambang | 108.0 | | R. Solida (Soft FM) |
| 133) | Kampong Thom | 108.0 | | R. Solida (Soft FM) |
| 133) | Phnom Penh | 108.0 | 10 | R. Solida (Soft FM) |
| 133) | Siem Reap | 108.0 | | R. Solida (Soft FM) |

(b)=Battambang Prov. (kc)=Kampong Cham Prov. (kt)=Kampong Thom Prov. (m)=Banteay Meanchey Prov. (mk)=Mondulkiri Prov (om)=Oddar Meanchey Prov. (r)=Ratanakiri Prov. (t)=Tbong Khmoum Prov.

**Addresses & other information:**
**1)** 87 Street 16BT, Sangkat Boeng Tompong, Meanchey District, Phnom Penh – **2)** No 25B, Street 320, Sangkat Boeng Keng Kang 3, Chamkar Mon District, Phnom Penh 12304 – **3)** 7 Makara Village, Sangkat Labansiek, Ban Lung City, Ratanakiri– **5)** No 13B Street 70, Phnom Penh **W:** vayofm.com – **6)** Vat Preah Neang, Stoung District, Kampong Thom – **8)** Thmey Village, Chamkar Dong, Phnom Penh 12410 – **9)** Romchek IV Village, Sangkat Rotanak, Battambang – **10)** Phum Wattamem, Khum O Dombong I, Sangkae District, Battambang Province. – **11)** Street 208, Romchek IV Village, Sangkat Rotanak, Battambang. Roung Masin Village, Sangkat O'Ambel, Sisophon – **12)** Vat Ta Meum Village, O Dombong Commune I, Sangkae District, Battambang – **13)** Slaket Village, Phum Tahou Commune, Steung Sen District, Kampong Thom – **14)**.National Highway 6, Tavean Village, Sala Kamkreuk, Siem Reap – **17)**Trasak phum Street (Street 63) no 246, Sangkat Boeng

Keng 1, Chamkar Mon District, Phnom Penh – **18)** No. 627 Street 69, Sala Kanseng Village, Svay Dangkum Commune, Siem Reap – **20)** No 131B, Street 271, Boeung Salang, Toul Kork, Phnom Penh – **25)** No 73 Street 271 (Yothapol Khemarek Phoumin), Phnom Penh 12160 **W:** abccambodia.com – **27)** PO Box 1426 Phnom Penh. Operated by Final Frontiers Foundation – **28)** Chong Kaosou Village, Slor Kram Commune, Siem Reap – **29)** No 37 Street 87BT, Phnom Penh 12351 – **31)** Chamkadong, Phnom Penh 12401 – **32)** Wat Thmey Street, Palelay Village, Poipet, Banteay Meanchey. Romchek III Village, Sangkat Rotanak, Battambang – **33)** Phsar Dam Rong Street, Mong Barang Village, Sangkat Boer, Kampong Chhnang – **35)** Slaeng Roleung Village, Sangkat Tuek Thla, Sen Sok District, Phnom Penh – **37)** Prek Mohatep Village, Sangkat Svay Por, Battambang – **38)** Vat Koltoteng, Kaoh Krabei Village, Sangkat Prey Thmey, Chbar Ambov District, Phnom Penh – **40)** Vat Damnak Village, Sangkat Salakamreuk, Siem Reap – **41)** Former National Route 7, Boeng Kok Village, Sangkat Boeng Kok, Kampong Cham – **45)** 15A, Street 371, Sangkat Tuek Thla, Sen Sok District, Phnom Penh – **49)** Lot 35, Street 1709, Sangkat KmNo 6, Russey Keo District, Phnom Penh 12401 – **50)** Vat Chbar Ambouv, Chbar Ampouv District, Phnom Penh. Vat Than, Sangkat Tonle Basak, Chamkar Mon District, Phnom Penh – **54)** Chong Kao Sou Village, Slorkram Commune, Siem Reap – **57)** Borey New Town #L14, Street 113KF, Sangkat Chaom Chao, Pou Senchey District, Phnom Penh – **62)** Chork Village, Sangkat Roka Knong, Doun Kaev City, Takeo – **63)** Vat Sankor, Sankor Commune, Kampong Svay District, Kompong Thom – **65)** 7th Floor, 216B Norodom Boulevard, Srah Chak Commune, Khan Daun Penh, Phnom Penh – **66)** Romchek IV Village, Sangkat Rotanak, Battambang – **67)** Wat Luong, Mongkul Borey, Banteay Meanchey – **68)** Romchek IV Village, Sangkat Rotanak, Battambang – **69)** Dewey International University, Street 207, Battambang – **70)** Group 10, Chong Kaosou Village, Slorkram Commune, Siem Reap – **73)** No 20 Street 592, Sangkat Tuol Sangke, Russei Keo District, Phnom Penh – **75)** No 33, Street 115, Phnom Penh 12258 – **78)** Kou Than Village, Sangkat O'Ambel, Sisophon, Banteay Meanchey Province – **79)** No 69, Street No 57 (Corner Street No 370), Phnom Penh – **80)** Boeng Kok II Village, Sangkat Boeng Kok, Kampong Cham – **81)** National Highway 4, Chbar Mon City, Kampong Speu– **82)** Vat Pothivan, Sangkat Snaor, Pou Senchey District, Phnom Penh – **83)** Vat Prasat Nengkmoa, Rovieng Commune, Samraong District, Takeo. Khnar Village, Sralab Commune, Suong, Tbong Khmum District – **84)** Chamkar Cafe Village, Sangkat Tuol Lvea, Pailin – **85)** Romchek IV Village, Sangkat Rotanak, Battambang – **87)** Rue de Tchechoslovaquie (Street 164), Phnom Penh – **89)** National Road 6, Chong Kaosou Village, Slorkram Commune, Siem Reap – **90)** Sangkat I, Sihanoukville – **91)** Km 4, Poipet, Banteay Meanchey Province – **94)** Romchek IV Village, Sangkat Ratana, Battambang. Chong Kaosou Village, Sangkat Slor Kram, Siem Reap **W:** sovannangkorfm106.com – **97)** Phum Otakam II, Sangkat Toul Ta Ek, Battambang – **98)** No 41 Street 360, Phnom Penh – **101)** No 8D Street 355, Sangkat Tuol Sangkei, Russei Keo District, Phnom Penh 12105 – **103)** Kleang Prak Village, Sangkat Boer, Kampong Chhnang. Chork Village, Sangkat Roka Knong, Doun Kaev City, Takeo – **105)** Wat Leap, Wat Leap Village, Battambang **W:** vodfm.com – **106)** Boeng Kok II Village, Kampong Cham – **108)** see 33) – **109)** 597, National Road 1, Daeum Slaeng Village, Chbar Ampov District, Phnom Penh – **112)** No 150 Street 516, Phnom Penh – **113)** Evocam Freedom International Cambodia, No 507J Tuol Kok Village, Tuol Kok District, Phnom Penh – **114)** Vat Phteah Kandal, Phteah Kandal Commune, Srey Santhor District, Kampong Cham – **115)** Tay Seng Building, Phumi 4 Village, Sangkat Kachanh, Ban Lung City, Ratanakiri – **116)** Women's Media Center of Cambodia, 19A Street 564, Sangkat Boeng Kok, Tuol Kok District, Phnom Penh **W:** wmc.org.kh – **117)** No. 627, Street 99, Sala Kanseng Village, Sangkat Svay Dangkum, Siem Reap – **119)** Phum Otakam II, Sangkat Toul Ta Ek, Battambang – **120)** see 33) – **121)** No 80 Street 136 (Entrance Street 15), Sangkat Psar Kandal 1, Daun Penh District, Phnom Penh – **130)** Psar Takeo Village, Sangkat Roka Knong, Doun Kaev City, Takeo – **131)** No 29, Street 210, Phnom Penh 12158 – **133)** 69 Choeng Ek Village, Sangkat Choeng Ek, Dangkao District, Phnom Penh 12415 – **134)** No 33, Street 115, Phnom Penh 12258 – **139)** No 33, Street 26BT, Thnort Chrum Village, Sangkat Boeng Thumpon, Meanchey District, Phnom Penh 12351 **W:** sbk.com. kh – **141)** No 45A, Boulevard Federation de Russie, Phnom Penh – **142)** Wat Bo, Sangkat Sala Kamroek, Siem Reap – **145)** Sangkat Tuol Svay Prey I, Chamkar Mon District, Phnom Penh 12308 – **147)** Wat Po Veal, Battambang – **148)** No 18, Rd. 562, Phnom Penh 12151 – **149)** National Road 6, Borey Seang Nam, Khnar Thmey Village, Sangkat Chreav, Siem Reap – **150)** Old National Highway 7, Veal Vong Village, Sangkat Veal Vong, Kampong Cham – **151)** Damnak Thom Village, Steung Meanchey Commune, Meanchey District, Phnom Penh 12352

**Relays of International Broadcasters**
**BBC World Service:** Phnom Penh 100.0MHz 1kW in English.
**Radio France Internationale. RFI Cambodge:** Battambang 94.5MHz

0.25kW, Kampong Cham 94.5MHz 0.25kW, Phnom Penh 92.0MHz 10kW, Siem Reap 92.0MHz 1kW, Sihanoukville 94.5MHz 0.5kW 24h n French and Khmer. **RFI Monde:** Phnom Penh 88.5MHz 24h in French

## CAMEROON

**L.T:** UTC +1h — **Pop:** 25 million — **Pr.L:** French, English, ethnic — **E.C:** 50Hz, 220V — **ITU:** CME

### NATIONAL COMMUNICATIONS COUNCIL (CNC)
🖳 Siège CNC Yaoundé, Quartier Bastos, B.P. 12 535, Yaoundé Centre 237 ☎+237 22 210309 🖷 +237 22 210308 **W:** cnc.gov.cm **E:** contact@cnc.gov.cm **L.P:** Prof. Laurent Charles Boyomo.

### CAMEROON RADIO TELEVISION (CRTV, Gov.)
🖳 B.P. 1634, Yaoundé +237 22214077 🖷 +237 22204340 **W:** crtv.cm **E:** infos@crtv.cm **L.P:** GM: Charles Ndongo.
**FM** (MHz):
**CRTV R. Nationale:** Yaoundé 88.8 10kW, Douala 89.2 10kW, Bertoua 89.8 10kW, Bafoussam 91.1 10kW, Ngaoundéré 92.5. Buéa 98.6.
**Regional stations:**
**CRTV Yaoundé FM:** 94.0, **CRTV Centre,** Yaoundé: 101.9 – **CRTV Littoral,** Douala: 91.3, **Suelaba FM:** 104.9 10kW – **CRTV Sud-Ouest,** Buea 94.5, **CRTV Mont Cameroun,** Buea 98.0 – **CRTV Nord,** B.P. 103, Garoua: 101.2 10kW – **CRTV Est,** B.P. 230, Bertoua: 92.9 10kW – **CRTV Ouest,** B.P. 970, Bafoussam: 93.5 10kW, Pouala FM 104.5 – **CRTV Nord-Ouest,** B.P. 4049, Bamenda: 93.5 10kW – **CRTV Sud,** Ebolowa 97.6 10kW, **Kaze FM** 91.1 – **CRTV Adamaoua,** Ngaoundéré: 102.5 10kW – **CRTV Extrême-Nord,** Maroua 94.8, Kousseri 95.5.

**Other FM Stations** (MHz):
**Dynamic FM,** Douala: 103.9 – **Kalak FM,** Yaoundé: 94.5 **W:** facebook.com/KalakOnline – **Magic FM,** Yaoundé: 100.1 – **R. Bon Berger,** Kaélé 99.0 – **R. Bonne Nouvelle:** Yaoundé 97.7, Ngaoundére 98.5, Douala 102.5, Ebolowa 102.7 – **R. Campus,** Ngaoundéré: 99.0 – **R. Environnement,** Yaoundé: 107.7 – **R. Equinoxe,** Douala: 93 **W:** lanouvelleexpression.net – **R. Le Lauréat,** Douala: 90.5 – **R. Lumière,** Yaoundé: 91.9 – **R. Noor,** Ngaoundéré: 106.1 – **R. Nostalgie,** Douala: 96.0 **W:** facebook.com/nostalgie.cm – **R. Reine:** Yaoundé 103.7 1kW, Buéa 97.7 1kW – **R. Salaaman,** Garoua: 89.0 – **R. Sawtu Linjiila,** Ngaoundéré: 95.7 1kW (SW relays see Target Broadcasts section) – **R. Siantou,** Yaoundé: 90.5 – **R. Venus,** Yaoundé: 95.4 – **R. Veritas,** Douala: 96.8 – **R. Vie Nouvelle,** Douala: 100.5 – **Real Time Music,** Douala: 103.5, Yaoundé 106.0 – **Sky One R,** Yaoundé: 104.5, Douala 100.1. **W:** skyonecameroun.com– **Sweet FM,** Douala: 88.7 – **TBC FM,** Yaoundé: 93.0.
**BBC African Sce:** Garoua 94.4, Bamenda 95.7, Yaoundé 98.4, Douala 101.3.
**Medi 1 Afrique Internationale:** Yaoundé 96.2
**RFI Afrique:** Douala 97.8, Bafoussam 101.1, Maroua 101.6, Garoua 104.8, Yaoundé 105.5, Bamenda 105.8MHz

## CANADA

**L.T:** see World Time Table (DST where applicable 10 Mar-3 Nov) — **Pop:** 37 million — **Pr.L:** English, French — **E.C:** 60Hz, 120V — **ITU:** CAN

### CANADIAN RADIO-TELEVISION AND TELECOMMUNICATIONS COMMISSION - CRTC
🖳 Ottawa, ON K1A 0N2 ☎+1 819 997 0313 🖷+1 819 994 0218 **W:** crtc.gc.ca **L.P:** Chair and CEO: Ian Scott. Exec. Dir., Broadcasting: Scott Hutton
The CRTC is an independent public organization that regulates and supervises Canadian broadcasting and telecommunications systems.

**Provinces & Territories:** AB=Alberta, BC=British Columbia, MB=Manitoba, NB=New Brunswick, NL=Newfoundland & Labrador, NS=Nova Scotia, NT=Northwest Territories, NU=Nunavut, ON=Ontario, PE=Prince Edward Island, QC=Québec, SK=Saskatchewan, YT=Yukon

### CANADIAN BROADCASTING CORPORATION/RADIO-CANADA (Pub)
🖳 Box 3220 Stn C, Ottawa ON K1Y 1E4 ☎+1 613 288 6033 **W:** cbc.radio-canada.ca **L.P:** Chair, Board of Dir: Michael Goldbloom. Pres. and CEO: Catherine Tait. Exec. VP, Media Technology and Infrastructure Sces: Steven Guiton. VP, Legal Sces. General Counsel and Corp. Secretary: Sylvie Gadoury. Exec. VP and CFO: Judith Purves. VP, People and Culture: Monique Marcotte. Exec. Dir. Enterprise Comm: Martine Ménard
**English Networks:** 🖳 Box 500 Stn A, Toronto ON M5W 1E6 ☎+1 416 205 3311 **W:** cbc.ca **L.P:** Exec. VP, English Sces: Heather

Conway. GM and Ed. in Chief, CBC News, English Sces: Jennifer McGuire. Exec. Dir. Marketing and Brand Comms, English Sces: Bonnie Brownlee
**French Networks:** ✉ Box 6000, Montréal PQ H3C 3A8 ☎+1 514 597 6000 **W:** ici.radio-canada.ca **LP:** Exec. VP, French Sces: Michel Bissonnette. Exec. Dir. News and Current Affairs: Luce Julien. Exec. Dir. Comm. and Branding: Guylaine Bergeron

## English Radio
### CBC Radio One

| MW | Location | Prov. | kHz | kW | N | Call |
|---|---|---|---|---|---|---|
| 1) | Grand Falls-Windsor | NL | 540 | 10 | | CBT |
| 2) | Watrous | SK | 540 | 50 | | CBK |
| 16) | St. Anthony | NL | 600 | 10 | c | CBNA |
| 4) | St. John's | NL | 640 | 10 | | CBN |
| 5) | Vancouver | BC | 690 | 25 | | CBU |
| 7) | Edmonton | AB | 740 | 50 | | CBX |
| 1) | Bonavista Bay | NL | 750 | 10 | | CBGY |
| 10) | Prince Rupert | BC | 860 | 10/2.5 | | CFPR |
| 11) | Inuvik | NT | 860 | 1 | | CHAK |
| 15) | Winnipeg | MB | 990 | 50/46 | | CBW |
| 16) | Corner Brook | NL | 990 | 10 | | CBY |
| 17) | Calgary | AB | 1010 | 50 | | CBR |
| 19) | Sydney | NS | 1140 | 10 | | CBI |
| 21) | Iqaluit | NU | 1230 | 1 | | CFFB |
| 1) | Gander | NL | 1400 | 4 | | CBG |

| FM | Location | Prov. | MHz | kW | Call |
|---|---|---|---|---|---|
| 7) | Bonnyville | AB | 92.9 | 55.5 | CBX-FM |
| 17) | Calgary | AB | 99.1 | 7 | CBR-1-FM |
| 7) | Edmonton | AB | 93.9 | 3.9 | CBX-2-FM |
| 7) | Grand Prairie | AB | 102.5 | 100 | CBXP-FM |
| 17) | Lethbridge | AB | 100.1 | 100 | CBRL-FM |
| 28) | Kamloops | BC | 94.1 | 4.8 | CBYK-FM |
| 30) | Kelowna | BC | 88.9 | 5.2 | CBTK-FM |
| 33) | Prince George | BC | 91.5 | 59.6 | CBYG-FM |
| 5) | Vancouver | BC | 88.1 | 97.6 | CBU-2-FM |
| 31) | Victoria | BC | 90.5 | 6.3 | CBCV-FM |
| 15) | Brandon | MB | 97.9 | 90 | CBWV-FM |
| 15) | Dauphin/Baldy Mtn. | MB | 105.3 | 95 | CBWW-FM |
| 15) | Winnipeg | MB | 89.3 | 2.8 | CBW-1-FM |
| 18) | Allardville | NB | 97.9 | 100 | CBAA-FM |
| 14) | Bon Accord | NB | 103.3 | 38.5 | CBZC-FM |
| 32) | Edmundston | NB | 99.5 | 24 | CBAN-FM |
| 14) | Fredericton | NB | 99.5 | 3.2 | CBZF-FM |
| 18) | Moncton | NB | 106.1 | 69.5 | CBAM-FM |
| 32) | Saint John | NB | 91.3 | 89 | CBD-FM |
| 22) | Happy Valley-Goose Bay | NL | 89.5 | 4.5 | CFGB-FM |
| 4) | Marystown | NL | 90.3 | 100 | CBNM-FM |
| 4) | St. John's | NL | 88.5 | 3.6 | CBN-1-FM |
| 9) | Halifax | NS | 90.5 | 91 | CBHA-FM |
| 9) | Middleton | NS | 106.5 | 93.4 | CBHM-FM |
| 9) | Mulgrave | NS | 106.7 | 100 | CBHB-FM |
| 19) | Sydney | NS | 92.1 | 8.2 | CBIS-FM |
| 9) | Yarmouth | NS | 92.1 | 94.3 | CBHY-FM |
| 11) | Yellowknife | NT | 98.9 | 4.1 | CFYK-FM |
| 6) | Huntsville | ON | 94.3 | 70 | CBLU-FM |
| 6) | Kingston | ON | 107.5 | 100 | CBCK-FM |
| 34) | Kitchener/Brantford | ON | 89.1 | 10.4 | CBLA-FM-2 |
| 39) | London | ON | 93.5 | 100 | CBCL-FM |
| 20) | North Bay | ON | 96.1 | 100 | CBCN-FM |
| 12) | Ottawa | ON | 91.5 | 84 | CBO-FM |
| 6) | Owen Sound | ON | 98.7 | 100 | CBCB-FM |
| 12) | Pembroke | ON | 92.5 | 100 | CBCD-FM |
| 6) | Peterborough | ON | 98.7 | 12.4 | CBCP-FM |
| 20) | Sault Ste. Marie | ON | 89.5 | 46 | CBSM-FM |
| 20) | Sudbury | ON | 99.9 | 50 | CBCS-FM |
| 8) | Thunder Bay | ON | 88.3 | 23.7 | CBQT-FM |
| 6) | Toronto | ON | 99.1 | 98 | CBLA-FM |
| 25) | Windsor | ON | 97.5 | 19 | CBEW-FM |
| 23) | Charlottetown | PE | 96.1 | 100 | CBCT-FM |
| 13) | Amos/Val-d'Or | QC | 101.1 | 50 | CBMN-FM |
| 13) | Montréal | QC | 88.5 | 25 | CBME-FM |
| 13) | Québec | QC | 104.7 | 65.8 | CBVE-FM |
| 29) | Saguenay | QC | 102.7 | 30 | CBJE-FM |
| 13) | Sherbrooke | QC | 91.7 | 15.9 | CBMB-FM |
| 2) | Regina | SK | 102.5 | 2.7 | CBKR-FM |
| 35) | Saskatoon | SK | 94.1 | 4.1 | CBK-1-FM |
| 3) | Whitehorse | YT | 104.7 | 6.3 | CFWH-FM |

-approx 360 mono relay txs **NB:** calls not announced

### CBC Music

| FM | Location | Prov. | MHz | kW | Call |
|---|---|---|---|---|---|
| 1) | Calgary | AB | 102.1 | 100 | CBR-FM |
| 7) | Edmonton | AB | 90.9 | 100 | CBX-FM |

| FM | Location | Prov. | MHz | kW | Call |
|---|---|---|---|---|---|
| 17) | Lethbridge | AB | 91.7 | 100 | CBBC-FM |
| 17) | Red Deer | AB | 99.9 | 71.5 | CBR-FM-1 |
| 5) | Kamloops | BC | 105.3 | 4.8 | CBU-FM-4 |
| 5) | Kelowna | BC | 89.7 | 5 | CBU-FM-3 |
| 5) | Vancouver | BC | 105.7 | 95.8 | CBU-FM |
| 31) | Victoria | BC | 92.1 | 88.5 | CBU-FM-1 |
| 15) | Brandon | MB | 92.7 | 90 | CBWS-FM |
| 15) | Winnipeg | MB | 98.3 | 160 | CBW-FM |
| 18) | Moncton | NB | 95.5 | 68 | CBA-FM |
| 32) | St. John/Fredericton | NB | 101.5 | 86.9 | CBZ-FM |
| 4) | Baie Verte | NL | 95.5 | 49 | CBN-FM-6 |
| 1) | Grand Falls-Windsor | NL | 90.7 | 100 | CBN-FM-1 |
| 4) | Marystown | NL | 91.7 | 100 | CBN-FM-5 |
| 4) | St. John's | NL | 106.9 | 100 | CBN-FM |
| 9) | Halifax | NS | 102.7 | 92 | CBH-FM |
| 9) | Mulgrave | NS | 103.1 | 81.7 | CBH-FM-2 |
| 19) | Sydney | NS | 105.1 | 68 | CBI-FM |
| 11) | Yellowknife | NT | 95.3 | 0.1 | CBNY-FM |
| 6) | Huntsville | ON | 106.9 | 70 | CBL-FM-1 |
| 6) | Kitchener/Brantford | ON | 90.7 | 8.2 | CBL-FM-2 |
| 6) | London | ON | 100.5 | 15.3 | CBBL-FM |
| 12) | Ottawa | ON | 103.3 | 84 | CBOQ-FM |
| 6) | Peterborough | ON | 103.9 | 12.4 | CBBP-FM |
| 20) | Sudbury | ON | 90.1 | 50 | CBBS-FM |
| 8) | Thunder Bay | ON | 101.7 | 25 | CBQ-FM |
| 6) | Toronto | ON | 94.1 | 38 | CBL-FM |
| 25) | Windsor | ON | 89.9 | 100 | CBE-FM |
| 23) | Charlottetown | PE | 104.7 | 100 | CBCH-FM |
| 13) | Montréal | QC | 93.5 | 100 | CBM-FM |
| 13) | Québec | QC | 96.1 | 0.8 | CBM-FM-2 |
| 13) | Sherbrooke | QC | 89.7 | 16.9 | CBM-FM-1 |
| 2) | Regina | SK | 96.9 | 100 | CBK-FM |
| 2) | Saskatoon | SK | 105.5 | 98 | CBKS-FM |
| 2) | Warmley | SK | 101.5 | 100 | CBK-FM-2 |
| 2) | Yorkton | SK | 91.7 | 57 | CBK-FM-3 |
| 3) | Whitehorse | YT | 104.5 | 0.5 | CBU-FM-8 |

+16 relay txs **NB:** calls not announced

## French Radio – Ici Radio Canada
### Ici Radio-Canada Première

| MW | Location | Prov. | kHz | kW | Call |
|---|---|---|---|---|---|
| 2) | Gravelbourg | SK | 690 | 5 | CBKF-1 |
| 6) | Toronto | ON | 860 | 50 | CJBC |
| 2) | Saskatoon | SK | 860 | 10 | CBKF-2 |
| 25) | Windsor | ON | 1550 | 10 | CBEF |

| FM | Location | Prov. | MHz | kW | Call |
|---|---|---|---|---|---|
| 7) | Calgary | AB | 103.9 | 22 | CBRF-FM |
| 7) | Edmonton | AB | 90.1 | 100 | CHFA-10-FM |
| 5) | Vancouver | BC | 97.7 | 95.8 | CBUF-FM |
| 5) | Victoria | BC | 99.7 | 1.2 | CBUF-FM-9 |
| 15) | Winnipeg | MB | 88.1 | 100 | CKSB-10-FM |
| 18) | Allardville | NB | 105.7 | 100 | CBAF-FM-2 |
| 18) | Bon Accord | NB | 91.7 | 60.2 | CBAF-FM-21 |
| 18) | Caraquet | NB | 90.3 | 100 | CBAF-FM-18 |
| 18) | Edmundston | NB | 100.3 | 20.9 | CBAF-FM-4 |
| 18) | Moncton | NB | 88.5 | 50 | CBAF-FM |
| 18) | St. John/Fredericton | NB | 102.3 | 93.1 | CBAF-FM-1 |
| 4) | St. John's | NL | 105.9 | 45.6 | CBAF-FM-17 |
| 9) | Halifax | NS | 92.3 | 91 | CBAF-FM-5 |
| 9) | Mulgrave | NS | 107.5 | 100 | CBAF-FM-11 |
| 20) | North Bay | ON | 95.1 | 100 | CBON-FM-17 |
| 12) | Ottawa | ON | 90.7 | 84 | CBOF-FM |
| 20) | Sudbury | ON | 98.1 | 50 | CBON-FM |
| 23) | Charlottetown | PE | 88.1 | 88 | CBAF-FM-15 |
| 36) | Amos/Val-d'Or | QC | 91.5 | 100 | CHLM-FM-1 |
| 24) | Gaspé | QC | 89.3 | 4.3 | CBGA-10-FM |
| 40) | Harve-Saint-Pierre | QC | 92.5 | 50 | CBSI-FM-7 |
| 24) | Matane | QC | 102.1 | 42.9 | CBGA-FM |
| 13) | Mont-Laurier | QC | 91.9 | 40.4 | CBF-FM-9 |
| 13) | Montréal | QC | 95.1 | 100 | CBF-FM |
| 27) | Québec | QC | 106.3 | 52.5 | CBV-FM |
| 26) | Rimouski | QC | 89.1 | 38.8 | CJBR-FM |
| 26) | Rivière-du-Loup | QC | 89.5 | 100 | CJBR-FM-1 |
| 36) | Rouyn-Noranda | QC | 90.7 | 11.4 | CHLM-FM |
| 29) | Saguenay | QC | 93.7 | 50 | CBJ-FM |
| 24) | Sainte-Anne-des-Monts | QC | 101.1 | 91 | CBGA-FM-7 |
| 40) | Sept Îles | QC | 98.1 | 96.8 | CBSI-FM |
| 38) | Sherbrooke | QC | 101.1 | 31.4 | CBF-FM-10 |
| 37) | Trois-Rivières | QC | 96.5 | 100 | CBF-FM-8 |
| 36) | Ville-Marie | QC | 89.1 | 66.4 | CBFY-FM |
| 2) | Regina | SK | 97.7 | 22.3 | CBKF-FM |

+148 mono relay txs

## Ici musique

| FM Location | Prov. | MHz | kW | Call |
|---|---|---|---|---|
| 7) Calgary | AB | 89.7 | 10 | CBCX-FM |
| 7) Edmonton | AB | 101.1 | 3.9 | CBCX-FM-1 |
| 5) Vancouver | BC | 90.9 | 2.8 | CBUX-FM |
| 5) Victoria | BC | 88.9 | 6.7 | CBUX-FM-1 |
| 15) Winnipeg | MB | 89.9 | 61 | CKSB-FM |
| 18) Allardville | NB | 101.9 | 100 | CBAL-FM |
| 18) Caraquet | NB | 88.3 | 100 | CBAL-FM-2 |
| 18) Edmundston | NB | 94.3 | 100 | CBAL-FM-5 |
| 18) Moncton | NB | 98.3 | 67.6 | CBAL-FM |
| 18) St. John/Fredericton | NB | 88.1 | 76.7 | CBAL-FM-4 |
| 9) St. John's | NL | 101.9 | 90.2 | CBAX-FM-2 |
| 9) Halifax | NS | 91.5 | 77.5 | CBAX-FM |
| 12) Ottawa | ON | 102.5 | 84 | CBOX-FM |
| 20) Sudbury | ON | 90.9 | 50 | CBBX-FM |
| 6) Toronto | ON | 90.3 | 10 | CJBC-FM |
| 9) Charlottetown | PE | 88.9 | 88 | CBAX-FM-1 |
| 36) Amos/Val-d'Or | QC | 88.3 | 100 | CBFX-FM-3 |
| 24) Gaspé | QC | 90.1 | 6.2 | CBFX-FM-5 |
| 24) Matane | QC | 107.5 | 31.7 | CBRX-FM-1 |
| 13) Mont-Laurier | QC | 91.1 | 82.8 | CBFX-FM-6 |
| 13) Montréal | QC | 100.7 | 100 | CBFX-FM |
| 27) Québec | QC | 95.3 | 64.6 | CBVX-FM |
| 26) Rimouski | QC | 101.5 | 100 | CBRX-FM |
| 26) Rivière-du-Loup | QC | 90.7 | 100 | CBRX-FM-3 |
| 36) Rouyn-Noranda | QC | 89.9 | 10.9 | CBFX-FM-4 |
| 29) Saguenay | QC | 100.9 | 50 | CBJX-FM |
| 40) Sept îles | QC | 96.1 | 84.8 | CBFX-FM-2 |
| 38) Sherbrooke | QC | 90.7 | 33.2 | CBFX-FM-2 |
| 37) Trois-Rivières | QC | 104.3 | 100 | CBFX-FM-1 |
| 2) Regina | SK | 88.9 | 96.4 | CKSB-FM-1 |
| 2) Saskatoon | SK | 88.7 | 100 | CKSB-FM-2 |

+7 relay txs

**NB:** Full list of E and F freqs at **W:** cbc.ca/frequency

**Addresses & other information:**
**1)** 132 Bennett Dr, Gander NL A1V 2H2 **W:** cbc.ca/centralmorning – **2)** 2440 Broad St, Regina SK S4P 4A1 **W:** cbc.ca/sask **W: (F):** ici.radio-canada.ca/saskatchewan – **3)** 3103 3rd Ave, Whitehorse YT Y1A 1E5 **W:** cbc.ca/north – **4)** Box 12010 Stn A, St. John's NL A1B 3T8 **W:** cbc.ca/nl **W: (F):** ici.radio-canada.ca/terre-neuve-et-labrador – **5)** 700 Hamilton St, Vancouver BC V6B 4A2 **W:** cbc.ca/bc **W: (F):** ici.radio-canada.ca/colombie-britannique-et-yukon – **6)** Box 500 Stn A, Toronto ON M5W 1E6 **W:** cbc.ca/toronto **W: (F):** ici.radio-canada.ca/toronto – **7)** 123 Edmonton City Centre 10062-102 Ave, Edmonton AB T5J 2Y8 **W:** cbc.ca/edmonton **W: (F):** ici.radio-canada.ca/alberta – **8)** 213 Miles St E, Thunder Bay ON P7C 1J5 **W:** cbc.ca/thunderbay **W: (F):** as 20) – **9)** 6940 Mumford Rd Suite 100, Halifax NS B3L 0B7 **W:** cbc.ca/ns **W: (F):** ici.radio-canada.ca/nouvelle-ecosse – **10)** Unit 1 222 3rd Ave W, Prince Rupert BC V8J 1L1 **W:** cbc.ca/daybreaknorth – **11)** 5002 Forrest Dr, Yellowknife NT X1A 2A9 **W:** as 3) – **12)** Box 3220 Stn C, Ottawa ON K1Y 1E4 **W:**. cbc.ca/ottawa **W: (F):** ici.radio-canada.ca/ottawa-gatineau – **13)** Box 6000, Montréal QC H3C 3A8 **W:** cbc.ca/montreal **W: (F):** ici.radio-canada.ca/montreal – **14)** Box 2200, Fredericton NB E3B 5G4 **W:** cbc.ca/informationmorningfredericton **W: (F):** as 18) – **15)** 541 Portage Ave, Winnipeg MB R3C 2H1 **W:** cbc.ca/manitoba **W: (F):** ici.radio-canada.ca/manitoba – **16)** 1 Mt Bernard Ave, Corner Brook NL A2H 6Y5 **W:** cbc.ca/cornerbrook – **17)** Box 2640, Calgary AB T2P 2M7 **W:** cbc.ca/calgary **W: (F):** as 7) – **18)** 165 Main St Suite 15, Moncton NB E1C 1B8 **W:** cbc.ca/informationmorningmoncton **W: (F):** ici.radio-canada.ca/nouveau-brunswick – **19)** 500 George St, Sydney NS B1P 1K6 **W:** cbc.ca/informationmorningcb – **20)** 43 Elm St Unit 120, Sudbury ON P3C 1S4 **W:** cbc.ca/sudbury **W: (F):** as 3) – **22)** as 4) **W:** cbc.ca/labradormorning – **23)** Box 2230, Charlottetown PE C1A 8B9 **W:** cbc.ca/pei **W: (F):** ici.radio-canada.ca/ile-du-prince-edouard – **24)** 303 avenue Saint-Jérôme, Matane QC G4W 3A8 **W:** ici.radio-canada.ca/gaspesie-iles-de-la-madeleine – **25)** 825 Riverside Dr W, Windsor ON N9A 5K9 **W:** cbc.ca/windsor **W: (F):** ici.radio-canada.ca/windsor – **26)** 185 boul René-Lepage Est, Rimouski QC G5L 1P2 **W: (F):** ici.radio-canada.ca/bas-saint-laurent – **27)** 888 rue Saint-Jean, Québec QC G1R 5H6 **W: (F):** ici.radio-canada.ca/quebec – **28)** 218 Victoria St, Kamloops BC V2C 2A2 **W:** cbc.ca/kamloops – **29)** 500 rue des Sagenéens, Chicoutimi QC G7H 6N4 **W: (F):** ici.radio-canada.ca/saguenay-lac-saint-jean – **30)** 243 Lawrence Ave, Kelowna BC V1Y 6L2 **W:** cbc.ca/daybreaksouth – **31)** CHEK Media Centre 780 Kings Rd, Victoria BC V8T 5A2 **W:** cbc.ca/ontheisland – **32)** Box 2358, Saint John NB E2L 3V6 **W:** cbc.ca/informationmorningsaintjohn **W: (F):** as 18) – **33)** Unit 1 890 Victoria St, Prince George BC V2L 5P1 **W:** as 10) – **34)** 117 King St W, Kitchener ON N2G 1A7 **W:** cbc.ca/kitchener-waterloo – **35)** 100 128 4th Ave S, Saskatoon SK S7K 1M8 **W:** cbc.ca/saskatoon – **36)** 70 avenue Principale, Rouyn-Noranda QC J9X 4P2 **W:**

**(F):** ici.radio-canada.ca/abitibi-temiscamingue – **37)** 225 des Forges bureau 101, Trois-Rivières QC G9A 2G7 **W: (F):** ici.radio-canada.ca/mauricie – **38)** 1335 rue King Ouest, Sherbrooke QC J1J 2B8 **W: (F):** ici.radio-canada.ca/estrie – **39)** 251 Dundas St, London ON N6A 6H9 **W:** cbc.ca/london – **40)** 350 rue Smith Bureau 30, Sept îles QC G4R 3X2 **W: (F):** ici.radio-canada.ca/cote-nord

**PRIVATE STATIONS** Txs with day power 100W and higher

| MW | kHz | Call | kW | N | Location | Prov. |
|---|---|---|---|---|---|---|
| 705) | 530 | CIAO | 1/0.25 | m | Brampton | ON |
| 701) | 560 | CFOS | 7.5/1 | | Owen Sound | ON |
| 204) | 570 | CKWL | 1 | | Williams Lake | BC |
| 500) | 570 | CFCB | 10/1 | | Corner Brook | NL |
| 702) | 570 | CKGL | 10 | | Kitchener | ON |
| 912) | 570 | CKSW | 10 | | Swift Current | SK |
| 703) | 580 | CFRA | 50/30 | | Ottawa | ON |
| 706) | 580 | CKWW | 0.5 | | Windsor | ON |
| 207) | 590 | CFTK | 1 | | Terrace | BC |
| 302) | 590 | CFAR | 10/1 | | Flin Flon | MB |
| 402) | 590 | CJCW | 1/0.25 | | Sussex | NB |
| 501) | 590 | VOCM | 20 | | St. John's | NL |
| 707) | 590 | CJCL | 50 | | Toronto | ON |
| 708) | 600 | CKAT | 10/5 | | North Bay | ON |
| 803) | 600 | CFQR | 10/5 | | Montréal | QC |
| 900) | 600 | CJWW | 25/8 | | Saskatoon | SK |
| 209) | 610 | CHNL | 25/5 | | Kamloops | BC |
| 303) | 610 | CHTM | 1 | | Thompson | MB |
| 709) | 610 | CKTB | 10/5 | | St. Catharines | ON |
| 501b) | 620 | CKCM | 10 | r | Grand Falls-Windsor | NL |
| 901) | 620 | CKRM | 10 | | Regina | SK |
| 102) | 630 | CHED | 50 | | Edmonton | AB |
| 711) | 630 | CFCO | 10/6 | | Chatham-Kent | ON |
| 712) | 640 | CFMJ | 50 | | Toronto | ON |
| 208) | 650 | CISL | 20/4 | | Vancouver | BC |
| 501d) | 650 | CKGA | 5 | | Gander | NL |
| 908) | 650 | CKOM | 10 | | Saskatoon | SK |
| 108) | 660 | CFFR | 50 | | Calgary | AB |
| 305) | 680 | CJOB | 50 | | Winnipeg | MB |
| 714) | 680 | CFTR | 50 | | Toronto | ON |
| 810) | 690 | CKGM | 50 | | Montréal | QC |
| 105) | 700 | CJLI | 50/20 | | Calgary | AB |
| 501e) | 710 | CKVO | 10 | | Clarenville | NL |
| 213) | 730 | CHMJ | 50 | | Vancouver | BC |
| 306) | 730 | CKDM | 10/5 | | Dauphin | MB |
| 804) | 730 | CKAC | 50 | F | Montréal | QC |
| 501a) | 740 | CHCM | 10 | r | Marystown | NL |
| 717) | 740 | CFZM | 50 | | Toronto | ON |
| 911) | 750 | CKJH | 25 | | Melfort | SK |
| 224a) | 760 | CFLD | 1 | r | Burns Lake | BC |
| 103) | 770 | CHQR | 50 | | Calgary | AB |
| 206) | 800 | CKOR | 10/0.5 | | Penticton | BC |
| 502) | 800 | VOWR | 10/2.5 | | St. John's | NL |
| 704) | 800 | CJBQ | 10 | | Belleville | ON |
| 713) | 800 | CKLW | 50 | | Windsor | ON |
| 811) | 800 | CJAD | 50/10 | | Montréal | QC |
| 902) | 800 | CHAB | 10 | | Moose Jaw | SK |
| 307) | 810 | CKJS | 10 | c m | Winnipeg | MB |
| 723) | 820 | CHAM | 50/10 | | Hamilton | ON |
| 104) | 840 | CFCW | 50/40 | | Camrose | AB |
| 205) | 840 | CKBX | 1/0.5 | | 100 Mile House | BC |
| 206c) | 870 | CKIR | 1/0.25 | r | Invermere | BC |
| 224) | 870 | CFSX | 1/0.5 | | Smithers | BC |
| 500a) | 870 | CFSX | 0.5 | r | Stephenville | NL |
| 114) | 880 | CHQT | 50 | | Edmonton | AB |
| 312) | 880 | CKLQ | 10 | | Brandon | MB |
| 230) | 890 | CJDC | 10 | | Dawson Creek | BC |
| 725) | 900 | CHML | 50 | | Hamilton | ON |
| 903) | 900 | CKBI | 10/2.8 | | Prince Albert | SK |
| 106) | 910 | CKDQ | 50 | | Drumheller | AB |
| 308) | 920 | CFRY | 25/15 | | Portage la Prairie | MB |
| 728) | 920 | CKNX | 10/1 | | Wingham | ON |
| 107) | 930 | CJCA | 50 | | Edmonton | AB |
| 405) | 930 | CFBC | 50 | | Saint John | NB |
| 503) | 930 | CJYQ | 25/3.5 | | St. John's | NL |
| 805) | 940 | CFNV | 50 | F | Montréal | QC |
| 904) | 940 | CJGX | 50/10 | | Yorkton | SK |
| 309) | 950 | CFAM | 10 | | Altona | MB |
| 406) | 950 | CKNB | 10/1 | | Campbellton | NB |
| 109) | 960 | CFAC | 50 | | Calgary | AB |
| 726) | 960 | CKNT | 2/0.28 | | Mississauga | ON |
| 214) | 980 | CKNW | 50 | | Vancouver | BC |
| 731) | 980 | CFPL | 10/5 | | London | ON |
| 806) | 980 | CHRF | 50/10 | F | Montréal | QC |

| MW | kHz | Call | kW | N | Location | Prov. |
|---|---|---|---|---|---|---|
| 905) | 980 | CJME | 10/5 | | Regina | SK |
| 733) | 1010 | CFRB | 50 | * | Toronto | ON |
| 215) | 1040 | CKST | 50 | | Vancouver | BC |
| 820) | 1040 | CJMS | 5/1.07 | F | Saint-Constant | QC |
| 734) | 1050 | CHUM | 50 | | Toronto | ON |
| 906) | 1050 | CJNB | 10 | | North Battleford | SK |
| 111) | 1060 | CKMX | 50 | * | Calgary | AB |
| 220) | 1070 | CFAX | 10 | | Victoria | BC |
| 736) | 1070 | CHOK | 10 | | Sarnia | ON |
| 221) | 1130 | CKWX | 50 | | Vancouver | BC |
| 122) | 1140 | CHRB | 50/46 | | High River | AB |
| 222) | 1150 | CKFR | 10 | | Kelowna | BC |
| 724) | 1150 | CKOC | 50/20 | | Hamilton | ON |
| 909) | 1150 | CJSL | 10 | | Estevan | SK |
| 907) | 1190 | CFSL | 10/5 | | Weyburn | SK |
| 225) | 1200 | CJRJ | 25 | m | Vancouver | BC |
| 710) | 1200 | CFGO | 50 | | Ottawa | ON |
| 505) | 1210 | VOAR | 10 | c | St. John's | NL |
| 910a) | 1210 | CFYM | 1/0.25 | r | Kindersley | SK |
| 313) | 1220 | CJRB | 10 | | Boissevain | MB |
| 209c) | 1230 | CJNL | 1 | r | Merritt | BC |
| 223) | 1240 | CKMK | 1 | r | Mackenzie | BC |
| 206b) | 1240 | CJOR | 1 | | Osoyoos | BC |
| 233) | 1240 | CFNI | 1 | | Port Hardy | BC |
| 304) | 1240 | CJAR | 1 | | The Pas | MB |
| 501c) | 1240 | CKIM | 1 | r | Baie Verte | NL |
| 310) | 1250 | CHSM | 10 | | Steinbach | MB |
| 721) | 1250 | CJYE | 10 | | Oakville | ON |
| 119) | 1260 | CFRN | 50 | | Edmonton | AB |
| 410) | 1260 | CKHJ | 10 | | Fredericton | NB |
| 605) | 1270 | CJCB | 10 | | Sydney | NS |
| 807) | 1280 | CFMB | 50 | m | Montréal | QC |
| 311) | 1290 | CFRW | 10 | | Winnipeg | MB |
| 751) | 1290 | CJBK | 10 | | London | ON |
| 753) | 1310 | CIWW | 50 | | Ottawa | ON |
| 229) | 1320 | CHMB | 50 | m | Vancouver | BC |
| 722) | 1320 | CJMR | 10 | m | Oakville | ON |
| 910) | 1330 | CJYM | 10 | | Rosetown | SK |
| 209a) | 1340 | CINL | 1 | r | Ashcroft | BC |
| 210) | 1340 | CFKC | 0.25 | r | Creston | BC |
| 612) | 1350 | CKAD | 1 | | Middleton | NS |
| 812) | 1350 | CHFO | 1/0.18 | F | Gatineau | QC |
| 758) | 1380 | CKPC | 25 | | Brantford | ON |
| 209b) | 1400 | CHNL-1 | 1 | r | Clearwater | BC |
| 206a) | 1400 | CIOR | 1 | r | Princeton | BC |
| 216) | 1410 | CFTE | 50 | | Vancouver | BC |
| 836) | 1410 | CJWI | 10 | F | Montréal | QC |
| 606) | 1420 | CKDY | 1 | | Digby | NS |
| 764) | 1430 | CHKT | 50 | m | Toronto | ON |
| 121) | 1440 | CKJR | 10 | | Wetaskiwin | AB |
| 607) | 1450 | CFAB | 1 | | Windsor | NS |
| 834) | 1450 | CHOU | 2/1 | m | Montréal | QC |
| 768) | 1460 | CJOY | 10 | | Guelph | ON |
| 234) | 1470 | CJVB | 50 | m | Vancouver | BC |
| 912a) | 1490 | CJSN | 1 | | Shaunavon | SK |
| 773) | 1540 | CHIN | 50/30 | m | Toronto | ON |
| 835) | 1570 | CJLV | 10 | F | Laval/Montréal | QC |
| 756) | 1580 | CKDO | 10 | | Oshawa | ON |
| 774) | 1610 | CHHA | 6.25 | m | Toronto | ON |
| 825) | 1610 | CHRN | 1 | m | Montréal | QC |
| 729) | 1650 | CINA | 5/0.68 | m | Mississauga | ON |
| 837) | 1650 | CJRS | 1 | F | Montréal | QC |
| 823) | 1670 | CJEU | 1 | F | Gatineau | QC |
| 720) | 1690 | CHTO | 6/1 | m | Toronto | ON |
| 831) | 1690 | CJLO | 1 | | Montréal | QC |

| SW | kHz | Call | kW | | Location | Prov. | Relays |
|---|---|---|---|---|---|---|---|
| 111) | 6030 | CFVP | 0.1 | | Calgary | AB | CKMX |
| 733) | 6070 | CFRX | 1 | | Toronto | ON | CFRB |

**B**: Stns that broadcast a common prgr during part of the day have a letter as part of the reference number

### Addresses & other information:

**Alberta**

**102)** 5204 84th St NW, Edmonton T6E 5N8 **W:** 630ched.com – **103)** 100-3320 17th Ave SW, Calgary T3E 0B4 **W:** newstalk770.com – **104)** 5708-48 Ave, Camrose T4V 0K1 **W:** cfcw.com – **105)** 100-4510 MacLeod Trail S, Calgary T2G 0A4 **W:** cjli.ca – **106)** Box 1480, Drumheller T0J 0Y0 **W:** realcountry910.com – **107)** 5316 Calgary Trail NW, Edmonton T6H 4J8 **W:** am930thelight.com – **108)** 535 7th Ave SW, Calgary T2P 0Y4 **W:** 660news.com – **109)** 240-2723 37th Ave NE, Calgary T1Y 5R8 **W:** sportsnet.ca/960 – **111)** 300-1110 Centre St NE, Calgary T2E 2R2 **W:** funny1060.com. Rpt: qslcalgary@gmail. com – **114)** as 102) **W:** 880edmonton.ca – **119)** 100-18520 Stony Plain Rd NW, Edmonton T5S 2E2 **W:** tsn.ca/radio – **121)** 5214A-50th Ave, Wetaskiwin T9A 0S8 **W:** w1440.com – **122)** 11-5th Ave SE, High River T1V 1G2 **W:** highriveronline.com

**British Columbia**

**204)** 83 First Ave S, Williams Lake V2G 1H4 **W:** mycariboonow.com – **205)** Box 1834, 100 Mile House V0K 2E0 **W:** as 204) – **206)** 33 Carmi Ave, Penticton V2A 3G4 **W:** penticton.myezrock.com – **206a)** Box 1400, Princeton V0X 1W0 – **206b)** 203 – 8309 Main St, Osoyoos V0H 1V0 – **206c)** Box 1403, Golden V0A 1H0 – **207)** 4625 Lazelle Ave, Terrace V8G 1S4 **W:** terrace.myezrock.com – **208)** as 221) **W:** sportsnet.ca/650 – **209)** 611 Lansdowne St, Kamloops V2C 1Y6 **W:** radionl.com – **209a)** Ashcroft – **209b)** Clearwater – **209c)** Merritt – **210)** Box 310, Creston V1R 1M4 **W:** kootenays.myezrock.com – **213)** as 214) **W:** am730.ca – **214)** 2000-700 W Georgia St, Vancouver V7Y 1K9 **W:** cknw.com – **215)** 500-969 Robson St, Vancouver V6Z 1X5 **W:** tsn.ca/radio – **216)** as 215) **W:** bnnbloomberg.ca – **220)** 1420 Broad St, Victoria V8W 2B1 **W:** cfax1070.com – **221)** 2440 Ash St, Vancouver V5Z 4J6 **W:** news1130. com – **222)** 3800-435 Bernard Ave, Kelowna V1Y 6N8 **W:** am1150.ca – **223)** 2nd flr – 1810 3rd Ave, Prince George V2M 1G4 **W:** 993thedrive. com – **224)** Box 335, Smithers V0J 2N0 **W:** mybulkeylakesnow.com – **224a)** Burns Lake – **225)** 110-3060 Norland Ave, Burnaby V5B 3A6 **W:** spiceradio1200am.com. Mostly langs – **229)** 100-1200 73rd Ave W, Vancouver V6P 6G5 **W:** am1320.ca. Mostly Chinese – **230)** 901 102nd Ave, Dawson Creek V1G 2B6 **W:** cjdccountry.com – **233)** 7035A Market St, Port Hardy V0N 2P0 **W:** mytriportnow.com – **234)** 2090 Aberdeen Centre 4151 Hazelbridge Way, Richmond V6X 4J7 **W:** am1470.com. Mostly langs.

**Manitoba**

**302)** Box 430 Stn Main, Flin Flon R8A 1N3 **W:** flinflononline.com – **303)** 103 Cree Rd, Thompson R8N 0B9 **W:** thompsononline.ca – **304)** Box 2980 Stn Main, The Pas R9A 1R7 **W:** thepasonline.com – **305)** 200-1440 Jack Blick Ave, Winnipeg R3G 0L4 **W:** cjob.com – **306)** 1735 Main St S, Dauphin R7N 2V4 **W:** 730ckdm.com – **307)** 520 Corydon Ave, Winnipeg R3L 0P1 **W:** ckjs.com. Mostly langs – **308)** 2390 Sissons Dr, Portage la Prairie R1N 3B2 **W:** portageonline.com – **309)** Box 950, Altona R0G 0B0 **W:** pembinavalleyonline.com – **310)** 105-32 Brandt St, Steinbach R5G 2J7 **W:** steinbachonline.com – **311)** 1445 Pembina Hwy, Winnipeg R3T 5C2 **W:** tsn.ca/radio – **312)** 624 14th St E, Brandon R7A 7E1 **W:** qcountryfm.ca – **313)** 420 S Railway St, Boissevain R0K 0E0 **W:** discoverwestman.com

**New Brunswick**

**402)** 6 Marble St, Sussex E4E 5M2 **W:** 590cjcw.com – **405)** 226 Union St, Saint John E2L 1B1 **W:** cfbcradio.com – **406)** 74 Water St, Campbellton E3N 1B1 **W:** 95cknb.ca – **410)** 206 Rookwood Ave, Fredericton E3B 2M2 **W:** khj.ca

**Newfoundland & Labrador**

**500)** Box 570 Stn Main, Corner Brook A2H 6H5 **W:** vocm.com – **500a)** 60 West St, Stephenville A2N 1C6 – **501)** Box 8590 Stn A, St. John's A1B 3P5 **W:** as 500) – **501a)** Box 560, Marystown A0E 2M0 – **501b)** Box 620 Stn Main, Grand Falls-Windsor A2A 2K2 – **501c)** Baie Verte – **501d)** Box 650 Stn Main, Gander A1V 1X2 – **501e)** Gen. Delivery, Clarenville A5A 2C1 – **502)** 101 Patrick St, St. John's A1E 3Y5 **W:** vowr. org – **503)** as 501) **W:** 930kixxcountry.ca – **505)** 1041 Topsail Rd, Mt. Pearl A1N 5E9 **W:** voar.org

**Nova Scotia**

**605)** Box 1270 Stn A, Sydney B1P 6K2 **W:** cjcbradio.com – **606)** Box 1420, Digby B0V 1A0 **W:** avrnetwork.com – **607)** 169-A Water St, Windsor B0N 2T0 **W:** as 606) – **612)** Box 550, Middleton B0S 1P0 **W:** as 606)

**Ontario**

**701)** Box 280 Stn Main, Owen Sound N4K 5P5 **W:** 560cfos.ca – **702)** 230 The Boardwalk 2nd flr, Kitchener N2N 0B1 **W:** 570news.com – **703)** 87 George St, Ottawa K1N 9H7 **W:** cfra.com – **704)** Box 488 Stn Main, Belleville K8N 5B2 **W:** cjbq.com – **705)** 5312 Dundas St W, Toronto M9B 1B3 **W:** am530.ca. Mostly langs – **706)** as 713) **W:** am580radio. com – **707)** 1 Ted Rogers Way 5th flr, Toronto M4Y 3B7 **W:** sportsnet. ca/590 – **708)** Box 3000, North Bay P1B 8K8 **W:** country600.com – **709)** Box 977 Stn Main, St. Catharines L2R 6Z4 **W:** 610cktb.com – **710)** as 703) **W:** tsn.ca/radio – **711)** Box 100 Stn Main, Chatham-Kent N7M 5K1 **W:** country929.com – **712)** Corus Quay 25 Dockside Dr, Toronto M5A 0B5 **W:** 640toronto.com – **713)** 1640 Ouellette Ave, Windsor N8X 1L1 **W:** am800cklw.com – **714)** as 707) **W:** 680news.com – **717)** 70 Jefferson Ave, Toronto M6K 1Y4 **W:** zoomerradio.ca – **720)** 437 Danforth Ave Suite 300, Toronto M4K 1P1 **W:** am1690.ca. Mostly Greek – **721)** 284 Church St, Oakville L6J 7N2 **W:** joy1250.com – **722)** as 721) **W:** cjmr1320.ca – **723)** 883 Upper Wentworth St Suite 401, Hamilton L9A 4Y6 **W:** funny820.com – **724)** as 723) **W:** tsn.ca/radio – **725)** 875 Main St W #900, Hamilton L8S 4R1 **W:** 900chml.com – **726)** 605-1 City Centre Dr, Mississauga L5B 1M2 **W:** sauga960am.ca – **728)** 215 Carling Terrace, Wingham N0G 2W0 **W:** cknx.ca – **729)** 1515 Britannia Rd Suite 315, Mississauga L4W 4K1 **W:** cinaradio.com. Mostly langs – **731)** Box

2580 Stn B, London N6A 4H3 **W:** am980.ca – **733)** 250 Richmond St W 3rd flr, Toronto M5V 1W4 **W:** newstalk1010.com. Rpt: cfrbcfrxreport@ gmail.com – **734)** as 733) **W:** tsn.ca/radio – **736)** 1415 London Rd, Sarnia N7A 1P9 **W:** chok.com – **751)** 743 Wellington Rd S, London N6C 4R5 **W:** cjbk.com – **753)** 2001 Thurston Dr, Ottawa K1G 6C9 **W:** 1310news.com – **756)** 207-1200 Airport Blvd, Oshawa L1J 8P5 **W:** ckdo.ca – **758)** 571 West St, Brantford N3R 7C5 **W:** am1380.ca – **764)** 8-135 East Beaver Creek Rd, Richmond Hill L4B 1E2 **W:** am1430.com. Mostly Chinese – **768)** 75 Speedvale Ave E, Guelph N1E 6M3 **W:** cjoy. com – **773)** 622 College St, Toronto M6G 1B6 **W:** chinradio.com. Mostly Italian – **774)** 22 Wenderly Dr, Toronto M6B 2N9 **W:** chha1610am.ca. Mostly Spanish

**Québec**
**803)** 6322 Jean-Talon St E, Montréal H1M 1S8 – **804)** 800 rue de la Gauchetière Ouest Bureau 1100, Montréal H5A 1M1 **W:** radiocirculation.net – **805)** as 803) **W:** cfnv940.com – **806)** 5877 ave Papineau, Montréal H2G 2W3 **W:** montrealam980.com – **807)** as 806) **W:** cfmbradio.com. Mostly langs – **810)** as 811) **W:** tsn.ca/radio – **811)** 1717 boulevard René-Lévesque Est, Montréal H2L 4T9 **W:** cjad.com – **812)** Gatineau – **820)** 143 rue Saint-Pierre, Saint-Constant J5A 2G9 **W:** cjms1040.ca – **823)** 855 boul. de Gappe pièce 310, Gatineau J8T 8H9 **W:** radiojeunesse.ca – **825)** 7655 rue Cordner, LaSalle H8N 2X2 **W:** radiohumsafar.com. Mostly langs – **831)** 7141 Sherbrooke St Ouest Room CC430, Montréal H4B 1R6 **W:** cjlo.com – **834)** 11876 rue de Meulles, Montréal H4J 2E6 **W:** grouprmo.ca. Mostly langs – **835)** 2040 Autoroute Laval, Laval H7S 2M9 **W:** radiomieuxetre.com – **836)** 3390 blvd Crémazie est, Montréal H2A 1A4 **W:** cpam1410.com – **837)** 4835 Côte St. Catherine Rd #2, Montréal H3W 1M4 **W:** laradiogospel.ca

**Saskatchewan**
**900)** 366 3rd Ave S, Saskatoon S7K 1M5 **W:** cjwwradio.com – **901)** 1900 Rose St, Regina S4P 0A9 **W:** 620ckrm.com – **902)** Box 800 Stn Main, Moose Jaw S6H 4P5 **W:** discovermoosejaw.com – **903)** 1316 Central Ave, Prince Albert S6V 6P5 **W:** 900ckbi.com – **904)** Broadc Place 120 Smith St E, Yorkton S3N 3V3 **W:** gx94radio.com – **905)** 210-2401 Saskatchewan Dr, Regina S4P 4H8 **W:** cjme.com – **906)** Box 1460 Stn Main, North Battleford S9A 2Z5 **W:** cjnb.com – **907)** Box 340 Stn Main, Weyburn S4H 2K2 **W:** discoverweyburn.com – **908)** 715 Saskatchewan Cres W, Saskatoon S7M 5V7 **W:** ckom.com – **909)** Box 1280 Stn Main, Estevan S4A 2H8 **W:** discoverestevan.com – **910)** Box 490, Rosetown S0L 2V0 **W:** westcentralonline.com – **910a)** Box 1330, Kindersley S0L 1S1 – **911)** Box 750, Melfort S0E 1A0 **W:** ck750.com – **912)** 300 - 198 1st Ave, Swift Current S9H 2B2 **W:** swiftcurrentonline. com – **912a)** Box 1176, Shaunavon S0N 2M0

| FM | Prov. | MHz | kW | N | Call |
|---|---|---|---|---|---|
| Airdrie | AB | 106.1 | 6 | | CFIT-FM |
| Athabasca | AB | 94.1 | 9 | | CKBA-FM |
| Bonnyville | AB | 98.7 | 12.3 | F | CHFB-FM |
| Bonnyville | AB | 99.7 | 50 | | CFNA-FM |
| Bonnyville | AB | 101.3 | 27 | | CJEG-FM |
| Brooks | AB | 101.1 | 8.6 | | CIXF-FM |
| Brooks | AB | 105.7 | 14 | | CIBQ-FM |
| Calgary | AB | 88.1 | 100 | m | CJWE-FM |
| Calgary | AB | 88.9 | 100 | | CJSI-FM |
| Calgary | AB | 90.3 | 100 | | CKMP-FM |
| Calgary | AB | 90.9 | 18 | | CJSW-FM |
| Calgary | AB | 92.1 | 100 | | CJAY-FM |
| Calgary | AB | 92.9 | 100 | | CFEX-FM |
| Calgary | AB | 93.7 | 100 | | CKUA-FM-1 |
| Calgary | AB | 94.7 | 53 | | CHKF-FM |
| Calgary | AB | 95.3 | 100 | | CKWD-FM |
| Calgary | AB | 95.9 | 100 | | CHFM-FM |
| Calgary | AB | 96.9 | 100 | | CJAQ-FM |
| Calgary | AB | 97.7 | 100 | | CHUP-FM |
| Calgary | AB | 98.5 | 100 | | CIBK-FM |
| Calgary | AB | 101.5 | 100 | | CKCE-FM |
| Calgary | AB | 103.1 | 100 | | CFXL-FM |
| Calgary | AB | 105.1 | 100 | | CKRY-FM |
| Calgary | AB | 106.7 | 8 | m | CKYR-FM |
| Calgary | AB | 107.3 | 100 | | CFGQ-FM |
| Camrose | AB | 98.1 | 50 | | CFCW-FM |
| Cold Lake | AB | 95.3 | 100 | | CJXK-FM |
| Drayton Valley | AB | 92.9 | 50 | | CIBW-FM |
| Drumheller | AB | 91.3 | 100 | | CKUA-FM-13 |
| Edmonton | AB | 91.7 | 96 | | CHBN-FM |
| Edmonton | AB | 92.5 | 97 | | CKNG-FM |
| Edmonton | AB | 94.9 | 100 | | CKUA-FM |
| Edmonton | AB | 95.7 | 100 | | CKEA-FM |
| Edmonton | AB | 96.3 | 100 | | CKRA-FM |
| Edmonton | AB | 97.3 | 100 | | CIRK-FM |
| Edmonton/Spruce Grove | AB | 98.5 | 100 | m | CFWE-FM-4 |
| Edmonton | AB | 99.3 | 100 | | CIUP-FM |

| FM | Prov. | MHz | kW | N | Call |
|---|---|---|---|---|---|
| Edmonton | AB | 100.3 | 97 | | CFBR-FM |
| Edmonton | AB | 101.7 | 100 | m | CKER-FM |
| Edmonton | AB | 102.3 | 100 | | CKNO-FM |
| Edmonton | AB | 102.9 | 100 | | CHDI-FM |
| Edmonton | AB | 103.9 | 98 | | CISN-FM |
| Edmonton | AB | 104.9 | 100 | | CFMG-FM |
| Edmonton | AB | 105.9 | 100 | | CJRY-FM |
| Edmonton | AB | 107.1 | 40 | | CJNW-FM |
| Edson | AB | 94.3 | 20 | | CFXE-FM |
| Fort McMurray | AB | 91.1 | 25 | | CKOS-FM |
| Fort McMurray | AB | 93.3 | 43.5 | | CJOK-FM |
| Fort McMurray | AB | 94.5 | 23.5 | m | CFWE-FM-5 |
| Fort McMurray | AB | 97.9 | 43.5 | | CKYX-FM |
| Fort McMurray | AB | 100.5 | 50 | | CHFT-FM |
| Fort McMurray | AB | 103.7 | 50 | | CFVR-FM |
| Fort Saskatchewan | AB | 107.9 | 20 | | CKFT-FM |
| Grande Prairie | AB | 93.1 | 100 | | CJXX-FM |
| Grande Prairie | AB | 96.3 | 70 | | CJGY-FM |
| Grande Prairie | AB | 97.7 | 100 | | CFGP-FM |
| Grande Prairie | AB | 98.9 | 100 | | CIKT-FM |
| Grande Prairie | AB | 100.9 | 100 | | CKUA-FM-4 |
| Grande Prairie | AB | 104.7 | 100 | | CFRI-FM |
| Grande Prairie | AB | 105.7 | 100 | m | CFWE-FM-7 |
| High Level | AB | 102.1 | 29 | | CKHL-FM |
| High Level | AB | 106.1 | 29 | | CFKX-FM |
| High Prairie | AB | 93.5 | 29 | | CKVH-FM |
| High River/Okotoks | AB | 99.7 | 16 | | CFXO-FM |
| High River/Okotoks | AB | 100.9 | 100 | | CKUV-FM |
| Joussard | AB | 91.7 | 4.2 | m | CFWE-FM-1 |
| Lac La Biche | AB | 90.5 | 19.6 | m | CFWE-FM-6 |
| Lacombe | AB | 94.1 | 55 | | CJUV-FM |
| Leduc | AB | 93.1 | 3.2 | | CJLD-FM |
| Lethbridge | AB | 94.1 | 100 | | CJOC-FM |
| Lethbridge | AB | 95.5 | 100 | | CHLB-FM |
| Lethbridge | AB | 98.1 | 20 | | CKBD-FM |
| Lethbridge | AB | 99.3 | 100 | | CKUA-FM-2 |
| Lethbridge/Taber | AB | 106.7 | 100 | | CJRX-FM |
| Lethbridge | AB | 107.7 | 100 | | CFRV-FM |
| Lloydminster | AB | 95.9 | 100 | | CKSA-FM |
| Lloydminster | AB | 106.1 | 100 | | CKLM-FM |
| Medicine Hat | AB | 94.5 | 100 | | CHAT-FM |
| Medicine Hat | AB | 96.1 | 100 | | CFMY-FM |
| Medicine Hat | AB | 97.3 | 100 | | CKUA-FM-3 |
| Medicine Hat | AB | 102.1 | 40 | | CJCY-FM |
| Medicine Hat | AB | 105.3 | 100 | | CKMH-FM |
| Moose Hills | AB | 96.7 | 100 | m | CFWE-FM-3 |
| Olds | AB | 96.5 | 35 | | CKLJ-FM |
| Olds | AB | 104.5 | 35 | | CKJX-FM |
| Peace River | AB | 94.9 | 100 | | CKYL-FM |
| Peace River | AB | 96.9 | 22 | | CKUA-FM-5 |
| Peace River | AB | 106.1 | 50 | | CKKX-FM |
| Piikani/Blood First Nation | AB | 89.3 | 10.2 | m | CFWE-FM-2 |
| Pincher Creek | AB | 92.7 | 6 | | CJPV-FM |
| Red Deer | AB | 90.5 | 38 | | CKRD-FM |
| Red Deer | AB | 95.5 | 100 | | CKGY-FM |
| Red Deer | AB | 98.9 | 100 | | CIZZ-FM |
| Red Deer | AB | 100.7 | 100 | | CKEX-FM |
| Red Deer | AB | 101.3 | 50 | | CKIK-FM |
| Red Deer | AB | 105.5 | 100 | | CHUB-FM |
| Red Deer | AB | 106.7 | 100 | | CFDV-FM |
| Red Deer | AB | 107.7 | 100 | | CKUA-FM-6 |
| Slave Lake | AB | 92.7 | 5 | | CHSL-FM |
| St. Paul | AB | 97.7 | 45 | | CHSP-FM |
| Stettler | AB | 93.3 | 23 | | CKSQ-FM |
| Strathmore | AB | 104.5 | 7 | | CKOV-FM |
| Suffield | AB | 104.1 | 4.3 | | CKBF-FM |
| Taber | AB | 93.3 | 100 | | CJBZ-FM |
| Vegreville | AB | 106.5 | 13 | | CKVG-FM |
| Wabasca-Desmarais | AB | 94.3 | 6 | | CHSL-FM-1 |
| Wainwright | AB | 93.7 | 50 | | CKWY-FM |
| Wainwright | AB | 101.9 | 50 | | CKKY-FM |
| Westlock | AB | 97.9 | 48 | | CKWB-FM |
| Whitecourt | AB | 96.7 | 9 | | CFXW-FM |
| Whitecourt | AB | 105.3 | 42.3 | | CIXM-FM |
| Campbell River | BC | 99.7 | 6 | | CIQC-FM |
| Chilliwack | BC | 98.3 | 5 | | CKSR-FM |
| Courtenay | BC | 97.3 | 11.6 | | CKLR-FM |
| Courtenay | BC | 98.9 | 5 | | CFCP-FM |
| Duncan | BC | 89.7 | 3.5 | | CJSU-FM |
| Fort St. John | BC | 98.5 | 50 | | CHRX-FM |
| Fort St. John | BC | 101.5 | 40 | | CKNL-FM |
| Gibsons | BC | 107.5 | 4.6 | | CISC-FM |

| FM | Prov. | MHz | kW | N | Call | FM | Prov. | MHz | kW | N | Call |
|---|---|---|---|---|---|---|---|---|---|---|---|
| Houston | BC | 105.5 | 3.5 | | CJFW-FM-7 | Inkerman/Pokemouche | NB | 97.1 | 44.4 | F | CKRO-FM |
| Kamloops | BC | 97.5 | 4.3 | | CKRV-FM | Kedgwick | NB | 90.1 | 3 | F | CFJU-FM |
| Kamloops | BC | 98.3 | 4.3 | | CIFM-FM | Miramichi | NB | 93.7 | 11 | F | CKMA-FM |
| Kamloops | BC | 100.1 | 3.5 | | CKBZ-FM | Miramichi | NB | 95.9 | 25 | | CHHI-FM |
| Kamloops | BC | 103.1 | 5 | | CJKC-FM | Miramichi | NB | 99.3 | 17.8 | | CFAN-FM |
| Kelowna | BC | 96.3 | 31 | | CKKO-FM | Moncton | NB | 90.7 | 30 | F | CFBO-FM |
| Kelowna | BC | 99.9 | 35 | | CHSU-FM | Moncton | NB | 91.9 | 70 | | CKNI-FM |
| Kelowna | BC | 101.5 | 33.3 | | CILK-FM | Moncton | NB | 94.5 | 19 | | CKCW-FM |
| Kelowna | BC | 103.1 | 35 | | CKQQ-FM | Moncton | NB | 96.9 | 100 | | CJXL-FM |
| Kelowna | BC | 103.9 | 32.9 | | CKOO-FM | Moncton | NB | 99.5 | 9.5 | F | CHOY-FM |
| Kelowna | BC | 104.7 | 36 | | CKLZ-FM | Moncton | NB | 103.1 | 46.8 | | CJMO-FM |
| Nanaimo | BC | 101.7 | 3 | | CHLY-FM | Moncton | NB | 103.9 | 70 | | CFQM-FM |
| Nanaimo | BC | 102.3 | 3 | | CKWV-FM | Saint John | NB | 88.9 | 25 | | CHNI-FM |
| Nanaimo | BC | 106.9 | 3 | | CHWF-FM | Saint John | NB | 94.1 | 100 | | CHSJ-FM |
| Penticton | BC | 100.7 | 14.1 | | CIGV-FM | Saint John | NB | 97.3 | 100 | | CHWV-FM |
| Port Alberni | BC | 93.3 | 6 | | CJAV-FM | Saint John | NB | 98.9 | 12 | | CJYC-FM |
| Powell River | BC | 95.7 | 5.8 | | CFPW-FM | Saint John | NB | 100.5 | 100 | | CIOK-FM |
| Prince George | BC | 94.3 | 11.5 | | CIRX-FM | Shediac | NB | 89.5 | 38 | F | CJSE-FM |
| Prince George | BC | 97.3 | 12 | | CJCI-FM | St. Stephen | NB | 98.1 | 40 | | CHTD-FM |
| Prince George | BC | 99.3 | 9.3 | | CKDV-FM | Woodstock | NB | 104.1 | 10 | | CJCJ-FM |
| Prince George | BC | 101.3 | 9.1 | | CKKN-FM | Argentia | NL | 100.3 | 3.7 | | CFOZ-FM |
| Squamish | BC | 107.1 | 30 | | CISQ-FM | Bonavista | NL | 92.1 | 6.7 | | CJOZ-FM |
| Terrace | BC | 103.1 | 3.2 | | CJFW-FM | Carbonear | NL | 103.9 | 30 | | CHVO-FM |
| Trail | BC | 95.7 | 14 | | CJAT-FM | Clarenville | NL | 100.7 | 4.1 | | VOCM-FM-1 |
| Vancouver | BC | 93.1 | 8 | m | CKYE-FM | Clarenville | NL | 105.3 | 4.7 | | CJMY-FM |
| Vancouver | BC | 93.7 | 71 | | CJJR-FM | Clarenville | NL | 107.5 | 25.5 | | CKSJ-FM-1 |
| Vancouver | BC | 94.5 | 90 | | CFBT-FM | Corner Brook | NL | 92.3 | 7.7 | | CKOZ-FM |
| Vancouver | BC | 95.3 | 57 | | CKZZ-FM | Corner Brook | NL | 103.9 | 35.6 | | CKXX-FM |
| Vancouver | BC | 96.1 | 100 | m | CHKG-FM | Gander | NL | 97.7 | 3.1 | | CFAZ-FM |
| Vancouver | BC | 96.9 | 70 | | CJAX-FM | Gander | NL | 98.7 | 6 | | CKXD-FM |
| Vancouver | BC | 99.3 | 100 | | CFOX-FM | Grand Falls-Windsor | NL | 95.9 | 46.6 | | CKMY-FM |
| Vancouver | BC | 100.5 | 11 | | CFRO-FM | Grand Falls-Windsor | NL | 102.3 | 36 | | CKXG-FM |
| Vancouver | BC | 101.1 | 100 | | CFMI-FM | Marystown | NL | 96.3 | 27 | | CIOZ-FM |
| Vancouver | BC | 102.7 | 95 | | CKPK-FM | Port au Choix | NL | 96.7 | 4.3 | | CFNW-FM |
| Vancouver | BC | 103.5 | 100 | | CHQM-FM | St. John's | NL | 94.7 | 100 | | CHOZ-FM |
| Vancouver | BC | 104.3 | 9.1 | | CHLG-FM | St. John's | NL | 97.5 | 100 | | VOCM-FM |
| Vancouver | BC | 104.9 | 31 | | CKKS-FM-2 | St. John's | NL | 99.1 | 100 | | CKIX-FM |
| Vancouver | BC | 106.3 | 9 | m | CJNY-FM | St. John's | NL | 101.1 | 20 | | CKSJ-FM |
| Vernon | BC | 105.7 | 100 | | CICF-FM | Stephenville | NL | 98.5 | 3 | | CIOS-FM |
| Vernon | BC | 107.5 | 100 | | CJIB-FM | Amherst | NS | 101.7 | 50 | | CKDH-FM |
| Victoria | BC | 91.3 | 3.5 | | CJZN-FM | Amherst | NS | 107.9 | 6.5 | | CFTA-FM |
| Victoria | BC | 98.5 | 100 | | CIOC-FM | Antigonish | NS | 98.9 | 75.4 | | CJFX-FM |
| Victoria | BC | 100.3 | 100 | | CKKQ-FM | Barrington | NS | 96.3 | 5.5 | | CJLS-FM-2 |
| Victoria | BC | 103.1 | 20 | | CHTT-FM | Bridgewater | NS | 98.1 | 32 | | CKBW-FM |
| Victoria | BC | 107.3 | 20 | | CHBE-FM | Bridgewater | NS | 100.7 | 10 | | CJHK-FM |
| Brandon | MB | 91.5 | 100 | | CKLQ-FM | Chéticamp | NS | 106.1 | 3 | F | CKJM-FM |
| Brandon | MB | 94.7 | 100 | | CKLF-FM | Glace Bay | NS | 89.7 | 6 | | CKOA-FM |
| Brandon | MB | 96.1 | 100 | | CKX-FM | Halifax | NS | 89.9 | 100 | | CHNS-FM |
| Brandon | MB | 101.1 | 100 | | CKXA-FM | Halifax | NS | 92.9 | 100 | | CFLT-FM |
| Nepawa | MB | 97.1 | 3.2 | | CJBP-FM | Halifax | NS | 93.9 | 3.1 | | CJLU-FM |
| Portage la Prairie | MB | 93.1 | 27 | | CHPO-FM | Halifax | NS | 95.7 | 65 | | CJNI-FM |
| Portage la Prairie | MB | 96.5 | 24 | | CJPG-FM | Halifax | NS | 96.5 | 100 | | CKUL-FM |
| Steinbach | MB | 96.7 | 100 | | CILT-FM | Halifax | NS | 100.1 | 100 | | CIOO-FM |
| Steinbach | MB | 107.7 | 27 | | CJXR-FM | Halifax | NS | 101.3 | 100 | | CJCH-FM |
| Winkler | MB | 88.9 | 100 | | CKMW-FM | Halifax | NS | 101.9 | 91 | | CHFX-FM |
| Winkler/Morden | MB | 93.5 | 100 | | CJEL-FM | Halifax | NS | 103.5 | 100 | | CKHZ-FM |
| Winnipeg | MB | 91.1 | 61 | F | CKXL-FM | Halifax | NS | 104.3 | 100 | | CFRQ-FM |
| Winnipeg | MB | 92.1 | 140 | | CITI-FM | Halifax | NS | 105.1 | 100 | | CKHY-FM |
| Winnipeg | MB | 94.3 | 100 | | CHIQ-FM | Inverness | NS | 102.5 | 10 | | CJFX-FM-1 |
| Winnipeg | MB | 95.1 | 100 | | CHVN-FM | Kentville | NS | 89.3 | 30 | | CIJK-FM |
| Winnipeg | MB | 97.5 | 310 | | CJKR-FM | Kentville | NS | 94.9 | 100 | | CKWM-FM |
| Winnipeg | MB | 99.1 | 100 | | CFPG-FM | Kentville | NS | 97.7 | 18 | | CKEN-FM |
| Winnipeg | MB | 99.9 | 100 | | CFWM-FM | Liverpool | NS | 94.5 | 8.7 | | CKBW-1-FM |
| Winnipeg | MB | 100.5 | 100 | | CFJL-FM | New Glasgow | NS | 94.1 | 80 | | CKEC-FM |
| Winnipeg | MB | 102.3 | 100 | | CKY-FM | New Tusket | NS | 93.5 | 3 | | CJLS-FM-1 |
| Winnipeg | MB | 103.1 | 100 | | CKMM-FM | Petit-de-Grat | NS | 104.1 | 5.8 | F | CITU-FM |
| Winnipeg | MB | 104.1 | 100 | | CFQX-FM | Pictou | NS | 97.9 | 100 | | CKEZ-FM |
| Winnipeg | MB | 104.7 | 3 | | CIUR-FM | Port Hawkesbury | NS | 101.5 | 38.1 | | CIGO-FM |
| Winnipeg/Selkirk | MB | 105.5 | 100 | | CICY-FM | Shelburne | NS | 93.1 | 8.6 | | CKBW-2-FM |
| Winnipeg | MB | 106.1 | 40 | | CHWE-FM | Sydney | NS | 94.9 | 61 | | CKPE-FM |
| Winnipeg | MB | 107.1 | 100 | | CKCL-FM | Sydney | NS | 98.3 | 100 | | CHER-FM |
| Bathurst | NB | 92.9 | 100 | F | CKLE-FM | Sydney | NS | 101.9 | 58 | | CHRK-FM |
| Bathurst | NB | 104.9 | 33.5 | | CKBC-FM | Sydney | NS | 103.5 | 26.5 | | CKCH-FM |
| Campbellton | NB | 103.9 | 11.3 | F | CIMS-FM | Truro | NS | 99.5 | 16.8 | | CKTY-FM |
| Caraquet | NB | 94.1 | 100 | F | CJVA-FM | Truro | NS | 100.9 | 50 | | CKTO-FM |
| Edmundston | NB | 92.7 | 40.8 | F | CJEM-FM | Weymouth | NS | 103.3 | 3 | | CKDY-1-FM |
| Fredericton | NB | 92.3 | 100 | | CFRK-FM | Yarmouth | NS | 95.5 | 18 | | CJLS-FM |
| Fredericton | NB | 93.1 | 100 | | CIHI-FM | Yarmouth | NS | 104.1 | 39.3 | F | CIFA-FM |
| Fredericton | NB | 105.3 | 78 | | CFXY-FM | Ajax | ON | 95.9 | 50 | | CJKX-FM |
| Fredericton | NB | 106.9 | 78 | | CIBX-FM | Bancroft | ON | 97.7 | 50 | | CHMS-FM |
| Grand Falls/Grand-Sault | NB | 93.5 | 5.3 | | CIKX-FM | Barrie | ON | 93.1 | 100 | | CHAY-FM |
| Grand Falls/Grand-Sault | NB | 105.1 | 3 | F | CFAI-FM-1 | Barrie | ON | 95.7 | 100 | | CFJB-FM |

| FM | Prov. | MHz | kW | N | Call | FM | Prov. | MHz | kW | N | Call |
|---|---|---|---|---|---|---|---|---|---|---|---|
| Barrie | ON | 100.3 | 32.8 | | CJLF-FM | North Bay | ON | 106.3 | 10 | | CFXN-FM |
| Barrie | ON | 101.1 | 7.5 | | CIQB-FM | Ohsweken | ON | 100.3 | 5 | | CKRZ-FM |
| Barrie | ON | 107.5 | 50 | | CKMB-FM | Orangeville | ON | 103.5 | 30.7 | | CIDC-FM |
| Barry's Bay | ON | 106.5 | 12 | | CHBY-FM | Orillia | ON | 105.9 | 20 | | CICX-FM |
| Belleville | ON | 91.3 | 3.2 | | CJLX-FM | Oshawa | ON | 94.9 | 50 | | CKGE-FM |
| Belleville | ON | 95.5 | 35 | | CJOJ-FM | Ottawa | ON | 88.5 | 90 | | CILV-FM |
| Belleville | ON | 97.1 | 50 | | CIGL-FM | Ottawa | ON | 89.1 | 18.1 | | CHUO-FM |
| Belleville | ON | 100.1 | 32 | | CHCQ-FM | Ottawa | ON | 89.9 | 27 | | CIHT-FM |
| Belleville | ON | 102.3 | 15 | | CKJJ-FM | Ottawa | ON | 93.1 | 12 | | CKCU-FM |
| Bluewater | ON | 91.7 | 6 | | CIBU-FM-1 | Ottawa | ON | 93.9 | 95 | | CKKL-FM |
| Bracebridge | ON | 99.5 | 12 | | CFBG-FM | Ottawa | ON | 95.7 | 9.1 | m | CFPO-FM |
| Bracebridge | ON | 102.3 | 23 | | CJMU-FM | Ottawa | ON | 97.9 | 6.8 | m | CJLL-FM |
| Brantford | ON | 92.1 | 80 | | CKPC-FM | Ottawa | ON | 99.1 | 66 | | CHRI-FM |
| Brockville | ON | 103.7 | 100 | | CJPT-FM | Ottawa | ON | 99.7 | 100 | | CJOT-FM |
| Brockville | ON | 104.9 | 7.7 | | CFJR-FM | Ottawa | ON | 100.3 | 100 | | CJMJ-FM |
| Cambridge | ON | 107.5 | 6 | | CJDV-FM | Ottawa | ON | 101.7 | 19.3 | | CIDG-FM |
| Chatham-Kent | ON | 89.3 | 18.7 | | CKGW-FM | Ottawa | ON | 105.3 | 84 | | CISS-FM |
| Chatham-Kent | ON | 94.3 | 50 | | CKSY-FM | Ottawa | ON | 106.1 | 100 | | CHEZ-FM |
| Chatham-Kent | ON | 95.1 | 42 | | CKUE-FM | Ottawa | ON | 106.9 | 84 | | CKQB-FM |
| Cobourg | ON | 93.3 | 15.5 | | CKSG-FM | Owen Sound | ON | 92.3 | 9.4 | | CJOS-FM |
| Cobourg | ON | 103.1 | 86.7 | | CFMX-FM | Owen Sound | ON | 93.7 | 22 | | CKYC-FM |
| Cobourg | ON | 107.9 | 20 | | CHUC-FM | Owen Sound | ON | 106.5 | 28 | | CIXK-FM |
| Collingwood | ON | 102.9 | 23 | | CFMO-FM | Parry Sound | ON | 103.3 | 46.6 | | CKLP-FM |
| Cornwall | ON | 92.1 | 45.6 | F | CHOD-FM | Pembroke | ON | 96.7 | 100 | | CHVR-FM |
| Cornwall | ON | 101.9 | 3.2 | | CJSS-FM | Pembroke | ON | 99.9 | 7.5 | | CKQB-FM-1 |
| Cornwall | ON | 104.5 | 28.2 | | CFLG-FM | Pembroke | ON | 104.9 | 34 | | CIMY-FM |
| Dryden | ON | 92.7 | 39 | | CKDR-FM | Penetanguishene | ON | 88.1 | 40 | F | CFRH-FM |
| Elliot Lake | ON | 94.1 | 90 | | CKNR-FM | Perth | ON | 88.1 | 5.4 | | CHLK-FM |
| Englehart | ON | 105.7 | 3.4 | | CJTK-FM-7 | Peterborough | ON | 96.7 | 7 | | CJWV-FM |
| Fort Erie | ON | 101.1 | 50 | | CFLZ-FM | Peterborough | ON | 99.7 | 11 | | CKPT-FM |
| Fort Frances | ON | 93.1 | 21 | | CFOB-FM | Peterborough | ON | 100.5 | 15 | | CKRU-FM |
| Gananoque | ON | 99.9 | 4.5 | | CJGM-FM | Peterborough | ON | 101.5 | 15.2 | | CKWF-FM |
| Goderich | ON | 104.9 | 12.6 | | CHWC-FM | Peterborough | ON | 105.1 | 7.5 | | CKQM-FM |
| Guelph | ON | 106.1 | 50 | | CIMJ-FM | Prescott | ON | 107.9 | 4.2 | | CKPP-FM |
| Haldimand | ON | 92.9 | 15 | | CHTG-FM | Prince Edward | ON | 99.3 | 3 | | CJPE-FM |
| Haliburton | ON | 93.5 | 6 | | CFZN-FM | Quinte West | ON | 107.1 | 15 | | CJTN-FM |
| Haliburton | ON | 100.9 | 3.4 | | CKHA-FM | Renfrew | ON | 96.1 | 7.1 | | CHMY-FM |
| Hamilton/Burlington | ON | 94.7 | 100 | | CHKX-FM | Renfrew | ON | 98.7 | 20 | | CJHR-FM |
| Hamilton | ON | 95.3 | 100 | | CING-FM | Sarnia | ON | 99.9 | 26 | | CFGX-FM |
| Hamilton | ON | 102.9 | 40.3 | | CKLH-FM | Sarnia | ON | 103.3 | 6 | | CKCI-FM |
| Hamilton/Burlington | ON | 107.9 | 26.1 | | CJXY-FM | Sarnia | ON | 106.3 | 50 | | CHKS-FM |
| Hearst | ON | 91.1 | 5.5 | F | CINN-FM | Saugeen Shores | ON | 90.9 | 3.1 | | CIYN-FM-2 |
| Huntsville | ON | 88.7 | 5.7 | | CKAR-FM | Saugeen Shores | ON | 97.9 | 9 | | CFPS-FM |
| Huntsville | ON | 105.5 | 43.4 | | CFBK-FM | Sault Ste. Marie | ON | 100.5 | 13.9 | | CHAS-FM |
| Kapuskasing | ON | 89.7 | 3 | F | CKGN-FM | Sault Ste. Marie | ON | 104.3 | 100 | | CJQM-FM |
| Kapuskasing | ON | 100.9 | 12 | | CKAP-FM | Shelburne | ON | 104.9 | 36.2 | | CFDC-FM |
| Kawartha Lakes | ON | 91.9 | 11.4 | | CKLY-FM | Simcoe | ON | 98.9 | 50 | | CHCD-FM |
| Kenora | ON | 89.5 | 50 | | CJRL-FM | Simcoe | ON | 99.7 | 18 | | CKNC-FM |
| Kincardine | ON | 95.5 | 5.7 | | CIYN-FM | Smiths Falls | ON | 92.3 | 17 | | CJET-FM |
| Kingston | ON | 93.5 | 7.5 | | CKXC-FM | Smiths Falls | ON | 101.1 | 100 | | CKBY-FM |
| Kingston | ON | 96.3 | 28 | | CFMK-FM | St. Catharines | ON | 97.7 | 50 | | CHTZ-FM |
| Kingston | ON | 98.3 | 95.5 | | CFLY-FM | St. Catharines | ON | 105.7 | 50 | | CHRE-FM |
| Kingston | ON | 98.9 | 15 | | CKLC-FM | St. Thomas | ON | 94.1 | 4.4 | | CKZM-FM |
| Kingston | ON | 101.9 | 3 | | CFRC-FM | St. Thomas | ON | 103.1 | 60 | | CFHK-FM |
| Kingston | ON | 104.3 | 8 | | CKWS-FM | Stratford | ON | 107.1 | 4 | | CJCS-FM |
| Kingston | ON | 105.7 | 50 | | CIKR-FM | Stratford | ON | 107.7 | 6 | | CHGK-FM |
| Kirkland Lake | ON | 101.5 | 23 | | CJKL-FM | Sudbury | ON | 91.7 | 50 | | CICS-FM |
| Kitchener/Waterloo | ON | 88.3 | 8.2 | | CJIQ-FM | Sudbury | ON | 92.7 | 100 | | CJRQ-FM |
| Kitchener/Waterloo | ON | 91.5 | 10 | | CKBT-FM | Sudbury | ON | 93.5 | 100 | | CIGM-FM |
| Kitchener | ON | 96.7 | 80 | | CHYM-FM | Sudbury | ON | 95.5 | 8.1 | | CJTK-FM |
| Kitchener | ON | 99.5 | 4.3 | | CKKW-FM | Sudbury | ON | 98.9 | 3.8 | F | CHYC-FM |
| Kitchener | ON | 105.3 | 100 | | CFCA-FM | Sudbury | ON | 103.9 | 100 | | CHNO-FM |
| Kitchener/Waterloo | ON | 106.7 | 5 | | CIKZ-FM | Sudbury | ON | 105.3 | 100 | | CJMX-FM |
| Leamington | ON | 92.7 | 4 | | CJSP-FM | Sunderland | ON | 89.9 | 5 | | CJKX-FM-1 |
| Leamington | ON | 96.7 | 27 | | CHYR-FM | Tamiskaming Shores | ON | 104.5 | 10 | | CJTT-FM |
| London | ON | 92.7 | 50 | | CJBX-FM | Thunder Bay | ON | 91.5 | 100 | | CKPR-FM |
| London | ON | 94.9 | 6 | | CHRW-FM | Thunder Bay | ON | 94.3 | 93 | | CJSD-FM |
| London | ON | 95.9 | 300 | | CFPL-FM | Thunder Bay | ON | 105.3 | 100 | | CKTG-FM |
| London | ON | 97.5 | 50 | | CIQM-FM | Tillsonburg | ON | 101.3 | 26 | | CKOT-FM |
| London | ON | 98.1 | 40 | | CKLO-FM | Tillsonburg | ON | 107.3 | 7.8 | | CJDL-FM |
| London | ON | 102.3 | 100 | | CHST-FM | Timmins | ON | 92.1 | 40 | | CJQQ-FM |
| London | ON | 106.9 | 3 | | CIXX-FM | Timmins | ON | 93.1 | 16.4 | | CHMT-FM |
| Manitoulin Island | ON | 100.7 | 15 | | CFRM-FM | Timmins | ON | 99.3 | 40 | | CKGB-FM |
| Manitoulin Island | ON | 103.1 | 24.8 | | CHAW-FM | Timmins | ON | 104.1 | 3.5 | F | CHYK-FM |
| Marathon | ON | 93.1 | 50 | | CFNO-FM | Toronto | ON | 88.1 | 4 | | CIND-FM |
| Markham | ON | 105.9 | 3 | m | CFMS-FM | Toronto | ON | 88.9 | 4.2 | m | CIRV-FM |
| Midland | ON | 104.1 | 20 | | CICZ-FM | Toronto | ON | 89.5 | 15 | | CIUT-FM |
| Napanee | ON | 88.7 | 11.1 | | CKYM-FM | Toronto | ON | 91.1 | 40 | | CJRT-FM |
| New Tecumseth | ON | 92.1 | 3.8 | | CIMA-FM | Toronto | ON | 91.9 | 5 | m | CHIN-1-FM |
| Newmarket | ON | 88.5 | 30 | | CKDX-FM | Toronto | ON | 92.5 | 13 | | CKIS-FM |
| Niagara Falls | ON | 105.1 | 15 | | CJED-FM | Toronto | ON | 93.5 | 3.7 | | CFXJ-FM |
| North Bay | ON | 100.5 | 100 | | CHUR-FM | Toronto | ON | 96.3 | 60 | | CFMZ-FM |
| North Bay | ON | 101.9 | 100 | | CKFX-FM | Toronto | ON | 97.3 | 28.9 | | CHBM-FM |

| FM | Prov. | MHz | kW | N | Call | FM | Prov. | MHz | kW | N | Call |
|---|---|---|---|---|---|---|---|---|---|---|---|
| Toronto | ON | 98.1 | 44 | | CHFI-FM | Montréal | QC | 98.5 | 100 | F | CHMP-FM |
| Toronto | ON | 99.9 | 40 | | CKFM-FM | Montréal | QC | 99.5 | 8.7 | F | CJPX-FM |
| Toronto | ON | 100.7 | 8.5 | m | CHIN-FM | Montréal | QC | 105.7 | 48 | F | CFGL-FM |
| Toronto | ON | 102.1 | 35.4 | | CFNY-FM | Montréal | QC | 107.3 | 42.9 | F | CITE-FM |
| Toronto | ON | 104.5 | 40 | | CHUM-FM | Natashquan | QC | 104.1 | 6.6 | F | CKNA-FM |
| Toronto | ON | 107.1 | 40 | | CILQ-FM | Nemaska | QC | 103.1 | 18.5 | | CJNM-FM |
| Wallaceburg | ON | 99.1 | 3 | | CKXS-FM | New Carlisle | QC | 97.1 | 5.6 | F | CHNC-FM |
| Welland | ON | 89.1 | 4.3 | | CKYY-FM | Pikogan | QC | 100.1 | 3.7 | m | CKAG-FM |
| Welland | ON | 91.7 | 50 | | CIXL-FM | Port-Cartier | QC | 99.1 | 45 | F | CIPC-FM |
| West Nipissing | ON | 97.1 | 6.5 | F | CHYQ-FM | Québec | QC | 90.9 | 5.7 | F | CION-FM |
| Windsor | ON | 88.7 | 100 | | CIMX-FM | Québec | QC | 91.9 | 31 | F | CJEC-FM |
| Windsor | ON | 90.5 | 7.5 | | CJAH-FM | Québec | QC | 93.3 | 33 | F | CJMF-FM |
| Windsor | ON | 93.9 | 100 | | CIDR-FM | Québec/Sainte-Foy | QC | 94.3 | 6 | F | CHYZ-FM |
| Windsor | ON | 95.9 | 11.8 | | CJWF-FM | Québec | QC | 98.1 | 40 | F | CHOI-FM |
| Windsor | ON | 100.7 | 9 | | CKUE-FM-1 | Québec | QC | 98.9 | 41 | F | CHIK-FM |
| Windsor | ON | 102.3 | 5 | m | CINA-FM | Québec/Lévis | QC | 102.1 | 33.9 | F | CFEL-FM |
| Wingham | ON | 94.5 | 75 | | CIBU-FM | Québec/Lévis | QC | 102.9 | 32.8 | F | CFOM-FM |
| Wingham | ON | 101.7 | 100 | | CKNX-FM | Québec | QC | 107.5 | 37 | F | CITF-FM |
| Woodstock | ON | 103.9 | 51 | | CKDK-FM | Rimouski/Mont-Joli | QC | 93.3 | 27.3 | F | CFYX-FM |
| Woodstock | ON | 104.7 | 20 | | CIHR-FM | Rimouski | QC | 96.5 | 5.8 | F | CKMN-FM |
| Charlottetown | PE | 93.1 | 75 | | CHLQ-FM | Rimouski | QC | 98.7 | 100 | F | CIKI-FM |
| Charlottetown | PE | 95.1 | 100 | | CFCY-FM | Rimouski | QC | 102.9 | 33.6 | F | CJOI-FM |
| Charlottetown | PE | 100.3 | 88 | | CHTN-FM | Rivière-du-Loup | QC | 103.7 | 60 | F | CIEL-FM |
| Charlottetown | PE | 105.5 | 88 | | CKQK-FM | Rivière-du-Loup | QC | 107.1 | 100 | F | CIBM-FM |
| Elmira | PE | 99.9 | 3.4 | | CHTN-FM-1 | Roberval | QC | 99.5 | 50 | F | CHRL-FM |
| Elmira | PE | 103.7 | 3.4 | | CKQK-FM-1 | Rouyn-Noranda | QC | 88.7 | 3.4 | F | CHIC-FM |
| St. Edward | PE | 89.9 | 5 | | CHTN-FM-2 | Rouyn-Noranda | QC | 95.7 | 44 | F | CJGO-FM-1 |
| St. Edward | PE | 91.1 | 5 | | CKQK-FM-2 | Rouyn-Noranda | QC | 96.5 | 61.1 | F | CHOA-FM |
| Summerside | PE | 102.1 | 50 | | CJRW-FM | Rouyn-Noranda | QC | 99.1 | 3 | F | CJMM-FM |
| Alma | QC | 95.7 | 100 | F | CKYK-FM | Saguenay | QC | 92.5 | 14.2 | F | CKAJ-FM |
| Alma | QC | 104.5 | 20 | F | CFGT-FM | Saguenay | QC | 94.5 | 100 | F | CJAB-FM |
| Amos/Val d'Or | QC | 103.5 | 100 | F | CHOA-FM-1 | Saguenay | QC | 96.9 | 100 | F | CFIX-FM |
| Amos/Val d'Or | QC | 104.3 | 91.8 | F | CHGO-FM | Saguenay | QC | 98.3 | 100 | F | CILM-FM |
| Amos | QC | 105.3 | 32.2 | F | CHOW-FM | Saguenay | QC | 106.7 | 46.2 | F | CION-FM-2 |
| Amqui | QC | 99.9 | 23.8 | F | CFVM-FM | Sainte-Marie | QC | 101.5 | 72 | F | CHEQ-FM |
| Asbestos | QC | 99.3 | 11.1 | F | CJAN-FM | Saint-Georges | QC | 99.7 | 100 | F | CHJM-FM |
| Baie-Comeau | QC | 97.1 | 4.2 | F | CHLC-FM | Saint-Georges | QC | 103.5 | 15 | F | CKRB-FM |
| Bécancour | QC | 90.5 | 60 | F | CKBN-FM | Saint-Hyacinthe | QC | 106.5 | 3 | F | CFEI-FM |
| Cap-aux-Meules | QC | 92.7 | 6.3 | F | CFIM-FM | Saint-Jérôme | QC | 103.9 | 39.3 | F | CIME-FM |
| Carleton-sur-Mer | QC | 94.9 | 37.6 | F | CIEU-FM | Salaberry-de-Valleyfield | QC | 103.1 | 3 | F | CKOD-FM |
| Chandler | QC | 96.3 | 22.9 | F | CFMV-FM | Sept-îles | QC | 94.1 | 11.3 | F | CKCN-FM |
| Chibougamau | QC | 93.5 | 56.2 | F | CKXO-FM | Shawinigan | QC | 92.9 | 3.8 | F | CFUT-FM |
| Chisasibi | QC | 101.1 | 3 | m | CHFG-FM | Sherbrooke | QC | 93.7 | 25.5 | F | CFGE-FM |
| Dégelis | QC | 95.5 | 12.5 | F | CFVD-FM | Sherbrooke | QC | 102.7 | 92 | F | CITE-FM-1 |
| Dolbeau-Mistassini | QC | 100.3 | 50 | F | CHVD-FM | Sherbrooke | QC | 107.7 | 25 | F | CKOY-FM |
| Drummondville | QC | 92.1 | 3 | F | CJDM-FM | Sorel-Tracy | QC | 101.7 | 3 | F | CJSO-FM |
| Drummondville | QC | 105.3 | 5.3 | F | CHRD-FM | St-Gabriel-de-Brandon | QC | 99.1 | 9.8 | F | CFNJ-FM |
| Eastmain | QC | 104.1 | 38.1 | m | CJEQ-FM-1 | Témiscouata-sur-le-Lac | QC | 98.3 | 3 | F | CIEL-FM-3 |
| Forestville | QC | 100.5 | 6 | F | CFRP-FM | Thetford Mines | QC | 97.3 | 100 | F | CFJO-FM |
| Fort-Coulonge | QC | 101.9 | 11.9 | F | CHIP-FM | Thetford Mines | QC | 105.5 | 6 | F | CKLD-FM |
| Gaspé | QC | 94.5 | 6 | F | CJRG-FM | Trois-Rivières | QC | 89.1 | 3 | F | CFOU-FM |
| Gatineau | QC | 94.9 | 84 | F | CIMF-FM | Trois-Rivières | QC | 89.9 | 3.2 | F | CIRA-FM-2 |
| Gatineau | QC | 97.1 | 11.2 | F | CHLX-FM | Trois-Rivières | QC | 94.7 | 100 | F | CHEY-FM |
| Gatineau | QC | 104.1 | 19 | F | CKTF-FM | Trois-Rivières | QC | 100.1 | 64.1 | F | CJEB-FM |
| Gatineau | QC | 104.7 | 100 | F | CKOF-FM | Trois-Rivières | QC | 102.3 | 5.8 | F | CIGB-FM |
| Granby | QC | 104.9 | 4.3 | F | CFXM-FM | Trois-Rivières | QC | 106.9 | 100 | F | CKOB-FM |
| Joliette | QC | 103.5 | 4.5 | F | CJLM-FM | Val-d'Or | QC | 102.7 | 96 | F | CJMV-FM |
| La Baie | QC | 105.5 | 6 | F | CKGS-FM | Ville-Marie | QC | 93.1 | 34 | F | CKVM-FM |
| La Pocatière | QC | 97.5 | 25.2 | F | CHOX-FM | Waskaganish | QC | 92.5 | 38 | m | CJRH-FM |
| La Sarre | QC | 92.5 | 6 | F | CJMM-FM-1 | Waswanipi | QC | 93.9 | 6.2 | m | CFNE-FM |
| La Sarre | QC | 102.1 | 4.1 | F | CJGO-FM | Wemindji | QC | 99.7 | 24.7 | m | CHPH-FM |
| La Tuque | QC | 97.1 | 28.4 | F | CFLM-FM | Buffalo Narrows | SK | 89.3 | 6 | | CIBN-FM |
| Lac-Etchemin | QC | 100.5 | 8.6 | F | CFIN-FM | Dafoe | SK | 100.3 | 100 | | CJVR-FM-1 |
| Lachute | QC | 104.9 | 3 | F | CJLA-FM | Estevan | SK | 102.3 | 100 | | CHSN-FM |
| Lac-Mégantic | QC | 106.7 | 4.3 | F | CJIT-FM | Estevan | SK | 106.1 | 100 | | CKSE-FM |
| Les Escoumins | QC | 94.9 | 4.7 | F | CHME-FM | Gravelbourg | SK | 107.1 | 97 | | CJME-2-FM |
| Louisville | QC | 103.1 | 4.2 | F | CHHO-FM | Humboldt | SK | 107.5 | 100 | | CHBO-FM |
| Maliotenam | QC | 104.5 | 6 | m | CKAU-FM | Kindersley | SK | 104.9 | 100 | | CKVX-FM |
| Maniwaki | QC | 97.3 | 16.9 | F | CHGA-FM | Meadow Lake | SK | 102.3 | 45 | | CJNS-FM |
| Matane | QC | 95.3 | 14.6 | F | CHOE-FM | Meadow Lake | SK | 104.5 | 45 | | CJCQ-FM-1 |
| Matane | QC | 105.3 | 30 | F | CHRM-FM | Melfort | SK | 105.1 | 100 | | CJVR-FM |
| Mistissini | QC | 95.3 | 50 | m | CINI-FM | Moose Jaw | SK | 100.7 | 100 | | CILG-FM |
| Mont-Laurier | QC | 104.7 | 16.9 | F | CFLO-FM | Moose Jaw | SK | 103.9 | 100 | | CJAW-FM |
| Montmagny | QC | 90.3 | 40.7 | F | CIQI-FM | Nipawin | SK | 94.7 | 14.8 | | CJNE-FM |
| Montréal | QC | 89.3 | 10 | F | CISM-FM | North Battleford | SK | 93.3 | 100 | | CJHD-FM |
| Montréal | QC | 90.3 | 5 | | CKUT-FM | North Battleford | SK | 95.5 | 28 | m | CJLR-FM-6 |
| Montréal | QC | 91.3 | 36.2 | F | CIRA-FM | North Battleford | SK | 97.9 | 100 | | CJCQ-FM |
| Montréal | QC | 91.9 | 4.7 | F | CKLX-FM | Okanese First Nation | SK | 95.3 | 50 | | CHXL-FM |
| Montréal | QC | 92.5 | 100 | | CKBE-FM | Prince Albert | SK | 88.1 | 49 | m | CJLR-FM-3 |
| Montréal | QC | 94.3 | 41.4 | F | CKMF-FM | Prince Albert | SK | 90.1 | 3 | F | CKSF-FM |
| Montréal | QC | 95.9 | 41.2 | | CJFM-FM | Prince Albert | SK | 91.1 | 100 | | CFMM-FM |
| Montréal | QC | 96.9 | 148 | F | CKOI-FM | Prince Albert | SK | 101.5 | 100 | | CHQX-FM |
| Montréal | QC | 97.7 | 41.2 | | CHOM-FM | Regina | SK | 90.3 | 43 | m | CJLR-FM-4 |

| FM | Prov. | MHz | kW | N | Call |
|---|---|---|---|---|---|
| Regina | SK | 92.1 | 100 | | CHMX-FM |
| Regina | SK | 92.7 | 100 | | CHBD-FM |
| Regina | SK | 94.5 | 100 | | CKCK-FM |
| Regina | SK | 98.9 | 100 | | CIZL-FM |
| Regina | SK | 104.9 | 100 | | CFWF-FM |
| Saskatoon | SK | 92.9 | 100 | | CKBL-FM |
| Saskatoon | SK | 95.1 | 100 | | CFMC-FM |
| Saskatoon | SK | 96.3 | 100 | | CFWD-FM |
| Saskatoon | SK | 98.3 | 100 | | CJMK-FM |
| Saskatoon | SK | 102.1 | 100 | | CJDJ-FM |
| Swift Current | SK | 94.1 | 100 | | CIMG-FM |
| Swift Current | SK | 97.1 | 100 | | CKFI-FM |
| Swift Current | SK | 101.7 | 100 | | CJME-1-FM |
| Wapella | SK | 102.9 | 14 | | CFGW-FM-2 |
| Warmley | SK | 107.3 | 87 | | CJME-3-FM |
| Waskesiu Lake | SK | 106.3 | 11 | | CJVR-FM-2 |
| Weyburn | SK | 103.5 | 100 | | CKRC-FM |
| Weyburn | SK | 106.7 | 100 | | CHWY-FM |
| Yorkton | SK | 94.1 | 100 | | CFGW-FM |
| Yorkton | SK | 98.5 | 50 | | CJJC-FM |
| Whitehorse | YT | 96.1 | 4.4 | | CKRW-FM |
| Whitehorse | YT | 98.1 | 4.3 | | CHON-FM |

**NB:** c=moving to FM F=French m=ethnic/multilingual r=relay *=also on SW +=F.Pl. Txs 3kW and higher. Most stns identify using a name rather than calls. Stns with calls containing numbers are relays. Industry Canada stn list database **W:** ic.gc.ca/eic/site/smt-gst.nsf/eng/h_sf01842.html. Stn history & web **W:** broadcasting-history.ca

**BRITISH FORCES BROADC. SCE.** Suffield AB
☎+1 403 544 4104 **W:** forces.net/radio **BFBS 1: FM:** 104.1 CKBF-FM

## CANARY ISLANDS (Spain)

**L.T:** UTC (31 Mar-27 Oct: +1h) — **Pop:** 2.1 million — **Pr.L:** Spanish — **E.C:** 50Hz, 230V — **ITU:** CNR

| | MW | kHz | kW | Net | Location | Island |
|---|---|---|---|---|---|---|
| 1) | 576 | 20 | RNE-1 | Las Palmas | GC |
| 2) | 621 | 300 | RNE-1 | Santa Cruz | TF |
| 2) | 720 | 10 | RNE-5 | Santa Cruz | TF |
| 1) | ‡747 | 25 | RNE-5 | Las Palmas | GC |
| 3) | ‡837 | 10 | COPE | Las Palmas | GC |
| 4) | 882 | 20 | COPE | Santa Cruz | TF |
| 5) | ‡1008 | 10 | Grupo R. | Las Palmas | GC |
| 6) | 1179 | 25 | SER | R. Clube Tenerife | |

**Addresses & other information**
**Abbreviations:** GC=Gran Canaria, GCF=Fuerteventura, GCL=Lanzarote, TF=Tenerife, TFP=Isla de la Palma, TFG=Isla de la Gomera, TFH=Hierro. (For network abbreviations refer to Spain)
**1)** R. Nacional de España, Av. Escaleritads 300-340, prolongacion Pedro Infinito, 35013 Las Palmas ☎ +34 928 364 088 📠 +34 928 362 754 — **2)** R. Nacional de España, San Martín 1, 38001 Sta. Cruz de Tenerife ☎ +34 (922) 288400 📠 +34 922 283363 **R.1:** 24h on 621kHz **N:** On the h. **R.2:** (classical music) 24h. **R.3:** 24h. **R.5:** 24h — **3)** R. Popular de Las Palmas, Av. Escaleritas 60-1°, Las Palmas 35011 ☎ +34 928 286970 **E:** direccion.laspalmas@cadenacope.net Dir: Antonio Miguel Díaz **D.Prgr:** 24h. **FM** :90.1MHz — **4)** R. Popular de Tenerife, Darías y Padron, 1-2°-38003 Santa Cruz de Tenerife ☎ +34 922 236900/05/09 📠 +34 922 2369121 **E:** tenerife@cadenacope.net Dir: José Carlos Marrero Gonzales. **D.Prgr:** 24h FM only — **5)**GRUPO Radio Las Palmas, C/ Profesor Lozano 5, 2°, Urb. Industrial El Sebadal, 35008 Las Palmas de Gran Canaria **W:** radiolaspalmas.com **FM** :100.3MHz **E:** informacion@radiolaspalmas.com ☎ +34 928 462052 📠 +34 928 462057 Dir:María Enma Hernández Martín. **D.Prgr:** 24h — **6)** R. Club Tenerife, Av. de Anaga 35, Santa Cruz de Tenerife 38001 ☎ +34 922 270400 📠 +34 922 281043 **E:** radioclubtenerife@unionradio.es Dir:Juan Ramon Hernandez. **FM** 101.1MHz — **7)** Av. Escaleritas 64 1°, 35011 Las Palmas de Gran Canaria **W:** radioecca.org **E:** info@radioecca.org **FM:** 99.5MHz

**Dial FM Networks:**
**Gran Canaria Las Palmas (MHz):** Cope Más Las Palmas 87.6 – R.T.I. Insular 87.7 – R. Maria 87.9 – R. Marca 88.2 – RNE5 INF.88.6 – Hit FM 88.9 –FUN R 89.9 – ECCA 90.4 – R.ECCA 90.7– COPE 91.0 – esRadio 91.1 – Canaras R. 91.4 – C100 91.8 – R. Top 21 92.0 –RNE1 92.8 – Aire Radio 93.4– R. Juventud 94.1 – Los 40 94.4 – RNE2 95.1 – Gestiona R. Las Palmas 95.4 - Inolvidable FM 95.8 – Tamaran FM Formula Hits 96.2 – R.Las Palmas 97.3 – Europa FM 98.0 – RNE3 98.5 – COPE FM 99.1 – Infierno FM 99.5 – SER Las Palmas 100.3 – Global FM 100.6 – Canarias R. 100.8 – Gestiona R. 101.2 – Cadena Dial 101.7 – Maxima FM 102.7

– Cope Más Las Palmas 103.0 – UD Radio 103.4 – R.Univerdance 103.8 – R. Faycan 104.2 – M80 105.4 – R. Guiniguada 105.9 – OCR 106.8
**Gran Canaria Maspalomas Playa del Ingles (MHz):** 9 Radio 87.9 –RNE1 88.5 - R.Arguineguin 89.4 – 7,7 Radio 89.6 – COPE FM 90.7 – ECCA Sur 91.4 – R.TOP 21 92.0 – R.Faro 92.5 – Onda Islena 93.8 – R.Sol 94.8 – esRadio 95.3 – R.Faro Sur 97.2 – R.Rondo 98.2 –RNE2 99.1 - SER Maspalomas 99.6 –RNE3 100.9 – R.Maria 102.7 – R.Abrisajac 103.5 – RNE5 INF. 106.5 – R.Dunas 107.6
**Fuerteventura (MHz):** RNE2 87.7 – R.Sintonia 88.2 – RNE5 89.8 - Nueve R. OCR 90.7 – COPE 91.2 – COPE 91.6 – R.Maxorata 92.1 – RNE1 92.6 - ECCA 93.0 – Atlantica FM 94.2 – Dunas FM 94.4 – RNE1 94.6 – Europa FM 95.6 –RNE2 96.0 - Canarias R. 96.9 – Nueve R. 97.7 – Q FM Corralejo 98.0 – R.Agua Cabra 99.6 Morro Jable – RNE3 100.6- Canarias R. 104.4 – RNE5 INF. 104.8 – R.Archipielago 105.0 – C.100 Puerto del Rosario 105.3 – MCM Mision Cristiana Moderna Radio 106.9
**Lanzarote (MHz):** O2 Radio 88.5 – esRadio 89.0 – SER 89.7 – Alo FM 90.1 – OCR 90.7 – OCR 91.1 – R.Cristal 92.0 – RNE1 92.5 – ECCA 93.0 – R.Marca 93.6 – R.Maria 93.9 – RNE2 94.9 – O2 Radio 96.4 – R.Insular 96.7 – COPE 98.3 – R. Las Arenas 98.6 – RNE5 99.0 - Onda Conejera 99.1 – RNE1 99.6 - RNE5 INF. 100.2 – Guapa FM 100.9 – Canarias R. 101.2 – RNE3 102.3 - RNE3 102.8 – Mi Tierra FM 103.1 – Los 40 104.0 – Cronicas R. 105.5 – Europa FM 106.5 – Latina Stereo 107.7
**Tenerife Norte (MHz):** R.Decibelios FM 87.5 – Cadena Dial 87.8 – MM Radio La Laguna 88.1 – Onda CIT 88.5 – RNE5 INF. 88.8 – Cadena Dial Sur 88.9 – ROCK FM 89.1 – C100 89.4 – ECCA La Laguna 89.6 – Marcha FM 89.8 – RNE3 90.0 – Onda 7 90.2 – R.El Dia La Laguna 90.8 – Maxima FM 91.1 –Gestiona R. Tenerife 91.3 - R.Marca Tenerife 91.5 – R.Atlantida 91.9 – RNE1 92.3 – Los 40 Tenerife 93.2 – Antena de Canarias 93.5 – Marcha FM La Laguna 93.8 – Teide OCR 94.0 R.Marca La Laguna 94.5 – RNE1 94.8 – Onda CIT R. Turismo La Laguna 95.2 – Gente R. 95.6 –Fun FM La Laguna 95.8 – RNE2 96.2 – Inter Magica FM 96.8 – COPE La Laguna 97.1 – Gestiona R. Tenerife 97.2 - R.Maria 97.5 – R.Marca 97.7 – Onda 7 La Laguna 97.9 – RNE5 INF. 98.1 – Onda Tenerife 98.5 – Canal 4 98.8 – Los 40 99.1 – Kiss FM 99.4 – esRadio 99.5 - SER R.Club Norte 99.8 – M80 100.1 – R.Pimienta La Orotava 100.3 – Orquestras del Atlantico La Laguna R. 100.5 – R.Taoro 100.7 – SER R.Clube Tenerife101.1 – COPE 101.4 – R.Majuelos La Laguna 101.7 – RNE2 102.1 – esRadio 102.3 – Kiss FM 102.5 – R.Maria La Laguna 103.2 – R.ECCA Los Cristianos 103.4 – RKM R. 103.8 – RNE5 INF.104.0 – Canarias R. 104.2 – La Mega Latina La Laguna 104.5 – Canarias R. 104.7 – esRadio 104.9 – Gestiona R. Valle Güimar 104.9 - Cope Más Tenerife 105.1 – R.Union Tenerife 105.3 – RNE3 105.7 – Canal 4 R. 106.1 – ECCA 106.6 – Exito R. 107.0 – R.La Guancha 107.2 – R.Realejos Los Realejos 107.9
**Tenerife Sur (MHz):** R. Gigante 87.7 – El Faro FM 87.9 – Canarias R. 88.1 – Cadena Dial Playa de las Americas 88.9 – R.ECCA 90.4 – RNE2 92.6 - Inter Magica FM 91.1 – RNE 2 92.6 – Los 40 Playa de las Americas 93.3 – R.Costa 93.8 – Gestiona R. 94.0 - Canal 4 R. 94.8 – esRadio 94.9 - RNE3 95.4 – SER R.Club Sur Playa de las Americas 95.9 – Fun R. 96.2 – Fun Radio 96.8 – Atlantico FM 97.1 – R.Marca 97.7 – Onda Nueva 99.7 – Onda Tenerife Arona 100.1 – Astrovision Magica FM 101.9 – Bomba FM R. 102.4 – Hit R. S.Miguel de Abona 103.0 – RNE1 105.7 – Teide OCR S.Miguel de Abona 106.3 – R.Decibelios FM Arona 107.5
**Isla de la Palma (MHz):** RNE5 88.4 - RNE5 INF. 89.6 – RNE1 90.8 – R.Murion 91.0 – R.Isla Bonita OCR 92.7 – RNE1 92.9 – Canarias R. 93.0 – COPE 95.1 – C100 95.6 – RNE2 96.1 -RNE2 96.7 – Gestiona R. 97.2 - Los 40 97.4 – Canarias R. 97.5 – R.21 Musica 98.0 – RNE5 INF.98.4 –RNE3 98.7 - ECCA 99.5 – Canarias R. 100.5 – SER R.La Palma 101.6 – RNE1 102.7 – R.Maria 103.1 – RNED3 103.8 - Cadena Dial 104.1 – RNE2 104.5 – RNE3 106.1 – R.Isla Bonita OCR 106.4 – Radio LUZ Garafia 107.0 Onda Taburiente El Paso 107.0
**La Gomera (MHz):** Intersur R. 88.0 – Onda Tagoror Gomera R. 88.5 – R.CLM 90.2 – RNE5 91.7 – R.Insular de la Gomera 92.2 – R.Insular de la Gomera 92.2 – RNE1 94.3 – R.Cantera 94.7 – R.Atlantico Sur 95.6 – Canarias R. 96.7 – Gestiona R. 98.0 - SER R.Garoè 98.8 – RNE2 101.8 – R.Gigante 102.2 – R.Garajonay 102.6 – ECCA 103.4 –Gestiona R. 103.5 - Formula Hit 103.7 – RNE3 105.2 – R.Insular de la Gomera 105.9 – R.Vallehermoso 107.4 – R.Agulo 107.6 – R.Ipalan 107.7
**El Hierro (MHz):** RNE5 89.8 – ECCA Valverde 90.6 – SER R.Garoè La Frontera 92.0 – RNE1 92.5 – RNE2 93.9 – RNE3 96.4 – RNE2 97.0 – RNE5 98.2 – Onda Herrena Valverde100.8 – RNE1 101.2 – Canarias R. Frontera 102.3 – Canarias R. Valverde 103.2 – RNE3 104.9 – R.Tajaraste Valverde 105.2 – Onda Herrena Frontera 107.0
**NB:** For LPFM stns on all islands: **W:** lalistadelafm.com/canarias.htm

**Tourist Radio FM Stations**
These stns broadcast in German, English and other languages to tourists visiting the Canary Islands. Most operate 24h
**Atlantis FM** (GCF) 98.0 (GCL) 101.7MHz **W:** atlantisfm.de – **Buzz**

**FM** (GCL) 88.6, 88.8MHz **W:** buzzfm.fm – **Coast FM** (TF) 89.9, 106.6MHz **W:** coastfmtenerife.com –**Energy FM** (TFG) 89.2, 95.7MHz **W:** dancemusicradio.net **Express FM** (TFG) 105.3, 94.6MHz **W:** express-fm.net – **Hola FM** (GCF) 95.1MHz **W:** holafm.de – **Holiday FM** (GC, TF) 95.3, 98.2, 99.0, 100.0MHz **W:** holidayfm.com – **Holland FM** (GC) 90.7MHz **W:** hollandfm906.nl – **Horizon FM** (TFG) 89.9, 104.5MHz **W:** horizon.fm – **Mix 101 FM Radio** (GC) 101.0, 104.8MHz **W:** mix-radio.net – **Oasis FM** (TFG) 101.0, 101.2 (TF) 91.3, 98.1MHz **W:** oasisfm.com – **On Life FM** (TF) ,90-5,99.7 **W:** onlifefm.tenerife.com – **QFM** (TF) 94.3MHz **W:** qmusica.com – **R. Europa FM (TF)** 100.6 (GCL) 102.5 **W:** radio-europa.fm **R. Mega Welle** (TF) 88.3, 102.0, 104.7MHz (GC) 88.3, 102.0MHz **W:** megawelle.radio.de – **Russkoe R.** 105 FM (TF) 105.0MHz **W:** russkoe-105fm.ru **Spectrum FM** (TF) 105.3MHz **W:** canaries.spectrumfm.net – **R. Syd** (TF) 90.0, 100.6MHz **W:** radiosyd. net – **UK Away FM** (GCL) 99.4, 99.9MHz **W:** ukawayfm.uk – **Vaughan Radio** (GC) 96.7 **W:** vaughanradio.com – **Volna FM** (TF) 102.9MHz **W:** volnafm.ru – **Yumbo FM** (GC) 105.1MHz **W:** yumbofm.com

## CAPE VERDE

**See CABO VERDE**

## CAYMAN ISLANDS (UK)

**L.T:** UTC -5h — **Pop:** 62,000 — **Pr.L:** English — **E.C:** 60Hz, 120V — **ITU:** CYM

### THE UTILITY REGULATION AND COMPETITION OFFICE (OFREG)
✉ 3rd Floor, Alissta Towers, 85 North Sound Rd., Grand Cayman ☎ +1 345 9464282 🖷 +1 345 9458284 **E:** info@ofreg.ky **W:** www.ofreg. ky **L.P:** Chair: Magda Embury

### RADIO CAYMAN (Gov. Comm.)
✉ 71B Elgin Av, PO Box 1110, George Town, Grand Cayman KY1-1102 ☎ +1 345 949 7799 🖷 +1 345 949 6536 **W:** radiocayman.gov.ky **L.P:** Dir: Norma McField
**FM: R. Cayman One:** Grand Cayman 89.9MHz 5kW Cayman Brac: 93.9MHz 0.3kW music, current affairs, news: 24h Relays BBCWS 0500-1100 – **Breeze FM:** Grand Cayman 105.3MHz 5kW Cayman Brac: 91.9MHz 0.3kW music and news

### CAYMAN ISLANDS WEATHER SERVICE (Gov.)
✉ Ministry of District Adm, Works, Lands & Agriculture, Gov't Adm Bldg, George Town, Grand Cayman KY1-9000
**FM:** Cayman Weather Radio ZFGT: 107.9MHz 1kW

### HURLEYS MEDIA LTD. (Comm.)
✉ 18 Forum Lane, Suite 5106, PO Box 30110, KY1-1201 Red Bay, Grand Cayman ☎ +1 345 233 9898/9494/9999/1019 **W:** z99.ky, rooster101.ky, bobfm.ky & iriefm.ky. **L.P:** Pres. & GM: Randy Merren. PD: Jason Howard **FM: Z99:** George Town 99.9MHz 5kW CHR – **Rooster 101.9:** 101.9MHz 5kW Cayman Brac 101.9MHz 1kW country – **Bob 94.9:** George Town 94.9MHz 1kW oldies – **Irie 98.9:** George Town 98.9MHz 2kW Cayman Brac 98.9MHz 0.3kW reggae

### ICCI-FM (Educ.)
✉ International College of the Cayman Islands, Newlands, 595 Hirst Rd, PO Box 136, Grand Cayman KY1-1501. College ☎ +1 345 947 1100 🖷 +1 345 947 1230 **W:** icci.edu.ky/icci-fm-101-1-radio/ **L.P:** Robert Lynch **FM:** 101.1MHz 0.5kW **D.Prgr:** 24h locally prod. prgrs for residents, or continuous jazz, classical and easy listening music, acc. to availability of student volunteers.

### DMS BROADCASTING LTD. (Comm.)
✉ 38 Godfrey Nixon Way, PO Box 31910, Grand Cayman KY1-1208 ☎ + 1 345 943 1367 🖷 +1 345 943 1368 **E:** info@dmsbroadcasting.ky **W:** dmsbroadcasting.ky **L.P:** MD: Don Seymour. GM: Dan Charleston
**FM: CayRock** George Town: 96.5MHz (1kW) Cayman Brac: 96.5MHz (0.3kW) – **HOT FM** George Town: 104.1kHz – **KISS FM** George Town 106.1MHz – **X 107.1** George Town 107.1MHz

### PRAISE 87.9 RADIO (Rlg.)
✉ 209 Walkers Rd, PO Box 515, George Town, Grand Cayman KY1-1106 ☎ + 1 345 640 2647 **W:** caymanadventist.org **FM:** 87.9MHz Adventist

### INTERACTIVE BROADCASTING & MEDIA LTD. (Comm.)
✉ 42 Edward St., Unit #2, PO Box 976, George Town KY-1102 ☎ + 1 345 943 3600 **W:** star927cayman.ky **L.P:** John Watler.

**FM: Star FM** 92.7MHz 2.5kW Urban

### BIG FISH (Rlg.)
✉ PO Box 1408, Prospect KY-1501 ☎ + 1 345 925 9550 **E:** pam@bigfish955.ky **W:** bigfish955.ky **L.P:** Pamela Norton. **FM:** 95.5MHz 3kW Contemp. Christian

### THE VOICE (Rlg.)
✉ PO Box 12099, George Town KY1-1010 ☎ + 1 345 746 9797 **E:** info@thevoicefm.ky **W:** thevoicefm.ky **FM:** 97.7MHz Gospel

## CENTRAL AFRICAN REPUBLIC

**L.T:** UTC +1h — **Pop:** 5.1 million — **Pr.L:** French, Sango — **E.C:** 50Hz, 220V — **ITU:** CAF.

### MINISTÈRE DE LA COMMUNICATION
✉ B.P. 940, Bangui ☎+236 21610437. **L.P:** Minister: Abdou Karim Meckassolia

### RADIO CENTRAFRIQUE (Gov.)
✉ B.P. 940, Bangui ☎+236 75503632. **W:** facebook.com/pages/RADIO-CENTRAFRIQUE/128958907146671 **E:** radio.centrafrique@yahoo.fr **L.P:** DG: Aimé-Christian Ndotah. PD: Mrs. Pauline Gbianza.
**FM:** Bangui 106.9MHz 1kW 24h.
**D.Prgr in French/Sango:** 24h. **N. in French:** 0600, 0700, 1300, 1800. **Ann:** F: "Ici Bangui, Radio Centreafricaine". **IS:** Repeated piano chord.

### RADIO MAÏNGO (Rlg.)
✉ B.P. 1035, PK 11 Route de Damara, Bangui **W:** radiomaingo.com **E:** info@waterforgood.org **L.P:** Dir: Wilfried Ouilibona, Coordinator: Mr. Farel Ndango Zekewane.
**SW:** Boali 6030 1kW. **D.Prgr.** in French, Sango, Bayaka and Fulfulde: Mon-Sat 0600-1100, daily 1300-1500 on 6030kHz.

### RADIO NDEKE LUKA
(joint initiative between the UN Development Programme, CAF government and Hirondelle Foundation)
✉ c/o PNUD, Av. de l'Indépendance, B.P. 872, Bangui ☎+236 72295252. **W:** radiondekeluka.org **L.P:** Dir: Martin Faye.
**FM:** Bambari/Bangui/Bouar 100.9MHz 1kW. **D.Prgr:** 24h in Sango/French. Also rel. by R. Maïngo, Boali on 6030 kHz between 1500-1700.
**Hirondelle-aided community radios (MHz):**
**R. Barangbaké,** Bria: 100.1 – **R. Be Oko,** Bambari: 103.5 – **R. Kuli Ndounga,** Nola: 98.0 – **R. Linga,** Bangui: 96.5 – **R. Magbadja,** Alindao – **R. Maïgaro,** Bouar: 108.0 – **R. Voix de la Pende,** Paoua: 102.6 – **R. Zoukpana,** Berbérati: 105.9 – **Voix de l'Ouham,** Bossangoa: 99.7.

**Other stations (MHz):**
**Guira FM,** Bangui: 93.3 **W:** minusca.unmissions.org/en/guira-fm **F.PI:** more transmitters – **Fréquence RJDH,** Bangui: 100.5 **W:** rjdh.org/tag/frequence-rjdh – **Hit R,** Bangui: 96.1 **W:** facebook.com/hitradiorca – **Leko Ti La Ouaka,** Bambari: 88.1 – **R. Anidussa,** M'Boki: 100.5 – **R. ESCA La Voix de la Grâce,** Bangui: 98.5 **E:** radiovoixdelagrace@yahoo.fr – **R. Notre Dame,** Bangui: 103.3 1kW **W:** radionotredame. org – **R. Sewa,** Bangui: 101.1 **W:** facebook.com/Radiosewa – **R. Siriri,** Bouar: 103.6 **W:** facebook.com/RadioSiriri – **R. Zereda,** Obo: 100.6 **W:** facebook.com/Radio-Zereda-45348407141418 – **R. Yemusse,** Djéma: 103.5.
**BBC African Sce,** Bangui: 90.2MHz.
**RFI Afrique,** Bangui: 99.8MHz.
**Voice of America,** Bangui: 102.4MHz

## CHAD

**L.T:** UTC +1h — **Pop:** 15 million — **Pr.L:** French, Arabic, 8 ethnic — **E.C:** 50Hz, 220V — **ITU:** TCD

### HAUT CONSEIL DE LA COMMUNICATION (HCC)
✉ N'Djamena. **L.P:** President: Wawa Dahab.

### OFFICE NATIONAL DE RADIO ET TÉLÉVISION DU TCHAD (ONRTV, Gov.)
✉ B.P. 892, Av. Mobutu, N'Djamena. ☎+235 22521513 🖷 +235 22521517 **W:** onrtv.td **L.P:** DG: Doubaye Kieoutuin.
**Station:** N'Djamena-Gredia.
**SW:** ‡6165kHz 100kW 0430-1900 (inactive).
**FM:** 94.5MHz 0.1kW. **D.Prgr:** in French/Arabic/others:24h. Local prgr. for N'djamena on 92.5MHz. **Ann:** "Ici N'Djamena, Office National de Radio et Télévision du Tchad".

## REGIONAL FM STATIONS

**R. Moundou,** B.P. 122, Moundou: 94.05/98.3MHz 200/450W – **R. Sarh,** B.P. 270, Sarh: 94.0MHz – **R. Abéché,** B.P. 105, Abéché: 101.0MHz – **R. Faya-Largeau:** 99.1MHz.
**F.PI:** 13 more regional stations.

## RADIO NDARASON INTERNATIONAL

N'Djamena ☎+235 62935528 **W:** ndarason.com **E:** info@ndara-son.com **L.P:** MD: David Smith. Mgr: Fiacre Munezero.
**FM:** Liwa 96.0, Bol 98.8, N'Djamena 107.1MHz.
**D.Prgr.** 24h in Kanuri, Kanembu & others.
**F.PI:** Ngouri 96.8, Doum Doum 97.2, Baga Sola 97.6MHz.
**Relays on shortwave:** see International Radio section.

**Other stations:**
**Al-Bayan FM,** N'Djamena: 93.7MHz – **Al-Nasr,** N'Djamena: 102.1MHz – **Dja FM,** N'Djamena: 96.9MHz 0.5kW – **R. Al-Quran,** N'Djamena: 91.0MHz – **R. Arc en Ciel,** N'Djamena: 107.7MHz – **R. Duji Lokar,** Mondou: 101.8MHz 0.5kW – **R. Effata,** Lai: 98.0MHz **W:** dioceselai.com – **R. Évangile Développement,** Pala: 88.5MHz – **FM Liberté,** N'Djamena: 105.3MHz – **R. Harmonie FM,** N'Djamena: 106.3MHz 0.5kW – **R. Lotiko:** Koumra 100.1MHz, Sarh 97.6MHz 0.5kW **W:** sarh.info/membres/nangadoumbaye/Lotiko Radio.html – **R. Terre Nouvelle,** Bangor 99.4MHz 1.1kW – **La Voix du Paysan,** Doba: 96.2MHz 1kW.
**BBC African Sce:** N'Djamena 90.6MHz
**RFI Afrique:** N'Djamena 100.2, Moundou 100.3, Sarh 100.4, Abéché 100.5MHz 1kW.
**R. Sawa:** N-Djamena 93.1MHz

## CHILE

**L.T:** UTC -4h (12 Aug 18-7 Apr 19, 8 Sep 19-5 Apr 20: -3h; dates subject to confirmation) — **Pop:** 18 million — **Pr.L:** Spanish — **E.C:** 50Hz, 220V — **ITU:** CHL — **Int. dialling code:** +56

## SUBSECRETARIA DE TELECOMUNICACIONES

**Offices:** Amunátegui 139, Santiago Clasificador 120, Correo 21, Santiago ☎ 2 24213500 2 26995138 **W:** subtel.cl

## ASOCIACION DE RADIODIFUSORES DE CHILE (ARCI)

Pasaje Matte 966, Piso 8. Of. 801 Santiago ☎2 28898900 2 26394205 **W:** archi.cl

° = on-air stn name not confirmed ‡ = inactive ± = varying freq.

| MW | Call | kHz | kW | Station, location, h of tr |
|---|---|---|---|---|
| MS01) | CB54 | 540 | 1 | R. Ignacio Serrano, Melipilla |
| BB01) | CC55 | 550 | 2 | R. Corporación, Concepción |
| AR02) | CD55 | 550 | 1 | R. Voz de la Tierra, Angol:1000-0200 |
| MS02) | CB57 | 570 | | R. Salud 570, Santiago |
| BB26) | CC59 | 590 | | CARACOL 590, Concepción: 24h |
| MC01) | CC59 | 590 | 10 | R. Pingüino, Punta Arenas |
| MS03) | CB60 | 600 | 10 | R. Vida Nueva, Santiago: 1100-0500 |
| CO01) | CA62 | 620 | 1 | R. Norte Verde, Ovalle |
| BB03) | CC62 | 620 | 10 | R. Bío-Bío, Concepción: 24h |
| VA01) | CB63 | 630 | 10 | R. Stela Maris, Valparaíso: 1200-0600 |
| AR03) | CD64 | 640 | 1 | R. Cooperativa, Temuco: 24h |
| MA13) | CC64 | 640 | 0.25 | R. Portales, Curico |
| MS26) | CB66 | 660 | 50 | R. UC, Santiago |
| BB04) | CC68 | 680 | 1 | R. Cooperativa, Concepción: 24h |
| MS05) | CB69 | 690 | 10 | R. Santiago, Santiago |
| LL02) | CD69 | ‡690 | 10 | R. Estrella del Mar (R.Maria), Ancud: 24h |
| LR01) | CD70 | 700 | 1 | Nueva R. Valdivia, Valdivia |
| MC02) | CD70A | 700 | 5 | R. Magallanes, Punta Arenas: 24h |
| BB07) | CC72 | 720 | 1 | R. Interamericana, Concepción |
| TA09) | CA72 | 720 | 1 | R. Portales, Iquique |
| VA02) | CB73 | 730 | 10 | R. Cooperativa AM, Valparaíso: 24h |
| BB19) | CD73 | 730 | 1 | R. Angelina, Los Angeles |
| MS06) | CB76 | 760 | 50 | R. Cooperativa, Santiago: 24h |
| AR10) | CD127 | 770 | 5 | R. Agricultura, Temuco: 24h |
| LL04) | CD77 | 770 | 1 | R. Cooperativa, Castro: 24h |
| LL05) | CD78 | 780 | 10 | R. Sago, Osorno |
| VA03) | CB80 | 800 | 5/1 | R. Maria, Viña del Mar: 24h |
| CO02) | CA82B | ‡820 | 10/1 | R. Portales, La Serena |
| BB05) | CC82 | 820 | 1 | R. UCSC, Concepción |
| LR02) | CD82 | 820 | 1 | R. Concordia, La Unión: 24h |
| MS07) | CB82 | 820 | | R. Carabineros, Santiago |
| VA04) | CB84 | ‡840 | 10 | R. Portales, Valparaíso |
| AS03) | CD84 | 840 | 1 | R. Santa María, Coyhaique |
| BB06) | CC86 | 860 | 10 | R. Inés de Suárez, Concepción: 24h |
| MS08) | CB88 | 880 | 10 | R. Colo Colo, Santiago: 24h |
| VA05) | CB90 | ‡900 | 1 | R. Portales, Viña del Mar |

| MW | Call | kHz | kW | Station, location, h of tr |
|---|---|---|---|---|
| BB08) | CC90 | ‡900 | 1 | R. Nuble, Chillán: 1100-0400 |
| LL07) | CD90 | 900 | 1 | R. LV de la Costa, Osorno:0930-0300 |
| MA14) | CC91 | 910 | 1 | R. Tropical Latina (RTL), Talca |
| AR04) | CD92 | 920 | 1 | R. 920, Temuco: 1000-0300 |
| MS09) | CB93 | ‡930 | 10 | R. Nuevo Mundo, Santiago: 24h |
| LL08) | CD93 | 930 | 10 | R. Reloncaví (R. Cooperativa), Puerto Montt: 24h |
| VA06) | CB94 | 940 | 1 | R. Valentín Letelier, Valparaíso |
| MS10) | CB96 | 960 | 10 | R. Carrera, Santiago |
| MC04) | CD96 | 960 | 10 | R. Polar, Punta Arenas |
| MA01) | CC97 | 970 | 1 | R. Lautaro, Talca: 1000-0500 |
| AS04) | CD97A | 970 | 1 | R. Patagonia Chilena, Coyhaique |
| LR03) | CD97 | 970 | 1 | R. Austral, Valdivia |
| CO11) | CA98 | 980 | 1 | La Serena |
| VA07) | CB98 | ‡980 | 5 | Valparaíso |
| MS11) | CB100 | 1000 | 10 | BBN R., Santiago |
| AR22) | CD101 | ‡1010 | 10 | R. Nielol, Temuco |
| MA02) | CC102 | 1020 | 5 | R. Amiga,Talca |
| BB25) | CC103 | 1030 | 10 | R. Chilena, Concepción: 1000-0300 |
| MS12) | CB103 | 1030 | 1 | R. Progreso, Talagante |
| LL10) | CD103 | 1030 | 10 | R. Chiloé, Castro:1100-0330 |
| MC05) | CD103A | 1030 | 1 | R. Payne AM, Puerto Natales |
| MS13) | CB106 | 1060 | 100 | R. Maria, Santiago |
| CO03) | CA108 | ‡1080 | 1 | Vicuña |
| AR07) | CD108 | 1080 | 1 | R. Los Confines, Angol |
| LL23) | CD109 | 1090 | 5 | Castro |
| MA11) | CC109 | 1090 | 5/1 | R. Chilena del Maule, Talca: 1000-0300 |
| VA08) | CB110 | 1100 | 10 | BBN R. Viña del Mar |
| AR08) | CD111 | 1110 | 10 | R. La Frontera, Temuco: 0900-0400 |
| MS14) | CB114 | 1140 | 100 | R. Nal., Santiago |
| MA04) | CC116 | ‡1160 | 1 | R. Ancoa, Linares |
| AR01) | CD116A | 1160 | 1 | R. Baha'i, Temuco: 0930-0130 |
| MC06) | CD117 | 1170 | 5 | R. Natales, Puerto Natales: 24 |
| MS15) | CB118 | ‡1180 | 50 | R. Portales, Santiago: 24h |
| BB20) | CD120 | 1200 | 10 | R. Agricultura, Los Angeles |
| LL12) | CD121 | ‡1210 | 1 | Puerto Montt |
| MA05) | CC121 | 1210 | 1 | R. Universidad de Talca, Talca: 24h |
| VA20) | CB121 | ‡1210 | | R. Valparaíso, Valparaíso |
| AR09) | CD122 | 1220 | 10 | R. Maria, Temuco |
| AN08) | CA124 | 1240 | 0.25 | R. Club Chuquicamate, Calma |
| MS16) | CB124 | 1240 | 25 | R. Universidad de Santiago, Santiago |
| LR04) | CD125 | 1250 | 10 | R. Pilmaiquen, Valdivia: 24h |
| MA06) | CC126 | 1260 | 1 | R. Condell, Curicó |
| MC07) | CD126 | ‡1260 | 10 | R. Maria, Punta Arenas |
| VA09) | CC126 | ±1270 | 5 | R. Festival, Viña del Mar: 1000-0400 |
| LL14) | CD128 | 1280 | 1 | R. la Palabra, Osorno |
| AN07) | CA129 | ‡1290 | 0.25 | R. Coya, Los Angeles |
| MS25) | CB130 | 1300 | 5 | R. Conexiones, Santiago: 1200-0300 |
| BB21) | CD132 | ‡1320 | 1 | R. Lincoyan, Mulchén |
| MS17) | CB133 | 1330 | 3 | R. La Perla del Dial, Santiago: 24h |
| LL16) | CD133 | 1330 | 3/15 | R. Vicente Pérez Rosales, Puerto Montt |
| VA10) | CB134 | 1340 | 10 | R. Colo Colo, Valparaíso: 24h |
| BB11) | CC134 | ‡1340 | 1 | R. La Discusión, Chillán: 24h |
| LR06) | CD134 | 1340 | 1 | R. Vida Nueva, Panguipulli |
| CO06) | CA135 | ‡1350 | 1 | R. Riquelme, Coquimbo: 1030-0430 |
| LL24) | CD135 | ‡1350 | 0.02 | Puerto Montt |
| BB12) | CC136 | 1360 | 5 | R. Universidad Bio Bio, Concepcion: 24h |
| AR11) | CD137 | 1370 | 1 | R. Vida Nueva, Temuco: 1100-0500 |
| MS18) | CB138 | 1380 | 50 | R. Corporación, Santiago: 24h |
| BB22) | CD140 | 1400 | 5 | R. La Amistad, Los Angeles |
| LL18) | CD140A | 1400 | 5 | R. Maria, Puerto Montt |
| VA11) | CB141 | 1410 | 5 | R. Amor, Viña del Mar |
| AR12) | CD141 | 1410 | 1 | R. Loncoche, Loncoche |
| MS19) | CB142 | ±1420 | 1 | R. Panamericana, Santiago: 1000-0200 |
| GB06) | CC143 | ‡1430 | 1 | Rancagua |
| BB13) | CC144 | 1440 | 1 | R. El Sembrador, Chillán: 1000-0230 |
| CO07) | C144A | ‡1440 | 1 | R. Coquimbo Stereo, La Serene: 24h |
| VA12) | CB145 | 1450 | 1 | R. Universidad Técnica "Federico Santa María, Valparaíso |
| MA08) | CC145 | 1450 | 4 | R. Tropical Latina – RTL, Curicó: 24h |
| MS20) | CB146 | 1460 | 1 | R. Palabra Viva, Santiago |
| BB14) | CC146 | 1460 | 1 | R. Armonía, Talcahuano |
| VA13) | CB147 | 1470 | 1 | R. Sargento Aldea, San Antonio |
| BB15) | CC148 | 1480 | 1 | R. La Amistad de Tomé, Tomé |
| CO08) | CA148 | 1480 | 1 | R. Comunicativa, Ovalle |
| AT06) | CA149 | ‡1490 | 1 | R. Alicanto, El Salvador |
| MS21) | CB149 | ‡1490 | 0.25 | Hola Radio, San Bernardo |
| MA09) | CC150 | ‡1500 | 1 | R. Centenario |
| MC08) | CD150 | 1500 | 1 | R. Tierra del Fuego, Porvenir |
| VA14) | CB150 | 1500 | 1 | R. Trasandina, Los Andes: 24h, Sun 2000-2200 |
| CO09) | CA151 | 1510 | 1/0.5 | R. Luís Alvarez Sierra, Illapel: 1000-0100 |

| MW | Call | kHz | kW | Station, location, h of tr |
|---|---|---|---|---|
| | | | | (Sat: -0400), Sun 1100-0100 |
| GB02) | CC151 | 1510 | 1 | R. Poder Pentecostal, Rancagua: 24h |
| MA10) | CC152 | 1520 | 1 | R. Soberanía, Linares: 0930-0005 |
| VA15) | CB152 | ‡1520 | 1 | R. Integración, San Antonio |
| AT05) | CA153 | 1530 | 1 | R. Vida Nueva, Copiapó: 1100-0500 |
| VA16) | CB153 | 1530 | 1 | R. Nexo, Quillota: 1000-0300 |
| BB17) | CC154 | ‡1540 | 1 | R. Portales, Chillán |
| LR05) | CD154 | ±1540 | 1 | R. San José de Alcudia, Río Bueno: |
| MS22) | CB144 | 1540 | | R.Sud America, Santiago |
| VA17) | CB155 | 1550 | 1 | R. Provincial AM, Putaendo |
| GB03) | CB155 | ±1550 | 1 | R. Manuel Rodríguez, San Fernando: |
| AP01) | CA156 | 1560 | 5/3 | R. Parinacota, Putre: 24h |
| MS23) | CB160 | 1560 | 1 | R. Manantial, Talagante: 1000-0300 |
| | | | | (Sat: -0500) |
| AR16) | CD156 | 1560 | 1 | R. Parque, Villarrica |
| GB04) | CC157 | ±1570 | 1 | R. Cristo Llama Al Pecador, Rancagua: 24h |
| MA11) | CC157A | 1570 | 1 | R. Familia del Maule, Talca: 1000-0300 |
| GB05) | CC158 | 1580 | 1 | R. Colchagua, Santa Cruz |
| VA18) | CB159 | ±1590 | 1 | R. Aconcagua, San Felipe: 1000-2300 |
| MA15) | CC159A | ‡1590 | 0.1 | Parral |
| MS24) | CB160 | 1600 | 0.25 | R. Nuevo Tiempo, Santiago: 24h |
| VA19) | CB160A | ‡1600 | 0.25 | R. Positiva, Viña del Mar |
| BB18) | CC160 | ±1600 | 0.25 | R. Llacolén, Concepción |
| AR23) | CD160 | 1600 | 0.25 | R. Alternativa, Temuco: 1000-0100 |

| SW | kHz | kW | Station, location, h of tr |
|---|---|---|---|
| MS27) | 5825 | 0.5 | R.Triunfal Evangelica, Talagante: 2200-0000 exc. Thu. |
| MS28) | 69250.45 | | RCW, R. Compañía Worldwide, San Francisco |

## Addresses & other information:

**AN00 (ANTOFAGASTA – Region II):**
**AN07)** Av Ignacio Carrera Pinto No 401-A, María Elena ☎55 641176 E: contacto@radiocoya.cl - FM: 92.5 MHz – **AN08)** P.O.Box 13630, Calama E: ce1rch.cl E: contacto@ce1rch.cl

**AP00 (ARICA Y PARINACOTA – Region XV)**
**AP01)** Calle José Miguel Carrera 350 esquina Av. Circulación O'Higgins, Putre ☎58 2252803 W: imputre.cl E: prensaputre@hotmail.com – FM: 94.5MHz

**AR00 (ARAUCANIA – Region IX):**
**AR01)** Cl 1Norte 0684, Labranza, Temuco ☎45 2375142 W: radio.bahai.cl **AR02)** Av. Bernardo O'Higgins 297, piso 2, Angol ☎45 2712331 E: radiovozdelatierra@gmail.com – **AR03)** Temuco W: cooperativa.cl E: internet@cooperativa.cl - FM: 103.1 MHz – **AR04)** Portales 527, Temuco ☎45 2277148 W: radionueveveinte.com E: radionueveveinte@gmail.com – **AR07)** Lautaro 124 Piso 2, Angol ☎45 2413647 W: losconfines.cl - FM: 94.9MHz – **AR08)** Av Caupolicán 110 Of 2003 Piso 20, Temuco ☎45 2213166 ☒45 2210309 W: araucanayfrontera.cl E: araucanaradio@gmail.com - FM: 95.9MHz «La Araucana» – **AR09)** Temuco W: radiomaria.cl E: contacto@radiomaria.cl – **AR10)** Lynch 6464, Temuco ☎45 213854 W: radioagricultura.cl – **AR11)** Av. Maquehue 1115 - Parte las Casas, Temuco ☎452 734948 W: radiovidanuevaencristojesus.cl – **AR12)** Ignacio Serrano 264, Loncoche ☒45 2471052 W: radioloncoche.cl E: radiocd141@gmail.com - FM: 105.9MHz «Vibración» – **AR16)** Vicente Reyes 528, Villarrica ☎45 411567 W: radioparque.cl E: radiopnacional@gmail.com – **AR22)** Temuco – **AR23)** Manuel Montt 381-C, Temuco ☎45 2483356 W: radioalternativa.cl

**AS00) (AISÉN – Region XI)**
**AS03)** Francisco Bilbao 691, Coyhaique ☎67 2232398 ☒67 2231306 W: radiosantamaria.cl E: contacto@radiosantamaria.cl - FM: 102.3MHz – **AS04)** Av Francisco Bilboa 457 ☎67 245632 W: radiopatagoniachilena.cl E: radiopatagoniachilena@gmail.com - FM: 99.3MHz «Acro Iris»

**AT00 (ATACAMA – Region III):**
**AT05)** Colipi371, Copiapo ☎52212031 W: radiovidanuevaencristojesus.com – **AT06)** Av. El Tofo 535, Diego de Almagro ☎52 2475023

**BB00 (BIO BIO – Region VIII):**
**BB01)** Angol 648, 2° piso, Concepción ☎41 2738650 W: radio-corporacion.cl E: contacto@radio-corporacion.cl – **BB03)** O'Higgins 680, Piso 3, Concepción ☎41 2620620 W: radiobiobio.cl E: biobio@laradio.cl - FM: 98.1MHz – **BB04)** Paicavi 119, 2° piso, (Plaza Peru) (or Cas. 2337), Concepción W: cooperativa.cl E: internet@cooperativa.cl - FM: 93.3 MHz– **BB05)** Campus San Andres, Alonso de Ribera 2850, Concepción ☎41 2345000 ☒41 2345001W: ucsc.cl/ucsc-radio – **BB06)** Castellón 477, 3° piso, Concepción ☎41 246 0486 W: radioinesdesuarez.cl E: contacto@radioinesdesuarez.cl – **BB07)** Calle Barros Arana 871, 5° piso, Of. 51, Concepción ☎41 2214450 W: radiointeramericana.cl E: contacto@radiointeramericana.cl – **BB08)** 5 de Abril 655, Chillán ☎42 2215530 W: radionuble.cl/ E: radiocontigo@gmail.com - FM: 89.7MHz "R.Nuble" – **BB11)** 18 de Septiembre 721, Chillán ☎42 2211667 W: ladiscusion.cl E: radiotv@ladiscusion.cl - FM: 94.7MHz – **BB12)** Avd Collao 1202, Casilla 5-C,

Concepción ☎41 3111 1040 W: radioubb.cl E: ubb@ubiobio.cl – **BB13)** Arauco 447, Chillán ☎41 2224603 W: radioelsembrador.cl E: administracion@radioelsembrador.cl - FM: 104.7MHz «Aurora FM» – **BB14)** Av.Los Carrera N° 464, Concepcion ☎41 2854594 W: armonia.cl E: concepcion@armonia.cl - FM: 99.5 MHz – **BB15)** Sotomayor 1184 2° piso of 203, Tomé ☎41 2650657 W: radiolaamistaddetome.cl E: contacto@radiolaamistaddetome.cl – **B17)** Chillán – **BB18)** Calle Barros Arana, Concepción ☎41 2244354 W: radiollacolen.com E: radiollacolen@gmail.com – **BB19)** Colo-Colo 451 Of. 120, Nivel 2, Los Angeles ☎43 2349920 E: contacto@radiocamila.cl - FM: 98.3 MHz – **BB20)** Calle Janequeo 615, Los Angeles ☎43 324212 W: radioagricultura.cl – **BB21)** Mulchén – **BB22)** Lautaro 279, Departemento 301, Los Angeles ☒43 2329834 W: radiolaamistad.cl E: radiolaamistad@gmail.com – **BB25)** Arzobispado de la Santísima Concepción, Barros Arana 544, 3° piso, Concepción ☎41 2626167 W: radiochilenaconcepcion.cl E: contacto@radiochilenaconcepcion.cl – **BB26)** Castellón 746, 2° piso, Concepcion ☎41 2460193 W: radiocaracol590.cl

**CO00 (COQUIMBO – Region IV):**
**CO01)** Ca Santiago 355, Ovalle ☎53 2620359 W: radionorteverde.cl E: radionorteverde@gmail.com – **CO02)** Av. Trancisco de Aguirre 337 of. 6, La Serena ☎94 5689365 W: laserena.cl E: portaleslaserena@gmail.com – **CO03)** Vicuña – **CO06)** Aldunate 1619, Coquimbo ☎51 2321051 W: radioriquelme.cl – **CO07)** Merceds Alvarez 3140 Sindempar , La Serena ☎6353 6299 W: quimbostereo.cl E: prensa@quimbostereo.cl – **CO08)** Pedro Montt 181, Ovalle W: radiocomunicativa.cl E: radiocomunicativa@gmail.com - FM: 93.7 MHz – **CO09)** Independencia 175, Illapel ☒53 2522831W: las.co.cl/Radio.htm E: direccionlas@entelchile.net - FM: 100.9MHz – **CO11)** Benavente 1141, La Serena

**GB00 (O'HIGGINS – Region VI):**
**GB02)** Santa María n° 61, Rancagua ☎72 2229586 W: poderpentecostal.org E. pastorclaudioespinoza@hotmail.com – **GB03)** Altos Mercado, calle Chacabuco esq. España, San Fernando ☎☒72 714267 E: cc155laradio@hotmail.com – **GB04)** Ca Santa Maria 126, Rancagua ☎72 242741 – **GB05)** Rafael Casanova 146, Santa Cruz ☎☒72 2822193 - FM: 105.5MHz «Ensueño» – **GB06)** Rancagua

**LL00 (LOS LAGOS – Region X):**
**LL02)** Elutero Ramírez 207, Ancud ☎56 65622722 W: radioestrelladelmar.cl/ – **LL04)** Thompson 255 (Cas. 174), Castro W: cooperativa.cl E: internet@cooperativa.cl – **LL05)** Juan Mckenna 904, Osorno ☎64 2321601 W: radiosago.cl E: mcifuentes@radiosago.cl - FM: 94.5 MHz – **LL07)** Cochrane 746, Osorno ☎64 312525 W: radiovozdelacosta.cl E: radiolavozdelacosta@hotmail.com – **LL08)** Egana 29, Puerto Montt ☎65 2252234 W: radioreloncavi.cl – **LL10)** Bernardo O'Higgins 486 (Cas. 106), Castro ☎ 65 2632260 W: radiochiloe.cl E: contacto@radiochiloe.cl - FM: 90.1MHz «Martin Ruiz de Gamboa» – **LL12)** Av Presidente Ibañez No 872 Piso 2, Puerto Montt ☎65 383290 W. armonia.cl E: puertomontt@armonia.cl – **LL14)** Eleuterio Ramírez 1050 Dpto.41,, Osorno ☎64 2237440 W: radiolapalabra.cl E: tuprogramas@radiolapalabra.cl - FM: 101.5MHz «La Palabra» – **LL16)** Talca 72 piso2, Puerto Montt ☎65 258439 – **LL18)** Puerto Montt W: radiomaria.cl E: contacto@radiomaria.cl - FM: 103.5 MHz – **LL22)** Pedro Lagos 295, Río Bueno ☎64 2341531 W: radiosanjosedealcudia.cl E: radio@radiosanjosedealcudia.cl – **LL23)** Castro – **LL24)** Puerto Montt

**LR00 (LOS RIOS – Region XIV):**
**LR01)** Arauco 340 Piso 3 Of. 307, Valdivia W: FB: Radio Nueva Valdivia – **LR02)** Arturo Prat 466, La Unión ☎64 2322275 W: radioconcordia.cl – **LR03)** Arauco 363 3° piso, Valdivia ☎63 2202642 W: radioaustralvaldivia. E: radioaustral@surnet.cl – **LR04)** Arauco No 340 4 Piso, Valdiva ☎63 2202642 W: radiopilmaiquen.cl - FM: 98.9 MHz – **LR05)** Pedro Lagos 295, Río Bueno ☎64 2341531 W: radiosanjosedealcudia.cl E: radio@radiosanjosedealcudia.cl – **LR06)** Bernard O'Higgins 793, Panguipulli. ☎63 2310796 W: radiovidanuevaencristojesus.com

**MA00 (MAULE – Region VII):**
**MA01)** Tres Sur 767 1 Ote y Pte., Talca ☎71 2970758 W: Facebook.com/RadioLautaro E: radiolautaro@gmail.com – **MA02)** Avenida Diagonal Isidoro Del Solar 28, Talca W: rangers.cl/radioamiga.html E: contacto@rangers.cl – **MA04)** Independencia 631, Linares ☎76 2612320W: radioancoa.cl - FM: 103.5MHz – **MA05)** Casa 2 Norte 685, Talca ☎71 200160 W: radioemisoras.utalca.cl E: storres@utalca.cl - FM: 102., 93.7MHz – **MA06)** Carmen 714, Curicó. ☎75 2453520 W: radiocondell.cl E: direccion@radiocondell.cl - FM: 92.7MHz – **MA08)** 157 Manuel Montt, Curicó ☎75 2328021 W: radiortl.cl E: publicidadrtl@gmail.com - FM: 95.5MHz – **MA09)** San Javier – **MA10)** Diputado Dario Dueñas 777, Linares ☎73 2210277 W: radiosoberania.es.tl E: soberania@hotmail.com – **MA11)** 5 Poniente No 1150, Talca W: radiofamiliachilena.cl E: info@radiofamiliachilena.cl ☎71 613756 – **MA13)** Villouta N° 558, Curico W: radiocorporacioncurico.

cl – **MA14)** Manuel Montt 198, Curico ☎75 328021 **W:** radiortl.cl **E:** publicidadrtl@gmail.com – **MA15)** Parral

**MC00 (MAGALLANES Y DE LA ANTARCTICA CHILENA – Reg. XII):**
**MC01)** Av España 959, 6200 623 Punta Arenas ☎61 2292900 **W:** elpinguino.com **E:** secretaria@elpinguino.com - **FM:** 95.3MHz – **MC02)** José Nogueira 1370, Punta Arenas ☎61 2243551 **W:** radiomagallanes. cl **E:** prensa@radiomagallanes.cl – **MC04)** Bories 871 Piso 2, Punta Arenas ☎61 2241417 **W:** radiopolar.com **E:** secretaria@radiopolar. com - **FM:** 96.5-98.5-105.7MHz «Finísima» – **MC05)** Cl Bulnes 819, Puerto Natales ☎61 2411450 **E:** famm1605@hotmail.com - **FM:** 89.5 MHz – **MC06)** Eberhard 212, Puerto Natales ☎61 2410157 ☎61 2414746 **W:** radionatales.com – **MC07)** Punta Arenas **W:** radiomaria. cl - **FM:** 88.9 MHz – **MC08)** Bulnes 449, Porvenir ☎61 2580100 **W:** radiotierradelfuego.cl **E:** director@radiotierradelfuego.cl

**MS00 (METROPOLITANA DE SANTIAGO – Region RM):**
**MS01)** Cla Ortuzar 935, Melipilla ☎ 2 28323440 **E:** radio.claudia@gmail.com - **FM:** 104.5MHz R.Carica – **MS02)** Santiago ☎32 3172827 **W:** radiosalud.cl **E:** contacto@radiosalud.cl – **MS03)** Av. Condell 910, Santiago ☎2 2224500 **W:** radiovidanuevaencristojesus.com - **FM:** 104.5 MHz – **MS05)** Triana 868, Providencia, Santiago. ☎2 2236 0096 **W:** radiosantiago.cl **E:** gerenciageneral@radiosantiago. cl – **MS06)** Maipú 525, Santiago 8350372 **W:** cooperativa.cl **E:** internet@cooperativa.cl – ☎2 32648000 ☎2 22360535 – **MS07)** Av. Bernardo O´Higgins 1196 **W:** carabineros.cl **E:** radioemisora@carabineros.cl – MS08) Almeda 4263, Estaciob Central ☎2 277 64839**W:** radiocolocolo.cl – **MS09)** San Pablo 2271, Santiago ☎2 26883175 **W:** radionuevomundo.cl – **W:** info@radionuevomundo.cl – **MS10)** Eleodoro Flores 2475, Nunoa, Santiago ☎2 23611894 **W:** radiocarrera.com – **MS11)** Paseo Bulnes 120, Oficina 72, Santiago Centro a metros de la Alameda ☎2 26718602 **W:** bbnradio.org **E:** red@bbnmedia.org – **MS12)** Enrique Alcalde 1081, Talagante ☎2 8153279 **W:** radioprogresoycontacto.cl **E:** ventas@radioprogresoycontacto.cl – **MS13)** Santiago ☎2 22258544 **W:** radiomaria.cl **E:** contacto@radiomaria.cl – **MS14)** Dardignac 196 Oficina 22, Bellavista-Patronato, Santiago ☎2 17370101 **W:** nacionaldechile.cl **F.** radio@nacionaldechile.cl – **MS15)** Fanor Velasco 11, Santiago ☎2 26712703 **W:** radioportales.cl **E:** administracion@radioportales.cl. – **MS16)** Alameda 3363, Estación Central, Santiago ☎2 7181922 **W:** radiousach. cl **E:** radio@usach.cl – **MS17)** Los Leones 668, Providencia, Santiago ☎2 25836602 **W:** 3radio.cl **E:** santiago@laperladeldial.cl – **MS18)** Av Salvador Allende 92, Santiago ☎2 25529266 **W:** radiocorporacion. cl – **MS19)** Gran Avenida Jose Miguel Carrera 5848, 4° piso, San Miguel, Santiago ☎2 24160725 **W:** radiopanamericanachile.tk – **MS20)** Ubicado en Carmen No 1436, Santiago Central ☎2 25511378 **W:** radiopalabraviva.cl – **MS21)** Av. Portales 3020, San Bernardo ☎2 2841 4135 **W:** Facebook: Radio Canelo **E:** caneloradio@gmail. com – **MS22)** Santiago ☎22 548 1257 **W:** radiosudamerica.cl **E:** contacto@radiosudamerica.cl – **MS23)** Av. Lib.Bdo. O'Higginsa 854, Talagante ☎2 28151374 **W:** radiomanantial.cl **E:** radiomanantial@tie.cl - **FM:** 102.9MHz «Embrujo FM» – **MS24)** Los Cerezos No 6251, Peñalolén, Santiago ☎2 22844921 **W:** nuevotiempo.cl **E:** contactos@nuevotiempo.cl – **MS25)** Purisima 251, Recoleta, Santiago ☎2 27351790 **W:** radioconexiones.cl – **MS26)** Casa Central de la Universidad Católica, Alameda 340, Santiago ☎2 23542320 ☎2 23542054 **W:** radiouc.cl **E:** radio@uc.cl – **MS27)** Barraza Baja, Talagante ☎ 2 28154375 **W:** FB **E:.** radiotriunfal@gmail.com – **MS28)** San Francisco

**TA00 (TARAPACA – Region I):**
**TA09)** Iquique **W:** radioportales.cl

**VA00 (VALPARAISO – Region V):**
**VA01)** Pedro Montt 1766 (Cas. 3304), Valparaíso ☎32 274 5537 **W:** radiostellamaris.cl **E:** contacto@radiostellamaris.cl – **VA02)** Morris No 106, Depto. 155, Piso 15, Valparaiso **W:** cooperativa.cl **E:** internet@cooperativa.cl – **VA03)** Viña del Mar **W:** radiomaria.cl **E:** contacto@radiomaria.cl – **VA04)** Condell 1190 Of 21, Valparaíso ☎32 2214115 **W:** portalesfm.cl **E:** portalesgerencia@gmail.com - **FM:** 89.5MHz – **VA05)** Valparaíso – **VA06)** Av. Errazuriz 2120, Valparaíso ☎32 2507657 **W:** rvl.uv.cl **E:** radio@uv.cl - **FM:** 97.3MHz – **VA07)** Valparaíso – **VA08)** Paseo Bulnes 120, Oficina 72 , Santiago Centro a metros de la Alameda ☎32 2885524 **W:** bbnradio.org **E:** red@bbnmedia.org – **VA09)** Ca Quinta 124 Segundo Nivel Oficina A, Viña del Mar ☎32 2684251 **W:** radiofestival.cl **E:** servicios@festival.cl – **VA10)** Plaza de la Justicia 45, Piso 7 Of. 704, Valparaíso ☎32 2566664 **W:** radiocolocolovalparaiso. cl – **VA11)** 1 ½ Poniente #443 (Entre 4 y 5, Vina del Mar ☎32 3172827 **W:** radioamor.cl – **VA12)** Av. España 1680, Valparaíso ☎32 2797511 **W:** radio.utfsm.cl - **FM:** 99.7MHz – **VA13)** Av. Barros Luco 1678 (✉ Cas. 68,Correo 2) San Antonio ☎35 211321 - **FM:** 90.9 MHz – **VA14)** Papudo 155, Los Andes ☎34 2421425 **W:** radiotrasandina1500.cl **E:** transandinaradioam@gmail.com – **VA15)** San Antonio – **VA16)** Blanco 185, Quillota ☎33 2268001 **W:** radiolibra.cl **E:** gerencia@radiolibra.cl - **FM:** 104.7MHz «Libra Stereo FM» – **VA17)** Arturo Prat Poniente no 565,

Of 5 Piso 2, Putaendo ☎34 502762 **W:** radioprovincialdeputaendo. cl – **VA18)** Santo Domigo 99 – oficina 4, San Felipe ☎34 2510198 **W:** radioaconcagua.cl **E:** ecornejo@radioaconcagua.cl - **FM:** 91.7MHz – **VA19)** Viña del Mar – **VA20)** Eusebio Lillo 520, local 12, edifico Torre Valparaiso, Valparaiso ☎32 3148080 **W:** radiovalparaiso.cl **E:** prensa@radiovalparaiso.cl - **FM:** 97.7 & 102.5 MHz

**FM in Santiago (all MHz) Power** 1-10kW **Slogans:** Name + «FM»: MS26) 88.1 Aurora – 88.5 Concierto – MS14) 88.9 R. Futuro – MS13) 89.3 R.Maria – MS26) 89.7 Duna – 90.5 Pudahuel – 91.3 El Conquistador – 91.7 Amistad – 92.5 Radioactiva – 92.9 Romance – 93.3 La Cooperativa – 93.7 Universo – VA02) 94.1 Rock & Pop – 95.3 40 principales – MS25) 95.9 Tiempo – 96.5 Beethoven – 97.1 Caracol – 97.7 Zero – 98.5 FM 2 – MS08) 99.3 Carolina – 99.7 Bío Bío – MS25) 100.1 Infinita – MS26) 100.9 – 101.3 Corazón – 101.7 FM Hit – 102.1 Oasis – 102.5 Univ. de Chile – 103.3 Horizonte – **MS12)** 103.9 R.Contacto – 104.1 Romantica – MS03) 104.5 Monumental – 104.9 Nina – 105.7 Para ti – 106.3 Armonía – MS11) 106.9 Sintonía – 107.5 Fantasía

## CHINA (People's Rep. of)

**LT:** UTC +8h — **Pop:** 1,394 million — **Pr.L:** Mandarin, Amoy, Cantonese, Chaozhou, Hakka, Kazakh, Korean, Mongolian, Tibetan, Uighur, Zhuang, a.o. — **E.C:** 50Hz, 220V — **ITU:** CHN

**MINISTRY OF INDUSTRY AND INFORMATION TECHNOLOGY**
⌕ 13 Xi Chang'an Jie, Beijing 100804 **W:** miit.gov.cn **L.P:** Minister: Miao Wei

**STATE ADMINISTRATION OF PRESS, PUBLICATION, RADIO, FILM AND TELEVISION) (Gov.)**
⌕ 2 Fuxingmenwai Dajie, Beijing 100866 or P.O.Box 4501, Beijing ☎ +86 10 6809 2707 ▤ +86 10 6851 2174 **W:** sapprft.gov.cn **L.P:** Dir: Nie Chenxi

**CHINA MEDIA GROUP (Gov.)**
(Zongyang Guangbo Dianshi Zongdai, Central Radio Television General Station)
⌕ 11 Fuxing Lu, Beijing 100859, Beijing. **L.P:** Dir: Shen Haixiong
Founded in 2018 as the administrator of China National Radio (CNR), China Central Television and China Radio International (see International radio section).

**Official P.R.C. Abbreviations:** The 31 regions of the People's Republic of China, with their abbreviations and names in Pinyin (Chinese Phonetic Alphabet) version followed by the old spelling in brackets: AH: Anhui (Anhwei) – BJ: Beijing M. (Peking) – CQ: Chongqing M. (Chungking) – EB: Hebei (Hopeh) – EN: Henan (Honan) – FJ: Fujian (Fukien) – GD: Guangdong (Kwangtung) – GS: Gansu (Kansu) – GX: Guangxi Zhuang A.R. (Kwangsi) – GZ: Guizhou (Kweichow) – HAN: Hainan (Hainan) – HB: Hubei (Hupeh) —HL: Heilongjiang (Heilungkiang) – HN: Hunan (Hunan) – JL: Jilin (Kirin) – JS: Jiangsu (Kiangsu) – JX: Jiangxi (Kiangsi) – LN: Liaoning (Liaoning) – NM: Nei Menggu A.R. (Inner Mongolia) – NX: Ningxia Hui A.R. (Ningsia) – QH: Qinghai (Tsinghai) – SC: Sichuan (Szechwan) – SD: Shandong (Shantung) – SH: Shanghai M. (Shanghai) – SN: Shaanxi (Shensi) – SX: Shanxi (Shansi) – TJ: Tianjin M. (Tientsin) – XJ: Xinjiang Uighur A.R. (Sinkiang) – XZ: Xizang A.R.(Tibet) – YN: Yunnan (Yunnan) – ZJ: Zhejiang (Chekiang).

**Regional Services:** Add "Renmin Guangbo Diantai" (People's Broadcasting Station) to the stn name shown in the table below to obtain the full name in Standard Chinese.
**Abbreviations:** 1 = 1st prgr, 2 = 2nd prgr, 3 = 3rd prgr; EBS = Economic Broadcasting Station.
**Languages:** Standard Chinese (Putonghua), based on the Beijing dialect, is used in broadcasts throughout China. Various dialects and minority languages are included in the relevant regional services and in broadcasts to Taiwan.
**Abbreviations:** Ch = Standard Chinese, Kg = Kirghiz, Ko = Korean, Kz = Kazakh, Mo = Mongolian, Tb = Tibetan, Ug = Uighur.

| MW | kHz | kW | Station | Tx Location |
|---|---|---|---|---|
| ZJ1) | 531 | 10 | Zhejiang | Jinhua |
| 1) | 540 | 50 | CNR 1 | Shenyang/Hefei |
| NM1) | 540 | 1 | Nei Menggu | Wuhai |
| NM18) | 540 | | Genhe | |
| QH4) | 540 | 10 | Haixi | Da Qaidam |
| 1) | 549 | 1200 | CNR 5 | Putian, FJ |

| MW | kHz | kW | Station | Tx Location |
|---|---|---|---|---|
| EN2) | 549 | 25 | Zhengzhou | |
| NM12) | 549 | 10 | Alxa | Bayanhot |
| EB1) | 558 | 3 | Hebei | Shijiazhuang |
| FJ1) | 558 | 5010 | Fujian | Jianyang |
| FJ1) | 558 | 10 | Fujian | Longyan |
| FJ1) | 558 | 10 | Fujian | Pingtan |
| FJ1) | 558 | 10 | Fujian | Putian |
| FJ1) | 558 | 10 | Fujian | Xiamen |
| FJ1) | 558 | 10 | Fujian | Xiapu |
| NM17) | 558 | 1 | Zalantun | |
| XJ1) | 558 | 120 | Xinjiang | Hutubi |
| YN16) | 558 | 10 | Nujiang | Lushui |
| 1) | 567 | 10 | CNR 1 | Lianyungang, JS |
| EN17) | 567 | 10 | Zhoukou | |
| TJ1) | 567 | 20 | Tianjin | |
| EN4) | 576 | 10 | Luoyang | |
| FJ5) | 576 | 3 | Quanzhou | |
| YN1) | 576 | 200 | Yunnan | Kunming |
| ZJ1) | ±576 | 1 | Zhejiang | Linhai |
| 14) | 585 | 200 | Southeast BC | Fuzhou, FJ |
| EB11) | 585 | 10 | Langfang | |
| EN14) | 585 | 10 | Nanyang | |
| GS3) | 585 | 3 | Jinchang | |
| HB8) | 585 | 10 | Jingzhou | |
| HL3) | 585 | 10 | Qiqihar | |
| JL2) | 585 | 10 | Changchun | |
| JL10) | 585 | 1 | Yanbian | Hunchun |
| JS1) | 585 | 50 | Jiangsu | Nanjing |
| JX5) | 585 | 10 | Xinyu | |
| LN1) | 585 | | Liaoning | Suizhong |
| LN16) | 585 | 1 | Chaoyang | Beipiao |
| SX6) | 585 | 10 | Jincheng | |
| SD1) | 594 | 50 | Shandong | Jinan/Yantai |
| XZ1) | 594 | 300 | Xizang | Lhasa |
| 1) | 603 | 10 | CNR 1 | Zhanjiang, GD |
| 13) | 603 | 10 | VO Pujiang | SH |
| AH1) | 603 | 10 | Anhui | Hefei |
| BJ1) | 603 | 25 | Beijing | |
| EB1) | 603 | 1 | Hebei | Shijiazhuang |
| EB6) | 603 | | Zhangjiakou | |
| EN13) | 603 | 10 | Sanmenxia | |
| EN1A) | 603 | 100 | Henan | Zhengzhou |
| GD1) | 603 | 10 | Guangdong | Guangzhou |
| GZ1) | 603 | 10 | Guizhou | Guiyang |
| HB3) | 603 | 10 | Wuhan | |
| HL5) | 603 | | Shuangyashan | |
| JL1) | 603 | | Jilin | Songyuan |
| JL10) | 603 | | Yanbian | Dunhua |
| JL3A) | 603 | | Jilin-shi EBS | |
| JS1) | 603 | | Jiangsu | Yangzhou |
| JS12) | 603 | | VO Jiangnan | |
| JS16) | 603 | 5 | Suzhou | |
| JS9) | 603 | 5 | Nantong | |
| JX9) | 603 | 10 | Ji'an | |
| LN1) | 603 | | Liaoning | |
| LN10) | 603 | | Yingkou | |
| LN7) | 603 | 10 | Dandong | |
| NM1) | 603 | 1 | Nei Menggu | Chifeng |
| NM19) | 603 | | Morin Dawa | |
| SD1) | 603 | 1 | Shandong | Zibo |
| SD3) | 603 | 10 | Qingdao | |
| SD10) | 603 | 10 | Jining | |
| SD5) | 603 | 10 | Zaozhuang | |
| SH1) | 603 | 10 | Shanghai | |
| SN1) | 603 | 25 | Shaanxi | Xi'an |
| SN7) | 603 | | Yan'an | |
| SX1) | 603 | 50 | Shanxi | Taiyuan |
| SX4) | 603 | 1 | Yangquan | |
| XJ10) | 603 | 1 | Shihezi | |
| XJ9) | 603 | 1 | Ili | Yining |
| YN1) | 603 | 1 | Yunnan | Zhaotong/Gejiu |
| ZJ1) | 603 | 1 | Zhejiang | Hangzhou/Wenzhou |
| ZJ4) | 603 | 10 | Ningbo | |
| FJ1) | 612 | 100 | Fujian | Ningde |
| GD6) | 612 | | Zhuhai | |
| LN1) | 612 | 10 | Liaoning | Chaoyang/Dandong |
| SC1) | 612 | 10 | Sichuan | Neijiang/Yibin |
| HB9) | 621 | 10 | Yichang | |
| HL1) | 621 | 200 | Heilongjiang | Harbin |
| QH4) | 621 | 20 | Haixi | Da Qaidam |
| SC9) | 621 | 3 | Guangyuan | |
| SD1) | 621 | 10 | Shandong | Liaocheng |

| MW | kHz | kW | Station | Tx Location |
|---|---|---|---|---|
| 1) | 630 | 200 | CNR 2 | Nanchang, JX |
| 1) | 630 | 100 | CNR 2 | Xingyang, EN |
| 1) | 639 | 200/400 | CNR 1 | BJ |
| 1) | 639 | 100 | CNR 1 | Chengdu, SC |
| AH3) | 648 | 1 | Huainan | |
| GD1) | 648 | 50 | Guangdong | Guangzhou |
| LN16) | 648 | 3 | Chaoyang | |
| SH1) | 648 | 10 | Shanghai | |
| XJ7) | 648 | | Kashi | |
| 1) | 657 | 5 | CNR 1 | Nanping, FJ |
| EN1) | 657 | 300 | Henan | Zhengzhou |
| JL7) | 657 | 1 | Baishan | |
| ZJ6) | 657 | | Jiaxing | |
| 11) | 666 | 600 | VO Strait | Fuzhou, FJ |
| AH2) | 666 | 10 | Hefei | |
| GZ5) | 666 | 1 | Anshun | |
| HL10) | 666 | 10 | Jiamusi | |
| JL4) | 666 | 10 | Siping | |
| LN8) | 666 | 2 | Jinzhou | |
| NM1) | 666 | 10 | Nei Menggu | Hailar/Xilinhot |
| QH1) | 666 | 200 | Qinghai | Xining |
| SD10) | 666 | 1 | Jining | |
| TJ1) | 666 | 50 | Tianjin | |
| ZJ5) | 666 | 10 | Wenzhou | |
| NM1) | 675 | 200 | Nei Menggu | Hohhot |
| XJ1) | 675 | 1 | Xinjiang | Altay |
| YN12) | 675 | 1 | Gejiu | |
| YN15) | 675 | 10 | Diqing | Shangri-la |
| ZJ9) | 675 | 1 | Jinhua | |
| 1) | 684 | 1200 | CNR 6 | Putian, FJ |
| AH1) | 684 | | Anhui | Xuancheng |
| AH13) | 684 | | Suzhou | |
| EB8) | 684 | 10 | Tangshan | |
| GS1) | 684 | 200 | Gansu | Lanzhou |
| HB1) | 684 | 10 | Hubei | Jingmen |
| HB1) | 684 | | Hubei Chutian | Huangshi |
| HL9) | 684 | 10 | Mudanjiang | |
| LN5) | 684 | 10 | Fushun | |
| XJ1) | 684 | 10 | Xinjiang | Hotan |
| ZJ11) | 684 | 10 | Zhoushan | |
| HL3) | 693 | 10 | Qiqihar | |
| SN1) | 693 | 300 | Shaanxi | Xianyang |
| 2) | 702 | | CRI DS | Zhuhai, GD |
| JL3) | 702 | 10 | Jilin-shi | |
| JS1) | 702 | 200 | Jiangsu | Nanjing |
| LN16) | 702 | 3 | Chaoyang | Lingyuan |
| NM15) | 702 | 1 | Manzhouli | |
| SC11) | 702 | 1 | Neijiang | |
| XJ1) | 702 | 10 | Xinjiang | Urumqi |
| YN5) | 702 | 10 | Honghe | Gejiu |
| AH12) | 711 | 3 | Fuyang | |
| EN2) | 711 | 10 | Zhengzhou | |
| QH1) | 711 | 10 | Qinghai | Golmud |
| GZ3) | 711 | 1 | Liupanshui | |
| SC5) | 711 | 1 | Panzhihua | |
| SC8) | 711 | 1 | Mianyang | |
| ZJ10) | 711 | 3 | Quzhou | |
| ZJ12) | 711 | 1 | Lishui | |
| 1) | 720 | 10 | CNR 2 | Minhou, FJ |
| 1) | 720 | 50 | CNR 2 | Xiamen, FJ |
| 1) | 720 | 10 | CNR 8 | Yanji, JL |
| 1) | 720 | 10 | CNR 13 | Yining/Kashi, XJ |
| 1) | 720 | 200 | CNR 16 | BJ |
| AH1) | 720 | | Anhui | Hefei/Chuzhou |
| SC7) | 720 | 1 | Deyang | |
| EN16) | 729 | 10 | Shangqiu | |
| JX1) | 729 | 200 | Jiangxi | Nanchang |
| EB12) | 738 | | Hengshui | |
| EN1) | 738 | | Henan | Anyang |
| HN1) | 738 | 200 | Hunan | Changsha |
| JL1) | 738 | 150 | Jilin | Changchun |
| XJ1) | 738 | 120 | Xinjiang | Hutubi |
| ZJ8) | 738 | 5 | Shaoxing | |
| 1) | 747 | 10 | CNR 1 | Haifeng, |
| GD1) | 747 | 10 | CNR 12 | |
| BJAH2) | 747 | 1 | Hefei | |
| EB1) | 747 | 25 | Hebei | Yincun Zhen |
| EB5) | 747 | 10 | Baoding | |
| EN5) | 747 | 10 | Pingdingshan | |
| FJ6) | 747 | | Longyan | |
| GD2) | 747 | 1 | Zhujiang EBS | Chenghai |
| HB1) | 747 | 30 | Hubei | Qichun |

| MW | kHz | kW | Station | Tx Location | MW | kHz | kW | Station | Tx Location |
|---|---|---|---|---|---|---|---|---|---|
| JS11) | 747 | 3 | Changzhou | | LN1) | 810 | 5 | Liaoning | Panjin |
| JS6) | 747 | | Yancheng | | LN15) | 810 | | Tieling | |
| JX8) | 747 | | Ganzhou | | LN16) | 810 | 10 | Chaoyang | |
| LN1) | 747 | | Liaoning | Dandong | SN2) | 810 | 50 | Xi'an | |
| LN10) | 747 | | Yingkou | | ZJ1) | 810 | 200 | Zhejiang | Hangzhou |
| LN12) | 747 | | Fuxin | | SD3) | 819 | | Qingdao | |
| LN16) | 747 | 3 | Chaoyang | Jianping | SX1) | 819 | 200 | Shanxi | Yuci |
| LN5) | 747 | | Fushun | | XJ11) | 819 | 1 | Kuytun | |
| NM1) | 747 | 1 | Nei Menggu | Erenhot | XJ12) | 819 | | Bayingolin | Korla |
| NM3) | 747 | 10 | Baotou | | 1) | 828 | 10 | CNR 2 | Shuangyashan, HL |
| NM4) | 747 | 1 | Wuhai | | BJ1) | 828 | 50 | Beijing | |
| NM5) | 747 | 10 | Chifeng | | EN1) | 828 | 10 | Henan | |
| NM9) | 747 | 10 | Tongliao | | EN17) | ±828 | 10 | Zhoukou | |
| NM6) | 747 | 10 | Ulanqab | Jining | EN6) | 828 | 10 | Jiaozuo | |
| NX1) | 747 | 10 | Ningxia | Yinchuan | GD1) | 828 | 40 | Guangdong | |
| SC1) | 747 | 200 | Sichuan | Chengdu | GD1) | 828 | 50 | Guangdong | Dongyuan |
| SC13) | 747 | 1 | Nanchong | | HB23) | ±828 | 1 | Xiantao | |
| SD11) | 747 | 10 | Rizhao | | HB8) | 828 | 10 | Jingzhou | |
| SD13) | 747 | 10 | Linyi | | 1) | 837 | 1000 | CNR 5 | Quanzhou, FJ |
| SN1) | 747 | 50 | Shaanxi | Xianyang | AH1) | 837 | | Anhui | Bengbu |
| SN6) | 747 | 1 | Weinan | | EN15) | 837 | 25 | Xinyang | |
| SX1) | 747 | 10 | Shanxi | Luliang | FJ1) | 837 | 3 | Fujian | Fuding |
| TJ1) | 747 | 50 | Tianjin | | FJ1) | 837 | | Fujian | Pucheng |
| YN6) | 747 | 100 | Xishuangbanna | Jinghong | HL2) | 837 | 50 | Harbin | |
| ZJ4) | 747 | | Ningbo | | LN14) | 837 | 10 | Liaoyang | |
| SX8) | 750 | 1 | Xinzhou | | 2) | 846 | 10 | CRI DS 4 | BJ |
| 1) | 756 | 50 | CNR 1 | Guangzhou, GD | AH1) | 846 | 10 | Anhui | Suzhou |
| 1) | 756 | 10 | CNR 1 | Jieyang, GD | AH2) | 846 | 1 | Hefei | Chaohu |
| 1) | 756 | 50 | CNR 1 | Zhuhai, GD | EB1) | 846 | | Hebei | Hengshui/Tangshan |
| 1) | 756 | 150 | CNR 1 | Harbin, HL | EB10) | 846 | 10 | Cangzhou | |
| 1) | 765 | 600 | CNR 5 | Fuzhou, FJ | EB11) | 846 | 10 | Langfang | |
| AH7) | 765 | 1 | Bengbu | | EB3) | 846 | | Handan | |
| EN23) | 765 | 10 | Gongyi | | | | | | |
| GD8) | 765 | 10 | Shaoguan | Wujiang | EN5) | 846 | 3 | Pingdingshan | |
| GZ1) | 765 | 10 | Guizhou | Zunyi | EN7) | 846 | | Hebi | |
| NM1) | 765 | 10 | Nei Menggu | Baotou/Xilinhot | GD1) | 846 | 10 | Guangdong | Raoping |
| BJ1) | 774 | 10 | Beijing | | GD1) | 846 | 10 | Guangdong | Zhaoqing |
| HB1) | 774 | 200 | Hubei | Wuhan | GX1) | 846 | 10 | Guangxi | Qinzhou |
| LN8) | 774 | 2 | Jinzhou | | HB1) | 846 | 30 | Hubei | Qichun |
| SX2) | 774 | | Taiyuan | | HB1) | 846 | 10 | Hubei | Xianning/Yichang |
| XJ6) | 774 | 10 | Hotan | | JL1) | 846 | 10 | Jilin | Changchun |
| 11) | 783 | 600 | VO Strait | Zhangpu, FJ | JS1) | 846 | 5 | Jiangsu | Nanjing |
| EB1) | 783 | 100 | Hebei | Baoding | JS11) | 846 | 10 | Changzhou | |
| EB1) | 783 | 10 | Hebei | Chengde | JS13) | 846 | 5 | Suzhou | |
| EB1) | 783 | | Hebei | Langfang/Handan | LN13) | 846 | 10 | Fuxin Mo BS | |
| GD10) | 783 | 20 | guangdong | Meizhou | LN8) | 846 | | Jinzhou | |
| EN2) | 792 | 1 | Zhengzhou | | SD2) | 846 | 10 | Jinan | |
| GS5) | 792 | 1 | Jiayuguan | | SD7) | 846 | 5 | Weifang | |
| GX1) | 792 | 200 | Guangxi | Nanning | SD9) | 846 | 10 | Weihai | |
| LN2) | 792 | 10 | Shenyang | | SX1) | 846 | 20 | Shanxi | Changzhi |
| SC3) | 792 | 10 | Chengdu | | XJ1) | 846 | 3 | Xinjiang | Hotan |
| SH1) | 792 | 50 | Shanghai | | XZ1) | 846 | 10 | Xizang | Lhasa |
| XJ2) | 792 | | Urumqi | | YN1) | 846 | 1 | Yunnan | Longchuan/Fugong |
| AH1) | 801 | 10 | Anhui | Hefei | YN11) | 846 | 1 | Zhaotong | |
| AH12) | 801 | 3 | Fuyang | | 1) | 855 | 50 | CNR 2 | Anning, YN |
| AH15) | 801 | 1 | Chizhou | | 1) | 855 | 10 | CNR 13 | Urumqi |
| EB10) | 801 | 25 | Cangzhou | | NM1) | 855 | | Nei Menggu | Alxa Zuoqi |
| EB8) | 801 | 10 | Tangshan | | AH1) | 864 | 50 | Anhui | Hefei |
| EN8) | 801 | | Xinxiang | | EB20) | 864 | | Renqiu | |
| FJ3) | 801 | 10 | Xiamen | Jimei | EN19) | 864 | | Qinyang | |
| GD2) | 801 | 50 | Zhujiang EBS | Maoming | SD15) | 864 | 10 | Binzhou | |
| GS1) | 801 | | Gansu | Lanzhou | ZJ1) | 864 | 1 | Zhejiang | Ninghai |
| HB1) | 801 | 10 | Hubei | Jingmen/Macheng | ZJ15) | 864 | 1 | Jiangshan | |
| HB1) | 801 | 10 | Hubei | Chongyang | 15) | 873 | 200 | China Huayi BC | Xiamen, FJ |
| JS1) | 801 | 1 | Jiangsu | Zhenjiang | EB13) | ±873 | | Xinji | |
| JS3) | 801 | | Xuzhou | | EN3) | ±873 | 10 | Kaifeng | |
| JS5) | 801 | 10 | Huai'an | | GS1) | 873 | 50 | Gansu | Linxia |
| JS7) | 801 | | Yangzhou | | HB3) | 873 | 50 | Wuhan | |
| LN1) | 801 | | Liaoning | Dandong/Gaizhou | HL1) | 873 | 100 | Heilongjiang | Harbin |
| LN16) | 801 | 1 | Chaoyang | Lingyuan | SD13) | 873 | 10 | Linyi | |
| NX2) | 801 | 10 | Yinchuan | | XJ8) | 873 | 1 | Changji | |
| SD10) | 801 | 10 | Jining | | ZJ7) | 873 | | Huzhou | |
| SD14) | 801 | 10 | Liaocheng | | EB2) | 882 | 20 | Shijiazhuang | |
| SD4) | 801 | 10 | Zibo | | EN22) | 882 | | Ruzhou | |
| SD8) | 801 | 10 | Yantai | | EN9) | 882 | | Anyang | |
| SD13) | 801 | 10 | Linyi | | FJ1) | 882 | 10 | Fujian | Fu'an |
| SN1) | 801 | 1 | Shaanxi | Weinan | FJ1) | 882 | 200 | Fujian | Minhou |
| SN2) | 801 | | Xi'an | | FJ1) | 882 | 10 | Fujian | Sanming |
| XJ7) | 801 | 1 | Kashi | | GZ6) | 882 | 1 | Qiannan | Duyun |
| ZJ5) | 801 | 10 | Wenzhou | | LN1) | 882 | 10 | Liaoning | Shenyang |
| EN18) | 810 | 25 | Zhumadian | | LN3) | 882 | 50 | Dalian | |
| JL5) | 810 | 10 | Liaoyuan | | NM2) | 882 | 10 | Hohhot | |

China

| MW | kHz | kW | Station | Tx Location | MW | kHz | kW | Station | Tx Location |
|---|---|---|---|---|---|---|---|---|---|
| QH3) | 882 | 10 | Yushu | | XJ2) | 927 | 10 | Urumqi | |
| XJ4) | 882 | | Karamay | | YN1) | 927 | | Yunnan | Kaiyuan |
| XJ9) | 882 | 1 | Ili | Yining | YN17) | 927 | 1 | Lufeng | |
| LN7) | 891 | 10 | Dandong | | ZJ7) | 927 | | Huzhou | |
| NM13) | 891 | 10 | Hinggan | Ulanhot | ZJ1) | 930 | | Zhejiang | |
| NX1) | 891 | 200 | Ningxia | Yinchuan | AH1) | 936 | 200 | Anhui | Hefei |
| SD1) | 891 | 10 | Shandong | Dongying | 1) | 945 | 400 | CNR 1 | Jiaohe, JL |
| XJ10) | 891 | 10 | Shihezi | | 1) | 945 | 10 | CNR 13 | Hami/Kuqa, XJ |
| 1) | 900 | 10 | CNR 2 | Golmud, QH | HB1) | 945 | 10 | Hubei | Qichun |
| 2) | 900 | | CRI DS 5 | BJ | HB1) | 945 | 10 | Hubei | Jingzhou |
| AH1) | 900 | | Anhui | Lu'an/Bengbu/Haungshan | HL1) | 945 | 50 | Heilongjiang | Harbin/Fujin |
| | | | | | NM7) | 945 | 10 | Xilingol | Xilinhot |
| EB1) | 900 | | Hebei | Shijiazhuang | NM10) | 945 | 10 | Ordos | |
| EB6) | 900 | 10 | Zhangjiakou | | NM10) | 945 | 10 | Ordos | Otog |
| EB7) | 900 | 1 | Chengde | | EB12) | 954 | 10 | Hengshui | |
| EB8) | 900 | | Tangshan | | GS2) | 954 | 10 | Lanzhou | |
| EB9) | 900 | | Qinhuangdao | | HA1) | 954 | 30 | Hainan | Haikou |
| EN1) | 900 | 25 | Henan | Zhoukou/Yima | LN4) | 954 | 10 | Anshan | |
| EN12A) | 900 | | Luohe EBS | | NM8) | 954 | 50 | Hulun Buir | Hailar |
| FJ1) | 900 | 3 | Fujian | Youxi | NM9) | 954 | 1 | Tongliao | |
| GD5) | 900 | 11 | Shenzhen | Bao'an | SC1) | 954 | 10 | Sichuan | Chengdu |
| GD6) | 900 | | Zhuhai | | SC6) | 954 | 1 | Luzhou | |
| HB1) | 900 | 10 | Hubei | Enshi | ZJ2) | 954 | 25 | Hangzhou | |
| HB1) | 900 | 10 | Hubei | Xiangyang | EB3) | 963 | 10 | Handan | |
| HL1) | 900 | 50 | Heilongjiang | Bei'an/Jiamusi | HB5) | 963 | 10 | Huangshi | |
| HN1) | 900 | | Hunan | Changsha | LN1) | 963 | 50 | Liaoning | Dalian |
| JL16) | 900 | 1 | Yanji | | XJ1) | 963 | 10 | Xinjiang | Qoqek/Gulja |
| JL2) | 900 | 10 | Changchun | | EN1) | 972 | 150 | Henan | Xingyang |
| JL4) | 900 | 1 | Siping | | HL2) | 972 | 10 | Harbin | |
| JS10) | 900 | 1 | Zhenjiang | | XJ1) | 972 | | Xinjiang | Altay |
| JS12) | 900 | | Wuxi | | 1) | 981 | 200 | CNR 1 | Changchun, JL |
| JS2) | 900 | 10 | Nanjing | | 1) | 981 | 50 | CNR 1 | Heyuan, GD |
| JS4) | 900 | 10 | Lianyungang | | 1) | 981 | 50 | CNR 1 | Maoming, GD |
| JS6) | 900 | | Yancheng | | 1) | 981 | 200 | CNR 1 | Nanchang, JX |
| LN1) | 900 | | Liaoning | Chaoyang/Huludao | 1) | 981 | 10 | CNR 1 | Shenzhen, GD |
| LN12) | 900 | | Fuxin | | SD7) | 981 | 5 | Weifang | |
| LN19) | 900 | 1 | Haicheng | | EB9) | 990 | 1 | Qinhuangdao | |
| LN6) | 900 | 1 | Benxi | | NM1) | 990 | 10 | Nei Menggu | Hohhot/Chifeng |
| NM1) | 900 | 10 | Nei Menggu | Ulanqab | SH1) | 990 | 100 | Shanghai | |
| NM5) | 900 | 10 | Chifeng | | YN1) | 990 | 10 | Yunnan | Hekou/Gejiu |
| SD3) | 900 | 10 | Qingdao | | AH19) | 999 | 1 | Bozhou | |
| SD4) | 900 | 10 | Zibo | | GD1) | 999 | 10 | Guangdong | Guangzhou |
| SN1) | 900 | 30 | Shaanxi | Xi'an | GZ2) | 999 | 10 | Guiyang | |
| SN4) | 900 | 1 | Baoji | | HL15) | 999 | | Aihui | |
| SX1) | 900 | 10 | Shanxi | Jincheng | LN1) | 999 | 200 | Liaoning | Shenyang |
| SX3) | 900 | 10 | Datong | | NM1) | 999 | 1 | Nei Menggu | Ulanhot |
| YN9) | 900 | 100 | Dehong | Luxi | SD1) | 999 | 10 | Shandong | Jining |
| ZJ1) | 900 | 1 | Zhejiang | Jinhua | XJ1) | 999 | 10 | Xinjiang | Hami/Bortala |
| ZJ11) | 900 | | Zhoushan | | XZ1) | 999 | 10 | Xizang | Lhasa |
| 1) | 909 | 300 | CNR 6 | Quanzhou, FJ | 1) | 1008 | 200 | CNR 1 | Anning, YN |
| CQ1) | 909 | 10 | Chongqing | Fuling | 2) | 1008 | 1 | CNR DS 3 | BJ |
| HL8) | 909 | 7.5 | Yichun | | 2) | 1008 | 3 | CNR DS | Urumqi, XJ |
| JL6) | 909 | 10 | Tonghua | | AH1) | 1008 | | Anhui | Suzhou/Fuyang |
| QH1) | 909 | 10 | Qinghai | Xining | EB11) | 1008 | | Langfang | |
| SC1) | 909 | 50 | Sichuan | Xichang | EB3) | 1008 | 10 | Handan | |
| TJ1) | 909 | 50 | Tianjin | | EN13) | 1008 | | Sanmenxia | |
| XJ1) | 909 | 10 | Xinjiang | Bortala | EN5) | 1008 | 1 | Pingdingshan | |
| GX2) | 918 | | Nanning | | EN2) | 1008 | 25 | Zhengzhou | |
| SD1) | 918 | 200 | Shandong | Jinan | FJ1) | 1008 | 1 | Fujian | Zhangping |
| 1) | 927 | 100 | CNR 6 | Xiamen, FJ | GJ3) | 1008 | 10 | Xiamen | Haicang |
| BJ1) | 927 | 50 | Beijing | | GD1) | 1008 | 10 | Guangdong | Zhongshan |
| EB4) | 927 | 12.5 | Xingtai | | GD2) | 1008 | 3 | Zhujiang EBS | Xinhui |
| EN11) | 927 | | Xuchang | | GS1) | 1008 | | Gansu | |
| EN14) | 927 | 10 | Nanyang | | HB1) | 1008 | 50 | Hubei | Jingmen |
| EN16) | 927 | 10 | Shangqiu | | HB22) | 1008 | 10 | Suizhou | |
| GD1) | 927 | 10 | Guangdong | Guangzhou | HN7) | ±1008 | 1 | Yueyang | |
| GD2) | 927 | 10 | Zhujiang EBS | Zhanjing | JS12) | 1008 | | Wuxi | |
| GZ1) | 927 | 200 | Guizhou | Kaili | JS2) | 1008 | 10 | Nanjing | |
| HB1) | 927 | 10 | Hubei | Suizhou | NX1) | 1008 | 1 | Ningxia | Guyuan |
| HB1) | 927 | 10 | Hubei | Xianning | SD12) | 1008 | 10 | Dezhou | |
| HB10) | 927 | | Jingmen | | SD3) | 1008 | 10 | Qingdao | |
| HB12) | 927 | 3 | Xiaogan | | SN1) | 1008 | 10 | Shaanxi | Hanzhong/Yan'an |
| HL1) | 927 | 10 | Heilongjiang | Shuangyashan | SN1) | 1008 | | Shannxi | Xi'an |
| HL2) | 927 | 1 | Harbin | Hulan | SX1) | 1008 | 10 | Shanxi | Xinzhou |
| JL19) | 927 | 1 | Hunchun | | TJ1) | 1008 | 50 | Tianjin | |
| JL3) | 927 | 10 | Jilin-shi | | 1) | 1017 | 1 | CNR 1 | Dongtou, ZJ |
| JS11) | 927 | 3 | Changzhou | | EB5) | 1017 | 10 | Baoding | |
| JS16) | 927 | 1 | Changshu | | GD1) | 1017 | 10 | Guangdong | Jieyang |
| JS8) | 927 | | Taizhou | | GD1) | 1017 | 50 | Guangdong | Shaoguan |
| JX1) | 927 | 10 | Jiangxi | Nanchang | QH1) | 1017 | 1 | Qinghai | Gonghe |
| LN1) | 927 | 50 | Liaoning | Shenyang | BJ1) | 1026 | 50 | Beijing | |
| SH1) | 927 | | Shanghai | | GZ1) | 1026 | 200 | Guizhou | Guiyang |

| MW | kHz | kW | Station | Tx Location | MW | kHz | kW | Station | Tx Location |
|---|---|---|---|---|---|---|---|---|---|
| JS14) | 1026 | 1 | Yizheng | | SD10) | 1116 | 1 | Jining | |
| JS6) | 1026 | 10 | Yancheng | | EB1) | 1125 | 10 | Hebei | Shijiazhuang |
| LN10) | 1026 | 2 | Yingkou | | HB1) | 1125 | | Hubei | Xiantao |
| XJ6) | 1026 | 10 | Hotan | | HB3) | 1125 | 50 | Wuhan | |
| 1) | 1035 | 50 | CNR 1 | Dalian/Wuhan | GS9) | 1134 | 1 | Yumen | |
| XJ1) | 1044 | 10 | Xinjiang | Urumqi/Korla | SN3) | 1134 | 10 | Tongchuan | |
| YN8) | 1044 | 1 | Dali | | XJ9) | 1134 | 1 | Ili | Yining |
| ZJ1) | 1050 | | Zhejiang | | ZJ1) | 1134 | 10 | Zhejiang | Wenzhou/Ningbo |
| 1) | 1053 | 10 | CNR 10 | BJ | 1) | 1143 | 10 | CNR 8 | BJ |
| AH2) | 1053 | 1 | Hefei | | EB18) | 1143 | 1 | Dingzhou | |
| EB10) | 1053 | 10 | Cangzhou | | EB8) | 1143 | | Tangshan | |
| EB15) | 1053 | 1 | Shahe | | EN1) | 1143 | 50 | Henan | Zhengzhou |
| EB17) | 1053 | 1 | Zhuozhou | | GS4) | 1143 | 10 | Tianshui | |
| EN18) | 1053 | 10 | Zhumadian | | GZ5) | 1143 | | Anshun | |
| EN3) | 1053 | 10 | Kaifeng | | HA1) | 1143 | | Hainan | Haikou |
| EN4) | 1053 | 10 | Luoyang | | HB1) | 1143 | | Hubei | Chanchun |
| HB1) | 1053 | 50 | Hubei | Qianjiang | HB1) | 1143 | 10 | Hubei | Shiyan |
| HN7) | 1053 | | Yueyang | | HL10) | 1143 | 1 | Jiamusi | |
| HN9) | 1053 | | Yiyang | | JL1) | 1143 | 1 | Jilin | Liaoyuan |
| JL10) | 1053 | 20 | Yanbian | Yanji | JL17) | 1143 | 1 | Tumen | |
| JS1) | 1053 | 10 | Jiangsu | Nanjing | JL3) | 1143 | 10 | Jilin-shi | |
| LN1) | 1053 | 50 | Liaoning | Shenyang | JL8) | 1143 | | Songyuan | |
| SD2) | 1053 | 10 | Jinan | | JS11) | 1143 | 3 | Changzhou | |
| YN1) | 1053 | | Yunnan | Zhaotong | JS9) | 1143 | | Nantong | |
| YN4) | 1053 | 10 | Wenshan | | LN10) | 1143 | | Yingkou | |
| GD2) | 1062 | 150 | Zhujiang EBS | Huadu | LN14) | 1143 | 1 | Liaoyang | |
| GD2) | 1062 | 50 | Zhujiang | Zhuhai | LN5) | 1143 | | Fushun | |
| HL11) | 1062 | 1 | Qitaihe | | NM1) | 1143 | | Nei Menggu | Ulanqab |
| FJ1) | ±1071 | | Fujian | | NM1) | 1143 | | Nei Menggu | Horqin |
| GX1) | 1071 | 10 | Guangxi | Ningming | NM16) | 1143 | 1 | Yakeshi | |
| HN5) | 1071 | 10 | Hengyang | | QH1) | 1143 | | Qinghai | Xining |
| LN4) | 1071 | 2 | Anshan | | SC11) | 1143 | | Neijiang | |
| SD16) | 1071 | 10 | Heze | | SC15) | 1143 | 1 | Dazhou | |
| SN4) | 1071 | 10 | Baoji | | SC9) | 1143 | | Guangyuan | |
| TJ1) | 1071 | 50 | Tianjin | | SD13) | 1143 | 10 | Linyi | |
| XJ3) | 1071 | 100 | Urumqi | | SD14) | 1143 | 10 | Liaocheng | |
| ZJ1) | 1071 | 10 | Zhejiang | Hangzhou | SD4) | 1143 | 10 | Zibo | |
| GD7) | 1080 | 5 | Shantou | | SN1) | 1143 | 1 | Shaanxi | Baoji/Weinan |
| HL7) | 1080 | 1 | Daqing | | SN9) | 1143 | 1 | Yulin | |
| HL12) | 1080 | 1 | Suihua | | XJ1) | 1143 | 10 | Xinjiang | Altay |
| JS13) | 1080 | 10 | Suzhou | | YN1) | 1143 | 1 | Yunnan | Kunming |
| ZJ1) | ±1080 | 1 | Zhejiang | Xiangshan | YN1) | 1143 | | Yunnan | Gejiu |
| 1) | 1089 | 600 | CNR 6 | Fuzhou, FJ | ZJ1) | 1143 | 1 | Zhejiang | Yuhuan |
| HN3) | 1089 | 1 | Zhuzhou | | HN1) | 1152 | 150 | Hunan | Changde |
| LN1) | 1089 | 200 | Liaoning | Shenyang | LN3) | 1152 | 10 | Dalian | |
| 1) | 1098 | 1000 | CNR 1/11 | Golmud, QH | NM11) | 1152 | 10 | Bayannur | Linhe |
| AH1) | 1098 | | Anhui | Hefei/Wuhu | NM13) | 1152 | 10 | Hinggan | Ulanhot |
| AH18) | 1098 | | Dangtu Xian | | 1) | 1161 | | CNR 1 | |
| AH7) | ±1098 | 1 | Bengbu | | GD2) | 1161 | 1 | Zhujiang EBS | Taishan |
| EB1) | 1098 | 1 | Hebei | Zhangjiakou | HB10) | 1161 | 10 | Jingmen | |
| EB12) | 1098 | | Hengshui | | JS12) | 1161 | 10 | Wuxi | |
| EN1) | 1098 | | Henan | Zhoukou | SD7) | 1161 | 10 | Weifang | |
| EN5) | 1098 | | Pingdingshan | | 1) | 1170 | 10 | CNR 1 | Huizhou, GD |
| GD4) | 1098 | 10 | Guangzhou | | 1) | 1170 | 600 | CNR 1 | Ji'an, JX |
| GX1) | 1098 | | Guangxi | | AH16) | 1170 | 1 | Lu'an | |
| HB1) | 1098 | 10 | Hubei | Jingzhou/Suizhou | AH17) | 1170 | 3 | Xuancheng | |
| HB8) | 1098 | 10 | Xiangyang | | AH2) | 1170 | 10 | Hefei | |
| JS1) | 1098 | 1 | Jiangsu | Zhenjiang | GD3) | 1170 | 10 | Guangzhou | |
| JS17) | 1098 | 1 | Zhangjiagang | | GS1) | 1170 | 10 | Gansu | Zhangye |
| JS3) | 1098 | | Xuzhou | | GX1) | 1170 | | Guangxi | |
| LN8) | 1098 | | Jinzhou | | JS2) | 1170 | 10 | Nanjing | |
| LN12) | 1098 | | Fuxin | | JS9) | 1170 | 10 | Nantong | |
| NM1) | 1098 | 10 | Nei Menggu | | NM5) | 1170 | 50 | Chifeng | |
| SD12) | 1098 | 10 | Dezhou | | NM6) | 1170 | 10 | Ulanqab | Jining |
| SX1) | 1098 | | Shanxi | Yangzhou/Changzhi | NM7) | 1170 | 10 | Xilingol | Xilinhot |
| TJ1) | 1098 | 50 | Tianjin | | NM8) | 1170 | 50 | Hulun Buir | Hailar |
| XJ5) | 1098 | 1 | Hami | | NM9) | 1170 | 50 | Tongliao | |
| YN1) | 1098 | 1 | Yunnan | Kaiyuan | SD15) | 1170 | 10 | Binzhou | |
| ZJ11) | 1098 | 10 | Zhoushan | | SD5) | 1170 | 10 | Zaozhuang | |
| AH6) | 1107 | 3 | Tongling | | HB1) | 1179 | 100 | Hubei | Wuhan |
| EN7) | 1107 | 10 | Hebi | | HL5) | 1179 | 10 | Shuangyashan | |
| FJ3) | 1107 | 10 | Xiamen | Jimei | JS7) | 1179 | 10 | Yangzhou | |
| HA1) | 1107 | 10 | Hainan | Tongshi | XJ4) | 1179 | 10 | Karamay | |
| JL1) | 1107 | 10 | Jilin | Yushu/Hunchun | EB19) | 1188 | 1 | Botou | |
| JX4) | 1107 | 1 | Pingxiang | | EB4) | 1188 | 10 | Xingtai | |
| XJ1) | 1107 | 100 | Xinjiang | Hutubi | JL10) | 1188 | | Yanbian | Longjing |
| ZJ6) | 1107 | 10 | Jiaxing | | FJ5) | 1197 | | Quanzhou | |
| 1) | 1116 | 120 | CNR 2 | Harbin, HL | HL3) | 1197 | 10 | Qiqihar | |
| 1) | 1116 | 600 | CNR 5 | Shaowu, FJ | SD16) | 1197 | 10 | Heze | |
| AH12) | 1116 | 10 | Fuyang | | SH1) | 1197 | 10 | Shanghai | |
| HA1) | 1116 | 30 | Hainan | Ledong | YN1) | 1197 | 1 | Yunnan | Ximeng |
| SC1) | 1116 | 200 | Sichuan | Chengdu | 1) | 1206 | 10 | CNR 2 | Sanming, FJ |

| MW | kHz | kW | Station | Tx Location |
|---|---|---|---|---|
| EB10) | 1206 | 25 | Cangzhou | |
| EB3) | 1206 | 10 | Handan | |
| EN20) | 1206 | 1 | Huixian | |
| GD1) | 1206 | 50 | Guangdong | Bao'an |
| HN1) | 1206 | 10 | Hubei | Xiangyang |
| JL10) | 1206 | 200 | Yanbian | Longjing |
| JS1) | 1206 | 1 | Jiangsu | Nanjing |
| NX1) | 1206 | 1 | Ningxia | Zhongning |
| SD9) | 1206 | 10 | Weihai | |
| SX1) | 1206 | 10 | Shanxi | Shuozhou |
| QH1) | 1206 | 1 | Qinghai | Dulan |
| 1) | 1215 | 20 | CNR 2 | Shenyang, LN |
| 1) | 1215 | 50 | CNR 7 | Zhuhai, GD |
| HB1) | 1215 | 10 | Hubei | Yichang |
| HB26) | 1215 | 1 | Enshi | |
| HL14) | 1215 | 50 | Heihe | |
| 1) | 1224 | 100 | CNR 6 | Xiamen, FJ |
| GX1) | 1224 | 100 | Guangxi | Nanning |
| JS10) | 1224 | 10 | Zhenjiang | |
| NM1) | 1224 | 10 | Nei Menggu | Ulanqab |
| HN1) | 1233 | 10 | Hunan | Yueyang/Shaoyang |
| JS9) | 1233 | 25 | Nantong | |
| XJ1) | 1233 | 120 | Xinjiang | Hutubi |
| XJ1) | 1233 | 10 | Xinjiang | Bortala |
| XJ1) | 1233 | 10 | Xinjiang | Urumqi |
| HB20) | 1242 | 1 | Macheng | |
| HB24) | 1242 | 1 | Qianjiang | |
| JX9) | 1242 | | Ji'an | |
| LN9) | 1242 | 1 | Huludao | |
| YN1) | 1242 | 100 | Yunnan | Kunming |
| ZJ10) | 1250 | 1 | Quzhou | |
| 2) | 1251 | | CRI DS 1 | BJ |
| AH13) | 1251 | 1 | Suzhou | |
| EB1) | 1251 | | Hebei | Qinhuangdao |
| EB2) | 1251 | 25 | Shijiazhuang | |
| EN10) | 1251 | 10 | Puyang | |
| EN12) | 1251 | 10 | Luohe | |
| EN21) | 1251 | 1 | Yima | |
| EN6) | 1251 | | Jiaozuo | |
| EN9) | ±1251 | | Anyang | |
| HB1) | 1251 | 5 | Hubei | Jingmen |
| JL3A) | 1251 | | Jilin-shi EBS | |
| JS12) | 1251 | 10 | Wuxi | |
| JS2) | 1251 | | Nanjing | |
| JS4) | 1251 | | Lianyungang | |
| JS5) | 1251 | 10 | Huai'an | |
| LN4) | 1251 | | Anshan | |
| QH1) | 1251 | 200 | Qinghai | Xining |
| SD1) | 1251 | 10 | Shandong | Jinan/Zibo |
| SD13) | 1251 | 10 | Linyi | |
| SD18) | 1251 | | Longkou | |
| SD3) | 1251 | 10 | Qingdao | |
| SD7) | 1251 | 10 | Weifang | |
| SN8) | 1251 | 10 | Hanzhong | |
| YN1) | 1251 | 1 | Yunnan | Kaiyuan |
| YN14) | 1251 | | Yuxi | |
| ZJ1) | 1251 | 1 | Zhejiang | Jinhua |
| ZJ4) | 1251 | | Ningbo | |
| ZJ7) | 1251 | | Huzhou | |
| HN8) | 1260 | 1 | Changde | |
| LN1) | 1260 | 10 | Liaoning | Fengcheng |
| XZ3) | 1260 | 1 | Shannan | Nedong |
| JL18) | 1269 | 1 | Dunhua | |
| JS3) | 1269 | 10 | Xuzhou | |
| SX1) | 1269 | 10 | Shanxi | Taiyuan/Xinzhou |
| EB1) | 1278 | 100 | Hebei | Shijiazhuang/Tangshan |
| FJ3) | 1278 | 10 | Xiamen | Jimei |
| HL13) | 1278 | 7.5 | Daxing'anling | Jagdaqi |
| JX2) | 1278 | 10 | Nanchang | |
| 1) | 1287 | 10 | CNR 1 | Ningde, FJ |
| EB20) | 1287 | 1 | Renqiu | |
| EN11) | 1287 | 1 | Xuchang | |
| DG5) | 1287 | 25 | Shenzhen | Bao'an |
| JS12) | 1287 | | Wuxi | |
| LN12) | 1287 | 20 | Fuxin | |
| NX1) | 1287 | 10 | Ningxia | Guyuan |
| SD7) | 1287 | 5 | Weifang | |
| YN7) | 1287 | 10 | Chuxiong | |
| ZJ1) | 1287 | 1 | Zhejiang | Dongtou |
| EB16) | 1296 | 1 | Qinghe | |
| LN20) | 1296 | 1 | Xingcheng | |
| LN6) | 1296 | 20 | Benxi | |
| SC10) | 1296 | 1 | Suining | |
| SH1) | 1296 | 25 | Shanghai | |
| SN5) | 1296 | 10 | Xianyang | |
| 1) | 1305 | 10 | CNR 2 | Xining, QH |
| NM1) | 1305 | | Nei Menggu | Ulanhot |
| SD2) | 1305 | 10 | Jinan | |
| CQ1) | 1314 | 50 | Chongqing | |
| HB14) | 1314 | 3 | Xianning | |
| HB6) | 1314 | 10 | Xiangyang | |
| JS1) | 1314 | 10 | Jiangsu | Suzhou/Huai'an |
| SD8) | 1314 | 10 | Yantai | |
| ZJ1) | 1314 | | Zhejiang | |
| HN2) | 1323 | 10 | Changsha | |
| JL9) | 1323 | 10 | Baicheng | |
| LN17) | 1323 | 1 | Wafangdian | |
| SD16A) | 1323 | 10 | Mudan | Heze |
| SN1) | 1323 | 10 | Shaanxi | Xi'an |
| ZJ4) | 1323 | 10 | Ningbo | |
| EN1) | 1332 | 10 | Henan | Zhengzhou |
| EN1) | 1332 | 10 | Henan | Hebi/Luoyang |
| EN1) | 1332 | | Henan | Anyang |
| FJ1) | 1332 | 10 | Fujian | Yunxiao |
| FJ2) | 1332 | 10 | Fuzhou | Minhou |
| GS6) | 1332 | 10 | Gannan | Hezuo |
| JL2) | 1332 | 10 | Changchun | |
| 1) | 1341 | 100 | CNR 1 | GD |
| HB19) | 1341 | 1 | Yingcheng | |
| HB21) | 1341 | 1 | Chibi | |
| HL1) | 1341 | 100 | Heilongjiang | Heihe |
| JS8) | 1341 | 10 | Taizhou | |
| LN1) | 1341 | 10 | Liaoning | Shenyang |
| SD12) | 1341 | 1 | Dezhou | |
| SD19) | 1341 | 1 | Qufu | |
| JX1) | 1350 | 50 | Jiangxi | Ji'an |
| JX1) | 1350 | 10 | Jiangxi | Shangrao/Yichun |
| JX1) | 1350 | 1 | Jiangxi | Jiujiang |
| LN19) | 1350 | | Haicheng | |
| NM9) | 1350 | 50 | Tongliao | |
| YN2) | 1350 | 50 | Kunming | |
| 1) | 1359 | 10 | CNR 1 | Xiamen/Sanming, FJ |
| 1) | 1359 | 10 | CNR 1 | Nanjing, JS |
| FJ1) | ±1368 | 3 | Fujian | Changding |
| HB8) | 1368 | | Jingzhou | |
| HB18) | 1368 | 1 | Guangshui | |
| HL6) | 1368 | 10 | Jixi | |
| 1) | 1377 | 600 | CNR 1 | Xingyang, EN |
| AH11) | 1377 | 1 | Chuzhou | |
| FJ1) | 1377 | 5 | Fujian | Nanping |
| NX5) | 1377 | 1 | Qingtongxia | |
| QH1) | 1377 | | Qinghai | Xining |
| SD3) | 1377 | 10 | Qingdao | |
| XZ1) | 1377 | 100 | Xizang | Lhasa |
| FJ1) | 1386 | 10 | Fujian | Quanzhou |
| GX3) | 1386 | 5 | Liuzhou | |
| HB11) | 1386 | 1 | Ezhou | |
| HB17) | 1386 | 1 | Shishou | |
| JS15) | 1386 | 1 | Jiangyin | |
| SD10) | 1386 | 1 | Jining | |
| TJ1) | 1386 | 50 | Tianjin | |
| AH1) | 1395 | 50 | Anhui | Hefei |
| AH1) | 1395 | 50 | Anhui | Fuyang/Chizhou |
| FJ1) | 1395 | 3 | Fujian | Yongchun |
| NM1) | 1395 | | Nei Menggu | |
| YN1) | 1395 | 1 | Yunnan | Pu'er |
| FJ1) | 1404 | 50 | Fujian EBS | Minhou |
| FJ1) | 1404 | 3 | Fujian | Fuqing |
| HB1) | 1404 | 10 | Hubei | Jingzhou |
| HB1) | 1404 | 10 | Hubei | Suizhou/Chongyang |
| LN7) | 1404 | 10 | Dandong | |
| HL4) | 1413 | 1 | Hegang | |
| JS1) | 1413 | 10 | Jiangsu | Yancheng/Wuxi |
| LN15) | 1413 | 1 | Tieling | |
| NM1) | 1413 | 10 | Nei Menggu | Tongliao/Ordos |
| NX4) | 1413 | 10 | Wuzhong | |
| XJ1) | 1413 | 10 | Xinjiang | Hami/Bortala |
| 1) | 1422 | 600 | CNR 1/13 | Kashi, XJ |
| 13) | 1422 | 20 | VO Pujiang | SH |
| SC4) | 1422 | 10 | Zigong | |
| SX1) | 1422 | 10 | Shanxi | Linfen |
| SX2) | 1422 | 10 | Taiyuan | |
| AH10) | 1431 | 2 | Huangshan | |

| MW | kHz | kW | Station | Tx Location |
|---|---|---|---|---|
| AH4) | 1431 | 10 | Huaibei | |
| EB2) | 1431 | 10 | Shijiazhuang | |
| HB16) | 1431 | 1 | Danjiangkou | |
| HN10) | 1431 | 1 | Jinshi | |
| JL8) | 1431 | 2 | Songyuan | |
| NM14) | 1431 | 1 | Fengzhen | |
| 1) | 1440 | 10 | CNR1 | Putian |
| GX1) | 1440 | 50 | Guangxi | Bose |
| LN18) | 1440 | 10 | Zhuanghe | |
| NM12) | 1440 | 10 | Alxa | Bayanhot |
| FJ1) | 1449 | 3 | Fujian | Dongshan |
| JX1) | 1449 | 20 | Jiangxi | |
| SD11) | 1449 | 10 | Rizhao | |
| SD6) | 1449 | 10 | Dongying | |
| EN2) | 1458 | 5 | Zhengzhou | |
| JS4) | 1458 | 10 | Lianyungang | |
| LN4) | 1458 | | Anshan | |
| NM1) | 1458 | 200 | Nei Menggu | Hohhot |
| EB5) | 1467 | 10 | Baoding | |
| FJ1) | 1476 | 3 | Fujian | Longhai |
| JX3) | 1467 | 7.5 | Jingdezhen | |
| SD1) | 1467 | 5 | Shandong | Dezhou |
| HB15) | 1476 | 1 | Laohekou | |
| HL1) | 1476 | 50 | Heilongjiang | Qiqihar/Fujin |
| HL9) | 1476 | | Mudanjiang | |
| JL14) | 1476 | 1 | Qian Gorlos | |
| LN7) | 1476 | | Dandong | |
| QH2) | 1476 | 10 | Xining | |
| SC12) | 1476 | 1 | Leshan | |
| SD4) | 1476 | 10 | Zibo | |
| ZJ1) | 1476 | 1 | Zhejiang | Leqing |
| GS1) | 1485 | | Gansu | |
| GX1) | 1485 | 1 | Guangxi | Lingshan |
| GX4) | 1485 | 1 | Guilin | |
| GX5) | 1485 | 3 | Wuzhou | |
| HB7) | 1485 | 10 | Shiyan | |
| HL6) | 1485 | 1 | Jixi | |
| JL11) | 1485 | 1 | Gongzhuling | |
| JX6) | 1485 | 1 | Jiujiang | |
| LN11) | 1485 | 1 | Panjin | |
| SC3) | 1485 | 1 | Chengdu | |
| SD1) | 1485 | 1 | Shandong | Weihai/Liaocheng |
| SX10) | 1485 | 1 | Shuozhou | |
| XJ11) | 1485 | 1 | Kuytun | |
| XJ5) | 1485 | 1 | Hami | |
| YN13) | 1485 | 1 | Chuxiong | |
| YN5) | 1485 | 1 | Honghe | Jinping |
| AH5) | 1494 | 1 | Wuhu | |
| FJ1) | 1494 | 1 | Fujian | Lianjiang/Fu'an |
| NM1) | 1494 | 1 | Nei Menggu | Erenhot |
| NM1) | 1494 | | Nei Menggu | Hailar |
| XJ1) | 1494 | 10 | Xinjiang | Yining/Tacheng |
| AH12) | 1503 | 1 | Fuyang | |
| HN4) | 1503 | 10 | Xiangtan | |
| SX1) | 1503 | 10 | Shanxi | Datong/Jincheng |
| GS7) | 1512 | 10 | Linxia | |
| SD2) | 1512 | 10 | Jinan | |
| EB1) | 1521 | | Hebei | Xingtai |
| EB11) | 1521 | 25 | Langfang | |
| EN5) | 1521 | 3 | Pingdingshan | |
| EN8) | 1521 | 10 | Xinxiang | |
| FJ3) | 1521 | 3 | Xiamen | |
| GD20) | 1521 | 1 | Zhaoqing | |
| GZ5) | 1521 | | Anshun | |
| HB25) | 1521 | 10 | Xiangzhou | |
| HL1) | 1521 | 1 | Heilongjiang | Jingbohu |
| JL1) | 1521 | 1 | Jilin | Taonan |
| JS11) | 1521 | 3 | Changzhou | |
| JS12) | 1521 | | Wuxi | |
| JS13) | 1521 | 5 | Suzhou | |
| JS17) | 1521 | | Zhangjiagang | |
| JS5) | 1521 | 10 | Huai'an | |
| JS7) | 1521 | | Yangzhou | |
| NM1) | 1521 | | Nei Menggu | Ordos |
| SD2) | 1521 | | Jinan | |
| SN1) | 1521 | 1 | Shaanxi | Shangluo |
| SX5) | 1521 | 1 | Changzhi | Qinxian |
| YN3) | 1521 | 1 | Qujing | |
| YN5) | 1521 | 1 | Honghe | Gejiu |
| ZJ1) | 1521 | 1 | Zhejiang | |
| ZJ7) | 1521 | | Huzhou | |
| JL1) | 1530 | 10 | Jilin | Yanji/Fuyuan |

| MW | kHz | kW | Station | Tx Location |
|---|---|---|---|---|
| SX7) | 1530 | 1 | Jinzhong | |
| ZJ1) | 1530 | 50 | Zhejiang | Hangzhou |
| 1) | 1539 | 100 | CNR 1 | Golmud, QH |
| QH1) | 1539 | 1 | Qinghai | Maqin |
| SD1) | 1548 | 200 | Shandong | Linyi |
| EB10) | 1557 | 25 | Cangzhou | |
| EB14) | 1557 | 1 | Nangong | |
| EB6) | 1566 | 10 | Zhangjiakou | |
| JL10) | 1566 | 1 | Yanbian | Longjing |
| GS8) | 1566 | 1 | Pingliang | |
| HB1) | 1566 | 10 | Hubei | Jingmen |
| SD14) | 1566 | 1 | Liaocheng | |
| SX9) | 1566 | 1 | Yuncheng | |
| GX1) | 1575 | | Guangxi | Yulin |
| JL12) | 1575 | | Lishu | |
| LN3) | 1575 | 2 | Dalian | |
| AH8) | 1584 | 1 | Ma'anshan | |
| AH9) | 1584 | 1 | Anqing | |
| EB7) | 1584 | 1 | Chengde | |
| GZ4) | 1584 | 1 | Zunyi | |
| JL13) | 1584 | 1 | Meihekou | |
| NM1) | 1584 | 1 | Nei Menggu | Tongliao |
| NM1) | 1584 | | Nei Menggu | Zalantun |
| SX1) | 1584 | | Shanxi | Taiyuan |
| SX3) | 1584 | | Datong | |
| SX5) | 1584 | 10 | Changzhi | |
| YN1) | 1584 | 1 | Yunnan | Gongshan |
| ZJ14) | 1584 | 1 | Rui'an | |
| 1) | 1593 | 600 | CNR 1 | Changzhou, JS |
| HL1) | 1593 | 10 | Heilongjiang | |
| XJ1) | 1593 | 10 | Xinjiang | Korla |
| JS1) | 1602 | 1 | Jiangsu | Hongze |

| SW | kHz | kW | Station | Tx Loc. | Times |
|---|---|---|---|---|---|
| NM8) | 3900 | 10 | Hulun Buir | Hailar | 2130-0700, 0900-1440 |
| XJ1) | 3950 | 100 | Xinjiang | Urumqi | Nov-Apr only |
| 1) | 3985 | 100 | CNR 2 | Golmud | 1200-1605 |
| GS6) | 3990 | 15 | Gannan | Hezuo | 2250-0100, 1020-1410 |
| XJ1) | 3990 | 100 | Xinjiang | Urumqi | Nov-Apr only |
| XJ1) | 4500 | 50 | Xinjiang | Urumqi | Nov-Apr only |
| 1) | 4750 | 10 | CNR 1 | Hailar | 2025-1805 |
| 1) | 4800 | 100 | CNR 1 | Golmud | 2025-1805 |
| XZ1) | 4820 | 100 | Xizang | Lhasa | 2000-1800 |
| XJ1) | 4850 | 100 | Xinjiang | Urumqi | Nov-Apr only |
| 11) | 4900 | 50 | VO Strait | Fuzhou | 1300-1600 |
| XZ1) | 4905 | 50 | Xizang | Lhasa | 2050-1805 |
| XZ1) | 4920 | 50 | Xizang | Lhasa | 2050-1805 |
| 11) | 4940 | 50 | VO Strait | Fuzhou | 2230-2400, 1300-1600 |
| XJ1) | 4980 | 100 | Xinjiang | Urumqi | Nov-Apr only |
| HN1) | 4990 | 10 | Hunan | Changsha | 2100-1710 |
| XJ1) | 5060 | 100 | Xinjiang | Urumqi | Nov-Apr only |
| 1) | 5925 | 100 | CNR 5 | Beijing | 2055-2400, 1000-1705 |
| XZ1) | 5935 | 100 | Xizang | Lhasa | 2000-1800 |
| 1) | 5945 | 100 | CNR 1 | Beijing | 2025-2300, 1300-1805 |
| XJ1) | 5960 | 100 | Xinjiang | Urumqi | 2300-0300, 1200-1800 |
| GS6) | 5970 | 15 | Gannan | Hezuo | 2250-0100, 1020-1410 |
| 1) | 5975 | 100 | CNR 8 | Beijing | 0600-1505 |
| QH1) | 5990 | 50 | Qinghai | Xining | 2250-1600 |
| 1) | 6000 | 100 | CNR 1 | Beijing | 2025-2330, 1100-1805 |
| 1) | 6010 | 100 | CNR 11 | Baoji-Sif. | 2155-2400, 1300-1605 |
| XJ1) | 6015 | 100 | Xinjiang | Urumqi | 2300-0345, 1150-1800 |
| XZ1) | 6025 | 100 | Xizang | Lhasa | 2050-1805 |
| 1) | d6030 | 30 | CNR 1 | Beijing | 2025-1805 |
| 1) | 6040 | 150 | CNR 2 | Beijing | 2055-2300 |
| NM1) | 6040 | 50 | Nei Menggu | Hohhot | 2150-1605 |
| XZ1) | 6050 | 100 | Xizang | Lhasa | 2000-1800 |
| SC1) | 6060 | 50 | Sichuan | Xichang | 2155-0135, 1000-1515 |
| 1) | 6065 | 100 | CNR 2 | Beijing | 2055-2230, 1200-1605 |
| 1) | 6080 | 100 | CNR 1 | Golmud | 2025-2400, 1100-1805 |
| NM8) | 6080 | 10 | Hulun Buir | Hailar | 2150-0530, 0935-1600 |
| 1) | 6090 | 100 | CNR 2 | Golmud | 2055-0100, 1100-1605 |
| XZ1) | 6110 | 100 | Xizang | Lhasa | 2050-1805 |
| 11) | 6115 | 50 | VO Strait | Fuzhou | 0940(W 0950)-1200 |
| XJ1) | 6120 | 100 | Xinjiang | Urumqi | 2300-0300, 1200-1800 |
| 1) | 6125 | 100 | CNR 1 | Beijing | 2025-2300, 1100-1805 |
| 1) | 6125 | 100 | CNR 1 | Shijiazhuang | 2025-2300, 1100-1805 |
| XZ1) | 6130 | 100 | Xizang | Lhasa | 2050-1805 |
| QH1) | 6145 | 50 | Qinghai | Xining | 2200-1600 |
| 1) | 6155 | 150 | CNR 2 | Beijing | 2055-2300, 1000-1605 |
| 1) | 6165 | 100 | CNR 6 | Beijing | 2155-0100, 0900-1605 |
| 1) | 6175 | 100 | CNR 1 | Beijing | 2025-2300, 0900-1805 |

| SW | kHz | kW | Station | Tx Loc. | Times |
|---|---|---|---|---|---|
| 15) | 6185 | 15 | China Huayi BC | Fuzhou | 0955-1600 |
| 1) | 6190 | 100 | CNR 2 | Golmud | 2055-2400 |
| XJ1) | 6190 | 50 | Xinjiang | Urumqi | 2305-0330, 1210-1800 |
| XZ1) | 6200 | 100 | Xizang | Lhasa | 2050-1805 |
| 12) | 6200 | 100 | VO Jinling | Nanjing | 1230-1500 |
| XJ1) | 7205 | 100 | Xinjiang | Urumqi | 2300-0230, 1400-1800 |
| YN1) | 7210 | 20 | Yunnan | Kunming | 0630-0830, 1100-1500, 2255-0300 |
| 1) | 7215 | 100 | CNR 1 | Shijiazhuang | 2025-2400 |
| 1) | 7220 | 100 | CNR 2 | Golmud | 0000-1200 |
| SC1) | 7225 | 50 | Sichuan | Xichang | 2155-0135, 1000-1515 |
| 1) | 7230 | 150 | CNR 1 | Xianyang | 2025-1805 |
| XJ1) | 7230 | 50 | Xinjiang | Urumqi | 2300-0330, 0510-1030, 1150-1700 |
| XZ1) | 7240 | 100 | Xizang | Lhasa | 2000-0300, 0900-1800 |
| 1) | 7245 | 150 | CNR 2 | Beijing | 2055-2300, 1300-1605 |
| XZ1) | 7255 | 100 | Xizang | Lhasa | 2050(Tu 2100)-0200, 1000-1805 |
| XJ1) | 7260 | 100 | Xinjiang | Urumqi | 2300-1800, Tu1 |
| 1) | 7265 | 100 | CNR 2 | Baoji-Sif | 2055-0100, 1230-1605 |
| NM1) | 7270 | 50 | Nei Menggu | Hohhot | 2150-1605 |
| 1) | 7275 | 100 | CNR 1 | Beijing | 2025-2300, 1100-1805, Tu 0800-1100 |
| XJ1) | 7275 | 100 | Xinjiang | Urumqi | 2300-1800 |
| GZ1) | 7275 | 10 | Guizhou | Guiyang | 0135-0855 |
| 1) | 7290 | 100 | CNR 1 | Beijing | 2025-2300, 1100-1805 |
| XJ1) | 7295 | 50 | Xinjang | Urumqi | Nov-Apr only |
| 1) | 7305 | 100 | CNR 1 | Shijiazhuang | 2025-2200, 1000-1805 |
| XJ1) | 7310 | 100 | Xinjiang | Urumqi | 2300-0200, 1400-1800 |
| 1) | 7315 | 150 | CNR 2 | Xianyang | 2055-0100, 1100-1605 |
| 1) | 7335 | 100 | CNR 2 | Baoji-Sif. | 2055-0030, 1300-1605 |
| XJ1) | 7340 | 100 | Xinjiang | Urumqi | 2300-1800 |
| 1) | 7345 | 100 | CNR 1 | Beijing | 2025-2400, 1100-1805 |
| 1) | 7350 | 100 | CNR 11 | Baoji-Sif. | 2155-2400, 1300-1605 |
| 1) | 7365 | 100 | CNR 1 | Shijiazhuang | 1200-1805 |
| 1) | 7370 | 150 | CNR 2 | Beijing | 2055-2300, 1300-1605 |
| 1) | 7375 | 150 | CNR 2 | Beijing | 1200-1605 |
| 1) | 7385 | 100 | CNR 5 | Beijing | 2055-2300, 0900-1705 |
| XZ1) | 7385 | 100 | Xizang | Lhasa | 2050(Tu2100)-0200, 0930-1805 |
| 1) | 7395 | 150 | CNR 2 | Xianyang | 2055-2400 |
| NM1) | 7420 | 50 | Nei Menggu | Hohhot | 2150-1605 |
| 1) | 7425 | 100 | CNR 2 | Xianyang | 1300-1605 |
| XZ1) | 7450 | 100 | Xizang | Lhasa | 2000(Tu2100)-0300, 0900-1800 |
| 1) | 9420 | 100 | CNR 6 | Beijing | 2155-0100, 0900-1605 |
| 1) | 9420 | 100 | CNR 13 | Lingshi | 1100-1805 |
| XJ1) | 9470 | 100 | Xinjiang | Urumqi | 0345-1150 |
| 1) | 9480 | 100 | CNR 11 | Baoji-Sif. | 2155-2400, 1100-1605 |
| XZ1) | 9490 | 100 | Xizang | Lhasa | 0200-1000 |
| 1) | 9500 | 100 | CNR 1 | Shijiazhuang | 2025-1805 |
| 11) | 9505 | 100 | VO Strait | Fuzhou | 0000-1300, W1 |
| XJ1) | 9510 | 50 | Xinjiang | Urumqi | 0510-1030 |
| 1) | 9515 | 100 | CNR 2 | Beijing | 2055-2400, 0900-1605 |
| NM1) | 9520 | 50 | Nei Menggu | Hohhot | 2150-1605, Tu2 |
| 1) | 9530 | 100 | CNR 11 | Baoji-Sif. | 0000-1300 |
| XJ1) | 9560 | 100 | Xinjiang | Urumqi | 0245-1200, Tu3 |
| 1) | 9570 | 100 | CNR 2 | Golmud | May-Oct 0100-1100, Tu 0600-0855 |
| XZ1) | 9580 | 100 | Xizang | Lhasa | 0200-0930, Tu4 |
| XJ1) | 9600 | 100 | Xinjiang | Urumqi | 0200-1400, Tu1 |
| 1) | 9610 | 100 | CNR 8 | Beijing | 2055-0600 |
| 1) | 9620 | 150 | CNR 2 | Beijing | May-Oct 2300-1300 |
| 1) | 9630 | 100 | CNR 1 | Golmud | 0000-1100, Tu5 |
| 1) | 9630 | 100 | CNR 17 | Lingshi | 1200-1805 |
| 1) | 9645 | 100 | CNR 1 | Beijing | 2330-1100, Tu5 |
| 1) | 9665 | 100 | CNR 5 | Beijing | 2055-2400, 1000-1705 |
| 1) | 9675 | 100 | CNR 1 | Beijing | 2300-1000, Tu5 |
| 1) | 9685 | 100 | CNR 5 | Beijing | 0000-1000, Tu5 |
| XJ1) | 9705 | 100 | Xinjiang | Urumqi | 0305-0530, 1005-1230 |
| 1) | 9710 | 100 | CNR 1 | Shijiazhuang | 2025-2330, 1100-1805 |
| 1) | 9720 | 150 | CNR 2 | Baoji-Xinjie | 0000-1000, Tu5 |
| NM1) | 9750 | 50 | Nei Menggu | Hohhot | 2150-1605 |
| 1) | 9755 | 100 | CNR 2 | Baoji-Sif. | 2055-2400, 1000-1605 |
| 1) | 9775 | 150 | CNR 2 | Beijing | 2055-0100, 0900-1605 |
| QH1) | 9780 | 50 | Qinghai | Xining | 2200-1600, Tu5 |
| 1) | 9785 | 100 | CNR 8 | Beijing | 0600-1505, Tu5 |
| 1) | 9810 | 150 | CNR 1 | Nanning | 2025-2300, 1300-1805 |
| 1) | 9810 | 100 | CNR 2 | Baoji-Sif. | 0100-1230, W2 |
| 1) | 9820 | 150 | CNR 2 | Xianyang | 2055-2400, 1100-1605 |
| 1) | 9830 | 100 | CNR 1 | Beijing | 2025-0100, 0730-1805, Tu 0730-0900 |
| XJ1) | 9835 | 100 | Xinjiang | Urumqi | May-Oct 0300-1200, Tu 0800-1100 |
| 1) | 9845 | 100 | CNR 1 | Beijing | May-Oct 2025-2400, 1200-1805 |
| QH1) | 9850 | 50 | Qinghai | Xining | 0215-1600, Tu6 |
| 1) | 9860 | 100 | CNR 1 | Beijing | 2025-2300, 1200-1805 |
| 1) | 9890 | 100 | CNR 13 | Lingshi | 1400-1805 |
| 1) | 11610 | 150 | CNR 2 | Beijing | May-Oct 2300-1300, We 0600-0900 |
| 1) | 11620 | 100 | CNR 5 | Beijing | 0000-1000, W2 |
| 1) | 11630 | 100 | CNR 17 | Lingshi | May-Oct 2355-1805, Tu 0600-0900 |
| 1) | 11660 | 150 | CNR 2 | Xianyang | May-Oct 0100-1100, We 0600-0900 |
| 1) | 11670 | 100 | CNR 2 | Beijing | May-Oct 2230-1200, We 0600-0900 |
| 1) | 11685 | 100 | CNR 11 | Baoji-Sif. | 0000-1300, W2 |
| 1) | d11695 | 30 | CNR1 | Dongfang | 0100-0900v (DRM test) |
| 1) | 11710 | 100 | CNR 1 | Beijing | 2025-0030, 1000-1805 |
| 1) | 11720 | 100 | CNR 1 | Shijiazhuang | 2330-1100, Tu5 |
| 1) | 11740 | 100 | CNR 2 | Lingshi | 2055-0100, 1100-1605 |
| 1) | 11750 | 100 | CNR 1 | Shijiazhuang | 2200-1000, Tu5 |
| 1) | 11760 | 100 | CNR 1 | Shijiazhuang | 0000-1200, Tu5 |
| XJ1) | 11770 | 100 | Xinjiang | Urumqi | 2300-1800, Tu1 |
| 1) | 11800 | 150 | CNR 2 | Beijing | May-Oct 2300-1200, We 0600-0900 |
| 1) | 11810 | 100 | CNR 8 | Beijing | 2055-0600 |
| 1) | 11835 | 150 | CNR 2 | Xianyang | 0000-1300, W2 |
| 1) | 11845 | 150 | CNR 2 | Xianyang | 0000-1100, W2 |
| XZ1) | 11860 | 100 | Xizang | Lhasa | 0300-0900, Tu5 |
| XJ1) | 11885 | 100 | Xinjiang | Urumqi | 2300-1800, Tu1 |
| 1) | 11905 | 100 | CNR 6 | Beijing | 0100-0900, W2 |
| 1) | 11915 | 100 | CNR 2 | Baoji-Sif. | 0030-1300, W2 |
| 1) | 11925 | 100 | CNR 1 | Lingshi | 2025-2330, 1200-1805 |
| 1) | 11935 | 100 | CNR 5 | Beijing | 2300-0900, W2 |
| XZ1) | 11950 | 100 | Xizang | Lhasa | 0300-0900, Tu5 |
| 1) | 11960 | 100 | CNR 1 | Beijing | 0000-0900, Tu5 |
| XJ1) | 11975 | 100 | Xinjiang | Urumqi | May-Oct 0305-0530, 1005-1230 |
| 1) | 12045 | 100 | CNR 1 | Beijing | 2300-1200, Tu5 |
| 1) | 12055 | 100 | CNR 17 | Lingshi | 2355-1200, Tu5 |
| 1) | 12080 | 100 | CNR 2 | Baoji-Sif. | 0000-1000, W2 |
| 1) | 13610 | 150 | CNR 1 | Nanning | 2300-1300, Tu5 |
| XJ1) | 13670 | 100 | Xinjiang | Urumqi | 0230-1400, Tu1 |
| 1) | 13700 | 100 | CNR 13 | Lingshi | May-Oct 2355-1400, Tu 0600-0900 |
| 1) | 15270 | 150 | CNR 2 | Beijing | 0100-0900, W2 |
| 1) | 15370 | 100 | CNR 1 | Shijiazhuang | 0000-1100, Tu5 |
| 1) | 15380 | 100 | CNR 1 | Beijing | 2300-1100, Tu5 |
| 1) | 15390 | 100 | CNR 13 | Lingshi | 2355-1100, Tu5 |
| 1) | 15480 | 100 | CNR 1 | Beijing | May-Oct 2300-1300, Tu 0600-0900 |
| 1) | 15500 | 150 | CNR 2 | Beijing | May-Oct 2300-1000, We 0600-0900 |
| 1) | 15540 | 100 | CNR 2 | Lingshi | 0100-1100, W2 |
| 1) | 15550 | 100 | CNR 1 | Beijing | 0000-1100, Tu5 |
| 1) | 15570 | 100 | CNR 11 | Baoji-Sif. | 0000-1100, W2 |
| 1) | d15580 | 30 | CNR1 | Dongfang | 0100-0900v (DRM test) |
| 1) | 15710 | 100 | CNR 6 | Beijing | 0100-0900, W2 |
| 1) | 17550 | 100 | CNR 1 | Beijing | 0000-1200, Tu5 |
| 1) | 17565 | 100 | CNR 1 | Beijing | 0100-0730(Tu -0600) |
| 1) | 17580 | 100 | CNR 1 | Lingshi | 2330-1200, Tu5 |
| 1) | 17595 | 100 | CNR 1 | Shijiazhuang | 2300-1100, Tu5 |
| 1) | 17605 | 100 | CNR 1 | Beijing | 0030-1000, Tu5 |
| 1) | 17625 | 150 | CNR 2 | Beijing | 0000-0900, W2 |
| 1) | 17890 | 100 | CNR 1 | Beijing | 2300-1100, Tu5 |

**NB:** Baoji-Sif. = Baoji-Sifangshan. ‡=inactive, ±=variable, d=DRM. Tu1= Tuesdays 0800-1100, Tu2=0600-0950, Tu3=0630-1100, Tu4= 0700-0800, Tu5= 0600-0900, Tu6= 0600-0855. W1=Wednesdays 0400-0945, W2= 0600-0900

| FM(MHz) | CNR 1 | CNR 2 | CNR 3 | Prov.T | Prov.M | City.T | City.M |
|---|---|---|---|---|---|---|---|
| Anshan | 101.0 | 105.1 | 98.3 | 97.5 | - | 99.5 | 93.6 |
| Baoding | 98.3 | 89.7 | 105.3 | 99.2 | 106.4 | 104.8 | - |
| Baotou | 96.9 | 99.3 | - | 95.7 | 107.4 | 89.2 | 100.1 |
| Beihai | 102.5 | - | 97.1 | 100.3 | 95.5 | 99.1 | - |
| Beijing | 106.1 | 96.6 | 90.0 | - | - | 103.9 | 97.4 |
| Benxi | 94.8 | 100.3 | - | 97.5 | 98.6 | 107.4 | - |

| FM(MHz) | CNR 1 | CNR 2 | CNR 3 | Prov.T | Prov.M | City.T | City.M |
|---|---|---|---|---|---|---|---|
| Changchun | 99.1 | 104.7 | 94.3 | 103.8 | 92.7 | 96.8 | 106.3 |
| Changde | 94.7 | 102.9 | - | 89.5 | 102.1 | 97.1 | 98.5 |
| Changsha | 95.0 | 87.6 | 107.7 | 91.8 | 89.3 | 106.1a | 102.2 |
| Chengdu | 103.7 | - | 107.6 | 101.7 | 95.5 | 91.4 | 105.6 |
| Chifeng | 101.2 | 107.1 | 88.5 | 105.6 | 94.5 | 101.8 | - |
| Chongqing | 102.9 | 100.0 | 90.6 | - | - | 95.5 | 88.1 |
| Dalian | 89.1 | 104.3 | 107.8 | 97.5 | - | 100.8 | 106.7 |
| Daqing | 97.3 | - | 102.3 | 99.8 | 102.9 | 95.0 | 106.0 |
| Fuzhou | 93.5 | - | 92.6 | 100.7 | 91.3 | 87.6 | 89.3 |
| Guangzhou | 89.3 | 106.6 | 87.4 | 105.2 | 99.3 | 106.1 | 102.7 |
| Guilin | 89.8 | 94.1 | - | 100.3 | 95.0 | 88.3a | - |
| Guiyang | 93.6 | 105.6 | 107.3 | 95.2 | 91.6 | 102.7 | 90.9 |
| Haikou | 105.8 | 87.8 | 89.8 | 100.0 | 94.5 | - | 91.6 |
| Handan | 88.7 | - | 93.9 | 99.2 | 102.4 | 106.8 | 102.8 |
| Hangzhou | 90.2 | 97.9 | 103.2 | 93.0 | 96.8 | 91.8 | 105.4 |
| Harbin | 89.9 | 88.1 | 100.9 | 99.8 | 95.8 | 92.5 | 90.9 |
| Hefei | 93.5 | 104.7 | 91.1 | 90.8 | 89.5 | 102.6 | 87.6 |
| Hengyang | 95.0 | 105.9 | - | 100.3 | 96.9 | 101.8 | - |
| Hohhot | 97.1 | - | 99.1 | 105.6 | 93.6 | 107.3 | - |
| Jiamusi | 94.4 | - | - | 99.8 | 105.8 | 98.0 | - |
| Jilin-shi | 98.0 | - | 104.5 | 103.8 | 93.4 | 105.3 | 91.3 |
| Jinan | 89.8 | 96.5 | 95.5 | 101.1 | 99.1 | 103.1 | 88.7 |
| Jinzhou | 104.9 | 101.2 | 106.0 | 97.5 | - | 100.3 | - |
| Jiujiang | 102.4 | - | - | 105.4 | 107.9 | 88.4 | 91.6 |
| Kaifeng | 106.3 | 100.8 | - | 104.1 | 88.1 | 105.1 | - |
| Kunming | - | 107.0 | 88.7 | 93.0 | 91.8 | 97.0 | - |
| Lanzhou | 94.8 | 90.3 | 88.3 | 103.5 | - | - | 99.5 |
| Lhasa | 89.2 | 104.3 | 96.1 | - | - | - | - |
| Lianyungang | 93.6 | 97.2 | - | 101.1 | - | 102.1 | - |
| Lijiang | 95.1 | - | 107.2 | 93.1 | 100.7 | - | - |
| Nanchang | 89.1 | 93.8 | 87.2 | 105.4 | 103.4 | 95.1 | 90.6 |
| Nanjing | 95.8 | 107.5 | 98.9 | 101.1 | 89.7 | 102.4 | 105.8 |
| Nanning | 106.2 | 93.6 | 99.0 | 100.3 | 95.0 | 107.4a | - |
| Ningbo | 95.7 | 101.2 | 107.7 | 93.0 | 103.2 | 97.4 | 93.9 |
| Qingdao | 96.7 | 104.1 | 98.0 | 106.0 | 106.6 | 89.7 | 91.5 |
| Qinhuangdao | 96.5 | - | - | 99.3 | 106.4 | 100.4 | 97.3 |
| Qiqihar | 97.7 | 101.8 | - | 99.8 | 90.4 | 94.1 | - |
| Quanzhou | 96.9 | 98.3 | 102.5 | 100.7 | - | 90.4 | 92.3 |
| Rizhao | 89.4 | 106.9 | - | 106.0 | - | 88.1 | - |
| Shanghai | 99.0 | 91.4 | 107.7 | - | - | 105.7 | 101.7 |
| Shenyang | 94.8 | 93.5 | 99.8 | 97.5 | 98.6 | - | - |
| Shenzhen | 95.8 | - | 101.2 | 105.2 | 93.9 | 106.2 | 97.1 |
| Shijiazhuang | 96.5 | 97.2 | 105.1 | 92.7 | 102.4 | 94.6 | 106.7 |
| Suzhou | 100.0 | 98.7 | - | 101.1 | 89.7 | 104.8 | 94.8 |
| Taiyuan | 97.0 | 99.0 | 89.3 | 88.0 | 94.0 | 107.0 | 102.6 |
| Tangshan | 93.2 | 107.4 | - | 99.3 | 89.5 | 96.8 | 94.0 |
| Tianjin | 102.9 | 98.0 | 92.5 | - | - | 106.8 | 99.0 |
| Urumqi | 88.7 | 90.6 | - | 94.9 | 103.9 | 97.4 | 106.5 |
| Weifang | 96.7 | - | - | 106.0 | 106.6 | 95.9 | 88.7 |
| Wenzhou | 103.1 | - | 92.1 | 93.0 | 104.7 | 103.9 | 100.3 |
| Wuhan | 95.6 | 97.8 | 90.7 | 92.7 | 105.8 | 89.6 | 101.8 |
| Wuhu | 103.8 | - | - | 90.8 | 91.8 | 96.3 | 98.2 |
| Wuxi | 89.4 | 98.7 | - | 101.1 | 89.7 | 106.9 | 91.4 |
| Xiamen | 102.6 | 87.5 | 105.2 | 100.7 | - | 107.0 | 90.9 |
| Xi'an | 96.4 | 103.0 | 95.5 | 91.6 | 98.8 | 104.3 | 93.1 |
| Xining | 91.6 | 105.6 | 100.6 | 97.2a | - | - | 104.3 |
| Yantai | 98.8 | 98.1 | - | 106.9 | 107.8 | 103.0 | 91.2 |
| Yinchuan | 96.4 | 107.8 | 99.7 | 98.4 | - | 100.6a | - |
| Yueyang | 103.2 | 87.6 | 107.7 | 91.8 | - | 104.1 | 106.1 |
| Zhangjiakou | 88.9 | - | - | 101.6 | 93.9 | - | 98.6 |
| Zhangzhou | 102.6 | 98.3 | 100.2 | 100.7 | - | 96.6 | 99.1 |
| Zhengzhou | 101.2 | 96.7 | - | 104.1 | 88.1 | 91.8 | 94.4 |
| Zhuhai | 99.1 | - | 101.2 | 105.2 | 93.9 | 87.5a | 91.5 |

**Prov.T**=Provincial traffic stn **Prov.M**=Provincial music stn **City.T**=City traffic stn **City.M**=City music stn a) Traffic music stn
**NB:** Official FM band 87.0-108.0MHz. Low power college stns exist 60-87MHz, some spread over 50-108MHz

**Addresses & other information:**
**1) CHINA NATIONAL RADIO (CNR)**
(Zhongyang Renmin Guangbo Diantai, which means Central People's Broadcasting Station)
✉ 2 Fuxingmenwai Dajie, Xicheng Qu, Beijing 100866 ☎ +86 10 8609 2636 **W:** cnr.cn **LP:** Gen. Dir: Yan Xiaoming. CE: Qian Yuelin
**V.O. China (1st Prgr News R.):** MW/SW/FM 24h (exc. Mon 1805-2025). MW/SW mostly 2025-1805 exc. Tues 0600-0850. SW detail see list. **V.O. the Economy (2nd Prgr China Business R.):** MW/SW/FM 24h (exc. Mon 1600-2100). MW/SW mostly 2055-1605 exc. Wed 0600-0900. SW detail see list. **V.O. the Music (3rd Prgr Music R.):** 2155-1605 (exc. Tue 0600-0900) on FM. **Scripture Music Sce**

**(4th Prgr"Golden R.):** 2055-1705 (exc. Tue 0500-0900) on 101.8MHz **V.O. Zhonghua (5th Prgr Zhonghua News R.):** 2100-1700 on MW/SW/102.3/94.9MHz (Fuzhou/Xiamen). **V.O. Shenzhou (6th Prgr Shenzhou Easy R.)** in Ch, Amoy and Hakka: 2200-1600 on MW/SW/106.2/107.9MHz (Fuzhou/Xiamen). **V.O. Huaxia (7th Prgr Huaxia R.)** for the Zhujiang Delta: Ch. on 1215kHz/87.8/92.3/104.9MHz 2105-1805 in Ch and Cantonese. **V.O. the Literary (9th Prgr Story R.):** 2100-1800 (exc. Tues 0500-0900) on 106.6MHz. **V.O. Old Age (10th Prgr Senior Citizen R.):** 2025-1805 (exc. Tue 0600-0900) on 1053kHz. **V.O. the Entertainment (12th Prgr Happy R.):** 2100-1800 (exc. Tue 0500-0900) on 747kHz. **V.O. Hong Kong (14th Prgr)** for Hong Kong Special Administrative Region: 24h (exc. Mon 1600-2100) in Ch and Cantonese see Hong Kong. **China Traffic Sce (15th Prgr):** on 99.6MHz (Beijing), 90.5 (Hubei Province), 101.2 (Hebei Province) 24h (exc. Mon 1600-2100). **V.O. China Country (16th Prgr):** on 720kHz (Beijing) 24h (exc. Mon 1600-2100). **China National Emergency Broadcasting:** in an emergency including a wide range earthquake on 9800/12000kHz/FM 24h.
**V.O. Minorities (8th Prgr Ethnic Minority R.)** 2055-1505 (exc. Wed 0600-0900) on MW/SW/104.5MHz (Hohhot), 106.5MHz(Yanji)

**Korean**

| | | | | |
|---|---|---|---|---|
| 0600-1000 | 9785, 5975, 1143, 720 | | | |
| 1000-1100+JL | 9785, 5975, 1143, 720 | | | |
| 1100-1505 | 9785, 5975,1143,720 | | | |

**Mongolian**

| | | |
|---|---|---|
| 2100-2330 | 11810, 9610, 1143 | |
| 2330-0030+ MN | 11810, 9610, 1143 | |
| 0030-0600 | 11810, 9610, 1143 | |

**11th Prgr. Tibetan Service** 2155-1605 on MW/SW (exc. Wed 0600-0855)/105.7MHz (Lhasa)

**Tibetan**

| | | | | |
|---|---|---|---|---|
| 2155-2300 | 9480, 7350, 6010, 1098 | | | |
| 2300-2400+XZ | 9480, 7350, 6010, 1098 | | | |
| 0000-0900 | 15570, 11685, 9530, 1098 | | | |
| 0900-1100 | 15570, 11685, 9530, 1098 | | | |
| 1100-1300 | 11685, 9530, 9480, 1098 | | | |
| 1300-1605 | 9480, 7350, 6010, 1098 | | | |

**13th Prgr. Uighur Service** 2355-1805 on MW/SW (exc. Tues 0600-0855) /FM

**Uighur**

| | | | | | |
|---|---|---|---|---|---|
| 2355-0600 | 15390, 13700, 945, 855, 720 | | | | |
| 0600-0630+XJ | 15390, 13700, 1422, 945, 855, 720 | | | | |
| 0630-0900 | 15390, 13700, 1422, 945, 855, 720 | | | | |
| 0900-1100 | 15390, 13700, 945, 855, 720 | | | | |
| 1100-1400 | 13700, 9420, 945, 855, 720 | | | | |
| 1400-1430+XJ | 9890, 9420, 945, 855, 720 | | | | |
| 1430-1805 | 9890, 9420, 945, 855, 720 | | | | |

**17th Prgr.Kazakh Service** 2355-1805 on SW (exc. Tues 0600-0855)

**Kazakh**

| | | |
|---|---|---|
| 2355-0900 | 12055, 11630 | |
| 0900-0930+XJ | 12055, 11630 | |
| 0930-1200 | 12055, 11630 | |
| 1200-1400 | 11630, 9630 | |
| 1400-1430+XJ | 11630, 9630 | |
| 1430-1805 | 11630, 9630 | |

**NB** +) relayed by regional stns

**2) CHINA RADIO INTERNATIONAL (CRI)**
(Zhongguo Guoji Guangbo Diantai)
🖳 Jia 16, Shijingshan Lu, Shijingshan Qu, Beijing 100040 ☎ +86 10 6889 1001 **W:** cri.cn **LP:** Gen. Dir: Wang Gengnian
**Domestic Sce:**
**Beijing 1 Easy FM** (1251kHz/91.5MHz): 24h in English – **Beijing 2 Hit FM** (88.7MHz): 24h in English – **Beijing 3 Round the Clock** (1008kHz): 24h in English – **Beijing 4 News Plus** (846kHz) 24h in English – **Beijing 5 News R.** (900kHz/90.5MHz): 24h in Chinese – **Tianjin News R.** (105.4MHz): 24h in Chinese – **Shijiazhuang News R.** (92.2MHz): 24h – **Shanghai 1 Hit FM** (87.9MHz): 2200-2400, 0300-1730 – **Shanghai 2 Easy FM** (100.1MHz): 24h – **Shanghai 3 News R.** (102.5MHz): 24h – **Hefei 1 Easy FM** (92.4MHz): 2200-1700 – **Hefei 2 News R.** (90.1MHz): 2200-1700 – **Chizhou News R.** (101.9MHz) – **Xinzhou News R.** (98.1MHz) – **Wuhu News R.** (89.4MHz) – **Xiamen 2 Easy FM** (95.8MHz): 2200-1700 – **Xiamen 3 News R.** (90.1MHz): 24h – **Qingdao News R.** (89.8MHz):24h – **Yantai News R.** (88.4MHz): 2300-2400, 0400-0430, 0900-1000 – **Wuhan News R.** (98.6MHz): 24h – **Changsha News R.** (99.5MHz): 24h – **Guangzhou 1 Hit FM** (88.5MHz): 24h – **Guangzhou 2 News R.** (107.1MHz): 24h – **Guangzhou 3 Easy FM** (98.0MHz) – **Shenzhen News R.** (107.1MHz):24h – **Zhuhai News R.** (702kHz): 24h – **Haikou News R.** (104.4MHz): 24h – **Chengdu News R.** (88.9MHz) – **Chongqing 1**

**Easy FM** (89.8MHz): 2200-1600 – **Chongqing 2 News R.** (91.7MHz): 24h – **Lhasa Easy FM** (100.0MHz): 1930-1600 – **Guiyang News R.** (102.1MHz): 24h – **Lanzhou Easy FM** (98.5MHz): 2200-1600 – **Urumqi News R.** (1008kHz): 24h

**DAB: China Digital Multimedia Broadcasting (CDMB), Beijing** on 208.720, 210.432, 212.144, 213.856MHz 2200-1600 (exc. Tues 0400-1000). Each freq. contains 5 audio ch and 3 video ch at maximum. Currently there are only one regular regional mux, one trial regional mux and four regular local mux on air.

**EXTERNAL SERVICES: China Radio International, Voice of Beibu Bay Radio, Yunnan Broadcasting Station**
See International Broadcasting section

## BROADCASTS TO TAIWAN
**11) Voice of the Strait** (Haixia zhi Sheng), 15 Yuandang Jie, Gulou Qu, Fuzhou, Fujian 350025. Operated by the People's Liberation Army of China **W:** vos.com.cn News Sce in Ch and Hakka on 666/4940/9505kHz 2230-1600 (exc. Wed 0400-0945).Including Hakka Prgr: 1115-1145 exc. Sat & Sun and English Prgr. "Focus on China": Sun1500-1530 - Automobile Life Sce in Amoy on 90.6MHz 24h - Dialect Sce in Amoy on 783/4900/6115kHz 2230-1600 (exc. Wed 0400-0953) - City Sunshine FM on 99.6MHz 24h (exc. Wed 0400-1000) – General Sce on 97.9MHz(Xiamen) 2230-1600 English Prgr. "Focus on China": Sat & Sun1500-1530 – **12) Voice of Jinling** (Jinling zhi Sheng), 132 Zhongshan Donglu, Nanjing, Jiangsu 210002. **W:** vojs.cn/2014new/c/n/ On 6200kHz 1200-1500 - Automobile FM 99.7MHz 24h – **13) Voice of Pujiang** (Pujiang zhi Sheng), 1376 Hongqiao Lu, Shanghai or P.O.Box 518, Shanghai 200051 **W:** yicai.com/show_topic/642116. On 1422kHz 2200-1600 **NB:** All SW and FM services have closed since 1 May 2013 – **14) Southeast Broadcasting Company**, B-10F, Fujian Radio & TV Center, 28 Xihuan Nan Lu, Fuzhou, Fujian350004 **W:** fjtv.net/folder526/folder617 On 585kHz/97.6/106.2MHz 2200-1600 in Ch and Amoy – **15) China Huayi Broadcasting Corporation**, 15 Yuandang Jie, Gulou Qu, Fuzhou or P.O.Box 251, Fuzhou, Fujian 350001 **W:** chbcnet.com On 873/6185kHz/107.1MHz(Fuzhou) for Taiwan, Hong Kong, Macao and Southeast Asia. 2200-1600 exc. Wed 0400-0953

## ANHUI PROVINCE
**AH1)** Anhui Radio and TV St, 666 Longtu Lu, Hefei, Anhui 230071 **W:** ahrtv.cn News General Sce "V.O. Anhui": on 936/846kHz/103.6MHz 2000-1800(Tues 1500) - Economic Sce on 864kHz/97.1MHz 24h (exc. Mon 1500-2100) - Travel Sce "FM1065 Anhui Private Car Sce"on 1098/837/900kHz/96.1/106.5MHz 24h exc. Tues 1500-2000) - Traffic Sce "Automobile 908": on 90.8MHz 24h (exc. Tues 1500-2150) - Life Sce on 603kHz/105.5MHz 2100-1600 - Farm Sce on 720/1008kHz/95.5MHz on 2000-1600(Mon 1500) - Music Sce "Changxiang 895": on 89.5MHz 24h - Novel and Storytelling Sce on 1395kHz/102.9/107.4MHz 2000-1800(Tues 1500) - Chinese Opera Sce on 801kHz/99.5MHz 24h (exc. Tues 1500-2000) "Hefei My FM": on 96.1MHz 24h – **AH2)** Hefei Radio and TV St, 558 Tian'ehu Lu, Hefei, Anhui 230011. News General Sce on 666kHz/91.5MHz 2050-1700 - Traffic Sce on 1053kHz/102.6MHz 24h (exc. Tues 0600-0850) - Automobile Music Sce "Hot FM": on 747kHz/87.6MHz 2200-1700 - Story Sce on 1170kHz/98.8MHz 2100-1700 - Hui Merchant Sce on 100.3MHz 2200-1800 - Xincheng Information Sce on 846kHz/88.1MHz 2125-1500 - Xincheng Traffic and Music Sce on 93.8MHz 2200-1600 – **AH2A)** 327 Jinzhai Lu, Luyang Qu, Hefei, Anhui 230061. Charm Music Sce on 88.6MHz 24h – **AH3)** 11 Dongshan Zhonglu, Huainan, Anhui 232001. News General Sce on 648kHz/103.7MHz 2125-1500 - Traffic and Literary Sce on 97.9MHz 2140-1500 - Music and Story Sce on 104.9MHz 24h(exc. Tues 0600-0900) – **AH4)** Huaibei Radio and TV St, 316 Renmin Zhonglu, Xiangshan Qu, Huaibei, Anhui 235000. News General Sce on 1431kHz/94.9MHz 2155-1600 - Traffic Sce on 100.4MHz 2150-1600 (exc. Tues 0630-0900) - Music Sce on 89.3MHz 2150-1600 – **AH5)** 197 Beijing Donglu, Wuhu, Anhui 241000. News General Sce on 100.4MHz 2100-1600 - Life Sce on 1494kHz - Traffic and Economic Sce on 96.3MHz 2128-1630 (Sun -1600) - Music and Story Sce on 98.2MHz 2200-1600 – **AH6)** Tongling Radio and TV St, Yi'an Beilu, Tongling, Anhui 244000. News General Sce on 1107kHz/95.9MHz 2155-1505 - Traffic and Life Sce on 88.7MHz 2230-1500 - Music and Story Sce on 92.4MHz 2225-1505 – **AH7)** Bengbu Radio and TV St, Xuehua Shan, Shengli Donglu, Bengbu, Anhui 233000. News General Sce on 765kHz/107.9MHz 2200-1400 - Economic Sce on 1098kHz/104.2MHz 2150-1430 - Traffic and Literary Sce on 98.4MHz 2200-1500 – **AH8)** Ma'anshan Radio and TV St, 46 Yushan Zhonglu, Ma'anshan, Anhui 243011. News Sce on 1584kHz/105.1MHz 2150-1500 (exc. Tues 0600-0850) - Traffic Sce on 92.8MHz 2130-1500 (exc. Tues 0600-0850) - Music FM "Xindong (Heart) 954": on 95.4MHz 2130-1500 – **AH9)** Anqing Radio and TV St, 23 Guanyue Miao, Anqing, Anhui 246004. News General Sce on 1584kHz/90.3MHz 2200-1500 - Traffic and Music Sce on 97.7MHz 2200-1500 (exc. Tues 0600-0925) - Story Sce on 93.7MHz 2200-1500 (exc. Tues 0600-0925) – **AH10)** Huangshan Radio and TV St, 9 Tiandu Dadao, Tunxi Qu, Huangshan, Anhui 245000. News General Sce on 1431kHz/93.3MHz 2200-1500 - Traffic and Travel Sce on 100.4MHz 2200-1500 – **AH11)** 225 Langxie Lu, Chuzhou, Anhui 239000. News General Sce on 95.0/97.3MHz 2125-1440 (exc. Tues 0500-0930) - Traffic and Music Sce on 105.4MHz 2125-1530 - Literary and Story Sce on 1377kHz/97.0MHz 2100-1500 – **AH12)** Nan 2 Huan Lu, Fuyang, Anhui 236034. News Sce on 1116kHz/91.6MHz 2130-1610 - Economic Sce on 711/801/1503kHz 2145-1550 (exc. Tues 0700-0830) - Traffic Sce on 90.0/103.5MHz 2130-1530 - Story Sce on 94.1MHz 2120-1530 – **AH13)** Suzhou Radio and TV St, Baihuiyuan, Huaihai Lu, Suzhou, Anhui 234000. News General Sce on 1251kHz/100.8/100.2MHz 2155-1450 (exc. Tues 0600-0850) - Traffic Sce, on 96.1MHz/95.1MHz 24h - City Music Sce on 97.1/107.3MHz 2130-1600 - Story Sce on 102.3MHz 2200-1600 – **AH15)** Changjiang Nanlu, Guichi Qu, Chizhou, Anhui 247100. News General Sce on 801kHz/98.1MHz 2200-1405 - Traffic and Travel Sce on 96.6MHz – **AH16)** Meishan Nanlu, Lu'an, Anhui 237001. News General Sce on 1170kHz/102.1MHz 2155-1505 - Traffic and Music Sce on 96.4MHz 2155-1505 - Music Ch. on 92.4MHz – **AH17)** 10 Zhuangyuan Lu, Xuancheng, Anhui 242000. News General Sce on 1170kHz/100.6MHz 2155-1500 - Traffic and Literary Sce on 106.1MHz 2155-1500 – **AH18)** 8 Chengguan Ximen, Dangtu Xian, Anhui 243100. Automobile Music BS: on 1098kHz/90.1MHz 2155-1400 (exc. Wed 0600-0900) – **AH19)** 62 Renmin Zhonglu, Bozhou, Anhui 236800 - News General Sce on 999kHz/88.2MHz 2130-1530 - Traffic and Music Sce on 107.2MHz 2130-1530

## BEIJING MUNICIPALITY
**BJ1)** 14 Jianguomenwai Dajie, Chaoyang Qu, Beijing 100022 **W:** rbc.cn/ News Sce on 828kHz/100.6MHz 24h exc. Mon 1600-2200 - Public Sce on 1026kHz/107.3MHz 2300-1500 - Sports Sce on 102.5MHz 2300-1530 - Traffic Sce on 103.9MHz 24h exc. Mon 1600-2100 - Story Sce on 603kHz/95.4MHz 0000-0730, 0900-1600 - Foreign Language Sce "Radio 774", "Radio Beijing International": on 774kHz/92.3MHz 2200-1600 - Literary Sce "Joy FM" on 87.6MHz 24h exc. Mon 1630-2100 - Music Sce on 97.4MHz 24h exc. Mon 1600-2100 – Mobile Sce "Metro Radio": on 94.5MHz 2300-1700 – Young Sce on 2200-1600 on 927kHz/98.2MHz.

## CHONGQING MUNICIPALITY
**CQ1)** 159 Zhongshan 3 Lu, Yuzhong Qu, Chongqing 400015 **W:** cbg.cn/ News Sce on 1314kHz/96.8MHz 24h - Economic Sce on 101.5MHz 24h - Traffic Sce on 95.5MHz 24h - City Sce on 93.8MHz 2130-1800 - Music Sce on 88.1MHz 24h - Literary Sce on 103.5MHz 24h

## HEBEI PROVINCE
**EB1)** 63 Yuhua Donglu, Shijiazhuang, Hebei 050012 **W:** hebradio.com News Sce on 1278/783kHz 2030-1700; on 104.3MHz/FM 24h - Economic Sce on 846kHz 24h - Life Sce on 747/783kHz/89.0/91.0MHz 24h (exc. Tues 1700-2030) - Traffic Sce on 99.2/101.6MHz 24h - Literary Sce "Private Car 907": on 900kHz/90.7/94.8MHz 24h - Music Sce on 102.4MHz/FM 24h (exc. Tues 1700-2015) - Farmer Sce on 558/1251kHz/98.1/88.3MHz 24h (exc. Tues 1700-2030) - Travel Culture Sce "Top Radio": on 603/1521kHz/100.3/88.1MHz 24h - Storytelling Ch on 1125/1521kHz - "Shijiazhuang My FM": on 102.9MHz 24h – **EB2)** 302 Tiyu Nan Dajie, Shijiazhuang, Hebei 050021. News Sce on 882kHz/88.2MHz 2125-1700 - Economic Sce "V.O. the City" on 1431kHz/100.9MHz 2125-1600 (exc. Tues 0600-0825) - Farm Sce on 1251kHz/96.1MHz 2100-1600 - Traffic Sce on 94.6MHz 2130-1700 - Taxi Sce on 92.2MHz 2230-1600 - Music Sce "NuStar Radio": on 106.7MHz 24h - Pinwei (Taste) Music Sce on 87.6MHz 24h – **EB3)** 246 Renmin Lu, Handan, Hebei 056002. News General Sce on 963kHz/96.4MHz 2100-1600 - Life Sce on 1206kHz 2100-1600 - Traffic Sce on 1008kHz/106.8MHz 2100-1600 - Music Sce on 102.8MHz 2100-1600 - Chinese Opera and Storytelling Sce on 846kHz/104.8MHz 2100-1600 – **EB4)** 15 Yejin Lu, Xingtai, Hebei 054000. News General Sce on 1188kHz/89.6/90.3MHz 2125-1600 (exc. Tues 0530-0930) - Economic Life Sce on 927kHz/102.0MHz 2120-1500 (exc. Tues 0530-0930) - Traffic and Music Sce on 91.8/101.2MHz 2225-1500 (exc. Tues 0630-0930) - Kuaile (Happy) Sce on 96.8MHz – **EB5)** 1620 Yangguang Bei Dajie, Baoding, Hebei 071051. News Sce on 1467kHz/93.7MHz 24h (exc. Tues 0600-0855) - Private Car Sce on 1017kHz/99.7MHz 2145-1600 (exc. Tues 0600-0900) - Traffic Sce on 747kHz/104.8MHz 1850-1600 (exc. Tues 0600-0900) - City Service Sce on 101.6MHz 2200-1400 - City and Country Alliance Sce on 101.3/103.2/105.6MHz - News General Sce on 90.9/92.6MHz – **EB6)** 17 Jianguo Lu, Qiaodong Qu, Zhangjiakou, Hebei 075000. News General Sce on 1566kHz/101.0/107.4MHz 2125-1505 - Traffic Sce on 900kHz/100.0MHz 2130-1600 - Private Car Sce on 603kHz/104.3MHz 2130-1300 (exc. Tues 0500-0900) - Pinwei (Taste) Music Sce on 98.6MHz 2130-1530 (exc. Tues 0600-0900) – **EB7)** 120 Guangdian Lu, Shuangqiao Qu, Chengde, Hebei 067000. News General Ch. on 1584kHz/89.1MHz 2155-0540, 0950-1400 - Traffic and Literary Ch. on 900kHz/97.6MHz 2155-1600 (exc. Tues 0600-0900) - Travel

Life Ch. on 100.6MHz 2225-1600 – **EB8)** 1 Guangda Jie, Wenhua Lu, Tangshan, Hebei 063000. News General Sce on 684kHz/91.7MHz 2030-1605 (exc. Tues 0705-0855) - Economic Life Sce on 801kHz/95.5MHz 2130-1530 (exc. Tues 0700-0830) - Traffic and Literary Sce on 1143kHz/96.8MHz 2135-1505 - Music Sce "NuStar Radio": on 94.0MHz 2200-1600 (exc. Tues 0700-0900) - "V.O. Cao Jidian" Novel Sce on 900kHz 2200-1600 (exc. Tues 0630-0900) - Cultural and Entertainment Sce on 105.9MHz – **EB9)** 9 Yingbin Lu, Haigang Qu, Qinhuangdao, Hebei 066000. News General Sce on 990kHz/89.1MHz 24h - Private Car Sce on 900kHz/103.8MHz 24h - Traffic Sce on 100.4MHz 24h (exc. Tues 0700-0800) - Sports and Music Sce on 97.3MHz 24h - Farm Sce "Huanle (Joy) FM": on 92.4/89.9MHz 24h – **EB10)** 12 Jiefang Xilu, Cangzhou, Hebei 061001. News General Sce on 1557kHz/97.0MHz 2057-1500 - Agricultural Economic Sce on 1053kHz/91.7MHz - Traffic and Music Sce on 1206kHz/93.8MHz 2200-1600 - Automobile Music Sce on 105.8MHz 24h - Music Sce on 846kHz/103.6MHz 2200-1500 - Storytelling Sce on 801kHz 2200-1500 – **EB11)** 8 Yongfeng Dao, Langfang, Hebei 065000. News General Sce on 1008/846kHz/95.1MHz 2055-1700 - Storytelling Sce on 585kHz/100.3MHz 24h - Chinese Opera Sce on 1521kHz/105.0MHz 2055-1700 – **EB12)** 693 Hongqi Dajie, Taocheng Qu, Hengshui, Hebei 053000. News General Sce on 954kHz/101.9MHz 2225-0535, 0825-1630 - Traffic Sce on 1098kHz/105.3MHz 2125-1500 - Literary Sce on 738kHz/96.1MHz 2230-1400 – **EB13)** 167, Bei Duan, Xinghua Lu, Xinji, Hebei 052360. 2225-2355, 0255-0500, 1025-1250 – **EB14)** Xitou, Shengli Dajie, Nangong, Hebei 055750. 2225-0045, 1005-1400 – **EB15)** 36 Yingxin Dajie, Shahe, Hebei 054100. 2200-1600 – **EB16)** Sanyang Dongjie, Qinghe Xian, Hebei 054800. 2100-1550 – **EB17)** Beiguan, Zhuozhou, Hebei 072750 – **EB18)** Zhongshan Xilu, Dingzhou, Hebei 073000. 2200-1500 – **EB19)** 393 Xiguan Xijie, Botou, Hebei 062150. 2225-2355, 0345-0450, 1025-1230 – **EB20)** 12-1 Xihuan Lu, Renqiu, Hebei 062550. General Ch. on 1287kHz/92.8MHz 2225-1600 - Storytelling Ch. on 864kHz 2255-1400

## HENAN PROVINCE

**EN1)** 2 Wei Yilu, Jinshui Qu, Zhengzhou, Henan 450003 **W:** radiohenan. com News Sce on 657kHz/95.4MHz/FM. 24h - Economic Sce on 738/972kHz/103.2MHz 24h - Traffic Sce on 104.1MHz 24h - Farm Sce "Green Ch.": on 900/107.4MHz 24h – Travel Sce "Private Car 999" on 99.9MHz 24h - Music Sce: on 88.1MHz/FM 24h - Visual Sce "My Radio": on 90.0MHz 24h - Entertainment Sce : on 1143kHz/97.6MHz 24h - Education Sce "UpRadio 1066": on 1332kHz/106.6MHz 24h - Leling (Senior Citizen) Sce on 603/1098kHz/105.6MHz 24h - Tianlai (Natural music) Sce on 93.6MHz 24h– **EN2)** 17 Shangwu Neihuan Lu, Zhengzhou, Henan 450018. News Sce on 549kHz/98.6MHz 24h (exc. Tues 0600-1000, Thurs 1600-2200) - Economic Sce "Chedao (Lane) 931": on 711kHz/93.1MHz 24h - "FM889": on 1008/792kHz/88.9MHz 24h - City Sce "Automobile 912": on 91.2MHz 24h - Music Sce "Huoli (Vitality) 944": on 94.4MHz 24h - Private Car Sce on 1458kHz/91.8MHz 24h - "Classic 1079": on 107.9MHz 24h – **EN3)** 78 Songcheng Lu, Kaifeng, Henan 475004. General Sce on 873kHz/98.6MHz 24h - News Sce on 101.4MHz 2200-1530 - Economic Sce on 100.2MHz 2155-1530 - Traffic Sce on 105.1MHz - New Farm Sce on 1053kHz/96.6MHz 2200-1530 (exc. Tues 0630-0955)– **EN4)** 67, Jiudu Lu, Luoyang, Henan 471009. News Sce "V.O. Heluo": on 576kHz/88.1MHz 2150-1600 - Economic Sce on 1053kHz/106.5MHz 2155-1600 - Traffic Sce on 92.7MHz 2155-1600 - Private Car Sce on 102.1MHz 2200-1600 – **EN5)** Zhong Duan, Jianshe Lu, Pingdingshan, Henan 467000. News Ch. on 747kHz/98.9MHz 2055-1500 - Private Car Sce on 1008kHz/105.8MHz 2155-1600 - Literary Sce on 846kHz 2200-1600, on 99.6MHz 24h - Traffic Sce on 1521kHz/96.4MHz 24h – **EN6)** 217 Jiefang Zhonglu, Jiaozuo, Henan 454002. News General Sce on 828kHz/103.0MHz 2200-1700 - Traffic and Travel Sce on 99.5MHz - Life and Literary Sce on 1251kHz/89.4MHz 2200-1700 (exc. Tues 0600-0955) – **EN7)** Zhong Duan, Huashan Lu, Hebi, Henan 458030. On 1107kHz/100.3MHz 2155-0535, 0955-1430 - Economic Ch. on 846kHz 2155-0535, 0955-1330 – **EN8)** 173 Renmin Lu, Weibin Qu, Xinxiang, Henan 453000. News General Sce on 801kHz/92.9MHz 2125-1600 (exc. Tues 0530-0955) - Traffic Sce on 1521kHz/99.1MHz 2155-1500 (exc. Tues 0500-0955) - Music Sce on 89.2MHz 24h - Private Car Sce on 90.3MHz 2200-1600 – **EN9)** Zhong Duan, Wenfeng Dadao, Anyang, Henan 455000. News Sce on 882kHz/94.2MHz 2155-1530 - Traffic Sce on 1251kHz/89.0MHz 2200-1400. - Automobile Music Sce on 100.8MHz 2155-1600 – **EN10)** Puyang Radio and TV St, 379 Zhongyuan Lu, Puyang, Henan 457000. News General Sce on 1251kHz/100.1MHz 2130-1535 (exc. Tues 0600-0900) - Economic Life Sce on 91.0MHz 2130-1530 - Traffic Sce on 89.5MHz 2100-1600 – **EN11)** 72 Balong Lu, Xiao Nanhai, Xuchang, Henan 461000. News Sce on 1287kHz/102.0MHz 2200-1500 - Traffic Sce on 92.6MHz 2130-1800 - Farm Sce on 927kHz 2150-1500 - Automobile Music Sce on 93.8MHz 2130-1800 – **EN12)** 152 Daxue Lu, Luohe, Henan 462000. News Sce on 1251kHz/89.0MHz 2055-1620 - Traffic and Music Sce on 106.7MHz 2155-1600 - City Sce "Car Radio": on 98.1MHz 2155-1600 – **EN12A)** 243 Haihe Lu, Luohe, Henan 462000

– **EN12B)** Luohe FM BS, 215 Shuanghui Lu, Luohe, Henan 462000. Life and Literary Sce on 93.6MHz 2230-1400 - Story Sce on 87.5MHz 2155-1430 – **EN13)** Zhong Duan, Jianshe Lu, Sanmenxia, Henan 472000. News General Ch. on 603kHz/90.8MHz 2155-1605 (exc. Tues 0530-0955) - Literary and Traffic Ch. on 1008kHz/104.0MHz 2255-1500 (exc. Tues 0530-1000) - Story Sce on 100.0MHz 24h - New Farm Sce on 98.9MHz – **EN14)** Zhong Duan, Funiu Lu, Nanyang, Henan 473000. News Sce on 104.2MHz 2130-1605 - General Sce on 585kHz/93.6MHz 2130-1605 - Literary Sce on 927kHz/106.0MHz 2130-1605 - Traffic Sce on 97.7/101.0MHz 2155-1605 - Story Sce on 106.0MHz 2130-1605 – **EN15)** Xinyang Radio and TV St, 19 Dongfanghong Dadao, Xinyang, Henan 464000. General Sce on 837kHz 2155-1500 - News Sce on 99.8MHz 2155-1600 - Economic Sce on 106.8MHz 2155-1600 - Traffic Sce on 94.8MHz 2155-1600 - Automobile Sce on 105.8MHz 2300-1600 - Music Sce on 88.8MHz – **EN16)** 35 Xinjian Nanlu, Shangqiu, Henan 476000. News Sce on 729kHz/89.0MHz 2100-1500 - City Sce on 927kHz/100.7MHz 2155-1605 - Traffic Sce on 94.5MHz 2200-1700 - Music Sce on 91.4MHz 24h – **EN17)** 10, Dong Duan, Jianshe Lu, Zhoukou, Henan 466000. News Sce on 828kHz 2050-1515 - Economic Life Sce on 567kHz 2050-1600 - Traffic Sce on 89.3MHz - Music Sce on 96.0MHz – **EN18)** 209 Wenhua Lu, Zhumadian, Henan 463000. News Sce on 810kHz 2125-? - Traffic and Travel Sce on 102.4MHz 2200-1600 - City Sce on 97.2MHz - Literary Sce on 1053kHz – **EN19)** Lianmeng Xiaoqu, Chengguan Zhen, Qinyang, Henan 454550 – **EN20)** 25 Xi Dajie, Huixian, Henan 453600 – **EN21)** 10 Qianqiu Lu, Yima, Henan 472300 – **EN22)** 30 Guangyu Lu, Ruzhou 467500 – **EN23)** Dufu Lu, Gongyi, Henan 451200. On 765kHz/98.2MHz 2155-1600 - Sunshine Ch. on 107.5MHz 2155-1530

## FUJIAN PROVINCE

**FJ1)** 128 Xihuan Nan Lu, Fuzhou, Fujian 350004 **W:** fjrtv.net News General Sce on 558/612/837/882/900/1368/1377/ 1386/1395/1404 /1449/1494/5040kHz/ 91.0/94.4/96.5/96.7/103.6/103.7/103.9/105.1/ 106.7MHz 24h (exc. Tues 0630-0855) in Ch and Amoy - City Life Sce on 98.7/101.5MHz 24h - Traffic Sce on 87.6/100.7MHz 24h (exc. Tues 0600-0850) - Automobile Music FM on 91.3/101.2/101.5MHz 24h (exc. Tues 0600-0900) - Fujian EBS "Caijing 961": on 1404/1467kHz/88.5/89 .6/95.5/96.1/96.8/ 98.6/103.1/104.8/104.9/105.4MHz 2200-1600 in Ch and Amoy – **FJ2)** Fuzhou Radio and TV, 1 Yuanyang Lu, Fuzhou, Fujian 350004. News Sce on 1332kHz/94.4MHz 24h (exc. Wed 0605-0925) in Ch and Fuzhou dialect — Music Sce on 89.3MHz 24h (exc. Thurs 0600-0900) - V.O. the Traffic: on 87.6MHz 24h - V.O. Zuohai: on 90.1MHz 24h in Fuzhou dialect – **FJ3)** 121 Hubin Beilu, Xiamen, Fujian 361012. News Sce on 1107kHz/99.6MHz 2130-1700 (exc. Tues 0600-0900) in Ch and Amoy - Economic and Traffic Sce on 1278kHz/107.0MHz 2200-1700 (exc. Tues 0600-0900) - V.O. Minnan: on 801kHz/101.2MHz 2200-1600 in Amoy - Music Sce on 90.9MHz 24h (exc. Tues 0600-0830) - Travel Sce on 1008kHz/94.0MHz 2200-1600 – **FJ4)** Putian PBS, 95 Dongzhen Lu, Licheng Qu, Putian, Fujian 351100. News General Sce on 93.7MHz 2130-1800 in Ch and Puxian dialect - Music and Traffic Sce on 103.0MHz 2130-1800 – **FJ5)** Quanzhou Radio and TV St, 1 Guangdian Lu, Quanzhou, Fujian 362000. News Sce on 576kHz/88.9MHz 24h - Economic and Life Sce on 92.3MHz 24h - Traffic Sce on 90.4MHz 24h (exc. Tues 0500-0900) V.O.the Music on 88.1MHz 24h - V.O. Citong: on 105.9MHz 24h in Quanzhou dialect– **FJ6)** Longyan PBS, Longyan Dadao, Longyan, Fujian 364000. News General Ch. on 92.5/106.0MHz 2158-1650 (exc. Tues 0630-0900) - V.O. the Travel: on 94.6MHz 2158-1600 (exc. Tues 0600-0900) – **FJ7)** Zhangzhou PBS, 1199, Jiulong Dadao, Xiangcheng District, Zhangzhou, Fujian 363000. News General Sce on 89.6/96.2MHz 2200-1700 in Ch and Amoy - Traffic Sce on 96.6/92.7MHz 2200-1700 (exc. Tues 0600-1000) – **FJ8)** Sanming PBS, 32 Zhuang, Liedong Shuangyuan Xincun, Sanming, Fujian 365000. News General Ch. on 97.5/103.4MHz 2155-1600 - Traffic and Music Sce on 105.6MHz

## GUANGDONG PROVINCE

**GD1)** 686 Renmin Beilu, Guangzhou, Guangdong 510012 **W:** rgd.com. cn Satellite Sce (News Ch.) on 648/828/846/1017/1206kHz/91.4/9 1.8/94.9/ 98.5/100.4/101.0/101.7/102.2MHz 24h - V.O. the City: on 103.6/92.6MHz 24h - Yangcheng Traffic St. on 105.2MHz 24h in Ch and Cantonese - Southern Life Sce on 999kHz/93.6MHz 24h - Stock Sce "Finance and Economics 927" on 927kHz/95.3MHz 2300-1600 - V.O. the Music: on 1008kHz/99.3/93.9/96.8/96.9/99.2/MHz 2100-1600 - Literary and Sports Sce on 603kHz/102.0/104.2/107.5/107.7MHz 24h – **GD2)** Zhujiang EBS, 686 Renmin Beilu, Guangzhou, Guangdong 510012. **W:** e974.com On 1062/747/801/ 927/1008/1062/1161kHz/ 92.0/97.4/98.7/103.0/103.8MHz 24h in Cantonese – **GD3)** 231 Huanshi Zhonglu, Guangzhou, Guangdong 510010 **W:** gztv.com News Information Sce "Fengyun 962": on 96.2/99.8MHz 24h in Cantonese-Automobile and Music Sce "Golden Melody" on 102.7MHz 24h in Cantonese - Traffic Sce "Jiaotong 1061": on 1098kHz/106.1MHz 24h (exc. Mon 1600-2200) - Youth Sce "Feiyang 88":on 1170kHz/88.0MHz 24h (exc. Mon Sun-Fry1600-2300) – **GD4)** 18F, Block 1, Phoenix

Building 2008 Shennan Road, Futian Qu, Shenzhen, Guangdong 518026 **W**: uradio.cc U Radio on 105.7MHz 24h in Ch –**GD5)** 1 Pengcheng 1 Lu, Futian Qu, Shenzhen, Guangdong 518026 **W**: szmg. com.cn News Ch. on 900kHz/89.8MHz 24h (exc. Tues 0530-0930) in Ch and Cantonese - Life Sce on 1287kHz/94.2MHz 24h in Ch and Cantonese - – Music Sce "Feiyang 971": on 97.1MHz 24h in Ch - Traffic Ch. on 106.2MHz 2230-1900 – **GD6)** 1129 Dong, Jiuzhou Dadao, Xiangzhou Qu, Zhuhai, Guangdong 519015. "Xianfeng 951": on 95.1MHz 24h in Ch and Cantonese - Traffic and Literature Sce "Jiaotong 875" on 900kHz87.5MHz 24h in Ch and Cantonese -"V.O. Lark" on 612kHz/91.5MHz 24h – **GD7)** Shantou Radio and TV St, 48 Chaoshan Lu, Shantou, Guangdong 515021. V.O. News Information: on 1080kHz/99.3MHz 24h in Ch and Chaozhou dialect - Music Ch. and Automobile Sce on 102.5MHz 24h –V.O. the Traffic: on 107.2MHz 24h (exc. Wed 0600-0900) in Ch and Chaozhou dialect – **GD8)** 57 Huimin Beilu, Shaoguan, Guangdong 512026. General Ch. on 105.7MHz 2030-1600 in Ch - Traffic and Travel Sce "V.O. Beijing" on 765kHz/97.5MHz 2030-1600 in Ch and Cantonese – **GD9)** Heyuan PBS, 1 Xingyuan Donglu, Yuancheng Qu, Heyuan, Guangdong 517000. General Sce on 91.1MHz in Ch and Cantonese - Travel and Traffic Sce on 97.8MHz – **GD10)** 42 Dong Jiaochang Bei, Meizhou, Guangdong 514011. News St. on 94.8/97.8MHz 2200-1600 in Ch and Hakka - Traffic St. on 105.8MHz 2200-1600 – **GD11)** Huizhou Radio and TV St, 13 Nantan Beilu, Huicheng Qu, Huizhou, Guangdong 516001. News and General- Ch.: on 100.0/88.3MHz 2230-1630 (exc. Tues 0030-0830) in Ch and Cantonese - Traffic and Economic Environment St. on /98.8MHz 2230-1600 - Music St.: on 90.7MHz 2230-1730 – **GD12)** Shanwei PBS, Zhong Duan, Shanwei Dadao, Shanwei, Guangdong 516600. News General Sce on 103.5MHz 0030-1600 in Ch and Hakka - Farm Sce on 91.3MHz 0033-1600– **GD13)** Dongguan PBS, 35 Xizheng Lu, Cheng Qu, Dongguan, Guangdong 523000. General Ch. on 100.8MHz 24h in Ch and Cantonese - Traffic Ch. on 107.5MHz 24h in Ch and Cantonese – Music Ch. on 104.0MHz 2300-1600– **GD14)** Zhongshan PBS, 4 Xingzhong Dao, Dong Qu, Zhongshan, Guangdong 528403. General Ch. on 96.7MHz 2200-1800 in Ch and Cantonese - Environment and Travel Sce on 88.8MHz 2200-1800 in Ch and Cantonese – **GD15)** Jiangmen PBS, 178 Fazhan Dadao, Jiangmen, Guangdong 529000. News General St. on 100.2MHz 2300-1630 in Ch and Cantonese - Music St. on 93.3MHz 2200-1500 in Ch and Cantonese – **GD16)** Foshan PBS, Jihua 6 Lu, Chancheng Qu, Foshan, Guangdong 528000. General Sce True Love 946 Sce on 94.6MHz 24h in Cantonese - Thousand Colors 985 Sce on 98.5MHz 24h (exc. Sun 1500-2400) in Cantonese - Traffic Ch. on 92.4MHz 24h - Be Jumbled Together 906 Sce on 90.6MHz 24h - Shunde 901 Sce on 90.1MHz 2225-1600 - Enjoy a Sightseeing Tour 883 Sce on 88.3MHz 24h – **GD17)** Yangjiang PBS, 114 Mojiang Lu, Jiangcheng Qu, Yangjiang, Guangdong 529500. General Sce: on 91.6MHz 2200-1700 in Ch and Cantonese –Education and Music Sce: on 96.4MHz 2200-1700 in Ch and Cantonese – **GD18)** Zhanjiang Radio and TV St, 123 Haibin Dadao Bei, Chikan Qu, Zhanjiang, Guangdong 524044. News Sce on 98.1MHz 2220-1700 in Ch, Cantonese and Leizhou dialect Economic Sce on 95.1MHz 2220-1700 - Traffic and Music Sce on 102.1MHz 2300-1600 – **GD19)** Maoming Radio and TV St, 1 Yingbin 4lu, Maoming, Guangdong. General Sce: on 101.1MHz 2250-1600 in Ch and Cantonese - VO Farming Area on 106.1MHz 2220-1600 – Traffic Sce on 93.5MHz 2245-1600 – **GD20)** Xinghu Dadao, Zhaoqing, Guangdong 526060. General Sce on 1521kHz/92.9MHz 2250-1600 in Ch and Cantonese - Traffic and Music Sce on 94.9MHz 2200-1600 in Ch and Cantonese – **GD21)** Qingyuan PBS, 18 Yinquan Lu, Qingcheng District, Qingyuan, Guangdong 511515. News General Sce on 88.7MHz 2225-1600 in Ch and Cantonese – Traffic and Travel Sce on 97.8MHz 2225-1600 in Ch and Cantonese –**GD22)** Jieyang PBS, Jinxianmen Dadao, Jieyang, Guangdong 522000.General Sce: on 103.9MHz 2230-1700 - Agricultural Sce: on 106.5MHz 2330-1600 in Jieyang dialect - Traffic and Travel Sce: on 95.2MHz – **GD23)** Jiedong PBS, Zhongxin Dadao, Jiedong, Guangdong 515500. On 100.2MHz 2220-1700 – **GD24)** Yunfu PBS, Baoma Lu, Yunfu, Guangdong 527300. General Sce on 100.6MHz 2220-1600 – Traffic and Music Sce on 96.4MHz 2220-1600

## GANSU PROVINCE

**GS1)** 561 Zhangsutan, Chengguan Qu, Lanzhou, Gansu 730010. **W**: gstv.com.cn News Sce on 684/873/1008kHz/96.0MHz 2150-1605 (exc. Tues 0600-0850) - City FM "Happy Radio" on 106.6MHz 24h –City FM "Heart FM 102.2" on 102.2MHz 2200-1700 - Economic Sce "U Radio" on 801kHz/93.4MHz 2255-1700 - Traffic Sce on 103.5/104.8MHz 24h - Youth FM: on 104.8MHz 2250-1600 - Farm Sce "Gansu Rural Radio" on 1170kHz/92.2MHz 2225-1700 (exc. Tues 0600-0850) – **GS2)** 92 Qingyang Lu, Lanzhou, Gansu 730030. News Sce on 954kHz/97.3MHz 2125-1700 - Traffic and Music Sce on 99.5MHz 2200-1900 (exc. Mon 0600-1000) - Private Car Sce "Happy FM 1008" on 100.8MHz 2055-1630 – **GS3)** 6 Yan'an Xilu, Jinchang, Gansu 737100. News General Sce on 585kHz/101.4MHz 2150-1600 - Traffic and Literary Sce on 103.8MHz 24h **GS4)** Tianshui Radio and TV St, 11-5 Huancheng

Zhonglu, Qincheng Qu, Tianshui, Gansu 741000. News General Sce on 1143kHz/98.2MHz 2220-1600 - Music and Literary Sce on 93.7MHz 2225-1600 – **GS5)** 10 Fuqiang Xilu, Jiayuguan, Gansu 735100 – **GS6)** Gannan Radio and TV St, 49 Xi 2 Lu, Hezuo, Gansu 747000. On 1332/3990/5970kHz/97.2MHz 2250-0100, 1020-1410 in Ch and Tb – **GS7)** 45 Tuanjie Lu, Linxia, Gansu 731100. 2255-0130(Sun 0230) – **GS8)** 45 Hongqi Jie, Kongtong Qu, Pingliang, Gansu 744000. 2200-1500 – **GS9)** Gongyuan Lu, Zhongping Qu, Yumen, Gansu 735200

## GUANGXI ZHUANG AUTONOMOUS REGION

**GX1)** 75 Minzu Dadao, Nanning, Guangxi 530022. **W**: gxradio.com Satellite Sce on 792/1071/1440/1485/1575kHz/FM. 91.1/91.4/91.9 24h (exc. Tues 0500-0930) - Anchorwomen BS "Hostess Radio" on 1224kHz/97.0/97.4/105.1MHz 24h (exc. Tues 0500-0830) in Ch and Guangxi dialect - Private Car 930: on 93.0/88.5/90.1/92.3/96.9MHz 2200-1700 (exc. Tues 0500-0930) in Ch and Zhuang - Traffic St. on 100.3/106.3MHz 2200-1700 (exc. Tues 0500-0930) - Literary Sce on 95.0/105.0MHz 24h (exc. Tues 0500-0930) - Modern 104 on 104.0MHz – **GX2)** Nanning PBS, 25 Gecun Lu, Nanning, Guangxi 530012. News General Ch. on 101.4MHz 2055-1700 in Ch and Guangxi dialect - Scripture Sce on 104.9MHz 24h - Traffic and Music Sce on 107.4MHz 2240-1600 - Story Sce "Success 895" on 89.5MHz 24h – **GX3)** 1 Guizhou Dadao, Liuzhou, Guangxi 545006. News Sce on 1386kHz/102.9MHz 2200-1700 in Ch and Liuzhou dialect - Traffic Sce "Love Radio": on 99.1MHz 2200-1700 - Country Life Sce on 105.9MHz 2200-1700 – **GX4)** 1 Anxin Beilu, Xiangshan Qu, Guilin, Guangxi 541002." V.O. the City" on 1485kHz/97.7MHz 2200-1600, - "Take off FM" on 88.3MHz 2200-1600 – Beloved 912 on 91.2MHz 2200-1600 – **GX5)** 69 Xinxing 3 Lu, Wuzhou, Guangxi 543002. News Sce on 1485kHz/100.8MHz 2200-1630 in Ch and Guangxi dialect - V.O. the Music and Traffic on 107.5MHz 2200-1300 (exc. Mon) – **GX6)** Beihai PBS, 36 Guizhou Nanlu, Beihai, Guangxi 536000. News General Sce on 93.5/88.4MHz 2200-1700 (exc. Tues 0500-0930) in Ch and Guangxi dialect - Economic Music and Traffic Sce on 99.1MHz 2200-1700 (exc. Tues 0500-0930) – **GX7)** Qinzhou PBS, 18 Liqiao Jie, Qinzhou, Guangxi 535000. News General Sce on 98.6MHz 2220-1645 (exc. Tues 0500-0930) - Music Sce on 88.9MHz 2220-1645 (exc. Tues 0500-0930) – **GX8)** Yulin PBS, 1 Guangdian Lu, Yulin, Guangxi 537000. News Sce on 97.8MHz 2200-1700 (exc. Tues 0600-0900) - Traffic and Music St. on 99.2MHz 2200-1700 – **GX9)** Bose PBS, Huochezhan Jinzhan Dadao, Bose, Guangxi 533000. News and General Sce on 105.2MHz 2200-1700 – Music Sce on 87.6MHz 2200-1700 – **GX10)** Hechi PBS, 457 Jincheng Zhong Lu, Hechi, Guangxi 547000. News and General Sce on 98.7MHz – **GX11)** Fangchenggang PBS, Xianren Shanding, Fangchenggang, Guangxi 538001. General Sce on 101.9MHz in Ch Vietnamese and Zhuang

## GUIZHOU PROVINCE

**GZ1)** Guizhou Radio and TV St, 302 Qingyun Lu, Guiyang, Guizhou 550002 **W**: gzstv.com General Sce on 765/927/1026kHz/7275kHz/94.6MHz/FM 24h - Economic Sce on 603kHz/98.9MHz 24h - Travel Sce on 97.2MHz 24h - Traffic Sce on 95.2MHz 24h - City Sce on 106.2MHz 24h - Music Sce on 91.6MHz 24h (exc. Tues 0600-0900) - Chinese IntellectualStory Sce on 90.0MHz 24h – **GZ2)** 15 Zunyi Lu, Nanming Qu, Guiyang, Guizhou 550002. **W**: qguiyang.cn General Sce on 999kHz/88.9MHz 24h - Female Sce on 104.0MHz 24h - Traffic Sce on 102.7MHz 24h - Music Sce "Dynamic 909" on 90.9MHz 24h – **GZ3)** 31 Minghu Lu, Zhongshan Qu, Liupanshui, Guizhou 553001. News General Ch. on 711kHz/99.8MHz 2225-1800 - Traffic Ch. on 93.8MHz - Music Ch. on 102.1MHz 2225-1800 – **GZ4)** 11 Daxing Lu, Honghuagang Qu, Zunyi, Guizhou 563000. General Sce, on 1584kHz/98.2MHz 2227-1600 - Traffic and Literary Sce on 94.1MHz 2225-1805 - Travel Life Sce on 88.0MHz 2230-1800 – **GZ5)** 34 Guihuang Xilu, Anshun, Guizhou 561000. News General Sce, on 666kHz/105.9MHz - Traffic Sce on 102.9MHz – **GZ6)** Qiannan PBS, 267 Huandong Zhonglu, Duyun, Guizhou 558000. News General Ch. on 882kHz/98.0MHz 2200-1530 - Traffic and Travel Ch. on 93.3/92.2MHz 2225-1600 – **GZ7)** Qiandongnan PBS, 34 Beijing Donglu, Kaili, Guizhou 556000, On 104.9MHz/FM 2230-1600 – **GZ8)** Qianxinan PBS, Xingyi Guangchang Pang, Xingyi, Guizhou 562400. News General Sce on 107.9MHz 2225-1700(Sun 1600) in Ch, Buyi and Miao - Traffic and Travel Sce on 88.3MHz 2225-1700 (Sun 1600)

## HAINAN PROVINCE

**HA1)** Hainan Radio and TV St, 61 Nansha Lu, Haikou, Hainan 570206 **W**: channel bluehm.com News Sce on 954/1107/1116kHz/88.6MHz/ FM 24h in Ch and Hainan dialect - V.O. International Tour Island: on 103.8/95.0/99.0/106.8MHz 2200-1700 - Traffic Sce on 1143kHz/100.0/89.3MHz 2255-1805 - Music Sce "Dongting 945": on 94.5/91.3/91.6MHz 2200-1700 - People Life Sce on 101.0MHz 2200-1700 in Ch and Hainan dialect – **HA2)** Haikou Radio and TV St, 15 Zhongsha Lu, Haikou, Hainan 570206. News General Sce on 101.8MHz 2155-1800 in Ch and Hainan dialect - City and Country Sce on 95.4MHz - Music Sce "Simul Radio" : on 91.6MHz 2155-1800 – **HA3)** Sanya Radio and TV St, Jiefang 4 Lu, Sanya, Hainan 572000. V.O. Tianya: on

104.6MHz 2200-1700 - Traffic Ch. on 100.3MHz

## HUBEI PROVINCE

**HB1)** 1237 Jiefang Dadao, Hankou, Wuhan, Hubei 430022 **W:** hbtv.com.cn News General Sce "V.O. Hubei": on 774/1404/1566kHz/104.6MHz/FM 2000-1735 (exc. Tues 0700-0850) - Information Sce on 1179/927/945/1008kHz 1955-1700 (exc. Tues 0630-0855) - Economic Sce on 1053/1251kHz/99.8MHz/FM 1940-1800 - Life Sce on 801/846/900/927/1098/ 1143/1215kHz/96.6MHz 24h - Farm Sce on 684/801/846/900/945/1125/1143kHz/91.2MHz/FM 24h (exc. Tues 0630-0855) - Private Car (Sports and Travel) Sce on 107.8/88.0/90.4MHz 24h - Fashion and Women Sce on 747/1206kHz/97.1/102.6MHz 2000-1700 - Classic Music Sce on 103.8MHz 24h - Chutian Traffic Sce on 92.7MHz 24h (exc. Tues 0630-0855) - Chutian Music Sce on 684kHz/105.8MHz/FM 24h (exc. Tues 0630-0855).– **HB3)** 620 Jianshe Dadao, Hankou, Wuhan, Hubei 430015. **W:** whtv.com.cn/audio/ General Sce on 873kHz/88.4MHz 2030-1700 - Changjiang Economic Sce on 1125kHz/100.6MHz 2030-1700 - Traffic Sce on 603kHz/89.6MHz 2100-1700 - Music Sce on 101.8MHz 2100-1700 - Children Sce "Pinwei 936" "i Radio": on 93.6MHz 2100-1600 – **HB5)** Guanghui Lu, Huangshi, Hubei 435000. News Sce on 963kHz/101.2MHz 2200-1600 - Traffic Sce on 103.3MHz 2200-1600 - Automobile Sce on 106.8MHz 2000-1800 – **HB6)** 200 Tanxi Lu, Fancheng Qu, Xiangyang, Hubei 441021. V.O. Xiangyang (News Sce): on 1098kHz/104.0MHz 2120-1635 (exc. Tues 0700-0830) - Music Sce on 1314kHz/90.9MHz 2130-1600. - Automobile Sce on 105.3MHz 2155-1635 (exc. Tues 0700-0830) - Traffic Sce "Dongli (Power) 890": on 89.0MHz 2155-1635 (exc. Tues 0700-0830) – **HB7)** 4 Renmin Beilu, Shiyan, Hubei 442000. News St. on 1485kHz/94.1MHz 2100-1600 - V.O. Checheng (Mobile City): on 99.1MHz 2200-1600 - Music and Traffic St. on 101.9MHz 2200-1700 (exc. Tues 0600-1000) – **HB8)** 266 Jiangjin Xilu, Shashi Qu, Jingzhou, Hubei 434000. V.O. Jingzhou: on 585kHz/97.2MHz 2200-1600 - General Sce on 828/1368kHz/98.4MHz 2030-1630 - 963 Beauty Music Sce on 96.3MHz 2200-1700 (exc. Tues 0700-0900) - 901 Automobile Sce on 90.1MHz 2130-1600. – **HB9)** 2 Guoyuan 1 Lu, Yichang, Hubei 443000. News General St. on 621kHz/95.6MHz 2100-1615 (exc. Tues 0600-0700) - Automobile St. on 106.6MHz 2130-1600 (exc. Tues 0600-0700) - Traffic and Music St. on 105.9MHz 2225-1645 (exc. Tues 0600-0700) – **HB10)** 100 Xiangshan Dadao, Dongbao Qu, Jingmen, Hubei 448000. News General Sce on 927kHz/96.6MHz 2150-1500 (exc. Tues 0600-1000) - City Life Sce on 1161kHz/89.7MHz 2130-1600 (exc. Tues 0600-1000) - Traffic and Music Sce on 99.3MHz 2200-1500 (exc. Tues 0600-1000) – **HB11)** 157 Binhu Lu, Ezhou, Hubei 436000. 2100-1600 – **HB12)** 116 Changzheng Lu, Xiaogan, Hubei 432100. News General Ch. on 927kHz/91.8MHz 2155-1530 (exc. Tues 0500-1000) - Traffic and Music Sce on 87.7MHz 2255-1505 – **HB13)** Huanggan PBS, 169 Dongmen Lu, Huangzhou Qu, Huanggang, Hubei 438000. News St. on 91.4MHz 2220-1600 - Traffic Sce on 107.6MHz 2220-1530 – **HB14)** 38 Wenquan Lu, Xianning, Hubei 437100. News Sce on 1314kHz/88.1MHz 2150-1505 (exc. Tues 0705-0905) - Traffic Sce on 95.9MHz 2220-1505 (exc. Tues 0705-0905) – **HB15)** 32 Xuefu Lu, Laohekou, Hubei 441800. 2220-0500, 0800-1400 – **HB16)** 4 Renmin Lu, Danjiangkou, Hubei 441900. News General Ch. on 1431kHz 2220-1600 – **HB17)** 2 Shannan Xiaoqu, Shishou, Hubei 434400. 2200-0005, 0955-1235 – **HB18)** 56 Guang'an Lu, Yingshan Zhen, Guangshui, Hubei 432700. 2155-0115, 0955-1305 – **HB19)** 146 Puyang Dadao, Yingcheng, Hubei 432400. 2200-0600, 0900-1305 – **HB20)** 199 Nanhuan Lu, Macheng, Hubei 436100. Educational and Music St. on 1242kHz/92.5/105.0MHz 2155-1430 – **HB21)** 50 Chunchuan Daqiao Lu, Chibi, Hubei 437300. 0950-1340 – **HB22)** 359 Lieshan Dadao, Suizhou, Hubei 441300. News St. on 1008kHz 2150-1600 - Traffic and Economic St. on 96.2MHz 2150-1600 – **HB23)** 117 Mianyang Dadao, Xiantao, Hubei 433000. 2130-1600 – **HB24)** 42 Zhanghua Nanlu, Yuanlin Zhen, Qianjiang, Hubei 433100. On 1242kHz/100.0MHz 2205-0445, 0930-1600 – **HB25)** 201 Hangkong Lu, Xiangzhou Qu, Xiangyang, Hubei 441104. On 1521kHz/96.5MHz 2155-1600 – **HB26)** 278 Dongfeng Dadao, Enshi, Hubei 445000. News General Sec on 1215kHz/99.0MHz- Traffic and Music Sce on 94.0MHz

## HEILONGJIANG PROVINCE

**HL1)** 333 Hanshui Lu, Nangang Qu, Harbin, Heilongjiang 150090 **W:** hljradio.com News St. on 621/900/927/1341/94.6MHz 2055-1800 - Private Car Ch. (Life Sce) on 104.5MHz/FM 24h (exc. Tues 1600-2100) - Traffic Sce on 99.8MHz/FM 2030-1700 - City Women Sce on 102.1MHz 24h - Favorite Home Ch. (Children Sce) on 97.0MHz/FM 24h - Music St. on 95.8MHz 24h (exc. Tues 1600-2100) - Country Sce on 945kHz/94.3MHz/FM 24h - University St. "Radio Young": on 99.3MHz/FM 2200-1600 - "873 Story Hour": on 873/1476kHz/FM 0000-1300 - Korean Sce on 873/1476kHz/FM 2100-2400, 1300-1500 in Ko - V.O. Beidahuang (Great Northern Wilderness): on 1476kHz/FM 2055-1600 – **HL2)** Harbin Radio and TV St, 1 Huashan Lu, Xiangyang Qu, Harbin, Heilongjiang 150036. News General Sce on 837kHz/94.1/105.6MHz 24h - Literary Sce on 98.4/97.8MHz 24h - Economic Sce on 972kHz. 24h (exc. Tues 0500-0900) - Traffic Sce on 92.5/95.3MHz 24h - Music

Sce on 927kHz/90.9/103.0MHz 24h - Automobile FM "Kuaile (Happy) 973": on 97.3/88.8MHz 24h – **HL3)** 99 Yong'an Dajie, Longsha Qu, Qiqihar, Heilongjiang 161005. News Sce on 1197kHz/87.8MHz 2000-1600(Tues 1405) - Life and Literary Sce on 693kHz/89.4/90.0MHz 2020-1505 - Traffic Sce on 94.1/98.0MHz 2050-1605 - Country Sce on 585kHz/103.4/87.5MHz – **HL4)** Jiuma Lu, Xiangyang Qu, Hegang, Heilongjiang 154100. News Sce on 1413kHz/97.2/101.4/107.6MHz 2055-1400 - Traffic and Literary Sce on 106.1MHz 2145-1400 - Life Sce on 93.3MHz – **HL5)** Shuangyashan Radio and TV St, 240 Xinxing Dajie, Jianshan Qu, Shuangyashan, Heilongjiang 155100. News Sce on 1179kHz/103.2/101.5MHz 2120-1230 - Traffic and Literary Sce on 99.5/98.1MHz - Country Life Sce on 98.6/104.2MHz - Storytelling Sce on 603kHz/88.6/94.6MHz – **HL6)** 11 Diantai Lu, Jiguan Qu, Jixi, Heilongjiang 158100. News General Sce on 1368kHz/94.5MHz 2130-0600, 0850-1350 - Traffic Sce on 1485kHz/95.9MHz - Literary and Life Sce on 1143kHz/98.6MHz - Storytelling Sce on 103.9MHz 2055-1500 – **HL7)** Jia 1, Dongfeng Lu, Sa'ertu Qu, Daqing, Heilongjiang 163311. General Sce on 1080kHz/96.7/97.5MHz 24h - Traffic Sce on 95.0MHz 24h - Music Sce on 106.0MHz 1955-1600.- Storytelling Sce on 90.9MHz 24h - V.O. Baihu: on 91.9MHz 2000-1600 – **HL8)** 16 Linshan Lu, Yichun Qu, Yichun, Heilongjiang 153000. News General Sce on 909kHz/92.4/102.1MHz 2130-0810 (exc. Mon 0725-1000) - Traffic and Life Sce on 98.5MHz 2200-1400 – **HL9)** 138 Taiping Lu, Mudanjiang, Heilongjiang 157000. News Sce on 684kHz/87.9MHz 2105-1400 (exc. Tues 0800-0855) - Life and Story Sce on 1476kHz/91.6MHz 2200-1530 - Traffic and Literary Sce on 98.2MHz 2300-1300 – **HL10)** 35 Shunhe Lu, Jiamusi, Heilongjiang 154002. News General Sce on 666kHz/101.7MHz 2055-0530, 0855-1400 - Economic Sce on 1143kHz/95.0MHz 2055-1600 - Traffic and Literary Sce on 98.0/93.8MHz 2225-1600 – **HL11)** 2 Shanhu Dajie, Taoshan Qu, Qitaihe, Heilongjiang 154600. News General Ch. on 1062kHz/89.9MHz 2300-1545 - Traffic Ch. on 98.8MHz – **HL12)** 255 Huanghe Beilu, Suihua, Heilongjiang 152054, Traffic Sce on 90.7MHz 2155-1400 - Farm Sce on 101.1MHz 2150-?- Music Sce on 1080kHz/97.4MHz - Storytelling Sce on 107.0MHz – **HL13)** 2 Xing'an Dajie, Jagdaqi Zhen, Heilongjiang 165000. Peoples Sce on 1278kHz/100.1MHz 2125-1400 (exc. Tues 0600-0955) – **HL14)** 310 Shengdao, Aihui Qu, Heihe, Heilongjiang 164300. General Sce on 1215kHz/103.8/107.3MHz 2100-1400 – **HL15)** 89 Xing'an Jie, Aihui Qu, Heihe, Heilongjiang 164300. V.O.Ai-Guang: on 999kHz/91.2MHz 2220-1500 (exc. Tues 0600-0850)

## HUNAN PROVINCE

**HN1)** Hunan Radio & TV St. Liuyang He Daqiao Dong, Changsha, Hunan 410003 **W:** hnradio.com News General Ch. on 738/1152/1233/4990kHz/102.8MHz 2100-1700 (exc. Tues 0500-0900) - V.O. Xiaoxiang "News 938": on 900kHz/93.8/100.7MHz 24h - Economic Sce "Meili (Charm) 901": on FM 2130-1700 (exc. Tues 0500-0900) - Literary Sce "Qingchun 975": on 97.5/87.5/90.6/90.8/96.9MHz 24h (exc. Tues 0500-0900) - Traffic Ch. on 91.8MHz/FM 24h - V.O. the Music: on 89.3/102.1MHz 24h - Travel Ch. on 106.9MHz 2100-1600 - Jinying (Golden Hawk) 955 BS."Big Eye BS": on 95.5/91.3/100.5MHz 24h – **HN2)** Changsha Broadcast &TV Group, 989 1duan Xiangfu Donglu, Changsha, Hunan 410016. City News Sce on 1323kHz/105.0MHz 24h (exc. Tues 0600-0900). - Economic Sce "Hi 886": on 88.6MHz 24h - Traffic and Music Sce "i Radio": on 106.1MHz 24h - Sound of City on 101.7MHz 24h – **HN2A)** Changsha Pinwei (Taste) Music BS . 52 Xiangjiang Zhonglu, Changsha, Hunan 410008. On 102.2MHz 24h – **HN2B)** Changsha 925 Yue BS "U Radio", 3 Laodong Zhonglu, Changsha, Hunan 410007. On 92.5MHz 24h – **HN3)** Zhuzhou Radio and TV St, 658 Taishan Lu, Tianyuan Qu, Zhuzhou, Hunan 412000. News Ch. on 1089kHz/101.2MHz 24h - Traffic Ch. on 98.4MHz 24h – **HN4)** Xiangtan Radio and TV St, Donghu Lu, Xiangtan, Hunan 411104. Mango Radio "V.O. Xiangtan": on 1503kHz/98.6MHz 24h - Traffic Ch. on 104.2MHz 2200-1600 - Da Yanjing (Big Eye) BS: on 106.5MHz 24h - Le Shenghuo (Happy Life) FM on 97.8MHz – **HN5)** 114 Xianfeng Lu, Hengyang, Hunan 421001. News Ch. on 1071kHz/98.9MHz 24h - Traffic Ch. on 101.8MHz 24h – **HN6)** Shaoyang Radio and TV St, 373 Zhangshulong, Baoqing Xilu, Daxiang Qu, Shaoyang, Hunan 422000. Traffic Ch. on 95.4/87.7MHz 2200-1700 - Music Ch. "Feiyang 928": on 92.8MHz 2300-1700 – **HN7)** Yueyang Radio and TV St, 421 Nanhu Dadao, Yueyang, Hunan 414000. News General Ch. on 1053kHz/104.1MHz 2120-1700 - Traffic and Music Ch. on 1008kHz/106.1/104.5MHz 2155-1700 – **HN8)** Changde Radio and TV St, 267 Wuling Dadao, Changde, Hunan 415000. News Ch. on 1260kHz/105.6MHz 2225-1705 - Traffic Ch. on 97.1MHz 2200-1600 - City Traffic and Music Sce on 98.5MHz – **HN9)** Chaoyang Lu, Yiyang, Hunan 413000. Mango Radio "V.O. Yiyang": on 1053kHz/99.7MHz 2200-1600 (exc. Wed 0800-1000) - Traffic Ch. on 88.1MHz 2200-1600 – **HN10)** 51 Renmin Lu, Jinshi, Hunan 415400 – **HN11)** Chenzhou PBS, 7 Li Dadao, Chenzhou, Hunan 423000. Automobile and Music Ch. on 99.2/89.9MHz 2200-1730 - Traffic Ch. on 102.8MHz 2200-1730 - Private Car Ch on 105.5MHz 24h - "Chenzhou My FM": on 88.3MHz – **HN12)** Huaihua PBS, Tianxing Lu, Huaihua,

Hunan 418000. City Control Sce on 97.2/107.6MHz 2230-1600 (exc. Tues 0400-0900) - Traffic Ch. on 103.8MHz 2220-1600

## JILIN PROVINCE

**JL1)** 2066 Weixing Lu, Changchun, Jilin 130033 **W:** jlradio.cn News General Sce on 738/1107/1521/1530kHz/91.6MHz 24h (exc. Tues 0500-0900) - Economic Sce on 603/846/1143kHz/93.3MHz 24h - Health and Entertainment Sce on 101.9MHz 24h (exc Tues 1500-1800) - Traffic Sce on 103.8MHz 24h - Information Sce on 100.1MHz 24h (exc. Tues 1500-1800) - Music Sce on 92.7MHz 24h (exc Tues 1500-1800) - Country Sce on 97.6MHz/FM 24h - Travel Sce on 103.3/94.7/107.7MHz 24h - Educational Sce "Gushi (Story) 963": on 96.3MHz 24h — **JL2)** 149 Baicao Lu, Chaoyang Qu, Changchun, Jilin 130061. News Sce on 900kHz/88.9MHz 24h - Life and Story Sce on 1332kHz/90.0MHz 24h "Changchung My FM": on 88.0MHz 24h (exc. SS1602-2200) - V.O. the Traffic: on 96.8/100.6MHz 24h - City Music Sce "Private Car Radio": on 106.3MHz 24h - City Elite Sce "Top Radio": on 585kHz/99.6MHz 24h— **JL3)** Nanjing Lu, Chuanying Qu, Jilin-shi, Jilin 132011. News Ch. on 927kHz/102.6MHz 24h - V.O. Old Age: on 702kHz/97.0MHz 24h - Traffic Ch. on 105.3MHz 24h - Music and Story St. on 1143kHz/94.0MHz 24h - Automobile Life St. on 88.3MHz 24h — **JL3A)** Jilin EBS, 2 Nanjing Lu, Chuanying Qu, Jilin-shi, Jilin 132011. Dushi (city) 110: on 1494kHz/90.3MHz 24h - V.O. the Health: on 603kHz/92.6MHz 24h - City Life Sce on 89.3MHz 2030-1700 - V.O. Jiangcheng Music: on 1251kHz/91.3MHz 24h — **JL4)** 39 Nan Xinhua Dajie, Siping, Jilin 136000. News General Ch. on 666kHz/93.9MHz 2100-1600 - Traffic and Literary St. on 99.5MHz 24h - Public Storytelling St. on 900kHz/90.5MHz 2100-1500 — **JL5)** Liaoyuan Radio and TV St, 20 Hebin Lu, Longshan Qu, Liaoyuan, Jilin 136200. General Ch. on 810kHz/99.2MHz - Traffic and Literary Sce on 96.2MHz 2125-1500 — **JL6)** Radio St Tong Hua, 199 Cuiquan Lu, Longquan Jie, Tonghua, Jilin 134001. **W:** 909radio.com News Sce on 909kHz/102.8MHz 2100-1500 (exc. Tues 0705-0855) - City Sce on 90.9MHz 2200-1400 - Traffic Sce on 104.7MHz 2140-1700 - Story Sce on 97.9MHz 2150-1400 — **JL7)** 36 Hunjiang Dajie, Badaojiang Qu, Baishan, Jilin 134302. News General Sce on 657kHz/107.7/95.8MHz 2100-1530 - Traffic Sce on 98.4MHz 2100-1500 — **JL8)** 1295 Linjiang Donglu, Ningjiang Qu, Songyuan, Jilin 138000. News General Sce on 1431kHz/89.9MHz 2100-1500 - Traffic and Literary Sce on 1143kHz/100.0MHz 24h - Public Life Sce on 98.6/96.8MHz 24h - Story Sce on 102.5MHz 24h — **JL9)** Baicheng Radio and TV St, 86 Xingfu Nan Dajie, Baicheng, Jilin 137000. News General Sce on 1323kHz/103.0MHz 24h (exc. Tues 0630-0940) - Traffic Sce on 96.5MHz - Literary Sce on 105.8MHz - Storytelling Sce on 98.5MHz — **JL10)** 166 Juzi Jie, Yanji, Jilin 133000. **W:** cn.iybtv.com Ch Satellite Sce on 1053/603/1566kHz/FM 2130-1630 in Ch & Ko - Ch News Sce on 88.2/91.7/92.2/98.3MHz in Ch - Ko News General Sce on 1206kHz/94.9MHz 2040-1600 (exc. Tues 0540-0900) in Ko & Ch - Ko Cultural Life Sce on 585/1188kHz/104.6MHz in Ko 2130-1510 - Traffic and Literary Sce on 105.9MHz 2130-1600 in Ch — **JL11)** 45 Dong Huancheng Lu, Gongzhuling, Jilin 136100. V.O. the Public: on 1485kHz 2050-1420 - V.O. the Traffic: on 101.3MHz — **JL12)** 18 Nan Dalu, Lishu Xian, Jilin 136500. V.O. the Northern Traffic: on 1575kHz/102.4MHz — **JL13)** 70 Henan Jie, Meihekou, Jilin 135000. V.O. the Traffic: on 1584kHz/95.7MHz 2155-1130 — **JL14)** 628 Qingzhen Jie, Qian Gorlos, Jilin 131100. On 1476kHz/91.0MHz 2125-2330, 0325-0500, 0955-1230 in Ch and Mo — **JL15)** Taonan PBS, 298 Tuanjie Xilu, Taonan, Jilin 137100 On 104.6MHz 2055-1500 — **JL16)** 7 Yongle Jie, Yanji, Jilin 133000. Ko Prgr. "Arirang Radio": on 900kHz/88.0MHz 2030-1600 - Yanji V.O. the Traffic BS: on 93.5MHz — **JL17)** 75 Yingchun Lu, Tumen, Jilin. 2155-1230 in Ch and Ko — **JL18)** 1-8 Xinhua Xilu, Dunhua, Jilin 133700. 2130-1500 in Ch and Ko — **JL19)** Jinghe Jie, Hunchun, Jilin 133300. Storytelling St. on 927kHz 2030-1530 in Ch and Ko - North East Asia V.O. Hunchun on 101.0MHz

## JIANGSU PROVINCE

**JS1)** Jiangsu Prov. Radio and TV Headquarters, 132 Zhongshan Donglu, Nanjing, Jiangsu 210002 **W:** jsbc.com News General Ch. on 702/801/1314/1413/1602kHz 2000-1700 (exc. Tues/Thurs 0600-0850) - News Sce on 93.7MHz/FM 2100-1600 - Home Sce on 107.1MHz 24h (exc. Tues 0600-0900, Wed 1700-2100) - Health Sce on 846/603/1098kHz/87.7/88.5MHz 24h (exc. Tues 0600-0900) - Financial and Economic Sce on 585kHz/95.2MHz 2000-1800 - Traffic Sce on 101.1MHz 24h (exc. Tues 1800-2000) - Story Sce on 1206kHz 24h - Music St. "Meili (Charm) 897": on 89.7/107.8MHz 24h (exc. Tues 0600-0900) - Classic Music St. on 97.5MHz 24h - Chinese Opera Sce on 1053kHz 2100-1600 — **JS2)** Nanjing Radio and TV Group, 358 Baixia Lu, Nanjing, Jiangsu 210001. News Sce on 1008kHz/106.9/88.8MHz 1900-1700 (exc. Tues 0600-0800) - Economic Sce on 900kHz/98.1MHz 24h - City Control Sce on 1170kHz/96.6MHz 2200-1600 - Traffic Sce on 102.4MHz 24h - Music Sce on 105.8MHz 24h - Sports Sce on 1251kHz/104.3MHz 24h - Private Car Sce on 98.1MHz 24h — **JS2A)** 359 Hongwu Lu, Baixia Qu, Nanjing, Jiangsu 210002. "Nanjing My FM": on 103.5MHz 24h — **JS3)** 223 Zhongshan Nanlu, Xuzhou, Jiangsu 221003. News Sce

on 1269kHz/93.0/89.3MHz 2000-1730 - Life Sce on 801kHz/91.6MHz 2025-1730 - Traffic Sce on 103.3MHz 2030-1700 - Literary Sceon 1098kHz/89.6MHz 2015-1600 - Music Sce on 99.6MHz 24h — **JS4)** 221 Jiefang Xilu, Xinpu Qu, Lianyungang, Jiangsu 222003. News Sce on 1458kHz/93.6/98.3MHz 2100-1600 (exc. Tues 0600-0855) - Economic Sce on 1251kHz/90.7MHz 2045-1600 - Traffic Sce on 92.7/96.0MHz 2155-1600 - V.O. the Music: on 90.2MHz 2050-1600 - Story Sce on 900kHz/104.8MHz 2200-1600 — **JS5)** 6 Dazhi Lu, Huai'an, Jiangsu 223001. News General Sce on 801kHz/94.1MHz 2000-1600 (exc. Tues 0600-0900) - Economic Life Sce on 1251kHz/105.0MHz 2000-1600 (exc. Tues 0600-0840) - Traffic and Literary Sce on 1521kHz/94.9MHz 2100-1600 - Public (Chengshi Guanli) Sce on 106.7MHz 2055-1600 - Automobile Music Sce on 104.2MHz 2100-1600 — **JS6)** Yancheng Radio and TV St, 4 Shengyuan Lu, Yancheng, Jiangsu 224001. News Sce on 1026kHz/91.5MHz 2100-1600 - Traffic Sce on 747kHz/105.3MHz 2200-1700 - Private Car Sce on 900kHz/88.2MHz 2100-1600 - V.O. the Music "Hi FM": on 98.0MHz — **JS7)** Yangzhou Radio and TV Media Group, 168 Weiyang Lu, Yangzhou, Jiangsu 225009. News Sce on 98.5/105.5MHz 2120-1800 (exc. Tues 0600-0930) - Traffic Sce on 103.5MHz 2120-1800 - Music Sce "Yes FM": on 94.9MHz 2100-1600 (exc. Tues 0645-0800) - Health Life Sce on 1179kHz/96.7MHz 2100-1600 - Classic Music Sce on 801/1521kHz - 2100-1600 — **JS8)** 20 Qingnian Lu, Taizhou, Jiangsu 225300. News Sce on 1341kHz/103.7/106.2MHz 2120-1525 (exc. Tues 0530-0855) - Music Sce on 927kHz/93.7MHz 2145-1600 - Traffic Sce on 92.1MHz 2200-1600 — **JS9)** 100 Renmin Zhonglu, Nantong, Jiangsu 226001. News Sce on 1233kHz/97.0MHz 2130-1600 - Private Car Sce on 603kHz/103.0/102.6MHz 2130-1600 - Traffic Sce on 1170kHz/92.9MHz 2200-1600 - Xingfu (Happy) Sce on 88.5/88.3MHz 2130-1600 - Music Sce on 91.8MHz 2130-1600 — **JS10)** 94 Zhongshan Xilu, Zhenjiang, Jiangsu 212004. News Sce on 104.0MHz 2055-1600. - Health Life Ch. on 1224kHz/94.0MHz 2000-1800 - Traffic Sce on 88.8MHz 2130-1600 - Music Sce "V.O. Jinshan Lake Music": on 96.3MHz 2100-1800 - City Sce on 90.5MHz 2030-1800 - Private Car BS "Donggan (Dynamic) 102.7": on 900kHz/102.7MHz 2130-1600 — **JS11)** Changzhou Radio and TV St, 10 Xiheng Jie, Changzhou, Jiangsu 213003. News General Sce on 846kHz 24h (exc. Tues 0600-0850) - News Sce on 103.4MHz 24h - Xi Opera Sce on 1143kHz 24h - Fortune Life Sce on 105.2MHz 24h - Traffic Sce on 90.0MHz 24h - Chinese Opera Sce on 747kHz 24h (exc. Tues 0600-0900) - Music Sce "Aiting 935": on 93.5MHz 24h - Classic Music Sce on 927kHz 24h - Literary St. (First Popular Ch): on 1521kHz/100.1MHz 2100-1600 — **JS12)** Wuxi Radio and TV Group, 4 Hubin Lu, Wuxi, Jiangsu 214061. News General Sce on 1161kHz/89.4MHz 2020-1600 (exc. Tues 0500-0900) - News Sce on 93.7MHz 2020-1600 - Economic Sce on 1251kHz/104.0MHz 2020-1600 - Story and Chinese Opera Sce on 1008kHz 24h - Traffic Sce on 106.9MHz 24h - Automobile Music Sce on 900kHz/91.4MHz 2130-1600 - City Life Sce on 1521kHz/98.7/88.1MHz 2130-1600 - V.O. Liangxi: on 603kHz/92.6MHz 2100-1600 — **JS13)** Suzhou Radio and TV Headquarters, 4 Gongyuan Lu, Suzhou, Jiangsu 215006. News General Sce on 1080kHz 2030-1600 (exc. Tues 0600-0730) in Ch and Suzhou dialect - V.O. the City "My Radio": on 91.1MHz 2030-1630 - Traffic Sce on 1521kHz/104.8MHz 2130-1600 - V.O. Old Age: on 603kHz - Life Sce on 96.5MHz 2130-1600(Tues 1525) - Music Sce "Dongting 948": on 94.8MHz 24h (exc. Tues 0600-1000) - Chinese Opera Sce on 846kHz - Automobile Sce on 102.8MHz 2200-1600 — **JS14)** 43 Gongnong Lu, Yizheng, Jiangsu 211400. On 1026kHz/94.3MHz 2155-0535, 0725-1350 — **JS15)** 79 Zhongshan Nanlu, Jiangyin, Jiangsu 214400. Happy Life Ch. on 1386kHz/106.0MHz 2200-1530 - T Automobile Ch. on 90.7MHz 2200-1500 — **JS16)** 29 Haiyu Beilu, Changshu, Jiangsu 215500. News Sce on 1116kHz/99.6MHz 2130-1405 (exc. Sat 0630-0830) - Traffic Sce on 747kHz/100.8MHz 2130-1405 (exc. Sat 0600-0800) — **JS17)** Zhangjiagang Radio and TV St, Chenjiachang Nong, Yangshe Zhen, Zhangjiagang, Jiangsu 215600. News Sce on 1098kHz 2140-1455 (exc. Wed 0600-0830) - Traffic Sce on 102.0MHz 2155-1500 (exc. Wed 0530-0955) - Music Sce on 1521kHz 2155-1500 — **JS18)** 7 Fazhan Dadao, Sucheng Qu, Suqian, Jiangsu 223800. News Sce on 92.1MHz 2110-1600 - Traffic Sce on 101.9MHz 2150-1700 - Aixin Netw. "Love Radio": on 106.3MHz

## JIANGXI PROVINCE

**JX1)** 207 Hongdu Zhong Dadao, Nanchang, Jiangxi 330046 **W:** radio.jxntv.cn News Sce on 729/1350/1449kHz/104.4MHz/FM 2000-1700 (exc. Tues 0600-0855) - V.O. the City: on 927kHz106.5MHz/FM 2100-1800 (exc. Tues 0600-0900) - Financial and Economic Sce "Chenggong (Success) 992": on 99.2MHz 2200-1600 - People Life Sce on 101.9MHz/FM 2100-1800 - Farm Sce "V.O. Green": on 1350kHz/98.5MHz/FM 2200-1600 (exc. Tues 0600-0900) - Traffic Sce on 105.4MHz 24h (exc. Tues 1730-2030) - Music Sce "i Radio": on 103.4MHz/FM 24h - Travel Sce on 97.4MHz 2200-1600 -"Nanchang My FM":on 96.9MHz 24h— **JX2)** 241 Ruzi Lu, Nanchang, Jiangxi 330009. News General Ch. on 1278kHz/91.7MHz 24h (exc. Tues 0500-0900) - Traffic Sce

"Hi Radio": on 95.1MHz 24h (exc. Tues 0500-0900) - "Big Eye 897": on 89.7MHz 24h - Music and Story Sce "Xinyi 906": on 90.6MHz 2130-1600 - "Phoenix 879": on 87.9MHz 24h - V.O. Qingshan Lake on 93.4MHz – **JX3)** 1073 Cidu Dadao, Jingdezhen, Jiangxi 333000. News General Sce on 1467kHz/96.5/107.3MHz 2200-1600 – **JX4)** Jiangwan Li, Binhe Xilu, Pingxiang, Jiangxi 337005. News General Ch. on 1107kHz/96.8/106.8MHz 2155-1500 - Traffic and Literary Ch. on 88.8MHz 24h – **JX5)** 49 Xianlai Zhong Dadao, Xinyu, Jiangxi 338000. News Sce on 585kHz/94.0MHz 2130-1800 - Traffic Sce on 96.2MHz 2200-1800 – **JX6)** 84 Changhong Dadao, Jiujiang, Jiangxi 332000. News Sce on 1485kHz/90.0MHz 2155-1600 - Traffic Sce on 88.4/88.9MHz 2255-1500 (exc. Tues 0530-0855) - Automobile Music Sce on 91.6MHz 2155-1600 - V.O. Ganbei: on 94.1MHz 2200-1600 – **JX7)** Yingtan PBS, 3 Jianshe Lu, Yingtan, Jiangxi 335200. V.O. Xinjiang (Xin River): on 103.2MHz 2200-1605 - V.O. the Traffic and Music: on 95.6MHz 2200-1800 – **JX8)** Zhong Duan, Ganjiang Yuan Dadao, Ganzhou, Jiangxi 341000. News Sce on 747kHz/93.7MHz 2200-1700 (exc. Tues 0600-0830) in Ch and Hakka - Music Sce on 94.5/103.4MHz 2200-1700 - Traffic Sce on 99.2/97.5MHz 2200-1700 – **JX9)** Ji'an Radio and TV St, 19 Beimen Jie, Ji'an, Jiangxi 343000. News Sce on 603/1242kHz/95.6/102.1MHz 2125-1430 - Traffic Sce on 100.6/94.3MHz 2200-1600 – **JX10)** Shangrao PBS, 51 Qingfeng Lu, Shangrao, Jiangxi 334000. News General Ch. on 93.4MHz 2200-1630 - Traffic and Music Ch. on 96.6/95.9MHz 2200-1630

### LIAONING PROVINCE

**LN1)** Liaoning Radio and TV St, 10 Guangrong Jie, Heping Qu, Shenyang, Liaoning 110003 **W:** lntv.com.cn or lntv.cn General Sce on 1089/603/612/963/1260kHz/102.9MHz 24h (exc. Tues 0605-0855). - Economic Sce on 999/585/801/900kHz/88.8MHz/FM 24h (exc. Tues 0540-0855) - Country Sce on 927kHz/96.9/103.4/107.1MHz 24h (exc. Tues 0500-0800) - Traffic Sce on 97.5MHz 24h (exc. Tues 0540-0850) - Literary Sce on 1053/747/801/810kHz/95.9/99.5/101.8MHz 24h (exc. Tues 0540-0900). - Life Sce on 882kHz/103.4/90.4MHz 24h (exc. Tues 0500-0855) - City Sce on 1341kHz/92.1MHz 24h - Music Sce on 98.6MHz 24h (exc. Thurs 0500-0855) - Information Sce (Dalian Blanch): on 90.6/90.4MHz 24h – **LN2)** Shenyang Radio and TV St, 89 Sanhao Jie, Heping Qu, Shenyang, Liaoning 110004. News Sce on 792kHz/104.5/107.0MHz 24h – **LN3)** Dalian Radio and TV St, 162 Minquan Jie, Shahekou Qu, Dalian, Liaoning 116022. News Sce on 882kHz/103.3MHz 1955-1605 (exc. Tues 0600-0800) - Financial Sce on 1152kHz/93.1MHz 24h (exc. Tues 0630-0800) - Automobile Sce "V.O. the City": on 99.1MHz 2025-1605 (exc. Tues 0630-0800) - Traffic Sce on 100.8MHz 24h (exc. Tues 0600-0800) - Sports Sce on 105.7MHz 2025-1605 (exc. Tues 0600-0800) - New City and Country Sce "Xingfu (Happy) 956": on 1575kHz/95.6MHz 2025-1600 (exc. Tues 0600-0800) - Music Sce on 106.7MHz 24h (exc. Tues 0600-0800) – **LN4)** Anshan Radio and TV St, 3, 219 Lu, Tiedong Qu, Anshan, Liaoning 114002. News Sce on 954kHz/95.3MHz 24h - Economic Sce on 89.7MHz 24h - Old Age Sce on 1071kHz/88.5MHz - Traffic Sce on 1458kHz/99.5MHz 24h - Music Sce on 93.8MHz 2100-1500 - Storytelling Sce on 1251kHz/87.9MHz – **LN5)** Fushun Radio and TV St, 2 Hunhe Beilu, Shuncheng Qu, Fushun, Liaoning 113006. News Sce on 684kHz/93.0/93.8MHz 2000-1500 - Traffic Sce "i Radio": on 747kHz/106.1MHz 24h - Music Sce "U Radio": on 100.6MHz 2030-1600 - Storytelling Sce on 1143kHz/88.2MHz – **LN6)** 15 Tiyu Lu, Mingshan Qu, Benxi, Liaoning 117000. News General St. on 1296kHz/94.0MHz 2030-1605 - Traffic and Economic St. on 900kHz/107.4MHz 24h (exc. Tues 0700-0900) - Life St. on 98.0MHz 2000-1600 - Storytelling St. on 104.1MHz 2055-1505 – **LN7)** Dandong Radio and TV St, 1 Shanshang Jie, Zhenxing Qu, Dandong, Liaoning 118000. **W:** 10001723438.qymgc.com News Sce on 1404kHz/103.6MHz 24h - Traffic Sce on 891kHz/101.7MHz 2000-1600 - City Sce on 1476kHz/104.3MHz 2000-1500 in Ch and Korean - Entertainment Sce (Story Sce) on 603kHz/88.0MHz 2128-1600 – **LN8)** 3, 4 Duan, Beijing Lu, Jinzhou, Liaoning 121000. News Sce Shiyuan (World Park) Ch. on 666kHz/92.7MHz 2125-1500 (exc. Tues 0530-0855) - Economic Sce on 774kHz/96.6MHz 2125-1500 (exc. Tues 0530-0855) - People Life Sce on 1098kHz/90.9/97.7MHz 2125-1500 (exc. Tues 0530-0855) - Traffic Sce on 846kHz/100.3MHz 2125-1500 (exc. Tues 0530-0855) – **LN9)** Huludao Radio and TV St, 23 Haixing Li, Longwan Dajie, Huludao, Liaoning 125000. News General Sce on 1242kHz/93.1/95.2MHz 2130-1535 - Traffic and Literary Sce on 87.8MHz 2150-1330 (exc. Tues 0540-0955) – **LN10)** Yingkou Radio and TV St, 10, Dong, Bohai Dajie, Zhanqian Qu, Yingkou, Liaoning 115000. News General Sce on 1026kHz/88.4/106.2MHz 2055-1500 - Economic Life Sce on 747kHz/89.0/92.8MHz 2100-1500 - Traffic and Literary Sce on 1143kHz/95.1MHz 2130-1600 - Storytelling and Entertainment Sce on 603kHz/94.1MHz 2125-1500 – **LN11)** Panjin Radio and TV St, 7 Shifu Dajie, Xinglongtai Qu, Panjin, Liaoning 124010. News General Sce on 1485kHz/104.2MHz 2100-1600 - Traffic and Literary Sce on 90.1MHz 2100-1500 - Economic Life Sce on 97.1MHz 2100-1600 - Storytelling and Chinese Opera Sce on 101.8MHz 2100-1550 - Music

Sce "V.O. Hexiang": on 95.3MHz – **LN12)** 61 Zhonghua Lu, Haizhou Qu, Fuxin, Liaoning 123000. News General Sce on 1287kHz/89.3MHz 2100-1510 - Economic and Storytelling Sce on 747kHz 2100-1600 - Literary Sce on 900kHz/105.3MHz 24h - Traffic Sce on 1098kHz/88.7MHz 2100-1600 – **LN13)** Fuxin Mongolian BS, 84 Shanbei Jie, Haizhou Qu, Fuxin, Liaoning 123000. 2155-0610, 1040-1300 in Mo – **LN14)** Liaoyang Radio and TV St, 59 Qingnian Dajie, Taizihe Qu, Liaoyang, Liaoning 111000. News General Sce on 837kHz/106.0MHz 2030-1530 (exc. Tues 0600-0800) - Economic Sce on 1143kHz/102.0MHz 2025-1530 – **LN15)** Tieling Radio and TV St, 45 Gongren Jie, Yinzhou Qu, Tieling, Liaoning 112000. V.O. Tieling: on 1413kHz/101.2MHz 2150-1300 - Traffic Sce on 102.8MHz 2200-1300 - Country Sce on 810kHz/90.8MHz 2130-1430 - Literary Sce on 95.9MHz – **LN16)** Chaoyang Radio and TV St, 88, 1 Duan, Xinhua Lu, Shuangta Qu, Chaoyang, Liaoning 122000. News General Sce on 585kHz/96.1/106.0MHz 2125-1600 - New Farm Sce on 810/702/747kHz/99.5MHz 1955-1600 (exc. Tues 0600-0900) - Traffic and Entertainment Sce on 93.8/103.1MHz 1955-1600 (exc. Tues 0600-0900) - Feiyang FM on 648/801kHz/106.5MHz 1955-1600 – **LN17)** 67 Jinluan Lu, Wafangdian, Liaoning 116300. News General Sce on 1323kHz/89.8/106.2MHz 2125-1345 – **LN18)** 385, 1 Duan, Huanghai Dajie, Zhuanghe, Liaoning 116400. 2100-0100, 0855-1200 – **LN19)** Haicheng Radio and TV St, 14 Huancheng Xilu, Haicheng, Liaoning 114200. News General Sce on 900kHz/90.4MHz 2135-1500 - Traffic and Entertainment Sce on 1350kHz/106.9MHz 2135-1500 – **LN20)** 18, 2 Duan, Xinghai Beilu, Xingcheng, Liaoning 121600 – **LN21)** 6 Qingnian Lu, Nanshan Jie, Beipiao, Liaoning 122100. V.O. Beipiao: on 91.2MHz 2125-1500 (exc. Tues 0500-0930) – **LN22)** Donggang PBS, 122 Huanghai Dajie, Dongguang, Liaoning. News Sce on 93.3/94.3MHz - Traffic and Life Sce on 98.0MHz - New Country Sce on 107.9MHz .

### NEI MENGGU AUTONOMOUS REGION

**NM1)** Nei Menggu PBS "V.O. Chinese Grassland", 55 Xinhua Dajie, Hohhot, Nei Menggu 010058 **W:** nmrb.cn Ch News General Sce on 675/540/603/ 747/765/855/900/999/1143/1494/1521/1584 /7420/9520kHz/89.0MHz 2150-1605 (exc. Tues 0600-0950) - Ch News Sce on 95.0MHz/FM 2150-1605 - Mongolian News General Sce on 1458/1098/1143/1395/6040/7270/9750kHz/FM 2150-1605 (exc. Tues 0600-0950) - Economic Life Sce on 101.4/103.8MHz 2100-1700 - V.O. the Traffic: on 105.6MHz/FM 24h - V.O. the Music: on 93.6MHz/FM 2150-1600 - Storytelling and Folk Art Sce on 102.8MHz 24h - Farm and Pastoral Sce "V.O. the Green Field": on 990/666/1224/1305/1413/1584kHz/91.9MHz/FM 2150-1605 (exc. Tues 0600-0950) **F.PI:** All MWs will be merged into 1044kHz - "V.O. the Grassland": on 105.0MHz – **NM2)** 159 Gongyuan Xilu, Hohhot, Nei Menggu 010035. Ch News General Sce on 882kHz/92.9MHz 24h- Mo General Sce on 105.9MHz 2225-1530 - Traffic Sce on 107.4MHz 2250-1600 - City Life Sce on 90.1MHz 24h - Literary Sce on 99.8MHz 24h - Favorite Car Information Sce "Happy Radio": on 103.9/98.5MHz 24h – **NM3)** 12 Gangtie Dajie, Hondlon Qu, Baotou, Nei Menggu 014030. General Sce on 747kHz/94.9MHz 2040-1600 - Mongolian Sce on 105.9MHz 1955-1605 - Traffic Sce on 89.2MHz 24h - Urban and Rural Sce "Automobile Music 100.1": on 100.1MHz 24h - Literary Sce on 98.1MHz 2055-1800 – **NM4)** Wuhai Radio and TV St, Huanghe Lu, Haibowan Qu, Wuhai, Nei Menggu 016000. General Sce on 747kHz/94.4MHz 2125-1600 - Mo General Sce on 104.2MHz 2125-1600 -Traffic and Music Sce on 99.2MHz 2125-1600 – **NM5)** Chifeng Radio and TV St, 12, Xi Duan, Gangtie Xijie, Hongshan Qu, Chifeng, Nei Menggu 024001. Ch General Sce on 747kHz/96.3MHz 2030-1600 - Mo General Sce on 1170kHz/89.4MHz 2130-1800 - Traffic Sce on 101.8MHz 24h (exc. Tues 0700-1000) - Farm and Pastoral Area Sce on 900kHz/102.4MHz 2100-1600 – **NM6)** 86 Qiaoxi Shahe Lu, Jining Qu, Ulanqab, Nei Menggu 012000. Ch News General Sce on 747kHz99.9MHz 2200-1600 - Mo Sce on 1170kHz/105.3MHz 2230-1210 - Traffic Sce on 92.3MHz in Ch 2155-1700 - Literary Sce on 94.3MHz in Ch 2155-1600 – **NM7)** 89 Xilin Dajie, Xilinhot, Nei Menggu 026000. Ch General Sce on 945kHz/99.4MHz 2225-1455 - Mo General Sce on 1170kHz/ 102.1MHz 2220-1505 - General Literary Sce on 106.9MHz 2255-1505 - Traffic and Literary Sce on 97.5MHz 2225-1455 – **NM8)** 43 Manzhouli Lu, Hailar Qu, Hulun Buir, Nei Menggu 021008. Ch General Ch. on 1170/3900kHz/99.9MHz 2130-1600 - Mo General Sce on 954/6080kHz/97.3MHz 2140-1430 – Trafiic and Literary Sce on 104.6MHz 2200-1600 – **NM9)** Tongliao Radio and TV St, 29 Heping Lu, Horqin Qu, Tongliao, Nei Menggu 028001. V.O. Tongliao: on 747kHz/97.2/87.8MHz 2110-1730 (exc. Tues ?-0855) - Traffic and Literary Sce on 954kHz/91.3MHz 2110-1530 (exc. Tues 0600-0855) - Mo Prgr. "V.O. Horqin": on 1170kHz/93.7/94.4/100.3MHz 2110-1730 – **NM10)** Ordos Radio and TV St, Manduhai Xiang, Dongsheng Qu, Ordos, Nei Menggu 017000. Ch News General Sce on 1170kHz/89.6MHz 2115-1600 - Mo News General Sce on 945kHz/93.5MHz 2220-1430 - Traffic Literary and Sports Sce on 100.8/ 87.9/90.7MHz 2130-1600 - Variety Sce on 97.3/95.3MHz 2155-1600 – **NM11)** 26 Xinhua Xijie, Linhe Qu, Bayannur, Nei Menggu

015000. News General Sce (V.O. Hetao): on 1152kHz/107.0MHz 2000-1600 - Traffic and Literary Sce (V.O. the Yellow River): on 97.7MHz 2200-1600 - V.O. the Traffic: on 95.8MHz 2200-1600 – **NM12)** Alxa Radio and TV St, 1 Elute Donglu, Bayanhot Zhen, Alxa Zuoqi, Nei Menggu 750306. Ch General Sce on 549/6025kHz/91.0MHz2225-1500 - Mo General Sce on 1440kHz/88.8MHz 2220-1500 – **NM13)** 73 Hinggan Bei Dalu, Ulanhot, Nei Menggu 137400. V.O. Hinggan: on 891kHz/89.1MHz 2125-1430 in Ch - V.O. Alateng Hinggan: on 1152kHz/94.7/96.4/96.6/97.7/103.3/107.0MHz 2200-1600 in Ch (0600-0655 in Mo) - V.O. the Traffic: on 99.0MHz 2125-1500 (exc. Tues 0600-0800) - V.O. the City: on 106.8MHz 2200-1500 – **NM14)** Xuegang Shan, Xinchengwan Xiang, Fengzhen, Nei Menggu 012100. 2225-0020, 0355-0505, 0955-1215 – **NM15)** 1 Dianshi Jie, Manzhouli, Nei Menggu 021400. On 702kHz/94.9MHz 2225-1600 in Ch, Mo and Russian – **NM16)** 1 Xing'an Dongjie, Yakeshi, Nei Menggu 022150 – **NM17)** 3 Shengli Lu, Shiqiao Jie, Zalantun, Nei Menggu 162650. On 558kHz/98.6/102.7MHz 2155-1400 – **NM18)** Zhongyang Dajie, Genhe, Nei Menggu 022350. 2130-0700, 0900-1430 – **NM19)** 129 Nawenxi Dajie, Nirji Zhen, Morin Dawa, Nei Menggu 162850

## NINGXIA HUI AUTONOMOUS REGION
**NX1)** Ningxia Radio and TV St, 66 Beijing Zhonglu, Jinfeng Qu, Yinchuan, Ningxia 750002 **W:**nxtv.cn/radio/ News Sce on 891/1206/1287kHz/106.1MHz/FM 2100-1700 (exc. Tues 0600-0955) - Economic Sce on 747kHz/92.8MHz 24h - Travel Sce on 104.7MHz 2215-1605 - Traffic Sce on 98.4MHz 24h - Music Sce on 104.7MHz 24h – **NX2)** Yinchuan Radio and TV St, 11 Zhongshan Beijie, Xingqing Qu, Yinchuan, Ningxia 750004. News General Ch. on 801kHz/90.5MHz 2300-1600 - City Economy Sce "Pinwei 950": on 95.0MHz 24h - Traffic and Music Sce on 100.6MHz 2200-1800– **NX3)** Shizuishan PBS, 363 Youyi Xijie, Dawukou Qu, Shizuishan, Ningxia 753000. On 95.4MHz – **NX4)** 54 Yumin Dongjie, Litong Qu, Wuzhong, Ningxia 751100. On 1413kHz/89.3MHz 2230-1600 – **NX5)** Wenhua Jie, Xiaoba Zhen, Qingtongxia, Ningxia 751600

## QINGHAI PROVINCE
**QH1)** Qinghai Radio and TV St, 81 Xiguan Dajie, Xining, Qinghai 810008 **W:** qhradio.com News General Ch. (Satellite Sce) on 666/711/909/1017/4750/ 6145/9780kHz/91.6MHz 2200-1600 (exc. Tues 0600-0900) - Tibetan Sce on 1206/1251/1539/4220/5990/9850kHz/98.3MHz 2250-1600 - Economic Sce on 1143kHz/107.5MHz 2255-1600 (exc. Tues 0600-0855) - Traffic and Music Sce on 1377kHz/97.2MHz 2255-1600 - Life Sce on 90.3MHz in Ch and Qinghai dialect – **QH2)** 43 Nanguan Jie, Xining, Qinghai 810000. News General Sce on 1476kHz/95.6MHz 2200-1630 - Traffic and Literary Sce on 104.3MHz 2230-1905 - City Life Sce "Easy FM": on 101.3MHz - City Service and Control Sce "Sunshine FM": on 102.7MHz – **QH3)** 139 Hongwei Lu, Jiegu Zhen, Yushu Xian, Qinghai 815000. On 882kHz 2255-0100, 1025-1230 in Ch and Tb. Rel. CNR 1: 1135-1230 – **QH4)** Haixi PBS, 7 Changjiang Lu, Delingha, Qinghai 817000. Ch Prgr. on 621kHz - Mo/Tb Prgr. on 540kHz

## SHANDONG PROVINCE
**SD1)** Shandong Radio and TV St, 81 Jing 10 Lu, Lixia Qu, Jinan, Shandong 250062 **W:** v.iqilu.com General Sce on 603/891/918/1467/1485/1548kHz/95.0MHz/FM 1940-1700 (exc. Tues 0530-0900) - Economic Sce on 594kHz/98.6MHz/FM 24h - Economic Ch. "FM96" on 96.0MHz 24h - Life Information Sce on 105.0/88.6/104.7/104.9/107.8MHz 24h - Traffic Sce on 101.1/106.0/106.9MHz 24h - Anchorwomen BS "i Radio": on 97.5MHz/FM 24h (exc. Tues 0500-0900) - Country Sce on 1251/621/999kHz/91.9MHz/FM 24h - Music Sce "City FM":on 99.1/92.9/96.9/106.6/107.8MHz 24h - Sports and Leasure Sce on 102.1MHz 24h – **SD2)** Jinan Radio and TV St, 32 Jing 11 Lu, Lixia Qu, Jinan, Shandong 250014. News Sce on 1053kHz/89.3/106.6MHz 24h (exc. Tues 0410-0850) - Economic Sce on 846kHz/90.9/95.7MHz 24h - Traffic Sce on 103.1/91.2MHz 24h (exc. Tues 0400-0850) - Music Sce on 88.7/105.8MHz 24h - Literary Sce "Xingfu (Happy) FM": on 1305kHz/105.8MHz 24h (exc. Tues 0400-0900) - Story Sce on 1512kHz/104.3/87.8MHz 24h - Private Car Sce on 93.6MHz 24h – **SD3)** 200 Ningxia Lu, Qingdao, Shandong 266071. **W:** guangdian.qtv.com.cn/ News Sce on 1377kHz/107.6MHz 1050-1700 – News & Life Sce 819, 97.3MHz Economic Sce Automobile Life Ch. on 1251kHz/102.9MHz 24h - Economic Sce Storytelling Ch. "Happy 603": on 603kHz/100.7MHz 24h - Traffic Sce on 900kHz/89.7MHz 24h - Private Car BS: on 1008kHz/96.4MHz 24h - Music and Sports Sce "Simul Radio": on 91.5MHz 24h - Story Sce on 95.2MHz 24h – **SD4)** Zibo Radio and TV Headquarters, 52 Huaguang Lu, Zhangdian Qu, Zibo, Shandong 255047. **W:** zbradio.com/General Sce on 89.0MHz 2100-1700 - News Sce Story Ch. on 1143kHz - Economy Sce on 801kHz/106.7MHz 2155-1700 - Traffic and Literary Sce on 1476kHz/100.0MHz 2145-1700 - Music Sce "i Radio":on 92.6MHz 2145-1700 - Private Car Sce "Yuedong 106.7" on 106.7MHz 2045-1700 Life Sce 900kHz/89.7MHz – **SD5)** Zaozhuang Radio and TV St, 88 Guangming Xilu, Zaozhuang, Shandong 277102. News Sce on 1170kHz/99.0MHz 2155-1600 - Life and Entertainment

Sce on 603kHz/101.4MHz 2200-1600 - Traffic and Literary Sce on 105.2MHz 2200-1600 - Music Sce on 100.6MHz 2200-1600 – **SD6)** 1229 Dongcheng Nan 1 Lu, Dongying, Shandong 257091. News Sce on 1449kHz/91.0MHz 2155-1430 - General Sce on 105.3MHz 2150-1435 - Traffic and Music Sce on 88.1/98.4MHz 2150-1435 – **SD7)** Weifang Radio and TV St, 85 Shengli Dongjie, Kuiwen Qu, Weifang, Shandong 261061. **W:** radio.wfcmw.cn News Sce on 1161kHz/100.2/88.1MHz 2055-1600 - Private Car Sce on 1287kHz/93.3MHz 2100-1600 - Traffic Sce on 846kHz/95.9MHz 2100-1600 - Beloved Home Sce on 98.3MHz 2055-1700 - Music Sce on 90.8MHz 24h - Story Sce on 981kHz/107.1MHz 2055-1600 - Huanle (Joy) FM "New Radio": on 89.9MHz 2200-1300 - Music Sce "Simul Radio": on 88.7MHz 24h – **SD8)** Yantai Radio and TV St, 32 Wenhua Xiang, Zhifu Qu, Yantai, Shandong 264000. General Sce on 1314kHz/101.0/94.3/98.6MHz 2000-1600 - Private Car Sce on 801kHz/105.9/92.8/102.7MHz 2000-1600 - Traffic Sce on 103.0/89.0/95.3MHz 2000-1600 - Music Sce "i Radio" on: 91.2/90.5MHz 24h Global Sce on 88.4/96.6/102.4MHz 24h. Rel. CRI "News Radio": 2300-2400, 0400-0430, 0900-1000 – **SD9)** 66 Wenhua Zhonglu, Weihai, Shandong 264200. News General Ch. on 1206kHz/99.6/105.1MHz 2100-1600 (exc. Tues 0600-0825). Ko Prgr: 0530-0600, 1430-1500 - Traffic and Literary Ch. on 846kHz/95.0/102.2MHz 2125-1500 (exc. Tues 0600-0855) - Story Ch. on 96.1MHz 2100-1600 - Music Fashion Sce on 90.7MHz – **SD10)** 11 Hongxing Zhonglu, Jining, Shandong 272037. **W:** jnnews. tv News Sce on 666kHz/101.8MHz 2200-1700 – Private Car Sce on 1116kHz/107.0MHz 2200-1700 - Traffic Sce on 801kHz/104.2MHz 2200-1700 - Music Sce on 1386kHz/103.1MHz 2200-1700 - Scripture Music Sce on 89.0MHz 24h – **SD11)** Rizhao Radio and TV St, Beishou, Yantai Lu, Rizhao, Shandong 276826. News General Ch. on 1449kHz/95.0MHz 2130-1600 (exc. Tues ?-0945) - Traffic and Life Ch. on 747kHz/88.1MHz 2130-1530 - Music Ch. on 104.0MHz 2130-1530 - City Ch. on 103.5MHz 2130-1530 – **SD12)** Dezhou Radio and TV St, 1288 Dongfanghong Xilu, Dezhou, Shandong 253012. News Sce on 1098kHz/104.1MHz 2150-1600 - Traffic and Music Sce on 1341kHz/94.1MHz 2150-1600 - Literary and Life Sce on 1008kHz/92.9MHz 2150-1600 - Private Car Sce on 98.9MHz 2150-1600 - Music FM on 97.9MHz – **SD13)** Linyi Radio and TV St, 21 Jinqueshan Lu, Lanshan Qu, Linyi, Shandong 276004. News General Sce on 873kHz/97.6MHz 2105-1600 (exc. Tues 0530-1020) – Fortune Ch on 1143kHz/93.2MHz 2125-1600 - V.O. the City: on 747kHz/101.0MHz 2130-1600 - Traffic Sce on 801kHz/89.9MHz 2125-1600 (exc. Tues 0600-0950) - Music Sce on 1251kHz/104.5MHz 2155-1600 – **SD14)** Liaocheng Radio and TV Headquaters, 41 Liuyuan Beilu, Liaocheng, Shandong 252000. News Sce on 1143kHz/96.8MHz 2125-1600 - Traffic Sce on 1566kHz/98.9MHz 2200-1600 - Music Sce "I Music" on 801kHz/92.4MHz 2300-1600 – **SD15)** Binzhou Radio and TV St, 358 Huanghe 5 Lu, Binzhou, Shandong 256603. News Sce on 864kHz/107.6MHz 2155-1600 - Life Sce on 1170kHz/99.4MHz 2155-1530 - Traffic Sce on 93.1MHz 2150-1600 - Music Sce on 87.8MHz 2200-1400 Private Car Sce 106.9MHz 24h – **SD16)** 28 Zhonghua Donglu, Heze, Shandong 274033. News Ch. on 1197kHz/93.9MHz 2055-1600 - Traffic Ch. on 94.8MHz 2055-1600 - Private Car Ch. on 1071kHz/96.8MHz 2055-1500 Music Ch. on 89.1MHz – **SD16A)** Mudan PBS, 2093 Changjiang Lu, Heze, Shandong 274000. V.O. Heze on 1323kHz/97.2MHz 2155-1700 - Heze V.O. the City: on 104.0MHz 2155-1700 - Story Sce on 88.0MHz 2300-1800 – **SD17)** Qingzhou PBS, 21 Fangongting Xilu, Qingzhou, Shandong 262500. On 95.4MHz 2155-1600 – **SD18)** Huangcheng Xihuan Lu, Longkou, Shandong 265701. On 101.6MHz - Yantai Longkou Economic and Literary BS: on 1251kHz 2228-0200, 0500-0700 – **SD19)** 4 Gulou Beijie, Qufu, Shandong 273100. On 1341kHz/98.4MHz 2155-0510(SS0450), 0955-1430(SS1410) – **SD20)** Tai'an PBS, 200 Yingxuan Dajie, Taishan Qu, Tai'an, Shandong 271000. News St. on 93.2MHz 2125-1600 - Economic St. on 90.1MHz 2130-1600 (exc. Tues 0600-1000) - Story Sce on 91.6MHz 2130-1600 - Traffic Information Sce on 106.2MHz 2125-1600 (exc. Tues 0600-1000) - V.O. City Music: on 104.4MHz

## SHANGHAI MUNICIPALITY
**SH1)** Shanghai Radio and TV St (SMG), 1376 Hongqiao Lu, Shanghai 200051 **W:** smg.cn, smgradio.cn News Sce on 990kHz/93.4MHz 24h - Traffic Sce on 648kHz/105.7MHz 24h - Chinese Opera and Folk Art Sce on 1197kHz/97.2MHz 2130-1500 in Ch and Shanghai dialect - Story Sce on 927kHz/107.2MHz 2200-1600 – Wuxing (Five Stars) Sports Sce on 94.0MHz 2200-1600 - Dong-Guang News St. on 1296kHz/90.9MHz 24h - Dongfang (Eastern) City Sce on 792kHz/89.9MHz 24h - First Financial and Ecomonic Sce on 603kHz/97.7MHz 24h - Popular Music Sce: on 101.7MHz 2200-1800 - Popular Music Sce "Love Radio": on 103.7MHz 24h - Classical Music Sce on 94.7MHz 24h(exc. Thurs 1600-2200) - Contemporary Hit Music Sce "KFM 98.1" on 98.1MHz 24h(exc. Thurs 1700-2200)

## SHAANXI PROVINCE
**SN1)** 336 Chang'an Nanlu, Xi'an, Shaanxi 710061 **W:** sxtvs.com News Sce on 693/1008/1143/1521/6176kHz/106.6MHz/FM 24h (exc. Tues

0600-0900) - News Prgr. (City Sce) on 1008kHz/101.8MHz 2058-1630 - Automobile FM on 89.6MHz 24h - Traffic Sce on 801/1323kHz/91.6MHz 24h - Farm Sce on 900kHz 24h - Youth Sce "Hi Radio": on 105.5MHz 24h - Chinese Opera Sce on 747kHz/107.8MHz 24h - Music Sce on 98.8/94.8/97.5MHz 24h - Story Sce on 603kHz 24h (exc. Tues 1700-2000) - Qin Melody Sce on 101.1MHz 2300-1600 - City Express Sce 99.9MHz 24h – **SN2)** Xi'an Radio and TV St, 100, Zhenxing Lu, Xi'an, Shaanxi 710068. News Sce on 810kHz/90.4MHz 2055-1700 - Private Car Sce on 106.1MHz 24h - Traffic and Travel Sce on 104.3MHz 24h - Music Sce on "i Radio":801kHz/93.1MHz 24h - Variety Sce on 102.4MHz 2155-1710 – **SN3)** Miaopu Lu, Hongqi Jie, Tongchuan, Shaanxi 727000. News General Sce on 1134kHz/103.7MHz 2210-0015, 0330-0515, 0915-1405 – **SN4)** 47 Hongqi Lu, Baoji, Shaanxi 721000. News Sce on 1071kHz 2055-1700 - Music Sce on 105.3MHz 2155-1700 - Economic Sce on 900kHz/102.8MHz 2155-1700 - Traffic and Travel Sce on 99.7MHz 2230-1400 – **SN5)** Nan Duan, Fu'an Lu, Xianyang, Shaanxi 712000. News General Sce on 1296kHz/100.7/107.6MHz 2150-1740 - City Music Sce on 99.9MHz 2200-1740 – **SN6)** Xi Duan, Dongfeng Jie, Weinan, Shaanxi 714000. News Sce on 747kHz/101.3/102.6MHz 2100-1600 (exc. Tues 0430-0700) - Life Sce on 96.4MHz 2250-1400 (exc. Tues 0500-0850) - Traffic Sce on 90.9MHz 2157-1600 – **SN7)** Dongguan Jie, Yan'an, Shaanxi 716000. News Sce on 603kHz/100.1/104.6MHz 2210-1500 (exc. Wed 0630-0910) - Traffic Sce on 98.7MHz – **SN8)** 14 Dong Jianshe Xiang, Hanzhong, Shaanxi 723000. News Sce on 1251kHz/95.6MHz 2130-1620 - Music St. on 97.1/99.5MHz 24h (exc. Wed 0700-0930) - Traffic and Travel Sce on 93.0/94.3/101.8MHz – **SN9)** 7 Zhonglou Xiang, Yulin, Shaanxi 719000. News Sce on 1143kHz/99.4MHz - Traffic and Literary Sce on 95.9MHz – **SN10)** Ankang PBS, 113 Bashan Zhonglu, Ankang, Shaanxi 725000. News Sce on 89.7MHz - Traffic Travel and Music Sce on 95.9MHz 2155-1600

**SHANXI PROVINCE**

**SX1)** Shanxi Radio and TV St, 318 Yingze Dajie, Taiyuan, Shanxi 030001 **W:** sxrtv.com General Sce on 819/846/900/1269kHz/90.4MHz/ FM 2100-1600 (exc. Tues 0600-0900) - Economic Sce on 95.8MHz 24h (exc. Tues 0600-0900) - V.O. the Health: on 1584kHz/105.9MHz 24h (exc. Mon 0600-0900) - Traffic Sce on 88.0MHz 24h - Farm Sce on 603/747/1008/1098/1206/1422/1503kHz /100.9MHz 24h - Music Sce on 94.0MHz 24h - Entertainment Sce on 101.5MHz 24h - Story Sce on 88.6MHz 24h – **SX2)** Taiyuan Radio and TV St, 2 Yifen Jie, Taiyuan, Shanxi 030024. News Sce on 91.2MHz 24h - V.O. Old Age: on 1422kHz/97.5MHz 2155-1600 - Private Car Sce on 774kHz/104.4MHz 24h - Traffic Sce on 107.0MHz 24h - Music Sce "i Radio": on 102.6MHz 24h – **SX3)** Datong Radio and TV St, 178 Yingbin Xilu, Datong, Shanxi 037006. News General Sce on 1584kHz/103.5MHz 2200-1805 - Music Sce on 91.1MHz 2200-1605 - Traffic Sce on 99.6MHz 2200-1805 - Variety Sce 900kHz/88.5MHz 24h – **SX4)** Yangquan Radio and TV St, Ningbo Lu, Yangquan, Shanxi 045000. News General Sce on 603kHz/102.7MHz 2150-1355 - Traffic Sce on 90.1MHz 2200-1600 – **SX5)** 87 Yingxiong Zhonglu, Changzhi, Shanxi 046000. News General Sce on 1584kHz/98.8MHz 2120-0600, 0915-1530 - Traffic Sce on 94.9/101.1MHz 2225-1600 (exc. Tues 0500-0900) – **SX6)** Fengtai Xijie, Jincheng, Shanxi 048000. News General Sce on 585kHz/89.8MHz 2155-1600 - Traffic Sce on 93.5MHz 2155-1600 – **SX7)** 3 Xiaoyuan Lu, Yuci Qu, Jinzhong, Shanxi 030600. News General Sce on 1530kHz/103.4MHz 2200-1600 - Traffic and Literary Sce on 92.1MHz 2300-1500 – **SX8)** Cangcheng Xijie, Xinzhou, Shanxi 034000 – **SX9)** 233 Hongqi Dongjie, Yuncheng, Shanxi 044000. News General Sce on 1566kHz/93.2MHz 2200-1600 - Traffic and Literary Sce on 101.9MHz 2200-1600 – **SX10)** Shuozhou Radio and TV St, 1 Minfu Xijie, Shuozhou, Shanxi 036002. News General Sce on 1485kHz/100.9MHz - Traffic and Literary Sce on 93.7MHz – **SX11)** Linfen Radio and TV St, 10 Guangxuan Jie, Linfen, Shanxi 041000. News General Sce on 95.1MHz 2200-1600 - Traffic and Literary Sce on 88.9MHz 2200-1600

**SICHUAN PROVINCE**

**SC1)** Sichuan Radio and TV St, 119-1 Hongxing Zhonglu, Chengdu, Sichuan 610017 **W:** sctv.com News Ch. "News FM": on 612/909/1116kHz/98.1/90.0/93.7/ 95.7/103.9/106.6MHz 24h - News Information Sce on 106.1MHz 24h - Economic Ch. Fortune Sce on 88.4/94.0MHz 2200-1700 - Economic Ch. People Life Sce on 89.4MHz 24h - Traffic Sce on 101.7MHz 2300-1600 - Travel Life Sce "i Radio":on 97.0MHz 2200-1700 - Private Car Sce "Auto Radio": on 92.5MHz 2300-1700 - Minority Sce on 954/6060/7225kHz 2155-1700 in Ch, Tb, Kham (Tb dialect) and Yi -Pleasure Sce : on 747kHz/90.0MHz 24h - Minjiang Music Sce "i Radio": on 95.5MHz 24h (exc. Tues 0700-1000) - Sound of City "City FM": on 102.6MHz 24h –**SC3)** 99 Shuanglin Jie, Chengdu, Sichuan 610021. News Sce on 792kHz/99.8MHz 2130-1700 - Traffic Sce on 1485kHz/91.4MHz 2200-1700 (exc. Tues 0500-0800) - Economic Sce "Excellence 1056": on 105.6MHz24h - Cultural and Leisure Sce "Scripture 946": on 94.6MHz 24h – Unique Music Sce "Only Radio": on 103.2MHz 24h – Private Car Music Sce on 105.1MHz 2200-1700

- V.O.Global: on 96.3MHz 2155-1605 – Story Sce "Happy Radio": on 88.2MHz 2100-1700 – **SC4)** Zigong Radio and TV St, 122 Dangui Dajie, Huidong Xinqu, Zigong, Sichuan 643000. News General Sce on 1422kHz/97.7MHz 2100-1500 - Cultural and Travel Sce on 90.8MHz 2300-1700 – **SC5)** Panzhihua Radio and TV St, 43, Zhong Duan, Jinshajiang Dadao, Dong Qu, Panzhihua, Sichuan 617000. Gerenal Sce on 711kHz/88.5MHz 2120-1700 - Farm Sce (Automobile St) on 91.0MHz 2230-1700 – **SC6)** Datong Lu, Chengbei Xinqu, Luzhou, Sichuan 646000. News General Sce on 954kHz/89.8/97.0MHz 2155-1600 - Traffic and Music Sce on 96.0/100.6MHz 2155-1600 – **SC7)** 63, 1 Duan, Taishan Nanlu, Deyang, Sichuan 618000. News Sce on 720kHz/95.9MHz 2200-1600 - Music and Traffic Sce on 107.8MHz 2300-1600 – **SC8)** Mianyang Radio and TV St, 232, Nan Duan, 1 Huan Lu, Fucheng Qu, Mianyang, Sichuan 621000. News Sce "V.O. Fujiang": on 711kHz/96.7/102.0MHz 2200-1600 - Traffic Sce on 103.3MHz 2200-1600 - Music Sce on 91.2/92.6MHz 2200-1600 – **SC9)** 585, Xi Duan, Hezhou Donglu, Guangyuan, Sichuan 628017. News General Ch. on 621/1143kHz/102.7MHz 2200-1700 - City and Country Ch. on 104.8MHz 2220-1600 – **SC10)** Suining Radio and TV St, 686 Suizhou Zhonglu, Chuanshan Qu, Suining, Sichuan 629000. News and Story Sce on 1260kHz/99.7MHz 2150-1800 - Traffic and Music Sce on 87.8MHz 2150-1800 – **SC11)** 33, 1 Xiang, Xianglong Lu, Neijiang, Sichuan 641000. Economic Sce on 1143kHz/101.4MHz – **SC12)** 639, Nan Duan, Chunhua Lu, Shizhong Qu, Leshan, Sichuan 614000. News General Ch. on 1476kHz/102.8MHz 2225-1800 - Music and Traffic Ch. "Big Eye": on 100.5MHz 2300(SS 2330)-1700 – **SC13)** 12 Sichou Lu, Nanchong, Sichuan 637000. News Information Sce on 747kHz/100.4/97.5MHz 2130-1630 - Traffic and Music Sce on 91.5MHz 2330-1630 – **SC14)** Yibin Radio and TV St, 7, Zhong Duan, Nan'an Changjiang Dadao, Cuiping Qu, Yibin, Sichuan 644000. News Sce on 92.8/97.0/101.4MHz 2200-1700 - Traffic Sce on 94.2/105.9MHz 2200-1700 - Jiudu (Wine City) Music Sce on 104.2MHz 2100-1600 – **SC15)** 92 Zhangjiawan, Tongchuan Qu, Dazhou, Sichuan 635000. News General Ch. on 1143kHz 2200-1600

**TIANJIN MUNICIPALITY**

**TJ1)** 143 Weijin Lu, Heping Qu, Tianjin 300070 **W:** radiotj.com News Sce on 909kHz/89.0MHz, 97.2MHz 2100-1800(FM 24h) - Economic Sce on 1071kHz/101.4MHz 2100-1500 - Crosstalk Sce on 567kHz/92.1MHz 2200-1600 - Traffic Sce on 106.8MHz 24h(exc. Tue 1600-2100) - Life Sce on 1386kHz/91.1MHz 2100-1700 - Literary Sce on 1098kHz/104.6MHz 24h(exc. Tue 1600-2100) - Music Sce "Nice Radio": on 99.0MHz 24h - Music Health Sce on 1008kHz 2300-1800 - Binhai Sce "Radio BH": on 747kHz/87.8MHz 2055-1600 Rural Sce 2200-1600 on 88.5MHz - Novel Sce on 666kHz 2200-1600

**XINJIANG UIGHUR AUTONOMOUS REGION**

**XJ1)** 830 Tuanjie Lu, Urumqi, Xinjiang 830044 **W:** xjbs.com.cn Ch General Sce "Sunshine 895" on 702/738/999/1494/3950wi./ 5060wi./5960/7260/7310/9600/9835su./11770kHz/89.5MHz 2300-1800 (SW exc. Tues 0800-1100) - Ug General Sce on 558/855/1044/1413/3990wi./4980wi./ 6120/7205/7275/9560/11885/ 13670kHz/101.7MHz 2300-1800 (exc. Tues 0800-1100) - Kz Prgr. on 963/1233/1107/4850wi./6015/7340/9470kHz 2300-1800 - Mo Prgr. on 909/1233/1593/4500wi./6190/7230/9510kHz 2300-1800 (SW: 2300-0330, 0510-1030, 1150-1800) - Kg Prgr. on 1233/7295wi./9705/11975su. kHz/98.2MHz 2300-1800 (SW: 0305-0530, 1005-1230) - Ch News Sce "Pioneer 961" on 96.1MHz 2300-1800 - Ch Private Car Sce (City Sce) on 837/1215kHz/92.9MHz 2300-1800 - Ch Traffic Sce on 94.9/101.8MHz 2300-1800 Ch Music Sce "MY FM": on 103.9MHz 2300-1800 - Ch Story Sce on 102.8MHz 2300-1800 Ch People Life Sce "WIFI Radio" on 92.4MHz 2300-1800 - Ug Traffic and Literary Sce on 107.4MHz 2300-1800 (exc. Tues 0800-1100) **NB:** wi.:Nov-Apr only, su.:May-Oct only – **XJ2)** 54, Bei 4 Xiang, Hongshan Lu, Urumqi, Xinjiang 830092. **W:** wlmqradio.com News Sce on 100.7MHz 2300-1800 - Economic Sce on 927kHz 2300-1700 - General Sce: on 792kHz 2300-1700 - Traffic Sce on 97.4MHz 2300-1800 - Taste (Travel and Music) Sce on 106.5MHz 24h - Ug General Sce on 1071kHz/104.6MHz 2300-1700.. –**XJ3)** 100 Tianshan Lu, Karamay, Xinjiang 834000. Ch News General Sce on 1179kHz 2355-1800 (exc. Tues 0800-0930) - Ug Sce on 882kHz 2355-1800 - City Sce on 92.6MHz 2355-2000 (exc. Tues 0830-0930) – **XJ5)** 2 Hongxing Xilu, Hami, Xinjiang 839000. Ch News and Traffic Sce "V.O. Hami": on 1485kHz/103.5MHz 2300-1800 - Ug FM on 1098kHz/107.9MHz 2300-1600 - V.O. Tianmi (Honey): on 98.1MHz 2300-1800 - Legend Story Sce "Green Ch": on 91.1MHz 2255-1800 - Music Sce "Touch Radio": on 99.9MHz 24h – **XJ6)** 13 Urumqi Nanlu, Hotan, Xinjiang 848000. Ch Prgr. on 1026kHz - Ug Prgr. on 774kHz/92.2MHz 2300-1800 – **XJ7)** Tiyu Lu, Kashi, Xinjiang 844000. Ch Sce on 648kHz/101.2MHz 2355-0215, 0455-0710, ?-1335 - Ug Sce on 801kHz/103.0MHz 2355-? – **XJ8)** 66 Shangcheng Lu, Changji, Xinjiang 831100. General Sce on 873kHz 2300-1700 - Traffic Sce on 96.9MHz - Story Sce on 107.4MHz 2330-1800 - Legal Sce on 105.3MHz - Music Sce on 103.3MHz – **XJ9)** Ili PBS, 1 Hongqi Lu, Yining, Xinjiang 835000. News General

Sce on 1134kHz/96.3/105.9/107.4MHz2255-1805 – Economic Sce on 90.5MHz 2325-1835 - Traffic and Music Sce on 100.8MHz - Ug Prgr. on 882kHz/88.4MHz 2350-0200, 0550-0700, 1150-1600 - Kz Prgr. on 603kHz/93.4MHz 2350-0200, 0550-0700, 1220-1500 – **XJ10)** 184 Bei 2 Lu, Shihezi, Xinjiang 832000. News Ch. on 891kHz/103.5MHz 0030-0730, 1130-1600 - Literary Ch. on 603kHz/89.3MHz – **XJ11)** 8 Kashi Xilu, Kuytun, Xinjiang 833200. Ch Prgr. on 1485kHz W2355-0230, Sun0025-0335, Sun0528-0740, W0558-0740, D1123-1425 - Kz Prgr. on 819kHz – **XJ12)** Bayingolin PBS, 1 Jianguo Nanlu, Korla, Xinjiang 841000. News Sce on 819kHz/96.6MHz - Music Sce on 92.2MHz 2300-1800 - Story Sce on 89.5MHz - Mo Sce on 104.7MHz - Traffic and Literary Sce on 107.7MHz 2330-1700

## XIZANG AUTONOMOUS REGION

**XZ1)** 41 Beijing Zhonglu, Lhasa, Xizang 850000 **W**: vtibet.com/ Ch Sce on 999/1377/4820/5935/6050/7240/7450/11860/11950kHz/93.3MHz 2000(Tues 2100)-1800 (exc. Tues 0600-1000) - Tibetan Sce on 594/846/49 05/4920/6025/6010/6110/6130/ 6200/7255/7385/9490/9580kHz/101.6MHz 2050 (Tues 2100)-1805 (exc. Tues 0600-1000). English Prgr. "Holy Tibet": 0700-0800, 1600-1700 - Kham (Tibetan dialect) General Sce on 594kHz/91.4MHz 2200-1605 (exc. Tues 0600-1000) - City Life Sce on 98.0MHz 2300-1700 (exc. Tues 0600-1000) Tibetan Science Education Sce on 106.3MHz – **XZ2)** Lhasa PBS, Lhasa, Xizang 850000. General Ch. on 91.4MHz 2350-1410 in Tb and Ch – **XZ3)** 25 Nedong Lu, Zetang Zhen, Nedong, Xizang 856000. 2335-0135, 0405-0535, 1005-1340 in Ch and Tb

## YUNNAN PROVINCE

**YN1)** 182 Renmin Xilu, Kunming, Yunnan 650031. News Sce on 576/846/990/1098/1197/1395/1584kHz/105.8MHz    2200-1600 – "Shangri-La 99": on 99.0MHz 0230-1430 - Economic Sce on 1143/88.7MHz 24h. Rel. CRI English prgr: 1300-1500 - Minority Sce on 7210kHz 2255-0300, 0630-0830, 1100-1500 in Lahu, Jingpo, Lisu, Dehong Dai, Xishuangbanna Dai etc - V.O. the Traffic: on 603/1098kHz/91.8MHz 2300-1700. - Music Sce "Binfen 97": on 846/1053/1251kHz/97.0MHz 2300-1600 (exc. Tues 0600-0900) - Knowledge Person Sce "Xinzhi 100": on 100.0MHz 2245-1700 - Children Sce on 101.7MHz 2250-1700 - Farm Sce on 1242kHz 2300-1600 (exc. Tues 0600-0800) - Int Sce see International Broadcasting section – **YN2)** 198 Danxia Lu, Kunming, Yunnan 650118. City News Sce "Sunlight Ch." on 1350kHz/100.8MHz 24h (exc. Tues 0400-0800) - New FM on 102.8MHz 24h - Automobile Sce "954 Car Netw.": on 95.4MHz 24h - Knowledge Person Sce on 105.0MHz 24h – **YN3)** 225 Qilin Xilu, Qilin Qu, Qujing, Yunnan 655000. V.O. Zhujiang Yuan: on 1521kHz/104.0MHz 2225-1600 - V.O. the Traffic: on 91.0MHz 2250-1600 – **YN4)** 32 Xinwen Lu, Wenshan, Yunnan 663000. Minority Language Ch. on 1053kHz/105.3MHz 2225-0030, 0355-0530, 0955-1400 in Ch, Zhuang, Miao and Yao - News General Ch. on 103.0/102.2MHz 2220-1500 - Qihua FM on 97.3MHz 2220-1600 – **YN5)** Honghe PBS, Jinhua Lu, Gejiu, Yunnan 661000. News Sce on 1521/1485kHz/101.4MHz 2200-1700 - Traffic Sce on 99.7MHz 2200-1730 - Minorities Sce on 702kHz/97.5MHz 2225-1830 in Ch, Hani and Yi – **YN6)** Xishuangbanna PBS, 4 Guangdian Lu, Jinghong, Yunnan 666100. Ch Prgr. on 98.9MHz 2225-1620 - Minority Language Prgr. on 747kHz/90.6MHz 2225-1625 in Ch, Xishuangbanna Dai and Hani – **YN7)** Chuxiong Autonomous Prefecture PBS, 144 Lucheng Donglu, Chuxiong, Yunnan 675000. General Sce on 1287kHz/106.1MHz 2225-1605 in Ch and Yi - Music Sce on 90.6/96.3MHz 2225-1605 – **YN8)** Wanhua Lu, Xiaguan Zhen, Dali, Yunnan 671000. News General Sce on 1044kHz/102.7MHz 2230-1500 - Traffic Sce on 99.9MHz 2230-1600 - Cang'er FM on 105.5MHz 2200-1600 – **YN9)** Dehong Radio and TV St, 51 Nanbeng Lu, Mang Shi, Yunnan 678400. Minority Language Sce on 900kHz/106.1MHz 2230-0110, 0330-0700, 1030-1530 in Ch, Dehong Dai, Jingpo and Zaiwa - General Sce on 104.3MHz 2215-1600 –**YN11)** 6 Longquan Lu, Zhaotong, Yunnan 657000. News General Sce "V.O. Wumeng": on 846kHz/97.5MHz 2225-1600 (exc. Tues 0710-0900) - Traffic and Travel Sce "V.O. Hedu (Crane City)": 2225-1600 – **YN12)** Baohua Lu, Gejiu, Yunnan 661400. V.O. Jinhu (Golden Lake): on 675kHz/102.7MHz – **YN13)** 38 Xueqiao Jie, Chuxiong, Yunnan 675000. W2225-2400, Sun2325-0200, D0325-0600, D0955-1405 – **YN14)** 29 Guihua Lu, Yuxi, Yunnan 653100. Green FM on 1251kHz/102.4MHz 2225-1600 – **YN15)** Diqing PBS, 67 Changzheng Dadao, Jiantang Zhen, Shangri-la Xian, Yunnan 674400. On 675kHz/104.7MHz in Ch and Tb – **YN16)** Nujiang Radio and TV St, 5 Weiyuan Xiang, Liuku Zhen, Lushui Xian, Yunnan 673100. On 558kHz/105.6MHz in Ch and Lisu – **YN17)** Longcheng Lu, Jinshan Zhen, Lufeng Xian, Yunnan 651200. 2225-1230

## ZHEJIANG PROVINCE

**ZJ1)**Zhejiang Radio & TV Group, 111 Moganshan Lu, Hangzhou, Zhejiang 310005 **W**: zrtg.com V.O. Zhejiang: on 810kHz/88.0/101.6MHz 24h (exc. Tues 0600-0800) - News Sce "Xinrui 988": on 1530kHz/98.8MHz 24h - Economic Sce on 95.0MHz 24h - V.O. the City: on 107.0/88.6/89.4/92 .5/98.2/100.7/101.7MHz 24h – V.O. the Traffic: on 93.0/93.6MHz 24h

- Music FM: on 1071kHz/96./89.8/94.5/96.8/102.5/106.4/107.8MHz 24h (exc. Tues 0600-0800) - Life Sce "Minsheng 996": on 900/930/1050/1314kHz /99.6/92.3/93.6/104.2/104.7MHz 24h - Anchorwomen BS: on 603/1251/1521kHz/104.5MHz 24h – **ZJ2)** 888 Zhijiang Lu, Hangzhou, Zhejiang 310016. **W**: radiohz.com "AM 954" Old Friends R. on 954kHz/69.0MHz 2000-1600 - V.O. Hangzhou "News 89": on 89.0MHz 24h – **ZJ2A)** Hangzhou Traffic and Economic Sce, 5 Qingchun Donglu, Hangzhou, Zhejiang 310016. On 91.8MHz 24h – **ZJ3)** City Music "V.O. Xihu", 86 Moganshan Lu, Hangzhou, Zhejiang 310005. On 105.4MHz 24h in Ch and Hangzhou dialect – **ZJ4)** Ningbo Radio and TV Group, 109 Heyi Lu, Ningbo, Zhejiang 315000. News Sce "V.O. Ningbo": on 1323kHz/92.0MHz 2055-1610. English N: D1600-1610 - "Yangguang (Sunshine) 904": on 1251kHz/90.4MHz 2155-1605 - Economic Sce "i Radio": on 747kHz/102.9MHz 2100-1600 (exc. Tues 0600-0730) - Traffic Sce on 603kHz/93.9MHz 24h - Music Sce "Private Car 986": on 98.6MHz 2300-1600 – **ZJ4A)** 36 Nan Dajie, Zhenhai Qu, Ningbo, Zhejiang 315200. Ningbo Private Car Music St. on 104.7MHz 24h (exc. Mon 0500-0830) - V.O. Yong River: on 100.1MHz – **ZJ5)** Wenzhou Radio and TV Media Group, Xincheng Dadao, Lucheng Qu, Wenzhou, Zhejiang 325027. News Sce "V.O. Wenzhou": on 666kHz/94.9/102.6MHz 24h (exc. Tues 0600-0900) in Ch and Wenzhou dialect - Economic Life Sce "Xingyun (Fortunate) 888": on 801kHz/88.8MHz 24h - Traffic Sce "Automobile FM": on 97.2/103.9MHz 24h - Private Car Music Sce "i Radio":on 100.3MHz 24h (exc. Tues 0600-0900) - V.O. Green: on 93.8MHz 24h – **ZJ6)** Jiaxing Radio and TV Group, 6 Dongsheng Lu, Jiaxing, Zhejiang 314001. News Sce on 1107kHz/104.1MHz 2125-1505 - Traffic Sce on 657kHz/92.2MHz 2130-1505 (exc. Tues 0530-0700) - Life Sce "Kuaile (Happy) 882" on 88.2MHz 2130-1500 (exc. Tues 0500-0700) – **ZJ7)** Huzhou Radio and TV Headquarters, 628 Xinhua Lu, Huzhou, Zhejiang 313000. News Sce on 873kHz/105.0MHz 2155-1600 (exc. Tues 0600-0730) - Traffic Sce on 927/1521kHz/103.5MHz 2155-1600 - Music Sce on 1251kHz/98.5MHz 2200-1600 – **ZJ8)** Shaoxing Radio and TV Headquarters, 508 Yan'an Donglu, Shaoxing, Zhejiang 312000. News General Sce on 738kHz/93.6MHz 2100-1600 - Traffic Sce on 94.1MHz 2130-1600 (exc. Tues 0600-0830) - Chinese Opera Sce on 102.5MHz 2130-0300 - Music Sce "i Music": on 103.5MHz 2100-1500 (exc. Tues 0600-0900) – **ZJ9)** 238 Renmin Xilu, Jinhua, Zhejiang 321000. News Sce on 675kHz/104.4MHz 2100-1600 (exc. Tues 0600-0900) - Economic Sce "Private Car 101": on 101.4MHz 2200-1700 - Traffic Sce on 94.2MHz 24h – **ZJ10)** Quzhou Radio and TV Headquarters, 35 Nanjie, Quzhou, Zhejiang 324000. News Sce "V.O. Quzhou": on 711kHz/105.3MHz 2155-1600 (exc. Tues 0500-0725) - Traffic and Music Sce on 1250kHz/97.5MHz 2200-1700 – **ZJ11)** Zhoushan Radio and TV Headquarters, 137 Changguo Lu, Dinghai Qu, Zhoushan, Zhejiang 316000. News General Ch. "V.O. Dinghai": on 684kHz/99.8MHz 2130-1500 (exc. Tues 0530-0855) - Traffic and Economic Sce on 1098kHz/97.0MHz 2155-1500 (exc. Tues 0500-0900) - Automobile Music FM "V.O. the City": on 900kHz/91.0/102.6MHz 2155-1500 (exc. Tues 0530-0855) – **ZJ12)** Lishui Radio and TV Headquarters, 2 Huayuan Lu, Liandu Qu, Lishui, Zhejiang 323000. News General Ch. on 711kHz/94.0/96.4MHz 2155-1600 - Traffic and Music Ch. on 106.9MHz 2155-1600 - New Farm Sce on 88.3MHz 24h – **ZJ13)** Xiaoshan PBS, Nanduan, Yucai Lu, Xiaoshan Qu, Hangzhou, Zhejiang 311200. On 107.9MHz 2155-1400 – **ZJ14)** Xishan, Chengguan, Rui'an, Zhejiang 325200. On 1584kHz/91.0MHz ?-1305 – **ZJ15)** 121 Zhongshan Lu, Jiangshan, Zhejiang 324100 – **ZJ16)** Taizhou PBS, 315 Zhongxin Dadao, Jiaojiang Qu, Taizhou, Zhejiang 318000. News General Ch. "987 Ch.": on 98.7/87.5/90.0MHz 24h - Traffic Sce on 102.7MHz - Music Sce on 100.1MHz.

## CHRISTMAS ISLAND (Australia)

**L.T:** UTC +7h — **Pop:** 1,843 — **Pr.L:** English, Malay, Cantonese, Hokkien, Mandarin — **E.C:** 50Hz, 240V — **ITU:** CHR

| MW kHz | Call | kW | Network, location |
|--------|------|-----|-------------------|
| 1) 1422 | 6ABCRN | 0.5 | ABC R. National, Phosphate Hill |

| FM MHz | Call | kW | Network, location |
|--------|------|-----|-------------------|
| 1) 89.3 | 6ABCRR | 0.02 | ABC Local R. (Kimberley), Phosphate Hill |
| 1) 90.1 | 6ABCRN | 0.02 | ABC R. National, Rocky Point |
| 1) 90.9 | 6FMS | 0.02 | Red FM, Phosphate Hill |
| 1) 91.7 | 6JJJ | 0.02 | ABC Triple J, Rocky Point |
| 2) 92.5 | 6RCI | 0.02 | Christmas Island Cmty R., Phosphate Hill |
| 1) 93.3 | 6ABCRR | 0.02 | ABC Local R. (Kimberley), Rocky Point |
| 1) 94.1 | 6ABCRN | 0.02 | ABC R. National, Phosphate Hill |
| 1) 95.7 | 6ABCRR | 0.1 | ABC Local R. (Kimberley), Drumsite |
| 1) 97.3 | 6ABCRN | 0.02 | ABC Radio National, Drumsite |
| 2) 98.9 | 6FMS | 0.02 | Red FM, Drumsite |
| 1) 100.5 | 6JJJ | 0.02 | ABC Triple J, Drumsite |
| 3) 102.0 | 16RCI | 0.02 | Christmas Island Cmty R., Drumsite |

| FM | MHz | Call | kW | Network, location |
|---|---|---|---|---|
| 1) | 103.7 | 6JJJ | 0.02 | ABC Triple J, Phosphate Hill |
| 3) | 105.3 | 6RCI | 0.02 | Christmas Island Cmty R., Rocky Point |
| 2) | 106.9 | 6FMS | 0.02 | Red FM, Rocky Point |

**Addresses & other information:**
All ABC and RedFM services are 24hr retransmissions via VAST satellite platform – **1)** Dept Infrastructure & Regional Development (Policy Section, Territories Reform & Service Delivery), 111 Alinga St, Canberra ACT 2601 (✉GPO Box 594, Canberra ACT 2601) ☎ +61 2 2674 7111 **E:** clientservice@infrastructure.gov.au – **2)** RedFM, 50 Hasler Rd, Osborne Park WA 6017 ☎ +61 8 9482 9500 🖹 +61 8 9482 9454 **E:** admin@redfm.com.au **W:** redfm.com.au – **3)** Broadcast House, Nursery Road, Drumsite (PO Box 474) Christmas Island WA 6798 ☎ +61 8 9164 7121 🖹 +61 8 9164 8615 **E:** 6rci@pulau.cx **W:** facebook.com/6RCIradio Local community stn. AKA VLU2-FM.

## COCOS (KEELING) ISLANDS (Australia)

**L.T:** UTC +6½h — **Pop:** 540 — **Pr.L:** English, Cocos Malay — **E.C:** 50Hz, 240V — **ITU:** ICO

| FM | MHz | Call | kW | Network (West Island) |
|---|---|---|---|---|
| 3) | 96.6 | 6CKI | 0.1 | Voice of the Cocos (Keeling) Isl. |
| 2) | 100.5 | 6FMS | 0.1 | Red FM |
| 1) | 102.1 | 6ABCRR | 0.1 | ABC Local R. Kimberley |
| FM | MHz | Call | kW | Network (Home Island) |
| 3) | 102.7 | 6CKI | 0.02 | Voice of the Cocos (Keeling) Isl. |
| 1) | 105.7 | 6ABCRR | 0.02 | ABC Local R. Kimberley |

**Addresses & other information:**
All ABC and Red FM services are 24hr retransmissions via VAST satellite platform **1)** Dept Infrastructure & Regional Development (Policy Section, Territories Reform & Service Delivery), 111 Alinga St, Canberra ACT 2601 (✉GPO Box 594, Canberra ACT 2601) ☎ +61 2 2674 7111 **E:** clientservice@infrastructure.gov.au **2)** Red FM, 50 Hasler Rd, Osborne Park WA 6017 ☎ +61 8 9482 9500 🖹 +61 8 9482 9454 **E:** admin@redfm.com.au **W:** redfm.com.au **3)** PO Box 1093, Cocos (Keeling) Islands WA 6799 ☎+61 8 9162 6666 **E:** 6cki@cki.cc **W:** facebook.com/6CKI-Voice-of-the-Cocos-Keeling-Islands-570321973012338/ **Prgr:** 24h with local news 0700 UTC M-F local community stn.

## COLOMBIA

**L.T:** UTC -5h — **Pop:** 49 million — **Pr.L:** Spanish — **E.C:** 60Hz, 110V — **ITU:** CLM

**MINISTERIO DE TECNOLOGIAS DE LA INFORMACION Y LAS COMUNICACIONES (MINTIC)**
✉ Edificio Murillo Toro, Cra 8a entre Calles 12 y 13, Bogotá, DC ☎ +57 1 344 3460 **W:** mintic.gov.co

**Call** HJ—, ‡ = inactive, rel. = relay, ± = varying freq †=irregular. The letters preceding the stn number indicate the departamento. Addresses are listed by departamento in alphabetical order.
**Hr of tr**. usually 24h, see address section for variations.

| MW | Call | kHz | kW | Station, location |
|---|---|---|---|---|
| DC01) | KA | 540 | 10 | R. Auténtica Básica, Bogotá |
| DC02) | HF | 550 | 50 | R. Nac. de Colombia, Medellín (Marinilla) |
| VP01) | R36 | 550 | 30 | Cadena Radial Vida, Mitú (r. 1130) |
| DC02) | QS | 560 | 10 | R. Nac. de Colombia, Tunja |
| GU01) | PF | 560 | 25/10 | LV de la Pampa, Maicao |
| DC02) | ND | 570 | 100 | R. Nac. de Colombia, Bogotá (El Rosal) |
| VI01) | C61 | 570 | 30 | Cadena Radial Vida, Puerto Carreño |
| DC02) | HP | 580 | 50/10 | R. Nac. de Colombia, Cali |
| AN01) | CR | 590 | 50 | Volvamos a Dios Radio, Medellín |
| AT01) | KU | 600 | 50 | R. Libertad, Barranquilla |
| NA13) | Z95 | 600 | 1 | LV de los Awas, Ricaurte el Diviso |
| DC02) | D90 | 610 | 50 | R. Nac. de Colombia, Riohacha |
| DC03) | KL | 610 | 30 | La Cariñosa, Bogotá |
| BO01) | VP | 620 | 10 | Colmundo Radio, Cartagena |
| VA01) | EL | 620 | 50/20 | Colmundo Radio, Cali |
| CL01) | FD | 630 | 10 | R. Manizales, Manizales |
| MA01) | BJ | 640 | 10 | RCN, Santa Marta |
| DC03) | KH | 650 | 50 | RCN Antena 2, Bogotá |
| NS01) | QS | 660 | 25 | Colmundo Radio, Cúcuta |
| VA02) | EZ | 660 | 10 | R. Auténtica, Cali |
| AN02) | PL | 670 | 50 | RCN Antena 2, Medellín |
| SS28) | R33 | 670 | 10 | UIS AM "La Nueva Radio", Bucaramanga |
| DC02) | ZO | 680 | 50 | R. Nac. de Colombia, Barranquilla |
| AN56) | Z73 | 690 | 1 | Emisora Embera Chami y Zenu de la Palma, Apartadó |

| MW | Call | kHz | kW | Station, location |
|---|---|---|---|---|
| DC04) | CZ | 690 | 35 | W Radio, Bogotá (r. 99.9) |
| VA03) | CX | 700 | 30 | W Radio, Cali |
| AN03) | NX | 710 | 10 | R. Red RCN, Medellín |
| BY14) | YD | 710 | 1 | R. La Paz, Paipa |
| AT01) | AN | 720 | 30 | Emisoras Unidas, Barranquilla |
| QU01) | VO | 720 | 25 | Transmisora Quindío, Armenia |
| CO03) | TJ | 730 | 15 | R. Uno, Montería |
| DC05) | CU | 730 | 10 | Melodía Estéreo, Bogotá |
| CE01) | NS | 740 | 50 | R. Guatapurí, Valledupar |
| NA01) | HB | 740 | 10 | Ecos de Pasto, Pasto |
| AN01) | DK | 750 | 50 | Caracol R., Medellín |
| CS01) | LH | 750 | 5 | LV de Yopal, Yopal |
| AT02) | AJ | 760 | 25 | RCN La Radio, Barranquilla |
| DC03) | JX | 770 | 100 | RCN La Radio, Bogotá (r. 93.9) |
| NA15) | FV | 780 | 5 | R. Viva, Pasto |
| SS30) | C21 | 780 | 10 | Antena del Río, Barrancabermeja |
| VA04) | ZG | 780 | 10 | LV del Valle, Cali |
| AN01) | DC | 790 | 10 | Múnera Eastman R, Medellín |
| TO03) | NC | 790 | 1 | Ecos del Combeima, Ibagué |
| QU06) | JH | 800 | 1 | R. Ciudad Milagro, Armenia |
| SS01) | BW | 800 | 100 | RCN, Bucaramanga |
| DC04) | CY | 810 | 60 | Caracol R., Bogotá (r. 100.9) |
| BO02) | AD | 820 | 10 | R. Vigía, Cartagena |
| VA03) | ED | 820 | 50 | Caracol R., Cali |
| AN01) | DM | 830 | 15 | O'hubo Radio AM/R. Reloj, Medellín |
| HU01) | KK | 840 | 30 | HJKK Sistema INRAI, Neiva |
| MA02) | BI | 840 | 10 | Ondas del Caribe, Santa Marta |
| VA24) | NA | 840 | 5 | R. Robledo (RCN), Cartago |
| DC04) | KC | 850 | 35 | Candela "La del Amor y el Despecho", Bogotá |
| CE02) | NJ | 860 | 50 | LV del Cañaguate/W Radio, Valledupar |
| VA05) | DV | 860 | 10 | Voces de Occidente, Buga |
| AN09) | ZH | 870 | 5 | Cadena Radial Vida, Medellín |
| BY16) | GD | 870 | 1 | Em. Reina de Colombia, Chiquinquirá |
| CL04) | FH | 880 | 10 | R. Regional Independiente, Anserma |
| TO01) | IA | 870 | 10 | LV del Tolima, Ibagué |
| SS02) | GE | 880 | 20 | Caracol R., Bucaramanga |
| DC06) | CE | 890 | 10 | Cadena Radial Vida, Bogotá |
| MA03) | PM | 890 | 20 | Caracol R., Santa Marta |
| NS02) | DD | 900 | 10 | RCN Fiesta, Cúcuta |
| VA04) | EY | 900 | 10 | LV de Cali, Cali |
| AN04) | DO | 910 | 10 | LV del Río Grande, Medellín |
| BY12) | TT | 910 | 1 | Ondas del Porvenir, Samacá |
| DC24) | S52 | 910 | 15 | Colombia Estereo, Florencia |
| GU02) | C84 | 910 | 20 | Cadena Radial Vida, Puerto Inírida |
| IS01) | MY | 910 | 30 | RCN, San Andrés (rel. 770 Bogotá) |
| BO03) | AA | 920 | 10 | Em. Fuentes, Cartagena |
| NA02) | JN | 920 | 10 | HSB Radio, Pasto |
| TO02) | SJ | 920 | 10 | Colmundo Radio, Ibagué |
| CL01) | IA | 930 | 5 | Bésame, Manizales (r. 91.7) |
| DC07) | CS | 930 | 10 | LV de Bogotá, Bogotá |
| AN59) | A76 | 940 | 5 | Frecuencia U, Medellín |
| NS03) | TL | 940 | 25 | RCN, Cúcuta |
| VA04) | GB | 940 | 10 | R. Calima, Cali |
| BY18) | UJ | 950 | 5 | Armonías Boyacenses, Tunja |
| RI01) | FN | 950 | 15 | Caracol Radio, Pereira |
| BO08) | HN | 960 | 10 | Caracol Radio, Magangué |
| IS05) | R31 | 960 | 15 | Candela, San Andrés: (r. 101.9 Bogotá) |
| SS23) | HX | 960 | 5 | Bluradio, Bucaramanga |
| CA01) | VK | 970 | 15 | Armonias del Caquetá, Florencia |
| DC08) | CI | 970 | 10 | R. Red RCN, Bogotá |
| NS04) | JV | 980 | 15 | Bésame, Cúcuta (r. 100.7) |
| VA06) | ES | 980 | 100 | RCN, Cali |
| AN02) | CH | 990 | 50 | RCN, Medellín |
| BY07) | HI | 990 | 5 | LV de Garagoa, Garagoa |
| BO04) | AQ | 1000 | 15 | RCN, Cartagena |
| DC02) | JG | 1000 | 10 | R. Nac. de Colombia, Manizales |
| GV01) | Q98 | 1000 | 20 | Vida, San José del Guaviare (r. 1130) |
| AT04) | OP | 1010 | 10 | Sistema Cardenal, Barranquilla |
| CO01) | ZD | 1010 | 15 | R. Panzenú, Montería |
| DC04) | CC | 1010 | 10 | Acuario Estéreo, Bogotá |
| HU02) | JR | 1010 | 15 | Caracol R., Neiva |
| NA03) | BN | 1010 | 10/5 | LV del Galeras, Pasto |
| SS03) | IX | 1010 | 10 | R. Yarima, Barrancabermeja |
| AN04) | DQ | 1020 | 10 | Emisora Claridad, Medellín |
| ME01) | KS | 1020 | 10 | La Cariñosa/LV del Llano, Villavicencio |
| RI02) | FQ | 1020 | 10 | RCN, Pereira |
| SS04) | DZ | 1020 | 15 | R. Primavera, Bucaramanga |
| TO03) | FT | 1020 | 10 | La FM, Ibagué |
| BY01) | DJ | 1030 | 10 | La Cariñosa, Duitama |
| CE03) | RF | 1030 | 15 | Ondas del Cesar, Aguachica |
| CO02) | GX | 1030 | 1 | RPC Radio, Lorica |

| MW | Call | kHz | kW | Station, location |
|---|---|---|---|---|
| VA06) | DT | 1030 | 30 | RCN Antena 2, Cali |
| VP02) | | ‡1030 | 5 | Ondas del Vaupés, Mitú |
| AT01) | AI | 1040 | 15 | R. Tropical, Barranquilla |
| CC02) | SY | 1040 | 10 | R. 1040, Popayán |
| DC10) | CJ | 1040 | 15 | Colmundo Radio, Bogotá |
| NA04) | UB | 1040 | 15 | Colmundo Radio, Pasto |
| NS05) | BF | 1040 | 15 | LV del Norte/Blu Radio, Cúcuta |
| QU02) | FM | 1040 | 15 | LV de Armenia, Armenia |
| AN04) | DR | 1050 | 10 | Vida, Medellín |
| AR01) | E73 | 1050 | 10 | LV del Cinaruco/Caracol, Arauca |
| CE04) | BB | 1050 | 10 | Sistema Cardenal, Valledupar |
| CO04) | AW | 1050 | 10 | RCN La Radio, Montería |
| CS03) | S62 | 1050 | 10 | Cusiana R., Yopal |
| ME02) | IO | 1050 | 5 | LV de la Conquista, Granada |
| SS05) | GU | 1050 | 10 | R. Bucarica, Bucaramanga |
| T004) | FZ | 1050 | 10 | La Cariñosa del Centro, Espinal |
| VA07) | NG | 1050 | 5 | R. Palmira, Palmira |
| AN05) | MG | 1060 | 1 | R. Litoral, Turbo |
| BY02) | MV | 1060 | 10 | R. Furatena, Chiquinquirá |
| CL02) | FJ | 1060 | 15 | RCN, Manizales |
| GU04) | LY | 1060 | 10 | R. Delfín, Riohacha |
| HU03) | OV | 1060 | 15 | R. Surcolombiana, Neiva |
| SU11) | YX | 1060 | 1 | R. Caracolí, Sincelejo |
| AT06) | AH | 1070 | 20 | Em. Atlántico, Barranquilla |
| CC03) | VR | 1070 | 10 | Nueva R. Super, Popayán |
| DC11) | CG | 1070 | 30 | R. Santa Fe, Bogotá |
| AN01) | AX | 1080 | 10 | LV de Antioquia, Medellín |
| CL03) | JS | 1080 | 10 | R. Uno, La Dorada |
| CO04) | AW | 1080 | 10 | LV de Montería, Montería |
| ME03) | KT | 1080 | 10 | R. Autentica, Villavicencio |
| SS06) | MH | 1080 | 10 | R. Melodía, Bucaramanga |
| VA04) | JF | 1080 | 10 | Vida, Cali |
| BO05) | OM | 1090 | 5 | Bluradio, Cartagena |
| BY03) | IH | 1090 | 8 | Caracol R., Sogamoso |
| CA02) | IG | 1090 | 10 | R. Autentica, Florencia |
| CL01) | IA | 1090 | 10 | W Radio, Manizales (r. 101.7) |
| NS06) | BC | 1090 | 15 | Caracol R., Cúcuta |
| T005) | JB | 1090 | 10 | Click Radio/Blu Radio, Guamo |
| AN06) | GQ | 1100 | 5 | Transmisora Surandes, Andes |
| AT04) | AT | 1100 | 15 | Caracol R., Barranquilla |
| CO05) | MK | 1100 | 5 | Emisora Ideal, Planeta Rica |
| DC27) | CN | 1100 | 10 | BBN R, Bogotá |
| HU04) | YZ | 1100 | 15 | R. Uno, Neiva |
| SS07) | GI | 1100 | 1 | LV de Colombia, Socorro |
| AN07) | DI | 1110 | 9 | R. Bolivariana, Medellín |
| AR02) | GP | 1110 | 5 | LV del Río Arauca, Arauca |
| ME04) | JP | 1110 | 10 | RCN, Villavicencio |
| SU02) | ZE | 1110 | 10 | R. Piragua, Sincelejo |
| VA03) | EW | 1110 | 10 | Tropicana FM, Cali |
| BY04) | KQ | 1110 | 10 | Caracol R., Tunja |
| DC24) | Q92 | 1120 | 5 | Colombia Mía, Yopal, CS |
| NS01) | TI | 1120 | 10 | Vox Dei, Cúcuta |
| RI03) | JC | 1120 | 1 | Cadena Radial Vida, Pereira |
| SS02) | GH | 1120 | 15 | 24 Horas Radio, Bucaramanga |
| AT07) | AC | 1120 | 10 | Em. Riomar, Barranquilla |
| DC09) | VA | 1130 | 15 | Cadena Radial Vida, Bogotá |
| NA05) | QQ | 1130 | 10 | Bésame, Pasto (r. 94.9) |
| AN02) | DL | 1140 | 10 | R. Paisa La Cariñosa, Medellín |
| B007) | KO | 1140 | 10 | R. Esperanza, Cartagena |
| CC12) | | ‡1140 | | R. Piendamo, Piendamo |
| CU01) | CL | 1140 | 10 | R. Panamericana, Girardot |
| ME05) | E67 | 1140 | 10 | Caracol R., Villavicencio |
| SS08) | RN | 1140 | 10 | RCN, Barbosa |
| BY05) | GJ | 1150 | 1 | W Radio, Duitama |
| HU05) | FP | 1150 | 10 | RCN, Neiva |
| NS07) | BT | 1150 | 10 | Catatumbo Radio/Blu Radio, Ocaña |
| QU03) | FI | 1150 | 15 | Caracol R., Armenia |
| AT01) | BL | 1160 | 10 | R. Aeropuerto, Barranquilla |
| CA03) | AU | 1160 | 15 | Ondas del Orteguaza, Florencia |
| CO06) | AZ | 1160 | 10 | Frecuencia Bolivariana, Montería |
| DC13) | OC | 1160 | 15 | Fuego AM, Bogotá |
| NA06) | ZV | 1160 | 5 | RCN R. Las Lajas, Ipiales |
| NS08) | EC | 1160 | 10 | R. San José de Cúcuta, Cúcuta |
| SS09) | S31 | 1160 | 10 | Colombia Mía, Barrancabermeja |
| VA04) | EV | 1160 | 10 | R. Eco, Cali |
| AN04) | FW | 1170 | 10 | R. Nutibara, Medellín |
| AR04) | E74 | 1170 | 10 | Meridiano 70, Arauca |
| B008) | NW | 1170 | 10 | Caracol R., Cartagena |
| BY04) | GA | 1170 | 10 | Cadena Radial Vida, Tunja |
| ME06) | BX | 1170 | 10 | Ondas del Meta, Villavicencio |
| VA08) | JE | 1170 | 1 | RCN, Tuluá |
| AN08) | | 1180 | | Em. Coorpurabá, Apartadó |
| CL05) | FX | 1180 | 15 | Caracol R., Manizales |
| GV02) | WA | 1180 | 5 | LV del Guaviare, San José del Guaviare |
| SS10) | GK | 1180 | 20 | La Cariñosa, Bucaramanga |
| T006) | JT | 1180 | 10/5 | RCN, Ibagué |
| AT05) | CT | 1190 | 1 | LV de la Costa, Barranquilla |
| DC07) | CV | 1190 | 10 | R. Cordillera, Bogotá |
| NA07) | KG | 1190 | 10 | R. Mira, Tumaco |
| GU05) | | ‡1195 | | Ondas del Ranchería, Barrancas |
| AN49) | IJ | 1200 | 15 | LV de la Raza, Medellín |
| BY06) | GC | 1200 | 10 | RCN Radio, Sogamoso |
| CU02) | CD | 1200 | 10 | Em. Nueva Epoca, Fusagasugá |
| GU06) | BZ | 1200 | 10 | Ondas del Riohacha, Riohacha |
| VA10) | NF | 1200 | 10 | R. Red RCN, Cali |
| HU02) | FR | 1210 | 10 | Bésame, Neiva |
| NS03) | E65 | 1210 | 15 | La Cariñosa, Cúcuta |
| RI02) | BQ | 1210 | 10 | La Cariñosa, Pereira |
| CO07) | AV | 1220 | 10 | R. Uno, Montería |
| DC22) | KR | 1220 | 10 | R. María, Bogotá |
| NA08) | NM | 1220 | 10 | R. Viva Cultural Bolívar, Ipiales |
| SS11) | MT | 1220 | 10 | RCN La Radio, San Gil |
| AN10) | IL | 1230 | 10 | Minuto de Dios, Medellín |
| BY04) | BR | 1230 | 6 | Emisora Radio Recuerdos, Tunja |
| CU03) | TP | 1230 | 1 | R. Colina Caracol, Girardot |
| SS12) | EH | 1230 | 15 | Colmundo Radio, Bucaramanga |
| VA06) | LK | 1230 | 10 | R. Calidad, Cali |
| QU04) | FG | 1240 | 10 | RCN, Calarcá |
| SS13) | GN | 1240 | 5 | R. Barrancabermeja, Barrancabermeja |
| VA11) | JA | 1240 | 3 | R. Buenaventura, Buenaventura |
| AT07) | OK | 1250 | 10 | Em. ABC, Barranquilla |
| DC14) | CA | 1250 | 10 | Capital Radio, Bogotá |
| NS06) | HS | 1250 | 15 | W Radio, Cúcuta (r. 99.9) |
| SU03) | EM | 1250 | 1 | LV de Corozal, Corozal |
| AM01) | OU | 1260 | 2 | Ondas del Amazonas, Leticia |
| AN11) | DA | 1260 | 5 | R. Auténtica, Medellín |
| BY05) | NO | 1260 | 5 | Torre Fuerte Radio, Duitama |
| CE08) | OH | 1260 | 5 | RCN Cesar, Valledupar |
| IS03) | HU | 1260 | 1 | Caracol R., San Andrés (rel 810 Bogotá) |
| ME07) | LX | 1260 | 5 | Minuto de Dios Eco Llanero, Villavicencio |
| NS10) | TM | 1260 | 5 | R. Sonar, Ocaña |
| T007) | CO | 1260 | 5 | Caracol R., Ibagué |
| VA28) | ET | 1260 | 5 | R. María, Cali |
| BO04) | AR | 1270 | 2 | La Cariñosa, Cartagena |
| CE05) | KJ | 1270 | 1.5 | LV de Curumaní, Curumaní |
| CU04) | XQ | 1270 | 1 | Cadena Radial Vida, Ubaté |
| DC24) | Q99 | 1270 | 5 | Colombia Mía, San José del Guaviare |
| PU01) | SV | 1270 | 1 | LV de Orito, Orito |
| RI05) | IM | 1270 | 1 | Colmundo Radio, Pereira |
| SS02) | TX | 1270 | 5 | W Radio, Bucaramanga |
| T012) | BM | 1270 | 5 | R. Internacional, Honda |
| AN12) | MB | 1280 | 5 | R. Suroeste, Concordia |
| AT01) | SO | 1280 | 5 | R. Playa Mendoza, Barranquilla |
| DC20) | KN | 1280 | 5 | Aviva2, Bogotá |
| GU07) | NO | 1280 | 5 | Impacto Popular, San Juan del Cesar |
| HU06) | CM | 1280 | 5 | HJKK Sistema INRAI, Pitalito |
| NA05) | LP | 1280 | 5 | Caracol R., Pasto |
| NS11) | RP | 1280 | 5 | Ecos de Tibú, Tibú |
| SS14) | NQ | 1280 | 1 | LV del Río Suárez, Barbosa |
| AN13) | TH | 1290 | 5 | LV de las Estrellas, Medellín |
| DC24) | SZ | 1290 | 5 | Colombia Mía, Saravena, AR |
| CU05) | KY | 1290 | 5 | RCN, Girardot |
| MA04) | EB | 1290 | 5 | LV del Turismo, Santa Marta |
| ME08) | NE | 1290 | 5 | LV del Ariari, Granada |
| SU04) | OI | 1290 | 5 | ConecZión Radio, Sampués |
| VA13) | MC | 1290 | 5 | R. Viva 12-90, Cali |
| BO10) | OG | 1300 | 5 | Aviva2, Cartagena |
| BY08) | RB | 1300 | 5 | CRB Cadena Radial Boyacense, Tunja |
| CC04) | IN | 1300 | 5 | R. Eucha, Belalcázar |
| RI01) | LD | 1300 | 5 | Bésame, Pereira |
| SS02) | NB | 1300 | 5 | Onda 5, Bucaramanga |
| T008) | EA | 1300 | 5 | R. Lumbí, Mariquita |
| AN14) | LM | 1310 | 5 | R. Santa Bárbara |
| AN15) | IR | 1310 | 5 | RCN Urabá, Apartadó |
| AT08) | AK | 1310 | 5 | LV de la Patria Celestial, Barranquilla |
| CO08) | DG | 1310 | 5 | Caracol R., Monteria |
| DC23) | JZ | 1310 | 5 | Radio 3:16, Bogotá |
| HU07) | WD | 1310 | 5 | Micrófono Cívico, Palermo |
| NS12) | TQ | 1310 | 5 | G12 Radio, Cúcuta (r. 1550) |
| AN16) | NW | 1320 | 5 | R. María, Medellín |
| BY09) | HT | 1320 | 5 | R. Guateque, Guateque |
| CU06) | NV | 1320 | 5 | La Cariñosa, Girardot |
| MA05) | LV | 1320 | 5 | R. Onda Fantastica, Fundación |
| SS15) | MS | 1320 | 5 | La Cariñosa, Barrancabermeja |

| MW | Call | kHz | kW | Station, location |
|---|---|---|---|---|
| VA14) | NK | 1320 | 1 | R. Luna, Palmira |
| AN17) | RD | 1330 | 1 | R. Fénix de Oriente 1330 AM, El Peñol |
| BO02) | AP | 1330 | 5 | R. Auténtica, Cartagena |
| CE09) | MP | 1330 | 1 | LV de Aguachica/R. María, Aguachica |
| CC05) | LS | 1330 | 5 | Caracol R., Popayán |
| RI02) | FE | 1330 | 5 | Antena 2, Pereira |
| SS16) | NR | 1330 | 1 | La Caliente 13-30, San Gil |
| AN18) | NP | 1340 | 1 | R. Comunal, Nariño |
| AT03) | FA | 1340 | 5 | R. Alegre, Barranquilla |
| DC03) | FB | 1340 | 5 | Años Maravillosos, Bogotá |
| HU05) | KD | 1340 | 5 | La Cariñosa, Neiva |
| NA10) | HA | 1340 | 5 | RCN Nariño, Pasto |
| NS04) | PY | 1340 | 5 | R. Lemas, Cúcuta |
| NS13) | VL | 1340 | 0.5 | Brisas del Catatumbo, Tibú |
| SS05) | NY | 1340 | 4 | R. Unica, Bucaramanga |
| SU05) | HY | 1340 | 5 | RCN Sucre, Sincelejo |
| VA15) | IS | 1340 | 5 | R. El Sol, Buenaventura |
| AN19) | DS | 1340 | 5 | Ondas de la Montaña, Medellín |
| AN20) | LO | 1350 | 5 | La Cariñosa, Caucasia |
| CE10) | MN | 1350 | 1 | R. Perijá, Codazzi |
| MA01) | OA | 1350 | 5 | R. Uno, Santa Marta |
| TO09) | HL | 1350 | 5 | Bésame, Ibagué |
| VA16) | EN | 1350 | 5 | R. Armonía, Cali |
| AN21) | PK | 1360 | 10/5 | LV de Abejorral, Abejorral |
| AN22) | | ‡1360 | 0.5 | R. Segovia, Segovia |
| BO08) | UO | 1360 | 5 | Sistema Cardenal, Cartagena |
| RI06) | RA | 1360 | 5 | Ecos 1360 R./R. María, Pereira |
| SS17) | KV | 1360 | 1 | R. Láser, Zapatoca |
| TO18) | MI | 1360 | 5 | R. Auténtica, Melgar |
| AN23) | NU | 1370 | 2.5 | RCN, Rionegro |
| AT09) | BO | 1370 | 5 | Minuto de Dios, Barranquilla |
| CC06) | KI | 1370 | 5 | RCN Cauca, Popayán: 24h |
| DC01) | KI | 1370 | 5 | R. Mundial/Auténtica, Bogotá |
| NS15) | BD | 1370 | 1 | R. Guaimaral, Cúcuta |
| SU14) | NI | 1370 | 1 | R. Sabanas/Blu Radio, Sincelejo |
| AN57) | JD | 1380 | 3 | NSE Radio, Medellín |
| BY11) | EE | 1380 | 5 | RCN, Tunja |
| CE13) | MM | 1380 | 5 | Cadena Radial Vida, Valledupar |
| CL06) | LG | 1380 | 3 | LV de La Dorada, La Dorada |
| HU08) | ID | 1380 | 5 | R. Potencia Latina, La Plata |
| VA18) | EJ | 1380 | 1 | Armonías del Palmar, Palmira |
| CL07) | FO | 1390 | 5 | LV de los Andes, Manizales |
| CU07) | YW | 1390 | 5 | R. Auténtica, Pacho |
| SS18) | ZY | 1390 | 1 | R. María, Bucaramanga |
| TO10) | FY | 1390 | 5 | Olímpica, Espinal |
| AN26) | LL | 1400 | 1 | RCN Antena 2, Santa Bárbara |
| AT02) | AS | 1400 | 5 | RCN Antena 2, Barranquilla |
| CC07) | WY | 1400 | 1 | LV de los Samanes: Quilichao |
| CC13) | | ‡1400 | 0.45 | R. Cañaveral, Morales |
| CHO2) | ER | 1400 | 1 | Ecos del Atrato/W Radio, Quibdó |
| CO09) | | 1400 | 0.25 | Brisas del Sinú, Tierralta |
| DC16) | KM | 1400 | 5 | Em. Mariana, Bogotá |
| NA11) | JJ | 1400 | 1 | R. Ipiales, Ipiales |
| NA12) | | ‡1400 | 1.5 | LV de Samaniego, Samaniego |
| NS16) | BK | 1400 | 1 | LV de la Gran Colombia, Cúcuta |
| QU04) | HM | 1400 | 5 | La Cariñosa de Armenia, Calarcá |
| SS19) | D31 | 1400 | 1 | LV de Cimitarra, Cimitarra |
| AN27) | DU | 1410 | 1 | Em. Cultural Univ. de Antioquia, Medellín |
| GU08) | P79 | 1410 | 2 | R. Evangélica, Uribia |
| SS20) | TY | 1410 | 1 | LV del Carare, Vélez |
| VA19) | EI | 1410 | 5 | R. Minuto de Dios, Buga |
| AN28) | D23 | 1420 | 1 | Ecos de Frontino, Frontino |
| CL05) | HK | 1420 | 5 | Cadena Radial Vida, Manizales |
| MA06) | BH | 1420 | 5 | R. Magdalena, Santa Marta |
| SS21) | SN | 1420 | 2 | R. Lenguerque, Zapatoca |
| TO06) | LE | 1420 | 1 | La Cariñosa, Ibagué |
| AN29) | CK | 1430 | 1 | R. Sensación, Yarumal |
| AN30) | MF | 1430 | 5 | La Ribereña, Puerto Berrío |
| AN47) | G42 | 1430 | 0.5 | R. Alejandría, Alejandría |
| AT10) | PW | 1430 | 5 | Colmundo Radio, Barranquilla |
| DC17) | KU | 1430 | 5 | Uniminuto Radio, Bogotá |
| NS17) | BP | 1430 | 2 | R. Cariongo, Pamplona |
| QU08) | X61 | 1430 | 0.25 | La U FM Estéreo, Armenia |
| SU07) | QX | 1430 | 5 | R. Majagual, Sincelejo |
| AN46) | NZ | 1440 | 5 | Colmundo Radio, Medellín |
| BY06) | GM | 1440 | 5 | RCN Antena 2, Sogamoso |
| CA04) | IB | 1440 | 5 | R. Uno, Florencia |
| VA20) | EN | 1440 | 5 | Caracol R., Tuluá |
| AN31) | E20 | 1450 | 1 | R. María, Urrao |
| CC09) | | 1450 | 0.5 | LV del Cauca, El Bordo |
| CL02) | NL | 1450 | 5 | La Cariñosa, Manizales |
| SS22) | HH | 1450 | 5 | R. Católica Metropolitana, Bucaramanga |

| MW | Call | kHz | kW | Station, location |
|---|---|---|---|---|
| TO13) | BY | 1450 | 5 | Olímpica, Flandes |
| AN33) | TN | 1460 | 5 | R. María, Turbo |
| AN34) | MU | 1460 | 1 | LV de Amalfi "La Primera", Amalfi |
| AN45) | E26 | 1460 | 1 | R. Capiro, La Ceja |
| AT02) | VH | 1460 | 5 | R. Uno, Barranquilla |
| DC18) | JW | 1460 | 5 | ENC R. (Em. Nuevo Continente), Bogotá |
| HU09) | FL | 1460 | 1 | Agustiniana Minuto de Dios, San Agustín |
| NA10) | ZU | 1460 | 5 | La Cariñosa, Pasto |
| NS18) | IW | 1460 | 1 | R. Monumental, Cúcuta |
| SU08) | AL | 1460 | 1 | R. Sincelejo, Sincelejo |
| AN04) | II | 1470 | 5 | Aviva2, Medellín |
| CU09) | HQ | 1470 | 5 | R. Futurama, Pacho |
| TO14) | TB | 1470 | 5 | Ondas de Ibagué/R. María, Ibagué |
| VA26) | NT | 1470 | 5 | R. Huellas, Cali |
| AN35) | TC | 1480 | 1 | R. Sonsón, Sonsón (n.f.1490) |
| MA07) | OD | 1480 | 5 | R. Rodadero, Santa Marta |
| RI04) | FC | 1480 | 5 | R. Única, Pereira |
| SS10) | TZ | 1480 | 5 | RCN Antena 2, Bucaramanga |
| AT11) | AY | 1490 | 5 | R. Vida Nueva, Barranquilla |
| DC19) | BS | 1490 | 4 | Em. Punto Cinco, Bogotá |
| HU10) | E62 | 1490 | 1 | R. Garzón, Garzón |
| SU09) | JO | 1490 | 1 | LV de San Marcos, San Marcos |
| VA21) | ZB | 1490 | 5 | Robles 14-90, La Nueva, Tuluá |
| CL09) | UW | 1500 | 5 | R. María, Manizales |
| CU10) | TW | 1500 | 5 | Kirios R, Fusagasugá |
| VA22) | LJ | 1500 | 5 | Sonora AM, Cali |
| AN37) | D24 | 1510 | 5 | LV de La Unión, La Unión |
| BY15) | A22 | 1510 | 1 | LV de San Luis, San Luis de Gaceno |
| QU07) | ZA | 1510 | 1 | R. Cristal, Armenia |
| SS23) | HX | 1510 | 1 | Candela AM, Bucaramanga |
| AN38) | | 1520 | 0.3 | Brisas del Palmar, Caucasia |
| AN39) | MA | 1520 | 1 | LV de Suroeste, Jericó |
| AT03) | LQ | 1520 | 5 | La Radio del Príncipe de Paz, Barranquilla |
| CL10) | | ‡1520 | | Sonoradio 1520 AM, Viterbo |
| DC09) | LI | 1520 | 5 | Su Presencia Radio, Bogotá |
| DC24) | T21 | 1520 | 0.25 | Colombia Mía, Tierralta, CO |
| NS19) | J98 | ‡1520 | 1 | Em. Una Voz de la Frontera, Puerto Santander |
| RI07) | RL | 1520 | 1 | Antena de los Andes, Sta Rosa de Cabal |
| SU10) | MZ | 1520 | 1 | Ecos de la Sierra Flor, Sincelejo |
| TO17) | AM | ‡1520 | 1 | R. Altamizal, Dolores |
| AN58) | DN | 1530 | 5 | Yeshu'a LV de Jesucristo, Medellín |
| CC14) | | ‡1530 | | R. Integración, Morales |
| GU09) | OZ | 1530 | 5 | LV de la Prov. de Padilla, San Juan del Cesar |
| ME10) | HKV82° | 1530 | 1 | Alcaraván Radio, Puerto Lleras |
| VA23) | EU | 1530 | 1 | Caracol Sevilla, Sevilla |
| AN41) | A26 | 1540 | 1 | Em. Brisas del Río Chico, Belmira |
| CL11) | ZF | 1540 | 5 | R. Cóndor, Manizales |
| NA09) | RQ | 1540 | 2 | R. Austral, Túquerres |
| SS25) | HD | 1540 | 1 | LV del Petróleo, Barrancabermeja |
| AT02) | CB | 1550 | 5 | R. El Sol "La Cariñosa", Barranquilla |
| DC21) | ZI | 1550 | 5 | G12 Radio, Bogotá |
| QU03) | QD | 1550 | 5 | Cadena Radial Vida, Calarcá |
| VA31) | LT | 1550 | 5 | Em. Revivir en Cristo, Cali |
| AN52) | XZ | 1560 | 5 | Santa María de la Paz R., Medellín |
| SS26) | HE | 1560 | 1 | Voces Rovirenses, Málaga |
| VA08) | LP | 1560 | 5 | La Cariñosa, Tuluá |
| CL12) | E70 | 1570 | 1 | R. Auténtica, Manizales |
| DC22) | TG | 1570 | 1 | R. María, Machetá |
| DC24) | E96 | 1570 | 1 | Colombia Mía, Palmira, VA |
| AT12) | QZ | 1580 | 5 | R. María, Barranquilla |
| DC25) | QT | 1580 | 5 | Wepa Salsa/Verdad Radio, Bogotá |
| MA08) | LC | 1580 | 1 | LV del Banco, El Banco |
| SU01) | RM | 1580 | 5 | Sistema Cardenal, Sincelejo |
| TO19) | E66 | 1580 | 1 | LV del Café, Rovira |
| AN44) | IP | 1590 | 5 | BBN 15-90 R., Envigado |
| SS27) | WB | 1590 | 5 | R. María/Em. Nuestra Sra, Socorro |
| CU13) | HV | 1600 | 5 | Emisora Armoniaz, Zipaquirá |
| VA27) | F33 | 1600 | 0.25 | R. Restauración, Cali |

| SW | Call | kHz | kW | Name and h of tr |
|---|---|---|---|---|
| DC26) | DH | †5910 | 5 | Alcaraván R, Pto Lleras: 2300-1000 (r. 1530) |
| DC26) | DH | †6010 | 5 | LV de tu Conciencia, Pto Lleras: 2300-1000 |

## Major Networks:

**RADIO NACIONAL DE COLOMBIA (Pub.)**
✉ Av. El Dorado Cr. 45 # 26 - 33 Bogotá, D.C. ☎ +571 2200727 📠 +571 2200700/230 **W:** radionacional.co **E:** info@rtvc.gov.co

**CARACOL (Primera Cadena Radial Colombiana)**
✉ Calle 67 N° 7-37, Bogotá, D.C. ☎ +57 1 348 7600 📠 +57 1 337 7126
**W:** caracol.com.co **E:** caracolcolombia@caracol.com.co - **Local prgr:** weekdays 1100-1200 & 2300-2400.

**RCN (Radio Cadena Nacional)**
✉ Cra. 13A N° 37-32, Bogotá, DC ☎ +57 1 314 7070 📠 +57 1 314

7070 **W:** rcnmundo.com
All "La Cariñosa" stations relay sport trs regularly from Antena 2.
**TODELAR (Circuito Todelar de Colombia)**
▣ Ap. 27344 (Av. Cra 20, N° 83-64), Bogotá, DC ☎ +57 1 621 6621 ▤
+57 1 616 0056 **W:** todelar.com **E:** todelar@telesat.com.co
**COLMUNDO RADIO**
▣ Diagonal 58 N° 26A-29, Bogotá, DC ☎ +57 1 217 8911 ▤ +57 1
348 2746 **W:** colmundoradio.com.co **E:** correo@colmundoradio.com
**SISTEMA VIDA INTERNACIONAL (Rlg.)**
▣ Avenida Calle 13 No 79-70, Bogotá, DC ☎ +57 1 294 8300
**W:** sistemavida.net
**CADENA RADIAL AUTENTICA DE COLOMBIA (Rlg.)**
▣ Ap. 18350, (Calle 32 N° 16-12), Bogotá, DC. Carrera 38D # 1-52,
Barrio Santa Isabel, Cali ☎ +57 1 285 3360 ▤ +57 1 285 2505
**W:** cmbflorestacali.org

**State abbreviations:** (Departamentos) AM = Amazonas, AN = Antioquia,
AR = Arauca, AT = Atlántico, BO = Bolívar, BY = Boyacá, CA = Caquetá, CC =
Cauca, CE = Cesar, CH = Chocó, CL = Caldas, CO = Córdoba, CS = Casanare,
CU = Cundinamarca, DC = Distrito Capital, GN = Guainía, GU = Guajira, GU =
Guaviare, HU = Huila, IS = Islas San Andrés y Providencia, MA = Magdalena,
ME = Meta, NA = Nariño, NS = Norte de Santander, PU = Putumayo, QU =
Quindío, RI = Risaralda, SS = Santander del Sur, SU = Sucre, TO = Todelar, VA
= Valle del Cauca, VI = Vichada, VP = Vaupés.
**N.B:** These abbreviations are not officially recognized by the
Colombian Post Office. Letters should therefore carry full name.

**Addresses & other information:**
**AM00) AMAZONAS**
**AM01)** Cra. 6A N° 10-104 (or Ap. 236), Leticia 1100-0500.
**AN00) ANTIOQUIA**
**AN01)** Cra. 81 No. 48A-39, Medellín **W:** volvamosadios.org cadenara-
dialjupiter.com **FM:** 88.9 – **AN02)** Edificio Coltejer, Calle 52 #47-42,
Medellín - 1100-0500 **W:** rcnmundo.com/radiopaisa – **AN03)** Calle 50
Colomb N° 67-141, Medellín **W:** radiored.com.co – **AN04)** Av.13 N°
84-42 (or Ap. 1431), Medellín **W:** cadenaradialvida.co – **AN05)** Cra.
19 N° 20-66, Turbo – **AN06)** Ap. 1431, Andes 1000-0200 – **AN07)**
Circular 1a N° 70-01, Bloque 6, P7 U.P.B. Laureles, Medellín. **W:** radi-
obolivarianavirtual.com - **FM:** 92.4MHz – **AN08)** Apartadó. – **AN09)**
Cra. 77B N° 48-144, Medellín **W:** vidaam.comco – **AN10)** Calle 56 N°
41-57, Medellín. **W:** rccradio.fm/minutodedios – **AN11)** Calle 41 N°
80B-46, P2, Medellín – **AN12)** Cra. 3 Calles 2 y 3, Concordia – **AN13)**
Ap. 4300, Medellín – **AN14)** Cra. 51 N° 51-38 (or Ap. 3854) , Medellín
- 1000-0500 – **AN15)** Calle 94 N° 99-51, Apartadó – **AN16)** Calle
50 N° 67-141 (or Ap. 65103), Medellín – **AN17)** Centro Cooperativo,
Parque Principal, El Peñol – **AN18)** Cra. 11 N° 10-34, Nariño - 1100-
0100 – **AN19)** Calle 44 N° 94-15, P3, Medellín. **W:** ondasdelamontana.
net – **AN20)** Cra. 2 N° 21-54, Caucasia – **AN21)** Cra. 51 N° 50-09,
Abejorral - 0900-0500 – **AN22)** Segovia - 1100-0300 – **AN23)** Cra. 51
N° 49-09, Rionegro – **AN24)** Calle 48B N° 79-38, Medellín – **AN26)**
Cra. Bolívar, Calle López, Santa Bárbara – **AN27)** Ap. 1226 (or Cra.
44 N° 48-72), Medellín - 1100-0500 **W:** emisora.udea.edu.co - **FM:**
101.9MHz – **AN28)** Cra. 32 N° 30-05, Frontino **W:** ecosdefrontino.es.tl
- 1000-2300 – **AN29)** Cra. 20 N° 20-21, Yarumal – **AN30)** Calle 6 N°
4-23, Puerto Berrio – **AN31)** Urrao **W:** radiomariacol.otg - 0900-0300
– **AN33)** Ap. 1289, Medellín - 1000-0400 – **AN34)** Cra. 19 Restrepo
N° 19-61, Amalfi - 1000-0300 **W:** lavozdeamalfi.com - **FM:** 103.9MHz –
**AN35)** Calle 8 N° 6-60, Sonsón – **AN37)** Calle 10 N° 9-37, La Unión (or
Ap. 4897, Medellín) – **AN38)** **E:** emivozunion@epm.net.co – **AN38)**
Batallón de Infantería N° 29 "Rifles", Barrio El Palmar, Caucasia - 1130-
0400 – **AN39)** Calle 7, Cras. 3 y 4, Jericó - 1000-0500 – **AN41)** Cra. 20
N° 20-14, Belmira – **AN44)** Ap. 81095 (or Cra. 44A N° 31 Sur-16,Barrio
San Marcos, Medellín), Envigado – **AN45)** Calle 20 N° 27-20, La Ceja
- 1100-0300 (Sun -0100) **W:** radiocapiro.jimdo.com – **AN46)** Cra. 80 N°
46-74, Medellín. **E:** mpecolmundo@gmail.com - 1100-0600 – **AN47)**
Junta de Acción, Comunal Central, Alejandría – **AN49)** Cra.73 N°
47-35, Medellín **W:** lavozdelaraza.com – **AN52)** Calle 10 N° 42-22,
Medellín **W:** santamariadelapaz.org – **AN56)** Calle 105F No. 51-16,
Barrio 20 de Enero, Apartadó – **AN57)** Calle 43 No. 67a-16, Barrio San
Joaquín, Medellín. **W:** nseradio.com – **AN58)** Cra 81A No. 48-B – 71,
Barrio Calasanz, Medellín – **AN59)** Cra 87 No. 65, Univ. de Medellín,
Medellín. **W:** webapps.udem.edu.co/FrecuenciaU
**AR00) ARAUCA**
**AR01)** Calle 19 N° 19-62 P2, Arauca – **AR02)** Cra. 20 N° 19-09, P5,
Arauca (or Ap. 16555, Bogotá) – **AR04)** Cra 20 N° 17-57, P3, Arauca
**W:** meridiano70.co
**AT00) ATLÁNTICO**
**AT01)** Cra. 53 N° 55-166,Edificio Diario La Libertad, Barranquilla.
**W:** cadenaradiallibertad.com.co – **AT02)** Cr 52 84-78 Alto Prado,
Barranquilla **W:** radiouno.com.co facebook.com/Radio-el-Sol-1550-
AM-1588250628078472 - 1000-0300 – **AT03)** Calle 82 N° 42H-54,

2do piso, Barranquilla - 0900-0400 **W:** principedepaz.com – **AT04)**
Cra. 53 # 74 - 56, Edificio Torre Banco de Occidente, Oficina 905,
Barranquilla **W:** facebook.com/SistemaCardenal – **AT05)** Cra. 53 N°
82-132, Barranquilla 1030-0200 **W:** emisoralavozdelacosta.net – **AT06)**
Organización Radial Olímpica, Calle 72 No 48-37, Barranquilla - 1000-
0500 – **AT07)** Cra. 48 N° 72-25, Ofc. 306, (or Ap. 2010), Barranquilla
todelar.com **W:** todelar.com - 1000-0200 – **AT08)** Cra. 45 No. 76-125,
Barranquilla - 0900-0500 **W:** vozdelapatriacelestial1310.com – **AT09)**
Calle 53 N° 50-11, P2, Barranquilla **W:** minutodedios.org – **AT10)** Cra.
44 N° 70-61, Barranquilla – **AT11)** Cra. 26, No 75B-07, Barranquilla -
1100-0500 **W:** radiovidanueva.net – **AT12)** Calle 60 N° 47-70, Centro
Cultural Santa Catalina, Barranquilla - 0930-0130
**BO00) BOLÍVAR**
**BO01)** Av. Venezuela, Edif. Banco Internacional, La Matuna 8B-05,
Cartagena – **BO02)** Calle Real 20-217, Cartagena - 1000-0500 – **BO03)**
Calle Mayor N° 6-34 (or Ap. 1771), Cartagena **W:** cadenaradiallibertad.
com.co - 1000-0420 – **BO04)** Ap. 246, Cartagena **W:** lacariñosa.com
– **BO05)** W: bluradio.com – **BO07)** Calle Sta Fe, N° 13-113, Torices,
Cartagena. **W:** radioesperanza1140.net – **BO08)** Matuna, Calle 32 No.
8-21, Of. 1106, Edificio Banco Popular, Cartagena **W:** caracol.com.co/
emisora/f/magangue – **BO09)** Av. 3 N° 21-62, La Manga, Cartagena
– **BO10)** Cra. 21 N° 29B-10, Cartagena **W:** avivamiento.com/aviva2.
php – **BO12)** Av, Venezuela, Edif. Suramericana, Of. 801, Cartagena
**BY00) BOYACÁ**
**BY01)** Calle 16 N° 15-21, P8, Edif.Camara de Comercio, Duitama **W:**
lacarinosa.com – **BY02)** Cra. 10 N° 16-36, Chiquinquirá - 0900-0600
– **BY03)** Ap. 282, Sogamoso - **FM:** 88.5MHz, 107.3MHz – **BY04)** Av.
Calle 13 No. 79 – 70, Tunja **W:** cadenaradialvida.com/emisora-cristi-
ana-online-vida-tunja-1-170-am – **BY05)** Cra. 15 N° 14-47, Duitama.
**W:** torrefuerteradio.co – **BY06)** Ap. 019, Sogamoso **W:** rcnmundo.
com - 1000-0500 - **FM:** 106.1MHz – **BY07)** Cra. 9 No. 8-65, Garagoa
- 1000-0330 – **BY08)** Calle 20 N° 10-64, Tunja – **BY09)** Cra. 7 N°
9-57, Guateque (or Ap. 17387, Bogotá) - 1000-0300 – **BY11)** Cra. 10
N° 17-50, P5, Tunja – **BY12)** Calle 5,N° 5-25, P2, Parque Santander,
Samacá. **W:** ondasdelporvenir.com 0900-0300 – **BY14)** Cra. 6 N° 6-93,
Paipa - 1000-0400 – **BY15)** Calle 6 N° 5-42, San Luis de Gaceno - 0900-
0300 – **BY16)** Calle 18 N° 12-81, P2, Chiquinquirá - **FM:** 92.6MHz –
**BY18)** Calle 20 N° 10-64, Ofc.307, Tunja **W:** armoniasboyacenses.com
**CA00) CAQUETÁ**
**CA01)** Cra.14 N° 12-129, Casa Episcobal, P2 (Ap. 285), Florencia -
1000-0300 – **CA02)** Ap. 465, Florencia. – **CA03)** Calle 17 N° 10-40,
P2, (Ap. 209), Florencia - 1030-0300 – **CA04)** Ap. 150, Florencia **W:**
radiouno.com.co
**CC00) CAUCA**
**CC02)** Cra 8 N° 3-17 (or Ap. 1321), Popayán - 1000-0400 **W:** redson-
oraam.com – **CC03)** Cra. 8 N° 5-41, Popayán **W:** radiosuperpopayan.
com – **CC04)** Casa Cural, Parque Principal, Belalcázar (or Ap. 987,
Bogotá) - 1000-2400 – **CC05)** Calle 5A N° 11-25, Popayán – **CC06)** Ap.
535, Popayán – **CC07)** Cra. 13 N° 9-20, Santander de Quilichao - 1100-
2400 – **CC09)** Batallón José Hilario López, Bordo – **CC12)** Cra. 4 N°
9-42, Piendamo – **CC13)** Barrio Sagrada Familia, Cra. 3 esq., Morales
- 1130-1700, 1900-2200 – **CC14)** Casa de la Cultura, Morales
**CE00) CESAR**
**CE01)** Calle 17 N° 15-67, Valledupar - 0900-0300 **W:** radioguatapuri.
com – **CE02)** Cra. 5 N° 13-52, Valledupar. **W:** lavozdelcanaguate.
com – **CE03)** Calle 5 N° 1-76, Local 210, Aguachica - 1000-0200 **W:**
caracol.com.co – **CE04)** Cl. 15 # 11A-56,, Valledupar **W:** facebook.com/
SistemaCardenal - 0900-0500 – **CE05)** Calle 6 N° 19-66, Curumaní -
1000-0100 - **FM:** 95. 7MHz – **CE08)** Ap. 250, Valledupar **W:** rcnradio.
com/seccion/locales/cesar – **CE09)** Cra. 10a N° 4-38, P2, Aguachica
**W:** facebook.com/lavozdeaguachica – **CE10)** Cra. 16 N° 11-102,
Codazzi – **CE13)** Calle 11 # 12 10 Barrio San Joaquin, Valledupar **W:**
cadenaradialvida.co
**CH00) CHOCÓ**
**CH02)** Cra. 4 N° 25-18, P2, (or Ap. 196), Quibdó - 1000-0400 – **CH03**
Choco.
**CL00) CALDAS**
**CL01)** Ap. 67, Manizales **W:** wradio.com.co besame.fm – **CL02)** Ap.
244, Manizales **W:** lacariñosa.com - 1000-0500 – **CL03)** Cra. 2 N°
13-31, P3, La Dorada **W:** radiouno.com.co - 1000-0500 – **CL04)** Cra.
4 N° 8-58, P3, Anserma - 0900-0300 – **CL05)** Ap. 2000, Manizales.
– **CL06)** Calle 11 N° 3-58 (or Ap. 34), La Dorada - 0930-0500 – **CL07)**
Calle 22 N° 21-40, Plaza Bolívar, Manizales **W:** redsonoraam.com –
**CL09)** Cra. 23 N° 71-03 (or Ap. 990), Manizales 1015-0500 – **CL10)**
Viterbo – **CL11)** Antigua Estación del Ferrocaril, Manizales - 1200-0400
**W:** radiocondor.fundeca.org.co – **CL12)** Cra. 23 N° 71-03, Av.Sant,
Manizales
**CO00) CÓRDOBA**
**CO01)** Cra. 3A N° 30-12, P2, Montería - 1000-0400 – **CO02)** Av. Olaya
Herrera, Edif. Jatin, Lorica **W:** rpcradio.com - 1000-0400 – **CO03)**
Calle 23 N° 1-53, Montería – **CO04)** Cra 2 N° 28-53, P2, (or Ap. 497),

Montería **W:** rcnradio.com - 1000-0300 – **CO05)** Cra. 8 N° 17-56, Planeta Rica – **CO06)** Ap. 148, Montería – **CO07)** Calle 27 N° 8-25, Montería **W:** radiouno.com.co – **CO08)** Ap. 364, Montería – **CO09)** Brigada N° 11, Tierralta

**CS00) CASANARE**
**CS01)** Calle 9 N° 22-63, Edif. Cine Casanare, P2, Yopal - 1000-0500. **FM:** 97.7MHz – **CS03)** Yopal

**CU00) CUNDINAMARCA**
**CU01)** Calle 14 N° 11-23, P2, Ofc.202, Girardot – **CU02)** Av. Las Palmas N° 5-08, P5, Fusagasugá - 0900-0400 – **CU03)** Terminal de Transportes, Girardot. **W:** radiocolina.com – **CU04)** Cra. 6 N° 6-38, Ubaté **W:** cadenaradioalvida.com – **CU05)** Ap. 416, Girardot – **CU06)** Calle 16 N° 10-38, P3, Girardot. **W:** lacarinosa.com 1030-0300 – **CU07)** Calle 7 N° 14-83, Pacho – **CU09)** Calle 3 N° 16-39, Pacho - 0930-0400 – **CU10)** Calle 8 N° 5-59, Fasagasugá **W:** facebook.com/KIRIOS-RADIO-102082222235 - 0900-0300 – **CU13)** Calle 3 N° 7-56, Zipaquirá. **W:** armoniaz.webcindario.com/html/somos.html

**DC00) DISTRITO CAPITAL**
**DC01)** Calle 32 N° 16-12, Bogotá **W:** radiomundialbogota.com – **DC02)** Cra. 45 No. 26-33, Bogotá **W:** senalradiodecolombia.gov.co – **DC03)** Cra. 13A N° 37-32, Bogotá **W:** rcnmundo.com/anosmaravillosos – **DC04)** Calle 67 No. 7-37, Bogotá **W:** wradio.com.co radiopolis.fm wepa.com.co candelaestereo.com – **DC05)** Calle 45 N° 13-70 , Ap. 19823, Bogotá. **W:** cadenamelodia.com – **DC06)** Calle 48 N° 18-77, Bogotá **W:** todelar.com cadenaradialvida.co – **DC07)** Av. 13 N° 84-42, Bogotá **W:** todelar.com – **DC08)** Calle 39A N° 18-12, Bogotá **W:** radiored.com.co – **DC09)** Calle 95 Bis No. 50-36, Bogotá, DC - 1100-0300 **W:** cadenaradialvida.co supresencia.com/su-presencia-radio – **DC10)** Diagonal 58 N° 26A-29, Bogotá – **DC11)** Calle 57 N° 17-48, Bogotá **W:** radiosantafe.com – **DC12)** Cra. 16 N° 43-09, Bogotá. **W:** mci12.com/noticias/108-g12-radio – **DC13)** Calle 25ª No. 32, 46 Barrio Gran América, Ap. 2086350, Bogotá D.C. **W:** fuegoam.com.co – **DC14)** Cra. 30 N° 91-84 (or Ap. 250649), Bogotá **W:** 1250amcapitalradio.com – **DC15)** Ap. 9291, Bogotá – **DC16)** Calle 6 N° 7-22, (or Ap. 3201), Bogotá. (alt.address: Calle 385 N° 75-31, Cd. Kennedy, Bogotá) - 1100-0130 **W:** emisoramariana.org – **DC17)** Calle 81B N° 72 B - 70, Barrio Minuto de Dios, Bogotá **W:** uniminutoradio.com – **DC18)** Cra. 27 N° 49-48, Bogotá **W:** nuevocontinente.co – **DC19)** Av. 15 N° 123-61, Of. 408, Bogotá **W:** emisorapunto5.com.co - 1100-2300 – **DC20)** **W:** avivamiento.com/aviva2.php – **DC21)** Calle 22C N° 31-01, Bogotá. – **DC22)** Carrera 21A, No. 151-23, Bogotá **W:** radiomariacol.org – **DC23)** Carrera 49, No. 127d-59, Bogotá **W:** radio316.com.co – **DC24)** Escuela de Cadetes José María Cordoba, Calle 80 N° 38-00, Bogotá – **DC25)** Diagonal 46A Sur 51-40, Centro Comercial Venecia Plaza 2do piso, Bogotá **W:** verdadradio.com wepa.com.co – **DC26)** Librería Colombia para Cristo, Calle 46 N° 13-36, Blg C, Ap.to 215, (or Apartado Aéreo 67751) Bogotá. (Reports c/o Rafael Rodríguez R., Apartado Aéreo 67751, (oficina Red 4-72 Unicentro), Bogotá, DC. Return postage required for QSL reply) **W:** facebook.com/Fuerza-de-Paz-106687386081261 **E:** 6010lavozdetuconciencia@gmail.com or (for reports) rafaelcoldx@yahoo.com – **DC27)** Av. Boyacá 48 A 11, Edificio Castillo Dorado, Of. 301, Bogotá. **W:** bbnradio.org

**GN00) GUAINÍA**
**GN02)** Inírida **W:** manantialvida.org

**GU00) GUAJIRA**
**GU01)** Cra. 9 N° 12-31, Maicao - 0900-0300 – **GU04)** Calle 15, Salida a Maicao, Riohacha - 0930-0400 – **GU05)** Barrancas – **GU06)** Cra 8A N° 3-27 (or Ap. 3), Riohacha – **GU07)** Cra. 6 N° 6-60, San Juan del César – **GU08)** Cra. 18 N° 13-54, Uribia – **GU09)** Calle 1 N° 5-63, San Juan del Cesar **W:** ondasdelaprovinciadepadilla.blogspot.com - 1000-0400

**GV00) GUAVIARE**
**GV01)** Transversal 23 No. 10–69, Barrio El Dorado, San José del Guaviare **W:** cadenaradioalvida.com – **GV02)** Cra 22 con Calle 9, San José del Guaviare. **W:** rcnradioguaviare.com

**HU00) HUILA**
**HU01)** Calle 7 N° 10-36, Neiva - 1000-0300 **W:** sistemainrai.net/hjkk840 – **HU02)** Ap. 150, Neiva **W:** besame.fm – **HU03)** Ap. 496 (or Cra. 7, Calles 21 y 22), Neiva - 1000-0530 – **HU04)** Cra. 13 N° 3A-24, Neiva. **W:** rcnmundo.com/radiounoneiva – **HU05)** Cra. 4 N° 2-21, Of. 501-502, Neiva. – **HU06)** Calle 6 N° 1A-31, Pitalito - 0900-0400 **W:** sistemainrai.net/hjkk1280 – **HU07)** Cra 8 N° 8-60, P2, Palermo - 0900-0300 – **HU08)** Calle 4a N° 5-59, La Plata - 1000-0100 – **HU09)** Cra. 14 N° 2-47, San Agustín – **HU10)** Cra. 7 N° 7-05, Garzón **W:** radiogarzon.com - 1000-0300

**IS00) ISLAS SAN ANDRÉS Y PROVIDENCIA**
**IS01)** Ap. 354, San Andrés Isla – **IS03)** Edif. Bermuda, P2, Av. de las Américas, San Andrés Isla – **IS5)** San Andrés Isla.

**MA00) MAGDALENA**
**MA01)** Av. Libertadores 27-101, Santa Marta. **W:** radio1.com.co – **MA02)** Cra. N° 18-32 (or Ap. 757), Santa Marta 0945-0500 – **MA03)** Calle 17 N° 5-83 (or Ap. 103), Santa Marta **W:** caracol.com.co/emisora/f/santa_marta – **MA04)** Calle 18 N° 5-58, Santa

Marta - 1000-0200 – **MA05)** Cra. 9 N° 14-13, Fundación – **MA06)** Ap. 1240, Santa Marta **W:** radiomagdalena1420am.com – **MA07)** Calle 11 C N° 18a-34, Santa Marta - 1100-0300 – **MA08)** Ap. 45, E Banco - 1000-0400

**ME00) META**
**ME01)** Calle 38 30 A-106 Centro, Villavicencio **W:** rcnmundo.com/lavozdelllano – **ME02)** Cra. 13 N° 15-52, Granada – **ME03)** Calle 38 N° 32-41, P7, Edif. Prollano, Ofc 702, Villavicencio **W:** autenticavillavicencio.com – **ME04)** Cra. 30 N° 36-14, P4, Villavicencio – **ME05)** Cra. 31 N° 37-71, Of.1001, (Ap. 2472), Villavicencio - 0900-0500 – **ME06)** Calle 41B N° 30-11, Barrio La Grama, Villavicencio **W:** ondasdelmeta.com – **ME07)** Cra. 40 N° 34-34, Baltazar Alto, Villavicencio – **ME08)** Calle 13 N° 28-05 (Ap. 001), Granada – **ME10)** (See DC26). **W:** fuerzadepaz com – **FM:** 88,8MHz Marfil Stereo

**NA00) NARIÑO**
**NA01)** Cra. 29 N° 17-30 (or Ap. 375), Pasto - 1000-0200 – **NA02)** Calle 20 N° 22-82, Pasto **W:** hsbradio.com.co – **NA03)** Ap. 454, Pasto – **NA04)** Calle 20 N° 24-73, Of 603, P6, Pasto - 0900-0500 – **NA05)** Cra. 27 N° 19-30, Pasto. **W:** besame.fm – **NA06)** Ap. 1005, Ipiales - 1100-0200 – **NA07)** Parque Colón (or Ap. 165), Tumaco - 1100-0400 – **NA08)** Cra. 8 N° 4-48, Ipiales - 1100-0200 – **NA09)** Calle 20 N° 15-13, Túquerres - 0900-0400 – **NA10)** Ap. 516, Pasto **W:** lacarinosa.com – **NA11)** Cra. 6A N° 9-14, P2, Ipiales – **NA12)** Cra. 5 N° 3-15, Samaniego – **NA13)** Fundación Tomás Cipriano de Mosquera, Ricaurte el Divisc 1300-2300 – **NA14)** Nevado Cumbal – **NA15)** Calle 15 N° 14-24 Pasto - 1100-0500 **W:** radioviva.com.co – **NA17)** Cra. 1 N° 21-36, Pasto

**NS00) NORTE DE SANTANDER**
**NS01)** Calle 5 N° 3-26 (or Ap. 1650), Cúcuta – **NS02)** Centro Comercia Bolívar, Local E4 y E5, Cúcuta **W:** rcnmundo.com - 1000-0400 – **NS03)** Ap. 400, Cúcuta.– **NS04)** Calle 5A N° 0-45, Cúcuta. **W:** besame. fm – **NS05)** Av. O. N° 10-54, P2 (or Ap. 624), Cúcuta **W:** lavozdelnorte1040am.com – **NS06)** Ap. 519, Cúcuta. **W:** oxigeno.fm – **NS07)** Cra. 13 N° 9-10, P7, Ocaña **W:** catatumboradio.blogspot.com – **NS08)** Calle 7N N° 4-117 (or Ap. 2284), Cúcuta – **NS10)** Calle 11 N° 15-24, Ocaña - 1030-0300 – **NS11)** Calle 7 N° 4-50, Tibú - 1000-2400 – **NS12)** Calle 17N No. 5-101, Cúcuta **W:** mci12.com – **NS13)** Base Militar "San Jorge", Tibú - 1030-1700, 2100-0200 – **NS15)** Calle 12 N° 4-19, Ofc. 214, (or Ap. 2582), Cúcuta - 1000-0500 – **NS16)** Av. OA N° 12-75, Ofc. 101 (or Ap. 1303), Cúcuta - 1000-0500 – **NS17)** Cra. 6 N° 4-59, P3 (or Ap. 1074), Pamplona - 0900-0300 – **NS18)** Av. 4 N° 11-17, Ofc. 303, Cúcuta - 1000-0400 – **NS19)** Cra. 2 N° 1-10, Puerto Santander - 1000-2200

**PU00) PUTUMAYO**
**PU01)** Calle Pricnpal, Orito - 1100-2300

**QU00) QUINDÍO**
**QU01)** Cra 16 N° 19-23, P10, Armenia – **QU02)** Calle 9 N° 13-50 (or Ap. 2361), Armenia – **QU03)** Ap. 2481, Armenia – **QU04)** Ap. 556, Calarcá – **QU06)** Cra. 14 N° 21-26, P2, (or km 2 via al Aeropuerto), Armenia **W:** facebook.com/Radio-ciudad-milagro-800-am-193845027308179 1000-0500 – **FM:** 104.7MHz Robles FM Stereo – **QU07)** Calle 21 N° 16-31, Ofc 702, (or Ap. 617), Armenia – **QU08)** Universidad del Quindío, Av.Bolívar Cra.15 Calle 12 Norte, Armenia **W:** uniquindio.edu.co/uniquindio/laufm – **FM:** 102.1MHz – **QU10)** Palacio Municipal, Armenia.

**RI00) RISARALDA**
**RI01)** Ap. 354, Pereira **W:** caracol.com.co/emisora/pereira besame. fm – **RI02)** Ap. 045, Pereira – **RI03)** Ap. 221, Pereira **W:** vidaam.com co – **RI04)** **W:** todelar.com – **RI05)** Cra. 7a N° 18-80, Of. 705, Edificio Centro Financiero, Pereira - 0930-0515 – **RI06)** Cra. 6a N° 16-42, Ofic. 205A, C.Cial. Los Arcos (or Ap. 1262), Pereira **W:** ecos1360.com radiomariacol.org – **RI07)** Cra. 15 N° 11-80, Santa Rosa de Cabal (or Calle 19 N° 8-74, Pereira) - 1000-0300

**SS00) SANTANDER**
**SS01)** Ap. 915, Bucaramanga – **SS02)** Ap. 223, Bucaramanga. **W:** 24horasradio.com.co **FM:** 90.7 – **SS03)** Calle 50 N° 17-71, P3 Barrancabermeja – **SS04)** Cra. 27 N° 45-80, Bucaramanga - 0900-0400 – **SS05)** Ap. 007, Bucaramanga - 1000-0200 – **SS06)** Calle 36 N° 14, 58 Piso 2, Bucaramanga **W:** melodiaenlinea.com – **SS07)** Calle 16 N° 15-01, Esquina, Socorro - 0930-0300 – **SS08)** Transv. 6 N° 9-56, Barbosa – **SS09)** Batallón de Artillería de Defensa Aerea N° 2 "Nueva Granada" (or Ap. 036), Barrancabermeja – **SS10)** Ap. 1100, Bucaramanga **W:** lacarinosa.com – **SS11)** Calle 11 N° 9-80, p. 3, San Gil – **SS12)** Calle 48 N° 35A-25, Bucaramanga – **SS13)** Edif.Súper Estrellas, Ofc.409 (or Ap. 23), Barrancabermeja - 1000-0300 – **SS14)** Calle 7 N° 17-44, Barbosa 0730-2330 – **SS15)** Ap 578, Barrancabermeja. **W:** rcnmundo.com/lacarinosabarranca 0900-0400 – **SS16)** Calle 12 N° 10-30, Centro, San Gil - 0900-0300 **W:** lacaliente1330.com – **SS17)** Calle 16 N° 4-47, Zapatoca – **SS18)** Calle 35 N° 20-39 (or Ap. 3104), Bucaramanga **W:** radiomariacol.org – **SS19)** Cra. 4 N° 4-118, P2, Cimitarra - 0900-0300 – **SS20)** Calle 9 N° 3-21 2° Piso, Vélez **W:** lavozdelcarare.com – **SS21)** Calle 20 N° 6-36, Zapatoca – **SS22)** Av. 36, No. 19-76, Piso 9, Bucaramanga **W:** rcm1450.com - 1100-0300 – **SS23)** Calle 41 N° 19-87, Bucaramanga

**W**: bluradio.com – **SS25)** Calle 12 N° 17-10, Ofc.302 (or Ap. 250), Barrancabermeja - 1000-0400 – **SS26)** Calle 11 N° 6A-11, Edif. San Gabriel, P2, Málaga - 1000-0200 – **SS27)** Diócesis del Socorro y San Gil, Cra. 13 N° 34, Esquina Socorro **W**: diocesisdesocorroysangil.org – 0500-2300 – **SS28)** Cra.27, Calle 9, Televis, Bucaramanga **W**: radio.uis.edu.co – **SS30)** Diócesis de Barrancabermeja, Calle Octava, entre Carreras 15 y 16, Barrancabermeja.
**SU00) SUCRE**
**SU01)** Ap. 167, Sincelejo **W**: facebook.com/SistemaCardenal – **SU02)** Cra. 18 N° 20-48 (or Ap. 448), Sincelejo – **SU03)** Cra. 24 N° 29-50 (or Ap. 100), Corozal - 1100-0500 – **SU04)** Cra. 20 N° 16-40 (or Ap. 191), Sincelejo - 1100-0300 **W**: coneczionradio.com – **SU05)** Calle 20 N° 24-93, Av. las Penitas, Sincelejo – **SU07)** Cra. 20 N° 25-92 piso 2, Sincelejo – **SU08)** Cra. 20 N° 21-46 (or Ap. 303), Sincelejo - 1000-0400 – **SU09)** Cra. 28 Calle 18, San Marcos – **SU10)** Calle 25A N° 18, Sincelejo - 1030-0430 – **SU11)** Cra. 20 N° 25-92, P2, Sincelejo - 1030-0200 **W**: radiocaracoli.com – **SU14)** Calle 24 No 18-31, Sincelejo **W**: facebook.com/radiosabanas
**TO00) TOLIMA**
**T001)** Calle 12 N° 1-17, P5, Ibagué **W**: lavozdeltolima.com – **T002)** Calle 14 N° 2A-14, P2, Ibagué – **T003)** Parque Murillo Toro N° 3-29, P4, Ibagué **W**: lafm.com.co - 1000-0400 – **T004)** Cra 7 con Calle 10, Espinal – **T005)** Calle 9 # 12-02, Guamo **W**: clickradio1090am.com – **T006)** Ap. 2419, Ibagué – **T007)** Ap. 1094, Ibagué **FM**: 93.9MHz – **T008)** Calle 5 N° 6-25, Mariquita – **T009)** Calle 9 N° 1-124, P3, Ibagué. **W**: besame. fm – **T010)** Calle 11 N° 4-26 (or Ap. 64), Espinal **W**: olimpicastereo. com.co – **T012)** Ap. 509, Honda - 1000-0300 – **T013)** Cra. 2 N° 11-27, Flandes **W**: olimpicastereo.com.co – **T014)** Cra 3 N° 12-76, Ofc.801 (or Ap. 589), Ibagué **W**: ondasdeibague.com - 1000-0000, r. R. María 0000-1000 – **T017)** Cra. 7a N° 5-36, Dolores - 0945-0300 – **TO 18)** Calle 7a No. 20-70, Melgar - 0900-0500 – **T019)** Cra. 2 N° 3-74, Rovira **W**: lavozdelcafeam.com
**VA00) VALLE DEL CAUCA**
**VA01)** Cra. 26 N° 5C-25, San Fernando, Cali - 1100-0300 – **VA02)** Cra. 38D Diagonal 37A-52B/Santa Isabel, Cali – **VA03)** Ap. 1941, Cali **W**: tropicanafm.com **FM**: 93.1 – **VA04)** Ap. 4666, Cali **W**: todelarcali.com – **VA05)** Cra. 14 N° 2-25, P2 (or Ap. 96), Buga - 1100-0500 – **VA06)** Av. 5B Norte N° 21-02, Cali **W**: rcnmundo.com/calidadcali – **VA07)** Cra. 33 N° 28-51 (Ap. 280), Palmira - 1000-0500. **W**: radiopalmira.com – **VA08)** Ap. 126, Tuluá - 1000-0300 – **VA10)** Calle 21 Nte N° 3N-49, P5, Cali **W**: radiored.com.co – **VA11)** Calle 12-39, Ofc 301, Edif.R.Buenaventura (Ap 383), Buenaventura 1030-0500. Rel. R. Maria 0200-1000. **W**: radiobuenaventura.com – **VA13)** Cra 19 N° 2N-29, Ofc 21B, Cali **W**: radiovivafenix.com – **VA14)** Cra. 30 N° 29-09, Palmira - 1000-0400 – **VA15)** Cra 6 N° 54-08, Av. Simon Bolívar, Buenaventura – **VA16)** Carrera 66B, No. 6-68, Barrio El Limonar, Cali **W**: armoniacali.com – **VA18)** Cra. 29 N° 32-88/90 (or Ap. 201), Palmira - 1130-0300 – **VA19)** Cra. 14 N° 5-77, Buga **W**: minutodedios.org – **VA20)** Cra. 26 N° 28-72, Tuluá. **W**: caracol.com.co – **VA21)** Calle 27 N° 33-35, Tuluá - 1100-0500 – **VA22)** Av. Roosevelt N° 34-37, Cali **W**: emisoras.redsonoraam.com/sonora-1500-am-cali – **VA23)** Cra. 51 N° 49-21, Sevilla – **VA24)** Calle 10 N° 6-87, P3, Cartago **W**: radiorobledo.com - 1100-0500 – **VA26)** Calle 13, No. 19-59, Barrio Guayaquil, Cali **W**: sistemahuellasinternacional.com 1100-0500 – **VA27)** Cra. 13 N° 10-58, Cali – **VA28)** Av.Roosevelt N° 28, Cali. (Or: Transversal 34 N° 149-23, Cedro Golf, Bogotá) – **VA31)** Cra. 13 N° 10-62, Cali. **W**: sistemahuellasinternacional.com - 1100-0400
**VI00) VICHADA**
**VI01)** Puerto Carreño **W**: manantialvida.org
**VP00) VAUPÉS**
**VP01)** Mitú – **VP02)** Mitú.
**FM in Bogotá (MHz)**: 88.9 R. Uno (RCN) – 89.9 40 Principales (Caracol) – 90.4 La UD (University) – 90.9 La Mega (RCN) – 91.9 Javeriana Estereo (University) – 92.4 Policía Nacional (Police) – 92.9 El Sonido de la Ciudad (Todelar) – 93.4 Colombia Estéreo (Colombian Army) – 93.9 RCN La Radio (rel. 770) – 94.9 La FM (RCN) – 95.9 R. Nac. de Colombia – 96.9 Blu R. – 97.4 La Vallenata (Caracol) – 97.9 Radioactiva (Caracol) – 98.5 Universidad Nacional (University) – 99.1 Radionica (RTVC) – 99.9 W Radio (Caracol) – 100.4 Oxígeno Urbano (Caracol) – 100.9 Caracol R (rel. 810kHz) – 101.9 Candela Estéreo – 102.9 Tropicana (Caracol) – 103.9 La X (Todelar) – 104.4 Fantástica – 104.9 Vibra Bogotá (W Radio) – 105.4 Rumba Stereo (RCN) – 105.9 Olímpica – 106.9 Universidad Jorge Tadeo Lozano (University) – 107.9 Minuto de Dios (Rlg)

## COMOROS

**L.T**: UTC +3h — **Pop**: 830,000 — **Pr.L**: French, Comorian, Arabic — **E.C**: 50Hz, 220V — **ITU**: COM

**OFFICE DE RADIO TÉLÉVISION DES COMORES (ORTC, Gov.)**
BP 452, Moroni, Grand Comoro ☎+269 7732531 🖷 +269 7730303

**W**: radiocomores.km **LP**: Tech. Dir: Abdulkader Radjab.
**FM**: Moroni, R.Studio 1 101.2MHz. Nkazi, R.Nkazi 107.0MHz. 6 x 1kW, 3 x 0.5kW txs. **D.Prgr**: 0300-1900. **Ann**: F: "Ici Radio Comoro".

Other stations:
**R. Dziyalandze**, Anjouan: 90.0MHz (rel. RFI 1700-1030).
**R. Ocean Indien**, Ngazidja: 100.5MHz. **W**: radioceanindien.km
**RFI Afrique**: Moroni 103.0, Mitsamiouli/Moheli/Mutsamundu 103.2MHz

## CONGO (Dem. Rep.)

**L.T**: Kinshasa & western part: UTC +1h, eastern part: UTC +2h — **Pop**: 82 million — **Pr.L**: French, Lingala, Swahili, Tshiluba, Kikongo — **E.C**: 50Hz, 220V — **ITU**: COD

**CONSEIL SUPÉRIEUR DE L'AUDIOVISUEL ET DE LA COMMUNICATION (CSAC)**
Kinshasa **LP**: President: Jean Bosco Bahala.

**RADIO-TÉLÉVISION NATIONALE CONGOLAISE (RTNC, Gov.)**
B.P. 3164, Kinshasa-Gombe ☎+243 81 9970699 🖷+243 81 123 7691 **W**: rtnc.cd **E**: info@rtnc-rdc.com **LP**: DG: Mr. E. Kipolongwa Mukambilwa, Dep. DG: M. Makaula.
**FM**: Kinshasa: **RTNC1 Radio Nationale**: 100.0MHz, **RTNC2 Radio Kinshasa**: 91.8MHz, **Channel for national languages**: 97.0MHz.
**D.Prgr**: 24h in French/Swahili/Lingala/Tshiluba/Kikongo. Also relayed by other stns. **Ann**: "RTNC, Radio-Télévision Nationale Congolaise, émettant de Kinshasa".

Provincial Stations:
**FM (MHz)**: 2) 94.5 3kW – 3) 88.9/92.0 1.5kW – 4) 93.3 1.5kW/90.0 0.05kW – 5) 93.5/98.5 – 6) 89.1 50kW – 7) 90.0 – 8) 92.5 1kW – 9) 94.8 – 10) 90.1 – 11) 93.7
**Addresses**: 2) B.P. 7296, Lubumbashi – 3) RTNC Kivu, B.P. 475, Bukavu – 4) B.P. 1061, Mbandaka – 5) B.P. 1232, Mbuji-Mayi – 6) B.P. 708, Kananga, Western Kasai – 7) B.P. 704, Matadi – 8) B.P. 1745, Kisangani – 9) Butembo, Nord-Kivu – 10) Goma, Nord-Kivu. **E**: rtncnordkivu@yahoo.fr – 11) Uvira, Sud-Kivu.

**RADIO TÉLÉ CANDIP**
B.P. 373, Bunia ☎+243 81 7363753 **E**: radiotelecandipisp@gmail.com **LP**: Dir: Freddy Lorima Dz'bo.
**SW**: Bunia 5066v kHz 1kW (inactive). **FM**: 98.0MHz 1kW.
**D.Prgr in French/Ethnic**: 0250v-0700, 1300-1900v.

**BEST RADIO (RADIO KAHUZI) (Rlg.)**
2 Ave. Masikita/Muhumba Ave, Bukavu or B.P. 42, Cyangugu, Rwanda. **W**: radiokahuzi.com **E**: radiokahuzi@gmail.com **LP**: Dir: Richard McDonald. National Dir: Kalangwa Dieudone. St. Mgr: Kathleen McDonald.
**SW**: Bukavu 6210kHz 0.8kW (irregular). **FM**: 91.1/102.1MHz 0.2kW.
**D.Prgr**: 0700-1600v in French, English, Kicongo, Kinyarwanda, Lingala, Mashi, Swahili and Tshiluba.

**RADIO OKAPI**
(joint initiative between the UN Mission in the DRC [MONUC] and Hirondelle Foundation)
QG Monuc, 12 Av. des Aviateurs, Kinshasa-Gombe ☎+243-81-890-6747 **W**: radiookapi.net **E**: info@hirondelle.org
**LP**: Dir: Yves Laplume.
**FM** (MHz): (powers 1-5kW): Isiro 90.1, Beni 92.0, Butembo 92.9, Gbadolite/Kananga/Lisala 93.0, Mbuji-Mayi 93.8, Kisangani 94.8, Bukavu 95.3, Gemena 95.4, Lubumbashi 95.8, Kanyabayonga/Mahagi 96.0, Aru 98.0, Bundundu 99.0, Matadi 102.0, Baraka/Kindu/Mbandaka 103.0, Kikwit/Kinshasa/Mbuji Mayi 103.5, Kamina 104.3, Manono 104.5, Bunia/Walikale 104.9, Kalemie 105.0, Goma/Uvira 105.2, Shabunda 105.4, Tshomo Ini 106.5.
**D.Prgr**: 0430-2200 in French/Lingala/Swahili/Tshiluba.

Other stations (all MHz):
**Business R. Africa**, Kinshasa: 98.6. **W**: brt-africa.com – **Canal Congo pour Christ**, Bukavu: 97.3 – **Canal Futur**, Kinshasa-Gombe: 107.4 – **CEBS**, Kinshasa: 93.7 – **RATELKI**, Kinshasa: 90.2 – **R. Artemis**, Bunia: 90.2 – **R. Boboto**, Isiro: 100.6 100W – **R. Butembo**: 100 – **R. Canal CVV**, Kinshasa: 102.3 – **R. Canal Révélation**, Bunia: 100.7 0.3kW – **R. Congo FM**, Kinshasa: 96.4 – **R. ECC**, Kinshasa: 104.0 – **R. Elikya**, Kinshasa: 97.5 – **R. Lwenge**, Baraki-Fizi: 88.9 150W – **R. Liberté Kinshasa (RALIK)**, 96.8 – **R. Maendeleo**: Bukavu 88.7 1kW, Chomuhini 103.3 1kW – **R. Malebo Broadcast**

**Channel** (MBC), Kinshasa: 98.3 – **R. Maria Malkia wa Amani** (Rlg.): Bukavu 94.0 & 97.0. **W:** pamojanakakaluigi.org/radio_maria. htm – **R. Méthodiste Lokole,** Kinshasa-Gombe: 100.8 – **R. Moto** (Rlg.): Kivu 103 1.2kW, Butembo 106.0 – **R. Neno la Uzima,** Bukavu: 100.2 – **R. Parole Eternelle,** Kinshasa: 103.8 **W:** facebook.com/ rpe2004 – **R. Raga FM:** Kinshasa-Binza 90.5 4kW. **W:** raga.cd – **R. Rehema:** Chamuhini 89.5 0.25kW, Bukavu 99.7 1kW – **R. Réveil FM,** Kinshasa-Gombe: 105.4 **W:** reveilfm.itgo.com – **R. Sango Malamu:** Boma 102.5, Kinshasa 104.5 – **R. Tangazeni Kristo** (Rlg.): Bunia 88.6, Aru/Kwandruma 90.0 **E:** buero@diguna.de – **R. Télé Armée de l'Eternel,** Kinshasa: 94.5 – **R. Télé Amani,** Kisangani; 100.1 25W, 103.1 0.5kW. – **R. Téle Boma** (RTB), Boma: 98.0 – **R. Télé Graben,** Beni/Butembo 98 – **R. Télé Groupe l'Avenir (RTGA),** Kinshasa 88.1 –**R. Télé Kin Malebo** (RTKM): Kinshasa 95.1, Kananga 97.5 – **R. Télé Kintuadi** (RTK): Boma 91.1, Kinshasa 97.1, Mbanza Ngungu 103.4, Matadi 107.5 – **R. Télé Message de Vie,** Kinshasa: 88.7 – **R. Télé Mosaïque,** Likasi: 88.5 – **R. Télé Puissance,** Kinshasa 101.0 – **RTV Bukavu Liberté,** Ibanda 107.3 – **RTV Mulangane,** Bukavu: 100.1 0.25kW – **R. Sentinelle,** Kinshasa: 97.1 – **R. Tomisa,** Kikwit: 97.5 0.5kW – **R. Veritas** (Rlg.), Kabinda: 105.0 – **R. Vuvu Kietu,** Mbanza Ngungu: 101.0 – **RCLS,** Kirumba: 91.0 – **REB,** Butembo: 90.7 – **RTIV,** Kisangani: 89.4 0.5kW – **Sauti ya Mkaaji,** Makongo: 87.85 – **Top Congo,** Kinshasa: 88.4.

**BBC African Sce:** Mbandaka/Mbuji-Mayi 90.5, Kisangani/ Lubumbashi 92.0, Kinshasa 92.6, Goma 93.8, Kolwezi 95.9, Kananga 96.8, Bunia 100.7, Bukavu 102.2
**RFI Afrique:** Bunia 90.2, Bukavu/Goma/Lubumbashi/Matadi 98.0, Mbandaka/Mbuji-Mayi 104.9, Kinshasa/Kisangani 105.0MHz.
**RTBFi** (Belgium), Kinshasa: 99.2MHz.
**VOA African Sce:** Kananga/Matadi/Mbuji-Mayi 93.5, Goma 96.2, Bukavu 97.4, Kisangani 97.7, Lubumbashi 102.8MHz

## CONGO (Rep.)

**L.T:** UTC +1h — **Pop:** 4.9 million — **Pr.L:** French, Lingala, Kikongo — **E.C:** 50Hz, 220V — **ITU:** COG

### CONSEIL SUPÉRIEUR DE LA LIBERTÉ DE LA COMMUNICATION (CSLC)
Rte de l'Auberge de Gascogne, Brazzaville ☎+242 06 9159898 **W:** cslc-congo.esy.es **E:** cslccongobz@gmail.com

### RADIO CONGO (Gov.)
Direction Générale, B.P. 2241, Brazzaville ☎+242 22 2810608
**SW:** Brazzaville 6115kHz 50kW 0500-1900 (irreg.)
**FM:** Dolisie 90.1MHz, Djambala 94.0MHz, Brazzaville 96.4MHz, Pointe-Noire 99.9MHz.
**National Network:** 0420-2300 in French & ethnic except Pointe-Noire carrying regional programme. **N. in English:** 1900 (approx.)

**Other stations:**
**Canal FM,** Brazzaville: 99.3MHz – **Hit R:** Brazzaville 89.0MHz, Pointe Noire 97.7MHz **W:** hitradio.ma – **R. Maria,** Pointe-noire: 88.7MHz. **W:** radiomaria.cg/home.aspx – **R. Mucodec,** Brazzaville: 100.3MHz. **W:** mucodec.com – **R. Liberté,** Brazzaville: 106.0MHz
**RFI Afrique:** Brazzaville/Pointe-Noire 93.2MHz
**VOA Africa:** Pointe-Noire 98.3MHz, Brazzaville 104.3MHz

## COOK ISLANDS

**L.T:** UTC-10h — **Pop:** 17,400 — **Pr.L:** English, Cook Island Maori — **E.C:** 50Hz, 240V — **ITU:** CKH

| MW | kHz | kW | Station | Location |
|---|---|---|---|---|
| 1) | 630 | 2.5 | R. Cook Islands AM | Rarotonga |
| FM | MHz | kW | Station | Location |
| 2) | 88.0 | | 88 FM Boom Boom R. | Aitutaki |
| 2) | 88.0 | | 88 FM Boom Boom R. | Rarotonga |
| 1) | 89.0 | | R. Cook Islands | Mitiaro |
| 1) | 89.0 | | R. Cook Islands | Pukapuka |
| 1) | 89.9 | | R. Cook Islands AM | Rarotonga |
| 3) | 90.3 | | Life FM | Rarotonga |
| 1) | 90.6 | | R. Cook Islands | Mangaia |
| 1) | 90.6 | | R. Cook Islands | Rakahanga |
| 1) | 90.6 | | R. Cook Islands | Palmerston |
| 7) | ‡91.8 | | Araura FM | Aitutaki |
| 4) | 91.9 | | Matariki FM | Rarotonga |
| 1) | 92.2 | | R. Cook Islands | Atiu |
| 1) | 92.2 | | R. Cook Islands | Penrhyn |
| 1) | 93.8 | | R. Cook Islands | Mauke |

| FM | MHz | kW | Station | Location |
|---|---|---|---|---|
| 1) | 93.8 | | R. Cook Islands | Nassau |
| 1) | ‡95.4 | | R. Cook Islands | Aitutaki |
| 1) | 95.4 | | R. Cook Islands | Manihiki |
| 4) | 96.7 | | Matariki FM | Rarotonga |
| 8) | 97.9 | | Maranatha FM | Rarotonga |
| 5) | ‡98.7 | | Adventist R. TK3ANA | Rarotonga |
| 4) | 99.9 | | Matariki FM | Rarotonga |
| 1) | ‡101.1 | | HITZ FM | Rarotonga |
| 6) | ‡103.3 | 1 | R. Ikurangi KCFM | Rarotonga |

‡ Station reported as inactive
**Addresses & other information**
**1)** The Voice of the Nation, Elijah Communications, PO Box 126, Avarua Rarotonga ☎+682 29460 📠+682 21907 **W:** www.radio-cook-islands. com/radio-cook-islands-the-voice-of-the-nation **E:** tunein@radio.co.ck **R. Cook Islands** AM, M-F 1600-0900 [Fri 1000] Sat 1600-1000 Su 1700-0900 **N:** Local news hourly M-F 1700-0200 **RNZI** 1600, 1700, 1800 M-F **Prgr:** Talkback, news, rlg srvcs and music in English and Cook I. Maori. **LP:** CEO Jeane Matenga. **HITZ FM** 24h **Prgr:** contemporary hit music). **Outer Island Network:** Txs outside Rarotonga are owned by the Cook Islands govt and relay R. Cook Islands AM and in some cases also originate prgrs as local community stns (many are reported inactive) – **2)** The Digital Factory, Avarua, Rarotonga ☎+682 23633 **W:** 88fmcookislands.com **E:** 88fmradio@gmail.com **LP:** George (GDub) Williams **Prgr:** 24h – **3)** United Christian Broadcasters, Matavera Rarotonga. **Prgr:** Religious **FPI:** Additional outlet on 88.0 – **4)** Matariki FM Ltd, PO Box 511, Avarua, Rarotonga ☎+682 25997 **W:** matarikifm. co.ck and streaming also at matarikifm.radio.net **E:** onair@matarikifm. co.ck **LP:** William Framhein **Format:** local Polynesian music Associated local community station: R.Enua Manu, Enuamanu School, Mapumai, Atiu **Format:** local talkback, community affairs, music and school news – **5)** PO Box 31, Avarua, Rarotonga ☎+682 22851 **E:** office@adventist. org.ck **Prgr:** Rlg – **6)** Kia Orana Country R., PO Box 521, Avarua, Rarotonga ☎+682 23203 – **7)** Aitutaki. Same family ownership as #2 with joint marketing and sales – **8)** Rarotonga. **Prgr:** Religious

## COSTA RICA

**L.T:** UTC -6h — **Pop:** 4.9 million — **Pr.L:** Spanish — **E.C:** 60Hz, 120V — **ITU:** CTR

### SUPERINTENDENCIA DE TELECOMUNICACIONES (SUTEL)
Guachipelín de Escazú, Oficentro Multipark, edificio Tapantí, 3er piso, 1000 San José ☎ +506 40000000 📠 +506 22156821 **E:** info@ sutel.go.cr **W:** sutel.go.cr **LP:** Chmn: Carlos Raúl Gutiérrez

### CAMARA NACIONAL DE RADIO (CANARA)
Ap.1583, 1002 San José ☎ +506 2256 2338 📠 +506 2255 4483 **W:** canara.cr **E:** info@canara.org

**Call:** TI–, ‡ = inactive, r. = relay, ± = varying freq

| MW | Call | kHz | kW | Station, location and h. of tr |
|---|---|---|---|---|
| 2) | SCL | 550 | 5 | R. Santa Clara, Cd. Quesada: 1100-0130 |
| 3) | ELR | ‡570 | 5 | R. Libertad, San José: 1200-0400 |
| 4) | ALY | 640 | 20 | R. Rica, San José: 1130-0400 |
| 5) | TNT | 670 | 10 | R. Managua, San José |
| 6) | JC | 700 | 10 | R. Sonora, San José |
| 7) | | 730 | 1 | R. Pacífico, Puntarenas: 1400-0200 |
| 8) | LX | 760 | 5 | R. Columbia, San José |
| 9) | RA | 780 | 10 | R. América, San José |
| 10) | SD | 800 | 3 | R. La Gigante, San José |
| 11) | GC | ‡820 | 2.5 | R. Tigre, San José: 1130-0600 |
| 12) | RDR | 850 | 2 | R. Cartago, Cartago: 1100-0400 |
| 13) | UCR | 870 | 10 | R. 870 UCR, San Pedro Montes de Oca |
| 15) | UM | 910 | 10 | BBN, San José/San Carlos |
| 16) | RCR | 930 | 5 | R. Costa Rica, Guadalupe |
| 14) | MIL | 1000 | 1 | R. 2 Rock, San José |
| 1) | | 1020 | | R. Metrópoli, Cartago |
| 19) | FC | 1080 | 1 | Faro del Caribe AM, San José |
| 20) | SCR | 1100 | 5 | R. Chorotega, Santa Cruz: 1315-0000 |
| 21) | ACE | 1120 | 1 | R. Alajuela, Alajuela: 1100-0300 |
| 22) | DKN | 1140 | 5 | R. Nueva, Guápiles |
| 23) | PJ | 1180 | 5 | R. Victoria, Heredia: 1100-0400 |
| 24) | TQ | 1200 | 5 | R. Cucu, San José: 1000-0600 |
| 25) | Q | 1220 | 5 | R. Fe y Poder, Limón |
| 27) | DIO | 1260 | 5 | R. Emaús, San Vito de Coto Brus:1100-0300 |
| 29) | GL | 1300 | 1 | R. La Fuente Musical, Cartago |
| 30) | HR | 1340 | 5 | R. Sideral, San Ramón: 1000-0400 |
| 31) | MS | 1380 | 1 | R. Guanacaste, Liberia: 1000-0500 |
| 32) | RPN | 1420 | 5 | R. Pampa, Liberia: 1100-0100 |

| MW Call | kHz | kW | Station, location and h. of tr |
|---|---|---|---|
| 33) RDVC | 1430 | 3 | R. San Carlos, Cd. Quesada: 1100-0300 |
| 28) RC | 1500 | 1 | R. Cima, Ciudad Quesada: 1100-0100 |
| 34) OAR | 1560 | 5 | R. Nicoya, Nicoya: 1000-0300 |
| 35) LGJ | 1590 | 1.5 | R. 16, Grecia: 1100-0400 |
| 36) CC ‡1600 | | 2.5 | R. Buenísima, Puerto Golfito |
| 37) MQ | 1600 | 1.5 | R. Pococí, Guápiles: 1100-0400 |

Hrs of tr. 24h except where shown.

**Addresses & other information:**
**1)** Cartago **W:** facebook.com/radio.metropoli – **2)** Ap. 221, 4400 Edificio Cenco, Cd. Quesada, San Carlos, Alajuela **W:** radiosantaclara.cr – **3)** Cadena Radial Costarricense, 100m oeste de Taca, La Uruca, 1000 San José or Ap. 301-2400, Desamparados **W:** libertadcr.com – **4)** Ap. 1695, 1000 San José **W:** radiorica640.net – **5)** Ap. 800-1000 (or Costado Oeste del Puente Juan Pablo II), 1000 San José. **W:** facebook.com/pages/Radio-Managua-AM/145937732087541 – **6)** San José **W:** radio-osonoracr.com – **7)** San José **W:** facebook.com/RadioPacifico730AM – **8)** De Casa Presidencial 400 metros oeste, Zapote, San Jose, 1000 San José **W:** columbiadeportiva.com – **9)** Edificio de la Prensa Libre, Calle 4, Avenida 4 (or Ap. 177-1009) San José **W:** 780america.com – **10)** Calles 15-13, Av. 11, Barrio Aranjuez (or Ap. 1735) 1000 San José **W:** radioalagigante800am.com – **11)** Ap. 6133, 1000 San José **W:** facebook.com/Radio-Tigre-105149222909252 – **12)** Altos de Apolo, frente a Palacio Municipal, Cartago **W:** radiocartago.org – **13)** Cd. Universitaria Rodrigo Facio, San Pedro Montes de Oca, 2060-1000 San José **W:** radios.ucr.ac.cr – **14)** **W:** rock2.am – **15)** De la Municipalidad de Tibas 100 mtrs al Norte y 75 metrs al Oeste, casa blanca a mano derecha (Ap. 2006), 1100 San José **W:** radioperola.com – **16)** Barrio Córdoba, Autos Bohío 100 sur y 100 este, 894-2200 Coronado **W:** radiocr.net – **19)** Ap. 2710, 1000 San José **W:** farodelcaribe.org – **20)** 700 mts este de Almacén Jiménez y Chaverrí, (or Ap. 92), 5175 Santa Cruz **W:** radio-chorotega.com – **21)** 300 metros Norte y 50 Oeste del Antiguo Hospital de Alajuela, Alajuela (or Ap. 233-4060, Moll International, Alajuela) **W:** radioalajuela.com – **22)** Limón, Pococí, Guápiles, 50 metros norte de Correos de CR **W:** radionueva.org – **23)** Universidad Nacional, 100 metros norte y 100 metros oeste, Heredia **W:** facebook.com/RadioVictoria1180AM – **24)** Ap. 1128, 1000 San José **W:** radiocucucr.com – **25)** Iglesia Maranatha, 7300 Puerto Limón **W:** feypoderradio.com – **27)** Ap.262, 8257 San Vito de Coto Brus **W:** emaus1260.com – **28)** Ciudad Quesada **W:** radiocimacr.com – **29)** 1 km este de la Basilica de los Angeles, Carr. a Paraíso, 7050 Cartago **W:** lafuentemusical.com – **30)** Ap. 73, 4250 San Ramón **W:** facebook.com/radiosideral – **31)** Residencial Las Brisas, Casa #11A, Buscando la quebrada (Ap. 27), 5600 Liberia, (or Ap. 6462, 1000 San José) **W:** radioguanacaste.com – **32)** Ap. 248, 5000 Liberia **W:** radiopampa.com – **33)** 500 Sur 25 Este del Parque de Ciudad Quesada (Ap. 25), 4400 Cd. Quesada **W:** radiosancarlos.co.cr – **34)** Ap. 50, 5200 Nicoya **W:** facebook.com/radionicoya1560 – **35)** 200 mtrs Sur de la Bomba Alvarado y Molina en Grecia Centro (or Ap. 16), 4100 Grecia, Alajuela **W:** radio16.com – **36)** Barrio El Invú, La Rotonda, Pto. Golfito **W:** 88stereo.com/grupo-88 – **37)** Costado Oeste del Estadio de Guápiles (or Ap. 160), 7210 Guápiles **W:** facebook.com/RADIO-POCOCI-647397988634486

**FM in San José and vicinity (MHz):** 88.7 Lira – 89.1 La Super Estación – 89.9 R. 899 – 89.5 Life FM Una Senda de Vida – 90.3 Sinfonola – 90.7 R. Ritmo 90.7 – 91.1 911 La Radio – 91.5 R. 915 – 91.9 Puntarenas – 92.3 Onda Radial – 92.7 Columbia Stereo – 93.1 R. Fides – 93.5 Monumental – 93.9 Sonido Latino – 94.3 Reloj – 94.7 R. 94.7 – 95.1 Z-FM – 95.5 R. 95 Cinco Jazz – 95.9 R. Romance – 96.3 Centro – 96.7 Universidad – 97.1 Faro del Caribe – 97.5 R. Musical – 97.9 R. 979 – 98.3 Stéreo Visión – 98.7 Columbia – 99.1 La Mejor FM – 99.5 R. Dos – 99.9 R. Azul – 100.3 FM Globo – 100.7 R. María – 101.1 R. Disney – 101.5 R. Nacional FM – 101.9 "U" – 102.3 La Super – 102.7 Exa FM – 103.1 Cientotres – 103.5 Best FM – 103.9 Sinai – 104.3 Oxígeno – 104.7 R. Hit – 105.1 Omega – 105.5 Ten Fifty-Five/Omega – 105.9 Beatz 106 – 106.3 R. Peninsular – 106.7 Premium – 107.1 R. Actual FM – 107.5 R. 107.5 Real Rock

**L.T:** UTC — **Pop**: 24 million — **Pr.L:** French, Diola, 12 ethnic — **E.C:** 50Hz, 220V — **ITU:** CTI

**HAUTE AUTORITÉ DE LA COMMUNICATION AUDIOVISUELLE (HACA)**
2 Plateaux Vallons, Rue J93, lot n°2460, B.P. V56, Abidjan ☎+225 22 419658 📠 +225 22 411455 **W:** haca.ci **E:** infos@haca.ci **L.P:** Chmn: Ibrahim Sy Savane.

**RADIODIFFUSION-TÉLÉVISION IVOIRIENNE (RTI, Gov.)**
B.P. 191, Abidjan ☎+225 20 214800 📠 +225 20 215038

**W:** rti.ci **L.P:** Acting DG: Lazare Saye Aka. Deputy DG for Radio: Jean-Claude Bayala.

| FM (MHz) | 1 | 2 | kW | FM (MHz) | 1 | 2 | kW |
|---|---|---|---|---|---|---|---|
| Abobo-Abidjan | 88.0 | 92.0 | 5 | Koun Fao | 94.2 | 101.0 | |
| Bouaflé | 99.0 | 102.6 | | Man | 96.9 | 100.2 | |
| Bouaké | 92.1 | 98.6 | | Naingbo | 93.0 | 103.0 | |
| Dabakala | 91.0 | 101.0 | | Niangue | 93.0 | 95.9 | |
| Dimbokro | 99.0 | 102.9 | | Séguéla | 89.0 | 95.0 | |
| Divo | 88.0 | 90.8 | 10 | Tengréla | 96.3 | 99.6 | |
| Grabo | 88.0 | 91.0 | 0.5 | Tiémé | 88.0 | 91.0 | 5/1 |
| Kouakoussikro | 89.3 | 92.4 | | Touba | 94.7 | 101.5 | |

**R. Côte d'Ivoire (1):** 0500-2400. **Fréquence Deux (2):** 24h.
**Ann:** "R. Côte d'Ivoire" or "Fréquence Deux". **IS:** s/on with clock chimes.

**Other stations:**
**Alpha Blondy FM,** Abidjan: 97.9MHz **W:** alphablondyfm.net – **Bassam FM,** Grand Bassam: 104.2MHz **W:** bassamfm.com – **CNews FM,** Abidjan: 88.6MHz **W:** radiocnews.com – **Cocody FM,** Abidjan: 98.5MHz 1kW **W:** facebook.com/radio-cocody-fm-380951067163 – **Fréquence Vie:** Abidjan 89.4 1kW, Bouaké 94.5, Man 99.2, Abengourou 100.2, Yamoussoukro 103.1MHz **W:** radiofrequencevie.com – **Hit R,** Abidjan: 93.3MHz. **W:** hitradio.ci – **Ivoire FM,** Abidjan: 103.4MHz **W:** ivoirefm.ci – **La Voix de l'Esperance,** Abidjan: 101.6MHz **W:** lavoixdelesperance.org – **Life R,** Yamoussoukro: 107.1MHz **W:** lavoixdelesperance.org – **Onuci FM:** Yamoussoukro 94.4MHz, Bouaké 95.3MHz, Abidjan 96.0MHz & 19 other sites **W:** onucifm.net – **R. Ado FM,** Bouaké: 97.9MHz – **R. Al Bayane,** Gagnoa 88.6, Seguela 89.6, Yamoussoukro 91.2, Abidjan 95.7, Bouna 96.0, Bouaké 100.7, Korhogo 102.2, Daloa 102.6, San-Pédro 102.7MHz. **W:** radio-albayane.com – **R. Arc-en-ciel,** Abidjan: 102.0MHz **W:** facebook.com/RadioArcEnCiel22 – **R. City FM,** Abidjan: 106.1MHz **W:** radiocityfm.ci – **R. Jam:** Yamoussokro 88.1 1kW, Korhogo 92.2, San-Pédro 94.0, Man 95.5, Abengourou 96.9, Abidjan 99.3 3kW, Bouaké 104.3, Gagnoa 105.3MHz **W:** radiojam.biz – **R. Maria,** Yamoussoukro: 104.8MHz. **W:** radiomaria.ci – **R. N'Gowa FM,** Abidjan: 89.7MHz **W:** facebook.com/Radio-NGowa-897FM-172371509804556 – **R. Nationale Catolique:** Aboisso 89.2, Man 96.7, Abengourou 99.0, San-Pédro 99.2, Yamoussoukro 101.2, Abidjan 102.5, Gagnoa 104.7, Daloa 105.0, Bondoukou 107.2MHz **W:** rnc-ci.net – **R. Nostalgie:** Abidjan 101.1, Bouaké 106.5MHz. **W:** nostalgie.ci – **Trace R,** Abidjan 95.0MHz **W:** trace.ci – **Vibe R,** Abidjan 94.6MHz **W:** viberadio.ci – **Zenith FM,** Abidjan: 92.8MHz **W:** facebook.com/Zenith-FM-221020288020468
**BBC African Sce**: Man 89.2, Bouaké 93.9, Abidjan 94.3, Yamoussoukro 97.7, San Pedro 103.1MHz.
**Medi 1 Afrique Internationale**: Abidjan 97.2MHz.
**RFI Afrique:** San Pedro 94.4, Yamoussoukro 96.0, Abidjan/Bouaké/Korhogo 97.6MHz.
**Voice of America,** Abidjan: 99.0MHz

**L.T:** UTC +2h (31 Mar-27 Oct: +3h) — **Pop:** 4.2 million — **Pr.L:** Croatian — **E.C:** 230V/50Hz — **ITU:** HRV

**HRVATSKA REGULATORNA AGENCIJA ZA MREŽNE DJELATNOSTI (HAKOM) (Croatian Regulatory Authority for Network Industries)**
Roberta Frangeša Mihanovica 9, 10010 Zagreb ☎ +385 1 7007007 📠 +385 1 7007070 **E:** ravnatelj_hakom@hakom.hr **W:** hakom.hr
**L.P:** DG: Miran Gosta

**HRVATSKA RADIOTELEVIZIJA (HRT) (Pub)**
Prisavlje 3, 10000 Zagreb ☎ +385 1 6342634 **E:** hrt@hrt.hr **W:** hrt.hr **L.P:** DG: Kazimir Bacic

| FM (MHz) | 1 | 2 | 3 | kW |
|---|---|---|---|---|
| Belje | 93.3 | 98.1 | - | 50 |
| Biokovo | 89.7 | 98.9 | - | 80 |
| Borinci | 88.3 | 96.1 | - | 3 |
| Brac | 99.8 | - | 88.8 | 3 |
| Buje | 91.3 | 103.7 | 93.2 | 1 |
| Celavac | 95.1 | 98.1 | - | 80 |
| Drenovci | 92.1 | 104.4 | - | 3 |
| Gruda | 101.7 | 106.1 | - | 2 |
| Ivanščica | 102.4 | 106.4 | 96.1 | 2x15/30 |
| Kalnik | 90.8 | 105.8 | 107.8 | 15 |
| Labinštica | 91.3 | 96.1 | 100.4 | 30 |
| Licka Plješivica | 87.7 | 90.5 | 100.3 | 50 |
| Limski kanal | 90.2 | 102.6 | - | 1 |
| Mirkovica | 91.3 | 93.3 | - | 30 |
| Murter | 92.7 | 99.4 | 104.1 | 1 |

| FM (MHz) | 1 | 2 | 3 | kW |
|---|---|---|---|---|
| Pag | 98.5 | 103.4 | - | 3 |
| Papuk | 94.9 | 106.8 | 97.7 | 10 |
| Psunj | 97.3 | 99.7 | - | 80 |
| Pula | 91.4 | 94.4 | 102.1 | 5 |
| Slavonski Brod | 91.3 | 105.1 | 107.9 | 15 |
| Sljeme | 92.1 | 98.5 | - | 120 |
| Srdj | 88.9 | 98.5 | - | 30 |
| Ştipanov Gric | 102.3 | 97.5 | 89.7 | 15 |
| Šubicevac | 94.0 | 90.0 | 102.3 | 1 |
| Ucka | 99.3 | 105.3 | 100.5 | 80 |
| Ugljan | 91.6 | 87.6 | - | 5 |
| Uljenje | 95.1 | 89.3 | 105.6 | 3 |
| Zagreb | - | - | 94.3 | 1 |

+ txs below 1kW.
**D.Prgr: Prgr 1 (Prvi program):** 24h. – **Prgr 2 (Drugi program):** 24h.
– **Prgr 3 (Treci program):** 24h.

### Hrvatski Radio (HR) Regional Stations

**D.Prgr:** all stns 24h (incl. rel. of HR Prgr 1). **HR R. Dubrovnik:** Branitelja Dubrovnika 21, 20000 Dubrovnik. **E:** radiodubrovnik@hrt.hr. On (MHz) 88.2 (Rota 1.7kW), 89.5 (Ilija 1.7kW), 97.2 (Blato 0.3kW), 101.1 (Vela Luka 0.3kW), 103.7 (Slano 0.05kW), 103.8 (Korcula 0.2kW), 105.0 (Srdj 30kW), 106.2 (Lastovo 2.7kW & Ston 0.05kW), 106.5 (Lopud 0.03kW). – **HR R. Knin:** Krešimirova 30, 23300 Knin. **E:** radio.knin@hrt.hr. On (MHz) 88.1 (Šubicevac 0.1kW), 90.2 (Knin 0.6kW), 94.4 (Promina 5kW). – **HR R. Osijek:** Šamacka 13, 31000 Osijek. **E:** radioosijek@hrt.hr. On (MHz) 99.3 (Drenovci 3kW), 102.0 (Psunj 80kW), 102.4 (Osijek), 102.8 (Beli Manastir 50kW), 105.3 (Borinci 3kW), 105.6 (Zlatarevac 0.1kW), 105.8 (Ilok). For ethnic minorities: Hungarian ("Eszéki Rádió"): 1805-1830. – **HR R. Pula:** Riva 10, 52100 Pula. **E:** radiopula@hrt.hr. On (MHz) 93.8 (Novigrad 0.15kW), 93.9 (Limski kanal 1kW), 94.2 (Vrsar 0.16kW), 96.3 (Koromacno 0.3kW), 96.4 (Buje 1kW), 100.0 (Pula 5kW), 101.3 (Ucka 80kW), 103.8 (Raša 0.1kW). For ethnic minorities: Italian ("R. Pola"): MF 1000-1003, 1300-1303, 1530-1555 (Sun 1645). – **HR R. Rijeka:** Korzo 24, 51000 Rijeka. **E:** redakcija@radio-rijeka.com. On (MHz) 94.5 (Brgud 0.1kW), 95.1 (Pulac 0.5kW), 97.9 (Cres 0.3kW & Kupjacki Vrh 0.3kW), 101.7 (Prezid 0.06kW), 102.7 (Mirkovica 30kW), 104.0 (Fužine 0.3kW), 104.7 (Ucka 80kW), 107.4 (Mali Lošinj 0.1kW), 107.5 (Mrkopalj 0.03kW). For ethnic minorities: Italian ("R. Fiume"): W 0930-0935, W 1130-1135, W 1330-1335, W 1500-1510. – **HR R. Sljeme:** Prisavlje 3, 10000 Zagreb. **E:** radio_sljeme@hrt.hr. On 88.1MHz (Sljeme 5kW). – **HR R. Split:** Mažuranicevo šetalište 24a, 21000 Split. **E:** radio.split@hrt.hr. On (MHz) 88.4 (Komiza 0.5kW), 100.2 (Hvar 0.05kW), 101.0 (Labinštica 30kW), 102.0 (Biokovo 80kW), 104.5 (Brac 3kW), 105.3 (Orlovaca 0.1kW), 105.8 (Vrlika 0.3kW). – **HR R. Zadar:** Poljana Šime Budinica 3, 23000 Zadar. **E:** radio_zadar@hrt.hr. On (MHz) 101.8 (Ugljan 5kW), 103.0 (Celevac 80kW), 105.9 (Pag 3kW).

### OTHER STATIONS

| | FM | MHz | kW | Location | Station |
|---|---|---|---|---|---|
| 4) | | 87.5 | 1 | Krk | Lagagini FM |
| 13) | | 87.8 | 10 | Brac | R. Dalmacija |
| 7) | | 88.0 | 3 | Beli Manastir | R. Baranja |
| 21) | | 88.3 | 3 | Virovitica | R. Marija |
| 13) | | 88.3 | 2 | Celevac | R. Dalmacija |
| 16) | | 88.6 | 4 | Velika Gorica | City R. |
| 26) | | 88.6 | 5 | Slavonski Brod | R. Slavonija |
| 38) | | 88.6 | 1 | Šibenik | R. Šibenik |
| 26) | | 89.1 | 2 | Nova Gradiška | R. Slavonija |
| 30) | | 89.3 | 3 | Ugljan | Novi R. |
| 51) | | 89.4 | 2 | Sisak | R. Sisak |
| 11) | | 89.6 | 7 | Porec | R. Centar Porec |
| 5) | | 89.7 | 4.7 | Sljeme | Antena Zagreb |
| 49) | | 89.9 | 1 | Koprivnica | R. Kraj |
| 42) | | 90.1 | 3 | Martinšcak | Prvi Karlovacki R. |
| 28) | | 90.2 | 1 | Požega | R. Vallis Aurea |
| 34) | | 90.2 | 1 | Vinkovci | Radio Postaja Vincovci |
| 1) | | 90.4 | 1 | Slatina | Narodni R. |
| 3) | | 90.4 | 3 | Kuna Pelješka | Hrvatski Katolicki R. |
| 1) | | 90.5 | 1 | Slavonski Brod | Narodni R. |
| 41) | | 90.5 | 1 | Komiža | Nautic R. Vis |
| 1) | | 90.6 | 1 | Buje | Narodni R. |
| 2) | | 90.8 | 1 | Šibenik | Otvoreni R. |
| 4) | | 91.0 | 1 | Veprinac | Laganini FM |
| 35) | | 91.0 | 1 | Djakovo | Slavonski R. |
| 2) | | 91.1 | 1 | Moslavacka Gora | Otvoreni R. |
| 19) | | 91.7 | 5 | Koprivnica | R. Koprivnica |
| 50) | | 91.7 | 5 | Moslavacka Gora | R. Quirinus |
| 9) | | 91.8 | 1 | Brac | R. Brac |
| 1) | | 92.0 | 5 | Celevac | Narodni R. |
| 4) | | 92.4 | 2 | Požega | Laganini FM |
| 2) | | 92.6 | 1 | Zagreb | Otvoreni R. |

| | FM | MHz | kW | Location | Station |
|---|---|---|---|---|---|
| 32) | | 92.9 | 1.9 | Virovitica | R. Virovitica |
| 37) | | 93.0 | 1 | Samobor | R. Samobor |
| 2) | | 93.2 | 1.7 | Gruda | Otvoreni R. |
| 11) | | 93.6 | 7 | Porec | R. Centar Porec |
| 12) | | 93.6 | 1 | Sveta Nedelja | Extra FM |
| 6) | | 93.6 | 30 | Labinštica | Ultra FM |
| 1) | | 93.7 | 13 | Otocac | Narodni R. |
| 32) | | 93.7 | 1 | Slatina | R. Virovitica |
| 18) | | 93.8 | 1 | Jastrebarsko | R. Jaska |
| 10) | | 93.9 | 3 | Bjelovar | R. Terezija |
| 26) | | 94.3 | 1 | Lužani | R. Slavonija |
| 1) | | 94.5 | 3 | Rijeka | Narodni R. |
| 57) | | 94.7 | 1 | Hvar | Megamix R. Hvar |
| 52) | | 94.8 | 1 | Rovinj | Rovinj FM |
| 54) | | 94.8 | 1 | Krapina | R. Kraj |
| 20) | | 94.9 | 5 | Velika Gorica | Gold FM |
| 58) | | 95.2 | 1 | Slunj | R. Slunj |
| 1) | | 95.3 | 3 | Osijek | Narodni R. |
| 23) | | 95.4 | 1 | Duga Resa | R. Mrežnica |
| 45) | | 95.4 | 5 | Drenovci | Hrvatski R. Vukovar |
| 1) | | 95.5 | 1 | Virovitica | Narodni R. |
| 3) | | 95.5 | 1 | Ugljan | Hrvatski Katolicki R. |
| 59) | | 95.6 | 1 | Trogir | Gradski R. Trogir |
| 27) | | 95.6 | 2 | Donja Stubica | R. Stubica |
| 1) | | 95.8 | 1 | Hvar | Narodni R. |
| 1) | | 95.9 | 1 | Pula | Narodni R. |
| 32) | | 96.3 | 1 | Pitomaca | R. Virovitica |
| 40) | | 96.3 | 3 | Lastovo | Soundset Ragusa |
| 13) | | 96.4 | 1 | Ugljan | R. Dalmacija |
| 21) | | 96.4 | 1 | Zagreb | R. Marija |
| 4) | | 96.5 | 1 | Varaždin | Laganini FM |
| 6) | | 96.5 | 1 | Rijeka | Totalni FM |
| 31) | | 96.8 | 5 | Petrova Gora | R. Banovina |
| 6) | | 96.8 | 10 | Brac | Ultra FM |
| 17) | | 96.9 | 80 | Ucka | R. Istra |
| 55) | | 97.1 | 4 | Gospic | R. Gospic |
| 2) | | 97.3 | 1 | Pula | Otvoreni R. |
| 56) | | 97.6 | 4 | Hvar | R. Makarska Rivijera |
| 2) | | 97.7 | 3 | Pag | Otvoreni R. |
| 17) | | 98.0 | 5 | Pula | R. Istra |
| 4) | | 98.0 | 3 | Zagreb | Laganini FM |
| 47) | | 98.0 | 1.5 | Cakovec | Hrvatski R. Cakovec |
| 43) | | 98.1 | 1 | Nova Gradiška | R. Nova Gradiška |
| 56) | | 98.4 | 2 | Makarska | R. Makarska Rivijera |
| 3) | | 98.6 | 1 | Osijek | Hrvatski Katolicki R. |
| 4) | | 99.1 | 1 | Osijek | Laganini FM |
| 15) | | 99.3 | 1 | Maruševec | R. Max |
| 33) | | 99.5 | 1 | Zaprešic | Z FM |
| 13) | | 100.0 | 3 | Žuljana | R. Dalmacija |
| 3) | | 100.0 | 15 | Promina | Hrvatski Katolicki R. |
| 39) | | 100.1 | 5 | Moslavacka Gora | Bjelovarsko-Bilogorski R. |
| 38) | | 100.7 | 3 | Žirje | R. Šibenik |
| 44) | | 101.0 | 120 | Sljeme | R. 101 |
| 1) | | 101.2 | 3 | Metkovic | Narodni R. |
| 4) | | 101.3 | 1 | Slavonski Brod | Laganini FM |
| 1) | | 101.2 | 3 | Metkovic | Narodni R. |
| 48) | | 101.3 | 1 | Ilok | R. Ilok |
| 4) | | 101.3 | 1 | Slavonski Brod | Laganini FM |
| 46) | | 101.4 | 1.5 | Kutina | R. Moslavina Kutina |
| 36) | | 101.5 | 1 | Vukovar | R. Dunav |
| 25) | | 101.7 | 5 | Buje | R. Eurostar |
| 22) | | 101.8 | 1 | Zagreb | R. Martin |
| 29) | | 102.1 | 6 | Lovic | Trend R. |
| 53) | | 102.5 | 5 | Zagreb | Yammat FM |
| 2) | | 102.6 | 1.5 | Mali Lošinj | Otvoreni R. |
| 9) | | 102.7 | 1 | Brac | R. Brac |
| 49) | | 103.2 | 1 | Jazbina | R. Kraj |
| 2) | | 103.3 | 13 | Otocac | Otvoreni R. |
| 1) | | 103.5 | 30 | Labinštica | Narodni R. |
| 3) | | 103.5 | 120 | Sljeme | Hrvatski Katolicki R. |
| 2) | | 103.6 | 1 | Krk | Otvoreni R. |
| 3) | | 103.9 | 80 | Psunj | Hrvatski Katolicki R. |
| 3) | | 104.1 | 50 | Licka Plješivica | Hrvatski Katolicki R. |
| 45) | | 104.1 | 5 | Županja | Hrvatski R. Vukovar |
| 2) | | 104.2 | 1 | Komor | Otvoreni R. |
| 6) | | 104.2 | 1 | Veprinac | Totalni FM |
| 40) | | 104.2 | 1.7 | Gruda | Soundset Ragusa |
| 2) | | 104.4 | 10 | Papuk | Otvoreni R. |
| 12) | | 104.5 | 1 | Zagreb | Extra FM |
| 3) | | 104.5 | 5 | Otocac | Hrvatski Katolicki R. |

| FM | MHz | kW | Location | Station |
|---|---|---|---|---|
| 24) | 104.9 | 1 | Vidovec | R. Megaton |
| 38) | 104.9 | 5 | Šibenik | R. Šibenik |
| 13) | 105.5 | 5 | Promina | R. Dalmacija |
| 8) | 105.5 | 1 | Okucani | R. Bljesak |
| 14) | 105.6 | 1.5 | Cakovec | R. 1 |
| 2) | 105.6 | 2 | Zagreb | Otvoreni R. |
| 55) | 105.7 | 1.5 | Otocac | R. Gospic |
| 1) | 106.1 | 30 | Mirkovica | Narodni R. |
| 35) | 106.2 | 50 | Beli Manastir | Slavonski R. |
| 2) | 106.5 | 3 | Brac | Otvoreni R. |
| 3) | 106.7 | 80 | Ucka | Hrvatski Katolicki R. |
| 13) | 106.9 | 4 | Labinštica | R. Dalmacija |
| 27) | 106.9 | 2 | Marija Bistrica | R. Stubica |
| 29) | 106.9 | 2 | Karlovac | Trend R. |
| 40) | 107.0 | 20 | Srdj | Soundset Ragusa |
| 45) | 107.2 | 5 | Vinkovci | Hrvatski R. Vukovar |
| 1) | 107.3 | 1 | Kutina | Narodni R. |
| 13) | 107.3 | 1 | Komiža | R. Dalmacija |
| 2) | 107.3 | 80 | Celevac | Otvoreni R. |
| 1) | 107.5 | 2 | Zagreb | Narodni R. |
| 2) | 107.5 | 1 | Slavonski Brod | Otvoreni R. |
| 1) | 107.9 | 3 | Pag | Narodni R. |
| 3) | 107.9 | 80 | Biokovo | Hrvatski Katolicki R. |
| 3) | 107.9 | 1 | Slatina | Hrvatski Katolicki R. |

+ txs below 1kW.

**Addresses & other information:**
**1)** Avenija Veceslava Holjevca 29, 10000 Zagreb. – **2)** Cebini 28/III, 10000 Zagreb – **3)** Vocarska c. 106, 10000 Zagreb – **4)** Slavonska avenija 2, 10000 Zagreb – **5)** Avenija Veceslava Holjevca 29, 10000 Zagreb – **6)** Kralja Zvonimira 14/III 21000 Split – **7)** Trg slobode 32/3, 31300 Beli Manastir – **8)** Blazenog kardinala A. Stepinca 24, 35430 Okucani – **9)** Mladena Vodanovica 3, 21400 Supetar – **10)** Jurja Haulika 23, 43000 Bjelovar – **11)** Vitomira Širole Paje 18, 52440 Porec – **12)** Avenija Veceslava Holjevca 29, 10000 Zagreb – **13)** Kralja Zvonimira 14/2, 21000 Split – **14)** Nova ulica 7, 40305 Nedelišce – **15)** Cerje Nebojse 151, 42243 Maruševec – **16)** Zagrebacka 19, 10410 Velika Gorica – **17)** Jurja Dobrile 6, 52000 Pazin – **18)** Trg Strossmayerov 5, 10450 Jastrebarsko – **19)** Zagrebacka b.b., 48000 Koprivnica – **20)** Zagrebacka 6, 10410 Velika Gorica, – **21)** Jordanovac 110, 10000 Zagreb. – **22)** Bjelovarska 62, 10360 Zagreb – **23)** Jozefinska c. 8, 47250 Duga Resa – **24)** Varaždinska 49/a, 42205 Vidovec – **25)** Rozag 23, 52470 Umag – **26)** Mile Budaka 1, 35000 Slavonski Brod – **27)** Toplicka 5, 49240 Donja Stubica – **28)** Cehovska 81, 34000 Pozega – **29)** Trg J. Broza 2, 47000 Karlovac – **30)** Zrinsko Frankopanska 13, 23000 Zadar – **31)** Slatina Pokupska 80, 44400 Glina – **32)** F. Rusana 1/9, 33000 Virovitica – **33)** Trg zrtava fašizma 6, 10290 Zapresic – **34)** Jurja Dalmatinca 29, 32100 Vinkovci – **35)** Hrvatske Republike 20, 31000 Osijek – **36)** Kvarternika 1, 32000 Vukovar – **37)** Djure Basariceka 4, 10432 Bregana – **38)** Božidara Petranovica 3, 22000 Šibenik – **39)** Trg E. Kvarternika 7a, 43000 Bjelovar – **40)** Dr. Ante Starcevica 20, 20000 Dubrovnik – **41)** V. Nazora 19, 21480 Vis – **42)** Ambroza Vraniczanya 2, 47000 Karlovac – **43)** Gunduliceva 7, 35400 Nova Gradiška – **44)** Gajeva 10, 10000 Zagreb – **45)** Dr. Franje Tudjmana 13, 32000 Vukovar – **46)** Ivana Gorana Kovacica 25, 44320 Kutina – **47)** Trg republike 5, 40000 Cakovec – **48)** Trg Nikole Ilockog 13, 32236 Ilok – **49)** Zagrebacka bb, 48000 Koprivnica – **50)** A.Starcevica 46, 44600 Sisak – **51)** Stjepana i Antuna Radica 2, 44000 Sisak – **52)** Zagrebacka 12a, 52210 Rovinj – **53)** Baruna Filipovica 23a, 10000 Zagreb – **54)** Haendelova 4 , 10000 Zagbreb – **55)** Budacka 12, 53000 Gospic – **56)** Don Mihovila Pavlinovica 1, 21300 Makarska – **57)** Šime Ljubica 30, 21000 Hvar – **58)** Trg Dr. Franje Tudjmana 14, 47240 Slunj – **59)** Put Mulina 2, 21220 Trogir.

**DAB Transmitters (Trial)** (DAB+)
**Tx Operator: OIV M:** R. Kraj, Sjeverni FM, Koprivnica Zupan, R. Istria, Antena Zagreb, Zagorski R., Narodni R., R. Dalmacija, Gold FM, R. Banovina, Enter Zagreb, Trend R., R. Martin, R. 101, Lagagini FM.

| Bl | kW | Location | Bl | kW | Location |
|---|---|---|---|---|---|
| 9C | 1.25 | Ivancica | 9C | 5 | Sljeme |
| 9C | 1 | Mirkovica | 11C | 8 | Ucka |

## CUBA

**L.T:** UTC -5h (10 Mar-3 Nov: -4h) — **Pop:** 11.4 million — **Pr. L:** Spanish — **E.C:** 60Hz, 110V — **ITU:** CUB

**MINISTERIO DE COMUNICACIONES (MC)**
**Dirección General de Telecomunicaciones**
✉ Plaza de la Revolución, Ciudad de la Habana

**INSTITUTO CUBANO DE RADIO Y TELEVISION (ICRT)**
✉ Edif.Radiocentro, Av. 23 N° 258, Vedado, Habana 4 ☎ +53 7

8324648. Radio Cubana has links to most national and local stns:
**W:** radiocubana.cu
Hrs of tr. usually 24h – see address section for variations. Call CM—

| MW | Call | kHz | kW | Primary network, location |
|---|---|---|---|---|
| N1) | BA | 530 | 1 | R. Rebelde, Guantánamo-R.Reloj, GU |
| N1) | BA | 530 | | R. Rebelde, Caribe, IJ |
| N5) | BQ | 530 | 10 | R. Enciclopedia, Villa María, CH |
| N1) | BA | 540 | 10 | R. Rebelde, Santa Rita, Maisí, GU |
| N1) | BA | 540 | 1 | R. Rebelde, Sancti Spíritus-Progreso, SS |
| N1) | BA | 550 | 12 | R. Rebelde, Pinar del Río-San Juan, PR |
| N1) | BA | 560 | 10 | R. Rebelde, Ciego de Avila-Rebelde/Reloj, CA |
| N1) | BA | 570 | 1 | R. Rebelde, Pilón-Siguanea, GR |
| N2) | BD | 570 | 25 | R. Reloj, Santa Clara-Reloj, VC |
| N1) | BA | 580 | 2.5 | R. Rebelde, Mabujabo, GU |
| N1) | BA | 590 | 10 | R. Rebelde, Guantánamo-Burenes, GU |
| N3) | BF | 590 | 25 | R. Musical Nacional, La Julia, MB |
| N1) | BA | 600 | 50 | R. Rebelde, San Germán, HO |
| N1) | BA | 610 | 1 | R. Rebelde, Cienfuegos-Malecón, CI |
| N1) | BA | 610 | 10 | R. Rebelde, Bueycito, GR |
| N1) | BA | 610 | 10 | R. Rebelde, Guane, PR |
| N2) | BD | 610 | 1 | R. Reloj, Trinidad- R. Trinidad, SS |
| N1) | BA | 620 | 25 | R. Rebelde, Colón, MA |
| N4) | BC | 630 | 5 | R. Progreso, Camagüey-Isabel Hortensia, CM |
| N4) | BC | 640 | 10 | R. Progreso, Guanabacoa-Progreso, CH |
| N4) | BC | 640 | 10 | R. Progreso, Las Tunas-Progreso, LT |
| N4) | BC | 650 | 10 | R. Progreso, Ciego de Avila-Surco/Progreso, CA |
| N1) | BA | 650 | 5 | R. Rebelde, Santiago de Cuba-Eide, SC |
| N4) | BC | 660 | 12 | R. Progreso, Jovellanos, MA |
| N1) | BA | 670 | 5 | R. Rebelde, Bahía Honda, AR |
| N1) | BA | 670 | 10 | R. Rebelde, Central Brasil, Jaronú, CM |
| N1) | BA | 670 | 10 | R. Rebelde, Camagüey-Villa Rosita, CM |
| N1) | BA | 670 | 50 | R. Rebelde, Arroyo Arenas, CH |
| N1) | BA | 670 | 5 | R. Rebelde, Morón, CA |
| N1) | BA | 670 | 10 | R. Rebelde, El Coco, HO |
| N1) | BA | 670 | | R. Rebelde, Mayarí, HO |
| N1) | BA | 670 | | R. Rebelde, Caribe, IJ |
| N1) | BA | 670 | 10 | R. Rebelde, Las Tunas-Rebelde1180, LT |
| N5) | BQ | 670 | 1 | R. Enciclopedia, Cárdenas-2, MA |
| N1) | BA | 670 | 5 | R. Rebelde, Matanzas-Circunvalación, MA |
| N1) | BA | 670 | 1 | R. Rebelde, Los Palacios, PR |
| N1) | BA | 670 | 1 | R. Rebelde, Pinar del Río-Coloma, PR |
| N1) | BA | 670 | 1 | R. Rebelde, Santa Lucía, PR |
| N1) | BA | 670 | 50 | R. Rebelde, Santa Clara-Rebelde670, VC |
| N4) | BC | 690 | 5 | R. Progreso, Santiago de Cuba-Sta. María, SC |
| N4) | BC | 690 | 10 | R. Progreso, Santa Clara-Progreso, VC |
| N1) | BA | 710 | 25 | R. Rebelde, Camagüey-Tagarro, CM |
| N1) | BA | 710 | 200 | R. Rebelde, Chambas-Centro 6, CA |
| N1) | BA | 710 | 50 | R. Rebelde, Cacocúm, HO |
| N1) | BA | 710 | 50 | R. Rebelde, Martí-Centro 5, MA |
| N1) | BA | 710 | 50 | R. Rebelde, La Julia, MB |
| PR01) | AM | 710 | 1 | R. Guamá, La Palma, PR |
| N1) | BA | 710 | 1 | R. Rebelde, Yaguajay, SS |
| N1) | BA | 710 | 50 | R. Rebelde, Santa Clara-Reloj, VC |
| N1) | BC | 720 | 2.5 | R. Progreso, Mabujabo, GU |
| N4) | BC | 730 | 10 | R. Progreso, La Fe-Progreso, IJ |
| HO01) | KO | 740 | 10 | R. Angulo, Sagua de Tánamo, HO |
| N4) | BC | 750 | 10 | R. Progreso, Palmira, CI |
| N4) | BC | 760 | 10 | R. Progreso, Guane, PR |
| N4) | BC | 760 | | R. Progreso, Mayarí Arriba-II Frente1, SC |
| N1) | BA | 770 | 10 | R. Rebelde, Las Tunas-Victoria, LT |
| AR01) | CW | 770 | 10 | R. Artemisa, La Salud, AR |
| N2) | BD | 790 | 10 | R. Reloj, Holguín, HO |
| N2) | BD | 790 | 25 | R. Reloj, Pinar del Río-Politécnico, PR |
| N4) | BC | 810 | 10 | R. Progreso, Guantánamo-Burenes, GU |
| N2) | BD | 820 | 10 | R. Reloj, Ciego de Avila-Rebelde/Reloj, CA |
| CH02) | BU | 820 | 10 | R. Ciudad Habana, Arroyo Arenas, CH |
| N4) | BC | 820 | 1 | R. Progreso, Moa-Rolo Monterrey, HO |
| N2) | J | 830 | | CMKC R. Revolucion, Mayarí Arriba-II Frente2, SC |
| SC01) | J | 840 | 1 | CMKC R. Revolucion, Palma Soriano, SC |
| VC01) | E | 840 | 10 | R. CMHW, Santa Clara-CMHW, VC |
| N2) | BD | 850 | 1 | R. Reloj, Nueva Gerona, IJ |
| N4) | BC | 850 | 1 | R. Progreso, Trinidad-Tetraplexer, SS |
| N2) | BD | 850 | | R. Reloj, Bolondrón, MA |
| N2) | BD | 870 | 1 | R. Reloj, Bueycito, GR |
| N2) | BD | 870 | 10 | R. Reloj, Baracoa-Van Van, GU |
| N2) | BD | 870 | 1 | R. Reloj, Sancti Spíritus-Reloj, SS |
| N4) | BC | 880 | 12 | R. Progreso, Pinar del Río-San Juan, PR |
| N4) | BC | 890 | 200 | R. Progreso, Chambas-Centro 6, CA |
| SC01) | J | 890 | | CMKC R. Revolucion, Santiago de Cuba, SC |
| N4) | BC | 900 | 50 | R. Progreso, San Germán, HO |
| CM01) | HA | 910 | 25 | R. Cadena Agramonte, Camagüey-Tagarro, CM |
| CH03) | BL | 910 | 5 | R. Metropolitana, Villa María, CH |
| N2) | BD | 910 | 5 | R. Reloj, Bolondrón, MA |

| MW | Call | kHz | kW | Primary network, location |
|---|---|---|---|---|
| N4) | BC | 920 | 1 | R. Progreso, Pilón-Siguanea, GR |
| N2) | BD | 930 | 1 | R. Reloj, Cienfuegos-Malecón, CI |
| N2) | BD | 930 | 1 | R. Reloj, La Jaiba, MA |
| N2) | BD | 930 | 1 | R. Reloj, Stgo de Cuba-Sta.María, SC |
| N4) | BC | 940 | 1 | R. Progreso, Sancti Spíritus-Progreso, SS |
| N2) | BD | 950 | 10 | R. Reloj, Camagüey-Isabel Hortensia, CM |
| N2) | BD | 950 | 10 | R. Reloj, Arroyo Arenas, HA |
| N2) | KC | 950 | 1 | R. R. Reloj, Mayarí Arriba-II Frente1, SC |
| N2) | BD | 960 | 10 | R. Reloj, Guantánamo-La Piña, GU |
| PR01) | AM | 970 | 5 | R. Guamá, Los Palacios, PR |
| N1) | BA | 970 | 1 | R. Rebelde, Trinidad-Tetraplexer, SS |
| CH04) | B | 980 | 2.5 | R. COCO, El Sapo, CH |
| N2) | BD | 980 | 1 | R. Reloj, Moa-Rolo Monterrey, HO |
| PR01) | AM | 990 | 25 | R. Guamá, Pinar del Río-Politécnico, PR |
| AR01) | CW | 1000 | 10 | R. Artemisa, Artemisa, AR |
| GR02) | NM | 1000 | 1 | R. Granma, Media Luna, GR |
| AR01) | CW | 1020 | 5 | R. Artemisa, Bahía Honda AR |
| GU01) | M | 1020 | 10 | CMKS R. Trinchera Antiimp., Baracoa-Van Van, GU |
| N2) | BD | 1020 | 1 | R. Reloj, Las Tunas-Progreso, LT |
| PR01) | AM | 1020 | 1 | R. Guamá, Santa Lucía, PR |
| MB01) | CL | 1040 | 10 | R. Mayabeque, Güines, MB |
| LT01) | LL | 1050 | 10 | R. Victoria, Las Tunas-Victoria, LT |
| MA02) | DL | 1060 | 25 | CMGW R. 26, Jovellanos, MA |
| GU01) | M | 1070 | 10 | CMKS R. Trinchera Antiimp., Guant.-Burenes, GU |
| PR01) | AM | 1070 | 10 | R. Guamá, Guane, PR |
| CA01) | IP | 1080 | 10 | R. Surco, Ciego de Ávila-Surco/Progreso, CA |
| CH01) | CH | 1080 | 5 | R. Cadena Habana, Villa María, CH |
| LT01) | LL | 1090 | 1 | R. Victoria, Amancio, LT |
| HO01) | KO | 1100 | 1 | R. Angulo, Mayarí, HO |
| HO01) | KO | 1110 | 10 | R. Angulo, Holguín, HO |
| N1) | BA | 1130 | | R. Rebelde, Imías, GU |
| CA01) | IP | 1140 | 25 | R. Surco, Morón, CA |
| CI01) | FL | 1140 | | R. Ciudad del Mar, Cienfuegos-Malecón, CI |
| CM02) | BQ | 1140 | 1 | R. Camagüey, Camagüey-Isabel Hortensia,CM |
| GR01) | NL | 1140 | 1 | R. Bayamo, Media Luna, GR |
| MA02) | DP | 1140 | 1 | R. Ciudad Bandera, Cárdenas-2, MA |
| MB01) | CL | 1140 | 25 | R. Mayabeque, La Salud, MB |
| N1) | BA | 1140 | 10 | R. Rebelde, Aguada, CI |
| N1) | BA | 1140 | | R. Rebelde, Guantánamo-La Piña, GU |
| N1) | BA | 1140 | | R. Rebelde, Caribe, IJ |
| N1) | BA | 1140 | 5 | R. Rebelde, Matanzas-Circunvalación, MA |
| N3) | BF | 1140 | 10 | R. Musical Nacional, Santa Clara-Progreso, VC |
| GR01) | NL | 1150 | 10 | R. Bayamo, Entronque Bueycito, GR |
| GR01) | NL | 1160 | 1 | R. Bayamo, Pilón-Siguanea, GR |
| GU01) | M | 1170 | 10 | CMKS R. Trinchera Antiimp., Sta. Rita, Maisí, GU |
| N1) | BA | 1180 | 10 | R. Rebelde, Artemisa, AR |
| N1) | BA | 1180 | 5 | R. Rebelde, Bahía Honda, AR |
| N1) | BA | 1180 | 1 | R. Rebelde, San Cristóbal, AR |
| N1) | BA | 1180 | 10 | R. Rebelde, Central Brasil, Jaronú CM |
| N1) | BA | 1180 | 50 | R. Rebelde, Camagüey-Villa Rosita, CM |
| N1) | BA | 1180 | | R. Rebelde, Guámaro, CM |
| N1) | BA | 1180 | 10 | R. Rebelde, Arroyo Arenas, CH |
| N1) | BA | 1180 | 50 | R. Rebelde, Guanabacoa, CH |
| N1) | BA | 1180 | 10 | R. Rebelde, Santa Catalina, CH |
| N1) | BA | 1180 | 1 | R. Rebelde, Ciego de Avila-Rebelde/Reloj, CA |
| N1) | BA | 1180 | 50 | R. Rebelde, Chambas-Centro 6, CA |
| N1) | BA | 1180 | 5 | R. Rebelde, Cienfuegos-1ra Tulipán, CI |
| N1) | BA | 1180 | 10 | R. Rebelde, Guantánamo-Radio Reloj, GU |
| GU02) | DX | 1180 | 1 | CMDX R. Baracoa "LV del Toa", Mabujabo, GU |
| N1) | BA | 1180 | 1 | R. Rebelde, Banes, HO |
| N1) | BA | 1180 | 50 | R. Rebelde, Cacocúm, HO |
| N1) | BA | 1180 | 10 | R. Rebelde, Moa-Rolo Monterrey, HO |
| N1) | BA | 1180 | 5 | R. Rebelde, Sagua de Tánamo, HO |
| N1) | BA | 1180 | 1 | R. Rebelde, Nueva Gerona, IJ |
| N1) | BA | 1180 | 1 | R. Rebelde, Puerto Padre, LT |
| N1) | BA | 1180 | 10 | R. Rebelde, Las Tunas-Rebelde1180, LT |
| N1) | BA | 1180 | | R. Rebelde, Bolondrón, MA |
| N1) | BA | 1180 | 5 | R. Rebelde, Cárdenas-1, MA |
| N1) | BA | 1180 | 25 | R. Rebelde, Colón, MA |
| N1) | BA | 1180 | 5 | R. Rebelde, Matanzas-La Jaiba, MA |
| N1) | BA | 1180 | 200 | R. Rebelde, Martí-Centro 5, MA |
| N1) | BA | 1180 | 10 | R. Rebelde, Güines, MB |
| N1) | BA | 1180 | | R. Rebelde, Hectométrico, MB |
| N1) | BA | 1180 | 10 | R. Rebelde, Sta Cruz del Norte-La Sierrita, MB |
| N1) | BA | 1180 | | R. Rebelde, Pinar del Río-Coloma, PR |
| N1) | BA | 1180 | 10 | R. Rebelde, La Palma, PR |
| N1) | BA | 1180 | 10 | R. Rebelde, Los Palacios, PR |
| N1) | BA | 1180 | 1 | R. Rebelde, Santa Lucía, PR |
| N1) | BA | 1180 | 1 | R. Rebelde, Sancti Spíritus-Progreso, SS |
| N1) | BA | 1180 | 1 | R. Rebelde, Mayarí Arriba-II Frente1, SC |
| N1) | BQ | 1180 | | R. Rebelde, Santiago de Cuba-Eide, SC |
| N1) | BA | 1180 | | R. Rebelde, Corralillo, VC |
| N1) | BA | 1180 | 10 | R. Rebelde, Sagua la Grande, VC |
| N1) | BA | 1180 | 10 | R. Rebelde, Santa Clara-CMHW, VC |
| SC02) | JD | 1190 | 10 | R. Coral/R. Revolución, Chivirico, SC |
| SS01) | GL | 1190 | 1 | R. Sancti Spíritus, Trinidad-Tetraplexer, SS |
| SS01) | GL | 1200 | 1 | R. Sancti Spíritus, Yaguajay, SS |
| N1) | BA | 1210 | | R. Rebelde, Las Tunas-Progreso, LT |
| SS01) | GL | 1210 | 10 | R. Sancti Spíritus, Sancti Spíritus-Reloj, SS |
| IJ01) | BY | 1220 | 10 | R. Caribe, La Fe-Progreso, IJ |
| N4) | BC | 1230 | | R. Progreso, Bayamo, GR |
| GU01) | M | 1250 | 1 | CMKS R. Trinchera Antimperialista, Imías, GU |
| N4) | BC | 1260 | 2.5 | R. Progreso, Media Luna, GR |
| N5) | BQ | 1280 | | R. Enciclopedia, Trinidad-RadioTrinidad, SC |
| SC03) | JN | 1280 | 1 | R. Mambí, Santiago de Cuba-Sta.María, SC |
| SC04) | JB | 1300 | | R. Titán, Palma Soriano, SC |
| N5) | BQ | 1310 | 1 | R. Enciclopedia, Nueva Gerona, IJ |
| AR01) | CW | 1320 | | R. Artemisa, San Cristóbal, AR |
| HO02) | KA | 1320 | | Ecos de Sagua, Sagua de Tánamo, HO |
| MA01) | DL | 1320 | 1 | CMGW R. 26, Matanzas-La Jaiba, MA |
| CI01) | FL | 1340 | 10 | R. Ciudad del Mar, Palmira, CI |
| CI01) | FL | 1350 | 10 | R. Ciudad del Mar, Aguada, CI |
| LT03) | LM | 1350 | 1 | R. Libertad, Puerto Padre, LT |
| GU03) | MA | 1370 | 1 | R. Playita, Imías, GU |
| HO01) | KO | 1380 | 1 | R. Angulo, Banes, HO |
| VC02) | ES | 1400 | 1 | R. Sagua, Sagua la Grande, VC |
| LT02) | LN | 1450 | 1 | R. Maboas, Amancio Rodríguez, LT |
| MB01) | CL | 1450 | 1 | R. Mayabeque, Sta. Cruz del Norte-La Sierrita, MB |
| SC05) | JL | 1460 | | R. 8SF, Mayarí Arriba-II Frente2, SC |
| LT04) | LB | 1470 | 1 | R. Chaparra, Puerto Padre, LT |
| HO03) | KN | 1490 | 1 | R. Mayarí, Mayarí, HO |
| SC06) | KZ | 1520 | | R. Baraguá "LV del Cauto", Palma Soriano, SC |
| N1) | BA | 1550 | | R. Rebelde, San Cristóbal, AR |
| N1) | BA | 1550 | 5 | R. Rebelde, Cienfuegos-1ra Tulipán, CI |
| N1) | BA | 1550 | | R. Rebelde, Guáimaro, CM |
| N1) | BA | 1550 | | R. Rebelde, Jayamá, CM |
| N1) | BA | 1550 | 10 | R. Rebelde, Santa Catalina, CH |
| N1) | BA | 1550 | | R. Rebelde, Guantánamo-La Piña, GU |
| N1) | BA | 1550 | 5 | R. Rebelde, Cárdenas-2, MA |
| N1) | BA | 1550 | 5 | R. Rebelde, Matanzas-Circunvalación, MA |
| N1) | BA | 1550 | | R. Rebelde, Hectométrico, MB |
| N4) | BC | 1550 | | R. Progreso, La Palma, PR |
| N1) | BA | 1550 | 1 | R. Rebelde, Yaguajay, SS |
| N1) | BA | 1550 | | R. Rebelde, Corralillo, VC |
| N4) | BA | 1550 | 1 | R. Progreso, Sagua La Grande, VC |
| N1) | BA | 1550 | 10 | R. Rebelde, Santa Clara-Rebelde670, VC |
| N1) | BA | 1620 | | R. Rebelde, El Sapo, CH |
| N1) | BA | 1620 | 1 | R. Rebelde, Guantánamo-R.Reloj, GU |
| N1) | BA | 1620 | | R. Rebelde, El Coco, HO |
| N1) | BA | 1620 | | R. Rebelde, Amancio Rodríguez, LT |
| GR01) | NL | 1620 | | R. Rebelde, Bayamo, GR |

| SW | Call | kHz | kW | Primary network, location |
|---|---|---|---|---|
| N4) | | 4765 | 50 | R. Progreso, La Habana (Bejucal): 0130-0500 |
| N1) | BA | 5025 | 100 | R. Rebelde, La Habana (Bauta) |

**Provinces:** AR=Artemisa CA=Ciego de Avila CH=Ciudad Habana CI=Cienfuegos CM=Camagüey GR=Granma GU=Guantánamo HA=Habana HO=Holguín IJ=Isla de laJuventud LT=Las Tunas MA=Matanzas MB=Mayabeque PR=Pinar del Río SC=Santiago de Cuba SS=Sancti Spíritus VC=Villa Clara

**NB:** Esp. at night stns rel. an upper level stn, i.e. municipal stn rel. provincial stn and provincial stn rel. nat. stn. Own prgrm for smallest stns is only few hrs per day. R. Rebelde carries sports events which are rel. by many other stns and other rel. may occur. Most txs operate 24h.

| FM | MHz | Call | Station | Location |
|---|---|---|---|---|
| N6) | 89.1 | BV | R. Taíno | Loma de la Cruz, HO |
| N1) | 90.3 | BA | R. Rebelde | El Mamey, GR |
| N4) | 90.3 | BC | R. Progreso | Loma de la Cruz, CH |
| N5) | 90.3 | BQ | R. Enciclopedia | Cienfuegos, CI |
| N2) | 90.5 | BD | R. Reloj | TV Guanito, PR |
| N6) | 90.5 | BV | R. Taíno | Guardalavaca, HO |
| N1) | 91.1 | BA | R. Rebelde | Guamá, SC |
| N5) | 91.1 | BQ | R. Enciclopedia | Cumbre, MA |
| N5) | 91.1 | BQ | R. Enciclopedia | San Isidro, SS |
| N6) | 91.5 | BV | R. Taíno | TV Tunas, LT |
| N4) | 91.7 | BC | R. Progreso | La Vigía, SS |
| N2) | 91.9 | BD | R. Reloj | TV Miraflores, HO |
| N7) | 91.9 | BR | Habana R. | Plan Mangos, CI |
| N1) | 92.1 | BA | R. Rebelde | El Brinco, MA |
| N4) | 92.3 | BC | R. Progreso | El Mamey, GR |
| N5) | 92.5 | BQ | R. Enciclopedia | Cayo Santa María, VC |
| N7) | 92.5 | BR | Habana R. | San Isidro, SS |
| N1) | 92.7 | BA | R. Rebelde | Topes de Collantes, SS |

| FM | MHz | Call | Station | Location |
|---|---|---|---|---|
| N3) | 92.7 | BF | R. Musical Nacional | Bayamo, GR |
| N3) | 92.7 | BF | R. Musical Nacional | Cienfuegos, CI |
| N5) | 92.7 | BQ | R. Enciclopedia | Sierra Caballos, IJ |
| N6) | 92.9 | BV | R. Taíno | Cunagua, CA |
| N7) | 92.9 | BR | Habana R. | Loma dos Hermanas, VC |
| N4) | 93.3 | BC | R. Progreso | Los Guineos, GU |
| N6) | 93.3 | BV | R. Taíno | Loma de la Cruz, CH |
| N6) | 93.3 | BV | R. Taíno | TV FM Camagüey, CM |
| N6) | 93.3 | BV | R. Taíno | Viñales, PR |
| N1) | 93.7 | BA | R. Rebelde | La Vigía, SS |
| N3) | 93.7 | BF | R. Musical Nacional | Cumbre, MA |
| N5) | 93.7 | BQ | R. Enciclopedia | Bayamo, GR |
| N5) | 93.7 | BV | R. Taíno | Sierra Caballos, IJ |
| N3) | 93.9 | BF | R. Musical Nacional | San Isidro, SS |
| N4) | 93.9 | BC | R. Progreso | TV Miraflores, HO |
| N6) | 93.9 | BV | R. Taíno | Corralillo -CMHW, VC |
| N5) | 94.1 | BQ | R. Enciclopedia | Estudio Manzanillo, GR |
| N5) | 94.1 | BQ | R. Enciclopedia | Loma de la Cruz, CH |
| N2) | 94.3 | BD | R. Reloj | Los Guineos, GU |
| N2) | 94.5 | BD | R. Reloj | TV Tunas, LT |
| N4) | 94.5 | BC | R. Progreso | El Brinco, MA |
| N1) | 94.7 | BA | R. Rebelde | Corralillo -CMHW, VC |
| N1) | 94.7 | BA | R. Rebelde | TV Cajalbana, PR |
| N2) | 94.7 | BD | R. Reloj | Cienfuegos, CI |
| N6) | 94.7 | BV | R. Taíno | S.Miguel Baños Jacán, MA |
| N7) | 94.7 | BR | Habana R. | Sierra Caballos, IJ |
| N7) | 94.9 | BR | Habana R. | TV FM Camagüey, CM |
| N6) | 95.1 | BV | R. Taíno | Majayara, GU |
| N7) | 95.1 | BR | Habana R. | TV Guanito, PR |
| N1) | 95.5 | BA | R. Rebelde | Candelaria-TV Salón, AR |
| N1) | 95.5 | BA | R. Rebelde | TV la Capitana, PR |
| N4) | 95.7 | BC | R. Progreso | Corralillo, VC |
| N2) | 95.9 | BD | R. Reloj | San Isidro, SS |
| N7) | 95.9 | BR | Habana R. | TV Tunas, LT |
| N5) | 96.3 | BQ | R. Enciclopedia | Cueva Arriba, GU |
| N3) | 96.5 | BF | R. Musical Nacional | Sierra Caballos, IJ |
| N1) | 96.7 | BA | R. Rebelde | Bayamo, GR |
| N1) | 96.7 | BA | R. Rebelde | Loma de la Cruz, CH |
| N1) | 96.7 | BA | R. Rebelde | TV Miraflores, HO |
| N2) | 96.7 | BD | R. Reloj | Loma dos Hermanas, VC |
| N5) | 97.1 | BQ | R. Enciclopedia | Los Guineos, GU |
| N6) | 97.1 | BV | R. Taíno | Puerto Boniato, SC |
| N1) | 97.5 | BA | R. Rebelde | Bartolomé Masó, GR |
| N3) | 97.5 | BF | R. Musical Nacional | TV FM Camagüey, CM |
| N4) | 97.5 | BC | R. Progreso | Candelaria-TV Salón, AR |
| N4) | 97.5 | BC | R. Progreso | Cueva Arriba, GU |
| N5) | 97.5 | BV | R. Taíno | Loma dos Hermanas, VC |
| N1) | 97.9 | BA | R. Rebelde | Los Guineos, GU |
| N2) | 98.1 | BD | R. Reloj | TV Ciego de Ávila, CA |
| N3) | 98.1 | BF | R. Musical Nacional | Los Guineos, GU |
| N5) | 98.1 | BQ | R. Enciclopedia | Puerto Boniato, SC |
| N2) | 98.3 | BF | R. Musical Nacional | TV Tunas, LT |
| N3) | 98.5 | BF | R. Musical Nacional | Cueva Arriba, GU |
| N2) | 98.7 | BD | R. Reloj | Loma de la Cruz, HO |
| N3) | 98.7 | BF | R. Musical Nacional | TV Guanito, PR |
| N7) | 98.7 | BR | Habana R. | Cumbre, MA |
| N7) | 98.7 | BR | Playa Habana R. | Caibarién Playa, VC |
| N1) | 99.1 | BA | R. Rebelde | TV Tunas, LT |
| N3) | 99.1 | BF | R. Musical Nacional | Loma de la Cruz, CH |
| N3) | 99.3 | BA | R. Rebelde | TV Ciego de Ávila, CA |
| N1) | 99.3 | BC | R. Progreso | Puerto Boniato, SC |
| N1) | 99.5 | BA | R. Rebelde | TV Guanito, PR |
| N4) | 99.9 | BC | R. Progreso | Loma de la Cruz, HO |
| N6) | 100.1 | BV | R. Taíno | La Vigía, SS |
| N1) | 100.3 | BA | R. Rebelde | S.Miguel Baños Jacán, MA |
| N3) | 100.3 | BF | R. Musical Nacional | Puerto Boniato, SC |
| N4) | 100.3 | BC | R. Progreso | TV Las Llamadas, SS |
| N4) | 100.5 | BC | R. Progreso | Sierra Caballos, IJ |
| N5) | 100.5 | BQ | R. Enciclopedia | TV FM Camagüey, CM |
| N1) | 100.7 | BA | R. Rebelde | Cueva Arriba, GU |
| N3) | 100.7 | BF | R. Musical Nacional | Loma Dos Hermanas, VC |
| N5) | 100.7 | BQ | R. Enciclopedia | Candelaria-TV Salón, AR |
| N4) | 100.9 | BC | R. Progreso | TV Ciego De Ávila, CA |
| N5) | 101.1 | BQ | R. Enciclopedia | TV Tunas, LT |
| N1) | 101.5 | BA | R. Rebelde | TV FM Camagüey, CM |
| N2) | 101.5 | BD | R. Reloj | Televilla, CH |
| N6) | 101.5 | BV | R. Taíno | Guisa, GR |
| N7) | 101.5 | BR | Habana R. | Puerto Boniato, SC |
| N4) | 101.9 | BC | R. Progreso | S.Miguel Baños Jacán, MA |
| N4) | 101.9 | BC | R. Progreso | TV Guanito, PR |
| N4) | 101.9 | BC | R. Progreso | TV Tunas, LT |
| N7) | 101.9 | BR | Habana R. | Cueva Arriba, GU |
| N2) | 102.1 | BD | R. Reloj | TV Punta Alegre, CA |
| N1) | 102.3 | BA | R. Rebelde | Puerto Boniato, SC |
| N2) | 102.3 | BD | R. Reloj | TV FM Camagüey, CM |
| N5) | 102.3 | BQ | R. Enciclopedia | Loma dos Hermanas, VC |
| N5) | 102.7 | BQ | R. Enciclopedia | Loma de la Cruz, HO |
| N5) | 102.7 | BQ | R. Enciclopedia | TV Guanito, PR |
| N7) | 102.9 | BR | Habana R. | La Vigía, SS |
| N2) | 103.1 | BD | R. Reloj | Puerto Boniato, SC |
| N4) | 103.1 | BC | R. Progreso | Bartolomé Masó, GR |
| N4) | 103.1 | BC | R. Progreso | Loma dos Hermanas, VC |
| N4) | 103.1 | BC | R. Progreso | TV FM Camagüey, CM |
| N1) | 103.5 | BA | R. Rebelde | Loma de la Cruz, CH |
| N2) | 103.5 | BD | R. Reloj | S.Miguel Baños Jacán, MA |
| N7) | 103.5 | BR | Habana R. | TV Ciego de Ávila, CA |
| N1) | 103.9 | BA | R. Rebelde | Plan Mangos, CI |
| N1) | 103.9 | BA | R. Rebelde | San Antonio del Sur, GU |
| N2) | 104.1 | BD | R. Reloj | Sierra Caballos, IJ |
| N7) | 104.1 | BR | Habana R. | Bayamo, GR |
| N6) | 104.5 | BV | R. Taíno | Bartolomé Masó, GR |
| N1) | 104.7 | BA | R. Rebelde | Loma dos Hermanas, VC |
| N2) | 105.1 | BD | R. Reloj | Cueva Arriba, GU |
| N1) | 105.7 | BA | R. Rebelde | Sierra Caballos, IJ |
| N1) | 105.7 | BA | R. Rebelde | TV Tamarindo, CA |
| N3) | 105.7 | BF | R. Musical Nacional | Loma de la Cruz, HO |
| N6) | 105.9 | BV | R. Taíno | Cueva Arriba, GU |
| N6) | 105.9 | BV | R. Taíno | Cumbre, MA |
| N1) | 106.3 | BA | R. Rebelde | TV Ciego de Ávila, CA |
| N4) | 106.3 | BC | R. Progreso | Cumbre, MA |
| N4) | 106.3 | BC | R. Progreso | Focsa, CH |
| N4) | 106.3 | BC | R. Progreso | TV St. Cruz del Norte, MB |
| N5) | 106.3 | BQ | R. Enciclopedia | S.Miguel Baños Jacán, MA |
| N7) | 106.9 | BR | Habana R. | Loma de la Cruz, CH |
| N7) | 106.9 | BR | Habana R. (e) | Habana Radio, CH |
| N1) | 107.9 | BA | R. Rebelde | Cumbre, MA |
| N1) | 107.9 | BA | R. Rebelde | Sagua la Grande, VC |
| N1) | 107.9 | BA | R. Rebelde | TV St. Cruz del Norte, MB |
| N1) | 107.9 | BA | R. Rebelde | Alamar San Pedro, CH |
| N3) | 107.9 | BF | R. Musical Nacional | S.Miguel Baños Jacán, MA |
| N6) | 107.9 | BV | R. Taíno | Plan Mangos, CI |
| N6) | 107.9 | BV | R. Taíno | San Isidro , SS |
| N6) | 107.9 | BV | R. Taíno | TV Ciego de Ávila, CA |

**Provincial & Municipal FM Stations** (MHz):

**AR) R. Artemisa:** 90.7 Candelaria, 90.9 Bahía Honda, 91.5 San Cristóbal, 92.1 Artemisa, 92.9 Alquízar, 93.7 Mariel, 94.5 Guanajay, 96.1 Bauta, 102.3 Candelaria-TV Salón, 104.1 Güira de Melena, 105.7 Caimito – **R. Ariguanabo:** 105.3 & 107.5 S.Antonio de los Baños

**CA) R. Surco:** 91.5 TV Ciego de Ávila, 93.7 Ciro Redondo, 94.1 Bolivia, 95.3 TV Ciego de Ávila, 96.1 Baraguá, 101.3 Tamarindo, 101.7 Majagua, 102.7 TV Ciego de Ávila, 107.9 TV Punta Alegre – **R. Morón:** 90.1 TV Tamarindo, 98.9 Morón – **R. Chambas:** 90.7 Estudios Chambas – **R. Amanecer:** 96.9 Primero de Enero

**CH) R. Cadena Habana:** 99.9 Televilla – **R. Ciudad Habana:** 94.7 Habana Libre, 94.7 Televilla – **R. Metropolitana:** 98.3 Habana Libre – **R. Coco:** 91.7 Habana Libre – **R. Habana Cuba:** 102.5 Focsa, 103.2 La Habana

**CI) R. Ciudad del Mar:** 91.1 Palmira, 95.9 Rodas, 98.5 Lajas, 98.9 Estudio Cienfuegos, 101.1 Abreus, 106.3 Plan Mangos – **R. Cumanayagua:** 95.1 Estud. Cumanayagua, 105.5 Crucecitas – **R. Cruces** "LV de los Molinos": 99.3 Cruces – **Aguada R.:** 105.1 Aguada

**CM) R. Cadena Agramonte:** 92.5 Jimaguayú, 96.7 Sibanicú, 99.7 Najasa, 105.3 TV FM Camagüey, 105.9 FM Sta. Cruz del Sur – **R. Guáimaro:** 90.3 Estudios Guáimaro – **R. Cubitas:** 95.7 Estudios Cubitas – **La Voz del Bayatabo:** 98.5 Minas – **R. Nuevitas:** 103.5 TV Nuevitas – **R. Santa Cruz:** 104.3 Sta. Cruz del Sur – **R. Florida:** 104.5 Florida Etecsa – **R. Esmeralda:** 105.9 Esmeralda – R. Vertientes: 104.1 Vertientes

**GR) CMKX R. Bayamo:** 90.1 Cauto Cristo, 90.7 Yara, 91.7 Campechuela, 96.3 Media Luna, 99.5 Bartolomé Masó, 100.3 Río Cauto, 102.1 Comunitaria Masó, 104.7 Comunitaria, 105.9 Buey Arriba – **R. Granma:** 96.5 Estudio Manzanillo – **CMND R. Jiguaní:** 91.9 Estudios Jiguaní – **R. Portada de la Libertad:** 95.1 El Mamey, 100.7 Niquero – **R. Ciudad Monumento:** 95.3 Bayamo

**GU) CMKS R. Trinch.Antiimp:** 92.1 Niceto Pérez, 93.1 Manuel Tames, 93.7 El Salvador, 94.7 Yateras, 95.5 Cueva Arriba, 99.9 Los Guineos, 100.3 Imías – **CMDX R. Baracoa:** 90.1 Los Guineos – **La Voz del Sol:** 91.1 Estudio Maisí – **R. Bahía:** 104.3 Estudios Caimanera

**HO) R. Angulo:** 91.7 Cueto, 92.9 Báguanos, 93.9 Rafael Freyre, 94.1 Cacocum, 95.1 Antillas, 97.7 Loma de la Cruz, 102.1 Frank País – **Ecos de Sagua:** 102.9 TV Miraflores – **La Voz del Níquel:** 92.7 TV Miraflores – **R. Juvenil:** 93.7 Calixto García, 93.7 Estudios C. García – **R. Gibara:** 94.9 Velasco, 107.9 Gibara – **R. Holguín:** 96.1 Loma de la Cruz

– **R. SG** "LV del Azucar": 106.9 Estudios San Germán
**IJ) R. Caribe:** 93.5 Cocodrilo, 101.7 Sierra Caballos
**LT) R. Victoria:** 95.5 Puerto Padre, 103.9 Jobabo, 104.9 TV Tunas – **R. Libertad:** 93.3 Puerto Padre, 93.3 Puerto Padre – **R. Chaparra:** 90.9 Jesús Menéndez – **R. Manatí** "LV del Faro": 92.9 Estudios Manatí
**MA) CMGW R. 37:** 90.1 Jovellanos, 90.5 Los Arabos, 91.5 Perico, 92.1 Limonar, 92.7 Pedro Betancourt, 93.1 Martí, 96.3 Unión de Reyes, 97.3 Estudios Matanzas, 97.7 Calimete, 99.5 Ciénaga de Zapata, 99.9 El Brinco, 104.3 S.Miguel Baños Jacán – **R. Ciudad Bandera:** 99.7 Cárdenas – **R. Victoria de Girón:** 93.7 Ciénaga de Zapata, 95.3 Jagüey Grande – **R. Varadero:** 98.1 Varadero – **La Voz de la Victoria:** 99.5 Ciénaga de Zapata, 99.9 El Brinco – **R. Llanura de Colón:** 101.1 Colón
**MB) R. Mayabeque:** 90.7 Nueva Paz, 91.3 Madruga, 91.9 San Nicolás, 92.5 Batabanó, 95.9 Güines, 102.7 Bejucal, 104.7 Televilla, CH, 105.9 Melena del Sur – **R. Jaruco:** 92.3 Jaruco, 105.1 Loma Travieso – **CMCW R. Camoa:** 97.9 TV Loma la Candela, 103.9 S. José de Las Lajas – **La Voz del Litoral:** 102.5 TV St. Cruz del Norte
**PR) R. Guamá:** 90.1 La Palma, 91.3 San Juan y Martínez, 92.3 Los Palacios, 92.5 Viñales, 93.1 San Luis, 96.3 Cajalbana, 96.7 Consolación del Sur, 96.7 Mantua, 103.5 TV Guanito, 105.1 Guane – **R. Sandino:** 98.5 Estudios Sandino – **R. Minas:** 104.9 Estudios Minas de M
**SC) CMKC R. Revolución:** 95.1 Puerto Boniato – **CMKW R. Mambí:** 93.7 Puerto Boniato – **R. Titán:** 96.9 Estudios Mella – **R. 8SF:** 92.3 Estudios II Frente – **CMKZ R. Baraguá:** 91.3 Palma Soriano – **CMDV R. Siboney:** 90.5 Puerto Boniato – **R. Triple M/CMKC:** 92.5 Estudios III Frente – **R. Grito de Baire:** 103.9 Estudios Cotramestre – **R. Majagüabo:** 104.7 Estudios San Luis – **Sonido SM:** 105.5 Estud. Songo-La Maya
**SS) R. Sancti Spíritus:** 90.5 Fomento, 90.7 Topes de Collantes, 93.1 Taguasco, 96.5 La Vigía, 106.3 San Isidro, 106.3 TV las Llamadas, – **R. Trinidad:** 90.1 Trinidad – **R. Vitral/R.Sancti Spíritus:** 101.1 San Isidro – **R. Jatibonico:** 105.1 Jatibonico – **La Voz de Cabaiguán:** 105.5 Cabaiguán – **R. Yaguajay:** 91.3 Yaguajay, 94.5 TV las Llamadas
**VC) CMHW:** 92.3 Camajuani, 92.3 Corralillo, 94.3 Ranchuelo, 95.5 Santo Domingo, 99.1 Encrucijada, 99.7 Cifuentes, 101.5 Loma dos Hermanas, 105.7 Manicaragua – **R. Sagua:** 105.9 Quemado de Güines, 106.3 Sagua la Grande – **CMHS R. Caibarién:** 90.9 & 94.1 TV Caibarién, 95.7 Caibarién Playa, 107.1 Remedios – **Estereocentro:** 93.5 Loma dos Hermanas – **R. Placetas:** 94.9 Placetas

**Addresses: & Other Information**
**National networks: N1)** R. Rebelde, Ap. 6277, La Habana 10600 (or Edif. Del ICRT, Av. 23 N° 258, Vedado, La Habana 10400) **W:** radiorebelde.cu – **N2)** R. Reloj, Ap. 6277, Ciudad de La Habana (or Ed. Radiocentro, Calle 23 No. 258, (8avo piso), entre Ly M, Vedado, La Habana 10400 **W:** radioreloj.cu – **N3)** R. Musical Nacional, Edificio N, Calle N, entre 23 y 21, Vedado La Habana 10400 **W:** cmbfradio.cu – **N4)** R. Progreso, Ap. 4042, La Habana 10300 (or Infanta 105, Esq. A 25, Centro Habana) **W:** radioprogreso.cu – **N5)** R. Enciclopedia, Edificio N, Calle N. N° 266 (bajos), entre 21 y 23, Vedado, La Habana 10400 **W:** radioenciclopedia.cu – **N6)** R. Taíno, Ap. 6277, La Habana 10400 (or Av. 23 N° 258, Vedado, La Habana 10400) - FM only – **N7)** Lamparilla No. 2 Edificio Lonja del Comercio, 10100 La Habana **W:** habanaradio.cu - FM only
**Provincial & Municipal Stations:**
**ARTEMISA: AR01)** Calle 50 No. 2310, entre 23 y 25, Artemisa 33800 **W:** artemisaradioweb.icrt.cu
**CIEGO DE ÁVILA: CA01)** Ap. 183 (or Chicho Valdés 66), Ciego de Ávila 65100 **W:** radiosurco.icrt.cu
**CIUDAD DE LA HABANA: CH01)** Calle 15, esq. a J, No. 210, Vedado, Plaza de la Revolución, La Habana 10400 **W:** cadenahabana.cu – **CH02)** Ap. 6599, La Habana 10600 (or Calle N No. 266 (5to piso), entre 21 y 23, Vedadado, Plaza de la Revolución, La Habana 10400) **W:** radiociudadhabana.icrt.cu – **CH03)** Ed. Focsa, Calle N No. 301 (1er piso), esq. A 17, Vedado, Plaza de la Revolución, La Habana 10400 **W:** radiometropolitana.cu – **CH04)** Ed. Focsa, Calle N No. 301, esq. A 17, Vedado, Plaza de la Revolución, La Habana 10400 **W:** radiococo.icrt.cu
**CIENFUEGOS: CI01)** Calle 37 No. 3602, entre 36 y 38, Cienfuegos 55100 **W:** rcm.cu
**CAMAGÜEY: CM01)** Calle Cisneros # 310 entre Ignacio Agramonte y General Gómez, Camagüey 70100 **W:** cadenagramonte.cu – **CM02) W:** radiocamaguey.wordpress.com Camagüey 1200-1800, Cadena Agramonte 1800-1200
**GRANMA: GR01)** Ap. 74 (or Calle General Calixto García 156, entre Figueredo y Luz Vásquez 74) Bayamo 85100 **W:** radiobayamo.icrt.cu – **GR02)** Ap. 220 (or Calle Martí 341, entre Quintin Banderas y León), Manzanillo 87510 **W:** radiogranma.co.cu
**GUANTÁNAMO: GU01)** "Trinchera Antiimperialista", Ap. 96 (or Donato Mármol 409, entre José Martí y Pedro A. Pérez), Guantánamo 95100 **W:** radioguantanamo.icrt.cu – **GU02)** Calle Martí #122, % Frank País y Maraví, Baracoa 97310. H of tr: 1000-0200 **W:** radiobaracoa.icrt.cu –

**GU03)** Calle B No. 2050, Imías 97500
**HOLGUÍN: HO01)** Ap. 14 (or Calle Máximo Gómez 298 (3er piso) entre Frexes y Martí), Holguín 80100 **W:** radioangulo.cu – **HO02)** Sagua de Tánamo 83200 **W:** facebook.com/RadioEcosDeSagua – **HO03)** Calle Martí 46, Mayarí 83300
**ISLA DE LA JUVENTUD: IJ01)** Calle 26, entre 41 y 43, Nueva Gerona 25100 **W:** radiocaribe.icrt.cu
**LAS TUNAS LT01)** Ap. 211 (or Calle Colón 157, entre Julián Santana y Francisco Vega), Las Tunas 75100 **W:** tiempo21.cu – **LT02)** Avenida Sergio Reynó 19, Amancio Rodriguez 77700 **W:** radiomaboas.cu – **LT03)** Calle Donato Mármol # 65 Entre Avenida Máximo Gómez y Ángel Ameijeiras. Puerto Padre, Las Tunas 77210. **W:** radiolibertad.cu – **LT04)** Emisora Radio Chaparra. Municipio Jesús Menéndez. Las Tunas. **W:** twitter.com/cmlbradio
**MATANZAS: MA01)** Ap. 51 (or Milanés final, esq. a Guachinango), Matanzas 40100 **W:** radio26.icrt.cu – **MA02)** Calzada, esq. a Calvo, Cárdenas 42100 **W:** radiociudadbandera.wordpress.com
**MAYABEQUE: MB01)** Calle 76 No. 7707, entre 77 y 81, Güines 33900. 1100-0500 exc. 24h in July/August. **W:** radiomayabeque.icrt.cu
**PINAR DEL RÍO: PR01)** Calle Colón 14, entre Adela Azcuy y Juan Gualberto Gómez, Pinar del Río 20100 **W:** rguama.icrt.cu
**SANTIAGO DE CUBA: SC01)** Ap. 232 (or Aguilera 554, entre San Augustín y Barnada), Santiago de Cuba 90100 **W:** crnkc.cu – **SC02)** R. Coral, Calle C No. 64, Chivirico, Guamá 92800 – **SC03)** Calle 8 No. 56, entre A e Independencia, Reparto Sueño, Santiago de Cuba 90900 **W:** radiomambi.icrt.cu – **SC04)** Radio Titán, Calle Central - Esq. 3ra S/N, Mella, Santiago de Cuba **W:** radiotitan.icrt.cu – **SC05)** Mayarí Arriba, Stgo. de Cuba **W:** radio8sf.icrt.cu – **SC06)** Calle Massó # 59 esquina Agramonte, Palma Soriano, Stgo. de Cuba **W:** radiobaragua.cu
**SANCTI SPÍRITUS: SS01)** Circunvalación s/n, Los Olivos 1, Sancti Spíritus 60100. **W:** radiosanctispiritus.cu
**VILLA CLARA: VC01)** Ap. 376 (or Parque Leoncio Vidal 4, entre Martha Abreu y Pao Chao), Santa Clara 50100 **W:** cmhw.cu – **VC02)** Libertadores 100, esq. a Carmen Ribalta, Sagua la Grande, Villa Clara 52310 **W:** radiosagua.icrt.cu

**Guantánamo Bay (leased to USA)**

**AFN GUANTÁNAMO BAY**
☞ Naval Media Center Broadcasting Detatchment, Guantánamo Bay, Cuba, PSC 1005, Box 22, FPO AE 09593, USA **W:** navy.mil/local/gtmo
**MW:** Talk Radio: Guantánamo Bay 1340kHz 0.25kW.
**FM:** The Mix: 102.1MHz 0.5kW, The Blitz: 103.1MHz 0.5kW

## CURAÇAO (Netherlands)

**L.T:** UTC -4h — **Pop:** 150,560 — **Pr.L:** Dutch (official), Papiamentu, English, Spanish — **E.C:** 50Hz, 127/220V — **ITU:** CUW

**Bureau Telecommunicatie en Post**
☞ Beatrixlaan 9, Emmastad; P.O. Box 2047, Curaçao ☎ +599 9 463 1700 📠 +599 9 736 5265 **W:** btnp.org **E:** gen.affairs@burtel.cw

| MW Call | kHz | kW | Station, location |
|---|---|---|---|
| 1) PJZ-86 | 860 | 10 | Z-86 R. Curom, Willemstad |
| **FM** | **MHz** | **kW** | **Station, location** |
| 1) | 88.3 | | Rockorsou, Willemstad |
| 23) | 88.9 | | Curaçao News R., Willemstad |
| 12) | 89.7 | | R. Krioyo, Willemstad |
| 22) | 91.5 | 0.75 | Hit R. 915 , Willemstad |
| 11) | 92.1 | | Direct Life 92.1 FM, Willemstad |
| 9) | 92.7 | | R. Edukativo, Deltha 92, Willemstad |
| 20) | 93.3 | 0.5 | Tele Curaçao FM, Willemstad |
| 3) | 93.9 | 20 | R. Korsou FM, Willemstad |
| 19) | 94.5 | 0.5 | R. 94, Willemstad |
| 8) | 95.1 | 0.5 | Clazz FM, Willemstad |
| 1) | 95.7 | 4 | Mi-95FM, Willemstad |
| 13) | 96.5 | 0.5 | New Song, Willemstad |
| 10) | 97.3 | 1 | Dolfijn FM, Willemstad |
| 8) | 97.9 | 0.5 | Easy 97.9 FM, Willemstad |
| 4) | 98.5 | 0.5 | R. Semiya, Willemstad |
| 21) | 99.1 | 0.5 | R. Lighthouse, Willemstad |
| 15) | 99.7 | | R. MAS, Santa Maria |
| 7) | 100.3 | | Hit 100.3, Willemstad |
| 3) | 101.1 | 5 | Laser 101, Willemstad |
| 2) | 101.9 | 2,5 | R. Hoyer 1, Willemstad |
| 5) | 103.1 | 0.75 | Paradise FM, Willemstad |
| 8) | 103.9 | 0.5 | R. One FM, Willemstad |
| 14) | 104.5 | 1 | R. Active FM, Willemstad |
| 2) | 105.1 | 2,5 | R. Hoyer 2, Willemstad |
| 16) | 106.3 | | Fiesta FM, Willemstad |

| FM | MHz | kW | Station, location |
|---|---|---|---|
| 11) | 107.1 | | R. Direct, Willemstad |
| 6) | 107.9 | 1 | Rumbera Network, Willemstad |

**Addresses & other information:**
**1)** Curom Broadcasting Curaçao, Roodeweg 62, Willemstad, Curaçao ☎ +599 9 462 2020 88Rockorsou: hip hop and R&B Mi-95FM: adult contemporary music Z86: news talk **W**: curom.cw **E**: contact@curomcuracao.com – **2)** Plasa Horacio Hoyer 21, Willemstad, Curaçao ☎ +599 9 461 1678 ≣ +599 9 461 6528 **E**: sales@radiohoyer.com **W**: radiohoyer.com MD: Mrs. Helen Hoyer. R. Hoyer 1 in Papiamentu 0930-0400, R. Hoyer 2 in Dutch 1000-0400 – **3)** Bataljonweg 7, Willemstad, Dir.Dianthe Isa-Oosterhof ☎ +599 9 737 3012 ≣ +599 9 737 2888. 24h. **E**: studio@korsou.com Separate prgrs ("Laser 101") on 101.1MHz ☎ +599 9 738 5670 **W**: laser-101.com – **4)** Parmantierweg 2, Willemstad ☎ +599 9 462 4000/4002/4004/4005 Dir: Saïd R. Flores. Rlg 24h programs in English, Dutch, Spanish and Papiamentu **E**: info@radiosemiya.org **W**: radiosemiya.org– **5)** Fokkerweg 26, Willemstad or PO Box 6103, Willemstad ☎ +599 9 462 8103 ≣ +599 9 462 9103 **W**: paradisefmcuracao.com **E**: info@paradisefm.cw Dutch with every h and half h Dutch news. Owner: C.L. Baas – **6)** Caracasbaaiweg 194, Willemstad ☎ +599 9 461 5027 **W**: rumberacuracao.com **E**: contacto@rumberanetwork.com.ve – **7)** Compleho Deportivo Casa Grandi Z/N Willemstad ☎ +599 9 747 3333 ≣ +599 9 747 1003 Manager: Elmer Cijntje. 24h Prgrs in Papiamentu, Spanish, Creole and English – **8)** Arikokweg 19A, Willemstad ☎ +599 9 462 3162 ≣ +599 9 462 8712. GM: Quintus Fliervoet ClazzFM ☎ info@clazzfm.com **W**: clazzfm.com 24h light music & jazz in E, Papiamentu & Dutch, R. One FM **E**: quintus@radioone.cw **W**: radioone.cw 24h dance & Top 40 music in E, & Dutch. Easy FM **W**: easyfm.com **E**: radio@easyfm.com 24h adult contemporary – **9)** Suffisantweg 18, Willemstad ☎ +599 9 868 8892≣ +599 9 888 5260 and + 599 9 869 3878 **W**: radiodeltha927.com **E**: info@radiodeltha927.com – **10)** Mambo Beach Blvd #21B, Willemstad ☎ +599 9 465 9975 ≣ 599 9 461 9975 Station Manager: Egon Sybrandy **D.Prgr.** 24 hours in Dutch **E**: info@dolfijnfm.com **W**: dolfijnfm.com – **11)** F.D Rooseveltweg 214, Tesoro Shopping Center, Willemstad Dir. Mrs. Jachmin Pinedo R. Direct: in Papiamentu and Spanish 1000-0400, other times music ☎ +599 9 888 5107 ≣ +599 9 888 8407 **W**: direct107.com Direct Life 92.1FM in Papiamentu and Dutch, interviews also in Dutch, English and Spanish 1030-1300 and 1800-2400 , other times music ☎+599 9 888 4107 ≣ +599 9 888 8407 **E**: 921local@gmail.com **W**: direct92.com – **12)** Gosieweg 133,Willemstad ☎ +599 9 736 4915 ≣ +599 9 736 4914 **E**: radiokrioyo@live.com – **13)** New Song Building, Muizenberg z/n ☎ +599 9 888 0965 ≣ +599 9 868 4343 **Dir.** Welton F.A. Esprit ; Christian prgrs 24h in English, French, Papiamentu, Dutch, Spanish,– **14)** Kaya Simon Pieters Kwiers 67, Willemstad, Curaçao ☎+599 9 560 3302 Dir. Arthur Zimmerman 24h in Papiamentu **W**: active.fm **E**: info@active.fm – **15)** Fosfaatweg 8, Sta. Maria ☎+599 9 888 4997 ≣ +599 9 888 6997 mass99.com **E** administratie@mas.com– **16)** Fatimaweg 2, Suffisant, Willemstad ☎+599 9 869 6606 ≣ +599 9 869 6613 Dir. Carlos S. de Abreu Ribeiro **E**: info@fiesta.fm and fiesta@fiesta.fm– **19)** Arikokweg 30, Charo Dir: Feliciano da Silva Piloto ☎+599 717 5947 ≣ +599 717 8220 **W**: vozdibonaire.com **E**: vozdibonaire@gmail.com Music and information, 24 hrs in Papiamentu – **20)** Berg Arafat z/n, Willemstad , GMr: Hugo Lew Jen Tai ☎+599 9 777 1688 ≣ +599 9 461 4138 and +599 9 777 1650– **21)** Totonakenweg z/n, Groot Kwartier ☎+599 9 973 64805 Dir. Robert Braumuller **E**: radiolh01@gmail.com **D.Prgr.** 24h in Dutch, Papiamentu, English and Spanish –**22)** Fokkerweg 26, PO Box 6103, Willemstad ☎+599 9 462 8103 ≣ +599 9 462 9103, Dir. **C.L. Baas W**: hitradio915.com **E**: info@hitradio915.com **D.Prgr.** 24h in Dutch, non-stop hits -23) ☎+599 9 463 6490 **E**:masterdpro@gmail.com

## CYPRUS

**L.T:** UTC +2h (31 Mar-27 Oct: +3h) — **Pop:** 1.2 million — **Pr.L:** Greek, Turkish, Armenian — **E.C:** 50Hz, 230V — **ITU:** CYP

### CYPRUS RADIO-TELEVISION AUTHORITY
◻ 32 Nikis Ave, P.O.Box 23377, 1682 Nicosia ☎+357 22 512468 ≣ F+357 22 512473 **W**: crta.org.cy **E**: crtauthority@cytanet.com.cy

### CYPRUS BROADCASTING CORPORATION (CYBC) (Pub)
◻ CyBC Street, Athalassa, P.O. Bxo 24824, CY-1397 Nicosia ☎+357 22 862000 ≣ +357 22 314050 **W**: cybc.com.cy **E**: info@cybc.com.cy
**L.P:** DG: Themis Themistocleous. Deputy DG: Michael Stylianou.

| MW | kHz | kW | Ch. | MW | kHz | kW | Ch. |
|---|---|---|---|---|---|---|---|
| Nicosia | 603 | 100 | 3 | Nicosia | 963 | 100 | 1 |

| FM (MHz) | Ch. 1 | Ch. 2 | Ch. 3 | Ch.4 | kW |
|---|---|---|---|---|---|
| Armenochori | 105.0 | 93.1 | 106.7 | 90.5 | 2 |

| FM (MHz) | Ch. 1 | Ch. 2 | Ch. 3 | Ch.4 | kW |
|---|---|---|---|---|---|
| Mt. Olympos | 97.2 | 91.1 | 94.8 | 88.2 | 30 |
| Paphos | 92.4 | 97.9 | 94.0 | 90.2 | 7 |
| Paralimni | 91.4 | 94.2 | 96.0 | 100.9 | 4 |

**Ch. 1 (Proto)** in Greek: 24h – **Ch. 2 (Deutero)** Multilingual: 24h. Prgrs in English 1030-1040, 1500-0300; Turkish 0300-1400; Armenian 1400-1500 – **Ch. 3 (Trito)** in Greek: 24h – **Ch. 4 (Classic)** in Greek: 24h.
**Ann:** Greek: "Radiofonikon Idryma Kyprou". Turkish: "Burasi Kibris Radyo Yayin Korporasyonu". **IS:** "Avkoritssa" (guitar).

**Other Stations (all MHz):**
**ANT1 FM:** Larnaca 102.7, Paphos 103.7. **W:** ant1iwo.com/fm – **Dromos FM:** Larnaca 100.5, Limassol 100.3, Nicosia 106.7. **W:** facebook.com/dromosfmcy – **Kanali 6:** Limassol 98.6, Nicosia 106.0, Mount Phanos 107.0 **W:** kanali6.com.cy – **Kanali 7:** Nicosia 98.4, Limassol 102.1 **W:** kanali7.com – **Kiss FM:** Limassol 88.5, Nicosia 89.0. **W:** kissfm.com.cy – **Klik FM:** Limassol 89.6, Larnaca 98.2, Nicosia 105.5 **W:** klikfm.com.cy – **Logos R:** Mount Olympos 101.1, Larnaca 101.6 **W:** logosradio.com.cy – **Mix FM:** Limassol 90.8, Larnaca 102.2, Nicosia 102.3 **W:** mixfmradio.com – **R. Astra:** Mount Olympos 92.8, Larnaca 105.3 **W:** astra.com.cy – **R. Athina:** Limassol 88.7, Nicosia 100.7 **W:** radioathina.com – **R. Proto:** Agia Napa 87.9, Larnaca 89.4, Mount Olympos 99.3 **W:** radioproto.com.cy – **R. Sfera:** Paphos 96.8, Limassol 106.4 **W:** radiosfera.com.cy – **Rock FM:** Limassol 89.2, Paphos 98.5, Latchi 106.7 **W:** rockfmcyprus.com – **Russian Wave:** Larnaca 98.6, Limassol 105.6 **W:** russianwave.com.cy – **Super FM:** Larnaca 95.7, Paphos 103.4, Mount Olympos 104.8 **W:** superfmradio.com – **Super Sport FM:** Limassol 100.3, Larnaca 103.0, Nicosia 106.7 **W:** sport-fm.com.cy

**MW:** Monte Carlo Doualiya & Trans World R. rel. on **MW:** 1233kHz 0200-2115 – **R. Sawa: MW:** 990kHz 24h.
For further details on these stns see International Radio section.

### NORTHERN CYPRUS

### SUPREME BROADCASTING BOARD (YYK)
◻ Memduh Asaf St. 9, Kösklüçiftlik, Lefkosa, Northern Cyprus ☎+90 392 228 1368 ≣+90 392 228 1272
**W:** kktcyyk.org **E:** info@kktcyyk.org

### BAYRAK RADYO TELEVIZYON KURUMU (BRTK, Gov.)
◻ BRT Sitesi, Dr. Fasil Küçük Bulvari, Lefkosa, Northern Cyprus, via Mersin 10, Turkey ☎+90 392 225 5555 ≣ +90 392 225 4991
**W:** brtk.net **E:** brt@brtk.net
**L.P:** DG: Mete Tümerkan. Head Tr. Dept: Mustafa Tosun.

| FM | R.1 | B.FM | B.Int. | R.Klasik | BTM | BRH | kW |
|---|---|---|---|---|---|---|---|
| Kantara | 90.6 | 98.1 | 87.8 | 93.4 | | | 10/1 |
| Selvilitepe | 102.0 | 92.1/88.8 | 105.0 | 88.4/102.5 | 94.6 | 100.1 | 20/1 |
| Lefkosa | 89.6 | 94.2 | | | | | 0.3/10 |

**R.1 (Bayrak Radyosu)** in Turkish: 24h – **Bayrak FM** in Turkish: 24h – **Bayrak International** in English (also news in Turkish/Greek/German/Russian/French/Arabic): 24h – **Radyo Klasik:** 24h – **Bayrak Türk Müzigi:** 24h – **Bayrak Radyo Haber** (Turkish): 24h.

**OTHER STATIONS FM** (MHz):

| | Station | W | E | kW | Location |
|---|---|---|---|---|---|
| 1) | R. Odtü | 103.1 | | 1 | Kalkanli |
| 2) | Cool FM | 92.6 | 97.5 | 1 | Magosa |
| 3) | As FM | 97.7 | 95.2 | 1 | Lefkosa |
| 4) | Sim FM | 98.6 | 89.5 | 2.5/0.3 | Lefkosa |
| 5) | Süper FM | 98.9 | | 1 | Lefkosa |
| 6) | Metro FM | 104.0 | | 1 | Lefkosa |
| 7) | Kral FM | 106.9 | | 1 | Lefkosa |
| 8) | Kibris FM | 103.4 | 100.2 | 5/2.5 | Lefkosa |
| 9) | First FM | 90.0 | 96.6 | 1/0.3 | Lefkosa |
| 10) | Akdeniz FM | 88.6 | | 1 | Lefkosa |
| 11) | R. Vatan Türkü | 104.5 | 94.4 | 5/1 | Lefkosa |
| 12) | R. Vatan Nihavent | 100.4 | 89.8 | 5/3 | Lefkosa |
| 13) | Dance FM | 95.5 | 95.1 | 1 | Lefkosa |
| 14) | Radyo T | 96.6 | | 1 | Lefkosa |
| 15) | R. Güven | 90.4/89.2 | 90.8 | 5/2/5 | Lefkosa |
| 16) | R. Plus | 106.2 | 105.8 | 1 | Magosa |
| 17) | Laü FM | 97.4 | | 1 | Lefke |
| 18) | Mayis FM | 96.0 | 101.3 | 1 | Lefkosa |
| 19) | Gaü FM | 105.8 | | 1 | Gime |
| 20) | Ciu FM | 107.2 | | 1 | Lefkosa |
| 21) | Daü FM | | 106.5 | 2 | Magosa |
| 22) | R. Enerji | 93.1 | 100.0 | 1 | Lefkosa |
| 23) | R. Havadis | 107.8 | | 2 | Lefkosa |
| 24) | Ada FM | 96.2 | 93.8 | 1 | Lefkosa |
| 25) | Capital R. | 93.8 | 99.4 | 1 | Lefkosa |

| | Station | W | E | kW | Location |
|---|---|---|---|---|---|
| 26) | R. Vatan | 87.5 | 104.3 | 5 | Lefkosa |
| 27) | Ydü FM | 88.0 | | 1 | Lefkosa |
| 28) | R. Juke | 90.9 | 99.8 | 2.5/1 | Lefkosa |
| 29) | Dream Live FM | 104.2 | 102.8 | 2 | Lefkosa |
| 30) | TRT FM | 101.3 | | 5 | Lefkosa |
| 31) | R. Play FM | 102.9 | 107.2 | 2/1 | Lefkosa |

**Tx sites:** W (west) = Selvilitepe, E (east)= Kantara-Sinan Dagi. All stns 24h.
**1)** radyoodtu.com.tr – **5)** superfm.gen.tr – **7)** kralfm.com.tr – **9)** kibrisfirstfm.net – **13)** dancefm.com.tr – **15)** radyoguven.com – **17)** radyo.eul.edu.tr – **18)** radyomayis.com – **20)** ciu.edu.tr/ciu-fm-2 – **21)** dautv.emu.edu.tr – **22)** radyoenerji.com – **23)** radyohavadis.com – **24)** adafmkibris.com – **25)** capitalcyprus.com – **27)** neu.edu.tr – **28)** radyoujuke.com – **29)** dreamfmlivecyprus.com – **31)** playfm.com.tr

### AKROTIRI & DHEKELIA (UK)

**Pop:** 15,700 — **Pr.L:** English, Greek — **E.C:** 50Hz, 240V — **ITU:** CYP

### FORCES RADIO BFBS CYPRUS (Mil.)
✉ BFBS Akrotiri, BFPO 57, UK ☎ +357 2527 8518 🖷 +357 2527 8580
**W:** forces.net/radio/stations/bfbs-cyprus **E:** cyprus@bfbs.com

| FM (MHz) | Forces R. CY | BFBS2 | kW |
|---|---|---|---|
| Akrotiri | 89.9 | 92.1 | 25 |
| Ayios Nikolaos | 107.3 | 89.7 | |
| Dhekelia | 99.6 | 95.3 | 25 |
| Nicosia | 91.7 | 89.7 | 1.5 |

**D.Prgr:** 24h. **Ann:** "Forces Radio BFBS"

**Other stations:**
**BBC World Sce: MW:** Zakaki 639 & 720kHz: Arabic 0300-0700, 1800/1500-2100

## CZECHIA

**L.T:** UTC +1h (31 Mar-27 Oct: +2h) — **Pop:** 10.5 million — **Pr.L:** Czech — **E.C:** 50Hz, 230V — **ITU:** CZE

### RADA PRO ROZHLASOVÉ A TELEVIZNÍ VYSÍLÁNÍ (RRTV) (Council for Radio and Television Broadcasting)
✉ Škrétova 44/6, 12000 Praha 2 ☎ +420 274813830 🖷 +420 274810885 **E:** podatelna@rrtv.cz **W:** www.rrtv.cz
**L.P:** Chmn: Martin Bezouška

### CESKÉ RADIOKOMUNIKACE, a.s.
✉ U nákladového nádraží 4, 130 00 Praha 3 ☎ +420 267 005 111 **E:** info@radiokomunikace.cz **W:** radiokomunikace.cz
Operates the TV and radio transmission facilities.

### CESKY ROZHLAS (CZECH RADIO) (Pub)
✉ Vinohradská 12, 120 99 Praha 2 ☎ +420 221 551 111 🖷 +420 221 551 300 **E:** info@rozhlas.cz **W:** rozhlas.cz
**L.P:** DG: René Zavoral PD: Ondrej Nováček TD: Karel Zyka

| LW & MW: | kHz | kW | Prgr. |
|---|---|---|---|
| Uherské Hradište | 270 | 50 | CRo 1 |
| Praha (Liblice) | 639 | 750 | CRo 2 |
| Ostrava-Svinov | 639 | 30 | CRo 2 |
| Brno (Dobrochov) | 954 | 200 | CRo 2 |
| Ceské Budejovice | 954 | 30 | CRo 2 |
| Karlovy Vary | 954 | 20 | CRo 2 |
| Ceské Budejovice | 1071 | 5 | CRo Plus |
| Ostrava-Svinov | 1071 | 5 | CRo Plus |
| Moravské Budejovice | 1332 | 50 | CRo 2 |

| FM (MHz) | CRo 1 | CRo 2 | CRo 3 | CRo 5 | CRoPlus | kW |
|---|---|---|---|---|---|---|
| 9) As | 107.9 | - | - | 96.7 | - | 0.1/0.2 |
| 1) Benešov | - | - | - | 99.0 | - | 1(5) |
| 6) Brno | 95.1 | 102.0 | - | 106.5 | - | 72/91/72 |
| 6) Brno (city) | - | - | 90.4 | 93.1 | 92.6 | 6/6/2 |
| 2) C. Budejovice | 91.1 | 103.7 | 96.1 | 106.4 | - | 80/1/40/80 |
| Cesky Krumlov | - | - | - | - | 98.2 | 0.2 |
| 9) Cheb | - | 88.2 | 106.2 | 100.8 | 89.5 | 1 |
| 4) Chomutov | 98.9 | 94.2 | 96.3 | 103.1 | - | 10 |
| Decín | - | 105.4 | - | - | 100.8 | 0.1 |
| 3) Domazlice | 98.0 | - | - | 105.3 | - | 10 |
| 13) Frydlant | - | - | - | 97.4 | - | 0.2 |
| 9) Hodonín | 106.2 | 107.8 | 100.4 | 93.6 | - | 9/3/9 |
| 5) Hradec Králové | - | - | - | 95.3 | - | 1 |
| 11) Hradec Králové | - | - | - | 104.7 | - | 10 |
| 8) Hulín | - | - | - | 101.6 | - | 1 |
| 13) Jablonné | - | - | - | 105.4 | - | 0.1 |
| 9) Jáchymov | - | - | - | 103.4 | - | 1 |

| FM (MHz) | CRo 1 | CRo 2 | CRo 3 | CRo 5 | CRoPlus | kW |
|---|---|---|---|---|---|---|
| 8) Jeseník | 91.3 | 88.7 | 98.2 | 106.8 | - | 20/0.2/20/20 |
| Jicín | - | 106.9 | - | - | - | 1 |
| 10) Jihlava | 90.7 | 107.1 | 88.4 | 87.9 | 95.4 | 20/10/20/10 |
| Kaplice | - | - | 105.9 | - | - | 0.2 |
| 9) Karlovy Vary | 102.6 | - | 105.7 | 91.0 | 97.8 | 0.1/0.2/1 |
| Kašperské Hory | - | - | 107.2 | - | - | 0.5 |
| 1) Kladno | - | - | - | 100.5 | - | 0.2 |
| 3) Klatovy | 99.8 | 90.3 | 88.6 | 102.4 | - | 10 |
| 1) Kutná Hora | - | 102.2 | - | 100.5 | - | 1/3 |
| 13) Liberec | 95.9 | 89.9 | 103.9 | 102.3 | - | 20/20/20/1 |
| Liberec | - | - | - | - | 91.3 | 0.5 |
| 8) Lipník n.Becvou | - | - | - | 88.7 | - | 0.1 |
| Litomerice | - | 100.0 | - | - | 92.8 | 0.1 |
| 9) Marián.Lázne | 97.6 | - | - | 100.8 | - | 1 |
| 1) Mladá Boleslav | - | - | - | 100.3 | - | 0.5 |
| Nové Hrady | - | 102.2 | - | - | - | 1 |
| 8) Olomouc | - | - | - | 92.8 | 107.2 | 1 |
| 7) Opava | - | 101.7 | - | 102.6 | - | 1/0.5 |
| 7) Ostrava | 101.4 | 101.9 | 104.8 | 107.3 | - | 43/0.5/43/3 |
| 11) Pardubice | 89.7 | 100.1 | 102.7 | 101.0 | - | 90/90/90/1 |
| Písek | 97.0 | 98.9 | 105.2 | - | - | 1 |
| Plzen (North) | 89.1 | 101.7 | 95.6 | - | - | 80 |
| 3) Plzen (East) | 99.2 | - | - | 106.7 | 93.3 | 10 |
| 3) Plzen (city) | - | - | - | 91.0 | - | 1 |
| Prachatice | - | - | - | - | 98.0 | 0.1 |
| 1) Praha | - | - | - | 100.7 | - | 50 |
| Praha (city) | 94.6 | 91.2 | 105.0 | - | 92.6 | 5/3/5/7 |
| 1) Príbram | 102.2 | 107.0 | - | 100.0 | 103.6 | 0.4/1/1 |
| 13) Prosec n.N. | - | - | - | 102.3 | - | 1 |
| 1) Rakovník | - | - | - | 100.4 | - | 1 |
| 5) Rychnov n.K. | - | - | - | 96.5 | - | 1 |
| 2) Slavonice | - | 103.3 | - | 88.2 | - | 1 |
| 3) Sokolov | 94.3 | - | - | 98.2 | - | 0.4 |
| Sušice | 90.6 | 89.7 | - | - | 97.9 | 0.1 |
| 11) Svitavy | - | - | - | 102.4 | - | 1 |
| 3) Tachov | - | - | - | 106.3 | - | 0.4 |
| Teplice | - | - | - | - | 103.6 | 0.1 |
| 10) Trebíc | - | - | - | 90.1 | - | 0.2 |
| 7) Trinec | 92.1 | - | - | 105.3 | - | 1 |
| 5) Trutnov | 88.5 | 93.4 | - | 90.5 | 101.9 | 10/10/20 |
| 13) Turnov | - | - | - | 91.5 | - | 0.1 |
| 12) Uher. Hradište | - | - | - | 99.1 | - | 0.2 |
| 12) Uhersky Brod | 93.0 | - | - | 107.3 | - | 1 |
| 4) Ustí nad Labem | 90.9 | - | 104.5 | 88.8 | - | 80 |
| Ustí n.L.(city) | - | 98.6 | - | - | 93.9 | 1 |
| 1) Ustí n. Orlicí | - | - | - | 98.6 | - | 1 |
| 7) Val. Mezirící | 92.5 | 89.9 | 96.8 | 99.0 | - | 7/1/7/7 |
| 4) Varnsdorf | - | - | 88.4 | 98.5 | - | 0.2 |
| 11) Velké Opatovice | - | - | - | 93.7 | 101.5 | 0.2 |
| Votice | 93.1 | 103.2 | - | - | - | 95 |
| 13 Vratislavice | - | - | - | 91.3 | - | 0.5 |
| 7) Vrbno pod Prad. | - | 103.6 | - | 95.5 | - | 1 |
| 12) Vsetín | 92.1 | 102.9 | 98.3 | 99.5 | - | 1 |
| 11) Vysoké Myto | - | - | - | 88.9 | - | 0.2 |
| 11) Zamberk | - | - | - | 103.3 | - | 0.5 |
| 3) Zelezná Ruda | - | - | - | 95.8 | - | 0.2 |
| 12) Zlín | 99.5 | 107.7 | 94.8 | 97.5 | - | 6 |
| 6) Znojmo | 101.2 | 89.6 | 99.2 | 97.3 | - | 1/3/3/1 |

**CRo 1 (Radiozurnál):** 24h (LW: Mon-Sat 0400-2300, Sun 0500-2300). **N:** on the h — **CRo 2 (Dvojka):** 24h (MW: Mon-Fri 0300-2300, Sat+Sun 0400-2300) — **CRo 3 (Vltava):** 24h — **CRo 4 (Radio Wave):** 24h (on internet only **W:** rozhlas.cz/radiowave/portal) — **CRo 5 REGIONAL STATIONS:** 24h own prgrs and relays of other regional stations (esp. in the night) — **CRo Plus:** 24h **N:** on the h
**Addresses & other information:**
CRo Regina Praha, Hybešova 10, 186 72 Praha 8 **W:** rozhlas.cz/regina (On DAB+ only) – **1)** CRo Region - Strední Cechy, Hybešova 10, 186 72 Praha 8 **W:** rozhlas.cz/strednicechy – **2)** CRo Ceské Budejovice, U Trí lvu 1, 370 29 Ceské Budejovice **W:** rozhlas.cz/cb – **3)** CRo Plzen, Nám. Míru 10, 320 70 Plzen **W:** rozhlas.cz/plzen – **4)** CRo Sever (=North), Na schodech 10, 400 91 Ústí nad Labem **W:** rozhlas.cz/sever – **5)** CRo Hradec Králové, Havlíckova 292, 501 01 Hradec Králové **W:** rozhlas.cz/hradec – **6)** CRo Brno, Beethovenova 4, 657 42 Brno **W:** rozhlas.cz/brno – **7)** CRo Ostrava, Dr. Šmerala 2, 729 91 Ostrava (Polish: Mon-Fri 1804-1830) **W:** rozhlas.cz/ostrava – **8)** CRo Olomouc, Horní námestí 21, 771 06 Olomouc **W:** rozhlas.cz/ol – **9)** CRo Karlovy Vary, Zítkova 3, 360 00 Karlovy Vary: Mon-Fri 1300-1500, otherwise CRo Plzen **W:** vary.rozhlas.cz – **10)** CRo Vysocina, Masarykovo nám 42, 586 01 Jihlava **W:** vysocina.rozhlas.cz – **11)** CRo Pardubice, Sv. Anežky Ceské 29, 530 02 Pardubice **W:** rozhlas.cz/pardubice – **12)** CRo Zlín, Osvoboditelu 187,

760 01 Zlín **W:** zlin.rozhlas.cz – **13)** CRo Liberec, Modrá 1048, 460 06 Liberec **W:** rozhlas.cz/liberec/portal

**EXTERNAL SERVICE: Radio Prague**
See International Broadcasting section.

**MAJOR PRIVATE STATIONS/NETWORKS:**
**RADIO IMPULS (Comm.)**
✉ Ortenovo nám. 15a, 170 00 Praha 7 ☎ +420 255 700 700 🖷 +420 255 700 727 **E:** impuls@radioimpuls.cz **W:** radioimpuls.cz
**FM:** see list below. **D.Prgr:** 24h

**RADIO FREKVENCE 1 (Comm.)**
✉ Wenzigova 4, 120 00 Praha 2 ☎ +420 257 001 111 🖷 +420 257 314 183 **E:** frekvence1@frekvence1.cz **W:** frekvence1.cz
**FM:** see list below. **D.Prgr:** 24h

**EVROPA 2 (Comm.)**
✉ Wenzigova 4, 120 00 Praha 2 ☎ +420 257 001 111 🖷 +420 257 001 807 **E:** info@evropa2.cz **W:** evropa2.cz
**FM:** see list below. **D.Prgr:** 24h

**KISS (Comm.)**
✉ Rícanská 3, 101 00 Praha 10-Vinohrady ☎ +420 601 111 601
**E:** studio@kiss.cz, program@kiss.cz **W:** kiss.cz **FM:** see list below.
**D.Prgr:** 24h

**RADIO PROGLAS (Relg)**
✉ Barvicova 85, 602 00 Brno ☎ +420 543 217 241-3 🖷 +420 543 217 245 **E:** radio@proglas.cz **W:** proglas.cz **FM:** see list below. **D.Prgr:** 24h

**COUNTRY RADIO (Comm.)**
✉ Ricanská 3, 101 00 Praha 10-Vinohrady ☎ +420 251 024 111 🖷 +420 251 024 224 **E:** info@countryradio.cz **W:** countryradio.cz
**MW:** Praha 1062kHz 20kW (0500-1800), 1kW (1800-0500) **FM:** see list below. **D.Prgr:** 24h

**RADIO DECHOVKA (Comm.)**
✉ U Prutníku 232, 250 72 Predboj ☎ +420 311 280 281 **E:** pusova@radiodechovka.cz **W:** radiodechovka.cz

| MW: | kHz | kW | MW: | kHz | kW |
|-----|-----|----|-----|-----|----|
| Hradec Králové | 792 | *1 | Ceské Budejovice | 1233 | 2 |
| Praha-Zbraslav | 1233 | 10 | Ostrava-Svinov | 1233 | 2 |
| Brno/Dobrochov | 1233 | 5 | Brno-Reckovice | 1233 | 0.5 |

**\*) F.PI.** 5-10kW **FM:** see list below. **D.Prgr:** 24h

**RADIO CESKY IMPULS (Comm.)**
✉ Ortenovo nám. 15a, 170 00 Praha 7 ☎ (studio) +420 255 700 701 **E:** moderator@ceskyimpuls.cz **W:** ceskyimpuls.cz
**MW:** Praha (Libeznice-Boranovice) 981kHz 10kW, Moravské Budejovice (Domamil) 981kHz 5kW, Litomysl 981kHz **(F.PI.)**, Hradec Králové 981kHz **(F.PI.)**. **D.Prgr:** 24h

**RADIO ZET (Comm.)**
✉ Wenzigova 4, 120 00 Praha 2 ☎ +420 257 001 240 **E:** info@zet.cz **W:** zet.cz **FM:** see list below. **D.Prgr:** 24h. Own prgr in Czech: 0600-1700; BBC WS relay in English: 1700-0600.

**Commercial FM Stations:**

| MHz | kW | Station | Location |
|-----|----|---------|----------|
| 87.6 | 70 | R. Impuls | Brno |
| 87.8 | 1 | R. Blaník | Praha |
| 87.8 | 1 | Hitrádio Cerná hora | Králíky |
| 88.1 | 1 | R. Evropa 2 | Liberec |
| 88.1 | 10 | Hitrádio Orion | Jeseník |
| 88.2 | 5 | R. Evropa 2 | Praha |
| 88.3 | 10 | Kiss | Brno |
| 88.4 | 1 | R. Blaník | Ceské Budejovice |
| 88.7 | 1 | R. Proglas | Tábor |
| 88.9 | 10 | R. Jih | Breclav |
| 89.0 | 1 | R. Práchen | Písek |
| 89.0 | 45 | R. Impuls | Ostrava |
| 89.3 | 5 | HEY R. | Benešov/Lbosín |
| 89.5 | 1 | R. Cas | Trinec |
| 89.5 | 5 | Country R. | Praha |
| 89.6 | 1 | R. Frekvence 1 | Plzen |
| 89.6 | 7 | Rock Max | Zlín |
| 89.8 | 1 | R. Zet | Ceské Budejovice* |
| 90.0 | 1 | Hitrádio Dragon | Cheb |
| 90.0 | 1 | R. Rubi | Sumperk |
| 90.0 | 10 | Kiss | Plzen |
| 90.2 | 1 | Kiss | Kutná Hora |
| 90.3 | 5 | Expres FM | Praha |
| 90.3 | 3 | Kiss | Zlín |

| MHz | kW | Station | Location |
|-----|----|---------|----------|
| 90.5 | 1.6 | R. Evropa 2 | Ceské Budejovice |
| 90.6 | 4 | Hitrádio FM Most | Chomutov |
| 90.6 | 1 | R. Proglas | Bystrice pod Hostynem |
| 91.0 | 70 | R. Frekvence 1 | Ostrava |
| 91.0 | 1 | R. Evropa 2 | Mariánské Lázne |
| 91.1 | 2 | Kiss | Pardubice |
| 91.4 | 66 | R. Impuls | Plzen |
| 91.6 | 1 | R. Blanik | Decín |
| 91.6 | 5 | Fajn R. | Opatovice |
| 91.7 | 4 | R. Zlín | Zlín |
| 91.9 | 1 | R. 1 | Praha |
| 92.1 | 10 | R. Impuls | Trutnov |
| 92.3 | 1 | R. Relax | Kladno |
| 92.3 | 5 | R. Haná | Pohorany |
| 92.5 | 5 | R. Egrensis | Mariánské Lázne |
| 92.8 | 5 | R. Cas | Ostrava |
| 92.8 | 1 | Hitradio Magic | Náchod |
| 92.9 | 1 | Kiss | Mladá Boleslav |
| 92.9 | 1 | R. Ceská Kanada | Dacice |
| 93.2 | 1 | R. Egrensis | Cheb |
| 93.3 | 20 | R. Proglas | Jeseník |
| 93.4 | 20 | R. Frekvence 1 | Jihlava |
| 93.5 | 50 | R. Frekvence 1 | Ustí nad Labem |
| 93.6 | 1 | Hitrádio Faktor | Písek |
| 93.7 | 5 | Hitrádio City | Praha |
| 93.7 | 45 | R. Hellax | Ostrava |
| 93.8 | 1 | R. Evropa 2 | Karlovy Vary |
| 93.9 | 80 | R. Blaník | Pardubice |
| 94.0 | 10 | R. Impuls | Klatovy |
| 94.1 | 10 | R. Frekvence 1 | Valašské Mezirící |
| 94.1 | 50 | R. Frekvence 1 | Ceské Budejovice |
| 94.3 | 10 | Hitrádio Vysocina | Jihlava |
| 94.5 | 0.1 | R. Dechovka | Tábor |
| 94.7 | 1 | Country R.Mor.Sev. | Ostrava |
| 95.0 | 95 | R. Blaník | Votice |
| 95.2 | 5 | Fajn North Music | Ustí nad Labem |
| 95.2 | 1 | Rock R. | Klatovy |
| 95.3 | 2.5 | R. Beat | Praha |
| 95.5 | 0.4 | R. Dechovka | Cesnovice |
| 95.7 | 2 | Signál R. Praha | Praha |
| 95.8 | 1 | Hitrádio Vysocina | Trebíc |
| 96.2 | 1 | R. Spin | Praha |
| 96.2 | 1 | R. Zlín | Uherský Brod |
| 96.4 | 4 | Hitrádio Orion | Ostrava |
| 96.5 | 1 | Kiss | Sumperk |
| 96.6 | 5 | R. Impuls | Praha |
| 96.7 | 5 | R. Zet | Jihlava* |
| 96.8 | 1 | Country R.Mor.Jih | Brno |
| 96.8 | 0.2 | R. Dechovka | C.Budejovice |
| 96.9 | 1 | Country R.Vychod | Pardubice |
| 97.1 | 5 | R. Rubi | Pohorany |
| 97.1 | 1 | Country R.Sever | Liberec |
| 97.2 | 5 | Fajn Radio | Praha |
| 97.4 | 50 | R. Frekvence 1 | Pardubice |
| 97.5 | 50 | Kiss | Votice |
| 97.7 | 1 | Evropa 2 | Ostrava |
| 97.9 | 20 | R. Proglas | Liberec |
| 98.1 | 1 | Fajn R. | Chomutov |
| 98.1 | 2 | Kiss | Praha |
| 98.1 | 1 | R. Orchidej | Brno |
| 98.3 | 1 | R. Cas | Trinec |
| 98.4 | 20 | R. Frekvence 1 | Trutnov |
| 98.4 | 5 | R. Impuls | Kašperské Hory |
| 98.6 | 1 | R. Zet | Plzen* |
| 98.7 | 1 | Hitrádio Orion | Trinec |
| 98.7 | 5 | R. Classic FM | Praha |
| 99.0 | 1 | Hitradio Brno | Brno |
| 99.1 | 1 | R. Zet | Pardubice* |
| 99.2 | 1 | R. Zet | Liberec* |
| 99.3 | 1 | Kiss | Cesky Krumlov |
| 99.3 | 10 | R. Evropa 2 | Jeseník |
| 99.3 | 1 | R. France Int./Fr. Mus. | Praha |
| 99.4 | 0.1 | R. Dechovka | Písek |
| 99.5 | 1 | R. Evropa 2 | Pardubice |
| 99.7 | 1 | Hitradio Dragon | Karlovy Vary |
| 99.7 | 1 | Rock R. | Ceské Budejovice |
| 99.7 | 5 | R. Bonton | Praha |
| 99.8 | 5 | Hitradio Apollo | Valašské Mezirící |
| 99.9 | 1 | Hitrádio Crystal | Ceská Lípa |
| 100.3 | 20 | R. Impuls | Jihlava |
| 100.5 | 7 | R. Impuls | Valašské Mezirící |
| 100.6 | 2 | R. Blaník | Teplice |

| MHz | kW | Station | Location |
|---|---|---|---|
| 100.8 | 1 | R. Beat | Slavonice |
| 100.9 | 20 | R. Impuls | Jeseník |
| 101.1 | 1 | Kiss | Frydek-Místek |
| 101.1 | 0.2 | R. Dechovka | Strakonice |
| 101.1 | 3 | R. Zet | Praha* |
| 101.3 | 10 | R. Evropa 2 | Plzen |
| 101.4 | 20 | R. Contact (RCL) | Liberec |
| 101.8 | 1 | Country R. | Tábor |
| 102.0 | 50 | R. Impuls | Ustí nad Labem |
| 102.5 | 5 | R. Frekvence 1 | Praha |
| 102.8 | 5 | Hitradio Dragon | Mariánské Lázne |
| 102.8 | 1 | Hitrádio FM Labe | Ustí nad Labem |
| 102.9 | 50 | R. Impuls | Ceské Budejovice |
| 103.0 | 10 | R. Krokodyl | Brno |
| 103.4 | 1 | R. Blaník | Hradec Králové |
| 103.4 | 5 | R. Petrov | Brno |
| 103.6 | 1 | Country R.Vychod | Chotebor |
| 103.6 | 1 | R. Ceská Kanada | Jindrichuv Hradec |
| 103.7 | 1 | Oldies R. Olympic | Praha |
| 103.8 | 10 | R. Frekvence 1 | Klatovy |
| 103.9 | 7 | Hitrádio Orion | Valašské Mezirící |
| 104.1 | 50 | R. Frekvence 1 | Plzen |
| 104.2 | 1 | R. Blaník | Znojmo |
| 104.3 | 20 | R. Frekvence 1 | Jeseník |
| 104.3 | 32 | Hitrádio Faktor | Ceské Budejovice |
| 104.5 | 50 | R. Frekvence 1 | Brno |
| 104.7 | 10 | R. Blaník | Plzen |
| 105.0 | 10 | R. Frekvence 1 | Zlín |
| 105.3 | 3 | Hitrádio Cerná hora | Trutnov |
| 105.4 | 1 | R. Rubi | Vrbno pod Pradedem |
| 105.5 | 95 | R. Evropa 2 | Votice |
| 105.5 | 1.5 | R. Evropa 2 | Brno |
| 105.7 | 1 | Signál R. | Mladá Boleslav |
| 105.8 | 8 | Hitrádio FM Plus | Klatovy |
| 105.8 | 1 | R. Zet | Ustí nad Labem* |
| 105.9 | 1 | R. Cas | Frenštát p. Radh. |
| 106.0 | 50 | R. Impuls | Pardubice |
| 106.1 | 3 | Hitrádio FM Plus | Plzen |
| 106.3 | 1 | R. Zet | Ostrava* |
| 106.4 | 1 | R. Evropa 2 | Vrchlabí |
| 106.5 | 10 | R. Blaník | Chomutov |
| 106.6 | 1 | Fajn R. | Kutná Hora |
| 106.7 | 1 | R. Evropa 2 | Znojmo |
| 107.2 | 1 | R. Evropa 2 | Ustí nad Labem |
| 107.4 | 1 | Hitrádio FM Plus | Jáchymov |
| 107.5 | 3 | R. Proglas | Brno |
| 107.5 | 2 | R. Proglas | Nové Hrady |

+ more than 70 txs below 1kW. *) rel. BBCWS at night

### DIGITAL RADIO (DAB+)
CRo on Blocks: **12C** Praha (20kW), Plzen (10kW), Ustí nad Labem (10kW), Trutnov (10kW); **12D** Ostrava (10kW), Brno (5kW), Jihlava (5kW) + 7 low power repeaters (0.1 – 0.3kW) with various CRo sces Ceské radiokomunikace on Blocks: **5D** Liberec (0.2), **10D** Praha (0.2kW), Ustí nad Labem (1kW; F.PI. 11B); **11C** Zlín (0.5kW; F.PI. 10B); **12B** Olomouc (1kW) with various private stations.
TELEKO on Blocks: **5D** Trutnov (1kW); **10A** Litomerice (1kW); **11A** Praha (0.2kW), Príbram (1kW) with various CRo and private stations RTI cz on Blocks: **5D** Ceské Budejovice (1kW); **10A** Plzen (0.2kW) with various CRo and private stations.

## DENMARK

**L.T:** UTC +1h (31 Mar-27 Oct: +2h) — **Pop:** 5.75 million — **Pr.L:** Danish — **EC:** 50Hz, 230/380V — **ITU:** DNK

### RADIO- OG TV-NÆVNET (Radio and TV Board)
✉ H.C. Andersens Boulevard 2, 1553 København V ☎ +45 33954200 **E:** rtv@slks.dk **W:** slks.dk/medier/radio-og-tv-naevnet
**L.P:** Chair: Caroline Heide-Jørgensen

### TERACOM A/S
✉ Banestrøget 19-21, 2630 Taastrup ☎+45 70118011 Teracom is responsible for the operation of txs carrying prgrs of DR and TV 2.

### DR RADIO (Pub.)
✉ DR Byen, Emil Holms Kanal 20, 0999 Copenhagen C ☎+45 35203040 **W:** dr.dk **L.P:** Chairman: Marianne Bedsted, DG: Maria Rørbye Rønn, News Dir.: Sandy French, Head of Radio: Gustav Lützhøft.
**LW:** Kalundborg 243kHz 50kW

| FM | P1/P2 | P3 | P4 | kW |
|---|---|---|---|---|
| Bornholm | 96.2 | 90.0 | 99.3 | 30 |
| Copenhagen | 90.8 | 93.9 | 96.5 | 60 |
| Funen | 89.0 | 92.6 | 96.8 | 60 |
| Holstebro | 90.2 | 92.9 | 98.5 | 60 |
| Nakskov | 89.4 | 94.1 | 92.2 | 30 |
| Næsted | 94.8 | 99.6 | 97.5 | 100 |
| Skamlebæk | 88.4 | 94.3 | 92.0 | 3 |
| So. Jutland | 95.1 | 97.2 | 99.9 | 60 |
| Thisted | 91.4 | 99.2 | 95.6 | 2 |
| Tolne, N.Jutland | 91.0 | 96.6 | 94.4 | 8 |
| Varde | - | - | 99.0 | 8 |
| Vejle | 95.5 | 90.7 | 94.0 | 10 |
| Ølgod | 88.7 | 92.3 | 97.7 | 10 |
| Aalborg | 93.3 | 89.7 | 98.1 | 60 |
| Aarhus | 88.1 | 91.7 | 95.9 | 60 |

+ 18 FM txs below 1kW. A full list is available at dr.dk/hjaelp/radio/sendemaster-og-frekvenser
**DAB+:** All prgrs from DR are also available on the internet and on DAB+: ch.11C on Sealand & Funen, ch. 8B in southern and western Jutland and ch.13B in northern and central Jutland

**P1** on FM (MF 0500-1700, Sat 0500-1700, Sun 0854-1700) + DAB+ (24h). **N:** on the h (except Su 0900 & 1000). N in Danish from KNR, Greenland: MF 1755-1800 – **P2** on FM (MF 1700-0500, Sat 1700-0700, Sun 1700-0854) + DAB+ (24h): Classical music – **P3** on FM (24h) + DAB+ (24h): Popular music, news and sport. N: on the h + MF: 0530, 0630, 0730 – **P4** on FM + DAB+. News, entertainment and regional prgrs. **N:** nat. news on the h and regional news on the half h – **P5** on DAB+. Music etc. for +60, at times relays P4 – **P6 Beat** on DAB+. Indie/alternative music – **P7 Mix** on DAB+. A/C chart hits – **P8 Jazz** on DAB+. Jazz – **DR Nyhedskanalen** on DAB+. News and sports – **DR Langbølge** on LW 243kHz. 0445-0505, 0700-0805, 1045-1135, 1645-1710. Special prgrs.: Wrp: 0445-0500, 0745-0800, 1045-1100 & 1645-1700 & navigational warnings: 1703-1710. Also news from P4 or P1 at 0500-0505, 0700-0705, 0800-0805, 1100-1115 & 1700-1703
**Regional stations:**
MF: 0505-0600, 0605-0700, 0705-0800, 0805-0900, 1130-1133, 1406-1500, 1510-1550 & 1610-1700. Sat 0603-0700, 0707-0800, 0807-0900 & 1130-1132. Sun: 0603-0700, 0703-0800, 0807-0900 & 1130-1132. P4 Trekanten and P4 Esbjerg are on the air at a reduced schedule. At other times national P4 prgrs are carried.
**DR Nordjylland**, Frederik Bajers Vej 9, 9220 Aalborg Ø: on 89.1/94.4/96.7/98.1MHz – **DR Midt- & Vest**, Vestergade 1, 7500 Holstebro: on 95.6/ 97.7/98.5/102.2MHz – **DR Østjylland**, Olof Palmes Alle 10-12, 8200 Aarhus N: on 88.9/95.9/96.4/102.0MHz – **DR Trekanten**, Den Hvide Facet 1, 4., 7100 Vejle: on 94.0MHz – **DR Syd**, H.P. Hansensgade 9-11, 6200 Aabenraa: on 94.0/96.0/99.9/103.7MHz – **DR Esbjerg** (cf. DR Syd) on 99.0/103.7MHz – **DR Fyn**, Lille Tornbjerg Vej 9-10, 5220 Odense SØ: on 96.4/96.8MHz – **DR Sjælland**, Vadestedet 1, 4700 Næsted: on 92.0/92.2/97.5MHz – **DR København**, Emil Holms Kanal 20, 0999 Copenhagen: on 96.5MHz – **DR Bornholm**, Aakirkebyvej 52, 3700 Rønne: on 93.2/99.3MHz
**Ann:** FM: "Du lytter til P et/to/tre/fire" (1st, 2nd, 3rd & 4th prgr.) etc. LW: "Du lytter til DRs langbølgesender på 243 kHz"

### RADIO 24SYV (Pub.)
✉ Vester Farimagsgade 41, 1606 Copenhagen V ☎ +45 31 247 247 **E:** kontakt@radio24syv.dk **W:** radio24syv.dk
**L.P:** Dir: Jørgen Ramskov
**FM (all MHz):** Nakskov 98.8 30kW, Holstebro 100.3 60kW, Funen 100.5 60kW, Tolne N. Jutland 100.7 10kW, Vejle 100.9 10kW, Skamlebæk 101.1 5kW, Thisted 101.3 3kW, Næsted 101.6 100kW, So.Jutland 102.1 60kW, Copenhagen 102.3 60kW, Varde 102.5 10kW, Aalborg 102.7 60kW, Aarhus 103.0 60kW, Bornholm 103.5 30kW + 4 FM tx below 1 kW. Also nationwide on DAB+ ch.12C
**Format:** News/talk

### BAUER MEDIA (Comm.)
✉ HC Andersens Blvd 1, 1553 Copenhagen ☎ +45 33376666 🖷 +45 33930807 **W:** bauermedia.dk
**L.P:** MD: Jim Receveur. CEN: Jan Andersen
**Nova:** AC. Varde 87.8MHz 10kW, So. Jutland 89.3MHz 3kW, Copenhagen 91.4MHz 12kW, Bornholm 92.2MHz 1kW, Funen 93.4MHz 1kW, Vejle 99.3MHz 1kW, Tolne N. Jutland 102.4MHz 1kW, Holstebro 103.4MHz 60kW, Næsted 103.9MHz 100kW, Aalborg 106.0MHz 6kW + 11 stns below 1kW (nominally). Also nationwide on DAB+ ch.12C – **The Voice:** CHR. On 40 FM txs + nationwide on DAB+ ch.12C – **Pop FM:** Classic hits. On 26 FM txs + nationwide on DAB+ ch.12C – **Radio 100:** Hot AC: Copenhagen 100.0MHz 75kW, Randers 99.9MHz 0.5kW + nationwide on DAB+ ch.12C – **Radio Klassisk:** Classical Music

on DAB+ Ch. 12C – **Radio Soft**: A/C Soft non-stop. On 22 FM txs – **MyRock**: Rock. On 24 FM txs + nationwide on DAB+ ch.12C.

### HARTVIG MEDIA (Comm.)
✉ PO Box 112, 8960 Randers SØ. **E:** wmr@wmr.dk. **W:** nb24.dk, wmr.dk & radio208.dk **L.P:** Dir: Stig Hartvig Nielsen
**World Music Radio (WMR):** Copenhagen 927kHz (0.3kW), 5840kHz (0.1kW) and 15805kHz (0.3kW) Tropical world music
**F.PI.: NB24:** Copenhagen 846kHz (0.3kW) News – **Radio208:** Copenhagen 1440kHz (0.5kW), 5800kHz (0.3kW) and 11440kHz (0.1kW) Progressive classic rock (1964-84).
All prgrs are also available on the internet

### RADIO OZ-VIOLA (Priv.)
✉ Engparken 35, 3400 Hillerød **E:** jansteendk@hotmail.com. **W:** www.ozviola.dk **L.P:** Jan Sørensen
**SW:** Hillerød 5825kHz (0.15kW) 1300-1600 Sat/Sun, irr

### EKSTRA BLADET (Comm)
✉ Rådhuspladsen 37, 1785 København V. ☎ +45 33111313. **W:** ekstrabladet.dk/radio/ **Ekstra Bladet Radio:** DAB+ ch. 12C (nationwide). Also available on the internet

### BBC WORLD SERVICE: DAB+ ch.12C (nationwide)

### PRIVATE STATIONS (all MHz):
Approx. 200 organizations are operating low-powered FM txs. (Nominal power: 0.16-0.5kW at 40m. height). Approx. 500 txs are on the air. Frequency lists by region: dkradio.dk. Major stns in the main cities are as follows (only main frequencies mentioned):
**Aabenraa:** Skala FM: 102.6/104.5 – Globus Guld: 106.7 – Classic FM: 92.0/104.0 – Radio Globus: 98.2
**Aalborg:** ANR, Langagervej 1, 9220 Aalborg Ø: 87.6/103.2/103.8 – Radio Nordjyske (same 🔲): 97.1/93.8 – The Voice: 100.2 – Radio Nord, Sigsgaardsvej 16, 9490 Pandrup: 95.1/98.9/102.2 – Radio 100: 101.4 – Grassroots/community stns: 92.2 &101.7
**Aarhus:** Radio go!FM, Jens Baggesens Vej 90K, 8200 Aarhus N: 92.2/94.6/106.5 – The Voice: 93.1/93.7 – Radio 100: 99.9 – MyRock: 90.9 – Radio Soft: 96.9 – Pop FM: 98.3 – Øst FM/Radio Hinnerup: 95.0/105.1 – Radio ABC: 98.9/107.0 – Radio Alfa Aarhus: 104.2 – Din Radio, Ravnsøvej 7, 8240 Risskov: 105.6/107.6 – Grassroots/community stns 89.5/98.7
**Copenhagen:** The Voice: 96.1/104.9/105.4 – Classic Rock: 88.2 – Radio Soft: 95.0/101.8 – MyRock: 92.7/103.6/104.4/105.6 – Pop FM: 89.4/97.2/101.2/104.1 – Radio Nord: 88.6/98.6/107.1/107.9 – Grassroots/community stns: 87.6, 89.6, 90.2, 90.4, 92.9, 94.5, 95.2, 95.5, 97.7, 98.9, 100.9, 102.9, 103.4, 105.9, 106.3, 107.4
**Esbjerg:** Radio Victoria, Borgergade 66, 6700 Esbjerg: 96.5/106.3 – Skala FM: 101.7/105.4/106.8 – Globus Guld: 101.3 – VLR Esbjerg: 100.7 – Radio 100: 90.4 – Radio Soft: 93.5 – The Voice: 91.2 – Classic FM: 105.9 – Rlg. stations: 93.5
**Frederikshavn:** Vendsyssel FM, Sønderjyllands Allé 35, 9900 Frederikshavn: 106.6 – ANR: 107.5 – Radio Nordjyske: 89.0 – Radio Nord: 96.1 – Radio 100: 90.1 – MyRock: 104.4 – The Voice: 99.6 – Radio Soft: 106.3
**Haderslev:** Skala FM: 88.4 – Classic FM: 107.4 – Norea Radio, Porsevej 6, 6100 Haderslev: 98.6 (rlg.) – Globus Guld: 101.7 – Radio Globus: 97.6/103.5
**Herning:** Radio M, Østergade 21, 7400 Herning: 99.7/105.8 – Radio Alfa (same 🔲): 89.5/107.4 – Radio Solo (same 🔲): 91.2/105.3 – Radio Classic, Gl. Kirkevej 33, 7400 Herning: 96.2 – Pop FM: 104.3
**Hjørring/Hirtshals:** Skaga FM, Jørgen Fibigers Gade 20, 9850 Hirtshals: 105.6/106.7 – ANR: 104.7 – Radio Nordjyske: 88.6 – Nova 107.0 – Radio Nord: 88.0 – Radio Soft: 107.8
**Holbæk:** Holbæk Radio, Anders Larsens Vej 7, 1., 4300 Holbæk: 104.7 – SLR: 106.1 – The Voice: 104.3 – MyRock: 90.1
**Holstebro:** Classic FM, Lægårdvej 86, 7500 Holstebro: 105.1/106.2 – Radio Max Holstebro, Enghaven 3, 7500 Holstebro: 97.4
**Horsens:** Radio VLR Horsens, Nørregade 42, 8700 Horsens: 91.1 – Classic FM: 95.3/105.3 – The Voice: 107.9 – MyRock: 107.0 – Nova 103.6 – Radio 100: 106.2 – Pop FM: 98.3
**Kolding:** Radio Viva, Skovvangen 42, 6000 Kolding: 98.0/106.3 – Skala FM, Dalbygade 40, 6000 Kolding: 87.6/105.2 – VLR/VLR Kolding: 103.2 – Radio Globus: 103.8 – Globus Guld: 100.3/102.7 – The Voice: 90.0 – Radio 100: 104.7
**Køge:** Radio Køge, Astersvej 23B, 4600 Køge: 98.2/106.2/106.8 – The Voice: 93.6 – Pop FM: 103.1 – MyRock: 95.6 – Radio Soft: 105.7
**Nyborg:** VLR: 95.3 – Skala: 90.1 – Radio Alfa: 87.6
**Nykøbing F:** Radio Sydhavsøerne, Tværgade 18, 4800 Nykøbing F: 87.8 – Pop FM: 93.0 – The Voice: 106.6 – Nova: 107.2 – MyRock: 106.1 – Radio Soft: 104.6

**Nykøbing M/Thisted:** Radio Limfjord, Gasværksvej 10, 7900 Nykøbing Mors: 104.7/106.9/107.8 – Limfjord Mix (same 🔲): 94.7 – Limfjord Slager (same 🔲): 107.3 – ANR: 97.4 – Radio Nordjyske: 106.7 – Radio Nord: 92.1 – Nova 87.9 – Radio 100: 96.5 – The Voice 106.2
**Næstved/Ringsted/Slagelse:** Radio SLR, Dania 38, 4700 Næstved: 91.6/100.7/101.0/106.5 – The Voice: 104.9/107.5 – MyRock: 95.6/107.5 – Radio 100: 93.7/106.2 – Pop FM: 88.7/106.2 – Radio Soft: 107.1
**Odense:** Skala FM: 91.1/99.1 – The Voice: 98.0/105.1/107.6 – Classic FM: 98.7/103.5 – Radio 100: 101.2 – MyRock: 100.1 – Pop FM: 90.6 – VLR: 98.4 – Radio Soft: 104.2 – Radio Diablo: 106.7 – Grassroots/community stations: 87.9 & 107.1
**Randers:** Radio ABC, Brotoften 10, 8940 Randers SV: 95.3/105.7 – Radio Alfa (same 🔲): 89.4/102.4 – Radio Solo (same 🔲): 93.5/96.4 – Radio Randers, Garnisonsvej 17, 8930 Randers : 104.9 – The Voice: 101.8 – Radio 100: 99.0 – Nova: 92.5 – Pop FM: 99.1 – Radio Soft: 87.6
**Roskilde:** The Voice: 104.3/106.6 – Pop FM: 93.0 – MyRock: 92.7 – Radio Soft: 107.7 – Roskilde Dampradio, Møllehusvej 22, 4000 Roskilde: 97.8
**Rødding:** Radio Globus, Herredfogedvej 2, 6630 Rødding: 104.4 – Globus Guld (same 🔲): 90.1/93.0 – Radio Victoria: 95.7 – Skala FM: 107.5
**Silkeborg:** Radio Silkeborg, Papirfabrikken 18, 8600 Silkeborg: 101.2/107.7 – Radio Alfa: 94.5 – Radio Solo: 104.6/105.9 – Radio ABC: 97.4 – The Voice: 97.8 – Radio Soft: 107.1
**Skive:** Radio Skive, Nordbanevej 1A, 7800 Skive: 104.0 – Radio Alfa Skive (same 🔲): 101.8 – Radio Solo (same 🔲): 107.9 – Radio Viborg: 105.6 – Classic FM: 106.5
**Skjern:** Radio Max, Bækgårdsvej 35C, 6900 Skjern: 105.0 – Skala FM: 107.5 – Grassrot stns: 96.4
**Svendborg:** Radio Diablo, Voldgade 9,1., 5700 Svendborg: 107.7 – Radio Alfa: 88.3 – Skala FM: 90.1/101.0
**Sønderborg:** Classic FM Als, Peblingestien 1, 6430 Nordborg: 88.0 – Globus Guld: 95.4 – Skala FM: 104.4 – Nova: 98.9
**Vejle:** VLR, Bugattivej 8, 7100 Vejle: 88.5/101.7 – Classic FM: 98.2 – The Voice: 105.9 – MyRock: 89.9 – Radio 100: 106.9 – Radio Soft: 98.8 – Globus Guld: 89.5 – Grassroot stn: 105.6
**Viborg:** Radio Viborg, Vesterbrogade 8, 8800 Viborg: 105.0 – Classic FM: 93.8 – Radio Alfa Viborg: 87.6/95.2 – Grassrot stn: 90.9

**DAB+:** Some local/regional, commercial stns are also using DAB+: ch.6A in Nykøbing S, 6D in W.Jutland (Ringkøbing & Herning), 7A in S.Jutland (Rødding), 7C in Vejle, 8A in E.Jutland (Randers, Langaa, Grenaa, Aarhus & Silkeborg), 8C in Thisted, 9B in Copenhagen, 9D in Nivaa (local mux), 11A in Esbjerg, 11B in Aalborg, 11D in Viborg & Skive, 12A in Svendborg and 12A in Bornholm.

## DJIBOUTI

**L.T:** UTC +3h — **Pop:** 910,000 — **Pr.L:** Arabic, French (official), Somali, Afar — **E.C:** 50Hz, 220V — **ITU:** DJI

### MINISTÈRE DE LA COMMUNICATION CHARGÉ DES POSTES ET DE TÉLÉCOMMUNICATIONS (MCPT)
✉ B.P. 32, 1 Rue de Moscou, Djibouti ☎+253 21 353928 🖷 +253 21 353957 **W:** mccpt.dj **E:** mccpt@intnet.dj **L.P:** Minister: Abdi Youssouf Sougueh.

### RADIODIFFUSION TÉLÉVISION DE DJIBOUTI (Gov.)
✉ B.P. 97, 1 Rue St. Laurent du Var, Djibouti ☎+253 21 352294 🖷 +253 21 356502 **W:** rtd.dj **E:** rtd@intnet.dj
**L.P:** DG: Abdoulkader Ahmed Idriss. Dir. Tech. Affairs: Ahmed Doualé. PD: Adoyata Daoud. Dir. Inf: Omar Ali Egueh.

| FM (MHz) | 1 | 2 | Q | kW |
|---|---|---|---|---|
| Ali Sabieh | 90.3 | 94.2 | 103.0 | 0.5 |
| Arta | 93.5 | 89.5 | 104.0 | 3 |
| Ballembaley | 95.3 | 91.3 | - | 1 |
| Dikhil | 96.6 | 98.8 | 104.0 | 0.5/ |
| Djibouti | 89.5/91.3/100.5 | 90.9/93.5/95.3 | 103.0 | 1 |

**Channel 1** in Arabic/Somali: 24h on FM.
**Channel 2** in Afar/French: 24h on FM.
**Q**=Quran prgr. **Ann:** "Radio Djibouti".

### OTHER STATIONS:
**BBC African Sce:** Djibouti 99.2MHz 1kW.
**Monte-Carlo Doualiya:** Arta 97.2MHz 2kW.
**R. Sawa: MW:** Djibouti (Pk 12) 1431kHz 600kW 1600-0400, **FM:** Arta 100.8MHz 5kW 24h.
**Voice of America:** Djibouti 102.0MHz 1kW

## DOMINICA

**L.T:** UTC -4h — **Pop:** 74,000 — **Pr.L:** English, Creole — **E.C:** 50Hz, 230V — **ITU:** DMA

### MINISTRY OF INFORMATION, SCIENCE, TELE-COMMUNICATIONS AND TECHNOLOGY
3rd Floor, Government Headquarters, Kennedy Avenue, Roseau ☎ +1 767 2663294 🖷 +1 767 4480182 **E:** information@dominica.gov. dm **W:** information.gov.dm **L.P:** Minister: Kelver Darroux

### DOMINICA BROADCASTING CORP. (Gov. Comm.)
Victoria St./58 Independence St., PO Box 148, Roseau ☎ +1 767 448 3282/3 🖷 +1 767 448 2918 **W:** dbcradio.net **L.P:** Chairman: Bennette Thomas. GM: Cecil Joseph
**DBS Radio:** Eggleston Roseau 88.1MHz 1kW, Marigot 103.5MHz 0.3kW, Petite Soufriere 103.1MHz 0.1kW, Grand Bay 103.5MHz 0.1kW, Portsmouth 104.1MHz. Own prgrs: 0900-0300. Creole: 1800-2000MF. BBC relay: 1200-1205 & 0300-0900.
**DBS Blaze FM:** Roseau: 89.5MHz. Portsmouth: 104.7

### OTHER STATIONS (FM in MHz):
**DOMINICA CATHOLIC RADIO,** Turkey Lane, Roseau ☎ +1 767 440 7985 **W:** dominicacatholicradio.org FM 96.1. Format: Rlg. – **KAIRI FM**, 42 Independence St., PO Box 331, Roseau ☎ +1 767 448 7330 🖷 +1 767 448 7332 **W:** kairifm.com L.P: CEO: Frankie Bellot. PD: Steve Vidal. FM: **Kairi FM:** 88.7/93.1/107.9 **Hot FM:** 91.1 – **POSSIE VIBRATIONS - FRESH 88.5**, Bay St., Portsmouth ☎ +1 767 616 1512 **W:** possievibrations.org FM: 88.5. Format: Community – **RADIO EN BA MANGO**, Grand Bay ☎ +1 767 446 3207 **W:** southcityagain.webs.com FM: 93.5/96.9. D.Prgr: Fr-Mo 2200-0300. Format: Community – **VIBES RADIO**, 36 Great George St., 2ⁿᵈ floor, Roseau ☎ +1 767 440 8152 🖷 +1 767 448 7376 **W:** vibesradio995. com L.P: Dir: Lennox Lawrence. FM 93.9 & 99.5 (different music formats) – **VOICE OF LIFE RADIO-ZGBC RADIO**, PO Box 205, Madrelle, Loubiere, Roseau ☎ +1 767 448 7017 🖷 +1 767 440 0551 **E:** volradio@cwdom.dm. L.P: GM: Clementina Munro. CEN: Kurt Matthew. FM: 24h Portsmouth 90.7 Roseau 102.1 Marigot 106.1. Format: Rlg. – **WICE Q95**, 10 Hanover Str., PO Box 861, Roseau ☎ +1 767 448 5822 🖷 +1 767 448 5828 **W:** wiceqfm.com L.P: CEO: Sheridan G. Gregoire FM: 90.5/92.3/95.1/95.7/97.5/98.3/105.7

## DOMINICAN REPUBLIC

**L.T:** UTC -4h — **Pop:** 11 million — **Pr.L:** Spanish — **E.C:** 60Hz, 110V — **ITU:** DOM

### INDOTEL - INSTITUTO DOMINICANO DE LAS TELECOMUNICACIONES
Abrahan Lincoln N° 962, Edif. Osiris 1, Planta, 10148 Santo Domingo ☎ +1 829 732 5555 🖷 +1 809 732 3904 **W:** indotel.gob.do **E:** info@indotel.gob.do **L.P:** DG: Luís Henry Molina.

Hrs of tr. 24h unless otherwise stated. Call HI—

| MW | Call | kHz | kW | Station, location and hr of tr. |
|---|---|---|---|---|
| 1) | B20 | 540 | 5 | R. ABC, Santo Domingo: 0900-0400 |
| 2) | B22 | 570 | 10/5 | R. Cristal/LV de la Liberación, Santo Domingo |
| 3) | B24 | 590 | 10/5 | R. Santa María, La Vega: 0900-0300 |
| 4) | C85 | ‡600 | | Celestial 600, Santo Domingo |
| 5) | B28 | 620 | 10 | R. Santo Domingo, Santo Domingo: 1100-0400 |
| 6) | B31 | 650 | 15/5 | R. Universal, Santo Domingo |
| 7) | B32 | 660 | 3 | R. Visión Cristiana, Santiago |
| 8) | B33 | 670 | 5 | R. Dial, San Pedro de Macorís |
| 9) | B38 | 680 | 3 | R. Zamba, San Ignacio de Sabaneta: 0930-0400 |
| 10) | | 710 | | Red Nacional Cristiana, Santo Domingo |
| 11) | B41 | ‡710 | | Ondas del Caribe, San Cristóbal |
| 12) | B42 | 720 | 1.5 | R. Norte, Santiago: 0900-0500 |
| 13) | B48 | ‡720 | 5 | R. Cayacoa, Higüey: 0900-0400 |
| 14) | B44 | 750 | 5 | R. Jesús, Santiago |
| 15) | B47 | ‡780 | 0.5 | R. Constanza, Constanza: 1100-0200 |
| 16) | B50 | 800 | 1 | R. Bonao Bendición, Bonao: 1000-0400 |
| 17) | B52 | 810 | 5 | R. Salvación Internacional, Baní: 1100-0300 |
| 18) | B54 | 830 | 10 | Emisora HIJB, Santo Domingo: 1000-0300 |
| 19) | B59 | 870 | 4 | R. La Vega, La Vega: 1000-0300 |
| 20) | | 890 | 3 | Consentida, Mao: 1000-0300 |
| 21) | B68 | 950 | 10 | R. Popular, Santo Domingo: 1000-0300 |
| 22) | B71 | ‡970 | 6 | R. Olímpica, La Vega |
| 23A) | B72 | 970 | 5/1 | R. Barahona, Barahona |
| 24) | C84 | 990 | 5/1 | R. Eternidad, Sto Domingo: 1100-2400 |
| 25) | B80 | ‡1050 | 1.5 | R. Hispaniola, Santiago |
| 26) | B83 | 1070 | 5/1 | HIBI Radio, San Francisco de Macorís: 0900-0400 |
| 46) | B84 | ‡1080 | 1 | R. RPQ Sport, Santo Domingo |
| 27) | B85 | 1090 | 2.5 | R. Amistad, Santiago |
| 28) | B86 | 1100 | 1 | Aliento FM, San Pedro de Macorís |
| 29) | B91 | 1110 | 1/0.5 | R. Marién, Dajabón: 0930-0200 |
| 30) | B96 | 1150 | 5 | Onda Musical, Sto Domingo: 1100-0500 |
| 31) | C23 | 1200 | | R. VEN - Voz Evangélica Nacional, Sto Domingo |
| 32) | | 1210 | 5 | R. Merengue, San Francisco de Macorís |
| 10) | | 1240 | 1 | Red Nacional Cristiana, Puerto Plata |
| 33) | C26 | ‡1240 | 1 | R. María de la Altagracia, Santo Domingo |
| 34) | C32 | 1270 | 1 | R. Ambiente, Baní: 1000-0400 |
| 35) | C36 | 1310 | 1 | R. Real AM, La Vega: 1100-0400 |
| 7) | C38 | 1330 | 3 | R. Visión Cristiana, Santo Domingo |
| 36) | C41 | 1350 | 1 | Ondas del Yuna, Bonao |
| 37) | C47 | 1380 | 1 | R. Nacional, Santiago: 1000-0300 |
| 38) | | 1380 | | Antena 13-80, Santo Domingo |
| 47) | C50 | ‡1410 | 1 | R. Tricolor, Santo Domingo |
| 39) | C54 | 1430 | 5 | R. Emanuel, Santiago |
| 40) | C55 | 1440 | 5 | R. Impactante, Sto Domingo: 1100-0400 |
| 10) | C60 | 1470 | 1 | Red Nal. Cristiana, San Francisco de Macorís |
| 23B) | | 1470 | | R. Barahona, Duvergé |
| 41) | C67 | 1510 | 10/3 | R. Pueblo, Sto Domingo: 1000-0400 |
| 23C) | C76 | 1580 | 1 | R. Neyba, Neyba: 0900-0400 |
| 42) | C78 | ‡1600 | 1 | R. Revelación en América, Santo Domingo |
| 43) | C80 | 1640 | 1/0.5 | R. Juventus Don Bosco, Santo Domingo |
| 44) | C81 | 1670 | 3 | LV del Yuna, Bonao |
| 45) | C82 | 1680 | 1 | R. Senda, San Pedro de Macorís |

‡ = inactive, (r) = repeater, ± = varying fq.

### Addresses & other information:
**1)** Av Rómulo Betancourt N° 2078, (or Ap 517), Sto Domingo **W:** radio-abc.org – **2)** Av. 27 de Febrero # 514, Edif. Manuel Arsenio Ureña, 6to Piso, Santo Domingo **W:** cristal570.com – **3)** Avenida Pedro A Rivera km 1.5 (or Ap 55), La Vega **W:** radiosantamaria.net – **4)** Avenida Las Américas Esquina España, Santo Domingo – **5)** Ap. 869 (or Dr.Tejada Florentino N° 8), Sto Domingo **W:** radiosantodomingord.com – **6)** Av 27 de Febrero, Edificio Kira, Sto Domingo **W:** radiouniversalam. com – **7)** Calle Sabana Larga #64, Santiago / Calle César Dargán #26, El Vergel (Frente a la Plaza Criolla), Sto Domingo (or P.O. Box 2908, Paterson, NJ 07509-2908, USA) **W:** radiovision.net **Local prgr**: Mon-Fri 2000-2300 – **8)** Av. Independencia No. 169, San Pedro de Macorís **W:** facebook.com/RADIODIAL – **9)** Calle Restauración N° 60 (or: Ap 2), San Ignacio de Sabaneta **W:** radiozamba.com – **10)** Avenida Lope de Vega, Santo Domingo **W:** rednacionalcristiana.org – **11)** San Cristóbal **W:** bocasondasdelcaribe.mex.tl – **12)** Urb. Las Hortensias (or Ap 454), Santiago **W:** norte720.com – **13)** Diócesis de la Alta Gracia, Calle General Santana 65, Higüey **W:** radiocayacoa.com – **14)** Calle Sánchez Esq Pedro F Bonó, Santiago **W:** radiojesus750am.com – **15)** Calle V. M de Robiou N° 18, Constanza **W:** radioconstanza.net – **16)** Calle Libertad N° 15, Bonao **W:** radiobonaobendicion.com - **FM:** 88.7MHz Latina 88 – **17)** Calle Mella esquina Calle 27 de Febrero, Baní **W:** facebook. com/RadioSalvacionInternacional810am – **18)** Edif. Teleantillas, Carr Duarte km 7.5, Sto Domingo **W:** facebook.com/pages/Emisora-HIJB-830-AM/173438096006789 – **19)** Av. Pedro A. Rivera, km 0 (or Ap 203), La Vega **W:** radiolavega.com – **20)** Calle 27 de Febrero Esq. Agustin Cabral (Ap 80), Valverde **W:** consentida890am.com – **21)** Av. Charles Summer N° 33, Los Prados (or Ap 928), Sto Domingo **W:** radiopopularam.com – **22)** Av. Pedro A. Rivera, km 0, (or Ap 203), La Vega **W:** olimpica970.com – **23A-F)** Empresas Radiofónicas SA, Av. Tiradentes #35, Naco. Torre Marmer, Santo Domingo or C/ María Montés #24, Edificio Rodolfo Lama, Barahona **W:** empresasradiofon-icas.com.do/medios/#panel-1 – **24)** Luís Amiama Tió # 105, Arroyo Hondo, Santo Domingo **W:** radioeternidad.com – **25)** Av. Rafael Vidal, Urb. Las Hortensias, Santiago **W:** radiohispaniola.com – **26)** Av 27 de Febrero N° 51 (orAp 201), San Francisco de Macorís **W:** hibiradio1070. blogspot.com – **27)** C/Dr. Arturo Grullon, Edificio Cablenet, Jardines Metropolitanos, Santiago **W:** amistad1090.com - **FM:** 101.9MHz – **28)** **W:** facebook.com/aliento95.5fm – **29)** Pres Henriquez 53, Dajabón **W:** radiomarien.org.do - **FM:** 93.3MHz – **30)** Calle Palo Incado N° 161, Sto Domingo **W:** ondamusical1150.com – **31)** Ap. 2217 (Av. Leopoldo Navarro #34, Esq. Juan E. Dunant, Ensanche Miraflores), Sto Domingo **W:** radioven.org – **32)** Calle 27 de Febrero N° (or Ap 57), San Francisco de Macorís **W:** radiomerengue.net - **FM:** Digital 94.7MHz – **33)** Unicentro Plaza, 2do Nivel, Ave Abraham Lincoln esq. 27 de Febrero, Santo Domingo **W:** facebook.com/radiomariadelalta-gracia – **34)** Sánchez esq Mella, Baní **W:** radioambiente.com.do - **FM:** 96.7MHz – **35)** Juan Rodríguez 76-A, La Vega **W:** radiorealam.net – **36)** Calle Duarte Esq Mella, Edif Fantino (2da planta), Bonao **W:** ondas-delyuna.com – **37)** Av Las Carreras, Esq Mella (4ta Planta), Santiago **W:** radionacional.net – **38)** Avenida Abraham Lincoln 1015, Paraíso,

Santo Domingo – **39)** Calle Cuba No. 46, 3ra planta, Los Pepines, (or Ap. 897) Santiago **W:** radioemanuel.org – **40)** Ave Sarasota esquina Winston Churchill, Plaza Universitaria, Local 9B, Santo Domingo **W:** facebook.com/Radio-Impactante-1440-AM-339671216065657 – **41)** Av. Los Proceres #46, Suite 203, Arroyo Hondo, Santo Domingo **W:** radiopueblo.net – **42)** Santo Domingo **W:** radiorevelacionam.net – **43)** Calle Juan Evangelista Jiménez # 49, Barrio María Auxiliadora, (or Ap. 4848), Santo Domingo **W:** juventusdonbosco.com– **44)** 16 de Agosto esq. Luperón, Bonao **W:** lavozdeluna.org - **FM:** 91.9MHz – **45)** Calle René del Risco Bermúdez No.17, Villa Progreso, San Pedro de Macorís **W:** radiosenda1680.org – **46)** Ave. Abraham Lincoln No. 476, Plaza Lincoln, Santo Domingo **W:** piodeportes.com – **47)** Av. 25 de Febrero 144, Ensanche Las Américas, P3 Hotel Hostal Puerto Rico, Santo Domingo

**FM in Sto Domingo (MHz):**
88.1 Primera FM – 88.5 Studio 88 – 88.9 Escape – 89.3 Neón – 89.7 Renuevo FM – 90.1 Fuego 90 – 90.5 Estrella 90 – 90.9 R. France Int. - 91.3 La 91 FM – 91.7 La Roka FM – 92.1 Hits 92 – 92.5 CDN R. - 92.9 Pura Vida 92.9 – 93.3 Independencia FM – 93.7 Latidos FM – 94.1 Fidelity – 94.5 KQ94 – 94.9 Kiss 95 – 95.3 Ministerio de Educación – 95.7 La Nota Diferente – 96.1 Quisqueya FM – 96.5 Ritmo 96 – 96.9 Exa FM – 97.3 R. Disney – 97.7 Estación 97.7 – 98.1 R. Amanecer – 98.5 Rumba FM – 98.9 Dominicana FM – 99.3 Sonido Suave – 99.7 Listín – 100.1 "100.1" – 100.5 Cima – 100.9 Súper Q – 101.3 Z101 Digital – 101.7 Top Lantina – 102.1 La X 102 – 102.5 Escándalo FM – 102.9 Raíces FM - 103.3 Los 40 Principales – 103.7 Power FM – 104.1 R. Caliente – 104.5 Mixx - 105.3 ABC – 105.7 La Bakana FM – 106.1 Disco 106 – 106.5 Zol FM – 106.9 LV Cultural de las FF AA – 107.3 La Kalle – 107.7 La Súper 7

**FM in Santiago (MHz):**
88.1 Primera FM – 88.5 Comando FM – 88.9 Sistema 89 – 89.3 R. Disney – 89.7 CDN R. – 90.1 Primor FM – 90.5 Fuego 90 – 90.9 R. Amanecer – 91.3 La 91 FM (relay) – 91.7 Contacto FM – 92.1 ZOL FM (relay) – 92.7 Lider FM – 93.1 Concierto FM – 93.7 R. Luz – 94.1 Full FM – 94.7 KV 94 – 95.1 Raices – 95.5 Digital FM – 95.9 Clave FM – 96.3 La Kalle – 97.1 Caliente – 97.5 Tremenda – 98.3 Turbo 98 – 99.1 Mortal FM (relay) – 100.3 Monumental FM – 101.1 Premium – 101.5 Z-101 (relay) – 101.9 Amistad FM – 103.1 Super 103 – 103.5 La N – 103.9 Super Regional – 104.3 Sonido HD – 104.7 Matrix – 105.5 Ke Buena – 105.9 La Bakana FM – 106.1 Criolla 106 – 106.5 R. Luz FM – 106.9 La Nueva 107 – 107.3 Suave 107 – 107.9 Mix 107.9

**FM in Puerto Plata (MHz):**
88.7 Zona FM – 89.3 La 89.3 FM - 90.5 Fantasía FM – 91.7 Melody FM – 92.5 L'arena – 92.9 Orbita FM – 95.3 Arca de Salvación – 96.3 La Kalle – 97.3 La 97.3 FM – 99.7 La 99 FM – 101.7 Romance FM – 104.9 La 104.9 FM – 106.3 Perla FM – 106.9 Master FM

## EASTER ISLAND (Chile)

**L.T:** UTC -6h (12 Aug 18-7 Apr 19, 8 Sep 19-5 Apr 20: -5h; dates subject to confirmation) — **Pop:** 5,700 — **Pr.L:** Spanish, Rapanui — **E.C:** 50Hz, 220V — **ITU:** PAQ

| AM | KHz | kW | Station | | | |
|---|---|---|---|---|---|---|
| 2) | 580 | 0.4 | R. Manukena | | | |

| FM | MHz | kW | Station | FM | MHz | kW | Station |
|---|---|---|---|---|---|---|---|
| 1) | 88.3 | - | ADN R. | 2) | 88.9 | 1 | R. Manukena |
| 2) | 99.1 | - | R. Rapanui | 3) | 104.3 | - | Los 40 Principales |
| 5) | 99.9 | - | R. Maria | 4) | 107.3 | - | R. Nuevo Tiempo |

**Addresses & other information**
**1)** 24h satellite rel. ADN Santiago **W:** adnradio.cl – **2)** La Misma Municipalidad de Isla de Pascua, Calle Atamu Tekena, Hangaroa. Correo Isla de Pascua, Chile ☎+56 32 2255 1245 **W:** portalrapanui.cl/rapanui/radiomanukena & facebook.com/oficial-radio-manukena **LP:** Dir: Juan Herrera Torres. Local community radio stn. **D.Prgr:** 24h – **3)** 24h satellite relay from Santiago **W:** los40.cl – **4)** 24h satellite relay from Santiago (Rlg.) **W:** nuevotiempo.org – **5)** 24h satellite relay from Santiago **W:** radiomaria.cl

## ECUADOR

**L.T:** UTC -5h — **Pop:** 17 million — **Pr.L:** Spanish, Quichua — **E.C:** 60Hz, 120V — **ITU:** EQA

**AGENCIA DE REGULACIÓN Y CONTROL DE LAS TELECOMUNICACIONES (ARCOTEL)**
🖳 Av. Diego de Almagro N31-95 entre Whymper y Alpallana, Quito ☎ +593 2 294 6400 **W:** arcotel.gob.ec **E:** comunicacion@arcotel.gob.ec

| MW | Call | kHz | kW | Station, location, hr. of tr. |
|---|---|---|---|---|
| GU01) | FA2 | 540 | 25 | R. Santiago, Guayaquil: 1100-0600 |
| GU02) | AK2 | 560 | 10 | CRE Satelital, Guayaquil |
| PI03) | CE1 | ‡570 | 1 | R. El Sol, Quito |
| GU03) | FC2 | ‡580 | 10 | R. Uno, Guayaquil |
| PI04) | RF1 | 590 | 5 | R. Super K800, Quito (r. 800kHz) |
| GU04) | XY2 | 600 | 40 | R. Ciudadana, Guayaquil: 1100-0400 |
| PI05) | MJ1 | 610 | 10 | R. Caravana, Quito |
| LO01) | XY3 | 620 | 7 | R. Ciudadana, Loja: 1100-0400 |
| GU05) | BI2 | 640 | 10 | R. Morena, Guayaquil |
| MA01) | FD4 | 650 | 5 | R. Visión, Manta: 0900-0500 |
| PI07) | FF1 | ‡670 | 10 | R. Jesus del Gran Poder, Quito |
| GU06) | VP2 | 680 | 10 | R. Atalaya, Guayaquil |
| GU07) | RS2 | 700 | 50 | R. Sucre, Guayaquil |
| EO01) | PR2 | 720 | 10 | R. Única, Machala |
| MA03) | GB4 | 720 | 5 | LV de Portoviejo, Portoviejo |
| PI09) | IC1 | 720 | 5 | R. Municipal, Quito |
| PI15) | GC1 | ‡740 | 10 | R. Melodía, Quito |
| GU09) | RC2 | 750 | 30 | R. Caravana, Guayaquil |
| PI10) | QE1 | 760 | 10 | R. Quito, Quito |
| GU10) | MF2 | 770 | 25/12 | R. Revolución, Guayaquil |
| GU08) | ML2 | 800 | 10 | R. Super K800, Guayaquil |
| CA01) | VI5 | 820 | 5 | R. LV de Ingapirca, Cañar: 0900-0330 |
| GU12) | RM2 | 830 | 10 | R. Huancavilca, Guayaquil |
| PI16) | PN1 | 840 | 25 | R. Vigía "LV de la Policía Nacional", Quito |
| GU13) | YS2 | 850 | 20 | R. San Francisco, Guayaquil |
| PI17) | PC1 | 860 | 10 | R. Positiva, Quito: 1015-0400 |
| GU14) | LY2 | 870 | 16 | R. Cristal, Guayaquil: 1000-0600 |
| TU02) | GS6 | ‡870 | 0.5 | R. Píllaro, Píllaro |
| PI18) | FJ1 | 880 | 10 | R. Católica Nacional, Quito: 1000-0200 |
| PI19) | VA1 | ‡900 | 10 | R. Sucre, Quito |
| GU15) | BO2 | 910 | 10 | La Radio Redonda, Guayaquil |
| EO02) | RU3 | 920 | 10 | CRO - Compañía Radiofónica Orense, Machala |
| PI40) | AB1 | 920 | 10 | R. Democracia, Quito |
| TU03) | BA6 | 930 | 5 | R. Ambato, Ambato |
| AZ21) | CP5 | 940 | 3 | R. Caravana, Cuenca |
| PI21) | BZ1 | 940 | 10 | R.CCE-Casa de la Cultura Ecuatoriana, Quito |
| CR05) | UE5 | 950 | 3 | LV de AIIECH, Colta |
| IM02) | AV1 | 950 | 3 | R. Chaskis del Norte, Ibarra |
| AZ02) | SA5 | 960 | 1.5 | R. Sonoonda Internacional, Cuenca:0900-0300 |
| TU04) | JX6 | ‡960 | 1 | LV del Santuario, Baños |
| IM03) | MB1 | 970 | 1 | R. Imperio, Ibarra: 1030-0300 |
| CR06) | JI5 | 980 | 1 | R. El Prado, Riobamba: 0900-0300 |
| TU05) | NR6 | 1010 | 10 | R. Líder TSB, Ambato: 0930-0300 |
| EO3) | GO3 | 1020 | 5 | Radio Estelar, Santa Rosa |
| GU21) | RF2 | 1030 | 5 | R. Ecuantena, Guayaquil: 1100-0500 |
| AZ05) | EV5 | 1040 | 10 | R. Splendid, Cuenca |
| TU06) | GB6 | 1040 | 1 | R. Colosal, Ambato: 0930-0500 |
| GU49) | RQ2 | 1050 | 5 | R. Águila, Guayaquil: 1030-0400 |
| CP01) | MG6 | ‡1060 | 1.5 | R. Ecos del Pueblo, Saquisilí |
| EO19) | CH2 | 1060 | 3 | R. Fiesta, Machala: 1100-0500 |
| AZ06) | CJ5 | 1070 | 5 | LV del Tomebamba, Cuenca: 1000-0500 |
| CP02) | BH6 | 1080 | 10 | R. Latacunga AM, Latacunga: 0900-0230 |
| GU22) | KD2 | 1080 | 10 | Sistema 2, Guayaquil |
| MA11) | AB4 | 1080 | 1 | R. Contacto, Manta: 0900-0300 |
| PI30) | VC1 | 1090 | 3 | R. Irfeyal "LV de Fe y Alegría", Quito |
| CP03) | GR6 | 1100 | 1 | R. Novedades, Latacunga |
| NA02) | LE7 | 1100 | 1 | R. Oriental, Tena: 0900-0400 |
| AZ07) | FC5 | 1110 | 5 | R. Ondas Azuayas, Cuenca: 1100-0200 |
| PI31) | JR1 | ‡1110 | 7 | R. Arpeggio, Quito |
| EO20) | CC3 | 1130 | 1 | R. Romántica, Machala |
| TU08) | PV6 | 1130 | 3 | R. Centro, Ambato |
| AZ08) | AZ5 | 1140 | 3 | R. Alpha Musical, Cuenca: 1100-0600 |
| PI33) | IR1 | ‡1140 | 3 | R. Raíz, Quito |
| CA02) | CY5 | 1160 | 3 | LV del Pueblo, Azogues |
| CP04) | UR6 | 1160 | 1 | R. Runatacuyac, Latacunga |
| EO05) | VR3 | 1160 | 1 | R. Vía, Machala |
| GU26) | RV2 | 1170 | 5 | R. Filadelfia, Guayaquil |
| AZ09) | DP5 | ‡1180 | 2 | R. Cuenca "LV de los 4 Ríos", Cuenca |
| CP05) | RF6 | 1190 | 1 | R. Nueva Sol, Pujilí: 1100-0200 |
| GU24) | DE2 | 1190 | 2 | UCSG Radio, Guayaquil: 1100-0500 |
| AZ10) | RM5 | ‡1200 | 2 | R. El Mercurio, Cuenca |
| PI36) | CS1 | 1200 | 3 | R. Super K 1200, Sangolquí: 1000-0100 |
| GU27) | BJ2 | ‡1210 | 10 | R. El Mundo, Guayaquil |
| LO07) | VC3 | 1210 | 10 | La Hechichera, Loja |
| TU09) | JM6 | 1210 | 5 | R. SIRA, Ambato: 1000-0600 |
| PI32) | PA1 | 1220 | 5 | R. Marañón, Quito |
| GU48) | RO2 | 1220 | 5 | R. Galáctica, Guayaquil: 1000-0400 |
| IM06) | RI1 | ‡1230 | 1.5 | CRI-Centro Radiofónico de Imbabura, Ibarra |
| PI37) | PA1 | 1240 | 1 | R. Metropolitana, Yaruquí: 1200-0300 |
| CC01) | EM1 | 1250 | 2 | R. Ondas Carchenses, Tulcán: 1000-0400 |
| AZ12) | CL3 | 1260 | 2 | R. Contacto XG, Cuenca: 1100-0400 |
| TU10) | RO6 | 1260 | 1 | R. Calidad, Ambato: 0930-0600 |

| MW | Call | kHz | kW | Station, location, hr. of tr. |
|---|---|---|---|---|
| GU23) | UM2 | 1270 | 10 | R. Universal, Guayaquil |
| MA15) | LD4 | 1270 | 2 | R. Junín, Junín: 1100-0500 |
| PI61) | | ‡1280 | 1 | R. Universitaria, Quito |
| AZ13) | JA5 | 1290 | 3 | LV del Río Tarqui, Cuenca: 0900-0200 |
| IM07) | NS1 | ‡1290 | 1 | R. Popular, Atuntaqui: 1100-0300 |
| BO04) | AK6 | 1300 | 3.5 | R. La Paz, Guaranda |
| SD04) | RU1 | 1300 | 2.5 | R. Festival, Sto Domingo de los Colorados |
| CA03) | CI5 | 1310 | 3 | R. Internacional TVO, Biblián |
| CR20) | AI5 | ‡1310 | 0.5 | Eco de los Andes, Cumandá: 1000-0200 |
| EO11) | CP3 | 1310 | 0.5 | LV de El Oro, Pasaje |
| LR05) | FR2 | 1320 | 1 | R. Guayacal, Babahoyo: 1030-0300 |
| MA24) | VO4 | ‡1320 | 1 | R. Carrizal, Calceta: 1130-0300 |
| TU11) | JD6 | 1320 | 3 | R. Continental, Ambato: 0930-0400 |
| EO12) | RV3 | ‡1330 | 2 | R. Nacional El Oro, Machala: 1000-0600 |
| ES03) | CO4 | 1340 | 5 | LV de su Amigo, Esmeraldas |
| LO08) | RG3 | ‡1340 | 1 | Ondas de Esperanza, Loja |
| AZ15) | SF5 | 1350 | 1 | San Fernando Radio, San Fernando |
| GU47) | VR2 | 1350 | 3 | Teleradio 1350 AM , Guayaquil |
| CA04) | AO5 | 1370 | 7 | R. El Rocio, Biblián |
| GU32) | VO2 | 1370 | 5 | LV de Milagro, Milagro |
| PI45) | CV1 | 1380 | 5 | R. Cristal "RCQ", Quito: 0830-0300 |
| TU13) | JR6 | 1380 | 1 | R. Mera, Ambato |
| AZ16) | EA5 | 1390 | 1.5 | R. Tropicana, Cuenca: 1200-0300 |
| GU16) | FL2 | 1400 | 3 | R. Z Uno, Guayaquil |
| AZ17) | KD5 | 1410 | 1 | R. Centro Gualaceo, Gualaceo |
| ES05) | FB4 | ‡1410 | 1 | LV de Quinindé, Quinindé |
| GU33) | CQ2 | ‡1410 | 1 | R. San Francisco, Milagro |
| PI59) | VE1 | 1410 | 1 | R. El Tiempo "La Emisora del Amor", Quito |
| EO15) | IM3 | 1420 | 2 | R. Corazón, Machala |
| NA06) | MJ7 | ‡1420 | 2 | LV del Napo, Tena |
| PI46) | GF1 | ‡1430 | 3.5 | R. Futura, Quito |
| CA05) | OV5 | 1440 | 2 | Ondas del Volante, Azogues: 1000-1800 |
| IM11) | BA1 | 1440 | 1 | R. Panorama, Ibarra: 1030-0400 |
| SE01) | SE2 | ‡1450 | 1 | R. Santa Elena, Santa Elena: 2200-0200 |
| PI47) | SC1 | 1450 | 1 | AS La Radio, Tabacundo |
| CP12) | IC6 | 1460 | 3 | R. Nuevos Horizontes, Latacunga: 1000-0200 |
| GU37) | LD2 | 1470 | 1.5 | R. Ecos de Naranjito, Naranjito |
| PI48) | ED1 | 1470 | 1 | Rdif. Ecos de Cayambe, Cayambe |
| MA20) | HV4 | 1480 | 1 | R. LV de Jipijapa, Jipijapa: 1100-0400 |
| CA06) | AM5 | 1490 | 2 | R. Santa María, Azogues |
| GU38) | VY2 | 1490 | 1 | R. Dinámica, Guayaquil |
| PI60) | MV1 | ‡1490 | 3 | R. La Poderosa, Quito |
| BO07) | RY6 | 1510 | 1 | R. Runacunapac Yachana, Simiátug |
| CA07) | MC5 | ‡1510 | 2 | LV de la Juventud, Cañar |
| GU39) | IO2 | 1510 | 0.5 | R. Naval, Guayaquil |
| PI56) | BD1 | 1510 | 3 | R. Monumental, Quito: 1300-0400 |
| CR18) | RI5 | 1520 | 1 | LV de Guamote, Guamote |
| CA08) | CC5 | 1530 | 5 | Ondas Cañaris AM, Azogues |
| CR19) | VP5 | ‡1530 | 1 | LV de Pallatanga, Pallatanga |
| SE02) | MP2 | ‡1530 | 1 | LV de la Península, La Libertad: 1100-0300 |
| TU15) | MZ6 | 1530 | 3 | R. Dorado Deportes, Pelileo: 1130-0230 |
| LR10) | FM2 | 1540 | 3 | R. Cristal de Ventanas, Babahoyo |
| AZ18) | AD5 | ‡1550 | 1 | R. Chaguarurco, Santa Isabel |
| GU42) | AD2 | 1550 | 1 | LV de El Triunfo, El Triunfo: 1100-0400 |
| IM15) | ZD1 | 1560 | 1.5 | R. Ecos Culturales de Urcuquí, Urcuquí |
| MA23) | CC4 | 1570 | 20 | R. La Voz, Manta |
| PI52) | LF1 | ‡1580 | 1 | R. Orellana, Machachi |
| PI53) | RZ1 | 1590 | 1 | R. Mensaje, Cayambe |
| TU17) | QT6 | 1590 | 1 | R. Panamericana, Quero |

Hrs of tr. 24h unless stated otherwise. Call HC—
° = also on SW, ‡ = inactive, (r) = repeater, ± = varying fq.

| SW | Call | kHz | kW | Station, location, h of tr |
|---|---|---|---|---|
| PI08) | | 6050 | 1 | R. HCJB, Quito: 0925-1400, 2100-0235 |

**Province-abbreviations:** AZ=Azuay BO=Bolívar CA=Cañar CC=Carchi CP=Cotopaxi CR=Chimborazo EO=El Oro ES=Esmeraldas GU=Guayas IM=Imbabura LO=Loja LR=Los Ríos MA=Manabí MS=Morona Santiago,NA=Napo PA=Pastaza PI=Pichincha SD=Santo Domingo de los Tsáchilas SE=Santa Elena SU=Sucumbíos TU=Tungurahua ZC=Zamora Chinchipe **N.B.:** These abbreviations are not recognized by the Ecuadorian Post Office. Letters should carry the full name.

**Addresses & other information:**
**AZ00) AZUAY**
**AZ02)** Av.Remigio Crespo y Calle La Libertad, Cuenca **W:** sonoondainternacional.com – **AZ05)** Cas 01-01-1352, Cuenca **W:** radiosplendid.com.ec – **AZ06)** Cas 01-01-0493, Cuenca **W:** www.lavozdeltomebamba.com – **AZ07)** Cas 01-01-4980 (or Av Héroes de Verdeloma 9-15), Cuenca **W:** facebook.com/ondas.azuayas – **AZ08)** Simon Bolívar 226, Cuenca **W:** facebook.com/RadioAlphaMusical1140Am – **AZ09)**

Bomboiza 1-83, entre Loja-Pastaza, Cuenca **W:** facebook.com/Radio-Cuenca-516150911750972 – **AZ10)** Av.de las Américas, Edif.Mercurio, Cuenca **W:** radioelmercurio.com.ec – **AZ12)** J. Dávila y C. Merchán, Cuenca **W:** 1260am.blogspot.com – **AZ13)** Manuel Vega 653 y Presidente Córdoba, Cuenca **W:** lavozdelriotarqui.com – **AZ15)** Av. José María Quito y Santiago de San Fernando, San Fernando **W:** san-fernandoradio.com – **AZ16)** Cas 830 (or Pumapungo 5-50), Cuenca **W:** tropicanalasuper.myl2mr.com – **AZ17)** Gran Colombia y 9 de Octubre 3102, Frente al Parque Central, Gualaceo **W:** radiocentrogualaceo.com – **AZ18)** Cas 01-01-46 (or Calle Bolívar 7-64), Aperado (or Calle 24 de Mayo y Abdon Calderón, Cuenca) **W:** facebook.com/radio-chaguarurco – **AZ21)** J. Roldos 480, Edif El Consorcio, Cuenca **W:** radiocaravana.com
**BO00) BOLÍVAR**
**BO03)** 10 de Agosto 612, Guaranda - **FM:** 93.9MHz – **BO04)** G Moreno y 7 de Mayo, Guaranda **W:** radiolapaz1300am.com – **BO07)** Echeandia s/n y Barragán, 020108 Simiátug Guaranda **W:** radiorunacunapac.org
**CA00) CAÑAR**
**CA01)** Av Ingapirca, Cdla El Vergel, Cañar (or Cas 01-01-0447, Cuenca) **Quichua:** 0900-1300, 2100-0200 - **FM:** 94.5MHz mostly different programming **W:** radioingapirca.com.ec – **CA02)** General Vintimilla 1-10 y Oriente, Azogues **W:** radiolavozdelpueblo.com – **CA03)** Mariscal Sucre 722 y B Ochoa, Biblián (or Cas 729, Azogues) **W:** radiointernacionaltvo.com – **CA04)** Calle Mariscal Sucre 202 y Tarquí, Biblián **W:** radioelrocio1370.com – **CA05)** Bolivar y Azuay, Azogues **W:** facebook.com/ondasdelvolante – **CA06)** Cas 03-01-730, Azogues **W:** facebook.com/RadioSantaMariaAM – **CA07)** Bolívar y Borrero (Junto Parque Central), Cañar – **CA08)** Universidad Católica de Cuenca - sede Azogues, Calle Rivera 613, Azogues **W:** ondascanaris.com.ec
**CC00) CARCHI**
**CC01)** Olmedo 52-025 y Ayacucho (or Cas. 30), Tulcán **W:** ondascarchenses.com
**CP00) COTOPAXI**
**CP01)** Imbabura 2333 y 9 de Octubre, Saquisilí **W:** ecosdelpueblo.com – **CP02)** Cas 05-01-392 (or Calle Quito 14-56, Pasaje La Catedral), Latacunga **W:** radiolatacunga.com – **FM:** 97.1/102.1MHz – **CP03)** 2 de Mayo 438, entre Tarquí y General Maldonado, Latacunga **W:** facebook.com/SoloDeportesRadioNovedadesAm1100khz – **CP04)** Bel.Quevedo Caserío Illuchi, Latacunga **W:** radiorunatacuyac.org In Quichua/Spanish – **CP05)** B Quevedo 555, Pujilí – **CP12)** Faustino Sarmiento 5046 y Vela, Latacunga **W:** rnh146.wix.com/rnh146
**CR00) CHIMBORAZO**
**CR05)** Cas.87A, Majipamba, Colta **W:** lavozdeaiiech.org.ec Prgrs in Quichua only - **FM:** 101.7MHz – **CR06)** Francia 1857 y Villaroel, Riobamba **W:** radioelprado.blogspot.com In Quichua&Spanish – **CR18)** Comunidad Sta Cruz, Guamote **W:** lavozdeguamote.org – **CR19)** Panamericana y Eloy Alfaro, Pallatanga – **CR20)** 1 Constituyente y G Rendon, Cumanda.
**EO00) EL ORO**
**EO01)** Bolívar Madero 1313, via Pto Bolívar, Machala **W:** facebook.com/radiounica720 – **EO02)** Bolívar 601, Edif.Encasa, Machala **W:** radiocro920am.com – **EO03)** Av. General Eloy Alfaro, a una cuadra de la Terminal Terrestre Binacional, Santa Rosa **W:** radioestelaram.wixsite.com/1020-khz – **EO05)** Cas 01-01-0086, Machala (or 9 de Octubre y Paéz), Machala **W:** viaradio.globalmediahd.net – **EO11)** San Martín 720, Entre Municipalidad y Och, Pasaje **W:** facebook.com/lavozdeeloro – **EO12)** 9 de Octubre y Sta Rosa, Machala **W:** facebook.com/pages/Radio-Nacional-El-ORO/570938789584764 – **EO15)** Av Buena Vista 742 y 4ta Norte, Machala – **EO19)** Av 9 de Octubre y 23 de Abril, Machala **W:** radiofiestamachala.com – **EO20)** Av 12va Norte y Buena Vista, Machala **W:** radioromanticamachala.blogspot.com
**ES00) ESMERALDAS**
**ES03)** Manuela Cañizares y Olmedo, Esmeraldas **W:** vozdesuamigo.com - **FM:** 96.3MHz – **ES05)** Simon Plata Torres y Maclovio Velazco, Quinindé **W:** radiosteroquininde.wixsite.com/radiosteroquininde - **FM:** 94.9MHz
**GU00) GUAYAS**
**GU01)** Cdla. Bolivariana, Avda. del Libertador Mz K Villa 8, Guayaquil **W:** radiosantiago.com.ec – **GU02)** Boyacá 642 y Padre Solano, Edificio El Torreón, 8vo. piso, Guayaquil **W:** radiocre.com – **GU03)** Cas 2119, Guayaquil (or Amazonas 743 y Veintemilla, P8, Quito) **W:** radiouno-580am.com – **GU04)** Quisquis 316 y Garaicoa, Edif Huancavelica, Guayaquil **W:** laciudadana.gob.ec – **GU05)** Av. Quito 1200 y Aguirre, Guayaquil **W:** radiomorena640.com – **GU06)** Rumichaca 934 y Velez, Guayaquil **W:** radioatalaya.net – **GU07)** Cas 11714 (or Av.Francisco de Orellana y Juan Tanca Marengo), Guayaquil **W:** radiosucre.com.ec – **GU08)** Av. Americas y Av. Constitución, dentro de TC Televisión, Guayaquil **W:** superk800.com – **GU09)** Cas 716, (or Av Juan Tanga Marengo km 3), Guayaquil **W:** radiocaravana.com/reproductores.php – **GU10)** Cas 09-01-4203 (or Colón 548 y Boyacá, P7), Guayaquil – **GU12)** Cas 856 (or Av. Guillermo Pareja Rolando, (Principal de la Alborada) y

la novena (esquina), Cdla. IETEI, Mz 2, solar 7), Guayaquil **W:** radio-huancavilca.com.ec – **GU13)** Cas 09-01-5762, Guayaquil **W:** radiosanfrancisco850am.com – **GU14)** Cas 5062 (or Laque 1407 y Antepara), Guayaquil **W:** radiocristal.com.ec – **GU15)** Malecón 206 entre Juan Montalvo y Loja, Guayaquil - **W:** laradioredonda.ec/AM/ – **GU16)** radioz1.ec – **GU18)** 10 de Agosto 504 y Chimborazo, P3), Guayaquil **E:** servidor1000@hotmail.com – **GU21)** Los Ríos 609, Cond Orellana, P4, Ofc 2, Guayaquil **W:** radioecuantena.com.ec – **GU22)** Ciudadela Albatros Calle Fragata # 203, atrás de la Sociedad Italiana Garibaldi, Avenida de las Américas, Guayaquil **W:** radiosistema2.com Also r. R. Sucre 700kHz – **GU23)** Chimborazo 3407 Y El Oro, Guayaquil **W:** radiouniver-salgye.com – **GU24)** Universidad Católica de Santiago de Guayaquil, Av. Carlos Julio Arosemena Km. 1 1/2 Vía Daule, Guayaquil **W:** ucsgrtv.com/radio – **GU26)** Veléz 905, Edif.Forum, P16 (or Cas 8729), Guayaquil. Also in Quchua **W:** radiofiladelfiamundial.com – **GU27)** Jiguas 500 y V.Emilio Estrada, Guayaquil **W:** angelfire.com/nt2/radioelmundo – **GU32)** Av. 17 de Septiembre y Azogues, esq. Edif. Radio, Milagro **W:** radiolavozdemilagro.com – **GU33)** Calle García Moreno y Bolívar 1013, Milagro **W:** facebook.com/RadioSanFranciscoMilagro – **GU37)** Av 5 de Octubre 150, Naranjito **W:** radioecosdenaranjito.com – **GU38)** Av 25 de Julio cdla 7 Lagos C, Guayaquil **W:** facebook.com/RadioDinamicaEcuador1490 – **GU39)** Cas 5940, Guayaquil **W:** inocar.mil.ec/web/index.php/boletines/avisos-navegantes/27-radio-naval/117-radio-naval-on-line – **GU42)** Jaime Roldos 700 y Av.8 de Abril, El Triunfo **W:** lavozdeltriunfo.com – **GU43)** Cdla.Belén Piedrahita y 1era, Daule – **GU47)** 9 de Octubre y Baquerizo Moreno, Edif.Plaza, P1, Guayaquil **W:** teleradio.com.ec – **GU48)** Edif El Forum, P5, Ofic 508, Guayaquil **W:** radiogalactica1230am.jimdo.com – **GU49)** Eloy Alfaro Duran en la Av. Samuel Cisneros, via el Secap, Guayaquil **W:** radioaguila1050am.com

### IM00) IMBABURA
**IM02)** Celiano Aguinaga y Panamericana Sur, Atuntaqui, Ibarra – **IM03)** Cas 413 (or Olmedo 1178 y Av.Peréz Guerrero), Ibarra **W:** radioimperio970.com – **IM06)** Río Chinchipe 397 y Río Daule, Ibarra – **IM07)** Cas 3, Atuntaqui **W:** wecyhpt.wixsite.com/radiopopular/social-media – **IM11)** Juan José Flores 11-26 y Jaime Rivadeneira, Ibarra **W:** radiopanorama1440.com – **IM15)** Antonio Ante s/n, Urcuquí **W:** ecosculturales.com – **IM16)** Jirón Roldos Aguilera y Panamericana Norte, Otavalo **E:** radiochaskis@hotmail.com

### L000) LOJA
**L001)** Av.J.A Eguuigurren y Bolívar, Loja **W:** laciudadana.gob.ec – **L003)** 24 de Mayo y Eloy Alfaro, Catamayo - **FM:** 93.7MHz – **L007)** Cas 196 (or Olmedo 11-56 y Mercadillo), Loja - **FM:** 88.9MHz – **L008)** Olmedo 1146 entre Azuay y Mercadillo, Loja **W:** oeradio.org – **L015)** Asociación Cristiana de Indigenas Saraguros, Saraguro - **FM:** 93.1MHz

### LR00) LOS RÍOS
**LR05)** Cdla El Mamey, Babahoyo – **LR10)** 28 de Mayo 1412 y 6 de Octubre, Babahoyo **W:** radiocristal.com.ec

### MA00) MANABÍ
**MA01)** Av.10ma y Calle 17, P2, Manta **W:** radiovisiondemanta.com – **MA03)** Ricaurte y P. Moreira, Portoviejo – **MA11)** 9 y Malecón, Edif "Jacob Vera", P1 Ofc 7, Manta **W:** radiocontactoam.com.ec – **MA15)** 10 de Agosto 180 y Eloy Alfaro, Junín **W:** radiojunin1270.com – **MA20)** Noboa y Colón, Jipijapa – **MA23)** Edificio Jacob Vera 1, Primer Piso Alto Of. 1, Manta **W:** lavoz1570.com – **MA24)** Flavio Alfaro 718 Ciudadela San Bartolo, Calceta **W:** radiocarrizalfm.com - **FM:** 96.1 – **MA25)** Cas 13-02-0629 (or Montufar N° 1014 y Aguilera), Bahía de Caráquez - **FM:** 95.3

### MS00) MORONA SANTIAGO
**MS06)** Federación de Centros Shuar, Domingo Comín 17-38, Sucúa (or Cas 17-01-4122, Quito).

### NA00) NAPO
**NA02)** Cas 260 (or Av.Jumandy 536, Barrio 2 Rios), Tena **W:** radioorientaltena.com - **FM:** 89.7MHz – **NA06)** Misión Josefina, Juan Montalvo s/n y P Central, Tena **W:** lavozdelnapo.com - **FM:** 88.5MHz

### PI00) PICHINCHA
**PI03)** 18 de Septiembre y Ulpiano Páez, Quito **W:** radioelsol.net – **PI04)** see GU08) – **PI05)** see GU09) – **PI07)** Cuenca 477 y Sucre (El convento de San Francisco), Quito 7 **W:** radiojesusdelgranpoder.com – **PI08)** Cas 17-17-691(or Villalengua 884 y Av.10 de Agosto), Quito. **D.Prgr.** in Spanish, Quichua, Cofan, Waorani and Cha'palaa. For exact schedule see Internatina Radio section **W:** radiohcjb.org – **PI09)** García Moreno 751 entre Sucre y Bolívar, P3, Quito **W:** www.radiomunicipal.gob.ec – **PI10)** Cas 17-21-1971 (or La Coruña 2104 y Whimper, Edif.Aragones) Quito **W:** ecuadoradio.ec – **PI15)** Panamericana Sur km 14.5, Quito – **PI16)** Ramírez Dávalos 612 y 10 de Agosto, Quito **W:** radiovigiafm.com – **PI17)** Av.Amazonas y Colón, Edif.España, P4, Ofc.42, Quito **W:** radiopositiva.com.ec – **PI18)** Cas 17-03-540 (or Av.América 1830 y Mercadillo),Quito **W:** radiocatolica.org.ec – **PI19)** Palacio 303 y Av La Gasca, Quito (see also GU07) – **PI21)** Cas 17-01-67, Quito **W:** radio.casadelacultura.gob.ec – **PI26)** Edif Sevilla, P9, J L Mera 565 y Carrión,

Quito **W:** rtunoticias.com – **PI30)** Cas 17-03-31 (or Carrión 1288 y Av 10 de Agosto), Quito **W:** irfeyal.org – **PI31)** Av. América 4829 y Naciones Unidas, Quito **W:** Cas. 17-11-2263 (or Bolívar 359 entre García Moreno y Venezuela), Quito **W:** facebook.com/RadioMaranon925Fm – **PI33)** Cas 17-01-638 (or Av Amazonas N35-89 y Corea, P4), Quito **W:** radioraiz.com – **PI36)** Cas 17-23-47 (or Av General Enríquez N° 29-35 y Río Chinchipe), Sangolquí **W:** radiosuperk1200.com – **PI37)** 12 de Octubre 227, Quito **W:** facebook.com/Radio-Metropolitana-1240-AM-Yaruqui-Quito-Ecuador-274116546327076 – **PI40)** Edif Doral Mariscal, Of 86, Páez y Mercadillo, Quito **W:** democracia.ec – **PI45)** Av. de la Prensa N°60-22 y Av.de la Prensa, Quito **W:** rcq1380.wix.com/1380 – **PI46)** Av.Amazonas 3911 y Corea, Unicormio 2, P10, Ofc.1008, Quito **W:** radiofuturaecuador.com.ec – **PI47)** Calle Bolívar y Alfredo Boada (sobre el Banco del Pichincha), Tabacundo **W:** facebook.com/Aslaradio1450am – **PI48)** Cas.17-25-5 (or Terán 409 y Av 10 de Agosto, Cayambe **W:** facebook.com/RadiodifusoraEcos – **PI52)** Luis Cordero 557 y J.Mejia, Machachi **W:** radioorellana.es.tl – **PI53)** Av.Natalia Jarrín 2-77 y Vivar, Cayambe **W:** facebook.com/radiomensajeam – **PI56)** Manuel Cajias E 14-09 y Toribio Hidalgo, Quito **W:** radiomonumental1510am.com – **PI59)** Gonzalo Díaz de Pineda 290 y Pedro del Alfaro, Quito **W:** radioeltiempo.com – **PI60)** Av Colón OE3-331 y Versalles, Edificio Villarre, Quito **W:** facebook.com/LaPoderosa1490Am – **PI61)** Universidad Central del Ecuador, Avenida América, Ciudadela Universitaria, Quito **W:** uce.edu.ec/web/facso

### SD00) SANTO DOMINGO DE LOS TSÁCHILAS
**SD04)** Quito e Ibarra, Santo Domingo de los Colorados **W:** radiofestivalfm.com

### SE00) SANTA ELENA
**SE01)** Guayaquil s/n y 9 de Octubre, Santa Elena **W:** facebook.com/fmsantaelena – **SE02)** 4a Av 619 y Robles, La Libertad **W:** vozpeninsula.com – **W:** 93.3MHz

### TU00) TUNGURAHUA
**TU02)** Bolívar 537 y Fund.del Canton, Píllaro (or Cas 18-01-244, Ambato) **W:** facebook.com/pages/Radio-Pillaro/202664373117501 – **TU03)** Cas 18-01-181 (or Sucre 09-42 y Quito), Ambato **W:** radioambato.com.ec - **FM:** 96.7MHz Amor – **TU04)** 12 de Noviembre y Ambato, Edif.El Pelegrino, Baños **W:** radiosantuario.com – **TU05)** Cas 18-01-0674 (or Av.Cevallos 15-57 y Mera, P10, Ofc 1001), Ambato **W:** radioliderambato.com – **TU06)** Bolívar y Martinez, Ambato **W:** radiocolosal.com – **TU08)** Cas 18-01-0574 (or Castillo entre 12 de Noviembre y Olmedo, Edif.R.Centro), Ambato **W:** radiocentroambato.com - **FM:** 91.7MHz – **TU09)** Cas. 498, Imbabura 1652, Ciudadela Bellavista, Ambato **W:** radiosira.com – **TU10)** Cevallos 754 y Martinez (or Cas 18-01-0198), Ambato **W:** radiocalidadambato.com – **TU11)** Cotacachi 176 e Iliniza, Ambato **W:** gruporadialcontinental.com – **TU13)** Cas 618 (or Calle Ayllón 1753 y Darquea), Ambato **W:** radiomera.net – **TU15)** Av Padre Chancon s/n y Juan Velasco, Pelileo **W:** radiodoradodeportes.com – **TU17)** Montalvo 106, Quero **W:** radiopanamericana.com.ec

### FM in Quito (MHz):
88.1 Latina FM – 88.5 Metro – PI08) 89.3 HCJB – 89.7 Majestad – 90.1 Tropicalida – 90.5 Disney – 90.9 Platinum – 91.3 Sabormix – PI17) 91.7 Visión – 92.1 Contacto Nuevo Tiempo – 92.5 Genial Exa FM – 92.9 Música y Sonido - PI33) 93.3 Eres 93.3 – 93.7 Galaxia – PI18) 94.1 Católica Nacional FM – 94.5 Rumba – 94.9 La Gitana – 95.3 Universal – 95.7 R. Legislativa – 96.1 Joya – 96.5 BBN - 96.9 Armónica FM - PI31) 97.3 La Otra FM – 97.7 Centro – 98.1 Proyección – 98.5 Alfa – 98.9 Colón – 99.3 La Luna – 99.7 Añoranza La Rumbera – 100.1 María – PI23) 100.5 Stereo Zaracay – 100.9 Nacional del Ecuador – 101.1 R. Pública – 101.3 Onda Azul – 101.7 Sucesos – 102.1 R.La Red – PI07) 102.5 Francisco Estéreo – 102.9 Distrito FM – 103.3 Onda Cero FM - 103.7 Sonorama – 104.1 Cobertura - 104.5 América – 104.9 Ecuashyri – 105.3 Kiss – 105.7 CRE – 106.1 Hot 106 R. Fuego – 106.5 Canela – 106.9 R. Genial – 107.3 JC – 107.7 Más Candela

### FM in Guayaquil (MHz):
88.1 María – 88.5 Galaxia Stereo – 88.9 Di Blu – 89.3 R. City – 89.7 Punto Rojo FM – 90.1 Romance FM – 90.5 Canela – 90.9 Kiss – 91.3 Tropicalida Stereo – 91.7 Antena Tres – 92.1 Estrella – 92.5 Forever Music FM – 92.9 Colón FM – 93.3 Majestad – 93.7 Disney – 94.1 Onda Positiva – 94.5 Platinum FM – 94.9 La Otra FM – 95.3 Cupido – 95.7 Metro Stereo – 96.1 Onda Cero FM – 96.5 Pasión – 96.9 Más Candela – 97.3 Nuevo Tiempo – 98.1 Morena – 98.5 J C R. – 98.9 Impacto FM – 99.3 Sabormix FM – 99.7 Elite – 100.1 R. La Prensa – 100.5 RSN FM Stereo – 100.9 Mundial – 101.3 La Estación Musical – 101.7 Telequil R. Stereo – 102.1 WQ Dos – 102.5 HCJB – 102.9 Armónia Musical – 103.3 Joya Stereo – 103.7 Sonorama FM – 104.1 Alfa Stereo – 104.5 Corazón – 104.9 Once Q FM – 105.3 Nacional del Ecuador, R. Pública – 105.7 Fabustereo – 106.1 BBN – 106.5 Fuego – 106.9 Ciudadana – 107.3 Rumba – 107.7 Visión FM

## EGYPT

**L.T:** UTC +2h — **Pop:** 80 million — **Pr.L:** Arabic — **E.C:** 50Hz, 220V — **ITU:** EGY

### NATIONAL MEDIA AUTHORITY (Gov)
⌨ P.O. Box 1186, Cairo 11511 (Street: Radio & TV Building, Cornish El Nil, Cairo) ☎ +20 2 25757715, 25789145 📠 +20 2 25789461
**E:** freqmeg@yahoo.com **W:** ertu.org (Arabic), egradio.eg (live audio)
**L.P:** Pres: Mr Husein Zein, Head Eng. Sector: Miss Mervat Ali, Head Broadcasting Sector: Mrs Nadya Mabrook

| MW | kHz | kW | P | Times |
|---|---|---|---|---|
| Cairo | 558 | 100 | 2i | 1200-0200 |
| Cairo | 558 | 100 | 10 | 0800-1100 |
| Sohag | 603 | 50 | 4 | 0200-2200 |
| Batra | 621 | 1000 | 6a | 24h |
| Tanta | 621 | 100 | 6a | 0800-1300 |
| Asswan | 702 | 10 | 2e | 0600-1300, 1500-2000 |
| Asswan | 702 | 10 | 4 | 0200-0400, 2000-2000 |
| El Kharga | 702 | 10 | 2g | 0600-1300, 1500-2200 |
| El Kharga | 702 | 10 | 4 | 0200-2200 |
| Tanta | 711 | 100 | 10 | 24h |
| Qena | 756 | 10 | 2e | 0600-1300, 1500-2200 |
| Qena | 756 | 10 | 4 | 0200-0400, 2000-2200 |
| Abis | 774 | 500 | 5 | 24h |
| Batra | 819 | 1000 | 1a | 24h |
| Santah | 864 | 400 | 4 | 24h |
| Matruh | 882 | 10 | 1a | 24h |
| Bawti | 918 | 10 | 1a | 24h |
| Cairo | 936 | 50 | 11 | 1700-2200 |
| Salum | 936 | 10 | 1a | 24h |
| Abu Simbel | 981 | 1 | 1a | 24h |
| Assiut | 981 | 10 | 2d | 0600-1300, 1500-2000 |
| Assiut | 981 | 10 | 4 | 0200-0400, 2000-2000 |
| Baris | 981 | 1 | 1a | 0300-2400 |
| Abu Simbel | 981 | 1 | 1a | 24h |
| El Arish | 1008 | 100 | 6b | 0800-1700 |
| El Arish | 1008 | 100 | 7 | 1700-2400 |
| El Fayoum | 1008 | 10 | 2d | 0600-1300, 1500-2000 |
| Cairo | 1071 | 100 | 1b | 0300-1500 |
| Cairo | 1071 | 100 | 6d | 1700-2300 |
| El Minya | 1080 | 10 | 1a | 0300-2400 |
| Luxor | 1080 | 10 | 1a | 0300-2400 |
| Tanta | 1161 | 100 | 2b | 0600-2400 |
| Qena | 1179 | 10 | 1a | 0300-2400 |
| Asswan | 1278 | 10 | 1a | 0300-2400 |
| Assiut | 1305 | 10 | 1a | 0300-2400 |
| Abu Simbel | 1314 | 1 | 2e | 0600-1300, 1500-2000 |
| Abu Simbel | 1314 | 1 | 4 | 0200-0400, 2000-2000 |
| Nag Hamadi | 1314 | 1 | 1a | 0300-2400 |
| Cairo | 1341 | 100 | 3c | 1900-0300 |
| Cairo | 1341 | 100 | 8a | 0700-1900 |
| Bawiti | 1341 | 10 | 2i | 1500-2000 |
| Bawiti | 1341 | 10 | 4 | 0200-0500, 2000-2200 |
| Bawiti | 1341 | 10 | 10 | 0700-1500 |
| Idfu | 1341 | 10 | 1a | 0300-2400 |
| Siwa | 1341 | 10 | 1a | 24h |
| Quseir | 1350 | 10 | 1a | 0300-2400 |
| El Kharga | 1368 | 10 | 1a | 0300-2400 |
| Luxor | 1386 | 10 | 2e | 0600-1300, 1500-2000 |
| Luxor | 1386 | 10 | 4 | 0200-0400, 2000-2000 |
| Salum | 1422 | 10 | 2h | 0600-1300, 1500-2000 |
| Salum | 1422 | 10 | 4 | 0200-0400, 2000-2200 |
| El Minya | 1476 | 10 | 2d | 0600-1300, 1500-2000 |
| El Minya | 1476 | 10 | 4 | 0200-0400, 2000-2000 |
| El Arish | 1503 | 25 | 4 | 0600-2000 |
| Quseir | 1575 | 10 | 2i | 1500-2000 |
| Quseir | 1575 | 10 | 4 | 0200-0500, 2000-2200 |
| Quseir | 1575 | 10 | 10 | 0700-1500 |
| Baris | 1584 | 1 | 2g | 0600-1300, 1500-2000 |
| Baris | 1584 | 1 | 4 | 2000-2200 |
| Idfu | 1584 | 10 | 2e | 0600-1300, 1500-2000 |
| Idfu | 1584 | 10 | 4 | 0200-0400, 2000-2000 |
| Matruh | 1593 | 10 | 2h | 0600-1300, 1500-2000 |
| Matruh | 1593 | 10 | 4 | 0200-0400, 2000-2000 |
| Nag Hamadi | 1602 | 10 | 2e | 0600-1300, 1500-2000 |
| Nag Hamadi | 1602 | 1 | 4 | 0200-0400, 2000-2000 |
| Siwa | 1602 | 10 | 2h | 0600-1300, 1500-2000 |
| Siwa | 1602 | 10 | 4 | 0200-0400, 2000-2200 |

**MW Prgrs:** 1a=General Prgr, 1b=Adults Prgr, 2=Local Prgrs (2b=Mid Delta, 2d=North Upper Egypt, 2e=South Upper Egypt, 2g=El Wady El Gadid, 2h=Matruh, 2i=Educational), 3c=Cultural Prgr, 4=Holy Koran Prgr, 5=Middle East Comm. Prgr, 6a=Voice of the Arabs, 6b=Palestine Prgr, 6d=Wadi el Nil, 7=Hebrew Prgr, 8a=Nile R. Netw. Songs Prgr, 10=Youth & Sports Prgr, 11=Om Kalthoum Prgr.

**FM (MHz):**

| Site | D | E | G | K | M | N | R | S | Y |
|---|---|---|---|---|---|---|---|---|---|
| Abh | - | - | - | - | - | - | 95.7 | - | - |
| Abu | - | - | 101.7 | 90.6 | - | - | - | - | - |
| Ala | - | - | - | - | - | 88.7 | - | - | - |
| Alx | - | 94.3 | 104.7 | 90.1 | 88.0 | 88.7 | 101.1 | 97.6 | - |
| Al F | 87.6 | - | 94.9 | 98.2 | - | 88.6 | 91.7 | - | 87.6 |
| Al O | - | - | - | 93.5 | - | - | 97.4 | - | - |
| Asy | 104.0 | - | 104.0 | 95.3 | 89.0 | 88.7 | - | 102.0 | 104.0 |
| Asw | 98.6 | - | 98.6 | 95.3 | - | 92.1 | - | - | 98.6 |
| Baris | - | - | - | 88.8 | - | - | - | - | - |
| Bawiti | - | - | 87.6 | - | - | 88.7 | - | - | - |
| Ben | - | - | - | - | - | 88.7 | 101.4 | - | - |
| Cairo [a] | - | 95.4 | 107.4 | 98.2 | 98.8 | 88.7 | 102.2 | 105.8 | 108.0 |
| Dahab | - | - | 98.5 | 92.0 | - | - | - | - | - |
| Dum | - | - | - | 93.8 | - | 88.7 | - | - | - |
| El A [b] | 87.8 | - | 94.1 | 87.8 | 97.4 | 90.9 | 97.4 | - | 87.8 |
| El D | - | - | 91.1 | 88.0 | - | - | 94.3 | - | - |
| El Db | - | - | - | - | - | 88.7 | - | - | 90.5 |
| El F | - | - | - | - | - | - | - | - | - |
| El K | - | - | - | 88.4 | - | - | - | - | - |
| El M | 91.0 | - | 91.0 | 97.5 | 101.0 | 87.9 | 94.2 | 104.6 | 91.0 |
| El Tur | 89.4 | - | 95.7 | 89.4 | 92.5 | - | 99.0 | - | 89.4 |
| Hal | - | - | 96.6 | - | - | 88.7 | 93.7 | - | - |
| Ham | - | - | - | - | - | 88.7 | - | - | - |
| Hga | 101.7 | 94.9 | 105.3 | 91.7 | - | 88.6 | - | 98.2 | 101.7 |
| Idfu | - | - | 101.7 | - | - | - | - | - | 98.2 |
| Ism | - | - | - | 93.5 | 90.4 | 96.7 | - | - | - |
| Isna | - | - | 90.3 | - | - | - | - | - | - |
| Kat | - | 90.0 | 87.6 | - | - | - | - | - | - |
| Kom | - | - | 92.8 | - | - | - | - | - | - |
| Lux | 93.1 | - | 93.1 | 103.1 | 90.0 | 96.3 | - | - | 93.1 |
| Mah | - | - | 99.6 | 93.1 | 89.8 | - | 89.2 | - | - |
| Man | - | - | 96.3 | - | - | - | - | - | - |
| Mat | - | - | 99.1 | - | 95.8 | 102.6 | 92.6 | - | - |
| Nag | - | 90.9 | 87.8 | - | - | - | 94.1 | - | - |
| Nakhl | - | - | 94.1 | - | - | - | - | - | - |
| Nat | - | - | - | - | - | 88.7 | - | - | - |
| Nuw | 99.1 | - | 92.6 | 99.1 | 89.5 | - | 95.8 | - | 99.1 |
| Pt S | - | - | 98.0 | 101.5 | 88.7 | 91.5 | - | - | - |
| Qena | 100.1 | - | 93.6 | 90.5 | - | 88.7 | - | 96.8 | 100.1 |
| Qus | - | - | 97.2 | - | 88.7 | - | - | - | - |
| Ras | 97.3 | - | 90.8 | 94.0 | - | 87.7 | - | - | 97.3 |
| Saf | - | - | 96.1 | 92.9 | - | - | 89.8 | - | - |
| Salum | - | - | 89.1 | - | - | 89.1 | - | - | - |
| SeS [c] | 97.6 | - | 91.1 | 97.6 | 88.0 | - | 94.3 | - | 97.6 |
| Sha | - | - | 103.5 | 93.5 | - | - | - | - | - |
| Sid | - | - | 101.2 | - | - | - | - | - | - |
| Siwa | - | - | 96.9 | 90.6 | - | - | 93.7 | - | - |
| Soh | 99.3 | - | 96.0 | 89.7 | - | 88.7 | 102.8 | 92.8 | 99.3 |
| Suez | - | - | 94.4 | 91.2 | 88.1 | 97.7 | - | - | - |

[a]=Site at Mokattem, also Cultural Prgr on 91.5MHz 100kW, Middle East Prgr on 89.5MHz 100kW and Voice of the Arabs on 106.3MHz 100kW, [b]=Also Palestine Prgr on 94.1MHz 54.5kW [c]=Koran Prgr also on 101.1MHz 7kW

**FM Prgrs:** D=Educational Prgr, E=European Prgr, G=General Prgr, K=Koran Prgr, M=Musical Prgr, N=Radio Misr Prgr, R=Regional Prgr, S=Songs Prgr, T=Middle East Prgr, Y=Youth & Sport

**Stations & powers:** Abu=Abu Simbel 0.3kW, Abh=Abu Homus 4kW, Ala=Alamain 11.9kW, Alx=Alexandria 58.6kW/N 11.9kW, Al F=Al Farfra 10kW/Y,D 0.3kW, Al O=Al Oga 10kW, Asy=Assyout 11.2kW/N 11.9kW Asw=Aswan 11.9kW, Baris 0.3kW, Bawiti 0.3kW, Ben=Beni Suef 10kW/N 0.3kW, Cairo 100kW, Dahab 0.3kW, Dum=Dumyat 0.3kW, El A=El Arish 54.5kW, El D=El Dakhla 4kW/K 0.3kW, El Db=El Dabaa 11.9kHz, El F=El Fayoum 10kW, El K=El Kharga 7kW, El M=El Minyah 18kW/K 10kW/S 4kW, El Tur 11.9kW, Hal=Halayeb 4kW/ 0.3kW, Ham=Hammam 11.9kW, Hga=Hurghada 7.96kW/Y,D 4kW/G 10kW, Idfu 0.3kW, Ism=Ismailia 61.5kW, Isna 0.3kW, Kat=Katherina 0.3kW, Kom=Kom Ombo 4kW, Lux=Luxor 11.7kW, Mah=Mahalla 155kW/N 10kW, Man=Managem Bahariya 0.3kW, Mat=Matruh 9.77kW, Nag=Naga Hamadi 10kW, Nakhl 0.3kW, Nat=Natron 11.9kW, Nuw=Nuweiba 9.53kW, Pt S=Port Said 10kW, Qena 28.6kW/N 4kW, Qus=Quseir 10kW/K 4kW, Ras=Ras Gharb 10kW, Saf=Safaga 10kW,

Salum 10kW, SeS=Sharm El Sheikh 7.41kW, Sha=Shalatin 0.3kW, Sid=Sidi Barani 10kW, Siwa 10kW/R 0.3kW, Soh=Sohag 38kW/N 4kW/N 0.3kW, Suez 8.71kW

**Ann:** General Prgr: "Idha'atu jumhuriya misr al'arabbiya min al-qa-hira". Voice of the Arabs: "Saut al-'arab, min al-qahira". Holy Koran prgr: "Idha'atu-l-Quran min al-qahira"

**Other FM Stations:**
**Nogoom FM,** Cairo 100.6MHz 100kW. Arabic music, 24h – **Nile FM,** Cairo 104.2MHz 100kW. Mainly English pop & rock, 24h **W:** nilefmonline.com – **Radio Hits,** Cairo 88.2MHz 100kW – **Mega FM,** 92.7MHz, Cairo 100kW, Natron, Alexandria, Hamman, Alamain 11.9kW– **Nagham FM,** Cairo 105.3MHz 100kW – **Radio 9090,** Cairo 90.9MHz 100kW – **Shaaby FM,** Cairo 95.0MHz 100kW – **NRJ Radio,** Cairo 92.1MHz 100kW – **DRN Radio,** Cairo 93.7MHz 100kW
**R7** rebroadcasts R. Misr Prgr on 88.7MHz and Mega FM on 92.7MHz, Cairo 11.9kW
**Maspero FM** rep. active Cairo on 91.5MHz and **Energy FM** 92.1MHz

**EXTERNAL SERVICES: Radio Cairo**
see International Broadcasting Section.

**Other Stations:**
**AFRTS** Low-power broadcasts of NPR and AFN to US contingent of UN MFO in Sinai rep. on wide range of freqs from 92.7 to 106.1. Also 107.0 at Gebel Musa.

## EL SALVADOR

**L.T:** UTC -6h — **Pop:** 6.2 million — **Pr.L:** Spanish — **E.C:** 60Hz, 115V — **ITU:** SLV

**SUPERINTENDENCIA GENERAL DE ENERGÍA Y TELECOMUNICACIONES (SIGET)**
✉ Sexta Décima Calle Poniente y 3°Av.Sur N° 2001, Colonia Flor Blanca, San Salvador ☎ +503 2257-4438 **W:** siget.gob.sv **E:** info@siget.gob.sv

**ASOCIACION SALVADORENA DE RADIODIFUSION (ASDER)** ✉ Calle La Ceiba # 261, Col. Escalon, San Salvador **W:** asder.com.sv

| MW Call | | kHz | kW | Station, location |
|---|---|---|---|---|
| 1) | HV | 540 | 5 | La Estación de la Palabra, San Salvador |
| 3) | NK | 600 | 3 | R. Alabanza, San Salvador |
| 4) | LN | 630 | 10 | R. Santa Sion, San Salvador |
| 5) | UES | 660 | 10 | R. Universitaria, San Salvador |
| 6) | JW | 700 | 12 | R. Cadena Mi Gente, San Salvador |
| 7) | RA | 720 | 1 | Radio Qué Buena, San Salvador (r:88.9) |
| 8) | KL | 760 | 5 | YSKL La Poderosa, San Miguel |
| 8) | KL | 760 | 1 | YSKL La Poderosa, Sonsonate (r:770) |
| 8) | KL | 760 | | YSKL La Poderosa, Zacateluca (r:770) |
| 8) | KL | 770 | 10 | YSKL La Poderosa, San Salvador: 1030-0530 |
| 8) | KL | 780 | 1 | YSKL La Poderosa, Usulután (r:770) |
| 8) | KL | 780 | 1 | YSKL La Poderosa, Sta Ana (r:770) |
| 10) | AX | 800 | 12 | R. María El Salvador, San Salvador: 1230-0600 |
| 11) | FA | 810 | 2 | R. Lorenzana, San Vicente |
| 12) | DA | ‡810 | 1.5 | R. Imperial, Sonsonate: 1100-0300 |
| 13) | FB | 840 | 10 | R. Santa Biblia, San Salvador: 1030-0300 |
| 14) | AR | †870 | 2 | R. Renacer, San Salvador |
| 22) | LA | 890 | 3 | R. Elohim, Santa Ana |
| 2) | QJ | 900 | 2 | R. Tiempo, San Salvador |
| 16) | TG | 930 | 3 | R. San José, San Salvador: 1130-0330 |
| 17) | HG | 950 | 1 | R. Chaparrastique, San Miguel |
| 18) | CA | 1020 | 5 | R. Máxima - LV de la Liberación, San Salvador |
| 19) | RM | 1030 | 1 | R. Frontera, Ahuachapán: 1200-0400 |
| 9) | U | 1050 | 10 | R. Evangélica Sinaí, San Salvador |
| 20) | ME | 1080 | 6 | R. Cadena CRET, San Salvador |
| 21) | MG | 1090 | 3 | R. Cadena CRET, Atiquizaya |
| 15) | RF | 1100 | 6 | R. Cristo Viene, San Salvador |
| 22) | LR | 1120 | 3 | R. Elohim, San Salvador: 1045-0500 |
| 23) | AJ | 1130 | 1 | R. Moderna, Sta Ana: 1200-0400 |
| 22) | CF | 1150 | 1 | R. Elohim, San Miguel |
| 25) | VG | 1180 | 5 | R. VEA-Voz Evangélica de América, San Salvador: 1200-2400 |
| 26) | CG | 1210 | 2 | R. Salem, Zacateluca |
| 28) | QN | 1240 | 1 | R. Norteña, San Miguel |
| 29) | AA | 1260 | 12 | R. Abba, San Salvador |
| 27) | QZ | 1270 | 3.5 | R. Visión, San Miguel |
| 30) | MQ | 1280 | 1 | R. Emaús, San Vicente |
| 31) | MA | 1290 | 1 | R. Chalatenango, Chalatenango: 1000-0300 |
| 33) | KG | 1300 | 1 | R. Llanera "La Campechana", San Miguel |

| MW Call | | kHz | kW | Station, location |
|---|---|---|---|---|
| 45) | FG | ‡1330 | | R. Cristo Te Llama, San Salvador |
| 35) | KO | 1370 | 1 | R. Lluvias de Bendición, San Miguel: 1100-0300 |
| 36) | JU | 1390 | 1 | R. Getsemani, La Unión: 1100-0400 |
| 37) | | ‡1390 | | R. LV de la Palabra Que Cambia, Chalchuapa |
| 38) | JS | 1390 | 1 | Sinaí R, LV del Rey de Gloria, Soyapango |
| 39) | JI | 1400 | 1 | LV del Litoral, Usulután: 1100-0400 |
| 40) | KR | 1450 | 1 | R. Restauración, San Miguel: 1000-0400 |
| 41) | CS | 1500 | 1 | R. Pentecostal Bethel, Usulután |
| 42) | DA | 1500 | 1 | R. Peniel, San Salvador |
| 43) | CZ | ‡1550 | 5 | R. Sanidad Divina, San Salvador: 1000-0600 |
| 44) | MV | 1600 | | R. Maya Visión, San Salvador |
| 22) | | 1630 | | R. Elohim, San Salvador: -0600 |

**Call YS**—, ‡ = inactive, (r) = repeater, ± = varying fq, † = irregular

**Addresses & other information:**
**1)** Misión Cristiana Elim, Ap. 2854 (or Calle al Matazano N° 1, A cien metros al occidente de bomba de ANDA), San Salvador **W:** elim.org.sv/540am – **2)** Colonia San Miguel, Cl Principal Pasaje Castillo, San Ramón Mejicanos, San Salvador. **W:** radiotiempoelsalvador.com – **3)** Edif. Antiguo Cine Apolo, 2ª. Av. Sur y 8ª Calle Oriente, San Salvador **W:** radioalabanzaelsalvador.org – **4)** 75 Av Norte, Prolongación Juan Pablo II, Col Jardines de Escalón, final Pasaje KL, San Salvador **W:** radiosantasion.org – **5)** Ciudad Universitaria "Dr. Fabio Castillo Figueroa", Final de Av.Mártires y Héroes del 30 julio, San Salvador **W:** ues.edu.sv/radio-ysues – **6)** 14 Calle Poniente, entre 43 y 45, Avenida Sur No. 2309, Col. Flor Blanca, San Salvador. **W:** migenteinforma.org – **7)** Ap., 720, San Salvador – **8)** 65 Av. Sur #192, , San Salvador **W:** radioyskl.com – **9)** Colonia Ciudad Real, Recidencial La Floresta, Pligono "E" N° 2, Calle Elizabeth, San Miguel **W:** ministerioradiosinai.com – **10)** Urb. General Escalon, Pasaje Beethoven 8/E, San Salvador **W:** radiomaria.org.sv – **11)** Carretera a Tecoluca, Col. Najarro, San Vicente – **12)** Ap.56, Sonsonate – **13)** Iglesia San Pablo, Final 5a Calle Poniente, Colonia Escalón, San Salvador **W:** radiosantabiblia.webnode.es – **14)** Jardines de la Cima, San Salvador **W:** facebook.com/RenacerAM – **15)** Centro de San Salvador, San Salvador **W:** radiocristoviene1100am.org – **16)** 1er Calle Josniente, San Salvador 503 **W:** radiosanjose.org – **17)** Bo El Calvario 4 Av Sur No 303 San Miguel **W:** radiochaparrastique.net – **18)** Avenida España Y 21 Calle Poniente Ex Cine Fausto #114, Esquina Opuesta Al Mercado San Miguelito, San Salvador **W:** facebook.com/Iglesia-Pentecostal-Dios-Es-Amor-El-Salvador-724523677666407 – **19)** Áv.2 de Abril y 8a Calle Poniente, Ahuachapán – **20)** Barrio La Cruz, 10 Av Norte N° 203-Bis, San Miguel **W:** radiocadenacret.com – **21)** Santa Ana **W:** radiocadenacret.com/?page_id=391 – **22)** 8a Av. Norte #225, atrás de la Despensa Familiar, por el parque San José, San Salvador **W:** radioelohim.com Mostly separate programming on 1120 and 1630kHz. – **23)** 8a Calle Poniente 11A, Sta Ana – **24)** Colonia Monte Carmelo, Calle a Los Naranjos, Frente Antena de la YSU, Sonsonate – **25)** Calle 5 de Noviembre y final 6 Av. Norte, Frente a Banco de Famila, San Martín, San Salvador. **W:** facebook.com/radiovea Also r. UPA 90.9 – **26)** 2a Calle Poniente 22, Zacatecoluca **FM:** 92.5 **W:** radiosalem.org – **27)** San Miguel **W:** radiovisionministeriosunidos.com – **28)** 14 Calle Poniente, San Miguel **W:** facebook.com/Radio-Norteña-El-Salvador-164392333624699 – **29)** Antigua Calle Ferrocarril, #2106, Colonia 3 de Mayo, San Salvador **W:** radioabba.org – **30)** 2 Av N N° 10, San Vicente **W:** facebook.com/radioemaus1280am – **31)** Calle a San Francisco Lempa, Col. Veracruz, Chalatenango **W:** radiochalatenango.com.sv – **33)** Col. Hirleman, 14 Calle Poniente, Bloque 6, N° 9, San Miguel – **34)** Bo El Centro, C.Bolivar y 4 Av.S, Stgo de María, Usulután – **35)** Carr.Panamericana, Crio El Alto, 300 mts al Norte, El Jalacatal, San Miguel. **W:** radiolluviasdebendicion.com – **36)** Calle General Menéndez No. 2-3, La Unión **W:** radiogetsemani.net – **37)** Calle al trapiche, Chalchuapa, Santa Ana **W:** lavozdelapalabraquecambia.blogspot.com – **38)** Carretera al Plan del Pino. Una cuadra antes de la Ciudadela Don Bosco, Soyapango, San Salvador **W:** lavozdelreydegloria.com – **39)** 12 Av.Sur y final 5a Calle Oriente, Col.Santa Rosa, Usulután **W:** lavozdellitoral.com – **FM:** 90.1MHz – **40)** Iglesia Elim, 8a Calle Poniente, San Miguel **W:** elimsanmiguel.org – **41)** Kilómetro 112½, Carretera El Litoral, Frente a Desvío El Mora, Usulután **W:** radiopentecostalbethel.org – **42)** San Salvador **W:** radiopeniel1500am.com – **43)** Calle 25 de Abril Poniente, Barrio San José # 22B, San Marcos, San Salvador **W:** radiosanidaddivina.com – **44)** Calle a San Antonio Abad No. 2209, Col. Centroamérica, San Salvador **W:** radiomayavision.com – **45)** Carretera de Oro km. 8 1/2 Colonia Altavista Ilopango, San Salvador **W:** radiocristotellama.net

**FM in San Salvador** (MHz): 87.75 Canal 6 – 88.1 AL Radio – 88.5 Paz – 88.9 Qué Bueno – (9) 89.3 Cool – 89.7 Bautista – 90.1 Láser (Spanish) – 90.5 Progreso – 90.9 UPA – 91.3 Exa – 91.7 YSUCA – 92.1 La Klave – 92.5 Club – 92.9 Láser (English) – 93.3 Globo – 93.7 El Mundo – 94.1 Super Estrella – 94.5 Vox FM – 94.9 Astral – (9) 95.3 R. Eco – 95.7 Verdad – 96.1 Scan – 96.5 R. Adventista – 96.9 R. Nacional

**W**: radionacional.gob.sv – 97.3 Corazón – 97.7 Luz – 98.1 Gospel FM – 98.5 Cuscatlán – 98.9 La Mejor FM – 99.3 Mesías – 99.7 Full FM – 100.1 ABC – 100.5 Restauración – 100.9 La Chévere – (9) 101.3 Monumental – 101.7 Mil 80 –102.1 102 Uno –102.5 Femenina – 102.9 102 Nueve – 103.3 Clásica – 103.7 Cadena Central – (8) 104.1 YSKL La Poderosa – 104.5 Sonora – 104.9 Fiesta – 105.3 Punto 105 – 105.7 YXY – 106.1 El Camino – 106.5 Ranchera – 106.9 R. Maya Visión – 107.3 R. María – 107.7 Fuego.

**FM in San Miguel** (MHz): 90.1 Stereo Caliente - 90.5 Siglo 21– 90.9 Popular – 92.5 YSUCA – 92.5 Monseñor Romero – 94.1 Cadena Central – 96.5 Agape R. – 97.3 Carnaval – 98.1 La Pantera – 99.7 Mi Consentida - 102.9 102 Nueve – 104.1 YSKL La Poderosa – 106.1 La Grande – 107.3 R. María.

**FM in Santa Ana** (MHz): 90.5 Supra Stereo - 91.7 YSUCA - 92.1 Fe y Alegría – (9) 92.5 R. Doremix – 93.3 Shabach – 95.3 Amor – 97.3 La Campirana – 97.9 Real FM – 99.7 Doble H - 102.9 102 Nueve – 104.1 YSKL La Poderosa – 105.3 Soda Stereo – 106.1 Bautista

## EQUATORIAL GUINEA

**L.T**: UTC +1h — **Pop**: 900,000 — **Pr.L**: Spanish, French, ethnic — **E.C**: 50Hz, 220V — **ITU**: GNE

**MINISTERIO DE INFORMACIÓN, TURISMO Y CULTURA**
✉ Barrio Nzalang (antiguo África 2000), Malabo. ☎+240 333 078221 🖷 +240 333 072444. **LP**: Minister: Purificación Opo Barila. Dir R & TV: Hermenesildo Moliko Djele.

**RADIO TELEVISIÓN DE GUINEA ECUATORIAL (RTVGE, Gov.)**
✉ Ap. 749, Bata ☎+240 333 082592 🖷 +240 333 082093 ✉ Av. 3 de Agosto 90, Ap. 195, Malabo ☎+240 333 072260 🖷 +240 333 072097 **W**: rtvge.com **LP**: Dir. Tech: Barila Sota.

| SW | kHz | kW | Times |
|---|---|---|---|
| Bata | 5005 | 50 | 0430-1730/2300v (irregular) |
| Malabo(Semu) | ‡6250 | 20 | 0500-2300 (inactive) |

**FM**: Bata 98/99.9MHz 1kW, Malabo 90.9MHz 12kW.
**D.Prgr**: in Spanish/ethnic.
**Rural radio**: La Voz de Kie-Ntem at Ebibeyín, Ecos de Wele Nzás at Mongomo and La Voz de Centro Sur at Evinayong.

**Other Stations:**
**R. Asonga**, Malabo 90.0/107.0MHz. **W**: radio.asonga.com
**BBC World Sce**: Malabo 92.5MHz in English/French.
**RFI Afrique**: Bata 88.5, Malabo 88.0/97.5MHz in French/Spanish

## ERITREA

**L.T**: UTC +3h — **Pop**: 5.5 million — **Pr.L**: Afar, Amharic, Arabic, Tigrinya, Tigre, others — **E.C**: 50Hz, 230V — **ITU**: ERI.

**MINISTRY OF INFORMATION**
✉ P.O. Box 872, Asmara ☎+291 1 120478/201820 🖷 +291 1 126747 **W**: shabait.com **E**: nesredin@tse.com.er

**VOICE OF THE BROAD MASSES OF ERITREA (Gov.)**
✉ P.O. Box 242, Asmara ☎+291 1 117111/118711 🖷 +291 1 124847 **LP**: DG: Ghirmay Berhe. TD: Mehreteab Tesfagiorgis. PD: Abdu Heji. Dir. Radio Eng.: Berhane Gerezgiher.
**Station**: Asmara (Selai Dairo).
**MW**: 837kHz 100kW (Prgr. 2), 945kHz 100kW (Prgr. 1). Alt. fq's used are 840 and 950 kHz.
**SW**: 7140kHz 100kW (Prgr. 1), 7180 kHz 100kW (Prgr. 2). Both irregular and frequency variable.
**Prgr. 1** in Tigrinya/Tigre/Kunama: 0300-1000, 1300-2000 – **Prgr. 2** in Arabic/Afar/Amharic/Oromo/Saho/Bilen: 0300-1000, 1430-2000.
**Zara FM**: 100MHz + others. **Numa FM**: 90MHz.
**Ann**: Amharic:"Yeh be Asmera ketema yemigegne yesifiw Yeritrea hezeb demts yeamarigna agelgilot new". Arabic: "Huna Asmara, Idha'at Sawt al-Jamahir al-Iritriyyah". Tigrigna: "Ezi kab Asmara Zemehalalef Medeber Radio Demtsi Hafash Eritrea Eyu".

## ESTONIA

**L.T**: UTC +2h (31 Mar-27 Oct: +3h) — **Pop**: 1.3 million — **Pr.L**: Estonian, Russian — **E.C**: 230V/50Hz — **ITU**: EST

**KULTUURIMINISTEERIUM (Ministry of Culture)**
✉ Suur-Karja 23, 15076 Tallinn ☎ +372 6282222 **E**: min@kul.ee **W**: kul.ee **LP**: Minister: Indrek Saar

**NB**: The Ministry of Culture issues broadcasting licenses.

**EESTI RAHVUSRINGHÄÄLING (ERR) (Pub)**
✉ F.R. Kreutzwaldi 14, 10124 Tallinn ☎ +372 6284100 **E**: err@err.ee
**W**: err.ee **LP**: Chmn: Erik Roose

| FM (MHz) | 1 | 2 | 3 | 4 | kW |
|---|---|---|---|---|---|
| Koeru | 105.1 | 102.6 | 107.6 | 93.4 | 3x30/7.8 |
| Kohtla-Nõmme | 105.4 | 102.9 | 90.4 | 95.3 | 11.2 |
| Kuressaare | 105.6 | 103.1 | 107.0 | - | 1 |
| Kõrgessaare | 91.2 | 99.1 | 94.9 | - | 1 |
| Möksi | - | - | - | 99.9 | 3 |
| Orissaare | 105.9 | 103.4 | 107.8 | - | 20/2x10 |
| Pärnu | 104.8 | 102.3 | 107.3 | 94.8 | 10 |
| Tallinn | 104.1 | 101.6 | 106.6 | 94.5 | 30 |
| Valga | - | - | - | 92.5 | 1.8 |
| Valgjärve | 106.1 | 103.6 | 105.7 | - | 2x40/12.5 |
| Viiratsi | 105.8 | 103.3 | 107.0 | 95.5 | 1 |

+ sites with only txs below 1kW.
**D.Prgr**: **Prgr 1 (Vikerraadio)**: 24h – **Prgr 2 (Raadio 2)**: 24h – **Prgr 3 (Klassikaraadio)**: 24h – **Prgr 4 (Raadio 4)** for ethnic minorities: 24h in Russian (exc. irreg. SS 1715-1800 for other ethnic communities (rotating): Armenian, Belarusian, Georgian, Romanian, Ukrainian) – **ERR Raadio Tallinn** 103.5MHz (1kW): 24h. Own prgrs 0500-2000; relays: 0300-0500 & 2000-2300 BBCWS (UK), 2300-0300 RFI (France).

**OTHER STATIONS**

| MW | kHz | kW | Location | Station |
|---|---|---|---|---|
| 6B) | 1035 | *100 | Tartu (Kavastu) | R. Eli |

| FM | MHz | kW | Location | Station |
|---|---|---|---|---|
| 2B) | 87.7 | 1 | Kehtna | Sky Plus |
| 3A) | 88.1 | 2 | Paide | Star FM |
| 2C) | 88.2 | 1 | Kõmsi | Retro FM |
| 11) | 88.3 | 2 | Tallinn | Hit FM |
| 4) | 88.6 | 3 | Pärnu | Raadio 7 |
| 8) | 88.8 | 1 | Tallinn | R. Mania |
| 6A) | 89.0 | 2.4 | Vanamõisa | Pereraadio |
| 6A) | 89.0 | 3 | Tartu | Pereraadio |
| 6A) | 89.4 | 1 | Härma | Pereraadio |
| 6A) | 89.6 | 3 | Tallinn | Pereraadio |
| 1C) | 89.8 | 1.1 | Vinni | MyHits |
| 1A) | 89.9 | 1 | Pärnu | Raadio Kuku |
| 9) | 90.1 | 1 | Kärdla | Raadio Kadi |
| 9) | 90.5 | 1 | Aste | Raadio Kadi |
| 1C) | 91.0 | 3 | Pärnu | MyHits |
| 1B) | 91.2 | 6.5 | Valgjärve | Raadio Elmar |
| 5A) | 91.3 | 1 | Raikküla | Tre Raadio |
| 1B) | 91.5 | 1.5 | Tallinn | Raadio Elmar |
| 1B) | 91.5 | 1 | Kuressaare | Raadio Elmar |
| 1B) | 91.7 | 7.5 | Koeru | Raadio Elmar |
| 1B) | 92.2 | 1 | Haapsalu | Raadio Elmar |
| 3A) | 92.2 | 2.9 | Padaorg | Star FM |
| 1C) | 92.3 | 1 | Parksepa | MyHit |
| 3B) | 92.5 | 1 | Rakvere | Power Hit R. |
| 5A) | 92.7 | 1.5 | Pärnu | Tre Raadio |
| 3A) | 92.9 | 3 | Haapsalu | Star FM |
| 2E) | 93.2 | 1.5 | Tallinn | NRJ FM |
| 3A) | 93.3 | 2.2 | Kuressaare | Star FM |
| 2B) | 93.8 | 3 | Holsta | Sky Plus |
| 2B) | 95.2 | 1 | Tartu | Sky Plus |
| 2B) | 95.4 | 2 | Tallinn | Sky Plus |
| 2C) | 95.4 | 1 | Aste | Retro FM |
| 4) | 96.1 | 3 | Tamsalu | Raadio 7 |
| 1D) | 96.3 | 9.5 | Kohtla-Järve | Narodnoe R. |
| 2B) | 96.3 | 1.9 | Vätta | Sky Plus |
| 3A) | 96.6 | 1.5 | Tallinn | Star FM |
| 7) | 96.6 | 1 | Sangaste | Ruut FM |
| 2B) | 96.8 | 1.6 | Pärnu | Sky Plus |
| 2B) | 96.9 | 1.5 | Palade | Sky Plus |
| 1C) | 97.2 | 2 | Tallinn | MyHits |
| 1C) | 97.2 | 1 | Tartu | MyHits |
| 1C) | 97.4 | 3 | Kuressaare | MyHits |
| 1C) | 97.4 | 2.5 | Koeru | MyHits |
| 3C) | 97.7 | 1 | Sillamäe | R. Volna |
| 2C) | 97.8 | 4 | Tallinn | Retro FM |
| 2C) | 97.9 | 1 | Viljandi | Retro FM |
| 2C) | 98.3 | 1.2 | Pärnu | Retro FM |
| 2A) | 98.4 | 3 | Tallinn | Sky R. |
| 2C) | 98.6 | 2.5 | Tartu | Retro FM |
| 1B) | 99.0 | 3 | Pärnu | Raadio Elmar |
| 3A) | 99.4 | 2 | Tartu | Star FM |
| 1A) | 99.6 | 3.2 | Padaorg | Raadio Kuku |
| 1C) | 99.8 | 2.5 | Linnamäe | MyHits |

| FM | MHz | kW | Location | Station |
|----|-----|-----|----------|---------|
| 1D) | 100.0 | 1 | Narva | Narodnoe R. |
| 1A) | 100.2 | 2 | Tartu | Raadio Kuku |
| 3A) | 100.3 | 2 | Pärnu | Star FM |
| 1A) | 100.4 | 1 | Kärdla | Raadio Kuku |
| 1A) | 100.5 | 2.2 | Paide | Raadio Kuku |
| 1A) | 100.6 | 3 | Kuressaare | Raadio Kuku |
| 10) | 100.7 | 3 | Põlva | R. Marta |
| 1A) | 100.7 | 1.9 | Tallinn | Raadio Kuku |
| 1A) | 100.8 | 1.5 | Viljandi | Raadio Kuku |
| 1A) | 100.9 | 2.5 | Linnamäe | Raadio Kuku |
| 5A) | 101.0 | 3 | Paide | Tre Raadio |
| 2D) | 101.2 | 1.3 | Tartu | Russkoe R. |
| 5B) | 101.7 | 1 | Möksi | Ring FM |
| 3A) | 101.9 | 3 | Sadaküla | Star FM |
| 3B) | 102.1 | 1.5 | Tallinn | Power Hit R. |
| 3A) | 102.8 | 1 | Valga | Star FM |
| 11) | 103.0 | 1 | Tartu | Hit FM |
| 3A) | 103.2 | 3 | Parksepa | Star FM |
| 2B) | 103.3 | 1 | Maidla | Sky Plus |
| 1C) | 104.5 | 1 | Liiva | MyHits |
| 5B) | 104.7 | 1 | Tartu | Ring FM |
| 5B) | 105.8 | 1 | Tallinn | Ring FM |
| 2B) | 106.8 | 1 | Kullamaa | Sky Plus |

+ txs below 1kW. *) 200kW during TWR relays (see International Radio section)

**Addresses & other information:**
**1A-D)** Veerenni 58a, 11314 Tallinn, exc. 1B) Õpetaja 9a, 51003 Tartu. 1E) in Russian. – **2A-E)** Pärnu mnt. 139f, 11317 Tallinn. 2A,C,D) in Russian. – **3A-C)** Peterburi 81, 11415 Tallinn. 3C) in Russian. – **4)** Välja 18, 10616 Tallinn – **5A,B)** Asula 4c, 11315 Tallinn; 5B) Peterburi 49, 11415 Tallinn – **6A)** Annemõisa 8, 50708 Tartu; **6B)** Vestervalli 20, 20306 Narva. In Russian (incl. TWR relays). **E:** raadioeli@gmail.com – **7)** Pikk 3a, 68206 Valga – **8)** Tartu mnt. 80d,10112 Tallinn – **9)** Kohtu 1, 93819 Kuressaare – **10)** Kesk 42, 63304 Põlva – **11)** Estonia puiestee 9, 10143 Tallinn

## ESWATINI

**L.T:** UTC +2h — **Pop:** 1.3 million — **Pr.L:** English, Siswati — **E.C:** 50Hz, 230V — **ITU:** SWZ

### SWAZILAND COMMUNICATIONS COMMISSION(SCCOM)
✉ Mbabane Office Park, Fourth Floor North Wing, P.O. Box 7811, Mbabane **W:** www.sccom.org.sz **E:** info@sccom.org.sz
**L.P:** CEO: Mvilawemphi Dlamini.

### SWAZILAND BROADCASTING AND INFORMATION SERVICES (Gov)
✉ P.O. Box 338, Corner Gwamile & Dzeliwe Streets, Mbabane H100 ☎+268 24042761 🖷 +268 24042774 **W:** gov.sz/index.php/ministries-departments/ministry-of-ict/swaziland-braodcating-a-information-services **E:** sbisnews@africaonline.co.sz
**L.P:** Dir: Percy Simelane. Asst. Principal prgrs Officer: Phesheya Dube. A/Prgr. Coordinator: Austin Dlamini. A/Tr. Engineer: Christopher Motsa.
**FM:** 88.5/91.6/93.6/105.2MHz 10kW + 4 low power relays.
**English Sce:** 0255-1800 on FM 91.6/93.6MHz. **N:** 0400, 0500, 1600.
**Siswati Sce:** 0255-2100 on FM 88.5/105.2MHz.
**Ann:** E: "This is the English sce. of Radio Swaziland". Siswati: "Lona ngu Mawakato waka Ngwane".
**IS:** at s/on, Cilongo (Swazi instrument). English Sce: cock crow, fanfare, spoken ID, instrumental theme.

### TRANS WORLD RADIO - VOICE OF THE CHURCH
✉ P.O. Box 4544, Corner Martin & Tenbergen St, Manzini **W:** vocfm.org **W:** info@voc.org.sz ☎+268 25054845 🖷 +268 25054809 **L.P:** Nat. Dir: Nelson Vilakati, Adm: Tryphinah Dlamini, PM: Abel Vilakati.
**FM:** Mbabane 95.0, Siteki 96.0, Mankayane/Pigg's Peak 97.0, Manzini 97.1, Hlatikhulu 101.0MHz.
**MW:** TWR Africa, Mpangela Ranch 1170kHz 1800-2155 100kW & SW. For further details see Int. Radio section

## ETHIOPIA

**L.T:** UTC +3h — **Pop:** 105 million — **Pr.L:** Amharic, Oromo, Sidamo, Somali, Tigrinya — **E.C:** 50Hz, 220V — **ITU:** ETH

### ETHIOPIAN BROADCASTING AUTHORITY (EBA)
✉ P.O. Box 43142, Hailalem Bldg. Kazanchis, Addis Ababa ☎+251 11 5538755 🖷 +251 11 5536767
**W:** www.eba.gov.et **E:** e.b.a1@ethionet.et

### ETHIOPIA BROADCASTING CORPORATION - RADIO ETHIOPIA (Gov.)
✉ P.O. Box 1020, Addis Ababa ☎+251 11 5516977
**W:** ebc.et **E:** ebc@ebc.et **L.P:** GM: Ato Solomon Tesfaye. SM: Kasa Miloko. CE: Kebede Gobena. Head of English Prgrs: Melesse Edea Beyi.

| MW | kHz | kW | MW | kHz | kW |
|----|-----|-----|----|-----|-----|
| Metu | 684 | 100 | Robe (Bale) | 972 | 100 |
| Arba Minch | 828 | 100 | Addis Ababa | 989 | 1 |
| Harar | 855 | 100 | Mekele | 1044 | 200 |
| Addis Ababa | 873 | 100 | Negele Borana | 1485 | 10 |
| Dese | 891 | 100 | | | |

**FM**(MHz): Addis Ababa 93.1 2.5kW, 96.3 3.5kW, 97.1, 104.7, Bahir Dar 94.5MHz, unknown sites: 88.7, 90.3, 91.9, 93.5, 98.7, 102.2.

**National Sce in Amharic/Others:** 0300-2100.
**Reg. prgrs** and **BBC relays** at times. External Sce relay on 989kHz 1200-1830. **FM Addis** in Amharic on 97.1MHz. **EBC R.** in English on 104.7MHz 0300-2100. Also rel. RFI.
**Ann:** (National Sce) "Yeh Ethiopia Broadcasting Corporation".
**EXTERNAL SERVICE:** see International Radio section.

### FANA BROADCASTING CORPORATE - RADIO FANA
✉ P.O.Box 30702, near Black Lion Hospital, in front of Sweden Embassy, Addis Ababa. **W:** fanabc.com **E:** fanabc@fanabc.com
**L.P:** GM: Woldu Yemessel. Tech. Dir: Mulugeta Mehari.
**MW:** Addis Ababa (Repi) 1080kHz 3kW.
**SW:** Addis Ababa (Geja) 6110kHz 100kW.
**FM (MHz):** Haromaya/Mekele 94.8, Dese 96.0, Nekemit 96.1, Addis Ababa/Gonder/Jimma 98.1, Wolayita 99.9, Shashemenie 103.4.
**D.Prgr. "Fana National"** in Afar/Amharic/Oromo/Somali/Tigrinya: 0255-2100 on MW & SW. **Fana FM:** on FM.

**Regional government stations:**
**RADIO OROMIYA (Oromiya Radio & TV Organisation, ORTO)**
✉ P.O. Box 2919, Adama. **W:** orto.et **L.P:** Mr. Abarra Hailu, Mgr. Mr. Habtamu Dargie Gudeta, Head Eng. Dept.
**MW:** Robe (Bale) 837kHz 100kW, Adama (Nazret) 1035kHz 10kW, Nekemte 1053kHz 100kW.
**SW:** Addis Ababa (Geja) 6030kHz 100kW.
**FM:** Addis Ababa (Intoto) 92.3MHz.
**D.Prgr. in Oromo** (some Amharic&English): Mon-Fri 0300-0600, 0900-1100, 1530-2000, SS 0300-1900. **Ann:** Oromo: "Kun Radio Oromiya".

**VOICE OF TIGRAY REVOLUTION (Gov)**
✉ P.O.Box 450, Mekele, Tigray ☎+251 34 4410544/5 **W:** dimtsiwoyane.com **L.P:** Dir: Abera Tesfay.
**MW:** Mekele 1359kHz 100kW.
**SW:** Addis Ababa 5950kHz 100kW.
**FM: DWET FM:** Axum 90.7, Shire 91.4, Humera 95.5, Mekele 102.2MHz 3kW.
**D.Prgr** in Tigrinya/Afar: MF 0300-2000, SS 0300-1730 (DWET FM 0300-2100). **Ann:** Tigrinya: "Dimtsi Woyane Tigray". **IS:** Melody played on washint (Ethiopian flute).

**AMHARA RADIO (Gov)**
✉ Amhara Mass Media Agency, P.O. Box 955, Bahir Dar. **L.P:** Dir: Chalacew Achamyehe. **W:** amma.gov.et **E:** ammawebmaster@yahoo.com
**MW:** Bahir Dar (Zege) 801kHz 100kW.
**SW:** Addis Ababa 6090kHz 100kW.
**D. Prgr** in Amharic/Awinya/Himtinya/Oromo: 0300-0600, 0900-1100, 1400-2100. **Ann:** Amharic: "Yeh ye Amhara Radio".

**ETHIOPIAN SOMALI REGIONAL STATE RADIO (Gov.)**
**SW:** Jigjiga (presumed loc.) 5940kHz 50kW.
**FM:** Jigjiga (presumed loc.) 99.1MHz
**D. Prgr** in Somali: 0400-0600, 1300-1500, 1800-2100 (times variable).
**Ann:** Somali: "Halkan wa Raadiyaha Dowlad Deegaanka Somalida Itoobia".

**SOUTH FM (Gov)**
✉ Southern Nations & Nationalities Mass Media Agency, P.O. Box 1080, Awassa.
**FM:** Awassa 96.9MHz, Arba Minch 90.9, Bensa 92.3, Bonga 97.4, Dire Dawa 106.1 2kW, Gedio 99.4, Jinka 87.8, Mizan 104.5, Waka 94.1, Wolkitie 89.2MHz.

**Other governmental stations:**
**Addis Ababa R:** 96.3MHz 4kW – **Bahir Dar FM:** 96.9MHz – **Debub FM,** Awassa: 100.6MHz – **Dire Dawa FM:** 106.1MHz 2kW – **Finfine FM:** Adama 92.3MHz – **Harari FM:** Harar: 101.4MHz – **Mekele FM:** 104.4MHz – **Somali FM,** Jigjiga 99.1MHz.

**Other stations:**
**Abay FM,** Addis Ababa: 102.9MHz **W:** facebook.com/Abayfm102.9 – **Afro FM,** Addis Ababa: 105.3MHz 2.5kW. **W:** afro105fm.com – **Ahadu R,** Addis Ababa: 94.3MHz **W:** ahaduradio.com – **Bisrat R,** Addis Ababa: 101.1MHz **W:** bisratfm.com – **ECSU R,** Addis Ababa: 100.5MHz **W:** facebook.com/ECSU.FM.RADIO – **Ethio FM,** Addis Ababa: 107.8MHz **W:** ethiofmradio.com – **Ravos FM,** Awasa: 100.9MHz – **R. Sidama,** c/o Furra Institute of Development Studies, P.O. Box 69, Yirgalem: **MW:** 954kHz 2.5kW; MF 0500-1400, SS 0400-1700 – **Sheger FM,** Addis Ababa: 102.1MHz. **W:** shegerfm.com – **Zami R,** Addis Ababa: 90.7MHz 2kW. **W:** zami.com.et

**Community Radio:**
**Finote Selam Community R:** 91.5MHz **W:** facebook.com/Finote-selam-community-Radio-FM-988-1928324040812967
**Haramaya** 91.5MHz **W:** www.haramaya.edu.et/community/radio
**Korie** 92.3MHz, **Argoba** 98.6MHz, **Jimma** 102.0MHz, **Keffa** 102.5, **Kombolcha** 104.8, **Kembata** 105.8MHz

## FALKLAND ISLANDS (UK)

**L.T:** UTC -3h — **Pop:** 3,100 (excl. military personnel) — **Pr.L:** English — **E.C:** 50Hz, 230V — **ITU:** FLK

### FALKLANDS RADIO (Pub)
John Street, Stanley FIQQ 1ZZ (PO Box 786) ☎+500 27277. **W:** www.radio.co.fk **E:** stationmanager@radio.co.fk **LP:** Stn Man.: Corina Goss, News Editor: Liz Roberts, Engineer.: Jason Lewis
**MW:** 530kHz 15kW. **FM**(MHz)**:** Stanley 88.3 2kW, Stanley-MPA 96.5, Sussex Mt 97.2 30W, Byron Heights 97.4 300W, Mt Alice 97.6 300W, Mt William 97.8 1kW, Port Howard & Mt Kent 101.0. **NB:** Rel. BBC World Service when Falklands R. off air

### BRITISH FORCES BROADCASTING SERVICE
Rockhopper Road, RAF Mount Pleasant. BFPO 655. ☎+500 73003. +500 32193. **E:** falklands@bfbs.com **W:** forces.net/radio
**LP:** SM: Anthony Ballard. Eng. Mgr: Callum Pilkington.
**BFBS Radio 1: FM**(MHz)**:** Mt Pleasant 98.5 2kW, Sapper Hill 91.1 300W, Byron Heights/Mt Alice/Mt Kent/ 102.4 10W
**BFBS Radio 2: FM**(MHz)**:** Mt Sussex 88.2, Mt William 88.8, Mt Pleasant 93.8 2kW, 300W, Sapper Hill 94.5 300W, Port Howard 100.4, Byron Heights/Mt Alice/Mt Kent 104.2 10W
**BFBS Falkland Radio: FM**(MHz)**:** Mt Sussex 106.2, Mt William 106.8, Port Howard 101.6
**BFBS Gurkha Radio: FM**(MHz)**:** Mt Pleasant 96.0 2kW, Byron Heights/Mt Alice/Mt Kent 106.0 10W
**D.Prgr:** 24h **N:** Every hour from BFBS Radio UK News by satellite from London. **Ann:** "This is BFBS in the Falklands". **V.** by QSL-card. Rp.

## FAROE ISLANDS (Denmark)

**L.T:** UTC (31 Mar-27 Oct: +1h) — **Pop:** 49,000 — **Pr.L:** Faroese — **E.C:** 50Hz, 230V — **ITU:** FRO

### KRINGVARP FØROYA ÚTVARPIÐ (Pub.)
Norðari Ringvegur 20, POBox 1299, FO 100 Tórshavn ☎ +298 347500 +298 347501 **E:** netvarp@kvf.fo **W:** kvf.fo
**LP:** SM: vacant. Head of admin: Jákupe Mikkelsen. Head of news: Liljan Weihe. TD: Hjallgrím P. Hentze.
**MW:** Akraberg 531kHz 10kW
**FM**(MHz)**:** Tórshavn 89.9 31kW, Klaksvík 94.3 41kW, Hesturin Suðurðy 97.5 27kW, Støðlafjall 100.0 3kW, Knukur 92.1 1kW + 25 LP stns
**D.Prgr:** 24h. All prgrs are in Faroese. **Ann:** 'Útvarpið'

### MIÐLAR (Comm.)
Grønlandsvegur 38, FO 100 Tórshavn ☎ +298 223910 **E:** midlar@midlar.fo **W:** midlar.fo. **L.P:** Jonhard Hammer.
**FM1:** Tórshavn 91.1/98.7, Klaksvík 88.7, Streymoy 95.9, Varmakelda 90.9, Høganesi 93.1. **D.Prgr:** 24h
**VoxPop** Tórshavn 91.7/104.1, Klaksvík 90.7, Streymoy 104.8, Varmakelda 90.3, Høganesi 93.9. **D.Prgr:** 24h

### R7 KRINGVARP (Comm.)
PO Box 226, FO 600 Saltangará ☎ +298 207777 **E:** r7@r7.fo **W:** r7.fo. **FM**(MHz)**:** Tórshavn 102.0 1kW, Suðuroy 102.9 1kW, Streymoy 106.0 1kW, Klaksvík: 107.0 1kW + 11 LP stns.

### LINDIN KRISTILIGT KRINGVARP (Rlg.)
Bøkjaragøta 9, POBox 2063, FO 165 Argir (Tórshavn) ☎ +298 321377 +298 321379 **E:** lindin@lindin.fo **W:** lindin.fo
**L.P:** Chairman: Preben Hansen. **FM**(MHz)**:** Tórshavn 101.0 3kW, Klaksvík: 103.0 500W, Suduroy 105.5 2.5kW, Norðourstreymoy 98.0 1kW + 10 LP stns. **D.Prgr:** 24h

### LOCAL STATIONS (in MHz):
**STAÐIÐ FM,** Ungdómshúsið, FO 350 Vestmanna. **W:** www.vestmanna.fo/stadid+fm.html. **Prgr:** Su&Th at 2100 LT. **FM:** 101.0 – **STREAM 98.7,** Skáltavehur 29, PO Box 242, FO 700 Klaksvík. **W:** stream.fo. **L.P.:** Johnny Olsen. **FM:** 98.7MHz

## FIJI

**L.T:** +12h (4 Nov 18-13 Jan 19, 3 Nov 19-19 Jan 20: +13h) — **Pop:** 912,200 — **Pr.L:** English, Fijian, Hindi — **E.C:** 50Hz, 240V — **ITU:** FJI

### DEPARTMENT OF COMMUNICATIONS
1st Floor, Credit Corporation Building, Suva ☎ +679 330 0766 +679 331 5167 **W:** communications.gov.fj **LP:** Dep. Secretary: Josua Turaganivalu

### TELECOMMUNICATIONS AUTHORITY OF FIJI
76 Gordon Street, GPO Box 13413, Suva ☎+679 3310105 +679 3310110 **W:** taf.org.fj **E:** contact@taf.org.fj
Regulator of radio broadcasting in Fiji

### FIJI BROADCASTING CORPORATION LTD (Pub/Comm)
PO Box 334, Suva ☎ +679 331 4333 +679 330 1643 **W:** fbc.com.fj **E:** infocenter@fbc.com.fj **LP:** CEO: Riyaz Saiyed Khaiyum C.E: Apisai Bakani
**Netw.: RF1 (R.Fiji One Na Domoiviti)** Fijian ☎ +679 330 2588 **W:** rf1.fbc.com.fj & facebook.com/radio-fiji-one-domoiviti – **RF2 (R.Fiji Two Desh ki Dhadkan)** Hindi ☎ +679 330 2588 **W:** rf2.fbc.com.fj & facebook.com/radio-fiji-two – **R.Mirchi** Hindi ☎ +679 330 2588 **W:** mirchifm@fbc.com.fj & facebook.com/mirchifm – **RFGold (R.Fiji Gold)** English ☎ +679 330 4500 **W:** goldfm@fbc.com.fj & facebook.com/goldfmfiji – **Bula FM** Fijian ☎ +679 331 4211 **W:** bulafm@fbc.com.fj & facebook.com/bula-fm – **2dayFM** English ☎ +679 331 6415 **W:** 2dayfm@fbc.com.fj & facebook.com/2dayfm-fiji **Prgr:** All 24/7 audio streaming via individual station websites

| MW | kHz | kW | Netw. | | |
|----|-----|----|----|----|----|
| Suva | 558 | 10 | RF1 | | |
| Suva | 990 | 10 | RFGold | | |
| FM | RF1 | RF2 | Bula FM | R.Mirchi | RFGOLD | 2dayFM |

| FM | RF1 | RF2 | Bula FM | R.Mirchi | RFGOLD | 2dayFM |
|----|-----|-----|---------|----------|--------|--------|
| 1) | 93.0 | 105.0 | 102.6 | 97.8 | 100.2 | 95.4 |
| 2) | 92.8 | 104.8 | 102.4 | 97.6 | 100.0 | 95.2 |
| 3) | 93.2 | 105.4 | 102.8 | 98.0 | 100.4 | 95.6 |
| 4) | 93.4 | 105.4 | 103.0 | 98.2 | 100.6 | 95.8 |

**1)** Deuba, Navua, Lami, Suva, Nausori, Korovou, Nadi, Lautoka, Yasawas, Mamanuca, Savusavu, Tavenui – **2)** Coral Coast, Nabau, Serua, Ba – **3)** Tavua – **4)** Rakiraki

**Private commercial network**
### COMMUNICATIONS FIJI LTD (Comm)
231 Waimanu Road [Private Mail Bag], Suva ☎ +679 331 4766 +679 330 3748 **W:** fijivillage.com [audio streaming needs registration and annual fee] **E:** info@fm96.com.fj **LP:** Man.Dir: William Parkinson, GM Fiji: Ian Jackson **E:** ian@fm96.com.fj CE: Philip Wilikibau **E:** philip@fm96.com.fj
**Netw.: FM96** (English) PD: Tony Rahiman **E:** tony@fm96.com.fj – **Legend FM** (English) PD: Alex Elbourne **E:** alex@fm96.com.fj – **Viti FM** (Fijian) PD: Malakai Veisamasama **E:** mala@fm96.com.fj – **Navtarang** (Hindi) PD: Satya Nand **E:** satya@fm96.com.fj – **R. Sargam** (Hindi) PD: Roneel Narayan **E:** roneel@sargam.com.fj **Prgr:** All 24/7

| FM | FM96 | Navtarang | Viti FM | Legend FM | R.Sargam |
|----|------|-----------|---------|-----------|----------|
| 1) | 96.2 | 101.0 | 92.2 | 98.6 | 103.4 |
| 2) | 96.0 | 100.8 | 92.0 | 98.4 | 103.2 |
| 3) | 96.6 | 101.4 | 92.6 | 99.0 | 103.8 |

**1)** Suva, Nausori, Central Division, Nadi, Lautoka, Labassa – **2)** Sigatoka, Coral Coast, Ba, Tavua, Vatukoula – **3)** Rakiraki

### OTHER STATIONS:

| FM | MHz | Station | Location |
|----|-----|---------|----------|
| 1) | 88.2 | BBC | Nadi |
| 1) | 88.2 | BBC | Suva |
| 3) | 89.0 | fem'TALK 89 FM | Suva |
| 3) | 89.0 | fem'TALK 89 FM | Labasa |
| 2) | 89.4 | R. Pasifik | Suva |

| FM | MHz | Station | Location |
|---|---|---|---|
| 8) | 89.8 | WHBN Harvest R. | Suva |
| 4) | 91.8 | R. France Int. | Suva |
| 5) | 93.6 | MIX 94FM | Sigatoka |
| 5) | 93.8 | MIX 94FM | Suva/Lautoka/Nadi/ Mamanucas/Yasawas |
| 5) | 94.2 | MIX 94FM | Ba/Tavua/Ra |
| 6) | 94.6 | R. Naya Jiwan | Suva |
| 6) | 103.4 | Nai Talai FM | Suva |
| 6) | 104.0 | R. Light | - |
| 6) | 104.2 | R. Light | Suva |
| 4) | 105.8 | R. France Int. | Suva |
| 10) | 106.6 | R. Australia | Suva |
| 10) | 106.6 | R. Australia | Nadi |
| 9) | 107.0 | Hope FM | Suva |
| 9) | 107.4 | Hope FM | Ba/Tavua/Vatukaola |

**Addresses and other information:**
**1)** 24/7 Pacific stream via satellite from London – **2)** School of Law, Arts & Media, University of the South Pacific, Private Mail Bag, Laucala, Suva ☎ +679 3232795 🖷+679 3231500 **LP:** SM: Allan Stevens **W:** usp.ac.fj **D:Prgr:** 2000-1200 includes prgrs in English, Pidgin, Hindi and iTaukei languages. As all staff are volunteers, stn only on-air during academic year. – **3)** Community Media Center, 54 Ratu Sukuna Road, Suva ☎ + 679 3318160/3310307 🖷 +679 33077207 **W:** femlinkpacific.org.fj **LP:** Exec.Dir: Sharon Bhagwan Rolls. Stations: Suva **Prgr:** 24/7 Labasa : **Prgr:** 2200-0200 M-F Mobile: Also operates a mobile community radio stn studio for women on Viti Levu – **4)** 24/7 English language stream via satellite from Paris – **5)** 11 Nasoki St, Lautoka ☎ +679 666 8900 **W:** mix.com.fj **E:** info@mix94.fm **ID:** "Fiji's Best Mix" 24h/7 – **6)** Pacific Islands Christian Network [PICN], Evangelical Bible Missions Trust Board. Studio:15 Tower Street, Suva. PO Box 2525, Gov.Bldgs, Suva. Stations: **R.Light** (English) **W:** radiolight.org **E:** radiolight@connect.com.fj ☎ +679 331 9536, **R. Naya Jiwan** (Hindi) **W:** www.nayajiwan.org ☎ +679 331 9535 **R. Nai Talai** (Fijian) **W:** naitalai.listen2myradio.com [audio streaming] **E:** revival@naitalai.org Currently inactive on FM – **8)** World Harvest Centre, Lot 1 Khalsa Rd, Kinoya, Suva. PO Box 1499, Nabua, Suva ☎ +679 3398901 **W:** whbn.info@gmail.com **LP:** Mktg Mgr: Rajiv Puran **D.Prgr:** 24/7 rlg – **9)** Seventh Day Adventist Church Mission, 37 Queens Road, Suva ☎ +679 336 3703 **W:** facebook.com/ hopefm107 – **10)** 24/7 relay of ABC R. in English via satellite.

## FINLAND

**LT:** UTC +2h (31 Mar-27 Oct: +3h) — **Pop:** 5.6 million — **Pr.L:** Finnish, Swedish — **E.C:** 50Hz, 230V — **ITU:** FIN

**VIESTINTÄVIRASTO
(FICORA, Finnish Communications Regulatory Authority)**
📠 PL 313, FI-00181 Helsinki ☎+358 295390100 🖷 +358 295390270 **W:** ficora.fi **E:** info@ficora.fi

**DIGITA OY (programme distributor)**
📠 Jämsänk. 2, FI-00520 Helsinki ☎+358 20411711 🖷 +358 204117234 **W:** digita.fi **E:** info@digita.fi

**YLEISRADIO (YLE, Pub.)**
📠 FI-00024 Yleisradio ☎+358 9 14801 🖷 +358 9 14803216 **W:** yle.fi
**LP:** DG: Mrs. Merja Ylä-Anttila.

| FM (MHz) | 1 | 2 | 3 | 4 | 5 | 6 | 7 | kW |
|---|---|---|---|---|---|---|---|---|
| Aavasaksa | 87.9 | 89.8 | 94.7 | | | | | 3 |
| Ahvenanmaa | | | 100.3 | | 104.9 | 93.1 | | 10/3 |
| Anjalankoski | 88.5 | 92.8 | 96.9 | 91.4 | | 99.5 | | 30 |
| Enontekiö | 88.5 | 91.4 | 98.7 | 104.6 | | | 101.2 | 5 |
| Espoo | 87.9 | 91.9 | 94.0 | 103.7 | 98.9 | 101.1 | | 60 |
| Eurajoki | 87.7 | 103.5 | 94.8 | 92.0 | 99.4 | 103.0 | | 30 |
| Fiskars | 90.9 | 93.1 | 97.0 | 105.0 | 102.5 | 99.7 | | 3 |
| Haapavesi | 89.0 | 96.1 | 98.4 | 101.9 | | | | 30 |
| Hämeenlinna | | | 99.2 | | | | | 1 |
| Iisalmi | 87.7 | 92.8 | 96.5 | 107.9 | | | | 2 |
| Ilomantsi | | | | 106.1 | | | | 1 |
| Inari | 88.4 | 92.8 | 98.8 | 105.3 | | | 101.9 | 50/30 |
| Joensuu | | | 106.9 | 101.2 | | | | 1 |
| Joutseno | 88.0 | 90.9 | 98.5 | 100.7 | | | | 30 |
| Jyväskylä | 89.9 | 87.6 | 99.3 | 92.5 | 103.5 | | | 3/30 |
| Karigasniemi | 89.5 | 93.4 | 96.8 | 103.7 | | 100.8 | | 2 |
| Kerimäki | 90.5 | 95.8 | 99.1 | 103.2 | | | | 30 |
| | | | 97.7 | | | | | 6 |
| Kiihtelysvaara | 88.4 | 94.9 | 97.2 | 100.4 | | | | 5 |
| Koli | 90.2 | 93.4 | 99.6 | 106.4 | | 102.4 | | 30/5 |

| FM (MHz) | 1 | 2 | 3 | 4 | 5 | 6 | 7 | kW |
|---|---|---|---|---|---|---|---|---|
| Kruunupyy | 91.4 | 94.0 | 97.6 | 88.8 | 99.7 | 102.7 | | 60/3 |
| Kuopio | 91.6 | 93.9 | 98.1 | 88.1 | | 100.2 | | 50 |
| Kuttanen | 94.1 | 97.2 | 99.6 | 105.6 | | | 102.2 | 3 |
| Lahti | 93.2 | 95.5 | 97.9 | 90.5 | | 100.6 | | 50/0.2 |
| Lapua | 88.2 | 90.1 | 93.1 | 97.5 | 95.2 | 101.5 | | 60/2 |
| Lohja | | | 96.1 | 105.0 | | | | 3 |
| Mikkeli | 88.9 | 92.1 | 94.6 | 101.8 | | | | 30 |
| Nuorgam | 88.6 | 93.9 | 97.7 | 107.8 | | | 101.2 | 3 |
| Oulu | 90.4 | 93.2 | 97.3 | 107.7 | | 100.3 | | 50/5 |
| Parikkala | | | 95.1 | | | | | 1 |
| Pello | 90.2 | 97.0 | 99.7 | 103.4 | | | | 3 |
| Perho | | | 95.9 | 92.2 | | | | 3 |
| Pernaja | 89.5 | 92.3 | 95.0 | 96.4 | 102.2 | 98.3 | | 3/1 |
| Pieksämäki | 89.4 | 95.3 | 97.4 | 104.9 | | | | 2/0.5 |
| Pihtipudas | 88.6 | 91.1 | 97.0 | 94.7 | | 100.8 | | 50/2.5 |
| Posio | 87.6 | 91.5 | 98.6 | 104.0 | | | | 30/3 |
| Pyhätunturi | 91.0 | 97.6 | 99.9 | 102.4 | | | | 50 |
| Pyhävuori | 88.9 | 91.0 | 94.2/97.2 | 96.1 | 98.6 | 102.6 | | 30/2 |
| Rovaniemi | 88.2 | 94.0 | 96.7 | 106.8 | | | 103.0 | 30/10 |
| Ruka | 90.7 | 92.8 | 95.1 | 104.3 | | | | 3/2 |
| Sievi | | | 90.3 | | | | | 1 |
| Sodankylä | 87.8 | 90.1 | 94.3 | 106.5 | | | 101.3 | 3 |
| Taivalkoski | 89.2 | 91.9 | 992/1036 | 106.5 | | | | 60 |
| Tammela | 89.2 | 91.3 | 96.0 | 105.4 | | | | 5 |
| Tampere | 90.7 | 93.7 | 99.9 | 88.3 | | 102.1 | | 60/6 |
| Tenola(NOR) | 89.0 | 94.1 | 95.8 | | | 100.5 | | 0.02 |
| Tervola | 88.6 | 92.6 | 95.6 | 101.6 | | | | 30 |
| Turku | 89.8 | 92.6 | 94.3 | 96.7 | 98.2 | 101.4 | | 60/6 |
| Utsjoki | 90.7 | 93.1 | 99.4 | 107.1 | | | 102.6 | 2/5 |
| Vaasa | 87.8 | 89.6 | 94.8 | 105.2 | 97.3 | 101.0 | | 1 |
| Vuokatti | 92.3 | 94.3 | 98.9 | 101.2 | | | | 60 |
| Ylläs | 92.2 | 95.3 | 98.1 | 100.7 | | | 103.8 | 50 |
| Ähtäri | 91.9 | 94.6 | 96.6 | 102.9 | | | | 3 |

+ approx. 30 transmitters under 1 kW.

**D.Prgr: FM1 "YLE Radio 1"** (classical music, culture, actualities): 24h (also on digital TV) – **FM2 "YleX"** (rock & pop culture for youth): 24h. (r. R. Suomi at night). **N:** on the h – **FM3 "Radio Suomi"** (news, sports, popular music and regional prgrs): 24h. **N:** on the h – **FM4 "YLE Puhe"** (news & talk prgr.): 24h. Also on digital TV. – **FM5 "X3M"** (Swedish language prgr for young people). 24h (simultaneous night prgr. with R Vega) – **FM6 "YLE Vega"** (Swedish language prgr for grown-up people and regional prgrs). 24h – **FM7 "Yle Sámi Radio"** (Sámi language network). 24h. Carries YLE, SR & NRK Sámi Radio daytime weekdays, at other times relays FM3 – **"YLE Mondo"** (digital network carried also via Espoo 97.5MHz 5kW): 24h.

**Regional prgrs:**
**In Finnish on FM3 Radio Suomi** network): Mon-Fri 0430-0800, 1200-1600 excl. nationwide news on the h. Addit. reg. news at 0830, 0930 & 1130. Also Sat 0710-0950 divided to 10 regions. – **YLE Helsinki:** 88.4 /90.3/94.0/95.0/96.1/97.0/99.1MHz – **YLE Tampere:** 99.9MHz – **YLE Lahti:** 97.9MHz – **YLE Hämeenlinna:** 96.0/99.2/107.1/107.8MHz – **YLE Turku:** 94.3/99.2/100.3/105.8/107.1MHz – **YLE Pori:** 94.8/97.2/106.9MHz – **YLE Jyväskylä:** 97.0/99.3MHz – **YLE Kotka:** 96.9MHz – **YLE Lappeenranta:** 89.1/95.1/97.2/98.5MHz – **YLE Joensuu:** 97.2/97.7/98.3/99.6/106.9MHz – **YLE Mikkeli** 94.6/97.4/99.1MHz – **YLE Kuopio:** 96.5/98.1MHz – **YLE Pohjanmaa:** 93.1/94.2/94.8/96.6MHz – **YLE Kokkola** 87.6/90.3/90.7/95.9/96.0/9 7.6MHz – **YLE Oulu:** 95.1/97.3/98.4/99.2/102.5MHz – **YLE Kajaani:** 98.9/103.6MHz – **YLE Kemi:** 94.7/95.6/103.7MHz – **YLE Rovaniemi:** 96.7MHz + 15 more freqs.
**In Swedish on FM6:** MF 0430-1000. **YLE Vega Huvudstadsregionen:** Helsingfors: 100.2/101.1/102.1/103.5/104.4 MHz – **YLE Vega Östnyland,** Borgå: 95.9/98.3/99.5/100.6MHz – **YLE Vega Västnyland:** Ekenäs: 99.7/101.9MHz – **YLE Vega Åboland,** Åbo: 87.6/93.1/101.4/103.0MHz – **YLE Vega Österbotten,** Vasa: 98.5 /100.3/100.8/101.0/101.5/102.6/102.7MHz.

**OTHER STATIONS; main nationwide networks:**

| FM (MHz) | 1) | 2) | 3) | 4) | 5) | 6) | 7) | 8) | 9) |
|---|---|---|---|---|---|---|---|---|---|
| Alajärvi | | 104.3 | | | | 102.2 | | | |
| Anjalankoski | 105.7 | | 102.7 | 90.0 | 89.3 | | 104.9 | 96.2 | |
| Espoo | 106.2 | | | | | | 92.5 | | |
| Eurajoki | | 90.4 | 105.1 | 104.5 | 96.5 | 106.0 | | 101.7 | 95.7 |
| Forssa | | | 98.5 | 103.6 | 107.5 | 103.3 | | 90.1 | |
| Haapavesi | 104.1 | 100.1 | 96.8 | | 105.6 | 93.4 | 106.1 | | |
| Hanko | | 107.5 | 96.2 | | 104.5 | 95.7 | 95.3 | | |
| Harjavalta | | | | | | 93.9 | | | |
| Heinola | | 87.6 | | | | | | | |
| Helsinki | | 96.2 | 104.6 | 94.9 | 98.1 | 96.8 | 90.0 | 89.0 | 88.6 |

| FM (MHz) | 1) | 2) | 3) | 4) | 5) | 6) | 7) | 8) | 9) |
|---|---|---|---|---|---|---|---|---|---|
| Huittinen | 93.0 | | | | | | | | |
| Hyvinkää | | | 95.7 | | 104.0 | | | | 89.4 |
| Hämeenlinna | 100.2 | 101.7 | 106.5 | 92.3 | | 97.3 | | 105.9 | 95.2 |
| Iisalmi | | 89.5 | 103.1 | 104.7 | 89.1 | | 95.6 | | 102.5 |
| Ikaalinen | 99.0 | | | | | | | | |
| Imatra | 105.3 | | | 101.5 | 102.5 | | | | |
| Inari | | | | 104.1 | | | | | |
| Inkoo | | | | | | 105.5 | | | |
| Joensuu | 92.8 | 87.9 | 103.7 | 102.9 | 96.4 | 101.9 | | | 98.7 |
| Joutseno | 103.8 | | 94.2 | | | | 96.0 | | |
| Juuka | 103.3 | | | | | | | | |
| Jyväskylä | 105.8 | 107.1 | 101.6 | 97.7 | 95.1 | 97.3 | 101.0 | 94.1 | 107.8 |
| Jämsä | 100.3 | 94.4 | | | 88.8 | 89.6 | | | |
| Järvenpää | | | | | | 101.8 | | | |
| Kajaani | | 102.8 | 107.0 | 96.3 | 93.7 | 94.8 | | | |
| Kalajoki | | | 104.6 | | | | | | |
| Kemi | | 105.2 | 98.8 | | | | | | |
| Kemijärvi | 104.7 | | | | | | | | |
| Kerimäki | 107.7 | 104.2 | | | | 91.3 | | | |
| Kitee | 102.2 | | | | | | | | |
| Kokkola | | 99.1 | 106.3 | | 99.1 | | | | |
| Koli | 104.3 | 95.7 | 94.7 | | 107.4 | | | | |
| Kotka | 87.7 | | 101.5 | | | | | | |
| Kouvola | 100.1 | 90.0 | 93.8 | 107.7 | 9 6 . 2 | | | | |
| Kristiinankaup. | 105.1 | 93.4 | | | | | | | |
| Kruunupyy | 98.8 | 107.2 | 105.3 | 104.9 | 104.3 | | | | |
| Kuopio | 106.7 | 96.7 | 93.0 | 100.9 | 107.3 | 101.6 | 89.1 | 106.1 | 92.0 |
| Kurikka | 92.3 | 100.1 | | | | | | | |
| Köyliö | | | 107.9 | | | | | | |
| Lahti | 102.4 | 103.0 | 105.0 | 89.7 | 104.4 | 96.6 | 94.2 | 106.4 | 103.8 |
| Lappeenranta | 93.5 | 105.0 | 94.8 | 96.5 | 100.2 | 96.0 | 97.4 | | |
| Lapua | 106.5 | 96.9 | 105.4 | 100.4 | | 89.4 | | | |
| Lempäälä | | | | 102.8 | | | | | |
| Lohja | 96.5 | 104.8 | 88.8 | 1 0 7 . 2 | | | | | |
| Loimaa | 98.5 | | | 91.8 | | | | | |
| Loviisa | | | 104.6 | 105.2 | | | | | |
| Luumäki | | | 96.0 | | | | | | |
| Mikkeli | 106.9 | 89.7 | 100.5 | 93.0 | 104.8 | 106.3 | 100.9 | 87.8 | |
| Mäntyharju | | | 93.0 | | | | | | |
| Nilsiä | | | 97.5 | | | | | | |
| Orivesi | 103.8 | 101.2 | 89.3 | | | | | | |
| Oulu | 104.8 | 89.4 | 101.4 | 95.8 | 96.4 | 99.1 | 106.2 | 106.9 | 101.0 |
| Outokumpu | 101.7 | | | | | | | | |
| Padasjoki | 87.8 | | | | | | | | |
| Parkano | 99.0 | 100.2 | | | | | | | |
| Pieksämäki | 102.2 | 101.3 | 103.0 | 96.5 | | | | | |
| Pihtipudas | 105.1 | 107.0 | 98.5 | 104.5 | 101.7 | 102.3 | | | |
| Pohja | 95.1 | | | | | | | | |
| Pori | 91.6 | 100.4 | 104.5 | 96.5 | 90.4 | 98.7 | 95.7 | 101.0 | |
| Porvoo | 99.8 | 107.9 | 93.5 | | | | | | |
| Pyhätunturi | 105.8 | 106.2 | | | | | | | |
| Pyhävuori | 107.6 | | | | | | | | |
| Raahe | 92.5 | 107.0 | 89.9 | 105.8 | 87.7 | | | | |
| Rauma | 105.1 | 103.6 | 93.9 | | | | | | |
| Riihimäki | 99.6 | 94.7 | | | | | | | |
| Rovaniemi | 105.5 | 89.3 | 102.0 | 106.3 | 103.3 | 101.1 | 93.4 | | |
| Ruka | 100.8 | 96.3 | | | | | | | |
| Ruovesi | 103.8 | | | | | | | | |
| Salo | 99.1 | 107.7 | 88.2 | | | | | | |
| Savonlinna | 96.7 | 104.2 | 101.4 | 105.2 | 91.3 | 93.6 | | | |
| Seinäjoki | 96.9 | 100.4 | 103.3 | 91.2 | 89.4 | 101.8 | | | |
| Sievi | 107.7 | | | | | | | | |
| Siilinjärvi | 102.0 | | | | | | | | |
| Sonkajärvi | 107.1 | | | | | | | | |
| Suomussalmi | | | 88.8 | 104.5 | | | | | |
| Sysmä | 90.2 | 106.8 | 101.3 | 93.5 | 96.1 | 89.1 | | | |
| Taivalkoski | 106.5 | 94.6 | | | | | | | |
| Tammisaari | 95.1 | 100.2 | 91.4 | 103.2 | 107.0 | | | | |
| Tampere | 104.7 | 100.9 | 89.6 | 104.2 | 91.6 | 90.0 | 105.6 | 98.8 | 94.1 |
| Tervola | 107.5 | 96.2 | 100.1 | | | | | | |
| Tornio | 98.8 | 92.0 | 98.3 | | | | | | |
| Turku | 103.9 | 100.1 | 98.7 | 97.6 | 103.4 | 104.6 | 102.4 | 107.3 | 89.0 |
| Uusikaupunki | 96.2 | 91.1 | 88.5 | | | | | | |
| Vaasa | 104.4 | 91.6 | 102.0 | 93.9 | 91.2 | | | | |
| Valkeakoski | 95.0 | 94.4 | | | | | | | |
| Vammala | 101.2 | 97.7 | 88.0 | | | | | | |
| Varkaus | 92.7 | 91.0 | 105.5 | 102.8 | | | | | |
| Vihti | 105.6 | | | | | | | | |
| Vilppula | 95.4 | | | | | | | | |
| Vuokatti | 105.7 | 107.0 | 88.8 | | | | | | |

| FM (MHz) | 1) | 2) | 3) | 4) | 5) | 6) | 7) | 8) | 9) |
|---|---|---|---|---|---|---|---|---|---|
| Ylivieska | 88.3 | | | | | | | | |
| Ylläs | 107.9 | 91.6 | | | | | | | |
| Ähtäri | 97.8 | 102.9 | 104.9 | 98.4 | 105.5 | | | | |

### Addresses: & Other Information

**1) Nova,** Tallberginkatu 1C, PL 123, 00180 Helsinki **W:** radionova.fi Powers 1-60kW — **2) Iskelmä,** Kehräsaari B5. 33200 Tampere. **W:** iskelma.fi Powers 0.1-3kW – **3) KISS FM,** Tallbergink. 1C 7. krs, 00180 Helsinki **W:** voice.fi Powers 0.1-60kW – **4) R. Rock,** Töölönlahdenkatu 2, PL 350, 00100 Helsinki **W:** radiorock.fi Powers 0.1-4kW – **5) R. Suomipop,** Lintulahdenk. 10, 00500 Helsinki **W:** radiosuomipop.fi Powers 0.1-3kW – **6) R. NRJ (Energy),** Kiviaidankatu 2 i, 00210 Helsinki **W:** nrj.fi Powers 0.1-30kW – **7) R. Aalto,** PL 350, Tehtaankatu 27-29 A, 00151 Helsinki. **W:** radioaalto.fi Powers 0.1-10kW – **8) R. Dei** (Rlg.), Ilmalankuja 2 i, 00240 Helsinki. **W:** radiodei.fi Powers 0.2-5kW – **9) Helmiradio,** PL 95, 00089 Sanoma **W:** helmiradio.fi Powers 0.2-2kW.
About 50 more stations are in operation.

### ÅLAND (autonomous province)

**SVERIGES RADIO** cf. Sweden

| FM (MHz) | P1 | P2 | P3 | P4 | kW |
|---|---|---|---|---|---|
| Mariehamn | 95.0 | 97.1 | 88.6 | 102.3 | 10 |

**Steel FM,** Mariehamn: 95.9MHz 0.2kW. **W:** steelfm.net – **Rix FM** (cf. Sweden), Mariehamn: 101.8MHz 3kW – **R. Harmonica,** Mariehamn: 102.8MHz 1kW – **Soft FM,** Mariehamn: 107.2MHz 0.2kW. **W:** softfm.net – **Ålands R. (Gov.),** Mariehamn: 91.3MHz 10kW. **W:** alandsradio.ax

## FRANCE

**L.T:** UTC +1h (31 Mar-27 Oct: +2h) — **Pop:** 65 million — **Pr.L:** French — **E.C:** 50Hz, 230V — **ITU:** F

### CONSEIL SUPÉRIEUR DE L'AUDIOVISUEL (CSA)
✉ 39/43 quai André Citroën, 75739 Paris cedex 15 ☎ +33 1 40583800 ▤ +33 1 45790006 **W:** csa.fr **LP:** Pres: Olivier Schrameck
The CSA regulates TV and radio, and issues broadcast licences

### TDF
✉ 155 bis avenue Pierre Brossolette, 92541 Montrouge cedex ☎ +33 1 55951000 **W:** tdf.fr **LP:** Pres & DG: Olivier Huart
TDF operates the majority of radio and TV txs

### TOWERCAST
✉ 46/50 avenue Théophile Gautier, 75016 Paris ☎ +33 1 40714071 **W:** towercast.fr **LP:** Pres: Jacques Roques
Towercast operates radio and TV txs

### OUTRE-MER 1ère (Pub)
✉ 35/37 rue Danton, 92240 Malakoff ☎ +33 1 55227100 **W:** la1ere.francetvinfo.fr **LP:** Dir.: Walles Kotra.
Outre-Mer 1ère is a part of France Télévisions and produces public service prgrs (radio & TV) in the French overseas territories

### RADIO FRANCE (Pub)
✉ 116 Av. du Président Kennedy, 75220 Paris cedex 16 ☎ +33 1 56402222 **W:** radiofrance.fr **LP:** Pres. & DG: Sybile Veil

### HOME SERVICES:

| FM: Station (MHz) | A | B | C | D | kW |
|---|---|---|---|---|---|
| Abbeville | 93.1 | 97.4 | 89.8 | - | 2.5 |
| Ajaccio | 92.4 | 97.6 | 88.0 | - | 10 |
| Ajaccio (La Punta) | 88.6 | 103.9 | - | 105.6 | 4 |
| Albi | - | - | - | 105.5 | 1 |
| Alençon | 93.0 | 88.0 | 91.0 | - | 13 |
| Ales | 87.6 | 96.1 | 98.6 | 105.1 | 1 |
| Amiens (St Just) | 95.4 | 102.5 | 99.4 | - | 20 |
| Amiens (Dury) | 92.6 | 97.0 | 89.3 | 105.5 | 2 |
| Angers | 93.2 | 91.4 | 97.4 | - | 10 |
| Angers (La Ballue) | - | - | - | 105.5 | 1 |
| Angoulême | 92.4 | 87.6 | 95.1 | 105.5 | 2 |
| Arcachon | 88.3 | 97.0 | 91.0 | 105.5 | 1.2 |
| Argenton sur Creuse | 101.9 | 89.8 | 97.2 | - | 5 |
| Arles | - | - | - | 105.0 | 1 |
| Arnay le Duc | 94.6 | 90.3 | 100.3 | 105.5 | 3 |
| Aurillac | 94.5 | 98.0 | 91.9 | - | 7 |
| Autun | 88.1 | 97.3 | 94.1 | - | 10 |
| Auxerre | 99.5 | 89.5 | 92.8 | - | 5 |
| Auxerre (Venoy) | - | - | - | 105.5 | 1 |
| Avallon | - | - | - | 105.6 | 1 |

| FM: Station (MHz) | A | B | C | D | kW |
|---|---|---|---|---|---|
| Avignon | 97.4 | 90.7 | 93.2 | - | 4 |
| Avignon (Sorgues) | - | - | - | 105.2 | 2 |
| Bar le Duc | 90.9 | 88.4 | 92.7 | 104.5 | 10 |
| Bastia | 95.9 | 89.2 | 93.9 | 105.5 | 10 |
| Bayonne | 89.0 | 96.1 | 92.7 | 105.5 | 16 |
| Beaucaire | - | - | - | 105.2 | 1 |
| Bergerac | 92.3 | 94.0 | 97.1 | - | 26 |
| Besançon (Montfaucon) | 98.7 | 89.3 | 95.0 | - | 10 |
| Besançon (Lomont) | 90.0 | 97.7 | 92.9 | - | 18 |
| Beziers | - | - | - | 105.1 | 1 |
| Bordeaux | 89.7 | 97.7 | 93.5 | 105.5 | 6 |
| Boulogne sur Mer | 103.3 | 99.9 | 89.4 | 106.5 | 1 |
| Bourges | 94.9 | 88.5 | 91.8 | - | 74 |
| Bourges (town) | - | - | - | 105.5 | 1 |
| Brest | 95.4 | 97.8 | 89.4 | - | 200 |
| Brest (town) | - | - | - | 105.5 | 3 |
| Briançon | 91.5 | 97.8 | 89.5 | 105.4 | 1 |
| Brignoles | 106.7 | 104.0 | 105.5 | - | 1.5 |
| Caen | 99.6 | 91.5 | 95.6 | - | 100 |
| Caen (town) | - | - | - | 105.5 | 1 |
| Calais | 104.7 | - | - | 105.6 | 1 |
| Cannes | - | - | - | 105.9 | 1 |
| Carcassone | 88.3 | 96.5 | 90.9 | - | 80 |
| Castres | - | - | - | 105.5 | 2 |
| Chambéry | 93.5 | 90.5 | 98.6 | - | 8 |
| Chambéry (town) | - | - | - | 105.1 | 1 |
| Champagnole | 88.5 | 91.7 | 98.3 | - | 1 |
| Charleville-Mézières | 95.8 | 90.1 | 93.5 | 105.9 | 10 |
| Chartres | 94.6 | 98.1 | 89.7 | - | 32 |
| Chartres (town) | - | - | - | 105.7 | 4 |
| Chateaubriant | - | - | - | 105.5 | 1 |
| Châteauroux | - | - | - | 105.5 | 1 |
| Chaumont | 96.5 | 90.4 | 93.3 | - | 15 |
| Chaumont (town) | - | - | - | 105.5 | 1 |
| Cherbourg-Octeville | 94.1 | 89.2 | 92.3 | 105.6 | 1 |
| Cholet | - | - | - | 105.9 | 1 |
| Clermont-Fd | 90.4 | 98.4 | 95.5 | 105.5 | 35 |
| Compiègne | - | - | - | 105.3 | 1 |
| Corse (East) | 96.8 | 92.3 | 99.8 | - | 17 |
| Corte | 98.2 | 91.0 | 94.8 | 105.5 | 1.3 |
| Cosne Cours s.Loire | - | - | - | 105.3 | 1 |
| Creil | 87.6 | 93.3 | 91.9 | 105.6 | 1 |
| Dijon | 95.9 | 93.7 | 99.2 | - | 25 |
| Dunkerque | - | - | - | 106.5 | 1 |
| Epinal | 98.6 | 92.4 | 89.4 | 106.5 | 10 |
| Evreux | 88.5 | 98.9 | 97.3 | 105.5 | 1 |
| Falaise | - | - | - | 105.3 | 1 |
| Fontainebleau | - | - | - | 105.5 | 2 |
| Gap | 98.3 | 88.5 | 95.3 | 105.5 | 5 |
| Gex | 94.4 | 96.7 | 89.6 | 101.1 | 25 |
| Grenoble (Chamrousse) | 99.4 | 88.2 | 91.8 | - | 1 |
| Grenoble (T. s. Venin) | 89.9 | 92.8 | 107.3 | 105.1 | 1 |
| Guéret | 100.7 | 98.8 | 90.8 | 105.5 | 12 |
| Hirson | 94.4 | 99.7 | 97.2 | - | 5 |
| Hyères | 91.6 | 97.5 | 94.5 | 107.1 | 1.5 |
| Laon | - | - | - | 105.3 | 1 |
| Laval | 95.1 | 88.3 | 92.1 | 105.5 | 5 |
| La Rochelle | - | - | - | 105.5 | 1 |
| Le Havre | 88.9 | 93.3 | 98.5 | 105.5 | 1 |
| Le Mans | 92.6 | 89.0 | 97.0 | 105.5 | 128 |
| Le Puy | 99.3 | 89.3 | 92.8 | - | 10 |
| Lesparre | 92.4 | 90.3 | 95.1 | - | 1.6 |
| Lille (Bouvigny) | 103.7 | 98.0 | 88.7 | 105.2 | 125 |
| Limoges | 93.0 | 89.5 | 97.5 | - | 150 |
| Limoges (town) | - | - | - | 105.5 | 2 |
| Longwy | 98.1 | 88.3 | 91.0 | 104.3 | 5 |
| Lourdes | - | - | - | 105.3 | 3.5 |
| Lyon (Mont Pilat) | 99.8 | 88.8 | 92.4 | 103.4 | 150 |
| Lyon (Town) | 101.1 | 94.1 | 98.0 | 105.4 | 4 |
| Mantes la Jolie | 95.0 | 92.4 | 97.1 | - | 5 |
| Marseille | 91.3 | 99.0 | 94.2 | - | 400 |
| Marseille | - | - | - | 105.3 | 13 |
| Marseille (town) | 91.7 | 98.6 | 94.7 | - | 1 |
| Maubeuge | - | - | - | 106.2 | 2 |
| Melun | - | - | - | 105.7 | 1 |
| Mende | 90.1 | 96.9 | 93.7 | - | 10 |
| Menton | 97.0 | 89.6 | 91.7 | 105.5 | 5 |
| Metz | 99.8 | 94.5 | 89.7 | 106.8 | 145 |
| Millau | 94.9 | 99.2 | 88.9 | - | 6 |
| Mont de Marsan | - | - | - | 105.5 | 6 |
| Montargis | 102.9 | 98.8 | 94.1 | 105.5 | 1 |
| Montauban | - | - | - | 105.7 | 1 |
| Montereau | - | - | - | 105.7 | 1 |
| Montlieu la Garde | 88.3 | 104.8 | 98.8 | - | 3.5 |
| Montluçon | - | - | - | 105.5 | 1 |
| Montpellier | 89.4 | 97.8 | 92.9 | - | 18 |
| Montpellier (Town) | 89.1 | - | 96.4 | 105.1 | 1 |
| Morosaglia | 97.1 | 88.8 | 93.4 | - | 1 |
| Mulhouse | 95.7 | 88.6 | 91.6 | 105.5 | 100 |
| Nancy | 96.9 | 88.7 | 91.7 | 105.9 | 5 |
| Nantes | 90.6 | 94.2 | 98.9 | 105.5 | 125 |
| Neufchateau | 96.3 | 100.3 | 91.5 | - | 1 |
| Neufchatel-en-Bray | 92.7 | 96.0 | 90.2 | - | 5 |
| Nevers | - | - | - | 105.5 | 1 |
| Nice | 100.2 | 101.9 | 92.2 | 105.7 | 100 |
| Nimes | 88.7 | - | - | 105.1 | 1/1.5 |
| Niort | 99.4 | 96.4 | 91.1 | - | 190 |
| Niort (town) | - | - | - | 105.5 | 1 |
| Noyon | - | - | - | 107.4 | 1 |
| Orléans | 99.2 | 95.8 | 90.7 | - | 4 |
| Orléans (town) | - | - | - | 105.5 | 1 |
| Paris | 87.8 | 93.5 | 91.7 | 105.5 | 10 |
| Parthenay | 93.8 | 87.9 | 98.5 | 105.5 | 12 |
| Pau | - | - | - | 105.5 | 1 |
| Perpignan | 92.1 | 99.8 | 97.2 | 105.1 | 10 |
| Poitiers | 97.7 | 92.3 | 95.5 | 105.5 | 1 |
| Porto Vecchio (Col de Mela) | 96.8 | 90.8 | 98.9 | - | 1.5 |
| Porto Vecchio (Punto di a Varra) | 92.6 | 87.9 | 94.6 | 100.4 | 1 |
| Privas | 89.8 | 96.5 | 94.7 | 105.2 | 1 |
| Redon | - | - | - | 95.8 | 1 |
| Reims | 96.8 | 98.8 | 89.2 | 105.5 | 135 |
| Rennes | 93.5 | 98.3 | 89.9 | - | 100 |
| Rennes (town) | - | - | - | 105.5 | 1 |
| Roanne | - | - | - | 105.5 | 1 |
| Rochefort | - | - | - | 95.7 | 1 |
| Rouen | 96.5 | 94.0 | 92.0 | - | 100 |
| Rouen (town) | - | - | - | 105.7 | 2.7 |
| Ruffec | - | - | - | 105.3 | 1 |
| Saint Brieuc | - | - | - | 105.5 | 1 |
| Saint Etienne | 99.5 | 89.1 | 92.7 | 105.6 | 2 |
| Saint-Nazaire | 95.2 | 92.2 | 102.6 | 105.5 | 1.5 |
| Saint-Quentin | - | - | - | 105.6 | 1 |
| Saint-Raphaël | 96.3 | 88.7 | 99.6 | - | 40 |
| Saint-Raphaël (town) | - | - | - | 106.0 | 1 |
| Sainte Foy la Grande | - | - | - | 105.5 | 1 |
| Saintes | - | - | - | 105.4 | 1 |
| Sarrebourg | 93.1 | 99.4 | 90.3 | - | 10 |
| Sens | 96.3 | 98.5 | 93.8 | - | 10 |
| Sens (town) | - | - | - | 105.7 | 1.3 |
| Soissons | - | - | - | 105.7 | 1 |
| Strasbourg | 97.3 | 87.7 | 95.0 | 104.4 | 48 |
| Toulon | 92.0 | 97.1 | 94.9 | 105.8 | 5 |
| Toulouse (town) | 88.1 | 96.3 | 91.1 | 105.5 | 2 |
| Toulouse (Pic du Midi) | 87.9 | 95.7 | 91.5 | - | 72 |
| Tours | 99.9 | 97.8 | 92.2 | - | 8 |
| Tours (town) | - | - | - | 105.5 | 1 |
| Troyes | 95.3 | 97.9 | 91.4 | - | 50 |
| Troyes (town) | - | - | - | 105.5 | 1 |
| Ussel | 96.0 | 88.2 | 99.7 | - | 10 |
| Valence | - | - | - | 105.4 | 3 |
| Vannes | 88.6 | 96.0 | 91.8 | 105.5 | 20 |
| Verdun | 92.1 | 99.3 | 97.4 | 106.3 | 6 |
| Villebon sur Yvette | 95.4 | 98.0 | 97.1 | - | 1 |
| Villers-Cotterets | 91.1 | 89.6 | 92.9 | - | 13 |
| Vittel | 98.2 | 89.0 | 94.0 | - | 8 |
| Voiron | 91.5 | 89.2 | 107.2 | 105.4 | 1 |

+ 1486 stns under 1kW. RDS on all txs.

**France Inter** (Network A) (stereo) : **D.Prgrs**:24h **N:** Hourly, plus 0630 – **France Culture** (Network B) (stereo) **D.Prgrs**:24h **N:** 0530, 0600, 0630, 0700, 0800, 1130, 1700, 1800, 2100 – **France Musique** (Network C) (stereo): **D.Prgrs**:24h **N:** 0600, 07000, 0800, 1700 – **France Info** (Network D) (mono) News and informations **D.Prgrs**:24h

**Mouv'**

| Station | MHz | kW | Station | MHz | kW |
|---|---|---|---|---|---|
| Ajaccio | 92.0 | 4 | Bordeaux | 87.7 | 1 |
| Amiens | 91.0 | 1 | Brest | 94.0 | 3 |
| Angers | 96.0 | 1 | Caen | 87.8 | 1 |
| Annecy | 99.4 | 1 | Cannes | 101.0 | 0.2 |
| Besançon | 93.5 | 1 | Carcassonne | 90.0 | 1 |

| Station | MHz | kW | Station | MHz | kW |
|---|---|---|---|---|---|
| Clermont-Fd | 97.5 | 2 | Mende | 107.2 | 0.2 |
| Dijon | 88.9 | 1 | Montpellier | 102.7 | 3 |
| Grenoble | 95.5 | 1 | Nantes | 96.1 | 3 |
| Lille | 91.0 | 2 | Nice | 101.0 | 2.5 |
| Toulouse | 95.2 | 5 | Paris | 92.1 | 8 |
| Tours | 94.1 | 2 | Reims | 101.1 | 0.5 |
| Limoges | 107.6 | 2 | Rennes | 107.3 | 2 |
| Lorient | 103.3 | 0.5 | Rouen | 95.8 | 1 |
| Lyon | 87.8 | 4 | St Etienne | 88.0 | 2 |
| Marseille | 96.8 | 2.5 | Valence | 100.7 | 0.5 |
| Marseille (town) | 96.4 | 1 | | | |

**D.Prgrs:** 24h RDS on all txs (stereo)

## Local Stations "FIP"

**FIP Bordeaux,** 12 allée Serr, 33100 Bordeaux ☎ +33 5 56241515 - Bordeaux 96.7MHz 2.5kW, Arcachon 96.5 0.5 kW
**FIP Nantes,** 2 bis quai François Mitterrand, 44100 Nantes ☎ +33 2 40444555 - Nantes 95.7MHz 2.5kW, St Nazaire 97.2MHz 1.5kW
**FIP Paris,** 116 avenue du Président Kennedy, 75220 Paris Cedex 16 – Paris 105.1MHz 10kW
**FIP Strasbourg,** 4 rue Joseph Massol, 67080 Strasbourg Cedex ☎ +33 3 88352400 - 92.3MHz 4kW
**Sts without local news:** Marseille 90.9MHz 4kW, Montpellier 99.7MHz 1kW, Rennes 101.2MHz 1kW, Toulouse 103.5MHz 2kW
RDS on all txs **D.Prgrs:** 24h Prgrs consist of music and news

## France Bleu

🖃 17/21 av du Général Mangin, 75016 Paris **D.Prgrs:** 24h uninterrupted music 2300-0358 (can vary on each France Bleu stn)
**France Bleu Local Stations** (F.B = France Bleu) - At certain times, local stns relay national France Bleu prgrs. 1200-1300, 1800-0500
**F.B Alsace,** 4 rue Joseph Massol, 67000 Strasbourg ☎ +33 3 88762000 **FM:** Strasbourg 101.4MHz 48kW, Mulhouse 102.6MHz 100kW
**F.B Armorique,** 14 av Jean Janvier, 35031 Rennes Cedex ☎ +33 2 99674321 **FM:** Vannes 101.3MHz 20kW, Rennes 103.1MHz 100kW
**F.B Auxerre,** 12 place Saint Amâtre, B.P 101, 89002 Auxerre Cedex ☎ +33 3 86723456 **FM:** Sens 100.5MHz 10kW, Auxerre 101.3MHz 5kW, Nevers 104.0MHz 1kW
**F.B Azur,** 2 place Grimaldi, 06000 Nice ☎ +33 4 97033636 **FM:** Nice 103.8MHz 10kW, Menton 94.8MHz 5kW, Saint Raphaël 100.7MHz 10kW
**F.B Béarn,** 5 place Clémenceau, 64000 Pau ☎ +33 5 59980909 **FM:** Oloron Sainte Marie 93.2MHz 1.5kW, Pau 102.5MHz 10kW
**F.B Belfort Montbéliard,** 10 rue des Capucins, 90000 Belfort ☎ +33 3 84579090 **FM:** Belfort 106.8MHz 2kW
**F.B Berry,** 10/12 rue de la République, 36000 Châteauroux ☎ +33 2 54273636 **FM:** Argenton 93.5MHz 5kW, Bourges 103.2MHz 19kW
**F.B Besançon,** 2 Place Granvelle, BP 591, 25027 Besançon Cedex ☎ +33 3 81212525 **FM:** Besançon 101.4MHz 18kW + 102.8MHz 10kW
**F.B Bourgogne,** 29 rue Guillaume Tell, BP 11888, 21018 Dijon Cedex ☎ +33 3 80592121 **FM:** Troyes 87.8 60kW, Arnay le Duc 103.4MHz 3kW, Dijon 103.7MHz 25kW
**F.B Breizh Izel,** 12 esplanade François Mitterrand, 29000 Quimper ☎ +33 2 98552929 **FM:** Brest 93.0MHz 200kW
**F.B Champagne-Ardenne,** 28 bd du Maréchal Joffre, BP 1094, 51054 Reims Cedex ☎ +33 3 26845151 **FM:** Charleville-Mézières 100.9MHz 10kW, Reims 95.1MHz 2kW, Châlons en Champagne 94.8MHz 1kW, Troyes 100.8MHz 1kW
**F.B Cotentin,** Hôtel Atlantique, impasse Piedagnel, 50100 Cherbourg-Octeville ☎ +33 2 33885050 **FM:** Cherbourg-Octeville 100.7MHz 4kW
**F.B Creuse,** 7 avenue de la République, BP 249, 23005 Guéret ☎ +33 5 55612323 **FM:** Guéret 94.3MHz 12kW
**F.B Drôme Ardèche,** 70 avenue de Romans, CS 10519, 26005 Valence Cedex ☎ +33 4 75401010 **FM:** Valence 87.9MHz 10kW, Privas 98.4MHz 1.5kW, Vals les Bains 103.8MHz 1kW
**F.B Gard Lozère,** 10 bd des Arènes, 30000 Nîmes ☎ +33 4 66363030 **FM:** Nîmes 90.2MHz 5kW, Alès 91.6MHz 2kW, Mende 104.9MHz 10kW
**F.B Gascogne,** 13 place Jean Jaurès, BP 289, 40005 Mont de Marsan Cedex ☎ +33 5 58465050 **FM:** Mont de Marsan 98.8MHz 20kW, Bayonne 100.5MHz 26kW, Mimizan 103.4MHz 20kW
**F.B Gironde,** 91 rue Nuyens, CS 91882, 33072 Bordeaux Cedex ☎ +33 5 57812020 **FM:** Bordeaux 100.1MHz 6kW, Lesparre 101.6MHz 1.6kW
**F.B Hérault,** 474 allée Henri II de Montmorency, 34060 Montpellier ☎ +33 4 67066565 **FM:** Montpellier 101.1MHz 18kW + 100.6MHz 1kW
**F.B Isère,** 27 av Félix Viallet, BP 154, 38003 Grenoble Cedex ☎ +33 4 76503838 **FM:** Chambéry 99.1MHz 5kW, Lyon 101.8MHz 25kW, Grenoble 102.8MHz 1kW + 98.2MHz 1.2kW, Voiron 101MHz 1kW

**F.B La Rochelle,** 5 av Michel Crépeau, 17025 La Rochelle Cedex 01 ☎ +33 5 46351717 **FM:** Royan 103.6MHz 1kW, Saintes 103.9MHz 60kW, Angoulême 101.5MHz 2kW, La Rochelle 98,2MHz 1kW
**F.B Limousin,** 23 bd Gambetta, BP 3603, 87036 Limoges Cedex ☎ +33 5 55113811 **FM:** Chateauponsac 92.5MHz 1kW, Ussel 101.4MHz 10kW, Limoges 103.5MHz 150kW
**F.B Loire Océan,** 2 bis quai François Mitterrand, 44200 Nantes ☎ +33 2 40444546 **FM:** Saint Nazaire 88.1MHz 1.5kW, Nantes 101.8MHz 200kW, Angers 88.5MHz 1k W
**F.B Lorraine Nord,** 5 rue d'Austrasie, B.P 50071, 57003 Metz cedex 03 ☎ +33 3 87682222 **FM:** Metz 98.5MHz 1kW, Sarreguemines 104 MHz 1kW
**F.B Maine,** 17 avenue Pierre Mendès France, 72000 Le Mans ☎ +33 2 43297272 **FM:** La Flèche 91.7MHz 1kW, Le Mans 96MHz 2.5 kW, Sablé sur Sarthe 105.7MHz 1kW
**F.B Mayenne,** 41 av Robert Buron, 53000 Laval ☎ +33 2 43495050 **FM:** Laval 96.6MHz 5kW
**F.B Nord,** 507 avenue du Président Hoover, 59000 Lille ☎ +33 3 20135962 **FM:** Lille (town) 87.8MHz 1kW, Lille (Bouvigny) 94.7MHz 125kW, Boulogne sur Mer 95.5MHz 1kW, Le Touquet 97.8MHz 2kW, Calais 106.2MHz 1kW
**F.B Normandie (Calvados-Orne),** 12 rue Rosa Parks, 14053 Caen Cedex 04 ☎ +33 2 31444844 **FM:** Le Havre 102.2MHz 2.5kW, Caen 102.6MHz 100kW
**F.B Normandie (Seine Maritime-Eure),** Hangar A, quai Boisguilbert, 76000 Rouen ☎ +33 2 35076666 **FM:** Le Havre 95.1MHz 1kW, Rouen 100.1MHz 100kW, Neufchâtel en Bray 101.6MHz 5kW, Evreux 89.5MHz 1kW
**F.B. Occitanie,** 78 allée Jean Jaurès, BP 50901, 31009 Toulouse ☎ +33 5 34417000 **FM:** Toulouse 91.8MHz 5 kW, Albi 103.7MHz 1 kW, Cahors 97.3MHz 1kW, Castres 91.8MHz 1kW, Mazamet 90.4MHz 1kW, Montauban 97.2 1kW, Rodez 106.2MHz 1kW, Saint Gaudens 96.4MHz 1kW
**F.B Orléans,** 3/5 place du Châtelet, 45000 Orléans ☎ +33 2 38714545 **FM:** Blois 93.9MHz 1kW, Orléans 100.9MHz 4kW, Montargis 106.8MHz 1kW
**F.B Paris,** 17/21 av du Général Mangin, 75016 Paris☎ +33 1 42301010: **FM:** Paris 107.1MHz 10kW, Chartres 97.3MHz 4kW.
**F.B Pays Basque,** 46 allées Marines, 64116 Bayonne Cedex ☎ +33 5 59466464 **FM:** Bayonne 101.3MHz 15kW
**F.B Pays d'Auvergne,** 80 bd François Mitterrand, 63000 Clermont-Ferrand ☎+33 4 73346363 **FM:** Clermont-Fd 102.5MHz 37kW, Aurillac 100.2MHz 1kW, Montluçon 96.7MHz 1kW
**F.B Pays de Savoie,** 256 rue de la République, 73000 Chambéry ☎ +33 4 79707374 **FM:** Annecy 95.2MHz 1kW, Chambéry 103.9MHz 8kW, Gex 106.1MHz 20kW
**F.B Périgord,** 1 cours Saint Georges, 24003 Périgueux Cedex ☎ +33 5 53538282 **FM:** Limoges 91.7MHz 100kW, Bergerac 99.0MHz 26kW
**F.B Picardie,** 2 rue du Maréchal de Lattre de Tassigny, 80000 Amiens ☎ +33 3 22711515 **FM:** Amiens 100.2MHz 2kW, Abbeville 100.6MHz 5kW, Beauvais 106,8MHz 1kW, Hirson 101.3MHz 5kW, Noyon 94,4MHz 1kW, Sailly Saillisel 102.8MHz 15kW
**F.B Poitou,** 27, bd de Solférino, 86000 Poitiers ☎ +33 5 49605000 **FM:** Parthenay 106.4MHz 12kW, Niort 101.0MHz 1kW
**F.B Provence,** 560 av Mozart, 13100 Aix en Provence. ☎ +33 4 42991313 **FM:** Brignoles 102.1MHz 1.5kW, Hyères 102.5MHz 1.5kW, Toulon 102.9MHz 5kW, Marseille 103.6MHz 200kW
**F.B RCFM,** 1 Place du Donjon – 1 Piazza di a Corte, BP 130, 20292 Bastia Cedex ☎ +33 4 95329532 **FM:** Corse (east) 88.2MHz 17kW, Ajaccio 100.5MHz 10kW, + 97.0MHz 4kW + 1404kHz 20kW, Canavaggia 101.7MHz 1kW, Corte 100.0MHz 1.33kW, Bastia 101.7MHz 10kW, Porto Vecchio 101.8MHz 1.5kW + 105.4MHz 1kW, Morosaglia 104.6MHz 1kW
**F.B Roussillon,** 24 av du Maréchal Leclerc, 66000 Perpignan ☎ +33 4 68519000 **FM:** Perpignan 101.6MHz 10kW
**F.B Saint-Étienne Loire,** 5 rue Pablo Picasso, CS 10091, 42003 Saint-Étienne Cedex 1 ☎ +33 4 77520808 **FM:** Saint-Étienne 97.1MHz 2kW
**F.B Sud Lorraine,** 21/23 bd du Recteur Senn, 54042 Nancy Cedex ☎ +33 3 83362020 **FM:** Epinal 100.0MHz 1.5kW, Nancy 100.5MHz 5kW, Vittel 102.6MHz 1kW, Neufchateau 103.0MHz 1kW
**F.B Touraine,** 40 rue James Watt, 37206 Tours Cedex 3 ☎ +33 2 47363737 **FM:** Tours 105.0MHz 8kW +98.7MHz 1kW
**F.B Vaucluse,** 25 rue de la République, 84000 Avignon ☎ +33 4 90140404 **FM:** Avignon 100.4MHz 2kW
+ 335 txs less than 1kW not mentioned. Stereo and RDS on all txs

## RADIO FRANCE INTERNATIONALE (Pub)

🖃 80 rue Camille Desmoulins, 92130 Issy les Moulineaux ☎ +33 1 84228484 **W:** rfi.fr **LP:** Marie-Christine Saragosse

RFI1 (French service): Paris **FM** 89.0MHz 10kW (stereo)
**EXTERNAL SERVICE** see International Broadcasting section

**PRIVATE MW STATION**
**BRETAGNE 5** ☞ Le Pôle, Parc d'activités de l'Espérance Ouest, 10 rue de la Doucine, 22120 QUESSOY ☎ +33 2 96330504 **W**: bretagne5.fr **MW**: Saint Gouéno 1593kHz 5kW. **D.Prgrs**:24h

**PRIVATE FM STATIONS:**

| FM Station | MHz | kW |
|---|---|---|
| 25) Auxerre | 87.6 | 1 |
| 23) Bayonne | 87.6 | 3 |
| 20) Bernay | 87.6 | 1 |
| 17) Besançon | 87.6 | 1 |
| 23) Castres | 87.6 | 1 |
| 26) Laval | 87.6 | 1 |
| 20) Le Havre | 87.6 | 1 |
| 26) Le Mans | 87.6 | 1 |
| 22) Niort | 87.6 | 1 |
| 7) Orléans | 87.6 | 2 |
| 17) Romilly sur Seine | 87.6 | 1 |
| 22) Vannes | 87.6 | 1 |
| 8) Yssingeaux | 87.6 | 1 |
| 23) Bourges | 87.7 | 1 |
| 13) Clermont Ferrand | 87.7 | 1 |
| 7) Corte | 87.7 | 1 |
| 5) Figeac | 87.7 | 1 |
| 19) Nice | 87.7 | 2 |
| 21) Saint Omer | 87.7 | 1 |
| 5) Tours | 87.7 | 2 |
| 20) Verneuil sur Avre | 87.7 | 1 |
| 19) La Flèche | 87.8 | 1 |
| 17) Le Blanc | 87.8 | 1 |
| 19) Mayenne | 87.8 | 1 |
| 23) Mazamet | 87.8 | 1 |
| 6) Montluçon | 87.8 | 1 |
| 14) Nantes | 87.8 | 1 |
| 17) Verdun | 87.8 | 1 |
| 6) Dijon | 87.9 | 1 |
| 21) Menton | 87.9 | 1 |
| 6) Montreuil | 87.9 | 1 |
| 17) Reims | 87.9 | 2 |
| 10) Saint Brieuc | 87.9 | 1 |
| 17) Saint Raphaël | 87.9 | 1 |
| 2) Toulon | 87.9 | 1 |
| 17) Yvetot | 87.9 | 1 |
| 10) Calais | 88.0 | 1 |
| 17) Châteauroux | 88.0 | 1 |
| 23) Colmar | 88.0 | 1 |
| 6) Noyon | 88.0 | 1 |
| 6) St Gilles Croix de Vie | 88.0 | 1 |
| 17) Vesoul | 88.0 | 1 |
| 3) Villefranche/Saône | 88.0 | 1 |
| 9) Vitry le François | 88.0 | 1 |
| 17) Angers | 88.1 | 1 |
| 3) Avignon | 88.1 | 1 |
| 6) Brive la Gaillarde | 88.1 | 1 |
| 18) Châtellerault | 88.1 | 1 |
| 23) Dole | 88.1 | 1 |
| 6) Nice | 88.1 | 5 |
| 17) Rouen | 88.1 | 1 |
| 6) Soissons | 88.1 | 1 |
| 3) Fontenay le Comte | 88.2 | 1 |
| 1) Le Havre | 88.2 | 1 |
| 10) Lille | 88.2 | 1 |
| 10) Metz | 88.2 | 1 |
| 10) Nancy | 88.2 | 1 |
| 6) Saint Quentin | 88.2 | 1 |
| 6) Strasbourg | 88.2 | 4 |
| 22) Tours | 88.2 | 1 |
| 13) Bonifacio | 88.3 | 1 |
| 13) Brioude | 88.3 | 1 |
| 17) Dijon | 88.3 | 1 |
| 9) L'Île Rousse | 88.3 | 1 |
| 8) Lorient | 88.3 | 1 |
| 17) Moulins | 88.3 | 1 |
| 17) Roanne | 88.3 | 1 |
| 17) Saint Flour | 88.3 | 1 |
| 14) Amiens | 88.4 | 1 |
| 12) Corte | 88.4 | 1 |
| 5) Laon | 88.4 | 1 |
| 9) Luxeuil les Bains | 88.4 | 1 |
| 4) Lyon | 88.4 | 4 |
| 6) Mont de Marsan | 88.4 | 1 |
| 19) Nantes | 88.4 | 2 |
| 5) Sarrebourg | 88.4 | 1 |

| FM Station | MHz | kW |
|---|---|---|
| 21) Sarreguemines | 88.4 | 1 |
| 6) Thouars | 88.4 | 1 |
| 5) Tonnerre | 88.4 | 1 |
| 8) Bordeaux | 88.5 | 1 |
| 10) Compiègne | 88.5 | 1 |
| 10) Gournay en Bray | 88.5 | 1 |
| 6) Nogent le Rotrou | 88.5 | 1 |
| 20) Quimper | 88.5 | 1 |
| 17) Annecy | 88.5 | 1 |
| 17) Châlons en Champ. | 88.6 | 1 |
| 6) Châteaubriant | 88.6 | 1 |
| 8) Chaumont | 88.6 | 1 |
| 19) Confolens | 88.6 | 1 |
| 22) Pamiers | 88.6 | 1 |
| 16) Paris | 88.6 | 4 |
| 23) Porto Vecchio | 88.6 | 1 |
| 18) Vichy | 88.6 | 1 |
| 10) Alençon | 88.7 | 1 |
| 7) Avallon | 88.7 | 1 |
| 25) Bastia | 88.7 | 1 |
| 8) Caen | 88.7 | 2 |
| 19) Chartres | 88.7 | 1 |
| 13) Châteauroux | 88.7 | 1 |
| 19) Étampes | 88.7 | 1 |
| 25) Ghisonaccia | 88.7 | 4 |
| 3) Gray | 88.7 | 1 |
| 18) Saint Flour | 88.7 | 1 |
| 22) Saint Gaudens | 88.7 | 1 |
| 22) Saintes | 88.7 | 1 |
| 22) Toulouse | 88.7 | 5 |
| 6) Bonnières sur Seine | 88.8 | 1 |
| 12) Clermont Ferrand | 88.8 | 1 |
| 4) Laval | 88.8 | 1 |
| 8) Nantes | 88.8 | 3 |
| 6) Reims | 88.8 | 2 |
| 17) Saint Dizier | 88.8 | 1 |
| 6) Verneuil sur Avre | 88.8 | 1 |
| 4) Bagnères de Bigorre | 88.9 | 1 |
| 8) Bordeaux | 88.9 | 1 |
| 13) Montluçon | 88.9 | 1 |
| 23) Rennes | 88.9 | 1 |
| 6) Aurillac | 89.0 | 1 |
| 6) Avignon | 89.0 | 1 |
| 6) Avranches | 89.0 | 1 |
| 17) Brest | 89.0 | 3 |
| 17) Clamecy | 89.0 | 1 |
| 13) Moulins | 89.0 | 1 |
| 23) Bernay | 89.1 | 1 |
| 1) Bourges | 89.1 | 1 |
| 18) Gien | 89.1 | 1 |
| 18) Perpignan | 89.1 | 3 |
| 8) Saint Nazaire | 89.1 | 1 |
| 22) Saint Quentin | 89.1 | 1 |
| 22) Valenciennes | 89.1 | 1 |
| 19) Brive la Gaillarde | 89.2 | 1 |
| 23) Châteaubriant | 89.2 | 1 |
| 9) Châtellerault | 89.2 | 1 |
| 22) Decazeville | 89.2 | 1 |
| 22) Lille | 89.2 | 2 |
| 18) Marseille | 89.2 | 10 |
| 13) Montbard | 89.2 | 1 |
| 17) Nevers | 89.2 | 1 |
| 33) Ussel | 89.2 | 1 |
| 23) Verneuil sur Avre | 89.2 | 1 |
| 17) Vichy | 89.2 | 1 |
| 17) Castres | 89.3 | 1 |
| 17) Cholet | 89.3 | 1 |
| 13) Longwy | 89.3 | 1 |
| 17) Niort | 89.3 | 1 |
| 9) Nogaro | 89.3 | 1 |
| 23) Rouen | 89.3 | 2 |
| 25) Arras | 89.4 | 1 |
| 17) Aurillac | 89.4 | 1 |
| 18) Bayeux | 89.4 | 1 |
| 18) Bayonne | 89.4 | 1 |
| 6) Chambéry | 89.4 | 1 |

| FM Station | MHz | kW |
|---|---|---|
| 23) Marmande | 89.4 | 1 |
| 6) Roanne | 89.4 | 1 |
| 8) Saint Dizier | 89.4 | 1 |
| 15) Toulon | 89.4 | 2 |
| 5) Saintes | 89.4 | 1 |
| 23) Chaumont | 89.5 | 1 |
| 6) Strasbourg | 89.5 | 4 |
| 18) Ajaccio | 89.6 | 8 |
| 14) Angers | 89.6 | 2 |
| 4) Auch | 89.6 | 1 |
| 6) Clermont Ferrand | 89.6 | 2 |
| 10) La Rochelle | 89.6 | 1 |
| 23) Le Havre | 89.6 | 1 |
| 17) Marseille | 89.6 | 4 |
| 21) Mende | 89.6 | 1 |
| 7) Vierzon | 89.6 | 1 |
| 5) Aubusson | 89.7 | 1 |
| 23) Bastia | 89.7 | 1 |
| 13) Nevers | 89.7 | 1 |
| 10) Nîmes | 89.7 | 1 |
| 23) Perpignan | 89.7 | 3 |
| 18) Saint Nazaire | 89.7 | 1 |
| 2) Tours | 89.7 | 2 |
| 6) Troyes | 89.7 | 1 |
| 6) Agen | 89.8 | 1 |
| 6) Brioude | 89.8 | 1 |
| 23) Corte | 89.8 | 1 |
| 23) Gray | 89.8 | 1 |
| 14) Lyon | 89.8 | 1 |
| 18) Quimper | 89.8 | 1 |
| 21) Roanne | 89.8 | 1 |
| 28) Rouen | 89.8 | 1 |
| 6) Sablé sur Sarthe | 89.8 | 1 |
| 18) Toulon | 89.8 | 4 |
| 18) Alès | 89.9 | 1 |
| 23) Cognac | 89.9 | 1 |
| 18) Douai | 89.9 | 1 |
| 17) Verdun | 89.9 | 1 |
| 19) Montpellier | 89.9 | 3 |
| 20) Nancy | 89.9 | 1 |
| 28) Paris | 89.9 | 10 |
| 3) Périgueux | 89.9 | 1 |
| 8) Saint Dizier | 89.9 | 1 |
| 20) Saint Girons | 89.9 | 1 |
| 18) Saint Raphaël | 89.9 | 1 |
| 20) Bagnères de Bigorre | 90.0 | 1 |
| 17) Bayeux | 90.0 | 1 |
| 22) Brest | 90.0 | 3 |
| 13) Cosne Cours/Loire | 90.0 | 1 |
| 23) Marseille | 90.0 | 10 |
| 21) Quimperlé | 90.0 | 1 |
| 9) Royan | 90.0 | 1 |
| 3) Vichy | 90.0 | 1 |
| 6) Béthune | 90.1 | 1 |
| 22) Évreux | 90.1 | 1 |
| 18) Nantes | 90.1 | 3 |
| 9) Neufchâteau | 90.1 | 1 |
| 19) Perpignan | 90.1 | 3 |
| 9) Poligny | 90.1 | 1 |
| 9) Toul | 90.1 | 1 |
| 7) Angoulême | 90.2 | 1 |
| 23) Bar le Duc | 90.2 | 1 |
| 3) Bergerac | 90.2 | 1 |
| 9) La Ferté s/Jouarre | 90.2 | 1 |
| 13) Melun | 90.2 | 1 |
| 18) Mimizan | 90.2 | 1 |
| 28) Nevers | 90.2 | 1 |
| 14) Pau | 90.2 | 1 |
| 20) Porto Vecchio | 90.2 | 1 |
| 20) Thionville | 90.2 | 1 |
| 17) Vannes | 90.2 | 2 |
| 6) Bastia | 90.3 | 4 |
| 13) Compiègne | 90.3 | 1 |
| 18) Decazeville | 90.3 | 1 |
| 10) Montargis | 90.3 | 1 |
| 17) Montmorillon | 90.3 | 1 |
| 22) Pamiers | 90.3 | 1 |
| 3) Saumur | 90.3 | 1 |
| 19) Valence | 90.3 | 1 |
| 3) Vivario | 90.3 | 1 |
| 20) Abbeville | 90.4 | 1 |
| 18) Auch | 90.4 | 1 |
| 13) Beauvais | 90.4 | 1 |
| 5) Bourg en Bresse | 90.4 | 1 |
| 10) Caen | 90.4 | 2 |
| 5) Calvi | 90.4 | 1 |

| FM Station | MHz | kW |
|---|---|---|
| 13) Châteaudun | 90.4 | 1 |
| 22) Dinan | 90.4 | 1 |
| 21) Longwy | 90.4 | 1 |
| 23) Paris | 90.4 | 10 |
| 23) Sablé sur Sarthe | 90.4 | 1 |
| 3) Alès | 90.5 | 1 |
| 9) Bourges | 90.5 | 1 |
| 26) Brest | 90.5 | 1 |
| 13) Chartres | 90.5 | 1 |
| 23) Le Mans | 90.5 | 2 |
| 24) Limoges | 90.5 | 1 |
| 9) Mont de Marsan | 90.5 | 1 |
| 13) Narbonne | 90.5 | 1 |
| 13) Rodez | 90.5 | 1 |
| 23) Tours | 90.5 | 2 |
| 4) Lourdes | 90.6 | 3 |
| 7) Maubeuge | 90.6 | 1 |
| 20) Melun | 90.6 | 1 |
| 8) Millau | 90.6 | 1 |
| 3) Noyon | 90.6 | 1 |
| 26) Creil | 90.7 | 2 |
| 7) Dijon | 90.7 | 1 |
| 18) Figeac | 90.7 | 1 |
| 4) Laon | 90.7 | 1 |
| 4) Laval | 90.7 | 1 |
| 21) Périgueux | 90.7 | 1 |
| 6) Soustons | 90.7 | 1 |
| 6) Troyes | 90.7 | 1 |
| 6) Avallon | 90.8 | 1 |
| 1) Bastia | 90.8 | 1 |
| 9) Château Thierry | 90.8 | 1 |
| 9) La Flèche | 90.8 | 1 |
| 9) Vannes | 90.8 | 1 |
| 23) Vesoul | 90.8 | 1 |
| 17) Annonay | 90.9 | 1 |
| 26) Brest | 90.9 | 3 |
| 9) Brive la Gaillarde | 90.9 | 1 |
| 13) Montreuil | 90.9 | 1 |
| 14) Poitiers | 90.9 | 1 |
| 17) Segré | 90.9 | 1 |
| 7) Villefranche/Saône | 90.9 | 1 |
| 18) Ajaccio | 91.0 | 8 |
| 19) Besançon | 91.0 | 1 |
| 6) Bourges | 91.0 | 1 |
| 10) Chambéry | 91.0 | 1 |
| 9) Colmar | 91.0 | 1 |
| 13) Fleurance | 91.0 | 1 |
| 24) Le Puy en Velay | 91.0 | 1 |
| 17) Sarrebourg | 91.0 | 1 |
| 7) Sens | 91.0 | 1 |
| 9) Vichy | 91.0 | 1 |
| 25) Boulogne sur Mer | 91.1 | 1 |
| 23) Dunkerque | 91.1 | 1 |
| 19) Malataverne | 91.1 | 1 |
| 3) Metz | 91.1 | 1 |
| 19) Montélimar | 91.1 | 1 |
| 9) Nancy | 91.1 | 1 |
| 19) Orange | 91.1 | 1 |
| 23) Pau | 91.1 | 1 |
| 3) Villeneuve sur Lot | 91.1 | 1 |
| 7) Aubusson | 91.2 | 1 |
| 6) Épinal | 91.2 | 1 |
| 6) Grenoble | 91.2 | 1 |
| 6) Laval | 91.2 | 1 |
| 22) Mulhouse | 91.2 | 1 |
| 17) Orléans | 91.2 | 2 |
| 6) Saint Tropez | 91.2 | 1 |
| 19) Agen | 91.3 | 1 |
| 19) Cahors | 91.3 | 1 |
| 9) Cambrai | 91.3 | 1 |
| 3) Clermont | 91.3 | 1 |
| 5) Dinan | 91.3 | 1 |
| 3) Paris | 91.3 | 10 |
| 27) Reims | 91.3 | 1 |
| 6) Valence | 91.3 | 1 |
| 3) Verneuil sur Avre | 91.3 | 1 |
| 19) Amiens | 91.4 | 1 |
| 13) Bastia | 91.4 | 4 |
| 10) Béziers | 91.4 | 1 |
| 9) Brive la Gaillarde | 91.4 | 1 |
| 18) Jonzac | 91.4 | 1 |
| 21) Morlaix | 91.4 | 1 |
| 7) Beaune | 91.5 | 1 |
| 5) Blois | 91.5 | 1 |
| 6) Boulogne sur Mer | 91.5 | 1 |
| 8) La Ferté s/Jouarre | 91.5 | 1 |

| FM | Station | MHz | kW | FM | Station | MHz | kW | FM | Station | MHz | kW | FM | Station | MHz | kW |
|---|---|---|---|---|---|---|---|---|---|---|---|---|---|---|---|
| 22) | Le Puy en Velay | 91.5 | 1 | 1) | Aix en Provence | 92.6 | 1 | 6) | Vic Fezensac | 93.4 | 1 | 17) | Parthenay | 94.4 | 1 |
| 26) | Roanne | 91.5 | 1 | 3) | Calvi | 92.6 | 1 | 22) | Ajaccio | 93.5 | 8 | 18) | Pau | 94.4 | 1 |
| 17) | Clermont Ferrand | 91.6 | 1 | 3) | Charolles | 92.6 | 1 | 13) | Béthune | 93.5 | 1 | 6) | St Gilles Croix de Vie | 94.4 | 1 |
| 9) | Corte | 91.6 | 1 | 10) | Clermont Ferrand | 92.6 | 1 | 18) | Dax | 93.5 | 1 | 9) | Saintes | 94.4 | 1 |
| 5) | Dunkerque | 91.6 | 1 | 3) | Corte | 92.6 | 1 | 14) | Metz | 93.5 | 1 | 19) | Toulouse | 94.4 | 1 |
| 17) | Épernay | 91.6 | 1 | 9) | Cosne Cours/Loire | 92.6 | 1 | 20) | Neufchâteau | 93.5 | 1 | 29) | Corte | 94.4 | 1 |
| 17) | La Châtre | 91.6 | 1 | 23) | Nîmes | 92.6 | 1 | 6) | Amiens | 93.6 | 1 | 5) | Creil | 94.5 | 2 |
| 5) | Lens | 91.6 | 1 | 17) | Quimper | 92.6 | 1 | 10) | Angers | 93.6 | 1 | 5) | Gournay en Bray | 94.5 | 1 |
| 5) | Perpignan | 91.6 | 3 | 7) | Saint Raphaël | 92.6 | 1 | 8) | Brest | 93.6 | 1 | 7) | La Rochelle | 94.5 | 1 |
| 13) | Royan | 91.6 | 1 | 3) | Bastia | 92.7 | 4 | 4) | Calvi | 93.6 | 1 | 7) | Laval | 94.5 | 1 |
| 3) | Tours | 91.6 | 2 | 23) | Boulogne sur Mer | 92.7 | 1 | 18) | Évreux | 93.6 | 1 | 9) | Mazamet | 94.5 | 1 |
| 4) | Agen | 91.7 | 1 | 3) | Dreux | 92.7 | 1 | 23) | La Roche sur Yon | 93.6 | 1 | 9) | Montmorillon | 94.5 | 1 |
| 23) | Cholet | 91.7 | 1 | 26) | Lorient | 92.7 | 1 | 19) | Laon | 93.6 | 1 | 9) | Nevers | 94.5 | 1 |
| 18) | La Tour du Pin | 91.7 | 1 | 13) | Montélimar | 92.7 | 1 | 17) | Mazamet | 93.6 | 1 | 7) | Rennes | 94.5 | 2 |
| 17) | Mortagne au Perche | 91.7 | 1 | 22) | Rennes | 92.7 | 1 | 6) | Montbard | 93.6 | 1 | 17) | Arcachon | 94.6 | 1 |
| 14) | Saint Étienne | 91.7 | 2 | 9) | Béthune | 92.8 | 1 | 9) | Pau | 93.6 | 1 | 13) | Chambéry | 94.6 | 1 |
| 17) | Villefranche/Saône | 91.7 | 1 | 10) | Blois | 92.8 | 1 | 18) | Verneuil sur Avre | 93.6 | 1 | 6) | Colmar | 94.6 | 1 |
| 7) | Amiens | 91.8 | 1 | 22) | Castres | 92.8 | 1 | 22) | Grenoble | 93.7 | 1 | 18) | Lannemezan | 94.6 | 1 |
| 7) | Bordeaux | 91.8 | 5 | 8) | Châteauroux | 92.8 | 1 | 10) | Le Havre | 93.7 | 1 | 22) | Perpignan | 94.6 | 3 |
| 7) | Brioude | 91.8 | 1 | 25) | Marseille | 92.8 | 4 | 17) | Nancy | 93.7 | 1 | 13) | Pouzauges | 94.6 | 1 |
| 18) | La Rochelle | 91.8 | 1 | 22) | Nice | 92.8 | 5 | 13) | Orléans | 93.7 | 2 | 12) | Reims | 94.6 | 1 |
| 21) | Montélimar | 91.8 | 1 | 23) | Vannes | 92.8 | 1 | 25) | Reims | 93.7 | 1 | 23) | Romilly sur Seine | 94.6 | 1 |
| 7) | Montpellier | 91.8 | 3 | 3) | Cambrai | 92.9 | 1 | 20) | Saint Nazaire | 93.7 | 1 | 7) | Saint Lô | 94.6 | 1 |
| 7) | Saint Dizier | 91.8 | 1 | 20) | Château Gontier | 92.9 | 1 | 6) | Saintes | 93.7 | 1 | 5) | Béziers | 94.7 | 1 |
| 7) | Saint Malo | 91.8 | 1 | 26) | Colmar | 92.9 | 1 | 13) | Toulon | 93.7 | 4 | 7) | Fougères | 94.7 | 1 |
| 7) | Saint Quentin | 91.8 | 1 | 13) | Lyon | 92.9 | 10 | 17) | Alençon | 93.8 | 1 | 18) | La Ferté Macé | 94.7 | 1 |
| 2) | Vichy | 91.8 | 1 | 22) | Menton | 92.9 | 1 | 6) | Chaumont | 93.8 | 1 | 13) | Le Havre | 94.7 | 1 |
| 7) | Bressuire | 91.9 | 1 | 7) | Montauban | 92.9 | 3 | 27) | Marseille | 93.8 | 4 | 2) | Limoges | 94.7 | 2 |
| 9) | Chalon sur Saône | 91.9 | 1 | 10) | Orléans | 92.9 | 2 | 18) | Montauban | 93.8 | 3 | 7) | Mende | 94.7 | 1 |
| 19) | Chaumont | 91.9 | 1 | 25) | Roanne | 92.9 | 1 | 7) | Orange | 93.8 | 1 | 6) | Nantes | 94.7 | 3 |
| 4) | Civray | 91.9 | 1 | 7) | Rochefort | 92.9 | 1 | 21) | Avallon | 93.9 | 1 | 17) | Poitiers | 94.7 | 1 |
| 9) | Épinal | 91.9 | 1 | 5) | St Amand Montrond | 92.9 | 1 | 6) | Bar le Duc | 93.9 | 1 | 8) | Quimper | 94.7 | 1 |
| 7) | Le Puy en Velay | 91.9 | 1 | 13) | Ajaccio | 93.0 | 8 | 17) | Bourg en Bresse | 93.9 | 1 | 17) | Saint Étienne | 94.7 | 2 |
| 9) | Lessay | 91.9 | 1 | 22) | Bonifacio | 93.0 | 1 | 19) | Bourges | 93.9 | 1 | 22) | Sarrebourg | 94.7 | 1 |
| 9) | Porto Vecchio | 91.9 | 1 | 5) | Cosne Cours/Loire | 93.0 | 1 | 7) | Carcassonne | 93.9 | 1 | 3) | Vesoul | 94.7 | 1 |
| 8) | Salon de Provence | 91.9 | 1 | 5) | Courtenay | 93.0 | 1 | 13) | Château Gontier | 93.9 | 1 | 6) | Angers | 94.8 | 1 |
| 5) | Vivario | 91.9 | 1 | 18) | Hirson | 93.0 | 1 | 20) | Condom | 93.9 | 1 | 23) | Annecy | 94.8 | 1 |
| 8) | Aix en Provence | 92.0 | 1 | 21) | Lille | 93.0 | 2 | 9) | Épernay | 93.9 | 1 | 20) | Chalon sur Saône | 94.8 | 1 |
| 8) | Albi | 92.0 | 1 | 9) | Lourdes | 93.0 | 3 | 18) | Guéret | 93.9 | 1 | 9) | Chaumont | 94.8 | 1 |
| 7) | Arcachon | 92.0 | 1 | 22) | Saint Raphaël | 93.0 | 1 | 20) | Jonzac | 93.9 | 1 | 22) | Forbach | 94.8 | 1 |
| 23) | Auxerre | 92.0 | 1 | 7) | Verdun | 93.0 | 1 | 3) | Lille | 93.9 | 1 | 6) | Longwy | 94.8 | 1 |
| 6) | Lille | 92.0 | 2 | 13) | Annecy | 93.1 | 1 | 25) | Nogent le Rotrou | 93.9 | 1 | 5) | Mulhouse | 94.8 | 1 |
| 23) | Montargis | 92.0 | 1 | 13) | Arcachon | 93.1 | 1 | 13) | Saint Brieuc | 93.9 | 1 | 22) | Nancy | 94.8 | 1 |
| 13) | Pamiers | 92.0 | 1 | 7) | Bayeux | 93.1 | 1 | 20) | Vannes | 93.9 | 1 | 5) | Nîmes | 94.8 | 1 |
| 8) | Saint Affrique | 92.0 | 1 | 13) | Bourg en Bresse | 93.1 | 1 | 7) | Verdun | 93.9 | 1 | 20) | Riscle | 94.8 | 1 |
| 7) | Saint Brieuc | 92.0 | 1 | 21) | Châlons en Champ. | 93.1 | 1 | 7) | Avignon | 94.0 | 1 | 5) | Avignon | 94.9 | 1 |
| 10) | Saintes | 92.0 | 1 | 6) | Châteaudun | 93.1 | 1 | 9) | Rochefort | 94.0 | 1 | 12) | Bastia | 94.9 | 1 |
| 19) | Soissons | 92.0 | 1 | 7) | Coutances | 93.1 | 1 | 22) | Saint Flour | 94.0 | 1 | 14) | Bordeaux | 94.9 | 1 |
| 3) | Brive la Gaillarde | 92.1 | 1 | 13) | Dole | 93.1 | 1 | 17) | Thionville | 94.0 | 1 | 17) | Caen | 94.9 | 1 |
| 21) | Cambrai | 92.1 | 1 | 8) | Ernée | 93.1 | 1 | 1) | Troyes | 94.0 | 1 | 13) | Hirson | 94.9 | 1 |
| 6) | Menton | 92.1 | 1 | 23) | Fontenay le Comte | 93.1 | 1 | 21) | Ussel | 94.0 | 1 | 9) | La Roche sur Yon | 94.9 | 1 |
| 18) | Nontron | 92.1 | 1 | 13) | La Tour du Pin | 93.1 | 1 | 6) | Arcachon | 94.1 | 1 | 13) | Le Puy en Velay | 94.9 | 1 |
| 19) | Troyes | 92.1 | 1 | 20) | Mulhouse | 93.1 | 1 | 25) | Chartres | 94.1 | 1 | 19) | Lyon | 94.9 | 1 |
| 13) | Amiens | 92.2 | 1 | 23) | Royan | 93.1 | 1 | 13) | Creil | 94.1 | 2 | 5) | Montpellier | 94.9 | 3 |
| 22) | Béthune | 92.2 | 1 | 13) | Saint Étienne | 93.1 | 2 | 19) | Decazeville | 94.1 | 1 | 8) | Rennes | 94.9 | 1 |
| 10) | Bordeaux | 92.2 | 1 | 7) | Toulon | 93.1 | 4 | 12) | Dijon | 94.1 | 1 | 24) | Alès | 95.0 | 1 |
| 7) | Colmar | 92.2 | 1 | 19) | Avallon | 93.2 | 1 | 18) | Grenoble | 94.1 | 1 | 21) | Autun | 95.0 | 1 |
| 7) | Dunkerque | 92.2 | 1 | 6) | Bergerac | 93.2 | 1 | 8) | Mayenne | 94.1 | 1 | 7) | Chambéry | 95.0 | 1 |
| 4) | Lannemezan | 92.2 | 1 | 5) | Commercy | 93.2 | 1 | 24) | Mont de Marsan | 94.1 | 1 | 6) | Cholet | 95.0 | 1 |
| 9) | Laon | 92.2 | 1 | 5) | Évreux | 93.2 | 1 | 13) | Montmorillon | 94.1 | 1 | 19) | Clermont Ferrand | 95.0 | 1 |
| 7) | Limoges | 92.2 | 2.2 | 8) | Guéret | 93.2 | 1 | 5) | Narbonne | 94.1 | 1 | 8) | Dinan | 95.0 | 1 |
| 22) | Metz | 92.2 | 1 | 22) | Nevers | 93.2 | 1 | 4) | Saint Gaudens | 94.1 | 1 | 19) | Grenoble | 95.0 | 1 |
| 22) | Mont de Marsan | 92.2 | 1 | 21) | Provins | 93.2 | 1 | 13) | Soissons | 94.1 | 1 | 10) | Lorient | 95.0 | 1 |
| 5) | Montélimar | 92.2 | 1 | 21) | Romilly sur Seine | 93.2 | 1 | 13) | Châlons en Champ. | 94.2 | 1 | 13) | Mimizan | 95.0 | 1 |
| 7) | Mulhouse | 92.2 | 1 | 22) | Saint Tropez | 93.2 | 1 | 3) | Chaumont | 94.2 | 1 | 9) | Montauban | 95.0 | 3 |
| 9) | Noyon | 92.2 | 1 | 5) | Ussel | 93.2 | 1 | 13) | Reims | 94.2 | 1 | 7) | Nice | 95.0 | 5 |
| 18) | Carcassonne | 92.3 | 1 | 13) | Arras | 93.3 | 1 | 5) | Saint Omer | 94.2 | 1 | 5) | Niort | 95.0 | 1 |
| 30) | Melun | 92.3 | 1 | 5) | Dreux | 93.3 | 1 | 23) | Tarbes | 94.2 | 1 | 13) | Porto Vecchio | 95.0 | 1 |
| 7) | Mimizan | 92.3 | 1.1 | 13) | Grenoble | 93.3 | 1 | 5) | Vierzon | 94.2 | 1 | 3) | Aubusson | 95.1 | 1 |
| 10) | Rennes | 92.3 | 1 | 7) | Lyon | 93.3 | 1 | 6) | Bordeaux | 94.3 | 5 | 17) | Douai | 95.1 | 1 |
| 13) | Vitry le François | 92.3 | 1 | 5) | Marmande | 93.3 | 1 | 21) | Cosne Cours/Loire | 94.3 | 1 | 23) | Épinal | 95.1 | 1 |
| 23) | Albi | 92.4 | 1 | 23) | Meaux | 93.3 | 3 | 18) | La Côte Saint André | 94.3 | 1 | 11) | Mâcon | 95.1 | 1 |
| 20) | Brest | 92.4 | 1 | 4) | Montauban | 93.3 | 3 | 23) | Le Mans | 94.3 | 2 | 24) | Marseille | 95.1 | 4 |
| 14) | Montpellier | 92.4 | 3 | 8) | Montluçon | 93.3 | 1 | 23) | Lille | 94.3 | 1 | 17) | Pithiviers | 95.1 | 1 |
| 22) | Romilly sur Seine | 92.4 | 1 | 18) | Orléans | 93.3 | 2 | 23) | Lorient | 94.3 | 1 | 10) | Saint Étienne | 95.1 | 2 |
| 5) | Saint Quentin | 92.4 | 1 | 5) | Pamiers | 93.3 | 1 | 15) | Paris | 94.3 | 4 | 9) | Saint Raphaël | 95.1 | 1 |
| 6) | Vannes | 92.4 | 1 | 3) | Poitiers | 93.3 | 1 | 23) | Saint Dizier | 94.3 | 1 | 3) | Ussel | 95.1 | 1 |
| 23) | Avignon | 92.5 | 1 | 17) | Argentan | 93.4 | 1 | 1) | Saint Étienne | 94.3 | 2 | 5) | Béziers | 95.2 | 1 |
| 7) | Brive la Gaillarde | 92.5 | 1 | 25) | Bourges | 93.4 | 1 | 10) | Saint Raphaël | 94.3 | 1 | 21) | Dunkerque | 95.2 | 1 |
| 4) | Cahors | 92.5 | 1 | 5) | Épernay | 93.4 | 1 | 21) | Sens | 94.3 | 1 | 21) | Fontenay le Comte | 95.2 | 1 |
| 17) | Fontenay le Comte | 92.5 | 1 | 6) | Le Chambon s/Lignon | 93.4 | 1 | 8) | Clermont Ferrand | 94.4 | 1 | 1) | Jussey | 95.2 | 1 |
| 17) | Issoudun | 92.5 | 1 | 13) | Lille | 93.4 | 1 | 8) | Le Puy en Velay | 94.4 | 1 | 9) | Périgueux | 95.2 | 1 |
| 9) | Le Havre | 92.5 | 1 | 8) | Marseille | 93.4 | 4 | 22) | Loches | 94.4 | 1 | 24) | Tarascon | 95.2 | 1 |
| 5) | Lille | 92.5 | 2 | 7) | Moulins | 93.4 | 1 | 19) | Orléans | 94.4 | 1 | 5) | Vivario | 95.2 | 1 |
| 7) | Lourdes | 92.5 | 3 | 10) | Narbonne | 93.4 | 1 | | | | | 21) | Argentan | 95.3 | 1 |
| 19) | Rodez | 92.5 | 1 | 23) | Quimper | 93.4 | 1 | | | | | 3) | Bordeaux | 95.3 | 5 |

| FM Station | MHz | kW |
|---|---|---|
| 20) Chartres | 95.3 | 1 |
| 20) Château Thierry | 95.3 | 1 |
| 7) Dax | 95.3 | 1 |
| 10) Le Puy en Velay | 95.3 | 1 |
| 21) Lisieux | 95.3 | 1 |
| 2) Lyon | 95.3 | 10 |
| 3) Mirande | 95.3 | 1 |
| 3) Montélimar | 95.3 | 1 |
| 13) Nancy | 95.3 | 1 |
| 3) Tarbes | 95.3 | 1 |
| 3) Toulon | 95.3 | 4 |
| 18) Cahors | 95.4 | 1 |
| 18) Chambéry | 95.4 | 1 |
| 13) Commercy | 95.4 | 1 |
| 19) Le Mans | 95.4 | 2 |
| 21) Orléans | 95.4 | 2 |
| 17) Pouzauges | 95.4 | 1 |
| 17) Ruffec | 95.4 | 1 |
| 21) Verneuil sur Avre | 95.4 | 1 |
| 8) Angers | 95.5 | 1 |
| 3) Annonay | 95.5 | 1 |
| 24) Bergerac | 95.5 | 1 |
| 23) Besançon | 95.5 | 1 |
| 13) Calvi | 95.5 | 1 |
| 5) Corte | 95.5 | 1 |
| 17) La Rochelle | 95.5 | 1 |
| 6) Mâcon | 95.5 | 1 |
| 19) Marseille | 95.5 | 10 |
| 9) Millau | 95.5 | 1 |
| 6) Nogent le Rotrou | 95.5 | 1 |
| 6) Niort | 95.6 | 1 |
| 11) Paris | 95.6 | 4 |
| 9) Saint Tropez | 95.6 | 1 |
| 9) Vannes | 95.6 | 1 |
| 23) Le Puy en Velay | 95.7 | 1 |
| 19) Lorient | 95.7 | 1 |
| 22) Lyon | 95.7 | 4 |
| 23) Metz | 95.7 | 1 |
| 23) Nancy | 95.7 | 1 |
| 6) Perpignan | 95.7 | 3 |
| 17) St Amand Montrond | 95.7 | 1 |
| 13) Angoulême | 95.8 | 1 |
| 13) Chambéry | 95.8 | 1 |
| 6) Montpellier | 95.8 | 3 |
| 3) Nice | 95.8 | 5 |
| 21) Saint Brieuc | 95.8 | 1 |
| 23) Thionville | 95.8 | 4 |
| 6) Toulon | 95.8 | 4 |
| 23) Beauvais | 95.9 | 1 |
| 13) Béthune | 95.9 | 1 |
| 10) Bourges | 95.9 | 1 |
| 13) Brioude | 95.9 | 1 |
| 13) Cavaillon | 95.9 | 1 |
| 18) Commercy | 95.9 | 1 |
| 17) La Tour du Pin | 95.9 | 1 |
| 10) Limoges | 95.9 | 2 |
| 22) Mazamet | 95.9 | 1 |
| 23) Montélimar | 95.9 | 1 |
| 9) Saint Étienne | 95.9 | 2 |
| 3) Annecy | 96.0 | 1 |
| 3) Brignoles | 96.0 | 1 |
| 23) Châteaudun | 96.0 | 1 |
| 13) Châtillon sur Seine | 96.0 | 1 |
| 3) Cognac | 96.0 | 1 |
| 23) Grenoble | 96.0 | 1 |
| 18) Lille | 96.0 | 2 |
| 6) Lisieux | 96.0 | 1 |
| 13) Marseille | 96.0 | 4 |
| 23) Paris | 96.0 | 10 |
| 23) Strasbourg | 96.0 | 1.5 |
| 22) Valence | 96.0 | 2 |
| 22) Auxerre | 96.1 | 1 |
| 22) Béziers | 96.1 | 2 |
| 13) Chartres | 96.1 | 1 |
| 8) Decazeville | 96.1 | 1 |
| 6) Le Puy en Velay | 96.1 | 1 |
| 23) Lyon | 96.1 | 4 |
| 23) Montauban | 96.1 | 3 |
| 19) Moulins | 96.1 | 1 |
| 13) Nancy | 96.1 | 1 |
| 13) Saint Dizier | 96.1 | 1 |
| 12) Tours | 96.1 | 2 |
| 17) Vire | 96.1 | 1 |
| 25) Aix en Provence | 96.2 | 1 |
| 19) Alençon | 96.2 | 1 |
| 13) Bagnères de Bigorre | 96.2 | 1 |
| 13) Bar le Duc | 96.2 | 1 |
| 18) Brive la Gaillarde | 96.2 | 1 |
| 22) Châteauroux | 96.2 | 1 |
| 23) Clermont Ferrand | 96.2 | 1 |
| 23) Compiègne | 96.2 | 1 |
| 6) Douai | 96.2 | 1 |
| 6) Dunkerque | 96.2 | 1 |
| 23) Montbard | 96.2 | 1 |
| 6) Saint Brieuc | 96.2 | 1 |
| 13) Sedan | 96.2 | 1 |
| 12) Amiens | 96.3 | 1 |
| 6) Bourg en Bresse | 96.3 | 1 |
| 7) Caen | 96.3 | 2 |
| 9) L'Aigle | 96.3 | 1 |
| 23) Le Péage/Roussillon | 96.3 | 1 |
| 9) Montluçon | 96.3 | 1 |
| 9) Morlaix | 96.3 | 1 |
| 7) Nogent le Rotrou | 96.3 | 1 |
| 17) Rennes | 96.3 | 1 |
| 13) Rodez | 96.3 | 1 |
| 7) Saint Étienne | 96.3 | 2 |
| 7) Annecy | 96.4 | 1 |
| 22) Bastia | 96.4 | 4 |
| 13) Blois | 96.4 | 1 |
| 22) Calvi | 96.4 | 1 |
| 22) Corte | 96.4 | 1 |
| 20) Cosne Cours/Loire | 96.4 | 1 |
| 13) Épernay | 96.4 | 1 |
| 13) Granville | 96.4 | 1 |
| 6) Lille | 96.4 | 2 |
| 6) Lorient | 96.4 | 1 |
| 13) Mont de Marsan | 96.4 | 1 |
| 2) Paris | 96.4 | 4 |
| 9) Saint Quentin | 96.4 | 1 |
| 20) Sarrebourg | 96.4 | 1 |
| 20) Bourges | 96.5 | 1 |
| 6) Brest | 96.5 | 3 |
| 7) Colmar | 96.5 | 1 |
| 10) Lyon | 96.5 | 4 |
| 20) Marmande | 96.5 | 1 |
| 23) Saint Flour | 96.5 | 1 |
| 23) Saint Nazaire | 96.5 | 1 |
| 23) Saint Omer | 96.6 | 1 |
| 5) Auxerre | 96.6 | 1 |
| 23) Châteauroux | 96.6 | 1 |
| 7) Clermont Ferrand | 96.6 | 2 |
| 14) Coulommiers | 96.6 | 1 |
| 17) Nice | 96.6 | 1 |
| 3) Nîmes | 96.6 | 1 |
| 3) Noyon | 96.6 | 1 |
| 3) Toulon | 96.6 | 4 |
| 6) Yssingeaux | 96.6 | 1 |
| 23) Abbeville | 96.7 | 1 |
| 23) Limoges | 96.7 | 1 |
| 13) Montargis | 96.7 | 1 |
| 17) Saint Lô | 96.7 | 1 |
| 22) Thionville | 96.7 | 1 |
| 23) Angoulême | 96.8 | 1 |
| 23) Brive la Gaillarde | 96.8 | 1 |
| 6) Caen | 96.8 | 2 |
| 6) Cahors | 96.8 | 1 |
| 20) Châtellerault | 96.8 | 1 |
| 14) Dreux | 96.8 | 1 |
| 7) Lille | 96.8 | 1 |
| 18) Mont de Marsan | 96.8 | 1 |
| 13) Nantes | 96.8 | 3 |
| 13) Redon | 96.8 | 1 |
| 13) Roanne | 96.8 | 1 |
| 13) Rochefort | 96.8 | 1 |
| 13) Valence | 96.8 | 1 |
| 13) Arras | 96.9 | 1 |
| 13) Guéret | 96.9 | 1 |
| 7) Montbard | 96.9 | 1 |
| 3) Montpellier | 96.9 | 3 |
| 17) Moulins | 96.9 | 1 |
| 13) Rennes | 96.9 | 1 |
| 1) Toulouse | 96.9 | 1 |
| 25) Calvi | 97.0 | 1 |
| 21) Chambéry | 97.0 | 1 |
| 9) Condom | 97.0 | 1 |
| 3) Mazamet | 97.0 | 1 |
| 3) Albi | 97.1 | 1 |
| 9) Bar le Duc | 97.1 | 1 |
| 21) La Ferté s/Jouarre | 97.1 | 1 |
| 26) Montélimar | 97.1 | 1 |
| 6) Montluçon | 97.1 | 1 |
| 6) Pouzauges | 97.1 | 1 |
| 7) Bagnères de Bigorre | 97.2 | 1 |
| 10) Bourg en Bresse | 97.2 | 1 |
| 3) Chaumont | 97.2 | 1 |
| 19) Épinal | 97.2 | 1 |
| 23) Propriano | 97.2 | 1 |
| 18) Saint Omer | 97.2 | 1 |
| 20) Alençon | 97.3 | 1 |
| 21) Auch | 97.3 | 1 |
| 13) Beauvais | 97.3 | 1 |
| 13) Bordeaux | 97.3 | 5 |
| 22) Le Havre | 97.3 | 1 |
| 25) Lyon | 97.3 | 1 |
| 23) Noyon | 97.3 | 1 |
| 9) Poitiers | 97.3 | 1 |
| 8) Rodez | 97.3 | 1 |
| 6) Vire | 97.3 | 1 |
| 21) Agen | 97.4 | 1 |
| 22) Bayeux | 97.4 | 1 |
| 13) Brest | 97.4 | 3 |
| 21) Grenoble | 97.4 | 1 |
| 23) Mont de Marsan | 97.4 | 1 |
| 17) Morhange | 97.4 | 1 |
| 21) Nice | 97.4 | 5 |
| 19) Paris | 97.4 | 4 |
| 18) Saint Malo | 97.4 | 1 |
| 3) Toulouse | 97.4 | 2 |
| 23) Argentan | 97.5 | 1 |
| 18) Béziers | 97.5 | 1 |
| 23) Carmaux | 97.5 | 1 |
| 13) Corte | 97.5 | 1 |
| 13) Dijon | 97.5 | 1 |
| 9) Mayenne | 97.5 | 1 |
| 21) Neufchâteau | 97.5 | 1 |
| 3) Nogent le Rotrou | 97.5 | 1 |
| 7) Royan | 97.5 | 2 |
| 7) Alès | 97.6 | 1 |
| 18) Avallon | 97.6 | 1 |
| 23) Caen | 97.6 | 2 |
| 12) Fontenay le Comte | 97.6 | 1 |
| 3) Le Mans | 97.6 | 2 |
| 7) L'Ile Rousse | 97.6 | 1 |
| 6) Menton | 97.6 | 1 |
| 6) Metz | 97.6 | 1 |
| 13) Montauban | 97.6 | 3 |
| 7) Pamiers | 97.6 | 1 |
| 3) Perpignan | 97.6 | 1 |
| 13) Rennes | 97.6 | 3 |
| 6) Bayonne | 97.7 | 5 |
| 9) Castres | 97.7 | 1 |
| 7) Compiègne | 97.7 | 1 |
| 4) Dreux | 97.7 | 1 |
| 7) Figeac | 97.7 | 1 |
| 28) Laval | 97.7 | 1 |
| 5) Maubeuge | 97.7 | 1 |
| 7) Montargis | 97.7 | 1 |
| 22) Nantes | 97.7 | 3 |
| 8) Ussel | 97.7 | 1 |
| 15) Vienne | 97.7 | 1 |
| 24) Brive la Gaillarde | 97.8 | 1 |
| 6) Chalon sur Saône | 97.8 | 1 |
| 1) Grenoble | 97.8 | 1 |
| 17) Porto Vecchio | 97.8 | 1 |
| 2) Reims | 97.8 | 2 |
| 6) Saint Étienne | 97.8 | 2 |
| 4) Bastia | 97.9 | 1 |
| 3) Cholet | 97.9 | 1 |
| 13) Parthenay | 97.9 | 1 |
| 4) Toulouse | 97.9 | 5 |
| 9) Angers | 98.0 | 1 |
| 18) Mirande | 98.0 | 1 |
| 3) Montélimar | 98.0 | 1 |
| 23) Montluçon | 98.0 | 1 |
| 23) Moulins | 98.0 | 1 |
| 9) Vannes | 98.0 | 1 |
| 23) Ajaccio | 98.1 | 8 |
| 18) Besançon | 98.1 | 1 |
| 3) Castres | 98.1 | 1 |
| 6) Dax | 98.1 | 1 |
| 6) Nice | 98.1 | 5 |
| 5) Périgueux | 98.1 | 1 |
| 9) Saint Flour | 98.1 | 2 |
| 20) Saintes | 98.1 | 1 |
| 13) Samatan | 98.1 | 1 |
| 13) Sens | 98.1 | 1 |
| 12) Strasbourg | 98.1 | 1 |
| 5) Annonay | 98.2 | 1 |
| 13) Auxerre | 98.2 | 1 |
| 9) Avignon | 98.2 | 1 |
| 19) Bernay | 98.2 | 1 |
| 19) Bordeaux | 98.2 | 1 |
| 22) Bourges | 98.2 | 1 |
| 12) Compiègne | 98.2 | 1 |
| 12) Gournay en Bray | 98.2 | 1 |
| 19) Limoges | 98.2 | 2 |
| 13) Lourdes | 98.2 | 3 |
| 13) Mâcon | 98.2 | 1 |
| 12) Narbonne | 98.2 | 1 |
| 22) Nevers | 98.2 | 1 |
| 12) Niort | 98.2 | 1 |
| 12) Paris | 98.2 | 4 |
| 8) Quimperlé | 98.2 | 1 |
| 1) Sablé sur Sarthe | 98.2 | 1 |
| 14) Tours | 98.2 | 2 |
| 13) Aix en Provence | 98.3 | 1 |
| 18) Bar le Duc | 98.3 | 1 |
| 9) Gien | 98.3 | 1 |
| 13) Montpellier | 98.3 | 3 |
| 22) Rouen | 98.3 | 2 |
| 21) Saint Affrique | 98.3 | 1 |
| 23) Saint Quentin | 98.3 | 1 |
| 20) Sarrebourg | 98.3 | 1 |
| 23) Amiens | 98.4 | 1 |
| 13) Chaumont | 98.4 | 1 |
| 21) Falaise | 98.4 | 1 |
| 3) La Flèche | 98.4 | 1 |
| 18) Mazamet | 98.4 | 1 |
| 18) Meaux | 98.4 | 1 |
| 5) Mirande | 98.4 | 1 |
| 9) Royan | 98.4 | 1 |
| 18) Agen | 98.5 | 1 |
| 3) Alençon | 98.5 | 1 |
| 13) Bastia | 98.5 | 1 |
| 17) Béziers | 98.5 | 1 |
| 28) Bourg en Bresse | 98.5 | 1 |
| 21) Hirson | 98.5 | 1 |
| 3) Laval | 98.5 | 1 |
| 3) Albi | 98.6 | 1 |
| 22) Bergerac | 98.6 | 1 |
| 9) Cognac | 98.6 | 1 |
| 6) Dax | 98.6 | 1 |
| 18) La Roche sur Yon | 98.6 | 1 |
| 18) Vannes | 98.6 | 1 |
| 21) Auch | 98.7 | 1 |
| 12) Caen | 98.7 | 1 |
| 13) Chartres | 98.7 | 1 |
| 13) La Rochelle | 98.7 | 1 |
| 6) Le Puy en Velay | 98.7 | 1 |
| 6) Niederbronn l. Bains | 98.7 | 1 |
| 3) Argentan | 98.8 | 1 |
| 20) Cannes | 98.8 | 1 |
| 21) Castres | 98.8 | 1 |
| 7) Grenoble | 98.8 | 1 |
| 20) Lorient | 98.8 | 1 |
| 20) Nice | 98.8 | 1 |
| 5) Rodez | 98.8 | 1 |
| 19) Toulon | 98.8 | 4 |
| 7) Valence | 98.8 | 1 |
| 3) Arcachon | 98.9 | 1 |
| 6) Auxerre | 98.9 | 1 |
| 7) Brest | 98.9 | 3 |
| 21) Gournay en Bray | 98.9 | 1 |
| 6) Le Creusot | 98.9 | 1 |
| 3) Lyon | 98.9 | 1 |
| 9) Mende | 98.9 | 1 |
| 3) Montauban | 98.9 | 3 |
| 21) Nemours | 98.9 | 1 |
| 6) Sens | 98.9 | 1 |
| 9) Vierzon | 98.9 | 1 |
| 9) Amiens | 99.0 | 1 |
| 22) Bayonne | 99.0 | 2 |
| 22) Carcassonne | 99.0 | 1 |
| 5) La Ferté Macé | 99.0 | 1 |
| 12) Metz | 99.0 | 1 |
| 29) Paris | 99.0 | 4 |
| 22) Poitiers | 99.0 | 1 |
| 7) Royan | 99.0 | 1 |

| FM | Station | MHz | kW |
|---|---|---|---|
| 17) | Saint Raphaël | 99.0 | 1 |
| 6) | Ussel | 99.0 | 1 |
| 3) | Aurillac | 99.1 | 1 |
| 9) | Cervione | 99.1 | 2 |
| 7) | Châteauroux | 99.1 | 1 |
| 5) | Châtillon sur Seine | 99.1 | 1 |
| 9) | Limoges | 99.1 | 2 |
| 20) | Provins | 99.1 | 1 |
| 18) | Toulouse | 99.1 | 5 |
| 3) | Abbeville | 99.2 | 1 |
| 25) | Alençon | 99.2 | 1 |
| 23) | Aubusson | 99.2 | 1 |
| 7) | Bourges | 99.2 | 1 |
| 13) | Brive la Gaillarde | 99.2 | 1 |
| 22) | Calais | 99.2 | 1 |
| 4) | Châtellerault | 99.2 | 1 |
| 7) | Condom | 99.2 | 1 |
| 7) | Mont de Marsan | 99.2 | 1 |
| 20) | Narbonne | 99.2 | 1 |
| 6) | Nice | 99.2 | 5 |
| 25) | Saint Lô | 99.2 | 1 |
| 23) | Vichy | 99.2 | 1 |
| 13) | Argentan | 99.3 | 1 |
| 22) | Cambrai | 99.3 | 1 |
| 13) | L'Aigle | 99.3 | 1 |
| 14) | Laval | 99.3 | 1 |
| 18) | Montpellier | 99.3 | 3 |
| 6) | Saint Nazaire | 99.3 | 1 |
| 10) | Avignon | 99.4 | 1 |
| 7) | Bastia | 99.4 | 4 |
| 7) | Calvi | 99.4 | 1 |
| 8) | Charolles | 99.4 | 1 |
| 25) | Clermont Ferrand | 99.4 | 1 |
| 5) | Fontainebleau | 99.4 | 2 |
| 3) | Mâcon | 99.4 | 1 |
| 7) | Mazamet | 99.4 | 1 |
| 27) | Metz | 99.4 | 1 |
| 13) | Mulhouse | 99.4 | 1 |
| 5) | Saint Malo | 99.4 | 1 |
| 3) | Châteaudun | 99.5 | 1 |
| 13) | Eauze | 99.5 | 1 |
| 27) | Paris | 99.5 | 4 |
| 13) | Toulouse | 99.5 | 1 |
| 6) | Abbeville | 99.6 | 1 |
| 25) | Aurillac | 99.6 | 1 |
| 18) | Bordeaux | 99.6 | 5 |
| 6) | Bourges | 99.6 | 1 |
| 3) | Carcassonne | 99.6 | 1 |
| 17) | Carmaux | 99.6 | 1 |
| 22) | Cholet | 99.6 | 1 |
| 24) | Corte | 99.6 | 1 |
| 18) | Dijon | 99.6 | 1 |
| 5) | Ile de Ré | 99.6 | 1 |
| 17) | Limoges | 99.6 | 2 |
| 5) | Porto Vecchio | 99.6 | 1 |
| 17) | Quimperlé | 99.6 | 1 |
| 7) | Salon de Provence | 99.6 | 1 |
| 9) | Vichy | 99.6 | 1 |
| 9) | Bagnères de Bigorre | 99.7 | 1 |
| 3) | Brest | 99.7 | 3 |
| 13) | La Flèche | 99.7 | 1 |
| 7) | Marseille | 99.7 | 4 |
| 22) | Montauban | 99.7 | 3 |
| 6) | Nevers | 99.7 | 1 |
| 2) | Orléans | 99.7 | 1 |
| 3) | Troyes | 99.7 | 1 |
| 9) | Ajaccio | 99.8 | 8 |
| 21) | Chartres | 99.8 | 1 |
| 9) | Guéret | 99.8 | 1 |
| 17) | Lavaur | 99.8 | 1 |
| 9) | Menton | 99.8 | 1 |
| 18) | Montargis | 99.8 | 1 |
| 6) | Mulhouse | 99.8 | 1 |
| 21) | Noyon | 99.8 | 1 |
| 21) | Parthenay | 99.8 | 1 |
| 19) | Argentan | 99.9 | 1 |
| 9) | Mimizan | 99.9 | 1 |
| 9) | Nîmes | 99.9 | 1 |
| 24) | Paris | 99.9 | 4 |
| 9) | Quimper | 99.9 | 1 |
| 9) | Argentan | 100.0 | 1 |
| 7) | Belfort | 100.0 | 1 |
| 23) | Béziers | 100.0 | 1 |
| 9) | Fontenay le Comte | 100.0 | 1 |
| 2) | Laval | 100.0 | 1 |
| 3) | L'Île Rousse | 100.0 | 1 |
| 13) | Limoges | 100.0 | 2 |
| 9) | Montélimar | 100.0 | 1 |
| 9) | Pithiviers | 100.0 | 1 |
| 9) | Poitiers | 100.0 | 1 |
| 22) | Porto Vecchio | 100.0 | 1 |
| 3) | Rodez | 100.0 | 1 |
| 13) | Romilly sur Seine | 100.0 | 1 |
| 23) | Toulouse | 100.0 | 2 |
| 18) | Angers | 100.1 | 1 |
| 9) | Bagnères de Bigorre | 100.1 | 1 |
| 3) | Bayonne | 100.1 | 3 |
| 19) | Carcassonne | 100.1 | 1 |
| 13) | Châteauroux | 100.1 | 1 |
| 3) | Marseille | 100.1 | 4 |
| 3) | Meaux | 100.1 | 1 |
| 9) | Melun | 100.1 | 1 |
| 22) | Reims | 100.1 | 2 |
| 20) | Saint Brieuc | 100.1 | 1 |
| 9) | Sens | 100.1 | 1 |
| 23) | Alès | 100.2 | 1 |
| 14) | Brest | 100.2 | 1 |
| 7) | Chinon | 100.2 | 1 |
| 5) | Coutances | 100.2 | 1 |
| 13) | Gien | 100.2 | 1 |
| 6) | Guéret | 100.2 | 1 |
| 9) | La Rochelle | 100.2 | 1 |
| 23) | Montpellier | 100.2 | 3 |
| 3) | Orthez | 100.2 | 1 |
| 9) | Troyes | 100.2 | 1 |
| 3) | Valence | 100.2 | 2 |
| 14) | Agen | 100.3 | 1 |
| 6) | Angoulême | 100.3 | 1 |
| 9) | Clermont | 100.3 | 1 |
| 7) | Le Mans | 100.3 | 2 |
| 6) | Lyon | 100.3 | 4 |
| 13) | Mende | 100.3 | 1 |
| 3) | Mont de Marsan | 100.3 | 1 |
| 9) | Narbonne | 100.3 | 1 |
| 9) | Paris | 100.3 | 10 |
| 19) | St Gilles Croix de Vie | 100.3 | 1 |
| 3) | Soissons | 100.3 | 1 |
| 24) | Arcachon | 100.4 | 1 |
| 9) | Besançon | 100.4 | 1 |
| 21) | Bourges | 100.4 | 1 |
| 9) | Chartres | 100.4 | 1 |
| 3) | Chaumont | 100.4 | 1 |
| 4) | Corte | 100.4 | 1 |
| 13) | Lens | 100.4 | 1 |
| 6) | Limoges | 100.4 | 2 |
| 9) | Niort | 100.4 | 1 |
| 9) | Orléans | 100.4 | 2 |
| 22) | Royan | 100.4 | 1 |
| 21) | Toulon | 100.4 | 4 |
| 9) | Toulouse | 100.4 | 5 |
| 17) | Tours | 100.4 | 2 |
| 9) | Alençon | 100.5 | 1 |
| 21) | Brive la Gaillarde | 100.5 | 1 |
| 6) | Château Gontier | 100.5 | 1 |
| 6) | Compiègne | 100.5 | 1 |
| 3) | La Tour du Pin | 100.5 | 1 |
| 3) | Marseille | 100.5 | 2 |
| 23) | Mulhouse | 100.5 | 1 |
| 18) | Nogent le Rotrou | 100.5 | 1 |
| 18) | Rodez | 100.5 | 1 |
| 9) | Rouen | 100.5 | 2 |
| 9) | Ruffec | 100.5 | 1 |
| 22) | Saint Étienne | 100.5 | 2 |
| 9) | Saint Nazaire | 100.5 | 1 |
| 9) | Albi | 100.6 | 1 |
| 7) | Avallon | 100.6 | 1 |
| 7) | Blois | 100.6 | 1 |
| 6) | Bourg en Bresse | 100.6 | 1 |
| 3) | Brioude | 100.6 | 1 |
| 3) | Carcassonne | 100.6 | 1 |
| 3) | Dijon | 100.6 | 1 |
| 3) | Douarnenez | 100.6 | 1 |
| 3) | Ghisonaccia | 100.6 | 4 |
| 5) | Parthenay | 100.6 | 1 |
| 3) | Reims | 100.6 | 2 |
| 17) | Saint Brieuc | 100.6 | 1 |
| 20) | Villeneuve sur Lot | 100.6 | 1 |
| 13) | Béziers | 100.7 | 1 |
| 13) | Decazeville | 100.7 | 1 |
| 13) | Laon | 100.7 | 1 |
| 13) | Laval | 100.7 | 1 |
| 13) | Le Mans | 100.7 | 2 |
| 9) | Le Puy en Velay | 100.7 | 1 |
| 4) | Paris | 100.7 | 10 |
| 9) | Aiti | 100.8 | 1 |
| 9) | Bastia | 100.8 | 4 |
| 9) | Calvi | 100.8 | 1 |
| 20) | Castres | 100.8 | 1 |
| 23) | Chambéry | 100.8 | 1 |
| 3) | Clermont Ferrand | 100.8 | 1 |
| 2) | Grenoble | 100.8 | 1 |
| 5) | Lisieux | 100.8 | 1 |
| 9) | Nîmes | 100.8 | 1 |
| 12) | Perpignan | 100.8 | 1 |
| 7) | Saint Gaudens | 100.8 | 1 |
| 8) | Thouars | 100.8 | 1 |
| 9) | Verneuil sur Avre | 100.8 | 1 |
| 20) | Vire | 100.8 | 1 |
| 6) | Alençon | 100.9 | 1 |
| 9) | Bayonne | 100.9 | 5 |
| 9) | Besançon | 100.9 | 1 |
| 13) | Coulommiers | 100.9 | 1 |
| 10) | Marseille | 100.9 | 10 |
| 3) | Nancy | 100.9 | 1 |
| 22) | Rodez | 100.9 | 1 |
| 3) | Amiens | 101.0 | 1 |
| 24) | Aurillac | 101.0 | 1 |
| 14) | Avignon | 101.0 | 1 |
| 23) | Bergerac | 101.0 | 1 |
| 13) | Château Thierry | 101.0 | 1 |
| 9) | L'Aigle | 101.0 | 1 |
| 5) | Lourdes | 101.0 | 3 |
| 6) | Quimper | 101.0 | 1 |
| 9) | Agen | 101.1 | 1 |
| 9) | Aubusson | 101.1 | 1 |
| 8) | Bar le Duc | 101.1 | 1 |
| 10) | Beauvais | 101.1 | 1 |
| 9) | Châteauroux | 101.1 | 1 |
| 9) | Ghisonaccia | 101.1 | 1 |
| 6) | La Roche sur Yon | 101.1 | 1 |
| 10) | Laval | 101.1 | 1 |
| 11) | Le Havre | 101.1 | 1 |
| 13) | Metz | 101.1 | 1 |
| 9) | Paris | 101.1 | 10 |
| 23) | Poitiers | 101.1 | 1 |
| 9) | Saint Malo | 101.1 | 1 |
| 9) | Ajaccio | 101.2 | 8 |
| 24) | Albi | 101.2 | 1 |
| 9) | Arras | 101.2 | 1 |
| 13) | Blois | 101.2 | 1 |
| 21) | Chaumont | 101.2 | 1 |
| 3) | Clermont Ferrand | 101.2 | 1 |
| 7) | Épinal | 101.2 | 1 |
| 3) | Chambéry | 101.3 | 1 |
| 21) | Châtellerault | 101.3 | 1 |
| 22) | Dreux | 101.3 | 1 |
| 13) | Dunkerque | 101.3 | 1 |
| 17) | Forbach | 101.3 | 1 |
| 6) | Jonzac | 101.3 | 1 |
| 22) | La Rochelle | 101.3 | 1 |
| 7) | La Tour du Pin | 101.3 | 1 |
| 21) | Le Blanc | 101.3 | 1 |
| 3) | Lille | 101.3 | 2 |
| 5) | Menton | 101.3 | 1 |
| 20) | Orange | 101.3 | 1 |
| 19) | Saint Étienne | 101.3 | 2 |
| 9) | Sarlat la Canéda | 101.3 | 1 |
| 10) | Amiens | 101.4 | 1 |
| 9) | Caen | 101.4 | 2 |
| 21) | Marseille | 101.4 | 10 |
| 5) | Nice | 101.4 | 5 |
| 9) | Noyon | 101.4 | 1 |
| 21) | St Gilles Croix de Vie | 101.4 | 1 |
| 12) | Toulouse | 101.4 | 1 |
| 9) | Vic Fezensac | 101.4 | 1 |
| 18) | Alès | 101.5 | 1 |
| 9) | Cahors | 101.5 | 1 |
| 9) | Évreux | 101.5 | 1 |
| 5) | Montbard | 101.5 | 1 |
| 8) | Nevers | 101.5 | 1 |
| 14) | Paris | 101.5 | 10 |
| 13) | Poitiers | 101.5 | 1 |
| 21) | Redon | 101.5 | 1 |
| 21) | Rodez | 101.5 | 1 |
| 17) | Valence | 101.5 | 1 |
| 19) | Vendôme | 101.5 | 1 |
| 18) | Cambrai | 101.6 | 1 |
| 5) | Chaumont | 101.6 | 1 |
| 18) | Issoudun | 101.6 | 1 |
| 10) | Le Mans | 101.6 | 2 |
| 5) | Mâcon | 101.6 | 1 |
| 20) | Montargis | 101.6 | 1 |
| 23) | Périgueux | 101.6 | 1 |
| 10) | Quimper | 101.6 | 1 |
| 21) | Saint Malo | 101.6 | 1 |
| 13) | Valence | 101.6 | 1 |
| 21) | Albi | 101.7 | 1 |
| 6) | Bayeux | 101.7 | 1 |
| 5) | Bayonne | 101.7 | 5 |
| 18) | Compiègne | 101.7 | 1 |
| 6) | Cosne Cours/Loire | 101.7 | 1 |
| 17) | Le Puy en Velay | 101.7 | 1 |
| 22) | Limoges | 101.7 | 2 |
| 21) | Mazamet | 101.7 | 1 |
| 18) | Montluçon | 101.7 | 1 |
| 22) | Montpellier | 101.7 | 1 |
| 23) | Morlaix | 101.7 | 1 |
| 9) | Provins | 101.7 | 1 |
| 7) | Reims | 101.7 | 2 |
| 9) | Romilly sur Seine | 101.7 | 1 |
| 22) | Tarascon | 101.7 | 1 |
| 6) | Aubusson | 101.8 | 1 |
| 9) | Auxerre | 101.8 | 1 |
| 9) | Bergerac | 101.8 | 1 |
| 23) | Brest | 101.8 | 3 |
| 7) | Laon | 101.8 | 1 |
| 6) | Le Havre | 101.8 | 1 |
| 24) | Toulouse | 101.8 | 1 |
| 17) | Aix en Provence | 101.9 | 1 |
| 3) | Cahors | 101.9 | 1 |
| 5) | Châtillon sur Seine | 101.9 | 1 |
| 6) | Cognac | 101.9 | 1 |
| 9) | Coutances | 101.9 | 1 |
| 9) | Évreux | 101.9 | 1 |
| 17) | Martigues | 101.9 | 1 |
| 9) | Mayenne | 101.9 | 1 |
| 18) | Moulins | 101.9 | 1 |
| 7) | Paris | 101.9 | 10 |
| 9) | Tonnerre | 101.9 | 1 |
| 17) | Vendôme | 101.9 | 1 |
| 7) | Abbeville | 102.0 | 1 |
| 6) | Bar le Duc | 102.0 | 1 |
| 17) | Beaune | 102.0 | 1 |
| 7) | Épinal | 102.0 | 1 |
| 6) | Falaise | 102.0 | 1 |
| 23) | La Rochelle | 102.0 | 1 |
| 7) | Metz | 102.0 | 1 |
| 5) | Neufchâteau | 102.0 | 1 |
| 22) | Quimper | 102.0 | 1 |
| 6) | Rennes | 102.0 | 3 |
| 21) | Saint Quentin | 102.0 | 1 |
| 24) | Toulouse | 102.0 | 60 |
| 7) | Annecy | 102.1 | 1 |
| 20) | Avallon | 102.1 | 1 |
| 20) | Calvi | 102.1 | 1 |
| 9) | Charolles | 102.1 | 1 |
| 26) | Coulommiers | 102.1 | 1 |
| 12) | Limoges | 102.1 | 2 |
| 26) | Melun | 102.1 | 1 |
| 9) | Mulhouse | 102.1 | 1 |
| 6) | Nîmes | 102.1 | 1 |
| 7) | St Amand Montrond | 102.1 | 1 |
| 18) | Strasbourg | 102.1 | 4 |
| 3) | Arcachon | 102.2 | 1 |
| 9) | Blois | 102.2 | 1 |
| 21) | Dole | 102.2 | 1 |
| 17) | La Ferté Macé | 102.2 | 1 |
| 7) | Montargis | 102.2 | 1 |
| 7) | Thouars | 102.2 | 1 |
| 7) | Troyes | 102.2 | 1 |
| 9) | Avranches | 102.3 | 1 |
| 13) | Cahors | 102.3 | 1 |
| 17) | Chambéry | 102.3 | 1 |
| 6) | Forbach | 102.3 | 1 |
| 21) | Le Puy en Velay | 102.3 | 1 |
| 6) | Marseille | 102.3 | 10 |
| 3) | Montbard | 102.3 | 1 |
| 18) | Nancy | 102.3 | 1 |
| 23) | Nevers | 102.3 | 1 |
| 26) | Paris | 102.3 | 4 |
| 3) | Quimperlé | 102.3 | 1 |
| 9) | Saint Brieuc | 102.3 | 1 |

| FM | Station | MHz | kW |
|---|---|---|---|
| 9) | Saint Omer | 102.3 | 1 |
| 10) | Tours | 102.3 | 2 |
| 7) | Auxerre | 102.4 | 1 |
| 9) | Bordeaux | 102.4 | 5 |
| 9) | Brest | 102.4 | 1 |
| 6) | Castres | 102.4 | 1 |
| 3) | Chalon sur Saône | 102.4 | 1 |
| 20) | Chaumont | 102.4 | 1 |
| 3) | Decazeville | 102.4 | 1 |
| 10) | Grenoble | 102.4 | 1 |
| 6) | Haguenau | 102.4 | 1 |
| 5) | Montmorillon | 102.4 | 1 |
| 9) | Nantes | 102.4 | 3 |
| 7) | Perpignan | 102.4 | 3 |
| 4) | Rennes | 102.4 | 1 |
| 9) | Romorantin Lanthen. | 102.4 | 1 |
| 5) | Thionville | 102.4 | 1 |
| 6) | Toulouse | 102.4 | 5 |
| 3) | Vienne | 102.4 | 1 |
| 22) | Angers | 102.5 | 1 |
| 18) | Calais | 102.5 | 1 |
| 24) | Carmaux | 102.5 | 1 |
| 5) | Chartres | 102.5 | 1 |
| 6) | Commercy | 102.5 | 1 |
| 5) | Dijon | 102.5 | 1 |
| 18) | Gourdon | 102.5 | 1 |
| 8) | Les Sables d'Olonne | 102.5 | 1 |
| 1) | Melun | 102.5 | 1 |
| 8) | Niort | 102.5 | 1 |
| 5) | Sarrebourg | 102.5 | 1 |
| 18) | Angoulême | 102.6 | 1 |
| 13) | Bergerac | 102.6 | 1 |
| 21) | Carcassonne | 102.6 | 1 |
| 21) | Montauban | 102.6 | 3 |
| 27) | Orléans | 102.6 | 1 |
| 3) | Quimper | 102.6 | 1 |
| 9) | Saint Gaudens | 102.6 | 1 |
| 20) | Troyes | 102.6 | 1 |
| 9) | Abbeville | 102.7 | 1 |
| 22) | Avallon | 102.7 | 1 |
| 3) | Limoges | 102.7 | 2 |
| 5) | Morlaix | 102.7 | 1 |
| 4) | Nérac | 102.7 | 1 |
| 8) | Paris | 102.7 | 10 |
| 20) | Rochefort | 102.7 | 1 |
| 9) | Saint Dizier | 102.7 | 1 |
| 5) | Saint Flour | 102.7 | 1 |
| 18) | Valence | 102.7 | 1 |
| 8) | Verneuil sur Avre | 102.7 | 1 |
| 13) | Alès | 102.8 | 1 |
| 9) | Annecy | 102.8 | 1 |
| 18) | Annonay | 102.8 | 1 |
| 13) | Avignon | 102.8 | 1 |
| 23) | Bordeaux | 102.8 | 5 |
| 9) | Bourg en Bresse | 102.8 | 1 |
| 22) | Brive la Gaillarde | 102.8 | 1 |
| 21) | Dax | 102.8 | 1 |
| 17) | Lorient | 102.8 | 1 |
| 20) | Parthenay | 102.8 | 1 |
| 5) | Saint Étienne | 102.8 | 2 |
| 2) | Saint Raphaël | 102.8 | 3 |
| 7) | Tours | 102.8 | 2 |
| 9) | Vitré | 102.8 | 1 |
| 5) | Canavaggia | 102.9 | 1 |
| 13) | Charolles | 102.9 | 1 |
| 14) | Clermont Ferrand | 102.9 | 1 |
| 4) | Confolens | 102.9 | 1 |
| 5) | Guéret | 102.9 | 1 |
| 1) | Le Mans | 102.9 | 2 |
| 21) | Lourdes | 102.9 | 3 |
| 5) | Lunéville | 102.9 | 1 |
| 23) | Nantes | 102.9 | 3 |
| 5) | Saint Lô | 102.9 | 1 |
| 24) | Villeneuve sur Lot | 102.9 | 1 |
| 9) | Chambéry | 103.0 | 1 |
| 9) | Châteaudun | 103.0 | 1 |
| 13) | Colmar | 103.0 | 1 |
| 6) | Condom | 103.0 | 1 |
| 18) | Le Puy en Velay | 103.0 | 1 |
| 5) | Lyon | 103.0 | 10 |
| 3) | Metz | 103.0 | 1 |
| 21) | Moulins | 103.0 | 1 |
| 9) | Neufchâtel en Bray | 103.0 | 1 |
| 12) | Poitiers | 103.0 | 1 |
| 21) | Saint Gaudens | 103.0 | 1 |
| 7) | Tonnerre | 103.0 | 1 |
| 23) | Angoulême | 103.1 | 1 |
| 21) | Arcachon | 103.1 | 1 |
| 3) | Bar le Duc | 103.1 | 1 |
| 20) | Bergerac | 103.1 | 1 |
| 17) | Charensat | 103.1 | 1 |
| 2) | Marseille | 103.1 | 4 |
| 20) | Paris | 103.1 | 10 |
| 5) | Roanne | 103.1 | 1 |
| 24) | Saint Affrique | 103.1 | 1 |
| 3) | Saint Dizier | 103.1 | 1 |
| 13) | Saint Flour | 103.1 | 1 |
| 10) | Toulouse | 103.1 | 5 |
| 22) | Amiens | 103.2 | 1 |
| 21) | Belfort | 103.2 | 1 |
| 21) | Cervione | 103.2 | 1 |
| 17) | Dole | 103.2 | 1 |
| 6) | Douarnenez | 103.2 | 1 |
| 9) | Grenoble | 103.2 | 1 |
| 9) | Mirande | 103.2 | 1 |
| 20) | Montmorillon | 103.2 | 1 |
| 19) | Niort | 103.2 | 1 |
| 20) | Nogent le Rotrou | 103.2 | 1 |
| 24) | Perpignan | 103.2 | 10 |
| 20) | Albi | 103.3 | 1 |
| 21) | Annecy | 103.3 | 1 |
| 18) | Aurillac | 103.3 | 1 |
| 21) | Avesnes sur Helpe | 103.3 | 1 |
| 6) | Carpentras | 103.3 | 1 |
| 5) | Chartres | 103.3 | 1 |
| 5) | Compiègne | 103.3 | 1 |
| 5) | Guingamp | 103.3 | 1 |
| 20) | La Rochelle | 103.3 | 1 |
| 20) | Lille | 103.3 | 2 |
| 7) | Nancy | 103.3 | 1 |
| 7) | Nérac | 103.3 | 1 |
| 20) | Orthez | 103.3 | 1 |
| 19) | Rouen | 103.3 | 2 |
| 20) | Sarlat la Canéda | 103.3 | 1 |
| 5) | Strasbourg | 103.3 | 4 |
| 10) | Toulon | 103.3 | 1 |
| 7) | Vichy | 103.3 | 1 |
| 25) | Cahors | 103.4 | 1 |
| 13) | Carcassonne | 103.4 | 1 |
| 7) | Metz | 103.4 | 1 |
| 5) | Nantes | 103.4 | 3 |
| 12) | Orléans | 103.4 | 1 |
| 20) | Rodez | 103.4 | 1 |
| 21) | Saint Lô | 103.4 | 1 |
| 25) | Tours | 103.4 | 2 |
| 6) | Beauvais | 103.5 | 1 |
| 7) | Dinan | 103.5 | 1 |
| 19) | Le Havre | 103.5 | 1 |
| 6) | Le Mans | 103.5 | 2 |
| 9) | Morlaix | 103.5 | 1 |
| 6) | Paris | 103.5 | 10 |
| 9) | Saint Affrique | 103.5 | 1 |
| 23) | Angers | 103.6 | 2 |
| 21) | Blois | 103.6 | 1 |
| 25) | Corte | 103.6 | 1 |
| 7) | Longwy | 103.6 | 1 |
| 5) | Montluçon | 103.6 | 1 |
| 20) | Saint Gaudens | 103.6 | 1 |
| 7) | Saint Nazaire | 103.6 | 1 |
| 23) | Alençon | 103.7 | 1 |
| 6) | Creil | 103.7 | 2 |
| 6) | Fontainebleau | 103.7 | 2 |
| 17) | Grenoble | 103.7 | 1 |
| 23) | Laval | 103.7 | 1 |
| 6) | Meaux | 103.7 | 3 |
| 9) | Mirande | 103.7 | 1 |
| 18) | Niort | 103.7 | 1 |
| 21) | Bastia | 103.8 | 4 |
| 21) | Bergerac | 103.8 | 1 |
| 17) | Chinon | 103.8 | 1 |
| 24) | Figeac | 103.8 | 1 |
| 12) | Lorient | 103.8 | 1 |
| 20) | Lourdes | 103.8 | 3 |
| 4) | Nantes | 103.8 | 2 |
| 5) | Saint Brieuc | 103.8 | 2 |
| 18) | Troyes | 103.8 | 1 |
| 11) | Ussel | 103.8 | 1 |
| 24) | Bayonne | 103.9 | 5 |
| 18) | Beauvais | 103.9 | 1 |
| 21) | Calvi | 103.9 | 1 |
| 18) | Épinal | 103.9 | 1 |
| 18) | Le Havre | 103.9 | 1 |
| 20) | Le Mans | 103.9 | 2 |
| 13) | Montpellier | 103.9 | 3 |
| 18) | Paris | 103.9 | 10 |
| 9) | Rennes | 103.9 | 3 |
| 21) | Saint Dizier | 103.9 | 1 |
| 19) | Saint Flour | 103.9 | 1 |
| 5) | Cazevile | 103.9 | 1 |
| 3) | Saint Quentin | 103.9 | 1 |
| 21) | Toulouse | 103.9 | 5 |
| 21) | Vierzon | 103.9 | 1 |
| 20) | Arcachon | 104.0 | 1 |
| 21) | Avignon | 104.0 | 1 |
| 21) | Besançon | 104.0 | 1 |
| 3) | Cervione | 104.0 | 2 |
| 21) | Mauriac | 104.0 | 1 |
| 2) | Metz | 104.0 | 1 |
| 18) | Millau | 104.0 | 1 |
| 21) | Pamiers | 104.0 | 1 |
| 21) | Romorantin Lanthen. | 104.0 | 1 |
| 18) | St Gilles Croix de Vie | 104.0 | 1 |
| 21) | Tours | 104.0 | 2 |
| 24) | Villefranche Rouerg. | 104.0 | 1 |
| 21) | Abbeville | 104.1 | 1 |
| 9) | Bressuire | 104.1 | 1 |
| 18) | Chartres | 104.1 | 1 |
| 20) | Compiègne | 104.1 | 1 |
| 21) | Confolens | 104.1 | 1 |
| 21) | Coulommiers | 104.1 | 1 |
| 21) | Laval | 104.1 | 1 |
| 20) | Mâcon | 104.1 | 1 |
| 24) | Mazamet | 104.1 | 1 |
| 21) | Melun | 104.1 | 1 |
| 8) | Menton | 104.1 | 1 |
| 20) | Montauban | 104.1 | 3 |
| 20) | Montélimar | 104.1 | 1 |
| 21) | Montluçon | 104.1 | 1 |
| 2) | Nancy | 104.1 | 1 |
| 5) | Rouen | 104.1 | 2 |
| 20) | Annecy | 104.2 | 1 |
| 20) | Bordeaux | 104.2 | 5 |
| 21) | Dijon | 104.2 | 1 |
| 20) | Grenoble | 104.2 | 1 |
| 20) | Lyon | 104.2 | 4 |
| 20) | Mende | 104.2 | 1 |
| 4) | Mirande | 104.2 | 1 |
| 21) | Nogent le Rotrou | 104.2 | 1 |
| 21) | Troyes | 104.2 | 1 |
| 20) | Ajaccio | 104.3 | 8 |
| 21) | Amiens | 104.3 | 1 |
| 21) | Angers | 104.3 | 1 |
| 21) | Bastia | 104.3 | 4 |
| 20) | Bayonne | 104.3 | 5 |
| 21) | Beauvais | 104.3 | 1 |
| 21) | Béziers | 104.3 | 1 |
| 20) | Bonifacio | 104.3 | 1 |
| 21) | Brest | 104.3 | 3 |
| 21) | Clermont Ferrand | 104.3 | 2 |
| 13) | Épinal | 104.3 | 1 |
| 5) | La Ferté Macé | 104.3 | 1 |
| 21) | La Rochelle | 104.3 | 1 |
| 21) | Le Havre | 104.3 | 1 |
| 21) | Le Mans | 104.3 | 2 |
| 21) | Limoges | 104.3 | 2 |
| 21) | Lorient | 104.3 | 1 |
| 20) | Marseille | 104.3 | 10 |
| 17) | Montbard | 104.3 | 1 |
| 13) | Montpellier | 104.3 | 1 |
| 21) | Nantes | 104.3 | 3 |
| 21) | Neufchâteau | 104.3 | 1 |
| 20) | Nîmes | 104.3 | 1 |
| 21) | Orléans | 104.3 | 2 |
| 21) | Pau | 104.3 | 10 |
| 21) | Péronne | 104.3 | 1 |
| 21) | Perpignan | 104.3 | 3 |
| 21) | Poitiers | 104.3 | 1 |
| 21) | Quimper | 104.3 | 1 |
| 21) | Rennes | 104.3 | 3 |
| 21) | Saint Affrique | 104.3 | 1 |
| 21) | St Amand Montrond | 104.3 | 1 |
| 21) | Saint Nazaire | 104.3 | 1 |
| 21) | Soissons | 104.3 | 1 |
| 20) | Toulon | 104.3 | 4 |
| 20) | Toulouse | 104.3 | 5 |
| 20) | Valence | 104.3 | 1 |
| 21) | Vannes | 104.3 | 1 |
| 21) | Aubusson | 104.4 | 1 |
| 21) | Auxerre | 104.4 | 1 |
| 7) | Bourg en Bresse | 104.4 | 1 |
| 21) | Jonzac | 104.4 | 1 |
| 20) | Le Puy en Velay | 104.4 | 1 |
| 19) | Montargis | 104.4 | 1 |
| 2) | Nice | 104.4 | 5 |
| 21) | Reims | 104.4 | 2 |
| 24) | Rodez | 104.4 | 1 |
| 18) | Romorantin Lanthen. | 104.4 | 1 |
| 13) | Ruffec | 104.4 | 1 |
| 20) | Saint Étienne | 104.4 | 1 |
| 20) | Agen | 104.5 | 1 |
| 5) | Alençon | 104.5 | 1 |
| 5) | Arles | 104.5 | 1 |
| 20) | Avignon | 104.5 | 1 |
| 7) | Baccarat | 104.5 | 1 |
| 20) | Chambéry | 104.5 | 1 |
| 11) | Chartres | 104.5 | 1 |
| 21) | Compiègne | 104.5 | 1 |
| 5) | Coulommiers | 104.5 | 1 |
| 19) | Forbach | 104.5 | 1 |
| 5) | Gien | 104.5 | 1 |
| 17) | La Roche sur Yon | 104.5 | 1 |
| 5) | Laval | 104.5 | 1 |
| 5) | Le Creusot | 104.5 | 1 |
| 5) | Melun | 104.5 | 1 |
| 17) | Redon | 104.5 | 1 |
| 21) | Rouen | 104.5 | 2 |
| 5) | Tours | 104.5 | 2 |
| 1) | Alès | 104.6 | 1 |
| 3) | Avallon | 104.6 | 1 |
| 5) | Bayeux | 104.6 | 1 |
| 5) | Bordeaux | 104.6 | 5 |
| 5) | Grenoble | 104.6 | 1 |
| 5) | L'Aigle | 104.6 | 1 |
| 5) | Lyon | 104.6 | 4 |
| 5) | Nevers | 104.6 | 1 |
| 5) | Nogent le Rotrou | 104.6 | 1 |
| 22) | Propriano | 104.6 | 1 |
| 20) | Saint Flour | 104.6 | 1 |
| 21) | Saint Raphaël | 104.6 | 1 |
| 22) | Zonza | 104.6 | 1 |
| 5) | Amiens | 104.7 | 1 |
| 5) | Angers | 104.7 | 1 |
| 5) | Beauvais | 104.7 | 1 |
| 5) | Brest | 104.7 | 3 |
| 24) | Carcassonne | 104.7 | 80 |
| 5) | Cholet | 104.7 | 1 |
| 5) | Clermont Ferrand | 104.7 | 2 |
| 5) | Dijon | 104.7 | 1 |
| 22) | Ghisonaccia | 104.7 | 2 |
| 5) | La Rochelle | 104.7 | 1 |
| 5) | Le Havre | 104.7 | 1 |
| 5) | Le Mans | 104.7 | 2 |
| 5) | Limoges | 104.7 | 2 |
| 5) | Lorient | 104.7 | 1 |
| 24) | Montpellier | 104.7 | 1 |
| 5) | Nantes | 104.7 | 3 |
| 5) | Orléans | 104.7 | 2 |
| 5) | Paris | 104.7 | 10 |
| 5) | Poitiers | 104.7 | 1 |
| 5) | Quimper | 104.7 | 1 |
| 5) | Rennes | 104.7 | 2 |
| 5) | Saint Nazaire | 104.7 | 1 |
| 5) | Soissons | 104.7 | 1 |
| 5) | Toulon | 104.7 | 4 |
| 5) | Troyes | 104.7 | 1 |
| 5) | Vannes | 104.7 | 1 |
| 5) | Annecy | 104.8 | 1 |
| 5) | Arcachon | 104.8 | 1 |
| 5) | Argentan | 104.8 | 1 |
| 20) | Aubusson | 104.8 | 1 |
| 20) | Auxerre | 104.8 | 1 |
| 5) | Bernay | 104.8 | 1 |
| 5) | Cambrai | 104.8 | 1 |
| 5) | Châlons en Champ. | 104.8 | 1 |
| 5) | Gourdon | 104.8 | 1 |
| 5) | La Tour du Pin | 104.8 | 1 |
| 5) | Marseille | 104.8 | 10 |
| 21) | Metz | 104.8 | 1 |
| 18) | Neufchâteau | 104.8 | 1 |
| 13) | St Amand Montrond | 104.8 | 1 |

| FM | Station | MHz | kW | FM | Station | MHz | kW | FM | Station | MHz | kW | FM | Station | MHz | kW |
|---|---|---|---|---|---|---|---|---|---|---|---|---|---|---|---|
| 5) | Saint Étienne | 104.8 | 2 | 22) | Paris | 105.9 | 10 | 22) | Lourdes | 106.5 | 1 | 2) | Clermont Ferrand | 107.0 | 1 |
| 18) | Saint Lô | 104.8 | 1 | 7) | Pau | 105.9 | 1 | 13) | Nogent le Rotrou | 106.5 | 1 | 23) | La Ferté Macé | 107.0 | 1 |
| 5) | Valence | 104.8 | 1 | 9) | Perpignan | 105.9 | 3 | 22) | Périgueux | 106.5 | 1 | 6) | L'Aigle | 107.0 | 1 |
| 5) | Abbeville | 104.9 | 1 | 18) | Poitiers | 105.9 | 1 | 5) | Reims | 106.5 | 2 | 19) | Le Puy en Velay | 107.0 | 1 |
| 5) | Agen | 104.9 | 1 | 13) | Saint Nazaire | 105.9 | 1 | 23) | Saint Étienne | 106.5 | 2 | 21) | Mont de Marsan | 107.0 | 1 |
| 5) | Besançon | 104.9 | 1 | 21) | Saintes | 105.9 | 1 | 26) | Strasbourg | 106.5 | 1.5 | 8) | Montauban | 107.0 | 1 |
| 7) | Chartres | 104.9 | 1 | 7) | Toulouse | 105.9 | 5 | 17) | Yvetot | 106.5 | 1 | 17) | Montluçon | 107.0 | 1 |
| 5) | Compiègne | 104.9 | 1 | 23) | Troyes | 105.9 | 1 | 22) | Albi | 106.6 | 1 | 23) | Nice | 107.0 | 5 |
| 7) | La Roche sur Yon | 104.9 | 1 | 21) | Valence | 105.9 | 1 | 10) | Brest | 106.6 | 3 | 9) | Nîmes | 107.0 | 1 |
| 22) | Laval | 104.9 | 1 | 21) | Ajaccio | 106.0 | 8 | 20) | Cahors | 106.6 | 1 | 18) | Porto Vecchio | 107.0 | 1 |
| 5) | Mont de Marsan | 104.9 | 1 | 22) | Besançon | 106.0 | 1 | 5) | Châtellerault | 106.6 | 1 | 7) | Rouen | 107.0 | 1 |
| 7) | Montereau F/Yonne | 104.9 | 1 | 22) | Blois | 106.0 | 1 | 17) | Châtillon sur Seine | 106.6 | 1 | 18) | Saint Quentin | 107.0 | 1 |
| 5) | Moulins | 104.9 | 1 | 24) | Bordeaux | 106.0 | 5 | 21) | Commercy | 106.6 | 1 | 1) | Valence | 107.0 | 1 |
| 7) | Parthenay | 104.9 | 1 | 7) | Cahors | 106.0 | 1 | 5) | Dreux | 106.6 | 1 | 5) | Abbeville | 107.1 | 1 |
| 24) | Périgueux | 104.9 | 1 | 17) | L'Aigle | 106.0 | 1 | 9) | Gournay en Bray | 106.6 | 1 | 10) | Arcachon | 107.1 | 1 |
| 5) | Rouen | 104.9 | 2 | 8) | Limoges | 106.0 | 2 | 18) | La Flèche | 106.6 | 1 | 5) | Bourges | 107.1 | 1 |
| 21) | Royan | 104.9 | 1 | 10) | Lorient | 106.0 | 1 | 6) | La Rochelle | 106.6 | 1 | 2) | Caen | 107.1 | 2 |
| 20) | Angoulême | 105.0 | 1 | 3) | Martigues | 106.0 | 1 | 5) | Le Puy en Velay | 106.6 | 1 | 21) | Carmaux | 107.1 | 1 |
| 20) | Auch | 105.0 | 1 | 21) | Mauriac | 106.0 | 1 | 25) | Montélimar | 106.6 | 1 | 23) | Dijon | 107.1 | 1 |
| 21) | Bar le Duc | 105.0 | 1 | 21) | Mayenne | 106.0 | 1 | 20) | Montluçon | 106.6 | 1 | 8) | Laval | 107.1 | 1 |
| 5) | Caen | 105.0 | 2 | 21) | Montargis | 106.0 | 1 | 23) | Quimperlé | 106.6 | 1 | 21) | Mulhouse | 107.1 | 1 |
| 24) | Cahors | 105.0 | 1 | 21) | Niort | 106.0 | 1 | 13) | Saint Malo | 106.6 | 1 | 9) | Nancy | 107.1 | 1 |
| 21) | L'Aigle | 105.0 | 1 | 22) | Noyon | 106.0 | 1 | 8) | Toulon | 106.6 | 1 | 10) | Poitiers | 107.1 | 1 |
| 13) | Luxeuil les Bains | 105.0 | 1 | 20) | Rennes | 106.0 | 3 | 9) | Vire | 106.6 | 1 | 7) | Quimper | 107.1 | 1 |
| 21) | Lyon | 105.0 | 4 | 8) | Roanne | 106.0 | 1 | 18) | Alençon | 106.7 | 1 | 18) | Saint Étienne | 107.1 | 2 |
| 7) | Morlaix | 105.0 | 1 | 13) | St Gilles Croix de Vie | 106.0 | 1 | 5) | Angoulême | 106.7 | 1 | 21) | Saint Flour | 107.1 | 1 |
| 23) | Reims | 105.0 | 2 | 23) | Agen | 106.1 | 1 | 18) | Bourges | 106.7 | 1 | 5) | St Méen le Grand | 107.1 | 1 |
| 22) | Alençon | 105.1 | 1 | 3) | Albi | 106.1 | 1 | 6) | Calvi | 106.7 | 1 | 21) | Alès | 107.2 | 1 |
| 3) | Angers | 105.1 | 2 | 27) | Amiens | 106.1 | 1 | 10) | Carcassonne | 106.7 | 1 | 2) | Angers | 107.2 | 1 |
| 21) | Bayonne | 105.1 | 5 | 13) | Angers | 106.1 | 2 | 5) | Chalon sur Saône | 106.7 | 1 | 19) | Avignon | 107.2 | 1 |
| 9) | Bonifacio | 105.1 | 1 | 8) | Aubusson | 106.1 | 1 | 5) | Condom | 106.7 | 1 | 6) | Bastia | 107.2 | 1 |
| 21) | Bordeaux | 105.1 | 5 | 19) | Bastia | 106.1 | 4 | 18) | Laval | 106.7 | 1 | 20) | Blois | 107.2 | 1 |
| 21) | Charolles | 105.1 | 1 | 5) | Brive la Gaillarde | 106.1 | 1 | 5) | Lisieux | 106.7 | 1 | 21) | Figeac | 107.2 | 1 |
| 20) | Clermont Ferrand | 105.1 | 2 | 5) | Calvi | 106.1 | 1 | 15) | Lyon | 106.7 | 1 | 14) | Limoges | 107.2 | 2 |
| 6) | Corte | 105.1 | 1 | 22) | Chartres | 106.1 | 1 | 5) | Mende | 106.7 | 1 | 19) | Mâcon | 107.2 | 1 |
| 9) | Dinan | 105.1 | 1 | 5) | Commercy | 106.1 | 1 | 22) | Moulins | 106.7 | 1 | 2) | Nantes | 107.2 | 3 |
| 25) | Le Puy en Velay | 105.1 | 1 | 22) | Melun | 106.1 | 1 | 10) | Nantes | 106.7 | 4 | 10) | Pau | 107.2 | 1 |
| 20) | Limoges | 105.1 | 2 | 9) | Montpellier | 106.1 | 3 | 1) | Paris | 106.7 | 4 | 8) | Rochefort | 107.2 | 1 |
| 21) | Nancy | 105.1 | 1 | 10) | Rouen | 106.1 | 2 | 3) | Roanne | 106.7 | 1 | 7) | Soissons | 107.2 | 1 |
| 20) | Niort | 105.1 | 1 | 5) | Saint Dizier | 106.1 | 1 | 5) | Royan | 106.7 | 1 | 2) | Toulouse | 107.2 | 1 |
| 17) | Toulon | 105.1 | 4 | 5) | Sarrebourg | 106.1 | 1 | 5) | Saint Gaudens | 106.7 | 1 | 20) | Tours | 107.2 | 1 |
| 7) | Ajaccio | 105.2 | 8 | 5) | Tarbes | 106.1 | 1 | 20) | Ussel | 106.7 | 1 | 24) | Ussel | 107.2 | 1 |
| 20) | Brive la Gaillarde | 105.2 | 1 | 21) | Angoulême | 106.2 | 1 | 5) | Vitry le François | 106.7 | 1 | 7) | Arnay le Duc | 107.3 | 1 |
| 21) | Épinal | 105.2 | 1 | 7) | Argentan | 106.2 | 1 | 4) | Alès | 106.8 | 1 | 3) | Arras | 107.3 | 1 |
| 9) | Issoudun | 105.2 | 1 | 19) | Avignon | 106.2 | 1 | 8) | Avallon | 106.8 | 1 | 10) | Auxerre | 107.3 | 1 |
| 3) | Lons le Saunier | 105.2 | 1 | 18) | Bergerac | 106.2 | 1 | 22) | Bordeaux | 106.8 | 5 | 2) | Bordeaux | 107.3 | 1 |
| 5) | Montauban | 105.2 | 3 | 18) | Étampes | 106.2 | 1 | 20) | Brioude | 106.8 | 1 | 2) | Brest | 107.3 | 2.8 |
| 21) | Saint Étienne | 105.2 | 2 | 20) | Laval | 106.2 | 1 | 4) | Chartres | 106.8 | 1 | 10) | Brive la Gaillarde | 107.3 | 1 |
| 13) | Saint Lô | 105.2 | 1 | 13) | Morlaix | 106.2 | 1 | 13) | Château Renault | 106.8 | 1 | 1) | Carcassonne | 107.3 | 1 |
| 21) | Vitré | 105.2 | 1 | 3) | Nantes | 106.2 | 2 | 20) | Grasse | 106.8 | 1 | 10) | Chantilly | 107.3 | 1 |
| 3) | Chartres | 105.3 | 1 | 6) | Neufchâteau | 106.2 | 1 | 17) | La Côte Saint André | 106.8 | 1 | 3) | Châteauroux | 107.3 | 1 |
| 19) | Cholet | 105.3 | 1 | 18) | Tonnerre | 106.2 | 1 | 22) | Marseille | 106.8 | 4 | 21) | Colmar | 107.3 | 1 |
| 5) | Metz | 105.3 | 1 | 22) | Toulon | 106.2 | 1 | 5) | Niort | 106.8 | 1 | 18) | Corte | 107.3 | 1 |
| 13) | Rouen | 105.3 | 2 | 13) | Vendôme | 106.2 | 1 | 5) | Pau | 106.8 | 1 | 8) | Dax | 107.3 | 1 |
| 22) | Sens | 105.3 | 1 | 13) | Arras | 106.3 | 1 | 13) | Perpignan | 106.8 | 1 | 23) | Évreux | 107.3 | 1 |
| 13) | Strasbourg | 105.3 | 4 | 13) | Bourges | 106.3 | 1 | 3) | Rennes | 106.8 | 3 | 3) | Lens | 107.3 | 1 |
| 18) | Dole | 105.4 | 1 | 5) | Castres | 106.3 | 1 | 5) | Rethel | 106.8 | 1 | 5) | Lorient | 107.3 | 1 |
| 9) | Nancy | 105.5 | 1 | 25) | Dijon | 106.3 | 1 | 18) | Saint Affrique | 106.8 | 1 | 18) | Lyon | 107.3 | 4 |
| 12) | Lens | 105.6 | 1 | 13) | Ghisonaccia | 106.3 | 1 | 23) | Béthune | 106.9 | 1 | 6) | Mazamet | 107.3 | 1 |
| 9) | Béziers | 105.7 | 1 | 6) | Laon | 106.3 | 1 | 21) | Bourg en Bresse | 106.9 | 1 | 2) | Menton | 107.3 | 1 |
| 23) | Bonifacio | 105.7 | 1 | 20) | Moulins | 106.3 | 1 | 20) | Châteauroux | 106.9 | 1 | 9) | Metz | 107.3 | 1 |
| 7) | Lannemezan | 105.7 | 1 | 21) | Pau | 106.3 | 1 | 8) | Cholet | 106.9 | 1 | 5) | Millau | 107.3 | 1 |
| 21) | Le Creusot | 105.7 | 1 | 22) | Quimper | 106.3 | 1 | 22) | Compiègne | 106.9 | 1 | 10) | Montpellier | 107.3 | 3 |
| 20) | Lesparre Médoc | 105.7 | 1 | 22) | Saint Brieuc | 106.3 | 1 | 14) | Corte | 106.9 | 1 | 20) | Orléans | 107.3 | 1 |
| 17) | Loches | 105.7 | 1 | 5) | Sarlat la Canéda | 106.3 | 1 | 8) | Grenoble | 106.9 | 1 | 7) | Parthenay | 107.3 | 1 |
| 14) | Marseille | 105.7 | 1 | 5) | Toulouse | 106.3 | 5 | 8) | La Roche sur Yon | 106.9 | 1 | 21) | Perpignan | 107.3 | 3 |
| 7) | Neufchâteau | 105.7 | 1 | 13) | Tours | 106.3 | 2 | 7) | Le Havre | 106.9 | 1 | 23) | Saint Brieuc | 107.3 | 1 |
| 9) | Redon | 105.7 | 1 | 8) | Vannes | 106.3 | 1 | 8) | Le Mans | 106.9 | 2 | 23) | Saint Raphaël | 107.3 | 1 |
| 5) | Saint Flour | 105.7 | 2 | 5) | Avallon | 106.4 | 1 | 5) | Lorient | 106.9 | 1 | 7) | Verdun | 107.3 | 1 |
| 19) | Sancerre | 105.7 | 1 | 15) | Bordeaux | 106.4 | 5 | 9) | Mantes la Jolie | 106.9 | 2 | 23) | Dreux | 107.4 | 1 |
| 21) | Strasbourg | 105.7 | 4 | 13) | Caen | 106.4 | 2 | 5) | Mazamet | 106.9 | 1 | 5) | Granville | 107.4 | 1 |
| 13) | Vesoul | 105.7 | 1 | 8) | Chambéry | 106.4 | 1 | 22) | Melun | 106.9 | 1 | 7) | Lisieux | 107.4 | 1 |
| 17) | Argenton sur Creuse | 105.8 | 1 | 18) | Clermont Ferrand | 106.4 | 2 | 3) | Mers les Bains | 106.9 | 1 | 2) | Nevers | 107.4 | 1 |
| 5) | Carcassonne | 105.8 | 1 | 5) | Marseille | 106.4 | 10 | 21) | Montpellier | 106.9 | 3 | 18) | Provins | 107.4 | 1 |
| 10) | Dijon | 105.8 | 1 | 5) | Montargis | 106.4 | 1 | 6) | Périgueux | 106.9 | 1 | 28) | Arcachon | 107.5 | 1 |
| 8) | Grenoble | 105.8 | 1 | 10) | Troyes | 106.4 | 1 | 18) | Poligny | 106.9 | 1 | 4) | Château Gontier | 107.5 | 1 |
| 9) | Nîmes | 105.8 | 1 | 10) | Valence | 106.4 | 1 | 6) | Propriano | 106.9 | 1 | 20) | Châteaudun | 107.5 | 1 |
| 23) | Segré | 105.8 | 1 | 5) | Agen | 106.5 | 1 | 5) | Provins | 106.9 | 1 | 21) | Cherbourg Octeville | 107.5 | 1 |
| 8) | Bourges | 105.9 | 1 | 5) | Aurillac | 106.5 | 1 | 5) | Romilly sur Seine | 106.9 | 1.2 | 30) | Paris | 107.5 | 4 |
| 18) | Brest | 105.9 | 3 | 5) | Blois | 106.5 | 1 | 28) | Saint Brieuc | 106.9 | 1 | 20) | Saint Dizier | 107.5 | 1 |
| 5) | Caen | 105.9 | 2 | 5) | Châteauroux | 106.5 | 1 | 26) | Saint Lô | 106.9 | 1 | 5) | Canavaggia | 107.7 | 1 |
| 22) | Clermont Ferrand | 105.9 | 1 | 19) | Corte | 106.5 | 1 | 2) | Strasbourg | 106.9 | 1 | 12) | Lorient | 107.7 | 1 |
| 21) | Corte | 105.9 | 1 | 15) | Évreux | 106.5 | 1 | 5) | Bar le Duc | 107.0 | 1 | 23) | La Ferté Macé | 107.9 | 1 |
| 20) | Ghisonaccia | 105.9 | 2 | 9) | Fougères | 106.5 | 1 | 8) | Bressuire | 107.0 | 1 | 20) | L'Aigle | 107.9 | 1 |
| 9) | Le Mans | 105.9 | 2 | 17) | Lons le Saunier | 106.5 | 1 | 8) | Cahors | 107.0 | 1 | | | | |
| 18) | Mende | 105.9 | 1 | | | | | 7) | Château Thierry | 107.0 | 1 | | | | |

**NB:** Includes stns 1kW and over.
As of September 2018, 5400 licences (txs) were allocated to private commercial and non-commercial FM stns. Approx. 3690 stns are affiliated to one of the following private commercial national networks.

**Addresses & other information:**
**1) Beur FM** ▣ 2 rue du Nouveau Bercy, 94220 Charenton le Pont ☎ +33 1 53483030 **W:** beurfm.net + 4 txs less than 1kW – **2) BFM Business** ▣ 12 rue d'Oradour sur Glane, 75015 Paris ☎ +33 1 71191181 **W:** bfmbusiness.bfmtv.com + 6 txs less than 1kW – **3) Chérie** ▣ 22 rue Boileau, 75016 Paris ☎ +33 1 40714000 ▤ +33 1 40714040 **W:** cheriefm.fr+ 68 txs less than 1kW – **4) COFRAC-Radio Notre Dame** ▣ 6 bd Edgard Quinet, 75014 Paris ☎+33 1 56564444 **W:** radionotredame.net + 18 txs less than 1kW – **5) Europe 1** ▣ 28 rue François 1er, 75008 Paris ☎ +33 1 44319000 **W:** europe1.fr **LW:** 183kHz 1500kW see Germany. + 157 txs less than 1kW – **6) Virgin Radio** ▣ 28 rue François 1er, 75008 Paris ☎ +33 1 47231000 **W:** virginradio.fr + 104 txs less than 1kW– **7) Fun Radio** ▣ 56 av Charles de Gaulle, 92200 Neuilly sur Seine ☎ +33 1 41924030. **W:** funradio. fr + 111 txs less than 1kW – **8) M Radio** ▣ 50 avenue Daumesnil, 75012 Paris **W:** mradio.fr + 38 txs less than 1kW – **9) NRJ** ▣ 22 rue Boileau, 75016 Paris ☎ +33 1 40714000 ▤ +33 1 40714040 **W:** nrj.fr + 151 txs less than 1kW – **10) Radio Classique** ▣ 12 bis place Henri Bergson, 75382 Paris. Cedex 08 ☎ +33 1 40085000 ▤ +33 1 40085080 **W:** radioclassique.fr + 28 txs less than 1kW – **11) Radio Courtoisie** ▣ 61 bd Murat 75016 Paris ☎ +33 1 46510085 ▤ +33 1 46512182 **W:** radiocourtoisie.fr + 3 txs less than 1kW – **12) Radio FG** ▣ 51 rue de Rivoli, 75001 Paris ☎ +33 1 40137531 **W:** radiofg.com + 10 txs less than 1kW – **13) Nostalgie** ▣ 22 rue Boileau, 75016 Paris ☎ +33 1 40714000. ▤ +33 1 40714040 **W:** nostalgie.fr + 120 txs less than 1kW – **14) Radio Nova** ▣ 127 avenue Ledru Rollin, 75011 Paris ☎ +33 1 53333300 **W:** nova.fr + 6 txs less than 1kW – **15) Radio Orient** ▣ 98 bd Victor Hugo, 92110 Clichy ☎ +33 1 41061600 **W:** radioorient.com + 4 tx less than 1kW – **16) Radio Soleil** ▣ 57 rue Avron, 75020 Paris ☎ +33 1 43484343 **W:** radio-soleil.com + 2 txs less than 1kW – **17) RCF** ▣ 7 place Saint Irénée, 69321 Lyon Cedex 05 ☎ +33 4 72386210. **W:** rcf.fr + 126 txs less than 1kW – **18) RFM** ▣ 28 rue François 1er, 75008 Paris ☎ +33 1 47232400 **W:** rfm.fr + 93 txs less than 1kW – **19) Rire et Chansons** ▣ 22 rue Boileau, 75016 Paris ☎ +33 1 40714000 ▤ +33 1 40714040 **W:** rireetchansons.fr + 52 txs less than 1kW – **20) RMC** ▣ 12 rue d'Oradour sur Glane, 75740 Paris Cedex 15 ☎ +33 1 71191191 ▤ +33 01 71191190 **W:** rmc.bfmtv.com **LW:** Roumoules 216kHz 1400kW See Monaco. + 151 txs less than 1kW – **21) RTL** ▣ 56 av Charles de Gaulle, 92200 Neuilly sur Seine. ☎ +33 1 41924040 **W:** rtl.fr **LW:** 234kHz 1500kW see Luxembourg. + 125 txs less than 1kW – **22) RTL 2** ▣ 56 av Charles de Gaulle, 92200 Neuilly sur Seine ☎ +33 1 41924020 **W:** rtl2.fr + 74 txs less than 1kW – **23) Skyrock** ▣ 37 bis rue Greneta, 75002 Paris ☎ +33 1 44888200 **W:** skyrock. fm + 115 txs less than 1kW – **24) Sud Radio** ▣ 104 avenue du Pdt Kennedy, Paris ☎ +33 1 53 92 07 20 **W:** sudradio.fr + 31 txs less than 1kW – **25) Jazz Radio** ▣ 40 quai Rambaud, 69002 Lyon ☎ +33 4 72101535 **W:** jazzradio.fr + 26 txs less than 1 kW – **26) Ouï FM** ▣ 2 rue de la Roquette, 75011 Paris ☎ +33 1 55281414 **W:** ouifm.fr + 14 txs less than 1kW – **27) France Maghreb 2** ▣ 84 rue des Couronnes, 75020 Paris ☎ +33 1 40339081 **W:** francemaghreb2.fr + 3 txs less than 1kW – **28) TSF Jazz** ▣ 127 avenue Ledru Rollin, 75011 Paris ☎ +33 1 53333300 **W:** tsfjazz.com + 8 txs less than 1kW – **29) Latina** ▣ 167 rue du Chevaleret 75013 Paris ☎ +33 1 53600109 **W:** latina.fr + 3 txs less than 1kW – **30) Africa n°1** ▣ 33 rue du Faubourg Saint Antoine, 75011 Paris ☎ +33 1 55075801 **W:** africa1.com + 1 tx less than 1kW

**DAB+:** Calais: 5B. Douai: 11D. Dunkerque: 8D. Lille: 7C, 7D, 8A. Marseille: 7A, 8A, 8C, 8D. Nice: 8D, 9D, 11A, 11C. Paris: 6A, 6D, 9A, 9B, 9D, 11A. Valenciennes: 7A.. Tests Rambouillet: 5C. **F.PI:** DAB+ in Arcachon, Bordeaux, Bourg en Bresse, Bourgoin Jallieu, Colmar, Hagueneau, La Roche sur Yon, Le Havre, Lyon, Mâcon, Mulhouse, Nantes, Rouen, Saint Nazaire, Sélestat, Tarare, Toulouse.

## FRENCH GUIANA

**L.T:** UTC -3h, — **Pop:** 283,000 — **Pr.L:** French — **E.C:** 50Hz, 127/220V — **ITU:** GUF — **Int. dialling code:** +594

**Guyane Première (Pub)**
▣ B.P. 7013, 97305 Cayenne ☎ 594 301500 ▤ 594 302649 **W:** http// guyane.la1ere.fr **L.P:** Dir: Anastasie Bourquin. Dir. Tec: Serge Sulpice-Timothe. PD: Jean-Pierre Karam
**FM:** Cacao, Ouanary 90.0MHz – Sinnamary Corossony, Saint Lauren, Grand Saint, Maripasoula 91.0MHz – Cayenne, Iracubo 92.0MHz – Mana, Kourou, Saint-Georges, Apatou, Kourou 94.0MHz – Papaichton, Camopi - 95.0MHz **D.Prgr:** 24h **Ann:** "Ici Cayenne, RFO Guyane" **IS:** "Nos richesses" on guitar. **V.** by QSL-folder. Rec. acc.

**Other stations in Cayenne:** R. Mosaique 88.1MHz – Ouest FM 89.4MHz – R. Metis 90.6MHz – R. Jam 96.2MHz – R. 2000 96.9MHz – NRJ, 97.3MHz – RVLD 98.3MHz – Nostalgie Guyane 99.6MHz – Vinyl R. 102.9MHz – RTM 103.3MHz – Trace 104.3MHz – Chéri 104.7MHz – R. RMP 105.9MHz

**RADIO FRANCE INTERNATIONALE RELAY STATION**
▣ TDF Montsinery, B.P. 97307, Cayenne Cedex
**FM:** Cayenne & Saint-Laurent 98.7MHz

## FRENCH POLYNESIA

**L.T: Tahiti:** UTC-10h, **Marquesas Is:** -9½h **Gambier Is:** -9h — **Pop:** 294,935 — **PR. L:** French, Tahitian — **E.C:** 60Hz, 220V — **ITU:** OCE

**CONSEIL SUPERIOR DE L'AUDIOVISUEL**
Regulator of broadcasting for French Polynesia.
**Comité territorial de l'audiovisuel de Polynésie française**
▣ Immeuble Charles Levy, Boulevard Pomaré, B.P. 20659, Papeete, 98713 Polynésie Française ☎689 40543888 **W:** csa.fr **E:** cta. polynesie-francaise@csa.fr

| FM MHz | Location | kW | Station |
|---|---|---|---|
| **Iles du Vent** | | | |
| 15) 87.6 | Papeete | 1 | R. Turiva |
| 2) 88.2 | Mont Marau | 3 | R. Maohi |
| 3) 88.6 | Moorea | 4 | R. NRJ Polynésie |
| 4) 89.0 | Moorea | 10 | R. Polynésie 1ère |
| 4) 89.0 | Moorea/Papetoai | 0.3 | R. Polynésie 1ère |
| 5) 90.9 | Afaahiti | 1 | R. 1 |
| 6) 91.4 | Mont Marau | 1 | R. Te Vevo o Te Tiaturiraa |
| 4) 91.8 | Mont Marau | 1 | R. Polynésie 1ère |
| 2) 92.3 | Moorea | 3.6 | R. Maohi |
| 9) 92.8 | Mont Marau | 3 | R. Te Reo O Tefana |
| 7) 93.2 | Papara | 1.3 | R. Hiti FM |
| 2) 94.8 | Pueu | 1 | R. Maohi |
| 4) 95.2 | Mahaena | 0.2 | R. Polynésie 1ère |
| 4) 95.2 | Papara | 0.2 | R. Polynésie 1ère |
| 4) 95.2 | Pic Rouge | 0.2 | R. Polynésie 1ère |
| 8) 95.6 | Mont Marau | 2 | R. La Voix de l'Espérance |
| 16) 96.0 | Mont Marau | 3 | R. Heipuni FM |
| 1) 96.4 | Mont Marau | 3 | R. Maria no Te Hau |
| 9) 97.4 | Maatea | 4.2 | R. Te Reo o Tefana |
| 10) 97.8 | Moorea | 6 | R. Taui FM |
| 5) 98.3 | Afaahiti | 1 | R. Tiare FM |
| 4) 99.0 | Papeete | 0.3 | R. Polynésie 1ère |
| 4) 99.0 | Pueu | 0.3 | R. Polynésie 1ère |
| 8) 99.5 | Maatea | 3 | R. La Voix de l'Espérance |
| 5) 100.0 | Maatea | 3 | R. 1 |
| 11) 101.1 | Moorea | 1.5 | Rire et Chansons Tahiti |
| 1) 101.5 | Moorea | 2 | R. Maria no Te Hau |
| 8) 102.2 | Papeete | 1 | R. La Voix de l'Espérance |
| 11) 102.6 | Mont Marau | 1 | Rire et Chansons Tahiti |
| 3) 103.0 | Mont Marau | 1.6 | R. NRJ Polynésie |
| 7) 103.4 | Faaa | 3 | R. Hiti FM |
| 5) 103.8 | Mont Marau | 3 | R. 1 |
| 5) 103.8 | Mont Marau | 3 | R. Tiare FM |
| 12) 104.7 | Moorea | 2 | R. Paofai |
| 5) 105.5 | Moorea | 3 | R. Tiare FM |
| 17) 106.4 | Moorea | 5 | R. Manotahi |
| 10) 107.3 | Mont Marau | 1 | R. Faa'a Taui FM |
| + 35 stations less than 1kW | | | |
| **Iles Sous le Vent** | | | |
| 4) 94.0 | Raiatea | 0.1 | R. Polynésie 1ère |
| 8) 96.2 | Raiatea | 0.2 | R. La Voix de l'Espérance |
| 4) 96.6 | Bora Bora | 0.1 | R. Polynésie 1ère |
| 1) 105.4 | Bora Bora | | R. Maria no Te Hau |
| + 18 stations less than 1kW | | | |
| **Archipel des Australes** | | | |
| 4) 89.6 | Raivavae/Rurutu | 0.1 | R. Polynésie 1ère |
| 4) 99.4 | Rapa/Rimatara/Tubuai | 0.1 | R. Polynésie 1ère |
| + 7 stations less than 1kW | | | |
| **Les Isles Marquises** | | | |
| 4) 88.2 | Hiva Oa | 0.05 | R. Polynésie 1ère |
| 4) 89.0 | Nuku Hiva | 0.5 | R. Polynésie 1ère |
| 4) 89.5 | Hiva Oa | 0.1 | R. Polynésie 1ère |
| 4) 90.5 | Nuku Hiva | 0.05 | R. Polynésie 1ère |
| 4) 91.5 | Ua Huka | | R. Polynésie 1ère |
| 18) 92.5 | Hiva | 6 | R. Te Oko Nui |
| 6) 93.5 | Nuku Hiva | 3 | R. Te Vevo o Te Tiaturiraa |
| 18) 94.5 | Nuku Hiva | 6 | R. Te Oko Nui |
| 10) 100.0 | Nuku Hiva | 1 | R. Taui FM |
| + 9 stations less than 1kW | | | |

| FM MHz | Location | kW | Station |
|---|---|---|---|
| **Iles des Tuamotu Gambier** | | | |
| 4) 90.5 | Arutua/Rautini | 0.1 | R. Polynésie 1ère |
| 4) 93.6 | Ahe/Hao/Kaukura/Mataiva/Napuka/Takaroa | | |
| | | 0.1 | R. Polynésie 1ère |
| 4) 94.0 | Faaite/Makemo//Mangareva/Nukutavake/Puka Puka/Rangiroa | | |
| | | 0.1 | R. Polynésie 1ère |
| 4) 94.4 | Fakahina/FakaravaHikueru/Manihi/Mururoa/Reau | | |
| | | 0.1 | R. Polynésie 1ère |
| 4) 94.8 | Anaa/Fangatau/Takapoto/Tatakoto/Tikehau/Tureia | | |
| | | 0.1 | R. Polynésie 1ère |
| 4) 95.2 | Apataki/Pukarua | 0.1 | R. Polynésie 1ère |
| 13) 96.0 | Marutea Sud | 1 | R. Marutea Sud |
| 1) 98.0 | Rangiroa | 0.2 | R. Maria no Te Hau |
| 14) 101.0 | Rangiroa | 1 | R. Te Reo Tuamotu |

+ 9 stations less than 1kW

**Addresses & other information:**
**1)** BP 94, 98713 Papeete ☎+689 40420011 📠+689 40420635 **E:** radiomarianotehau@mail.pf **W:** radiomarianotehau.com & facebook.com/radiomarianotehau – **2)** BP 5038, 98716 Pirae ☎+689 40501616 **E:** courrier@radiomaohi.pf **W:** radiomaohi.pf – **3)** BP 50, 98713 Papeete ☎+689 40475283 📠+689 40464346 **E:** contact.nrj@pacfm.fr **W:** nrj.pf – **4) POLYNESIE LA PREMIÈRE (Pub)** ☑ Centre Pamatai, BP 60-125, 98702 Faaa ☎+689 40861600 📠+689 40861621 **W:** polynesie1ere.fr **E:** polynesie1ere@francetv.fr **Prgr:** 24h **LP:** Dir. Regional: Gérald Prufer – **5)** BP 3601, 98713 Papeete ☎+689 40434100 📠+689 40422421 (R.1) ☎+689 423403406 (R. Tiare FM) **E:** contact@radio1.pf **Brands:** Radio 1: **W:** radio1.pf & facebook.com/radio1tahiti/ Radio Tiare: **W:** tiarefm.pf & facebook.com/pages/tiare-fm – **6)** BP 1817, 98713 Papeete, 51, rue Dumont D'Urville, Orovini, Papeete ☎+689 40412341 📠+689 40412322 **E:** contacts@mail.pf **W:** facebook.com/Rtv-Tahiti-103877699955813 – **7)** Punaauia, ☎+689 89932932 **W:** hitifm.pf, facebook.com/hiti-fm-tahiti **E:** hitifmtahiti@gmail.com – **8)** 55 Cours de l'Union sacrée, Papeete (BP 140593, 98701 Arue) ☎+689 40508259 📠+689 40451427 **E:** direction@lvdl.pf – **9)** BP 6295, 98703 Faaa ☎+689 40819797 📠+689 40825493 **E:** tereo@mail.pf **W:** facebook.com/tereootefana – **10)** BP 60076, Faaa-Centre, Papeete ☎+689 40854747 📠+689 40412555 **E:** tauifm@mail.pf **W:** tauifm.net – **11)** SARL Pac FM ☎+689 40421414 **E:** community-rpp@rpp.pf **W:** facebook.com/rire.et.chansons – **12)** BP 113, 98713 Papeete ☎ +689 40460624 📠+689 40419357 **E:** radiopaofai@epm.pf **W:** radio.radiopaofai.org – **13)** [atoll has no permanent population] – **14)** Cultural Association Iva Manu-Manu Arii, Avatoru, Rangiroa, Tuamotu-Gambier [r. silent] – **15)** No details available – **16)** No details available – **17)** No details available – **18)** BP 20, Nuku Hiva, Iles Marquises ☎ +689 40910155 📠+689 40910157 **W:** facebook.com/Radio-TE-OKO-NUI-539567206195327/ **E:** teokonuiradio@Outlook.fr

## FRENCH SOUTHERN & ANTARCTIC LANDS

**L.T:** UTC+5h — **Pop:** 150 (wi), 300 (su) — **Pr.L:** French — **E.C:** 50Hz, 220V — **ITU:** none (**WRTH:** FSA); Isles Kerguelen: ITU: KER

| FM | MHz | Station | FM | MHz | Station |
|---|---|---|---|---|---|
| 1) | 98.0 | Radio Ker | 3) | 100.0 | RTL |
| 2) | 100.0 | France Inter | | | |

**Addresses & other information:**
**1)** Port-aux-Francais, District de Kerguelen, Terres Australes & Antarctiques Francaises [via Reunion, Indian Ocean]. 24h community station. – **2)** 24h satellite relay from Paris, Mon-Fri. – **3)** 24h satellite relay from Paris, weekends

## GABON

**L.T:** UTC +1h — **Pop:** 1.8 million — **Pr.L:** French, Fang, Bopounou, Obamba, Djebi — **E.C:** 50Hz, 220V — **ITU:** GAB

### CONCEIL NATIONAL DE LA COMMUNICATION(CNC)
☑ B.P. 6437, Libreville ☎+241 1762796 **L.P:** Pres: Pierre-Marie Dong.

### RADIODIFFUSION-TÉLÉVISION GABONAISE(RTG,Gov.)
☑ B.P. 10150, Libreville ☎+241 1732459 📠 +241 1739775. **L.P:** DG RTG-1: Willy Kombény. DG RTG-2: Jules Legnongo. Asst. DGs: Radio: Gilles Terence Nzoghe. Tech: Claude Nganga. Provincial Stns: Robert Aloli.

| MW | kHz | kW | N | Times |
|---|---|---|---|---|
| Oyem | 549 | 20 | 2 | 0430-0630, 1030-1430, 1600-2230 |

**FM**(MHz): Libreville 87.7/96.5 (**1**), 92.5 (**2**), Franceville 87.9 (**2**), Makokou 100.5 (**2**), Oyem 87.9 (**2**), Pt. Gentil 88.0 (**2**), Tchibanga 91.0 (**2**).

**1** = RTG Chaîne 1 in French. **2** = RTG Chaîne 2 (provincial netw.) in French & ethnic languages**.**
**Ann:** 1: "Ici Libreville, vouz écoutez Radio Gabon, chaîne 1".
**IS:** Indigenous instruments. Opens and closes with National Anthem.

**OTHER STATIONS:**
**Hit R**, Libreville/Port Gentil 98.5MHz **W:** facebook.com/HITRADIOGabon – **R. Émergence,** B.P. 06, Libreville: 91.6MHz 30W **W:** f-i-a.org/emergence – **R. Génération Nouvelle,** B.P. 727, Libreville: 97.4MHz – **R. Mandarine,** B.P. 511, Libreville: 106.6MHz – **R. Nostalgie,** B.P. 13050, Libreville: 93.0MHz – **R. Notre-Dame de Sainte-Marie,** B.P 20348, Libreville: 99MHz – **R. Soleil FM,** B.P. 5420, Libreville: 107.7MHz – **Top FM,** B.P. 6554, Libreville: 105.5MHz (also rel. VOA) – **R. Unité,** B.P. 2676, Libreville: 100.5MHz.
**Africa No. 1**, Libreville 94.5MHz 1kW **W:** africa1.com
**BBC African Sce,** Libreville: 94.0MHz 4kW
**Medi 1 Afrique Internationale,** Libreville: 101.5MHz
**RFI Afrique** in Franceville/Libreville/Port-Gentil on 104.0MHz

## GALAPAGOS ISLANDS (Ecuador)

**L.T:** UTC -6h — **Pop:** 25,000 — **Pr.L:** Spanish — **E.C:** 60Hz 110/220V — **ITU:** EQA (**WRTH:** GAL)

### LA VOZ DE GALAPAGOS (Rlg)
Prefectura Apostólica de Galápagos, Puerto Baquerizo Moreno ☎ +593 5 459435 **W:** lavozdegalapagos.net
**FM: Galápagos Stereo** 97.1MHz.
**FM in Pto Baquerizo Moreno (MHz):** 91.1 R. Pública/Nacional del Ecuador FM – 94.7 R. Mar – 97.1 LV de Galápagos FM – 100.7 R. María – 101.9 Encantada FM – 104.3 Telegalápagos FM
**FM in Pto Ayora (MHz):** 88.7 R. Santa Cruz – 89.9 Caravana AM – 93.5 Pacífica FM - 94.7 R. Mar – 95.9 Antena 9 FM – 98.3 Stereo Zaracay – 101.9 Encantada FM

## GAMBIA

**L.T:** UTC — **Pop:** 1.8 million — **Pr.L:** English, Mandinka, Fula, Wolof, Jola, Serahuleh, Manjago, Aku — **E.C:** 50Hz, 230V — **ITU:** GMB

### PUBLIC UTILITIES REGULATORY AUTHORITY (PURA)
☑ 94 Kairaba Ave, Bakau, KSMD, Banjul ☎ +220 4399601 📠 +220 4399905 **W:** pura.gm **E:** info@pura.gm

### GAMBIA RADIO & TELEVISION SERVICE (GRTS) (Gov)
☑ Mile 7 Studios, P.O. Box 387, Banjul ☎+220 4495101/4497419 📠 +220 4495102 **W:** grts.gm **LP:** DG: Mr. Modou Sanyang. Deputy DG: Mr. Alhaji Modou Joof.
**FM:** Serrekunda 96.0MHz, Abuko 98.6MHz, Bonto 102.6MHz, Banjul 106.7MHz.
**D.Prgr:** in E/local langs: 0600-2400. N. in E: 0700, 1300, 1800, 2200. **Ann:** "GRTS Radio". **IS:** Cora (harp).

**Other stations (all** MHz):
**Afriradio,** Banjul: 107.6 **W:** africell.gm/FM.php – **Capital FM,** Banjul: 100.4 **W:** capitalfm.gm – **Choice FM,** Banjul: 106.4 **W:** choicefm.gm – **City Limits R,** Serrekunda: 93.6 0.25kW – **Hill Top R,** Serrekunda: 104.7 100W – **Hot FM,** Banjul: 104.3 **W:** hotfmgambia.gm – **Kora FM,** Banjul: 103.9 **W:** korafm.gm – **Paradise FM:** Farafenni105.5, Serrekunda 105.7, Basse 105.8 1kW. **W:** paradisefm.gm – **Star FM,** Banjul: 96.6 **W:** starfm.gm – **Unique FM,** Banjul/Basse: 100.7 **W:** uniquefm.gm Also r. VOA – **West Coast R,** Serrekunda: 92.1 & 95.3 (different prgr.) **W:** westcoast.gm – **Vibes FM,** Banjul: 106.1 **W:** vibesfm.gm
**RFI Afrique:** Banjul 89.0MHz

## GEORGIA

**L.T:** UTC +4h; Abkhazia and South Ossetia (de facto): UTC +3h — **Pop:** 4 million — **Pr.L:** Georgian, Abkhaz, Ossetic — **E.C:** 230V/50Hz — **ITU:** GEO

### SAKARTVELOS KOMUNIKATSIEBIS EROVNULI KOMISIA (Georgian National Communications Commission)
☑ Ave. Ketevan Tsamebuli/Bochorma St. 50/18, 0144 Tbilisi ☎ +995 32 2921667 📠 +995 32 2921625 **E:** post@gncc.ge **W:** gncc.ge **L.P:** Chmn: Kakhi Bekauri

### SAKARTVELOS SAZOGADOEBRIVI MAUTSQEBELI (Pub) (Georgian Public Broadcaster)
☑ M.Kostava St. 68, 0171 Tbilisi ☎ +995 32 2409477 **E:** info@gbp.ge **W:** gpb.ge **L.P:** DG: Vasil Maghlaperidze

| FM | 1 | 2 | kW | FM | 1 | 2 | kW |
|---|---|---|---|---|---|---|---|
| Akhaltsikhe | 102.4 | - | 1 | Kutaisi | 100.3 | - | 2 |
| Batumi* | 102.4 | - | 1 | Tbilisi | 102.4 | 100.9 | 10/5 |
| Telavi | 100.6 | - | 1 | Zugdidi | 101.3 | - | 1 |

+ sites with only txs below 1kW. *) Located in Ajara (autonomous republic)

**D.Prgr: Prgr 1 (Radio 1):** 24h. – **Prgr 2 (Radio 2):** 0400-2200. – **Regional Branch** in Ajara: see below.

## OTHER STATIONS

| FM | MHz | kW | Location | Station |
|---|---|---|---|---|
| 25) | 92.3 | 1 | Tbilisi | R. Tanamgzavri |
| 22B) | 93.1 | 1 | Tbilisi | Qartuly Vinili |
| 20) | 93.5 | 1 | Tbilisi | R. Tbilisi 93.5FM |
| 14) | 93.9 | 1 | Tbilisi | Star FM |
| 15) | 94.3 | 1 | Tbilisi | R. GIPA |
| 1) | 94.3 | 1 | Dedoplistskaro | R. Iveria |
| 22A) | 94.7 | 1 | Tbilisi | R. Maestro |
| 5E) | 95.1 | 1 | Tbilisi | Avtoradio |
| 3) | 95.5 | 1 | Tbilisi | R. Komersant |
| 17) | 96.3 | 1 | Tbilisi | R. Jako |
| 5C) | 96.7 | 1 | Tbilisi | R. Ar Daidardo |
| 18) | 97.1 | 1 | Tbilisi | Dardimandi FM |
| 34) | 97.5 | 1 | Akhaltsikhe | FM 97.5 |
| 31) | 97.5 | 1 | Kutaisi | 42nd parallel |
| 26) | 97.5 | 1 | Tbilisi | R. Kubrik |
| 33) | 97.8 | 1 | Gori | R. Mosaic |
| 10) | 98.0 | 1 | Tbilisi | R. Utsnobi |
| 21) | 98.5 | 1 | Tbilisi | Shokoladi FM |
| 7) | 98.9 | 1 | Kutaisi | Apkhazetis khma |
| 7) | 98.9 | 1 | Tbilisi | Apkhazetis khma |
| 23) | 99.3 | 1 | Tbilisi | R. Chveneburi |
| 5D) | 99.7 | 1 | Tbilisi | R. Vinil |
| 22A) | 99.9 | 1 | Kutaisi | R. Maestro |
| 9) | 100.0 | 1 | Gori | R. Imedi |
| 5E) | 100.2 | 1 | Dmasisi | Avtoradio |
| 27) | 100.3 | 1 | Tbilisi | Beat FM 100.3 |
| 9) | 100.9 | 1 | Kutaisi | R. Imedi |
| 12) | 101.0 | 1 | Dmanisi | R. Tavisupleba |
| 9) | 101.2 | 1 | Akhalkalaki | R. Imedi |
| 2) | 101.4 | 1 | Tbilisi | R. Monte-Karlo |
| 12) | 101.5 | 1 | Gori | R. Tavisupleba |
| 19) | 101.9 | 1 | Tbilisi | R. Kalaki |
| 5E) | 102.3 | 1 | Kutaisi | Avtoradio |
| 5C) | 102.7 | 1 | Kutaisi | R. Ar Daidardo |
| A) | 102.9 | 1 | Tbilisi | RFI relay |
| 29) | 102.9 | 1 | Zugdidi | R. Odishi+ |
| 22A) | 103.0 | 1 | Tkibuli | R. Maestro |
| 5B) | 103.4 | 1 | Tbilisi | R. Fortuna+ |
| 5B) | 103.4 | 1 | Gori | R. Fortuna+ |
| 5B) | 103.4 | 1 | Kutaisi | R. Fortuna+ |
| 12) | 103.6 | 1 | Zugdidi | R. Tavisupleba |
| 22) | 103.8 | 1 | Dmansi | R. Maestro |
| 6) | 104.1 | 1 | Tbilisi | R. Palitra |
| 9) | 104.1 | 5 | Chiatura | R. Imedi |
| 9) | 104.2 | 1 | Zugdidi | R. Imedi |
| 4) | 104.3 | 1 | Tbilisi | R. Positive |
| 9) | 104.7 | 1 | Dedoplistskaro | R. Imedi |
| 28) | 104.7 | 1 | Tbilisi | NRJ |
| 16) | 104.8 | 1 | Gori | R. Trialeti |
| 18) | 105.0 | 1 | Kutaisi | Dardimandi FM |
| 8) | 105.1 | 1 | Tbilisi | R. Obieqtivi |
| 9) | 105.1 | 5 | Dmansi | R. Imedi |
| 22A) | 105.2 | 1 | Ozurgeti | R. Maestro |
| 30) | 105.5 | 1 | Kutaisi | R. Rioni |
| 1) | 105.5 | 1 | Tbilisi | R. Iveria |
| 9) | 105.9 | 1 | Tbilisi | R. Imedi |
| 22A) | 106.3 | 1 | Gori | R. Maestro |
| 11) | 106.4 | 1 | Tbilisi | Pirveli R. |
| 11) | 105.4 | 1 | Kutaisi | Pirveli R. |
| 5A) | 106.9 | 1 | Tbilisi | R. Fortuna |
| 5A) | 106.9 | 1 | Gori | R. Fortuna |
| 5A) | 106.9 | 1 | Kutaisi | R. Fortuna |
| 7) | 107.2 | 1 | Zugdidi | Apkhazetis khma |
| 12) | 107.4 | 1 | Tbilisi | R. Tavisupleba |
| 12) | 107.4 | 2 | Tbilisi | R. Tavisupleba |
| 13) | 107.9 | 1 | Tbilisi | Saqartvelos khma |
| 24) | 107.9 | 1 | Kutaisi | R. Dzveli Kalaki |

+ txs below 1kW.

**Addresses & other information:**
**1)** Erekle II square 1, 0105 Tbilisi – **2)** M.Kostava St. 14, 0169 Tbilisi. In Russian. – **3)** Nadiradze St. 8, 0102 Tbilisi – **4)** Dadiani 21, 0101 Tbilisi – **5A-D)** Beliashvili St. 9, 0159 Tbilisi – **6)** Iosebidze St. 49,

0160 Tbilisi – **7)** Kindzmarauli St. 15, 0121 Tbilisi – **8)** Agladze St. 31, 0119 Tbilisi – **9)** Lubliana St. 5, 0159 Tbilisi – **10)** M.Kostava St. 68, 0171 Tbilisi – **11)** Aleksidze St. 1, 0193 Tbilisi – **12)** Vazha-Pshavela Ave. 45, 0177 Tbilisi – **13)** Tashkenti St. 51, 0160 Tbilisi – **14)** Vazha-Pshavela Ave. 16, 0160 Tbilisi – **15)** Marie Brosset St. 2, 0108 Tbilisi – **16)** Chavchavadze St. 45, 1400 Gori – **17)** Tbilisi – **18)** Kindzmarauli St. 15, 0168 Tbilisi – **19)** Melikishvili St. 1, 0179 Tbilisi – **20)** Sanapiro St. 1, 0114 Tbilisi – **21)** M. Kostava St. 47/57, 0179 Tbilisi – **22A,B)** Akaki Beliashvili St. 8, 0159 Tbilisi – **23)** Gagarin St. 24, 0160 Tbilisi – **24)** Gaponov St. 30, 4600 Kutaisi – **25)** Tbilisi – **26)** Tbilisi – **27)** Tsinamdzgvrishvili St. 95, 0112 Tbilisi – **28)** Dolidze St. 2, 0171 Tbilisi – **29)** Zviad Gamsakhurdia 19, 2100 Zugdidi – **30)** Paliashvili St. 2, 4600 Kutaisi – **31)** Kutaisi – **32)** Tbilisi – **33)** Gori – **34)** Akhaltsikhe – **A)** Rel. RFI (France).

## AJARA
(Autonomous republic)

### AJARA RADIO & TV (Pub)
Memed Abashidze Ave. 41, 6010 Batumi ☎ +995 422 274370 📠 +995 422 274384 **E:** info@radioajara.ge **W:** radioajara.ge; ajaratv.ge
**L.P:** Dir: Natia Kapanadze
**FM:** Batumi 104.5MHz (0.5kW)
**D.Prgr: R. Ajara** 24h.
**NB:** Ajara Radio & TV is a branch of Georgian Public Broadcaster.
**OTHER STATIONS**

| FM | MHz | kW | Location | Station |
|---|---|---|---|---|
| 22A) | 90.9 | 1 | Batumia | R. Maestro |
| 9) | 100.1 | 1 | Batumi | R. Imedi |
| 5C) | 101.9 | 1 | Batumi | R. Ar Dadaido |
| 5B) | 103.4 | 1 | Batumi | R. Fortuna+ |
| 1) | 105.4 | 1 | Batumi | R. Iveria |
| 5A) | 106.9 | 5 | Batumi | R. Fortuna |

+ txs below 1kW.
**Addresses & other information:** see main tx table.

## ABKHAZIA
(Self-proclaimed "Republic of Abkhazia")

### APSNYTWI AXWYNTKARRATW TELERADIO-EILAXWYRA (Gov*) (Abkhaz State Radio & TV Co.)
(* Run by the administration of the "Republic of Abkhazia")
V.Ardzinba St. 16, Sokhumi, Abkhazia (mail: via Russia) ☎ +7 840 2264867 📠 +7 840 2266144 **E:** apsua.radio@gmail.com **W:** apsua.tv
**L.P:** DG: Ronald Bganba

| MW | kHz | kW |
|---|---|---|
| Sokhumi | 1350 | 30 |

| FM | MHz | kW | FM | MHz | kW |
|---|---|---|---|---|---|
| Tkvarcheli | 102.2 | - | Ochamchire | 104.0 | - |
| Sokhumi | 103.7 | - | Gagra | 107.1 | - |

**D.Prgr: Apsua R.** with own prgrs in Abkhaz, Russian. Outside of own prgrs, various other stns may be relayed (mainly Avtoradio). On MW: limited schedule, changing frequently.

**OTHER STATIONS**

| FM | MHz | kW | Location | Station |
|---|---|---|---|---|
| 1) | 91.2 | - | Ochamchire | R. Soma |
| A) | 100.7 | - | Ochamchire | R. Sputnik relay |
| 3) | 101.1 | - | Sokhumi | R. Xara Xradio |
| A) | 101.3 | - | Gagra | R. Sputnik relay |
| 3) | 101.7 | - | Gagra | R. Xara Xradio |
| 4) | 101.9 | - | Sokhumi | R. Rio Rita |
| 4) | 102.2 | - | Gagra | R. Rio Rita |
| A) | 102.5 | - | Sokhumi | R. Sputnik relay |
| A) | 103.2 | - | Sokhumi | R. Sputnik relay |
| 2) | 103.6 | - | Gagra | Pervoye R. |
| A) | 105.4 | - | Gagauta | R. Sputnik relay |
| 1) | 106.1 | - | Tkvarcheli | R. Soma |
| 2) | 106.5 | - | Sokhumi | Pervoye R. |
| 1) | 107.9 | 0.3 | Sokhumi | R. Soma |

**Addresses & other information:**
**1)** Zvanba St. 9, Sokhumi **E:** info@radiosoma.com – **2)** Rel. Pervoye R. (Russia) – **3)** pr. Leona 17, Sokhumi **E:** reklama.sukhum@gmail.com – **4)** Sokhumi – **A)** Rel. R. Sputnik (Russia).

## SOUTH OSSETIA
(Self-proclaimed "Republic of South Ossetia")

### GTRK "IR" (Gov*)
(* Run by the administration of the "Republic of South Ossetia")
Geroev St. 37, Tskhinvali, South Ossetia (mail: via Russia) ☎ +7 929 8066070 **E:** radio-ir@yandex.ru **W:** 102-3fm.ru

**L.P:** Dir (Radio): Alan Yskhovrebov
**FM:** Tskhinvali 102.3MHz.
**D.Prgr: R. Ir-FM** in Russian, Ossetic: 24h.

### OTHER STATIONS

| FM | MHz | kW | Location | Station |
|---|---|---|---|---|
| 3) | 104.1 | - | Tskhinvali | R. City |
| B) | 104.5 | - | Kaysa | Vesti FM relay |
| 1) | 105.9 | - | Tskhinvali | Volna FM |
| A) | 106.3 | - | Tskhinvali | R. Sputnik relay |
| 2) | 107.3 | - | Tskhinvali | R. Yuzhnyy gorod |

**Addresses & other information:**
**1)** Tskhinvali – **2)** Geroev St. 1, Tskhinvali **E:** info@yugfm.ru – **2)** Tskhinvali. Incl. rel. R. Sputnik (Russia) – **A)** Rel. R. Sputnik (Russia) – **B)** Rel. Vesti FM (Russia)

## GERMANY

**L.T:** UTC +1h (31 Mar-27 Oct: +2h) — **Pop:** 83 million — **Pr.L:** German — **E.C:** 50Hz, 230V — **ITU:** D

### BUNDESNETZAGENTUR

✉ Postfach 8001, 53105 Bonn (office location: Tulpenfeld 4) ☎ +49 228 14 0 🖷 + 49 228 14 8872 **W:** bnetza.de
**NB:** Broadcasting regulation, except aspects of spectrum use/transmitter operations regulated by Bundesnetzagentur, is in Germany the sole responsibility of the federal states. Some of the public broadcasting institutions shown in section I are common operations by various states. Some states have also agreed a common regulation of the private sector as shown in section II.

### I. PUBLIC STATIONS

### ARBEITSGEMEINSCHAFT DER ÖFFENTLICH-RECHTLICHEN RUNDFUNKANSTALTEN DEUTSCHLANDS (ARD)

Formalised co-operation of institutions B)-J), Deutschlandradio and Deutsche Welle (see International Broadcasting section) are associated members.
**Radio operations under ARD umbrella:** Common overnight prgr. ARD-Hitnacht (2205-0500, oldies, produced by SR), ARD-Popnacht (2305-0400, AC, produced by SWR), Die junge Nacht der ARD (2300-0400/0000-0500, produced by WDR), ARD-Nachtkonzert (2305-0500, classical, produced by BR), ARD-Infonacht (2200-0500, news, produced by MDR). Common summertime evening prgr. ARD-Radiofestival mid July to mid September daily 1900-2300.
**Satellite radio:** Most radio stations of member institutions B)-J) are carried on Astra 1M, 12.266 GHz

### A) DEUTSCHLANDRADIO

Common operation of all federal states
**Cologne seat:** ✉ Raderberggürtel 40, 50968 Köln ☎ +49 221 345 0 🖷 +49 221 345 4803
**Berlin seat:** ✉ Hans-Rosenthal-Platz, 10825 Berlin ☎ +49 30 8503 0 🖷 +49 30 8503 6168 **W:** deutschlandradio.de

| FM (MHz) | DLF | DK | kW |
|---|---|---|---|
| **Baden-Württemberg** | | | |
| Baden-Baden | - | 107.9 | 0.1 |
| Baden-Baden | - | 107.9 | 0.1 |
| Biberach | 100.5 | - | 0.5 |
| Blauen | 105.1 | - | 10 |
| Esslingen | 96.7 | - | 0.1 |
| Freiburg | - | 90.6 | 0.2 |
| Geislingen | - | 87.7 | 0.2 |
| Göppingen | 99.8 | - | 0.1 |
| Heidelberg | 106.5 | - | 0.4 |
| Heidenheim | 94.0 | 100.8 | 0.1 |
| Heilbronn | 91.3 | 97.3 | 0.1 |
| Hornisgrinde | 106.3 | - | 80 |
| Kirchheim | 91.3 | - | 0.1 |
| Konstanz | - | 94.5 | 0.2 |
| Lörrach | - | 95.0 | 0.1 |
| Ludwigsburg | 94.1 | 97.3 | 0.5/0.1 |
| Pforzheim | 89.2 | 95.2 | 0.1/0.5 |
| Rottweil | 106.0 | - | 0.1 |
| Schwäb. Hall | 95.8 | - | 0.1 |
| Schw. Gmünd | - | 95.9 | 0.2 |
| Stuttgart | 96.0 | 87.9 | 0.5/1 |
| Tübingen | 93.9 | 99.4 | 0.5/1 |
| Ulm | 103.5 | 91.5 | 0.5/1 |

| FM (MHz) | DLF | DK | kW |
|---|---|---|---|
| Witthoh | 100.6 | - | 40 |
| Wörth | - | 96.6 | 0.2 |
| **Bayern** | | | |
| Amberg | - | 107.9 | 0.1 |
| Ansbach | 92.7 | 102.7 | 0.2 |
| Aschaffenbg. | - | 94.8 | 0.1 |
| Augsburg | 97.8 | 100.0 | 0.3/15 |
| B. Reichenhall | - | 92.6 | 0.1 |
| Bad Tölz | 87.8 | 93.2 | 0.1 |
| Berchtesgd. | 91.6 | 103.4 | 0.1 |
| Brotjacklrieg. | 100.1 | - | 100 |
| Burgbernhm. | 106.3 | 94.3 | 0.2/0.3 |
| Burglengenf. | - | 107.3 | 0.1 |
| Cham | - | 101.4 | 0.1 |
| Freilassing | 100.3 | - | 15 |
| Füssen | 87.6 | 103.4 | 0.1 |
| Hof Waldst. | - | 89.3 | 20 |
| Hohe Linie | - | 101.3 | 0.2 |
| Hohenpeißbg. | 94.7 | - | 0.1 |
| Ingolstadt | 107.0 | 88.6 | 0.5 |
| Kaufbeuren | - | 107.3 | 0.1 |
| Kempten | 89.3 | 89.8 | 0.1 |
| Landsberg | 90.3 | 107.9 | 0.1 |
| Landshut | 95.9 | 100.5 | 0.2 |

| FM (MHz) | DLF | DK | kW |
|---|---|---|---|
| München | 101.7 | 96.8 | 0.3 |
| Nürnberg | 90.1 | 105.6 | 0.1 |
| Oberstdorf | 92.0 | 96.5 | 0.1 |
| Ochsenkopf | 100.3 | - | 100 |
| Passau | - | 97.7 | 0.5 |
| Pfronten | 96.5 | - | 0.02 |
| Regensburg | 95.5 | 101.3 | 0.2 |
| Rhön | 103.3 | - | 100 |
| Rosenheim | 97.2 | 96.2 | 0.1 |
| Rosenh.-D'bg. | 97.7 | - | 0.1 |
| Starnberg | 87.9 | 94.7 | 0.1 |
| Straubing | - | 88.7 | 0.4 |
| Traunstein | - | 88.3 | 0.1 |
| Weiden | - | 103.7 | 0.1 |
| Weilheim | 94.7 | - | 0.05 |
| Würzburg | 100.3 | 101.3 | 0.1 |
| **Berlin & Brandenburg** | | | |
| Berlin A'platz | 97.7 | 89.6 | 100 |
| Calau | - | 90.8 | 20 |
| Casekow | 105.2 | - | 6 |
| Cottbus | 88.6 | - | 3 |
| Eisenhütt.st. | 100.2 | - | 1 |
| Frankfurt (Bo.) | 97.3 | 92.7 | 0.5/5 |
| Herzberg/Els. | 94.5 | - | 0.3 |
| Rhinow | - | 103.7 | 0.2 |
| **Bremen** | | | |
| Bremen | 107.1 | 100.3 | 100/1 |
| Bremerhaven | 103.4 | 106.2 | 0.5/5 |
| **Hamburg** | | | |
| Hamburg | 88.7 | 89.1 | 3/0.1 |
| **Hessen** | | | |
| Darmstadt | - | 98.2 | 0.3 |
| Eschwege | 100.6 | - | 0.5 |
| Feldberg | 98.7 | - | 60 |
| Frankfurt/M. | - | 91.2 | 0.3 |
| Fritzlar | - | 96.0 | 0.1 |
| Fulda | - | 90.7 | 0.3 |
| Gießen | - | 107.5 | 0.3 |
| Hanau | - | 107.7 | 0.3 |
| Heusenstamm | - | 99.8 | 0.2 |
| Hofgeismar | 106.9 | - | 0.3 |
| Kassel | 92.7 | - | 0.1 |
| Korbach | 92.8 | - | 0.1 |
| Limburg | - | 105.1 | 0.3 |
| Mainz-Kastel | - | 107.2 | 0.4 |
| Marburg | - | 93.3 | 0.1 |
| Michelstadt | 100.5 | 107.2 | 0.2 |
| Oberursel | - | 101.8 | 0.1 |
| Rimberg | 91.3 | - | 50 |
| Wetzlar | - | 97.3 | 0.3 |
| **Mecklenburg-Vorpommern** | | | |
| Anklam | 107.4 | - | 1 |
| Barth | 100.3 | - | 0.1 |
| Dargun | 89.8 | - | 0.5 |
| Demmin | 89.8 | 106.2 | 1/0.5 |
| Greifswald | 104.3 | 96.9 | 0.2 |
| Güstrow | 106.0 | - | 0.8 |
| Helpterberg | 96.5 | 97.1 | 10/30 |
| Heringsdorf | 98.4 | 107.1 | 0.5 |
| Neukloster | 90.6 | - | 0.3 |
| Neustrelitz | 97.9 | - | 1 |
| Ribn.-Damg. | 102.1 | - | 0.2 |
| Röbel | 102.4 | 90.0 | 3 |
| Rostock | 97.3 | 96.7 | 5/40 |
| Sassnitz | 104.0 | 101.4 | 8 |
| Schwerin | 106.3 | 95.3 | 2/100 |
| Stralsund | 89.3 | 92.1 | 0.4 |
| Waren/Mü. | 91.3 | - | 0.2 |
| **Niedersachsen** | | | |
| Aurich | 101.8 | 106.9 | 100/1 |
| Cloppenbg. | - | 95.5 | 0.1 |
| Cuxhaven | 101.6 | 107.7 | 2/20 |
| Damme | 95.4 | 97.5 | 0.3 |
| Emden | - | 93.4 | 1 |
| Göttingen | 101.0 | - | 0.1 |
| Hannover | 94.0 | - | 0.1 |
| Hann. Münd. | 98.5 | - | 0.5 |
| Höhbeck | 102.2 | - | 100 |
| Jever | - | 89.0 | 0.5 |
| Leer | - | 91.5 | 0.5 |

| FM (MHz) | DLF | DK | kW |
|---|---|---|---|
| Lingen | 102.0 | | 25 |
| | | 91.6* | 0.4 |
| | | 102.9* | 0.3 |
| Lübbecke | - | 97.7 | 0.2 |
| Lüneburg | - | 97.9 | 0.5 |
| Meppen | - | 100.7 | 0.3 |
| Norden | - | 105.3 | 0.3 |
| Nordhorn | - | 97.1 | 0.2 |
| Oldenburg | - | 102.8 | 0.1 |
| Osnabrück | 101.8 | - | 0.5 |
| Seesen | 88.0 | - | 0.1 |
| Soltau | 89.3 | - | 0.1 |
| Stadthagen | 106.1 | - | 1 |
| Tecklenburg | - | 101.1 | 0.5 |
| Torfh./Harz | 103.5 | - | 100 |
| Uelzen | 107.5 | 97.1 | 0.5/0.2 |
| Visselhövede | - | 88.8 | 1 |
| Warendorf | 107.2 | - | 1 |
| **Nordrhein-Westfalen** | | | |
| Aachen | 102.7 | - | 0.5 |
| B. Oeynhsn. | 93.9 | - | 0.1 |
| Beckum | 91.5 | - | 0.2 |
| Bielefeld | 95.5 | 106.2 | 0.1 |
| Bonn | 89.1 | 98.9 | 5/0.1 |
| Eifel-Bärbelk. | - | 106.1 | 20 |
| Gronau | - | 94.6 | 0.2 |
| Kleve | - | 90.1 | 1 |
| Köln | 91.3 | - | 0.1 |
| Langenberg | - | 96.5 | 35 |
| Lemgo | 92.2 | 88.9 | 0.3 |
| Lennestadt | - | 96.9 | 0.1 |
| Lübbecke | - | 97.7 | 0.2 |
| Münster | 104.5 | 97.5 | 0.3/0.1 |
| Nordhelle | 102.7 | - | 20 |
| Olpe | - | 96.3 | 0.1 |
| Olsberg | - | 106.1 | 10 |
| Paderborn | 94.5 | - | 0.2 |
| Schwerte | 104.4 | - | 0.2 |
| Siegen | 94.2 | 100.2 | 0.1 |
| Stadthagen | 106.1 | - | 1 |
| Steinfurt | - | 91.0 | 0.2 |
| Tecklenburg | - | 101.1 | 0.5 |
| Warendorf | 107.2 | - | 1 |
| Warburg | 106.6 | - | 0.2 |
| Wesel | 102.8 | - | 50 |
| Wuppertal | 90.0 | - | 0.3 |
| **Rheinland-Pfalz** | | | |
| B. Kreuznach | 106.5 | - | 0.1 |
| Bingen | - | 106.3 | 0.2 |
| Bitburg | - | 95.3 | 0.1 |
| Boppard | 90.5 | 88.9 | 0.1 |
| Idar-Oberst. | 89.5 | 94.7 | 0.2 |
| Kaiserslaut. | 105.1 | 98.1 | 0.2 |
| Koblenz | 99.8 | 105.3 | 0.5 |
| Limburg | 103.3 | 105.1 | 0.3 |
| Linz | - | 98.3 | 0.1 |
| Lorch | 88.1 | - | 0.1 |
| Ludwigshafen | - | 97.3 | 0.1 |
| Mayen | 100.8 | - | 0.2 |
| Pirmasens | 106.1 | 94.4 | 0.4 |
| Prüm | 95.4 | - | 0.1 |
| Saarburg | 104.6 | 105.3 | 20/0.1 |
| Traben-Trarb. | 88.7 | 106.2 | 0.3 |
| Trier | - | 94.3 | 0.2 |
| Wörth | - | 96.6 | 0.2 |
| **Saarland** | | | |
| Lebach | - | 107.9 | 0.1 |
| Neunkirchen | - | 105.0 | 1 |
| Oberperl | - | 106.2 | 1 |
| Saarbrücken | 90.1 | 107.5 | 1/0.4 |
| Saarlouis | - | 96.3 | 0.1 |
| Völklingen | - | 88.6 | 0.1 |
| **Sachsen** | | | |
| Bad Düben | - | 99.4 | 0.2 |
| Bärenstein | - | 104.3 | 1 |
| Belgern | - | 101.1 | 1 |
| Chemnitz | - | 106.3 | 0.3 |
| Collmberg | - | 96.1 | 0.3 |
| Döbeln | - | 101.3 | 1 |
| Dresden | 97.3 | 93.2 | 100/1 |

| FM (MHz) | DLF | DK | kW | | FM (MHz) | DLF | DK | kW |
|---|---|---|---|---|---|---|---|---|
| Eilenburg | – | 92.0 | 0.2 | | Itzehoe | 102.2 | 97.5 | 0.4/0.1 |
| Freiberg | – | 100.7 | 1 | | Kaltenkirchen | – | 105.5 | 0.1 |
| Geyer (Erzg.) | 97.0 | – | 100 | | Kiel | – | 104.7 | 0.3 |
| Grimma | – | 91.6 | 0.1 | | Lauenburg | – | 95.8 | 0.1 |
| Hoyerswerda | – | 89.7 | 0.5 | | Neumünster | – | 107.8 | 0.5 |
| Leipzig-Holzh. | – | 100.4 | 2 | | Niebüll | – | 104.2 | 0.3 |
| Löbau | 99.5 | 103.0 | 5/2 | | Rendsburg | – | 95.2 | 0.3 |
| Pulsnitz | – | 106.7 | 0.5 | | Schleswig | – | 105.0 | 0.2 |
| Schöneck | 94.5 | – | 3 | | Sylt | 90.3 | 103.9 | 0.2 |
| Weißwasser | – | 97.7 | 2 | | **Thüringen** | | | |
| Wiederau | 96.6 | – | 100 | | Altenburg | – | 97.3 | 0.4 |
| Zwickau | – | 104.6 | 0.2 | | Bleßberg | – | 94.2 | 100 |
| **Sachsen-Anhalt** | | | | | Eisenach | 106.5 | – | 0.5 |
| Brocken/Harz | – | 97.4 | 100 | | Erfurt | 103.1 | – | 2 |
| Dessau | 107.1 | – | 0.3 | | Gera | 94.3 | 93.6 | 0.3 |
| Dequede | – | 96.9 | 7 | | Gotha | 94.0 | – | 0.1 |
| Eisleben | 103.8 | – | 0.5 | | Ilmenau | 99.9 | – | 0.1 |
| Schönebeck | 102.0 | – | 20 | | Inselsberg | – | 97.2 | 100 |
| Wittenberg | 89.3 | 107.7 | 1/0.5 | | Jena | 104.5 | 98.2 | 0.3 |
| Zeitz | – | 91.8 | 0.5 | | Mühlhausen | 107.0 | – | 1 |
| **Schleswig-Holstein** | | | | | Nordhausen | 96.4 | – | 0.1 |
| Bungsberg | 101.9 | 103.1 | 95/0.2 | | Pößneck | 89.2 | – | 0.1 |
| Flensburg | 93.3 | 92.1 | 20/0.2 | | Saalfeld | 98.7 | – | 0.1 |
| Garding | 102.3 | 101.7 | 0.5 | | Sondershaus. | 101.9 | – | 0.1 |
| Güby | – | 105.0 | 0.2 | | Suhl | 98.8 | – | 0.1 |
| Heide | 104.4 | 92.2 | 1/0.1 | | Weimar | 89.7 | – | 0.5 |
| Husum | – | 101.0 | 0.1 | | | | | |

*) directional with different beams
**F.P.I.:** Closing down low power txs with limited reach.
**DAB:** See section II.
**Satellite:** Astra 1N, 11.954GHz h (operated by ZDF, see TV section).
**D.Prgr: Deutschlandfunk** from Köln studios, full sce. with strong emphasis on information – **Deutschlandfunk Kultur** from Berlin studios, culture, during daytime music format Alternative – **Deutschlandfunk Nova**, from Köln studios, for young audiences – **Dokumente & Debatten**, parliament coverage, audio of TV talkshows and other special prgrs.

## B) BAYERISCHER RUNDFUNK (BR)
Public broadcasting institution of Bayern
📧 Bayerischer Rundfunk, 80300 München (location of radio operations: Rundfunkplatz 1) ☎ +49 89 5900 01 🖷 +49 89 5900 2375 **W:** br-online.de

| FM (MHz) | B1 | B2 | B3 | BR K | B5 | kW |
|---|---|---|---|---|---|---|
| Augsburg | – | – | – | – | 105.3 | 0.5 |
| Bad Reichenhall | 91.8 | 89.9 | 96.7 | 98.3 | 105.0 | 0.3 |
| Bamberg | 94.8N | 98.6 | 99.8 | 102.9 | 97.4 | 25/5 |
| Berchtesgaden | 90.4 | 94.6 | 96.9 | 94.2 | 106.4 | 0.3/0.1 |
| Brotjacklriegel | 92.1R | 96.5 | 94.4 | 100.9 | 106.9 | 100/50 |
| Büttelberg | 91.4N | 88.2 | 99.3 | 95.5 | 104.0 | 25/10 |
| Coburg | 93.5N | 88.3 | 99.2 | 97.7 | 92.8 | 5/0.3 |
| Dillberg | 88.9N | 92.3 | 97.9 | 87.6 | 102.0 | 25 |
| | 104.5R | | | | | 5 |
| Eichstätt | 101.6 | 90.5 | 97.6 | 89.0 | 106.1 | 25/10 |
| Garmisch-Partenk. | 89.2 | 93.5 | 97.7 | 95.9 | 104.9 | 0.1 |
| Grünten (Allgäu) | 90.7U | 88.7 | 95.8 | 101.0 | 106.9 | 50/100 |
| Herzogstand | 88.1 | 97.0 | 91.0 | – | 106.7 | 0.1 |
| Hochberg-Traunst. | 98.0 | 91.5 | 95.9 | 97.0 | 107.1 | 5/0.5 |
| Hohenpeißenberg | 92.8 | 94.2 | 99.2 | 100.4 | – | 25 |
| Hoher Bogen | 96.8R | 91.6 | 94.7 | 88.3 | 104.4 | 50/5 |
| Hühnerberg | 91.9U | 96.1 | 99.5 | 93.1 | 107.5 | 25/11 |
| Kreuzberg (Rhön) | 98.3W | 93.1 | 96.3 | 107.9 | 105.3 | 100/50 |
| Landshut | 90.2R | 97.8 | 95.3 | 93.2 | 106.6 | 0.1 |
| Lindau | 88.1U | 92.0 | 94.0 | 87.6 | 100.4 | 0.5/0.1 |
| München-Ismaning | 91.3 | 88.4 | 97.3 | 103.2 | 90.0 | 25 |
| Ochsenkopf | 90.7N | 96.0 | 99.4 | 102.3 | 107.1 | 100/50 |
| | 91.2R | | | | | 20 |
| Passau | 87.7R | 93.2 | 90.4 | 95.6 | 105.9 | 0.5/0.3 |
| Pfaffenberg | 95.6W | 88.4 | 93.4 | 98.0 | 106.4 | 25/1 |
| Regensburg | 95.0R | 93.0 | 99.6 | 97.0 | 105.0 | 25/5 |
| Untersb. Geiereck*) | 87.8 | 92.9 | 96.1 | 100.7 | – | 0.1 |
| Wallberg | 94.0 | 87.7 | 99.7 | 97.9 | 101.8 | 0.1 |
| Wendelstein | 93.7 | 89.5 | 98.5 | 102.3 | 105.7 | 100 |
| Würzburg | 90.9W | 90.0 | 97.6 | 89.0 | 105.7 | 5/0.2 |

*) site in Austria
**DAB:** See L).
**D.Prgr: Bayern 1**, oldies, rel. ARD-Hitnacht, Mon-Fri 1105-1200 and 1805-1855 regional prgr. from Nürnberg (N), Regensburg (R), Würzburg (W) and Ulm (U) – **Bayern 2**, various prgr., rel. ARD-Nachtkonzert – **Bayern 3**, AC, 24h – **BR Klassik**, classical music, 24h – **B5 aktuell,**

news, on FM mono signal, rel. ARD-Infonacht – **Bayern Plus**, German "Schlager" music, 24h – **BR Heimat**, German/Bavarian folk music, 24h – **BR Puls**, for young listeners, 24h – **B5 Plus**, coverage of parliament, sports and other special prgr. – **BR Verkehr**, traffic announcements

## C) HESSISCHER RUNDFUNK (HR)
Public broadcasting institution of Hessen
📧 60222 Frankfurt am Main (office and studio location: Bertramstraße 8) ☎ +49 69 155 1 🖷 +49 69 155 2900 **W:** hr-online.de

| FM (MHz) | hr1 | hr2 | hr3 | hr4 | kW |
|---|---|---|---|---|---|
| Alsfeld-Homberg | – | – | 105.6 | – | 0.1 |
| Bad Hersfeld | 88.9 | – | 102.9 | – | 0.3 |
| Bingen | – | – | 91.1 | – | 0.3 |
| Feldberg (Taunus) | 94.4 | 96.7 | 89.3 | 102.5R | 100 |
| Frankfurt (HR headq.) | – | 87.9 | – | – | 0.1 |
| Fulda | – | 106.6 | 88.5 | 103.9N | 0.3 |
| Habichtswald | – | – | 101.2 | 103.2N | 20 |
| Hardberg (Odenw.) | 90.6 | – | 92.7 | 101.6R | 50 |
| Heidelstein (Rhön) | 104.8 | – | 106.2 | 107.3N | 50 |
| Hoher Meißner | 99.0 | 95.5 | 89.5 | 101.7N | 100 |
| Kassel | 94.3 | 93.7 | – | – | 0.5 |
| Limburg | – | 100.8 | – | 97.1M | 0.3/0.2 |
| Marburg | – | – | – | 102.8M | 1 |
| Rimberg | – | – | – | 91.9N | 50/20 |
| Rotenburg | – | – | 105.7 | – | 0.3 |
| Sackpfeife | 91.0 | – | 87.6 | 104.3M | 100 |
| Schlüchtern | – | – | 88.9 | – | 0.3 |
| Weilburg | – | – | – | 97.9M | 0.1 |
| Wetzlar | – | – | – | 90.5M | 0.3 |
| Wiesbaden | 98.3 | 93.1 | – | – | 0.1 |
| Würzberg (Odenw.) | 88.1 | 97.4 | 89.7 | 103.8R | 5 |

| FM (MHz) | You FM | hr-info | kW |
|---|---|---|---|
| Alsfeld | – | 104.0 | 0.1 |
| Bad Hersfeld | – | 106.9 | 0.3 |
| Bad Nauheim | – | 88.9 | 0.3 |
| Bad Orb | – | 89.8 | 0.3 |
| Bensheim | 90.2 | 91.2 | 0.2/0.1 |
| Bingen | 92.3 | – | 0.3 |
| Darmstadt | 104.3 | 107.0 | 0.8/5 |
| Eltville | 96.2 | – | 0.5 |
| Eschwege | 106.6 | – | 0.1 |
| Frankfurt/Main | 90.4 | 103.9 | 0.5 |
| Friedberg | 94.0 | 92.1 | 0.3 |
| Fritzlar | – | 106.6 | 0.1 |
| Fulda | 93.6 | 89.7 | 0.3/0.2 |
| Gelnhausen | 99.4 | – | 0.3 |
| Gießen | 97.9 | 99.2 | 0.5/0.3 |
| Hardberg | 95.3 | – | 50 |
| Herborn | 103.4 | – | 0.5 |
| Kassel-Wilhelmsh. | 100.1 | 107.5 | 0.5/1 |
| Korbach | 91.6 | 102.6 | 0.5/1 |
| Limburg | 90.7 | 99.2 | 0.2/0.3 |
| Marburg | 93.9 | 98.5 | 1/0.3 |
| Michelstadt | 91.0 | – | 0.2 |
| Reinhardshain | – | 92.9 | 0.2 |
| Rimberg | 97.7 | 95.0 | 50 |
| Rotenburg | – | 96.8 | 0.3 |
| Sackpfeife | 102.3 | 99.6 | 10/100 |
| Schlüchtern | 88.2 | 91.5 | 0.3 |
| Seeheim | – | 88.2 | 0.1 |
| Sontra | – | 90.8 | 0.1 |
| Wetzlar | 105.5 | 93.2 | 0.3 |
| Wiesbaden | 99.7 | 97.2 | 0.2/0.1 |
| Witzenhausen | 91.1 | – | 0.3 |

**DAB:** 6 txs on ch. 7B.
**D.Prgr: hr1**, oldies, rel. ARD-Popnacht – **hr2**, culture and classical music, rel. ARD-Nachtkonzert, ARD-Radiofestival – **hr3**, AC, rel. ARD-Popnacht – **hr4**, produced at Kassel (Wilhelmshöher Allee 347, 34131 Kassel), light music format, rel. ARD-Hitnacht, regional news Nordhessen (N; Kassel/Fulda), Mittelhessen (M; Gießen) and Rhein-Main (R; Frankfurt/Darmstadt) – **You FM**, CHR, rel. Die junge Nacht – **hr-info**, news, rel. ARD-Infonacht with own insertions.

## D) MITTELDEUTSCHER RUNDFUNK (MDR)
Public broadcasting institution of Sachsen, Sachsen-Anhalt and Thüringen. 📧 Kantstraße 71-73, 04360 Leipzig (TV, MDR Aktuell, administration) **W:** mdr.de
📧 Gerberstraße 2, 06110 Halle/Saale ☎ +49 345 300 0 🖷 +49 345 300 5544 (MDR Kultur, MDR Jump, MDR Sputnik)

| FM (MHz) | MDR 1 | Jump | Kult | Akt | Sputnik | kW |
|---|---|---|---|---|---|---|
| **Txs in Sachsen:** | | | | | | |
| Altenburg | – | – | – | 101.5 | – | 1 |
| Annaberg-Buchholz | – | – | – | 91.2 | – | 0.2 |
| Aue | – | – | – | 95.1 | – | 1 |
| Auerbach | – | – | – | 101.7 | – | 0.4 |
| Bautzen | – | 98.8 | – | 87.9 | – | 0.2/0.1 |
| Chemnitz-Reichenh. | – | – | – | 94.7 | – | 0.5 |
| Collmberg | 101.8L | 103.7 | 98.9 | 105.9 | – | 2x5/0.5/30 |
| Döbeln-Mockritz | – | – | – | 99.6 | – | 0.1 |
| Dresden-Wachwitz | 92.2 | 90.1 | 95.4 | 106.1 | – | 3x100/0.5 |
| Eilenburg | – | – | – | 92.4 | – | 0.2 |
| Freiberg | 99.1C | – | – | 93.7 | – | 1/0.2 |
| Freital | – | – | – | 95.9 | – | 0.2 |
| Geyer (Erzgebirge) | 92.8C | 89.8 | 87.7 | – | – | 100 |
| Grimma-Hohnstädt | – | – | – | 100.6 | – | 0.2 |
| Görlitz | – | – | – | 106.9 | – | 1 |
| Hoyerswerda | 93.0B | 89.0 | 94.7 | 94.2 | – | 1/0.5/1/1 |
| | 100.4 | | | | | 30 |
| Kamenz | – | – | – | 93.9 | – | 1 |
| Klingenthal | 93.7C | – | 98.4 | – | – | 0.2 |
| Leipzig city | – | – | – | 95.6 | – | 0.5 |
| Löbau | 98.2B | 91.8 | 96.2 | – | – | 5 |
| Markneukirchen | 104.8C | – | 106.4 | – | – | 0.5 |
| Meißen-Korbitz | – | – | – | 94.9 | – | 1 |
| Neustadt | – | – | – | 89.6 | – | 0.2 |
| Plauen | – | – | – | 102.0 | – | 1 |
| Raschau | – | – | – | 91.6 | – | 0.2 |
| Seifhennersdorf | 94.5B | 96.9 | 103.4 | – | – | 0.25/0.3 |
| Schöneck | 88.7C | 101.2 | 98.7 | – | – | 3/30/3 |
| Stollberg | – | – | – | 89.3 | – | 0.1 |
| Torgau | 88.9L | – | 93.0 | – | – | 0.5/0.2 |
| Weißwasser | – | – | – | 90.5 | – | 1 |
| Wiederau (Leipzig) | 93.9L | 90.4 | 88.4 | – | – | 100 |
| | 106.5H | | | | | *30 |
| Zittau | 87.7B | 107.1 | 95.4 | 106.4 | – | 0.2/0.5 |
| Zschopau | – | – | – | 99.5 | – | 0.2 |
| Zwickau | – | – | – | 91.4 | – | 1 |
| **Txs in Sachsen-Anhalt:** | | | | | | |
| Aschersleben | – | – | – | 102.8 | – | 1 |
| Brocken | 94.6 | 91.5 | 107.8 | – | – | 60/100/10 |
| Burg | – | – | – | 89.6 | – | 1 |
| Dequede | 94.9St | 98.9 | 89.4 | – | – | 10 |
| Dessau-Mildensee | – | – | – | 90.0 | – | 0.3 |
| Fleetmark | – | – | – | 90.1 | 105.0 | 2/1 |
| Gernrode | – | – | – | 91.0 | – | 0.1 |
| Haidberg | – | – | – | – | 100.7 | 5 |
| Haldensleben | – | – | – | 99.1 | – | 1 |
| Halle Petersberg | 100.8H | – | – | 95.3 | 104.4 | 5/2/10 |
| Halle city | – | 89.6 | 107.3 | – | – | 0.1 |
| Hergisdorf | 92.9H | – | – | – | – | 1 |
| Jerichow | – | – | – | – | 90.5 | 1 |
| Jessen | – | – | – | 87.6 | – | 1 |
| Klötze | – | – | – | – | 100.7 | 5 |
| Köthen | – | – | – | 106.4 | – | 0.3 |
| Magdeburg | 96.1 | – | 107.4 | – | – | 10/30 |
| Naumburg | 92.3H | – | – | – | 93.1 | 1/0.5 |
| Sangerhausen | 101.1H | – | 99.9 | – | – | 0.1/1 |
| Schneidlingen | – | – | – | 106.7 | – | 0.5 |
| Schönebeck | – | – | – | 91.1 | 105.2 | 2/1.5 |
| Stendal-Borstel | – | – | – | 87.8 | 104.8 | 1 |
| Weißenfels | – | – | – | 88.8 | – | 1 |
| Wernigerode | – | – | – | 98.6 | – | 1 |
| Wittenberg | 88.1D | 101.6 | 104.0 | – | – | 30/2x55 |
| Zeitz-Hainichen | – | – | – | – | 89.4 | 0.5 |
| **Txs in Thüringen:** | | | | | | |
| Apolda | – | – | – | 91.2 | – | 1 |
| Arnstadt | – | – | – | 106.1 | – | 0.5 |
| Bad Salzungen | – | – | – | 94.0 | – | 0.1 |
| Bleßberg | 91.7S | 96.9 | – | – | – | 100/20 |
| Eisenach | – | – | – | 100.0 | – | 0.2 |
| Erfurt | 94.4 | – | – | 97.8 | – | 2/1 |
| Gera | – | – | – | 91.1 | – | 1 |
| Gotha | – | – | – | 88.8 | – | 0.1 |
| Greiz | – | – | – | 93.3 | – | 0.2 |
| Heiligenstadt | 93.6He | – | – | 90.5 | – | 0.1 |
| Ilmenau | – | – | – | 93.0 | – | 0.1 |
| Inselsberg | 92.5 | 90.2 | 87.9 | – | – | 100/100/60 |
| Jena-Oßmaritz | 88.2B | 101.9 | 96.4 | 89.5 | – | 1/0.2 |
| Keula | 98.5He | – | – | – | – | 20 |
| Lobenstein | 95.5G | – | – | 101.8 | – | 2/0.5 |
| Magdala | 92.9 | – | – | 99.2 | – | 0.01/0.05 |
| Meiningen | – | – | – | 94.7 | – | 0.2 |

| FM (MHz) | MDR 1 | Jump | Kult | Akt | Sputnik | kW |
|---|---|---|---|---|---|---|
| Mühlhausen | – | – | – | 105.8 | – | 0.1 |
| Nordhausen | 88.3He | – | – | 93.7 | – | 0.1 |
| Pößneck | – | – | – | 101.6 | – | 0.2 |
| Remda | 103.6 | 105.6 | 100.7 | – | – | 60 |
| Ronneburg | 97.8G | 100.9 | 103.9 | – | – | 10/30/30 |
| Saalfeld | – | – | – | 104.6 | – | 0.1 |
| Schleiz | – | – | – | 105.1 | – | 0.2 |
| Schmalkalden | – | – | – | 100.0 | – | 0.1 |
| Schmölln | – | – | – | 107.9 | – | 0.2 |
| Sondershausen | 100.1He | – | – | 95.1 | – | 0.05/0.1 |
| Sonneberg | – | – | – | 105.8 | – | 0.1 |
| Suhl Erleshügel | 93.7S | 91.1 | 89.8 | 97.5 | – | 1/0.1/0.2/5 |
| Weimar Ettersberg | 93.3 | – | – | – | – | 5 |
| Weimar Belvedere | – | – | – | 102.6 | – | 2 |

*) Directional, to north and west only

**DAB:** 6 txs in Sachsen-Anhalt on ch. 6B, 7 txs in Thüringen on ch. 8B, 7 txs in Sachsen on ch. 9A. Carry central prgr. plus respective MDR 1 stn. in all regional versions.

**D.Prgr: MDR 1 Radio Sachsen**, Königsbrücker Str. 88, 01099 Dresden, regional prgr. from studios Bautzen (freq. marked (B), Chemnitz (C) and Leipzig (L); **MDR Sachsen-Anhalt**, Stadtparkstr. 8, 39114 Magdeburg, regional prgr. Dessau (D), Halle (H) and Stendal (St); **MDR Thüringen**, Gothaer Str. 36, 99094 Erfurt; regional prgr. Gera (G), Heiligenstadt (He) and Suhl (S). 2200-0400 on all MDR 1 stns common prgr. – **MDR Jump**, AC – **MDR Kultur**, culture, rel. ARD-Nachtkonzert, ARD-Radiofestival – **MDR Aktuell**, news – **MDR Sputnik**, CHR, rel. Die junge Nacht – **MDR Klassik**, classical music, at times rel. **MDR Kultur** – **MDR Schlagerwelt**, German "Schlager" music – **Serbske Rozhlas**, Am Postplatz 2, 02607 Bautzen. Prgr. in Upper Sorbian on 100.4MHz Mon-Fri 0405-0700, Sat 0505-0800, Sun 1000-1130. Radio Satkula for young listeners Mon 1900-2100. Also rel. Bramborske Serbske Radio, see G).

## E) NORDDEUTSCHER RUNDFUNK (NDR)

Public broadcasting institution of Hamburg, Mecklenburg-Vorpommern, Niedersachsen and Schleswig-Holstein
✉ Rothenbaumchaussee 132, 20149 Hamburg ☎ +49 40 4156 0 🖷 +49 40 447 602 **W:** ndr.de

| FM (MHz) | NDR 1 | NDR 2 | NDR-K | Info | N-Joy | kW |
|---|---|---|---|---|---|---|
| **Txs in Hamburg:** | | | | | | |
| Moorfleet | 90.3 | 87.6 | 99.2 | 92.3 | 94.2 | 80/5/1 |
| | 89.5No | | | | | 10 |
| **Txs in Mecklenburg-Vorpommern:** | | | | | | |
| Anklam | 94.6Gr | – | – | – | 103.0 | 6.3/1.25 |
| Bad Doberan | 94.3R | – | – | – | 103.7 | 0.2/5 |
| Barth | 87.6Gr | – | – | – | 95.0 | 0.4/0.3 |
| Demmin | 97.6N | 92.5 | 91.8 | 101.5 | 95.1 | 0.1/1 |
| Dömitz | 88.3 | – | – | – | – | 1 |
| Garz/Rügen | 102.5Gr | 99.8 | 91.5 | 88.6 | 95.5 | 50/10 |
| Greifswald | 101.0Gr | – | – | – | – | 0.16 |
| Grevesmühlen | 100.7W | – | – | – | 103.4 | 0.5/5 |
| Güstrow-Strentz | 92.5R | – | – | – | 104.4 | 1.25/0.63 |
| Helpterberg | 90.5N | 99.1 | 96.0 | 101.8 | 103.2 | 100/1.25 |
| | 94.2Gr | | | | | 6.3 |
| Heringsdorf | 97.6Gr | 94.0 | 102.7 | 100.5 | 92.3 | 1 |
| Malchin | – | – | – | 103.5 | 94.4 | 1 |
| Neubrandenburg | – | – | – | – | 89.5 | 1 |
| Pasewalk | 93.7Gr | – | – | – | 94.8 | 2.5/1.25 |
| Ribnitz-Damgarten | – | – | – | – | 99.4 | 0.3 |
| Röbel | 88.5N | 107.0 | 94.7 | 100.4 | 97.4 | 10/60/4 |
| Rostock | 91.0R | 93.5 | 88.2 | 102.8 | 88.9 | 160/40/5 |
| Schwerin | 92.8 | 98.5 | 89.2 | 105.3 | 99.5 | 30/100/2 |
| Stralsund | 92.1Gr | – | – | – | – | 4 |
| Ueckermünde | 90.1Gr | – | – | – | 104.1 | 4/1.5 |
| Wismar | 96.2W | – | – | – | – | 0.2 |
| Wolgast-Moeckow | 89.0Gr | – | – | – | 93.2 | 0.4/0.3 |
| **Txs in and for Niedersachsen:** | | | | | | |
| Alfeld | 87.8B | 93.6 | 96.5 | 91.1 | 92.9 | 0.05 |
| Aurich-Popens | 95.8OI | 98.1 | 90.0 | 96.4 | 92.7 | 25/10/1 |
| Bad Pyrmont | 88.6 | 92.6 | 95.7 | 98.5 | – | 0.05 |
| Bad Rothenfelde | – | – | – | 97.9 | 91.2 | 0.2/0.1 |
| Braunlage | – | – | – | – | 96.1 | 0.02 |
| Braunschweig | – | – | – | – | 93.0 | 40 |
| Bremen-Walle | – | – | 95.0 | – | – | 1 |
| Bremerhaven | – | – | 98.9 | 92.8 | – | 0.5/0.05 |
| Cloppenburg | – | – | 103.7 | 93.5 | – | 1 |
| Cuxhaven | 105.4OI | 97.9 | 94.6 | 93.1 | 91.6 | 20/10/1/10 |
| | 98.4 | | | | | 1 |
| Damme | – | – | 106.5 | 105.0 | – | 0.5/1 |
| Dannenberg | 91.2L | 96.4 | 93.3 | 90.7 | 94.0 | 25/10/3/1 |
| Goslar | 88.2B | 93.7 | 95.1 | 96.0 | 96.5 | 0.1 |

| FM (MHz) | NDR 1 | NDR 2 | NDR-K | Info | N-Joy | kW |
|---|---|---|---|---|---|---|
| Göttingen | 88.5B | 94.1 | 96.8 | 99.9 | 95.9 | 5/0.5/5/0.5 |
| Hann. Münden | 88.2B | 96.1 | 90.8 | 92.9 | 94.8 | 0.05 |
| Hannover-Hemm. | 90.9 | 96.2 | 98.7 | 88.6 | 92.6 | 15/5/15/0.5/25 |
| Hildesheim | – | – | – | – | 95.7 | 0.5 |
| Holzminden | 92.7B | 96.0 | 98.4 | 88.6 | 99.7 | 0.5/0.1 |
| Jever | – | – | – | – | 97.3 | 0.3 |
| Königslutter-Elm | – | – | – | 88.7 | – | 0.2 |
| Lingen | 92.8O | 97.8 | 90.2 | 88.9 | 96.6 | 15/0.2/0.5 |
| Meppen | – | – | – | – | 93.3 | 0.05 |
| Osnabrück | 92.4O | 89.2 | 98.8 | 87.6 | 96.4 | 8/2x0.2 |
| Rinteln | – | – | – | 95.3 | 105.2 | 0.1/0.04 |
| Rosengarten | 103.2L | – | – | – | 91.4 | 20/0.3 |
| Seesen | – | – | – | 90.4 | 96.6 | 0.2/0.05 |
| Stadthagen | 100.8 | 102.6 | 104.4 | 98.2 | 91.3 | 25/1 |
| Steinkimmen | 91.10I | 99.8 | 94.4 | 98.6 | 92.9 | 100/3/1 |
| Torfhaus | 98.0B | 92.1 | 89.9 | 99.5 | – | 100/50 |
| Visselhövede | 91.8L | 95.9 | 87.8 | 98.4 | 97.6 | 5/2/5/1/30 |
| Wedel | – | – | – | – | 95.6 | 0.2 |
| Wolfsburg | – | – | – | 88.2 | – | 0.1 |

**Txs in Schleswig-Holstein:**

| FM (MHz) | NDR 1 | NDR 2 | NDR-K | Info | N-Joy | kW |
|---|---|---|---|---|---|---|
| Bungsberg | 97.8Lb | 91.9 | 89.9 | 96.6 | 99.0 | 50/1/0.5 |
| Flensburg | 89.6F | 93.2 | 96.1 | 87.7 | 91.0 | 25/10/0.5 |
| Garding-Katingsiel | – | – | – | – | 88.8 | 0.5 |
| Heide-Welmbüttel | 90.5H | 96.3 | 99.4 | 87.9 | 94.9 | 15/0.5 |
| Helgoland island | 88.9H | 93.4 | 97.0 | 92.5 | 91.5 | 0.01 |
| Husum | – | – | – | – | 93.7 | 0.05 |
| Kiel-Kronshagen | 91.3 | 98.3 | 95.7 | 99.7 | 94.5 | 15/1/0.4/15 |
| Lauenburg | 94.7Lb | – | – | 96.8 | 99.8 | 0.3 |
| Lübeck | 93.1Lb | 90.7 | 88.0 | 95.9 | 94.0 | 0.5/0.1/0.5 |
| Mölln | 104.5Lb | – | – | – | 90.9 | 20/0.5 |
| Neumünster | 106.4No | – | – | 90.8 | 98.7 | 20/1/0.5 |
| Niebüll-Süderlügum | – | – | – | – | 91.5 | 0.2 |
| Sylt | 90.9F | 98.7 | 94.3 | 92.7 | 95.6 | 5 |
| Wedel | – | – | – | – | 95.6 | 0.2 |

**DAB:** Visselhövede tx on ch. 6A, Hannover tx on ch. 6D , Hamburg txs on ch. 7A, Kiel tx on ch. 9C, Braunschweig tx on ch. 11B, Steinkimmen tx on ch. 12A, Schwerin tx on ch. 12B

**D.Prgr: NDR 90,3** from Hamburg studios, on 90.3/98.4MHz – **NDR 1 Radio MV**, Schloßgartenallee 61, 19061 Schwerin; via txs in Mecklenburg-Vorpommern, regional prgr. Greifswald (Gr), Neubrandenburg (N), Rostock (R) and Wismar (W, from Schwerin studios) – **NDR 1 Niedersachsen**, Rudolf-von-Bennigsen-Ufer 22, 30169 Hannover; via txs in Niedersachsen, regional prgr. Braunschweig (B), Göttingen (G), Lüneburg area (L, from Hannover studios), Oldenburg (Ol) and Osnabrück (O) – **NDR 1 Welle Nord**, Postfach 34 80, 24033 Kiel (studio location: Eggerstr. 16); via txs in Schleswig-Holstein and 89.5MHz; regional prgr. Flensburg (F), Heide (H), Lübeck (Lb) and Norderstedt (No). 2110-0430 common prgr. on all NDR 1 stns – **NDR 2**, AC – **NDR Kultur**, classical music, rel. ARD-Nachtkonzert, ARD-Radiofestival – **NDR Info**, Mon-Fri 0500-1850 and Sat 0500-1700 news format, other times diverse prgr., at night music specials – **NDR Info Spezial**, special prgr., rel. ARD-Infonacht, Mon-Fri 1500-2000 Cosmo (see J), Sun 0500-0700 NDR 90,3 former Hamburger Hafenkonzert prgr., broadcast since 1929). Sea weather forecasts at 2305 (also via NDR Info FM txs in Mecklenburg-Vorpommern), 0730 and 2105 – **N-Joy**, CHR, rel. Die junge Nacht – **NDR Blue**, alternative – **NDR Plus**, German "Schlager" music

## F) RADIO BREMEN (RB)

Public broadcasting institution of Bremen
✉ Diepenau 10, 28195 Bremen ☎ +49 421 246 0 📠 +49 421 246 1010 **W:** radiobremen.de

| FM (MHz) | Eins | Zwei | Vier | Next | Cosm | kW |
|---|---|---|---|---|---|---|
| Bremen-Walle | 93.8 | 88.3 | 101.2 | 96.7 | 95.6 | 60/4/0.5 |
| Bremerhaven | 89.3 | 95.4 | 100.8 | 92.1 | 94.9 | 25/0.5 |

**DAB:** Bremen-Walle tx on ch. 7B, incl. also Kiraka, see J).

**D.Prgr: Bremen Eins**, oldies, rel. 2305-0400 (Sun to 0500) SWR1 – **Bremen Zwei**, culture, rel. ARD-Nachtkonzert – **Bremen Vier**, AC, rel. ARD-Popnacht – **Bremen Next**, for youth – **Cosmo**, see J)

## G) RUNDFUNK BERLIN-BRANDENBURG (RBB)

Public broadcasting institution of Berlin and Brandenburg, operating from two main seats:
**Potsdam:** ✉Marlene-Dietrich-Allee 20, 14482 Potsdam-Babelsberg ☎ +49 331 731 0 📠 +49 331 731 3571
**Berlin:** ✉14046 Berlin (studio/office location: Masurenallee 8-14) ☎ +49 30 3031 0 📠 +49 30)3015 062 **W:** rbb-online.de

**Txs in Berlin:**

| MHz | kW | Site | Program |
|---|---|---|---|
| 88.8 | 80 | Scholzplatz | R. Berlin |
| 92.4 | 80 | Scholzplatz | Kulturradio |
| 93.1 | 25 | Scholzplatz | Inforadio |
| 95.8 | 100 | Alexanderplatz | radioeins |
| 96.3 | 80 | Scholzplatz | Cosmo |
| 99.7 | 100 | Alexanderplatz | Antenne Brandenburg |
| 102.6 | 20 | Alexanderplatz | Fritz |

**Txs in Brandenburg:**

| FM (MHz) | Ant.B. | Eins | Fritz | Kultur | Info | kW |
|---|---|---|---|---|---|---|
| Belzig-Lütte | 106.2 | 99.3 | 91.9 | 100.2 | – | 100/10 |
| Booßen | 87.6F | 89.1F | 101.5 | 96.8 | 102.0 | 5/30/1,5 |
| Calau | 98.6C | 95.1C | 103.2 | 104.4 | 93.4+ | 100/30 |
| Casekow | 91.1Pr | 106.1 | 100.1 | 104.4 | – | 60/10 |
| Cottbus | – | – | – | – | 99.9 | 1 |
| Guben | 100.9C | – | – | – | – | 6 |
| Lübben | – | – | – | – | 92.4 | 0.4 |
| Perleberg | – | – | – | – | 92.3 | 1 |
| Prenzlau | 99.4Pr | – | – | – | 98.6 | 0.5 |
| Pritzwalk | 106.6Pe | 99.9 | 103.1 | 91.7 | – | 100/10 |
| Wittstock | – | – | – | – | 97.7 | 1.3 |

+) Bramborske Serbske Radio

**DAB:** Berlin txs on ch. 7D, also rel. Bayern 2, BR Klassik (see B), MDR Jump (see D), SWR3 (see I), WDR 2 (see J). Cottbus tx on ch. 10B.
**D.Prgr from Berlin studios: Radio Berlin**, Berlin city prgr., rel. ARD-Popnacht – **Inforadio**, news, rel. ARD-Infonacht with local insertions – **Kulturradio**, classical music, rel. ARD-Nachtkonzert, ARD-Radiofestival
**D.Prgr from Potsdam studios: Antenne Brandenburg**, light music, regional prgr. from studios Perleberg (Pe), Prenzlau (Pr), Frankfurt/Oder (F) and Cottbus (C), 2100-2305 common prgr. with Radio Berlin, rel. ARD-Nachtexpress – **radioeins**, progressive-style rock/pop and information, regional prgr. from Frankfurt/Oder and Cottbus – **Fritz**, youth, rel. Die junge Nacht
**Cosmo:** (see J)
**Bramborske Serbske Radio**: RBB, Studio Cottbus, Berliner Straße 155, 03046 Cottbus. Prgr. in Lower Sorbian Mon-Fri 1100-1200 and repeat at 1800-1900, Sundays and holidays 1130-1300. 93.4MHz otherwise rel. Inforadio and Serbske Rozhlas (see D)

## H) SAARLÄNDISCHER RUNDFUNK (SR)

Public broadcasting institution of Saarland
✉ Funkhaus Halberg, 66100 Saarbrücken ☎ +49 681 602 0 📠 +49 681 602 3874 **W:** sr-online.de

| FM (MHz) | SR 1 | SR 2 | SR 3 | UnserDing | kW |
|---|---|---|---|---|---|
| Bliestal-Webenheim | 92.3 | – | 89.1 | 98.0 | 5 |
| Göttelborner Höhe | 88.0 | 91.3 | 95.5 | 103.7 | 100/20 |
| Homburg | – | 98.6 | – | – | 0.2 |
| Merzig-Hilbringen | 89.3 | 92.1 | 98.0 | – | 0.1 |
| Neunkirchen | – | – | – | – | 5 |
| Oberperl | 91.9 | 88.6 | 96.1 | – | 5 |
| Sankt Wendel | – | – | – | 90.3 | 0.1 |

**DAB:** 5 txs on ch. 9A, also rel. Kiraka (see J), R. Salü (see U)
**D.Prgr: SR 1 Europawelle Saar**, AC, rel. ARD-Popnacht – **SR 2 KulturRadio**, culture, rel. ARD-Nachtkonzert, ARD-Radiofestival – **SR 3 Saarlandwelle**, light music, news in French at 0805 – **Unser Ding**, CHR, at times rel. Das Ding (SWR) – **Antenne Saar**, rel. of SR 2, SWR Info and Radio France Internationale

## I) SÜDWESTRUNDFUNK (SWR)

Public broadc.institution of Baden-Württemberg and Rheinland-Pfalz
✉ 76522 Baden-Baden (Location: Hans-Bredow-Straße) ☎ +49 7221 929 0 📠 +49 7221 929 2010
**Broadcasting house Mainz:** ✉ Postfach 3740, 55122 Mainz (Location: Am Fort Gonsenheim 39) ☎ +49 6131 929 0
**Broadcasting house Stuttgart:** ✉ Postfach 106040, 70049 Stuttgart (Location: Neckarstraße 230) ☎ +49 711 929 0 **W:** swr.de

| FM (MHz) | SWR1 | SWR2 | SWR3 | SWR4 | DasDing | kW |
|---|---|---|---|---|---|---|
| Txs in and for Baden-Württemberg: | | | | | | |
| Aalen Braunenberg | 95.1 | 91.1 | 98.1 | 96.9U | – | 50/5 |
| Albstadt-Mahlesfeld | – | – | – | 99.5Tü | 87.8 | 0.1/0.3 |
| Bad Bellingen | – | – | – | 96.6F | – | 0.1 |
| Bad Mergentheim | 87.8 | 93.2 | 99.7 | 105.5H | 100.5 | 10/0.1 |
| Baden-Baden | 90.9 | 98.9 | 99.6 | 88.5Ka | 91.7 | 0.8/0.4 |
| Baiersbronn | – | – | – | 87.90 | – | 0.1 |
| Basel St. Crischona* | 87.9 | 92.0 | 98.3 | 89.5L | – | 5 |
| Blauen-Hochblauen | 89.2 | 92.6 | 97.0 | – | – | 8.4 |
| Buchen | 91.9 | 97.1 | 94.1 | 107.5M | 100.6 | 0.1/25 |
| Elzach Hörnleberg | – | – | – | 101.8F | – | 0.1 |
| Feldberg | 89.8 | 97.9 | 93.8 | 104.0F | – | 5 |
| Freiburg-Lehen | 107.0 | 91.1 | 90.2 | 100.7F | – | 0.1/1 |
| Freudenberg | 90.3 | 97.2 | 94.9 | 91.6H | – | 0.01 |

| FM (MHz) | SWR1 | SWR2 | SWR3 | SWR4 | DasDing | kW |
|---|---|---|---|---|---|---|
| Geislingen | 93.0 | 88.5 | 95.5 | 107.9 | – | 0.5/0.1 |
| Grünten* | 98.7 | – | 103.0 | – | – | 30 |
| Hausach Brandenkopf | 95.4 | – | 99.7 | 97.60 | – | 0.5/0.1 |
| Heidelberg Königstuhl | 97.8 | 88.8 | 99.9 | 104.1M | – | 100 |
| Heilbronn | – | – | – | 99.5H | – | 2 |
| Hornisgrinde | 93.5 | 96.2 | 98.4 | 94.00 | – | 80/5 |
| Karlsruhe-Ettlingen | – | – | – | 97.0Ka | – | 20 |
| Klettgau | 95.1 | 92.8 | 98.5 | 87.7Lö | – | 2.6 |
| Lichtenstein | 99.1 | – | – | 89.0Tü | – | 0.1 |
| Mannheim | – | – | – | – | 91.5 | 4 |
| Mötzingen | – | – | 97.2 | 87.6Tü | 90.5 | 1 |
| Mühlacker | – | – | – | 95.7B | – | 2 |
| Pforzheim | 92.9 | 88.1 | 99.3 | 87.6Ka | – | 5/0.2/0.5 |
| Raichberg | 88.3 | 91.8 | 94.3 | 107.3Tü | – | 40/25 |
| Ravensburg | 99.0 | – | 87.9 | – | 107.2 | 0.1 |
| Reutlingen | – | – | – | – | 97.7 | 2 |
| Schiltach-Simonsberg | 90.8 | – | 94.5 | 99.20 | – | 0.1 |
| Schwäbisch Gmünd | – | – | – | 100.9U | – | 0.1 |
| Sigmaringen | – | – | – | 101.2Fr | – | 0.1 |
| Strasbourg* | – | – | – | 88.90 | – | 1 |
| Stuttgart-Degerloch | 94.7 | 105.7 | 92.2 | 90.1 | 90.8 | 100/2 |
| Stuttgart (town) | 99.6 | 93.1 | – | – | – | 0.5/0.2 |
| | | | | | †91.5 | 0.3 |
| Tübingen | – | – | – | – | 97.3 | 2 |
| Ulm Kuhberg | 92.6 | 89.2 | 97.4 | 94.5U | 98.9 | 10/1 |
| Vaihingen | – | 98.6 | – | – | – | 0.1 |
| Villingen-Schwenningen | – | – | – | 91.1F | – | 1 |
| Waldenburg | 98.8 | 93.8 | 96.5 | 106.6H | – | 100/50 |
| Waldburg | – | 94.9 | – | 99.5H | – | 60 |
| | | | | 91.2Fr | | 25 |
| Weinheim | 97.1 | – | 99.5 | 100.7M | – | 0.04/0.1 |
| Wertheim | 96.9 | 91.8 | 94.6 | 101.2H | – | 0.1 |
| Witthoh | 92.4 | 90.4 | 97.1 | 89.0Fr | – | 40/5 |
| Zell Hohe Möhr | 87.6 | – | 96.8 | 100.2F | – | 0.1 |
| Zwiefalten | 93.7 | – | 92.8 | 87.6Fr | – | 0.1 |

†) SWR Info. *Basel site in Switzerland, Strasbourg site in France, Grünten site in Bayern.

**Txs in and for Rheinland-Pfalz:**

| FM (MHz) | SWR1 | SWR2 | SWR3 | SWR4 | DasDing | kW |
|---|---|---|---|---|---|---|
| Bad Kreuznach | – | – | – | – | 90.9 | 0.1 |
| Bleialf-Buchet | 88.3 | 99.7 | 98.9 | 94.6T | – | 0.1 |
| Daun | 91.1 | – | 98.5 | 93.6T | – | 8 |
| Diez-Geisenberg | 88.4 | 93.4 | 98.2 | 87.9K | – | 0.01/0.1 |
| Donnersberg | 99.1 | 92.0 | 101.1 | 105.6Kl | – | 60 |
| Haardtkopf | 97.7 | 93.0 | 90.0 | 107.1T | – | 50/25 |
| Hohe Wurzel | – | – | – | 107.9M | – | 6.2 |
| Idar-Oberstein | 88.5 | 95.1 | 98.1 | 106.4T | – | 0.01/1 |
| Kaisersl. Bomberg | 90.8 | 93.9 | 97.5 | 99.6Kl | 92.5 | 25/0.3 |
| Koblenz-Waldesch | 96.1 | 94.0 | 91.6 | 107.4K | 99.4 | 10/40/0.2 |
| Kreuzweiler | – | – | – | 97.3T | – | 0.3 |
| Linz | 92.4 | – | 94.8 | 97.4K | – | 50 |
| Mainz-Kastel* | 87.7 | 103.2 | 93.7 | 91.4M | 105.2 | 1 |
| Mainz-Wolfsheim | – | – | – | 94.9M | – | 5 |
| Marienberger Höhe | 89.8 | 95.4 | 92.8 | 106.3K | 91.3 | 25/0.1 |
| Nierstein-Oppenheim* | – | – | – | 92.9M | 98.4 | 0.1/0.3 |
| Pirmasens Kettrichhof | 100.8 | – | 107.2 | 104.2Kl | – | 5 |
| Rüdesheim* | – | 99.4 | 93.3 | 88.6M | – | 0.1/0.5 |
| Saarburg | 99.2 | 93.8 | 90.6 | 101.2T | – | 5 |
| Trier | 94.9 | 89.4 | 98.2 | 98.8T | 91.7 | 0.1/0.3 |
| Tübingen Herrenberg | – | – | 97.2 | 87.6Tü | 90.5 | 1 |
| Weinbiet | 89.9 | 102.2 | – | 95.9L | – | 25 |
| Zweibrücken | – | – | – | 90.5Kl | – | 0.2 |

*) Site in Hessen. +20 stns below 0.1kW

**DAB:** 12 txs on ch. 8D, 10 txs on ch. 9D, 9 txs on ch. 11A.
**D.Prgr. from Stuttgart studios,** via txs in Baden-Württemberg: **SWR1 Baden-Württemberg**, oldies, at night common SWR1 prgrs from Baden-Baden; **SWR4 Baden-Württemberg**, light music, with local prgr. from Freiburg (F), Friedrichshafen (F), Heilbronn (H), Karlsruhe (Ka), Lörrach (Lö), Mannheim (M), Offenburg (O), Tübingen (T) and Ulm (U), rel. ARD-Hitnacht
**D.Prgr. from Mainz studios,** via txs in Rheinland-Pfalz: **SWR1 Rheinland-Pfalz**, oldies, at night common SWR1 prgrs from Baden-Baden; **SWR4 Rheinland-Pfalz**, light music, with local prgrs from Kaiserslautern (Kl), Koblenz (K), Ludwigshafen (L) and Trier (T), rel. ARD-Hitnacht
**D.Prgr. from Baden-Baden studios: SWR2**, culture, 1740-1800 prgr. from Mainz/Stuttgart, at night rel. ARD-Nachtkonzert; **SWR3**, AC; **Das Ding**, youth, rel. Die junge Nacht; **SWR Info**, news, rel. ARD-Infonacht

## J) WESTDEUTSCHER RUNDFUNK (WDR)
Public broadcasting institution of Nordrhein-Westfalen
✉ 50600 Köln (location: Appellhofplatz 1) ☎ +49 221 220 1 📠 +49

221 220 4800 **W:** wdr.de

| FM (MHz) | ELive | WDR 2 | WDR 3 | WDR4 | WDR5 | kW |
|---|---|---|---|---|---|---|
| Aachen-Stolberg | 106.4 | 100.8A | 95.9 | 93.9 | 101.9 | 20 |
| Arnsberg | 96.0 | 99.4S | 97.5 | 91.7 | 88.5 | 0.1 |
| Bad Oeynhausen | 107.7 | 99.1B | 92.7 | 90.1 | 87.7 | 0.1 |
| Bergheim | – | 88.4K | – | – | – | 2 |
| Bonn Venusberg | 102.4 | 100.4K | 93.1 | 90.7 | 88.0 | 50 |
| Dortmund | – | 87.8D | – | – | – | 2 |
| Ederkopf | 107.2 | 101.8S | – | 100.7 | 95.8 | 15/20 |
| Eifel-Bärbelkreuz | 105.5 | 101.0 | 96.3 | 104.4 | 89.6 | 20/10/20/10 |
| Gummersbach | – | 91.8W | – | – | – | 10 |
| Hallenberg | 105.7 | – | – | 96.1 | 88.3 | 0.1 |
| Höxter Hasselberg | 107.3 | 96.4B | 95.2 | 87.8 | 93.9 | 0.5 |
| Ibbenbüren | 102.5 | 96.0M | 97.3 | 99.5 | 88.5 | 0.5 |
| Klever Berg | 103.7 | 93.3Dü | 98.1 | 101.7 | 99.7 | 2 |
| Köln | 87.6 | 98.6K | – | – | – | 0.3/0.5 |
| Langenberg | 106.7 | 99.2Dü | 95.1 | 101.3 | 88.8 | 100 |
| | | | | | 103.3+ | 100 |
| Lübbecke | 93.6 | 96.0B | 91.7 | 99.6 | 88.6 | 0.1 |
| Münster-Baumberge | 107.9 | 94.1M | 89.7 | 100.0 | 92.0 | 25 |
| Nordhelle | 104.7 | 93.5S | 98.1 | 103.8 | 90.3 | 35 |
| Olsberg | 107.0 | 102.1S | – | 104.1 | 98.6 | 10 |
| Remscheid | – | 95.7W | – | – | – | 1 |
| Schmallenberg | 100.1 | 93.8S | 97.8 | 101.1 | 90.0 | 0.1 |
| Siegen | 107.5 | 97.1S | 98.4 | 101.2 | 97.6 | 0.5/1/0.5/1 |
| Teutoburger Wald | 105.5 | 93.2B | 97.0 | 100.5 | 90.6 | 100 |
| Warburg | 98.2 | 91.8B | 94.3 | 104.5 | 88.4 | 0.5 |
| Wittgenstein | – | 92.3S | 88.7 | – | – | 15 |
| Wuppertal | – | 99.8W | – | – | – | 1 |

*) Funkhaus Europa
**DAB:** 23 txs on ch. 11D, also rel. Domradio (see S)
**D.Prgr: 1 Live**, CHR – **WDR 2**, AC, incl. local news from Aachen (A), Bielefeld (B), Köln (K), Dortmund (D), Düsseldorf (Dü), Münster (M), Siegen (S), Wuppertal (W); at night rel. NDR 2 – **WDR 3**, culture, rel. ARD-Nachtkonzert, ARD-Radiofestival – **WDR 4**, light music, ARD-Hitnacht – **WDR 5**, information, repeats overnight – **Cosmo**, for migrants, also via RBB and RB txs (see F/G) – **VERA**, continuous traffic jam information – **WDR Event**, live coverage of various events, otherwise silent – **1 Live Diggi**, continuous CHR music – **Kiraka**, for childrens

## II. COMMERCIAL AND OTHER STATIONS

### K) BADEN-WÜRTTEMBERG
**Media institution:** Landesanstalt für Kommunikation (LfK) ✉ Postfach 102927, 70025 Stuttgart (office location: Reinsburgstraße 27 ☎ +49 711 669910 📠 +49 711 6699111 **W:** lfk.de

**Commercial stations:**

| FM | MHz | kW | Site | Station |
|---|---|---|---|---|
| 2) | 87.8 | 1 | Mannheim | big FM |
| 6) | 88.6 | 2 | Langenburg | R. Ton |
| 3) | 89.1 | 0.5 | Heilbronn | Hit-R. Antenne 1 |
| 3) | 89.3 | 0.1 | Bad Urach | Hit-R. Antenne 1 |
| 2) | 89.5 | 10 | Stuttgart Frauenkopf | big FM |
| 3) | 89.5 | 0.1 | Wertheim | Hit-R. Antenne 1 |
| 2) | 89.7 | 1 | Tübingen | big FM |
| 11) | 90.4 | 2 | Karlsruhe | Klassik R. |
| 9) | 90.5 | 2 | Achern | Hitradio Ohr |
| 2) | 90.9 | 0.1 | Heidelberg city | big FM |
| 15) | 91.4 | 3 | Lützenhardt | R. TV R. |
| 7) | 91.4 | 0.5 | Pforzheim | die neue welle |
| 19) | 92.4 | 1 | Hockenheimring | Rennradio |
| 2) | 92.7 | 1 | Horb | big FM |
| 9) | 93.0 | 0.1 | Haslach | Schwarzwald R. |
| 16) | 93.1 | 1 | Rottweil-Zimmern | R. Neckarburg |
| 15) | 94.7 | 0.5 | Freiburg-Lehen | baden.fm |
| 17) | 95.4 | 0.1 | Stuttgart SWR bldg. | Metropol FM |
| 5) | 95.6 | 1 | Balingen | Neckaralb Live |
| 6) | 96.0 | 0.1 | Künzelsau | R. Ton |
| 10) | 96.4 | 1 | Überlingen | R. Seefunk |
| 6) | 96.8 | 0.3 | Eppingen | R. Ton |
| 4) | 96.9 | 0.1 | Schussental | R. 7 |
| 12) | 97.2 | 1 | Stuttgart-Münster | egoFM |
| 2) | 97.2 | 0.5 | Sinsheim-Dühren | big FM |
| 13) | 97.5 | 0.5 | Esslingen | Die Neue 107.7 |
| 8) | 97.6 | 0.3 | Rudersberg | Energy Stuttgart |
| 2) | 99.0 | 0.5 | Rottweil | big FM |
| 5) | 99.0 | 0.1 | Bad Urach | Neckaralb Live |
| 15) | 99.2 | 0.2 | Herrenberg | R. TV R. |
| 9) | 99.2 | 0.1 | Oberkirch | Hitradio Ohr |
| 10) | 99.3 | 5 | Friedrichshafen | R. Seefunk |
| 2) | 99.7 | 1 | Ulm | big FM |
| 3) | 100.1 | 50 | Schwäbisch Hall | Hit-R. Antenne 1 |

| FM | MHz | kW | Site | Station |
|---|---|---|---|---|
| 6) | 100.1 | 0.1 | Hechingen | R. Ton |
| 2) | 100.3 | 5 | Geislingen | big FM |
| 1) | 100.4 | 80 | Hornisgrinde | R. Regenbogen |
| 8) | 100.7 | 20 | Güglingen | Energy Stuttgart |
| 5) | 100.9 | 1 | Tübingen | Neckaralb Live |
| 7) | 100.9 | 0.8 | Baden-Baden | die neue welle |
| 1) | 101.1 | 8.4 | Blauen-Müllheim | R. Regenbogen |
| 8) | 101.2 | 0.1 | Villingen-Schwenningen | R. 7 |
| 3) | 101.3 | 75 | Stuttgart Frauenkopf | Hit-R. Antenne 1 |
| 9) | 101.6 | 0.5 | Brandenkopf | Hit-R. Ohr |
| 8) | 101.8 | 25 | Karlsruhe | die neue welle |
| 4) | 101.8 | 10 | Ulm-Ermingen | R. 7 |
| 10) | 101.8 | 10 | Konstanz | R. Seefunk |
| 8) | 101.8 | 1 | Backnang | Energy Stuttgart |
| 10) | 101.9 | 0.1 | Schopfheim | R. Seefunk |
| 16) | 102.0 | 3 | Villingen-Schwenningen | R. Neckarburg |
| 1) | 102.1 | 25 | Mudau | Regenbogen Zwei |
| 10) | 102.4 | 0.2 | Laufenburg [Switzerl.] | R. Seefunk |
| 4) | 102.5 | 40 | Witthoh-Tuttlingen | R. 7 |
| 6) | 102.6 | 0.5 | Schwäbisch Hall | R. Ton |
| 10) | 102.6 | 0.3 | Ravensburg | R. Seefunk |
| 8) | 102.6 | 0.1 | Bad Wildbad | die neue welle |
| 8) | 102.7 | 0.1 | Nagold | die neue welle |
| 1) | 102.8 | 50 | Heidelberg.Königstuhl | R. Regenbogen |
| 2) | 102.8 | 0.5 | Freiburg | big FM |
| 11) | 103.0 | 1 | Göppingen | Klassik R. |
| 8) | 103.0 | 0.3 | Calw | die neue welle |
| 10) | 103.1 | 5 | Rheinfelden | R. Seefunk |
| 3) | 103.1 | 0.1 | Reutlingen | Hit-R. Antenne 1 |
| 6) | 103.2 | 25 | Heilbronn | R. Ton |
| 3) | 103.4 | 50 | Raichberg | Hit-R. Antenne 1 |
| 6) | 103.5 | 20 | Bad Mergentheim | R. Ton |
| 4) | 103.7 | 50 | Aalen | R. 7 |
| 16) | 103.7 | 0.1 | Schramberg | R. Neckarburg |
| 2) | 103.8 | 2 | Baden-Baden | big FM |
| 10) | 103.9 | 10 | Iberger Kugel | R. Seefunk |
| 11) | 103.9 | 2 | Stuttgart-Münster | Klassik R. |
| 10) | 104.2 | 1 | Sigmaringen | R. Seefunk |
| 6) | 104.2 | 0.1 | Heidenheim | R. Ton |
| 8) | 104.3 | 2 | Sindelfingen | Energy Stuttgart |
| 10) | 104.3 | 0.1 | Lörrach | R. Seefunk |
| 8) | 104.5 | 2 | Waiblingen | Energy Stuttgart |
| 8) | 104.5 | 0.1 | Winnenden | Energy Stuttgart |
| 16) | 104.6 | 1 | Oberndorf | R. Neckarburg |
| 14) | 104.6 | 0.3 | Biberach | Donau 3 FM |
| 1) | 104.6 | 0.1 | Buchen | R. Regenbogen |
| 2) | 104.7 | 0.2 | Heilbronn | big FM |
| 6) | 104.7 | 0.1 | Wertheim | R. Ton |
| 13) | 104.7 | 0.1 | Geislingen | Die Neue 107.7 |
| 5) | 104.8 | 1 | Reutlingen | Neckaralb Live |
| 9) | 104.9 | 5 | Offenburg-Ohlsbach | Hit-R. Ohr |
| 18) | 104.9 | 1 | Stuttgart-Münster | sunshine live |
| 4) | 105.0 | 50 | Grünenbach | R. 7 |
| 2) | 105.1 | 0.2 | Aalen | big FM |
| 2) | 105.2 | 20 | Pforzheim | big FM |
| 10) | 105.3 | 0.5 | Singen | R. Seefunk |
| 3) | 105.4 | 1 | Geislingen | Hit-R. Antenne 1 |
| 3) | 105.4 | 0.3 | Balingen | Hit-R. Antenne 1 |
| 10) | 105.4 | 0.1 | Waldshut-Tiengen | R. Seefunk |
| 9) | 105.5 | 0.5 | Bühl | Hit-R. Ohr |
| 14) | 105.9 | 5 | Ulm-Ermingen | Donau 3 FM |
| 15) | 106.0 | 8.4 | Blauen-Müllheim | baden.fm |
| 3) | 106.0 | 0.1 | Bad Mergentheim | Hit-R. Antenne 1 |
| 1) | 106.1 | 1 | Heidelberg-Königstuhl | Regenbogen Zwei |
| 13) | 106.1 | 1 | Göppingen | Die Neue 107.7 |
| 14) | 106.2 | 0.5 | Riedlingen | Donau 3 FM |
| 13) | 106.5 | 0.1 | Kirchheim | Die Neue 107.7 |
| 15) | 106.6 | 0.1 | Titisee-Neustadt | baden.fm |
| 13) | 106.8 | 1 | Nürtingen | Die Neue 107.7 |
| 3) | 106.9 | 0.1 | Leonberg | Hit-R. Antenne 1 |
| 10) | 107.0 | 5 | Wannenberg-Klettgau | R. Seefunk |
| 3) | 107.0 | 1 | Pforzheim | Hit-R. Antenne 1 |
| 6) | 107.1 | 20 | Aalen | R. Ton |
| 1) | 107.1 | 0.1 | Wiesloch | Regenbogen Zwei |
| 7) | 107.3 | 0.1 | Bruchsal | die neue welle |
| 9) | 107.4 | 5 | Lahr | Hit-R. Ohr |
| 13) | 107.4 | 0.1 | Gosbach | Die Neue 107.7 |
| 13) | 107.7 | 4 | Stuttgart Frauenkopf | Die Neue 107.7 |
| 15) | 107.7 | 0.5 | Freiburg-Littenweiler | baden.fm |
| 1) | 107.7 | 0.1 | Weinheim | Regenbogen Zwei |
| 5) | 107.9 | 1 | Sickingen | Neckaralb Live |
| 1) | 107.9 | 0.1 | Mosbach | Regenboen Zwei |

| FM | MHz | kW | Site | Station |
|---|---|---|---|---|
| 7) | 107.9 | 0.1 | Bretten | die neue welle |

**Addresses & other information:**
**1)** P.O.-Box 10 26 55, 68026 Mannheim (studio location: Dudenstr. 12-26); **W:** regenbogenweb.de AC, separate Regenbogen Zwei prgr. rock – **2)** Kronenstr. 24, 70173 Stuttgart; **W:** bigfm.de CHR, further txs see T), U) – **3)** Plieningerstr. 150, 70567 Stuttgart; **W:** antenne1. de AC – **4)** Gaisenbergstr. 29, 89073 Ulm; **W:** radio7.de AC – **5)** Obere Wässere 6-8, 72764 Reutlingen; **W:** neckaralblive.de AC – **6)** Allee 2, 74072 Heilbronn; **W:** radio-ton.de AC – **7)** Albert-Nestler-Str. 26, 76131 Karlsruhe; **W:** meine-neue-welle.de AC – **8)** Anton-Schmidt-Str. 36, 71332 Waiblingen; **W:** energy-stuttgart.de CHR – **9)** Postfach 20 80, 77610 Offenburg (studio location: Hauptstr. 83a); **W:** hitradio-ohr. de schwarzwaldradio.com AC – **10)** Konzilstr. 1, 78462 Konstanz; **W:** radio-seefunk.de AC – **11)** see O) – **12)** see L) – **13)** Königstr. 2, 70173 Stuttgart; **W:** dieneue1077.de Rock – **14)** Basteistr. 37, 89073 Ulm; **W:** donau3fm.de AC – **15)** Munzingerstr. 1, 79111 Freiburg; **W:** baden.fm AC – **16)** August-Schuhmacher-Str. 10, 78664 Eschbronn-Mariazell; **W:** radio-neckarburg.de – **17)** see M), stn. 15 – **18)** Grunewaldstr. 3, 12165 Berlin (studio); W: sunshine-live.de Techno, also via Astra 1N, 12.148GHz – **19)** during Hockenheimring races only

**Non-commercial stations:**

| FM | MHz | kW | Site | Station |
|---|---|---|---|---|
| 10) | 88.4 | 0.3 | Freiburg univ. | echo-fm |
| 6) | 88.6 | 1 | Stuttgart-Münster | Hochschulr. Stuttg. |
| 9) | 89.2 | 0.1 | Horb | Freies R. Freudens. |
| 1) | 89.6 | 0.1 | Mannheim | bermuda.funk |
| 4) | 91.2 | 0.1 | Bruchsal | LernR. |
| 8) | 96.6 | 1 | Tübingen | Wüste Welle |
| 2) | 97.5 | 0.1 | Schwäbisch Hall | R. StHörfunk |
| 5) | 99.2 | 0.3 | Stuttgart-Münster | Freies R. f. Stuttg. |
| 9) | 100.0 | 0.5 | Freudenstadt | Freies R. Freudens. |
| 10) | 102.3 | 1 | Freiburg Vogtsberg | R. Dreyeckland |
| 7) | 102.6 | 1 | Ulm-Ermingen | R. FreeFM |
| 9) | 104.1 | 0.1 | Baiersbronn | Freies R. Freudens. |
| 12) | 104.5 | 0.5 | Hohe Möhr | R. Kanal Ratte |
| 3) | 104.8 | 1 | Karlsruhe | Querfunk |
| 2) | 104.8 | 0.1 | Crailsheim | R. StHörfunk |
| 1) | 105.4 | 1 | Heidelberg Königstuhl | bermuda.funk |

**Addresses & other information:**
**1)** Brückenstr. 2-4, 68167 Mannheim; **W:** bermudafunk.org. Also rel. R. Aktiv (Universität Mannheim, Postfach 144, 68131 Mannheim); **W:** radioaktiv-online.de Mon-Wed 0600-1000 and 1700-1900, Thu-Fri 2300-1000 and 1700-1900, Sun 1900-2100 – **2)** Haalstr. 9, 74523 Schwäbisch Hall; **W:** sthoerfunk.de – **3)** Steinstr. 23, 76133 Karlsruhe; **W:** querfunk.de rel. Mon-Fri 0600-1100 and Mon-Thu 1600-2100 stn. 4) – **4)** Hochschule für Musik, Postfach 6040, 76040 Karlsruhe (studio location: Wolfartsweierer Str. 7a); **W:** lernradio.de – **5)** Freies R. für Stuttgart, Rieckestr. 24, 70190 Stuttgart; **W:** freies-radio.de – **6)** Hochschulradio Stuttgart, Nobelstr. 10, 70569 Stuttgart; **W:** horads.de – **7)** Söflinger Str. 206, 89077 Ulm; **W:** freefm.de – **8)** Hechinger Str. 203, 72072 Tübingen; **W:** wueste-welle.de Rel. Tue-Thu 0700-0800 Helle Welle (religious) – **9)** Freies R. Freudenstadt, Forststr. 23, 72250 Freudenstadt; **W:** radio-fds.de – **10)** Adlerstr. 12, 79098 Freiburg; **W:** rdl.de – **11)** Georges-Köhler-Allee Geb. 076, 79110 Freiburg; **W:** echo-fm.uni-freiburg.de – **12)** Bahnhofstr. 3, 79650 Schopfheim; **W:** kanalrattefm.de

**DAB:** 13 txs on ch. 5C Deutschlandfunk, Deutschlandfunk Kultur, Deutschlandfunk Nova, Dokumente & Debatten, Absolut Relax, Energy, ERF Plus, Klassik Radio, Radio Bob, Radio Horeb, Schlagerparadies, Sunshine Live, Schwarzwaldradio – 11 txs on ch. 11B, Bürgermedien (mixed prgr. of non-commercial stns), Radio VHR and rel. of 12 commercial FM stns

## L) BAYERN
**Media institution:** Bayerische Landeszentrale für Neue Medien (BLM) ✉ Heinrich-Lübke-Straße 27, 81737 München ☎ +49 89 638 080 🖷 +49 89 63808140; **W:** blm.de
**FM networks:**

| Location | Ant.B. | Rock. | Klass | egoFM | Galaxy | kW |
|---|---|---|---|---|---|---|
| Amberg | – | – | – | – | 105.5 | 0.1 |
| Ansbach | – | – | – | – | 105.8 | 0.1 |
| Aschaffenburg | 103.0 | – | – | – | 91.6 | 25/0.1 |
| Augsburg | 104.2 | 87.9 | 92.2 | 94.8 | – | 0.1/0.3 |
| Bad Reichenhall | 103.7 | – | – | – | – | 0.3 |
| Bamberg | 101.1 | – | – | – | 104.7 | 25/0.5 |
| Bayreuth | – | – | – | – | 92.7 | 0.1 |
| Bayrischzell | 106.7 | – | – | – | – | 0.1 |
| Berchtesgaden | 107.9 | – | – | – | – | 0.3 |
| Breithart | 101.5 | – | – | – | – | 25 |
| Brotjacklriegel | 103.5 | – | – | – | – | 100 |

| Location | Ant.B. | Rock. | Klass | egoFM | Galaxy | kW |
|---|---|---|---|---|---|---|
| Coburg | 103.8 | – | – | – | 90.4 | 5/0.2 |
| Dillberg | 100.6 | – | – | – | – | 25 |
| Eichstätt | 100.2 | – | – | – | – | 25 |
| Enterbach | 101.1 | – | – | – | – | 0.5 |
| Erding | – | 87.9 | – | – | – | 0.1 |
| Erlangen | – | – | – | 106.2 | – | 0.2 |
| Freising | – | 95,0 | – | – | – | 0.1 |
| Fürth | – | – | – | 91.0 | – | 0.2 |
| Grünten | 104.4 | – | – | – | – | 50 |
| Heidelstein | 101.9 | – | – | – | – | 100 |
| Herzogstand | 102.0 | – | – | – | – | 0.1 |
| Hochries | 107.7 | – | – | – | – | 50 |
| Hof | – | – | – | – | 94.0 | 0.2 |
| Högl-Freilassing | 105.3 | – | – | – | – | 1 |
| Hohenpeißenb. | 103.8 | – | – | – | – | 25 |
| Hoher Bogen | 101.9 | – | – | – | – | 50 |
| Ingolstadt | – | – | – | – | 107.9 | 0.1 |
| Isen | – | 88.8 | – | – | – | 0.5 |
| Kirchseeon | – | 93.0 | – | – | – | 0.6 |
| Kempten | – | – | – | – | 88.1 | 0.3 |
| Konradsreuth | – | – | – | – | 98.1 | 0.1 |
| Landshut | 99.3 | – | – | – | 99.8 | 0.2 |
| Lindau | 99.0 | – | – | – | – | 0.5 |
| Moosinning | – | 99.4 | – | – | – | 0.5 |
| Münchberg | – | – | – | – | 98.1 | 0.1 |
| München | 101.3 | 94.5 | 107.2 | 100.8 | – | 0.3 |
| Naila | – | – | – | – | 96.5 | 0.1 |
| Nördlingen | 103.3 | – | – | – | – | 25 |
| Nürnberg | – | – | 105.1 | 103.6 | – | 0.5/0.3 |
| Oberaudorf | 94.6 | – | – | – | – | 0.3 |
| Ochsenkopf | 103.2 | – | – | – | – | 100 |
| Passau | 102.1 | – | – | – | 91.7 | 1/0.2 |
| Pfaffenhofen | 92.6 | – | – | – | – | 0.5 |
| Regensburg | 103.0 | – | 91.1 | 107.5 | – | 25/0.3/0.3 |
| Reit im Winkel | 101.6 | – | – | – | – | 0.1 |
| Rosenheim | – | – | – | – | 106.6 | 0.1 |
| Selb | – | – | – | – | 93.4 | 0.1 |
| Sonthofen | 93.6 | – | – | – | – | 0.1 |
| Traunstein | 103.7 | – | – | – | – | 5 |
| Ulm | 104.8 | – | – | – | – | 0.1 |
| Weiden | – | – | – | – | 89.8 | 0.1 |
| Weiler Simm. | 106.0 | – | – | – | – | 0.1 |
| Wunsiedel | – | – | – | – | 97.3 | 0.2 |
| Würzburg | 104.4 | – | 92.1 | 95.8 | – | 5/0.3 |
| Zugspitze | 102.7 | – | – | – | – | 2 |

**Addresses & other information:**
**Antenne Bayern (AC), Rockantenne (rock):** Münchener Straße 101c, 85737 Ismaning; also via Astra 1N, 12.148GHz h; **W:** antenne. de rockantenne.de – **Klassik R.:** see O) – **egoFM:** Leopoldstraße 254, 80807 München; also via Astra 1M, 12.460GHz; **W:** egofm.de Alternative – **R. Galaxy:** Lilienthalstraße 3c, 93049 Regensburg, **W:** radiogalaxy.de CHR. Mon-Fri 1400-1800 local prgr, produced by stns 17), 26), 29), 30/31), 32), 33), 35) (R. Euroherz), 36), 41), 42), 43) and 48) listed below

**Local stations:**

| FM | MHz | kW | Site | Station |
|---|---|---|---|---|
| 39) | 87.9 | 0.3 | Straubing Bogenberg | R. AWN |
| 35) | 88.0 | 5 | Großer Waldstein | extra–rad. / Euroherz |
| 19) | 88.1 | 0.1 | Krumbach-Kirchberg | R. Prima 1 |
| 18) | 88.2 | 0.2 | Kaufbeuren | R. Ostallgäu |
| 51) | 88.2 | 0.1 | Bad Reichenhall | R. Untersberg |
| 32) | 88.5 | 0.5 | Bamberg Rothof | R. Bamberg |
| 36) | 88.5 | 0.1 | Tirschenreuth | R. Ramasuri |
| 27) | 88.6 | 0.1 | Karlstadt | R. Charivari |
| 5) | 89.0 | 0.3 | München Olympiaturm | 2DAY/Neues Europa |
| 42) | 89.0 | 0.1 | Dingolfing | R. Trausnitz |
| 51) | 89.0 | 0.1 | Högl-Freilassing | R. Untersberg |
| 26) | 89.1 | 0.1 | Wassertrüdingen | R. 8 |
| 31) | 89.2 | 0.5 | Coburg Eckardtsberg | R. EINS |
| 17) | 89.3 | 0.1 | Oberstdorf-Steinach | RSA R. |
| 40) | 89.3 | 0.2 | Regen Geiskopf | Unser R. Deggendorf |
| 26) | 89.4 | 0.5 | Ansbach Ludwigshöhe | R. 8 |
| 24) | 89.7 | 0.1 | Dillingen | RT.1 Nordschwaben |
| 38) | 89.7 | 0.3 | Regensburg Ziegetsberg | gong fm |
| 41) | 89.7 | 0.3 | Bad Griesbach | Unser R. Passau |
| 26) | 89.8 | 0.1 | Dinkelsbühl | R. 8 |
| 45) | 89.8 | 0.1 | Landsberg-Stoffen | R. 106.4 |
| 31) | 90.0 | 0.1 | Kronach-Neuses | R. EINS |
| 19) | 90.2 | 0.32 | Bad Grönenbach | R. Prima 1 |
| 26) | 90.2 | 0.1 | Gunzenhausen | R. 8 |
| 47) | 90.2 | 0.1 | Miesbach-Bergham | R. Alpenwelle |

| FM | MHz | kW | Site | Station |
|---|---|---|---|---|
| 21) | 90.3 | 0.1 | Günzburg | Hitradio X |
| 26) | 90.4 | 0.2 | Neuadstadt / Aisch | R. 8 |
| 27) | 90.4 | 0.1 | Gemünden / Lohr | R. Charivari |
| 49) | 90.4 | 0.1 | Mühldorf | Inn-Salzach-Welle |
| 30) | 90.5 | 0.1 | Bad Kissingen | R. PrimaTon |
| 29) | 90.8 | 0.2 | Alzenau | R. Primavera |
| 47) | 91.7 | 0.1 | Holzkirchen Jasberg | R. Alpenwelle |
| 42) | 91.8 | 0.2 | Pfeffenhausen-Stollnried | R. Trausnitz |
| 47) | 92.0 | 0.1 | Wolfratshausen | R. Alpenwelle |
| 6) | 92.4 | 0.3 | München Olympiaturm | (shared freq.) |
| 42) | 92.7 | 0.1 | Weiler Simmerberg | Welle Bodensee |
| 37) | 92.7 | 0.4 | Hoher Bogen | Charivari Regensbg. |
| 49) | 92.7 | 0.3 | Reichertsheim | Inn-Salzach-Welle |
| 13) | 92.9 | 0.3 | Nürnberg | Hi R. N1 |
| 17) | 93.0 | 0.1 | Immenstadt | RSA R. |
| 49) | 93.1 | 0.1 | Burgkirchen-Gendorf | Inn-Salzach-Welle |
| 2) | 93.3 | 0.3 | München Olympiaturm | Energy 93.3 |
| 33) | 93.3 | 0.1 | Pegnitz | R. Mainwelle |
| 23) | 93.4 | 0.3 | Augsburg | R. Fantasy |
| 9) | 93.6 | 0.3 | Erlangen | Energy Nürnberg |
| 36) | 93.6 | 0.1 | Waidhaus Fischerberg | R. Ramasuri |
| 19) | 93.9 | 0.3 | Mindelheim-Altensteig | R. Prima 1 |
| 41) | 93.9 | 0.3 | Vilshofen-Otterkirchen | Unser R. Passau |
| 30) | 94.0 | 0.1 | Bad Brückenau | R. PrimaTon |
| 37) | 94.0 | 1 | Seubersdorf Göschberg | Charivari Regensb. |
| 11) | 94.5 | 0.3 | Nürnberg | R. F / Jazztime |
| 43) | 94.6 | 0.1 | Schrobenhausen | R. IN / R. ND1 |
| 47) | 95.0 | 0.2 | Bad Tölz | R. Alpenwelle |
| 35) | 95.1 | 0.1 | Marktredwitz | extra–r. / Euroherz |
| 36) | 95.3 | 1 | Hirschberg Rothbühl | R. Ramasuri |
| 45) | 95.4 | 0.3 | Lichtenfels | R. EINS |
| 43) | 95.4 | 0.1 | Ingolstadt | R. IN |
| 3) | 95.5 | 0.3 | München Olympiaturm | Charivari 95.5 |
| 24) | 95.6 | 1 | Harburg Hühnerberg | RT.1 Nordschwaben |
| 30) | 95.7 | 0.1 | Haßfurt/Main | R. PrimaTon |
| 39) | 95.7 | 0.1 | Mallersdorf-Hofkirchen | R. AWN |
| 14) | 95.8 | 0.3 | Nürnberg | R. Z |
| 4) | 96.3 | 0.3 | München Olympiaturm | R. Gong 96,3 |
| 38) | 96.3 | 0.32 | Burglengenfeld | gong fm |
| 1) | 96.4 | 1 | Fürth | star fm |
| 32) | 96.6 | 0.1 | Forchheim Pinzberg | R. Bamberg |
| 45) | 96.6 | 0.1 | Starnberg | R. 106.4 |
| 17) | 96.7 | 0.1 | Kempten town | RSA R. |
| 22) | 96.7 | 0.3 | Augsburg | Kit R. RT.1 |
| 48) | 96.7 | 0.3 | Flintsbach Dandlberg | Charivari Rosenheim |
| 12) | 97.1 | 0.3 | Nürnberg | Gong 97.1 |
| 24) | 97.1 | 0.1 | Donauwörth | RT.1 Nordschwaben |
| 41) | 97.2 | 0.1 | Grafenau Liebersberg | Unser R. Passau |
| 26) | 97.3 | 0.3 | Feuchtwangen | R. 8 |
| 38) | 97.3 | 0.1 | Schwandorf Weinberg | gong fm |
| 46) | 97.5 | 0.1 | Weilheim | R. Oberland |
| 17) | 97.6 | 1 | Kempten Blender | RSA R. |
| 18) | 98.0 | 0.1 | Füssen | R. Ostallgäu |
| 51) | 98.1 | 0.1 | Berchtesgaden | R. Untersberg |
| 37) | 98.2 | 0.3 | Regensburg Ziegetsberg | Charivari Regensb. |
| 41) | 98.3 | 0.2 | Passau-Haidenhof | Unser R. Passau |
| 10) | 98.6 | 0.3 | Nürnberg | Charivari 98.6 |
| 40) | 98.7 | 0.1 | Deggendorf-Hochobernd. | Unser R. Deggendorf |
| 37) | 98.8 | 0.5 | Burglengenfeld | Charivari Regensbg. |
| 34) | 98.9 | 0.1 | Stadtsteinach | R. Plassenburg |
| 25) | 99.0 | 0.2 | Lauf Moritzberg | star fm |
| 27) | 99.0 | 0.1 | Marktheidenfeld | R. Charivari |
| 43) | 99.1 | 0.1 | Eichstätt-Seuversholz | R. IN |
| 50) | 99.4 | 0.3 | Haslach-Einham | R. Chiemgau |
| 36) | 99.9 | 0.2 | Weiden Fischerberg | R. Ramasuri |
| 47) | 99.9 | 0.1 | Herzogstand | R. Alpenwelle |
| 29) | 100.4 | 1 | Aschaffenburg | R. Primavera |
| 30) | 100.5 | 0.5 | Schweinfurth | R. PrimaTon |
| 26) | 100.8 | 0.1 | Burgbernheim | R. 8 |
| 43) | 101.2 | 0.2 | Neuburg/Donau | R. IN / R. ND1 |
| 46) | 101.2 | 0.1 | Oberammergau | R. Oberland |
| 46) | 101.4 | 0.3 | Sindelsdorf | R. Oberland |
| 30) | 101.5 | 0.1 | Bad Neustadt-Unsleben | R. PrimaTon |
| 41) | 101.5 | 0.1 | Freyung Geyersberg | Unser R. Passau |
| 50) | 101.5 | 0.3 | Trostberg | R. Chiemgau |
| 34) | 101.6 | 5 | Kulmbach Rehberg | R. Plassenburg |
| 27) | 102.4 | 0.3 | Würzburg | R. Charivari |
| 37) | 102.6 | 0.32 | Waldmünchen Perlhütte | Charivari Regensbg. |
| 16) | 103.6 | 0.5 | Lindau Hoyerberg | Welle Bodensee |
| 36) | 103.9 | 0.1 | Amberg Eisberg | R. Ramasuri |
| 37) | 103.9 | 0.5 | Kelheim Leitenberg | Charivari Regensbg. |
| 1) | 104.0 | 0.1 | München Blutenburgstr. | R. Arabella |

| FM | MHz | kW | Site | Station |
|---|---|---|---|---|
| 42) | 104.1 | 1 | Landshut | R. Trausnitz |
| 48) | 104.2 | 0.3 | Oberaudorf-Hölzelsau | Charivari Rosenheim |
| 33) | 104.3 | 10 | Oschenberg | R. Mainwelle |
| 47) | 104.3 | 0.5 | Enterbach-Ringberg | R. Alpenwelle |
| 46) | 104.6 | 0.1 | Herzogstand | R. Oberland |
| 43) | 104.8 | 0.2 | Pfaffenhofen Wolfsberg | R. IN |
| 36) | 105.1 | 0.5 | Wiesau-Fuchsmühle | R. Ramasuri |
| 1) | 105.2 | 25 | München-Isen | R. Arabella |
| 18) | 105.2 | 0.1 | Obergünzburg | R. Ostallgäu |
| 43) | 105.4 | 0.1 | Beilngries | R. IN |
| 37) | 105.5 | 0.3 | Lam-Koppenhof | Charivari Regensbg. |
| 42) | 105.5 | 0.32 | Landau | R. Trausnitz |
| 20) | 105.9 | 5 | Ulm-Ermingen | R. Donau 1 |
| 37) | 105.9 | 0.32 | Nabburg Galgenberg | Charivari Regensbg. |
| 32) | 106.1 | 0.1 | Burglesau Reisberg | R. Bamberg |
| 46) | 106.2 | 0.3 | Garmisch-Partenkirchen | R. Oberland |
| 47) | 106.2 | 0.1 | Schliersbergalm | R. Alpenwelle |
| 18) | 106.3 | 0.5 | Eisenberg Schloßberg | R. Ostallgäu |
| 36) | 106.4 | 0.1 | Königstein Gr. Ossinger | R. Ramasuri |
| 45) | 106.4 | 2 | Fürstenfeldbruck | R. 106.4 |
| 49) | 106.4 | 0.3 | Lohkirchen | Inn-Salzach-Welle |
| 8) | 106.5 | 0.1 | Nürnberg | afk max |
| 28) | 106.9 | 5 | Würzburg | R. Gong 106,9 |
| 9) | 106.9 | 0.3 | Nürnberg | Energy Nürnberg |
| 42) | 107.4 | 1 | Pfarrkirchen-Postm. | R. Trausnitz |
| 25) | 107.8 | 0.2 | Schwabach Heidenberg | star fm |
| 40) | 107.9 | 0.2 | Brotjacklriegel | Unser R. Deggendorf |
| + 28 txs less than 0.1kW | | | | |

### Addresses & other information:

**Dienstleistungsgesellschaft für Bayerische Lokal-Radioprogramme (BLR)** ✉ Rosenheimer Straße 145c, 81671 München **W:** blr.de Provides network prgr. and other content for many of the above listed stns
**1)** Paul-Heyse-Str. 2-4, 80336 München, **W:** radioarabella.de – **2)** Pestalozzistr. 15-19, 80469 München, **W:** energy.de/muenchen – **3)** Postfach 20 16 09, 80016 München (studio location as stn. 1), **W:** charivari.de – **4)** Franz-Joseph-Str. 14, 80801 München, **W:** radiogong.de – **5)** Schneemanstr. 25, 81369 München, **W:** radio2-day.de Rel. Sat 2300-Mon 0500 R. Neues Europa: Konviktstr. 1, 85049 Ingolstadt – **6)** Radio Horeb, Postfach 1165, 87501 Immenstadt; **W:** radiohoreb.de Religious. Also via Astra 1N, 12.604GHz h. On 92.4MHz Mon-Fri 0000-1300, Sat-Sun 2300-0500, Sun 0900-1200 and 1300-2300. Christliches Radio München, Postfach 310201, 80102 München; **W:** christlichesradio.de Religious, Mon-Fri 1300-1400, Sun 0800-0900 and 1200-1300. Lora München, Gravelottestr. 6, 81667 München, **W:** lora924.de Non-commercial. Mon-Thu 1500-2300, Fri 1500-2000. Feierwerk München, Hansastr. 39, 81373 München; **W:** feierwerk.de Non-commercial. Fr 2000-Sat 2300 and Sun 0500-0900 – **7)** M94.5 no longer on FM, freq. surrendered to Rockantenne – **8)** Fürther Str. 212, 90429 Nürnberg, **W:** afkmax.de Journalist training stn. – **9)** Ostendstr. 100, 90482 Nürnberg, **W:** energy.de/nuernberg – **10),11),12),13)** Funkhaus Nürnberg, Senefelder Str. 7, 90409 Nürnberg, **W:** funkhaus.de 92.0MHz also rel. Camillo 92.9 (Mon, Tue, Sun 2000-2200), R. AREF (Sun 0900-1100), Pater 92.9 (Sun 1100-1200), R. Meilensteine (Sun 0800-0900), 94.5MHz also rel. Jazztime Nürnberg (Mon 2100-2200, Thu 2000-2100). – **14)** Kopernikusplatz 12, 90459 Nürnberg, **W:** radio-z.net. 1300-0100 only, other times rel. stn. 25) – 15) left blank – **16)** W: welle-bodensee.de – **17)** Rottachstr. 17, 87439 Kempten, **W:** allgaeuseite.de/rsa_radio – **18) W:** roal.de – **19)** Hirschgasse 1, 87700 Memmingen, **W:** prima1.de – **20)** Leipzigstr. 26, 88400 Biberach, **W:** radiodonau1.de – **21)** Augsburger Str. 112, 89312 Günzburg, **W:** hitradiox.de – **22)** Curt-Frenzel-Str. 4, 86167 Augsburg, **W:** radio-rt1.de – **23)** Ludwigstr. 1, 86150 Augsburg, **W:** fantasy.de Rel. Mon 2100-2400 Kanal C (university stn.): Eichleitnerstr. 30, 86159 Augsburg, **W:** kanal-c.de – **24)** Artur-Proeller-Str. 1, 86609 Donauwörth, **W:** rt1-nordschwaben.de – **25)** O'Brien Str. 2, 91126 Schwabach; **W:** rocksender.de/rocksender_nuernberg/ – **26)** Postfach 8, 91510 Ansbach (studio location: Schalkhäuser Landstr. 5), **W:** radio8.de – **27), 28)** Semmelstr. 15, 97070 Würzburg, **W:** charivari.fm and gong.fm Also rel. Radio Opera – **29)** Am Funkhaus 1, 63743 Aschaffenburg, **W:** radio-primavera.de – **30),31)** Seifartshofstr. 21, 96450 Coburg, **W:** radioeins.com – **32)** Gutenbergstr. 5, 96050 Bamberg, **W:** radio-bamberg.de – **33)** Postfach 10 11 61, 95411 Bayreuth (studio location: Richard-Wagner-Str. 33), **W:** mainwelle.de – **34)** E.C.-Baumann-Str. 5, 95326 Kulmbach, **W:** radio-plassenburg.de – **35)** 0900-1000, 1200-1300 and 1800-2000 extra–radio, Postfach 1745, 95016 Hof (studio location: Kreuzsteinstr. 2-6), **W:** extra-radio.de otherwise: R. Euroherz, Pfarr 1, 95028 Hof, **W:** euroherz.de – **36)** Unterer Markt 35, 92637 Weiden, **W:** ramasuri.de – **37), 38)** Lilienthalstr. 3c, 93049 Regensburg **W:** radiocharivari.de and gongfm.de – **39), 40)** Bahnhofstr. 28, 94469 Deggendorf, **W:** unserradio.de – **41)** Medienstr. 5, 94036 Passau, **W:** as stn. 40) – **42)** Altstadt 361, 84028 Landshut, **W:** radio-trausnitz.de – **43)** Donaustr. 11, 85049 Ingolstadt, **W:** radio-in.de rel. 0500-0900 on 94.6/101.2MHz R. ND1 – **44)** Hitwelle no longer in FM, freq. surrendered to Rockantenne – **45)** Schöngeisingerstr. 11, 82256 Fürstenfeldbruck, **W:** radio1064.de – **46)** Postfach 1752, 82467 Garmisch-Partenkirchen (studio location: Marienplatz 17), **W:** radio-oberland.de – **47) W:** radio-alpenwelle.de – **48)** Hafnerstr. 5-7, 83022 Rosenheim, **W:** radio-charivari.de – **49)** Mozartstr. 3a, 84508 Burgkirchen/Alz, **W:** inn-salzach-welle.de – **50)** Rupertistr. 40-42, 83278 Traunstein, **W:** radio-chiemgau.de – **51)** untersrw.de **N.B** stns 49), 50), 51) also rel. prgr. of independent producers
**DAB:** 16 txs on ch. 5C, use see K) – Erlangen tx on ch. 6A Funklus – 3 txs on ch. 8C, 15 txs on ch. 10A, 4 txs on ch. 10B, 7 txs on ch. 12D Rockantenne, Absolut Hot, Kultradio, Ego FM and some BR prgr. – 47 txs on ch. 11D most BR prgr. and Antenne Bayernt – Augsburg tx on ch. 9C, Nürnberg tx on ch. 10C, Ingolstadt tx on ch. 11A, München txs on ch. 11C 11 stns – München tx on ch. 12A engineering tests

## M) BERLIN & BRANDENBURG
**Media institution:** Medienanstalt Berlin-Brandenburg (MABB) ✉ Kleine Präsidentenstraße 1, 10178 Berlin ☎ +49 30 264 9670 📠 +49 30 264 96730 **W:** mabb.de

**Berlin txs:**

| FM | MHz | kW | Site | Station |
|---|---|---|---|---|
| 14) | 87.9 | 1 | Alexanderplatz | Star FM |
| 27) | 88.4 | 2 | Winterfeldtstraße | (shared) |
| 24) | 89.2 | *0.5 | Schäferberg | R. Potsdam |
| 19) | 90.2 | 16 | Alexanderplatz | R. Teddy |
| 27) | 90.7 | 0.1 | Schäferberg | (shared) |
| 16) | 91.0 | 1 | Winterfeldtstraße | ALEX |
| 2) | 91.4 | 100 | Alexanderplatz | Berliner Rundfunk |
| 10) | 93.6 | 3 | Alexanderplatz | JAM FM |
| 3) | 94.3 | 20 | Alexanderplatz | rs2 |
| 12) | 94.8 | 4 | Schäferberg | BBC WS |
| 17) | 96.7 | 0.8 | Winterfeldtstraße | RFI |
| 13) | 97.2 | 0.2 | Winterfeldtstraße | R. Russkij |
| 9) | 98.2 | 8 | Scholzplatz | R. Paradiso |
| 11) | 98.8 | 1 | Alexanderplatz | KISS FM |
| 4) | 100.6 | 13 | Alexanderplatz | Flux FM |
| 8) | 101.3 | 5 | Alexanderplatz | Klassik R. |
| 15) | 101.9 | 0.5 | Alexanderplatz | Metropol FM |
| 5) | 103.4 | 10 | Alexanderplatz | Energy Berlin |
| 18) | 104.1 | 0.6 | Winterfeldtstraße | KCRW Berlin |
| 6) | 104.6 | 10 | Alexanderplatz | 104.6 RTL |
| 7) | 105.5 | 5 | Alexanderplatz | Spreeradio |
| 21) | 106.0 | 1 | Alexanderplatz | R. B2 |
| 12) | 106.8 | 2 | Scholzplatz | Jazz R. |
| 1) | 107.5 | 40 | Alexanderplatz | BB R. |
| *) directional towards Potsdam | | | | |

**Brandenburg txs:**

| FM | MHz | kW | Site | Station |
|---|---|---|---|---|
| 24) | 87.6 | 0.4 | Brandenburg/Havel | R. Potsdam |
| 5) | 87.6 | 0.2 | Prenzlau | Energy Berlin |
| 6) | 88.0 | 1 | Crinitz | 104.6 RTL |
| 20) | 88.3 | 0.5 | Neuruppin | Power R. |
| 6) | 89.5 | 0.5 | Elsterwerda-Hohenl. | 104.6 RTL |
| 23) | 90.3 | 0.5 | Spremberg | R. Cottbus |
| 9) | 90.4 | 0.2 | Guben-Reichenbach | R. Paradiso |
| 1) | 90.9 | 0.8 | Rhinow | BB R. |
| 3) | 91.3 | 1 | Lauchhammer West | rs2 |
| 5) | 91.6 | 1.3 | Casekow | Energy Berlin |
| 21) | 91.6 | 0.5 | Cottbus-Klein Oßnig | R. B2 |
| 5) | 91.7 | 0.1 | Herzberg/Elster | Energy Berlin |
| 23) | 92.1 | 1 | Guben-Reichenbach | R. Cottbus |
| 20) | 93.3 | 0.5 | Schwedt | Power R. |
| 22) | 93.9 | 3 | Fürstenwalde | HitRadio SKW |
| 20) | 94.4 | 1.3 | Perleberg | Power R. |
| 23) | 94.5 | 0.3 | Cottbus-Madlow | R. Cottbus |
| 3) | 94.7 | 3 | Booßen (Frankf./O.) | rs2 |
| 1) | 95.0 | 0.8 | Angermünde | BB R. |
| 20) | 95.2 | 0.4 | Belzig-Lütte | Power R. |
| 20) | 95.3 | 0.1 | Fürstenwalde | Power R. |
| 25) | 95.3 | 0.6 | Potsdam | BHeins |
| 1) | 95.4 | 0.8 | Eberswalde | BB R. |
| 9) | 95.5 | 0.2 | Eisenhüttenstadt | R. Paradiso |
| 3) | 95.6 | 1.3 | Cottbus-Klein Oßnig | rs2 |
| 5) | 96.6 | 0.5 | Wittstock | Energy Berlin |
| 3) | 96.7 | 1 | Crinitz | rs2 |
| 6) | 96.9 | 1 | Luckenwalde | 104.6 RTL |
| 21) | 97.0 | 0.6 | Potsdam | R. B2 |
| 28) | 98.0 | 0.7 | Booßen (Frankf./O.) | Pure FM |

| FM | MHz | kW | Site | Station |
|---|---|---|---|---|
| 20) | 99.1 | 0.5 | Erkner | Power R. |
| 19) | 99.3 | 0.8 | Booßen (Frankf./O.) | R. Teddy |
| 3) | 100.1 | 3 | Lübben | rs2 |
| 2) | 100.9 | 5 | Casekow | Berliner Rundfunk |
| 21) | 101.1 | 0.5 | Fürstenwalde | R. B2 |
| 1) | 102.1 | 20 | Casekow | BB-R. |
| 20) | 102.1 | 0.6 | Potsdam | Power R. |
| 2) | 102.2 | 3 | Cottbus-Klein Oßnig | Berliner Rundfunk |
| 23) | 102.7 | 0.5 | Forst | R. Cottbus |
| 1) | 103.7 | 0.6 | Eisenhüttenstadt | BB R. |
| 26) | 103.8 | 1.5 | Großräschen | Lausitzwelle |
| 3) | 103.9 | 6 | Forst | rs2 |
| 2) | 104.2 | 20 | Booßen (Frankf./O.) | Berliner Rundfunk |
| 1) | 104.3 | 100 | Pritzwalk-Buchholz | BB R. |
| 21) | 104.9 | 0.8 | Eberswalde | R. B2 |
| 1) | 105.0 | 3 | Brandenburg-Krahne | BB R. |
| 22) | 105.1 | 0.8 | Königs Wusterh. | HitRadio SKW |
| 9) | 105.9 | 1.6 | Booßen (Frankf./O.) | R. Paradiso |
| 3) | 106.3 | 4 | Spremberg | rs2 |
| 21) | 106.9 | 0.2 | Frankfurt/Oder | R. B2 |
| 1) | 107.2 | 100 | Calau | BB R. |
| 3) | 107.3 | 12 | Casekow | rs2 |
| 1) | 107.8 | 30 | Booßen (Frankf./O.) | BB R. |
| 1) | 107.9 | 5 | Gransee | BB R. |

**Addresses & other information:**
**1)** Großbeerenstr. 185, 14482 Potsdam; **W:** bbradio.de AC, with short local insertions – **2)** Grunewaldstr. 3, 12165 Berlin; **W:** berliner-rundfunk.de Oldies – **3)** as stn. 2); **W:** rs2.de AC – **4)** Pfuelstr. 5, 10997 Berlin; **W:** fluxfm.de Alternative – **5)** Hardenbergstr. 4-5, 10623 Berlin; **W:** energy.de/berlin. CHR – **6), 7)** Kurfürstendamm 207-208, 10719 Berlin; **W:** 104.6rtl.com (CHR), spreeradio.de (oldies) – **8)** see O) – **9)** Am Kleinen Wannsee 5, 14109 Berlin; **W:** paradiso.de Soft AC. Run by Protestant church – **10)** as stn. 9); **W:** jamfm.de Black, also via Astra 1M, 12.460GHz – **11)** as stn. 2); **W:** kissfm.de CHR – **12)** See International Broadcasting section under UK – **13)** Kochstr. 54, 10969 Berlin; **W:** radio-rb.de In Russian – **14)** Dircksenstr. 48, 10178 Berlin; **W:** starfm.de Rock – **15)** Markgrafenstr. 11, 10969 Berlin, **W:** metropolfm.de prgr. in Turkish. Further txs see K) and T) – **16)** Voltastr. 5, 13355 Berlin; **W:** alex-berlin.de Citizen radio, run by MABB – **17)** See International Broadcasting section under France – **18)** 1900 Pico Blvd., Santa Monica, CA 90405, USA; **W:** kcrw.com. Replaced Berlin operation of NPR in 2017 – **19)** August-Bebel-Str. 26-53, 14482 Potsdam; **W:** radioteddy.de childrens prgr., also via Astra 2C, 12.148GHz h. Further txs see P), Q), T) – **20)** Potsdamer Str. 131, 10783 Berlin; **W:** powerradio918.de Oldies – **21)** Pfalzburger Str. 43-44, 10717 Berlin; **W:** radiob2.de German "Schlager" – **22)** Karl-Marx-Str. 116, 15745 Wildau; **W:** hitradio-skw.de Oldies – **23)** Schloßkirchplatz 3, 03046 Cottbus; **W:** radiocottbus.de AC – **24)** Brandenburger Str. 48, 14467 Potsdam; **W:** radio-potsdam.de – **25)** August-Bebel-Str. 26-53, Fach 43, 14482 Potsdam; **W:** bheins.de – **26)** see V), stn. 8) – **27)** Shared use by various programmers, organized by stn. 16) **W:** 88vier. de – **28)** Wichertstr. 16, 10439 Berlin; **W:** pure-fm.de
**DAB:** 8 txs on ch. 5C see K) – Alexanderplatz tx on ch. 7B Mega R. SNA (rel. R. Sputnik, see International Broadcasting section under Russia), R. B2, R. Paradiso, R. Paloma, Pure FM, ERF Pop and other, frequently changing channels

## N) BREMEN
**Media institution:** Bremische Landesmedienanstalt (Brema) 🖃 Grünenweg 26, 28215 Bremen ☎ +49 421 334940 🖷 +49 421 323533 **W:** bremische-landesmedienanstalt.de

| FM | MHz | kW | Site | Station |
|---|---|---|---|---|
| 1) | 89.8 | 1 | Bremen-Walle | Energy Bremen |
| 4) | 90.7 | 0.2 | Bremerhaven | R. Weser TV |
| 4) | 92.5 | 0.2 | Bremen Neuenstr. | R. Weser TV |
| 3) | 97.2 | 0.5 | Bremen-Walle | Metropol FM |
| 1) | 104.3 | 8 | Bremerhaven | Energy Bremen |
| 2) | 104.8 | 0.1 | Bremen-Walle | R. Teddy |
| 5) | 107.6 | 0.2 | Bremen-Walle | R. 21 |
| 2) | 107.9 | 0.3 | Bremerhaven | R. Teddy |

**Addresses & other information:**
**1)** Erste Schlachtpforte, 28195 Bremen; **W:** energy.de/bremen CHR – **2)** see M), stn. 19 – **3)** see M) – **4)** Richtweg 14, 28195 Bremen; **W:** radioweser.tv Citizen radio – **5)** see R)
**DAB:** Txs on ch. 5C see K)

## O) HAMBURG & SCHLESWIG-HOLSTEIN
**Media institution:** Medienanstalt Hamburg / Schleswig-Holstein (MA HSH) 🖃 Rathausallee 72-76, 22846 Norderstedt ☎ +49 40 3690050 🖷 +49 40 36900555 **W:** ma-hsh.de

| FM | R.SH | delta | Bob | Klass. | kW |
|---|---|---|---|---|---|
| Ahrensburg | – | 96.5 | – | – | 2 |
| Bredstedt | – | – | 98.1 | – | 0.1 |
| Bungsberg (Eutin) | 100.2 | 104.1 | 106.2 | 97.2 | 2x50/0.2 |
| Flensburg-Freienwill | 101.4 | 105.6 | – | – | 20 |
| Flensburg-Harrislee | – | – | 88.5 | 106.5 | 0.5 |
| Garding | – | – | 94.1 | 91.7 | 0.5 |
| Hamburg-Bergedorf | 102.0 | 107.7 | 93.7 | – | 0.1 |
| Hamburg Hertz-T. | 100.0 | 93.4 | – | 98.1 | 2x2/0.1 |
| Heide-Welmbüttel | 103.8 | 100.4 | – | – | 15 |
| Heide (town) | – | – | 96.9 | – | 0.3 |
| Helgoland (island) | 100.0 | 103.5 | 101.6 | 89.8 | 0.1 |
| Husum | – | 92.0 | – | – | 0.1 |
| Itzehoe | – | – | 104.9 | 92.7 | 1/0.5 |
| Kaltenkirchen | 102.9 | 107.4 | 101.1 | – | 20 |
| Kiel | 102.4 | 105.9 | 97.0 | 97.4 | 2x15/0.3 |
| Lauenburg | 102.5 | 105.6 | 97.4 | – | 1/1/0.3 |
| Lübeck | – | – | 91.5 | – | 0.3 |
| Mölln-Berkenthin | 101.5 | 107.9 | 91.5 | 93.6 | 2x20/0.3 |
| Neumünster | – | – | 88.9 | – | 0.5 |
| Niebüll | – | – | 107.2 | 94.7 | 0.2 |
| Rendsburg | – | – | 93.6 | 92.9 | 0.5 |
| Schleswig (town) | – | – | 92.4 | 100.8 | 1/0.5 |
| Schleswig-Borgwedel | – | – | – | 93.9 | 0.5 |
| Westerland (Sylt) | 102.8 | 104.8 | 89.1 | 89.8 | 5/5/1/0.5 |

**Addresses & other information:**
**R.SH** (AC), **delta radio** (CHR), **R. Bob** (rock): Wittland 3, 24109 Kiel; **W:** rsh.de deltaradio.de radiobob.de – **Klassik R.**: Postfach 57 03 60, 22772 Hamburg (studio location: Planckstr. 15); **W:** klassikradio.de Light classical and lounge music. Further txs see K), L), M), R). Also via Astra 1M, 12.460GHz

**Hamburg area only:**

| FM | MHz | kW | Site | Station |
|---|---|---|---|---|
| 1) | 88.1 | 0.1 | Bergedorf | Hamburg Zwei |
| 1) | 88.5 | 2 | Otterndorf*) | R. Hamburg |
| 2) | 91.7 | 0.1 | H.-Hertz-Turm | 917xfm |
| 2) | 93.6 | 2 | Otterndorf*) | Alsterradio |
| 1) | 95.0 | 0.1 | H.-Hertz-Turm | Hamburg Zwei |
| 3) | 97.1 | 0.1 | H.-Hertz-Turm | Energy Hamburg |
| 3) | 100.9 | 0.1 | Bergedorf | Energy Hamburg |
| 3) | 101.6 | 0.1 | Wedel | Energy Hamburg |
| 1) | 103.6 | 80 | Moorfleet | R. Hamburg |
| 1) | 104.0 | 0.2 | H.-Hertz-Turm | R. Hamburg |
| 1) | 105.8 | 0.5 | Ahrensburg | Hamburg Zwei |
| 2) | 106.8 | 40 | Rahlstedt | 106!8 rock'n pop |

*) tx in Niedersachsen, serving Neuwerk and Scharhörn islands (belonging to Hamburg)

**Addresses & other information:**
**1)** Postfach 10 01 23, 20001 Hamburg (studio location: Spitalerstraße 10); **W:** radiohamburg.de (AC), hamburg-zwei.de (former Oldie 95, relaunched in 2014) – **2)** Messberg 4, 20095 Hamburg; **W:** 106acht. de (AC), 917xfm.de (alternative) – **3)** Winterhuder Marktplatz 6, 22299 Hamburg; **W:** energy.de/hamburg CHR

**Non-commercial stations:**

| FM | MHz | kW | Site | Station |
|---|---|---|---|---|
| 1) | 93.0 | 0.1 | Hamburg Hertz-Turm | Freies Sender Kombinat |
| 2) | 96.0 | 0.1 | Hamburg Hertz-Turm | TIDE 96.0 / HLR |
| 4) | 97.6 | 0.5 | Garding | OK Westküste |
| 5) | 98.8 | 0.5 | Lübeck-Stockelsdorf | OK Lübeck |
| 4) | 98.8 | 0.1 | Husum | OK Westküste |
| 3) | 101.2 | 0.1 | Kiel | Kiel FM |
| 5) | 105.2 | 0.1 | Heide | OK Westküste |

**Addresses & other information:**
**1)** Schulterblatt 23c, 20357 Hamburg; **W:** fsk-hh.org – **2)** TIDE 96.0, Uferstraße 2, 22081 Hamburg; **W:** tidenet.de Run by Hamburg Media School. Mon 0500-2300 and thorough Tue 0500 til Sun 0500. **Hamburger Lokalradio**, Kulturzentrum LOLA, Lohbrügger Landstraße 8, 21031 Hamburg; **W:** hhlr.de On 96.0MHz Sun 0500 til Mon 0500 and night Mon/Tue 2300-0500 – **3)** Hamburger Chaussee 36, 24113 Kiel; **W:** kielfm.de – **4)** Landvogt-Johannsen-Str. 11, 25746 Heide; **W:** okwestkueste.de – **5)** Kanalstr. 42-48, 23554 Lübeck; **W:** ok-luebeck.de **DAB:** Hamburg/Kiel txs on ch. 5C see K) – Hamburg tx on ch. 11C FSK, HLR, R. Paradiso, Mega R. (rel. R. Sputnik), Mauma FM, Pure FM, 80s80s.

## P) HESSEN
**Media institution:** Hessische Landesanstalt für Privaten Rundfunk (LPR) 🖃 Wilhelmshöher Allee 262, 34131 Kassel ☎ +49 561 935860 🖷 +49 561 9358630; **W:** lpr-hessen.de

| FM | FFH | plan. | Bob | Ant harm | kW |
|---|---|---|---|---|---|
| Alsfeld | 88.1 | – | 101.5 | – 94.1 | 4/0.1 |
| Bad Camberg | – | 99.8 | – | – 105.4 | 0.5 |

| FM | FFH | plan. | Bob | Ant | harm | kW |
|---|---|---|---|---|---|---|
| Bad Hersfeld | 95.9 | – | 99.8 | – | 88.4 | 0.1/0.3 |
| Bad Nauheim | – | 104.6 | 106.6 | 90.7 | 100.4 | 0.3/1 |
| Bensheim | – | – | 103.3 | – | 107.5 | 0.2 |
| Bingen | 106.9 | 103.4 | – | – | 101.8 | 0.2/0.3 |
| Butzbach | – | – | – | – | – | 0.1 |
| Darmstadt | – | 91.1 | 92.4 | 100.8 | 93.0 | 0.2/0.5 |
| Delkenheim | – | – | – | 88.0 | – | 0.3 |
| Dieburg | – | 90.1 | 99.5 | – | 104.7 | 1/0.2 |
| Dillenburg | 100.0 | – | – | – | – | 30 |
| Driedorf | 106.8 | – | – | – | – | 30 |
| Eisenberg | – | 100.3 | – | – | – | 50 |
| Eltville | 90.3 | – | – | – | – | 0.2 |
| Eschwege | – | 104.6 | 103.0 | – | 88.3 | 0.5/0.3 |
| Feldberg | 105.9 | – | – | – | – | 100 |
| Frankfurt | – | 100.2 | 101.4 | 95.1 | 97.6 | 1/0.1 |
| Fritzlar | – | – | 88.4 | – | 106.6 | 0.1 |
| Fulda | – | 99.9 | 105.7 | – | 95.7 | 0.2/0.3 |
| Gelnhausen | – | 93.9 | – | – | – | 0.2 |
| Gießen | – | 93.7 | 92.6 | 105.2 | 102.0 | 0.5/0.1 |
| Glashütten | – | – | – | – | 93.2 | 0.5 |
| Habichtsw. | 103.7 | – | – | – | – | 20 |
| Hanau | – | – | – | 97.3 | 106.8 | 0.5 |
| Heidelstein* | 100.9 | – | – | – | – | 50 |
| Hofgeismar | – | – | 88.8 | – | – | 0.1 |
| Hoherodskopf | – | – | 94.7 | – | – | 0.1 |
| Homberg | – | – | 99.3 | – | – | 0.1 |
| H. Meißner | 105.1 | – | – | – | – | 100 |
| Idstein | – | – | – | – | 93.2 | 0.5 |
| Kassel | – | 104.6 | 99.4 | – | 96.6 | 0.5/0.2 |
| Krehberg | 105.0 | – | – | – | – | 20 |
| Korbach | 107.7 | 94.0 | 96.5 | – | 107.4 | 20/0.2 |
| Limburg | – | 97.6 | 90.2 | – | 92.1 | 0.5/0.2 |
| Marburg | – | 101.0 | 103.9 | – | 96.2 | 0.3/0.1 |
| Michelstadt | 96.1 | – | 98.5 | – | 104.6 | 0.1/1 |
| Offenbach | – | – | – | – | 99.3 | 0.3 |
| Reinhardshain | – | 92.9 | – | – | – | 0.2 |
| Rimberg | – | – | 90.5 | – | – | 0.1 |
| Rotenburg | – | – | 96.8 | – | 104.5 | 0.3/0.1 |
| Schlüchtern | – | – | 101.3 | – | – | 0.2 |
| Schotten | – | – | 94.7 | – | – | 0.1 |
| Vogelsberg | – | – | 94.7 | – | – | 0.1 |
| Wetzlar | – | 103.7 | 88.2 | 105.0 | 101.3 | 0.3/0.5 |
| Wiesbaden | 102.0 | 90.1 | 101.4 | 95.1 | 88.2 | 0.1/0.5 |

**N.B.** Klassik Radio txs have been closed down.
**Addresses & other information:**
**Hit-R. FFH** (AC), **Planet R.** (black/CHR), **harmony.fm** (oldies): FFH-Platz 1, 61111 Bad Vilbel; **W:** ffh.de planet-radio.de harmonyfm.de also via Astra 1L, 12.633GHz – **R. Bob**, Friedrich-Ebert-Str. 2, 34117 Kassel; **W:** radiobob.de Rock – **Antenne Frankfurt**, Rüsselsheimer Str. 22, 60326 Frankfurt am Main; **W:** antenne-frankfurt.de

**Other stations:**

| FM | MHz | kW | Site | Station |
|---|---|---|---|---|
| 8) | 90.0 | 0.1 | Wetzlar | ERF Pop |
| 5) | 90.1 | 0.1 | Marburg-Lahnberge | R. Unerhört |
| 3) | 90.9 | 0.3 | Rüsselsheim | R. Rüsselsheim |
| 9) | 91.7 | 0.2 | Kassel | R. Teddy |
| 1) | 91.8 | 0.1 | Frankfurt-Ginnheim | R. X |
| 9) | 93.5 | 0.1 | Rotenburg | R. Teddy |
| 9) | 93.8 | 0.3 | Bad Hersfeld | R. Teddy |
| 2) | 92.5 | 0.1 | Wiesbaden | R. RheinWelle 92,5 |
| 7) | 96.5 | 0.3 | Witzenhausen | RundFunk Meißner |
| 10) | 99.2 | 0.3 | Fulda | Domradio |
| 9) | 99.4 | 0.1 | Sontra | RundFunk Meißner |
| 7) | 99.7 | 0.5 | Eschwege | RundFunk Meißner |
| 7) | 102.6 | 0.3 | Hessisch Lichtenau | RundFunk Meißner |
| 9) | 102.8 | 0.3 | Fulda | R. Teddy |
| 4) | 103.8 | 0.3 | Darmstadt | R. Darmstadt |
| 6) | 105.8 | 0.5 | Kassel Tannenwäldchen | Freies R. Kassel |

**Addresses & other information:**
**1)** Schützenstr. 12, 60311 Frankfurt; **W:** radiox.de – **2)** Postfach 49 20, 65039 Wiesbaden; **W:** rheinwelle.de – **3)** Ludwigstr. 13-15, 65428 Rüsselsheim; **W:** radio2r.de – **4)** Steubenplatz 12, 64293 Darmstadt; **W:** radiodarmstadt.de – **5)** Rudolf-Bultmann-Str. 2b, 35039 Marburg, **W:** radio-rum.de – **6), 7)** Niederhoner Str. 1, 37269 Eschwege, **W:** eschwege.de/rfm – **8)** Berliner Ring 62, 35576 Wetzlar, **W:** erf.de German affiliate of Trans World Radio (see International Broadcasting section under USA/Austria), now mostly using digital platforms – **9)** see M) – **10)** see S)
**DAB:** 7 txs on ch. 5C see K) – Feldberg/Frankfurt/Mainz txs on ch. 11C FFH, Harmony FM, Planet R., Absolut Hot, R. Teddy, Mega R. (rel. R. Sputnik)

## Q) MECKLENBURG-VORPOMMERN

**Media institution:** Medienanstalt Mecklenburg-Vorpommern ✉Bleicheufer 1, 19053 Schwerin ☎ +49 385 5588 10 🖷 +49 385 5588 130 **W:** medienanstalt-mv.de

| Location | A.MV | Osts | Parad | Tedd | B2 | kW |
|---|---|---|---|---|---|---|
| Ahrenshoop | – | – | 103.3 | – | – | 0.6 |
| Demmin | – | 107.9 | – | – | – | 0.2 |
| Garz (Rügen) | 105.1 | 107.6 | – | – | – | 50 |
| Greifswald | – | – | – | – | 87.8 | 0.8 |
| Grevesmühlen | 105.8 | 94.7 | – | – | – | 0.2/0.1 |
| Güstrow | 107.7 | 98.0 | – | – | – | 1/0.4 |
| Helpterberg | 103.8 | 105.8 | – | – | – | 100 |
| Heringsdorf | 105.4 | 103.3 | – | – | – | 10/2 |
| Röbel | 93.8 | 92.2 | – | – | – | 50/0.1 |
| Rostock | 100.8 | 104.8 | 89.7 | 95.8 | 106.5 | 130/0.1 |
| Schwerin | 101.3 | 107.3 | 103.9 | 102.9 | 90.1 | 100/0.2 |
| Stralsund | – | – | 103.6 | 93.0 | 98.9 | 0.1/0.4 |
| Waren | 98.3 | 93.0 | – | – | – | 0.2/0.1 |
| Wismar | 88.7 | 93.7 | – | (F.Pl.) | – | 0.2/0.1 |
| Wolgast | – | 100.0 | – | – | – | 0.5 |

**Addresses & other information:**
**Antenne MV**, Rosa-Luxemburg-Straße 25/26, 18055 Rostock; **W:** antennemv.de AC – **Ostseewelle**, Warnowufer 59a, 18057 Rostock; **W:** ostseewelle.de CHR – **Radio Paradiso, Radio Teddy, Radio B2** see M)

**Local stations:**

| FM | MHz | kW | Site | Station |
|---|---|---|---|---|
| 1) | 88.0 | 0.8 | Neubrandenburg | NB-Radiotreff |
| 3) | 90.2 | 0.1 | Rostock | LOHRO |
| 5) | 92.4 | 0.1 | Rostock | sunshine live |
| 2) | 98.1 | 0.2 | Greifswald | R. 98eins |
| 1) | 98.7 | 0.1 | Malchin | NB-Radiotreff |
| 4) | 105.6 | 0.2 | Rostock | Jazz Radio |

**Addresses & other information:**
**1)** Treptower Str. 9, 17033 Neubrandenburg; **W:** nb-radiotreff.de run by Medienanstalt, also prgr. from Malchin studio – **2)** Domstr. 12, 17489 Greifswald; **W:** 98eins.de run by university, Mon-Fri 1800-2200 only, otherwise rel. stn. 1) – **3)** Margaretenstr. 43, 18057 Rostock; **W:** lohro.de non-commercial – **4)** see M), stn. 12 – **5)** see K), stn. 18
**DAB:** Schwerin tx on ch. 5C (see K)

## R) NIEDERSACHSEN

**Media institution:** Niedersächsische Landesmedienanstalt für privaten Rundfunk (NLM), ✉Seelhorststraße 18, 30175 Hannover ☎ +49 511 28477 0 🖷 +49 511 28477 36 **W:** nlm.de

| FM | ffn | Ant. | R. 21 | Klass | kW |
|---|---|---|---|---|---|
| Aurich | 103.1 | 104.9 | 100.6 | – | 2x25/1 |
| Bad Rehburg | – | – | 89.4 | – | 0.5 |
| Barsinghausen | 101.9 | 103.8 | – | – | 25 |
| Braunschw.-Broitzem | 103.1 | 106.9 | 104.1 | – | 15/13/1 |
| Buxtehude | – | – | 106.0 | – | 1 |
| Celle | – | – | 93.5 | – | 0.2 |
| Cuxhaven | – | – | 106.6 | – | 0.6 |
| Cuxhaven-Otterndorf | 102.6 | 104.6 | – | – | 20 |
| Dannenberg-Zernien | 102.7 | 106.1 | – | – | 25 |
| Delmenhorst | – | – | 107.6 | – | 0.1 |
| Goslar | – | – | 87.7 | – | 0.5 |
| Göttingen | 102.8 | 106.0 | 93.4 | – | 2x5/1 |
| Hannoversch Münden | 100.7 | 106.7 | – | – | 0.5 |
| Hannover | – | – | 104.9 | 107.4 | 0.5/0.2 |
| Helmstedt | – | – | 94.1 | – | 0.5 |
| Hildesheim | – | – | 105.8 | – | 1 |
| Holzminden | 102.2 | 105.7 | – | – | 0.5 |
| Leer-Nüttermoor | – | – | 104.5 | – | 0.3 |
| Lingen-Damaschke | 101.5 | 104.3 | 106.9 | – | 2x15/0.5 |
| Lüneburg | – | – | 91.9 | – | 0.1 |
| Oldenburg | – | – | 104.1 | – | 0.2 |
| Osnabrück | 103.4 | 105.9 | 95.3 | – | 2x10/0.1 |
| Rosengarten | 100.6 | 105.1 | – | – | 20 |
| Seesen | – | 100.9 | – | – | 0.1 |
| Stade | – | – | 97.3 | – | 0.2 |
| Steinkimmen | 102.3 | 105.7 | – | – | 100 |
| Torfhaus (Harz) | 102.4 | 106.3 | – | – | 100 |
| Uelzen | – | – | 99.7 | – | 0.5 |
| Visselhövede | 101.7 | 104.2 | 90.1 | – | 2x10/1 |
| Wilhelmshaven | – | – | 99.1 | – | 0.3 |
| Wolfsburg | – | – | 99.1 | – | 0.5 |

**NB.** Bremen txs on Hit-R. Antenne and R. 21 see N). R. Hamburg / 106!8 rock'n pop txs at Cuxhaven see O)
**Addresses & other information:**
**R. ffn**, Stiftszenstr. 12, 30159 Hannover; **W:** ffn.de AC – **Hit-R. Antenne**, Goseriede 9, 30159 Hannover; **W:** antenne.com. AC –

**R. 21**, An der Feuerwache 3-5, 30823 Garbsen; **W:** radio21.de Rock, cooperates with Rockland Radio, see T) – **Klassik R.** see O)

**Regional stations:**

| FM | MHz | kW | Site | Station |
|----|------|-----|------|---------|
| 13) | 87.6 | 0.1 | Hannover Telemax | R. Hannover |
| 4) | 87.7 | 0.2 | Emden | R. Ostfriesland |
| 3) | 87.8 | 1 | Wilhelmshaven | R. Jade |
| 1) | 88.0 | 1 | Uelzen | R. ZuSa |
| 18) | 88.2 | 0.3 | Norden | R. Nordseewelle |
| 1) | 89.7 | 0.5 | Dannenberg-Zernien | R. ZuSa |
| 17) | 90.4 | (F.Pl.) | Oldenburg | R. Oldenburg |
| 18) | 90.6 | 0.2 | Borkum | R. Nordseewelle |
| 16) | 93.8 | 0.1 | Wolfsburg | R. 38 |
| 4) | 94.0 | 1 | Aurich-Haxtum | R. Ostfriesland |
| 8) | 94.8 | 0.1 | Bad Pyrmont | R. Aktiv |
| 2) | 95.2 | 0.2 | Nordhorn | Ems-Vechte-Welle |
| 1) | 95.5 | 1 | Lüneburg | R. ZuSa |
| 5) | 95.6 | 1 | Lingen-Schepsdorf | Ems-Vechte-Welle |
| 14) | 98.2 | 0.3 | Osnabrück | R. Osnabrück |
| 5) | 99.3 | 1 | Molbergen-Cloppenburg | Ems-Vechte-Welle |
| 18) | 99.5 | 1 | Aurich | R. Nordseewelle |
| 8) | 100.0 | 0.3 | Hameln | R. Aktiv |
| 12) | 100.0 | 0.1 | Hannover Bettfedernf. | R. Flora |
| 18) | 100.1 | 1 | Neuharlingersiel | R. Nordseewelle |
| 16) | 100.3 | 15 | Braunschweig Drachenb. | R. 38 |
| 15) | 103.3 | 0.6 | Nienburg | R. Mittelweser |
| 4) | 103.9 | 0.2 | Leer | R. Ostfriesland |
| 18) | 104.0 | 1 | Norderney | R. Nordseewelle |
| 10) | 104.6 | 0.5 | Braunschweig-Broitzem | R. Okerwelle |
| 6) | 104.8 | 1 | Osnabrück | OS R. 104,8 |
| 11) | 105.3 | 1 | Hildesheim | R. Tonkuhle |
| 2) | 106.5 | 1 | Oldenburg-Wahnbek | Oldenburg Eins |
| 7) | 106.5 | 0.3 | Hannover Telemaxx tower | Leinehertz |
| 9) | 107.1 | 1 | Göttingen | StadtR. Gött. |

**Addresses and other information:**
**1)** Ilmenauufer 47, 29525 Uelzen and Scharnhorststr. 1, 21335 Lüneburg; **W:** zusa.de – **2)** Bahnhofstr. 11, 26122 Oldenburg; **W:** oeins.de – **3)** Kieler Str. 31, 26382 Wilhelmshaven; **W:** radio-jade.de – **4)** VHS Emden, An der Berufsschule 3, 26721 Emden; **W:** radio-ostfriesland.com – **5)** Halle IV, Kaiserstr. 10a, 49809 Lingen; **W:** emsvechtewelle.de – **6)** Lohstr. 45a, 49074 Osnabrück; **W:** os-radio.de – **7)** Hildesheimer Str. 29, 30169 Hannover; **W:** leinehertz.de – **8)** Hefehof 23, 31785 Hameln; **W:** radio-aktiv.de – **9)** Groner Str. 2, 37073 Göttingen; **W:** stadtradio-goettingen.de – **10)** Rebenring 18, 38106 Braunschweig; **W:** okerwelle. de – **11)** Andreas-Passage 1, 31134 Hildesheim; **W:** tonkuhle.de – **12)** Zur Bettfedernfabrik 3, 30451 Hannover; **W:** radioflora.de on 100.0MHz during special events, otherwise via webstream only – **13)** Münzstr. 3/4, 30159 Hannover; **W:** radio-hannover.de – **14)** Jürgensort 10, 49074 Osnabrück; **W:** radioosnabrueck.com – **15)** Wölper Str. 122, 31582 Nienburg; **W:** radionienburg.de – **16)** Hintern Brüdern 23, 38100 Braunschweig; **W:** radio38.de – **17)** Annenheider Str. 159, 27755 Delmenhorst; **W:** radio-oldenburg.de – **18)** Am Markt 6, 26506 Norden; **W:** radio-nordseewelle.de

**Permanent special stns: R. S.A.S.** (**W:** radio-sas.de), Stadthagen 94.5MHz; **Lamberti-Kirchenfunk** (**W:** soerenkoenig.com/ Radlam) Aurich 106.0MHz; **Kirchenfunk Esterwegen**, 106.6MHz; **Kirchenfunk Lorup**, 107.6MHz; **Kirchenfunk Herzlake**, 106.1MHz; **Pfarrfunk Breitenberg**, 98.4MHz.; **Kirchenfunk Meppen**, 95.0MHz; **Pfarrradio Warsingsfehn**, Moormerland 95.2MHz; **DAB:** 6 txs on ch. 5C (see K)

## S) NORDRHEIN-WESTFALEN
**Media institution:** Landesanstalt für Medien Nordrhein-Westhalen (LFM) ✉Postfach 10 34 43, 40025 Düsseldorf (office location: Zollhof 2) ☎ +49 211 77 007 0 🖷 +49 211 727 170 **W:** lfm-nrw.de

**R. NRW**, Essener Str. 55, 46047 Oberhausen; **W:** radionrw.de The following stns are affiliates with some hours of own prgrs per day, other times rel. R. NRW with local IDs inserted automatically.

| FM | MHz | kW | Site | Station |
|----|------|-----|------|---------|
| 5) | 87.7 | 0.2 | Krefeld-Oppum | Welle Niederrhein |
| 26) | 88.1 | 4 | Eggegebirge | R. Hochstift |
| 19) | 88.2 | 0.5 | Lüdinghausen | R. Kiepenkerl |
| 37) | 88.2 | 0.5 | Siegen | R. Siegen |
| 35) | 88.3 | 0.1 | Meinerzhagen | R. MK |
| 16) | 88.4 | 1 | Bocholt | Westmünsterlandw. |
| 36) | 89.1 | 0.2 | Schmallenberg | R. Sauerland |
| 7) | 89.4 | 1 | Düsseldorf Rheinturm | NE-WS 89.4 |
| 6) | 90.1 | 0.3 | Mönchengladbach | R. 90,1 |
| 31) | 90.8 | 0.1 | Herne | Herne 90acht |
| 30) | 91.2 | 0.2 | Dortmund | R. 91.2 |
| 39) | 91.2 | 0.2 | Siegburg | R. Bonn/Rhein-Sieg |
| 42) | 91.4 | 0.1 | Bergheim | R. Erft |

| FM | MHz | kW | Site | Station |
|----|------|-----|------|---------|
| 35) | 91.5 | 0.1 | Altena | R. MK |
| 33) | 91.5 | 0.1 | Hattingen-Schierken | R. en |
| 3) | 91.7 | 0.1 | Moers-Meerbeck | R. K.W. |
| 23) | 91.7 | 0.1 | Vlotho | R. Herford |
| 4) | 92.2 | 0.1 | Duisburg | R. Duisburg |
| 35) | 92.5 | 0.3 | Iserlohn | R. MK |
| 20) | 92.6 | 1 | Sendenhorst | R. WAF |
| 43) | 92.7 | 0.5 | Düren-Hürtgenwald | R. Rur |
| 13) | 92.9 | 0.5 | Mülheim-Saarn | R. Mülheim |
| 29) | 92.9 | 0.1 | Selm | antenne unna |
| 16) | 93.0 | 0.5 | Ahaus | Westmünsterlandw. |
| 26) | 93.7 | 0.1 | Paderborn | R. Hochstift |
| 39) | 94.2 | 0.1 | Much-Wersch | R.Bonn/Rhein-Sieg |
| 9) | 94.3 | 0.2 | Solingen | R. RSG |
| 15) | 94.6 | 0.1 | Recklinghausen | Hit R. Vest |
| 20) | 94.7 | 0.2 | Warendorf | R. WAF |
| 36) | 94.8 | 0.1 | Marsberg | R. Sauerland |
| 23) | 94.9 | 0.5 | Herford | R. Herford |
| 18) | 95.1 | 0.1 | Rahden | R. Westfalica |
| 19) | 95.4 | 0.2 | Münster | Antenne Münster |
| 15) | 95.6 | 0.1 | Berghaltern | Hit R. Vest |
| 24) | 95.7 | 0.5 | Minden Jakobsberg | R. Westfalica |
| 20) | 95.7 | 0.3 | Beckum | R. WAF |
| 14) | 96.1 | 0.1 | Gelsenkirchen | REL |
| 36) | 96.2 | 0.4 | Olsberg-Antfeld | R. Sauerland |
| 20) | 96.3 | 0.3 | Oelde | R. WAF |
| 38) | 96.9 | 0.5 | Leverkusen-Opladen | R. Berg |
| 1) | 97.2 | 0.1 | Simmerath | Antenne AC |
| 35) | 97.2 | 0.1 | Werdohl | R. MK |
| 37) | 97.3 | 0.1 | Bad Laasphe | R. Siegen |
| 29) | 97.4 | 0.5 | Lünen | Antenne Unna |
| 11) | 97.6 | 4 | Langenberg | R. Neandertal |
| 16) | 97.6 | 1 | Borken | Westmünsterlandw. |
| 22) | 97.6 | 0.4 | Friedrichsdorf | R. Bielefeld |
| 39) | 97.8 | 0.5 | Bonn Venusberg | R. Bonn/Rhein-Sieg |
| 2) | 98.0 | 1 | Kleve | Antenne Niederrhein |
| 22) | 98.3 | 0.1 | Bielefeld | R. Bielefeld |
| 32) | 98.5 | 0.5 | Bochum | R. 98.5 |
| 14) | 98.5 | 0.1 | Bottrop | REL |
| 37) | 98.9 | 0.1 | Neunkirchen | R. Siegen |
| 35) | 99.5 | 0.1 | Plettenberg | R. MK |
| 44) | 99.7 | 0.1 | Euskirchen | R. Euskirchen |
| 38) | 99.7 | 0.5 | Gremberg | R. Berg |
| 39) | 99.9 | 0.5 | Bonn-Königswinter | R. Bonn/Rhein-Sieg |
| 1) | 100.1 | 0.4 | Aachen Karlshöhe | Antenne AC |
| 35) | 100.2 | 0.5 | Lüdenscheid | R. MK |
| 5) | 100.6 | 1 | Viersen | Welle Niederrhein |
| 27) | 100.9 | 1 | Soest-Möhnesee | Hellweg R. |
| 25) | 101.0 | 0.5 | Schieder-Schwalenbg. | R. Lippe |
| 7) | 102.1 | 0.3 | Grevenbroich | NE-WS 89.4 |
| 12) | 102.2 | 0.3 | Essen-Werden | R. Essen |
| 29) | 102.3 | 1 | Schwerte Sommerberg | Antenne Unna |
| 5) | 102.5 | 0.3 | Viersen Süchtelner Höhe | Welle Niederrhein |
| 16) | 103.6 | 0.1 | Gronau | Westmünsterlandw. |
| 27) | 103.6 | 0.1 | Lippstadt | Hellweg R. |
| 17) | 104.0 | 1 | Tecklenburg | R. RST |
| 8) | 104.2 | 1 | Düsseldorf | Antenne Düsseldorf |
| 33) | 104.2 | 0.1 | Witten-Stockum | R. en |
| 26) | 104.8 | 0.5 | Neuhaus-Hasselberg | R. Hochstift |
| 26) | 104.8 | 0.1 | Büren | R. Hochstift |
| 36) | 104.9 | 0.1 | Meschede | R. Sauerland |
| 1) | 105.0 | 0.1 | Monschau | Antenne AC |
| 12) | 105.0 | 0.1 | Essen-Holsterhausen | R. Essen |
| 28) | 105.0 | 0.2 | Hamm | R. Lippewelle |
| 38) | 105.2 | 4 | Lindlar | R. Berg |
| 17) | 105.2 | 4 | Schöppingen | R. RST |
| 15) | 105.2 | 0.1 | Dorsten | Hit Radio Vest |
| 37) | 105.4 | 4 | Aue-Kirchhundem | R. Siegen |
| 38) | 105.7 | 1 | Waldbröl | R. Berg |
| 2) | 105.7 | 0.5 | Geldern | Antenne Niederrhein |
| 33) | 105.7 | 0.1 | Gevelsberg | R. en |
| 42) | 105.8 | 1 | Köln-Ehrenfeld | R. Erft |
| 13) | 106.2 | 1 | Oberhausen | R. Oberhausen |
| 19) | 106.3 | 0.2 | Dülmen | R. Kiepenkerl |
| 36) | 106.5 | 0.5 | Hallenberg | R. Sauerland |
| 36) | 106.6 | 0.2 | Arnsberg | R. Sauerland |
| 25) | 106.6 | 1 | Lemgo | R. Lippe |
| 24) | 106.6 | 0.1 | Lübbecke | R. Westfalica |
| 21) | 106.8 | 0.4 | Borgholzhausen | R. Gütersloh |
| 45) | 106.9 | 4 | Schleiden (Eifel) | R. Euskirchen |
| 41) | 107.1 | 0.5 | Köln Neumarkt | R. Köln |
| 33) | 107.2 | 0.1 | Herdecke | R. en |

| FM | MHz | kW | Site | Station |
|---|---|---|---|---|
| 27) | 107.3 | 0.2 | Wickede | Hellweg R. |
| 19) | 107.4 | 1 | Coesfeld | R. Kiepenkerl |
| 25) | 107.4 | 1 | Linderhofe-Dörenberg | R. Lippe |
| 10) | 107.4 | 0.5 | Wuppertal | R. Wuppertal |
| 44) | 107.4 | 0.1 | Bad Münstereifel | R. Euskirchen |
| 21) | 107.5 | 1 | Oelde | R. Gütersloh |
| 43) | 107.5 | 0.1 | Linnich | R. Rur |
| 36) | 107.6 | 0.5 | Sundern | R. Sauerland |
| 3) | 107.6 | 0.2 | Wesel-Büderich | R. K.W. |
| 40) | 107.6 | 0.1 | Leverkusen-Wiesdorf | R. Leverkusen |
| 27) | 107.7 | 0.2 | Belecke-Sennhöfe | Hellweg R. |
| 34) | 107.7 | 0.2 | Hagen | R. Hagen |
| 1) | 107.8 | 0.4 | Aachen Stolberg | Antenne AC |
| 39) | 107.9 | 0.1 | Herchen-Rosbach | R. Bonn/Rhein-Sieg |
| 9) | 107.9 | 0.1 | Remscheid | R. RSG |

**Addresses & other information:**
**1)** Merzbrück 214, 52146 Würselen, **W:** antenne-ac.de – **2)** Stechbahn 2-8, 47533 Kleve, **W:** antenneniederrhein.de – **3)** Rheinstr. 24-26, 47495 Rheinberg, **W:** radiokw.de – **4)** Ruhrorter Str. 187, 47119 Duisburg, **W:** medien.freepage.de/guidojansen – **5)** Uerdinger Str. 543, 47800 Krefeld, **W:** welleniederrhein.de – **6)** Lüpertzender Str. 159, 41061 Mönchengladbach, **W:** radio901.de – **7)** Moselstr. 16, 41464 Neuss, **W:** news894.de – **8)** Kaistr. 7, 40221 Düsseldorf, **W:** antenneduesseldorf.de – **9)** Postfach, 42621 Solingen (studio location: Alleestr. 1) **W:** radiorsg.de – **10)** Friedrich-Engels-Allee 426, 42283 Wupperta, **W:** radiowuppertal.de – **11)** Elberfelder Str. 81, 40804 Mettmann **W:** radioneandertal.de – **12)** Sachsenstr. 36, 45128 Essen **W:** radio-essen.de – **13)** Essener Str. 99, 46047 Oberhausen **W:** 106.2.radiooberhausen.de and 92.9.radiomuelheim.de – **14)** Hochstr. 68, 45894 Gelsenkirchen, **W:** radio-emscher-lippe.de – **15)** Schaumburgstr. 14, 45657 Recklinghausen **W:** hitradiovest.de – **16)** Heinrich-Hertz-Str. 6, 46325 Borken **W:** radiowmw.de – **17)** Postnstr. 3, 48431 Rheine, **W:** radiorst.de – **18)** Nevinghoff 14/16, 48147 Münster, **W:** antennemuenster.de – **19)** Tiberstr. 21, 48249 Dülmen, **W:** radio-kiepenkerl.de – **20)** Am Schweinemarkt 3, 48231 Warendorf **W:** radiowaf.de – **21)** Feldstr. 14, 33330 Gütersloh **W:** radioguetersloh.de – **22)** Niedernstr. 21-27, 33602 Bielefeld **W:** radiobielefeld.de – **23)** Berliner Str. 30, 32052 Herford **W:** radioherford.de – **24)** Johanniskirchhof 2, 32423 Minden **W:** radiowestfalica.de – **25)** Lagesche Str. 17, 32756 Detmold **W:** radiolippe.de – **26)** Frankfurter Weg 22, 33106 Paderborn **W:** radiohochstift.de – **27)** Jakobistr. 46, 59494 Soest **W:** hellwegradio.de – **28)** Königstr. 39, 59065 Hamm **W:** lippewelle.de – **30)** Karl-Zahn-Str. 11, 44141 Dortmund **W:** radio912.de – **31)** Bahnhofstr. 45, 44623 Herne **W:** radio-herne.de – **32)** Westring 26, 44787 Bochum, **W:** ruhrwelle-bochum.de – **33)** Mühlenstr. 25, 58285 Gevelsberg **W:** radio-en.de – **34)** Rathausstr. 23, 58095 Hagen, **W:** radio-hagen.de – **35)** Vinckestr. 9-13, 58636 Iserlohn, **W:** radio-mk.de – **36)** Steinstr. 32, 59872 Meschede, **W:** radio-sauerland.de – **37)** Postfach 10 02 42, 57002 Siegen (studio location: Obergraben 33), **W:** radio-siegen.de – **38)** Friedrich-Ebert-Str., 51429 Bergisch Gladbach, **W:** radioberg.de – **39)** Kennedybrücke 4, 53225 Bonn, **W:** radio-bonn.de – **40)** Bismarckstr. 71, 51373 Leverkusen, **W:** radioleverkusen.de – **41)** Stolberger Str. 374, 50933 Köln, **W:** radiokoeln.de – **42)** Hürth Park, 50354 Hürth, **W:** radioerft.de – **43)** August-Klotz-Str. 21, 52349 Düren, **W:** radiorur.de – **45)** Rheinstr. 55, 53881 Euskirchen, **W:** radioeuskirchen.de

**Stns not affiliated to Radio NRW:**

| FM | MHz | kW | Site | Station |
|---|---|---|---|---|
| 12) | 87.9 | 0.05 | Bielefeld | Hertz 87.9 |
| 13) | 89.4 | 0.03 | Paderborn | L'Unico |
| 9) | 90.0 | 0.3 | Bochum | CT das radio |
| 11) | 90.9 | 0.05 | Münster university | R. Q |
| 1) | 92.0 | 0.05 | Pulheim | Domradio |
| 2) | 92.1 | 0.03 | Siegen university | Radius 92,1 |
| 8) | 93.0 | 0.05 | Dortmund university | Eldoradio |
| 3) | 94.3 | 0.05 | Bielefeld-Bethel | Antenne Bethel |
| 4) | 94.7 | 0.05 | Meschede | R. FH |
| 7) | 96.8 | 0.5 | Bonn | (shared freq.) |
| 6) | 97.1 | 0.04 | Düsseldorf-Bilk | Hochschul. Düsseld. |
| 15) | 89.4 | 0.03 | Paderborn university | L'Unico FM |
| 4) | 99.1 | 0.1 | Aachen | Hochschul. Aachen |
| 5) | 100.0 | 0.1 | Köln Sterngasse | Kölncampus |
| 1) | 101.7 | 0.03 | Köln Sterngasse | Domradio |
| 11) | 103.9 | 0.5 | Steinfurt college | R. Q |
| 10) | 104.5 | 0.2 | Essen university | Campus FM |
| 10) | 105.6 | 0.05 | Essen university | Campus FM |

**Addresses & other information:**
**1)** Domkloster 3, 50667 Köln; **W:** domradio.de further txs see P) and T), also via Astra 1L, 12.460GHz h. Run by Catholic church – **2)** Hölderlinstr. 3, 57068 Siegen; **W:** radius921.de – **3)** Quellenhofweg 25, 33617 Bielefeld-Bethel; **W:** antenne-bethel.de Run by diacony

– **4)** Wüllnerstr. 5, 52056 Aachen; **W:** hochschulradio-aachen.de – **5)** Albertus-Magnus-Platz, 50923 Köln; **W:** koelncampus.de – **6)** Universitätsstr. 1, 40225 Düsseldorf; **W:** hochschulradio.uni-duesseldorf.de – **7)** shared by six groups – **8)** Vogelpothsweg 74, 44227 Dortmund; **W:** eldoradio.de – **9)** 44780 Bochum (studio location: Ruhr university, room 04/452); **W:** radioct.de – **10)** Universitätsstr. 2, 45141 Essen; **W:** campusfm.info – **11)** Bismarckallee 3, 48151 Münster; **W:** radioq.de – **12)** Universitätsstr. 25, 33615 Bielefeld; **W:** radiohertz.de – **13)** Warburger Str. 100, 33098 Paderborn; **W:** l-unico.de – **14)** Jahnstr. 23, 59872 Meschede; **W:** radiofh.de – **15)** Warburger Str. 100, 33098 Paderborn; **W:** l-unico.de – **16)** Radio Triquency, Liebigstr. 87, 32657 Lemgo; **W:** triquency.de Via lp. txs on 95.9/96.1/99.4MHz **N.B** Stns 2) and 4)-16) university/college
**F.P.I.:** Radiopol FM (see M), stn. 15) on Essen 88.3MHz, Olpe 89.0MHz, Bochum 89.3MHz, Hagen 89.4MHz, Köln 89.9MHz, Krefeld 90.5MHz, Mülheim 93.7MHz, Dorsten 97.0MHz, Lennestadt 98.9MHz, Herdecke 107.2MHz, Attendorn 107.8MHz. Allocation was subject of legal action at time of editing.
**DAB:** 7 txs on ch. 5C see K). Domradio rel. by J)

## T) RHEINLAND-PFALZ
**Media institution:** Landesanstalt für Medien und Kommunikation (LMK) ✉Postfach 21 73 63, 67072 Ludwigshafen (office loc.: Turmstraße 8) ☎ +49 621 5252 0 🖷 +49 621 5252 152 **W:** lmk-online.de

| FM | RPR 1 | bigFM | Rockl. | Metrop | kW |
|---|---|---|---|---|---|
| Bad Bergzabern | 103.3 | – | – | – | 0.3 |
| Bad Dürkheim | 98.1 | 96.4 | – | – | 0.1 |
| Bad Kreuznach | 89.7 | 104.8 | – | – | 0.1/0.2 |
| Bad Marienberg | 102.9 | – | – | – | 25 |
| Bernkastel-Kues | – | 100.5 | – | – | 0.1 |
| Betzdorf | – | 107.7 | – | – | 0.5 |
| Bitburg | – | – | 107.9 | – | 0.1 |
| Bornberg-Eßweiler | 103.1 | 107.6 | – | – | 25 |
| Daun (Eifel) | 102.1 | 106.6 | – | – | 20 |
| Diezer Hain | 101.2 | 100.4 | – | – | 0.1 |
| Grünstadt/Mertesh. | 103.3 | – | – | – | 0.1 |
| Haardtkopf | 100.1 | – | – | – | 50 |
| Heckenbach | 103.5 | 104.9 | – | – | 30 |
| Hohe Wurzel | – | – | 107.9 | – | 6 |
| Idar-Oberstein | 100.3 | 101.9 | – | – | 1 |
| Kalmit | 103.6 | 106.7 | – | – | 25 |
| Kirchheimbolanden | – | – | 97.1 | – | 0.2 |
| Kleinkarlbach | 91.1 | – | – | – | 0.1 |
| Koblenz Kühkopf | 101.5 | 104.0 | – | – | 40 |
| Koblenz-Bendorf | – | – | 88.3 | 107.8 | 0.3 |
| Linz | – | 96.9 | – | – | 0.2 |
| Ludwigshafen | – | – | – | 88.4 | 0.1 |
| Mainz (San-Olm | 100.6 | 104.5 | – | – | 20 |
| Mainz (city) | 98.1 | 106.6 | – | 96.0 | 0.2/0.4 |
| Mannheim | – | – | 93.2 | – | 1 |
| Pirmas. Kettrichhof | 104.7 | – | – | – | 1 |
| Pirmasens (town) | – | 96.7 | – | – | 0.4 |
| Rivenich | – | 95.8 | – | – | 0.2 |
| Saarburg | 102.6 | 96.5 | – | – | 20 |
| Trier Petrisberg | 102.9 | 106.4 | 105.8 | – | 0.1/0.5 |
| Zweibrücken | 103.3 | 106.6 | – | – | 2/0.1 |

**Addresses & other information:**
**RPR 1**, Turmstr. 8, 67059 Ludwigshafen; **W:** rpr1.de – **bigFM:** see K), stn.2); rel. of adopted version in responsibility of RPR – **Rockland R.**, Wallstr. 1-5, 55122 Mainz; **W:** rockland.de cooperates with R. 21, see R) – **Metropol FM** see M), stn. 15

**Local stations:**

| FM | MHz | kW | Site | Station |
|---|---|---|---|---|
| 3) | 87.6 | 0.2 | Idar-Oberstein | R. Idar-Oberstein |
| 7) | 87.8 | 0.1 | Welschbillig | Cityradio Trier |
| 10) | 87.9 | 0.1 | Bretzenheim (church) | Studio Nahe |
| 2) | 88.3 | 0.1 | Bad Kreuznach | Antenne Bad Kreuznach |
| 7) | 88.4 | 0.5 | Trier Petrisberg | Cityradio Trier |
| 6) | 88.4 | 0.3 | Pirmasens | R. Pirmasens |
| 8) | 94.1 | 0.3 | Mommenheim | Antenne Mainz |
| 5) | 94.2 | 1 | Neustadt/Weinstr. | Antenne Pfalz |
| 9) | 94.7 | 0.2 | Wittlich | R. Wittlich |
| 7) | 94.7 | 0.1 | Trierweiler | Cityradio Trier |
| 5) | 94.8 | 0.1 | Landau | Antenne Landau |
| 4) | 96.9 | 0.5 | Kaiserslautern | Antenne Kaiserslautern |
| 8) | 97.1 | 0.1 | Bodenheim | Antenne Mainz |
| 11) | 87.8 | 0.1 | Koblenz | R. Teddy |
| 1) | 98.0 | 1 | Koblenz Moselw. Str. | Antenne Koblenz |
| 1) | 98.0 | 1 | Neuwied | Antenne Koblenz |
| 1) | 98.9 | 1 | Koblenz-Bendorf | Antenne Koblenz |
| 8) | 106.6 | 0.1 | Mainz | Antenne Mainz |

**Addresses & other information:**
**1)** Friedrich-Ebert-Ring 54, 56068 Koblenz; **W:** akoblenz.de – **2)**

Kreuzstr. 31-33, 55543 Bad Kreuznach; **W:** antenne-kh.de – **3)** Auf der Idar 2a, 55743 Idar-Oberstein; **W:** radio-io.de – **4)** Am Altenhof 11-13, 67655 Kaiserslautern; **W:** antenne-kl.de – **5)** Europastr. 3, 67433 Neustadt/Wstr.; **W:** antenne-landau.de antenne-pfalz.de – **6)** Schloßstr. 44, 66953 Pirmasens; **W:** radio-pirmasens.de – **7)** Paulinstr. 1, 54292 Trier; **W:** cityradio-trier.de – **8)** Hechtsheimer Str. 35, 55131 Mainz; **W:** antenne-mainz.de – **9)** Schloßstr. 7a, 54516 Wittlich; **W:** radio-wittlich.de – **10)** Obere Grabenstr. 29, 55450 Langenlonsheim; **W:** studio-nahe.de Run by Catholic church, mostly rel. Domradio, see S) – **11)** See M), stn. 19)
**DAB:** Koblenz/Scharteberg txs on ch. 5C see K). Rel. of Big FM World Beats see I)

## U) SAARLAND
**Media institution:** Landesmedienanstalt Saar (LMS) ✉Postfach 11 01 64, 66070 Saarbrücken (office location: Nell-Breuning-Allee 6) ☎ +49 681 389880; 🖷 +49 681 3898820; **W:** lmsaar.de

| LW | kHz | kW | Prgr. |
|---|---|---|---|
| Überherrn (Felsberg) | 183 | 1500 | Europe 1 (see under France) |

| FM | Salü | C.Ro. | bigFM | Saar. | kW |
|---|---|---|---|---|---|
| Homburg | – | – | – | 89.6 | 1 |
| Lebach-Hoxberg | – | 100.9 | – | – | 1 |
| Merzig | 103.0 | – | 92.6 | 105.1 | 0.1/0.5 |
| Mettlach | 104.2 | – | – | 106.1 | 0.1 |
| Neunkirchen | – | 99.3 | – | 94.6 | 1/0.6 |
| Oberperl | 100.3 | – | – | – | 5 |
| Saarbr. Schoksbg. | 101.7 | – | – | – | 100 |
| Saarbr. Halberg | – | – | 94.2 | – | 1 |
| Saarbr. Winterberg | – | 92.9 | – | – | 1 |
| Saarbr. Schwarzenbg. | – | – | – | 99.6 | 0.1 |
| Saarlouis | – | 102.8 | 99.5 | – | 1 |
| St. Ingbert | – | 100.6 | – | – | 0.1 |
| Sulzbach | – | – | 96.8 | – | 0.1 |
| Webenheim | 100.0 | – | – | – | 5 |

**Addresses & other information:**
**R. Salü, Classic Rock R.:** Postfach 10 08 44, 66008 Saarbrücken (studio location: Richard-Wagner-Str. 58-60); **W:** salue.de classic-rock-radio.de – **bigFM Saarland:** Gutenbergstr. 11-23, 66103 Saarbrücken; **W:** bigfm-saarland.de mostly rel. Stuttgart prgr. (see K), stn. 2) – **R. Saarbrücken, R. Merzig, R. Neunkirchen, R. Homburg:** Nell-Breuning-Allee 6, 66115 Saarbrücken; **W:** radio-sb.de radiomerzig.de antenneneunkirchen.de radio-homburg.de
**DAB:** Schoksberg tx on ch. 5C see K). Rel. of R. Salü see H)

## V) SACHSEN
**Media institution:** Sächsische Landesanstalt für privaten Rundfunk und neue Medien (SLM) ✉Postfach 10 16 62, 04016 Leipzig ☎ +49 341 22 59 0 🖷 +49 341 22 59 199; **W:** slm-online.de office location: Ferdinand-Lassalle-Straße 21

| FM | PSR | R.SA | RTL | Radio | Energ. | kW |
|---|---|---|---|---|---|---|
| Annaberg-Buchholz | – | 104.8 | – | – | – | 0.5 |
| Auerbach | – | 107.9 | – | – | – | 0.1 |
| Bärenstein | – | – | – | 107.2E | – | 0.2 |
| Beilrode | – | 99.6 | – | – | – | 1 |
| Borna | – | – | – | 99.5L | – | 0.1 |
| Chemnitz-Reichenh. | – | 91.0 | – | 102.1C | 97.5 | 3 |
| Collmberg | 98.0 | – | 104.7 | – | – | 5/10 |
| Döbeln | – | 107.9 | – | – | 98.3 | 1/0.2 |
| Dresden-Gompitz | – | – | – | 91.1D | – | 1 |
| Dresden-Wachwitz | 102.4 | 89.2 | 105.2 | 103.5D | 100.2 | 100/2 |
| Ebersbach | – | 106.1 | – | – | – | 0.5 |
| Elsterberg | – | 99.7 | – | – | – | 0.2 |
| Flöha | – | 98.4 | – | 99.0C | – | 0.1 |
| Freiberg | – | 90.6 | – | 104.2D | 96.4 | 0.2/0.5 |
| Freital | – | 88.3 | – | 107.0D | – | 0.2 |
| Geyer (Erzgebirge) | 100.0 | – | 105.4 | – | – | 100 |
| Görlitz | – | 105.1 | – | – | – | 1 |
| Grimma | – | 107.4 | – | 90.9L | 93.3 | 2/0.3 |
| Hoyerswerda-Zeißig | – | 96.9 | – | – | 87.6 | 0.2/0.3 |
| Kamenz | – | 106.2 | – | – | – | 0.2 |
| Leipzig-Holzhausen | – | – | – | 91.3L | 99.8 | 4 |
| Leipzig-Reudnitz | – | 98.2 | – | – | – | 1 |
| Leisnig | – | 100.5 | – | – | – | 1 |
| Limbach-Oberfrohna | – | – | – | 107.3C | – | 0.1 |
| Löbau Schafberg | 101.0 | – | 105.6 | 107.6G | – | 30 |
| Löbau town | – | 87.6 | – | – | – | 0.5 |
| Markneukirchen | – | 89.6 | – | – | – | 1 |
| Meerane | – | – | – | 89.2Z | – | 0.1 |
| Meißen-Korbitz | – | – | – | 107.5D | – | 0.2 |
| Mittelherwigsdorf | – | 100.0 | – | 94.3G | – | 0.5/0.3 |
| Mügeln | – | 91.2 | – | – | – | 0.5 |
| Neukirchen | – | – | – | 95.8C | – | 1 |

| FM | PSR | R.SA | RTL | Radio | Energ. | kW |
|---|---|---|---|---|---|---|
| Niederschöna | – | 94.4 | – | – | – | 0.5 |
| Niesky | – | 95.0 | – | – | – | 0.2 |
| Nossen | – | 91.4 | – | – | – | 0.2 |
| Oelsnitz (Vogtland) | – | 91.5 | – | – | – | 0.1 |
| Olbernhau | – | 101.0 | – | – | – | 0.5 |
| Oschatz | – | 89.1 | – | – | – | 0.3 |
| Pirna | – | – | – | 96.4D | – | 0.1 |
| Plauen | – | 93.5 | – | – | – | 1 |
| Reichenbach/Vogtl. | – | 92.4 | – | – | – | 0.2 |
| Riesa | – | 106.4 | – | – | 91.7 | 2/1 |
| Rothenburg | – | 100.0 | – | – | – | 0.2 |
| Schöneck | 92.0 | – | 106.0 | – | – | 10/30 |
| Sohland | – | 107.0 | – | – | – | 0.2 |
| Stollberg | – | 93.4 | – | – | – | 1 |
| Torgau | – | 91.1 | – | – | – | 0.2 |
| Weißwasser | – | 101.9 | – | – | – | 0.5 |
| Werdau | – | – | – | 90.9Z | – | 0.3 |
| Wiederau (Leipzig) | 102.9 | – | 106.9 | – | – | 100 |
| Wilkau-Haßlau | – | 92.3 | – | 103.4Z | – | 0.5 |
| Wilthen | – | 106.5 | – | – | 104.9 | 1/0.5 |
| Wurzen | – | 95.0 | – | – | – | 0.4 |
| Zittau | – | 100.0 | – | – | – | 0.5 |
| Zschopau | – | – | – | 91.7C | – | 0.3 |
| Zwickau-Ebersbrunn | – | – | – | 96.2Z | 98.2 | 0.5/0.3 |
| Zwickau-Planitz | – | 95.5 | – | – | – | 0.5 |

**Addresses & other information:**
**R. PSR** (AC), **R.SA** (oldie-based, specifically aiming at GDR-socialized audiences), **Energy Sachsen** (CHR): Thomasgasse 2, 04102 Leipzig; **W:** radiopsr.de rsa-sachsen.de nrj.de – **Hitradio RTL** (AC), **R. Chemnitz / Dresden / Erzgebirge / Lausitz / Leipzig / Zwickau** (AC, on freq. marked C, D, E, G, L, Z, with some content from local studios): Ammonstr. 35, 01067 Dresden; **W:** bcs-dresden.de

**Other stations:**

| FM | MHz | kW | Site | Station |
|---|---|---|---|---|
| 7) | 88.2 | 0.4 | Auerbach | Vogtland R. |
| 9) | 88.2 | 1 | Weißig (Bernsdorf) | Lausitzwelle |
| 1) | 88.9 | 1 | Chemnitz-Reichenhain | Apollo R. |
| 10) | 89.2 | 1 | Weißwasser | R. WSW |
| 2) | 89.2 | 0.1 | Leipzig-Reudnitz | R. Blau |
| 2) | 94.4 | 0.3 | Leipzig-Stahmeln | R. Blau |
| 10) | 94.9 | 0.2 | Wilthen | R. WSW |
| 7) | 95.4 | 2 | Plauen | Vogtland R. |
| 5) | 97.6 | 4 | Leipzig-Holzhausen | mephisto 97.6 |
| 3) | 98.4 | 0.1 | Dresden-Gompitz | coloRadio |
| 2) | 99.2 | 0.5 | Leipzig-Connewitz | R. Blau |
| 3) | 99.3 | 0.1 | Freital (Dresden) | coloRadio |
| 6) | 99.3 | 0.1 | Mittweida | R. Mittweida |
| 7) | 100.5 | 1 | Reichenbach/Vogtland | Vogtland R. |
| 1) | 102.7 | 1 | Chemnitz-Reichenhain | R. T |
| 9) | 102.8 | 1 | Hoyerswerda Neustadt | Lausitzwelle |
| 7) | 103.8 | 0.5 | Markneukirchen | Vogtland R. |
| 8) | 107.7 | 2 | Fichtelberg | R. Erzgebirge |

**Addresses & other information:**
**1)d** As Hitradio RTL; **W:** apolloradio.de ; classical music and jazz, also Mon-Fri 2200-1700, Sat-Sun 2300-1100 via txs of stns 2), 3), 4) – **2)** Paul-Gruner-Str. 62, 04107 Leipzig; **W:** radioblau.de – **3)** Jordanstr. 5, 01099 Dresden; **W:** coloradio.org – **4)** Karl-Liebknecht-Str. 19, 09111 Chemnitz; **W:** radiot.de rel. 1700-1800 Chemnitz university prgr. – **5)** Ritterstr. 9-13, 04109 Leipzig; **W:** mephisto976.uni-leipzig.de run by Leipzig university; Mon-Fri 0900-1100 and 1700-1900, other times rel. R.SA – **6)** Leisniger Str. 9, 09648 Mittweida; **W:** radio-mittweida.de run by Mittweida college – **7)** Haselbrunner Str. 114, 08225 Plauen; **W:** vogtlandradio.de **F.P.I.:** Txs in Altenburg, Gera and Schleiz – **8)** Vierenstr. 11, 09484 Oberwiesenthal; **W:** radioerzgebirge-online.de – **9)** Schulstr. 15, 02977 Hoyerswerda; **W:** lausitzwelle.de is 103.8MHz tx see M) – **10)** Werner-Seelenbinder-Str. 54a, 02943 Weißwasser; **W:** radiowsw.de
**DAB:** 5 txs on ch. 5C see K)

## W) SACHSEN-ANHALT
**Media institution:** Medienanstalt Sachsen-Anhalt (MSA) ✉ Reichardtstraße 9, 06114 Halle/Saale ☎ +49 345 52550 🖷 +49 345 5255 121 **W:** msa-online.de

| FM | R Bro | RTL | SAW | Rock | kW |
|---|---|---|---|---|---|
| Bernburg | – | – | – | 95.0 | 1 |
| Blankenburg | 99.9 | – | 95.7 | – | 0.3/0.1 |
| Brocken | – | 89.0 | 101.4 | – | 60/100 |
| Dequede | 101.0 | – | 95.6 | – | 60/1 |
| Dessau-Mildensee | 90.6 | – | 92.6 | 94.1 | 0.8/2/0.3 |
| Eisleben | 93.7 | – | – | – | 1 |
| Fleetmark-Lüge | – | – | 103.9 | – | 5 |

| FM | R Bro | RTL | SAW | Rock | kW |
|---|---|---|---|---|---|
| Halle Petersberg | 93.5 | – | 103.3 | – | 5 |
| Halle city | – | – | – | 98.3 | 0.5 |
| Hergisdorf-Wolferode | 93.7 | – | – | – | 1 |
| Köthen | – | – | – | 97.1 | 1 |
| Magdeburg-Buckau | – | – | – | 98.7 | 0.2 |
| Naumburg | 98.8 | – | 95.1 | 99.6 | 10/0.5/1 |
| Sangerhausen | 107.1 | – | 99.4 | – | 0.1 |
| Schneidlingen | – | – | – | 107.2 | 2.5 |
| Schönebeck | 105.7 | – | 100.1 | – | 15/20 |
| Stendal Tucholsky-Str. | – | – | 100.5 | – | 0.5 |
| Weißenfels | – | – | – | 88.0 | 1 |
| Wernigerode | 105.4 | – | 90.8 | – | 0.5/1 |
| Wiederau (Leipzig) | – | – | 104.9 | – | *90 |
| Wittenberg-Gallun | 102.3 | – | 98.4 | – | 4/5 |
| Zeitz-Hainichen | 99.1 | – | – | – | 0.5 |
| Ziesar | – | – | 102.8 | – | 2 |

*) tx in Sachsen, sharply directional towards Sachsen-Anhalt

**Addresses & other information:**
**R. Brocken** (oldie-based AC), **89.0 RTL** (CHR): Große Ulrichstr. 60D, 06108 Halle; **W:** brocken.de 89.0rtl.de – **R. SAW** (AC), **Rockland Sachsen-Anhalt:** Hansapark 1, 39116 Magdeburg; **W:** radiosaw.de rockland-digital.de

**Non-commercial stations:**

| FM | MHz | kW | Site | Station |
|---|---|---|---|---|
| 2) | 92.5 | 1 | Aschersleben | R. hbw |
| 1) | 95.9 | 0.6 | Halle Petersberg | R. Corax |

**Addresses and other information:**
**1)** Unterberg 11, 06108 Halle; **W:** radiocorax.de – **2)** Herrenbreite 9, 06449 Aschersleben; **W:** radio-hbw.de
**DAB:** 4 txs on ch. 5C see K) – 4 txs on ch. 11C and 3 txs on ch. 12C R. Brocken, 89.0 RTL, SAW, Rockland

## X) THÜRINGEN
**Media institution:** Thüringer Landesmedienanstalt (TLM) 🖃 P.O.-Box 90 03 61 (office location: Steigerstraße 10), 99096 Erfurt
☎ +49 361 211770 🖷 +49 361 2117755 **W:** tlm.de

| FM | Ant.T | LW | Top 40 | Teddy | kW |
|---|---|---|---|---|---|
| Altenburg | – | – | 98.4 | – | 0.5 |
| Apolda | – | – | – | 99.5 | 0.2 |
| Arnstadt | – | – | – | 96.5 | 0.1 |
| Bleßberg | 102.7 | 106.7 | – | – | 60 |
| Dingelstädt | 103.9 | – | – | – | 5 |
| Eisenach | – | – | 93.5 | 90.9 | 0.2 |
| Erfurt-Windischh. | 100.2 | 99.7 | – | – | 3/0.5 |
| Erfurt-Hochheim | – | – | 88.6 | 99.2 | 0.5 |
| Gera | 98.3 | 105.8 | 95.3 | – | 0.2/1 |
| Gotha | – | – | 90.8 | 99.3 | 0.1/0.2 |
| Heiligenstadt | – | 88.7 | – | – | 0.1 |
| Ilmenau | – | – | 94.8 | – | 0.1 |
| Inselsberg | 102.2 | 104.2 | – | – | 100 |
| Jena-Oßmaritz | 90.9 | 106.1 | – | – | 1 |
| Jena Kernberge | – | – | 94.8 | – | 0.2 |
| Keula | – | 104.5 | – | – | 10 |
| Kulpenberg | 104.7 | 96.8 | – | – | 3 |
| Lobenstein | 93.2 | 98.5 | – | – | 1/2 |
| Meiningen | – | – | 99.5 | 90.6 | 0.2/0.1 |
| Mühlhausen | – | – | 93.8 | 102.9 | 0.2/0.5 |
| Nordhausen | 106.8 | 105.8 | 103.0 | 107.4 | 0.1/0.2 |
| Pößneck | – | – | 98.9 | – | 0.2 |
| Remda Kalmberg | 107.6 | 95.7 | – | – | 60/10 |
| Ronneburg | 102.5 | 94.9 | – | – | 30/3 |
| Saalfeld | – | – | 97.6 | – | 0.1 |
| Sömmerda | – | – | 91.0 | – | 0.1 |
| Sondershausen | – | – | 90.7 | – | 0.2 |
| Sonneberg | – | – | 88.8 | – | 0.1 |
| Suhl | 101.3 | 88.6 | 92.1 | – | 2x1/0.1 |
| Weimar Ettersberg | 107.2 | 89.2 | – | – | 0.25 |
| Weimar Belvedere | – | – | 97.9 | 88.7 | 0.1 |

**Addresses & other information:**
**Antenne Thüringen** (AC), **Top 40** (rock): Belvederer Allee 25, 99425 Weimar; **W:** antennethueringen.de radiotop40.de – **LandesWelle Thüringen** (AC): Mehringstr. 5, 99086 Erfurt; **W:** landeswelle.de – **Radio Teddy** see M)

**Local stations:**

| FM | MHz | kW | Site | Station |
|---|---|---|---|---|
| 9) | 92.4 | 0.2 | Schleiz | Vogtland R. |
| 1) | 96.2 | 0.6 | Erfurt-Hochheim | F.R.E.I. |
| 4) | 96.5 | 0.2 | Eisenach | Wartburg-R. |
| 3) | 98.1 | 0.3 | Ilmenau | hsf Studentenradio |
| 6) | 100.4 | 0.1 | Nordhausen | R. Enno |
| 8) | 100.5 | 0.1 | Artern | R. Artern |
| 5) | 103.4 | 0.3 | Jena-Oßmaritz | R. OKJ |
| 9) | 104.5 | 0.1 | Gera | Vogtland R. |
| 7) | 105.2 | 0.3 | Saalfeld | SRB |
| 2) | 106.6 | 2 | Weimar Belvedere | R. Lotte |
| 9) | 107.5 | 0.5 | Altenburg | Vogtland R. |

**Addresses & other information:**
**1)** Gotthardstr. 21, 99084 Erfurt; **W:** radio-frei.de – **2)** Herderplatz 14, 99423 Weimar, **W:** radiolotte.de Rel. Bauhaus university prgr. Mon 1900-2300 – **3)** Postfach 100 565, 98684 Ilmenau; **W:** hsf.tu-ilmenau. de Run by Ilmenau university – **4)** Georgenstr. 43, 99817 Eisenach; **W:** wartburgradio.com – **5)** Helmboldstr. 1, 07749 Jena; **W:** radio-okj.de – **6)** August-Bebel-Platz 6, 99734 Nordhausen; **W:** radio-enno.de – **7)** Tiefer Weg 7, 07318 Saalfeld; **W:** srb.fm – **8)** Solsteg 1, 06556 Artern; **W:** radio-artern.com – **9)** see V), stn. 7)
**DAB:** 5 txs on ch. 5C see K)

## III. ARMED FORCES STATIONS

| FM | MHz | kW | Site | Prgr. |
|---|---|---|---|---|
| **Baden-Württemberg** | | | | |
| 2) | 102.3 | 100 | Stuttgart | AFN Stuttgart |
| **Bayern** | | | | |
| 3) | 89.9 | 0.2 | Amberg | AFN Bavaria |
| 3) | 90.3 | 0.1 | Garmisch-Partenk. | AFN Bavaria |
| 3) | 93.5 | 0.2 | Hohenfels | AFN Bavaria |
| 3) | 98.5 | 0.1 | Grafenwöhr | AFN Bavaria |
| 3) | 104.9 | 0.4 | Illesheim | AFN Bavaria |
| 3) | 107.3 | 1 | Ansbach | AFN Bavaria |
| 3) | 107.7 | 0.3 | Vilseck | AFN Bavaria |
| **Hessen** | | | | |
| 4) | 103.7 | 0.5 | Wiesbaden | AFN Wiesbaden |
| **Nordrhein-Westfalen** | | | | |
| 7) | 91.7 | 0.3 | Gütersloh | BFBS R. 2 |
| 7) | 101.6 | 0.3 | Bielefeld | BFBS R. 2 |
| 7) | 103.0 | 70 | Bielefeld | BFBS Germany |
| 7) | 105.0 | 0.3 | Paderborn | BFBS R. 2 |

**NB:** Geilenkirchen Air Base served by AFN and BFBS txs at Brunssum, see under Netherlands

| | | | | |
|---|---|---|---|---|
| **Rheinland-Pfalz** | | | | |
| 5) | 103.0 | 0.4 | Pirmasens | AFN Kaiserslautern |
| 5) | 105.1 | 2 | Kaiserslautern | AFN Kaiserslautern |
| 6) | 105.1 | 1 | Spangdahlem | AFN Spangdahlem |
| 5) | 106.1 | 0.1 | Baumholder | AFN Kaiserslautern |

**Addresses & other information:**
**1)** Bundeswehr, Zentrum Operative Information, Kürrenberger Steig 34, 56727 Mayen; **W:** radio-andernach.de Prgr. for Bundeswehr operations abroad presented as **Radio Andernach**, distributed via local FM txs – **2) AFN Stuttgart**, Robinson Barracks, 70376 Stuttgart; **W:** stuttgart.afneurope.net Own prgr. Mon-Fri 0400-0800 and 1400-1700 – **3) AFN Bavaria**, Rose Barracks, 92249 Vilseck; **W:** bavaria. afneurope.net Own prgr. Mon-Fri 0500-0800 and 1400-1700 – **4) AFN Wiesbaden**, Würgelstr. 1217, Flugplatz Erbenheim, 65205 Wiesbaden; **W:** wiesbaden.afneurope.net Own prgr. Mon-Fri 0500-0900 and 1300-1700 – **5) AFN Kaiserslautern**, Vogelweh, Bldg. 2058, 67661 Kaiserslautern; **W:** kaiserslautern.afneurope.net Own prgr. Mon-Fri 0500-1700, Sat 0700-1100 – **6) AFN Spangdahlem**, Spangdahlem Air Base, 54529 Spangdahlem; **W:** spangdahlem.afneurope.net Own prgr. Mon-Fri 0500-0900 and 1300-1600, Sat 0800-1100 – **7) BFBS Germany**, Otto-Hahn-Straße 20, 33104 Paderborn, Sennelager; **W:** forces.net/radio. Also via Eutelsat 10A, 11.221GHz v. To be closed until 2020 – **AFN Europe**, Sembach Kaserne, Building 166, 67681 Sembach-Heuberg, **W:** afneurope.net Produces network prgr., rel. by local AFN stns in Germany, Belgium and Italy.

## GHANA

**L.T:** UTC — **Pop:** 29 million — **Pr.L:** English, Akan, Dagbani, Ga, Ewe, Hausa, Nzema, others — **E.C:** 50Hz, 230V — **ITU:** GHA

### NATIONAL COMMUNICATIONS AUTHORITY (NCA)
🖃 P.O. Box CT 1568, 1st Rangoon Close, Switchback Rd, Cantonments, Accra ☎+233 30 2776621 🖷 +233 30 2763449 **W:** nca.org.gh **E:** info@nca.org.gh **L.P:** Acting DG: Major J. R. K. Tandoh.

### GHANA BROADCASTING CORPORATION (GBC, Pub.)
🖃 P.O. Box 1633, Broadcasting House, Ring Road Central, Kanda, Accra ☎+233 30 2786567 🖷 +233 30 2773247
**W:** gbcghana.com **E:** info@gbcghana.com **L.P:** DG: Albert Don Chebe. Dir. Radio: Theo Agbam. Dir. Eng: Mrs. Sarah Boye.

**GBC Regional & partnership stations:**

| FM | MHz | Name | Web/Addr./Area |
|---|---|---|---|
| Bolgatanga | 89.5 | URA R. | Upper East |

| FM | MHz | Name | Web/Addr./Area |
|---|---|---|---|
| Han | 90.1 | Upper West R. | Upper West |
| Tamale | 91.2 | R.Savannah | North |
| Ho | 91.5 | Volta Star R. | Volta |
| Kumasi | 92.1 | Garden City R. | Ashanti |
| Cape Coast | 92.5 | R.Central | Central |
| Accra | 93.7 | R. Ada | P.O. Box 9482, K.I.A |
| Wa | 93.9 | Upper West R. | Upper West |
| Sunyani | 94.7 | R. Bar | Brong Ahafo |
| Sekondi-Takoradi | 94.7 | Twin City R. | West |
| Dormaa-Ahenkro | 94.9 | R. Dormaa | Brong Ahafo |
| Accra | 95.7 | Uniiq FM | Greater Accra |
| Accra | 96.5 | Obonu FM | Greater Accra |
| Apam | 96.5 | Apam R. | Central |
| Swedru | 98.6 | Swedru R. | Central |
| Kumasi | 99.5 | Luv FM | P.O. Box 17207, Accra |
| Accra | 99.7 | Joy FM | myjoyonline.com |
| Koforidua | 106.7 | Sunrise FM | East |

**Network N. in E** (rel. by all GBC stations): 0600, 0700, 0900, 1100SS, 1300, 1400, 1800, 2000, 2200, 2345.

**Other FM stations in Accra:**
**Asempa FM,** P.O. Box 17013, Accra-North: 94.7MHz – **Atlantis R**, P.O. Box 14629, Accra: 87.9MHz 5kW – **Channel R**, P.O. Box AN 8135, Accra-North: 92.7MHz – **Choice FM,** Accra: 102.3MHz. **W:** choicefmghana. com – **Citi FM,** P.O. Box 30211, K.I.A, Accra: 97.3MHz – **Happy FM,** P.O. Box 1538, Dansoman, Accra: 98.9MHz – **Hot FM,** P.O. Box KD594, Kanda, Accra: 93.9MHz – **Peace FM,** Accra: 104.3MHz 5kW. **W:** peacefmonline. com – **R. Gold FM,** P.O. Box 17298, Accra: 90.5MHz – **R. Hit,** P.O. Box 17013, Accra-North: 103.7MHz – **R. Universe,** P.O. Box 25, Legon: 105.7MHz – **Sunny FM,** Box CT 3850, Cantonments, Accra: 88.7MHz – **Top R,** P.O. Box CT 4748, Cantonments, Accra: 103.1MHz – **Vibe FM,** Priv. Mailbag CT 183, Accra 91.9MHz.
+ 75 more stations elsewhere.
**BBC World Sce:** Accra 101.3MHz, Sekondi-Takoradi 104.7MHz.
**RFI Afrique:** Accra 89.5MHz, Kumasi 92.9MHz in French/English.
**VOA African Sce:** Accra 98.1MHz

## GIBRALTAR (UK)

**LT:** UTC +1h (31 Mar-27 Oct: +2h) — **Pop:** 32,500 — **Pr.L:** English, Spanish — **E.C:** 50Hz, 230V — **ITU:** GIB

### GIBRALTAR BROADCASTING CORPORATION
**Radio Gibraltar**
✉ Broadcasting House, 18 South Barrack Rd, Gibraltar GX11 1AA ☎ +350 200 79760 **W:** gbc.gi **E:** radiogibraltar@gbc.gi
**LP:** CEO: Gerard Teuma, Head of R.: Ian Daniels, Head of Eng.: Michael Corcoran
**MW:** 1458kHz 4kW
**FM:** 91.3MHz 0.2kW, 92.6MHz 1.0kW, 100.5MHz 1.0kW
**D. Prgr:** 24h **Radio Gibraltar Plus** opt out in Spanish M-F 1300-1500, English M-F 1500-1700 on 100.5 MHz and 1458 kHz **Ann:** "Radio Gibraltar"
**DAB:** DAB+ Mux on 225.648MHz Block 12B and 227.360MHz Block 12C with 4 GBC ch.

### BRITISH FORCES BROADCASTING SCE. GIBRALTAR
✉ BFBS Gibraltar, BFPO 52, BF1 2AR; Oyster Cottage, Four Corners, Gibraltar ☎ +350 200 55389 **W:** forces.net/radio/stations/bfbs-gibraltar **E:** gib@bfbs.com
**FM:** BFBS Gibraltar: North Mole 93.5MHz 0.2kW; O'Hara's Battery 97.8MHz 1kW (Relays BFBS UK when not carrying local prgs.)
BFBS Radio 2: North Mole 89.4MHz 0.2 kW; O'Hara's Battery 99.5MHz 0.25kW. **D. Prgr:** 24h

### ROCK RADIO (Comm)
✉ 61 Governors Str., Gibraltar GX11 1AA ☎ +350 225 0500 **W:** rockradio.gi **E:** hello@rockradio.gi
**FM:** 99.2 MHz **DAB:** DAB+ **D. Prgr:** 24h

## GREECE

**LT:** UTC +2h (31 Mar-27 Oct: +3h) — **Pop:** 11 million — **Pr.L:** Greek — **E.C:** 50Hz, 230V — **ITU:** GRC

### ETHNIKI EPITROPI TILEPIKOINONION KAI TAHIDROMION (EETT) (Hellenic Telecommunications & Post Commission)
✉ Leof. Kifisias 60, 151 25 Maroussi ☎ +30 210 6101500 🖷 +30 210 6105049 **W:** eett.gr **E:** info@eett.gr **LP:** President: Konstantinos Masselos.

### ETHNIKO SIMVOULIO RADIOTILEORASIS (ESR) (National Council for Radio & Television)
✉ Panepistimiou & Amerikis 5, 105 64 Athina ☎ +30 213 1502300 🖷 +30 210 3319881 **W:** esr.gr **E:** ncrtv@otenet.gr
**LP:** President: Athanasios Koutromanos.

### ELLINIKI RADIOFONIA (ERA) (Greek Public Radio)
✉ Leof. Mesogeion 432, 153 42 Agia Paraskevi, Athina ☎ +30 210 6066000 🖷+30 210 6002941 **W:** ert.gr **E:** info@ert.gr **LP:** CEO: Christos Leontis. Tech. Dir: Petros Filos. Dir. Tech. Op. Radio: Kanavas Kreon
**MW:** Athina 729kHz 70kW, Kerkira 1008kHz 50kW, Tripoli 1305kHz 1kW, Komotini1404 kHz 50kW, Volos 1485kHz 0.1kW, Hania 1512kHz 50kW(inactive).
**NB:** Stns except Athina carry ERA1, reg. prgrs & Kosmos in evening.

| FM | ERA1 | ERA2 | ERA3 | ERASp | Reg. | ERP |
|---|---|---|---|---|---|---|
| 16) Aetos | - | - | - | - | 104.4 | 1 |
| 5) Ahentrias | 94.4 | 96.4 | - | - | 105.6 | 10 |
| 3) Ainos | 96.9 | 98.9 | 104.2 | 106.8 | 93.2 | 20/10 |
| 2) Akarnanika | 88.9 | 91.3 | 102.5 | 97.3 | 100.3 | 20/10 |
| 9) Assea | 88.3 | 103.5 | 90.3 | 95.3 | 101.5 | 10/35 |
| Borsa | 90.5 | 102.6 | 96.7 | 106.6 | - | 2 |
| 1) Bournias | - | 104.8 | - | 106.8 | 89.7 | 2 |
| Delvinaki | - | 102.4 | - | - | - | 1 |
| Devas | 93.5 | - | - | - | - | 6 |
| Didima | 101.2 | 99.4 | 97.4 | 103.2 | - | 2 |
| 9) Doliana | - | - | - | - | 101.5 | 35 |
| 4) Dovroutsi | - | - | - | - | 98.3 | 10 |
| 12)Erateini | - | 96.5 | 94.5 | - | 89.9 | 10 |
| Finiki | 91.0 | 93.0 | - | 104.8 | - | 1 |
| Geraneia | 97.9 | 99.9 | - | 105.0 | - | 20/10 |
| Hamezi | - | 89.0 | - | 91.9 | 89.9 | 6/3 |
| Hlomo | - | 101.5 | - | 107.4 | - | 2 |
| Hortiatis | 88.0 | 90.0 | 92.0 | 93.9 | - | 20 |
| 1) Ikaria | - | - | - | - | 89.1 | 3 |
| Imittos | 105.8 | 103.7 | 90.9 | 101.8 | - | 20/2 |
| 17) Kagias | - | 91.2 | 105.1 | 87.6 | 89.6 | 2/1 |
| 12) Kalavrita | - | - | - | - | 93.9 | 2 |
| 1) Karfas | - | - | - | 102.1 | 100.1 | 1 |
| 19) Kastania | 103.6 | ‡88.2 | - | 105.6 | 100.2 | 2/10 |
| Katsikas | 107.0 | - | - | - | - | 35 |
| 17) Kefalohori | 96.4 | - | 105.8 | - | 101.5 | 3/1 |
| Korylovos | - | 99.5 | - | - | - | - |
| Lefkes | - | 98.9 | - | 102.7 | - | 10 |
| 7) Lefkimi | 89.8 | 91.8 | - | 107.7 | 87.8 | 6/5/2 |
| 1) Lepetimnos | - | - | - | - | 99.4 | 1 |
| Lidoriki | - | 99.5 | - | - | 90.4 | 1 |
| 2) Ligiades | 106.1 | 99.8 | 97.8 | 102.1 | 88.2 | 2 |
| Lihada | 88.7 | 104.2 | - | - | - | 10 |
| Manoliassa | 103.3 | - | - | - | - | 10 |
| 15) Malaxa | - | - | - | - | 100.6 | 2 |
| 14) Monte Smith | - | - | - | - | 93.1 | 1 |
| 18) Mousteni | 102.4 | 104.4 | 100.5 | 107.3 | 106.0 | 2 |
| 7) Olympos | 92.3 | 94.3 | 106.4 | - | 104.4 | 10 |
| Orfanio | 89.2 | 91.2 | 97.5 | 107.3 | - | 35 |
| 12) Panahaiko | - | 104.3 | 102.3 | 87.9 | 92.5 | 2 |
| 6) Pantokratoras | 91.8 | 93.8 | 89.8 | 101.1 | 99.3 | 20/10 |
| Parnitha | 91.6 | 102.9 | 95.6 | 100.9 | - | 20/10 |
| 16)Petalidi | 92.2 | 94.2 | 89.3 | 100.4 | 107.2 | 10/3 |
| 13)Pilio | 92.8 | 94.8 | 96.8 | 107.1 | 101.2 | 20/10 |
| 7) Pithio | 98.9 | 93.8 | 88.1 | 89.4 | 101.0 | 10 |
| 11) Plaka | 89.2 | 90.7 | 88.7 | 107.3 | 98.1 | 4/2 |
| 7) Plaka | - | - | - | - | 103.5 | 2 |
| 1) Prof. Ilias (L) | - | - | 97.2 | - | 103.0 | 1 |
| 14)Prof. Ilias (R) | 88.4 | 90.4 | 103.4 | 101.4 | 92.7 | 10 |
| 5) Rogdia | 104.8 | 99.2 | 91.3 | 93.9 | 97.5 | 2 |
| 15)Skloka | 92.9 | 94.9 | 106.0 | 90.1 | 104.0‡ | 10 |
| 3) Skopos | - | - | - | - | 95.2 | 2 |
| 10) Smerna | - | - | - | - | 102.4 | 10 |
| 13) Soros | - | - | - | - | 100.7 | 2 |
| 5) Stavros (Las.) | - | - | - | - | 105.3‡ | 1 |
| 14) Sympetro | 107.9 | 96.1 | - | - | 98.4 | 1 |
| 1) Thanos | - | - | - | - | 96.5 | 1 |
| 18)Thasos | 95.1 | - | 100.8 | 104.7 | 96.3 | 35 |
| 1) Thosolopotami | - | - | - | - | 95.2 | 1 |
| Tsotili | 89.1 | - | - | - | - | 1 |
| 1) Vathi | - | - | - | - | 89.7 | 1 |
| 8) Vitsi | 88.6 | 90.6 | 103.1 | 105.1 | 96.6 | 20/10 |
| 19) Vitsi | - | - | - | - | 100.5 | 3 |

+about 50 stations under 1 kW. ‡) Inactive.
**D.Prgr:** All 24h. **ERA1 (Proto):** News, talk, current affairs. **ERA2 (Deftero):** Music and culture. **ERA3 (Trito):** Classical music, arts. **ERA Sport:** sports.

## Other ERT Stations:

**Kosmos Radio:** Assea 93.6 1kW, Doliana 93.6 1kW, Parnitha 93.6 100kW, Borsa 94.0 1kW, Pithio 94.7 10kW, Moustheni 97.2 2kW, Kagias 97.5 1kW‡, Vasilaki 97.5 1kW, Skolka 104.4 10kW‡, Korilovos 104.2 1kW, Plaka 105.5 2kW, Imittos 107.0 6kW.

**DAB:** Mux featuring ERA1, ERA2, ERA3, ERA Sport, Kosmos, The Voice of Greece, and ERA7 (relaying audio from Vouli TV): Imittos 227.360MHz/12C 300w, Parnitha 227.360MHz/12C, Assea 213.360MHz/10C, Filippio (Thessaloniki) 174.928MHz/5C, Geraneia 206.352MHz/9C (90w), Panahaiko 188.928MHz/7A. **F.PI:** Network to be expanded nationwide.

## Regional station addresses:

**1) Northern Aegean:** E. Bostani 69, 811 00 Mitilini – **2) Ioannina:** N. Papadopoulou 2, 454 44 Ioannina – **3) Zakynthos:** Ampelokipoi, 291 00 Zakynthos – **4) Larissa** Iroon Politehniou 1, 1h Stratia, 412 22 Larissa – **5) Heraklion:** Maxis Kritis 161, 713 03 Iraklio – **6) Kerkiras:** Ethniki Lefkimis, 491 00 Kerkira – **7) Orestiada:** Euripidou 15, 682 00 Orestiada – **8) Florina:** Megarovou 20, 531 00 Florina – **9) Tripolis:** Nafpliou & Erithrou Staurou 1, 221 00 Tripoli – **10) Pirgos:** Olympion 70, GR-27100 Pirgos – **11) Komotinis:** P.O. Box 5, Kosmiou Terma, GR-69100 Komotini – **12) Patra:** Panahaidos Athinas 93, Dasyllio, 263 31 Patra – **13) Volou:** Pl. Agiou Konstantinou, 382 22 Volos – **14) Southern Aegean:** 50 km. Rodou-Kallitheas, 851 00 Rhodes – **15) Chanion:** Ellis 40, 732 00 Chania – **16) Kalamata:** Anataliko Kentro 10-11, 241 00 Kalamata – **17) Serres:** P.O. Box 91, Stratopedou Kolokotroni, 621 00 Serres – **18) Kavala:** Sof. Venizelou & Iokastis, Stratopedo Karakaosta, 654 03 Kavala – **19) Kozani:** I. Tranta 19, 501 00 Kozani. **W:** webradio.ert.gr/periferia

**IS:** The opening notes of the Greek folk song "Tsopanakos imouna" (Once I Was A Shepherd Boy) played on flute and sheep bells.

**EXTERNAL SERVICE:** see International Radio section.

## RADIOFONIKOS STATHMOS MAKEDONIAS (Gov.)

✉ Aggelaki 14, 546 36 Thessaloniki ☎+30 2310 299600 📠 +30 2310 299451 **W:** ert.gr **E:** makedonia@ert.gr
**Makedonia 1: FM:** Hortiatis 102.0MHz 20kW, 24h.
**Makedonia 2: FM:** Hortiatis 95.8MHz 20kW, 24h.
**Ann:** "Elliniki Radiophonia, Radiofonikos Stathmos Makedonias"

## ERT OPEN - ELLINIKI RADIOFONIA & TILEORASIS (ERA, Greek Public Radio)

✉ Leof. Mesogeion 463, Agia Paraskevi, 153 43 Athina ☎+30 210 6002909-10 📠 +30 210 6002941 **W:** ertopen.com **E:** ertopen@gmail.com
**FM:** Parnitha 106.7MHz.
**NB:** Operated by members of union of ERT administrative staff, using ERT transmission facilities and frequency assigned to ERT.

## ILIDA RADIO (Comm.)

✉ Ag. Trifonos 5, 27200 Amaliada. **W:** ilida911.gr **E:** info@ilida911.gr **D.Prgr:** 24h.
**MW:** Kastro 1584kHz 1kW. **FM:** Frangapidima 91.1MHz 2kW.

## 1431 AM (Educ.)

✉ Aristotle University of Thessaloniki, 2os Orofos Ptergas Ilektrologon, Politehniki Sholi, 54124 Thessaloniki. **W:** 1431am.org **D.Prgr:** 24h. **MW:** Thessaloniki 1431kHz 350W.

**UNOFFICIAL STATIONS** (Athens area, Voreios Ihos in Thessaloniki): Diavlos 1 693kHz, Studio 1 792kHz, Studio 54 828kHz, Black & White 927kHz, R. Galatsi 945kHz, R. Daffy 1044kHz, R. Mesogeia 1071kHz, R. 322 1107kHz, Mini Watt 1125kHz, R. Nikolaos Elata 1188kHz, R. Apollon 1242kHz, R. FBI 1269kHz, Smooth R. 1341kHz, Supersonic 1377kHz, R. Veteranos 1476kHz, Voreios Ihos 1539kHz and many others.

## PRIVATE FM STATIONS in Athina, Thessaloniki and Patra

### Athina

| FM | MHz | Station | kW | FM | MHz | Station | kW |
|---|---|---|---|---|---|---|---|
| 1) | 87.5 | Kriti FM | 1 | 11) | 90.4 | Kanali 1 | 5 |
| 2) | 87.7 | En Lefko | 10 | 12) | 90.6 | ART FM | 4 |
| 3) | 88.0 | Menta 88 | 10 | 13) | 91.2 | Peiraiki Ekkl. | 10 |
| 4) | 88.3 | Meraki FM | 2 | 14) | 91.4 | Lyra FM | 10 |
| 5) | 88.6 | News 24/7 | 8 | 15) | 92.0 | Galaxy 92 | 10 |
| 6) | 88.9 | Hit 88,9 | 14 | 16) | 92.3 | Lampsi 92,3 | 7 |
| 7) | 89.2 | Music 89,2 | 10 | 17) | 92.6 | Best 926 | 10 |
| 8) | 89.5 | Ekklesia Ell. | 15 | 18) | 92.9 | Kiss FM | 12 |
| 9) | 89.8 | Dromos 89,8 | 10 | 19) | 93.2 | Ellinikos 93,2 | 10 |
| 10) | 90.1 | Parapolitika FM | 10 | 20) | 93.8 | 93,8 FM | 1 |
| 21) | 94.0 | R. Epikoinonia | 1 | 43) | 101.3 | Diesi 101,3 | 10 |
| 22) | 94.3 | XFM | 5 | 44) | 101.6 | Paradise R. | 5 |
| 23) | 94.6 | Spor FM | 10 | 45) | 102.2 | Sfera 102,2. | 10 |
| 24) | 94.9 | Rythmos 949 | 10 | 46) | 102.5 | Athens Voice | 2 |
| 25) | 95.2 | Athens Deejay | 10 | 47) | 102.7 | Palmos On Air | 5 |
| 26) | 95.9 | Sevdas FM | 2 | 48) | 103.1 | R. Blackman | 5 |
| 27) | 96.1 | Dirla FM | 1 | 49) | 103.3 | Sport 24 R. | 10 |
| 28) | 96.3 | Red 96,3 | 10 | 50) | 104.0 | Party 104 FM | 2 |
| 29) | 96.6 | Pepper 96,6 | 10 | 51) | 104.3 | Hristianismos FM | 9 |
| 30) | 96.9 | Rock 969 | 10 | 52) | 104.6 | Thema 104.6 | 9 |
| 31) | 97.2 | Easy 97,2 | 10 | 53) | 104.9 | Styl FM | 4 |
| 32) | 97.5 | Love R. | 10 | 54) | 105.2 | Atlantis FM | 5 |
| 33) | 97.8 | Real FM | 12 | 55) | 105.5 | Sto Kokkino | 5 |
| 34) | 98.1 | Free R. | 1 | 56) | 106.2 | Mad R. | 10 |
| 35) | 98.3 | Athina 9,84 | 10 | 57) | 106.4 | R. Argosaronikos | 5 |
| 36) | 98.6 | Mousikos 98,6 | 5 | 58) | 106.5 | Laiko Radiofono | 3 |
| 37) | 98.9 | Alpha 989 | 10 | 59) | 107.2 | Blue Space FM | 3 |
| 38) | 99.2 | Melodia 99,2 | 9 | 60) | 107.4 | R. 107,4 | 2 |
| 39) | 99.5 | Peiratikos FM | 5 | 61) | 107.6 | Laikos 107,6 | 5 |
| 40) | 99.8 | Smooth 99,8 | 3 | 62) | 107.8 | Star FM | 5 |
| 41) | 100.3 | Skai 100,3 | 9 | 63) | 108.0 | Dias FM | 1 |
| 42) | 100.6 | Nostos 100,6 | 3 | | | | |

### Thessaloniki

| FM | MHz | Station | kW | FM | MHz | Station | kW |
|---|---|---|---|---|---|---|---|
| 63) | 87.6 | Laikos FM | 7 | 90) | 98.7 | R. Synora | 5 |
| 64) | 88.5 | 88miso | 1 | 91) | 99.0 | R. Ena | 5 |
| 65) | 89.0 | 89 Rainbow | 6 | 92) | 99.4 | Flash 99,4 | 2 |
| 66) | 89.4 | Arena FM | 6 | 93) | 99.8 | R. Ekrixi | 2 |
| 67) | 89.7 | Imagine 89,7 | 4 | 94) | 100.0 | FM 100 | 5 |
| 68) | 90.4 | 904 Aristera | 5 | 95) | 100.3 | Republic 100,3 | 5 |
| 69) | 90.8 | Zoo R. | 8 | 96) | 100.6 | FM 100,6 | 5 |
| 70) | 91.1 | VFM 91,1 | 3 | 97) | 101.0 | Dytika FM | 0.1 |
| 71) | 91.4 | Sto Mov | 4 | 98) | 101.3 | Lelevose FM | 5 |
| 72) | 91.7 | RSO 91,7 | 5 | 99) | 101.7 | Kalamaria FM | 5 |
| 73) | 92.4 | Karamela R. | 5 | 100) | 102.3 | R. Akrites | 1 |
| 74) | 92.8 | Yellow R. | 1 | 101) | 102.6 | Plus R. | 6 |
| 75) | 93.1 | Bee FM | 1 | 102) | ‡103.0 | More R. | 5 |
| 76) | 93.4 | Sto Kokkino | 5 | 103) | 103.6 | Focus FM | 5 |
| 77) | 93.7 | R. Gnomi | 1 | 104) | 104.0 | Fly 104 FM | 6 |
| 78) | 94.2 | R. Lydia | 6 | 105) | 104.4 | Radiokymata | 3 |
| 79) | 94.5 | R. Thessaloniki | 8 | 106) | 104.7 | Rock R. | 2 |
| 80) | 94.8 | Eroticos FM | 5 | 107) | 104.9 | Praktoreio FM | 1 |
| 81) | 95.1 | Cosmoradio | 8 | 108) | 105.2 | Live 105,2 | 0.5 |
| 82) | 95.5 | Metropolis FM | 8 | 109) | 105.5 | 1055 Rock | 5 |
| 83) | 96.1 | Fair Play 96,1 | 4 | 110) | 105.8 | Hroma FM | 3 |
| 84) | 96.5 | Alpha 96,5 | 4 | 111) | 106.1 | City International | 2 |
| 85) | 96.8 | Velvet 96,8 | 7 | 112) | 106.5 | Gold 106.5 | 5 |
| 86) | 97.1 | R. Almopia | 5 | 113) | 106.8 | Iera Mt. Langada | 2 |
| 87) | 97.5 | Easy 97,5 | 7 | 114) | 107.1 | Real FM | 4 |
| 88) | 98.0 | R. North | 6 | 115) | 107.4 | Libero 107,4 | 5 |
| 89) | 98.4 | Panorama 9,84 | 5 | 116) | 107.7 | Minima 107.7 | 5 |

**Patra FM (MHz):** Aroma 88.2 – Iera Mitropoli Patras 88.5 – Melody FM 88.8 – Skai Patras 89.4 – Mousikos FM 90.0 – Imera FM 90.4 – Yes R. 91.2 – Radio 91,5 91.5 – R. Enter 91.7 – Kiis Extra 92.2 – Top FM 93.0 – Max FM 93.4 – R. Gamma 94.0 – Alpha Patras 94.4 – Rythmos 94.9 – Oxygen 95.3 – Spor FM Patras 96.3 – Sfera Patras 96.6 – Wave R. 97.4 – R. Messatida 98.0 – Flash Patras 98.7 – R. Aigio 99.2 – Fasma FM 99.7 – You FM 100.1 – Melodia Patras 100.4 – Anoixi FM 100.7 – Free 101.1 – Hroma 102.1 – Loux FM 102.7 – Mousiki Lampsi 103.3 – Palmos FM 103.7 – Sport24 Patras 104.1 – Mythos FM 104.8 – Antenna Patras 105.3 – Derti 105.7 – Galaxy FM 106.1 – R. Patra 106.5 – Sto Kokkino 107.7. Powers 1–5kW.

+ approx 1100 additional private stns nationwide. ‡=inactive
**NB:** No official information available about powers of most Athina stations and Thessaloniki powers are mostly based on estimates.

**DAB:** Test broadcasts in Athens region by Digital Power (Gold, Pop, Jazz, Rock) on 216.928MHz/11A (Imittos).

## Addresses & other information:

**1)** Peloponissou 42, 18121 Koridallos **W:** kritifm.com – **2)** Fraggoklisias 8, 15125 Maroussi **W:** enlefko.fm – **3)** Mesogeion 174, 15125 Maroussi **W:** menta88.gr – **4)** Athina **W:** penies.gr – **5)** Leof. Siggrou 166, 17671 Kallithea **W:** news247.gr/radiofono24 – **6)** Fraggoklisias 8, 15125 Maroussi **W:** hit889.gr – **7)** Ifigenias 47, 14231 Neo Iraklio **W:** music892.gr – **8)** Iasiou 1, 11526 Athina **W:** ecclesia.gr/greek/ecclesiaradio/index.asp – **9)** Viltanioti 36, 14564 Kato Kifisia **W:** dromosfm.gr – **10)** Iasonos 2, 18537 Piraeus **W:** parapolitikaradio.gr – **11)** Evripidou 79, 18532 Piraeus **W:** kanaliena.gr – **12)** Praxitelous 58, 17674 Kallithea **W:** artfm906.gr – **13)** Deligiorgi 47, 18535 Piraeus

**W:** pe912fm.com – **14)** Athina **W:** lyrafm.gr – **15)** Pirronos 12, 16346 Ilioupoli **W:** galaxy92.gr – **16)** Viltanioti 36, 14564 Kato Kifisia **W:** lampsifm.gr – **17)** Perikleous 49, 15451 Neo Psyhiko **W:** best926. gr – **18)** Vas. Sofias 85, 15124 Maroussi **W:** kiss.gr – **19)** Leof. Kifisias 215, 15124 Maroussi **W:** ellinikos932.fm – **20)** Iroon Polytechniou, Polytechnoupoli, 15773 Zografou **W:** radio98fm.org – **21)** S. Karagiorgi 2 & M. Antypa, 14121 Iraklio **W:** 94fm.gr – **22)** Zitsis 54, 13123 Ilion. **W:** xfm943.gr **23)** Eth. Makariou/Delta Falireos 2, 18547 Neo Faliro **W:** sport-fm.gr – **24)** Theotokopoulou 4 & Astronafton, 15124 Maroussi **W:** rythmosfm.gr – **25)** Viltanioti 36, 14564 Kato Kifisia **W:** athensdeejay.gr – **26)** Athina **W:** sevdas.gr – **27)** Athina **W:** dirla.gr – **28)** Fraggoklisias 8, 15125 Maroussi **W:** redfm.gr – **29)** Mesogeion 174, 15125 Maroussi **W:** pepper966.gr – **30)** Viltanioti 36, 14564 Kato Kifisia **W:** rockfm. gr – **31)** Leof. Kifisias 10-12, 15125 Maroussi **W:** easy972.gr – **32)** Dimitros 31, 17778 Tavros **W:** loveradio.gr – **33)** Leof. Kifisias 215, 15124 Maroussi **W:** realfm.gr – **34)** Athina **W:** afradio.gr – **35)** Peiraios 100, 11854 Athina **W:** athina984.gr – **36)** Nikolaou Plastira 172, 13561 Agioi Anargiroi **W:** mousikos986.gr – **37)** Thesi Petsa-Vakalopoulou, 15351 Pallini **W:** alpha989.com – **38)** Fraggoklisias 8, 15125 Maroussi **W:** melodia.gr – **39)** Mihalakopoulou 80, 11528 Athina **W:** peiratikos. gr – **40)** A. Franzi & Ameinokleous 1, 11744 Neos Kosmos **W:** smooth. gr – **41)** Eth. Makariou/Delta Falireos 2, 18547 Neo Faliro **W:** skai. gr/1003 – **42)** Ag. Theklas 5, 153 43 Agia Paraskevi **W:** nostosradio. gr – **43)** Viltanioti 36, 14564 Kato Kifisia **W:** diesi.gr – **44)** Askeli Porou 18020 **W:** paradiseradio.gr – **45)** Nikolaou Plastira 172, 13561 Agioi Anargiroi **W:** sfera.gr – **46)** Harilaou Trikoupi 22, 10679 Athina **W:** athensvoice.gr/radio – **47)** 18020 Poros **W:** palmosradio.gr – **48)** Papanastasiou 25, 18755 Keratsini **W:** blackman.gr – **49)** Leof. Syggrou 166, 17671 Kallithea **W:** sport24radio.gr – **50)** Papagou 2 & Leof. Dimokratias 1A, 15127 Melissia **W:** partyfm104.gr – **51)** Sofocleous 52 & Menandrou, 10552 Athina **W:** christianity.gr/radio-christianity – **52)** Agrafon 5, 15123 Maroussi **W:** themaradio.gr – **53)** Athina **W:** stylfm. gr – **54)** Ag. Konstantinou 11, 18544 Piraeus **W:** atlantisfm.gr – **55)** Sarri 19, 10554 Athina **W:** stokokkino.gr – **56)** Eth. Antistaseos 253, 15351 Pallini **W:** mad.tv/mad-radio-106-2 – **57)** Dritseika Methanon, 18030 Methana **W:** radioargosaronikos.gr – **58)** Athina **W:** 1065radio. com – **59)** Athina **W:** bluespacefm.com – **60)** Athina – **61)** Athina **W:** laikosfm.gr – **62)** Athina **W:** starathens.gr – **63)** Athina **W:** diasfm. gr – **64)** G. Kranidioti 2, 57001 Pylaia Thessaloniki **W:** laikos.gr – **65)** Armenopoulou 9, 54635 Thessaloniki **W:** 88miso.gr – **66)** K. Karamanli 175, 54349 Thessaloniki **W:** 89rainbow.gr – **67)** Cavafi 1 & Solomou 4, 54250 Pylaia Thessaloniki **W:** arenafm.gr – **68)** Adrianoupoleos 20A, 55133 Kalamaria Thessaloniki **W:** imagine897.gr – **69)** Egnatias 69, 54631 Thessaloniki **W:** 902.gr – **70)** Kosti Palama 6G, 55535 Pylaia **W:** zooradio.gr – **71)** K. Karamanli 69, 4os Orofos, 54642 Thessaloniki **W:** 911.gr – **72)** 10 km. Filirou-Langada, 57010 Thessaloniki **W:** stokokkino.gr/kokkino-mov.php – **73)** 10 km. Filirou-Langada, 57010 Filiro, Thessaloniki **W:** rso.gr – **74)** Fanariou 13 & Mouson, 56429 Stavroupoli Thessaloniki **W:** karamelaradio.gr – **75)** K. Karamanli 171, Voulgari, 54249 Thessaloniki **W:** yellowradio.gr – **76)** 4hs Avgoustou 6, 57003 Agios Athanasios Thessaloniki **W:** ble.fm – **77)** Siggrou 11, 54625 Thessaloniki **W:** stokokkino.gr/kokkino-thes.php – **78)** Ag. Sofias 43, 54623 Thessaloniki **W:** gnominet.gr – **79)** Eleftherias 15, 56123 Ambelokipi Thessaloniki **W:** radiolydia.com – **80)** 170 km Moudianon, Kombos Risiou, 57001 Thermi Thessaloniki **W:** rthess.gr – **81)** 170 km Moudianon, Kombos Risiou, 57001 Thermi Thessaloniki **W:** eroticos. gr – **82)** Tsimiski 51, 6os Orofos, 54623 Thessaloniki **W:** cosmoradio. gr – **83)** K. Palama 6A, 54352 Pylaia Thessaloniki **W:** metropolisradio. gr – **84)** Tsalouhidi 20, 54249 Thessaloniki **W:** fairplayradio.gr – **85)** K. Kristalli 4, 54630 Thessaloniki **W:** alpha965.gr – **86)** Kosti Palama 6G, 54630 Thessaloniki **W:** velvet968.gr – **87)** Lohagou N. Papadopoulou 17, 58400 Aridaia **W:** aridaia-gegonota.blogspot.com – **88)** 26hs Oktovriou 90, 54627 Thessaloniki – **89)** Mitropoleos 34, 54623 Thessaloniki **W:** radionorth.gr – **90)** Andreou Georgiou 56, 54627 Thessaloniki **W:** panorama984.gr – **91)** Kentriki Plateia Polikastrou Kilkis & Ermou 4, 1os Orofos, 61200 Polikastro Kilkis **W:** synorafm.gr – **92)** K. Karamanli 175, 54249 Thessaloniki **W:** 99fm.gr – **93)** 26hs Oktovriou 46, 54627 Thessaloniki **W:** flash994.gr – **94)** Melenikou 31A, 56224 Evosmos Thessaloniki **W:** ekrixifm.gr – **95)** N. Germanou 1, 54645 Thessaloniki **W:** fm100.gr – **96)** Kosti Palama 6G, 55535 Pylaia **W:** republicradio.gr – **97)** N. Germanou 1, 54645 Thessaloniki **W:** fm100. gr – **98)** Thessaloniki **W:** dytikafm.weebly.com – **99)** Antigonidon 19, 54630 Thessaloniki **W:** lelevose.gr/radio.html – **100)** Andrianoupoleos 8 & Epanomis 26, 55133 Kalamaria Thessaloniki **W:** kalamariafm.gr – **101)** Vas. Othonos 12, 54629 Stavroupoli, Thessaloniki **W:** radioakrites. gr – **102)** Aristotelous 7, 54624 Thessaloniki **W:** plusradio.gr – **103)** Aristotelous 7, 54624 Thessaloniki W: moreradio.gr – **104)** Politehniou 21, 54623 Thessaloniki **W:** focusfm.gr – **105)** 26hs Oktovriou 90, 54627 Thessaloniki **W:** fly104.gr – **106)** A. Papandreou 27, 56334 Kordelio Thessaloniki **W:** radiokymata.gr – **107)** Kouskoura 5, 54625 Thessaloniki **W:** rockradio.gr – **108)** Egnatias 154, 54636 Thessaloniki **W:** praktoreio-

fm.gr – **109)** Promitheos 33 & Afroditis 12, 54630 Thessaloniki **W:** facebook.com/105.2live – **110)** Aggelaki 31, 54621 Thessaloniki **W:** 1055rock.gr – **111)** Kromnis 10, 54453 Toumpa Thessaloniki **W:** hroma. gr – **112)** Karatassou 31, 55132 Kalamaria Thessaloniki **W:** cityinterna-tional.gr – **113)** Aggelaki 31, 54621 Thessaloniki **W:** gold1065.gr – **114)** 57200 Langadas Thessaloniki **W:** imlagada.gr/default.aspx?catid=89 – **115)** Aristotelous 5, 54624 Thessaloniki **W:** realfm.gr – **116)** Leontos Sofou 18, 54625 Thessaloniki **W:** facebook.com/liberofm – **117)** Makedonikis Aminis 1, 54631 Thessaloniki. **W:** minima1077.gr

## AMERICAN FORCES RADIO & TV SERVICE (Mil.)
**W:** afneurope.net/Stations/Souda-Bay **FM:** "107.3 The Odyssey": Souda Bay 107.3MHz 0.5kW

## GREENLAND (Denmark)

**L.T:** UTC -3h (DST*: -2h). Qaanaaq & Thule Air Base: UTC -4h (DST*: -3h; not Thule AB), Ittoqqortoormiit: UTC -1h (DST*: UTC), Danmarkshavn: UTC. *) 31 Mar-27 Oct — **Pop:** 57,000 — **Pr.L:** Greenlandic, Danish — **E.C:** 50Hz, 230V — **ITU:** GRL

### KALAALIT NUNAATA RADIOA – KNR (Pub. Comm.)
✉ Issortarfimmut 1A, PO Box 1007, DK-3900 Nuuk ☎ +299 361500 🖶 +299 361502 **W:** knr.gl **E:** info@knr.gl
**L.P:** Chrmn: Nukaaraq Eugenius. MD: Karl Henrik Simonsen. Hd of Radio: Maasana Egede

| MW | kHz | kW | MW | kHz | kW |
|---|---|---|---|---|---|
| Nuuk | 570 | 5 | Qeqertarsuaq | 650 | 5 |
| Simiutaq | 720 | 10 | | | |

| FM | MHz | kW | FM | MHz | kW |
|---|---|---|---|---|---|
| Nuuk | 90.5 | 0.5 | Ilulissat | 96.0 | 0.1 |
| Sisimiut | 95.0 | 0.1 | Tasillaq | 96.0 | 0.08 |
| Uummannaq | 95.0 | 0.05 | Sanderson Hope | 96.0 | 0.1 |
| Upernavik | 95.0 | 0.05 | Aasiaat | 96.5 | 0.1 |
| Qaqortoq | 95.5 | 0.1 | Manitsoq | 97.0 | 0.08 |
| Kangerlussuaq | 96.0 | 0.08 | Dye Four | 98.7 | 0.08 |

+ 62 additional stns 0.1kW or less. On 88.1-99.0MHz. Most txs use 94.0, 95.0, 95.4, 95.5, 96.0 or 97MHz **KNR:** 24h in Greenlandic (approx. 90%) and in Danish. N on the h in Greenlandic and Danish. Main N in Greenlandic: 1500, 2100. Danish: 1515, 2115
**Ann:** "Kallaallit-Nunaata Radioa", "Grønlands Radio" **IS:** "Sunnia Kalippoq" (The Whaleboat "Sonja" drags whale) played on celeste

**DR P1**, Denmark. Satellite relay 24h Nuuk 98.0MHz 0.1kW
**RÚV Rás 2**, Iceland. Satellite relay 24h Narsaq 88.0MHz (0.01kW)

### INUUNERUP NIPAA (Rlg)
✉ Ilivinnguaq 1, PO Box 67, DK-3900 Nuuk ☎ +299 321382 🖶 +299 321226 **W:** inn.gl **E:** ino.nuuk@greennet.gl
**L.P:** Chrmn: John Østergaard Nielsen. Hd of Prgr.: Jan Berthelsen
**FM:** 88.5MHz (all txs are 0.05kW) in Aasiaat, Ilulissat, Kullorsuaq, Maniitsoq, Nanortalik, Nuuk, Qaanaaq, Qaqortoq, Sisimiut, Tasiilaq, Upernavik and Uummannaq
**D.Prgr:** 1030-1430, 1600-1930 and 2200-0230. Most prgrs in Greenlandic

### PRIVATE STATIONS – local radio FM (MHz):
**Ice FM**, Industrivej 18, Box 1082, 3900 Nuuk ☎ +299 522840 W: icefm.gl FM 93.5 (0.1 kW) – **Nanoq FM**, Box 1016, 3900 Nuuk ☎ +299 321911 **W:** nanoqmedia.gl/kl/radio-2/ FM 100.0 – **Nipi FM**, Box 279, 3921 Maniitsoq ☎ +299 547771 **W:** nipifm.gl FM 90.5/93.0 (Maniitsoq) & 99.0 (Kangaamiut) – **Qaanaap Duhaudaa**, Qaanaaq ☎ +299 191777 L.P. David Qujaukitsoq. FM 93.5 – **Radio Narsaq**, Josifip aqq. 543, 3961 Narsaq. L.P. Johan Henningsen. FM 93.0 (0.025kW) – **Seekon Radio**, Box 361, 3920 Qaqortoq ☎ +299 531994. L.P. Kelly Berthelsen. FM 103.0 – **Tusaataat**, Box 401, 3911 Sisimiut ☎ +299 864800 **W:** tusaataat.gl L.P. Jens Klaus Lennert. FM 93.0 (0.05kW).

## GRENADA

**L.T:** UTC -4h — **Pop:** 110,000 — **Pr.L:** English — **E.C:** 50Hz, 230/400V — **ITU:** GRD

### GRENADA BROADCASTING NETWORK – G.B.N. Radio (Gov, Comm.)
✉ Observatory Road, PO. Box 535, St. George's ☎ +1 473 440 3033 🖶 +1 473 444 4180 **W:** gbn.gd **E:** grenadabroadcastingnetwork@ gmail.com
**L.P:** GM: Odetta Campbell. CEN: Kennedy Bowen
**FM:** HOTT FM: 98.5/98.7MHz 1000-0300 – **K105:** 105.5MHz (South) /105.9MHz (North)

**HARBOUR LIGHT OF THE WINDWARDS (Rlg.)**
☞ Harbour Light Way, Hillsborough Post Office, Tarleton Point, Carriacou ☎ +1 473 443 7628 🖶 +1 473 443 7628 **W:** harbourlightradio. org **E:** harbourlight@spiceisle.com **LP:** SM: Randy Cornelius
**MW:** 1400kHz 5kW **FM:** 92.3MHz 0.25kW, 94.5MHz 0.25kW
**D.Prg:** MW: 0900-0400. FM: 24h. **N:** rel. BBC
**Ann:** "This is the Harbour Light of the Windwards broadcasting from beautiful and friendly Carriacou"

**PRIVATE STATIONS (FM in MHz):**
**Boss FM,** Bruce St. Mall St., St George's ☎+1 473 442 1177. W: bossfmgrenada.net. FM 104.1/104.9 – **Chime FM,** Grant Comm., PO Box 553, Tanteen, St George's ☎+1 473 440 7746. FM 100.9 – **City Sound,** River Road, St George's ☎+1 473 440 9616 🖶+1 473 440 7838 **W:** citysoundfm.com FM 96.5/97.5 – **CRFM Community Radio:** Morne Jaloux, St George's ☎+1 473 440 4848 🖶+1 473 440 4991 FM 89.5 – **Fresh FM,** Bruce St Mall, St George's. FM 102.7 – **GFN - Grenada Family Network,** Advent Ave, Grand Bras, PO Box 2747, St George's ☎+1 473 435 4297. FM 91.3. Format: Rlg. (Adventist) – **GNCN - Good News Catholic Radio,** Church St., Box 224, St George's ☎+1 473 435 0143 FM 99.5/99.9. Format: Rlg – **GTC Radio,** Morne Rouge, Grand Anse, St George's ☎+1 473 439 9700 **E:** gtc@ gtcfm.com **W:** gtcfm.com FM 89.9/90.5 – **Live Wire HD,** Ross Point, PO Box 90, St George's ☎/🖶+1 473 435 3563 FM 90.1 – **Magic 103,** Moving Target Co., Lagoon Road, St George's ☎+1 473 440 8171 🖶 +1 473 440 8505 **W:** magic103fm.com FM 98.9/95.7/103.3 – **Power 95.1,** Melville St., St George's ☎+1 473 435 9500 **W:** power95fm.com FM 95.1/95.3 – **Real FM Grenada,** High Street, Sauters, St Patrick ☎+1 473 442 0975 **W:** drealfmgrenada.com FM 91.5/91.9 – **Secret Radio,** L'anse aux Epines, St. Geroge's. ☎+1 473 410 4512 **W:** secretharbourgrenada.com/secret-radio FM: 92.7 – **SGU 107.5,** Office of University Communications, 2nd floor, Chancellery, St George's University, St George's ☎+1 473 444 4175 ext. 2191 🖶+1 473 444 3153 **W:** sgu.edu. FM 107.5. Format: Non-comm. community radio – **Sister Isle Radio,** Fort Hill, Hillsborough, Carriacou ☎+1 473 443 8141/8142 FM 92.9 – **Star FM 101.7,** Soubise St. Andrew **W:** starfmgrenada.com FM 101.7 – **The Soul of Grenada (TSOG),** Grand Roy, St. John's. FM 100.7 – **Vibes 101.3,** Church St, Hillsborough, Carriacou ☎+1 473 439 0101 FM 101.3 – **Wee FM,** Grenada Wireless Comm Network, Cross St, PO Box 555, St George's ☎+1 473 440 4933 🖶+1 473 440 8724 **W:** weefmgrenada.com FM 93.3/93.9

## GUADELOUPE (France)

**L.T:** UTC -4h — **Pop:** 350,000 — **Pr.L:** French, Créole Patois — **E.C:** 50Hz, 230V — **ITU:** GLP

**GUADELOUPE PREMIÈRE (Pub)**
☞ Morne Bernard-Destrellan, B.P. 180, F-97122 Baie-Mahault. ☎+590 590939696. 🖶+590 590939682 **W:** guadeloupe.la1ere.fr **LP:** Dir: R.Surjus. Editor-in-Chief: Philippe Goudé. PD: L.Francil. Head Comms Dept: Sonia Gémieux
**FM:** Point-à-Pitre 88.9MHz 1kW, Haut du Morne des Pères 89.1MHz 1kW, Deshaies 96.8MHz 0.1kW, Basse-Terre 97.0MHz 3kW, Pointe-Noire 97.4MHz 16kW
**D.Prg:** 24h. **N:** 1100, 1700, 2230, plus relays of France-Inter.
**Ann:** "Ici Point-à-Pitre, La Première Guadeloupe".
**IS:** "Biguin" (guitar) **V.** by QSL-card. Rp.

**RADIO CARAÏBES INTERNATIONAL (Comm.)**
☞ **RCI Guadeloupe,** B.P. 1309, 97187 Point-à-Pitre Cédex. ☎ +590 590839696 🖶 +590 590839697
**FM:** Basse-Terre 98.6MHz 1kW, Deshaies 98.6MHz 0.3kW, Morne-à-Louis 100.2MHz 2kW, Point-à-Pitre 106.6MHz 1kW, Haut du Morne 106.6MHz 0.05kW. **D.Prg:** 24h.

**RADIO BASSES INTERNATIONALE (Comm)**
☞ Stations de radio, Lieu-dit Les Basses, 97112 Grand Bourg ☎ +590 590977088 🖶 +590 590978062
**FM:** Haut du Morne des Pères 88.7MHz 1kW, Grand-Bourg 90.4MHz 1kW, Morne-à-Louis 98.2MHz 2kW, Basse-Terre 102.2MHz 1kW

**RADIO MASSABIELLE (RCF) (Rlg)**
☞ B.P. 607, 97168 Point-à-Pitre ☎+590 590832521 🖶 +590 590 834861. **LP:** Pres: José Colat-Jolivière, Dir: Père Silvère Numa
**W:** radiomassabielle.fr **E:** contact@radiomassabielle.fr
**FM:** Point-à-Pitre 91.8MHz 0.6kW, Pointe-Noire 101.8MHz 1kW

**RADIO SAPHIR FM**
☞ rue Bel Air Bourg, 97170 Petit-Bourg ☎+590 590352274
**E:** saphirfm@live.fr **W:** radiosaphir.fr
**FM:** Point-à-Pitre 89.4MHz 1kW

**Other stations (all FM** (MHz)**):**
**France Inter,** Pointe-à-Pitre 91.2 1kW, Haut du Morne des Pères 91.7 1kW, Morne-à-Louis 95.0 16kW, Basse-Terre 95.4 3kW – **NRJ Guadeloupe,** Pointe-à-Pitre, 100.6 1kW, Basse-Terre 102.6 1kW, Morne-à-Louis 107.2 2kW – **Antilles Infos,** 105.8 2kW, 106.5 1kW – **Bel'Radio,** 96.3 1kW, 106.9 1kW – **Fréquence Alizée,** 96.6 1kW, 103.4 2kW – **R. Éclair,** 96.0 1kW, 101.0 2kW – **R. Gaïac FM,** 99.8 1kW, 104.7 1kW – **R. Haute Tensi,** 89.8 1kW, 90.8 1kW – **R. Karata,** 90.6 1kW, 106.5 1kW – **Radio Madras FM,** 92.5 2kW, 92.9 1kW – **Radio Nostalgie,** 105.4 1kW, 107.6 2kW – **Trace FM,** 92.1 2kW, 94.1 1kW. **NB:** +11 other stations

## GUAM (USA)

**L.T:** UTC +10h — **Pop:** 165,718 — **Pr.L:** English, Chamorro, Filipino — **E.C:** 60Hz, 110/220V — **ITU:** GUM

**FEDERAL COMMUNICATIONS COMMISSION (FCC)**
see USA for details

| | MW | kHz | kW | | MW | kHz | kW |
|---|---|---|---|---|---|---|---|
| 1) | KGUM | 567 | 10 | 12) | KUSG | 1350 | 0.09 |
| 2) | KUAM | 630 | 10 | 13) | KVOG | 1530 | 0.25 |
| 3) | KTWG | 801 | 10 | | | | |
| | **FM** | **MHz** | **kW** | | **FM** | **MHz** | **kW** |
| 4) | KHMG | 88.1 | 8 | 12) | KUSG-FM | 98.3 | 0.25 |
| 5) | KPRG | 89.3 | 9.2 | 16) | KZGU | 99.5 | 17 |
| 6) | KKGU | 90.1 | 0.25 | 9) | KOKU | 100.3 | 50 |
| 5) | KOLG | 90.9 | 5.7 | 11) | KNUT | 101.1 | 8 |
| 7) | KSDA-FM | 91.9 | 3.8 | 10) | KTKB-FM | 101.9 | 46 |
| 9) | KMOY | 92.7 | 42 | 8) | KISH | 102.9 | 25 |
| 12) | KUSG-FM | 93.3 | 0.01 | 11) | KIJI | 104.3 | 8.6 |
| 2) | KUAM-FM | 93.9 | 5.2 | 1) | KGUM-FM | 105.1 | 10.5 |
| 3) | KVOG-FM | 94.7 | 0.25 | 3) | KTWG-FM* | 105.9 | 0.2 |
| 8) | KSTO | 95.5 | 2.5 | 14) | KGCA-LP | 106.9 | 0.07 |
| 1) | KGUM-FM* | 96.5 | 0.25 | 14) | KGCA-LP | 107.9 | 0.023 |
| 1) | KZGZ | 97.5 | 37 | | *) = CP | | |

**Addresses & other information:**
1) **Sorensen Pacific Broadcasting Inc** 111 Chalan Santa Papa, Suite 800; Hagatna, GU 96910-5193 ☎+1 671 477-5700, +1 808 524-6495, 🖶+1 671 477-3982 **Brands:** KGUM-AM Talk, news **W:** k57.com; KZGZ Power98 CHR **W:** power98guam.com [KZGU 99.5 currently licenced to Garapan-Saipan, N Marianas but serves Guam as 'The Shark'] **W:** guamshark.com KGUM-FM 'The Kat' **W:** facebook. com/105thekat – 2) **Pacific Telestations LLC** 600 Harmon Loop Road, Suite 102; Dededo, GU 96929-6536 ☎+1 671 637-KUAM (637-5826) 🖶+1 671 637-9865 **W:** kuam.com **Brands:** KUAM: Isla63 'Island Pride' contemporary island music; KUAM-FM: i94 Champion Radio CHR – 3) **Edward H Poppe Jr & Frances W Poppe,** Cornerstone 800AM, 1868 Halsey Drive; Asan, GU 96910-1505 ☎+1 671 477-5894 🖶+1 671 477-6411 **W:** ktwg.com **E:** am800guam@gmail.com Format: Protestant Christian talk and instruction, gospel music **NB:** Korean Mon & Fri 0800-0830, Tagalog Wed 0800-0830, Chamorro Thu 0800-0815 & Sun 0700-0730, Japanese Thu 0815-0830 – 4) **Harvest Christian Academy,** Harvest Family Radio, PO Box 23189 Barrigada, GU 96921 ☎ +1 671 477 6341🖶 +1 671 477 7136 **W:** hbcguam.net **E:** khmg@hbcguam.net **LP:** GM: John Collier **Prgr:** 24h religious– 5) **Guam Educational Radio Foundation** c/o University of Guam, 303 University Drive; UOG Station; Mangilao, GU 96923-1871 **NB:** BBCWS Daily 0700-0800, Sun 1900-2100, Mon 1900-2000, Tue 1400-2000, Wed & Thu 1400-1800 & 1900-2000, Fri 1400-1800, Sat 1700-2000 **W:** kprgfm.com STA 4.6kw because of typhoon damage and need to relocate tower – 6) **Catholic Educational Radio,** Chalan Santo Papa; P.O. 23006, Guam Mail Facility, Barrigada, GU 96921-3006 **W:** kolg.com **LP:** GM: Deacon Frank Tenorio, Dir. Prgr: Chuck White **Prgr:** 24h relig – 7) **Good News Broadcasting Corp,** Joy FM, 290 Chalan Palasyo, Hagatna Heights, GU 96910-6405 ☎ +1 671 472 1111 🖶 +1 671 477 4678 **W:** joyfmguam.com **LP:** GM: Matthew Dodd **Prgr:** 24h religious **Languages:** English, Chinese, Chuukese, Japanese, Korean, Tagalog – 8) **Inter-Island Communications Inc,** Nimitz Hill, 1868 Halsey Drive, Piti, GU 96910-1505 – 9) **Moy Communications,** Guam Hit Radio 100, 107 Julale Center, 424 West O'Brien Drive, Hagatna, GU 96910-5078 **W:** hitradio100.com **E:** marketing@hitradio100.com **KOKU:** "Guam's #1 Hit Music Station" CHR **KMOY** – 10) **KM Broadcasting of Guam LLC,** 177-B Ilipog Drive, Suite 203; Tamuning, GU 96913-4107 **E:** rolly@ ktkb.com **W:** ktkb.com **Brand:** Megamixx 101.9 Format: OPM Origil Pilipino Music **Prgr Language:** Tagalog – 11) **Choice Broadcasting Company** 543A Top-Plaza Building, N Marine Dr, Tamuning, GU 96913-4217☎+1 671 478-0104 🖶+1 671 647-7480 **KNUT** Fun 101 FM "Guam's Hottest OPM & US Hit Station" **Prgr:** Filippino **W:** facebook. com/fun101Guam **KIJI** 3F La Casa de Colina Building, Tamuning GU 96913 "The Boss 104.3FM" **Prgr:** Classic Rock **LP:** SM: Rich de Vera

**W:** kijifm104.com **E:** rich@kijifm104.com **Other:** sister company to iConnect – **13) MCS LLC**, 125 Tun Jesus, Crisotomo Street #308, Tamuning GU 96913 ☎+1 671 648-4262 – **12)** Hagatna. ☎+1 671 648-4262 **W:** kusgthepulse.com – **13) Guam Power II Inc**, 1100 Alakea #1800, Honolulu HI 96813-2839 ☎+1 808 521-4711 – **14) KGCA Inc**, Melodies of Prayer Inc, 154 Calachucha Ave, Barrigada GU 96913 ☎+1 671 637 5975 **W:** melodiesofprayer.com **E:** mail@melodiesofprayer. com **L.P:** Chair: Edwin Supit **Prgr:** 24h religious – **15) Hurao Inc**, 264 Calle de los Marteres St, Agat GU 96935 ☎ +1 671 482-4630 – **16)** SORENSEN PACIFIC BROADCASTING, INC. "The Shark" 962 Pale San Vitores Road, Suite 116, Tumon

**ADVENTIST WORLD RADIO - ASIA (Rlg.) and TRANS WORLD RADIO - ASIA (Rlg.):** See International Radio section

## GUATEMALA

**L.T:** UTC -6h — **Pop:** 17 million — **Pr.L:** Spanish — **E.C:** 60Hz, 120V — **ITU:** GTM

### SUPERINTENDENCIA DE TELECOMUNICACIONES
▣ 4a Avenida N° 15-51, Z-10, Guatemala ☎+502 2321100 ext. 101 **W:** sit.gob.gt

### CÁMARA DE RADIODIFUSION DE GUATEMALA
▣ 12 Calle 1-25, Zona 10, Edificio Geminis 10, Torre Norte, Of. 812, Guatemala ☎+502 23353077 **W:** camaraderadiodifusiongt.com
**Call** TG—, ‡ = inactive, (r) = repeater, ± = varying fq.

| MW Call | | kHz | kW | Station, location, h. of tr. |
|---|---|---|---|---|
| M01) | | 560 | 1 | R. Quetzal, Malacatán |
| ES01) | PA | 570 | 1 | R. Palmeras, Escuintla |
| GU01) | Y | 580 | 5 | R. Progreso, Guatemala: 1300-0100 |
| QU01) | RQ | 590 | 5 | R. Quiché, Sta Cruz del Quiché: 1100-0400 |
| GU02) | GA | 610 | 5 | R. Alianza, Guatemala: 1000-0500 |
| T001) | PQ | 620 | 5 | R. 6-20, San Cristóbal: 1200-0400 |
| PE01) | EL | 630 | | R. Cultural Porvenir, Sta Elena: (r. 730) |
| QE01) | Q | 660 | 3 | LV de Quetzaltenango: 1100-0400 |
| AV02) | VP | 680 | 10 | R. Norte, Cobán: 1000-0500 |
| JU01) | VB | 690 | 1 | R. Tamazulapa, Jutiapa |
| ES03) | AJ | 700 | 1 | R. Inspiración, Escuintla |
| GU03) | HR | ‡700 | 15 | R. Mundial, Guatemala |
| QE02) | XL | 710 | 1 | R. Tecún Umán, Quetzaltenango (r. 730) |
| GU05) | | 760 | | R. 760, Guatemala |
| ZA01) | CK | 780 | 1 | Sultana La Cristiana, Zacapa |
| PE02) | | 810 | | R. Moapán, Sta Elena |
| SA01) | | 810 | | R. Circuito San Juan, San Juan |
| GU06) | END | 810 | 1 | R. Constelación, Guatemala: 1200-0400 |
| SU01) | AV | 830 | 5 | R. Satélite, Mazatenango: 1100-0400 |
| AV06) | | 840 | 2.5 | R. Luz, San Pedro Carchá |
| JU04) | | 840 | | Idea Radio, Jutiapa: -0100 |
| SU02) | L | 870 | 0.5 | R. Victoria, Mazatenango |
| ES04) | HU | 890 | 1 | R. Escuintla, Escuintla |
| IZ02) | MA | 900 | 1 | R. Amatique, Puerto Barrios |
| GU30) | KL | ‡910 | 10 | R. Fe y Esperanza, Guatemala: 1130-0600 |
| ES05) | RS | 920 | 0.2 | R. Cultural, Escuintla (r. 730) |
| GU13) | LV | 940 | 10 | Eventos Católicos R., San Pedro Sacatepéquez, Guatemala: 1200-0500 |
| SU03) | AF | 950 | 1 | R. Indiana, Mazatenango |
| GU14) | AX | ‡970 | 5 | R. Continental, Guatemala: 1200-0430 |
| CH01) | AL | 990 | 1 | R. Perla de Oriente, Chiquimula |
| CM02) | | 1000 | | R. Cultural y Educativa, Patzún |
| GU32) | | 1000 | | R. Revelación y Verdad, Guatemala: 1055-0500 |
| IZ06) | | 1010 | 1 | R. Caribe, Izabal |
| QU03) | XI | 1010 | 1 | R. Ixil, Nebaj: 1100-0200 |
| SM05) | CM | 1020 | 5 | R. Frontera, Pajapita: 1100-0400 |
| GU15) | UX | 1030 | 10 | R. Panamericana, Guatemala: 1400-0000 |
| JA01) | JP | 1040 | 1 | R. Oriental, Jalapa |
| HU01) | SL | 1050 | 5/1 | LV de los Cuchumatanes, Huehuetenango: 1100-0600 |
| QE04) | D | 1070 | 3/2 | LV de Occidente, Quetzaltenango: 1200-0600 |
| ZA02) | LU | 1080 | 1 | R. Novedad, Zacapa |
| QE05) | SR | 1100 | 1 | R. Superior, Coatepeque |
| AV04) | MK | 1110 | 1 | R. Verapaz, Cobán |
| GU17) | C | ‡1120 | 0.5 | R. Poderosa, Guatemala |
| RE01) | VR | 1130 | 1 | Em. Unidas LV de la Costa Sur, Retalhuleu |
| GU17) | T | 1150 | 10 | R. Sonora, Guatemala: 1100-0600 |
| IZ03) | RI | 1160 | 1 | R. Izabal, Morales (r. 730): 1300-0300 |
| QE06) | RL | 1170 | 1 | R. Cadena Landivar, Quetzaltenango: 0900-0300 |
| JU02) | RJ | 1200 | 12 | R. Unción, Jutiapa |
| GU19) | MX | 1210 | 10/5 | R. Palabra Miel, Guatemala -0400 |
| IZ04) | AT | 1230 | 1 | R. Atlántida, Puerto Barrios: 1130-0500 |

| MW Call | | kHz | kW | Station, location, h. of tr. |
|---|---|---|---|---|
| SU04) | | 1230 | | R. América, Cuyotenango |
| CH02) | PY | 1250 | 1 | R. Payakí, Esquipulas: 1100-0300 |
| T004) | | 1250 | 1 | LV Cristiana, Totonicapán |
| GU21) | CQ | 1270 | 2.5 | R. Exclusiva, Guatemala |
| ZA03) | | 1290 | | R. Miramundo "LV del Ejercito", Zacapa |
| QE07) | AN | 1310 | 1 | R. LV de los Altos, Quetzaltenango: 1100-0700 |
| JU03) | ME | 1320 | 0.5 | R. Quezada, Jutiapa |
| GU22) | MU | 1330 | 5 | Unión R, Guatemala |
| AV05) | MC | 1350 | 1 | R. Monja Blanca, Cobán |
| GU23) | LK | 1360 | 10 | R. Tic Tac "LV del Evangelio", Guatemala |
| QE09) | AC | 1370 | 1 | LV de Colomba, Colomba |
| T003) | EB | 1380 | 0.5 | R. Momostenango Educativa, Momostenango:1100-0300 |
| QE10) | GH | 1410 | 5 | Nueva R. Xelajú, Quetzaltenango: 1200-0600 |
| GU29) | | ‡1420 | | R. Capital, Guatemala |
| HU02) | AG | 1430 | 1.2 | LV de Huehuetenango: 1100-0400 |
| SU05) | MS | 1440 | 0.5 | R. Nacional, Mazatenango: 0000-0400 |
| GU24) | LG | 1450 | 1 | R. Hosanna, Guatemala: 1000-0400 |
| PE04) | RN | 1460 | 2.5 | R. Petén, Flores: 1100-0500 |
| GU25) | HB | 1480 | 5 | R. Horizontes, Guatemala: 1030-0200 |
| RE02) | RE | 1490 | 1 | R. Modelo, Retalhuleu |
| GU26) | DX | 1510 | | R. Centroamericana, Guatemala |
| PE05) | | 1520 | | R. Taysal, Sta Elena de la Cruz |
| QE12) | | 1560 | | R. Inspiración, Quetzaltenango |
| GU27) | VE | 1570 | 10 | R. VEA-Voz Evangélica de América, Guatemala: 1030-0600 |
| CM01) | XC | 1590 | 1 | R. Triunfadora, Chimaltenango |

| SW Call | | kHz | kW | Station, location & h. of tr |
|---|---|---|---|---|
| CH04) | AV | ‡4055 | 0.7 | R. Verdad, Chiquimula: 0910-0600 |

**State abbreviations:** (Departamentos) AV = Alta Verapaz, BV = Baja Verapaz, CH = Chiquimula, CM = Chimaltenango, ES = Escuintla, GU = Guatemala, HU = Huehuetenango, IZ = Izabal, JA = Jalapa, JU = Jutiapa, PE = Petén, QE = Quetzaltenango, QU = Quiché, RE = Retalhuleu, SA = Sacatepéquez, SR = Santa Rosa, SM = San Marcos, SO = Solólá, SU = Suchitepéquez, TO = Totonicapán, ZA = Zacapa. **N.B:** These abbreviations are not recognized by the Post Office. Letters should therefore carry the full name.
**Addresses & other information:**
**AV00) ALTA VERAPAZ**
**AV01)** 5 Calle 1-06, Z-3, 16001 Cobán – **AV02)** 2 Calle 5-57, Z-3, 16001 Cobán – **AV04)** 2 Calle 5-57, Z-3, 16001 Cobán – **AV05)** Edif Municipalidad, 5a Calle 1-06, 16001 Cobán – **AV06)** 11 Av Zona 1, Colonia Cuatro Caminos, San Pedro Carchá (or Apartado Postal 14, 16001 Cobán)
**BV00) BAJA VERAPAZ**
**BV01)** Inst de Educación Básica, Barrio Abajo San Jerónimo, 15001 Salamá. Prgrs. in Spanish, Achi and Q'eqchí
**CH00) CHIQUIMULA**
**CH01)** 7 Calle Av 4-00, Z-1, 20001 Chiquimula (or 6 Av 0-60, Z-4, Torre Prof II, Of 904, 01004 Guatemala) – **CH02)** 5 Av 6-37, Z-1, 20007 Esquipulas – **FM:** 91.5MHz – **CH04)** Estación Educativa Evangélica, Ap. 5, 20901 Chiquimula. **W:** radioverdad.org
**CM00) CHIMALTENANGO**
**CM01)** 2 Calle 3-33, Z-3, 04001 Chimaltenango – **CM02)** 6ta Calle 3-88, Zona 5, Patzún 050, Chimaltenango.
**ES00) ESCUINTLA**
**ES01)** 15 Calle 2-48, Z-3, 05001 Escuintla – **ES02)** Col 15 de Junio, Z-3, Tiquisate, 05001 Escuintla – **FM:** 92.3MHz – **ES03)** 4 Av 12-27, Z-1, 05001 Escuintla. **W:** radioinspiracion@gmail.com – **ES04)** 4 Av 11-38, Z-1, 05001 Escuintla – **ES05)** Central American Benevolent Association, 05001 Escuintla – **FM:** 96.3MHz
**GU00) GUATEMALA**
**GU01)** 9 Av 0-32, Z-2, 01002 Guatemala. **W:** radioprogresoguatemala. com – **GU02)** 34 Av "A" 7-60 Tikal 2, Z-7, 01007 Guatemala. **W:** radioalianza.org – **GU03)** 8 C 10-54, Zona 11, Col. Roosevelt, 01011 Guatemala. **W:** radiomundial.com.gt – **GU05)** 3ª. Avenida 11-42, Zona 3 Mixco, Colonia El Rosario, Guatemala **W:** radio760online.com – **GU06)** Guatemala **W:** facebook.com/RadioConstelacion810Am – **GU08)** 20 Av 3-86, Z-11, Utatlán II, 01011 Guatemala – **GU09)** 11 Calle 2-43, Z-1, 01001 Guatemala – **GU11)** Calzada San Juan 7-90, Edif.Acuario, Z-7, 01007 Guatemala – **GU12)** 6a Av 0-60, Zona 4, Torre Profesional 1, Niv. 9, Of. 911, 01004 Guatemala **W:** eventoscatolicos.com.gt – **GU14)** 15 Calle 3-45, Z-1, 01001 Guatemala – **GU15)** 1 Av 35-48, Z-7, Col Toledo, 01007 Guatemala. **W:** panamericanadeguatemala.net – **GU16)** 10 Calle 5-20, Z-1, 01001 Guatemala – **GU17)** 2 Calle 18-07, Zona 15, Vista Hermosa 1, 01015 Guatemala. **W:** sonora.com.gt – **GU19)** 4 Av 1-14, Z-1, 01001 Guatemala. **W:** centralpalabramiel.com/home_radio – **GU21)** Carretera Vieja a Antigua Guatemala, 2da Calle 23-70, Zona 1, Mixco, Guatemala **W:** radioexclusiva.org – **GU22)** Ap 51-C, 18 avenida

0-75 zona 15, Vista Hermosa II, 01015 Guatemala. **W:** unionradiogt. org – **GU23)** 1a Calle 35-48, Zona 7, Colonia Toledo, Guatemala. **W:** radiotictac1360.com – **GU24)** 8a Calle 10-54, Zona-11, Col. Roosevelt, Guatemala **W:** radiohosanna1450.blogspot.com – **GU25)** 17 Av.21, Cnt.Com Las Pergolas, Z-11, 01011 Guatemala **W:** horizontesgt.com – **GU26)** 17 Av.21, Cnt.Com Las Pergolas, Z-11, 01011 Guatemala **W:** radiocentroamericana1510am.com – **GU27)** Ap 1213, (or 30 Av "A" 7-33, Z-7, Col Tikal, 01007 Guatemala), 01901 Guatemala. **W:** radiovea. org – **GU29)** Guatemala. **W:** radiocapital1420am.com.gt – **GU30)** 10a Avenida 0-61, Z-19, Colonia La Florida, 01019 Guatemala – **GU32)** 17 Av. 5-47, Zona 11, Col. Miraflores, 01011 Guatemala **W:** radiorevelacionyverdad.com

## HU00) HUEHUETENANGO
**HU01)** 2 Calle 4-42, Z-1, 13001 Huehuetenango – **HU02)** Ap 13, 13901 Huehuetenango **W:** lavozdehuehue.comlu.com – **HU04)** 13025 San Sebastián Coatán Programming in Spanish & Chuj Coatán. **FM:** 92.5MHz –**HU05)** 13020 San Sebastián H, Huehuetenango. **W:** tgmi-radiobuenasnuevas.com

## IZ00) IZABAL
**IZ01)** Calle Principal, Morales – **IZ02)** Ruta Atlántico km 291, 18001 Puerto Barrios – **IZ03)** Barrio El Carrizal, Morales – **IZ04)** Ap 425, 18901Puerto Barrios – **IZ05)** 8 Av 15 y 16 Calle, 18001 Puerto Barrios – **IZ06)** Izabal

## JA00) JALAPA
**JA01)** Barrio San Francisco, Una Cuadra Abajo de Incav, Jalapa **W:** facebook.com/pages/Radio-Oriental-Jalapa-Guatemala/234662116555928

## JU00) JUTIAPA
**JU01)** 4 Avenida 4-79, Zona 1, Colonia El Latino, 22001 Jutiapa – **JU02)** Carr Interamericana km 117, 22001 Jutiapa. **W:** radiouncion-jutiapa.com – **JU03)** Quezada – **JU04)** 6ta Calle 5-00, Zona 3, a un costado del puente del Incienso, 22001 Jutiapa **W:** facebook.com/radiomaranathajutiapa

## PE00) PETÉN
**PE01)** Sta Elena de la Cruz **FM:** 96.9MHz – **PE02)** Sta Elena de la Cruz – **PE04)** Isleta Sta Bárbara, 17001 Flores (or 1 Av 1-22, Z-1, Guatemala) **W:** radiopeten.com.gt - **FM:** 105.3MHz– **PE05)** Ministerio de la Defensa Nacional, Sta Elena de la Cruz

## QE00) QUETZALTENANGO
**QE01)** Ap 113 (or 13 Av 8-19, Z-1), 09901 Quetzaltenango – **QE02)** 6 Av 6-41, Z-1, 09001 Quetzaltenango – **QE03)** 5 C 13-56, Zona 3, Xelajú (Ap 90), 09901 Quetzaltenango - **FM:** 99.1MHz– **QE04)** 7 Av 0-26, Z-2, 09002 Quetzaltenango. **W:** radiotgd.com – **QE05)** 3 Calle 3-38, Z-1, Coatepeque – **QE06)** 14 Av "A" 0-78, Z-1, 09002 Quetzaltenango – **QE07)** Ap 107, 09901 Quetzaltenango – **QE09)** Calle Principal, Z-2, Colomba. - **FM:** 99.1MHz– **QE10)** 4 Calle 15A-62, Z-1, 09002 Quetzaltenango. **W:** nuevaradioxelaju.com – **QE11)** 3 Calle 3-38, Z-1, Coatepeque, Retalhuleu – **QE12)** Km 211, Aldea Duraznales, Concepción, Chjquirichapa, Quetzaltenango.

## QU00) QUICHÉ
**QU01)** 7 Calle 3-67, Z-5, 14001 Sta Cruz del Quiché **W:** radioscatolicasdequiche.com - **FM:** 90.7 MHz – **QU03)** 5 Av 1-32, Canton Batzbaca, 14013 Nebaj

## RE00) RETALHULEU
**RE01)** Ap 84, 11901Retalhuleu – **RE02)** 7 Av 6-72, 11001 Retalhuleu (or Ap 183-A, Guatemala): 0900-0300

## SA00) SACATEPÉQUEZ
**SA01)** San Juan Sacatepéquez. **W:** radiocircuitosanjuan.com

## SR00) SANTA ROSA
**SR01)** Edif Municipal, Chiquimulilla.

## SM00) SAN MARCOS
**SM01)** 4 Avenida 4-32, Z-1, Malacatán – **SM04)** 5 Calle 8-21, Z-1, San Pedro – **SM05)** Pajapita, 12001 San Marcos

## SU00) SUCHITEPÉQUEZ
**SU01)** 10001 Mazatenango - 1100-0400 – **SU02)** La Libertad 9-91, Z-1, 10001 Mazatenango – **SU03)** 6 Av 10-54, Z-1, 10001 Mazatenango – **SU04)** 13 Av 23-60, Z-12, 10012 Coyotenango – **SU05)** Calle 30 de Junio 1a y 2a, Z-5, 10001 Mazatenango

## T000) TOTONICAPAN
**T001)** Barrio La Cienaga, 08002 San Cristóbal Totonicapán – **T003)** Momostenango, 08001 Totonicapán – **T004)** Totonicapán

## ZA00) ZACAPA
**ZA01)** 4 Calle 12-54, Z-1, 19001 Zacapa – **ZA02)** 4 Calle 10-34, Z-1, 19001 Zacapa – **ZA03)** Zona Militar N° 7, 19001 Zacapa

**FM in Guatemala City (MHz):** 88.1 Fabuestereo - 88.5 Galaxia la Picosa – 88.9 Fabulosa 88.9 – 89.3 Estrella – 89.7 Em.Unidas – 90.1 Yo Sí Sideral – 90.5 Punto – 90.9 Exitos – 91.3 Furia Musical – 91.7 Fiesta – 92.1 Universidad – 92.5 40 Principales – 92.9 Disney – 93.3 FM Joya – 93.7 Mía – 94.1 94 FM – 94.5 La Sabrosita – 94.9 Nueve Cuatro Nueve – 95.3 Kyrios – 95.7 Ranchero – 96.1 Nuevo Mundo – 96.5 Atmósfera - 96.9 Sonora – 97.3 Alfa – 97.7 Kiss FM - 98.1

Doble S – 98.9 Globo – 99.3 La Grande - 99.7 Conga – 100.1 Infinita – 100.5 Cultural – 100.9 La Hit FM – 101.3 R. Extrema – 101.7 R. Activa – 102.1 Stereo 102 – 102.5 FM Fama – 102.9 Caliente – 103.3 R. María – 103.7 R. Fiesta – 104.1 Stereo Visión – 104.5 TGRF R. Faro Cultural – 104.9 Tropicálida – 105.3 Celebra FM – 105.7 Union – 106.1 Red Deportiva – 106.5 Clásica – 106.9 ¡UyUyUy! – GU04) 107.3 TGW LV de Guatemala – 107.7 Mega

**FM in Quetzaltenango (MHz):** 87.5 Estéreo Bendición – 88.1 Dinámica – 88.5 La Consentida – 89.5 Emisoras Unidas – 89.9 Prisima FM – 90.3 Tropicálida – 90.7 María – 91.1 La Nueva Mega – 91.7 La Rubia – 92.3 R. Cadena Sonora – 92.7 Cadena Caliente – 93.1 Nahual Estereo – 93.7 Fiesta – 94.3 Diamante – 94.7 Punto – 95.1 Ke Buena – 95.5 Evolución – 95.9 FM Globo – 96.3 FM Intima – 97.1 Exa FM – 97.5 Gaviota FM – 98.3 La Grande – 98.7 Yo Sí Sideral – 99.1 RTVA Arqueocesana – 99.5 Génesis – 99.9 Galaxia – La Picosa – 100.3 Stereo Cien – 100.7 R. Cultura – 101.1 R. Estéreo Tulán – 101.5 Estéreo Alegre – 102.3 Precencias R. – 102.9 Cristal – 103.3 La Voz de Dios – 104.3 Emisoras Unidas – 104.7 Razón – 105.3 La Voz del Evangelio – 105.9 FM Luna – 106.3 La Visión F – 106.7 Alfa – 107.1 R. Exitos – 107.5 TGQ La Voz de Quetzaltenango – 107.9 R. Estéreo Vida

## GUINEA

**L.T:** UTC — **Pop:** 13 million — **Pr.L:** French, Fulah, Maninké, Soussou — **E.C:** 50Hz, 220V — **ITU:** GUI

### CONSEIL NATIONAL DE LA COMMUNICATION (CNC)
📧 Conakry **W:** guinee.gov.gn **L.P:** Chmn: Mounir Camar.

### RADIO TÉLÉVISION GUINÉENNE (RTG, Gov.)
📧 B. P. 391, Conakry ☎+224 30 41 55 19 **W:** rtgkoloma.info **L.P:** DG: Alpha Kabinet Keita. Dir. Tech: Aladji Touré.
**SW:** Conakry (Sonfonia): 9650kHz 50kW (irregular): 0600-2400.
**FM:** Conakry 88.5/91.7MHz. **R. Kaloum Stereo:** 94.9MHz.
**D.Prgr.** in French/Ethnic: 24h.
**Ann:** F: "Radio Guineé". **IS:** Guitar.

### RADIO RURALE (RTG rural stations):
**Basse Guinée,** Kindia: 98.7/99.2/99.3MHz – **Beyla:** 94.4/98.2MHz – **Bissikirima:** 91.0MHz – **Boké:** 95.3MHz – **Dinguiraye:** 98.6MHz – **Faranah:** 88.2MHz – **Gaoual:** 98.6MHz – **Guinée Forestiere,** Nzérékoré: 89.0MHz – **Haute Guinée:** Mandiana 88.2MHz, Kankan 92.1MHz, Dabadou 93.0MHz, Siguiri 97.2MHz, Douabou 99.0MHz – **Kérouané:** 92.2MHz – **Kindia:** 88.3MHz, Kakoulima 98.7MHz, Koliadi 99.9MHz – **Kissidougou:** 95.4/98.1MHz – **Koundara:** 98.6MHz – **Macenta:** 88.6/98.2MHz – **Mali:** 101.6MHz – **Mamou:** 91.1/101.1MHz – **Moyenne Guinée,** Pita: 87.6MHz – **Siguiri:** 94.4MHz – **Télimélé:** 97.7MHz – **Tougué:** 98.3MHz.

### Private stations:
**Atlantic FM:** Conakry 96.5MHz – **Bambou FM:** Coyah/Faranah 89.3MHz– **Bolivar FM:** Mamou 99.4MHz **W:** bolivarmedia.webs.com – **Cherie FM:** Conakry 104.1MHz **W:** cheriefmguinee.com – **Djiguii FM,** Conakry: 105.7/107.7MHz. **W:** djiguii.com – **Djoliba FM:** Conakry/Siguiri 95.6MHz – **Espace FM:** Conakry 99.6MHz, Labé 99.7MHz **W:** espacefmguinee.info – **Gangan FM:** Conakry 101.1MHz – **Horizon FM:** Conakry/Kankan 103.4MHz – **R. Liberté FM:** Conakry/N'zérékoré 101.7MHz **W:** radiolibertefm.com – **R. Maria,** Conakry: 100.8MHz **W:** radiomaria.org – **R. Milo,** Kankan/Siguiri: 99.5MHz **W:** milo-fm.com – **R. Nostalgie Guinée:** Conakry 98.2MHz 1kW **W:** nostalgieguinee. net – **R. Renaissance:** Conakry 95.9MHz **W:** renaissancefmguinee. com – **Sabari FM,** Conakry: 97.3MHz 1kW. **W:** sabarifm.com – **Soleil FM:** Conakry 101.7MHz – **Swet FM:** Conakry 102.2MHz.
**BBC World Sce:** Conakry/Labé 93.9MHz.
**R. France Int:** Conakry 89.0, Kankan/Labé/Nzerékoré 89.9MHz

## GUINEA-BISSAU

**L.T:** UTC — **Pop:** 2 million — **Pr.L:** Portuguese, Crioulo, others — **E.C:** 50Hz, 220V — **ITU:** GNB

### AUTORIDADE REGULADORA NACIONAL (ARN)
📧 Enterramento/Traseiros do Hospital Militar, C.P. 1372, Bissau ☎+245 443204873 🖷 +245 443204876 **W:** arn.gw **E:** info@arn.gw

### RADIODIFUSÃO NACIONAL (RDN, Gov.)
📧 C.P. 191, Av. Domingos Ramos, Bissau ☎+245 443212426 **W:** rdngbissau.com
**FM:** Nhacra 91.5, Catió 93.7, Gabú 94.5, Bissau 104.1MHz.
**D.Prgr:** 0600-2400.
**Ann:** "Escutam a Radiodifusão Nacional da República da Guiné-Bissau"

**OTHER STATIONS:**
**R. Bombolom,** Bissau: 106.2MHz. Also rel. BBC & DW **W:** facebook.com/Radio-bombolom-1375960895959569 – **R. Capital FM,** Bissau: 87.7MHz **W:** radiocapital.caster.fm – **R. Cidade FM,** Bissau: 105.6MHz **W:** radiocidadefmgbissau.blogspot.com – **R. Evangélica FM,** Gabú: 92.4MHz **W:** evangelicafmgabu.caster.fm – **R. Gandal,** Gabú: 105.7MHz **W:** radiocidadefmgbissau.blogspot.com – **R. Jovem,** Bissau: 102.8MHz **W:** radiojovem.info – **R. Luz,** Bissau: 97.7MHz **W:** radioluzafrica.com – **R. Mavegro,** Bissau: 100.0MHz. Also rel. BBC – **R. Nossa** (Rlg.), Bissau: 98.9MHz **W:** radionossabissau.com – **R. Pindjiguiti,** Bissau: 95.0MHz. Also rel. VOA **W:** facebook.com/Rádio-galáxia-de-pindjiguiti-1195284467171089 – **R. Sol Mansi** (Rlg.), Mansôa/Gabú 90.0MHz, Bissau/Bafatá/Canchungo 101.8MHz. 0630-2300. Also rel. Vatican R. and UN prgrs. **W:** facebook.com/Radio.Sol. Mansi – **R. Voz de Quelélé,** Bissau: 104.8MHz **W:** radio-voz-quelele. blogspot.com
**RDP África:** Nhacra 88.4MHz 25kW, Catió 96.9 & Gabú 100.0MHz 1kW.
**RFI Afrique:** Gabú 93.6, Bissau 94.0, Catió 101.5MHz.
+30 community radio stations

## GUYANA

**L.T:** UTC -4h — **Pop:** 774 000 — **Pr.L:** Creole, English, Hindi, Urdu, Amerindian dialects — **E.C:** 110V/60Hz, 220V/50hZ — **ITU:** GUY

### PUBLIC UTILITIES COMMISSION
✉ Parliament Buildings, Brickdam, Georgetown ☎ +592 227 3293
🖷+592 227 3534

### NATIONAL COMMUNICATIONS NETWORK INC. (Gov)
✉ Broadcasting House, P.O. Box 10760, Georgetown ☎+592 223 6049, +592 223 1566/1577 🖷+592 226 2253 **W:** ncnguyana.com **E:** feedback@ncnguyana.com
**L.P:** SEO: Mohammed Sattaur GM: Mazrul Bacchus Prod. Mgr: Martin Goolsarran
**MW:** Georgetown 560 kHz
**FM:** Georgetown 100.1 MHz -Hot FM/98.1 MHz – VYBZ FM
**Voice of Guyana:** 24h on 560kHz **V.** by letter
**Other FM stations:** Megajams, Georgetown 87.7MHz – R. Guyana Incorporated, Georgetown 89.5MHz, Essequibo 89.3MHz, Berbice 89.3MHz **W:** radioguyanafm89.com

## HAITI

**L.T:** UTC -5h (10 Mar-3 Nov: -4h) — **Pop:** 11 million — **Pr.L:** Creole, French — **E.C:** 50+60Hz, 110V — **ITU:** HTI

### CONSEIL NATIONAL DES TELECOMMUNICATIONS (CONATEL)
✉ B.P.2002 (or Cité de l'Exposition 16), Port-au-Prince ☎ +509 25163325 🖷+509 22239229 **W:** conatel.gouv.ht **E:** info@conatel.gouv.ht

| MW | kHz | kW | Station, location |
|---|---|---|---|
| 1) | 660 | 5 | R. Lumière, Port-au-Prince |
| 1) | 720 | 1 | R. Lumière, Petite Riviere |
| 1) | 740 | 1 | R. Lumière, Pignon |
| 1) | 760 | 2 | R. Lumière, Les Cayes |
| 11) | 840 | 10 | R. 4VEH, Cap Haitien |
| 2) | 1030 | | R. Ginen, Port-au-Prince |

| FM | MHz | kW | Station, location |
|---|---|---|---|
| 1) | 88.1 | | R. Lumière, Gonaives |
| 3) | 88.5 | | Caraibes FM, Cap-Haitien |
| 6) | 88.5 | | R. Kiskeya, Port-au-Prince |
| 6) | 88.9 | | R. Kiskeya, Camp-Perrin |
| 34) | 89.7 | | Voix de l'Espérance, Port-au-Prince |
| 10) | 89.9 | | R. Parole de Vie, Fort-Liberté |
| 14) | 88.9 | | R. Télé Express Continental, Jacmel |
| 9) | 90.3 | | R. Timoun, Jacmel |
| 9) | 90.5 | | R. Timoun, Cap-Haitien |
| 40) | 90.5 | | Signal FM, Port-au-Prince |
| 9) | 90.7 | | R. Timoun, Les Cayes |
| 5) | 90.9 | | R. Vision 2000, Jacmel |
| 9) | 90.9 | | R. Timoun, Port-au-Prince |
| 44) | 91.3 | | Tropic FM, Port-au-Prince |
| 9) | 91.5 | | R. Timoun, Hinche/Port-de-Paix |
| 10) | 91.7 | | R. Ephphatha, Jacmel |
| 9) | 91.9 | | R. Timoun, Jérémie |
| 1) | 92.1 | | R. Lumière Stereo 92, Port-au-Prince |
| 2) | 92.1 | | R. Ginen, Cap-Haitien |
| 5) | 92.5 | | R. Vision 2000, Port-de-Paix |
| 21) | 92.5 | | R. Commerciale d'Haiti, Port-au-Prince |

| FM | MHz | kW | Station, location |
|---|---|---|---|
| 2) | 92.9 | | R. Télé Ginen, Port-au-Prince + 4 sites |
| 11) | 93.3 | | R. 4VEH, Pignon |
| 19) | 93.3 | | Canal du Christ, Port-au-Prince |
| 41) | 93.7 | | R. Vasco, Port-au-Prince |
| 11) | 94.1 | | R. 4VEH, Cap-Haitien |
| 29) | 94.1 | | R. Nouvelle Génération, Port-au-Prince |
| 3) | 94.5 | 3 | Caraibes FM, Port-au-Prince |
| 10) | 94.7 | | R. Voix de la Paix, Port-de-Paix |
| 4) | 94.9 | | R. Metropole, Jacmel |
| 9) | 94.9 | | R. MBC, Port-au-Prince |
| 27) | 95.3 | | La Voix de l'Evangile, Port-au-Prince |
| 10) | 95.5 | | R. Men Kontre, Les Cayes |
| 15) | 95.7 | | R. Horizon 2000, Port-au-Prince |
| 1) | 95.9 | | R. Lumière, Les Cayes/Jérémie |
| 20) | 95.9 | | R. Boukman, Port-au-Prince |
| 36) | 96.1 | | RCH 2000, Port-au-Prince |
| 30) | 96.5 | | Sky FM, Port-au-Prince |
| 11) | 96.7 | | R. 4VEH, Mirelabais |
| 19) | 96.9 | | R. Tele Antilles Internationale, Port-au-Prince |
| 16) | 97.3 | | R. Télémegastar, Port-au-Prince |
| 1) | 97.9 | | R. Lumière, Dame Marie |
| 5) | 98.1 | | R. Vision 2000, Gonaives |
| 28) | 98.1 | | Maxima FM, Port-au-Prince |
| 9) | 98.5 | | R. Timoun, Gonaives |
| 10) | 98.5 | | R. Voix Ave Maria, Cap-Haitien |
| 26) | 98.5 | | R. Ibo, Port-au-Prince |
| 10) | 98.7 | | R. Christ Roi, Gonaives |
| 13) | 98.9 | | Alleluia FM, Port-au-Prince |
| 5) | 99.3 | | R. Vision 2000, Port-au-Prince |
| 2) | 99.5 | | R. Ginen, Miragoâne |
| 32) | 99.7 | | Sweet FM, Port-au-Prince |
| 5) | 99.9 | | R. Vision 2000, Saint-Marc |
| 4) | 100.1 | 2 | R. Metropole, Port-au-Prince |
| 11) | 100.3 | | R. 4VEH, Ile de la Tortue |
| 45) | 100.3 | | R. Leve Kanpe, Hinche |
| 23) | 100.5 | | R. Eclair, Port-au-Prince |
| 2) | 100.7 | | R. Ginen, Miragoâne |
| 12) | 100.9 | | Magik 9, Port-au-Prince |
| 4) | 101.3 | | R. Metropole, Saint-Marc |
| 33) | 101.3 | | Univers FM, Port-au-Prince |
| 22) | 101.3 | | R. Télé Digital, Port-au-Prince |
| 5) | 101.7 | | R. Vision 2000, Les Cayes |
| 24) | 101.7 | | Energie FM, Port-au-Prince |
| 7) | 102.1 | | R. Nationale d'Haiti, Port-au-Prince |
| 3) | 102.5 | | Caraibes FM, Port-de-Paix |
| 4) | 102.5 | | R. Metropole, Les Cayes |
| 35) | 102.5 | | R. Télé Zenith, Port-au-Prince |
| 43) | 102.7 | | Trace FM, Port-au-Prince |
| 6) | 102.9 | | R. Kiskeya, Saint-Marc |
| 31) | 102.9 | | R. Super Star, Port-au-Prince |
| 4) | 103.3 | | R. Metropole, Gonaives |
| 17) | 103.3 | | R. Melodie, Port-au-Prince |
| 10) | 103.5 | | R. de l'Immaculée Conception, Hinche |
| 39) | 103.7 | | R. Shalom, Port-au-Prince |
| 25) | 104.5 | | R. Galaxie, Port-au-Prince |
| 37) | 104.9 | | RFM, Port-au-Prince |
| 7) | 105.1 | | R. Nationale d'Haiti, Cap-Haitien |
| 7) | 105.3 | | R. Nationale d'Haiti, Port-au-Prince |
| 5) | 105.7 | | R. Vision 2000, Cap-Haitien |
| 10) | 105.7 | | R. Soleil, Port-au-Prince |
| 10) | 105.9 | | R. Tet Ansamn, Jérémie |
| 7) | 106.3 | | R. Nationale d'Haiti, Cap-Haitien |
| 18) | 106.5 | | Planet Kreyol, Port-au-Prince |
| 6) | 106.9 | | R. Kiskeya, Sans Souci |
| 46) | 107.1 | | R. Ideal, Port-de-Paix |
| 42) | 107.3 | | R. Solidarité, Port-au-Prince |
| 38) | 107.7 | | Scoop FM, Port-au-Prince |

**Addresses & other information:**
**1)** Côte Plage 16, Carrefour, B.P .1050, Port-au-Prince **W:** radiolumiere. org – **2)** #28, Delmas 31, Port-au-Prince **W:** rtghaiti.com/radioginen – **3)** 45 Rue Chavannes, Port-au-Prince **W:** radiotelevisioncaraibes.com – **4)** 8, Delmas 52, B.P. 62, Port-au-Prince **W:** metropolehaiti.com – **5)** 184, Av. John Brown, Lalue, Port-au-Prince **W:** radiovision2000haiti.net – **6)** 42, Rue Villemenay, Bois Verna, Port-au-Prince **W:** radiokiskeya.com – **7)** Delmas 65, Impasse Orchidée, B.P. 1143, Port-au-Prince – **8)** 11, Rue Rigaud, P.V, Port-au-Prince **W:** freewebs.com/radiombc – **9)** **W:** radiosoleil.org radiovoixavemaria.com – **11)** Route Nationale 1, Morne Rouge, B.P. 1, Cap-Haitien **W:** radio4veh.org – **12)** **W:** magik9haiti. com – **13)** **W:** alleluiafmhaiti.com – **14)** #35, Rue de l'Eglise, Jacmel **W:** radioteleexpress.com – **15)** Rue Butte # 2, Bourdon, Port-au-Prince 6111 **W:** radiohorizon2000endirect.com – **16)** **W:** radiotelemegastar.com –

**17) W:** radiomelodiehaiti.com – **18)** Delmas 48 #34, Port-au-Prince **W:** planetkreyol.com – **19)** 77 Rue Metellus, Bas de la Montagne Noire, Pétionville, Port-au-Prince 6140 **W:** radioteleantilleshaiti.com – **20) W:** facebook.com/pages/Radio-Boukman/157901850906631 – **21)** 39 Blvd. 15 Octobre, Tabarre, Port-au-Prince **W:** radiocommercialedhaiti.com – **22) W:** radioteledigital.fr.ht – **23) W:** radioeclairhaiti.com – **24) W:** energiefm.com – **25) W:** radiogalaxiehaiti.com – **26) W:** radioibo.net – **27) W:** rvehaiti.org – **28)** facebook.com/maximafm.haiti – **29)** Delmas 64, No. 6, Port-au-Prince **W:** palimpalem.com/6/radionouvel-legeneration – **30) W:** haitiskyfm.com – **31)** Delmas 68, Angle rues Safran et C. Henri, Pétionville, Haïti **W:** superstarhaiti.com – **32)** Rue Dr Coles #8, Résidences du soleil, Delmas 25, Port-au-Prince **W:** sweetfmhaiti.com – **33)** Rue Villate, Pétionville, Port-au-Prince **W:** universfm.net – **34)** Diquini 63, Campus de l'Université Adventiste d'Haiti, B.P. 1339, Port-au-Prince **W:** 4vve.org – **35)** 33, Bon Repos, Route nationale #1,Port-Au-Prince **W:** radiotelezenith.net – **36) W:** rch2000.net – **37) W:** rfmhaiti.net – **38)** 93 Rue Vilatte, Pétionville, Port-au-Prince **W:** scoopfmhaiti.com – **39) W:** radioshalomhaiti.com **40)** #127 Rue Louverture, Pétionville, Port-au-Prince **W:** signalfmhaiti.com – **41) W:** radiovascohaiti.com – **42)** 6 Rue Fernand, Canape Vert, Port-au-Prince **W:** radiosolidaritehaiti.com – **43) W:** ht.trace.fm – **44) W:** tropicfmhaiti.com – **45)** radiolevekanpehaiti.com – **46)** 3 Rue Trois Grace, Port-de-Paix **W:** radioidealfm.com

## RADIO FRANCE INTERNATIONALE
**FM:** Port-au-Prince 89.3, Gonaïves 90.5, Jeremie 92.7, Jacmel 96.9, Cap Haïtien 100.5, Les Cayes 106.9MHz

## HAWAII (USA)

**L.T:** UTC -10h — **Pop:** 1.42 million — **Pr.L:** English, Japanese, Filipino — **E.C:** 60Hz, 120V — **ITU:** HWA

**FEDERAL COMMUNICATIONS COMMISSION (FCC)**
see USA for details

**THE HAWAII ASSOCIATION OF BROADCASTERS, INC.**
P.O. Box 61562, Honolulu HI 96839 **W:** hawaiibroadcasters com **E:** jamie@hawaiibroadcasters.com **L.P:** Pres: Chris Leonard, Exec. Dir: Jamie Hartnett

| | MW kHz | kW | Call | Location |
|---|---|---|---|---|
| 1) | 550 | 5 | KNUI | Kahului, Maui |
| 37) | 570 | 1 | KUAI | Eleele, Kauai |
| 3) | 590 | 7.5 | KSSK | Honolulu, Oahu |
| 43) | 650 | 10 | KPRP | Honolulu, Oahu |
| 6) | 670 | 5 | KPUA | Hilo, Hawaii |
| 7) | 690 | 10 | KHNR | Honolulu, Oahu |
| 35) | 740 | 5 | KCIK | Kihei, Maui |
| 7) | 760 | 10 | KGU | Honolulu, Oahu |
| 1) | 790 | 5 | KKON | Kealakekua, Hawaii |
| 3) | 830 | 10 | KHVH | Honolulu, Oahu |
| 1) | 850 | 5 | KHLO | Hilo, Hawaii |
| 7) | 880 | 2 | KHCM | Honolulu, Oahu |
| 1) | 900 | 5 | KMVI | Kahului, Maui |
| 5) | 940 | 10 | KKNE | Honolulu, Oahu |
| 3) | 990 | 5 | KIKI | Honolulu, Oahu |
| 9) | 1040 | 10 | KLHT | Honolulu, Oahu |
| 30) | ‡1060 | 5 | KIPA | Hilo, Hawaii |
| 11) | 1080 | 5 | KWAI | Honolulu, Oahu |
| 2) | 1110 | 5 | KAOI | Kihei, Maui |
| 12) | 1130 | 1 | KPHI | Honolulu, Oahu |
| 13) | 1210 | 1 | KZOO | Honolulu, Oahu |
| 2) | 1240 | 5 | KEWE | Wailuku, Maui |
| 14) | 1270 | 5 | KNDI | Honolulu, Oahu |
| 16) | 1370 | 6.2 | KUPA | Pearl City, Oahu |
| 17) | 1420 | 5 | KKEA | Honolulu, Oahu |
| 18) | 1460 | 5 | KHRA | Honolulu, Oahu |
| 17) | 1500 | 5 | KHKA | Honolulu, Oahu |
| 19) | 1540 | 5 | KREA | Honolulu, Oahu |
| 20) | 1570 | 15 | KUAU | Haiku, Maui |

| | FM MHz | kW | Call | Location |
|---|---|---|---|---|
| 21) | 88.1 | 39 | KHPR | Honolulu, Oahu |
| 21) | 88.1 | 4 | KHPR-FM1 | Makaha, Hawaii |
| 21) | 88.1 | 3 | KHPR-FM3 | Kailua, Hawaii |
| 21) | 88.7 | 6.5 | KHPH | Kailua, Hawaii |
| 9A) | 88.9 | 2.5 | KHJC | Lihue, Kauai |
| 21) | 89.1 | 12 | KANO | Hilo, Hawaii (CP) |
| 21) | 89.3 | 38.5 | KIPO-FM | Honolulu, Oahu |
| 21) | 89.3 | 4 | KIPO-FM1 | Makaha, Hawaii |
| 21) | 89.7 | 62 | KIPM | Waikapu, Maui |
| 38) | 89.9 | 1 | KIPL | Lihue, Kauai |
| 22) | 90.1 | 7 | KTUH | Honolulu, Oahu (CP) |
| 22) | 90.3 | 3 | KTUH | Honolulu, Oahu |

| | FM MHz | kW | Call | Location |
|---|---|---|---|---|
| 23) | 90.3 | 5 | KCIF | Hilo, Hawaii |
| 21) | 90.7 | 56 | KKUA | Wailuku, Maui |
| 26) | 90.9 | 0.9 | KKCR | Hanalei, Kauai |
| 21) | 91.1 | 30 | KANO | Hilo, Hawaii |
| 21) | 91.3 | 12 | KAHU | Pahala, Hawaii (CP) |
| 9) | 91.5 | 100 | KLHT-FM | Honolulu, Oahu (CP) |
| 44) | 91.7 | 1.2 | KMNO | Wailuku, Maui |
| 26) | 91.9 | 6 | KAQA | Kilauea, Kauai |
| 30) | 92.1 | 4.5 | KHWI | Holualea, Hawaii |
| 3) | 92.3 | 100 | KSSK-FM | Waipahu, Oahu |
| 1) | 92.5 | 1.7 | KLHI-FM | Kahului, Maui |
| 30) | 92.7 | 7.5 | KHBC | Hilo, Hawaii |
| 37) | 93.1 | 100 | KQMQ-FM | Honolulu, Oahu |
| 6) | 93.1 | 10 | KMWB | Captain Cook, Hawaii |
| 1) | 93.5 | 72 | KPOA | Lahaina, Maui |
| 37) | 93.5 | 51 | KQNG-FM | Lihue, Kauai |
| 3) | 93.9 | 100 | KHJZ | Honolulu, Oahu |
| 1) | 93.9 | 7.3 | KLUA | Kailua-Kona, Hawaii |
| 1) | 94.3 | 2 | KDLX | Makawao, Maui |
| 39) | 94.3 | 100 | KZZV | Hanapepe, Kauai (CP) |
| 37) | 94.7 | 100 | KUMU-FM | Honolulu, Oahu |
| 6) | 94.7 | 51 | KWXX-FM | Hilo, Hawaii |
| 2) | 95.1 | 3.5 | KAOI-FM | Wailuku, Maui |
| 2) | 95.5 | 100 | KAIM-FM | Honolulu, Oahu |
| 2) | 95.5 | - | KEWE-FM | Wailuku, Maui |
| 1) | 95.9 | 39 | KPVS | Hilo, Hawaii |
| 37) | 95.9 | 51 | KSRF | Poipu, Kauai |
| 5) | 96.3 | 75 | KRTR-FM | Kailua, Oahu |
| 29) | 96.9 | 100 | KFMN | Lihue, Kauai |
| 6) | 97.1 | 38 | KNWB | Hilo, Hawaii |
| 12) | 97.3 | 1.5 | KRKH | Wailea-Makena, Maui |
| 7) | 97.5 | 80 | KHCM-FM | Honolulu, Oahu |
| 1) | 97.9 | 51 | KKBG | Hilo, Hawaii |
| 12) | 98.1 | 51 | KJMQ | Lihue, Kauai |
| 1) | 98.3 | 9.4 | KJMD | Pukalani, Maui |
| 3) | 98.5 | 51 | KDNN | Honolulu, Oahu |
| 12) | 98.9 | 51 | KITH | Kapaa, Kauai |
| 1) | 99.1 | 7.3 | KAGB | Waimea-Kamuela, Hawaii |
| 7) | 99.5 | 100 | KGU-FM | Honolulu, Oahu |
| 1) | 99.9 | 72 | KJKS | Kahului, Maui |
| 12) | 99.9 | 51 | KTOH | Kalaheo, Kauai |
| 1) | 100.3 | 35 | KAPA | Hilo, Hawaii |
| 1) | 100.3 | 7.1 | KAPA-FM1 | Puueo, Hawaii |
| 5) | 100.3 | 100 | KCCN-FM | Honolulu, Oahu |
| 40) | 100.7 | 2.2 | KQMY | Kihei, Maui |
| 12) | 101.1 | 100 | KORL-FM | Waianae, Oahu |
| 12) | 101.1 | 0.98 | KORL-FM | Lahaina, Maui |
| 6) | 101.1 | 6.5 | KAOY | Kealakekua, Hawaii |
| 3) | 101.9 | 100 | KUCD | Pearl City, Oahu |
| 45) | 102.3 | 1.9 | KNIT | Kaunakakai, Molokai |
| 37) | 102.7 | 61 | KDDB | Waipahu, Oahu |
| 30) | 102.1 | 50 | KTBH-FM | Kurtistown, Hawaii |
| 30) | 102.9 | 1.5 | KMKV | Paia, Maui |
| 2) | 103.3 | 51 | KSHK | Hanamaulu, Kauai |
| 31) | 103.5 | 100 | KLUU | Wahiawa, Oahu |
| 2) | 103.9 | 100 | KNUQ | Paauilo,Maui |
| 5) | 104.3 | 75 | KPHW | Kaneohe, Oahu |
| 12) | 104.7 | 72 | KONI | Lanai City, Maui |
| 5) | 105.1 | 100 | KINE-FM | Honolulu, Oahu |
| 4) | 105.3 | 28 | KBGX | Keaau, Hawaii |
| 4) | 105.3 | 1 | KBGX-FM5 | Naalehu, Hawaii |
| 32) | 105.5 | 21 | KPMW | Haliimaile, Maui |
| 37) | 105.9 | 100 | KPOI-FM | Honolulu, Oahu |
| 1) | 106.1 | 7.3 | KLEO | Kahaluu-Kona, Hawaii |
| 12) | 106.5 | 72 | KRYL | Haiku, Maui |
| 33) | 106.7 | 25 | KNAN | Nanakali, Oahu |
| 34) | 106.9 | 5.5 | KWYI | Kawaihae, Hawaii |
| 4) | 107.7 | 28 | KKOA | Volcano, Hawaii |
| 4) | 107.7 | 1 | KKOA-FM1 | Hilo, Hawaii |
| 4) | 107.7 | 1 | KKOA-FM5 | Naalehu, Hawaii |
| 7) | 107.9 | 100 | KKOL | Aiea, Oahu |

Txs on air or CP less than 1kW not mentioned. ‡=inactive

**Addresses & other information:**
**Addresses:** Add state abbreviation **HI** before zip code except 31), 33), 35), 39), 40). **D.Prgr:** All stns 24h unless otherwise stated **1) Pacific Radio Group, Maui:** 311 Ano Street, Kahului, 96732-1304 KMVI **W:** espnmaui.com KNUI **W:** knuimaui.com KLHI-FM **W:** x925.fm KPOA **W:** kpoa.com KJMD **W:** dajam983.com KJKS **W:** kiss-99fm.com; **Hawaii:** 913 Kanoelehua Ave, Hilo, 96720-5116 KKON **W:** espnhawaii.com KHLO **W:** espnhawaii.com KLUA **W:** nativefm.com KPVS **W:** nativefm.com KKBG **W:** kbigfm.com KAGB **W:** kaparadio.com KAPA **W:** kaparadio.com KLEO **W:** kbigfm.com – **2) Visionary Related**

**Entertainment LLC, Molokai:** KMKK-FM ✉ 130 Kamehameha V Highway, Kaunakaka, 96748; **Maui:** KAOI **W:** kaoi1110.com KAOI-FM **W:** kaoifm.com KNUQ **W:** q103maui.com KDLX **W:** kdlx943.com ✉ 1900 Main Street, Wailuku, 96793-1900 KEWE **W:** kewe1240.com ✉ PO Box 1437, Wailuku, 96793-6437 – **3) Capstar TX Ltd Partnership, Oahu:** KSSK **W:** ksskradio.com KHVH **W:** khvhradio.com KHBZ **W:** khbz.com KSSK-FM KHJZ 939jamz.com KDNN **W:** island985.com KUCD **W:** star1019.com ✉ 400 Dole Cannery Plaza, 650 Iwilei Rd #400, Honolulu, 96817-5319 – **4) Mahalo Multi Media LLC, Hawaii:** KBGX **W:** lava1053.com KKOA ✉ 74-5606 Luhia St #B-7, Kailua-Kona, 96740-1678 – **5) Summit Media Corporation, Oahu:** KKNE **W:** n/a KRTR-FM **W:** krater96.com KCCN-FM **W:** kccnfm100.com KPHW **W:** power1043.com KINE **W:** hawaiian105.com **F.PL** 50kW ✉ 900 Fort St Mall #700, Honolulu, 96813-3797 **L.P:** Patti Milburn VP & CEO, TJ Malievsky President [KHPW] – **6) New West Broadcasting Corporation, Hawaii:** KPUA **W:** kpua.net KWXX-FM **W:** kwxx.com KNWB **W:** b97hawaii.com KMWB **W:** b97hawaii.com KAOY **W:** kwxx.com ✉ 1145 Kilauea Ave, Hilo, 96720-4203 – **7) Salem Media of Hawaii Inc, Oahu:** KHNR **W:** khnrtownhall.com KGU **W:** kguradio.com KGU-FM **W:** 995kgufm.com KHCM **Prgr:** 24h. China R. International relay in English, Chinese, Korean & Japanese KAIM-FM **W:** thefishhawaii.com KHCM-FM **W:** 975countrykhcm.com KKOL **W:** oldies1079honolulu.com ✉ 1160 N King St #200, Honolulu, 96817-3307 – **9) Calvary Chapel of Honolulu Inc, Oahu:** KLHT **W:** klight.org ✉ KLHT-FM (91.5) CP 98-1016 Komo Mai Drive, Aiea, 96701-1901 – **9A) Calvary Chapel of Twin Falls Inc:** KHJC **W:** csnradio.com/ stations/studiowaivered/khjc.php ✉: 2970 Kele St #117, Lihue, 96766-1803 – **11) Radio Hawaii Inc, Oahu:** KWAI **W:** kwai1080am.com ✉ 100 N Beretania St #401, Honolulu, 96817-4724 – **12) Hochman-McCain Hawaii Inc, Oahu:** KPHI **W:** pinoypowerkphiradio.com **Prgr:** Filipino "Today's Filipino Mix' KORL-FM **W:** korl1011.com KORL-FM HD2 **W:** korl1015.com KORL-FM HD3 **W:** korl971.com **Prgr:** Korean KORL-FM HD4 **W:** korl1075.com **Prgr:** Japanese ✉ 900 Fort St Mall #450, Honolulu, 96813-3713; **Maui:** KRKH **W:** krock973.com KONI **W:** koni1047.com KRYL **W:** kryl1065.com ✉ 300 Ohukai Road #C-318, Kihei, 96753-7040; **Kauai:** KJMQ **W:** 981jamz.com KITH **W:** islandradio989.com KTOH **W:** roostercountry.com ✉ 4334 Rice St #206, Lihue, 96766-1801 **W:** hhawaiimedia.net – **13) Polynesian Broadcasting Inc, Oahu:** KZOO **W:** kzoohawaii.com **Prgr:** Japanese. ✉ 203 Japanese Cultural Center, 2454 S Beretania St, Honolulu, 96826-1524– **14) Broadcast House of the Pacific Inc, Oahu:** KNDI **W:** kndi.com **Prgr:** multicultural, religious. ✉ 1734 S King St, Honolulu, 96826-2042 – **16) Broadcasting Corporation of America, Oahu:** KUPA ✉ 1015 Waiiki St, Honolulu, 96821-1234 – **17) Blow Up LLC, Oahu:** KKEA **W:** sportsradio1420.com KHKA **Format:** NBC Sports Radio Network ✉ 1088 Bishop St #LL2, Honolulu, 96813-3113 – **18) RK Media Group, Oahu:** KHRA **W:** radiokoreahawaii.com **Prgr:** Korean. ✉ 970 North Kalaheo Avenue #C-107, Kailua, HI 96734-1871 – **19) JMK Communications Inc, Oahu:** KREA **Prgr:** Korean. ✉ 1839 S King St #203, Honolulu, 96814-2137 – **20) First Assembly King's Cathedral & Chapel, Maui:** KUAU **W:** kingscathedral.com ✉ 777 Mokulele Hwy, Kahului, 96732-3000 – **21) Hawaii Public Radio Inc, Oahu:** KHPR **W:** hawaiipublicradio.org] KIPO [includes BBC relay] ✉ 738 Kaheka St #101, Honolulu, 96814-3726; **Simulcast: Maui:** KKUA **F.PL:** KIPM [KIPO relay] **Hawaii:** KANO **F.PL:** KIPH (KIPO relay) – **22) The University of Hawaii, Oahu:** KTUH **W:** ktuh.org ✉ 202 Hemenway Hall, University of Hawaii, 2445 Campus Road, Honolulu, 96822-2216 – **23) Hilo Christian Broadcasting Corporation, Hawaii:** KCIF **W:** kcifhawaii.org ✉ 180 Kinoole St, Hilo, 96720-2827 – **26) Kekuhu Foundation Inc, Kauai:** KKCR **W:** kkcr.org KAQA **W:** kkcr.com **F.PL:** 6kW ✉ 4520-D Hanalei Plantation Road, PO Box 825, Hanalei, 96714-0825 – **29) FM97 Associates, Kauai:** KFMN **W:** kfmn97.com ✉ 1860 Leleiona Road, Lihue, 96766-9000 – **30) Resonate Hawaii LLC, Hawaii:** KIPA KHBC **W:** khbcradio.com KHWI **W:** hawaiiswave.com KTBH-FM **W:** 1027thebeach.fm ✉ 688 Kino`ole St #112, Hilo, 96720-3868 – **31) Educational Media Foundation, Oahu:** KLUU **W:** air1.com **Maui:** KMKV **W:** mauifm.com ✉ 5700 W Oaks Blvd, Rocklin, CA 96765 – **32) Rey-Cel Broadcasting Inc, Maui:** KPMW **W:** mix1055.fm **Prgr:** Filipino ✉ 230 Hana Hwy, Kahului, 96732 – **33) Big D Consulting Ltd, Oahu:** KNAN: 3800 Howard Hughes Parkway 17th Floor, Las Vegas, NV 89109 – **34) Colin H Naito, Kauai:** KWYI ✉ 64-1040 Mamalahoa Hwy #4, Kamuela, 96743-6540 – **35) IHR Educational Broadcasters, Maui:** KCIK ✉ 3256 Penryn Road #100, Loomis, CA 95650-8052 – **37) Ohana Broadcast Company LLC, Kauai:** KQNG-FM **W:** kongradio.com KUAI KSRF **W:** surf959fm.com KSHK **W:** shaka103.com ✉ 4271 Halenani St, Lihue, 96766-1312 **Oahu:** KQMQ-FM **W:** 931thezone.net KUMU-FM **W:** kumu.com KDDB **W:** 1027dabomb.net KPOI-FM **W:** kpoifm.com 765 Amana St #206, Honolulu, 96814-3248 – **39) Virtues Communications Network, LLC: Kauai:** KZZV PO Box 215, Kings Park, NY 11754 – **40) Future Modulation Broadcasting, LLC: Maui:** KQMY ✉ 4700 Allan Road,

Cheyenne, WY 82009 – **43) SM-KRTR-AM LLC, Oahu:** KPRP [LMA]: ✉ Pinoy Power Media, Pioneer Plaza, 900 Fort Street Mall #700, Honolulu, 96813-3701 **W:** facebook.com/kprpam650/ **L.P:** Founder & CEO Imelda Ortega Anderson **Format:** Filipino – **44) Maui Media Initiative, Inc: Maui** KMNO ✉ 72 Kono Pl, Kahului, 96732-1326 – **45) Kona Coast Radio LLC, Molokai:** KNIT ✉ 130 Kamehameha V Highway, Kaunakakai, 96748 [associated with #37]

**L.T:** UTC -6h — **Pop:** 8.3 million — **Pr.L:** Spanish — **E.C:** 60Hz, 110V — **ITU:** HND

**COMISIÓN NACIONAL DE TELECOMUNICACIONES (CONATEL)**
✉ Ap. 15012, Edificio CONATEL, Colonia Modelo, Sexta Avenida Suroeste Contigua a Hondutel, Tegucigalpa ☎ +504 2552 7484 📠 +504 2236 8611 **W:** conatel.gob.hn **E:** transparencia@conatel.gob.hn Hrs of tr 24h unless otherwise stated.
**Call** HR—, ‡ = inactive, † =irregular

| MW | Call | kHz | kW | Station, location |
|---|---|---|---|---|
| 1) | XT | 550 | 1 | ABC Radio, Tegucigalpa |
| 2) | XD | †550 | 0.5 | R. Manantial, San Marcos: 1115-0300 |
| 3) | KL | 560 | 1 | R. Reloj, San Pedro Sula |
| 6) | ZQ | 580 | 3 | R. Cadena Voces, Tegucigalpa |
| 112) | EO | 580 | 3 | Super Estrella de Occidente, Sta Rosa de Copán |
| 5) | LP3 | 590 | 10 | R. América, San Pedro Sula |
| 5) | | 590 | 1 | R. América, Tela |
| | RE | 590 | | Catacamas |
| 5) | | 610 | 1 | R. América, Gracias |
| 5) | LD | 610 | 10 | R. América, Tegucigalpa: 1030-0400 |
| 5) | LP4 | 610 | 3 | R. América, Santa Rosa de Copán |
| 5) | LP | 620 | 1 | R. América, Juticalpa |
| 5) | | 620 | 10 | R. América, Siguatepeque |
| 5) | LP | 630 | 3.5 | R. América, Choluteca |
| 5) | LP7 | 630 | 5 | R. América, La Ceiba |
| 5) | LP | 650 | 1 | R. América, Danlí |
| 5) | | 650 | 2.5 | R. América, Olanchito |
| 5) | | 650 | 1 | R. América, Tocoa |
| 7) | VS | 650 | 2.5 | R. Católica de Olancho, Juticalpa |
| 8) | NN18 | 660 | 3 | LV de Honduras, La Ceiba |
| 8) | NN | 670 | 10 | LV de Honduras, Tegucigalpa |
| 8) | NN20 | 670 | 1 | LV de Honduras, Sta Rosa de Copán |
| 8) | NN8 | 680 | 10 | LV de Honduras, San Pedro Sula |
| 8) | NN2 | 680 | 10 | LV de Honduras, Siguatepeque |
| 8) | NN7 | 680 | 1 | LV de Honduras, Danlí |
| 8) | NN10 | 680 | 1 | LV de Honduras, Juticalpa |
| 8) | NN3 | 690 | 1 | LV de Honduras, Choluteca |
| 11) | SG | †710 | 2.5 | R. LV de la Libertad, Catacamas |
| 79) | NN3 | 720 | 1 | R. Caribe, La Ceiba |
| 10) | NN4 | 730 | 1 | R. Centro, Tegucigalpa |
| 12) | QQ | 740 | 1 | R. Intibucá, La Esperanza: 1100-0100 |
| 13) | IH | 740 | 5 | La Super Grande, Juticalpa: 1230-0400 |
| 9) | TG2 | 740 | 1 | R. Satélite, San Pedro Sula: 1100-0600 |
| 90) | VC | 740 | 2.5 | LV Evangélica, Olanchito (r. 1390) |
| 16) | XW | 760 | 2.5 | R. Comayagüela, Tegucigalpa |
| 14) | RD | 770 | 1 | R. Majestad, Juticalpa |
| 21) | DL | †800 | 1 | R. Corporación, Comayagua: 1100-0400 |
| 17) | XS2 | 800 | 3 | R. Moderna, San Pedro Sula (r. 820) |
| 90) | VC | 810 | 6 | LV Evangélica, La Ceiba (r. 1390) |
| 25) | LP24 | 810 | 3 | R. Valle, Choluteca: 1000-0400 |
| 17) | LP16 | 820 | 5 | R. Moderna, Tegucigalpa |
| 84) | KW | 820 | 7/3 | R. Sultana, Sta Rosa de Copán: 1100-0400 |
| 24) | RU | 830 | 1 | R. Uno, San Pedro Sula |
| 26) | JB | †830 | 1 | Cadena Radial Impacto, Comayagua |
| 90) | QW | 840 | 3 | LV Evangélica, Tela (r. 1390) |
| 19) | | 860 | 0.5 | R. Río de Dios, Olanchito |
| 20) | BV | 860 | 1.5 | R. Piedra Blanca, Catacamas |
| 3) | H | 880 | 10 | R. Nacional de Honduras, Tegucigalpa |
| 9) | UP6 | †900 | 1 | R. Satélite, La Ceiba |
| 29) | VS | 910 | 10 | La Voz de Suyapa, Tegucigalpa |
| 21) | RM | †920 | 1 | R. Sistema, Comayagua |
| 31) | ZV | 920 | 1 | Una Voz Que Clama en el Desierto, S. P. S. |
| 32) | SK | †920 | 5 | R. Catacamas, Catacamas: 1200-0400 |
| 91) | CQ | 930 | 4 | Cadena Radial Samaritano, La Ceiba |
| 18) | CR | 940 | 1 | DCR (Dif. Cristiana de R.), Tegucigalpa |
| 34) | QL | 950 | 5 | R. Centro de Honduras, Siguatepeque |
| 38) | LY | 970 | 2 | R. Millenium, Tegucigalpa |
| 41) | AO | †980 | 1 | R. Tocoa, Tocoa |
| 39) | ZC | 980 | 2 | R. Rhema, San Pedro Sula |
| 90) | VC | 980 | 5 | LV Evangélica, Comayagua (r. 1390) |

| MW | Call | kHz | kW | Station, location |
|---|---|---|---|---|
| 36) | PR | 990 | 3.5 | R. Paz, Choluteca: 1100-0200 |
| 30) | CY | †1000 | 3 | R. Congolón, Gracias: 1100-0500 |
| 44) | XZ | 1000 | 1 | HCH Radio, Tegucigalpa |
| 89) | CD | 1010 | 1 | R. Constelación. Juticalpa: 1200-0300 |
| 23) | LL | 1010 | 1 | R. Visión Cristiana, Tocoa |
| 27) | PN | 1020 | 3 | R. Visión Cristiana Internacional, Marcovia |
| 90) | VC | 1040 | 5 | LV Evangélica, Juticalpa |
| 90) | VC | 1040 | 1 | LV Evangélica, Danlí |
| 48) | KT | 1060 | | R. La Catracha, Tegucigalpa |
| 42) | BB | 1070 | 3 | R. Unidad Evangélica, Catacamas |
| 53) | LE | 1070 | 1 | R. Unica, San Pedro Sula |
| 43) | IE | 1080 | 3 | R. Senda de Vida, San Lorenzo: 1200-2300 |
| 91) | CQ | 1090 | 10 | Cadena Radial Samaritano, Tegucigalpa |
| 57) | AJ | 1100 | 1 | Radio Gualaco, Gualaco |
| 58) | ND | 1100 | 1.5 | R. La Esperanza, La Esperanza: 1100-0300 |
| 59) | VA | 1100 | 1 | R. Tiempo, San Pedro Sula |
| 38) | TL | †1120 | 2 | R. Fiesta, Tegucigalpa |
| 63) | BT | 1130 | 1 | Ritmo 1130, Juticalpa |
| 99) | HP | 1130 | 2 | Estéreo Pinares, Siguatepeque |
| 65) | UL | ‡1140 | 1 | R. Pico Bonito, La Ceiba |
| 90) | VC | 1140 | 3 | LV Evangélica, Choluteca |
| 5) | LP12 | 1150 | 1 | R. Universal, Tegucigalpa |
| 35) | VZ | 1160 | 1 | R. Juan Pablo II, Siguatepeque |
| 46) | FJ | ‡1160 | 5 | R. País, Progreso |
| 47) | | 1160 | | R. Nueva Palestina, Nueva Palestina |
| 45) | AF | 1170 | 2 | La Campeonísima, Choluteca |
| 19) | | 1180 | 1 | R. Río de Dios, Belén |
| 49) | AZ | 1180 | 1 | R. El Tigre, Tegucigalpa |
| 6) | VW3 | 1190 | 5 | R. Cadena Voces, El Progreso |
| 72) | SI | ‡1200 | 1 | R. Impacto, Tela: 1200-0400 |
| 71) | | 1220 | 1 | R. Destellos de Luz, Sabá |
| 74) | OP | †1220 | 1 | R. Costeña Ebenezer, San Pedro Sula:1100-0600 |
| 75) | YS | ‡1220 | 1 | R. Suari, Marcala |
| 148) | SD | ‡1220 | 3 | R. Destellos de Luz, Sabá |
| 91) | CQ | 1230 | 3 | Cad. R. Samaritano, San Marcos de Colón |
| 133) | ZC | ‡1240 | 1 | R. Vanguardia, Tegucigalpa |
| 37) | KF | 1250 | 1 | R. Garzel, Juticalpa |
| 51) | YF | ‡1250 | 1 | R. Renacimiento, Comayagua |
| 77) | FP | 1260 | 1 | R. Amistad, San Marcos de Colón |
| 107) | BN | 1280 | 1 | R. San Miguel, Marcala: 1000-0400 |
| 50) | OW | 1280 | 1 | LV de la Victoria, Juticalpa |
| 82) | LR | ‡1300 | 5 | Estéreo Emaus, Santa Rosa de Copán |
| 83) | IV | 1300 | 5 | CCI Radio, Tegucigalpa |
| 90) | VC | 1310 | 2.5 | LV Evangélica, San Pedro Sula |
| 52) | CM | 1310 | 5 | R. Universidad de Agricultura, Catacamas |
| 153) | TQ | 1340 | 10 | R. Adventista Maranatha, San Pedro Sula |
| 91) | CQ | 1340 | 5 | Cadena Radial Samaritano, Comayagua |
| 28) | BS | 1360 | 1 | R. San Pedro, Tegucigalpa: 1100-0600 |
| 85) | UN | 1370 | 5 | LVC Radio, Catacamas |
| 90) | VC | 1390 | 10/5 | LV Evangélica, Tegucigalpa |
| 90) | VC | 1390 | 1 | LV Evangélica, Sata Rosa de Copán |
| 80) | YT | ‡1400 | 1 | R. Estrella de Oro, San Pedro Sula |
| 86) | UV | 1400 | 1 | R. El Patrón, Catacamas |
| 90) | FO | 1430 | 1 | LV Evangélica, Puerto Cortés |
| 97) | VM | ‡1430 | 1 | R. Maranatha, La Paz |
| 98) | RD | 1440 | 1 | R. Belén, La Ceiba |
| 56) | GC | ‡1460 | 2.5 | R. Reino, San Pedro Sula |
| 102) | EZ | 1480 | 1 | R. Misiones Int. "R. MI", Comayagüela |
| 60) | HY | 1490 | 1 | R. Boquerón, Juticalpa |
| 106) | EM | 1510 | 1 | R. Emmanuel, Nueva Ocotepeque: 1100-2330 |
| 183) | DF | 1520 | 1 | R. Ríos de Agua Viva, Siguatepeque |
| 192) | MQ | †1520 | 5 | R. Manantial de Vida Eterna, Juticalpa |
| 40) | | 1550 | 1 | R. Miel, Sabá |
| 181) | BX | 1590 | 5 | R. Perla, El Progreso |

**Addresses & other information:**

**1)** Centro Sercano de Boulevard Suyapa, Tegucigalpa **W:** abcradiohn. com – **2)** San Marcos, Ocotepeque **W:** manantial550.radio12345.com – **3)** Ap 403, Barrio La Guadalupe, Ave. República de Chile, Edificio Loyola segundo nivel, frente a CEDAC, Tegucigalpa **W:** rnh.gob.hn – **4)** San Pedro Sula 94.1MHz – Ap 24, San Pedro Sula – **5)** Edif Audio Video, Ap 259, Tegucigalpa **W:** radiouniversalhn.net – **6)** Blvd Morazán, Edificio Classic, 2ndo piso, Frente a Banco Ficohsa, Tegucigalpa **W:** radiocadenavoceshn.com – **7)** Juticalpa, Olancho **W:** rcolancho.org – **8)** Emisoras Unidas, Col Florencia, Blv Suyapa (or Ap 642), Tegucigalpa **W:** radiopaz.hn – **9)** Emisoras Unidas, Col Florencia, Blv Suyapa (or Ap. 642), Tegucigalpa **W:** radiosatelite.hn – **10)** **W:** radiocentro.hn – **11)** **W:** facebook.com/RadioEvangelicaLaVozDeLaLibertad – **12)** Barrio El Way, Calle Principal, La Esperanza, Intibucá **W:** radiointibuca.webs.com – **13)** Ap 9, Barrio de Jésus, 4ta y 5ta Ave, 6ta Calle, Juticalpa **W:** grupocnc.net/radio740.html – **14)** Ap 15, 16101 Juticalpa - **FM:** 106.3MHz Prgrs in Sp and E – **15)** Atras de Gasolinera Shell, La Entrada, Copán –**16) W:** facebook.com/radiocomayaguelahn – **17)** Colonia Alameda, Calle Las Flores, una cuadra al norte del Bloque Materno Infantil, Hospital Escuela, Ap 259, Tegucigalpa **W:** radiomoderna.net – **18)** Ap 3448 (or Iglesia Amor Viviente, Col Godoy frente a F.H.I.S.), Tegucigalpa **W:** dcr940.net – **19) W:** radioriodedios.org riodedios.net (separate feeds) – **20)** Barrio de Jésus, Catacamas, Olancho **W:** radiopiedrablancahn.com – **21)** Barrio San Francisco, Fte Parque, Comayagua - **FM:** 99.9MHz – **22)** Danlí, El Paraíso – **23)** Tocoa, Colón **W:** radiovisioncristianahn. com – **24)** 2 calle 7 y 8 avenida S.O, San Pedro Sula **W:** radiouno830. es.tl – **25)** Ap 29, Choluteca **W:** radiovalle.net - **FM:** 90.7MHz – **26)** Ap. 33, Avenida José Santos Guardiola, Comayagua **W:** facebook.com/CadenaRadialImpactoLaVozDeComayagua - **FM** 93.9MHz – **27)** Barrio El Tamarindo, contigo al Restaurante Kig Palace, Choluteca **W:** rvci. org - **FM:** 93.5MHz – **28)** Ap 364, Av.New Orleans, San Pedro Sula **W:** radiosanpedrohn.net - **FM:** San Pedro Sula 88.9MHz – **29)** Ap. 480, Suyapa Medios, Edificio Pablo VI atras del Santuario de Suyapa 1, Tegucigalpa 3404 **W:** fundacioncatolica.org/lavozdesuyapa.html – **30)** Frente al Parque "Lempira", Gracias, Lempira (or Ap.1579, Tegucigalpa) – **W:** facebook.com/radiocongolon – **31)** Ap 2918 (or 5 Calle, 10 y 11 Av S.O 91), San Pedro Sula **W:** facebook.com/Una-Voz-Que-Clama-En-El-Desierto-Honduras-603677789818059 - **FM:** 102.1MHz Radio Fabulosa – **32)** Ap 50, Catacamas **W:** catacamas.net - **FM:** 104.5MHz – **33)** Ap 10, 12101 Comayagua 1100-2400 - **FM:** 89.1MHz R.Vida – **34)** Barrio Abajo, 2 Ave, 2da. y 3era. CII S.E, Siguatepeque **W:** lacentro.centrora-dialhn.net - **FM:** 96.3MHz – **35) W:** facebook.com/radiojuanpablo – **36)** Ap 40, B. El Hospital Edificio Obispado, frente a oficinas del sanaa, Choluteca **W:** radiopazhn.org - **FM:** 95 5MHz – **37)** Juticalpa, Olancho **W:** facebook.com/Radio-Garzel-151178541726267 – **38)** Ap 2821, Col. ave Guanacaste #1511, Tegucigalpa **W:** circuitopop.com – **39)** Ap 996 (or 9 CA, Entre 8 y 9 Av), San Pedro Sula **W:** rhema. ebenezer.hn **FM:** 98.5MHz Estéreo Mass – **40)** Barrio el Chorro, 2da. Avenida, entre 7 y 8 calle, Sabá, Colón **W:** radiomielsaba.com – **41)** Bo la Esperanza, 2 cuadras y media del Mercado municipal, Tocoa, Colón **W:** radiotocoa.com – **42)** Barrio La Cruz, Contiguo a la Iglesia el Encuentro, Catacamas, Olancho **W:** facebook.com/Radio-Unidad-Evangelica-254226874988732 – **43)** Colonia Morazan, San Lorenzo, Valle **W:** radiosendadevida.net – **44)** Ap. 614, Lomas del Mayab, calle San Marcos esquina opuesta a Novel Center, Casa # 1647, Tegucigalpa **W:** hchradio.com – **45)** Ap 78, Choluteca **W:** emisorasaliadashn. com/html/la-campeonisima.html – **FM:** 105.1MHz – **46)** Progreso, Yoro **W:** facebook.com/Radio-Pais-1160-AM-342357765898331– **47)** Nueva Palestina, Olanco **W:** facebook.com/Radio-Nueva-Palestina-Oficial-314955388985208 – **48)** Tegucigalpa – **49)** Tegucigalpa – **50)** Edif. Las Vegas 1/2 Cuadra al Norte de Banco Atlántidad, B° El Centro, Juticalpa, Olancho **W:** grupoecohn.com/vozvictoria.php – **51)** Barrio Cabañas 2 cuadras al Norte de la Planta de la ENEEE, Comayagua **W:** facebook.com/Radio-Renacimiento-374089842665596 – **52)** Kilometro 9 en la Carretera que conduce al Municipio Dulce Nombre de Culmi, Catacamas, Olancho **W:** unag.edu.hn – **53)** 9 Av 4 Calle, Edif Las Fuentes, San Pedro Sula **W:** radiounicahn.com – **56)** Misión Cristiana Internacional El Shaddai, San Pedro Sula **W:** facebook.com/RadioReino – **57)** Gualaco, Olancho **W:** facebook.com/1100AMRADIO – **58)** Ap 25, La Esperanza, Intibucá **W:** facebook.com/Radio-La-Esperanza-1970762733210863 – **59)** Ap 906, Bo. Lempira, 10 Calle, 8-9 Ave., S.O, San Pedro Sula **W:** radiotiempohn.com - **FM:** Stero Fama 97.7MHz – **60)** Juticalpa, Olancho 16101 **W:** radioboqueron. net – **63)** Juticalpa **W:** ritmo1130.com – **65)** Barrio La Isla, La Ceiba **W:** facebook.com/radio-pico-bonito-1140-am-165026650238268 – **71)** Sabá, Colón - **W:** facebook.com/RadioDestellosDeLuz – **72)** Calle José Trinidad Cabañas, Edif Hotel Presidente, Tela - **FM:** 88.9 – **74)** Iglesia de Cristo, Ministerio Ebenezer, 14 Calle A, Costado Sur de Wendy's Circunvalación (or Ap 34-76), San Pedro Sula **W:** ebenezer.hn – **75)** Calle Principal, Marcala, La Paz – **77)** Barrio Fátima, San Marcos de Colón, Choluteca **W:** radioamistad.biz – **79)** Emisoras Unidas, Solares Nuevos, Av. República, La Ceiba **W:** radiocaribe.hn – **80)** Ap 303, Barrio los Andes 9 calle B, 15 Avenida circunvalación, San Pedro Sula **W:** radioestrelladeoro.org - **FM:** 97.3MHz – **81)** Barrio Campo Luna, Choluteca **W:** emisorasunidas.net - **FM:** 88.7MHz – **82)** Ap. 203, Diócesis de Santa Rosa de Copan, Iglesia Católica. Barrio El Carmen, Costado Este del Parque Infantil, Santa Rosa de Copan **W:** radiosan-tarosa.net - **FM:** 94.5MHz – **83)** Residencial El Trapiche, Boulevard Suyapa, 30694 Tegucigalpa **W:** cciradio.org – **84)** Ap 204, Sta Rosa de Copán **W:** facebook.com/RadioSultanaHN - **FM:** 90.3MHz – **85)** Barrio La Cruz, cuadra y media al Este de la Municipalidad de Catacamas, Olancho **W:** facebook.com/lavozdecatacamas **FM** 97.9MHz – **86)** Catacamas, Olancho – **89)** Barrio Las Flores, Avenida La Trinidad, Casa 054, Juticalpa **W:** radioconstelacion.net - **FM:** 101.9MHz – **90)** Ap 3252, Tegucigalpa – (Owned and operated by Conservative Baptist Home Mission Society, Box 828, Wheaton, IL 60187, USA) **W:** hrvc. org – **91)** Colonia Payaqui, bulevar San Juan Bosco, frente a el segun-do porton del instituto San Miguel, Casa 3658, 504, Tegucigalpa **W:** radiosamaritano.net - 1100-0500 – **95)** 12 Calle 2a Ave 206, Barrio

La Curva, Puerto Cortés – **97)** Santiago de la Paz, La Paz (or Col.21 de Octubre, Sector 3, Bloque 2, Casa 5, Tegucigalpa) **W:** facebook.com/MaranathaHonduras – **98)** Ap. 614, Av San Isidro, Entre Calles 9 y 10, La Ceiba **W:** facebook.com/RadioBelenhn – **99)** Casa 269, Barrio Abajo, Siguatepeque 1155 **W:** pinares.centroradialhn.net - **FM:** 91.5MHz – **102)** Ap. 20583, Comayagüela (or IMF World Missions, 1115 S. Grove Ave. Ste. 104, Ontario, CA 91761) - 1100-0300 **W:** radiomi.com - **FM:** Talanga 99.3MHz – **106)** Barrio San Andrés, Ocotepeque **W:** facebook.com/Radio-Emmanuel-1510-AM-160416914020684 – **107)** Barrio Concepción, Marcala, La Paz (or Palacio Arzobispal, Av.Cervantes, Barrio El Centro, Tegucigalpa) **W:** radiosanmiguelhn.blogspot.com.en – **112)** Santa Rosa de Copán **W:** superestrella.org - **FM:** 93.1MHz – **128)** Radio Ensenanzas Evangelicas, Puerto Lempira – **133)** Ap 914, Tegucigalpa – **147)** Ap 888, (or Centro Comercial San José), La Ceiba **W:** applegatefellowship.org/missions/honduras.asp **E:** radiolitoral@psinet.hn – **148)** Barrio La Pava, Sabá, Colón **W:** radiodestellosdeluz.org – **153)** Ap 210 (or 5 Calle, 10 y 11 Av S.O., Barrio Beuque), San Pedro Sula **W:** 1340am.tk – **181)** 4 y 5 Ave, 3 Calle 442, Barrio Las Delicias, El Progreso, Yoro **W:** radioperla.com – **183)** Barrio El Centro, Valle del Boulevard, Contiguo a la Iglesia Adventista, Siguatepeque **W:** facebook.com/radioriosdeaguaviva.hn – **192)** Barrio de Jesús, Casa 7, Calle Principal, Juticalpa **W:** facebook.com/Radio-Manantial-de-Vida-Eterna-1520-AM/172815026105703

**FM in Tegucigalpa (MHz):** 88.1 Stereo Exitos – 88.7 Globo Grupera – 88.9 RDS R. – 89.3 Power – 89.9 R. Red de Radiodifusión Bíblica – 90.5 R. Corazón 90.5 – 91.1 R. Kairos FM – 91.7 R. Buenísima – 92.3 Rock n' Pop – 92.9 R. HRN – 93.3 Cadena Voces – 94.1 FM 94 – 94.7 América – 94.9 HCH Radio – 95.3 Digital – 95.9 R. Panamericana – 96.5 R. Estéreo Fiel – 97.1 EstéreoTic Tac – 97.7 Azul – 98.3 Estéreo Concierto – 98.9 Estéreo Fe – 99.5 Suprema – 100.1 Super 100 – 100.7 R. Exa FM – 101.3 Nacional de Honduras – 101.9 Vox – 102.5 Suave FM – 102.9 Tu Alternativa Siempre – 103.7 Luz – 104.5 Satélite – 104.9 Estéreo Amor – 105.5 Musiquera – 106.1 Romántica – 106.7 Stereo Rumba – 107.3 W107 Energía Estéreo – 107.9 Top Music con La Onda del Nuevo Mundo.

**AFRTS (Air Force)**
✉ JTF-B, APO AA 34042, USA **E:** PAO@jtfb-emh1.army.mil
**FM:** 106.3MHz Soto Cano Air Base, 0.25kW **D.Prgr:** 24h

## HONG KONG (China, SAR)

**L.T:** UTC +8h — **Pop:** 7.4 million — **Pr.L:** Cantonese, English — **E.C** 50Hz, 200/220V — **ITU:** HKG

### COMMUNICATIONS AUTHORITY
✉ Wu Chung House, 213 Queen's Road East, Wan Chai, Hong Kong ☎ +852 29616333 🖷 +852 25072219 **E:** webmaster@ofca.gov.hk **W:** www.coms-auth.hk **L.P:** Chair: Winnie Tam Wan-chi

### RADIO TELEVISION HONG KONG (Gov.)
✉ Broadcasting House, 30 Broadcast Drive, Kowloon, Hong Kong ☎ +852 2272 0000 🖷 +852 2336 9314 **E:** ccu@rthk.org.hk **W:** rthk.org.hk **L.P:** Dir. of Broadc: Leung Ka-wing, Asst. Dir. of Broadc. (Radio & Corporate Programming): Albert Cheung

| MW | Network | Location | kW |
|---|---|---|---|
| 567 | R. 3 | Golden Hill | 20 |
| 621 | P. Ch | Golden Hill | 20 |
| 675 | R. 6 | Peng Chau | 10 |
| 783 | R. 5 | Golden Hill | 20 |
| 1584 | R. 3 | Chung Hom Kok | 0.1 |

P. Ch = Putonghua Channel

| FM | Netw. | kW | Tx Location | Target Div. |
|---|---|---|---|---|
| 92.3 | R. 5 | 0.025 | Tin Shui Wai | |
| 92.6 | R. 1 | 3 | Mt. Gough | Kowloon |
| 92.9 | R. 1 | 0.1 | Golden Hill | Tsuen Wan |
| 93.2 | R. 1 | 0.5 | Cloudy Hill | Fan Ling |
| 93.4 | R. 1 | 0.7 | Castle Peak | Tuen Mun |
| 93.5 | R. 1 | 0.15 | Beacon Hill | Sha Tin |
| 93.6 | R. 1 | 0.05 | Hill 374 | Yuen Long |
| 94.4 | R. 1 | 1 | Kowloon Peak | HK Isl. north, Sai Kung |
| 94.8 | R. 2 | 3 | Mt. Gough | Kowloon |
| 95.2 | R. 5 | 0.02 | Mt. Nicholson | Jardine's Lookout |
| 95.3 | R. 2 | 0.5 | Cloudy Hill | Fan Ling |
| 95.6 | R. 2 | 0.05 | Hill 374 | Yuen Long |
| 96.0 | R. 2 | 0.5 | Lamma Isl. | HK Isl. south |
| 96.3 | R. 2 | 0.15 | Beacon Hill | Sha Tin |
| 96.4 | R. 2 | 0.7 | Castle Peak | Tuen Mun, |
| 96.9 | R. 2 | 1 | Kowloon Peak | HK Isl. north, Sai Kung |
| 97.6 | R. 4 | 3 | Mt. Gough | Kowloon |
| 97.8 | R. 4 | 0.5 | Cloudy Hill | Fan Ling |
| 97.9 | R. 3 | 0.02 | Mt. Nicholson | Jardine's Lookout |
| 98.1 | R. 4 | 0.15 | Beacon Hill | Sha Tin |
| 98.2 | R. 4 | 0.05 | Lamma Isl. | HK Isl. south |
| 98.2 | R. 4 | 0.05 | Hill 374 | Yuen Long |
| 98.4 | R. 4 | 0.1 | Golden Hill | Tsuen Wan |
| 98.7 | R. 4 | 0.7 | Castle Peak | Tuen Mun, |
| 98.9 | R. 4 | 1 | Kowloon Peak | HK Isl. north, Sai Kung |
| 99.4 | R. 5 | 0.015 | Tseung Kwan O | Jank Bay |
| 100.9 | P. Ch | 0.01 | Tai Hang Road | |
| 100.9 | P. Ch | 0.003 | Castle Peak | Tuen Mun |
| 103.3 | P. Ch | 0.015 | Tseung Kwan O | Jank Bay |
| 103.3 | P. Ch | 0.025 | Tin Shui Wai | |
| 106.8 | R. 5 | 0.03 | Castle Peak | Tuen Mun |
| 106.8 | R. 3 | 0.15 | Chung Hom Kok | HK Isl. south |
| 107.8 | R. 3 | 0.015 | Tseung Kwan O | Jank Bay |
| 107.8 | R. 3 | 0.025 | Tin Shui Wai | |

**RTHK Radio 1** in Cantonese/Chinese: 24h – **RTHK Radio 2** in Cantonese 24h, partly indonesian on Sat 2300-2400 – **RTHK Radio 3** in English: 24h, partly Nepali on Sun 1105-1200, partly Urdu on Sun 1205-1300 – **RTHK Radio 4** in English/Cantonese, partly relay BBCWS English 1500-2300: 24h – **RTHK Radio 5** in Cantonese/Chinese: 24h – **RTHK Radio 6** RelayV.O. Hong Kong, 14th Prgr of China National Radio (CNR) in Beijing, in Chinese and Cantonese: 24h – **RTHK Putonghua Channel** in Chinese: 24h
**Ann:** Cantonese: "Heunggong dintoi dai (number) toi"

### HONG KONG COMMERCIAL BROADC. CO. LTD
✉ 3 Broadcast Drive, Kowloon, Hong Kong ☎ +852 2336 5111 🖷+852 2338 0021 **E:** cs@881903.com **W:** 881903.com

| MW | | kW | Location | Prgr. |
|---|---|---|---|---|
| 864 | | 10 | Peng Chau | 24h music |
| FM | Netw. | kW | Tx Location | Target Div. |
| 88.1 | CR1 | 3 | Mt.Gough | Kowloon |
| 88.3 | CR1 | 0.5 | Cloudy Hill | Fan Ling |
| 88.6 | CR1 | 0.7 | Castle Peak | Tuen Mun |
| 88.9 | CR1 | 0.1 | Golden Hill | Tsuen Wan |
| 89.1 | CR1 | 0.5 | Lamma Isl. | HK Isl. south |
| 89.2 | CR1 | 0.15 | Beacon Hill | Sha Tin |
| 89.5 | CR1 | 1 | Kowloon Peak | HK Isl. north, Sai Kung |
| 90.3 | CR2 | 3 | Mt.Gough | Kowloon |
| 90.7 | CR2 | 0.5 | Cloudy Hill | Fan Ling |
| 90.9 | CR2 | 0.1 | Golden Hill | Tsuen Wan |
| 91.1 | CR2 | 0.15 | Beacon Hill | Sha Tin |
| 91.2 | CR2 | 0.7 | Castle Peak | Tuen Mun |
| 91.6 | CR2 | 0.5 | Lamma Isl. | HK Isl. south |
| 92.1 | CR2 | 1 | Kowloon Peak | HK Isl. north, Sai Kung |

**HKCR CR1** (Supercharged 881) in Cantonese. 24h **N:** half-hourly
**HKCR CR2** (Ultimate 903) in Cantonese 24h **N:** hourly **Ann:** "Chikja gaulingsaam"
**HKCR AM864** in English, partly Filipino on Fri and Sat 1300-1500. 24h **N:** On the h from 2300-1500

### METRO BROADCAST CORPORATION LTD.
✉ Basement 2, Site 6, Whampoa Gardens Hunghom, Kowloon, Hong Kong ☎ +852 3698 8000 🖷+852 2123 9889 **E:** prenquiry@metroradio.com.hk **W:** metroradio.com.hk

| MW | Network | kW | Location | |
|---|---|---|---|---|
| 1044 | Metro Plus | 10 | Peng Chau | |
| FM | Network | kW | Tx Location | Target Div. |
| 99.7 | Metro Info | 3 | Mt.Gough | Kowloon |
| 100.0 | Metro Info | 0.5 | Cloudy Hill | Fan Ling |
| 100.4 | Metro info | 0.7 | Castle Peak | Tuen Mun |
| 100.5 | Metro Info | 0.15 | Beacon Hill | Sha Tin |
| 101.0 | Metro Info | 0.01 | Stanley | |
| 101.6 | Metro Info | 0.1 | Golden Hill | Tsuen Wan |
| 101.8 | Metro Info | 1 | Kowloon Peak | HK Isl. north |
| 102.1 | Metro info | 0.5 | Lamma Isl. | HK Isl. south |
| 102.4 | Metro Finance | 0.15 | Beacon Hill | Sha Tin |
| 102.5 | Metro Finance | 0.7 | Castle Peak | Tuen Mun |
| 102.6 | Metro Finance | 0.01 | Stanley | |
| 104.0 | Metro Finance | 3 | Mt.Gough | Kowloon |
| 104.5 | Metro Finance | 0.5 | Lamma Isl. | HK Isl. south |
| 104.7 | Metro Finance | 0.5 | Cloudy Hill | Fan Ling |
| 105.5 | Metro Finance | 0.1 | Golden Hill | Tsuen Wan |
| 106.3 | Metro Finance | 1 | Kowloon Peak | HK Isl. north |

**Metro Plus** in English (Partly Cantonese, Mandarin, Hindi and Thai) 24h music, news and information **Metro Info** in Cantonese. 24h **Ann:** "Sansing jiseun toi" **Metro Finance** in Cantonese 24h

**DIGITAL RADIO (DAB)**
DAB has been discontinued since September 2017

## HUNGARY

**L.T**: UTC +1h (31 Mar-27 Oct: +2h) — **Pop**: 9.77 million — **Pr.L**: Hungarian — **E.C**: 50Hz, 230V — **ITU**: HNG

**NEMZETI MÉDIA- ÉS HÍRKÖZLÉSI HATÓSÁG (NMHH)**
**(National Media and Communications Authority)**
✉ 1015 Budapest, Ostrom u. 23-25 ☎ +36 1 4577100 🖷 +36 1 3565520 **E**: info@nmhh.hu **W**: nmhh.hu **L.P**: Pres: Monica Karas

**ANTENNA HUNGÁRIA ZRT.**
✉ 1119 Budapest, Petzvál József u. 31-33 ☎ +36 1 4642462 🖷 +36 1 4642525 **E**: antennah@ahrt.hu **W**: ahrt.hu **L.P**: CEO: András Kápolnai

**HELYI RÁDIÓK ORSZÁGOS EGYESÜLETE (HEROE)**
**(National Association of Local Radios)**
✉ 8000 Székesfehérvár, Donát u. 92 ☎ +36 22 505310 🖷 +36 22 505312 **E**: info@radetzky.hu **W**: heroe.hu **L.P**: Pres: András Radetzky

**MAGYAR RÁDIÓ**
✉ 1016 Budapest, Naphegy tér 8 ☎ +36 1 3287000 2 36 1 3287447 **W**: radio.hu **E**: info@radio.hu **L.P**: CEO: István Jónás
**Kossuth Rádió** ☎ +36 1 3287945 **W**: mediaklikk.hu/kossuth **Petöfi Rádió** ☎ +36 1 3288555 **W**: mediaklikk.hu/petofi **Bartók Rádió** ☎ +36 1 3288772 **W**: mediaklikk.hu/bartok

| MW | kHz | kW | Prg | MW | kHz | kW | Prg |
|---|---|---|---|---|---|---|---|
| Solt | 540 | 1000 | 1 | Marcali | 1188 | 300 | 4 |
| Lakihegy | 873 | 20 | 4 | Szolnok | 1188 | 100 | 4 |
| Pécs | 873 | 20 | 4 | Szombathely | 1251 | 25 | D |
| Miskolc | 1116 | 15 | D | Nyíregyháza | 1251 | 25 | D |
| Mosonmagyaróvár | 1116 | 5 | D | Györ | 1350 | 5 | 4 |

| FM (MHz): | MR1 | MR2 | MR3 | Dankó | kW(erp) |
|---|---|---|---|---|---|
| Aggtelek | 94.6 | | | | 2.3 |
| Balassagyarmat | 93.7 | | | | 3 |
| Barcs | 89.5 | | | | 2 |
| Budapest | 107.8 | 94.8 | 105.3 | 100.8 | 83/77/81/79 |
| Cegléd | 93.0 | | | | 1.1 |
| Csávoly | 96.7 | 89.4 | | | 6.1/6.3 |
| Debrecen | 99.7 | 89.0 | 106.6 | 91.4 | 1.4/1/1/1.2 |
| Dombóvár | | | | 100.2 | 1 |
| Fehérgyarmat | 105.9 | | | | 5.6 |
| Gerecse | 105.6 | | | | 10 |
| Györ | 87.6 | 93.1 | 106.8 | 106.4 | 7.6/7.5/7.5/0.8 |
| Kabhegy | 107.2 | 93.9 | 105.0 | 102.3 | 87/65/69/5.4 |
| Kaposvár | 96.7 | | | | 3.5 |
| Karcag | 97.9 | | | | 10 |
| Kecskemét | 104.9 | | | | 1.1 |
| Kékestetö | 95.5 | 102.7 | 90.7 | 99.8 | 20/30/28/0.3 |
| Keszthely | | | | 104.3 | 1 |
| Kiskörös | 88.4 | 95.1 | 105.9 | | 2/1.7/3 |
| Komádi | 103.0 | 96.7 | 105.1 | 89.9 | 39/37/30/5 |
| Miskolc | 97.1 | | 107.5 | 102.3 | 5.6/1.4/1.4 |
| Mosonmagyaróvár | 95.0 | | | | 0.8 |
| Nagykanizsa | 90.2 | 94.3 | 104.7 | 106.7 | 8.3/12/20/5 |
| Nyíregyháza | | | | 107.4 | 1 |
| Pécs | 95.9 | 103.7 | 107.6 | 104.6 | 25/50/10/5.6 |
| Rábaszentandrás | | | | 105.2 | 4.9 |
| Sátoraljaújhely | 91.9 | | | | 0.5 |
| Siófok | | | | 93.6 | 3 |
| Sopron | 96.8 | 99.5 | 107.9 | 101.6 | 9.3/9/7/5.1 |
| Szeged | 90.3 | 104.6 | 105.7 | 93.1 | 0.6/5/2.2/1 |
| Szekszárd | 99.0 | | | | 1.1 |
| Szentes | 100.4 | 98.8 | 107.3 | 91.6 | 34/32/34/2 |
| Szolnok | 94.3 | | | 101.2 | 6.3/2 |
| Telkibánya | 90.2 | | | | 3.6 |
| Tiszafüred | | | | 105.2 | 1 |
| Tokaj | 97.5 | 92.7 | 105.5 | 88.3 | 50/50/50/5 |
| Úzd | 101.5 | 90.3 | 106.9 | | 3/3/3 |
| Vasvár | 91.6 | 98.2 | 106.9 | 103.6 | 6.8/7.5/3/3 |

+ 16 Kossuth txs & + 16 Dankó txs below 1kW

**Programmes**: P1 = **Kossuth R.** (news-talk) P2 = **Petöfi R.** (pop) P3 = **Bartók R.** (classical) P4 = **Nemzetiségi adások** (Ethnic broadcasts), P5 = **Parlamenti adások** (Parliamentary broadcasts, internet/satellite only), P6 = **Duna World Rádió** (internet/satellite only) D = **Dankó Rádió** (folk+operetta)
**Daily pr**: 24h exc. **P1** MW: Mo-Fr 0330-2130, Sa-Su: 0400-2130 & **P4** MW: 0700-1900

**ANN**: **P1**: "Kossuth Rádió, otthon a világban" **P2**: "Petöfi Rádió - a Te slágered" **P3**: "Bartók Rádió, több, mint klasszikus"
**P4**: **Nemzetiségi (Ethnic pr)**: ☎ +36 (1) 328-8672 🖷 +36 (1) 328-8682. **W**: www.mediaklikk.hu/nemzetisegiradio/ **Daily**: Croatian 0700-0900, German 0900-1100, Bell at noon 1100-1103, Serbian 1300-1500, Romanian 1500-1700, Slovak 1700-1900 **Mon**: Hungarian 1103-1200, Slovenian 1200-1230, **Mon-Fri**: Music of nationalities 1230-1300 **Tue**: Rusyn 1200-1230 **Tue/Thu**: Roma (Lovari dialect) 1130-1200 **Tue-Fri**: Hungarian 1103-1130 **Wed**: Bulgarian 1200-1230 **Wed/Fri**: Roma (Boyash dialect) 1130-1200 **Thu**: Greek 1200-1230 **Fri**: Ukrainian 1200-1230, **Sat**: Armenian 1200-1230, Polish 1230-1300 **Sat/Sun**: Music of nationalities 1103-1200 **Sun**: Hungarian (In One Motherland) 1200-1300.
**Dankó Rádió**: ✉ Kunigunda útja 64, 1037 Budapest ☎ +36 1 7596071 **W**: mediaklikk.hu/danko/ **É**: dankoradio@mtva.hu
**Daily pr**: 24h on FM; **Mo-Fr**: 0330-2005, **Sa-Su**: 0400-2005 on MW, **Ann**: "Dankó Rádió, csendül a nóta, száll a muzsika"
**NB**: **DX data**: radiosite.hu, frekvencia.hu

**National network:**
**Retro Rádió (Comm.)**
✉ 1016 Budapest, Hegyalja út 7-13 ☎ +36 20 2222122 **W**: www.retroradio.hu **E**: info@retroradio.hu

| Location | MHz | kW | Location | MHz | kW |
|---|---|---|---|---|---|
| Kaposvár | 89.0 | 0.05 | Vasvár | 101.2 | 1 |
| Nagykanizsa | 93.6 | 0.25 | Györ | 101.4 | 10 |
| Szeged | 94.9 | 1 | Komádi | 101.6 | 30 |
| Szentes | 95.7 | 0.2 | Sopron | 102.0 | 30 |
| Miskolc | 98.3 | 5.6 | Fehérgyarmat | 102.8 | 2.5 |
| Szekszárd | 98.4 | 1 | Budapest | 103.3 | 100 |
| Gerecse | 100.0 | 0.05 | Tokaj | 103.5 | 50 |
| Kabhegy | 100.5 | 100 | Kékes | 104.7 | 30 |
| Debrecen | 101.1 | 3 | Pécs | 105.5 | 50 |

**Other Stations**

| FM | MHz | kW | Location | Station |
|---|---|---|---|---|
| 27) | 87.9 | 1 | Szeged | R. 1 |
| 9) | 88.1 | 1 | Budapest | InfoR. (news) |
| 2) | 88.3 | 1 | Komárom | Mária R. (rlg) |
| 2) | 88.3 | 1 | Cegléd | Mária R. (rlg) |
| 2) | 88.8 | 1.3 | Budapest | Mária R. (rlg) |
| 1) | 89.5 | 77 | Budapest | Music FM |
| 5) | 90.3 | 0.4 | Budapest | Tilos R. (community) |
| 11) | 90.5 | 1 | Komárom | Forrás R. |
| 7) | 90.6 | 1 | Sátoraljaújh. | Szent István R. (rlg) |
| 27) | 90.6 | 1.2 | Veszprém | R. 1 |
| 26) | 90.9 | 2 | Budapest | Jazzy (smooth jazz) |
| 14) | 91.7 | 1.2 | Kiskörös | Magyar Katolikus R. (rlg) |
| 7) | 91.8 | 0.5 | Eger | Szent István R. (rlg) |
| 28) | 92.1 | 1 | Budapest | Klasszik R. (classical) |
| 14) | 92.5 | 0.43 | Esztergom | Magyar Katolikus R. (rlg) |
| 4) | 92.6 | 1 | Siófok | Part FM |
| 24) | 92.9 | 2.6 | Budapest | Klubrádió (talk) |
| 14) | 92.9 | 1 | Zalaegerszeg | Magyar Katolikus R. (rlg) |
| 2) | 93.4 | 1 | Dabas | R. Dabas |
| 25) | 93.6 | 0.85 | Nagykörös | Gong R. |
| 18) | 94.2 | 1 | Budapest | Trend FM |
| 20) | 94.4 | 1 | Debrecen | Európa R. |
| 7) | 95.1 | 1 | Miskolc | Szent István R. (rlg) |
| 27) | 95.1 | 1 | Zalaegerszeg | R.1 |
| 7) | 95.4 | 1 | Encs | Szent István R. (rlg) |
| 29) | 95.7 | 1 | Balassagy. | Megafon R. |
| 22) | 95.8 | 2 | Budapest | Rock FM |
| 14) | 96.1 | 0.1 | Székesfehérv. | Magyar Katolikus R. (rlg) |
| 27) | 96.3 | 5 | Miskolc | R. 1 |
| 27) | 96.4 | 2.5 | Budapest | R. 1 |
| 25) | 96.5 | 1 | Kecskemét | Gong R. |
| 16) | 97.1 | 2 | Szombathely | Lánchíd R. ++ |
| 27) | 97.7 | 1 | Szombathely | R. 1 |
| 11) | 97.8 | 0.8 | Tatabánya | Forrás R. |
| 12) | 98.0 | 0.14 | Budapest | Civil R. (community) |
| 16) | 98.9 | 1 | Szigetvár | Lánchíd R. ++ |
| 8) | 99.5 | 5 | Budapest | Magyar FM |
| 10) | 100.0 | 0.5 | Kalocsa | Koronafm100 |
| 33) | 100.1 | 1 | Györ | Györ+ R. |
| 16) | 100.3 | 1 | Budapest | Lánchíd R. ++ |
| 20) | 100.5 | 1 | Nyíregyháza | Európa R. |
| 2) | 100.6 | 3 | Telkibánya | Mária R. (rlg) |
| 6) | 100.7 | 1 | Eger | FM7 |
| 14) | 101.2 | 2 | Pécs | Magyar Katolikus R. (rlg) |
| 27) | 101.3 | 1 | Eger | R. 1 |
| 21) | 101.6 | 1 | Miskolc | R. M |

| FM | MHz | kW | Location | Station |
|----|-----|-----|----------|---------|
| 22) | 101.6 | 0.1 | Budapest | Sola R. (protestant rlg) |
| 31) | 101.9 | 1 | Tamási | Tamási R. |
| 14) | 102.1 | 0.74 | Budapest | Magyar Katolikus R. (rlg) |
| 30) | 102.4 | 0.8 | Szolnok | Amadeus R. |
| 14) | 102.5 | 0.5 | Szekszárd | Magyar Katolikus R. (rlg) |
| 34) | 102.7 | 0.95 | Barcs | Dráva Hullám 102.7 |
| 17) | 103.0 | 1 | Miskolc | Csillagpont R. |
| 27) | 103.1 | 0.1 | Györ | R. 1 |
| 35) | 103.9 | 0.86 | Nyíregyháza | Best FM |
| 3) | 103.9 | 5 | Budapest | Sláger FM |
| 27) | 104.0 | 1 | Békéscsaba | R. 1 |
| 35) | 104.6 | 0.8 | Debrecen | Best FM |
| 14) | 104.6 | 1 | Sopron | Magyar Katolikus R. (rlg) |
| 2) | 104.9 | 0.8 | Dömös | Mária R. (rlg) |
| 36) | 105.1 | 0.74 | Szekszárd | R. Antritt |
| 13) | 105.9 | 3.2 | Budapest | Karc FM |
| 16) | 107.0 | 1 | Tatabánya | Lánchíd R. ++ |
| 15) | 107.0 | 0.8 | Kistelek | R. 7 |
| 19) | 107.0 | 0.76 | Szigetsz.mikl. | Lakihegy R. |
| 14) | 107.4 | 0.5 | Szombathely | Magyar Katolikus R. (rlg) |

+ approximately 170 additional FM txs from 50W to 1kW
++ ceased, only music since 13.04.2018

**Addresses & other information:**
**1)** ☑ 1138 Budapest, Népfürdö utca 22. B torony V. em. ☎+36 1 7998895 **W:** musicfm.hu **E:** info@musicfm.hu – **2)** ☑ 1133 Budapest, Gogol u. 28 ☎+36 1 3730701 **W:** www.mariaradio.hu **E:** info@mariaradio.hu **NB:** total 19 txs. 4 hours local px from many regional studios – **3)** ☑ 1012 Budapest, Márvány u. 17 ☎+36 1 2375300 **W:** slagerfm.hu **E:** online@slagerfm.hu – **4)** ☑ 8600 Siófok, Budai Nagy Antal u. 1-3 ☎+36 84 310168 **W:** partfm.hu **E:** info@partfm.hu **NB:** total 2 txs – **5)** ☑ 1085 Budapest, Mária u. 54. ☎+36 1 4768491 **W:** tilos.hu **E:** radio@tilos.hu **NB: English** every 2nd Sat 1400-1530 / **French** every 2nd Sat 1530-1630 / **German** every 2nd Sun 0600-0800 / **Spanish** every 2nd Sat 1400-1530 / **Russian+Hungarian** every 2nd Wed 1730-1830 / **Chinese** every 2nd Wed 1730-1830 / **Serbo-Croatian** every 2nd Tue 1900-2000 – **6)** ☑ 3300 Eger, Csákány u. 1. ☎ +36 36 782114 (Eger) / +36 37 302302 (Gyöngyös/Hatvan) **W:** fm7.hu/ **E:** info@fm7.hu **NB:** total 3 txs – **7)** ☑ 3300 Eger, Széchenyi utca 5. ☎+36 36 510-610 **W:** szentistvanradio.hu **E:** info@szentistvanradio.hu **NB:** total 8 txs – **8)** ☑ 1016 Budapest, Hegyalja út 7-13 ☎+36 20 5555155 **W:** magyarfm.eu **E:** info@magyarfm.eu – **9)** ☑ 1033 Budapest, Polgár u. 8-10 ☎+36 1 4832950 **W:** inforadio.hu **E:** info@inforadio.hu – **10)** ☑ 6300 Kalocsa, Szent István kir. út 34, ☎+36 78 567662 **W:** www.koronafm100.hu **E:** info@koronaradio.hu – **11)** ☑ 2800 Tatabánya, Stúdium tér 1. ☎+36 34 310021 **W:** forrasradio.hu **E:** forras@forrasradio.hu **NB:** total 2 txs – **12)** ☑ 1116 Budapest, Sztregova utca 3 ☎+36 1 489-0997 **W:** civilradio.hu **E:** civilradio@civilradio.hu – **13)** ☑ 1097 Budapest, Könyves Kálmán krt. 12-14 ☎+36 1 9111111 **W:** karcfm.hu **E:** info@karcfm.hu – **14)** ☑ 1062 Budapest, Délibáb u. 15-17 ☎+36 1 255-3366 **W:** katolikusradio.hu **E:** info@katradio.hu **NB:** total 20 txs – **15)** ☑ 6800 Hódmezövásárhely, Szabadság tér 71. ☎+36 62 533777 **W:** www.radio7.hu **E:** radio7@radio7.hu **NB:** total 3 txs – **16)** ☑ 1089 Budapest, Üllöi út 102 ☎+36 1 8148730 **W:** lanchidradio.hu **E:** info@lanchidradio.hu **NB:** total 14 txs – **17)** ☑ 3526 Miskolc, Szentpéteri Kapu 72-76 ☎/🖶 +36 46 515276 **W:** csillagpontradio.hu **E:** info@cspr.hu – **18)** ☑ 1133 Budapest, Váci út 78/B ☎+36 1 8881500 **W:** trendfm.hu/ **E:** info@trendfm.hu – **19)** ☑ 2310 Szigetszentmiklós, Csepeli út 15. ☎+36 20 2754003 **W:** lakihegyradio.hu **E:** sales@lakihegyradio.hu – **20)** ☑ 3530 Miskolc, Toronyalja utca 13. (main HQ) ☎+36 46 509904 **W:** refradio.hu/radio/euradio **E:** euradio@euradio.hu, ☑ 4026 Debrecen, Péterfia u. 1-7. ☎+36 30 9027041 **E:** debrecen@euradio.hu, ☑ 4400 Nyíregyháza, Eötvös u. 9/A ☎+36 42 401035 **E:** nyiregyhaza@euradio.hu **NB:** total 6 txs – **21)** ☑ 3525 Miskolc, Széchenyi István út 46. l/5 ☎/🖶+36 46 320075 **W:** fmradiom.hu/ **E:** reklam@fmradiom.hu **NB:** total 4 txs – **22)** ☑ 1064 Budapest,Vörösmarty u. 65 ☎+36 1 3850835 **W:** www.solaradio.hu **E:** info@solaradio.hu – **23)** ☑ 2370 Dabas, Szent István tér 1/b ☎+36 29 562562 **W:** radiodabas.hu **E:** radiodabas@radiodabas.hu – **24)** ☑ 1037 Budapest, Bokor u 1-3-5 ☎+36 1 2406953 **W:** klubradio.hu **E:** info@klubradio.hu – **25)** ☑ 6000 Kecskemét, Petöfi Sándor u 1/b ☎+36 76 414030 **W:** gongradio.hu **E:** titkarsag@gongradio.hu **NB:** total 7 txs – **26)** ☑ 1022 Budapest Detrekö u. 12. ☎+36 1 7876992 **W:** jazzyradio.hu **E:** info@jazzy.hu – **27)** ☑ 1016 Budapest, Hegyalja út 7-13 ☎+36 20 3111111 **W:** radio1.hu **E:** radio1@radio1.hu **NB:** total 33 txs. 20 hrs. main px of Budapest on all 33 frequencies + 4 hrs. local px in other cities. – **28)** ☑ 1022 Budapest, Detrekö u. 12 ☎+36 1 7866464 **W:** klasszikradio.hu **E:** info@klasszikradio.hu **NB: English** daily at 2300, 0000, 0100, 0200 & 0300 BBC news – **29)** ☑ 2660 Balassagyarmat, Rákóczi Fejedelem út 50 ☎+36 35 957957 **W:** www.megafonfm.hu **E:** megafonfm@

megafonfm.hu **30)** ☑ 5000 Szolnok, Baross út 3. ☎+36 56 221024 **W:** amadeusradio.hu **E:** amadeusradio@amadeusradio.hu – **31)** ☑ 7090 Tamási, Szabadság utca 41/B ☎+36 74 570260 **W:** tamasiradio.hu **E:** tamasiradio@tamasiradio.hu – **32)** ☑ 1152 Budapest, Szentmihályi út 167 ☎+36 1 9111958 **W:** www.rockfm958.hu **E:** info@rockfm958. hu – **33)** ☑ 9023 Györ, Kodály Zoltán u. 32/A ☎+36 96 777777 **W:** radio.gyorplusz.hu **E:** radio@gyorplusz.hu – **34)** ☑ 7570 Barcs, Köztársaság u. 2/1 ☎+36 82 462204 **W:** barcsihirek.hu/drava-hullam **E:** info@barcsmedia.hu – **35)** ☑ 4026 Debrecen, Darabos u. 35. ☎+36 52 450900 **W:** bestfm.hu **E:** info@bestfm.hu **NB:** total 2 txs – **36)** ☑ 7100 Szekszárd, Wesselényi u. 16. ☎+36 74 444444 **W:** radioantritt. hu **E:** szerk@radioantritt.hu

**Kisközösségi rádió (lowpower community radio)**
Non-profit low-power stns (0.1–10W) were granted licences in cities and country villages. In recent years the number of these stns has drastically decreased, mainly for financial reasons. Currently only 17 such stns are operating in the whole country. See **W:** frekvencia.hu/fmlist-hng.htm
**DAB+:** Budapest – Hármashatár-hegy, Budapest – Széchenyi-hegy, Budapest – Száva utca, MR1-3, Dankó Rádió, Magyar Katolikus R., InfoRádió, Klubrádió, Lánchíd R. on 222.064 MHz (ch 11D) 3 x 250W

**L.T:** UTC — **Pop:** 330,000 — **Pr.L:** Icelandic — **E.C:** 230V/50Hz — **ITU:** ISL

**FJÖLMIĐLANEFND (The Media Commission)**
☑ Borgartúni 21, 105 Reykjavík ☎ +354 4150415 🖶 +354 4150410 **E:** postur@fjolmidlanefnd.is **W:** fjolmidlanefnd.is
**L.P:** Dir: Elfa Ýr Gylfadóttir

**RÚV (Pub)**
☑ Efstaleiti 1, 150 Reykjavík ☎ +354 5153000 **E:** frettir@ruv.is **W:** ruv.is **L.P:** DG: Magnús Geir Þórðarsson

| LW | kHz | kW | Prgr | MW | kHz | kW | Prgr |
|----|-----|-----|------|-----|-----|-----|------|
| Gufuskálar | 189 | 150 | 1/2* | Reykjavík | 666 | 1 | (°) |
| Eiðar | 207 | 75 | 1/2* | | | | |

*) Each tx has automatic fallback to Prgr 1 if time-shared feed is lost
°) Temporary test license (nonstop mx or relay Rás 1/2)

| FM (MHz) | 1 | 2 | 3 | kW |
|----------|-----|-----|-----|-----|
| Almannaskarð | 90.3 | 104.8 | - | 1 |
| Auðsholt | 91.3 | 95.3 | - | 2.5 |
| Gagnheiði | 99.8 | 87.7 | - | 5 |
| Girðisholt | 92.9 | | - | 3.5 |
| Háfell | 93.8 | 98.7 | - | 14/34 |
| Hegranes | 90.6 | 98.8 | - | 3.1/5 |
| Hnjúkar | 89.1 | 95.5 | - | 6/6.2 |
| Reykjavík | 93.5 | 90.1 | 87.7 | 3.4/2/2 |
| Skálafell | 92.4 | 99.9 | - | 24 |
| Stykkishólmur | 88.0 | 96.3 | - | 3/3.5 |
| Vaðlaheiði | 91.6 | 96.5 | - | 9.3 |
| Vestmannaeyar | 97.1 | 88.1 | - | 17/24 |
| Viðarfjall | 88.1 | 96.1 | - | 3.3 |

+ sites with only txs below 1kW.
**D.Prgr: Prgr 1 (Rás 1):** 24h. – **Prgr 2 (Rás 2):** 24h. – **Prgr 3 (Rondó):** 24h. **On LW:** 0000-0625 Rás 1, 0625-0900 (MF) Rás 1+2 (joint tr), 0625-0900 (SS) Rás 1, 0900-1000 Rás 2, 1000-1400 (Tue/Wed) Rás 1, 1000-1017 (exc. Tue/Wed) Rás 1, 1017-1220 (exc. Tue/Wed) Rás 2, 1220-1400 (Mon/Thu/Fri) Rás 1, 1220-1300 (Sat/Sun) Rás 1, 1400 (Sat/Sun 1300)-1800 Rás 2, 1800-1900 Rás 1, 1900-2200 Rás 2, 2200-2220 Rás 1, 2220-2400 Rás 2.

**OTHER STATIONS**

| FM | MHz | kW | Location | Station |
|----|-----|-----|----------|---------|
| 5) | 88.5 | 1 | Reykjavík | XA Radió |
| 2) | 89.7 | 1 | Hafell | K100 |
| 6) | 89.9 | 1 | Hrafnafell | Áttan FM |
| 6) | 89.9 | 1.6 | Selfoss | Áttan FM |
| 1E) | 90.4 | 2 | Vestmannaeyjar | X997 |
| 1C) | 90.9 | 2 | Úlfarsfell | GullBylgjan |
| 6) | 91.3 | 1 | Hegranes | Áttan FM |
| 1A) | 92.7 | 2 | Vaðlaheiði | Bylgjan |
| 4) | 93.3 | 1 | Vestmannaeyjar | Suðurland FM |
| 1A) | 94.5 | 2 | Háfell | Bylgjan |
| 1B) | 94.7 | 1 | Egilsstaðir | FM957 |
| 1B) | 95.1 | 1 | Hegranes | FM957 |
| 1B) | 95.7 | 2 | Reykjavík | FM957 |
| 4) | 96.3 | 1 | Selfoss | Suðurland FM |
| 1D) | 96.7 | 2 | Úlfarsfell | LéttBylgjan |
| 4) | 97.3 | 1 | Reykjavík | Suðurland FM |

| FM | MHz | kW | Location | Station |
|----|-----|-----|----------|---------|
| 1E) | 97.7 | 2 | Úlfarsfell | X997 |
| 1A) | 97.9 | 1 | Hegranes | Bylgjan |
| 1A) | 98.9 | 2 | Reykjavík | Bylgjan |
| 1A) | 98.9 | 1 | Hnjúkar | Bylgjan |
| 2) | 100.5 | 1 | Bláfjöll | K100 |
| 1A) | 100.9 | 2 | Vestmannaeyjar | Bylgjan |
| 1B) | 101.7 | 2 | Vestmannaeyjar | FM957 |
| 2) | 101.7 | 1 | Þrándur | K100 |
| 7) | 102.1 | 1 | Reykjavík | Útvarp Saga |
| 1B) | 102.5 | 1 | Skáneyjarbunga | FM957 |
| 3) | 102.9 | 2.5 | Reykjavík | Lindin |
| 1B) | 103.2 | 1 | Selfoss | FM957 |
| 1A) | 103.3 | 1 | Skáneyjarbunga | Bylgjan |
| A) | 103.5 | 2 | Úlfarsfell | BBCWS relay |
| 1F) | 103.9 | 1 | Úlfarsfell | FMX Klassík |
| 1A) | 104.5 | 2 | Grenjadalsfell | Bylgjan |
| 2) | 104.9 | 1 | Strútur | K100 |

+ txs below 1kW.

**Addresses & other information:**
**1A-1F)** Suðurlandsbraut 8, 108 Reykjavík – **2)** Hádegismóum 2, 101 Reykjavík – **3)** Krókhálsi 4a, 110 Reykjavík – **4)** Hrísmýri 6, 800 Selfoss – **5)** Brávallagötu 18, 101 Reykjavík. Partly in English. – **6)** Víkurhvarf 2, 203 Kópavogur – **7)** Þverholti 14, 105 Reykjavík – **A)** Rel. BBCWS (UK)

## INDIA

**L.T**: UTC +5½h — **Pop**: 1.28 billion — **Pr.L**: Assamese, Bangla, Bodo, Dogri, English, Gujarati, Hindi, Kannada, Kashmiri, Maithili, Marathi, Malayalam, Nepali, Odia, Punjabi, Santhali, Sindhi, Tamil, Telugu & Urdu — **E.C**: 50Hz 230V — **ITU**: IND

### MINISTRY OF INFORMATION & BROADCASTING
Main Secretariat: ✉ A-Wing, Shastri Bhawan, New Delhi-110001 **W:** mib.nic.in **I.P:** Minister for Info. & Broadcasting: Col. Rajyavardhan Singh Rathore. Minister of State for Information & Broadcasting: [position vacant]

### PRASAR BHARATI (BROADCASTING CORPORATION OF INDIA) (Public Corporation)
✉ Prasar Bharati House, Copernicus Marg, New Delhi-110001 ☎ +91 11 23118400 **L.P:** Chairman: [position vacant] ☎ +91 11 23118801/23118802 **E:** chairman@prasarbharati.gov.in **W:** prasarbharati.gov.in CEO: Shashi S. Vempati ☎ +91 11 23118803/23118804 **E:** ceo@prasarbharati.gov.in

### AKASHVANI – ALL INDIA RADIO
Administration/Engineering: ✉ Directorate General, All India Radio, Akashvani Bhavan, Parliament Street, New Delhi-110001
☎ +91 11 23421006, 23715413 🖷 +91 11 23711956
**W:** allindiaradio.gov.in
**L.P:** DG: Fayyaz Sheheryar ☎ +91 11 23421300 🖷 91 11 23421956 **E:** dgair@prasarbharati.gov.in Eng. in Chief: C.B.S.Maurya ☎ +91 11 23421058 🖷 +91 11 23421459 **E:** einc@prasarbharati.gov.in
**Spectrum Management & Synergy:** Room No.204, All India Radio, Akashvani Bhavan, Parliament Street, New Delhi-110001 ☎ +91 11 23421062, 23421145 **E:** spectrum-manager@prasarbharati.gov.in
**Programming:** ✉ New Broadcasting House, 27 Mahadev Road, New Delhi-110 001 ☎ +91 (11) 23421218
✉ Akashvani Bhavan, Parliament Street, New Delhi-110001 ☎ +91 11 23715411
**News Services Division:** ✉ New Broadcasting House, 27 Mahadev Road, New Delhi-110 001 Newsroom ☎ +91 11 23421100 🖷 +91 11 23421219 **E:** nbhnews@prasarbharati.gov.in **W:** newsonair.nic.in **L.P.** Dir.Gen. (News): Sitanshu Kar ☎ +91 11 23421218 **E:** dgn.nsd@gmail.com News on phone: English ☎ +91 11 1259, Hindi +91 11 1258
**Entertainment Channel:** (Vividh Bharati): All India Radio, ✉ Gorai Road, Borivli West, Mumbai-400 091, Maharashtra ☎ +91 22 28692698 **E:** vbsmumbai@gmail.com **W:** vividhbharti.org
**National Channel:** ✉ All India Radio, Todapur, New Delhi 110012 ☎ +91 11 25843207 **E:** delhi.nationalchannel@prasarbharati.gov.in
**Research & Development:** ✉ Office of the Addl. Director General, R & D, All India Radio, 14-B, Indra Prashta Estate, Ring Road, New Delhi-110002 ☎ +91 11 23379329, 23379255, **E:** cerdairdd@gmail.com
**Monitoring:** ✉ International Monitoring Stn., All India Radio, Dr. K.S. Krishnan Rd, Todapur, New Delhi-110012 ☎ +91 11 25842939 **E:** delhi.todapur@prasarbharati.gov.in ✉ Central Monitoring Stn, All India Radio, Ayanagar, New Delhi-110047 **E:** delhi.ayanagarcms@prasarbharati.gov.in
**Audience Research:** ✉ Audience Research Unit, AIR, Akashwani Bhavan, Parliament Street, New Delhi 110001 ☎ +91 11 23421022
**Live streaming: W:** allindiaradio.gov.in

**Regional Headquarters:** (Office of the Additional Director General)
**North Zone:** AIR, Jamnagar House, Shahjahan Road, New Delhi-110011 ☎ +91 11 23382519
**East Zone:** AIR, 4th Floor, Akashvani Bhawan, Eden Garden, Kolkata-700001 ☎ +91 33 22480158
**North-East Zone:** AIR, Doordarshan Complex, KG Baruah Road, P.O. Zoo Road, Guwahati – 781024, Assam ☎ +91 361 2200326
**West Zone:** AIR, 101 M.K.Road, Mumbai-400020, Maharashtra ☎ +91 22 22014287
**South Zone:** AIR, Swami Sivanada Salai, Chepauk, Chennai-600005 ☎ +91 44 25383253
**NB:** Thiruvananthapuram is given in all cases as Trivandrum.

**MW:** c) Vividh Bharati, e) ext.sce., n) national channel, r) relay stn

| kHz | Station | kW | reg | kHz | Station | kW | reg |
|-----|---------|-----|-----|-----|---------|-----|-----|
| 531 | Jodhpur A | 300 | N | 1125 | Tezpur | 20 | NE |
| 540 | Aizawl | 20 | NE | 1125 | Udaipur | 20 | N |
| 549 | Ranchi A | 100 | E | 1134 † | Chinsurah | 1000 | E |
| 558 | Mumbai B | 100 | W | 1143 | Ratnagiri | 20 | W |
| 567 | Dibrugarh | 300 | NE | 1143 | Rohtak | 20 | N |
| 576 | Alappuzha | 200 | S, r | 1152 | Kavaratti | 10 | S |
| 585 | Nagpur A | 300 | W | 1161 | Trivandrum | 20 | S |
| 594 | Chinsurah | 1000 | E, e | 1179 | Rewa | 20 | W |
| 603 | Ajmer | 200 | N, r | 1188 | Mumbai C | 50 | W,c |
| 612 | Bengaluru A | 200 | S | 1197 | Tirunelveli | 20 | S |
| 621 | Patna A | 100 | E | 1206 | Bhawanipatna | 200 | E |
| 630 | Thrissur | 100 | S | 1215 | New Delhi | 20 | N, n |
| 639 | Kohima | 100 | NE | 1215 | Pudducherri | 20 | S |
| 648 | Indore A | 200 | W | 1224 | Srinagar C | 10 | N |
| 657 | Kolkata A | 200 | E | 1233 | Tura | 20 | NE |
| 666 | New Delhi B | 100 | N | 1242 | Varanasi | 100 | N |
| 675 | Bhadravathi | 20 | S | 1251 | Sangli | 20 | W |
| 675 | Chhatarpur | 20 | W | 1260 | Ambikapur | 20 | W |
| 675 | Itanagar | 100 | NE | 1269 | Agartala | 20 | NE |
| 684 | Kozhikode A | 100 | S | 1269 | Madurai | 20 | S |
| 684 | Port Blair | 100 | S | 1287 | Panaji A | 100 | W |
| 684 | Kargil A | 200 | N | 1296 | Darbhanga | 20 | E |
| 702 | Jalandhar A | 200 | N, e | 1305 | Parbhani | 20 | W |
| 711 | Siliguri | 200 | E | 1314 | Bhuj | 20 | W |
| 720 | Chennai A | 100 | S | 1323 | Kolkata C | 20 | E, c |
| 729 | Guwahati A | 100 | NE | 1332 | Tezu | 10 | NE |
| 747 | Hyderabad A | 200 | S | 1341 | Kohima | 1 | NE |
| 747 | Lucknow A | 300 | N | 1350 | Kupwara | 20 | N, r |
| 756 | Jagdalpur | 100 | W | 1377 | Hyderabad B | 20 | S |
| 765 | Dharwad A | 200 | S | 1386 | Gwalior | 20 | W |
| 774 | Shimla | 100 | N | 1395 | Bikaner | 20 | N |
| 792 | Pune A | 100 | W | 1404 | Gangtok | 20 | NE |
| 801 | Jabalpur | 200 | W | 1413 | Kota | 20 | N |
| 810 | Rajkot A | 300 | W | 1458 | Barmer | 20 | N |
| 819 | New Delhi A | 200 | N | 1458 | Bhagalpur | 20 | E |
| 828 | Panaji B | 20 | W, c | 1467 | Jeypore | 100 | E |
| 828 | Silchar | 20 | NE | 1485 | Ahwa | 1 | W |
| 837 | Vijayawada A | 100 | S | 1485 | Chamoli | 1 | N |
| 846 | Ahmedabad A | 200 | W | 1485 | Drass | 1 | N, cr |
| 864 | Shillong | 100 | NE | 1485 | Dunagrpur | 1 | N |
| 873 | Jalandhar B | 300 | N | 1485 | Joranda | 1 | E |
| 882 | Imphal | 300 | NE | 1485 | Khaltsi | 1 | N, cr |
| 891 | Rampur | 20 | N | 1485 | Nongstoin | 1 | NE |
| 900 | Kadapa | 100 | S | 1485 | Nyoma | 1 | N, cr |
| 909 | Gorakhpur | 100 | N | 1485 | Pithoragarh | 1 | N, r |
| 918 | Suratgarh | 300 | N | 1485 | Soro | 1 | E, r |
| 927 | Visakhapatnam | 100 | S | 1512 | Kokrajhar | 20 | NE |
| 936 | Tiruchirapalli A | 100 | S | 1521 | Tawang | 20 | NE |
| 945 | Sambalpur | 100 | E | 1530 | Agra | 20 | N |
| 954 | Najibabad | 200 | N | 1566 | Nagpur | 1000 | W, nr |
| 963 | Jalgaon | 20 | W | 1584 | Dharmanagar | 1 | NE |
| 972 | Cuttack A | 300 | E | 1584 | Diphu | 1 | NE |
| 981 | Raipur | 100 | W | 1584 | Himmat Nagar | 1 | W |
| 990 | Jammu A | 300 | N | 1584 | Kalpa | 1 | N, r |
| 999 | Almora | 1 | N | 1584 | Kargil B | 1 | N |
| 999 | Coimbatore | 20 | S | 1584 | Keonjhar | 1 | E |
| 1008 | Kolkata B | 100 | E | 1584 | Kota | 1 | N |
| 1017 | Chennai B | 100 | S | 1584 | Mon | 1 | NE |
| 1026 | Prayagraj A | 20 | N | 1584 | Padam | 1 | N,cr |
| 1035 | Guwahati B | 20 | NE | 1593 | Bhopal A | 10 | W |
| 1044 | Mumbai A | 100 | W | 1602 | Diskit | 1 | N cr |
| 1053 | Leh | 20 | N | 1602 | Pauri | 1 | N |
| 1053 | Tuticorin | 200 | S, e | 1602 | Saiha | 1 | NE |
| 1062 | Passighat | 100 | NE | 1602 | Tiesuru | 1 | N,cr |
| 1071 | Rajkot | 1000 | W, e | 1602 | Tuensang | 1 | NE |
| 1089 | Udipi | 20 | S, r | 1602 | Udhagamandalam | 1 | S |
| 1089 | Naushera | 20 | N, r | 1602 | Uttarkashi | 1 | N, r |
| 1107 | Kalaburgi | 20 | S | 1602 | William Nagar | 1 | NE |
| 1116 | Srinagar A | 300 | N | 1602 | Ziro | 1 | NE |

## DRM frequencies on MW:

| kHz | Station | kW | reg | kHz | Station | kW | reg |
|---|---|---|---|---|---|---|---|
| 558 | Ranchi | 100 | E | 846 | Vijayawada * | 100 | S |
| 567 | Mumbai B * | 100 | W | 855 | Ahmedabad * | 200 | W |
| 576 | Dibrugarh | 300 | NE | 882 | Jalandhar | 300 | N |
| 603 | Chinsurah | 1000 | E | 927 | Suratgarh | 300 | N |
| 612 | Ajmer * | 200 | N | 945 | Tiruchirapalli * | 100 | S |
| 621 | Bengaluru * | 200 | S | 999 | Jammu ** | 300 | N |
| 630 | Patna * | 200 | E | 1017 | Kolkata B * | 100 | E |
| 666 | Kolkata A * | 200 | E | 1044 | Guwahati B * | 20 | NE |
| 684 | Itanagar* | 200 | NE | 1053 | Mumbai A * | 100 | W |
| 720 | Siliguri* | 200 | E | 1071 | Passighat | 100 | NE |
| 729 | Chennai A * | 200 | S | 1080 | Rajkot | 1000 | W |
| 756 | Lucknow* | 300 | N | 1251 | Varanasi * | 100 | N |
| 774 | Dharwad* | 200 | S | 1296 | Panaji * | 100 | W |
| 783 | Chennai # | 20 | S | 1368 | New Delhi # | 20 | N |
| 801 | Pune * | 100 | W | 1404 | Bikaner* | 20 | N |
| 810 | Jabalpur* | 200 | W | 1467 | Barmer* | 20 | N |
| 819 | Rajkot* | 300 | W | 1530 | Tawang | 20 | NE |
| 828 | New Delhi A* | 200 | N | | | | |

**NB:** Full tx kW given but most txs use far fewer kW in DRM mode. DRM Schedule: Operates in Simulcast mode. # Pure DRM. * Operates on their respective analogue frequency (Digital frequency-9KHz) in pure DRM Mode during 1000-1100 hrs UTC every day except Sunday carrying 2 ch. ** Operates on 990 KHz (999-9KHz) in pure DRM Mode during 0500-0600 UTC every day except Sunday carrying 2 ch.

**D.Prgr:** Varies from stn to stn. Some stns have 1 or 2 transmissions while others have 3. Extended coverage during sports or special events. **National Ch.:** 1325-0043 on 1215, 1566, 9380 kHz

**F.PI: Replacement: 1kW MW to 1kW FM:** Almora, Joranda, Kalpa, Soro; **1 kW MW to 10kW FM:** Udhagamangalam

**Addresses of MW stations (See also SW stn addresses):**

**1000kW MW stations:**

**1)** AIR, Super Power Transmitter, Chinsurah-712102, Bangla – **2)** AIR, National Channel, Seminary Hills, Nagpur-440006, Maharashtra – **3)** AIR, Super Power Transmitter, Radio Colony, Jamnagar Road, Rajkot -360006, Gujarat

**Other MW stations:**

**Agarthala**-799001, Tripura – Vivbhav Nagar, **Agra**-282001, Uttar Pradesh – Ashram Rd, Navarangpura, **Ahmedabad**-380009, Gujarat – **Ahwa**-394710, Dangs Dist., Gujarat – 21/10 Vaishali Nagar, **Ajmer**-305001, Rajasthan – Pathirapally, **Alappuzha**-688521, Kerala – **Almora**-263601, Kumaon Dist., Uttarakhand – Kumar Palace, **Ambikapur**-497001, Surguja Dist., Chhatisgarh –Raj Bhavan Rd, **Bengaluru**-560001, Karnataka – Laxmi Nagar, **Barmer**-344001, Rajasthan – J.P.S.Colony, Paper Tower, **Bhadravati**-577302, Karnataka – Port Campus, **Bhagalpur**-812001, Bihar – **Bhawanipatna**-766001, Nektiguda, Kalahandi Dist., Odisha – **Bhuj**-370001, Kutch Dist., Gujarat – **Bikaner**-334001, Rajasthan – **Chamoli**-246424, Gopeshwar, Uttarakhand – 7, Kamarajar Salai, Mylapore, **Chennai**-600004, Tamilnadu – **Chhatarpur**-471001, Madhya Pradesh – Trichy Rd, Ramanathapuram, **Coimbatore**-641045, Tamilnadu – Madhupur House, Bakshi Bazar, Cantonment Rd, **Cuttack**-753001, Odisha – **Darbhanga**-846004, Bihar – **Dharmanagar**-799250, Tripura – Saptapur, **Dharwad**-580008, Karnataka – Malakhubasa, **Dibrugarh**-786001, Assam – **Diphu**-782460, Kabri Anglong Dist., Assam – **Diskit**-194401, Leh Dist., Jammu & Kashmir – **Drass**-194102, Kargil, Jammu & Kashmir – Dungarpur-314001, Rajasthan –Town Hall, **Gorakhpur**-273001, Uttar Pradesh – Chandmari, **Guwahati**-781003 Assam – Gandhi Rd, **Gwalior**-474002, Madhya Pradesh – **Himmat Nagar** – 383001, Gujarat – Malwa House, Residency Area, **Indore**-452001, Madhya Pradesh – 373 Napier Town, **Jabalpur**-482001, Madhya Pradesh – Collectorate Rd, **Jagdalpur**-494 001, Bastar Dist., Chhattisgarh – **Jalandhar**-144001, Punjab – Jilhapet, **Jalgaon**-425001, Maharashtra – R. Kashmir, Begum Haveli, Old Palace Road, **Jammu**-180001, Jammu & Kashmir — Paoata 'C' Road, **Jodhpur**-342006, Rajasthan – **Joranda**-759014, Dhenkanal Dist., Odisha – Cooperative Colony, **Kadapa**-516001, YSR Dist., Andhra Pradesh –Aiwan-e-Shahi, Municipal Garden, **Kalaburgi** -585103, Karnataka – **Kalpa**-172108, Kinnaur Dist., Himachal Pradesh – **Kargil**-194103, Jammu & Kashmir – **Kavaratti**-682555, Lakshadeep – **Khaltsi**-194106, Leh, Jammu & Kashmir – **Kokrajhar**-783370, Assam – Jawahar Rd, **Kota**-324001, Rajasthan – Beach Rd, **Kozhikode**-673001, Kerala – **Kupwara** – 193222, Jammu & Kashmir – Lady Doak College Rd, Chokkikulam, **Madurai**-625002, Tamilnadu – **Mon**-798621, Nagaland – Broadcasting House, Backbay Reclamation, Mumbai-400020, Maharashtra – Civil Lines, Palam Rd, **Nagpur**-440001, Maharashtra – Kotwali Rd, **Najibabad**-246763, Bijnor Dist., Uttar Pradesh – **Naushera**–193125, Jammu & Kashmir – **Nongstoin**-793119, West Khasi Hills, Meghalaya – **Nyoma**-194101, Leh Dist, Jammu & Kashmir – **Obra**-231219, Uttar Pradesh – **Padam**, Jammu & Kashmir

- Altinho, **Panaji**-403001, Goa – Jamakar Colony, Nawa Mondha, **Parbhani**-431401, Maharashtra – **Pasighat**-791102, East Siang Dist., Arunachal Pradesh – Frazer Road, Chhaju Bagh, **Patna**-800001, Bihar – **Pauri**-246001, Uttarakhand – **Pithorgarh**-262501, Uttarakhand – Z-9 Dayanand Marg, **Prayagraj** (Allahabad)-211001, Uttar Pradesh – Indira Nagar, Gorimedu, **Puducherri**-605006 – University Rd, Shivaji Nagar, **Pune**-411005, Maharashtra – Sitaram Pandit Marg, **Rajkot**-360001, Gujarat – **Rampur**-244901, Uttar Pradesh – 6 Ratu Rd, **Ranchi**-834001, Jharkhand –Thiba Palace Rd, **Ratnagiri**-415612, Maharashtra – 6 Civil Lines, **Rewa**-486001, Madhya Pradesh – Subhash Rd, **Rohtak**-124001, Haryana – **Saiha**-796901, Chhimtuipui Dist., Mizoram – 3, Kuchery Rd, **Sambalpur**-768001, Odisha – Market Yard, Kolhapur Rd, **Sangli**-416416, Maharashtra – **Silchar**-788001, Cachar Dist., Assam – 2 Mile Sevoke Rd, **Siliguri**-734401, Darjeeling Dist., Bangla –**Soro**-756045 , Balasore Dist, Odisha – **Suratgarh**-335804, Sriganganagar Dist., Rajasthan – **Tawang**-790104, Arunachal Pradesh – **Tezpur**-784001, Sonitpur Dist., Assam – **Tezu**-792001, Lohit Dist., Arunachal Pradesh – Ramavarmapuram, **Thrissur**-680631, Kerala – **Tiesuru**, Jammu & Kashmir, 28-3 Promenade Rd, **Tiruchirapalli**-620001, Tamilnadu – Sarojini Park, Palayamkottai, **Tirunelveli**-627006, Tamilnadu – **Tuensang**-798612, Nagaland – Lower Chandmari, **Tura**-794001, Meghalaya – Millerpuram, Playamkottai Road, **Tuticorin**-628008, Tamilnadu – Chetak Circle, **Udhagamandalam**-643001, Nilgris, Tamilnadu – **Udaipur**-313001, Rajasthan – Brahmavar, **Udipi**-576213, Dakshina Kanara Dist., Karnataka – **Uttar Kashi**-249193, Uttarakhand –Mahmoorganj, **Varanasi**-221010, Uttar Pradesh – Bandar Rd, Punnammathota, **Vijayawada**-520010, Andhra Pradesh – Siripuram, **Visakhapatnam**-530003, Andhra Pradesh – **William Nagar**, Meghalaya – **Ziro**-791120, Lower Subansiri Dist., Arunachal Pradesh.

**Web addresses of AIR stns:** **Bengaluru:** airbengaluru.com **Chennai:** airchennai.org **Cuttack:** aircuttack.com, cbscuttack.com **Guwahati:** airguwahati.gov.in **Kolkata:** airkolkata.gov.in **Jodhpur:** allindiaradiojodhpur.co.in **Kota:** airkota.com **New Delhi (Khampur):** wix.com/hptkhampur/airkhampur **Panaji:** airpanaji.gov.in **Raipur:** airraipur.org **Shimla:** airshimla.com **Sambalpur:** airsambalpur.com **Siliguri:** airsiliguri.in **Thiruvanathapuram:** airtvm.com **Email:** ID of AIR stns is normally location followed by @prasarbharati. gov.in e.g.: hyderabad@prasarbharati.gov.in

## Regional Domestic SW stations:

| kHz | kW | Station | H. of tr. |
|---|---|---|---|
| 4760 | 10 | Leh | s0130/w0213-0430, 1130-1630 |
| 4760 | 4 | Port Blair | 2355-0300, 1030-1700(SS -1730) |
| 4800 | 50 | Hyderabad | 0020-0215, 1130-1744 |
| 4810 | 50 | Bhopal | 0025-0215 1130-1742 |
| 4835 | 10 | Gangtok | 0100-0500 1030-1700 |
| 4870# | 100 | Delhi (Kingsway) | 0230-0330 1430-1530 (R. Sadaye Kashmir) |
| 4895 | 50 | Kurseong | 0055-0430 1130-1700 |
| 4910 | 50 | Jaipur | 0025-0430, 1130-1741 |
| 4920 | 50 | Chennai | 0015-0245 1200-1739 |
| 4950† | 50 | Srinagar | s0030/w0100-0215, 1120-1740 (2145v-2245v during Ramadan) |
| 4970 | 50 | Shillong | 0025-0400 1056-1741 |
| 5010 | 50 | Trivandrum | 0020-0205 1130-1745 |
| 5040 | 50 | Jeypore | 0025-0436,0700-0915 1130-1741 |
| 5050† | 10 | Aizawl | 0025-0400 1130-1630 |
| 6000 | 10 | Leh | 0700(Sun 0630)-0930 |
| 6030† | 250 | Delhi | 0200-0230, 0230-0300, 1215-1430, 1430-1530 |
| 6085 | 10 | Gangtok | For special broadcasts in daytime |
| 6100 | 250 | Delhi (Khampur) | 0730-0800 (R. Sadaye Kashmir) |
| 6100 | 250 | Delhi (Khampur) | 0900-1200 |
| 6110† | 50 | Srinagar | 0225-1115 |
| 7230 | 50 | Kurseong | 0620-1030 |
| 7250# | 100 | Delhi (Kingsway) | 1130-1140 |
| 7270# | 100 | Chennai | 0130-0430 (FM Gold) |
| 7290 | 50 | Trivandrum | 0230-0930 (Sat , Sun 1030) |
| 7295† | 10 | Aizawl | 0700-1000 |
| 7315 | 50 | Shillong | 0656-0931 |
| 7325 | 50 | Jaipur | 0630-0930 |
| 7340# | 100 | Mumbai | 1130-1140 |
| 7380 | 50 | Chennai | 0300-0930 (Sun 1130) |
| 7390 | 4 | Port Blair | 0315-0400(SS -0500), 0700-0931(Sun -1000) |
| 7420 | 50 | Hyderabad | 0225-0932 (Sun 1030) |
| 7430 | 50 | Bhopal | 0225-0932 (Sun 1030) |
| 7555 | 100 | Delhi (Kingsway) | 1515-1600 |
| 9380 | 250 | Aligarh | 0100-0435 0830-1200 (Vividh Bharati), 1320-0043 (National Channel) |
| 9865 | 500 | Benguluru | 0025-0435, 0900-1200, 1245-1740 (V. Bharati) |

| kHz | kW | Station | H. of tr. |
|---|---|---|---|
| 9950 | 100 | Delhi (Kingsway) | 1130-1140 |
| 11620# | 250 | Delhi (Khampur) | 1130-1140 |

s = summer, w = winter, v = timing/frequency varies. † = irregular/off air, #= frequency also used by External Services at other times

**N in English** originating in New Delhi and relayed by most stns: 0035-0040, 0245-0300, 0630-0635, 0730-0735, 0830-0845, 0935-0940, 1030-1035, 1135-1140, 1230-1235, 1430-1435, 1530-1545, 1730-1735. Extended broadc. for special events, important Parliament sessions, sports and on January 26 (Republic Day) and August 15 (Independence Day).
**V.** by QSL-card. Reception Reports to: ✉ Dy. Director General (Spectrum Management & Synergy), All India Radio, Room No.204, Akashvani Bhavan, New Delhi-110001 ☎ 91-11-23421062, 23421145: Use form in: pbinfo.air.org.in/feedback/ **E:** spectrum-manager@prasarbharati.gov.in .Local stns also verify directly in many cases by letter or email. No return postage necessary.
**Addresses of SW stations** (R. rpts may be sent to the Stn Engineer): **1) Aizawl:** R. Tila, Tuikhuahtlang, Box 13, Aizawl-796001 ☎+91 389 2322415 **E:** aizawl@prasarbharati.gov.in – **2) Aligarh:** Anoopshahar Road, Aligarh-202001, Uttar Pradesh ☎+91 571 2700972 **E:** aligarh@prasarbharati.gov.in – **3) Bengaluru:** Super Power Transmitters, Yelahanka New Town, Bengaluru-560064, Karnataka ☎+91 80 27601149 **E:** sptairynk@rediffmail.com – **4) Bhopal:** Shyamla Hills, Bhopal-462002, Madhya Pradesh ☎+91 755 2660088 **E:** bhopal@prasarbharati.gov.in – **5) Chennai:** S.M.Nagar PO, Avadi, Chennai-600062, Tamilnadu. Tel. 91 44 26383204. **E:** Chennai.avadi@prasarbharati.gov.in **W:** airchennai.org – **6) Gangtok:** Old MLA Hostel, Gangtok-737101, Sikkim ☎+91 3592 202636 **E:** airgtk@rediffmail.com – **7) Hyderabad:** Rocklands, Saifabad, Hyderabad-500004, Telangana ☎+91 40 23234904. **E:** airhyderabad@rediffmail.com – **8) Jaipur:** 5 Park House, Mirza Ismail Road, Jaipur-302001, Rajasthan ☎ +91 141 2366263 **E:** jaipur@prasarbharati.gov.in – **9) Jeypore:**764005, Odisha ☎+91 6854 232524 **E:** airjeypore@gmail.com – **10) Kurseong:** Mehta Club Bldg, Kurseong-734203, Darjeeling Dist., Bangla ☎+91 354 2344350 **E:** kurseong@prasarbharati.gov.in – **11) Leh:** Leh-194101, Ladakh Dist., Jammu & Kashmir ☎+91 1982 252063 **E:** leh@prasarbharati.gov.in – **12) Mumbai:** Marve Road, Malwani, Malad West, Mumbai 400095, Maharashtra. ☎+91 22 28882867. **E:** hptairmalad@gmail.com—**13A) New Delhi:** High Power Transmitters, Khampur, New Delhi -110036 ☎+91 11 27831474 **E:** hptkhampur@gmail.com **W:** wix.com/hptkhampur/airkhampur – **13B)** High Power Transmitters, Kingsway, New Delhi-110009 ☎+91 11 27606661 **E:** delhi.kingsway@prasarbharati.gov.in – **14) Panaji:** Goa University PO, Panaji-403206 ☎+91 832 2459096 **E:** panaji.spt@prasarbharati.gov.in – **15) Port Blair:** Haddo Post, Dilanipur, Port Blair-744102, Andaman & Nicobar Islands ☎+91 3192 230682 **E:** airportblair@rediffmail.com – **16) Shillong:** North Eastern Service, Pomdngiem, Opposite GPO, Shillong-793001, Meghalaya ☎+91 364 2224443 **E:** shillong@prasarbharati.gov.in – **17) Srinagar:** R. Kashmir, Sherwani Rd, Srinagar-190001, Jammu & Kashmir ☎+91 194 2452100 **E:** rksrinagar_sge@rediffmail.com – **18) Thiruvananthapuram:** Bhakti Vilas, Vazuthacaud, Thiruvanathapuram-695014, Kerala ☎+91 471 2325009 **W:** airtvm.com **E:** se_airtvm@rediffmail.com

**FM Stations:** b ) FM Rainbow c) Vividh Bharati g) FM Gold r) relay stn + about 200 relay stns of 100W operating mostly on 100.1 MHz

| MHz | location | kW | reg | MHz | location | kW | reg |
|---|---|---|---|---|---|---|---|
| 93.9 | Vadodara | 10 | W,C | 100.3 | Jammu A | 3 | N |
| 96.7 | Amedabad | 10 | W,C | 100.3 | Karaikal | 10 | S |
| 100.1 | Ahmednagar | 10 | W | 100.3 | Mangaluru | 10 | S |
| 100.1 | Bengaluru | 1 | S | 100.4 | Bareilly | 6 | N |
| 100.1 | Chennai | 20 | S, g | 100.4 | Cuttack | 10 | E,C |
| 100.1 | Gorakhpur | 10 | N,C | 100.4 | Mandla | 1 | W |
| 100.1 | Keonjhar | 10 | E | 100.5 | Chhatarpur | 5 | W |
| 100.1 | Kolkata | 20 | E, g | 100.5 | Dehradun | 10 | N |
| 100.1 | Kothagudem | 6 | S | 100.5 | Dhule | 10 | W |
| 100.1 | Ludhiana | 10 | N, g | 100.5 | Hospete | 10 | S |
| 100.1 | Mumbai | 20 | W, g | 100.5 | Kodaikanal | 10 | S,B |
| 100.1 | New Delhi | 20 | N,g | 100.5 | Ranchi | 10 | E |
| 100.2 | Adilabad | 10 | S | 100.5 | Ukhrul | 1 | NE r |
| 100.2 | Ambikapur | 5 | W | 100.6 | Berhampur | 10 | E |
| 100.2 | Darjeeling | 10 | E | 100.6 | Jalandhar | 10 | N,C |
| 100.2 | Haflong | 10 | NE | 100.6 | Mysuru | 10 | S |
| 100.2 | Patiala | 6 | N | 100.6 | Nagpur | 10 | W,C |
| 100.2 | Shivpuri | 1 | W | 100.6 | Sangli | 1 | W, C |
| 100.3 | Prayagraj | 10 | N,C | 100.6 | Varanasi | 10 | N, C |
| 100.3 | Asansol | 10 | E, r | 100.7 | Aizawl | 6 | NE |
| 100.3 | Bhawanipatna | 5 | E | 100.7 | Churu | 6 | N |
| 100.3 | Bomdila | 1 | NE | 100.7 | Lucknow | 10 | N,B |
| 100.3 | Jaipur B | 10 | N,C | 100.7 | Poonch | 6 | N |

| MHz | location | kW | reg | MHz | location | kW | reg |
|---|---|---|---|---|---|---|---|
| 100.7 | Raigarh | 6 | W | 102.2 | Murshidabad | 6 | E |
| 100.7 | Rajgarh | 3 | W | 102.2 | Vijayawada | 10 | S,B |
| 100.8 | Faizlka | 20 | N, r | 102.3 | Chautan Hill | 20 | N r |
| 100.8 | Guwahati | 10 | NE,C | 102.3 | Chennai | 20 | S, C |
| 100.8 | Jamshedpur | 10 | E,C | 102.3 | Daman | 5 | W |
| 100.9 | Kasauli | 10 | N, r | 102.3 | Guna | 10 | W |
| 100.9 | Mokokchung | 5 | NE | 102.3 | Hissar | 10 | N |
| 100.9 | Port Blair | 10 | S,C | 102.3 | Karimnagar | 5 | S, r |
| 101.0 | Balurghat | 10 | E, r | 102.3 | Karwar | 5 | S |
| 101.0 | Bhaderwah | 5 | N | 102.3 | Kochi A | 5 | S |
| 101.0 | Nagercoil | 10 | S | 102.3 | Kurseong | 5 | E,B |
| 101.0 | Pune | 10 | W,C | 102.3 | Lakhimpur Kheri | 10 | N r |
| 101.0 | Sambalpur | 5 | E | 102.4 | Akola | 10 | W |
| 101.0 | Suryapet | 1 | S, r | 102.4 | Gairsain | 1 | N |
| 101.1 | Bathinda | 6 | N | 102.4 | Jamshedpur | 10 | E |
| 101.1 | Jowai | 5 | NE | 102.4 | Kurnool | 10 | S |
| 101.1 | Nanded | 10 | W | 102.4 | Pithorgarh | 1 | N |
| 101.1 | Surat | 10 | W,C | 102.4 | Rajkot | 10 | W,C |
| 101.1 | Thrissur | 1 | S | 102.4 | Rewa | 10 | N |
| 101.1 | Tuticorin | 1 | S | 102.4 | Tezpur | 1 | NE |
| 101.2 | Banda | 10 | N, r | 102.5 | Dharmapuri | 10 | S |
| 101.2 | Jaipur | 10 | W | 102.5 | Kullu | 5 | N, r |
| 101.2 | Khandwa | 10 | W | 102.5 | Longtherai | 5 | NE |
| 101.2 | Mahabubnagar | 10 | S, r | 102.5 | Patna | 10 | E,C |
| 101.2 | New Tehri | 1 | N,c | 102.5 | Ujjain | 5 | W,r |
| 101.2 | Nutan Bazar | 1 | NE r | 102.6 | Chitradurga | 6 | S |
| 101.3 | Aligarh | 10 | N,B,r | 102.6 | Goalpara | 1 | NE r |
| 101.3 | Balaghat | 10 | W | 102.6 | Naushera | 10 | N |
| 101.3 | Banswara | 10 | N | 102.6 | New Delhi | 20 | N,B |
| 101.3 | Bengaluru | 10 | S,B | 102.6 | Rourkela | 6 | E |
| 101.3 | Cuttack | 6 | E,B | 102.6 | Sagar | 10 | W |
| 101.3 | Dibrugarh | 1 | NE | 102.6 | Srinagar | 10 | N,C |
| 101.3 | Osmanabad | 10 | W | 102.6 | Tirunelveli | 10 | S, B |
| 101.4 | Chennai | 20 | S,B | 102.7 | Jalandhar | 10 | N,B |
| 101.4 | Churachandpur | 5 | NE | 102.7 | Kolhapur | 10 | W |
| 101.4 | Devikulam | 5 | S | 102.7 | Manjeri | 3 | S,B |
| 101.4 | Kurukshetra | 10 | N | 102.7 | Nagaon | 6 | NE |
| 101.4 | Nashik | 10 | W | 102.7 | Obra | 6 | N |
| 101.4 | Siliguri | 10 | E,C | 102.7 | Srikakulam | 1 | S, r |
| 101.5 | Amravati | 10 | W,C,r | 102.7 | Yavatmal | 10 | W |
| 101.5 | Bageshwar | 5 | N | 102.8 | Hyderabad | 10 | S,C |
| 101.5 | Kannur | 10 | S | 102.8 | Mumbai | 20 | W,C |
| 101.5 | Lumding | 1 | NE r | 102.8 | Puducherry | 10 | S,B |
| 101.5 | Markapur | 10 | S | 102.8 | Rae Bareilly | 10 | N |
| 101.5 | Ratnagiri | 1 | W | 102.8 | Saraipalli | 1 | W |
| 101.5 | Sawai Madhopur | 10 | N | 102.9 | Baripada | 5 | E |
| 101.6 | Agartala | 10 | NE,C | 102.9 | Beed | 6 | W |
| 101.6 | Indore | 10 | W,C | 102.9 | Bengaluru | 10 | S,C |
| 101.6 | Lucknow | 10 | N,C | 102.9 | Chittorgarh | 10 | N |
| 101.6 | Patna | 10 | E | 102.9 | Jabalpur | 10 | W,C |
| 101.6 | Ratnagiri | 10 | W, C | 102.9 | Rampur | 1 | N |
| 101.7 | Anantapur | 10 | S | 103.0 | Chandrapur | 6 | W |
| 101.7 | Aurangabad | 10 | W,C | 103.0 | Coimbatore | 10 | S,B |
| 101.7 | Chaibasa | 10 | E | 103.0 | Daltonganj | 6 | E |
| 101.7 | Junagadh | 10 | W | 103.0 | Dharwad | 10 | S,C |
| 101.7 | Tura | 5 | NE | 103.0 | Gangtok | 10 | NE |
| 101.7 | Udaipur | 10 | N,C | 103.0 | Jhansi | 10 | N |
| 101.8 | Vijapura | 10 | S | 103.0 | Kohima | 10 | NE |
| 101.8 | Hamirpur | 5 | N | 103.1 | Alwar | 10 | N |
| 101.8 | Jaisalmer | 10 | N | 103.1 | Amethi | 5 | N |
| 101.8 | Kolkata | 10 | E,C | 103.1 | Betul | 10 | W |
| 101.8* | Wokha | 1 | NE | 103.1 | Chandigarh | 10 | N,C |
| 101.9 | Bolangir | 10 | E | 103.1 | Itanagar | 10 | NE |
| 101.9 | Faizabad | 6 | N | 103.1 | Macherla | 3 | S |
| 101.9 | Hyderabad | 10 | S,B | 103.1 | Madikeri | 10 | S |
| 101.9 | Lungleh | 5 | NE | 103.1 | Patnitop | 10 | N |
| 101.9 | Rajouri | 10 | N, r | 103.1 | Satara | 5 | W |
| 101.9 | Trivandrum | 10 | S,C | 103.1 | Shanthi Nikethan | 3 | E |
| 102.0 | Kota | 1 | N | 103.2 | Bilaspur | 6 | W |
| 102.0 | Rairangpur | 10 | E | 103.2 | Jhalawar | 10 | N |
| 102.0 | Parbhani | 1 | W | 103.2 | Kailashahar | 6 | NE |
| 102.0 | Shahdol | 10 | W | 103.2 | Nizamabad | 10 | S |
| 102.0 | Visakhapatnam | 10 | S,B | 103.2 | Tirupati-I | 10 | S |
| 102.1 | Hazaribagh | 6 | E | 103.3 | Ajmer | 10 | N |
| 102.1 | Jalgaon | 10 | W | 103.3 | Bellary | 10 | S |
| 102.1 | Jodhpur | 10 | N,C | 103.3 | Dhubri | 6 | NE, r |
| 102.1 | Mussoorie | 10 | N,Br | 103.3 | Madurai | 10 | S |
| 102.1 | Phek | 1 | NE r | 103.3 | Ranchi | 10 | E,C |
| 102.1 | Raichur | 10 | S | 103.4 | Agra | 10 | N |
| 102.2 | Tiruchirapalli | 10 | S,B,c | 103.4 | Dharamsala | 10 | N |
| 102.2 | Chindwara | 10 | W | 103.4 | Jorhat | 10 | NE |
| 102.2 | Godhra | 10 | W | 103.4 | Puri | 6 | E |
| 102.2 | Hassan | 10 | S | 103.4 | Sasaram | 10 | E |
| 102.2 | Kathua | 10 | N | 103.4 | Solapur | 10 | W |
| 102.2 | Mathura | 10 | N | 103.4 | Vijayawada | 1 | S,C |
| 102.2 | Maunath Bhanjan | 10 | Nr | 103.5 | Bhadravathi | 10 | S |

| MHz | location | kW | reg | MHz | location | kW | reg |
|---|---|---|---|---|---|---|---|
| 103.5 | Bhopal | 10 | W,C | 103.7 | Bhuj | 5 | W |
| 103.5 | Imphal | 10 | NE | 103.7 | Kalaburgi | 10 | S,C |
| 103.5 | Kurseong | 10 | E | 103.7 | Kanpur | 10 | N, C |
| 103.5 | Mount Abu | 6 | N | 103.7 | Nagaur | 6 | N |
| 103.5 | Rohtak | 10 | N,C | 103.7 | Purnea | 10 | E |
| 103.5 | Srinagar | 10 | N | 103.7 | Shimla | 10 | N |
| 103.5 | Warangal | 10 | S | 104.5 | Jammu B | 10 | N,C |
| 103.6 | Amritsar | 20 | N | 105.4 | Panaji | 6 | W,B |
| 103.6 | Jeypore | 1 | E | 106.4 | New Delhi | 20 | N, C |
| 103.6 | Kozhikode | 10 | S,C | 106.6 | Bikaner | 10 | N |
| 103.6 | Kadapa | 1 | S | 107.0 | Kolkata | 20 | E,B |
| 103.6 | Oros | 5 | W | 107.1 | Mumbai | 20 | W,B |
| 103.6 | Shillong | 10 | NE,B | 107.2 | Kasauli | 10 | N,C,R |
| 103.7 | Belonia | 10 | NE | 107.5 | Tirupati II | 3 | S |

**NB:** AWR, FEBA, R. Atmeeya Yatra, TWR etc. also broadcasting via AIR stns on MW/SW/ FM.

**F.PI: 1kW:** Anini, Bomdila, Champai, Champawat, Changlang, Daporijo, Khonsa, Kolasib, Tamenglong, Tuipang, Udaipur (Tripura), Zunheboto. **5kW:** Alappuzha, Almora, Gwalior, Silchar **6kW:** Replacement of 6kW txs at many locations. **6kW to 10kW:** at many places **10kW:** Amethi, Bardhaman, Bathanaha, Bundi, Dhanbad, Etawah, Gadania, Haldwani, Himbotingla, Kakinada, Kanpur, Krishna Nagar, Ludhiana, Meerut, Muzzafarpur, Narkatiaganj, Nanpara, Nellore, Panaji, Sitamarhi, Sultanpur, Udhampur, Vijayawada. Replacement of 10kW txs at many locations.

**Addresses of FM stations** (see also SW & MW stn addresses)**:**
**Adilabad**-504002, Telangana − **Ahmednagar**-414001, Maharashtra − **Akola**-444001, Maharashtra − Scheme No 6, Mangal Vihar, **Alwar**-301001, Rajasthan − **Amritsar**-143001, Punjab − **Amethi**, Uttar Pradesh – Tapovan Gate, Camp, **Amravati**-444602, Maharashtra − Near Collectorate, **Anantapur**-515001, Andhra Pradesh − **Asansol**-713301, Burdwan Dist., Bangla − Jalna Rd, **Aurangabad**-431005, Maharashtra − **Aurangabad**-842101, Bihar− **Bageshwar**, 263642, Uttarakhand − **Balaghat**-481001, Madhya Pradesh−**Balurghat**-733101, Bangla − **Banda**-210001, Uttar Pradesh − **Banswara**-327001, Rajasthan − No 15, Lal Phatak, Badaun Road, **Bareilly**-243004, Uttar Pradesh − **Baripada**-757001, Mayurbhanj Dist., Odisha − Khandeshwari Road, **Beed**-431122, Maharashtra − **Bellary**-583101, Karnataka − **Belonia**-799155, Tripura − **Berhampur**-760001, Ganjam Dist., Odisha − **Betul**-460001, Madhya Pradesh − **Bathinda**-151005, Punjab − **Bhaderwah**-182222, Doda Dist., Jammu & Kashmir− Nutan Colony, **Bilaspur**-495001, Chhattisgarh − **Bolangir**-767001, Odisha − Tungri Maidan, **Chaibasa**-833201, Singhbhum Dist., Jharkhand − **Chandrapur**-442401, Maharashtra − Sector-19B, **Chandigarh**-160019 − **Cherrapunji**-793108, East Khasi Hills, Meghalaya − **Chindwara**-480001, Madhya Pradesh − **Chitradurga**-577501, Karnataka − Sector 4, Gandhi Nagar, **Chittorgarh**-312001, Rajasthan − **Churu**-331001, Rajasthan − **Churachandpur**-795128, Manipur − **Daltonganj**-822101, Jharkhand − Opp. Varkunt, Mota Fliya, **Daman**-396210, Daman & Diu − **Darjeeling**-734101, Bangla − **Dehradun** 248001, Uttarakhand − **Devikulam**-685613, Idukki Dist., Kerala − **Dharmapuri**-636701, Tamilnadu − **Dharmasala**-176215, Kangra Dist., Himachal Pradesh − **Dhubri**-783301, Assam − **Dhule**-424001, Maharashtra − Begumganj Garahiya, **Faizabad**-224001, Uttar Pradesh − **Faizlka**-152123, Firozpur Dist., Punjab − **Gairsain**-246248, Chamoli Dist, Utarakhand − **Goalpara**-783101, Assam − **Godhra**-389001, Gujarat − **Guna**-473001, Madhya Pradesh − **Haflong**-788819, Assam − **Hamirpur**-177001, Himachal Pradesh − Salagame Road, **Hassan**-573201, Karnataka − Jail Road, **Hazaribagh**-825301, Jharkhand − **Hissar**-125001, Haryana − **Hospete**-583201, Karnataka − Vyas Colony, **Jaisalmer**-345001, Rajasthan − Adityapur, Gamharia Rd, **Jamshedpur**-831013, Jharkhand −Jungle Road, **Jhalawar**-326001, Rajasthan − Kanpur Road, **Jhansi**-284128, Uttar Pradesh − **Jorhat**-785001, Assam − **Jowai**-793150, Jaintia Hills, Meghalaya − **Junagadh**, Gujarat − **Kailashahar**-799277, Tripura − **Kannur**-670001, Kerala − Radio Avenue, Nehru Ngr., **Karaikal**-609606, Puducherri − **Kanpur**-208001, Uttar Pradesh − **Karimnagar**-505001, Telangana − **Karwar**-581301, Karnataka − **Kasauli**-173204, Solan Dist., Himachal Pradesh − **Kathua**-184104, Jammu & Kashmir − **Keonjhar**-758001, Odisha − **Khandwa**-450001, Nimar Dist., Madhya Pradesh − BMC PO, **Kochi**-682021, Ernakulam Dist., Kerala − Anandagiri, **Kodaikanal**-624101, Tamilnadu − Sardar Cly, Taravai Park, **Kolhapur**-416003, Maharashtra − Ramavaram, **Kothagudem**-507118, Telangana − **Kulu**-175101, Himachal Pradesh − Bellary Road, **Kurnool**-518003, Andhra Pradesh − **Kurushetra**-132118, Haryana − **Lakhimpur Kheri**-262701, Uttar Pradesh − **Longtherai**-799275, Dhalai Dist, Tripura − **Ludhiana**-141001, Punjab − **Lumding**-782447, Nagaon Dist, Assam − **Lungleh**-796701, Mizoram − **Macherla**-522426, Guntur Dist, Andhra Pradesh − **Madikeri**-571201, Kodagu Dist., Karnataka − **Mahabubnagar**-509001, Telangana −

Kadri Hills, **Mangaluru**-575004, Dakshin Kanara Dist., Karnataka − **Manjeri**-676121, Kerala − **Mandla**-481661, Madhya Pradesh − **Markapur**-523316, Prakasam Dist., Andhra Pradesh − Vrindavan Rd, Gayatri Tapobhumi, **Mathura**-281003, Uttar Pradesh − **Maunath Bhanjan**-275101, Mau Dist. Uttar Pradesh − **Mokokchung**-798601, Nagaland − **Mount Abu**-307501, Sirohi Dist., Rajasthan − **Murshidabad**-742101, Bangla − **Mussoorie**-248179, Dehradun Dist., Uttarakhand − Yadavagiri, **Mysuru**-570020, Karnataka − **Nagaon**-782002, Assam − Basni Rd, **Nagaur**-341001, Rajasthan − Konam, **Nagercoil**-629004, Kanya Kumari Dist., Tamilnadu − Vasrania, **Nanded**-431601, Maharashtra − **Nashik**-422001, Maharashtra − **New Tehri**-249001, Tehri Garhwal Dist, Utarakhand − **Nizamabad**-503012, Telangana − **Nutan Bazar**-788115, Cachar Dist, Assam − Tambri Vibhag, **Oros**-416812, Sindhudurg Dist, Maharashtra − **Osmanabad**-413501, Maharashtra − Phase-I, Urban Estate, Rajpura Rd, **Patiala**-147002, Punjab − Patnitop-182142, Jammu & Kashmir − **Phek**-797108, Nagaland − **Poonch**-185101, Jammu & Kashmir − **Puri**-751001, Odisha − **Purnea**-854302, Bihar − **Rae Bareilly**-229001, Uttar Pradesh − **Raichur**-584101, Karnataka − Chote Atarmude, **Raigarh**-496001, Chhattisgarh − Kamla Nehru Marg, Civil Lines, **Raipur**-492001, Chhattisgarh − **Rairangpur**-757043, Mayurbhanj Dist., Odisha − **Rajgarh**-465661, Madhya Pradesh − **Rajouri**-185131, Jammu & Kashmir − **Rourkela**-769001, Odisha − **Sagar**-470001, Madhya Pradesh − **Saraipalli**-493558, Raipur, Chhattisgarh − **Sasaram**-821115, Rohtas Dist., Bihar − **Satara**-415001, Maharashtra − Pali Road, **Shahdol**-484001, Madhya Pradesh − **Shanthi Nikethan**, Bangla − Physical College, **Shivpuri**-473551, Madhya Pradesh − **Solapur**-413006, Maharashtra − **Srikakulam**-532001, Andhra Pradesh − **Surat**-395001, Gujarat − **Suryapet**-508213, Telangana − **Swai Madhopur**-322001, Rajasthan − **Tirupati**-517501, Andhra Pradesh − **Ujjain**-456001, Madhya Pradesh − **Ukhrul**-795142, Manipur − Makarpura Rd, **Vadadora**-390009, Gujarat −**Vijapura**-586101, Karnataka−**Warangal**-506002, Telangana − **Yavatmal**-445001, Maharashtra.

**NB:** Bijapur is now **Vijapura**, Gulbargais now **Kalaburgi**, Hospet is now **Hospete**, Mangalore is now **Mangaluru**

**EXTERNAL SERVICES: All India Radio**
see International Broadcasting section

**Private FM Stations:**

| Location | MHz | Station | Location | MHz | Station |
|---|---|---|---|---|---|
| Agartala | 92.7 | Big FM | Aurangabad | 93.5 | Red FM |
| Agartala | 95.0 | Red FM | Aurangabad | 94.3 | My FM |
| Agra | 91.9 | R. City | Aurangabad | 98.3 | R. Mirchi |
| Agra | 92.7 | Big FM | Bareilly | 91.9 | R. City |
| Agra | 93.7 | Fever FM | Bareilly | 92.7 | Big FM |
| Agra | 94.5 | FM Tadka | Bareilly | 94.3 | Fever FM |
| Ahmedabad | 91.1 | R. City | Bengaluru | 91.1 | R. City |
| Ahmedabad | 93.5 | Red FM | Bengaluru | 91.9 | R. Indigo |
| Ahmedabad | 94.3 | My FM | Bengaluru | 92.7 | Big FM |
| Ahmedabad | 98.3 | R.Mirchi | Bengaluru | 93.5 | Red FM |
| Ahmedabad | 95.0 | R. One | Bengaluru | 94.3 | R. One |
| Ahmedabad | 104.0 | Mirchi Love | Bengaluru | 95.0 | R. Mirchi |
| Ahmednagar | 91.1 | R. City | Bengaluru | 98.3 | R. Mirchi |
| Ahmednagar | 92.7 | Big FM | Bengaluru | 104.0 | Fever FM |
| Ahmednagar | 104.0 | My FM | Bhaderwah | 94.3 | Top FM |
| Ahmednagar | 106.4 | R.Dhamaal | Bharuch | 92.3 | R.Mirchi |
| Aizawl | 92.7 | Big FM | Bharuch | 105.2 | Top FM |
| Aizawl | 93.5 | Red FM | Bhavnagar | 91.5 | R.Mirchi |
| Aizawl | 94.3 | R. Gup Shup | Bhavnagar | 93.1 | Top FM |
| Ajmer | 92.7 | Big FM | Bhopal | 92.7 | Big FM |
| Ajmer | 94.3 | My FM | Bhopal | 93.5 | Red FM |
| Ajmer | 104.8 | R. City | Bhopal | 94.3 | My FM |
| Ajmer | 106.4 | FM Tadka | Bhopal | 98.3 | R. Mirchi |
| Akola | 91.1 | R. City | Bikaner | 91.1 | R. City |
| Akola | 91.9 | R. Orange | Bikaner | 92.7 | Big FM |
| Akola | 94.3 | My FM | Bikaner | 94.3 | My FM |
| Akola | 95.0 | R. Mirchi | Bikaner | 95.0 | FM Tadka |
| Aligarh | 94.1 | Current FM | Bilaspur | 91.1 | FM Tadka |
| Aligarh | 92.7 | Big FM | Bilaspur | 91.9 | Radio Orange |
| Aligarh | 94.9 | Fever FM | Bilaspur | 92.7 | Radio Rangila |
| Aligarh | 104.6 | FM Tadka | Bilaspur | 94.3 | My FM |
| Alappuzha | 92.7 | R.Mango | Bareilly | 94.3 | Fever FM |
| Alappuzha | 104.8 | Club FM | Bareilly | 91.1 | FM Tadka |
| Amravati | 92.7 | R.Mirchi | Chandigarh | 92.7 | Big FM |
| Amritsar | 92.7 | Big FM | Chandigarh | 93.5 | Red FM |
| Amritsar | 93.5 | Red FM | Chandigarh | 94.3 | My FM |
| Amritsar | 94.3 | My FM | Chandigarh | 98.3 | R.Mirchi |
| Amritsar | 104.8 | R.Mirchi | Chennai | 91.1 | R. City |
| Asansol | 92.7 | Big FM | Chennai | 91.9 | Fever FM |
| Asansol | 93.5 | Red FM | Chennai | 92.7 | Big FM |
| Asansol | 95.0 | R.Mirchi | Chennai | 93.5 | Suryan FM |
| Aurangabad | 92.7 | Big FM | Chennai | 94.3 | R. One |

| Location | MHz | Station | Location | MHz | Station | Location | MHz | Station | Location | MHz | Station |
|---|---|---|---|---|---|---|---|---|---|---|---|
| Chennai | 95.0 | Suryan FM | Jhansi | 104.8 | R.Mirchi | Nagpur | 91.9 | Mirchi Love | Sangli | 91.1 | R. City |
| Chennai | 98.3 | R. Mirchi | Jhansi | 106.4 | Red FM | Nagpur | 92.7 | Big FM | Sangli | 91.9 | Aapla FM |
| Chennai | 104.8 | Chennai Live | Jodhpur | 92.7 | Big FM | Nagpur | 94.3 | My FM | Sangli | 93.5 | Radio Orange |
| Chennai | 106.4 | Hello FM | Jodhpur | 93.5 | Red FM | Nagpur | 98.3 | R. Mirchi | Sangli | 104.0 | My FM |
| Coimbatore | 91.1 | R. City | Jodhpur | 94.3 | My FM | Nanded | 91.1 | R. City | Shillong | 91.1 | R. Mirchi |
| Coimbatore | 93.5 | Suryan FM | Jodhpur | 98.3 | R. Mirchi | Nanded | 93.5 | Red FM | Shillong | 93.5 | Red FM |
| Coimbatore | 98.3 | R. Mirchi | Junagadh | 91.9 | Top FM | Nanded | 94.3 | My FM | Shillong | 98.3 | Big FM |
| Coimbatore | 106.4 | Hello FM | Junagadh | 95.0 | R.Mirchi | Nashik | 93.5 | Red FM | Shimla | 95.0 | Big FM |
| Cuttack | 91.9 | Sartak FM | Kalaburgi | 93.5 | Red FM | Nashik | 95.0 | R. City | Shimla | 98.3 | R. Mirchi |
| Cuttack | 92.7 | Big FM | Kannur | 91.9 | R. Mango | Nashik | 98.3 | R. Mirchi | Shimla | 106.4 | R. Dhamaal |
| Cuttack | 93.5 | Red FM | Kannur | 93.5 | Red FM | Nashik | 104.2 | My FM | Siliguri | 92.7 | High FM |
| Cuttack | 104.0 | R. Choklate | Kannur | 94.3 | Club FM | Nellore | 93.5 | Red FM | Siliguri | 93.5 | Red FM |
| Dehradun | 93.5 | Red FM | Kanpur | 91.9 | Mirchi Love | New Delhi | 91.1 | R. City | Siliguri | 94.3 | R. Misty |
| Dhubri | 94.3 | R. Gup Shup | Kanpur | 92.7 | Big FM | New Delhi | 92.7 | Big FM | Siliguri | 98.3 | R. Mirchi |
| Dhule | 93.5 | Red FM | Kanpur | 93.5 | Red FM | New Delhi | 93.5 | Red FM | Solapur | 91.1 | R. City |
| Dhule | 95.0 | My FM | Kanpur | 95.0 | Fever FM | New Delhi | 94.3 | R. One | Solapur | 92.7 | Big FM |
| Dhule | 106.4 | R.Dhamaal | Kanpur | 98.3 | R. Mirchi | New Delhi | 95.0 | Hit FM | Solapur | 95.0 | My FM |
| Durg | 91.9 | R.Mirchi | Kanpur | 104.8 | R. City | New Delhi | 98.3 | R. Mirchi | Solapur | 104.8 | FM Tadka |
| Erode | 91.9 | Suryan FM | Kargil | 91.1 | Top FM | New Delhi | 104.0 | Fever FM | Srinagar | 92.7 | Big FM |
| Erode | 92.7 | Hello FM | Kargil* | 98.3 | | New Delhi | 104.8 | Ishq FM | Srinagar | 93.5 | Red FM |
| Gangtok | 93.5 | Red FM | Karnal | 91.9 | R. City | New Delhi | 107.2 | R. Nasha | Srinagar | 95.0 | FM Tadka |
| Gangtok | 95.0 | R. Misty | Karnal | 94.5 | My FM | Palanpur | 93.7 | R.Mirchi | Srinagar | 98.3 | R. Mirchi |
| Godhra | 93.1 | Top FM | Karnal | 106.4 | R.City | Panaji | 91.9 | R. Indigo | Surat | 91.1 | R. City |
| Gorakhpur | 91.1 | FM Tadka | Kathua | 91.1 | Top FM | Panaji | 92.7 | Big FM | Surat | 91.9 | Mirchi Love |
| Gorakhpur | 91.9 | R. City | Kathua* | 106.4 | | Patiala | 91.1 | R. City | Surat | 92.7 | Big FM |
| Gorakhpur | 92.7 | Big FM | Kochi | 91.9 | R. Mango | Patiala | 92.7 | Big FM | Surat | 94.3 | My FM |
| Gorakhpur | 94.3 | Fever FM | Kochi | 93.5 | Red FM | Patiala | 104.8 | R. Mirchi | Surat | 95.0 | Red FM |
| Guwahati | 91.9 | R. City | Kochi | 94.3 | Club FM | Patiala | 106.4 | R.Dhamaal | Surat | 98.3 | R. Mirchi |
| Guwahati | 93.5 | Red FM | Kochi | 104.0 | R. Mirchi | Patna | 91.1 | R. City | Trivandrum | 92.7 | Big FM |
| Guwahati | 94.3 | R. Gup Shup | Kolhapur | 92.7 | Big FM | Patna | 93.5 | Red FM | Trivandrum | 93.5 | Red FM |
| Guwahati | 95.0 | R. Mirchi | Kolhapur | 94.3 | Tomato FM | Patna | 95.0 | Big FM | Trivandrum | 94.3 | Club FM |
| Gwalior | 91.9 | Suno Lemon | Kolhapur | 95.0 | R. City | Patna | 98.3 | R. Mirchi | Trivandrum | 98.3 | R. Mirchi |
| Gwalior | 92.7 | Big FM | Kolhapur | 98.3 | R. Mirchi | Poonch | 94.3 | Top FM | Thrissur | 91.1 | Red FM |
| Gwalior | 94.3 | My FM | Kolkata | 91.9 | Radio City | Poonch* | 106.4 | | Thrissur | 91.9 | R. Mango |
| Gwalior | 95.0 | Tadka 95 FM | Kolkata | 92.7 | Big FM | Porbandar | 93.5 | Top FM | Thrissur | 104.8 | Club FM |
| Haflong | 94.3 | R.Gup Shup | Kolkata | 93.5 | Red FM | Prayagraj | 92.7 | Big FM | Tiruchirapalli | 93.5 | Suryan FM |
| Hissar | 91.9 | R. City | Kolkata | 94.3 | R. One | Prayagraj | 93.5 | Red FM | Tiruchirapalli | 95.0 | R.Mirchi |
| Hissar | 92.7 | Big FM | Kolkata | 98.3 | R. Mirchi | Prayagraj | 94.3 | Fever FM | Tiruchirapalli | 106.4 | Hello FM |
| Hissar | 94.5 | My FM | Kolkata | 104.0 | Fever FM | Prayagraj | 106.4 | FM Tadka | Tirunelveli | 93.5 | Suryan FM |
| Hissar | 106.4 | R. Dhamaal | Kolkata | 104.8 | Ishq FM | Puducherry | 92.7 | Big FM | Tirunelveli | 95.0 | R.Mirchi |
| Hubli | 93.5 | Red FM | Kolkata | 106.2 | Amar FM | Puducherry | 93.5 | Suryan FM | Tirunelveli | 106.4 | Hello FM |
| Hubli | 98.3 | R.Mirchi | Kota | 91.1 | R. City | Puducherry | 104.0 | R.Mirchi | Tirupati | 92.7 | Big FM |
| Hyderabad | 91.1 | R. City | Kota | 92.7 | Big FM | Puducherry | 106.4 | Hello FM | Tirupati | 93.5 | Red FM |
| Hyderabad | 92.7 | Big FM | Kota | 94.3 | My FM | Pune | 91.1 | R. City | Tirupati | 104.0 | E FM |
| Hyderabad | 93.5 | Red FM | Kota | 95.0 | FM Tadka | Pune | 93.5 | Red FM | Tuticorin | 93.5 | Suryan FM |
| Hyderabad | 94.3 | Fever FM | Kozhikode | 91.9 | R. Mango | Pune | 94.3 | R. One | Tuticorin | 106.4 | Hello FM |
| Hyderabad | 95.0 | Mirchi 95 | Kozhikode | 92.7 | R. Mirchi | Pune | 95.0 | Big FM | Udaipur | 91.9 | R. City |
| Hyderabad | 98.3 | R. Mirchi | Kozhikode | 93.5 | Red FM | Pune | 98.3 | R. Mirchi | Udaipur | 92.7 | Big FM |
| Hyderabad | 104.0 | Kool FM | Kozhikode | 104.8 | Club FM | Pune | 104.2 | Mirchi Love | Udaipur | 94.3 | My FM |
| Hyderabad | 106.4 | Magic FM | Leh | 91.1 | Top FM | Raigarh | 91.1 | R.Mirchi | Udaipur | 95.0 | FM Tadka |
| Indore | 92.7 | Big FM | Leh | 93.5 | Red FM | Raipur | 94.3 | My FM | Ujjain | 91.9 | R.Mirchi |
| Indore | 93.5 | Red FM | Leh* | 98.3 | | Raipur | 95.0 | FM Tadka | Vadodara | 91.1 | R. City |
| Indore | 94.3 | My FM | Lucknow | 91.1 | R. City | Raipur | 98.3 | R. Mirchi | Vadodara | 92.7 | Big FM |
| Indore | 98.3 | R. Mirchi | Lucknow | 93.5 | Red FM | Raipur | 104.8 | Rangila FM | Vadodara | 93.5 | Red FM |
| Itanagar | 92.7 | Big FM | Lucknow | 94.3 | Big FM | Rajahmundry | 91.1 | R.Mirchi | Vadodara | 98.3 | R. Mirchi |
| Itanagar | 94.3 | R. Gup Shup | Lucknow | 98.3 | R. Mirchi | Rajahmundry | 92.7 | E FM | Varanasi | 91.9 | R. City |
| Jabalpur | 93.5 | Red FM | Lucknow | 104.0 | Fever FM | Rajahmundry | 93.5 | Red FM | Varanasi | 93.5 | Red FM |
| Jabalpur | 94.3 | My FM | Lucknow | 107.2 | Mirchi Love | Rajkot | 92.7 | Big FM | Varanasi | 95.0 | Big FM |
| Jabalpur | 98.3 | R. Mirchi | Madurai | 91.9 | R. City | Rajkot | 93.5 | Red FM | Varanasi | 98.3 | R. Mirchi |
| Jabalpur | 106.4 | R.Dhamaal | Madurai | 93.5 | Suryan FM | Rajkot | 98.3 | R. Mirchi | Vellore | 91.5 | Hello FM |
| Jaipur | 91.1 | R. City | Madurai | 98.3 | R. Mirchi | Rajkot | 94.3 | My FM | Vellore | 93.9 | Suryan FM |
| Jaipur | 93.5 | Red FM | Madurai | 106.4 | Hello FM | Ranchi | 91.9 | R. City | Veraval | 93.5 | Top FM |
| Jaipur | 94.3 | My FM | Mangaluru | 92.7 | Big FM | Ranchi | 92.7 | Big FM | Vijayawada | 91.9 | E FM |
| Jaipur | 95.0 | FM Tadka | Mangaluru | 93.5 | Red FM | Ranchi | 104.8 | R. Dhoom | Vijayawada | 93.5 | Red FM |
| Jaipur | 98.3 | R. Mirchi | Mangaluru | 98.3 | R. Mirchi | Ranchi | 106.4 | R. Dhamaal | Vijayawada | 98.3 | R. Mirchi |
| Jaipur | 104.0 | Mirchi Love | Mehsana | 91.9 | R.Mirchi | Rourkela | 91.9 | Sartak FM | Visakhapatnam | 91.1 | R. City |
| Jalandhar | 91.9 | R. City | Mehsana | 92.7 | Top FM | Rourkela | 92.7 | Big FM | Visakhapatnam | 93.5 | Red FM |
| Jalandhar | 92.7 | Big FM | Mokokchung* | 93.5 | | Rourkela | 98.3 | | Visakhapatnam | 98.3 | R. Mirchi |
| Jalandhar | 94.3 | My FM | Mumbai | 91.1 | R. City | Radiodisha | | | Warangal | 91.9 | R. Mirchi |
| Jalandhar | 98.3 | R. Mirchi | Mumbai | 91.9 | R. Nasha | Rourkela | 104.0 | R. Choklate | Warangal | 93.5 | Red FM |
| Jalgaon | 91.1 | R. City | Mumbai | 92.7 | Big FM | Salem | 91.5 | Hello FM | Warangal | 104.8 | E FM |
| Jalgaon | 94.3 | My FM | Mumbai | 93.5 | Red FM | Salem | 93.9 | Suryan FM | | | |
| Jalgaon | 98.3 | FM Tadka | Mumbai | 94.3 | R. One | | | | | | |
| Jalgaon | 106.4 | R.Dhamaal | Mumbai | 98.3 | R. Mirchi | | | | | | |
| Jammu | 91.9 | Red FM | Mumbai | 104.0 | Fever FM | | | | | | |
| Jammu | 92.7 | Big FM | Mumbai | 104.8 | Ishq FM | | | | | | |
| Jammu | 95.0 | FM Tadka | Mumbai | 106.4 | Magic FM | | | | | | |
| Jammu | 98.3 | R. Mirchi | Muzzafarpur | 94.3 | Red FM | | | | | | |
| Jamnagar | 91.9 | Top FM | Muzzafarpur | 91.9 | FM Tadka | | | | | | |
| Jamnagar | 95.0 | R.Mirchi | Muzzafarpur | 92.7 | Big FM | | | | | | |
| Jamshedpur | 91.1 | R. City | Muzzafarpur | 106.4 | R.Dhamaal | | | | | | |
| Jamshedpur | 92.7 | Big FM | Mysuru | 92.7 | Big FM | | | | | | |
| Jamshedpur | 93.5 | Red FM | Mysuru | 93.5 | Red FM | | | | | | |
| Jamshedpur | 104.8 | R. Dhoom | Mysuru | 104.8 | R.Mirchi | | | | | | |
| Jhansi | 91.1 | FM Tadka | Nagpur | 91.1 | R. City | | | | | | |
| Jhansi | 92.7 | Big FM | Nagpur | 93.5 | Red FM | | | | | | |

*= F.P.I. **NB:** Big FM rel. R. Japan in Hindi 1835-1900 UTC via Bengaluru, Hyderabad, Kolkata, Mumbai, New Delhi on 92.7 MHz.

**Web addresses: Amar FM:** aamar106fm.com **Best FM:** bestfm95. in **Chennai Live:** chennailive.fm **Club FM:** clubfm.in **E FM:** eenadufm.net **Fever FM:** fever.fm **Hit FM:** hit95fm.in **Ishq FM:** ishq.com **My FM:** myfmindia.com **R. Chaska:** radiochaska.com **R. Choklate:** radiochoklateonline.com **R.City:** radiocity.in/radiocity **R. Dhamaal:** dhamaal24.com **R. Gup Shup:** radiogupshup.com **R. High:** radiohigh927fm.com **R. Mango:** radiomango.in **R. Mirchi:** radiomirchi.com **R. Misty:** radiomisty.co.in **R. Nasha:** radionasha.com **R. One:** radioone.in **R. High:** radiohigh927fm.com **Red FM:** redfmindia. in **Suryan FM:** suryanfm.in **Top FM:** topfm.in

### Gyan Vani (Educational FM Channel)
Electronic Media Production Centre, Sanchar Kendra, Indira Gandhi National Open University (IGNOU), Maidan Garhi, New Delhi-110068 ☎ +91 11 29532163,29532164,29532165 **W:** ignou.ac.in

| Location | MHz | kW | Location | MHz | kW |
|---|---|---|---|---|---|
| Agra | 105.6 | 10 | Madurai | 105.6 | 10 |
| Ahmedabad | 105.6 | 6 | Mumbai | 105.6 | 10 |
| Aurangabad | 105.6 | 10 | Mysuru | 105.6 | 10 |
| Bengaluru | 106.4 | 10 | Nagpur | 105.6 | 10 |
| Bhopal | 105.0 | 10 | New Delhi | 105.6 | 10 |
| Chandigarh | 105.6 | 10 | Panaji | 107.8 | 10 |
| Chennai | 105.6 | 10 | Patna | 105.6 | 10 |
| Coimbatore | 91.9 | 10 | Prayagraj | 107.4 | 10 |
| Cuttack | 105.6 | 10 | Pune | 105.6 | 10 |
| Hyderabad | 105.6 | 10 | Raipur | 105.6 | 10 |
| Indore | 105.6 | 10 | Rajkot | 105.6 | 10 |
| Guwahati | 107.8 | 10 | Shillong | 103.6 | 10 |
| Jabalpur | 105.6 | 10 | Srinagar | 107.8 | 10 |
| Jaipur | 105.6 | 10 | Trivandrum | 105.6 | 10 |
| Jalandhar | 105.6 | 10 | Tiruchirapalli | 104.8 | 10 |
| Kanpur | 106.4 | 10 | Tirunelveli | 105.6 | 10 |
| Kochi | 105.6 | 10 | Varanasi | 105.6 | 10 |
| Kolkata | 105.4 | 10 | Visakhapatnam | 106.4 | 10 |
| Lucknow | 105.6 | 10 | | | |

**NB:** Txs located at and maintained by AIR. Some stations are currently off air. **F.PI:** 19 more new stations

**Community FM Radio Stations:** Around 250 stns run by educational institutions, NGOs and others with 50W on **FM (MHz):** 90.4, 90.7, 90.8, 91.2, 96.9, 106.8, 107.2, 107.4 and 107.8. **F.PI.** More community stns by different institutions.

## INDONESIA

**L.T**: We. Indonesia (Java, Sumatra, We. & Ce. Kalimantan): UTC +7h; Ce. Indonesia (So. & Ea. Kalimantan, Sulawesi, Bali, Nusa Tenggara): UTC +8h; Ea. Indonesia (Maluku, Papua): UTC +9h — **Pr.L:** Bahasa Indonesia (Indonesian), Acehnese, Balinese, Javanese, Madurese, Malay, Sundanese and over 700 others — **Pop:** 267 million — **E.C:** 50 Hz, 220V — **ITU:** INS

### DIRECTORATE GENERAL OF POSTS & TELECOMMUNICATIONS (Direktorat Jenderal Pos dan Telekomunikasi)
Gedung Sapta Pesona, Medan Merdeka Barat 17, Jakarta 10110 ☎ +62 21 3835955 ▤ +62 21 3860754 **W:** postel.go.id **E:** admin@postel.go.id

### INDONESIAN BROADCASTING COMMISSION (Komisi Penyiaran Indonesia, KPI)
Gedung Sekretariat Negara Lt VI, Jl. Gajah Mada 8, Jakarta 10120 ☎ +62 21 6340713 ▤ +62 21 6340667 **W:** kpi.go.id
**LP:** Head: Mr Yuliandre Darwis. Dep. Head: Mr Sujarwanto Ahmad Arifin.

### RADIO REPUBLIK INDONESIA (RRI) (Gov.)
**National Station:** RRI, Jakarta Jl. Medan Merdeka Barat 4-5, Jakarta 10110, or Tromolpos 1157 (or Kotak Pos 356), Jakarta 10001 ☎ +62 21 3842083 ▤ +62 21 3457132 **W:** rri.co.id **E:** info@rri.co.id
**LP:** Man. Dir.: Mr Muhammad Rohanudin, Dir. of Tech. & New Media: Mr Rahadian Gingging MK.
**Pro 1 (Prosatu):** Information and entertainment on 91.2MHz **Pro 2 (Produa)** on 105.0MHz **Pro 3 (Protiga):** National news network on 999kHz, 88.8MHz 24h, also relayed in full on FM by most regional stns. N: on the h. Sports N. (Berita Olahraga): 0400, 0800. **Pro 4 (Proempat):** Educational and cultural prgrs on 1332kHz, 92.8MHz 24h. Relays Pro 3 1700-2200
**Local Stations:** Pro 1 (music and information), Pro 2 (for young people), Pro 3 (relay of Pro 3 Jakarta), Pro 4 (education and culture). MW and SW freqs below carry the local Pro 1 sce except where marked '3' or '4'. **H of tr:** Pro 3 24h, others usually 0430/0500-2400 local time

| MW | kHz | kW | Station | MW | kHz | kW | Station |
|---|---|---|---|---|---|---|---|
| JB01) | 540 | 10 | Bandung 4 | PB02) | 774 | | Fak-Fak |
| JT01) | 585 | 50 | Surabaya 4 | NT02) | 783 | 10 | Ende |
| SL01) | 630 | 50 | Makassar | JH01) | 801 | 10 | Semarang |
| PB01) | 702 | 10 | Manokwari | PA02) | 810 | 7.5 | Merauke |
| MA01) | 720 | 10 | Ambon | NB01) | 855 | 10 | Mataram |
| PA06) | 729 | 10 | Nabire | JB03) | 864 | 5 | Cirebon |
| BE01) | 747 | 10 | Bengkulu | JT02) | 891 | 10 | Malang 4 |
| JH03) | 756 | 10 | Purwokerto | MU01) | 891 | 10 | Ternate |
| MA02) | 765 | 1 | Tual | PB03) | 909 | 10 | Sorong |

| MW | kHz | kW | Station | MW | kHz | kW | Station |
|---|---|---|---|---|---|---|---|
| RI01) | 927 | 25 | Pekanbaru 4 | SB01) | 1179 | 10 | Padang |
| SG01) | 954 | 10 | Kendari | ST01) | 1188 | 10 | Manado 4 |
| JT03) | ‡963 | 10 | Jember | KH01) | 1197 | 10 | Palangkaraya |
| JH02) | 972 | 50 | Surakarta | BA01) | 1206 | 10 | Denpasar |
| JK01) | 999 | 150 | Jakarta 3 | JB01) | 1215 | | Bandung 3 |
| G001) | 1008 | 10 | Gorontalo | KT01) | 1215 | 10 | Samarinda |
| JT04) | 1008 | 10 | Madiun | KB01) | 1233 | 5 | Pontianak |
| PA03) | 1026 | 5 | Serui | JB02) | 1242 | 10 | Bogor |
| LA01) | 1035 | 5 | Bandar Lampung | AC01) | 1251 | 10 | Banda Aceh 4 |
| SH01) | 1035 | | Palu | SS01) | 1287 | 25 | Palembang |
| PA04) | 1044 | 2 | Biak | JK01) | 1332 | 10 | Jakarta 4 |
| ST02) | ‡1044 | 10 | Tahuna | KR01) | ‡1341 | | Tanjung Pinang |
| SU02) | 1044 | 10 | Sibolga | KU01) | 1350 | 10 | Tarakan |
| BA02) | 1080 | 10 | Singaraja | SH02) | 1377 | 10 | Tolitoli |
| JA01) | 1098 | 10 | Jambi | PA05) | 1395 | 1 | Wamena |
| JT05) | 1098 | 10 | Sumenep | BB01) | 1413 | 5 | Sungai Liat |
| NT01) | 1107 | 5 | Kupang | SB02) | 1512 | 10 | Bukittinggi |
| YG01) | 1107 | 10 | Yogyakarta 4 | | | | |

| SW | kHz | kW | Station, h. of tr. |
|---|---|---|---|
| KH01) | $3325 | 10 | Palangkaraya. |
| MU01) | 3345 | 10 | Ternate irr. |
| PB02) | ‡4790 | | Fak-Fak irr. |
| PA05) | ‡4870 | | Wamena: 2000-2315, 0800-1500 |
| PA06) | ‡6125 | | Nabire |
| PA06) | ±7290 | | Nabire: 2200-2300, 0500-0830v |

**NB:** ‡=r. inactive at editorial deadline, ±=variable frq, v.=variable times. $ = carries VO Indonesia (Ext. Sce). During Ramadan several stns begin morning transmissions as early as 1800.

**Addresses** (JI = Jalan). All **FM:** in MHz. FM freqs are listed in order of prgr (Pro 1, Pro 2, Pro 3, Pro4) exc. where noted. Local FM relays are marked after + and generally carry Pro-1.
**AC01)** Jl Sultan Iskandar Muda 13, P.O Box 112, Banda Aceh 23423, Nanggroe Aceh Darussalam - **FM:** 97.7/92.6/87.8/88.6 + 90.5 Tapaktuan, 91.9 Langsa, 92.0 Sinabang, 92.3 Kutacane, 93.0 Subulussalam, 95.1 Lamno, 97.3 Jantho, 97.5 Calang, 99.7 Beuneuruen — **AC02)** Jl Peutua Ibrahim 75, Teumpok Teungoh, Lhokseumawe 24352, Nanggroe Aceh Darussalam - **FM:** 89.3/100.9/95.2 — **AC03)** RRI Sabang, Jl Yos Sudarso 65, Cot Bak U, Kecamatan Sukajaya, Sabang, Nanggroe Aceh Darussalam - **FM:** 94.0 — **AC04)** RRI Takengon, Jl Lembaga Kemili, Takengon, Aceh Tengah, Nanggroe Aceh Darussalam - **FM:** 93.0 — **AC05)** RRI Meulaboh, Meulaboh, Nanggroe Aceh Darussalam - **FM:** 97.0 (Pro 1)/88.7 (Pro 3) — **AC06)** RRI Singkil, Singkil, Nanggroe Aceh Darussalam — **FM:** 92.2
**BA01)** Jl Hayam Wuruk 70, Keladis, Denpasar 80233 (Kotak Pos 31, Denpasar 80001), Bali - **FM:** 88.6/95.3/93.0/100.0 + 99.5 Tamblingan, 100.9 Karangasem — **BA02)** Jl Gajah Mada 144, Tromolpos 153, Singaraja 81113, Bali - **FM:** 97.9/103.7/102.0
**BB01)** Jl Jend Ahmad Yani, Sungai Liat 33211, Bangka, Bangka Belitung - **FM:** 96.4/101.4/97.2 + 90.4 Toboali, 95.4 Mentok, 95.5 Tanjung Pandan, 99.8 Pangkalpinang
**BE01)** Jl Let Jend S Parman 25, Kotak Pos 13, Bengkulu 38227, Bengkulu - **FM:** 92.5/105.1/90.9 + 95.4 Muko-Muko, 97.0 Bintuhan, 98.0 Curup, 101.3 Ipuh
**BN01)** RRI Banten, Kompleks Pendopo Gubernur Banten, Serang, Banten - **FM:** 94.9
**G001)** Jl Jenderal Sudirman 30, Gorontalo 96128, Gorontalo - **FM:** 101.8/92.4/96.7 + 92.5 Baroko, 94.9 Paguyaman, 97.0 Marisa **JA01)** Jl Jendral A Yani 5, Telanaipura, Jambi 36122, Jambi - **FM:** 88.5/90.9/94.4 + 95.8 Bangko, 99.0 Kualatungkal, 99.0 Sarolangun, 99.8 Sungai Penuh, 99.8 Tungkal Ilir, 101.0 Muara Bungo — **JA02)** RRI Sungai Penuh, Sungai Penuh, Jambi - **FM:** 97.1/101.0
**JB01)** Jl Diponegoro 61, Bandung 40122 (Kotak Pos 1055, Bandung 40001), Jawa Barat - **FM:** 97.6/96.0 + 95.0 Gunung Malang, 97.0 Purwakarta/Subang, 97.8 Tasikmalaya, 98.0 Bayah, 98.2 Puncak Surangga, 98.9 Saketi, 102.5 Cikuray, 103.3 Garut — **JB02)** Jl Pangrango 30, P.O Box 232, Bogor 16161, Jawa Barat - **FM:** 93.7/106.8 — **JB03)** Jl Brigjen Dharsono/By Pass, Cirebon 45132, Jawa Barat - **FM:** 93.7/94.8/97.5
**JH01)** Jl Ahmad Yani 144-146, Kotak Pos 1307, Semarang 50241, Jawa Tengah - **FM:** 89.0/95.3/88.2/91.4 + 94.2 Colo, 96.7 Batang, 97.7 Gunung Gantungan) 99.4 Gunung Depok, 99.5 Gunung Periksa — **JH02)** Jl Abdul Rahman Saleh 51, Kotak Pos 40, Surakarta 57133, Jawa Tengah - **FM:** 101.0/105.5/105.9 + 96.3 Tawangmangu — **JH03)** Jl Jendral Sudirman 427, Kotak Pos 5, Purwokerto 53116, Jawa Tengah - **FM:** 93.1/99.0/107.3
**JK01)** Jl Medan Merdeka Barat 4-5, Jakarta 10110 (Tromolpos 1157, Jakarta 10001).
**JT01)** Jl Pemuda 82-90, Kotak Pos 239, Surabaya 60271, Jawa Timur - **FM:** 99.2/95.2/106.3/96.8 + 91.1 Cemoro Lawang, 97.9 Pacitan, 99.2 Alas Malang, 99.2 Pare, 102.3 Pulau Bawean; Studio 5 (additional

music sce for Surabaya area): 91.7MHz – **JT02)** Jl Candi Panggung 58, Kotak Pos 78, Mojolangu, Malang 65142, Jawa Timur - **FM:** 91.5/87.9/94.6/105.3 – **JT03)** Jl D.I Panjaitan 61, Jember 68110 (Kotak Pos 166, Jember 68101), Jawa Timur - **FM:** 95.4/89.5/87.9 + 91.6 Banyuwangi/Bondowoso, 95.8 Lumajang – **JT04)** Jl Mayjen Panjaitan 10-12, Madiun 63133, Jawa Timur - **FM:** 99.7/97.7/104.0 + 96.3 Kemiri – **JT05)** Jl Urip Sumoharjo 26, Sumenep 69411, Madura, Jawa Timur - **FM:** 101.3/94.6/93.0 – **JT06)** RRI Sampang, Jl Peliang Km 2, Torjun, Sampang, Madura, Jawa Timur - **FM:** 100.8 – **JT06)** RRI Kediri, Pare Kediri, Jawa Timur - **FM:** 100.2

**KB01)** Jl Jendral Sudirman 7, Kotak Pos 6, Pontianak 78111, Kalimantan Barat - **FM:** 104.2/101.8/90.3 + 95.0 Nangamerakai, 96.8 Ketapang, 97.0 Sanggau) 97.7 Sambas, 97.7 Singkawang, 98.0 Kendawangan, 98.2 Semitau, 99.3 Sanggau Ledo, 100.2 Balaikarangan – **KB02)** RRI Sintang, Jl Oevang Oeraya, Baning, Sintang, Kalimantan Barat - **FM:** 96.6/90.7/102.5 – **KB03)** RRI Entikong, Jl Lintas Negara Indonesia-Malaysia, Entikong Sanggau, Kalimantan Barat - **FM:** 100.2

**KH01)** Jl M Husni Thamrin 1, Palangkaraya 73112, Kalimantan Tengah - **FM:** 89.2/92.4/95.9 + 93.6 Kuala Kapuas, 93.6 Sampit, 96.0 Muara Teweh, 97.1 Pulang Pisau, 97.3 Buntok, 99.2 Pangkalan Bun

**KR01)** Jl Ahmad Yani Km 4, Kotak Pos 8, Tanjung Pinang 29133, Bintan, Kepulauan Riau - **FM:** 98.3/92.1/101.3 + 96.6 Karimun, 99.6 Tarempa – **KR02)** RRI Ranai, Jl Sepempang, Ranai, Pulau Natuna Besar 29183, Kepulauan Riau – **FM:** 90.0/105.9/104.0 – **KR03)** RRI Batam, Komplek Politeknik Batam, Batam Centre, Batam, Kepulauan Riau - **FM:** 105.1/105.5/90.9

**KS01)** Jl Jenderal A. Yani Km 3.5 No 234, Kotak Pos 117, Banjarmasin 70234, Kalimantan Selatan - **FM:** 97.6/95.2/92.5/87.7 + 89.4 Batu Licin, 90.2 Kotabaru, 90.7 Amuntai, 99.6 Banjarbaru,105.7 Kandangan

**KT01)** Jl Moh Yamin 8, P.O Box 45, Samarinda 75110, Kalimantan Timur - **FM:** 97.6/88.5/98.4 + 96.0 Penajam, 96.7 Berau, 96.8 Tanah Grogot, 97.0 Balikpapan, 97.4 Melak, 97.4 Bontang/Sangata, 99.0 Tenggarong – **KT02)** RRI Sendawar, Jl D.I. Panjaitan 61, Dusun Busur, Kampung Barong Tongkok, Sendawar, Kutai Barat, Kalimantan Timur - **FM:** 103.3 – **KT03)** RRI Long Bagun, Mahakam Hulu, Kalimantan Timur **FM:** freq. not yet conf.

**KU01)** Jl Sungai Mahakam 10, Kampung Empat, Tarakan Timur 77125, Kalimantan Utara - **FM:** 97.9/101.9/88.8 – **KU02)** Jl Pelajar Perumda II, Malinau, Kalimantan Utara - **FM:** 95.5 – **KU03)** Jl TVRI 77, Nunukan, Kalimantan Utara - **FM:** 97.1/89.6 + 95.5 Pulau Sebatik (Pro 3)

**LA01)** Jl Gatot Subroto 26, Kotak Pos 24, Pahoman, Bandar Lampung 35213, Lampung - **FM:** 90.9/92.5/87.7 + 94.7 Rajabasa (Pro 3), 95.8 Kotabumi, 97.0 Kota Agung, 99.0 Simpang Pematang, 99.4 Liwa, 99.7 Padang Cermin, 100.2 Tulungbawang – **LA02)** Way Kanan, Lampung-FM: 103.6

**MA01)** Jl Jendral Akhmad Yani 1, Ambon 97124, Maluku - **FM:** 95.4/98.4/102.0 + 92.0 Amahai/Masohi, 94.3 Saumlaki – **MA02)** Jl Sukarno-Hatta, Kec Wat Deh, Tual 97661, Pulau Kai, Maluku - **FM:** 93.2/97.6/103.6 – **MA03)** RRI Bula, Seram Bagian Timur, Maluku **FM:** 90.0.

**MU01)** Jl Sultan Khairun 2, Kedaton, Ternate 97720, Maluku Utara - **FM:** 101.8/96.7/104.1 + 92.8 Pulau Morotai, 93.7 Soasiu

**NB01)** Komplek Perumahan RRI Mataram, Jl Majapahit, P.O Box 2, Mataram, Lombok, Nusa Tenggara Barat - **FM:** 89.2/104.2/94.3 + 89.1 Dompu, 89.3 Sumbawa Besar, 92.7 Kuripan, 96.3 Aik Bukak, 97.9 Lombok Timur

**NT01)** Jl Tompello 8, Kupang 85225, Timor, Nusa Tenggara Timur - **FM:** 94.4/90.0/101.9 + 88.8 Soe, 90.7 Kefamenanu – **NT02)** Jl Durian, Ende 86317, Flores, Nusa Tenggara Timur - **FM:** 100.5/92.2 + 89.0 Bajawa (Pro 3), 89.2 Labuhan Baju (Pro 3) – **NT03)** RRI Rote Ndao, Baa, Rote 85371, Nusa Tenggara Timur - **FM:** 93.3 – **NT04)** RRI Atambua, Komplek Kantor Bupati Belu, Jl Eltari 1, Atambua, Timor, Nusa Tenggara Timur - **FM:** 91.5

**PA01)** Jl Tasangkapura 23, Kotak Pos 1077, Jayapura 99200, Papua - **FM:** 96.0/90.1/105.9/89.3 + 93.5 Sentani, 94.5 Timika, 96.5 Sarmi, 96.7 Sorendiweri, 97.6 South Jayapura, 100.0 Genyem – **PA02)** Jl Jendral Ahmad Yani 11, Mopa Baru, Merauke 99611 (Kotak Pos 111, Merauke 99601), Papua - **FM:** 90.0&95.4 (Pro-1)/98.1/105.0 – **PA03)** Jl Pattimura, Serui 98213, Papua – **FM:** 96.4/101.5/94.5 – **PA04)** Jl Majapahit, Kotak Pos 505, Biak 98117, Papua - **FM:** 96.9/95.3/95.8 + 96.3/97.6 Numfor – **PA05)** Jl Ahmad A Yani 64, Wamena 99511 (Kotak Pos 10, Wamena 99501), Papua - **FM:** 97.1/96.3/94.7 – **PA06)** Jl Merdeka 74, Nabire 98811 (Kotak Pos 110, Nabire 98801), Papua – **FM:** 96.0/90.1/94.4 – **PA07)** RRI Boven Digul, Jl Trans Papua 17, Tanah Merah, Papua – **FM:** 93.6 – **PA08)** RRI Oksibil, Jl. Perbukitan Okpol, Oksibil, Papua - **FM:** 90.0 – **PA09)** RRI Skow, Jl RRI Stasiun Perbatasan, Skow, Papua - **FM:** 98.3

**PB01)** Jl Merdeka 68, Manokwari 98311, Papua Barat - **FM:** 94.3/97.8/95.1 – **PB02)** Jl Kapt P Tendean, Kotak Pos 154, Fak-Fak 98612, Papua Barat - **FM:** 97.2/99.0/93.15 + 98.1 Kokas – **PB03)** Jl Sam Ratulangi 4, Kotak Pos 146, Sorong 98414, Papua Barat - **FM:**

102.6/95.9/95.1 + 95.9 Bintuni, 96.3 Teminabuan – **PB04)** Jl Air Merah, Kaimana, Papua Barat - **FM:** 96.3

**RI01)** Jl Jend Sudirman 440, Kotak Pos 51, Pekanbaru 28115, Riau - **FM:** 99.1/88.4/89.2/95.9 + 92.6 Pasir Pangaraian, 93.0 Dumai, 94.7 Selat Panjang, 96.5 Sei Pakning, 98.5 Baserah, 99.3 Tembilahan, 99.9 Siak – **RI02)** Bengkalis, Riau - **FM:** 90.6 (Pro-1)/89.8 (Pro-3)

**SB01)** Jl Jendral Sudirman 12, Kotak Pos 77, Padang 25124, Sumatera Barat - **FM:** 97.5/90.8/88.4 + 88.4 Pandai Sikek Padang Pariaman, 89.5 Bukit Gompong Solok, 92.0 Bungkit Palakat, 96.0 Lubuk Sikaping, 96.8 Pasaman Barat, 97.9 Bukit Langkisau Painan, 97.9 Dharma Seraya, 98.5 Mentawai – **SB02)** Jl.Prof Muhammad Yamin 199, Kotak Pos 3, Aurkuning, Bukittinggi 26131, Sumatera Barat - **FM:** 94.8/97.2/90.5 – **SB03)** Jl Diponegoro 48, Pariaman, Sumatera Barat - **FM:** 97.1

**SG01)** Jl Laute Mandonga 44, Kotak Pos 7, Kendari 93111, Sulawesi Tenggara - **FM:** 96.7/90.8/91.6 + 93.5 Boepinang, 97.0 Raha, 99.5 Lasolo

**SG02)** Bau-Bau, Sulawesi Tenggara - **FM:** 99.4

**SH01)** Jl R.A Kartini 39, Palu 94112, Sulawesi Tengah - **FM:** 90.8/105.0/92.4 + 95.4 Ampana, 95.5 Tanjung Santigi, 96.0 Banggai, 96.2 Poso, 97.1 Toboli, 99.2 Luwuk – **SH02)** Jl Jenderal Sudirman, Tolitoli 94514, Sulawesi Tengah - **FM:** 102.0/90.2/94.5 – **SH03)** RRI Ampana, Jl Tanjungulu Tojo Una-Una, Ampana, Sulawesi Tengah - **FM:** 93.0

**SL01)** Jl Riburane 3, Kotak Pos 103, Makassar 90111, Sulawesi Selatan - **FM:** 94.4/96.8/106.3/92.9 + 90.6 Bontu Tabang, 94.0 Baraka, 99.0 Parepare, 99.0 Bantaeng – **SL02)** RRI Bone, Jl Ahmad Yani, Watampone, Sulawesi Selatan - **FM:** 97.7

**SR01)** Jl H. Abdul Malik Pattana Endeng, Mamuju, Sulawesi Barat - **FM:** 96.0

**SS01)** Jl Radio 2 Km 4, Palembang 30128, Sumatera Selatan - **FM:** 92.4/91.6/97.1/88.4 + 90.3 Sekayu, 90.5 Baturaja, 90.5 Pagar Alam, 95.1 Lubuklinggau, 97.7 Prabumulih, 99.9 Muara Enim

**ST01)** Jl Radio 1, Kotak Pos 1110, Tikala Ares, Manado 95124, Sulawesi Utara - **FM:** 94.5/97.7/104.4/88.6 + 88.2 Pineleng, 92.0 Lirung, 92.5 Buroko, 98.1 Tondano, 99.5 Melonguane (Pro-3) – **ST02)** Jl Tona, Tahuna, Sangihe, Sulawesi Utara - **FM:** 98.7/92.0/105.4 – **ST03)** RRI Talaud - **FM:** 101.2

**SU01)** Jl Jend Gatot Subroto Km 5.6, Medan 20123, Sumatera Utara - **FM:** 94.3/92.4/88.8/88.4 + 90.0 Natal, 90.6 Rantau Prapat, 91.9 Kotanopan, 92.0 Prapat, 92.0 Sidikalang, 94.5 Simar Jarunjung, 96.1 Pematang Siantar, 96.3 Tarutung, 99.1 Sibuhan, 99.3 Pulau Raja – **SU02)** Jl Ade Irma Suryani Nasution 11, Sibolga 22513, Sumatera Utara - **FM:** 97.2/94.8/103.1 + 99.9 Padangsidempuan – **SU03)** RRI Gunungsitoli, Desa Iraonogeba, Gunungsitoli, Nias, Sumatera Utara - **FM:** 96.2/101.3/90.3– **SU04)** RRI Nias Selatan, Teluk Dalam, Nias Selatan, Sumatera Utara - **FM:** 93.1

**YG01)** Jl Ahmad Jazuli 4, Tromolpos 18, Kotabaru, Yogyakarta 55224, Daerah Istimewa Yogyakarta - **FM:** 91.1/102.5/102.9/106.6

**EXTERNAL SERVICES: The Voice of Indonesia**
see International Broadcasting section.

## FEDERATION OF INDONESIAN NATIONAL COMMERCIAL BROADCASTERS (Persatuan Radio Siaran Swasta Nasional Indonesia)
✉ Jl Raya Mabes Hankam 19-A, Setu, Cipayung, Jakarta Timur 13880 ☎ +62 21 84591855 📠 +62 21 29066878 **W:** radioprssni.com/ prssninew/ **E:** radioprssni@radioprssni.com or ppjkt@indosat.net.id
**LP:** Chmn: Rohmad Hadiwojoyo. Commercial stn permitted power: up to 1kW (MW) and 10kW (FM).

## LOCAL PUBLIC BROADCASTING STATIONS (Lembaga Penyiaran Publik Lokal)
Local government stns have made the transition to local government-owned but autonomous public broadcasters. As a result, the names of former local government radio stns (Radio Siaran Pemerintah Daerah) have been changed. Where occasionally still referred to, these stn headings apply: **RKPD:** Radio Khusus Pemerintah Daerah – **RPK:** Radio Pemerintah Kabupaten – **RSPD:** Radio Siaran Pemerintah Daerah – **RSPK:** Radio Siaran Pemerintah Kabupaten.

## INDONESIAN COMMUNITY RADIO NETWORK (Jaringan Radio Komunitas Indonesia)
✉ Sekretariat, Jaringan Radio Komunitas Indonesia, Jl Dwi Sri 10, Bandung, Jawa Barat ☎ +62 22 5224205 **W:** jrki.wordpress.com **E:** suara.jrki@gmail.com or jrk_kongres04@yahoo.com
**LP:** Chrmn: Bowo Usodo
The majority of community stns operate from 107.7 to 108.0 MHz. Maximum permitted power is 50W

| MW | kHz | kW | Station, location |
|---|---|---|---|
| JB04) | 549 | | Inyong R., Depok |

| MW | kHz | kW | Station, location |
|---|---|---|---|
| BN02) | ±576 | | R. Hutama Buana Suara (HBS), Ciledug |
| JK02) | 594 | | R. AM 594, Jakarta |
| KB04) | 621 | | R. Kijang Berantai (Kiber) Perkasa, Sambas |
| JK03) | 630 | 1 | R. Samhan, Jakarta |
| JB05) | 675 | | R. Syair Tauhid, Depok |
| JK04) | 693 | | R. Musik Asik Nusantara (R. Muara), Jakarta |
| YG02) | 711 | | R. Suara Konco Tani, Sidokarto |
| JB06) | 720 | | R. Silaturahim, Cibubur |
| JH05) | 720 | 0.25 | R. Lusiana Namberwan (R. Silaturahim), Semarang |
| BN03) | 738 | | R. Bharata Bhakti Nusa (Jakarta Music & News R.), Tangerang |
| JA03) | 740 | | RSPD Batanghari, Muarabulian |
| JB07) | 756 | | R. Rodja, Cileungsi - Bogor |
| SB04) | 774 | 0.35 | RSPD Kotamadya Payakumbuh |
| KS02) | ±783 | | R. Dakwah Masjid Raya Sabilal Muhtadin Banjarmasin |
| YG03) | 783 | | R. Swara Kenanga, Yogyakarta |
| JK05) | 792 | 1 | R. As Syafi'iyah, Jakarta |
| JB08) | 810 | | RSPD Kabupaten Bandung (R. Kandaga) |
| JH07) | 810 | | R. Suara Maung Sakti, Banjarnegara |
| JB09) | 828 | 0.25 | R. Leidya Swara Utama (R. Kharisma), Bandung |
| JK06) | 828 | | R. Berita Klasik (RBK), Jakarta |
| SL03) | 828 | | R. Swara Christy Ria, Makassar |
| JA04) | 837 | | R. Kelapa Indah (R. KIN), Tanjung Jabung Barat |
| JK07) | 837 | | R. Muslim Jakarta |
| JH08) | 846 | | R. Immanuel, Surakarta |
| JT08) | 846 | | R. Suara Al Iman, Surabaya |
| JB10) | 855 | | R. Kabar Empat, Bekasi |
| YG04) | ±855 | | R. Gemma Satunama, Gunung Kidul |
| JT09) | ‡864 | | R. Menara Tiga, Surabaya |
| JH09) | 873 | 0.5 | R. Buana Asri (R. Publik Kabupaten Sragen), Sragen |
| JB11) | 882 | | R. Suara Anggada Senatama (S.A.S.), Banjarsari |
| JK08) | 882 | | R. Pelangi Nusantara, Jakarta |
| JA05) | 900 | 0.25 | R. Gema Nugraha, Sungai Penuh |
| JH10) | 900 | | R. Darussalaf, Sukoharjo |
| JK09) | ±900 | | R. Sindajaya, Jakarta |
| KB05) | 900 | | R. Aries Sanggau Perkasa, Sanggau |
| SU05) | ±900 | | R. Aksi Bethany, Medan |
| JB12) | 909 | | R. Mustaqbal, Bekasi |
| BN04) | 909 | | R. Suara Guntur Laras, Tangerang |
| JB13) | 918 | | R. Siaran Gema Nury (R. Elnury), Bogor |
| YG05) | ±927 | | R. Suara Parangtritis, Parangtritis |
| JK10) | 936 | 0.25 | R. Puspa Dwi Swara Cipta (P2SC), Jakarta |
| JB14) | 936 | | R. Samhan Mulya, Sumedang |
| JH11) | 945 | | R. Swara Buana Asri, Wonosobo |
| BN05) | ±954 | | R. Benda Baru (RBB), Pamulang, Tangerang |
| JT10) | 954 | 0.25 | R. El Bayu, Gresik |
| SS02) | 954 | 0.15 | R. Garuda Kenten Jaya (Bazz R., Islamic R. Palembang), Palembang |
| SL04) | 954 | | R. Wadhatama Nusantara (Makkah AM), Makassar |
| BN06) | 972 | | R. Pusako Minangkabau, Tangerang |
| KS03) | 990 | | R. Bahana Al-Mursyidul Amin, Martapura |
| KB06) | 1008 | | R. Suara Pemangkat, Pemangkat |
| SL05) | 1008 | | R. Suara Adyafiri, Watansoppeng |
| BN07) | ±1017 | | R. Swara Angkasa Semesta (RASS), Teluknada, Tangerang |
| JK11) | 1026 | | R. Suara Khatulistiwa (SK), Jakarta |
| SS03) | 1026 | | R. Suara Enim Jaya Perkasa (En-J), Muara Enim |
| JB15) | 1044 | | R. Purna Yudha (i-Dream R.), Depok |
| JH12) | 1062 | | R. P.T.D.I. Unisa 205, Semarang |
| JT11) | 1062 | 1 | R. Sangkakala, Surabaya |
| PA10) | ±1062 | | R. Swara Lembah Baliem, Wamena |
| SU06) | 1062 | | R. Tembang Perbauangan Indah, Perbauangan |
| SL06) | 1080 | | R. Suara Viktori, Makassar |
| JK12) | ‡1098 | | Perkumpulan R. Siaran Pendidikan Tinggi Universitas Tarumanegara (VOMS) |
| JB16) | ±1116 | | R. Adhika Swara (R. Alawiyah), Bekasi |
| JB17) | 1116 | 1 | R. Barani, Bandung |
| JT12) | ±1117 | 0.25 | R. Carolina Arjuno, Surabaya |
| JH13) | 1125 | | R. Suara Diponegoro, Semarang |
| JK13) | 1134 | 2 | R. Swara Mega Asri (R. Safari), Jakarta |
| JH14) | ±1143 | | R. Swara Delanggu (Swadesi), Delanggu-Klaten |
| JK14) | 1152 | | R. Ikadi, Jakarta |
| JT13) | 1152 | | R. Yasmara, Surabaya |
| JB18) | ±1170 | | R. Dios (R. Paksi), Bandung |
| JK15) | ‡1170 | | R. Jalesviva Jayamahe (JJM, Suara Samudera), Jakarta |
| PA11) | 1170 | | R. Suara Nusa Bahagia, Jayapura |
| YG06) | 1179 | | R. Unisia Media Umat, Sleman |
| JH15) | ±1180 | 0.5 | RSPD Wonogiri |

| MW | kHz | kW | Station, location |
|---|---|---|---|
| JT14) | 1188 | | R. Swara Perak Jaya P.T.D.I., Surabaya |
| BN08) | 1197 | | R. Swara Mitra, Tangerang |
| BN09) | 1206 | | GES Radio, Tangerang |
| SB05) | 1206 | | R. Suara Dikara Bawana (Dirgan Bravo), Padang |
| JH16) | 1224 | | R. Angkasa Bahana Citra (A.B.C.), Surakarta |
| YG07) | 1251 | | R. Edukasi, Yogyakarta |
| JB19) | 1260 | | R. Suara Pekerja (SP), Bekasi |
| PA12) | 1278 | | R. Pikonane, Yahukimo |
| JH17) | 1314 | | Suara Sion Perdana, Karanganyar |
| YG08) | 1323 | | R. Kartini Indah Swara, Yogyakarta |
| BN10) | ±1440 | | R. Edukasi, Tangerang |
| JT15) | ±1449 | 0.7 | R. Pertanian Wonocolo, Surabaya |
| JB20) | 1458 | | R. Fajri, Bandung |
| SH05) | 1458 | 1 | R. Kareme Nuvula (RPK Parigi Moutong), Parigi |
| JB21) | 1475 | | RKDT Karawang (Studio Radio Daerah Pangkal Perjuangan) |
| BN11) | ±1476 | | R. Bhalqist, Tangerang |
| JB22) | 1476 | | R. Rodja Bandung, Bandung |
| ST04) | ‡1494 | | R. Suara Kasih, Tahuna |
| KT04) | 1512 | 0.25 | R. Swara Mitra Dirgantara (Rasmira), Balikpapan |
| JB23) | ±1523 | | R. Swara Primadona Mahardika, Cikampek |
| JK16) | 1530 | | R. Mesjid Sunda Kelapa, Jakarta |

**NB:** ‡ = r. inactive ± = variable. A number of unlicensed stns operating in the Tangerang area, Banten province, are not included in the list above.

## Addresses (JI = Jalan)
### BN00) BANTEN
**BN02)** JI Radeh Fatah, Perum Lembang Baru I/3, Ciledug, Tangerang 15151 – **BN03)** carries China Radio International prgr, address as stn BN03) – **BN04)** JI Kayu Gede 2, Paku Jaya, Serpong Utara, Tangerang – **BN05)** Benda Baru, Pamulang, Tangerang – **BN06)** JI KH. Hasyim Ashari, Gedung Berkah Motor Lt 3, Cipondoh, Tangerang – **BN07)** JI Kampung Melayu Barat, Teluknaga, Tangerang – **BN08)** JI Komplek Peruri, Ciledug, Tangerang – **BN09)** Tangerang **BN10)** Pusat Teknologi Informasi dan Komunikasi (PUSTEKKOM), Departemen Pendidikan Nasional (DEPDIKNAS), Ciputat, Tangerang – **BN11)** Pondok Serut, Serpong Utara, Tangerang Selatan.
### JA00) JAMBI
**JA03)** JI.Gajah Mada, Muarabulian 36610 – **JA04)** JI Panglima H Saman 297B, Kuala Tungkal, Tanjung Jabung Barat 36513 – **JA05)** JI Yos Sudarso 55, Sungai Penuh, Kerinci.
### JB00) JAWA BARAT (West Java)
**JB04)** JI Perintis I, Kalimulya, Depok – **JB05)** JI Rawakalong 122, Grogol, Limo, Depok – **JB06)** JI Masjid Silaturahim 36, Kalimanggis, Cibubur, Bekasi – **JB07)** Masjid Al Barkah, JI Pahlawan kp Tengah, Cileungsi - Bogor – **JB08)** JI Adikusumah, Bale Endah, Dayeuh Kolot, Bandung – **JB09)** JI Siliwangi 5, Bandung 40132 – **JB10)** JI Kain Raya 3, Rawa Lumbu, Bekasi – **JB11)** JI Raya Barat 98, Banjarsari, Ciamis 46383 – **JB12)** Kompleks Pondok Pesantren Al Binaa IBS, JI Raya Pebayuran, Kertasari, Pebayuran, Bekasi 17710 – **JB13)** JI Raya Kedunghalang 2, Warung Jambu, Bogor 16155 – **JB14)** Jalan Raya Jatinagor 138, Sumedang 45363 – **JB15)** JI Rawa Pule I, Kukusan, Beji, Depok 16425 – **JB16)** JI Raya Jatiwaringin 50, Bekasi 17411 – **JB17)** JI Raya Cinunuk 84, Cileunyi, Bandung 40393 – **JB18)** ITC Kosambi Blok G-16 Lt I, JI Baranangsiang, Bandung 40112 – **JB19)** JI Ahmad Yani 1, Bekasi – **JB20)** JI Nagrak Cangkuang RT 02/10, Soreang, Bandung – **JB21)** JI Siswa 56, Cikampek, Karawang 41373 – **JB22)** Masjid Umar Ibnul Khatab, Desa Selacau RT 02/05, Lembur Tengah, Batujajar, Bandung Barat 40561 – **JB23)** Jalan Brigpol Nasuha 2, Karawang.
### JH00) JAWA TENGAH (Central Java)
**JH05)** JI Raung 7, Candi Baru, Semarang – **JH06)** JI Kendeng (Pesayangan) 55, Kroya, Cilacap – **JH07)** JI Letjend S Parman 28, Banjarnegara – **JH08)** JI DI Panjaitan 3, Surakarta – **JH09)** JI Veteran 21, Sragen 57211 – **JH10)** Cemani, Sukoharjo – **JH11)** JI Raya Ketek-Kalikajar 33, Wonosobo 56311 – **JH12)** Yayasan Badan Wakaf Sultan Agung (YBWSA), Universitas Islam Sultan Agung, JI Raya Kaligawe Km 4, Semarang 50012 – **JH13)** JI Perentis Kemerdekaan, Watugong, Semarang – **JH14)** JI Raya Delanggu Utara 53, Delanggu, Klaten 57471 – **JH15)** Komplek Perluasan Kota, JI Plongkowati, Wonogiri – **JH16)** JI Kapt Mulyadi 117, Surakarta 57113– **JH17)** JI Dr Muwardi 47, Badranasri, Karanganyar.
### JK00) JAKARTA
**JK02)** JI Matraman 39, Jakarta – **JK03)** JI Swadaya Raya 26/143, Raden Inten, Jakarta – **JK04)** JI Cipinang Timur 15, Rawamangun, Jakarta 13240 – **JK05)** JI Masjid Al Barkah 17, Tebet, Jakarta Selatan – **JK06)** JI Danau Agung II/5-7, Sunter Agung, Podomoro, Jakarta 14350 – **JK07)** J Swadaya 1, Pondok Ranggon, Cipayung, Jakarta Timur – **JK08)** Gedung Sasana Kriya TMII Lantai 2, JI Pondok Gede Arena Taman Mini Indonesia Indah, Jakarta Timur – **JK09)** Kampung Beting, Jakarta Utara – **JK10)** JI Dakota V/1, Kemayoran, Jakarta 10630 –

**JK11)** Jl Tipar Cakung 9, Cilincing, Jakarta Utara – **JK12)** Kampus II Universitas Tarumanegara, Jl. Tanjung Duren Utara no 1 Blok D, Tanjung Duren, Jakarta 11470.– **JK13)** Gedung AKA, Jl Bangka Raya 2, Kebayoran Baru, Jakarta Selatan 12720 – **JK14)** Ikatan Da'i Indonesia, Jl Bambu Apus Raya 62, Jakarta Timur 13890 – **JK15)** Mabes TNI Angkatan Laut (Naval HQ, Indonesian Armed Forces), Jl Rayu Seru, Cilangkap, Jakarta Timur – **JK16)** Menteng, Jakarta.

**JT00) JAWA TIMUR (East Java)**
**JT08)** Komplek STAI Ali Bin Abi Thalib, Jl Sitopo Kidul 51, Surabaya – **JT09)** Jl Simolawang I/96, Surabaya 60144 – **JT10)** Jl Aipda Karel Sasuit Tubun 15, Gresik 61114 – **JT11)** Kompleks Manyar Indah Plaza, Jl Ngagel Jaya Selatan, Surabaya – **JT12)** Jl Ngagel Jaya Utara IV/21, Surabaya 60283 – **JT13)** Jl Amir Hamzah 18, Surabaya 60241 – **JT14)** Jl Teluk Aru 68, Surabaya 60165 – **JT15)** Jl Ahmad Yani 112, Wonokromo, Surabaya.

**KB00) KALIMANTAN BARAT (West Kalimantan)**
**KB04)** Jl Raya Sambas Bukitluwing 1, Sambas – **KB05)** Jl Kom Yos Sudarso 9, Sanggau 78582 – **KB06)** Jl Pembangunan RT 003/XIV, Desa Harapan, Pemangkat 79153.

**KS00) KALIMANTAN SELATAN (South Kalimantan)**
**KS02)** Jl Jend. Sudirman 1, Banjarmasin 70114 – **KS03)** Jl Barintik 35, P.O. Box 48, Martapura 70613

**KT00) KALIMANTAN TIMUR (East Kalimantan)**
**KT04)** Jl A Yani 50, Balikpapan 76123.

**PA00) PAPUA (formerly Irian Jaya)**
**PA10)** Jl Bhayangkara, Wamena – **PA11)** Jl Skyline, Jayapura – **PA12)** Anyelma, Kurima, Yahukimo

**SB00) SUMATERA BARAT (West Sumatra)**
**SB04)** Jl Jend Sudirman 18, Payakumbuh 26211 – **SB05)** Jl W.R Mongonsidi 4B, Lantai 2, Padang.

**SH00) SULAWESI TENGAH (Central Celebes)**
**SH05)** Jl Toraraga 234, Parigi 94371.

**SL00) SULAWESI SELATAN (South Celebes)**
**SL03)** Jl Manggis 16, Makassar 90112 – **SL04)** Masjid Wihdatul Ummah, Jl Abdullah Daeng Sirua 52J, Makassar – **SL05)** Jl Poros Cabenge 1, Watansoppeng – **SL06)** Kompleks Ruko Somba Opu Blok B/19, Tanjung Bunga - Makassar

**SS00) SUMATERA SELATAN (South Sumatra)**
**SS02)** Jl Dr M Isa 38, 8 Ilir, Palembang 30114 – **SS03)** Jl Pramuka I/15, Muara Enim.

**ST00) SULAWESI UTARA (North Celebes)**
**ST04)** Manente, Tahuna, Kepulauan Sangihe.

**SU00) SUMATERA UTARA (North Sumatra)**
**SU05)** Jl Pabrik Tenun 102, Medan – **SU06)** Jl Deli Gg Kereta Api 6, Perbaungan, Deli Serdang 20586.

**YG00) DAERAH ISTIMEWA YOGYAKARTA (Yogyakarta Special Reg.)**
**YG02)** Jl Godean Km 9, Dukuh Sidokarto Godean, Sleman – **YG03)** Jl Panti Wreda 5, Giwangan, Umbulharjo, Yogyakarta 55163 – **YG04)** JSC Satunama, Wiladeg, Gunung Kidul – **YG05)** Jl Parangtritis 22, Tegalsari RT46, Donotirto Kretek, Parangtritis 55772, Bantul – **YG06)** Universitas Islam Indonesia, Jl Demanangbaru 24, Sleman – **YG07)** Balai Pengembangan Media Radio, Pusat Teknologi Informasi dan Komunikasi Pendidikan, Departemen Pendidikan Nasional, Jl Sorowajan Baru 367, Banguntapan, Yogyakarta 55198 – **YG08)** Bantul, Yogyakarta.

**FM Stations:** A large number of FM stns operate throughout the country. See RRI address list for RRI FM freqs.
**Jakarta area FM (MHz):** 87.6 Antarnusa Jaya (Hard Rock) – 87.8 Bogor Swaratama (Sheba), Bogor – 88.0 Mustang Utama – 88.2 M2, Bekasi – 88.4 Arief Rahman Hakim (ARH/Global R.) – 89.2 Power R.– 89.4 Sipatahunan (RSPK Bogor), Bogor – 89.6 Mustika Abadi (I R.) – 90.0 Elshinta – 90.2 Harmoni FM, Bekasi – 90.4 Muara Abdi Nusa Cosmopolitan) – 90.6 RH56, Bekasi – 90.8 Suara Gema Pembangunan Utama (Oz R. Jakarta) – 91.0 Cherry Black R., Bogor – 91.6 Indika Millenia – 92.0 Sonora – 92.2 Radiotemen Nagaswara, Bogor – 92.4 Primaswara Adi Spirit Semesta (PAS/R. Bisnis Jakarta) – 93.0 Teman, Bogor – 93.2 Merpati Dharmawangsa (Hot FM) – 93.4 Kancah Irama Suara Indonesia (KISI), Bogor – 93.6 Gema Wargakarya Satnawa Gaya), Bekasi – 93.9 Swara Mersidiona (Mersi), Tangerang – 94.3 Gardia Asia Bumi (Woman) – 94.5 Ganadas, Bogor – 94.7 Agustina Yunior (U) – 95.1 Kirana Indah Suara (KIS) – 95.3 Pertanian Ciawi, Bogor – 95.5 Siaran Alaikassalam Sejahtera (RAS) – 95.7 Win FM, Bogor – 95.9 Smart Media Utama – 96.3 Pelita Kasih (RPK) – 96.7 Swara Rhadana Dunia (Hitz FM) – 97.1 Suara Monalisa (Dangdut Indonesia) – 97.5 Safari Bina Budaya (Motion) – 97.9 Bahana Sanada Dunia Female), Tangerang – 98.1 One Center, Bekasi – 98.3 Cakrawala Gita Swara (Mandarin Station) – 98.5 Islamic Centre Dakwah Al-Awwabin Rida) , Depok– 98.7 Attahiriyah (Gen) – 99.1 Delta Insani – 99.3 Fajri, Bogor – 99.5 Kayumanis (Smooth) – 99.7 Bahana Suara Alam WADI), Bogor – 99.9 Draba (Virgin Radio Jakarta)– 100.1 Lesmana,

Bogor – 100.3 Elgangga, Bekasi – 100.6 Jati Yaski Mandiri (Heartline), Tangerang – 100.8 Megaswara, Bogor – 101.0 Suara Irama Indah (Jak) – 101.4 Suara Kejayaan (Trax on Sky) – 101.8 Terik Matahari Bahana Pembangunan – 102.2 Prambors – 102.4 Media Akbar Zhapin (ZFM), Depok – 102.6 Camajaya Surya Nada – 102.8 Gema Annisa Persada, Cikarang-Bekasi – 103.0 Irnusa Ria, Depok – 103.2 Duta Swara Parahyangan, Bekasi – 103.4 Taman Mini (DFM) – 103.6 Swara Irama Kusuma Sena (Elpas), Bogor – 103.8 Pesona Gita Anindita (Brava) – 104.0 Forum 77 (8EH), Bekasi – 104.2 Media Suara Trisakti (MS-Tri) – 104.4 Swara Widya Sari (Puncak), Bogor – 104.6 Trijaya Sakti (Sindo Trijaya R.) – 105.4 Niaga Chakti Bhudi Bhakti (CBB) – 105.6 Suara Pendikikan Al-Ihya dan Insan Kamil, Bogor – 105.6 Gema Annisa, Cikarang-Bekasi – 105.8 Ramako Jaya Raya (Most R.) – 106.0 Siaran Gema Nury (Elnury), Bogor – 106.2 Bergaya Nyanyian Irama Sejati, Tangerang (Bens) – 106.4 R. Attaqwa FM, Bekasi – 106.6 Sabda Sosok Sohor (V Radio) – 107.0 Nada Komunikasi Utama (Dakta), Bekasi – 107.2 Cemerlang, Depok – 107.3 Suara Tunggal Angkasa Raya (Star), Tangerang – 107.5 Mitra Carita Enambelas (Music City / MC), Depok – 107.7 Prestasi – 107.7 Islamic R. – 107.7 Sahabat Pramuka (Scout R.), Cibubur – 107.7 UG, Depok – 107.7 Komunitas Institut Pertanian Bogor (Agri), Bogor – 107.9 Suara Sorak Kemenangan – 107.9 Telekomunikasi Cipta (UI FM), Depok – 107.9 Jalesvira Jayamahe (Suara Samudera).
**Bandung FM (MHz):** 87.7 Ekacita Swara Buana (Hard Rock FM) – 88.1 Swara Emas (SE) – 88.5 Mora Purna Karsa – 88.9 Hasil Era Reformasi (Auto Radio) – 89.3 Cipta Swara Global (Elshinta) – 89.7 Media Wisata Sariasih (Global R.) – 90.1 Karang Tumaritis (Zora) – 90.5 Cakra – 90.9 Lita Sari – 91.3 Manca Suara (Sindo R.) – 91.7 Citra Bahana Limbangan (INB) – 92.1 Bandung Suara Indah (Mei Sheng) – 92.5 Madah Ekaristi Swaratronika (Maestro) – 92.9 Arus Rizki (ARFM), Cimahi– 93.3 Ganesha Nada (Walagri) – 93.7 Paramuda – 94.1 Sanndy Qyu, Soreang – 94.4 Bandung Cipta Perdana (Delta FM) – 94.8 Galang Wahana Raya (Radio ON) – 95.2 Swara Pandawa Lima Shakti (Bandung R.) – 95.6 Suara Burinyay (B Radio) – 96.4 Swaratama Cicalengka (Bobotoh) – 96.8 Nada Kencana Agung – 97.2 Shinta Buana – 98.0 Maya Nada – 98.4 Suara Sembilan Delapan Lima (Prambors) – 98.8 Caandika Widya Swara (Sonora) – 99.2 Manggala Gemini Bandung (Kids FM) – 99.6 Thomson – 100.0 Swara Milliard Artha (Ninety-Niners) – 100.4 Ilnafir Karanglayung Citra Budaya Suara (KLCBS) – 100.7 RSPD Kabupaten Bandung (R. Kandaga), Bale Endah – 101.1 Swakarsa Megantara (MGT) – 101.5 Dahlia Flora – 101.9 Putramas Mulia Rahayu (Cosmo) – 102.3 Tiara Rase Perdana – 102.7 Madinatussalam Bandung (MQ) – 103.1 Mitragamma Swara (Oz FM) – 103.5 Citrahutama Eltravidya (Chevy) – 103.9 Antassalam Bagja (Hits) – 104.3 Generasi Muda (U FM) – 104.7 Salam Rama Dwihasta – 105.1 Gema Dwipa (I R.) – 105.5 Garuda Tunggal Angkasa – 105.9 Ardan Swaratama – 106.3 Bhakti Musik Wastukencana (Urban R) – 106.7 Mara Ghita – 107.1 Lintas Kontinental (K-Lite) – 107.5 Mustika Parahyangan (PR FM) – 107.9 Jabar One
**Batam FM (MHz):** 87.6 Discovery Minang – 91.7 Aljabar Serumpun – 100.7 Ramako Batam (Batam FM) – 101.6 Matra Komersial Batam (Zoo FM) – 102.3 Kencana Ria Indah Suara (Kei FM) – 103.2 Artha Media Juanesha (Juan FM) – 104.3 Lintas Sei Ladi (Silaturahim) – 104.7 Batam Indah Gelora Suara (BiGSFM) – 106.0 Media Hang Batam (Hang FM) – 106.5 Suara Marga Semesta (Sing FM) – 107.0 Be FM – 107.7 R. Alfa Omega– 107.8 Rabbani Generation (RG FM) – 107.9 R. Komunitas Hang Tuah
**Denpasar (Bali) FM (MHz):** 87.8 Baturiti Menara Swara (Hard Rock) – 89.4 Gema Sunari Indah – 89.8 Organik Lestari Sejahtera (Pak Oles), Tabanan – 90.2 Suara Yudha (Urban R. Bali) – 90.6 Gema Megantara Pratama (Megantara Bali), Tabanan – 91.0 Gita Bakti Persada (Phoenix) – 91.4 Beat – 91.8 Flamboyant Bali Indah (FBI) – 92.2 Gema Megantara Pesona (Heartline) – 92.6 RPKD Denpasar – 93.3 Berita Bagus Sejati (Thomson News R.), Kuta – 94.1 Swara Swarga (Thomson Dangdut) – 94.9 Click Gita Saraswati, Bangli – 96.1 Genta Suara Bali – 96.5 Suara Kinijani (Global), Tabanan – 96.9 Elang Kosa Gagana (Elkoga) – 97.3 Sonata Indah (Soni) – 97.7 Gema Merdeka – 98.1 Gia, Gianyar – 98.5 Plus – 98.9 Bali Kerta (Bali FM), Gianyar – 99.3 Duta Dewata (Duta Female) – 99.7 Srinadi FM, Klungkung – 100.5 Dunia Bokashi Raya, Klungkung – 101.2 Bali Swara Mitragama (D'Oz R. Bali), Kuta – 102.0 Suara Denpasar Chakti (Cassanova) – 102.4 R. Publik Kabupaten Bangli (RPKB) – 102.8 Menara – 103.2 Mega Nada, Tabanan – 103.6 Pinguin – 104.4 Aneka Rama (AR) – 104.8 R. Gelora Gianyar – 105.6 Bali Mandala Perkasa, Gianyar – 106.0 Swara Kreasi Utama (Kuta R.), Kuta – 106.9 Swara Bukit Bali Indah (BBI), Kuta – 107.2 Swara Smarapura Shakti, Klungkung – 107.7 Komunitas Dwijendra
**Medan FM (MHz):** 87.6 DASS FM, Lubuk Pakam – 88.0 Cikal Anugrah Fiesta (La Femme) – 88.9 RPDK Deli Serdang, Lubuk Pakam – 89.2 Pasopati Perkasa (P FM) – 89.6 Visi Orang Medan Sumatera – 90.0 Gebyar Nada Satuwarna (Hot 90 FM), Deli Serdang – 90.4 Swara Teladan Anugrah (Sonora) – 90.8 Garuda Pentasindo Hutama (Mix FM) – 91.2 Swara Belmera (Istana MBC) – 91.6 Surya Damusu (Umsu FM) – 92.0 Mom's 99, Binjai – 92.8 Suara Dirgantara (Lite FM),

Namorambe – 93.2 Berita Jaringan Global (Elshinta) – 94.7 Bonita Jaya (Suara Medan) – 95.1 Prapanca Buana Suara (Sindo Trijaya R.) – 95.5 Citra Buana Indah (CB) – 95.9 Mutiara Mandiri Buana Swara (City R.) – 96.3 Rhodesa (Medan FM) – 96.7 Citra Ayu Senada (R. Dangdut Indonesia, RDI) – 97.1 Sikamoni – 97.5 Swara Kencana Yuda (Prambors) – 97.9 Tuah Singalorlau (Narwastu FM), Deli Serdang – 98.3 Komersil Siaran Nusantara (I Radio) – 99.1 Khamasutra (Moze FM) – 99.5/106.2 Kardopa – 99.9 Istana Merpati Jaya (Istana MBC) – 100.5 Pelangi Lintas Nusa (Mutiara FM) – 101.0 Suara Binuang (Joy FM) – 101.4 Roris Shinta Rama – 101.8 Radio Media Indah Suara Handalan (Smart FM) – 102.2 Bonsita – 102.6 Alnora (Star News FM) – 103.4 Simponi – 103.8 Gitasukma Bahana (A R.) – 104.2 Mitramedia Dirgantara (R. Maria Indonesia) – 104.6 Anugrah Pradana Muda (Star FM), Deli Serdang – 105.0 Kindung Indah Seleras Suara (KISS FM) – 105.4 Pesona Ciptaswara (RPC), Binjai – 105.8 Medan Cipta Perdana (Delta FM) – 106.6 Sonya Portibi – 107.3 Lips FM– 107.8 Raja FM

**Surabaya FM (MHz):** 87.7 R. Zodiac (Colors) – 88.1 Kota Buaya Mandiri – 88.5 Metro Gema Mega – 88.9 JT-FM (Smart FM)– 89.3 Surabaya Pesona Femina (Prambors) – 89.7 Hafini Jaya Mandiri (Hard Rock FM) – 90.1 Media Caraka Angkasa – 90.4 Ampel Denta– 90.6 Swara Laras Varia Citra Torasih (Rosco R.)– 90.9 Global Nada Prima – 91.3 Suzana Suara Bhakti – 92.5 Kreasi Indah Dunia Swara (Kosmonita) – 92.9 BFM – 93.3 Eka Laras Vicaksana Torya (El Victor) – 93.8 Shamsindo Indonusa (Suara Muslim Surabaya) – 94.4 Suara Digital Indonesia (My Radio) – 94.8 Devina Jelita (DJ FM)– 95.6 TOC FM (R. Spirit) – 96.0 Mercury Masa Depan Sukses – 96.4 Bahtera Yudha – 97.1 Suara Masa Depan Cerah (Life R.) – 97.6 Shinta Warga Gemilang (Elshinta) – 98.0 Salvatore Surabaya (Sonora) – 98.4 Giri Swara Indah Sakti (Swara Giri FM), Gresik – 98.8 Kartika Bahari Dirgantara (M R.) – 99.6 Gitaya Gegana (She R.) – 100.0 Fiskaria Jaya Suara Surabaya – 100.5 Delta FM – 101.1 Laras Pancar Istana Suara (Istara) – 101.5 Cakrawala Bhakti – 101.9 Stratosfir (Strato) – 102.7 Suara Mahasiswa Turun Bekerja (MTB) – 103.1 Camar (Gen FM) – 103.5 Wijaya – 103.8 Rajawali Megah (Primaradio) – 104.3 Bisnis Surabaya (PAS FM) – 104.7 Cakra Awigra (Sindo Trijaya R.) – 105.1 Wahana Informasi Gemilang (JJ R.) – 105.5 Star Wibawa Anugrah, Pandaan – 105.9 Era Bimasakti Selaras (EBS) – 106.7 Merdeka Lokatama – 107.5 Media Assalam Surabaya (SAS FM) – 107.9 Suara An-Nida

## IRAN

**L.T:** UTC +3½h (22 Mar - 22 Sept: +4½h) — **Pop:** 81 million — Pr.L: Farsi (Persian) — **E.C:** 50Hz, 220V — **ITU:** IRN

### ISLAMIC REPUBLIC OF IRAN BROADCASTING (Gov.)
P O. Box 19395-333, Tehran ☎+98 21 2204 1093 🖷 +98 21 2222 1508 **W:** radio.ir **E:** radio@irib.ir **L.P:** President: Abdolali Ali Asgari.

| MW | Region, location | kHz | kW | N | Language, time |
|---|---|---|---|---|---|
| 24) | Iranshahr | 531 | 600 | I | |
| 13) | Sirjan | 549 | 400 | I | |
| 3) | Azarshahr | 558 | 500 | I | |
| 4) | Bushehr | 558 | 200 | I | |
| 5) | Shahr-e-Kord | 558 | 50 | I | |
| 6) | Habibabad | 558 | 200 | I | |
| 7) | Shiraz (Dehnow) | 558 | 400 | I | |
| 8) | Kiashahr | 558 | 100 | I | |
| 9) | Gonbad-e Kavus | 558 | 600 | I | |
| 10) | Hamadan | 558 | 100 | I | |
| 15) | Shushtar | 558 | 400 | I | |
| 21) | Tehran (Goldasteh) | 558 | 600 | I | |
| 24) | Chabahar | 558 | 50 | I | |
| 26) | Yazd | 558 | 50 | I | |
| 26) | Ardakan | 558 | 200 | I | |
| 27) | Zanjan | 558 | 50 | I | |
| 29) | Mashhad | 558 | 200 | I | |
| 30) | Birjand | 558 | 150 | I | |
| 15) | Mahshahr | 576 | 600 | E | Arabic 0330-1630 |
| 2) | Maku | 576 | 50 | I | Azeri |
| 21) | Tehran (Gheslagh) | 585 | 1000 | F | |
| 24) | Zahedan | 594 | 50 | I | |
| 29) | Bajgiran | 603 | 10 | R | |
| 14) | Qasr-e-Shirin | 612 | 600 | E | Arabic 0430-1630 |
| 11) | Bandar Abbas | 621 | 50 | R | |
| 3) | Bonab | 639 | 400 | E | Kur/Tur 0420-1920 |
| 8) | Kiashahr | 657 | 100 | R | |
| 24) | Zahedan | 657 | 100 | I | |
| 7) | Abadeh | 666 | 50 | R | |
| 7) | Darab | 666 | 60 | I | |
| 7) | Lamerd | 666 | 50 | R | |
| 7) | Lar | 666 | 50 | R | |
| 7) | Qir | 666 | 50 | R | |

| MW | Region, location | kHz | kW | N | Language, time |
|---|---|---|---|---|---|
| 7) | Shiraz (Dehnow) | 666 | 400 | R | |
| 29) | Kashmar | 684 | 50 | R | |
| 29) | Mashhad | 684 | 100 | R | |
| 11) | Bandar Lengeh | 693 | 100 | R | |
| 8) | Kiashahr | 702 | 500 | E | Aze/Tur 0320-2020 |
| 15) | Ahvaz | 711 | 600 | R | Arabic/Farsi |
| 14) | Mahidasht | 720 | 750 | I | |
| 29) | Taybad | 720 | 400 | R/E | r. Ardabil 0000-0050, IRIB Azeri 0050-1720 |
| 4) | Dayyer | 738 | 50 | R | |
| 9) | Gonbad-e Kavus | 747 | 600 | I | |
| 13) | Sirjan | 747 | 150 | R | |
| 5) | Shahr-e-Kord | 756 | 200/50 | R | |
| 24) | Chabahar | 765 | 600 | R/E | |
| 19) | Arak | 774 | 100 | R | |
| 24) | Iranshahr | 783 | 150 | R | Baluchi |
| 27) | Sohravard (Zanjan) | 792 | 50 | R | Azeri |
| 18) | Khorramabad | 810 | 100 | R | |
| 20) | Sari | 819 | 30 | R | |
| 30) | Tabas | 828 | 50 | R | |
| 6) | Habibabad | 837 | 300 | R | |
| 3) | Miyaneh | 846 | 50 | R | Azeri |
| 14)Qasr-e-Shirin | | 864 | 50 | R | |
| 28) | Bojnurd | 873 | 50 | R | |
| 32) | Mahabad | 882 | 60 | R | Kurdish |
| 16) | Dehdasht | 891 | 50 | R | Luri |
| 16) | Yasouj | 891 | 50 | R | Luri |
| 25) | Tehran (Goldasteh) | 900 | 600 | Q | Arabic |
| 13) | Jiroft | 918 | 50 | R | |
| 18) | Dorud | 927 | 50 | R | |
| 2) | Miandoab | 936 | 300 | R | Azeri/Kurdish |
| 2) | Urmia | 936 | 50 | R | Azeri/Kurdish |
| 17) | Dehgolan | 945 | 100 | R | |
| 30) | Birjand | 963 | 150 | R | |
| 12) | Ilam | 972 | 100 | R | |
| 10) | Hamadan | 981 | 100 | R | |
| 17) | Baneh | 999 | 50 | R | Kurdish |
| 23) | Semnan | 1008 | 100 | R | |
| 11) | Bandar Abbas | 1017 | 50 | I | |
| 3) | Azarshahr | 1026 | 200 | R | Azeri |
| 23) | Yazd | 1035 | 100 | R | |
| 12) | Dehloran | 1044 | 50 | R | |
| 18) | Khorramabad | 1053 | 100 | I | |
| 23) | Saravan | 1053 | 30 | R | |
| 13) | Kerman | 1062 | 200 | R | |
| 22) | Qom (Alborz) | 1071 | 100 | M | |
| 15) | Mahshahr | 1080 | 600 | E | Arabic 1630-0030 |
| 23) | Shahrud | 1089 | 50 | R | |
| 24) | Zabol | 1098 | 200 | E | Afghan langs. 0130-1720 |
| 29) | Sabzevar | 1107 | 50 | R | |
| 21) | Qazvin | 1125 | 50 | R | |
| 3) | Kaleybar | 1134 | 10 | R | Azeri |
| 16) | Yasuj | 1143 | 50 | I | |
| 14) | Qasr-e-Shirin | 1161 | 600 | E | Arab. 0130-0420,1630-2130 |
| 25) | Tehran | 1188 | 300 | P | |
| 1) | Moghan | 1197 | 50 | R | Azeri |
| 30) | Nehbandan | 1206 | 10 | R | |
| 20) | Chalus (Darya) | 1215 | 60 | R | |
| 11) | Kish Island | 1224 | 300 | E | Arabic |
| 13) | Kerman | 1224 | 50 | I | |
| 6) | Khur | 1260 | 10 | R | |
| 1) | Khalkhal | 1269 | 50 | R | Azeri |
| 14) | Kermanshah | 1278 | 300 | R | |
| 24) | Zabol | 1296 | 50 | R | |
| 4) | Bushehr | 1305 | 50 | R | |
| 1) | Ardabil | 1314 | 50 | I | |
| 3) | Jolfa | 1323 | 50 | E/R | Azeri 0030-2030 |
| 25) | Tehran (Goldasteh) | 1332 | 300 | T | |
| 13) | Bam | 1341 | 20 | R | |
| 9) | Gonbad-e Kavus | 1368 | 150 | R | |
| 24) | Chabahar | 1377 | 50 | R | Baluchi |
| 14) | Paveh | 1377 | 50 | R | |
| 11) | Hajiabad | 1395 | 50 | R | |
| 9) | Gorgan | 1395 | 50 | E | Turkmen 1420-1820 |
| 1) | Qir | 1404 | 10 | I | |
| 7) | Estahban | 1413 | 10 | R | |
| 9) | Bandar-e-Torkamen | 1449 | 400 | E | Turkmen 1220-1820 |
| 30) | Ghayen | 1458 | 10 | R | |
| 22) | Alborz | ±1467 | 100 | R | |
| 17) | Marivan | ±1476 | 20 | R | Kurdish |
| 2) | Khoy | 1485 | 10 | R | Azeri |
| 7) | Jahrom | 1485 | 10 | R | |

| MW | Region, location | kHz | kW | N | Language, time |
|---|---|---|---|---|---|
| 23) | Damghan | 1485 | 1 | I | |
| 29) | Taybad | 1494 | 10 | R | |
| 33) | Jamshidabad | 1485 | 400 | R | Arabic |
| 1) | Ardabil | 1512 | 50 | R | Azeri |
| 9) | Gorgan | 1539 | 50 | R | |
| 23) | Garmsar | 1539 | 10 | I | |
| 16) | Gachsaran | 1548 | 10 | R | |
| 17) | Sanandaj | 1548 | 10 | I | |
| 20) | Larijan | 1548 | 10 | R | |
| 22) | Eshtehard | 1548 | 10 | I | |
| 23) | Shahroud | 1548 | 50 | I | |
| 30) | Ferdows | 1548 | 10 | R | |
| 24) | Zabol | 1557 | 50 | I | |
| 13) | Bam | 1566 | 50 | I | |
| 15) | Abadan | 1575 | 800 | | 1430-0230 |
| 23) | Biyarjomand | 1584 | 50 | R | |
| 23) | [unk. location] | 1584 | 10 | R | |
| 7) | Kazerun | 1602 | 10 | R | |
| 15) | Dezful | 1602 | 1 | R | |
| 23) | Damghan | 1602 | 10 | R | |
| 23) | Garmsar | 1602 | 10 | R | |
| 26) | Bahabad | 1602 | 1 | I | |

± variable frequency. Other languages than Farsi mentioned. Time given, if known by monitoring not to be 24h.

| FM | Location | J | I | V | A | R | M |
|---|---|---|---|---|---|---|---|
| 1 | Ardabil | 88.0 | 90.3 | 92.3 | 102.3 | 94.3 | 96.3 |
| 2 | Urmia | 88.5 | 90.5 | 92.5 | 98.5 | 94.5 | 96.5 |
| 3 | Tabriz 1 | 88.0 | 90.0 | 92.0 | 102.0 | 94.0 | 96.0 |
| 3 | Tabriz 2 | - | 91.0 | 93.0 | 99.0 | - | 97.0 |
| 4 | Bushehr | - | - | - | - | 92.2 | - |
| 5 | Shahr-e-Kord | 88.0 | 90.0 | 92.0 | 102.0 | 94.0 | 96.0 |
| 6 | Isfahan 1 | 89.0 | 91.0 | 93.0 | 93.5 | 95.0 | 97.0 |
| 6 | Isfahan 2 | 88.5 | 90.5 | 92.5 | 107.5 | 94.5 | 96.5 |
| 7 | Shiraz | 88.0 | 90.0 | 92.0 | 93.5 | 94.0 | 96.0 |
| 8 | Rasht | 89.0 | 91.0 | 93.0 | 93.5 | 95.0 | 97.0 |
| 9 | Gorgan | 88.3 | 90.3 | 92.3 | 99.0 | 94.3 | 96.3 |
| 10 | Hamadan | 88.0 | 90.0 | 92.0 | 93.5 | 94.0 | 96.0 |
| 11 | Bandar Abbas | 87.9 | 90.1 | 91.8 | 93.4 | 94.2 | 96.0 |
| 11 | Kish Island | 87.6 | 89.9 | 93.0 | 93.5 | 99.2 | 96.8 |
| 12 | Ilam | 88.0 | 90.0 | 92.0 | - | 94.0 | 96.0 |
| 13 | Kerman | 88.0 | 90.0 | 92.0 | 93.5 | 94.0 | 96.0 |
| 14 | Kermanshah | 88.0 | 90.0 | 92.0 | - | 94.0 | 96.0 |
| 15 | Abadan | 87.6 | 89.7 | 92.7 | - | 93.8 | 95.6 |
| 15 | Ahwaz | 88.0 | 90.0 | 92.0 | 93.5 | 94.0 | 96.0 |
| 16 | Yasuj | 88.0 | 90.0 | 92.0 | - | 94.0 | 96.0 |
| 17 | Sanandaj | 88.0 | 90.0 | 92.0 | - | 94.0 | 96.0 |
| 18 | Khorramabad | 88.0 | 90.0 | 92.0 | - | 94.0 | 96.0 |
| 19 | Arak | 88.3 | 90.3 | 92.3 | 93.3 | 94.3 | 96.3 |
| 20 | Sari | 88.0 | 90.0 | 92.0 | 93.5 | 94.0 | 96.0 |
| 21 | Qazvin | 88.2 | 90.2 | 92.2 | - | 94.2 | 96.2 |
| 22 | Qom | 88.5 | 90.5 | 92.5 | - | 94.5 | 96.5 |
| 23 | Semnan | 88.0 | 90.0 | 92.0 | - | 94.0 | 96.0 |
| 24 | Zahedan | 88.0 | 90.0 | 92.0 | - | 94.0 | 96.0 |
| 25 | Tehran | 88.0 | 90.0 | 92.0 | 93.5 | 94.0 | 96.0 |
| 26 | Yazd | 88.0 | 90.0 | 92.0 | - | 94.0 | 96.0 |
| 27 | Zanjan | 88.5 | 90.5 | 92.5 | 93.5 | 94.5 | 96.5 |
| 28 | Bojnurd | 88.0 | 90.0 | 92.0 | - | 94.0 | 96.0 |
| 29 | Mashhad | 88.0 | 90.0 | 92.0 | 93.5 | 94.0 | 96.0 |
| 30 | Birjand | 88.0 | 90.0 | 92.0 | - | 94.0 | 96.0 |
| 31 | Karaj | 88.9 | 90.9 | 92.9 | - | 94.9 | 96.9 |
| 32 | Mahabad | 87.8 | 89.8 | 91.8 | - | 95.8 | - |

| FM | Location | Eg | Q | S | P | F |
|---|---|---|---|---|---|---|
| 1 | Ardabil | 98.3 | 100.3 | - | 104.3 | 106.3 |
| 2 | Urmia | 98.8 | 100.5 | 102.5 | 104.5 | 106.5 |
| 3 | Tabriz 1 | 98.0 | 100.0 | - | 104.0 | 106.0 |
| 3 | Tabriz 2 | - | - | 103.0 | - | 107.0 |
| 4 | Bushehr | | | | | |
| 5 | Shahr-e-Kord | 98.0 | 100.0 | - | 104.0 | 106.0 |
| 6 | Isfahan 1 | 99.0 | 101.0 | 103.0 | 105.0 | 107.0 |
| 6 | Isfahan 2 | 98.5 | 100.5 | 102.5 | 104.5 | 106.5 |
| 7 | Shiraz | 98.0 | 100.0 | 102.0 | 104.0 | 106.0 |
| 8 | Rasht | 99.0 | 101.0 | 103.0 | 105.0 | 107.0 |
| 9 | Gorgan | 98.3 | 100.3 | 102.3 | 104.3 | 106.3 |
| 10 | Hamadan | 98.0 | 100.3 | 102.0 | 104.0 | 106.0 |
| 11 | Bandar Abbas | 98.6 | 100.2 | 101.8 | 104.3 | 106.6 |
| 11 | Kish Island | 97.7 | 99.7 | 102.8 | 104.6 | 105.8 |
| 12 | Ilam | 98.0 | 100.0 | 102.0 | 104.0 | 106.0 |
| 13 | Kerman | 98.0 | 100.0 | 102.0 | 104.0 | 106.0 |
| 14 | Kermanshah | 98.0 | 100.0 | 102.0 | 104.0 | 106.0 |
| 15 | Abadan | 97.6 | 99.6 | 101.6 | 104.9 | 106.7 |
| 15 | Ahwaz | 98.0 | 100.0 | 102.0 | 104.0 | 106.0 |

| FM | Location | Eg | Q | S | P | F |
|---|---|---|---|---|---|---|
| 16 | Yasuj | 98.0 | 100.0 | 102.0 | 104.0 | 106.0 |
| 17 | Sanandaj | 98.0 | 100.0 | 102.0 | 104.0 | 106.0 |
| 18 | Khorramabad | 98.0 | 100.0 | 102.0 | 104.0 | 106.0 |
| 19 | Arak | 98.3 | 100.3 | 102.3 | 104.3 | 106.3 |
| 20 | Sari | 98.0 | 100.0 | 102.0 | 104.0 | 106.0 |
| 21 | Qazvin | 98.2 | 100.2 | 102.2 | 104.2 | 106.2 |
| 22 | Qom | 98.5 | 100.5 | 102.5 | 104.5 | 106.5 |
| 23 | Semnan | 98.0 | 100.0 | 102.0 | 104.0 | 106.0 |
| 24 | Zahedan | 98.0 | 100.0 | 102.0 | 104.0 | 106.0 |
| 25 | Tehran | 98.0 | 100.0 | 102.0 | 104.0 | 106.0 |
| 26 | Yazd | 98.0 | 100.0 | 102.0 | 104.0 | 106.0 |
| 27 | Zanjan | 98.5 | 100.5 | 102.5 | 104.5 | 106.5 |
| 28 | Bojnurd | 98.0 | 100.0 | 102.0 | 104.0 | 106.0 |
| 29 | Mashhad | 98.0 | 100.0 | 102.0 | 104.0 | 106.0 |
| 30 | Birjand | 98.0 | 100.0 | 102.0 | 104.0 | 106.0 |
| 31 | Karaj | 98.9 | 100.9 | 102.9 | 104.9 | 106.9 |
| 32 | Mahabad | - | 99.8 | - | 103.8 | 105.8 |

**NB:** Only main FM transmitter sites for each production studio listed. Iran authorities have not provided comprehensive update information regarding their transmitter network in recent years and all information is based on various web sources and monitoring observations.

**Stations of provincial or regional centres: 1)** Ardabil – **2)** West Azerbaijan **E:** 162-waz@irib.ir – **3)** East Azerbaijan **E:** tabriz@irib.ir – **4)** Bushehr **E:** prbushehr@irib.ir – **5)** Chaharmahal & Bakhtiari: R. Jahanbin – **6)** Isfahan **E:** isfahan@irib.ir – **7)** R. Fars **W:** fars.irib.ir – **8)** Gilan **E:** gilan@irib.ir – **9)** Golestan – **10)** Hamadan – **11)** Hormozgan: R. Khalij e Fars: **W:** khalijefars.irib.ir R. Kish: info@kish.irib.ir – **12)** Ilam – **13)** Kerman **E:** web@kerman.irib.ir – **14)** Kermanshah – **15)** R. Khuzestan, Ahvaz (also Arabic) – **16)** Kohgiluyeh & Boyerahmad: R. Dena – **17)** Kurdistan – **18)** Lorestan – **19)** Markazi – **20)** Mazandaran: R. Tabaristan **E:** 162-mzn@irib.ir – **21)** Qazvin – **22)** Qom **E:** info@qom.irib.ir – **23)** Semnan **E:** semnan@irib.ir – **24)** Sistan & Baluchestan **E:** zahedan@irib.ir – **25)** Tehran – **26)** Yazd **E:** taban@yazd.irib.ir – **27)** Zanjan – **28)** North Khorasan (R. Bojnurd) **E:** kh-shomali@irib.ir – **29)** Razavi Khorasan: R. Mashhad **E:** infoplanning-ksnr@irib.ir – **30)** South Khorasan: R. Khorasan-e Jonubi **E:** birjand@irib.ir – **31)** Alborz – **32)** Mahabad – **33)** Abadan **E:** prabadan@irib.ir
**NB:** Access to regional web pages also via **W:** dpp.irib.ir/radio

**Networks:**
**I=Radio Iran:** 24h, but hrs. of operation vary by station. Frequencies for R. Iran and provincial prgrs at the same transmitter site may be swapped. Gradually all R. Iran MW transmitters will be concentrated to 558 kHz synchronous frequency. **N:** on the half hour – **R=Regional (Provincial) network.** Studios in 33 centres producing prgrs in Farsi and local langs, including some locally produced Ext. Sce prgrs. Regional prgrs are usually 24h. Most provincial stations also carry "Shabhaye Iran" (Iran Nights) between 2030-2230, produced in turn by each studio. **E=External Service – J=R. Javan** (Youth): 24h on FM – **V=R. Varzesh** (Sports) on FM – **A=R Ava** (Music Radio): 24h on FM – **M=R. Ma'aref** ("Religious Knowledge", rlg.): 24h on MW 1071kHz & FM. – **Eg=R. Eghtesad** (Economy) on FM – **Q=R. Quran**(rlg.): 24h on MW 900kHz and FM – **S=R. Salamat** (Health R): 24h on FM – **P=R. Payam** ("Message", music, traffic, news): 24h on MW 1188kHz + FM – **F=R. Farhang** (cultural): 24h on MW 585kHz & FM – **T=Tehran Province Prgr**. 24h on MW 1332kHz & FM 94.0MHz – **R. Tartil** (Quran): Tehran 101.5MHz - **R. Goftogoo** (Dialogue), Tehran: 24h on 103.5MHz – **R. Saba** (Humour): Tehran 105.5MHz – **R. Namayesh** (Theatre): Tehran 107.5MHz.

**Foreign Language prgrs in Tehran:** English 91.5MHz, Arabic 97.5MHz, various languages 99.5MHz.

**Ann: J:** "Inja Tehran ast, Sedaye Jomhuriye Islamiye Iran, Shabakeye Radyoe-ye Javan". **I:** "Inja Tehran ast, Sedaye Jomhuriye Islamiye Iran, Shabakeye Radyoe-ye Iran". **V:** "Inja Tehran ast, Sedaye Jomhuriye Islamiye Iran, Shabakeye Radyoe-ye Varzesh". **A:** "Inja Tehran ast, Sedaye Jomhuriye Islamiye Iran, Radyoe Ava". **R:** "Inja (capital) ast, Sedaye Jomhuriye Islamiye Iran, shabakeye ostaniye (province)." **M:** "Inja Qom ast, Sedaye Jomhuriye Islamiye Iran, Shabakeye Radyoe-ye Ma'aref". **Eq:** "Inja Tehran ast, Sedaye Jomhuriye Islamiye Iran, Shabakeye Radyoe-ye Eghtesad". **Q:** "Inja Tehran ast, Sedaye Jomhuriye Islamiye Iran, Shabakeye Radyoe-ye Qur'an". **S:** "Inja Tehran ast, Sedaye Jomhuriye Islamiye Iran, Shabakeye Radyoe-ye Salamat". **P:** "Inja Tehran ast, Sedaye Jomhuriye Islamiye Iran, Shabakeye Radyoe-ye Payam". **F:** "Inja Tehran ast, Sedaye Jomhuriye Islamiye Iran, Shabakeye Radyoe-ye Farhang".

**EXTERNAL SERVICE: Pars Today:** see International Radio section

## IRAQ

**L.T:** UTC +3h — **Pop:** 39 million — **Pr.L:** Arabic, Kurdish, Assyrian, Turkoman — **E.C:** 50Hz, 230V — **ITU:** IRQ

### COMMUNICATIONS AND MEDIA COMMISSION (CMC)
✉ P.O. Box 2044, District 929, Street 32, Building 18 , Jadreiah, Baghdad ☎+964 1 7180009 🖷 +964 1 719 5839 **W:** cmc.iq **E:** enquiries@cmc.iq **L.P:** Deputy Dir: Ali Nasir.

### IRAQI MEDIA NETWORK (Gov)
✉ near Al-Mansoor Melia Hotel, Salihiya, Baghdad **W:** imn.iq **E:** info@imn.iq **L.P:** DG: Hassan Al-Musawi. Dir. Eng: Emad Aziz.

| MW | kHz | kW | Prgr. |
|---|---|---|---|
| Baghdad | 792 | 20 | Main |

| FM | MHz | kW | Prgr. | FM | MHz | kW | Prgr. |
|---|---|---|---|---|---|---|---|
| Diwaniya | 88.1 | | Provincial | Salah al-Din | 98.0 | | Al-Iraqiya |
| Mosul | 88.7 | | Main/Prov. | Baghdad | 98.3 | 1 | Main |
| Ninewa | 88.7 | | Main | Kut | 98.5 | 1 | Al-Iraqiya |
| Sinjar | 90.5 | | Main | Qaim | 98.5 | | Main |
| Ramadi | 90.8 | | Main | Rutba | 99.0 | | Main |
| Kirkuk | 91.5 | | Main | Nasiriya | 99.0 | | Quran |
| Hit | 92.0 | | Main | Babylon | 99.0 | | Provincial |
| Karbala | 92.2 | 1 | Main | Haditha | 99.0 | | Al-Iraqiya |
| Muthanna | 92.7 | | Main | Falluja | 99.9 | 1 | Main |
| Karbala | 93.3 | | Provincial | Basra | 100.5 | 5 | Main |
| Shomali | 94.2 | 10 | Main | Najaf | 101.0 | 5 | Provincial |
| Baquba | 94.8 | 10 | Provincial | Baghdad | 103.3 | | Al-Iraqiya |
| Ali Al-Garbi | 95.0 | | Main | Mosul | 103.3 | | Main/Prov. |
| Diyala | 96.0 | | Al-Iraqiya | Amara | 104.1 | | Quran |
| Maysan | 96.1 | | Al-Iraqiya | Baghdad | 105.0 | | Al Jel |
| Tikrit | 96.1 | | Main | Amara | 106.0 | | Main |
| Najaf | 96.5 | 5 | Quran | | | | |

**Main Prgr** (Republic of Iraq R.): 24h in Arabic on on MW and FM except for Provincial programmes on some transmitters during the day. **R. Al-Iraqiya:** 24h. **Quran prgr** (R. Furqan): 24h. **R. Al Jel** (for youth). **R. Nineva:** daytime on Mosul trs. **Ann:** Main prgr: "Idha'at Jumhuriyah al-Iraq min Baghdad".

**Other stations:**

| | MW | kHz | kW | Location | Station | H of tr |
|---|---|---|---|---|---|---|
| 5) | | 999 | 20 | Baghdad | R. Bilad | 0240-1810 |
| 6) | | 1008 | 20 | Najaf | Sowt al-Fadhila | |
| | | 1017 | 10 | Karbala | R. Karbala | |
| 7) | | 1053 | 3 | Baghdad | R. As-Salam | 0300-2100 |
| 10) | | 1116 | 20 | Baghdad | R. Dar as-Salam | 0230-2100 |
| 11) | | 1179 | 30 | Baghdad | R. Voice of Iraq | 0400-1800 |

| | FM | MHz | kW | Location | Station | H of tr |
|---|---|---|---|---|---|---|
| 14) | | 87.5 | | Penjwin | R. Garmiyan (Yekgirtu R.) | |
| 48) | | 87.5 | | Kirkuk | R. Vision | |
| 21) | | 87.7 | 1 | Baghdad | Monte-Carlo Doualiya | 24h |
| 9) | | 87.8 | | Kirkuk | Vo Kurdistan | 0300-2000 |
| 10) | | 88.0 | | Kirkuk | R. Dar as-Salam | 0400-2100 |
| 20) | | 88.0 | | Sulaimaniya | R. Sawa | 24h |
| 21) | | 88.1 | 1 | Mosul | Monte-Carlo Doualiya | 24h |
| 43) | | 88.2 | | Baghdad | R. Dijla | 0500-0100 |
| 22) | | 88.3 | 1 | Sulaimaniya | R. Nawxo | |
| 1) | | 88.4 | | Karbala | Imam Hussein FM | 0200-1900 |
| 22) | | 88.4 | | Erbil | R. Nawxo | |
| 43) | | 88.4 | | Basra | R. Dijla | 0500-0100 |
| 22) | | 88.4 | | Halabja | R. Nawxo | |
| 46) | | 88.5 | | Mosul | R. Nawa (Arabic) | |
| 18) | | 88.5 | | Sulaimaniya | Traffic FM | |
| 23) | | 88.6 | 1 | Baghdad | Panorama FM | 24h |
| 38) | | 88.6 | 1 | Halabja | R. Dênge Nwe | 0500-1700 |
| 20) | | 88.8 | | Sulaimaniya | VOA | 24h |
| 47) | | 88.9 | | Erbil | R. Duhok | 0400-2300 |
| 19) | | 89.0 | 2 | Baghdad +2 stns | BBC Arabic | 24h |
| 39) | | 89.0 | | Kirkuk | R. Ashur | |
| 47) | | 89.0 | | Amediye | R. Duhok | 0400-2300 |
| 46) | | 89.1 | | Penjwin | R. Nawa (Kurdish) | |
| 14) | | 89.1 | | Kalar | R. Garmiyan (Yekgirtu R.) | |
| 3) | | 89.1 | | Basra | R. Al-Amal | |
| 8) | | 89.1 | | Sulaimaniya | R. Al-Hayat Al-Jadida | 0300-2200 |
| 45) | | 89.3 | 10 | Amara | Al-Mirbad R. | 24h |
| 46) | | 89.3 | | Saidsadeq | R. Nawa (Kurdish) | |
| 46) | | 89.3 | | Halabja | R. Nawa (Kurdish) | |
| 10) | | 89.4 | | Mosul | R. Dar as-Salam | 0500-2100 |
| | | 89.4 | | | R. Melbend | |
| 46) | | 89.5 | 4 | Kirkuk | R. Nawa (Kurdish) | |

| | FM | MHz | kW | Location | Station | H of tr |
|---|---|---|---|---|---|---|
| 47) | | 89.5 | | Duhok | R. Duhok | 0400-2300 |
| 20) | | 89.6 | | Al-Amara | VOA | 24h |
| | | 89.6 | | | VO Islam (Kurdish) | |
| 31) | | 89.7 | | Karbala | Al-Huda Islamic R. | 24h |
| 4) | | 89.9 | | Mosul | R. Al-Ghad | |
| 46) | | 89.9 | 5 | Baghdad | R. Nawa (Kurdish) | |
| 46) | | 89.9 | 1 | Kalar | R. Nawa (Kurdish) | |
| 19) | | 90.0 | 1 | Basra | BBC Arabic | 24h |
| 24) | | 90.0 | | Kirkuk | Turkoman FM | 0510-2200 |
| 39) | | 90.0 | | Mosul | R, Ashur | |
| 27) | | 90.3 | | Baghdad | R. Al-Noor | (inactive) |
| 36) | | 90.3 | | Sulaimaniya | Ur FM | 24h |
| 36) | | 90.3 | | Kirkuk | Ur FM | 24h |
| 20) | | 90.4 | 1 | Hilla | R. Sawa | 24h |
| 26) | | 90.4 | | Baghdad | R. Al-Yauwm | -1500 |
| 42) | | 90.4 | | Basra | R. Al-Ahd | |
| 17) | | 90.6 | 0.1 | Kirkuk | R. Lawani Kurdistan | |
| 46) | | 90.7 | 1 | Sulaimaniya | R. Nawa (Arabic) | |
| 46) | | 90.7 | 2 | Duhok/Zakho | R. Nawa (Arabic) | |
| 46) | | 91.1 | 2 | Zakho | R. Nawa (Kurdish) | |
| 10) | | 91.1 | 1 | Baghdad/Tikrit | R. Dar as-Salam | 0500-2100 |
| 39) | | 91.1 | | Nineva | R. Ashur | |
| 3) | | 91.3 | | Najaf | R. Al-Amal | |
| 9) | | 91.4 | | Salah al Din | Vo Kurdistan | 0300-2000 |
| 28) | | 91.5 | 5 | Baghdad | Al-Rasheed R. | 0300-2300 |
| 9) | | 91.5 | | Erbil | VO Kurdistan | 0300-2000 |
| 47) | | 91.5 | | Zakho | R. Duhok | 0400-2300 |
| 20) | | 91.6 | | Al-Amara | R. Sawa | 24h |
| 28) | | 91.6 | 5 | Basra | Al-Rasheed R. | 0300-2300 |
| 19) | | 91.7 | | Nasiriya | BBC Arabic | 24h |
| 20) | | 91.7 | | Mosul | VOA | 24h |
| 34) | | 91.7 | | Sulaimaniya | Zed R. | |
| 46) | | 90.7 | 8 | Ramadi | R. Nawa (Arabic) | |
| 40) | | 91.8 | | Basra | Sumer FM | 24h |
| 7) | | 91.9 | 0.3 | Baghdad | R. As-Salam | 0700-2100 |
| 46) | | 91.9 | 3 | Duhok/Halabja | R. Nawa (Kurdish) | |
| 46) | | 91.9 | 9 | Sara-Dokan | R. Nawa (Kurdish) | |
| 21) | | 92.0 | 1 | Basra | Monte-Carlo Doualiya | 24h |
| 17) | | 92.0 | 0.1 | Ranye | R. Lawani Kurdistan | |
| 46) | | 92.0 | 9 | 4 locations | R. Nawa (Kurdish) | |
| 28) | | 92.1 | | Kirkuk | Al-Rasheed R. | 0300-2300 |
| 20) | | 92.2 | | Hilla | R. Sawa | 24h |
| 34) | | 92.3 | | Erbil/Duhok | Zed R. | |
| 46) | | 92.3 | 1 | Sulaiminiyah | R. Nawa (Music) | |
| 19) | | 92.5 | 2 | Sulaimaniya | BBC Arabic | 24h |
| 34) | | 92.5 | | Kirkuk | Zed R. | |
| 46) | | 92.5 | | Basra/Koya | R. Nawa (Arabic) | |
| 51) | | 92.5 | | Mosul | Start FM | |
| 46) | | 92.7 | | Erbil | R. Nawa (Arabic) | |
| 1) | | 92.7 | | Najaf/Wasit | Imam Hussein FM | 0200-1900 |
| 32) | | 92.8 | 0.6 | Basra | Al-Nakhil R. | 0300-2100 |
| 40) | | 92.8 | | Sulaimaniya | Sumer FM | 24h |
| 19) | | 92.9 | 2 | Kirkuk | BBC Arabic | 24h |
| 43) | | 93.1 | | Sulaimaniya | R. Dijla | 0500-0100 |
| 43) | | 93.1 | | Mosul | R. Dijla | |
| 45) | | 93.3 | 5 | Basra | Al-Mirbad R. | 24h |
| 9) | | 93.3 | | Dohuk | Vo Kurdistan | 0300-2000 |
| 5) | | 93.5 | | Baghdad | R. Bilad | 0400-1700 |
| 20) | | 93.6 | | Samawa | VOA | 24h |
| 1) | | 93.7 | | Baghdad | Imam Hussein FM | 0200-1900 |
| 52) | | 93.7 | | Sulaimaniya | R. Taxi | |
| 46) | | 93.9 | 17 | Kalak/Khanaqin | R. Nawa (Arabic) | |
| 20) | | 94.0 | | Baquba | VOA | 24h |
| 43) | | 94.0 | | Mosul | R. Dijla | 0500-0100 |
| 46) | | 94.6 | | Kirkuk | R. Nawa (Arabic) | |
| 4) | | 94.7 | | Mosul | R. Al-Ghad | |
| 2) | | 95.0 | | Baghdad | Sawt al-Khaleej | |
| 28) | | 95.5 | | Mosul | Al-Rasheed R | 0300-2300 |
| 4) | | 95.5 | | | R. Al-Ghad | |
| 12) | | 95.5 | | Kirkuk | VO People Kurdistan | 0500-2100 |
| 20) | | 95.6 | 10 | Samawa | R. Sawa | 24h |
| 43) | | 95.7 | | Erbil/Kirkuk | R. Dijla | |
| 53) | | 95.7 | | Sulaimaniya | Voice of Kurdsat (English) | |
| 19) | | 96.0 | 2 | Mosul | BBC Arabic | 24h |
| | | 96.1 | | Najaf | Al-Ghadeer R. | |
| 30) | | 96.1 | | Babylon | R. Al-Hilla | |
| 33) | | 96.1 | 5 | Baghdad | R. Al-Mahaba | |
| 35) | | 96.3 | | No. Iraq | Guven R. | |
| 53) | | 96.3 | | Sulaimaniya | Dengê Kurdsat (Kurdish) | |
| 43) | | 96.5 | | Samara | R. Dijla | 0500-0100 |
| 46) | | 96.5 | | Koya/Qaladezi | R. Nawa (Kurdish) | |
| 1) | | 96.6 | 5 | Baghdad | R. Al-Nas | 0400-1500 |

| FM | MHz | kW | Location | Station | H of tr |
|---|---|---|---|---|---|
| 20) | 96.8 | | Kirkuk | VOA | 24h |
| 19) | 96.9 | 2 | Baghdad | BBC English | 24h |
| 8) | 97.1 | | Sulaimaniya | R. Al-Hayat Al-Jadida | 0300-2200 |
| 20) | 97.1 | 2 | Tikrit | R. Sawa | 24h |
| 46) | 97.1 | | Ranya/Sara | R. Nawa (Kurdish) | |
| 37) | 97.3 | | Baghdad | Sowt al-Jam'ah | |
| 20) | 97.5 | | Baquba | R. Sawa | 24h |
| 28) | 97.5 | | Mosul | Al-Rasheed R | 0300-2300 |
| 46) | 97.5 | | Penjwin/Zmnako | R. Nawa (Kurdish) | |
| 20) | 97.6 | | Ramadi | VOA | 24h |
| 45) | 97.7 | 10 | Samawa | Al-Mirbad R. | 24h |
| 12) | 97.9 | | Baghdad | Al-Hurriyah R. | 0500-2100 |
| 36) | 97.9 | | Basra | Ur FM | 24h |
| 24) | 98.0 | 0.1 | Erbil | Turkoman FM | 0510-2200 |
| 40) | 98.2 | | Erbil | Sumer FM | 24h |
| 46) | 98.5 | | Mosul | R. Nawa (Arabic) | |
| 2) | 98.7 | | Basra | Sawt al-Khaleej | |
| 43) | 98.8 | | Erbil | R. Dijla | 0500-0100 |
| 20) | 98.8 | 1 | Kirkuk | R. Sawa | 24h |
| | 98.8 | | Babylon | University R. | |
| 36) | 98.9 | 5 | Baghdad | Ur FM | 24h |
| 36) | 98.9 | | Salah-al-Din | Ur FM | 24h |
| 36) | 98.9 | | Mosul | Ur FM | 24h |
| 36) | 98.9 | | Ramadi/Diyala | Ur FM | 24h |
| 25) | 99.1 | | Karbala | Karbala FM | 0300-1500 |
| 15) | 99.3 | 3 | Bahrez | Ind. RTV Netw. | 0500-2100 |
| 45) | 99.3 | 0.3 | Kut | Al-Mirbad R. | 24h |
| 54) | 99.3 | | Sulaimaniya | Babylon FM | |
| 39) | 99.4 | | Baghdad | R. Ashur | 0600-1700 |
| 20) | 99.6 | | Ramadi | R. Sawa | 24h |
| 22) | 99.9 | | Kirkuk | R. Nawxo | |
| 40) | 99.9 | 5 | Baghdad | Sumer FM | 24h |
| 40) | 99.9 | | Dohuk | Sumer FM | 24h |
| 14) | 100.2 | | Tawella | R. Garmiyan (Yekgirtu R.) | |
| 42) | 101.0 | | Baghdad | R. Al-Ahd | |
| 20) | 101.1 | | Tikrit | VOA | 24h |
| 45) | 101.4 | 10 | Nasiriya | Al-Mirbad R. | 24h |
| 17) | 101.5 | | Baghdad | VO Iraqi National Congress | |
| 41) | 102.0 | 3 | Baghdad | R. Shafaq | 0300-2300 |
| 55) | 102.1 | | Sulaimaniya | Nalia FM | |
| 20) | 102.4 | 10 | Baghdad | R. Sawa (alt. fq 100.5) | 24h |
| 20) | 103.0 | | Erbil | Monte-Carlo Doualiya | 24h |
| 29) | 103.3 | | Erbil | R. Runaky | |
| 30) | 103.3 | | Basra | R. Times Square | |
| 49) | 103.3 | | Kirkuk | R. Justice | |
| 14) | 103.4 | | Kifri | R. Garmiyan (Yekgirtu R.) | |
| 6) | 104.0 | | Kirkuk | R. Kirkuk | |
| 58) | 104.9 | | Erbil | R. Maria | |
| 20) | 105.0 | 10 | Basra | R. Sawa | 24h |
| 19) | 105.2 | | Nasiriya | BBC English | 24h |
| 14) | 105.4 | | Darbandikhan | R. Garmiyan (Yekgirtu R.) | |
| 56) | 105.5 | | Sulaimaniya | Al-Nujaba FM | |
| 57) | 105.7 | | Sulaimaniya | X FM Radio | |
| 20) | 105.8 | 1 | Najaf | R. Sawa | 24h |
| 40) | 105.8 | | Diwaniya | Sumer FM | 24h |
| 20) | 106.3 | | Tikrit | Monte-Carlo Doualiya | 24h |
| 44) | 106.0 | 1 | Baghdad | As-Salam 106 FM | 24h |
| 20) | 106.6 | 5 | Erbil/Mosul | R. Sawa | 24h |
| 20) | 107.0 | 10 | Basra | R. Sawa | 24h |
| | 107.7 | | Zakho | R. Hizal | |
| 20) | 107.8 | | Najaf | VOA | 24h |
| 20) | 108.0 | | Erbil | VOA | 24h |

**Addresses & other information:**
**1)** W: imamhussain-fm.com – **2)** See main entry under Qatar – **3)** ("Hope"). W: radioalamalfm.com – **4)** ("Tomorrow"). W: alghad.fm – **5)** R. Bilad ("Lands"). Operated by the Islamic Virtue Party. W: albilad.org E: albilad@albilad.org – **6)** Sowt al- Fadhila ("Voice of Virtue"), Najaf – **7)** R. As-Salam ("Peace") W: mail@tvalsalam.tv – **8)** R. Al-Hayat Al-Jadida (New Life Radio) W: laii.org –**9)** Operated by the Kurdistan Democratic Party W: kurdistanradio.net E: info@kurdistanradio.net Prgrs in Sorani Kurdish/Arabic – **10)** R. Dar As-Salam ("Haven of Peace"), The Voice of the Iraqi Islamic Party. W: darusalam.net – **11)** Operated by Imam Al-Shirazi International Association. W: voiraq. com E: voiceiraq@yahoo.com Prgrs in Arabic/English/Turkmen – **12)** Operated by the Patriotic Union of Kurdistan W: hurriya.net E: hur-riyanet@yahoo.com In Sorani Kurdish/Arabic – **13)** Operated by the Kurdistan Islamic Group. W: komalnews.net . Prgrs in Arabic/Kurdish/ Turkish – **14)** W: radiogarmyan.net – **15)** E: kahoofy2005@yahoo. com – **16)** W: facebook.com/RadioAlSalam – **17)** Kurdistan Youth R. W: mosy-krg.org – **18)** W: facebook.com/traffic.FM.Sulaimaniyah – **19)** BBC Arabic Service E: arabicservice@bbc.co.uk – **20)** R. Sawa

("Together"). Also on MW via Kuwait 1593kHz 150kW 24h. For more details see International Radio section (USA) – **21)** R. France Internationale & Monte-Carlo Doualiya. prgrs in Arabic/French. For details see International radio section (France) –**22)** facebook.com/ Radiorunaky.tk – **23)** See MBC entry under UAE – **24)** W: kerkuk. net Prgrs in Turkoman/Arabic – **25)** Shammasyia St. 29, Quarter 318, Line 55, House 31, Adhadmyia, Baghdad – **26)** R. Al-Yauwm ("Today Radio") – **27)** R. Al-Noor ("Light"). E: alnoor903fm@yahoo.com – **28)** W: alrasheedmedia.com E: alrasheedfm@yahoo.com . Different prgr. to each region – **29)** facebook.com/Radiorunaky.tk?fref=nf – **30)** face-book.com/btsfmradio – **31)** W: al-hodaonline.com E: alhodaonline@ gmail.com – **32)** Operated by the Islamic Supreme Council of Iraq. W: almejlis.org E: info@almejlis.org – **33)** R. Al-Mahaba ("Friendship"), Voice of Iraqi Women. Supported by the United Nations Development Fund for Women (UNIFEM). W: okiinc.org/vow_radio.html – **34)** W: zagrostv.com – **35)** Operated by the Turkish army – **36)** W: urradio.fm – **37)** Sawt al-Jam'ah ("Voice of the University") – **38)** R. Dênge Nwe ("New Voice"). W: halabja.info/Radio halabja.htm E: dangynwe@ yahoo.com – **39)** Operated by the Assyrian Democratic Movement (ADM/ZOWAA) W: zowaa.org E: info@zowaa.org .In Assyrian/Arabic – **40)** W: sumerfm.com – **41)** R. Shafaq ("Twilight"). W: shafaaq. com . In Kurdish/Arabic – **42)** R. Al-Ahd (Oath), Baghdad – **43)** R. Dijla (Tigris). W: radiodijla.com – **44)** As-Salam (Peace) 106 FM. W: peace106fm E-mail: peace106fm@yahoo.com – **45)** W: almirbad. com E: info@almirbad.com – **46)** W: radionawa E: info@radiona-wa.com – **47)** W: duhokradio.org – **48)** Operated by the Iraqi Turkmen Brotherhood Party – **49)** Operated by the Iraqi Turkmen Justice Party – **50)** W: uobabylon.edu.iq – **51)** W: start-fm.com/en – **52)** W: facebook.com/RadioTaxi93.7FM – **53)** W: kurdsat.tv – **54)** English W: babylonfm.net – **55)** W: nrttv.com – **56)** W: alnujaba.tv/tv.html – **57)** W: xfm.tv – **58)** W: radiomariam.org

## IRELAND

**L.T:** UTC (31 Mar-27 Oct: +1h) — **Pop:** 4.7 million — **Pr.L:** Irish Gaelic, English — **E.C:** 50Hz, 230V — **ITU:** IRL

### BROADCASTING AUTHORITY OF IRELAND (BAI)
▣ 2-5 Warrington Place, Dublin D02 XP29 ☎ +353 1 644 1200 🖷 +353 1 644 1299 **E:** info@bai.ie **W:** bai.ie **L.P:** Chief Exec: Michael O'Keeffe.
Responsible for regulation of commercial broadcasting in the Irish Republic. Full list of licensed stns can be found on BAI website.

### RAIDIÓ TEILIFÍS EIREANN (Statutory Corporation)
▣ Donnybrook, Dublin 4 ☎ +353 1 208 3111 🖷 +353 1 208 3080 **E:** info@rte.ie **W:** rte.ie
**L.P:** DG: Dee Forbes; Ch. Fin. Offr.: Breda O'Keeffe; Dir. Content: Jim Jennings; Dir Ops.: Frances Abeton, Dir. Tech.: Richard Waghorn, MD News: John Williams
**Raidió Na Gaeltachta:** Casla, Conamara, Co Galway ☎ +353 91 506677 🖷 +353 91 506666 **E:** rnag@rte.ie **W:** rte.ie/rnag
**Lyric FM:** Cornmarket Square, Limerick ☎ +353 61 410222 🖷 +353 61 310223 **E:** lyric@rte.ie **W:** rte.ie/lyricfm **Pub.:** RTE Guide

| LW | kHz | | kW | Prg. | |
|---|---|---|---|---|---|
| Summerhill | 252 | | 150/300 | 1 | |

| FM (MHz) | 1 | 2 | 3 | 4 | kW |
|---|---|---|---|---|---|
| Achill | 89.9 | 92.1 | 94.3 | 99.5 | 3 |
| Aranmore | 89.6 | 91.8 | 94.0 | 99.2 | 3 |
| Ballybofey | 89.7 | 91.9 | 94.1 | 99.3 | 0.5 |
| Bantry | 88.7 | 90.9 | 93.1 | 98.3 | 1 |
| Cahirciveen | 89.5 | 91.7 | 93.9 | 99.1 | 3 |
| Cairn HI (Longford) | 89.8 | - | - | - | 20 |
| Casla | 88.4 | 90.6 | 92.8 | 98.0 | 2 |
| Castlebar | 89.3 | 91.5 | 93.7 | 98.9 | 3 |
| Castletownbere | 88.3 | 90.5 | 92.7 | 97.9 | 3 |
| Clermont Carn | 87.8 | 97.0 | 102.7 | 95.2 | 40 |
| Clifden | 89.5 | 91.7 | 93.9 | 99.1 | 3 |
| Clonmel | 88.3 | 90.5 | 92.7 | 97.9 | 1 |
| Cnoc an Oir | 89.2 | 91.4 | 93.6 | 98.7 | 1 |
| Cork (Spur Hill) | 89.2 | 91.4 | 93.6 | 98.8 | 5 |
| Crosshaven | 88.2 | 90.4 | 92.6 | 97.8 | 3 |
| Dungarvan | 88.5 | 90.7 | 92.9 | 98.1 | 3 |
| Fanad | 89.8 | 92.0 | 94.2 | 99.4 | 1 |
| Greystones | 89.5 | 91.7 | 93.9 | 99.1 | 1 |
| Holywell Hill | 89.2 | 91.4 | 93.6 | 98.8 | 6 |
| Kilduff | 90.2 | 92.4 | 99.8 | - | 3 |
| Kippure | 89.1 | 91.3 | 93.5 | 98.7 | 50 |
| Knockmoyle | 88.4 | 90.6 | 92.8 | 98.0 | 1 |
| Limerick City | 89.4 | 91.6 | 93.8 | 99.0 | 2.5 |
| Maghera | 88.8 | 91.0 | 93.2 | 98.4 | 160 |

| FM (MHz) | 1 | 2 | 3 | 4 | kW |
|---|---|---|---|---|---|
| Malin | 89.9 | 91.1 | 93.3 | 98.5 | 2 |
| Monaghan | 88.9 | 91.1 | 93.3 | 98.5 | 2.5 |
| Moville | 88.3 | 90.5 | 92.7 | 97.9 | 1 |
| Mt. Leinster | 89.6 | 91.8 | 94.0 | 99.2 | 200 |
| Mullaghanish | 90.0 | 92.2 | 94.4 | 99.6 | 160 |
| Suir Valley | 89.0 | 91.2 | 93.4 | 98.6 | 3 |
| Three Rock | 88.5 | 90.7 | 92.9 | 96.7 | 10 |
| Truskmore | 88.2 | 90.4 | 92.6 | 97.8 | 120 |

+ 10 relays below 0.5kW

**1) RTE R. 1:** 24h mainly in English. **N. in English:** on the h **N. in Irish Gaelic:** 2150 – **2) 2FM:** 24h in English. – **3) Raidió Na Gaeltachta**: 24h in Irish Gaelic – **4) Lyric FM:** 24h classical music.

**DIGITAL RADIO (DAB):** DAB/DAB+ trs are on Band 3. **RTE national multiplex** Block 12C 227.360 MHz trs. in Dublin, NE Ireland, Cork, Limerick carrying RTE services: R1, R1+, R1 Extra, 2FM, 2FM+, 2XM, Chill, Gold, Junior, Lyric FM, Pulse, R Na Gaeltachta.

**2RN** (formerly RTE Network)
Block B, Cookstown Court, Old Belgard Road, Dublin 24 ☎ +353 1 208 2259 **E:** 2rntech@2rn.ie **W:** 2rn.ie
Distributes RTE radio and TV, Today FM and some local and regional broadcasters

**TODAY FM (Comm.)**
Marconi House, Digges Lane, Dublin D02 TD60 ☎ +353 1 804 9000 **E:** info@todayfm.com **W:** todayfm.com

| FM | MHz | kW | FM | MHz | kW |
|---|---|---|---|---|---|
| Crosshaven | 100.0 | 6 | Knockanore | 101.0 | 2 |
| Truskmore | 100.0 | 250 | Castlebar | 101.1 | 6 |
| Moville | 100.1 | 2 | Woodcock Hill | 101.2 | 5 |
| Clonmel | 100.1 | 2 | Greystones | 101.3 | 1 |
| Knockmoyle | 100.2 | 2 | Clifden | 101.3 | 6 |
| Dungarvan | 100.3 | 6 | Kilkeaveragh | 101.3 | 6 |
| Maghera | 100.6 | 320 | Mt. Leinster | 101.4 | 400 |
| Monaghan | 100.7 | 5 | Fanad | 101.6 | 8 |
| Suir Valley | 100.8 | 6 | Achill | 101.7 | 6 |
| Kippure | 100.9 | 100 | Mullaghanish | 101.8 | 320 |
| Holywell Hill | 101.0 | 12 | Three Rock | 101.8 | 2 |
| Spur Hill, Cork | 101.0 | 10 | Clermont Carn | 105.5 | 80 |

+ 5 trs.under 1kW
**D.Prgr:** 24h **N:** on the h, also on the half h at peak times

**NEWSTALK (Comm.)**
Marconi House, Digges Lane, Dublin D02 TD60 ☎ + 353 1 644 5100 📠 + 353 1 644 5101 **W:** newstalk.com **E:** info@newstalk.com
**L.P:** CE: Gerard Whelan

| FM | MHz | kW | FM | MHz | kW |
|---|---|---|---|---|---|
| Monaghan | 103.3 | 2.5 | Mohercrom | 107.4 | 10.0 |
| Capard | 105.8 | 4 | Waterford | 107.4 | 2.0 |
| Three Rock | 106.0 | 10 | Mullaghanish | 107.4 | 80.0 |
| Clonmel | 106.0 | 1 | Truskmore | 107.4 | 80.0 |
| Nagles | 106.4 | 4 | Fanad | 107.6 | 4 |
| Achill | 106.8 | 1.3 | Maghera | 107.6 | 32.0 |
| Holywell Hill | 106.9 | 12 | Saggart | 107.6 | 2.0 |
| Longford | 106.9 | 5 | Dungarvan | 107.6 | 5.0 |
| Limerick City | 107.0 | 2 | Cork City | 107.8 | 5 |
| Ballyguile | 107.0 | 2 | Cahirciveen | 107.8 | 4.0 |
| Clifden | 107.0 | 4 | Kilduff | 107.8 | 2.0 |
| Castlebar | 107.2 | 6 | Gorey | 107.8 | 1.0 |
| Mt Leinster | 107.2 | 2 | Wexford | 107.8 | 0.4 |
| Knockmoyle | 107.2 | 4 | Clermont Carn | 107.9 | 4 |

+4 trs. under 0.4 kW

**SPIRIT RADIO (Rlg.)**
Radio Centre, Killarney Rd., Bray, Co Wicklow A98 R6F6 ☎ + 353 1 272 4760 **W:** spiritradio.ie **E:** info@spiritradio.ie

| MW | kHz | kW |
|---|---|---|
| Carrickroe | 549 | 25 |

| FM | MHz | kW | FM | MHz | kW |
|---|---|---|---|---|---|
| Tralee | 88.0 | 0.4 | Carlow | 90.5 | 0.5 |
| Limerick | 89.8 | 0.4 | Cork | 90.9 | 0.5 |
| Dublin | 89.9 | 0.4 | Galway | 91.7 | 0.4 |
| Waterford | 90.1 | 0.4 | Saggart | 92.2 | 0.5 |
| Bray | 90.1 | 0.2 | Kilkenny | 93.1 | 0.2 |
| Ennis | 90.3 | 0.5 | Sligo | 93.4 | 0.2 |
| Dundalk | 90.4 | 0.1 | Wexford | 94.5 | 0.2 |

**D.Prgr:** 24h

**Local Stations:**

| FM | MHz | kW | Station, tx location |
|---|---|---|---|
| 31) | 87.8 | 1 | Connemara Community R., Clifden |
| 30) | 94.6 | 1 | Classic Hits 4FM, Saggart |
| 32) | 94.7 | 5 | Spin South West, Clifden |
| 18) | 94.8 | 4 | Northern Sound, Slieve Glah |
| 30) | 94.8 | 3 | Classic Hits 4FM, Churchfield (Mallow) |
| 1) | 94.9 | 9 | East Coast FM, Avoca |
| 30) | 94.9 | 3 | Classic Hits 4FM, Three Rock |
| 2) | 95.0 | 10 | Limerick's Live 95 FM, Woodcock Hill |
| 16) | 95.1 | 10 | WLR FM, Faha, Dungarvan |
| 10) | 95.2 | 2 | Highland R, Aran Mor |
| 30) | 95.4 | 9 | Classic Hits 4FM, Nowen Hill |
| 7) | 95.5 | 2 | Clare FM, Kilrush |
| 17) | 95.6 | 1 | Cork's 96 FM, Kilworth,NE Cork |
| 3) | 95.6 | 4 | South East R, Mt.Leinster |
| 4) | 95.8 | 10 | LM FM, Mt. Oriel |
| 17) | 95.8 | 10 | Cork's 96 FM, Nowen Hill |
| 7) | 95.9 | 2 | Clare FM, Woodcock Hill |
| 8) | 96.0 | 1 | KCLR, Corbally Wood |
| 5) | 96.1 | 10 | MWR FM, Kiltimagh |
| 17) | 96.1 | 2 | Cork's 96 FM, Mount Hillary |
| 20) | 96.2 | 6 | R. Kerry, Cahirciveen |
| 1) | 96.2 | 10 | East Coast FM, Bray |
| 18) | 96.3 | 10 | Northern Sound, Monaghan |
| 7) | 96.4 | 10 | Clare FM, Maghera |
| 17) | 96.4 | 10 | Cork's 96 FM, Holly Hill |
| 8) | 96.6 | 10 | KCLR, Johns Well |
| 9) | 96.8 | 10 | Galway Bay FM, Knockroe |
| 8) | 96.9 | 4 | KCLR, Rossmore |
| 34) | 96.9 | 9 | iRadio, Scalp Mountain |
| 20) | 97.0 | 40 | R. Kerry, Mullaghanish |
| 11) | 97.1 | 10 | Tipp FM, Scrouthea |
| 5) | 97.1 | 3 | MWR FM, Achill |
| 12) | 97.3 | 5 | KFM, Rossmore |
| 30) | 97.4 | 9 | Classic Hits 4FM, Bweeng Mountain |
| 9) | 97.4 | 2 | Galway Bay FM, Redmount Hl |
| 9) | 97.4 | 1 | Galway Bay FM, Seanafaistin |
| 16) | 97.5 | 10 | WLR FM, East Waterford |
| 20) | 97.6 | 2 | R. Kerry, Knockanore |
| 12) | 97.6 | 4 | KFM, Slieve Thuile |
| 13) | 98.1 | 5 | 98 FM, Three Rock |
| 1) | 99.9 | 5 | East Coast FM, Saggart Hill |
| 33) | 100.3 | 12 | R. Nova, Three Rock |
| 3) | 102.0 | 13 | Beat 102-103 FM, Mount Leinster |
| 34) | 102.1 | 9 | iRadio, South Galway |
| 10) | 102.1 | 1.3 | Highland R., Feirn Hill |
| 24) | 102.2 | 6 | Beat 102-103 FM, West Waterford |
| 26) | 102.2 | 5 | Q 102, Three Rock |
| 32) | 102.3 | 1 | Spin South West, Ennistymon |
| 24) | 102.4 | 10 | Beat 102-103 FM, Clonmel |
| 21) | 102.5 | 3 | Ocean FM, Truskmore |
| 32 | 102.5 | 5 | Spin South West, Knockmoyle |
| 17a) | 102.6 | 10 | C103, Cork City |
| 32) | 102.7 | 9 | Spin South West, Maghera |
| 24) | 102.8 | 10 | Beat 102-103 FM, East Waterford |
| 1) | 102.9 | 16 | East Coast FM, Ballyguile |
| 1) | 102.9 | 2 | East Coast FM, Baltinglass |
| 17) | 102.9 | 1 | C103, NE Cork |
| 32) | 102.9 | 2 | Spin South West, Cahirciveen |
| 32) | 103.0 | 2.5 | Spin South West, Woodcock Hill |
| 34) | 103.1 | 9 | iRadio, Longford |
| 34) | 103.1 | 9 | i102-104, Achill |
| 34) | 103.1 | 1 | iRadio, Senafaistin |
| 22) | 103.2 | 0.5 | Dublin City FM, Three Rock |
| 10) | 103.3 | 10 | Highland R, Scalp Mountain |
| 17a) | 103.3 | 10 | C103, Nowen Hill |
| 34) | 103.3 | 4 | iRadio, Clifden |
| 6) | 103.5 | 2.5 | Midlands 103, Sliabh Bloom |
| 32) | 103.5 | 1 | Spin South West, Knockanore |
| 17a) | 103.7 | 5 | C103, Mt. Hillary |
| 34) | 103.7 | 9 | iRadio, Castlebar |
| 25) | 103.8 | 5 | Spin 103.8, Three Rock |
| 11) | 103.9 | 3.2 | Tipp FM, Kilduff |
| 34) | 104.0 | 2 | iRadio, Aranmore |
| 14) | 104.1 | 2.5 | Shannonside 104FM, Sliabh Bawn |
| 30) | 104.2 | 9 | Classic Hits 4FM, Limerick |
| 15) | 104.4 | 5 | FM 104, Three Rock |
| 34) | 104.4 | 10 | iRadio, Sligo (Truskmore) |
| 28) | 104.5 | 10 | Red FM, W. Cork (Nowen Hill) |
| 10) | 104.5 | 2 | Highland R., Back Mountain |
| 30) | 104.6 | 10 | Classic Hits 4FM, Maghera,Co Clare |
| 34) | 104.7 | 1 | iRadio, Saggart |
| 19) | 104.8 | 10 | Tipperary Mid-West R, Dangandargan |
| 34) | 104.8 | 2.5 | iRadio, Cavan (Sliabh Giah) |

| FM | MHz | kW | Station, tx location |
|---|---|---|---|
| 30) | 104.9 | 9 | Classic Hits 4FM, Galway City |
| 21) | 105.0 | 10 | Ocean FM, Mt.Charles |
| 34) | 105.0 | 5 | iRadio, Mt Oriel (Louth) |
| 28) | 105.7 | 5 | Red FM, North Cork (Nagles) |
| 28) | 106.1 | 10 | Red FM, Churchfield, Cork |
| 34) | 106.2 | 5 | iRadio, Capard |
| 23) | 106.4 | 2 | Raidió Na Life, Three Rock |
| 34) | 106.7 | 10 | iRadio, Monaghan |
| 27) | 106.8 | 4 | Sunshine 106.8, Three Rock |

+ approx 110 additional txs of less than 1kW

**Addresses & other information:**
**1)** Radio Centre, Killarney Rd, Bray, Co Wicklow A98 R6F6 **E:** reception@eastcoast.fm **W:** eastcoast.fm – **2)** Radio House, Richard Court, Dock Rd, Limerick V94 HF91 **E:** info@live95fm.ie **W:** live95fm.ie – **3)** Custom House Quay, Wexford Town **E:** info@southeastradio.ie **W:** southeastradio.ie – **4)** Broadcasting House, Rathmullen Rd, Drogheda, Co Louth A92 T274 **E:** info@lmfm.ie **W:** lmfm.ie – **5)** Clare Str, Ballyhaunis, Co Mayo **W:** midwestradio.ie – **6)** Tindle House, Axis Business Park, Tullamore, Co Offaly R35 R588 **E:** info@midlandsradio.fm **W:** midlandsradio.fm – **7)** Abbeyfield Centre, Francis Str, Ennis, Co Clare **W:** clare.fm – **8)** Leggettsrath Business Park, Carlow Rd, Kilkenny **E:** info@kclr96fm.com **W:** kclr96fm.com – **9)** Unit 13, Sandy Rd, Galway **E:** info@galwaybayfm.ie **W:** galwaybayfm.ie – **10)** Pine Hill, Letterkenny, Co Donegal **E:** enquries@highlandradio.com **W:** highlandradio.com – **11)** Broadcast Centre, 4A Gurtnafleur Business Park, Clonmel, Co Tipperary **E:** reception@tippfm.com **W:** tippfm.com – **12)** KFM Broadcast Centre, M7 Business Park, Newhall, Naas, Co Kildare W91 HX03 **E:** info@kfmradio.com **W:** kfmradio.com – **13)** Marconi House, Digges Lane, Dublin D02 TD60 **E:** website@98fm.com **W:** 98fm.com – **14)** Unit 1E Master Tech Business Park, Athlone Rd, Longford N39 RR67 **W:** shannonside.ie – **15)** Macken House, Mayor Str Upper, Dublin 1 **E:** sales@fm104.ie **W:** fm104.ie – **16)** Broadcast Centre, Ardkeen, Dunmore Rd, Waterford X91 C4VN **E:** reception@wlrfm.com **W:** wlrfm.com – **17)** Broadcasting House, Patrick's Place, Cork T23 E183 **E:** info@96fm.ie **W:** 96fm.ie – **17a)** Majestic Business Park, Goulds Hill, Mallow, Co. Cork **E:** info@c103.ie **W:** c103.ie - **18)** Unit 3 Milltown Business Park, Monaghan **E:** reception@norththernsound.ie **W:** northernsound.ie – **19)** St Michael Str, Tipperary E34 K156 **W:** tippmidwestradio.com – **20)** Maine Str., Tralee, Co Kerry **E:** info@radiokerry.ie **W:** radiokerry.ie – **21)** Ocean FM Broadcasting Centre, North West Business Park, Collooney, Co Sligo F91 NX02 **E:** reception@oceanfm.ie **W:** oceanfm.ie – **22)** Docklands Innovation Park, Unit 6, 128-130 East Wall Rd, Dublin 3 **E:** admin@dublincityfm.ie **W:** dublincityfm.ie – **23)** 63-66 Amiens Str., Dublin 1 **E:** eolas@raidionalife.ie **W:** raidionalife.ie (Irish language stn) – **24)** Broadcast Centre, Ardkeen, Dunmore Rd, Waterford **E:** sales@beat102103.com **W:** beat102103.com – **25)** Marconi House, Digges lane, Dublin D02 TD60 **E:** info@spin1038.com **W:** spin1038.com – **26)** Macken House, 39-40 Upper Mayor Str, Dublin 1 **E:** info@q102.ie **W:** q102.ie – **27)** Castleforbes House, Castleforbes Rd., Dublin D01 A8NO **E:** mail@sunshineradio.ie **W:** sunshine1068.com – **28)** 1 University Technology Centre, Curraheen Rd., Bishopstown, Cork **E:** info@redfm.ie **W:** redfm.ie – **30)** Ground Floor, Castleforbes House, Castleforbes Rd., Dublin D01 A8NO. **E:** info@classichits.ie – **31)** Connemara West Centre, Letterfrack, Co Galway **E:** info@connemarafm.com – **32)** 2nd Floor Landmark Building, Raheen, Limerick **E:** info@spinsouthwest.com **W:** spinsouthwst.com – **33)** 1st Floor, Castleforbes House, Castleforbes Rd, Dublin D01 A8NO **E:** info@nova.ie **W:** nova.ie – **34)** iRadio, Level 3, Unit C, Monksland Business Park, Athlone. **E:** reception@iradio.ie **W:** iradio.ie

**Unofficial MW stations:**

| kHz | kW | Station, tx location |
|---|---|---|
| 846 | 3 | R. North, Redcastle, Co Donegal |
| 981 | 1 | R. Star Country, Emyvale, Co Monaghan |
| 1395 | 0.3 | Energy Power AM, Dublin (SS & public holidays) |

**Community/special interest stns:** 21 stns in operation at October 2018. **Hospital/Institutions:** 5 stns. **Temporary/Special Event services:** see BAI **W:** bai.ie **Wireless Public Address System (WPAS):** religious and other sces broadc. to the housebound via CB radio 27.600-27.995 MHz.

## ISRAEL

**L.T:** UTC +2h (29 Mar-27 Oct: +3h) — **Pop:** 8.3 million — **Pr.L:** Hebrew, Arabic — **E.C:** 50Hz, 230V — **ITU:** ISR

### KAN – Israel Public Broadcasting Corporation (IPBC)
⌂ Kanfei Nesharim 35, Jerusalem ☎+972 76 809 8000 **W:** kan.org.il **E:** info@kan.org.il kanenglish@kan.org.il

| MW | kHz | kW | Prgr | MW | kHz | kW | Prgr |
|---|---|---|---|---|---|---|---|
| Yavne | 531 | 50 | B | Yavne | 1080 | 50 | B |
| Yavne | 657 | 100 | B | Akko | 1206 | 50 | B |
| Akko | 738 | 10 | D | Eilat | 1458 | 10 | A |
| She'ar Yashuv | 882 | 10 | B | She'ar Yashuv | 1458 | 10 | A |

| FM (MHz) | A | H | B | C | D | M | X | R | kW |
|---|---|---|---|---|---|---|---|---|---|
| Akko | 104.9 | - | 95.0 | - | 99.3 | - | - | 101.3 | 40 |
| Arad | - | - | 95.0 | 89.7 | - | - | - | 101.3 | |
| Ariel | 105.3 | 90.5 | 95.2 | 97.5 | - | - | 88.2 | - | 4 |
| Atara | 105.3 | - | 95.2 | 97.5 | 93.7 | 103.7 | 88.2 | 100.5 | 16/40 |
| Bar Yehuda | - | - | 94.5 | - | - | - | - | - | |
| Beersheba | 104.7 | 100.7 | 94.5 | 105.5 | 92.3 | 98.5 | 88.5 | 101.8 | 4/80 |
| Bnei Yehuda | - | - | 94.5 | 105.5 | 92.3 | - | - | - | |
| Efrat | 105.3 | 90.5 | 95.2 | 97.5 | 93.7 | - | 88.2 | 100.5 | 8 |
| Eilat | - | - | 94.5 | 105.5 | 92.3 | 98.5 | 88.5 | - | 4 |
| Ein Yahav | - | - | 95.2 | 97.5 | - | - | 88.2 | - | 4 |
| Eitanim | 105.1 | 92.5 | 95.5 | 97.8 | 88.8 | 91.3 | 87.6 | 100.3 | 160/100 |
| Gidron | - | - | 94.5 | 105.5 | 92.3 | - | - | - | |
| Grofit | - | - | 95.5 | 97.8 | - | 91.3 | 87.6 | - | 16 |
| Haifa | 104.7 | 100.7 | 94.5 | 105.5 | 92.3 | 98.5 | 88.5 | - | 80 |
| Heletz | - | 90.8 | 95.0 | - | 99.3 | - | - | 101.3 | 20 |
| Jerusalem | 104.9 | 90.8 | 95.0 | 89.7 | 99.3 | 103.7 | 88.0 | 101.3 | 8/2 |
| Kalya | - | - | 95.5 | 97.8 | 88.8 | 91.3 | - | - | 8/0.5 |
| Katzir | - | - | 95.2 | - | 93.7 | - | - | - | 40 |
| Kohav Hayarden | 104.9 | 90.8 | 95.0 | 89.7 | - | 97.2 | - | 101.3 | 40 |
| Manara | - | - | 95.0 | 89.7 | - | 97.2 | - | 101.3 | 2 |
| Mitzpe Ramon | - | - | 95.0 | 89.7 | - | 97.2 | - | 88.0 | 20 |
| Nazareth | - | - | 95.2 | 97.5 | 93.7 | - | - | 100.5 | |
| Netanya | - | 90.5 | - | - | - | - | - | 100.5 | 8 |
| Safed | 105.1 | 92.5 | 95.5 | 97.8 | 88.8 | 91.3 | 87.6 | 100.3 | 40 |
| Tefen | - | 90.5 | 95.2 | 97.5 | - | - | 88.2 | - | |
| Tel Aviv | 104.9 | 90.8 | 95.0 | 89.7 | - | 97.2 | 88.0 | 101.3 | 10/4/2 |

**Prgrs** (in Hebrew if not mentioned otherwise):
**A: "Kan Tarbut"** (Culture Network): Talk & cultural programming 24h. **N.** in Hebrew: rel. Prgr. B. – **H: "Kan Moreshet"** (Heritage Network): 24h – **B: "Kan Bet":** 24h. News, current affairs & sports. **Ann** (for news): "Kan Kol Yisrael". **N.** on the h. – **C: "Kan Gimel":** 24h Israeli popular music. **N:** rel. Prgr. B. – **D: "Kan Dalet, Makan Radio"** (Arabic). 24h. – **X: "Kan 88 FM":** 24h. **N:** rel. Prgr. B. Light music, traffic reports – **R: Kan REQA** (Reshet Qlitat Aliya): immigrants network, 24h mostly in Russian but also in Amharic, French, Yiddish, Ladino, Romanian, Spanish, Moghrabi, Bukharian, Georgian and Hungarian, and in English 1800-1900. – **M: "Kol Ha Musica"** (VO Music): 24h, classical music and drama. – **Educational radio** "Kol HaCampus" is operating on 106.0MHz with 1kW in Holon, Tiberias, Beersheba, Haifa, Bet El and other trs in colleges around Israel. **W:** 106fm.co.il

### GALEI TZAHAL (Israel Defence Forces R, Mil.)
⌂ 1 Dror St, corner of Yehuda Hayamit St, Tel Aviv. Military ⌂ MPO Box 01005 Jaffa ☎+972 3 5126666 **W:** glz.co.il **E:** glz@galatz.co.il
**L.P:** Commander: Yaron Dekel.

| FM (MHz) | Main | kW | GalGalatz | kW |
|---|---|---|---|---|
| Beersheba | 102.3 | 10 | 99.8 | 10 |
| Beit She'an | 104.0 | 5 | 91.8 | 5 |
| Efrat | 102.3 | | 91.8 | |
| Eilat | 104.0 | 1 | 107.0 | 1 |
| Grofit | 96.6 | 10 | 93.5 | 10 |
| Haifa | 102.3 | 10 | 107.0 | 10 |
| Jerusalem | 104.0 | 1 | 107.1 | 1 |
| Kalya | 104.0 | 2 | 99.8 | 2 |
| Kiryat Shmona | 104.0 | 1 | 107.0 | 1 |
| Ma'ale Adumim | 104.0 | 0.3 | - | |
| Ma'ale Efraim | 96.6 | 1 | 107.0 | 1 |
| Mitzpe Ramon | 104.0 | 5 | 107.0 | 5 |
| Ramla | 96.6 | 20 | 91.8 | 10 |
| Safed | 96.6 | 5 | 93.5 | 5 |
| Sapir | 102.3 | 2 | 91.8 | 2 |
| Tel Aviv | 104.0 | 2 | 93.5 | 2 |
| Wadi Ara | 104.0 | 5 | 99.8 | 5 |

**Main Prgr:** 24h. (news, talk show, music). **N:** on the h.
**GalGalatz** (traffic reports and music): 24h.
**Ann:** Main Prgr: "Galei Tzahal, Shidure Tsva Hagana Le'Yisrael".

### SECOND AUTHORITY FOR TELEVISION & RADIO
⌂ 20 Beit Hadfus St, P.O.Box 3445, Jerusalem ☎+972 2 6556222 **W:** rashut2.org.il **E:** rashut@rashut2.org.il

Regional commercial FM radio (all in Hebrew except as noted):
**ECO99fm**, Hertzliyah: 99.0MHz **W:** echo99.fm – **Galey Israel:** Benjamin area 89.3MHz, Central Israel 94.0MHz, South 102.5MHz,

Dan area 106.5 MHz. **W:** srugim.co.il/galeyisrael – **Pervoye R,** Rishon Le'Zion. In Russian: Ashdod 89.1MHz. **W:** 891fm.co.il – **R. A´shams** (The Sun) in Arabic at Nazareth-Ein Hahoresh area. 98.1 & 101.1MHz. **W:** ashams.com – **R. Cham Esh,** Haifa: 99.5MHz. **W:** 995.co.il – **R. Darom** (Southern R.): Beersheba 97.0MHz, Kiryat Gat, Ashkelon. Arava & Dead Sea settlements: 95.8MHz. **W:** radiodarom.co.il **R. Darom** (Southern R.) :101.5MHz. **W:** radiodarom.co.il/?page_id=2880 – **R. Haifa,** Haifa: 107.5MHz. **W:** 1075.fm – **R. Jerusalem:** Jerusalem 101.0MHz, Bet Shemesh 89.5MHz. **W:** tapuz.co.il/minisites/radiojerusalem – **R. Kol Barama,** Tel Aviv 92.1MHz, Beersheva 104.3MHz, Jerusalem 105.7MHz. **W:** kol-barama.co.il – **R. Kol Chai:** Bene Brak 92.8, Jerusalem 93.0/102.5MHz **W:** 93fm.co.il – **R. Kol Rega:** Galilee 96.0MHz, Tiberias 91.5MHz. **W:** 96fm.co.il – **R. Lev Ha Medina:** Shfela 91.0MHz, Beersheba 93.3MHz. **W:** 91fm.co.il – **Kol Ha Yam Ha Adom** (VO the Red Sea): 101.1, 102.0MHz 1kW. **W:** fm102.co.il – **R. L'Lo Hafsaka** (Nonstop): Upper Galilee 101.5MHz, Ramat Gan 103.0MHz, Lower Galilee 104.5MHz. **W:** 103.fm – **R. Tel Aviv:** 102.0MHz. **W:** 102fm.co.il – **R. Tishim,** (90), Tel Aviv: 90.0, 94.7MHz. **W:** 90fm.co.il – **Radius 100 FM,** Tel Aviv: 100.0MHz. **W:** 100fm.co.il

### WEST BANK & GAZA STRIP
### (Palestinian Authority)

**L.T:** UTC +2h (23 Mar-26 Oct: +3h; suspended during month of Ramadan; dates subject to confirmation) — **Pop:** 5 million — **Pr.L:** Arabic — **E.C:** 50Hz, 230V — **ITU:** XWB (West Bank), XGZ (Gaza)

## PALESTINIAN BROADCASTING CORPORATION (Gov)
🖃 P.O. Box 984, Al-Bireh, Ramallah, West Bank ☎+970 2 2988888 **W:** vop.ps **E:** info@pbc.ps
**FM:** Jenin & Ramallah 90.7MHz, Gaza 99.4MHz. Regional service: Jenin 89.5MHz.
**D.Prgr. in Arabic:** 0400-2300 **Ann:** "Sawt Filastin".

## PRIVATE FM STATIONS:
**Al-Balad FM,** Jenin: 104.8/105.8MHz **W:** albaladfm.com – **Al-Horya R,** Ramallah: 104.5MHz **W:** alhorya.com – **Al-Manar R,** Gaza: 92.0MHz **W:** manarfm.com – **Al-Qamar R,** Jericho: 89.4MHz **W:** maannet.org – **Ajyal R:** Ramallah 103.4MHz, Bethlehem 106.9MHz, Gaza 107.2MHz **W:** arn.ps – **Amwaj R.,** Ramallah 91.5MHz, south 99.4MHz, north 104.8MHz **W:** amwaj.ps – **Angham R.,** Ramallah: 92.3MHz **W:** radioangham.com – **Besan R.,** Ramallah: 101.9MHz **W:** facebook.com/OfficialBesanFM – **Cool FM:** 104.0MHz, all English **W:** coolfm.ps – **Gaza FM:** 100.9MHz **W:** gazafm.net – **Hala FM:** 94.3MHz. See main entry under Jordan – **Hebron R:** 90.4MHz **W:** hebronradio.com – **Holy Quran R,** Hebron 88.2MHz, Jerusalem 88.4MHz, Nablus 96.9MHz **W:** quran-radio.com – **Iman R,** Gaza: 96.2MHz **W:** imanradio.com – **Kul Al-Nas R,** Tulkarem: 107.3MHz – **Najah FM,** Nablus: 88.5MHz **W:** najah.edu/en/about/nnu-offices/media-center/najah-fm – **Nas FM,** Jenin: 104.9MHz **W:** nasfm.ps – **Quds R,** Gaza: 102.7MHz **W:** qudsradio.ps – **R. Al-Shamal,** Qalqiliya: 96.6MHz **W:** alshamal.net – **Raya FM:**, North 103.9, Central, 98.3, Jericho 96.4, Gaza 96.8 **W:** raya.ps – **R. Bethlehem 2000,** Bethlehem: 102.9/106.3/107.6MHz 5kW **W:** rb2000.ps Also rel. BBC&DW – **R. Isis,** Bethlehem: 87.5MHz **W:** radioisis.net – **R. Marah,** Hebron: 100.4MHz **W:** marah-fm.ps – **R. Mawwal,** Bethlehem: 101.7MHz **W:** mawwal.ps – **R. Minbar Al-Hurriya,** Hebron: 92.7MHz **W:** hr.ps – **R. Nagham,** Qalqiliya: 99.6MHz **W:** radionagham.com – **R. Nisaa,** Ramallah: 96.0MHz, Gaza 96.2MHz. **W:** radionisaa.net – **R. Ray,** Gaza: 98.0MHz **W:** alrayradio.ps – **R. Tariq al-Mahabeh,** Nablus: 97.7/108.0MHz **W:** tnfm.net – **Sawt al-Aqsa,** Gaza: 106.7MHz **W:** alaqsavoice.ps – **Sawt al-Asra,** Gaza: 107.9MHz. **W:** asravoice.ps – **Sirajj R,** Hebron: 105.7MHz **W:** sirajfm.com – **24 FM:** Hebron 94.8MHz, Ramallah 97.9MHz **W:** 24fm.ps

**Monte-Carlo Doualiya:** Ramallah 94.6, Nablus 97.3, Hebron 99.7MHz
**R. Sawa:** Jenin 93.5, Ramallah 94.2, Nablus 94.5, Hebron 100.2MHz

## ITALY

**L.T:** UTC +1h (31 Mar-27 Oct: +2h) — **Pop:** 60.6 million — **Pr.L:** Italian — **E.C:** 50Hz, 230V — **ITU:** I

## AUTORITÀ PER LE GARANZIE NELLE COMUNICAZIONI (AGCOM)
### (Italian Communications Authority)
🖃 Centro Direzionale, Isola B5, 80143 Napoli ☎ +39 08 17507111 🖷 +39 08 17507616 **E:** info@agcom.it **W:** www.agcom.it
**L.P:** Dir: Camilla Sebastiani

## RAI-RADIOTELEVISIONE ITALIANA (Pub.)
🖃 Viale G. Mazzini 14, 00195 Roma ☎ +39 06 38781 🖷 +39 06

3622621 🖃 (Listeners) Centro Corrispondenza, C.P. 320, 00100 Roma ☎ +39 06 3317 2591 🖷 +39 06 3317 1895 **E:** service@rai.it **W:** rai.it **Tech. Dept:** RAI Teche: Via Cernaia 33, 10121 Torino, **Dir.** Maria Pia Ammirati **W:** teche.rai.it **E:** teche@rai.it **RAI Way:** Centro Ascolto e Qualità Controllo Servizio RAI Monza, Via Parco Mirabellino 1, 20900 Monza **L.P:** Pres.: Roberto Sergio **W:** raiway.rai.it **E:** raiway@rai.it **V:** QSL-card. No Rp. **W:** contattalarai.rai.it/dl/rai/contattalarai.html **Sedi Regionali: W:** sediregionali.rai.it **E:** sedi.regionali@rai.it **L.P:** Pres.: Marcello Foa, GM: Mario Orfeo, Dir. Reg. Radio: Luigi Meloni, Dir. RAI Italia: Mario Giudici.
**Regional Centres:** 🖃 **1** Abruzzo: Viale de Amicis 27, 65123 Pescara – **2** Alto Adige: Piazza Mazzini 23, 39100 Bolzano/Bozen – **3** Basilicata: Via dell'Edilizia 2, 85100 Potenza – **4** Calabria: Viale G. Marconi 1, 87100 Cosenza – **5** Campania: Via Marconi 11, 80125 Napoli – **6** Emilia-Romagna: Viale della Fiera 13, 40127 Bologna – **7** Friuli-Venezia-Giulia: Via Fabio Severo 7, 34133 Trieste – **8** Lazio: Largo Villy de Luca 4, 00188 Roma – **9** Liguria: Corso Europa 125, 16132 Genova – **10** Lombardia: Corso Sempione 27, 20145 Milano – **11** Marche: Piazza della Repubblica 1, 60121 Ancona – **12** Molise: Viale Principe di Piemonte 59, 86100 Campobasso – **13** Piemonte: Via G.Verdi 16, 10121 Torino – **14** Puglia: Via Dalmazia 104, 70121 Bari – **15** Sardegna: Via Barone Rossi 27, 09125 Cagliari – **16** Sicilia: Viale Strasburgo 19, 90146 Palermo – **17** Toscana: Largo Alcide de Gasperi 1, 50134 Firenze – **18** Trentino: Via Fratelli Perini 141, 38122 Trento – **19** Umbria: Via L. Masi 2, 06121 Perugia – **20** Valle d'Aosta: Loc.Grande Charriere 70, 11020 Saint Cristophe – **21** Veneto: Palazzo Labia, Campo S. Geremia,Sestiere Cannaregio 275, 30121 Venezia

| MW Station | kHz | kW | Prg |
|---|---|---|---|
| 17) Pisa (Coltano) | 657 | 100 | R1 |
| 10) Milano (Siziano) | 900 | 100/50 | R1 |
| 21) Venezia (Campalto) | 936 | 10/5 | R1 (+a) |
| 7) Trieste (Monte Radio) | 981 | 20/10 | S |
| 13) Torino (Volpiano) | 999 | 50/10 | R1 |
| 11) Ancona (Montagnolo) | 1062 | 10/6 | R1 |
| 15) Cagliari (Decimoputzu) | 1062 | 60/10 | Rp (d) |
| 16) Catania (Barriera del B) | 1062 | 20/2 | R1 (c) |
| 8) Roma (Monte Ciocci) | 1107 | 10 | R1 |
| 16) Palermo (Mte Pellegrino) | 1116 | 10 | R1 (c) |
| 14) Foggia | 1431 | 5/2 | R1 |
| 21) Belluno Cortina | 1449 | 2 | R1 (+a) |
| 9) Genova (Portofino) | 1575 | 50/30 | R1 |

| FM (MHz) | R1 | R2 | R3 | R4 | GRP | kW |
|---|---|---|---|---|---|---|
| 6) Bertinoro | 90.8 | 93.4 | 99.6 | - | 89.7 | 30 |
| 6) Bologna | 89.5 | 91.7 | 93.9 | - | 93.6 | 60 |
| 2) Bolzano | 91.5 | 93.7 | 97.1 | 99.6 | 95.1 | 14 |
| 6) Ca' del Vento | 92.1 | 96.5 | 98.5 | - | 90.6 | 40 |
| 8) Canepina-PNibbio | 93.7 | 99.4 | | - | | 12 |
| 4) Capo Spartivento | 95.6 | 97.6 | 99.7 | - | 104.2 | 10 |
| 21) Col Visentin | 91.1 | 93.1 | 95.5 | - | | 30 |
| 4) Crotone | 94.9 | 97.9 | 99.9 | - | 97.4 | 10 |
| 17) Firenze | 87.8 | 91.1 | 98.4 | - | 88.0 | 10 |
| 7) Friscano | 88.4 | 90.5 | 94.1 | - | | 10 |
| 4) Gambarie | 95.3 | 97.3 | 99.3 | - | | 40 |
| | - | 103.9 | | | | 40 |
| 9) Genova | 89.5 | 91.9 | 95.1 | - | 104.5 | 80 |
| 5) Golfo di Policastro | 88.5 | 90.5 | 92.5 | - | | 10 |
| 5) Golfo di Salerno | 95.1 | 97.1 | 99.1 | - | | 20 |
| 7) Gorizia | 89.5 | 92.3 | 94.6 | 98.3 | 90.3 | 10 |
| 14) Martina Franca | 89.1 | 91.1 | 93.1 | - | 90.3 | 100 |
| 10) Milano | 90.6 | 93.7 | 99.4 | 102.2 | 88.3 | 60 |
| 17) Monte Argentario | 90.1 | 92.1 | 94.3 | - | 99.6 | 70 |
| | - | 89.0 | | | - | 16 |
| 9) Monte Beigua | 91.5 | 94.6 | 98.9 | - | 100.5 | 40 |
| 14) Monte Caccia | 94.6 | 96.7 | 99.2 | - | 98.3 | 100 |
| 16) Monte Cammarata | 91.1 | 95.9 | 99.9 | - | 98.3 | 100 |
| 6) Monte Canate | - | 95.9 | | - | | 24 |
| 8) Monte Cavo | 87.6 | 91.2 | 98.4 | - | 99.3 | 80 |
| 11) Monte Conero | 88.3 | 90.3 | 92.3 | - | 105.2 | 100 |
| 5) Monte Faito | 94.1 | 96.1 | 98.1 | - | 91.0 | 100 |
| 16) Monte Lauro | 94.7 | 96.7 | 98.7 | - | 89.0 | 100 |
| 15) Monte Limbara | 88.9 | 95.3 | 99.3 | - | | 60 |
| 17) Monte Luco | 88.1 | 92.5 | 96.2 | - | 103.2 | 30 |
| 11) Monte Nerone | 94.7 | 96.6 | 98.7 | - | 88.1 | 100 |
| 19) Monte Miranda | 95.7 | 97.7 | 99.7 | - | 102.1 | 60 |
| | - | 88.3 | | | - | 30 |
| 10) Monte Penice | 94.2 | 97.4 | 99.9 | - | 88.2 | 120 |
| | - | 103.0 | | | - | 120 |
| 3) Monte Pierfaone | 88.1 | 90.1 | 92.1 | - | 91.2 | 45 |
| 19) Monte Sambuco | 88.6 | 90.7 | 93.5 | - | | 100 |
| | - | 100.7 | | | - | 100 |

| FM (MHz) | R1 | R2 | R3 | R4 | GRP | kW |
|---|---|---|---|---|---|---|
| 4) Monte Scuro | 88.5 | 90.5 | 92.5 | - | 98.4 | 30 |
| 15) Monte Serpeddi | 90.7 | 92.7 | 96.3 | - | 106.5 | 70 |
| 17) Monte Serra | 88.5 | 90.5 | 92.9 | - | 88.2 | 70 |
| 16) Monte Soro | 89.9 | 91.9 | 93.9 | - | 104.2 | 30 |
| 19) Monte Subasio | 89.3 | 91.4 | 93.5 | - | 104.6 | 30 |
| 21) Monte Venda | 88.1 | 89.0 | 89.9 | - | - | 160 |
| 5) Monte Vergine (AV) | 87.9 | 90.3 | 92.3 | - | 93.0 | 20 |
| 5) Napoli Camaldoli | 89.3 | 91.3 | 93.3 | 103.9 | 101.0 | 12 |
| 3) Nova Siri | - | - | 89.5 | - | - | 10 |
| 16) PalermoMtePellegri | 94.9 | 96.9 | 98.9 | - | 90.3 | 40 |
| 1) Pescara S. Silvestro | 89.2 | 94.3 | 96.4 | - | 102.0 | 70 |
| 3) Pomarico | 88.7 | 92.7 | 95.7 | - | - | 10 |
| 15) Punta Badde Urbara | 91.3 | 93.3 | 97.3 | - | - | 70 |
| 8) Roma M. Mario | 89.7 | 91.7 | 93.7 | - | 100.3 | 100 |
| 4) Roseto Capo Spulico | 94.4 | 96.5 | 98.5 | - | - | 10 |
| 14) Salento Turrisi | 90.7 | 95.5 | 97.5 | - | 91.0 | 60 |
| 17) San Cerbone | 95.3 | 97.3 | 99.3 | - | - | 12 |
| 21) San Zenodi Montagna | 93.2 | 96.5 | 98.5 | - | 89.5 | 10 |
| 10) Selva Piana | 88.4 | 90.3 | 92.4 | - | - | 20 |
| 13) Torino Eremo | 92.1 | 95.6 | 98.2 | 101.8 | 88.2 | 100 |
| 16) Trapani Erice | 88.4 | 90.5 | 92.5 | - | 90.8 | 60 |
| 7) Trieste Mte Belvedere | 91.5 | 93.6 | 95.8 | 103.9 | 106.7 | 30 |
| 7) Udine | 94.9 | 97.2 | 99.8 | - | - | 60 |
| 8) Velletri | 88.7 | 90.7 | 92.7 | - | - | 15 |

+ over 6000 stns below 1kW

**D.Prgr:** All stns transmit from 0500 to 2300, except Milano 900kHz, Roma 1107kHz 24h **R1**=Radiouno, **R2FM**=Radiodue, **R3FM**=Radiotre, **S**=Special Prgrs.

**Regional Prgrs:** 0620 -0628 Mon/Sat RAI1; 1110-1127 RAI1 Mon/ Sat ; 1730-1735 RAI1 Mon/Fri, 1115-1126 RAI1 Sun
**(a) Friuli:** 0618-0657 Mon-Sat RAI1, 1003-1157 Mon-Sat RAI1, 1130-1157 Sun RAI 1,1300-1415 Mon-Fri RAI1, 1330-1400 Sat RAI1, 1730-1756 Mon/Fri RAI1, 1715-1756 Sat RAI1, 0740-0910, 1108-1157, 1730-1756 Sun sport RAI1; (+a): "L'ora della Venezia Giulia" 1345-1445 Mon/Sat RAI1, 1330-1400 Sun RAI1 – **(b) Sicilia:** 1230-1245, Mon/ Sat RAI1 Arabic sce only on FM stns – **(c) Sicilia:** 0630-0657,1110-1127,1315-1400, 1730-1756 Mon/Sat; RAI1 1140-1157,1730-1756 Sun sport RAI1 – **(d) Sardegna:** 0630-0657,1315-1400, 1730-1756 Mon/ Sat RAI1, 1730-1756 Sun sport RAI1 – **(f) Valle D'Aosta:** 1315-1400 Mo/Sat, 1730-1756 Sun sport RAI1 (Bilingual) – **(e) Alto Adige** 0630-0657, 1315-1400, 1730-1756 Mon/Sat; 1730-1756 Sun sport RAI1
**NB:** All 1h earlier in summertime

**SPECIAL PRGRS:**
**ISO Radio:** 24h sce for motorway users on 103.3MHz FM (220 txs of 5kW or less);103.2MHz Milano,Como,Lecco area; 103.5MHz, Rome area **E:** isoradio@rai.it **W:** isoradio.it **Dir. :** Danilo Scarrone. **GR Parlamento:** 24h sce Italian Parliament channel. FM (150 txs of 5kW or less) **W:** grparlamento.rai.it **Dir.;** Gerardo Greco. **Sender Bozen (Bolzano):** Prgrs in German on FM (46 txs of 1kW or less) **DPrgr:** 0500 (Sun 0600)-2300. N. 0615 (W), 0800 (Sun), 1000 (W), 1100, 1200, 1300, 1700 (W), 1930 **E:** kontakt@rai.it **W:** senderbozen.rai.it
**Regional Prgr. in Slovene:** Trieste 981kHz 20 kW + 103.9MHz 20kW (and 22 additional FM-txs). **D. Prgr:** 0500 (Sun 0600)-1900. **N:** W 0500, 0700, 0900, 1200, 1300, 1600, 1800; Sun 0700, 1200, 1300, 1800. Dir. : Guido Corso. **N.** in German: 0900 (W). Night : RAI 1 FM 1900-0500.
**Ann:** Home Sce: "RAI Radiouno", "RAI Radiodue", "RAI Radiotre" as appropriate. Night Prgr: "RAI-Radiotelevisione Italiana stazioni a onda media di Milano kHz 900, di Roma kHz 1107, e di Pisa kHz 657" **W:** sedezfjk.rai.it

**R.A.S.**
✉ Europaallee 164/A, 39100 Bozen ☎ +39 0471 546666 🖷 +39 0471 200378 **E:** info@ras.bz.it **W:** ras.bz.it **L.P:** Pres: Rudi Gamper MD: Georg Plattner, Dir. Tec: Dr .Johann Silbernagl
**NB: R.A.S.** is a public body of the autonomous Region of Southern Tyrol whose purpose is to relay TV and radio from Germany, Austria and Switzerland to the German-speaking population.

| FM (MHz) | RAS 1 | RAS 2 | RAS 3 | kW |
|---|---|---|---|---|
| Kronplatz | 100.7 | 103.0 | 104.7 | 2 |
| Meransen | 101.3 | 103.9 | 107.3 | 1 |
| Obervinschgau | 100.5 | 103.0 | 106.1 | 0.6 |
| Penegal | 103.3 | 100.3 | 104.7 | 2 |
| Perdonig | 101.8 | 104.0 | 106.0 | 1 |
| Plose | 99.8 | 102.0 | 105.6 | 1 |
| Vinschgau | 101.1 | 102.9 | 105.0 | 2 |

+ 880 low power stns

**RAS 1:** rel. OE-3 (Austria) - **RAS-2:** rel. OE-R (Austria) - **RAS-3:** rel. OE-1 (Austria)

**DAB+:** RAI & RAS on Blocks 12A-12DA, 223.936MHz - 229.072MHz Consorzio DAB Italia on block 9D. 208.064MHz **W:** dab.it

**PRIVATE STATIONS**
Only stns with MW/SW broadcasts and FM networks are listed. A number of other stns are heard irr. There are approx. 600 FM stns

| | MW kHz | kW | Station, location and h of tr. |
|---|---|---|---|
| 1) | 567 | 1 | Challenger R., Villa Estense (PD): prgrs VOA IRRS-Nexus |
| 9) | †828 | 1 | Z100, Pavia area, irr. |
| 16) | †1098 | | Media R. Castellana, Castel San Pietro (BO) irr. |
| 11) | †1206 | | Amica R. Veneta, Peraga di Vigonza (PD), mx no stop |
| 15) | 1305 | 1 | R. Coltano Marconi, Coltano (PI) |
| 7) | †1350 | 1 | I AM R., north Milano irr. Fri/Sun* |
| 10) | †1377 | 1 | R. One, Pistoia area, irr. |
| 4) | †1404 | 0.1 | Gruppo R. Luna 106, Chiozza di Scandiano (RE): 0600-1900 |
| 12) | †1476 | 0.05 | R. Briscola, Lenta (VC) irr. |
| 17) | †1485 | 0.1 | R. Feltre Stereo, Belluno irr. |
| 3) | †1566 | 0.1 | R. Kolbe Sat, Schio (VI): irr. |
| 14) | 1584 | 5 | R. Diffusione Europea, Trieste |
| 13) | 1584 | 0.5 | Regional R., Otricoli (TR) |
| 2) | 1602 | 0.02 | R. 3 Network, Poggibonsi (SI) |
| 6) | 1602 | 0.02 | RTV R. Treviso, Treviso |
| 8) | 1602 | 0.02 | Dot R., Spello (PG) |

**Addresses & other information:**
**1)** Via Legnaro 6, 35040 Villa Estense (PD) 🖷 +39 0429 662280 **W:** challenger.it **E:** challenger@challenger.it **V.** by letter Rp. SM: Maurizio Anselmo – **2)** **W:** radio3.net **E:**redazione@radio3.net V: via mail SM: Mirko Roppolo – **3)** R. Kolbe Sat, Via Ischia 9, 36015 Schio (VI) ☎ +39 0445 505035 **W:** radiolkolbe.it **E:** segreteria@radiokolbe. net SM: Alberto De Pretto – **4)** **E:** rtv1602@libero.it – **5)** Via Brolo Sotto 52, 42019 Chiozza di Scandiano (RE ) ☎+39 0522 856598 🖷+39 0522 5263255 **W:** radio106.it **E:** info@radioluna.com – **FM:** 104.4,105.9MHz 5kW **SM:** Battista Francia – **7)** **E:** info@iamradio. am – **8)** **W:** www.dotradio.eu **E:** info@dotradio.eu – **9) E:** z100milano@ ondemedie.am – **11)** **W:** redazio44.wixsite.com/amicaradioveneta – **12)** **W:** facebook.com/FreeRadio-AM-465163190333643/ – **13)** **W:** facebook.com/radioregionalam – **14)** **W:** radiodiffusioneeuropea.net – **15)** via Palazzi 21, 56121 Coltano (PI) **W:** radiocoltanomarconi.it **E:**info@radiocoltanomarconi.it ☎+39 050 989318 – **16)** **W:** www. mediaradiocastellana.it **E:** info@mediaradiocastellana.it

**FM NETWORKS IN MAJOR CITIES (MHz):**

| | Network | To | Mi | Ve | Bo | Ge |
|---|---|---|---|---|---|---|
| 1) | Circuito Margherita | 91.8 | 89.5 | - | - | 90.1 |
| 2) | Kiss Kiss | 92.4 | 97.6 | - | 101.8 | 104.9 |
| 3) | InBlu R. | 89.0 | 94.6 | 94.6 | 97.0 | 88.8 |
| 4) | Latte Miele | 88.5 | 92.2 | 106.2 | 91.2 | - |
| 5) | m2o | 93.0 | 91.0 | 87.8 | 89.0 | 88.6 |
| 6) | Popolare Network | 97.6 | 107.6 | 97.3 | 96.2 | - |
| 7) | R. Capital | 90.3 | 90.1 | 98.5 | 99.4 | 93.9 |
| 8) | R. 105 | 99.6 | 99.1 | 98.9 | 103.5 | 99.5 |
| 9) | R. 101 | 101.0 | 100.9 | 107.3 | 96.0 | - |
| 10) | R. Classica | 98.7 | 94.0 | - | - | 101.1 |
| 11) | R. Cuore | 92.7 | 101.7 | - | - | - |
| 12) | R. Deejay | 106.9 | 99.7 | 94.8 | 99.7 | 96.9 |
| 13) | R. RDS | 96.4 | 107.3 | 99.8 | 104.2 | 95.7 |
| 14) | R. Italia Anni 60 | 103.7 | 106.3 | 101.7 | 102.1 | 91.3 |
| 15) | R. Italia | 106.6 | 98.4 | 98.1 | 100.6 | 106.3 |
| 16) | R. Maria | 107.5 | 107.9 | 106.5 | 90.5 | 106.6 |

| Network | To | Mi | Ve | Bo | Ge |
|---|---|---|---|---|---|
| 17) R. Mater | 105.7 | 95.3 | 100.1 | - | - |
| 19) R. Freccia | 90.9 | 91.4 | 99.0 | 97.7 | 96.0 |
| 20) R. Radicale | 102.8 | 96.8 | 104.7 | 92.0 | 95.4 |
| 21) R. RMC 1 | 105.5 | 105.3 | 100.4 | 101.3 | 104.2 |
| 22) R. RMCSport | 103.5 | 95.9 | 99.1 | 89.2 | 100.2 |
| 23) R. 24 | 105.0 | 104.8 | 106.8 | 107.0 | 97.2 |
| 24) RTL 102.5 | 102.5 | 102.5 | 102.5 | 101.6 | 102.4 |
| 25) Virgin R. | 90.9 | 104.5 | 93.1 | 106.5 | 105.5 |
| 26) R. Sportiva | 101.5 | 95.8 | - | 87.7 | 105.8 |
| 27) R. Subasio | - | 87.5 | - | - | - |

| Network | Fi | Rm | Na | Ba | Pa |
|---|---|---|---|---|---|
| 1) Circuito Margherita | 96.7 | 96.4 | 100.7 | 95.2 | 95.2 |
| 2) Kiss Kiss | 92.8 | 97.2 | 89.0 | 100.8 | 103.0 |
| 3) InBlu R. | 93.9 | 96.3 | 93,45 | 100.0 | 88.0 |
| 4) Latte Miele | 91.4 | 93.1 | 101.2 | - | 94.6 |
| 5) m2o | 105.8 | 97.0 | 98.3 | 88.5 | 107.8 |
| 6) Popolare Network | 93.6 | 103.3 | - | 97.3 | 96.0 |
| 7) R. Capital | 97.6 | 95.5 | 104.6 | 88.5 | 92.9 |
| 8) R. 105 | 105.0 | 96.1 | 99.7 | 87.9 | 105.1 |
| 9) R. 101 | 94.9 | 100.0 | 93.0 | 107.3 | 97.2 |
| 10) R. Classica | 99.4 | 89.5 | - | 105.0 | 99.5 |
| 11) R. Cuore | 100.2 | - | - | - | 89.1 |
| 12) R. Deejay | 100.6 | 101.0 | 92.3 | 93.2 | 107.5 |
| 13) R. RDS | 101.8 | 103.0 | 107.5 | 89.1 | 106.6 |
| 14) R. Italia Anni 60 | - | - | 104.1 | 89.6 | 95.8 |
| 15) R. Italia | 107.6 | 104.2 | 96.8 | 103.5 | 104.8 |
| 16) R. Maria | 88.8 | 95.1 | 98.8 | 102.0 | 89.4 |
| 17) R. Mater | 93.9 | 93.5 | - | 95.4 | - |
| 18) R. Norba | - | - | 92.7 | 105.5 | - |
| 19) R. Freccia | 90.2 | 102.1 | 95.2 | 105.2 | 97.8 |
| 20) R. Radicale | 97.0 | 88.6 | 101.6 | 89.3 | 92.0 |
| 21) R. RMC 1 | 106.6 | 106.3 | 91.6 | 92.0 | 90.0 |
| 22) R. RMCSport | 100.3 | 90.9 | 101.2 | 101.2 | 95.8 |
| 23) R. 24 | 103.8 | 107.9 | 103.5 | 88.2 | 104.5 |
| 24) RTL 102.5 | 100.9 | 102.1 | 102.6 | 102.5 | 102.3 |
| 25) Virgin R. | 107.2 | 98.7 | 93.5 | 106.6 | 93.2 |
| 26) R. Sportiva | 94.2 | 88.3 | 105.3 | 100.2 | 100.5 |
| 27) R. Subasio | 94.5 | 94.5 | 106.5 | - | - |

To=Torino Mi=Milano Ve=Venezia Bo=Bologna Ge=Genova Fi=Firenze Rm=Roma Na=Napoli Ba=Bari Pa=Palermo
Reference to Italian frequencies on **W:** fmdx.altervista.org

**Addresses & other information:**
**1)** Via Marchese di Villabianca 82, 90143 Palermo (PA) ☎+39 091 302712 📠+39 091 8724835 **W:** radiomargherita.com **E:** info@radiomargherita.com SM: Giuseppe Orobello **V.** by letter. Rp. – **2)** Via Sgambati 61, 80131 Napoli (NA) ☎+39 081 5461212 📠+39 081 5467789 **W:** kisskiss.it **E:** info@kisskiss.it, ufficiotecnico@kisskiss.it SM: Lucia Niespolo TM: Ugo Lombardi **V.** by letter. Rp. – **3)** Via Aurelia 796, 00165 Roma (RM) ☎+39 06 6650851 📠+39 06 66508516 **W:** radioinblu.it **E:** info@radioinblu.it TM: Paolo Ruffini. **V.** by letter. Rp – **4)** Via Andrea Costa 10, 40013 Castelmaggiore (BO) ☎+39 051 70928 📠+39 051 6325710 **W:** lattemiele.com **E:** info@lattemiele.com SM: Franco Mignani – **5)** Piazza della Repubblica 23/c, 00185 Roma (RM) ☎+39 06 492311 📠+39 06 4453758 **W:** m2o.it **E:** contatti@m2o.it PM: Fabrizio Tamburini **V.** by letter. Rp. – **6)** Via U.Olleoro 5, 20155 Milano (MI) ☎+39 02 392411 📠+39 02 39273125 **W:** radiopopolare. it **E:** Radiopop@radiopopolare.it SM: Marcello Lorrai **V.** by QSL-card. Rp. – **7)** Via C. Colombo 90, 00147 Roma (RM) ☎+39 06 494321 📠+39 06 44702290 **W:** capital.it **E:** infoline@capital.it SM: Vittorio Zucconi. **V.** by QSL-card. Rp. – **8)** Largo G. Donegani 1, 20121 Milano (MI) ☎+39 02 6596116 📠39 02 6592272 **W:** 105.net **E:** diretta@105. net, altafrequenza@radioengineering.net SM: Alberto Hazan **V.** QSL-Card. Rp. – **9)** Via Giovanni Ventura 3, 20134 , Milano (MI) ☎+39 02 210831 📠+39 02 210831210 **W:** r101.it **E:** infor101@r101.it SM: Mirko Lagonegro **V.** by QSL-card. Rp. – **10)** Via M.Burigozzo 5, 20122 Milano (MI) ☎+39 02 58219600 📠+39 02 58219407 **W:** radioclassica.fm **E:** radioclassica@class.it SM: Carla Signorile **V.** by letter. Rp. – **11)** Via Giovanni da Verrazzano 16, Localita Le Melorie, 56038 Ponsacco (PI) ☎+39 0587 2861 📠+39 0587 733861 **W:** mediahit.it **E:** info@mediahit.it SM: Italo Bessi **V.** by letter. Rp – **12)** Via Massena 2, 20154 Milano (MI) ☎+39 02 342522 📠+39 02 342888 **W:** deejay.it **E:** segnalazioni@deejay.it SM: Linus **V.** by QSL-card. Rp. – **13)** Via Pier Ruggero Piccio 55, 00136 Roma (RM) ☎+39 06 37704242 📠+39 06 37704250 **W:** rds.it **E:** ufficiotecnico@rds.it SM: Stefano Montefusco **V.** by letter. Rp. **W:** rds.it/frequenze/ – **14)** Via Zambra 11, 38121 Trento (TN) ☎ +39 0461 828990 📠+39 0461 428960 **W:** radioitaliaanni60.it **E:** info@radioitaliaanni60.it SM: Franco Nisi **V.** by letter – **15)** Viale Europa 49, 20093 Cologno Monzese (MI) ☎+39 02 25441 📠+39 02 25444220 **W:** radioitalia.it **E:** info@radioitalia.it SM: Mario Volanti **V.** by letter.

Rp. – **16)** Via Milano 12 , 22036 Erba (CO) ☎+39 031 610600 📠+39 031 611288 **W:** radiomaria.it **E:** info.ita@radiomaria.org SM: Don Livio Fanzaga **V.** by QSL-card. Rp. Rpt requested to **E:** QSL@radiomaria.org QSL Mgr. Giampiero Bernardini, St Eng, Claudio Re. – **17)** Via XXV Aprile 1, 22031 Albavilla (CO) ☎+39 031 645214 📠+39 031 6490527 **W:** radiomater.com **E:** redazione@radiomater.com SM: Don Mario Galbiati **V.** by letter. Rp. – **18)** Via Foggia 29, 70014 Conversano (BA) ☎+39 80 4951229 📠+39 80 4953079 **W:** radionorba.it **E:** radionorba@radionorba.it SM: Annamaria Fantasia **V.** by letter. Rp. – **19)** Via Scotti 11, 24122 Bergamo 📠+39 035 239385 **W:** radiofreccia.it/ **V.** by letter. Rp. – **20)** Centro di Produzione, Via Principe Amedeo 2, 00185 Roma (RM) ☎+39 06 488781 📠+39 06 4880196 **W:** radioradicale.it **E:** ioascolto@radioradicale.it SM: Alessio Falconio **V.** by letter. Rp. – **21)** Via Principe Amedeo 2, 20121 Milano (MI) ☎+39 02 29001636 📠 +39 02 6551451 **W:** radiomontecarlo.it **E:** rmc@radiomontecarlo. net, altafrequenza@radioengineering.net SM: Paolo Del Forno **V.** by QSL-card. Rp – **22)**RMC Sport via Cristoforo Colombo 112, 00149 Roma (RM) **W:** rmcsport.net **E:** redazione@rmcsport.net SM: Paolo Del Forno **V.** by QSL-card. Rp. – **23)** Via Monte Rosa 91, 20149 Milano (MI) ☎+39 02 30221 📠+039 02 30224462 **W:** radio24.it **E:** info@radio24.it SM: Roberto Napoletano **V.** Dario Arbulla (Ufficio Tecnico) by letter. Rp.– **24)** Viale Piemonte 61/63, 20093 Cologno Monzese (MI) ☎+39 02 251515 📠+39 02 25096201 **W:** rtl.it **E:** qualita@rtl.it SM Man.: Armando Finocchi (Chief Eng.) SM: Luigi Tornari **V.** QSL-card. Rp. – **25)** Largo Donegani 1, 20121 Milano (MI) ☎+39 02 6596116 📠 +39 02 62537460 **W:** virginradioitaly.it **E:** guastivirgin@virginradio. it altafrequenza@radioengineering.net SM: Francesco Migliozzi **V.** QSL-Card. Rp. – **26)** Via Giovanni da Verrazzano 16, Localita Le Melorie, 56038 Ponsacco (PI) ☎+39 0587 2861 📠+39 0587 733861 **W:** radiosportiva.com **E:**redazione@radiosportiva.it SM: Italo Bessi **V.** by letter. Rp – **27)** Localita Colle de Bensi, 06081 Assisi (PG) ☎+39 075 8060 📠+39 075 8065419 **W:** radiosubasio.it **E:** subasio@radiosubasio. it SM: Rita Settimi **V.** by letter. Rp.

**EXTERNAL SERVICES:**
**NEXUS - INTERNATIONAL BROADCASTING ASSOCIATION**
See International Broadcasting section
**BCL NEWS – STUDIO DX**
See International Broadcasting section

**AMERICAN FORCES NETWORK EUROPE (U.S. Mil.)**
**W:** afneurope.net/AFN-360/; **E:** harringtonj@afns.vicenza.army.mil
**FM** (MHz): **1)** The Eagle, 106.0 10kW, Vicenza. AFN,C/o Caserma Ederle,Via della Pace 100, 36100 Vicenza (VI) **W:** vicenza.afneurope. net ☎+039 0444 397111 **V.** by letter. No Rp. – **2)** LAVA 107.0 10kW, Naples. PSC 817, Box 31,FPO AE 09622, USA **W:** naples.afneurope.net **E:** ask.nsa@nsa.naples.navy.mil ☎+039 081 811 4242 **V.** by letter. No Rp. – **3)** 105.9 5kW, Sigonella. **E:** afnsigonella@mail.mil

## IVORY COAST

See CÔTE D'IVOIRE

## JAMAICA

**L.T:** UTC -5h — **Pop:** 2.9 million — **Pr.L:** English — **E.C:** 50Hz, 110/220V — **ITU:** JMC

**BROADCASTING COMMISSION OF JAMAICA**
✉ 5th Floor, Victoria Mutual Building, 53 Knutsford Boulevard, Kingston 5 ☎ 1 876 9209537 📠 +1 876 9291997 **E:** info@broadcom. org **W:** www.broadcastingcommission.org
**L.P:** Chmn: Anthony Clayton

**RJR GLEANER COMMUNICATIONS GROUP**
**RADIO JAMAICA LTD (Comm.)**
✉ 32 Lyndhurst Rd, Kingston 5 ☎ +1 876 926 1100 📠 +1 876 929 7467 **W:** rjrgleanergroup.com **L.P:** Chmn: Oliver F. Clarke. MD: Gary Allen. GM Radio: Dennis Howard.
**FM**(MHz): **RJR94**: 94.1/94.3/94.5/94.7/94.9 — **Fame95**: 95.1/ 95.3/95.5/95.7/95.9 — **Hitz92**: 92.1/92.3/92.5/92.2/92.9 — **Music99**: 99.1/99.3/99.5/99.7/99.9 — **Power106FM**: 106.1/106.3/ 106.5/106.7/106.9. **NB:** Music99 and Power106FM are still being run from 7 North St, Kingston.

**CORNWALL BROADCASTING COMPANY LTD**
✉ 63 Barnett St, Montego Bay ☎ +1 876 971 4163/9124 **W:** mellofmjamaica.com **L.P:** CEO Al Robinson. Ops Mgr Edwin George
**FM**(MHz): **Mello FM**: 88.1/88.3/88.5/88.7 — **Riddim 96 FM**: 96.5/96.7/96.9 — **Energy FM**: 102.1/102.3/102.5/102.7/102.9
**NB:** The company also operates from 3 Cargill Av, Kingston 10

**OTHER STATIONS** (FM in MHz):

**BBC FM:** 104.1/104.3/104.5/104.7/104.9. 24h relay of the BBC World Service — **Bess FM,** 4 East Bloomsbury Rd, Kingston 10 ☎ +1 876 754 1898 🖹 +1 876 920 4749 **W:** bessfm.com **L.P:** Antonio Shaw. FM: 100.1/100.3/100.5/100.7/100.9 — **Fyah 105,** 40-41 Beechwood Ave, Kingston 5 ☎ +1 876 754 4182 🖹 +1 876 920 1440 **W:** fyah105.com **L.P:** GM Ronald Sutherland FM: 105.3/105.5/105.7 — **Gospel JA,** Unit 5, Tri 7 Business Green Crescent, Kingston 10 ☎ +1 876 906 3423 **W:** gospelja.com FM: 91.7/91.9 — **Irie FM,** P.O Box 282, Coconut Grove, Ocho Rios ☎ +1 876 974 5051/968 5023 🖹 +1 876 974 5154 **E:** info@iriefm.net **W:** iriefm.net **L.P:** MD Debbian Dewar. FM: 107.1/107.3/107.5/107.7/107.9. Format: Reggae — **Klas FM,** 17 Haining Rd, Kingston 5 ☎ +1 876 929 1344 🖹 +1 876 906 0572 **W:** klassportsradio.com FM: 89.1/89.3/89.5/89.9. Format: Sport — **Kool 97 FM,** 1 Braemar Ave, Kingston 10 ☎ +1 876 818 7620 **W:** kool97fm.com **L.P:** GM Howard Armstrong. FM: 97.1/97.3/97.5/97.7/97.9 — **Love FM,** 81 Hagley Pk Rd, Kingston 11 ☎ +1 876 968 9596 **W:** love101.org FM: 101.1/101.3/101.5/101.7/101.9. Format: Rlg. — **Mega Jamz,** 40A Mannings Hill Rd, Kingston 8 ☎ +1 876 631 1510 🖹 +1 876 925 7625 **W:** megajamzfm.com **L.P:** MD Katherine Chong. FM: 98.1/98.3/98.5/98.7/98.9. Format: Oldies — **Nationwide News Network,** Bradley Av, Kingston ☎ +1 876 630 1210 **W:** nationwideradiojm.com **L.P:** Cliff Hughes. FM: 90.3/90.5/90.7 — **NCU 91 FM,** Northern Caribbean University, East Campus, Manchester Rd, Mandeville ☎ +1 876 963 7716 **W:** ncumediagroup.com FM: 91.1/91.3/91.5. Format: Rlg. (Adventist) — **Newstalk 93FM,** Universal Media Company, 18 Ring Rd., Mona, Kingston 7 ☎ +1 876 970 2345 🖹 +1 876 970 2472 **W:** newstalk93fm.com FM: 93.1/93.3/93.5/93.7/93.9 — **Radio France Internationale,** 80A Lady Musgrave Rd, Kingston 10: FM: 96.5 — **Roots FM,** 1 Mahoe Drive, Kingston 14 ☎ +1 876 923 6488 🖹 +1 876 923 6000. FM: Kingston 96.1 — **Stylz FM,** 4 Boundbrooke Ave, Port Antonio P.O. ☎ +1 876 453 1444 **W:** stylzfm.com **L.P:** Huel Jackson. FM: 96.1/96.3/96.7 — **SunCity Radio,** Shop #30-32, Portmore Pines Plaza, Portmore, St. Catherine ☎ +1 876 989 3318 🖹 +1 876 949 7991 **W:** suncityradio.fm **L.P:** CEO Doreen Billings. FM: 104.9 — **TBC FM (The Breath of Change),** 51 Molynes Rd, Kingston 10 ☎ +1 876 754 5120 🖹 +1 876 968 9159 **W:** tbcradio.org FM: Kingston 88.5. Format: Rlg (Baptist) — **Vybz FM,** 98 Great George Street, Savanna-la-Mar, Westmoreland ☎ +1 876 918 2521 🖹 +1 876 918 2394. **L.P:** Viannie Bedward Morgan. FM: 96.3 — **Zip 103,** 1B Courtney Walsh Drive, Kingston 10 ☎ +1 876 929 6233 🖹 +1 876 960 0523 **W:** zipfm.net **L.P:** MD Debbian Dewar. FM: 103.1/103.3/103.5/103.7/103.9.

**NB: +** 10 low-power stns not included.

## JAPAN

**L.T:** UTC +9h — **Pop:** 126 million — **Pr.L:** Japanese — **EC:** 50 & 60Hz, 100V — **ITU:** J

**INFORMATION AND COMMUNICATIONS BUREAU, MINISTRY OF INTERNAL AFFAIRS AND COMMUNICATIONS (SOUMU SHO)**

🖃 1-2, Kasumigaseki 2-chome, Chiyoda-ku, Tokyo 100-8926 ☎ +81 3 5253 5111 **W:** soumu.go.jp **L.P:** Minister: S.Noda

**NIPPON HOSO KYOKAI (NHK) (Pub)**
**(The Japan Broadcasting Corporation)**

🖃 2-1, Jinnan 2-chome, Shibuya-ku, Tokyo 150-8001 ☎ +81 3 3465 1111 **W:** nhk.or.jp
**L.P:** Chmn. (Board of Governors): S.Ishihara. Pres: R.Ueda. Exec. Vice-Pres: H.Doumoto. Exec. Dirs: Y.Kida, T.Sakamoto. Exec. Dir & Chief of Eng: A.Chigono. Sen. Dirs: Y.Matsubara, H.Araki, N.Ogi, Y.Kan, H.Nakata, I.Suzuki, C.Matsuzaka
**Pub:** NHK Nenkan (Japanese), NHK Update (English)

| MW Loc. & Prgr | Call | kHz | kW | | MW Loc. & Prgr | Call | kHz | kW |
|---|---|---|---|---|---|---|---|---|
| E2) Nago 1 | | 531 | 1 | | G3) Obihiro 1 | OG | 603 | 5 |
| F2) Morioka 1 | QG | 531 | 10 | | E1) Fukuoka 1 | LK | 612 | 100 |
| A2) Matsumoto 1 | | 540 | 1 | | A2) Iida 1 | | 621 | 1 |
| C2) Nanao 1 | | 540 | 1 | | E3) Nobeoka 1 | | 621 | 1 |
| E2) Ishigaki 1 | | 540 | 1 | | G4) Asahikawa 1 | CG | 621 | 3 |
| B3) Miyazaki 1 | MG | 540 | 5 | | C3) Shizuoka 1 | PB | 639 | 10 |
| E4) Kitakyushu 1 | SK | 540 | 1 | | E6) Oita 1 | IP | 639 | 5 |
| F3) Yamagata 1 | JG | 540 | 5 | | C4) Toyama 1 | IG | 648 | 5 |
| E2) Okinawa 1 | AP | 549 | 10 | | B1) Osaka 1 | BK | 666 | 100 |
| G1) Sapporo 1 | IK | 567 | 100 | | D3) Yamaguchi 1 | UG | 675 | 1 |
| C3) Hamamatsu 1 | DG | 576 | 1 | | G5) Hakodate 1 | VK | 675 | 5 |
| C5) Kagoshima 1 | HG | 576 | 10 | | E7) Nagasaki 1 | AG | 684 | 5 |
| G2) Kushiro 1 | PG | 585 | 10 | | A1) Tokyo 2 | AB | 693 | 500 |
| A1) Tokyo 1 | AK | 594 | 300 | | D1) Hiroshima 1 | FB | 702 | 10 |
| D2) Okayama 1 | KK | 603 | 5 | | G6) Kitami 2 | KD | 702 | 10 |

| MW Loc. & Prgr | Call | kHz | kW | | MW Loc. & Prgr | Call | kHz | kW |
|---|---|---|---|---|---|---|---|---|
| C1) Nagoya 1 | CK | 729 | 50 | | G7) Muroran 2 | IZ | 1125 | 1 |
| G1) Sapporo 2 | IB | 747 | 500 | | G2) Kushiro 2 | PC | 1152 | 10 |
| E8) Kumamoto 1 | GK | 756 | 10 | | H3) Kochi 2 | RB | 1152 | 10 |
| F4) Akita 2 | UB | 774 | 500 | | G6) Kitami 1 | KP | 1188 | 10 |
| A3) Takada 1 | | 792 | 1 | | C2) Kanazawa 1 | JK | 1224 | 10 |
| C5) Takayama 1 | | 792 | 1 | | D5) Matsue 1 | TK | 1296 | 10 |
| F2) Naze 1 | | 792 | 1 | | F2) Yamada 1 | | 1323 | 1 |
| G4) Enbetsu 1 | | 792 | 1 | | F5) Fukushima 1 | FP | 1323 | 1 |
| A2) Nagano 1 | NK | 819 | 5 | | E8) Minamata 1 | | 1341 | 1 |
| B3) Osaka 2 | BB | 828 | 300 | | F5) Iwaki 1 | | 1341 | 1 |
| A3) Niigata 1 | QK | 837 | 10 | | D4) Tottori 1 | LG | 1368 | 1 |
| G4) Nayoro 1 | | 837 | 1 | | F3) Tsuruoka 1 | | 1368 | 1 |
| E8) Hitoyoshi 1 | | 846 | 1 | | H4) Takamatsu 1 | HP | 1368 | 5 |
| F5) Koriyama 1 | | 846 | 5 | | D3) Yamaguchi 2 | UC | 1377 | 5 |
| H1) Uwajima 1 | | 846 | 1 | | E7) Nagasaki 2 | AC | 1377 | 1 |
| E8) Kumamoto 2 | GB | 873 | 500 | | E6) Hachinohe 2 | | 1377 | 1 |
| C3) Shizuoka 1 | PK | 882 | 10 | | C2) Kanazawa 2 | JB | 1386 | 10 |
| F1) Sendai 1 | HK | 891 | 20 | | D2) Okayama 2 | KB | 1386 | 5 |
| C1) Nagoya 2 | CB | 909 | 10 | | C5) Kagoshima 2 | HC | 1386 | 1 |
| A4) Kofu 1 | KG | 927 | 5 | | F2) Morioka 2 | QC | 1386 | 1 |
| C6) Fukui 1 | FG | 927 | 5 | | A2) Nagano 2 | NB | 1467 | 1 |
| D2) Tsuyama 1 | | 927 | 1 | | B3) Miyazaki 2 | MC | 1467 | 1 |
| G4) Wakkanai 1 | | 927 | 1 | | E6) Oita 2 | ID | 1467 | 1 |
| B3) Hikone 1 | QP* | 945 | 1 | | G4) Wakkanai 2 | | 1467 | 1 |
| E7) Fukue 1 | | 945 | 1 | | G5) Hakodate 2 | VB | 1467 | 1 |
| G7) Muroran 1 | IQ | 945 | 3 | | A2) Iida 2 | | 1476 | 1 |
| D2) Tokushima 1 | XK | 945 | 1 | | E8) Aso 1 | | 1503 | 1 |
| D3) Hagi 1 | | 963 | 1 | | F4) Akita 1 | UK | 1503 | 10 |
| D2) Yonago 1 | | 963 | 1 | | A2) Matsumoto 2 | | 1512 | 1 |
| E9) Saga 1 | SP | 963 | 1 | | F5) Koriyama 2 | | 1512 | 1 |
| F6) Aomori 1 | TG | 963 | 5 | | H1) Matsuyama 2 | ZB | 1512 | 5 |
| H1) Matsuyama 1 | ZK | 963 | 5 | | C3) Hamamatsu 2 | DC | 1521 | 1 |
| A2) Kisofukushima 1 | | 981 | 1 | | C6) Fukui 2 | FC | 1521 | 1 |
| E7) Sasebo 1 | | 981 | 1 | | D2) Yonago 2 | | 1521 | 1 |
| H3) Kochi 1 | RK | 990 | 10 | | E2) Ishigaki 2 | | 1521 | 1 |
| D1) Fukuyama 1 | | 999 | 1 | | F3) Yamagata 2 | JC | 1521 | 1 |
| F6) Hachinohe 1 | | 999 | 1 | | F6) Aomori 2 | TC | 1521 | 1 |
| H3) Nakamura 1 | | 999 | 1 | | H3) Nakamura 2 | | 1521 | 1 |
| E1) Fukuoka 2 | LB | 1017 | 50 | | A3) Niigata 2 | QB | 1593 | 10 |
| C4) Toyama 2 | IC | 1035 | 1 | | D5) Matsue 2 | TB | 1593 | 10 |
| F3) Tsuruoka 2 | | 1035 | 1 | | A4) Kofu 2 | KC | 1602 | 1 |
| H4) Takamatsu 2 | HD | 1035 | 1 | | D1) Fukuyama 2 | | 1602 | 1 |
| D1) Hiroshima 1 | FK | 1071 | 20 | | E3) Nobeoka 2 | | 1602 | 1 |
| F1) Sendai 2 | HB | 1089 | 10 | | E4) Kitakyushu 2 | SB | 1602 | 1 |
| C5) Takayama 2 | | 1125 | 1 | | E5) Naze 2 | | 1602 | 1 |
| D3) Hagi 2 | | 1125 | 1 | | E8) Hitoyoshi 2 | | 1602 | 1 |
| D4) Tottori 2 | LC | 1125 | 1 | | F5) Fukushima 2 | FD | 1602 | 1 |
| E2) Okinawa 2 | AD | 1125 | 10 | | G4) Asahikawa 2 | CC | 1602 | 1 |
| G3) Obihiro 2 | OC | 1125 | 1 | | G4) Enbetsu 2 | | 1602 | 1 |
| G4) Nayoro 2 | | 1125 | 1 | | H1) Uwajima 2 | | 1602 | 1 |

+ approx 240 stns below 1kW. There are multiple stns on 1026, 1161 and 1584kHz broadc. R. One, and on 1359 & 1539kHz, broadc. R. Two
**1:** NHK R. One, **2:** NHK R. Two. **Call:** JO(call). *stn announces its callsign as "JOBK"

| FM Location | Call | MHz | kW | | FM Location | Call | MHz | kW |
|---|---|---|---|---|---|---|---|---|
| A5) Utsunomiya | BP | 80.3 | 1 | | E1) Fukuoka | LK | 84.8 | 3 |
| A6) Chiba | MP | 80.7 | 5 | | E2) Miyakojima | | 85.0 | 1 |
| C4) Toyama | IG | 81.5 | 1 | | A10)Saitama | LP | 85.1 | 5 |
| A7) Maebashi | TP | 81.6 | 1 | | G1) Sapporo | IK | 85.2 | 5 |
| C7) Tsu | NP | 81.8 | 3 | | F5) Fukushima | FP | 85.3 | 1 |
| A8) Yokohama | GP | 81.9 | 5 | | E8) Kumamoto | GK | 85.4 | 1 |
| F3) Yamagata | JG | 82.1 | 1 | | A4) Kofu | KG | 85.6 | 1 |
| C2) Kanazawa | JK | 82.2 | 1 | | E5) Kagoshima | HG | 85.6 | 1 |
| A3) Niigata | QK | 82.3 | 1 | | D5) Hamada | | 85.8 | 1 |
| A1) Tokyo | AK | 82.5 | 10 | | F6) Aomori | TG | 86.0 | 3 |
| C1) Nagoya | CK | 82.5 | 10 | | H4) Takamatsu | HP | 86.0 | 1 |
| F1) Sendai | FK | 82.5 | 5 | | F4) Akita | UK | 86.7 | 3 |
| B2) Kyoto | OK | 82.8 | 1 | | H1) Matsuyama | ZK | 87.7 | 1 |
| F2) Morioka | QG | 83.1 | 1 | | B1) Osaka | BK | 88.1 | 10 |
| A9) Mito | EP | 83.2 | 1 | | E2) Okinawa | AP | 88.1 | 1 |
| C6) Fukui | FG | 83.4 | 1 | | G4) Nayoro | | 88.2 | 1 |
| F2) Tokushima | XK | 83.4 | 1 | | D1) Hiroshima | FK | 88.3 | 1 |
| A3) Yamato | | 83.5 | 1 | | D2) Okayama | KK | 88.7 | 1 |
| C5) Gifu | QP | 83.6 | 1 | | C3) Shizuoka | PK | 88.8 | 1 |
| B2) Otsu | OP | 84.0 | 1 | | E6) Oita | IP | 88.9 | 1 |
| B4) Himeji | | 84.2 | 1 | | G4) Chikoma | | 89.1 | 1 |
| E5) Tanegashima | | 84.4 | 1 | | G2) Nakashibetsu | | 89.9 | 1 |

+ approx 481 stns below 1kW. **Call:** JO(call)-FM

**Addresses of regional HQs and stns:**
**A)** Kanto-Koshinetsu area = Tokyo **A1)**: same as NHK general HQ

address – **A2)** Nagano: 210-2, Inaba, Nagano 380-8502 – **A3)** Niigata: 1-49, Kawagishi-cho, Chuo-ku, Niigata 951-8508 – **A4)** Kofu: 1-1-20, Marunouchi, Kofu 400-8552 – **A5)** Utsunomiya: 3-1-2, Chuo, Utsunomiya 320-8502 – **A6)** Chiba: 5-1, Chibaminato, Chuo-ku, Chiba 260-8610 – **A7)** Maebashi: 189, Motosojyamachi, Maebashi 371-8555 – **A8)** Yokohama: 281, Yamashita-cho, Naka-ku, Yokohama 231-8324 – **A9)** Mito: 3-4-4, Omachi, Mito 310-8567 – **A10)** Saitama: 6-1-21, Tokiwa, Urawa-ku, Saitama 330-9310 – **B)** Kinki area = Osaka – **B1)**: 1-20, Otemae 4-chome, Chuo-ku, Osaka 540-8501 – **B2)** Kyoto: 576,Torayacho, Nakakyo-ku, Kyoto 604-8515 – **B3)** Otsu: 3-30, Uchidehama, Otsu 520-0806 – **B4)** Kobe: 24-7, Nakayamate-dori 2-chome, Chuo-ku, Kobe 650-8515. **C)** Tokai-Hokuriku area = Nagoya **C1)**: 13-3, Higashisakura 1-chome, Higashi-ku, Nagoya 461-8725 – **C2)** Kanazawa: 14-1, Otemachi, Kanazawa 920-8644 – **C3)** Shizuoka: 6-1, Yahata 1-chome, Suruga-ku, Shizuoka 422-8787 – **C4)** Toyama: 3-1, Shinsogawa, Toyama 930-8502 – **C5)** Gifu: 2-3, Kyomachi, Gifu 500-8554 – **C6)** Fukui: 3-3-5, Hoei, Fukui 910-8680 – **C7)** Tsu: 4-8, Marunouchi Yousei-cho, Tsu 514-8531. **D)** Chugoku area = Hiroshima **D1)**: 11-10, Otemachi 2-chome, Naka-ku, Hiroshima 730-8672 – **D2)** Okayama: 15-1, Ekimotomachi, Kita-ku, Okayama 700-8621 – **D3)** Yamaguchi: 2-1, Nakazono-cho, Yamaguchi 753-8660 – **D4)** Tottori: 100, Teramachi, Tottori 680-8701 – **D5)** Matsue: 1-21, Nadamachi, Matsue 690-8601. **E)** Kyushu area = Fukuoka – **E1)**: 1-10, Ropponmatsu 1-chome, Chuo-ku, Fukuoka 810-8577 – **E2)** Okinawa: 2-6-21, Omoromachi, Naha 900-8535 – **E3)** Miyazaki: 2-2-15, Ehiranishi, Miyazaki 880-8633 – **E4)** Kitakyushu: 1-1-20, Muromachi 1-chome, Kokurakita-ku, Kitakyushu 803-8555 – **E5)** Kagoshima: 4-6, Honko Shinmachi, Kagoshima 892-8603 – **E6)** Oita: 2-36, Takasagomachi, Oita 870-8660 – **E7)** Nagasaki: 1-1, Nshirakamachi, Nagasaki 850-8603 – **E8)** Kumamoto: 5-1, Hanabatacho, Chuo-ku, Kumamoto 860-8602 – **E9)** Saga: 2-15-8, Jyonai, Saga 840-8601. **F)** Tohoku area = Sendai – **F1)**: 20-1, Honmachi 2-chome, Aoba-ku, Sendai 980-8435 – **F2)** Morioka: 1-3, Ueda 4-chome, Morioka 020-8555 – **F3)** Yamagata: 2-50, Sakura-cho, Yamagata 990-8575 – **F4)** Akita: 4-2, Higashidori Nakamachi, Akita 010-8501 – **F5)** Fukushima: 1-2, Wase-cho, Fukushima 960-8588 – **F6)** Aomori: 2-1-1, Matsumori, Aomori 030-8633. **G)** Hokkaido area = Sapporo – **G1)**: 1, Odori Nishi 1-chome, Chuo-ku, Sapporo 060-8703 – **G2)** Kushiro: 3-8, Nusamai-cho, Kushiro 085-8660 – **G3)** Obihiro: 2-2, Nishi 5-jyo Minami 7-chome, Obihiro 080-0015 – **G4)** Asahikawa: 27, 6-jyo Dori 6-chome, Asahikawa 070-8680 – **G5)** Hakodate: 13-1, Chitose-cho, Hakodate 040-8680 – **G6)** Kitami: 3-24, Hokutocho 2-chome, Kitami 090-0035 – **G7)** Muroran: 3-50, Yamatecho 1-chome, Muroran 051-0012. **H)** Shikoku area = Matsuyama – **H1)**: 5, Horinouchi, Matsuyama 790-8501 – **H2)** Tokushima: 1-28, Terashimahoncho Higashi, Tokushima 770-8544 – **H3)** Kochi: 3-12, Honmachi 3-chome, Kochi, 780-8512 – **H4)** Takamatsu: 1-12-7, Nishikimachi, Takamatsu, 760-8686.

**NHK R. One** (General prgr): 24h **N:** every h(exc Sun 0000, Mon-Fri 1400). Also at 2140(exc Sat). **Regional and local prgrs** (the amount of local prgrs varies between stns) 2055wrp, 2125N/wrp/inf, 2155wrp/inf, 2220(Fri&Sat 2215)N/wrp/inf, 2240(Sat 2255)N/wrp/inf, 0055(exc Sun)N/wrp/inf, 0250wrp/inf, 0315(SS 0310)N/wrp, 0355(exc Sun) wrp/inf, 0455N/wrp/inf, 0555N/wrp/inf, 0755N/wrp/inf, 0855N/wrp/inf, 0950N/wrp/inf, 1015(SS)N/wrp, 1055(SS)wrp/inf, 1255N/wrp/inf, 1410N/wrp. **IS:** Original music played by Celesta. **Ann:** "JO(call), NHK (location) Daiichi Hoso desu". Local ID's with call letters, network & location given by studio stns just before: 2000, 0300, 1000
**NHK R. Two** (Educational prgr): 2100-1540(Sun 1530). No regular regional and local prgrs. **Foreign language N** (rel. NHK World - R. Japan): **Chinese:** 0430(SS 0450). **Korean:** 0415(SS 0440). **English:** 0500. **Portuguese:** 1340(Sat 1425, Sun 1355). **Spanish:** 0400. Weather map: 0700. **IS:** Original music played by Celesta. Nat. Anthem at s/on on national holidays & s/off. **Ann:** "JO(call), NHK (location) Daini Hoso desu". Local IDs on certain stns (as 1st Netw) just before 2100, 0415(Mon-Fri), 0420(SS), 0720 and s/off.
**NHK FM Netw:** 24h. 1600-2000 relays R. One, **N:** 2200, 0300, 0950(local), 1000. **Ann:** "JO(call)-FM, NHK (location) FM Hoso desu". Local IDs just before 2000, 0300, 1000
**V:** NHK officially has no organised QSL sce. However, many local stns verify by QSL card or letter for DX reports.

**EXTERNAL SERVICES:**
**RADIO JAPAN, NHK WORLD NETWORK**
See International Broadcasting section

**THE JAPAN COMMERCIAL BROADCASTERS ASSOCIATION (NIPPON MINKAN HOSO RENMEI)**
✉ 3-23, Kioi-cho, Chiyoda-ku, Tokyo 102-8577 ☎ +81 3 5213 7711 🖷 +81 3 5213 7703 **W:** j-ba.or.jp
**L.P:** Pres: Y.Okubo. Vice-Presidents: M.Kato, T.Sasaki, Y.Kosugi, G.Sumami, M.Miyauchi, S.Komago, M.Yokoi, K.Miura. Exec. Dir:

S.Nagahara. **Pub:** Nippon Minkan Hoso Nenkan, Gekkan Minpo, Minkan Hoso (all Japanese) and NAB Handbook (English) etc.

| MW | Call | kHz | kW | ID | Station, location & h of tr |
|---|---|---|---|---|---|
| 1) | CR | 558 | 20 | CRK | R. Kansai, Kobe |
| 2) | WN | 639 | 5 | STV | STV R., Hakodate |
| 3) | DF | 684 | 5 | IBC | Iwate Hoso, Morioka |
| 3) | LO | 684 | 1 | IBC | Iwate Hoso, Ofunato |
| 4) | IL | 720 | 1 | KBC | Kyushu Asahi Hoso, Kitakyushu |
| 5) | LR | 738 | 5 | KNB | Kita Nihon Hoso, Toyama |
| 5) | | 738 | 1 | KNB | Kita Nihon Hoso, Takaoka |
| 6) | RR | 738 | 10 | RBC | Ryukyu Hoso, Naha |
| 7) | JF | 765 | 5 | YBS | Yamanashi Hoso, Kofu |
| 8) | PF | 765 | 5 | KRY | Yamaguchi Hoso, Shunan |
| 9) | XR | 864 | 10 | ROK | R. Okinawa, Naha: 2000-1800(Sun1530) |
| 10) | SO | 864 | 5 | SBC | Shin'etsu Hoso, Matsumoto |
| 11) | HE | 864 | 3 | HBC | Hokkaido Hoso, Asahikawa |
| 11) | QF | 864 | 3 | HBC | Hokkaido Hoso, Muroran |
| 11) | | 864 | 1 | HBC | Hokkaido Hoso, Enbetsu |
| 12) | FB | 864 | 5 | FBC | Fukui Hoso, Fukui |
| 13) | XN | 864 | 1 | CRT | Tochigi Hoso, Nasu |
| 2) | WS | 882 | 3 | STV | STV R., Kushiro |
| 2) | | 882 | 1 | STV | STV R., Esashi |
| 11) | HO | 900 | 5 | HBC | Hokkaido Hoso, Hakodate |
| 14) | HF | 900 | 5 | BSS | San'in Hoso, Yonago: (off air Sat1800-1955, Sun1500-1955) |
| 15) | ZR | 900 | 5 | RKC | Kochi Hoso, Kochi |
| 2) | VX | 909 | 5 | STV | STV R., Abashiri |
| 16) | EF | 918 | 5 | YBC | Yamagata Hoso, Yamagata |
| 16) | | 918 | 1 | YBC | Yamagata Hoso, Tsuruoka |
| 16) | | 918 | 1 | YBC | Yamagata Hoso, Yonezawa |
| 16) | | 918 | 1 | YBC | Yamagata Hoso, Shinjo |
| 8) | PM | 918 | 1 | KRY | Yamaguchi Hoso, Shimonoseki |
| 8) | PN | 918 | 1 | KRY | Yamaguchi Hoso, Iwakuni |
| 17) | TR | 936 | 5 | ABS | Akita Hoso, Akita |
| 18) | NF | 936 | 5 | MRT | Miyazaki Hoso, Miyazaki |
| 18) | | 936 | 1 | MRT | Miyazaki Hoso, Nobeoka |
| 18) | | 936 | 1 | MRT | Miyazaki Hoso, Nichinan |
| 18) | | 936 | 1 | MRT | Miyazaki Hoso, Kobayashi |
| 18) | | 936 | 1 | MRT | Miyazaki Hoso, Takachiho |
| 19) | KR | 954 | 100 | TBS | TBS R., Tokyo |
| 20) | NR | 1008 | 50 | ABC | Asahi Hoso, Osaka |
| 21) | AR | 1053 | 50 | CBC | Chubu Nippon Hoso, Nagoya: (S) |
| 2) | WM | 1071 | 5 | STV | STV R., Obihiro |
| 10) | SR | 1098 | 5 | SBC | Shin'etsu Hoso, Nagano |
| 10) | SW | 1098 | 1 | SBC | Shin'etsu Hoso, Iida |
| 22) | MF | 1098 | 5 | NBC | Nagasaki Hoso, Sasebo |
| 23) | GF | 1098 | 5 | OBS | Oita Hoso, Oita |
| 24) | WO | 1098 | 5 | RFC | R. Fukushima, Koriyama |
| 25) | CF | 1107 | 20 | MBC | Minami Nihon Hoso, Kagoshima |
| 25) | | 1107 | 1 | MBC | Minami Nihon Hoso, Akune |
| 25) | | 1107 | 1 | MBC | Minami Nihon Hoso, Oguchi |
| 25) | | 1107 | 1 | MBC | Minami Nihon Hoso, Sendai |
| 26) | MR | 1107 | 5 | MRO | Hokuriku Hoso, Kanazawa |
| 26) | | 1107 | 1 | MRO | Hokuriku Hoso, Nanao |
| 27) | AF | 1116 | 5 | RNB | Nankai Hoso, Matsuyama |
| 27) | AL | 1116 | 1 | RNB | Nankai Hoso, Niihama |
| 27) | AM | 1116 | 1 | RNB | Nankai Hoso, Uwajima |
| 28) | DR | 1116 | 5 | BSN | Niigata Hoso, Niigata |
| 29) | QR | 1134 | 100 | NCB | Bunka Hoso, Tokyo |
| 30) | BR | 1143 | 20 | KBS | KBS Kyoto, Kyoto |
| 31) | OR | 1179 | 50 | MBS | Mainichi Hoso, Osaka |
| 15) | | 1197 | 1 | RKC | Kochi Hoso, Nakamura |
| 32) | FO | 1197 | 5 | RKB | RKB Mainichi Hoso, Kitakyushu |
| 33) | BF | 1197 | 10 | RKK | Kumamoto Hoso, Kumamoto |
| 33) | | 1197 | 1 | RKK | Kumamoto Hoso, Hitoyoshi |
| 33) | | 1197 | 1 | RKK | Kumamoto Hoso, Aso |
| 33) | | 1197 | 1 | RKK | Kumamoto Hoso, Goshoura |
| 34) | YF | 1197 | 5 | IBS | Ibaraki Hoso, Mito: (off air Fri2000-2050, Sat2000-2100, Sun1500-2000) |
| 2) | WL | 1197 | 3 | STV | STV R., Asahikawa |
| 2) | | 1197 | 1 | STV | STV R., Wakkanai |
| 2) | | 1197 | 1 | STV | STV R., Nayoro |
| 2) | | 1197 | 1 | STV | STV R., Enbetsu |
| 30) | BO | 1215 | 2 | KBS | KBS Kyoto, Maizuru |
| 30a) | BW | 1215 | 1 | KBS | KBS Shiga, Hikone |
| 22) | UR | 1233 | 5 | NBC | Nagasaki Hoso, Nagasaki |
| 35) | GR | 1233 | 5 | RAB | Aomori Hoso, Aomori |
| 36) | LF | 1242 | 100 | NBS | Nippon Hoso, Tokyo: (S) |
| 37) | IR | 1260 | 20 | TBC | Tohoku Hoso, Sendai |
| 11) | HW | 1269 | 1 | HBC | Hokkaido Hoso, Obihiro |
| 11) | HM | 1269 | 1 | HBC | Hokkaido Hoso, Esashi |
| 38) | JR | 1269 | 5 | JRT | Shikoku Hoso, Tokushima |
| 38) | | 1269 | 1 | JRT | Shikoku Hoso, Ikeda |

| MW Call | kHz | kW | ID | Station, location & h of tr |
|---|---|---|---|---|
| 32) FR | 1278 | 50 | RKB | RKB Mainichi Hoso, Fukuoka |
| 11) HR | 1287 | 50 | HBC | Hokkaido Hoso, Sapporo |
| 39) UF | 1314 | 50 | OBC | R. Osaka, Osaka: (S) |
| 40) SF | 1332 | 50 | Tokai | R. Hoso, Nagoya |
| 41) ER | 1350 | 20 | RCC | Chugoku Hoso, Hiroshima |
| 11) TS | 1368 | 1 | HBC | Hokkaido Hoso, Wakkanai |
| 1) CE | 1395 | 1 | CRK | R. Kansai, Toyooka |
| 24) WE | 1395 | 1 | RFC | R. Fukushima, Wakamatsu |
| 11) QL | 1404 | 5 | HBC | Hokkaido Hoso, Kushiro |
| 42) VR | 1404 | 1 | SBS | Shizuoka Hoso, Shizuoka |
| 42) VO | 1404 | 1 | SBS | Shizuoka Hoso, Hamamatsu |
| 1) IF | 1413 | 50 | KBC | Kyushu Asahi Hoso, Fukuoka |
| 43) RF | 1422 | 50 | RF | RF R. Nippon, Yokohama |
| 14) HL | 1431 | 1 | BSS | San'in Hoso, Tottori: (as 900kHz) |
| 14) | 1431 | 1 | BSS | San'in Hoso, Izumo: (as 900kHz) |
| 22) | 1431 | 1 | NBC | Nagasaki Hoso, Fukue |
| 24) WW | 1431 | 1 | RFC | R. Fukushima, Iwaki |
| 45) VF | 1431 | 5 | WBS | Wakayama Hoso, Wakayama: (S) |
| 45) ZF | 1431 | 1 | GBS | Gifu Hoso, Gifu: 2100-1600 |
| 2) WF | 1440 | 50 | STV | STV R., Sapporo |
| 2) | 1440 | 3 | STV | STV R., Muroran |
| 2) | 1440 | 1 | STV | STV R., Tomakomai |
| 11) QM | 1449 | 5 | HBC | Hokkaido Hoso, Abashiri |
| 46) KF | 1449 | 1 | RNC | Nishi Nippon Hoso, Takamatsu |
| 46) | 1449 | 1 | RNC | Nishi Nippon Hoso, Marugame |
| 22a) UO | 1458 | 1 | NBC | Nagasaki Hoso, Saga |
| 24) WR | 1458 | 1 | RFC | R. Fukushima, Fukushima |
| 34) YL | 1458 | 1 | IBS | Ibaraki Hoso, Tsuchiura |
| 34) | 1458 | 1 | IBS | Ibaraki Hoso, Sekijo |
| 41) | 1458 | 1 | RCC | Chugoku Hoso, Shobara |
| 8) PL | 1485 | 1 | KRY | Yamaguchi Hoso, Hagi |
| 35) GO | 1485 | 1 | RAB | Aomori Hoso, Hachinohe |
| 11) TL | 1494 | 1 | HBC | Hokkaido Hoso, Nayoro |
| 47) YR | 1494 | 10 | RSK | Sanyo Hoso, Okayama |
| 47) | 1494 | 1 | RSK | Sanyo Hoso, Takahashi |
| 47) | 1494 | 1 | RSK | Sanyo Hoso, Tsuyama |
| 47) | 1494 | 1 | RSK | Sanyo Hoso, Niimi |
| 47) | 1494 | 1 | RSK | Sanyo Hoso, Bizen |
| 47) | 1494 | 1 | RSK | Sanyo Hoso, Ochiai |
| 28) DO | 1530 | 1 | BSN | Niigata Hoso, Joetsu |
| 13) XF | 1530 | 5 | CRT | Tochigi Hoso, Utsunomiya |
| 41) EO | 1530 | 1 | RCC | Chugoku Hoso, Fukuyama |
| 41) | 1530 | 1 | RCC | Chugoku Hoso, Mihara |

+ approx 125 relay stns below 1kW. Of these some exist multiply on 801, 1026, 1062 and 1557kHz.

## Simultaneous FM broadcasts of MW stns

| FM | MHz | kW | Stn, loc | FM | MHz | kW | Stn, loc |
|---|---|---|---|---|---|---|---|
| 17) | 90.1 | 1 | ABS, Akita | 14) | 92.2 | 0.5 | BSS, Matsue |
| | 90.2 | 1 | KNB, Toyama | 8) | 92.3 | 1 | KRY, Shunan |
| 4) | 90.2 | 1 | KBC, Fukuoka | 16) | 92.4 | 1 | YBC, Yamagata |
| 46) | 90.3 | | RNC, Takamatsu | 43) | 92.4 | | RF, Yokohama |
| 18) | 90.4 | 1 | MRT, Miyazaki | 22) | 92.6 | 1 | NBC, Nagasaki |
| 45) | 90.4 | 1 | GBS, Gifu | 28) | 92.7 | 1 | BSN, Niigata |
| | 90.4 | 5 | STV, Sapporo | 25) | 92.8 | 1 | MBC, Kagoshima |
| 19) | 90.5 | 7 | TBS, Tokyo | 40) | 92.9 | 7 | Tokai R., Nagoya |
| 3) | 90.6 | 1 | IBC, Morioka | 36) | 93.0 | 7 | NBS, Tokyo |
| 31) | 90.6 | 7 | MBS, Osaka | 38) | 93.0 | 1 | JRT, Tokushima |
| 15) | 90.8 | | RKC, Kochi | 9) | 93.1 | 1 | ROK, Naha |
| 24) | 90.8 | 0.5 | RFC, Fukushima | 20) | 93.3 | 7 | ABC, Osaka |
| | 90.9 | 1 | YBS, Kofu | 23) | 93.3 | 1 | OBS, Oita |
| 32) | 91.0 | 1 | RKB, Fukuoka | 37) | 93.5 | 5 | TBC, Sendai |
| | 91.1 | 1 | CRK, Kobe | 21) | 93.7 | 7 | CBC, Nagoya |
| 33) | 91.4 | 0.8 | RKK, Kumamoto | 42) | 93.9 | 1 | SBS, Shizuoka |
| 47) | 91.4 | 0.7 | RSK, Okayama | 26) | 94.0 | 1 | MRO, Kanazawa |
| 11) | 91.5 | 5 | HBC, Sapporo | 13) | 94.1 | 1 | CRT, Utsunomiya |
| 29) | 91.6 | 7 | NCR, Tokyo | 44) | 94.2 | 0.5 | WBS, Wakayama |
| 27) | 91.7 | 1 | RNB, Matsuyama | 12) | 94.6 | 1 | FBC, Fukui |
| 35) | 91.7 | 1 | RAB, Aomori | 34) | 94.6 | 1 | IBS, Mito |
| 39) | 91.9 | 7 | OBC, Osaka | 41) | 94.6 | 1 | RCC, Hiroshima |
| 6) | 92.1 | 1 | RBC, Naha | 30) | 94.9 | 3 | KBS, Kyoto |
| 10) | 92.2 | 1 | SBC, Nagano | | | | |

+ Relay stns below 1kW. **FPI:** Brank Power stns

**Call:** JO(call). **(S):** AM Stereo (C-QUAM System). **Schedule:** 24h unless otherwise indicated above. Most 24h stns are off the air for 1 to 5 hours until 1900 or 2000 on Sun unless mentioned. All other days a network prgr is aired 1600 or 1800 to 2000 on most stns. Network prgrs may also be broadcast at other times of day. **ID:** Company initials are usually used as stn identification

**Addresses & other information:**
**1)** R. Kansai Co., Ltd., 5-7, Higashi Kawasaki-cho 1-chome, Chuo-ku, Kobe 650-8580 **W:** jocr.jp – **2)** The STVradio Broadcasting Co., Ltd, 1-1,

Nishi 8-chome, Kita 1-jo, Chuo-ku, Sapporo 060-8705 **W:** stv.jp – **3)** Iwate Broadc Co., Ltd., 6-1, Shike-cho, Morioka 020-8566 **W:** ibc.co.jp – **4)** Kyushu Asahi Broadc Co., Ltd, 1-1, Nagahama 1-chome, Chuo-ku, Fukuoka 810-8571 **W:** kbc.co.jp – **5)** Kita-nihon Broadc Co., Ltd.,10-18, Ushijima-machi, Toyama 930-8585 **W:** knb.ne.jp – **6)** Ryukyu Broadc Corp., 3-1, Kumoji 2-chome, Naha 900-8711 **W:** rbc.co.jp – **7)** Yamanashi Broadc System, Inc., 6-10, Kitaguchi 2-chome, Kofu 400-8525 **W:** ybs. jp – **8)** Yamaguchi Broadc Co., Ltd., Koen-ku, Shunan 745-8686 **W:** kry. co.jp – **9)** R Okinawa Corp., 4-8, Nishi 1-chome, Naha 900-8604 **W:** rokinawa.co.jp – **10)** Shin-etsu Broadc Co., Ltd., 1200, Toigoshomachi, Nagano 380-8521 **W:** sbc21.co.jp – **11)** Hokkaido Broadc Co., Ltd., 2, Nishi 5-chome, kita 1-jo, Chuo-ku, Sapporo 060-8501 **W:** hbc.co.jp – **12)** Fukui Broadc Corp., 510, Owada 2-chome, Fukui 910-8588 **W:** fbc. jp –**13)** Tochigi Broadc Co., Ltd., 2-2-5, Showa, Utsunomiya 320-8601 **W:** crt-radio.co.jp – **14)** Broadc System of San-in, 1-71, Nishi-Fukubara 1-chome, Yonago 683-8670 **W:** bss.jp – **15)** Kochi Broadc Co., Ltd., 2-15, Hon-machi 3-chome, Kochi 780-8550 **W:** rkc-kochi.co.jp – **16)** Yamagata Broadc Co., Ltd., 5-12, Hatago-machi 2-chome, Yamagata 990-8555 **W:** ybc.co.jp – **17)** Akita Broadc System, 9-42, Sanno 7-chome, Akita 010-8611 **W:** akita-abs.co.jp – **18)** Miyazaki Broadc Co., Ltd., 6-7, Tachibanadori-nishi 4-chome, Miyazaki 880-8639 **W:** mrt.jp – **19)** TBS Radio, Inc., 3-6, Akasaka 5-chome, Minato-ku, Tokyo 107-8006 **W:** tbsradio.jp – **20)** Asahi Radio Broadc Corp., 1-30, Fukushima 1-chome, Fukushima-ku, Osaka 553-8503 **W:** abc1008.com – **21)** CBCradio Co., Ltd., 2-8, Shinsakae 1-chome, Naka-ku, Nagoya 460-8405 **W:** hicbc.com – **22)** Nagasaki Broadc Co., Ltd., 1-35, Uwa-machi, Nagasaki 850-8650 **W:** nbc-nagasaki.co.jp – **22a)** Nagasaki Broadc Co., Ltd Saga station, 1249, Honjo-machi, Saga 840-0027 **W:** nbc-saga.co.jp – **23)** Oita Broadc System, 1-1, Imazuru 3-chome, Oita 870-8620 **W:** e-obs.com – **24)** R Fukushima Broadc Co., Ltd., 8, Shimoaraki, Fukushima 960-8655 **W:** rfc. jp – **25)** Minaminihon Broadc Co., Ltd., 5-25, Korai-cho, Kagoshima 890-8570 **W:** mbc.co.jp – **26)** Hokuriku Broadc Co., Ltd., 2-1, Honda-machi 3-chome, Kanazawa 920-8560 **W:** mro.co.jp – **27)** Nankai Broadc Co., Ltd., 1-1, Honmachi 1-chome, Matsuyama 790-8510 **W:** rnb.co.jp – **28)** Broadc System of Niigata, Inc., 18, Kawagishi-cho 3-chome, Chuo-ku, Niigata 951-8655 **W:** ohbsn.com – **29)** Nippon Cultural Broadc., Inc.,31, Hamamatsu-cho 1-chome, Minato-ku, Tokyo 105-8002 **W:** joqr.co.jp – **30)** Kyoto Broadc System Co., Ltd., Kamichojamachi, Karasumadori, Kamigyo-ku, Kyoto 602-8588 **W:** kbs-kyoto.co.jp – **30a)** KBS Shiga Station, 6-19, Tachibana-cho, Hikone 522-0062 – **31)** Mainichi Broadc System, Inc., 17-1, Chayamachi, Kita-ku, Osaka 530-8304 **W:** mbs.jp – **32)** RKB Mainichi Broadc Corp., 3-8, Momochihama 2-chome, Sawara-ku, Fukuoka 814-8585 **W:** rkb.jp – **33)** Kumamoto Broadc Co., Ltd., 30, Yamasaki-machi, Kumamoto 860-8611 **W:** rkk.co.jp – **34)** Ibaraki Broadc System, 2084-2, Senba-cho, Mito 310-8505 **W:** ibs-radio.com – **35)** Aomori Broadc Corp., 8-1, Matsumori 1-chome, Aomori 030-8655 **W:** rab.co.jp – **36)** Nippon Broadc System, Inc., 9-3, Yurakucho 1-chome, Chiyoda-ku, Tokyo 100-8439 **W:** jolf.co.jp – **37)** Tohoku Broadc Co., Ltd., 26-1, Kasumi-cho, Yagiyama, Taihaku-ku, Sendai 980-8668 **W:** tbc-sendai.co.jp – **38)** Shikoku Broadc Co., Ltd., 5-2, Nakatokushima-cho 2-chome, Tokushima 770-8573 **W:** jrt.co.jp – **39)** Osaka Broadc Corp., 2-4, Benten 1-chome, Minato-ku, Osaka 552-8501 **W:** obc1314. co.jp – **40)** Tokai Radio Broadc Co., Ltd., 14-27, Higashisakura 1-chome, Higashi-ku, Nagoya 461-8503 **W:** tokairadio.co.jp – **41)** RCC Broadc Co., Ltd., 21-3, Moto-machi, Naka-ku, Hiroshima 730-8504 **W:** rcc.net – **42)** Shizuoka Broadc System, 1, Toro 3-chome, Suruga-ku, Shizuoka 422-8680 **W:** at-s.com – **43)** RF Radio Nippon Co., Ltd., 85, Choja-machi 5-chome, Naka-ku, Yokohama 231-8611 **W:** jorf.co.jp – **44)** Wakayama Broadc System, 3, Minato-honmachi 3-chome, Wakayama 640-8577 **W:** wbs.co.jp – **45)** Gifu Broadc System, 52, Hashimotocho 2-chome, Gifu 500-8588 **W:** zf-web.com – **46)** Nishi-nippon Broadc Co., Ltd., 8-15, Marunouchi, Takamatsu 760-8575 **W:** rnc.co.jp – **47)** Sanyo Broadc Co., Ltd., 1-3, Marunouchi 2-chome, Okayama 700-8580 **W:** rsk.co.jp.
**V:** Most stns verify by QSL-card. Rec acc. Rp

## NIKKEI RADIO BROADCASTING CORPORATION (RADIO NIKKEI)

2-8, Toranomon 1-chome, Minato-ku, Tokyo 105-8565 ☎ +81 3 6205 7810 🖷 +81 3 6205 7809 **W:** radionikkei.jp

| SW | kHz | kW | Prgr | SW | kHz | kW | Prgr |
|---|---|---|---|---|---|---|---|
| JOZ | ‡3925 | 50 | 1 | JOZ6 | 6115 | 50 | 2 |
| JOZ4 | *3925 | 10 | 1 | JOZ3 | ‡9595 | 50 | 2 |
| JOZ5 | 3945 | 10 | 2 | JOZ7 | ‡9760 | 50 | 2 |
| JOZ2 | 6055 | 50 | 1 | | | | |

*) Nemuro; others Nagara (Chiba), ‡ inactive
**1st Prgr:** 2155-1500 on 6055kHz, 2155-2300 & 0750-1500 on 3925kHz (Nemuro)
**2nd Prgr:** Sun-Thu 2300-1000 on 6115kHz, 1000-1400 on 3945kHz, Fri & Sat 2300- 0900 on 6115kHz.
**IS:** Slow tempo chime with Japanese instrument "Koto" at sign on and sign off - **V.** by QSL card. Rp.

## COMMERCIAL FM STATIONS:

| FM | Call | MHz | kW | Station, location & h of tr |
|----|------|-----|-----|------------------------------|
| 1) | QU | 76.1 | 1 | FM Iwate, Morioka |
| 2) | LU | 76.1 | 1 | FM Fukui, Fukui |
| 3) | FW | 76.1 | 1 | Love FM, Fukuoka |
| 4) | SV | 76.4 | 1 | R. Berry, Utsunomiya |
| 5) | AW | 76.5 | 10 | FM COCOLO, Osaka |
| 6) | VV | 76.8 | 1 | FM Okayama, Okayama |
| 7) | UV | 77.0 | 1 | E-R. LAKESIDE, Otsu |
| 8) | JU | 77.1 | 5 | Date FM, Sendai |
| 9) | SU | 77.4 | 1 | FM Kumamoto, Kumamoto |
| 10) | VU | 77.4 | 0.5 | V-air, Matsue |
| 11) | XU | 77.5 | 1 | FM Niigata, Niigata |
| 12) | | 77.6 | 1 | Kiss-FM Kobe, Himeji |
| 13) | QV | 77.8 | 10 | ZIP FM, Nagoya |
| 14) | NV | 77.9 | 0.5 | FM Saga, Saga |
| 15) | GV | 78.0 | 5 | bayfm, Chiba |
| 16) | GU | 78.2 | 1 | Hiroshima FM, Hiroshima |
| 17) | YU | 78.6 | 1 | FM Kagawa, Takamatsu |
| 18) | RV | 78.7 | 3 | CROSS FM, Kitakyushu (Fukuoka) |
| 19) | NU | 78.9 | 3 | R. Cube, Tsu |
| 20) | WV | 79.0 | 1 | FM Port, Niigata: (off air SS 1600-2053) |
| 21) | KU | 79.2 | 1 | K-MIX, Hamamatsu (Shizuoka) |
| 22) | UU | 79.2 | 1 | FM Yamaguchi, Yamaguchi |
| 23) | HU | 79.5 | 1 | FM Nagasaki, Nagasaki |
| 52a) | CW | 79.5 | 5 | Inter FM Nagoya, Nagoya |
| 24) | DV | 79.5 | 5 | NACK 5, Saitama |
| 25) | EU | 79.7 | 1 | FM Ehime, Matsuyama: 2057-1803 (v.) |
| 26) | ZU | 79.7 | 1 | FM Nagano, Matsumoto (Nagano) |
| 27) | OV | 79.8 | 1 | µ FM, Kagoshima |
| 28) | WU | 80.0 | 1 | FM Aomori, Aomori |
| 29) | AU | 80.0 | 10 | Tokyo FM, Tokyo |
| 30) | XV | 80.0 | 1 | FM Gifu, Ogaki (Gifu) |
| 31) | FV | 80.2 | 10 | FM 802, Osaka |
| 32) | FU | 80.4 | 5 | AIR-G', Sapporo |
| 33) | EV | 80.4 | 1 | Rhythm Station, Yamagata |
| 34) | HV | 80.5 | 1 | Hello Five, Kanazawa |
| 35) | CU | 80.7 | 10 | FM Aichi, Nagoya |
| 36) | MV | 80.7 | 1 | FM Tokushima, Tokushima |
| 37) | DU | 80.7 | 3 | FM Fukuoka, Fukuoka |
| 38) | AV | 81.3 | 7 | J-WAVE, Tokyo |
| 39) | LV | 81.6 | 0.5 | Hi-six, Kochi |
| 40) | TV | 81.8 | 1 | Fukushima FM, Koriyama(Fukushima) |
| 41) | PV | 82.5 | 5 | FM North Wave, Sapporo |
| 42) | OU | 82.7 | 1 | FM Toyama, Toyama |
| 43) | PU | 82.8 | 3 | FM Akita, Akita |
| 44) | CV | 83.0 | 1 | FM Fuji, Kofu: 1950-1730 (v.) |
| 45) | MU | 83.2 | 1 | Joy FM, Miyazaki |
| 46) | TU | 84.7 | 5 | FM Yokohama, Yokohama |
| 47) | BU | 85.1 | 10 | FM Osaka, Osaka |
| 48) | RU | 86.3 | 1 | FM Gunma, Maebashi |
| 11) | | 86.5 | 1 | FM Niigata, Yamato |
| 10) | | 86.6 | 1 | V-air, Hamada |
| 49) | IU | 87.3 | 1 | FM Okinawa, Naha |
| 50) | JV | 88.0 | 1 | Air R., Oita |
| 51) | KV | 89.4 | 3 | Alpha-Station, Kyoto |
| 52) | DW | 89.7 | 10 | Inter FM, Tokyo |
| 12) | IV | 89.9 | 1 | Kiss-FM Kobe, Kobe |

**NB:** Relay stns below 1kW and community stns are not included.
**Call: JO(call)-FM. Schedule:** 24h unless otherwise indicated above. Most 24h stns are off the air for 2 to 5 hours until 1900, 2000 or 2100 on Sun.

### Addresses & other information:
**1)** FM Iwate Broadc Co., 2-10, Uchimaru, Morioka 020-8512 **W:** fmi.co.jp – **2)** Fukui FM Broadc Co., Ltd., 1-1, Miyuki 1-chome, Fukui 910-8553 **W:** fmfukui.jp – **3)** LOVE FM International Broadc Co., Ltd., 12-23, Imaizumi 1-chome, Chuo-ku, Fukuoka 810-8516 Prgr in English, Chinese and Korean etc **W:** lovefm.co.jp – **4)** FM Tochigi Brordc co., Ltd., 2-1, Chuo 1-chome, Utsunomiya 320-8550 **W:** berry.co.jp – **5)** FM 802 Co., Ltd., See 32). Foreign language prgr in English, Chinese, Korean, etc. Since April 2012, the business has been transfered from Kansai Intermedia Corp. to FM 802 Co. Ltd. **W:** cocolo.jp – **6)** Okayama FM Broadc Co., Ltd., 1-8-45, Nakasange, Okayama 700-0821 **W:** fm-okayama.co.jp – **7)** FM Shiga Co., Ltd., 19-10, Nishinosho, Otsu 520-0818 **W:** e-radio.co.jp – **98)** Sendai FM Broadc., Inc., 10-28, Honcho 2-chome, Aoba-ku, Sendai 980-8420 **W:** datefm.co.jp – **9)** FM Kumamoto Broadc Co., Ltd., 5-50, Chibajomachi, Kumamoto 860-0001 **W:** fmk.fm – **10)** FM San-in Co., Ltd., 383, Tono-machi, Matsue 690-8508 **W:** fm-sanin.co.jp – **11)** FM Radio Niigata Co., Ltd., 3-5, Saiwainishi 4-chome, Chuo-ku, Niigata 950-8581 **W:** fmniigata.com – **12)** Kiss-FM KOBE Inc., 5-4 Hatoba-cho, Chuo-ku, Kobe 650-8589 **W:** kiss-fm.co.jp – **13)** ZIP-FM Inc., 20-17, Marunouchi 3-chome, Naka-ku, Nagoya 460-8578 **W:** zip-fm.co.jp –

**14)** FM Saga Co., Ltd., 286-5, Fukuro, Honjo-machi, Saga 840-0023 **W:** fmsaga.co.jp – **15)** bayfm78 Co., Ltd., 6-1, Nakase 2-chome, Mihama-ku, Chiba 261-7127 **W:** bayfm.co.jp – **16)** Hiroshima FM Broadc Co., Ltd., 8-2, Minamimachi 1-chome, Minami-ku, Hiroshima 734-8511 **W:** hfm.jp – **17)** FM Kagawa Broadc Co., Ltd., 4-23, Saiho-cho 1-chome, Takamatsu 760-8584 **W:** fmkagawa.co.jp – **18)** Cross FM Co., Ltd, 1-1, Kyomachi 3-chome, Kokurakita-ku, Kitakyushu 802-8570 **W:** crossfm.co.jp – **19)** Mie FM Broadc co., Ltd., 1043-1, Kannonji-cho, Tsu 514-8505 **W:** fmmie.jp – **20)** Niigata Kenmin FM Broadc Co., Ltd., 1-1, Bandai 2-chome, Chuo-ku, Niigata 950-8579 **W:** fmport.com – **21)** Shizuoka FM Broadc Co., Ltd, 133-24, Toshiwa-cho, Naka-ku, Hamamatsu 430-8575 **W:** k-mix.co.jp – **22)** FM Yamaguchi Co., Ltd., 3-31, Midori-cho, Yamaguchi 753-8521 **W:** fmy.co.jp – **23)** FM Nagasaki Co., Ltd., 5-5, Sakae-machi, Nagasaki 850-8550 **W:** fmnagasaki.co.jp – **24)** FM Nack 5 Co Ltd., 682-2, Nishiki-cho, Omiya-ku, Saitama 330-8579 **W:** nack5.co.jp – **25)** FM Ehime Broadc Co., 10-7, Takewara-machi 1-chome, Matsuyama 790-8565 **W:** joeufm.co.jp – **26)** Nagano FM Broadc Co., Ltd, 13-5, Honjo 1-chome, Matsumoto 390-8520 **W:** fmnagano.co.jp – **27)** FM Kagoshima Co., Ltd., 1-38, Higashisengoku-cho, Kagoshima 892-8579 **W:** myufm.jp – **28)** Aomori FM Broadc Co., Ltd., 7-19, Tsutsumi-machi 1-chome, Aomori 030-0812 **W:** afb.co.jp – **29)** Tokyo FM Broadc Co., Ltd., 7, Kojimachi 1-chome, Chiyoda-ku, Tokyo 102-8080 **W:** tfm.co.jp – **30)** Gifu FM Broadc Co., Ltd., 35-10, Kono 4-chome, Ogaki 503-8580 **W:** fmgifu.com – **31)** FM 802 Co., Ltd., Kita 2-6, Tenjinbashi 2-chome, Kita-ku, Osaka 530-8580 **W:** funky802.com – **32)** FM Hokkaido Broadc Co., Ltd., 1, Nishi 2-chome, kita 1-jo, Chuo-ku, Sapporo 060-8532 **W:** air-g.co.jp – **33)** FM Yamagata Co., Ltd., 14-69, Matsuyama 3-chome, Yamagata 990-9543 **W:** rfm.co.jp – **34)** FM Ishikawa Broadc Co., Ltd., 1-45, Hikoso-machi 2-chome, Kanazawa 920-8605 **W:** hellofive.jp – **35)** FM Aichi Broadc Co., Ltd., 15-18, Chiyoda 2-chome, Naka-ku, Nagoya 460-8388 **W:** fma.co.jp – **36)** FM Tokushima Broadc Co., 6, Saiwai-cho 1-chome, Tokushima 770-8567 **W:** fm807.jp – **37)** Fukuoka FM Broadc Co., Ltd., 9-19, Kiyokawa 1-chome, Chuo-ku, Fukuoka, 810-8575 **W:** fmfukuoka.co.jp – **38)** J-WAVE Inc., Roppongi Hills Mori Tower 33F, 10-1, Roppongi 6-chome,, Minato-ku, Tokyo 106-6188 **W:** j-wave.co.jp – **39)** FM Kochi Broadc Co., Ltd., 1-5, Takashocho 2-chome, Kochi 780-8532 **W:** fmkochi.com – **40)** FM Fukushima Inc., 4-4 Shinmei-cho, Koriyama, 960-8013 **W:** rfc.jp – **41)** FM North Wave Co., Ltd., 3-1, Nishi 4-chome, Kita 7-jo, Kita-ku, Sapporo 060-8557 **W:** fmnorth.co.jp – **42)** Toyama FM Broadc Co., Ltd., 2-11, Okuda-machi, Toyama 930-8567 **W:** fmtoyama.co.jp – **43)** FM Akita Broadc Co., Ltd., 7-10, Yabase-Honcho 3-chome, Akita 010-0973 **W:** fm-akita.co.jp – **44)** FM Fuji Co Ltd., Aria 105, Kawadamachi, Kofu 400-8550 **W:** fmfuji.jp – **45)** Miyazaki FM Broadc Co., Ltd., 78, Gion 2-chome, Miyazaki 880-8583 **W:** joyfm.co.jp – **46)** Yokohama FM Broadc Co., Ltd., 2-1, Minato-Mirai 2-chome, Nishi-ku, Yokohama 220-8110 **W:** fmyokohama.co.jp – **47)** FM Osaka Co., Ltd., 3-1, Minatomachi 1-chome, Naniwa-ku, Osaka 556-8510 **W:** fmosaka.net – **48)** FM Gunma Broadc Co., Ltd., 4-8, Wakamiyacho 1-chome, Maebashi 371-8533 **W:** fmgunma.com – **49)** FM Okinawa Broadc Corp., 40, Kowan, Urasoe, Okinawa 901-2525 **W:** fmokinawa.co.jp – **50)** FM Oita Broadc., Co., Ltd., 3-8-8, funai-machi, Oita 870-8558 **W:** fmoita.co.jp – **51)** FM Kyoto, Inc., CoCon Karasuma 8F, 620, Suiginya-cho, Karasuma-dori Shijo-sagaru, Shimogyo-ku, Kyoto 600-8566 **W:** fm-kyoto.jp – **52)** Inter FM 897 Co., Ltd., 3-3, Higashi-shinagawa 1-chome, Shinagawa-ku, Tokyo 140-0002 - Prgr in English & foreign languages **W:** interfm.co.jp – **52a)** Inter FM Nagoya, 1-33-2, Kitaharacho, Mizuho-ku, Nagoya 467-0811
**V.** Most stns verify by QSL card. Rec acc. Rp.

## AMERICAN FORCES NETWORK (AFN) (U.S. Mil.)
The network serves the members of the US forces. The stns in Japan broadcast by authority of Commander, US Forces, Japan, in cooperation with the Information and Communications Policy Bureau in Japan. Stns are linked by land line and microwave.

**AFN Tokyo,** Det 10, Unit 5091 Bldg 3266, Yokota Air Base, Fussa, Tokyo 197-0001 or Det 10, Unit 5091 Bldg 3266, APO/AP 96328-5091 ☎+81 42 552 2511 ext 52374 📠+81 42 552 2511 ext 52386 **E:** dma.Yokota.afn.list.publicity@mail.mil **W:** afnpacific.net/Local-Stations/Tokyo
**Other stns: AFN Okinawa:** Okinawa **E:** DMA.Kadena.AFN.list.publicity@mail.mil **W:** afnpacific.net/Local-Stations/Okinawa – **AFN Misawa:** Misawa, Aomori **E:** afn@misawa.af.mil **W:** afnpacific.net/Local-Stations/Misawa **AFN Iwakuni:** Iwakuni, Yamaguchi **W:** afnpacific.net/Local-Stations/Iwakuni – **AFN Sasebo:** Sasebo, Nagasaki **W:** afnpacific.net/Local-Stations/Sasebo

| MW | kHz | kW | MW | kHz | kW |
|----|-----|-----|-----|-----|-----|
| Okinawa | 648 | 10 | Misawa | 1575 | 1 |
| Tokyo | 810 | 50 | Sasebo | 1575 | 0.30 |
| Iwakuni | 1575 | 1 | | | |

**FM:** Okinawa 89.1MHz 20kW
**D. Prgr:** 24h **N:** on the h. **Ann:** "This is the American Forces Network" **V.** by QSL card or letter

## JORDAN

**L.T:** UTC +2h (29 Mar-25 Oct: +3h; dates subject to confirmation) — **Pop:** 7.9 million — **Pr.L:** Arabic — **E.C:** 50Hz, 230V — **ITU:** JOR

### AUDIOVISUAL COMMISSION (AVC)

✉ P.O.Box 142515, Amman 11814 ☎+ 962 6 5549720 📠 + 962 6 5535093 **W:** avc.gov.jo **E:** avc.inv@nic.jo **L.P:** Dir: Hussein Bani Bani.

### JORDAN RADIO & TELEVISION CORP. (JRTV, Gov.)

✉ Al-Shara Al-Musharrafah St, P.O.Box 909, JO-11118 Amman ☎+962 6 4773111 📠 +962 6 4778 578 **W:** jrtv.gov.jo **E:** rj@jrtv.gov.jo **L.P:** Dir. Radio: Naser Anani. Dir. Eng: Khalaf Khawaldah. CE of Radio: Haidar Abu Hmaid.

| MW | kHz | kW | Prgr | Times |
|---|---|---|---|---|
| Shobak | 612 | 100 | Main | 24h |
| Amman | 1035 | 20 | Main | 24h |

| FM | Main | Amman FM | R. Jordan | Quran | Hadaf | kW |
|---|---|---|---|---|---|---|
| Ajlun | 95.8 | 95.8 | 90.9 | - | - | 10/5 |
| Amman | 90.0 | 99.0 | 96.3 | 93.1 | 88.0 | 5/10 |
| Aqaba | 101.5 | 98.1/105.6 | 99.7 | 91.5 | - | 5/1 |
| Irbid | 103.8 | 95.4 | - | 98.7 | - | 1 |
| Karak | 103.6 | - | - | 98.7 | - | 1 |
| Salt | - | 105.0 | - | - | - | 1 |
| Tafeleh | 90.8 | - | - | - | - | 1 |

**Main Arabic sce:** 24h. Jordan Armed Forces R: 1400-1600. **Amman FM** in Arabic: 24h (Irbid with some local prgr). **R. Jordan 96.3:** 24h in English exc. **French** 1100-1300. **Quran Prgr:** 24h. **Hadaf** (sports prgr.): 24h.
**Ann:** Arabic: "Huna Amman, Idha'atu-I-Mamlaka al-Urdoniya al-Hashemi-ya". Armed forces R: "Idha'at Al-Quwaat Al-Musala al-Urdoniya, al-Gayish al-Arabi". E: "This is R. Jordan broadcasting from Amman".

**Other stations** (FM MHz):
**Amen FM:** Amman/Aqaba 89.5, Irbid 89.7 **W:** amenfm.jo — **Ayyam FM:** Amman 91.5, Irbid 91.9, Petra 92.1 **W:**ayaamfm.jo — **Beat FM,** Amman: 102.5 English. **W:** mybeat.fm — **Bliss FM,** Amman: 104.3 English. **W:** bliss.jo — **Energy FM,** Amman: 97.7 English. **W:** energyradio.jo — **Global FM:** Amman 94.5 2kW. **W:** globaljo.fm Also r. CRI — **Hala FM:** Aqaba 91.1, Irbid/Ruweished 91.3, Al-Karak 94.3, Al-Salt/Tafilaq 94.7, Ajlun 94.3, Amman 102.1, Petra 105.4 **W:** hala.jo — **Hawa FM,** Amman: 105.9MHz **W:** ammancity.gov.jo — **Hayat FM:** Irbid 94.7, Amman 104.7, Azraq 105.4 **W:** hayat.fm — **Mazaj FM:** Amman 95.3, Irbid 101.7 **W:** mazajfm.com — **Melody FM:** Amman 91.1, Zarqa 105.5 — **Mood FM,** Amman: 92.0 English. **W:** mood.fm — **Play FM:** Amman 99.6, Irbid 105.3. English **W:** play.jo — **R. Al-Balad,** Amman: 92.4 **W:** balad.fm — **R. Fann:** Aqaba 91.1, Irbid/Ruweished 91.3, Ajlun/Karak 94.3, Salt/Tafileh 94.7, Amman 102.1/104.2, Petra/Azraq 105.4 **W:** radiofann.com — **R. Farah Al-Nas,** Amman: 98.5 **W:** farahalnas.jo — **R. Yaqeen,** Amman: 103.7, Irbid 97.7 **W:** yaqeen.jo1jo.org — **Rotana R:** Irbid 90.5, Amman 99.9 **W:** rotana.net — **Sawt Al-Janoub,** Ma'an: 90.5 — **Sawt al-Madina:** Amman: 88.7 **W:** sawtalmadenah.net — **Sawt el-Ghad:** Amman 101.5 **W:** sawtelghad.com (see main entry under Lebanon) — **Spin Jordan:** Irbid 88.3, Ma'an 88.5, Amman 94.1, Aqaba 103.5 English. **W:** spin.jo — **Sunny,** Amman: 105.1 English. **W:** sunny.jo — **Watar FM:** Amman 88.3, Irbid 91.5, Aqaba 102.5 **W:** watar.fm — **Virgin R. Jordan,** Amman: 93.7 **W:** virginradiojordan.com — **Yarmouk FM,** Irbid: 105.7 **W:** yu.edu.jo

**BBC Arabic Sce:** Amman 103.1 5kW, Ajlun 89.1 10kW.
**Monte-Carlo Doualiya:** Amman 97.4, Ajlun 106.2MHz.
**R. Sawa:** Amman 98.1 10kW, Ajlun 107.4MHz

## KAZAKHSTAN

**L.T:** UTC +6h (Western Kazakhstan: +5h) — **Pop:** 18.1 million — **Pr.L:** Kazakh, Russian — **E.C:** 220V/50Hz — **ITU:** KAZ

### MÁDENIET JÁNE SPORT MINISTRLIGI
### (Ministry of Culture and Sport)

✉ House of Ministries, 010000 Astana ☎ +7 7172 740251 **W:** mks.gov.kz **L.P:** Minister: Arystanbek Muhamediýli
**NB.** The ministry issues broadcasting licenses.

### QAZAQ RADIOLARY JSS (Gov)

✉ Qonaev k. 4, 010000 Astana ☎ +7 7172 757302 **E:** qazaqradiolary@qazradio.kz **L.P:** DG: Mádi Manatbek
✉Almaty studios: Jeltoqsan k. 177, 050013 Almaty

| MW | kHz | kW | Prgr | MW | kHz | kW | Prgr |
|---|---|---|---|---|---|---|---|
| Aqtaý | 1341 | 25 | 1 | Lepsi° | 1557 | | 1 |

°) Status uncertain

| FM (MHz) | 1* | 2 | | FM (MHz) | 1* | 2 |
|---|---|---|---|---|---|---|
| Aiagóz | 101.0m | 103.2 | | Oktiabrskoe | 104.8i | - |
| Almaty# | 101.0a | 106.5 | | Oral | 101.2e | 103.2 |
| Amangeldi | 103.2e | - | | Óskemen | 104.0m | 105.6 |
| Aqadyr | 101.0j | - | | Pavlodar | 101.0i | 106.7 |
| Aqjal | 101.3j | - | | Petropavl | 106.8n | 104.7 |
| Aqqý | 106.4i | - | | Priozersk | 100.7j | - |
| Aqsai | 101.4e | - | | Qandyagash | 101.8c | - |
| Aqtaý## | 100.5g | 102.1 | | Qarabalyq | 103.2k | - |
| Aqtóbe | 102.2c | 105.7 | | Qarabutaq | 104.3c | - |
| Aral | 101.3l | - | | Qaragaily | 103.0j | - |
| Arqalyq | 105.7k | 101.4 | | Qaragandy | 103.4j | 102.3 |
| Astana### | 106.8 | 100.4 | | Qarajal | 102.1j | - |
| Atasý | 101.8j | - | | Qarataý | 103.0f | - |
| Atbasar | 104.5b | - | | Qaratóbe | 102.4e | - |
| Atyraý | 101.0d | 102.8 | | Qaraýlykeldi | 101.6c | - |
| Baianaýyl | 103.5i | - | | Qazygurt | 106.1h | - |
| Balqash | 101.0j | - | | Qorgaljyn | 101.6b | - |
| Baqanas | 104.4a | 100.6 | | Qostanai | 105.4k | 107.4 |
| Barshatas | 101.6o | - | | Qulsary | 102.2d | 106.0 |
| Chapaev | 101.9e | - | | Qushmuryn | 104.9k | - |
| Derzhavinsk | 100.3b | - | | Qyzylorda | 102.0l | 101.0 |
| Dostyq | 106.2h | - | | Rýzaevka | 101.2n | - |
| Ekibatuz | 106.9i | - | | Sarqan | 102.2a | 105.2 |
| Esil | 102.5b | - | | Saryagash | 102.3h | - |
| Hromtaý | 102.0c | - | | Semei | 100.1m | 104.4 |
| Inderbor | 101.5d | 103.2 | | Soldatovo | 101.3m | - |
| Jangyztóbe | 104.5m | 106.9 | | Stepniak | 101.0b | - |
| Jalpaqtal | 103.1e | - | | Stepnogor | 102.2b | 103.5 |
| Jarkent | 101.0a | 104.2 | | Taraz | 100.8f | 102.6 |
| Jaryq | 103.1j | - | | Tasqala | 105.6e | - |
| Jetisai | 107.9h | - | | Tolqyn | - | 105.0 |
| Jezqazgan | 103.1j | - | | Torgai | 100.9k | - |
| Jitiqara | 100.9h | - | | Túrkistan | 101.0h | 102.2 |
| Jolymbet | 104.5b | - | | Uzynkól | 104.7k | - |
| Jympity | 102.4e | - | | Shagan | 101.0a | 102.8 |
| Kárim Mynbaev | 105.2j | - | | Shalqar | 101.4c | - |
| Kishkenekól | 102.9n | - | | Shieli | 101.8l | - |
| Kókpekti | 102.2m | - | | Shý | 107.6f | - |
| Kókshetáý | 101.0b | 103.7 | | Shymkent | 106.4h | 102.7 |
| Lisakovsk | 107.2k | - | | Vozvyshenka | 101.0n | - |
| Maqanshy | 101.0m | 103.6 | | Yrgyz | 101.9c | - |
| Maqat | 101.2d | 102.5 | | Zaisan | 103.2m | - |
| Nikolaevka | 103.8n | - | | Zapadnaia | 104.7f | - |

**NB:** All txs 1kW. Additional txs below 1kW. *) incl. reg. prgrs a-o (see below). # Also Prgr 3 on 102.8MHz, ## also Prgr 3 on 103.0MHz, ### also Prgr 3 on 102.7MHz
**D.Prgrs: Prgr 1 (Qazaq radiosy):** 24h in Kazakh, Russian — **Prgr 2 (Shalqar radiosy)** 0000-1800 in Kazakh — **Prgr 3 (Classic FM)** 24h — **Local station:** R. Astana on Astana 101.4MHz (1kW) in Kazakh, Russian: 24h.

**Qazaqstan RTRK Regional Services**
The regional branches (filialy) of Qazaqstan RTRK (the holding enterprise of Qazaq Radiolary JSS) broadcast at various times via txs of Prgr 1 (see FM chart). In addition, some branches are also broadcasting on own FM frequencies in Kazakh and languages of ethnic minorities.
**a) Almaty qalaliq filialy:** Jeltoqsan k. 177, 050013 Almaty. **E:** almatytrk@kaztrk.kz — **b) Aqmola oblystyq filialy:** Kýibyshev k. 19, 020000 Kókshetáý. **E:** akmola@kaztrk.kz — **c) Aqtóbe oblystyq filialy:** Ahtanov k. 54, 030002 Aqtóbe. **E:** tvaktobe@gmail.com — **d) Atyraý oblystyq filialy:** Moldagaliev k. 29, 060005 Atyraý **E:** qazaqstan.atyrau@mail.ru. Own prgrs on Atyraý 102.0MHz (0.25kW) — **e) Batys Qazaqstan oblystyq filialy:** Sydyqov k. 1, 090000 Oral. **E:** oral.tv@mail.ru — **f) Jambil oblystyq filialy:** Súleimenov k. 6, 080000 Taraz. **E:** taraztv@kaztrk.kz — **g) Mangistaý oblystyq filialy:** 24 shagyn aýdan, 130000 Aqtaý. **E:** aktautrk@gmail.com — **h) Ontýstik Qazaqstan oblystyq filialy:** Qazybek bi k. 20, 160000 Shymkent. **E:** shymkenttv@kaztrk.kz — **i) Pavlodar oblystyq filialy:** Suraganov k. 21, 140006 Pavlodar. **E:** kaz.pavlodar@mail.ru. R. Jalyk on Pavlodar 100.5MHz (0.5kW) + translators. — **j) Qaragandy oblystyq filialy:** Jaýynger-internatsionalister k. 14, 100000 Qaragandy. **E:** kartv@kaztrk.kz — **k) Qostanai oblystyq filialy:** Ál-Farabi dangyly 126, 110003 Qostanai. **E:** office_kst@kaztrk.kz — **l) Qyzylorda oblystyq filialy:** Jeltoqsan k. 11, 120014 Qyzylorda — **m) Shygys Qazaqstan oblystyq filialy:** Stahanovskaia k. 70, 070010 Óskemen. **E:** oskementv@kaztrk.kz. **Local station (Semei qalalyq filialy):** Shýgaev k. 157, 071403 Semei. R. on Semei 106.9MHz (0.25kW). — **n) Soltýstik Qazaqstan oblystyq filialy:** Brýsilovskii k. 1, 150000 Petropavl. **E:** petropavltv@gmail.com.

**OTHER STATIONS**

| FM | MHz | kW | Location | Station |
|---|---|---|---|---|
| 3) | 89.6 | 1 | Shymkent | Gakku FM |
| 9) | 89.6 | 2 | Almaty | Business FM |
| 13) | 91.3 | 2 | Almaty | R. Dacha |

| FM | MHz | kW | Location | Station |
|---|---|---|---|---|
| 8) | 91.7 | 1 | Aqtóbe | Dala FM |
| 2) | 100.1 | 1 | Taraz | Avtoradio |
| 8) | 100.2 | 1 | Almaty | Dala FM |
| 13) | 100.3 | 1 | Shymkent | R. Dacha |
| 4B) | 100.4 | 1 | Taldyqorgan | Jýldyz FM |
| 4A) | 100.5 | 1 | Qaragandy | Tengri FM |
| 4B) | 100.8 | 1 | Astana | Jýldyz FM |
| 5) | 101.2 | 1 | Shymkent | Love R. |
| 11) | 101.2 | 1 | Qaragandy | Zhana FM |
| 2) | 101.4 | 1 | Shagan | Avtoradio |
| 4B) | 101.4 | 1 | Almaty | Jýldyz FM |
| 4A) | 101.4 | 1 | Aqtaý | Tengri FM |
| 4A) | 101.4 | 1 | Semei | Tengri FM |
| 13) | 101.4 | 1 | Qyzylorda | R. Dacha |
| 8) | 101.8 | 1 | Astana | Dala FM |
| 3) | 101.8 | 1 | Almaty | Gakku FM |
| 13) | 102.2 | 1 | Almaty | Energy FM |
| 13) | 102.3 | 1 | Óskemen | R. Dacha |
| 4B) | 102.4 | 1 | Qyzylorda | Jýldyz FM |
| 4A) | 102.7 | 1 | Aqtóbe | Tengri FM |
| 13) | 102.8 | 1 | Qyzylorda | Russkoye R. |
| 4B) | 102.9 | 1 | Óskemen | Jýldyz FM |
| 13) | 102.9 | 1 | Pavlodar | R. Dacha |
| 6) | 103.2 | 1 | Astana | Orda FM |
| 13) | 103.3 | 1 | Oral | R. Dacha |
| 5) | 103.5 | 2 | Almaty | Love R. |
| 4A) | 103.5 | 1 | Óskemen | Tengri FM |
| 10) | 103.6 | 1 | Taldyqorgan | Russkoye R. |
| 2) | 103.8 | 1 | Qostanai | Avtoradio |
| 1) | 104.0 | 1 | Qaragandy | Retro FM |
| 8) | 104.1 | 1 | Petropavl | Dala FM |
| 4A) | 104.5 | 1 | Astana | Tengri FM |
| 2) | 104.6 | 1 | Qyzylorda | Avtoradio |
| 2) | 104.7 | 1 | Óskemen | Avtoradio |
| 4A) | 104.7 | 1 | Shymkent | Tengri FM |
| 2) | 105.0 | 1 | Pavlodar | Avtoradio |
| 1) | 105.0 | 1 | Astana | Retro FM |
| 2) | 105.2 | 1 | Aqtóbe | Avtoradio |
| 2) | 105.2 | 1 | Shymkent | Avtoradio |
| 5) | 105.2 | 1 | Qyzylorda | Love R. |
| 10) | 105.4 | 1 | Aqtaý | Russkoye R. |
| 9) | 105.4 | 2 | Astana | Business FM |
| 2) | 105.6 | 1 | Pavlodar | Avtoradio |
| 12) | 105.6 | 1 | Qaragandy | R. NS |
| 2) | 105.8 | 1 | Ekibatuz | Avtoradio |
| 4A) | 105.8 | 1 | Oral | Tengri FM |
| 12) | 105.9 | 1 | Shymkent | R. NS |
| 3) | 106.0 | 1 | Óskemen | Gakku FM |
| 4B) | 106.1 | 1 | Kókshetaý | Jýldyz FM |
| 2) | 106.2 | 1 | Jezqazgan | Avtoradio |
| 8) | 106.2 | 1 | Atyraý | Dala FM |
| 2) | 106.3 | 1 | Qaragandy | Avtoradio |
| 8) | 106.3 | 1 | Shagan | Dala FM |
| 4B) | 106.3 | 1 | Petropavl | Jýldyz FM |
| 2) | 106.4 | 1 | Astana | Avtoradio |
| 13) | 106.5 | 1 | Kókshetaý | R. Dacha |
| 4B) | 106.5 | 1 | Semei | Jýldyz FM |
| 11) | 106.6 | 1 | Jezqazgan | Zhana FM |
| 4B) | 106.7 | 1 | Taraz | Jýldyz FM |
| 4A) | 106.7 | 1 | Shagan | Tengri FM |
| 4B) | 106.8 | 1 | Taraz | Jýldyz FM |
| 1) | 107.0 | 1 | Almaty | Retro FM |
| 8) | 107.2 | 1 | Qyzylorda | Dala FM |
| 4B) | 107.2 | 1 | Atyraý | Jýldyz FM |
| 13) | 107.3 | 2 | Astana | R. Dacha |
| 8) | 107.3 | 1 | Taraz | Dala FM |
| 4A) | 107.5 | 1 | Almaty | Tengri FM |
| 4A) | 107.6 | 1 | Kókshetaý | Tengri FM |
| 2) | 107.7 | 1 | Atyraý | Avtoradio |
| 8) | 107.7 | 1 | Qaragandy | Dala FM |
| 4A) | 107.7 | 1 | Taraz | Tengri FM |
| 5) | 107.8 | 1 | Aqkól | Love R. |
| 7) | 107.9 | 1 | Óskemen | R. Miks |

+ txs below 1kW.

**Addresses & other information:**
**1)** Respýblika alany 13, 050013 Almaty – **2)** Satpaev k. 30a, 050057 Almaty **E:** info@avtoradio.kz – **3)** Almaty – **4A,B)** Begalin k. 148, 050051 Almaty – **5)** Minbaev k. 53, 050057 Almaty **E:** radio@loveradio.kz – **6)** Jeltoqsan k. 49, 010000 Astana **E:** radio@astv.kz – **7)** Gagarin k. 11, 070000 Óskemen – **8)** Jetysu-2 39a, 050063 Almaty – **9)** Almaty – **10)** Lenin k. 10a, 100000 Qaragandi – **11)** M-n Samal-1 36, 050059 Almaty – **12)** Bórenbay batyr k. 154, 050000 Almaty – **13)** Seifullin dangyly 498, 050004 Almaty

---

## KENYA

**L.T:** UTC +3h — **Pop:** 48 million — **Pr.L:** English, Swahili, Kikuyu, Luhya, Luo, Kalenjin, Somali, others — **E.C:** 50Hz, 240V — **ITU:** KEN

### COMMUNICATIONS AUTHORITY OF KENYA
P.O. Box 14448, Nairobi 00800 ☎+254 20 4242000 **W:** ca.go.ke
**E:** info@ca.go.ke

### KENYA BROADCASTING CORPORATION (KBC, Pub.)
P.O. Box 30456, Nairobi 00100 ☎+254 20 2766000 +254 20 2220675 **W:** kbc.co.ke **E:** md@kbc.co.ke **L.P:** Chmn: Charles Musyoki Muoki. MD: Waithaka Waihenya.

| MW | kHz | kW | Netw. | MW | kHz | kW | Netw. |
|---|---|---|---|---|---|---|---|
| Kapsimotwa# | 558 | 25 | W | Maralal | 1107 | 100 | S |
| Garissa | 567 | 50 | S | Wajir | 1152 | 50 | S |
| Ngong§ | 612 | 100 | S | Marsabit | 1233 | 50 | N |
| Garissa | 639 | 50 | I | Wajir | 1305 | 50 | I |
| Marsabit | 675 | 50 | S | Maralal | 1386 | 100 | N |
| Ngong§ | 747 | 100 | C | #) near Kisumu, §) near Nairobi. | | | |

| FM | S | E | Co | Pw | Mi | Ki | Ma | Mw | I |
|---|---|---|---|---|---|---|---|---|---|
| Limuru* | 92.9 | 95.6 | 99.5 | - | - | 98.0 | - | - | 101.9 |
| Malindi | 96.5 | 93.3 | - | 93.7 | - | - | - | - | - |
| Meru** | 90.4 | 103.5 | - | - | - | - | - | 100.3 | - |
| Nyeri | 87.6 | 100.7 | 102.3 | - | - | - | - | - | - |
| Mombasa | 100.7 | 103.1 | - | 104.7 | - | - | - | - | - |
| Timboroa | 88.6 | 91.5 | - | - | - | - | - | - | - |
| Nakuru | 104.1 | 96.5 | - | - | - | - | - | - | - |
| Eldoret | - | - | - | - | - | 92.9 | - | - | - |
| Kapsimotwa | - | - | - | - | - | - | - | - | - |
| Kisumu | 88.6 | 91.5 | - | - | - | - | 93.5 | - | - |
| Kisii | 103.3 | - | - | - | 101.7 | - | - | - | - |
| Nyadundo | - | - | 99.7 | - | - | - | - | - | - |

*Limuru txs serve Greater Nairobi. **) also called Nyambene.

**Networks (from Nairobi studios unless stated):**
**S=Swahili Sce "Radio Taifa":** 0200-2110 on MW, 24h on FM. Also rel. China R. Int. 1905-2000 – **E=English Sce:** 0200-2105 (on FM, non-stop music 2105-0200). Includes relays of CRI 1700-1800 & BBC – **N= Northastern Sce:** 0230-2105: Turkana on 1386kHz, Borana, Burji & Rendille on 1233kHz – **C=** relays of Mwatu FM and Nosim FM: Mon-Sat 0200-2010 – **I=** Iftiin FM in Somali on 639/1305kHz & 101.9MHz – **W=Western Sce** from Kisumu studios in local langs Mon-Fri 0300-1905 on 558kHz – **Co=Coro FM** in Kikuyu – **Pw=Pwani FM** from Mombasa studios – **Mi=Minto FM** (from Keroka studios in Kisii) – **Ki=Kitwek FM** in Kalenjin – **Ma=Mayienga FM** (from Kisumu studios in Luo) – **Mw=Mwago FM** in Meru – **Ingo FM:** western Kenya on 100.5MHz in Luhya – **Mwatu FM:** Kibwezi 93.1MHz in Kamba – **Nosim FM:** Narok 90.5MHz in Masai.
**Ann:** E: "This is KBC English Service". **IS:** Flute & drum melody in some services.

### ROYAL MEDIA SERVICES LTD. (RMS)
P.O. Box 7468, Nairobi 00300 ☎+254 20 2721415/6 +254 20 2724211 **W:** royalmediaservices.co.ke **E:** info@royalmedia.co.ke **L.P:** Owner: Samuel K. Macharia. MD: Wachira Waruru.
**FM**(MHz): **R. Citizen** in Swahili/Eng: Eldoret 90.4, Voi 91.8, Chuka 93.1, Machakos 94.2, Meru 94.3, Kibwezi 95.4, Narok 95.5, Garissa 95.7, Maralal 95.9, Kapenguria 96.1, Kanyenyeini 96.5, Wajir 97.0, Mombasa 97.3, Malindi 97.4, Kisumu 97.6, Marsabit 98.0, Kitui 98.6, Nakuru 100.5, Nyadundo 103.6, Nyeri 104.3, Homa Bay 105.2, Nairobi/Namanga 106.7 – **Hot 96 FM** in Eng/Sheng/Swahili: Nairobi 96.0, Eldoret 87.6, Kisumu 103.1, Mombasa 90.4, Nakuru 102.5, Nyeri 88.6

**RMS** also operates the following stns for specific lang. communities:
**FM**(MHz): **Bahari FM (**in Swahili & coastal langs): Mombasa 94.2 – **Chamgei FM** (in Kalenjin): 90.4, Nakuru 95.0, Eldoret 97.5 – **Egesa FM** (in Kisii): Kisii 94.6, Nairobi 103.2 – **Inooro FM** (in Kikuyu): Nyadundo 88.9, Nakuru 89.8, Meru 95.1, Muranga 96.9, Nyeri 97.8, Nairobi 98.9, Mombasa 99.2, Chuka 102.0, Eldoret 107.0 – **Mulembe FM** (in Luhya): Webuye 89.6, Rift Valley 94.0, Eldoret 95.8, Nakuru 97.9 – **Musyi FM** (in Kamba): Nairobi 102.2, Kitui 103.6 – **Muuga FM** (in Meru): Meru 88.9, Nairobi 94.2 – **Ramogi FM** (in Luo): Nakuru 95.4, Mombasa 96.0, Homa Bay 97.0, Siaya 98.4, Nairobi 107.1, Kisumu 107.6 – **Wimwaro FM** (in Embu): Embu 93.0 – Vuuka FM (in Maragoli): Kisumu 100.4.

### RADIO AFRICA LTD.
P.O. Box 74497, Nairobi ☎+254 20 4244000 +254 20 4447410

**W:** the-star.co.ke **E:** info@kissfm.co.ke **LP:** MD: Patrick Quarcoo.
**FM**(MHz): **Kiss 100** in Eng/Swahili: Nairobi 100.3, Eldoret 89.1, Kisumu 92.5, Meru 93.5, Mombasa 88.7, Nakuru 98.1, Nyeri 100.1, Webuye 104.7 – **Classic 105 FM** in Eng/Swahili: Nakuru 95.7, Nairobi 105.2, Mombasa 107.5 – **East FM** (Asian): Nairobi 106.3, Mombasa 89.5 – R. **Jambo** (sports): Kisii 89.3, Mombasa 92.3, Meru 92.7, Webuye 95.3, Nakuru 96.9, Maralal/Narok/Nyahururu 97.3, Nairobi 97.5, Malindi 98.1, Nyeri 99.3, Eldoret 99.5, Kapenguria 99.7, Kisumu 100.1, Garissa 104.3, Kibwezi/Lamu 104.7, Kitui 104.9, Voi 105.7 – **X FM** (rock music): Nairobi 105.5 – **Relax FM** (R&B music): Nairobi 103.5.

## NATION MEDIA GROUP LTD.
🖃 P.O. Box 49010, Nairobi 00100 ☎ +254 20 3288000 **W:** nationmedia.com **LP:** Chmn: Wilfred Kiboro. CEO: Linus Gitahi. Managing Ed. Broadc. Div: Linus Kaikai.
**FM**(MHz): **Nation FM** in Eng/Swahili: Nairobi 96.3, Eldoret 102.7, Kisumu 102.1, Meru 93.9, Mombasa 101.5, Nakuru 97.7, Nyeri 104.9 – **QFM** in Swahili: Nairobi 94.4, Eldoret 96.7, Meru 107.1, Mombasa 87.9, Nakuru 103.3, Nyeri 90.9.

**OTHER FM STNS IN NAIROBI** (including relays elsewhere; freqs are in Nairobi unless stated, & in MHz): **1 FM**: 97.1, Meru 99.1, Nyeri 106.1, Nakuru 106.5, Mombasa 107.3 – **2 FM**: 87.7, Meru 99.1, Nyeri 106.1, Nakuru 106.5, Mombasa 107.3 – **ATG Radio**: 91.1, Voi 88.5, Kibwezi 95.1 – **Biblia Husema Broadcasting** (Christian): 96.7, Eldoret 96.3, Lokichokio 102.5, Nakuru 102.9, Machakos 96.7, Timboroa 101.5 – **Capital FM** (in Eng): 98.4, Garissa 102.7, Kitui 106.5, Malindi 104.5, Meru 103.9, Mombasa 98.4, Nakuru 98.5, Nyeri 98.5, Timboroa 93.0, Voi 104.9 – **Chamgei FM**: 90.4, Kericho 90.2, Nakuru 95.0, Eldoret 97.5 – **East Africa R.** (in Eng/Swahili - relay of Tanzanian stn): 94.7 – **Family R. 316** (Christian): 103.9, Kisumu 96.5, Mombasa 97.9, Nakuru 102.1 – **Gukena FM**: 92.2, Mt. Kenya/Nakuru 92.8 – **Ghetto R.** (in Sheng): 89.5 – **Homeboyz R.**: 103.5 – **Hope FM** (Pentecostal Church): 93.3, Mombasa 101.9, Timboroa 93.9 – **Iftiin FM** (Somali): 101.9 – **Iqra FM** (Islamic): 95.0 – **Kameme FM** (mainly in Kikuyu): 101.1, Eldoret 101.9, Nakuru 99.3, Nyeri 92.3, Meru 88.3. Also rel. BBC – **Kass FM** (in Kalenjin): 89.1, Eldoret 90.0, Kisumu 91.0, Nakuru 92.5, Kisii 99.3, Mombasa 102.7 – **Kubamba R.**: 91.6 – **Mbaitu FM**: 92.5, Kitui 100.4, Makueni 100.5 – **Meru FM**: 107.8, Meru 88.3, Central 101.3, Mombasa 100.3, Timau 101.3 Nanyuku 100.3 – **Milele FM** (in Swahili): 93.6, Kapenguria 88.3, Taita-Taveta (Voi) 89.7, Nakuru/Nyahururu 90.2, Kitui/Lamu 91.3, Nyeri 91.7, Webuye 92.7, Kisii 95.1, Mombasa 96.7, Maralal/Narok 98.7, Kisumu 99.7, Garissa 99.9, Malindi 101.3, Meru 101.5, Eldoret 103.1, Kibwezi 104.3 – **One FM**: 97.1, Mombasa 107.3, Nakuru 106.5, Nyeri 106.1, Meru 99.1 – **Pamoja FM/ECN R.:** Kibera 99.9 – **Qwetu R:** 95.3, Kisumu 99.1, Mombasa 92.0, Webuye 98.0 – **R. Maisha** 102.7, Nakuru 104.5, Mombasa/Meru 105.1, Kisumu 105.3, Nyeri 105.7 – **R. Nam Lolwe:** 101.5, Kisumu 97.3, Mombasa 94.7, Nakuru 87.7 – **Sound Asia:** 88.0, Mombasa 89.9 – **Star FM** (in Somali/Swahili/Eng): 105.9, Dadaab/Garissa 97.1, Wajir 97.3, Mandera 97.5. Also rel. BBC. **W:** starfm.co.ke – **Truth FM:** 90.7 – **Uptown Radio:** 91.1 – **R. Waumini:** 88.3. **W:** catholicchurch.or.ke
**NB:** 99.9MHz is assigned for use in Nairobi by several very low-powered community stns. There are many private FM stns outside Nairobi.

**Relays of international stations:**
**BBC WS** (E/Swahili): Kisumu 88.1, Nairobi/Mombasa 93.9MHz
**VOA** (E/Swahili): Nairobi 107.5MHz
**RFI Afrique** (F/E/Swahili): Nairobi 89.9, Mombasa 105.5MHz

## KIRIBATI

**L.T:** UTC +12h (Gilbert Islands), UTC +13h (Phoenix Islands), UTC +14h Line Islands) — **Pop:** 102,350 — **Pr.L:** I-Kiribati, English — **E.C:** 50Hz, 240V — **ITU:** KIR

### COMMUNICATIONS COMMISSION OF KIRIBATI
🖃 Box 529, Betio, Tarawa ☎ +686 75125431/75125488 **W:** cck.ki
**E:** enquiry@cck.ki
Regulator of broadcasting in Kiribati [including Kiritimati Island]

| MW | kHz | kW | Station |
|---|---|---|---|
| 1) London Settlement | 846 | 10 | R. Kiribati |
| 2) Bairiki | 1440 | 10 | R. Kiribati |
| **FM** | **MHz** | **kW** | **Station** |
| 1) Bairiki | 88.0 | 0.1 | Mauri FM 88 |
| 2) Betio | 89.0 | | Newair FM |
| 3) Bairiki | 90.0 | | R. Australia |
| 4) Ronton | 93.5 | 0.5 | R. Kiribati Kiritimati FM |
| 5) Bairiki | 95.0 | | BBC |

| FM | MHz | kW | Station |
|---|---|---|---|
| 4) Tarawa | 100.0 | | BBC |
| 2) Bairiki | 101.0 | | Newair FM |

**Addresses & other information**
**1) BROADCASTING & PUBLICATIONS AUTHORITY – RADIO KIRIBATI** 🖃 PO Box 78, Bairiki, Tarawa **LP:** CEO Teannaki Tongaua **E:** ceo@bpa.org.ki Mgr Program & Publications Mrs Reita Andrew **E:** program-publications@bpa.org.ki Engineering Netw. Mgr Babera Marewenimakin **E:** engineering-network@bpa.org.ki ☎ +686 75121457 📠 +686 75121096. **E:** radio.kiribati@gmail.com **W:** bpa.org.ki Audio streaming at Icecast 202.6.120.13:8000 **MW:** Bairiki 1440kHz 10kW **FM:** 88.0MHz 0.1kW [relays MW] **D.Prgr:** I-Kiribati (90%) English (10%): 1855-2030, 0000-0130, 0500-1000 **N. in English:** 2000, 0100, 1800 (RNZI) followed by local news bulletin [r.relaying other RNZI programs irregularly). Incl. sponsored programs from government agencies, international agencies on AM, with spot advertising only on FM. **Ann:** "This is Radio Kiribati, the national broadcasting service of Kiribati in the Central Pacific" "Aio bwanaan Kiribati te botaki ni kanako bwanaa I bukin Kiribati I nukan te Betebeke". **RADIO KIRIBATI KIRITIMATI FM** 🖃 Ronton, Kiritimati Island, Kiribati, Central Pacific **FM:** Ronton (London) 93.5MHz 0.5kW **Prgr:** Satellite feed from R. Kiribati 88.0 FM and local originated prgrs for Kiritimati (Christmas) Island in the Line Islands [Responsibility of Kiritimati Branch Broadcasting Services via Engineering Netw Mgr]. – **2)** PO Box 204, Bairiki, Tarawa. **L.P:** Sir Ieremia Tabai. **D.Prgr:** Local commercial prgrs in English & I-Kiribati ☎ +686 75121671 **E:** newairfm89kiribati@gmail.com – **3)** 24/7 Pacific stream in English via satellite from Melbourne – **4)** 24/7 Pacific stream in English via satellite from London.

## KOREA, North

**L.T:** UTC +9h — **Pop:** 25 million — **Pr.L:** Korean — **E.C:** 50Hz, 220V — **ITU:** KRE

### THE RADIO AND TELEVISION BROADCASTING COMMITTEE OF THE DEMOCRATIC PEOPLE'S REPUBLIC OF KOREA
🖃 Jonsung-dong, Moranbong District, Pyongyang ☎ +850 2 816035

### KOREAN CENTRAL BROADCASTING STATION
(Joson Jung-ang Pangsong)
🖃 Jonsung-dong, Moranbong District, Pyongyang ☎ +850 2 812301

| MW | kHz | kW | Prgr | MW | kHz | kW | Prgr |
|---|---|---|---|---|---|---|---|
| Chongjin | 702 | 50 | C/R | Sinuiju | 873 | 250 | C/R |
| Wiwon | *720 | 500 | C/R | Wonsan | *882 | 250 | C/R |
| Hyesan | ‡765 | 50 | C/R | Hwangju | +927 | 50 | C/R |
| Kaesong | 810 | 50 | C/R | Hamhung | ‡999 | 250 | C/R |
| Pyongyang | 819 | 500 | C | Pyongyang | 1368 | 2 | E |
| **SW** | **kHz** | | **Prgr** | **SW** | **kHz** | | **Prgr** |
| Sariwon | ‡2350 | | C/R | Wonsan | ‡3968 | | C/R |
| Pyongyang | 2850 | | C | Chongjin | ‡3980 | | C/R |
| Hamhung | 3220 | | C/R | Kanggye | 6100 | | C |
| Pyongyang | ‡3350 | | C/R | Pyongyang | 9665 | | C |
| Hyesan | ‡3920 | | C/R | Kanggye | 11680 | | C |
| Kanggye | 3959 | | C/R | | | | |

*= Kanggye, += Sariwon, ‡=inactive, C = Central Broadcast from Pyongyang, R = Regional Sce, E = rel. Ext. Sce
**NB:** all freqs variable **FM:** Kaesong 102.3MHz
**D.Prgr. in Korean:** 2000-1800 on all freqs exc. 6100 (2000-0850 & 1300-1800). **N:** 2100, 2200, 0100, 0300, 0600, 0800, 1100, 1200, 1300. Regional Prgrs: W0500-0600. Rel. Pyongyang Broadc. St: 1500-1800 on 702/720/864kHz 1500-2000 on 102.3MHz 1800-2000 on 3220kHz. **Ann:** "Joson Jung-ang Pangsong-imnida". Reg. Prgrs: "(location) Pangsong-imnida". **IS:** Song of General Kim Il Sung. Opening & closing music: Nat. Anthem. **V:** not verified

**EXTERNAL SERVICES: Voice of Korea, Pyongyang Broadcasting Station, Echo of Unification**– See International Radio section

### PYONGYANG FM BROADCASTING STATION
(Pyongyang FM Pangsong)

| FM | MHz | kW | FM | MHz | kW |
|---|---|---|---|---|---|
| Pyongsong | 90.1 | 2 | Sariwon | 103.0 | 2 |
| Kaesong | ‡92.5 | 2 | Haeju | ‡103.7 | 10 |
| Kanggye | 93.3 | 5 | Pyongyang | 105.2 | 20 |
| Hyesan | 93.8 | 2 | Chongjin | 105.5 | 10 |
| Wonsan | 95.1 | 5 | Hamhung | 106.1 | 20 |
| Sinuiju | ‡101.3 | 5 | Nampo | 107.2 | 2 |
| Komdok | 102.1 | 1 | | | |

‡=inactive
**D.Prgr:** 0700-2000, 2100-0000 (National holidays: 2100-2030) (music

and drama) **Ann:** "Pyongyang FM Pangsong-imnida". **IS:** Song of General Kim Jong Il. Opening music: Pyongyang Is My Heart

## KOREAN PEOPLE'S ARMY FM BROADCASTING STATION (Joson Inmingun FM Pangsong)
**FM:** 95.5MHz **Ann:** "Joson Inmingun FM Pangsong-imnida"

## KOREA, South

**L.T:** UTC +9h — **Pop:** 51 million — **Pr.L:** Korean — **E.C:** 60Hz, 110/220V — **ITU:** KOR

## KOREA COMMUNICATIONS COMMISSION
✉ 47 Gwanmun-ro, Gwacheon-si, Gyeonggi-do, Rep. of Korea
☎ +82 2 5009000 **W:** kcc.go.kr **L.P:** Chair: Lee Hyo-sung

## KOREAN BROADCASTING SYSTEM (KBS) (Hanguk Bangsong Gongsa) (Public Corporation)
✉13, Yeouidaebang-ro, Yeongdeungpo-gu, Seoul 07235 ☎ +82 2 781 1000 🖷 +82 2 761 2499 **W:** kbs.co.kr
**L.P:** Pres & CEO: Yang Sung-dong. Auditor Gen.: Jeon Hong-Gu. Exec.Vice Pres: Jung Pil Mo, Exec. Man. Dirs:Hwang Yong-Ho (Broadcast & Marketing), Lim Byung Kul (Future Business), Kim Eui-Chul (N & Sports), Kim Deock Jae (Content Production), Kim Yong-Duk (Production Tech), Park Jae Hong (Audience Rel.). Dir. Int. Rel. Div: Kim Jong-Myung

| MW | Location | Call | kHz | kW | | MW | Location | Call | kHz | kW |
|---|---|---|---|---|---|---|---|---|---|---|
| 10) | Jangheung | SM | 540 | 1 | | 19) | Jeju+ | KS | 963 | 10 |
| 13) | Daegu+2 | QH | 558 | 250 | | 14) | Andong+ | CR | 963 | 10 |
| 9) | Jeonju+ | KF | 567 | 100 | | 14) | Andong+ | CR | 963 | 10 |
| 12) | Suncheon 3 | | 576 | 1 | | K1) | Dangjin* | CA | 972 | 1500 |
| N2) | Namyang* | SA | 603 | 500 | | 4) | Gangneung 3 | - | 1008 | 50 |
| 19) | Seogwipo | - | 621 | 10 | | 15) | Pohang+ | CP | 1035 | 10 |
| 12) | Yeosu | - | 630 | 10 | | 6) | Cheongju+ | KQ | 1062 | 50 |
| 3) | Chuncheon+ | KM | 657 | 50 | | 18) | Jinju+ | CJ | 1098 | 20 |
| 9) | Jeonju 3 | - | 675 | 10 | | N3) | Hwaseong* | KC | 1134 | 500 |
| N1) | Sorae* | KA | 711 | 500 | | 5) | Wonju+ | CW | 1152 | 10 |
| 13) | Daegu+ | KG | 738 | 100 | | K2E) | Gimje* | SR | 1170 | 500 |
| 10) | Gwangju+ | KH | 747 | 100 | | 10) | Gwangju 3 | - | 1224 | 20 |
| 4) | Gangneung+ | KR | 864 | 100 | | 16) | Hapcheon | - | 1278 | 1 |
| 8) | Daejeon+ | KI | 882 | 20 | | 17) | Ulsan+ | QB | 1449 | 10 |
| 2) | Busan+ | KB | 891 | 250 | | 11) | Mokpo+ | KN | 1467 | 50 |
| 16) | Changwon 3 | - | 936 | 10 | | | | | | |

**MW:** N1 = KBS R. One, N2 = KBS R. Two, N3 = KBS R. Three, K1 = Global Korean Network 1, K2 = Global Korean Network 2, E = also used for Ext. sce., KBS WORLD R, N = Netw. or local stn. area, *) Key stn, +) = Regional key St, 2 = rel N2 exc. for local prgrs, 3 = rel N3 (other local st take N1 ), Call: HL(call)

**NB:** Global Korean Network stns and FM-stns do not use call letters (even if assigned). Other stns without call letters use the calls from their regional key stns.

| FM | Location | I | II | III | kW |
|---|---|---|---|---|---|
| 1) | Gwanaksan | 97.3* | 93.1 | 89.1a | 10/10/10 |
| 1) | Gwanaksan | | | 106.1b | -/-/10 |
| 1) | Gwanaksan | | | 104.9c | -/-/2 |
| 1) | Yongmunsan | 90.3* | | | 1 |
| 2) | Hwangnyeongsan | 103.7 | 92.7 | 97.1b | 3/5/3 |
| 3) | Hwaaksan | 99.5* | 91.1 | 98.7b | 5/5/3 |
| 4) | Gwaebangsan | 98.9* | 89.1 | 102.1b | 3/5/5 |
| 5) | Baegunsan | 97.1 | 89.5 | | 1/3 |
| 5) | Taegisan | 95.5* | | | 1 |
| 4) | Hambaeksan | 93.7* | 97.3 | | 1/3 |
| 6) | Sikhangsan | | 102.1 | | -/3 |
| 8) | Sikhangsan | | | 100.9b | -/-/3 |
| 6) | Heukseongsan | 89.9* | | | 1 |
| 6) | Uamsan | 89.3 | 94.1 | 90.9b | 1/3/3 |
| 7) | Gayeopsan | 92.1* | 100.3 | | 1/3 |
| 8) | Gyeryongsan | 94.7* | 98.5 | | 3/5 |
| 9) | Moaksan | 96.9* | 100.7 | 92.9b | 5/5/3 |
| 9) | Nogodan | 88.3* | 104.5 | | 1/3 |
| 10) | Mudeungsan | 90.5* | 92.3 | 95.5b | 5/5/3 |
| 11) | Yangulsan | | 98.3 | | -/1 |
| 11) | Daedunsan | 105.9 | | | 2 |
| 12) | Namsan | | | 102.7b | -/-/1 |
| 12) | Mangunsan | 95.7* | 94.5 | | 1/3 |
| 13) | Palgongsan | 101.3* | 89.7 | 102.3b | 5/5/3 |
| 14) | Ilwolsan | 90.5* | | | 1 |
| 14) | Hakkasan | | 88.1 | | -/3 |
| 15) | Johangsan | 95.9* | 93.5 | | 1/3 |
| 15) | Uljin | 93.9 | | | 1 |
| 16) | Bulmosan | 91.7* | 93.9 | 106.1b | 5/1/3 |

| FM | Location | I | II | III | kW |
|---|---|---|---|---|---|
| 17) | Muryongsan | 90.7* | 101.9 | | 1/3 |
| 18) | Gamaksan | | 92.1 | | -/3 |
| 18) | Mangjinsan | 90.3 | 89.3 | | 1/1 |
| 19) | Gyeonwolak | 99.1* | 96.3 | 91.9b | 3/3/3 |
| 19) | Sammaebong | 95.3 | 99.9 | 89.7b | 3/3/3 |

+ low power relay stns
Reg = region in MW section. I-Standard FM (R. One); II-KBS FM One; III a = KBS FM Two, b = R. Two, c=R. Three. *) also SCA (R. Three)

**KBS R. One** (KBS Je-il Radio, HLKA): 24h Non-commercial nationwide news sce. Key freqs 711kHz, 90.3/97.3MHz. Also rel. by Standard FM stns and most reg. stns. Reg. stns may broadcast local prgrs at designated times. **N:** hourly 2000-1500 except 1100(W). Local N: 2205(Sun), 2210(W), 0000(Sun), 0005(w), 0310(Sun), 0315(W), 0605, 0805(Mon-Fri), 0900(Sun), 0905(W)
**KBS R. Two** (KBS Je-i Radio, Happy FM, HLSA): 2000-1800 (558kHz to 1500). Commercial. Key freq's 603kHz/106.1MHz. Reg. stns may broadcast local prgrs at designated times. **N:** 2100(w), 2200(w), 0000, 0300, 0900, 1100(w). Local N: 0500, 0700. Global Korean Network prgr 1700-1800
**KBS R. Three** (KBS Je-sam Radio, Sarang-ui Sori Bangsong, HLKC): 2100-1800. Non-comm. sce. **N:** 0100(W), 0300(W), 0500(w), 1200.
**KBS FM One** (KBS Je-il Bangsong, Classic FM, HLKA-FM): 24h. Mainly Korean traditional and western classical music
**KBS FM Two** (KBS Je-i FM Bangsong, Cool FM, HLKC-FM): 24h. Mainly Korean and western popular and light classical music
**Ann: N1:** "AM Chilbaek-sib-il(711)kHz, FM Gusib-chil-jeom-sam(97.3) MHz, KBS II Radiomnida. HLKA". **N2:** "KBS Je-i Radiomnida". **N3:** "KBS Je-sam Radio, Sarang-ui Sori Bangsong-imnida. HLKC".

**Addresses of key regional stations:**
**2)** 429, Suyeong-ro, Suyeong-gu, Busan 48316 – **3)** 109, Bangsong-gil, Chuncheon-si, Gangwon-do 24363 – **4)** 13, Imyeong-ro 131beon-gil, Gangneung-si, Gangwon-do 25534 – **5)** 37, Wonil-ro, Wonju-si, Gangwon-do 26432 – **6)** 1428, Seobu-ro, Heungdeok-gu, Cheongju-si, Chungcheongbuk-do 28637 – **7)** 3448, Jungwon-daero, Chungju-si, Chungcheongbuk-do 27428 – **8)** 128, Dunsan-daero 117beon-gil, Seo-gu, Daejeon 35203 – **9)** 30, Majeonjungang-ro, Wansan-gu, Jeonju-si, Jeollabuk-do 54962 –**10)** 287, Uncheon-ro, Seo-gu, Gwangju 61946 – **11)** 221, Yangeul-ro, Mokpo-si, Jeollanam-do 58613 – **12)** 250, Jungang-ro, Suncheon-si, Jeollanam-do 57938 – **13)** 30, Dalgubeol-daero 496-gil, Suseong-gu, Daegu 42095 – **14)** 27, Gamnamu 3-gil, Andong-si, Gyeongsangbuk-do 36647 – **15)** 72, Jungseom-ro, Nam-gu, Pohang-si, Gyeongsangbuk-do 37771 – **16)** 178, Jungang-daero, Changwon-si, Gyeongsangnam-do 51444 – **17)** 212, Beonyeong-ro, Nam-gu, Ulsan 44702 – **18)** 85, Sinan-ro, Jinju-si, Gyeongsangnam-do 52695 – **19)** 8, Bokji-ro 1-gil, Jeju-si, Jeju 63220.
**Local identifications:** Within local prgrs. **N1:** just before the h. at 2000, 2200(Sun), 2300, 0000(W), 0200, 0300, 0500, 0700(Mon-Fri), 0800, 0900(Sun), 1000(W), 1100(Sun), 1300, 1400, 1500(Sun), 1600. **N2:** just before the h. 2000-1700. **N3:** just before the h. 2100-1700. **FM One:** just before the h. at 2000-2200, 0000, 0200, 0300, 0500, 0700-0900, 1100, 1300, 1500, 1600, 1800. **FM Two:** just before the h.

**Digital service (UKBS Music):** 177.008MHz(Daegu/Pohang/Suncheon), 183.008MHz(Gwangju/Mokpo/Seogwipo), 189.008MHz(Jinju/Andong), 201.008MHz(Daejeon/Cheongju/Chungju), 207.008MHz(Seoul/Busan/Ulsan/Changwon/Jeonju), 213.008MHz(Chuncheon/Gangneung/Wonju/Jeju-si): 24h

**EXTERNAL SERVICES: KBS WORLD RADIO, KBS Global Korean Network (Hanminjok Bangsong)** See International Radio section

## KOREA EDUCATIONAL BROADCASTING SYSTEM (EBS) (Gyoyuk Bangsong) (Pub.)
✉ 281, Hallyu world-ro, Ilsandong-gu, Goyang-si, Gyeonggi-do 10393
☎ +82 2 526 2000 🖷 +82 2 526 2419 **W:** ebs.co.kr
Call letters HLQL used for all the stns.

| FM | Tx location | MHz | kW |
|---|---|---|---|
| Chungju | Gayeopsan | 104.1 | 3 |
| Changwon | Bulmosan | 104.3 | 3 |
| Seoul | Gwanaksan | 104.5 | 10 |
| Jinju | Gamaksan | 104.7 | 3 |
| Gangneung | Gwaebangsan | 104.9 | 3 |
| Wonju | Baegunsan | 104.9 | 3 |
| Seogwipo | Sammaebang | 104.9 | 3 |
| Daegu | Palgongsan | 105.1 | 5 |
| Gwangju | Mudeungsan | 105.3 | 5 |
| Daejeon | Gyeryongsan | 105.7 | 5 |
| Ulsan | Muryongsan | 105.9 | 3 |

| FM | Tx location | MHz | kW |
|---|---|---|---|
| Yeosu | Mangunsan | 106.3 | 3 |
| Chuncheon | Hwaaksan | 106.5 | 3 |
| Pohang | Johangsan | 106.7 | 3 |
| Jeonju | Moaksan | 106.9 | 5 |
| Taebaek | Hambaeksan | 107.1 | 3 |
| Jeju | Gyeonwolak | 107.3 | 3 |
| Namwom | Nogodan | 107.5 | 3 |
| Daegu | Ilwolsan | 107.7 | 3 |
| Andong | Hakkasan | 107.7 | 3 |
| Busan | Hwangnyeongsan | 107.7 | 3 |
| Cheongju | Sikjangsan | 107.9 | 3 |

+ low power relay stns
**D.Prgr:** 2000-1700 **Ann:** "EBS, Gyoyuk Bangsong-imnida"

## GUGAK FM BROADCASTING SYSTEM
**(Gugak Bangsong) (Pub.)**
▣ DMS Bldg., 12, World Cup Buk-ro 54-gil, Mapo-gu, Seoul 03925
☎ +82 2 300 9990 🖷 +82 2 300 9959
**W:** gugakfm.co.kr
**Stations:** Seoul HLQA-FM 99.1MHz 5kW: 24h, Daejeon HLEK-FM 90.5MHz 1kW: 24h, Namwon 95.9MHz: 24h, Namdo 94.7MHz 0.5kW: 24h, Gyeongju/Pohang 107.9MHz 3kW: 24h, Jeonju 95.3MHz 1kW: 24h, Busan 98.5MHz 1kW: 24h, Gangneung 103.3MHz 1kW: 24h, Daegu 107.5MHz 1kW: 24h, Gwangju HLEG-FM 99.3MHz 1kw: 24h, Jeju(Hallasan) 91.3MHz 1kW: 24h, Jeju(Sammaebong) 106.9MHz 1kW: 24h. **Ann:** "Gugak Bangsong-imnida"

## MUNHWA BROADCASTING CORP. (MBC)
**(Munhwa Bangsong) Nationwide comm. netw.**
▣267, Seongam-ro, Mapo-gu, Seoul 03925 ☎ +82 2 789 0011 **W:** imbc.com

| | MW Call | kHz | kW | Station | | MW Call | kHz | kW | Station |
|---|---|---|---|---|---|---|---|---|---|
| 1) | CQ | 765 | 10 | Daejeon MBC | 11) | AT | 1080 | 10 | Yeosu MBC |
| 2) | AJ | 774 | 10 | Jeju MBC | 12) | AV | 1107 | 10 | Pohang MBC |
| 3) | AN | 774 | 10 | Chuncheon MBC | 13) | KU | 1161 | 20 | Busan MBC |
| 4) | CT | 810 | 10 | Daegu MBC | 14) | AK | 1215 | 10 | Jinju MBC |
| 5) | CN | 819 | 20 | Gwangju MBC | 15) | SB | 1242 | 10 | Wonju MBC |
| 6) | AU | 846 | 10 | Ulsan MBC | 16) | AF | 1287 | 10 | Gangneung MBC |
| 7) | CX | 855 | 10 | Jeonju MBC | 17) | AX | 1287 | 10 | Cheongju MBC |
| 8) | KV | 900 | 50 | Seoul MBC | 18) | AO | 1332 | 10 | Chungju MBC |
| 9) | AP | 990 | 10 | Changwon MBC | 19) | AQ | 1350 | 10 | Samcheok MBC |
| 10) | AW | 1017 | 10 | Andong MBC | 20) | AM | 1386 | 10 | Mokpo MBC |

**D.Prgr:** All 24h

| | | Music FM | | Standard FM | |
|---|---|---|---|---|---|
| | FM Location | MHz | kW | MHz | kW |
| 8) | Seoul | 91.9 | 10 | 95.9 | 10 |
| 13) | Busan | 88.9 | 5 | 95.9 | 3 |
| 4) | Daegu | 95.3 | 5 | 96.5 | 5 |
| 5) | Gwangju | 91.5 | 5 | 93.9 | 5 |
| | Gwangju | 95.1 | 3 | - | - |
| 1) | Daejeon | 97.5 | 5 | 92.5 | 3 |
| 7) | Jeonju | 99.1 | 5 | 94.3 | 2 |
| | Jeonju (Namwon) | | | 101.7 | 3 |
| 9) | Changwon | 100.5 | 1 | 98.9 | 3 |
| 3) | Chuncheon | 94.5 | 3 | 92.3 | 3 |
| 17) | Cheongju | 99.7 | 1 | 107.1 | 1 |
| 2) | Jeju | 90.1 | 3 | 97.9 | 1 |
| | Jeju(Seogwipo) | 102.9 | 3 | 97.1 | 1 |
| 6) | Ulsan | 98.7 | 3 | 97.5 | 1 |
| 16) | Gangneung | 94.3 | 5 | 96.3 | 3 |
| 14) | Jinju | 97.7 | 1 | 91.1 | 3 |
| | Jinju | 96.1 | 3 | 93.5 | 1 |
| 20) | Mokpo | 102.3 | 1 | 89.1 | 2 |
| 11) | Yeosu | 98.3 | 2 | 100.3 | 1 |
| 10) | Andong | 91.3 | 3 | 100.1 | 3 |
| 15) | Wonju | 98.9 | 3 | 92.7 | 1 |
| | Wonju | - | - | 102.5 | 1 |
| 18) | Chungju | 88.7 | 3 | 96.1 | 1 |
| 19) | Samcheok | 98.1 | 3 | 101.5 | 1 |
| | Samcheok | 99.9 | 1 | 93.1 | 3 |
| 12) | Pohang | 97.9 | 3 | 100.7 | 3 |
| | Pohang(Uljin) | 94.9 | 1 | 102.7 | 1 |

+low power rel. stns
**NB:** Standard FM stns simulcast with the MW stn in the same city. A separate sce. is provided to the Music FM stns. All regional stns broadcast a combination of a feed from Seoul and their own local prgrs. Standard FM stns follow the same schedule as their corresponding MW outlet. Music FM of Seoul MBC sched: 24h
**Ann:** "(freq. and location) Munhwa Bangsong-imnida. (Call)" or "Munhwa Bangsong-imnida" or "MBC". Seoul: "Jungpa Gubaek (900)

kHz, Pyojun FM Gushib-o-jeom-gu 95.9MHz Munhwa Bangsong-imnida"

**Addresses & other information:**
**NB:** Add "(location) Munhwa Broadc. Corp." to addr.
**1)** 161, EXPO-ro, Yuseong-gu, Daejeon 34125 **W:** tjmbc.co.kr – **2)** 35, Munyeon-ro, Jeju-si, Jeju Special Self-do 63120 **W:** jejumbc.co.kr – **3)** 54, Subyengongwon-gil, Chuncheon-si, Gangwon-do 24239 **W:** chmbc.co.kr – **4)** 400, Dongdaegu-ro, Suseong-gu, Daegu 42020 **W:** dgmbc.co.kr – **5)** 17, Wolsan-ro 116byeon-gil, Nam-gu, Gwangju 61629 **W:** kjmbc.co.kr – **6)** 65, Seowon 3-gil, Jung-gu, Ulsan 44512 **W:** usmbc.co.kr – **7)** 50, Sanneomeo 1-gil, Wansan-gu, Jeonju-si, Jeollabuk-do 54986 **W:** jmbc.co.kr – **8)** National addr. – **9)** 11-11, Yangdeokseo 9-gil, Masan Hoewon-gu, Changwon-si, Gyeongsangnam-do 51322 **W:** mbcgn.com – **10)** 20, Dangwon-ro, Andong-si, Gyeongsangbuk-do 36645 **W:** andongmbc.co.kr – **11)** 135, Munsu-ro, Yeosu-si, Jeollanam-do 59700 **W:** ysmbc.co.kr – **12)** 421, Saecheingnyeng-ro, Pohang-si, Gyeongsangbuk-do 37685 **W:** phmbc.co.kr – **13)** 69, Gamporo 8beon-gil, Suyeong-gu. Busan 48276 **W:** busanmbc.co.kr – **14)** 13, Gaho-ro, Jinju-si, Gyeongsangnam-do 52817 **W:** mbcgn.co.kr – **15)** 67, Hakseong-gil, Wonju-si, Gangwon-do 26412 **W:** wjmbc.co.kr – **16)** 267, Gajak-ro, Gangneung-si, Gangwon-do 25477 **W:** mbceg.co.kr – **17)** 1322, 2 Sunhwan-ro, Heungdeok-gu, Cheongju-si, Chungcheongbuk-do 28382 **W:** mbccb.co.kr – **18)** 3250, Jungwon-daero, Chungju-si, Chungcheongbuk-do 27480 **W:** mbccb.co.kr – **19)** 629-59, Saecheongnyeon-doro, Samcheok-si, Gangwon-do 25909 **W:** mbceg.co.kr – **20)** 334, Yeongsan-ro, Mokpo-si, Jeollanam-do 58700 **W:** mpmbc.co.kr

## CHRISTIAN BROADCASTING SYSTEM (CBS)
**(Gidokkyo Bangsong)**

| | MW Call | kHz | kW | Station and h.of tr. |
|---|---|---|---|---|
| 1) | KY | 837 | 50 | CBS Seoul: 24h |
| 2) | CL | 999 | 10 | CBS Gwangju: 2000-1600 |
| 4) | KT | 1251 | 10 | CBS Daegu: 2000-1600 |
| 5) | CM | 1314 | 10 | CBS Jeonbuk: 2000-1600 |
| 6) | KP | 1404 | 10 | CBS Busan: 2000-1600 |

| | CBS FM | Call | MHz | kW | h. of tr. |
|---|---|---|---|---|---|
| 1) | CBS-FM Seoul | HLKY-FM | 93.9 | 7 | 24h (Music FM) |
| | CBS Seoul | HLKY-SFM | 98.1 | 10 | 24h |
| 2) | CBS Gwangju | HLCL-SFM | 103.1 | 5 | 2000-1600 |
| 3) | CBS Jeonnam | HLCL-FM | 102.1 | 2 | 2000-1600 |
| 4) | CBS Daegu | HLKT-SFM | 103.1 | 5 | 2000-1600 |
| 4) | CBS-FM Daegu | HLKT-FM | 97.1 | 1 | 24h |
| 5) | CBS Jeonbuk | HLCM-SFM | 103.7 | 5 | 2000-1600 |
| 5) | CBS Jeonbuk | HLKP-SFM | 102.9 | 5 | 2000-1600 |
| 6) | CBS-FM Busan | HLKP-FM | 102.1 | 1 | 24h |
| 7) | CBS Cheongju | HLAC-FM | 91.5 | 3 | 2000-1600 |
| 8) | CBS Gangwon | HLDC-FM | 93.7 | 3 | 2000-1600 |
| 8) | CBS Gangwon | (W) | 94.9 | 1 | 2000-1600 |
| 9) | CBS Daejeon | HLDX-FM | 91.7 | 5 | 2000-1600 |
| 10) | CBS Pohang | HLCB-FM | 91.5 | 3 | 2000-1600 |
| 11) | CBS Gyeongnam | HLCC-FM | 106.9 | 5 | 2000-1600 |
| 12) | CBS Jeju | HLKO-FM | 93.3 | 3 | 2000-1600 |
| 12) | CBS Jeju | (S) | 90.9 | 1 | 2000-1600 |
| 13) | CBS Yeongdong | HLCO-FM | 91.5 | 3 | 2000-1600 |
| 14) | CBS Ulsan | HLKP-FM | 100.3 | 3 | 2000-1600 |

+low power relay stns. (W)=Wonju relay st. (S)= Seogwipo relay st

**Addresses & other information:**
**1)** 159-1, Mokdongseo-ro, Yangcheon-gu, Seoul 07997 ☎ +82 2 2650 7000 **W:** cbs.co.kr **Ann:** "Jeongjikhan Sesang-eul Gakkuneun AM Palbaek-samsip-chil(837)kHz, Pyojun FM Gusip-pal-jeom-il(98.1)MHz, CBS-mnida. HLKY." – **2)** 89, Uncheon-ro, Seo-gu, Gwangju 62002 ☎ +82 62 376 8500 – **3)** 166, Jungang-ro, Suncheon-si, Jeollanam-do 57939 ☎ +82 61 902 1000 – **4)** 612, Jungang-daero, Buk-ku, Daegu 41561 ☎ +82 53 426 8001 – **5)** 453, Beonyeong-ro, Deokjin-gu, Jeonju-si, Jeollabuk-do 54806 ☎ +82 63 256 1000 – **6)** 141, Sinam-ro, Busanjin-gu, Busan 47344 ☎ +82 51 636 0050 – **7)** 31, Sugok-ro 5beon-gil, Seowon-gu, Cheongju-si, Chungcheongbuk-do 28697 ☎ +82 43 292 4100 – **8)** 32, Wondae-ro 26beon-gil, Gangneung-si, Gangwon-do 25506 ☎ +82 33 643 1000 – **9)** 1712, Gyebaek-ro, Jung-gu, Daejeon 34956 ☎ +82 42 259 8888 – **10)** 10, Sanggong-ro, Nam-gu, Pohang-si, Gyeongsangbuk-do 37831 ☎ +82 54 277 5500 – **11)** Room 404, 510, Changi-daero, Uichang-gu, Changwon-si, Gyeongsangnam-do 51508 ☎ +82 55 224 5600 – **12)** 15, Singgwang-ro, Jeju-si, Jeju Teukbyeol Jachido 63125 ☎ +82 64 744 0933 – **13)** 32, Won-daero 26-gil, Gangneung-si, Gangwon-do 25506 ☎ +82 33 642 9131 – **14)** 216, Jungang-ro, Nam-gu, Ulsan44690 ☎ +82 52 256 3333
**Ann:** stns 2)-8): "Jeongjikhan Sesang-eul Kakkuneun (freq.), CBS (location) Bangsong-imnida (call)" or "Maeumgwa Maeumi Mannaneun Bangsong (freq.), CBS (location) Bangsong-imnida (call)"

**F.PI:** Relay stns in Chungju, Wonju, Jinju, Gongju, Seosan. Music FM in Daejeon, Gwangju, Jeju, Ulsan, Jeonbuk (Jeonju), Gyeongnam (Changwon)

## SEOUL BROADCASTING SYSTEM (SBS)

✉ 161, Mok-dong Seo-ro, Yangcheon-gu, Seoul 07996 ☎ +82 2 2061 0006 🖷 +82 2 2113 3169 **W:** sbs.co.kr
**MW:** HLSQ Goyang (near Seoul) 792kHz 50kW **D.Prgr:** 24h
**Standard FM** (Love FM): 103.5MHz HLSQ-SFM 10kW: 24h
**Music FM** (Power FM): 107.7MHz HLSQ-FM 10kW: 24h + lp rel. stn.
**Ann:** "AM Chilbaek-gusib-I 792kHz, FM Baek-sam-jeom-o 103.5MHz, SBS Love FM-imnida. HLSQ", "FM Baek-chil-jeom-chil 107.7MHz, Yeoreobune SBS Power FM-imnida. HLSQ"

## FAR EAST BROADCASTING CO., KOREA (Rlg.)

| MW | kHz | kW | Station, location |
|----|-----|----|----|
| 1) | 1188 | 100 | HLKX, Seoul |
| 2) | 1566 | 250 | HLAZ, Jeju |
| **FM** | **MHz** | **kW** | **Station, location** |
| 1) | 106.9 | 5 | HLKX-SFM, Seoul |
| 2) | 104.7 | 1 | HLAZ-SFM, Jeju |
| 3) | 93.3 | 5 | HLAD-FM, Daejeon |
| 4) | 98.1 | 5 | HLDD-FM, Changwon |
| 5) | 90.1 | 3 | HLDY-FM, Yeongdong |
| 6) | 100.5 | 1 | HLKW-FM, Mokpo |
| 7) | 90.3 | 3 | HLDZ-FM, Pohang |
| 8) | 107.3 | 3 | HLQR-FM, Ulsan |
| 9) | 93.3 | 1 | HLQQ-FM, Busan |
| 10) | 91.9 | 1 | HLKK-FM, Daegu |
| 11) | 93.1 | 1 | HLED-FM, Gwangju |
| 12) | 97.5 | 1 | HLEI-FM, Jeonnam Dongbu |

+ low power relay stns

**Addresses & other information:**
**1)** Far East Broadc. Co.(Geukdong Bangsong), 56, Wausan-ro, Mapo-gu, Seoul 04067 ☎ +82 2 320 0114 🖷 +82 2 320 0229 **W:** febc.net
**D.Prgr:** 24h. Korean: 1900-1000, 1600-1700 (Stangdard FM: 24h)
**English:** 1000-1100(1188kHz) **Chinese:** 1900-2000(1188kHz). **VOA Relay in Korean:** 1100-1500(1188kHz). **RFA Relay in Korean:** 1500-1900(1188kHz). **Ann:** Korean "Jungpa Cheonbaek-palsip-pal(1188)kHz, Pyojun FM Paeng-nyuk-jeom-gu(106.9)MHz, Areumdaun Chanyanggwa Gibbeun Sosigeul Jeonhaneun Geukdong Bangsong-imnida.". English: "This is HLKX Radio broadcasting with 100,000 watts of power on 1188kHz" **FI:** by contributions & free will offerings – **2)** Jeju Geukdong Bangsong, 67, Gamundongsan 4-gil, Aewol-up, Jeju-si, Jeju Teukbyeol Jachido 63050 ☎ +82 64 799 8100 **D.Prgr:** 24h. **Korean:** 1600-1700, 1900-1100 (Stangdard FM: 24h). **Chinese:** 1100-1230(1566kHz), 1345-1600(1566kHz). **Japanese:** 1230-1345(1566kHz). **Russian:** 1830-1900. **RFA Relay in Korean:** 1000-1100(1566kHz). **VOA Relay in Korean:** 1700-1800(1566kHz). **Voice of Wilderness,** see COTB North Korea, 1900-2000 on Sat. – **3)** Daejeon Geukdong Bangsong, 38-8, Jijok-ro 364-gil, Yuseong-gu, Daejeon 34076 ☎ +82 42 828 9330. **D.Prgr:** 24h – **4)** Changwon Geukdong Bangsong, 147, Du-daero, Seongsan-gu, Changwon-si, Gyeongsang-nam-do 51519 ☎ +82 55 269 9810 **D.Prgr:** 24h – **5)** Yeongdong Geukdong Bangsong, 465 Jungang-ro, Sokcho-si, Sokcho-si, Gangwon-do 24803 ☎ +82 33 638 9000 **D.Prgr:** 1900-1700 – **6)** Mokpo Geukdong Bangsong, 61, Bipa-ro, Mokpo-si, Jeollanam-do 58690 ☎ +82 61 284 9000 **D.Prgr:** 1900-1700 – **7)** Pohang Geukdong Bangsong, 164, Yongdang-ro, Buk-gu, Pohang-si, Gyeongsangnam-do 58690 ☎ +82 54 256 3000 **D.Prgr:** 24h – **8)** Ulsan Geukdong Bangsong, 145, Beonyeong-ro, Nam-gu, Ulsan-si 44695 ☎ +82 52 256 2000 **D.Prgr:** 24h – **9)** Busan Geukdong Bangsong, 105, Senteom Jungang-ro, Haeundae-gu, Busan 48058 ☎ +82 51 759 6000 **D.Prgr:** 24h – **10)** Daegu Geukdong Bangsong, 90, Hwarang-ro, Suseong-gu, Daegu 42037 ☎ +82 53 770 3000 **D.Prgr:** 24h – **11)** Gwangju Geukdong Bangsong, 73, Sangmubeonyeong-ro, Seo-gu, Gwangju 61946 ☎ +82 62 373 1000 **D.Prgr:** 24h – **12)** Jeonnam Dongbu Geukdong Bangsong, 14, Munsu-ro, Yeosu-si, Jeolla-nam-do 59706 ☎ +82 61 650 3800 **D.Prgr:** 24h

## CATHOLIC PEACE BROADCASTING CORP. (CPBC)
**(Gatollik Pyeonghwa Bangsong) Endowment by the Catholic Church.**
**Stations:**
**1)** Seoul HLQP-FM 105.3MHz 5kW: 1957-1702 – **2)** Gwangju HLDL-FM 99.9MHz 5kW, 99.5MHz 1kW(rel. stn in Yeosu): 1957-1702 – **3)** Deagu HLDK-FM 93.1MHz 3kW, 96.9MHz 0.5kW(rel. st. in Pohang), 100.7MHz 0.5kW(rel. stn in Andong): 1957-1702 – **4)** Busan HLDW-FM 101.1MHz 3kW, 94.3MHz 0.5kW(rel. st in Ulsan), 105.5MHz(rel. st in Changwon): 1957-1702 – **5)** Daejeon HLQO-FM 106.3MHz 3kW: 1957-1702 + low power rel. stn.

**Addresses:**
**1)** 330, Samil-daero, Jung-gu, Seoul 04552 ☎ +82 2 2270 2114 🖷 +82 2 2270 2210 **W:** pbc.co.kr **Ann:** " Gatollik Pyeonghwa FM Baeg-o-jeom-sam(105.3)MHz, Gibbeun Sosik, Balgeun Sesang, CPBC Gatollik Pyeonghwa Bangsong-imnida. HLQP." – **2)** 75, Sangmusimin-ro, Seo-gu, Gwangju 61951 – **3)** 20, Seoseong-ro, Jung-gu, Daegu 41933 – **4)** 71, Junggu-ro, Jung-gu, Busan 48968 – **5)** 471, Daejong-ro, Jung-gu, Daejeon 34915 ☎ +82 42 250 3200

## BUDDHIST BROADCASTING SYSTEM (BBS)
**(Bulgyo Bangsong) Owned and operated by the Buddhists**
**Stations:**
**1)** Seoul HLSG-FM 101.9MHz 5kW: 2000-1700 – **2)** Gwangju HLDB-FM 89.7MHz 3kW, 105.7MHz 0.5kW(rel. stn in Gwnagyang): 2000-1700 – **3)** Busan HLDA-FM 89.9MHz 5kW, 89.5MHz 0.5kW (rel. stn in Changwon), 88.1MHz 0.5kW(rel. stn in Jinju): 2000-1700 – **4)** Daegu HLDI-FM 94.5MHz 3kW, 105.5MHz 0.5kW (rel. stn in Pohang), 97.7MHz 1kW (rel. stn in Andong): 2000-1700 – **5)** Cheongju HLDJ-FM 96.7MHz 3kW: 2000-1700 – **6)** Chuncheon HLQM-FM 100.1MHz 3kW, 104.3MHz 1kW(rel. stn in Gangneung): 2000-1700 – **7)** Ulsan HLQU-FM 88.3MHz 1kW: 2000-1700 – **8)** Jeju HLEL-FM 94.9MHz 1kW, 100.5MHz 1kW(rel. stn in Seogwipo) + low power rel. stns
**Addresses:**
**1)** Dabo Building;20, Mapo-daero, Mapo-gu, Seoul 04175 ☎ +82 2 705 5114 🖷 +82 2 705 5229 **W:** bbsi.co.kr – **2)** Dongyang Bldg, 9, Sangmu Jungang-ro, Seo-gu, Gwangju 61962 ☎ +82 62 520 1114 – **3)** Boseong Bldg, 102, Beomil-ro, Dong-gu, Busan 48738 ☎ +82 51 520 5114 – **4)** Jingak Bldg, 261, Myeongdeok-ro, Jung-gu, Daegu 41956 ☎ +82 53 427 5114 – **5)** 101, Wolpyeong-ro 184beon-gil, Sangdang-gu, Cheongju-si, Chungcheongbuk-do 28776 ☎ +82 43 294 5114 – **6)** 10, Jungang-ro, Chuncheon-si, Gangwon-do 24270 ☎ +82 33 250 2114 – **7)** 201, Samsan-ro, Nam-gu, Ulsan 44703 ☎ +82 52 279 8114 – **8)** 14, Imhang-ro, Jeju-si, Jeju Teukbyeol Jachido 63277 ☎ +82 1811 0818
**Ann:** 1) "FM Baeg-il-jeom-gu (101.9)MHz, BBS Bulgyo Bangsong-imnida. HLSG."

## SEOUL TRAFFIC BROADCASTING SYSTEM (TBS)
**(Gyotong Bangsong)**
Municipal Station. This stn is operated by the Seoul Municipal Traffic Broadcast Headquarters to provide traffic information and education to the citizens of Seoul and surroundings.
🖳 S-PLEX Center, 31, Maebongsan-ro, Mapo-gu, Seoul 03909 ☎ +82 2 311 5114 🖷 +82 2 311 5219 **W:** tbs.seoul.kr
**Station:** HLST-FM(Live FM) 95.1MHz 5kW: 24h in Korean. HLSW-FM(Soul FM) 101.3MHz 1kW: 24h in English.
**Ann:** "FM Gusib-o-jeom-il(95.1)MHz, TBS Gyotong Bangsong-imnida","You're listening to 101.3 tbs-eFM"

## TRAFFIC BROADCASTING NETWORK (TBN)
**(Hanguk Gyotong Bangsong)**
🖳 2, Hyeoksin-ro, Wonju-si, Gangwon-do 26466 ☎ +82 33 749 5000 🖷 +82 33 749 5908 **W:** tbn.or.kr
**Stations:**
**1)** Busan 94.9MHz HLDN-FM 3kW: 24h – **2)** Gwangju 97.3MHz HLDM-FM 3kW, 103.5MHz 3kW (rel. st. in Gwangyang): 24h – **3)** Daejeon 102.9MHz HLDT-FM 3kW: 24h – **4)** Daegu 103.9MHz HLDU-FM 3kW: 24h – **5)** Incheon 100.5MHz HLSU-FM 1kW: 24h – **6)** Gangwon(Wonju) 105.9MHz HLSV-FM 3kW: 24h, Gangwon(Chuncheon) 103.7MHz 3kW: 24h , Gangwon(Gangneung) 105.5MHz 3kW: 24h, Gangwon(Donghae) 95.3MHz 1kW: 24h – **7)** Jeonju 102.5MHz HLCM-FM 3kW: 24h – **8)** Ulsan 104.1MHz HLCV-FM 1kW: 24h+ low power relay stns– **9)** Changwon 95.5MHz HLEE-FM 1kW: 24h, Changwon(Jinju) 100.1MHz 1kW: 24h – **10)** Gyeongbuk(Gyeongju) 103.5MHz HLEF-FM 1kW: 24h, Gyeongbuk(Uljin) 103.7MHz 1kW: 24h – **11)** Jeju 105.5MHz HLEH-FM 1kW, 105.9MHz 1kW(rel. st. in Seogwipo): 24h + low power rel. stns.
**Addresses & other information:**
**1)** 68, Yongso-ro, Nam-gu, Busan 48501 ☎ +82 51 6105 114 **Ann:** "FM Gusib-sa-jeom-gu(94.9)MHz, Busan Gyotong Bangsong-imnida. HLDN-FM" – **2)** 40, Cheomdanjungang-ro 182-gil, Gwangsan-gu, Gwangju 62274 ☎ +82 62 9701 114 **Ann:** "FM Gusib-chil-jeom-sam(97.3)MHz, Gwangju Gyotong Bangsong-imnida. HLDM" – **3)** 17, Singalma-ro, Seo-gu, Daejeon 35280 ☎ +82 42 6001 114 **Ann:** "FM Baeg-i-jeom-gu(102.9)MHz, Dallineun Radio Daejeon Gyotong Bangsong-imnida." – **4)** 120, Hyeonchug-ro, Nam-gu, Daegu 42420 ☎ +82 53 6060 114 **Ann:** "FM Baek-sam-jeom-gu(103.9)MHz, Daegu Gyotong Bangsong-imnida. HLDU-FM" – **5)** 251, Maesohol-ro, Nam-gu, Incheon 22201 ☎ +82 32 4531 114 **Ann:** "FM Baek-jeom-o(100.5) MHz, TBN Incheon Gyotong Bangsong-imnida. HLSU" – **6)** 183, Dongbusunhwan-ro, Wonju-si, Gangwon-do 26457 ☎ +82 33 7490 114 **Ann:** "Haengbogui Giljabi, Ggumi Inneun Bangsong, FM Baeg-

o-jeom-gu(105.9)MHz, Gangwon Gyotong Bangsong-imnida." – **7)** 1097-10, Jeogyeorip-ro, Deokjin-gu, Jeonju 54859 ☎ +82 63 2593 114 **Ann:** "FM Baeg-i-jeom-chil(102.7)MHz, TBN Jeonju Gyotong Bangsong-imnida. HLCM" – **8)** 11, Hamwol 7-gil, Jung-gu, Ulsan 44426. ☎ +82 52 290 8514 **Ann:** "FM Baeg-sa-jeom-il(104.1) MHz, TBN Ulsan Gyotong Bangsong-imnida. HLCV" – **9)** 82-4, Changwoncheon-ro 94-gil, Uichang-gu, Changwon-si 51409. ☎ +82 55 272 6114 **Ann:** "FM Gusib-o-jeom-o(95.5)MHz, Changwon Gyotong Bangsong-imnida. HLEE" – **10)** 95, Samheung-ro, Buk-gu, Pohang-si 37613. ☎ +82 54 240 6214 **Ann:** "FM Baek-sam-jeom-o(103.5) MHz, TBN Gyeongbuk Gyotong Bangsong-imnida. HLEF" – **11)** 17, Gwandeok-ro 11-gil, Jeju-si, Jeju 63277 ☎ +82 64 717 8114 **Ann:** "FM Baeg-o-jeom-o(105.5)MHz, TBN Jeju Gyotong Bangsong-imnida. HLEH"

## KOREA NEW NETWORK CORP. (KNN)
🖃 30, Senteomseo-ro, Haeundae-gu, Busan 48058 ☎ +82 51 850 9000 **W:** knn.co.kr **Station:** HLDG-FM(Power FM) 99.9MHz 3kW, 102.5MHz 1kw(rel. stn in Changwon), 105.5MHz 1kW(rel. stn in Jinju): 24h, HLDG-SFM(Love FM) 105.7MHz 1kW: 24h.
+low Power rel. stns
**Ann:** "Busan Guship-gu-jeom-gu(99.9), Gijang Yangsan Gusim-nyuk-jeom-sam(96.3), Changwon Baeg-i-jeom-o(102.5), Jinju Baeg-o-jeom-o(105.5), jeulgeoumeul cheongchwijawa hamgge mandeuneun KNN Power FM-imnida.", "Busan Baeg-o-jeom-chil(105.7)MHz. Saranghamyeom jeulgeopseumnida, saranghamyeon haengbokhamnida. Hamgge hamyeom deouk keojineun sarang. Love FM-imnida."

## TAEGU BROADCASTING CORPORATION (TBC)
**(Daegu Bangsong)**
🖃 23, Dongdaegu-ro, Susong-gu, Daegu 42175 ☎ +82 53 760 1900 **W:** tbc.co.kr **Station:** HLDE-FM(Dream FM) 99.3MHz 5kW: 24h. Relay stn: Pohang 99.7MHz 1kW, Andong 106.5MHz 0.5kW. **Ann:** "HLDE-FM TBC Dream FM-imnida"

## KWANGJU BROADCASTING CO., LTD. (KBC) (Gwangju Bangsong)
🖃 87, Jungang-ro, Nam-gu, Gwangju 61637 ☎ +82 62 650 3114 **W:** ikbc.co.kr **Station:** HLDH-FM(MY FM) 101.1MHz 5kW: 24h. Relay stn: Yeosu 96.7MHz 1kW. **Ann:** "HLDH, FM 101.1MHz, 96.7MHz, Yeollin Sesang, Joheun Chingu, KBC MY FM"

## TAEJON BROADCASTING CO., LTD. (TJB)
**(Daejeon Bangsong)**
🖃 131, EXPO-ro, Yuseong-gu, Daejeon 34125 ☎ +82 42 281 1101 **W:** tjb.co.kr **Station:** HLDF-FM(Power FM) 95.7MHz 5kW: 24h Relay stn: Seosan 96.5MHz 0.5kW. **Ann:** "Gusib-o-jeom-chil(95.7), Gusim-nyuk-jeom-o(96.5)MHz, TJB Power FM-imnida. HLDF"

## JEONJU TELEVISION CORPORATION (JTV)
**(Jeonju Bangsong)**
🖃 1083, Jeongyeorip-ro, Deokjin-gu, Jeonju-si, Jeollabuk-do 54859 ☎ +82 63 250 5200 **W:** jtv.co.kr **Station:** HLDQ-FM(Magic FM) 90.1MHz 5kW: 24h **Ann:** "FM Gusib-jeom-il(90.1)MHz, JTV Magic FM-imnida. HLDQ"

## CHEONGJU BROADCASTING CORPORATION (CJB)
**(Cheongju Bangsong)**
🖃 59-1, Saun-ro, Seowon-gu, Cheongju-si, Chungcheongbuk-do 28654 ☎ +82 43 265 7000 **W:** cjb.co.kr **Station:** HLDI-FM(Joy FM) 101.5MHz 5kW, 97.9MHz 2kW(rel. stn in Eumseong): 24h
**Ann:** "FM Baeg-il-jeom-o(101.5)MHz, CJB Joy FM-imnida. HLDI"

## ULSAN BROADCASTING CORPORATION (UBC)
**(Ulsan Bangsong)**
🖃 41, Gugyo-ro, Jung-gu, Ulsan 44520 ☎ +82 52 228 6000 **W:** ubc.co.kr **Station:** HLDP-FM(Green FM) 92.3MHz 3kW: 24h **Ann:** "Gusib-i-jeom-sam(92.3)MHz, UBC Green FM Bangsong-imnida. HLDP"

## JEJU FREE INTERNATIONAL CITY BROADCASTING SYSTEM (JIBS) (Jeju Gukje Jayu Dosi Bangsong)
🖃 95, Yeonsam-ro, Jeju-si, Jeju Teukbyeol Jachido 63148 ☎ +82 64 740 7800 **W:** jibstv.com **Station:** HLQC-FM(Power FM) 101.5MHz 3kW: 24h. Relay stn: Seogwipo 98.5MHz 1kW
**Ann:** "JIBS New Power FM Bangsong-imnida"

## GANGWON NO.1 BROADCASTING CO., LTD (G1)
**(Gangwon Minbang)**
🖃 274, Soyanggang-ro, Dong-myeon, Chuncheon-si, Gangwon-do 24210 ☎ +82 33 248 5000 **W:** g1tv.co.kr **Station:** HLCG-FM(Fresh FM) 105.1MHz 3kW: 24h. Relay stn: Gangneung 106.1MHz 1kW, Wongju 103.1MHz 0.5kW +low Power rel. stns

**Ann:** "Wonju Baeg-sam-jeom-il(103.1), Chuncheon Baeg-o-jeom-il(105.1), Gangneung Baeng-ryuk-jeom-il(106.1), Taebaek Gusib-gu-jeom-sam(99.3)MHz, G1 Fresh FM, HLCG"

## KYONGGI BROADCASTING CO. (KFM) (Gyeonggi Bangsong)
🖃 111, Maeyeong-ro 345-gil, Yeongtong-gu, Suwon-si, Gyeonggi-do 16703 ☎ +82 31 210 0999 **W:** kfm.co.kr
**Station:** HLDS-FM 99.9MHz 5kW: 24h **Ann:** "FM Gusib-gu-jeom-gu(99.9) MHz, Gyeonggi Bangsong-imnida. HLDS"

## Kyung-In Broadcasting (Gyeong-in Bangsong)
🖃 7, Aam-daero 287beon-gil, Nam-gu, Incheon 22196 ☎ +82 32 830 1000 **W:** ifm.co.kr **Station:** HLDO-FM 90.7MHz 5kW: 24h **Ann:** "FM Gusib-jeom-chil(90.7)MHz, Gyeong-In Bangsong"

## YTN RADIO(YTN FM)
🖃 76, Sangamsan-ro, Mapo-gu, Seoul 03926 ☎ +82 2 398 8000 **W:** ytnfm.co.kr **Station:** HLQV-FM 94.5MHz 3kW: 24h **Ann:** "FM Gusib-sa-jeom-o(94.5)MHz, YTN FM-imnida. HLQV"

## WON-BUDDHISM BROADCASTING SYSTEM (WBS)
**(Woneum Bangsong)**
🖃 **1)** 75, Hyeonchung-ro, Dongjak-gu, Seoul 06904 ☎ +82 2 2102 7700 **W:** wbsfm.com – **2)** 10, Gwangbokjungang-ro 33beon-gil, Jung-gu, Busan 48947 ☎ +82 51 247 3844 – **3)** 501, Iksan-daero, Iksan-si, Jeollabuk-do 54536 ☎ +82 63 837 0979 – **4)** 31, Sangmuowol-ro Seo-gu, Gwanju 61966 – **5)** 42, Jungang-daero 66-gil, Jung-gu, Daegu 41961 ☎ +82 53 425 0983.
**Stations: 1)** Seoul HLQK-FM 89.7MHz 3kW: 24h – **2)** Busan HLQJ-FM 104.9MHz 3kW: 24h – **3)** Jeonbuk(Iksan) HLDV-FM 97.9MHz 3kW: 24h – **4)** Gwangju HLQN-FM 107.9MHz 1kW: 24h – **5)** Daegu HLCS-FM 98.3MHz 1kW: 24h.
**Ann: 1)** FM Palsip-gu-jeom-chil(89.7)MHz, WBS Woneum Bangsong-imnida. HLQK" – **2)** "FM Baek-sa-jeom-gu(104.9)MHz, WBS Busan Woneum Bangsong-imnida. HLQJ" – **3)** "FM Gusip-chil-jeom-gu(97.9) MHz, WBS Jeonbuk Woneum Bangsong-imnida. HLDV" – **4)** "FM Baek-chil-jeom-gu(107.9)MHz, WBS Gwangju Woneum Bangsong-imnida. HLQN" – **5)** "FM Gusip-pal-jeom-sam(98.3)MHz, WBS Daegu Woneum Bangsong-imnida. HLCS"

## KOREA INTERNATIONAL BROADCASTING FOUNDATION
**(Arirang Radio)**
🖃 Arirang Tower, 2351, Nambusunhwan-ro, Seocho-gu, Seoul 06713 ☎ +82 2 3475 5000 **W:** arirang.co.kr **Station:** Jeju HLSE-FM 88.7MHz 3kW: 24h in English. Relay stn: Seogwipo 88.1MHz 1kW. **Ann:** "You're listening to Arirang Radio"

## GFN FOUNDATION
🖃 17, Sajik-ro, Nam-gu, Gwangju 61640 ☎ +82 62 460 0987 **W:** gfn.or.kr **Station:** HLSY-FM 98.7MHz 1kW, 93.7MHz 1kW(rel. stn in Yeosu): 2000-1700 in English. **Ann:** "Listen more Feel more! GFN 98.7 FM"

## BUSAN e-FM
🖃 Centum venture town 4F, 41, Centum dong-ro, Haeundae-gu, Busan 48059 ☎ +82 51 861 8601 **W:** befm.or.kr **Station:** HLSX-FM 90.5MHz 1kW: 2000-1700 in English. **Ann:** "Now you're listening to Busan e-FM 90.5"

## KOREAN FORCES NETWORK (Friends FM) (Gukpang FM)
🖃 54-99, Duteopbawi-ro, Yongsan-gu, Seoul 04353 **W:** dema.mil.kr/web/fm.do **Stations: FM** (operated by KBS): Namsan HLSF-FM 96.7MHz 2kW, Hwaaksan 96.7MHz 5kW, Yongmunsan 101.1MHz 3kW, Gwaebangsan 92.5MHz 3kW , Jeju 94.1MHz 3kW + 8 lp stns
**D.Prgr:** 24h. Own prgrs 2100-1500, other times relay KBS R. One (HLKA). prgrs for soldiers. Also 0832-0856(Sun) via KBS R. One network. **Ann:** "Yuneunghan anbo teunteunhan gukpang, yeoreobun-ui gukpang FM-imnida"

## AMERICAN FORCES NETWORK KOREA (AFN)
🖃 As below ☎ +82 2 7914 6495/6 **W:** afnkorea.com

| MW & FM Stations | | kHz | kW | MHz | kW |
|---|---|---|---|---|---|
| 1) | Pyeongtaek/Camp Humphreys | +1440 | *5 | 88.3 | 3 |
| 2) | Daegu/Camp Walker | - | - | 88.5 | 1 |
| 3) | Busan/Camp Hialeah | - | - | 88.1 | 0.25 |
|  | Chuncheon/Camp Page | 1044 | 1 | 88.5 | 0.1 |
|  | Uijeongbu/Camp Red Cloud | 1161 | 0.25 | 88.5 | 0.25 |
| 4) | Dongducheon/Camp Casey | +1197 | 1 | 88.3 | 0.3 |
| 5) | Songtan/Osan Air Base | - | - | 88.5 | 0.05 |
| 6) | Seoul/Yongsan | - | - | 102.7 | 5 |

## MW & FM Stations

| | | kHz | kW | MHz | kW |
|---|---|---|---|---|---|
| 7) | Gunsan/Gunsan Air Base | 1440 | 1 | 88.5 | 0.25 |
| | Waegwan/Camp Carrol | 1440 | 5 | - | - |
| | Pohang/Camp Libby | 1512 | 0.25 | - | - |
| | Jinhae/Naval St. | 1512 | 0.25 | 88.5 | 0.05 |
| | Gwanju/Gwangju Air Base | | | 88.5 | 0.05 |

+= local prgrs 2005-0000 Mon-Fri; otherwise rel.1). *= **F.PI:** 10kW
**D.Prgr:** 24h (MW/FM sep. prgrs). **N.** on the h. Formal sign on at 1505
**Ann:** AM: "American Forces Network Korea", FM (Seoul): "This is Eagle FM"
**Addresses: 1)** Headquarters, American Forces Network Korea, Unit #15877. APO AP 96271-0543, USA ☎ +82 2 7914 6495. Commanding Officer: LTC Eric Badger – **2)** Unit #15029, APO AP 96218-0186, USA – **3)** Unit #15184. APO AP 96259-0274, USA – **4)** Unit #15116, APO AP 96224-0380, USA – **5)** Unit #2034. APO AP 96278-5000, USA – **6)** Unit #15324, APO AP 96205-0097, USA – **7)** Unit #2011, APO AP 96264-5000, USA

# KOSOVO

**L.T:** UTC +1h (31 Mar-27 Oct: +2h) — **Pop:** 1.7 million — **Pr.L:** Albanian, Serbian — **E.C:** 230V/50Hz — **ITU:** pending (**WRTH:** RKS)

## KOMISIONI I PAVARUR PËR MEDIA (KPM)
### (Independent Media Commission)
✉ Rr. Perandori Justinian nr. 14, Qyteza Pejton, 10000 Prishtinë ☎ +383 38 245031 🖷 +383 38 245034 **E:** info@kpm-ks.org **W:** kpm-ks.org **L.P:** Chmn: Muja Ferati

## RADIOTELEVIZIONI I KOSOVËS (RTK) (Pub)
✉ Rr. Xhemail Prishtina nr. 12, 10000 Prishtinë ☎+383 38 230102 **E:** post@rtklive.com **W:** rtklive.com **L.P:** Chmn: Ismet Bexheti

| MW | kHz | kW | Prgr | | | |
|---|---|---|---|---|---|---|
| Prishtinë | 549 | 1 | 1 | | | |

| FM (MHz) | | 1 | 2 kW | FM | 1 | 2 kW |
|---|---|---|---|---|---|---|
| Cërnusha | 87.6 | 91.5 | 0.4 | Prishtinë | 91.9 | 93.3 0.5 |
| Maja e Gjelbërt | 88.5 | 90.5 | 0.4 | Prishtinë II | - | 99.2 0.5 |
| Golesh | 95.7 | 97.7 | 3.5 | Zatriq | 88.9 | 92.4 0.5 |
| Leposaviq* | | 97.3 | 0.3 | *) KFOR Camp Nothing Hill | | |

**D.Prgr: Prgr 1 (R. Kosova 1):** 24h in Albanian. – **Prgr 2 (R. Kosova 2):** 0600-1300, 2000-2400 in Albanian; prgrs for ethnic minorities: 1300-1500 Serbian, 1500-1700 Turkish, 1700-1900 Bosnian, 1900-2000 Romany.

### OTHER STATIONS

| FM | MHz | kW | Location | Station |
|---|---|---|---|---|
| 23) | 88.1 | 1 | Podujevë | R. Vizioni |
| 24) | 88.6 | 1 | Prishtinë | Glam R. |
| 12) | 89.1 | 1 | Zubin Potok | R. Kolašin |
| 4) | 89.4 | 1 | Ljubinjë e Epërme | R. Astra |
| 25) | 90.2 | 2 | Golesh | R. K4 (Albanian) |
| 11) | 92.2 | 1 | Mitrovicë | R. Kiss |
| 6) | 92.6 | 1 | Ferizaj | R. Ferizaj |
| 2) | 92.7 | 1 | Maja e Gjelbërt | R. Djukagjini |
| 15) | 92.9 | 1 | Leposaviq | R. Mir |
| 3) | 94.0 | 1 | Kamenicë | R. 24 |
| 2) | 94.5 | 2.5 | Zariq | R. Djukagjini |
| 1) | 94.8 | 1 | Maja e Gjelbërt | Virgin R. |
| 19) | 94.9 | 1 | Mitrovicë | R. Ylberi |
| 9) | 95.4 | 1 | Kaçanik | R. Kaçaniku |
| A) | 96.2 | 1 | Prishtinë | RFE-RL/VOA relay |
| 18) | 96.4 | 1 | Dragash | R. Sharri |
| 20) | 96.4 | 1 | Gjilan | R. Star |
| 25) | 96.6 | 2 | Golesh | R. K4 (Serbian) |
| 22) | 97.9 | 1 | Gjilan | R. Victoria |
| 17) | 98.4 | 1 | Gjilan | R. Rinia |
| B) | 98.6 | 1 | Golesh | BBCWS relay |
| 10) | 98.8 | 1 | Kamenicë | R. Kamenica |
| 16) | 99.0 | 1 | Mitrovicë | R. Mitrovica |
| 2) | 99.7 | 30 | Golesh | R. Djukagjini |
| 8) | 100.3 | 1 | Leposaviq | R. Impuls |
| 5A) | 100.9 | 1 | Gjilan | R. Shqip FM |
| C) | 101.0 | 1 | Prishtinë | RFI relay |
| 13) | 101.9 | 1 | Mitrovicë | R. Kontakt Plus |
| 14) | 102.4 | 1 | Shillovë | R. Max |
| 1) | 102.8 | 30 | Golesh | Virgin R. |
| 5B) | 103.3 | 1 | Gjilan | R. Energji |
| 1) | 103.9 | 2.5 | Zatriq | Virgin R. |
| 7) | 104.1 | 1 | Viti | R. Iliria |
| 21) | 104.5 | 1 | Vushtrri | R. Vicianum |

+ txs below 1kW.

**Addresses & other information:**
**1)** Pallati i mediave, aneks II, 10000 Prishtinë. **E:** radio21@rtv21.tv – **2)** Rr. Ismail Qemajli nr. 7, 30000 Pejë – **3)** 70000 Lagjja Liria – **4)** 20000 Ljubinjë e Epërme. In Bosnian. – **5A,B)** Rr. "Abdullah Presheva" nr. 63, 60000 Gjilan – **6)** Rr. Dëshmoret e Kombit, 70000 Ferizaj – **7)** Rr. Hoxhë Jonuzi p.n., 61000 Viti – **8)** Rr. 24 Novembar p.n., 40000 Leposaviq. In Serbian. – **9)** Rr. Vellezerit Çaka p.n., 71000 Kaçanik – **10)** Shtëpia e Kultures, 62000 Kamenicë – **11)** Rr. Kralj Petar I p.n., 40000 Mitrovicë – **12)** Rr. Arsenija Carnojevica nr. 48, 40650 Zubin Potok. In Serbian. – **13)** Rr. Lole Ribara nr. 58, 40000 Mitrovicë – **14)** 60000 Shillovë. In Serbian. – **15)** Rr. Vojske Jugoslavije nr. 26, 40000 Leposaviq. In Serbian. – **16)** Sheshi Jasharaj, 40000 Mitrovicë – **17)** Rr. Skenderbeu nr. 13, 60000 Gjilan – **18)** Rr. "Rruga e Dëshmorve", 22000 Dragash – **19)** Sheshi Agim Hajrizi p.n., 40000 Mitrovicë – **20)** Rr. Lagja Dardania nr. 1, 60000 Gjilan – **21)** Rr. Faruk Beqiri p.n., 42000 Vushtrri – **22)** Rr. Dardania I nr. 12/9, 60000 Gjilan – **23)** Rr. Zahir Pajaziti p.n., 11000 Podujevë – **24)** Rr. Enver Zymberi nr. 5, 10000 Prishtinë – **25)** HQ KFOR, Film City, 10000 Prishtinë – **A)** Rel. RFE-RL & VOA (USA) – **B)** Rel. BBCWS (UK) – **C)** Rel. RFI (France)

# KUWAIT

**L.T:** UTC +3h — **Pop:** 4.1 million — **Pr.L:** Arabic — **E.C:** 50Hz, 240V — **ITU:** KWT

## MINISTRY OF INFORMATION
✉ P.O. Box 193, 13002 Safat ☎+965 22415301 🖷 +965 22434511

## RADIO OF THE STATE OF KUWAIT
✉ P.O. Box 967, 13010 Safat ☎+965 22436193 🖷 +965 22417830 **W:** media.gov.kw **E:** kwtfreq@media.gov.kw
**L.P:** Mr. Hani Al-Naqi, Dir. Freq. Mgmt.
**Stations: MW:** Magwa 630/963/1341kHz, Kabd 540/1134/1269kHz.
**FM:** Madinat-al-Kywait

| MW(kHz) | kW | Prgr. | Times |
|---|---|---|---|
| 540 | 600 | Main Arabic | 24h |
| 630 | 10 | Quran prgr. | 24h |
| 963 | 20 | Main Arabic | 1200-1600, 2100-0500 |
| | | Multilingual | 0500-1200, 1600-2100 |
| 1134 | 100 | Main Arabic | 24h |
| 1269 | 100 | Arab Music | 24h |
| 1341 | 100 | Quran prgr. | 2200-0400 |
| | | 2nd Arabic | 0400-2200 |

| FM(MHz) | kW | Prgr. | Times |
|---|---|---|---|
| 87.9/101.0 | 20 | Arab Music | 24h |
| 89.5/95.3 | 20 | Main Arabic | 24h |
| 88.4/93.9 | 20/10 | OFM | 24h |
| 92.5/96.3 | 10/5 | Easy FM | 24h |
| 93.3 | 5 | Multilingual | 0500-1800 |
| 94.9 | 5 | Folklore prgr. | 24h |
| 98.9/105.1 | 20 | Quran | 24h |
| 97.5 | 20 | Quran 22-04 & | 2nd Arabic 04-22 |
| 94.5 | 20 | 2nd Arabic | 0400-2200 |
| 99.7 | 20 | Super Station | 24h |
| 100.5 | 10 | TV sound (Prgr. 1) | 24h |
| 103.2/103.7 | 20 | Modern Arab Music | 24h |

**Main Arabic prgr:** 24h. **N:** 0300, 0500, 1000, 1700, 2100 – **2nd Arabic prgr:** 0400-2200 – **Arab Music prgr:** 24h – **Modern Arab Music prgr:** 24h – **Multilingual prgr:** English 0500-0800, 1800-2100, Persian 0800-1000, Filipino 1000-1200, Urdu 1600-1800 – **OFM** (youth prgr.): 24h – **Quran prgr:** 24h – **"Easy FM" in English:** 24h – **"FM Super Station"** in English: 24h. **N:** on the hour.
**Ann:** "Idha'at al-Dawlat Al Kuwait".

**Other stations:**
**Arabian Gulf R**, 91.5MHz.
**Kuwait Pulse,** 88.8MHz. **W:** fm888.info
**Marina FM,** 90.4MHz 5kW. **W:** marinafm.com
**U FM,** 98.4MHz. **W:** ufm4u.com
**Sowt al-Khaleej,** 102.4MHz 5kW. See Qatar for main entry.
**Sowt al-Rayan,** 102.0MHz. See Qatar for main entry.
**AFN:** Al-Jabber/Camp Doha 101.5/107.9MHz 50W/5kW.
**BBC World Sce:** Arabic 90.1MHz, English 100.1MHz, both 5kW.
**Monte Carlo Doualiya:** 107.4MHz 2kW. **RFI:** 107.0MHz 2kW.
**R. Sawa:** 1548kHz 600kW, 1593kHz 150kW, 95.7MHz 5kW, all 24h.
**Voice of America:** 96.9MHz 5kW

# KYRGYZSTAN

**L.T:** UTC +6h — **Pop:** 6.1 million — **Pr.L:** Kyrgyz, Russian, Uzbek — **E.C:** 220V/50Hz — **ITU:** KGZ

**MADANIYAT, MAALYMAT JANA TURIZM MINISTRILIGI**
**(Ministry of Culture, Information and Tourism)**
✉ Pushkin St. 78, 720040 Bishkek ☎ +996 312 620482 📠 +996 312 623589 **E:** minculture.kg@gmail.com **W:** minculture.gov.kg
**L.P:** Minister: Jumagulov Sultanbek
**NB.** The Ministry is responsible for issuing broadcasting licenses.

**KOOMDUK TELERADIOBERÜÜ KORPORATSIYASY**
**(KTRK) (Pub) (Public Broadcasting Corp.)**
✉ Jash Gvardiya blvd. 59, 720010 Bishkek ☎ +996 312 392059
**E:** public@ktrk.kg **W:** ktrk.kg **L.P:** DG: Ilim Karypbekov

| MW | kHz | kW | Prgr | MW | kHz | kW | Prgr |
|---|---|---|---|---|---|---|---|
| Bishkek (a) | 612 | 150 | 1 | Aydarken° | 1404 | 7 | 1 |
| Osh° | 693 | 40 | 1 | Dödömöl° | 1404 | 20 | 1 |
| Naryn° | 1404 | 7 | 1 | Orgochor° | 1404 | - | 1 |
| Cholponata° | 1404 | 1 | 1 | Jalalabat° | 1431 | 40 | 1 |

° Status uncertain

| SW | kHz | kW | Prgr | SW | kHz | kW | Prgr |
|---|---|---|---|---|---|---|---|
| Bishkek (a) | 4010 | 100 | 1 | Bishkek (a) | 4820 | 100 | 2 |

| FM (MHz) | 1 | 2 | 3 | FM (MHz) | 1 | 2 | 3 |
|---|---|---|---|---|---|---|---|
| Balykchy | 105.3 | - | - | Karakol | 102.4 | 106.0 | 100.6 |
| Batken | 104.2 | - | 102.2 | Naryn | 100.5 | 103.2 | 107.7 |
| Bishkek | 104.1 | 106.9 | 103.7 | Osh | 100.7 | - | - |
| Jalalabat | 104.7 | 105.9 | 106.3 | Talas | 102.0 | 107.6 | 105.7 |

+ translators (a) Krasnaya Rechka

**D.Prgr: Prgr 1 (Birinchi radio):** 0000-1800 in Kyrgyz, Russian; Rel. Dostuk radiosu: 0230-0330 (Sat), 0430-0700 (Sat), 0710-0900 (Sat), 1000-1200 (Sat), 1100-1200 (Sun), 1300-1400 (SS), 1500-1530 (SS) — **Prgr 2 (Kyrgyz radiosu):** 24h in Kyrgyz. – **Prgr 3 (Ming kyyal FM)** 24h in Kyrgyz. – **Prgr 4 (Dostuk radiosu):** 0000-1800 via DTT & web-casting (+ via Birinchi R. on weekends). For ethnic minorities in Kyrgyz, Dungan, Polish, Russian, Tatar, Turkish, Uighur, Ukrainian, Uzbek.

**OTHER STATIONS**

| FM | MHz | kW | Location | Station |
|---|---|---|---|---|
| A) | 66.26 | 17 | Karakol | R. Rossii relay |
| A) | 67.94 | 17 | Bishkek | R. Rossii relay |
| A) | 68.66 | 17 | Karaköl | R. Rossii relay |
| A) | 69.92 | 17 | Osh | R. Rossii relay |
| A) | 69.95 | 17 | Kazarman | R. Rossii relay |
| A) | 70.07 | 17 | Arstanbap | R. Rossii relay |
| A) | 70.40 | 17 | Sülüktü | R. Rossii relay |
| A) | 70.82 | 17 | Naryn | R. Rossii relay |
| A) | 72.20 | 17 | Jalalabat | R. Rossii relay |
| A) | 72.44 | 17 | Sülüktü | R. Rossii relay |
| 5) | 87.5 | 6.3 | Kumaryk | Kyrgyzstan Obondoru |
| 13) | 87.5 | 3 | Bishkek | R. Mir |
| 2A) | 87.6 | 3.2 | Chon-Döbö | Evropa Plus |
| 22) | 87.6 | 6.3 | Mayly-Suu | R. Kaskad |
| 9) | 87.7 | 1 | Isfana | R. Almaz |
| 5) | 87.9 | 16 | Balykchy | Kyrgyzstan Obondoru |
| B) | 88.0 | 3 | Bishkek | Vesti FM relay |
| 6A) | 88.1 | 1.6 | Talas | Manas FM |
| 14) | 88.3 | 6.3 | Karaköl | R. OK |
| 7) | 88.5 | 3 | Bishkek | Maral FM |
| 14) | 88.8 | 4 | Cholponata | R. OK |
| 15) | 89.0 | 4 | Bishkek | R. Rekord |
| C) | 89.3 | 2 | Karabalta | R. Sputnik relay |
| 2B) | 89.3 | 6.3 | Kumaryk | Retro FM |
| 2B) | 89.4 | 3.2 | Chon-Döbö | Retro FM |
| 12) | 89.6 | 3 | Bishkek | El FM |
| 2B) | 89.7 | 10 | Balykchy | Retro FM |
| 14) | 89.8 | 1.6 | Talas | R. OK |
| 8) | 90.2 | 1 | Bishkek | Parlament R. |
| 8) | 90.3 | 6.3 | Kumaryk | Parlament R. |
| 20) | 90.6 | 2 | Kara-Balta | Next FM |
| 13) | 90.8 | 1.6 | Talas | R. Mir |
| 6B) | 90.9 | 2 | Bishkek | Manas Zhanyrygy |
| 13) | 91.1 | 4 | Karakol | R. Mir |
| 2A) | 91.3 | 6.3 | Kumaryk | Evropa Plus |
| 8) | 91.5 | 1.6 | Balykchy | Parlament R. |
| 1) | 92.6 | 1 | Talas | Avtoradio |
| 8) | 92.6 | 1.6 | Karakol | Parlament R. |
| 5) | 93.3 | 1 | Naryn | Kyrgyzstan Obondoru |
| 6A) | 93.7 | 1 | Naryn | Manas FM |
| C) | 95.1 | 3.2 | Naryn | R. Sputnik relay |
| 7) | 95.3 | 1 | Osh | Maral FM |
| B) | 96.2 | 1.6 | Karakol | Vesti FM relay |
| 11) | 96.9 | 4 | Naryn | Sanjyra R. |
| 11) | 98.0 | 4 | Karakol | Sanjyra R. |
| 8) | 98.7 | 1 | Naryn | Parlament R. |
| 11) | 99.7 | 1 | Jalalabat | Sanjyra R. |

| FM | MHz | kW | Location | Station |
|---|---|---|---|---|
| 8) | 100.0 | 1.6 | Chon-Döbö | Parlament R. |
| 14) | 100.5 | 3 | Bishkek | R. OK |
| 25) | 100.5 | 1.6 | Talas | Radiomost |
| 1) | 100.9 | 3 | Bishkek | Avtoradio |
| 15) | 101.1 | 1 | Cholponata | R. Rekord |
| C) | 101.1 | 1.6 | Talas | R. Sputnik relay |
| 16) | 101.3 | 3 | Bishkek | Tumar FM |
| 3) | 101.4 | 1 | Karakol | Hit FM |
| 3) | 101.4 | 3 | Balykchy | Hit FM |
| 8) | 101.4 | 1.6 | Sülüktü | Parlament R. |
| C) | 101.4 | 1 | Bishkek | R. Sputnik relay |
| 2B) | 101.4 | 1.6 | Osh | Retro FM |
| 8) | 101.5 | 2 | Batken | Parlament R. |
| 2B) | 101.5 | 8 | Naryn | Retro FM |
| 2A) | 101.7 | 1 | Bishkek | Evropa Plus |
| 17) | 101.8 | 1.6 | Karakol | Radio LW |
| 9) | 102.0 | 1 | Jalalabat | R. Almaz |
| 9) | 102.0 | 1 | Kochkor | R. Almaz |
| 9) | 102.1 | 3 | Bishkek | R. Almaz |
| 10) | 102.5 | 3 | Bishkek | Pyramida FM |
| 20) | 102.6 | 2 | Talas | Next FM |
| 3) | 102.7 | 1.6 | Cholponata | Hit FM |
| 6A) | 102.9 | 1 | Bishkek | Manas FM |
| 12) | 102.9 | 1.6 | Nookat | El FM |
| 16) | 103.2 | 1.6 | Cholponata | Tumar FM |
| 16) | 103.2 | 2 | Osh | Tumar FM |
| 11) | 103.3 | 3 | Bishkek | Sanjyra R. |
| 5) | 104.3 | 1.6 | Batken | Kyrgyzstan Obondoru |
| 11) | 104.4 | 1.6 | Talas | Sanjyra R. |
| 2B) | 104.5 | 4 | Bishkek | Retro FM |
| 4) | 104.6 | 20 | Sülüktü | Jash FM |
| 7) | 105.0 | 1.6 | Batken | Maral FM |
| 8) | 105.0 | 3 | Osh | Parlament R. |
| C) | 105.0 | 1 | Bishkek | R. Sputnik relay |
| 11) | 105.3 | 1 | Kara-Balta | Sanjyra R. |
| 11) | 105.3 | 2 | Batken | Sanjyra R. |
| 7) | 105.5 | 1.6 | Karakol | Maral FM |
| 9) | 105.5 | 3 | Naryn | R. Almaz |
| 3) | 105.6 | 1 | Bishkek | Hit FM |
| 11) | 105.6 | 1.6 | Osh | Sanjyra R. |
| 4) | 105.8 | 1.6 | Özgen | Jash FM |
| 4) | 105.8 | 2.5 | Gülchö | Jash FM |
| 8) | 105.9 | 1 | Kochkor | Parlament R. |
| 18) | 106.0 | 4 | Bishkek | Atom FM |
| 7) | 106.1 | 1.6 | Talas | Maral FM |
| 21) | 106.1 | 3 | Osh | Yntymak R. |
| 7) | 106.3 | 1.6 | Naryn | Maral FM |
| 24) | 106.4 | 2 | Batken | R. Salam |
| 5) | 106.5 | 1 | Bishkek | Kyrgyzstan Obondoru |
| 5) | 106.5 | 4 | Osh | Kyrgyzstan Obondoru |
| 2A) | 106.7 | 8 | Naryn | Evropa Plus |
| 9) | 106.8 | 1.6 | Cholponata | R. Almaz |
| 2A) | 107.1 | 1 | Balykchy | Evropa Plus |
| 19) | 107.4 | 2 | Bishkek | Ekho Moskvy |
| 26) | 107.5 | 1.6 | Cholponata | Volna Issykkulya |
| 8) | 107.7 | 1 | Kara-Kulja | Parlament R. |
| 12) | 107.7 | 2 | Osh | El FM |
| 11) | 107.7 | 3 | Jalalabat | Sanjyra R. |
| 23) | 107.8 | 1 | Bishkek | R. Romantika |
| 11) | 107.9 | 1.6 | Cholponata | Sanjyra R. |

+ txs below 1kW.

**Addresses & other information:**
**1)** Akhunbaev k. 119a, 720000 Bishkek – **2A,B)** Shabdan Baatyra k. 4b, 720000 Bishkek **E:** 2A) office@europa.kg, 2B) info@retrofm.ru – **3)** pr. Chuy 36, 720000 Bishkek **E:** advert@hitfm.kg – **4)** Akhunbaev k. 129, 720000 Bishkek **E:** office.jashfm@gmail.com – **5)** Shabdan Baatyra k. 4b, 720000 Bishkek **E:** radio@obondoru.kg – **6A,B)** 720000 Bishkek **E:** info@mediamanas.kg – **7)** Frunze k. 387, 720000 Bishkek **E:** info.maralfm@gmail.com – **8)** 720000 Bishkek – **9)** Chuykov k. 133a, 720000 Bishkek **E:** almazradio@gmail.com – **10)** Jantosheva k. 70, 720000 Bishkek – **11)** Tokumbaev k. 46a, 720000 Bishkek – **12)** Lenin k. 330, 723500 Osh **E:** elfm@gmail.com – **13)** Abdrakhmanov k. 170, 720000 Bishkek – **14)** Shabdan Baatyra k. 6, 720000 Bishkek **E:** okradio@elcat.kg – **15)** 720000 Bishkek **E:** office@mixmedia.kg – **16)** Jantoshev k. 70, 720000 Bishkek **E:** info@tumar.fm – **17)** 1 may k. 61, 722360 Karakol – **18)** Abdrakhmanov k. 192, 720000 Bishkek **E:** atomfm@gmail.com – **19)** 720000 Bishkek – **20)** Sataev k. 52/67, 722720 Talas – **21)** Nurmatov k. 3, 4-kabat, 723500 Osh **E:** yntymakunalgysy@gmail.com – **22)** 721600 Toktogul – **23)** Akhunbaev k. 119a, 720000 Bishkek **E:** romantika.bishkek@gmail.com – **24)** 8 Mart k, 25, 715100 Batken – **25)** 59-kvartal, 8-uy, 1-batir, 722720 Talas – **26)** 18 mkr Voskhod 66, 722200 Karakol – **A)** Rel. R. Rossii (Russia) – **B)** Rel. Vesti FM (Russia) – **C)** Rel. R. Sputnik (Russia).

**Radio via DTT:** see National TV section.

**Int. relays on MW:** (Tx operated by Kyrgyztelecom on behalf of TWR) Bishkek (Krasnaya Rechka) 1287kHz 150kW (F.pl), 1467kHz 500kW. See Int. Radio section

## LAOS

**L.T**: UTC +7h — **Pop:** 7.2 million — **Pr.L:** Lao (Lao Soung, Lao Theung dialects), Hmong, Khmu — **E.C:** 50Hz, 230V — **ITU:** LAO

### MINISTRY OF INFORMATION, CULTURE AND TOURISM
✉ Setthathilath Rd, Vientiane ☎ +856 21 212411 🖷 +856 21 212408 **L.P:** Minister: Bosengkham Vongdara

### LAO NATIONAL RADIO – LNR (Gov.)
✉ PO Box 310, Vientiane; Phaynam Rd, Ban Sisakhet, Chantabouly District, Vientiane ☎ +856 21 243250 🖷 +856 21 212430 **W:** lnr.org. la **L.P:** DG: Mr Phosy Keomanivong
**City and Provincial sces:** These are operated by the local governments + Sisavangvong Rd, Ban Pakhame, Luang Prabang – Km 2 Route 13 South, Oudomsavane Village, Pakse, Champassak Province - Manthatulat Road, Vientiane – Houamouangtai Village, Savannakhet, Khantabouly – Nongbouakham Village, Tha Khek, Khammouane

| MW | kHz | kW | S | H of tr |
|---|---|---|---|---|
| Vientiane* | 567 | 200 | N | 2200-0800, 0900-1630 |
| Khantabouly, Sa | 585 | 20 | P | 2230-1300 |
| Luang Prabang | 705 | 10 | P | 2200-0800, 1025-1500 |
| SW | kHz | kW | S | H of tr |
| Vientiane | 6130 | 50 | N | 2200-0800, 0900-1630 |

**S**=Sce, N=National, P=Provincial, Sa=Savannakhet prov.
*) Tx loc.: Kilometre 49 (GC: 18N20 102E27)
Reg. stns generally rel. national news at 0000, 0500, 1200
**National Sce in Lao:** 2300-0600, 0900-1330; **Hmong:** 2200-2230, 0600-0700, **Khmu:** 2230-2300, 0700-0800; **Foreign Language Sce in Chinese:** 1400-1430; **English:** 1430-1500; **French:** 1500-1530; **Khmer:** 1330-1400; **Thai:** 1530-1600; **Vietnamese:** 1600-1630; **N:** 2300, 0000, 0500, 0800, 1200
**Ann:** LNR: 'Thini Sathani Vitthayou Krachaisiang Hengsat'
**IS:** Music on Khéne (mouth organ) & Solo (bamboo instrument)

**LNR FM** (MHz): Vientiane FM 103.7 20kW: 2300-1600 – Happy Radio 97.3 20kW: 2300-1700 – Climax Radio 95.0: 2300-1700 – Butterfly Radio 94.3: 2300-1330, Foreign Language Sce 94.3 1330-1630 (as 567 & 6130kHz)
**Vientiane City FM** (MHz): Vientiane 105.5 1kW: 2330-1700 – Vientiane 98.8 10kW
**Provincial FM** (MHz): Attapeu: 95.0 10kW – Paksan, Bolikhamsay Prov: 101.5 5kW – Houai Xay, Bokeo Prov: 102.75 1kW – Khantabouly, S: 100.75 1kW Luang – Namtha Prov: 98.0 1kW Luang Prabang: 103.5MHz 0.3kW. Muang Hay, Oudomxay Prov: 100MHz 0.1kW – Pakse, Champassak Prov: 103.7 1kW – Phonsavan, Xieng Khuang Prov: 97.5 5kW – Phongsali Prov: 102 0.1kW – Sam Neua, Houa Phan Prov: 102.0 10kW – Saravane: 101.2 0.3kW – Saiyabouly: 96.5 5kW – Saysomboun Special Reg.: 100 5kW – Sekong: 102.7 1kW – Siphandon, Champassak Prov: 97.3 0.33kW – Tha Khek, Khammouane Prov: 95.5 0.1kW

### LAO YOUTH RADIO STATION
**Lao People's Revolutionary Youth Union**
✉ Phonthan Village, Xaysetha District, Vientiane
**FM:** Vientiane 90.0MHz 2.5kW.

### LAO PEOPLE'S ARMY BROADCASTING (Mil.)
✉ Phonkheng Village, Vientiane
**FM:** Vientiane 99.7MHz 10kW. Rel. on 99.7MHz: Attapeu, Bolikhamsay, Houai Xay, Houai Xe, Luang Prabang, Nam Bak, Pak Lay, Paksan, Pakse, Paksong, Phonsavan, Saiyabouly, Saravane, Savannakhet, Sekong, Siphandon, Tha Khek, Viengxay.

### PUBLIC SECURITY RADIO STATION (Gov.)
✉ Public Security Ministry, Sengsavang Village, Saysettha District, Vientiane
**FM:** Vientiane 101.5MHz 10kW

### OTHER STATIONS:
**China R. International:** Vientiane 93.0MHz 10kW D.Prgr: 0300-1530 rel. CRI from Beijing in Chinese, English & Lao

**R. France Internationale:** Vientiane 100.5 MHz 5kW D.Prgr: 24h rel. RFI from Paris in French

## LATVIA

**L.T:** UTC +2h (31 Mar-27 Oct: +3h) — **Pop:** 1.9 million — **Pr.L:** Latvian, Russian — **E.C:** 230V/50Hz — **ITU:** LVA

### NACIONALA ELEKTRONISKO PLAŠSAZINAS LIDZEKLU PADOME (NEPLP)
**(National Council for Electronic Media)**
✉ Doma laukums 8A, LV-1939 Riga ☎ +371 67221848 🖷 +371 67220448 **E:** neplpadome@neplpadome.lv **W:** neplpadome.lv
**L.P:** Chair: Dace Kezbere

### LATVIJAS RADIO (Pub)
✉ Doma laukums 8, LV-1505 Riga ☎ +371 67206722 **E:** radio@latvijasradio.lv **W:** latvijasradio.lsm.lv **L.P:** Chair: Una Klapkalne

| FM (MHz) | 1 | 2 | 3 | 4 | 5 | 6 | kW |
|---|---|---|---|---|---|---|---|
| Aluksne | 106.8 | 104.3 | - | 100.5 | - | - | 3.5 |
| Cesvaine | 102.5 | 105.0 | 103.5 | - | - | - | 2x20/4.5 |
| Dagda | 102.6* | 98.6 | - | 99.1 | - | - | 1.7/1/0.9 |
| Daugavpils | 90.6* | 100.7 | 88.1 | 88.7 | 104.0 | - | 4/7.9/1.3/6.3/3.2 |
| Dundaga | 91.1 | 106.7 | - | - | - | - | 4 |
| Kuldiga | 95.9 | 101.3 | 92.0 | - | - | - | 10/16.6/3.3 |
| Lielauce | 99.6 | - | - | - | - | - | 1 |
| Liepaja | 107.1 | 101.0 | 104.6 | 97.9 | 102.1 | - | 2x12.6/3.2/6.3/0.2 |
| Limbaži | 105.5 | - | - | - | - | - | 5.6 |
| Male | 100.3 | - | - | - | - | - | 1 |
| Piedruja | 87.6* | - | - | 94.5 | - | - | 1.6 |
| Rezekne | 107.5* | 101.0 | 101.8 | 104.2 | 103.8 | - | 2x20/5/20/0.4 |
| Riga | 90.7 | 91.5 | 103.7 | 107.7 | 93.1 | 95.8 | 2x35/9.5/6.6/8.9/0.7 |
| Valmiera | 104.0 | 101.5 | 87.6 | - | 89.5 | - | 2x20/2x2.4 |
| Ventspils | 99.2 | 103.0 | 89.8 | 95.3 | 96.5 | - | 3x0.3/1/0.2 |
| Viesite | 107.6 | 104.7 | 102.2 | 91.1 | - | - | 3x5/1.6 |
| Vilaka | - | - | 100.0 | - | - | - | 1.7 |

*) Incl. reg prgrs (see below)
**D.Prgr: Prgr 1 (Latvijas R.1):** 24h – **Prgr 2 (Latvijas R.2):** 24h – **Prgr 3 (Latvijas R.3 - Klasika):** 24h – **Prgr 4 (Latvijas R.4 - Doma laukums)** for ethnic minorities: 24h in Russian (exc. Mon-Wed 1810-1900 for other ethnic communities, rotating each day/week: Armenian, Belarusian, Estonian, Georgian, German, Lithuanian, Polish, Russian for the Jewish community, Russian for the Old Believers community, Tatar, Ukrainian). – **Prgr 5 (Latvijas R.5 - Pieci.lv):** 24h – **Prgr 6 (Latvijas R.6 - NABA):** 24h. This outlet provides a relay of the Latvijas Universitate student webradio station R. NABA (✉Aspazijas blvd. 5, LV-1050 Riga **E:** naba@radionaba.lv), and live broadcasts from parliament (Saeima). – **Regional prgr:** LR Latgales studija, Atbrivošanas aleja 90, LV-4601 Rezekne. On FM (see main tx table) in Latvian/Latgalian/Russian: MF 1305-1400.

### OTHER STATIONS

| MW | kHz | kW | Location | Station |
|---|---|---|---|---|
| 20A) | 1485 | 1.25 | Riga | R. Merkurs |
| 20B) | 1602 | 1 | Riga | R. Centrs # |
| **FM** | **MHz** | **kW** | **Location** | **Station** |
| 3C) | 87.7 | 1.6 | Liepaja | EHR Russkie Hity |
| 1B) | 87.9 | 1 | Ventspils | R. SWH+ |
| 2) | 87.9 | 2.5 | Madona | Star FM |
| 3A) | 88.4 | 1 | Gulbene | EHR |
| 9) | 88.4 | 1.3 | Liepaja | Kurzemes R. |
| 4C) | 88.6 | 1 | Riga | R. 88.6 FM |
| 2) | 89.1 | 2.5 | Selpils | Star FM |
| 1C) | 89.2 | 4 | Riga | R. SWH Rock |
| 1A) | 89.3 | 1 | Dundaga | R. SWH |
| 18) | 89.5 | 1.1 | Aizpute | R. Tev |
| 19) | 90.1 | 3.2 | Daugavpils | Divu Krastu R. |
| 3B) | 90.3 | 1 | Matiši | EHR Superhits |
| 18) | 90.4 | 2.2 | Kuldiga | R. Tev |
| 5) | 90.8 | 1 | Ventspils | Kristigais R. |
| 3B) | 90.9 | 3 | Madona | EHR Superhits |
| 2) | 91.0 | 1.9 | Liepaja | Star FM |
| 2) | 91.9 | 1.5 | Rezekne | Star FM |
| 8) | 91.9 | 2 | Iecava | Top R. |
| 2) | 92.0 | 1 | Vilkene | Star FM |
| 12A) | 92.3 | 1 | Liepaja | Retro FM |
| 8) | 92.4 | 1 | Daugavpils | Top R. |
| 9) | 92.4 | 1.3 | Tukums | Kurzemes R. |
| 3A) | 92.9 | 2 | Daugavpils | EHR |
| 16) | 93.5 | 2.2 | Liepaja | XOfm |
| 4D) | 93.9 | 2.8 | Riga | Baltkom R. |

| FM | MHz | kW | Location | Station |
|---|---|---|---|---|
| 1B) | 94.0 | 1 | Valka | R. Tev |
| 1B) | 94.0 | 1 | Valka | R. Tev |
| 1C) | 94.1 | 1.1 | Jekabpils | R. SWH Rock |
| 3B) | 94.3 | 1.6 | Talsi | EHR Superhits |
| 6B) | 94.6 | 1 | Valka | R. Skonto Vidzeme |
| 1A) | 94.7 | 1 | Broceni | R. SWH |
| 7) | 94.9 | 1.3 | Riga | Capital FM |
| 1B) | 95.0 | 2.5 | Dundaga | R. Tev |
| 17) | 95.2 | 6.3 | Daugavpils | Latgales R. |
| 3B) | 95.2 | 1.6 | Liepaja | EHR Superhits |
| 8) | 95.4 | 1 | Riteri | Top R. |
| 17) | 95.8 | 1 | Jekabpils | Latgales R. |
| 7) | 95.9 | 1 | Valmiera | Capital FM |
| 12B) | 96.1 | 2.1 | Kraslava | Russkoe Retro |
| 3A) | 96.1 | 1.6 | Liepaja | EHR |
| 3C) | 96.2 | 2 | Riga | EHR Russkie Hity |
| 3B) | 96.8 | 1 | Riga | EHR Superhits |
| 6B) | 97.0 | 1 | Valmiera | R. Skonto Vidzeme |
| 10) | 97.3 | 2.6 | Riga | R. Marija Latvija |
| 6A) | 97.5 | 3.2 | Liepaja | R. Skonto Kurzeme |
| 2) | 97.7 | 1.1 | Pure | Star FM |
| 8) | 97.7 | 1 | Livani | Top R. |
| 1B) | 98.1 | 1 | Valmiera | R. Tev |
| 8) | 98.3 | 2.3 | Riga | Top R. |
| 5) | 98.5 | 3.3 | Kuldiga | Kristigais R. |
| 1C) | 98.8 | 7.2 | Valmiera | R. SWH Rock |
| 13) | 99.0 | 1 | Jurmala | R. Jurmala |
| 12A) | 99.4 | 1.6 | Daugavpils | Retro FM |
| 17) | 99.5 | 2 | Balvi | Latgales R. |
| 4B) | 99.5 | 2.8 | Riga | Lounge FM |
| 6B) | 99.8 | 2 | Cesvaine | R. Skonto Vidzeme |
| 5) | 99.9 | 2 | Daugavpils | Kristigais R. |
| 15) | 100.0 | 2.5 | Riga | R. PIK |
| 1A) | 100.1 | 1.9 | Kuldiga | R. SWH |
| 6A) | 100.5 | 1 | Ventspils | R. Skonto Kurzeme |
| A) | 100.5 | 1.3 | Riga | BBCWS relay |
| 5) | 100.6 | 1.6 | Liepaja | Kristigais R. |
| 3A) | 100.8 | 1 | Talsi | EHR |
| 8) | 100.9 | 1 | Cesis | Top R. |
| 16) | 101.0 | 2.6 | Riga | XOfm |
| 1A) | 101.2 | 4.5 | Jekabpils | R. SWH |
| 5) | 101.3 | 1.1 | Kraslava | Kristigais R. |
| 14) | 101.6 | 3.2 | Daugavpils | Alise Plus |
| 5) | 101.8 | 5.6 | Riga | Kristigais R. |
| 3A) | 101.9 | 1 | Ventspils | EHR |
| 2) | 102.0 | 2.3 | Broceni | Star FM |
| 1A) | 102.2 | 4 | Talsi | R. SWH |
| 4A) | 102.7 | 2.8 | Riga | Mix FM |
| 5) | 102.8 | 1 | Jekabpils | Kristigais R. |
| 17) | 103.0 | 1.8 | Rezekne | Latgales R. |
| 2) | 103.2 | 5 | Svente | Star FM |
| 3B) | 103.2 | 1 | Kuldiga | EHR Superhits |
| 2) | 103.8 | 1.3 | Kuldiga | Star FM |
| 3A) | 104.3 | 4.8 | Riga | EHR |
| 16) | 104.7 | 1.1 | Cesis | XOfm |
| 2) | 105.0 | 1.6 | Pope | Star FM |
| 5) | 105.1 | 5 | Liepaja | R. SWH |
| 11) | 105.1 | 1.3 | Rezekne | R. Rezekne |
| 1A) | 105.2 | 3.6 | Daugavpils | R. SWH |
| 1A) | 105.2 | 13.2 | Riga | R. SWH |
| 1A) | 105.4 | 1.3 | Ventspils | R. SWH |
| 12A) | 105.5 | 2 | Rezekne | Retro FM |
| 1B) | 105.7 | 4.1 | Riga | R. SWH+ |
| 5) | 105.9 | 3.5 | Cesvaine | Kristigais R. |
| 6B) | 106.1 | 3.5 | Daugavpils | R. Skonto Vidzeme |
| 2) | 106.2 | 6.3 | Riga | Star FM |
| 9) | 106.4 | 11.5 | Kuldiga | Kurzemes R. |
| 1A) | 106.5 | 4 | Rezekne | R. SWH |
| 1A) | 106.5 | 1 | Valmiera | R. SWH |
| 2) | 106.6 | 1 | Bauska | Star FM |
| 1B) | 107.2 | 6.3 | Daugavpils | R. SWH+ |
| 6) | 107.2 | 4 | Riga | R. Skonto |
| 2) | 107.4 | 2 | Valmiera | Star FM |
| 3A) | 107.4 | 1.3 | Kuldiga | EHR |
| 8) | 107.6 | 1.6 | Liepaja | Top R. |
| 1A) | 107.9 | 5 | Cesvaine | R. SWH |
| 9) | 107.9 | 1 | Ventspils | Kurzemes R. |

+ txs below 1kW. #) Planned start: early 2019

**Addresses & other information:**
**A-C)** Ganibu dambis 24D, LV-1013 Riga. 1B) in Russian – **2)** Dzelzavas iela 120G, LV-1021 Riga – **3A-C)** Elijas iela 17, LV-1050 Riga. 3C) In Russian – **4A-D)** Kr.Valdemara iela 8, LV-1010 Riga. In Russian – **5)** Lacplesa iela 37, LV-1011 Riga – **6)** Kr.Valdemara iela

100, LV-1013 Riga. Reg. stns: **6A)** Graudu iela 27/29, LV-3401 Liepaja; **6B)** Rigas iela 13, LV-4201 Valmiera – **7)** L.Nometnu iela 62, LV-1002 Riga – **8)** Terbatas iela 83B, LV-1001 Riga. In Russian – **9)** Pilsetas laukums 4, LV-3301 Kuldiga – **10)** Ojara Vaciesa iela 6, LV-1004 Riga – **11)** Atbrivosanas aleja 108-1, LV-4601 Rezekne. In Russian – **12A,B)** Kr.Valdemara iela 76, LV-1013 Riga. In Russian. – **13)** Brivibas bulv. 30-6, LV-1050 Riga. In Russian – **14)** Raina iela 28, LV-5401 Daugavpils. In Russian. – **15)** Brivibas bulv. 30, LV-1050 Riga. In Russian – **16)** K.Valdemar iela 76-1A, LV-1013 Riga – **17)** Latgales iela 82, LV-4601 Rezekne. Partly in Latgalian – **18)** Kr.Valdemara iela 100, LV-1013 Riga – **19)** Atbrivosanas aleja 98, LV-4601 Rezekne – **20A,B)** P.O.Box 371, LV-1010 Riga **E:** rni@apollo.lv; 20B) in Russian – **A)** Rel. BBCWS (UK)

## LEBANON

**LT:** UTC +2h (31 Mar–27 Oct: +3h) — **Pop:** 6 million — **Pr.L:** Arabic, French, English, Armenian — **E.C:** 50Hz, 230V — **ITU:** LBN

**MINISTRY OF INFORMATION**
✉ Hamra, Beirut ☎ +961 1 754400 **W:** ministryinfo.gov.lb

**RADIO LEBANON (Gov.)**
✉ Rue Lyon, Sanayeh, P.O. Box 4848, Beirut ☎ +961 1 743531 **W:** radioliban.gov.lb **E:** radiolibanonline@hotmail.com
**L.P:** Dir: Mohammad Ibrahim. Tech. Dir: Nazih Chahine. Chief, Prgr. Dept: Waheed Jalal. Chief, Public Rel: Faouzi Fehmy.
**1st Prgr. in Arabic:** 0330-2330 on 98.1/98.5MHz. **2nd Prgr. in French/English:** 24h on 96.2MHz. **Rel. R. France Int:** 12h daily. **Ann:** A: "Iza'at Loubnan min Beirut". **IS:** Opening notes from the Lebanese National anthem played on guitar.

**OTHER STATIONS:**

| FM | MHz | Name | FM | MHz | Name |
|---|---|---|---|---|---|
| 41) | 87.5 | Irtiqaa Way | 26) | 97.5 | R. Strike |
| 43) | 87.9 | Vo Youth | 38) | 97.9 | Vo Grace |
| 20) | 88.1 | R. Nostalgie | 41) | 98.5 | Irtiqaa Way |
| 4) | 88.5 | R. Orient | 36) | 98.9 | R. Aghani Aghani |
| 44) | 88.5 | R. Liban Culture | 5) | 99.1 | NRJ |
| 7) | 89.1 | Risala R. | 15) | 99.7 | Fame FM |
| 32) | 89.5 | Virgin R. | 1) | 100.3 | Voice of Lebanon |
| 42) | 89.7 | Flash FM | 37) | 100.7 | R. Al-Fajir |
| 35) | 89.7 | Ciel FM | 25) | 101.0 | R. Jaras Scoop |
| 16) | 90.1 | Sawt al Hurriya | 24) | 101.3 | Power FM |
| 12) | 90.3 | Sawt al-Jadeed | 31) | 101.5 | R. Sevan |
| 17) | 90.5 | R. Light FM | 22) | 101.9 | R. Delta |
| 31) | 90.8 | R. Sevan | 9) | 102.5 | R. Free Lebanon |
| 33) | 91.0 | Sawt al-Injil | 21) | 103.0 | Pax R. |
| 8) | 91.3 | Nidaa al-Maarifa | 2) | 103.8 | Sawt al-Shaab |
| 3) | 91.9 | R. Al-Nour | 39) | 104.1 | Play FM |
| 47) | 92.1 | Sawt al-Huda | 19) | 104.5 | Mix FM |
| 44) | 92.3 | R. Liban Culture | 37) | 104.9 | R. Al-Fajir |
| 28) | 92.7 | Sawt el-Mada | 6) | 105.3 | R. One |
| 23) | 93.3 | Voice of Lebanon | 45) | 105.7 | Star FM |
| 13) | 94.0 | Holy Quran R | 14) | 106.1 | Voice of Charity |
| 33) | 94.5 | Sawt al-Injil | 27) | 106.7 | Al-Balad R. Station |
| 10) | 94.9 | Voice of Van | 18) | 107.3 | R. MBS |
| 34) | 95.5 | Al-Bachaer Radio | 30) | 107.7 | Sawt el-Noujoum |
| 30) | 95.9 | Sawt el-Noujoum | 37) | 107.7 | R. Al-Fajir |
| 41) | 96.5 | Irtiqaa Way Radio | 46) | 107.9 | Jabal Loubnan |
| 11) | 96.9 | Sawt el-Ghad | | | |

**NB:** most stns have been allocated 400kHz frequency range, of which mostly the centre freq. is listed above. In many cases the trs from various sites are placed on both upper and lower limits of the range.

**Addresses & other information:**
**1)** P.O. Box 165271, Ashrafieh, Bachir el Gemayel Ave, Beirut **W:** sawtlebnan.com – **2)** Jabal el Arab St, Wata el Mousaitbeh, P.O.Box 14/5425, Beirut **W:** sawtachaab.com – **3)** Al-Nour Bldg, Abdel Nour St, Haret Hreïk, P.O.Box 25-197, Ghbeiry, Beirut **W:** alnour.com.lb/ radio Also relayed via in Syria via Tartus on 1071kHz and Aleppo 98.7MHz – **4)** Annajah Centre, Mar Elias St, Karakol Druz, P.O. Box 11-6362, Beirut. **W:** radioorientlb.com – **5)** Studiovision Bldg, Naccache, Metn, Beirut. **W:** nrjlebanon.com 24h in English. – **6)** Zakhem Bldg, Beit Meri El Metn, Beirut. **W:** radioone.fm 24h in English – **7)** Fraiha Bld. 3rd Floor, Barbour Beirut. **W:** risalaradio.com – **8)** Shaykh Ahmad Iskandarani Centre, Bourj Abi Haidar, Beirut. **W:** nidaa.fm – **9)** Kebbe Bldg, Adonis, Zouk Mosbeh, P.O.Box 110, Zouk Mekhael, Jounieh **W:** rll.com.lb – **10)** 2nd floor, Shaghzoyan Centre, Borj Hammoud, Beirut. P.O. Box 80-860, Beirut. **W:** voiceofvan.net 24h in Armenian & Arabic – **11)** Jal el Dib 60073 **W:** sawtelghad.com – **12)** Watta al-Museitbeh, Ghbeiri, Beirut **W:** aljadeed.tv hawacom.

tv/radio – **13)** Dar al Fatwa, P.O. Box 14-5380, Al Mazraa-Beirut **W:** quranradio.com.lb – **14)** Couvent St. Jean, Fouad Chehab St, P.O. Box 850, Jounieh. **W:** voiceofcharity.org 24h in Arabic/French/others – **15)** 3rd floor, La Perla Centre, Sabra Highway, Jounieh. **W:** famefm.com – **16)** Achrafieh, Kobayate St, Tutunji Center 7th floor, Beirut 1100 **W:** facebook.com/SawtelhouriaRadio – **17)** cityrama, dekwaneh, sin el fil the private club, 3rd floor, Beirut **W:** radiolightfm.com 0500-2200 in English/French – **18)** 1st floor, Pères Paulistes building, Off Highway, Haret Sakhre, Kesrouane **W:** facebook.com/RadioMBS – **19)** Alfred Naccache Ave, P.O. Box 166-815, Achrafieh, Beirut. **W:** mixfm.com.lb 24h in English – **20)** Mont Liban Bldg, Ave. Fouad Chehab, Fassouh, P.O.Box 16-6000, Achrafieh, Beirut. **W:** nostalgie.com.lb 24h in French – **21)** P.O. Box 116-5104, Beirut. 24h in English. **W:** paxradio.net – **22)** Kahalé Bldg, Old St, P.O.Box 1306, Beit Meri el Metn. **W:** radiodelta. fm – **23)** c/o Modern Media Company, Dbayeh, Beirut. **W:** vdl.com. lb – **24)** powerfmlebanon.com – **25)** 4th Floor, Hawa Chicken Building, Damascus Highway, Hazmiyé **W:** jarasfm.com – **26)** Sin El Fil, Saydeh Str, Facing Saydeh Church ,Beirut **W:** radiostrike.com – **27)** Centre Nasrallah, Rue Al-Anwar, Jdeideh, P.O. Box 90-1119, Beirut. **W:** albaladonline.com – **28)** Mirna el Chalouhi Centre 2nd floor, Sin el-Fil, Beirut. **W:** sawtelmada.com – **29)** txs in Beirut/Tripoli/Tyros/Sidon. For details see IntRad under France – **30)** Kreshet Bldg. 7th floor, Suyoufi St, Algazlep, Achrafieh, Beirut. **W:** sawtelnoujoum.com – **31)** Khatchadurian Street, Khederlarian Building, Ground Floor, Beirut **W:** radiosevan.com – **32)** Jal al-Dib highway, Beirut **W:** virginradiolebanon.com – **33)** Sawt al-Injil, Maronite Archdiocese of Beirut **W:** facebook.com/voiceofgospel – **34)** Sawt al-Bachaer, Beirut **W:** albachaer. com – **35) W:** facebook.com/CielFMLebanon – **36)** Beirut Media Zone, Studiovision Bldg #1, Naccache, Beirut **W:** aghaniaghani.com – **37)** Beirut **W:** fajrradio.com – **38) W:** antiochpatriarchate.org/radio.php – **39) W:** playfmlebanon.com In Arabic & English – **41) W:** irtiqaaway. com – **42)** unlicensed **W:** facebook.com/flashfmlebanon – **43)** unlicensed **W:** yeridasartoutiantsayne.com – **44) W:** radiolibanculture. com – **45) W:**starfmlebanon.com – **46) W:** jaballebnan.fm– **47)** Beirut

**Monte-Carlo Doualiya:** Tripoli 103.0, Nabatyeh 103.1, Beirut/Saida/ Tyre/Zahlé 103.3, Jezzine 103.4MHz.
**R. Sawa:** Al-Qubayat/Beirut/Bekaa/Deir el-Acher/Jabal Safi/Tripoli 87.7MHz

## LESOTHO

**L.T:** UTC +2h — **Pop:** 2.2 million — **Pr.L:** Sesotho, English — **E.C:** 50Hz, 220V — **ITU:** LSO

### LESOTHO COMMUNICATIONS AUTHORITY (LCA)
P.O. Box 15896, 6th Floor, Moposo House, Kingsway Road, Maseru ☎+266 22224300 ▤ +266 22310984 **W:** lca.org.ls **E:** lca@lca.org.ls

### LESOTHO NATIONAL BROADCASTING SERVICES (LNBS) (Pub.)
P. O. Box 552, Lerotholi St, Opposite Royal Palace, Maseru 100 ☎+266 22321460 ▤ +266 22313980 **W:** lnbs.org.ls ultimaterado. co.ls **L.P:** D.G. Broadc: Mr. Lebohang Dada Mokasa. CE: Mr. Motlatsi Monyane.Sr. Tr. Eng MW: Mr. Khoabane Qhobela. Sr. Tr. Eng. FM&TV: Mr. Ncheme Sekhoane & Mr. Ntima Molete. CE: Mr. Motlatsi Monyane.
**MW:** Maseru (Lancer's Gap): 639kHz 100kW, 891kHz 50kW, 1197kHz 50kW.

| FM | MHz | kW(TRP) | FM | MHz | kW(TRP) |
|---|---|---|---|---|---|
| Leribe | 88.6 | | Likhoele | 97.2 | 1 |
| Katse | 90.8 | 0.3 | Maseru (Berea) | 99.8 | 5 |
| Ha-Sottho | 92.6 | 0.25 | Thaba-Putsoa | 100.2 | 1 |
| Lebelonyane | 93.2 | 1 | Sheep Stud Hill | 102.4 | 1 |
| Maseru (Berea) | 93.3 | 5 | Popa | 103.6 | 1 |
| Chafo | 96.0 | 1 | Souru | 105.4 | 1 |
| Matshoana | 96.8 | 1 | Sehong-hon | 106.1 | 0.25 |

**R. Lesotho** in Sesotho/English: 24h on 639kHz & FM excl. two Ultimate FM freq's.
**Ultimate FM** in English: 891 & 1197kHz and 88.6 & 99.8MHz 24h.
**Ann:** E: "This is Radio Lesotho" or "This is the Lesotho National Broadcasting Service, Maseru". Sesotho: "Se-ea-le-moea sa Lesotho, Maseru". **IS:** native horn instruments.

### OTHER STATIONS:
**Catholic R. FM:** Qoatsaneng, Maseru 103.3MHz – **Dope FM,** Maseru: 103.6 MHz – **Fill the Gap (Jesu ke Karabo):** Mafeteng 87.6MHz, Leribe 102.8MHz, Lancer's Gap 105.3MHz – **Harvest FM:** Lancer's Gap, Maseru 98.9MHz – **Joy FM,** Private Bag A68, Maseru 100: 106.9MHz 1kW **W:** joyfm.co.ls Also rel. VOA. **F.Pl:** trs in Mafeteng and Maputsoe – **LM R:** Maseru 104.0MHz **W:** lmradio.net – **Lesotho Evangelical Church R,** Lancer's Gap, Maseru: 102.4MHz

– **MoAfrika FM:** Leribe 89.7MHz, Mafeteng 90.7MHz, Lancer's Gap 99.3MHz. **W:** moafrika.co.ls – **People's Choice FM,** Development House, Block D, Floor 9, Kingsway Str, Maseru: 95.6MHz. **W:** pcfm. co.ls – **Thaha-Khube FM,** Ha Ts'osane, Maseru: 97.6MHz – **Tšenolo FM,** Khubetsoana: 91.3MHz.

**BBC African Sce,** Maseru (Berea): 90.2MHz.
**RFI Afrique,** Maseru (Berea): 96.5MHz in French/English

## LIBERIA

**L.T:** UTC — **Pop:** 4.7 million — **Pr.L:** English, 18 ethnic — **E.C:** 60Hz, 120V — **ITU:** LBR

### LIBERIA TELECOMMUNICATIONS AUTHORITY (LTA)
National Investment Commission Annex, 12th Street, Sinkor, Tubman Boulevard, Monrovia ☎+231 27302012 **W:** lta.gov.lr **E:** info@lta.gov.lr

### LIBERIA BROADCASTING SYSTEM (LBS, Pub.)
P.O. Box 594, Paynesville **W:** elbcradio.com **E:** lbs@yahoo.com **L.P:** DG: Darryl Ambrose Nmah, Sr. Deputy DG: Ledgerhood Rennie.
**FM: ELBC Radio** 99.9MHz 10kW **D.Prgr:** 0530-2400.

### RADIO ELWA (Rlg.)
P.O. Box 192, Monrovia **W:** elwaministries.org **E:** elwaradio54@ gmail.com **L.P:** GM: Moses T. Nyantee.
**SW:** Monrovia 4760 & 6050kHz 1kW (4760 kHz inactive).
**FM:** Monrovia 94.5MHz 2kW.
**D.Prgr** in English/local lang's: 0530-1000, 1700-2400 (SS -2230).

### ECOWAS RADIO (Economic Community of West African States)
Monrovia **W:** ecowas.int **W:** info@ecowas.int
**FM:** Gbarnga 90.5MHz, Harper/Monrovia/Zwedru 91.5MHz, Sanniquelle 95.1MHz. Greenville/Voinjama 97.1MHz (Harper/ Sanniquelle 1kW, others 5kW). **D.Prgr:** 24h in English/French/ Portuguese

### OTHER STATIONS:
**ABCU R,** Yekepa: 95.7MHz 0.6kW. **W:** africanbiblecolleges.org/ abcu_liberia.php – **City FM,** Monrovia: 90.2MHz – **Crystal FM,** Monrovia: 95.5MHz – **DC 101.1 FM,** Monrovia: 101.1MHz. Also rel. BBC African Sce – **King's FM,** Monrovia: 88.5MHz. Also rel. VOA. – **Liberian Christian Broadcasting Network,** Monrovia: 102.3MHz – **Love FM,** Monrovia: 105.5MHz – **Power FM,** Monrovia: 93.3MHz – **Magic FM,** Monrovia: 99.2MHz – **R. Monrovia:** 92.1MHz. **W:** radiomonrovia247.com – **Sky FM,** Monrovia: 107.0MHz. **E:** skyliberia@yahoo.com – **Truth FM,** Monrovia 96.1MHz. **W:** truthfm.com. lr – **United Metodist Church R,** Monrovia 98.7MHz 0.3kW.

**BBC African Sce,** Monrovia: 103.1MHz
**RFI Afrique:** Monrovia 106.0MHz in French/English/Mandinka.
About 35 community radio stations are in operation

## LIBYA

**L.T:** UTC +2h — **Pop:** 6.4 million — **Pr.L:** Arabic — **E.C:** 50Hz, 127/230V — **ITU:** LBY

### GENERAL AUTHORITY FOR COMMUNICATIONS AND INFORMATICS (GACI)
Zawia St., Tripoli ☎ +218 21 3619811 ▤ +218 21 3622452 **E:** info@cim.gov.ly **W:** www.cim.gov.ly **L.P:** Chmn: Sami Al-Fintazi

### LIBYAN RADIO & TELEVISION NETWORK (Gov)
El Fath Rd, P.O. Box 80237, Tripoli ☎+218 21 4442252 ▤ +218 21 3403458. **W:** ltv.ly facebook.com/radio.alwatania.ly facebook.com/ 966FM-1053AM-138800026297759/

| MW | kHz | kW | Prgr. |
|---|---|---|---|
| Benghazi | ‡675 | 100 | Vo Homeland |
| Tripoli | ‡1053 | 100 | Vo Homeland |

**FM:** El Beida 87.9MHz, Tripoli 88.8MHz (youth channel), Benghazi 89.3MHz (with 675kHz), Sultan 89.9MHz, Misrata 90.3MHz (regional), Tripoli 90.3MHz, Sabha 92.9MHz, Sabha 93.4MHz (with 1053kHz), Misrata 95.5MHz (Koran), Sabha 96.1MHz, Tripoli 96.6MHz (with 1053kHz), El Beida 98.1MHz, Benghazi 98.9MHz, Sirte 101.1 (Amwaj FM), Al-Zawiyah 101.3MHz, Tobruk 102.6MHz, Sabha 102.9MHz, Tripoli 103.4/105.3 (city council).
**Ann:** "Radio Libya al-Wataniya".

## Other stations:

| FM | MHz | Station, Prgr & other info |
|---|---|---|
| Tripoli | 87.7 | Tripolitana (**W:**facebook.com/TripolitanaFm) |
| Benghazi | 88.1 | R. Sawa |
| Surman | 88.1 | R. Aloula (W:facebook.com/radioloulasurman) |
| Misallata | 88.3 | R. Misallata (**W:** facebook.com/msallata.radio) |
| Benghazi | 88.5 | Libya FM (**W:** libya.fm) |
| Tripoli | 88.8 | Al-Shababiya: (Youth R. of 17th February) |
| Misrata | 89.1 | Tanasuh FM (**W:** facebook.com/TanasuhFM) |
| Derna | 89.3 | R. Free Derna |
| Zliten | 89.3 | Tanasuh FM (**W:** facebook.com/TanasuhFM) |
| Tripoli | 89.5 | Al-Qitab wa al-Sunna (**W:**facebook.com/alkitabwasuna) |
| Tripoli | 90.0 | Sama Libya FM (**W:** facebook.com/Sama-libya-fm-364785736977619) |
| Benghazi | 90.5 | BBN FM (**W:** facebook.com/EnglishforLibyaonbbn) |
| Misrata | 90.5 | Al-Furqan R. (**W:** furqan.ly) |
| Tripoli | 90.5 | Qimam al-Andalus Quran R. (**W:** facebook.com/qimam.fm) |
| Tripoli | 90.7 | R.Alsaa (**W:**facebook.com/RadioAlsaa90.7English) |
| Benghazi | 90.9 | Minhaj al-Sunna Facebook: MinhajAlssuna |
| Tripoli | 91.1 | Libo FM (**W:** facebook.com/LiboFm) |
| Benghazi/Misrata | 91.5 | BBC Arabic Sce (**W:** bbc.com/Arabic) |
| Garian | 91.9 | R. Garian (**W:** facebook.com/91.09fm) |
| Tripoli | 92.1 | R. Al-Amal (**W:** facebook.com/alamalfm) |
| Al-Marj | 92.3 | Marj FM |
| Ajdabiya | 92.4 | Al Jazeera (Arabic Sce TV sound relay) |
| Benghazi | 92.4 | Tribute FM (**W:** tributefm.com, in English) |
| Tripoli | 92.5 | Libya FM |
| Misrata | 92.5 | Flash FM |
| Benghazi | 92.9 | Sanabil Libya for Children |
| Tripoli | 93.8 | Lebda FM (**W:** facebook.com/Lebdafm) |
| Sirte | 94.3 | R. Al-Tawhid (Islamic State) |
| Benghazi | 95.5 | Jawak FM (**W:** facebook.com/jawakfm) |
| Tripoli | 95.5 | Al-Madena FM (**W:** facebook.com/ALmadenaFM) |
| Misrata | 96.5 | Tubaktes FM Koran prgr. |
| Tripoli | 96.9 | Ly FM (**W:** lyradio.webs.com) |
| Misrata | 97.5 | Tubaktes FM |
| Al-Khums | 97.9 | R. Biladi FM |
| Tripoli | 98.1 | Tribute FM (**W:** tributefm.com, in English) |
| Nalut | 98.2 | R. Free Nalut (in Tamazight) |
| 4 sites | 98.7 | Al-Wasat R. (live.alwasat.ly) |
| Tripoli | 99.0 | R.Tajoura (**W:** facebook.com/RTAJ99FM) |
| Misrata | 99.1 | R. Sawa |
| Benghazi | 99.5 | R.Madinaty (**W:** facebook.com/radiomycity) |
| Tripoli | 99.5 | R.Al Shorouk FM |
| Misrata | 99.9 | Misrata FM (**W:** misrata.fm) |
| Benghazi | 99.9 | Al-Iman R. (**W:** facebook.com/999.ly) |
| Benghazi | 100.1 | Libyana Hits (**W:** libyanahits.fm, English) |
| El Beida | 100.1 | R. Sowt Libya (**W:** facebook.com/radio.sout.libya.fm100.1) |
| Tripoli | 100.3 | Salaf Way FM (**W:** facebook.com/salafwayfm) |
| Tripoli | 100.7 | R. Zone (**W:** facebook.com/radiozonelibya) |
| Benghazi | 101.1 | Shabab FM (**W:** facebook.com/101.1FM) |
| Tripoli | 102.1 | Tanasuh FM (**W:** facebook.com/TanasuhFM) |
| Benghazi | 102.4 | Al-Iman R. (**W:** facebook.com/999.ly) |
| Tobruk | 102.5 | Nidaa al-Iman (**W:** neydaaalaeman.esy.es,) |
| Tripoli | 102.5 | Tripoli FM (**W:** tripolifm.ly) |
| Ajdabiya | 103.0 | Libya Free TV sound (**W:** libya.tv) |
| Zliten | 103.5 | Zliten FM (**W:**facebook.com/ZlitenFM) |
| Misrata | 104.0 | Sawt al-Medina |
| Tripoli/others | 105.3 | Al Aan FM (**W:** alaan.fm) |
| Benghazi/Tripoli | 105.5 | Monte-Carlo Doualiya |
| Benghazi | 105.9 | R. Power (**W:** facebook.com/radiopower105.9fm) |
| Yefren | 106.3 | R. Awal (**W:** awal.ly) |
| Benghazi | 106.5 | R.Zain (W:facebook.com/ZAIN106.5FM) |
| Tripoli | 106.6 | R. Sawa: 2kW |
| Benghazi | 106.9 | Sowt Libya al-Watan |
| Tripoli | 107.7 | Al-Jawhara FM |

## LIECHTENSTEIN

**L.T:** UTC +1h (31 Mar-27 Oct: +2h) — **Pop:** 38,000 — **Pr.L:** German, Alemannic German — **E.C:** 230V/50Hz — **ITU:** LIE

### LIECHTENSTEINISCHER RUNDFUNK (Pub)
🖃 Dorfstr. 24, 9495 Triesen, Fürstentum Liechtenstein ☎ +423 3991313 **E:** admin@radio.li **W:** radio.li **L.P:** Chair: Hildegard Hasler
**FM (MHz):** Balzers 88.8 (0.05kW), Buchs* 89.2 (0.5kW), Steg 96.6

(0.25kW), Vaduz 96.9 (0.1kW), Nendeln 100.2 (0.05kW), Vilters* 103.4 (0.1kW), Thal* 105.9 (0.2kW), Rüthi* 106.1 (1kW).
*) Located in Switzerland. Also on DAB Block 9D via txs in Eastern Switzerland (see Switzerland entry).
**D.Prgr: Radio L** 24h

## LITHUANIA

**L.T:** UTC +2h (31 Mar-27 Oct: +3h) — **Pop:** 2.8 million — **Pr.L:** Lithuanian, Polish, Russian — **E.C:** 230V/50Hz — **ITU:** LTU

### LIETUVOS RADIJO IR TELEVIZIJOS KOMISIJA (LRTK)
(Radio and TV Commission of Lithuania)
🖃 Šeimyniškiu g. 3a, 09312 Vilnius ☎ +370 5 2330660 🖷 +370 5 2647125 **E:** lrtk@rtk.lt **W:** rtk.lt **L.P:** Chmn: Mantas Martišius

### LIETUVOS NACIONALINIS RADIJAS IR TELEVIZIJA (LRT) (Pub)
🖃 S.Konarskio g. 49, 03123 Vilnius ☎ +370 5 2363000 **E:** lrt@lrt.lt
**W:** lrt.lt **DG:** Monika Garbaciauskaite-Budriene

| FM (MHz) | 1 | 2 | 3 | kW |
|---|---|---|---|---|
| Biržai | 100.8 | 87.5 | - | 5/1.3 |
| Bubiai | 100.9 | 103.4 | 90.5 | 2x20/0.8 |
| Druskininkai | 102.3 | 103.7 | 91.7 | 8.2/5/0.6 |
| Giruliai | 102.8 | 105.3 | 91.9 | 27.5/29/0.5 |
| Joniškis | 89.4 | 94.4 | - | 2/0.5 |
| Juragiai | 102.1 | 96.2 | 98.0 | 2x10/1.9 |
| Kalvarija | 104.8 | - | - | 1 |
| Mažeikiai | 93.3 | 101.8 | 89.9 | 2x2/0.7 |
| Pažagieniai | 107.5 | 105.3 | 93.7 | 2x1.5/1.7 |
| Plunge | 88.0 | 105.0 | - | 1/0.7 |
| Skuodas | 99.3 | 103.5 | - | 0.7/2 |
| Taurage | 98.8 | 107.4 | 104.2 | 13/2/1 |
| Viešintos | 101.9 | 104.4 | 106.5 | 17.4/18/0.9 |
| Vilnius | 89.0 | 105.1 | 98.3 | 20/6.5/3.5 |
| Visaginas | 102.9 | 100.4 | - | 5 |

+ sites with only txs below 1kW.
**D.Prgr: Prgr 1 (LRT Radijas):** 24h. For ethnic minorities: 1405-1530 Russian. – **Prgr 2 (LRT Klasika):** 24h. For ethnic minorities: 1300-1330 Belarusian (Tue), Russian (Wed/Thu/SS); Ukrainian (Fri), 1330 (Mon 1300)-1400 Polish. – **Prgr 3 (LRT Opus):** 24h.

### OTHER STATIONS

| FM | MHz | kW | Location | Station |
|---|---|---|---|---|
| 2D) | 87.8 | 5.3 | Vilnius | Rock FM |
| 2B) | 88.2 | 3.2 | Bubiai | ZIP FM |
| 16) | 88.3 | 1 | Utena | Relax FM |
| 19) | 88.5 | 5 | Vilnius | Extra FM |
| 23) | 88.8 | 4 | Bubiai | XXL FM |
| 19) | 89.1 | 1 | Marijampole | Extra FM |
| 2A) | 89.6 | 3 | Vilnius | Radiocentras |
| 9) | 89.7 | 3.5 | Bubiai | Power Hit R. |
| 3B) | 90.1 | 2 | Perkunai | Pukas 2 |
| 2D) | 90.3 | 20 | Juragiai | Rock FM |
| 2C) | 90.6 | 2.3 | Giruliai | Rusradio LT |
| 2A) | 91.2 | 4 | Tryškiai | Radiocentras |
| 22) | 91.4 | 3.2 | Klaipeda | XFM |
| 7) | 91.4 | 2.1 | Marijampole | Marijos radijas |
| 19) | 91.5 | 1 | Ukmerge | Extra FM |
| 2B) | 91.6 | 2 | Skuodas | ZIP FM |
| 7) | 91.8 | 2 | Bubiai | Marijos radijas |
| 2A) | 92.2 | 3.5 | Bubiai | Radiocentras |
| 4A) | 92.3 | 1.5 | Utena | Ziniu radijas |
| 3B) | 92.4 | 3.2 | Kaunas | Pukas 2 |
| 2B) | 92.5 | 4.5 | Giruliai | ZIP FM |
| 2B) | 92.7 | 2.1 | Mažeikiai | ZIP FM |
| 1A) | 92.8 | 11.7 | Krakes | M-1 |
| 7) | 93.1 | 1.3 | Vilnius | Marijos radijas |
| 4A) | 93.4 | 1 | Marijampole | Ziniu radijas |
| 5) | 93.5 | 1 | Utena | Gold FM |
| 3A) | 94.0 | 2.5 | Lelionys | Pukas |
| 3A) | 94.2 | 4.8 | Liktenai | Pukas |
| 3A) | 94.6 | 2 | Ukmerge | Pukas |
| 3A) | 94.8 | 2.5 | Daukšiai | Pukas |
| 15A) | 94.9 | 3.2 | Giruliai | Laluna |
| 7) | 95.0 | 4 | Viešintos | Marijos radijas |
| 3B) | 95.4 | 4 | Liepkalnis | Pukas 2 |
| A) | 95.5 | 3.2 | Vilnius | BBCWS relay |
| 3A) | 95.7 | 2 | Šiauliai | Pukas |
| 4) | 96.0 | 1.8 | Biržai | Ziniu radijas |
| 4) | 96.4 | 1.8 | Mažeikiai | Ziniu radijas |
| 10) | 96.6 | 1 | Panevežys | Pulsas |

| FM | MHz | kW | Location | Station |
|---|---|---|---|---|
| 9) | 96.7 | 2.3 | Giruliai | Power Hit R. |
| 1B) | 97.6 | 4 | Juragiai | M-1 Plius |
| 21) | 97.8 | 1.6 | Šiauliai | RS2 |
| 7) | 98.2 | 1.9 | Biržai | Marijos radijas |
| 1B) | 98.3 | 3.4 | Giruliai | M-1 Plius |
| 1B) | 98.7 | 1.6 | Utena | M-1 Plius |
| 12) | 99.0 | 3.2 | Alytus | FM 99 |
| 13) | 99.7 | 1 | Vilnius | European Hit R. |
| 6) | 99.8 | 2 | Giruliai | Kelyje |
| 2A) | 99.9 | 2 | Raseiniai | Radiocentras |
| 2B) | 100.1 | 4 | Vilnius | ZIP FM |
| 1B) | 100.2 | 5 | Pažagieniai | M-1 Plius |
| 19) | 100.2 | 1 | Klaipeda | Extra FM |
| 8) | 100.4 | 4 | Mažeikiai | Mažeikiu aidas |
| 2C) | 100.4 | 2.4 | Kaunas | Rusradio LT |
| 1B) | 100.5 | 3 | Bubiai | M-1 Plius |
| 15B) | 100.8 | 1.3 | Klaipeda | Raduga |
| 3B) | 100.9 | 1.1 | Vilnius | Pukas 2 |
| 2A) | 101.1 | 1.4 | Alytus | Radiocentras |
| 2A) | 101.4 | 3.8 | Pažagieniai | Radiocentras |
| 2A) | 101.5 | 2 | Giruliai | Radiocentras |
| 4B) | 101.5 | 2.3 | Vilnius | Easy FM |
| 3A) | 101.6 | 1.7 | Taurage | Pukas |
| 2A) | 101.6 | 1.9 | Druskininkai | Radiocentras |
| 16) | 101.7 | 1.6 | Bubiai | Relax FM |
| 2A) | 101.8 | 2 | Marijampole | Radiocentras |
| 3A) | 102.0 | 1 | Karlai | Pukas |
| 4A) | 102.2 | 1.6 | Giruliai | Žiniu radijas |
| 17) | 102.5 | 3.4 | Bubiai | Saules radijas |
| 3A) | 102.6 | 1 | Skuodas | Pukas |
| 5) | 102.6 | 5.8 | Vilnius | Gold FM |
| 2A) | 102.7 | 1.5 | Taurage | Radiocentras |
| 18) | 102.9 | 4 | Kaunas | Tau |
| 1C) | 103.0 | 2.2 | Pažagieniai | Lietus |
| 1C) | 103.0 | 1.1 | Tryškiai | Lietus |
| 1C) | 103.1 | 2.5 | Vilnius | Lietus |
| 1C) | 103.1 | 1.7 | Taurage | Lietus |
| 1C) | 103.3 | 1 | Biržai | Lietus |
| 1C) | 103.4 | 1.1 | Utena | Lietus |
| 1C) | 103.5 | 4.2 | Juragiai | Lietus |
| 1C) | 103.7 | 1.6 | Giruliai | Lietus |
| 4A) | 103.7 | 1.1 | Visaginas | Žiniu radijas |
| 20) | 103.8 | 1.8 | Vilnius | Znad Wilii |
| 1C) | 103.9 | 3.7 | Bubiai | Lietus |
| 5) | 104.1 | 4 | Giruliai | Gold FM |
| 2B) | 104.1 | 20 | Juragiai | ZIP FM |
| 1B) | 104.3 | 2 | Marijampole | M-1 Plius |
| 5) | 104.3 | 1.2 | Šiauliai | Gold FM |
| 5) | 104.5 | 4 | Kaunas | Gold FM |
| 14) | 104.7 | 1 | Vilnius | XFM |
| 5) | 104.8 | 1.2 | Panevežys | Gold FM |
| 4A) | 104.8 | 2.2 | Taurage | Žiniu radijas |
| 4A) | 104.9 | 1 | Juragiai | Žiniu radijas |
| 2B) | 105.0 | 1 | Utena | ZIP FM |
| 2B) | 105.2 | 1.3 | Raseiniai | ZIP FM |
| 19) | 105.4 | 3.9 | Kaunas | Extra FM |
| 2B) | 105.4 | 10 | Visaginas | ZIP FM |
| 2A) | 105.5 | 1.7 | Biržai | Radiocentras |
| 11) | 105.6 | 3.2 | Mažeikiai | Mažeikiai.FM |
| 2C) | 105.6 | 2.2 | Vilnius | Rusradio LT |
| 2B) | 105.7 | 2 | Taurage | ZIP FM |
| 2C) | 105.8 | 4.2 | Bubiai | Rusradio LT |
| 1A) | 105.9 | 3.2 | Ignalina | M-1 |
| 6) | 105.9 | 1 | Kaunas | Kelyje |
| 1A) | 106.0 | 2.2 | Pažagieniai | M-1 |
| 1A) | 106.0 | 2 | Tryškiai | M-1 |
| 1A) | 106.2 | 1.5 | Taurage | M-1 |
| 1B) | 106.2 | 4 | Vilnius | M-1 Plius |
| 1A) | 106.3 | 3.9 | Marijampole | M-1 |
| 1A) | 106.3 | 2.5 | Bubiai | M-1 |
| 1A) | 106.3 | 2 | Utena | M-1 |
| 1A) | 106.4 | 2 | Raseiniai | M-1 |
| 1A) | 106.5 | 3 | Giruliai | M-1 |
| 1A) | 106.6 | 4 | Juragiai | M-1 |
| 2B) | 106.7 | 2 | Laukuva | ZIP FM |
| 1A) | 106.8 | 1 | Vilnius | M-1 |
| 2A) | 107.1 | 3.9 | Juragiai | Radiocentras |
| 3A) | 107.3 | 2 | Vilnius | Pukas |
| 10) | 107.3 | 3.2 | Biržai | Pulsas |
| 3A) | 107.6 | 3.7 | Kaunas | Pukas |
| 3A) | 107.8 | 4.5 | Perkunai | Pukas |
| 4A) | 107.9 | 1 | Pažagieniai | Žiniu radijas |

+ txs below 1kW.

## Addresses & other information:

**1A-C)** Laisves pr. 60, 05120 Vilnius – **2A-D)** Laisves pr. 60, 05120 Vilnius. 2C) in Russian – **3A,B)** Šaldytuvu g. 25, 45123 Kaunas – **4A,B)** A.Smetonos g. 6, 01115 Vilnius – **5)** Gedimino pr. 50/2, 01110 Vilnius – **6)** Savanoriu pr. 151, 50174 Kaunas – **7)** M.Daukšos g. 21, 44282 Kaunas – **8)** Sodu g. 13-93, 89116 Mažeikiai – **9)** Kalvariju g. 143, 08221 Vilnius – **10)** Respublikos g. 28, 35174 Panevežys – **11)** Ventos g. 8a, 89111 Mažeikiai – **12)** Rotušes a. 2a, 62141 Alytus – **13)** Odminiu g. 8, 01112 Vilnius – **14)** Pylimo g. 20-10, 01118 Vilnius – **15A,B)** Taikos pr. 81, 94114 Klaipeda. 15B) in Russian – **16)** Laisves pr. 60, 05120 Vilnius – **17)** Aušros al. 64, 76240 Šiauliai – **18)** Draugystes g. 19, 51230 Kaunas – **19)** Konstitucijos pr. 7, 09308 Vilnius – **20)** Laisves pr. 60, 05120 Vilnius. In Polish. – **21)** Varpo g. 22, 76297 Šiauliai – **22)** Pylimo g. 20-10, 01118 Vilnius – **23)** Sauletekio g. 17-44, 87101 Telšiai – **A)** Rel. BBCWS (UK).

**Int. relays on MW:** (Upon demand; provided by R. Baltic Waves International; tx operated by LRTC) Viešintos 612/1386kHz 300kW (currently run at 75kW). See International Radio section

## LORD HOWE ISLAND (Australia)

**L.T:** UTC +10½ (7 Oct 18-7 Apr 19, 6 Oct 19-5 Apr 20: +11h) — **Pop:** 380 — **Pr.L:** English — **E.C:** 50Hz, 230V — **ITU:** AUS (**WRTH:** LHW)

### AUSTRALIAN BROADCASTING CORP. [ABC]

| FM | Call | kW | Station |
|---|---|---|---|
| 104.1 | 2ABCFM | 0.02 | ABC Classic FM |
| 105.3‡ | 2JJJ | 0.02 | Triple J |
| 106.1‡ | 2ABCFM | 0.02 | ABC Classic FM |

**NB:** ‡ ABC stns r. inactive with reception via satellite only

**LORD HOWE ISLAND RADIO**
✉ The Shack, New Jetty Complex, Lagoon Road [PO Box 52], Lord Howe Island NSW 2898 ☎ +61 2 6563 2123 🖷 +61 2 6563 2127
**FM:** 100.1MHz, 40W **Prgr:** Irr. Local prgr. Wed midday, and Thurs night 2130-0230. Local community stn

## LUXEMBOURG

**L.T:** UTC +1h (31 Mar-27 Oct: +2h) — **Pop:** 584,103 — **Pr.L:** Luxembourgish, French, German — **E.C:** 230V/50Hz — **ITU:** LUX

### AUTORITE LUXEMBOURGOISE INDEPENDENTE DE L'AUDIOVISUEL (ALIA)
✉ 19, rue du Fossé, L-1536 Luxembourg ☎ +352 24782089 🖷 +352 27858464 **E:** info@alia.etat.lu **W:** www.alia.lu
**L.P:** Chmn: Thierry Hoscheit

### RADIO 100,7 (Pub)
✉ 12a, Avenue J.F. Kennedy, L-1855 Luxemburg ☎ Tel: +352 4400441 🖷 Fax: +352 440044980 **E:** info@100komma7.lu **W:** www.100komma7.lu
**L.P:** Pres: Laurent Loschetter
**FM:** Neidhausen 95.9 MHz 3 kW, Dudelange 100.7 MHz 100 kW
**D.Prgr:** 24h in Luxembourgish

### RTL (Comm.)
✉ 45 blvd. Pierre Frieden, L-1543 Luxembourg ☎ +352 4214 22175 🖷 +352 4214 22756 **W:** radio.rtl.lu **L.P:** Pres: Jacques Santer.
**Luxembourg Sce: RTL Radio Lëtzebuerg:** ☎ +352 4214 23 🖷 +352 4214 22737 **W:** rtl.lu
**German Sce: RTL Radio:** ✉ Kurfürstendamm 207-208, D-10719 Berlin ☎ +49 30 88484120 🖷 +49 30 88484121 **W:** rtlradio.de **L.P:** Station Manager: Frank Jaeger
**LW:** 234kHz 1500kW (227° towards Paris) via Beidweiler, 24h Fr. sce

| FM | Station | Location | kW |
|---|---|---|---|
| 88.9 | R. Lëtzebuerg | Dudelange | 100 |
| 92.5 | R. Lëtzebuerg | Hosingen | 50 |
| 93.3 | RTL Radio | Dudelange | 100 |
| 97.0 | RTL Radio | Hosingen | 100 |

Also FM relays in France & Germany.
**RTL Radio Lëtzebuerg** 24h in Luxembourgish: 24h on 92.5MHz

### OTHER STATIONS (all MHz and 1 kW or more)
**R. Ara,** 2 rue de la Boucherie, 1247 Luxembourg **W:** ara.lu - **FM:** 87.8/102.9 – **R. Latina,** 2 rue Astrid, 1143 Luxembourg **W:** radiolatina.lu - **FM:** 91.7/101.2 – **Antenne Luxembourg - FM:** 94.3/103.4 – **R. Eldorado,** B.P. 1344, 1013 Luxembourg **W:** eldorado.lu - **FM:** 95.0 – **L'Essentiel R. - FM:** 107.7 **W:** lessentiel.lu
+ several other stations of less than 1kW

## MACAU (China, SAR)

**L.T:** UTC +8h — **Pop:**660,000 — **Pr.L:** Portuguese, Cantonese — **E.C:** 50Hz, 230V — **ITU:** MAC

### TELEDIFUSÃO DE MACAU, SARL (Priv. Comm.)
Avenida Dr. Rodrigo Rodrigues, No. 223-225, Edificio Nam Kwong 7°Andar, Macau ☎ +853 28713025 ▤ +853 28717194 **E:** rmacau@tdm.com.mo **W:** tdm.com.mo
**FM:** 98.0MHz 2.5kW **D.Prgr:** Portuguese 24h except Indonesian on Sun 1200-1300 and Tagalog on Sat 1200-1300, including relay RDP Antena 1 on Sun 1400-2300, Mon-Thu 1600-2300, Fri 1600-2400 and Sat 1300-2400. **FM:** 100.7MHz 2.5kW **D.Prgr:** Cantonese and Chinese 24h

### RÁDIO VILA VERDE LDA (Priv. Comm.)
Hipódromo da Taipa, Macau ☎ +853 28820338 ▤ +853 28820337 **E:** am738@am738.com **W:** am738.com
**FM:** 99.5MHz, suspended **D.Prgr:** Cantonese 24h

## MACEDONIA

**L.T:** UTC +1h (31 Mar-27 Oct: +2h) — **Pop:** 2.1 million — **Pr.L:** Macedonian, Albanian — **E.C:** 230V/50Hz — **ITU:** MKD

### AGENCIJA ZA AUDIO I AUDIOVIZUELNI MEDIUMSKI USLUGI (AVMU) (Agency for Audio and Audiovisual Media Services)
bul. Makedonija 38, 1000 Skopje ☎ +389 2 3103400 ▤ +389 2 3103401 **E:** contact@avmu.mk **W:** avmu.mk
**L.P:** Dir: Zoran Trajcevski

### MAKEDONSKO RADIO TELEVIZIJA (MRT) (Pub)
bul. Goce Delcev bb, 1000 Skopje ☎ +389 2 519899 **E:** direkcija@mrt.com.mk **W:** mrt.com.mk **L.P:** DG: Marjan Cvetkovski

| MW | kHz | kW | Prgr |
|---|---|---|---|
| Sveti Nikole | 810 | 100 | 1, International Service |

| FM (MHz) | 1 | 2 | 3 | kW |
|---|---|---|---|---|
| Belasica | 91.5 | 97.8 | 106.8 | 10 |
| Boskija | 95.3 | 98.1 | 105.4 | 10 |
| Bukovic | 89.2 | 95.9 | 104.3 | 1 |
| Cocon | 88.8 | 93.8 | 98.1 | 1 |
| Crn Vrv | 97.3 | 94.1 | 101.3 | 100 |
| Gevgelija | 99.2 | 102.4 | 96.5 | 10 |
| Golak | 94.5 | 97.0 | 107.7 | 10 |
| Mali Vlaj | 93.3 | 97.7 | 91.0 | 10 |
| Pelister | 92.3 | 96.1 | 102.6 | 20 |
| Popova Šapka | 88.8 | 96.3 | 98.3 | 5 |
| Stogovo | 95.3 | 101.0 | 91.3 | 3 |
| Tepavci | 94.9 | 103.4 | 91.5 | 1 |
| Turtel | 93.3 | 90.5 | 99.7 | 50 |
| Vodno | 98.9 | 92.4 | 87.8 | 10 |

+ txs below 1kW.
**D.Prgr: Prgr 1 (R. Skopje):** 24h – **Prgr 2 (R. 2):** 24h – **Prgr 3 (R. Shkupi):** 24h in Albanian & other ethnic minority languages (Bosnian, Romany, Serbian, Turkish, Vlakh).
**International Service (R. Makedonija):** see Int. Radio section.

### OTHER STATIONS
| FM | MHz | kW | Location | Station |
|---|---|---|---|---|
| 2) | 89.7 | 1 | Vodno | Kanal 77 |
| A) | 91.3 | 1 | Skopje | RFI relay |
| 1) | 92.9 | 1 | Pelister | Antena 5 |
| 1) | 95.5 | 1 | Vodno | Antena 5 |
| 1) | 104.8 | 1 | Turtel | Antena 5 |
| 1) | 106.3 | 1 | Boskija | Antena 5 |

+ txs below 1kW.
**Addresses & other information:**
**1)** ul. Tetovska 35, 1000 Skopje – **2)** ul. 5-ta Partiska konferencija bb, 2000 Štip – **A)** Rel. RFI (France)

## MADAGASCAR

**L.T:** UTC +3h — **Pop:** 26 million — **Pr.L:** Malagasy, French — **E.C:** 50Hz, 220V — **ITU:** MDG

### AUTORITÉ DE RÉGULATION DES TECHNOLOGIES DE COMMUNICATION (ARTEC)
Rue Ravoninahitriniarivo, Alarobia, 101 Antananarivo ☎ +261 20 2242119 **E:** artec@artec.mg **W:** www.artec.mg
**L.P:** Chmn: Jean Rakotomalala

### RADIO MADAGASIKARA - RADIO NATIONALE MALAGASY (RNM) (Pub.)
BP 4422, Anosy, 101 Antananarivo **W:** facebook.com/radio.madagasikara (stream on anio-info.com) **E:** r.radiomadagaskara@yahoo.fr ☎ +261 20 2221745 ▤ +261 20 2232715
**L.P:** Dir: Johary Ravoajanarahy.

| MW | kHz | kW | H of tr |
|---|---|---|---|
| Fenoarivo | 630 | 50 | 0300-1900 |

| SW | kHz | kW | H of tr |
|---|---|---|---|
| Ambohidrano | v5010 | 10 | 0300-0500, 1500-1900 |
| Ambohidrano | 6135 | 30 | 0500-1500 |

**NB:** All transmitters operate irregularly.
**FM:** Antananarivo 99.2MHz (0.5kW) & relay txs.
**D.Prgr:** 0300-1900 (SS 2200) in Malagasy & French.
**Ann:** Malagasy: "R. Madagasikara"; F: "R. Madagascar".

### OTHER STATIONS
| FM | MHz | kW | Location | Station |
|---|---|---|---|---|
| 2) | 88.6 | | Antananarivo | R. Fahazavana |
| | 89.2 | | Antananarivo | BBCWS relay |
| | 89.8 | | Fianarantsoa/Toamasina | BBCWS relay |
| 3) | 92.0 | | Antananarivo | Alliance FM (also r. RFI) |
| | 92.0 | | Antsirabé/others | R. France Int. |
| 4) | 93.4 | | Antananarivo | R. Don Bosco |
| 5A) | 94.4 | | Antananarivo | R. Tana |
| | 96.0 | | Antananarivo/others | Radio France Int. |
| 6) | 96.6 | | Antananarivo | R. Des Jeunes |
| 7) | 97.6 | | Antananarivo | R. Antsiva |
| | 98.0 | | Antsirana | R. France Int. |
| 8) | 98.2 | | Toamasina | R. Voanio |
| 5B) | 102.0 | | Antananarivo | R. 102 |
| 1) | 105.0 | 0.75 | Ambositra | R. Maria |
| 9) | 105.2 | | Antananarivo | Ma FM |
| 10) | 106.0 | | Antananarivo | R. Lazan Iarivo |
| 11) | 107.4 | | Antananarivo | R. FMFOI |

**NB:** Unlicensed stns are operating in many parts of the country.

**Addresses & other information:**
**1) W:** radiomaria.org – **2)** BP 623, Lot II J 11, Faravohitra, Rue Joël Rakotomalala, 101 Antananarivo. **W:** radiofahazavana.agilityhoster.com – **3)** Enceinte Maison Laborde, Andohalo, 101 Antananarivo. **W:** alliancefr.mg – **4)** BP 60, Maison Don Bosco, Ivato Airport, 105 Antananarivo. **W:** radiodonbosco.mg – **5A-B)** Enceinte Sitram, Ankorondrano, 101 Antananarivo. **W:** rta.mg . A) in Malagasy, B) in French –**6)** BP 4370, Immeuble Vitasoa, Analakely, 101 Antananarivo. **W:** rdeejay.net – **7)** BP 12170, Zone Zital Ankorondrano, Enceinte RTA, 101 Antananarivo. **W:** radio-antsiva.com –**8)** BP 489, 11 Rue Grandidier, 501 Toamasina. **W:** voanio.com – **9)** BP 1414, Ankorondrano, 101 Antananarivo. **W:** matv.mg – **10)** BP 6319, V.A 49 Andafiavaratra, 101 Antananarivo. **W:** rli106fm.com – **11)** Rue Docteur Ralarosy V W01, Ambohipotsy, 101 Antananarivo **W:** fmfoi.ifrance.com

## MADEIRA (Portugal)

**L.T:** UTC (31 Mar-27 Oct: +1h) — **Pop:** 300,000 — **Pr.L:** Portuguese — **E.C:** 50Hz, 230/380V — **ITU:** MDR

### ANACOM-Autoridade Nacional de Comunicações, Delegação da Madeira
Rua do Vale das Neves, 19, São Gonçalo, 9050-332 Funchal ☎ +351 291 79 02 00 ▤+351 291 79 02 01

### RÁDIO E TELEVISÃO DE PORTUGAL, S.A. (RTP) (Pub)
### Centro Regional da RTP-Madeira (radio & TV)
Caminho de Santo António, n.°145 , 9020-002 Funchal ☎ +351 291 20 20 00 ▤ +351 291 23 07 53 **W:** rtp.pt **E:** rdpmadeira@rtp.pt
**L.P:** Dir: Martim Santos

| FM(MHz) | Ant. 1 | Ant.2 | Ant. 3 | kW |
|---|---|---|---|---|
| Achada da Cruz | 104.3 | | 105.0 | 0.8 |
| Cabo Girão | 96.7 | 99.4 | 94.8 | 1/3/1 |
| Calheta | 105.4 | | 107.5 | 0.1 |
| Caniço | 101.6 | 99.0 | 89.3 | 0.5 |
| Encumeada | 93.1 | | 90.8 | 0.06 |
| Gaula | 98.5 | 106.3 | 91.3 | 1/0.7/1 |
| Maçapez | 92.0 | | 95.7 | 0.1 |
| Monte | 104.6 | 102.4 | 89.8 | 1/1/0.7 |
| Paúl da Serra | 101.9 | | 93.3 | 1 |
| Pico do Areeiro | 95.5 | 88.4 | 94.1 | 13/15 |
| Pico do Facho | 93.1 | | 90.8 | 0.03 |
| Ponta do Pargo | 90.2 | | 94.6 | 1 |
| Porto Santo | 100.5 | 103.3 | 96.5 | 10 |

| FM(MHz) | Ant. 1 | Ant.2 | Ant. 3 | kW |
|---|---|---|---|---|
| Ribeira Brava | 105.6 | | 103.1 | 1 |
| Santa Clara * | 104.6 | 102.4 | 89.8 | |

\* Tunnel tx at Funchal

**D.Prgr:** all networks 24h. Antena 1 of RDP Madeira provides regional prgrs M-F 0700-2000, Sat 0900-1900, Sun 1000-2300 LT; Antena 2 relays Lisboa 24h; Antena 3 Madeira carries own prgrs. M-F 0700-1900, Sat 0000-0300 & 0600-2400, Sun 0800-2400 LT. Technical info may be obtained from **W:** gabinete.tecnologias@rtp.pt
**V.** by QSL-card via RTP Lisboa

**RÁDIO RENASCENÇA – Em. Católica Portuguesa (Rlg/Comm)**
📺 (see Portugal) - **FM:** Pico do Silva 88.0MHz 44kW (RR), 93.6MHz 44kW (RFM)

**PEF – Posto Emissor de Radiodifusão do Funchal** (Priv., comm.)
📺 Rua Ponte de São Lázaro 3, 9000-027 Funchal ☎ +351 291 23 03 93 & +351 291 208 950 🖷 +351 291 22 17 97 **E:** radiopef@gmail.com, noticiaspef@gmail.com **W:** pef.pt
**MW:** Funchal 1530kHz 3kW (nominal power: 10kW)
**FM:** Funchal 92.0MHz 2kW **D.Prgr:** 24h Relays R. Renascença, Lisboa, at certain times **Ann:** "PEF - a sua rádio regional"

**Local FM stations:**

| FM | Island | Station & location | MHz | kW |
|---|---|---|---|---|
| 4) | Madeira | R. Jornal da Madeira, Funchal | 88.8 | 1 |
| 13) | Madeira | R. São Vicente, São Vicente | 89.2 | 0.5 |
| 6) | Madeira | R. Zarco, Machico | 89.6 | 1 |
| 9) | Pto Santo | R. Praia, Pto Santo | 91.6 | 0.5 |
| 12) | Madeira | Santana FM, Santana | 92.5 | 0.5 |
| 11) | Madeira | R. Palmeira, Santa Cruz | 96.1 | 0.5 |
| 10) | Madeira | R. Festival da Madeira, Ribeira Brava | 98.4 | 0.5 |
| 1) | Madeira | R. Calheta, Calheta | 98.8 | 0.5 |
| 5) | Madeira | TSF Madeira, Funchal | 100.0 | 2 |
| 2) | Madeira | R. Popular da Madeira, Câm. de Lobos | 101.0 | 2 |
| 8) | Madeira | R. Porto Moniz, Porto Moniz | 102.9 | 0.5 |
| 7) | Madeira | R. Sol, Ponta do Sol | 103.7 | 0.5 |
| 3) | Madeira | R.Clube da Madeira, Funchal | 106.8 | 0.4 |

+ five 50W repeaters used by three stns
**Addresses & other information** (add +351 to tel/fax nos)**:**
**1) & 12)** Edifício Ondaparque, Av.ª D. Manuel I, 9370-133 Calheta ☎ 291 820132/6 🖷 291 820138 **E:** radiocalheta@gmail.com, santanafm@gmail.com **W:** radiocalheta.pt, santanafm.com.pt – **2), 3) & 10)** Avenida Estados Unidos da América n.º 146-150, 9000-090 Funchal ☎291 766101/291 761068 **W:** popular.radiosmadeira.pt, clube. radiosmadeira.pt & festival.radiosmadeira.pt **E:** ssfranco75@gmail. com radiofestival98.4@gmail.com – **4)** Rua 31 de Janeiro, n.º 73 e 74. 9050-013 Funchal ☎ 291 210 408/9 🖷291 210 401 **E:** rjm@jm-madeira. pt, gerencia@jm-madeira.pt **W:** jm-madeira.pt/radio– **5)** Rua Fernão de Ornelas, 56-3º, 9050-021 Funchal ☎ 291 202300 🖷 291 20 23 87; relays TSF Lisboa – **6) & 11)** Conjunto Habitacional da Bemposta, Ap-A1/A2, Água de Pena, 9200-012 Machico ☎ 291 526896 & 291 526961 **E:** radiozarcomachico@gmail.com & radiopalmeira96.1@ gmail.com **W:** zarco.radiosmadeira.net **W:** palmeira.radiosmadeira.net –**7)** Estrada Murteiras-Canhas, 9360-303 Canhas ☎ 291 972 282 **E:** radiopontadosol@gmail.com **W:** sol.radiosmadeira.net – **8)** Bombeiros Voluntários de S. Vicente e Porto Moniz, Vila de S. Vicente, 9240 São Vicente ☎ 291 842135 🖷 291 842666 – **9)** Rua Goulart de Medeiros, 1, 9400 Porto Santo ☎ 291 980130 🖷 291 980137 **E:** radiopraia91.6fm@ gmail.com **W:** radiopraia.com – **13)** Bombeiros Voluntários de São Vicente e Porto Moniz, Sítio do Pé do Passo, 9240-225 São Vicente ☎ 291 842694 & 29184 2661 🖷 291 842393

## MALAWI

**LT:** UTC +2h — **Pop:** 18 million — **Pr.L:** English, Chichewa, Tumbuka, Lomwe, Sena, Yao, Nkhonde, Tonga — **E.C:** 50Hz, 230V — **ITU:** MWI

**MALAWI COMMUNICATIONS REGULATORY AUTHORITY (MACRA)**
📺 Salmon Amour Rd, Private Bag 261, Blantyre ☎+265 1 623611 🖷 +265 1 623890 **L.P:** DG: Allexon Chiwaya. Dir of Broadc: Fegus Lipenga. **W:** macra.org.mw **E:** info@macra.org.mw

**MALAWI BROADCASTING CORPORATION (MBC, Pub.)**
📺 P.O. Box 30133, Chichiri, Blantyre 3 ☎+265 1 871461 **W:** mbc.mw **E:** dgmbc@mbc.mw **L.P:** DG: Dr. Benson Tembo. Ag. Dir. Prgr. & News: Hamilton Chimala. Dir. of Signal Distr. &Projects: Joseph Chikagwa.

| MW | kHz | kW | MW | kHz | kW |
|---|---|---|---|---|---|
| Mangochi | 540 | 10 | Lilongwe | 594 | 30 |
| Karonga | 558 | 10 | Ekwendeni | 675 | 50 |

| MW | kHz | kW | MW | kHz | kW |
|---|---|---|---|---|---|
| Blantyre | 756 | 10 | Chitipa | 1404 | 10 |
| Bangula | ‡810 | 10 | Matiya | 1422 | 10 |

| FM | R1 | R2FM | kW | FM | R1 | R2FM | kW |
|---|---|---|---|---|---|---|---|
| Bangula | 104.5 | 88.1 | 1 | Mangochi | 98.3 | 91.8 | 1 |
| Chikangawa | 105.9 | 103.0 | 1 | Mchinji | 88.0 | 95.4 | 1 |
| Chitipa | 90.7 | 100.5 | 1 | Mpingwe | 95.4 | 92.2 | 1/5 |
| Dedza | 90.1 | 104.5 | 1 | Nkhotakota | 95.6 | - | 1 |
| Dwangwa | 103.6 | 93.6 | 1 | Nsanje | 95.5 | 94.4 | 0.05 |
| Ekwendeni | 92.2 | 100.5 | 1 | Ntchisi | 100.5 | 92.4 | 2 |
| Kanengo | 94.7 | 91.5 | 5/1 | Salima | 105.9 | 100.0 | 1 |
| Karonga | 95.5 | 98.7 | 2 | Zomba | 94.1 | 96.8 | 2/5 |
| Kasungu | 94.5 | 96.2 | 1 | | | | |

**Radio 1 in English/Chichewa/Others** on MW/FM: 24h.
**Radio 2FM in English/Chichewa** on FM: 24h.
**Ann:** E: R1: "Radio 1", R2: "Radio 2FM". Chichewa: "Kuno ndi ku Radio ya MBC".

**Other stations (FM MHz):**
**R. Alinafe,** Lilongwe: 97.1. **E:** radioalinafe@sdnp.org.mw – **Calvary Family Church R,** Blantyre 3: 105.8 0.25kW. **E:** calvaryministries@hotmail.com – **Capital R**: Blantyre/Mzuzu 102.5, Dedza 105.2, Lilongwe 102.8, Zomba 96.1, all 1kW. **W:** capitalradiomalawi.com – **Channel For All Nations,** Lilongwe: 101.5 – **FM 101 Power:** (all txs 0.5/1kW): Ntcheu 88.1, Livingstonia 93.2, Chintheche 98.6, Mzuzu 99.0, Nkhoma 100.3, Blantyre/Lilongwe/Nkhota-kota 101.0, Dedza 103.9, Ntchisi 104.0, Dwangwa 107.2. **W:** fm101.malawi.net – **Joy R,** Blantyre: 89.6 – **MIJ FM:** Blantyre/Lilongwe/Mzuzu: 90.3 **W:** mijmw.net – **R. Islam:** Blantyre 97.6, Dedza 105.7, Dowa 89.7, Karonga 97.7, Lilongwe 97.6, Mtengo Wa Ung'ono 99.7, Mangochi 101.8, Mzuzu 97.0, Namwera 97.4, Zomba 102.9, all 1kW. **W:** radioislam.org.mw – **R. Maria Malawi:** Mangochi 88.5 1kW, Dowa 94.0 1kW, Blantyre 99.2 1kW, Zomba 99.4 2kW, Dedza 99.7 2kW. **W:** radiomaria.mw – **Star FM,** Blantyre: 89.0 – **Trans World Radio Malawi:** Blantyre 89.1, Ntchis 90.7, Mvera 91.1, Dedza 96.4, Yawo 106.2, Chikangawa/Zomba 106.4, Lilongwe 106.5, Thyolo 107.1, all 2kW. **W:** twrmalawi.wordpress. com – **Ufulu FM:** Blantyre 92.5MHz **W:** ufulufm.com – **YONECO FM:** Lilongwe 90.0, Blantyre 101.9, Zomba 101.9, Mzuzu 104.0 **W:** yoneco. org – **Zodiak BS:** Chitipa 89.5, Dedza 89.0, Dowa 92.9, Karonga 93.7, Lilongwe 95.1, Livingstonia 95.0, Mpingwe 97.0, Mzuzu 95.1, Namwera 103.3, Zomba 89.3. **W:** zbsmw.com
**BBC African Sce:** Mzuzu 87.9, Lilongwe 98.0, Blantyre 98.7MHz

## MALAYSIA

**L.T:** UTC +8h — **Pop:** 32 million — **Pr.L:** Malay, English, Chinese. In West Malaysia also Tamil and various Orang Asli languages, East Malaysia also 12 local languages or dialects — **E.C:** 50Hz, 230V — **ITU:** MLA

**MALAYSIAN COMMUNICATIONS AND MULTIMEDIA COMMISSION (MCMC) (Suruhan Komunikasi dan Multimedia Malaysia, SKMM)**
Regulatory body for the communications & multimedia industries.
📺 MCMC Tower 1, Jalan Impact, Cyber 6, 63000 Cyberjaya, Selangor ☎ +60 3 8688 8000 🖷 +60 3 8688 1000 **W:** skmm.gov.my **L.P:** Acting Chairman: YBhg. Dato' Dr. Mohd Ali Mohamad Nor.

**JABATAN PENYIARAN MALAYSIA (Dept of Broadcasting of Malaysia) (Gov.)**
Parent body of RTM 📺 Angkasapuri, 50614 Kuala Lumpur ☎ +60 3 2282 5333 🖷 +60 3 2282 5103

**RADIO TELEVISION MALAYSIA - RTM (Gov.)**
📺 Dept. of Broadcasting, Angkasapuri, Bukit Putra, 50614 Kuala Lumpur ☎ +60 3 2282 5333 🖷 +60 3 2282 7146 **W:** rtm.gov.my **E:** aduan@rtm.net.my
**L.P:** DG: Dato' Haji Abu Bakar Abdul Rahim. Prgr Dir (Radio): YBhg. Dato' Hj. Mustafa Kamal Abd Razak.

| FM (MHz) | Site | 1 | 2 | 4 | 5 | 6 | kW |
|---|---|---|---|---|---|---|---|
| Alor Setar | a | 94.9 | 100.5 | 98.7 | 101.3 | 96.7 | 5 |
| Balik Pulau | b | 101.7 | 93.9 | 88.5 | 92.1 | 98.9 | 0.1 |
| Baling | c | 88.7 | 89.7 | 91.7 | 92.5 | 93.3 | 1 |
| Besut | d | 94.3 | 98.8 | 97.0 | 97.8 | 95.3 | 0.1 |
| Bukit Gantang | 88.3 | - | | | | | 0.1 |
| Cameron | e | 89.1 | 93.1 | 101.1 | 103.5 | 104.3 | 0.1 |
| Damak | f | | 89.4 | - | | | |
| Dungun | g | 95.9 | 96.9 | 98.9 | 99.7 | 100.7 | 1 |
| FELDA Tenang | 91.0 | 89.4 | 90.2 | 87.8 | | | |

| FM (MHz) | Site | 1 | 2 | 4 | 5 | 6 | kW |
|---|---|---|---|---|---|---|---|
| Gambang | | 89.2 | 88.3 | - | - | - | 0.5 |
| Gerik | h | 97.8 | 95.4 | 98.4 | 100.8 | 100.0 | 0.1 |
| Gua Musang | i | 89.7 | 91.1 | 94.1 | 94.9 | 93.2 | |
| Ipoh | j | 88.3 | 90.9 | 90.1 | 92.1 | 98.9 | 0.5 |
| Jeli | k | 88.4 | 89.2 | 90.8 | 91.6 | 92.4 | 0.1 |
| Jerantut | l | 88.1 | 93.5 | 89.9 | 90.7 | 91.9 | 0.1 |
| Johor Bahru | m | 106.7 | 105.7 | 102.9 | 104.9 | 101.1 | 0.5 |
| Kg Keruak | | 89.7 | 91.7 | 92.5 | 103.3 | - | |
| Kota Bharu | n | 101.1 | 101.9 | 104.7 | 105.7 | 106.7 | 1 |
| Kuala Lumpur | o | 87.7 | 88.5 | 90.3 | 89.3 | 92.3 | 1 |
| KL2 | | - | 95.3 | - | - | - | 5 |
| KL2 | p | 98.3 | - | 100.1 | 106.7 | 96.3 | 2 |
| KT | q | 92.5 | 91.7 | 89.7 | 90.5 | 87.9 | 1 |
| Kuantan | r | 107.9 | 107.1 | 105.3 | 106.1 | 103.3 | 1 |
| Lenggong | s | - | 92.3 | - | - | - | |
| Machang | t | 95.5 | 96.5 | 98.5 | 99.3 | 100.9 | 2 |
| Maran | u | 87.9 | 91.2 | 94.7 | 89.6 | 90.4 | 0.25 |
| Melaka | v | 93.6 | 96.6 | 97.4 | 100.4 | 103.3 | 0.5 |
| Mersing | w | 90.1 | 90.9 | 92.9 | 89.1 | 88.3 | 1 |
| Paloh | | - | 90.7 | - | - | - | 0.1 |
| Penang | x | 101.7 | 93.9 | 88.5 | 92.1 | 98.9 | |
| Raub | y | - | 106.2 | - | - | - | 0.5 |
| Rompin | | 93.7 | - | 90.7 | 88.9 | - | |
| Sedeli | | 100.5 | 96.5 | - | - | - | |
| Seremban | z | 87.9 | 91.7 | 88.7 | 89.7 | 90.5 | 0.1 |
| Sik | aa | 99.5 | 102.7 | 105.9 | 106.7 | 107.5 | 1 |
| Sintok (UUM) | | 99.5 | 102.7 | 105.9 | 106.7 | 107.5 | |
| Taiping | bb | 103.3 | 107.1 | 105.3 | 106.1 | 107.9 | 0.5 |
| Tapah | cc | 88.7 | - | - | - | - | 0.5 |
| U. Tembeling | dd | 90.1 | 89.3 | 88.5 | 87.7 | - | 0.1 |

**National networks 1-6**: see below. KL2=KL/Selangor/Pahang (West). KT=Kuala Terengganu.

**Sites**: a) Gunung Jerai, b) Bukit Genting (Penang) c) Bukit Palong, d) Bukit Bintang, e) Gunung Berinchang, f) Bukit Botak, g) Bukit Bauk, h) RTM Gerik (Mempelam Sari), i) Bukit Chupak, j) Bukit Keledang, k) Bukit Tangki Air, l) Bukit Istana, m) Gunung Pulai, n) Telipot, o) Menara KL (Bukit Nanas), p) Gunung Ulu Kali, q) Bukit Besar, r) Bukit Pelindung, s) Bukit Ladang Teh, t) Bukit Bakar, u) Bukit Senggora, v) Gunung Ledang (Mt Ophir), w) Bukit Tinggi, x) Bukit Penara, y) Bukit Fraser, z) Bukit Telapa Burok, aa) Bukit Dedap, bb) Bukit Larut (Maxwell Hill) cc) Changkat Rembian,dd) Kampung Bantal, Ulu Tembeling.

**Asyik FM/Salam FM:** Cameron Highlands (G. Berinchang) 105.1MHz 0.1kW, Damak (Bukit Botak) 99.9MHz, Gunung Ledang 95.6MHz 0.25kW, Gunung Ulu Kali 102.5MHz 5kW, Kuala Lumpur 91.1MHz 1kW, Lenggong 97.3MHz, RTM Gerik (Mempelam Sari) 96.7MHz 0.1kW
**NB:** All **FM** powers throughout are TRP

**RTM national services**
**1) Klasik FM (R. Klasik):** 24h news, information & Malay oldies in Malay. **2) Nasional FM:** 24h General sce in Malay. **4) Traxx FM:** 24h News, music and travel sce in English. **5) Ai FM:** 24h General Sce in Chinese (Mandarin exc. news at 0200 in Hakka, 0500 Cantonese, 0700 Hakka & 1300 Chaozhou). **6) Minnal FM:** 24h General sce in Tamil.
**Asyik FM:** 0000-1500 for Orang Asli in Jakun, Malay, Semai, Temiar & Temuan. **Salam FM:** Rlg. prgrs in Malay from Jabatan Kemajuan Islam Malaysia 1500-2400 **V.** occasionally by letter or Email. **Ann:** names of networks and regional sces are sometimes preceded by the words 'Radio Malaysia'.

**RTM regional services in West Malaysia:**
Most sces. operate 24h in Malay. Exceptions include Langkawi, which carries local & tourist information in English and Malay. Some sces relay RTM Klasik Nasional overnight. Refer to above lists for tx sites and powers for frequencies marked av a.
**Johor:** Johor FM (JFM), Karung Berkunci 716, 80990 Johor Bahru, Johor. On 92.1MHz w, 101.9MHz m, 105.3MHz v – **Kedah:** Kedah FM, Kompleks Penerangan dan Penyiaran Sultan Abdul Halim, KM 3, Jalan Kuala Kedah, 05400 Alor Setar, Kedah. On 88.5MHz Selama-Bandar Baru (site Bukit Sungai Kecil Hilir) 0.25kW, 90.5MHz c, 97.5MHz a, 105.1MHz aa, 105.1MHz Sintok (UUM), 105.7MHz Gunung Raya 1kW – **Kelantan:** Kelantan FM, Peti Surat 143, 15720 Kota Bharu, Kelantan. On 88.1MHz FELDA Paloh 1kW, 97.3MHz t 102.9MHz n, 92.0MHz i 0.1kW, 90.0MHz i, 107.1MHz d – **Kuala Lumpur:** KL.fm On 97.2MHz o – **Langkawi (Kedah):** Langkawi FM, Tingkat 2, Bangunan Tabung Haji, Jalan Padang Mat Sirat, 07000 Kuah, Langkawi. On 87.5MHz Kuah 0.1kW, 104.8MHz Gunung Raya 1kW **English:** 0100-0400, 0700-1000 Malay/English 1300-1600 – **Melaka:** Melaka FM (MFM), Jalan Taming Sari, 75614 Melaka. On 102.3MHz v – **Negeri Sembilan:** Negeri

FM, Jalan Raja Ali, 71000 Seremban, Negeri Sembilan. On 92.5MHz z, 95.7MHz Gunung Tampin 0.1kW, 107.7MHz v – **Pahang:** Pahang FM, Peti Surat 152, 25710 Kuantan, Pahang. On 88.0MHz Bandar Muadzam Shah (Bukit Sembilan), 91.9MHz Rompin 0.25kW, 92.0MHz Maran 0.25kW, 92.7MHz l, 100.3MHz e, 104.1MHz r, 107.2 f, 107.5MHz p – **Perak:** Perak FM, Jalan Dairy, 31400 Ipoh, Perak. On 89.6MHz Tanjung Malim (Bukit Asa) 0.25kW, 94.2MHz Lenggong (Bukit Ladang Teh) 0.025kW, 94.7MHz e, 95.6MHz j, 96.2MHz h, 96.7MHz Gerik, 97.3MHz Changkat Rembian 0.5kW, 104.1MHz bb – **Perlis:** Perlis FM, Tingkat 6, Bangunan WSP, Jalan Bukit Lagi, 01000 Kangar, Perlis. On 102.9MHz Pauh 2kW – **Pulau Pinang (Penang):** Mutiara FM, Jalan Burmah, Peti Surat 433, 10350 Pulau Pinang. On 90.9MHz b, 93.9MHz a, 95.7MHz Bukit Penara 1kW – **Selangor:** Selangor FM Bangunan Sultan Salehudin Abdul Aziz Shah, 40000 Shah Alam, Selangor. On 99.8MHz Hulu Langat, 100.9MHz p – **Terengganu:** Terengganu FM, Peti Surat 63, 20914 Kuala Terengganu, Terengganu. On 88.7MHz q, 88.9MHz FELDA Tenang, 90.0MHz FELDA Cerul, 96.2MHz d, 97.7MHz g,

**RADIO TELEVISION MALAYSIA SABAH (Gov)**
Kompleks Bersepadu Kementerian Komunikasi dan Multimedia, Off Jalan Lintas Kepayan, 88200 Kota Kinabalu ☎ +60 88 712344
**Addresses of local stns:** Tingkat 6, Wisma Persekutuan, W.D.T. 52, 90500 Sandakan – Jalan Chong Thien Vun, Peti Surat 606, 91008 Tawau - Aras Bawah Rumah Persekutuan Keningau, Peti Surat 424, 89008 Keningau
**LP:** Dir. Broadcasting: Mr Ali Haji Ngasio. Dir. Tech. (R.): Cyril Simon.

**RADIO TELEVISION MALAYSIA LABUAN (Gov)**
Jalan Tanjung Taras, Peti Surat 81311, 87023 WP Labuan ☎ +60 87 415677 🖷 +60 87 416658

| FM (MHz) | Tx | SF | SV | 1 | 2 | 4 | 5 | kW |
|---|---|---|---|---|---|---|---|---|
| FELDA S | a | 104.1 | 106.7 | 99.9 | 102.9 | 104.9 | 105.7 | 0.1 |
| Gadong | b | 89.3 | 92.6 | 88.0 | 88.9 | 90.7 | 91.6 | 0.1 |
| Kota Belud | c | 101.5 | 104.1 | 99.9 | 100.7 | 102.5 | 103.3 | 0.1 |
| K. Kinabalu | d | 89.9 | 92.7 | 88.1 | 88.9 | 90.7 | 91.9 | 1 |
| Kudat | e | 95.9 | 98.9 | 94.1 | 94.9 | 96.7 | 98.1 | 1 |
| Labuan | f | - | 93.3 | 87.6 | 88.5 | 90.3 | 92.3 | 0.1 |
| Lahad Datu | g | 89.7 | 92.6 | 87.9 | 88.7 | 90.5 | 91.7 | 1 |
| Langkon | | 97.1 | 91.1 | 101.6 | 90.1 | 89.0 | 87.7 | 0.1 |
| Layang-L. | h | 104.5 | 107.1 | 99.5 | 100.3 | 105.3 | 106.3 | 1 |
| Luasong | | - | - | 87.7 | 88.5 | 89.3 | 90.1 | 0.1 |
| Nabawan | | - | - | 88.3 | 89.1 | 89.9 | 90.6 | |
| Sandakan | j | 92.9 | 96.1 | 91.1 | 92.1 | 94.3 | 95.1 | 1 |
| Sipitang | k | 97.9 | 102.9 | 95.5 | 96.5 | 99.1 | 99.9 | 1 |
| Tawau | l | 95.7 | 99.3 | 93.9 | 94.7 | 97.1 | 98.1 | 1 |
| Tenom | m | 90.3 | 93.1 | 88.5 | 89.3 | 91.7 | 92.3 | 1 |

**Sites:** , a) FELDA Sahabat, b) Bukit Gadong, c) Bukit Pompoda d) Kota Kinabalu (Bukit Lawa Mandau) e) Bukit Kelapa, f) Bukit Timbalai, g) Gunung Silam, h) Layang-Layang (Mount Kinabalu) j) Bukit Trig, k) Bukit Tampulung, l) Gunung Andrassy, m) Bukit Sigapon
**National networks: 1-5:** see RTM national sces above
**State networks: SF=** Sabah FM in Malay 24h. **Reg. N:** 2200, 2330, 0400, 0530, 0830, 1400. **SV= Sabah V FM in English** 0400-0700 & 1700-1900, Mandarin 0100-0400 inc. news in Hakka at 0100, Bajau 0700-1100; Dusun 1300-1700, Kadazan 2030-0100 & 0600-0830, Murut 1100-1300. **N.** (English): 0500
**Local Sces:** Labuan FM on 89.4MHz 0.1kW (Bukit Timbalai) & 103.7MHz 0.1kW (RTM Labuan): 2145-1200 incl. English 0100-0300 – Tawau FM on 93.6MHz 1 kW (Guning Silam), 99.1MHz 0.1kW (FELDA Sahabat), 100.1MHz 1kW (Gunung Andrassy): 2245-1100 in Malay – Sandakan FM on 90.1MHz 1kW (Bukit Trig): 2150-1100 – Keningau FM on 94.7MHz (Tenom), 98.4MHz (Keningau): 2300-0900 in Malay, Dusun and Murut

**RADIO TELEVISION MALAYSIA SARAWAK (Gov.)**
Broadcasting House, Jalan P. Ramlee, 93614 Kuching ☎ +60 82 248422 🖷 +60 82 246523
**L.P:** Dir. Broadcasting: vacant
**Addresses of local stns:** Bangunan Penyiaran, 98700 Limbang – Bangunan Penyiaran, Jalan Brighton, 98000 Miri – Bangunan Penyiaran, 96009 Sibu – Bangunan Penyiaran, 95000 Sri Aman – Bangunan Penyiaran, Jalan Sommerville, Bintulu

**Stations:** Kajang (near Kuala Lumpur).

| SW | kHz | kW | Netw. | SW | kHz | kW | Netw. |
|---|---|---|---|---|---|---|---|
| Kajang | 9835 | 100 | SF | Kajang | 11665 | 100 | W |

| FM (MHz) | Tx | SF | Red | 1 | 2 | 4 | 5 | kW |
|---|---|---|---|---|---|---|---|---|
| Belaga | | 105.4 | 107.8 | 103.8 | 104.6 | 106.2 | 107.0 | 0.1 |
| Betong | a | 94.4 | 97.8 | 92.8 | 93.6 | 95.2 | 96.0 | 0.1 |
| Bintulu | b | 93.7 | 100.5 | 87.9 | 90.3 | 98.5 | 99.3 | 1 |
| Dalat | | - | 96.9 | - | - | - | - | 0.1 |

| FM (MHz) | Tx | SF | Red | 1 | 2 | 4 | 5 | kW |
|---|---|---|---|---|---|---|---|---|
| Kapit | d | 92.7 | 89.9 | 90.7 | 91.9 | 88.1 | 88.9 | 0.1 |
| Kuching | e | 88.9 | 91.9 | 92.9 | 88.1 | 89.9 | 90.7 | 10 |
| Lambir Hills | f | 88.1 | 90.7 | 91.9 | 92.7 | 88.9 | 89.9 | 1 |
| Lawas | g | 97.5 | 100.5 | 94.7 | 96.7 | 98.5 | 99.3 | 0.1 |
| Limbang | h | 101.5 | 104.1 | 97.1 | 98.1 | 102.3 | 103.3 | 1 |
| Limbang | j | 100.0 | 107.7 | 95.3 | 99.2 | 106.0 | 106.8 | 0.1 |
| Marudi | k | - | - | 102.9 | - | - | - | 0.1 |
| Miri | l | 100.3 | 106.3 | 107.1 | 99.3 | 104.5 | 105.3 | 0.1 |
| Mukah | | 88.9 | 92.3 | 88.3 | 89.1 | 90.7 | 91.5 | 0.5 |
| Sarikei | m | 91.5 | 89.2 | 87.9 | 90.3 | 92.3 | 93.6 | 10 |
| Serian | n | 94.8 | 97.2 | 98.0 | 94.0 | 95.6 | 96.4 | 0.5 |
| Sibu | o | 101.5 | 104.1 | 95.5 | 98.5 | 102.5 | 103.3 | 0.1 |
| Song | p | 95.7 | 99.0 | 91.1 | 92.2 | 96.7 | 97.5 | 1 |
| Sri Aman | q | 100.3 | 106.3 | 107.3 | 98.9 | 92.3 | 105.3 | 1 |
| Stapong | r | 95.1 | 101.1 | 93.3 | 94.1 | 95.9 | 97.1 | 1 |
| Suai | s | 97.1 | - | 95.1 | - | - | - | |

SF=Sarawak FM, W=Wai FM, Red=Red FM L=Limbang FM S=Sibu
**National networks:** 1, 2, 4, 5: see RTM national sces
**SW:** 9835kHz: 2200-1600 (rel. Sarawak FM). 11665kHz: 2200-1600 (rel. Wai FM)
**FM:** Additional local sce. freqs: Gunung Serapi (Kuching) 101.3MHz 10kW (Wai FM Iban) & 106.1MHz (Wai FM Bidayuh / Kayan-Kenyah), Bukit Ampangan 101.7MHz 0.5kW (Wai FM Bidayuh / Kayan-Kenyah) & 106.9MHz 0.5kW (Wai FM Iban).
**Sites:** a) Off. Spaoh b) Bukit Setiam c) Bukit Nyabau d) Bukit Kapit e) Gunung Serapi f) Bukit Lambir g) Bukit Tiong h) Bukit Mas j) Bukit Sagan Rudang, k) BukitDabei, l) RTM Miri, m) Bukit Dabei, n) Bukit Ampangan o) Bukit Lima p) Bukit Song q) Bukit Temunduk r) Bukit Singgalang s) Bukit TT 844.
**State networks: Sarawak FM** in Malay 24h. **N.** (Kuching): 2200, 0400, 1000, 1400. **Red FM** 2200-1600, in Chinese: 2200-0200, 0700-1300; English: 0200-0700, 1300-1600. Educational prgs during school terms: MF 0100-0300. **N.** (Kuching): English 0400, 0700, 1300; Chinese 0000, 0801, 1000, 1245; Hakka 1030; Hokkien 1045. **Wai FM** 2200-1600 in Iban. Relays Limbang FM Mon/Thurs 1300-1400. **Wai FM:** 2200-1600, in Bidayuh: 2200-0400 & 1000-1600; Kayan/Kenyah: 0400-1000. FM txs of all state networks relay Sarawak FM 1600-2200.
**Local sces: Bintulu FM:** 0100-1100 in Malay and Iban. RTM Bintulu 95.3MHz 1kW, Bukit Setiam 97.5MHz 1kW. **Limbang FM:** in Malay 0100-0400, 1000-1300; Lun Bawang (Murut) 0400-0700, also relayed via Kuching 7270kHz; Bisaya 0700-1000; Iban 1300-1400 also relayed by Wai FM Iban Mon/Thurs. Bukit Mas 104.9MHz 1kW, Bukit Tiong 101.1MHz 0.1kW, Bukit Sagan Rudang 94.5MHz 0.1kW. **Miri FM:** in Malay 0000-0300, 1000-1300, Chinese 0700-1000, Iban 0400-0700, Kenyah 0300-0400. Lambir Hills 95.7MHz 1kW, Miri (RTM Miri) 98.0MHz 0.1kW. **Sibu FM:** in Malay 0100-0400, 1000-1300, Chinese 0700-1000, Iban 0400-0700. Bukit Lima 87.6MHz 0.1kW, Bukit Kayu Malam 94.6MHz 1kW, Bukit Song 99.8MHz 1kW, Bukit Kapit 94.3MHz 0.1kW, Belaga 103.0MHz 0.1kW, Bukit Singgalang 102.1MHz 1kW, Mukah 98.7MHz 0.5kW. **Sri Aman (RaSa FM):** in Malay, Iban, Chinese. Bukit Temunduk 89.5MHz 1kW. **NB** Local sces relay Wai FM Iban 2200-0100 and from close of local prgrs until 1600, and relay Sarawak FM 1600-2200.
**IS:** A musical phrase (played on a native instrument, the Sape), alternating between A and F.

## ASTRO RADIO SDN. BHD. (Comm.)
✉ All Asia Broadcast Centre, Technology Park Malaysia, Bukit Jalil, 57000 Kuala Lumpur **W:** astroradio.com.my
**L.P:** CEO: Mr Jake Abdullah

| FM(MHz) | Tx | MY | ERA | Lite | Mix | Hitz | Sin | Mel | THR | Zay |
|---|---|---|---|---|---|---|---|---|---|---|
| Alor Setar | a | 99.7 | 103.6 | 104.4 | 91.0 | 92.8 | 97.1 | 106.5 | 102.4 | 98.1 |
| Ipoh | b | 100.6 | 103.7 | 101.5 | 94.3 | 92.7 | 96.9 | 98.5 | 102.7 | 106.4 |
| Johor Bahru | c | 95.4 | 104.5 | 94.6 | 99.1 | 97.6 | 87.8 | 98.4 | 103.7 | 92.8 |
| Johor Bahru | d | - | - | - | - | - | 103.3 | - | - | - |
| Kota Bharu | e | 102.3 | 103.3 | 104.3 | 94.6 | 92.8 | 93.8 | 99.8 | 88.1+ | |
| KK | f | 104.0 | 102.4 | 103.2 | 101.6 | 100.8 | 104.9 | 98.6 | - | - |
| KT | g | 101.2 | 102.8 | 105.9 | 98.3 | 94.8 | 97.5 | 104.0 | 100.2+ | |
| KL/Selangor | h | 101.8 | 103.3 | 105.7 | 94.5 | 92.9 | 96.7 | 103.0 | 99.3 | 104.9 |
| Kuantan | i | 101.1 | 98.0 | 104.7 | 94.1 | 93.2 | 97.2 | 100.0 | 88.8+ | 91.6 |
| Kuching | j | 96.9 | 96.1 | 100.1 | 97.7 | 95.3 | 102.1 | 103.7 | - | - |
| Langkawi | k | 100.1 | 90.7 | - | - | 92.4 | 100.9 | - | 101.9 | - |
| Melaka | | 106.4 | 90.3 | 92.2 | 91.1 | 93.0 | 96.0 | 107.3 | 99.7 | 98.9 |
| Miri | m | 103.2 | 101.3 | - | - | 105.8 | 87.7 | 102.4 | - | - |
| Penang | | - | - | - | - | - | - | - | 99.3 | - |
| Sandakan | o | 100.6 | 103.0 | - | - | 99.8 | 106.9 | 102.2 | - | - |
| Seremban | p | 100.6 | 103.6 | 104.6 | 94.2 | 96.6 | 96.9 | 97.9 | 101.5 | - |
| Taiping | q | 100.2 | 95.2 | 89.3 | 91.3 | 93.6 | 96.4 | 104.9 | 102.1 | - |
| Tapah | r | - | 102.0 | - | - | - | - | - | - | - |

**Prgrs: MY FM:** Music channel in Mandarin & Cantonese. **ERA:** Contemporary Malaysian music channel in Malay. **Lite FM:** Easy listening music in English. **Mix FM:** Music and variety in English. **Hitz.fm:** Top 40 presented in English. **Sinar FM:** Malay oldies. **Melody FM:** Programming in Chinese. **THR Raaga:**Music and traffic information presented in Tamil. 24h. **THR Gegar:** Separate prgrs in Malay for East Coast on freqs marked +. **Zayan FM:** Islamic music presented in Malay.
**GoXuan FM:** 24h in Chinese on Kuala Lumpur/Klang Valley (Gunung Ulu Kali) 88.9MHz 2kW, Penang (Bukit Penara & Batu Ferranghi) 107.6MHz.
**Sites:** a) Gunung Jerai b) Bukit Keledang c) Gunung Pulai d) Metropolis Tower, JB e) Bukit Panau f) Kota Kinabalu (Bukit Kokol) g) Kuala Terengganu (Bukit Jerung) h) Gunung Ulu Kali i) Bukit Pelindong j) Bukit Djin k) Gunung Raya l) Gunung Ledang m) Tanjong Lobang n) Bukit Penara o) Bukit Trig p) Telapa Barok q) Bukit Larut r) Changkat Rembian.
**TRP:** generally 2kW, exc. Sinar FM at sites e, f, j, k and l: 0.25kW, THR 1kW exc 0.5kW at sites b, n and q.

## BFM MEDIA (Comm.)
✉ 5.01 Wisma BU8, 11 Lebuh Bandar Utama, 47800 Petaling Jaya ☎ +60 3 7629 7112 **W:** bfm.my **L.P:** Exec. Dir: Malek Ali
**BFM:** Kuala Lumpur/Klang Valley (Gunung Ulu Kali) 89.9MHz, 24h business prgrs and music in E and Malay.

## CENSE MEDIA SDN. BHD. (Community Radio)
✉ L-72-3 Block L, KK Times Square, Off Coastal Highway, 88100 Kota Kinabalu, Sabah **W:** kupikupifm.my
**City Plus:** Seremban 106.0MHz (Gunung Telapa Burok), 24h in Chinese.
**Kupi-Kupi FM:** Kota Kinabalu (Bukit Keratong) 96.3 MHz, 24h in Malay & English.

## DIGITAL MEDIA BROADCASTING SDN. BHD. (Bernama News Agency) (Gov.)
✉ 15th Fl, Wisma Bernama, 28 Jalan 1/65A, off Jalan Tun Razak, 53300 Kuala Lumpur ☎+60 3 2692 7939 📠 +60 3 2692 8939
**W:** radio24.com.my
**Bernama Radio:** Kuala Lumpur/Klang Valley (Bukit Nanas), 93.9MHz 1kW, Johor Bahru (Gunung Pulai) 107.5MHz 1kW, Kota Kinabalu (Bukit Keratong) 107.9 MHz, Kuching (Bukit Antu) 100.9 MHz, 24h in E and Malay.

## GENMEDIA SDN. BHD. (1Malaysia for Youth) (Comm.)
✉ Unit C-06-11, Block C, Plaza Mont Kiara, 55100 Kuala Lumpur ☎ +60 3 6206 4848 **W:** 1m4youth.my
**1M4U FM:** Kuala Lumpur/Klang Valley (Bukit Sungai Besi) 107.9MHz, 24h prgr. for young people and volunteers in E and Malay.

## HUSA NETWORK SDN. BHD. (Comm.)
✉ Tingkat 2&3, Bangunan Epic Pavilion, Jalan Pejabat, 20200 Kuala Terengganu ☎ +60 9 6262255 📠 +60 9 6262266
**W:** manis.fm
**Manis FM:** Kota Bharu (Tunjung) 90.6MHz, Kuantan (Bukit Pelindong) 95.1MHz, Kuala Terengganu (Bukit Jerung) 102.0MHz. Prgrs in Malay.
**TRP:** all sites 2kW

## INSTITUT KEFAHAMAN ISLAM MALAYSIA (Institute of Islamic Understanding) (Gov., Rlg.)
✉ No 2, Langgak Tunku, Off Jalan Duta, 50480 Kuala Lumpur ☎+60 3 62046273 📠 +60 3 620462779 **W:** ikimfm.my
**L.P:** Dir. of R.: Nik Roskiman bin Abdul Samad

| FM | Tx | MHz | FM | Tx | MHz |
|---|---|---|---|---|---|
| Alor Setar | a | 89.0 | Kuching | h | 93.6 |
| Ipoh | b | 102.7 | Lahad Datu | n | 107.3 |
| Johor Bahru | c | 106.2 | Melaka | j | 89.5 |
| Kota Bharu | d | 89.9 | Miri | o | 104.0 |
| Kota Kinabalu | e | 93.9 | Negeri Sembilan | k | 102.7 |
| Kuala Lumpur | i | 91.5 | Penang (Balik Pulau) | l | 102.7 |
| Kuala Terengganu | f | 100.2 | Tawau | m | 100.7 |
| Kuantan | g | 89.5 | | | |

**Radio Ikim (IKIM.FM):** 24h in Malay with limited Arabic and English.
**Sites:** a) Gunung Jerai, b) Bukit Keledang, c) Gunung Pulai, d) Bukit Panau, e) Bukit Kokol, f) Bukit Besar, g) Bukit Pelindong 2, h) Pending, i) Bukit Cincin, j) Gunung Ledang, k) Gunung Telapa Burok l) Bukit Genting m) Gunung Andrassy. n)Gunung Silam o)Tanjung Lobang **TRP:** sites a-k: 2kW

## KRISTAL HARTA SDN. BHD. (CATS RADIO) (Comm.)
✉ Lot 287, Jalan Bako, Petra Jaya, 93050 Kuching, Sarawak ☎ +60 82 311799 📠 +60 82 254993 **W:** catsfm.my **L.P:** Chmn: Tan Sri

Datuk Amar Haji Bujang Mohd Nor. **GM:** Haji Mohd Iskandar Hajni Mohd Nawawi

| FM | Tx location | MHz | FM | Tx location | MHz |
|----|-------------|-----|----|-------------|-----|
| Bintulu | Bukit Setiam | 88.3 | Sarikei | Bt. K. Malam | 96.7 |
| Kuching | Gunung Serapi | 99.3 | Sibu | Bukit Lima | 88.4 |
| Limbang | Bukit Mas | 88.7 | Sibu | Bt. Singgalang | 99.9 |
| Miri | Lambir Hills | 93.3 | Sri Aman | Bt. Temudok | 88.7 |
| Mukah | Mukah | 95.7 | | | |

**Prgr.:** 24h in Malay, E and Iban. **TRP:** all sites 1kW

## MEDIA PRIMA BHD. (Comm.)

✉ Tingkat 2, South Wing, Sri Pentas, Persiaran Bandar Utama, 47800 Petaling Jaya, Selangor Darul Ehsan ☎ +60 3 77105022 🖷 +60 3 77107098 **W:** hotfm.com.my or flyfm.com.my or onefm.com.my
**L.P:** Head of Radio Ntwks: Ahmad Izham Omar

| FM(MHz) | Tx | Hot | Fly | One | FM(MHz) | Tx | Hot | Fly | One |
|---------|----|-----|-----|-----|---------|----|-----|-----|-----|
| Alor Setar | a | 88.2 | 99.1 | 87.8 | Kuantan | h | 92.4 | 87.6 | 100.4 |
| Ipoh | b | 104.5 | 87.9 | 87.6 | Kuching | | 94.3 | - | 98.3 |
| Johor Bahru | c | 90.1 | 102.5 | 105.3 | Melaka | j | 104.3 | 94.0 | 88.1 |
| Kota Bharu | d | 105.1 | 107.4 | - | Penang | k | - | 89.9 | - |
| Kota Kinabalu | e | 87.7 | - | 95.7 | Seremban | l | 99.5 | 98.6 | 88.3 |
| KL/Selangor | f | 97.6 | 95.8 | 88.1 | Taiping | m | 90.5 | - | - |
| KT | g | 105.0 | 107.5 | - | | | | | |

**Hot FM:** 24h in Malay. Hot FM freqs are licensed to Synchrosound Studios Sdn Bhd. **Fly FM:** 24h in English/Malay. FlyFM freqs are licensed to Malaysian Airports (Sepang) Sdn. Bhd. **One FM:** 24h in Mandarin and Cantonese **Kool FM:** 24h in Malay on 101.3MHz in KL area (Bukit Sungai Besi) 1kW, 90.2MHz in Penang area (Bukit Penara) 2kW, 88.6MHz Kota Bharu (Peringat), 93.6MHz Kuala Terengganu (g), 107.3MHz Alor Setar (Menara Alor Setar)
**Sites:** a) Gunung Jerai exc. 99.1MHz: Menara Alor Setar b) Bukit Keledang c) Gunung Pulai exc. 105.3MHz: Taman Sentosa, JB d) Peringat e) Hot FM: Bukit Kokol, One FM: Bukit Karatong f) Gunung Ulu Kali g) Kuala Terengganu (Bukit Besar) h) Bukit Pelindong i) Hot FM: Gunung Serapi, One FM: Bukit Djin j) Gunung Ledang k) Bukit Penara l) Bukit Telapa Burok exc. One FM: Bukit Gan m) Bukit Larut. **TRP:** Fly FM 0.25kW exc. Bukit Cincin: 2kW

## RIMAKMUR SDN. BHD. (Comm.)

✉ Tropicana City Office Towers, Level 2.01, No. 3, Jalan SS 20/27, 47400 Petaling Jaya, Selangor Darul Ehsan ☎ +60 3 78851188 🖷 +60 3 78851099 **W:** suriafm.com.my **L.P:** COO: Engku Emran Engku Zainal Abidin

| FM | Tx | MHz | FM | Tx | MHz |
|----|----|-----|----|----|-----|
| Alor Setar | a | 106.9 | Kuala Terengganu | g | 102.4 |
| Ipoh | b | 96.0 | Kuantan | h | 96.1 |
| Johor Bahru | c | 101.4 | Melaka | i | 88.5 |
| Klang Valley (KL) | d | 105.3 | Seremban | j | 107.0 |
| Kota Bharu | e | 106.1 | Taiping | k | 91.7 |
| Kota Kinabalu | f | 105.9 | | | |

**Suria FM:** 24h in Malay. **Sites:** a) Gunung Jerai b) Bukit Keledang c) Gunung Pulai d) Bukit Panau e) Bukit Kokol g) Bukit Besar h) Bukit Pelindong 2 i) Gunung Ledang j) Bukit Telapa Burok k) Bukit Larut. Kota Kinabalu 105.9MHz carries local prgrs at times.

## SENANDUNG SONIK SDN. BHD. (Comm.)

**Tea FM:** Kota Kinabalu (Bukit Keratong) 102.8MHz, Kuching (Bukit Antu) 102.7MHz, Sibu (Bukit Lima) 100.7MHz. 24h in Chinese.

## STAR RFM SDN. BHD. (Comm.)

✉ Tropicana City Office Towers Level 2.01 No 3, Jalan SS20/27, 47400 Petaling Jaya, Selangor Darul Ehsan ☎ +60 3 78851188 🖷 +60 3 78851099 **W:** 988.com.my **E:** rfm988@silicon.net.my

| FM(MHz) | Tx | 988 | FM(MHz) | Tx | 988 |
|---------|----|-----|---------|----|-----|
| Alor Setar | a | 96.1 | Kuantan | e | 90.4 |
| Ipoh | b | 99.8 | Melaka | f | 98.2 |
| Johor Bahru | c | 99.9 | Penang | g | 94.5 |
| KL/Selangor | d | 98.8 | Seremban | h | 93.3 |

**Red FM:** carrying test transmissions during 2017 **988** (jiu ba ba): 24h in Mandarin & Chinese dialects. **Sites:** a) Gunung Jerai b) Gunung Keledang c) Gunung Pulai d) Gunung Ulu Kali e) Bukit Pelindong f) Gunung Ledang g) Bukit Penara h) Bkt Telapa Burok

## SUARA JOHOR (Comm.)

✉ Bukit Pelangi, Jalan Pasir Pelangi, 80050 Johor Bahru, Johor ☎ +60 7 3314104 🖷 +60 7 3351104 **L.P:** CEO: Haji Bakhtiar Haji Arshad
**BEST 104:** Melaka & Segamat (Gunung Ledang) 94.8MHz, Johor Bahru (Gunung Pulai) 104.1MHz 10kW TRP, Kuala Lumpur/Selangor (Gunung Ulu Kali) 104.1MHz, Mersing (Bukit Tinggi) 102.5MHz
**D.Prgr:** 24h (Malay & E music)

---

**University stations:**
**Putra FM,** ✉ Tingkat 2 Jabatan Komunikasi, Fakulti Bahasa Moden dan Komunikasi, Universiti Putra Malaysia, 43400 UPM Serdang, Selangor **W:** putrafm.upm.edu.my
**Station:** 90.7MHz 1kW: Mon-Fri 0200-1600 in Malay & E
**Radio UiTM (UFM),** ✉ Level 13, Menara Ilmu Universiti Teknologi MARA, 40450 Bandaraya Shah Alam, Selangor **W:** uitm.edu.my/ufm
**Station:** 93.6MHz 1kW
**KK FM,** ✉ University Malaysia Sabah (UMS), Jalan UMS, 88400 Kota Kinabalu, Sabah **W:** kkfm.my **Station:** 91.1MHz

## MALDIVES

**L.T:** UTC +5h — **Pop:** 400,000 — **Pr.L:** Dhivehi (Maldivian) — **E.C:** 50Hz, 230V — **ITU:** MLD

## MALDIVES BROADCASTING COMMISSION

✉ G. Billoorijehige (3rd Floor), Majeedhee Magu, Malé ☎ +960 3334333 🖷 +960 3334334 **W:** broadcom.org.mv **E:** info@broadcom.org.mv **L.P:** DG: Ibrahim Khaleel.

## PUBLIC SERVICE MEDIA (Pub.)

✉ Radio Building, Ameenee Magu, 20331 Malé ☎ +960 3000300 🖷 +960 3317273 **W:** psm.mv **E:** info@psm.mv
**Dhivehi Raajjeyge Adu** (Voice of Maldives): **MW:** Thilafushi 1449kHz 10kW. **FM:** Malé 89.0MHz 1kW, Foahmula 89.0MHz 0.5kW, Addu 90.0MHz 0.5kW. **D.Prgr.** in Dhivehi: 24h. English: 1300-1315.
**Dhivehi FM:** Malé 91.0MHz 1kW. **Dheenuge Adu:** Malé 90.0MHz.

**Other stations:**
**Capital R,** Malé: 93.6MHz — **Dhi FM,** Malé: 95.2MHz — **Faraway FM,** Malé: 96.6MHz — **H FM,** Malé: 92.6MHz — **R. Atoll** (Rlg.), Malé: 96.0MHz **W:** radioatoll.com

## MALI

**L.T:** UTC — **Pop:** 19 million — **Pr.L:** French, Bambara, Peuls, Sonrhai, Sarakolé, Bobo, others — **E.C:** 50Hz, 220V — **ITU:** MLI

## HAUTE AUTORITÉ DE LA COMMUNICATION (HAC)

✉ B.P. 116, Bamako ☎ +223 20232101

## OFFICE DE RADIODIFFUSION TÉLÉVISION DU MALI (ORTM, Gov.)

✉ B.P. 171, Rue del Marne 287, Bamako ☎ +223 20212019 🖷 +223 20214205 **W:** ortm.ml **E:** info@ortm.info
**L.P:** DG: Baba Dagamaissa. Dir. Nat. Radio: Oumar Sangare. Dir. Rural Radio: Mamadou Niama Diarra. Dir. Transm. Netw.: Soumailou Aboubacrine Dicko.
**SW:** Bamako (Kati) 50/100kW

| kHz | Times | kHz | Times |
|-----|-------|-----|-------|
| †5995 | 0555-0800, 1800-2400 | †9635 | 0800-1800 |

**FM Stations:**
**National R.** Bamako: 92.0MHz 1 kW + 47 txs of 0.5/0.25kW
**Regional R. (Channel 2)**

| Location | MHz | kW | Location | MHz | kW |
|----------|-----|----|----------|-----|----|
| Mopti | 94.4 | 10 | Ségou | 96.8 | 1 |
| Bamako | 95.2 | 1 | Sikasso | 98.3 | 1 |
| Kayes | 95.4 | 10 | | | |

**National R. (Radio Mali)** in French/Arabic/English/Bambara/others: SW & FM. **D.Prgr:** 0555-2400. **N. in English:** Sat 1905-1920.
**Regional R. (Channel 2)** on FM only: **D.Prgr:** 0800-1945.
**Ann:** "Vous écoutez l'office de Radiodiffusion-Télévision Malienne émettant de Bamako". **E:** "This is Bamako, Mali Radio Telecommunications". **IS:** Guitar.

## MIKADO FM (United Nations' Minusma operation)

☎ +223 44927070 **W:** minusma.unmissions.org/mikado-fm-la-radio-de-la-paix **E:** radio.mikado@gmail.com
**FM**(MHz): Bamako 106.6, Gao 94.0, Mopti 91.8, Timbuktu 92.6.

**Other stations in Bamako:**
**R. Patriote FM** 88.1MHz — **R. Canal 2000:** 90.7MHz. **W:** membres.lycos.fr/canal2000 — **R. Mirador** 91.1MHz — **La Voix de la Verité** 91.5MHz — **Fréquence 3** 93.8MHz — **R. Tabalé** 94.3MHz — **R. Guintan** 94.7MHz — **R. Benkan** 97.1MHz — **R.Liberté** 97.7MHz **W:** comfm.com/live/radio/radioliberte **E:** liberte@mtelecom-mali.net — **R. Bamakan** 100.3MHz — **R. Klédu** FM 101.2MHz — **R Jekafo** 100.7MHz — **R. Kayira FM** 104.4MHz — **R. Voix de l'Islam** 107.4MHz.
**R. Rurale:** Kolondieba 93.7MHz, Koutiala, Macina and others.

**RFI Afrique**: Gao 92.1, Segou 93.6, Sikasso 95.0, Mopti 97.7, Bamako 98.5, Kayes 102.2MHz in French/Mandinka.
**BBC African Service**: Bamako 88.9MHz.
**VOA African Sce**: Timbuktu 90.3, Gao 92.9, Bamako 102.0MHz

## MALTA

**L.T:** UTC +1h (31 Mar-27 Oct: +2h) — **Pop:** 430,000 — **Pr.L:** English, Maltese — **E.C:** 50Hz, 230V — **ITU:** MLT

### MALTA BROADCASTING AUTHORITY
### (Regulatory Authority)
7 Mile-end Rd, Hamrun HMR1719 ☎ +356 21221281, 21247908 +356 21240855 **E:** info.ba@ba.org.mt **W:** ba-malta.org **LP:** Chrmn: Mr. M Micallef, Chief Exec: Dr. Pierre Cassar

### PUBLIC BROADCASTING SERVICES LTD
75, St. Luke's Road, Gwardamangia MSD 09 ☎ +356 21225051 +356 21244601 **E:** info@tvm.com.mt **W:** tvm.com.mt/mt/radio
**LP:** Head of News: Reno Bugeja. Chief Exec.: John Bundy, Consultant Manager: Costantino Abela
**RADIO MALTA**
**MW:** Bizbizja 999kHz 5kW **FM:** Bizbizja 93.7MHz 8kW, 107.5MHz 0.025kW **D.Prgr:** 24h. **N:** D.Prgr: 24h. N: 0700 - 0800 - 1000 - 1200 - 1600 - 1800 - 2230. BBC News 0900 - 1100. **RFI** News 1400
**RADJU MALTA 2: FM:** 105.9MHz 8kW
**MAGIC MALTA: FM:** 91.7MHz 8kW, 24h
**DIGI B NETWORK LTD:** 136, Alwetta Street, Mosta MST4508 ☎ +356 27420570 **E:** info@digibnetwork.com **W:** digibnetwork.com **LP:** Man. Dir: Sergio D'Amico.
**DAB+:** 6A, 6C, 12A, Bouquet includes local, gov. and international stns.

### COMMERCIAL STATIONS:
**89.7 BAY**, Eden Place, St. George's Bay, St. Julian's STJ3310 ☎+356 23710800 +356 23710845 **E:** bayproduction@bay.com.mt **W:** bay. com.mt **LP:** Stn Mngr: Kevin DeCesare Jnr - **FM:** 89.7MHz 8kW –
**CALYPSO TEN-18**, 28 New Street in Valletta Road, Luqa ☎+356 21578022/52102055 +35621578026 **E:** calypsoradio1@gmail.com **W:** calypsoradio.com **LP:** Dir.: Frank Camilleri-Freddie Cacciatolo - **FM:** 101.8MHz 8kW – **CAMPUS FM**, University Broadcasting Services, Old Humanities Building, University of Malta, Tal-Qroqq Msida MSD 06 ☎+356 21333313 +356 21314485 **E:** campusfm@um.edu.mt **W:** campusfm.um.edu.mt **LP:** Stn Mngr: Rev. Joseph Borg, Prod. Co-ord.: Ms. Celaine Buhagiar. - **FM:** 103.7MHz 8kW. Also rel. BBC WS – **ONE R.**, A28B, Industrial Estate, Marsa, LQA 06 ☎+35625682568 +35621248249 **E:** onenews@one.com.mt **W:** one.com.mt **LP:** Man. Dir.: Dr. Michael Vella-Haber, Senior Man. Broadc.: Ms. Ruth Vella Micallef, Man. R.: Pierre Borg - **FM:** 92.7MHz 8kW, 88.2MHz 200W, 88.0MHz 25W.(Operated by Maltese Labour Party) – **R. 101**, 2 Triq Herbert Ganado, Pieta' PTA1450 ☎+356 21230101 +356 21240261 **E:** studio@ radio101.com.mt **W:** radio101.com.mt - **FM:** 101.0MHz 8kW, 95.5MHz 300W. (Operated by Maltese Nationalist Partys) – **R. MARIJA**, Kunvent Patrijiet Dumnikani, Misrah San Duminku, Rabat RBT 2521 ☎+356 21453105/21452474 +356 21453103 **E:** info.mal@radiomaria.org **W:** radjumarija.org **LP:** Coordinator: Michael Amato - **FM:** 102.3MHz 8kW, 107.8MHz 200W – **RTK, MEDIA CENTRE**, Archdiocese of Malta and Diocese of Ghawdex, Triq Nazzjonali, Blata-Badja HMR02 ☎+356 2569 9400/2124 6714-5 +356 2569 9151/9160 **E:** info@rtk.org.mt **W:** rtk.org.mt **LP:** Chmn: Lino Casapinta, Stn Man.: Karl Wright (kwright@rtk.com.mt) Prgr Man.: Tonio Bonello (tbonello@rtk.com.mt). Technical Manager: George Pollacco (studios@rtk.com.mt). Head of News: Josianne Camilleri (josianne@newsbook.com.mt) - **FM:** 103.0MHz 8kW, Ghawdex 97.8MHz 400W, Malta 97.6MHz 250W – **SMASH R.**, 4 Thistle Lane, Paola PLA 19 ☎+356 21667777 +356 21697830 **E:** info@smashmalta.com **W:** smashmalta.com - **FM:** 104.6MHz 8kW – **VIBE FM**, Triq Tas-Sliema, Kappara, San Gwann, SGN4411 ☎+356 21385887 +356 21383826 **E:** info@vibefm.com. mt **W:** vibefm.com.mt **LP:** Head: Justin Chircop - **FM:** 88.7MHz 8kW – **XFM 100.2**, 15, Naxxar Road, Birkirkara, BKR 9043 ☎+356 21378871 **E:** info@ xfm.com.mt **W:** xfm.com.mt - **FM:** 100.2MHz 8kW
**Established Community Stations (all MHz):**
Bastjanizi FM 95.0, Big FM 107.1, BKR Radio 94.5FM 94.5, Deejays R. 95.6FM: 95.6, Energy FM 96.4, 96.5, Hearth 94.3FM 94.3, Kottoner 98 FM 98.0, La Salle FM 99.4, Lehen il-Belt Gorgjana 105.6, Lehen il-Belt Victoria 104.0, Mics R. 93.3, Pure Gold Christian R. 97.8, R. City 107.6FM: 107.6, R. Galaxy Network 105.0, Radju Bambina 98.3, Radju Elenjani 95.8FM: 95.8, Radju Hompesch 90.0, Radju Katidral 90.9, Radju Lehen il-Qala 106.3, Radju Luminarja 106.9, Radju Prekursur 99.3, Radju Sacro Cuor 105.2, Radju Santa Katarina 90.6, Radju Sokkors 95.1, Radju Vilhena 106.0, Radju Vizitazzjoni 92.4, Radju Xeb-er-ras 90.8, South End

FM 91.0, Trinitarji FM 89.3, Y4J Radio 105.4
**Temporary Community Stations (all MHz):**
Temp. licences up to 2 years and powers of 0.25-1W: Circuit Assembly of Jehovah's Witnesses 108.0, Guzeppini 891FM 89.1, Int. Bible Students Assoc. 108.0, Lehen il-Karmelitani 101.4, MMG FM 97.5, Radio 12th May 96.5, R. Leonardo 105.2, Radju 15 t'Awwissu 98.3, Radju Banda Fgura 93.1, Radju al Tarxien 99.0, Radju Kazin Banda San Filep 106.3, Radju Lauretana 89.3, Radju Margerita 96.1, Radju Maria Bambina 90.2FM: 90.2, Radju Marija Assunta 98.9, Radju Sant'Andrija 88.4, Tal-Gilju FM95.4: 95.4

## MARSHALL IS (USA associated)

**L.T:** UTC +12h — **Pop:** 53,167— **Pr.L:** English, Kajin Majol — **E.C:** 60Hz, 110/220V — **ITU:** MHL

### RADIO MARSHALL ISLANDS (Gov/Comm)
PO Box 19, Majuro 96960 ☎+692 625 8413 Studio ☎ + 692 625 8411 **E:** v7ab@ntamar.net **W:** www.v7abradio.info (audio streaming) **LP:** GM: Antari Elbon, PD: Arden Sorimle, CE: Stanny Wottokna
**MW:** V7AB 1098kHz 25kW **FM:** 88.9MHz **D.Prgr:** 1830(Sun 1900)-1130
**News:** Local bulletins, also RNZI & BBC.

**OTHER STATIONS:**

| MW | kHz | kW | Station |
|---|---|---|---|
| 1) Majuro | ‡1170 | 5 | Eagle Christian R. (Currently inactive) |

| FM | MHz | kW | Station | FM | MHz | kW | Station |
|---|---|---|---|---|---|---|---|
| 7) Majuro | 90.7 | 0.3 | Joy-FM | 5) Majuro | 103.5 | | Power 103.5 |
| 2) Majuro | 95.5 | | V7MI | 3) Majuro | 104.1 | | V7AA |
| 4) Majuro | 96.5 | 0.03 | WSO-FM | 6) Majuro | 105.0 | | V7WU |
| 8) Majuro | 98.5 | | BBC | | | | |

**Addresses & other information:**
**1)** Bukot Nan Jesus Church, Majuro 96960 ☎+692 625 7914 **E:** eagle1@ntamar.net **W:** facebook.com/1st-bnj-international-eagle-christian-radio-999fm-1170am **LP:** Pastor Paul & Laura Hensene **D.Prgr:** 1800-1200 **ID:** 'V7Eagle'– **2)** Pacific Media Services, Majuro 96960 ☎+692 625 2911 **E:** v7emon@ntamar.net **LP:** Mgr: Fred Pedro, CE: Benitito Kom **ID:** "V7Emon" (='V7Good') **Format:** music, local/ international news, talkback – **3)** Majuro Independent Baptist Church, PO Drawer H, Majuro 96960-1008 ☎+692 625 3141 +692 625 3141 **E:** v7aafm@ntamar.net **ID:** "The Change 104.1FM" – **4)** National Weather Radio, Majuro 96960. Live and recorded local weather and emergency information for the Majuro atoll area, 24h – **5)** "Power 103.5" Rairikku, Majuro Atoll, 96960 ☎+692 247 1035 **W:** www. facebook.com/majuropower103.5fm/ – **6)** WUTMI-FM, Women United Together Marshall Islands, PO Box 105, Majuro 96960 **W:** wutmirmi. com **Prgr:** women's prgrs 10.5 hours daily – **7)** Joy-FM C/- Delap Seventh-day Adventist School PO Box I, Majuro, MH 96960 – **8)** Broadcasting House, Portland Place, London W1A 1AA **E:** worldservice. letters@bbc.co.uk

## MARTINIQUE (France)

**L.T:** UTC -4h — **Pop:** 385,000 — **Pr.L:** French, Creole — **E.C:** 50Hz, 220V — **ITU:** MRT

### MARTINIQUE PREMIÈRE (Pub)
La Clairière, BP 662, 97263 Fort-de-France Cédex ☎+596 596595200 +596 596595226 **W:** la1ere.francetvinfo.fr/martinique/radio
**LP:** Dir. Régional: Augustin Hoareau, CE Hubert Louis-Sidney
**FM:** 92.0/93.0/93.2/94.3/98.9/100.9MHz
**D.Prgr:** 24h. on MW & FM. **Main N:** 1000, 1100, 1200, 1700, 2000. Rel. France-Inter & France Info

### RADIO CARAÏBES INTERNATIONAL MARTINIQUE (Comm)
2 Boulevard de la Marne, 97200 Fort-de-France ☎+596 596639870 +596 596632659 **W:** rci.fm **LP:** Dir: José Anelka
**FM:** 91.2/92.6/98.7/98.9/103.0/104.6MHz
**D.Prgr:** 24h **N:** on the h (rel. Europe 1). **Ann.:** RCI

**Other FM stations in Fort-de-France (in MHz):**
88.1 Radio Liberté – 88.9 FM Plus – 89.3 Radio Sud-Est – 89.7 ICS – 90.1 Radio Intertropicale – 90.6 Trace FM – 90.9 France Inter – 91.6 Radio Esperance – 92.4 Radio Transat – 92.8 Radio Actif – 93.6 RFA Radio Frequence Atlantique – 94.0 Bel Radio – 94.9 Radio APAL – 95.3 Radio Fusion FM – 95.8 France Inter – 96.2 Radio Imagine – 96.7 Nostalgie – 97.2 Louange FM – 97.5 RLDM Radio Lévé Doubout Matinik – 98.1 Super Radio – 99.1 REM Radio Evangile Martinique – 99.5 Radio Saint Louis – 100.6 Radio Canal Antilles & Radio France Internationale – 101.6 Chérie FM – 102.0 Ekla FM – 103.4 RBR Radio Banlieue Relax – 103.9 Fun Radio – 104.4 NRJ – 104.8 Mouv' FM

– 105.5 Campus FM – 105.7 Super Radio – 106.2 Radio AS & Radio France Internationale – 107.3 RMC Radio Maxxi – 107.6 Nostalgie

## MAURITANIA

**L.T:** UTC — **Pop:** 4.3 million — **Pr.L:** Arabic, French, Poular, Soninké, Wolof — **E.C:** 50Hz, 220V — **ITU:** MTN

### HAUTE AUTORITÉ DE LA PRESSE ET DE L'AUDIOVISUEL (HAPA)
✉ BP 3192, Ilot C Lot 406, Tevragh Zeina, Nouakchott ☎+222 45241088 🖷 +222 45241051 **W:** hapa.mr **L.P:** Dir: M. Imam Cheikh Ould Ely.

### RADIO MAURITANIE (RM, Gov.)
✉ Av. Gamal Abdel Nasser 387, BP 200, Nost Ksar, Nouakchott ☎+222 45253 266 🖷 +222 4525 4069 **W:** radiomauritanie.mr radiocoran.mr radiochabab.mr radioculturelle.com **E:** rm@radiomauritanie.mr
**L.P:** DG: Yeslem Ben Abdem.
**MW:** Nouakchott 783kHz 50kW (inactive).
**FM** (MHz, 2nd frequency for Quran prgr.): Aïoun 94.7/88.1, Akjoujt 90.4/98.7, Aleg 94.0/87.7 1kW + 90.8 1kW (local stn), Amourj 99.1/95.8, Aoujeft 92.4, Atar 98.0/90.2, Bababé 96.2/89.9, Barkéol 100.0, Bir-Moghrein 90.0, Boghe 88.1/90.2, Boutilimit 92.2/95.4, Boulenouar 97.5, Chami 88.2, Chinguitti 102.0, Djigueni 92.5/89.4, Guerou 99.3/103.8, Kaedi 97.2/89.0, Keur Macene 102.5/94.4, Kiffa 91.4/96.7, Maghama 92.7/90.7, Magta Lahjar 89.0/94.0, MBagne 90.8/103.8, M'Bout 98.4/93.2, Medredra 94.2/91.0, Moudjeria 96.9/93.7, Mounghel 94.8/88.5, N'Beiket Lahouach 97.0/93.4, Néma 98.5/90.1, Nouadhibou 94.7/91.5, Nouakchott 93.3 6kW/98.0 2kW, Ouadane 98.6, Oualata 98.0, R'Kis 104.3/96.1, Rosso 98.0/94.0, Sélibabi 97.7/92.4, Tembedra 96.9/107.3, Tichit 98.0, Tidjikja 98.5/90.2, Tintane 94.8/98.2, Zouérate 97.5/93.3.
**Regional Prgrs(FM** MHz): R. Aleg 90.8, R. Atar 98.0 , R. Aioun 94.0, R. Kaedi 97.2, R. Kiffa 91.4/96.7 , R. Nema 98.0 , R. Nouadhibou 93.0/98.0, R. Nouakchott 96.1, R. Zouérate 98.0.
**NB:** Where no power is shown, stns are 0.1kW.
**Youth R:** Nouakchott 98.0MHz 1kW.
**D.Prgr.** in **Arabic/French/others:** 24h. N: Arabic: 0700, 1100(not Fri), 1200, 1300, 1500(not Fri), 1600(Fri), 2200, 2400. French: 1330(Fri), 1430, 1800v. **Quran prgr:** 24h. **Ann:** A: "Huna Nouakchott, Idha'at al-Gumhuriyati al-Islamiyya al-Mauritaniya". F: "Ici Nouackchott, R. Mauritanie". **IS:** Mauritanian guitar.

**Other Stations:**
**R. Koubeni:** Nouakchott 94.2MHz **W:** facebook.com/R.koubeni
**Mauritanid FM:** Nouakchott 100.5MHz, Nouadhibou 101.5MHz **W:** facebook.com/mauritanidFM
**R. Nouakchott:** Nouadhibou 92.0, Nouakchott 99.5MHz
**R. Sahara Media:** Nouakchott 92.8MHz, Nouadhibou 95.6MHz **W:** saharamedias.net
**R. Tenwire:** Nouakchott 97.1MHz **W:** facebook.com/radiotenwire
**BBC Arabic Sce:** Nouadhibou 102.4MHz, Nouakchott 106.9MHz –
**Medi 1 Maghreb:** Nouakchott 102.4MHz – **Monte-Carlo Doualiya,** Nouakchott: 90.2MHz 2kW – **RFI Afrique:** Nouadhibou 88.0, Nouakchott 103.3MHz – **R. Sawa:** Nouakchott 93.8MHz

## MAURITIUS

**L.T:** UTC +4h — **Pop:** 1.3 million — **Pr.L:** English, French, 6 Indian langs, Chinese — **E.C:** 50Hz, 230V — **ITU:** MAU (Rodrigues: ROD)

### INDEPENDENT BROADCASTING AUTHORITY (IBA)
✉ Level 2, The Celi Court 6, Sir Celicourt Antelme Str, Port Louis ☎+230 213 3890 🖷 +230 213 3894 **W:** iba.mu **E:** iba@intnet.mu

### MAURITIUS BROADCASTING CORPORATION (MBC, Pub)
✉ 1 Louis Pasteur Str, Forest Side ☎+230 6021200 🖷 +230 6757332 **W:** mbcradio.tv
**R. Maurice,** Malherbes: 684kHz 10kW **D.Prgr:** 24h in Creole, French & Chinese.
**R. Mauritius,** Malherbes: 819kHz 10kW. **D.Prgr:** 24h in Indian languages.
**Rodrigues FM,** Citronelle: 1206kHz 1kW, 97.3MHz 0.5kW.
**Best FM** in English & Hindi: Jurançon 96.4MHz 0.5kW, Plaine Wilhelms 99.4MHz 1kW, Signal Mt. 103.5MHz 1kW.
**Kool FM** in Creole, English, French: Jurançon 89.3MHz 1kW, Signal Mt. 91.7MHz 1kW, Plaine Wilhelms 97.3MHz 1kW.
**Taal FM** in Bhojpuri, Chinese and Hindi: Plaine Wilhelms 94.0MHz 1kW, Jurançon 95.6MHz 0.5kW, Signal Mt. 98.2MHz 1kW.

**Other stations:**
**NRJ Maurice:** Curepipe 90.8, Jurançon 92.4, Signal Mt. 94.9 **W:** nrj.mu – **R. Plus:** Malherbes 87.7, Port Louis 88.6, Jurançon 98.9 **W:** radioplus.mu – **R. One:** Malherbes 100.8, Port Louis 101.7, Jurançon 102.4 **W:** r1.mu – **Top FM:** Malherbes 104.4, Port Louis 105.7, Jurançon 106.0 **W:** topfmradio.com
**BBC World Sce:** Bigara 1575kHz 2kW. 24h.
**RFi Afrique:** Curepipe/Jurançon/Port Louis/Rodrigues 93.2MHz

## MAYOTTE (France)

**L.T:** UTC +3h — **Pop:** 250,000 — **Pr.L:** French, Mahorian — **E.C:** 50Hz, 220V — **ITU:** MYT

### MAYOTTE PREMIÈRE (Pub)
✉ B.P. 103, Rue de Jardins, 97610 Dzaoudzi ☎+262 269601017 🖷 +262 269601852 **W:** mayotte.la1ere.fr **L.P:** DG: Georges Chow-Toun.
**FM:** Dzaoudzi 91.0MHz 0.1kW, M'lima Combani 92.0MHz 0.5kW, Kanikeli-Choungui 101.3MHz 0.5kW, Mtsanboro-Madjabalini 103.2MHz 0.5kW.
**D.Prgr** in French/Mahorian: Local prgr. Mon-Sat 0000-1900, Sun 0145-1830. Relays RFI overnight.
**Ann:** "Vous êtes à l'écoute de Mayotte Première".
**IS:** Melody on guitar.

**Europe 2:** Boueni 90.2MHz, Mamoudzou 99.1MHz, Pamandzi 97.7MHz
**France-Inter:** Dzaoudzi 101.0MHz 24h

## MEXICO

**L.T:** UTC -6h (DST*: -5h). QR: UTC -5h. BS, CH, NA, SN: UTC -7h (DST*: -6h). SO: UTC -7h. BC: UTC -8h (DST**: -7h) *) 7 Apr-27 Oct **) as (*) except 10 Mar-3 Nov in certain locations along the border with USA — **Pop:** 130 million — **Pr.L:** Spanish — **E.C:** 60Hz, 127V — **ITU:** MEX

### INSTITUTO FEDERAL DE TELECOMUNICACIONES (IFT)
**Unidad de Sistemas de Radio y Televisión**
✉ Insurgentes Sur #1143, Col. Noche Buena, Delegación Benito Juárez, CP 03720, México D.F. **W:** ift.org.mx **E:** quejas@ift.org.mx ☎ +52 55 50154000.

### DIRECCION DE RADIO
**Departamento de Asignación de Frecuencias**
✉ Eugenia 197, Col.Narvarte, 03020 Delg. Benito Juárez México, D.F ☎ +52 55 5015 4785.

**Call** XE–,° = also on SW, ‡= inactive, # = HD Radio (IBOC), d = daytime operation. The letters preceding the stn number indicate the state. Addresses are listed by state in alphabetical order. Hrs of tr usually 24h – see address section for variations.
**NB:** most stations carry "La Hora Nacional" (official prgr). Mon. 0400-0500 (Sun. local time); first half hour nationwide prgr, second regional programming.

| MW Call | kHz | kW | Station, location |
|---|---|---|---|
| BC01) SURF | 540 | 0.1 | R. Zion, Tijuana |
| CH15) TX | 540 | 4/1 | La Ranchera de Paquimé, Nuevo Casas Grandes (r. XHTX 90.5) |
| CS01) MIT | 540 | 5/1 | R. IMER, LV de Balún Canán, Comitán (r. XHEIMT 107.9 HD1) |
| ME01) WF | 540 | 20/2.5 | La Bestia Grupera, Tlalmanalco |
| NL01) WA | 540 | 1.5/1 | Los 40, Monterrey |
| SL01) WA | 540 | 150 | Los 40, San Luis Potosí (r. XHEWA 103.9) |
| SN01) HS | 540 | 5/2.5 | La Mejor, Los Mochis (r. XHHS 90.5) |
| CH01) PL | 550 | 5/0.15 | La Super Estación, Cd. Cuauhtémoc (r. XHEPL 91.3) |
| NA01) GNAY | 550 | 2.5/0.15 | R. Aztlán, "Nuestra Radio", Tepic |
| CO01) GIK | 560 | 1.4/0.25 | La Acerera, Monclova (r. XHGIK 88.1) |
| DF01) OC | 560 | 1.5/0.5 | R. Chapultepec, México |
| DG01) SRD | 560 | 10/1 | La Tremenda, Santiago Papasquiaro (r. XHSRD 89.3) |
| CL01) MZA | 560 | 10/1 | Sol FM, Manzanillo (Cihuatlán JL) (r. XHMZA 89.7) |
| MI01) LQ | 570 | 2/1.7 | Candela, Morelia (r. XHLQ 90.1) |
| NA02) TD | 570 | 5/1 | R. Red, Tecuala (r. XHETD 92.5) |
| NL02) BJB | 570 | 5/2 | BJB Regional Mexicana, Monterrey |
| OX02) OA | 570 | 5/2.5 | La Mexicana, Oaxaca (r. XHEOA 94.9) |
| PU01) VJP | 570 | 5/1 | R. Xicotepec, Xicotepec de Juárez (r. XHVJP 92.7) |
| CH08) FI | 580 | 5/0.7 | Fiesta Mexicana, Chihuahua (r. XHFI 96.5) |
| CO02) LRDA | 580 | 2.5/2.5 | La Rancheria del Aire, Piedras Negras (r. XHEMU 103.7) |

| MW Call | kHz | kW | Station, location |
|---|---|---|---|
| JL02) AV | 580 | 10/1 | Canal 58, Guadalajara |
| QR02) YI | 580 | 1/0.25 | Mix FM, Cancún (r. XHYI 93.1) |
| DF02) PH | 590 | 25/10 | Sabrosita 590, México |
| DG03) E | 590 | 1 | R. Fórmula Durango, Durango(r. XHE 105.3) |
| GJ01) GTO | 590 | 10/0.25 | Hits 95.5, León (r. XHGTO 95.9) |
| TM02) FD | 590 | 5/0.5 | La Mejor, Reynosa |
| CS05) OCH | 600 | 10/0.5 | K'in Radio, Ocosingo |
| GR02) BB | 600 | 5/1 | La Comadre, Puros Éxitos, Acapulco (r. XHBB 101.5) |
| NL03) MN | 600 | 1/0.5 | La Regiomontana, Monterrey |
| SN02) HW | 600 | 5/1 | La Mejor, Chametla (r. XHHW 102.7) |
| CO34) SORN | 610 | 1 | Viva Saltillo, Saltillo |
| MI03) UF | 610 | 5/1 | La Z, Uruapan (r. XHUF 100.5) |
| SN03) GS | 610 | 6/1 | Chavez R. GS, Guasave (r. XHGS 106.1) |
| YU04) UM | 610 | 10/0.2 | La Nueva Candela, Valladolid (r. XHUM 92.7) |
| BC02) SS | 620 | 2 | ESPN Deportes, Ensenada |
| DF03) NK | 620 | 50/5 | R. 6-20, México (Ecatepec ME) |
| TB15) GMSR | 620 | 2.5 | 620 AM, La R. Que Se Ve, Villahermosa |
| TM03) GH | 620 | 1/0.25 | La Lupe, Río Bravo (r. XHCAO 89.1) |
| JL05) PBGJ | 630 | 10/0.5 | Jalisco Radio, Guadalajara (r. XEJB 96.3) |
| NL03) FB | 630 | 10 | La F-B 6-30, Monterrey |
| QR03) CCQ | 630 | 5 | La Z, Cancún (r. XHCCQ 91.5) |
| SO05) FX | 630 | 1/0.25 | Amor 101, Guaymas (r. XHFX 101.3) |
| TM04) ERO | 630 | 1/0.15 | R. Tamaulipas, Esteros |
| VE03) FU | 630 | 10/0.75 | La Nueva Voz, Cosamaloapan (r. XHFU 103.3) |
| CH27) JUA | 640 | 5 | La Caliente, Cd.Juárez |
| HG01) NQ | 640 | 50/25 | La NQ, Tulancingo (r. XHNQ 90.1) |
| TM05) TAM | 640 | 5/1 | Ke Buena, Cd.Victoria (r. XHTAM 96.1) |
| GR05) CHH | 650 | 5/0.25 | Capital Máxima, Chilpancingo(r. XHCHH 97.1) |
| JL06) EJ | 650 | 10 | La Patrona, Puerto Vallarta (r. XHEJ 93.5) |
| OX05) PX | 650 | 5/0.2 | LV de Ángel, Puerto Ángel (r. XHEPX 99.9) |
| SN05) TNT | 650 | 5/1 | Chavez R. 65, Los Mochis (r. XHTNT 100.5) |
| SO40) HEEP | 650 | 1 | Acustik Radio, Hermosillo (F.P.I.) |
| YU03) VG | 650 | 2.5/0.02 | R. Fórmula, Primera Cad, Mérida (r. XHVG 94.5) |
| AG01) EY | 660 | 50/10 | La Kaliente, Aguascalientes(r. XHEY 102.9) |
| BS06) SJC | 660 | 2.5/0.25 | KVOZ, San José del Cabo (r. XHESJC 93.1) |
| DF04) DTL | 660 | 5/1 | R. Ciudadana, México |
| DG10) DGEP | 660 | 1 | Acustik Radio, Durango (F.P.I.) |
| NL02) FZ | 660 | 10/1 | ABC R., Monterrey |
| QR04) CPR | 660 | 30d | R. Chan Santa Cruz, Felipe Carrillo Puerto |
| GR06) CHG | 680 | 5/2.5 | Súper 107.1, Chilpancingo (r. XHCHG 107.1) |
| YU10) FCSM | 680 | 10/1 | R. María, Mérida |
| BC03) WW | 690 | 78/50 | La 690, Tijuana |
| DF05) N | 690 | 50/5 | R. Centro y El Fonógrafo, México (Tlalnepantla ME) |
| NL04) RG | 690 | 10/1 | RG La Deportiva, Monterrey (r. XHFMTU 103.7 HD2) |
| ZC03) MA | 690 | 50/2 | La Mejor Zacatecas, Fresnillo (r. XHEMA 107.9) |
| CA09) XPUJ | 700 | 5 | LV del Corazón de la Selva, X'pujil |
| JL08) DKR | 700 | 10/0.15 | R. Red, Guadalajara |
| MI02) LX | 700 | 5 | R. Zitácuaro, Zitácuaro (r. XHLX 95.1) |
| SO07) ETCH | 700 | 5d | LV de los Tres Ríos, Etchojoa |
| DF04) MP | 710 | 7 | R. 710, México |
| GR02) MAR | 710 | 1 | R. Disney, Acapulco (r. XHMAR 98.5) |
| OX24) OAEP | 710 | 5/0.5 | Acustik Radio, Oaxaca (F.P.I.) |
| SL13) SLEP | 710 | 1/0.25 | Acustik Radio, San Luis Potosí (F.P.I.) |
| SN08) BL | 710 | 5/0.25 | La Ke Buena, Culiacán (r. XHBL 91.9) |
| CH30) JCC | 720 | 1 | El Fonógrafo, Cd. Juárez |
| CO07) DE | ‡720 | 8/0.25 | La Kaliente, Saltillo (r. XHDE 105.7) |
| MI06) KN | 720 | 5d | La Ke Buena, Huetamo (r. XHKN 95.5) |
| ZC09) JAGC | 720 | 2 | La Bonita del Norte, Juan Aldama |
| BS07) LBC | 730 | 2.5 | La Giganta, Loreto (r. XHLBC 95.7) |
| CH07) HB | 730 | 50/1 | La Mexicana, Hidalgo del Parral (r. XHEHB 107.1) |
| DF06) X | 730 | 100 | W Deportes, México |
| JL10) GDL | 730 | 5/1 | @FM, Guadalajara (r. XHGDL 88.7) |
| SO41) SOS | 730 | 2/0.3 | La Ranchera, Agua Prieta (r. XHSOS 97.3) |
| YU07) PET | 730 | 10d | LV de los Mayas, Peto (r. XHPET 105.5) |
| CO09) QN | 740 | 10/1 | R. Fórmula, Torreón (r. XHQN 105.9) |
| JL11) VAY | 740 | 1 | Amor, Puerto Vallarta (r. XHVAY 92.7) |
| OX08) POR | 740 | 5/0.1 | T-Prende, Putla de Guerrero(r. XHPOR 98.7) |
| QR06) CAQ | 740 | 20/10 | R. Fórmula QR Cancún, Cancún(r. XHCAQ 92.3) |
| TBYY) KV | 740 | 10/1 | EXA FM, Villahermosa (r. XHKV 88.5) |
| GR23) ACEP | 750 | 5 | Acustik Radio, Acapulco (F.P.I.) |
| MI31) UORN | 750 | 10 | Acustik Michoacán, Uruapan (r. XEMEFM 1240) |
| NA06) JMN | 750 | 10d | LV de los Cuatro Pueblos, Jesús María |
| SN08) CSI | 750 | 5/0.25 | Romántica, Culiacán (r. XHCSI 89.5) |
| CS11) RA | 750 | 5/0.5 | R. Uno, San Cristóbal las Casas |
| DF07) ABC | 760 | 70/10 | ABC Radio, México (La Paz ME) |
| DG06) DGO | 760 | 5/0.5 | La Mejor, Durango (r. XHDGO 103.7) |
| JL12) ZZ | 760 | 5/1 | R. Gallito, Guadalajara |
| SO10) EB | ‡760 | 5/1 | La Zeta, Cd.Obregón (r. XHEB 98.5) |
| SO11) NY | 760 | 5/0.1 | R. Xeny, Nogales |
| MI08) ML | 770 | 5/1.5 | La Ranchera, Apatzingán (r. XHEML 98.3) |
| NL05) ACH | 770 | 25/1 | R. Fórmula Monterrey, Monterrey |
| SL07) ANT | 770 | 10 | LV de las Huastecas, Tancanhuitz de Santos |
| ZC08) FRTM | 770 | 25/1 | XEFRTM, Zacatecas (F.P.I.) |
| CO10) WGR | 780 | 10/0.25 | Exa FM, Monclova (r. XHWGR 101.1) |
| GJ03) ZN | 780 | 5/1 | Exa FM, Celaya (r. XHZN 104.5) |
| GR08) XY | 780 | 2.5/1 | La Poderosa Voz del Balsas, Cd.Altamirano |
| JL13) LD | 780 | 5/0.5 | R. Costa, Autlán (r. XHLD 103.9) |
| OX10) GLO | 780 | 10d | LV de la Sierra Juárez, Guelatao de Juárez |
| TM09) SFT | 780 | 5/1 | La Poderosa, San Fernando(r.XHSFT 103.7) |
| TM34) TMEP | 780 | 1/0.25 | Acustik Radio, Tampico (F.P.I.) |
| BC05) SU | 790 | 1/0.25 | La Dinámica, Mexicali (r. XHSU 105.9) |
| BS01) NT | 790 | 5/0.75 | R. La Paz/R. Fórmula, La Paz(r. XHNT 97.5) |
| DF05) RC | ‡790 | 50/1 | Formato 21, México |
| JL14) GAJ | 790 | 0.25 | Grupo Fórmula Jalisco 7-90 AM, Guadalajara |
| TM10) FE | 790 | 1/0.5 | La Radio de Nuevo Laredo, Nuevo Laredo |
| BC06) SPN | 800 | 0.5/0.25 | Cadena 800, Tijuana |
| CH12) ROK | 800 | 50 | R. Cañón/Onda Cristiana, Cd.Juárez |
| GR09) ZV | 800 | 5d | LV de la Montaña, Tlapa de Comonfort |
| NL06) DD | 800 | 10/2.5 | RG La Deportiva, Montemorelos(r. XHDD 92.9) |
| VE09) QT | 800 | 1 | La Poderosa, Veracruz (r. XHQT 106.9) |
| GJ05) EMM | 810 | 1/0.5 | R. La Salmantina, Salamanca |
| GR10) AGR | 810 | 7/0.6 | R. Fórmula, Acapulco (r. XHAGR 105.5) |
| QR07) RB | 810 | 2.5/0.25 | Sol Estéreo, Cozumel (r. XHRB 89.9) |
| SO12) RSV | 810 | 5d | Tribuna R., Cd. Obregón |
| TM11) RI | 810 | 10/0.1 | R. Rey, Reynosa |
| TM35) FW | 810 | 50/1 | Hits FM 106.3, Tampico (r. XHFW 106.3) |
| TX01) HT | 810 | 5/1 | R. Huamantla, Huamantla (r. XHHT 106.9) |
| BC07) ABCA | 820 | 3.5/0.5 | ABC Radio/R. Frontera, Mexicali |
| GR11) GRC | 820 | 1d | RTG R, Coyuca de Catalán |
| JL12) BA | 820 | 10/1 | La Consentida, Guadalajara |
| SL05) BM | 820 | 10/1 | Ke Buena, San Luis Potosí (r. XHBM 105.7) |
| DF08) ITE | 830 | 10/5 | R. Capital, México |
| MI09) PUR | 830 | 8d | LV de los P'urhepechas, Cheran |
| NL07) LN | 830 | 5/0.25 | La Caliente, Linares (r. XHLN 105.7) |
| OX11) TLX | 830 | 1/0.5 | La Poderosa, Tlaxiaco (r. XHTLX 100.5) |
| JL16) XXX | 840 | 5/1 | Fiesta Mexicana, Tamazula(r. XHXXX 97.5) |
| NA03) TEY | 840 | 1/0.25 | R. Sensación, Tepic (r. XHTEY 93.7) |
| TM13) MY | 840 | 1d | La Jefa, Cd.Mante (r. XHEMY 98.7) |
| VE11) PV | 840 | 2.5/0.1 | La Fiera Grupera, Papantla (r. XHPV 97.3) |
| BC10) ZF | 850 | 0.25d | Buenísima, Mexicali |
| JL17) MIA | 850 | 3/1 | R. Disney, Guadalajara (r. XHEMIA 90.3) |
| MI10) ZI | 850 | 5/1 | Maxistar, Zacapu (r. XHZI 98.5) |
| QE03) JAQ | 850 | 1/0.1 | La Ke Buena, Jalpan (r. XHJAQ 107.1) |
| BC08) MO | 860 | 10/7.5 | 8-60 La Poderosa/Uniradio, Tijuana |
| CH33) ZOL | 860 | 1/0.5 | R. Noticias 860, Cd.Juárez |
| CL05) AL | 860 | 1/0.5 | R. Fórmula, Manzanillo (r. XHAL 97.7) |
| DF09) UN | 860 | 45/10 | R. UNAM, México |
| NL04) NL | 860 | 5/1.5 | R. Recuerdo, Monterrey |
| QR08) CTL | 860 | 10/1 | R. Chetumal, Chetumal (r. XHCHE 100.9) |
| SN12) NW | 860 | 1/0.25 | Máxima 103, Culiacán (r. XHNW 103.3) |
| CH18) TAR | 870 | 10d | LV de la Sierra Tarahumara, Guachochi |
| GR12) GRO | 870 | 1 | RTG R, Chilpancingo (r. XHGRC 97.7) |
| OX12) ACC | 870 | 10/0.25 | LV del Puerto, Pto. Escondido(r. XHACC 93.3) |
| CH38) CHEP | 880 | 5/0.25 | XECHEP, Chihuahua (F. PI.) |
| JL18) AAA | 880 | 20/1 | R. Mujer, Guadalajara (r. XHEAAA 92.7) |
| SL04) EM | 880 | 5/1 | La M Mexicana, Río Verde(r. XHEEM 94.5) |
| GJ06) AK | 890 | 5/0.5 | La Mejor, Acámbaro (r. XHAK 89.7) |
| SN13) NZ | 890 | 10/0.5 | La Sinaloense, Culiacán (r. XHENZ 92.9) |
| DF06) W | 900 | 100 | W Radio, México (r. XEW 96.9) |
| NL08) OK | 900 | 10/2.5 | La OK, Monterrey |
| BC10) AO | 910 | 0.25 | R. Mexicana, Mexicali |
| GJ24) LNEP | 910 | 5/0.1 | Acustik Radio, León (F.P.I.) |
| CA10) STRC | 920 | 1.5/0.5 | Voces, Campeche |
| CO06) RCA | 920 | 5/0.2 | Planeta, Torreón (Gómez Palacio DG) (r. XHRCA 102.7) |
| GJ08) RE | 920 | 5/1 | La Comadre, Puros Éxitos, Celaya(r. XHRE 88.1) |
| JL21) LT | 920 | 10/1 | R. María, Tlaquepaque |
| MI11) LCM | 920 | 5/2.5 | La Poderosa, Cd.Lázaro Cárdenas |
| PU06) ZAR | 920 | 1 | @FM, Puebla |
| CO33) SAME | 930 | 1 | XESAME, Saltillo (F.P.I.) |
| OX14) TLA | 930 | 5d | LV de la Mixteca, Tlaxiaco |
| BC07) MMM | 940 | 1/0.1 | 940 AM Oldies, Mexicali |
| BS08) RLA | 940 | 10/1 | R. Surcalifornia, Santa Rosalía |
| CO17) YJ | 940 | 10/0.1 | La Fiera Musical, Nueva Rosita (r. XHYJ 105.1) |
| DF06) Q | 940 | 50 | Ke Buena 9-40, México |
| JL22) HE | 940 | 1 | Ke Buena, Atotonilco |
| TM15) RKS | 940 | 1d | Romántica, Reynosa |
| BC09) KAM | #950 | 20/5 | R. Fórmula Californias, Tijuana |

| MW Call | kHz | kW | Station, location |
|---|---|---|---|
| CA02) MAB | 950 | 3/0.9 | Retro FM, Cd. del Carmen (r. XHMAB 101.3) |
| CH02) FA | 950 | 1/0.5 | La Poderosa, Chihuahua (r. XHFA 89.3) |
| GR10) ACA | 950 | 5/1 | R. Fórmula, Acapulco (r. XHACA 106.3) |
| JL23) MEX | 950 | 5/0.5 | La Mexicana, Cd.Guzmán (r. XHMEX 104.9) |
| NL09) RN | 950 | 5/1 | R. Naranjera, Monterrey ((r. XHERN 100.9) |
| OX15) OJN | 950 | 10d | LV de la Chinantla, San Lucas Ojitlán |
| SO15) PB | 950 | 10/0.1 | Grupera 93.1, Hermosillo (r. XHEPB 93.1) |
| DG09) TPH | 960 | 5d | Las Tres Voces de Durango, Santa María de Ocotán |
| GR15) XC | 960 | 1.5/1 | ABC R. 960, Taxco (r. XHXC 96.1) |
| JL24) HK | 960 | 10/2.5 | HK 9-60, LV de Guadalajara, Guadalajara |
| SL08) CZ | 960 | 1 | ABC R., San Luis Potosí |
| SO16) IQ | 960 | 1 | Toño, Cd.Obregón (r. XHIQ 102.5) |
| TM16)K | 960 | 5/1 | La Estación Grande, Nuevo Laredo |
| VE08) OZ | 960 | 1/0.25 | Amor, Xalapa (r. XHOZ 91.7) |
| CH22) SW | 970 | 0.5 | R. Madera, Cd. Juárez (r. XHESW 96.1) |
| CH30) J | 970 | 5 | R. México Noticias, Cd.Juárez |
| DF10) RFR | 970 | 50/4 | Grupo Fórmula 970, México |
| GJ10) UG | 970 | 1 | R. Universidad de Guanajuato, Guanajuato |
| MI08) CJ | 970 | 1/0.25 | Los 40, Apatzingán (r. XHCJ 94.3) |
| SN15) VOX | 970 | 5/0.4 | Fiesta Mexicana, Mazatlán (r. XHVOX 98.7) |
| SO02) EZ | 970 | 5/0.25 | La Mejor, Caborca (r. XHEZ 90.7) |
| TM17)O | 970 | 1 | NotiGAPE, Matamoros |
| YU05) MH | 970 | 5/0.5 | Candela FM, Mérida (r. XHMH 95.3) |
| MI15) LC | 980 | 1/0.2 | Radio Pía, La Piedad (r. XELC FM 92.7) |
| PU07) FS | 980 | 5 | XELFFS, Izúcar de Matamoros (F.PI) |
| SO17) FQ | 980 | 2.5/0.5 | La FQ, Cananea (r. XFQ 103.1 HD) |
| BC05) CL | 990 | 1.4/3 | La Rocola 9-90, Mexicali |
| CS09) TG | ‡990 | 20/1 | Extremo, Tuxtla Gutiérrez (r. XHTG 90.3) |
| JL07) BCN | 990 | 1/0.1 | BC Radio, Guadalajara (r. XHBC 95.1) |
| NL04) T | 990 | 50 | La T Grande, Monterrey |
| OX16) IU | 990 | 2.5/1 | Stereo Cristal, Oaxaca (r. XHIU 105.7) |
| CH33) FV | 1000 | 1 | La Rancherita, Cd.Juárez |
| CS02) TAC | 1000 | 10/1 | Exa FM, Tapachula (r. XHTAC 91.5) |
| DF02) OY | 1000 | 50/20 | Mil AM, México |
| SN07) MMS | 1000 | 1 | La Ke Buena, Mazatlán (r. XHMMS 97.9) |
| TM19)NLT | 1000 | 1/0.1 | R. Fórmula Nuevo Laredo, Nuevo Laredo |
| YU01) MYL | 1000 | 5 | So Good, Mérida (r. XHMYL 92.1) |
| HG03) HGO | 1010 | 1d | Hidalgo R, Huejutla |
| JL12) HL | 1010 | 50/5 | W Deportes, Guadalajara |
| MI18) TUX | 1010 | 1d | LV de la Sierra Oriente, Tuxpan |
| PU08) PA | 1010 | 20/2 | Ke Buena, Puebla (r. XHEPA-FM 89.7 HD1) |
| SO19) XN | 1010 | 0.5/0.2 | R. Ures, Ures |
| CL11) COEP | 1020 | 1 | Acustik Radio, Colima (F.P.I.) |
| QR11) WO | 1020 | 1/0.25 | Sol Stereo, Chetumal (r. XHWO 97.7) |
| VE11) PR | 1020 | 5/0.5 | Éxtasis Digital, Poza Rica (r. XEPR 102.7) |
| BC02) SDD | 1030 | 5 | La Tremenda, Ensenada |
| CA06) BCC | 1030 | 25 | La Mejor, Cd. del Carmen (r. XHBCC 100.5) |
| CS18) VFS | 1030 | 10/0.25 | LV de la Frontera Sur, Las Margaritas |
| DF05) QR | ‡1030 | 50/5 | R. Centro, México |
| JL34) ROPJ | 1030 | 10/1 | XEROPJ, Lagos de Moreno (F.PI.) |
| QR14) FEL | 1030 | 5d | LV del Gran Pueblo, Felipe Carrillo Puerto (r. XHNKA 104.5) |
| SL09) IE | 1030 | 5/1 | Stereo 1030, Matehuala (r. XHIE 106.3) |
| TM18)PAV | 1030 | 1/0.5 | La Picuda, Tampico (r. XHPAV 91.7) |
| CS19) PLE | 1040 | 5 | R. Palanque, Palenque |
| GJ09) SAG | 1040 | 5/0.25 | R. Lobo Bajío, Irapuato |
| JL18) BBB | 1040 | 10/1 | ESNE R, Guadalajara |
| ME02)CH | 1040 | 5/0.75 | Pirata FM 89.3, Toluca (r. XHCH 89.3) |
| BC05) D | 1050 | 10d | La Gran D, Mexicali |
| BS05) BCS | 1050 | 10/1 | La Radio de Sudcalifornia, La Paz |
| MI07) IP | 1050 | 5 | La Poderosa, Uruapán (r. XHIP 89.7) |
| NL10) G | 1050 | 100 | La Ranchera 1050, Monterrey |
| VE25) JF | 1050 | 5d | R. Max, Tierra Blanca |
| DF11) EP | °1060 | 100/20 | R. Educación "Señal 1060 AM", México |
| TM30)RDO | 1060 | 7/2.5 | La Raza 1060, Reynosa |
| CA05) IT | 1070 | 1/0.25 | Exa FM, Cd. del Carmen (r. XHIT 99.7) |
| GR02) AGS | 1070 | 5/1 | Amor, Acapulco (r. XHAGS 101.3) |
| JL26) SP | 1070 | 10/1 | Rock & Soul, Guadalajara (r. XHESP 91.9) |
| BS09) PAB | 1080 | 0.5/0.25 | R. Celebridad, La Paz |
| CL08) UU | 1080 | 0.1/0.13 | La Mejor, Colima (r. XHUU 92.5) |
| JL27) PBPV | 1080 | 5d | Jalisco R., Puerto Vallarta (r. XHVJL 91.9) |
| ME03)TUL | 1080 | 5 | R. Mexiquense Valle de México, Tultitlán |
| BC12) PRS | 1090 | 50 | XX Sports 1090 AM/Mighty 1090, Rosarito |
| NL04) MU | 1090 | 5/0.1 | Milenio R, Monterrey (r. XHFMTU 103.7) |
| PU10) HR | 1090 | 1 | La HR, Puebla |
| TM20)WL | 1090 | 1d | La Romántica, Nuevo Laredo |
| VE50) MCA | 1090 | 10 | La Grande de las Huastecas, Pánuco (r. XHMCA 104.3) |
| BS10) BAC | 1100 | 1 | R. Asunción/R. Sur California, Bahía Asunción |
| GJ11) BV | 1100 | 5 | R. Alegría, Moroleón (r. XHBV 95.7) |
| GR17) GRM | 1100 | 1d | RTG R, Ometepec |
| ZC07) TGO | 1100 | 5/0.5 | R. Cañón, Tlaltenango (r. XHTGO 90.1) |
| CH33) WR | 1110 | 5/0.5 | Cristo Rey Radio, Ciudad Juarez |
| CO20) PU | 1110 | 0.25 | La P-U, Monclova |
| DF05) RED | 1110 | 100 | R. RED y Formato 21, México (Tlalnepantla ME) |
| JL20) PVJ | 1110 | 1/0.2 | Fiesta Mexicana, Puerto Vallarta |
| SO23) VS | 1110 | 1/0.25 | Maxima 96-3, Hermosillo (r. XHVS 96.3) |
| TM21)OQ | 1110 | 1 | NotiGAPE, Reynosa |
| BC13) MX | 1120 | 0.4/0.1 | Noticias 1120, Mexicali |
| JL29) UNO | 1120 | 0.5 | R. Uno La Popular , Guadalajara |
| PU10) POP | 1120 | 5 | Fórmula 11-20 AM, Puebla |
| TB14) TQE | 1120 | 5/0.5 | La R. de Tabasco, Tenosique (r. XETVH 1230kHz) |
| YU09) RUY | 1120 | 1d | R. Universidad, Mérida (r. XHRUY 103.9) |
| AG02) YZ | 1130 | 10/2.5 | La Poderosa, Aguascalientes (r. XHYZ 107.7) |
| ME10)CHAP | 1130 | 5 | R. Chapingo, Chapingo (F.P.I.) |
| MI19) FN | 1130 | 1/0.1 | Candela, Uruapan (r. XHFN 91.1) |
| NA11)LUP | 1130 | 1d | R. Lupita, Las Varas (r. XHLUP 89.1) |
| SO24) HN | 1130 | 1 | Toño, Nogales |
| CS20) TEC | 1140 | 1/0.5 | R. Tecpatán, Tecpatán |
| HG04) PEC | 1140 | 1 | Sonoarmonía, San Bartolo Tutotepec |
| NL02) MR | 1140 | 50 | R. Esperanza, Monterrey |
| PU11) TE | 1140 | 5 | 106.3 FM, Tehuacán (r. XHETE 106.3) |
| BC14) RM | #1150 | 1 | R. Fórmula, Mexicali |
| DF05) JP | ‡1150 | 50/10 | El Fonógrafo, México |
| JL10) AD | 1150 | 50/1 | R. Metrópoli, Guadalajara |
| OX20) XP | 1150 | 10/1 | La Mejor, Tuxtepec (r. XHESO 104.9) |
| SN17) UAS | 1150 | 10/0.15 | R. UAS, Culiacán (r. XHUAS 96.1) |
| VE24) TVR | 1150 | 1.5/0.5 | Azul 106.9, Tuxpan (r. XETVR 106.9) |
| BC15) QIN | 1160 | 10 | LV del Valle, San Quintín |
| ME05)RLK | 1170 | 1/0.25 | Super Stereo Miled, Atlacomulco (r. XHRLK 104.7) |
| PU06) CD | 1170 | 10/2.5 | La Romántica, Puebla (r. XHEDC 92.9 HD1) |
| SO26) FEM | 1170 | 5/0.1 | R. Disney, Hermosillo (r. XHFEM 99.5) |
| TM15) RT | 1170 | 5d | Ke Buena, Reynosa |
| VE46) ZS | ‡1170 | 2.5/1 | R. Hit, Coatzacoalcos (r. XHZS 92.3) |
| BS05) UBS | 1180 | 10 | R. Universidad Autonoma de Baja California Sur, La Paz |
| CH35) DCH | 1180 | 5/1.5 | Ke Buena, Cd. Delicias |
| DF12) FR | 1180 | 10/5 | R. Felicidad, México |
| BC16) MBC | 1190 | 0.25/0.1 | Cadena 1190 AM, Mexicali |
| CH30) PZ | 1190 | 1/0.1 | R. Centro, Cd.Juárez |
| JL12) WK | 1190 | 50/10 | W Radio/W Guadalajara, Guadalajara |
| MO02)JOEP | 1190 | 5 | Acustik Radio, Jojutla (F.P.I.) |
| NL10) CT | 1190 | 10/0.1 | Contacto 11-90, Monterrey |
| SL12) XQ | 1190 | 25/1 | R. Universidad, San Luís Potosí |
| VE32) PP | 1190 | 5 | La Comadre, Orizaba (r. XHPP 100.3) |
| BS11) PAS | 1200 | 1 | R. Punta Abreojos, Punta Abreojos |
| ME06)QY | 1200 | 2.5 | Retro FM, Toluca (r. XHQY 103.7) |
| QE07) QJAL | 1200 | 5 | R. Jalpan, Jalpan |
| CS21) COPA | 1210 | 5d | LV de los Vientos, Copainalá |
| PU10) PUE | 1210 | 5/1 | Pasion FM, Puebla (r. XHPUE 92.1 HD) |
| CO22) SAL | 1220 | 4.5d | R. Universidad Agraria, Saltillo |
| DF04) B | 1220 | 100 | La B Grande, México |
| JL14) DKN | 1230 | 0.5 | Fórmula Jalisco 12-30 AM, Guadalajara (r. XEDM 101.1) |
| NL05) IZ | 1230 | 10/1 | R. Fórmula Monterrey 1230, Monterrey |
| TB14) TGN | 1230 | 10/1 | La Radio de Tabasco, Villahermosa |
| SN23) CSEP | 1230 | 10 | Acustik Radio, Culiacán (F.P.I.) |
| CH12) WG | 1240 | 1 | Bengala 12-40, Cd.Juárez |
| HG05) RD | 1240 | 1 | La Comadre, Pachuca (r. XHRD 104.5) |
| MI31) MFM | 1240 | 25 | Acustik Michoacán, Morelia |
| SO24) CG | 1240 | 1 | Arroba FM, Nogales |
| JL24) DK | 1250 | 10 | DK 12-50, Guadalajara |
| ME07)TEJ | 1250 | 1/0.25 | R. Mexiquense, Tejupilco |
| PU13) ZT | 1250 | 5/0.5 | La Mejor, Puebla |
| VE55) VREP | 1250 | 1 | Acustik Radio, Veracruz (F.PI.) |
| DF12) L | 1260 | 20/10 | La Comadre, México |
| GJ14) ZH | 1260 | 1/0.25 | La Estación que se Escucha, Salamanca |
| JL31) JY | 1260 | 5/1 | La Mejor, Autlán (r. XHJY 101.5) |
| OX22) JAM | 1260 | 10d | LV de la Costa Chica, Santiago Jamiltepec |
| SO30) MW | 1260 | 1/0.25 | Río Digital 93.9, San Luis Río Colorado |
| VE22) MTV | 1260 | 1 | R. Lobo de Mina, Minatitlán (r. XHMTV 100.9) |
| BC17) AZ | 1270 | 0.5 | La Z, Tijuana |
| CO33) TGME | 1270 | 10 | XETGME, Torreón (F.PI.) |
| GJ16) RPL | 1270 | 10/0.15 | La Poderosa RPL, León (r. XHRPL 93.9) |
| SO31) GL | 1270 | 1/0.5 | La Verdad Radio, Navojoa |
| VE11) RRR | 1270 | 1/0.25 | La Huasteca, Papantla |
| GJ17) SQ | 1280 | 2.5/1 | R. San Miguel, S. M. de Allende (r. XHSQ 103.3) |
| JL14) BON | 1280 | 0.5/0.25 | R. Fórmula Jalisco, Guadalajara (r. XHBON 89.5) |

| MW Call | kHz | kW | Station, location |
|---|---|---|---|
| NL04) AW | 1280 | 10/1 | AW, Involvidable, Monterrey |
| PU14) EG | 1280 | 1/0.5 | ABC Radio, Puebla |
| TM24)TUT | 1280 | 1d | R. Tamaulipas, Tula |
| GJ18) FAC | 1290 | 5/0.25 | La Poderosa, Salvatierra (r. XHFAC 92.9) |
| MI24) IX | 1290 | 1/0.5 | La Pantera, Sahuayo |
| SO16) AP | 1290 | 1/0.25 | Romántica, Cd.Obregón (r. XHAP 96.9) |
| CH30) P | 1300 | 38/0.2 | Fiesta Mexicana, Cd.Juárez |
| GJ19) XV | 1300 | 1/0.75 | La Z, León (r. XHXV 88.9) |
| HG07) AWL | 1300 | 1/0.25 | El Corazón de la Sierra,Jacala |
| SO24) XW | 1300 | 1/0.1 | La Bestia Grupera, Nogales |
| BC18) C | 1310 | 1 | R. Enciso, Tijuana |
| CS25) RAM | 1310 | 1 | R. Amanecer, LV Indígena, Betania |
| GR18) GRT | 1310 | 1d | RTG R, Taxco |
| JL10) TIA | 1310 | 10/1 | R. Vital, Guadalajara |
| NL02) VB | 1310 | 5/0.25 | R. 13, Monterrey |
| PU15) HIT | 1310 | 5/1 | R. Felicidad, Puebla |
| QE10) QRMD | 1310 | 5 | XEQRMD, Querétaro (F.P.I.) |
| TM25)AM | 1310 | 1/0.25 | La Mandona, Matamoros |
| CO33) PNME | 1320 | 10 | XEPNME, Piedras Negras (F.P.I.) |
| BC19) AA | 1340 | | R. Variedades, Mexicali |
| HG08) QB | 1340 | 1 | Super Stereo Miled, Tulancingo(r. XHQB 97.1) |
| JL24) DKT | 1340 | 5/1 | Radiorama 13-40, Frecuencia Deportiva, Guadalajara |
| MI08) APM | 1340 | 1 | Candela, Apatzingán (r. XHAPM 95.1) |
| MI26) CR | 1340 | 1 | La Zeta, Morelia (r. XHCR 96.3) |
| NL02) NV | 1340 | 1 | Romántica 1340, Monterrey (r. XHXL 91.7) |
| PU17) LU | 1340 | 10/5 | Ke Buena Puebla, Cd. Serdán (r. XHLU 93.5) |
| TM25) MT | 1340 | 0.6 | R. Diamante, Matamoros |
| TM26) BK | 1340 | 1 | La Raza, Nuevo Laredo (r. XHBK 95.7) |
| CO06) TB | 1350 | 5/0.5 | R. Laguna, Torreón |
| CS23) CAH | 1350 | 5/1 | La Popular, LV de Soconusco, Cacahoatán (r. XHCAH 89.1) |
| DF04) QK | #1350 | 5/1 | Tropicalísima 13-50, México |
| PU18) CTZ | 1350 | 10d | LV de la Sierra Norte, Cuetzalán |
| SO30) LBL | 1350 | 8d | R. Centro, San Luis Río Colorado |
| TM27)ZD | 1350 | 0.25 | La Mandona, Camargo |
| CH02) DI | 1360 | 1/0.4 | @FM, Chihuahua (r. XHDI 88.5) |
| GR23) IGEP | 1360 | - | Acustik Radio, Iguala (F.P.I.) |
| VE42) ZON | 1360 | 10d | LV de la Sierra, Zongolica |
| BC10) HG | 1370 | 0.5 | Vida 13-70, Mexicali |
| DG08) RPU | 1370 | 1/0.25 | La Z, Durango (r. XHRPU 102.9) |
| JL24) PJ | 1370 | 10/1 | R. Ranchito, Guadalajara |
| MI27) SV | 1370 | 5/0.5 | R. Nicolaita, Morelia |
| NL05) MON | 1370 | 10/0.4 | R. Fórmula, Monterrey (r. Trión 89.3) |
| SO33) HF | 1370 | 5 | R. Fórmula, Nogales |
| TM20)GNK | 1370 | 5/0.5 | La La Ranchera Norteña, Nuevo Laredo |
| DF14) CO | 1380 | 50/5 | Romántica 13-80, México |
| VE27) TP | 1380 | 1/0.1 | Sensación FM, Xalapa (r. XHTP 95.5) |
| CL10) TY | ‡1390 | 10/2.5 | @FM, Tecomán (r. XHTY 91.3) |
| HG06) ZG | 1390 | 10/2.5 | R. Mezquital, Iximiquilpan (r. XHD 96.5) |
| M001) CTAM | 1390 | 1 | La R. de Morelos, Cuautla (r. XHYTE 90.9) |
| TM13)XO | 1390 | 5/1 | La Super Buena, Cd.Mante (r. XHXO 95.7) |
| TM21)OR | 1390 | 1 | NotiGAPE, Reynosa |
| ME08)XI | 1400 | 2.5/1 | Capital Máxima, Ixtapan de la Sal (r. XHXI 99.5) |
| NL11) SH | 1400 | 51 | R. Sabinas, Cd.Sabinas |
| OX23) UBJ | 1400 | 1 | R. Universidad, Oaxaca |
| CA13) CUA | 1410 | 1/0.25 | R. Universidad, Campeche |
| DF02) BS | 1410 | 25/1 | Bandolera 14-10, México |
| JL32) KB | 1410 | 25/10 | Canal 14-10, Guadalajara (r. XHKB 99.9) |
| TM20)AS | 1410 | 1/0.25 | Fiesta Mexicana, Nuevo Laredo (r. XHAS 101.5) |
| BC20) XX | 1420 | 10/2 | Vida, Tijuana |
| CH33) F | 1420 | 5/0.5 | Activa 14-20, Cd.Juárez |
| NL03) H | 1420 | 5/0.4 | La H, Antología Vallenata, Monterrey |
| TM21)EW | 1420 | 1 | W1420/LV del Bajo Bravo, Matamoros |
| TM29)WD | 1430 | 5/0.15 | R. X, Cd. Miguel Alemán |
| TX02) TT | 1430 | 1 | R. Tlaxcala, La Doble T, Tlaxcala |
| DF15) EST | 1440 | 25/5 | Quiéreme 14-40, México |
| JL33) ABCJ | 1440 | 10/1 | ABC Radio, Guadalajara (r. XHABCJ 95.9) |
| GR21) RY | 1450 | 2/1 | La Poderosa Voz del Sur, Arcelia |
| MI24) RNB | 1450 | 1 | R. Impacto, Sahuayo y Jiquilpan |
| NL04) JM | 1450 | 5/1 | U ERRE R., Monterrey |
| SO29) DJ | ‡1450 | 0.5 | R. Clave, Magdalena de Kino |
| VE55) PREP | 1450 | 1 | Acustik Radio, Poza Rica (F.P.I.) |
| CH32) YC | 1460 | 1 | R. Fórmula, Cd.Juárez |
| GR12) GRA | 1460 | 1 | RTG R., Acapulco (r. XHGRC 97.7) |
| OX07) KC | 1460 | 5/0.5 | Planeta, Oaxaca (r. XHKC 100.9) |
| SO30) CB | 1460 | 10/0.25 | R. Ranchito, San Luis Río Colorado |
| BC08) RCN | 1470 | 10/25 | RCN/Uniradio 14-70, Tijuana (r. CRI 12h) |
| CA11) BAL | 1470 | 2.5/0.5 | R. Voz Maya de México, Bécal |
| DF10) AI | 1470 | 50/5 | Grupo Fórmula 1470, México |
| HG10) IND | 1470 | 1/0.5 | Hidalgo R., Tlanchinol |

| MW Call | kHz | kW | Station, location |
|---|---|---|---|
| SN22) ACE | 1470 | 1/0.1 | Trión, Mazatlán (r. XHACE 91.3) |
| TM31)HI | 1470 | 10/0.25 | La Consentida, Ciudad Miguel Alemán |
| HG11) CARH | 1480 | 5 | LV del Pueblo Hña-hñu, Cárdonal (r. XHCARH 89.1) |
| JL24) ZJ | 1480 | 20/1 | Simplemente Supérate, Guadalajara |
| NL04) TKR | 1480 | 10/1 | La TKR, Rancherita y Regional, Monterrey |
| SO18) NS | 1480 | 1/0.25 | Z107.1, Navojoa (r. XHENS 107.1) |
| TM32)VIC | 1480 | 5/0.15 | R. Tamaulipas, Cd.Victoria |
| CH37) CJC | 1490 | 1 | R. Net, Cd.Juárez |
| TM33)MS | 1490 | 1 | R. Mexicana, Matamoros |
| VE28) YTM | 1490 | 1 | R. Teocelo, Teocelo |
| DF10) DF | 1500 | 50 | Grupo Fórmula 1500, México |
| GJ23) FL | 1500 | 1/0.5 | La FL, Guanajuato (r. XHFL 90.7) |
| HG12) HUI | 1510 | 0.25 | R. Huichapan, Huichapan |
| NL12) QI | 1510 | 10d | Opus 1510 R. Nuevo León, Monterrey |
| CO31) VUC | 1520 | 1d | La Norteñita, Allende (r. XHVUC 95.9) |
| ME07)ATL | 1520 | 1d | R. Mexiquense, Atlacomulco |
| SO38) EH | 1520 | 1d | La Primera, San Luis Río Colorado |
| VE35) VO | 1520 | 1d | La Mega, San Rafael (e. XHVO 94.3) |
| DF14) UR | 1530 | 50/1 | Éxtasis Digital, México |
| GJ01) SD | 1530 | 10/0.1 | La Lupe, Silao (r. XHSD 99.3) |
| NL13) STN | 1540 | 5/0.5 | R. Red, Monterrey (r. XERED 1110kHz) |
| SO39) HOS | 1540 | 5 | La Invasora, Hermosillo |
| BC06) BG | 1550 | 1 | Cadena 1550 AM, Tijuana |
| MI29) REL | 1550 | 1 | La R. del Sistema, Morelia (r. XHREL 106.9) |
| TM29)NU | 1550 | 5/0.25 | La Rancherita, Nuevo Laredo |
| VE36) RUV | 1550 | 1d | R. Universidad Veracruzana, Xalapa |
| CH33) JPV | 1560 | 1d | R. Deportiva 15-60, Cd. Juárez |
| CS24) CHZ | 1560 | 20/0.15 | R. Lagarto, Chiapa de Corzo (r. XHCHZ 107.9 HD) |
| DF05) INFO | ‡1560 | 50/10 | Aire Libre R., México (XHINFO 105.3) |
| GJ15) MAS | 1560 | 1/0.25 | La Estación Familiar, Salamanca |
| MI30) LAC | 1560 | 5/1 | Azul FM, Cd.Lázaro Cárdenas (r. XHLAC 107.9 HD) |
| CO32) RF | 1570 | 100 | La Poderosa, Cd.Acuña (r. XHRF 103.9 HD) |
| SO26) DM | 1580 | 10 | Mix, Hermosillo (r. XHDN 102.7) |
| CH24) BZ | 1590 | 5/0.25 | Éxtasis Digital, Cd.Delicias |
| DF14) VOZ | 1590 | 20/10 | Arroba 15-90, México (La Paz ME) |
| GR22) TPA | ‡1600 | 1d | RTG R, Tlapa de Comonfort |
| ME07)GEM | 1600 | 5 | R. Mexiquense, Metepec |
| BC21) UT | 1630 | 10/1 | UABC R, Mexicali |
| DF16) ARZ | 1650 | 5 | ZER R. 16-50, México |
| ME11)ANAH | 1670 | 1 | R. Anáhuac, Huixquilucan |
| BC12) PE | 1700 | 10 | ESPN R., Tecate |
| **SW Call** | **kHz** | **kW** | **Station, location & h of tr** |
| DF11) PPM | 6185 | 10 | Cultura México, Señal Internacional, México: 1400-0500 (separate prgr. 23-06) |

**State abbreviations:** AG = Aguascalientes; BC = Baja California; BS = Baja California Sur; CA = Campeche; CH = Chihuahua; CL = Colima; CO = Coahuila; CS = Chiapas; DF = Distrito Federal; DG = Durango; GJ = Guanajuato; GR = Guerrero; HG = Hidalgo; ME = Estado de México; MI = Michoacán; MO = Morelos; NA = Nayarit; NL = Nuevo León; OX = Oaxaca; PU = Puebla; QE = Querétaro; QR = Quintana Roo; SL = San Luis Potosí; SN = Sinaloa; SO = Sonora; TB = Tabasco; TM = Tamaulipas; TX = Tlaxcala; VE = Veracruz; YU = Yucatán; ZC = Zacatecas.

**N.B:** These abbreviations are not officially recognized by the Mexican Post Office. Letters should therefore carry the abbreviations in brackets or full state name.

**Addresses & other information:**
**AG00) AGUASCALIENTES (Ags.)**
**AG01)** Grupo Radiofónico Zer, San Miguel 117-A, Col. Salud, 20240 Aguascalientes **W:** grupozer.net – **AG02)** Morelos 222, Col. Centro, 20000 Aguascalientes **W:** radiogrupo.com.mx
**BC00) BAJA CALIFORNIA (B.C.)**
**BC01)** Calle Iluvia 2554, Fracc. Playas de Tijuana 22500, Tijuana (or: P.O. Box 40231 Downey, CA. 90239 USA) **W:** radiozion.net – **BC02)** Av. General Ferreira 3250, Col. Madero Sur, Tijuana. **W:** espn620am.com latremenda1030.com – **BC03)** Carr. Libre Tijuana- Ensenada No. 3100, 22710 Playas de Rosarito. (or: 3500 W. Olive Ave. Suite 250 Burbank, CA 91505 USA) **W:** wradio690.com – **BC05)** Radiorama · Mexicali, Pasaje Vallarta 1128, Centro Cívico, 21000 Mexicali. **W:** radioramamex-icali.com - 1400-0300 – **BC06)** Grupo Cadena, Av.de los Olivos 3401, Fracc. Cubillas, 22410 Tijuana. **W:** cadenanoticias.com – **BC07)** Grupo ABC Radio, Ave. Francisco I. Madero 4. Col. Nueva, 21100 Mexicali. **W:** radiofrontera820am.com facebook.com/ABCRadio820AMMexicali 940oldies.com – **BC08)** Uniradio, Gral. Manuel Márquez de León 950, Zona Urbana Río, 22010 Tijuana (or: 5030 Camino de la Siesta, Suite 403, San Diego, CA 92108, USA) **W:** uniradio.com – **BC09)** Radio Fórmula Tijuana, Blvd. Agua Caliente 8710. local 17 y 18. Plaza Pio Pico, Centro, 22000 Tijuana **W:** radioformulabc.com – **BC10)**

Audiorama Mexicali, Av. Calafia 519, Centro Cívico, 21000 Mexicali W: audioramabc.com – **BC12)** Blvd. Agua Caliente 10535-506, Fracc. Chapultepec, 22420 Tijuana (or: 6160 Cornerstone Court, East, Suite 100, San Diego, CA 92121, USA) W: mighty1090.com espnradio1700. com sandiego1700.com Prgrs in E – **BC13)** Francisco L. Montejano 2200, Fracc. Fovisste, 21030 Mexicali (or: P.O.Box 872125, Calexico, CA 92232) W: noticias1120am.com **BC14)** Pasaje Cozumel 1140, Centro Cívico, 21000 Mexicali W: radioformulabc.com – **BC15)** Calle Octava n° 139, Fracc. Cd San Quintín, 22930 San Quintín W: cdi. gob.mx/ecosgobmx/xequin.php - 1200-0200 (Sun –2200) Prgrs in Sp., Mixteco, Triqui and Zapateco – **BC16)** Grupo Cadena, Prolongación Alfareros No. 253 Centro Cívico, 21000 Mexicali W: cadenanoticias. com/radio/cadena.1190-am – **BC17)** Baja California 1310, Zona Norte, 22100 Tijuana (or: Box 430233, San Ysidro, CA 92073, USA) – **BC18)** Blvd. Agua Caliente esq. Blvd. Cuauhtémoc 2513-6, 22400 Tijuana (or P.O.Box 430521, San Ysidro, CA. 92143 USA) W: radioenciso1310.com – **BC19)** Boulevard Benito Juárez No 1990, Local 12, Plaza Fimbres, Col Jardines del Valle, 21270 Mexicali – **BC20)** Audiorama Tijuana, Carlos Robirosa 3110-B, Fracc. Aviación, 22420 Tijuana W: audioramabc. com – **BC21)** Edif. Rectoría, Av. Álvaro Obregón y Calle Julián Carrillo s/n, Col. Nueva, 21100 Mexicali (or: UABC Radio, 233 Paulin Avenue, P O Box MSC 5163, Calexico, CA 92231-2646, USA) W: radio.uabc. mx - 1400-0800.

**BS00) BAJA CALIFORNIA SUR (B.C.S.)**
**BS01)** Plaza Cuatro Molinos, Ignacio Manuel Altamirano 2790, Zona Central, 23000 La Paz W: centroderadiotelevision.weebly.com - 1300-0700 – **BS05)** Ap.19-B, 23010 La Paz W: centroderadiotelevision.weebly.com - 1300-0500 – **BS07)** Carretera Cd. Constitución, Sta. Rosalía, 23880 Loreto W: radiolagiganta.com – **BS08)** Av de Las Flores 1, 23920 Santa Rosalía – **BS10)** 23960 Bahía Asunción – **BS11)** 23970 Punta Abreojos
**CA00) CAMPECHE (Camp.)**
**CA02)** Calle 22 N° 131, 24100 Cd.del Carmen - 1200-0400 – **CA05)** Calle 32 N° 23-2 P.B., Centro, 24100 Cd.del Carmen W: exafm.com/ ciudaddelcarmen - 1200-0500 – **CA06)** Tamaulipas 15, Col.Santa Ana, 24050 Campeche - 1200-0600 – **CA09)** Domicilio Conocido, 24640 X'pujil W: cdi.gob.mx/ecosgobmx/xexpuj.php - 1100-1600, 2000-0000 - Prgrs in Sp., Maya and Chol – **CA10)** Prol.Calle 53, Esq.Av.16 de Septiembre s/n, 24000 Campeche W: vocescampeche.gob.mx - 1200-0600 – **CA11)** Calle 30 No. 269, Barrio Pablo García, 24930 Becal E: cadenacultural@prodigy.net
**CH00) CHIHUAHUA (Chih.)**
**CH01)** Calle Agustín Melgar 473, 31500 Cd.Cuauhtémoc W: xepl. com.mx – **CH02)** Julián Carrillo No 701, 31000 Chihuahua – **CH07)** Boulevard Ortíz Mena 54, 3er. piso, Col. Centro, 33800 Hidalgo del Parral – **CH08)** Julián Carrillo 705-A, 31000 Chihuahua W: radiorama. com.mx/secciones.php?sec_id=32 – **CH12)** Av.Insurgentes 2127, Col. Ex-Hipódromo, 33000 Cd Juárez W: gruposiete.com.mx/radio face-book.com/ondacristiana800 – **CH15)** Jesús Urueta 504, 31700 Nuevo Casas Grandes W: gbmradio.com - 1200-0400 – **CH18)** CDI, Francisco M. Plancarte y Felipe Ángeles, Col. El Salto, 31980 Guachochi W: cdi.gob.mx/ecosgobmx/xetar.php – **CH22)** Calle 3a N° 1204, 31940 Cd.Madero W: radiomadera.com – **CH24)** Ap.250, 33000 Cd.Delicias - 1300-0500 – **CH27)** Avenida Tecnológico 1770, Colonia Fuentes del Valle, Galería C, Local D-07, 32000 Cd.Juárez W: multimedios.com/ estaciones - 1200-0700 – **CH30)** Av Vicente Guerrero 2329, Col.Partido Romero, 32280 Cd.Juárez W: gradiomex.com radiorama.com.mx radio-centro991.com - 1200-0500 – **CH32)** Av. de la Raza 3585, Int. 503, Plaza Grande, Col. Mascareñas, 32340 Cd. Juárez W: radioformulajuarez. com – **CH33)** Mega Radio, Av. Chapultepec 316, Col Cuauhtémoc, Edificio Megaradio, 32010 Cd.Juárez W: megaradio.mx 860noticias. com.mx larancherita1000.com.mx cristoreyradio.com activa1420.mx radiodeportiva1560.com – **CH37)** Grupo NET, José Borunda 1178, 32000 Cd.Juárez W: radionet1490.com.mx – **CH38)** Escápate al Paraíso S.A. de C.V., N/A W: grupoacustik.com.mx/radio
**CL00 COLIMA (Col.)**
**CL01)** Grupo Radiofónico ZER, Blvd. Costero Miguel de la Madrid 505, Col. Playa Azul, 28218 Manzanillo E: xemza@hotmail.com W: grupozer.net – **CL05)** Blvd. Costera Miguel de la Madrid 801-3, Col. Las Brisas, 28260 Manzanillo - 1100-0700 – **CL08)** Ignacio Sandoval 13, Centro, 28000 Colima - 1200-0600 W: lamejor.com.mx/#!/colima/ home – **CL10)** Radiorama Tecomán, Av. Antonio Leaño del Castillo 663, Col. Ponciano Arriaga, 28160 Tecomán - 1100-0300 – **CL11)** Escápate al Paraíso S.A. de C.V., N/A W: grupoacustik.com.mx/radio
**C000) COAHUILA (Coah.)**
**CO01)** De la Fuente 223 Pte., Col. Los Telefonistas, 25700 Monclova W: laacerera.mx – **CO02)** San Juan 819, Fracc. San José, 26014 Piedras Negras W: rancherita.com.mx – **CO06)** Grupo Radio México, Priv. Eulogio Ortiz y Jesús Pamanes, Col. Ampl. Los Ángeles, 27140 Torreón W: grmtorreon.webs.com/radioranchito.htm, planetaradio.com.mx/ torreon – **CO09)** Grupo Radio Fórmula, Independencia 706, Mza 29, Col. Los Ángeles, 27140 Torreón W: radioformulatorreon.com – **CO10)**

Puebla y Washington s/n, Guadalupe, 25750 Monclova W: exafm.com/ monclova – **CO20)** GRM Radio, Venustiano Carranza 612-2 Ote., 25700 Monclova - W: grmradio.com – **CO22)** Universidad Autónoma Agraria, "Antonio Narro", Periférico Luis Echeverría S/N, Lourdes, 25070 Saltillo W: radionarro.com – **CO32)** Madero 600, Centro, 26200 Cd. Acuña W: imer.com.mx/lapoderosa – **CO33)** Media FM, S.A. de C.V., N/A – **CO34)** Grupo M, Hidalgo 2757 Norte, Col. República Norte, 25280 Saltillo W: gemradio.com.mx/vivasaltillo
**CS00 CHIAPAS (Chis.)**
**CS01)** Instituto Mexicano de la Radio, Av. Chichimá 405, (or A. P. 16) 30000 Comitán - 1100-0700 W: imer.mx/radioimer – **CS02)** 2ª Calle Poniente No. 4, 2° piso, 30700 Tapachula W: exafm.com/tapachula – **CS05)** Radio Chiapas, Segunda Sur Oriente 132, 29950 Ocosingo W: radiotvycine.chiapas.gob.mx E: xeoch@radiotvycine.chiapas.gob. mx – **CS09)** Radio Núcleo, Blvd. Belisario Domínguez 4820, 29000 Tuxtla Gutiérrez W: radionucleo.com - 1200-0600 – **CS11)** Radio Chiapas, Avenida Benito Juárez 48, Interior Altos, 29200 San Cristóbal las Casas E:xera@radiotvycine.chiapas.gob.mx – **CS18)** 14a Sur-Poniente s/n, Barrio San Sebastián, 30180 Las Margaritas W: cdi. gob.mx/ecosgobmx/xevfs.php - 1200-0030 (SS – 2400) Prgrs in Sp., Tojobal, Mame, Tzeltal and Tzotzil – **CS19)** Radio Chiapas, Av. 5 de Mayo entre Aldama y Allende s/n, Centro, 29960 Palenque 1000-0400 W: radiotvycine.chiapas.gob.mx – **CS20)** Radio Chiapas, 2ª Sur y 1ª s/n, 29610 Tecpatan W: radiotvycine.chiapas.gob.mx – **CS21)** Primera Oriente s/n, Barrio Siete Huesos, 29620 Copainalá 1230-2230 Prg in Sp., Zoque and Tzotzil – **CS23)** Instituto Mexicano de la Radio, Km. 1.5 Carr. Cacahoatán-Unión Juárez, Ejido Rosario Ixtal, 30890 Cacahoatán W: imer.mx/lapopular – **CS24)** Instituto Mexicano de la Radio, Km. 14 Libramiento Norte, 29160 Chiapa de Corzo W: imer.mx/radiolagarto – **CS25)** CS25) La Fuente de Poder Educativa Indígena de Chiapas, A.C., Sinaí 3, 29416 Betania, Prg in Sp. and Tzotzil.
**DF00) CIUDAD DE MÉXICO (D.F.)**
**DF01)** Grupo Radio Digital, Paseo de las Palmas 751, Col. Lomas de Chapultepec, 11000 México W: radiochapultepec.com - 1100-0700 – **DF02)** NRM Comunicaciones, Prolongación Paseo de la Reforma 115, Col. Paseo de las Lomas, 01330 México. W: nrm.com.mx ban-dolera1410.com – R. Mil: Ap.21-1000, 04021 México W: radiomil. com.mx – **DF03)** Radiodifusoras Asociadas, Durango 341, Planta Baja, Col. Roma, 06700 México W: radio620.com – **DF04)** Instituto Mexicano de la Radio, Real de Mayorazgo 83, Barrio Xoco, 03330 México W: imer.mx – **DF05)** Grupo R. Centro, Av. Constituyentes 1154, Col. Lomas Altas, 11950 México W: radiocentro.com redamf21. com – **DF06)** Televisa Radio, Calzada de Tlalpan 3000, Col. Espartaco, 04870 México. W: televisa.com wradio.com.mx los40.com.mx kebuena. com.mx xeqradio.mx deportes2.televisa.com/tdw – **DF07)** Grupo ABC Radio, Basilio Vadillo 29, Col Tabacalera, 06030 México. W: abcradio. com.mx – **DF08)** Grupo Radiodifusoras Capital, Montes Urales 425, Col. Lomas de Chapultepec, 11000 México. W: gruporadiocapital.com. mx – **DF09)** Universidad Nacional Autónoma de México, Adolfo Prieto 133, Col. del Valle, 03100 México. W: radiounam.unam.mx – **DF10)** Grupo R. Fórmula, Av. Universidad 1273, Col. del Valle, 03100 México. W: radioformula.com.mx – **DF11)** Radio Educación, Ángel Urraza 622, Col. del Valle 03100 México. W: radioeducacion.edu.mx emisorasre. gob.mx – **DF12)** Grupo ACIR, S.A., Pirineos 770, Lomas de Chapultepec, 11000; W: grupoacir.com.mx, 889noticias.com.mx, amorfm.com.mx, digital99.com.mx, mixfm.com.mx, radiofelicidad.com.mx, comadre.mx – **DF14)** Radiorama Valle de México, Paseo de la Reforma 56, P1, Col. Juárez, 06000 México. W: radioramavm.mx arroba.fm – **DF15)** Grupo 7 División Radio, Montecito 59, Col. Nápoles, 03810 México. W: gruposiete.com.mx, quiereme1440.mx – **DF16)** grupozer.net/ estados.php?estado=6 facebook.com/ZerRadio1650 – **DF17)** Grupo Imagen Multimedia, Av. Universidad 2014, Col. Copilco Universidad, 04350 México W: imagen.com.mx, imagenradio.com.mx, rmx.com. mx – **DF18)** Universidad Iberoamericana, Av. Prol. Paseo de la Reforma 880, Lomas de Santa Fe, 01219 México. W: ibero909.fm – **DF19)** Universidad Autónoma Metropolitana, Av. Constituyentes 1054, Col. Lomas Altas, 11950 México W: uamradio.uam.mx – **DF20)** Instituto Politécnico Nacional, Av. Santa Ana 1000, San Fco. Culhuacán, 04430, México. W: radio.ipn.mx – **DF21)** MVS Radio, Mariano Escobedo 532, Col. Anzures, 11300 México. W: mvsradio.com – **DF22)** XEFAJ, S.A. de C.V., Av. Bosques de Duraznos 65, Oficina 1009, Col. Bosques de las Lomas, 11700 México – **DF23)** Alianza por el Derecho Humano de las Mujeres a Comunicar W: violetaradio.org
**DG00) DURANGO (Dgo.)**
**DG01)** Fco. I. Madero y Heroico Colegio Militar s/n, Col. Altamira, 34600 Santiago Papasquiaro. W: santiago.latremenda.com.mx – **DG03)** Jesús Contreras 111, Col. Guillermina, 34279 Durango W: radioformuladurango.com – **DG06)** Blvd. Fco. Villa 3115, Fracc. Gpe. Victoria INFONAVIT, 34125 Durango W: xhdgofm.com,xedu860.com – **DG08)** Grupo Radio México, Capitán de Ibarra 1203 Ote., Fracc. del Lago, 34080 Durango. W: durango.lazradio.com.mx – **DG09)** DCI,

Domicilio conocido, 34985 Santa María de Ocotán **W:** cdi.gob.mx/ecosgobmx/xetph.php – **DG10)** Escápate al Paraíso S.A. de C.V., N/A **W:** grupoacustik.com.mx/radio
**GJ00) GUANAJUATO (Gto.)**
**GJ01)** Boulevard Algeciras 1504, Col. Lomas de Arbide, 37368, León **W:** bajio.multimedios.com – **GJ03)** Blvd.López Mateos Ote 1117, 38070 Celaya **W:** exafm.com/#!/celaya/home - 1200-0600 – **GJ05)** Morelos 110, 36500 Irapuato **W:** radioirapuato.com - 1200-0600 – **GJ06)** Allende 17, 38600 Acámbaro. **W:** radioconsentida.com - 1200-0400 – **GJ08)** Corporación ACIR Celaya, Guanajuato 106, Col Alameda, 38090 Celaya **W:** lacomadre.mx/la-comadre.881-1-celaya – **GJ09)** Corporación Bajío Comunicaciones, Av.Guerrero y Francisco Sarabia, Centro Plaza Magna, Locales 1,2 y 3 C, 36500 Irapuato **W:** ely-ella.mx radiolobobajio.mx – **GJ10)** Palacio Federal, Casa de Moneda, Sopeña 1, P2, 36000 Guanajuato **W:** radiouniversidad.ugto.mx - 1300-0500 – **GJ11)** Elodia Ledezma 658, Fracc. Las Flores, 38990 Moroleón **W:** radiomoroleon.mx - 1200-0600 – **GJ14)** Aldama 301(or Ap.24) , 36700 Salamanca - 1300-0500 – **GJ15)** Morelos 110, Centro, 36500 Salamanca **W:** radioirapuato.com/estaciones/wesalamanca - 1300-0500 – **GJ16)** Cañada 310, Esq.Roca, Col Jardines de Moral, 37160 León **W:** lapoderosa.com.mx – **GJ19)** 10 de Mayo No. 126, Centro, 37000 León **W:** lazradio.com.mx - 1200-2400 – **GJ23)** Municipio Libre 8, 36080 Guanajuato **W:** 907santafe.com - 1300-0300 – **GJ24)** Escápate al Paraíso S.A. de C.V., N/A **W:** grupoacustik.com.mx/radio
**GR00) GUERRERO (Gro.)**
**GR02)** Grupo ACIR, Av. La Suiza 19, Fracc. Las Playas, 39390 Acapulco **W:** 101.5acapulco.comadre.mx amor1031.mx – **GR05)** Zapata 28, 5to. Piso, esquina Galeana, Centro, 39000 Chilpancingo **W:** capitalmaxima.mx/chilpancingo - 1200-0400 – **GR06)** Audiorama Guerrero, Av. Del Sur 14, Col. Margarita Viguri, 39060 Chilpancingo. **W:** radiorama-guerrero.com.mx – **GR08)** Fray Bautista Moya 410, Centro, 40660 Cd. Altamirano. **W:** radioxexy.com.mx - 1200-0430 – **GR09)** Av. Heroico Colegio Militar No 234, Col Aviación, 41304 Tlapa de Comonfort **W:** cdi.gob.mx/ecosgobmx/xezv.php - 1200-0100 (SS -2000) Prgrs in Sp., Náhuatl, Mixteco and Tlapaneco – **GR10)** Carretera Escénica 109, Col. Villas Guitarrón, Acapulco **W:** radioformulaguerrero.com – **GR11)** Av. Revolución 6, 40700 Coyuca de Catalán. **W:** rtvgro.net – **GR12)** Monteblanco 37, Fracc. Hornos Insurgentes, 39350 Acapulco. **W:** rtvgro.net - 1200-0700 – **GR17)** Benito Juárez 19-A, Barrio del Carmen, 41700 Omotepec. **W:** rtvgro.net – **GR18)** Hacienda del Cernillo, Casa Gallos s/n, 40200 Taxco. **W:** rtvgro.net - 1200-0400 – **GR21)** Avenida Lázaro Cárdenas 54, Col Héroes Surianos, 40500 Arcelia. **W:** radioarcelia.com - 1200-0400 – **GR22)** 41300 Tlapa de Comonfort **W:** rtvgro.net – **GR23)** Escápate al Paraíso S.A. de C.V., N/A **W:** grupoacustik.com.mx/radio
**HG00 HIDALGO (Hgo.)**
**HG01)** Plaza de la Constitución y Manuel F Soto (or Ap.96), 43600 Tulancingo **W:** nqradio.com - 1200-0600 – **HG03)** R. y Televisión de Hidalgo, Blvd. Adolfo López Mateos s/n, Col. Aviación Civil, 43000 Huejutla **W:** radioytelevision.hidalgo.gob.mx - 1100-0300 – **HG05)** Plaza Juárez 103 (or Ap.123), 42000 Pachuca **W:** 104.5pachuca.comadre.mx - 1200-0600 – **HG08)** Hidalgo Ote.209, Col. Centro, 43600 Tulancingo **W:** facebook.com/miledtulancingo - 1200-0600 – **HG11)** Domicilio Conocido, Col Buenos Aires, 42370 Cárdonal **W:** cdi.gob.mx/ecosgobmx/xecarh.php - 1300-2300 Prgrs in Sp., Otomí and Náhuatl – **HG12)** Chávez Macotela 8, 42400 Huichapan **W:** radioytelevision.hidalgo.gob.mx
**JL00) JALISCO (Jal.)**
**JL02)** México Radio, Calzada Independencia Sur 324, Col. Centro, 44100 Guadalajara **W:** canal58.com.mx – **JL03)** Blvd. Francisco Medina Asencio km. 7.5, Plaza Marina Local 101, Col. Marina Vallarta, 48300 Puerto Vallarta **W:** kebuenapv.com – **JL05)** C7 Jalisco, Francisco Rojas González 155, Col. Ladrón de Guevara, 44600 Guadalajara. **W:** c7jalisco.com – **JL06)** Av. Francisco Villa 549, Col. Versalles, 48310 Puerto Vallarta **W:** lapatrona935fm.com – **JL07)** Hidalgo 158, Centro, 49000 Cd. Guzmán - 1200-0600 – **JL08)** Lorenzana 884, Col. Chapalita, 45040 Guadalajara. **W:** notisistema.com – **JL10)** Notisistema, Av. México 3150 Fracc. Moraz, 44670 Guadalajara. **W:** notisistema.com – **JL11)** Grupo ACIR, Paseo de Las Gaviotas 198, Col. Las Gaviotas, 48351 Puerto Vallarta – **JL12)** Televisa Radio, Rubén Darío 158, Circunvalación Vallarta, 44680 Guadalajara **W:** Av. Hidalgo 111, Centro, 48900 Autlán. **W:** radiocosta.com.mx **JL14)** Av. México 3370, Plaza Bonita, Local Subanda P, 45120 Guadalajara **W:** radioformulaguadalajara.com - 1300-0700 – **JL16)** Promomedios, Portal Hidalgo 13, Int.10, Centro, 49650 Tamazula **W:** promomediosjalisco.com – **JL17)** Grupo ACIR, Av. Lázaro Cárdenas 2820, Jardines del Bosque, 44520 Guadalajara - 1200-0600 – **JL20)** Radiorama Puerto Vallarta, Honduras 309, Int. 161, Col.5 de Diciembre, 48350 Puerto Vallarta – **JL21)** Calle San Juan Bosco 3623, Fracc. Jardines de San Ignacio, 45050 Zapopan. **W:** radiomariamexico.com – **JL23)** Primero de Mayo 126-8, 49000 Cd. Guzmán - 1200-0600 – **JL24)** Radiorama

de Occidente, Av. Niños Héroes 1555, 6to. Piso, Col. Moderna, 44190 Guadalajara. **W:** radioramadeoccidente.com – **JL26)** Mega Radio, Av. Pablo Casals 567, Col. Prados Providencia, 44670 Guadalajara. **W:** megaradio.mx 1070noticias.com – **JL27)** Océano Pacífico 201, Palmar de Aramara, 48300 Puerto Vallarta – **JL29)** Hidalgo 2055 Esq. Tomas de Gómez, Col Arcos Sur, 44500 Guadalajara – **JL32)** Av. Francia 1783, Col. Moderna, Sector Juárez, 44190 Guadalajara - 1200-0600 – **JL33)** c/o El Periódico el Occidental, Calzada Independencia Sur 324, Col Centro, 44100 Guadalajara – JL34) Radio Operadora Pegasso, S.A. de C.V., N/A
**ME00) ESTADO DE MÉXICO (Edo.Méx.)**
**ME01)** Radiorama del Valle de México, Paseo de la Reforma 56, P1, Col.Juárez, 06000 México, D.F. **W:** radioramavm.mx/labestiagrupera - 1200-0600 – **ME02)** Grupo R. Capital, Allende Sur 209, Col. Centro, 50000 Toluca **W:** radiocapital.mx/toluca - 1100-0600 – **ME03)** Sistema de R. y Televisión Mexiquense, Av. Quintana Roo 44, Col. Prado Sur, Tultitlan **W:** radioytvmexiquense.mx – **ME06)** Radiorama Toluca, Av. José María Morelos 903, esq. con Quintana Roo, Col. la Merced (Alameda), 50080 Toluca. **W:** radiorama.com.mx – **ME07)** Sistema de R. y TV Mexiquense, Av. Estado de México km 1, Col. La Virgen, 52140 Metepec **W:** radioytvmexiquense.mx - 1200-0600 – **ME08)** José María Morelos 948, Esq. Carretera a Tonatico, 51900 Ixtapan de la Sal. **W:** gruporadiocapital.mx/index.php/capital-maxima/ixtapan-de-la-sal - 1200-0600 – **ME10)** Universidad Autónoma de Chapingo, Carr. México-Texcoco km 38.5, 56235 Chapingo **W:** chapingo.mx/cultura/radio.php - 1800-0200 – **ME11)** Cabina 5, Edificio CAD, Escuela de Comunicación, Av. Universidad Anáhuac 46, Col. Lomas Anáhuac, Huixquilucan. **W:** anahuac.mx/radio
**MI00) MICHOACÁN (Mich.)**
**MI01)** Aqua 78, Col.Prados del Campestre, 58297 Morelia **W:** rasacandela.com - 1200-0300 – **MI02)** Av. Revolución Sur 66, Col. Mariano Matamoros, 61506 Zitácuaro **W:** radiozitacuaro.com - 1200-0600 (SS -0400) – **MI03)** Privada de Diligencias 53, Int. 1, Fraccionamiento El Mirador (or Ap.61), 60100 Uruapan **W:** lazeta.mx/Uruapan – **MI07)** Macarena 32, Inguambo, 60130 Uruapan **W:** radioramamichoacan.com – **MI08)** Av.Constitución de 1814 Norte 2 Altos, 60600 Apatzingan **W:** gruporadioapatzingan.com.mx - 1200-0500 – **MI09)** CDI, Av. Lázaro Cárdenas 30, Col. San Marcos, 60270 Cherán **W:** cdi.gob.mx/ecosgobmx/xepur.php - 1200-0200 Prgrs in Sp and Purépecha – **MI11)** CDI, Carr. Lázaro Cárdenas-La Mira, 5 de Mayo, 60990 Lázaro Cárdenas – **MI15)** Madero 116, Col. Centro, 59300 La Piedad **W:** radiopia.mx – **MI18)** Carretera Federal N° 15 Morelia-Zitácuaro km 125.6, 61420 Tuxpan **W:** cdi.gob.mx/ecosgobmx/xepur.php - 1200-2330 Prgrs in Sp., Mazahua, Otomí & Matlatzinca – **MI19)** Juan Ayala 10, Int 102, Centro, 60000 Uruapan **W:** candelauruapan.com – **MI24)** Av. Díaz Ordaz 225A (Ap.60), 59000 Sahuayo **W:** promoradio.com - 1300-0400 – **MI26)** Aquiles Serdán 548 , 58020 Morelia **W:** lazeta.mx/Morelia – **MI29)** José Rosas Moreno 200, Col. Vista Bella, 58090 Morelia **W:** sistemaichoacano.tv – **MI30)** . José María Morelos 14, Segundo Sector del Fidelac, 60950 Lázaro Cárdenas **W:** rimer.gob.mx/radioazul - 1100-0600 – **MI31)** Media Group, Torre Victoria, Av. Acueducto 2800, Piso 6, Col. Lomas de Hidalgo, 58241Morelia **W:** www.mediagroup.mx
**M000) MORELOS (MoR )**
**MO01)** 62746 Cuautla (alt.address: Hidalgo 109, Col. Cuauhtémoc, 62220 Ocotepec, Cuernavaca) **W:** imryt.org – **MO02)** Escápate al Paraíso S.A. de C.V., N/A **W:** grupoacustik.com.mx/radio
**NA00) NAYARIT (Nay.)**
**NA01)** Radio Aztlán, Av. Victoria 213 A Pte, 63940 Tepic. **W:** aztlanradio.com – **NA02)** Carretera Tecuala – Acaponeta km. 1, Tecuala (or Ap.7, 63440 Tecuala) **W:** alica-medios.com/radiored - 1200-0400 – **NA03)** Radiorama Nayarit, Puebla 64 Sur, Centro, 63060 Tepic. **E:**radioramanayarit@hotmail.com **W:** radioramanayarit.mx – **NA06)** Domicilio Conocido, 63530 Jesús María **W:** cdi.gob.mx/ecosgobmx/xejmn.php - 1200-2000 Prgrs in Sp., Cora, Huichol, Tepehuáno and Náhuatl
**NL00) NUEVO LEÓN (N.L.)**
**NL01)** Parque Industrial Regiomontano, 64540 Monterrey – **NL02)** Grupo Radio Alegría, Av. Madero Oriente 1110, 64000 Monterrey. **W:** epsilonmedia.mx/?page_id=15313 – **NL03)** Grupo Radio Centro, Juan Ignacio Ramón 506 Oriente, P20, Edif. Latino, 64000 Monterrey **W:** facebook.com/laregiomontana600 fb630.com – **NL04)** Paricutín Sur 316, Col. Roma, (or. Ap.203) 64700 Monterrey **W:** mmradio.com - 1200-0700 – **NL05)** Edificio Santos, Francisco I. Madero 1955, Int. 210, 64000 Monterrey **W:** radioformulamonterrey.com – **NL06)** Capitán Alonso de León s/n o Antigua Carretera Nacional km 904, Barrio Zaragoza, 67500 Montemorelos. **W:** delta929fm.com – **NL07)** Carr. Nacional Km. 856, Col. La Amistad, 67700 Linares (or. Ap.81), 67700 Linares - 1200-0600 – **NL08)** Radio ACIR, Monterrey 698, Esq. Cerralvo, Col. Libertad, 64130 Guadalupe **W:** radioacir.net – **NL10)** NRM Comunicaciones, Av. Cuauhtémoc 725 Nte., Centro, (or. Ap.118) 64000 Monterrey. **W:** nucleoradio.com – **NL11)** Grupo Radio Alegría, Reforma s/n, Col.

Enrique Lozano, 65290 Cd. Sabinas Hidalgo - 1200-0600 – **NL12)** Av. San Francisco y Loma Grande, Col. Loma Grande, 64000 Monterrey **W:** nl.gob.mx/radio-y-television-de-nuevo-leon – **NL13)** Grupo Radio Centro, Padre Mier Poniente 439, Centro, 64000 Monterrey

**OX00) OAXACA (Oax.)**
**OX05)** Cerro El Panteón, Ap.35, 70900 Puerto Ángel **W:** lavozdelangel.com.mx - 1200-0200 – **OX06)** Aquiles Serdán y Mina 502, Col. Benito Juárez Norte, 70301 Matías Romero **W:** encuentroradiotv.com - 1200-0100 – **OX07)** Grupo Radio México, Netzahualcóyotl 216, Col Reforma, 68050 Oaxaca - 1200-0600 – **OX08)** Morelos 6-2, 71000 Putla de Guerrero - 1200-0130 – **OX10)** Lázaro Cárdenas s/n, 68770 Guelatao de Juárez **W:** cdi.gob.mx/ecosgobmx/xeglo.php - 1200-0130 Prgrs in Sp., Zapoteco, Mixe and Chinanteco – **OX12)** Carr. Puerto Escondido-Pochutla Km. 143, 71980 Puerto Escondido **W:** lavozdelpuerto.mx - 1300-0600 – **OX14)** CDI, Blvd. Rafael Reyes Spíndola 1, 69800 Tlaxiaco **W:** cdi.gob.mx/ecosgobmx/xetla.php - 1200-2400 Prgrs in Sp., Mixteco and Triqui – **OX15)** Independencia s/n, Sección Segunda, 68470 San Lucas Ojitlán **W:** cdi.gob.mx/ecosgobmx/xeojn.php - 1400-2200 Prgrs in Sp., Mazateco, Cuicateco and Chinanteco – **OX16)** Amapolas 808, Col. Reforma, 68050 Oaxaca - 1200-0600 – **OX22)** Plaza de la Constitución y Negrete s/n, 71700 Santiago Jamiltepec. Prgrs in Sp., Mixteco, Amuzgo and Chatino **W:** cdi.gob.mx/ecosgobmx/xejam.php - 1200-2400 – **OX24)** Escápate al Paraíso de C. de V., N/A **W:** grupoacustik.com.mx/radio

**PU00) PUEBLA (Pue.)**
**PU01)** Plaza de la Constitución 102, altos 1, 73080 Xicotepec de Juárez **W:** radioxicotepec570am.com – **PU06)** Teziutlán Sur 17, Col. La Paz, 72160 Puebla **W:** radiooro.com.mx – **PU08)** Blvd. Atlixco 37, Local 218, Plaza JV, Col. San José, 72170 Puebla. **W:** kebuena1010.com.mx – **PU10)** Av. 15 de Mayo 2939, Col. Las Hadas, 72070 Puebla. **W:** cincoradio.com.mx mx – **PU11)** Cinco Radio, Manuel Pereyra Mejía 417, Col. Ignacio Zaragoza, 75770 Tehuacán **W:** cincoradio.com.mx - 1300-0100 – **PU13)** Calle Matamoros 77, esq. San Martin Texmelucan, Col. La Paz, 72160 Puebla. **W:** lamejorpuebla.mx – **PU14)** 3 Oriente no, 201, col. Centro Histórico, 72000 Puebla. **W:** abcradiopuebla.com.mx – **PU15)** Av. 15 Pte. 1306, Col. Santiago, 72000 Puebla. **W:** grupoacir.com.mx – **PU18)** Priv. Miguel Alvarado s/n, 73560 Cuetzalán. **W:** cdi.gob.mx/ecosgobmx/xectz.php - 1200-0100 prgrs in Sp, Náhuatl and Totonaco.

**QE00) QUERÉTARO (Qro.)**
**QE07)** Camino de Piedras Anchas 100, Cabecera Municipal de Jalpan de Serra, 76000 Jalpan **W:** rtq.com.mx – **QE10)** Medios Digitales RMX, S.A. de C.V., N/A

**QR00) QUINTANA ROO (Q.Roo.)**
**QR02)** Calle 63, Supermanzana 61, Mzna 7, Lote 1, 77500 Cancún **W:** mixfm.mx/mix-93-1-cancun - 1100-0600 – **QR03)** Grupo Radio México, Av. López Portillo, Supermanzana 59, Manzana 8 Lote 2, Local 1433-A, Col. Benito Juárez, 77515 Cancún **W:** lazradio.com.mx/cancun - 1200-0300 – **QR04)** Sistema Quintanarroense de Comunicación Social, Carretera a Tulum, Km. 1.5, 77200 Félipe Carillo Puerto. **W:** sqcs.com.mx – **QR06)** Plaza Hollywood local 86, Supermanzana 35, 77508 Cancún **W:** radioformulaqr.com – **QR07)** 20 Av. Sur 965, Entre 13 y 15, Sur. Col. Andrea Quintana Roo. (or:Ap.299) 77600 Cozumel,**W:** sol899.com – **QR08)** Av. Miguel Hidalgo 201, 77000 Chetumal **W:** sqcs.com.mx - 1100-0700 – **QR09)** Av. Uxmal 30, Supermanzana 62, 77513 Cancún **W:** sqcs.com.mx - 1100-0500 – **QR11)** Prol. Av.Héroes 680, 77000 Chetumal **W:** sol899.com - 1200-0400 – **QR14)** CDI, Av. Altamirano 83, Col. Emiliano Zapata, 77200 Felipe Carrillo Puerto - 1200-0000 Prgrs in Sp. and Maya **W:** cdi.gob.mx/ecosgobmx/xenka.php

**SL00) SAN LUIS POTOSÍ (S.L.P.)**
**SL01)** Radiorama San Luis Potosí, Eucaliptos 565, Col. Jardín, 78270 San Luis Potosí **W:** globalmedia.mx/los40 – **SL05)** Globalmedia, Av. Dr. Salvador Nava Martínez No 278, Col El Paseo, 78320 San Luis Potosí **W:** globalmedia.mx – **SL07)** CDI, Josefa Ortíz de Domínguez 5, 79800 Tancanhuitz de Santos **W:** cdi.gob.mx/ecosgobmx/xeant.php - 1200-0700. Prgrs in Sp., Náhuatl, Pame and Huasteco – **SL09)** Betancourt No 401, Col. Centro, 78700 Matehuala **W:** stereo1030.com - 1155-0405 – **SL12)** General Mariano Arista 245, Centro Histórico, 78000 San Luis Potosí. **W:** radiouniversidad.uaslp.mx – **SL13)** Escápate al Paraíso S.A. de C.V., N/A **W:** grupoacustik.com.mx/radio

**SN00) SINALOA (Sin.)**
**SN01)** Aquiles Serdán 860 Pte, Col. Scally, 81200 Los Mochis - 1300-0700 **W:** lamejor.com.mx/#!/losmochis/home – **SN02)** RSN, Av. Rafael Buelna 202, Fracc. Hacienda Las Cruces, 82126 Mazatlán **W:** lamejor.com.mx/#!/mazatlan/home – **SN03)** Grupo Chávez R., Ignacio Zaragoza 200, 2do.piso, Centro, 81000 Guasave **W:** grupochavezradio.com - 1230-0800 – **SN04)** Av. Benemérito de las Américas 400, Lomas del Mar, 82010 Mazatlán **W:** exafm.com/#!/mazatlan/home – **SN05)** Cjon. Sinaloa 442 Pte., Centro, 81200 Los Mochis **W:** grupochavezradio.com – **SN07)** Radiorama Mazatlán, Av. Miguel Alemán 619 Ote, Centro, 82000 Mazatlán – **SN08)** Radiorama Culiacán, Av. Álvaro Obregón 24

Sur, Local 53 2do. piso, Plaza Paladio, Centro, 80000, Culiacán – **SN12)** Megamedios, Paseo Niños Héroes 802 Pte., Centro, 80000 Culiacán - 1300-0600 **W:** maxima103.com – **SN17)** Radio Universidad Autónoma de Sinaloa, Agustina Ramírez 1249, Col. Gabriel Leyva, 80030 Culiacán **W:** radiouas.org - 1300-0200 – **SN22)** Insurgentes 313, Col. Flamingos, 82149 Mazatlán **W:** radioformulamazatlan.com – **SN23)** Escápate al Paraíso S.A. de C.V., N/A **W:** grupoacustik.com.mx/radio

**SO00) SONORA (Son.)**
**SO02)** Grupo R. Palacios, Álvaro Obregón 184, Centro, 83600 Caborca **W:** lauk.com.mx – **SO05)** Av. Serdán, y Calle 29 N° 415, Centro, (or: Ap.630) 85480 Guaymas **W:** amor101.mx – **SO07)** Carr. a Novojoa km 27, 85280 Etchojoa **W:** cdi.gob.mx/ecosgobmx/xeetch.php - 1300-0100. Prgrs in Sp., Mayo, Yaqui and Guarijío – **SO10)** Uniradio, Norte 811 Oriente, Centro, 85000 Cd. Obregón **W:** uniradio.com/radio/obregon/preciosa985 – **SO11)** Obregón 38, 1 Altos, Centro, 84000 Nogales (or: Box 1472, Nogales, AZ 85628, USA) **W:** xenygenial.com – **SO12)** Durango 901 Sur Altos, Col. Campestre, 85160 Cd. Obregón **W:** tribunaradio.com.mx - 1300-0200 – **SO15)** Radio SA, Heriberto Aja 96, Centro, 83000 Hermosillo **W:** grupera931.mx – **SO17)** IMER, Av. Juárez 9ª Este, 84620 Cananea **W:** imer.mx/lafq - 1200-0700 – **SO19)** Pino Suarez 99, 84900 Ures - 1300-0500 – **SO24)** Larsa Comunicaciones, Vázquez 127, Col. Fundo Legal, 84000 Nogales **W:** larsavision.tv/2017/nogales.php - 1200-0200 – **SO29)** Radio SA, Nayarit y Heriberto Aja 96, Centro, 83000 Hermosillo. **W:** activa897.com – **SO30)** Ave. Francisco Eusebio Kino y Calle 5 No 470, Barrio Comercial (Ap.44), 83449 San Luis Río Colorado **W:** radiogrupooir.com/zeta radiogrupooir.com/centro - 1300-0100 – **SO31)** Av. Morelos y Ramón Corona s/n, Col. Constitución, 85830 Navojoa - 1200-0700 – **SO33)** Grupo Radio Fórmula, Váquez 127 Altos, Col. Fundo Legal, 84000 Nogales – **SO38)** Carr. del Valle y Prol. Ave. Madero, 83449 San Luis Río Colorado – **SO39)** Uniradio, Blvd Navarrete 38, Local 2, Col. Valle Hermoso, 83209 Hermosillo **W:** uniradionoticias.com/invasora1019 – **SO40)** Escápate al Paraíso S.A. de C.V., N/A – **SO41)** Grupo Radiofónico ZER, Calle Internacional y Av. 5 Int. 8-C, 84200 Agua Prieta

**TB00) TABASCO (Tab.)**
**TB14)** Comisión de Radio y Televisión de Tabasco, Prolongación 27 de Febrero No.1001, 86035 Villahermosa **W:** corat.mx – **TB15)** Grupo Multimedios Sin Reservas, Prol. Av. 27 de Febrero 3117, Fracc. Galaxias 86035 Villahermosa **W:** sinreservas.mx

**TM00) TAMAULIPAS (Tamps.)**
**TM02)** Blvd. Miguel Hidalgo 200 A, Col. Polanco, 88710 Reynosa **W:** notigape.com/estaciones.html - 1300-0100 – **TM03)** BMP Radio, Lázaro Cárdenas 210, Local 19,20 y 21, Col. Centro, 88500 Reynosa **W:** es-la.facebook.com/lalupe891 – **TM04)** Altamira Calle Principal de Esteros, Carr. Tampico-González, 89600 Altamira **W:** radio.tamaulipas.gob.mx - 1200-0400 – **TM05)** Grupo AS, Carretera Victoria-Mante Km 2 s/n, Col Las Brisas, 87180 Cd. Victoria **W:** grupoasradio.com/victoria – **TM09)** Zaragoza 85, 87600 San Fernando **W:** facebook.com/La-Poderosa-Xesft-San-Fernando-1044458185603049 - 1200-0600 – **TM10)** Grupo Mi Radio, Paseo Colón 3822. 2do. piso, local 16, Plaza Cristal Colonia Jardín. 88060 Nuevo Laredo **W:** gcorporativoradiofonicodemexico.com – **TM11)** Tiburcio Garza Zamora 335, Rodríguez, 88630 Reynosa **W:** radio.notireytamaulipas.mx/web – **TM15)** Radiorama Reynosa, Tiburcio Garza Zamora No 1245, Col Beatty, 88630 Reynosa **W:** radioramareynosa.com.mx - 1200-0400 – **TM16)** González 2409 3er. Piso, 88000 Nuevo Laredo **W:** xek.com.mx – **TM17)** Calle 14 y Abasolo, No 76, 87300 Matamoros **W:** notigape.com/estaciones.html - 1200-0600 – **TM19)** Morelos 2513, Juárez, 88209 Nuevo Laredo - 1200-0600 – **TM20)** Radiorama Nuevo Laredo, Mendoza 747, Centro, 88000 – **TM21)** Blvd. Hidalgo 22 A, Fracc. Polanco, 88710 Reynosa **W:** notigape.com/estaciones.html – **TM24)** Diego Acuña, 87900 Cd. Tula - 1200-0400 – **TM25)** Sexta 75, Centro, (or Ap.540), 87300 Matamoros **W:** corporativoradiofonicodemexico.com - 1200-0700 – **TM26)** Morelos 2513, Col. Juárez, (or. Ap.232), 88000 Nuevo Laredo **W:** laraza957.com - 1155-0600 (Sat –0800, Sun –0200) – **TM27)** Carretera Ribereña KM 62, 88440 Cd. Camargo - 1200-0400 **W:** grupomiradio.mx/portal/estaciones/reynosa – **TM29)** Quinta 226, Centro, (or Ap.13), 83000 Cd. Miguel Alemán **W:** notigape.com/estaciones.html - 1155-0400 – **TM30)** Grupo R. Avanzado, Ignacio Zaragoza 660, Local 4, 88500 Reynosa **W:** laraza1060.com - 1200-0600 – **TM31)** Séptima 233 Altos, Centro, 88300 Ciudad Miguel Alemán **W:** grupomiradio.mx/portal/estaciones/miguelaleman - 1155-0200 – **TM32)** Calle 8 y Cuauhtémoc 125, Col. Pedro Sosa, 87120 Cd Victoria **W:** radio.tamaulipas.gob.mx - 1200-0800 – **TM33)** Sexta y Fuerza Aérea, Edif. María Rebeca, 87300 Matamoros – **TM34)** Escápate al Paraíso S.A. de C.V., N/A **W:** grupoacustik.com.mx/radio – **TM35)** Grupo Flores Radio, Cristóbal Colón 207 Norte, Centro, 89000 Tampico

**TX00) TLAXCALA (Tlax.)**
**TX01)** Av.Juárez Norte 203, 90500 Huamantla - 1200-0600 – **TX02)** Calle Uno 420, Col. Xicohtencatl, 90070 Tlaxcala **W:** radiotlaxcala1430.mx - 1200-0600

**VE00) VERACRUZ (Ver.)**
**VE03)** Ruíz Cortines 303, Col. Centro, 95400 Cosamaloapan **W:** xefuradio.com.mx – **VE08)** Moctezuma 77, Bis Col. Centro, 91000 Xalapa **W:** amorfm.mx/amor-91-7-xalapa – **VE09)** Benjamín Franklin 4, Col. Centro, 91700 Veracruz **W:** lapoderosaveracruz.fm/site – **VE11)** Av. Unión esq. Michoacan 101, Col. Lazaro Cardenas, 93200 Poza Rica **W:** radioramapozarica.mx – **VE22)** Eulalio Vela 15, Col. Obrera, 96700 Minatitlán **W:** gruporadiomina.com – **VE24)** Morelos No. 37 Altos 3er. Piso Frente al Parque Reforma, Col. Centro, 92800 Tuxpan **W:** facebook.com/Azul106.9fm – **VE27)** Plaza Crystal, Local 20, 91150 Xalapa **W:** 955sensacionfm.com - 1200-0600 – **VE28)** Bernarda Soto Mercado 2, 91615 Teocelo **W:** radioteocelo.org.mx - 1100-0200 – **VE32)** Sur 31 N° 336, 94300 Orizaba **W:** lacomadreorizaba.com - 1200-0600 – **VE42)** CDI, Callejón de las ánimas s/n, Col. Centro, 95000 Zongolica **W:** cdi.gob.mx/ecosgobmx/xezon.php – **VE55)** Escápate al Paraíso S.A. de C.V., N/A **W:** grupoacustik.com.mx/radio
**YU00) YUCATÁN (Yuc.)**
**YU01)** Grupo Rivas, Calle 62 N° 465, Entre 53 y 55, Centro, 97000 Mérida **W:** gruporivas.com.mx - 1130-0100 – **YU03)** Calle 33-B No. 513, Col. García Gineres, 97070 Mérida **W:** radioformulayucatan.com – **YU04)** Cadena RASA, Km 1 Carr. Valladolid-Carillo Puerto, 97780 Valladolid **W:** cadenarasa.com/candela_valladolid - 1100-0500 – **YU05)** Cadena RASA, Edificio Publicentro, Calle 62, No 508 Altos, (Ap.217), 97001 Mérida **W:** cadenarasa.com - 1200-0600 – **YU07)** Carretera Peto-Tzucacab Km 2, 97930, Peto **W:** cdi.gob.mx/ecosgobmx/xepet.php - 1100-0100 (Sun - 1300-2200) Prgrs in Sp And Maya – **YU09)** Universidad Autónoma de Yucatán, Calle 60 No. 491-A, Esquina con 57, Centro, 97000 Mérida **W:** radio.uady.mx - 1200-0600 – **YU10)** Fundación Cultural para la Sociedad Mexicana A.C., Calle 43, No. 499, Centro, 97000 Mérida **W:** radiomariamexico.com
**ZC00) ZACATECAS (Zac.)**
**ZC03)** Blvd. Paseo del Mineral 746 Sur, Col. Venustiano Carranza, 99099 Fresnillo **W:** lamejor.com.mx – **ZC07)** Josefa Ortiz de Dominguez 51, P3, 99700 Tlaltenango **W:** radiotr.com - 1200-0600 – **ZC08)** Transmisiones MIK, S.A. de C.V., N/A – **ZC09)** Domicilio conocido, 98300 Juan Aldama **W:** www.comunicacionesjfj.com

**FM in México City (MHz):** (HD Radio): **DF05)** 88.1 (HD1: Universal) – **DF12)** 88.9 Noticias – **DF02)** 89.7 Oye 89.7 – **DF17)** 90.5 (HD1: Imagen) – **DF18)** 90.9 ((HD1: Ibero 90.9, HD2: Ibero 90.9.2) – **DF05)** 91.3 (HD1: Alfa 91.3) – **DF05)** 92.1 Red FM – **DF06)** 92.9 La Ke Buena – **DF05)** 93.7 (HD1: Joya) – **DF19)** 94.1 UAM R. – **DF04)** 94.5 (HD1: Opus 94, HD2: XEB 1220 La B Grande, HD3: Jazz Digital) – **DF12)** 95.3 Amor – **DF20)** 95.7 R. IPN – **DF09)** 96.1 R. UNAM – **DF11)** 96.5 (R.Educación, F.PI) – **DF06)** 96.9 W Radio – **DF05)** 97.7 (HD1: R. Centro 97-7) – **DF17)** 98.5 (HD1: RMX) – **DF12)** 99.3 R. Disney – **DF02)** 100.1 Stereo Cien – **DF02)** 100.9 Beat – **DF06)** 101.7 Los 40 – **DF21)** 102.5 MVS – **DF10)** 103.3 (HD1: Grupo Fórmula Digital HD 103.3, HD2: Grupo Fórmula Digital HD 103.3 – 1hr., HD3: Grupo Fórmula Digital HD 1470, HD4: Grupo Fórmula Trión) – **DF10)** 104.1 (HD1: Grupo Fórmula Digital HD 104.1, HD2: Grupo Fórmula Digital HD 104.1 – 1hr., HD3: Grupo Fórmula Digital HD 1470, HD4: Jazz FM) – **DF21)** 104.9 Exa FM – **DF22)** 105.3 (HD1: Aire Libre) – **DF04)** 105.7 (HD1: Horizonte, HD2: RMI, R. México Internacional, HD3: Interferencia HD3) – **DF23)** 106.1 (XHCDMX R. Violeta, F.PI.) – DF12) 106.5 Mix 106 – **DF05)** 107.3 (HD1: La Z) – **DF04)** 107.9 (HD1: Horizonte 108, HD2: R. Ciudadana, HD3: Música del Mundo)

## MICRONESIA (USA associated)

**L.T:** Chuuk, Yap: UTC +10h; Kosrae, Pohnpei: UTC +11h — **Pop:** 106,227 — **Pr.L:** Yapese, Trukese, Ponapean, Kosraean, English — **E.C:** 60Hz, 120V — **ITU:** FSM

### FEDERATED STATES OF MICRONESIA BROADCASTING SERVICE (Gov.)
🖂 Public Information Office, P.O. Box 34, Palikir Station, Pohnpei State FSM 96941 **L.P:** Chairman: Shelten G Neth **E:** chairman@mail.fm ☎ +691 320 2548 🖷 +691 320 4356

### CHUUK STATE

| MW Call | kHz | kW | MW Call | kHz | kW |
|---|---|---|---|---|---|
| 1) V6A | 1350 | 1(‡) | 2) V6AK | 1593 | 5 |
| **FM Call** | **MHz** | **kW** | **FM Call** | **MHz** | **kW** |
| 2) BWXX | 88.5 | - | 4) V6CWS | 89.5 | - |

**Addresses & other information**
**1)** Baptist Mid-Missions P.O. Box 819, Weno, Chuuk State FSM 96942 **L.P:** Pastor Jody J Colson ☎ +691 330 3453 **E:** jtcolson@mail.fm – **2)** FSMBS R. Chuuk, PO Box 189, Weno, Chuuk State FSM 96942 **L.P:** Mgr Ennis Timothy ☎+691 3302374 🖷 +691 3302593 **W:** fm/chuuk/radio **ID:** "Ach nenien appio V6AK ion Chuuk" **D.Prgr:** 1900-0700 daily BWXX-FM repeater [currently inactive] – **3)** Baptist Church, Weno,

Chuuk State FSM 96942 **L.P:** Rev.Tom Phillips **Prgr:** conservative religious music and supplied paid prgrs – **4)** National Weather R. [WSO FM], PO Box A, Weno, Chuuk State, FSM 96942. Live and recorded local weather and emergency information for Chuuk Lagoon area 24h

### KOSRAE STATE

| MW | Call | kHz | kW |
|---|---|---|---|
| 1) | V6AJ | 1503 | 1 |

**Addresses & other information**
**1)** FSMBS R. Kosrae, PO Box 147, Tofol, Kosrae State FSM 96944 **L.P:** Mgr Keitson Jonas ☎ +691 370 3040 🖷 +691 370 3880 **W:** fm/kosrae/radio **E:** v6aj@mail.fm **ID:** "Painge station V6AJ, fwin an Kosrae" **D.Prgr:** 2000-1400, 24h during adverse weather.

### POHNPEI STATE

| SW | Station | kHz | kW | | |
|---|---|---|---|---|---|
| 4) | V6MP | 4755 | 1 (currently inactive) | | |
| **MW** | **Station** | **kHz** | **kW** | **MW Station** | **kHz kW** |
| 1) | V6AF | 999 | 1 | 2) V6AH | 1449 10 |
| **FM** | **Station** | **MHz** | **kW** | **FM Station** | **MHz kW** |
| 7) | Magic FM | 100.3 | - | | |
| 4) | V6MA | 88.5 | 0.3 | 8) BBC | 101.1 - |
| 6) | V6WI | 89.5 | - | 1) V6AF | 104.1 - |

**Addresses & other information**
**1)** Baptist R. Pohnpei, PO Box H, Kolonia, Pohnpei State FSM 96941. ☎+691 3202475 **E:** v6afpohnpei@gmail.com **LP:** Gabe Eiben **D.Prgr:** 24h – **2)** FSMBS R. Pohnpei, PO Box 1086, Kolonia, Pohnpei State FSM 96941 **L.P:** Commissioner Shelten G Neth ☎+691 320 2296 🖷+691 320 5212 **W:** fm/pohnpei/radio **E:** v6ah_radio@mail.fm **ID:** "Met Station V6AH nan Pohnpei" **D.Prgr:** 1900-1105, 24h during adverse weather – **3)** Bernard's Enterprises, Kolonia, Pohnpei State FSM 96941 ☎+691 320 2441 🖷+691 320 2444 – **4)** the Cross, Pacific Missionary Aviation, Radio Station, PO Box 517, Kolonia, Pohnpei State FSM 96941 ☎ +691 320 1122/2496 **W:** pmapacific.org **E:** radio@pmapacific.org **SW:** Ninseitamw, Kolonia, simulcast of 88.5MHz – **6)** R. Paradise, Paradise Media, PO Box 1748, Kolonia, Pohnpei State FSM 96941 **W:** paradisemediapni.com **E:** paradiseradiopni@gmail.com **L.P:** GM: William Hoffman **Format:** hiphop & reggae music, community news – **7)** Kolonia, Pohnpei State FSM 96941, joint ownership with KWAW Saipan CNM – **8)** 24h BBC Pacific stream satellite rel from London

### YAP STATE

| MW | Station | kHz | kW |
|---|---|---|---|
| 2) | V6AG | 1260 | 1 |
| 1) | V6AI | 1494 | 5 |
| **FM** | **Station** | **MHz** | **kW** | **FM Station** | **MHz kW** |
| 1) | KUTE FM | 88.1 | - | 2) V6JY | 88.9 0.25 |

**Addresses & other information**
**1)** FSMBS R. Yap, PO Box 117, Colonia, Yap State FSM 96943 **L.P:** Mgr Sebastian Tamagken ☎ +691 350 2174 🖷 +691 350 2160 **W:** fm/yap/radio **E:** s_tamagken@yahoo.com **ID:** "Pary e radio station V6AI nu Waab" **D.Prgr:** 2000-1400, 24h during adverse weather. KUTE-FM is repeater – **2)** Joy Family R., PO Box 1219, Yap State FSM 96943 ☎ +691 350 8483 **D.Prgr:** 24h religious.

## MOLDOVA

**L.T:** UTC +2h (31 Mar-27 Oct: +3h) — **Pop:** 4 million — **Pr.L:** Romanian, Ukrainian, Russian, Gagauz — **E.C:** 230V/50Hz — **ITU:** MDA

### CONSILIUL COORDONATOR AL AUDIOVIZUALULUI (CCA) (Coordinating Audio-Visual Council)
🖂 str. Vlaicu Parcalab 46, 2012 Chisinau ☎ +373 22277551 🖷 +373 22277471 **E:** office@cca.md **W:** cca.md **L.P:** Pres: Dragos Vicol

### TELERADIO MOLDOVA (Pub)
🖂 str. Miorita 1, 2028 Chisinau ☎ +373 22721388 **E:** trm@trm.md **W:** trm.md **L.P:** Pres: Olga Bordeianu

| MW | kHz | kW | Prgr | MW | kHz | kW | Prgr |
|---|---|---|---|---|---|---|---|
| Chisinau (Codru) | 873 | 50 | 1 | Edinet | 1494 | 20 | 1 |
| Cahul | 1494 | 20 | 1 | | | | |

| FM (MHz) | 1 | 2 | kW | FM | 1 | 2 | kW |
|---|---|---|---|---|---|---|---|
| Balti | - | 99.4 | 4 | Mindrestii Noi | 104.9 | - | 2 |
| Cahul | 100.7 | - | 4 | Straseni | 100.5 | - | 5 |
| Causeni | 106.8 | - | 4 | Trifesti | 103.3 | - | 4 |
| Cimislia | 103.5 | - | 2 | Ungheni | 102.0 | - | 4 |
| Edinet | 101.3 | - | 4 | | | | |

+ sites with only txs below 1kW.
**D.Prgr:** Prgr 1 (R. Moldova Actualitati) 24h. For ethnic minorities: 0700-0710 Russian, 0900-0910 (SS 0905) Russian, 1200-1210 (SS 1205)

Russian, 1600-1610 Russian; 1815-1835 Romany (Tue), Various (Wed); 1815-1855 Gagauz (Mon), Ukrainian (Thu), Bulgarian (Fri); 1835-1900 Russian (Tue/Wed); W 1900-1930 (Sat 1905, Mon 1945) Russian. – **Prgr 2 (R. Moldova Tineret):** 24h. – **Prgr 3 (R. Moldova Muzical):** 24h via webcasting.

## OTHER STATIONS

| FM | MHz | kW | Location | Station |
|----|-----|----|----------|---------|
| A) | 67.46 | 17 | Edinet | BBCWS relay |
| C) | 68.48 | 17 | Straseni | RFE-RL relay |
| C) | 69.53 | 17 | Ungheni | RFE-RL relay |
| C) | 70.31 | 17 | Edinet | RFE-RL relay |
| 3) | 71.57 | 2.5 | Chisinau | Vocea Basarabiei |
| 6) | 87.9 | 1.2 | Edinet | R. Noroc |
| 2) | 88.0 | 1 | Chisinau | Muz FM |
| 19) | 88.7 | 4 | Edinet | Publika FM |
| 14) | 89.1 | 2 | Chisinau | Retro FM |
| 9) | 89.4 | 1 | Leova | R. Plai |
| 2) | 89.5 | 4 | Edinet | Muz FM |
| 17) | 89.6 | 1 | Chisinau | R. Chisinau |
| 15) | 90.4 | 1.8 | Cahul | Radio.md |
| 2) | 90.5 | 2 | Balti | Muz FM |
| 21) | 90.7 | 3.2 | Chisinau | Aquarelle FM |
| 20) | 91.0 | 3.2 | Balti | Maestro FM |
| 8) | 91.2 | 7.9 | Rezina | Jurnal FM |
| 3) | 91.9 | 2 | Causeni | Vocea Basarabiei |
| 2) | 92.3 | 1.25 | Ungheni | Muz FM |
| 2) | 92.6 | 2 | Cahul | Muz FM |
| 2) | 94.7 | 1 | Varnita | Muz FM |
| 16) | 96.7 | 2 | Chisinau | Comedy R. |
| 9) | 97.2 | 3.1 | Chisinau | R. Plai |
| 9) | 98.8 | 2.5 | Cimislia | R. Plai |
| 7) | 98.5 | 2 | Stefan Voda | Eco FM |
| 6) | 99.7 | 1.4 | Chisinau | R. Noroc |
| 6) | 99.9 | 3.2 | Causeni | R. Noroc |
| 18) | 99.9 | 3.2 | Glodeni | R. Prim |
| 8) | 100.1 | 3.2 | Chisinau | Jurnal FM |
| 3) | 100.3 | 1 | Glodeni | Vocea Basarabiei |
| 9) | 100.5 | 1 | Briceni | R. Plai |
| 9) | 100.6 | 1 | Stefan Voda | R. Plai |
| 5) | 100.7 | 1.3 | Mîndrestii Noi | Micul Samaritean |
| 12) | 100.9 | 2 | Chisinau | Kiss FM |
| 6) | 100.9 | 1.6 | Iargara | R. Noroc |
| 1) | 101.1 | 1.3 | Proteagailovca | Hit FM |
| 22) | 101.3 | 2 | Chisinau | Magic FM |
| 9) | 101.5 | 16 | Causeni | R. Plai |
| 1) | 101.7 | 1 | Chisinau | Hit FM |
| 5) | 102.0 | 1 | Causeni | Micul Samaritean |
| 7) | 102.3 | 10 | Straseni | Vocea Basarabiei |
| 13) | 102.7 | 1 | Chisinau | Virgin R. |
| 9) | 102.9 | 16 | Mîndrestii Noi | R. Plai |
| 10) | 102.9 | 1.1 | Nisporeni | Cultura Divina |
| 4) | 103.0 | 3.2 | Causeni | Novoye R. |
| 6) | 103.4 | 2.2 | Calarasi | R. Noroc |
| 4) | 103.5 | 1.6 | Balti | Vocea Basarabiei |
| 4) | 103.7 | 1.6 | Chisinau | Novoye R. |
| 5) | 103.8 | 10 | Edinet | Micul Samaritean |
| 5) | 104.2 | 1 | Chisinau | Micul Samaritean |
| 6) | 104.3 | 5 | Floresti | R. Noroc |
| 1) | 104.5 | 20 | Ungheni | Hit FM |
| 1) | 105.2 | 20 | Cahul | Hit FM |
| 5) | 105.4 | 10 | Trifesti | Micul Samaritean |
| 11) | 105.6 | 1.6 | Balti | Megapolis FM |
| 3) | 105.7 | 5 | Nisporeni | Vocea Basarabiei |
| 17) | 106.1 | 2.5 | Proteagailovca | R. Chisinau |
| 9) | 106.8 | 1.6 | Floresti | R. Plai |
| 5) | 107.0 | 20 | Ungheni | Micul Samaritean |
| B) | 107.3 | 10 | Straseni | RFI relay |
| 1) | 107.6 | 20 | Mîndrestii Noi | Hit FM |
| 5) | 107.8 | 20 | Cahul | Micul Samaritean |
| 8) | 107.9 | 10 | Edinet | Jurnal FM |

+ txs below 1kW.

**Addresses & other information:**
**1)** str. Bucovinei nr 9, 2075 Chisinau. Rel. Hit FM (Russia) – **2)** str. Ghiceorilor nr. 1, 2008 Chisinau – **3)** 4829 Magdacesti – **4)** sos. Hîncesti 59/1, 2028 Chisinau – **5)** str. Bucuresti 68, 2012 Chisinau – **6)** bd. Negruzzi 6, 2001 Chisinau – **7)** sos. Balcani nr. 7/7, 2069 Chisinau – **8)** str. M. Sadoveanu nr. 21, 2044 Chisinau – **9)** str. Inculet Ion 105, 2025 Chisinau – **10)** 6421 Cioresti – **11)** str. Alba Iulia 75, 2028 Chisinau – **12)** str. Ismail 33, 2011 Chisinau. Rel. Kiss FM (Romania) – **13)** str. Alecu Russo 1, 2068 Chisinau. Rel. Virgin R. (Romania) – **14)** str. Frumusica 1, 2002 Chisinau. Rel. Retro FM (Russia) – **15)** str. Independentei nr. 50, 2072 Chisinau – **16)** str. Bucuresti 68, 2012 Chisinau. Rel. R. Sputnik (Russia) – **17)** str. Bucuresti 42A, ap. 3,

2012 Chisinau. Own prgrs & rel. R.România Actualitati (Romania) – **18)** str. Suveranitati 5, 2901 Glodeni – **19)** str. Ghioceilor 1, 2071 Chisinau – **20)** bd. Moscovei 21, 2068 Chisinau – **21)** str. Puskin 47/1C, 2012 Chisinau – **22)** str. Gradinilor 25-13, 2001 Chisinau – **A)** Rel. BBCWS (UK) – **B)** Rel. RFI (France) – **C)** Rel. RFE-RL (USA).

## GAGAUZIA
(Autonomous territorial unit)

### GAGAUZIYA RADIO TELEVISIONU (GRT) (Pub)
☐ str. Lenin 164, 3805 Comrat ☎ +373 29823086 🖷 +373 29826934
**E:** grt.efir@mail.ru **W:** grt.md **L.P:** Chmn: Vladimir Kilçik

| FM | MHz | kW | FM | MHz | kW |
|----|-----|----|----|-----|----|
| Comrat | 102.1 | 5 | Baurci | 104.6 | 1.25 |
| Vulcanesti | 103.6 | 0.2 | | | |

**D.Prgr: GRT FM** in Gagauz, Russian: 0500-2200.

## OTHER STATIONS

| FM | MHz | kW | Location | Station |
|----|-----|----|----------|---------|
| 19) | 98.0 | 2.5 | Comrat | Publika FM |
| 6) | 99.5 | 2.5 | Comrat | R. Noroc |
| 23) | 100.3 | 1 | Comrat | PRO 100 R. |
| 5) | 103.2 | 1 | Ciadîr-Lunga | Micul Samaritean |
| 1) | 106.6 | 5 | Comrat | Hit FM |
| 2) | 107.5 | 1 | Baurci | Muz FM |

+ txs below 1kW.

**Addresses & other information:** see main tx table. **23)** str. Lenin nr. 204a, 3800 Comrat.

## TRANSNISTRIA
(Self-proclaimed "Pridnestrovian Moldavian Republic")

### PRIDNESTROVSKAYA GTRK (PGTRK) (Gov*)
(* Run by the administration of the "Pridnestrovian Moldavian Republic")
☐ per. Khristoforova 5, 3300 Tiraspol, Transnistria ☎ +373 53373074
**E:** radio1@pgtrk.ru **W:** radio.pgtrk.ru **L.P:** Dir: Igor Nikitenko

| MW | kHz | kW | Prgr | | |
|----|-----|----|------|---|---|
| Maiac | 621 | 150 | 2 | | |
| **FM** (MHz) | **1** | **2** | **kW** | **FM** | **1** | **2** | **kW** |

| FM (MHz) | 1 | 2 | kW | FM | 1 | 2 | kW |
|----------|---|---|----|----|---|---|----|
| Camenca | 105.0 | 106.4 | - | Tiraspol | 104.0 | 105.0 | 0.2 |
| Caterinovca | 104.0 | - | - | Valea Adinca | 100.1 | - | - |
| Dnestrovsc | 100.3 | - | - | Voroncovo | 106.0 | - | 1 |
| Maiac | 106.0 | - | 1.5 | | | | |

**D.Prgr: Prgr 1 (R. 1):** 24h – **Prgr 2 (R. 1 plyus):** 24h on FM, limited schedule on MW.

## OTHER STATIONS

| FM | MHz | kW | Location | Station |
|----|-----|----|----------|---------|
| 3) | 88.8 | 3 | Tiraspol[1] | R. Shanson |
| 6) | 89.3 | - | Varnita | R. Novaya volna |
| 2) | 89.6 | - | Tiraspol | Hit FM |
| 7) | 90.1 | - | Slobozia | Retro FM |
| 12) | 90.5 | - | Tiraspol | R. Rekord |
| 8) | 91.2 | - | Tiraspol | Russkoye R. |
| 9) | 91.5 | - | Slobozia | R. Maksimum |
| 14) | 91.7 | - | Dubasari | Dubossary FM |
| 11) | 96.2 | - | Ribnita | Beat FM |
| A) | 100.1 | - | Tiraspol[1] | R. Sputnik relay |
| 10) | 100.3 | 0.03 | Dubasari | Dubossarskoye R. |
| B) | 100.7 | - | Tiraspol | R. Rossii relay |
| 5) | 100.9 | - | Voroncovo | Dorozhnoye R. |
| 4) | 102.5 | - | Tiraspol | Nik FM |
| A) | 104.6 | - | Ribnita | R. Sputnik relay |
| C) | 104.6 | 0.1 | Slobozia | Mayak relay |
| 5) | 105.4 | 2 | Bender | Dorozhnoye R. |
| A) | 106.5 | - | Maiac | R. Sputnik relay |
| A) | 105.8 | - | Slobozia | R. Sputnik relay |
| 13) | 107.1 | - | Tiraspol | Avtoradio |
| 1) | 107.7 | 1 | Tiraspol[1] | R. Inter FM |

[1] Synchro-network with txs in several towns

**Addresses & other information:**
**1)** ul. K.Libnikhta 1/2, 3300 Tiraspol – **2)** Rel. Hit FM* – **3)** ul. K.Libnikhta 1/2, 3300 Tiraspol. Rel. R. Shanson* – **4)** 3300 Tiraspol – **5)** 3300 Tiraspol. Rel. Dorozhnoye R.* – **6)** ul. Internatsionalistov 13, Bender. Rel. Love R.* – **7)** Rel. Retro FM* – **8)** ul. Yunosti 1, 3300 Tiraspol. Rel. Russkoye R.* – **9)** Rel. R. Maksimum* – **10)** ul. Dzerzhinskogo 4, 4501 Dubasari. Rel. Dorozhnoye R.* – **11)** ul. Kirova 130, 5500 Ribnita – **12)** Rel. R. Rekord* – **13)** Rel. Avtoradio* – **14)** 4501 Dubasaril – **A)** Rel. R. Sputnik* – **B)** Rel. R. Rossii* – **B)** Rel. Mayak* (*= Relays from Russia).

**Int. relays on MW:** (Upon demand; txs operated by Pridnestrovskiy radioteletsentr) Grigoriopol (Maiac) 999/1413kHz 1000kW. See Int. Radio section

## MONACO

**L.T:** UTC +1h (31 Mar-27 Oct: +2h) — **Pop:** 33,000 — **Pr.L:** French — **E.C:** 50Hz, 230V — **ITU:** MCO

### MONACO MEDIA DIFFUSION (Comm.)
📧 10-12 Quai Antoine 1er, MC-98000 Monaco ☎ +377 97974700 🖷 +377 97974707 **W:** mmd.mc **E:** contact@mmd.mc
**L.P:** Jean Pastorelli

| LW & MW | kHz | kW | Prgr. |
|---|---|---|---|
| Roumoules (France) | 216 | *1500 | RMC |
| Col de la Madone (France) | 702 | 200 | ‡ (inactive) |
| Roumoules (France) | 1467 | 1000 | TWR relay** 2045-2245, |
| | | | Sat. 2115-2245 |
| Col de la Madone (France) | 1467 | 40 | ‡ (inactive) |

*) 900kW from 1900 **) mainly Polish & Arab Prgs

### RMC (Comm.)
📧 HQ: 15 rue Général Alain de Boissieu 75015 Paris, France ☎ +33 1 71191191 🖷 +33 1 71191190 **W:** rmc.bfmtv.com
**L.P:** Roumoules (France) 216kHz 1500kW RMC 0356-2308 (IDs as "RMC" only). **FM:** Col de la Madone 98.5MHz 50kW; Monaco Herculis 98.8MHz 0.1kW 24h.

### RADIO MONACO (Comm.)
📧 HQ: 7 Rue du Gabian, Gildo Pastor Centre, MC-98000 Monaco ☎ +377 97700700 🖷 +377 97700701 **W:** radio-monaco.com
**FM:** Monaco Mont Agel Site 1 98.2MHz 0.5 kW; Mont Agel Site 1 95.4MHz 1kW, Grasse (France) 103.2MHz 0.5kW **E:** info@radio-monaco.com

### RADIO MONTE CARLO ITALIE (Comm.)
📧 8 Quai Antoine 1er, MC-98000 Monaco ☎ +377 97976666 🖷 +377 97708661 **W:** radiomontecarlo.net **E:** rmc@radiomontercarlo.net
**FM: RMC1** Monaco Mont Agel Site 1 106.8MHz 1kW **RMC2** Ventimiglia (IM) Italy 101.6 MHz

### RIVIERA RADIO (Comm)
📧 10 Quai Antoine 1er, MC-98000 Monaco ☎ +377 97979494 🖷 +377 97979495 **W:** rivieraradio.mc **E:** info@rivieraradio.mc
**L.P:** MD: Paul Kavanagh. Tech. Manager: Peter Miller
**FM:** Monaco Musée Océanographique 106.3MHz 1kW; Col de la Madone 106.5MHz 50kW **D.Prgr.** in English: 24h Rel. BBCWS N every h

**Other FM stations (all sces. 24h):**

| FM | MHz | kW | Station, location |
|---|---|---|---|
| 1) | 88.2 | 0.01 | R. Maria Italia, Escorial |
| 2) | 90.3 | 50 | M R., Col de la Madone |
| 3) | 90.6 | 0.2 | Médi 1, Mont Agel Site 2 |
| ) | 91.4 | 0.16 | Mont Agel Site 2 |
| ) | 92.7 | 0.1 | Herculis |
| 4) | 93.2 | 0.2 | Jazz R.,Mont Agel Site 2 |
| 5) | 93.5 | 50 | R. Nostalgie, Col de la Madone |
| 5) | 93.8 | 1 | R. Nostalgie, Mont Agel Site 1 |
| 6) | 94.5 | 0.1 | R. Pitchoun, Escorial |
| 7) | 95.1 | 0.1 | RTL 2 Musée Océanographique |
| 4) | 95.7 | 0.16 | Jazz R., Mont Agel Site 2 |
| 8) | 96.1 | 0.7 | R. FG Mont Agel Site 2 |
| 9) | 96.4 | 0.3 | Chérie, Mont Agel Site 1 |
| 10) | 96.7 | 0.05 | R. Ethic , Escorial |
| 11) | 97.9 | 0.2 | Sud R., Mont Agel Site 2 |
| 12) | 99.1 | 0.03 | R. 105 Italia, Escorial |
| 13) | 101.1 | 0.16 | Fun R., Mont Agel Site 1 |
| 6) | 102.1 | 0.1 | R. Pitchoun, Mont Agel Site 2 |
| 14) | 102.4 | 0.3 | R. Rire & Chansons, Mont Agel Site 1 |
| 15) | 102.7 | 50 | R .Classique, Col de la Madone |
| 16) | 103.0 | 1 | RFM, Mont Agel Site 1 |
| 17) | 103.3 | 0.4 | RDS Italia, Musée Océanographique |
| 9) | 104.5 | 0.1 | Cherie, Musée Océanographique |

**Addresses and other information:**
**1) W:** radiomaria.it – **2) W:** mradio.fr – **3) W:** medi1.com – **4) W:** jazzradio.fr – **5) W:** nostalgie.fr – **6) W:** tvradio-pitchoun.fr – **7) W:** rtl2.fr – **8) W:** radiofg.com – **9) W:** cheriefm.fr – **10) W:** radioethic.com – **11) W:** sudradio.fr – **12) W:** radio105.net – **13) W:** funradio.fr – **14) W:** rireetchansons.fr – **15) W:** radioclassique.fr – **16)W:** rfm.fr – **17)** rds.it

**DAB+** (Mont Agel): 8A 195.936 MHz 10kW Radio 105 – RMC Italie – Riviera Radio. – R. Maria (France) – Médi 1 – RMC 2 – R. Latina – R.

Ethic – Crooner Radio – Swigg FM – MC Doualiya – R. Monaco 12B ( 225.648 MHz) 10kW Fréquence Mistral – R. Pitchoun – R. Orient – BZD Radio

## MONGOLIA

**L.T:** UTC +8h (Western Mongolia: +7h) — **Pop:** 3 million — **Pr.L:** Mongolian — **E.C:** 220V/50Hz — **ITU:** MNG

### KHARILTSAA KHOLBOONY ZOKHITSÜÜLAKH KHOROO (Communications Regulatory Commission)
📧 Sükhbaatar district, Metro Business Center, Sükhbaatar St. 13, 5th floor, Ulaanbaatar 14201 ☎ +976 1 1304257 🖷 +976 1 1327720 **E:** info@crc.gov.mn **W:** crc.gov.mn
**L.P:** Chmn/CEO: Adiyasuren Saikhanjargal (Mongolian: Saikhanjargal Adiyasüren)

### MONGOLYN ÜNDESNII OLON NIITIIN RADIO TELEVIZ (MÜONRT) (Pub)
**(Mongolian National Broadcaster)**
📧 Bayangol district, 11th subdistrict, Khuvisgalyn Rd. 3, Ulaanbaatar 16061 ☎ +976 91 915575 **E:** contact@mnb.mn **W:** mnb.mn **L.P:** DG: Ninjjamts Luvsandash (Mongolian: Luvsandash Ninjjamts)

| LW | kHz | kW | Prgr | LW/MW | kHz | kW | Prgr |
|---|---|---|---|---|---|---|---|
| Ulaanbaatar (a) | 164 | 500 | 1 | Ölgii | 209 | 75 | 1+R |
| Choibalsan | 209 | 75 | 1 | Altai | 227 | 75 | 1+2* |
| Dalanzadgad | 209 | 75 | 1+1* | Mörön | 882 | 75 | 1 |

(a) Khonkhor; R=incl. MÜONRT regional prgr (see below); *=Txs also carry prgrs of non-affiliated regional public broadcasters (see under "Regional Public Service Stations"): [1] Goviin Dolgion Büsiin Olon Niitiin R. [2] Govi-Altain Olon Niitiin R.

| SW | kHz | kW | Prgr | SW | kHz | kW | Prgr |
|---|---|---|---|---|---|---|---|
| Altai | 4830 | 10 | 3 | Ulaanbaatar (a) | 7260 | 50 | 3 |
| Mörön | 4895 | 10 | 3 | (a) Khonkhor | | | |

**NB:** All SW txs are scheduled to be on the air on a regular basis. However, the txs on 4830/4895 appear to propagate only periodically outside of their domestic target areas. All sites have backup txs for each SW freq to secure uninterrupted operation.

| FM (MHz) | 1 | 3 | kW | FM | 1 | 3 | kW |
|---|---|---|---|---|---|---|---|
| Altai | 107.0 | - | 0.05 | Ölgii | 107.0 | - | 0.05 |
| Choibalsan | 101.5 | 106.7 | 0.05 | Sainshand | 100.9 | - | 1 |
| Dalanzadgad | 107.5 | - | 1 | Ulaanbaatar | 106.0 | 100.9 | 1 |
| Mörön | 103.0 | 103.6 | 0.05 | Zamyn-Üüd | 105.2 | - | 0.1 |

+ translators
**D.Prgr: Prgr 1 (Mongolyn R.):** 2200-1500 – **Prgr 3 (R3):** 2300-1500
**MÜONRT Regional Branch: Bayan-Ölgii R.** on Ölgii 209kHz. Incl. prgrs in Kazakh.
**External Service (Voice of Mongolia):** See Int. Radio section.
**NB:** The External Service (Voice of Mongolia) has been redesignated "Prgr 2" by MÜONRT instead of the former domestic channel Altan san Radio. Altan san R. was discontinued in 2017.

### REGIONAL PUBLIC SERVICE STATIONS
**Govi-Altain Olon Niitiin R.:** Yesönbulag district (Altai), Badsuuriin Rd. On Altai 227kHz*. – **Goviin Dolgion Büsiin Olon Niitiin R.:** Dalanzadgad. On Dalanzadgad 209kHz* + 103.6MHz. – **Züün Büsiin Olon Niitiin R.:** Choibalsan. On Choibalsan 106.4MHz.
*Timeshared with Prgr 1 of Mongolian National Broadcaster (MÜONRT).
**NB:** These stns are not part of, or affiliated with MÜONRT.

### OTHER STATIONS

| FM | MHz | kW | Location | Station |
|---|---|---|---|---|
| 22) | 88.8 | 1 | Ulaanbaatar | Medee medeelliin R. |
| 23) | 89.7 | 1 | Ulaanbaatar | Zokhist ayalguu R. |
| 24) | 90.5 | 1 | Ulaanbaatar | VIP R. |
| 25) | 91.1 | 1 | Ulaanbaatar | Tsag üe zaluus R. |
| 2) | 91.7 | 1 | Ulaanbaatar | Metro Lounge R. |
| 1) | 92.1 | 1 | Ulaanbaatar | Toim R. 92.1 |
| 3) | 92.5 | 1 | Ulaanbaatar | Star FM |
| 4) | 95.1 | 1 | Ulaanbaatar | Khamag Mongol R. |
| 5) | 95.7 | 1 | Ulaanbaatar | Arga bilig R. |
| 26) | 96.3 | 1 | Ulaanbaatar | Avto R. |
| 6) | 96.9 | 1 | Ulaanbaatar | Elgen nutag R. |
| 7) | 97.5 | 1 | Ulaanbaatar | Lavain egshig R. |
| 8) | 98.1 | 1 | Ulaanbaatar | Formula FM |
| 9) | 98.5 | 1 | Ulaanbaatar | Best R. |
| 10) | 98.9 | 1 | Ulaanbaatar | Business R. |
| 11) | 99.3 | 1 | Ulaanbaatar | Ineemseglel R. |
| 12) | 99.7 | 1 | Ulaanbaatar | Ikh Mongol |
| 13) | 100.1 | 1 | Ulaanbaatar | Kiss FM |
| 14) | 100.5 | 1 | Ulaanbaatar | Giingoo R. |

| FM | MHz | kW | Location | Station |
|---|---|---|---|---|
| 15) | 101.7 | 1 | Ulaanbaatar | Shine Mongol R. |
| 27) | 102.1 | 1 | Ulaanbaatar | MGL R. |
| 16) | 102.5 | 1 | Ulaanbaatar | R. UB |
| 21) | 102.5 | 1 | Darkhan | Shine dolgion R. |
| A) | 103.1 | 1 | Ulaanbaatar | BBCWS relay |
| 17) | 103.6 | 1 | Ulaanbaatar | Tani R. |
| 18) | 104.0 | 1 | Ulaanbaatar | Mongolyn duu kholoi |
| 19) | 104.0 | 1 | Khovd | Ger büüliin R. |
| 19) | 104.0 | 1 | Erdenet | Ger büüliin R. |
| 19) | 104.5 | 1 | Ulaanbaatar | Ger büüliin R. |
| 19) | 104.5 | 1 | Darkhan | Ger büüliin R. |
| 19) | 104.5 | 1 | Mörön | Ger büüliin R. |
| 28) | 105.0 | 1 | Ulaanbaatar | Övör Mongolyn R. |
| 20) | 105.5 | 1 | Ulaanbaatar | Vibe 105.5 |
| 6) | 106.5 | 1 | Bayankhongor | Ger büüliin R. |
| 19) | 106.5 | 1 | Bulgan | Ger büüliin R. |
| 19) | 106.5 | 1 | Sainshand | Ger büüliin R. |
| B) | 106.6 | 1 | Ulaanbaatar | VOA Relay |
| 29) | 107.0 | 1 | Ulaanbaatar | Smart FM |
| 21) | 107.5 | 1 | Ulaanbaatar | Shine dolgion R. |

+ txs below 1kW.

### Addresses & other information:
**1)** Chingeltei district, 2nd subdistrict, Sansar Cable LLC Building, Ulaanbaatar – **2)** Bayangol district, 11th subdistrict, Khuvisgalyn Rd. 3, Ulaanbaatar **E:** info@evsegmongol.mn – **3)** Ulaanbaatar – **4)** Sükhbaatar district, 5th subdistrict, N&N center, 3rd floor, Room 302, Ulaanbaatar 14192 **E:** hamagmongol@yahoo.com – **5)** Sükhbaatar district, 8th subdistrict, Independence Palace, Amar St., 1st floor, Ulaanbaatar 14200 **E:** argabillg_fm@yahoo.com – **6)** Khan-Uul district, 15th subdistrict, Narkhan khotkhon 61-r Building, Room 32, Ulaanbaatar 13380 **E:** dnaba_d@yahoo.com – **7)** Chingeltei district, 2nd subdistrict, Khudaldaa St., Javzandamba Center, 3rd floor, Ulaanbaatar **E:** info@lavain-egshig.mn – **8)** Chingeltei district, 5th subdistrict, Narny Titem Building, 2nd floor, Ulaanbaatar **E:** ubradio@mail.mn – **9)** Chingeltei district, 4th subdistrict, Business Development Centre, Ulaanbaatar Bank Building, 2nd floor, Ulaanbaatar 15160 **E:** best_985@yahoo.com – **10)** Ulaanbaatar **E:** info@business-radio.mn – **11)** Sükhbaatar district, 8th subdistrict, Amar St., CT House, 5th floor, Room 433, Ulaanbaatar 14200 – **12)** Bayangol district, Enkhtaivan Ave., Grand Plaza, 14th floor, Room 1404, Ulaanbaatar 16050 **E:** fm_997@yahoo.com – **13)** Chingeltei district, 1st subdistrict, Ulaanbaator Bank bair, 13th floor, Room 1302, Ulaanbaatar **E:** gerlees2002@yahoo.com – **14)** Ulaanbaatar – **15)** Ulaanbaatar **E:** shine_mongolradio@yahoo.com – **16)** Bayangol district, Enkhtaivan Ave., Grand Plaza, 14th floor, Room 1108, Ulaanbaatar 16050 **E:** fmub1025@yahoo.com – **17)** Ulaanbaatar – **18)** Ulaanbaatar – **19)** Bayanzürkh district, 2nd subdistrict, 15th microdistrict, 10A-r Building, Ulaanbaatar **E:** windfm1045@yahoo.com – **20)** Ulaanbaatar **E:** hulan@bproduction.mn – **21)** Bayanzürkh district, 6th subdistrict, 13th microdistrict, Namiianjugiin St., Ereliin 40-r Building, Ulaanbaatar – **22)** Ulaanbaatar – **23)** Ulaanbaatar – **24)** Ulaanbaatar – **25)** Ulaanbaatar – **26)** Chingeltei district, 4th subdistrict, 4th District City Administration, Ulaanbaatar **E:** mongol_media@yahoo.com – **27)** Sükhbaatar district, 14th subdistrict, Altai St., New World Tower, 5th floor, Room 501, Ulaanbaatar **E:** info@mglradionews.com – **28)** Ulaanbaatar. Incl. rel. CRI (P.R. China) – **29)** Sükhbaatar district, 8th subdistrict, STÖ Building, 4th floor, Ulaanbaatar 13381 – **A)** Rel. BBCWS (UK) – **B)** Rel. VOA (USA).

**Int. relays on MW:** (Upon demand; tx operated by RTBN) Choibalsan 1431kHz 500kW. See Int. Radio section

## MONTENEGRO

**L.T:** UTC+1h (31 Mar-27 Oct: +2h) — **Pop:** 630,000 — **Pr.L:** Montenegrin, Serbian — **E.C:** 50Hz, 230V — **ITU:** MNE

### AGENCIJA ZA ELEKTRONSKE MEDIJE CRNE GORE (AEM) (Agency for Electronic Media of Montenegro)
✉ Bulevar Svetog Petra Cetinjskog 9, 81000 Podgorica ☎ +382 20 201430 🖷 +382 20 201440 **E:** aem@aemcg.org **W:** aemcg.org
**L.P:** Chmn: Ranko Vujovic

### RADIO TELEVIZIJA CRNE GORE (Pub)
✉ Bul. Revolucije 19, 81000 Podgorica ☎ +382 20 245595 **W:** rtcg.me **E:** marketing@rtcg.org **L.P:** DG: S. Sestic

| FM (MHz) | RCG 1 | R. 98 | kW | FM (MHz) | RCG 1 | R. 98 | kW |
|---|---|---|---|---|---|---|---|
| Bjelasica | 92.1 | 99.3 | 54 | Podgorica | 96.5 | 89.3 | 10 |
| Durmitor | 96.1 | 91.3 | 10 | Tovic | 88.0 | 98.9 | 10 |
| Lovcen | 94.9 | 98.0 | 54 | Velji Grad | 99.8 | 89.6 | 10 |
| Mozura | 97.3 | 93.4 | 10 | | | | |

+ 11 txs.less than 1kW

**Local/private stations**
**R. Antena M,** Podgorica 87.6MHz + 5 relays – **R. Cetinje** 94.5MHz + 1 relay – **R. Elmag,** Podgorica 96.0MHz + 7 relays – **R. Bar** 91.8MHz + 1 relay – **R. Berane** 88.2MHz + 1 relay – **R Bijelo,** Polje 101.1MHz + 1 relay – **R. Budva** 98.7MHz + 1 relay – **R. Corona,** Bar 88.9MHz +1 relay – **R. D,** Podgorica 88.6MHz + 2 relays – **R. Danilovgrad** 92.9MHz – **R. Fokus,** Bijelo Polje 93.9MHz – **R. Free Montenegro,** Podgorica 103.0.MHz – **R. Glas** Plava, Plav 102.9.MHz – **R. Gorica,** Podgorica 93.3MHz – **R. Herceg** Novi 90.0MHz +1 relay – **R. Jupok,** Rozaje 98.7MHz + 1 relay – **R. Kotor** 95.3MHz + 1 relay – **R. Max,** Danilovgrad 107.5MHz + 1 relay – **R. Mir,** Tuzi 106.1MHz + 1 relay – **R. Mojkovac** 92.8MHz – **R. Montena,** Podgorica 105.7MHz + 5 relays – **R. Niksic** 89.8MHz + 2 relays – **R. Ozon,** Kolasin 97.6MHz – **R. Panorama,** Pljevlja 89.2MHz – **R. Pljevlja** 94.8MHz – **R. Rozaje** 104.4MHz – **R. Svetigora,** Cetinje 101.0.MHz – **R. Tivat** 88.5.MHz – **R. Ulcinj** 91.3MHz + 1 relay – **R. Zeta,** Podgorica 93.8.MHz – **R. City,** Podgorica 107.3MHz

## MONTSERRAT (UK)

**L.T:** UTC -4h — **Pop:** 5,000 — **Pr.L:** English — **E.C:** 60Hz, 120/230V — **ITU:** MSR

### ZJB RADIO MONTSERRAT (Gov. Comm.)
✉ PO Box 51, Sweeneys ☎ +1 664 491 2885 **E:** zjb@gov.ms **W:** zjbradio.com **L.P:** SM: Herman Sargeant. Techn: Ivor Greenaway
**FM:** 88.3MHz, 0.1kW (Isles Bay Hill), 95.5MHz, 5kW (Silver Hills)
**D.Prgr:** 24h BBC relay at night 0400-0930
**Ann:** "ZJB Radio Montserrat, the Voice of Montserrat"

**OTHER STATIONS** (MHz)
**ETERNAL LIFE RADIO** ✉ Cavalla Hill ☎ +1 664 496 6982 **W:** eternal-liferadio.com FM: 106.1 – **CSS CARIBBEAN SUPER STATION - FM:** 93.9 (relay Trinidad) – **VIBZ FM - Family Radio Network** ✉ P.O Box 350, Baker Hill ☎ +1 664 491 7331 **W:** vibzfm.com FM: 89.9 (relay Antigua)

## MOROCCO

**L.T:** UTC +1h — **Pop:** 35 million — **Pr.L:** Arabic, French, Berber languages, Hassania — **E.C:** 50Hz, 127/220V — **ITU:** MRC

### HAUTE AUTORITÉ DE LA COMMUNICATION AUDIO-VISUELLE (HACA)
✉ Espace les Palmiers, Lot 26,Angle Avenues Anakhil et Mehdi Ben Barka, B.P. 20590, Rabat Ryad ☎+212 53 7579600 🖷 +212 53 7714274 **W:** haca.ma **E:** info@haca.ma **L.P:** DG: Ahmed Akhchichine.

### SOCIÉTÉ NATIONALE DE RADIODIFFUSION ET DE TÉLÉVISION (SNRT) - RADIO MAROCAINE (Pub.)
✉ 1, Rue El Brihi, B.P. 1042, MA-10000 Rabat ☎+212 53 7700 319 🖷 +212 53 772 2047 **W:** snrt.ma **E:** lemediateur@snrt.ma **Reg.** ✉ B.P. 459, Laayoune. **L.P:** DG: Mohamed Ayad. Dir. Tech: Allal Kacimi.

| LW/MW | kHz | kW | N | LW/MW | kHz | kW | N |
|---|---|---|---|---|---|---|---|
| Azilal | ‡207 | 400 | A | Sebaa-Aioun | 612 | 300 | A |
| Sidi Bennour | 540 | 600 | A/R | Laâyoune | 711 | 300 | R |
| Oujda | 595 | 50 | A/R | Agadir | 936 | 100 | A/R |

**F.PI:** two new 400 kW MW transmitters in Agadir

| FM (MHz) | A | B | C | Q&R | kW |
|---|---|---|---|---|---|
| Agadir | 91.0 | 94.2 | 97.5 | 87.9 | 20 |
| Beni Mellal | 92.9 | 89.8 | 96.1 | | 10 |
| Bouarfa | 88.0 | 91.1 | 94.3 | | 20 |
| Casablanca | 96.0 | 90.0 | 95.3 | 98.6 | |
| Dakhla | 93.5 | 91.8 | | 98.3 | |
| El Houceima | 105.7 | 92.1 | 95.3 | 89.0 | 8 |
| El Jadida | 90.4 | | | | |
| Erfoud | 91.8 | | 98.3 | | 12 |
| Errachidia | 91.3 | 97.8 | 94.5 | | 20 |
| Essaouira | 97.9 | 91.4 | | | |
| Fès | 88.8 | 95.1 | 101.9 | 98.4 | 10 |
| Figuig | 91.9 | 95.1 | 98.4 | | 5 |
| Ifrane | 90.5 | 93.6 | 96.8 | | |
| Kenitra | 91.6 | | 87.7 | | 12 |
| Khenifra | 91.6 | 87.9 | 104.6 | 94.2 | 10 |
| Khouribga | 87.6 | | | | |
| Lâayoune | 93.9 | 97.9 | 91.1 | 91.0 | 10 |
| Marrakech | 94.9 | 98.8 | 89.7 | 91.7 | 30 |
| Meknès | 88.8 | 95.1 | 101.9 | 92.5 | 10 |
| Nador | 87.6 | 93.9 | 97.2 | | 12 |
| Ouarzazate | 90.3 | 93.4 | 96.6 | | 6 |

| FM (MHz) | A | B | C | Q&R | kW |
|---|---|---|---|---|---|
| Oujda | 89.9 | 99.4 | 91.3 | 96.1 | 12 |
| Rabat | 91.0 | 87.9 | 104.6 | 94.2 | 20 |
| Safi | 90.9 | | 94.1 | | 5 |
| Settat | 92.1 | 89.0 | 107.3 | | 5 |
| Tanger | 88.7 | 91.8 | 95.0 | 88.7 | 20 |
| Tantan | 90.3 | | | | |
| Taounate | 96.1 | | | | |
| Taourirt | 96.6 | 93.4 | 90.3 | | 10 |
| Taroudant | 92.2 | | | | |
| Taza | 91.7 | 98.2 | | | 12 |
| Tétouan | 90.6 | 100.2 | 96.9 | 93.7 | 12 |
| Zougara | 94.3 | 97.6 | 91.1 | | 5 |

| FM | 1) | 2) | 3) | 4) | 5) | 6) | 7) | 8) | 9) | 10) |
|---|---|---|---|---|---|---|---|---|---|---|
| Smara | 93.5 | 93.1 | 95.0 | 106.0 | 95.4 | - | 91.8 | 105.4 | - | - |
| Tafraoute | 88.5 | - | - | 99.2 | 89.6 | 95- | 9 102.7 | 93.3 | - | - |
| Tantan | 103.5 | 93.1 | 99.9 | - | 97.0 | 95.2 | 91.8 | 101.3 | - | - |
| Tanger | 102.3 | 93.3 | 104.7 | 105.4 | 96.4 | 103.3 | 89.6 | 94.3 | 92.3 | 91.1 |
| Taounate | 91.5 | 93.9 | 105.8 | 93.1 | 103.6 | 95.6 | - | 90.0 | - | 99.6 |
| Taourirt | 91.5 | - | 106.0 | - | 98.8 | - | 105.1 | 94.8 | 94.2 | - |
| Tarfaya | 95.9 | - | 95.0 | 102.7 | 97.2 | - | 89.6 | - | - | - |
| Targuist | - | 104.5 | 95.8 | 106.2 | 90.8 | 103.7 | 92.7 | - | - | |
| Taroudante | 101.3 | 93.9 | 87.7 | 99.9 | 104.9 | 97.8 | - | 88.1 | - | - |
| Taza | 95.8 | 93.5 | 105.3 | 88.0 | 99.5 | 103.0 | 88.6 | 89.9 | 100.1 | 101.7 |
| Tétouan | 105.9 | 93.9 | - | 104.5 | 97.8 | 87.8 | 101.1 | 107.3 | - | 93.0 |
| Tiznit | 90.6 | - | 104.2 | - | 91.5 | 103.1 | 88.4 | 105.1 | - | - |
| Zagora | 104.7 | 93.1 | 95.8 | - | 91.8 | - | 88.0 | 105.9 | - | - |

**A: Al-Idaa al-Watania in Arabic:** 24h. **N:** on the h. – **B: Chaîne Inter:** 24h. **Spanish:** 1330-1345, **English:** 1345-1300. Other times in French. – **C: Al-Idaa al-Amazighia in Berber/Arabic dialects:** 0800-2400. **Q: Quran R. "R. Mohammed VI":** 24h.

**Regional Prgrs** (FM on Q network). **MW: Agadir,** Avenue Hassan II, Agadir: on 936kHz. **Casablanca,** Ain Chock, Casablanca: **Laâyoune/ Dakhla:** on 711kHz. **Marrakech:** 40 Ave. Yugoslavie, Marrakech: on 540kHz. **Fès & Meknès:** on 612kHz (Fès 0600-1200, Meknès 1200-1800). **Oujda,** Avenue Omar Errifi, Oujda: on 595kHz/104.0MHz. **Tanger:** 33, Avenue Amir Moulay Abdallah, Tanger: on 540kHz. **Tetouan,:**30, Avenue Mohammed V, Tetouan.

**Ann:** Arabic: "Huna Ribat, Idha'atu-l-Mamlaka al Maghribiyya" or "Idha'at al-Wataniya". French: "Ici Rabat, Radiodiffusion Télévision Marocaine". Berber: "Dahab Rbad al-idaa al-Amazighia Li Mamlaka L'Maghrib".

### MEDI 1 RADIO (Comm, Semi-Gov.)
B.P. 2055, 3/5 rue Emsallah, 90000 Tanger ☎&🖨 +212 539936363 **W:** medi1.com **E:** technique@medi1.com **LP:** Dir: Hassan Kiyar.
Two separate streams acc. to target area: Antenne Maghreb in Arabic/French and Antenne Afrique Internationale in French.
**LW:** Nador 171kHz 1600kW
**FM** (MHz):Agadir 104.6 20kW, Al Hoceima 88.5 16kW, Beni Mellal/ Oujda 102.9 12kW, Bouarfa 97.2 1kW, Casablanca 99.6 9kW, Dakhla 96.4, El Jadida 96.7, Enjil/Erfoud/Figuig 97.0, Errachadia 96.0 16kW, Essaouira 94.6 12kW, Fès 101.4 2kW, Goulmima 96.8 16kW, Ifrane 97.9 3kW, Khenifra 97.6 16kW, Kenitra 97.7, Khouribga 104.4, Laâyoune 101.0 10kW, Larache 91.3, Marrakech 105.3 1kW, Meknès 105.5 10kW, Merchiche 87.6, Nador 89.6 10kW, Ouarzazate/Zaio 99.9, Rabat 97.5 20kW, Safi 97.0, Slokia 95.3, Semara 96.8, Taliouine 92.2, Tanger 101.0 1kW, Tantan 93.4, Taounate 103.1, Taourirt 97.5 16kW, Tarfaya 97.9, Taroudante 95.4, Taza 96.2 16kW, Tetouan 103.7 12kW, Tiznit 96.9, Zagora 97.0.
**D.Prgr.** in Arabic/French: 24h. **Ann:** "Médi 1".

**Other stations, main networks:**

| FM | 1) | 2) | 3) | 4) | 5) | 6) | 7) | 8) | 9) | 10) |
|---|---|---|---|---|---|---|---|---|---|---|
| Agadir | 100.4 | 93.1 | 96.5 | - | 95.6 | - | 89.3 | 103.7 | - | - |
| Al Hoceima | 97.7 | 93.3 | 98.6 | 102.1 | 90.8 | - | - | 103.3 | 94.4 | - |
| Béni Mellal | 94.0 | 93.5 | 89.2 | - | 98.1 | - | - | 94.7 | 91.6 | 105.1 |
| Bouarfa | 89.1 | 93.1 | 106.5 | - | 89.9 | - | 95.9 | 105.6 | 90.6 | - |
| Boujdour | - | 93.1 | 88.0 | 106.0 | 102.0 | - | 88.9 | 105.6 | - | - |
| Casablanca | 104.3 | 93.1 | 88.7 | - | 100.3 | 92.5 | 88.2 | 100.8 | 91.2 | 102.1 |
| Dakhla | 89.7 | 93.1 | 93.9 | 106.0 | 99.7 | - | 88.7 | 88.0 | - | - |
| El Jadida | 95.1 | 93.1 | 102.5 | 92.7 | 100.5 | 97.3 | 89.3 | 96.2 | 91.5 | 101.3 |
| Erfoud | - | - | - | 88.7 | - | - | 105.4 | 104.5 | - | - |
| Errachadia | 102.5 | 93.5 | 102.9 | - | 104.1 | - | 100.5 | 105.6 | - | - |
| Essaouira | 92.8 | 93.3 | 99.9 | 104.1 | 96.1 | - | 89.8 | 98.5 | - | - |
| Fès | 103.9 | 93.7 | 106.9 | - | 94.1 | 98.8 | 88.3 | 91.4 | 89.4 | 100.4 |
| Figuig | 101.9 | 93.1 | 88.1 | 105.5 | 97.8 | - | 106.4 | 91.3 | 88.8 | - |
| Guelmin | 91.9 | 93.1 | 100.3 | - | 98.5 | 96.8 | 88.7 | 94.3 | - | - |
| Goulmima | 96.4 | 93.2 | 105.0 | 97.5 | - | - | 91.0 | 103.2 | - | - |
| Ifrane | 103.6 | - | 106.7 | - | 94.6 | - | - | 89.9 | - | 103.2 |
| Kenitra | - | 93.3 | 101.6 | - | 107.6 | 106.9 | - | 98.1 | - | 99.5 |
| Khenifra | 102.4 | - | - | 101.2 | - | - | 104.7 | 95.6 | - | - |
| Khouribga | 106.6 | - | 97.2 | - | 101.4 | - | - | 92.3 | 93.9 | - |
| Laâyoune | 104.6 | 93.1 | 107.1 | 106.3 | 91.6 | - | 89.4 | 98.6 | 94.8 | - |
| Larache | 99.3 | 93.1 | 100.8 | 104.4 | 96.7 | - | 92.8 | - | - | - |
| Marrakech | 100.6 | 93.8 | 97.7 | 106.5 | 94.4 | 90.5 | 88.6 | 97.1 | 98.2 | - |
| Meknès | 99.9 | 93.7 | 102.5 | 106.1 | 96.6 | 97.2 | 104.2 | 90.3 | 90.7 | 92.9 |
| Nador | 104.3 | 91.9 | 105.3 | 90.7 | 92.6 | - | - | 95.7 | 100.7 | 101.4 |
| Oujda | 102.0 | 93.5 | 101.0 | 92.9 | 98.5 | - | 92.2 | 106.5 | 97.7 | 103.4 |
| Ouarzazate | 91.2 | 93.1 | 105.6 | - | 92.0 | - | 88.9 | 103.4 | - | - |
| Rabat | 95.7 | 93.5 | 100.5 | - | 99.8 | 106.9 | 90.2 | 103.7 | 96.5 | 97.0 |
| Safi | 103.6 | 93.5 | 105.4 | - | 99.2 | 92.3 | 90.3 | 104.5 | - | - |
| Settat | 103.8 | 92.9 | 102.9 | 105.7 | 98.9 | 106.4 | 93.4 | 97.9 | 94.7 | 96.4 |
| Skhour | 102.2 | - | 102.6 | - | 95.8 | 92.2 | 88.0 | 103.7 | - | - |

**1) Aswat FM:** Ghandi Mall, Imm 9, Bd. Ghandi, Casablanca. **W:** aswat. ma – **2) Radio 2M** (Semi-Gov.): Km 7300 route de Rabat Ain Seeba, Casablanca. **W:** radio2m.ma – **3) MFM Atlas/Oriental/Sahara/ Saïss/Souss & Casa FM:** Groupe New Publicity, 58 Av. des FAR, Tour des Habous, 13ème étage, Casablanca. **W:** mfmradio.ma radiocasafm. ma – **4) Cap Radio:** Zone industrielle, Route de Tétouan, Allée principale lot n°123, Tanger. **W:** capradio.ma – **5) Hit Radio:** 3 rue Assouhaili, Agdal, Rabat. **W:** hitradio.ma Also transmitters in many West & Central African French speaking countries – **6) R. Atlantic:** Eco-Médias, 70 Bd. Massira Khadra, Casablanca. **W:** atlanticradio.ma – **7) Med Radio:** 55, intersection Blvd Zerktouni et rue Sebta, 5ème étage n° 20, Casablanca. **W:** medradio.ma – **8) R. Chada FM:** Société R. Kolinass, 42 Bd. Idriss 1er quartier des Hôpitaux, Casablanca. **W:** chadafm.net – **9) R. Mars:** 30 Ave. des Far 13ème étage, Casablanca 20000. **W:** radiomars.ma – **10) Medina FM:** Rue Oued ziz imm 51 appt 4 agdal, Rabat. **W:** radiomedinafm.ma
**R. Sawa:** Meknès 91.9MHz, Fès 97.9MHz 2kW, Rabat/Agadir 101.0MHz 20kW, Casablanca 101.5MHz 10kW, Marrakech 101.7MHz 12kW, Tanger 101.8MHz 20kW.

### CEUTA (Spain)
**L.T:** see Spain — **Pop:** 85,000 — **Pr.L:** Spanish

**R. Nacional de España,** Real 90, E-51001 Ceuta. **FM:** RNE-1 97.2MHz, R. Clásica 100.8MHz, RNE5TN 101.9MHz, RNE-3 106.8MHz, all 1kW.
**SER Radiolé - R. Ceuta,** Poblado Marinero, Local 32, E-51001 Ceuta. **MW:** 1584kHz 5kW 24h rel. of Radiolé netw. **FM:** 96.2MHz R. Ceuta
**COPE,** Sargento Mena 5-8,1°izq, E-51001 Ceuta. **FM:** 89.8MHz.
**Onda Cero R,** Calle Delgado Serrano 1, 1°, E-51001 Ceuta. **FM:** 101.4MHz 3kW.
**RTV Ceuta,** Paseo Alcalde Sánchez Prado, 5 entreplanta, 51001 Ceuta. **FM:** 99.0MHz. **W:** rtvce.es
**R. Solidaria:**107.1MHz **W:** radiosolidaria.com
**Radio Adventista:** 107.8 MHz **W:** adventistaes.radio.es

### MELILLA (Spain)
**L.T:** see Spain — **Pop:** 85,000 — **Pr.L:** Spanish

**R. Nacional de España,** Altos de la Vía 3, E-52004 Melilla. **MW: RNE1** 972kHz 5kW. **FM:** (0.3kW): 97.7MHz (R1), 100.1MHz (RNE5TN), 105.3MHz (R3), 106.8MHz (R. Clásica).
**SER R. Melilla,** Calle Cardenal Cisneros 8 bajo, E-52001 Melilla **W:** cadenaser.com/tag/melilla/a/ . **MW:** 1485kHz 1kW 24h. **FM:** (MHz): 92.2MHz, 96.3 Los 40 Melilla, 100.1 Dial Melilla.
**COPE,** C/ Pablo Vallescá 6 "Edificio Ánfora"2° - 1, E-52001 Melilla. copemelilla.com **FM:** 102.2MHz Cadena 100, 98.4MHz COPE Melilla.
**Onda Cero R,** Calle de Musico Granados 2, E-52004 Melilla **FM:** 89.6MHz
**RTV Melilla,** C/ General Macías, 11, 1° izquierda – 52001 Melilla . **W:**inmusa.es **FM:** 104.0 MHz .
**R. Maria:** 92.9 MHz. **W:** radiomaria.es
**R. Adventista W:** adventistaes.radio.es **FM:** 103.2/106.2MHz

## MOZAMBIQUE

**L.T:** UTC +2h — **Pop:** 30 million — **Pr.L:** Portuguese, 20 ethnic languages — **E.C:** 50Hz, 220V — **ITU:** MOZ

### INSTITUTO NACIONAL DAS COMUNICAÇÕES (INCM)
Av. Eduardo Mondlane, 123/127, PO Box 848, Maputo ☎+258 21 490131 🖨 +258 21 494435. **W:** incm.gov.mz **E:** info@incm.gov.mz

### RÁDIO MOÇAMBIQUE (Pub.)
Rua da Rádio n.º 2, C.P. 2000, Maputo ☎+258 21 431687 🖨 +258 21 321816 **W:** rm.co.mz **E:** caprimoe@zebra.uem.mz
**L.P:** Chmn/CEO: Ricardo Malate, TD: Hermenegildo Basílio Mula, Int.

Rel. Dir: Maria Cremilda Massingue, Fin. Dir: Arlindo Piedade de Sousa

| MW | kHz | kW | N | | MW | kHz | kW | N |
|---|---|---|---|---|---|---|---|---|
| 1) Maputo | 738 | 50 | AN | | 4) Chimoio | 1026 | 50 | EP |
| 3) Nampula | 765 | 50 | EP | | 7) Quelimane | 1179 | 50 | EP |
| 10) Xai-Xai | 810 | 50 | EP | | 5) Inhambane | 1206 | 50 | EP |
| 2) Beira Dondo | 873 | 50 | EP | | 8) Pemba | 1224 | 50 | EP |
| 9) Tete | 963 | 50 | EP | | 6) Lichinga | 1260 | 50 | EP |
| 1) Maputo | 1008 | 50 | EP | | | | | |

| FM | MHz | kW | N | | FM | MHz | kW | N |
|---|---|---|---|---|---|---|---|---|
| 10) Chicumbane | 87.8 | 1 | AN | | 10) Chokwe | 96.7 | 1 | AN |
| 4) Chimoio | 88.5 | 1 | D | | 8) Palma | 97.4 | 1 | EP |
| 6) Metangula | 88.5 | 1 | AN | | 2) Beira | 97.6 | 1 | AN |
| 9) Tete | 88.5 | 0.3 | D | | 7) Quelimane | 97.8 | 1 | EP |
| 5) Vilaculos | 88.9 | 1 | AN | | 1) Maputo | 97.9 | 1 | C |
| 6) Lichinga | 89.1 | 0.25 | AN | | 10) Massangena | 97.9 | 1 | EP |
| 4) Mossorize | 89.2 | 1 | AN | | 5) Inhambane | 98.1 | 0.25 | D |
| 7) Milange | 89.2 | 1 | AN | | 6) Matchedje | 98.2 | 1 | AN |
| 2) Gorongosa | 89.9 | 1 | AN | | 2) Caia | 98.6 | 1 | D |
| 2) Masinga | 89.9 | 1 | AN | | 7) Beira | 99.2 | 1 | D |
| 8) Pemba | 89.9 | 0.25 | D | | 7) Quelimane | 99.5 | 1 | AN |
| 6) Cuamba | 90.4 | 1 | AN | | 8) Metoro | 100.7 | 5 | AN |
| 8) Macomia | 90.4 | 1 | EP | | 9) Tete | 100.7 | 0.2 | EP |
| 8) M. da Praia | 90.6 | 1 | EP | | 8) Montepuez | 100.9 | 1 | AN |
| 10) Xai-Xai | 90.9 | 1 | EP | | 5) Maxixe | 101.6 | 1 | AN |
| 5) Mabote | 91.2 | 1 | AN | | 6) Lichinga | 101.7 | 1 | AN |
| 6) Mecanhelas | 91.3 | 1 | AN | | 10) Massingir | 101.7 | 1 | AN |
| 2) Dondo | 91.6 | 5 | AN | | 5) Homoíne | 102.1 | 2 | AN |
| 7) Mocuba | 91.7 | 1 | EP | | 1) Maputo | 102.3 | 1 | EP |
| 7) Namacata | 92.1 | 1 | AN | | 9) Ulónque | 103.7 | 1 | AN |
| 1) Maputo | 92.3 | 5 | AN | | 4) Catandica | 104.8 | 1 | AN |
| 1) Maputo | 93.1 | 1 | D | | 5) Inhambane | 105.1 | 0.3 | EP |
| 3) Nampula | 93.6 | 0.25 | D | | 2) Beira | 105.2 | 1 | C |
| 3) Nampula | 95.1 | 1 | AN | | 3) Nampula | 105.5 | 0.25 | EP |
| 2) Beira | 96.5 | 1 | EP | | 6) Marrupa | 105.6 | 1 | AN |
| 4) Chimoio | 96.6 | 0.25 | EP | | 1) Maputo | 105.9 | 1 | E |

+22 more tx's under 1kW.

**Antena Nacional (AN)** in Portuguese: 24h.
**Cidade FM (C)** in Portuguese: 24h. Also rel. BBC.
**RM Desporto (D)** in Portuguese: 0300-2200.
**Maputo Corridor R. (E)** in English: 1000-2200. Also rel. BBC.
**Emissão Provincial (EP)** in Portuguese/ethnic: Provincial prgrs Mon-Fri 0240-2100, 24h weekends and rel. of Antena Nacional overnight on weekdays.
**1)** EP de Maputo – **2)** EP de Sofala, C.P. 1942, Beira – **3)** EP de Nampula, C.P. 93, Nampula – **4)** EP de Manica, C.P. 390, Chimoio – **5)** EP de Inhambane, C.P. 196, Imhambane – **6)** EP do Niassa, C.P. 171, Lichinga – **7)** EP de Zambézia, C.P. 333, Quelimane – **8)** EP de Cabo Delgado, C.P. 45, Pemba – **9)** EP de Tete, C.P. 384, Tete – **10)** EP de Gaza, C.P. 130, Xai-Xai.
**Ann:** "Rádio Moçambique, Antena Nacional", EP: "Rádio Moçambique, (province)". **IS:** Mbira (indigenous xylophone). Opens and closes with National Anthem.

**Other Stations (FM MHz):**
**A Voz do Islão,** Maputo: 96.3 – **KFM,** Maputo: 88.3 – **Lifetime Music R,** Maputo: 87.8 1kW **W:** lmradio.net – **R. Capital,** Maputo: 90.7 (also rel. TWR) – **R. Haq,** Nampula: 104.4 – **R. Índico:** Maputo 89.5, Inhambane 89.7, Quelimane 88.2, Beira/Chimoio/Lichinga/Nampula/Pemba/Tete/Xai-Xai 90.0 **W:** teste.radioindico.fm – **R. Maria Moçambique:** Maputo 103.1, Villankulo/Xai Xai 102, Chokwe 101.4, Govure 102.5, Quissico 106.4, Maxixe 104.2, Nova Mambone 104.0 **W:** radiomaria.org.mz – **R. Miramar,** Maputo: 101.4, Beira 98.1, Nampula 98.4 **W:** radiomiramarfm.blogspot.com – **R. N'tyana,** Maputo: 93.5 – **R. Savana,** Maputo: 100.2 **W:** savana.co.mz – **R. SFM,** Maputo: 94.6 – **R. Terra Verde,** Maputo: 98.6 – **99FM:** Maputo 99.3, Beira 89.3, Tete/Xai-Xai 95.0, Inhambane 96.0, Nampula 97.3, Pemba 99.5 **W:** 99fm.co.mz – **R. Viva:** Maputo 99.6 1kW, Nampula 90.8. **W:** radioviva.fm – **Top R,** Maputo: 104.2 **W:** topradiomoz.blogspot.com

**BBC African Service:** Tete 87.8, Nampula 88.3, Beira 88.5, Quelimane 95.3, Maputo 95.5, Chimoio 99.0, Xai-Xai 100.9MHz – **RDP Africa:** Beira 94.8, Maputo 89.2, Nampula 91.9, Quelimane 89.0 (all 50kW) – **RFI Afrique:** Maputo 105.0 2kW in French/Portuguese.
In addition about 100 community radio stations are in operation

## MYANMAR

**L.T:** UTC + 6½h — Pop: 55 million — **Pr.L:** Burmese (Bamar), English. Major minority languages: Kachin, Kayah, Kayin (Po & Sakaw), Chin, Mon, Rakhine, Shan — **E.C:** 50Hz, 230V — **ITU:** BRM

### MINISTRY OF INFORMATION
✉ Yaza Thingaha Rd, Zeya Theiddhi Ward, Naypyidaw ☎ +95 67 412323 **W:** moi.gov.mm

### MYANMA RADIO AND TELEVISION DEPT, MRTV (Gov.) MYANMA RADIO
✉ Tatkon Township, Naypyidaw ☎ +95 67 79483 📠 +95 67 79403 **Yangon centre:** Pyay Rd, Kamayut-11041, Yangon ☎+95 1 527119 📠+95 1 534211 **W:** mrtv.gov.mm **E:** mrtv@mptmail.net.mm **LP:** DG: U Myint Htway, Dir. R.: U Zay Yar. CE: U Myo Win, Dir TV: U Myo Myint Aung

| MW (kHz) | kW | Loc | Pr | H. of tr. |
|---|---|---|---|---|
| 576 | 100 | Y | N | 2300-1700 |
| 594 | 200 | N | N | 2300-1700 |
| 729 | 100 | Y | Y | 2330 (SS 2300)-1630 |
| SW (kHz) | kW | Loc | Pr | H. of tr. |
| 5915 | 50 | N | Mi | 2300-1700 |
| 5985 | 50 | Y | N | 2300-0130, 1130-1700 |
| 7200± | 50 | Y | Y | 2330-1500v |
| 9730 | 50 | Y | N | 0130-1130 |

| FM | MHz | kW | Region/State |
|---|---|---|---|
| Yangon | 87.6 | | Yangon Region |
| Hsipaw | 88.0 | 0.3 | Shan State |
| Nyaunglaybin | 88.3 | 2 | Bago Region |
| Pyin U Lwin | 88.3 | | Mandalay Region |
| Taungdwingyi | 88.3 | 2 | Magwe Region |
| Theinni | 88.3 | 0.15 | Shan State |
| Ye-U | 88.3 | 2 | Sagaing Region |
| Maungdaw (Buthidaung) | 88.9 | 2 | Rakhine State |
| Taunggyi | 88.9 | | Shan State |
| Myawaddy | 89.0 | | Kayin State |
| Tachilek | 89.0 | | Shan State |
| Naypyidaw (Tatkon) | 89.2 | 2 | Union Territory |
| Yanbye | 89.2 | 2 | Rakhine State |
| Kanbalu | 89.5 | 0.3 | Sagaing Region |
| Sittwe | 89.8 | 2 | Rakhine State |
| Maungdaw (Buthidaung) | 90.1 | | Rakhine State |
| Kennedy Peak | 90.4 | 2 | Chin State |
| Loikaw | 90.7 | 2 | Kayah State |
| Lashio | 91.3 | | Shan State |
| Mawlamyine | 91.3 | | Mon State |
| Bago | 92.5 | 2 | Bago Region |
| Minbu | 92.5 | | Magwe Region |
| Pathein | 92.5 | | Pathein District |
| Magwe (Popa) | 94.3 | | Magwe Region |
| Sagaing | 94.6 | | Sagaing Region |
| Pyinmana | 94.9 | | Union Territory |

**NB:** Other FM freqs are in operation, details not available. FM network carries N prgr, but some FM freqs opt out to carry Mi or Y prgrs in minority languages at times.
**Loc=Location:** N=Naypyidaw. Y=Yangon. **Pr=Prgr:** N=National prgr in Burmese, English., also language lessons in English and Japanese from Voic eof America, Australian Broadcasting Corporation and NHK World. Mi=minorities prgrs in Kachin, Shan, Phalan Chin, Mindat Chin, Rakhine, Wa and Kokang. Y=Yangon prgr in Sakaw Kayin, Po Kayin, Mon, Kayah, Gekho and Gebo. E=Educational prgr in Burmese and English. **English** (in N Prgr): 0230-0330, 0700-0730, 1530-1630.
**N:** Generally 30 mins past the UTC h on N prgr; in English on N prgr at 0230, 0700, 1530. **Mayu FM:** 2330-0330, 0930-1330 in Burmese, Rakhine and Rohingya on Maungdaw 90.1MHz.
**Ann: E:** 'This is Myanma Radio' IS: Myanma Orchestral Music

### THAZIN RADIO (Mil.)
✉ Tatmadaw Broadcasting, Thin Village, Pyin U Lwin ☎ +95 33 60165 **W:** thazinfm.com.mm
Operated by the Directorate of Public Relations and Psychological Warfare, Ministry of Defence

| MW | kW | Pr | H. of tr. | | | | |
|---|---|---|---|---|---|---|---|
| 639 | 400 | M | 2330-0200, 0430-0700, 0930-1500 | | | | |
| SW | kW | Pr | H. of tr. | SW | kW | Pr | H. of tr. |
| 6030 | 100 | M | 2330-0200 | 7435 | 100 | M | 0930-1330 |
| 6165 | 100 | Mi | 2330-0130 | 9460 | 100 | M | 0430-0700 |
| 6165 | 100 | M | 0930-1500 | 9590 | 100 | Mi | 0130-0330, 0430-0830 |

**Thazin FM:** 2230-1630 in Burmese. Bago/Magwe/Naypyidaw/Taunggyi 87.6MHz, Hakha/Lashio/Meikhtila/Myeik/Sagaing/Sittwe/Yangon 88.6MHz, Myitkyina 89.2MHz, Monywa/Pathein/Pyin U Lwin/Tachilek 89.5MHz, Dawei/Muse 91.0MHz.
**Pr=Prgr:** M=Main prgr in Burmese, exc.English 0130-0200, 0630-0700, 1430-1500. Mi=minorities prgr in Chin, Kachin, La, Po, Geba, Kokang, Karen, Shan, Kayah, Gekho and Mon.

**Other Stations:**
**Cherry FM (Comm.)** ✉ Mya Yeik Nyo Hotel, Yangon **W:** cherryfmmym.com Operated by Zay Kaba Co. **FM:** Hpa-an/Kawkareik 88.3MHz, Yangon 89.3MHz, Loikaw/Muse 89.5MHz, Hsipaw/Kunlong/ Kyaingtong/Lashio/Laukkaing/Pyin U Lwin/Tachilek/Taunggyi 89.8MHz, Pathein 91.3MHz, Sagaing 92.2MHz, Naypyidaw/Pyay 92.5MHz, Popa 93.1MHz – **City FM (FM-89) (Gov.)** ✉ 573 Pyay Rd, Kamayut Township, Yangon ☎ +95 1 536042 **FM:** Yangon 89.0MHz – **FM Bagan (Comm.)** ✉ A-2, Min Dhama Road, Mayangone Township, Yangon ☎ +95 1 655301-3 Operated by Htoo Co. **FM:** Popa 88.3MHz, Ganga/Kennedy Peak 89.2MHz, Hakha/Minbu 89.8MHz, Yangon 89.9MHz, Sagaing 93.4MHz, Pyinmana/Taunggyi 93.7MHz, Pathein 94.9MHz – **Khayae FM (Community R.)** ✉ Htantabin 104.8MHz – **Mandalay FM (Gov.)** ✉ Mandalay. Yangon office: Rm 1402-3, Olympic Twr, Bo Aung Kyaw St, Yangon **W:** mandalayfm.com Joint venture of Forever Group and Mandalay City Development Committee (MCDC). **FM:** Mandalay (Sagaing Hill)/Taungoo/Yangon 87.9MHz, Naypyidaw 88.3MHz, Hpa-an 90.4MHz, Minhla 90.7MHz, Bago 96.1MHz – **Myanmar International Radio (MIRadio) (Comm.)** ✉ Room 05-05, 53 Strand Rd, Yangon **W:** miradio.com.mm. Operated by Monnect Group Co. Ltd **FM:** Yangon 96.1MHz, Mandalay 96.5MHz, Naypyidaw 96.7MHz in English – **Padamyar FM (Comm.) (Ruby FM)** ✉ Shop House 4, 3rd Floor & 4th Floor, Junction Square Compound, Between Kyun Taw Street and Pyay Road, Kamayut Township, Yangon ☎ +95 1 2306011 **W:** padamyarfm.com Operated by Thein Kyaw Kyaw Co. **FM:** Yangon 88.2, Kanbalu/Monywa 88.6MHz, Bhamo/ Katha/Myitkyina/Nam Mar/Sagaing 88.9MHz, Naypyidaw 89.5MHz, Bilin/Minbu/Popa 90.7MHz, Bago/Pyay 91.3MHz, Taunggyi 92.2MHz, Mawlamyine 92.5MHz, Pathein 93.7MHz – **Pyinsawaddy FM (Teen Radio) (Comm.)** ✉ Rm 1402-3, Olympic Twr, Bo Aung Kyaw St, Yangon Operated by Forever Group ✉ Sittwe, Rakhine State. **FM:** Labutta 87.9MHz, Sitwe 88.3MHz, Pathein/Thandwe 88.9MHz, Bogale 90.4MHz, Yangon 91.0MHz, Kyaungon 100.6MHz – **Shwe FM (Comm.) (Gold FM)** Operated by Shwe Thanlwin Co. ✉ 131/133 Botahtaung Pagoda Road, Yangon ☎ +95 1 9010082 **W:** shwefmradio. com **FM:** Bilin/Nyaunglaybin/Pyay 89.5MHz, Yangon 89.6MHz, Bago/ Dawei/Hpa-an/Kawthaung/Kyaikto/Mawlamyine/Myawaddy/Myeik/ Taungoo 89.8MHz, Shaung/Taunggyi 91.0MHz, Naypyidaw 91.3MHz, Popa 91.9MHz

## NAMIBIA

**L.T:** UTC +2h — **Pop:** 2.6 million — **Pr.L:** English, Afrikaans, German, local languages — **E.C:** 50Hz, 220V — **ITU:** NMB

**COMMUNICATIONS REGULATORY AUTHORITY OF NAMIBIA (CRAN)**
✉ Private Bag 13309, Communication House, 56 Robert Mugabe Ave, Windhoek ☎+264 61 222666 🖷 + 264 61 238646 **W:** ncc.org. na **E:** info@cran.na **L.P:** CEO: Stanley Shanapinda. Head Eng.: Ronel le Grange.

**NAMIBIAN BROADCASTING CORPORATION (Pub)**
✉ P.O. Box 321, Pettenkofer Str, Windhoek West 9000 ☎+264 61 2919111 🖷 + 264 61 2913325 **W:** nbc.na **E:** pr@nbc.na

| FM (MHz) | Hart. | Nat. | Funk. | Kati | Omu. | Kai. | Nwa. | TYS | Wat. |
|---|---|---|---|---|---|---|---|---|---|
| Aminuis | 88.9 | 92.0 | - | - | 95.2 | - | - | 98.5 | - |
| Andara | - | 92.5 | - | 95.7 | - | - | 102.5 | - | - |
| Arendsnes | 88.7 | 90.1 | 91.8 | 96.4 | 99.7 | 106.8 | 95.0 | 98.3 | 103.2 |
| Aroab | 87.9 | 94.2 | - | - | - | 104.6 | - | - | - |
| Aus | 92.5 | - | 95.8 | 102.6 | - | 106.2 | - | - | - |
| Aussenkehr | 92.5 | 95.7 | - | 98.7 | - | 102.5 | - | - | - |
| Bethanien | 88.1 | 91.2 | 94.4 | 97.7 | 101.2 | 104.8 | - | - | - |
| Brukkaros | 90.2 | 96.5 | - | - | - | 106.9 | - | - | - |
| Buitepos | - | 95.0 | - | 98.3 | 101.8 | - | - | - 105.4 | - |
| Ekuli | - | 91.5 | - | 88.4 | - | - | 98.0 | - | - |
| Epukiro | 91.6 | 98.1 | - | - | 101.6 | - | - | - 105.2 | - |
| Erongo | 90.6 | 93.7 | 96.9 | 100.2 | 103.7 | 107.3 | - | - | - |
| Gam | - | 92.6 | - | 102.6 | 99.1 | - | - | - | - 95.8 |
| Gibeon | - | - | - | - | - | 100.7 | - | - | - |
| Gobabis | 87.6 | 90.7 | 93.9 | 102.9 | 100.7 | 104.3 | 92.9 | 97.2 | - |
| Grossherzog Fr. | 88.6 | 91.7 | 94.9 | 98.2 | 101.7 | 105.3 | - | - | - |
| Kamanjab | 89.7 | - | - | - | - | 106.4 | - | - | - |
| Katima Mulilo | 98.5 | 92.6 | 90.9 | 99.1 | 94.1 | 106.2 | - | 95.8 | 87.8 |
| Keetmanshoop | 87.6 | 90.7 | 93.9 | 97.2 | 89.3 | 104.3 | - | - | - |
| Kl. Waterberg | 89.6 | 92.7 | 95.9 | 99.2 | 102.7 | 106.3 | - | - | - |
| Koës | 88.8 | 95.1 | - | - | - | 105.5 | - | - | - |
| Kongola | - | 88.3 | - | 91.4 | - | - | 97.9 | - | - |
| Lüderitz | 89.7 | 92.8 | 96.0 | 99.3 | 100.2 | 103.7 | - | - | - |
| Maltahöhe | 88.5 | - | 94.8 | - | - | 105.2 | - | - | - |

| FM (MHz) | Hart. | Nat. | Funk. | Kati | Omu. | Kai. | Nwa. | TYS | Wat. |
|---|---|---|---|---|---|---|---|---|---|
| Mariental | 87.7 | 90.8 | 94.0 | 101.8 | 105.4 | 104.4 | - | - | - |
| Nakop | 90.6 | 93.7 | - | 100.2 | - | 103.7 | - | - | - |
| Nkurenkuru | - | 90.7 | - | 87.6 | 97.2 | - | 93.9 | - | - |
| Noordoewer | 87.7 | 90.8 | - | 97.3 | - | 100.8 | - | - | - |
| Okongo | - | 89.0 | - | 92.1 | - | 95.3 | - | - | - |
| Omega | - | 89.4 | - | 92.5 | - | - | - | 99.0 | - |
| Omuthiya | - | 89.2 | - | 98.8 | 102.3 | 105.9 | - | - | - |
| Opuwo | - | 91.1 | - | 97.6 | 101.1 | - | - | - | - |
| Oranjemund | 90.0 | 93.1 | - | 99.6 | - | 106.7 | - | - | - |
| Oshakati | 89.2 | 87.8 | 96.4 | 97.4 | 98.8 | 105.9 | 90.9 | 99.7 | - |
| Otjimbingwe | - | - | - | - | 102.3 | 105.9 | - | - | - |
| Otjinene | 90.2 | 93.5 | - | - | 96.7 | - | - | - 103.5 | - |
| Pareisis | 88.7 | 91.8 | 95.0 | 98.3 | 101.8 | 105.4 | - | - | - |
| Renosterkop | 87.9 | 91.0 | - | - | 101.0 | 104.6 | - | - | - |
| Rietfontein | - | 92.2 | - | 89.1 | 95.4 | - | - | - 98.7 | - |
| Rosh Pinah | 90.3 | 93.4 | - | 96.6 | - | 99.9 | - | - | - |
| Rössing | 89.7 | 92.8 | 96.0 | 99.3 | 101.1 | 106.4 | - | - | - |
| Rundu | - | 89.6 | - | - | - | - | - | - | - |
| Sesfontein | - | 91.6 | - | 98.1 | 101.6 | 105.2 | - | - | - |
| Shamvura | - | 91.3 | - | 97.8 | - | - | - | 104.9 | - |
| Signalberg | 87.7 | 90.8 | 94.0 | 97.3 | 100.8 | 104.4 | - | - | - |
| Stampriet | 89.7 | 92.8 | 96.0 | - | - | 106.4 | - | - | - |
| Terrace Bay | - | 104.3 | - | - | - | - | - | - | - |
| Tsumeb | 88.6 | 91.7 | 94.9 | 98.2 | - | 105.3 | - | - | - |
| Tsumkwe | - | 90.4 | - | 100.0 | 93.5 | - | - | - | - 103.5 |
| Ur | 89.8 | 92.9 | 96.1 | 99.4 | 102.9 | 106.5 | - | - | - |
| Windhoek | 89.5 | 92.6 | 95.8 | - | - | - | 93.5 | 90.4 | - |

**Hartklop FM in Afrikaans:** 24h– **National FM in English:** 24hrs – **Funkhaus Namibia in German:** 24h – **Kati FM in Oshivambo:** 0350-2200 – **Omurari FM in Otjihero:** 0300-2200 – **Kaisames FM in Damara/Nama:** 0500-2000 – **Nwanyi FM in Lozi:** 0400-2200 (SS 1900) – **Tirelo ya Setswana (TYS) in Tswana:** 0500-2000 – **Wato FM in Kwangali, Rumanyo, Rugciriku, Thimbukushu:** 0400-2200 (SS 1900) – **R. Opuwo,** Arendesnes: 103.2MHz 5kW.

**OTHER STATIONS (FM MHz):**
**Base FM,** Katarura 106.2 **W:** basefm.com.na – **E FM:** Klein Windhoek 91.3 0.25kW, Swakopmund 91.5MHz 0.5kW **W:** efmnamibia.weebly. com – **Energy 100FM:** Walvis Bay 88.8 0.5kW, Klein Windhoek 100.0 0.5kW, Oshakati 100.9 2kW **W:** energy100fm.com – **Fresh FM,** Windhoek 102.9 **W:** freshfm.na – **Hitradio Namibia:** Swakopmund 97.5 1kW, Windhoek 99.5 1kW **W:** hitradio.com.na . In German – **JACC FM:** Otjiwarongo 90.9 0.1kW, Tsumeb 92.6 0.1kW, Rundu 92.7 0.1kW, Gobabis 92.9 0.1 kW, Lüderitz 93.7 0.1kW, Arandis/ Swapakopmund 94.3 0.5kW, Karibib/Omaruru/Usakos 94.6 0.1kW, Henties Bay/Swapakopmund/Walvis Bay 95.1 0.1kW, Grootfontein 95.2MHz, Eenhana/Ondangwa/Ongwediva/Oshakati/Outapi 95.5 1kW, Keetmanshoop 95.6 0.1kW, Oranjemund/Mariental 97.3 0.1kW, Rosh Pinah 103.4 0.1kW, Okahandja/Rehoboth/Windhoek 103.5 1kW, Katima Mulilo 107.4 0.1kW **W:** jacc.rocks . In English. – **Kanaal 7,** Windhoek 102.3 + 18 FM fq's. **W:** k7.com.na – **Kosmos,** Klein Windhoek 94.1 **W:** kosmos.com.na – **Live FM,** Rehoboth 90.3 **W:** facebook.com/ RadioLiveFm – **R. 99:** Walvis Bay & Swakopmund 96.5, Windhoek 99.0, Otjiwarango 99.9, Tsumeb 101.7, Oshakati & Ondangwa 104.5 **W:** 99fm.com.na – **Omulunga R:** Otjiwarongo 87.8 0.1kW, Grootfontein 92 0.1kW, Mariental 95.0 0.1kW, Rundu 99.2 0.1kW, Rehoboth/Windhoek 100.9 1kW, Ongwediva/Oshakati 102.3 1kW, Swakopmund/Walvis Bay 105.5 0.1kW, Keetmanshoop 106 0.1kW, Lüderitz 106,4 0.1kW, Gobabis 107.5 0.1kW **W:** omulunga.com – **Radiowave FM:** Otjimbingwe 87.8 1.5kW, Grootfontein 88.9 0.1kW, Lüderitz 90.6 0.1kW, Rössing 91.1 0.25kW, Walvis Bay 91.9 0.1kW, Usakos 92.2, Keetmanshoop 92.4 0.1kW, Tsumeb 95.8 0.1kW, Klein Windhoek 96.7 1.5kW, Otjiwarongo 100.9 0.1kW, Katima Mulilo 104.5 0.35kW, Rundu 105.4 0.35kW, Oshakati 106.8 0.35kW **W:** radiowave.com.na – **UNAM R,** Windhoek 97.4 0.1kW **W:** unam.edu.na/faculty-of-humanities-and-social-scienc-es/unam-radio – **West Coast FM,** Swakopmund 107.7 0.25kW **W:** westcoastfmnamibia.com
**R. France Int,** Windhoek: 107.9MHz in English/French

## NAURU

**L.T:** UTC +12h — **Pop:** 11,302 — **Pr.L:** English, Nauruan — **E.C:** 50Hz, 110/240V — **ITU:** NRU

**NAURU BROADCASTING SERVICE (Gov)**
**Nauru Media Bureau, Home Affairs Department**
✉ P O Box 429, Rep. of Nauru, Ce. Pacific ☎ +674 444 3190 🖷 +674 4443153 **E:** radionaurufm@hotmail.com (email bounces) **L.P:** SM: Dominic Appi, Tech.Mgr: Max Gadaloa

**FM:** 105.1MHz **D.Prgr:** 1800-1100 now includes local health, sports and education prgrs. Other times carries **Radio Australia** English for the Pacific satellite relay from Melbourne 1100-1800 **N:** on the h local and R. Australia.

## NEPAL

**LT:** UTC +5¾h — **Pop:** 25.3 million — **Pr.L:** Nepali, English — **E.C:** 50Hz, 230V — **ITU:** NPL

### MINISTRY OF INFORMATION AND COMMUNICATIONS
✉ Kathmandu ☎ +977 1 4211556 🖷 +977 1 4211729 **E:** info@moic. gov.np **W:** moic.gov.np **LP:** Minister: Gokul Prasad Baskota

### RADIO NEPAL (Pub, Comm.)
✉ Radio Broadcasting Service, G.P.O. Box 634, Singha Durbar, Kathmandu ☎+977 1 4231804 🖷+977 1 4221952 **W:** radionepal.gov. np **E:** program@radionepal.gov.np **E:** engg@wlink.com.np (Eng. div: ☎+977 1 4211842)
**LP:** Exec. Dir: Er. R.S. Karki. Dep. Exec. Dirs: Mr Rajendra Prasad Sharma & Mr Sushil Koirala. Chief Eng.: Er. Ramesh Jung Karkee

| MW | kHz | kW | MW | kHz | kW |
|---|---|---|---|---|---|
| Surkhet | 576 | 100 | Kathmandu | 792 | 100 |
| Dhankuta | 648 | 100 | Dipayal | 810 | 10 |
| Pokhara | 684 | 100 | Bardibas | 1143 | 10 |

**SW:** Khumaltar 5005kHz 100kW/5kW (‡, but irr.15-20kW test with open carrier or dummy load 0815-1115) **F.P.I.:** New 100kW DRM-capable tx.
**D.Prgr** on MW/SW: 2315-1720. **N.** in **Nepali** at 0015, 0115, 0315, 0415, 0515, 0615, 0715, 0915, 1015, 1115, 1315, 1515, 1715; **Other language N.** in **English:** 0215, 0815, 1415; in **Sanskrit** 0010; in **Sherpa** 1020; in **Magahi** 1025, for **Children** 1110; in **Tamang** 1120; in **Bhojpuri** 1205; in **Urdu** 1215; in **Maithili** 1215; in **Hindi** 1615; **Youth** 0140 ; **Variation at Regional Centres:** 0400-0415 & 1215-1300. **Sponsored Prog** on Thu and Sat at 1625
**Ann:** Nepali: 'Yo Radio Nepal Ho'; English: 'This is Radio Nepal'
**IS:** Instruments used are conch shell, violin, piano and jal tarang
**V.** by QSL-card

### FM STATIONS:

| FM | MHz Station | FM | MHz Station |
|---|---|---|---|
| Achhaam | 88.2 R. Vaijnath FM | Bharatpur | 97.9 Image FM |
| Achhaam | 92.0 R. Ramaroshan † | Bhedetar | 90.0 Saptakoshi FM † |
| Arghakhanchi | 101.0 R. Deurali † | Bhedetar | 96.8 V. of Youth FM |
| Arghakhanchi | 105.8 R. Argakhanchi † | Bhedetar | 97.9 Image FM |
| Baglung | 91.6 Saypatri FM † | Bhojpur | 98.6 R. Chomolungma |
| Baglung | 96.4 Baglung FM | Bhojpur | 103.6 R. Bhojpur |
| Baglung | 98.6 Dhaulagiri FM † | Biratnagar | 88.2 Kankai Sangeet |
| Baglung | 104.1 R. Dhorpatan | Biratnagar | 91.2 Birat FM |
| Baglung | 107.4 Sarathi FM | Biratnagar | 94.3 Koshi FM |
| Baitadi | 103.6 Saugat FM | Biratnagar | 105.6 SaptaKoshi FM |
| Baitadi | 106.6 R. Sansher | Biratnagar | 106.7 Sky FM |
| Bajhang | 93.6 Seti FM | Birgunj | 91.4 Gadimai FM † |
| Bajhang | 98.0 R. Nepal | Birgunj | 92.2 Kalika FM |
| Bajhang | 100.6 Saipal R. | Birgunj | 96.1 Kantipur FM |
| Bajura | 104.0 R. Bajura | Birgunj | 96.8 V. of Youth FM |
| Banke | 88.4 R. Xpress FM | Birgunj | 97.0 Image FM |
| Banke | 94.0 R. Krishnasar † | Birgunj | 97.6 Indreni FM |
| Banke | 94.6 R Bageshori | Birgunj | 99.0 Birgunj FM † |
| Banke | 95.6 R Bheri Aawaj | Birgunj | 100.0 R. Nepal |
| Banke | 96.8 Youth FM | Birgunj | 103.8 Narayani FM † |
| Banke | 97.3 R Jana Aawaj | Birgunj | 105.4 Star FM |
| Banke | 97.9 Image FM | Birtamod | 92.6 Kanchanjunga FM |
| Banke | 101.2 R. Kohalpur † | Birtamod | 105.0 Kankai Samaaj |
| Banke | 101.8 Kantipur FM | Buditola | 100.2 R. Nepal |
| Banke | 102.4 R. Pratibodh | Butwal | 92.2 Kalika FM |
| Banke | 104.2 Naya Nepal Sanchar | Butwal | 92.8 R. Namaste |
| Banke | 104.5 R. Rubaru † | Butwal | 93.6 Jagaran R. † |
| Banke | 104.8 Nepalgunj FM | Butwal | 94.4 Butwal FM † |
| Banke | 105.4 Bheri FM | Butwal | 96.1 Kantipur FM |
| Bara | 88.8 Sanskar FM | Butwal | 97.9 Image FM |
| Bara | 106.0 R. Simara | Butwal | 98.2 Tinau FM † |
| Bardiya | 100.6 Fulbari FM | Butwal | 99.4 R. Jagran |
| Bardiya | 106.0 R. Babai | Byash | 105.8 Madi Seti FM |
| Bardiya | 106.4 R. Gurubaba † | Chainpur | 100.6 Saipal R. † |
| Besisahar | 95.0 R. Marsyangdi | Chainpur | 105.2 R. Kailash |
| Bhairahawa | 98.8 Siddhartha FM | Chainpur | 106.6 Saipal R. |
| Bhairahawa | 102.0 Rupandehi FM † | Charpane | 103.6 R. Kechana |
| Bhaktapur | 88.8 NepaliKo R. | Chitawan | 89.8 R. Dhruvatara |
| Bhaktapur | 105.4 Bhaktapur FM † | Chitawan | 91.0 Kalika FM |
| Bharatpur | 91.0 Kalika FM 2 | Chitawan | 91.6 Synergy FM |
| Bharatpur | 91.6 Synergy FM | Chitawan | 94.0 Hamro FM |
| Bharatpur | 94.0 Hamro FM | Chitawan | 94.6 R Chitawan |
| Bharatpur | 94.6 Chitawan FM † | Chitawan | 95.2 Kalika FM |
| Bharatpur | 95.2 Kalika FM | Chitawan | 96.1 Kantipur FM |
| Bharatpur | 96.1 Kantipur FM | Chitawan | 96.8 Youth FM |
| Bharatpur | 96.8 V. of Youth FM | Chitawan | 97.9 Image FM |

| FM | MHz Station | FM | MHz Station |
|---|---|---|---|
| Chitawan | 100.6 R. Triveni | Hetauda | 92.9 Manakamana FM |
| Chitawan | 103.0 R. Nepal | Hetauda | 96.6 Hetauda FM † |
| Chitawan | 104.5 R. Arpan | Hetauda | 103.4 Shakti FM |
| Chitawan | 105.2 R. Narayani † | Humla | 94.2 Ekikrit Vikash Kendra |
| Chitawan | 107.6 R. Madi | Humla | 96.8 V. of Youth FM |
| Dadeldhura | 95.0 R. Sudur Aawaj | Humla | 100.0 R. Nepal |
| Dadeldhura | 96.0 Paschim Nepal Media | Humla | 101.4 Sarkegad FM |
| Dadeldhura | 97.4 Vikash Nyaya March | Humla | 103.4 R. Kailash † |
| Dadeldhura | 104.8 Aafno FM † | Illam | 90.6 R. Fikkal FM |
| Dailekh | 89.8 R. Dhurbatara FM | Illam | 93.0 Illam FM † |
| Dailekh | 104.0 R. Panchakoshi FM† | Illam | 94.9 R. Nepalbani † |
| Damak | 91.8 Star FM | Illam | 100.0 R. Nepal |
| Damak | 93.6 Pathibhara FM † | Illam | 104.0 Sandakpur FM |
| Damak | 101.6 Saptarangi FM | Itahari | 107.2 Namaste FM |
| Daman | 97.0 Prathidhwani FM | Jajarkot | 97.9 Asal Sashan Jilla |
| Damauli | 94.2 Damauli FM | | Samiti |
| Dang | 88.0 R. Jharana | Jajarkot | 105.0 R. Paila |
| Dang | 89.0 R. Hamro Pahuch | Jajarkot | 107.6 Khalanga FM |
| Dang | 91.4 R Madhya. | Jalweshwor | 106.7 R. Appan Mithila |
| Dang | 92.4 Indreni FM | Janakpur | 91.0 R. Today † |
| Dang | 93.4 R. Prakriti | Janakpur | 97.0 R. Janakpur † |
| Dang | 95.1 R. Ganatantra Rapti | Janakpur | 100.8 R. Mithila † |
| Dang | 98.0 R. Nepal | Janakpur | 101.8 Janakpur FM † |
| Dang | 100.2 R Tulsipur | Janakpur | 105.0 Mithilanchal FM |
| Dang | 102.8 R Swargadwari | Janakpur | 106.0 Janaki FM |
| Dang | 103.5 R. Highway | Jhapa | 88.8 R. Saragam |
| Dang | 104.0 R. Saryu Ganga | Jhapa | 89.1 Hamro Sanchar |
| Dang | 106.4 Super FM | | Samuha |
| Dang | 107.0 Dang FM † | Jhapa | 92.6 Kanchanjungha FM |
| Dang | 107.3 R. Naya Yug | Jhapa | 96.8 FM Mechi Tunes |
| Darchula | 98.0 R. Nepal | Jhapa | 101.6 Saptarangi FM † |
| Darchula | 102.2 Kalapani FM † | Jhapa | 103.9 R. Sandesh |
| Darchula | 104.5 R. Naya Nepal | Jhapa | 105.0 Birta FM |
| Daunne | 100.0 R. Nepal | Jhapa | 105.9 R. Sunrise |
| Dhading | 89.4 R. Loktranta FM† | Jhapa | 106.9 Seemana FM |
| Dhading | 92.1 Rajmarga | Jhapa | 107.5 Nagarik FM |
| | Sanchar Kendra | Jomsom | 100.0 R. Nepal |
| Dhading | 97.6 Shree Sahid | Jumla | 100.0 R. Nepal |
| | Smriti Sanchar | Jumla | 100.6 Hamro Aawaj |
| Dhading | 105.0 Krishi R. † | | Hamro Sarokar |
| Dhading | 105.6 R. Trishuli | Jumla | 105.2 R. Karnali FM |
| Dhading | 106.0 R. Dhading † | Kailali | 87.9 Godavari FM |
| Dhangadi | 89.4 R. Jana Aawaj | Kailali | 88.8 Paschim Today FM |
| Dhangadi | 91.4 Khaptad FM | Kailali | 91.4 Ghodaghodi FM |
| Dhangadi | 93.8 Dinesh FM † | Kailali | 93.2 Fulbari FM † |
| Dhangadi | 101.8 Kantipur FM | Kailali | 93.8 Dinesh FM? |
| Dhankuta | 87.6 Heart FM | Kailali | 98.2 Khaptad FM |
| Dhankuta | 92.2 R. Makalu † | Kailali | 101.0 Tikapur FM |
| Dhankuta | 96.1 R Kantipur | Kailali | 101.8 Kantipur FM |
| Dhankuta | 96.8 Youth FM | Kailali | 103.0 R. Nepal |
| Dhankuta | 97.9 Image FM | Kailali | 103.7 R. Kailali FM |
| Dhankuta | 105.2 R. Laliguransh | Kailali | 105.3 Sita Sanchar |
| Dhankuta | 106.2 R. Dhankuta † | | Samuha |
| Dhanusha | 91.0 R Today | Kailali | 105.6 Ujyalo Sudur |
| Dhanusha | 93.8 City Sahakari R. | | Paschhim |
| Dhanusha | 95.0 Kamalamai FM | Kailali | 107.0 Hamra Malika FM |
| Dhanusha | 97.0 R Janakpur | Kailali | 107.3 Hamro Fulbari FM |
| Dhanusha | 99.4 Mithilanchal FM | Kalikot | 100.0 R. Nepal |
| Dhanusha | 106.0 Janaki FM | Kalikot | 101.2 R. Bhek Aawaj † |
| Dhanusha | 106.6 Mithila Sanchar | Kalikot | 101.8 R. Chulimalika † |
| | Samuha | Kalikot | 102.8 R. Malika † |
| Dharan | 95.1 R. Ganatantra | Kalyanpur | 106.8 Nuwakot FM |
| Dharan | 95.6 Star FM | Kamalamai | 103.6 R. Sindhuligadi |
| Dharan | 106.6 Budasubba FM | Kanchanpur | 104.3 Angel FM |
| Dhulikhel | 104.0 Madhya. FM † | Kapilvastu | 89.6 R. Buddha Aawaj |
| Dolakha | 103.4 Hamro R. † | Kapilvastu | 104.2 R. Kapilvastu † |
| Dolakha | 104.0 R. Sailung | Kapilvastu | 105.4 R. Samanata |
| Dolakha | 106.0 Gaurishankar FM | Kapilvastu | 106.1 Janakpur Sanchar |
| Dolakha | 106.4 R. Kalinchowk † | | Samuha |
| Dolakha | 108.8 Chyomongmo | Kaski | 107.6 Tilarakot R. FM |
| | Media Pvt. Ltd. | Kaski | 87.9 R. Chhunumunu |
| Dolpa | 100.0 R. Nepal | Kaski | 90.6 R. Gandaki |
| Dolpa | 106.3 Se Foksundo Sanchar | Kaski | 91.0 Machhapuchhre FM |
| Doti | 94.4 Triveni FM | Kaski | 92.2 Himchuli FM |
| Doti | 105.9 R. Shaileshwari FM | Kaski | 93.4 R Annapurna |
| Gaidakot | 101.6 Vijay FM | Kaski | 95.8 Pokhara FM |
| Ghorahi | 91.4 R. Madhya. | Kaski | 96.8 Youth FM |
| Ghorahi | 102.8 R. Swargadwari FM† | Kaski | 97.9 Image FM |
| Godawari | 104.2 ECR FM | Kaski | 99.6 Annapurna Music FM |
| Gorkha | 102.4 R. Manakamana | Kaski | 101.2 Big FM |
| Gorkha | 103.6 Gorakhkali FM | Kaski | 101.8 Kantipur FM |
| Gorkha | 103.9 R. Manaslu † | Kaski | 102.2 Sunaulo FM |
| Gorkha | 104.6 R. Lamjung | Kaski | 102.6 R. Apostle |
| Gorkha | 105.4 R. Harmi | Kaski | 103.4 R. Safalta |
| Gorkha | 106.4 Deurali FM | Kaski | 106.0 Gorkhali R. |
| Gorkha | 107.2 Mero Saathi | Kaski | 106.6 R. Lekhnath |
| Gulariya | 100.6 Phoolbari FM | Kaski | 107.6 Tarang Pvt. Ltd |
| Gulmi | 88.4 R. Sky FM | Kathmandu | 87.6 R. Upatyaka † |
| Gulmi | 91.2 R. Gulmi | Kathmandu | 88.2 Jana Sandesh |
| Gulmi | 94.8 Ruru FM | Kathmandu | 88.8 Nepaliko R. |
| Gulmi | 100.0 R. Nepal | Kathmandu | 89.4 R. Mirmire |
| Gulmi | 106.2 R Resunga | Kathmandu | 90.6 Times FM |
| Hetauda | 90.4 National FM | Kathmandu | 91.2 Hits FM |

| FM | MHz | Station |
|---|---|---|
| Kathmandu | 91.8 | Nepal FM |
| Kathmandu | 92.4 | Capital FM |
| Kathmandu | 93.0 | Gorkha FM |
| Kathmandu | 93.5 | R. Jana Sandesh |
| Kathmandu | 94.0 | HBC FM |
| Kathmandu | 94.6 | Metro FM |
| Kathmandu | 95.2 | Star FM |
| Kathmandu | 96.8 | V. of Youth FM |
| Kathmandu | 97.9 | Image FM |
| Kathmandu | 98.3 | Keeps Media |
| Kathmandu | 98.8 | R. City FM |
| Kathmandu | 99.4 | Maittri FM |
| Kathmandu | 100.0 | R. Nepal |
| Kathmandu | 100.6 | RBC FM |
| Kathmandu | 101.8 | GopiKrishna FM |
| Kathmandu | 103.0 | R Nepal or BBC# |
| Kathmandu | 103.6 | R. Bagmati |
| Kathmandu | 104.8 | FM Adhyatma Jyoti |
| Kathmandu | 105.1 | Good News FM |
| Kathmandu | 106.2 | CJMC FM |
| Kathmandu | 106.3 | R. Audio |
| Kathmandu | 107.0 | TU FM |
| Kavre | 87.9 | R. Masti |
| Kavre | 88.4 | R. Shepherd |
| Kavre | 89.8 | R ABC |
| Kavre | 104.0 | Madhyapurva FM† |
| Kavre | 104.5 | R. Naya Sandesh |
| Kavre | 106.7 | R. Namobuddha† |
| Kavre | 107.3 | R. Janasanchar |
| Kavre | 107.6 | Grace FM |
| Khalanga | 92.0 | R. Pyuthan † |
| Khalanga | 101.0 | R. Salyan |
| Khanigau | 103.6 | R. Parbat |
| Khotang | 102.4 | R. Haleshi † |
| Khotang | 105.0 | Rupakot R. † |
| Kirtipur | 106.7 | Newa FM |
| Kohalpur | 101.2 | R. Kohalpur |
| Lahan | 102.6 | Samad FM |
| Lahan | 105.4 | Fulbari R. |
| Lalitpur | 90.0 | Ujyaalo FM |
| Lalitpur | 96.1 | Kantipur FM |
| Lalitpur | 97.2 | Headlines&MusicFM |
| Lalitpur | 100.0 | R. Nepal |
| Lalitpur | 100.9 | R. Lalipur |
| Lalitpur | 101.2 | Classic FM |
| Lalitpur | 102.4 | R. Sagarmatha † |
| Lalitpur | 104.2 | Paryawaran Chakra R. |
| Lalitpur | 105.7 | BFBS or R Nepal # |
| Lamahi | 105.8 | R. Deukhuri |
| Lamjung | 88.4 | R. Lamjung |
| Lamjung | 95.0 | R. Marsyangdi † |
| Liwang | 93.8 | R. Rolpa † |
| Mahend. | 90.2 | Kanchanpur FM |
| Mahend. | 96.2 | R. Mahakali † |
| Mahend. | 99.4 | Suklafanta FM † |
| Mahottari | 88.4 | R. Darpan † |
| Mahottari | 90.4 | Jaleshwarnath FM† |
| Mahottari | 94.4 | R. Appan Mithila† |
| Mahottari | 103.4 | R. Rudraksha |
| Mahottari | 103.7 | R. Gunjan |
| Mahottari | 107.0 | R. Sungava FM† |
| Makwanpur | 88.0 | Hetauda Media |
| Makwanpur | 88.5 | R. Aakash Ganga |
| Makwanpur | 96.6 | Hetauda FM |
| Makwanpur | 97.0 | R. Pratidhwani |
| Makwanpur | 98.0 | R. Nepal |
| Makwanpur | 99.6 | R. Thaha Sansar |
| Makwanpur | 101.3 | R. Makwanpur |
| Makwanpur | 103.4 | R. Sakti |
| Makwanpur | 106.6 | R. Asmita |
| Makwanpur | 107.2 | R. Palung |
| Mechinagar | 96.8 | FM Mechi Tunes |
| Morang | 87.9 | Jagriti FM |
| Morang | 91.2 | B FM † |
| Morang | 94.3 | Koshi FM |
| Morang | 95.1 | Janasanchar Kendra |
| Morang | 101.0 | R. Chamatkar |
| Morang | 102.1 | R. Makalu |
| Morang | 102.6 | R. Sunakhari |
| Morang | 104.4 | R. Purwanchal † |
| Morang | 104.8 | Sajha R. |
| Morang | 105.6 | Saptakoshi FM |
| Morang | 106.3 | R. Suseli FM |
| Morang | 106.6 | Sky FM |
| Mugu | 100.0 | R. Nepal |
| Mugu | 102.2 | R. Suryadaya FM |
| Mugu | 104.6 | R. Rara |
| Mugu | 106.6 | Mugali Chalchitra Vikash Sang |
| Mugu | 107.4 | R. Mugu |
| Musikot | 92.8 | R. Sisne FM |
| Mustang | 89.0 | Gramin Suchana Vikash Kendra |

| FM | MHz | Station |
|---|---|---|
| Mustang | 96.8 | V. of Youth FM |
| Mustang | 103.0 | R. Nepal |
| Myagdi | 88.2 | Myagdakali FM |
| Myagdi | 104.4 | R. Myagdi † |
| Myanglung | 104.2 | R. Samhaltung |
| Nawalparasi | 90.2 | R. Parasi |
| Nawalparasi | 100.0 | R. Nepal |
| Nawalparasi | 101.0 | R.Madhyavindu FM† |
| Nawalparasi | 101.6 | Vijaya FM |
| Nawalparasi | 103.4 | Daunne FM |
| Nepalgunj | 94.6 | R. Bageshwori |
| Nepalgunj | 95.6 | R. Bheri Aawaj † |
| Nepalgunj | 96.8 | V. of Youth FM |
| Nepalgunj | 97.3 | R. Jana Aawaj |
| Nepalgunj | 97.9 | Image FM |
| Nepalgunj | 101.8 | Kantipur FM |
| Nepalgunj | 104.8 | R. Nepalgunj |
| Nilkantha | 106.0 | Dhading FM |
| Nuwakot | 104.5 | R. Jalapa |
| Nuwakot | 107.4 | R. Abhiyan |
| Okhaldhunga | 100.6 | Ramailo Com. R. |
| Okhaldhunga | 104.8 | Afno FM † |
| Okhaldhunga | 107.6 | R. Okhaldhunga |
| Palpa | 90.8 | Muktinath FM |
| Palpa | 93.2 | Shrinagar FM |
| Palpa | 99.4 | R Paschimanchal |
| Palpa | 103.6 | R. Rampur |
| Palpa | 103.9 | R. Palpa |
| Palpa | 106.9 | R. Madanpokhara † |
| Palung | 107.2 | R. Palung FM |
| Panchthar | 97.3 | Simhalila FM |
| Panchthar | 99.2 | Eagle FM |
| Panchthar | 104.2 | Sumhatlung FM† |
| Parbat | 95.2 | R. Didi Bahini † |
| Parbat | 100.6 | R. Shaligram † |
| Parsa | 91.4 | Gadimai FM |
| Parsa | 92.8 | Bhojpuriya FM |
| Parsa | 96.1 | R. Kantipur |
| Parsa | 96.8 | Youth FM |
| Parsa | 97.6 | Indreni FM |
| Parsa | 97.9 | Image FM |
| Parsa | 99.0 | R Birganj |
| Parsa | 100.0 | R. Nepal |
| Parsa | 101.9 | Aakas FM |
| Parsa | 103.8 | Narayani FM |
| Parsa | 105.8 | Birgunj Musical FM |
| Parsa | 107.0 | R. Tarang |
| Pokhara | 91.0 | Madhhapuchhre FM |
| Pokhara | 92.2 | Himchuli FM † |
| Pokhara | 93.4 | R. Annapurna † |
| Pokhara | 95.8 | Pokhara FM |
| Pokhara | 96.8 | V. of Youth FM |
| Pokhara | 97.9 | Image FM |
| Pokhara | 99.2 | R. Barahi FM |
| Pokhara | 104.6 | R. Sarangkot |
| Prithivinarayan | 92.8 | R. Gorkha † |
| Putalibazar | 90.2 | Syangja FM † |
| Pyuthan | 90.0 | R. Mahila Aawaj |
| Pyuthan | 92.0 | R Pyuthan |
| Pyuthan | 97.0 | R. Mandhawi † |
| Pyuthan | 103.6 | R. Lishne Aawaj |
| Rajbiraj | 105.8 | R. Rajbiraj |
| Ramechhap | 88.6 | R. Tinlal |
| Ramechhap | 102.1 | Hajurko R. |
| Rasuwa | 100.9 | Durgam FM |
| Rasuwa | 102.1 | Rasuwa FM |
| Rautahat | 89.6 | R. Madhes |
| Rautahat | 90.4 | R. Jivan Jyoti |
| Rautahat | 90.8 | Rautahat FM † |
| Rautahat | 93.2 | Rajdevi FM † |
| Rautahat | 98.2 | R. Sanskriti |
| Rautahat | 98.6 | Madhesh Jana Aawaj |
| Rautahat | 102.2 | Gaur FM |
| Rautahat | 102.6 | R. Nunthar FM |
| Rolpa | 93.8 | R. Rolpa |
| Rolpa | 104.5 | R. Jaljala |
| Rukum | 89.2 | R. Sani Bheri |
| Rukum | 92.8 | R. Sisne † |
| Rukum | 100.8 | R. SanoBheri |
| Rukum | 102.0 | Uttarjganga Sanchar Kendra |
| Rupandehi | 88.2 | R. Republic |
| Rupandehi | 88.6 | R. Malmala |
| Rupandehi | 92.8 | Star FM |
| Rupandehi | 93.6 | R. Jagaran |
| Rupamdehi | 94.4 | Butwal FM |
| Rupandehi | 95.5 | R. Mukti † |
| Rupandehi | 96.1 | R. Kantipur |
| Rupandehi | 96.8 | R. Lumbini † |
| Rupandehi | 97.6 | Image FM |
| Rupandehi | 98.2 | Tinau FM |

| FM | MHz | Station |
|---|---|---|
| Rupandehi | 98.8 | Siddhartha FM |
| Rupandehi | 102.0 | Rupandehi FM |
| Rupandehi | 105.0 | R. Samabesi |
| Rupandehi | 106.6 | R. Devdaha |
| Rupandehi | 107.2 | Aasha ko Sandesh |
| Salleri | 94.6 | R. Dudhkoshi |
| Salleri | 102.2 | Solu FM |
| Salyan | 101.0 | R. Salyan † |
| Salyan | 102.2 | R. Sharada FM |
| Salyan | 103.8 | R. Sahara |
| Salyan | 104.8 | R. Rapti FM † |
| Salyan | 106.1 | R. Kapurkot |
| Sankhuwa. | 100.8 | R. Arun Sandesh |
| Sankhuwa. | 107.5 | Gurans FM |
| Sankhuwa. | 105.8 | Khadbari FM † |
| Saptari | 91.8 | Today FM |
| Saptari | 92.8 | Bhorukawa |
| Saptari | 101.4 | R. Chhinnamasta |
| Saptari | 102.1 | Janak Sanchar Samuha |
| Saptari | 104.6 | Appan FM |
| Sarlahi | 89.3 | R. Madhes † |
| Sarlahi | 94.6 | R. Ekata |
| Sarlahi | 104.8 | Malangwa FM |
| Sarlahi | 105.6 | R. Sarlahi † |
| Sarlahi | 107.4 | Mai FM † |
| Siligadi | 96.8 | V. of Youth FM |
| Simikot | 100.0 | R. Nepal |
| Sindhuli | 92.0 | R. Sindhuligadi † |
| Sindhuli | 104.2 | R. Sahara |
| Sindhup. | 89.1 | R. Avarv |
| Sindhup. | 96.8 | Youth FM |
| Sindhup. | 102.8 | Sindhu FM |
| Sindhup. | 105.0 | R. Sindhu † |
| Siraha | 88.1 | R. Saugat |
| Siraha | 88.8 | Bhaluwahi Samudaik R. |
| Siraha | 107.8 | R. Samagra |
| Solukhumbu | 94.6 | R. Dudhkoshi |
| Solukhumbu | 101.2 | Solu FM |
| Solukhumbu | 105.3 | R. Everest |
| Sunsari | 88.5 | Dantakali FM |

| FM | MHz | Station |
|---|---|---|
| Sunsari | 89.4 | R. Jaya Nepal |
| Sunsari | 90.0 | Saptakoshi FM † |
| Sunsari | 95.1 | Ganatantra FM |
| Sunsari | 95.6 | Star FM |
| Sunsari | 96.1 | R. Kantipur |
| Sunsari | 98.8 | Vijaypur FM |
| Sunsari | 99.5 | Popular FM |
| Sunsari | 103.6 | Jana Sanchar Kendra Nepal |
| Sunsari | 107.2 | Namaste FM |
| Surkhet | 90.2 | R. Surkhet † |
| Surkhet | 90.8 | Jagaran FM † |
| Surkhet | 92.6 | R. Himal |
| Surkhet | 98.6 | R. Bheri |
| Surkhet | 101.2 | R. Bheka Aawaj |
| Surkhet | 103.4 | Bulbule FM † |
| Surkhet | 106.7 | Himal FM |
| Syangja | 89.2 | R. Waling |
| Syangja | 89.6 | R. Syangja † |
| Tamghas | 106.2 | R. Resunga |
| Tanahu | 88.2 | Dhorbarahi FM |
| Tanahu | 88.8 | R. Bandipur † |
| Tanahu | 94.2 | Damauli FM |
| Tanahu | 97.2 | R. Tanahun † |
| Tanahu | 102.6 | R. Devghat |
| Tanahu | 104.2 | R. Bhanubhakta† |
| Tansen | 96.8 | Muktinath FM † |
| Tansen | 93.2 | Shreenagar FM |
| Tansen | 99.4 | R Paschimancha |
| Taplejung | 94.6 | R. Taplejung |
| Taplejung | 102.0 | Tamor † |
| Tawlihawa | 104.2 | R. Kapilbastu |
| Tehrathum | 102.6 | R.Menchhyayam |
| Thulasen | 92.0 | R. Ramaroshan † |
| Tikapur | 101.0 | Tikapur FM † |
| Tribhuwan. | 92.4 | Indreni FM |
| Tulsipur | 100.2 | R. Tulsipur FM † |
| Udaypur | 91.6 | Amurta FM † |
| Udaypur | 92.4 | R. Udayapur |
| Udaypur | 104.0 | R. Triyuga |
| Udaypur | 106.8 | UK FM |
| Walling | 105.4 | R. Aandhikhola † |

**NB:** Madhya. = Madhyapashchim Mahend. = Mahendranagar, Sankhuwa. = Sankhuwasabha, Sindhup. = Sindhupalchok, Tribhuwan. = Tribhuwannagar, † BBC Nepali rel. daily 0130-0145,1500-1545 # BFBS on 105.7 & BBC WS on 103.0 FM rel. 24hrs or R. Nepal.

**Other Stations**
**Guru-Baba FM:** Bansgadi, 106.4MHz 0.1kW. Prgrs in Tharu
**BFBS: Gurkha R./R.2, W:** forces.net/radio Kathmandu
**FM:** 105.7MHz (Nepali & English) #

## NETHERLANDS

**L.T:** UTC +1h (31 Mar-27 Oct: +2h) — **Pop:** 17.2 million — **Pr.L:** Dutch — **E.C:** 50Hz, 230V — **ITU:** HOL

### COMMISSARIAAT VOOR DE MEDIA
Hoge Naarderweg 78, 1217 AH Hilversum ☎ +31 35 7737700 **E:** cvdm@cvdm.nl **W:** www.cvdm.nl
**L.P:** Chair: Madeleine de Cock Buning

### NEDERLANDSE OMROEP STICHTING (NOS)
Mediapark, Journaalplein 1, 1217 ZK Hilversum; Postbus 26600, 1202 JT Hilversum ☎ +31 35 6779222
**W:** nos.nl **E:** publieksvoorlichting@nos.nl

### NTR (PUBLIEKE TAAKOMROEP)
Mediapark, Wim T. Schippersplein 5-7, 1217WD Hilversum or P.O. Box 29000, 1202 MA Hilversum ☎ +31 88 7799 999 **W:** ntr.nl **E:** info@ntr.nl

### NEDERLANDSE PUBLIEKE OMROEP (NPO)
Bart de Graaffweg 2, 1217ZL Hilversum or P.O. Box 26444, 1202 JJ Hilversum ☎ +31 35 677 8899 **W:** npo.nl
Representing the following broadcasting organisations: AVROTROS, BNNVARA, EO, Human, KRO-NCRV, MAX,NOS, NTR, VPRO, WNL, PowNed
Dutch national public prgrs are provided by the **NOS**, **NTR** and the broadcasting organisations of the **NPO**.

| FM | NPO1 | NPO2 | NPO3 | NPO 4 | kW |
|---|---|---|---|---|---|
| Alphen ad Rijn- | - | | 96.5 | | 0.06 |
| Amsterdam | 98.6 | 92.3 | 96.5 | 94.5 | 0.03/0.03/0.03/0.03 |
| Arnhem | 98.6 | 92.9 | 96.5 | 92.1 | 0.06/0.06/0.06/0.06 |
| Den Haag | 105.5 | 92.9 | 96.5 | 94.1 | 0.013/0.05/0.008 |
| Emmaberg | 105.3 | 93.4 | 103.9 | 98.7 | 10/10/10/10 |

| FM | NP01 | NP02 | NP03 | NPO 4 | kW |
|----|------|------|------|-------|-----|
| Eys | - | 97.2 | - | - | 10 |
| Goes | 104.4 | 94.4 | 99.8 | 95.0 | 40/0.1/10/10 |
| Hoogersmilde | 91.8 | 88.0 | 88.6 | 94.8 | 100/100/40/10 |
| Hoorn | 98.6 | 105.1 | 96.5 | - | 0.4/0.01/0.4 |
| Hulst | - | 107.1 | - | - | 0.05 |
| IJsselstein | 98.9 | 92.6 | 96.8 | 94.3 | 70/70/70/50 |
| Jirnsum | 104.3 | - | - | - | 0.07 |
| Loon op Zand | - | - | - | 98.2 | 55 |
| Markelo | 98.4 | 104.6 | 96.2 | 91.4 | 80/80/80/80 |
| Mierlo | 104.6 | 92.3 | 97.1 | - | 0.03/0.07/0.07 |
| Roermond | 104.8 | 88.2 | 90.9 | 94.5 | 100/100/100/100 |
| Roosendaal | 92.1 | 95.9 | 96.5 | 87.6 | 0.06/0.02/0.03/0.02 |
| Rotterdam | 98.6 | 92.9 | 97.1 | 94.7 | 0.08/0.08/0.04/13 |
| Wageningen | - | - | - | 94.7 | 0.05 |
| West Terschelling | - | 89.9 | - | - | 0.05 |
| Westdorpe | - | 97.8 | - | - | 100 |
| Wieringerwerf | 95.0 | 92.9 | 97.1 | 101.6 | 15/15/15/35 |

**Ann:** "Dit is de VARA", "Dit is de VPRO" etc. **NPO R. 1:** news, sport; **NPO R. 2** and **NPO 3 FM:** music; **R. 4:** classical music

**Regional stations:**

| FM | Mhz | kW | Location | Station |
|----|-----|-----|----------|---------|
| 2) | 87.6 | 8 | Mierlo | Omroep Brabant |
| 4) | 87.9 | 15 | Goes | Omroep Zeeland |
| 9) | 88.7 | 1 | Alkmaar | NH R. |
| 9) | 88.9 | 10 | Amsterdam | NH R. |
| 6) | 89.1 | 40 | Megen | R. Gelderland |
| 13) | 89.3 | 20 | Rotterdam | R West |
| 10) | 89.4 | 10 | Hengelo | R. Oost |
| 12) | 89.8 | 25 | Lelystad | Omroep Flevoland |
| 6) | 90.4 | 10 | Ruurlo | R. Gelderland |
| 5) | 90.8 | 3 | Hoogersmilde | R. Drenthe |
| 2) | 91.0 | 15 | Roosendaal | Omroep Brabant |
| 2) | 91.9 | 2 | Loon op Zand | Omroep Brabant |
| 3) | 92.2 | 25 | Jirnsum | Omrop Fryslân |
| 3) | 92.5 | 1 | Hoogersmilde | Omrop Fryslân |
| 7) | 93.1 | 4 | IJsselstein | R. M Utrecht |
| 11) | 93.4 | 10 | Rotterdam | R. Rijnmond |
| 9) | 93.9 | 11 | Wieringerwerf | NH R. |
| 1) | 95.3 | 10 | Emmaberg | L1 R. |
| 10) | 95.6 | 5 | Markelo | R. Oost |
| 2) | 95.8 | 5 | Megen | Omroep Brabant |
| 8) | 97.5 | 20 | Groningen | R. Noord |
| 7) | 97.9 | 3 | Rhenen | R. M Utrecht |
| 10) | 99.4 | 25 | Zwolle | R. Oost |
| 6) | 99.6 | 4 | Zaltbommel | R. Gelderland |
| 1) | 100.3 | 100 | Roermond | L1 R. |
| 6) | 103.5 | 20 | Ugchelen | R. Gelderland |

+8 low-power relays

**Addresses: & other information:**
**1)** Postbus 31, 6200 AA Maastricht ☎ +31 43 850 60 00 🖷 +31 43 850 61 01 **E:** redactie@L1.nl **W:** l1.nl – **2)** Postbus 108, 5600 AC Eindhoven ☎ +31 40 2949494 **E:** contact@omroepbrabant.nl **W:** omroepbrabant. nl – **3)** Postbus 7600, 8903 JP Leeuwarden ☎ +31 58 299 7799 **E:** direksje@omropfryslan.nl **W:** omropfryslan.nl – **4)** Postbus 1090, 4388 ZH Oost-Souburg ☎ +31 118 499900 **E:** nieuws@omroepzeeland.nl **W:** omroepzeeland.nl – **5)** Postbus 999, 9400 AZ Assen ☎ +31 592 338080 **E:** redactie@rtvdrenthe.nl **W:** rtvdrenthe.nl – **6)** Postbus 747, 6800 AS Arnhem ☎ +31 26 3713713 **E:** omroep@gld.nl **W:** omroepgelderland.nl – **7)** Postbus 1012, 3500 BA Utrecht ☎ +31 30 8500600 🖷 +31 30 8500601 **E:** vraag@rtvutrecht.nl **W:** rtvutrecht.nl – **8)** Postbus 30101, 9700 RP Groningen ☎ +31 50 3199999 **E:** info@rtvnoord. nl **W:** rtvnoord.nl – **9)** Postbus 9823, 1006AM Amsterdam ☎ +31 88 850 5050 **E:** nieuws@nhnieuws.nl **W:** nhnieuws.nl – **10)** Postbus 1000, 7550BA Hengelo (Ov) ☎ +31 74 2456456 **E:** info@rtvoost.nl **W:** rtvoost.nl – **11)** Postbus 1515, 3000 BM Rotterdam ☎ +31 10 7075 707 **E:** communicatie@rijnmond.nl **W:** rijnmond.nl – **12)** Postbus 567, 8200 AN Lelystad ☎ +31 320 285085 **E:** rtv@omroepflevoland.nl **W:** omroepflevoland.nl – **13)** Postbus 24025, 2490 AA Den Haag ☎ +31 70 3078888 **E:** online@omroepwest.nl **W:** omroepwest.nl

**Public local stations in major cities: FM(MHz):**
**Amsterdam** 96.1 FUN X, 99.4 Stads FM (SALTO), 105.2 Radio Zuid Oost (RAZO), 106.8 Stads FM (SALTO), 107.9 Caribbean FM – **Den Haag** 92.0 Den Haag FM,98.4 FUN X – **Rotterdam** 91.8 FUN X– **Utrecht** 96.1 FUN X, 105.7 Bingo FM, 107.7 Bingo FM
**Addresses & other information:**
**FUN X Rotterdam**, Lloydstraat 21,3024EA Rotterdam ☎ +31 10 22 14 900 🖷 +31 10 22 14 918 – **FUN X Amsterdam**, Piet Heinkade 181K, 1019HC Amsterdam ☎ +31 20 530 4960 – **FUN X Utrecht**, Hengeveldstraat 29, 3572KH Utrecht ☎ +31 30 303 1250 **W:** funx.

nl – **Radio Zuid ,Oost,(RAZO),Stads FM (SALTO),Caribbean FM** Piet Heinkade 181E, 1019HC Amsterdam ☎ +31 20 638 6386 **W:**salto. nl – **Den Haag FM:** Laan van 's-Gravenmade 4, 2495AJ, Den Haag ☎ +31 70 307 8899 **W:** denhaagfm.nl **E:** info@denhaagfm.nl – **Bingo FM,** postbus 1012, 3500BA Utrecht ☎ +31 30 850 0600 🖷 +31 30 850 0601 **W:** rtvutrecht.nl/bingofm **E:** vraag@rtvutrecht.nl
**Digital services DAB+ and DMB on Band III:** National DAB+ on 220.352MHz and 227.360MHz. Regional DAB+ on 195.936MHz (West), 208.064MHz (Noordwest), 183.648MHz (Oost) 188.928MHz (Zuid), 208.064MHz (Zuidwest), Public Local Radio DAB+ on 190.640Mhz

**OTHER STATIONS**

| MW | kHz | kW | Location | Station |
|----|-----|-----|----------|---------|
| 53) | 1008 | 100 | Zeewolde | Groot Nieuws R.* |
| 60) | 1566 | 1 | Den Haag | Vahon Hindustani R. |
| 51) | 1602 | 0.5 | Harlingen | Cyber Gold R./R.Seagull |

* until 1 January 2019
**LPAM** stns on **675kHz:** Hotradio Classics, Emmeloord 0.1kW, Hotradio Hits, Bornerbroek 0.1kW, Radio Nostalgie, Kollumerzwaag, 0.1 kW, Radio Babylona, Musselkanaal, 0.1kW, Unique, Wijchen,0.1kW, Stichting Middengolf, Utrecht 0.05kW* **747kHz:** Cupra Radio, Emmer-Compascuum , 0.1kW, Radio 4 Brainport, Waalre, 0.1kW, Groeistad R, Wassenaar, 0.1kW, Different Radio 747 AM, Nijkerk, 0.05kW, R. Overland, Maastricht, 0.1kW, Salland 747AM, Deventer, 0.1kW, R. Seagull, Harlingen, (06.00-18.00),0.1kW, Radio 0511, Harlingen (18.00-06.00), 0.1kW , **828kHz:** Hotradio Hits, Huissen, 0.1kW, Wereldstad Radio AM828 , Rotterdam, 0.1kW, Quality RTV, Utrecht, 0.05kW*, R. Bontekoe, Hoorn, 0.1kW **891kHz:** Euregio Radio, Baexem, 0.1kW, Fidelio Radio, Driebergen-Rijsenburg, 0.1kW, Radio City International, Zeeland, 0.1kW, **1035kHz:** Neverland AM, Venlo, 0.1kW. **1224kHz:** United AM, Neede 0.1kW, Extra AM, Amsterdam, 0.1kW, Radio Eldorado, Damwâld, 0.05kW, Radio Emmeloord, Emmeloord, 0.1kW, Radio T-POT, Gasselternijveen, 0.1kW, Radio Overland, Lunteren, 0.1kW, Radio 1224, Lunteren, 0.1kW, Kilrock 1224AM, s-Gravendeel, 0.1kW, Nostalgie AM, Siddeburen, 0.1kW, **1251kHz:** Memories 1251 AM, Geffen, 0.1kW. **1332kHz:** R.Transparant, Creil 0.1kW, Radio Flandria, Hemelum, 0.1kW, Sterrekijker AM, Elim, 0.1kW, Citrus AM, Emst, 0.1kW, De Witte Bizon, Emst 0.1kW, Alfa Radio, Haaksbergen, 0.05 kW, Impact AM, Wassenaar, 0.1kW, Radio 0511, Ternaard, 0.1kW (0600-1800), Radio Seagull, Ternaard, 0.1kW (1800-0600) **1395kHz:** Barkey, Almere Buiten, 0.05kW, Westcoast AM, Katwijk aan Zee, 0.1kW, R. Seabreeze AM, Grou, 0.1kW, Cupra R., Emmer-Compascuum, 0.1kW, Q-AM 1395, Waardenburg, 0.1kW, Loostad R., Apeldoorn, 0.1kW, Studio Denakker, Klazienaveen, 0.1kW, Happy AM, Middelburg 0.1kW **1485kHz:** Radio Jong Europa, Alphen aan den Rijn,(fri-sun) 0.001kW, Flashback 1485AM, Baarn,0.001kW, Radio Beilen, Beilen, 0.001kW, Radio 220, Buitenpost, 0.001kW, Amplivier Radio, Dâmwald, 0.001kW, Engelen, Goor, 0.001kW, Radio Hoogeveen AM, Hoogeveen, 0.001kW, AMsterdam 1485, Amsterdam, 0.001kW, , Wijkradio, Waalwijk, 0.001kW, Veluwe Centraal, Apeldoorn, 0.001kW, Veluwe AM, Ermelo, 0.001kW, Veluws Genot, Oldebroek, 0.001kW, Monti Radio,'s-Heerenberg, 0.001kW, More R, Sneek, 0.001kW, R. 0511, Rhederbrug, 0.001kW, ,Quality RTV, Utrecht, 0.001kW*, Wereldstad, Rotterdam, 0.001kW, R. Koekoek, Rijswijk, 0.001kW, , R. Impuls, Amersfoort, 0.001kW, Columbia AM, Aalst, 0.001kW, , EyeRadio, Tiel, 0.001kW,Vintage Music Radio,Vlissingen, 0.001kW, Voorburgse Radio Centrale West, Voorburg, 0.001kW*, Vrij Radio Zwolle, Zwolle, 0.001kW, Mol, Katwijk, 0.001kW* **1584kHz:** Antenne Domstad, Utrecht 0.001kW,
* licensed, but off the air

| FM | MHz | kW | Location | Station |
|----|-----|-----|----------|---------|
| 20) | 87.6 | 1 | Enschede | Joy R. |
| 61) | 87.6 | 45 | Hoogersmilde | R. 10 |
| 61) | 87.7 | 115 | Lelystad | R. 10 |
| 61) | 87.9 | 10 | Den Bosch | R. 10 |
| 61) | 88.1 | 4 | Hilversum | R. 10 |
| 23) | 88.2 | 1 | Ugchelen | 100%NL |
| 23) | 88.3 | 2 | Wieringerwerf | 100%NL |
| 9) | 88.4 | 43 | Roosendaal | Slam! |
| 3) | 88.6 | 26 | Mierlo | BNR Nieuws R. |
| 57) | 88.8 | 1 | Vlissingen | Sublime |
| 15) | 88.9 | 1 | Den Bosch | R. 8FM Noordoost Brabant |
| 23) | 89.0 | 3 | Lochem | 100%NL |
| 26) | 89.1 | 4 | Groningen | R NL Grunn FM |
| 19) | 89.1 | 2 | Wieringerwerf | R. Veronica |
| 9) | 89.2 | 1 | Venlo | Slam! |
| 9) | 89.2 | 3 | Zwolle | R. NL |
| 62) | 89.2 | 1 | Amersfoort | EVA R. |
| 15) | 89.2 | 1 | Breda | R. 8FM West Brabant |
| 15) | 89.3 | 1 | Eindhoven | R. 8FM West Brabant |
| 23) | 89.5 | 10 | Alkmaar | 100%NL |

| FM | MHz | kW | Location | Station | FM | MHz | kW | Location | Station |
|---|---|---|---|---|---|---|---|---|---|
| 23) | 89.5 | 5 | Utrecht | 100%NL | 77) | 95.9 | 5 | Alphen ad Rijn | Fresh FM |
| 3) | 89.6 | 5 | Hoogersmilde | BNR NieuwsR. | 76) | 96.0 | 2 | Wieringerwerf | Coastline FM |
| 30) | 89.6 | 1 | Nieuwbergen | Maasland R. | 66) | 96.2 | 1 | Zoetermeer | ZFM |
| 57) | 89.7 | 2.5 | Mierlo | Sublime | 19) | 96.3 | 20 | Loon op Zand | R. Veronica |
| 57) | 89.7 | 2 | Breda | Sublime | 29) | 96.3 | 1 | Alkmaar | Wild Hitradio |
| 11) | 89.9 | 1 | Emmen | R. NL | 19) | 96.6 | 1 | Goes | R. Veronica |
| 23) | 90.0 | 3 | Breskens | 100%NL | 11) | 96.6 | 1 | Leeuwarden | R. NL |
| 23) | 90.0 | 17 | Loon op Zand | 100%NL | 11) | 97.0 | 2 | Hoogeveen | R. NL |
| 69) | 90.1 | 1 | Ujala Radio | Diemen | 11) | 97.1 | 1 | Assen | R. NL |
| 23) | 90.2 | 50 | Roosendaal | 100%NL | 19) | 97.1 | 1 | Vlissingen | R. Veronica |
| 11) | 90.3 | 4 | Eindhoven | R.NL | 29) | 97.3 | 2 | Haarlem | Wild Hit R. |
| 57) | 90.3 | 10 | Groningen | Sublime | 63) | 97.6 | 2 | Maastricht | Q-Music Limburg |
| 57) | 90.4 | 25 | Hoorn | Sublime | 11) | 97.6 | 36 | Rotterdam | R. NL |
| 57) | 90.5 | 8 | Rotterdam | Sublime | 19) | 97.7 | 10 | Arnhem | R. Veronica |
| 57) | 90.5 | 15 | Hoogersmilde | Sublime | 19) | 97.7 | 6 | Mierlo | R. Veronica |
| 57) | | 5 | Hoogezand | Sublime | 63) | 97.7 | 15 | Landgraaf | Q-Music Limburg |
| 11) | 90.5 | 4 | Helmond | R.NL | 19) | 97.8 | 2 | Ijsselstein | R. Veronica |
| 57) | 90.7 | 50 | Ijsselstein | Sublime | 58) | 97.9 | 3 | Tjerkgaast | R Continu |
| 57) | 90.7 | 6 | Enschede | Sublime | 36) | 98.0 | 12 | Amsterdam | R. Decibel |
| 57) | 90.8 | 2 | Terneuzen | Sublime | 36) | 98.3 | 15 | Alkmaar | R. Decibel |
| 9) | 91.0 | 10 | Tjerkgaast | Slam! | 20) | 98.5 | 2 | Groningen | Joy R. |
| 9) | 91.0 | 1 | Markelo | Slam! | 20) | 98.5 | 1 | Tjerkgaast | Joy R. |
| 61) | 91.1 | 2 | Maastricht | R. 10 | 63) | 98.5 | 1 | Weert | Q-Music Limburg |
| 9) | 91.1 | 40 | Hilversum | Slam! | 20) | 98.7 | 20 | Hoogersmilde | Joy R. |
| 48) | 91.1 | 1 | Gemert | Centraal FM | 23) | 99.1 | 15 | Enschede | 100%NL |
| 9) | 91.2 | 4 | Jirnsum | Slam! | 23) | 99.1 | 3 | Hoogezand | 100%NL |
| 18) | 91.3 | 1 | Hoogezand | Simone FM | 23) | 99.1 | 5 | Tjerkgaast | 100%NL |
| 18) | 91.3 | 1 | Stadskanaal | Simone FM | 32) | 99.1 | 1 | Geleen | Streekomroep START |
| 3) | 91.3 | 70 | Rotterdam | BNR Nieuws R. | 9) | 99.2 | 26 | Breskens | Slam! |
| 3) | 91.3 | 1 | Tilburg | BNR Nieuws R. | 9) | 99.4 | 30 | Mierlo | Slam! |
| 3) | 91.5 | 3 | Driewegen | BNR Nieuws R. | 9) | 99.4 | 1 | Breda | Slam! |
| 3) | 91.5 | 10 | Eys | BNR Nieuws R. | 36) | 99.4 | 2 | Den Haag | R. Decibel |
| 19) | 91.6 | 5 | Amsterdam | R. Veronica | 68) | 99.5 | 2 | Hengelo | R. Ideaal |
| 23) | 91.9 | 1 | Venlo | 100%NL | 9) | 99.6 | 25 | Hoorn | Slam! |
| 23) | 92.1 | 10 | Emmaberg | 100%NL | 36) | 99.6 | 3 | Rotterdam | R. Decibel |
| 11) | 92.4 | 8 | Westdorpe | R. NL | 9) | 99.6 | 6 | Hoogersmilde | Slam! |
| 58) | 92.4 | 4 | Hoogezand | R. Continu | 3) | 99.9 | 1 | Dedemsvaart | BNR Nieuws R. |
| 58) | 92.4 | 1 | Ommen | R. Continu | 3) | 99.9 | 3 | Ugchelen | BNR Nieuws R. |
| 58) | 92.6 | 1 | Emmen | R. Continu | 3) | 99.9 | 27 | Wormer | BNR Nieuws R. |
| 47) | 92.9 | 1 | Wellerooi | Maasland R. | 3) | 100.1 | 60 | IJsselstein | BNR Nieuws R. |
| 44) | 93.0 | 1 | Meppel | R. TV Meppel | 3) | 100.1 | 4 | Nijmegen | BNR Nieuws R. |
| 18) | 93.0 | 2 | Assen | Simone FM | 3) | 100.2 | 20 | Lochem | BNR Nieuws R. |
| 61) | 93.0 | 12 | Westdorpe | R. 10 | 13) | 100.4 | 25 | Westdorpe | QMusic |
| 9) | 93.1 | 1 | Emmen | Slam! | 13) | 100.4 | 7 | Roosendaal | QMusic |
| 11) | 93.1 | 1 | Ommen | R. NL | 13) | 100.4 | 20 | Rotterdam | QMusic |
| 26) | 93.2 | 20 | Jirnsum | Waterstad FM | 13) | 100.4 | 95 | Hoogersmilde | Qmusic |
| 71) | 93.2 | 1 | Eindhoven | R. JND | 13) | 100.4 | 25 | Doetinchem | QMusic |
| 11) | 93.3 | 1 | Enschede | R. NL | 13) | 100.5 | 5 | Wieringerwerf | QMusic |
| 11) | 93.3 | 1 | Loon op Zand | R. NL | 13) | 100.5 | 2 | Nijmegen | QMUsic |
| 61) | 93.3 | 2 | Breskens | R. 10 | 13) | 100.7 | 25 | Breskens | QMusic |
| 69) | 93.3 | 1 | Amsterdam | Ujala R. | 13) | 100.7 | 6 | Hengelo | QMusic |
| 11) | 93.5 | 3 | Markelo | R. NL | 13) | 100.7 | 68 | IJsselstein | QMusic |
| 75) | 93.5 | 1 | Beers | Omroep Land van Cuijk | 13) | 100.7 | 10 | Lichtenvoorde | Qmusic |
| 29) | 93.6 | 3 | Amsterdam | Wild Hit R. | 24) | 101.0 | 93 | Hoogersmilde | Sky R. 101 FM |
| 11) | 93.6 | 1 | Eindhoven | R. NL | 24) | 101.1 | 5 | Nijmegen | Sky R. 101 FM |
| 9) | 93.6 | 6 | Zwolle | Slam! | 24) | 101.2 | 200 | Hilversum | Sky R. 101 FM |
| 9) | 93.7 | 2 | Hoogezand | Slam! | 24) | 101.2 | 20 | Terneuzen | Sky R. 101 FM |
| 9) | 93.7 | 2 | Hengelo | Slam! | 24) | 101.2 | 1 | Driewegen | Sky R. 101 FM |
| 40) | 93.7 | 2 | Leiden | Sleutelstad FM | 24) | 101.2 | 32 | Enschede | Sky R. 101 FM |
| 9) | 93.8 | 17 | Megen | Slam! | 24) | 101.3 | 5 | Roosendaal | Sky R. 101 FM |
| 23) | 93.8 | 1 | Haarlem | 100%NL | 24) | 101.4 | 10 | Deventer | Sky R. 101 FM |
| 15) | 93.9 | 4 | Roosendaal | R. 8FM West Brabant | 24) | 101.5 | 4 | Arnhem | Sky R. 101 FM |
| 19) | 94.0 | 1 | Emmen | R. Veronica | 24) | 101.5 | 8 | Rotterdam | Sky R. 101 FM |
| 72) | 94.0 | 1 | Favoriet FM | Zevenaar | 24) | 101.5 | 7 | Vught | Sky R. 101FM |
| 11) | 94.1 | 1 | Den Bosch | R. NL | 24) | 101.6 | 5 | Mierlo | Sky R. 101 FM |
| 11) | 94.1 | 2 | Tjerkgaast | R. NL | 24) | 101.6 | 3 | Roermond | Sky R. 101 FM |
| 23) | 94.2 | 1 | Hoogersmilde | 100%NL | 24) | 101.7 | 2 | Gilze | Sky R. 101 FM |
| 11) | 94.5 | 1 | Den Helder | R. NL | 18) | 101.7 | 2 | Emmen | Simone FM |
| 23) | 94.9 | 12 | Mierlo | 100%NL | 24) | 101.8 | 2 | Boxtel | Sky R. 101 FM |
| 23) | 95.0 | 2 | Amersfoort | 100%NL | 24) | 101.9 | 8 | Tilburg | Sky R. 101 FM |
| 23) | 95.0 | 4 | Nijmegen | 100%NL | 24) | 101.9 | 36 | Goes | Sky R. 101 FM |
| 9) | 95.2 | 25 | Alphen aan den Rijn | Slam! | 11) | 101.9 | 1 | Zieuwent | R. NL |
| 15) | 95.2 | 1 | Weert | R. 8FM Eindhoven | 14) | 101.9 | 3 | Megen | R. 538 |
| 3) | 95.3 | 20 | Zwolle | BNR Nieuws R. | 14) | 102.1 | 100 | Hilversum | R. 538 |
| 43) | 95.3 | 2 | Scharmer | Regio FM | 14) | 102.2 | 10 | Hoogersmilde | R. 538 |
| 3) | 95.4 | 1 | Emmen | BNR Nieuws R. | 14) | 102.3 | 13 | Alkmaar | R. 538 |
| 3) | 95.4 | 15 | Gilze | BNR Nieuws R | 14) | 102.3 | 40 | De Mortel | R. 538 |
| 3) | 95.5 | 30 | Tjerkgaast | BNR Nieuws R. | 14) | 102.3 | 15 | Lochem | R. 538 |
| 15) | 95.5 | 1 | Mierlo | R. 8FM Eindhoven | 14) | 102.3 | 2 | Roermond | R. 538 |
| 77) | 95.6 | 1 | Rijswijk | Fresh FM | 14) | 102.4 | 1 | Arnhem | R. 538 |
| 77) | 95.7 | 5 | Alphen ad Rijn | Fresh FM | 14) | 102.4 | 1 | Amsterdam | R. 538 |
| 11) | 95.7 | 2 | Meppel | R. NL | 14) | 102.4 | 20 | Westdorpe | R. 538 |

| FM | MHz | kW | Location | Station |
|---|---|---|---|---|
| 14) | 102.4 | 1 | Dedemsvaart | R. 538 |
| 14) | 102.5 | 8 | Tilburg | R. 538 |
| 14) | 102.5 | 100 | Tjerkgaast | R. 538 |
| 14) | 102.5 | 1 | Utrecht | R. 538 |
| 14) | 102.6 | 2 | Nijmegen | R. 538 |
| 14) | 102.6 | 13 | Hengelo | R. 538 |
| 14) | 102.7 | 10 | Emmen | R. 538 |
| 14) | 102.7 | 100 | Rotterdam | R. 538 |
| 14) | 102.9 | 3 | Stadskanaal | R. 538 |
| 19) | 103.0 | 40 | Hilversum | R. Veronica |
| 19) | 103.1 | 20 | De Lutte | R. Veronica |
| 190 | 103.1 | 11 | Markelo | R. Veronica |
| 19) | 103.1 | 8 | Megen | R. Veronica |
| 19) | 103.2 | 40 | Rotterdam | R. Veronica |
| 19) | 103.2 | 3 | Hoorn | R. Veronica |
| 19) | 103.2 | 25 | Hoogersmilde | R. Veronica |
| 19) | 103.2 | 2 | Emmeloord | R. Veronica |
| 19) | 103.3 | 6 | Terneuzen | R. Veronica |
| 19) | 103.4 | 3 | Hoogezand | R. Veronica |
| 19) | 103.5 | 5 | Roosendaal | R. Veronica |
| 61) | 103.6 | 15 | Amsterdam | R. 10 |
| 15) | 103.6 | 10 | Tilburg | R. 8 FM Tilburg |
| 61) | 103.8 | 5 | Emmen | R. 10 |
| 61) | 103.8 | 1 | Goes | R. 10 |
| 61) | 103.8 | 20 | Rotterdam | R. 10 |
| 61) | 103.8 | 10 | Tjerkgaast | R. 10 |
| 61) | 103.9 | 1 | Enschede | R. 10 |
| 61) | 104.0 | 1 | Haarlem | R. 10 |
| 61) | 104.1 | 100 | Arnhem | R. 10 |
| 11) | 104.2 | 3 | Alkmaar | R. NL |
| 11) | 104.3 | 1 | Breda | R. NL |
| 23) | 104.4 | 50 | Hilversum | 100%NL |
| 11) | 104.4 | 2 | Groningen | R. NL |
| 23) | 104.6 | 87 | Rotterdam | 100%NL |
| 45) | 104.8 | 1 | Zuidwolde | DNO. |
| 75) | 105.4 | 1 | Coevorden | ZO!34 |
| 74) | 106.6 | 1 | Hippolytushoef | Noordkop R. |
| 34) | 106.7 | 1 | Lochem | Achterhoek FM |
| + 445 stns below 1kW | | | | |

**Addresses and other information:**
**3)** Prins Bernhardplein 173 1097BL Amsterdam or Postbus 651, 1000 AR Amsterdam ☎ +31 20 592 8500 **E:** info@bnr.nl **W:** bnr.nl **–9)** Postbus 34 1400AA Bussum ☎ +31 88 101 00 10 **E:** info@slam.nl **W:** slam.nl – **11)** Postbus 248, 8600AE Sneek ☎ +31 515 432360 **W:** radionl.fm **E:** info@radionl.fm and techniek@radionl.fm **–13)** De Kauwgomballenfabriek, Paul van Vlissingenstraat 10D, 1096BK Amsterdam ☎ +31 20 7970 500 **E:** info@qmusic.nl **W:** qmusic.nl **–14)** Postbus 2538, 1200 CM Hilversum ☎ +31 35 5385538 **W:** 538.nl **– 15)** Postbus 8, 5201 AA Den Bosch ☎ +31 73 6312003 **W:** radio8fm.nl **E:** techniek@radio8fm.nl and info@radio8fm.nl **–** 18) Nijbracht 138, 7821CE Emmen ☎ +31 591 652 025 **E:** info@simonefm.nl **W:** simone.nl **– 19)** Postbus 2538, 1200CM Hilversum ☎ +31 35 625 2700 **E:** info@radioveronica.nl **W:** radioveronica.nl **– 20)** Postbus 248, 8600AE Sneek ☎ +31 515 432360 **W:** joyradio.nl **E:** techniek@joyradio.nl **– 23)** Postbus 34, 1400AA Bussum ☎ +31 88 101 00 10 **E:** info@100p.nl **W:** 100p.nl **– 24)** Postbus 2538, 1200CM Hilversum ☎ +31 35 skyradio.nl **W:** skyradio.nl **26)** Postbus 248, 8600AE Sneek ☎ +31 515 432 360 **E:** info@waterstadfm.nl techniek@waterstadfm.nl **W:** waterstadfm.nl**–** **29)** Maalderij 21E, Amstelveen ☎ +31 20 447 0030 **W:** wildhitradio.nl **E:** info@wildhitradio.nl **– 30)** Raadhuisstraat 5, 5854AX Nieuwbergen ☎ +31 485 34 1939 **W:** maaslandradio.nl **E:** kantoor@maaslandradio.nl **– 32)** Postbus 114, 6160AC Geleen ☎ +31 46 4747555 🖃 +31 4748493 **W:** streekomroepstart.nl **E:** redactie@streekomroepstart.nl **– 34)** Wiersserbroekweg 5a, 7251LG Vorden ☎ +31 575 556560 **E:** info@achterhoekfm.nl **W:** achterhoekfm.nl **– 36)** Postbus 94443, 1090GK Amsterdam ☎ +31 62 064 2229 **W:** radiodecibel.nl **E:** info@radiodecibel.nl **–40)** Evertsenstraat 69/Y 2315SK Leiden ☎ +31 71 523 5907 **W:** sleutelstad.nl **E:** info@sleutelstad.nl **– 43)** Kapelstraat 9, 9781GK Bedum **W:** regiofm.info **E:** studio@regiofm.info ☎ +31 50 2059 205**– 44)** Postbus 510, 7940AM Meppel ☎ +31 522 241404 **W:** rtvmeppel.nl **E:** secretariaat@rtvmeppel.nl **– 45)** Postbus 8, 7920AA Zuidwolde ☎ +31 528 373444 **W:** wijzijndno.nl **–48)** St. Annastraat 60, 5421KC Gemert ☎ +31 492 366833 **W:** omroepcentraal.nl **E:** redactie@omroepcentraal.nl (06.00-18.00); **W:** cyberradio.co.uk **E:** captain@cyberhothits.com ; **Radio Seagull** in English(1800-0600) PO Box 24 8860AA Harlingen **W:** radioseagull.com **E:** info@radioseagull.com **– 53)** Zandstraat 36, 3901CM Veenendaal 24h rlg pgr.☎ +31 909 123 1008 **W:** grootnieuwsradio.nl **E:** info@grootnieuwsradio.nl.**Transmissions will end on January 1ˢᵗ, 2019– 57)** Tractieweg 41, Studio E, , 3534AP Utrecht ☎ +31 303 5443 **W:** sublimefm.nl **E:** info@sublime.nl **– 58)** Exloërkijl Zuid 38, 9571AC

Tweede Exloërmond ☎ +31 909 9223 🖃 +31 599 67 11 02 **W:** radiocontinu.nl **E:** studio@radiocontinu.– **59)** Lloydstraat 23, 3024EA Rotterdam ☎ +31 10 820 1702 **W:** openrotterdam.nl **E:** info@openrotterdam.nl **- 60)** Newtonstraat 25, 2562KC Den Haag ☎ +31 70 365 2247 and +31 70 362 2077 24 hr in Sarnami Hindustani and Dutch **W:** vahonfm.nl **E:** info@vahonfm.nl QSL-manager: Koos Wijnants, qsl.vahon@ziggo.nl**– 61)** Postbus 2538, 1200CM Hilversum ☎ +31 909 300 10 10 **W:** radio10.nl **E:** info@radio10.nl**– 62)** Van Persijnstraat 19a, 3811LS Amersfoort ☎ +31 33 8893 492 **W:** amersfoort-eemland1.nl **E:** redactie@mediagroep-eva.nl **–66)** Postbus 841, 2700AV Zoetermeer ☎ +31 79 331 7287 **E:** studio@zfmzoetermeer.nl **W:** zfmzoetermeer.nl **– 68)** Postbus 50, 7020AB Zelhem .☎ +31 314 62 40 02 🖃 +31 314 624 202 **W:** radioideaal.nl **E:** redactie@ideaal.org and info@ideaal.org **– 69)** Hoogoord 51B 1102CC Amsterdam ☎ +31 20 4 09 08 07 **E:** info@ujala.nl **W:** ujala.nl **–71)** IBCweg 3n, 5683PK Best ☎ +31 85 760 99 32 **W:** radiojnd.nl **– 72)** Ringbaan Zuid 8b, , 6905DB Zevenaar ☎ +31 316 342 242 **W:** rtv-favoriet.nl **E:** redactie@rtv-favoriet.nl **–74)** Rozenlaantje 8, 1777HR Hippolytushoef, ☎ +31 227 591 629 **W:** noordkopnieuws.nl **E:** info@rtvnoordkop.nl **– 75)** Breestraat 1D, 5845AX Sint Anthonis, ☎ +31 485 381 777 **W:** omroeplvc.nl **E:** info@omroeplvc.nl - **75)** Postbus 34, 7800AA Emmen ☎ +31 591 392 220 **W:** zo34.nl **E:** info@zo34.nl techniek@zo34.nl - **76)** **W:** coastlinefm.nl **E:** studio@coastlinefm.nl info@coastlinefm.nl **– 77)** **W:** sbradio.nl

**Military stations**

| FM | MHz | kW | Location | Station |
|---|---|---|---|---|
| 2) | 87.7 | 0.05 | Maastricht | BFBS * |
| 1) | 96.9 | 1.6 | Brunssum, Schinnen | AFN The Eagle |
| 2) | 90.2 | 0.05 | Brunssum | BFBS |
| 1) | 99.7 | 0.3 | Brunssum, Schinnen | AFN The Eagle |
| 1) | 107.9 | 0.1 | Zeeland, Volkel | AFN The Eagle |
| * reported to be off the air | | | | |

**Addresses & other information:**
**1) W:** afneurope.net **D.Prgr:** 24h – **2)** ☎ +44 1494 874 461 🖃 +44 2037 550 **E:** info@bfbs.com **W:** forces.net/radio **D.Prgr:** Relays BFBS prgrs Germany

## NEW CALEDONIA (France)

**L.T:** UTC +11h — **Pop:** 256,275 — **Pr.L:** French, New Caledonian languages — **E.C:** 50Hz, 220V — **ITU:** NCL

### CONSEIL SUPÉRIEUR DE L'AUDIOVISUEL
**Comité territorial de l'audiovisuel de Nouvelle-Calédonie et des Iles Wallis-et-Futuna**
🖃1, rue du Contre-Amiral Joseph Bouzet-Nouville, B.P. 739, 98845 Nouméa ☎+687 254051 🖃 +687 254085 **W:** csa.fr **E:** ctr.noumea.csa@lagoon.nc
Regulator of broadcasting for New Caledonia & Wallis and Futuna

| FM | | MHz | kW | Station |
|---|---|---|---|---|
| 1) | Port Boisé-Oungoné | 88.0 | 1 | Nouvelle Calédonie la 1ère |
| 1) | Mont Do-Boulouparis | 88.0 | 2.2 | Nouvelle Calédonie la 1ère |
| 1) | Ouaco/Tsiba | 88.0 | 1.2 | Nouvelle Calédonie la 1ère |
| 1) | Aoupinie/Ponerihouen | 89.0 | 3 | Nouvelle Calédonie la 1ère |
| 1) | Nouméa-Mt Coffyn | 89.0 | 2.3 | Nouvelle Calédonie la 1ère |
| 1) | Ouvéa-Pte Gervaise | 89.5 | 1.3 | Nouvelle Calédonie la 1ère |
| 1) | Koné-Kaféaté | 90.0 | 3 | Nouvelle Calédonie la 1ère |
| 1) | Nouméa -Mont Koghis | 90.0 | 5 | Nouvelle Calédonie la 1ère |
| 1) | Kone/Mont Kafeate | 90.0 | 3.5 | Nouvelle Calédonie la 1ère |
| 1) | Lifou/Nawagued | 90.5 | 11 | Nouvelle Calédonie la 1ère |
| 1) | Koumac/Dôme de Tiebaghi | 91.0 | 4 | Nouvelle Calédonie la 1ère |
| 1) | Houaïlou/Pic Ba | 91.0 | 2 | Nouvelle Calédonie la 1ère |
| 1) | Lifou-Waé | 91.5 | 2 | Nouvelle Calédonie la 1ère |
| 1) | Noumea/Mont Coffyn | 91.5 | 2.2 | RFO 3 |
| 1) | Houailou-Pic Ba | 91.0 | 2.1 | Nouvelle Calédonie la 1ère |
| 1) | Koumac-Tiébaghi | 91.0 | 4.3 | Nouvelle Calédonie la 1ère |
| 1) | Bourail-Château d'Eau | 91.0 | 1.3 | Nouvelle Calédonie la 1ère |
| 2) | Bouloupari | 92.0 | 2.2 | France Inter |
| 2) | Yaté | 92.0 | 3 | France Inter |
| 2) | Ponerihouen | 93.0 | 3 | France Inter |
| 2) | Nouméa -Mont Coffyn | 93.0 | 2.2 | France Inter |
| 3) | Nouméa -Mont Coffyn | 93.5 | 2 | NRJ |
| 2) | Kone | 94.0 | 3.5 | France Inter |
| 2) | Nouméa -Mont Koghis | 94.0 | 5 | France Inter |
| 2) | Lifou | 94.5 | 11 | France Inter |
| 5) | Dumbéa (Nouméa) | 95.0 | 1 | R. Océane |
| 5) | Mont Do/ Boulupari | 96.0 | 2.2 | R. Djiido |
| 5) | Aoupinie/Ponerihouen | 97.0 | 1.5 | R. Djiido |
| 5) | Nouméa/Tour de Montravel | 97.4 | 1.5 | R. Djiido |
| 6) | Koné | 98.0 | 1 | R. Rythme Bleu |
| 6) | Nouméa -Mont Koghis | 98.0 | 1.5 | R. Rythme Bleu |
| 5) | Lifou | 98.5 | 1.5 | R. Djiido |

| FM | MHz | kW | Station |
|---|---|---|---|
| 6) Koumac | 99.0 | 1.5 | R. Rythme Bleu |
| 6) Bouloupari | 100.0 | 1 | R. Rythme Bleu |
| 6) Goro | 100.0 | 1 | R. Rythme Bleu |
| 6) Nouméa | 100.4 | 1.5 | R. Rythme Bleu |
| 6) Poya | 101.0 | 1 | R. Rythme Bleu |
| 5) Dumbéa (Nouméa) | 102.0 | 1.5 | R. Djiido |
| 5) Kone/Mont Kafeate | 102.0 | 1 | R. Djiido |
| 5) Lifou | 102.5 | 1.5 | R. Rythme Bleu |
| 5) Koumac | 103.0 | 1.5 | R. Djiido |

+ 55 stations less than 1kw

**Addresses & other information:**
**1) Nouvelle Calédonie La Première (Pub)** 1 rue Maréchal Leclerc, Mt Coffyn, B.P. G3, 98848 Nouméa Cedex ☎ +687 239907 ▤ +687 239975 **W:** la1ere.francetvinfo.fr/nouvellecaledonie/rado (live streaming) **L.P:** Reg. Dir: Jean Phillipe Pascal **D.Prgr:** 24h in French and local languages (local and Réseau Outre-Mer Première common prgr satellite feed) – **2) Radio France Inter (Pub):** satellite relay from Paris 24h in French – **3) NRJ,** 41 rue de Sébastopol, B.P G5, 98848 Nouméa Cedex ☎ +687 279592 ▤ +687 279447 **W:** nrj.nc; facebook.com/NRJ. Nouvelle.Caledonie 24h – **4) R. Océane,** 282 rue Jacques Lékawé, 7KM, 98800 Nouméa ☎ +687 410095 ▤+687 410099 **L.P:** President, Dumbéa Communications – Robert Lucas, Dir: Lucia Alikifaitunu **E:** contact@oceanefm.nc **W:** oceanefm.nc 24h – **5) R. Djiido,** 31 rue Édouard Unger, 98800 Nouméa ☎ + 687 253515 ▤ +687 272187 **W:** radiodjiido.nc; facebook.com/RDK.kanalk/ **E:** radiodjiido@radiodjiido. nc **L.P:** Thierry Kameremoin 24h – **6) R. Rythme Bleu,** 4 Avenue de Sebastopol, 98800 Nouméa, B.P 578, 98845 Nouméa Cedex ☎ +687 254646 ▤ +687 284928 **W:** rrb.nc **E:** rrb@lagoon.nc **L.P:** Dir: Elizabeth Nouar **Prgr:** local + prgrs from Europe 1. 24h

## NEW ZEALAND

**L.T:** UTC +12h (30 Sep 18-7 Apr 19, 29 Sep 19-5 Apr 20: +13h) — **Pop:** 4.75million — **Pr.L:** English, Maori, Samoan — **E.C:** 50Hz, 230V — **ITU:** NZL

### RADIO SPECTRUM MANAGEMENT GROUP
**Ministry of Business, Innovation & Employment**
▤ P.O. Box 2847, Wellington 6140 ☎ +64 4 962 2603 NZ Freephone 0508 776 463 ▤ +64 4 978 3162 **W:** rsm.govt.nz **E:** info@rsm.govt. nz **L.P:** Mgr Policy Planning: Len Starling Mgr Licensing: Siegmund Wieser. **RSMG** is the statutory authority responsible for radio spectrum licensing & administration.

### BROADCASTING STANDARDS AUTHORITY
▤ P.O. Box 9213, Marion Square, Wellington 6141 ☎ +64 4 382 9508 ▤+64 4 382 9543 NZ Freephone 0800 366 996 **W:** bsa.govt.nz **E:** info@ bsa.govt.nz **L.P:** CE: Belinda Moffat. The BSA statutory authority has codes of broadc. practice and a complaints procedure.

### NEW ZEALAND ON AIR
▤ P.O. Box 9744, Marion Square, Wellington 6141 ☎ +64 4 382 9524 ▤ +64 4 382 9546 **W:** nzonair.govt.nz **E:** info@nzonair.govt.nz **L.P:** CE: Jane Wrightson. **NZOA** is the operational funding agency for R. New Zealand, Community Access R., R. Reading Service, National Pacific R. Trust, Samoan Capital R., [bNet] and TV and New Media.

### RADIO NEW ZEALAND (Non-commercial, Pub)
▤ P.O. Box 123, Wellington 6140 ☎ +64 4 474 1999 ▤ +64 4 474 1730 **W:** radionz.co.nz **L.P:** CE: Paul Thompson; Infrastructure Mgr: Matthew Finn; Trs: Gary Fowles
**Network Stations:** RNZ National (**N**), RNZ Concert (**C**), RNZ AM Network (**AM**). For full FM listings see website. **Prgr:** 24h from Wellington studios except for RNZ AM Network which only broadc. when Parliament in session [rel. commercial stn Star at other times]. **N:** RNZ News bulletins.
**Network Stations:**

| MW | kHz | kW | Net | MW | kHz | kW | Net |
|---|---|---|---|---|---|---|---|
| Wellington | 567 | 50 | N | Whangarei | 837 | 2.5 | N |
| Hawkes Bay | 630 | 10 | N | Auckland | 882 | 10 | AM |
| Alexandra | 639 | 2 | N | Dunedin | 900 | 6 | AM |
| Tauranga | 657 | 10 | AM | Hawkes Bay | 909 | 5 | AM |
| Wellington | 657 | 50 | AM | New Plymouth | 918 | 2.5 | N |
| Christchurch | 675 | 10 | N | Timaru | 918 | 2.5 | N |
| Invercargill | 720 | 10 | N | Christchurch | 963 | 10 | AM |
| Tokoroa | 729 | 2.5 | N | Kaikohe | 981 | 2 | N |
| Auckland | 756 | 10 | N | Masterton | 1071 | 2.5 | N |
| Dunedin | 810 | 10 | N | Nelson | 1116 | 2.5 | N |
| Tauranga | 819 | 10 | N | Queenstown | 1134 | 2 | N |
| Kaitaia | 837 | 2 | N | Hamilton | 1143 | 2.5 | N |

| MW | kHz | kW | Net | MW | kHz | kW | Net |
|---|---|---|---|---|---|---|---|
| Rotorua | 1188 | 0.4 | N | Palmerston Nth | 1449 | 2 | N |
| Gisborne | 1314 | 2 | N | Westport | 1458 | 2.5 | N |
| Invercargill | 1314 | 6 | AM | Hamilton | 1494 | 3 | AM |

+ = synchronised

| FM (MHz) | N | C | FM (MHz) | N | C |
|---|---|---|---|---|---|
| Far North | 101.1/101.5 | 100.3/98.3 | Kapiti Coast | 101.5 | 98.3 |
| Whangarei | 101.2/104.4 | 100.4/105.2 | Wairarapa | 101.5 | 99.1 |
| Auckland | 101.4 | 92.6 | Wellington | 101.3/101.7 | 92.5/96.1 |
| Hamilton | 101.0 | 91.4 | Blenheim | 101.7 | 99.3 |
| Tauranga | 101.0 | 91.4 | Nelson | 101.6 | 91.2 |
| Whakatane | 101.7 | 95.3 | Christchurch | 101.7 | *89.7 |
| Rotorua | 101.5 | 90.3 | Greymouth | 101.0 | 95.5 |
| Gisborne | 101.3 | 97.3 | Westport | - | 98.9 |
| Taupo | 101.6/104.8 | 98.4 | Ashburton | 101.3 | - |
| New Plymouth | 101.0 | 91.6 | Timaru | 101.1 | 99.5 |
| Hawkes Bay | 101.5 | 91.1 | Dunedin | 101.4 | **92.6 |
| Whanganui | 101.6 | 99.2 | Queenstown | 101.6 | 98.4 |
| Palmerston N. | 101.0 | 89.0 | Invercargill | 101.2 | 90.0 |

*also on 99.7, 95.1, **also on 99.0, 99.4
Low powered network stations at Russell (C), Te Kuiti (N), Kapiti Coast (N), Takaka (N), Tekapo (N), Twizel (N), Omarama (N), Wanaka (C), Alexandra (N), Te Anau (N) & Milford Sound (N).

**EXTERNAL SERVICE: Radio New Zealand Int.**
- see International broadcasting section

### COMMUNITY ACCESS RADIO
12 independent stns affiliated to the **Association of Community Access Broadcasters [ACAB]** **W:** acab.org.nz **E:** info@acab.org. nz. Each stn serves local urban communities with a variety of ethnic language, cultural and comm. group prgrs. BBC WS is carried overnight on several stns. **H. of tr:** 24h

| MW | KHz | kW | Station |
|---|---|---|---|
| 2) Palmerston Nth | 999 | 1.5 | Manawatu Peoples R. |
| 4) Hawkes Bay | 1431 | 2 | R. Kidnappers |
| 5) Dunedin | 1575 | 2.5 | OAR 105.4FM |
| **FM** | **MHz** | **kW** | **Station** |
| 6) Blenheim | 88.9 | 0.1 | Fresh FM |
| 3) Hamilton | 89.0 | 5 | Free FM89 |
| 7) Masterton | 92.7 | 0.8 | Arrow FM |
| 6) Takaka | 95.0 | 0.1 | Fresh FM |
| 9) Invercargill | 96.4 | 3.2 | R. Southland |
| 8) Christchurch | 96.9 | 3.5 | Plains FM |
| 12) New Plymouth | 104.4 | 5 | Access R. Taranaki |
| 10) Auckland | 104.6 | 15.8 | Planet FM |
| 4) Hawkes Bay | 104.7 | 4 | R. Kidnappers |
| 11) Kapiti Coast | 104.7 | 0.63 | Coast Access R. |
| 6) Nelson | 104.8 | 1.6 | Fresh FM // 107.2 |
| 5) Dunedin | 105.4 | 8 | OAR 105.4FM |
| 1) Wellington | 106.1 | 2.5 | Wellington Access R. |

**Addresses & other information**
**1)** P.O. Box 9073, Marion Square, Wellington 6141 ☎ +64 4 385 7210 **W:** accessradio.org.nz **E:** info@accessradio.org.nz – **2)** P.O. Box 4666, Manawatu Mail Centre, Palmerston North 4442 ☎+64 6 357 9340 **W:** accessmanawatu.co.nz **E:** info@MPR.nz **Prgr:** BBC WS overnight 1200-2100 overnight daily – **3)** P.O. Box 110, Waikato Mail Centre, Hamilton 3240 ☎ +64 7 834 2170 **W:** freefm.org.nz **E:** info@freefm.org.nz – **4)** P.O. Box 680, Hastings 4156 ☎+64 6 878 8710 **W:** radiokidnappers.org. nz **E:** chris@radiokidnappers.org.nz – **5)** 301 Moray Place, Dunedin ☎ +64 3 471 6161 **W:** oar.org.nz **E:** manager@oar.org.nz **Mgr: Prgr:** BBC WS overnight 1100-1800 daily – **6)** 87 Atawhai Drive, Nelson 7010 ☎ +64 3 546 9891 **W:** freshfm.net **E:** nelson@freshfm.net – **7)** 92 Queen Street, Masterton ☎ +64 6 378 0255 **W:** arrowfm.co.nz **E:** quiver@ arrowfm.co.nz – **8)** 154 Madras Street, Christchurch ☎ +64 3 365 7997 **W:** plainsfm.org.nz **E:** info@plainsfm.org.nz **Prgr:** BBC WS overnight Su-Th 1200-1900 Fri-Sat -1800 – **9)** P.O. Box 1, Invercargill ☎ +64 3 218 9891 ▤ +64 3 214 1425 **W:** radiosouthland.org.nz **E:** darren@ radiosouthland.org.nz **Prgr:** BBC WS overnight Su-Th 1200-1900 Fri -1930, Sat -2000 – **10)** P.O. Box 44215, Pt Chevalier, Auckland 1246 ☎ +64 9 815 8600 **W:** planetaudio.org.nz **E:** info@planetaudio.org.nz – **11)** P.O. Box 213, Waikanae ☎/▤ +64 4 293 4838 **W:** coastaccessradio. org.nz **E:** accessradio.kapiti@xtra.co.nz – **12)** PO Box 445, Taranaki Mail Centre, New Plymouth 4340 ☎ 06 751 3720 **W:** accessradiotaranaki. com **E:** alessandra@accessradiotaranaki.com

### COMMUNITY RADIO
Independent unaffiliated community stns.

| FM | MHz | kW | Station |
|---|---|---|---|
| 1) Raglan | 98.1 | 0.06 | Raglan Community R. |
| 4) Dargaville | 98.6 | 0.5 | Big River FM |

| FM | MHz | kW | Station |
|---|---|---|---|
| 2) Hamner | 103.7 | 0.3 | Compass FM |
| 2) Rangiora | 104.9 | 4 | Compass FM |
| 3) Eketahuna | 106.5 | 0.5 | R. Eketahuna |

**Addresses & other information**
**1)** Municipal Bldgs, 41 Bow St, Raglan ☎ +64 7 825 2981 **W:** raglanradio.com **E:** manager@raglanradio.com – **2)** P.O. Box 27, Rangiora 7440 ☎ +64 3 313 7101 **W:** compassfm.org.nz **E:** manager@compassfm.org.nz **Ann:** 'The Voices of North Canterbury' – **3)** Main St, Eketahuna ☎ 06 375 8080 **W:** radioeketahuna.co.nz **E:** admin@radioeketahuna.co.nz **Net:** 88.3 – 4) P O Box 199, Dargaville 0310 ☎ +64 9 439 3003 **W:** bigriverfm.co.nz **E:** office@bigriverfm.co.nz

## TE MANGAI PAHO
✉ P.O. Box 10004, Wellington 6143 ☎ +64 4 915 0700 🖷 +64 4 915 0701 **W:** tmp.govt.nz **E:** radio@tmp.govt.nz **L.P:** Mgr Radio Portfolio: Carl Goldsmith.
Te Mângai Pâho is the broadc. funding agency providing operational funding to 21 independent community Mâori radio stns connected to the iwi radio distribution system, Punga.net: an internet distribution system for sharing radio prgrs, audio and data between the netw. of Mâori radio stns, Mâori TV Service and other system users.

## MAORI RADIO STATIONS (Comm.)

| MW | KHz | kW | Station |
|---|---|---|---|
| 1) Ruatoria | 585 | 2 | R.Ngâti Porou |
| 2) Auckland | 603 | 5 | R. Waatea |
| 3) Hawkes Bay | 765 | 2.5 | R. Kahungunu |
| 4) Wellington | 1161 | 5 | Te Úpoko o te Ika |
| 5) Tauranga | 1440 | 0.2 | Moana Radio |

| FM | MHz | kW | Station |
|---|---|---|---|
| 6) Rotorua | 88.7 | 0.8 | Te Arawa FM |
| 8) Timaru | 89.1 | 5 | Tahu FM |
| 7) Palmerston Nth | 89.8 | 1 | Kia Ora FM |
| 8) Christchurch | 90.5 | 15.8 | Tahu FM |
| 8) Kaikoura | 90.7 | 0.16 | Tahu FM |
| 11) Gisborne | 91.7 | 0.8 | Turanga FM |
| 17) Taupo | 92.0 | 4 | Tüwharetoa FM |
| 20) Coromandel | 92.2 | 0.2 | Nga Iwi FM |
| 20) Thames | 92.4 | 4 | Nga Iwi FM |
| 20) Waihi | 92.8 | 0.2 | Nga Iwi FM |
| 11) Gisborne | 93.3 | 1.6 | Turanga FM |
| 6) Rotoiti | 93.9 | 0.4 | Te Arawa FM |
| 3) Hawkes Bay | 94.3 | 4 | R. Kahungunu |
| 14) New Plymouth | 94.8 | 2 | Te Korimako o Taranaki |
| 16) Lower Hutt | 94.9 | 1 | Atiawa Toa FM |
| 8) Dunedin | 95.0 | 3 | Tahu FM |
| 15) Ngaruwahia | 95.4 | 7.9 | R.Tainui |
| 9) Tokoroa | 95.7 | 1 | Raukawa FM |
| 18) Whakatane | 96.9 | 4 | Tümeke FM |
| 13) Kaitaia | 97.1 | 4 | Te Hiku 97.1 FM |
| 10) Mangamuka | 97.5 | 6.3 | Tautoko FM |
| 17) Turangi | 97.6 | 4 | Tüwharetoa FM |
| 5) Tauranga | 98.2 | 0.8 | Moana Radio |
| 14) Opunake | 98.4 | 2 | Te Korimako o Taranaki |
| 19) Whangarei | 99.1 | 10 | Ngâti Hine FM |
| 10) Mangamuka | 99.5 | 6 | Tautoko FM |
| 19) Whangarei | 99.6 | 0.8 | Ngâti Hine FM |
| 12) Te Kuiti | 99.6 | 0.8 | Maniapoto FM |
| 8) Invercargill | 99.6 | 8 | Tahu FM |
| 20) Paeroa | 99.6 | 0.1 | Nga Iwi FM |
| 21) Whanganui | 100.0 | 0.8 | Awa FM |
| 16) Wellington | 100.9 | 1.6 | Atiawa Toa FM |
| 13) Kaitaia | 104.3 | 4 | Sunshine FM |
| 18) Whakatane | 106.5 | 1.6 | Sun FM |

**Addresses & other information (all MHz):**
**1)** P.O. Box 55, Ruatoria 4043 ☎ +64 6 864 8020 **W:** radiongatiporou.com **E:** manager@radiongatiporou.co.nz **FM:** 89.3/90.5/98.5/105.3/106.5 – **2)** P.O. Box 43157, Mangere, Manukau 2153 ☎ +64 9 275 9070 **W:** waateanews.com **E:** bernie@waatea603am.co.nz **FM:** 96.6 – **3)** P.O. Box 2613, Hastings 4153 ☎ +64 6 872 8943 **W:** radiokahungunu.co.nz **E:** pat@radio-kahungunu.co.nz **FM:** 94.3 – **4)** P.O. Box 11812, Manners Street, Wellington 6142 ☎ +64 4 801 5002 **W:** teupoko.co.nz **E:** info@teupoko.co.nz – **5)** P. O. Box 382, Seventh Avenue, Tauranga 3140 ☎ +64 7 571 0009 **W:** moanaradio.co.nz **E:** charlie@moanaradio.co.nz **FM:** Moana 98.2 FM – **6)** P.O. Box 883, Rotorua 3040 ☎ +64 7 349 2959 **W:** tearawaonline.com **E:** rawiri@tearawafm.com – **7)** P.O. Box 1341, Palmerston North Central, Palmerston North 4440 ☎ +64 6 353 1881 **W:** kiaorafm898.maori.nz **E:** danielle@rangitaane.co.nz – **8)** P.O. Box 13469, Armagh, Christchurch 8141 ☎ +64 3 371 3905 🖷 +64 3 371 3901 **W:** tahufm.com **E:** blade_jones@ngaitahu.iwi.nz **FM Netw.:** 89.1/90.7/95.0/99.6 – **9)** P.O. Box 842, Tokoroa 3444 ☎ +64 7 886

---

0127 **W:** raukawafm.co.nz **E:** - **FM Netw.:** 90.6/93.2 – **10)** 4317 SH1, Mangamuka, Okaihau 0476 ☎+64 9 401 8991 **W:** tautokofm.com **E:** radiotautoko@tautokofm.com **FM Netw.:** 97.2/97.5/98.1/99.5 – **11)** P.O. Box 1224, Gisborne 4040 ☎ +64 6 868 6821 **W:** turangafm.co.nz **E:** fred@turangafm.maori.nz **FM Netw.:** 95.7/98.1 – **12)** P.O. Box 416, Te Kuiti 3941 ☎ +64 7 878 1160 **W:** mfmradio.co.nz **E:** jaqui@mfmradio.co.nz **FM Netw.:** 91.8/92.7/99.6/106.0 – **13)** P.O. Box 458, Kaitaia 0441 ☎ +64 9 408 3944 **W:** te-hiku-radio/ **E:** peterlucas@tehiku.co.nz **FM:** 97.1FM, 104.3FM – **14)** P.O. Box 4232, Taranaki Mail Centre, New Plymouth 4340 ☎+ 64 6 757 9055 🖷+64 6 757 9093 **W:** tekorimako.co.nz **E:** tipene@tekorimako.co.nz – **15)** P.O. Box 208, Ngaruawahia 3742 ☎ +64 7 824 5650 **W:** facebook.com/radiotainui **E:** trina@radiotainui.co.nz **FM Netw.:** 96.5/106.4 – **16)** P.O. Box 36111, Wellington Mail Centre, Lower Hutt 5043 ☎+64 4 569 7993 **W:** atiawatoafm.co.nz **E:** info@atiawa.co.nz – **17)** PO Box 198, Turangi 3334 ☎+64 7 386 0935 **W:** tuwharetoafm.co.nz **E:** manager@tuwharetoafm.co.nz **FM Netw.:** 89.4/95.1/Taupo 97.6/Taihape 100.6 – **18)** P.O. Box 2090, Kopeopeo, Whakatane 3159 ☎+64 7 308 0403 **W:** tumekefm.co.nz **E:** jarrod@sunfm.co.nz – **19)** P.O. Box 1127, Whangarei 0140 ☎ +64 9 438 6115 **W:** ngatihinefm.co.nz **E:** manager@ngatihinefm.co.nz – **20)** P.O. Box 135, Paeroa 3640 ☎+ 64 7 862 6247 **W:** ngaiwifm.co.nz **E:** nifm@ngaiwifm.co.nz **FM Netw.:** 92.2/92.4/92.7/92.8/99.6/105.1 – **21)** PO Box 430, Whanganui 4540 ☎+ 64 6 347 1402 **W:** awafm.co.nz **FM Netw.:** 91.0/93.5

## NATIONAL PACIFIC R. TRUST (PACIFIC MEDIA NETW., Comm)
✉ 2 Osterley Way, Manukau, Auckland, NZ, 2241 ☎+64 9 361 6656 🖷+64 9 361 3966 **W:** niufm.com **E:** info@niufm.com **LP:** CE in Command Tony Amos CE on Watch Lefoa Henry Jenkins Dep CE Patrick Lino **Stns: 531PI W** 531pi.com **E:** info@radio531pi.com Market: older Pacific people **NiuFM Auckland 103.8** Market: Pacific youth in Auckland **NiuFM Network** Market: Pacific youth nationwide **Prgr: 531PI** 24/7 English/individual Pacific languages **NiuFM** 24/7pan-Pacific English 1800-0600 daily 10 Pacific languages 0600-1800 daily. **Other:** Pacific R. News **W:** pacificradionews.com Independent charitable trust funded by NZ On Air and Ministry for Culture & Heritage.
**MW: 531PI** Auckland 531Khz 5kW
**FM: NiuFM Network**

| FM | MHz | kW | FM | MHz | kW |
|---|---|---|---|---|---|
| Whangarei | 103.6 | 0.4 | Manawatu | 103.4 | 10 |
| Auckland | 103.8 | 15.8 | Wellington | 103.7 | 7.9 |
| Hamilton | 103.4 | 79.4 | Christchurch | 104.1 | 15.8 |
| Rotorua | 103.9 | 0.8 | Wellington | 104.1 | 0.8 |
| Taupo | 104.0 | 1.6 | Dunedin | 103.8 | 4 |
| Taranaki | 103.6 | 5 | Invercargill | 103.6 | 4 |
| Hawkes Bay | 103.9 | 6.3 | | | |

## RADIO BROADCASTERS ASSOCIATION
✉ PO Box 8049, Auckland, New Zealand, 1150 ☎ +64 9 378 0788 **W:** rba.co.nz **E:** jana@rba.co.nz **L.P:** CE: Jana Rangooni. **RBA** represents NZ commercial radio industry and sponsors NZ Radio Awards.

## MAJOR COMMERCIAL NETWORKS
Full FM listings at individual netw. or local brand websites.

**MEDIAWORKS,** Level 2, 239 Ponsonby Road, Ponsonby, Auckland 1011. ✉ P.O. Box 8880, Symonds Street, Auckland 1150 ☎ 64 9 928 9300 🖷 +64 9 373 4000 **W:** mediaworks.co.nz **LP:** Group CEO Mark Wheldon, CEO MediaWorks Radio: Wendy Palmer.
**Prgrs:** 24h **Owner: MediaWorks Holdings Ltd**
**Netw. Brands** ✉ P.O. Box 47560, Ponsonby, Auckland 1144 ☎ +64 9 928 9000 🖷 +64 9 361 1677 **Radio LIVE:** ✉ P.O. Box 8880, Symonds Street, Auckland 1150 ☎+64 9 928 9270 🖷 +64 9 360 0390 **W:** radiolive.co.nz **George FM:** ✉ P.O. Box 47664, Ponsonby, Auckland 1144 ☎ +64 9 928 9150 🖷 +64 9 360 0044 **W:** georgefm.co.nz. **Prgr:** 24h from Auckland studios. **N:** R. LIVE. **Other netw. brands: The Edge W:** theedge.co.nz – **The Rock W:** therock.co.nz – **The Sound W:** thesound.co.nz – **Mai FM W:** maifm.co.nz – **Magic W:** magic.co.nz.

| MW | Khz | kW | Station | | MW | Khz | kW | Station |
|---|---|---|---|---|---|---|---|---|
| Alexandra | 531 | 2 | MORE FM | L | Tauranga | 1107 | 1 | R. Live | N |
| Auckland | 702 | 10 | Magic | N | Wellington | 1233 | 1 | R.LIVE | N |
| Christchurch | 738 | 5 | Magic | N | Dunedin | 1305 | 2.5 | R. Dunedin | L |
| Wellington | 891 | 5 | Magic | N | Queenstown | 1359 | 1 | MORE FM | L |
| Rotorua | 1107 | 1 | R. Live | N | Hawkes Bay | 1368 | 1 | R.LIVE | N |

**L** = Local **N** = Network

| FM | 1 | 2 | 3 | 4 | 5 | 6 | 7 |
|---|---|---|---|---|---|---|---|
| Far North | 94.0 | - | - | 90.0 | - | - | - |
| Kerikeri | - | - | - | - | 92.0 | - | - |
| Whangarei | 94.0 | 90.8/100.7 | - | 90.0 | 107.3 | - | 98.0 |
| Rodney | - | 92.9 | 104.9 | 100.1 | - | - | - |
| Auckland | 94.2 | 100.6 | - | 90.2 | 93.8 | 96.6 | 88.6 |

| FM | 1 | 2 | 3 | 4 | 5 | 6 | 7 |
|---|---|---|---|---|---|---|---|
| Hamilton | 97.8 | 100.2 | - | 93.0 | 93.8 | 107.3 | 105.8 |
| Tauranga | 99.8 | 100.6 | 88.6 | 94.2 | 92.6 | 107.4 | 96.6 |
| Whakatane | 104.1 | 92.1 | - | - | 105.7 | - | - |
| Rotorua | 99.9 | 95.1 | 100.7 | 92.7 | 91.1 | - | 105.5 |
| Taupo | 88.8 | 99.2 | - | 94.4 | 100.0 | - | - |
| Gisborne | 99.7 | 94.9 | - | 94.1 | 96.5 | - | 89.3 |
| Hawkes Bay | 98.3 | 106.3 | 92.7 | 95.1 | 91.9 | - | 105.5 |
| New Plymouth | 94.0 | 89.2 | - | 95.6 | 98.0 | - | - |
| Whanganui | 88.8 | 96.0 | 90.4 | 95.2 | 94.4 | - | - |
| Palmerston Nth | 93.0 | 93.8 | 104.2 | 95.4 | 94.6 | 107.1 | 97.0 |
| Wairarapa | 95.9 | 98.3 | 105.5 | - | 93.5 | - | - |
| Kapiti Coast | 97.5 | 99.1 | 95.1 | 91.9 | 94.3 | - | - |
| Wellington | 91.7 | 98.9 | - | 96.5 | 97.3 | 104.5 | 100.5 |
| Marlborough | 104.9 | 95.3 | 105.7 | 91.3 | 96.1 | - | - |
| Nelson | 88.8 | 96.0 | 99.2 | 94.4 | 98.4 | 95.2 | - |
| Kaikoura | - | 89.1 | - | - | - | - | - |
| Christchurch | 88.9 | 99.3 | - | 93.7 | 92.9 | 106.9 | 95.3 |
| West Coast | - | 90.1 | 95.7/105.9 | - | §97.1 | - | - |
| Ashburton | 93.3 | - | 103.7 | 97.3 | 95.7 | - | - |
| Timaru | 92.3/95.5 | 105.9 | 103.5 | 91.5 | **90.7 | - | - |
| Wanaka | 98.6 | - | - | 89.8 | 93.8 | - | - |
| Oamaru | 96.0 | 100.8 | 94.4 | 104.8 | 99.2 | - | - |
| Dunedin | 91.8 | 96.6 | 99.8 | 93.4 | 90.2 | 107.1 | - |
| Queenstown | 95.2 | 91.2 | 104.0 | 100.0 | 97.6 | 96.8 | - |
| Central Otago | 88.7/98.6 | 95.9 | 106.0 | 89.8/98.3 | 93.5 | | |
| Invercargill | 97.2 | 94.0 | 106.0 | 90.8 | 98.0 | - | - |

**1**=The Edge, **2**=R.LIVE, **3**=Magic, **4**=The Rock, **5**=The Sound **6**=George **7** =Mai FM  § also on 91.5, 92.5, 98.7 ** Also on 97.1, 104.6

**Local Brands: The Breeze: W:** thebreeze.co.nz – **MORE FM W:** morefm.co.nz – **R. Dunedin W:** radiodunedin.co.nz **NB:** Overnight and weekends often networked from Auckland except for R. Dunedin. **Prgr:** 24h **N:** R.Live bulletins.

| FM Location | 1 | 2 | FM Location | 1 | 2 |
|---|---|---|---|---|---|
| 4) Northland | - | 91.6 | 18) Kapiti | 100.7 | 89.3/90.3 |
| 4) Bay of Isl. | - | 95.2 | 2) Wellington | 94.1/98.5 | 94.7[a] |
| 24) Orewa | - | 92.9/88.9 | 19) Nelson | 97.6 | 92.8 |
| 5) Auckland | 93.4 | 91.8 | 20) Marlborough | 89.7[b] | 92.9 |
| 6) Waikato | 99.4 | 92.2 | 21) Kaikoura | 97.1 | 89.9 |
| 7) Tauranga | 95.8 | 93.4 | 21) Christchurch | 94.5 | 92.1[c] |
| 8) Whitianga | 96.7 | 90.3[d] | 25) Ashburton | 106.1 | 98.9 |
| 9) Rotorua | 91.9 | 95.9 | 25) Timaru | 89.9 | 92.1[e] |
| 10) Taupo | 100.8 | 93.6 | 25) Oamaru | 97.6 | 100.0 |
| 11) Gisborne | 106.7 | 98.9/90.1 | 3) Dunedin[f] | 98.2 | 97.4/100.6 |
| 12) Hawkes Bay | 97.5 | 88.7 | 1) Cent..Otago | 96.7[g] | 90.3/94.3 |
| 13) Taranaki | 94.4 | 93.2 | 13) Balclutha | - | 92.9/93.7 |
| 14) Whanganui | 97.6 | 92.8 | 22) Queenstown | 99.2 | 92.0 |
| 15) Manawatu | 98.6 | 92.2 | 23) Southland | 91.6 | 89.2 |
| 16) Wairarapa | 99.9 | 89.3 | | | |

**1**= The Breeze, **2**= MORE FM
[a] also on 95.3/99.7, [b] also 94.7/98.7, [c] also on 94.9/99.1, [d] also on 89.1/89.9/90.6/93.2/93.9/90.0/97.2/104.2/106.7, [e] also on 93.1/97.9, [f] R. Dunedin also 95.4 & 106.7, [g] also 93.8/97.8/99.4.

**Addresses & other information**
**1)** P.O. Box 143, Alexandra 9340 ☎ +64 3 901 6200 ▤ +64 3 448 6502 – **2)** P.O. Box 11441, Manners Street, Wellington 6142 ☎+64 4 915 1000 ▤ +64 4 915 1009 – **3)** P.O. Box 1957, Dunedin 9054 **R. Dunedin:** ☎ +64 3 477 6934 **FM:** 106.7MHz **The Breeze/MORE FM:** ☎ +64 3 951 3600 ▤ +64 3 477 6874 – **4)** P.O. Box 100, Whangarei 0140 ☎ +64 9 986 9990 ▤ +64 9 438 2348 – **5)** The Breeze/MORE FM: P.O. Box 8880, Symonds Street, Auckland 1150 ☎+64 9 928 9300 ▤ +64 9 373 4000 **Mai FM:** P.O. Box 68886, Newton, Auckland ☎ +64 9 977 7800 ▤ +64 9 977 7801 – **6)** P.O. Box 19293, Hamilton 3244 ☎ +64 7 958 7050 ▤ +64 7 838 2893 – **7)** P.O. Box 13344, Tauranga 3141 ☎ +64 7 928 7300 ▤ +64 7 577 0294 – **8)** P.O. Box 16, Whitianga +64 7 866 5696 ▤ +64 7 866 2553 – **9)** P.O. Box 92, Rotorua 3040 ☎ +64 7 921 7630 ▤ +64 7 348 3830 – **10)** P.O. Box 393, Taupo 3351 ☎+64 7 906 7500 ▤ +64 7 378 2701 – **11)** P.O. Box 468, Gisborne 4040 ☎+64 6 986 3700 ▤ +64 6 869 0037 – **12)** P.O. Box 1957, Hastings 4156 ☎ +64 6 974 6150 ▤ +64 6 876 5626 – **13)** P.O. Box 869, Taranaki Mail Centre, New Plymouth ☎ +64 6 968 6200 ▤ +64 6 757 5020 – **14)** P.O. Box 928, Whanganui 4540 ☎ +64 6 965 6300 ▤ +64 6 345 5592 – **15)** P.O. Box 446, Palmerston North Central, Palmerston North 4440 ☎+64 6 952 6420 ▤ +64 6 356 1317 – **16)** P.O. Box 881, Masterton ☎+64 6 370 2548 ▤ +64 6 378 8877 – **17)** P.O. Box 603, Levin ☎+64 6 368 2827 ▤ +64 6 368 0415 – **18)** P.O. Box 132, Paraparaumu 5254 ☎ +64 4 903 0400 ▤ +64 4 297 2999 – **19)** P.O. Box 907, Nelson 7040 ☎+64 3 546 9670 ▤ +64 3 546 9427 – **20)** P.O. Box 930, Blenheim ☎+64 3 579 0393 – **21) The Breeze:** Private Bag 4750, Christchurch 8140 ☎ +64 3 961 3102 ▤ +64 3 366 5301 **MORE FM:** P.O. Box 25209, Victoria Street, Christchurch 8144 ☎+64 3 961

3322 ▤ +64 3 377 1993 – **22)** P.O. Box 224, Queenstown ☎+64 3 901 0810 ▤ +64 3 442 7799 – **23)** P.O. Box 1740, Invercargill ☎ +64 3 948 3900 ▤ +64 3 218 8015 – **24)** The Village, 292 Hibiscus Coast Highway, Orewa 0931 ☎+64 9 928 9940 ▤ +64 9 427 0251 – **25)** 56 Woollcombe Street, Timaru ☎ +64 3 6889886.

## NZ MEDIA & ENTERTAINMENT [NZME]

✉ **NZME:** 2 Graham Street, Auckland 1010, New Zealand. ✉ **Postal:** Private Bag 92198, Victoria St West, Auckland 1142 ☎ +64 9 379 5050 **W:** nzme.co.nz **L.P:** CEO: Michael Boggs
**Netw. Brands: Prgr:** 24h from Auckland studios **N:** Newstalk ZB bulletins.
**Brands:** Coast **W:** thecoast.net.nz – Flava **W:** flava.co.nz - Radio Hauraki **W:** hauraki.co.nz – Mix **W:** mixonline.co.nz – Newstalk ZB **W:** newstalkzb.co.nz - Radio Sport **W:** radiosport.co.nz - ZM **W:** zmonline.com

### Radio Sport

| MW | kHz | kW | MW | KHz | kW |
|---|---|---|---|---|---|
| Nelson | 549 | 1 | Hawkes Bay | 1125 | 1 |
| Invercargill | 558 | 5 | Auckland | 1332 | 10 |
| Dunedin | 693 | 5 | Rotorua | 1350 | 1 |
| Ashburton | 702 | 1 | Levin/Kapiti | 1377 | 2 |
| Whangarei | 729 | 3 | Timaru | 1494 | 2.5 |
| New Plymouth | 774 | 5 | Christchurch | 1503 | 2.5 |
| Hamilton | 792 | 5 | Wellington | 1503 | 5 |
| Whanganui | 1062 | 1 | Tauranga | 1521 | 1 |
| Palmerston N | 1089 | 2.5 | | | |

### NewstalkZB

| MW | kHz | kW | MW | KHz | kW |
|---|---|---|---|---|---|
| Rotorua | 747 | 0.4 | New Plymouth | 1053 | 2 |
| Masterton | 846 | 2 | Auckland | 1080 | 10 |
| Invercargill | 864 | 10 | Christchurch | 1098 | 5 |
| Ashburton | 873 | 1 | Timaru | 1152 | 2 |
| Palmerston N. | 927 | 2 | Whanganui | 1197 | 2 |
| Gisborne | 945 | 2 | Kaikohe | 1215 | 2 |
| Tauranga | 1008 | 10 | Napier-Hastings | 1278 | 2 |
| Christchurch | 1017 | 10 | Westport | 1287 | 2 |
| Kaitaia | 1026 | 2 | Hamilton | 1296 | 2.5 |
| Whangarei | 1026 | 2 | Nelson | 1341 | 2 |
| Wellington | 1035 | 20 | Oamaru | 1395 | 2 |
| Dunedin | 1044 | 10 | Tokoroa | 1413 | 2 |

### Coast

| MW | kHz | kW | MW | KHz | kW |
|---|---|---|---|---|---|
| Whangarei | 900 | 2.5 | New Plymouth | 1359 | 2.5 |
| Dunedin | 954 | 1 | Palmerston North | 1548 | 1 |
| Hawera | 1323 | 3 | Christchurch | 1593 | 2.5 |

### Radio Hauraki

| MW | kHz | kW |
|---|---|---|
| Dunedin | 1125 | |
| Hawkes Bay | 1584 | 1 |

| FM | 1 | 2 | 3 | 4 | 5 | 6 | 7 |
|---|---|---|---|---|---|---|---|
| Far North | - | -93.2/105.1 | - | - | - | - | 89.2 |
| Russell | 89.6 | - | - | - | - | - | - |
| Whangarei | - | 106.0 | 93.2 | - | - | 94.8 | 89.2 |
| Auckland | 105.4 | 95.8 | 99.0 | 89.4 | - | 91.0 | 98.2 |
| Whangamata | 97.9 | - | - | - | - | - | - |
| Hamilton | 105.0 | - | 96.2 | 97.0 | - | 89.8 | - |
| Tauranga | 97.4 | - | 91.0 | 90.2 | - | 89.4 | 99.0 |
| Rotorua | 96.7 | 89.5 | - | - | - | 98.3 | 94.3 |
| Taupo | - | - | 92.8 | 96.0 | 107.7 | 90.4 | - |
| Gisborne | 88.3 | 106.1 | 105.3 | - | - | 107.4 | - |
| Hawkes Bay | 99.9 | 96.7 | - | 90.3 | - | 95.9 | - |
| New Plymouth | - | - | 90.8 | 96.4 | - | 98.8 | 106.0 |
| Whanganui | 98.4 | - | - | - | - | 96.8 | - |
| Palmerston Nth | 105.8 | - | - | 100.2 | - | 90.6 | - |
| Masterton | - | - | - | - | 91.9 | 94.3 | - |
| Kapiti Coast | 95.9 | - | - | 89.5 | - | 91.1 | - |
| Wellington | 95.7 | - | 93.3 | 89.3 | - | 90.9 | 93.7 |
| Nelson | 100.8 | - | 90.4 | - | - | 96.8 | 104.0 |
| Ashburton | - | - | 98.1 | - | - | - | - |
| Blenheim | - | - | 94.5 | 92.1 | 98.5 | - | - |
| Christchurch | 90.1 | 93.3 | 106.5 | 100.1 | - | 91.3 | 91.7 |
| | - | 88.0 | - | - | - | 90.9 | - |
| Greymouth | - | - | 105.1 | 105.9 | 89.9 | - | - |
| | 91.5/97.1 | | | | | | |
| Timaru | - | - | - | - | - | 96.3 | - |
| Wanaka | 94.6 | - | - | 90.6 | - | 100.2 | - |
| Dunedin | 104.6 | 88.6 | 106.2 | - | - | 95.8 | - |
| Queenstown | - | - | - | 89.6 | - | 88.8 | - |
| Alexandra | - | - | 95.1 | - | - | - | - |
| Invercargill | 92.4 | - | 93.2 | - | - | 95.6 | - |

**1**=Coast, **2**=Flava, **3**=R.Hauraki, **4**=NewstalkZB, **5**=R.Sport, **6**=ZM **7** = Mix
**Local Brand: The Hits W:** thehits.co.nz

**MW:** 1) Takaka 1269kHz

| FM | MHz | FM | MHz | FM | MHz |
|---|---|---|---|---|---|
| 27) Picton | 89.1 | 12) S Taranaki | 91.2 | 4) Auckland | 97.4 |
| 20) Ashburton | 89.3 | 19) Kaikoura | 91.5 | 7) Rotorua | 97.5 |
| 23) Dunedin | 89.4 | 18) Westport | 92.5 | 18) Reefton | 97.5 |
| 11) Hawkes Bay | 89.5 | 16) Kapiti | 92.7 | 19) Christchurch | 97.7 |
| 1) Nelson | 89.6 | 18) Hokitika | 93.1 | 14) Manawatu | 97.8 |
| 13) Whanganui | 89.6 | 21) Timaru | 94.7 | 22) Oamaru | 98.4 |
| 12) Taranaki | 90.0 | 6) Tauranga | 94.9 | 5) Waikato | 98.6 |
| 17) Wellington | 90.1 | 3) Northland | 95.6 | 21) Timaru | 98.7 |
| 15) Masterton | 90.3 | 24) Wanaka | 96.2 | 25) Southland | 98.8 |
| 24) Queenstown | 90.4 | 23) Dunedin | 96.2 | 10) Wairoa | 99.7 |
| 25) Te Anau | 90.4 | 3) Far North | 96.4 | 18) Reefton | 99.9 |
| 18) Westland | *90.5 | 19) Sumner | 96.5 | 24) Alexandra | 99.9 |
| 18) Greymouth | 90.7 | 9) Taupo | 96.8 | 6) Whangamata | 100.3 |
| 10) Gisborne | 90.9 | 2) Blenheim | 96.9 | 3) Doubtless Bay | 105.9 |
| 18) Westport | 90.9 | 8) Tokoroa | 97.3 | 3) Russell | 106.1 |

* Also on 97.1, 99.9 FM

**Addresses & other information**

**1)** P.O. Box 43, Nelson 7043 ☎ +64 3 546 2557 – **2)** P.O. Box 225, Blenheim ☎+64 3 578 0129 – **3)** P. O. Box 845, Whangarei ☎ +64 9 430 4950 – **4)** Private Bag 92198, Auckland ☎ +64 9 379 5050 – **5)** P.O. Box 489, Hamilton ☎+64 7 858 0700 – **6)** P.O. Box 642, Tauranga ☎ +64 7 578 9139 – **7)** P.O. Box 1147, Rotorua ☎ +64 7 348 9089 – **8)** P.O. Box 272, Tokoroa ☎ +64 7 886 8399 – **9)** P.O. Box 967, Taupo ☎ +64 7 376 0550 – **10)** P.O. Box 1040, Gisborne ☎+64 6 867 2139 – **11)** P.O. Box 241, Napier ☎ +64 6 833 8400 – **12)** P.O. Box 141, New Plymouth ☎ +64 6 759 2460 – **13)** P.O. Box 632, Wanganui ☎ +64 6 345 8564 – **14)** P.O. Box 1045, Palmerston North ☎ +64 6 350 3550 – **15)** P.O. Box 220, Masterton ☎+64 6 370 5014 – **16)** P.O. Box 462, Paraparaumu ☎+64 4 296 1201 – **17)** P.O. Box 300, Wellington ☎+64 4 802 4710 #NewstalkZB 1035MW/90.1FM carries local breakfast show – **18)** P.O. Box 378, Greymouth ☎+64 3 768 7068 – **19)** P.O. Box 1484, Christchurch ☎ +64 3 379 9600 #NewstalkZB 1098MW/89.3FM carries local breakfast show – **20)** P.O. Box 465, Ashburton ☎+64 3 307 8927 – **21)** P.O. Box 275, Timaru ☎ +64 3 684 8152 – **22)** P.O. Box 426, Oamaru ☎ +64 3 433 1090 – **23)** P.O. Box 888, Dunedin ☎+64 3 474 8400 – **24)** PO Box 1769, Queenstown ☎ +64 3 447 3175 – **25)** P.O. Box 802, Invercargill ☎+64 3 211 1500 – **26)** P.O. Box 292, Gore ☎ +64 3 208 9325 – **27)** P.O. Box 43, Nelson ☎ +64 3 546 2557

**Associated local NZME station - Hokonui R.**

**MW:** Hawera 1557KHz 2kW

**FM:** Mid-Canterbury 92.5 FM & 96.5 FM, Southland 94.8 FM, West Otago 95.2 FM, South Otago 91.3 FM (and in town on 88.3 FM)

✉ PO Box 292, Gore 9700 ☎+64 3 208 9325 **W:** hokonui.co.nz **Prgr:** 24/7 breakfast live from local studios in Gore, Balclutha & Ashburton then networked from Dunedin/Gore **N:** NewstalkZB **NB:** Hokonui is privately owned but under long-term lease to NZME

## RHEMA MEDIA

🖳 **Corporate:** 53 Upper Queen Street, Eden Tce, Auckland.1010 🖳 **Postal:** Private Bag 92636, Symonds Street, Auckland 1150. ☎ +64 9 307 1251 🖳 +64 9 309 6888 **W:** rhemamedia.co.nz **L.P:** Chief Exec: Andrew Fraser **Dir.Prgr-Radio:** Gary Hoogvliet **Other Media:** Shine TV, NZ charitable organization.

**Netw. Stns: Prgr:** 24h from Auckland studios. Star also broadc. on RNZ AM Netw. txs when Parliament not in session. A duplicate network in several markets carries Star 24/7 so that listeners can hear it without interruption when Parliament is in session. **N:** NZME bulletins. **Netw. Brands:** Life **W:** lifefm.co.nz – Rhema: rhema. co.nz – Star **W:** star.net.nz – Full FM listings at individual netw. brand websites.

### Rhema

| MW | kHz | kW | MW | KHz | kW |
|---|---|---|---|---|---|
| Tauranga | 540 | 5 | Nelson | 801 | 1.5 |
| New Plymouth | 540 | 2 | Hamilton | 855 | 2 |
| Christchurch | 540 | 1 | Wellington | 972 | 5 |
| Kaitaia | 549 | 2 | Auckland | 1251 | 5 |
| Whangarei | 621 | 2 | Invercargill | 1404 | 5 |
| Dunedin | 621 | 2 | | | |

### Star

| MW | kHz | kW | MW | KHz | kW |
|---|---|---|---|---|---|
| Hamilton | 576 | 2.5 | Auckland | 882 | *10 |
| Whanganui | 594 | 2 | Dunedin | 900 | *10 |
| Timaru | 594 | 2 | Hawkes Bay | 909 | *5 |
| Nelson | 612 | 2 | Christchurch | 963 | *10 |
| Christchurch | 612 | 2 | Invercargill | 1026 | 2.5 |
| New Plymouth | 612 | 5 | Invercargill | 1314 | *5 |
| Tauranga | 657 | *10 | Dunedin | 1377 | 2 |
| Wellington | 657 | *50 | Hamilton | 1494 | *3 |

*shares freq with RNZ AM Netw. Duplicate freqs in same market carry Star 24/7 when alternate * freq carrying RNZ AM Netw.

| FM | 1 | 2 | 3 | FM | 1 | 2 | 3 |
|---|---|---|---|---|---|---|---|
| Kaitaia | - | - | 103.5 | Blenheim | 104.1 | - | 93.7 |
| Kaikohe | 99.9 | - | - | Nelson | - | - | 93.6 |
| Whangarei | - | - | 98.8 | Kaikoura | 105.1 | - | - |
| Auckland | - | - | 99.8 | Christchurch | - | - | 87.6 |
| Hamilton | - | - | 94.6 | Westport | 94.9 | 103.7 | 104.5 |
| Tauranga | 104.6 | - | 94.6 | Greymouth | 92.3 | 104.3 | 94.7 |
| Whakatane | - | - | 104.9 | Ashburton | - | - | 91.7 |
| Rotorua | 93.5 | - | 106.3 | Timaru | 104.3 | - | 105.1 |
| Taupo | 95.2 | - | 105.6 | Oamaru | 106.4 | - | 95.2 |
| Taumarunui | 97.5 | 95.9 | 96.7 | Dunedin | - | - | 94.2 |
| Raetihi | 95.0 | 92.6 | 98.2 | Wanaka | 89.0 | 87.6 | 105.0 |
| Gisborne | 103.7 | 92.5 | 100.5 | Cromwell | 89.5 | 87.6 | 91.1 |
| Hawkes Bay | 99.1 | - | 93.5 | Alexandra | 92.7 | 100.7 | 103.9 |
| Taranaki | - | - | 99.6 | Queenstown | 94.4 | 107.0 | - |
| Whanganui | 104.8 | - | 100.8 | Gore | 99.2 | - | 105.6 |
| Palmerston Nth | 91.4 | - | 96.2 | South Otago | 96.1 | 88.9 | 92.1 |
| Masterton | 97.5 | 100.7 | 88.7 | Invercargill | - | - | 100.0 |
| Kapiti Coast | 103.9 | - | 96.7 | | | | |

**1** = Rhema, **2** = Star, **3** = Life FM

## TAB TRACKSIDE RADIO

PO Box 38899, Wellington Mail Centre, Lower Hutt 5045 ☎+64 4 576 6999 NZ Freephone 0800 102 106 Freephone from Australia: 0011 800 10 20 30 44 **W:** tab.co.nz/help/tv-radio/radio-trackside.html **E:** helpdesk@ tab.co.nz **Other:** Totalisator Agency Board operated betting and race reporting services by NZ Racing Board.

| MW | kHz | kW | MW | kHz | kW |
|---|---|---|---|---|---|
| Hawkes Bay | 549 | 1 | Dunedin | 1206 | 2 |
| Wellington | 711 | 5 | Invercargill | 1224 | 2 |
| Palmerston Nth | 828 | 2 | Timaru | 1242 | 1 |
| Tauranga | 873 | 1 | Christchurch | 1260 | 2 |
| Hamilton | 954 | 2 | Auckland | 1476 | 5 |
| Nelson | 990 | 1 | Gisborne | 1485 | 1 |
| Ashburton | 1071 | 1 | Rotorua | 1548 | 0.9 |
| **FM** | **MHz** | **kW** | **FM** | **MHz** | **kW** |
| Northland | 92.4 | - | Kapiti Coast | 93.5 | 0.63 |
| Whakatane | 96.1 | 1 | Wairarapa | 91.1 | 1 |
| Taupo | 91.2 | 2 | Oamaru | 89.6 | 0.1 |
| New Plymouth | 97.2 | 5 | Queenstown | 93.6 | 0.8 |

+ 6 other stns in minor markets

## STUDENT RADIO (bNet affiliated stations)

| FM | MHz | kW | Station |
|---|---|---|---|
| 1) Wellington | 88.6 | 0.5 | R. Active |
| 2) Dunedin | 91.0 | 2.5 | R. One |
| 3) Auckland | 95.0 | 12.6 | 95bFM |
| 4) Christchurch | 98.5 | 1.6 | RDU 98.5FM |
| 5) Palmerston North | 99.4 | 0.16 | R. Control |

**1)** PO Box 11971 Wellington **W:** radioactive.fm **E:** ross@radioactive.fm – **2)** PO Box 1436, Dunedin **W:** r1.co.nz **E:** r1@r1.co.nz – **3)** c/o AUSA, Private Bag 92019, Auckland 1142 **W:** 95bfm.com **E:** 95bfm@95bfm. com – **4)** PO Box 699, Christchurch Central **W:** rdu.org.nz **E:** james@rdu. org.nz – **5)** c/o MUSA, Students Centre Bldg, Massey University, Private Bag 11-222, Palmerston North **W:** radiocontrol.org.nz **E:** manager@ radiocontrol.org.nz

## INDEPENDENT STATIONS

| MW | kHz | kW | Station |
|---|---|---|---|
| 1) Ranfurly | 729 | 0.1 | Burn729am |
| 2) Palmerston | 756 | 0.8 | Puketapu R. |
| 4) Auckland | 810 | 2 | BBC World Service NZ |
| 5) Auckland | 936 | 1 | AM936 Chinese R. |
| 6) Auckland | 990 | 1 | Apna 990 |
| 7) Auckland | 1179 | 5 | Ake |
| 8) Whakatane | 1242 | 2 | One Double X |
| 9) Tauranga | 1368 | 0.8/0.1 | Village R. |
| 10) Auckland | 1386 | 10 | R. Tarana |
| 11) Christchurch | 1413 | 1 | R. Ferrymead |
| 17) Hawkes Bay | 1530 | 1 | The Wireless Station |
| 13) Auckland | 1593 | 5 | R. Samoa |
| 14) Levin | 1602 | 2.5 | R. Reading Service |
| **FM** | **MHz** | **kW** | **Station** |
| **Northland** | | | |
| 12) Mangawhai | 90.4 | 0.1 | The Wireless |
| 15) Waipu | 105.6 | 0.02 | Smooth FM |
| 12) Mangawhai | 106.4 | 0.05 | Heads FM |
| **Auckland** | | | |
| 18) Auckland | 90.6 | 1.6 | Chinese R 90.6FM |
| 19) Station Rock GBI | 94.6 | 1 | Aotea FM |

| FM Auckland | MHz | kW | Station |
|---|---|---|---|
| 5) Auckland | 99.4 | 1.6 | Chinese R. FM99.4 |
| 19) Port Fitzroy GBI | 104.0 | 0.1 | Aotea FM |
| 5) Auckland | 104.2 | 3 | Chinese R. FM104.2 |
| 20) Auckland | 106.2 | 15.8 | Humm FM |
| **Waikato** | | | |
| 24) Pio Pio | 88.7 | 0.8 | Cruise FM |
| 24) Te Kuiti/Mangakino | 104.4 | 0.8/0.1 | Cruise FM |
| 24) Tokoroa | 105.3 | 0.3 | Cruise FM |
| **Bay of Plenty & Lakes** | | | |
| 27) Waihi Beach | 89.0 | 0.008 | The Rhythm |
| 8) Whakatane | 89.7 | 3w | One Double X |
| 8) E.BOP | 90.5 | 16 | One Double X |
| 26) Opotiki | 91.7 | 0.1 | Bridge 91.7FM |
| 8) Whakatane | 92.9 | 0.16 | One Double X |
| 8) E. BOP | 93.7 | 1.6 | Bayrock |
| -) Whitianga | 95.1 | 0.1 | R. Whitianga (FPI) |
| 21) Waihi/Tokatea | 96.4 | 0.1/0.1 | Gold FM |
| -) Whitianga | 97.5 | 0.1 | Classic Gold |
| 8) E. BOP | 97.7 | 2 | Q97 |
| 21) Whitianga | 99.1 | 0.1 | Gold FM |
| 27) Rotorua | 99.1 | 0.25 | The Heat |
| 8) Whakatane | 99.3 | 0.16 | Q97 |
| 21) Waihi Beach | 99.4 | 0.06 | Gold FM |
| 8) Ohope Beach | 100.1 | 0.1 | Bayrock |
| 28) Rotorua | 104.7 | 0.6 | Good News Community R |
| 22) Tauranga | 105.4 | 8 | The Station |
| 25) Taupo | 106.4 | 6 | Timeless Taupo |
| **Central North** | | | |
| 16) Taupo | 89.6 | 6 | Cool Blue Taupo |
| 32) Taihape | 90.0 | 0.6 | Ski FM |
| 33) Raetihi | 90.2 | 1.6 | Brian FM |
| 32) Taumarunui | 91.1 | 1 | Ski FM |
| 33) Whanganui | 91.2 | 0.8 | Brian FM |
| 32) South Ruapehu | 91.8 | 1.6 | Ski FM |
| 33) Whanganui | 92.0 | 0.8 | Reelworld R. |
| 32) Taumarunui | 92.7 | 1.6 | Peak FM |
| 33) Taihape | 93.2 | 0.16 | Brian FM |
| 32) Whanganui | 93.6 | 0.16 | Ski FM |
| 24) Taumarunui | 94.3 | 1 | Cruise FM |
| 34) Waipuna | 95.8 | 1.6 | Peak FM |
| 24) Waipuna | 99.0 | 1.6 | Cruise FM |
| 34) Taihape | 99.6 | 0.1 | Peak FM |
| 34) Taumarunui | 99.9 | 0.1 | Peak FM |
| 36) New Plymouth | 100.4 | 1.6 | The Most |
| 33) Ruapehu | 104.6 | 1.6 | Reelworld R. |
| 38) New Plymouth | 105.2 | 5 | Cruize FM |
| 39) Foxton | 105.4 | 0.16 | R.Foxton |
| 32) National Park | 105.4 | 0.8 | Ski FM |
| 40) Whanganui | 105.6 | 0.8 | The Avenue |
| 32) Ohakune | 106.2 | 0.1 | Ski FM |
| **HB-East Coast** | | | |
| 31) Dannevirke | 99.4 | 0.03 | Central FM |
| 35) Woodville | 99.6 | 0.05 | R. Woodville |
| 30) Hawkes Bay | 100.7 | 4 | R. Bay FM |
| 31) Tourere | 105.2 | 2 | Central FM |
| 31) Waipukurau | 106.0 | 2 | Central FM |
| **Wellington** | | | |
| 58) Wellington | 105.3 | 2 | Wellington 105.3FM |
| 59) Kapiti Coast | 106.3 | 0.6 | Beach FM |
| **Nelson/Marlborough** | | | |
| 29) Takaka | 95.8 | 0.1 | XS80s |
| 33) Havelock | 100.1 | 0.8 | Brian FM |
| 33) Blenheim | 100.9 | 0.1 | Brian FM |
| 33) Seddon | 104.3 | 0.3 | Brian FM |
| 33) Nelson | 105.6 | 5 | Brian FM |
| 33) Picton | 105.9 | 0.16 | Brian FM |
| 33) Blenheim | 106.5 | 0.8 | Reelworld FM |
| **Canterbury** | | | |
| 42) Akaroa | 90.3 | 0.3 | Akaroa R. |
| 42) Akaroa | 91.1 | 0.3 | Akaroa R. |
| 44) Mt Hutt Skifield | 94.1 | 0.16 | Mt Hutt R. Ski |
| 45) Twizel | 95.8 | 0.08 | R.Twizel |
| 46) Christchurch | 96.1 | 15.8 | EMBR 96.1 |
| 33) Twizel | 99.0 | 0.08 | Brian FM |
| 33) Ashburton | 99.7 | 8 | Brian FM |
| 33) Kaikoura | 100.3 | 0.5 | Brian FM |
| 48) S.Canterbury | 100.3 | 1 | Kiwi Access 100FM |
| 49) Christchurch | 100.9 | 5 | V. of the South Pole |
| 50) Christchurch | 105.7 | 5 | Pulzar FM |
| 33) Hamner | 106.1 | 0.3 | Brian FM |
| **West Coast** | | | |
| 43) Reefton | 90.3 | 0.5 | Coast FM |

| FM West Coast | MHz | kW | Station |
|---|---|---|---|
| 43) Westport | 96.5 | 1.6 | Coast FM |
| 43) Greymouth | 97.9 | 0.5 | Coast FM |
| 43) Karamea | 99.3 | 1.6 | Coast FM |
| 43) Greymouth | 99.5 | 1.6 | Coast FM |
| 43) Hokitika | 100.3 | 2.5 | Coast FM |
| **Otago & Southland** | | | |
| 33) Oamaru | 88.8 | 0.6 | Brian FM |
| 51) Glenorchy | 89.2 | 0.3 | Glenorchy Country R. |
| 52) Alexandra | 90.3 | 0.8 | Local R.Central |
| 33) Wanaka | 91.4 | 0.5 | Brian FM |
| 52) Cromwell | 91.9 | 0.1 | Local R.Central |
| 52) Alexandra | 91.9 | 0.5 | Local R.Central |
| 53) Wanaka | 92.2 | 0.5 | R. Wanaka |
| 52) Roxburgh | 94.3 | 0.02 | Local R.Central |
| 53) Wanaka | 97.0 | 0.5 | R. Wanaka |
| 23) Te Anau | 99.2 | 0.1 | The Basin |
| 29) Wanaka | 103.4 | 0.1 | XS80s |
| 61) Oamaru | 104.0 | 0.6 | Real R. |
| 53) Wanaka | 104.2 | 0.5 | Roy FM |
| 52) Ranfurly | 104.3 | 0.6 | Local R. Central |
| 55) Invercargill | 105.2 | 4 | Country R. |
| 33) Cromwell | 105.5 | 0.1 | Brian FM |
| 33) Alexandra | 105.5 | 1.6 | Brian FM |
| 56) Gore | 106.4 | 0.8 | Cave FM |

**Addresses & other information**

**1)** 10 Pery St, Ranfurly 9332 **E:** burn729am@xtra.co.nz– **2)** 118 Ronaldsay St, Palmerston 9430 **E:** puketapuradio@xtra.co.nz **Prgr:** local community radio – **4)** Auckland Radio Trust, PO Box 28622, Remuera, Auckland **W:** worldservice.co.nz **E:** vince@worldservice. co.nz **Prgr:** BBC World Service satellite relay from London 24/7, RNZI Dateline Pacific and local advertising & prgrs achieved by trimming seconds per minute off the satellite feed and 'saving' about 3 minutes per hour – **5)** PO Box 12743, Penrose, Auckland 1642 **W:** chinesevoice. co.nz **E:** info@wtv.co.nz **Prgr:** 936AM Mandarin [incl satellite services from China & Taiwan], 99.4 FM Cantonese [incl satellite services from Hong Kong], **104.2 FM** Mandarin [12h daily], China R. International English [12h daily] – **6)** Level 3, 362 Great North Rd, Henderson, Waitakere 0612 **W:** apna990.co.nz **E:** info@apna990.com **Prgr:** Hindi – **7)** Te Reo o Ngati Whenua, Te Runanga o Ngati Whatua, PO Box 1784, Whangarei. **W:** ngatiwhatua.iwi.nz/manaakitanga/ake-1179am **E:** ake1179@ngatiwhatua.iwi.nz **Prgr:** Maori reggae favorites, soul, R&B music – **8)** Radio Bay of Plenty Ltd, PO Box 383, Whakatane 3158 **Brands:** 1XX **W:** 1xx.co.nz facebook.com/radio1xx – Bayrock **W:** bayrock.co.nz facebook.com/bayrockonline – Q97 **W:** q97.co.nz & facebook.com/q97hits **E:** reception@1xx.co.nz – **9)** PO Box 841 Seventh Avenue, Tauranga 3140 **W:** villageradio.co.nz **E:** info@villageradio. co.nz **Prgr:** Nostalgia Mon-Fri 2200-0400 Sat-Sun 2100-0500 – **10)** PO Box 5956, Wellesley Street, Auckland 1141 **W:** tarana.co.nz **E:** info@ tarana.co.nz **Prgr:** Hindi – **11)** PO Box 19090, Woolston, Christchurch 8241 **W:** radioferrymead.co.nz **Prgr:** Fri 2000-Mon 1200 non-stop including automated prgrs, Statutory Holidays & Christmas New Year period –**12)** Perryscope Productions Ltd, PO Box 180, Mangawhai 0540 **Brands:** Heads FM **W:** facebook.com/heads106.4fm The Wireless **W:** facebook.com/thewirelessfm **E:** mark@perryscope.co.nz – **13)** PO Box 200105, Papatoetoe Central, Manukau 2156 **W:** radiosamoa. co.nz **E:** sales@samoatimes.co.nz **Prgr:** Samoan **Other:** Samoa Times newspaper – **14)** PO Box 360, Levin 5500 **W:** radioreading.org.nz & facebook.com/radioreading **E:** rrsinfo@radioreading.org.nz **Prgr:** RNZ National relay Sat 0500-2359, Sun 0800-2000, all other times own programs + 107.3 FM –**15)** 88 The Centre, Waipu **W:** facebook. com/radiowaveswaipu **E:** info@radiowaveswaipu.co.nz **Prgr:** Mon-Fri 2100-0530 Sat/Sun 0000-0700 – **16)** PO Box 8947, Havelock North **Prgr:** mostly automated standards, rock & roll music, obs. with some live anncrs in primetime. – **18)** 194 Marua Road, Mt Wellington, Auckland 1051 **W:** fm906.co.nz **E:** info@fm906. co.nz **Prgr:** 24/7 Mandarin **Other:** owned by Global CAMG Media Group [includes 3CW 1241/1620 Melbourne] **W:** camg-media.com –**19)** Hector Sanderson Road, Claris, Great Barrier Island **W:** aoteafm. org & facebook.com/aoteafm **E:** aoteafm@xtra.co.nz **Prgr:** 1930-0600 daily – **20)** PO Box 27647, Mt Roskill, Auckland 1440 **W:** hummfm. com & facebook.com/hummfm **E:** connect@hummfm.com **Prgr:** 24/7 Hindi – **21)** PO Box 341, Waihi 3641 **W:** goldfm.co.nz **E:** info@ goldfm.co.nz **Other:** 88.0/88.3 – **22)** 52 Devonport Road, Tauranga **W:** vinyldestination.co.nz – **23)** – **E:** thebasinfm@gmail.com – **24)** Level 1, 203 Leith Place, Tokoroa **W:** cruisefm.co.nz & facebook.com/cruise-fm **E:** johnnydryden@xtra.co.nz – **25)** Great Lake Taupo R Ltd, 23 Scannell Street, Taupo **W:** timelesstaupo.co.nz **E:** radio@timelesstaupo.co.nz – **26)** PO Box 593, Opotiki **W:** wwt.org.nz **E:** wwt@xtra.co.nz –**27)** 7 The Crescent Waihi Beach **W:** wtd.net.nz/the-rhythm-89fm-waihi-beach/ – **28)** Rotorua Gospel Broadc. Charitable Trust, 42 Mount View Dr,

Mangakakahi, Rotorua 301 3 **E:** comrad@xtra.co.nz – **29)** **W:** xs80s. com **E:** studio@xs80s.com – **30)** PO Box 720, Hastings **W:** radiobayfm. co.nz & facebook.com/radiobayfm **E:** radiobayfm@xtra.co.nz – **31)** PO Box 195, Waipukurau **W:** centralfm.co.nz & facebook.com/central.fm.3 **E:** centralfm@xtra.co.nz – **32)** PO Box 661, Taupo **W:** skifmnetwork. co.nz & facebook.com/skifm **E:** info@skifmnetwork.com **Other:** FPL 1251 MW Taupo – **33)** 268 Broadway Ave, Palmerston North **Brands:** Brian FM **W:** brianfm.com & facebook.com/brianfm Reelworld FM **E:** brian@brianfm.com studios in Blenheim & Springvale [Whanganui] – **34)** PO Box 37, Raetihi. **W:** peakfm.nz & facebook.com/peak-fm **E:** geoff@peakfmruapehu.co.nz – **35)** 79 Vogel Street, Woodville **W:** radiowoodville.co.nz **E:** station@radiowoodville.co.nz + 88.3 – **36)** 12 Bell Street, New Plymouth 4310 **W:** mostfm.co.nz **E:** mostfm@mostfm. com – **38)** 38 Liardet Street, New Plymouth **W:** cruizefm.co.nz **E:** info@ bigmedia.co.nz – **39)** MAVTECH The National Museum of Audio Visual Technology, Avenue Road, Foxton **W:** mavtech.co.nz & facebook. com/mavtechnz **E:** mavtech@xtra.co.nz – **40)** 180 Upper Roberts Avenue, RD14, Whanganui **W:** theavenue.co.nz – **42)** 1 Edwards Road, Wainui, Banks Peninsula, Christchurch **W:** akaroaradio.co.nz **E:** dave@akaroaradio.co.nz – **43)** 171 Palmerston Street, Westport **W:** coastfm.net.nz & facebook.com/coast.fm **E:** studio@coastfm.net. nz **Other:** Westport News newspaper r – **44)** seasonal only station based at Mt Hutt Skifield associated with Radioworks – **45)** Twizel Promotion & Development Assoc. Inc, PO Box 4, Market Place, Twizel **E:** radiotwizel@gmail.com – **46)** NZ Broadcasting School, CPIT Campus, 150 Madras Street, Christchurch **W:** nzbs.co.nz/ **NB:** each year the NZBS rebrands its station on 96.1 to give students broadcasting experience. – **48)** James Valentine, 8 Lisava Street, Timaru. Automated music only – **49)** 12 Walters Road, Marshland, Christchurch **W:** tvo.co.nz **E:** vsp@tvo.cc **Prgr:** 24/7 mainly Chinese including programs from China R.International in various languages on weekends – **50)** PO Box 13209, Christchurch **W:** pulzarfm.co.nz & facebook.com/pulzarfm **E:** info@pulzarfm.co.nz – **51)** PO Box 52, Glenorchy **W:** glenorchycommunity.nz/community-services/glenorchy-country-radio **E:** glenorchycountry@gmail.com – **52)** Alexandra: 2/22 Centennial Ave, Alexandra 9320 Cromwell: 34 Ree Crescent, Cromwell **W:** localradiocentral.nz & facebook.com/localradiocentral facebook.com/localradiocromwell **E:** diack@xtra.co.nz Roxburgh + 88.0 – **53)** PO Box 825, Wanaka **W:** wanakalive.com & facebook. com/radiowanaka **E:** info@radiowanaka.co.nz **E:** jamie@radiowanaka. co.nz – **55)** 145 Islington Street, Invercargill **W:** countryradio.co.nz **E:** countryradio@xtra.co.nz + 88.1/87.7 – **56)** 6 North Tce, Dunedin **W:** caveman4music.vpweb.co.nz & facebook.com/caveman – **58)** 18 Ashwood Street, Woodridge, Newlands, Wellington **W:** facebook.com/ wellington105.3fm/ **E:** info@wellington105.3fm.co.nz **Prgr:** 24/7 Hindi – **60)** Lindale Complex, Paraparaumu **W:** beachfm.co.nz & facebook. com/beachfm106.3 – **61)** PO Box 504, Oamaru **W:** 104fm.co.nz

**NB:** New Zealand FM List at **W:** radiodx.com is regularly updated by members of the NZ Radio DX League. LPFM [1w or less] stns broadcast on 87.6-88.3 and 106.7-107.7MHz throughout the country and ALL stns less than 1kw are included in a regularly updated free NZ Radio Guide from the Radio Heritage Foundation **W:** radioheritage.net

## NICARAGUA

**L.T:** UTC -6h — **Pop:** 6.2 million — **Pr.L:** Spanish — **E.C:** 60Hz, 120V — **ITU:** NCG

### TELCOR – INSTITUTO NICARAGÜENSE DE TELECOMUNICACIONES Y CORREOS
✉ Ave. Bolívar Esquina Diagonal a la Cancillería, Managua
☎ +505 2222 7350 **W:** telcor.gob.ni

| MW Call | | kHz | kW | Station, location & h. of tr. |
|---|---|---|---|---|
| MA01) | A3OW | 540 | 25 | R. Corporación, Managua: 0950-0505 |
| CH01) | A2RQ | 570 | 5 | R. Stereo Veritas, Chinandega: 1030-0250 |
| MA02) | A3LP | 580 | 10 | R. 580, Managua: 1030-0000 |
| MA03) | A3MD | 600 | 10 | La Nueva R. Ya, Managua: 1000-0600 (SS 24h) |
| MA04) | N | 620 | 10 | R. Nicaragua, Managua: 1000-0400 |
| MA05) | AM | 680 | 10/2 | R. La Primerísima, Managua: 1045-0500 |
| MT01) | RH | ‡690 | 10/5 | R. Hermanos, Matagalpa: 1000-0400 |
| CT01) | | ‡720 | | R. Asunción, Juigalpa |
| MA07) | A3LS | 740 | 50 | La Sandino "La S Grande", Managua |
| MA08) | A3RO | 800 | 50 | R. Cadena 800, Managua: 0800-0500 |
| MA10) | A3NT | 840 | 5 | R. Fe 840, Managua |
| CT02) | CD | 870 | 10 | R. Centro, Juigalpa: 1100-0200 |
| MA11) | A3EP | ‡880 | 10 | R. El Pensamiento, Managua: 1100-0300 |
| JI01) | | 910 | 5 | R. Jinotega, Jinotega |
| MA13) | W | 920 | 10 | R. Mundial, Managua: 1100-0400 |
| RS01) | ACTH | 960 | 2.5 | R. Trópico Húmedo, San Carlos: 1000-0300 |
| MA15) | FF | 1000 | 10 | R. Hosanna, Managua: 1200-0400 |
| NS01) | FAVP | 1010 | 5 | R. LV del Pinar, Ocotal: 1100-0400 |
| MA17) | A3CP | 1120 | 5 | R. CEPAD "El Arco Iris del Amor", Managua |
| LE01) | | 1150 | | R. Darío, León |
| CH03) | A6RB | ‡1190 | 1 | R. Bendición, Cayanlipe |
| AS01) | MNG | ‡1230 | 5 | R. Manantial, Nueva Guinea: 1000-0300 |
| MA20) | A3RR | 1240 | 5 | R. Vida, Managua |
| MA21) | A2CC | ‡1300 | 1 | Canal 130 AM, Managua: 1200-2330 |
| MA24) | A3MR | 1440 | 25 | R. Maranatha, Managua: 1000-0500 |
| B001) | RY | ‡1470 | 1 | R. Yarrince, Boaco |
| CA02) | A4TS | ‡1530 | 0.5 | R. LV de Teresa, Santa Teresa: 1400-2200 |

Hrs of tr 24h except where shown. Call YN__ . ‡ = inactive, ± = varying fq

**Addresses & other information:**

**AS00) ATLANTICO SUR**
**AS01)** TELCOR, 1½ c este, Nueva Guinea **W:** radiomanantialnicaragua. blogspot.com **FM:** 102.5

**B000) BOACO**
**B001)** Casa del Finquero, 20 vrs al este, Boaco

**CA00) CARAZO**
**CA02)** Entrada II Calle, ½ c abajo, Sta Teresa **W:** lavozdeteresa.es.tl

**CH00) CHINANDEGA**
**CH01)** Frente Iglesia de Guadalupe (or Ap. 12), Chinandega **FM:** 102.5 **W:** radioveritas.es.tl – **CH03)** Cayanlipe

**CT00) CHONTALES**
**CT01)** de Catedral 1/2c al Sur, Juigalpa **W:** facebook.com/estereo. juigalpanicaragua **FM:** 93.7 – **CT02)** Caracoles negros, Juigalpa **W:** radiocentro870am.com

**JI00) JINOTEGA**
**JI01)** Escuela Gabriela Mistral, ½ al Norte, Avenida Ernesto Rosales, Jinotega. **W:** radiojinotega.com **FM:** 102.1

**LE00) LEÓN**
**LE01)** frente al parque Posada del Sol, casa #93. León **W:** radiodario893.com **FM:** 89.3

**MA00) MANAGUA**
**MA01)** Cd. Jardín Q-20, Av. Ponciano Lombillo (Apartado Postal 2442), Managua **W:** radio-corporacion.com – **MA02)** Reparto El Carmen, Costado Oeste del Parque, Managua **W:** radiola580.com – **MA03)** Frente a la Universidad Centroamericana, Managua **W:** nuevaya. com.ni – **MA04)** Villa Fontana, Contiguo a TELCOR, Managua **W:** radionicaragua.com.ni – **MA05)** Apartado Postal 4003 (or Barrio Bolonia, de Tica bus, 100 metros al sur, 100 metros al este), Managua **W:** radiolaprimerisima.com – **MA06)** Altamira D'Este 621, Managua **W:** radiocatolica.org – **MA07)** Av. Colón, Managua 11121 **W:** lasandino.com.ni – **MA08)** Semáforos de Lozelsa 1c al lago, ½ abajo, Managua **W:** radio800ni.com – **MA10)** Mansión Teodolinda 6C. al sur, ½ C. al oeste M/I, Managua **W:** fe840.com – **MA11)** Distribuidora Vicky, 4C Al lago, Casa 73, Managua **W:** facebook.com/Radio-El-Pensamiento-334434523643149 – **MA13)** Reparto Miraflores, Rest. Munich 4c Al lago 1 c al Oe, Managua **W:** radiomundialdenicaragua. com – **MA15)** Rotonda Jean Paul Genie 300 mts al oeste sobre la pista, Comunidad Hosanna 2821, Managua **W:** facebook.com/ RadioHosanna – **MA17)** Apartado 3091, Managua **W:** radiocepad. org – **MA20)** Carret. Vieja a León, km 10 ¾, 500 m al N 200 al Oe, Managua **W:** facebook.com/RadioVida1240Am – **MA21)** Carretera a Masaya, Km 12 ¾, 450 Metros al este, Managua – **MA22)** Bo La Cruz, Cine Blanca, 5c al N, ½ c al E, Casa 1112, Managua – **MA24)** Rotonda Metrocentro 1 c al sur, ½ C Abajo, Casa 41, Managua **W:** facebook. com/radiomaranatha

**MS00) MASAYA**
**MS01)** Carr. a Managua km 24½, Masaya

**MT00) MATAGALPA**
**MT01)** Bo. Liberación Igl. Catedral. 1c al N 25 vs al Oe, Matagalpa **FM:** 92.3 **W:** radiohermanos.net

**NS00) NUEVA SEGOVIA**
**NS01)** En el Centro Histórico de la ciudad, del Templo Nuestra Señora de la Asunción una cuadra al norte, Ocotal **W:** radiolavozdelpinar.com **FM:** 100.9MHz Stereo Mogotón

**RS00) RIO SAN JUAN**
**RS01)** Costado Norte de la Iglesia Católica, San Carlos **W:** facebook. com/tropicohumedo.tk **FM:** 89.3

**FM in Managua (MHz):** 87.7 Canal 6 – 88.9 Israel – 89.5 Enlace – 89.9 Tropicálida – 90.5 R. Nicaragua – 90.9 La Marka – 91.3 Futura – 91.7 R. La Primerísima – 92.1 Estación X – 92.7 Advent Estéreo – 93.1 La Buenísima – 93.5 Alfa Radio – 93.7 La Gran Cadena – 93.9 La Tigre – 94.3 Ondas de Luz – 94.7 Mujer – 95.1 La Pachanguera – 95.5 Amor – 95.9 Estéreo Ritmo – 96.3 La Gran Cadena – 96.7 Furia Magic – 96.9 La Nueva R. Ya – 97.1 Estéreo Mía – 97.5 Corporación – 97.9 Salsa 98 – 98.3 R. Viva – 98.7 Romántica – 99.1 La Nueva R. Ya – 99.5

Universidad – 99.9 María – 100.3 R. Tuani – 100.7 Disney – 101.1 Güegüense – 101.5 Juvenil – 101.9 R. Clásica – 102.3 Universidad – 102.7 Magic – 103.1 Bautista – 103.5 Maranatha – 103.9 Joya FM – 104.3 Estrella del Mar – 104.7 Hit – 105.1 Mi Preferida – 105.5 Rock FM – 105.9 Rica – 106.3 Galaxia, La Picosa – 106.7 Eco Romántico – 107.1 Sol – 107.5 La Sandino – 107.9 Restauración

## NIGER

**LT:** UTC +1h — **Pop:** 22 million — **Pr.L:** French, Hausa, Zarma, Tamashek, Fulfulde, Arabic etc. — **E.C:** 50Hz, 220V — **ITU:** NGR

**CONSEIL SUPÉRIEUR DE LA COMMUNICATION (CSC)**
✉ Plateau I, Niamey ☎+227 20 722356 ⊟ +227 20 722667 **L.P:** Chmn: Daouda Diallo. Vice Chmn: Hamidou Kô.

**LA VOIX DU SAHEL – OFFICE DE RADIODIFFUSION-TÉLÉVISION DU NIGER (ORTN, Gov.)**
✉ Maison de la Radio, B.P. 361, Niamey ☎+227 20 722272 ⊟ +227 20 722548 **W:** ortn.ne **E:** ortny@ortn-niger.com **L.P:** DG: Amadou Harouna Yayé. Dir. Voix du Sahel: Mahaman Chamsou Maïgary. Gen. Secr: Mrs. Diaffra Fadimou Moumouni. Tech. Dir: Maraka Laouali.
**FM** (MHz): Maradi 88.4, Doutchi 89.7, Niamey 91.3, Zinder 91.3 2.5kW, Diffa 92.0, B. Konni 96.2, Madaoua 97.2, Tillaberi 99.0 10kW, Dosso 99.8, Tahoua 100.0, Agadez 106.8. All 1kW if not given otherwise. In addition 16 txs under 1kW.
**D.Prgr in French/ethnic:** 0500-2300 (Sun -2200). Local prgrs: 0700-1130 & 1500-1700. **N. in French:** 0545, 1200, 1900. **IS:** Local flute. **Ann:** F:"Ici la Voix du Sahel", A: "Idha'at al-Jumhuriya al-Niger, Sawt as-Sahel min Niamey".

**Other Stations:**
**Alternative FM:** Niamey/Agadez/Zinder: 99.4MHz. **W:** alternativeniger.org — **Anfani FM:** Niamey/Birni Nkonni/Diffa/Maradi/Zinder 100.0MHz 1.5kW. **W:** anfani-info.com — **Dounia FM,** Niamey: 89.0MHz 3kW. **E:** radioteledounianiger@yahoo.fr — **Espoir FM,** Niamey: 101.0MHz **E:** espoirfm@iniger.ne — **Hit R,** Niamey: 88.7MHz **W:** hitradio.co —**La Voix de l'Hemicycle,** Niamey: 95.1MHz —**Radio & Musique (R&M),** Niamey: 104.5MHz 1kW **E:** retm@intnet.ne — **R. Bonferey,** Niamey: 105.0MHz 1kW **W:** sites.google.com/a/bonferey.com/www — **R. Dounia,** Niamey: 99.0MHz 1kW **E:** nodiabaoba@yahoo.fr — **R. Saraounia,** Niamey/Birnin Konni/Madoua/Maradi/Tahoua: 102.1MHz — **Sahara FM,** Agadez: 97.0MHz 1kW **W:** radiosahara.blog.fr — **Tambara FM,** Niamey: 107.0MHz 0.5kW **E:** tambarafm@yahoo.fr — **Ténéré FM,** Niamey/Agadez/Diffa/Dosso/Maradio/Tahoua/Tillaberi/Zinder: 98.0MHz 1kW.
**R. Rurale** stations on FM in Agadez, Bankilaré, Diffa, Dosso, Gaya, Maradi, Niamey, Tahoua, Tillabéri, Zinder.
**BBC African Sce,** Niamey: 100.4MHz.
**RFI Afrique:** Agadez 94.5, Diffa/Maradi/Niamey/Tahoua/Zinder 96.2MHz in French/Hausa.
**VOA African Sce:** Niamey 102.5MHz

## NIGERIA

**LT:** UTC +1h — **Pop:** 192 million — **Pr.L:** English, Yoruba, Hausa, Igbo — **E.C:** 50Hz, 240V — **ITU:** NIG

**NATIONAL BROADCASTING COMMISSION (NBC)**
✉ Road 14, Badagry Rd, Gwarinpa, Abuja ☎+234 1 2647867 **W:** nbc.gov.ng **L.P:** DG: Yomi Bolarinwa **L.P:** DG: Mr. Emeka Mba. Dir. Pub. Aff: Malam Awwal Salihu.

**FEDERAL RADIO CORPORATION OF NIGERIA (FRCN) - RADIO NIGERIA (Gov.)**
✉ Radio House, Herbert Macauley Way, Area 10, PMB 452, Garki, Abuja, Federal Capital Territory ☎+234 9 2341103 ⊟ +234 9 2346486 **W:** radionigeria.gov.ng **E:** kns@radionigeria.net **LP:** DG: Malam Muhammad Ladan Salihu. Dir. Eng. Sces: Ibrahim Abdullahi.
**1) R. Nigeria Lagos,** Broadcasting House, P.M.B. 12504, Ikoyi Road, Ikoyi, Lagos, Lagos State. ☎+234 1 2690301-5. L.P: Exec. Dir: Prince Atilade Atoyebi. R. One in English. NB: Nigerian N. from Lagos or Abuja at 0600, 1500 & 2100 is relayed by all FRCN stations and most state stations. Ann: "This is R. Nigeria, Lagos". Metro FM, Ikeja in English: 0500-2300 on 97.7MHz 20kW. Bond FM, Ikeja in Pidgin/English/Yoruba/Hausa/Igbo on 92.9MHz 20kW: 0430-2300. R. One, Ikoyi: 103.5Mhz. – **2) R. Nigeria Abuja,** 12th Floor, Radio House, Garki, P.M.B. 7, Abuja, Federal Capital Territory ☎+234 9 88210410 L.P: Exec. Dir: Shuaibu Ibrahim. D.Prgr: 0530-2305 in English/Hausa/Igbo/Yoruba and others. Kapital FM, Abuja: 92.9MHz.Ann: "This is

R. Nigeria, Abuja". – **3) R. Nigeria Enugu,** Broadcasting House, Onitsha Rd, P.M.B. 1051, Enugu, Enugu State ☎+234 42 254400 ⊟ + 234 42 254173 L.P: Exec. Dir: Eddy Agwuegbo. 0500-2315 in English/Igbo/Tiv/Efik/Izon. Coal City FM, Enugu: 92.8MHz – **4) R. Nigeria Ibadan,** Broadcasting House, Oba Adebimpe Rd, P.M.B. 5003, Dugbe, Ibadan, Oyo State ☎+234 2 2400660-3 ⊟ + 234 2 2413930 **W:** radionigeriaibadan.org.ng **E:** radionigeriaibadan@gmail.com L.P: Exec. Dir: Princess Banke Ademola. D.Prgr: 0430-2305 in English/Yoruba/Edo/Igala/Urhobo. Premier FM, Ibadan: 93.5MHz. Amuludun FM, Ibadan: 96.3MHz. Ann: "R. Nigeria Ibadan, Station with distinction". – **5) R. Nigeria Kaduna,** Broadcasting House, No. 7 Yakubu Gowon Way, P.O.Box 250, Kaduna, Kaduna State ☎+234 62 235390 ⊟ + 234 62 245392 L.P: Ag. Zonal Dir: Alhaji Muhammad Sani Suleiman. Chief Tech. Officer: Shehu A. Muhammad. Ch. 1 in Hausa: 0430-2300 on 594/6090kHz. Ch. 2 in English/Hausa/Fulfulde/Kanuri/Nupe: 0430-2300 on 1107kHz. Supreme FM in English: 0500-2400 on 96.1MHz. Karama FM in Hausa: 92.1MHz. Ann: "This is R. Nigeria, Kaduna".

| MW | kHz | kW | | MW | kHz | kW |
|---|---|---|---|---|---|---|
| 4) Moniya | 576 | 25 | 3) Enugu | | 828 | 100 |
| 5) Jaji | 594 | 200 | 5) Jaji | | 1107 | 25 |
| 4) Ibadan | 657 | 100 | | | | |
| **SW** | kHz | kW | | | | |
| 5) Kaduna | 16090 | 10 | | | | |

**FM** (MHz): **1)** 92.9/97.7 **2)** 92.9 **3)** 92.8 **4)** 93.5/96.3 **5)** 92.1/96.1.

**Further federal FM stations (MHz):** Abakaliki 101.5, Abeokuta 94.5, Ado-Ekiti 100.5, Akure 102.5, Asaba 104.4, Awka 105.5, Bauchi 98.5, Benin 101.5, Bida (Minna) 100.5, Birnin-Kebbi 103.5, Calabar 99.5, Damaturu 104.5, Dutse 100.5, Gombe 103.5, Gusau 102.5, Ilesha 95.5, Idofian (Ilorin) 103.5, Jalingo 104.5, Jos 101.5, Kano 103.5, Katsina 104.5, Kwara 103.5, Lafia 102.5, Lokoja 98.1, Maiduguri (Borno) 102.5, Makurdi (Benue) 91.1, Osogbo 93.5, Owerri 100.5, Port-Harcourt 98.5, Sokoto 101.5, Umuahia 103.5, Uyo 104.5, Yenagoa 106.5, Yola 101.5.
**Aso FM:** Abuja: 93.5MHz. **W:** asoradioonline.com

**STATES RADIO STATIONS:**

| MW Location | kHz | kW | MW Location | kHz | kW |
|---|---|---|---|---|---|
| 17) Sokoto | 540 | 50 | 43) Yola | 917 | 50 |
| 37) Ado | 549 | 25 | 10) Makurdi | 918 | 50 |
| 13) Owerri | 567 | 50 | 27) Birnin Kebbi | 945 | 10 |
| 40) Gusau | 567 | 50 | 25) Katsina | 972 | 25 |
| 9) Maiduguri | 603 | 50 | 20) Ikeja | 990 | 10 |
| 18) Abeokuta | 603 | 25 | 21) Bauchi | 990 | 50 |
| 16) Ilorin | 612 | 50 | 12) Kontagora | 1008 | 10 |
| 8) Katabu | 639 | 50 | 34) Iree | 1008 | 10 |
| 14) Jogana | 729 | 50 | 33) Dutse | 1026 | 25 |
| 42) Kaduna | 747 | 60 | 23) Ugaga | 1134 | 20 |
| 15) Ibadan | 756 | 100 | 24) Jos | 1224 | 50 |
| 27) Zuru | 801 | 1 | 31) Jalingo | 1269 | 10 |
| 30) Damaturu | 801 | 20 | 11) Yola | 1440 | 10 |

**FM** (MHz): **6)** 96.1 **7)** 95.8 **8)** 89.9/90.9 **9)** 95.3 **10)** 95.0 **11)** 95.8 **12)** 91.3 **13)** 94.4 **14)** 89.3 **15)** 98.5 **16)** 99.0 **17)** 96.4 **18)** 90.5 **19)** 96.5 **20)** 107.5 **21)** 94.6 **22)** 99.1 **23)** 92.7 **24)** 90.5 **26)** 90.5 **28)** 88.5 **29)** 88.6/97.9 **31)** 90.6 **32)** 88.1 **34)** 89.5 **35)** 94.0 **36)** 97.1 **37)** 91.5 **38)** 97.3 **39)** 96.8 **41)** 98.1

**States Radio information:**
**6)** Enugu State Broadc. Sce (ESBS), Broadcasting House, Independence Layout, P.M.B. 01600, Enugu, Enugu State. Prgr 1 on MW: 0430-2300 in English/others. Prgr. 2 on FM ("Sunrise 96"): 0500-2100 – **7)** Edo State Broadc. Sce, P.M.B. 1012, Aduwawa, Benin City, Edo State. 0400-2305 in English + 12 local languages – **8)** Kaduna State Media Corp. (KSMC), Wurno/Rabah Road, PMB 2013, Kaduna North, Kaduna State. Kada 1 AM: 0430-2315 in English/Hausa on 639kHz. Kada 2 on 89.9MHz. Capital Sound on 90.9MHz **W:** ksmc.com.ng – **9)** Borno Radio & TV Corp., P.M.B. 1020, Broadcasting House, Along Shehu Laminu Way, Maiduguri, Borno State **E:** brtvnews@yahoo.com 0400-2305 in English/Hausa/Kanuri/Marghi/Suwa/Babur-Bura – **10)** R. Benue, P.M.B. 102202, Makurdi, Benue State. Prgr. 1: 0430-2305 in English/others. Prgr. 2 on FM: 0500-2105. Ann: "This is R. Benue, Makurdi" – **11)** Adamawa Broadc. Corp. (ABC), P.M.B. 2123, Yola, Adamawa State. 0500-2300 in English/Hausa + 6 Nigerian languages. On MW: 0500-2100. Ann: "This is ABC Yola, your No. 1 radio station" – **12)** Niger State Media Corp., Radio House, Ibrahim Babangida St, P.M.B. 88, Minna, Niger State **E:** radioniger@yahoo.com 0430-2130 in English/others – **13)** Imo Broadc. Corp, Ebu Rd, P.O. Box 329, Owerri, Imo State. Prgr. 1: 0425-2305 on MW. Prgr. 2: 0440-2305 on FM. English: 0430-0630, 1100-1830, 2100-2300 (Sat/Sun 0100), other times Igbo – **14)** Kano State BC, 1 Ibrahim Taiwo

Rd, Gidan Bello Dandago, P.M.B. 3014, Kano, Kano State. **W:** radioka-noonline.com Prgr. 1 on MW: 0430-2320. Prgr. 2: on FM: 0550-2320 in English/Hausa. **Ann:** "Radio Kano" – **15)** Broadc. Corp. of Oyo State, P.M.B. 1, Akodi Post Office, Ibadan, Oyo State. Prgr. 1: 0400-2200 in English/Yoruba. Prgr 2: on FM: 0700-2100. **Ann:** "R. O-y-o" – **16)** Kwara State Broadc. Corp, Akpata Yakuba, P.M.B. 1345, Ilorin, Kwara State. 0400-2305 in English/others – **17)** Sokoto State BC, Moliba Adamawa Rd, Tudua Wada, P.M.B. 2156, Sokoto, Sokoto State. 0430-2305 in English/Hausa. **Ann:** "Rima Radio" – **18)** Ogun State BC, Ibara Housing Estate, P.M.B. 2084, Abeokuta, Ogun State. OGBC1 on MW, OGBC2 on 90.5 FM: 0400-2400 in English/Yoruba – **19)** Ondo State Radio Corp, Broadcasting House, Oba-Ile, P.M.B. 709, Akure, Ondo State. 0400-2300 in English/others – **20)** Lagos State Broadc. Corp, Obafemi Awolowo Way, P.M.B. 21035, Ikeja, Lagos State. 0430-0005 in English/Yoruba. **Ann:** "NBC" – **21)** Bauchi Radio Corp, 18 Ahmadu Bello Way, P.M.B. 0133, Bauchi, Bauchi State. **W:** brcbauchi.info Prgr 1: 0430-2300 on MW, Prgr. 2: 24h on 94.6MHz and 10 other txs. 846 kHz being renovated – **22)** Rivers State Broadc. Corp, 4 Degema St, P.M.B. 5170, Port Harcourt, Rivers State. Prgr. 1: 0450-2310 on MW, Prgr. 2: 0450-2310 on FM in English/others – **23)** Cross River State Broadc. Corp. (CRBC), No. 8 IBB Way, P.M.B. 1035, Calabar, Cross River State **E:** crbc@skannet.com 0430-2315 in English/others – **24)** Plateau Radio & TV Corp. (PRTVC), 5 Joseph Gomwalk Rd, P.M.B. 2043, Jos, Plateau State. Ch. 1 on MW: 0500-2300, Ch. 2 on FM: 0500-2300 in English/others. **Ann:** "This is Radio Plateau 1 AM", "This is Radio Plateau 2, 90.5 FM Stereo" – **25)** Katsina State Radio & TV Sces (KSRTV), Former SDP State Headquarters, Batsari Rd, P.M.B. 2163, Katsina, Katsina State. 0430-2300 in English/others. **Ann:** "This is Katsina State R." – **26)** Akwa Ibom Broadc. Corp, 205 Aka Rd, P.M.B. 1122, Uyo, Akwa Ibom State. 0500-2300 in English/others – **27)** R. Kebbi, km 9 Kalgo Rd, Birnin Kebbi, Kebbi State. 0500-2300 in English/others – **28)** Anambra Broadc. Sce (ABS), off Arroma Junction, P.M.B. 5070, Awka, Anambra State. 0500-2300 in English/Igbo – **29)** Delta State Broadc. Sce, Broadc. House P.M.B. 5032, Asaba, Delta State. 0500-2300 in English/others – **30)** Yobe Broadc. Corp, km 6 Gujba Rd, P.M.B. 1044, Damaturu, Yobe State. 0500-2300 in English/others – **31)** Taraba State Broadc. Sces, Broadc. House, adjacent Gen. Sani Abacha State Secretariat, P.M.B. 1038, Jalingo, Taraba State. 0500-2305 in English/others, 25 kW tx on MW, operated at 10 kW: 0500-1100, 1430-2300 – **32)** Broadc. Corp. of Abia State (BCA), Broadc. House, Government Station Layout, B.M.P. 7276, Umuahia, Abia State. **W:** bcanigeria.com 0500-2300 in English/Igbo – **33)** Jigawa Broadc. Corp, Broadc. House, Kiyawa Rd, P.M.B. 7032, Dutse, Jigawa State. 0500-2205 **W:** facebook.com/pages/Radio-Jigawa/1537960919805870?fref=ts – **34)** Osun State Broadc. Corp, Studio 1, Ita-Akogun St, P.M.B. 4425, Osogbo, Osun State. 0500-2300 in English/others – **35)** Kogi State Broadc. Corp, 1 Danladi Zakari Rd, P.M.B. 1095 GRA, Lokoja, Kogi State. 0500-2300 in English/others. **Ann:** "R. Kogi" – **36)** Nasawara Broadc. Sce (NBS), Tudun K. Nasarawa auri, Makurdi Rd, P.M.B. 97, Lafia, Nasarawa State. 24h in English/others – **37)** Broadc. Sce of Ekiti State, Old Ado Ekiti Local Government Secretariat, Okeyinmi, P.M.B. 5343, Ado, Ekiti State – **38)** Bayelsa State Broadc. Corp, P.M.B. 56, Ekeki, Yenagoa, Bayelsa State. "Glory FM" in English/others – **39)** Gombe State Broadc. Sce, Buhari Estate Rd, GRA, Gombe, Gombe State. 0500-2300 in English/others – **40)** Zamfara State R, Mall. Yahaya Secretariat, Off Zaria Road, P.M.B. 01007, Gusau, Zamfara State – **41)** Ebonyi Broadcasting Service (EBBS), Ministry of Information Building, Government House Annex, Abakaliki, Ebonyi State – **42) Nagarta R,** Nagarta Communications Complex, Katabu, Mararraban, Jos, P.O. Box 574, Kaduna. **W:** face-book.com/Nagarta-Radio-341166022644111 D.Prgr: 0430-2305 – **43) R. Gotel,** P.O. Box 5759, Modire (After Yola Bridge), Off Yola-Mubi Expressway, Jimeta-Yola, Adamawa State. **W:** radiogotelyola.com **E:** info@radiogotelyola.com D.Prgr: 24h in English/French.

**EXTERNAL SCE: Voice of Nigeria:** see International Radio section.

**Private FM stations:**
**Alheri R:** Kaduna 97.7MHz **W:** ditvalheriradiokaduna.9f.com – **Brila FM:** Abuja/Lagos/Kaduna/Onitsha 88.9MHz **W:** brilafm.net – **Choice FM:** 103.5MHz – **Cool FM,** 267A, AIM Plaza, Etim Inyang Crescent Victoria Island Annex.P.M.B. 10096, Victoria Island, Lagos:   Port Harcourt 95.9, Abuja/Lagos 96.9MHz. **W:** coolfm.us – **Cosmo FM,** Plot 18, Pocket Estate, Independence Layout, Enugu: 105.5MHz – **Defence FM** (Mil), Abuja: 107.7MHz – **Eko-FM,** Lagos: 89.75MHz – **Freedom R:** Kaduna 92.9MHz, Dutse/Kano 99.5MHz **W:** freedom-radionig.com – **Independent R,** Benin City: 92.3MHz **W:** itvradionigeria.com – **Lafiya Dole R,** Maiduguri: 108.0MHz **W:** facebook.com/lafiyadoleradio – **Liberty R,** Kaduna: 91.7MHz – **Naija FM,** Ibadan: Lagos: 102.7MHz **W:** naija102.com – **Ray Power 1:** Lagos/Abuja 100.5MHz **Ray Power 2:** Lagos/Kano 106.5MHz + rel. in other towns

(Incl. rel. of BBC African Sce in English/Hausa) – **Rhythm FM,** 17A Commercial Ave, Yaba, Lagos: 93.7MHz – **Rhythm 94.7,** Hilltop, Karu, Abuja: 94.7MHz – **Rockcity FM,** Abeokuta 101.9MHz **W:** srockcity-fmradio.com –**Space FM,** Ibadan: 90.1MHz **W:** spacefm901.org.ng – **Splash FM,** Ibadan: 105.5MHz **W:** splashfm1055.com – **Sweet FM,** Abeokuta: 107.1MHz **W:** facebook.com/sweetfm1071 – **The Beat:** Ibadan: 97.9MHz. Lagos 99.9MHz **W:** thebeat97.com thebeat99.com – **Wazobia FM:** for addr. see Cool FM above. Port Harcourt 94.1MHz, Lagos 95.1MHz, Abuja 99.5MHz. **W:** wazobiafm.com – **We FM:** Abuja 106.3MHz. **W:** facebook.com/wefmng – **Vo Women:** Lagos 91.7MHz **W:** wfm917.com **F.PI:** transmitters in other states.
**NB:** about 20 community radio stations also in operation

## NIUE

**L.T:** UTC -11h — **Pop:** 1,600 — **Pr.L:** Niuean, English — **E.C:** 50Hz, 230V — **ITU:** NIU

### BROADCASTING CORPORATION OF NIUE (BCN)
✉ P.O. Box 68, Alofi, Niue, South Pacific. Studio: Fonuakula, Alofi ☎ +683 4226 **E:** sunshine@mail.gov.nu
**LP:** CEO: Trevor Tiakia
**FM:** 88.6MHz 0.1kW, 91.0MHz 0.5kW
**D.Prgr:** Mon-Sat. **N:** international news bulletins from R. Australia/RNZI 1800, 1900, 0200 **Ann:** "This is Radio Sunshine"

**Other Stations:**
Oka Rock FM, Alofi 107.9MHz , OKA-KOA Multimedia Systems, Commercial Centre, PO Box 5, Alofi, Niue, South Pacific ☎ +683 4379 **W:** niuemusic.com **E:** sales@niuemusic.com **D.Prgr:** 24/7 incl. **Sunday** gospel music and evening jazz

## NORFOLK ISLAND (Australia)

**L.T:** UTC +11h — **Pop:** 1,750 — **Pr.L:** English, Pitcairn Norfolk — **E.C:** 50Hz, 230V — **ITU:** NFK

**NB:** Since 1 July 2016, Norfolk Island has been transitioning to greater integration with Australia. The Broadcasting Section of the Norfolk Island Regional Council (R Norfolk) manages all broadcasting services on the island including R Norfolk and the Australian Broadcasting Corporation (ABC) radio retransmissions.

| AM | kHz | Call | kW | Programme |
|---|---|---|---|---|
| 1) | 1566 | VL2NI | 0.1 | R. Norfolk |
| **FM** | **MHz** | **Call** | **kW** | **Programme** |
| 1) | 89.9 | VL2NI | 0.25 | R. Norfolk [stereo] |
| 1) | 91.9 | 2ABCRN | 0.15 | ABC R. National [stereo] |
| 1) | 93.9 | 2ABCFM | 0.05 | ABC Classic FM [stereo] |
| 1) | 95.9 | 2ABCRR | 0.15 | ABC Local R. (Western Plains, Dubbo, NSW) |
| 1) | 98.2 | 2JJJ | 0.25 | ABC Triple J [stereo] |
| 2) | 99.9 | | | Pines FM (Local community programming) |

**Addresses & other information:**
**1)** R Norfolk, New Cascade Road (PO Box 95), Norfolk Island 2899, Australia ☎ +6723 22137 🖷 +6723 23298 **E:** manager@radio.gov.nf & news@radio.gov.nf **LP:** Louci Reynolds ASM Gary Summerscales Contract Tech. **D.Prgr:** 1930-0500 M-F, 1930-0030 Sat-Sun **MW:** relay R. New Zealand National rnz.co.nz from Wellington via satellite overnight daily 0500-1930 **FM:** relay MW during the day, pre-programmed music nightly M-F from 0500 but volunteer announcers with individual prgrs daily evenings (except Wed) at various times otherwise pre-programmed music. **V:** responds promptly to email reports – **2)** Norfolk Island Community Radio ☎+6723 22899 **E:** Pinefm999@outlook.com, **FB:** facebook.com/NIcommunityradio/

## NORTHERN MARIANA ISLANDS (USA Commonwealth)

**L.T:** UTC +10h — **Pop:** 55,194 — **Pr.L:** English, Chamorro, Carolinian, Filipino — **E.C:** 60Hz, 120V — **ITU:** MRA

### FEDERAL COMMUNICATIONS COMMISSION (FCC)
see USA for details

| MW | kHz | kW | Station | MW | kHz | kW | Station |
|---|---|---|---|---|---|---|---|
| 1) | 1080 | 1.1 | KCNM | 2) | 1440 | 1.1 | KKMP |
| **FM** | **MHz** | **kW** | **Station** | **FM** | **MHz** | **kW** | **Station** |
| 3) | 88.1 | 1.8 | KRNM | 3) | 91.5 | 0.6 | KMOP |
| 3) | 89.1 | 0.25 | KRNM | 2) | 92.1 | 0.01 | KKMP |
| 6) | 89.9 | 1.8 | KORU | 4) | 97.9 | 6.5 | KPXP |
| 3) | 90.7 | 0.6 | KCKD | 4) | 99.5 | 17 | KZGU |

| FM | MHz | kW | Station | FM | MHz | kW | Station |
|----|-----|-----|---------|----|-----|-----|---------|
| 5) | 100.3 | 1.1 | KWAW | 1) | 106.3 | 0.25 | KCNM |
| 1) | 103.9 | 3.2 | KZMI | | | | |

**Addresses & other information:**
**1) Choice Broadcasting Company LLC**, PO Box 500914, Saipan 96950-0914 ☎+1 671 2347239 ≣+1 671 2340447 **KCNM**: News/Talk **KZMI**: Adult Contemporary **LP**: GM Bob Webb **Prgr**: 24h – **2) Blue Continent Communications Inc.** PO Box 500815, Saipan 96950-0815 ☎+1 670 233 1440 **W**: cnmiradio.com **E**: kkmp670@gmail.com **LP**: CEO: Rosemond Santos, VP: Gary Sword **Format**: 'Strickly Island' Islands Music – **3) Marianas Educational Media Services Inc** Sunny Plaza, 125 Tun Jesus Crisostomo St #301, Tamuning GU 96913 **E**: darryl@guamtech.com **LP**: CEO: Robert F Kelly, Community Radio Mgr: Darryl Taggerty **KRNM 88.1**: Chalan Kanoa simulcast 24h KPRG Guam, **KRNM 89.1**: Capital Hill simulcast 24h KPRG Guam **Format**: NPR, Public Radio International and BBC World Service, **KCKD**: **Format**: relay WCPE Wake Forest NC **W**: theclassicalstation.org 24h classical music, **KMOP**: **Format**: Melodies of Prayer **W**: melodiesofprayer.com 24h religious – **4) Sorensen Pacific Broadcasting Inc.** PPP415 Box 10000, Saipan 96950 ☎+1 670 2357996 ≣+1 670 2357998 **W**: sorensenmediagroup.com **LP**: SM: Tina Palacios **KZGU** and **KPXP**: 'Power99' Top 40/Islands Music [STA 1.5kw because of typhoon damage] **D.Prgr**: 24h – **5) Magic 100FM** 1st Fl, Naru Building, Susupe, Saipan 96950 ☎+1 670 2345929 ≣+1 670 2342262 **W**: magic100radio. com **E**: kwaw100.3@magic100radio.com **D.Prgr**: 24h – **6) Good News Broadcasting Corp.** 290 Chalan Palasyo, Agana Heights, GU 96910 ☎+1 671 472 1111 ≣+1 671 4774678 **W**: joyfmguam.com **LP**: GM: Matthew Dodd **Format**: simulcast 24h KSDA-FM Guam religious Joy FM Family Friendly Radio.

## NORWAY

**L.T**: UTC +1h (31 Mar-27 Oct: +2h) — **Pop**: 5.3 million — **Pr.L**: Norwegian — **EC**: 50Hz, 230V — **ITU**: NOR

**MEDIETILSYNET (Norwegian Media Authority)**
⌨ Nygata 4, N-1607 Fredrikstad ☎ +47 69301200 ≣ +47 69301201 **E**: post@medietilsynet.no **W**: www.medietilsynet.no **LP**: DG: Mari Velsand

**NORWEGIAN COMMUNICATIONS AUTHORITY**
⌨ PB 93, NO-4791 Lillesand ☎+47 22824600 ≣ +47 22824640 **W**: nkom.no

**NORKRING (Transmission provider)**
⌨ PB 1, NO-1331 Fornebu ☎+47 67892000 ≣ +47 67893611 **W**: norkring.no

**NRK - NORSK RIKSKRINGKASTING AS (Pub.)**
⌨ NO-0340 Oslo ☎+47 23047000 ≣+47 23047575 **Inf.Dpt**: ☎+47 81565900 **E**: info@nrk.no **W**: nrk.no
**LP**: DG: Thor Gjermund Eriksen

| LW | kHz R | kW |
|----|-------|-----|
| Ingøy | 153 b | 100 |

**DAB**: Oslo, Akershus, Østfold 12C. Hedmark, Oppland 13E, Buskerud, Telemark, Vestfold 13A. Trøndelag, Møre og Romsdal 12C. Agder, Rogaland 13F. Nordland, Sør-Troms 13E, Hordaland, Sogn og Fjordane 12B, Nord-Troms, Finnmark12B
**Programmes:**
**P1:**⌨ NO-7005 Trondheim ☎+47 73881400 ≣+47 73881809 24h. **N**: MF on the h also 0530, 0630, 0730, 1130, 1530, 1630. Sat on the h also 0630, 1130. Sun on the h also 0430. Reg. prgrs: see below
**P2:** ⌨ NO-0340 Oslo ☎+47 23047297 ≣+47 23047480 24h cultural prgr. **N**: MF on the h 0500-0000 except 1800, 1900 2000 and 2200. Also 0530, 0630, 0730, 1130, 1630. Sat: on the h. 0500-0000 except 0900, 1200, 1800, 1900, 2000. Also 0630, 1130, 1530. Sun: on the h 0500-2300 except 1200, 1300, 1600, 1800, 1900. Also 1530.
**P3:** ⌨ NO-7005 Trondheim ☎+47 73881600 ≣+47 73881609 24h youth prgr. Rly P1 2300-0500. **N**: MF on the h 0500-2300 except 1600, 1800, 2000, 2200, also 0530, 0630, 0730, 0830. Sat: on the h except 1600, 1800, 2000, 2100, 2200. Sun: on the h except 2200
**Sápmi:** ⌨ PB 183, NO-9730 Karasjok ☎+47 78469200 ≣+47 78469223; 24h in Sami language. Also on P2 MF 1230-1300. Additional prgrs on P2 in northern Norway and Oslo MF 0600-0800, 1300-1630, (Fri also 1200-1230, 1630-1700), Sat/Sun 1700-1800
**Klassisk:** ⌨ NO-0340 Oslo ☎+47 23047882 ≣ +47 23048575. 24h classical music. Some rly P2
**Alltid Nyheter:** ⌨ NO-0340 Oslo ☎+47 23047000 ≣ +47 23045141 24h rolling news. Rly BBC World Service most of the day Sat/Sun and 2100-0500 weekdays
**MP3:** NRK MPETRE: ⌨ NO-7005 Trondheim ☎+47 73881600 ≣ +47

73881609. 24h teenage ch. with techno/dance music. Some rly of P3

**NRK REGIONAL SERVICES:**
On **P1**. **D.Prgr**: MF 0503-0530, 0533-0600, 0603-0630, 0640-0700, 0703-0730, 0733-0800, 0903-0905, 1003-1005, 1103-1105, 1203-1205, 1303-1400, 1405-1500, 1503-1600. Sat: 0703-0705, 0803-0805, 0903-0905
**a)** NRK Buskerud, PB 733 Strømsø, NO-3003 Drammen: Some shared prgr with Telemark and Vestfold, as NRK Østafjells. – **b)** NRK Finnmark, PB 1333, NO-9506 Alta: **153kHz**. Some shared prgr with Troms and Nordland. – **c+h)** NRK Hedmark og Oppland, PB 174, NO-2601 Lillehammer and NO-2418 Elverum. Separate news hrly, remaining prgrs shared – **d)** NRK Hordaland, PB 7777, NO-5020 Bergen – **e)** NRK Møre og Romsdal, PB 1516, NO-6025 Ålesund – **f)** NRK Nordland, PB 1446, NO-8038 Bodø. Some shared prgr with Finnmark and Troms. – **g+l)** NRK Trøndelag, PB 2450 Sluppen, NO-7005 Trondheim and Løshalla 15, NO-7712. Some separate newsbulletins, remaining prgrs shared – **i)** NRK Rogaland, PB 614, NO-4090 Hafrsfjord – **j)** NRK Sogn og Fjordane, PB 100, NO-6801 Førde – **k)** NRK Sørlandet, PB 413, NO-4664 Kristiansand – **m)** NRK Telemark, PB 284, NO-3901 Porsgrunn. Some shared prgr with Buskerud and Vestfold, as NRK Østafjells. – **n)** NRK Troms, PB 6138 Langnes, NO-9291 Tromsø. Some shared prgr with Finnmark and Nordland. – **o)** NRK Vestfold, PB 120, NO-3101 Tønsberg. Some shared prgr with Buskerud and Telemark, as NRK Østafjells. – **p)** NRK Østfold, PB 33, NO-1629 Gamle Fredrikstad – **q)** NRK Østlandssendingen, PB 4555 Nydalen, NO-0421 Oslo.
**Ann**: 1st Prgr: "P1". 2nd Prgr: "P2". 3rd Prgr: "Petre". Sami: "Datlae Sámeradio, Kárássjagás"

**OTHER STATIONS:**
**RADIO NORGE** (Comm.)
⌨ Jernbanetorget 4, NO-0154 Oslo ☎+47 07270 **W**: bauermedia.no / radionorge.no **LP**: MD: Lasse Kokvik
**D.Prgr**: 24h on **DAB**. **N**: M-F: on the h. 0500-2300, also 0630, 0730, 1430, 1530. Sat: on the h. 0800-2300. Sun: on the h.0800-2300
**P4 – RADIO HELE NORGE** (Comm.)
⌨ PB 817, NO-2626 Lillehammer ☎+47 61248444 ≣ +47 61248445 **W**: p4.no **LP**: MD: Trygve Rønningen
**D.Prgr**: 24h on **DAB**. **N**: M-F: on the h 0500-2300, also 0530, 0630, 0730, 1430, 1530, 1630. Sat-Sun: on the h 0700-2300
**RADIO 1 HITS** (Comm.)
⌨ PB 1102 Sentrum, NO-0104 Oslo ☎+47 22023300 ≣+47 22952202 **W**: radio1.no **FM**(MHz): Oslo: 103.4, Bergen: 90.4, 97.1, 106.4, 107.1, Stavanger: 107.2, Trondheim: 96.3. All txs below 1 kW
**RADIO METRO** (Comm.)
⌨ Akersgata 45, NO-0158 Oslo ☎+47 21555910 **W**: radiometro.no **FM** Main freqs (MHz): Oslo: 106.8, Askim: 105.4, Lillestrøm: 107.9, Drammen: 103.8, Hønefoss: 103.5, Gjøvik: 105.8, Lillehammer: 105.0, Elverum/Hamar: 102,9, Trondheim: 104.2/107.0, Stjørdal: 97.5, Levanger: 99.8, Steinkjer: 95.2. All txs below 1 kW
**NRJ NORGE** (Comm.)
⌨ Akersgata 73, NO-0180 Oslo ☎+47 22797500 ≣ +47 22797501 **W**: nrj.no **FM** Main freqs (MHz): Oslo: 90.5, Drammen: 95.3, Kristiansand: 93.2/106.9, Stavanger: 99.3, Bergen: 98.2, Trondheim: 95,5/105.1/106.7 All txs below 1 kW

**Internet**: Most stns provide webstreams and/or on-demand audio sces. **Satellite**: Most NRK-channels, radio and TV (incl NRK regional TV), Radio Norge and P4 are available through satellite.

**LOCAL FM STATIONS**
Around 300 low power FM commercial stns are in operation, some sharing freqs. Many of them organised through Lokalradioforbundet. **DAB**: Almost all local FM stns have been granted an extension until 2022 for using FM. **W**: lokalradioforbundet.no

**AFRTS (U.S. Mil.)**
**FM**: Lifjell 101.5MHz (Stavanger). D.Prgr: 24h rly AFN Europe

**SVALBARD (SPITSBERGEN) (Norwegian Territory)**
**L.T**: UTC +1h (24 Mar-27 Oct: UTC +2h) — **Pr.L**: Norwegian — **E.C**: 50Hz, 230V

**NRK - NORSK RIKSKRINGKASTING AS (Pub.)**
**MW**: Longyearbyen: 1485kHz 1kW
**D.Prgr**: 24h relay NRK P1 on DAB and FM (incl. regional prgr NRK Troms)

| FM | P1 | P2 | P3 | kW |
|----|-----|-----|-----|-----|
| Isfjord R. | 89.7 | 93.6 | 97.3 | 0.05 |
| Ny-Ålesund | 91.3 | 94.8 | | 0.12 |
| Svea | 89.1 | 92.0 | | 0.025 |

**DAB**: Svalbard (Platåfjellet and Longyearbyen) 12B

## OMAN

**L.T:** UTC +4h — **Pop:** 4.8 million — **Pr.L:** Arabic — **E.C:** 50Hz, 240V — **ITU:** OMA

### MINISTRY OF INFORMATION

Omanet Team, Oman Electronic Network, P.O.Box 600, 113 Masqat ☎+968 24603222 🖷 +968 24693770 **W:** omanet.om **E:** omanet@omantel.net.om **L.P:** Minister: Hamad bin Mohammed Al Rashdi

### PUBLIC AUTHORITY FOR RADIO AND TV - RADIO SULTANATE OF OMAN (RSO, Gov.)

P.O. Box 1130, Madinat Al Ilam, 133 Masqat ☎+968 24 601538 🖷+968 24 602831 **W:** part.gov.om **L.P:** DG Radio: Nasser Al-Sybani. DG Eng.: Mohd Salim Al Marhouby. Dir. Freq: Salim Al-Nomani. Dir. Trs: Saif Al-Rasheedi

| MW | kHz | kW | MW | kHz | kW |
|---|---|---|---|---|---|
| Bidiya | 558 | 500 | Salalah | 738 | 100 |
| Haima | 576 | 100 | Barka (Seeb) | 1242 | 500 |
| Buraimi | 639 | 100 | Bahla | 1278 | 100 |

| FM | G | Q | Y | E | kW(TRP) |
|---|---|---|---|---|---|
| Bahla | 107.3 | 96.5 | - | - | 1 |
| Barka | 101.8 | 107.3 | - | - | 5 |
| Batina | - | - | 91.7 | - | |
| Buraimi | 96.1 | 93.0 | - | - | 5 |
| Dhalkut | - | - | 94.5 | - | |
| Dhank | - | - | 91.2 | - | |
| Haima | - | 106.5 | 98.8 | - | |
| Hasikiya | 96.5 | - | - | - | 1 |
| Dakhiliya | - | - | 98.8 | - | |
| Ibra | 93.2 | - | 98.8 | - | 2 |
| Ibri | 99.1 | 106.9 | - | - | 5 |
| Jalan Bani Buali | 88.1 | 97.7 | - | - | 5 |
| Khasab | 100.6 | - | - | - | 1 |
| Madha | 97.4 | - | - | - | 0.1 |
| Masqat | 94.4 | 93.2 | 100.0 | 90.4 | 5 |
| Mazyunah | 88.2 | 88.5 | - | - | 1 |
| Murbat | - | - | 100.0 | - | |
| Nizwa | 88.5 | 100.5 | - | - | 1 |
| Quriyat | 100.4 | - | - | - | 2.5 |
| Sadah | 88.2 | - | 100.0 | - | 1 |
| Saham | 91.1 | 93.6 | - | - | 5 |
| Salalah | - | - | 100.0 | 90.4 | |
| Sayq | 89.3 | 94.0 | - | - | 5 |
| Sur | 97.2 | 87.6 | - | - | 1 |
| Taqah | - | - | 100.0 | - | |
| Thumrait | - | 93.0 | 100.0 | 91.3 | |

**G=General Arabic prgr:** 24h on MW & FM. **N:** 0300, 0700 (Fri 0830), 1300, 1600, 1700, 1900, 2000. **Q=Quran prgr:** 24h. **Al-Shabab (Youth) channel:** 24h. **R. Oman FM in English:** 24h.
**Ann:** A: "Idha'atul Saltanat al-Oman min Masqat." E: "This is the English Service of Radio Sultanate of Oman from Masqat".

**EXTERNAL SERVICE:** See International Broadcasting section.

**Other Stations:**
**Al Wisal FM,** Masqat: 96.5MHz. **W:** wisal.fm — **Hala FM,** Masqat: 102.7MHz. **W:** halafm.com — **Hi FM,** Masqat: 95.9MHz. **W:** hifmradio.com — **Merge FM,** Masqat: 104.8MHz. **W:** radiomerge.com — **Sowt al-Khaleej,** Masqat: 107.7MHz. See Qatar for main entry.
**BBC relay:** Masqat 89.8 (Arabic), 103.2MHz (English).
**R. France Int:** Masqat 92.2MHz in Arabic.
**BBC relay station:** MW (702kHz 1500-2100 & 1413kHz 0030-0400, 1300-2100) & SW: for details see International Broadcasting section

## PAKISTAN

**L.T:** UTC +5h — **Pop:** 208 million — **Pr.L:** Urdu, Punjabi, Sindhi, Pushto, Balochi, English — **E.C:** 50Hz, 230V — **ITU:** PAK

### PAKISTAN ELECTRONIC MEDIA REGULATORY AUTHORITY (PEMRA)

Green Trust Tower, 6th Floor F-6, Jinnah Ave, Blue Area, Islamabad **W:** pemra.gov.pk **E:** info@pemra.gov.pk **L.P:** Chairman: Mr. Absar Alam.

### PAKISTAN BROADCASTING CORPORATION (PBC, Gov.) RADIO PAKISTAN

Broadcasting House, Constitution Avenue, Islamabad 44000 ☎+92 51 9214278 🖷 +92 51 9223827 **W:** radio.gov.pk **E:** info@radio.gov.pk **L.P:** DG: Mr. Shiraz Latif. Dir. of Eng.: Mr. Mohammad Khan.

| MW | kHz | kW | R | MW | kHz | kW | R |
|---|---|---|---|---|---|---|---|
| Peshawar-I | 540 | 300 | K | Peshawar-III | 1170 | 100 | K |
| Khuzdar | 567 | *300 | B | Loralai | 1251 | 10 | B |
| Islamabad | 585 | 500 | F | Peshawar-II | 1260 | 400 | K |
| Lahore-I | 630 | 100 | P | Lahore (city) | 1332 | 100 | P |
| Karachi (Landhi) | 639 | 10 | S | Bhawalpur | 1341 | 10 | P |
| Dera Ismail Khan | 711 | 100 | K | Zhob | 1449 | 10 | B |
| Quetta (Yaru) | 756 | *100 | B | Faisalabad | 1476 | 10 | P |
| Turbat | 981 | *100 | B | Gilgit | 1512 | 10 | K |
| Hyderabad (city) | 1008 | 100 | B | Skardu | 1557 | 10 | K |
| Multan | 1035 | 100 | S | Chitral | 1584 | 10 | N |
| Larkana | 1053 | 100 | S | Sibi | 1584 | 0.25 | B |
| Quetta (city) | 1134 | 100 | P | Abbotabad | 1602 | 0.25 | K |
| Rawalpindi | 1152 | 100 | B | *running on low power. | | | |

**R=Region:** N=North, K=Khyber Pakhtoonkhawa & Northern tribal areas, F=Federal District of Islamabad, P=Punjab, S=Sindh, B=Balochistan.
**NCAC:** News & Current Affairs Channel on MW: 0200-1810/1900 in Urdu & English. Also regional programmes in other languages. Times vary by frequency. **N. in English:** 0300, 0800, 1100, 1300, 1600, 1700. 585/630/756kHz carry Voice of Quran 0200-0700.
**FM93 (community radio stations):** on 93.0MHz in Abbottabad, Bannu, Chitral, Dera Ismail Khan, Faisalabad, Gilgit, Gwadar, Hyderabad, Islamabad, Karachi, Kohat, Lahore, Muzaffarabad, Mianwali, Mithi, Multan, Larkana, Quetta, Skardu and Sargodha. Powers 2-5 kW. (Also r. CRI in Urdu & English).
**Voice of Quran:** 93.4MHz in Islamabad, Karachi, Lahore, Narowal, Peshawar, Quetta, Multan, Bannu, Gwadar, Sibb, Gilgit and Skardu.
**Dhanak FM 94** (music): Islamabad, Karachi and Lahore on 94.0MHz.
**FM101:** information and entertainment channel on 101.0MHz in Abbottabad, Faisalabad, Hyderabad, Islamabad, Kalarkahar, Karachi, Lahore, Larkana, Multan, Muree, Peshawar, Quetta and Sialkot. Powers 2kW except Karachi 5kW.
**Regional prgr:** Khairpur 93.3MHz, Bhit Shah & Rawalpindi 93.5MHz. In tribal areas: R. Paktunhkhwa 92.2MHz. R. Swat 96.0MHz.
**D.Prgr:** as above in Urdu, English and regional languages. Local IDs are usually heard at sign on/off.
**Ann:** "This is Radio Pakistan".
**F.PI: SW:** 1x100kW to be added at Karachi (Landhi).
**FM93:** is being extended to Umerkot, Sukkur, Nawabshah, Jacobabad, Dadu, Badin, Mirpurkhas, Sanghar and Thatta. In total the network will have 47 stns. Prgrs will be 40% English/Urdu and 60% regional. 20 new DRM+ transmitters ordered.

**EXTERNAL SERVICE:** See International Broadcasting section.

### AZAD KASHMIR RADIO (AKR, Gov.)

Broadcasting House, Muzaffarabad (AJK) 13100, via Pakistan. **W:** fm93mirpur.com
**L.P:** Dir: Javed Iqbal.
**MW:** Mirpur 936kHz 100kW.
**SW:** Islamabad (Rewat) ‡7265kHz 100kW.
**FM:** Mirpur 101.4MHz, Muzaffarabad 93.0MHz.
**D.Prgr:** Muzaffarabad channel: 0045-0445 & 1000-1810 on FM. Mirpur: MW: 0045-0515 & 1100-1810, FM: 0045-1900. Rawalpindi-III ("Trakhel") channel (from Islamabad 100kW): 7265kHz: 1100-1300 & 1600-1810 (inactive). Prgrs on all channels also include R. Pakistan NCAC relays.
**Ann:** "Yeh Azad Kashmir Radio Muzaffarabad hay". 936kHz: "Mediumwave na-sau-chattis (936) khz par. Yeh Azad Kashmir Radio hay". SW: "Yeh Azad Kashmir Radio Trakhal hay".
**IS:** "Azad Kashmir" anthem at open and close.

**Other, non-PBC stations** (FM in MHz). Powers normally in Islamabad/Karachi/Lahore 2kW, other cities 1kW and university/public radio 200-500W):
**Apna Karachi 107:** Karachi 107.0. **W:** apnakarachi107.fm — **City FM 89:** Karachi/Lahore/Islamabad/Faisalabad 89.0 **W:** cityfm89.com — **FM 100 Pakistan:** Abbottabad/Gujrat/Hyderabad/Islamabad/Jhelum/Karachi/Lahore/Multan/Rahim Yar Khan 100.0 **W:** fm100pakistan.com — **FM Sunrise Pakistan:** Jhelum 95.0, Sardogha/Sahiwal 96.0, Islamabad 97.0 **W:** fmsunrise.com — **Hamara FM Network:** Kharian 97.0, Mandi Bahuddin 98.0 **W:** hamarafm.com.pk — **Hot FM 105,** Karachi & 13 other cities on 105.0MHz **W:** hotfm.com.pk — **Hum FM,** Islamabad & 5 other cities: 106.2 **W:** hum.fm — **Humara FM,** Faisalabad: 90.0 **W:** humara.fm — **Josh FM,** Hyderabad/Karachi/Lahore: 99.0 — **KUST FM 99,** Kohat: 98.0 **W:** radio.kust.edu.pk — **Mast FM 103,** Faisalabad/Karachi/Lahore/Multan: 103.0 **W:** mastfm103.com.pk — **Power FM,** Abbottabad/Islamabad/Vehari: 99.0 **W:** power99.com.pk — **Punjab Univ. FM,** Lahore: 104.6 0.1kW **W:** pu.edu.pk/news/

fm_schedule2007.asp – **Radioactive 96,** Karachi: 96.0 **W:** radioactive96.fm – **R. Awaz:** Gujranwala & 11 other sites in Punjab on 105.0 **W:** radioawaz.com.pk – **R. Buraq:** Abbottabad/Mardan/Peshawar/Sialkot: 104.0 **W:** radio-buraq.com – **R. One,** Gwadar/Islamabad/Karachi/Lahore: 91.0 **W:** fm91.com.pk – **Suno FM,** 50 transmitters on 89.4MHz **W:** superfmnetwork.com – **Super FM,** Bahawalnagar: 90.0 **W:** sunofm.pk – **VO Kashmir,** Muzaffarabad: 105.0 **W:** vokfm105.com – **Zab FM,** Islamabad/Karachi/Larkana: 106.6 0 **W:** zabfm.org
**China R. Int.** (Urdu/English): Karachi/Islamabad 98.0, Kohat/Lahore/Multan 93.0.
**VOA R. Aap ki Dunyaa:** via Orzu TJK 972kHz 800kW 1400-0200

## PALAU (USA associated)

**L.T:** UTC +9h — **Pop:** 21,964 — **Pr.L:** Palauan, English — **E.C:** 60Hz, 120V — **ITU:** PLW

### T8AA BROADCASTING STATION (Gov)
**Bureau of Domestic Affairs**
PO Box 279, Koror State, Republic of Palau 96940 ☎ +680 4882417 +680 4881932 **L.P:** SM: Ms Eunice Akiwo **E:** ecoparadise@palaugov.net
**FM:** Voice of Palau 87.9 1900-1300 **N:** includes R. Australia via satellite. **Format:** local news, music and talkback

**Other Stations:**

| FM | MHz | kW | Station | FM | MHz | kW | Station |
|----|-----|------|--------|----|------|-----|---------|
| 2) | 88.5 | 0.45 | WWFM | 4) | 89.9 | 0.6 | PWFM |
| 1) | 88.9 | - | KRFM | 3) | 102.5 | 0.2 | T8WH-FM |
| 2) | 89.5 | 0.45 | WWFM | | | | |

**Addresses & other information:**
**1)** Rudimich Enterprises, Sure Save Store, PO Box 2000, Koror 96940 ☎+680 4881359 **E:** rudimch@palaunet.com **ID:** "Island Rhythm" **Format:** Contemporary Top 40 **D.Prgr:** 24h in English/Palauan – **2)** Diaz Broadcasting Co, PO Box 1327, Koror 96940 ☎+680 4884848 +688 5874420 **L.P:** GM Alfonso Diaz, WWFM English & Palaun, KDFM Filipino, classical, jazz, easy listening format **W:** brouhaha.net/palau/wwfm **E:** wwfm@palaunet.com **D.Prgr:** 24h – **3)** Christian Radio 102 5, Palau. World Harvest R., PO Box 12, South Bend IN 46614, USA ☎ (574) 2918200 (574) 2919043 **E:** whr@lesea.com **W:** whr.org **Prgr:** Music and other in-house LeSEA programs in English, also available via Intelsat 19 – **4)** 1A Building [above Dollar 99 store], Room S, Floor 3, Medalai hamlet, Koror ☎ +680 4885350, +680 488 5250 **TXT:** +680 778 5490 US based message line +1 503 928 7718 **W:** palauwaveradio.com **ID:** "Palau Wave Radio" **L.P:** Sha Merirei Ongelungel, GM **Format:** social, cultural & political news, information and music. **D.Prgr:** 24h
**NB:** Calls beginning K and W are unofficial as Palau regulates its own broadc. spectrum. American-style calls are more familiar to locals.

**EXTERNAL SERVICES: T8WH (Rlg.)** See Int. Broadcasting section

## PANAMA

**L.T:** UTC -5h — **Pop:** 4.1 million — **Pr.L:** Spanish — **E.C:** 60Hz, 110V — **ITU:** PNR

### AUTORIDAD NACIONAL DE LOS SERVICIOS PUBLICOS
Vía España, Edificio Office Park, Ciudad de Panamá (Apartado Postal 0816-01235, Zona 5, Panamá ☎ + 507-508 4500 **W:** asep.gob.pa **E:** atencionalusuario@asep.gob.pa

Call HO–, ‡ = inactive, (r) = repeater, ± = varying fq.
Hr of tr 24h unless otherwise stated.

| MW | Call | kHz | kW | Station, location, hr. of tr. |
|------|------|-----|-----|--------------------------------|
| VE01) | | 550 | | R. Estéreo Universidad, Santiago |
| PA03) | H2 | 560 | 3 | RPC Radio, Colón |
| PA03) | H4 | 580 | 10 | RPC Radio, David |
| PA03) | H3 | 590 | 10 | RPC Radio, Chitré |
| PA03) | HM | 610 | 10 | RPC Radio, Panamá |
| HE01) | J35 | 630 | 2 | R. Provincias, Chitré |
| CN01) | K22 | 640 | 2.5 | CPR, Colón |
| PA14) | | 640 | 2.5 | R. Panamá, La Palma |
| PA02) | S22 | 650 | 5 | R. Mía "Cadena Nacional", Panamá |
| PA03) | H5 | 660 | 1 | RPC Radio, Bocas del Toro |
| PA09) | | 660 | 5 | La Nueva Exitosa, Sabana Grande (r: 930) |
| PA06) | LY | 670 | 5 | R. Hogar, Panamá |
| PA26) | F32 | 680 | 5 | Bendición Radio, David |
| DA01) | | 680 | 5 | Voz sin Fronteras, Metetí: 1000-2400 |

| MW | Call | kHz | kW | Station, location, hr. of tr. |
|------|------|-----|-----|--------------------------------|
| PA18) | | 690 | 5 | R. Evangelio Vivo, Panamá |
| PA08) | Q51 | 710 | 10 | KW Radio Continente, Panamá |
| BT01) | B52 | 710 | 5 | Ondas del Caribe, Bocas del Toro: 1000-0400 |
| HE04) | B50 | 720 | 10 | R. República, Chitré: 1100-0300 |
| PA37) | R44 | 740 | 2.6 | La Exitosa, La Chorrera |
| CH03) | N26 | 740 | 5 | R. Cristal, David |
| HE07) | | 750 | 5 | R. Inolvidable, Chitré: 1000-2300 |
| PA10) | XO | 760 | 5 | LV del Istmo, Panamá: 1145-0300 |
| HE05) | L83 | 770 | 10 | R. Nacional, Chitré: 1100-0100 |
| PA07) | | 780 | 5 | MQV Radio, Panamá |
| PA14) | | 790 | 6 | R. Panamá, Santiago |
| CE02) | | 800 | 3 | Tropical 800, Los Santos: 1030-0300 |
| PA11) | G | 810 | 1 | R. 10, Panamá |
| CH05) | F28 | 820 | 3 | R. Ritmo Chiriquí, David: 1100-0400 |
| LS01) | R56 | 830 | 5 | R. Península, Macaracas: 1000-0200 |
| PA12) | L80 | ‡840 | 10 | R. Nacional, Panamá |
| PA09) | | 850 | 1 | La Exitosa, Colón |
| PA09) | T61 | 850 | 5 | La Exitosa de Chiriquí, David (r: 930) |
| HE03) | L55 | 860 | 10 | R. Reforma, Chitré: 1030-0400 |
| PA13) | HO | 870 | 5.5 | R. Libre, Panamá |
| CN02) | B51 | 880 | 1 | R. Visión Panamá, Colón |
| PA14) | | 880 | 2.5 | R. Panamá, Bocas del Toro |
| PA14) | | 880 | 2.5 | R. Panamá, Chiriquí |
| HE02) | Q62 | 890 | 2 | R. Ritmo Stereo, Chitré |
| PA14) | HA | 900 | 10 | CD Radio, Panamá |
| PA02) | S56 | 920 | 5 | R. Mía, Los Santos |
| PA09) | R46 | ‡930 | 10 | La Exitosa, Panamá |
| CH06) | K85 | 930 | 2 | R. Mi Preferida,Pto Armuelles:1000-0400 |
| CH07) | M33 | 960 | 1 | AM Tropical, David |
| PA05) | | 960 | 1 | R. Capital, Panamá |
| VE02) | S97 | 970 | 3 | Ondas Centrales, Santiago: 1000-0300 |
| PA15) | | 990 | 5 | COC Radio (W Radio aff.), Panamá |
| CE01) | K36 | 1000 | 10 | R. Poderosa "La Fuerte", Aguadulce |
| PA16) | | 1020 | 5 | R. Ancón, Panamá: 1000-0400 |
| LS02) | J2 | 1040 | 2.5 | Canajagua AM Stereo, Las Tablas |
| PA17) | WK | 1060 | 10 | R. Metrópolis, Panamá |
| CE02) | | 1070 | 3 | R. Estéreo Mi Favorita, Penonomé |
| PA07) | J24 | 1080 | 5 | R. Mundo Internacional, Panamá |
| PA23) | M92 | 1100 | 5 | LV de la Liberación, Panamá |
| PA19) | M21 | 1120 | 5 | R. Sonora, Panamá: 1030-0300 |
| CE03) | U80 | 1130 | 2.5 | Vox MN, Aguadulce |
| PA20) | B49 | 1140 | 5 | R. Panamericana, Panamá: 1100-0500 |
| CH08) | C20 | 1160 | 5 | Ondas Chiricanas, David |
| PA21) | | 1180 | 10 | R. Chinavisión, Panamá |
| VE03) | U | 1180 | 5 | AM Original, Santiago: 1100-0200 |
| PA11) | E91 | 1210 | 1 | R. Diez, Panamá |
| PA17) | | 1230 | 1 | R. Infantil, Panamá |
| CH09) | M56 | 1240 | 3 | Ondas de Vida, David |
| CE04) | LY | 1250 | 5 | R. Hogar, Penonomé: 0955-0300 |
| PA22) | J22 | 1270 | 3 | R. Tipy Q, Panamá |
| CH13) | | 1290 | 5 | R. Única, Panamá |
| CH13) | S23 | 1290 | 3 | R. Única, Chiriqui |
| CH13) | | 1290 | 5.5 | R. Única, Los Santos |
| CH10) | I417 | 1300 | 5 | R. Baha'ís, Boca del Monte |
| PA25) | | 1330 | 5 | Stereo Fe (Voz Poderosa), Panamá |
| LS05) | | 1340 | 2.5 | Tipikal 13-40, Las Tablas |
| PA36) | Z38 | 1350 | 5 | BBN R., Panamá |
| PA26) | | 1380 | 10 | Bendición Radio, Panamá |
| PA07) | | 1390 | 5 | R. Mundo Internacional, Colón |
| PA27) | T40 | 1400 | 10 | Digital R. Luz, La Chorrera |
| LS03) | H779 | 1410 | 5 | R. Mensabé, Las Tablas: 1000-0300 |
| PA28) | | 1430 | 7.5 | R. Kids, Panamá |
| PA29) | | 1450 | 5 | R. Melodía, Panamá: 1000-0330 |
| BT02) | D42 | 1460 | 0.5 | LV de Almirante, Bocas del Toro: 1400-0400 |
| PA30) | | 1470 | 5 | La Primerísima, Panamá |
| PA38) | | 1490 | 3 | Asamblea Nacional, Cocle |
| PA31) | A95 | 1510 | 5 | Hosanna R., Panamá |
| PA32) | | 1530 | 10 | R. Avivamiento, Panamá |
| VE04) | | 1540 | 4 | Festival 1540 AM, Santiago |
| PA33) | | 1560 | 10 | Cadena Radial Adventista, Panamá |
| PA34) | | 1580 | 1 | Hosanna Manantial, Panamá |

**Province abbreviations:** (Provincias) BT = Bocas del Toro, CE = Coclé, CH = Chiriquí, CN = Colón, DA = Darién, HE = Herrera, LS = Los Santos, PA = Panamá, VE = Veraguas. **N.B:** These abbreviations are not recognized by the Post Office. Letters should carry the full name.
**Addresses & other information:**
**BT00) BOCAS DEL TORO**
**BT01)** Finca 13, Empalme, Changuinola - **FM:** 90.1MHz **W:** bocasondasdelcaribe.com – **BT02)** Calle 6 y Av. N. Almirante.

**CE00) COCLÉ**
**CE01)** Ap. 090 (or Vía al Puerto), Aguadulce **W:** radiopoderosa99.com - **FM:** 99.9MHz – **CE02)** Av. Juan Demóstenes Arosemena, Galerías Aro, Penonomé - **FM:** 91.7MHz – **CE03)** Calle Rodolfo Chiari, Edificio Don Chopo, planta alta, Aguadulce **W:** voxpanama.com - **FM:** 103.7MHz. – **CE04)** La Esperanza, Penonomé **W:** radiohogar.org

**CH00) CHIRIQUÍ**
**CH02)** Ap. 540 (or Av. 8 y Calle A Norte, Barrio Bolívar), David - **FM:** 98.1MHz – **CH05)** Av. D.Noreste, Medio Oeste, David - **FM:** 93.1MHz – **CH06)** Ap. 44 (or Barriada San José), Puerto Armuelles - **FM:** 105.3MHz – **CH07)** Calle Central, David - **FM:** 107.9MHz – **CH08)** Ap. 172 (or Calle Elisandro Calvo, Doleguita), David - **FM:** 100.1MHz – **CH09)** Av.Estudiante, Calle 4 final, Edif.Hermanos Pinzón, David – **CH10)** Ap. 1187, David – **CH13)** Zahita SA, Calle 45, Bella Vista, Ed. El Conquistador, Panamá. Belongs to Sistema Metrópolis **W:** facebook. com/Radio-Unica-Las-Tablas-448956025239635

**CN00) COLÓN**
**CN01)** Calle 2da detras de Panamá All Brown, Colón - **FM:** 101.5MHz, 103.5MHz – **CN02)** Calle 1 Paseo Washington, Colón - **FM:** 105.3MHz

**DA00) DARIÉN**
**DA01)** Calle Principal de Metetí, Metetí. (or Ap. 87-0871 Panamá 7) **W:** facebook.com/RADIO-VOZ-SIN-FRONTERAS-274034529294042 - **FM:** 100.1MHz

**HE00) HERRERA**
**HE01)** Ap. 423 (or Urb.Las Mercedes), Chitré **W:** radioprovincias630. com – **HE02)** Paseo Enrique Geenzier, Chitré. **W:** ritmostereo975.com - **FM:** 97.5 – **HE03)** Ap. 194, Chitré - **FM:** 98.5MHz – **HE04)** Ap. 191, Chitré - **FM:** 103.3MHz – **HE05)** Av. Pérez, Chitré – **HE07)** Ap. 375 (or Calle Francisco Audia), Chitré.

**LS00) LOS SANTOS**
**LS01)** Calle Central, Macaracas - **FM:** 93.7MHz – **LS02)** Ap. 10 (or Av. Belisario Porras, final), Las Tablas **W:** canajaguaamstereo. com – **LS03)** Ap. 20 (or Av. Agustín Cano Castillero), Las Tablas **W:** radiomensabe.com – **LS05)** Los Cerritos, Las Tablas **W:** tipikal-1340am.com

**PA00) PANAMÁ**
**PA02)** Ap. 5117, Panamá 5 **W:** radiomiapanama.com radiomials-s920am.com – **PA03)** Ap. 0827-00116, Avenida 12 de Octubre, Panamá **W:** rpcradio.com – **PA04)** Ap. 6-2323, El Dorado or Calle 63B, Casa N° 2), Panamá **W:** radio-soberana.com – **PA05)** Edif. Orion, P8, Via España frente al PIEX, Panamá – **PA06)** Ap. 102 (or San Francisco de la Caleta, via Cincuentario y Av. José Matilde Pérez), Panamá 9-A **W:** radiohogar.org – **PA07)** Alcalde Díaz, Calle Principal, Panamá **W:** imqv.com – **PA08)** Ap. 87-1324, Panamá 7 (or Vía Argentina, Edif. Carillón, Panamá) **W:** kwcontinente.com **E:** kwcontinente@cableonda. net – **PA09)** Ap. 7462, Panamá 5 **W:** laexitosapanama.com – **PA10)** Ap. 6-1192, (or 66 Oeste N° 641) El Dorado, Panamá. **E:** atrd@panama.c-com.net – **PA11)** Av. 21C norte 31B, Bethania, Panamá **W:** radio10pty.com – **PA12)** Ap. 4950 (or Edif.Dorchester, P5), Panamá 5 **W:** sertv.gob.pa – **PA13)** Edif. Dorchester, Vía España, Panamá 4 – **PA14)** Calle 54 Obarrio, Edificio Plaza Globus, 2do piso, Panamá **W:** radiopanama.com.pa – **PA15)** Edificio Casa de Oración Cristiana, Santa Elena, Parque Lefevre, Panamá **W:** cocradio.com – **PA16)** Calle Cuba y Calle 37, Panamá **W:** radioancon.com – **PA17)** Vía España y Calle 45, Edif. El Conquistador PB, Panamá **W:** radiometropolis. com.pa – **PA18)** Condomino Dorado N° 2, Ofc. 10A, Vía Ricardo J. Alfaro, Panamá – **PA19)** Ap. 87-1165 (or Calle 63 Oeste N° E-21, Urb. Los Angeles), Panamá 7 **W:** sonora1120.com – **PA20)** Ap. 6956 (or Vía José Agustín Arango), Panamá 7 – **PA21)** Sun Tower Mall, Av. Ricardo J.Alfaro, Panamá **W:** chinavision1180am.com – **PA22)** Calle 45, Edif. Conquistador, Bella Vista, P2, Panamá – **PA23)** Rua Estudiante, Antiguí Cine Central, 1861, Santa Ana, Panamá – **PA25)** Iglesia Internacional del Evangélico Cuadrangular, Los Andes N° 2, Panamá **W:** stereoferadio.com – **PA26)** Entrada de Nuevo Chorrillo, frente a la Barriada Fundavico, Distrito de Arraiján, Panamá **W:** bendicion-radio.com – **PA27)** Ap. 473, La Chorrera – **PA28)** Río Abajo, Panamá – **PA29)** Ap. 87-3541 (or Vía Fernández de Córdoba, Jardin Cosita Buena), Panamá 7 **E:** lizbethcardenas@hotmail.com – **PA30)** Edif.La Marqueta, Vía Porras, Panamá **W:** laprimerisimadepanama. com – **PA31)** Ap. 6-8229 (or Calle Erick del Valle y Vía Argentina, Edif. Vicky 2), El Dorado, Panamá **W:** hosanna.pma.org/sradio.htm – **PA32)** Av. Ernesto T. Lefevre, Panamá **W:** avivamiento.com – **PA33)** Ap. 3244, Panamá 3 (or Carrasquilla, Calle 2da N° 39, Panamá) **W:** lavozdepanama.org - **FM:** Colón 105.3 – **PA34)** Sky Phone S.A., Cerro Peñon, Panamá **W:** hosannamanantial.net – **PA36)** Ap. 0860-00356, (or Vía Cincuentenario final, a 300 metros del McDonald's de Río Abajo, después del Edificio La Reina) Panamá – **PA37)** Av. Las Américas, La Chorrera.

**VE00) VERAGUAS**
**VE01) W:** up.ac.pa/portalup/radioestereoup.aspx – **VE02)** Ap. 131, Santiago – **VE03)** Ap. 286 (or Calle 10), Santiago – **VE04)** Calle Calidonia, Ave B Norte, Mercado Público, Santiago **W:** festival1540am.com

**FM in Panamá City (MHz):** 88.1 R. 10 – 88.5 88.5 FM Stereo – 88.9 Sol 88.9 – 89.3 Cool FM – 90.1 Estéreo 89 – 90.5 Super Q – 90.9 RPC Radio – 91.3 Besame – 91.7 Máxima – 92.1 Power 921 – 92.5 La KY – 92.9 YXY – 93.3 Metrópolis – 93.7 María – 94.5 W Radio Panamá – 94.9 Hosanna Capital – 95.3 La Nueva Exitosa – 95.7 KW Continente – 96.1 Stereo Fe – 96.5 TVN R. – 96.9 Caliente Panamá –97.3 WAO 97½ – 97.7 Mix – 98.1 La Mega – 98.9 Ultra Estéreo – 99.3 La 99 – 99.7 Tropic Q – 100.1 Antena 8 – 100.5 Fabulosa Estereo – 100.9 Estéreo Azul – 101.3 R. Disney – 101.7 R. Nacional/SERTV – 102.1 Lo Nuestro – 102.5 FM Corazón – 102.9 Blast – 103.3 Quiubo Estéreo – 103.7 Play FM – 104.1 Telemetro Radio – 104.5 K-Latin – 104.9 Estéreo Vida – 105.7 40 Principales – 106.1 Boom! – 106.5 Rock & Pop – 107.3 Omega Stereo – R. Estéreo Universidad 107.7

## PAPUA NEW GUINEA

**L:T:** UTC +10h; Bougainville: +11h — **Pop:** 8.25million — **Pr.L:** English, Tok Pisin, Motu + 860 ethnic langs — **E.C:** 50Hz, 240V — **ITU:** PNG

**NATIONAL INFORMATION & COMMUNICATIONS TECHNOLOGY AUTHORITY (Gov)**
✉ P.O Box 8444, Boroko, NCD ☎ +675 3033200 🖷 +675 3256868, 3004829 **W:** nicta.gov.pg **E:** licensing@nicta.gov.pg **LP:** CEO: Charles Punaha. Regulator of broadc. and communications (2016)

**NB:** In February 2018 PNG was hit by a 7.5 magnitude earthquake, the epicentre was in the Southern Highlands Province and the surrounding provinces of Hela, Western Province, Sandaun and Enga also suffered considerable damage. This resulted in many of the radio stations in these areas being out of action. There is still much work to be done which means the situation regarding which stations are on the air changes all the time. These listings are as accurate as possible.

**NATIONAL BROADCASTING CORPORATION (Gov)**
✉ P.O. Box 1359, Boroko NCD ☎ +675 325 5233 🖷 +675 325 6296 **E:** - info@nbc.com.pg **W:** nbcpng.com.pg/- **L.P:** MD: Memafu Kapera, Dir.Engineering: Robin Vuvut.
**Netw.: NBC National** (English/Tok Pisin), **NBC Kundu** (Prov.: English/ Tok Pisin & local vernaculars), **Tribe FM** (Nat. English/Tok Pisin)
**NBC National (Voice of Papua New Guinea):**

| MW | kHz | kW |
|---|---|---|
| Port Moresby | 585 | 10 |

| FM | MHz | kW | FM | MHz | kW |
|---|---|---|---|---|---|
| Port Moresby | 90.7 | 1 | Rabaul | 100.8 | 0.3 |

**D.Prgr:** 1900-1400 daily **N:** on the h 1900-1400 **Format:** National public service prgr. **V:** card or letter **F.PL:** FM coverage of NBC National is being expanded nationwide at existing NBC Kundu transmitter sites. **NB:** A full list of NBC National FM stns is available at nbcpng.com radio-frequencies.
**NBC Kundu Network** (local provincial stns often funded in partnership with provincial govs): 90.7MHz from Port Moresby carries some prgrs for the Voice of Blessed Peter Tarot which used to be heard on FM from several locations.

| MW | kHz | kW | Station, slogan, location |
|---|---|---|---|
| 7) | 585 | 2 | NBC Gulf, Kerema |
| 1) | 585 | 2 | NBC Karai, "Maus Bilong Sandaun", Vanimo |
| 18) | 585 | 2 | NBC Western Daru |
| 2) | 585 | 2 | NBC Northern Popondetta |
| 1) | 585 | 2 | NBC Vanimo, "Maus Bilong Sandaun", Vanimo |
| 4) | 675 | 2 | NBC Wewak,"Maus Bilong Sepi", Wewak |
| 10) | 810 | 10 | NBC Morobe, "Maus Bilong Kund", Lae |
| 9) | 810 | 10 | NBC Rabaul, "Maus Bilong Tavuvu", Rabaul |
| 13) | 864 | 2 | NBC Madang, "Maus Bilong Garamut", Madang |
| 2) | 900 | 10 | NBC Kimbe, "Singaut Bilong Tavur", Kimbe |
| 6) | 900 | 10 | NBC Eastern Highlands, Goroka |
| 20) | 1107 | 10 | NBC Alotau, "Maus Bilong Caauka, V. of Kula |
| | 1494 | 10 | NBC National, Wabag |
| 1) | 1593 | 10 | NBC Vanimo, "Maus Bilong Sandaun", Vanimo |

**NB:** None of these MW stations has been heard recently but they are still listed on NBC's webpage.

| SW | kHz | kW | Station, slogan, location |
|---|---|---|---|
| 4) | ‡2410 | 10 | NBC Enga, Wabag |
| 1) | ‡3205 | 10 | NBC Vanimo, "Maus Bilong Sandaun", Vanimo |
| 10) | ‡3220 | 10 | NBC Morobe, "Maus Bilong Kundu", Lae |
| 2) | ‡3235 | 10 | NBC West New Britain, "Singaut Bilong Tavur", Kimbe |
| 7) | ‡3245 | 10 | NBC Gulf, "V. of the Seagull", Kerema |
| 13) | 3260 | 10 | NBC Madang, "Maus Bilong Garamut", Madang |

| SW | kHz | kW | Station, slogan, location |
|---|---|---|---|
| 17) | ‡3275 | 10 | NBC Southern Highlands, Mendii |
| 18) | ‡3305 | 10 | NBC Western, "V. of the Sunset", Daru |
| 11) | ‡3315 | 10 | NBC Manus, "Maus Bilong Chauka", Lorengau |
| 19) | 3325 | 10 | NBC Bougainville, "Maus Bilong Sankamap", Buka ARB |
| 14) | ‡3335 | 10 | NBC East Sepik, "Maus Bilong Sepik", Wewak |
| 12) | ‡3345 | 10 | NBC Northern, "V. of the People of Oro", Popondetta |
| 15) | ‡3355 | 10 | NBC Chimbu, "Karai Bilong Mumbu", Kundiawa |
| 20) | ‡3365 | 10 | NBC Milne Bay, "V. of Kula", Alotau |
| 8) | ‡3375 | 10 | NBC Western Highlands, "Eagle FM", Mt Hagen |
| 9) | ‡3385 | 10 | NBC East New Britain, "Maus Bilong Tavuvur", Rabaul |
| 6) | ‡3395 | 10 | NBC Eastern Highlands, "Karai Bilong Kumul", Goroka |
| 3) | ‡3905 | 10 | NBC New Ireland, "Singaut Bilong Drongo", Kavieng |
| 5) | ‡4890 | 10 | NBC Central, "V. of the Conch-Shell", Pt Moresby |
| 8) | *‡5985 | 10 | NBC Western Highlands, "Eagle FM", Mt Hagen |
| 9) | *‡5985 | 10 | NBC East New Britain, "Maus Bilong Tavuvur, Rabaul |
| 19) | *‡6020 | 10 | NBC Bougainville, "Maus Bilong Sankamap", Buka ARB |
| 20) | *‡6040 | 10 | NBC Milne Bay, "V. of Kula", Alotau |
| 18) | *‡6080 | 10 | NBC Western, "V. of the Sunset", Daru |
| 14) | *‡6140 | 10 | NBC East Sepik, "Maus Bilong Sepik", Wewak |

**NB:** Stns may operate irr. schedules or have long periods of silence because of technical, power, funding or other issues. Broadcasts are sometimes heard during local sports or political events or special anniversaries with little or no advance notice. ‡ Currently inactive on SW but could reactivate without notice. *‡ Licensed but inactive: may be used irr. for events of nat. importance but not necessarily from the same location because of the lack of reliable SW transmission facilities. 3260 & 3325kHz are heard regularly, and 6080kHz is soon to be reactivated according to NBC announcement August 2018

| FM | MHz | kW | Station, slogan, location |
|---|---|---|---|
| 20) | 90.4 | - | NBC Milne Bay, "V. of Kula", Alotau |
| 13) | 90.4 | - | NBC Madang, "Maus Bilong Garamut", Madang |
| 12) | 90.5 | - | NBC Northern, "V. of the People of Oro", Popondetta |
| 4) | 90.6 | - | NBC R. Enga Wabag |
| 1) | 90.7 | - | NBC Vanimo, "Maus Bilong Sandaun", Vanimo |
| 15) | 90.7 | - | NBC Chimbu, "Karai Bilong Mumbu", Kundiawa |
| 14) | 90.8 | - | NBC East Sepik, "Maus Bilong Sepik", Wewak |
| 3) | 90.9 | - | NBC New Ireland, "Singaut Bilong Drongo", Kavieng |
| 7) | 90.9 | - | NBC Gulf, "V. of the Seagull", Kerema |
| 6) | 91.1 | - | NBC Eastern Highlands, "Kam Gud FM", Kainantu |
| 8) | 91.5 | - | NBC Western Highlands, "Eagle FM", Mt Hagen |
| 6) | 91.9 | 3 | NBC Eastern Highlands, "Kam Gud FM", Goroka |
| 9) | 98.3 | - | NBC East New Britain, "Maus Blong Tavuvur", Kenabot |
| 11) | 100.3 | - | NBC Manus, "Maus Bilong Chauka", Lorengau |
| 9) | 101.3 | - | NBC East New Britain, "Maus Blong Tavuvur", Kenabot |
| 9) | 103.3 | - | NBC East New Britain, "Maus Blong Tavuvur", Kenabot |
| 9) | 104.3 | - | NBC East New Britain, "Maus Blong Tavuvur", Kenabot |
| 10) | 105.0 | - | NBC Morobe, "Maus Bilong Kundu", Lae |

**D.Prgr:** 2000-2200, 0800-1200v. **Format:** Non-commercial local music and health, education, public safety and sports prgrs. **N:** NBC National Network. **V:** card or letter, email; send reports direct to stn.
**FM:** An increasing number of Kundu stns now also broadcast locally on FM from existing transmitter sites. **NB:** A full list of current Kundu FM stns is currently still unavailable.
**NBC Tribe FM:** c/o NBC, 1359 Boroko NCD, Port Moresby. 92.3 FM Nationwide. New youth netw. delivered via satellite. **W:** facebook. com/tribefm **F.PL:** FM coverage being expanded nationwide with local relays broadc. from Kundu tx sites but locations currently unavailable.
**NB:** A recent review of provincial stns may result in consolidation of NBC stns; some SW stns are not being repaired or replaced when equipment fails. Satellite delivery of NBC National and Tribe FM to be expanded via local FM txs as funding allows. Local NBC Kundu studio prgrs continue on FM (and SW only as necessary) giving 3 NBC prgr streams (2 national 1 local) at all proposed remaining locations as FM equipment also installed in association with national expansion of Kundu2 TV sce. Funding for provincial Kundu stns allocated at provincial level. National NBC services are centrally funded but need provincially funded infrastructure to be available.

**Addresses & other information:**
**Regions:** ARB=Autonomous Region of Bougainville, Cen=Central, Chi=Chimbu, EHP=Eastern Highlands, ENB=East New Britain, Eng=Enga, ESP=East Sepik, Gul=Gulf, Mad=Madang, Man=Manus, MBP=Milne Bay, Mor=Morobe, NCD=National Capital District, NIP=New Ireland, Or=Oro, SHP=Southern Highlands, WHP=Western Highlands, WNB=West New Britain, WP=Western, WSP=West Sepik
**1)** P.O Box 37, Vanimo, WSP ☎ +675 857 1144/1149 🖹 +675 8571305 – **2)** P.O.Box 412, Kimbe, WNB ☎ +675 983 5600/5185/5010 🖹 +675 9835600 – **3)** P.O.Box 477, Kavieng, NIP ☎ +675 9842077 🖹 +675

984 2191 – **4)** P.O.Box 300, Wabag, Eng ☎ +675 5471013 🖹 +675 5471069 – **5)** P.O Box 1359, Boroko NCD ☎ +675 3217155 🖹 +675 3217110 **FM:** 90.7 carries Karai Network including Tribe FM [youth prgr] Sa 2100-0000 local; **SW:** carries FM 95.5 'Radio Gadona' – **6)** P.O Box 311, Goroka, EHP ☎ +675 732 1618/1733/1607 🖹 +675 7321533 – **7)** P.O.Box 36, Kerema, Gul. ☎ +675 6481076 🖹 +675 6481003 – **8)** P.O.Box 311, Mount Hagen WHP ☎ +675 5421000 🖹 +675 5421001 – **9)** P.O.Box 393, Rabaul, ENB ☎ +675 982 8966/67/68/69/70 🖹 +675 9828971 – **10)** P.O.Box 1262, Lae, Mor ☎ +675 472 1311/7520/4209 🖹 +675 4726423 – **11)** P.O Box 505, Lorengau, Man ☎ +675 4709079 🖹 +675 4709079 – **12)** P.O.Box 137, Popondetta, Or ☎ +675 329 7037/38 🖹 +675 3297362 – **13)** P.O Box 2036, Jomba, Mad. ☎ +675 852 2415/2301/2360 🖹 +675 8522360 – **14)** P.O Box 65, Wewak, ESP ☎ +675 856 2316/2398 🖹 +675 8562405 – **15)** P.O.Box 228, Kundiawa, Chi ☎ +675 7351012 🖹 +675 7351012 – **17)** P.O.Box 104, Mendi SHP ☎ +675 549 1017/1020 🖹 +675 5491017 – **18)** P.O.Box 23, Daru WP ☎ +675 645 9234/9151 🖹 +675 6459319 – **19)** P.O.Box 35 Buka, ARB ☎ +675 9739911 🖹 +675 9739912 – **20)** P.O.Box 111, Alotau MBP ☎ +675 641 1028/1334 🖹 +675 6411028

**MAJOR COMMERCIAL NETWORKS:**
**FM 100 Kalang Advertising Ltd (Telikom PNG subsidiary)**
🖃 P.O. Box 1534, Boroko, NCD ☎ +675 300 4300 🖹 +675 300 4316 **L.P:** CEO: John Mong, Ops Mgr: Bonner Tito **D.Prgr:** 24h via satellite **F.PL:** Continued FM expansion nationwide
**FM(MHz): Brands FM100:** W: fm100.com.pg (No web Page updates since 2016) **E:** info@fm100.com (Unable to make contact with station) **Format:** Contemporary music "PNG's Information & Music Leader" **Sports** relay 2GB Sydney NRL Live Fri/Sat/Sun - 100.1 Kandrian, 100.2 Kavieng/Goroka/Tabubil, 100.3 1kW Pt Moresby/Lorengau/Kimbe/ Tabubil/Finschafen/Mendi, 100.4 Mt Hagen, 100.5 Popondetta/Lae/ Namatanai/Daru/Tari, 100.6 Pomio/Buka, 100.8 1kW Rabaul/Madang/ Wewak, 101.1 Kundiawa, 102.0 Paga Hill, 107.1 Mt Horeatoa/Mt Kainguma, 107.3 Mt Boregoro/Mt Waterholes, 107.7 Mt Dimodimo
**Hot FM:** W: facebook.com/hot97fm E: sashahot97fm@gmail.com
**Format:** youth oriented contemporary music - Port Moresby 97.0 and other locations

**PNGFM**
🖃 P.O. Box 774, Port Moresby NCD ☎ +675 323 4288 🖹 +675 323 1628 **L.P:** MD: Adrian Au, CE: Clezy Rakole **W:** cfl.com.fj/radiopng **E:** aau@naufm.com.pg **D.Prgr:** 24h via satellite
**Netw.: Nau FM** PD: Turner Arifeae **Format:** E, urban westernized youth market **Yumi FM** PD: Rosemary Botong **Format:** Tok Pisin, local and adult contemporary music **Legend FM Bikpla 101:** E, Hits of 1970s-2000s. **F.PL:** Continued FM expansion nationwide
**FM(MHz): Nau FM:** 96.1 1kW Goroka, 96.3 1kW Lae/Madang, 96.5 1kW Kimbe/Port Moresby/Lihir/Rabaul/Lorengau, 96.7 Alotau, 96.9 1kW Mt Hagen. **Yumi FM:** W: facebook.com/pages/93fm-yumi-fm 93.1 1kW Pt Moresby/Lihir, 93.3 Tinputz, 93.5 Mt Hagen, 93.7 1kW Lae/Madang, 93.9 Rabaul/Goroka, 95.0 Kundiawa, 96.3 Balimo **Legend FM Bikpla:** W: facebook.com/pages/legend-fm-png 101.1 Port Moresby/Lae/Madang/Goroka/Mt Hagen/Rabaul/Kokopo

**MAJOR NON-COMMERCIAL NETWORKS**
**Wantok Radio Light – PNG Bible Church**
🖃 Papua New Guinea Christian Broadcasting Network, P.O. Box 1273, Port Moresby NCD ☎ +675 326 2933 🖹 +675 326 1104 **L.P:** GM: Pawa Warena **W:** wantokradio.org **E:** admin@wantokradio. org **D.Prgr:** 24h via satellite **N:** NBC National bulletins 0700, 1900 **Format:** religious **F.PL:** Continued FM expansion nationwide via satellite **Affiliation:** HCJB/Evangelical Bible Missions through Life Radio Ministries, Griffin GA, USA
**SW:** ‡7325kHz1kW Pt Moresby WSP **QSL:** r. to **E:** qsl@wantokradio.org (SW transmitter has been off the air but is due to resume broadcasting in October 2018)
**FM(MHz):** 93.9 1kW Port Moresby, 105.9 Wewak/Kimbe/Buka/ Popondetta/Lae/Kokopo/Kiunga/Goroka/Mt Hagen/Ialibu/Wabag/ Alotau/Mendi/Kainantu/Madang

**CRN (Catholic Radio Network) – Radio Maria**
🖃 Radio Maria PNG Inc, PO Box 8719, Boroko, NCD ☎ +675 325 9178 **L.P:** Father Peter Kote **W:** radiomaria.org **E:** director.pg@ radiomaria.org **Format:** religious **D.Prgr:** 24h via satellite **F.PL:** continued FM expansion nationwide via satellite
**SW:** ‡4960 KHz 1kW Vanimo WSP **ID:** R.St.Gabriel **Address:** P.O Box 205, Vanimo WSP ☎ +675 857 1305 **Prgr:** local studio and network prgrs from Port Moresby **QSL:** qsl@radiomaria.org (Inactive)
**FM(MHz):** 98.1 Mt Hagen 101.0 Kimbe/Mendi 103.5 Port Moresby/ Wewak 103.7 Lae

## OTHER STATIONS:

| FM | MHz | kW | Location | Station |
|----|-----|----|----------|---------|
| 1) | 89.1 | | Port Moresby NCD | Lalokau FM |
| 2) | 89.9 | 1 | Port Moresby NCD | FM Central |
| 3) | 90.0 | 1 | Hela SHP | ECPNG FM |
| 4) | 94.7 | 0.5 | Lae Mor | FM Morobe |
| 5) | 95.3 | | Buka ARB | New Dawn FM |
| 6) | 97.9 | 1 | Port Moresby NCD | 2G 97.9 FM |
| 7) | 101.9 | 0.3 | Port Moresby NCD | R. Australia |
| 7) | 101.9 | 0.3 | Arawa | R .Australia |
| 7) | 101.9 | 0.3 | Lae Mor | R. Australia |
| 7) | 101.9 | 0.3 | Goroko | R. Australia |
| 7) | 101.9 | 0.3 | Mt Hagen | R. Australia |
| 7) | 106.9 | 0.1 | Lae Mor | BBC |
| 7) | 107.6 | 0.1 | Port Moresby NCD | BBC |

### Addresses & other information:

**1)** Port Moresby, NCD ☎+675 320 1888 **W:** facebook.com/lalokau891 **LP:** Dir.Prg5: Peter Heni – **2)** HIRAD Ltd, P.O Box 333, Port Moresby NCD ☎+675 321 0533 – **3)** Evangelical Church of PNG**)** – **4)** Intouch Media, PO Box 3310, Lae Mor ☎+675 479 1477 – **5)** Buka ARB ☎+675 973 9319 🖷+675 973 9285 **LP:** Stn Mgr Aloysius Laukai **W:** bougainville.typepad.com/newdawn **E:** tambolema@daltron.com. pg – **6)** Pacific Adventist University (PAU), PMB, Boroko NCD ☎+675 328 0400 **W:** pau.ac.pg facebook.com/2g.97.9fm **E:** 2g@pau.ac.pg **ID:** "Exalting God above all the earth. Psalms 97.9" NBPOL – **7)** TEPNG, PO Box 1388, Boroko NCD ☎+675 325 6322 🖷+675 325 0350 **L.P:** Mgr Ops Wayne Wilson **E:** wwilson@tepng.com **R. Australia:** 24/7 Pacific stream via satellite from Melbourne, **BBC:** 24/7 Pacific stream via satellite from London.

## PARAGUAY

**L.T:** UTC -4h (7 Oct 18-24 Mar 19, 6 Oct 19-22 Mar 20: -3h) — **Pop:** 6.81 million — **Pr.L:** Spanish, Guaraní — **E.C:** 50Hz, 220V — **ITÚ:** PRG — **Int. dialling code:** +595

### COMISIÓN NACIONAL DE TELECOMUNICACIONES (CONATEL)

🖳 Presidente. Franco N° 780 y Ayolas, Edif. Ayfra, Asunción ☎ 21 438 2000 **W:** conatel.gov.py **L.P:** Pres: Mirian Teresita Palacios Ferreira

| MW | Call | kHz | kW | Station, location, h. of tr |
|----|------|-----|----|-----------------------------|
| AP01) | ZP16 | 550 | 20/12 | R. Parque, Ciudad del Este: 0800-0100 |
| AM01) | ZP15 | 570 | 1 | R. LV del Amambay, Pedro Juan Caballero: 0900-0200 Sun 1100-0020 |
| SP01) | ZP32 | 590 | 5 | R. Ycuámandyyú, San Pedro: 0900-0200 |
| BO01) | ZP30 | 610 | 50 | LV del Chaco Paraguayo, Filadelfia: 0900-0230, SS 1000-0130 |
| SP02) | ZP40 | ±620 | 5 | R. Nasaindý, San Estanislao: 0900-0300(Sat -0000, Sun -2300) |
| CG01) | ZP19 | ±640 | 15 | R. Caaguazú, Coronel Oviedo: 0900-0500 |
| CA01) | ZP4 | 650 | 50 | R. Uno, Asunción: 0900-0430, Sat:24h, Sun 1000-0300 |
| CO05) | ZP74 | 660 | 10 | R. Regional, Concepción |
| AP02) | ZP26 | 660 | 5 | R. Itapirú, Cd. del Este |
| CA02) | ZP11 | 680 | 50 | R. Caritas, Asunción: 24h |
| NE01) | ZP12 | 700 | 12 | R. Carlos Antonio López, Pilar: (rel. R. Nal 920): 0800-0300 |
| PH01) | ZP17 | 720 | 50 | R. Pai Puku, Teniente Irala Fernández: 0900-0100 Sun; silent |
| CA03) | ZP7 | 730 | 50 | R. ABC Cardinal, Lambaré: 24h |
| CZ01) | ZP38 | 740 | 1/0.5 | R. Hechizo, Caazapá |
| CA04) | ZP42 | 750 | 5 | R. LV de la Policía Nacional, Asunción |
| IP01) | ZP80 | 760 | 25/10 | R. Encarnación, Encarnación |
| CA05) | ZP70 | 780 | 30 | R. Primero de Marzo, Asunción: 24h |
| CN01) | ZP27 | 800 | 5/3 | R. Mbaracayú, Salto del Guairá: 24h |
| CA13) | ZP23 | 800 | 5 | La Union R800, Asunción: 1000-0300 Sat: 1400-2100 Sun: 1100-2000 |
| GU01) | ZP6 | 840 | 5 | R. Guairá, Villarrica: 0900-2400 |
| CR01) | ZP28 | ±860 | 1 | LV de la Cordillera, Caacupé: 0900(SS 1000)-0400 |
| CE01) | ZP33 | ±890 | 5/0.5 | R. Tres de Febrero, Itá (895 at night) |
| CA06) | ZP1 | 920 | 20/100 | R. Nal del Paraguay, Chaco-i: 0800-0300 |
| CA07) | ZP9 | 970 | 80 | R. 9-70 , Asunción: 0800-0300 |
| AM02) | ZP31 | 980 | 5 | R. Mburucuyá, Pedro Juan Caballero: 0900-0130 |
| CE02) | ZP36 | 1000 | 5/0.5 | R. Mil, San Antonio: 0930-0400 |
| CA08) | ZP14±1020 | | 25 | R. Ñanduti, Asunción: 24h |
| MI01) | ZP43 | 1040 | 5 | R. Arapysandú, San Ignacio: 0900-0200 |
| CE03) | ZP25 | 1080 | 10 | R. Monumental, Caco-i: 1100(Sun 0900)-2330 |
| AM03) | ZP71 | 1100 | 5 | R. Ñú Verá, Capitán Bado |
| CE04) | ZP24 | 1120 | 10 | La Deportiva, San Lorenzo: 0900-0300 |
| CR02) | CP22 | 1140 | 5/2 | R. Central de Notícias, Atyrá |

| MW | Call | kHz | kW | Station, location, h. of tr |
|----|------|-----|----|-----------------------------|
| CA09) | ZP72 | 1160 | 10 | R. Antena Dos, Asunción |
| CG02) | ZP52 | 1180 | 5/1 | R. Coronel Oviedo – RCO-AM, Coronel Oviedo |
| AP03) | ZP45 | 1190 | 5 | LV de la Libertad, Henendarias |
| CE05) | ZP44 | 1200 | 10 | R. Libre, Fernando de la Mora:0930-0130, |
| CA10) | ZP3 | 1250 | 5 | R. Asunción, Asunción |
| GU03) | ZP34 | 1260 | 5 | R. Panambi Vera, Villarrica |
| AP04) | ZP53 | 1280 | 10/025 | LV del Este, Cd. del Este (F.PI. to 1310) |
| CA11) | ZP53 | 1300 | 5 | R. Fe y Alegria, Villa Hayes |
| AP04) | ZP53 | 1310 | 10/025 | LV del Este, Cd. del Este |
| CA12) | ZP13 | 1330 | 10 | R. Chaco Boreal, Asunción: 24h |
| CO01) | ZP37 | 1360 | 5 | R. Yby Ya'u, Ybu Ya'u |
| CO02) | ZP8 | 1380 | 1 | R. Concepción, Concepción |
| CO03) | ZP42 | 1400 | 5 | R. Güyrá Campana, Horqueta |
| MI02) | ZP35 | 1430 | 2 | R. Mangore, S. Juan Bautista: 0900-0200 (Sun -0000) |
| CO04) | ZP29 | 1450 | 5 | R. Vallemi, Vallemi |
| AM04) | ZP23 | 1480 | 1 | R. Dos Fronteras, Bella Vista Norte |
| CE06) | ZP20 | 1480 | 5 | R. América, Nemby: 24h |

| SW | Call | kHz | kW | Name, location and h of tr |
|----|------|-----|----|----------------------------|
| BO1) | ZP30 | 6884 | 0.1 | LV del Chaco Paraguayo, Filadelfia: (USB) |
| PH1) | ZP17 | 6890 | 0.1 | R. Pa'i Puku, Tte. Irala Fernández: (USB) |
| CE7) | | 12000 | 0.001 | R. LICEMIL, Ypané (Comms Training Prgr) |

**NB:** ± = varying freq.

### Addresses & other information:

**AM00 (AMAMBAY)**
**AM01)** 14 de Mayo 485 esq Cerro León, Pedro Juan Caballero ☎336 272537 **W:** amambay570.com.py **E:** amambay570@gmail.com - **FM:** 100.5MHz – **AM02)** Villa María Victoria, Fracción San Jorge, Pedro Juan Caballero ☎336 272528 **W:** mburucuya.com.py – **AM03)** Estrella c/4 de Enero, Capitán Bado, Amambay ☎337 230262 **W:** capitanbadonoticias.com/radio1100 **E:** radiozp71@gmail.com – **AM04)** Calle Iturbe 146, Bella Vista Norte ☎ **FM:** 92.5MHz

**AP00 (ALTO PARANA)**
**AP01)** Km 10 Av San Blas.. Ciudad del Este **W:** Facebook: RadioParqueFm1025 – **FM:** 102.5 MHz – **AP02)** Av Coronel Sánchez 3800, Cd del Este **W:** radioitapiru.com **E:** radioitapiru@hotmail.com - **FM:** 96.1MHz – **AP03)** Juan E.O´Leary 152, 1a piso, Oficina 5, Hernandarias **W:** radiolavozdelalibertad1190.jimdo.com – **AP04)** Avenida San Blás No 353, Ciudad del Este ☎61 512 583 **W:** lavoz.com. py **E:** lavozam@hotmail.com

**B000 (BOQUERÓN)**
**BO01)** 29 Filadelfia, 9300 Fernheim ☎491 432330 🖷491 432501 **W:** zp30.com.py **E:** info@zp30.com.py

**CA00 (CAPITAL)**
**CA01)** Av Mariscal López 2948 c/MacArthur, Asunción ☎ 21 603400 **W:** hoy.com.py/radio-uno **E:** info@radiouno.com.py – **CA02)** Kubischek 661 y Azara, (Cas 1313), Asunción **W:** caritas.com.py **E:** caritas@caritas.com.py ☎21 213570 🖷21 204161 – **CA03)** Yegros 745, Asunción ☎21 415 1730 **W:** abc.com.py/730am/ **E:** 730am@abc.com.py – **CA04)** Comandancia de la Policia Nacional, El Paraguayo Independiente c/Chile, Asunción ☎ 21 492 515 **W:** fmenvivo.com/la_voz_de_la_policia **E:** rrpnacional@gmail.com – **CA05)** Av Perón y Concepción Prieto Yegros, Asunción ☎21 300380 **W:** 780am.com.py **E:** administracion@780am.com.py – **CA06)** Av Blas Garay 241e/Yegros e Iturbe, Asunción ☎21 390 376 🖷21 390 375 **W:** radionacional. gov.py **E:** contacto@radionacional.com.py – **CA07)** Av Rodriguez de Francia 34, Asunción ☎21 450 283 **W:** radio970am.com.py **E:** info@radio970am.com.py – **CA08)** Choferes del Chaco 1194, Asunción ☎21 604308 **W:** nanduti.com.py **E:** publicidad@holdingderadio.com. py – **CA09)** Estados Unidos 2019, Asunción – **CA10)** Capitán Lombardo 174 y Av Artigas, Asunción ☎21 282 661 – **CA11)** O´Leary 1847 c/ Séptima Proyectada, Asunción ☎21 371659 **W:** radiofeyalegriapy. org **E:** comunicaciones@feyalegria.org.py – **CA12)** Alejo Garcia 2589 con Rio de la Plata, Asuncion ☎21 425 589 **W:** chacoboreal.com. py **E:** info@chacoboreal.com.py – **CA13)** Av Republica Argentina 316 (con Souza), Asunción ☎21 611 370 **W:** launionr800.com.py **E:** info@launionr800.com.py

**CE00 (CENTRAL)**
**CE01)** Av Enrique Doldán Ibieta y Presidente Franco, Itá ☎24 32543 **Guaraní:** 0900-1000, 1330-1430, 1800-1845 – **CE02)** ☎21 674000 **W:** radio1000.com.py **E:** info@radio1000.com.py – **CE03)** Av General Aquino 9999 y José Bonifacio, Luque ☎21 644330 **W:** monumental. com.py **E:** mensajes@monumental.com.py – **FM:** 91.9 MHz Estación 40 – **CE04)** Av Médicos del Chaco 6229 – Asuncion ☎21 307 1012 **W:** ladeportiva.com **E:** info@ladeportiva.com – **CE05)** Av Zavalaa Cué 1620, Fernando de la Mora Zona Sur ☎21 509 087 🖷21 509076 **W:** rllibre.wordpress.com/la-fundacion-libre **E:** radiolibre@gmail.com – **CE06)** Cas 2220, Asunción ☎21 964 100 **W:** radioiglesia.com **E:** iglesiaradio@gmail.com – **CE07)** Liceo Militar "Acosta Ñur" Ypané

**CG00 (CAAGUAZÚ)**
**CG01)** Jóvenes por la democracia c/ Km 131, Coronel Oviedo ☎521 1202251**W:** FB: - Radio Caaguazú – **FM:** 102.3MHz R.Más – **CG02)** Av Mariscal Estigarribia 304 casi Yrendague, Coronel Oviedo ☎521 202579 **W:** FB: - Radio Coronel Oviedo **E:** rco1180@hotmail.com - **Guaraní:** 50% of prgr 0900-0100 - **FM:** 91.9MHz FM del Sol
**CN00 (CANINDEYÚ)**
**CN01)** Eduardo López Moreira 5155, Salto del Guairá ☎462 42 350
**CO00 (CONCEPCIÓN)**
**CO01)** Av San Juan y alas Paraguayo, Ybu Ya'u ☎39 210 263 **W:** Facebook: Radio Yby Yby ZP37 **E:** carlosescobar777@hotmail. es – **CO02)** Panchito López 241 entre Prof.Cabral y Screiber, (Cas 78), Concepción ☎31 242318 🖷31 242254 – **CO03)** José Luís Arbues c/ Ruta 5, Horqueta ☎32 222364 – **CO04)** Zona Urbana, Vallemi ☎351 230329 – **CO05)** Av Pinedo y Mayor Lorenzo Medina, Concepción ☎331 243589 **W:** Facebook: Radio Regional 660 AM **E:** contacto@radioregional660.com
**CZ00 (CAAZAPA)**
**CZ01)** Mariscal Estigarribia esquina Boulevard Villarica,Caazapá ☎542 232607 **E:** causacomunpy@hotmail.com
**CR00 (CORDILLERA)**
**CR01)** Dr Venancio Pino y 3ra Proyectada, Caacupé ☎511 423326 **W:** radiozp28.com **E:** cordillera860am@hotmail.com – **CR02)** Atyrá
**GU00 (GUAIRA)**
**GU01)** Pte Franco 788 y Alejo Garcia, Villarrica ☎🖷 54 142385 **W:** radioguaira.com.py **E:** info@radioguaira.com.py – **FM:** 103.5MHz – **GU03)** Angostura y Olimpio, Bo Ybarotu, Villarrica ☎541 42229 **W:** Facebook: Radio Panambivera **E:** panambivera@grupopanambi.com
**IP00 (ITAÚA)**
**IP01)** Mcal Estigarribia – casi 14 de Mayo – Centro, Encarnación ☎71 205195 **W:** radioencarnacion.com **E:** gerencia@radioencarnacion.com – **FM:** 95.7 MHz
**MI00 (MISIONES)**
**MI01)** Av Mariscal López y Capitan del Puerto, San Ignacio ☎82 232374 **W:** arapysanduam.blogspot.no **E:** arapysanduam@gmail.com – **MI02)** Coronel Alfredo A Ramos esq San Juan, San Juan Bautista, Misiones ☎81 212 306 **W:** radiomangore.com/index **E:** mangoream@hotmail.es
**NE00 (ÑEEMBUCÚ)**
**NE01)** Alberdi y Av Iralda, Pilar ☎786 232219 **W:** radionacionaldelparaguay.com.py **E:** zp12pilar@gmail.com
**PH00 (PRESIDENTE HAYES)**
**PH01)** Tta. Irala Fernández, Ruta Transchaco km-. 389, Chaco ☎424 270349 (In Asuncion J. Eulogio Estigarribia c/ M. Molas ☎21 605754) **W:** radiopaipuku.org.py **E:** rppuku@tigo.com.py
**SP00 (SAN PEDRO)**
**SP01)** Ruta 11 Juana M de Lara, Villa de San Pedro ☎34 2222300 **W:** Facebook: Radio Ycuamandyyu **E:** radioycuamandyyu@gmail.com – **SP02)** Av Cnl. Zoilo González e/ Pedro Juan Caballero y Mauricio José Troche, San Pedro ☎43 4342 2095 🖷43 4342 0292 **W:** radionasaindy.com.py

**FM in Metro Asunción (MHz):** 88.3 R. Ñemby – 89.1 R. Conquistador – 90.1 R.Viva – 90.7 Ysapy – 91.1 Estacion 40 – 91.5 R. Top Milenium – 91.9 Hit FM – **CA3:** 92.3 Los 4o Principales – 92.7 R. Fernando de la Mora – 94.7 R. Azul y Oro – **CA6:** 95.1 R.Nacional – 95.5 Rock & Pop – 95.9 R. Amor – 96.5 R. Disney – **CA5:** 97.1 FM Latina – 97.9 R. Nuevo Tiempo – 98.5 Yacyretá – 99.1 R. Corazón – 100.1 Canal 100 – 100.5 Arpa –100.9 Monte Carlo – 101.3 R. Farra – 101.7 FM Puerto Elsa – 102.1 R. Obedira – 102.7 Aspen Classic FM – 103.1 FM Popular – 103.7 R. Lambaré 2000 – 105.1 R. Venus– 106.1 FM Paraguay – 106.9 R. Urbana – 107.3 R. Maria – 25) 107.7 FM Concert

## PERU

**LT:** UTC -5h — **Pop:** 32 million — **Pr.L:** Spanish, Quechua, Aymara — **E.C:** 60Hz, 220V — **ITU:** PRU — **Int. dialling code:** +51

## MINISTERIO DE TRANSPORTES, COMUNICACIONES, VIVIENDA Y CONSTRUCCION
Dirección General de Telecomunicaciones
✉ Jr. Zorritos N° 1203, Lima 1 ☎ 1 1 6157800 **W:** mtc.gob.pe **E:** estadistica@mtcgob.pe **L.P:** Viseministro de comunicaciones: Raúl Ricardo Pérez – Reyes Espejo

## ASOCIACION DE RADIO Y TELEVISION DEL PERU (ARTV)
✉ Av. Manco Capac N° 333, Lima 13 ☎ 1 3321656

| MW | Call | kHz | kW | Station, location, h of tr. |
|---|---|---|---|---|
| LM01) | OBX4E | 540 | 10 | R. Inca del Perú, Lima: 24h |

| MW | Call | kHz | kW | Station, location, h of tr. |
|---|---|---|---|---|
| LL01) | OCX2D | 540 | 1 | R. San Antonio, El Porvenir |
| TC20) | OBU6W | 550 | 1 | R. Bacan Sat // 750, Pocollay |
| JN49) | OBU4M | 560 | 1 | R. Bacan Sat, Sicaya |
| LM02) | OBZ4L | ±560 | 5 | R. Oriente, Lima |
| LB01) | OBX1H | 560 | 5 | Radiomar, Chiclayo |
| IC33) | OAM5I | 570 | 1 | R. OAM5I, Salas |
| LB02) | OAU1M | 570 | 3 | R. Univ. Nal. Pedro Ruiz Gallo, Lambayeque |
| LL51) | OAM2M | 570 | 3 | R. Antena 9, Huamachuco |
| CJ01) | OAX2E | 580 | 10 | R. Marañón, Jaén: 24h |
| LL02) | OCY2L | 580 | 1 | R. El Sol, La Esperanza |
| LM03) | OAX4M | 580 | 12 | R. Maria, Lima: 24h |
| PU58) | OAM7N | 580 | 1 | R. Publica, Puno |
| AQ02) | OCX6V | 590 | 1 | NSE R., Arequipa |
| IC28) | OAM5E | 590 | 1 | R. Sembrador, Chincha |
| LL03) | OBX2B | 600 | 1 | R. Onda de Paz (IPDA), Trujillo: 24h |
| LM04) | OBZ4W | ‡600 | 10 | R. Cora, Lima: 24h |
| MQ19) | OCU6S | 600 | 1 | R. OCU6S, Marsical Nieto |
| PI55) | OCU1K | 600 | 1 | R. Frias, Frias |
| CJ32) | OCY2I | 610 | 6 | R. Santa Monica, Chota: 1100-0100, Sun 1145-1700 |
| PU61) | OAM7M | 610 | 1 | R. Continental, Ayaviri |
| TC19) | OBU6V | 610 | 1 | R. OBU6V, Pocollay |
| AQ53) | OCX6K | 620 | 1 | R. Maria, Uchumayo, Aqp |
| LL04) | OAX2M | 620 | 0.4 | R. Chepen, Chepen |
| LM05) | OBU4B | 630 | 1 | R. Ovación, san Isidro |
| CU72) | OBU7I | 630 | 1 | Chaski R., Urubamba: 1000-1500, 1700-0100 |
| PI04) | OBX1U | 630 | 18 | R. Cutivalú "LV del Desierto", Castilla: 1000-0100 Sat/Sun 1100 |
| LB03) | OAU1Y | 640 | 3 | R. La Luz, José Leonardo Ortiz |
| LM06) | OAZ4K | 640 | 10 | R. Del Pacifico, Lima: 1030-0430 |
| PU01) | OBX7B | 640 | 10 | R. Onda Azul, Puno. 0800-0400, S/S -0300 |
| AM11) | OAU9D | ‡650 |  | R. Kampgakis, Nieva |
| CJ67) | OBU2P | 650 | 1.5 | R. Bendición Cristiana, Huambos: 1000-0400 |
| IC25) | OCU5Q | 650 | 1 | R. OCU5Q, Pueblo Nuevo |
| LL05) | OAX2N | 650 | 1 | R. Regional del Norte, Trujillo |
| PU57) | OBM7C | 650 | 1 | R. OBM7C, Sandia |
| TC24) | OCU6L | 650 | 1 | R. OCU6L, Alto de la Alianza |
| CU35) | OAZ7J | 660 | 3 | R. Santa Monica, Wanshaq |
| LB04) | OCX1U | 660 | 3 | R. J.H.C., Chiclayo |
| LM07) | OCX4R | 660 | 10 | R. La Inolvidable, Lima: 1100-0700 |
| PU02) | OAX7H | 670 | 10 | R. Nal.. del Perú, Puno |
| CJ03) | OCY2Y | 680 | 1 | R. San Luis, Jaén |
| CU73) | OBU7G | 680 | 1 | R. Vida, Cusco |
| IC01) | OAX5E | 680 | 1 | Emisora del Pacifico, Ica: 1100-0100 |
| LL06) | OBX2L | 680 | 0.5 | R. Amauta, Chócope |
| LM08) | OBX4A | 680 | 20 | R. RBC, San Isidro |
| MQ20) | OCU6Q | 680 |  | R. Americana, Moquegua |
| PA13) | OAM4B | 680 | 5 | R. OAM4B, Chaupimarca |
| CU74) | OAM7C | 690 | 1 | R. Altiva, Yanaoca |
| CU04) | OBU7K | 700 | 1 | R. La Salle, Maras |
| JN01) | OBU4J | 700 | 3 | R. La Luz, El Tambo |
| LL07) | OBU2T | 700 | 1 | R. Sausal Superior, Ascope |
| LM09) | OBZ4H | 700 | 25 | R. R. Integridad, San Miguel |
| SM15) | OAU9A | 700 | 10 | R. Maria, Moyobamba |
| AQ04) | OAU6L | 710 | 1 | R. Amor, Socabaya, Aqp |
| CJ63) | OCU2X | 710 | 5 | R.TurboMix, Cajamarcal |
| CO2) | OBX5Q | 710 | 5 | R. Programas del Perú, Ica |
| MD01) | OCX7I | ‡710 | 10 | R. Nacional del Peru, Puerto Maldonado |
| CU05) | OBU7D | 720 | 3 | NSE R., Santiago |
| JN04) | OAU4E | 720 | 10 | R. Sideral, La Oroya: 24h |
| LL08) | OAX2J | ‡720 | 25 | R. Nal.. del Perú, Trujillo |
| LB06) | OAU1O | 720 | 0.5 | R. Frecuencia Oceánica, San José |
| PU45) | OCU7J | 720 | 2 | R. Noticias, Puno |
| CJ05) | OBU2Q | 730 | 2.5 | R. Maria, Cajamarca |
| LM10) | OAX4G | 730 | 50 | R. Programas del Perú - RPP, San Isidro:24h |
| PI05) | OAX1D | 730 | 10 | R. del Pacifico, Piura: 1100-0500 |
| PU52) | OAM7X | 730 | 1 | R. Altura, Macusani: 0900-0100 |
| TC20) | OCU6G | 730 | 1 | R. OCU6G, Tacna |
| AQ05) | OAX6C | 740 | 10 | R. Continental, Paucarpat Aqp |
| CJ38) | OBX2U | 740 | 5 | R. Ilucan, Cutervo: 1000-0400 |
| CU06) | OBU7C | 740 | 1 | R. Rede, Cusco |
| JN46) | OCU4X | 740 | 3 | R. Vision, Huancayo |
| LL09) | OCX2X | 740 | 1 | R. El Puerto, Pascamayo |
| PU50) | OAM7R | 740 | 1 | R. Publica, Juliaca |
| CU75) | OCU7O | 750 | 1 | R. Tupac Amaru/FM, Yanaoca Canas: 0900-0200 |
| PA01) | OCX4X | 750 | 10 | R. Los Andes, Cerro de Pasco: 1000-0400 |
| IC27) | OAM5D | 750 | 1 | R. OAM5D, Chincha |
| TC14) | OBU6I | 750 | 1 | R. Bacan Sat, Pocollay |
| SM19) | OAU9G | 750 | 5 | R. OAU9G, Bellavista |
| AP11) | OBU5B | 760 | 1 | R. Municipal, Chincheros |
| CU91) | OCX7V | 760 |  | R. Cadena Los Andes, Chaski |
| LL10) | OBX2K | 760 | 0.5 | R. Andino, Otuzco |

| MW Call | kHzkW | Station, location, h of tr. |
|---|---|---|
| LM11) OCU4Q | 760 10 | R. Bienstar, Chorillos //1360 : 24h |
| MD10) OBM7K | 760 1 | R. OBM7K, Mazuku |
| PU59) OAM7Q | 760 1 | R. Azángaro, Azángaro |
| AQ06) OBX6H | 770 2.5 | R. La Inolvidable, Caiama, Aqp |
| CU76) OCU7K | 770 1 | R. LV Evangelica, Urcos |
| LB31) OCX1T | 770 3 | R. Vision, José Leonardo Ortiz: 24h |
| PU03) OAU7D | 770 2.5 | R. Allinccapac, Macusani |
| AY31) OCU5L | 780 2 | R. OCU5L, Ayacucho |
| CJ07) OBU2N | 780 1 | R. Coremarca, Bambamarca: 1000-0200 |
| LM12) OAX4X | 780 3 | R. Victoria,Lima: 24h |
| PU04) OAZ7S | 780 10 | R. Nuevo Tiempo, Juliaca: 24h |
| TB01) OAX1K | 780 10 | R. Nal. del Perú, Tumbes |
| CU07) OAZ7H | 790 3 | R. La Luz, Cusco |
| CL11) OAX2I | 790 10 | R. Programas del Perú - RPP, Trujillo |
| TC16) OBU6D | 790 2.5 | R. Uno, Tacna |
| AQ07) OBX6A | 800 0.3 | Contacto Sur, Cerro Colorado, Aqp |
| CJ71) OCU2Y | 800 3 | R. Vision, Cajamarca: 24h |
| IC03) OBX5B | ‡800 0.5 | R. Sur, Ica |
| JN05) OBU4D | 800 1 | R. Vida, Huancayo |
| LM13) OAU4H | 800 0.5 | R. La Luz, Huaral |
| PI06) OCX1P | 800 1 | Telecom del Norte, Piura |
| AY19) OBU5E | 810 1.5 | ABC Radio TV, Huamanga |
| AP19) OCU5Z | 810 3 | R. Asociación Cultural Tintaya, Cotabambas |
| CJ80) OCU2V | 810 1 | R. Nor Andina, Jaen |
| CU70) OAM7E | ‡810 5 | R. Jerusalen, Cusco |
| LL12) OAU2G | 810 1 | R. Apocali, Trujillo |
| MQ14) OCU6Q | 810 2 | R. R.Santa Cruz, Moquegua |
| MQ16) OCU6R | 810 1 | R. OCU6R, General Sanchec |
| PU05) OAX7T | 810 10 | R. Programas del Perú - RPP, Juliaca: 24h |
| CJ43) OBX2J | 820 0.5 | R. Nuevo Continente, Cajamarca |
| PI54) OBU1X | 820 | R. Vision, Piura |
| LM14) OAX4O | 820 20 | R. Libertad, Lima: 1000-0900 |
| CU08) OAZ7U | 830 1 | R. Inti Raymi, Santiago: 0900-0100 |
| CJ62) OCU2M | 830 1 | R. Universo, Bambamarca |
| JN06) OAU4C | 830 10 | R. Capital, El Tambo |
| LL52) OAM2A | 830 5 | R. Educacion, Trujillo |
| PU53) OAM7W | 830 1 | R. OAM7W, Macusani |
| TC02) OAX6D | 830 10 | R. Nacional del Perú, Tacna |
| AN01) OAU3Q | 840 1 | R. Vision, Casma: 24h |
| AN25) | 840 | R. Campesina, Huari: 24h |
| AP15) OCU5N | 840 1 | R. OCU5N, Abancay |
| AQ01) OBX6Y | 840 1 | R. Azul, Cayama Aqp: 24h |
| CJ08) OAU2E | 840 1 | R. Nuevo Continente, San Ignacio |
| CU58) OCU7I | 840 1 | R. Santa Cruz, Kunturkanki |
| PI50) OCU1C | 840 1 | R. Campesina de Ayabaca), Ayabaca |
| AM12) OBX9W | 850 1 | R. OBX9W, Chachapoyas |
| CU77) OAM7I | 850 5 | R. Lorena, San Sebastian |
| HN19) OBU3B | 850 1 | R. OBU3B. Cerro Jactay |
| HV08) OAM5L | 850 1 | R. OAM5L, Acori |
| LB49) OCU1Y | 850 1 | R. OCU1Y, Chiclayo |
| LM15) OAX4A | 850 40 | R. Nal. del Perú, Lima: 24h |
| PI56) OBU1M | 850 1 | R. Nal. del Peru, Ayabaca |
| TC11) OAU6S | ‡850 | R. Nal. del Peru, Tarata |
| PU35) OBU7Z | 850 | R. Pachamama, Puno: 0830-0300 |
| PI08) OCX1M | 860 3 | R. Nuevo Norte, Sullana |
| PU609 OBM7B | 860 | R. OBM7B, Sandia |
| AQ52) OCX6F | 870 2.5 | R. Impacto Universal, Uchumayo Aqp |
| CU10) OCX7R | 870 1 | R. Mundo, Wanchaq: 24h |
| JN34) OCX4D | 870 2.5 | R. Huancayo, El Tambo: 24h |
| LB08) OBX1F | 870 10 | R. Programas del Perú - RPP, Chiclayo: 24h |
| PU06) OAU7O | 870 5 | R. Libertad, Puno |
| AY22) OBU5W | 880 5 | R. OBU5W |
| LL15) OAX2P | 880 2 | R. Sintonia, Trujillo |
| LM16) OBZ4N | 880 50 | R. Union, Lima: (IPDA) 24h |
| PU09) OCU4S | 880 5 | R. Cumbre, Chaupimarca |
| AP16) OCU5J | 890 1 | R. Cielo, San Pedro de Cachora |
| CU56) OCU7C | 890 1 | R. Laramani, Espinar |
| IC29) OCU5W | 890 1 | R. OCU5W, Ica |
| PU07) OBX7S | 890 3 | R. Bahá´í del Lago Titicaca, Chiucuito: 0900-0200 |
| CJ10) OAU2N | 890 1 | R. Nor Andina, Celendin |
| AQ11) OBX6K | 900 3 | R. Nevada, Uchumayo, Aqp: 24h |
| HN02) OAX3E | 900 | R. Ribereña, Aucaycu |
| LM17) OBX4X | ‡900 10 | R. Felicidad, Lima: 24h |
| PI52) OCU1P | 900 1 | R. Huarmaca, Huarmaca |
| AY02) OAU5M | 910 1 | R. Estacion Wari, Ayacucho |
| CU40) OAU7M | 910 1 | R. Regional – R.Quechua, Sicuani |
| PU08) OAU7G | 910 1 | R. Frontera, Juliaca |
| CJ66) OAM2G | 920 3 | R. Vision, Samangay: 24h |
| CU66) OAM7H | 920 1 | CVC La Voz, Cusco |
| IC04) OCX5C | 920 1 | R. Stelar, Chinca Alta |
| MD07) OCU7W | 920 1 | R. OCU7W, Tambopata |

| MW Call | kHzkW | Station, location, h of tr. |
|---|---|---|
| LL16) OBX2S | 920 1 | R. Ollantay, Virú |
| PI10) OBX1J | 920 10 | R. Programas del Peru - RPP, Piura: 24h |
| PU42) | 920 | R. Campesina, Juli: 0900-0300 |
| SM01) OAX9V | 920 1 | R. Marginal, Tocache |
| TC16) OBU6M | 920 2.5 | R. Uno, Tacna: 24h |
| AM13) OBX9V | 930 1 | R. OBX9V, Huambo |
| AQ12) OBX6T | 930 5 | R. Yaravi, Cerro Colorado, Aqp. |
| AY23) OBU5S | 930 1 | R. OBU5S, Pucar del Sara Sara |
| CU67) OAM7J | 930 1 | R. Cadena Sur, Espinar |
| LB40) OCU1O | 930 3 | R. Nor Andina, Olmos: 0900-0300 |
| LL17) OCX2V | 930 1 | R. Inti, Chepén |
| LM18) OAX4E | 930 5 | Moderna - R.Papa, Lima: 24h |
| PU09) OBU7T | 930 3 | R. Cadena Colca, Juliaca |
| AQ55) OBU6G | 930 1 | R. OBU6G, Cotahuasi |
| CJ58) OBX2G | 940 | R. Cutervo, Cutervo - 0500 |
| CU13) OBX7P | 940 1.5 | R. Las Vegas – W Radio, Wanchaq: 24h |
| JN08) OBU4E | 940 1 | R. Luz, Jauja |
| PI47) OBU1Y | 940 1 | R. Studio Satelite, Tambo Grande |
| AN02) OBX3S | 950 1 | R. Programas del Perú - RPP, Chimbote |
| AP12) OBU5R | 950 1 | R. OBU5R, Cotabambas |
| AY24) OBU5N | 950 1 | R. OBU5N, Paucar del Sara Sara |
| CJ72) OAM2H | 950 1.5 | Onda Popular, Bambamarca |
| PU46) OAM7S | 950 1 | R. OAM7S, Juliaca |
| TC13) | 950 | R. Campesina, Tarata |
| AQ13) OBX6S | 960 18 | R. El Pueblo 960, Mariano Melgar, Aqp |
| CU14) OBU7P | 960 1 | R. Concierto Santa Monica, Espinar |
| JN09) OCY4V | 960 1 | R. Manantial, Chilca |
| LB11) OBX1Y | ±960 3 | R. WSP, Chiclayo: (r. on 958): 0900-0400 |
| LM19) OAX4D | 960 10 | R. Panamericana, Lima: 24h |
| CJ13) OAU2K | 970 1 | R. Lider del Norte, Cajamarca |
| CU15) OAU7A | 970 5 | R. Tropicana, Wanchaq |
| IC05) OBX5A | 970 1 | R. Comericial Sonora, Ica |
| PI11) OBX1V | 970 1.5 | R. La Capullana, Sullana |
| PU11) OBU7B | 970 1 | R. Union Qollasuyo, Juliaca |
| AQ14) OAU6F | 980 1.5 | R. Universidad, Arequipa: 1000-0100 |
| AM14) | 980 | R. Comercial Cosmos, La Peca |
| AY14) OBU5K | 980 1 | R. LV de Huamanga, Huamanga |
| CJ42) OCX2R | 980 1 | Andina R., Chota |
| CU78) OCU7X | 980 1 | R. Caden Sur, Sicuani |
| JN10) OBU4H | 980 1 | R. OBU4H, Huancayo |
| LB12) OAU1N | 980 1 | R. Primavera, Lambayeque |
| PI51) OBU1N | 980 1 | R. Campesina, Huancabamba |
| AN04) OBX3L | 990 | R. Peruana, Chimbote |
| CJ14) OBX2M | 990 0.5 | R. Concordia, Contumaza |
| LM20) OBX4J | 990 12 | R. Latina, Miraflores: 24h |
| PA07) OCU4A | 990 | R. Oro, Huayllay |
| PI57) OCU1H | 990 3 | R. Bendicion Cristiana, Piura |
| PU47) OCU7T | 990 2.5 | R. Milagros, Juliaca |
| TC04) OAX6K | ‡990 10 | R. Continental, Tacna |
| AQ15) OBX6R | 1000 2.5 | R. Edesa, Cerro Colorado, Aqp |
| CU16) OAZ7P | ‡1000 2 | R. Prensa al Dia, Cusco |
| HV01) OBX5W | 1000 1 | R. Lircay, Lircay |
| HN03) OBX3V | 1000 1 | R. Huanuco |
| JN50) OBU4Z | 1000 1 | R. OBU4Z, Pariahuanaca |
| LB44) OCU1N | 1000 7 | R. OCU1N, San José |
| LM75) OAM4N | 1000 1 | R.OAM4N, Barranca |
| AM10) OBX9T | 1010 1 | R. Fé, Bagua Grande |
| AQ56) OBU6L | 1010 1 | R. Orcopampa, Orcopampa |
| AP13) OBU5T | 1010 1 | R. OBU5T, Cotabambas |
| CJ15) OBX2P | ‡1010 1.5 | R. San Francisco, Cajamarca |
| CJ86) | 1010 | R. Cajamarca, Cajamarca |
| LM54) OAX4U | 1010 10 | R. Cielo, Lima: 24h |
| PI13) OBU1L | 1010 1 | LV de las Huaringas, Huancabamba |
| PU48) OCU7P | 1010 1 | R. Nac. del Peru, Juli |
| TB02) OBZ1C | 1010 1 | R. Sonora, Tumbes |
| AY25) OBU5M | 1020 0.5 | R. AM Vida, Huamanga |
| CJ41) OAU2J | 1020 2 | R. Bambamarca, Bambamarca |
| LB45) OCU1M | 1020 1 | R. OCU1M, José Leonardo Ortiz |
| CU17) OBU7O | 1020 1 | R. Informes, Sicuani |
| CU85) OAM7Y | 1020 5 | R. Kinsachata Tintaya, Espinar |
| JN11) OBU4F | 1020 1 | R. Cristo Vive, Huancayo |
| PI14) OBU1D | 1020 1 | R. La Luz, Piura |
| TC05) OAU6J | ‡1020 1 | R. Internacional, Tacna |
| AQ16) OCX6L | 1030 1 | R. Cumbia, Arequipa |
| CJ73) OAM2E | 1030 5 | R. La Beta Cajamarca |
| CU18) OCX7O | 1030 1 | R. HG-AM, Cusco |
| LL19) OAU2U | 1030 5 | R. Los Andes, Huamachuco |
| PU12) OAX7N | 1030 1 | R. LV del Altiplano, Puno |
| SM16) OBX9Z | 1030 1 | R. OBX9Z, San Ramon |
| AN29) OAU3P | 1040 1 | R. Nueva Vida, Chimbote |
| CJ74) OAM2L | 1040 1 | R. OAM2L, Pomahuaca |
| CU19) OAU7H | 1040 1 | R. Los Andes, Espinar |

| MW | Call | kHz | kW | Station, location, h of tr. |
|---|---|---|---|---|
| IC06) | OBX5U | 1040 | 1 | R. La Luz, Ica |
| LM21) | OBX4O | 1040 | 10 | R. Metropolitana, Miraflores |
| PI15) | OAZ1D | 1040 | 1 | R. Vecinal, Piura |
| AQ17) | OBX6B | 1050 | 3 | Bethel R., Uchumayo, Aqp |
| CJ89) | | 1050 | 1 | R. Tigre, Rejoapampa, Sorochuco |
| JN12) | OBZ4J | 1050 | 1 | Bethel R., Huancayo |
| LB42) | OCU1E | 1050 | 3 | R. Bendición Cristiana, Chiclayo |
| LL20) | OCX2B | 1050 | 1 | R. San Sebastian (R. Maria), Chepen |
| PI58) | OAZ1C | 1050 | 1 | R. Superior, Chulucanas |
| PU13) | OAZ7Q | 1050 | 1 | R. Noticias, Juliaca: 24h |
| AN27) | OAU3S | 1060 | 3 | R. R.Cielo, Chimbote |
| AP14) | OBU5Q | 1060 | 2 | R. Restauracion, Andahuaylas |
| AY26) | OAU5P | 1060 | 1 | Estacion Wari, Huamanga |
| CJ17) | OCY2O | ±1060 | 5 | R. Sudamerica, Cutervo |
| CU20) | OAU7U | 1060 | 1 | R. Estudio 1060, Cusco |
| LM22) | OCY4D | 1060 | 1 | R. Exito, Lima |
| MD04) | OCU7V | 1060 | 1 | Tambopata |
| MQ10) | OBU6O | 1060 | 1 | R. Municipilidad, Omate |
| PI41) | OBU1F | 1060 | 1 | R. Studio 1060. Piura |
| PI16) | OBX1D | ±1060 | 1 | R. La Luz, Piura |
| TU10) | OCU1V | 1060 | 2 | R. OCU1V, Tumbes |
| AQ18) | OAU6K | 1070 | 1 | R. Trinidad, Paucarpata, Aqp.: 1000-0200 |
| HN13) | OAU3N | 1070 | 1 | R. OAU3N, Huánuco |
| HV09) | OAM5K | 1070 | 1 | R. OAM5K, Huancavelica |
| IC07) | OAX5A | 1070 | 0.2 | R. San Juan, San Juan de Marcona |
| JN13) | OBX4G | 1070 | 1 | R. Visión, San Ramón |
| LB14) | OAU1J | 1070 | 1 | R. Vida, José Leonardo Ortiz |
| SM03) | OBX9J | 1070 | 3 | R. Andes, Tarapoto |
| CJ18) | OAU2L | 1080 | 1 | R. Nueva Vida, Cajamarca |
| CU21) | OAX7S | 1080 | 2.2 | R. Salkantay, Cusco |
| JN51) | OBU4W | 1080 | 1 | R. OBU4W, Huancayo |
| LM23) | OAU4I | 1080 | 10 | R. La Luz, Lima: 24h |
| MQ11) | OBU6H | 1080 | 1 | R. LV del Sur, Moquegua |
| PA10) | OCU4O | 1080 | 5 | R. Mineria, Chaupimarca |
| PI16) | OBX1D | ±1080 | 1.5 | R. La Luz, Piura |
| PU14) | OCU7O | 1080 | 1 | R. Nacional, Ayaviri |
| AQ61) | OBX6X | 1090 | 1 | R. Amistad (IPDA), Arequipa |
| AY05) | OAU5F | 1090 | 1 | R. Inti Andina, Aucara |
| JN14) | OCY4G | 1100 | 1 | Sonorama R., Huancayo |
| LB15) | OBX1L | 1100 | 1 | R. Ondas de Paz (IPDA), Chiclayo |
| LM64) | OAZ4W | 1100 | 1 | R. Programas del Peru - RPP, Barranca |
| LM71) | OCU4N | 1100 | 1 | R. OCU4N, Cañete |
| LL46) | OCU2E | 1100 | 1 | R. 1000, Lima |
| PU15) | OBX7Z | 1100 | 1 | R. LTC, Juliaca |
| CJ20) | OCX2U | 1110 | 1 | R. Jaén, Jaén: 1030-0600 |
| CU22) | OCX7T | 1110 | 5 | R. Machupicchu, Cusco |
| HN17) | OAU3R | 1110 | 3 | R. Cielo, Huánuco |
| LM24) | OAU4J | 1110 | 1 | R. Feliz, Lima: 24h |
| MQ04) | OBU6F | 1110 | 1 | R. Austral, Ilo |
| PI17) | OCX1R | 1110 | 0.5 | R. Centro Popular, La Union |
| AQ20) | OCX6U | 1110 | 1 | R. Municipal, Cerro Colorado, Aqp |
| AY06) | OAU5H | 1120 | 1 | R. Quispillaccta, Ayacucho: 0900-1400. 2100-0100 |
| CJ61) | OAM2F | 1120 | 3 | R. Paz, Chota |
| HV03) | OAU5W | 1120 | 0.5 | R. Huayllahuara |
| JN58) | | 1120 | 1 | R. San Bartolome, Junin |
| LL21) | OBX2I | 1120 | 1.5 | R. Dinamica, Trujillo |
| LM67) | OCU4E | 1120 | 1 | R. Bendición, Barranca |
| LT05) | OAX8A | 1120 | 5 | R. Nacional, Iquitos |
| UC09) | OBX8R | ±1125 | 1 | R. Nuevo Tiempo, Campoverde (nf 1120) |
| AQ63) | OCU6I | 1130 | 1 | R. OCU6I, Camaná |
| CJ21) | OAX2V | 1130 | 1.2 | R. Los Andes (RPP), Cjamarca |
| CU65) | OAM7F | 1130 | 5 | R. Ondas de Paz, Cuzco (IPDA) |
| JN60) | OAM4K | 1130 | 1 | R. OAM4K, Junin |
| LM27) | OAX4N | 1130 | 2.6 | R. Bacán Sat., Lima: 24h |
| MQ09) | OBU6Q | 1130 | 1 | R. OBU6Q, Moquegua |
| PI53) | OCU1R | 1130 | 1 | R. OCU1R,Huarmaca) |
| PU16) | OAU7B | 1130 | 1 | R. Onda Popular, Juliaca |
| AN07) | OAU3C | 1140 | 1 | R. Bahia, Chimbote: 1000-0200(Sun -2200) |
| AQ21) | OAX6L | 1140 | 1 | R. Capital, Cerro Colorado, Aqp: (rel. Lima) |
| CJ83) | OAM2O | 1140 | 5 | R. Maria, Chota |
| IC08) | OAX5W | 1140 | 0.5 | R. Chinchaysuyo, Chinca Alta |
| JN16) | OCY4C | 1140 | 1 | R. Programas del Perú - RPP, Pilcomayo |
| LB16) | OAU1T | 1140 | 5 | R. Fraternal, Ferreñafe |
| LL48) | OCU2D | 1140 | | Chami R., Otuzco |
| PI18) | OBX1W | 1140 | 1.5 | R. Piura, Piura |
| CJ22) | OCY2E | 1150 | 0.5 | R. Chasquillacta, Pedro Galvez: 1030-2200 |
| CU23) | OCX7Q | 1150 | 2.5 | R. Universal, Wanchaq: Mon-Sat 0900-1200 |
| PA02) | OBU4K | 1150 | 5 | R. Mineria, Cerro de Pasco |
| PU17) | OAU7X | 1150 | 2.5 | R. La Sureña, Juliaca |
| AY07) | OBX5O | 1160 | 1 | R. Huanta 2000, Huanta : 1030-0130 |
| JN52) | OCU4V | 1160 | 1 | R. Maranatha, Huancayo |
| LL22) | OAX2C | 1160 | 0.3 | R. Libertad Mundo, Trujillo: 24h |

| MW | Call | kHz | kW | Station, location, h of tr. |
|---|---|---|---|---|
| LB17) | OCX1S | 1160 | 1 | Radiales Nor Oriental del Marañon, Chiclayo |
| LM56) | OAX4C | 1160 | 5 | R. 1160/R.Onda Cero Lima: 24h |
| MD02) | OCX7Z | 1160 | 1 | R. del Sur, Tambopata |
| MQ05) | OBX6G | ‡1160 | 1 | R. Nac. del Perú, Moquegua |
| PI59) | OCU1Q | 1160 | 1 | R. LV Campesino, Huamarca |
| AN08) | OAZ3K | ‡1170 | 1 | R. Nor Peruana Chimbote |
| AQ22) | OBX6L | 1170 | 10 | R. Programas del Perú, Uchumayo, Aqp |
| CJ24) | OAU3A | 1170 | 1 | R. Jerusalen, Cajamarca (IPDA 24/7) |
| CU24) | OBU7F | 1170 | 1 | Bethel R., Cusco |
| HV06) | OAM5B | 1170 | 2 | R. OAM5B, Acobamba |
| IC19) | OAU4N | 1170 | 1 | R. Horizonte La Voz del Agro, Pueblo Nuevo |
| JN58) | OAM4I | 1170 | 1 | R. COSAT, Satipo |
| LM72) | OAM7A | 1170 | 1 | R. OAM4E, Paramonga |
| PU18) | OCX7Y | 1170 | 0.5 | R. Constelación, Puno |
| CJ25) | OAM2K | 1180 | 1 | Municipalidad Provincial de Jaen, Jaen |
| CJ23) | OAU2T | 1180 | 1 | R. Siglo 21, Chota |
| JN18) | OCY4Z | 1180 | 1 | R. Libertad , Junin |
| LM62) | OCU4K | 1180 | 10 | NSE Radio, Lima |
| PI60) | OAZ1H | 1180 | 2.5 | R. Vencinal, Piura |
| TC14) | OCU6N | 1180 | 1 | R. Bacan Sat 2, Pocollay |
| AN09) | OBX3D | 1190 | 5 | R. Ancash, Huaraz |
| AQ23) | OCX6G | 1190 | 1 | R. Central de Noticias, Miraflores Aqp |
| AY27) | OBU5U | 1190 | 2 | R. OBU5U, Huamanga |
| LB18) | OAX1E | 1190 | 10 | Bravasa R., Chiclayo |
| CU25) | OAX7B | 1190 | 2 | R. Tawantinsuyo, Cusco |
| MD08) | OAM7V | 1190 | 3 | R. Cielo, Tambopata |
| TB08) | OCU1S | 1190 | 3 | R. Cielo. Tumbes |
| AP03) | OBX5X | 1200 | 1 | R. Comercial, Abancay |
| CJ26) | OAU2A | 1200 | 1 | LV de Cumbe, Cajamarca: 1000-0200 |
| JN19) | OAU4G | 1200 | 3 | R. Andes, Huancayo |
| LM60) | OAX4B | 1200 | 3 | Cadena R. 1200, Lima |
| PI61) | OCU1A | 1200 | 1 | R. Fe, Piura |
| PU19) | OCX7S | 1200 | 1 | R. Continental, Juliaca |
| PU55) | OAM7O | 1200 | 1 | R. Universidad, Puno |
| TC06) | OAU6P | 1200 | 3 | R. La Luz, Tacna |
| HV05) | | 1200 | 1 | R. Master Mix, Huancavelica |
| AN34) | OBU3D | 1210 | 1 | R. OBU3D, Chimbote |
| CJ75) | OCU2W | 1210 | 1 | R. OCU2W, Querocoto |
| CU26) | OAX7M | 1210 | 1 | R. Quillabamba, Quillabamba: 1000-0300 |
| CU55) | OCU7B | 1210 | 1 | R. Qorilazo, Chumbivilcas |
| HN12) | OBX3X | 1210 | 1 | R. Ondas de Paz, Huanuco |
| JN20) | OCY4T | 1210 | 1 | R. Galaxia, Satipo |
| LL24) | OAX2Q | 1210 | 1 | R. Universo, Trujillo: 24h |
| AQ24) | OAX6X | 1220 | 10 | R. Melodia, Hunter, Aqp: 24h |
| CU02) | OAU7N | 1220 | 1 | R. Universidad de San Antonio Abad , Cusco: 24h |
| IC20) | OBU5I | 1220 | 1 | R. Bethel, San Clemente |
| JN53) | OCU4W | 1220 | 1.5 | R. Cora, Huancayo |
| LB19) | OCX1X | 1220 | 1 | R. Libertad, Chiclay: 0900-0400 |
| LM63) | OCU4H | 1220 | 1 | R. Fe, Lima: 24h |
| CJ76) | OAM2B | 1220 | 1 | R. Fé, Cajamarca |
| JN21) | OBZ4Y | 1230 | 1 | R. Selecciones,Tarma: 1100-0200(Sun -1800) |
| LM65) | OCU4C | 1230 | 1 | R. La Luz, Huacho |
| MD06) | OAM7T | 1230 | 2.5 | R. Tambopata, Tambopata |
| MQ12) | OBU6T | 1230 | 1 | R. OBU6T, Moquequa |
| PA03) | OBX4Z | ‡1230 | 1 | R. LV de Oxapampa, Oxapampa |
| PU20) | OAU7V | 1230 | 1 | R. Surupana, Caminca |
| PU62) | | 1230 | 1 | R. Frecuencia Amistad, Juliaca |
| AM01) | OAU9B | 1240 | 1 | R. Bagua Grande, Chachapoyas |
| AN10) | OAU3L | 1240 | 1 | R. La Luz, Chimbote |
| AQ25) | OAU6D | 1240 | 15 | R. Lider, Socabaya, Aqp |
| CU27) | OCU7Z | 1240 | 5 | R. Pachatusán, Sicuani |
| IC10) | OAU5U | 1240 | 1 | R. Eco, Ica |
| JN22) | OAU4V | 1240 | 12 | R. Cumbre, Huancayo -0000 |
| LB21) | OAZ1A | 1240 | 1 | R. Ferreñafe, Ferreñafe |
| LL26) | OAU2Y | 1240 | 1 | R. Nor Andino, Santiago de Chuco |
| PI69) | OCX1C | 1240 | 1 | R. Sechura, Sechura |
| PU44) | OCX1C | 1240 | 1 | R. Campesina, Ayaviri |
| CJ27) | OAU2V | 1250 | 1 | R. HGV, Santa Cruz |
| CU28) | OBX7A | 1250 | 3 | R. Solar, Cusco: 1000-0500 |
| LM30) | OAX4L | 1250 | 5 | R. Cora, Lima |
| MQ08) | OAU6I | 1250 | 1 | R. Campesina, Omate |
| PI23) | OBZ1B | 1250 | 1.5 | R. Dif. BNS, Talara Alta |
| SM07) | OAX9C | 1250 | 1 | R. Americana, Nueva Cajamarca |
| UC10) | OBX8S | 1250 | 3 | R. Cielo, Calleria |
| AN11) | OAU3B | 1260 | 3 | R. El Pregonero, Chimbote |
| AQ26) | OBX6D | 1260 | 1 | R. Manahaim, Uchumayo Aqp |
| HN04) | OAU3F | 1260 | 1 | R. La Luz, Huanuco |
| JN54) | OCU4F | 1260 | 1 | R. Corazón Andino, El Tambo |
| LB20) | OCX1O | 1260 | 1 | R. Nova, Chiclay |
| LL49) | OBX2C | 1260 | | R. Otuzco, Otuzco |
| LL56) | | 1260 | | R. Cielo, Trujillo – relay of R.Cielo, Lima (r) |
| LM68) | OCU4B | 1260 | 3 | R. La Luz, San Vicente de Cañete |

| MW | Call | kHz | kW | Station, location, h of tr. |
|---|---|---|---|---|
| AY08) | OBX5S | 1260 | 0.3 | R. Nal. del Perú, Ayacucho |
| AQ46) | OBU6P | 1270 | 1 | R. San Antonio, Callalli |
| CU30) | OAU7S | 1270 | 2 | R. Horizonte – LV de Agro, Cusco |
| HV07) | OAM5A | 1270 | 2 | R. OAM5A, Huancavelica |
| JN23) | OBZ4T | 1270 | 0.4 | R. La Merced, Chanchamayo |
| LL28) | OCX2Z | 1270 | 1 | R. Estacion Latina, Cepén |
| LM31) | OAZ4H | 1270 | 0.4 | R. Huacho, Huacho |
| PI24) | OAU1S | 1270 | 1 | R. Nor Peru, Paita |
| TC21) | OBU6N | 1270 | 3 | R. OBU6N, Tacna |
| AN12) | OBX3C | ‡1280 | | R. El Puerto, Chimbote |
| AQ27) | OBX6P | 1280 | 0.5 | R. Fénix, Camaná |
| CJ28) | OBX2F | 1280 | 1 | R. Moderna, Cajamarca: 1000-0400(Sun -0300) |
| CU61) | OCU7R | 1280 | 1 | R. Fé, Sicuani |
| HN01) | OAX3Y | 1280 | 1 | R. La Selva, Rupa-Rupa |
| IC21) | OBU5J | 1280 | 3 | Yeshua R., Chinca Alta |
| LB22) | OAU1R | 1280 | 1 | R. Bethel, San Jose |
| PA11) | | 1280 | | R. Bethel, Chaquimarca |
| PU49) | OCU7S | 1280 | 2.5 | R. Continental, Macusani |
| AQ28) | OCX6B | 1290 | 5 | R. Cielo, Cerro Colorado Aqp |
| AY20) | OBU5V | 1290 | 1 | R. OBU5V, Ayacucho |
| CJ69) | OAM2C | 1290 | 1 | R. Estelar, Chota: 1000-0200 |
| JN24) | OBU4S | 1290 | 1 | R. Exito, La Oroya |
| LM32) | OBU4Q | 1290 | 1 | S & RD, Hualmay |
| LM69) | OCU4P | 1290 | 1 | San Vicente de Cañete |
| LL53) | OBU2D | 1290 | 1 | R. Sonorama, Trujillo |
| TB04) | OCX1Q | 1290 | 1 | R. Programas del Perú - RPP, Tumbes: 24h |
| AN13) | OAX3O | 1300 | 0.5 | R. Huascarán, Independencia: 1100-0300 |
| CJ29) | OAU2I | 1300 | 1 | R. Paraiso, Cajabamba |
| CU31) | OAX7P | ‡1300 | 5 | R. Onda Imperial, Cusco: 1200-2130 |
| CU89) | | 1300 | | R. Chumpiwilkas, Santo Tomas Chumbivilcas |
| JN55) | OCU4R | 1300 | 2.5 | R. OCU4R, Ahuac |
| LB23) | OAU1U | 1300 | 1 | R. Frecuencia Lider, Morro |
| LM33) | OAX4S | 1300 | 5 | R. Comas, Comas: 24h |
| PU21) | OAX7X | 1300 | 0.35 | R. La Decana – R.Juliaca, Juliaca |
| SM08) | OBX9P | ‡1300 | 1 | R. La Luz, Tarapoto |
| TC18) | OBU6X | 1300 | 3 | R. Candarave, Ilabaya |
| UC03) | OAZ8B | 1300 | 1 | R. Nuevo Mundo, Pucallpa |
| AQ50) | OAU6N | 1310 | 6 | R. Libertad, Alto Selva Alegre Aqp |
| AY21) | OBU5X | 1310 | 3 | Ayacucho |
| CJ30) | OBX2D | 1310 | 1 | R. Chota, Chota: 1100-0300 |
| LM34) | OBX4L | 1310 | 1 | R. Irvisa, Huacho |
| HN15) | OAU3T | 1310 | 5 | R. OAU3T, Rupa Rupa |
| LT09) | OBX8L | 1310 | 12 | R. Vision Amazonia (R. MIVIA), Iquitos |
| PI62) | OCU1D | 1310 | 3 | Bethel R., Piura |
| AN31) | OAU3W | 1320 | 5 | R. OAU3W, La Caleta |
| AP19) | OCU5V | 1320 | 5 | R. Cultural Tintaya, Cotabambas |
| AQ60) | OBU6B | 1320 | 0.5 | R. Majes |
| IC22) | OBU5L | 1320 | 1 | La Luz del Mundo, Pueblo Nuevo |
| JN26) | OCU4T | 1320 | 2.5 | R. Bacan Sat., Huancayo |
| LB24) | OBU1S | 1320 | 1 | R. Frecuencia Popular, Olmos |
| LM55) | OAX4I | 1320 | | R. La Cronica, Lima |
| PU22) | OAU7W | 1320 | 3 | R. TV Peru, Juliaca: 1000-0300 |
| TC17) | OBU6A | 1320 | 1 | R. OBU6A, Tacna |
| AQ30) | OVX6E | 1330 | 1 | Frequencia 1330, Arequipa |
| AY09) | OBU5P | 1330 | 0.5 | R. Bethel, Huamanga |
| CU32) | OCX7K | 1330 | 1 | R. San Miguel, Wanchaq |
| JU61) | OAM4L | 1330 | 2 | R. OAM4L, Chiclayo |
| LB25) | OAU1A | 1330 | 1 | R. Amistad, Chiclayo |
| LL54) | OAM2D | 1330 | 1 | R. Fé, La Esperanza |
| PI63) | OCU1J | 1330 | 1 | R. Frecuencia Ideal, Frias |
| SM17) | OBX9Y | 1330 | 1 | R. Fé, Tarapoto |
| AN33) | OBU3C | 1340 | 1 | R. OBU3C, Casma |
| CJ31) | OAU2S | 1340 | 1 | R. Shalom, Cajamarca |
| CU87) | | 1340 | | R. Choque, Chumbivilcas |
| IC11) | OAX5D | 1340 | 0.5 | R. Chincha, Chincha Alta |
| JN27) | OAU4N | 1340 | 1 | R. Jauja, Jauja |
| LM35) | OAU4Q | 1340 | 10 | R. Alegria, Pucasana |
| PI64) | OBX1K | 1340 | 1 | R. San Francisco, Piura |
| PU23) | OBU7V | 1340 | 1 | R. Sudamericana, Juliaca |
| AY18) | OBU5O | 1350 | 1 | R. Atlantis, Huamanga |
| HN16) | OAU3X | 1350 | 1 | R. OAU3X, Pillco Marca |
| LB31) | OAU1H | 1350 | 1 | R. Vision, Chiclayo: 24h |
| LM73) | OAM4H | 1350 | 1 | R. Paraiso, Huacho |
| MQ1) | OCU6D | 1350 | 3 | R. Municipal, Ichuña |
| TB09) | OCU1I | 1350 | 1 | R. Fé, Tumbes |
| UC04) | OBX8D | 1350 | | R. Super, Pucallpa |
| AN16) | OAU3A | 1360 | 1 | R. Intercontinental, Yungay |
| AQ32) | OCX6T | 1360 | 7.5 | R. Popular, Mariano Melgar |
| CJ77) | OCU2Z | 1360 | 2 | R. Las Palmas, Querocotillo: 1100-0200 |
| CU34) | OAX7R | ‡1360 | 2.5 | R. Sicuani, Sicuani |
| IC12) | OBZ5Z | 1360 | 1 | R. Cruz del Sur, Palpa |
| JN28) | OAU4O | 1360 | 1 | R. Sudamericana, Tarma |
| LM58) | OCU4I | 1360 | 10 | R. Bienestar, Lima: 24h |
| PI25) | OBZ1A | 1360 | 1 | R. del Norte, Sullana |
| PU24) | OUA7L | 1370 | 2.5 | R. Andina, Juliaca |
| AP05) | OCX5A | 1370 | 1 | Inti R., Abanacy |
| AP17) | OCU5Y | 1370 | 3 | R. Chalhuahuacho, Chalhuahuacho |
| AQ62) | OBU6Y | 1370 | 1 | R. OBU6Y, Viraco |
| CU79) | OAM7G | 1370 | 3 | R. Qosqo Wayra, Cusco |
| MQ07) | OAX6T | ‡1370 | | R. Moquegua, Moquegua |
| SM18) | OAU9E | 1370 | 5 | R. OAU9E, Moyobamba |
| PA01) | OCU4U | 1370 | 10 | R. Los Andes, Cerro de Pasco |
| AN32) | OAU3U | 1380 | 1 | R. R.dif San Juan, Chimbote |
| AQ33) | OAX6O | 1380 | 3 | R. San Martin, Arequipa: 1055-0500 |
| CJ33) | OAX2W | ‡1380 | 1 | R. Atahualpa, Cajamarca |
| CJ34) | OAU2H | 1380 | 1 | R. Campesina, Cajamarca |
| JN29) | OBU4L | 1380 | | R. Chilca,Chilca |
| HN06) | OBX3I | ±1380 | 1 | R. Pilco Mozo, Huanuco |
| IC31) | OAM5E | 1380 | 1 | R. OAM5E, Salas |
| LM38) | OCY4U | 1380 | 1 | R. Nuevo Tiempo, Lima: 24h |
| MD05) | OCU7U | 1380 | 1 | R. OCU7U, Tambopata |
| PI26) | OBZ1D | 1380 | 1 | RB - R. Bellavista, Bellavista |
| AY28) | OCU5C | 1390 | 2.5 | R. Cielo, Ayacucho |
| CJ70) | OBU2U | 1390 | 0.5 | Frequencia del Norte, Santa Cruz |
| CU36) | OAU7T | 1390 | 1 | R. Enlace, Kunturkanki |
| CU69) | OAM7A | 1390 | 3 | R. Exitosa, Sicuani: 24h |
| LL32) | OAU2Z | 1390 | 3 | R. La Luz, Trujillo |
| LB41) | OCU1G | 1390 | | R. Fe, Pimentel |
| AN35) | OBU3E | 1400 | 1 | R. OBU3E, Chimbote |
| CJ88) | OAU2H | 1400 | 1 | R. Agricultura, Cajamarca |
| CU37) | OAX7I | 1400 | 1 | R. La Hora, Cuzco |
| HV10) | OCU5S | 1400 | 1 | R. OCU5S, Preov |
| IC30) | OAM5G | 1400 | 1 | R. OAM5G, Ica |
| JN30) | OBX4H | 1400 | 1 | R. Luz, Tarma |
| LM39) | OBX4W | 1400 | 2.5 | R. Ecco, Lima: 24h |
| TC22) | OCU6F | 1400 | 1 | R. Candaravena, Candaravna |
| AY33) | OCU5G | 1410 | 3 | R. Genesis, Huanta |
| CJ64) | OCU2Q | 1410 | 1 | R. Huracana, Pedro Galvez |
| HN18) | OAU3Y | 1410 | 1 | R. Ke Buena, Paucarbambilia |
| LB29) | OBU1G | 1410 | 1 | R. Olmos, Olomos |
| LM40) | OBZ4V | 1410 | 1 | R. Bethel, Huacho |
| PU26) | OBU7A | 1410 | 1 | R. Corporacion Wayra, Juliaca |
| TB05) | OBU1H | 1410 | 3 | R. La Luz, Tumbes |
| UC05) | OBX8I | 1410 | 1 | Dif. Comercial, Pucallpa |
| AQ57) | OBU6C | 1420 | 1 | R. Fe, Arequipa |
| IC23) | OBU5H | 1420 | 0.5 | R. la Luz, Salas |
| CJ85) | OAM2P | 1420 | 5 | R. La Positiva, Bambamarca |
| CU88) | OAM7K | 1420 | 1.5 | R. San Luis, Pallpata |
| LM41) | OBZ4G | 1420 | 1 | R. San Isidro, Lima |
| PI65) | OCU1F | 1420 | 2 | R. OCU1F, Tambo Grande |
| AM03) | OBX9H | 1430 | 1 | R. Utcubamba, Bagua Grande |
| AN18) | OAZ3H | ‡1430 | 1 | R. Chavin, Chimbote |
| CJ78) | OCU2U | 1430 | 1 | R. Vision, Jaén |
| CJ39) | OAZ7M | 1430 | 1 | R. OAZ7M, Cusco |
| JN31) | OAZ4V | 1430 | 0.5 | R. Universal, El Tambo: 1100-0500 |
| LM42) | OCU4L | 1430 | 1 | R. Chilca, Cañete |
| PU27) | OBU7U | 1430 | 1 | R. Red Andina, Juliaca |
| TC08) | OAU6M | ‡1430 | 1 | R. Lider, Tacna |
| AQ19) | OAX6R | 1440 | 2.5 | R. Santa Monica, Hunter, Aqp: |
| AY32) | OCU5K | 1440 | 2.5 | R. OCU5K, Ayacucho |
| CU71) | OAM7L | 1440 | 3 | R. Solar, Espinar |
| CJ35) | OAU2O | 1440 | 2 | R. Frecuencia VH, Celendín |
| IC26) | OCU5P | 1440 | 3 | R. Cielo, Ica |
| LB30) | OBX1T | 1440 | 2 | R. Cooperativa Tumán, , Tumán |
| LM43) | OAX4K | 1440 | 1 | R. Imperial 2, Lima |
| PI66) | OBU1Z | 1440 | 1 | R. OBU1Z, Vice |
| AQ58) | OBU6K | 1450 | 1 | R. OBU6K, Chivay |
| CJ81) | OAU2W | 1450 | | R. Manantial de Vida, Cajamarca:1100-0100 (Sun -1300) |
| CJ82) | | 1450 | | R. Libertad, Bambamarca |
| JN45) | OBU4Y | 1450 | 1 | R. La Nueva Andina (IPDA) Huancayo |
| LL35) | OCX2J | 1450 | 1 | R. San Juan, Trujillo |
| LM44) | OBX4K | 1450 | 1 | R. Fortaleza, Barranca |
| MO15) | OCU6E | 1450 | 1 | R. Santa Cruz, Ichuña |
| PA08) | OAM4A | 1450 | 1 | R. Vida, Tinyahuarco |
| AN30) | OAU3V | 1450 | 2.5 | R. Municipal, Cabana |
| AQ37) | OBU6R | 1460 | 1 | R. Bahia, Mollendo |
| CU42) | OBU7M | 1460 | | R. OBU7M, Marcapata |
| IC32) | OAM5C | 1460 | 1 | Rdif. Disaga, Pueblo Nuevo |
| JN32) | OCY4I | 1460 | 0.5 | R. Imperial, Junin |
| JN33) | OAZ4F | 1460 | 1 | R. La Oroya, La Oroya: 1000-0300 |
| JN48) | OCU4Y | 1460 | 1 | R. Voz Cristiana, Chongo Bajo: 24h (n.f. 1470) |
| PI29) | OAX1V | 1460 | 1 | R. Sullana "LV de Chira", Sullana |
| PU28) | OAX7W | 1460 | 10 | R. Sol de los Andes, Juliaca: 0900-0300 |

| MW | Call | kHzkW | Station, location, h of tr. |
|---|---|---|---|
| AQ38) | OAU6E | 1470 2.5 | R. Victoria, Alto Selva Alegre Aqp |
| CU43) | OAX7G | 1470 1 | R. Cusco, Cusco |
| JN48) | OCU4Y | 1470 1 | R. Voz Cristiana, Chongo Bajo: 24h (r. 1460) |
| LB46) | OAU1P | 1470 1 | R. California, Lambayeque |
| LL37) | OCY2G | 1470 1 | R. Oliversa, Quiruvilca |
| LM45) | OAU4B | 1470 20 | R. Capital, Lima |
| TC09) | OAX6M | ‡1470 0.8 | R. Tacna, Tacna: 24h |
| CU44) | OAZ7G | 1480 1 | R. Espinar, Yauri |
| CJ44) | OBU2H | 1480 0.2 | R. Santa Ana, Cuervo: 1000-0100 |
| JN35) | OAU4A | 1480 1 | R. Mineria, Santa Rosa de Sacco: 1100-2300 |
| LL38) | OCX2C | 1480 0.6 | R. Comercial San Pedro, Virú |
| LM70) | OAM4F | 1480 1 | R. OAM4F, Barranca |
| MD09) | OBM7F | 1480 1 | R. OBM7F, Tambopata |
| AQ39) | OAX6Q | 1490 1.3 | R. Fidelidad, Cerro Colorado, Aqp |
| AP10) | OBU5C | 1490 2.5 | Radiodifusora los Chankas, Andahuaylas |
| AP18) | | 1490 | R. Patron Santiago, Challhuacho |
| CU80) | OCU7Y | 1490 2.5 | Cadena Sur del Peru, Cusco (IPDA) |
| IC15) | OAX5N | 1490 1 | R. Nazca, Nazca |
| LB47) | OAX1L | ±1490 1 | R. Imperio, Chiclayo |
| LT14) | OAX8F | 1490 1 | R. Atlántiada, Iquitos |
| PA15) | OCX4P | 1490 0.5 | R. La Luz, Cerro de Pasco |
| PU51) | OAM7P | 1490 1 | R. OAM7P, Capachica |
| CJ39) | OBU2J | 1500 2 | R. San Pablo, San Pablo |
| CU81) | OAM7B | 1500 1 | R. TV Cristiana, Sicuani |
| HN07) | OBX3J | 1500 1 | R. Luz y Sonido, Huanuco: 0900-0300 |
| JN56) | OCU4Q | 1500 1 | R. Scala de Oro, Huancayo |
| LL39) | OBX2X | 1500 0.5 | R. Comercial, Trujillo |
| LM47) | OBX4I | ±1500 18 | R. Santa Rosa, Lima: 24h |
| TC10) | OAU6B | ‡1500 1 | R. Bulevar, Tacna |
| AQ40) | OCX6Q | ±1510 3 | R. Alegria, Mariano Melgar, Aqp |
| CU82) | OBX7P | 1510 1 | R. Las Vegas, Wanchaq |
| JN37) | OCX4J | 1510 1 | R. Tarma, Tarma: 1000-0200, Sun 1100-2300 |
| LB32) | OBU3I | 1510 1 | R. Super Real, Olmos |
| LM66) | OCU4M | 1510 1 | R. OCU4M, San Vicente de Cañete |
| TB06) | OCX1V | 1510 1 | R. Tumbes, Tumbes |
| UC06) | OBX8K | 1510 1 | R. Centro de los Medios, Sepahua |
| CJ84) | OAM2Q | 1516 1 | R. Charles, Bambamarca (nf 1530) |
| AY29) | OCU5F | 1520 2 | R. OCU5F, Huanta |
| CU48) | OBU7X | 1520 1 | R. Avance - Voz Evangelica, Espinar |
| LB26) | OAX1C | 1520 1 | R. Cristal, Chiclayo |
| HV04) | OBU5Z | 1520 1 | R. Municipal, Castrovirreyna |
| MQ13) | OBU6Z | 1520 6 | R. OBU6Z, Mascal Nieto |
| PA12) | OAM4C | 1520 1 | R. OAM4C, San Juan |
| PI68) | OCU1T | 1520 1 | R. LV del Campesino, Ayabacha |
| PU56) | | 1520 | R. Andina, Lampa |
| CJ06) | OBX2R | 1530 3 | R. Oriental, Jaén |
| CJ84) | OAM2Q | 1530 1 | R. Charles, Bambamarca |
| CU49) | OAZ7F | 1530 0.5 | Rdif. Espinar, Yauri |
| CU50) | OBU7N | 1530 1 | R. Ondas del Sur Oriente, Quillabamba |
| IC17) | OAU3D | 1530 1 | R. Universidad San Juan Bautista, Subtanjalla |
| JN38) | OBZ4S | 1530 1 | R. 15-50, Huancayo: 24h |
| LM49) | OBU4C | 1530 10 | R. Milenia, Lima |
| PI70) | | 1530 1 | R. La Jefa, Sullana |
| AQ41) | OAU6A | 1540 1 | R. Milenio Universal, Alto Selva Alegre |
| CU51) | OCX7V | ‡1540 1 | R. Los Andes, Cusco |
| LL42) | OBU2A | 1540 2 | R. Mundial, Trujillo |
| LM74) | OAM4G | 1540 1 | R. Angie@Net, Barranca |
| PA05) | OBX4N | 1540 0.3 | R. Corporacion, Cerro de Pasco: 0900-0500 |
| TB07) | OBX1B | 1540 1 | R. LV de la Frontera, Tumbes |
| TC23) | OCU6H | 1540 1 | R. OCU6H, Pocollay |
| AN22) | OAU3D | ‡1550 1 | R. Cruz, Chimbote |
| AY10) | OBX5J | 1550 1 | R. Maria, Huamanaga |
| CJ88) | | 1550 | R. Integracion, Cuervo |
| CU83) | OAM7D | ±1550 1 | R. San Sebastian, Livitaca |
| IC24) | OAU5Z | 1550 3 | R. La Luz del Mundo, Subtanjalla |
| LB48) | OCU1W | 1550 1 | R. OCU1W, Monsefú |
| LM51) | OBX4P | 1550 5 | R. Independencia, Independencia |
| PI67) | OCU1B | 1550 1 | R. La Clave, Castilla |
| AQ42) | OCX6N | 1560 1 | R. Sabor, Arequipa |
| CJ79) | OAM2I | 1560 1 | R. R. Antena Norte, Cajabamba |
| CU52) | OAZ7N | 1560 1 | R. Maria, Wanchaq |
| JN57) | OCU4Z | 1560 2.5 | R. R. Rumba, Hualhuas |
| TC25) | OCU6K | 1560 1 | R. OCU6K, Alto de la Alianza |
| AY34) | OCU5O | 1570 2.5 | R. Musuq Chaski Radio, Huamanga |
| CJ54) | OBU2L | 1570 1 | R. Colonial, Contumaza |
| CU62) | OCU7L | 1570 1 | R. Vilcanota, Sicuani |
| HN20) | OBU3A | 1570 1 | R. OBU3A. Cerro Jactay |
| IC31) | OAM5H | 1570 1 | R. OAM5H, Chinca Alta |
| LM59) | OCU4J | 1570 25 | R. Bethel, Lima |
| LL47) | OCU2C | 1570 1 | Rdif. Julcan, Otuzco |
| PI32) | OCX1Z | 1570 1 | R. La Nueva Esperanza, Tambo Grande |
| PU32) | OAU7Z | 1570 1 | R. Carraviz, Juliaca (IPDA) |

| MW | Call | kHzkW | Station, location, h of tr. |
|---|---|---|---|
| AQ59) | OBU6S | 1580 1 | R. OBU6S, Orcopampa |
| CJ87) | OAM2R | 1580 1 | R. OAM2R, Jaen |
| HV02) | OAU5J | 1580 1 | R. Virgen del Carmen, Huancavelica: 24h |
| JN40) | OAU4P | 1580 1 | R. San Juan, Tarma |
| LB36) | OBX1M | 1580 1 | R. Naylamp, Lambayeque |
| LM76) | OAM4O | 1580 1 | R. Andina, Huachoa |
| TC27) | OCU6M | 1580 1 | R. Bacan Sat., Tacna |
| AQ44) | OCX6S | 1590 1 | R. Mundo, Arequipa |
| AY30) | OBU5F | 1590 1 | R. OBU5F, Lucanas |
| CJ68) | OAM2S | 1590 1 | R. Municipal, San Marcos |
| IC34) | OAM5J | 1590 3 | R. OAM5J, Ica |
| LL43) | OBU2C | 1590 1 | R. Bendicion, Trujillo |
| LM52) | OAZ4Z | ‡1590 1.5 | R. Vida, Lima |
| PU33) | OAU7C | 1590 1 | R. Asillo, Azangaro |
| CU86) | OBM7A | 1600 3 | R. OBM7A, Wanchaq |
| JN44) | OBU4R | 1600 2.5 | R. Nuevo Tiempo, Huancayo: 24h |
| MO18) | OCU6C | 1600 1 | R. OCU6C Moquequa |
| AQ45) | OAU6O | 1610 0.5 | R. El Sol, Arequipa |
| PU54) | | 1610 | R. Inka, Acora |
| CU90) | | 1620 | R. Choquechamaca, Chamaca |
| LL57) | | 1650 | R. Santa Roas, San Ignacio, Otuzco (r) |

| SW | Call | kHzkW | Station, location, h of tr. |
|---|---|---|---|
| AY07) | OAZ5B | 4747 0.5 | R. Huanta 2000, Huanta: (n.f: 4755): 1100-0100 |
| JN37) | OCX4E | 4775 0.5 | R. Tarma, Tarma: 1000-1400 2000-0200, Sun: 1100-1400 2000-2300 |
| CU64) | OAW7I | 4780 | R. OAW7I, Cusco (F.PI) |
| CU68) | OAW7J | 4800 1 | R. OAW7J, Cusco (F.PI) |
| SM14) | OAW9A | 4810 1 | R. Logos, Chazuta |
| LT01) | OAX8R | 4824 10 | LV de la Selva, Iquitos 1030 – 1400 |
| LL55) | OAW2H | 4920 1 | R. LV Del Pueblo, Santiago de Chuco |
| AY13) | OAX5S | 4955 1 | R. Cultural Amauta, Huanta: 1000-1400, 2100-0100 |
| CU26) | OAX7Q | 5025 5 | R. Quillabamba, Quillabamba: 1000-0200 |
| CU72) | OBX4M | 5980 1 | R. Chaski R., Urubamba: 1000-1500, 2200-0100 |
| AN36) | OAD3A | 6090 1 | R. OAD3A, Independencia (F.PI) |
| CU25) | OAX7C | 6174 1 | R. Tawantinsuyo, Cusco |

**NB:** ‡ = inactive, ± = varying freq., † = irregular
° = on-air stn name not confirmed, Aqp = Provincia de Arequipa

**Addresses & other information:**
**NB:** Names of *departamentos* should be added to addresses.
**AMOO (AMAZONAS):**
**AM01)** Jr.Grau N° 617, 01001 Chachapoyas – **AM03)** Jr F Villareal N° 400, 01671 Bagua Grande – **FM:** 96.9MHz – **AM04)** Jr Amazonas N° 1717 ( Ap 69), 01001 Chachapoyas ☎41 777793 **W:** horizonteperu. com **E:** rhorizonte@hotmail.com - **FM:** 99.9MHz –**AM10)** Calle Higos Urcos 651, 01671 Bagua Grande, Utcubamba – **AM11)** Av.Gonzalo Puerta s/n, 01131 Nieva, Condorcanqui – **FM.** 91.7 MHz – **AM12)** Jr Salamanca N° 1183, 01001 Chachapoyas - **AM13)** Jr Amazonas s/n, Urb. Tupac Amaru, 01321 Huambo – **AM14)** Av La Circunvalacion N° 1249, 01651 La Peca
**AN00 (ANCASH):**
**AN01)** Tabon Alta, Fundo El Milagro, 02661 Casma ☎43 711266 **W:** visionradioperu.com - **FM:** 93.7 MHz – **AN02)** Av Francisco Pizarro, 02741 Chimbote – **FM:** 95.5MHz – **AN04)** Urb. el Trapecio 2da etapa, MZ G, Lote 18, 02741 Chimbote – **FM:** 97.5MHz – **AN07)** Jr Elias Aguirre N° 755 cerca a Panamericana Television, 02741 Chimbote ☎44 272639 – **AN08)** Pasaje Los Jardines N° 129, 02741 Chimbote - **FM:** 104.3MHz – **AN09)** Jr Francisco Araoz 146, Independencia 02001 Huaraz ☎43 421359 **W:** invierteenhuaraz.com.pe/radioa/ **E:**radioancashhuaraz@gmail.com - **FM:** 101.3MHz – **AN10)** Av Enrique Meiggs N° 2013, 02741 Chimbote ☎43 805591 **W:** radiolaluz.com **E:** programacion@radiolaluz.com - **FM:** 89.9MHz – **AN11)** Jr Elias Aguirre N° 549, 2do Piso Oficina 205, 02741 Chimbote – **AN12)** Jr Alfonso Ugarte N° 554, 02741 Chimbote - **FM:** 89.9MHz – **AN13)** Jr San Martin N° 655, 02001 Huaraz – **FM:** 104.5MHz – **AN16)** Casero el Rayan, 02816 Yungay – **AN18)** Urb. San Juan ZN 5, 02741 Chimbote - **FM:** 92.3MHz – **AN22)** Jr Alfonso Ugarte N° 627 4° piso, 02741 Chimbote – **AN25)** Huari **W:** agrorural.gob.pe/pagina/huari-ancash – **AN27)** Jr Jorge Chávez N° 364, 02741 Chimbote **W:** radiocielo.pe – **AN29)** Jr John F.Kennedy MZ. 36, Lote 1, Miraflores Alto, 02741 Chimbote – **AN30)** Plaza de Armas N° 106, Cabana– **AN31)** Av Malecón s/n, La Caleta – **AN32)** Av Santa Cruz 397, Chimbote – **AN33)** Av Peru 1263, Casma – **AN34)** Av Jorge Chavez 364, Chimbote – **AN35)** Jr Francisco Pizarro 610, Chimbote – **AN36)** Jr Los Jardines 670, Independencia
**AP00 (APURIMAC):**
**AP03)** Av Nuñez 401, 03001 Abancay – **AP05)** Av Seoane 375, Region Inca, 03001 Abancay ☎8 332 4087 **W:** corporacionsolar.com **E:** intiradio@corporacionsolar.com - **FM:** 103.3 Solar FM – **AP10)** Jr. Juan Antonio Trellers N° 278, 03281 Andahuaylas ☎83 721511 - **FM:** 94.9 MHz – **AP11)** Tres Cruces, 03141 Ocobamba – **AP12)**

Av Cristo de Los Andes, Barrio El Salvador, 03301 Challhuahuacho, Cotabamba – **AP13)** Barrio Pampaña Calle Apurimac s/n, 03341 Cotabambas – **AP14)** Jr Los Sauces N° 283, U.V. Pochccota, 03281 Andahuaylas **W:** restauracionandahuaylas.com **AP15)** Jr Manuel Seone 320, Abancay **W:** radiocielo.pe – **AP17)** Comunidad de Fuerobamba, Chalhuahuacho **☎**953 283062 **W:** facebook.com/ rchallhuahuachooficial **E.:** radiochallhuahuacho@gmail.com – **AP18)** Ca 8 de Agosto, 03301 Challhuahuacho – **AP19)** Comunidad de Fuerabamba, Dist. Callhuahuach, Cotabambas

**AQ00 (AREQUIPA):**
**AQ01)** Ca San Juan de Dios N° 210, Zona Alto, 04001 Arequipa **☎**54 200982 **W:** radioazularequipaperu.com **E:** radioazulamfm@hotmail. com – **FM:** 89.5MHz – **AQ02)** Ca San Juan de Dios 210, 04001 Arequipa **W:** nseradio.com **E:** nsearequipa@nseradio.com – **AQ04)** Av. Salaverry 103, Socabaya, 04051 Arequipa **☎**54 507362 – **AQ05)** Centro Comercial, Av Independencia 600, Of 401-A, Cercado, 04001 Arequipa **☎**54 406175 - **FM:** 93.5MHz – **AQ06)** Jr.Palacio Viejo 216, Cayma, 04016 Arequipa – **FM:** 89.5 MHz – **AQ07)** Av Emmel 216, Yanahuara, 04020 Arequipa **W:** radiohuanta2000fm **E:** radioportena@hotmail. com – **AQ11)** Av Victor A Belaúnde C-8, Umacollo, 04001 Arequipa **☎**54 255888 📠54 251822 - **FM:** 97.1MHz – **AQ12)** Ca Los Robles 139, Urb. Orrantia, 04001 Arequipa **☎**54 289952 – Quechua: Sat.2h **W:** radioyaravi.org.pe **E:** direccion@radioyaravi.org.pe - **FM:** 106.3MHz – **AQ13)** Calle Palacio Viejo 401, 04001 Arequipa **☎**54 223080 **W:** radioelpueblo960.pe - **FM:** 98.5MHz in Majes, 102.1 in Tacna – **AQ14)** Av Independencia s/n 2° piso, Pabellón de la Cultura, Ciudad Universitaria (Cas 23), 04001 Arequipa. **☎**54 287717 **W:** unsa.edu. pe and radiouniversidadaqp.blogspot.no **E:** radiouniversidad@unsa. edu.pe – **AQ15)** At 200 Millas La Pino, 04039 Paucarpata – **AQ16)** Av Independencia 905 - 2do piso, 04001 Arequipa **☎**54 204904 - **FM:** 107.7MHz – **AQ17)** Av Union 225, Miraflores, 04009 Arequipa (Also in Lima: LI59) **W:** betheltradio.fm **E:** betheltradio@bethelradio. fm – **AQ18)** Av La Paz 504, 04001 Arequipa **☎**54 204847 **Quechua:** 1000-1200 – **AQ19)** Av Independencia 905 2° piso, Ur. Municipal 04001 Arequipa **☎**54 204904 **W:** radiosantamonicaarequipa.com **E:** gerencia@radiosantamonicaarequipa.com – **AQ20)** Calle 28 de Julio N° 129 – La Libertad, Cerro Colorado, 04023 Arequipa – **AQ21)** Av.La Paz 521, Costado Grifo Repsol, 04001 Arequipa **☎**54 446053 - **FM:** 95.8MHz – **AQ22)** Av La Paz 511 "A", Of 312 – 3er piso, 04001 Arequipa **☎**54 287821 **W:** rpp.com.pe – **AQ23)** Av La Salle 124, Urb. Daniel Alcides Carrión 14, 04044 José Luis Bustamente y Rivero 04001 Arequipa **☎**54 431051 – **AQ24)** Calle San Camilo 501-A Cercado, 04001 Arequipa **☎**54 204420 **W:** radiomelodia.com.pe - **FM:** 104.3MHz – **AQ25)** Av Independencia 1819, 04001 Arequipa **☎**54 286438 **E:** lideraqp@gmail.com – **AQ26)** Ca Pierola 209, Of 205, 04001 Arequipa **☎**54 284411 – **AQ27)** Esq Av Lima y Calle Bolognesi, 04446 Camaná – **AQ28)** Av. Independencia 600, Edifico C.C. Independencia N° 321D, 04001 Arequipa **W:** radiocielo.pe – rel. of R.Cielo, Lima 24h – **AQ30)** Sebastian Luna 105a, Parque Azángaro 2° Pisa, Miraflores, 04009 Arequipa **☎**54 221262 **W:** frecuencia1330arequipa.blogspot. com – **AQ32)** Av.Independencia N° 600, Oficina 302-A, 04001 Arequipa **W:** Facebook: Radio Popular Arequipa – **AQ33)** Calle Deán Valdivia 221, Cercado, 04001 Arequipa **W:** radiosanmartin.pe **E:** director@ radiosanmartin.pe **☎**54 215190 - **FM:** 97.7MHz – **AQ37)** C.Baca Flor 410, (Cas 128), 04466 Mollendo **☎**54 532521 **W:** radiobahiaperu. es.tl **E:** radiobahiadelvalle@hotmail.com – **FM:** 101.5MHz – **AQ38)** Dean Valdivia 418, Piso 3, Cercado, 04001 Arequipa **☎**54 405480 **W:** radiovictoriaperu.com **E:** radiovictoria_aqp@hotmail.com – **AQ39)** Santo Domingo 113 , Galerias Gamesa Of 700, 04001 Arequipa, (Ap 2330) **☎**54 214997 **E:** radiominuto@terra.com.pe - **FM:** 99.9MHz – **AQ40)** Centro Comercial Independencia, Av Independencia N° 403-A, Ofic 433, 4° piso, 04001 Arequipa **☎**54 287211 - **FM:** 95.1 MHz – **AQ41)** Ca Puente Grau 122, 04001 Arequipa **☎**54 507643 **W:** radiomileniouniversal.blogspot.no **E:** radiomileniouniversal@hotmail. com – **AQ42)** Sebastian Luna 105a, Parque Azángaro 2° Pisa, Miraflores, 04009 Arequipa , Arequipa – **AQ44)** Ca Castilla 39, Urb. Municipal, 04001 Arequipa – **AQ45)** C.C Héroes Anónimos tercer piso, Oficina 301-a,. Ca Independencia, 04001 Arequipa **☎**54 299887 **W:** facebook.com/radioelsolaqp/ **E:** radioelsol1610@gmail.com – **AQ46)** Parroquia San Antonio de Padua, Plaza Principal s/n, 04201 Callalli, Prov de Caylloma **E:** rsan_antonio14@hotmail.com - **FM:** 94.5MHz – **AQ50)** Ca Trabada 105, VI Centenario, 04001 Arequipa **☎**54 202022 **W:** radiolibertadaqp.com **E:** radiolibertadaqp@hotmail.com – **AQ52)** Calle Puente Arnao 705, 3 Cdras de la Av. Progreso, 04001 Arequipa – **AQ53)** 04001 Arequipa **W:** radiomariaperu.org – **AQ55)** Casinino Peralta 102, 04101 Cotahuasi, La Union – **AQ56)** Ca 22 de Octubre s/n, Urb. Los Miradores, 04231 Orcopampa – **AQ57)** Av Del Ejercito 1013, 04001 Arequipa – **AQ58)** Sector Escalera, 04341 Chivay – **AQ59)** Av Buena Ventura s/n, 04231 Orcopampa – **AQ60)** Mz. 3E Lte. 18 Pedregal, 04426 Majes – **AQ61)** Av Independecia 905, 04001 Arequipa **☎**54

288787 **W:** ipda.com.pe/radioarequipa.htm – **AQ62)** Plaza de Armas s/n, 04556 Viraco – **AQ63)** Jr. Pizarro N° 121, Camaná

**AY00 (AYACUCHO):**
**AY02)** Ca Nazarena 108H, 05001 Ayacucho **E:** macebu90@hotmail. com - **FM:** 95.3MHz – **AY05)** Plaza Mayor Felipe Guzman Poma, 05411 Aucara, Lucanas **E:** radioia1090@hotmail.com – **AY06)** Jr Chorro 274 – Int "A", 05001 Ayacucho, **☎**66 326042 **W:** radioquispillaccta.com Prgr mainly in **Quechua AY07)** Jr Gervasio Santillana 455, 05111 Huanta **☎**66 322105 **W:** radiohuanta2000fm.com **E:** webmaster@ radiohuanta2000fm.com - **FM:** 92.9MHz – **AY08)** Jr Piura s/n, 05001 Ayacucho – **FM:** 97.9MHz – **AY09)** Jr. Los Girasoles 194, Canan Bajo, 05001 Ayacucho – **FM:** 93.9 MHz – **AY10)** Local de Obispado, 05021 Carmen Alto, **W:** radiomariaperu.com – **FM:**106.7MHz – **AY13)** Jr Cahuide 278, 05111 Huanta (Cas 24) **☎**66 322153 **W:** radioamautafm. net/ **E:** radioamauta@hotmail.com – **FM:** 99.9MHz – **AY14)** Ca El Nazareno, 2do Pasaje 159, Cercado, 05001 Ayacucho **☎**66 528523 **W:** diariolavozdehuamanga.com **E:** diariolavozdehuamanga@yahoo.com. ar - **FM:** 91.1MHz – **AY18)** Ca Manco Capac 157, 05001 Ayacucho **W:** Facebook: R.Atlantis - **FM:** 99.3 MHz – **AY19)** Jr Angel del Señor MZ C Lote 01A, Asociacion Los Mecanicos **☎**528594, Huamanga – **AY20)** Av Mariscal Cáceres 641, 05001 Ayacucho – **AY21)** Jr Arequipa N° 231, 05001 Ayacucho – **AY22)** Av Mariscal Cáceres 641, 05001 Ayacucho – **AY23)** Jr Bolognes 147-149, Barrio Huánuco, 05571 Pausa, Paúcar del Sara Sara – **AY24)** Av 28 de Julio s/n, 05571 Pausa – **AY25)** Jr Dos de Mayo 610, 05001 Ayacucho **W:** radioamvida1020khz. blogspot.no **E:** radioamvida1020@yahoo.com.pe – **AY26)** Urb. Mariscal Cáceres, Mz. K Lote 12, 05001 Ayacucho **☎**966 905992 **W:** Facebook: Estacion Wari 1060 khz A.M.– **AY27)** Jr Primavera 175, Santa Ana, 05001 Ayacucho – **AY28)** Av.Miguel Grau 256, 05001 Ayacucho **W:** radiocielo.pe – **AY29)** Jr Miller 177, 05111 Huanta – **AY30)** Jr Tacna N° 617, 05601 Pucuio – **AY31)** Jr Cesar Vallejo 325 – San Juan Bautista, 05001 Ayacucho – **AY32)** Av. Los Andes 624, 05001 Ayacucho – **AY33)** Jr. Libertad 153, 05111 Huanta – **AY34)** Av. Javier Pérez de Cuellar 546, Urb. José Ortiz Vergara Mx. "S", Ayacucho **☎**97 8465290 **W:** FB: Musuq Chaski Radio 1570 AM

**CJ00 (CAJAMARCA)**
**CJ01)** Jr Francisco de Orellana 343 ( Apt 50), 06101 Jaén **W:** radiomaranon.org.pe **E:** correo@radiomaranon.org.pe **☎**76 431147 - **FM:** 96.1 & 97.5 MHz – **CJ03)** Km 5 Carretera Jaen-San Ignacio, 06101 Jaen - **FM:** 90.9MHz – **CJ05)** Predio Coliga, 06001 Cajamarca **W:** radiomariaperu.org – **CJ06)** Av Mesones Muro 157, 06101 Jaén – **CJ07)** Jr 28 de Julio 712, 06115 Bambamarca **☎**76 353462 **W:** radiocoremarca.com **E:** coremarca@radiocoremarca.com - **FM:** 100,5 – **CJ08)** Jr Villanueva Pinillos N°N330, 06151 San Ignacio – **CJ10)** Celendin **☎**76 639577 **W:** radionorandina.com **E:** norandina101.9@ hotmail.com - **FM.** 101.9 MHzz – **CJ13)** Jr Huánuco 2361, 06001 Cajamarca **☎**76 341347 **W:** Facebook: Radio Líder Cajamarca **E:** radiolider970cajamarca@hotmail.com - **FM:** 90.3MHz – **CJ14)** Jr David León N° 601, 06001 Contumazá – **CJ15)** Jr Dos de Mayo 271, 06001 Cajamarca **☎**76 369915 **W:** radiosanfranciscoperu. com **E:** radiosanfrancisco@gmail.com - **FM:** 91.9MHz – **CJ17)** Jr Orozco 320, 06858 Cutervo **☎**76 737090 **W:** radiosudamerica. net – **CJ18)** Av Via de Evitamiento Norte 280, 06001 Cajamarca **☎**76 343725 **W:** radionuevavidacomunicaciones.com **E:** radiotvnc@ radionuevavidacomunicaciones.com or radiotvnvc@hotmail.com – **CJ20)** Jr Mariscal Castilla 439, 06101 Jaén – **CJ21)** Av San Martin De Porres s/n, 06001 Cajamarca **☎**76 828566– **CJ22)** Jr Leoncio Prado 330, 06501 San Marcos **☎**76 858083 – **CJ23)** Av Inca Garcilazo de la Vega 473, 05301 Chota – **CJ24)** Jr Mariano Melgar 138 , Cajamarca **☎**76 368975 **W:** layzonradio.com **E:** radiolayzon@yahoo.es - **FM:** 90.5MHz – **CJ25)** Ca. San Martin 1371, Jaèn **☎**76 433414 – **CJ26)** Jr. Huanuco 100, Barrio San Pedro, 06001 Cajamarca **☎**76 368952 **W:** radiolavozdelcumbe.net **E:** cia.radioytvlavozdelcumbe@hotmail. com – **CJ27)** Jr Simon Bolivar 280, 06813 Santa Cruz – **CJ28)** Jr. Revilla Peréz 540, Barrio Pueblo Nuevo, 06001 Cajamarca **☎**76 344465 **W:** radiomoderna.pe **E:** radio_moderna@yahoo.es - **FM:** 98.1 & 106.5 MHz – **CJ29)** Jr Silva 673, 06001 Cajabamba **☎**76 551421 **E:** radioparaiso1300@hotmail.com – **CJ30)** Jr Santa Rosa 674-680, 06301 Chota **☎**76 351240 **W:** radiochota.com **E:** radiochota@hotmail. com – **CJ31)** Ca La Paz N° Cd Int 11, 06001 Cajamarca **☎**76 885580 – **CJ32)** Jr. 27 de Noviembre 557, 06301 Chota **W:** radiosantamonica.org **E:** radiosantamonica2@hotmail.com **☎**76 351477 📠76 351132 - **FM:** 95.7MHz – **CJ33)** Juan XXIII s/n (Plaza Bolognesi), 06001 Cajamarca - **FM:** 89.9MHz – **CJ34)** Av. Independencia 102 – 3er piso, 06001 Cajamarca **☎**999491668 **W:** radiocampesina.pe **E:** campesinaradio@ hotmail.com – **CJ35)** Jr. Arica cuadra. 5 s/n, Celendin **☎**76 555115 **E:** frecuenciavh_1440@hotmail.com – **CJ36)** Jr. Alfonso Ugarte N° 668, 06001 Cajamarca **☎**7655 7075 **W:** facebook.com Radio San Miguel Cajamarca **E:** sanmiguelradioradio@hotmail.com - **FM:** 101.1MHz – **CJ38)** Jr. Lima 290, 06858 Cutervo **☎**76 437010 **W:** radioilucan.com **E:** radioilucan@hotmail.com - **FM:** 96.5MHz – **CJ39)** Av Bolognesi 501,

06652 San Pablo - **FM:** 95.3 MHz – **CJ41**) Jr Jorge Chávez 416, 06115 Bambamarca ☎76 501297 **W:** radiobambamarca.com - **FM:** 101.3 MHz "Stereo Líder" – **CJ42**) Anaximandro Vega 481, Plaza de Armas, 06031 Chota ☎76 351442 ☐76 352027 **W:** andinaradio.net **E:** webmaster@andinaradio.net – **CJ43**) Jr Manuel Seoane 285, Cajamarca ☎976 017576 **W:** radiocontinente.pe – **CJ44**) Av San Juan 835, 06858 Cutervo. ☎76 437272 **W:** www.radiosantaana.com **E:** info@radiosantaana.com –**CJ54**) Jr Jose Galvez 698, 06631 Contumaza –**CJ58**) Cutervo ☎65 4654 5454 **W:** radiocutervo.com **E:** radiocutervo@hotmail.com – **FM:** 101.1 MHz – **CJ61**) Jr Santa Ros No 399, 06115 Bambamarca ☎76 501297 **W:** radiobambamarca.com - **FM:** 98.5 MHz – **CJ62**) Jr Los Libertadores 250, 06115 Bambamarca **W:** universobambamarca.com – **FM:** 98.5 MHz – **CJ63**) Jr Miguel Iglesia 483-489, 06001 Cajamarca ☎76 366985 **W:** turbomix.com.pe - **FM:** 92.5MHz – **CJ64**) Jr Leonico Prado 550, 06501 Pedro Galvez, San Marcos **W:** Facebook.com/Radio-Huracan-San-Marcos-600351456767398 – **CJ66**) 06115 Samangay **W:** visionradioperu.com – **CJ67**) José Osores 331, 06301 Chota ☎97 6163606 **W:** corporacionrior.org **E:** carranzamori@hotmail.com – **CJ68**) Jr Leoncios Prado 360, 06501 San Marcos **W:** radiomunicipalsanmarcos@hotmail.com – **FM:** 106.1 MHz – **CJ69**) Jr Anaximandro"Vega 688, 06301 Chota ☎97 68011212 **E:** digitelssac@hotmail.com – **FM:** 105.9 MHz – **CJ70**) Jr Cutervo 543, 06813 Santa Cruz ☎76 844068 **W:** frecuenciadelnorte.globered.com – **CJ71**) Carretera Agocucho s/n, Parimarca Baja, Zona Rural Marcopampa, 06001 Cajamarca **W:** visionradioperu.com – **CJ72**) Jr. San Martin 950 & Av Miguel Carducci 101, 06115 Bambamarca ☎97 6407575**W:** ondapopular.pe/bambamarca **E:** ondapopular.radio@hotmail.com – **FM:** 96.5 MHz – **CJ73**) Jr Eten 152, 06001 Cajamarca ☎976 372920 **W:** radiolabeta.com **E:** envivo@radiolabeta.com - **FM:** 101.3 MHz – **CJ74**) Cerro Chamusco, 06873 Pomahuaca – **CJ75**) Vista Alegre, Querocoto ista Alegre, 06846 Querocoto – **CJ76**) Las Dalias 147, 06001 Cajamarca – **CJ77**) Prolongacion Arequipa s/s, Barrios Altos,06861 Querocotillo ☎995 583160 **W:** radiolaspalmasdequerocotillo.com **E:** radiolaspalmas1360@hotmail.com – **CJ78**) Iglesia Pentecostal La Cosecha, Caserio San Lorenzo de Shumba km 46 Carretera San Ignacio, Jaen – **CJ79**) Jr Marañon 345, Tacshana, 06536 Cajabamba ☎76 774441 **W:** Facebook – **CJ80**) Ca Lambayeque 156, 06101 Jaen ☎949 917090 **W:** radionorandinajaen.com – **CJ81**) Jr. Teresa de Journet 131, Urb. Alameda, 06001 Cajamarca ☎94 2021465 **W:** manantialdevida1450.com **E:** manantialdevidaradio@hotmail.com – **CJ82**) Bambamarca **W:** Facebook.com/radiolibertadbambamarca – **FM:** 104.1 MHz – **CJ83**) Jr.Juan XXIII 287, 06031 Chota – **CJ84**) Jr Alfonso Ugarte 212, Bambamarca ☎76 353642 **W:**.radiocharles.com **E:** radiocharles91.1@hotmail.com - **FM:** 91.1 MHz – **CJ85**) Jr Fray Juose Arana 738, Chota ☎97 5801485 **W:** facebook.com/lapositiva.chota.bambamarca/ **E:** loloperiiodista@hotmail.com – **FM:** 90.1 MHz – **CJ86**) Jr Huancavelica No 387, Urb. Las Margaritas – Barrio San José, Cajamarca ☎76 601795 **W:** radiotvcajamarca.com – **CJ87**) Pasaje Shililique s/n, Jaen – **CJ88**) Cutervo **W:** FB - **FM.:** 91.1 MHz – **CJ88**) **W:** radioagriculturacajamarca.com **E:** Francisco.cortez@radioagricultura.com – **CJ89**) Rejopampa, Sorochuco

**CU00 (CUSCO:)**
**CU02**) Universidad Nacional de San Antonio Abad del Cusco, Av. de la Cultura 733, 08001 Cusco ☎84 786874 **W:** abel-ww.wix.com/radiouniversidad-unsaac-cusco **E:** radio_universidad@hotmail.com – **CU04**) Av Charcahuaylla s/n, 08028 Maras, Prov Urubamba ☎84 201410 **W:** radiolasalle.com.pe **E:** webmaster@radiolasalle.com.pe – **FM:** 91.7MHz – **CU05**) Prolongacion Av. Grau 30, Huancaro, 08001 Cusco ☎84 221045 **W:** nseradio.com **E:** nsecusco@nseradio.com – **CU06**) Ca Tres Cruces de Oro 430, 3er piso, 08001 Cusco ☎84 232717 **W.:** facebook.com/radioredecusco **E.:** redecusco@yahoo.com – **CU07**) Ca Puputi K-3B, Cercado de Cusco, 08001 Cusco ☎84 505364 **W:** radioluzcusco.com – **CU08**) Ca Inca 650, Santiago, 08001 Cusco ☎84 228649 **W:**radiointiraymi.com **E:** intiraymiradio@hotmail.com - **Quechua:** 2 hrs: - 1100, 1500 – **CU10**) Ca Daniel A Carrioón 602, Urb. Fideranda, 08006 Wanchaq ☎84 255491 – **CU13**) Av Tupac Amaru, Urb. Progreso D3, 08006 Wanchaq ☎84 504961 **W:** radiolasvegas.pe **E:** administracion@grupovegas.com.pe - **FM:** 100.1 MHz – **CU14**) Jr Cusco 805 - Yauri, 08451 Espinar ☎84 773692 **W:** http//radioconciertocusco.galeon.com – **FM:** 103.9MHz – **CU15**) Asoc. Pro-Vivendi el Periodista Lt B-13, 08006 Wanchaq ☎84 261556 **W:** radiotropicanacusco.blogspot.no – **E:** RadioTropicanaCusco@gmail.com – **CU16**) Urb. Villa el Periodista Lote E-1, 08001 Cusco ☎84 239514 **W:** cuscoctv47.com **E:** prensaaldiaperu@gmail.com – **CU17**) Ca Sucre 107, 08351 Sicuaní – **CU18**) Jr Ricardo Palma M 2, Wanchaq, 08001 Cusco ☎84 246201 - **FM:** 100.7MHz – **CU19**) Ca Anta s/n, Antanampa, 08541 Espinar **W:** radiolosandesdelperu.es.tl - **FM :** 98.9MHz – **CU20**) Jr Juan Espinoza Medrano P-13, Urb Rosas Pata, 08001 Cusco **E:** sernaquem@hotmail.com – **CU21**) Ca Retiro 296-A, 08001 Cusco ☎84 224567 - **FM:** 92.7MHz – **CU22**)

Lote E-11, Urb Bancopata, 08001 Cusco **W:** machupicchuradio.com **E:** machupicchuradio@hotmail.com - **FM:** 100.1MHz – **CU23**) Jr José Santos Chocano, Bloque G-11, Urb. Santa Monica, 08001 Cusco ☎84 226765 ☐84 234494 **W:** radiouniversalcusco.com.pe **E:** radiouniversal@speedy.com.pe - **FM:** 103.3MHz – **CU24**) Ca Meloc 417, 08001 Cusco **W:** bethelradio.fm – **CU25**) Av El Sol N° 830, 08001 Cusco ☎84 228411 **W:** facebook.com/www.radiotawantinsuyo- **FM:** 91.3MHz – **CU26**) Av Martin Pio Concha 339, 08141 Santa Ana **Quechua:** 1300-1430, 2100-0100 ☎84 281002 **W:** radioquillabamba.com - **FM:** 91.1MHz – **CU27**) Jr Bolivar 217, 08351 Sicuani **W:** radiopachatusan.com**E:** pachatusanradio1240@hotmail.com – **CU28**) Pasaje Constancia 102, Of 410, 08006 Wanchaq **W:** solimperiotvradio.blogspot.com – **CU30**) Jr José Olaya Mz H-9, Urb Bancopata, 08009 Santiago ☎84 252591 – **CU31**) Ca Sacsaywaman K-10, Urb. Manuel Prado, 08001 Cusco - **FM:** 104.1MHz – **CU32**) Av. Garcilazo de la Vega 604, 08006 Wanchaq ☎84 226912 **E:** campesinaprensa@gmail.com – **CU34**) Jr 2 de Mayo 206, 08351 Sicuani ☎84 351136 **W:** radiosicuani.org.pe **E:** radiosicuani@gmail.com - **Quechua:** 0930-1100, 2300-0300 0900-0300 - **FM:** 91.1MHz – **CU35**) Urb. Marcavalle, P-20, 08002 Wanchaq ☎84 226555 **W:** rtvsantamonica.com **E:** radiosantamonica@gmail.com - **FM:** 93.9MHz – **CU36**) Plaza de Armas s/n, El Descanso, 08371 Kunturkanki Canas, Prov. de Canas **E:** cpmaldonado@caritas.org.pe – **CU37**) Conjunto Habitacional Pachacútec A-105, 08001 Cusco ☎84 211371 **W:** radiovidacusco.org – **CU39**) Jr Matara 526, 08001 Cusco - **FM:** 106.5MHz – **CU40**) Av Manuel Callo Zevallos 161, 08351 Sicuani ☎84 351700 **W:** radioquechua.pe **E:** radioquechus@gmail.com - **FM:** 97.7MHz – **CU42**) Plaza de Armas s/n, 08281 Marcapata, Provincia de Quispicanchi – **CU43**) Ca Saphi 601, Cusco ☎84 225851 - **FM:** 90.1MHz – **CU44**) Av El Sol 230, Yauri, 08451 Espinar - **FM:** 103.1MHz – **CU48**) Av Panamericana 105, Yauri, 08451 Espinar – **CU49**) Av Cusco s/n, Yauri, 08451 Espinar – **CU50**) Jr Ricardo Palma 516, 08141 Quillabamba - **FM:** 96.5MHz – **CU51**) Ca Choquechaca 152, 08001 Cusco ☎84 802444 – **CU52**) Ca Heladeros 220, 08006 Wanchaq **W:** radiomariaperu.org - **FM:** 102.1MHz – **CU55**) Comunidad de Usañaje, Ca 28 de Junio 507, 08551 Santo Tomas, Chumbivilcas **W:** radioqorilazo.zragteam.com – **CU56**) Av San Martin 305, Yauri, 08451 Espinar ☎84 301099 **W:** radiolaramani.com **E:** radiolaramani@latinmail.com – **CU58**) Plaza de Armas s/n, El Descanso, 08371 Kunturkanki, Prov de Canas **E:** radiosantacruz@peru.com - **FM:** 97.7MHz – **CU61**) Ca Arequipa 590, 08351 Sicuani – **CU62**) Av Arequipa s/n, 08351 Sicuani ☎84 352373 **W:** radiovilcanotasicuani.com **E:.** rperzquispe@hotmail.com – **CU64**) Ca Monjaspata 745, 08001 Cusco – **CU65**) Sede Nacional Cusco, Av Huayarurupata 1707, Wanchaq, Cusco – **CU66**) Puputi 208, Int. N° 01, 08001 Cusco – **CU67**) Av San Martin 311, 08451 Espinar ☎84 250132 **W:** radiocadenasurespinar.blogspot.com **E:** waldervalero@hotmail.com - **FM:** 103.1 MHz – **CU68**) Av Cuzco 117, 08058 San Sebastian – **CU69**) Malecón Cusco s/n, 08351 Sicuani,**W:** radioexitosa.pe – **CU70**) Av Infancia 551, 08001 Cusco ☎84 784397 **W:** facebook.com R. Jerusalen – **CU71**) Huánuco 113, 08451 Espinar ☎84 301125 **W:** radiosolarespinar.com – **CU72**) Ca Belen 600, 08031 Urubamba ☎99 6783273 **W:** radiochaski.com **E:** chaskiradio@hotmail.com - **FM:** 94.9 MHz – **CU73**) Av Ejercito 200, 08001 Cusco ☎84 775511 **W:** radiovidacusco.org – **CU74**) Av Tupac Amaru 526, 08386 Yanaoca **W:** Facebook Radio Altiva Canas – **CU75**) Av Tupac Amaru 321 08386 Yanaoca Canas ☎968666649 **W:** radiotupacamaru.blogspot.no – **CU76**) Urb. Tambillo L-5, 08086 Urcos – **CU77**) Av de la Cultura 3035 A-1, 08058 San Sebastian – **CU78**) Av Carrion 313, 08351 Sicuani **W:** redinformativadelsur.blogspot.se – **CU79**) Ca Mojospata 745, Cusco ☎98 665 5540 **W:** radiowayraperu.com – **CU80**) Av Huayruropata 1707, Cusco **W:** ipda.com.pe – **CU81**) Esquina Calle Alegria 205 con Av.Arequipa No 119, 08351 Sicuani – **CU82**) Av Tupac Amaru D-3, Urb. Progreso, 08006 Wanchaq ☎84 246832 **W:** radiolasvegas.pe – **CU83**) Ca Concepcion MZ J-4, Lote 4, 08531 Livitica – **CU85**) Yauri, Espinar ☎973 583596 **W:** radiokinsachata.pe **E:** info@radiokinsachata.pe – **CU86**) Av. Diagonal (R.Zavaleta) 117 5° piso, Wanchaq –**CU87**) Chumbbivilcas – **CU88**) Pallpata, Espinar – **CU89**) Bolivar esq. Bolognesi, Santo Tomás, Chumbbivilcas ☎84 612178 **W:** radiochumpiwillkas.com – **CU90**) Chamaca, Chumbivilcas – **CU91**) Av Cultura No 2405, Oficina 203, Cusco **W:** radio760cuscoam.com **E:** radiolosandes760cusco@gmail.com

**HN00 (HUANUCO):**
**HN01**) Av Raymondi N° 432, 10221 Rupa-Rupa ☎6256 2024 – **HN02**) Malecón Huallaga 1038, 10261 Aucayacu – **HN03**) Jr Tacna 693, 10001 Huanuco ☎62 517996 **W:** radiohuanuco.com – **HN04**) Jr Hermilio Valdiz 272,10001 Huanuco ☎62 516360 **W:** radioluz.com – **HN06**) Ruben Dario 128, 10051 Amarilis, 10001 Huánuco ☎62 512428 – **HN07**) Jr Dos de Mayo 218, 208, 10001 Huánuco **E:** luzysonido@hotmail.com ☎62 518500 ☐62 511985 **Quechua:** 1000-1200, 2300-0200 - **FM:** 105.7MHz – **HN12**) Jr. Aguilar N° 560, 2do Piso, 10001 Huanuco – **HN13**) Sector San Cristóbal de Huayllabamba, 10066 San

Francisco de Cayran – **HN15)** Pasaje Uchiza 170, Int 7, 10221 Rupa-Rupa – **HN16)** Sector Mesepata, 10061 Pilco Marca – **HN17)** Jr Leonicio con Libertad, 10001 Huanuco **W:** radiocielo.com – **HN18)** Jr. Ambo 112, Amarilis **W:** kebuenaradioytv.com – **FM:** 99.7 – **HN19)** Jr Colonial 312, 10021 Amarilis – **HN20)** Jr Colonial N° 312, 10021 Amarilis

## HV00 (HUANCAVELICA):

**HV01)** Puno 110, 09481 Lircay, Prov de Angaraes – **HV02)** Plaza Bolognesi 142, Cercado,09001 Huancavelica ☎67 451257 **E:** jlopez_alvarado@hotmail.com – **FM:** 99.1MHz – **HV03)** Ca Arequipa S/N, 09841 Huayllahuara – **HV04)** Av Los Libertadores s/n, Castrovirreina – **HV05)** Cl Mercurio 101, Urb. Santa Bárbara, Huancavelica ☎67 451376 **W:** radiomastermixfm.com **E:** mastermixfm@hotmail.com – **HV06)** Jr Armado Revorredo 588, Acobamba – **HV07)** Jr Sebastián 353, Huancavelica – **HV08)** Plaza San Lorenzo S/N,Acoria – **HV09)** Av Andrés Avelino Cáceres No 381, Huancavelica – **HV10)** Ca. Lima s/n, Preov

## IC00 (ICA):

**IC01)** Conde de Nieva 125, 11001 Ica – **IC02)** Av Ayacucho Esq Grau s/n, 11001 Ica ☎56 231956 – **FM:** 105.3MHz – **IC03)** Av Conde de Nieva, Urb Luren, 11001 Ica – **FM:** 90.7MHz – **IC04)** Av San Martín 305, 2° piso, 11101 Chincha Alta – **IC05)** Ca Cajamarca 195, 11001 Ica – **FM:** 103.3MHz – **IC06)** Av Leon de Bivero 100 2do Piso, 11001 Ica ☎56 237326 **W:** radioluluz.com – **IC07)** Zona M-6, San Juan de Marcona, 111521 Marcona ☎56 525268 – **IC10)** Ca Bolivar 473, 11001 Ica. ☎56 219300 – **IC11)** Calle Grocio Prado 122, 11101 Chincha Alta – **IC12)** Los Portales de Escribanos 167, Plaza de Armas, Palpa **E:** radiocruzdelsur@hotmail.com – **FM:** 99.7 MHz – **IC15)** San Martín 120, Urb Pencal, 11521 Nazca – **IC17)** Km 300, Panamericana Sur, 11011 Subtanjalla **E:** epcc@upsjb.edu.pe – **IC19)** Jr Los Ángeles 296 3er Piso, Publo Nuevo, 11141 Chincha ☎56 263278 – **IC20)** Ca San Francisco 301, 11241 San Clemente ☎56 312416 **W:** facebook.com/carlosalberto.bautistagutierrez – **IC21)** Jr Lima 529,11141 Chincha Alta **W:** yeshuaradiofm.blogspot.es – **FM:** 107.5 MHz – **IC22)** Urb. Fernando de Leon de Vivero R` 1-7, 11146 Pueblo Nuevo **W:** bethelradio.fm **E:** bethelradio@bethelradio.fm – **IC23)** Ca Camino Real s/n, Sector Guadeloupe, 11021 Salas **W:**radiolaluz.com – **IC24)** Programa de Vivienda Vallea Hermoso, 11011 Subtanjalla – **IC25)** Jirón Miraflores 342, 4588 Pueblo Nuevo – **IC26)** Av Arenales 697, Ica – **IC27)** Ca San Francisco s/n – Sector Colorado, Chincha – **IC28)** Av. Las Gaviotas Cdra. 17 A27, Urb. Sagitario, Santiago de Surco, Lima ☎1 2577315 **W:** elsembrador.com **E.:** elsembradortv@gmail.com – **IC29)** Av Arenales 685, Ica – **IC30)** Av Arenales 685, Ica – **IC31)** Av Progreso 168, Chinca Alta – **IC31)** Prolongación Cañete Mz. D- 1, LT21-A, Salas – **IC32)** Jr. Ica 357, Pueblo Nuevo – **IC33)** Prolongación Cañete s/n, Salas – **IC34)** Ica

## JN00 (JUNIN):

**JN01)** Jr Los Manzanos 695, 12009 El Tambo ☎64 789459 **W:** radioluluz.com – **FM:** 101.7MHz – **JN04)** Av Tayacaja 324, Of 202, 12851 La Oroya – **JN05)** Av Jorge Chavez 851, Anexo Zaños Grande, 12009 El Tambo **E:** radiovida@hotmail.com – **JN06)** Ca Ancash 543, Of 208, 12001 Huancayo – **FM:** 103.1MHz – **JN08)** Jr Bolognesi 484 2de Piso, 12417 Jauja **W:** radioluzdetarma.com – **JN09)** Av Calmell del Solar 469-481, Sn Carlos Hye, 12001 Huancayo ☎64 211312 **W:** rmanantial.webcindario.com **E:** manantialradio960@hotmail.com – **FM:** 94.9 MHz – **JN10)** Jr. Huancas 251, a San Carlos, 12001 Huancayo – **JN11)** Esquina Prolongación Pachitea 136 y Pasaje Andaluz 106 4° piso, 12001 Huancayo – **JN12)** Paraje Aliguata, Anexo A Azapampa, 12014 Chilca **W:** bethelradio.fm – **JN13)** Ca Mercado 194, 12321 San Ramón – **JN14)** Ca Real 270, El Tambo, 12001 Huancayo ☎64 245396 ░64 253921 – **FM:** 96.7MHz "R Futura" – **JN16)** Paseo La Breña 174 2 piso Of 202, 12001 Huancayo ☎64 219990 – **JN18)** Jr Cerro de Pasco 582, ( Ap 2), 12101 Junín ☎64 344029 **W:** rlibertadjunin.com **E:** radiolibertadjunin@yahoo.es – **FM:** 98.9MHz – **JN19)** Av Ayacucho 7300, 12001 Huancayo – **FM:** 105.7MHz – **JN20)** Av Manuel Prado 239,12411 Satipo – **JN21)** Jr Moquegua 648, 12221 Tarma – **JN22)** Jr Puno 430, Huancayo ☎64 218080 **W:** radiocumbre.org.pe **E:** radiocumbre985fmcom@gmail.com – **FM:** 98.5MHz – **JN23)** Jr Junín 163, 12331 La Merced Chanchamayo – **JN24)** Jr Dario Leon 198, 4° piso, 12851 La Oroya **W:** Facebook – **FM:** 91.7 MHz – **JN26)** Ca Real 1453, 12001 Huancayo **W:** radiobacan.com **E:** corpluss@radiobacan.com – **JN27)** Jr Junin 843 , 2° piso, 12741 Jauja ☎64 362428 ░64 361850 – **JN28)** Jr Jauja 494, 12221 Tarma – **JN29)** Prolongacion los Proceres s/n, Barrio Las Lomas, 12014 Chilca – **JN30)** Jr Moquegua 642, 12221 Tarma ☎64 321864 **W:** radioluzdetarma.com – **JN31)** Av Jose Carlos Mariátegui 699, Urb Tambo, 12001 Huancayo ☎64 241941 ░64 252840 – **FM:** 102.5MHz – **JN32)** Ca Bolivar 481, 12101 Junin – **JN33)** Marcavelle Block "F" 191,Santa Rosa de Sacco, 12851 La Oroya **W:** Facebook – Radio La Oroya **E:** radio_la_oroya@hotmail.com ☎64 391401 ░64 391748 – **FM:** 100.1MHz – **JN34)** Ca Real 517, Of 403, 12001 Huancayo ☎64 231831 **W:** radiohuancayo.com.pe – **FM:** 104.3MHz – **JN35)** Av Arevaldo 484, Anexo Chuccus, 12841 Santa Rosa de Sacco, Prov de Yauli – **JN37)** Jr Molino del Amo 167 (Cas.167), 12221 Tarma ☎64 321510 ░6432 1167 **W:** radiotarma.com **E:** informacion@grupomonteverde.com – **FM:** 99.3 & 101.7MHz "R Tropicana" in La Merced – **JN38)** Av Huancavelica 430, 2° piso (Ap 230), 12001 Huancayo ☎64 233851 **W:** radio1550.com **E:** radio@radio1550.com – **FM:** 88.9MHz – **JN40)** Jr Pasco y Amazonas 420 2 piso Edifico San Juan, 12221 Tarma ☎64 321820 – **FM:** 106.5 MHz – **JN44)** Ca Principal de Lama, Pariahuanca, 12001 Huancayo **W:** nuevotiempo.org.pe – **JN45)** Av.Huancavelica 439 4to pisi, 12001 Huancyo – **JN46)** Prolongacion ICA y Ca. Real s/n, 12001 Huancayo **W:** visionradioperu.com – **JN48)** Jr Santa Cecilia 107 12014 Chilca ☎64 201011 **W:** radiovozcristianaperu.com **E:** radiovozcristiana1470am@hotmail.com – **JN49)** Pasaje Omacoto, 12072 Sicaya – **JN50)** Ca Principal de Lampa s/n, 12006 Pariahuanca – **JN51)** Jr Ayacucho 297, 12001 Huancayo – **JN52)** Av los Incas 421, Huancán ☎64 248362 **W:** ministerioevangelicoapocalipsis.com – **JN53)** Conjunto Habitacional Villa Mercedes, Block 03, Tiends 1, 12001 Huancayo **W:** radiocora.net – **JN54)** Av Deusta 548,12009 El Tambo – **JN55)** Jr La Victoria 322, Costado Colegio Casillo, 12009 El Tambo ☎64 249121 – **JN56)** Jr Cajamarca 178, Huancayo ☎64 215038 **W:** radioscaladeoro.com **E:** escalaradio@hotmail.com – **FM:** 107.1 MHz – **JN57)** Jr Ayacucho 297,12001 Huancayo **W:** FB- **E:** rumbaradioactiva@hotmail.com – **FM:** 91.1 MHz – **JN58)** Centro Poblado de Tzancuvatziari, Satipo – **JN59)** Junin – **JN60)** Altura de Puente Chacachimpa, Carretera Junin Ondores, Junin – **JN61)** Pasaje Las Orquidias s/n, Tarma

## LB00 (LAMBAYEQUE):

**LB01)** Km 4 de la Carretera Pimentel, 14001 Chiclayo – **FM:** 105.1MHz – **LB02)** Ca Juan XXXIII 391 (Ciudad Universitaria), 14601 Lambayeque **W:** unprg.edu.pe **E:** universitariaradio@hotmail.com – **LB03)** Psje. Woyke 179,Oficina Radio, Edifico Angelica, 14011 San José ☎74 237850 **W:** radioluluz.com – **LB04)** Juan Cuglievan 984, 14001 Chiclayo – Quechua: **Sun:** 0600-1100 – **LB06)** Alfonso Ugarte 505, 14011 San José ☎74 608991 – **LB08)** Ca San José 462, Of 207, 14001 Chiclayo ☎74 204786 – **FM:** 96.7MHz – **LB11)** Av Pedro Ruiz 1123, 3° piso, 14001 Chiclayo – **LB12)** Calle 28 de Julio 440, 14041 San Jose ☎74 650332 **W:** radioprimaverachiclayo.com – **LB14)** Colombia 1637, Urb. V.R.Haya de la Torre, 14001 Chiclayo ☎74 208523 – **LB15)** Av Saenz Peña 1046, 14001 Chiclayo ☎74 208872 – **FM:** 98.3MHz – **LB16)** Av Tupac Amaru 532, 14301 Ferreñafe ☎73 286044 **E:** aflff@hotmail.com – **LB17)** Ca San José 1084, 14001 Chiclayo – **LB18)** Av. Lora y Lora 1505, Urb. San Isidro, 14001 Chiclayo ☎74 320616 – **FM:** 94.1MHz – **LB19)** Ca Manuel Seano 918, 14001 Chiclayo ☎74 236363 – **LB20)** Ca Las Violetas s/n, 14001 Chiclayo **W:** radionova.com.pe/nova_chiclayo.html – **FM:** 94.9MHz – **LB21)** Ca Francisco Gonzales Burgán 717, 14301 Ferreñafe ☎74 286351 **E:** radioferrenafe@hotmail.com – **LB22)** Ca 1 de Mayo 278, Urrunaga, 14001 Chiclayo – **LB23)** Caserio Tranca Falupe, 14101 Morrope – **LB24)** Ca San Francisco 1499 – P.J.Cruz de Chalpo, 14161 Olmos – **LB25)** Jr. Juan Cuglievan 984, 14001 Chiclayo ☎98 1877701 **W:** radioamistadperu.net – **LB26)** Empresa Capimag S.R.L., Calle Justicia 102, Urb. Túpac Amaru, 14001 Chiclayo – **LB29)** Ca San José 148, 14161 Olmos **E:** clori1009@yahoo.es – **LB30)** Av el Tren s/n, 14001 Chiclayo – **LB31)** Ca Juan Fanning N° 457, Urb San Juan, 14001 Chiclayo ☎74 239889 **W:** visionradioperu.com **E:** informes@visionradioperu.com – **LB32)** Ca Tarata 931, 14161 Olmos **W:** Facebook – Radio Super Real 1510 – **LB36)** Av Huamaucho 1080, 14601 Lambayeque ☎74 284085 **W:** radionaylamp.com **E:** naylamp@llampallec.rep.net.pe – **FM:** 96.1MHz – **LB40)** Ca Amadeo Ruiz 320, 14161 Olmos **W:** radionorandinaolmos.com – **FM:** 102.7 MHz – **LB41)** Ca Nazca 300, 14021 La Victoria ☎74 232559 **W:** radiofechiclayo.tk **E** jesusmiguela1077@hotmail.com att.: Pastor José Huamán – **LB42)** Ca Vicente de la Vega 873, 14001 Chiclayo ☎74 224287 **W:** corporacionrbc.org **E:** carranzamori@hotmail.com – **LB44)** Av Lora y Lora 399, Urb. Patazca, 14001 Chiclayo – **LB45)** Av Los Andes No 950, 14021 La Victoria – **LB46)** Prolongacion 8 de Octubre No 263, 14601 Lambayeque – **LB47)** Av Pedro Ruiz 1250, 14001 Chiclayo ☎74 229494 – **LB48)** Ca Diego Ferre 637, Monsefú – **LB49)** Av Pacifico 483, Chiclayo

## LL00 (LA LIBERTAD):

**LL01)** Av.Gonzales Prada 695-12, 13001 Trujillo ☎44 436007 – **LL02)** Jr Benito Juarez 1753, 13009 La Esperanza – **LL03)** Daniel Alcides Carrión 306,13001 Trujillo ☎44 291058 – **FM:** 98.3MHz – **LL04)** Ca Lima 599, 13171 Chepén – **LL05)** San Martín 472, 13001 Trujillo ☎44 251792 – **LL06)** Av Los Incas s/n, Anexo Facala, Ascope – **LL07)** Ca Junín 23, Sausal, 13261 Ascope – **LL08)** Francisco Pizarro 532, Of 205, 13001 Trujillo – **LL09)** Jr Ayacucho 65, 13111 Pacasmayo ☎44 583042 – **LL10)** Jr San Antonio 880 Piso 2, 13301 Otuzco ☎44 436007 – **LL11)** Jr Marcelo Corne 224, Urb San Andrés, 13001 Trujillo ☎44 294050 – **FM:** 90.9MHz – **LL12)** Av V Belaunde MZ.L lote 15, Urb Santo Dominguito, 13001 Trujillo – **LL15)** Av Gran Chimu 1791 – Esperanza Alta, 13009 La Esperanza – **LL16)** Alfonso Ugarte 222, 13052 Virú ☎44 371046 **W:** radioollantayperu.com **E:** viru@radioollantayperu.

com – **FM:** 102.3MHz – **LL17)** Ca Trujillo 699-A, 13171 Chepén – **LL19)** Psje. Damián Niculau 108, 13501 Huamachuco. ☎44 441502 **W:** radiolosandesdehuamachuco.com **E:** radiolosandesdireccion@yahoo. es – **LL20)** Psje. Rosa Elvira Farro Solis 3, Urb. Ignacioa Reaño, 13171 Chepen ☎44 561430 **W:** sansebastianradio.com **E:** info@ sansebastianradio.com - **FM:** 103.3 MHz – **LL21)** Miguel Grau 439, Of. 213, 13001 Trujillo ☎44 217885 – **LL22)** Zepita 452, 13001 Trujillo ☎44 249326 📠44 252970 **W:** radiolibertadmundo.com **E:** contactanos@radiolibertadmundo.com – **LL24)** Bolívar 780 ( Cas 1029), 13001 Trujillo ☎44 233981 – **LL26)** Ca Cáceres 1338, 13761 Santiago de Chuco ☎44 230277 – **LL28)** Jr Progreso 987, 13171 Chepén - **FM:** 98.7MHz – **LL32)** Av. Geronimo La Torre 175, Urb. Las Quintanas, 13001 Trujillo ☎44 803207 **W.:** Facebook – Radio La Luz 1390 – **LL35)** Pasaje San Martin 300, Urb Alto Mochica, ( Ap 352) 13001 Trujillo ☎44 201606 **W:** sanjuansuperradio.com **E:** radiosanjuan@ hotmail.com **LL37)** Jr Trujillo 350, 13701 Quiruvilca ☎949 611963 **W:** radiooliversa.com – **LL38)** Av. Virú N° 1205, 13052 Virú – **LL39)** Av. España 1238 – oficina 305, 13001 Trujillo ☎44 210494 – **LL42)** Av. Cesar Vallejo 390, 13001 Trujillo **W:** radiomundialam.com - **FM:** 96.9MHz – **LL43)** Av España 1210, 13001 Trujillo ☎44 295214 **W:** Facebook **E:** pastormamerto@hotmail.com – **LL46)** Ca Victor Julio Rossel 324, 13831 Julcan – **LL47)** Ca Progreso 551, 13301 Otuzco ☎44 220221 – **LL48)** Ca La Libertad 120, 13301 Otuzco ☎44 436565 **W:** chamiradio.org.pe **E:** direccion@chamiradio.org.pe – **LL49)** Ca Progreso 551, 13301 Otuzco **W:** radiootuzco.blogspot.no – **LL51)** Jr Lara 591, 13501 Huamachuco **W:** radioantena9.com – **LL52)** Av America Sur 3145, Urb. Monserrat (Apt. 1075), 13001 Trujillo ☎44 604444 **W:** upao.edu.pe/radio **E:** cceli@upao.edu.pe – **LL53)** Jr Francisco Pizarro 970, 13001 Trujillo – **LL54)** Panamericana Norte Km 570 – El Milagro, 13009 La Esperanza – **LL55)** Ca Simón Bolivar 675, Santiago de Chuco **FB:** Radio-La-Voz-Del-Pueblo-Santiago-De-Chuco-137302053483702 – **LL56)** Trujillo – **LL57)** San Ignacio, Otuzco

**LM00 (LIMA):**
**LM01)** Juan Vargas 147, Chorrillos, Lima 09 ☎1 4388850 **W:** radioinca. com.pe – **LM02)** Jr Camana 615 of 605, Lima 01 ☎1 4272639 **W:** radiooriente.com **E:** radiooriente@hotmail.es – **LM03)** Av Garzón 2031, Jesús Maria, Lima 11 ☎1 7001600 ☎1 4333276 **W:** radiomariaperu. org **E:** info.per@radiomaria.org – **LM04)** Jr, Contunaz No 933 Ofic 601, Lima 15001 ☎1 4280938 **W:** radiocora.net **E:** soporteradiocora@gmail. com – **LM05)** Ca Miguel Dasso 144, Of 2A, San Isidro, Lima 27 ☎1 5922291 **W:** ovacion.com.pe/radio/ **E:** radioovacion@ovacion.com. pe – **LM06)** Av Guzman Blanco 465, oficina 203-701, (Ap 4236) Lima 01 ☎1 4333275 **W:** pacificocomunicaciones.com/radio640.html **E:** informes@pacificocomunicaciones.com – **LM07)** Justo Pastor Davila 197, Chorillos, Lima 09 ☎1 6176600 **W:** radiolainolvidable.com.pe **E:**crpradio@crpradio.com – **LM08)** Los Robles 297, San Isidro, Lima **W:** rbcradio.pe **E:** contacto@rbcradio.pe – **LM09)** Jr. Alejandro Tirado 508, Urb. Santa Beatriz, Lima 01 (✉ C.P. 138, La Molina, Lima 12) ☎1 2653291 **W:** redradiointegridad.com **E:** redradiointegridad. org – **LM10)** Av Paseo de la República 3866, 2° piso, San Isidro, Lima 27 ☎1 2150200 **W:** rpp.com.pe **E:** info@gruporpp.com.pe – **LM11)** Justo Pastor Dávila 197, Chorillos, Lima 09 ☎1 6176600 📠1 2513324 **W:** radiomar.com.pe – **LM12)** Alfonso Ugarte 1428 of 904, Lima ☎1 4241805 – **LM13)** Prolongación los Angeles 676, Huaral, Lima 18 ☎1 2465296 **W:** Facebook Radio la Luz Huaral **E:** radiolaluzhuaral@hotmail. com - **FM:** 94.7 MHz – **LM14)** Jr Mayta Cápac 1385, Jesús Maria Central, Lima 11 **W:** radiolibertad.com.pe **E:** info@radiolibertad.com. pe ☎1 2660777 – **LM15)** Av Petit Thouars 447, Santa Beatriz, Lima 01 **W:** radionacional.com.pe **E:** webmaster@irtp.com.pe ☎1 4338956 – **LM16)** Av José Pardo 138, Of. 1501, Miraflores, Lima 18 ☎1 7120145 **W:** radiounion.pe **E:** informes@unionradio.com – **LM17)** Av Paseo de la Republica 3866, San Isidro Lima 27 ☎1 2210941 **W:** felicidad.com. pe – **LM18)** Av Republica de Chile 295, Of. 1104, Santa Beatriz, Lima 01 ☎1 3327779 **W:** modernaradiopapa.com.pe **E:** correomoderna@ hotmail.com – **LM19)** Paseo Parodi 340, San Isidro, Lima 27 **W:** radiopanamericana.com **E:** radio@panamericana.com ☎1 4388585 📠1 4221223 – **LM20)** Jr Ignacio Merino 230, Santa Cruz, Miraflores, Lima 18 ☎1 4428810 **W:** radiolatina.com.pe **E:** contacto@radiolatina. com.pe – **LM21)** Julio C.Tello 152, Lince, Lima 14 ☎1 4714291 **W:** metropolitanaradioperuana.com **E:** metropolitanaradioperuana@ gmail.com – **LM22)** Julio C.Tello 152, Lince, Lima 14 ☎1 4714291 **W:** radioexitoperu.com **E:** radioexitoperu@gmail.com – **LM23)** Av Alfonso Ugarte 1465, 01 Lima ☎1 3320080 **W:** radiolaluz.com **E:**dr. davidlozano@hotmail.com – **LM24)** Gerardo Unger 6347, San Martin de Porres, Lima 31 ☎1 5373204 **W:** radiofelizperu.com – **LM27)** Jr Bernardo Alcedo 375, Lince, Lima 14 ☎1 2652333 **W:** radiobacan. com **E:** corplus@radiobacan.com – **LM30)** Jr. Contunaz No 933 Ofic 601, Lima 15001 ☎1 4280938 **W:** radiocora.net **E:** soporteradiocora@ gmail.com **LM31)** Jr Echenique 140, 15140 Huacho – **LM32)** Mz L, Lt 7, Urb La Esperanza, 15146 Hualmay – **LM33)** Av Estados Unidos 327, Urb Huaquillay, Comas, Lima 07 **W:** radiocomas.com **E:** comas@

radiocomas.com ☎1 5250094 📠1 5250859 – **LM34)** Ca MCDO Sur 105, 15140 Huacho – **LM35)** Cl Felipe Arancibia 861, San Juan de Miraflores Lima ☎1 368 6829 **W:** radioalegria1340am.com – **LM38)** Av Comandante Espinar N° 680, Miraflores, Lima 18 ☎1 6107760 📠1 6107761 **W:** nuevotiempo.org.pe **E:** radio@nuevotiempo.org.pe – **LM39)** Av. Paseo de la Republica 3832 – Oficina 602, 01 San Isidro, Lima ☎1 4405790 **W:** eccoradio.pe **E:** eccoradiopropusa@gmail. com – **LM40)** Av 28 de Julio 1781, La Victoria. Lima 13 ☎1 6131701 **W:** bethelradio.fm **E:** bethelradio@bethelradio.fm – **LM41)** Av Petit Thouars 1806, Lince, Lima 14 ☎1 4711278 **W:** radiosanisidroam. com – **LM42)** Mz C, Lte. 5, Asoc. Virgen de la Familia, 15857 Chilca – **LM43)** Av Separadora Industrial s/n, Lote 4, MZ5, M25, Parcela 1, Villa El Salvador, Lima 42 ☎1 2913012**W:** radioimperial2peruam. com – **LM44)** Alfonso Ugarte 149, 15170 Barranca ☎1 2354238 – **FM:** 101.5 MHz – **LM45)** A.Paseo de la República 3866, San Isidro **W:** capital.com.pe – **LM47)** Jr Camaná 170, (Apt 4451 San Miguel), El Cercado, Lima 01 **W:** radiosantarosa.com.pe **E:** contacto@ radiosantarosa.com.pe ☎1 4277488 – **LM49)** Calle Las Lucumas 4168 4to.Piso Urb. Naranjal – Independencia, Antes San Martin de Porres, Lima ☎1 7153268 **W:** radiomileniaperu.com – **LM51)** Jr. Napo 3916, Independencia, Lima 28 ☎1 5234319 **W:** radioindependenciaperu. com.pe **E:** wbaldeon@radioindependenciaperu.com.pe – **LM52)** Av Colombia 325, Pueblo Libre, Lima ☎1 4236201 **W:** radiovida1590. com/public_html/ – **LM54)** Av. Almirante Guisse N° 1885, Lince, Lima 14 ☎1 4723110 **W:** radiocielo.com.pe – **LM55)** Av Petit Thouars 447, Santa Beatriz, Lima 01 **W:** radionacional.com.pe ☎1 4331404 – **LM56)** Av. Paseo Parodi 340, San Isidro, Lima 43 ☎1 4413050 **W:** radio1160. com.pe – **LM58)** CRP – Justo Pastor Davila 197, Chorrillos, Lima 09 ☎1 617 6606 **W:** radiobienestar.pe – **LM59)** Av 28 de Julio 1781, La Victoria. Lima 13 ☎1 6131701 **W:** bethelradio.fm **E:** bethelradio@ bethelradio.fm – **LM60)** Jr. Morales Bermúdez 140, Pueblo Libre, Lima 21 ☎1 4248122 **W:** cadena1200.org **E:** contacto@cadena1200. org – **LM62)** Av.Salaverry 862, Jesus Maria, Lima 11 **W:** nseradio. com **E:** nselima@nseradio.com ☎1 4714172 – **LM63)** Av.Gerardo Unger 6995, Independencia, Lima 28 ☎1 5331848 **W:** radiofeperu.com **E:** gerencia@radiofeperu.org – **LM64)** KM 193 Panamericana Norte, Barranca, Lima 04 – **LM65)** Urb. Lever Pacocha "D" 13 Av. San Martin 1 Piso, 15140 Huacho ☎1 3045427 **W:** radioluz.com – **LM66)** Luis Alberto Lizarraga Alva, Cerro Laguna, 15703 San Vicente de Cañete, Provinca de Cañete – **LM67)** Jr Mariano Melgar 235, 15173 Barranca **W:** radiobendicionbarranca.blogspot.no – **LM68)** Mz. E Lt. 1 AAHH Cocharcas Asuncion 8, 15708 Imperial – **LM69)** Ca Tupac Amaru 140, Urb. Casuarina, 15703 San Vicente de Cañete – **LM70)** Jr. Lima 1398, 15173 Barranca – **LM71)** Jr.Cusco s/n, Cuadra 1, Quilmana, 15875 Cañete – **LM72)** Av Miguel Grau s/n, Paramonga – **LM73)** Av Grau 592, Oficina 502, Huacho ☎1 3970739 **W:** radioparaisofm.com - **FM:** 103.5 MHz – **LM74)** Pampa de Lara s/n, Barranca ☎992 619756 **W:** angienetradio.com **E:** alzejara@hotmail.com – **LM75)** Av Arics S/n, Barranca – **LM76)** Sector Pampa Colorado, Huacho, Huara

**LT00 (LORETO):**
**LT01)** Jr Abtao 255, 16001 Iquitos ☎65 265244 **W:** radiolavozdelaselva. org **E:** administracion@radiolavozdelaselva.org - **FM:** 93.9 MHz – **LT05)** Av Antonio Raymondi 331, 16001 Iquitos - **FM:** 101.3MHz – **LT09)** Jr Arica 737, 16001 Iquitos – **LT10)** Ca Progreso 112-114, 16421 Yurimaguas, Alto Amazonas **W:** roriente.org **E:** oriente995@yahoo.com ☎65 351611 - **FM:** 99.5MHz – **LT14)** Arica 441, 16001 Iquitos

**MD00 (MADRE DE DIOS):**
**MD01)** Jr Guillermo Billingurst 406 PTO, 17001 Puerto Maldonado - **FM:** 101.3MHz – **MD02)** Nueva Plaza de Armas 200, 17001 Puerto Maldonado – **MD04)** Av Fitzcarrald 130, 17001 Madre de Dios – **MD05)** Av Andres Avelino Caceres km 4.5, Carreter de Tambopata a Cusco – Zona La Pastora, 17001 Madre de Dios – **MD06)** Jr Apurimac Psj. Tacna Lt.10 Mz.B5, 17001 Tambopata – **MD07)** Sector Triunfo s/n, Tambopata – **MD08)** Jr Lerón 368, Tambopata **W:** radiocielo.pe – **MD09)** Jr Apurimac s/n, Tambopata – **MD10)** Pasaje Túpac Amaru S/N, Mazuko

**MQ00 (MOQUEGUA):**
**MQ04)** PP.JJ. John F. Kennedy, Mz. E Lte. 48, 18311 Ilo – **MQ05)** Jr Tarapaca 260, 18001 Moquegua - **FM:** 101. – **MQ07)** Jr Ayacucho N° 639 ( Ap 22), 18001 Moquegua ☎53 461542 - **FM:** 105.3MHz – **MQ08)** Mollejo s/n, 18401 Omate **W:** agrorural.gob.pe/escuchar-radios-campesinas – **MQ09)** Marsical Andrés A.Cáceres 193, 18001 Moquegua – **MQ10)** Ca Grau 101 – Frenta a la Plazade Armas, 18401 Omate – **MQ11)** Ca Libertad 1015, 18001 Cercado Moquegua ☎53 463276 **W:** radiolavozdelsurmoquegua.com **E:** radiolavozdelsur@gmail. com – **MQ12)** Sector Charsawa-Centro Poblado Menor Los Angeles, 18001 Moquegua – **MQ13)** Pse San Antonio s/n, Mascal Nieto – **MQ14)** Jr Ancash 555-2, Moquegua **W:** radiosantacruzmoquegua - **FM:** 94.7 MHz – **MO15)** Calle Moquegua S/N, Ichuña, ☎53 338433 **W.:** facebook.com/radioo.cruzichuna – **MO16)** Ca 2 de Enero S/N, Ichuña ☎9990 25026 **W:** mdi.gob.pe **E:** munichuna@gmail.com –

**MO17)** Anexo Santa Cruz Oyo Oyo, Prov. General Sanchez – **MO18)** Plaza de Armas s/n, Moquegua – **MO19)** Sector Chojasirca Alta, Distr. de San Cristobal, Prov de Mariscal Nieto – **MO20)** Calle Áncash No 556, Cercado, Moquegua ☎953 601958 **W.:** radioamericana.com.pe **E.:** americanafm@hotmal.com - **FM.:** 95.7, 101.7MHz

**PA00 (PASCO):**

**PA01)** Plazuela Gamaniel Blanco, 127- 2°Nivel - Ninguno, 19001 Chaupimarca ☎63 422398 **W:** radioaltourtv.org **E:** radiotalturatv@hotmail.com - **FM:** 90.9MHz R.Alrura;: 97.7 MHz R.Los Andes – **PA02)** Jr Puno s/n, 19001 Chaupimarca - **FM:** 102.5MHz – **PA03)** Jr Mullembruck 468, Urb Cercado, 1921100xapampa ☎63 762689 - **FM:** 101.5MHz – **PA05)** Jr Huamachuco 214, Cerro de Pasco ☎63 330109 **W:** radiocorporacion.com.pe – **PA07)** Jr Daniel Alcids Carrion 250, 19026 Huayllay – **PA08)** Av Tupac Amaru 1066, Colquijirca, 19016 Tinyahuarco – **PA09)** Jr.Pedro Caballero y Lira s/n, Galeria Mina de Oro, 19001 Chaupimarca **W:** radiocumbre.com.pe - **FM:** 103.1 MHz – **PA10)** Jr.Bolognesi 225, 19001 Chaupimarca **W:** radiomineria.com.pe/radiominera - **FM:**102.5 MHz – **PA11)** Jr Lima 365, 19001 Chaupimarca – **PA12)** Av Simon Bolivar 410, San Juan, 19151 Yanacancha – **PA13)** Pasajae Jauja 106, Chaupimarca – **PA14)** Oxapampa – **PA15)** Cerro de Pasco

**PI00 (PIURA):**

**PI04)** Jr San Ignacio de Loyola 300, 20011 Castilla ☎73 342802 **W:** radiocutivalu.org **E:** cutivalu@radiocutivalu.org - **FM:** 100.5MHz – **PI05)** Ica 419, Of 206, 20001Piura - **FM:** 92.1MHz – **PI06)** Santa Maria C., 20001 Piura - **FM:** 94.5MHz.– **PI08)** Ugarteche 490, 20201 Sullana - **FM:** 99.3MHz.– **PI10)** Ca Tacna 260 4 piso, (frente al banco de la nación), 20001 Piura ☎73 303369 – **PI11)**Ca San Martin 1041, 20201 Sullana ☎73 503071 **W:** Facebook Radio Capullana **E:** capullanaradio@latinmail.com.pe - **FM:** 95.7MHz – **PI13)** Calle el Altillo 282, 20541 Huancabamba ☎73 473259 **W:** lavozdelashuaringas.com **E:** radio@lavozdehuarinjas.com - **FM:** 103.7 MHz – **PI14)** Av Sánches Cerro 582 2do Piso, 20001 Piura ☎73 304221 **W:** radioluaz.com - **FM:** 107.9MHz – **PI15)** Carretera Piura-Chulucanas km 4, 20011 Castilla ☎73 324180 – **PI16)** Av. Sanches Cerro 582 - 2° piso, 20001 Piura ☎73 304221 **W:** radioluaz.com - **FM:** 107.9 MHz – **PI17)** Ca Unión 515 – b, Barrio Punta Arena, 20001 Piura ☎73 374106 – **PI18)** Zona Industrial Mz D Km 5, Carretera Piura, 20201 Sullana **E:** piuraradio@terra.com.pe - **FM:** 101.9MHz – **PI23)** Ca 8 s/n, 20131 Talara Alta, ☎383 750 **W:** radiobns.com **E:** radiobns1992@hotmail.com – **PI24)** Mz "E" Lote 8, Urb. Isabel Barreto I Etapa, 20801 Paita ☎73 211885 **W:** radionorperu.blogspot.ne - **FM:** 102.9MHz – **PI25)** Jr Leoncio Prado 425, 20201 Sullana – **PI26)** Madre de Dios 258, 20201 Sullana ☎73 505026 – **PI32)** Av Grau Cuadra N° 5, Cruceta San Lorenzo, 20701 Tambo Grande – **PI41)** Km 993,8, Carretera Panamericana, Predio Don Bosco, Sector Coscomba, 20001 Piura – **PI47)** Av Principal, Caserio La Peñita, 20701 Tambo Grande – **PI50)** Av.Miguel F. Cerro s/n, AA HH, San Jose, 20046 Vice **W:** agrorural.gob.pe/radio-ayabaca-de-piura.html – **PI51)** Jr 9 de Octubre 110, 20571 Huarmaca **W:** agrorural.gob.pe/radio-huancabamba-de-piura.html – **PI52)** Jr 9 de Octubre 110, 20571 Huarmaca **W:** radiohuarmaca.com.pe – **FM:** 98.1 MHz – **PI53)** Bolivar 114, 20441 Ayabaca – **PI54)** Km. 248 Panamericana Carretera a Chulucanas, 20011 Castilla **W:** visionradioperu.com – **PI55)** Ca Piura 508, 20611 Frias ☎73 631459 **W:** Facebook: R.Frias - **FM:** 96.5 MHz– **PI56)** Barrio Santa Rosa s/n, 20441 Ayabaca – **PI57)** Jr Morro Solar, Block F, 20001 Piura **W:** corporacionrbc.com – **PI58)** Jr Pisagua 812, 20601 Chulucanas ☎73 378627 **E:** radiosup263@hotmail.com – **PI59)** Esq. Calle Jorge Chavez y 9 de Octubre, 20571 Huarmaca **W:** rvclagrande1160am.es.tl – **PI60)** MZ. H. LT 14 – Urb. San Eduardo, 20001 Piura – **PI61)** Av Circunvalacion Lopez Albujar MZ. B.LT. 8, 20001 Piura – **PI62)** Predio de Mercedec Vite Quezada s/n, San Miguel – Valle Medio, 20001 Piura **W:** bethelradio.fm – **PI63)** Cl. Piura 311, 20611 Frias 944360440 **W:** radiofrecuenciaideal.com **E:** contacto@radiofrecuenciaideal.com – **PI64)** Calle Atahualpa No 235 – Edif. El Sol – 3er Piso, 20001 Piura – **PI65)** Parcela T15.8 – 42 Sector 7, 20701 Tamboa Grande – **PI66)** Calle Alfonso Ugarte 118, 20046 Vice – **PI67)** Av Progreso 101, Castilla ☎73 340301 **W:** laclave.com.pe **E:** laclave100mail.com - **FM:** 104.5 MHz – **PI68)** Ca Bolognesi 515-b, Sullana ☎73 507979 **W:** radiolajefa1530.com

**PU00 (PUNO):**

**PU01)** Jr Conde Lemos 212, 21001 Puno ☎51 351562 **W:** radioondaazul.com **E:** ondazul@radioondaazul.com - Quechua & Aymara: 6h daily - **FM:** 95.7MHz "Stereo Azul" – **PU02)** Jr Arequipa 385, 21001 Puno – **PU03)** Jr Miraflores MZ E-1, Lt-4 – Barrio Jorge Chavez, 21111 Macusani ☎51 51837009 **E:** rvamacusani@terra.com.pe - **FM:** 90.5MHz – **PU04)** Jr Jauregui 966, 21621 Juliaca ☎51 800601 **W:** nuevotiempo.org **E:** nuevotiempojuliaca@gmail.com – **PU05)** Ca San Román 116, 21621 Juliaca ☎51 325357 – **PU06)** Simon Bolivar 442, 21001 Puno – **PU07)** "Lugar Denominado ""Barco Chuco"",21061 Chucuito **Aymara & Quechua** 0900-1400, 1900-0100

– **PU08)** Jr.Huanaynacapac T4,Centro Comerical No2, 21621 Juliaca ☎51 322313 **W:** radiofronterajuliaca.blogspot.no - **FM:** 107.9MHz – **PU09)** Jr. San Isidro MZ. S, Lote 14-.B, Urb. Señor de Huanca, 21621 Juliaca ☎51 502319 – **PU11)** Jr 2 de Mayo 418 – 4to nivel, 21621 Juliaca **W.** 24horasradionoticias **E:** radionoticias24horasamotmail.com – **PU12)** Jr. Moquegua 180, 21001 Puno ☎51 351502 **W:** Facebook – Radio La Voz Del Altiplano – **PU13)** Ca Mariano Pandía 166, 2° piso, 21621 Juliaca – **PU14)** Jr.Leonicio Prado, 21001 Puno – **PU15)** Jr Unión 242, 21621 Juliaca **E:** radioltcj@latinmail.com ☎51 322452 ▤51 369450 – **PU16)** Jr Apurimac 640, 21621 Juliaca ☎51 207007 **W:** radioondapopular.pe - **FM:** 88.9Mhz – **PU17)** Jr Antonio (Sierra) 178, prolongación Ramón Castilla, a dos cuadras del Cuartel Bolognesi, 21621 Juliaca ☎+51 793059 – **PU18)** Jr Piura 167, 21001 Puno ☎51 9731663 - **Aymara & Quechua:** 0900-1100 – **PU19)** Jr. Carabaya 998, Juliaca **E:** andino.pe **E:** info@radiotvcontinental.com – **PU20)** Jr Lima s/n, 21666 Caminaca **E:** trebol34@mixmail.com – **PU21)** Ramon Castilla 949, 21621 Juliaca ☎51 321372 **W:** ladecana.pe **E:** guadalupee8@hotmail.com - **FM:** 90.9MHz – **PU22)** Jr Apurimac 644 Juliaca, 21621 Juliaca ☎51 641342 **W:** radiotvperu.pe **E:** radiotvperu@hotmail.com - **FM:** 106.7 MHz – **PU23)** Jr 2 de Mayo 790, 21621 Juliaca **W:** Jr 2 de Mayo, 21621 Juliaca ☎51 470000 **W:** radioandinajuliaca.com **E:** gerencia@radioandinajuliaca.com – **PU26)** Jr Raúl Porras 210, 21621 Juliaca ☎51 502005 **W:** radiocorporacionwayrajuliaca.com – **PU27)** Jr Chachani 220, , 21621 Juliaca ☎51 324846 **W:** radioredandina.com **E:** radioredandina@hotmail.com – **PU28)** Jr 2 de Mayo 209, Oficina 406, 21621 Juliaca ☎51 321115 **W:** radiosoldelosandes.com - **FM:** 104.5MHz "El Sol de los Andes FM" – **PU32)** Jr 2 de Mayo , 21621 Juliaca **E:** carraviz@gmail.com or carraviz@hotmail.com - Listeners correspondence to: Iván Tito Vizcarra – **PU33)** Azangaro **W:** radioasillo.com – **PU35)** Jr Acora 222, 21001 Puno ☎51 366222 **W:** pachamamaradio.org **E:** info@pachamamaradio.org – **PU42)** Túpac Amaru Altura Coliseo Juli s/n, 21401 Juli ☎51 554173 **W:** agrorural.gob.pe/radio-juli-de-puno **E:** radiocampesinajuli@hotmail.com – **PU44)** 21701 Ayaviri **W:** agrorural.gob.pe/radio-ayaviri-de-puno.html– **PU45)** Jr Jose Galvez 542, Urb Bellavista, 21001 Puno ☎51 323546 **W.** 24horasradionoticias.com **E:** radionoticias24horasamotmail.com – **PU46)** Jatun Pampa Chejollani Cupi-Esquen, 21621 Juliaca – **PU47)** Ca s/n – Sector Taparachi Zona Industrial, Urb. la Rinconada 3ra E-17, 21621 Juliaca **W:** radiomilagros.com – **PU48)** Zona Fortaleza Pucara, Sector Chuñawi, 21401 Juli – **PU49)** Jr Ayacucho 679, 21601 Caracoto **E: W.:** coorporativocontinental.com **E..** informes@coorporativocontinental.com – **PU50)** Jr Tumbes 220 3ere nivel, Juliaca ☎51 1327311 **W:** radiopublica.pe **E:** webmaster@radiopublica.pe – **PU51)** Jr Arequipa 403, 21051 Capachica – **PU52)** Jr. Alfonso Ugarte N° 608 Macusani, Carabaya, 21 111 Macusani ☎950 300420 **W:** coorporativocontinental.com **E:** informes@coorporativocontinental.com - **FM:** 100.9MHz – **PU53)** Pasaje Echenique 110, Cercado, 21 111 Macusani **W:** Facebook: R. Inca-Acora – **PU55)** Jr Lima 317, Puno **W:** Facebook: R.Universidad Puno – **FM:** 92.9 – **PU56)** Jr 2 de Mayo s/n, Lampa ☎950 984 787 **W:** actiweb.es/radioandinalampa – **PU57)** Jr Pedro de Candida s/n, Sandia – **PU58)** Juliaca **W:** radiopublica.pe **E:** radiopublica.580@gmail.com – **PU59)** Azángaro – **PU60)** Cl Sandia s/n, Cuyocuyo, Sandia – **PU61)** Jr. Carabaya No 998 – 5to piso (esquina con Benigno Ballón), Juliaca ☎51 323030 **W:** coorporativocontinental.com **E:** informes@coorporativocontinental.com – **PU62)** Jr Azangaro 575, Juliaca **W:** radiofrecuenciaamistad.blogspot.com

**SM00 (SAN MARTIN):**

**SM01)** Jr San Martín 257, 22411 Tocache ☎42 551031 - **FM:** 100.1 MHz – **SM03)** Av Compagñón 410, 22221 Tarapoto – **SM07)** Jr Imperio 764, 22056 Nueva Cajamarca– **FM:** 100.3 MHz – **SM08)** Jr Bolognesi 180 Altos, 22221 Tarapoto **W:** radioluluz.com – **SM14)** Jr Loreto 300, 22251 Chazuta **W:** ethnicradio.org **E:** agiazo@hotmail.com – **SM15)** Jr Callao 650 (Apt. 133), 22001 Moyobamba ☎42 562353 – **SM16)** Av Celedin s/n, 22066 San Fernando – **SM17)** Av Alfonso Ugarte Cdra 18, Los Olivos, 22221 Tarapoto – **SM18)** Jr Libertad 157, Moyobamba – **SM19)** Jr Las Dalias s/n Mz 17, Lt E, Bellavista

**TC00 (TACNA)**

**TC02)** Prolong Unanue 1041 ( Cas 113), 23001 Tacna - **FM:** 99.9MHz – **TC04)** Jr Sir Jones s/n (Cas 281), 23001 Tacna – **TC05)** Arias y Araguez 584, 23001 Tacna – **TC06)** Cl Tarata 665, Urb San José - Bacigalup, 23001 Tacna **W:** radioluluz.com – **TC08)** Av Internacional 484, Alto de la Alianza, 23001 Tacna ☎52 804100 – **FM:** 106.7 MHz – **TC09)** Av.Dos de Mayo 2-A 23001 Tacna ☎52 414871 **W:** radiotacna.com.pe **E:** gerencia@radiotacna.com.pe - **FM:** 104.3 & 104.7MHz – **TC10)** Av San Martín de Porras 209, Natividad, 23001 Tacna **E:** radiobulevar@hotmail.com ☎5284 8537 – **TC11)** Jose Olaya s/n 2° piso, 23341 Tarata – **TC13)** 23341 Tarata **W:** agrorural.gob.pe/escuchar-radios-campesinas.html – **TC14)** Villa Universitaria Capannique A 20, 23031 Pocoally **W:** radiobacan.com – **TC16)** Ca 2 de Mayo 263, 23001 Tacna

☎52 428184 **W:** radiouno.pe **E:** prensa@radiouno.pe - **FM:** 93.7 MHz
– **TC17)** Ca Progreso 43, Vigila, 23001 Tacna – **TC18)** Barrio Azul S-27, Ilabaya **W:** Facebook. Radio Candarave – **TC19)** Sector Buganvillas – A 200m. Cruze de Tarapaca con Buganvillas, Distr. de Pocollay, Dept. de Tacna – **TC19)** Villa Universitaria Capanique A-20, Pocollay – **TC20)** Calle Gil de Herrera 186, Tacna – **TC21)** Av El Sol 427, Tacna – **TC22)** Candarave **W:** FB radiocandaravena.com – **TC23)** Calle Gil de Herrera 186, Pocoally – **TC24)** Pampa de Layagache – Alt. Km 25 Carretera a Tarata, Alto de la Alianza – **TC26)** Prolongación Hermanos Reynosa s/n, Pocollay – **TC27)** Carretera Calana, Sector Santa Rita,Tacna **W:**radiobacan.com

**TB00 (TUMBES):**
**TB01)** Pza Alipio Rosales s/n, 24001 Tumbes - **FM:** 99.7MHz – **TB02)** Ca Tarapaca 163, 24001 Tumbes – **TB04)** Panamericana Norte Km 1321, 24001 Tumbes **W:** rpp.com.pe - **FM:** 100.5MHz – **TB05)** Av.Mayor Novoa 814 2° piso, 24001 Tumbes ☎72 527002 – **TB06)** Jr Bolívar 117, 24001 Tumbes ☎72 523003 – **TB07)** Jr Piura 1010, 24001 Tumbes – **TB08)** Av.Mariscal Castilla 432, 24001 Tumbes **W:** radiocielo.pe – **TB09)** Paseo Concordia y Bolognesi 2° piso, 24001 Tumbes – **TU10)** Zona Rural de Pampa Grande, Tumbes

**UC00 (UCAYALI):**
**UC03)** Av 9 de Diciembre 646, Pucallpa – **UC04)** Jr Coronel Portillo 448-A, Pucallpa ☎61 573876 **W:** radiousa.com **E:** radiosuper103.3@gmail.com - **FM:** 103.3MHz – **UC05)** Zona San Fernando, Callería – **UC06)** Ca Padre Francisco Alvares s/n, Sephua – **FM:** 100.5MHz **UC09)** Carretera Federale Basadre Km 37, Los Pinos, Campoverde **W:** nuevotiempo.org.pe **E:** radio@nuevotiempo.org.pe – **UC10)** Av Tupac Amaru 957, Calleria **W:** radiocielo.pe

**FM in Lima (MHz):** 88.3 R.Magica,San Isidro – **LM17)** 88.9 R.Felicidad – 89.7 Emisoras Peruanos (RPP), San Isidro – 90.1 Cieneguilla – 90.1 R:Bethel, Ate-Amauta – 90.1 R.Silde, Lurigancho – 90.5 R.La Zona, Lurigancho – 91.1 R.San Borja – 91.5 R.Planicie – 91.5 R.del Sur, Lurin – 91.5 R.Chalaca, Cieneguilla – 91.5 R.Andina, Ate-Huayacan - 91.9 Okey Radio, San Isidro – 92.5 R.Studio 92, San Isidro – 93.1 R.Ritmo Romantico, Chorrillos – **LM07)** 93.7 La Inolvidable – 94.3 R.Bravaza, San Isidro – 94.9 R.La Karibeña, Chorillos – 94.9 R.A, Corillos – 95.5 R.La Exitosa, Chorillos – 96.1 Z Rock & Pop, Chorillos – **LM45)** 96.7 R.Capital – 97.3 R.Moda, Chorillos – 97.7 R.Kandela, Ate – 97.7 R.Canto Grande, San Juan de Lurigancho – LM03) 97.7 R.Maria – 97.7 R.Sencación, Chaclayo – 97.7 R.Vitarte, Cieneguilla – **LM56)** 98.1 R.1160 – 98.7 R.Magica, Punta Hermosa – 98.7 R.Karibeña, San Luis – 99.1 R.Doble Nueve, Jesus Maria – 99.5 Ate-Huaycan – 99.5 Comas – 99.5 Cieneguilla – 99.5 Chaclacayo – **LM43)** 99.5 R.Imperial 2 – **LM22)** 100.1 R.Exito – 100.1 R.Oasis, San Isidro – 100.5 R.Enmanuel, Ate – 100.7 R.Satelite, Ventanilla – 100.7 R.La Familia, Carabayllo – **LM19)**101.1 R.Panamericana – **LM54)** 101.7 R.Cielo – **LM33)** 101.7 R.Comas – **LM54)** 101.7 R.Cielo – 101.7 R.Stereo Villa, Villa El Salvador – 101.7 Chaclavayo – 101.7 San Juan – **LM33)** 102.1 R.Oxigeno, San Isidro **LM51)** R.Nacional, Barranco – 103.3 R.Unión, Miraflores – **LM15)**103.9 R.Nacional, Lima –104.7 Viva FM, San isidro – **LM47)**105.1 R.Santa Rosa, Carabayllo – 105.5 R.Fiesta, Lince – **LM11)**106.3 R. Mar Plus, Chorillios – **LM58)** 107.1 R.Nueva Q, Chorillos – 107.7 R. Planeta, Chorillos

## PHILIPPINES

**L.T:** UTC +8h — **Pop:** 107 million — **Pr.L:** Pilipino (Tagalog), English, Cebuano, Ilocano, Hiligaynon, Bicol — **E.C:** 50Hz, 230V — **ITU:** PHL

### NATIONAL TELECOMMUNICATIONS COMMISSION (NTC) (Dept. of Transportation and Communications)
🖳 NTC Bldg., BIR Road, East Triangle, Diliman, Quezon City 1104 ☎ +63 2 9254651 or 9267722 **W:** ntc.gov.ph
**L.P:** Commissioner: Gamaliel A. Cordoba. Dep. Commissioners: Delilah F. Deles, Edgardo V. Cabarios. Chief Broadcast Sces Div: Alvin Bernard N. Blanco

### KAPISANAN NG MGA BRODKASTER NG PILIPINAS (KBP) (Assoc. of Broadcasters of the Philippines)
🖳 6th Flr, LTA Bldg, 118 Perea Str, Legaspi Village, Makati C, 1226 NCR ☎ +63 2 8151990/1/2 🖷 +63 2 8151993 **W:** kbp.org.ph
**L.P:** Chmn: Ruperto S. Nicdao, Jr. Pres: Herman Z. Basbaño. Most stns are KBP members

### CATHOLIC MEDIA NETWORK (CMN)
🖳 Unit 201 Sunrise Condominium, 226 Ortigas Ave, North Greenhills, San Juan, Manila 1503 NCR ☎ +63 2 7249850 🖷 +63 2 7249962
**L.P:** Pres: Fr. Francis B. Lucas. Chmn: Bishop Bernardino Cortez. (28 affiliated stns on MW, 20 on FM)

### PHILIPPINE BROADCASTING SERVICE (PBS, 'Radyo Pilipinas') (Gov.)
🖳 4/F Government Media Center Bldg., Vasra, Quezon C, 1128 NCR ☎ +63 2 9242607 **W:** pbs.gov.ph **L.P:** Dir. Gen: Rizal Giovanni "Bong" Aportadera, Jr.
**Manila stns:** DZRB "RP1" (news sce) 738 kHz, DZSR "RP3" Sports Radio 918 kHz, DZRM "RP2" Radyo Magasin 1278 kHz, DWFO-FM "FM-1" 87.5MHz, DWBR-FM "FM2" 104.3MHz
**Regional MW stns on MW: DWBT**, San Antonio, Basco, 3900 Batanes. **DWFB**, Mariano Marcos State University Campus, Laoag C, 2900 Ilocos Norte. **DWFR**, Multipurpose Bldg, Provincial Capitol Compound, Bontoc, 2616 Mountain Province. **DWHC**, Perez Park, Lucena C, 4301 Quezon Province. **DWPE**, CSU Campus, Caritan Highway, Tuguegarao, 3500 Cagayan. **DWRB**, City Civic Center, Taal Ave, Naga C, 4400 Camarines Sur. **DWRM**, City Hall Compound, Puerto Princesa C, 5300 Palawan. **DWRS**, Poblacion, Tayug, 2445 Pangasinan. **DXBN**, City Hall Compound, Brgy. Doongan, Butuan C, 8600 Agusan del Norte. **DXIM**, A. Velez Str, Cagayan de Oro C, 9000 Misamis Oriental. **DXJS**, Capitol Hills, Tandag, 8300 Surigao del Sur. DXJT, Brgy Maloro,Tangub C, 7214 Misamis Occidental. **DXMR**, Baliwasan Chico, Zamboanga C, 7000 Zamboanga del Sur. **DXPT**, Tubig Boh, Bongao, 7500 Tawi-Tawi. **DXRG**, Dugenio Str, Gingoog C, 9014 Misamis Oriental. **DXRP**, Door 5, PTA Complex, Magsaysay Park, 2nd District, Agdao, 8000 Davao C. **DXSM**, Camp Asturias, Jolo, 7400 Sulu. **DXSO**, Satellite Office, MSU Campus, Marawi C, 9700 Lanao del Sur. **DYES**, Capitol Compd, Borongan, 6800 Eastern Samar. **DYLL**, PNRC Youth Center Bldg, Bonifacio Drive, Iloilo C, 5000 Iloilo. **DYMP**, Govt Center, Candahug, Palo, Leyte. **DYMR**, CSCST Compound, Vicente Sotto, 6000 Cebu C. **DYOG**, Butel Building, Calbayog C, 6710 W. Samar. **DYSL**, Southern Leyte State University Compound, Sogod, 6606 Southern Leyte. **DZAG**, Don Mariano Marcos Memorial State University, Agoo, 2504 La Union. **DZEQ**, Polo Field, Pacdal Circle, Baguio C, 2600 Benguet. **DZER**, Boac, 4900 Marinduque. **DZMQ**, Tondaligan Beach, Dagupan C, 2400 Pangasinan. **DZRK**, Capitol Compound, Tabuk, 3800 Kalinga. **DZVC** Virac, State College Campus, 4800 Catanduanes
See **PB)** entries in the MW frequency list below for frequencies and powers. Regional stns usually relay news from Manila on the h., and also carry networked prgrs at times.

**NB:** A number of stns are operating irr or are inactive
**Callsigns:** _____ -AM

| | MW Call | kHz | kW | Net | | MW Call | kHz | kW | Net |
|---|---|---|---|---|---|---|---|---|---|
| 67) | DXGH | 531 | 5 | dz | 50) | DZRH | 666 | 35 | |
| 118) | DYDW | ‡531 | 10 | cm | 103) | DXGD | 675 | 1 | cm |
| 4) | DZBR | 531 | 10 | | 85) | DYKC | 675 | 5 | |
| 83) | DYRB | 540 | 1 | | 43) | DWJJ | 684 | 5 | |
| 54) | DZWT | 540 | 10 | cm | 50) | DYEZ | 684 | 10 | ak |
| PB) | DWRB | 549 | 10 | | 33) | DZCV | 684 | 5 | |
| 16) | DXHM | 549 | 5 | | 84) | DXBC | 693 | 10 | ag |
| 84) | DZXL | 558 | 40 | | 85) | DXDX | 693 | 1 | |
| 67) | DXCH | 567 | 5 | dz | 50) | DYKX | 693 | 1 | dz |
| 73) | DXMF | 576 | 10 | | 50) | DYPH | 693 | 10 | dz |
| PB) | DYMR | 576 | 10 | | 106) | DZTP | 693 | 10/5 | |
| PB) | DZMQ | 576 | 10 | | 31) | DZAS | 702 | 50 | |
| 17) | DZHR | 576 | 5 | dz | 58) | DXIC | 711 | 5 | ag |
| 16) | DXCP | 585 | 5 | cm | 84) | DXRD | 711 | 5 | ss |
| PB) | DYLL | 585 | 1 | su | 29) | DYBR | ‡711 | 5 | |
| 16) | DXDB | 594 | 5 | cm | 50) | DZVR | 711 | 5 | bo |
| 60) | DYWR | ‡594 | 10 | bo | 58) | DZYI | 711 | 5 | ss |
| 36) | DZBB | 594 | 20 | su | 50) | DYOK | 720 | 5 | ak |
| 10) | DZLL | 603 | 10 | | 7) | DZJO | 720 | 5 | |
| 84) | DXPR | ‡603 | 5 | | 60) | DZSO | 720 | 5 | bo |
| 22) | DZVV | 603 | 5 | bo | PB) | DWPE | 729 | 10 | |
| 75) | DWSP | 612 | 5 | dz | 60) | DXIF | 729 | 10 | bo |
| 84) | DYHP | 612 | 10 | | 84) | DXMY | 729 | 5 | |
| 84) | DXDC | 621 | 10 | | 70) | DXOR | 729 | 5 | |
| PB) | DZVC | 621 | 5 | | 72) | DZGB | 729 | 5 | |
| 85) | DZTG | 621 | 5 | | PB) | DZRB | 738 | 10 | |
| 2) | DZMM | 630 | 50 | | 62) | DXND | 747 | 5 | cm |
| 22) | DYWB | 630 | 10/5 | bo | 84) | DYHB | 747 | 5 | |
| 84) | DXKR | 639 | 5 | | 50) | DZJC | 747 | 10 | ak |
| 85) | DZRL | 639 | 5 | | PB) | DWRS | 756 | 5 | |
| 67) | DWRH | 648 | 10 | dz | 9) | DWHL | 756 | 1 | |
| PB) | DWRM | 648 | 10 | | 121) | DXBZ | 756 | 10 | |
| 84) | DXMB | 648 | 3 | | 82) | DXJM | 756 | 2 | |
| 50) | DYRC | 648 | 5 | ak | 83) | DXGS | 765 | 5 | |
| 77) | DWRN | 657 | 10 | | 58) | DYAP | 765 | 10 | |
| 130) | DXDD | 657 | 5 | cm | 58) | DYAR | 765 | 5 | ss |
| PB) | DYES | 657 | 5 | | 58) | DZYT | 765 | 5 | ss |
| 84) | DYVR | 657 | 5 | | 41) | DWWW | 774 | 25 | |
| 98) | DZLU | 657 | 1 | | PB) | DXSM | 774 | 10 | |
| PB) | DXRP | ‡666 | 10 | | PB) | DXSO | 774 | 10 | |

| MW | Call | kHz | kW | Net | | MW | Call | kHz | kW | Net | | MW | Call | kHz | kW | Net | | MW | Call | kHz | kW | Net |
|---|---|---|---|---|---|---|---|---|---|---|---|---|---|---|---|---|---|---|---|---|---|---|
| 84) | DYRI | 774 | 10 | ag | | 42) | DYBQ | 981 | 10 | | | 28) | DXED | 1224 | 10 | dz | | 17) | DYCH | 1395 | 10 | dz |
| 94) | DXRA | 783 | 10 | | | 58) | DZRD | 981 | 10 | ss | | PB) | DZAG | 1224 | 10 | | | 132) | DZVT | 1395 | 5 | cm |
| 51) | DYME | 783 | 5 | | | 107) | DZIQ | 990 | 10 | | | 87) | DWRV | 1233 | 5 | cm | | 58) | DXAQ | ‡1404 | - | ss |
| 75) | DZNL | 783 | 5 | ak | | 91) | DXBM | 990 | 5 | su | | 31) | DYVS | 1233 | 5 | | | 85) | DYKB | 1404 | 1 | |
| 95) | DWES | 792 | 5 | | | 67) | DYTH | 990 | 5 | dz | | 32) | DWBL | 1242 | 20 | | | 91) | DWRA | 1413 | 5 | su |
| 38) | DWGV | 792 | 5 | | | 67) | DZMT | 990 | 5 | dz | | 105) | DXSY | 1242 | 5 | | | 33) | DYXW | 1413 | 5 | |
| PB) | DXBN | 792 | 10 | | | 45) | DWMI | 999 | 5 | D | | 27) | DXZB | 1242 | 5 | | | 11) | DYZD | ‡1422 | 5 | |
| 73) | DXPD | 792 | 5 | bo | | 84) | DXHP | 999 | 1 | | | 42) | DYRG | 1251 | 1 | | | 89) | DYRS | ‡1431 | 5 | |
| 66) | DYRR | 792 | 5 | | | PB) | DXPT | 999 | 1 | | | 72) | DZMS | 1251 | 2.5 | | | 50) | DWDH | 1440 | 10 | dz |
| 58) | DXBL | 801 | 1 | ss | | 91) | DYSS | 999 | 5 | su | | 49) | DWMC | 1260 | 5 | | | 100) | DXSI | 1440 | 0.01 | |
| 22) | DXES | 801 | 5 | bo | | PB) | DZEQ | 999 | 5 | | | 50) | DXRF | 1260 | 5 | dz | | 52) | DXSA | 1449 | 5 | |
| 16) | DYKA | 801 | 5 | | | 16) | DWBS | 1008 | 5 | cm | | 91) | DYDD | 1260 | 10 | | | 97) | DYZZ | 1458 | 10 | |
| 35) | DYWC | 801 | 5 | cm | | 102) | DWGO | 1008 | 5 | | | 28) | DZEL | 1260 | 5 | | | 120) | DZJV | 1458 | 10 | |
| 60) | DZNC | 801 | 10 | bo | | 85) | DXXX | ‡1008 | 10 | | | 91) | DWRC | 1269 | 10 | | | 87) | DWVR | 1467 | 1 | cm |
| PB) | DXRG | 810 | 1 | | | 42) | DWDC | 1017 | 10 | | | PB) | DZRM | 1278 | 10 | | | 131) | DXVP | 1467 | 5 | cm |
| 90) | DZRJ | 810 | 10 | | | PB) | DWLC | 1017 | 5 | | | 50) | DZZH | 1287 | 5 | dz | | 92) | DWRB | 1476 | 1 | |
| 58) | DWAR | 819 | 5 | ss | | 44) | DXPR | 1017 | 10 | | | 133) | DWPR | 1296 | 5 | | | 90) | DXRJ | 1476 | 10 | |
| 114) | DWMG | 819 | 1 | | | 138) | DXSN | 1017 | 5 | cm | | 2) | DXAB | 1296 | 10 | | | 88) | DZYA | 1476 | 1 | |
| 101) | DXSC | ‡819 | 1 | | | 73) | DXMC | 1026 | 5 | bo | | 42) | DYJJ | 1296 | 5 | | | 67) | DYDH | 1485 | 5 | dz |
| 53) | DXUM | 819 | 10 | | | 58) | DZAR | 1026 | 10 | ss | | 25) | DWXI | 1314 | 10 | | | 108) | DWSS | 1494 | 10 | |
| 58) | DYVL | 819 | 10 | ak | | 139) | DXUZ | ‡1035 | 5/1 | | | 57) | DXAD | ‡1322 | 5 | | | 83) | DXOC | 1494 | 5 | |
| 39) | DWZR | 828 | 5 | | | 88) | DYRL | 1035 | 10 | | | 19) | DXHR | ‡1323 | 10 | | | 2) | DYAB | 1512 | 10 | |
| 84) | DXCC | 828 | 10 | ag | | 22) | DZWX | 1035 | 5 | bo | | 36) | DYSI | 1323 | 10 | su | | 125) | DZAT | 1512 | 10 | |
| 135) | DZTC | 828 | 1 | | | 88) | DXCO | 1044 | 5 | | | PB) | DZRK | 1323 | 10 | | | 14) | DZME | 1530 | 25 | |
| PB) | DXJS | 837 | 10 | | | 81) | DXLL | 1044 | 5 | uk | | 58) | DWAY | 1332 | 5 | ss | | 77) | DZYM | 1539 | 5 | |
| 58) | DXRE | 837 | 5 | ss | | 17) | DYMS | ‡1044 | 5 | ak | | 85) | DZKI | 1332 | 1 | | | 36) | DZSD | 1548 | 10 | su |
| 22) | DYFM | 837 | 10 | bo | | 60) | DZNG | ‡1044 | 10 | bo | | 91) | DXRL | ‡1341 | 10 | su | | 16) | DYDM | 1548 | 5 | cm |
| 30) | DZXE | ‡837 | 5 | | | 85) | DXKD | 1053 | 10 | | | 48) | DWUN | 1350 | 50 | | | 5) | DXID | 1566 | 10 | |
| 58) | DZRV | 846 | 50 | cm | | 112) | DYSA | 1053 | 5 | cm | | PB) | DZER | ‡1350 | 5 | | | PB) | DYMP | ‡1566 | 7.8 | |
| 67) | DXGO | 855 | 5 | ak | | 31) | DXKI | 1062 | 5 | | | 129) | DYSJ | 1359 | 1 | | | 18) | DXJR | 1575 | 10 | |
| 42) | DXWG | ‡855 | 1 | | | 46) | DYEC | 1062 | 10/5 | | | 77) | DZYR | 1359 | 5 | | | 24) | DWBR | 1584 | 1 | |
| 17) | DXZH | 855 | 5 | dz | | 28) | DZEC | 1062 | 40 | | | 58) | DWTT | ‡1368 | 5 | | | 124) | DXSK | 1593 | 10 | |
| 33) | DZGE | 855 | 10 | | | 85) | DXKT | 1071 | 5 | | | 85) | DXKO | 1368 | 10 | | | 113) | DZUP | 1602 | 1 | |
| 58) | DWSI | 864 | 5 | ss | | 110) | DYXT | 1071 | 1 | | | 85) | DZBS | 1368 | 2.5 | | | 84) | DWNX | 1611 | 10 | |
| 97) | DYHH | 864 | 10 | | | 123) | DZSL | 1071 | 1 | | | 15) | DZRA | 1368 | 1 | | | 37) | DWGI | 1638 | 0.6 | |
| 140) | DZIP | 864 | 10 | | | 28) | DWIN | 1080 | 5 | | | 85) | DXKP | 1377 | 10 | | | 56) | DZBF | 1674 | 1 | |
| 58) | DZSP | 864 | 5 | ss | | 83) | DWRL | 1080 | 5 | | | 55) | DXCR | 1386 | 10 | | | ‡ = r. inactive, ± = variable | | | | |
| 134) | DZWM | 864 | 5 | cm | | 85) | DXKS | 1080 | 1 | | | 16) | DYVW | 1386 | 5 | cm | | | | | | |
| 58) | DXRB | 873 | 5 | ss | | 67) | DYBH | 1080 | 5 | dz | | | | | | | | | | | | |
| 58) | DXRT | ‡873 | 5 | | | 111) | DXCM | 1089 | 10 | uk | | | | | | | | | | | | |
| 127) | DZYUP | 873 | 5 | | | 39) | DYCR | ‡1089 | 1 | | | | | | | | | | | | | |
| 1) | DZPA | 873 | 5 | cm | | 23) | DWAD | 1098 | 10 | | | | | | | | | | | | | |
| 33) | DZRC | 873 | 5 | | | 58) | DXCL | 1098 | 5 | ss | | | | | | | | | | | | |
| 3) | DWIZ | 882 | 50 | | | 61) | DWDY | 1107 | 10 | | | | | | | | | | | | | |
| 62) | DXMS | 882 | 10 | cm | | 141) | DXBB | 1107 | 5 | | | | | | | | | | | | | |
| PB) | DYOG | 882 | 5 | | | 129) | DYIN | 1107 | 5 | bo | | | | | | | | | | | | |
| 73) | DZGR | 891 | 5 | | | 8) | DZOM | 1107 | 1 | | | | | | | | | | | | | |
| 63) | DWNE | 900 | 5 | | | 13) | DYAG | 1116 | 5 | | | | | | | | | | | | | |
| 84) | DXRZ | 900 | 5 | ag | | 31) | DXAS | 1116 | 5 | | | | | | | | | | | | | |
| 22) | DYOW | 900 | 5 | bo | | 104) | DYTR | 1116 | 10 | | | | | | | | | | | | | |
| 115) | DYLA | 909 | 5 | | | 113) | DZLB | 1116 | 5 | | | | | | | | | | | | | |
| 91) | DYSP | 909 | 5 | su | | 69) | DXGL | 1125 | 10 | | | | | | | | | | | | | |
| 16) | DZEA | 909 | 5 | cm | | 91) | DXGM | 1125 | 5 | su | | | | | | | | | | | | |
| 84) | DXRS | 918 | 5 | ag | | 22) | DZWN | 1125 | 5 | bo | | | | | | | | | | | | |
| PB) | DZSR | 918 | 50 | | | 26) | DWDD | 1134 | 10 | | | | | | | | | | | | | |
| 122) | DWRS | 927 | 5 | | | 95) | DWJS | 1134 | 5 | | | | | | | | | | | | | |
| 64) | DXDA | 927 | 5 | | | 111) | DXMV | 1134 | 5 | uk | | | | | | | | | | | | |
| 84) | DXMD | 927 | 5 | ag | | 79) | DXOS | 1134 | 10 | | | | | | | | | | | | | |
| 103) | DXMM | 927 | 5 | cm | | 77) | DYRM | ‡1134 | 1 | | | | | | | | | | | | | |
| 73) | DZLG | 927 | 5 | bo | | PB) | DWBT | 1134 | 1 | | | | | | | | | | | | | |
| 40) | DWIM | 936 | 5 | | | 137) | DYAF | 1143 | 10 | cm | | | | | | | | | | | | |
| 111) | DXDN | 936 | 5 | uk | | 31) | DZMR | 1143 | 10 | | | | | | | | | | | | | |
| PB) | DXIM | 936 | 10 | | | 51) | DYCM | 1152 | 5 | | | | | | | | | | | | | |
| 84) | DYCC | 936 | 1 | | | 75) | DWCM | 1161 | 10 | | | | | | | | | | | | | |
| 85) | DYKW | 936 | 1 | | | 111) | DXDS | 1161 | 5 | uk | | | | | | | | | | | | |
| 84) | DZXT | 936 | 1 | | | 84) | DXKR | 1161 | 5 | ag | | | | | | | | | | | | |
| 116) | DXDV | 945 | 10 | | | 11) | DYRD | 1161 | 5 | | | | | | | | | | | | | |
| 58) | DXRO | 945 | 5 | ak | | 72) | DZMD | 1161 | 5 | | | | | | | | | | | | | |
| 4) | DYRO | ‡945 | 5 | | | PB) | DXMR | 1170 | 10 | | | | | | | | | | | | | |
| PB) | DWFB | 954 | 10 | | | PB) | DYSL | 1170 | 10 | | | | | | | | | | | | | |
| PB) | DXJT | 954 | 1 | | | 65) | DZCA | ‡1170 | 10 | | | | | | | | | | | | | |
| 110) | DYMM | ‡954 | 5 | | | 142) | DWET | 1179 | 10 | | | | | | | | | | | | | |
| 20) | DZEM | 954 | 40 | | | 91) | DXYK | 1179 | 5 | su | | | | | | | | | | | | |
| 62) | DXOM | 963 | 10 | | | 60) | DYCX | 1179 | 5 | | | | | | | | | | | | | |
| 58) | DXYZ | 963 | 5 | ss | | 36) | DYSB | 1179 | 5 | su | | | | | | | | | | | | |
| 73) | DYMF | 963 | 10 | bo | | 23) | DZRS | 1179 | 1 | | | | | | | | | | | | | |
| 136) | DZNS | 963 | 5 | cm | | 22) | DXLX | 1188 | 5 | bo | | | | | | | | | | | | |
| PB) | DWFR | 972 | 5 | | | 2) | DYRV | ‡1188 | 1 | | | | | | | | | | | | | |
| 45) | DWTI | 972 | 5 | | | 82) | DZLT | 1188 | 5 | | | | | | | | | | | | | |
| 17) | DXKH | 972 | 5 | dz | | 114) | DZXO | 1188 | 5 | | | | | | | | | | | | | |
| 17) | DYSM | 972 | 1 | ak | | 98) | DWBA | 1197 | 5 | | | | | | | | | | | | | |
| 58) | DWMT | 981 | 5 | dz | | 31) | DXFE | 1197 | 10 | | | | | | | | | | | | | |
| 22) | DXBR | 981 | 10 | bo | | 4) | DYRH | ‡1197 | 5 | | | | | | | | | | | | | |
| 84) | DXDR | 981 | 5 | ag | | 118) | DYRF | 1215 | 10 | cm | | | | | | | | | | | | |
| 88) | DXOW | 981 | 10 | | | 50) | DWSR | 1224 | 5 | dz | | | | | | | | | | | | |

**GENERAL NOTES:**

**Station identifications:** Generally, stn IDs are given on the h and half h. The English alphabet is used for the call letters, while the freq. is usually expressed in Spanish- or English-language numerals. Extensive stn details are included in sign on and sign off Anns.

**Callsign assignments:** DU = Shortwave only; DW = Luzon; DX = Mindanao and Sulu; DY = Visayas and Palawan; DZ = Luzon

**Administrative divisions:** Level 1: regions, 2: provinces, cities (C.), 3: municipalities, 4: barangays (brgy.). The National Capital Region (NCR) is also known as Metropolitan Manila or Metro-Manila.

**NB:** Cities may be referred to with or without 'City', e.g. Baguio City or Baguio. Quezon City is always referred to by its full name.

**Prgr. networks:** ag=R. Agong, ak=Aksyon R. bo=Bombo R., cm=Catholic Media Network (CMN, see above and entry **16)** below), dz=DZRH (key: 666kHz), ss=Sonshine R. (key: 1026kHz), su=Super R., uk=Radyo Ukay

**Web addresses for broadcast networks:** FEBC: **W:** febc.org – Bombo R. **W:** bomboradyo.com – R. Mindanao Netw **W:** rmn.ph – Manila Broadc. Co **W:** manilabroadcasting.com – Sonshine R. **W:** sonshineradio.com – DZRH: dzrh.com.ph

**FM:** A large number of FM stns are operating throughout the country. **Callsigns:** \_\_\_\_-FM

**Manila FM**(MHz): – **PB)** 87.5 DWFO 'FM1' – 88.3 DWCT 'Jam 88.3' (Raven Broadc. Corp.) – 89.1 DWAV 'Wave 89.1' (Blockbuster Broadc. System) – 89.9 DWTM 'Magic 89.9' (Quest Broadc. Inc.) – **50)** 90.7 DZMB 'Love R.' – 91.5 DWKY 'Win R.' (Mabuhay Broadc. System Inc.) – 92.3 DWFM 'Radyo5 92.3 News FM' (Nation Broadc. Corp.) – 93.1 DWRX 'Monster R.' (Audiovisual Communicators Inc.) – **84)** 93.9 DWKC 'iFM' – **32)** 94.7 DWLL 'Mellow 947' – **28)** 95.5 DWDM 'Pinas FM' – **17)** 96.3 DWRK 'Easy Rock' – **36)** 97.1 DWLS 'Barangay LS' – **3)** 97.9 DWQZ '97dot9 Home R.' – **31)** 98.7 DZFE 'The Master's Touch' – 99.5 DWRT 'Play FM' (Real R. Network Inc.) – **90)** 100.3 DZRJ 'RJ 100' – **67)** 101.1 DWYS 'Yes the Best' – **2)** 101.9 DWRR 'MOR 101.9 For Life!' – **73)** 102.7 DWSM 'Star FM' – 103.5 DWKX 'K-Lite' (Advanced Media Broadc. Syst.) – **PB)** 104.3 DWBR 'FM2.' – 105.1 DWBM 'Crossover' (Mareco Broadc. Network) – 105.9 DWLA 'Like FM' (Bright Star Broadc Network) – 106.7 DWET 'Energy FM' (Ultrasonic Broadc. Syst. Inc.) – **141)** 107.5 DWNU 'Wish FM.'

**Cebu City FM**(MHz): – 88.3 DYAP 'Mom's R.' (Southern Broadc. Network) –**16)** 89.1 DYDW 'Power 89' – 89.9 DYKI 'MemoRies FM' (Primaxx Broadc. Network) – 90.7 DYAC 'Crossover' (Mareco Broadc. Network) –**17)** 91.5 DYHR 'Yes the Best' – 92.3 DYBN 'Magic 92.3' (Quest Broadc., Inc.) – **115)** 93.1 DYWF 'Brigada News FM'– **84)**

93.9 DYXL 'iFM'– 94.7 DYLL 'Energy FM' (Ultrasonic Broadc. System) – **22)** 95.5 DYMX 'Star FM' – 96.3 DYRK 'W- Rock' (Exodus Broadc. Co.) – **2)** 97.1 DYLS 'MOR for Life!' – **50)** 97.9 DYBU 'Love R.' – **31)** 98.7 DYFR 'FR FM' – **91)** 99.5 DYRT 'Barangay RT' – **90)** 100.3 DYRJ 'RJ 100' – 101.1 DYIO 'Y 101' (GVM Radio/TV Corp.) – 101.9 DYNC 'Radyo5 News FM' (Nation Broadc. Corp.) – **17)** 102.7 DYTC 'Easy Rock' – 103.5 DYCD 'Retro Cebu' (Ditan Communications/Univ. of Mindanao Broadc. Network) – 105.1 DYUR 'Halo-Halo 105.1' (Ultimate Entertainment) – 105.9 DYBT 'Monster R.' (Capricorn Production & Management Corp.) – **3)** 106.7 DYQC 'Home R.' – 107.5 DYNU 'Win R.' (Progressive Broadc. Corp.)

**Davao City FM (MHz): – PB)** 87.5 DXRP R. Pilipinas – 88.3 DXDR 'Energy FM' (Ultrasonic Broadc. System) – 89.1 DXBE 'Magic 89.1' (Quest Broadc. Inc) – **16)** 89.9 DXGN – **50)** 90.7 DXBM 'Love R.' – **82)** 91.5 DXKX 'Brigada News FM' – **111)** 92.3 DXWT 'Wild 92.3' – 93.1 DXAC 'Crossover' (Mareco Broadc. Network) – **84)** 93.9 DXXL 'iFM' – **32)** 94.7 DXLL 'One Radio Davao' – **107)** 95.5 DXKR 'Retro 95.5' – **22)** 96.3 DXFX 'Star FM' – 97.1 DXUR 'Halo-Halo R. 97.1' (Ultimate Entertainment Inc.) – 97.9 DXSS 'Mom's R.' (Southern Broadc. Network) – **3)** 98.7 DXQM 'Home R.' – 99.5 DXBT 'Monster R.' (Ausiovisual Communicators Inc. – **90)** 100.3 DXDJ 'RJ 100' – **2)** 101.1 DXRR 'MOR for Life!' – 101.9 DXFM 'Radyo5 News FM' (Nation Broadc. Corp.) – 102.7 DXDM 'Mango Radyo' (Multipoint Broadc. Network) – **91)** 103.5 DXRV 'Barangay 103.5' – 104.3 DXMA 'Hope Radio' (United Christian Broadcasters) – **17)** 105.1 DXYS 'Easy Rock' – 105.9 DXMX 'Balita FM' (Omarco Broadc. Corp.) – 106.7 DXET 'Dream FM' (ABC Development Corp.) – 107.5 DXNU 'Win R.' (Progressive Broadc. Corp.)

**Addresses:**
For each entry the organisation or company name is followed by the call letters (in alphabetical order) and addresses of the stns licensed to the organisation. When contacting a stn, use Radio Station + the call letters as stn name. In some cases the stn may be operated by a different organisation than the licensee mentioned below

**PB)** See separate listing for Philippine Broadc. Sce Above. – **1)** Abra Community Btcg. Corp. DZPA R. Totoo, Blessed Arnold Janssen Communication Center, Zamora Str corner Rizal Str, Bangued, 2800 Abra – **2)** ABS-CBN Broadc. Corp (R. Patrol). DXAB, KM-4, Shrine Hills, Matina, 8000 Davao C. DYAB, ABS-CBN Broadc. Center, Jagobiao, Mandaue C, 6014 Cebu. DYRV, Catbalogan, 6700 Samar. DZMM, ABS-CBN Broadcast Center, Sergeant Esquerra Avenue corner of Mother Ignacia Street, Barangay South Triangle, Quezon C, 1103 NCR – **3)** Aliw Broadc. Corp. DWIZ, 5th Floor, Citystate Center, 809 Shaw Boulevard, Barangay Oranbo, Pasig C, 1600 NCR – **4)** Allied Broadc. Center, Inc. DYRH, JTL Bldg, North Drive, Bacolod C, 6100 Negros Occidental. DYRO. Roxas C., Capiz – DZBR Bible R., President Jose P. Laurel Highway, Batangas C, 4200 Batangas – **5)** Association of Islamic Dev't. Cooperative. DXID, Banale Dist, Pagadian C, 7016 Zamboanga del Sur – **7)** Bayanihan Broadc. Corp. DZJO, Infanta, 4336 Quezon Province – **8)** Ben Viduya (OMARCO). DZOM, Calapan C, 5200 Mindoro Oriental – **9)** Beta Broadc. Syst. DWHL R. Apo, 8 Kessing Str, Olongapo C, 2200 Zambales – **10)** Bicol Broadc. Syst. DZLL, BBS Bldg, Balagtas Road, Magsaysay Ave, Naga C, 4400 Camarines Sur – **11)** Bohol Chronicle Radio Corp. DYRD, Dejaresco Bldg, 56 Bernardino Inting Str, Tagbilaran C, 6300 Bohol. DYZD, Brgy Tapon, Ubay, 6315 Bohol – **13)** Cadiz Radio & TV Netw. DYAG, Cadiz C, 6121 Negros Occidental – **14)** Capitol Broadc. Center. DZME Kinze Trenta, OMM-Citra Bldg, Ortigas Center, Padig C, 1309 NCR – **15)** Catanduanes State College. DZRA, Virac, 4800 Catanduanes – **16)** Catholic Media Network (CMN). Most MW sts ID as R. Totoo. DWBS Radio Veritas, 2/F Landco Business Park, Legaspi C, 4500 Albay. DXCP, Lagao, Gen. Santos C, 9500 South Cotabato. DXDB Radyo Bandilyo, Communications Media Center, San Isidro Cathedral Compound, Malaybalay C, 8700 Bukidnon. DXHM, Clergy House Compound, Madang, Mati C., Davao Oriental. DYDM, SJC Extension Campus, Mambajao, Maasin C, 6600 Southern Leyte. DYKA, St Joseph Bldg, San Jose de Buenavista, 5700 Antique. DYWW, Clergy House, Baybay Blvd, Borongan, 6800 Eastern Samar. DZEA, Brgy. Nalbo, Laoag C, 2900 Ilocos Norte – **17)** Cebu Broadc. Co. DXKH, Bayabas, Cagayan de Oro C, 9000 Misamis Oriental. DXZH, Zamboanga C, 7000 Zamboanga del Sur. DYCH, Tanke, Talisay C, 6045 Cebu. DYMS, San Bartolome Str, Catbalogan, 6700 Samar. DYSM, Brgy. Cawayan, Catarman, 6400 Northern Samar. DZHR, Carig, Tuguegarao, 3500 Cagayan. – **18)** Cagayan de Oro Media Corp. DXJR R. Higala, Manolo Fortich, Bukidnon – **19)** Gateway UHF Broadcasting (Seventh Day Adventist). DXHR Hope R., km 43 Baan Hwy, Butuan C., 8600 Agusan del Norte – **20)** Christian Era Broadc. Sce DZEM, Barn Studio Bldg, New Era Studio Campus, 9 Central Avenue, Quezon C, 1107 NCR – **22)** Consolidated Broadc. Syst, Inc. DXBR, Bombo R. Broadc. Center, Arujville Subd, Brgy. Libertad, Butuan C, 8600 Agusan del Norte. DXES Bombo R. Broadc. Center, Amao Rd, Brgy. Bula, Gen. Santos C, 9500

South Cotabato. DXLX, Tambo, Brgy. Hinaplon, Iligan C, 9200 Lanao del Norte. DYFM, Sky City Tower, Mapa Str, Jaro, Iloilo C, 5000 Iloilo. DYOW, Bombo R. Broadc. Center, Arnaldo Blvd, Roxas C, 5800 Capiz. DYWB, Bombo R. Broadcast Center, Lacson Str, Mandalagan, Bacolod C, 6100 Negros Occidental. DZVV, Bombo R. Broadc. Center, Brgy. Tamag, Vigan, 2700 Ilocos Sur. DZWN, Bombo R. Broadc. Center, Maramba Bankers' Village, Bonuan Catacdang, 2400 Dagupan C, Pangasinan. DZWX, Bombo R. Broadc. Center, 87 Lourdes Subdivision Rd, Baguio C, 2600 Benguet – **23)** Crusaders Broadc. Syst, R. Ngayon. DWAD, 209 E. de la Paz Str, Mandaluyong C, 1550 NCR – **24)** Dawnbreaker's Foundation. DWBR R. Baha'i, Bulac, Talavera, 3114 Nueva Ecija or P. O.Box 27, San José City 3121 – **25)** Delta Broadc. Syst. DWXI, Mathew Str, Multinational Village, Parañaque C, 1708 NCR – **26)** Dept. of National Defense, Armed Forces R.. DWDD, PVAO Building, Camp Aguinaldo, EDSA, Quezon C, 1110 NCR – **27)** DXZB/TV13 Cooperative, Inc. DXZB, Zamboanga C, 7000 Zamboanga del Sur – **28)** Eagle Broadc. Corp. DWIN, Bo. Lucao, Dagupan C, 2400 Pangasinan. DXED, Cabiguio Ave, Agdao, 8000 Davao C. DZEC, EBC Building, 25 Central Avenue, Quezon C, 1107 NCR. DZEL, Bo. Mayao, Lucena C, 4301 Quezon Province – **29)** East Visayan Broadc. DYBR, Sagcahan Rd, P.O. Box 80, Tacloban C, 6500 Leyte – **30)** Fairwaves Broadc. Netw. DZXE R. Tirador, Mira Hills, Vigan, 2700 Ilocos Sur – **31)** Far East Broadc. Co. . DXAS, P.O. Box 349, Tugbungan, Zamboanga C, 7000 Zamboanga del Sur. DXFE, Circumferential Rd, Dona Vicente Village, 8000 Davao C. DXKI, P.O. Box 8004, Brgy Morales, Koronadal C, 9506 South Cotabato. DYVS, P.O. Box 393, Km. 7, Pahanocoy, Bacolod C, 6100 Negros Occidental. DZAS, 46th Floor, One Corporate Center, Meralco Avenue corner Dona Julia Vargas Avenue, Ortigas Center, Pasig C, 1600 NCR. DZMR Missions Radio, Maharlika Highway, Sefton Village, Santiago City, 3311 Isabela – **32)** FBS Radio Netw., Unit 908, Paragon Plaza, EDSA corner Reliance Str, Mandaluyong C, 1554 NCR – **33)** Filipinas Broadc. Netw. DYXW, Baruyan, San Jose, Tacloban C, 6500 Leyte. DZCV, Ugac Norte, Tuguegarao, 3500 Cagayan. DZGE R. Numero Uno, Nordia Resort, Baras, Canaman, Naga C, 4400 Camarines Sur. DZRC R. Champion, Capt. Aquendes Drive, Legaspi C, 4500 Albay – **35)** Franciscan Broadc. Corp. DYWC R. Bandilyo, Parish Compound, St Anthony of Padua Parish, Sibulan, Dumaguete C, 6201 Negros Oriental – **36)** GMA Netw, Inc. DZSD, Arellano St., Dagupan C, 2400 Pangasinan. DYSB, Bacolod C, 6100 Negros Occidental. DYSI, GMA Compound, MacArthur Drive, Jaro, Iloilo C, 5000 Iloilo. DZBB, GMA Netw. Center, EDSA corner Timog Ave, Diliman, 1103 Quezon C – **37)** Guzman Institute of Tech. DWGI, 509 Z.P. de Guzman, Quiapo, Manila, NCR – **38)** GV Broadc. Syst. DWGV R. Centro, Rizal Extension, Cut-Cut, Angeles C, 2009 Pampanga – **39)** Hypersonic Broadc. Center. DWZR Zoom Radio, Penaranda Str, Legaspi C, 4500 Albay. DYHR, Calbayog C, 6710 W. Samar – **40)** Insular Broadc. Syst. DWIM R. Mindoro, Brgy. Bayanihan, Calapan, 5200 Mindoro Oriental – **41)** Interactive Broadcast Media, Inc. DWWW, Units 807-808 Atlanta Center, Annapolis Street, Greenhills, San Juan C, 1502 NCR – **42)** Intercontinental Broadc. Corp, R. Budyong. DWDC, A.B. Fernandez Ave, Dagupan C, 2400 Pangasinan. DXWG, Iligan C, 9200 Lanao del Norte. DYBQ, Datu Puti Subdivision, ,Cubay, Jaro, Iloilo C, 5000 Iloilo. DYJJ, Roxas Ave, Roxas C, 5800 Capiz. DYRG, Roxas Ave Extension, Andagao, Kalibo, 5600 Aklan – **43)** Kaissar Broadc. Netw. DWJJ R.bisyon (Double J Ad Ventures), Celcor Compound, Bitas, Cabanatuan C, 3100 Nueva Ecija – **44)** Kalayaan Broadc. Syst. DXRR R. Rapido, Bug-ac, Matina, 8000 Davao C – **45)** Katigbak Enterprises (ConAmor Broadcasting Systems). DWMI, Calapan, 5200 Mindoro Oriental. DWTI, Broadcast Village, Ibabang Dupay, Lucena C, 4301 Quezon Province – **46)** Puerto Princesa Broadc. Co. DYEC Environment Radio, Puerto Princesa C, 5300 Palawan – **48)** Progressive Broadcasting Corporation. DWUN UNTV Radio La Verdad, UNTV Bldg, 907 EDSA, Brgy Philam, Quezon C, 1104 NCR – **49)** Magiliw Community Broadc. Co. DWMC, Tomana, Rosales, 2441 Pangasinan – **50)** Manila Broadc. Co. DWDH, Lucao District, Dagupan C, 2400 Pangasinan. DWSR, Talipan, Pagbilao, Lucena C, 4301 Quezon Province. DXRF, Matina, 8000 Davao C. DYEZ, Wilrose Building, Burgos Str, Bacolod C, 6100 Negros Occidental. DYKX, Kalibo, 5600 Aklan. DYOK, Suite 301Carlos Uy Bldg, Diversion Rd, Manurriao, Iloilo C, 5000 Iloilo. DYPH, Gabinete Rd, Bancao-Bancao, Puerto Princesa C, 5300 Palawan. DYVL, J. Romualdez corner Real Streets, Tacloban C, 6500 Leyte. DYRC Radyo Cebu, 3rd Floor, Cinco Centrum Building, Fuente Osmeña Blvd, 6000 Cebu C. DZJC, Brgy. 29, Rizal Street, St. Joseph District, Laoag C, 2900 Ilocos Norte. DZRH, MBC Bldg, Vicente Sotto Str, CCP Complex, Pasay C, 1300 NCR. DZZH, Cabit-an, Sorsogon C, 4700 Sorsogon – **51)** Masbate Community Broadc. Co. DYCM, 201 Dona Luisa Bldg, Fuente Osmena Ave, Cebu City, 6000 Cebu. DYME, Tugbo Str, Masbate C, 5400 Masbate – **52)** Mindanao Broadc. Co, Inc. DXSA, Marawi C, 9700 Lanao del Sur – **53)** Univ. of Mindanao Broadcasting Netwk. DXUM R. Ukay, UMBN Broadcast Center, Multi-test Bldg, Ponciano Reyes St, 8000 Davao C – **54)** Mt. Province Broadc. Corp. DZWT, P.O. Box 156, Mount Beckel, La Trinidad, Baguio C, 2600 Benguet – **55)** Mt. View

College. DXCR Hope R., MVC, Valencia, 8709 Bukidnon – **56)** Municipality of Marikina, DZBF, R. Marikina, Second Floor, City Hall, Shoe Avenue, Marikina C, 1800 NCR – **57)** Mindanao Dev. Multi-Purpose Coop. DXAD Radio Ranao, Marcos Blvd, Saduc, Marawi C, 9700 Lanao del Sur – **58)** Swara Sug Media Corporation. DWAR, Laoag C, 2900 Ilocos Norte. DWAY, Cabanatuan C, 3100 Nueva Ecija. DWSI, North Eastern Foundation College, Santiago, 3311 Isabela. DWTT, Tarlac C, 2300 Tarlac. DXBL, Mangagoy, Bislig C, 8311 Surigao del Sur. DXAQ, Philippine-Japan Friendship Hwy, Catitipan, Davao C. DXCL, Cagayan de Oro C, 9000 Misamis Oriental. DXRB, Brgy Libertad, Butuan C, 8600 Agusan del Norte. DXRD, J.P Laurel Ave, Bajada, 8000 Davao C. DXRE, Lagao, Gen. Santos C, 9500 South Cotabato. DXRO, Don Roman Vilo Str, Cotabato C, 9600 Maguindanao. DXRT, Jolo, 7400 Sulu. DXYZ, San Jose Rd, Baliwasan, 7000 Zamboanga C. DYAR, 3$^{rd}$ Fl. Astron Gestus Bldg, Gorordo Ave, 6000 Cebu C. DZAR, 3rd Floor, ACQ Tower, Santa Rita Street, Barangay Guadelupe Nuevo, Makati C, 1212 NCR. DZRD, Banuan Guesset, Dagupan C, 2400 Pangasinan. DZSP, San Pablo C, 4000 Laguna. DZYI, Calamagui 2nd, Ilagan, 3300 Isabela. DZYT, Cagayan Teachers College, Tuguegarao, 3500 Cagayan – **60)** Newsounds Broadc. Netw. DXIF, Bombo R. Broadc. Center, Corrales Ave, Cagayan de Oro C, 9000 Misamis Oriental. DYCX, San Jose de Buenavista, Antique. DYWR, Bombo R. Broadc. Center, Sto. Nino cor. Imelda Ave, Tacloban C, 6500 Leyte. DZNC, Bombo R. Broadc. Center, Barrio Menante ll, Cauayan, 3305 Isabela. DZNG, Bombo R. Broadc. Center, Diversion Road, Brgy. Tabuko, Naga C, 4400 Camarines Sur. DZSO, Bombo R. Broadcast Center, Pennsylvania Ave, Parian, San Fernando C, 2500 La Union. DZVR, Bombo R. Broadcast Center, 48 A, Cabungaan Airport Ave, Laoag C, 2900 Ilocos Norte – **61)** Northeastern Broadc. Sce DWDY, Ground Floor, Isabela Hotel, Mirante Uno, Cauayan, 3305 Isabela – **62)** Notre Dame Broadc. Corp. DXMS, Sinsuat Ave cor. Rizal Ave, Cotabato C, 9600 Maguindanao. DXND, Daang Maharlika, Kidapawan C, 9400 North Cotabato. DXOM R. Bida, General Santos Drive, Morales, Koronadal C., S, Cotabato – **63)** Nueva Ecija Provincial Gov. DWNE, Brgy Singalat, Palayan C, 3132 Nueva Ecija – **64)** Office of the Governor, Prov. of Agusan del Sur. DXDA R. Agusan, Patin-ay, Prosperidad, 8500 Agusan del Sur – **65)** Office of the Civil Defense. DZCA, Agham Rd. Science Garden, Pag-asa Planetarium, NCR – **66)** Ormoc Broadc. Co. DYRR, Bantigue, Ormoc C, 6541 Leyte – **67)** Pacific Broadc. Syst (subsidiary of Manila Broadc. Co.) DWRH, Rizal, Santiago C, 3311 Isabela.. DXCH, Krislamville, Kakar, Cotabato C, 9600 Maguindanao. DXGH, Purok Malakas, Lagao, Gen. Santos C, 9500 South Cotabato. DXGO, MBC Compound, Brgy. Duterte, R. Castillo Str, Agdao, 8000 Davao C. DYBH, Bacolod C, 6100 Negros Occidental. DYDH, Iloilo Cadastre, Iloilo C, 5000 Iloilo. DYTH, Real Str, Tacloban C, 6500 Leyte. DZMT, Santo Tomas, Laoag C, 2900 Ilocos Norte – **68)** Palawan Broadc. Corp. DYAP, Rey Olivar Bldg., 61 Mabini St. Puerto Princesa C, 5300 Palawan. – **69)** PEC Broadc. Corp. DXGL, Butuan C, 8600 Agusan del Norte – **70)** Pedro N. Roa Broadc. DXOR, Don A. Velez Str, Cagayan de Oro C, 9000 Misamis Oriental – **72)** People's Broadc. Netw. DZGB, Mayona Building, Imperial Court Subdivision, Legaspi C, 4500 Albay. DZMD, Vinzons Ave, Daet, 4600 Camarines Norte. DZMS, Balobo Str, Sorsogon C, 4700 Sorsogon – **73)** People's Broadc. Sce DXMC, Bombo R. Broadc. Center, Km 4 General Santos Drive, Koronadal C, 9506 South Cotabato. DXMF, Bombo R. Broadc. Center, San Pedro Str, 8000 Davao C. DXPD, Bombo R. Broadc. Center, North Diversion Road, Brgy. Banale, Pagadian C, 7016 Zamboanga del Sur. DYMF, 87-A. Borromeo Str, 6000 Cebu C. DZGR, Bombo R. Broadc. Center, Taft Str Extension, Brgy 5, Tuguegarao, 3500 Cagayan. DZLG, Bombo R. Broadc. Center, Tahao Road, Legaspi C, 4500 Albay. – **75)** Philippine Broadc. Corp. DWCM, Caranglaan District, Dagupan C, 2400 Pangasinan. DWMT, San Isidro, Magarao, Naga C, 4400 Camarines Sur. DWSP, Tuding, Itogon, nr Baguio City, Benguet. DZNL, Brgy. Pagdalagan, San Fernando C, 2500 La Union. – **77)** Philippine Radio Corp. DWRN R. Asenso, Manipit Rd, Queborac Bagumbayan, Naga C, 4400 Camarines Sur. DYRM, Bo. Calindangan, Dumaguete C, 6200 Negros Oriental. DZYM R. Asenso, Puerto Gallenero, Pag-asa, San Jose, 5100 Mindoro Occidental. DZYR, Catbangen, San Fernando C, 2500 La Union – **79)** Public Affairs Sce, Armed Forces of the Philippines. DXOS, Basilan Island, Basilan – **81)** R.T. Broadc. Specialistns Philippines. DXLL, Campaner Str, Zamboanga C, 7000 Zamboanga del Sur – **82)** Radio Corp. of the Philippines. DXJM, J & M Bldg, Villakananga, Butuan C, 8600 Agusan del Norte. DZLT, Bo. Ibabang Dupay, Lucena C, 4301 Quezon Province. DZXT, MacArthur H-way, Tarlac C, 2300 Tarlac – **83)** DWRL Radio, Inc (subsidary of 82 above). DWRL, Purok 5, Rawis, Legaspi C, 4500 Albay. DXGS R. Asenso, NLSA Rd, Lagao, Gen. Santos C, 9500 South Cotabato. DXOC R. Asenso, Manabay, Catadman, Ozamis C, 7200 Misamis Occidental. DYRB, C. Padilla St., 6000 Cebu C – **84)** Radio Mindanao Netw. DWNX, 2/F Ramaida Centrum, East Angeles Str, Naga City, 4400 Camarines Sur. DXBC, Montilla Blvd, Butuan C, 8600 Agusan del Norte. DXCC, Canoy Bldg., Don Apolinar Velez Str, Cagayan de Oro C, 9000 Misamis Oriental. DXDC, San Vincente Bldg,

cor. Anda & Bonifacio Stns, 8000 Davao C. DXDR, Bo. Mario Turno, Dipolog C, 7100 Zamboanga del Norte. DXHP, Flomencia Bldg. P. Castillo Mangagoy, Bislig C, 8311 Surigao del Sur. DXIC, Pafs Mejia Bldg, Roxas Str. cor Aguinaldo Str, Iligan C, 9200 Lanao del Norte. DXKR, Gen. Santos Drive, Koronadal C, 9506 South Cotabato. DXMB, Fortich Str, Malaybalay C, 8700 Bukidnon. DXMD, Bo. Obrero National Highway, Gen. Santos C, 9500 South Cotabato. DXMY, Esteros, RH 10, Cotabato C, 9600 Maguindanao. DXPR, Mercedes Str, San Jose Dist, Pagadian C, 7016 Zamboanga del Sur. DXRS, Km. 1 Rizal Str, Surigao C, 8400 Surigao del Norte. DXRZ, Zamaveco Bldg, Pilar Str, Zamboanga C, 7000 Zamboanga del Sur. DYCC, Brgy. Obrero, Calbayog C, 6710 W. Samar. DYHB, 4th Flt, SSS Bldg. Lacson Str, Bacolod C, 6100 Negros Occidental. DYHP, 2nd Flr, Gold Palace Bldg, 168 Osmeña Blvd, 6000 Cebu C. DYKR, C. Laserna Str, Kalibo, 5600 Aklan. DYRI, St Anne Bldg, Luna Str, La Paz, Iloilo C, 5000 Iloilo. DYVR, Punta, Tabuc, Roxas C, 5800 Capiz. DZXL, 4/F, Guadelupe Commerical Complex, Guadelupe Nuevo, Makati C, 1200 NCR – **85)** Radio Philippines Netw. DXDX R. Ronda, Acharon Blvd, Gen. Santos C, 9500 South Cotabato. DXKD, Gonzales corner Lopez Jaena Str, Biasong, Dipolog C, 7100 Zamboanga del Norte. DXKO R. Ronda, Gusa, National Hwy, Cagayan de Oro C, 9000 Misamis Oriental. DXKP R. Ronda, Araulio Str, Brgy Datoc, Pagadian C, 7016 Zamboanga del Sur. DXKS, Capitol Rd, Surigao C, 8400 Surigao del Norte. DXKT R. Ronda, Marfori Heights, 8000 Davao C. DXXX R. Ronda, Brgy Tugbungan, 7000 Zamboanga C. DYKB R. Ronda, Bo. Sumag, Bacolod C, 6100 Negros Occidental. DYKC, Barangay Maguikay, Mandaue C, 6014 Cebu. DYKW R. Ronda, Cagamayan, Binalbagan, 6107 Negros Occidental. DZBS R. Ronda, Agrix Supermarket cor. Magsaysay Ave. & Bakawkan, Baguio C, 2600 Benguet. DZKI R. Ronda, San Agustin, Iriga C, 4431 Camarines Sur. DZRL R. Ronda, Bo. Kawayan, Batac, 2906 Ilocos Norte. DZTG, 46 Rizal Str, Tuguegarao, 3500 Cagayan – **86)** Radio Sorsogon Netw, Inc. DZRS, Don Luis Lee Bldg, Plaza Bonifacio, Sorsogon, 4700 Sorsogon – **87)** Radio Veritas Global Broadc. Syst. DWRV, Maharlika Highway, Bayombong, 3700 Nueva Vizcaya. DWVR, San Jose C, 3121 Nueva Ecija. DZRV, R. Veritas, 20/F The Centerpoint Bldg 1, 162 West Ave corner EDSA, Ortigas Center, Pasig C, 1600 NCR – **88)** R. Pilipino Corp (R. Asenso). DXCO, Atco Bldg, Capistrano & Gomez Str, Cagayan de Oro C, 9000 Misamis Oriental. DXOW, Mapa, 8000 Davao C. DYRL, Camaroli Av, Lupit Subd, Bacolod C, 6100 Negros Occidental. DZYA 2/F Tanglao Bldg, Balibago, Angeles C, 2009 Pampanga. – **89)** Ragde, Vicente & Sons. DYRS, Ragde Comp, Corner M. Endrinda Str and Broce Str, San Carlos C, 6127 Negros Occidental – **90)** Rajah Broadc. Netw (R. Bandido). DXRJ, RJ Clubhouse, Sta. Filomena, Iligan C, 9200 Lanao del Norte. DZRJ (The Voice of the Philippines), Ventures Bldg 1, Gen. Luna Str, Makati C, NCR – **91)** Republic Broadc. Syst. (owned by GMA Network Inc.) DWRA, Baguio C, 2600 Benguet. DWRC, San Nicolas, 2901 Ilocos Norte. DXBM, Cotabato C, 9600 Maguindanao. DXGM, Shrine Hills, Matina, 8000 Davao C. DXRL, 3/F Carisma Bldg., General Santos Drive, Koronadal C, 9506 South Cotabato. DXYK, Butuan C, 8600 Agusan del Norte. DYSP, Solid Rd, Brgy San Manuel, Puerto Princesa C, 5300 Palawan. DYSS, GMA Network Center, Nivel Hills, Apas, 6000 Cebu C – **92)** Ribbon Broadc. Netw. DWRB, 5/F, LCC Bldg, Lipa C, 4217 Batangas – **94)** RMC Broadc. Co, Inc (Rizal Memorial Colleges). DXRA R. Arangkada, A. Pichon Sr., 8000 Davao C – **95)** Rolin Broadc. Enterprises (sts relay RMN DWAR 103.9MHz, Puerto Princesa). DWES, Narra, 5303 Palawan. DWJS, Roxas, 5308 Palawan – **97)** Sarraga Integration and Management Corp. (SIAM), El Nuevo Bantay R. DYHH Bantay R.DYDD, Martinez, Cebu C, 6000 Cebu. DYZZ, Bogo, 6010 Cebu. DYZZ, Guihulngan, 6214 Negros Oriental – **98)** Satellite Broadc. Corp. DWBA, Bangued, 2800 Abra. DZLU, National College of Technology Campus, Barangay 1, San Fernando C, 2500 La Union –**100)** Southern Institute of Tech. DXSI, Cagayan de Oro C, 9000 Misamis Oriental – **101)** Southern Philippines Mass Comm. DXSC, Camp Navarro, Calarian, 7000 Zamboanga C – **102)** Subic Broadc. Corp. DWGO Gabay ng Olangapo, 1 Kasarinlan Rd, Olongapo, 2200 Zambales – **103)** Sulu Tawi-Tawi Broadc. Foundation. DXGD Radio for Peace, Bongao, 7500 Tawi-Tawi. DXMM R. Totoo, Gandasuli Str, Jolo, 7400 Sulu – **104)** Tagbilaran Broadc. Corp. DYTR, CAP Bldg, CPG Ave crnr Borja Str, Dampas, Tagbilaran C, 6300 Bohol – **105)** Times Broadc. Corp. DXSY, Mariano Marcos, Ozamis C, 7200 Misamis Occidental – **106)** Tirad Pass R/TV Broadc. Netw. DZTP R. Tirad Pass, San Nicolas, Candon, 2710 Ilocos Sur – **107)** Trans-Pacific Broadc. Corp. (operated by Philippine Daily Inquirer). R. Inquirer, 2/F Media Resources Plaza, Pasong Tirad cor. Mola Str, Brgy La Paz, Makati C, 1204 NCR – **108)** Supreme Broadc. Systems. DWSS, Paragon Plaza, EDSA, Mandaluyong C, 1554 NCR – **110)** Universal Broadc. Syst (owned by Radio Mindanao Network). DYMM, Sunshine Village, Esperos Str, Tacloban C, 6500 Leyte. DYXT, Luna Str, Tagbilaran C, 6300 Bohol – **111)** University of Mindanao Broadc. Netwk (UMBN). DXCM, UM School Compound, Cotabato C, 9600 Maguindanao. DXDN, UM Tagum School Compound, Tagum C, 8100 Davao del Norte. DXDS, Digos C, 8002 Davao del Sur. DXMV, Mt. Kitangcad Cor. Kanlaon Street,

Valencia, 8709 Bukidnon. – **112)** University of San Agustin. DYSA R. San Agustin, 2/F Univ. of S. Agustin, Gen. Luna Str, Iloilo C, 5901 Iloilo – **113)** University of the Philippines. DZLB, UP Los Banos College, 4031 Laguna. DZUP, Media Center, College of Mass Comunications, UP Campus Diliman, R, Magasay Ave corner Apacible Str, Quezon C, 1104 NCR – **114)** Vanguard Radio Netw (Radio Vanguard). DWMG, Solano, 3709 Nueva Vizcaya. DZXO, Ground Floor Diego Building, Maharlika Highway, Cabanatuan C, 3100 Nueva Ecija – **115)** Visayas Mindanao Confederation of Trade Unions. DYLA, Alu-Vimcontu Welfare Center, Pier Area, 6000 Cebu C – **116)** Vismin Radio & TV Broadc. Net. DXDV, Baan, Butuan C, 8600 Agusan del Norte – **118)** Word Broadc. Corp. DYDW Radio Diwa, Burayan, San José, Tacloban C, 6500 Leyte. DYRF R. Fuerza, Univ. of San Carlos, Pelaez Str, 6000 Cebu C – **120)** ZOE Broadc. Netw. DZJV, 140 Brgy Parian, Calamba, 4027 Laguna – **121)** Baganian Broadc. Corp. DXBZ R. Bagting, Bana Str, Sta Maria District, Pagadian C., 7015 Zamboanga del Sur – **122)** Solidnorth Broadcasting System. DWRS Commando Radio, Tamag, Vigan, 2700 Ilocos Sur – **123)** S.O.L. Telebroadcasting Station. DZSL, Purok 2, Talisay, Camarines Norte – **124)** Ranao Radio & TV Broadcast System Corp. DXSK R. Ranaw, Pangarungan Village, Marawi C, 9700 Lanao del Sur – **125)** End Time Mission (Pentecostal Missionary Church of Christ 4th Watch). DZAT, Purok Rosal, Bo. Silangan Mayao, Lucena C., 4301 Quezon Province – **127)** University of the Philippines in the Visayas. DYUP UPV Radio, Miagao, Iloilo – **129)** Inter-Island Broadc. Corp. (IBC), owned by 73) above. DYIN, Bombo R. Broadcast Center, Oyo Torong Str, cor. J. Magno. Str, Kalibo, 5600 Aklan. DYSJ, San José de Buenavista, Antique – **130)** Dan-ag sa Dakbayan Broadc. Corp. DXDD R. Kampana, New DXDD Bldg, Rizal. Str, Ozamis C, 7200 Misamis Occidental – **131)** Roman Catholic Archdiocese of Zamboanga Broadc. Network (RCA-ZBN). DXVP R. Verdadero, Sacred Heart Center, R.T. Lim Bvd, Zamboanga C, 7000 Zamboanga del Sur – **132)** Apostolic Vicariate of San José de Mindoro. DZVT R. Totoo, Labangan Poblacion, San José, 5100 Mindoro Occidental – **133)** Multipoint Broadc. Netwk. DWPR Power Radio, A.B. Fernandez Ave, Bolosan District, Dagupan C, 2400 Pangasinan – **134)** Alaminos City Broadc. Corporation. DZWM R. Totoo, St Joseph Cathedral Compound, Alaminos, 2404 Pangasinan – **135)** Government of Tarlac Province. DZTC, MacArthur Hwy, Tarlac C, 2300 Tarlac – **136)** Archdiocese of Nueva Segovia. DZNS R. Totoo, Brgy Pantay Fatima, Vigan, 2700 Ilocos Sur – **137)** Diocese of Bacolod. DYAF R. Veritas Bacolod, Rizal Str corner San Juan Str, Brgy. 11, Bacolod C, 6100 Negros Occidental – **138)** Silangan Broadcasting Corporation. DXSN R. Magbalantay or R. Totoo, 55 Jules Chevalier Str, Surigao C, 8400 Surigao del Norte – **139)** Universidad de Zamboanga. DXUZ R. Lipay, Ipil, 7001 Zamboanga Sibugay – **140)** Itransmission, Inc. DZIP R. Palaweño, Dimalanta Bldg, Rizal Ave, Puerto Princesa, Palawan – **141)** Sarangani Broadcasting Netwk. DXBB R. Alerto, Yumang Str, Brgy San Isidro, Gen. Santos C, 9500 South Cotabato – **142)** End-Time Mission Broadcasting Service. DWET Life R, Batal, Santiago C, 3311 Isabela.

**EXTERNAL SERVICES: R. Pilipinas, Radio Veritas Asia, FEBC International Service, VOA/IBB**
see International Broadcasting section

## PITCAIRN ISLANDS (UK)

**L.T:** UTC -8h — **Pop:** 50 — **Pr.L:** Pitcairn English — **E.C:** 50Hz, 240V — **ITU:** PTC

### PITCAIRN ISLAND RADIO
☎ Adamstown, Pitcairn Island **L.P:** Paul Warren. **FM:** 87.5MHz 0.0025kW. **Prgr:** local community radio. **NB:** Inactive

## POLAND

**L.T:** UTC +1h (31 Mar-27 Oct: +2h) — **Pop:** 38.5 million — **Pr.L:** Polish — **E.C:** 230V/50Hz — **ITU:** POL

### KRAJOWA RADA RADIOFONII I TELEWIZJI (KRRiT)
**(National Broadcasting Council)**
☎ Skwer kard. S.Wyszynskiego 9, 01-015 Warszawa ☎ +48 225973000 🖷 +48 225973180 **E:** krrit@krrit.gov.pl **W:** krrit.gov.pl
**L.P:** Pres: Witold Kolodziejski

### RADA MEDIÓW NARODOWYCH (RMN)
**(National Media Council)**
☎ Kancelaria Sejmu, ul. Wiejska 4/6/8, 00-902 Warszawa.
**L.P:** Chmn: Krzysztof Czabanski

### POLSKIE RADIO S.A. (PR) (Pub)
☎ al. Niepodleglosci 77/85, 00-977 Warszawa ☎ +48 226459212 🖷

+48 226453993 **E:** public.relations@polskieradio.pl **W:** polskieradio.pl
**L.P:** Chmn: Andrzej Rogoyski

| LW | kHz | kW | Prgr | | |
|---|---|---|---|---|---|
| Solec Kujawski | 225 | 1200* | 1 | | *) 700kW at night |
| FM (MHz) | 1 | 2 | 3 | 5 | kW |
| Bialogard (Slawoborze) | 106.0 | 98.2 | 101.5 | - | 10/2x15 |
| Bialystok (Krynice) | 92.3 | - | 96.0 | - | 30 |
| Bielawa | - | - | - | 103.5 | 1 |
| Bogatynia (G.Wysoka) | 92.8 | - | - | - | 1 |
| Bydgoszcz | - | - | - | 96.2 | 1 |
| Bydgoszcz (Trzeciewiec) | 106.6 | 97.6 | 102.1 | - | 60/2x120 |
| Czestochowa | - | - | - | 98.9 | 2 |
| Czestochowa (Wreczyca) | 87.5 | 90.6 | 91.7 | - | 10/2x60 |
| Elblag (Jagodnik) | - | 102.3 | - | 101.2 | 5/0.25 |
| Gdansk (Chwaszczyno) | 95.7 | - | 99.9 | - | 120 |
| Gdynia | - | 97.2 | - | - | 2 |
| Gizycko (Milki) | 97.1 | 92.6 | 94.4 | - | 6/2x10 |
| Golancz | 101.3 | - | - | - | 3 |
| Gorlice | 105.4 | - | 91.6 | - | 10/0.2 |
| Gorzów Wlkp. | - | - | - | 105.4 | 1 |
| Ilawa (Kisielice) | 94.8 | 102.7 | - | 104.8 | 2x10/5 |
| Jelenia Góra (Sniezne Kotly) | 92.5 | - | 94.0 | - | 10 |
| Kalisz (Mikstat) | 100.0 | 95.6 | 102.5 | 94.2 | 10 |
| Katowice (Kosztowy) | 97.9 | 105.6 | 99.7 | - | 60 |
| Kielce (Swiety Krzyz) | 92.3 | - | 96.2 | - | 60 |
| Kielce | - | 102.7 | - | 87.6 | 1/0.1 |
| Klodzko (Czarna Góra) | 97.6 | - | 89.2 | - | 10 |
| Klodzko | - | 92.4 | - | - | 2 |
| Konin (Zólwieniec) | 87.7 | - | 103.3 | - | 30 |
| Koszalin (Gologóra) | 107.9 | 93.8 | 97.4 | - | 60 |
| Kraków (Choragwica) | 89.4 | - | 99.4 | - | 60 |
| Kraków (Krzemionki) | - | 102.0 | - | 97.2 | 1/0.4 |
| Krosno (Sucha Góra) | 88.0 | - | 92.0 | - | 120 |
| Krynica (G.Jaworzyna) | 106.4 | 89.6 | - | 98.4 | 1/0.1/1 |
| Kutno | 101.8 | 96.9 | - | - | 8.9/0.8 |
| Lebork (Skórowo Nowe) | 100.5 | 88.2 | 106.3 | 107.5 | 2x10/5/10 |
| Legnica | - | 105.3 | - | 103.3 | 2/0.3 |
| Leszno | - | 88.7 | - | 107.9 | 0.25/1 |
| Lezajsk (Giedlarowa) | 96.8 | - | 98.9 | - | 10 |
| Lobez (Toporzyk) | - | - | - | 100.6 | 3 |
| Lódz | 107.8 | 91.4 | 103.8 | 107.3 | 30/2x10/1.5 |
| Lowicz | 101.6 | - | - | - | 10 |
| Lubaczów (Boble) | 100.0 | 88.4 | 96.0 | - | 10 |
| Luban (Nowa Karczma) | 99.0 | - | 91.5 | - | 10/60 |
| Lublin (Piaski) | 90.8 | - | 104.2 | - | 30/90 |
| Nowy Tomysl (Bolewice) | - | 107.7 | - | - | 10 |
| Olsztyn (Pieczewo) | 93.0 | 93.7 | 99.1 | 97.9 | 30/2/120/0.1 |
| Opole (Chrzelice) | 88.3 | 94.5 | 90.3 | - | 60/10/60 |
| Ostroleka (Lawy) | 106.7 | 96.3 | 98.5 | 93.4 | 10/5/10/0.2 |
| Pila (Staszyce) | - | 102.5 | - | - | 10 |
| Plock (Rachocin) | 92.2 | 98.1 | 96.1 | - | 60/2.5/60 |
| Poznan (Srem) | 92.3 | - | 96.4 | - | 120 |
| Przasnysz | 105.9 | 107.1 | - | - | 10 |
| Przemysl (Tatarska Góra) | 87.8 | 94.1 | 99.6 | 91.0 | 5/1/5/1 |
| Przysucha (Kozlowiec) | 92.0 | 104.8 | - | - | 10 |
| Rabka (G.Lubon Wielki) | 93.4 | 90.4 | - | - | 5 |
| Radom (Wacyn) | - | 100.3 | - | 97.5 | 1/0.1 |
| Ryki | 105.1 | 88.7 | - | - | 10 |
| Rzeszów | - | 105.8 | - | 91.5 | 1 |
| Siedlce (Losice) | 88.3 | - | 90.5 | - | 30 |
| Slupsk | 104.3 | - | - | 106.8 | 2.8/5 |
| Solina (G.Jawor) | 90.7 | - | 96.3 | - | 30 |
| Stargard | - | 107.6 | - | - | 1 |
| Suwalki (G.Krzemianucha) | 105.5 | 92.0 | 96.6 | 88.7 | 20/2x30/0.2 |
| Swieradów-Zdrój | - | 93.2 | - | 90.5 | 10/1 |
| Swinoujscie (Chrobrego) | 107.7 | - | - | - | 10 |
| Szczawnica (G.Prehyba) | 88.0 | - | 94.7 | - | 10/5 |
| Szczecin (Kolowo) | 100.3 | - | 102.3 | - | 60 |
| Szczecin (Warszewo) | - | 96.3 | - | 88.4 | 1 |
| Tarnów (G.Sw. Marcina) | - | - | - | 99.9 | 2.5 |
| Tarnów (Lichwin) | 91.1 | 88.6 | - | - | 10 |
| Torun | - | - | - | 89.7 | 1 |
| Walbrzych (G.Chelmiec) | - | 87.9 | 99.8 | 94.3 | 2x5/0.5 |
| Walcz (Rusinowo) | 101.9 | - | 90.9 | - | 30 |
| Warszawa | 92.4 | 104.9 | 99.1 | 92.0 | 0.3/2.5/0.1/0.2 |
| Warszawa (Raszyn) | 102.4 | - | 98.8 | - | 120 |
| Wisla (G.Skrzyczne) | 91.5 | - | 100.8 | - | 10 |
| Wloclawek (Szpetal Górny) | - | 93.9 | - | - | 1 |
| Wlodawa (Zolnierzy) | - | 102.5 | - | - | 10 |
| Wloszczowa (Dobromierz) | 88.9 | - | - | - | 3.2 |
| Wroclaw (G.Sleza) | 98.8 | - | 100.2 | - | 120 |
| Wroclaw (Zórawina) | - | 87.7 | - | 107.5 | 10/5 |
| Zagan (Wichów) | 91.2 | 104.7 | 87.8 | - | 30 |

**FM** (MHz)

| | 1 | 2 | 3 | 5 | kW |
|---|---|---|---|---|---|
| Zakopane (G.Gubalówka) | 92.8 | 90.9 | 98.2 | - | 10/0.3/10 |
| Zamosc (Feliksówka) | 105.7 | - | - | 95.3 | 10/1 |
| Zamosc (Tarnawatka) | - | 87.6 | 91.3 | - | 30 |
| Zielona Góra (Jemiolów) | 105.0 | 89.9 | 94.1 | - | 60 |
| Zielona Góra (Wilkanowo) | - | - | - | 104.0 | 2 |

+ sites with only txs below 1kW.

**D.Prgr: Prgr 1 (Jedynka):** 24h – **Prgr 2 (Dwójka):** 24h – **Prgr 3 (Trójka):** 24h. – **Prgr 4 (Czwórka):** 24h via DAB. – **Prgr 5 (PR24):** 24h. **International Service (R. Poland):** see Int. Radio section.

## PR Regional Stations

**D.Prgr:** All stations broadcast 24h. **PR R.Bialystok:** ul. Swierkowa 1, 15-328 Bialystok **E:** radiobia@radio.bialystok.pl. On (MHz) 87.9 (Lomza 0.2kW), 89.4 (Bialowieza 0.1kW), 98.6 (G.Krzemianucha 30kW), 99.4 (Krynice 30kW), 104.1 (Makarki 10kW), DAB 5C (Krynice 2kW). – **PR R.Dla Ciebe (RDC):** ul. Mysliwiecka 3/5/7, 00-977 Warszawa **E:** radio@rdc.pl. On (MHz) 87.6 (Ostrów Mazowiecka 1kW), 89.1 (Wacyn 5kW), 100.8 (Ostroleka 0.25kW), 101.0 (Warszawa 12.9kW), 101.9 (Rachocin 60kW), 103.4 (Losice 120kW), DAB 6B (Warszawa PKiN 6kW). – **PR R.Gdansk:** ul. Grunwaldzka 18, 80-006 Gdansk **E:** poczta@radio.gdansk.pl. On (MHz) 91.1 (Skórowo Nowe 10kW), 102.0 (Slupsk 1kW), 103.7 (Chwaszczyno 120kW), 106.0 (Kwidzyn 1kW), 107.0 (Bytów 10kW), DAB 5B (Chwaszczyno 10kW). – **PR R.Katowice:** ul. Ligonia 29, 40-953 Katowice **E:** sekretariat@radio.katowice.pl. On (MHz) 89.3 (Zabrze 0.5kW), 97.0 (Racibórz 1kW), 98.4 (Wreczyca 60kW), 101.2 (Bytków 1kW), 102.2 (Kosztowy 60kW), 103.0 (G.Skrzyczne 10kW), DAB 11A (Kosztowy 6kW). – **PR R.Kielce:** ul. Radiowa 4, 25-317 Kielce. **E:** radio@radio.kielce.com.pl. On (MHz) 90.4 (Kielce 0.25kW), 100.0 (Wloszczowa 1kW), 101.4 (Swiety Krzyz 120kW), DAB 11C (SFN). – **PR R.Koszalin:** ul. Pilsudskiego 43-49, 75-502 Koszalin. **E:** radio@radio. koszalin.pl. On (MHz) 88.1 (Rusinowo 3kW), 91.0 (Kolobrzeg 0.1kW), 92.5 (Slawoborze 15kW), 95.3 (Slupsk 2kW)*, 97.8 (G.Chelmska 0.1kW), 103.1 (Gologóra 60kW), DAB 11B (SFN). *) incl. prgrs from Slupsk studio. – **PR R.Kraków:** al. Slowackiego 22, 30-007 Kraków. **E:** radio@ radio-krakow.pl. On (MHz) 87.6 (G. Lubon Wielki 5kW), 90.0 (G.Prehyba 10kW), 97.4 (Gorlice 2kW), 98.8 (Andrychów 1kW), 100.0 (G.Gubalówka 10kW), 101.0 (G. Sw. Marcina 10kW), 101.6 (Choragwica 60kW), 102.1 (G.Jaworzyna 1kW), DAB 11B (Choragwica 10kW). – **PR R.Lódz:** ul. Narutowicza 130, 90-146 Lódz. **E:** studio@radiolodz.pl. On (MHz) 96.7 (Sieradz 0.5kW), 99.2 (Lódz 30kW), 104.0 (Wieruszów 1kW), DAB 5C (Lodz 10kW). – **PR R.Lublin:** ul. Obronców Pokoju 2, 20-030 Lublin. **E:** poczta@radio.lublin.pl. Prgr 1 (R. Lublin): on (MHz) 93.1 (Biala Podlaska 5kW), 102.2 (Piaski 90kW), 103.1 (Ryki 10kW), 103.2 (Feliksówka 30kW), DAB 11B (SFN). Prgr 2 (R. Freee): on 89.9MHz (Lublin 10kW). – **PR R.Poznan:** ul. Berwinskiego 5, 60-765 Poznan. **E:** office@radio-merkury. pl. Prgr 1 (R. Poznan): On (MHz) 91.1 (Mikstat 10kW), 91.9 (Zólwieniec 30kW), 100.9 (Srem 120kW), 102.4 (Bolewice 3kW), 103.6 (Rusinowo 60kW), DAB 12A (SFN). Prgr 2 (MC R.): on 102.7MHz (Piatkowo 2kW). – **PR R.Olsztyn:** ul. Radiowa 24, 10-206 Olsztyn. **E:** radio@ro.com.pl. On (MHz) 99.6 (Milki 10kW), 103.2 (Pieczewo 120kW), 103.4 (Jagodnik 0.5kW), DAB 11B (Pieczewo 5.5kW). – **PR R.Opole** ul. Strzelców Bytomskich 8, 45-084 Opole. **E:** pro_fm@radio.opole. pl. On (MHz) 88.0 (Brzeg 1kW), 89.1 (Olesno 1kW), 92.6 (Paczków 1kW), 94.8 (Glubczyce 1kW), 96.3 (Kluczbork 30kW), 101.2 (Opole 1kW), 103.2 (Chrzelice 1kW), 105.1 (Strzelce Opolskie 1kW), 107.7 (Namyslów 1kW), DAB 11C (SFN). – **PR R.PiK:** ul. Gdanska 48-50, 85-006 Bydgoszcz. **E:** radio@ radiopik.pl. On (MHz) 100.1 (Trzeciewiec 120kW), 100.3 (Wloclawek 1kW), 106.9 (Brodnica 10kW), DAB 11C (SFN). – **PR R.Rzeszów:** ul. Zamkowa 3, 35-032 Rzeszów. **E:** radiorz@radio.rzeszow.pl. On (MHz) 90.3 (Machów 1kW), 90.5 (Sucha Góra 120kW), 96.4 (Mielec 1kW), 99.2 (G.Jawor 5kW), 102.0 (Tatarska 20kW), 102.9 (Giedlarowa 30kW), 103.7 (Boble 10kW), 106.7 (Magdalenka 2kW), DAB 11A (SFN). – **PR R.Szczecin:** al. Wojska Polskiego 73, 70-481 Szczecin. **E:** sekretariat@ radio.szczecin.pl. Prgr 1 (R. Szczecin): on (MHz) 92.0 (Kolowo 60kW), 98.7 (Slawoborze 10kW), 106.3 (Chrobrego 10kW), DAB 11A (SFN). Prgr 2 (R. Szczecin Extra): on 94.4MHz (Warszewo 0.5kW) + DAB. – **PR R.Wroclaw:** ul. Karkonoska 8-10, 53-015 Wroclaw. **E:** sekretariatzarza-du@prw.pl. Prgr 1 (R. Wroclaw): on (MHz) 89.0 (G.Wysoka 1kW), 95.5 (G.Chelmiec 5kW), 96.0 (Czarna Góra 10kW), 96.7 (Sniezne Kotly 10kW), 98.0 (G.Parkowa 0.1kW), 102.3 (G.Sleza 10kW), 103.6 (Nowa Karczma 60kW), DAB 5B (Zórawina 5kW). Prgr 2 (R. RAM): on 89.8MHz (Zórawina 6kW). Prgr 3 (RW Kultura): on DAB. – **PR R.Zachód:** ul. Kukulcza 1, 65-472 Zielona Góra. **E:** radio@zachod.pl. Prgr 1 (R. Zachód): on (MHz) 103.0 (Jemiolów 120kW), 106.0 (Wichów 30kW), DAB 11C (SFN). Prgr 2 (R. Zielona Góra): on 97.1MHz (Zielona Góra 1kW) + DAB.

## OTHER STATIONS

| MW | kHz | kW | Location | Station |
|---|---|---|---|---|
| 70A) | 963 | 0.1 | Lipsko | Twoje R. Lipsko/R. AM |
| 70B) | 1062 | 0.8 | Cmolas | Twoje R. Cmolas/R. AM |

| MW | kHz | kW | Location | Station |
|---|---|---|---|---|
| 70C) | 1584 | 0.8 | Andrychów | R. Andrychów/R. AM |
| 70) | 1602 | 0.8 | Kraków | R. AM |

| FM | MHz | kW | Location | Station |
|---|---|---|---|---|
| 27) | 87.7 | 1.2 | Bialystok | R. Akadera |
| 3) | 87.7 | 3 | Miedzyzdroje | R. Maryja |
| 1B) | 87.8 | 1 | Kraków | R. RMF Classic |
| 3) | 87.8 | 1 | Biala Podlaska | R. Maryja |
| 4) | 87.9 | 25 | Lublin | R. Plus |
| 3) | 87.9 | 10 | Lódz | R. Maryja |
| 2A) | 88.0 | 3 | Golancz | R. ZET |
| 1C) | 88.1 | 1 | Zabrze | R. RMF MAXXX |
| 36) | 88.1 | 1 | Wielun | R. Fiat |
| 1A) | 88.2 | 120 | Kielce | R. RMF FM |
| 3) | 88.2 | 1 | Polkowice | R. RMF FM |
| 3) | 88.2 | 1 | Ostrów Wlkp. | R. Maryja |
| 6A) | 88.2 | 1 | Torun | R. TOK FM |
| 2A) | 88.3 | 60 | Zielona Góra | R. ZET |
| 3) | 88.3 | 1 | Kutno | R. Maryja |
| 3) | 88.4 | 10 | Bielsko-Biala | R. Maryja |
| 6B) | 88.4 | 5 | Poznan | R. Zlote Przeboje |
| 3) | 88.5 | 10 | Slupsk | R. Maryja |
| 3) | 88.5 | 1 | Bydgoszcz | E. Maryja |
| 61) | 88.6 | 1 | Skierniewice | R. RSC |
| 3) | 88.7 | 1 | Koszalin | R. ZET |
| 3) | 88.7 | 1.6 | Golancz | R. Maryja |
| 3) | 88.7 | 1.6 | Wagrowiec | R. Maryja |
| 7) | 88.8 | 1 | Krakow | R. WAWA |
| 3) | 88.9 | 2 | Gdansk | R. Maryja |
| 3) | 88.9 | 120 | Wroclaw | R. Maryja |
| 4) | 88.9 | 15 | Szczecin | R. Plus |
| 3) | 89.0 | 1 | Warszawa | R. Maryja |
| 39) | 89.2 | 5 | Bialystok | R. Jard |
| 6A) | 89.2 | 1 | Elblag | R. TOK FM |
| 1A) | 89.3 | 60 | Koszalin | R. RMF FM |
| 1A) | 89.3 | 30 | Lublin | R. RMF FM |
| 2A) | 89.4 | 10 | Luban | R. ZET |
| 3) | 89.4 | 2 | Stargard | R. Maryja |
| 3) | 89.5 | 10 | Gniezno | R. Plus |
| 5A) | 89.5 | 1 | Sanok | R. Eska |
| 3) | 89.5 | 1 | Wegrów | R. Maryja |
| 2D) | 89.6 | 1 | Lodz | Antyradio |
| 33) | 89.6 | 1 | Opole | R. DOXA |
| 3) | 89.8 | 1 | Mielec | R. Maryja |
| 30) | 89.8 | 1 | Poznan | R. Emaus |
| 6B) | 89.8 | 1 | Szczecin | R. Zlote Przeboje |
| 19) | 90.0 | 2 | Rybnik | R. 90 |
| 6B) | 90.0 | 4 | Legnica | R. Zlote Przeboje |
| 13) | 90.1 | 10 | Zamosc | Katolickie R. Zamosc |
| 5A) | 90.1 | 2 | Lodz | R. Eska |
| 9) | 90.1 | 1 | Koscierzyna | R. Kaszëbe |
| 3) | 90.2 | 10 | Kamiensk | R. Maryja |
| 43) | 90.2 | 1 | Kolobrzeg | R. Kolobrzeg |
| 63) | 90.2 | 1 | Bielsko-Biala | R. Aniol Beskidów |
| 3) | 90.3 | 1 | Zielona Góra | R. Maryja |
| 66) | 90.3 | 2 | Stargard | Twoje R. |
| 6B) | 90.4 | 1 | Wroclaw | R. Zlote Przeboje |
| 3) | 90.6 | 5 | Kraków | R. Maryja |
| 32) | 90.6 | 1 | Slupsk | R. FAMA |
| 4) | 90.7 | 2 | Gryfice | R. Plus |
| 4) | 90.7 | 5 | Radom | R. Plus |
| 5A) | 90.7 | 2 | Gdynia | R. Eska |
| 16) | 90.8 | 1 | Mlawa | R. 7 |
| 1C) | 90.8 | 1 | Inowroclaw | R. RMF MAXXX |
| 14) | 90.9 | 1 | Jelenia Góra | Muzyczne R. |
| 14) | 90.9 | 5 | Walbrzych | Muzyczne R. |
| 1A) | 91.0 | 120 | Warszawa | R. RMF FM |
| 6B) | 91.2 | 2 | Katowice | R. Zlote Przeboje |
| 1A) | 91.3 | 10 | Lobez | R. RMF FM |
| 38) | 91.4 | 1 | Pelplin | R. Glos |
| 1A) | 91.5 | 15 | Ostroleka | R. RMF FM |
| 4) | 91.6 | 10 | Ryki | R. ZET |
| 4) | 91.7 | 1 | Zielona Góra | R. Plus |
| 3) | 91.7 | 2 | Golancz | R. RMF FM |
| 2A) | 91.8 | 10 | Swinoujscie | R. ZET |
| 3) | 91.8 | 1 | Ciechanów | R. Maryja |
| 1A) | 91.9 | 30 | Siedlce | R. RMF FM |
| 2D) | 92.0 | 1 | Gdansk | Antyradio |
| 59) | 92.0 | 2.5 | Wroclaw | R. Rodzina |
| 2A) | 92.1 | 1 | Wlodawa | R. ZET |
| 6B) | 92.1 | 1 | Bydgoszcz | R. Zlote Przeboje |
| 15) | 92.1 | 4 | Zdunska Wola | Nasze R. |
| 4) | 92.2 | 10 | Opole | R. ZET |
| 55) | 92.3 | 1 | Laziska Gorna | R. Express FM |

| FM | MHz | kW | Location | Station |
|---|---|---|---|---|
| 9) | 92.3 | 2 | Gdansk | R. Kaszëbë |
| 7) | 92.4 | 1 | Nowy Sacz | R. WAWA |
| 6B) | 92.5 | 1 | Kraków | R. Zlote Przeboje |
| 2A) | 92.6 | 120 | Lodz | R. ZET |
| 42) | 92.6 | 1 | Sepólno Kraj. | R. Weekend |
| 7) | 92.6 | 1 | Krosno | R. WAWA |
| 3) | 92.7 | 10 | Lebork | R. Maryja |
| 2C) | 92.8 | 1 | Torun | Meloradio |
| 6B) | 92.8 | 1 | Opole | R. Zlote Przeboje |
| 6B) | 92.8 | 2 | Tarnów | R. Zlote Przeboje |
| 1A) | 92.9 | 10 | Wroclaw | R. RMF FM |
| 2A) | 92.9 | 10 | Gryfice | R. ZET |
| 32) | 92.9 | 1 | Tomaszów Maz. | R. FAMA |
| 1A) | 93.0 | 60 | Katowice | R. RMF FM |
| 5A) | 93.0 | 10 | Poznan | R. Eska |
| 3) | 93.1 | 1 | Krynica | R. Maryja |
| 6B) | 93.2 | 5 | Jedrzejów | R. Zlote Przeboje |
| 7) | 93.2 | 2 | Szczecin | R. WAWA |
| 1A) | 93.3 | 120 | Bydgoszcz | R. RMF FM |
| 5C) | 93.3 | 1 | Warszawa | R. Eska Rock |
| 25) | 93.4 | 2 | Gliwice | R. CCM |
| 1A) | 93.5 | 10 | Lódz | R. RMF FM |
| 2A) | 93.6 | 120 | Wroclaw | R. ZET |
| 2B) | 93.7 | 1 | Kraków | R. Chillizet |
| 1A) | 93.8 | 60 | Luban | R. RMF FM |
| 52) | 93.8 | 1 | Kutno | R. Victoria |
| 5A) | 93.8 | 10 | Gorzów Wlkp. | R. Eska |
| 65) | 93.8 | 1 | Czestochowa | R. Jura |
| 54) | 93.9 | 1 | Kedzierzyn-Kozle | R. Park FM |
| 4) | 94.0 | 1 | Konskie | R. Plus |
| 6B) | 94.0 | 1 | Tokarnia | R. Zlote Przeboje |
| 12) | 94.1 | 1 | Jaslo | VIA - Kat. R. Rzeszów |
| 5A) | 94.1 | 1 | Elblag | R. Eska |
| 38) | 94.2 | 1 | Kartuzy | R. Glos |
| 1A) | 94.3 | 60 | Plock | R. RMF FM |
| 3) | 94.3 | 1 | Racibórz | R. Maryja |
| 3) | 94.4 | 1 | Tarnobrzeg | R. Maryja |
| 5A) | 94.4 | 5 | Bydgoszcz | R. Eska |
| 6B) | 94.4 | 1 | Zary | R. Zlote Przeboje |
| 23) | 94.5 | 1 | Grodzisk Maz. | R. Bogoria |
| 3) | 94.5 | 1 | Ustrzyki Dolne | R. Maryja |
| 1A) | 94.6 | 120 | Poznan | R. RMF FM |
| 5A) | 94.6 | 1 | Gdansk | R. Eska |
| 36) | 94.7 | 10 | Czestochowa | R. Fiat |
| 52) | 94.7 | 1 | Rawa Maz. | R. Victoria |
| 1A) | 94.8 | 30 | Zagan | R. RMF FM |
| 59) | 94.8 | 2 | Strzelin | R. Rodzina |
| 25) | 94.9 | 1 | Oswiecim | R. CCM |
| 31) | 94.9 | 1 | Sochaczew | R. Sochaczew |
| 4) | 94.9 | 1 | Jelenia Góra | R. Plus |
| 6A) | 94.9 | 1 | Kielce | R. TOK FM |
| 2A) | 95.0 | 20 | Lezajsk | R. ZET |
| 3) | 95.0 | 3 | Szczecinek | R. Maryja |
| 1A) | 95.1 | 1.6 | Suwalki | R. RMF FM |
| 2C) | 95.1 | 1 | Zabrze | Meloradio |
| 2A) | 95.2 | 60 | Szczecin | R. ZET |
| 3) | 95.2 | 1 | Swieradów-Zdrój | R. Maryja |
| 3) | 95.2 | 1 | Sieradz | R. Maryja |
| 6A) | 95.2 | 1 | Gdynia | R. TOK FM |
| 1A) | 95.3 | 60 | Olsztyn | R. RMF FM |
| 1A) | 95.3 | 60 | Opole | R. RMF FM |
| 1A) | 95.4 | 10 | Tarnów | R. RMF FM |
| 3) | 95.4 | 5 | Skierniewice | R. Maryja |
| 3) | 95.4 | 1 | Gniezno | R. Maryja |
| 39) | 95.5 | 4 | Bielsk Podl. | R. Jard |
| 2A) | 95.6 | 120 | Bydgoszcz | R. ZET |
| 6B) | 95.6 | 1 | Lublin | R. Zlote Przeboje |
| 2A) | 95.7 | 10 | Wisla | R. ZET |
| 5B) | 95.7 | 1 | Szczecin | R. VOX FM |
| 6B) | 95.7 | 1 | Rzeszów | R. Zlote Przeboje |
| 1C) | 95.8 | 1 | Warszawa | R. RMF MAXXX |
| 3) | 95.8 | 1 | Hrubieszów | R. Maryja |
| 48) | 95.8 | 1 | Krapkowice | R. Vanessa |
| 1C) | 95.8 | 2 | Konin | R. RMF MAXXX |
| 57) | 95.9 | 1 | Olsztyn | R. UWM FM |
| 5A) | 95.9 | 1 | Koszalin | R. Eska |
| 1A) | 96.0 | 60 | Kraków | R. RMF FM |
| 1C) | 96.0 | 1 | Olesnica | R. RMF MAXXX |
| 53) | 96.0 | 6 | Lódz | R. Parada |
| 1A) | 96.1 | 1 | Gorzów Wlkp. | R. RMF FM |
| 1A) | 96.1 | 1 | Legnica | R. RMF FM |
| 10) | 96.2 | 2 | Zabrze | R. Silesia |
| 1A) | 96.4 | 15 | Bialogard | R. RMF FM |
| 1C) | 96.4 | 1 | Gdansk | R. RMF MAXXX |
| 3) | 96.5 | 10 | Zamosc | R. Maryja |
| 4) | 96.5 | 10 | Warszawa | R. Plus |
| 1A) | 96.6 | 30 | Walcz | R. RMF FM |
| 2A) | 96.6 | 10 | Lebork | R. ZET |
| 6B) | 96.6 | 1 | Zabrze | R. Zlote Przeboje |
| 6B) | 96.6 | 1 | Czestochowa | R. Zlote Przeboje |
| 1C) | 96.7 | 2 | Kraków | R. RMF MAXXX |
| 52) | 96.7 | 1 | Skierniewice | R. Victoria |
| 7) | 96.7 | 3 | Torun | R. WAWA |
| 3) | 96.9 | 7.5 | Ilawa | R. Maryja |
| 5A) | 96.9 | 1 | Szczecin | R. Eska |
| 2A) | 97.0 | 30 | Poznan | R. ZET |
| 3) | 97.0 | 1 | Lublin | R. Maryja |
| 3) | 97.0 | 2 | Ciechanowiec | R. Maryja |
| 1A) | 97.1 | 12 | Wloszczowa | R. RMF FM |
| 54) | 97.1 | 1 | Brzeg | R. Park FM |
| 24) | 97.2 | 1 | Pulawy | R. Pulawy 24 |
| 2A) | 97.2 | 1 | Walbrzych | R. ZET |
| 67) | 97.2 | 1 | Wagrowiec | Wasze R. FM |
| 2A) | 97.3 | 60 | Plock | R. ZET |
| 5A) | 97.3 | 1 | Zamosc | R. Eska |
| 6A) | 97.4 | 1 | Katowice | R. TOK FM |
| 1C) | 97.5 | 1 | Lomza | R. RMF MAXXX |
| 2A) | 97.5 | 30 | Zagan | R. ZET |
| 5A) | 97.7 | 1 | Kraków | R. Eska |
| 2A) | 97.8 | 2.5 | Szczawnica | R. ZET |
| 2A) | 97.9 | 60 | Walcz | R. ZET |
| 1A) | 98.0 | 10 | Kalisz | R. RMF FM |
| 22) | 98.1 | 120 | Bialystok | R. Racja |
| 2C) | 98.1 | 1 | Inowroclaw | Meloradio |
| 52) | 98.1 | 1 | Mszczonów | R. Victoria |
| 5A) | 98.1 | 2 | Tarnów | R. Eska |
| 34) | 98.2 | 1 | Przemysl | R. Fara |
| 28) | 98.3 | 1 | Polkowice | R. Elka |
| 1A) | 98.4 | 120 | Gdansk | R. RMF FM |
| 6A) | 98.5 | 1 | Bydgoszcz | R. TOK FM |
| 28) | 98.5 | 1 | Leszno | R. Elka |
| 2A) | 98.6 | 1 | Nysa | R. ZET |
| 51) | 98.6 | 2 | Lodz | R. Niepokalanów |
| 2A) | 98.7 | 10 | Ilawa | R. ZET |
| 3) | 98.8 | 10 | Gorzów Wlkp. | R. Maryja |
| 1A) | 98.9 | 30 | Konin | R. RMF FM |
| 9) | 98.9 | 2 | Reda | R. Kaszëbë |
| 1B) | 99.0 | 1 | Kielce | R. RMF Classic |
| 5A) | 99.0 | 1 | Szczecinek | R. Eska |
| 22) | 99.2 | 10 | Biala Podlaska | R. Racja |
| 42) | 99.3 | 2 | Chojnice | R. Weekend |
| 2C) | 99.4 | 2.5 | Poznan | Meloradio |
| 68) | 99.4 | 1 | Wloclawek | R. Kujawy |
| 1A) | 99.5 | 1 | Kluczbork | R. RMF FM |
| 3) | 99.5 | 1 | Lipiany | R. Maryja |
| 4) | 99.5 | 1 | Slupsk | R. Plus |
| 6B) | 99.5 | 1 | Zmudz | R. Zlote Przeboje |
| 2C) | 99.6 | 1 | Konin | Meloradio |
| 1C) | 99.7 | 1 | Koszalin | R. RMF MAXXX |
| 3) | 100.0 | 5 | Zielona Góra | R. Maryja |
| 1A) | 100.1 | 120 | Krosno | R. RMF FM |
| 6B) | 100.1 | 4 | Warszawa | R. Zlote Przeboje |
| 1A) | 100.2 | 120 | Bialystok | R. RMF FM |
| 3) | 100.2 | 1 | Gizycko | R. Maryja |
| 64) | 100.2 | 5 | Zabrze | R. Fest |
| 3) | 100.3 | 1 | Bogatynia | R. Maryja |
| 48) | 100.3 | 3 | Racibórz | R. Vanessa |
| 3) | 100.4 | 5.5 | Ostrów Maz. | R. Maryja |
| 3) | 100.4 | 1 | Nysa | R. Maryja |
| 4) | 100.4 | 5 | Lódz | R. Plus |
| 3) | 100.6 | 10 | Torun | R. Maryja |
| 3) | 100.6 | 10 | Krosno | R. Maryja |
| 3) | 100.6 | 10 | Glogów | R. Maryja |
| 3) | 100.6 | 5 | Parczew | R. Maryja |
| 40) | 100.6 | 60 | Czestochowa | R. Jasna Góra |
| 2A) | 100.7 | 2 | Zamosc | R. ZET |
| 3) | 100.7 | 5 | Rabka | R. Maryja |
| 4) | 100.7 | 10 | Gorzów Wlkp. | R. Plus |
| 1A) | 100.8 | 10 | Jelenia Góra | R. RMF FM |
| 32) | 100.8 | 5 | Kielce | R. FAMA |
| 1A) | 100.9 | 10 | Slupsk | R. RMF FM |
| 3) | 100.9 | 1 | Wloclawek | R. Maryja |
| 2D) | 101.0 | 1 | Kraków | Antyradio |
| 1A) | 101.1 | 30 | Solina | R. RMF FM |
| 1C) | 101.1 | 5 | Walbrzych | R. RMF MAXXX |
| 3) | 101.1 | 10 | Zlotów | R. Maryja |
| 5A) | 101.1 | 2 | Kalisz | R. Eska |
| 1A) | 101.2 | 5 | Swinoujscie | R. RMF FM |
| 1C) | 101.2 | 1 | Bytów | R. RMF MAXXX |
| 69) | 101.2 | 1 | Lubaczów | Katolickie R. Zamosc |

| FM | MHz | kW | Location | Station |
|---|---|---|---|---|
| 3) | 101.2 | 10 | Zagan | R. Maryja |
| 58) | 101.2 | 2.5 | Szczawnica | R. RDN |
| 6A) | 101.2 | 1 | Plock | R. TOK FM |
| 2C) | 101.3 | 1 | Kraków | Meloradio |
| 3) | 101.3 | 1 | Lomza | R. Maryja |
| 6B) | 101.3 | 10 | Pabianice | R. Zlote Przeboje |
| 2A) | 101.4 | 30 | Suwalki | R. ZET |
| 3) | 101.4 | 10 | Czersk | R. Maryja |
| 5B) | 101.5 | 1 | Wroclaw | R. VOX FM |
| 1A) | 101.6 | 10 | Klodzko | R. RMF FM |
| 2D) | 101.6 | 1 | Poznan | Antyradio |
| 3) | 101.6 | 10 | Pisz | R. Maryja |
| 3) | 101.6 | 1 | Szczecin | R. Maryja |
| 4) | 101.7 | 120 | Gdansk | R. Plus |
| 46) | 101.7 | 35 | Siedlce | Katolickie R. Podlasie |
| 62) | 101.7 | 1 | Kepno | R. Sud |
| 28) | 101.7 | 1 | Jarocin | R. Elka |
| 1A) | 101.8 | 60 | Lezajsk | R. RMF FM |
| 1A) | 101.8 | 10 | Zakopane | R. RMF FM |
| 28) | 101.8 | 1 | Jarocin | R. Elka |
| 1A) | 102.0 | 10 | Gizycko | R. RMF FM |
| 3) | 102.0 | 10 | Bielsk Podl. | R. Maryja |
| 5A) | 102.0 | 1 | Leszno | R. Eska |
| 3) | 102.3 | 10 | Lubaczów | R. Maryja |
| 3) | 102.4 | 1 | Kartuzy | R. Maryja |
| 6D) | 102.4 | 1 | Kraków | R. Pogoda |
| 8) | 102.4 | 1 | Mielec | R. Leliwa |
| 18) | 102.6 | 1 | Elk | R. 5 Elk |
| 1C) | 102.6 | 1 | Czestochowa | R. RMF MAXXX |
| 3) | 102.6 | 10 | Tarnów | R. Maryja |
| 4) | 102.6 | 1 | Bydgoszcz | R. Plus |
| 4) | 102.6 | 1 | Koszalin | R. Plus |
| 4) | 102.6 | 20 | Polkowice | R. Plus |
| 37) | 102.7 | 1 | Bialystok | R. Ortodoxia |
| 4) | 102.7 | 5 | Rabka | R. Plus |
| 51) | 102.7 | 1 | Skierniewice | R. Niepokalanów |
| 2A) | 102.8 | 10 | Ostroleka | R. ZET |
| 2A) | 102.8 | 5 | Katowice | R. ZET |
| 3) | 102.8 | 1 | Chelm | R. Maryja |
| 3) | 102.8 | 10 | Kluczbork | R. Maryja |
| 4) | 102.8 | 1 | Swieradów-Zdrój | R. Plus |
| 1A) | 102.9 | 8 | Walbrzych | R. RMF FM |
| 1C) | 102.9 | 1 | Lebork | R. RMF MAXXX |
| 2A) | 102.9 | 12 | Przysucha | R. ZET |
| 2C) | 102.9 | 1 | Slupca | Meloradio |
| 3) | 102.9 | 10 | Gryfice | R. Maryja |
| 6A) | 102.9 | 1 | Kraków | R. TOK FM |
| 44) | 103.0 | 3 | Warszawa | R. Kolor 103 FM |
| 6B) | 103.0 | 2 | Gdansk | R. Zlote Przeboje |
| 2A) | 103.1 | 13 | Solina | R. ZET |
| 60) | 103.1 | 1 | Kalisz | R. Rodzina Kalisz |
| 1A) | 103.2 | 10 | Szczawnica | R. RMF FM |
| 41) | 103.3 | 1 | Bialystok | R. i |
| 5A) | 103.3 | 1 | Kielce | R. Eska |
| 1A) | 103.4 | 7 | Lebork | R. RMF FM |
| 1A) | 103.4 | 10 | Przemysl | R. RMF FM |
| 2A) | 103.4 | 60 | Czestochowa | R. ZET |
| 3) | 103.5 | 3 | Trzcinsko-Zdrój | R. Maryja |
| 52) | 103.5 | 5 | Lowicz | R. Victoria |
| 6D) | 103.5 | 1 | Bydgoszcz | R. Pogoda |
| 21) | 103.6 | 2 | Nysa | R. Nysa FM |
| 50) | 103.6 | 10 | Lomza | R. Nadzieja |
| 58) | 103.6 | 30 | Tarnów | R. RDN |
| 3) | 103.7 | 3 | Katowice | R. Maryja |
| 56) | 103.7 | 1 | Wroclaw | R. MUZO.FM |
| 6C) | 103.7 | 1 | Warszawa | Rock Radio |
| 12) | 103.8 | 10 | Rzeszów | VIA - Kat. R. Rzeszów |
| 2A) | 103.8 | 10 | Klodzko | R. ZET |
| 6C) | 103.8 | 1 | Kraków | Rock R. |
| 45) | 103.9 | 1.5 | Ciechanów | Kat. R. Diecezji Plockiej |
| 2C) | 103.9 | 2 | Kielce | Meloradio |
| 2A) | 104.0 | 10 | Gizycko | R. ZET |
| 3) | 104.0 | 10 | Swiecie | R. Maryja |
| 1C) | 104.1 | 5 | Pila | R. RMF MAXXX |
| 2A) | 104.1 | 60 | Kraków | R. ZET |
| 32) | 104.1 | 1 | Zyrardów | R. FAMA |
| 2A) | 104.2 | 10 | Bialogard | R. ZET |
| 2A) | 104.2 | 10 | Jelenia Góra | R. ZET |
| 3) | 104.2 | 10 | Elblag | R. Maryja |
| 4) | 104.3 | 1 | Myslibórz | R. Plus |
| 45) | 104.3 | 1 | Plock | Kat. R. Diecezji Plockiej |
| 2A) | 104.4 | 10 | Kalisz | R. ZET |
| 3) | 104.4 | 1 | Stalowa Wola | R. Maryja |
| 5A) | 104.4 | 1 | Gdansk | R. VOX FM |
| 2C) | 104.5 | 1 | Lodz | Meloradio |

| FM | MHz | kW | Location | Station |
|---|---|---|---|---|
| 3) | 104.5 | 10 | Wlodawa | R. Maryja |
| 3) | 104.5 | 5 | Wielen | R. Maryja |
| 34) | 104.5 | 1 | Krosno | R. Fara |
| 3) | 104.6 | 2 | Opole | R. Maryja |
| 5A) | 104.6 | 1 | Torun | R. Eska |
| 15) | 104.7 | 2 | Sieradz | Nasze R. |
| 1A) | 104.7 | 3 | Rabka | R. RMF FM |
| 3) | 104.7 | 120 | Bialystok | R. Maryja |
| 3) | 104.7 | 10 | Lobez | R. Maryja |
| 11) | 104.9 | 1 | Chelm | Bon Ton R. |
| 1A) | 104.9 | 1 | Koszalin | R. RMF FM |
| 2C) | 104.9 | 1.5 | Mragowo | Meloradio |
| 56) | 104.9 | 1 | Kraków | R. MUZO.FM |
| 5A) | 104.9 | 10 | Krosno | R. Eska |
| 5A) | 104.9 | 60 | Wroclaw | R. Eska |
| 2A) | 105.0 | 120 | Gdansk | R. ZET |
| 2D) | 105.0 | 1 | Bielsko-Biala | Antyradio |
| 3) | 105.1 | 1 | Przemysl | R. Maryja |
| 3) | 105.1 | 30 | Konin | R. Maryja |
| 3) | 105.1 | 10 | Elk | R. Maryja |
| 20) | 105.2 | 1 | Zakopane | R. Alex |
| 3) | 105.2 | 5 | Wielun | R. Maryja |
| 2A) | 105.3 | 60 | Kielce | R. ZET |
| 2A) | 105.3 | 30 | Koszalin | R. ZET |
| 3) | 105.3 | 1 | Plonsk | R. Maryja |
| 2A) | 105.4 | 30 | Siedlce | R. ZET |
| 6C) | 105.4 | 1 | Poznan | Rock R. |
| 6A) | 105.4 | 2 | Zdunska Wola | R. TOK FM |
| 7) | 105.5 | 1.3 | Wroclaw | R. WAWA |
| 3) | 105.6 | 1 | Kalisz | R. Maryja |
| 5A) | 105.6 | 1 | Pila | R. Eska |
| 5A) | 105.6 | 5 | Warszawa | R. Eska |
| 5B) | 105.6 | 1 | Gdynia | R. VOX FM |
| 6B) | 105.6 | 1 | Miedzyzdroje | R. Zlote Przeboje |
| 2A) | 105.7 | 20 | Olsztyn | R. ZET |
| 7) | 105.7 | 1 | Opole | R. WAWA |
| 67) | 105.8 | 2 | Golancz | Wasze R. FM |
| 14) | 105.8 | 10 | Jelenia Góra | Muzyczne R. |
| 1A) | 105.9 | 1 | Krynica | R. RMF FM |
| 1A) | 105.9 | 60 | Czestochowa | R. RMF FM |
| 46) | 106.0 | 1 | Garwolin | Katolickie R. Podlasie |
| 1C) | 106.1 | 5 | Bydgoszcz | R. RMF MAXXX |
| 4) | 106.1 | 10 | Kraków | R. Plus |
| 9) | 106.1 | 1 | Hel | R. Kaszëbë |
| 6D) | 106.1 | 10 | Wroclaw | R. Pogoda |
| 2C) | 106.2 | 1 | Opole | Meloradio |
| 3) | 106.2 | 10 | Lidzbark Warm. | R. Maryja |
| 30) | 106.2 | 1.5 | Poznan | R. Emaus |
| 35) | 106.2 | 1 | Warszawa | R. Warszawa |
| 6B) | 106.2 | 1 | Jelenia Góra | R. Zlote Przeboje |
| 17) | 106.2 | 1 | Radom | R. Rekord FM |
| 2A) | 106.3 | 8 | Zakopane | R. ZET |
| 3) | 106.3 | 60 | Plock | R. Maryja |
| 3) | 106.3 | 5 | Klodzko | R. Maryja |
| 3) | 106.3 | 20 | Lezajsk | R. Maryja |
| 1A) | 106.4 | 60 | Zielona Góra | R. RMF FM |
| 26) | 106.4 | 1 | Radom | R. Centrum |
| 2D) | 106.4 | 1 | Zabrze | Antyradio |
| 1A) | 106.5 | 10 | Elk | R. RMF FM |
| 1C) | 106.5 | 20 | Kielce | R. RMF MAXXX |
| 5A) | 106.5 | 1 | Lobez | R. Eska |
| 5A) | 106.6 | 5 | Zary | R. Eska |
| 6C) | 106.6 | 4 | Opole | Rock R. |
| 14) | 106.7 | 5 | Swieradów-Zd. | Muzyczne R. |
| 1A) | 106.7 | 60 | Szczecin | R. RMF FM |
| 1C) | 106.7 | 3 | Gdynia | R. RMF MAXXX |
| 47) | 106.7 | 1 | Bielsko-Biala | R. Bielsko |
| 3) | 106.8 | 110 | Poznan | R. Maryja |
| 5A) | 106.8 | 1 | Bochnia | R. Eska |
| 5A) | 106.9 | 10 | Radom | R. Eska |
| 2D) | 106.9 | 2 | Wroclaw | Antyradio |
| 2A) | 107.0 | 40 | Lublin | R. ZET |
| 2C) | 107.0 | 2 | Gizycko | Meloradio |
| 3) | 107.0 | 10 | Czestochowa | R. Maryja |
| 5B) | 107.0 | 1.6 | Kraków | R. VOX FM |
| 1B) | 107.1 | 1 | Gdynia | R. RMF Classic |
| 2A) | 107.1 | 30 | Konin | R. ZET |
| 3) | 107.2 | 120 | Kielce | R. Maryja |
| 59) | 107.2 | 2 | Bystrzyca Klodzka | R. Rodzina |
| 2A) | 107.3 | 75 | Bialystok | R. ZET |
| 1A) | 107.4 | 10 | Ilawa | R. RMF FM |
| 2A) | 107.4 | 30 | Krosno | R. ZET |
| 3) | 107.4 | 2.5 | Walbrzych | R. Maryja |
| 3) | 107.4 | 1 | Koszalin | R. Maryja |
| 2A) | 107.4 | 1 | Kluczbork | R. ZET |

| FM | MHz | kW | Location | Station |
|---|---|---|---|---|
| 5B) | 107.4 | 1 | Poznan | R. VOX FM |
| 2A) | 107.5 | 30 | Warszawa | R. ZET |
| 49) | 107.5 | 1 | Naklo | R. Naklo |
| 29) | 107.6 | 60 | Katowice | R. eM |
| 1A) | 107.7 | 15 | Zamosc | R. RMF FM |
| 3) | 107.7 | 10 | Siedlce | R. Maryja |
| 3) | 107.7 | 20 | Olsztyn | R. Maryja |
| 2A) | 107.8 | 10 | Tarnów | R. ZET |
| 29) | 107.9 | 1 | Kielce | R. eM |
| 2A) | 107.9 | 10 | Przemysl | R. ZET |
| 3) | 107.9 | 20 | Suwalki | R. Maryja |
| 3) | 107.9 | 10 | Ryki | R. Maryja |
| 33) | 107.9 | 10 | Opole | R. DOXA |

+ txs below 1kW.

**Addresses & other information:**
**1A-C)** al. Waszyngtona 1, 30-204 Kraków – **2A-D)** ul. Zurawia 8, 00-503 Warszawa – **3)** ul. Zwirki i Wigury 80, 87-100 Torun – **4)** ul. Zarawia 8, 00-503 Warszawa – **5A-C)** ul. Senatorska 13/15, 00-075 Warszawa – **6A-D)** ul. Czerska 14, 00-732 Warszawa – **7)** ul. Senatorska 12, 00-082 Warszawa – **8)** ul. Wyspianskiego 5 39-400 Tarnobrzeg – **9)** ul. Dabrowskiego 14D, 84-230 Rumia – **10)** Park Hutniczy 3-5, 41-800 Zabrze – **11)** ul. Wojslawicka 7, 22-100 Chelm – **12)** ul. Zamkowa 4, 35-032 Rzeszów – **13)** ul. Hetmana J. Zamoyskiego 1, 22-400 Zamosc – **14)** pl. Ks. K. Wyszynskiego 45, 58-500 Jelenia Góra – **15)** ul. Rynek 14, 98-200 Sieradz – **16)** pl. Pilsudskiego 27, 09-300 Zuromin – **17)** ul. Okulickiego 39, 26-600 Radom – **18)** ul. Bulwarowa 5, 16-400 Suwalki – **19)** Os. Dabrówki 1b, 44-286 Wodzislaw Sl. – **20)** ul. Smrekowa 26A, 34-500 Zakopane – **21)** ul. Podolska 22, 48-300 Nysa – **22)** ul. Ciepla 1/7, 15-472 Bialystok – **23)** ul. Kilinskiego 14, 05-825 Grodzisk Mazowiecki – **24)** Generala Stefana Grota-Roweckiego 4, 24-100 Pulawy – **25)** ul. Jana Pawla II 2, 44-100 Gliwice – **26)** ul. Lazienna 6, 62-800 Kalisz – **27)** ul. Zwierzyniecka 4, 15-333 Bialystok – **28)** ul. Spóldzielcza 6, 64-100 Leszno – **29)** ul. Jordana 39, 40-953 Katowice. – **30)** ul. Zielona 2, 61-851 Poznan – **31)** ul. Narutowicza 1/1, 96-500 Sochaczew – **32)** ul. Piotrkowska 12/522, 25-510 Kielce – **33)** ul. Koraszewskiego 7-9, 45-011 Opole – **34)** pl. Katedralny 4, 37-700 Przemysl – **35)** ul. Floriranska 3, 03-707 Warszawa – **36)** al. Najswietszej Marii Panny 54, 42-200 Czestochowa – **37)** ul. Antoniuk Fabryczny 13, 15-762 Bialystok – **38)** ul. Biskupa Dominika 11, 83-130 Pelplin – **39)** ul. Rzemieslnicza 4a, 15-703 Bialystok – **40)** ul. O. Augustyna Kordeckiego 2, 42-225 Czestochowa – **41)** Ks. A.Abramowicza 1a, 15-872 Bialystok – **42)** ul. Jana Pawla II 1B, 89-804 Chojnice – **43)** ul. Janusza Korczaka 2, 78-100 Kolobrzeg – **44)** ul. Narbutta 41/43, 02-536 Warszawa – **45)** ul. Ks.Piotra Sciegiennego 18, 06-400 Ciechanów – **46)** ul. Pilsudskiego 62, 08-110 Siedlce – **47)** ul. Olszówka 62, 43-309 Bielsko-Biala – **48)** ul. Batorego 5, 47-400 Racibórz – **49)** ul. Mickiewicza 3, 89-100 Naklo nad Notecia – **50)** ul. Sadowa 3, 18-400 Lomza – **51)** ul. Zakroczymska 1, 00-225 Warszawa – **52)** ul. Seminaryjna 6A, 99-400 Lowicz – **53)** ul. Pilsudskiego 141, 92-318 Lódz – **54)** ul. Piastowska 1, 47-200 Kedzierzyn-Kozle – **55)** ul. Pilsudskiego 12, 43-100 Tychy – **56)** ul. Ostrobramska 77, 04-175 Warszawa – **57)** ul. Kanafojskiego 1/14, 10-724 Olsztyn – **58)** ul. Bema 14, 33-100 Tarnów – **59)** ul. Katedralna 13, 50-328 Wroclaw – **60)** ul. Zlota 144, 62-810 Kalisz – **61)** ul. Wita Stwosza 2/4, 96-100 Skierniewice – **62)** ul. Jankowy 55, 63-600 Kepno – **63)** ul. Sw. Jana Chrzciciela 14, 43-346 Bielsko-Biala – **64)** ul. Jana Pawla II 2, 44-100 Gliwice – **65)** ul.Wilsona 6, 42-200 Czestochowa – **66)** ul. Pilsudskiego 105, 73-110 Stargard – **67)** ul. Przemyslowa 7a, 62-100 Wagrowiec – **68)** ul. Piaski 9, 87-800 Wloclawek – **69)** ul. Hetmana J. Zamoyskiego 1, 22-400 Zamosc – **70)** ul. Fatimska 13a, 31-831 Kraków. Affiliates with own prgrs at times: **70A)** ul. Ilzecka 6a, 27-300 Lipsko **E:** radio@lipsko. eu; **70B)** ul. Cmolas 212a, 36-105 Cmolas **E:** radiocmolas@o2.pl; **70C)** ul. Krakowska 74, 34-120 Andrychów **E:** radio@andrychow.eu.

**DAB Transmitters** (DAB+)
**Muxes 1+2:** currently not assigned. **Licensee Mux 3:** Polskie R. **M:** PR1-4, PR24, PR R. Chopin, PR R. Dzieciom, PR Regional stns, PR R. Poland/BBCWS relay. – **Local/Experimental Muxes:** not shown.

| Block | kW | Location | Mux |
|---|---|---|---|
| 5B | 10 | Gdansk (Chwaszczyno) | 3 |
| 5B | 5 | Wroclaw (Zórawina) | 3 |
| 5C | 2 | Bialystok (Krynice) | 3 |
| 5C | 10 | Lodz | 3 |
| 6B | 6 | Warszawa (PKiN) | 3 |
| 10D | | SFN (Kielce) | 3 |
| 11A | 6 | Katowice (Kosztowy) | 3 |
| 11A | | SFN (Rzeszów) | 3 |
| 11A | 15 | Szczecin (Kolowo) | 3 |
| 11B | | SFN (Kolobrzeg, Koszalin) | 3 |
| 11B | 10 | Kraków (Choragwica) | 3 |
| 11B | | SFN (Lublin) | 3 |
| 11B | 5.5 | Olsztyn (Pieczewo) | 3 |

| Block | kW | Location | Mux |
|---|---|---|---|
| 11C | | SFN (Bydgoszcz, Torun) | 3 |
| 11C | | SFN (Opole) | 3 |
| 11C | | SFN (Zielona Góra) | 3 |
| 12A | | SFN (Poznan) | 3 |

## PORTUGAL

**L.T:** UTC (31 Mar-27 Oct: +1h) — **Pop:** 10.3 million — **Pr.L:** Portuguese — **E.C:** 50Hz, 230V — **ITU:** POR

**ANACOM – Autoridade Nacional de Comunicações.**
HQ: Avenida José Malhoa, 12, 1099-017 Lisboa ☎+351 21 721 10 00 +351 21 721 10 01 **W:** anacom.pt **E:** info@anacom.pt
Gov. body responsible for licensing & monitoring radio & TV txs

**APR – Associação Portuguesa de Radiodifusão (Assoc. of Portuguese Broadcasters)**
Avenida Defensores de Chaves, n.º 65 - 3º 1000-113 Lisboa ☎+351 213 015 453/+351 213 015 459/ +351 213 016 999 +351 21 301 65 36 **W:** apradiofusao.pt **E:** apr@apradiofusao.pt

**RTP-Rádio e Televisão de Portugal, SGPS (Pub)**
Av. Marechal Gomes da Costa, 37, 1849-030 Lisboa ☎ +351 21 794 70 00 +351 21 794 75 70 **W:** rtp.pt **E:** info@rtp.pt **LP:** Chmn: Gonçalo Reis
**Antena 1/Antena 2/Antena 3/RDP Africa/RDP Açores/RDP Madeira/RDP Internacional:** ☎ +351 21 382 00 00. Antena 1 +351-21-382 00 70 +351-21-382 00 05, Antena 2 ☎+351-21-382 02 82 +351-21-382 01 99, Antena 3 +351-21-382 02 02 ☎ +351-21-382 00 17, RDP África ☎ +351-21-382 02 12 +351-21 382 00 81.
**News Dept:** ☎ +351-21 382 00 02 +351-21 382 01 83
**L.P:** Chmn. bd of Dirs: Gonçalo Reis, Dir. of Antena 1/2/RDPi: Rui Fernandes Pêgo, Dir. of Antena 3: Nuno Reis, Dir. of RDP África: Jorge Oliveira Gonçalves , Reg. Dir. Açores & Madeira: see respective country entries, Technical info. & support may be obtained from **E:** gabinete.tecnologias@rtp.pt
**Ann:** "Antena 1, a rádio que liga Portugal", "Antena 2, a rádio clássica", "Antena 3, a alternativa pop"

| MW Antena 1 | kHz | kW | MW Antena 1 | kHz | kW |
|---|---|---|---|---|---|
| Miranda do Douro | 630 | 2 | Viseu | 666 | 10 |
| Montemor-o Velho | 630 | 10 | Elvas | 720 | 10 |
| Bragança | 666 | 2 | Guarda | 720 | 10 |
| Castanheira do Ribatejo* | 666 | 10 | Castelo Branco | 720 | 10 |
| Covilhã | 666 | 10 | Mirandela | 720 | 10 |
| Valença | 666 | 10 | Lamego | 756 | 2 |
| Vila Real | 666 | 10 | Portalegre | 1287 | 2 |

*) north of Lisbon; also known as "CEN" (Centro Emissor Nacional)

| FM (MHz) | Ant. 1 | Ant. 2 | Ant. 3 | kW |
|---|---|---|---|---|
| Alcoutim | 88.9 | 91.5 | 101.9 | 0.2 |
| Arestal (Aveiro) | 106.7 | 95.2 | | 0.5 |
| Bornes (Bragança) | 92.8 | 91.1 | 102.1 | 10 |
| Braga (Sameiro) | 91.3 | 88.0 | 103.0 | 10/2/10 |
| Bragança | 96.4 | 98.2 | 104.2 | 9 |
| Castelo Branco | 88.9 | 94.9 | 104.3 | 0.5 |
| Coimbra C (a) | 94.9 | - | | 4 |
| Elvas (Vª Boim) | 103.8 | 93.2 | 101.6 | 5.4 |
| Faro (S.Miguel) (b) | 97.6 | 93.4 | 100.7 | 10 |
| Gardunha | 96.4 | 93.9 | 101.3 | 10 |
| Grândola | 99.2 | 90.6 | 103.6 | 10 |
| Gravia (S. Pº do Sul) | 104.5 | 106.8 | 107.9 | 0.1 |
| Guarda | 94.7 | 88.4 | 100.6 | 6.4 |
| Janas (Sintra) | 96.9 | 96.0 | 103.8 | 0.2 |
| Leiria | 98.7 | 104.2 | 106.4 | 1 |
| Lisboa (Banática) | 99.4 | 88.9 | 100.0 | 1/0.3/0.3 |
| Lisboa (Monsanto) (c) | 95.7 | 94.4 | 100.3 | 10 |
| Lousã | 87.9 | 89.3 | 102.2 | 34/34/39 |
| Manteigas | 104.8 | 91.6 | 100.3 | 0.5 |
| Marão (Vila Real) | 95.2 | 99.8 | 101.5 | 9 |
| Marofa § | 97.2 | 93.4 | 104.6 | 20/20/10 |
| Mendro | 87.7 | 91.1 | 102.4 | 20/20/44 |
| Mértola | 90.9 | 92.2 | 100.1 | 0.4 |
| Minhéu (V. P. Aguiar)* | 94.9 | 88.0 | 104.7 | 10 |
| Miranda do Douro | 90.3 | 95.7 | 98.9 | 0.05 |
| Moledo | 102.9 | 88.0 | 92.3 | 0.5 |
| Monchique (Fóia) | 88.9 | 91.5 | 101.9 | 25 |
| Montargil | 93.6 | 99.6 | 105.0 | 3 |
| Montejunto | 98.3 | 88.7 | 105.2 | 10 |
| Muro | 88.3 | 94.6 | 102.0 | 10 |
| Paredes de Coura | 102.9 | - | 92.3 | 0.1 |
| Pte. de Lima (Rendufe) | 89.2 | 92.2 | 104.9 | 0.3 |
| Portalegre | 97.9 | 92.9 | 102.8 | 10 |

| FM (MHz) | Ant. 1 | Ant. 2 | Ant. 3 | kW |
|---|---|---|---|---|
| Porto (Mte. da Virgem) | 96.7 | 92.5 | 100.4 | 44/44/50 |
| Santarém | 98.8 | - | - | 0.4 |
| S. Domingos | 87.9 | 89.3 | 103.7 | 0.2 |
| Serra de Ossa | 88.4 | 95.0 | 102.1 | 2/0.5/0.5 |
| Tróia (Setúbal) | 106.7 | 99.7 | 107.9 | 0.07 |
| Túnel do Marão # | 95.2 | - | 101.5 | |
| Valença | 98.2 | 89.6 | 104.0 | 10 |
| Viseu | 88.2 | 97.5 | 101.8 | 0.5/0.5/0.7 |

* District of Vila Real; § District of Guarda
# Tunnel tx in motorway A4 between Amarante and Vila Real

**RDP África: a)** 103.4MHz 1kW, **b)** 99.1MHz 1kW, **c)** 101.5MHz 4kW
**D.Prgrs:** 24h **Ant. 1**=Antena 1 (general pt rgrs, sport), **Ant. 2**=Antena 2 (classical music, culture), **Ant. 3**=Antena 3 (pop/rock music), **RDP Africa** (general prgrs for the Portuguese-speaking African community. **RDP abroad:** txs in Cape Verde, Guinea-Bissau, São Tomé e Príncipe, Mozambique, all relaying RDP África, in Timor, relaying RDPi and airing a local prgr, and in Bosnia for the Portuguese peace-keeping force: this tx operated by the military (see respective country entries).
**RDP África:** ✉ Av. Marechal Gomes da Costa, 37, 1849-030 Lisboa ☎ +351 21 382 00 00 🖳 +351 21 382 00 81 **LP:** Dir: Jorge Oliveira Gonçalves **E:** rdpafrica@rtp.pt

**Web Radio:** Audio feeds at **W:** rtp.pt Antenas 1, 2 & 3 and RDP-África, RDP-Madeira and RDP-Açores. RTP web-only radios: 15 stns selectable in **W:** rtp.pt/play
**SATELLITE: Europe, N. Africa & Mid. East:** Hot Bird 13C (13° E), Transponder 7 (11.33433 GHz), Ku Band, H. Pol., FEC: ¾, SyR: 27.5 Ms/s, RDPi: PID 2502 (stereo), RDP Ant. 1: PID 2602 (mono), 24h. **Africa:** Intelsat 907 (27.5° W), DVB-S2 standard, Transponder 23/23, C Band, Right Circ. Pol., Symbol Rate 5.879 kSps. Freq. 3924.928 MHz; prgrs: RDP África: audio PID d 412 (mono), RDPi: audio PID d 413 (stereo), Ant. 1: audio PID d 411 (mono). **Asia & Oceania:** Asiasat 5 (digital) (100.5°E), DVB-S2 standard, "European Bouquet", Transponder C2V (3700 MHz), C Band, Ver. Pol. on 30.000 Ms/s, FEC ¾. RDP Int. stereo on the audio ch. 29, RDP Ant. 1 aired on the audio ch. 30. **N.America & Hawaii:** Galaxy 19 (digital) (97° W), Transponder K26, Frequency 12125.5 MHz, Ku Band, H. Pol., SyR 20.4667 Ms/s, FEC ¾. RDP Int. audio PID: 4001 (stereo). **The Americas:** Intelsat 34 (55.5° W), DVB-S2 standard, Transponder AE17C/AE17C (4100.6 MHz), C Band, V. Pol., SyR 2.2222 Ms/s, FEC 8/9. RDP Int.: PID 413. **S.America:** Telstar 14 / Estrela do Sul 2 (63°W), transponder 13, 11710MHz, ku Band, Vert. Pol., Sy.Rate 3200, FEC 2/3. RDP Int.: PID 268 (stereo).
**DAB:** RDP halted T-DAB broadcasts in June 2011. The network may be restored but there are no current plans to reactivate this service.

**RÁDIO COMERCIAL, S.A. (Priv., comm.)**
Owned by Media Capital Rádio – Radiofonia e Publicidade, S.A. **W:** mcr.iol.pt **E:** contacto@mcr.iol.pt
✉ Rua Sampaio e Pina, 24-26, 1099-044 Lisboa ☎ +351 21 382 15 00 🖳 +351 21 382 15 89 **E:** programas@radiocomercial.iol.pt, Northern office: Rua Tenente Valadim, 181, 4100 Porto ☎ +351 22 605 75 00 **W:** radiocomercial.clix.pt **LP:** Dir. Gen. MCR Rádios: Luís Cabral

| FM | MHz | kW | FM | MHz | kW |
|---|---|---|---|---|---|
| Fóia (Monchique) | 88.1 | 10 | Guarda | 96.1 | 10 |
| Moledo | 88.5 | 0.2 | São Miguel (Faro) | 96.1 | 10 |
| Lamego | 88.7 | 5 | Grândola | 96.8 | 10 |
| Minhéu (Vila Real) | 88.9 | 10 | Monsanto (Lisboa) | 97.4 | 44 |
| Leiria | 89.0 | 1 | Monte de Virgem (Porto) | 97.7 | 44 |
| Viana do Castelo | 89.3 | 0.4 | Gardunha | 98.2 | 10 |
| Lousã | 90.8 | 44 | Valongo | 98.2 | 0.1 |
| Bornes | 91.9 | 10 | Sintra | 98.5 | 0.3 |
| Mendro | 92.0 | 50 | Portalegre | 98.9 | 10 |
| Aveiro | 92.2 | 0.2 | Valença | 99.0 | 10 |
| Bragança | 93.9 | 10 | Montejunto | 99.8 | 10 |
| Braga | 99.2 | 10 | Pico da Pena (Vouzela) | 103.1 | 0.2 |
| Viseu | 94.3 | 0.5 | Vila Boim (Elvas) | 105.9 | 1 |
| Mértola | 95.8 | 0.4 | | | |

**D.Prgr:** 24h **Ann:** Rádio Comercial. **Format:** music stn
**Local FM stns in the same group:**
**M80:** (see Southern network) – **Cidade** (**W:** cidade.iol.pt): txs in Lisboa 91.6MHz 5kW, Vila Nova de Gaia (Monte da Virgem, near Porto) 107.2MHz 0.5kW, Redondo (Alentejo province) 97.2MHz 0.5kW, Alcanena (Santarém) 99.3MHz 2kW, Penacova (Coimbra) & Loulé (Algarve province), 99.7MHz 1/2kW, Vale de Cambra (near Aveiro) 101.0 MHz 0.5kW, Viseu 102.8 MHz 2kW, Amares (Braga) 104.4MHz 1kW, Montijo (Lisboa region) 106.2MHz 1kW – **Smooth FM** (**W:** smoothfm. iol.pt): txs in Lisboa 96.6 MHz 5kW, Barreiro (Lisboa region) 103.0MHz 2kW, Matosinhos (near Porto) 89.5MHz 1.5kW, Figueiró dos Vinhos

(near Coimbra) 92.8MHz 1kW & Santarém 97.7MHz 2kW – **Vodafone FM** (**W:** vodafone.fm): txs in Amadora (Lisboa reg.) 107.2MHz 1.5kW, Moita (near Lisboa) 101.1MHz 1.5kW, Maia (near Porto) 94.3MHz 1.5kW & Cantanhede (near Coimbra) 103.0MHz 2 kW

**RÁDIO RENASCENÇA – Em. Católica Portuguesa (Rlg/Comm)**
✉ Quinta do Bom Pastor,Estrada da Buraca 8-12, 1549-025 Lisboa ☎ +351 21 323 92 00 🖳 +351 21 323 92 99 **E:** mail@rr.pt (**PR: E:** rp@rr.pt) **W:** rr.pt & rfm.pt & radiosim.pt
**LP: News Dir.:** Drª Graça Franco, **PD** (R. Renascença): Dr Nelson Ribeiro, **PD** (RFM): Dr. António Mendes, **PD** (Rádio Sim): Dina Isabel

| MW: Rádio Sim | kHz | kW | MW: Rádio Sim | kHz | kW |
|---|---|---|---|---|---|
| Castelo Branco | 1251 | 1 | Seixal | 963 | 1 |
| Chaves | 1251 | 1 | Vilamoura# | 891 | 2.5 |
| Coimbra# | 981 | 3 | | | |

* 1x10 kW main tx; 1x1kW standby unit. R. Sim has been broadcasting using the latter. ‡ inactive # 10kW nominal
**NB:** R. Sim has a number of inactive MW transmitters. As of August 2018, there are currently no plans to reactivate any of them.

| FM (MHz) | RR | RFM | R. Sim | kW |
|---|---|---|---|---|
| Aveiro | 102.5 | 97.4 | - | 0.2 |
| Arrábida | 105.8 | 89.9 | - | 10/12 |
| Bornes | 89.6 | 101.1 | - | 10 |
| Braga | - | 89.7 | 101.1 | 1/10 |
| Bragança | 105.7 | 99.5 | - | 10 |
| Elvas | - | - | 102.3 | 0.1 |
| Elvas/V.ª Boim | - | 107.1 | 99.8 | 1 |
| Fóia (Monchique) | 98.6 | 104.9 | - | 12 |
| Gardunha | 103.4 | 99.5 | - | 10 |
| Guarda | 90.2 | 104.0 | - | 10 |
| Lamego | 98.6 | 106.2 | - | 12 |
| Leiria | - | 107.7 | 95.1 | 3/2 |
| Lisboa | 103.4 | 93.2 | - | 50 |
| Lousã | 106.0 | 91.7 | - | 50/56 |
| Marofa | 94.2 | 103.0 | - | 16/10 |
| Mendro | 96.5 | 100.9 | - | 50 |
| Minhéu | 89.8 | 102.6 | - | 10 |
| Monte da Virgem | 93.7 | 104.1 | - | 50 |
| Montejunto | 90.2 | 106.8 | - | 10 |
| Muro | 103.4 | 90.4 | - | 10/20 |
| Pena (Vouzela) | 93.8 | 95.0 | - | 0.4 |
| Penafiel | 90.2 | 102.3 | - | 1 |
| S. Mamede | 95.3 | 101.1 | - | 10 |
| São Miguel | 103.8 | 89.6 | - | 10 |
| Serra de Ossa | 98.5 | 89.7 | - | 2 |
| Sintra | 105.0 | 106.6 | - | 0.3 |
| Túnel do Marão | 94.2 | | | |
| Valença | 100.0 | 95.4 | - | 10 |
| Valongo | 104.5 | 106.2 | - | 0.4/1 |
| Viseu | 103.6 | 99.4 | - | 1 |

**D.Prgr.:** 24h. **Ann:** "Renascença - música e informação dia-a-dia.", "RFM - só grandes músicas"
Some prgs are simulcast on RR Canal 1 & R. Sim
**Local FM stns of the R. Renascença group: Mega Hits** (**W:** mega. fm): txs in Lisboa 92.4MHz 5kW, Sintra (west of Lisboa) 88.0MHz 1 kW, Coimbra 90.0MHz 5kW, Aveiro 96.5MHz 2kW, Gondomar (Porto region) 90.6MHz 2kW and Braga 92.9MHz 2kW
**Local FM stns relaying Rádio Sim: R. Sim Pal** Palmela (near Lisboa): 102.2MHz 2kW; **R. Sim Porto** Maia (near Porto): tx in Valongo 100.8MHz 1.5kW; **R. Sim Rio Maior** Rio Maior (near Santarém): 92.6MHz 1kW, 99.5MHz 0.05kW; **R.Sim NoAr** Viseu: 106.4 MHz 2kW; **R. Sim Alentejo** Portel (near Évora): 97.5 MHz 0.5kW

**Regional FM networks:**
**Northern network**
**RÁDIO NOTÍCIAS, PRODUÇÕES E PUBLICIDADE, S.A.**
✉ Rua Tomás da Fonseca, Torres de Lisboa, Torre E - 4° Piso, 1600-209 Lisboa ☎ +351 21 861 25 00 🖳 +351 21 861 25 07/8/10 **LP:** Chmn.: Daniel Proença de Carvalho, TD: Alberto Santos, Dir tx network: José de Sousa
TSF Northern office & Radiopress HQ: ✉ Rua Gonçalo Cristóvão, 195, 4017-001 Porto ☎ +351 22 206 28 00 🖳 +351 22 206 28 03 **E:** tsf@tsf.pt **W:** tsf.pt
**Station: TSF (priv., comm.)**

| FM | MHz | kW | FM | MHz | kW |
|---|---|---|---|---|---|
| Pena (Vouzela) | 102.5 | 0.1 | Guarda | 106.6 | 10 |
| Bornes | 103.2 | 10 | Minhéu | 106.7 | 10 |
| Gardunha | 105.1 | 10 | Braga | 106.9 | 10 |
| Valongo (Porto) | 105.3 | 50 | Bragança | 107.0 | 10 |
| Marofa | 105.4 | 10 | Lousã | 107.4 | 50 |
| Valença | 105.7 | 10 | Marão | 107.6 | 10 |
| Muro | 106.5 | 10 | Túnel do Marão | 107.6 | |

**NB:** the whole netw. relays key stn TSF 89.5MHz 5kW Lisboa . TSF broadcasts 24 hours/day via **R. Jovem** 105.4MHz 2kW Évora , **R. Santa Maria** 101.6MHz 2kW Faro (Algarve) and **R. Caldas** 103.1 MHz 1kW Caldas da Rainha; in the Açores via **R. Comercial dos Açores-TSF** 99.4MHz 3kW Ponta Delgada (São Miguel isl.) and in Madeira via **R. Notícias-TSF** 100.0MHz 2kW Funchal.
**Format:** mainly news. **D.Prgr:** 24h

**Southern network**
**LICENSEE: RÁDIO REGIONAL DE LISBOA, S.A.**
(Owned by Média Capital Rádio) ⌨ see R.Comercial **W:** m80.iol.pt
**Station: M80 Rádio (priv., comm.)**

| FM | MHz | kW | FM | MHz | kW |
|---|---|---|---|---|---|
| Bragança# (Nogueira) | 89.2 | 1 | Coimbra # | 98.4 | 5 |
| Bragança# | 90.0 | 0.05 | Fafe # | 103.8 | 1 |
| Porto # | 90.0 | 5 | Monsanto (Lisboa) | 104.3 | 50 |
| Leiria# | 93.0 | 2 | Manteigas# | 104.4 | 0.5 |
| Mogadouro# | 93.1 | 1 | Valongo# | 105.8 | 1.5 |
| Aveiro# | 94.4 | 2 | São Miguel (Faro) | 106.1 | 10 |
| Penalva do Castelo# | 95.6 | 0.5 | Mendro | 106.4 | 50 |
| Montejunto | 96.4 | 10 | Portalegre | 106.7 | 10 |
| Sabugal# | 96.8 | 0.5 | Fóia (Monchique) | 107.1 | 10 |
| Vila Real # | 97.4 | 1 | Grândola | 107.5 | 10 |

**#** ) txs of associated local stns. **Format:** music oldies from 1970s-2000s. **N:** every h on the h. **D.Prgr:** 24h **Ann:** "M80 Rádio"

**Other Networks:**
**Rádio 5FM (Priv., comm.)**
⌨ Avenida Visconde de Barreiros, 89, 5°, 4470-151 Maia ☎+351 229 439 380 **E:** geral@radio5.pt **W:** radio5.pt
**FM:** txs in Póvoa de Varzim 89.0MHz 2kW & Monte da Virgem (V. N. Gaia) 88.4 MHz 1kW (both near Porto) **D.Prgr:** 24h
**Rádio Meo Sudoeste (Priv., comm.)**
⌨ Rua Viriato n°25, 4°/6°-1050-234 Lisboa ☎+351 210 105 765 ▤+351 210 105 769 **W:** radiomeosudoeste.pt **E:** geral@radiomeomusic.pt
**FM:** Almada (near Lisboa) 100.8MHz 2kW & Monte da Virgem (V. N. Gaia) 102.7MHz 2kW **D.Prgr:** 24h **Format:** pop/dance music
**Rádio SBSR (Priv., comm.)**
⌨ Rua Viriato n° 25 , 3°, 1050-234 Lisboa ☎+351 210 105 730 **W:** sbsr.fm **FM:** Lisboa 90.4MHz 5kW & Porto 91.0MHz 1.5kW **D.Prgr:** 24h **Format:** indie rock/ independent music
**Rádio Amália (Priv., comm.)**
⌨ Rua Viriato n° 25 , 3° Esq°- 1050-234 Lisboa ☎+351 210 105 740 ▤+351 210 105 769 **W:** amalia.fm **E:** geral@amalia.fm
**FM:** Loures (near Lisboa) 90.2MHz 2kW & Setúbal 100.6MHz 2kW **D.Prgr:** 24h **Format:** Portuguese music (Fado)
**Rádio Nova Era (Priv., comm.)**
⌨ Rua das Camélias, 134 B, 4430-038 Vila Nova de Gaia ☎+351 223 770 180▤+351 223 759 675 **W:** radionovaera.pt **E:** geral@radionovaera.pt **FM:** Monte da Virgem (V. N. Gaia) 101.3MHz 2kW & Paredes 100.1MHz 2kW (both near Porto) **D.Prgr:** 24h **Format:** dance music
**Rádio Dom Bosco (Priv., comm.)**
⌨ Vilarinho do Tanha, 5000-011 Abaças - Vila Real ☎+351 254 905 108/+351 967 453 017 (☎+351 259 010 069 - studios in Abaças & +351 254 090 144 - studios in Régua) ▤+351 223 759 675 **W:** radiodombosco.pt **E:** radiodombosco@sapo.pt
**FM:** Lamego 94.1MHz 2kW & Trancoso 92.1MHz 1kW (near Guarda) **D.Prgr:** 24h **Format:** general
**Golo FM (Priv., comm.)**
⌨ R. Francisco Carqueja, 179 - 3° E, 4350-185 Porto ☎+351 221 450 010 **E:** correio@golo.fm **W:** golo.fm **FM:** 89.2MHz 2kW Amarante (near Porto), Bombarral 94.8MHz 1kW & Ponte de Sor (near Portalegre) 96.0MHz 2kW + 105.6MHz 0.050kW. All frequencies carry also local prgs. **D.Prgr:** 24h **Format:** sports
**Record FM (Priv., Rlg/Comm)**
⌨ Rua Dr. Coutinho Pais 25-A, 2770-180 Paço de Arcos ☎+351 214 406 380/1 **E:** geral@recordfm.pt **W:** www.recordfm.pt
**FM:** Sintra (near Lisboa) 107.7MHz 1kW, Monte da Virgem (V. N. Gaia) 95.5MHz 2kW, Silves (Algarve region) 91.8MHz 2kW, Leiria 101.3MHz 2kW, Santarém 101.7MHz 2kW & 105.5MHz 0.05kW. All frequencies carry also local prgs . **D.Prgr:** 24h **Format:** general, religious prgrs. **NB:** Associated local VHF-FM stns relaying prgs from Record FM: **Antena Sul:** Viana do Alentejo (near Évora) 95.5MHz 0.5kW & Almodôvar 90.4MHz 0.5kW

**Local Stations** (all priv. & comm.)
**Rádio Altitude**
⌨ Rua Batalha Reis, 6300-668 Guarda +351 271 22 19 95 ▤ +351 271 22 14 92 **E:** altitude@altitude.fm **W:** altitude.fm **L.P** Dir: Rui Isidro
**FM:** 90.9MHz 2kW 24h **Ann:** "Altitude FM"

**NB:** R. Altitude owns a MW license (1584kHz 1kW), but broadcasts only on VHF-FM. As the MW tower had to be dismantled, there are no current plans to reactivate the service soon.
**Rádio Elvas**
⌨ Rua dos Chilões, n.° 1 R/C 7350-078 Elvas ☎+351 268 62 20 44 ▤ +351 268 62 20 46 **E:** radioelvas@radioelvas.com **W:** radioelvas.com
**FM:** 91.5MHz 0.5kW Vila Boim (Elvas), 103.0MHz 0.05kW São Vicente (Elvas), 104.3MHz 0.05kW Elvas **D.Prgr:** 24h
**NB:** Associated local VHF-FM stns relaying Rádio Elvas: **R. Nova Antena (Montemor-o-Novo):** 101.3MHz 2kW (**W:** radionovaantena. com); **Rádio Campo Maior:** 95.9MHz 0.5kW Campo Maior (near Elvas) **W:** radiocampomaior.com)

**Other FM stations:**

| | FM | MHz | kW | Station, location |
|---|---|---|---|---|
| 45) | | 88.2 | 2 | Ultra FM, Vila Franca de Xira |
| 37) | | 88.6 | 2 | R. Jornal de Setúbal, Setúbal: (effective 0.03kW) |
| 46) | | 89.1 | 2 | R. Lezíria, Vila Franca de Xira |
| 1) | | 89.7 | 2 | R. Antena Livre, Abrantes |
| 41) | | 90.5 | 2 | R. Cidade de Tomar, Tomar |
| 42) | | 90.8 | 2 | R. Geice, Viana do Castelo |
| 10) | | 91.4 | 2 | R. Iris FM, Benavente |
| 30) | | 91.8 | 2 | R. Clube de Penafiel, Penafiel |
| 6) | | 91.9 | 2 | R. Barcelos, Barcelos |
| 13) | | 92.0 | 2 | R. Castelo Branco, Castelo Branco |
| 20) | | 92.1 | 2 | R. Maiorca, Figueira da Foz |
| 5) | | 92.7 | 2 | ERA FM-Emissora Reg. de Amarante, Amarante |
| 28) | | 92.8 | 2 | R. Horizonte Tejo, Bobadela (Loures) |
| 3) | | 93.9 | 2 | R. Telefonia do Sul, Alcácer do Sal |
| 48) | | 94.0 | 2 | R. Cidade Hoje, Vila Nova de Famalicão |
| 25) | | 94.0 | 2 | R. 94 FM, Leiria |
| 17) | | 94.1 | 2 | Diana FM, Évora |
| 16) | | 94.5 | 2 | R. Despertar, Estremoz |
| 15) | | 94.7 | 2 | Voz do Sorraia, Coruche |
| 32) | | 94.8 | 5 | R. Festival, Porto |
| 39) | | 94.8 | 2 | R. Gilão, Tavira |
| 22) | | 95.8 | 2 | R. Fundação, Guimarães |
| 34) | | 96.1 | 2 | R. Onda Viva, Póvoa de Varzim |
| 7) | | 96.2 | 2 | R. MFM, Barreiro |
| 38) | | 96.9 | 2 | R. Horizonte Algarve, Tavira |
| 24) | | 97.0 | 2 | R. Clube de Lamego, Lamego |
| 4) | | 97.8 | 2 | Radar, Almada |
| 23) | | 98.0 | 2 | R. Santiago, Guimarães |
| 40) | | 98.0 | 2 | R. Hertz, Tomar |
| 12) | | 98.1 | 3 | R. Marginal, Cascais |
| 43) | | 98.4 | 2 | R. XL FM, Vila do Conde |
| 33) | | 98.9 | 5 | R. Nova, Porto |
| 36) | | 98.9 | 2 | R. Azul, Setúbal: (effective power 0.3 kW) |
| 19) | | 99.1 | 2 | Foz do Mondego Rádio, Figueira da Foz |
| 29) | | 99.3 | 2 | R. Soberania, Águeda |
| 31) | | 100.5 | 2 | R. Portalegre, Portalegre |
| 8) | | 101.4 | 2 | R. Pax, Beja |
| 27) | | 101.9 | 2 | Estação Orbital, Sacavém (Loures) |
| 35) | | 102.7 | 2 | Antena Miróbriga, Santiago do Cacém |
| 26) | | 103.1 | 2 | Total FM, Loulé |
| 18) | | 103.2 | 2 | R. Telefonia do Alentejo, Évora |
| 29) | | 103.7 | 2 | R. Canção Nova, Ourém |
| 9) | | 104.5 | 2 | R. Voz da Planície, Beja |
| 44) | | 104.6 | 2 | R. Linear, Vila do Conde |
| 47) | | 105.0 | 2 | Digital FM, Vila Nova de Famalicão |
| 49) | | 105.5 | 2 | RCI-R. Clube do Interior, Viseu |
| 21) | | 105.8 | 2 | R. "F", Guarda |
| 11) | | 106.0 | 2 | R. Antena Minho, Braga |
| 14) | | 107.9 | 2 | R. Universidade de Coimbra, Coimbra |

Some stns use 0.05kW repeaters + over 200 stns of less than 2kW

**Addresses & other information:**
Many stns have websites and may also have webcasting; most, if not all, have an email address. Add country code to tel. & fax nos
**1)** Rua General Humberto Delgado, Edifício Mira Rio cv / Apartado 65, 2204-909 Abrantes ☎ 241 360170/1 ▤ 241 360179 **E:** geral@antenalivre.pt **W:** antenalivre.pt – **2)** Rua José Sucena, 120-3°, 3750-157 Águeda ☎ 234 602133 ▤ 241-624334 **W:** soberania.com – **3)** Travessa João Rosa 5A, 7005-665 Évora ☎ 266 702 926 **E:** dialogohabil@gmail.com **W:** radiotds.pt– **4)** Rua Pêro da Covilhã 34, Restelo, 1400-296 Lisboa ☎ 213 011 899 / 933 948 670 **E:** geral@radarlisboa.fm **W:** radarlisboa.fm – **5)** Edifício de Sta. Luzia, Apartado 64, 4600-035 São Gonçalo, Amarante, ☎ 255 136 045 **W:** erafm927.com **E:** geral.erafm@gmail.com – **6)** Centro Comercial Bolívar, lojas 45-49 / Apartado 129, 4750-180 Arcozelo, Barcelos ☎ 253 823530 /1 ▤ 253 823 531 **E:** geral@radiobarcelos.com **W:** radiobarcelos. pt – **7)** Rua Oliveira ao Carmo, 8, 1200-309 Lisboa **W:** radiomfm.

pt – **8)** Rua de Angola, Torre C-11°, 7800-468 Beja ☎ 284 325 011 🖷 284 326312 **E:** radio@radiopax.com **W:** radiopax.com – **9)** Rua da Misericórdia, 4 / Apartado 368, 7800-285 Beja ☎ 284 311 330 🖷 284 321446 **E:** radio@vozdaplanicie.pt **W:** vozdaplanicie.pt – **10)** Rua dos Operários Agrícolas, 5B, 2135-322 Samora Correia ☎ 263 650 730 🖷 263 650 739 **E:** director@irisfm.pt, informacao@irisfm.pt **W:** irisfm.pt – **11)** Praceta Escola do Magistério, 36 / Apartado 2186, 4700-222 Braga ☎ 253 309560 🖷 253 309569 **E:** rui.sequeira@antena-minho.pt, antonio.jose@antena-minho.pt **W:** antena-minho.pt – **12)** Rua Viriato n° 25 4°E -105-234 Lisboa ☎ 21 0105742/63 🖷 21 0105769 **E:** geral@marginal.fm **W:** marginal.fm – **13)** Av° 1° de Maio, 89, 1° Esquerdo, 6000-086 Castelo Branco ☎ 272 347 346 **E:** racabgeral@gmail.com , racabcomercial@gmail.com **W:** radiocastelobranco.pt – **14)** Apartado 1178, 3001-501 Coimbra ☎ 239 851 058/80 🖷239 835 446 **E:** info@ruc.pt, tecnica@ruc.pt **W:** ruc.pt – **15)** Rua do Couço, 29-r/c frt, 2100-169 Coruche ☎ 243 617436 & 243 617 100 🖷 243 617100 **E:** radiovozsorraia@sapo.pt,rvsinformacao@gmail.com **W:** radiovozsorraia.blogspot.com – **16)** Rua Bento de Jesus Caraça, Bloco C 1° Andar - Apartado 76 , 7100-104 Estremoz ☎ 268 339454 🖷 268 339 456 **E:** geral@radiodespertar.net **W:** radiodespertar.net – **17)** MARÉ, EE08, 7000-500 Évora ☎ 266 700333 🖷 266 700555 **E:** geral@dianafm.com **W:** dianafm.com – **18)** Estrada de Arraiolos, km 2, Arcos da Cartuxa. 7001-951 Évora☎ 266 730 415 🖷 266 730411 **E:** administracao@diariodosul.com.pt **W:** radiotelefoniadoalentejo.com.pt– **19)** Rua Detrás da Alfândega n.° 1-A ☎ 233 040 620 🖷 233 428184 **E:** fozdomondego.secretariado@gmail.com – **20)** Rua Poeta João de Lemos, 6, 3080-476 Maiorca ☎233930500 🖷233 930 499 – **21)** Rua Soeiro Viegas, 2-B, 6300-758 Guarda ☎ 271 221468 🖷 271 221482 **E:** radiof@gmpress.pt **W:** radiof.gmpress.pt – **22)** Rua Arqueólogo Mário Cardozo, Ed. Guimarães Palace 411, Apartado 358, 4800-116 Guimarães ☎ 253 420520/2/5/6 🖷 253 420529 **E:** geral@radiofundacao.net **W:** radiofundacao.net – **23)** Edifício Santiago, Rua Dr. José Sampaio, 264, Apartado 485, 4810-275 Guimarães ☎ 253 421700 🖷 253 421709 **E:** santiago@guimaraesdigital.com, geral@guimaraesdigital.com **W:** guimaraesdigital.com – **24)** Urbanização da Urtigosa, Bloco 6 - R/C, 5100-183 Lamego ☎ 254 609300/1 🖷 254 609309 **E:** geral@rclamego.pt **W:** rclamego.pt – **25)** Av. dos Combatentes da Grande Guerra, Edifício Liz – 10° / Apartado 1113, 2400-122 Leiria ☎ 244 860090/4 🖷 244 860098 **E:** geral@radio94fm.pt **W:** radio94fm.pt –**26)** Rua da Rádio, Sítio do Troto, 8135-030 Almancil ☎ 289 391 031& 289 397 666🖷 289 397110 **E:** rp.totalfm@gmail.com, totalfm@totalfm.pt – **27)** Travessa do Olival, 6, 2685-086 Sacavém ☎ 21 9401019 & 21 9427750 🖷 21 9427757 **E:** orbital@orbital.pt – **28)** Rua da Boa Vista, N.° 2-B, 2685-027 Bobadela, Loures ☎ 21 9559215 & 21 9553113 /219 🖷 21 9558465 **E:** geral@horizontefm.pt **W:** horizontefm.pt – **29)** Estrada da Batalha, 68, Edifício Canção Nova/ Apartado 199, 2495-405 Fátima ☎249 530600/3 🖷249 530609 **E:** direcaoradio@cancaonova.pt **W:** radio.cancaonova.pt – **30)** Rua Alfredo Pereira, 14-2° / Apartado 14, 4564-909 Penafiel ☎ 255 710040 🖷 255 710049 **E:** info.mail@radioclube-penafiel.pt,jose.ferreira@radioclube-penafiel.pt **W:** radioclube-penafiel.pt – **31)** Av. de Santo António, 22 , Edifício Régio 1, Atelier "A" e "B" /Apartado 154, 7300 -074 Portalegre ☎ 245 300550 🖷 245 331630 **E:** geral@radioportalegre.pt **W:** radioportalegre.pt – **32)** Rua da Alegria, 582 - 9 esq°, 4000-037 Porto ☎22 5370177 & 22 5101008 **E:** geral@radiofestival.pt **W:** radiofestival.pt – **33)** Rua Júlio Dinis, 270 Bloco A, 3° piso, 4050-318 Porto ☎ 226 151 000🖷 22 6151001 **E:** nova@radionova.fm **W:** radionova.fm – **34)** Praça dos Combatentes, 15, 4990-439 Póvoa de Varzim ☎ 252 613686/888/878 & 252 299 570 🖷252 613898 **E:** radioondaviva@sapo.pt **W:** radioondaviva.com – **35)** Rua Condes de Avillez, 19-21, Apartado 45, 7540-152 Santiago do Cacém ☎ 269 750600 **E:** noticiasmirobriga@gmail.com and direcao.radio240@gmail.com **W:** antenamirobriga.pt – **36)** & **37)** Av. Dr. António Rodrigues Manito, 58 - r/c "B", 2900-061 Setúbal ☎ 265 112023 & 265 119 947 🖷 265 089053 & 265 573639 **E:** geral@radioazul.pt, radiojornalsetubal@gmail.com **W:** radioazul.pt– **38)** Quinta de S. Pedro, E.N. 125, 8800-903 Tavira ☎ 281 380 240 🖷 281 380 249/ 59 **E:** horizontealgarve@gmail.com, horizontesecretaria@gmail.com **W:** radiohorizonte.com – **39)** Largo de Santana, 1, 8800-701 Tavira ☎ 281 320240 🖷281 325523 **E:** radiogilao@net.vodafone.pt, radiogilao@gmail.com **W:** radiogilao.com – **40)** Rua Centro Republicano, 135, Apartado 133, 2300-909 Tomar ☎ 249 323100/20 🖷 249 316995 **E:** radiohertz@radiohertz.pt **W:** radiohertz.pt – **41)** Travessa da Cascalheira, n.° 27, 2300 Tomar ☎ 249 310010 🖷 249 310016 **E:** geral@cidadetomar.pt **W:** radio.cidadetomar.pt – **42)** Rua José Espregueira N°23 R/C, 4900-459 Viana do Castelo ☎ 258 800400 🖷 258 800409 **E:** geral@radiogeice.com **W:** radiogeice.com – **43)** Av. Visconde Barreiros, 89 - 5° - 4470-151 Maia ☎ 229 439 393/5 🖷 229 439 394 **W:** radioxlfm.pt – **44)** Rua das Donas, 3, 4480-910 Vila do Conde ☎ 252 642426/7/8/9 🖷 252 642303 **E:** radiolinear@gmail.com **W:** radiolinear.pt – **45)** R. Dr. Sousa Martins, Lote 2, 2725-461 Algueirão-Mem Martins☎ 218 007 558 **E:** geral@

ultrafm.pt **W:** ultrafm.pt – **46)** Praça Marquês de Pombal, 2-7°,2600-222 Vila Franca de Xira ☎ 263 3286000 / 263 272 089 🖷 263 3286007 **E:** radioleziria@gmail.com **W:** radioleziria.com– **47)** Rua 8 de Dezembro, 214, Antas S. Tiago, Apartado 410, 4760-016 Vila Nova de Famalicão ☎ 252 308143/5/7 🖷 252 308144/9 **E:** geral@famatv.pt, informacao@famatv.pt **W:** famatv.pt– **48)** R. 5 de Outubro, Edifício Vilarminda, loja 20-4 / Apartado 218, 4764-976 Vila Nova de Famalicão ☎ 252 301 783 🖷 252 301789 **E:** geral@cidadehoje.pt **W:** cidadehoje.pt – **49)** R. Dom Duarte 13, 3500-135 Viseu ☎ 232 431 249 & 969 574 194 🖷 213 519 134 **E:** info@rci.pt **W:** rci.pt

**Military Stations:**
**CINCSOUTHLANT**-Commander-in-Chief South Atlantic Area/
**CINCIBERLANT**-Commander-in-Chief Iberian Atlantic Area: ⊡ 2780 OEIRAS ☎. PR: +351 214 404106 - **FM** 88.4MHz 0.1kW (inactive)
**D. Prgr:** AFN in English

**L.T:** UTC -4h — **Pop**: 3.7 million — **Pr.L:** Spanish, English — **E.C:** 60Hz, 120V — **ITU:** PTR

**FEDERAL COMMUNICATIONS COMMISSION (FCC)**
see USA for details

**ASOCIACIÓN DE RADIODIFUSORES DE PUERTO RICO**
⊡ P.O. Box 11208,The Atrium Business Center, Ave. Constitución 530, San Juan 00922 ☎+1 787 783 8810 **W:** radiodifusorespr.com **E:** radiodifusorespro@gmail.com
Most stns broadcast in Sp. only °=EE or mainly EE. d=directional antenna ‡ = inactive. Hrs of tr 24h except where indicated.

| MW Call | kHz | kW | Station, location, h. of tr. |
|---|---|---|---|
| 1) WPAB | 550 | 5 | WPAB 550 "La Radio del Sur", Ponce |
| 2) WKAQ | 580 | 4.5 | R. KAQ "La Numero Uno", San Juan |
| 3) WYEL | 600 | 5 | Mayagüez (r. WKAQ 580) |
| 4) WEXS | 610 | 1/0.25 | X-61, Patillas |
| 5) WUNO | 630 | 5 | NotiUno 6-30, San Juan |
| 6) WAPA | 680 | 10 | Cadena WAPA R. "La Poderosa", San Juan |
| 7) WKJB | 710 | 10/0.75 | KJB "Radio Isla", Mayagüez: 0915-0400 |
| 8) WIAC | 740 | 10 | WIAC La Original, San Juan: 0700-0300 |
| 8) WIAC | 740 | 0.5/0.1 | WIAC La Original, Ponce: 0700-0300 |
| 9) WORA | 760 | 5 | NotiUno, Mayagüez (r. 630) |
| 10) WKVM | 810 | 25 | R. Paz 810, San Juan: 0900-0500 |
| 11) WXEW | 840 | 5/1 | R. Victoria "La Reina del Caribe", Yabucoa |
| 12) WABA | 850 | 5/1 | WABA "La Grande", Aguadilla |
| 13) WQBS | 870 | 1.25 | WQBS Radio, San Juan: 0900-0400 |
| 14) WYKO | 880 | 1/0.5 | La Poderosa 880, Sabana Grande |
| 15) WFAB | 890 | 0.25 | R. Unidad Cristiana "La Nave 890", Ceiba |
| 16) WPRP | 910 | 4.4 | NotiUno, Ponce (r. 630) |
| 17) WYAC | 930 | 2.5 | WIAC La Original, Cabo Rojo (r. 740) |
| 18) WIPR | 940 | 10/2.5 | Máxima 940 AM, San Juan |
| 19) WDNO | 960 | 1/1.7 | Cima Norte, Quebradillas (r. 1600) |
| 20) WPRA | 990 | 0.91 | La Primera, Mayagüez: 0900-0400 |
| 21) WOQI | 1020 | 1/0.3 | R. Casa Pueblo, Adjuntas: 1000-0200 |
| 22) WOSO | 1030 | 0.3/0.3 | San Juan (F.P.I.) |
| 23) WNVI | 1040 | 9/0.25 | R. Nueva Vida, Moca |
| 24) WCGB | 1060 | 5/0.5 | Rock R. Network, Juana Díaz (r. 1190)° |
| 25) WMIA | 1070 | 0.5/2.5 | Cadena WAPA R. "La Poderosa", Arecibo |
| 26) WLEY | 1080 | 0.25 | R. Ley, Cayey |
| 27) WSOL | 1090 | 02/07 | R. Sol, San Germán: 0930-0400 |
| 28) WVJP | 1110 | 2.5/0.5 | Z101 Digital, Caguas |
| 29) WMSW | 1120 | 2.6/5 | R. Once, Hatillo: 1000-0200 |
| 30) WOIZ | 1130 | 02/0.7 | R. Antillas, Guayanilla: 0900-0200 |
| 31) WQII | 1140 | 10 | Once Q Cadena Nac., San Juan:1000-0400 |
| 32) WBQN | 1160 | 5/2.5 | R. Borinquén, Barceloneta-Manatí: 1100-0200 |
| 33) WLEO | 1170 | 0.5 | R. Leo, Ponce |
| 34) WBMJ | 1190 | 10/5 | Rock R. Netw./"La Rocca", San Juan° |
| 35) WGDL | 1200 | 0.25/1 | La Mejor AM, Lares |
| 36) WHOY | 1210 | 5 | R. Hoy "La Señal Activa", Salinas |
| 37) WNIK | 1230 | 1 | Única Radio, Arecibo |
| 38) WALO | 1240 | 5 | Walo Radio, Humacao |
| 39) WJIT | 1250 | 0.25/1 | R. Hit, Sabana |
| 40) WISO | 1260 | 2.5/2 | Cadena WAPA R, Ponce (r. 680) |
| 41) WCMN | 1280 | 5/1 | NotiUno, Arecibo (r. 630) |
| 42) WTIL | 1300 | 1 | Cadena WAPA Radio, Mayagüez (r. 680) |
| 43) WSKN | 1320 | 5/2.3 | R. Isla 1320, San Juan |
| 44) WENA | 1330 | 1.5 | La Buena 1330, Yauco |
| 45) WWNA | 1340 | 0.95 | R. Una 1340, Aguadilla: 0900-0300 |
| 46) WEGA | 1350 | 2.5 | Candelita 7, Vega Baja |
| 47) WIVV | 1370 | 5/1.2 | Rock R. Network,Vieques Island (r. 1190)° |

| MW Call | kHz | kW | Station, location, h. of tr. |
|---|---|---|---|
| 49) WOLA | 1380 | 1 | R. Prócer "Voz de la Montaña", Barranquitas |
| 50) WISA | 1390 | 1 | WIAC La Original, Isabela (r. 740) |
| 51) WIDA | 1400 | 1 | Cadena R. Vida, Carolina |
| 52) WRSS | 1410 | 1 | R. Progreso, San Sebastián |
| 2) WUKQ | 1420 | 1 | Ponce (r. WKAQ 580) |
| 54) WNEL | 1430 | 5 | R.Tiempo, Caguas |
| 55) WCPR | 1450 | 1 | Coamomall Radio, Coamo |
| 56) WRRE‡ | 1460 | 0.5/0.3 | Maranatha Radio Ministries, Juncos |
| 57) WLRP | 1460 | 0.5 | R. Raíces, San Sebastián: 0900-0400 |
| 58) WKUM | 1470 | 2/4 | Cumbre, Orocovis: 0900-0200 |
| 59) WMDD | 1480 | 5 | El 14-80, Fajardo |
| 60) WDEP | 1490 | 5/1 | R. Isla, Ponce (r. 1320) |
| 61) WMNT | 1500 | 1/0.25 | R. Atenas, Manatí: 1030-0200 |
| 62) WBSG | 1510 | 1 | R. Voz, Lajas |
| 63) WRSJ | 1520 | 25 | IBC News Network, San Juan |
| 64) WUPR | 1530 | 1/0.25 | Exitos 1530, Utuado: 1000-0400 |
| 65) WIBS | 1540 | 1d | Caribe 1540 AM, Guayama |
| 66) WKFE | 1550 | 0.25 | R. Café Dinámica, Yauco |
| 67) WBYM | 1560 | 5/0.75 | La Mas Z Radio, Bayamón |
| 68) WPPC | 1570 | 1/0.1 | R. Felicidad, Peñuelas: 1300-2300 |
| 6) WVOZ | 1580 | 5/2 | Cadena WAPA R, Morovis |
| 6) WXRF | 1590 | 1 | Cadena WAPA R, Guayama (r. 680) |
| 69) WCMA | 1600 | 5 | Cima 103.7, Bayamón: 1100-0500 |
| 70) WGIT | 1660 | 10/1 | Faro de Santidad, Canóvanas |

**Addresses & other information:**
**1)** Box 7243, Ponce 00732-7243 **W:** pab550.com - **FM:** WOQI 93.3MHz, WIOC 105.1MHz, WOYE 94.1MHz, Mayagüez **– 2)** Box 364668, San Juan 00936-4668 **W:** wkaq580.univision.com - **FM:** KQ-105 La Primera 104.7MHz **– 3)** Box 1370, Mayagüez 00681-1370 - **FM:** WAEL-FM 96.1MHz, Maricao **– 4)** Box 640, Patillas 00723-0640 **W:** x61radio.com **– 5)** Box 363222, San Juan 00936-3222 **W:** notiuno. com **– 6)** Urb Baldrich, 134 Domenech Ave, Hato Rey 00918-3502 **W:** waparadiopr.com **– 7)** Box 1293, Mayagüez 00709-1293 **W:** radiois-la1320.com **– 8)** Box 9023916, San Juan 00902-3916 **W:** wiac740. com **– 9)** Box 43, Mayagüez 00681-0043 (or P.O.Box 363222, San Juan, PR 00936) **W:** notiuno **– 10)** Urb. Roosevelt, 415 Calle Carbonell, Hato Rey 00918-2866 **W:** radiopaz810.com **– 11)** Box 100, Yabucoa 00767 **W:** victoria840.com **– 12)** 6 Calle Munoz Rivera St., Aguadilla 00603-5154 (or P.O.Box 188, Aguadilla, PR 00605) **W:** waba850.com **– 13)** Calle Bori 1508, Urb Autonsanti, San Juan 00927 **W:** wqbsradio.com **– 14)** Calle Dr. Felix Tio 34, Sabana Grande, PR 00637 **W:** wyko880am.com **– 15)** P.O.Box 318, Río Blanco, PR 00744. **W:** radiounidadcristiana.com **– 16)** Box 7771, Ponce 00732-7771 **W:** notiuno.com **– 17)** Box 681, Cabo Rojo 00623-0681 **W:** wiac740.com **– 18)** Box 190909, Hato Rey 00918-0909 **W:** wipr.pr **– 19)** P.O.Box 846, Aguada, PR 00602. **W:** cima103.com - **FM:** 103.7MHz **– 20)** Box 1293, Mayagüez 00681-1293 **W:** wpra990.com **– 21)** Box 704, Adjuntas 00601-0704 **W:** casapueblo.org **– 23)** Box 846, Aguada, PR 00602-0846 **W:** nuevavida.fm - **FM:** 104.5MHz **– 24)** Box 1414, Juana Díaz 00795-1414 (or P.O.Box 367000, San Juan, PR 00936) - Mon-Fri 1300-1700 local prgrs in Spanish **– W:** rockradionetwork.org **– 26)** Box 1186, Cayey 00737-1186 (or 100 Gran Bulevar Paseo #403A, San Juan, PR 00926) **W:** radioisla1320.com/radio-ley-1080-am **– 27)** Box 5000, Suite 442, San Germán 00683-0442 **W:** radiowsol.com **– 28)** Box 207, Caguas 00726-0207. Relays Z101 Digital 101.3MHz from Santo Domingo, Dom. Rep. **W:** z101digital.com **– 29)** 550 Calle Truncado, Hatillo 00659-2712 (or P.O.Box 140961, Arecibo, PR 00614) **W:** radi-oonce.com **– 30)** Box 561130, Guayanilla 00656-1130 **W:** radioanti-llas.4t.com **– 31)** Cobian's Plaza, Santurce 00909-1820 (or Box 193779, San Juan, PR 00919) **W:** 11qradio.com **– 32)** Box 1625 (or Calle 16 H-6 Urb. Flamboyán), Manatí 00674-1625 **– 33)** Box 7213, Ponce 00732-7213 **W:** unoradio.com **– 34)** Box 367000, San Juan 00936-7000 (or Av Ponce de León N° 1409, P4, Santurce 00907) – Mon-Fri 2300-0540 Spanish, 0540-2300 English, Sun English 24h **W:** rockradionetwork. org **– 35)** Box 872, Lares, PR 00669 **– W:** wgdl1200am.com **– 36)** Box 1148, Salinas 00751-1148 **W:** radiowhoy.com **– 37)** Box 141526, Arecibo 00614 **W:** unicaradio1230.com - **FM:** 106.5MHz **– 38)** Box 1240 (or P.O.Box 9230), Humacao 00792 **W:** waloradio.com **– 39)** Box 316, Coamo 00769-0316 (or P.O.Box 878, Vega Alta, PR 00692) **W:** radiohit1250.com **– 41)** Box 436, Arecibo 00613-0436 **W:** notiuno.com **– 42)** Box 1360, Mayagüez 00681-1360 **W:** waparadiopr.com - **FM:** 106.9MHz **– 43)** Box 363222, San Juan 00936-3222 **W:** radioisla1320. com **– 44)** Box 1330, Yauco 00698-1330 **W:** labuena1330.com **– 45)** Box 7, Moca 00676-0007 **W:** radiouna1340.com **– 46)** BHC 03 Box 12110, Carolina, P.R. 00987 **W:** candelita7.com **– 48)** HC02 Box 13903, Vieques Island, PR 00765 – Sat 1000-1300 local programming in English **W:** rockradionetwork.org 34 **– 49)** Box 669-A, Barranquitas, PR 00794 **– 50)** Box 750, Isabela 00662-0750 **W:** wisa1390.com - **FM:** WKSA 101.5MHz **– 51)** Box 188, Carolina 00986-0188 **W:** cadenara-diovida.net - **FM:** 90.5MHz **– 52)** Box 1410, San Sebastián 00685-1410

**W:** radioprogreso1410.com **– 54)** Box 487, Caguas 00726-0487 **W:** radiotiempo.net **– 55)** Box 1863, Coamo 00769-1863 **W:** coamomall. com/coamomallradio **– 56)** Box 1460, Las Piedras, PR 00771-1460 **W:** maranatharadioministries.com **– 57)** Box 1670, San Sebastián 00685-1670 **W:** wlrpam.net **– 58)** 10 Calle Pedro Arroyo, Orocovis 00720-2202 (or P.O.Box 1210, Orocovis, PR 00720) **W:** cumbre1470.com **– 59)** Box 948, Fajardo 00738-0948 **W:** wmdd.radio.net **– 60)** Box 7213, Ponce 00732-7213 **W:** radioisla1320.com **– 61)** Box 6, Manatí 00674-0006 **W:** radioatenas1500.net **– 62)** Box 593, Lajas 00667-0593 (has requested permission to move to San Germán) **– 63)** Calle Bori 1554, San Juan, PR 00927. **W:** ibcnewsnetwork.com **– 64)** Box 868, Utuado 00641-0868 **W:** exitos1530radio.com **– 65)** Box 1540, Guayama 00785-1540 **W:** caribe1540am.com **– 66)** Box 324, Yauco 00698-0324 (or 100 Gran Bulevar Paseo #403A, San Juan, PR 00926) **W:** facebook. com/radiocafe1550 **– 67)** Box 4036, Carolina 00984-4036 (or Calle Bori 1554, San Juan, PR 00927) **W:** metroradio1560.com **– 68)** Box 9064, Ponce 00732-9064 **W:** radiofelicidadpr.com **– 69)** Box 9394, Santurce 00908-9394 **W:** cima103.com - **FM:** 103.7MHz **– 70)** Calle Bori 1554, San Juan, PR 00927 **W:** farodesantidad.com

**FM in San Juan (MHz):** 89.7 WRTU University of San Juan – 91.3 WIPR "Allegro" – 93.7 WZNT – 96.5 WRXD Play FM – 99.1 WPRM-FM – 99.9 WIOA – 102.5 WTOK – 104.7 WKAQ-FM – 105.7 WCAD

## QATAR

**L.T:** UTC +3h — **Pop:** 2.3 million — **Pr.L:** Arabic — **E.C:** 50Hz, 240V — **ITU:** QAT

### SUPREME COUNCIL OF INFORMATION & COMMUNICATION TECHNOLOGY
P.O. Box 23264, Al Nassr Tower, Post Office Roundabout, Al Corniche St., Doha ☎+974 44 995333 🖷 +974 44 935913 **W:** ictqatar.qa **E:** info@ict.gov.qa

### QATAR MEDIA CORPORATION (QMC, Gov.)
🖃 P.O. Box 1414, Doha ☎+974 44 894444 🖷 +974 44 882888 **W:** qatarradio.qa **E:** info@qatarradio.qa **LP:** Exec. Chmn: Sheikh Jabor Bin Yusuf Bin Jasim Al Thani. Dir. of Broadc: Mubarak Jaham Al-Kawari.
**Main Arabic Prgr. (A):** 24h. **MW:** Al-Arish 675kHz 600kW. **FM:** Al-Jumailiya 90.8MHz 40kW, Umm Said 93.4MHz, Al-Markhiyah 96.0MHz 10kW, Al Kohr 97.6MHz 10kW, Al-Khaisah 103.4MHz, Al Ruwais 106.0MHz.
**English prgr:** Doha 97.5MHz 10kW. **W:** qbsradio.qa
**Quran prgr:** Khawr al-Udayd 103.4MHz 0.5kW, Doha 105.7Mhz.
**Urdu prgr:** Doha 107.0MHz 5kW. **W:** urduradio.qa
**Oryx FM,** Doha, 94.0MHz (joint QMC and RFI project in French.) **W:** oryxradio.qa
**Sowt al-Khaleej** (Vo the Gulf): Doha 88.0/93.4/99.0/100.8MHz. **W:** skr.fm
**Al-Jazeera Arabic TV audio:** Doha 102.6MHz.
**Al-Kass TV audio:** Doha 100.3MHz 20kW. **W:** alkass.net
**Qatar TV Arabic audio:** Al-Khaisah 104.6MHz 20kW.
**Ann:** Main Arabic prgr: "Idha'at Qatar min al-Doha".

**OTHER STATIONS:**
**Emarat FM,** Doha: 104.0MHz. See UAE **– Malayalam FM,** Doha: 98.6MHz **W:** radio986.com **– Middle East BC,** Markhiya 92.0MHz **– One FM,** Doha 89.6MHz. In Hindi **W:** facebook.com/oneFMQatar **– R. Olive,** Doha 106.3MHz. In Hindi **W:** olive.qa **– R. Suno,** Doha 98.6MHz. In Malayalam **W:** suno.qa **– QF Radio,** Doha: 91.7MHz English, 93.7MHz Arabic. **W:** qfradio.org.qa **– Sowt Al-Rayyan-Souq Waqif:** Doha 97.0MHz 20kW, Markhiyah 102.0MHz 10kW. **W:** soutalrayyan.com
**AFN,** Al Udeid Airbase: 98.9/101.3MHz **– BBC World Sce,** Doha: 107.4MHz 8kW **– Monte Carlo Doualiya,** Doha: 99.6MHz 5kW **– R. Sawa,** Al-Jumailiya: 92.6MHz 20kW

## RÉUNION (France)

**L.T:** UTC +4h — **Pop:** 900,000 — **Pr.L:** French — **E.C:** 50Hz, 220V — **ITU:** REU

### RÉUNION LA PREMIÈRE (Pub)
🖃 12 rue René Demarne, BP 47716, 97804 Saint-Denis Cedex 9 ☎+262 262406767 🖷 +262 262216484 **W:** reunion.la1ere.fr/radio **LP:** Directrice Regional: Dominique Richard.

| FM | MHz | kW | FM | MHz | kW |
|---|---|---|---|---|---|
| Petite-Ile | 87.8 | 2 | Plaine des Cafres | 90.7 | 2 |
| Saint-Denis | 89.2 | 2 | Saint-Paul | 90.7 | 1 |
| Le Tampon | 89.6 | 3 | Saint-Leu | 90.9 | 1 |

| FM | MHz | kW | FM | MHz | kW |
|---|---|---|---|---|---|
| Le Port | 91.0 | 2 | Saint-Benoît | 106.7 | 2 |

+6 trs under 1kW.
**D.Prgr:** 24h. During nighttime 2000-0100 relay of RFI.
**Ann:** "Réunion Première". **IS:** "Séga & Maloya" (Réunion folklore).

**Other Stations:**

| FM (MHz) | 1 | 2 | 3 | 4 | 5 | 6 | 7 | 8 | kW |
|---|---|---|---|---|---|---|---|---|---|
| Cilaos | 103.5 | 98.8 | 107.4 | - | - | - | 88.5 | 100.7 | 0.2 |
| Etang-Salé | | 89.3 | | - | - | - | - | 94.7 | 1 |
| La Possession | | 93.4 | | - | - | - | 103.0 | - | 1 |
| Le Port | 91.6 | 93.4 | 94.2 | 105.2 | 93.8 | | 103.3 | - | 1-2 |
| Le Tampon | 99.2 | 97.4 | | 98.6 | 104.0 | 105.7 | - | - | 1-3 |
| Petite-Ile | 91.1 | - | - | 105.5 | - | - | - | - | 1-2 |
| Plaine des-Chafres | 91.3 | - | - | 105.1 | 96.5 | 93.0 | - | - | 1-2 |
| Plaine des-Palm. | 99.2 | 88.2 | 100.1 | - | - | - | 93.6 | - | 1-3 |
| Saint-André | - | - | 94.2 | - | - | - | - | - | 2 |
| Saint-Benoit | 97.5 | 101.3 | - | - | 88.5 | - | - | 105.2 | 0.2-1 |
| Saint-Denis | 98.8 | 97.8 | 101.5 | 95.1 | 107.7 | 103.4 | 95.5 | 91.3 | 0.2-2 |
| Sainte-Rose | 99.8 | - | 87.6 | 107.5 | 89.0 | 93.6 | 102.1 | - | 0.2-1 |
| Sainte-Suzanne | 99.6 | 106.2 | - | 101.1 | - | 95.7 | - | 0.1-1 |
| Saint-Joseph | 91.7 | - | 98.8 | 98.0 | 107.0 | 90.5 | 103.5 | 88.3 | 0.1-1 |
| Saint-Leu | 91.5 | 95.0 | | 105.3 | 96.7 | 92.8 | 103.1 | 106.8 | 1 |
| Saint-Paul | - | 107.1 | 103.7 | 105.7 | 96.6 | 89.6 | 90.0 | 87.6 | 1-2 |
| Saint-Philippe | 101.1 | 91.6 | - | - | - | - | 102.6 | 90.3 | 0.1-1 |
| Salazie | 93.2 | 101.7 | 89.0 | 104.4 | - | 103.2 | - | 105.7 | 0.2 |
| Saline-les-Hauts | - | 95.2 | - | 105.5 | 106.6 | 89.4 | 103.3 | - | 1 |
| Trois Bassins | 91.3 | - | 107.9 | - | - | - | - | 95.6 | 1 |
| Vincendo | - | - | - | - | - | 101.6 | 105.8 | - | 1 |

**1) France Inter W:** franceinter.fr – **2) R. Freedom W:** freedom.fr – **3) Kréol FM W:** radiokreol.com – **4) RER** (Radio ést Réunion) **W:** rer.re – **5) R. Festival W:** radiofestival.re – **6) Antenne Réunion Radio W:** antennereunion.fr – **7) Fun R. W:** funradio.re – **8) R. Arc en Ciel W:** 7afm.com

## ROMANIA

**L.T:** UTC +2h (31 Mar-27 Oct: +3h) — **Pop:** 19.2 million — **Pr.L:** Romanian, Hungarian, German — **E.C:** 230V/50Hz — **ITU:** ROU

### CONSILIUL NATIONAL AL AUDIOVIZUALULUI (CNA) (National Audiovisual Council)
✉ Bd. Libertatii nr. 14, sector 5, 050706 Bucuresti ☎ +40 213055350
🖷 +40 213055354 **E:** cna@cna.ro **W:** cna.ro
**L.P:** Pres: Laura Corina Georgescu

### SOCIETATEA ROMÂNA DE RADIODIFUZIUNE (SRR) (Pub)
✉ Str. Berthelot nr. 60-64, sector 1, 010171 Bucuresti ☎ +40 213031777 **E:** relatii.public@radioromania.ro **W:** radioromania.ro
**L.P:** DG: Georgica Severin

| LW/MW | kHz | kW | Prgr | MW | kHz | kW | Prgr |
|---|---|---|---|---|---|---|---|
| Brasov (Bod) | 153 | 200 | AS | Miercurea Ciuc | 945 | 15 | 1 |
| Petrosani | 531 | 15 | 1 | Iasi (Uricani) | 1053 | 400 | R |
| Urziceni | 531 | 15 | AS | Cluj (Jucu) | 1152 | 400 | 1 |
| Târgu Jiu | 558 | 400 | 1 | Bacau (Galbeni) | 1179 | 400 | 1 |
| Brasov (Bod) | 567 | 50 | 1 | Resita (Vascau) | 1179 | 10 | 1 |
| Satu Mare | 567 | 50 | 1 | Brasov (Bod) | 1197 | 15 | R/L+M |
| Botosani | 603 | 50 | 1 | Constanta (d) | 1314 | 50 | AS |
| Bucuresti (a) | 603 | 30 | AS+M | Craiova | 1314 | 15 | R |
| Oradea | 603 | 50 | 1 | Timisoara | 1314 | 25 | AS+M |
| Drobeta-T. Severin | 603 | 15 | R | Târgu Mures | 1323 | 15 | R+M |
| Timisoara (b) | 630 | 400 | R | Galati | 1332 | 50 | 1 |
| Voinesti | 630 | 50 | AS | Sighetul M. | 1404 | 50 | R/L+M |
| Sighetul M. | 711 | 50 | 1 | Sibiu | 1404 | 15 | 1 |
| Baia Mare | 720 | 10 | 1 | Olanesti | 1422 | 10 | 1 |
| Nufarul | 720 | 15 | 1 | Constanta (d) | 1458 | 100 | 1 |
| Sinaia | 720 | 15 | R | Nufarul | 1530 | 15 | R |
| Lugoj (Boldur) | 756 | 400 | 1 | Radauti | 1530 | 15 | 1 |
| Bucuresti (c) | 855 | 400 | 1 | Miercurea Ciuc | 1593 | 15 | R+M |
| Cluj (Jucu) | 909 | 200 | R+M | Ioan Corvin | 1593 | 15 | 1 |
| Timisoara | 909 | 50 | 1 | Oradea | 1593 | 15 | R+M |
| Constanta (d) | 909 | 25 | R | Sibiu | 1593 | 15 | R/L+M |

(a) Herastrau (b) Ortisoara (c) Tâncâbesti (d) Valul lui Traian
R=Regional prgrs, L=Local prgr (substudio), M=Ethnic Minority Service in Hungarian/German

| FM (MHz) | 1 | 2 | 4 | kW |
|---|---|---|---|---|
| Alexandria | 91.8 | 89.7 | - | 10 |
| Arad (Siria) | 103.8 | 106.8 | - | 60 |
| Bacau (Turn) | 98.8 | 101.8 | - | 10 |
| Baia Mare (Mogosa) | 102.5 | 100.1 | - | 60 |
| Baneasa (Dobrogea Sud) | 106.6 | 89.1 | - | 30 |

| FM (MHz) | 1 | 2 | 4 | kW |
|---|---|---|---|---|
| Bârlad (Popeni) | 103.9 | 102.8 | - | 10 |
| Bihor (Curcubata Mare) | 91.0 | 105.8 | - | 60 |
| Bistrita (Heniu) | 103.9 | 101.3 | - | 40 |
| Botosani (Saveni) | 100.8 | 106.0 | - | 10 |
| Bucuresti (Herastrau) | 105.3 | 101.3 | 104.8 | 2x100/2 |
| Buzau (Dealul Istrita) | 107.0 | 103.7 | - | 14 |
| Calafat (Plenita) | 90.2 | 101.1 | - | 10 |
| Câmpulung M. (Rarau) | 96.0 | 98.7 | - | 30 |
| Cluj-Napoca (Feleac) | 88.8 | 101.0 | - | 30 |
| Comanesti (Laposi) | 104.7 | 101.4 | - | 30 |
| Constanta (Techirghiol) | 105.5 | - | - | 60 |
| Craiova | 88.7 | - | - | 30 |
| Deva (Magura Boiu) | 103.4 | 105.0 | - | 30 |
| Drobeta - T. Severin (Balota) | 91.4 | 105.8 | - | 30 |
| Faget | 89.8 | - | - | 5 |
| Focsani (Magura Odobesti) | 102.5 | 101.0 | - | 60 |
| Galati (Vacareni) | 106.4 | 101.6 | - | 60 |
| Gheorgheni (Harghita-Bai) | 103.4 | 106.8 | - | 60 |
| Iasi (Pietrarie) | 101.1 | 103.1 | - | 100 |
| Mahmudia | 100.5 | 102.0 | - | 10 |
| Novaci (Cerbu) | 92.9 | 89.5 | - | 100 |
| Oradea | 104.1 | 96.1 | - | 10/60 |
| Petrosani (Parâng) | 88.1 | 90.6 | - | 10 |
| Piatra Neamt (Pietricica) | 103.6 | 100.3 | - | 30/10 |
| Ploesti (Costila) | 102.2 | 104.1 | 97.6 | 30 |
| Ramnicu Vâlcea (Cozia) | 103.4 | 102.5 | - | 30 |
| Resita (Semenic) | 102.5 | - | - | 100 |
| Sibiu (Paltinis) | 101.8 | 103.7 | - | 60 |
| Suceava (Mihoveni) | 99.6 | 101.6 | - | 30 |
| Târgu Mures | 93.6 | 104.9 | - | 10 |
| Timisoara (Urseni) | 106.4 | 100.7 | - | 10 |
| Tulcea | 99.4 | 105.4 | - | 10 |
| Tulcea (Topolog) | 105.0 | 103.0 | - | 30 |
| Turnu Magurele | 105.1 | 101.1 | - | 30 |
| Varatec | 91.2 | 100.8 | - | 10 |
| Zalau (Meses) | 88.1 | 105.0 | - | 10 |

+ sites with only txs below 1kW.

**D.Prgr: Prgr 1 (România Actualitati):** 24h. – **Prgr 2 (România Cultural):** 24h. – **Prgr 3 (România 3 Net „Florian Pittis"):** 24h via webcasting. – **Prgr 4 (România Muzical „George Enescu"):** 24h. – **Antena Satelor (AS):** 24h. – **Service for Hungarian & German ethnic minorities (Programul maghiar-german):** W 1200-1300 German & 1300-1400 Hungarian; Sun 0800-0820 Hungarian & 0820-0830 German.
**International Service (R. Romania Int.):** see Int. Radio section.

### SRR Regional Stations
✉ **R. România Regional,** Str. Berthelot nr. 60-64, sector 1, 010171 Bucuresti ☎ +40 21 3031469 **E:** radio.regional@radioromania.ro **W:** romaniaregional.ro **NB:** All reg. stns relay news from national networks at times.
**R. Bucuresti FM:** Str. Berthelot nr. 60-64, 010171 Bucuresti. **E:** radio-bucuresti@srr.ro. On 98.3MHz (Bucuresti 100kW): 24h – **R. Romania Brasov FM (F.pl):** B-dul. Eroilor nr. 29, 500036 Brasov. On (MHz) 93.3 (Negresti-Oas 2kW) + (kHz) 1107 (Brasov), 1593 (Sibiu) in Romanian, Hungarian, German. NB: Brasov FM is planned to unite the substudios Antena Brasovului (currently under R. Targu Mures) and Antena Sibiului (currently under R. Cluj). – **R. Romania Cluj:** Str. Donath nr. 160, 400293 Cluj-Napoca. **E:** office@radiocluj.ro. On (MHz) 87.6 (Satu Mare 2kW), 93.3 (Negresti-Oas 2kW), 95.4 (Paltinis 0.1kW)*, 95.6 (Feleac 20kW), 101.7 (Sighetul 2kW): 24h; on (kHz) 909 (Cluj), 1404 (Sighetul M.)*, 1593 (Oradea & °Sibiu): 0400-2000 (*= except for prgrs from local substudios; °= W until 1900). For ethnic minorities: Hungarian ("Kolozsvári Rádió"): 0000-0200 (MF), 0600-0800 (W), 1300 (Sun 1200)-1600. Local substudios with own prgrs (otherwise rel. R. Cluj): **"Antena Sibiului"** Str. Brutarilor nr. 3, 550251 Sibiu. **E:** antena.sibiului@gmail.com. On 95.4MHz (Paltinis 0.1kW): 0900-1600 (MF); **"R. Sighet"** Str. Plevnei nr. 8, 435500 Sighetul Marmatiei. **E:** radiosighet@yahoo.com. On 1404kHz: 0400-0600 (MF), 0800 (Sun 0830)-1200, 1600-1900; for ethnic minorities: Hungarian ("Máramarosszigeti Rádió"): 0440-0450 (Mon), 0520-0525 (W), 1620-1630 (Tue), 1730-1755 (Thu); Ukrainian 1700-1755 (Fri). – **R. Romania Constanta:** Vila nr. 1, 900001 Mamaia. **E:** secretariat@radioconstanta.ro. Prgr 1 ("R. Constanta FM") on (MHz) 90.8 (Techirghiol 30kW), 93.0 (Tulcea 0.5kW), 100.1 (Constanta 5kW, Mangalia 5kW), 106.2 (Sulina 2kW): 24h. Jul/Aug incl. prgr "R. Vacanta" 0800-1600 (for tourists; incl. N. produced by SRR's "R.Romania International" service in English, French, German, Italian, Russian); Prgr 2 ("R. Constanta AM") on (kHz) 909 (Valul lui Traian), 1530 (Mahmudia): 0400-2200. For ethnic minorities: MF 1905-2000 Greek (Mon), Armenian (Tue), Russian (for the Russio-Lipovanian ethnic minority) (Wed), Tatar (Thu), Turkish (Fri); Aromanian: 1610-1700 (Sun). – **R. Romania Iasi:** Str. Lascar Catargi nr. 44, 700107 Iasi. **E:**

secretariat@radioiasi.ro. Prgr 1 ("R. Iasi FM") on (MHz) 90.8 (Rarau 30kW), 94.5 (Husi 1kW), 96.3MHz (Pietrarie 100kW) 24h; Prgr 2 ("R. Iasi AM") on 1053kHz 0400-2000. For ethnic minorities (on Prgr 1+2): Mon-Thu 1830-1900 Romany (Mon), Yiddish (Tue), Russian (for the Russio-Lipovanian ethnic minority) (Wed), Ukrainian (Thu). – **R. Romania Oltenia Craiova:** Bd. Stirbei Voda nr. 3, 200352 Craiova. **E:** office@radiocraiova.ro. On (kHz) 603 (Drobeta-Turnu Severin), 1314 (Craiova) + (MHz) 99.8 (Râmnicu Vâlcea 0.2kW), 102.9 (Craiova 10kW), 105.0 (Cerbu 100kW): 24h. – **R. Romania Resita:** Str. Petru Maior nr. 71, 320111 Resita. **E:** contact@radioresita.ro. On 105.6MHz (Semenic 100kW): 24h. For ethnic minorities: 1710-1740 Ukrainian (Mon), Serbian (Tue), Hungarian (Wed), German (Thu), Croatian (Fri), Slovak (Sat), Czech (Sun). – **R. Romania Târgu Mures:** Bd. 1 Decembrie 1918 nr. 109, 540445 Târgu Mures. **E:** office@radiomures.ro. Prgr 1 on (MHz) 98.9 (Harghita-Bai 60kW), 102.9 (Târgu Mures 10kW): 0400-2000; Prgr 2 on (kHz) 1197 (Brasov) 1323 (Târgu Mures), 1593 (Miercurea Ciuc) + 106.8MHz (Harghita 60kW): 0400-2200. For ethnic minorities: Hungarian ("Marosvásárhelyi Rádió"): W 0400 (Sat 0500)-1900, Sun 0500-2000; German ("R. Neumarkt"): W 1900-2000 (also via Sibiu 1593kHz). – **R. Romania Timisoara:** Str. Pestalozzi nr. 14A, 300115 Timisoara. **E:** secretariat@radiotimisoara.ro. Prgr 1 ("R. Timisoara FM") on (MHz) 101.5 (Parang 10kW), 102.9 (Arad 2kW)*, 103.8 (Faget 5kW)*, 105.9 (Urseni 0.3kW): 24h (*= exc. for prgrs from substudio Arad); Prgr 2 ("R. Timisoara") on 630kHz: 24h. For ethnic minorities: German ("R. Temeswar"): 1100-1200 on MW & 1700-1800* on 105.9MHz (*= Italian on 1st Mon); Hungarian ("Temesvári Rádió"): 1200-1300 on MW & 1800-1900 on 105.9MHz; Serbian: 1300-1400 on MW & 1900-2000 on 105.9MHz; Sun, only on MW: 1430-1500 Czech, 1500-1600 Slovak, 1600-1700 Ukrainian, 1700-1800 Bulgarian, 1800-1900 Romany. Local substudio with own prgr **"Arad FM"** (otherwise rel. R.Timisoara FM): Bd. Revolutiei nr. 77, 310130 Arad. On (MHz) 102.9 (Arad 2kW), 103.8 (Faget 5kW): MF 1600-2000.

## OTHER STATIONS

| MW | kHz | kW | Location | Station |
|---|---|---|---|---|
| 10) | 1485 | 1 | Rotunda | R. Maria |
| 3) | 1485 | 1 | Botosani | R. Vocea Sperantei |
| 3) | 1485 | 1 | Medias | R. Vocea Sperantei |
| 3) | 1485 | 1 | Oradea | R. Vocea Sperantei |
| 3) | 1584 | 1 | Iasi | R. Vocea Sperantei |
| 3) | 1584 | 1 | Tecuci | R. Vocea Sperantei |
| 3) | 1584 | 1 | Vatra Dornei | R. Vocea Sperantei |
| 45) | 1602 | 1 | Arad | ALT FM |
| 3) | 1602 | 1 | Piatra Neamt | R. Vocea Sperantei |

| FM | MHz | kW | Location | Station |
|---|---|---|---|---|
| 4) | 88.0 | 30 | Bârlad | Kiss FM |
| 1) | 88.2 | 5 | Botosani | Europa FM |
| 43) | 88.2 | 1 | Oltenita | Stil FM |
| 22) | 88.3 | 1 | Ploiesti | Best FM |
| 6) | 88.3 | 3 | Topolog | Itsy Bitsy |
| 2A) | 88.4 | 10 | Varatec | Digi FM |
| 2A) | 88.5 | 100 | Semenic | Digi FM |
| 4) | 88.5 | 2 | Vaslui | Kiss FM |
| 7A) | 88.5 | 1 | Constanta | Virgin R. |
| 22) | 88.6 | 1 | Campina | Best FM |
| 6) | 88.7 | 2 | Satu Mare | Itsy Bitsy |
| 5) | 88.9 | 2 | Mahmudia | R. ZU |
| 5) | 89.0 | 3 | Bucuresti | R. ZU |
| 2A) | 89.1 | 10 | Târgu Mures | Digi FM |
| 1) | 89.2 | 2 | Brasov | Europa FM |
| 9) | 89.2 | 1 | Sulina | R. Trinitas |
| 1) | 89.3 | 4.5 | Siria | Europa FM |
| 5) | 89.3 | 1 | Pietricica | R. ZU |
| 41) | 89.3 | 2 | Sighetul M. | Sighet FM |
| 1) | 89.4 | 2 | Giurgiu | Europa FM |
| 2D) | 89.5 | 6 | Bucuresti | Dance FM |
| 6) | 89.5 | 5 | Tulcea | Itsy Bitsy |
| 14) | 89.7 | 22 | Harghita-Bai | Mária Rádió Erdély |
| 16) | 89.8 | 2 | Slobozia | Magic FM |
| 2B) | 89.9 | 1 | Brasov | Pro FM |
| 2B) | 89.9 | 2 | Medgidia | Pro FM |
| 2A) | 90.0 | 60 | Magura Odobesti | Digi FM |
| 1) | 90.0 | 4.5 | Bistrita | Europa FM |
| 9) | 90.1 | 2 | Toplita | R. Trinitas |
| 5) | 90.3 | 30 | Laposi | R. ZU |
| 1) | 90.4 | 2 | Râmnicu Vâlcea | Europa FM |
| 1) | 90.5 | 4.5 | Baia Mare | Europa FM |
| 5) | 90.6 | 5 | Topolog | R. ZU |
| 7B) | 90.6 | 1 | Bacau | Vibe FM |
| 1) | 90.7 | 4 | Târgu Mures | Europa FM |
| 13) | 90.7 | 30 | Turnu Magurele | National FM |
| 4) | 90.8 | 2 | Târgu Bujor | Kiss FM |
| 16) | 90.8 | 2 | Bucuresti | Magic FM |
| 1) | 90.9 | 5 | Satu Mare | Europa FM |

| FM | MHz | kW | Location | Station |
|---|---|---|---|---|
| 13) | 90.9 | 5 | Mahmudia | National FM |
| 5) | 90.9 | 2 | Slobozia | R. ZU |
| 4) | 91.1 | 1 | Constanta | Kiss FM |
| 42) | 91.1 | 1 | Saveni | Sport Total FM |
| 2A) | 91.3 | 10 | Urseni | Digi FM |
| 4) | 91.3 | 30 | Dealul Istrita | Kiss FM |
| 2A) | 91.4 | 60 | Harghita-Bai | Digi FM |
| 39) | 91.4 | 2 | Tulcea | R. Impuls |
| 7A) | 91.5 | 5 | Cozia | Virgin R. |
| 13) | 91.7 | 1 | Bucuresti | National FM |
| A) | 91.7 | 30 | Feleac | RFI relay |
| 2A) | 91.8 | 10 | Turn | Digi FM |
| 2A) | 92.0 | 60 | Vacareni | Digi FM |
| 4) | 92.0 | 10 | Heniu | Kiss FM |
| 2A) | 92.0 | 6 | Simnic | R. Impuls |
| 1) | 92.1 | 4.5 | Petrosani | Europa FM |
| 7B) | 92.1 | 2 | Bucuresti | Vibe FM |
| 25) | 92.2 | 1 | Onesti | Dream FM |
| 2A) | 92.4 | 60 | Paltinis | Digi FM |
| 10) | 92.5 | 10 | Meses | R. Maria |
| 9) | 92.5 | 2 | Giurgiu | R. Trinitas |
| 5) | 92.5 | 30 | Dealul Istrita | R. ZU |
| 9) | 92.7 | 1 | Iasi | R. Trinitas |
| 4) | 92.8 | 1 | Galati | Kiss FM |
| 23) | 92.9 | 2 | Constanta | C FM |
| 9) | 93.0 | 60 | Harghita-Bai | R. Trinitas |
| 1) | 93.2 | 4.5 | Oradea | Europa FM |
| 35) | 93.2 | 2 | Negresti | Smile FM |
| 4) | 93.3 | 1 | Slobozia | Kiss FM |
| 9) | 93.3 | 3 | Ceahlau | R. Trinitas |
| 1) | 93.4 | 2 | Alexandria | Europa FM |
| 13) | 93.4 | 30 | Heniu | National FM |
| A) | 93.5 | 1 | Bucuresti | RFI relay |
| 9) | 93.5 | 2 | Comanesti | R. Trinitas |
| 9) | 93.6 | 30 | Cozia | R. Trinitas |
| 3) | 93.6 | 1 | Tulcea | R. Vocea Sperantei |
| 4) | 93.8 | 1 | Draganesti-Olt | Kiss FM |
| 2A) | 93.9 | 30 | Dobrogea Sud | Digi FM |
| 13) | 94.0 | 2 | Zimnicea | National FM |
| 37) | 94.2 | 1 | Bucuresti | R. Vocea Evangheliei |
| 2A) | 94.3 | 30 | Cozia | Digi FM |
| 9) | 94.3 | 1 | Mogosa | R. Trinitas |
| 14) | 94.4 | 2 | Toplita | Mária Rádió Erdély |
| 12) | 94.6 | 10 | Meses | R. Transilvania |
| 38) | 94.7 | 10 | Pietricica | Viva FM |
| 26) | 94.8 | 1 | Bucuresti | R. Guerilla |
| 16) | 94.9 | 2 | Satu Mare | Magic FM |
| 2B) | 94.9 | 60 | Paltinis | Pro FM |
| 6) | 95.0 | 10 | Saveni | Itsy Bitsy |
| 5) | 95.1 | 2 | Medgidia | R. ZU |
| 9) | 95.3 | 100 | Costila | R. Trinitas |
| 8) | 95.5 | 1 | Craiova | R. Galaxy |
| 2A) | 95.7 | 10 | Bârlad | Digi FM |
| 31) | 95.8 | 1 | Tulcea | R. Delta |
| 2A) | 95.9 | 30 | Magura Boiu | Digi FM |
| 19) | 95.9 | 2 | Basarabi | R. Neptun |
| 7A) | 96.0 | 2 | Negresti-Oas | Virgin R. |
| 4) | 96.1 | 5 | Bucuresti | Kiss FM |
| 13) | 96.1 | 2 | Timisoara | National FM |
| 7B) | 96.1 | 2 | Zimnicea | Vibe FM |
| 2A) | 96.2 | 60 | Techirghiol | Digi FM |
| 8) | 96.4 | 5 | Cozia | R. Galaxy |
| 9) | 96.4 | 1 | Nucet | R. Trinitas |
| 2B) | 96.5 | 2 | Satu Mare | Pro FM |
| 9) | 96.5 | 60 | Vacareni | R. Trinitas |
| 5) | 96.6 | 60 | Paltinis | R. ZU |
| 2A) | 96.7 | 10 | Saveni | Digi FM |
| 27) | 96.8 | 2 | Dabuleni | Favorit FM |
| 4) | 96.8 | 2 | Mahmudia | Kiss FM |
| 28) | 96.9 | 3.5 | Bucuresti | Gold FM |
| 32) | 96.9 | 30 | Baia Mare | Social FM |
| 15) | 97.0 | 10 | Magura Odobesti | Focus FM |
| 7A) | 97.1 | 30 | Mihoveni | Virgin R. |
| 8) | 97.2 | 30 | Turnu Magurele | R. Galaxy |
| 5) | 97.2 | 2 | Brasov | R. ZU |
| 5) | 97.3 | 30 | Bârlad | R. ZU |
| 24) | 97.4 | 2 | Sighetul M. | City Rádíó |
| 7) | 97.5 | 2 | Medgidia | R. Terra |
| 7A) | 97.7 | 10 | Meses | Virgin R. |
| 6) | 97.8 | 6 | Constanta | Itsy Bitsy |
| 2A) | 97.9 | 3 | Bucuresti | Digi FM |
| 7A) | 97.9 | 2 | Voineasa | Virgin R. |
| 25) | 98.0 | 1 | Bacau | Dream FM |
| 3) | 98.0 | 2 | Negresti-Oas | R. Vocea Sperantei |
| 16) | 98.1 | 1 | Botosani | Magic FM |
| 13) | 98.1 | 10 | Varatec | National FM |

| FM | MHz | kW | Location | Station |
|---|---|---|---|---|
| 9) | 98.1 | 1 | Hârsova | R. Trinitas |
| 9) | 98.2 | 1 | Bailesti | R. Trinitas |
| 2A) | 98.5 | 30 | Laposi | Digi FM |
| 2A) | 98.5 | 10 | Parâng | Digi FM |
| | 98.5 | 30 | Canlia | Kiss FM |
| 9) | 98.5 | 10 | Balota | R. Trinitas |
| 9) | 98.5 | 60 | Mogosa | R. ZU |
| 7A) | 98.7 | 6 | Dealul Istrita | Virgin R. |
| 1) | 98.8 | 1 | Slatina | Europa FM |
| 16) | 99.1 | 3 | Galati | Magic FM |
| 4) | 99.2 | 30 | Cozia | Kiss FM |
| 2A) | 99.2 | 100 | Pietrarie | Digi FM |
| 46) | 99.2 | 1 | Ploesti | R. Prahova |
| 6) | 99.3 | 2.5 | Bucuresti | Itsy Bitsy |
| 16) | 99.3 | 30 | Heniu | Magic FM |
| 1) | 99.5 | 5 | Calarasi | Europa FM |
| 2A) | 99.6 | 30 | Costila | Digi FM |
| 44) | 99.7 | 2 | Târgu Bujor | R. 1 |
| 1) | 100.0 | 5 | Bârlad | Europa FM |
| 1) | 100.0 | 2 | Balota | Europa FM |
| 1) | 100.2 | 5 | Harghita-Bai | Europa FM |
| 7A) | 100.2 | 25 | Bucuresti | Virgin R. |
| 1) | 100.3 | 2 | Buzau | Europa FM |
| 1) | 100.3 | 1 | Vaslui | Europa FM |
| 13) | 100.6 | 2 | Târgu Mures | National FM |
| 18) | 100.6 | 30 | Turnu Magurele | R. Sud |
| 17) | #100.6 | 6 | Bucuresti | Rock FM |
| 2A) | 100.7 | 2 | Brasov | Digi FM |
| 2A) | 100.7 | 100 | Cerbu | Digi FM |
| 1) | 100.9 | 2 | Slobozia | Europa FM |
| 13) | 100.9 | 5 | Faget | National FM |
| 2A) | 101.6 | 10 | Meses | Digi FM |
| 34) | 101.7 | 2 | Ploiesti | R. S.O.S. |
| 40) | 101.9 | 3 | Bucuresti | Romantic FM |
| 1) | 102.0 | 2.5 | Nucet | Europa FM |
| 2A) | 102.3 | 2 | Toplita | Digi FM |
| 1) | 102.7 | 1.5 | Câmpulung M. | Europa FM |
| 1) | 102.7 | 5 | Meses | Europa FM |
| 2B) | 102.8 | 5 | Bucuresti | Pro FM |
| 9) | 103.1 | 2 | Dabuleni | R. Trinitas |
| 47) | 103.4 | 3 | Bucuresti | R. 7 |
| 2A) | 103.4 | 10 | Mihoveni | Digi FM |
| 1) | 103.4 | 10 | Galati | Europa FM |
| 3) | 103.5 | 2 | Cobadin | R. Vocea Sperantei |
| 2C) | 103.8 | 5 | Bucuresti | Music FM |
| 2A) | 104.0 | 2 | Satu Mare | Digi FM |
| 4) | 104.1 | 10 | Parâng | Kiss FM |
| 7A) | 104.1 | 1 | Mangalia | Virgin R. |
| 1) | 104.2 | 2 | Voineasa | Digi FM |
| 1) | 104.2 | 4 | Turn | Europa FM |
| 36) | 104.3 | 2 | Toplita | R. Son |
| 1) | 104.4 | 5 | Timisoara | Europa FM |
| 2A) | 104.5 | 30 | Feleac | Digi FM |
| 1) | 104.5 | 2 | Craiova | Europa FM |
| 3) | 104.5 | 1 | Zimnicea | R. Vocea Sperantei |
| 2A) | 104.8 | 30 | Rarau | Digi FM |
| 1) | 104.8 | 2 | Negresti-Oas | Europa FM |
| 17) | 104.8 | 3 | Galati | Rock FM |
| 1) | 105.1 | 4.5 | Pietricica | Europa FM |
| 7A) | 105.2 | 30 | Dobrogea Sud | Virgin R. |
| 2A) | 105.3 | 60 | Siria | Digi FM |
| 2A) | 105.3 | 60 | Mogosa | Digi FM |
| 5) | 105.3 | 2 | Hârlau | R. ZU |
| 2A) | 105.5 | 30 | Craiova | Digi FM |
| 1) | 105.5 | 5 | Mihoveni | Europa FM |
| 5) | 105.5 | 2 | Negresti | R. ZU |
| 1) | 105.8 | 7.5 | Odobesti | Europa FM |
| 13) | 105.9 | 10 | Parâng | National FM |
| 1) | 106.1 | 5 | Constanta | Europa FM |
| 1) | 106.2 | 6 | Paltinis | Europa FM |
| 48) | 106.2 | 1 | Bucuresti | 3FM |
| 1) | 106.3 | 5 | Comanesti | Europa FM |
| 33) | 106.3 | 1 | Botosani | Viva FM |
| 24) | 106.4 | 2 | Satu Mare | City Rádió |
| 1) | 106.5 | 5 | Iasi | Europa FM |
| 21) | 106.6 | 2 | Moldova Noua | 9FM |
| 1) | 106.6 | 12 | Feleac | Europa FM |
| 7A) | 106.6 | 2 | Draganesti-Olt | Virgin R. |
| 1) | 106.7 | 40 | Bucuresti | Europa FM |
| 1) | 107.1 | 10 | Cerbu | Europa FM |
| 1) | 107.1 | 2.5 | Varatec | Europa FM |
| 2B) | 107.1 | 2 | Mangalia | Pro FM |
| 11) | 107.2 | 10 | Rarau | Impact FM |
| 7A) | 107.3 | 2 | Zimnicea | Virgin R. |
| 20) | 107.3 | 5 | Bucuresti | Smart FM |
| 2A) | 107.4 | 2 | Negresti-Oas | Digi FM |

| FM | MHz | kW | Location | Station |
|---|---|---|---|---|
| 1) | 107.4 | 5 | Tulcea | Europa FM |
| 1) | 107.5 | 100 | Costila | Europa FM |
| 1) | 107.5 | 5 | Resita | Europa FM |
| 2A) | 107.6 | 60 | Oradea | Digi FM |
| 9) | 107.6 | 2 | Voineasa | R. Trinitas |
| 1) | 107.7 | 5 | Magura Boiu | Europa FM |
| 2A) | 107.8 | 30 | Heniu | Digi FM |
| 2B) | 107.8 | 10 | Turn | Pro FM |
| 30) | 107.8 | 2 | Moldova Noua | Popular FM |
| 2A) | 107.9 | 60 | Curcubata Mare | Digi FM |
| 2A) | 107.9 | 30 | Balota | Digi FM |
| 4) | 107.9 | 2 | Satu Mare | Kiss FM |
| 7A) | 107.9 | 1 | Tulcea | Virgin R. |

+ txs below 1kW. #) HD Radio trial

**Addresses & other information:**
**1)** Str. Horia Macelariu nr. 36-28, sector 1, 013932 Bucuresti – **2A-D)** Sos. Panduri nr. 71, sector 5, 061344 Bucuresti – **3)** Str. Erou Iancu Nicolae nr. 38-38A, 077190 Voluntari **E:** rvs@rvs.ro – **4)** Splaiul Independentei nr. 202A, sector 6, 060022 Bucuresti – **5)** Str. Maior Gheorghe Sontu nr. 8, sector 1, 011448 Bucuresti – **6)** Str. Leonida nr. 19, sector 2, 20556 Bucuresti – **7A,B)** Str. Horia Macelariu nr. 36-28, sector 1, 013932 Bucuresti – **8)** Bd. Carol nr. 43, 318688 Drobeta-Turnu Severin – **9)** Aleea Dealul Mitropoliei nr. 25, sector 4, 040163 Bucuresti – **10)** Str. Spartacus nr. 33, 410466 Oradea **E:** contact@radiomaria. ro – **11)** Str. Petru Rares nr. 19, 720011 Suceava – **12)** Bd. Dacia nr. 103, 410457 Oradea – **13)** Str. Fabricii nr. 46B, sector 6, 060823 Bucuresti – **14)** Str. Bârsei nr. 18, 410423 Oradea. In Hungarian – **15)** Bd. Nicolae Balcescu nr. 48, 120260 Buzau – **16)** Bd. Libertatii nr. 14, sector 5, 050706 Bucuresti – **17)** Splaiul Independentei nr. 319, sector 6, 060044 Bucuresti – **18)** Str. Campia Islaz nr. 97A, 200420 Craiova – **19)** Str. Ion Roata nr. 3, 900178 Constanta – **20)** Str. Horia Macelariu nr. 36-38, sector 1, 013937 Bucuresti – **21)** Str. Clabucet nr. 13, ap. 15, 300145 Timisoara – **22)** Str. Teilor nr. 11, 105600 Campina – **23)** Bd. Alexandru Lapusneanu nr. 104, 900648 Constanta – **24)** Str. I.C. Bratianu nr. 1, 440010 Satu Mare. In Hungarian – **25)** Str. Drumul Muntele Gaina nr. 107-109, sector 1, 013913 Bucuresti – **26)** Str. G-ral Dimitrie Salmen, Nr. 20, Ap.7, Sector 2, 021371 Bururesti – **27)** Str. Ianus Pannonius nr. 25A, 410150 Oradea – **28)** Bd. Iuliu Maniu nr. 51, sector 6, 061077 Bucuresti – **29)** Str. 24 Ianuarie nr. 9E, 905200 Cernavoda – **30)** Str. Grisellini nr. 43, 325550 Moldova Noua – **31)** Str. Podgoriilor nr. 32, 820185 Tulcea – **32)** Bdul. Traian nr. 14, 430212 Baia Mare – **33)** Str. Cuza Voda nr. 4, 710095 Botosani – **34)** Str. DN1 Ploiesti-Campina km 5C, 107070 Blejoi – **35)** Str. Spiru Haret nr. 5, 730148 Vaslui – **36)** Str. Baratilor nr. 18, 545400 Sighisoara – **37)** Str. Orzari nr. 84, sector 2, 021554 Bucuresti – **38)** Str. Marasti nr. 18, 720188 Suceava – **39)** Str. Octavian Goga nr.42, 400000 Cluj-Napoca – **40)** Bd. Ficusului nr. 44A, sector 1, 013975 Bucuresti – **41)** Str. Xenopol nr. 46C, 435500 Sighetul M. – **42)** Str. Torentului nr. 2, sector 2, 012320 Bucuresti – **43)** Str. Bucuresti nr. 149-151, 910011 Calarasi – **44)** Str. 1 Decembrie 1918 nr. 91A, 805300 Tecuci – **45)** Str. Sinaia nr. 17, 310084 Arad **E:** contact@altfm.ro. In Romanian & Hungarian. – **46)** Str. Democratiei 28a 100558 Ploiesti – **47)** Str. Doamnei 17, 030056 Bucuresti – **48)** Bdul. Dimitrie Pompeiu nr. 9-9A, Complex Iride Business Park, Cladirea 14, Sector 2, 020335 Bucuresti – **A)** Rel. RFI (France).

**DAB Transmitter** (Trial)
**Tx Operator:** Radiocom **M:** România Actualitati, România Cultural, România Muzical, R. 3Net, Bucuresti FM **Tx:** Block 12A (Bucuresti (Herastrau) 0.5kW)

**L.T:** KA: UTC +2h; AD, AR, BE, BR, CC, CV, DA, IN, IV, KB, KC, KD, KL, KO, KS, KT, KU, KV, KX, LI, MD, ME, MO, MU, NE, NN, NO, OL, PS, PZ, RO, RY, SM, SO, SP, ST, TA, TL, TS, TV, VL, VN, VO, YA: +3h; AS, SA, SR, UD, UL: +4h; OB, PR, SV, TY, VG, YN: +5h; BA, CB, KG, KY: +5h; OM: +6h; AK, KE, KN, NS, RA, RK, RT, TO: +7h; BU, IR: +8h; RS (Western), YV, ZB: +9h; AM, KH, PM, RS (Central): +10h; MA, RS (Eastern), SL: +11h; CK, KM: +12h. Resp. Krym & Sevastopol: +3h. — **Pop:** 143.5 million — **Pr.L:** Russian; additional official languages in the republics: Abaza, Adyghe, Altay, Avar, Azeri, Bashkir, Buryat, Chechen, Chuvash, Erzya, Ingush, Kabardian, Kalmyk, Karachay-Balkar, Khakas, Komi-Zyrian, Lezgi, Mansi, Mari, Moksha, Nogai, Ossetic, Tatar, Tuvan, Udmurt, Yakut. Resp. Krym & Sevastopol: Ukrainian, Crimean Tatar. — **E.C:** 230V/50Hz — **ITU:** RUS

**FEDERALNAYA SLUZHBA PO NADZORU V SFERE SVYAZI, INFORMATSIONNYKH TEKHNOLOGIY I MASSOVYKH KOMMUNIKATSII (ROSKOMNADZOR) (Federal Service for the Supervision of Communications, Information Technology, and Mass Media)**
▣ 109074 Moskva, Kitaygorodskiy proyezd 7 ☎ +7 495 9876800 ▤

+7 495 9876801 **E:** rsoc_in@rsoc.ru **W:** rkn.gov.ru
**L.P:** Head: Aleksandr A.Zharov

**VSEROSSIYSKAYA GOSUDARSTVENNAYA
TELEVIZIONNAYA I RADIOVESHCHATELNAYA
KOMPANIYA (VGTRK) (Gov)**
✉ 125040 Moskva, Yamskogo polya 5-ya ul. 19/21 ☎ +7 495
2514050🖷 +7 495 2142347 **E:** vgtrk@vgtrk.com **W:** vgtrk.com
**L.P:** GD: Oleg B.Dobrodeyev
**FM** (MHz) **R. Rossii (RR):** tx list see VGTRK Regional Services – **R.
Kultura:** Moskva 91.6MHz 5kW.

| Rg | Location | RM* | VFM* | kW |
|----|----------|-----|------|-----|
| AD | Maykop | 104.0 | - | 4 |
| AK | Barnaul | 101.0 | 101.5 | 2/1 |
| AR | Arkhangelsk | 106.0 | 90.8 | 1 |
| AR | Severodvinsk | 90.4 | - | 1 |
| AS | Astrakhan | 101.2 | 107.4 | 1 |
| BA | Steplitamak | 106.7 | - | 2 |
| BA | Ufa | 100.6 | 102.1 | 1 |
| BE | Belgorod | 88.7 | 105.9 | 1 |
| BR | Bryansk | 90.6 | 104.0 | 1 |
| BU | Ulan-Ude | 103.2 | 88.4 | 1 |
| CB | Chelyabinsk | 93.6 | 92.6 | 1 |
| CB | Kartaly | 104.0 | - | 1 |
| CB | Magnitogorsk | 101.8 | - | 1 |
| CC | Goragorskiy | 104.1 | 103.3 | 1 |
| CC | Gudermes | 104.9 | 102.6 | 1/0.1 |
| DA | Makhachkala | 98.6 | 100.3 | 1 |
| IR | Angarsk | 103.5 | - | 1 |
| IR | Bratsk | 99.9 | p105.8 | 1/0.5 |
| IR | Irkutsk | 88.1 | 101.7 | 1/2 |
| KA | Kaliningrad | 102.5 | 95.1 | 4/1 |
| KB | Nalchik | 101.1 | 107.4 | 1 |
| KD | Krasnodar | 91.4 | 100.6 | 1 |
| KE | Kemerovo | 102.3 | 90.6 | 1/0.5 |
| KE | Novokuznetsk | 103.0 | 95.2 | 1 |
| KG | Kurgan | 102.0 | - | 1 |
| KH | Khabarovsk | 90.6 | 104.8 | 1 |
| KL | Kaluga | 98.7 | 107.1 | 1/0.5 |
| KM | Petropavlovsk-Kam. | 103.5 | 107.0 | 1 |
| KN | Krasnoyarsk | 106.6 | 94.0 | 1 |
| KO | Syktyvkar | 90.8 | - | 1 |
| KO | Ukhta | p91.0 | 103.9 | 0.5/1 |
| KT | Petrozavodsk | 107.9 | p106.3 | 0.5/1 |
| KU | Kursk | 95.3 | 102.9 | 1 |
| KX | Elista | 102.2 | - | 1 |
| KY | Surgut | 107.0 | 100.7 | 1/0.5 |
| LI | Lipetsk | 106.6 | - | 1 |
| MA | Magadan | 105.0 | - | 1 |
| MD | Saransk | 102.6 | 90.6 | 1 |
| ME | Yoshkar-Ola | 102.7 | - | 1 |
| MO | Moskva | 103.4 | 97.6 | 5 |
| MU | Murmansk | 103.5 | 107.8 | 1 |
| NN | N.Novgorod | 92.4 | 98.6 | 4/1 |
| NO | Pestovo | 103.2 | - | 1 |
| NO | V.Novgorod | 101.2 | - | 5 |
| NS | Novosibirsk | 93.2 | 104.6 | 1/2 |
| OB | Buguruslan | 102.8 | - | 1 |
| OB | Orenburg | 106.3 | 90.5 | 1 |
| OB | Orsk | 101.1 | - | 1 |
| OM | Omsk | 88.6 | 107.8 | 1 |
| OR | Oryol | 99.2 | - | 1 |
| PE | Penza | 95.2 | 96.0 | 1 |
| PM | Vladivostok | 88.8 | 89.8 | 1 |
| PR | Berezniki | (p) | p107.0 | 1 |
| PR | Perm | 96.2 | 88.5 | 1 |
| PS | Pskov | 104.1 | - | 1 |
| RA | Gorno-Altaysk | 104.2 | - | 1 |
| RO | Dyoktevo | (p) | 104.5 | 1 |
| RO | Rostov-na-Donu | 91.8 | 90.2 | 0.1/1 |
| RO | Salsk | (p) | 102.8 | 1 |
| RO | Shakhty | 100.5 | 106.8 | 1/0.1 |
| RS | Yakutsk | 89.7 | - | 1 |
| RT | Kyzyl | 103.4 | - | 1 |
| RY | Mosolovo | 107.5 | - | 1 |
| RY | Ryazan | 99.1 | 97.7 | 1 |
| SA | Samara | 92.1 | 93.5 | 1 |
| SA | Zhigulyovsk | 106.4 | 87.5 | 1 |
| SL | Yuzhno-Sakhalinsk | 103.5 | 107.2 | 5/1 |
| SM | Roslavl | 102.5 | - | 1 |
| SM | Vyazma | 104.6 | - | 1 |
| SO | Vladikavkaz | 89.6 | 106.3 | 1 |
| SP | St.Peterburg | 107.0 | 89.3 | 5 |

| Rg | Location | RM* | VFM* | kW |
|----|----------|-----|------|-----|
| SR | Balakovo | 101.3 | - | 1 |
| ST | Pyatigorsk | 102.5 | - | 1 |
| ST | Stavropol | 104.3 | 96.3 | 1 |
| TA | Tambov | 89.8 | - | 1 |
| TL | Tula | 103.9 | 100.9 | 1 |
| TO | Tomsk | 106.6 | 91.1 | 1 |
| TS | Kazan | 93.9 | 94.3 | 1 |
| TS | Nab.Chelny | 99.4 | 91.1 | 1 |
| TY | Tyumen | 100.0 | 103.6 | 1 |
| UD | Izhevsk | 94.4 | 104.9 | 1 |
| UL | Ulyanovsk | 100.6 | 102.5 | 1 |
| VG | Volgograd | 95.3 | 106.8 | 1 |
| VL | Vladimir | p103.9 | - | 1 |
| VN | Rossosh | 106.5 | 101.9 | 1 |
| VN | Voronezh | 105.7 | 96.3 | 1 |
| VO | Vologda | 102.3 | - | 1 |
| YA | Yaroslavl | 107.9 | 99.9 | 1 |
| ZB | Chita | 104.5 | 101.5 | 1 |

+ sites with only txs below 1kW. Rg=Region (see VGTRK Regional
Services chapter) *) Txs may carry local/regional opt-outs (produced
by the regional VGTRK branches) p=Planned
All remaining txs of RM in the OIRT-FM band are being phased out and
replaced by frqs in the CCIR-FM band: Abakan 68.63 (4kW), Cherkessk
72.11 (4kW), Khanty-Mansiysk 68.60 (2kW), Moskva 67.22 (5kW),
Saratov 72.65 (4kW), Sochi 70.07 (2kW), Smogiri 67.13 (4kW).
**D.Prgr: R. Rossii (RR):** 24h. There are several time-shifted editions
for time zones outside of the European part of Russia: these editions
are not announced on-air, and some prgrs may be carried simultaneously in several editions. – **Mayak (RM), R. Kultura, Vesti FM
(VFM):** 24h – **MW relay of Vesti FM for listeners in Ukraine:** see
International Radio section.

**VGTRK Regional Services**
**D.Prgr:** Reg. prgrs produced by the regional VGTRK branches are
generally broadcast at local prime time hours (morning/noon/early
evening) on freqs shared with R. Rossii on FM (txs see below) & via
the national DVB-T2 multiplex 1 (txs see National TV section). In
addition, some branches broadcast short news bulletins and/or local
advertsing via the freqs of Mayak or Vesti FM. A few branches also
have separate local or reg. outputs on exclusive freqs (txs see below).
(NB: GTRK=gosudarstvennaya teleradiokompaniya, state broadcasting
company).
**AD)** Respublika Adygeya (Adygeya): GTRK "Adygeya", 385000 Maykop,
ul. Zhukovskogo 24. **E:** trkra@radnet.ru **Reg:** On (MHz) Guzeripl
68.00, Krasnogvardeyskoye 69.38, Khamyshki 70.70, Koshekhabl
71.93, Takhtamukay 73.76, Maykop 98.8, Sevastopolskaya 100.2,
Ust-Sakhrayskiy 100.3, Dakhovskaya 100.8, Kamennomostskiy 101.1,
Novoprokhladnoye (+1 tx) 103.9 in Russian, Adyghe. Also on Krasnodar
(KD) 107.2MHz. **SW prgr for the Circassian ethnic minority in the
Near East:** see International Radio section.
**AK)** Altayskiy kray: GTRK "Altay", 656045 Barnaul, Zmeinogorskiy trakt
27a. **E:** altai@gtrk.ttb.ru **Reg:** On (MHz) Yeltsovka 100.1, Kytmanovo
100.2, Ovsyannikovo (+1) 100.3, Tyumenskoye 100.7, Shipunovo
100.9, Ust-Kalmanka 101.2, Reprikha 101.3, Mayak 101.4, Burla (+1)
101.5, Alekseyevka (+2) 102.0, Kurya 102.4, Pospelikha 102.5, Ust-
Charyshskaya Pristan 102.6, Verkh-Suyetka 102.7, Kulunda (+3) 102.8,
Mikhaylovskoye 102.9, Gornyak (+1) 103.0, Klyuchi (+1) 103.2, Zalesovo
(+1 tx) 103.3, Barnaul (+3) 103.4, Maralikha (+3) 103.5, Berezovka
103.6, Novichikha 103.7, Galbshtadt 103.9, Pavlovsk (+1) 104.2,
Krasnoshchekovo 104.3, Aleysk 104.6, Biysk 104.7, Bayevo 104.8,
Blagoveshchenka (+1) 105.1, Topchikha 105.2, Shelabolikha 105.7,
Rubtsovsk 106.0, Krasnogorskoye 106.8, Tabuny 106.9, Talkmenka
107.1, Zmeinogorsk 107.2, Belokurikha 107.4, Bystryy Istok (+1) 107.5,
Local channel "Heart FM" on (MHz) Barnaul 69.80/105.9, Kamen-na-
Obi 100.6, Zarinsk 101.2.
**AM)** Amurskaya oblast: GTRK "Amur", 675000 Blagoveshchensk,
per. Svyatitelya Innokentiya 15. **E:** info@gtrkamur.ru **Reg:** On (MHz)
Skovorodino 67.22, Belogorsk 67.82, Zeya 68.24, Progress 68.36,
Shimanovsk 68.72, Svobodnyy 69.92, Tynda 70.64, Blagoveshchensk
91.0.
**AR)** Arkhangelskaya oblast: GTRK "Pomorye", 163061 Arkhangelsk, ul.
Popova 2. **E:** agtrk@pomorie.ru **Reg:** "R. Pomorye" on (MHz) Urdoma
66.38, Nizhneye Ustye 66.98, Kozmogorodskoye 67.10, Nyandoma
67.31, Karpogory 67.76, Konosha 67.91, Rogachevo 68.00, Pinega
68.30, Glubokiy 68.45, Mezen 68.48, Verkhneozersk 69.11, Plesetsk
69.23, Lekushonskoye 69.50, Vazhskiy 69.56, Sorga 69.71, Kizema
69.80, Pogost 69.92, Svetlyy 70.04, Pogor 70.19, Alferovskaya 70.34,
Okulovskaya 70.55, Malozhma 70.64, Siya 70.73, Pervomayskiy 72.14,
Stroyevskoye 72.38, Vershinino 72.50, Skarlakhta 73.10, Shangaly
73.19, Samkovo 73.37, Morshchikhinskaya 73.52, Severodvinsk 88.7,

Arkhangelsk 102.0 (also relayed via txs in region NE).

**AS)** Astrakhanskaya oblast: GTRK "Lotos", 414000 Astrakhan, ul. Molodoy Gvardii 17. **E:** tvlotos@astranet.ru **Reg:** "R. Lotos" on (MHz) Tambovka 103.4, Astrakhan 104.5, Chernyy Yar 105.3.

**BA)** Respublika Bashkortostan: GTRK "Bashkortostan", 450076 Ufa, ul. Gafuri 9/1. **E:** gtrk@gtrk.tv **Reg:** "R. Bashkortostana" on (MHz) Tolbazy 65.96, Neftekamsk 66.47, Mesyagutovo (+1) 66.86, Salavat 67.04, Baymak 67.16, Verkhneyarkeyevo (+1) 68.00, Karaidel (+1) 68.42, Isyangulovo 68.66, Sharan 68.78, Uchaly 69.53, Inzer 70.01, Oktyabrskiy 70.28, Idelbakovo 70.58, Belebey 70.61, Birsk 70.76, Abzanovo 70.82, Bizhbulak 71.21, Starosubkhangulovo 71.36, Kugarchi 71.63, Burayevo 71.90, Beloretsk 72.05, Komsomolskiy 72.35, Krasnousolskiy 72.74, Tuymazy 73.37, Ufa 89.5, Oktyabrskiy 90.6, Bizhbulyak 100.8, Abzanovo 101.1, Idelbakovo 101.3, Karaidel 101.7, Isyangulovo 102.0, Starosubkhangulovo 102.1, Sharan 102.2, Mesyangutovo 102.3, Inzer 102.4, Verkhneyarkeyevo 102.6, Salavat 102.9, Baymak 103.4, Bakaly 103.7, Komsomolsk 104.1, Kugarchi 104.6, Verkhniy Avzyan 105.4, Krasnousolskiy 105.6, Tolbazy 107.3 in Bashkir, Russian.

**BE)** Belgorodskaya oblast: GTRK "Belgorod", 308009 Belgorod, pr. Slavy 60. **E:** trcblg@gtrktv.ru **Reg:** On (MHz) Staryy Oskol 107.0, Belgorod 107.2.

**BR)** Bryanskaya oblast: GTRK "Bryansk", 241033 Bryansk, ul. Stanke Dimitrova 77. **E:** radio@br-tvr.ru **Reg:** On (MHz) Navlya 67.37, Shvedchiki 70.04, Unecha 70.55, Pocheb 71.54, Belaya Beryozka 73.19, Trubchevsk 73.94, Novozybkov 89.5, Bryansk 91.6.

**BU)** Respublika Buryatiya: GTRK "Buryatiya", 670000 Ulan-Ude, ul. Yerbanova 7. **E:** bgtrk@bgtrk.ru **Reg:** On (MHz) Kurumkan 66.08, Severobaykalsk 66.29, Zakamensk (+6) 66.68, Kyren 66.86, Gusinoozersk 67.16, Petropavlovka 67.46, Sulkhara (+1) 68.00, Mikhaylovka (+1) 68.24, Altsak (+1) 68.48, Babushkin (+6) 68.60, Ashanga (+1) 69.08, Sosnovo-Ozerskoye (+5 ) 69.56, Kyakhta 70.16, Balakta 71.12, Bagdarin (+1) 71.66, Kyakhta 71.96, Botsiy 72.44, Ulan-Ude 90.0, B.Rechka (+6) 101.0, Ust-Barguzin 101.1, Barykino 101.5, Bardarin (+2) 102.0, Ust-Muya 102.2, Mukhorshibir (+1) 102.5, Taksimo 102.7, Bichura 103.0, Kabansk 104.0, Turuntayevo 104.1, Kika (+1) 104.5, Tashir 105.0, Barguzin 105.5, Yelan 106.0, Gremyachinsk (+2) 106.5, Novoilinsk 107.1, Bayangol Barg (+7) 107.5 in Russian, Buryat.

**CB)** Chelyabinskaya oblast: GTRK "Yuzhnyy Ural", 454000 Chelyabinsk, ul. Ordzhonikidze 54b. **E:** radio@cheltv.ru **Reg:** "R. Yuzhnyy Ural" on (MHz) Kartaly 66.65, Kyshtym 67.13, Yuryuzan 67.25, Stepnoye 68.36, Mezhozernyy 68.68, Novoburino 70.82, Oktyabrskoye 70.91, Miass 95.0, Chelyabinsk 97.8, Magnitogorsk 99.3, Zlatoust 107.2.

**CC)** Chechenskaya respublika: GTRK "Vaynakh", 364000 Groznyy, ul. B. Khmelnitskogo 147. **E:** gtrkvainah@mail.ru **Reg:** "R. Vaynakh" on (MHz) Gvardeyskoye 68.84, Goragorskiy 72.44, Dargo 95.2, Guni 98.7, Zony (+1) 100.0, Naurskaya 101.2, Zandak 101.6, Znamenskoye 101.7, Tazbichi 102.5, Shelkovskaya (+1) 103.1, Assinovskaya 103.2, Groznyy 103.6, Khal-Kiloy 104.3, Kharachoy 105.0, Borzoy (+1) 105.1, Kargalinskaya 106.0, Terskoye 106.4, Dabrankhi 106.8, Benoy 106.9, Gudermes 107.3 in Russian, Chechen.

**CK)** Chukotskiy avtonomnyy okrug: GTRK "Chukotka", 686710 Anadyr, ul. Lenina 18. **E:** gtrk@anadyr.ru **Reg:** On (MHz) Lorino (+6) 100.5, Alkatvaam (+5) 101.6, Beringovskiy (+4) 102.8, Anadyr (+24) 104.7 in Russian, Chukchi.

**CV)** Chuvashskaya respublika - Chuvashiya: GTRK "Chuvashiya", 428003 Cheboksary, ul. Nikolayeva 4. **E:** chradio@tvr.chtts.ru **Reg:** "R. Chuvashii" on (MHz) Ibresi 70.85, Yadrin 71.12, Tsivilsk 99.9 in Russian, Chuvash.

**DA)** Respublika Dagestan: GTRK "Dagestan", 367032 Makhachkala, ul. M.Gadzhiyeva 182. **E:** gtrk_dagestan@mail.ru **Reg:** On (MHz) Kochubey 67.04, Gergebil 69.95, Dubki 100.1, Derbent 104.9, Makhachkala 105.6 in Russian, Avar, Chechen, Kumyk, Lak, Nogai, Rutul, Tsakhur; Aghul, Azeri, Dargwa, Lezgi, Tabassaran, Tat.

**IN)** Respublika Ingushetiya: GTRK "Ingushetiya", 386100 Nazran, per. Naberezhnyy 8 **E:** pressari@mail.ru **Reg:** On (MHz) Nazran 101.3, Karabulak 104.0 in Russian, Ingush.

**IR)** Irkutskaya oblast: GTRK "Irkutsk", 664025 Irkutsk, ul. Gorkogo 15. **E:** news@vesti.irk.ru **Reg:** On (MHz) Zhmurovo 66.32, Ulan-Ude 66.62, Yerbogadzen 66.68, Tulun 66.74, Bodaybo (+1) 66.98, Chuna 67.10, Novaya Igirma 67.76, Cheremkhovo 67.88, Zheleznogorsk 68.12, Zhigalovo 68.24, Ust-Ilimsk 68.48, Mama 69.29, Tayshet 69.80, Baykalsk 69.86, Bayanday (+1) 70.64, Bokhan (+1) 70.82, Kachug 71.15, Zima 72.14, Yelantsy 72.26, Ust-Ilimsk 91.3, Bratsk 99.1, Magistralnyy 101.0, Kirensk 101.9, Ust-Ordynskiy 103.5, Irkutsk 105.0, Angarsk 107.9.

**IV)** Ivanovskaya oblast: GTRK "Ivteleradio", 153000 Ivanovo, ul. Teatralnaya 31. **E:** admin@ivtele.ru **Reg:** On (MHz) Rodniki 70.13, Furmanov 73.64, Ivanovo 89.1.

**KA)** Kaliningradskaya oblast: GTRK "Kaliningrad", 236016 Kaliningrad, ul. Klinicheskaya 19. **E:** sekretar1@kaliningrad.rfn.ru **Reg:** On (MHz) Veselovka 65.90, Bolshakovo 70.19, Kaliningrad 103.9.

**KB)** Kabardino-Balkarskaya respublika: GTRK "Kabardino-Balkariya", 360030 Nalchik, pr. Lenina 3. **E:** vestikbr@mail.ru **Reg:** On (MHz) Samarkovo (+5) 66.62, Tyrnyauz (+4) 71.51, Gerperezh (+1) 72.50, Zayukovo 73.49, Bulundu 73.70, Nalchik 101.8 in Russian, Kabardian, Karachay-Balkar.

**KC)** Karachayevo-Cherkesskaya respublika: GTRK "Karachayevo-Cherkesiya", 369000 Cherkessk, ul. Krasnoarmeyskaya 51. **E:** gtrk_kchr@rambler.ru **Reg:** On (MHz) Krasnogorskaya 66.98, Karachayevsk (+1 tx) 67.34, Kavkazkiy 68.21, Adyge-Khabl 68.66, Zelenchuskaya 68.81, Pregradnaya 69.80, Ispravnaya 69.83, Ust-Dzheguta 69.89, Teberda 69.98, Arkhyz 70.07, Dombay 70.25, Cherkessk 70.31, V.Mara 71.06, Storozhevaya 71.72, Kurdzhinovo 71.81, Khabez 71.84, Urup 72.44, Cherkessk 91.2 in Russian, Abaza, Karachay-Balkar, Nogai.

**KD)** Krasnodarskiy kray: GTRK "Kuban", 350038 Krasnodar, ul. Radio 5. **E:** owl@kubantv.ru **Reg:** On (MHz) Tbilisskaya 66.20, Goryachiy Klyuch 66.41, Abrau-Dyurso 66.62, Novorossiysk (+1) 67.97, Gelendzhik 68.30, Kanevskaya 68.36, Armavir 68.57, Vyshestebliyevskaya 68.72, Primorsko-Ahktarsk 69.08, Kropotkin (+1) 69.23, Pavlovskaya 69.59, Temryuk 70.22, Krasnyy Kut (+1) 70.43, Tuapse 70.46, Yeysk 71.15, Gubskaya 71.21, Arkhipo-Osipovka 71.93, Sochi 71.93*, Apsheronsk 72.26, Imretinskaya 72.37, Otradnaya 72.98, Armavir 100.4, Tuapse 101.4, Belaya Glina 102.0, Kushchevskaya 103.5, Krasnodar 107.2, Yeysk 107.4. **NB:** *) Tx also carries prgrs by reg. substudio (Territorialnoye otdeleniye GTRK "Kuban"): 354000 Sochi, ul. Teatralnaya 11a. **E:** tv@sochi.com.

**KE)** Kemerovskaya oblast: GTRK "Kuzbass", 650000 Kemerovo, ul. Krasnoarmeyskaya 137a. **E:** director@gtrk.kuzbass.net **Reg:** "R. Kuzbassa" on (MHz) Yurga 66.11, Klyuchevaya 67.04, Tashtagol 69.80, Anzhevo-Sudzhensk 70.40, Novokuznetsk 97.9, Kiselyovsk 100.0, Mezhdurechensk 100.8, Kemerovo 103.7, Leninsk-Kuznetskiy 103.8. Reg. channel "Kuzbass FM" on (MHz) Kemerovo 91.0, Klyuchevaya 101.2, Leninsk-Kuznetskiy 101.3, Anzhevo-Sudzhensk 101.6, Mezhdurechensk 101.8, Novokuznetsk 102.0, Guryevsk 102.5, Yurga 103.6, Belovo 104.5, Sheregesh 105.7, Prokopyevsk 107.4.

**KG)** Kurganskaya oblast: GTRK "Kurgan", 640018 Kurgan, ul. Sovetskaya 105. **E:** report@gtrk-kurgan.ru **Reg:** On (MHz) Shumikha 66.89, Makushino 68.48, Shadrinsk 69.23, Shatrovo 71.18, Kurgan 105.0.

**KH)** Khabarovskiy kray: GTRK "Dalnevostochnaya", 680632 Khabarovsk, ul. Lenina 4. **E:** tv@dvtrk.com **Reg:** On (MHz) Tyrma 66.32, Sovetskaya Gavan (+1) 66.74, Sukpay 67.31, Bogorodskoye 67.52, Troitskoye 67.73, Ayan (+1) 68.00, Chumikan 68.12, Duki 68.30, Arka 69.20, Okhotsk 69.32, Glebovo 69.47, Vyazemskiy 69.83, Bikin 69.92, Chegdomyn 70.16, im. P.Osipenko 70.64, Novaya Inya 71.42, De-Kastri 72.71, Khabarovsk 91.4, Nikolayevsk-na-Amure 101.6, Komsomolsk-na-Amure 105.2* (also via txs in region YV). Local channel "R. 101.8" on Khabarovsk 101.8MHz. **NB:** *) Tx also carries reg. prgrs by reg. substudio (Territorialnoye otdeleniye GTRK "Dalnevostochnaya"): 681000 Komsomolsk-na-Amure, ul. Molodogvardeyskaya 7 **E:** studio@kmscom.ru.

**KL)** Kaluzhskaya oblast: GTRK "Kaluga", 248021 Kaluga, Pole Svobody 40a. **E:** mail@gtrk-kaluga.ru **Reg:** On (MHz) Lyudinovo 67.91, Medyn 68.03, Baryatino 70.79, Mosalsk 71.39, Spassk-Demensk 72.05, Zhizdra 72.92, Khvastovichi 73.07, Sukhinichi 101.3, Kaluga 104.3, Yukhnov 104.9, Obninsk 106.4.

**KM)** Kamchatskiy kray: GTRK "Kamchatka", 683000 Petropavlovsk-Kamchatskiy, ul. Sovetskaya 62. **Reg:** On (MHz) Ust-Bolsheretsk 69.56, Palana (+7) 69.68, Ust-Kamchatsk 71.12, Klyuchi 71.90, Milkovo 71.96, Sobolevo 72.9, Petropavlovsk-Kamchatskiy 102.0. Incl. prgrs in Koryak, Itelmen, Evenki produced by substudio (Territorialnoye otdeleniye GTRK "Kamchatka"): 684620 Palana, ul. Obukhova 4.

**KN)** Krasnoyarskiy kray: GTRK "Krasnoyarsk", 660028 Krasnoyarsk, ul. Mechnikova 44a. **E:** referent@kgtrk.ru **Reg:** On (MHz) Balakhta 66.32, Motygino 66.44, Karatuzskoye 67.37, Zelenogorsk 68.21, Solyanka 68.84, Uzhur 69.56, Pirovskoye 70.76 Tyukhtet 71.42, Krasnoturansk 71.48, Kodinsk 71.66, Igarka 72.00, Yeniseysk 72.74, Krasnoyarsk 94.5, Kansk 100.9, Norilsk 101.4*, Tura (+1) 101.5**, Borodino 101.8, Anash 102.7, Lesosibirsk 102.8, Dudinka*** 103.7, Achinsk 104.0, Nazarovo 104.8, Sukhobuzimskoye 104.9, Kozulka 106.3, Divnogorsk (+1) 107.9. **NB:** *) Tx also carries reg. prgrs by GTRK "Norilsk", 663300 Norilsk, nab. Urvantseva 10. **E:** secr@norilsk-tv.ru; **) Tx also carries prgrs by reg. substudio (Territorialnoye otdeleniye GTRK "Krasnoyarsk") in Russian, Evenki: 663370 Tura, ul. 50 let Oktyabrya 28. **E:** heglen@tura.evenkya.ru; ***) Tx also carries prgrs by reg. substudio (Territorialnoye otdeleniye GTRK "Norilsk") in Russian, Nenets: 647000 Dudinka, ul. Gorkogo 15. **E:** gtrktaimyr@dudinka.krasnet.ru.

**KO)** Respublika Komi: GTRK "Komi Gor", 167005 Syktyvkar, Oktyabrskiy pr. 164. **E:** komigor@komi.rfn.ru **Reg:** On (MHz) Yarashyu 65.90, Storozhevsk 66.32, Priuralsk 66.35, Ukhta 66.44, Vorkuta 66.60, Pechora 66.92, Ust-Tsilma 67.10, Sludka 67.16, Pomozdino 67.85, Kadzherom 68.30, N.Odes (+1) 68.36, Troitsko-Pechorsk 68.60, Shoshka

68.72, Aykino 68.78, Kartayol (+2) 68.93, Meshchura 69.02, Mordino 69.05, Inta 69.08, Krasnobor 69.11, Okunevo 69.20, Usogorsk 69.56, Koygorodok 69.74, Myyeldino (+1) 69.83, Ust-Kulom 70.16, Petrun 70.28, Vetyu 70.40, Voyvozh 70.64, Spasporub 70.73, Vuktyl 71.06, Kuratovo 71.09, B.Pyssa 71.15, Chukhlom 73.19, Usinsk (+1) 73.31, Syktyvkar 91.6 in Russian, Komi-Zyrian.

**KS)** Kostromskaya oblast: GTRK "Kostroma", 156961 Kostroma, pl. Konstitutsii 1. **E:** mail@kostroma.rfn.ru **Reg:** On (MHz) Galich 66.74, Sharya 67.10, Kologriv 68.66, Soligalich 69.02, Makaryev 71.60, Nerekhta 89.3, Kostroma 91.6, Pyshchuk 103.5, Vokhma 103.7, Chukhloma 103.8, Pavino 103.9, Parfenevo 104.0, Ostrovskoye 107.3.

**KT)** Respublika Kareliya: GTRK "Kareliya", 185002 Petrozavodsk, ul. Pirogova 2. **E:** gtrk@petrozavodsk.rfn.ru **Reg:** "R. Karelii" on (MHz) Kostomuksha 70.28, Petrozavodsk 102.2, Muyezerskiy 102.7, Loukhi 103.0, Medvezhyegorsk 103.7, Naiystenyarvi 105.0, Sortavala 105.6, Segezha 106.0 in Russian, Finnish, Karelian, Vepsian.

**KU)** Kurskaya oblast: GTRK "Kursk", 305016 Kursk, ul. Sovetskaya 32. **E:** gtrk@kursk.rfn.ru **Reg:** On (MHz) Kshenskiy 72.41, Kursk 101.7

**KV)** Kirovskaya oblast: GTRK "Vyatka", 610000 Kirov, ul. Uritskogo 34. **E:** tv@gtrk-vyatka.ru **Reg:** On (MHz) Vyatskiye Polyarny 66.35, Kirs 66.86, Sovetsk 67.07, Klyuchi 67.91, Falyonki 68.33, Pinyug (+1) 70.55, Shmelevo 70.73, Urzhum 71.06, Omutninsk 71.33, Sanchursk 73.28, Kirov 106.3.

**KX)** Respublika Kalmykiya: GTRK "Kalmykiya", 358000 Elista, ul. M.Gorkogo 34. **E:** kalmykiagtrk@mail.ru **Reg:** On (MHz) Utta 68.24, Ulan-Kholl 69.59, Elista 102.7 in Russian, Kalmyk.

**KY)** Khanty-Mansiyskiy avtonomnyy okrug - Yugra (NB: KY is subordinated to region TY): GTRK "Yugoriya", 628012 Khanty-Mansiysk, ul. Gagarina 4. **E:** gtrk@ugoria.tv **Reg:** "R. Yugry" on (MHz) Agirish 65.96, Khanty-Mansiysk 66.08, Kondinskoye 66.20, Kommunisticheskiy 66.32, Beloyarskiy 66.44, Oktyabrskoye 66.68, Bobrovskaya 66.77, Uray 67.22, Langepas 67.28, Kuminskiy 67.52, Igrim (+1) 68.33, Batovo 69.47, Mezhdurechenskiy 70.28, Vakhovsk 70.67, Nyagan 70.82, Gornopravdinsk 71.00, Kogalym 71.30, Beryozovo 71.42, Yugorsk 71.78, Raduzhnyy 72.08, Pyt-Yakh 72.86, Surgut 89.9, Nizhnevartovsk 107.8 in Russian, Khanti, Mansi. Txs also relay reg. prgrs by GTRK "Region-Tyumen", TY.

**LI)** Lipetskaya oblast: GTRK "Lipetsk", 398050 Lipetsk, pl. Plekhanova 1. **E:** teleradio@lipetsk.rfn.ru **Reg:** On (MHz) Chernava 69.26, Izmalkovo 73.79, Lipetsk 89.1, Yelets 101.7, Terbuny 101.9, Dankov 102.4, Ploty 102.6, Dobrinka 102.7, Dolgorukovo 102.9, Chaplygin 103.3, Lev Tolstoy 103.8, Usman 104.0, Volovo 104.4.

**MA)** Magadanskaya oblast: GTRK "Magadan", 685024 Magadan, ul. Kommuny 8/12. **E:** center@magtrk.ru **Reg:** On (MHz) Susuman 70.16, Evensk 100.5, Orotukan (+3) 101.0, Ola 101.3, Myaundzha 102.0, Omchak (+3) 102.5, Stekolnyy 102.9, Magadan 103.5.

**MD)** Respublika Mordoviya: GTRK "Mordoviya", 430030 Saransk, ul. Dokuchayeva 29. **E:** radiomordovii@mail.ru **Reg:** On (MHz) Tengushevo 66.35, Vechkusy 66.95, Dubenki 67.28, Krasnoslobodsk 67.31, B.Ignatovo 67.34, Ruzayevka 67.46, Yavas 67.67, Umet 68.33, B.Berezniki 68.42, Atyashevo 68.51, Torbeyevo 68.69, Chamzinka 68.75, Yelniki 68.78, Lyambir 68.96, Temnikov 68.99, Kadoshkino 69.41, Ardatov 69.53, St.Shaygovo 69.65, Insar 71.03, Romodanovo 71.12, Saransk 91.2, Atyuryevo 106.0 in Russian, Erzya, Moksha.

**ME)** Respublika Mariy El: GTRK "Mariy-El", 424031 Yoshkar-Ola, ul. Mashinostroiteley 7a. **E:** tv@tv.mari.ru **Reg:** On (MHz) Volzhsk 69.29, Sovetskiy 71.21, Kozmodemyansk 72.20, Zvenigovo 73.16, Yoshkar-Ola 106.0 in Russian, Mari.

**MO)** Moskva (Federal City) & Moskovskaya oblast: no regional branch of VGTRK.

**MU)** Murmanskaya oblast: GTRK "Murman", 183032 Murmansk, per. Rusanova 7. **E:** radio@tvmurman.com **Reg:** On (MHz) Kandalaksha 67.70, Revda 67.94, Alakurtti 69.50, Teriberka (+2) 69.74, Kaneva (+1) 70.01, Tumannyy 70.19, Kirovsk (+1) 70.34, Lovozero 70.73, Krasnoshchelye 72.38, Ostrovnoy 106.1, Murmansk 107.4.

**NE)** Nenetskiy avtonomnyy okrug (NB: NE is subordinated to region AR): Territorialnoye otdeleniye GTRK "Pomorye", 164700 Naryan-Mar, ul. Smidovicha 19. **E:** zapolyarie@mail.ru **Reg:** On (MHz) Naryan-Mar 66.20 in Russian, Nenets. Tx also relays reg. prgrs by GTRK "Pomorye", Arkhangelsk, AR.

**NN)** Nizhegorodskaya oblast: GTRK "Nizhniy Novgorod", 603950 Nizhniy Novgorod, ul. Belinskogo 9a. **E:** radio@nnov.rfn.ru **Reg:** On (MHz) Vacha 66.65, Sokolskoye 66.92, Sergach 67.16, Semyonov 67.43, Pavlovo 67.85, Uren 68.84, Kovernino 69.53, Shakhunya 69.59, Diveyevo 69.80, Lyskovo 70.43, Lukoyanov 70.52, Krasnyye Baki 70.64, Vyksa 71.09, Kstovo 73.97, N.Novgorod 93.9, Arzamas 106.6.

**NO)** Novgorodskaya oblast: GTRK "Slaviya", 173620 Velikiy Novgorod, ul. B.Moskovskaya 106. **E:** slavia-wn@yandex.ru **Reg:** "R. Slaviya" on (MHz) Borovichi 69.02, Zaluchye 71.93, Pestovo 100.0, Novgorod 102.2.

**NS)** Novosibirskaya oblast: GTRK "Novosibirsk", 630048 Novosibirsk, ul. Rimskogo-Korsakova 9. **E:** rrkc5@nsktv.ru **Reg:** On (MHz) B.Izyrak

(+1) 66.26, Novotroitsk 66.32, Vengerovo (+3) 66.35, Balman 66.44, Severnoye (+1) 66.50, Ust-Tarka 66.62, Suzun 66.68, Ordynskoye 66.74, Vdovino 66.86, Kargat 66.89, Maray 66.92, Kyshtovka 66.98, Novopreobrazhenka 67.01, Verkh-Iki 67.04, Chistoozernoye (+1) 67.04, Kurilovo (+1) 67.13, B.Chernaya (+1) 67.25, Dovolnoye 67.28, Kreshchenskoye 67.37, B.Kuliki 67.40, Biaza 67.43, Ichkala 67.49, Proletarskiy 67.52, Novoabyshevo 67.67, Gruzdeyevka 68.00, Bobrovka 68.18, Kordon 68.21, Aleksandro-Nevskoye 68.24, Vinograd 68.27, Boltovo 68.30, Bagan 68.36, Nikolayevka 68.54, Ogneva Zaimka 68.57, Ubinskoye 68.63, Bazovo 68.69, Korolevka 68.81, Ozero Karachi 68.84, Barabo-Yudino 68.90, Karasuk (+1) 68.93, Zdvinsk 68.96, Varvarovka (+1) 68.99, Maslyanino 69.05, Vladimirovka 69.08, Vassino 69.11, Novosilish 69.32, Alekseyevka 69.44, Kuybyshev 69.68, Bitki 69.74, Mikhaylovka 69.77, Bolshenikolskoye (+1) 69.83, Aksenikha 69.86, Zavyalovo 69.89, Kochki (+1) 69.95, Listvyanka 69.98, Novo-Baganenok 70.01, Cherepanovo 70.10, Moshkovo 70.22, Yermolayevka 70.40, Novokrasnoye 70.46, Musy 70.58, Kargan 70.61, Verkh-Miltyushi 70.67, Kruglikovo 70.70, Bergul 70.76, Minino (+1) 71.00, Krivoyazh 71.03, Krasnyy Yar (+1) 71.06, Lebedevo 71.48, Tatarsk 71.60, Bolotnoye 71.66, N.Matrenka 71.78, Novodubrovskoye 71.84, Bobrovichinsk 71.91, Beloye 72.08, Bortsovo 72.17, Zyryanka 72.23, Orlovka 72.26, Raduga 72.29, Krugloozernoye 72.32, Verkh-Krasnoyarka 72.41, Zonovo 72.62, Novobibeyevo 72.71, Kourak 72.95, Novosibirsk 97.8

**OB)** Orenburgskaya oblast: GTRK "Orenburg", 460024 Orenburg, per. Televizionnyy 3. **E:** gtrc@orenburg.rfn.ru **Reg:** On (MHz) Buzuluk 66.62, Yasnyy 69.71, Kuvandyk 70.04, Orenburg 91.0, Uralskoye 101.9, Sorochinsk 102.0, Bikkulovo (+1) 102.1, Tashla 102.6, Svetlyy 102.9, Pervomayskiy 103.0, Kvarkeno 103.1, Saraktash 103.3, Izobilnoye 103.5, Ilek 103.6, Novosergiyevka 103.9, Sol-Iletsk 104.6, Abdulino 105.1, Pleshanovo 105.2, Akbulak 105.5, Sharlyk 106.4, Alekseyevo 106.5, Tyulgan 106.6, Ponomarevka 106.9, Severnoye 107.0, Buguruslan (+1) 107.5, Aleksandrovka 107.8 in Russian, Chuvash, Tatar.

**OL)** Orlovskaya oblast: GTRK "Oryol", 302028 Oryol, ul. 7 Noyabrya 43. **E:** post@ogtrk.oryol.ru **Reg:** On (MHz) Livny 67.19, Oryol 102.3.

**OM)** Omskaya oblast: GTRK "Irtysh", 644050 Omsk, pr. Mira 2. **E:** reklama@omsk.rfn.ru **Reg:** (MHz) Isilkul 66.50, Ust-Ishim 67.04, Nazyvayevsk 67.28, Tara 68.39, Khutora 70.43, Cherlak 71.06, Omsk 87.7.

**PM)** Primorskiy kray: GTRK "Vladivostok", 690091 Vladivostok, ul. Uborevicha 20a. **E:** ptr@ptr-vlad.ru **Reg:** "R. Primorskogo kraya" on (MHz) Nakhodka 66.74/101.4, Olga 67.58, Permskoye 67.79, Arsenyev 68.60, Kraskino 68.84, Kavalerovo 69.20, Dalnerechensk 69.32, Dalnegorsk 70.04, Novozhatkovo 70.64, Plastun (+1) 71.00, Chkalovka 72.08, Kamenka (+4) 101.5, Rudnyy 101.9, Moryak-Rybolov (+2) 102.0, Vladivostok (+3) 102.1, Agzu (+5) 103.5, Ussuriysk 106.0.

**PR)** Permskiy kray: GTRK "Perm", 614090 Perm, ul. Tekhnicheskaya 7. **E:** main@t7.ru **Reg:** "R. Permskogo kraya" on (MHz) Kungur 66.65, Barda 67.10, Kudymkar 67.19*, Gayny 67.34*, Kizel 67.67, Keros 67.88*, Chastye 68.63, Oktyabrskiy 68.72, Vaya 68.78, Ust-Chernoye 68.84*, Ilyinskiy 68.93, Serebryanka 69.14, Uinskoye 69.38, Karagay 69.53, Osa 70.55, Chusovoy 70.67, Chernushka 70.70, Siva 70.73, Kochevo 70.82*, Krasnovishersk 71.33, Chaykovskiy 71.42, Berezniki 71.87, Ochyor 72.02, Kosa 73.10*, Yelovo* (+1 tx) 73.58, Perm 90.2, Gayny 100.6, Siva 101.8, Berezniki 104.2. NB: *) Txs also carry prgrs by reg. substudio (Territorialnoye otdeleniye GTRK "Perm") in Russian, Komi-Permyak 617240 Kudymkar, ul. Volodarskogo 18. **E:** kudtv@mail.ru.

**PS)** Pskovskaya oblast: GTRK "Pskov", 180000 Pskov, ul. Nekrasova 50. **E:** tv@pvi.ru **Reg:** On (MHz) Trutnevo 67.34, Novosokolniki 67.94, Sebezh 68.12, Dedovichi 69.86, Glubokoye 70.01, Pskov 91.1, V.Luki 103.8.

**PZ)** Penzenskaya oblast: GTRK "Penza", ul. Lermontova 39, 440602 Penza. **E:** gtrk@penza-trv.ru **Reg:** On (MHz) Pachelma 66.80, Sosnovoborsk 68.51, Meshcherskoye 68.84, Blagodatka 69.08, Lopatino 70.22, Penza 70.67, Narovchat 70.88, Belinskiy 71.21, Issa 100.2, Gorodishche 100.4, Lunino 101.0, Neverkino 101.1, Nikolsk 106.1, Malaya Serdoba 106.4.

**RA)** Respublika Altay: GTRK "Gornyy Altay", 659000 Gorno-Altaysk, pr. Kommunisticheskiy 37. **E:** info@elaltay.ru **Reg:** On (MHz) Turochak 66.02, Tashanta (+1) 67.10, Gorno-Altaysk 67.22, Onguday (+1) 74.65, Ust-Kan 102.8, Ulagan 103.3, Kosh-Agach 103.5, Ust-Koksa 104.8 in Russian, Altai.

**RK)** Respublika Khakasiya: GTRK "Khakasiya", 655017 Abakan, ul. Vyatkina 12. **E:** vgtrk2003@mail.ru **Reg:** "R. Khakasiya" on (MHz) Kopyevo 68.00, Priiskovyy 68.51, Chernogorsk 69.50, Shira 70.16, Tashtyp (+1) 71.00, Bogdan 72.50, Askiz 72.59, Cheremushki 73.01, Sorsk 73.19, Sonskiy 73.52, Beya (+1) 73.61, Kommunar 73.85, Abakan 91.0, Sayanogorsk 102.7, Abaza 103.3 in Russian, Khakas.

**RO)** Rostovskaya oblast: GTRK "Don-TR", 344101 Rostov-na-Donu, ul. 1-ya Barrikadnaya 18. **E:** dontr2@dontr.ru **Reg:** On (MHz) Morozovsk 67.07, Kamensk 70.28, Rostov-na-Donu 89.0, Volgodonsk 99.0, Veshenskaya 101.4, Shakhty 102.9, Morozovsk 104.0, Novocherkassk

105.4, Salsk 105.9.

**RS)** Respublika Sakha (Yakutiya): GTRK "Sakha", 677892 Yakutsk, ul. Ordzhonikidze 48. **E:** gtrksakha@yandex.ru **Reg:** "R. Yakutii" on (MHz) Neryungri 66.68, Aldan 69.38, Lensk 70.28, Batagay 100.5, Namtsy 101.2, Olyokminsk 101.4, Pokrovsk 101.7, Belaya Gora (+2) 102.0, Yakutsk 104.9 in Russian, Yakut.

**RT)** Respublika Tyva: GTRK "Tyva", 667003 Kyzyl, ul. Gornaya 31. **Reg:** On (MHz) Shagonar 70.64, Kyzyl 105.5 in Russian, Tuvinian.

**RY)** Ryazanskaya oblast: GTRK "Oka", 390006 Ryazan, ul. Skomoroshinskaya 20. **E:** zavtv@ryazan.rfn.ru **Reg:** "R. Ryazani" on (MHz) Kadom 68.03, Yermish 69.35, Lesnoye-Konobeyevo 72.35, Ryazan 99.7, Miloslavskoye 101.8, Mosolovo 103.5, Ryazhsk 105.2, Skopin 106.9.

**SA)** Samarskaya oblast: GTRK "Samara", 443011 Samara, ul. Sovetskoy Armii 205. **E:** info@tvsamara.ru **Reg:** On (MHz) Tolyatti 88.9, B. Glushitsa 91.7, Podlesnyy 94.8, Kurumoch 95.0, Samara 95.3, Borskoye 96.1, Novyy Kutuluk 98.5, Petrovka 99.0, Kinel 99.5, Bereznyaki (+1) 100.0, Beregovoy 100.3, Oktyabrsk 100.4, Chapayev 100.7, Chetyrla 101.2, Kamyshla 102.6, Mordovo-Adelyakovo 103.0, Syzran (+1) 103.4, Chelno-Vershiny 103.5, Androsovka (+1) 103.9, Alekseyevka (+1) 104.0, Pokhvistnevo 104.1, Yelkhovka 104.2, Klyavlino (+1) 104.4, Koshki 105.1, Neftegorsk 105.2, Isakly 105.3, Staraya Racheyka 105.4, Novokurovka 105.5, Krasnoarmeyskoye 105.8, Sergiyevsk 105.9, Khvorostyanka 107.1, Kinel-Cherkassy 107.7.

**SL)** Sakhalinskaya oblast: GTRK "Sakhalin", ul. Komsomolskaya 209, 693000 Yuzhno-Sakhalinsk. **E:** gtrksakhalin@gmail.com **Reg:** On (MHz) Tymovskoye 66.08, Khoe 66.80, Golovino 68.00, Malokurilskoye 68.24, Pyatirechye 68.39, Smirnykh 68.69, Okha 69.20, Aleksandrovsk-Sakhalinskiy 69.44, Gornozavodsk 69.50, Nogliki 69.56, Okhotskoye 69.65, Poronaysk 69.92, Tomari 70.16, Uglegorsk 70.40, Yuzhno-Kurilsk 70.94, Novikovo 71.12, Shebunino 71.63, Nevelsk 101.7, Dolinsk 102.0, Chekhov 104.0, Kholmsk 104.8, Yuzhno-Sakhalinsk 106.0, Korsakov 107.6. Incl. prgr in Korean.

**SM)** Smolenskaya oblast: GTRK "Smolensk", 214025 Smolensk, ul. Nakhimova 1. **E:** rukovodstvo@smolgtrk.rfn.ru **Reg:** On (MHz) Smolensk 68.54, Smogiri 68.96, Vyazma 69.20, Roslavl 70.91.

**SO)** Respublika Severnaya Osetiya - Alaniya: GTRK "Alaniya", 362007 Vladikavkaz, Osetinskaya gorka 2. **E:** mail@alaniatv.ru **Reg:** On (MHz) Verkhniy Fiagdon 69.47, Mozdok 71.78, Vladikavkaz 90.0 in Russian, Ossetic. Local channel "Alaniya FM" on Vladikavkaz 104.5MHz.

**SP)** Sankt Peterburg (Federal City) & Leningradskaya oblast: GTRK "Sankt-Peterburg", 197022 St.Peterburg, nab. reki Karpovki 43. **E:** info@rtr.spb.ru **Reg:** On (MHz) Tikhvin 66.14, St.Peterburg 66.30/99.0, Kingisepp 67.67, Podporozhye 69.95, Luga 70.88.

**SR)** Saratovskaya oblast: GTRK "Saratov", 410004 Saratov, 2-ya Sadovaya ul. 7. **E:** top@gtrk.renet.ru **Reg:** On (MHz) Perelyub 66.44, Yershov 68.48, Aleksandrov Gay 69.68, Balashov 70.16, Saratov 71.09, Balakovo 100.4.

**ST)** Stavropolskiy kray: GTRK "Stavropolye", 355000 Stavropol, ul. Artema 35a. **E:** referent@stavropolye.tv **Reg:** On (MHz) Ipatovo 66.77, Pyatigorsk 68.96, Stavropol 69.53, Neftekumsk 70.01, Pyatigorsk 107.8

**SV)** Sverdlovskaya oblast: GTRK "Ural", 620026 Yekaterinburg, ul. Lunacharskogo 212. **E:** radio@sgtrk.ru **Reg:** "R. Urala" on (MHz) Talitsa 65.93, Novaya Lyalya 66.08, Petrokamenskoye 66.32, Alapayevsk 66.50, Talitsa 66.71, Zaykovo 66.83, Nevyansk 66.92, Nizhniye Sergi 67.01, Ivdel 67.76, Sankino 68.66, Basyanovskiy 68.69, Propokyevskaya Salda 68.72, Serebryn Bugalysh 68.93, Rezh (+2) 69.17, Bisert 69.29, Baranchinskiy 69.29, Serov 69.65, Klevakinskoye 69.74, Useninovo 69.80, Andronovo 70.16, Andryushino 70.34, Afanasyevskoye (+1) 70.43, Pelym 70.58, Arti 70.73, Pyshma 71.24, Kamyshlov 72.53, Severouralsk 73.25, Turinsk 73.85, Yekaterinburg 95.5, Krasnoufimsk 101.7.

**TA)** Tambovskaya oblast: GTRK "Tambov", 392000 Tambov, ul. Michurinskaya 8a. **E:** gtrk@intmb.ru **Reg:** On (MHz) Tambov 100.9.

**TL)** Tulskaya oblast: GTRK "Tula", 300600 Tula, Staronikitskaya ul. 1. **E:** info@tula.rfn.ru **Reg:** On (MHz) Novomoskovsk 72.35, Tula 90.2, Suvorov 102.4.

**TO)** Tomskaya oblast: GTRK "Tomsk", 634050 Tomsk, ul. Pushkina 19. **E:** adm@tvtomsk.ru **Reg:** "R. Tomsk" on (MHz) Aleksandrovskoye 66.02, Pudino 66.74, Nadym 66.80, Kozhevnikovo 67.01, Krivosheino 67.31, Beregayevo (+2) 67.40, Staraya Yuvala (+1) 68.15, Voznesenka (+1) 68.33, Malinovka 68.39, Parabel 68.45, Kolpashevo 68.87, Klyukvinka 68.33, Strezhevoy 68.51, Vysokiy Yar 68.54, Teguldet 68.60, Yagodnyy 68.66, Koplashevo 68.87, Ulu-Yul 69.08, Podgornoye 69.20, Kyonga 69.29, Baturino 69.50, Belyy Yar 69.56, Parbig 69.80, Bakchar (+1) 70.01, Malinovka 70.55, Novaya Tyuvinka 70.70, Komsomolsk 70.82, Novyy Vasyugan 71.00, Novonikolskoye 71.21, Oktyabrskiy (+1) 71.33, Kargasok 71.42, Asino 71.67, Molchanovo 71.84, Krasnyy Yar 72.17, Chilino 72.20, Podgornoye 72.44, Zyryanskoye 73.01, Plotinkovo 73.22, Volodino 73.40, Novyy Tevriz (+1) 102.0, Tomsk 102.9, Turuntayevo 106.3.

**TS)** Respublika Tatarstan (Tatarstan): GTRK "Tatarstan", 420015 Kazan, ul. M. Gorkogo 15. **E:** secret@trttv.ru **Reg:** "R.Tatarstana"/ "Tatarstan radiosi" on (MHz) Abdakhmanovo 72.59, Nurlat 87.6, Bilyarsk (+1) 92.1, Muslyumovo 92.4, Aznakayevo 95.3, Sarmanovo 96.4, Sovkhoz im. Kirova 98.2, Novosheshminsk 98.8, B.Atnya 98.9, Kazan (+1) 99.2, Leninogorsk 99.9, Bavly 100.3, Nizhnekamsk 101.1, Kushmany 101.6, Cheremshan 102.6, Kutlu-Bukash 103.5, Buinsk 103.8, Almetyevsk 103.9, Tetyushi 104.8, Shemordan 107.5, Bazarnye Mataki 107.8, Aktanysh (+1) 107.9 in Russian, Tatar.

**TV)** Tverskaya oblast: GTRK "Tver", 170000 Tver, ul. Vagzhanova 9. **E:** gtrktver@tvcom.ru **Reg:** On (MHz) V.Volochyok 87.5, Selizharovo 88.2, Tver 93.5, Bologoye 99.2, Maksatikha (+1) 99.5, Krasnyy Kholm 100.5, Olenino 101.5, Spirovo 101.7, Nelidovo 102.5, Staritsa 103.1, Rameshki 103.5, Toropetsk 104.0, Zharkovskiy 104.1, Zap. Dvina 105.1, Belyy (+1) 107.1, Kashin 107.7, Vesyegonsk 107.9.

**TY)** Tyumenskaya oblast: GTRK "Region-Tyumen", 625013 Tyumen, ul. Permyakova 6. **E:** gtrk@region-tyumen.ru **Reg:** On (MHz) Berdyuzhye 66.41, Aromashevo 66.68, Gagarino 66.89, Yarkovo 66.95, Vagay 68.60, Armizonskoye 68.84, Masali 68.96, Yurginskoye 69.11, Demyanskoye 69.32, B.Sorokino 69.95, Nizhnyaya Tavda 70.34, Shabanovo 70.55, Uvat 71.42, Tobolsk 71.90, Uporovo 73.19, Tyumen 90.8, Zavodoukovsk 104.1 (also relayed via txs in region KY).

**UD)** Udmurtskaya respublika: GTRK "Udmurtiya", 426004 Izhevsk, ul. Komunarov 216. **E:** adm@udmtv.ru **Reg:** On (MHz) Kizner 71.81, Balezino 96.3, Izhevsk 96.6, Sarapul 96.8, Alnashi 98.3, Karakulino 98.4, Debyosy 101.0, Vavozh 102.7, Kambarka (+1) 103.6, Mozhga 104.0, Krasnogorodskoye 104.7, Valamaz 105.0, Syumsi 107.2 in Russian, Udmurt, Tatar, Mari.

**UL)** Ulyanovskaya oblast: GTRK "Volga", 432030 Ulyanovsk, ul. Simbirskaya 5. **E:** volgarek@mail.ru **Reg:** On (MHz) Veshkayma 70.40, Gladchikha 73.49, Ulyanovsk 89.6, Dimitrovgrad 107.2

**VG)** Volgogradskaya oblast: GTRK "Volgograd-TRV", 400066 Volgograd, ul. Mira 9. **E:** radioinfo@volgograd-trv.ru **Reg:** (MHz) Mikhaylovka 66.83, Elton 66.95, Uryupinsk 67.17, Kamyshin 69.14, Chilekovo 69.44, Loboykovo (+1) 70.40, Yelan 70.49, Kletskiy 70.94, Surovikino 71.00, Zhirnovsk 71.51, Volgograd 98.3, Yelan 102.7, Uryupinsk 103.4, Zhirnovsk 103.6, Uspenka 103.9, Kamyshin 105.2, Novoanninskiy 106.1, Mikhaylovka 106.5, Kletskiy 107.0. Local channel "Volgograd 24" on Volgograd 93.5MHz.

**VL)** Vladimirskaya oblast: GTRK "Vladimir", 600000 Vladimir, ul. Bol. Moskovskaya 62. **E:** adm@vladtv.ru **Reg:** On (MHz) Petushki 66.71, Aleksandrov 67.67, Suzdal 68.72, Gorokhovets 69.08, Sudogda 69.47, Melenki 70.25, Vyazniki 70.28, Sobinka 70.61, Kovrov 70.67, Kirzhach 71.03, Kolchugino 73.55, Murom 88.7, Kovrov 98.3, Gus-Khrustalnyy 103.1.

**VN)** Voronezhskaya oblast: GTRK "Voronezh", 394625 Voronezh, ul. Karl Marksa 114. **E:** tv@vgtv.vrn.ru **Reg:** On (MHz) Bobrov 67.04, Kalach 67.37, Borisoglebsk 70.82, Boguchar 71.90, Voronezh 95.9, Ertil 101.5.

**VO)** Vologodskaya oblast: GTRK "Vologda", 160000 Vologda, ul. Predtechenskaya 32. **E:** secretar@grk35.ru **Reg:** On (MHz) Sludno 66.77, Vitegra (+1) 66.86, Syamzha 67.88, Nyuksenitsa 68.03, Vologda 69.05, Verkhovazhye 69.08, Lipin Bor 69.65, Totma 69.71, Kurilovo 70.07, Vologda 98.0, Andomskiy Pogost 100.8, Tarnogorskiy Gorodok 101.5, Kharovsk 102.2, Vozhega 102.5, Novaya Derevnya (+1) 102.7, Shuyskoye 102.9, Cherepovets 103.4.

**YA)** Yaroslavskaya oblast: GTRK "Yaroslaviya", 150014 Yaroslavl, ul. Bogdanovicha 20. **E:** gtrk@yaroslavl.rfn.ru **Reg:** On (MHz) Yaroslavl 99.1, Volga 102.8, Lyubim 103.6, Danilov 104.3.

**YN)** Yamalo-Nenetskiy avtonomnyy okrug - Yugra (NB: YN is subordinated to region TY): GTRK "Yamal", 626600 Salekhard, ul. Lambinykh 3. **E:** gtrk@gtrk-yamal.ru **Reg:** On (MHz) Gubkinskiy 66.75, Muzhi 68.90, Yar-Sale 69.32, Kharp 70.76, Noyabrsk 70.46, Nadym 71.78, Salekhard (+1) 100.6, Muravlenko 104.7. Txs also relay reg. prgrs by GTRK "Region-Tyumen", Tyumen, TY.

**YV)** Yevreyskaya avtonomnaya oblast: GTRK "Bira", 679016 Birobidzhan, ul. Oktyabrskaya 15. **E:** gtrkbira@biratv.rfn.ru **Reg:** On (MHz) Obluchye 66.32, Birobidzhan 67.88, Khingansk 68.33, Birakan 68.60, Pashkovo 69.89, Bidzhan (+1) 70.07, Kuldur 73.64, Amurzet 101.3.

**ZB)** Zabaykalskiy kray: GTRK "Chita", 672090 Chita, ul. Kostyushko-Grigorovicha 27. **E:** chrtv@chita.ru **Reg:** On (MHz) Kokuy (+1) 66.14, Nerchinskiy Zavod 66.44, Krasnyy Chikoy 66.53, Kyra 68.00, Khilok 68.09, Karymskoye 68.81, Novopavlovka 69.05, Baley 69.17, Ulety 69.41, Khada-Bulak 69.56, Kholbon 69.80, Verkh-Usugli 69.98, Orlovskiy 70.07*, Krasnokamensk 70.67, Priargunsk 73.85, Chita 91.6, Narasun 101.9, Kurulga (+1) 102.4, Aleksandrovskiy Zavod (+6 txs) 102.5, Kokuy 102.6, Tokhtor 102.8, Chara 103.0, Duldurga 103.3, Gazimurskiy Zavod (+2) 103.6, Maleta (+1) 103.7, Darasun (+1) 104.1, Batakan (+6) 104.2, Novokurgatay (+1) 104.4 in Russian, Buryat. NB: *) Tx also carries prgrs by reg. substudio (Territorialnoye otdeleniye GTRK

"Chita"): ul. Bazara Rinchino 7, 687000 Aginskoye. **E:** abgtrk_agi@
aginsk.chita.ru.

## RADIO ORFEY (Gov)
✉ 115326 Moskva, ul. Pyatnitskaya 25 ☎ +7 495 9514340 🖨 +7 495
9594067 **E:** rgmc@muzcentrum.ru **W:** muzcentrum.ru
**LP:** DG: Irina Gerasimova

| Rg | Location | MHz | kW | Rg | Location | MHz | kW |
|----|----------|-----|-----|----|----------|-----|-----|
| PR | Perm | 66.80 | 4 | TL | Tula | 71.93 | 4 |
| SV | Yekaterinburg | 69.92 | 1 | MO | Moskva | 99.2 | 5 |
| LI | Lipetsk | 70.07 | 4 | SM | Smolensk | 104.3 | 0.5 |
| VG | Volgograd | 71.33 | 2 | KG | Kurgan | 106.0 | 1 |
| SP | St.Peterburg | 71.66 | 5 | | | | |

**D.Prgr:** 24h.

**OTHER STATIONS** (¦=time-shared)

| MW | kHz | kW | Rg | Location | Station |
|----|-----|-----|----|----------|---------|
| 86) | ¦ 612 | 20 | MO | Kurkino, E | Narodnoye R. |
| 172) | ¦ 612 | 20 | MO | Kurkino, E | R. Radonezh |
| 172) | 684 | 10 | SP | Olgino, E | R. Radonezh |
| A) | 738 | 5 | MO | Kurkino, E | Vsemirnaya radioset |
| 117) | 765 | 20 | KH | Khabarovsk, FE | R. Vostok Rossii |
| 117) | 765 | 20 | KH | Komsomolsk-na-A., FE | R. Vostok Rossii |
| 117) | 765 | 5 | KH | Chegdomyn, FE | R. Vostok Rossii |
| 117) | 765 | 5 | KH | De-Kastri, FE | R. Vostok Rossii |
| 117) | 765 | 5 | KH | Sovetskaya Gavan, FE | R. Vostok Rossii |
| 117) | 765 | 5 | KH | Troitskoye, FE | R. Vostok Rossii |
| 117) | 765 | 5 | KH | Tsimmermanskoye, FE | R. Vostok Rossii |
| 117) | 765 | 5 | KH | Vyazemskiy, FE | R. Vostok Rossii |
| 117) | 765 | 5 | KH | Yekaterinoslavka, FE | R. Vostok Rossii |
| 117) | 765 | 5 | KH | Yagodnyy, FE | R. Vostok Rossii |
| 121) | ¦ 828 | 10 | SP | Olgino, E | Radiogazeta Slovo |
| 123) | ¦ 828 | 10 | SP | Olgino, E | Pravoslavnoye R. |
| 128) | 1053 | 10 | SP | Olgino, E | R. Mariya |

| FM | MHz | kW | Rg | Location | Station |
|----|-----|-----|----|----------|---------|
| 12) | 66.23 | 1 | TS | Nab.Chelny | Brezhnev FM |
| 124C) | 66.68 | 1 | BA | Ufa | R. Ashkadar |
| 134A) | 67.70 | 1 | CB | Magnitogorsk | Studio 21 |
| 178) | 67.70 | 1 | UL | Ulyanovsk | Tatarskoye R. |
| 148) | 67.79 | 1 | TS | Nab.Chelny | R. Kunel |
| 1) | 68.00 | 5 | MO | Moskva | Avtoradio |
| 4) | 68.09 | 1 | PZ | Penza | Europa plus |
| 60) | 68.51 | 4 | SV | Irbit | Kanal Voskreseniye |
| 168) | 68.84 | 5 | MO | Moskva | R. 1 |
| 60) | 68.87 | 4 | SV | Nizhniye Sergi | Kanal Voskreseniye |
| 5) | 68.90 | 1 | KN | Krasnoyarsk | Hit FM |
| 3) | 69.11 | 1 | AK | Barnaul | Ekho Moskvy |
| 108) | 69.68 | 1 | BA | Ufa | R. 1-y Kanal |
| 7) | 69.74 | 1 | UL | Ulyanovsk | Militseyskaya volna |
| 15) | 70.70 | 1 | CB | Chelyabinsk | DFM |
| 16) | 70.85 | 1 | KV | Kirov | Retro FM |
| 3) | 71.06 | 1 | RK | Abakan | Ekho Moskvy |
| 60) | 71.21 | 4 | SV | Nizhniy Tagil | Kanal Voskreseniye |
| 197A) | 71.30 | 1 | RS | Yakutsk | R. Viktoriya-Sakha |
| 2) | 71.30 | 5 | MO | Moskva | Russkoye R. |
| 60) | 71.69 | 4 | SV | Serov | Kanal Voskreseniye |
| 14) | 71.72 | 2 | KL | Kaluga | R. Shanson |
| 14) | 72.11 | 1 | KA | Kaliningrad | R. Shanson |
| 60) | 72.11 | 4 | SV | Afanasyevskoye | Kanal Voskreseniye |
| 60) | 72.11 | 4 | SV | Tavda | Kanal Voskreseniye |
| 99) | 72.29 | 1 | ZB | Chita | Populyarnoye R. |
| 87) | 72.41 | 4 | CV | Ibresi | Nats. R. Chuvashii |
| 14) | 72.44 | 1 | KV | Kirov | R. Shanson |
| 60) | 72.83 | 4 | SV | Yekaterinburg | Kanal Voskreseniye |
| 172) | 72.92 | 10 | MO | Moskva | R. Radonezh |
| 56) | 73.10 | 10 | SP | Sankt-Peterburg | Grad Petrov |
| 2) | 73.22 | 1 | IR | Bratsk | Russkoye R. |
| 16) | 73.25 | 1 | KL | Kaluga | Retro FM |
| 86) | 73.25 | 1 | KD | Krasnodar | Narodnoye R. |
| 130B) | 73.55 | 1 | VN | Voronezh | R. Blagovestiye |
| 2) | 73.76 | 1 | IR | Angarsk | Russkoye R. |
| 26) | 73.88 | 1 | MD | Saransk | R. Rekord |
| 3) | 73.94 | 1 | YA | Yaroslavl | Ekho Moskvy |
| 3) | 73.97 | 1 | CB | Chelyabinsk | Ekho Moskvy |
| 11) | 87.5 | 1 | SR | Saratov | R. Maksimum |
| 134A) | 87.5 | 1 | BR | Bryansk | Studio 21 |
| 178) | 87.5 | 1 | TS | Nab.Chelny | Tatarskoye R. |
| 19) | 87.5 | 1 | RO | Salsk | Dorozhnoye R. |
| 19) | 87.5 | 5 | SP | Sankt-Peterburg | Dorozhnoye R. |
| 28) | 87.5 | 5 | MO | Moskva | Biznes FM |
| 6) | 87.5 | 1 | KY | Surgut | Love R. |
| 134A) | 87.6 | 1 | BE | Belgorod | Studio 21 |
| 19) | 87.6 | 1 | IV | Kineshma | Dorozhnoye R. |

| FM | MHz | kW | Rg | Location | Station |
|----|-----|-----|----|----------|---------|
| 21) | 87.6 | 1 | SV | Yekaterinburg | R. Zvezda |
| 23) | 87.6 | 1 | PR | Perm | Detskoye R. |
| 25) | 87.6 | 1 | KE | Kemerovo | R. Mir |
| 1) | 87.7 | 1 | AM | Blagoveshchensk | Avtoradio |
| 134A) | 87.7 | 1 | SM | Smolensk | Studio 21 |
| 134A) | 87.8 | 1 | BA | Ufa | Studio 21 |
| 134A) | 87.8 | 1 | PM | Vladivostok | Studio 21 |
| 183) | 87.8 | 1 | KY | Nizhnevartovsk | R. Sibir |
| 31) | 87.9 | 5 | MO | Moskva | Like FM |
| 6) | 87.9 | 1 | BR | Bryansk | Love R. |
| 6) | 87.9 | 1 | IV | Ivanovo | Love R. |
| 8) | 87.9 | 1 | AS | Astrakhan | Nashe R. |
| 23) | 88.2 | 1 | RO | Rostov-na-Donu | Detskoye R. |
| 24) | 88.2 | 1 | BA | Ufa | NRJ |
| 5) | 88.2 | 1 | KY | Surgut | Hit FM |
| 97) | 88.2 | 1 | KE | Leninsk-Kuznetskiy | Pioner FM |
| 1) | 88.3 | 2 | PM | Vladivostok | Avtoradio |
| 16) | 88.3 | 5 | MO | Moskva | Retro FM |
| 16) | 88.3 | 1 | SL | Yu-Sakhalinsk | Retro FM |
| 17) | 88.3 | 1 | TS | Kazan | Serebryanyy dozhd |
| 18) | 88.3 | 1 | TY | Tyumen | Yumor FM |
| 19) | 88.3 | 1 | AK | Barnaul | Dorozhnoye R. |
| 22) | 88.3 | 1 | KH | Khabarovsk | R. KP |
| 23) | 88.3 | 1 | SR | Saratov | Detskoye R. |
| 23) | 88.3 | 1 | AS | Astrakhan | R. Dacha |
| 27) | 88.3 | 1 | KD | Krasnodar | R. Dacha |
| 5) | 88.3 | 1 | SV | Yekaterinburg | Hit FM |
| 24) | 88.4 | 1 | SA | Tolyatti | NRJ |
| 36) | 88.4 | 5 | SP | Sankt-Peterburg | Avtoradio S-Peterburg |
| 6) | 88.4 | 1 | KE | Kemerovo | Love R. |
| 1) | 88.5 | 1 | KH | Komsomolsk-na-A. | Avtoradio |
| 1) | 88.5 | 1 | MO | Yegoryevsk | Avtoradio |
| 21) | 88.5 | 1 | TO | Tomsk | R. Zvezda |
| 35) | 88.5 | 5 | IR | Irkutsk | R. Vera |
| 17) | 88.6 | 1 | IV | Ivanovo | Serebryanyy dozhd |
| 5) | 88.6 | 1 | UL | Dimitrovgrad | Hit FM |
| 1) | 88.7 | 2 | KH | Khabarovsk | Avtoradio |
| 134A) | 88.7 | 1 | MU | Murmansk | Studio 21 |
| 14) | 88.7 | 1 | AM | Blagoveshchensk | R. Shanson |
| 174) | 88.7 | 1 | AS | Astrakhan | R. Astrakhan |
| 18) | 88.7 | 10 | MO | Moskva | Yumor FM |
| 25) | 88.7 | 1 | KD | Krasnodar | Detskoye R. |
| 25) | 88.7 | 1 | SA | Samara | R. Mir |
| 26) | 88.7 | 1 | SR | Saratov | R. Rekord |
| 7) | 88.7 | 1 | AK | Barnaul | Militseyskaya volna |
| 9A) | 88.7 | 1 | SM | Safonovo | R. Vanya |
| 134A) | 88.8 | 1 | UL | Ulyanovsk | Studio 21 |
| 17) | 88.8 | 1 | SV | Yekaterinburg | Serebryanyy dozhd |
| 185) | 88.8 | 1 | IN | Nazran | R. Ingushetiya |
| 22) | 88.8 | 1 | ST | Pyatigorsk | R. KP |
| 26) | 88.8 | 1 | TY | Tyumen | R. Rekord |
| 9A) | 88.8 | 1 | BU | Ulan-Ude | R. Vanya |
| 18) | 88.9 | 1 | PR | Perm | Yumor FM |
| 18) | 88.9 | 1 | KM | Petropavlovsk-K. | Yumor FM |
| 18) | 88.9 | 5 | SP | Sankt-Peterburg | Yumor FM |
| 19) | 88.9 | 1 | TS | Kazan | Dorozhnoye R. |
| 26) | 88.9 | 1 | SL | Yu-Sakhalinsk | R. Rekord |
| 3) | 88.9 | 1 | IR | Irkutsk | Nashe R. |
| 14) | 89.0 | 1 | UL | Dimitrovgrad | R. Shanson |
| 18) | 89.0 | 1 | BA | Ufa | Yumor FM |
| 139) | 89.1 | 5 | MO | Moskva | R. Jazz |
| 24) | 89.1 | 1 | OM | Omsk | NRJ |
| 9A) | 89.1 | 1 | MU | Murmansk | R. Vanya |
| 176) | 89.2 | 1 | SR | Saratov | Taksi FM |
| 23) | 89.2 | 1 | SV | Yekaterinburg | Detskoye R. |
| 27) | 89.2 | 1 | KE | Kemerovo | R. Dacha |
| 27) | 89.2 | 1 | UL | Ulyanovsk | R. Dacha |
| 6) | 89.2 | 1 | BU | Ulan-Ude | Love R. |
| 25) | 89.3 | 1 | IR | Irkutsk | R. Mir |
| 45) | 89.3 | 1 | KD | Krasnodar | Novoye R. |
| 19) | 89.4 | 1 | PM | Vladivostok | Dorozhnoye R. |
| 27) | 89.4 | 1 | RK | Abakan | R. Dacha |
| 4) | 89.4 | 1 | PR | Perm | Europa plus |
| 134A) | 89.5 | 1 | OM | Omsk | Studio 21 |
| 25) | 89.5 | 1 | MU | Murmansk | R. Mir |
| 76) | 89.5 | 10 | MO | Moskva | Megapolis FM |
| 2) | 89.6 | 1 | KH | Khabarovsk | Russkoye R. |
| 24) | 89.6 | 1 | SV | Yekaterinburg | NRJ |
| 27) | 89.6 | 1 | TY | Tyumen | R. Dacha |
| 176) | 89.7 | 1 | TS | Kazan | Taksi FM |
| 202) | 89.7 | 4 | SP | Sankt-Peterburg | R. Zenit |
| 18) | 89.8 | 1 | RK | Abakan | Yumor FM |

| FM | MHz | kW | Rg | Location | Station |
|---|---|---|---|---|---|
| 21) | 89.8 | 1 | IR | Irkutsk | R. Zvezda |
| 22) | 89.8 | 1 | KE | Kemerovo | R. KP |
| 46) | 89.8 | 1 | PR | Perm | Comedy R. |
| 26) | 89.9 | 1 | SV | Serov | R. Rekord |
| 49) | 89.9 | 5 | MO | Moskva | Strana FM |
| 19) | 90.2 | 2 | KY | Surgut | Dorozhnoye R. |
| 16) | 90.4 | 1 | SA | Tolyatti | Retro FM |
| 19) | 90.4 | 1 | KE | Leninsk-Kuznetskiy | Dorozhnoye R. |
| 22) | 90.4 | 1 | BU | Ulan-Ude | R. KP |
| 22) | 90.4 | 2 | PM | Vladivostok | R. KP |
| 46) | 90.4 | 1 | TY | Tyumen | Comedy R. |
| 35) | 90.5 | 1 | OM | Omsk | R. Vera |
| 22) | 90.6 | 1 | SR | Saratov | R. KP |
| 23) | 90.6 | 1 | BA | Ufa | Detskoye R. |
| 24) | 90.6 | 1 | KD | Krasnodar | NRJ |
| 28) | 90.6 | 1 | SA | Samara | Biznes FM |
| 98B) | 90.6 | 5 | SP | Sankt-Peterburg | R. dlya dvoikh |
| 1) | 90.7 | 1 | PR | Perm | Avtoradio |
| 124A) | 90.7 | 1 | BA | Verkhneyakeyevo | R. Yuldash |
| 19) | 90.7 | 1 | TL | Tula | Dorozhnoye R. |
| 2) | 90.7 | 1 | TS | Kazan | Russkoye R. |
| 208) | 90.7 | 1 | NN | Arzamas | Rock FM |
| 23) | 90.7 | 2 | IR | Irkutsk | Detskoye R. |
| 70) | 90.7 | 1 | LI | Lipetsk | Lipetsk FM |
| 8) | 90.7 | 1 | KY | Surgut | Nashe R. |
| 8) | 90.7 | 1 | TO | Tomsk | Nashe R. |
| 207) | 90.8 | 5 | MO | Moskva | Relaks FM |
| 27) | 90.8 | 1 | MU | Murmansk | R. Dacha |
| 35) | 90.8 | 1 | KV | Kirov | R. Vera |
| 45) | 90.8 | 1 | SV | Yekaterinburg | Novoye R. |
| 54) | 90.8 | 1 | BU | Ulan-Ude | Buryaad FM |
| 61) | 90.8 | 1 | SO | Vladikavkaz | Kavkaz R. |
| 17) | 90.9 | 1 | AS | Astrakhan | Serebryanyy dozhd |
| 25) | 90.9 | 1 | OM | Omsk | R. Mir |
| 25) | 90.9 | 1 | PM | Vladivostok | R. Mir |
| 27) | 90.9 | 1 | TA | Tambov | R. Dacha |
| 6) | 90.9 | 1 | RS | Yakutsk | Love R. |
| 9A) | 90.9 | 1 | BR | Unecha | R. Vanya |
| 131) | 91.0 | 1 | TS | Alyoshkin Saplyk | R. Bolgar |
| 21) | 91.0 | 1 | KG | Kurgan | R. Zvezda |
| 22) | 91.0 | 1 | KD | Krasnodar | R. KP |
| 24) | 91.0 | 1 | KH | Khabarovsk | NRJ |
| 27) | 91.0 | 1 | SR | Saratov | R. Dacha |
| 45) | 91.0 | 1 | SA | Samara | Novoye R. |
| 9A) | 91.0 | 1 | KS | Kostroma | R. Vanya |
| 10) | 91.1 | 1 | BR | Bryansk | R. 7 |
| 18) | 91.1 | 1 | TS | Kazan | Yumor FM |
| 18) | 91.1 | 1 | KY | Surgut | Yumor FM |
| 19) | 91.1 | 1 | IR | Irkutsk | Dorozhnoye R. |
| 27) | 91.1 | 1 | LI | Lipetsk | R. Dacha |
| 3) | 91.1 | 1 | BA | Ufa | Ekho Moskvy |
| 45) | 91.1 | 1 | AK | Barnaul | Novoye R. |
| 45) | 91.1 | 10 | SP | Sankt-Peterburg | Novoye R. |
| 8) | 91.1 | 1 | KN | Norilsk | Nashe R. |
| 14) | 91.2 | 1 | KV | Kirov | R. Shanson |
| 17) | 91.2 | 1 | TY | Tyumen | Serebryanyy dozhd |
| 18) | 91.2 | 1 | ZB | Chita | Yumor FM |
| 18) | 91.2 | 1 | RO | Rostov-na-Donu | Yumor FM |
| 18) | 91.2 | 1 | BU | Ulan-Ude | Yumor FM |
| 19) | 91.2 | 1 | SO | Vladikavkaz | Dorozhnoye R. |
| 3) | 91.2 | 5 | MO | Moskva | Ekho Moskvy |
| 3) | 91.2 | 1 | PR | Perm | Ekho Moskvy |
| 14) | 91.3 | 1 | KE | Belovo | R. Shanson |
| 19) | 91.3 | 1 | VL | Murom | Dorozhnoye R. |
| 4) | 91.3 | 1 | SA | Tolyatti | Europa plus |
| 1) | 91.4 | 1 | MO | Shatura | Avtoradio |
| 16) | 91.4 | 1 | AS | Astrakhan | Retro FM |
| 23) | 91.4 | 1 | UD | Izhevsk | Detskoye R. |
| 23) | 91.4 | 1 | OM | Omsk | Detskoye R. |
| 24) | 91.4 | 1 | UL | Ulyanovsk | NRJ |
| 27) | 91.4 | 1 | KG | Kurgan | R. Dacha |
| 3) | 91.4 | 1 | SV | Yekaterinburg | Ekho Moskvy |
| 4) | 91.4 | 1 | TS | Almetyevsk | Europa plus |
| 43) | 91.4 | 1 | BE | Belgorod | Marusya FM |
| 6) | 91.4 | 1 | AM | Blagoveshchensk | Love R. |
| 131) | 91.5 | 1 | TS | Kazan | R. Bolgar |
| 14) | 91.5 | 1 | SA | Samara | R. Shanson |
| 15) | 91.5 | 1 | BA | Ufa | DFM |
| 17) | 91.5 | 1 | KE | Kemerovo | Serebryanyy dozhd |
| 25) | 91.5 | 1 | TO | Tomsk | R. Mir |
| 3) | 91.5 | 5 | SP | Sankt-Peterburg | Ekho Moskvy |
| 8) | 91.5 | 1 | SR | Saratov | Nashe R. |
| 139) | 91.6 | 1 | AR | Arkhangelsk | R. Jazz |
| 18) | 91.6 | 1 | UL | Dimitrovgrad | Yumor FM |
| 25) | 91.6 | 1 | TS | Nab.Chelny | R. Mir |
| 25) | 91.6 | 1 | SO | Vladikavkaz | R. Mir |
| 27) | 91.6 | 1 | KV | Kirov | R. Dacha |
| 27) | 91.6 | 1 | KY | Surgut | R. Dacha |
| 27) | 91.6 | 1 | BU | Ulan-Ude | R. Dacha |
| 97) | 91.8 | 1 | PR | Perm | Pioner FM |
| 134A) | 91.9 | 1 | TS | Kazan | Studio 21 |
| 159) | 91.9 | 1 | SV | Yekaterinburg | R. Narodnaya volna |
| 220) | 91.9 | 1 | SA | Tolyatti | Samarskoye gub. R. |
| 25) | 92.0 | 1 | UD | Izhevsk | R. Mir |
| 80A) | 92.0 | 5 | MO | Moskva | Moskva FM |
| 22) | 92.3 | 1 | SV | Yekaterinburg | R. KP |
| 24) | 92.3 | 2 | TS | Kazan | NRJ |
| 27) | 92.4 | 5 | MO | Moskva | R. Dacha |
| 35) | 92.4 | 1 | TY | Tyumen | R. Vera |
| 220) | 92.5 | 1 | SA | Samara | Samarskoye gub. R. |
| 1) | 92.6 | 1 | MO | Orekhovo-Zuyevo | Avtoradio |
| 1) | 92.6 | 1 | MO | Taldom | Avtoradio |
| 134A) | 92.7 | 1 | SV | Yekaterinburg | Studio 21 |
| 46) | 92.7 | 2 | KN | Krasnoyarsk | Comedy R. |
| 10) | 92.8 | 3 | NS | Novosibirsk | R. 7 |
| 141) | 92.8 | 5 | MO | Moskva | R. Karnaval |
| 22) | 92.8 | 1 | NN | N.Novgorod | R. KP |
| 39) | 92.9 | 2 | SP | Sankt-Peterburg | IZ.RU |
| 8) | 92.9 | 1 | SA | Samara | Nashe R. |
| 218) | 93.1 | 1 | TS | Kazan | R. Iskatel |
| 134A) | 93.2 | 5 | MO | Moskva | Studio 21 |
| 134A) | 93.2 | 1 | KE | Novokuznetsk | Studio 21 |
| 28) | 93.5 | 1 | TS | Kazan | Biznes FM |
| 45) | 93.5 | 1 | KN | Krasnoyarsk | Novoye R. |
| 8) | 93.5 | 1 | NN | N.Novgorod | Nashe R. |
| 10) | 93.6 | 1 | KA | Kaliningrad | R. 7 |
| 64) | 93.6 | 5 | MO | Moskva | Kommersant FM |
| 35) | 93.7 | 1 | SV | Yekaterinburg | R. Vera |
| 25) | 93.8 | 1 | VG | Volgograd | R. Mir |
| 154) | 94.0 | 5 | MO | Moskva | Vostok FM |
| 18) | 94.0 | 1 | KA | Kaliningrad | Yumor FM |
| 25) | 94.0 | 1 | CB | Chelyabinsk | R. Mir |
| 6) | 94.2 | 2 | NS | Novosibirsk | Love R. |
| 35) | 94.6 | 1 | NS | Novosibirsk | R. Vera |
| 6) | 94.6 | 1 | CB | Chelyabinsk | Love R. |
| 15) | 94.7 | 1 | NN | N.Novgorod | DFM |
| 212) | 94.8 | 5 | MO | Moskva | Govorit Moskva |
| 8) | 94.8 | 1 | SV | Yekaterinburg | Nashe R. |
| 10) | 94.9 | 1 | VG | Volgograd | R. 7 |
| 209) | 95.0 | 1 | KN | Krasnoyarsk | Russkiye pesni |
| 24) | 95.0 | 4 | SP | Sankt-Peterburg | NRJ |
| 25) | 95.0 | 2 | NS | Novosibirsk | R. Mir |
| 35) | 95.0 | 1 | PR | Perm | R. Vera |
| 208) | 95.2 | 5 | MO | Moskva | Rock FM |
| 22) | 95.3 | 1 | CB | Chelyabinsk | R. KP |
| 134A) | 95.4 | 1 | UD | Izhevsk | Studio 21 |
| 19) | 95.4 | 1 | SV | Svetogorsk | Dorozhnoye R. |
| 25) | 95.4 | 1 | PR | Perm | R. Mir |
| 8) | 95.4 | 1 | NS | Novosibirsk | Nashe R. |
| 134A) | 95.5 | 5 | SP | Sankt-Peterburg | Studio 21 |
| 134A) | 95.5 | 1 | SA | Tolyatti | Studio 21 |
| 16) | 95.5 | 1 | KA | Kaliningrad | Retro FM |
| 212) | 95.5 | 1 | TV | Tver | Govorit Moskva |
| 14) | 95.6 | 1 | VL | Vladimir | R. Shanson |
| 16) | 95.6 | 1 | PZ | Penza | Retro FM |
| 21) | 95.6 | 10 | MO | Moskva | R. Zvezda |
| 23) | 95.6 | 1 | KE | Novokuznetsk | Detskoye R. |
| 64) | 95.6 | 1 | NN | N.Novgorod | Kommersant FM |
| 171) | 95.7 | 1 | BE | Rakitnoye | R. Radio |
| 18) | 95.7 | 1 | SA | Samara | Yumor FM |
| 21) | 95.7 | 1 | RY | Ryazan | R. Zvezda |
| 23) | 95.7 | 1 | VG | Volgograd | Detskoye R. |
| 6) | 95.7 | 1 | TO | Tomsk | Love R. |
| 158) | 95.8 | 1 | KA | Gusev | R. na Vostoke |
| 21) | 95.8 | 1 | TY | Tyumen | R. Zvezda |
| 23) | 95.8 | 1 | NS | Novosibirsk | Detskoye R. |
| 45) | 95.8 | 1 | PR | Perm | Novoye R. |
| 46) | 95.8 | 1 | UD | Izhevsk | Comedy R. |
| 46) | 95.9 | 4 | SP | Sankt-Peterburg | Comedy R. |
| 46) | 95.9 | 1 | SV | Yekaterinburg | Comedy R. |
| 1) | 96.0 | 1 | SA | Tolyatti | Avtoradio |
| 19) | 96.0 | 5 | MO | Moskva | Dorozhnoye R. |
| 24) | 96.0 | 1 | CB | Chelyabinsk | NRJ |
| 25) | 96.0 | 1 | KE | Novokuznetsk | R. Mir |

| FM | MHz | kW | Rg | Location | Station |
|---|---|---|---|---|---|
| 47) | 96.0 | 1 | NN | N.Novgorod | Dinamit N.Novgorod |
| 23) | 96.1 | 1 | RY | Ryazan | Detskoye R. |
| 5) | 96.1 | 1 | TV | Tver | Hit FM |
| 6) | 96.1 | 1 | VG | Volgograd | Love R. |
| 193) | 96.2 | 1 | KN | Krasnoyarsk | Krasnoyarsk FM |
| 2) | 96.2 | 2 | NS | Novosibirsk | Russkoye R. |
| 22) | 96.2 | 1 | YA | Yaroslavl | R. KP |
| 24) | 96.2 | 1 | UD | Izhevsk | NRJ |
| 27) | 96.2 | 1 | CB | Magnitogorsk | R. Dacha |
| 45) | 96.2 | 1 | SV | Nizhniy Tagil | Novoye R. |
| 2) | 96.3 | 1 | KA | Kaliningrad | Russkoye R. |
| 204) | 96.3 | 1 | SA | Samara | Radiola |
| 46) | 96.3 | 1 | KE | Belovo | Comedy R. |
| 14) | 96.4 | 1 | PZ | Penza | R. Shanson |
| 16) | 96.4 | 1 | CB | Chelyabinsk | Retro FM |
| 176) | 96.4 | 5 | MO | Moskva | Taksi FM |
| 22) | 96.5 | 1 | VG | Volgograd | R. KP |
| 27) | 96.5 | 1 | RY | Ryazan | R. Dacha |
| 45) | 96.5 | 1 | TV | Tver | Novoye R. |
| 21) | 96.6 | 1 | KN | Krasnoyarsk | R. Zvezda |
| 22) | 96.6 | 1 | SV | Nizhniy Tagil | R. KP |
| 22) | 96.6 | 1 | PR | Perm | R. KP |
| 38) | 96.6 | 1 | PR | Berezniki | Beloye R. |
| 8) | 96.6 | 1 | SA | Tolyatti | Nashe R. |
| 27) | 96.7 | 1 | KE | Belovo | R. Dacha |
| 9A) | 96.7 | 1 | SP | Lyuban | R. Vanya |
| 23) | 96.8 | 1 | CB | Chelyabinsk | Detskoye R. |
| 23) | 96.8 | 5 | MO | Moskva | Detskoye R. |
| 24) | 96.8 | 1 | NN | N.Novgorod | NRJ |
| 35) | 96.8 | 1 | SA | Samara | R. Vera |
| 8) | 96.8 | 1 | TS | Kazan | Nashe R. |
| 129) | 96.9 | 1 | RY | Ryazan | R. Den |
| 17) | 96.9 | 1 | KE | Novokuznetsk | Serebryanyy dozhd |
| 16) | 97.0 | 2 | NS | Novosibirsk | Retro FM |
| 23) | 97.0 | 1 | KN | Krasnoyarsk | Detskoye R. |
| 27) | 97.0 | 4 | SP | Sankt-Peterburg | R. Dacha |
| 116) | 97.2 | 1 | KA | Neman | Russkiy kray |
| 22) | 97.2 | 10 | MO | Moskva | R. KP |
| 8) | 97.2 | 1 | VG | Volgograd | Nashe R. |
| 134A) | 97.3 | 1 | RY | Ryazan | Studio 21 |
| 19) | 97.3 | 1 | SA | Samara | Dorozhnoye R. |
| 25) | 97.4 | 1 | KN | Krasnoyarsk | R. Mir |
| 46) | 97.4 | 2 | NS | Novosibirsk | Comedy R. |
| 8) | 97.5 | 1 | TV | Tver | Nashe R. |
| 17) | 97.6 | 1 | KE | Belovo | Serebryanyy dozhd |
| 24) | 97.6 | 1 | PR | Perm | NRJ |
| 27) | 97.6 | 1 | VG | Volgograd | R. Dacha |
| 17) | 97.7 | 1 | KA | Kaliningrad | Serebryanyy dozhd |
| 22) | 97.7 | 1 | VN | Voronezh | R. KP |
| 10) | 97.8 | 1 | KN | Krasnoyarsk | R. 7 |
| 139) | 97.8 | 1 | SA | Samara | R. Jazz |
| 6) | 97.8 | 1 | UD | Izhevsk | Love R. |
| 67) | 97.8 | 1 | VG | Leninsk | Belyy lebed |
| 27) | 97.9 | 1 | VL | Vladimir | R. Dacha |
| 4) | 97.9 | 1 | SA | Syzran | Europa plus |
| 161) | 98.0 | 1 | NN | N.Novgorod | R. Obraz |
| 18) | 98.0 | 1 | SV | Nizhniy Tagil | Yumor FM |
| 181) | 98.0 | 5 | MO | Moskva | R. Shokolad |
| 22) | 98.0 | 1 | TS | Kazan | R. KP |
| 22) | 98.2 | 1 | SA | Samara | R. KP |
| 22) | 98.3 | 1 | NS | Novosibirsk | R. KP |
| 15) | 98.4 | 1 | TY | Tyumen | DFM |
| 45) | 98.4 | 5 | MO | Moskva | Novoye R. |
| 134A) | 98.5 | 1 | OL | Oryol | Studio 21 |
| 21) | 98.5 | 1 | TV | Tver | R. Zvezda |
| 6) | 98.5 | 2 | SV | Yekaterinburg | Love R. |
| 79) | 98.5 | 1 | BE | Borisovka | Mir Belogorya |
| 9A) | 98.5 | 1 | RY | Mosolovo | R. Vanya |
| 1) | 98.5 | 1 | MO | Zaraysk | Avtoradio |
| 111) | 98.6 | 5 | SP | Sankt-Peterburg | Royal R. |
| 16) | 98.6 | 1 | SA | Samara | Retro FM |
| 1) | 98.7 | 2 | NS | Novosibirsk | Avtoradio |
| 16) | 98.7 | 2 | KN | Krasnoyarsk | Retro FM |
| 18) | 98.7 | 1 | BA | Salavat | Yumor FM |
| 25) | 98.7 | 1 | ST | Stavropol | R. Mir |
| 27) | 98.7 | 1 | CB | Chelyabinsk | R. Dacha |
| 27) | 98.7 | 1 | TS | Nab.Chelny | R. Dacha |
| 65) | 98.7 | 1 | KE | Novokuznetsk | PIFM |
| 97) | 98.7 | 1 | PR | Berezniki | Pioner FM |
| 11) | 98.8 | 1 | TO | Tomsk | R. Maksimum |
| 20) | 98.8 | 10 | MO | Moskva | R. Romantika |
| 24) | 98.8 | 1 | VG | Volgograd | NRJ |
| 8) | 98.8 | 1 | VO | Vologda | Nashe R. |
| 17) | 98.9 | 1 | PR | Perm | Serebryanyy dozhd |
| 19) | 98.9 | 1 | SV | Yekaterinburg | Dorozhnoye R. |
| 24) | 98.9 | 1 | KS | Kostroma | NRJ |
| 25) | 98.9 | 1 | SA | Tolyatti | R. Mir |
| 26) | 98.9 | 1 | KE | Leninsk-Kuznetskiy | R. Rekord |
| 4) | 98.9 | 1 | PM | Arsenyev | Europa plus |
| 9A) | 98.9 | 1 | SM | Gagarin | R. Vanya |
| 164) | 99.0 | 1 | DA | Makhachkala | Kristall FM |
| 18) | 99.0 | 1 | MO | Taldom | Yumor FM |
| 25) | 99.0 | 2 | KB | Nalchik | R. Mir |
| 4) | 99.0 | 1 | TS | Chistopol | Europa plus |
| 1) | 99.1 | 2 | CB | Chelyabinsk | Avtoradio |
| 113) | 99.1 | 1 | KN | Krasnoyarsk | R. 99.1 FM |
| 18) | 99.1 | 1 | VN | Voronezh | Yumor FM |
| 23) | 99.1 | 1 | NN | N.Novgorod | Detskoye R. |
| 23) | 99.1 | 1 | PZ | Penza | Detskoye R. |
| 24) | 99.1 | 2 | NS | Novosibirsk | NRJ |
| 3) | 99.1 | 1 | SA | Samara | Ekho Moskvy |
| 11) | 99.2 | 1 | VG | Volgograd | R. Maksimum |
| 19) | 99.2 | 1 | SR | Balakovo | Dorozhnoye R. |
| 22) | 99.2 | 1 | VO | Vologda | R. KP |
| 27) | 99.2 | 1 | KT | Petrozavodsk | R. Dacha |
| 6) | 99.2 | 1 | TS | Almetyevsk | Love R. |
| 6) | 99.2 | 1 | SV | Nizhniy Tagil | Love R. |
| 8) | 99.2 | 1 | TY | Tyumen | Nashe R. |
| 21) | 99.3 | 1 | KO | Syktyvkar | R. Zvezda |
| 22) | 99.3 | 1 | TV | Tver | R. KP |
| 27) | 99.3 | 1 | BA | Steplitamak | R. Dacha |
| 4) | 99.3 | 1 | SP | Kingisepp | Europa plus |
| 5) | 99.3 | 1 | KE | Leninsk-Kuznetskiy | Hit FM |
| 6) | 99.3 | 1 | KU | Kursk | Love R. |
| 6) | 99.3 | 1 | VL | Vladimir | Love R. |
| 112) | 99.4 | 1 | TY | Golyshmanovo | R. 7 Tyumen |
| 16) | 99.4 | 5 | PR | Perm | Retro FM |
| 18) | 99.4 | 1 | LI | Lipetsk | Yumor FM |
| 19) | 99.4 | 1 | SA | Tolyatti | Dorozhnoye R. |
| 28) | 99.4 | 2 | SV | Yekaterinburg | Biznes FM |
| 4) | 99.4 | 1 | MO | Kolomna | Europa plus |
| 45) | 99.4 | 1 | TS | Chistopol | Novoye R. |
| 140) | 99.5 | 2 | KB | Nalchik | R. Kabardino-Balkariya |
| 18) | 99.5 | 1 | NS | Novosibirsk | Yumor FM |
| 203) | 99.5 | 1 | RS | Aldan | Radiogora |
| 21) | 99.5 | 1 | KA | Kaliningrad | R. Zvezda |
| 22) | 99.5 | 1 | IR | Bratsk | R. KP |
| 23) | 99.5 | 1 | VN | Voronezh | Detskoye R. |
| 23) | 99.5 | 1 | CB | Chelyabinsk | Ekho Moskvy |
| 4) | 99.5 | 1 | KE | Novokuznetsk | Europa plus |
| 45) | 99.5 | 1 | YA | Yaroslavl | Novoye R. |
| 93) | 99.5 | 1 | NN | N.Novgorod | NN-Radio |
| 139) | 99.6 | 1 | TO | Tomsk | R. Jazz |
| 16) | 99.6 | 1 | VO | Vologda | Retro FM |
| 169) | 99.6 | 1 | SR | Balakovo | R. Aktivnoye |
| 19) | 99.6 | 1 | SP | Lyuban | Dorozhnoye R. |
| 19) | 99.6 | 1 | OL | Oryol | Dorozhnoye R. |
| 22) | 99.6 | 1 | TY | Tyumen | R. KP |
| 24) | 99.6 | 1 | PZ | Penza | NRJ |
| 35) | 99.6 | 1 | TS | Almetyevsk | R. Vera |
| 53) | 99.6 | 5 | MO | Moskva | R. Russkiy khit |
| 24) | 99.8 | 1 | TV | Tver | NRJ |
| 27) | 99.8 | 1 | CB | Asha | R. Dacha |
| 27) | 99.8 | 1 | KE | Mezhdurechensk | R. Dacha |
| 6) | 99.8 | 1 | SP | Vyborg | Love R. |
| 102) | 99.9 | 5 | MO | Kurovskoye | Prosto R. |
| 2) | 99.9 | 1 | KD | Vyshestebliyevskaya | Russkoye R. |
| 25) | 99.9 | 1 | VN | Voronezh | R. Mir |
| 4) | 99.9 | 1 | SA | Samara | Europa plus |
| 10) | 100.0 | 1 | NN | N.Novgorod | R. 7 |
| 104) | 100.0 | 1 | CB | Chelyabinsk | R. 100 |
| 14) | 100.0 | 1 | VG | Volgograd | R. Shanson |
| 16) | 100.0 | 1 | RY | Mosolovo | Retro FM |
| 16) | 100.0 | 1 | SV | Yekaterinburg | Retro FM |
| 2) | 100.0 | 1 | OL | Oryol | Russkoye R. |
| 217) | 100.0 | 1 | KA | Sovetsk | Mediakit FM |
| 45) | 100.0 | 1 | NS | Novosibirsk | Novoye R. |
| 7) | 100.0 | 1 | OB | Akbulak | Militseyskaya volna |
| 8) | 100.0 | 1 | PR | Perm | Nashe R. |
| 1) | 100.1 | 1 | PR | Berezniki | Avtoradio |
| 1) | 100.1 | 1 | KA | Kaliningrad | Avtoradio |
| 1) | 100.1 | 1 | PZ | Penza | R. 7 |
| 17) | 100.1 | 5 | MO | Moskva | Serebryanyy dozhd |
| 18) | 100.1 | 1 | CB | Magnitogorsk | Yumor FM |

| FM | MHz | kW | Rg | Location | Station |
|---|---|---|---|---|---|
| 45) | 100.1 | 1 | VL | Vladimir | Novoye R. |
| 5) | 100.1 | 1 | RO | Rostov-na-Donu | Hit FM |
| 6) | 100.1 | 1 | SA | Tolyatti | Love R. |
| 83) | 100.1 | 1 | UD | Izhevsk | Moya Udmurtiya |
| 14) | 100.2 | 1 | LI | Khlebnoye | R. Shanson |
| 18) | 100.2 | 1 | TS | Almetyevsk | Yumor FM |
| 2) | 100.2 | 1 | SM | Vyazma | Russkoye R. |
| 4) | 100.2 | 1 | VO | Vologda | Europa plus |
| 4) | 100.2 | 1 | KU | Zheleznogorsk | Europa plus |
| 10) | 100.2 | 1 | TA | Tambov | R. 7 |
| 18) | 100.3 | 2 | KN | Krasnoyarsk | Yumor FM |
| 2) | 100.3 | 1 | SA | Samara | Russkoye R. |
| 24) | 100.3 | 1 | KE | Mariinsk | NRJ |
| 25) | 100.3 | 1 | IR | Angarsk | R. Mir |
| 36) | 100.3 | 1 | SP | Kingisepp | Avtoradio S-Peterburg |
| 4) | 100.3 | 1 | BR | Bryansk | Europa plus |
| 4) | 100.3 | 1 | KS | Kostroma | Europa plus |
| 4) | 100.3 | 1 | KO | Syktyvkar | Europa plus |
| 4) | 100.3 | 1 | VN | Voronezh | Europa plus |
| 7) | 100.3 | 1 | OB | Sol-Iletsk | Militseyskaya volna |
| 146) | 100.4 | 2 | CB | Chelyabinsk | R. Kontinental |
| 166) | 100.4 | 5 | SV | Yekaterinburg | R. Pilot |
| 17) | 100.4 | 4 | NN | N.Novgorod | Serebryanyy dozhd |
| 2) | 100.4 | 1 | UL | Dimitrovgrad | Russkoye R. |
| 24) | 100.4 | 1 | KT | Petrozavodsk | NRJ |
| 27) | 100.4 | 1 | SM | Gagarin | R. Dacha |
| 51) | 100.4 | 1 | OL | Oryol | Ekspress R. |
| 1) | 100.5 | 1 | TY | Tobolsk | Avtoradio |
| 16) | 100.5 | 1 | TL | Tula | Retro FM |
| 177) | 100.5 | 1 | RS | Aldan | R. Sakha |
| 178) | 100.5 | 1 | TS | Kazan | Tatarskoye R. |
| 182) | 100.5 | 1 | SV | Nizhniy Tagil | R. Si |
| 19) | 100.5 | 1 | VN | Bobrov | Dorozhnoye R. |
| 2) | 100.5 | 1 | KS | Buy | Russkoye R. |
| 2) | 100.5 | 1 | UD | Izhevsk | Russkoye R. |
| 215) | 100.5 | 1 | PR | Solikamsk | SK FM |
| 34) | 100.5 | 1 | KE | Novokuznetsk | Apeks-Radio |
| 4) | 100.5 | 10 | SP | Sankt-Peterburg | Europa plus |
| 69) | 100.5 | 5 | MO | Moskva | Zhara FM |
| 7) | 100.5 | 1 | VL | Kovrov | Militseyskaya volna |
| 16) | 100.6 | 1 | VL | Murom | Retro FM |
| 18) | 100.6 | 1 | SR | Saratov | Yumor FM |
| 184) | 100.6 | 2 | TY | Tyumen | R. Siti |
| 2) | 100.6 | 1 | BA | Kumertau | Russkoye R. |
| 2) | 100.6 | 1 | TV | Tver | Russkoye R. |
| 218) | 100.6 | 1 | RA | Gorno-Altaysk | R. Iskatel |
| 22) | 100.6 | 1 | AM | Blagoveshchensk | R. KP |
| 23) | 100.6 | 1 | AK | Barnaul | Detskoye R. |
| 24) | 100.6 | 1 | KE | Kemerovo | NRJ |
| 26) | 100.6 | 1 | MD | Saransk | R. Rekord |
| 4) | 100.6 | 1 | VG | Volgograd | Europa plus |
| 6) | 100.6 | 1 | KL | Kaluga | Love R. |
| 8) | 100.6 | 1 | OM | Omsk | Nashe R. |
| 10) | 100.7 | 1 | ST | Stavropol | R. 7 |
| 115) | 100.7 | 1 | RO | Rostov-na-Donu | FM-na Donu |
| 120) | 100.7 | 1 | SA | Otradnyy | R. Aprel |
| 124B) | 100.7 | 1 | BA | Davlekanovo | Sputnik FM |
| 137) | 100.7 | 1 | VN | Voronezh | R. Guberniya |
| 170) | 100.7 | 1 | DA | Makhachkala | R. Priboy |
| 19) | 100.7 | 1 | MU | Apatity | Dorozhnoye R. |
| 19) | 100.7 | 1 | ZB | Chita | Dorozhnoye R. |
| 19) | 100.7 | 1 | KT | Peldozha | Dorozhnoye R. |
| 200) | 100.7 | 3 | NS | Novosibirsk | R. Yuniton |
| 24) | 100.7 | 1 | KB | Nalchik | NRJ |
| 26) | 100.7 | 1 | OB | Orsk | R. Rekord |
| 27) | 100.7 | 1 | KU | Kursk | R. Dacha |
| 4) | 100.7 | 1 | BR | Unecha | Europa plus |
| 4) | 100.7 | 1 | PM | Ussuriysk | Europa plus |
| 5) | 100.7 | 1 | PR | Perm | Hit FM |
| 6) | 100.7 | 1 | RY | Ryazan | Love R. |
| 9A) | 100.7 | 1 | SM | Vyazma | R. Vanya |
| 124A) | 100.8 | 1 | BA | Burayevo | R. Yuldash |
| 16) | 100.8 | 1 | BR | Bryansk | Retro FM |
| 18) | 100.8 | 1 | VL | Vladimir | Yumor FM |
| 19) | 100.8 | 1 | KN | Krasnoyarsk | Dorozhnoye R. |
| 26) | 100.8 | 1 | OB | Orenburg | R. Rekord |
| 28) | 100.8 | 1 | CB | Chelyabinsk | Biznes FM |
| 51) | 100.8 | 1 | OL | Livny | Ekspress R. |
| 6) | 100.8 | 1 | AR | Arkhangelsk | Love R. |
| 6) | 100.8 | 1 | KM | Petropavlovsk-K. | Love R. |
| 1) | 100.9 | 1 | KD | Kushchyovskaya | Avtoradio |
| 10) | 100.9 | 1 | IR | Irkutsk | R. 7 |
| 157) | 100.9 | 1 | KA | Kaliningrad | R. Monte-Karlo |
| 16) | 100.9 | 1 | KD | Novorossiysk | Retro FM |
| 183) | 100.9 | 1 | ZB | Aginskoye | R. Sibir |
| 19) | 100.9 | 1 | LI | Lipetsk | Dorozhnoye R. |
| 22) | 100.9 | 1 | AK | Biysk | R. KP |
| 25) | 100.9 | 1 | TS | Kazan | R. Mir |
| 25) | 100.9 | 1 | YA | Rybinsk | R. Mir |
| 26) | 100.9 | 4 | NN | N.Novgorod | R. Rekord |
| 35) | 100.9 | 5 | MO | Moskva | R. Vera |
| 4) | 100.9 | 1 | OL | Oryol | Europa plus |
| 45) | 100.9 | 1 | UD | Izhevsk | Novoye R. |
| 46) | 100.9 | 1 | RK | Abakan | Comedy R. |
| 79) | 100.9 | 1 | BE | Belgorod | Mir Belogorya |
| 94) | 100.9 | 1 | PR | Kudymkar | Okrug FM |
| 98A) | 100.9 | 10 | SP | Sankt-Peterburg | Piter FM |
| 126) | 101.0 | 1 | PM | Artyom | R. AVN |
| 14) | 101.0 | 1 | TY | Ishim | R. Shanson |
| 14) | 101.0 | 1 | SV | Nizhniy Tagil | R. Shanson |
| 14) | 101.0 | 1 | TY | Tyumen | R. Shanson |
| 176) | 101.0 | 1 | SA | Samara | Taksi FM |
| 19) | 101.0 | 1 | VO | Belozersk | Dorozhnoye R. |
| 19) | 101.0 | 1 | CB | Magnitogorsk | Dorozhnoye R. |
| 19) | 101.0 | 1 | VO | Vologda | Dorozhnoye R. |
| 2) | 101,0 | 2 | TS | Bugulma | Russkoye R. |
| 21) | 101.0 | 1 | PR | Berezniki | R. Zvezda |
| 27) | 101.0 | 1 | OM | Omsk | R. Dacha |
| 29) | 101.0 | 1 | KD | Otradnaya | Pervoye R. |
| 3) | 101.0 | 1 | KV | Kirov | Ekho Moskvy |
| 34) | 101.0 | 2 | KE | Kemerovo | Apeks-Radio |
| 35) | 101.0 | 5 | RY | Mosolovo | R. Vera |
| 35) | 101.0 | 1 | KT | Petrozavodsk | R. Vera |
| 4) | 101.0 | 1 | MU | Murmansk | Europa plus |
| 9A) | 101.0 | 1 | KO | Ukhta | R. Vanya |
| 9B) | 101.0 | 5 | SP | Vyborg | Populyarnaya klassika |
| 1) | 101.1 | 1 | KD | Sochi | Avtoradio |
| 1) | 101.1 | 1 | RS | Yakutsk | Avtoradio |
| 10) | 101.1 | 1 | PR | Perm | R. 7 |
| 124A) | 101.1 | 1 | BA | Neftekamsk | R. Yuldash |
| 16) | 101.1 | 1 | ZB | Chita | Retro FM |
| 187) | 101.1 | 1 | NS | Kuybyshev | R. 54 |
| 19) | 101.1 | 1 | ME | Yoshkar-Ola | Dorozhnoye R. |
| 20) | 101.1 | 1 | DA | Makhachkala | R. Romantika |
| 207) | 101.1 | 1 | SR | Saratov | Relaks FM |
| 217) | 101.1 | 1 | KA | Chernyakhovsk | Mediakit FM |
| 24) | 101.1 | 1 | VN | Voronezh | NRJ |
| 3) | 101.1 | 1 | VG | Volgograd | Ekho Moskvy |
| 35) | 101.1 | 1 | KD | Yeysk | R. Vera |
| 7) | 101.1 | 1 | KE | Novokuznetsk | Militseyskaya volna |
| 15) | 101.2 | 10 | MO | Moskva | DFM |
| 16) | 101.2 | 1 | KD | Krasnodar | Retro FM |
| 18) | 101.2 | 1 | CB | Chelyabinsk | Yumor FM |
| 19) | 101.2 | 1 | MU | Monchegorsk | Dorozhnoye R. |
| 213) | 101.2 | 1 | SA | Tolyatti | Samara-Maksimum |
| 24) | 101.2 | 1 | IV | Ivanovo | NRJ |
| 27) | 101.2 | 1 | AR | Arkhangelsk | R. Dacha |
| 4) | 101.2 | 5 | SV | Yekaterinburg | Europa plus |
| 5) | 101.2 | 1 | KO | Pechora | Hit FM |
| 16) | 101.3 | 1 | BA | Tuymazy | Retro FM |
| 16) | 101.3 | 1 | VL | Vladimir | Retro FM |
| 18) | 101.3 | 1 | UD | Izhevsk | Yumor FM |
| 19) | 101.3 | 1 | RK | Abakan | Dorozhnoye R. |
| 2) | 101.3 | 1 | AK | Biysk | Russkoye R. |
| 2) | 101.3 | 1 | MD | Saransk | Russkoye R. |
| 25) | 101.3 | 1 | AK | Rubtsovsk | R. Mir |
| 3) | 101.3 | 1 | OB | Orenburg | Ekho Moskvy |
| 4) | 101.3 | 1 | LI | Lipetsk | Europa plus |
| 45) | 101.3 | 1 | TS | Kazan | Novoye R. |
| 6) | 101.3 | 2 | KN | Krasnoyarsk | Love R. |
| 6) | 101.3 | 1 | ST | Pyatigorsk | Love R. |
| 8) | 101.3 | 1 | KA | Kaliningrad | Nashe R. |
| 9A) | 101.3 | 1 | TO | Tomsk | R. Vanya |
| 1) | 101.4 | 1 | VN | Rossosh | Avtoradio |
| 1) | 101.4 | 1 | BA | Sterlitamak | Avtoradio |
| 1) | 101.4 | 1 | TV | Tver | Avtoradio |
| 11) | 101.4 | 1 | PR | Berezniki | R. Maksimum |
| 131) | 101.4 | 2 | TS | Bilyarsk | R. Bolgar |
| 14) | 101.4 | 1 | KH | Khabarovsk | R. Shanson |
| 16) | 101.4 | 1 | KS | Kostroma | Retro FM |
| 17) | 101.4 | 1 | PZ | Penza | Serebryanyy dozhd |
| 18) | 101.4 | 1 | KT | Petrozavodsk | Yumor FM |
| 19) | 101.4 | 1 | TY | Omutinskoye | Dorozhnoye R. |
| 19) | 101.4 | 1 | ST | Stavropol | Dorozhnoye R. |

| FM | MHz | kW | Rg | Location | Station | FM | MHz | kW | Rg | Location | Station |
|---|---|---|---|---|---|---|---|---|---|---|---|
| 24) | 101.4 | 1 | OL | Oryol | NRJ | 124B) | 101.9 | 2 | BA | Steplitamak | Sputnik FM |
| 24) | 101.4 | 1 | TL | Tula | NRJ | 14) | 101.9 | 1 | AK | Barnaul | R. Shanson |
| 27) | 101.4 | 1 | PM | Ussuriysk | R. Dacha | 17) | 101.9 | 5 | KD | Sochi | Serebryanyy dozhd |
| 27) | 101.4 | 1 | VO | Vologda | R. Dacha | 19) | 101.9 | 1 | KO | Ukhta | Dorozhnoye R. |
| 5) | 101.4 | 5 | IR | Angarsk | Hit FM | 2) | 101.9 | 1 | DA | Makhachkala | Russkoye R. |
| 5) | 101.4 | 1 | NN | N.Novgorod | Hit FM | 23) | 101.9 | 1 | BU | Ulan-Ude | Detskoye R. |
| 52) | 101.4 | 10 | SP | Sankt-Peterburg | Eldoradio | 23) | 101.9 | 1 | VO | Vologda | Detskoye R. |
| 55) | 101.4 | 2 | NS | Novosibirsk | Gorodskaya volna | 26) | 101.9 | 1 | TS | Kazan | R. Rekord |
| 81) | 101.4 | 1 | KO | Ukhta | R. Kabriolet | 4) | 101.9 | 1 | TS | Nab.Chelny | Europa plus |
| 1) | 101.5 | 1 | BR | Bryansk | Avtoradio | 4) | 101.9 | 1 | KD | Novorossiysk | Europa plus |
| 1) | 101.5 | 1 | CV | Cheboksary | Avtoradio | 4) | 101.9 | 1 | OM | Omsk | Europa plus |
| 1) | 101.5 | 1 | TS | Nab.Chelny | Avtoradio | 5) | 101.9 | 1 | IR | Tulun | Hit FM |
| 1) | 101.5 | 1 | KY | Nyagan | Avtoradio | 8) | 101.9 | 5 | TL | Tula | Nashe R. |
| 110B) | 101.5 | 3 | VG | Volgograd | Volgograd FM | 1) | 102.0 | 1 | VN | Beguchar | Avtoradio |
| 14) | 101.5 | 1 | SR | Saratov | R. Shanson | 1) | 102.0 | 1 | SR | Pugachyov | Avtoradio |
| 18) | 101.5 | 3 | OM | Omsk | Yumor FM | 1) | 102.0 | 1 | RY | Ryazan | Avtoradio |
| 18) | 101.5 | 1 | IR | Tayshet | Yumor FM | 1) | 102.0 | 1 | TV | Zapandaya Dvina | Avtoradio |
| 19) | 101.5 | 1 | RY | Ryazan | Dorozhnoye R. | 10) | 102.0 | 1 | ST | Ipatovo | R. 7 |
| 2) | 101.5 | 1 | KE | Yurga | Russkoye R. | 101) | 102.0 | 1 | CV | Cheboksary | R. Rodnykh dorog |
| 219) | 101.5 | 1 | PR | Perm | R. Nostalzhi | 14) | 102.0 | 1 | OB | Orsk | R. Shanson |
| 24) | 101.5 | 1 | KE | Novokuznetsk | NRJ | 17) | 102.0 | 1 | KY | Khanty-Mansiysk | Serebryanyy dozhd |
| 26) | 101.5 | 2 | SA | Samara | R. Rekord | 17) | 102.0 | 1 | MU | Kirovsk | Serebryanyy dozhd |
| 27) | 101.5 | 1 | DA | Makhachkala | R. Dacha | 177) | 102.0 | 1 | RS | Sangar | R. Sakha |
| 3) | 101.5 | 1 | AM | Blagoveshchensk | Ekho Moskvy | 18) | 102.0 | 1 | SV | Yekaterinburg | Yumor FM |
| 4) | 101.5 | 1 | SV | Nizhniy Tagil | Europa plus | 183) | 102.0 | 1 | ZB | Kholbon | R. Sibir |
| 46) | 101.5 | 1 | MO | Shatura | Comedy R. | 183) | 102.0 | 1 | ZB | Krasnokamensk | R. Sibir |
| 62) | 101.5 | 2 | AD | Maykop | Kazak FM | 19) | 102.0 | 1 | BR | Bryansk | Dorozhnoye R. |
| 85) | 101.5 | 1 | NO | Malaya Vishera | MV Diapazon | 19) | 102.0 | 1 | NS | Novosibirsk | Dorozhnoye R. |
| 1) | 101.6 | 1 | AR | Arkhangelsk | Avtoradio | 19) | 102.0 | 1 | PR | Perm | Dorozhnoye R. |
| 10) | 101.6 | 1 | VN | Voronezh | R. 7 | 19) | 102.0 | 1 | AR | Velsk | Dorozhnoye R. |
| 108) | 101.6 | 1 | BA | Ufa | R. 1-y Kanal | 26) | 102.0 | 1 | MU | Murmansk | R. Rekord |
| 14) | 101.6 | 1 | SV | Krasnoturinsk | R. Shanson | 4) | 102.0 | 1 | ZB | Chita | Europa plus |
| 16) | 101.6 | 1 | IV | Ivanovo | Retro FM | 4) | 102.0 | 1 | MD | Saransk | Europa plus |
| 19) | 101.6 | 1 | PZ | Kuznetsk | Dorozhnoye R. | 4) | 102.0 | 1 | SM | Smolensk | Europa plus |
| 2) | 101.6 | 1 | MU | Apatity | Russkoye R. | 4) | 102.0 | 1 | SO | Vladikavkaz | Europa plus |
| 24) | 101.6 | 1 | VG | Mikhaylovka | NRJ | 45) | 102.0 | 1 | CB | Chelyabinsk | Novoye R. |
| 4) | 101.6 | 1 | CB | Chelyabinsk | Europa plus | 49) | 102.0 | 10 | SP | Sankt-Peterburg | Strana FM |
| 6) | 101.6 | 1 | RO | Rostov-na-Donu | Love R. | 92) | 102.0 | 2 | VG | Volgograd | Novaya volna |
| 7) | 101.6 | 1 | OB | Pleshanovo | Militseyskaya volna | 1) | 102.1 | 1 | LI | Lipetsk | Avtoradio |
| 7) | 101.6 | 1 | OB | Saraktash | Militseyskaya volna | 1) | 102.1 | 1 | SR | Saratov | Avtoradio |
| 1) | 101.7 | 1 | AS | Astrakhan | Avtoradio | 11) | 102.1 | 1 | SV | Nizhniy Tagil | R. Maksimum |
| 1) | 101.7 | 1 | VN | Borisoglebsk | Avtoradio | 131) | 102.1 | 2 | TS | Leninogorsk | R. Bolgar |
| 10) | 101.7 | 1 | YA | Yaroslavl | R. 7 | 14) | 102.1 | 1 | IR | Bratsk | R. Shanson |
| 131) | 101.7 | 1 | TS | Bugulma | R. Bolgar | 14) | 102.1 | 2 | KY | Nizhnevartovsk | R. Shanson |
| 14) | 101.7 | 2 | KN | Krasnoyarsk | R. Shanson | 157) | 102.1 | 5 | MO | Moskva | R. Monte-Karlo |
| 14) | 101.7 | 1 | SL | Yu-Sakhalinsk | R. Shanson | 2) | 102.1 | 1 | TO | Tomsk | Russkoye R. |
| 15) | 101.7 | 1 | RK | Abakan | DFM | 27) | 102.1 | 1 | SA | Samara | R. Dacha |
| 15) | 101.7 | 1 | BA | Neftekamsk | DFM | 33) | 102.1 | 1 | UL | Ulyanovsk | 2x2 R. |
| 19) | 101.7 | 1 | VO | Babayevo | Dorozhnoye R. | 4) | 102.1 | 1 | PS | Pskov | Europa plus |
| 195) | 101.7 | 4 | PM | Vladivostok | R. VBC | 88) | 102.1 | 1 | IR | Irkutsk | R. MSM |
| 2) | 101.7 | 1 | YV | Birobidzhan | Russkoye R. | 9A) | 102.1 | 1 | KE | Belovo | R. Vanya |
| 204) | 101.7 | 1 | SR | Balakovo | Radiola | 9A) | 102.1 | 1 | KE | Mariinsk | R. Vanya |
| 27) | 101.7 | 1 | IR | Bratsk | R. Dacha | 1) | 102.2 | 1 | MO | Serebryanyye Prudy | Avtoradio |
| 36) | 101.7 | 1 | SP | Lyuban | Avtoradio S-Peterburg | 1) | 102.2 | 1 | SM | Vyazma | Avtoradio |
| 4) | 101.7 | 1 | UL | Ulyanovsk | Europa plus | 16) | 102.2 | 1 | RY | Sasovo | Retro FM |
| 45) | 101.7 | 1 | BE | Belgorod | Novoye R. | 16) | 102.2 | 1 | TV | Tver | Retro FM |
| 7) | 101.7 | 1 | AK | Kamen-na-Obi | Militseyskaya volna | 16) | 102.2 | 1 | YA | Yaroslavl | Retro FM |
| 8) | 101.7 | 10 | MO | Moskva | Nashe R. | 17) | 102.2 | 3 | KN | Krasnoyarsk | Serebryanyy dozhd |
| 1) | 101.8 | 1 | VN | Bobrov | Avtoradio | 171) | 102.2 | 1 | AK | Blagoveshchenka | R. Radio |
| 1) | 101.8 | 1 | PR | Chusovoy | Avtoradio | 182) | 102.2 | 1 | SV | Kamensk-Uralskiy | R. Si |
| 1) | 101.8 | 1 | KO | Syktyvkar | Avtoradio | 19) | 102.2 | 1 | NO | Valday | Dorozhnoye R. |
| 10) | 101.8 | 1 | OL | Oryol | R. 7 | 19) | 102.2 | 1 | AR | Vazhskiy | Dorozhnoye R. |
| 105) | 101.8 | 1 | PZ | Penza | R. 101.8 | 19) | 102.2 | 1 | SP | Volkhov | Dorozhnoye R. |
| 134A) | 101.8 | 1 | KV | Kirov | Studio 21 | 2) | 102.2 | 1 | RK | Abakan | Russkoye R. |
| 134A) | 101.8 | 1 | KT | Petrozavodsk | Studio 21 | 2) | 102.2 | 1 | BE | Belgorod | Russkoye R. |
| 14) | 101.8 | 1 | TS | Chistopol | R. Shanson | 4) | 102.2 | 1 | KD | Krasnodar | Europa plus |
| 15) | 101.8 | 1 | KE | Kemerovo | DFM | 4) | 102.2 | 1 | KB | Nalchik | Europa plus |
| 16) | 101.8 | 1 | UD | Izhevsk | Retro FM | 6) | 102.2 | 2 | AS | Astrakhan | Love R. |
| 16) | 101.8 | 1 | OB | Orenburg | Retro FM | 1) | 102.3 | 1 | KD | Armavir | Avtoradio |
| 16) | 101.8 | 1 | NO | V. Novgorod | Retro FM | 1) | 102.3 | 1 | AM | Belogorsk | Avtoradio |
| 19) | 101.8 | 2 | VL | Vladimir | Dorozhnoye R. | 1) | 102.3 | 2 | OB | Orenburg | Avtoradio |
| 2) | 101.8 | 1 | KD | Krasnodar | Russkoye R. | 1) | 102.3 | 1 | PZ | Penza | Avtoradio |
| 2) | 101.8 | 1 | ST | Stavropol | Russkoye R. | 112) | 102.3 | 1 | TY | Ivat | R. 7 Tyumen |
| 25) | 101.8 | 1 | SA | Syzran | R. Mir | 125) | 102.3 | 1 | SA | Tolyatti | R. Avgust |
| 28) | 101.8 | 1 | KA | Kaliningrad | Biznes FM | 129) | 102.3 | 1 | MO | Kolomna | R. Blago |
| 4) | 101.8 | 1 | KD | Tuapse | Europa plus | 131) | 102.3 | 2 | TS | Shemordan | R. Bolgar |
| 4) | 101.8 | 1 | TV | Tver | Europa plus | 19) | 102.3 | 1 | VN | Voronezh | Dorozhnoye R. |
| 4) | 101.8 | 1 | TY | Tyumen | Europa plus | 2) | 102.3 | 1 | BA | Neftekamsk | Russkoye R. |
| 7) | 101.8 | 1 | OB | Buzuluk | Militseyskaya volna | 25) | 102.3 | 1 | KH | Khabarovsk | R. Mir |
| 1) | 101.9 | 1 | AK | Biysk | Avtoradio | 27) | 102.3 | 1 | IR | Usolye-Sibirskoye | R. Dacha |
| 1) | 101.9 | 4 | NN | N.Novgorod | Avtoradio | 4) | 102.3 | 1 | BU | Ulan-Ude | Europa plus |
| 10) | 101.9 | 1 | KY | Surgut | R. 7 | 6) | 102.3 | 1 | KO | Syktyvkar | Love R. |

| FM | MHz | kW | Rg | Location | Station |
|---|---|---|---|---|---|
| 9A) | 102.3 | 1 | TL | Bogoroditsk | R. Vanya |
| 1) | 102.4 | 1 | PM | Dalnegorsk | Avtoradio |
| 112) | 102.4 | 1 | TY | Vikulovo | R. 7 Tyumen |
| 134A) | 102.4 | 1 | CB | Chelyabinsk | Studio 21 |
| 15) | 102.4 | 1 | AK | Barnaul | DFM |
| 15) | 102.4 | 1 | TS | Nurlat | DFM |
| 15) | 102.4 | 1 | VL | Vladimir | DFM |
| 152) | 102.4 | 5 | IN | Nazran | ITT-veshchaniye |
| 16) | 102.4 | 1 | TS | Kazan | Retro FM |
| 179) | 102.4 | 1 | PM | Luchegorsk | Vladivostok FM |
| 19) | 102.4 | 1 | KS | Galich | Dorozhnoye R. |
| 19) | 102.4 | 1 | PS | Sebezh | Dorozhnoye R. |
| 2) | 102.4 | 1 | KO | Ukhta | Russkoye R. |
| 27) | 102.4 | 1 | UD | Izhevsk | R. Dacha |
| 29) | 102.4 | 1 | KD | Yeysk | Pervoye R. |
| 35) | 102.4 | 1 | TV | Rzhev | R. Vera |
| 4) | 102.4 | 1 | DA | Makhachkala | Europa plus |
| 4) | 102.4 | 1 | PM | Nakhodka | Europa plus |
| 46) | 102.4 | 1 | NN | N.Novgorod | Comedy R. |
| 6) | 102.4 | 1 | TA | Tambov | Love R. |
| 62) | 102.4 | 5 | KD | Novorossiysk | Kazak FM |
| 1) | 102.5 | 1 | MU | Murmansk | Avtoradio |
| 1) | 102.5 | 4 | IV | Rodniki | Avtoradio |
| 122) | 102.5 | 1 | BA | Kumertau | R. Aris |
| 14) | 102.5 | 1 | KD | Sochi | R. Shanson |
| 14) | 102.5 | 1 | BA | Ufa | R. Shanson |
| 146) | 102.5 | 1 | CB | Magnitogorsk | R. Kontinental |
| 16) | 102.5 | 1 | SV | Serov | Retro FM |
| 16) | 102.5 | 5 | KY | Surgut | Retro FM |
| 16) | 102.5 | 1 | TO | Tomsk | Retro FM |
| 18) | 102.5 | 1 | VN | Beguchar | Yumor FM |
| 19) | 102.5 | 1 | SM | Safonovo | Dorozhnoye R. |
| 19) | 102.5 | 1 | KT | Kotkozero | Dorozhnoye R. |
| 199) | 102.5 | 1 | KY | Yugorsk | R. Yugra |
| 2) | 102.5 | 1 | OM | Omsk | Russkoye R. |
| 2) | 102.5 | 1 | TY | Tyumen | Russkoye R. |
| 24) | 102.5 | 2 | SA | Samara | NRJ |
| 27) | 102.5 | 1 | KM | Petropavlovsk-K. | R. Dacha |
| 35) | 102.5 | 1 | RY | Ryazan | R. Vera |
| 4) | 102.5 | 1 | AK | Biysk | Europa plus |
| 4) | 102.5 | 1 | CV | Cheboksary | Europa plus |
| 4) | 102.5 | 1 | RS | Yakutsk | Europa plus |
| 4) | 102.5 | 1 | SL | Yu-Sakhalinsk | Europa plus |
| 46) | 102.5 | 5 | MO | Moskva | Comedy R. |
| 50) | 102.5 | 5 | SV | Yekaterinburg | Dzhem FM |
| 62) | 102.5 | 1 | KD | Psebay | Kazak FM |
| 1) | 102.6 | 1 | IR | Sayansk | Avtoradio |
| 10) | 102.6 | 1 | SR | Saratov | R. 7 |
| 131) | 102.6 | 2 | TS | Nizhnekamsk | R. Bolgar |
| 134B) | 102.6 | 5 | ST | Stavropol | R. dlya druzey |
| 16) | 102.6 | 1 | VG | Volgograd | Retro FM |
| 18) | 102.6 | 1 | VN | Ostrogozhsk | Yumor FM |
| 183) | 102.6 | 1 | ZB | Chita | R. Sibir |
| 19) | 102.6 | 1 | KT | Leppyasilta | Dorozhnoye R. |
| 19) | 102.6 | 1 | KS | Makaryev | Dorozhnoye R. |
| 19) | 102.6 | 4 | SP | Tikhvin | Dorozhnoye R. |
| 2) | 102.6 | 1 | BR | Bryansk | Russkoye R. |
| 2) | 102.6 | 1 | YA | Yaroslavl | Russkoye R. |
| 26) | 102.6 | 1 | NS | Novosibirsk | R. Rekord |
| 27) | 102.6 | 1 | KE | Novokuznetsk | R. Dacha |
| 3) | 102.6 | 1 | PS | Pskov | Ekho Moskvy |
| 4) | 102.6 | 1 | KL | Kaluga | Europa plus |
| 45) | 102.6 | 1 | IR | Irkutsk | Novoye R. |
| 72) | 102.6 | 1 | PS | V.Luki | Luki FM |
| 1) | 102.7 | 1 | AM | Progress | Avtoradio |
| 1) | 102.7 | 1 | KU | Zheleznogorsk | Avtoradio |
| 10) | 102.7 | 1 | BE | Belgorod | R. 7 |
| 124A) | 102.7 | 1 | BA | Baymak | R. Yuldash |
| 124A) | 102.7 | 1 | BA | Oktyabrskoye | R. Yuldash |
| 14) | 102.7 | 1 | MU | Kandalaksha | R. Shanson |
| 14) | 102.7 | 1 | VO | Vologda | R. Shanson |
| 15) | 102.7 | 5 | PR | Perm | DFM |
| 150) | 102.7 | 4 | PM | Vladivostok | R. Lemma |
| 171) | 102.7 | 1 | AK | Zaraysk | R. Radio |
| 196) | 102.7 | 1 | KH | Khabarovsk | Mix FM |
| 214) | 102.7 | 1 | IR | Nizhneudinsk | Udachnoye R. |
| 24) | 102.7 | 1 | IR | Ust-Ilimsk | NRJ |
| 29) | 102.7 | 5 | KD | Krasnodar | Pervoye R. |
| 4) | 102.7 | 1 | AS | Astrakhan | Europa plus |
| 5) | 102.7 | 1 | KO | Syktyvkar | Hit FM |
| 96) | 102.7 | 1 | TV | Tver | Pilot R. |
| 9A) | 102.7 | 2 | SA | Tolyatti | R. Vanya |
| 1) | 102.8 | 1 | PM | Arsenyev | Avtoradio |
| 1) | 102.8 | 1 | RA | Gorno-Altaysk | Avtoradio |
| 1) | 102.8 | 1 | NS | Kuybyshev | Avtoradio |
| 11) | 102.8 | 10 | SP | Sankt-Peterburg | R. Maksimum |
| 124B) | 102.8 | 1 | BA | Uchaly | Sputnik FM |
| 14) | 102.8 | 1 | IR | Cheremkhovo | R. Shanson |
| 14) | 102.8 | 1 | VN | Voronezh | R. Shanson |
| 19) | 102.8 | 1 | KS | Ostrovskoye | Dorozhnoye R. |
| 2) | 102.8 | 1 | AM | Belogorsk | Russkoye R. |
| 21) | 102.8 | 1 | SO | Vladikavkaz | R. Zvezda |
| 3) | 102.8 | 1 | BU | Ulan-Ude | Ekho Moskvy |
| 4) | 102.8 | 1 | PR | Berezniki | Europa plus |
| 4) | 102.8 | 1 | OB | Orsk | Europa plus |
| 4) | 102.8 | 1 | OM | Takmyk | Europa plus |
| 40) | 102.8 | 1 | TS | Kazan | BIM-R. |
| 63) | 102.8 | 5 | KN | Krasnoyarsk | Krasnoyarsk glavnyy |
| 79) | 102.8 | 1 | BE | Valuyki | Mir Belogorya |
| 82) | 102.8 | 1 | PZ | Penza | Most R. |
| 9A) | 102.8 | 1 | KE | Kemerovo | R. Vanya |
| 1) | 102.9 | 1 | IR | Bratsk | Avtoradio |
| 1) | 102.9 | 1 | PM | Nakhodka | Avtoradio |
| 1) | 102.9 | 1 | RS | Neryungri | Avtoradio |
| 1) | 102.9 | 1 | TA | Tambov | Avtoradio |
| 15) | 102.9 | 1 | SA | Samara | DFM |
| 18) | 102.9 | 1 | KO | Ukhta | Yumor FM |
| 19) | 102.9 | 1 | SP | Podporozhye | Dorozhnoye R. |
| 2) | 102.9 | 5 | NN | N.Novgorod | Russkoye R. |
| 208) | 102.9 | 1 | SL | Yu-Sakhalinsk | Rock FM |
| 4) | 102.9 | 1 | VG | Mikhaylovka | Europa plus |
| 4) | 102.9 | 1 | VL | Vladimir | Europa plus |
| 46) | 102.9 | 1 | AK | Barnaul | Comedy R. |
| 58) | 102.9 | 1 | CB | Chelyabinsk | Intervolna |
| 6) | 102.9 | 1 | KA | Kaliningrad | Love R. |
| 62) | 102.9 | 4 | KD | Armavir | Kazak FM |
| 75) | 102.9 | 1 | KV | Kirov | Mariya FM |
| 1) | 103.0 | 1 | MA | Magadan | Avtoradio |
| 124A) | 103.0 | 1 | BA | Belyanka | R. Yuldash |
| 14) | 103.0 | 1 | TS | Bugulma | R. Shanson |
| 14) | 103.0 | 10 | MO | Moskva | R. Shanson |
| 15) | 103.0 | 1 | CB | Magnitogorsk | DFM |
| 160) | 103.0 | 1 | YN | Noyabrsk | R. Noyabrsk |
| 175) | 103.0 | 1 | BA | Ufa | R. Roksana |
| 19) | 103.0 | 1 | VN | Borisoglebsk | Dorozhnoye R. |
| 19) | 103.0 | 1 | IV | Ivanovo | Dorozhnoye R. |
| 19) | 103.0 | 1 | SP | Kirishi | Dorozhnoye R. |
| 2) | 103.0 | 1 | UL | Ulyanovsk | Russkoye R. |
| 204) | 103.0 | 1 | SR | Saratov | Radiola |
| 23) | 103.0 | 1 | CV | Cheboksary | Detskoye R. |
| 4) | 103.0 | 1 | UD | Izhevsk | Europa plus |
| 5) | 103.0 | 2 | OB | Orenburg | Hit FM |
| 8) | 103.0 | 1 | YV | Birobidzhan | Nashe R. |
| 8) | 103.0 | 1 | MU | Murmansk | Nashe R. |
| 8) | 103.0 | 1 | KM | Petropavlovsk-K. | Nashe R. |
| 8) | 103.0 | 1 | PS | Pskov | Nashe R. |
| 1) | 103.1 | 1 | CB | Ozersk | Avtoradio |
| 1) | 103.1 | 1 | KT | Petrozavodsk | Avtoradio |
| 1) | 103.1 | 3 | PM | Spassk-Dalniy | Avtoradio |
| 1) | 103.1 | 1 | VG | Volgograd | Avtoradio |
| 112) | 103.1 | 1 | TY | Tyumen | R. 7 Tyumen |
| 16) | 103.1 | 1 | SV | Krasnoturinsk | Retro FM |
| 16) | 103.1 | 1 | ST | Stavropol | Retro FM |
| 18) | 103.1 | 1 | AK | Biysk | Yumor FM |
| 197B) | 103.1 | 1 | RS | Yakutsk | R. Viktoriya |
| 2) | 103.1 | 1 | KD | Sochi | Russkoye R. |
| 4) | 103.1 | 1 | BE | Staryy Oskol | Europa plus |
| 6) | 103.1 | 1 | KS | Kostroma | Love R. |
| 62) | 103.1 | 1 | KD | Primorsko-Akhtarsk | Kazak FM |
| 7) | 103.1 | 1 | OB | Abdulino | Militseyskaya volna |
| 7) | 103.1 | 1 | MU | Apatity | Militseyskaya volna |
| 7) | 103.1 | 1 | OB | Kuvandyk | Militseyskaya volna |
| 7) | 103.1 | 1 | AK | Slavgorod | Militseyskaya volna |
| 89) | 103.1 | 1 | KL | Kaluga | Nika FM |
| 1) | 103.2 | 1 | KD | Krasnodar | Avtoradio |
| 11) | 103.2 | 1 | PR | Perm | R. Maksimum |
| 112) | 103.2 | 1 | TY | B.Sorokino | R. 7 Tyumen |
| 124A) | 103.2 | 1 | BA | Davlekanovo | R. Yuldash |
| 14) | 103.2 | 1 | IR | Tayshet | R. Shanson |
| 14) | 103.2 | 4 | PM | Vladivostok | R. Shanson |
| 14) | 103.2 | 1 | SV | Yekaterinburg | R. Shanson |
| 15) | 103.2 | 1 | SA | Tolyatti | DFM |
| 18) | 103.2 | 1 | TS | Nab.Chelny | Yumor FM |
| 18) | 103.2 | 1 | VN | Pavlovsk | Yumor FM |

| FM | MHz | kW | Rg | Location | Station |
|---|---|---|---|---|---|
| 19) | 103.2 | 1 | MD | Saransk | Dorozhnoye R. |
| 19) | 103.2 | 1 | SM | Vyazma | Dorozhnoye R. |
| 2) | 103.2 | 1 | AS | Astrakhan | Russkoye R. |
| 2) | 103.2 | 1 | ST | Pyatigorsk | Russkoye R. |
| 21) | 103.2 | 1 | AR | Plesetsk | R. Zvezda |
| 21) | 103.2 | 1 | ME | Yoshkar-Ola | R. Zvezda |
| 38) | 103.2 | 1 | PR | Krasnovishersk | Beloye R. |
| 4) | 103.2 | 1 | MO | Kashira | Europa plus |
| 4) | 103.2 | 1 | VL | Kovrov | Europa plus |
| 4) | 103.2 | 3 | NS | Novosibirsk | Europa plus |
| 4) | 103.2 | 1 | RY | Ryazan | Europa plus |
| 5) | 103.2 | 1 | KG | Kurgan | Hit FM |
| 1) | 103.3 | 2 | TS | Kazan | Avtoradio |
| 1) | 103.3 | 2 | KY | Surgut | Avtoradio |
| 124A) | 103.3 | 1 | BA | Bakaly | R. Yuldash |
| 14) | 103.3 | 1 | KE | Kemerovo | R. Shanson |
| 14) | 103.3 | 1 | OL | Livny | R. Shanson |
| 15) | 103.3 | 1 | PR | Berezniki | DFM |
| 15) | 103.3 | 1 | VL | Murom | DFM |
| 179) | 103.3 | 1 | PM | Dalnerechensk | Vladivostok FM |
| 2) | 103.3 | 1 | AM | Blagoveshchensk | Russkoye R. |
| 2) | 103.3 | 1 | MU | Kandalaksha | Russkoye R. |
| 2) | 103.3 | 1 | IR | Sayansk | Russkoye R. |
| 24) | 103.3 | 1 | OB | Buzuluk | NRJ |
| 24) | 103.3 | 2 | KN | Krasnoyarsk | NRJ |
| 27) | 103.3 | 1 | SR | Balakovo | R. Dacha |
| 27) | 103.3 | 1 | UD | Balezino | R. Dacha |
| 27) | 103.3 | 1 | OB | Orsk | R. Dacha |
| 27) | 103.3 | 1 | RO | Rostov-na-Donu | R. Dacha |
| 27) | 103.3 | 1 | YA | Yaroslavl | R. Dacha |
| 29) | 103.3 | 4 | KD | Tbilisskaya | Pervoye R. |
| 37) | 103.3 | 1 | KA | Dobrovolsk | Baltik Plyus |
| 7) | 103.3 | 1 | TL | Tula | Militseyskaya volna |
| 73) | 103.3 | 1 | BA | Salavat | M R. |
| 99) | 103.3 | 1 | ZB | Chita | Populyarnoye R. |
| 1) | 103.4 | 1 | KV | Kirov | Avtoradio |
| 1) | 103.4 | 1 | KL | Obninsk | Avtoradio |
| 1) | 103.4 | 1 | NO | Valday | Avtoradio |
| 1) | 103.4 | 1 | VN | Voronezh | Avtoradio |
| 1) | 103.4 | 1 | KV | Vyatskiye Polyarny | Avtoradio |
| 15) | 103.4 | 5 | SP | Sankt-Peterburg | DFM |
| 173) | 103.4 | 4 | NN | N.Novgorod | R. Randevu |
| 19) | 103.4 | 1 | AR | Arkhangelsk | Dorozhnoye R. |
| 19) | 103.4 | 1 | RA | Gorno-Altaysk | Dorozhnoye R. |
| 2) | 103.4 | 1 | VL | Vladimir | Russkoye R. |
| 1) | 103.5 | 1 | KA | Chernyakhovsk | Avtoradio |
| 1) | 103.5 | 1 | KD | Labinsk | Avtoradio |
| 1) | 103.5 | 1 | SO | Vladikavkaz | Avtoradio |
| 109) | 103.5 | 5 | OM | Omsk | R. 3 |
| 147) | 103.5 | 1 | RS | Aldan | STV-R. |
| 15) | 103.5 | 1 | BR | Bryansk | DFM |
| 16) | 103.5 | 1 | CV | Cheboksary | Retro FM |
| 16) | 103.5 | 1 | MU | Kirovsk | Retro FM |
| 16) | 103.5 | 1 | KT | Petrozavodsk | Retro FM |
| 179) | 103.5 | 1 | PM | Dalnegorsk | Vladivostok FM |
| 179) | 103.5 | 5 | PM | Novozhatkovo | Vladivostok FM |
| 19) | 103.5 | 1 | UL | Ulyanovsk | Dorozhnoye R. |
| 2) | 103.5 | 1 | SM | Smolensk | Russkoye R. |
| 206) | 103.5 | 1 | AR | Velsk | Region 29 |
| 207) | 103.5 | 1 | BA | Ufa | Relaks FM |
| 4) | 103.5 | 1 | SR | Saratov | Europa plus |
| 4) | 103.5 | 1 | KO | Ukhta | Europa plus |
| 7) | 103.5 | 1 | AK | Aleysk | Militseyskaya volna |
| 7) | 103.5 | 1 | OB | Tyulgan | Militseyskaya volna |
| 76) | 103.5 | 1 | KN | Norilsk | Megapolis FM |
| 8) | 103.5 | 1 | CB | Chelyabinsk | Nashe R. |
| 9A) | 103.5 | 1 | OL | Oryol | R. Vanya |
| 132) | 103.6 | 2 | PR | Perm | Nashi pesni |
| 134A) | 103.6 | 1 | SV | Nizhniy Tagil | Studio 21 |
| 155) | 103.6 | 1 | SA | Samara | R. Megapolis |
| 18) | 103.6 | 1 | RS | Yakutsk | Yumor FM |
| 19) | 103.6 | 1 | VG | Volgograd | Dorozhnoye R. |
| 19) | 103.6 | 1 | TV | Vyshniy Volochyok | Dorozhnoye R. |
| 2) | 103.6 | 1 | TS | Nab.Chelny | Russkoye R. |
| 24) | 103.6 | 1 | CB | Magnitogorsk | NRJ |
| 27) | 103.6 | 1 | VL | Kolchugino | R. Dacha |
| 4) | 103.6 | 1 | BE | Belgorod | Europa plus |
| 4) | 103.6 | 1 | VL | Gus-Khrustalnyy | Europa plus |
| 4) | 103.6 | 1 | ST | Stavropol | Europa plus |
| 88) | 103.6 | 1 | IR | Cheremkhovo | R. MSM |
| 1) | 103.7 | 1 | MD | Saransk | Avtoradio |
| 1) | 103.7 | 1 | NO | V. Novgorod | Avtoradio |
| 11) | 103.7 | 10 | MO | Moskva | R. Maksimum |
| 117) | 103.7 | 2 | KH | Khabarovsk | R. Vostok Rossii |
| 134A) | 103.7 | 1 | VO | Vologda | Studio 21 |
| 14) | 103.7 | 1 | AS | Astrakhan | R. Shanson |
| 143) | 103.7 | 1 | OB | Orsk | R. Khit |
| 149) | 103.7 | 1 | KU | Kursk | R. Kurs |
| 157) | 103.7 | 1 | RO | Rostov-na-Donu | R. Monte-Karlo |
| 16) | 103.7 | 1 | AK | Biysk | Retro FM |
| 16) | 103.7 | 1 | KX | Elista | Retro FM |
| 16) | 103.7 | 1 | AM | Shimanovsk | Retro FM |
| 16) | 103.7 | 1 | PM | Vladivostok | Retro FM |
| 18) | 103.7 | 1 | SR | Balakovo | Yumor FM |
| 182) | 103.7 | 5 | SV | Yekaterinburg | R. Si |
| 183) | 103.7 | 1 | RK | Abakan | R. Sibir |
| 19) | 103.7 | 1 | KD | Krasnodar | Dorozhnoye R. |
| 19) | 103.7 | 1 | KG | Kurgan | Dorozhnoye R. |
| 19) | 103.7 | 1 | BU | Ulan-Ude | Dorozhnoye R. |
| 19) | 103.7 | 1 | NN | Vorotynets | Dorozhnoye R. |
| 2) | 103.7 | 1 | KE | Mezhdurechensk | Russkoye R. |
| 220) | 103.7 | 1 | SA | Isakly | Samarskoye gub. R. |
| 27) | 103.7 | 1 | KD | Sochi | R. Dacha |
| 4) | 103.7 | 1 | OB | Orenburg | Europa plus |
| 103) | 103.8 | 1 | ME | Yoshkar-Ola | Puls R. |
| 124A) | 103.8 | 1 | BA | Steplitamak | R. Yuldash |
| 14) | 103.8 | 1 | PR | Berezniki | R. Shanson |
| 15) | 103.8 | 1 | TO | Tomsk | DFM |
| 16) | 103.8 | 1 | KO | Syktyvkar | Retro FM |
| 17) | 103.8 | 1 | TV | Tver | Serebryanyy dozhd |
| 177) | 103.8 | 1 | RS | Neryungri | R. Sakha |
| 19) | 103.8 | 1 | NO | Borovichi | Dorozhnoye R. |
| 19) | 103.8 | 1 | YA | Yaroslavl | Dorozhnoye R. |
| 2) | 103.8 | 4 | AR | Arkhangelsk | Russkoye R. |
| 2) | 103.8 | 1 | RT | Kyzyl | Russkoye R. |
| 25) | 103.8 | 1 | KN | Yeniseysk | R. Mir |
| 4) | 103.8 | 1 | IR | Irkutsk | Europa plus |
| 4) | 103.8 | 2 | KN | Krasnoyarsk | Europa plus |
| 4) | 103.8 | 1 | PZ | Penza | Europa plus |
| 4) | 103.8 | 1 | ST | Pyatigorsk | Europa plus |
| 6) | 103.8 | 1 | VN | Voronezh | Love R. |
| 8) | 103.8 | 1 | UD | Izhevsk | Nashe R. |
| 89) | 103.8 | 1 | KL | Sukhinichi | Nika FM |
| 1) | 103.9 | 1 | AK | Barnaul | Avtoradio |
| 1) | 103.9 | 1 | PM | Dalnerechensk | Avtoradio |
| 134A) | 103.9 | 1 | TA | Tambov | Studio 21 |
| 15) | 103.9 | 1 | MO | Lukhovitsy | DFM |
| 15) | 103.9 | 2 | NS | Novosibirsk | DFM |
| 16) | 103.9 | 1 | VG | Mikhaylovka | Retro FM |
| 18) | 103.9 | 1 | OL | Oryol | Yumor FM |
| 183) | 103.9 | 1 | OM | Omsk | R. Sibir |
| 2) | 103.9 | 3 | PM | Dalnegorsk | Russkoye R. |
| 2) | 103.9 | 1 | KV | Kirov | Russkoye R. |
| 2) | 103.9 | 1 | KM | Petropavlovsk-K. | Russkoye R. |
| 4) | 103.9 | 1 | SV | Irbit | Europa plus |
| 4) | 103.9 | 5 | NN | N.Novgorod | Europa plus |
| 45) | 103.9 | 1 | PM | Partizansk | Novoye R. |
| 45) | 103.9 | 1 | SR | Saratov | Novoye R. |
| 7) | 103.9 | 5 | UL | Veshkayma | Militseyskaya volna |
| 1) | 104.0 | 1 | SV | Kamensk-Uralskiy | Avtoradio |
| 112) | 104.0 | 1 | TY | Ishim | R. 7 Tyumen |
| 124B) | 104.0 | 1 | BA | Kugarchi | Sputnik FM |
| 14) | 104.0 | 1 | TS | Kazan | R. Shanson |
| 14) | 104.0 | 1 | KE | Novokuznetsk | R. Shanson |
| 16) | 104.0 | 1 | MU | Murmansk | Retro FM |
| 16) | 104.0 | 1 | BA | Ufa | Retro FM |
| 19) | 104.0 | 1 | TV | Rzhev | Dorozhnoye R. |
| 19) | 104.0 | 1 | RS | Yakutsk | Dorozhnoye R. |
| 26) | 104.0 | 1 | SA | Tolyatti | R. Rekord |
| 4) | 104.0 | 1 | KY | Nizhnevartovsk | Europa plus |
| 45) | 104.0 | 1 | VG | Volgograd | Novoye R. |
| 8) | 104.0 | 10 | SP | Sankt-Peterburg | Nashe R. |
| 91) | 104.0 | 1 | KD | Novorossiysk | Novaya Rossiya |
| 9A) | 104.0 | 1 | PZ | Pachelma | R. Vanya |
| 1) | 104.1 | 1 | AR | Plesetsk | Avtoradio |
| 1) | 104.1 | 1 | RO | Rostov-na-Donu | Avtoradio |
| 118) | 104.1 | 5 | PR | Perm | R. Alfa |
| 15) | 104.1 | 1 | TS | Chistopol | DFM |
| 15) | 104.1 | 1 | OB | Orsk | DFM |
| 15) | 104.1 | 1 | CB | Tryokhgornyy | DFM |
| 188) | 104.1 | 1 | AS | Astrakhan | Yuzhnaya volna |
| 19) | 104.1 | 1 | AM | Shimanovsk | Dorozhnoye R. |
| 2) | 104.1 | 1 | IR | Bratsk | Russkoye R. |
| 2) | 104.1 | 1 | CB | Chelyabinsk | Russkoye R. |

| FM | MHz | kW | Rg | Location | Station |
|---|---|---|---|---|---|
| 24) | 104.1 | 1 | RY | Ryazan | NRJ |
| 26) | 104.1 | 1 | ME | Gornyak | R. Rekord |
| 27) | 104.1 | 1 | SV | Yekaterinburg | R. Dacha |
| 4) | 104.1 | 2 | KY | Khanty-Mansiysk | Europa plus |
| 6) | 104.1 | 1 | SV | Krasnoturinsk | Love R. |
| 8) | 104.1 | 1 | NO | V. Novgorod | Nashe R. |
| 9A) | 104.1 | 1 | SM | Roslavl | R. Vanya |
| 9A) | 104.1 | 1 | MD | Saransk | R. Vanya |
| 1) | 104.2 | 1 | KG | Kurgan | Avtoradio |
| 133) | 104.2 | 1 | UL | Ulyanovsk | Ulyanovsk FM |
| 14) | 104.2 | 1 | KY | Surgut | R. Shanson |
| 161) | 104.2 | 4 | NN | Arzamas | R. Obraz |
| 18) | 104.2 | 2 | TO | Tomsk | Yumor FM |
| 18) | 104.2 | 1 | SM | Vyazma | Yumor FM |
| 19) | 104.2 | 1 | SP | Kingisepp | Dorozhnoye R. |
| 192) | 104.2 | 2 | VO | Babayevo | R. Transmit |
| 192) | 104.2 | 1 | VO | Totma | R. Transmit |
| 2) | 104.2 | 1 | CB | Magnitogorsk | Russkoye R. |
| 23) | 104.2 | 1 | TY | Tyumen | Detskoye R. |
| 24) | 104.2 | 1 | BE | Belgorod | NRJ |
| 24) | 104.2 | 15 | MO | Moskva | NRJ |
| 28) | 104.2 | 1 | KN | Krasnoyarsk | Biznes FM |
| 4) | 104.2 | 1 | RK | Abakan | Europa plus |
| 4) | 104.2 | 1 | MU | Apatity | Europa plus |
| 4) | 104.2 | 3 | PM | Vladivostok | Europa plus |
| 5) | 104.2 | 1 | KD | Krasnodar | Hit FM |
| 6) | 104.2 | 1 | CV | Cheboksary | Love R. |
| 6) | 104.2 | 1 | IR | Irkutsk | Love R. |
| 69) | 104.2 | 1 | AR | Arkhangelsk | Zhara FM |
| 7) | 104.2 | 1 | OB | Tashla | Militseyskaya volna |
| 1) | 104.3 | 1 | OL | Oryol | Avtoradio |
| 11) | 104.3 | 1 | KT | Petrozavodsk | R. Maksimum |
| 15) | 104.3 | 2 | OB | Orenburg | DFM |
| 15) | 104.3 | 1 | VN | Voronezh | DFM |
| 16) | 104.3 | 1 | SR | Saratov | Retro FM |
| 19) | 104.3 | 1 | KE | Kemerovo | Dorozhnoye R. |
| 19) | 104.3 | 1 | KH | Khabarovsk | Dorozhnoye R. |
| 19) | 104.3 | 1 | PZ | Penza | Dorozhnoye R. |
| 2) | 104.3 | 1 | BA | Steplitamak | Russkoye R. |
| 2) | 104.3 | 1 | KD | Tikhoretsk | Russkoye R. |
| 213) | 104.3 | 2 | SA | Samara | Samara-Maksimum |
| 22) | 104.3 | 1 | VL | Vladimir | R. KP |
| 75) | 104.3 | 1 | NN | Krasnyye Baki | Mariya FM |
| 9A) | 104.3 | 1 | KV | Kirov | R. Vanya |
| 1) | 104.4 | 5 | TL | Tula | Avtoradio |
| 10) | 104.4 | 1 | BE | Ivnya | R. 7 |
| 14) | 104.4 | 5 | SP | Sankt-Peterburg | R. Shanson |
| 16) | 104.4 | 1 | AK | Barnaul | Retro FM |
| 16) | 104.4 | 1 | TA | Tambov | Retro FM |
| 19) | 104.4 | 1 | AM | Blagoveshchensk | Dorozhnoye R. |
| 19) | 104.4 | 1 | NO | Khoynaya | Dorozhnoye R. |
| 19) | 104.4 | 1 | PS | Pushkinskiye gory | Dorozhnoye R. |
| 192) | 104.4 | 1 | VO | Nikolsk | R. Transmit |
| 192) | 104.4 | 2 | VO | Vologda | R. Transmit |
| 2) | 104.4 | 1 | PR | Chusovoy | Russkoye R. |
| 24) | 104.4 | 1 | KE | Yurga | NRJ |
| 26) | 104.4 | 1 | OM | Omsk | R. Rekord |
| 27) | 104.4 | 1 | BA | Tuymazy | R. Dacha |
| 4) | 104.4 | 1 | YN | Noyabrsk | Europa plus |
| 4) | 104.4 | 5 | KD | Sochi | Europa plus |
| 6) | 104.4 | 1 | KA | Sovetsk | Love R. |
| 6) | 104.4 | 1 | SL | Yu-Sakhalinsk | Love R. |
| 7) | 104.4 | 1 | VL | Murom | Militseyskaya volna |
| 75) | 104.4 | 2 | TS | Shemordan | Mariya FM |
| 9A) | 104.4 | 1 | KE | Novokuznetsk | R. Vanya |
| 1) | 104.5 | 1 | KM | Petropavlovsk-K. | Avtoradio |
| 1) | 104.5 | 1 | SM | Safonovo | Avtoradio |
| 1) | 104.5 | 1 | BE | Staryy Oskol | Avtoradio |
| 1) | 104.5 | 1 | YA | Yaroslavl | Avtoradio |
| 100) | 104.5 | 1 | MU | Murmansk | Power Hit R. |
| 114) | 104.5 | 1 | UD | Izhevsk | R. Adam |
| 16) | 104.5 | 1 | MU | Kandalaksha | Retro FM |
| 163) | 104.5 | 1 | CB | Chelyabinsk | R. Olimp |
| 167) | 104.5 | 1 | MD | Saransk | Start FM |
| 170) | 104.5 | 1 | DA | Kizilyort | R. Priboy |
| 18) | 104.5 | 1 | VG | Volgograd | Yumor FM |
| 19) | 104.5 | 1 | KT | Lakhdenpokhya | Dorozhnoye R. |
| 190) | 104.5 | 1 | PM | Nakhodka | R. Svob. Nakhodka |
| 197A) | 104.5 | 1 | RS | Yakutsk | R. Viktoriya-Sakha |
| 199) | 104.5 | 1 | KY | Nyagan | R. Yugra |
| 2) | 104.5 | 1 | BA | Ufa | Russkoye R. |
| 210) | 104.5 | 5 | SV | Yekaterinburg | Rok-Arsenal |
| 25) | 104.5 | 1 | NO | V. Novgorod | R. Mir |
| 27) | 104.5 | 2 | NN | N.Novgorod | R. Dacha |
| 29) | 104.5 | 5 | KD | Kanevskaya | Pervoye R. |
| 33) | 104.5 | 1 | UL | Dimitrovgrad | 2x2 R. |
| 35) | 104.5 | 1 | TV | Vyshniy Volochyok | R. Vera |
| 4) | 104.5 | 1 | KA | Kaliningrad | Europa plus |
| 4) | 104.5 | 1 | ME | Yoshkar-Ola | Europa plus |
| 45) | 104.5 | 1 | RY | Ryazan | Novoye R. |
| 5) | 104.5 | 1 | KO | Ukhta | Hit FM |
| 7) | 104.5 | 1 | OB | Sharlyk | Militseyskaya volna |
| 1) | 104.6 | 1 | KV | Kilmez | Avtoradio |
| 1) | 104.6 | 1 | KD | Tuapse | Avtoradio |
| 124A) | 104.6 | 1 | BA | Akyar | R. Yuldash |
| 15) | 104.6 | 1 | RO | Rostov-na-Donu | DFM |
| 16) | 104.6 | 5 | IR | Irkutsk | Retro FM |
| 179) | 104.6 | 1 | PM | Arsenyev | Vladivostok FM |
| 183) | 104.6 | 1 | IR | Bratsk | R. Sibir |
| 183) | 104.6 | 1 | TO | Tomsk | R. Sibir |
| 192) | 104.6 | 1 | VO | Cherepovets | R. Transmit |
| 24) | 104.6 | 1 | SA | Syzran | NRJ |
| 27) | 104.6 | 2 | KN | Krasnoyarsk | R. Dacha |
| 40) | 104.6 | 1 | TS | Almetyevsk | BIM-R. |
| 42) | 104.6 | 1 | VN | Liski | Pervoye setevoye |
| 6) | 104.6 | 1 | PR | Berezniki | Love R. |
| 6) | 104.6 | 1 | LI | Lipetsk | Love R. |
| 66) | 104.6 | 1 | TY | Tyumen | Krasnaya Armiya |
| 7) | 104.6 | 1 | AK | Zaraysk | Militseyskaya volna |
| 1) | 104.7 | 1 | RK | Abakan | Avtoradio |
| 1) | 104.7 | 1 | CB | Magnitogorsk | Avtoradio |
| 1) | 104.7 | 1 | KY | Nizhnevartovsk | Avtoradio |
| 10) | 104.7 | 5 | MO | Moskva | R. 7 |
| 124A) | 104.7 | 1 | BA | Belebey | R. Yuldash |
| 124B) | 104.7 | 1 | BA | Neftekamsk | Sputnik FM |
| 131) | 104.7 | 1 | TS | Nurlat | R. Bolgar |
| 15) | 104.7 | 1 | TS | Kazan | DFM |
| 16) | 104.7 | 1 | KH | Komsomolsk-na-A. | Retro FM |
| 19) | 104.7 | 1 | BR | Shvedchiki | Dorozhnoye R. |
| 2) | 104.7 | 1 | KT | Petrozavodsk | Russkoye R. |
| 24) | 104.7 | 1 | KE | Mezhdurechensk | NRJ |
| 26) | 104.7 | 1 | PR | Perm | R. Rekord |
| 27) | 104.7 | 5 | PM | Vladivostok | R. Dacha |
| 46) | 104.7 | 1 | BE | Belgorod | Comedy R. |
| 8) | 104.7 | 1 | AR | Arkhangelsk | Nashe R. |
| 8) | 104.7 | 1 | KD | Krasnodar | Nashe R. |
| 97) | 104.7 | 1 | KS | Sharya | Pioner FM |
| 98A) | 104.7 | 1 | SP | Luga | Piter FM |
| 1) | 104.8 | 1 | SA | Samara | Avtoradio |
| 1) | 104.8 | 1 | VL | Vladimir | Avtoradio |
| 134A) | 104.8 | 1 | KD | Sochi | Studio 21 |
| 14) | 104.8 | 1 | TV | Tver | R. Shanson |
| 16) | 104.8 | 1 | SM | Smolensk | Retro FM |
| 16) | 104.8 | 1 | BA | Steplitamak | Retro FM |
| 17) | 104.8 | 1 | SR | Saratov | Serebryanyy dozhd |
| 18) | 104.8 | 1 | MO | Kolomna | Yumor FM |
| 19) | 104.8 | 1 | KB | Nalchik | Dorozhnoye R. |
| 19) | 104.8 | 1 | OB | Orenburg | Dorozhnoye R. |
| 19) | 104.8 | 1 | KO | Syktyvkar | Dorozhnoye R. |
| 194) | 104.8 | 1 | DA | Makhachkala | R. Assa |
| 2) | 104.8 | 1 | KE | Kemerovo | Russkoye R. |
| 2) | 104.8 | 1 | KS | Kostroma | Russkoye R. |
| 2) | 104.8 | 1 | PZ | Penza | Russkoye R. |
| 2) | 104.8 | 1 | VN | Voronezh | Russkoye R. |
| 2) | 104.8 | 1 | TY | Zavodoukovsk | Russkoye R. |
| 24) | 104.8 | 1 | TS | Nab.Chelny | NRJ |
| 5) | 104.8 | 1 | OL | Oryol | Hit FM |
| 6) | 104.8 | 1 | MU | Monchegorsk | Love R. |
| 7) | 104.8 | 1 | UL | Sengiley | Militseyskaya volna |
| 77) | 104.8 | 5 | SP | Sankt-Peterburg | R. Baltika |
| 1) | 104.8 | 1 | YN | Noyabrsk | Avtoradio |
| 124A) | 104.9 | 1 | BA | Beloretsk | R. Yuldash |
| 131) | 104.9 | 1 | TS | Kutlu-Bukash | R. Bolgar |
| 16) | 104.9 | 1 | KV | Kirov | Retro FM |
| 18) | 104.9 | 1 | MD | Saransk | Yumor FM |
| 2) | 104.9 | 1 | VO | Vologda | Russkoye R. |
| 23) | 104.9 | 1 | TA | Tambov | Detskoye R. |
| 29) | 104.9 | 5 | KD | Novorossiysk | Pervoye R. |
| 4) | 104.9 | 1 | TL | Tula | Europa plus |
| 6) | 104.9 | 1 | TS | Bavly | Love R. |
| 6) | 104.9 | 1 | NN | N.Novgorod | Love R. |
| 62) | 104.9 | 1 | KD | Yeysk | Kazak FM |
| 7) | 104.9 | 2 | UL | Novospasskoye | Militseyskaya volna |
| 71) | 104.9 | 1 | CB | Chelyabinsk | L-Radio |

| FM | MHz | kW | Rg | Location | Station | FM | MHz | kW | Rg | Location | Station |
|---|---|---|---|---|---|---|---|---|---|---|---|
| 95) | 104.9 | 1 | SO | Vladikavkaz | R. MSS | 29) | 105.4 | 4 | KD | Armavir | Pervoye R. |
| 1) | 105.0 | 1 | KE | Novokuznetsk | Avtoradio | 46) | 105.4 | 1 | SA | Samara | Comedy R. |
| 1) | 105.0 | 1 | KA | Sovetsk | Avtoradio | 57) | 105.4 | 1 | CC | Groznyy | R. Groznyy |
| 1) | 105.0 | 2 | SV | Yekaterinburg | Avtoradio | 7) | 105.4 | 1 | OB | Pervomayskiy | Militseyskaya volna |
| 10) | 105.0 | 1 | RY | Ryazan | R. 7 | 1) | 105.4 | 1 | YA | Rybinsk | Avtoradio |
| 131) | 105.0 | 1 | PR | Barda | R. Bolgar | 1) | 105.5 | 1 | MO | Uvarovka | Avtoradio |
| 147) | 105.0 | 1 | RS | Mirnyy | STV-R. | 106) | 105.5 | 1 | SL | Yu-Sakhalinsk | R. ASTV |
| 15) | 105.0 | 1 | OB | Buguruslan | DFM | 124A) | 105.5 | 1 | BA | Ufa | R. Yuldash |
| 16) | 105.0 | 1 | BU | Ulan-Ude | Retro FM | 131) | 105.5 | 2 | TS | Nab.Chelny | R. Bolgar |
| 18) | 105.0 | 1 | VN | Arkhangelskoye | Yumor FM | 144) | 105.5 | 1 | SP | Kirishi | R. Kirishi |
| 18) | 105.0 | 1 | AS | Astrakhan | Yumor FM | 147) | 105.5 | 1 | RS | Neryungri | STV-R. |
| 198) | 105.0 | 1 | RS | Neryungri | R. Voyazh | 15) | 105.5 | 1 | OL | Oryol | DFM |
| 199) | 105.0 | 5 | KY | Surgut | R. Yugra | 16) | 105.5 | 1 | UL | Ulyanovsk | Retro FM |
| 216) | 105.0 | 5 | MO | Moskva | R. Kniga | 171) | 105.5 | 2 | SV | Nizhniy Tagil | R. Radio |
| 24) | 105.0 | 1 | KD | Tuapse | NRJ | 171) | 105.5 | 1 | AK | Rubtsovsk | R. Radio |
| 26) | 105.0 | 1 | KO | Ukhta | R. Rekord | 183) | 105.5 | 1 | RA | Gorno-Altaysk | R. Sibir |
| 27) | 105.0 | 1 | BA | Ufa | R. Dacha | 19) | 105.5 | 1 | MA | Magadan | Dorozhnoye R. |
| 29) | 105.0 | 1 | KD | Belaya Glina | Pervoye R. | 192) | 105.5 | 4 | VO | Belogorsk | R. Transmit |
| 29) | 105.0 | 1 | KD | Psebay | Pervoye R. | 2) | 105.5 | 1 | MU | Murmansk | Russkoye R. |
| 3) | 105.0 | 1 | TO | Tomsk | Ekho Moskvy | 2) | 105.5 | 1 | KB | Nalchik | Russkoye R. |
| 6) | 105.0 | 1 | OM | Omsk | Love R. | 2) | 105.5 | 1 | KE | Novokuznetsk | Russkoye R. |
| 7) | 105.0 | 1 | KU | Kursk | Militseyskaya volna | 2) | 105.5 | 1 | BE | Staryy Oskol | Russkoye R. |
| 8) | 105.0 | 1 | ST | Kislovodsk | Nashe R. | 211) | 105.5 | 1 | IR | Ust-Kut | Lena FM |
| 87) | 105.0 | 2 | CV | Tsivilsk | Nats. R. Chuvashii | 25) | 105.5 | 1 | BU | Ulan-Ude | R. Mir |
| 1) | 105.1 | 1 | ST | Stavropol | Avtoradio | 59) | 105.5 | 1 | VN | Ertil | Kanal Melodiya |
| 110A) | 105.1 | 1 | VG | Volgograd | R. Sputnik | 6) | 105.5 | 1 | KD | Tuapse | Love R. |
| 124A) | 105.1 | 1 | BA | Kumertau | R. Yuldash | 6) | 105.5 | 1 | TV | Tver | Love R. |
| 134A) | 105.1 | 1 | LI | Lipetsk | Studio 21 | 7) | 105.5 | 1 | OB | Kvarkeno | Militseyskaya volna |
| 14) | 105.1 | 1 | PR | Perm | R. Shanson | 77) | 105.5 | 1 | SP | Vyborg | R. Baltika |
| 14) | 105.1 | 1 | RO | Rostov-na-Donu | R. Shanson | 84) | 105.5 | 1 | ME | Yoshkar-Ola | R. Mariy El |
| 16) | 105.1 | 1 | TY | Tyumen | Retro FM | 14) | 105.6 | 5 | IR | Irkutsk | R. Shanson |
| 1) | 105.1 | 1 | IR | Ust-Ilimsk | Retro FM | 171) | 105.6 | 1 | TY | Ishim | R. Radio |
| 168) | 105.1 | 1 | MO | Shatura | R. 1 | 2) | 105.6 | 2 | VG | Volgograd | Russkoye R. |
| 2) | 105.1 | 1 | PR | Berezniki | Russkoye R. | 220) | 105.6 | 2 | SA | Kinel-Cherkassy | Samarskoye gub. R. |
| 4) | 105.1 | 1 | YA | Yaroslavl | Europa plus | 25) | 105.6 | 1 | KO | Syktyvkar | R. Mir |
| 9A) | 105.1 | 1 | TV | Vyshniy Volochyok | R. Vanya | 26) | 105.6 | 1 | TS | Almetyevsk | R. Rekord |
| 1) | 105.2 | 1 | ZB | Chita | Avtoradio | 29) | 105.6 | 1 | KD | Primorsko-Akhtarsk | Pervoye R. |
| 1) | 105.2 | 2 | KN | Krasnoyarsk | Avtoradio | 3) | 105.6 | 1 | LI | Lipetsk | Ekho Moskvy |
| 10) | 105.2 | 1 | CB | Magnitogorsk | R. 7 | 30) | 105.6 | 1 | TS | Shemordan | Dulkyn radiosy |
| 135) | 105.2 | 1 | PZ | Penza | R. Ekspress | 4) | 105.6 | 2 | KH | Khabarovsk | Europa plus |
| 149) | 105.2 | 1 | KU | Zheleznogorsk | R. Kurs | 48) | 105.6 | 1 | TY | Tyumen | Dipol FM |
| 2) | 105.2 | 1 | KO | Syktyvkar | Russkoye R. | 6) | 105.6 | 1 | CB | Magnitogorsk | Love R. |
| 23) | 105.2 | 1 | KT | Petrozavodsk | Detskoye R. | 7) | 105.6 | 1 | OB | Novosergiyevka | Militseyskaya volna |
| 27) | 105.2 | 1 | SA | Tolyatti | R. Dacha | 7) | 105.6 | 1 | MD | Saransk | Militseyskaya volna |
| 27) | 105.2 | 1 | OB | Yasnyy | R. Dacha | 1) | 105.7 | 1 | MU | Apatity | Avtoradio |
| 37) | 105.2 | 1 | KA | Kaliningrad | Baltik Plyus | 1) | 105.7 | 1 | BR | Unecha | Avtoradio |
| 4) | 105.2 | 1 | SM | Vyazma | Europa plus | 124B) | 105.7 | 1 | BA | Oktyabrskoye | Sputnik FM |
| 46) | 105.2 | 2 | KY | Megion | Comedy R. | 14) | 105.7 | 1 | RK | Abakan | R. Shanson |
| 5) | 105.2 | 2 | NS | Novosibirsk | Hit FM | 14) | 105.7 | 1 | UD | Izhevsk | R. Shanson |
| 62) | 105.2 | 5 | KD | Krasnodar | Kazak FM | 147) | 105.7 | 1 | RS | Yakutsk | STV-R. |
| 8) | 105.2 | 1 | KD | Sochi | Nashe R. | 16) | 105.7 | 1 | OM | Omsk | Retro FM |
| 1) | 105.3 | 1 | KE | Kemerovo | Avtoradio | 18) | 105.7 | 1 | SA | Tolyatti | Yumor FM |
| 131) | 105.3 | 1 | TS | Absalyamovo | R. Bolgar | 19) | 105.7 | 1 | PR | Berezniki | Dorozhnoye R. |
| 138) | 105.3 | 1 | SO | Vladikavkaz | R. Ir | 19) | 105.7 | 4 | NO | V. Novgorod | Dorozhnoye R. |
| 15) | 105.3 | 5 | PM | Vladivostok | DFM | 2) | 105.7 | 10 | MO | Moskva | Russkoye R. |
| 16) | 105.3 | 1 | VN | Voronezh | Retro FM | 2) | 105.7 | 1 | SV | Yekaterinburg | Russkoye R. |
| 17) | 105.3 | 1 | NO | V. Novgorod | Serebryanyy dozhd | 22) | 105.7 | 1 | ST | Stavropol | R. KP |
| 17) | 105.3 | 1 | VO | Vologda | Serebryanyy dozhd | 28) | 105.7 | 2 | NS | Novosibirsk | Biznes FM |
| 171) | 105.3 | 1 | IR | Usolye-Sibirskoye | R. Radio | 29) | 105.7 | 1 | KD | Sochi | Pervoye R. |
| 18) | 105.3 | 1 | VN | Rossosh | Yumor FM | 4) | 105.7 | 1 | RO | Rostov-na-Donu | Europa plus |
| 19) | 105.3 | 1 | UD | Izhevsk | Dorozhnoye R. | 4) | 105.7 | 1 | SV | Serov | Europa plus |
| 2) | 105.3 | 1 | SR | Saratov | Russkoye R. | 5) | 105.7 | 2 | PM | Vladivostok | Hit FM |
| 2) | 105.3 | 1 | TL | Tula | Russkoye R. | 78) | 105.7 | 1 | KD | Krymsk | R. Elektron |
| 207) | 105.3 | 1 | TS | Kazan | Relaks FM | 10) | 105.8 | 1 | VL | Vladimir | R. 7 |
| 27) | 105.3 | 1 | KS | Kostroma | R. Dacha | 124A) | 105.8 | 1 | BA | Mesyagutovo | R. Yuldash |
| 27) | 105.3 | 1 | OB | Orenburg | R. Dacha | 14) | 105.8 | 1 | BA | Neftekamsk | R. Shanson |
| 6) | 105.3 | 5 | SP | Sankt-Peterburg | Love R. | 14) | 105.8 | 1 | ST | Pyatigorsk | R. Shanson |
| 8) | 105.3 | 1 | RS | Yakutsk | Nashe R. | 19) | 105.8 | 1 | SM | Roslavl | Dorozhnoye R. |
| 80B) | 105.3 | 5 | MO | Moskva | Capital FM | 2) | 105.8 | 1 | KN | Krasnoyarsk | Russkoye R. |
| 1) | 105.4 | 1 | NO | Borovichi | Avtoradio | 201) | 105.8 | 1 | KG | Shardinsk | R. Za oblakami |
| 1) | 105.4 | 1 | TO | Tomsk | Avtoradio | 205) | 105.8 | 1 | KS | Kostroma | RDV-FM |
| 10) | 105.4 | 1 | CB | Chelyabinsk | R. 7 | 27) | 105.8 | 1 | KO | Ukhta | R. Dacha |
| 124A) | 105.4 | 1 | BA | Fyodorovka | R. Yuldash | 3) | 105.8 | 1 | TS | Kazan | Ekho Moskvy |
| 124A) | 105.4 | 1 | BA | Uchaly | R. Yuldash | 5) | 105.8 | 1 | OB | Orsk | Hit FM |
| 134A) | 105.4 | 1 | IV | Ivanovo | Studio 21 | 59) | 105.8 | 1 | VN | Borisoglebsk | Kanal Melodiya |
| 16) | 105.4 | 1 | AR | Arkhangelsk | Retro FM | 6) | 105.8 | 4 | TL | Tula | Love R. |
| 16) | 105.4 | 1 | RY | Ryazan | Retro FM | 62) | 105.8 | 4 | KD | Tbilisskaya | Kazak FM |
| 177) | 105.4 | 1 | RS | Mirnyy | R. Sakha | 7) | 105.8 | 1 | OB | Buguruslan | Militseyskaya volna |
| 18) | 105.4 | 1 | VN | Kalach | Yumor FM | 7) | 105.8 | 1 | OB | Orenburg | Militseyskaya volna |
| 19) | 105.4 | 1 | NN | N.Novgorod | Dorozhnoye R. | 8) | 105.8 | 1 | IR | Usolye-Sibirskoye | Nashe R. |
| 19) | 105.4 | 1 | KG | Shardinsk | Dorozhnoye R. | 1) | 105.9 | 1 | TS | Bugulma | Avtoradio |
| 2) | 105.4 | 1 | AK | Barnaul | Russkoye R. | 14) | 105.9 | 2 | CB | Chelyabinsk | R. Shanson |

| FM | MHz | kW | Rg | Location | Station |
|---|---|---|---|---|---|
| 14) | 105.9 | 1 | RY | Ryazan | R. Shanson |
| 142) | 105.9 | 1 | KC | Karachayevsk | R. Kavkaz Khit |
| 157) | 105.9 | 5 | SP | Sankt-Peterburg | R. Monte-Karlo |
| 16) | 105.9 | 1 | RT | Kyzyl | Retro FM |
| 16) | 105.9 | 1 | SO | Vladikavkaz | Retro FM |
| 18) | 105.9 | 1 | TV | Tver | Yumor FM |
| 187) | 105.9 | 2 | NS | Raduga | R. 54 |
| 19) | 105.9 | 1 | VN | Kalach | Dorozhnoye R. |
| 19) | 105.9 | 1 | KA | Kaliningrad | Dorozhnoye R. |
| 199) | 105.9 | 1 | KY | Nizhnevartovsk | R. Yugra |
| 2) | 105.9 | 1 | TA | Tambov | Russkoye R. |
| 4) | 105.9 | 1 | KY | Surgut | Europa plus |
| 62) | 105.9 | 1 | KD | Tuapse | Kazak FM |
| 7) | 105.9 | 1 | NN | N.Novgorod | Militseyskaya volna |
| 79) | 105.9 | 1 | BE | Svistovka | Mir Belogorya |
| 1) | 106.0 | 1 | MO | Kolomna | Avtoradio |
| 10) | 106.0 | 1 | KB | Nalchik | R. 7 |
| 134A) | 106.0 | 1 | VG | Volgograd | Studio 21 |
| 15) | 106.0 | 1 | KD | Krasnodar | DFM |
| 16) | 106.0 | 1 | SV | Nizhniy Tagil | Retro FM |
| 171) | 106.0 | 1 | IR | Nizhneudinsk | R. Radio |
| 18) | 106.0 | 1 | IR | Irkutsk | Yumor FM |
| 19) | 106.0 | 1 | AS | Astrakhan | Dorozhnoye R. |
| 19) | 106.0 | 1 | MU | Murmansk | Dorozhnoye R. |
| 2) | 106.0 | 1 | SR | Balakovo | Russkoye R. |
| 27) | 106.0 | 1 | PM | Nakhodka | R. Dacha |
| 4) | 106.0 | 1 | IV | Ivanovo | Europa plus |
| 4) | 106.0 | 1 | CB | Magnitogorsk | Europa plus |
| 4) | 106.0 | 1 | KM | Petropavlovsk-K. | Europa plus |
| 4) | 106.0 | 1 | BA | Ufa | Europa plus |
| 4) | 106.0 | 1 | SP | Vyborg | Europa plus |
| 5) | 106.0 | 1 | TS | Nab.Chelny | Hit FM |
| 1) | 106.1 | 1 | UD | Izhevsk | Avtoradio |
| 1) | 106.1 | 1 | TY | Tyumen | Avtoradio |
| 1) | 106.1 | 1 | VO | Vologda | Avtoradio |
| 124A) | 106.1 | 1 | BA | Bikkulovo | R. Yuldash |
| 124A) | 106.1 | 1 | BA | Kugarchi | R. Yuldash |
| 124A) | 106.1 | 1 | BA | Verkhniye Tatyshly | R. Yuldash |
| 17) | 106.1 | 1 | KL | Kaluga | Serebryanyy dozhd |
| 19) | 106.1 | 1 | AM | Belogorsk | Dorozhnoye R. |
| 2) | 106.1 | 1 | RS | Yakutsk | Russkoye R. |
| 21) | 106.1 | 1 | KX | Elista | R. Zvezda |
| 24) | 106.1 | 1 | KE | Belovo | NRJ |
| 24) | 106.1 | 1 | KD | Sochi | NRJ |
| 24) | 106.1 | 1 | TO | Tomsk | NRJ |
| 25) | 106.1 | 1 | ZB | Chita | R. Mir |
| 27) | 106.1 | 1 | OL | Oryol | R. Dacha |
| 98A) | 106.1 | 1 | SP | Kirishi | Piter FM |
| 9A) | 106.1 | 2 | SA | Samara | R. Vanya |
| 10) | 106.2 | 1 | LI | Lipetsk | R. 7 |
| 14) | 106.2 | 1 | OM | Omsk | R. Shanson |
| 16) | 106.2 | 1 | OB | Orsk | Retro FM |
| 16) | 106.2 | 1 | ST | Pyatigorsk | Retro FM |
| 179) | 106.2 | 5 | PM | Spassk-Dalniy | Vladivostok FM |
| 18) | 106.2 | 1 | KG | Shardinsk | Yumor FM |
| 187) | 106.2 | 2 | NS | Novosibirsk | R. 54 |
| 19) | 106.2 | 1 | AK | Biysk | Dorozhnoye R. |
| 19) | 106.2 | 1 | KS | Kostroma | Dorozhnoye R. |
| 19) | 106.2 | 1 | KU | Kursk | Dorozhnoye R. |
| 19) | 106.2 | 1 | KE | Novokuznetsk | Dorozhnoye R. |
| 19) | 106.2 | 1 | PZ | Pachelma | Dorozhnoye R. |
| 2) | 106.2 | 5 | PR | Perm | Russkoye R. |
| 204) | 106.2 | 5 | SV | Yekaterinburg | Radiola |
| 21) | 106.2 | 1 | NO | V. Novgorod | R. Zvezda |
| 27) | 106.2 | 1 | KH | Khabarovsk | R. Dacha |
| 29) | 106.2 | 1 | KD | Pavlovskaya | Pervoye R. |
| 4) | 106.2 | 10 | MO | Moskva | Europa plus |
| 45) | 106.2 | 1 | RK | Abakan | Novoye R. |
| 6) | 106.2 | 1 | VL | Murom | Love R. |
| 6) | 106.2 | 1 | UL | Ulyanovsk | Love R. |
| 10) | 106.3 | 1 | TV | Tver | R. 7 |
| 124B) | 106.3 | 1 | BA | Baymak | Sputnik FM |
| 13) | 106.3 | 1 | RO | Taganrog | Donskoye R. |
| 15) | 106.3 | 1 | KY | Nizhnevartovsk | DFM |
| 15) | 106.3 | 1 | MD | Saransk | DFM |
| 16) | 106.3 | 1 | BE | Belgorod | Retro FM |
| 19) | 106.3 | 1 | IR | Bratsk | Dorozhnoye R. |
| 19) | 106.3 | 1 | CB | Chelyabinsk | Dorozhnoye R. |
| 19) | 106.3 | 1 | SR | Saratov | Dorozhnoye R. |
| 2) | 106.3 | 1 | KD | Goryachiy Klyuch | Russkoye R. |
| 2) | 106.3 | 1 | SM | Roslavl | Russkoye R. |
| 220) | 106.3 | 1 | SA | Khvorostyanka | Samarskoye gub. R. |

| FM | MHz | kW | Rg | Location | Station |
|---|---|---|---|---|---|
| 25) | 106.3 | 1 | AM | Blagoveshchensk | R. Mir |
| 26) | 106.3 | 5 | SP | Sankt-Peterburg | R. Rekord |
| 41) | 106.3 | 1 | DA | Khasvyurt | Khas FM |
| 1) | 106.4 | 1 | YV | Birobidzhan | Avtoradio |
| 11) | 106.4 | 1 | AS | Astrakhan | R. Maksimum |
| 11) | 106.4 | 1 | KA | Kaliningrad | R. Maksimum |
| 11) | 106.4 | 1 | TL | Tula | R. Maksimum |
| 127) | 106.4 | 10 | IR | Irkutsk | R. Fresh |
| 16) | 106.4 | 1 | NN | N.Novgorod | Retro FM |
| 16) | 106.4 | 1 | TS | Nab.Chelny | Retro FM |
| 179) | 106.4 | 5 | PM | Vladivostok | Vladivostok FM |
| 19) | 106.4 | 1 | TA | Tambov | Dorozhnoye R. |
| 216) | 106.4 | 1 | VG | Volgograd | R. Kniga |
| 26) | 106.4 | 1 | KY | Surgut | R. Rekord |
| 4) | 106.4 | 1 | RA | Gorno-Altaysk | Europa plus |
| 59) | 106.4 | 4 | VN | Bobrov | Kanal Melodiya |
| 8) | 106.4 | 1 | AK | Barnaul | Nashe R. |
| 9A) | 106.4 | 1 | PZ | Kuznetsk | R. Vanya |
| 9A) | 106.4 | 1 | KE | Mezhdurechensk | R. Vanya |
| 9A) | 106.4 | 1 | SV | Nizhniy Tagil | R. Vanya |
| 1) | 106.5 | 1 | BA | Ufa | Avtoradio |
| 15) | 106.5 | 1 | SR | Balakovo | DFM |
| 16) | 106.5 | 1 | TS | Chistopol | Retro FM |
| 16) | 106.5 | 1 | KG | Kurgan | Retro FM |
| 16) | 106.5 | 2 | AD | Maykop | Retro FM |
| 16) | 106.5 | 1 | KM | Petropavlovsk-K. | Retro FM |
| 16) | 106.5 | 1 | ME | Yoshkar-Ola | Retro FM |
| 168) | 106.5 | 1 | MO | Zaraysk | R. 1 |
| 171) | 106.5 | 1 | KN | Achinsk | R. Radio |
| 171) | 106.5 | 2 | IR | Zima | R. Radio |
| 18) | 106.5 | 1 | BR | Bryansk | Yumor FM |
| 183) | 106.5 | 1 | VO | Vologda | Yumor FM |
| 19) | 106.5 | 1 | BU | Ulan-Ude | R. Sibir |
| 19) | 106.5 | 1 | SP | Luga | Dorozhnoye R. |
| 19) | 106.5 | 1 | KD | Tuapse | Dorozhnoye R. |
| 19) | 106.5 | 1 | SL | Yu-Sakhalinsk | Dorozhnoye R. |
| 23) | 106.5 | 1 | SM | Smolensk | Detskoye R. |
| 27) | 106.5 | 1 | OB | Kuvandyk | R. Dacha |
| 3) | 106.5 | 1 | YA | Yaroslavl | Ekho Moskvy |
| 4) | 106.5 | 1 | BA | Neftekamsk | Europa plus |
| 45) | 106.5 | 1 | MU | Murmansk | Novoye R. |
| 6) | 106.5 | 1 | TY | Tyumen | Love R. |
| 68) | 106.5 | 1 | RS | Yakutsk | Lena R. |
| 8) | 106.5 | 1 | MA | Magadan | Nashe R. |
| 15) | 106.6 | 1 | AK | Biysk | DFM |
| 153) | 106.6 | 1 | SP | Kirishi | Volkhov FM |
| 19) | 106.6 | 1 | KS | Sharya | Dorozhnoye R. |
| 199) | 106.6 | 2 | KY | Khanty-Mansiysk | R. Yugra |
| 2) | 106.6 | 1 | ZB | Chita | Russkoye R. |
| 24) | 106.6 | 1 | RO | Rostov-na-Donu | NRJ |
| 25) | 106.6 | 1 | UL | Ulyanovsk | R. Mir |
| 27) | 106.6 | 1 | PR | Berezniki | R. Dacha |
| 6) | 106.6 | 10 | MO | Moskva | Love R. |
| 6) | 106.6 | 3 | SA | Samara | Love R. |
| 1) | 106.7 | 1 | KD | Kropotkin | Avtoradio |
| 1) | 106.7 | 1 | KD | Yeysk | Avtoradio |
| 119) | 106.7 | 4 | IV | Rodniki | Ivanovo FM |
| 134B) | 106.7 | 1 | RY | Ryazan | R. dlya druzey |
| 157) | 106.7 | 1 | PM | Nakhodka | R. Monte-Karlo |
| 16) | 106.7 | 1 | RK | Abakan | Retro FM |
| 176) | 106.7 | 1 | TS | Bugulma | Taksi FM |
| 18) | 106.7 | 2 | PZ | Penza | Yumor FM |
| 19) | 106.7 | 1 | PR | Chaykovskiy | Dorozhnoye R. |
| 19) | 106.7 | 1 | KV | Kirov | Dorozhnoye R. |
| 19) | 106.7 | 1 | TV | Tver | Dorozhnoye R. |
| 19) | 106.7 | 1 | SP | Vyborg | Dorozhnoye R. |
| 26) | 106.7 | 1 | MU | Apatity | R. Rekord |
| 27) | 106.7 | 1 | NS | Novosibirsk | R. Dacha |
| 29) | 106.7 | 1 | KD | Temryuk | Pervoye R. |
| 4) | 106.7 | 1 | KV | Vyatskiye Polyarny | Europa plus |
| 42) | 106.7 | 1 | VN | Borisoglebsk | Pervoye setevoye |
| 6) | 106.7 | 1 | KO | Ukhta | Love R. |
| 8) | 106.7 | 1 | KE | Kemerovo | Nashe R. |
| 88) | 106.7 | 1 | IR | Listvyanka | R. MSM |
| 1) | 106.8 | 1 | SV | Nizhniy Tagil | Avtoradio |
| 1) | 106.8 | 1 | OM | Omsk | Avtoradio |
| 101) | 106.8 | 1 | PS | V.Luki | R. Rodnykh dorog |
| 124B) | 106.8 | 1 | BA | Bakaly | Sputnik FM |
| 139) | 106.8 | 1 | IR | Irkutsk | R. Jazz |
| 14) | 106.8 | 1 | KD | Krasnodar | R. Shanson |
| 168) | 106.8 | 1 | MO | Taldom | R. 1 |
| 168) | 106.8 | 1 | MO | Volokalamsk | R. 1 |

| FM | MHz | kW | Rg | Location | Station |
|---|---|---|---|---|---|
| 19) | 106.8 | 1 | VN | Beguchar | Dorozhnoye R. |
| 19) | 106.8 | 5 | BE | Belgorod | Dorozhnoye R. |
| 2) | 106.8 | 1 | SV | Serov | Russkoye R. |
| 218) | 106.8 | 1 | CB | Chelyabinsk | R. Iskatel |
| 22) | 106.8 | 1 | AK | Barnaul | R. KP |
| 24) | 106.8 | 1 | AS | Astrakhan | NRJ |
| 25) | 106.8 | 1 | MD | Saransk | R. Mir |
| 4) | 106.8 | 2 | TS | Kazan | Europa plus |
| 4) | 106.8 | 1 | VL | Murom | Europa plus |
| 45) | 106.8 | 2 | KH | Khabarovsk | Novoye R. |
| 59) | 106.8 | 1 | VN | Voronezh | Kanal Melodiya |
| 6) | 106.8 | 8 | SR | Saratov | Love R. |
| 8) | 106.8 | 1 | KE | Novokuznetsk | Nashe R. |
| 90) | 106.8 | 1 | KY | Yugorsk | Nord FM |
| 134A) | 106.9 | 1 | VL | Vladimir | Studio 21 |
| 14) | 106.9 | 1 | NN | N.Novgorod | R. Shanson |
| 151) | 106.9 | 1 | VO | Vologda | R. 10/69 |
| 19) | 106.9 | 1 | KD | Sochi | Dorozhnoye R. |
| 2) | 106.9 | 1 | SP | Tikhvin | Russkoye R. |
| 27) | 106.9 | 1 | TL | Tula | R. Dacha |
| 32) | 106.9 | 1 | SA | Tolyatti | 106.9 FM |
| 44) | 106.9 | 1 | MU | Murmansk | Bolshoye R. |
| 45) | 106.9 | 1 | TS | Nab.Chelny | Novoye R. |
| 8) | 106.9 | 1 | BU | Ulan-Ude | Nashe R. |
| 9A) | 106.9 | 1 | KE | Yurga | R. Vanya |
| 1) | 107.0 | 1 | KE | Belovo | Avtoradio |
| 124B) | 107.0 | 1 | BA | Ufa | Sputnik FM |
| 131) | 107.0 | 1 | TS | Novosheshminsk | R. Bolgar |
| 14) | 107.0 | 1 | SR | Balakovo | R. Shanson |
| 15) | 107.0 | 1 | UD | Izhevsk | DFM |
| 165) | 107.0 | 2 | SV | Yekaterinburg | Sputnik 107 FM |
| 19) | 107.0 | 1 | TY | Tyumen | Dorozhnoye R. |
| 2) | 107.0 | 1 | CV | Cheboksary | Russkoye R. |
| 2) | 107.0 | 5 | PM | Vladivostok | Russkoye R. |
| 23) | 107.0 | 1 | YA | Yaroslavl | Detskoye R. |
| 39) | 107.0 | 5 | MO | Moskva | IZ.RU |
| 62) | 107.0 | 5 | KD | Kanevskaya | Kazak FM |
| 9A) | 107.0 | 1 | BR | Bryansk | R. Vanya |
| 1) | 107.1 | 1 | IR | Irkutsk | Avtoradio |
| 124B) | 107.1 | 1 | BA | Kumertau | Sputnik FM |
| 131) | 107.1 | 1 | TS | Aznakayevo | R. Bolgar |
| 131) | 107.1 | 2 | TS | Bazarnyye Mataki | R. Bolgar |
| 136) | 107.1 | 1 | PS | Pskov | Sedmoye nebo |
| 14) | 107.1 | 1 | KG | Kurgan | R. Shanson |
| 177) | 107.1 | 2 | RS | Yakutsk | R. Sakha |
| 189) | 107.1 | 1 | DA | Makhachkala | R. Stolitsa |
| 22) | 107.1 | 1 | KN | Krasnoyarsk | R. KP |
| 27) | 107.1 | 1 | IV | Ivanovo | R. Dacha |
| 27) | 107.1 | 1 | TO | Tomsk | R. Dacha |
| 7) | 107.1 | 1 | AK | Rubtsovsk | Militseyskaya volna |
| 124B) | 107.2 | 1 | BA | Belebey | Sputnik FM |
| 124B) | 107.2 | 1 | BA | Beloretsk | Sputnik FM |
| 130A) | 107.2 | 1 | VN | Voronezh | R. Borneo |
| 14) | 107.2 | 1 | MD | Saransk | R. Shanson |
| 16) | 107.2 | 1 | KO | Ukhta | Retro FM |
| 162) | 107.2 | 1 | RY | Ryazan | R. OK |
| 19) | 107.2 | 1 | KT | Petrozavodsk | Dorozhnoye R. |
| 19) | 107.2 | 1 | SM | Smolensk | Dorozhnoye R. |
| 2) | 107.2 | 1 | OB | Orenburg | Russkoye R. |
| 22) | 107.2 | 1 | KA | Kaliningrad | R. KP |
| 23) | 107.2 | 1 | SA | Samara | Detskoye R. |
| 35) | 107.2 | 1 | IR | Bratsk | R. Vera |
| 8) | 107.2 | 1 | CB | Snezhinsk | Nashe R. |
| 1) | 107.3 | 1 | PM | Luchegorsk | Avtoradio |
| 131) | 107.3 | 1 | TS | Menzelinsk | R. Bolgar |
| 15) | 107.3 | 1 | CB | Chelyabinsk | DFM |
| 156) | 107.3 | 1 | TS | Kazan | R. Millenium |
| 19) | 107.3 | 1 | PS | Novosokolniki | Dorozhnoye R. |
| 2) | 107.3 | 1 | VL | Murom | Russkoye R. |
| 220) | 107.3 | 1 | SA | Sergiyevsk | Samarskoye gub. R. |
| 26) | 107.3 | 1 | SP | Luga | R. Rekord |
| 45) | 107.3 | 1 | OM | Omsk | Novoye R. |
| 5) | 107.3 | 1 | KE | Kemerovo | Hit FM |
| 1) | 107.4 | 1 | KS | Kostroma | Avtoradio |
| 134A) | 107.4 | 1 | SA | Tolyatti | Studio 21 |
| 14) | 107.4 | 2 | TA | Tambov | R. Shanson |
| 18) | 107.4 | 5 | NN | N.Novgorod | Yumor FM |
| 191) | 107.4 | 1 | PM | Ussuriysk | Primorskaya volna |
| 199) | 107.4 | 1 | TY | Tyumen | R. Yugra |
| 2) | 107.4 | 5 | KD | Novorossiysk | Russkoye R. |
| 2) | 107.4 | 1 | VN | Rossosh | Russkoye R. |
| 206) | 107.4 | 1 | AR | Arkhangelsk | Region 29 |
| 21) | 107.4 | 1 | ZB | Chita | R. Zvezda |
| 27) | 107.4 | 1 | AK | Barnaul | R. Dacha |
| 28) | 107.4 | 10 | SP | Sankt-Peterburg | Biznes FM |
| 5) | 107.4 | 1 | KN | Achinsk | Hit FM |
| 5) | 107.4 | 3 | MO | Moskva | Hit FM |
| 7) | 107.4 | 1 | OB | Ilek | Militseyskaya volna |
| 74) | 107.4 | 1 | KD | Sochi | Maks FM |
| 79) | 107.4 | 1 | BE | Staryy Oskol | Mir Belogorya |
| 98A) | 107.4 | 1 | SR | Balakovo | R. dlya dvoikh |
| 1) | 107.5 | 1 | SM | Roslavl | Avtoradio |
| 10) | 107.5 | 1 | RK | Abakan | R. 7 |
| 131) | 107.5 | 1 | TS | Bavly | R. Bolgar |
| 134A) | 107.5 | 1 | KC | Karachayevsk | Studio 21 |
| 134A) | 107.5 | 1 | KH | Khabarovsk | Studio 21 |
| 14) | 107.5 | 1 | TL | Tula | R. Shanson |
| 15) | 107.5 | 1 | TS | Nizhnekamsk | DFM |
| 186) | 107.5 | 1 | SV | Irbit | R. Skit |
| 19) | 107.5 | 1 | SM | Gagarin | Dorozhnoye R. |
| 2) | 107.5 | 1 | VL | Kovrov | Russkoye R. |
| 2) | 107.5 | 1 | BU | Ulan-Ude | Russkoye R. |
| 27) | 107.5 | 1 | IR | Irkutsk | R. Dacha |
| 28) | 107.5 | 1 | BA | Ufa | Biznes FM |
| 3) | 107.5 | 1 | PZ | Penza | Ekho Moskvy |
| 45) | 107.5 | 1 | RO | Rostov-na-Donu | Novoye R. |
| 5) | 107.5 | 1 | AK | Rubtsovsk | Hit FM |
| 8) | 107.5 | 1 | KG | Kurgan | Nashe R. |
| 1) | 107.6 | 1 | KD | Kanevskaya | Avtoradio |
| 11) | 107.6 | 1 | KE | Leninsk-Kuznetskiy | R. Maksimum |
| 14) | 107.6 | 1 | BR | Bryansk | R. Shanson |
| 16) | 107.6 | 1 | RS | Yakutsk | Retro FM |
| 17) | 107.6 | 1 | KU | Kursk | Serebryanyy dozhd |
| 18) | 107.6 | 1 | PZ | Pachelma | Yumor FM |
| 180) | 107.6 | 1 | SV | Yekaterinburg | Gorod FM |
| 19) | 107.6 | 1 | SP | Priozersk | Dorozhnoye R. |
| 22) | 107.6 | 1 | UD | Izhevsk | R. KP |
| 4) | 107.6 | 1 | TO | Tomsk | Europa plus |
| 1) | 107.7 | 1 | BE | Belgorod | Avtoradio |
| 1) | 107.7 | 1 | KE | Mezhdurechensk | Avtoradio |
| 107) | 107.7 | 1 | KD | Krasnodar | R. 107 |
| 124B) | 107.7 | 1 | BA | Burayevo | Sputnik FM |
| 124B) | 107.7 | 1 | BA | Mesyagutovo | Sputnik FM |
| 134A) | 107.7 | 1 | OB | Orenburg | Studio 21 |
| 14) | 107.7 | 2 | NS | Novosibirsk | R. Shanson |
| 16) | 107.7 | 1 | KD | Armavir | Retro FM |
| 18) | 107.7 | 1 | IR | Bratsk | Yumor FM |
| 18) | 107.7 | 1 | SM | Smolensk | Yumor FM |
| 2) | 107.7 | 1 | IV | Ivanovo | Russkoye R. |
| 26) | 107.7 | 1 | VL | Murom | R. Rekord |
| 27) | 107.7 | 1 | SV | Nizhniy Tagil | R. Dacha |
| 45) | 107.7 | 1 | PM | Vladivostok | Novoye R. |
| 7) | 107.7 | 1 | OB | Yasnyy | Militseyskaya volna |
| 8) | 107.7 | 1 | KO | Ukhta | Nashe R. |
| 10) | 107.8 | 1 | KD | Novorossiysk | R. 7 |
| 16) | 107.8 | 1 | PR | Berezniki | Retro FM |
| 16) | 107.8 | 1 | KN | Norilsk | Retro FM |
| 19) | 107.8 | 1 | TY | Ishim | Dorozhnoye R. |
| 19) | 107.8 | 1 | VN | Rossosh | Dorozhnoye R. |
| 2) | 107.8 | 10 | SP | Sankt-Peterburg | Russkoye R. |
| 27) | 107.8 | 1 | AK | Biysk | R. Dacha |
| 28) | 107.8 | 1 | NN | N.Novgorod | Biznes FM |
| 29) | 107.8 | 1 | KD | Kushchyovskaya | Pervoye R. |
| 4) | 107.8 | 1 | SR | Volsk | Europa plus |
| 6) | 107.8 | 1 | TS | Kazan | Love R. - |
| 7) | 107.8 | 5 | MO | Moskva | Militseyskaya volna |
| 1) | 107.9 | 1 | SV | Krasnoturinsk | Nashe R. |
| 1) | 107.9 | 5 | PM | Novozhatkovo | Avtoradio |
| 10) | 107.9 | 1 | BE | Staryy Oskol | R. 7 |
| 145) | 107.9 | 1 | VL | Vladimir | Vladimir - Novaya volna |
| 16) | 107.9 | 1 | KE | Kemerovo | Retro FM |
| 16) | 107.9 | 1 | KD | Sochi | Retro FM |
| 19) | 107.9 | 1 | KM | Petropavlovsk-K. | Dorozhnoye R. |
| 19) | 107.9 | 1 | BA | Ufa | Dorozhnoye R. |
| 2) | 107.9 | 1 | RY | Ryazan | Russkoye R. |
| 2) | 107.9 | 1 | SO | Vladikavkaz | Russkoye R. |
| 21) | 107.9 | 1 | AK | Barnaul | R. Zvezda |
| 23) | 107.9 | 1 | KV | Kirov | Detskoye R. |
| 24) | 107.9 | 2 | KY | Surgut | NRJ |
| 25) | 107.9 | 1 | KD | Tikhoretsk | R. Mir |
| 3) | 107.9 | 1 | SA | Tolyatti | Ekho Moskvy |
| 35) | 107.9 | 1 | KH | Khabarovsk | R. Vera |
| 35) | 107.9 | 1 | TV | Mednoye | R. Vera |

| FM | MHz | kW | Rg | Location | Station |
|---|---|---|---|---|---|
| 36) | 107.9 | 1 | SP | Vyborg | Avtoradio S-Peterburg |

+ txs below 1kW. MW/SW txs: E = European part of Russia, S = Siberia, FE = Far Eastern part of Russia.

**Addresses and other information:**

**1)** 127083 Moskva, ul. 8-go Marta 8 – **2)** 123298 Moskva, 3-ya Khoroshevskaya ul. 12 – **3)** 119992 Moskva, ul. Novyy Arbat 11 – **4)** 109004 Moskva, ul. Stanislavskogo 21 – **5)** 123298 Moskva, 3-ya Khoroshevskaya ul. 12 – **6)** 127299 Moskva, ul. Bolshaya Akademicheskaya 5a – **7)** 109180 Moskva, 3-y Golutinskiy per. 8/10 – **8)** 123060 Moskva, ul. Narodnogo Opolcheniya 39 – **9)** 199406 St.Peterburg, ul. Shevchenko 28 – **10)** 109004 Moskva, ul. Stanislavskogo 21 – **11)** 123298 Moskva, 3-ya Khoroshevskaya ul. 12 – **12)** 423822 Nab.Chelny, Naberezhnochelinskiy pr. 21 – **13)** 347936 Taganrog, Noviy 17-y per. 108 – **14)** 119049 Moskva, ul. Shabolovka 10 – **15)** 123298 Moskva, 3-ya Khoroshevskaya ul. 12 – **16)** 109004 Moskva, ul. Stanislavskogo 21 – **17)** 109004 Moskva, ul. Stanislavskogo 21 – **18)** 127083 Moskva, ul. 8-go Marta 8 – **19)** 199406 St.Peterburg, ul. Shevchenko 28 – **20)** 127083 Moskva, ul. 8-go Marta 8 – **21)** 129164 Moskva, pr. Mira 126 – **22)** 127993 Moskva, Staryy Petrovsko-Razumovskiy proyezd 1/23 – **23)** 129226 Moskva, ul. Vilgelma Pika 3 – **24)** 127083 Moskva, ul. 8-go Marta 8 – **25)** 107076 Moskva, ul. Krasnobogatyrskaya 44 – **26)** 198303 St.Peterburg, pr. Stachek 105 – **27)** 127299 Moskva, ul. B. Akademicheskaya 5a – **28)** 127287 Moskva, 2-ya Khutorskaya ul. 38a – **29)** 350038 Krasnodar, ul. Korolenko 2/1 – **30)** 420066 Kazan, ul. Dekrabristov 2 – **31)** 129226 Moskva, ul. Vilgelma Pika 3 – **32)** 445051 Tolyatti, Primorskiy bul. 28 – **33)** 432030 Ulyanovsk, ul. Narimanova 75 – **34)** 650007 Novokuznetsk, ul.Ordzhonikidze 35 – **35)** 107553 Moskva, B.Cherkizovskaya ul. 17 – **36)** 197376 St.Peterburg, ul. Ak.Pavlova 5 – **37)** 236000 Kaliningrad, ul. Narvskaya 58 – **38)** 618400 Berezniki, Klyuchevaya ul. 19 – **39)** 115093 Moskva, Partiynyy per. 1 – **40)** 420021 Kazan, ul. Gabdully Tukaya 91 – **41)** 368000 Khasavyurt, Energeticheskaya ul. 1 – **42)** 398059 Lipetsk, ul. Sovetskaya 64c – **43)** 308023 Belgorod, Studencheskaya ul. 28 – **44)** 183038 Murmansk, ul. Lenina 68 – **45)** 123308 Moskva, ul. D. Bednogo 24 – **46)** 129272 Moskva, Trifonovskaya 57 – **47)** 603022 N.Novgorod, Okskiy syezd 8 – **48)** 625000 Tyumen, ul. Geologorazvedchikov 28 – **49)** 123290 Moskva, 1-y Magistralnyy proyezd 11 – **50)** 620075 Yekaterinburg, pr. Lenina 41 – **51)** 302028 Oryol, ul. 7-ye Noyabrya 43 – **52)** 197376 St.Peterburg, ul. Prof.Popova 47 – **53)** 129164 Moskva, Zubarev per. 15 – **54)** 670000 Ulan-Ude, ul. Borsoyeva 105 – **55)** 630087 Novosibirsk, ul. Nemirovicha-Danchenko 122 – **56)** 199034 St.Peterburg, nab. L. Shmidta 39 – **57)** 364014 Groznyy, ul. Mayakovskogo 92 – **58)** 454091 Chelyabinsk, ul. Ordzhonikidze 81 – **59)** 394000 Voronezh, ul. Lenina 73 – **60)** 620086 Yekaterinburg, ul. Repina 6a – **61)** 362047 Vladikavkaz, ul. Vesennaya 5 – **62)** 350038 Krasnodar, ul.Korolenko 2/1 – **63)** 660075 Krasnoyarsk, ul. Severo-Yeniseyskaya 33 – **64)** 125080 Moskva, ul. Vrubelya 4 – **65)** 650001 Kemerovo, ul. Sevastopolskaya 6 – **66)** 625019 Tyumen, ul. Respubliki 211a – **67)** 400081 Volgograd, ul. Angarskaya 71 – **68)** 677000 Yakutsk, ul. Bestuzheva-Marlinskogo 9/3 – **69)** 143402 Krasnogorsk, ul. Mezhduradrodnaya 12 – **70)** 398050 Lipetsk, ul. Plekhanova 1 – **71)** 454091 Chelyabinsk, ul. Ordzhonikidze 41 – **72)** 182106 Velikiye Luki, pl. Chapayeva 5 – **73)** 453124 Steplitamak, ul. Khudayberdina 17 – **74)** 354000 Sochi, ul. Severnaya 12 – **75)** 610000 Kirov, Oktyabrskiy pr. 120 – **76)** 127015 Moskva, Bolshaya Novodmitrovskaya ul. 36 – **77)** 97046 Sankt-Peterburg, Petrogradskaya nab. 18a – **78)** 353380 Krymsk, ul. K.Libknekhta 21 – **79)** 308000 Belgorod, pr. Slavy 60 – **80A,B)** 127137 Moskva, ul. Pravdy 24/2. 80B) in English – **81)** 746903 Ukhta, Oktyabrskkaya ul. 21 – **82)** 440026 Penza, ul. Lermontova 39 – **83)** 426069 Izhevsk, ul. Pesochnaya 9 – **84)** 424038 Yoshar-Ola, pr. Tsargradskiy 37 – **85)** 174260 Malaya Vishera, ul. Moskovskaya 21 – **86)** 125009 Moskva, ul. Tverskaya 7. **E:** narodnoe-radio@mail.ru – **87)** 428003 Cheboksary, pr. Lenina 15 – **88)** 664047 Irkutsk, ul. Baykalskaya 105 – **89)** 248021 Kaluga, ul. Moskovskaya 189 – **90)** 628260 Yugorsk, ul. Lenina 18 – **91)** 353915 Novorossiysk, ul. Revolutsii 1905 goda 19 – **92)** 400131 Volgograd, ul. Komsomolskaya 8 – **93)** 603155 N.Novgorod, ul. B.Pecherskaya 33-1 – **94)** 619001 Kudymkar, ul. Polevaya 3 – **95)** 362013 Vladikavkaz, ul. Nikolayeva 84 – **96)** 170000 Tver, ul. Mednikovskaya 55/25 – **97)** 115035 Moskva, Sofiyskaya nab. 30 – **98A,B)** 99155 St.Peterburg, pr. KIMa 5/34 – **99)** 672010 Chita, ul. Amurskaya 36 – **100)** 183038 Murmansk, ul. Yegorova 14 – **101)** 428018 Cheboksary, ul. Nizhegorodskaya 6 – **102)** 142672 Likino-Dulevo, ul. Oktyabrskaya 42 – **103)** 424038 Yoshkar-Ola, ul. Voinov-Internatsionalistov 37 – **104)** 454084 Chelyabinsk, ul. Kalinina 21 – **105)** 440046 Penza, ul. Mira 1a – **106)** 693023 Yuzhno-Sakhalinsk, ul. Komsomolskaya 213a – **107)** 350000 Krasnodar, ul. Gimnazicheskaya 51 – **108)** 450075 Ufa, ul. Blyukhera 15 – **109)** 644010 Omsk, ul. Dekabristov 130 – **110A,B)** 400131 Volgograd, ul. Krasnoznamenskaya 25 – **111)** 191186 Sankt-Peterburg, ul. Italyanskaya 15 – **112)** 625013 Tyumen, ul. Tekstilnaya 1 – **113)** 620151 Krasnoyarsk, ul. Baumana 22 – **114)** 426035 Izhevsk, ul. Avangardnaya 4b – **115)** 344006 Rostov-na-Donu, ul. Suvorova 26 – **116)** 236022 Kaliningrad, pr. Sovetskiy 12 – **117)** 680000 Khabarovsk ul. Lenina 4 – **118)** 514017 Perm, ul. Turgeneva 33a – **119)** 153003 Ivanovo, ul. Parizhskoy Kommuny 16 – **120)** 403348 Mikhaylovka, ul. Mira 81 – **121)** 197022 St.Peterburg, P.O.Box 122.

**E:** radioslovo@mail.ru – **122)** 453300 Kumertau, PKiO im. Gagarina – **123)** 196084 St.Peterburg, ul. Tsvetochnaya 16b **E:** radio_rusk@mail.ru – **124A-C)** 450076 Ufa, ul. Gafuri 9 124A,B) in Bashkir. – **125)** 445010 Tolyatti, ul. Sovetskaya 74a – **126)** 692760 Artyom, ul. Kirova 68 – **127)** 665831 Angarsk ul. Vesennyaya 2 – **128)** 190068 St.Peterburg, P.O.Box 732. **E:** pr@radiomaria.ru – **129)** 140400 Kolomna, ul. Shilova 9 – **130A,B)** 394071 Voronezh, ul. 20-letnaya Oktyabrya 66 – **131)** 420015 Kazan, ul. Gorkogo 15 – **132)** 614060 Perm, ul. Uralskaya 119 – **133)** 432000 Ulyanovsk – **134A,B)** 109004 Moskva, ul. Stanislavskogo 21 – **135)** 440434 Penza, ul. Markina 1 – **136)** Paromenskaya ul. 21/32, 180007 Pskov – **137)** 394036 Voronezh, ul. K.Marksa 67b – **138)** 362007 Vladikavkaz, ul. Osetinskaya gorka 2a – **139)** 125190 Moskva, Leningradskiy pr. 80 – **140)** 360000 Nalchik, pr. Lenina 5 – **141)** 115054 Moskva, ul. Valovaya 32/75 – **142)** 369200 Karachayevsk – **143)** 462411 Orsk, ul. Leninskogo Komsomola 4b – **144)** 187110 Kirishi, ul. Sovetskaya 20 – **145)** 600000 Vladimir, Vorontsovskiy per. 4 – **146)** 454080 Chelyabinsk, ul. Ordzhonikidze 58a – **147)** 677007 Yakutsk, ul. Kirova 17/3 – **148)** 423827 Nab.Chelny, bul. Yunykh Lenintsev 9 – **149)** 305004 Kursk, ul. Dimitrova 76 – **150)** 690091 Vladivostok, ul. Pologaya 53 – **151)** 160000 Vologda, ul. Oktyabrskaya 44 – **152)** 386102 Nazran, ul. Moskovskaya 29a – **153)** 187401 Volkhov, ul. Kommunarov 18 – **154)** 29164 Moskva, Zubarev per. 15 – **155)** 443070 Samara, ul. Partizanskaya 19 – **156)** 420032 Kazan, ul. Tabeykina 19a – **157)** 123298 Moskva, 3-ya Khoroshevskaya ul. 12 – **158)** 238050 Gusev, ul. Shkolnaya 11 – **159)** 420053 Yekaterinburg, ul. Volgogradskaya 193 – **160)** 629807 Noyabrsk, ul. Lenina 47 – **161)** 603068 N.Novgorod, Yarmarochnyy proyezd 10 – **162)** 390023 Ryazan, ul. Tsiolkovskogo 20 – **163)** 454090 Chelyabinsk, ul. Tsvillinga 46a – **164)** 367000 Makhachkala – **165)** 620026 Yekaterinburg, ul. Vazhova 162 – **166)** 620075 Yekaterinburg, ul. Lenina 41 – **167)** 430000 Saransk, ul. Kommunisticheskaya 89 – **168)** 123007 Moskva, 5-ya Magistralnaya ul. 6 – **169)** 413851 Balakovo, ul. Volzhskaya 74a – **170)** 368120 Kyzylyurt, pr. Imama Shamilya 43/13 – **171)** 123001 Moskva, Vspolnyy per. 18 – **172)** 113326 Moskva, ul. Pyatnitskaya 25. **E:** radonezh@radonezh.ru – **173)** 603006 N.Novgorod, ul. Semashko 37 – **174)** 414040 Astrakhan, ul. Lyakhova 4 – **175)** 450075 Ufa, ul. Blyukhera 15 – **176)** 127299 Moskva, ul. B.Akademicheskaya 5a – **177)** 677027 Yakutsk, ul. Ordzhonikidze 48 – **178)** 420094 Kazan, ul. Golubyatnikova 20a – **179)** 690091 Vladivostok, ul. Pologaya 66 – **180)** 620014 Yekaterinburg, ul. Lenina 24a – **181)** 127287 Moskva, 2-ya Khutorskaya ul. 38a – **182)** 620014 Yekaterinburg, ul. Lenina 41 – **183)** 634003 Tomsk, per. Marininskiy 8 – **184)** 625013 Tyumen, ul. Permyakova 7 – **185)** 386245 Stanitsa Troitskaya, ul. Krestyanskaya 4 – **186)** 623850 Irbit, ul. Zhukova 6a – **187)** 630011 Novosibirsk, ul. Kirova 3 – **188)** 414000 Astrakhan, ul. Nab. 1-ya Maya 75 – **189)** 367000 Makhachkala, ul. Gamidova 18 – **190)** 367032 Makhachkala, ul. M.Gadzhiyeva 188 – **191)** 690065 Vladivostok, ul. Strelnikova 7 – **192)** 162610 Cherepovets, ul. Lenina 151 – **193)** 660028 Krasnoyarsk, ul. Baumana 22 – **194)** 367020 Makhachkala, ul. Nuradilova 2 – **195)** 690091 Vladivostok, ul. Uborevicha 20a – **196)** 680000 Krasnoyarsk, ul. Frunze 58 – **197A,B)** 677027 Yakutsk, ul. Oktyabrskaya 16/2 – **198)** 678960 Neryungi, teletsentr – **199)** 628011 Khanty-Mansiysk, ul. Gagarina 4 – **200)** 630087 Novosibirsk, ul. Nemirovicha-Danchenko 122 – **201)** 640021 Kurgan, ul. Tobolnaya 54 – **202)** 197101 St.Peterburg, ul. Kronverskaya 23 – **203)** 678901 Aldan, Sportivnyy per. 2 – **204)** 620144 Yekaterinburg, ul. Khokhryakova 104 – **205)** 156005 Kostroma, ul. Lagernaya 15 – **206)** 163002 Arkhangelsk, Novgorodskiy pr. 32 – **207)** Varshavskoye shosse 9, 117105 Moskva – **208)** 123060 Moskva, ul. Narodnogo Opolcheniya 39 – **209)** 660000 Krasnoyarsk – **210)** 620075 Yekaterinburg, ul. Lenina 41 – **211)** 666784 Ust-Kut, ul. Kirova 88 – **212)** 123298 Moskva, 3-ya Khoroshevskaya ul. 12 – **213)** 443110 Samara, ul. Novo-Sadovaya 44 – **214)** 680000 Khabarovsk, ul. Frunze 58 – **215)** 618551 Solikamsk, ul. Vseobucha 80 – **216)** 127238 Moskva, Lokomotivnyy proyezd 21 – **217)** 236010 Kaliningrad, pr. Mira 136 – **218)** 649002 Gorno-Altaysk, pr. Kommunisticheskiy 1 – **219)** 614990 Perm, ul. Lenina 50-141 – **220)** 443068 Samara, ul. Novo-Sadovaya 106 – **A)** Rel. Encompass Digital Media (UK) Russian language feed (branded "WRN"). Full schedule: **W:** wrn.ru.

## NON-PROFESSIONAL RADIO STATIONS

Upon application, the regulator Roskomnadzor may issue temporary, short-term licenses to non-professional radio stations ("Individualnoye (Lyubitelskoye) veshchaniye"). These stns may operate with low power on specifically assigned MW frqs, usually 1584 (e.g. Moskva), 1593 (e.g. St.Peterburg) or 1602kHz or/and (if requested) on low power SW frqs. The txs are typically self-made, or modified amateur radio equipment. Primarily technical universities have been organising this type of transmitting activity (partly in cooperation with local amateur radio clubs), providing studio facilities and technical logistics. The prgrs are usually produced in the studio of an existing in-house (closed circuit) student radio station in these institutions.

**Radio via DTT:** see National TV section.

## CRIMEA

**NB:** The station listing can be found at the end of the Ukraine entry

## RWANDA

**L.T:** UTC +2h — **Pop:** 12 million — **Pr.L:** Kinyarwanda, Swahili, French, English — **E.C:** 50Hz, 230V — **ITU:** RRW

### RWANDA UTILITIES REGULATORY AGENCY (RURA)
✉ B.P. 6929, Kigali ☎+250 252584562 🖷 +250 252584563 **W:** rura.gov.rw **E:** info@rura.gov.rw

### RWANDA BROADCASTING AGENCY (RBA) (Gov)
✉ B.P. 83, Kigali ☎+250 252572276 **W:** rba.co.rw **E:** radiorwanda@yahoo.com **L.P:** Dir. Broadc: Mweusi Karake. Dir. Prgrs: Paul Ndamage. Ag. Ch.Editor: Willy Rukundo. Tech. Dir: Charles Nahayo.
**FM: Channel I** (MHz): 89.8 Kinanira 0.5kW, 93.5 Nyarupfubire 0.5kW, 95.1 Mugogo/Rushaki 0.5kW, 97.6 Karongi 1kW, 100.7 Mt. Jali 5kW, 103.2 Byumba 0.5kW, 103.9 Butare 0.5kW + 8 trs under 0.5kW.
**Channel II (Magic FM):** Kigali 90.7MHz 5kW.
**D.Prgr** in Kinyarwanda/Swahili/French/English: 24h. N. in English: 0515, 1830. **Ann:** F: "Vous écoutez Radio Rwanda émettant de Kigali".

**OTHER STATIONS FM**(MHz)
**City R,** Kigali: 88.3 1kW — **Contact FM:** Kigali 89.7 0.5kW — **Flash FM,** Kigali: 89.2 0.5kW — **KT R,** Kigali: 96.7 W: ktradio.rw — **R. Izuba,** Kibungo: 100.0 0.25kW –**R. Isango Star,** Kigali: 91.5 **W:** isangostar.rw – **R. Maria Rwanda:** Gitarama 88.6 1kW, Kigali 97.3 2kW, Karongi 99.8 **E:** radiomariar@yahoo.fr – **R. 10 FM:** Kigali (Mont Jari) 87.6 0.5kW **W:** danslevent.com/rwanda **E:** contact@danslevent.com – **R. Salus** (University R.), Butare: 97.0 1kW, Kigali 101.9 1kW. **W:** salus.nur.ac.rw – **R. Sana uRwanda** (Rlg.): Kigali 98.0 – **R. Umucyo,** Kigali: 102.8 0.1kW
**Rwanda Community Radio Network:** Rubavu, 94.6, Nyagatare 95.5, Musanze 98.4, Huye 100.4, Rusizi 103.2MHz **W:** rwandaradioscommunautaires.org

**AWR:** 106.4 0.3kW – **BBC African Sce:** Kibuye 93.3, Kigali (Mont Jari) 93.9 3kW, Butare 106.1 3kW – **RFI Afrique:** Kigali 92.1 in French/Swahili – **Voice of America:** Kigali 104.3 2kW – **Deutsche Welle:** Kigali 96.0MHz 2kW

## SABA (Netherlands)

**L.T:** UTC -4h — **Pop:** 1,950 — **Pr.L:** Dutch (official), English — **E.C:** 60Hz, 110V — **ITU:** BES

### AGENTSCHAP TELECOM Bonaire, Sint Eustatius, Saba
✉ Kaya Grandi 69, P.O. Box 791, Bonaire ☎ + 599 717 3140 🖷 +599 717 3554 **W:** agentschaptelecom.nl **E:** bes@agentschaptelecom.nl

### SABA RADIO
✉ PO Box 27,The Bottom, Saba ☎ +599 4 16 3213 🖷 +599 416 3525 **L.P:** Dir. Michael Nicholson **W:** q939.fm **E:** sabaradiopjf2@yahoo.com
**FM:** PJF2 93.9MHz 0.6 kW 24h in English; Dutch Saturdays 2200-2300 and Sundays 1615-1715; Spanish Thursdays 1800-2200; Papiamentu Mondays to Thursdays 1600-1800, Fridays and Saturdays 1600-2200.

## SAMOA

**L.T:** UTC +13h (30 Sep 18-7 Apr 19, 29 Sep 19-5 Apr 20: +14h)— **Pop:** 195,000 — **Pr.L:** Samoan, English — **E.C:** 50Hz, 230V — **ITU:** SMO

### OFFICE OF THE REGULATOR [Gov]
✉ Private Bag, Apia, Samoa. First Flr, G.Meredith Bldg, Tamaligi, Apia ☎ +685 30282 🖷 +685 30281 **W:** regulator.gov.ws **E:** admin@regulator.gov.ws **L.P:** Regulator: Donnie de Freitas. Mgr Spectrum & Tech. Scs: Untoa Auelua Fonoti

| MW | kHz kW | MW | kHz kW |
|---|---|---|---|
| 1) 2AP Apia | #540  5 | 1) 2AP Apia | #747  5 |
| **FM** | **MHz kW** | **FM** | **MHz kW** |
| 2) Showers of Blessings FM88.1 | | 9) Power FM | 96.9 |
| 3) Talofa FM | 88.5 0.25 | 2) Showers of Blessings FM 97.5  0.5 | |
| 4) Mai FM | 89.1  1 | 3) Magik FM | 98.1  0.3 |
| 3) Magik FM | 89.1 | 6) EFKS FM | 98.9 |
| 2) Showers of Blessings FM89.9 | | 3) Talofa FM | 99.9 0.25 |
| 5) Aiga Fesilafa'i | 90.5  1 | 10) China R. Int. | 100.4 |
| 6) EFKS FM* | 90.9 | 3) K-Lite FM | 101.1 0.25 |
| 3) Talofa FM* | 91.5 0.25 | 11) R. Australia | 102.0 |
| 7) Samoa FM | 93.7 | 8) Laufou o le Talaleilei103.1 | |
| 8) Laufou o le Talaleilei | 95.1  1 | 7) Samoa FM* | 104.1 |
| 3) Star FM | 96.1 0.25 | 12) NUS Campus R. | 105.0 |

| FM | MHz kW | FM | MHz kW |
|---|---|---|---|
| 9) Power FM | 106.7 | 6) EFKS FM | 106.9 |

**NB:** Location Apia & Upoulu except *) Savai'i. #) 2AP Apia is replacing its transmission mast and may be off air.

**Addresses & other information:**
1) **NATIONAL RADIO 2AP (Gov)** ✉ Ministry of Communications and Information Technology, Government of Samoa, Level 1, CA & CT Plaza, Savalolo, Apia, Samoa ☎ +685 26177 🖷 +685 24671 **W:** mcit.gov.ws **E:** mcit@mcit.gov.ws ☎ 2AP Studio, Mulinu'u, Apia: +685 21422 **E:** a.ahsam@mcit.gov.ws **L.P:** CEO: Tua'imalo Asamu Ah Sam, Senior Programmer: Vaasiliega Lupati Lagaia Samoan/English: 1700 (Sun 2200)-1000 on 540kHz Edu: broadcs on some weekdays for Samoa and Tokelau 1930-2030 on 747kHz World N: 1800W, 1900W, 1930W. Local N: 1630W, 1730W, 1830W, 0730W Ann: "National Radio 2AP" or "Voice of the Nation" – 2) Samoa Worship Centre Church, PO Box 3026, Apia. ☎ +685 21447/23887/29153 🖷 +685 20657 **W:** samoa.worshipcentre-worldwide.org & facebook.com/uagaofaamanuiago/info incl live streaming audio. Prgr: Samoan/English religious – 3) R. Polynesia Ltd, P.O.Box 762, Svalalo, Apia ☎+685 25148/49/50 🖷 +685 25147 Brands: Magik FM - "Samoa's #1 Hit Music Station" (English) ☎ Studio +685 33981, Talofa FM "100% Local" (Samoan) Studio ☎+685 33999, K-Lite FM "Memories are Good" (English) ☎+685 33101 **N:** RNZI throughout the day, Star FM "Absolute Music Variety" (English) ☎ +685 33961 **W:** fmradio.ws **E:** corey@fmradio.ws **L.P:** CEO Corey Keil D.Prgr: 24h – 4)Samoa Quality Broadcasters, Mulinu'u, Apia ☎+685 24790/91, 21735 🖷 +685 24789 CEO: Galuemalemana Ms Faresea Matafeo **E:** ceo@sbcl.ws **D.Prgr:** 24h (Samoan/English) Other: technical services for R. Australia 102.0FM – 5) Catholic Archdiocese of Samoa, PO Box 532, Muli'vai, Apia. ☎ +685 21156/21051/7521051 **E:** daman-auisavelio@yahoo.com Prgr: Samoan religious – 6) Ekalesia Faapotopototoga Kerisiano Samoa [EFKS] - Congregational Christian Church in Samoa, 5th Floor, John Williams Building, Tamalagi, Apia. ☎ +685 24414 **F:** +685 20429 **W:** cccs.org.ws Prgr: Samoan religious Other: EFKS-TV – 7) Talamua Media & Publications Ltd, Level 2, Nia Mall, Fugalei, Apia. PO Box 1321, Apia. ☎ +685 7777937, 7513937 **W:** talamua.com **E:** samoafm93.7@gmail.com L.P: MD: Angela Kronfeld-Polu. **ID:** "The People's Station" D.Prgr: 24h in Samoan/English – 8) Youth for Christ Samoa, PO Box 3706, Apia. ☎ +685 22663 **W:** yfcsamoa.org **L.P:** Manasa Aloalii Prgr: Samoan religious – 9) Silver & Gold Radio Imaging Ltd, Vaea Street, Apia. ☎ 685 28894 **W:** facebook.com/power-969-1067-fm-samoa **ID:** 'The Station that Rocks the Nation' Prgr: Samoan/English – 10) 24/7 English language via satellite from Beijing – 11) 24/7 Pacific English stream via satellite from Melbourne – 12) Faculty of Arts, Media & Journalism program, National University of Samoa, Le Papaigalagala Campus, To'omatgi ☎+685 20072 🖷 +685 25489 **E:** info@nus.edu.ws **W:** nus.edu.ws **L.P:** Nora Tumua **E:** n.tumua@nus.edu.ws Vicky Lepou **E:** v.lepou@nus.edu.ws Prgr: student campus radio in Samoan/English.

## SAMOA (AMERICAN) (USA)

**L.T:** UTC -11h — **Pop:** 56,625— **Pr.L:** Samoan, English — **E.C:** 60Hz, 120V — **ITU:** SMA

### FEDERAL COMMUNICATIONS COMMISSION (FCC)
see USA for details

| FM | MHz Call | kW | FM | MHz Call | kW |
|---|---|---|---|---|---|
| 6)Tafuna | 88.1 KGIF | 1.5 | 10)Tafuna | 94.5 KKAS-LP | 0.1 |
| 7)PagoPago | 88.9 KKBT | 0.3 | 4) Ili'Ili | 95.1 KULA-LP | 0.1 |
| 8)Nu'uuli | 89.7 KMOA | 1.5 | 4) W. District | 97.1 KULA-LP | 0.011 |
| 9)Mapusaga | 90.5 KPPO | 0.75 | 4) C. District | 99.1 KULA-LP | 0.011 |
| 6)Utulei | 91.3 KIOE | 1.5 | 4) E. District | 102.5 KULA-LP | 0.023 |
| 3)Pago Pago | 92.1 KSBS-FM | 15.5 | 2) Fagaitua | 103.1 WVUV-FM | 1.3 |
| 2)Pago Pago | 93.1 KKHJ-FM | 1.1 | 5) Pago Pago | 104.1 KNWJ | *0.01 |
| 2)Pavaiai | 93.7 KKHJ-FM | 0.01 | 5) Leone | 104.7 KNWJ | 0.28 |

* reported silent

**Addresses & other information:**
2) South Seas Broadcasting Inc, PO Box 6758, Pago Pago, American Samoa 96799. L.P: Joey Cummings, GM ☎+1 684 633 4493 **W:** KKHJ-FM: khjradio.com **ID:** '93KHJ' **W:** WVUV-FM: wvuv.com **ID:** "WVUV-FM is V103 The People's Station' in Samoan/English, D.Prgr: both 24h **Other Media:** KKHJ-TV Island TV Cable 10 – 3) Samoa Technologies Inc, PO Box 793, Pago Pago, American Samoa 96799-0793 ☎+1 684 633 7000 🖷+1 684 633 5727 **W:** ksbsfm92.com **E:** info@ksbsfm92.com L.P: Esther Prescott, GM **ID:** 'Island 92 - The Station That Belongs to You' **News:** hourly bulletins from RNZI, R. Australia, BBC, NPR, VOA. D.Prgr: 24h – 4) Pacific Islands Bible School, PO Box 1268, Pago Pago, American Samoa 96799 – 5) Showers of Blessings R., PO Box 997777, Pago Pago, American Samoa 96799 ☎+1 684 699 8123. 🖷+1 684 699 8126 **W:** fm104.org **E:** info@fm104.org – 6) Leone Church of Christ, PO Box 5093,

Pago Pago, American Samoa 96799 **–7)** Rev Shannon Cummings dba Pure Truth Ministries, PO Box 6008, Pago Pago, American Samoa 96799 **– 8)**Teen Challenge American Samoa P.O.Box 277, Pago Pago, American Samoa 96789. **L.P:** Otto and Vickie Haleck ☎ +1 684 699 2635 **W:** globaltc.org **– 9)** Second Samoan Congregational Church of Long Beach, 655 Cedar Ave, Long Beach CA 90802-1222 **– 10)** Life Inc Ministry, PO Box 1744, Pago Pago, American Samoa 96799.

## SAN MARINO

**L.T.** UTC +1h (31 Mar-27 Oct: +2h) — **Pop**. 32,500 — **Pr.L:** Italian — **E.C:** 230V/50Hz — **ITU:** SMR

### SAN MARINO RTV (Gov)
🖃 Viale J.F. Kennedy 13, 47890 Repubblica di San Marino ☎ +378 0549 882000 🖷 +378 0549 882840 **E:** radio@sanmarinortv.sm **W:** smtvsanmarino.sm/radio **L.P:** Dir. Carlo Romeo, Prgr.Dir.: Giuseppe Cesetti, T.Dir.: Fabio Pelliccioni
**FM:** 102.7MHz 30kW **D.Prgr:** 24h
**DAB+ :** Channel 73 SD , Channel 573 SD.
**San Marino Classic**, **E:** classic@sanmarinortv.sm **LP:** Prgr. Dir. Stefano Coveri **FM:** 103.2MHz 30kW **D.Prgr:** 24h. Also carries govt meetings, live service.
**F.PI.** no plans to start on MW assigned freq. 711kHz
**V:** by QSL-card. Rpts to **E:** ufficiotecnico@sanmarinortv.sm

## SÃO TOMÉ E PRÍNCIPE

**L.T.** UTC +1h — **Pop:** 210,000 — **Pr.L:** Portuguese, Crioulo — **E.C:** 50Hz, 220V — **ITU:** STP

### RÁDIO NACIONAL DE SÃO TOMÉ E PRÍNCIPE (RNSTP, Gov)
🖃 Avenida Marginal 12 de Julho, C.P. 44, São Tomé ☎/🖷 +239 222 13 42 **W:** rnstp.st **E:** atendimento@rnstp.st
**L.P:** Dir: Artur Meneses de Pinho. CE: Felisberto Garcia.
**MW:** Pinheira: 945kHz 20kW **FM:** 89.7/95.4/99.3MHz.
**D.Prgr:** 24h in Portuguese. **N:** 0700, 1300, 1630, 1930.
**IS:** one note gong, guitar.

**RDP África:** São Tomé 92.8MHz 3kW, Príncipe 101.9MHz 70W.
**RFI Afrique:** 102.8MHz in French/Portuguese.
**VOA Africa:** São José 105.5MHz 0.2kW in English/Portuguese.
**VOA relay station:** MW 1530kHz 600kW 0300-0630, 1600-2200 & SW. For further details see International Radio section under USA

## SAUDI ARABIA

**L.T.** UTC +3h — **Pop:** 33 million — **Pr.L:** Arabic — **E.C:** 60Hz, 127/220V — **ITU:** ARS

### MINISTRY OF CULTURE & INFORMATION (MOCI)
🖃 Nasseriya Str, Riyadh 11161 ☎+966 1 4014440 🖷 +966 1 402 3570. **W:** moci.gov.sa **L.P:** Dep. Min. of Eng. Affairs: Dr. Riyadh Najm.

### SAUDI BROADCASTING AUTHORITY (SBA, Gov.)
🖃 P.O. Box 61718, Riyadh 11575 or P.O. Box 8525, Riyadh 11492 ☎+966 1 4425170 🖷 +966 1 4041692 **W:** sba.sa **E:** saudi-radio@moci.gov.sa

| MW | kHz | kW | H of tr & Prgr. |
|---|---|---|---|
| Bisha | 531 | 10 | 24h (Q) |
| Ar-Rass | 549 | 10 | 0300-2300 (R) |
| Jizan | 549 | 1 | 24h (A) |
| Qurayyat | 549 | 2000 | 0300-1500 (R) |
| Rafha | 549 | 20 | 24h (R) |
| Abha | 558 | 5 | 24h (Q) |
| Jeddah (Bahrah) | 567 | 200 | 24h (Q) |
| Afif | 567 | 15 | 24h (Q) |
| Jizan | 576 | 20 | 24h (Q) |
| Riyadh | 585 | 1200 | 24h (R) |
| Hofuf | 594 | 10 | 0300-2300 (R) |
| Duba | 594 | 2000 | 0300-1500 (R) |
| Makkah | 594 | 50 | 24h (I) |
| Aflaj | 612 | 15 | 24h (Q) |
| Hail | 612 | 5 | 24h (J) |
| Jizan | 630 | 20 | 0300-2200 (J) |
| Najran | 630 | 10 | 24h (Q) |
| Jeddah (Khumra) | 648 | 2000 | 0300-2300 (R) |
| Rafha | 657 | 20 | 24h (Q) |
| Abha | 675 | 5 | 0300-2300 (R) |

| MW | kHz | kW | H of tr & Prgr. |
|---|---|---|---|
| Afif | 675 | 20 | 0300-2300 (R) |
| Jeddah (Bahrah) | 684 | 200 | 24h (J) |
| Riyadh | 684 | 10 | 24h (J) |
| Bisha | 702 | 10 | 24h (J) |
| Duba | 702 | 40 | 24h (J) |
| Najran | 747 | 10 | 24h (A) |
| Buraidah | 747 | 10 | 0300-2300 (J) |
| Aflaj | 765 | 20 | 24h (J) |
| Hofuf | 765 | 10 | 24h (J) |
| Qurayyat | 765 | 20 | 24h (Q) |
| Ras al-Khair | 783 | 100 | 24h (I) |
| Jeddah (An-Nuziah) | 792 | 50 | 24h (Q) |
| Abha | 810 | 5 | 24h (Q) |
| Hafar al-Batin | 810 | 20 | 24h (Q) |
| Buraida | 846 | 20 | 24h (Q) |
| Ras al-Khair | 855 | 100 | 24h (Q) |
| Ar-Rass | 873 | 10 | 24h (Q) |
| Dammam | 882 | 100 | 24h (Q) |
| Qurayyat | 900 | 1000 | 1500-0300 (R) |
| Hofuf | 927 | 20 | 24h (J) |
| Makkah | 936 | 50 | 24h (Q) |
| Riyadh | 936 | 50 | 24h (Q) |
| Hail | 945 | 5 | 24h (R) |
| Madinah | 981 | 20 | 24h (Q) |
| Duba | 999 | 20 | 24h (Q) |
| Rafha | 1035 | 20 | 24h (J) |
| Afif | 1044 | 20 | 0300-2300 (J) |
| Bisha | 1071 | 50 | 24h (R) |
| Najran | 1080 | 10 | 0300-2200 (J) |
| Qurayyat | 1089 | 20 | 24h (J) |
| Dammam | 1098 | 100 | 24h (J) |
| Madinah | 1116 | 20 | 24h (J) |
| Aflaj | 1206 | 20 | 24h (J) |
| Hafar al-Batin | 1215 | 20 | 24h (J) |
| Madinah | 1215 | 20 | 24h (R) |
| Dammam | 1260 | 500 | 24h (R) |
| Riyadh | 1422 | 20 | 24h (I) |
| Ras al-Khair | 1440 | 1600 | 24h (R) |
| Jeddah (Bahrah) | 1449 | 200 | 24h (R) |
| Hafar al-Batin | 1467 | 50 | 24h (R) |
| Jeddah (Khumra) | 1512 | 1000 | 1500-0300 (Q) |
| Duba | †1521 | 2000 | 1500-0300 (R) |

Some transmitters running on lower power.

| FM(MHz) | R | J | Q | I/M | E |
|---|---|---|---|---|---|
| Abha | - | - | - | - | 89.0 |
| Aflaj | 93.3 | 96.5 | 99.8 | - | - |
| Almandaq | - | - | - | - | 99.1 |
| Al-Artawiya | - | - | - | - | 102.9 |
| Al-Bad' | - | - | - | - | 107.3 |
| Al-Bahah | 98.0 | 88.4 | 91.5 | - | 104.1 |
| Al-Duwadimi | - | - | - | - | 98.1 |
| Al-Henakiya | - | - | - | - | 98.4 |
| Al-Huwayd | - | - | - | - | 102.0 |
| Al-Kharj | - | - | - | - | 94.2 |
| Al-Madha | - | - | - | - | 97.7 |
| Al-Musayjid | - | - | - | - | 97.7 |
| Al-Nuhaitiya | - | - | - | - | 98.0 |
| Al-Ula | - | - | - | - | 103.6 |
| Al-Uwayqilah | - | - | - | - | 99.2 |
| Al-Wajh | - | - | - | - | 105.5 |
| Ar-Rass | 96.1 | 102.9 | 99.4 | - | - |
| Arafat | 92.2 | 94.0 | 90.8 | 92.2 | 95.4 |
| Arar | 94.1 | 97.4 | 88.4 | - | - |
| Buraydah | 99.3 | 95.6 | 93.2 | - | 98.9 |
| Dammam | 92.8/93.8 | 94.7 | 90.0 | - | 103.6 |
| Darma | - | - | - | - | 102.3 |
| Duba | 89.5 | 95.8 | 92.6 | - | - |
| Ethnen | - | - | - | - | 107.3 |
| Farasan Island | - | - | - | - | 99.3 |
| Halat Ammar | - | - | - | - | 97.5 |
| Haradh | - | - | - | - | 101.3 |
| Hubuna | - | - | - | - | 98.6 |
| Huraymila | - | - | - | - | 95.5 |
| Jeddah | 92.0/99.5 | 93.0 | 89.9 | - | 96.2 |
| Jizan | 95.1 | 88.8 | 91.9 | - | - |
| Jubail | 107.8 | 105.6 | 95.3 | - | - |
| Khamis Mushait | - | - | - | - | 107.3 |
| Kharj | 94.0 | 96.0 | 90.0 | 95.2 | - |
| Makkah | 94.7 | 98.0 | 91.5 | - | 87.7 |
| Medina | 90.5 | 93.6 | 96.8 | - | 100.1 |

| FM(MHz) | R | J | Q | I/M | E |
|---|---|---|---|---|---|
| Rabigh | - | - | - | - | 96.8 |
| Rafha | - | - | - | - | 100.2 |
| Riyadh | 91.2 | 94.4 | 100.0 | - | 97.0 |
| Sabt Alalayah | - | - | - | - | 98.3 |
| Sajir | - | - | - | - | 102.7 |
| Taif | 96.5 | 93.3 | 99.8 | - | 106.9 |
| Turaif | - | - | - | - | 101.5 |
| Turbah | - | - | - | - | 98.2 |
| Uqlat as-Suqur | - | - | - | - | 101.7 |
| Wadi Al-Fora'a | - | - | - | - | 98.8 |
| Yanbu | 97.4 | 93.6 | 90.9 | - | - |

+ numerous low power stations under 10kW for local coverage.
**R=R. Riyadh in Arabic:** 24h. – **J=R. Jeddah in Arabic:** 24h, on most MW fqs 0300-2200. – **Q=Quran prgr:** 24h incl. Call of Islam 0100-0300 – **I=Call of Islam prgr:** 24h. – **E=English prgr. "Saudia Radio"** (from either Riyadh or Jeddah studios): 24h. – **M=Music prgr:** 24h. **A:** "R. Al-Azm", a programme for Yemen (also FM Dhahran al-Janub 94.9, Fayfa 99.0, Jizan/Najran 107.0MHz. For more details see International section.
**Ann:** R. Riyadh: "Idha'at ar-Riyadh", "Idha'atu'l-mamlakah al-arabiyah t'il-saudiayh min al-Riyadh". R. Jeddah: "Idha'at al-Jiddah", "Idha'atu'l-mamlakah al-arabiyah t'il-saudiayh min Jiddah". 'Quran prgr: "Idha-atu'l-Koran al-Kareem min al-mamlakah al-arabiyah t'il-saydiah". Call of Islam: "Idha'at Nidaa Al-Islam min Makka Al-Mukaram". E: "This is Saudia Radio".
**IS:** 'Ud' (oriental lute). Opens and closes with National Anthem.
**F.PI:** separate FM network for Call of Islam prgr.

**EXTERNAL SERVICE: Saudi Radio International:** see International Radio section.

**SAUDI ARAMCO RADIO (**Serving the staff of Saudi Aramco Co.)
✉ P.O.Box 5000, Dhahran 31311 **W:** saudiaramco.com **E:** webmaster@aramco.com.sa
**Studio 1** (pop, rock and country music): Udhailiyah 88.8MHz, Dhahran 91.4MHz, Safaniya/Tanajib/Haradh 103.8MHz – **Studio 2** (easy listening, jazz and classical music): Udhailiyah 91.9MHz, Dhahran 101.4MHz, Safaniya/Tanajib/Haradh 107.9MHz. **D.Prgr:** 24h in English.

**Other stations (FM MHz):**
**Alif Alif FM:** Riyadh 94.0, Jeddah 101.0, Dammam 107.5. **W:** alifaliffm.com – **MBC FM:** Dammam 101.9, Riyadh 102.0, Jeddah/ Medina 103.0. **W:** mbc.net/mbcfm – **Mix FM:** Tabuk 93.0MHz, Riyadh & 5 sites 98.0, Jubayl 98.4, Nazran 101.0, Taif 101.4, Kharj/ Skaka 103.0, Breida/Jeddah 105.5, Makkah & 3 sites 106.0, Majmaa 106.2, Baha/Rabegh 106.9. **W:** mixfm-sa.com – **Panorama FM:** Dammam 91.9, Riyadh 96, Tabuk 101.7, Jeddah 102, Madinah 102.3, Buraidah (Al Qassim) 103.3, Abha/Taif 104. See main entry under UAE – **R. Rotana:** Jeddah/Riyadh 88.0, Dammam 100.0. **W:** rotanafm.com – **uFM R.:** Riyadh 90.0, Madina 91.0, Al-Kharj/Ara'ar/ Al-Dawadimi 91.5. **W:** ufmradio.com. **American Forces Network:** 93.7/100.7/103.9/107.8, Dammam 95.5, Makkah 95.8, Jeddah 97.0. New FM licenses granted to: Ghayat Al-Ibdah, Rotana, Electronic Resources and Shams R.

## SENEGAL

**L.T:** UTC — **Pop:** 16 million — **Pr.L:** French, Wolof, Mandinga, Soninké, Pular, others — **E.C:** 50Hz, 230V — **ITU:** SEN

### CONSEIL NATIONAL DE REGULATION DE L'AUDIOVISUEL (CNRA)
✉ 15ème étage, Immeuble Fahd, Blvd Djily Mbaye, B.P. 50059, Dakar RP ☎+221 33 8499120 🖷 +221 33 8234785 **W:** cnra.sn
**L.P:** Chairperson: Nancy Ngom Ndiaye.

### RADIODIFFUSION TÉLÉVISION SÉNÉGALAISE (Gov.)
✉ Triangle Sud x Avenue El-Hadj Malick SY, B.P. 1765, Dakar ☎+221 33 8491212 🖷 +221 33 8223490 **W:** rts.sn **E:** rts@rts.sn
**L.P:** DG: Babacar Diagne. Dir. Radio: Oumar Seck. Dir. New Tech. & Development: Papa Abdou Diallo.

| FM | N | I | R | M | kW |
|---|---|---|---|---|---|
| Bakel | 95.9 | 107.3 | - | - | 5 |
| Dakar | 95.7 | 92.5 | 94.5 | 95.2 | 10 |
| Diourbel | 97.6 | 96.6 | 101.1 | - | 2 |
| Fatick | 95.7 | - | 92.8 | - | 0.5/2 |
| Goudiry | 106.0 | - | 91.1 | - | 0.5 |
| Kaolack | 103.0 | 107.0 | 97.9 | - | 5 |
| Kédougou | 94.6 | 97.7 | 100.0 | - | 2 |

| FM | N | I | R | M | kW |
|---|---|---|---|---|---|
| Kolda | 100.0 | 102.2 | 92.2 | - | 2 |
| Koungheul | 89.7 | - | 107.0 | - | 1 |
| Linguère | 92.1 | 89.0 | - | - | 5 |
| Louga | 95.0 | 101.8 | 88.7 | - | 5/2 |
| Matam | 95.6 | 89.1 | 100.6 | - | 2 |
| Ndioum | - | 98.4 | 92.7 | - | 5 |
| Ourossogui | 96.5 | 89.1 | 105.3 | - | 5/2 |
| Podor | - | - | 100.6 | - | 0.25 |
| Richard Toll | - | - | 89.6 | - | 0.1 |
| Saint-Louis | 91.9 | 90.1 | 96.3 | - | 10/5 |
| Tambacounda | 102.0 | 88.1 | 92.0 | - | 5 |
| Thiès | 96.9 | 94.9 | 100.6 | - | 5 |
| Touba | - | - | 99.2 | - | 0.25 |
| Vélingara | 99.0 | 89.1 | 92.2 | - | 2 |
| Ziguinchor | 95.2 | 100.2 | 98.9 | - | 5 |

**N=Chaîne Nationale:** 24h in French, Wolof and other national languages – **I=R. Sénégal Internationale:** 24h in French, Arabic, Portuguese and other languages – **M=RTS Mag FM:** 24h in French – **R=Chaîne Régionale:** 0600-2400, regional programming for 9 to 18 hours a day depending on station.
**Ann:** N: "Radiodiffusion Télévision Sénégalaise émettant de Dakar". Int: "Radio Sénégal Internationale". **IS:** Melody on "Cora" (local harp).

**OTHER STATIONS (main networks):**

| FM | 1) | 2) | 3) | 4) | 5) | 6) | 7) |
|---|---|---|---|---|---|---|---|
| Bakel | - | - | 93.7 | 100.8 | - | - | - |
| Banlieue | 91.7 | - | - | - | - | - | - |
| Bignona | - | 91.4 | - | 88.3 | - | - | - |
| Dagana | - | - | - | 91.7 | - | - | - |
| Dakar | 98.5 | 94.0 | 88.9 | 101.0 | 103.9 | 98.7 | 97.8 |
| Diourbel | 91.1 | 92.4 | 90.9 | - | - | 106.0 | 105.5 |
| Fatick | - | 99.3 | 102.5 | - | 99.3 | - | 102.8 |
| Joal | - | - | 92.4 | - | - | - | - |
| Kaffrine | - | 95.0 | 102.4 | - | - | - | - |
| Kaolack | 94.6 | 93.9 | 105.0 | 92.7 | 99.7 | 93.1 | 91.9 |
| Kébémer | - | - | 91.5 | 101.3 | - | - | - |
| Kédogou | - | 99.7 | 98.6 | 106.4 | - | - | - |
| Kidira | - | - | 105.0 | - | - | - | - |
| Kolda | 95.4 | 93.2 | 98.7 | 91.9 | 102.2 | 99.7 | 88.1 |
| Linguere | - | - | 102.8 | - | - | - | - |
| Louga | - | 88.3 | 91.8 | - | 98.3 | 107.0 | 103.4 |
| Matam | 98.4 | 95.0 | - | 89.3 | 96.9 | 91.8 | 88.7 |
| Mboro | - | - | 98.6 | - | - | - | - |
| Mbour | 106.9 | 95.8 | 102.8 | - | - | 104.1 | - |
| Ndioum | 93.9 | - | - | - | - | - | - |
| Nioro | - | 98.4 | - | - | - | - | - |
| Ourossogui | - | - | 99.5 | - | - | - | - |
| Podor | - | 100.0 | 98.7 | - | 95.4 | - | - |
| Richard Toll | - | 99.0 | 106.0 | - | - | - | - |
| Saint-Louis | 93.2 | 99.3 | 106.3 | 88.3 | 94.6 | 88.9 | 88.1 |
| Sédhiou | 88.0 | - | 95.3 | - | - | - | - |
| Tambacounda | 98.5 | 93.2 | 91.0 | 94.0 | 105.6 | 100.5 | 90.3 |
| Thiès | 102.2 | 102.5 | 93.7 | 106.9 | 92.3 | 107.1 | 105.1 |
| Toubambacké | 92.8 | 92.4 | - | 89.1 | 106.2 | - | - |
| Velingara | - | 96.4 | 102.4 | - | - | - | - |
| Ziguinchor | 95.6 | 92.0 | 92.4 | - | - | 106.0 | 103.4 |

**Addresses: 1)** Sud FM Sen R, Immeuble Fahd, Bld. Djily Mbaye x rue Macodou Ndiaye (5ème étage), Dakar ☎+221 33 8650888 🖷 +221 33 8220250 **W:** sudfm.net **– 2)** R. Futurs Medias (RFM), Rue 15x Corniche, Immeuble Elimane Ndour , B.P. 17795, Dakar ☎+221 33 8491640 **W:** futursmedias.net **– 3)** R. Dunyaa: HLM 1, Rue 14 prolongée, Dakar ☎+221 33 8242424 **E:** dunyaa@sentoo.sn **– 4)** Express An-Nour FM **– 5)** Convergence FM, Immeuble Lambert, Avenue Bourguiba, Dakar ☎+221 33 8253989 **W:** convergencefm. wordpress.com **– 6)** Océan FM **– 7)** Sénégal Info
**Community radio FM (MHz):**
**Afia FM**, Dakar: 93.0 5kW – Biyen FM, Thiès 89.5 2kW – Ferlo FM, Dahra: 94.0 2kW – Gaynaako FM, Podor 99.0 0.5kW. **W:** gaynaakofm. org – Jéeri FM, Keur Momar Sarr 97.0 0.3kW – Manoore FM, Dakar: 89.4 5kW – R. Penc Mi, Fissel: 90.6 1kW. **E:** pencmi_fm@yahoo.fr – R. Tim-Timol, Matam: 91.8 1kW.

**Other stations (MHz):**
**BBC African Sce:** Dakar 105.6 10kW in French.
**Medi 1 Afrique Internationale:** Dakar 93.8
**RFI Afrique:** Ziguinchor 87.6, Tambacounda 88.9, Kaolack 91.4, Dakar 92.0, Richard Toll 94.3, Mbacké 94.4, Bakel 98.2, St.-Louis 99.7, Thiès 100.2MHz.
**VOA Africa:** Dakar 102.0MHz in French & Wolof

## SERBIA

**L.T:** UTC +1h (31 Mar-27 Oct: +2h) — **Pop:** 7.1 million — **Pr.L:** Serbian — **E.C:** 50Hz, 230V — **ITU:** SRB

**REGULATORNO TELO ZA ELEKTRONSKE MEDIJE (REM) (Regulatory Authority of Electronic Media)**
⌨ Trg Nikole Pasica 5, 11003 Beograd ☎ +381 11 2028700 🖷 +381 11 2028745 **E:** office@rem.rs **W:** www.rem.rs
**L.P:** Vice Pres: Goran Petrovic

**JP. EMISIONA TEHNIKA I VEZE/ETV (PUBLIC ENTERPRISE BROADCASTING AND COMMUNICATION)**
⌨ Kneza Viseslava 88, 11030 Beograd ☎ +381 11 3693251 🖷 +381 11 3693260, Tech.: ☎ +381 11 3212650 **W:** etv.rs **E:** etv@etv.rs, tehnika@etv.rs, etv@etv.rs **L.P:** Branko Gogic

**RADIO-TELEVIZIJA SRBIJE (Pub)**
⌨ Takovska 10, 11000 Beograd ☎ +381 11 3212000 **E:** kontaktcentar@rts.rs **W:** rts.rs **L.P:** DG: Dragan Bujosevic
**R. Beograd:** Hilendarska 2, 11000 Beograd ☎ +381 11 3248888 **L.P:** Dir: Milivoje Mihajlovic **W:** radiobeograd.co.rs

| MW | kHz | kW | Prgr | |
|---|---|---|---|---|
| Sjenica | 1602 | 0.5 | rel. Radio Beograd 1 | |
| **FM (MHz)** | **I** | **II/III** | **202** | **kW** |
| Avala | 95.3 | 97.6 | 104.0 | 75/75/130 |
| Bajina Basta | 91.9 | 93.0 | 94.0 | 2 |
| Beograd | 88.3 | - | - | 2 |
| Besna Kobila | 91.7 | 95.3 | 100.1 | 25/25/40 |
| Bitovik | 91.7 | 92.9 | 104.3 | 25 |
| Crni Vrh | 89.7 | 99.3 | 101.0 | 25 |
| Crveni Cot | 94.5 | 96.5 | 101.8 | 75/75.130 |
| Deli Jovan | 87.7 | 94.9 | 98.9 | 25/25/40 |
| Jastrebac | 96.9 | 89.3 | 103.5 | 100 |
| Kopaonik | 90.9 | 93.7 | 102.1 | 50/50/100 |
| Ljubovija | 104.0 | 94.0 | 105.6 | 25 |
| Maljen | 104.5 | 107.9 | 93.4 | 25 |
| Ovcar | 88.1 | 90.1 | 101.6 | 25 |
| Pirot | 98.5 | 102.5 | 101.0 | 15 |
| Subotica | 88.9 | 101.1 | 98.5 | 50/50/0.3 |
| Tornik | 90.6 | 97.5 | 100.2 | 15 |
| Trgoviste | 90.1 | 92.3 | 96.9 | 15 |
| Tupiznica | 92.5 | 96.1 | 100.4 | 25 |
| Vrsac | 95.7 | 98.1 | 103.0 | 30 |

Additional low power local stns not mentioned.
**R. Beograd 1:** 24h **N:** W 0303, 0330, 0400, 0430, 0500, 0540, 0700, 0800, 0900, 1000, 1100, 1200, 1300, 1400, 1600, 1700, 1830, 2100, 2200, 2300; Sun 0430, 0500, 0530, 0600, 0700, 0800, 0900, 1000, 1100, 1200, 1400, 1600, 1830, 2000, 2200, 2300 — **R. Beograd 2:** W 0400-1900 (Sun 0600-1900). **N:** W 1130, 1230, 1330, 1500, 1600, 1850. Sun 0630, 0730, 0930, 1055, 1130, 1330, 1730, 1850 — **R. Beograd 3:** 1900-2300 (Serious prgr.) — **R. Beograd 202:** 24h on 104.0MHz + FM 202 – **Stereorama:** 0700-1900SS on FM 202. Other times rel. Beograd 202

**Local stations:**

| FM | MHz | FM | MHz | FM | MHz |
|---|---|---|---|---|---|
| Arandjelovac | 98.9 | Leskovac | 99.0 | Smed. Palanka | 88.3 |
| Bor | 91.7 | Loznica | 107.4 | Smederevo | 96.1 |
| Cacak | 92.8 | Majdanpek | 96.7 | Soko Banja | 90.5 |
| Jagodina | 97.3 | Mladenovac | 97.0 | Uzice | 92.0 |
| Kladovo | 89.0 | Novi Pazar | 90.0 | Valjevo | 88.6 |
| Kragujevac | 88.9 | Pirot | 95.8 | Vranje | 96.5 |
| Kraljevo | 87.6 | Pozarevac | 90.1 | Vrnjacka Banja | 96.5 |
| Krusevac | 92.2 | Priboj | 88.7 | Zajecar | 98.1 |
| Lazarevac | 89.3 | Prijepolje | 98.9 | | |

**E: R. Bella Amie:** belami.rs **R. Vranje:** rtv-vranje.rs **R. Leskovac:** radioleskovac.rs **R. Kragujevac:** rtk.co.rs **R. Valjevo:** patak.co.rs

**FM stations with national coverage:**

| FM | MHz | FM | MHz |
|---|---|---|---|
| Radio S2 | 88.9 | Play | 92.5 |
| FM Hit Radio | 98.5 | R. S1 | 94.9 |

All stns have relays.
**E: Index:** indexradio.rs **Play:** b92.net **R.S:** radios.rs **Hit Music:** hitmusicfm.rs

**Local FM stations in Beograd:**

| FM | MHz | FM | MHz | FM | MHz |
|---|---|---|---|---|---|
| R. S2 | 88.9 | Bum Bum | 89.4 | R. JAT | 90.2 |

| FM | MHz | FM | MHz | FM | MHz |
|---|---|---|---|---|---|
| R. S3 | 90.9 | Rock R. | 96.2 | Novosti | 104.7 |
| Pink | 91.3 | Naxi | 96.9 | Nostalgie | 105.2 |
| TDI | 91.8 | FM Hit R. | 98.5 | Karolina | 106.3 |
| Play | 92.5 | Studio B | 99.1 | Top FM | 106.8 |
| Laguna | 93.7 | Sport FM | 100.4 | S.Ljubve | 107.3 |
| R. S1 | 94.9 | R. S4 | 102.2 | AS FM R. | 107.9 |
| TRI | 95.8 | | | | |

There are numerous local FM stns.

### VOJVODINA (Autonomous Province)

**RADIO TELEVIZIJA NOVI SAD**
⌨ Ignjata Pavlasa 3, 21000 Novi Sad ☎ +381 21 210-1420 🖷 +381 21 423348 **E:** office@rtv.rs **W:** rtv.rs

| FM (MHz) | I | II | III | kW |
|---|---|---|---|---|
| Novi Sad | 87.7 | 90.5 | 100.0 | 50 |
| Subotica | 99.3 | 92.5 | | 50 |
| Vrsac | 99.6 | 91.7 | 107.1 | 30 |

I) in Serbian, II) in Hungarian, III) prgrs for national minorities
**R. Novi Sad 1:** 24h in Serbian **R. Novi Sad 2:** 24h in Hungarian
**R.Novi sad** 3: 24h for national minorities

**Local stations:**

| FM | MHz | FM | MHz | FM | MHz |
|---|---|---|---|---|---|
| Apatin | 98.7 | Kovin | 89.5 | St. Pazova | 91.5 |
| B. Palanka | 95.1 | Odzaci | 89.7 | Subotica | 91.5 |
| B. Topola | 97.8 | Pancevo | 92.1 | Temerin | 93.5 |
| B. Petrovac | 91.4 | Ruma | 102.7 | Vrbas | 95.5 |
| Beocin | 97.8 | Sid | 89.1 | Vrsac | 94.0 |
| Indjija | 96.0 | Sombor | 97.5 | Zrenjanin | 103.6 |
| Kovacica | 93.2 | Srbobran | 102.6 | | |

There are numerous low-power local FM stns.
**E: R. Pancevo:** rtvpancevo.rs **R. Panon:** pannonrtv.com **R. Zrenjanin:** radiozrenjanin.rs

## SEYCHELLES

**L.T:** UTC +4h — **Pop:** 98,000 — **Pr.L:** Creole, English, French — **E.C:** 50Hz, 240V — **ITU:** SEY

**DEPARTMENT OF INFORMATION COMMUNICATIONS TECHNOLOGY (DICT)**
⌨ P.O. Box 737, Third Floor, Caravelle House, Manglier St, Victoria, Mahé ☎ +248 4286609 🖷 +248 4324643 **W:** www.ict.gov.sc **E:** psoffice@ict.gov.sc **L.P:** Principal Secretary: Benjamin Choppy

**SEYCHELLES BROADCASTING CORPORATION(SBC, Pub.)**
⌨ P.O. Box 321, Hermitage, Mahé ☎ +248 4289600 🖷 +248 4225641 **W:** sbc.sc **E:** ceo.secretary@sbc.sc
**L.P:** DCEO: Mr. Jude Louange. Head of Marketing & Corporate Affairs: Ms. Cindy Wirtz Head of Eng. & Tech.: Mr. Jean-Paul Gamatis. Head of Radio Prgr: Mrs. Jeannette Julienne

**MW:** Victoria 1368kHz 10kW.
**FM:** St. Louis 93.6MHz 1kW, Praslin 100.8MHz 0.03kW.
**D.Prgr: MW: Radyo Sesel** (spoken word): 0200-1800. **N:** English: 0300, 0600, 0900, 1500. **French:** 0330, 0700, 1300, 1700. **Creole:** 0230, 0500, 0800, 1600.
**FM: Paradise FM** (musical prgr.): 24h.
**Ann:** E: "This is SBC Radio". F: "Ici la Radio SBC". C: "Isi Radyo Sesel"
**IS:** Instrumental music.

**Other Stations:**
**K-Radio:** 96.8/97.0/97.2/99.0MHz. **W:** k-ent.sc
**Pure FM:** Anse Soleil 90.0MHz, St. Louis 90.7MHz, Praslin 95.7MHz. **W:** purefm.sc
**RFI Afrique:** Anse Soleil 102.8MHz 0.25kW, Pointe au Sel 103.2MHz, Victoria 103.8MHz 1kW.
**BBC World Sce:** Anse Soleil 105.2MHz, Pointe au Sel 105.6MHz, St. Louis/Victoria 106.2MHz

## SIERRA LEONE

**L.T:** UTC — **Pop:** 6.7 million — **Pr.L:** English, Krio, Limba, Mende, Temne, others — **E.C:** 50Hz, 230V — **ITU:** SRL

**INDEPENDENT MEDIA COMMISSION (IMC)**
⌨ Kissy House, 54 Siaka Stevens Street, Freetown ☎+232 22 221835 **W:** imc-sl.org **E:** info@imc-sl.org
**L.P:** Commissioner: Augustine Garmoh.

## SIERRA LEONE BROADCASTING CORPORATION (SLBC, Pub.)
New England, Freetown ☎+232 22 241919 ▯ +232 22 240922 **W:** slbc.sl
**L.P:** DG: Elvis Gbanabom Hallowell. Dir. Eng.: Alhajie Bangura.
**FM:** Freetown 100.0MHz 8kW. Regional stations (mostly own programming): Bo 96.5MHz 2kW, Kenema 93.5MHz 2kW, Kono 90.2MHz 1kW, Makeni 88.0MHz 1kW. In addition 4 trs under 1kW.
**D.Prgr:** 0600-2400.

### Other Stations FM (MHz):
**Africa Young Voices (AYV),** Freetown: 101.6. **W:** ayvnews.com – **Believers Broadcasting Network (BBN)** (Rlg.), Freetown: 93.0 2kW. **W:** bbn-sl.org – **Capital R:** Freetown 104.9 8kW, Bo 102.3 50W, Kenema 104.9 30W, Makeni 103.3 30W. **W:** capitalradio.sl – **Eastern R:** Kenema 101.9, Kono 96.5 – **Joy FM,** Segbwema 88.5 – **Kids Radio Network,** Freetown 103.0 **W:** facebook.com/kidsradionetwork – **Kiss FM,** Bo: 104.0 (Also rel. VOA) – **R. Bintumani,** Kabala: 93.7 – **R. Bontico,** Bonthe: 96.9 – **R. Democracy,** Freetown: 98.1 **W:** radiodemocracy.sl – **R. Galaxy,** Mahera: 106.1 – **R. Gbafth,** Mile 91: 91.0 – **R. Kolenten,** Kambia: 92.4 – **R. Mankneh,** Makeni: 95.1 – **R. Moa,** Kailahun: 105.5 – **R. Modcar,** Moyamba: 94.8 – **R. Maria,** Makeni 101.1 0.5kW – **R. Mount Aureol,** Fourah Bay College, Freetown: 107.3MHz – **Njala University R,** Njala 92.5 – **R. Numbura,** Bumbuna: 102.5 – **R. Wanjei,** Pujehun: 101.1 – **R. Viascity,** Waterloo: 100.6 – **Star R,** Freetown 103.5 – **Skyy R,** Freetown: 106.6 – **Unity R,** Freetown: 98.4 – **Voice of Islam,** Freetown: 102.0 – **VO the Handicapped,** Freetown: 96.2 (mostly rel. BBC) – **VO the Peninsula,** Tombo: 96.0 – **VO Women,** Mattru Jong: 88.5.

**BBC African Sce:** Freetown 94.3 8kW, Makeni 91.7 60W, Bo 94.35120W, Kenema 95.3MHz 60W – **RFI Afrique:** Freetown: 89.9 in French/English/Mandinka – **VOA Africa:** Freetown 102.4MHz

## SINGAPORE

**L.T:** UTC +8h — **Pop:** 5.80 million — **Pr.L:** English, Chinese, Malay, Tamil — **E.C:** 50Hz, 230V — **ITU:** SNG

### INFO-COMMUNICATIONS MEDIA DEVELOPMENT AUTHORITY OF SINGAPORE (IMDA) (Government statutory board)
3 Fusionopolis Way, #16-22 Symbiosis, Singapore 138633 ☎ +65 6377 3800 ▯ +65 6577 3888 **W:** imda.gov.sg
**L.P:** Chmn: Mr Chan Yeng Kit, CEO: Mr Tan Kiat How.

### MEDIACORP RADIO SINGAPORE PTE LTD (Comm.)
Mediacorp Campus, 1 Stars Avenue, Ayer Rajah, Singapore 138507 ☎ +65 6333 3888 ▯ +65 6251 5828 **W:** mediacorp.sg (corporate), toggle.sg/en (programming)
**L.P:** Chmn: Chiang Meng Niam. CEO: Ms Tham Loke Kheng.
**Stations:** FM tx centre at Bukit Batok

| FM | MHz | kW | Network | Format | Lang. |
|---|---|---|---|---|---|
| 1) | 89.7 | 6 | Ria 89.7FM | CHR | Malay |
| 2) | 90.5 | 6 | Gold 90FM | Gold | English |
| 3) | 92.4 | 10 | Symphony 92FM | Classical | English |
| 4) | 93.3 | 6 | Y.E.S. 93.3FM | AC | Chinese |
| 5) | 93.8 | 6 | 938LIVE | N./Info | English |
| 6) | 94.2 | 10 | Warna 94.2FM | N./Info | Malay |
| 7) | 95.0 | 6 | Class 95FM | AC | English |
| 8) | 95.8 | 10 | Capital 95.8FM * | N./Info | Chinese |
| 9) | 96.8 | 10 | Oli 96.8FM | Full sce | Tamil |
| 10) | 97.2 | 6 | Love 97.2FM ** | Easy | Chinese |
| 11) | 98.7 | 6 | 987FM | CHR | English |

*) in Chinese: 'Chengshi Pindao' **) in Chinese: 'Zui'ai Pindao'
**D.Prgr:** all networks 24h Tr. powers shown are TRP
**Ownership:** MediaCorp is wholly owned by Temasek Holdings, an investment company of the Government of Singapore.

### SO DRAMA! ENTERTAINMENT (Comm.)
Operated by the Singapore Armed Forces Reservists' Ass.
Tower B #12-04, Defence Technology Towers, 5 Depot Rd, Singapore 109681 ☎ +65 6373 1920 ▯ +65 6278 3039 **W:** sodrama.sg
**883JiaFM:** 88.3MHz 5kW, 24h in Chinese
**Power98FM:** 98.0MHz 12kW, 24h in English

### SPH RADIO PTE LTD (Singapore Press Holdings, Comm.)
1000 Toa Payoh North, News Centre Podium Block Level 3, Singapore 318994 ☎ +65 6319 1900 ▯ +65 6319 1099 **W:** sphradio.sg **L.P:** Deputy CEO & Chairman: Mr Patrick Daniel. Gen. Mgr: Mr Sim

Hong Huat. Senior Prgr Dir. 91.3 & 92: Jamie R. Meldrum. Senior Prgr Dir 96.3 & 100.3: Ms Carine Ang. Ass Prgr Dir 89.3: Ms Loretta Lopez.
**Money FM.:** 24h in English on 89.3 MHz **One FM:** 24h in English on 91.3MHz **Kiss92 FM:** 24h in English on 92.0MHz **96.3 Hao FM:** 24h in Chinese on 96.3MHz **UFM 1003:** 24h in Chinese on 100.3MHz

### BBC SINGAPORE 88.9 FM
24h rel. of BBCWS in English. The 5kW FM tx at Bukit Batok is operated by MediaCorp.

**FAR EASTERN RELAY STATION** (Babcock Communications Ltd)
51 Turut Track, Singapore 718930 ☎ +65 6793 7511
See International Radio section

## SLOVAKIA

**L.T:** UTC +1h (31 Mar-27 Oct: +2h) — **Pop:** 5.5 million — **Pr.L:** Slovak — **E.C:** 50Hz, 230V — **ITU:** SVK

### RADA PRE VYSIELANIE A RETRANSMISIU (RVR) (Council for Broadcasting and Retransmission)
Palisády 36, 81106 Bratislava ☎ +421 22090650 ▯ +421 220906535 **E:** office@rvr.sk **W:** www.rvr.sk
**L.P:** Chair: Marta Danielová

### ROZHLAS A TELEVÍZIA SLOVENSKA (Radio and Television of Slovakia) - RTVS (Pub) SLOVENSKY ROZHLAS (SLOVAK RADIO)
Mytna 1 (P.O.Box 55), 817 55 Bratislava 15 ☎ + 421 2 57273111 ▯ +421 2 57273559 **W:** rozhlas.sk **E:** info@rozhlas.sk **Radio FM: W:** radiofm.sk **E:** info@radiofm.sk **L.P:** DG: Jaroslav Rezník. PD: Michal Dzurjanin. TD: Igor Zachar

| MW | kHz | kW | Prgr |
|---|---|---|---|
| Kosice | 702 | 5 | S5 (daytime) + S3 (nighttime) |
| Nitra (Jarok) | 1098 | 25 | S5 (daytime) + S3 (nighttime) |
| Rimavská Sobota | 1521 | 10 | S5 (daytime) + S3 (nighttime) |

| FM (MHz) | S1 | S2 | S3 | S4 | kW |
|---|---|---|---|---|---|
| Banská Bystrica | 90.1 | 101.5 | 102.0 | 105.4 | 100/100/0.1/2 |
| Banská Stiavnica | 99.0 | - | 102.6 | - | 20/20 |
| Bardejov | 93.5 | 89.3 | 88.8 | 101.7 | 10/1/10/10 |
| Borsky Mikulás | - | - | 95.6 | 102.8 | 1 |
| Bratislava | 96.6 | 99.3 | 104.4 | 89.3 | 100/10/10/10 |
| Cadca | - | - | - | 91.8 | 0.5 |
| Dolny Kubin | - | - | - | 91.7 | 1 |
| Dubnica n.V. | 92.2 | - | - | - | 0.5 |
| Kosice | 96.6 | 100.3 | - | - | 100/35 |
| Kosice (city) | - | - | 96.2 | 101.2 | 0.5/1 |
| Lucenec | 103.6 | 88.2 | - | 98.0 | 10/2/10 |
| Modry Kamen | 90.9 | 88.5 | 103.1 | 98.3 | 10 |
| Námestovo | 102.4 | 100.4 | 88.7 | - | 10 |
| Nitra | 91.2 | 102.2 | - | - | 10/10 |
| N. Mesto n.V. | 103.2 | 100.7 | 90.8 | - | 10 |
| Nové Zámky | - | - | 94.6 | 102.8 | 1 |
| Poprad | 92.2 | 96.9 | 94.2 | 104.3 | 30 |
| Presov | - | - | 106.7 | 101.5 | 0.5 |
| Rim. Sobota | - | 95.0 | - | - | 1 |
| Roznava | 97.3 | 88.6 | 90.0 | 105.9 | 1/1/1/1 |
| Ruzomberok | 103.8 | 100.6 | 104.6 | 102.1 | 5 |
| Snina | 91.2 | - | 102.2 | 107.6 | 10 |
| Stará Lubovna | 89.1 | 102.3 | 96.1 | - | 10 |
| Sturovo | 96.3 | 91.7 | 106.2 | 103.7 | 10 |
| Trebisov | - | 89.2 | 106.7 | 101.3 | 10 |
| Trencín | - | 95.9 | 97.8 | 101.2 | 10 |
| Trnava (F.Pl.) | 90.8 | - | - | - | 10 |
| Trstená | - | - | - | 91.9 | 10 |
| Zilina | 103.5 | 100.1 | 97.2 | 94.5 | 20/20/30/20 |
| Zvolen | - | 99.8 | 89.0 | - | 0.5/1 |

### Addresses & other information:
**S1** = Radio Slovensko: 24h (national prgr news) **S2** = Radio Regina: 24h (regional prgrs + prgrs for national minorities in Hungarian, Ukrainian, Ruthenian, German, Czech, Polish and Gypsy/Roma + relays of Radio Slovensko – S1) **S2 BA** = Radio Regina Bratislava, Mytna 1, 817 55 Bratislava 15 **S2 BB** = Radio Regina Banská Bystrica L. Sáru 1, 975 68 Banská Bystrica **S2 KE** = Radio Regina Kosice Masarykova 7, 041 61 Kosice **S3** = Radio Devín: 24h (cultural prgr) on FM and 1700-0500 on 702, 1098 and 1521kHz **S4** = Radio FM: 24h (rock, pop and alternative music). N: on the h **S5** = Radio Patria – production of prgrs for national minorities in Hungarian, Ukrainian, Ruthenian, German, Czech, Polish, Gypsy/Roma relayed on S2 and S5 txs Slovensky Rozhlas, HRNEV, Moyzesova 7, 040 01 Kosice **E:** nev@slovakradio.

sk Prgrs for minorities (S5): Hungarian 0500-1700 on 702, 1098 and 1521kHz). Prgrs for national minorities (S5) on Radio Regina (S2): Mon+Wed+Fri+Sat+Sun 1700-1800, Tue+Thu 1700-1800, 1900-2000

**EXTERNAL SERVICE: Radio Slovakia International**
See International Broadcasting section

**MAJOR PRIVATE STATIONS/NETWORKS:**
**ASOCIÁCIA NEZÁVISLYCH ROZHLASOVYCH A TELEVÍZNYCH STANÍC (Association of Independent Radio Stations)**
✉ Gröslingova 63, 811 09 Bratislava ☎ +421 2 5296 2370 **W:** anrts. sk **E:** anrts@anrts.sk

**FUN RADIO (Comm.)** ✉ Leskova 5, 815 25 Bratislava ☎ +421 2 52494601 ▤ +421 2 52495535 **W:** funradio.sk – **RADIO JEMNÉ (Comm.)** ✉ Dr. Vladimíra Clementisa 10, 815 25 Bratislava ☎ +421 2 48484811 ▤ +421 2 52492701 **W:** jemne.sk **FM:** see list below **D.Prgr:** 24h – **RADIO EXPRES (Comm.)** ✉ Lamacská cesta 1, 841 04 Bratislava ☎ +421 2 59308900 ▤ +421 2 59308991 **W:** expres.sk **FM:** see list below **D.Prgr:** 24h – **EUROPA 2 (Comm.)** ✉ Seberíniho 1, 821 03 Bratislava ☎ +421 2 48224201 **W:** europa2.sk **FM:** see list below **D.Prgr:** 24h – **RADIO LUMEN (Relig.)** ✉ Kapitulská 2, 974 01 Banská Bystrica ☎ +421 48 4710800 ▤ +421 48 4710840 **W:** lumen.sk **FM:** see list below **D.Prgr:** 24h – **RADIO ANTÉNA ROCK (Comm.)** ✉ Dr. Vladimira Clementisa 10, 821 02 Bratislava ☎ +421 2 48484811 **W:** antenarock.sk **FM:** see list below **D.Prgr:** 24h – **RADIO VLNA (Comm.)** ✉ Siberiniho 1, 821 02 Bratislava ☎ +421 2 48484855 **W:** radiovlna.sk **FM:** see list below **D.Prgr:** 24h

**Private Commercial FM Stations:**

| FM | MHz | kW | Station |
|---|---|---|---|
| Kosice | 87.7 | 80 | Fun R. |
| Banská Bystrica | 87.7 | 10 | R. Jemné |
| Nové Mesto n.V. | 88.0 | 8.5 | R. Jemné |
| Hlohovec | 88.4 | 2 | R. Expres |
| Ruzomberok | 88.4 | 1 | R. Expres |
| Snina | 88.5 | 10 | R. Vlna |
| Banská Bystrica | 88.6 | 1 | R. Jazz |
| Nitra | 88.8 | 10 | R. Anténa Rock |
| Trencín | 89.1 | 10 | Fun R. |
| Rimavská Sobota | 89.3 | 1 | R. Expres |
| Ruzomberok | 89.7 | 1 | R. Lumen |
| Nitra | 89.7 | 1 | R. Expres |
| Banská Bystrica | 90.5 | 2 | R. One BB |
| Prievidza | 90.5 | 1 | R. WOW |
| Presov | 90.8 | 2 | R. Kosice |
| Zilina | 90.8 | 1 | R. One Rock |
| Moldava nad Bodvou | 91.0 | 1 | R. Expres |
| Ruzomberok | 91.1 | 1 | R. Vlna |
| Lucenec | 91.6 | 10 | Fun R. |
| Stropkov | 92.4 | 1 | R. Vlna |
| Zvolen | 92.6 | 1 | R. Expres |
| Zámky | 92.7 | 1 | R. Expres |
| Zilina | 92.7 | 1 | R. Vlna |
| Ruzomberok | 92.8 | 1 | R. Vlna |
| Trencín | 93.3 | 10 | R. Lumen |
| Banská Stiavnica | 93.3 | 2 | R. Lumen |
| Bratislava | 93.8 | 6 | R. Lumen |
| Košice | 93.8 | 2 | R. Best FM |
| Lehota p.Vtác. | 93.9 | 1 | R. Beta |
| Bratislava | 94.3 | 100 | Fun R. |
| Banská Bystrica | 94.7 | 1 | R. One Retro |
| Košice | 94.8 | 1 | R. Anténa Rock |
| Liptovsky Mikuláš | 95.0 | 1 | Fun R. |
| Nitra | 95.2 | 10 | Europa 2 |
| Kosice | 95.2 | 2 | R. Expres |
| Levoca | 95.3 | 1 | R. Expres |
| Bardejov | 95.6 | 1 | R. Vlna |
| Roznava | 95.7 | 1 | R. Expres |
| Snina | 95.9 | 10 | R. Anténa Rock |
| Lucenec | 96.0 | 5 | R. Vlna |
| Cadca | 96.1 | 1 | R. Frontinus |
| Martin | 96.2 | 1 | R. Frontinus |
| Partizánske | 96.4 | 1 | R. One Rock |
| Trstená | 96.5 | 2 | R. Expres |
| Zilina | 96.5 | 1 | R. Expres |
| Strázske | 97.0 | 5 | R. Kosice |
| Banská Bystrica | 97.6 | 100 | R. Anténa Rock |
| Stropkov | 97.8 | 1 | R. Lumen |
| Handlová | 98.1 | 1 | R. Lumen |
| Bardejov | 98.2 | 1 | R. Expres |
| Nové Mesto n.V. | 98.5 | 8.8 | Europa 2 |

| FM | MHz | kW | Station |
|---|---|---|---|
| Kosice | 98.6 | 50 | R. Jemné |
| Nové Zámky | 98.7 | 1 | R. Max |
| Ruzomberok | 98.8 | 5 | R. Anténa Rock |
| Michalovce | 99.0 | 2 | R. Vlna |
| Bardejov | 99.1 | 1 | R. Lumen |
| Zilina | 99.2 | 20 | Fun R. |
| Sturovo | 99.4 | 10 | R. Expres |
| Vychodna | 99.5 | 1 | R. Expres |
| Cadca | 99.6 | 1 | R. Vlna |
| Bratislava | 100.3 | 1 | R. Anténa Rock |
| Poprad | 100.9 | 30 | Europa 2 |
| Lucenec | 101.1 | 5 | R. Expres |
| Roznava | 101.4 | 1 | R. Vlna |
| Bratislava | 101.8 | 100 | R. Vlna |
| Trencín | 102.5 | 1 | R. Expres |
| Poprad | 102.5 | 1 | Fun R. |
| Roznava | 102.8 | 1 | R. Vlna |
| Strbské Pleso | 102.9 | 2 | R. Lumen |
| Kosice | 102.9 | 1 | Fun R. |
| Michalovce | 103.3 | 2 | R. Lumen |
| Presov | 103.7 | 8 | Europa 2 |
| Banská Bystrica | 104.0 | 100 | Fun R. |
| Presov | 104.1 | 1 | R. Kiss |
| Prievidza | 104.5 | 1 | R. One Rock |
| Zilina | 104.6 | 1 | R. Frontinus |
| Bratislava | 104.8 | 50 | Europa 2 |
| Poprad | 104.8 | 1 | R. Vlna |
| Martin | 104.9 | 1 | R. Vlna |
| Banská Stiavnica | 105.1 | 20 | R. Vlna |
| Povazská Bystrica | 105.2 | 1 | R. Expres |
| Prešov | 105.2 | 1 | R. Anténa Rock |
| Trencín | 105.5 | 10 | R. Vlna |
| Stará Lubovna | 105.7 | 10 | R. Expres |
| Námestovo | 105.8 | 10 | R. Lumen |
| Presov | 105.8 | 2 | R. Vlna |
| Banská Bystrica | 106.0 | 50 | Europa 2 |
| Kosice | 106.2 | 20 | R. Expres |
| Lucenec | 106.3 | 3 | R. Lumen |
| Roznava | 106.3 | 1 | R. Lumen |
| Prievidza | 106.4 | 1 | R. Jazz |
| Modry Kamen | 106.5 | 1 | R. Expres |
| Bratislava | 106.6 | 10 | R. Jemné |
| Banská Bystrica | 106.6 | 1 | R. Vlna |
| Partizánske | 106.7 | 1 | R. WOW |
| Zilina | 106.9 | 3 | R.Jemné |
| Dobsiná | 107.0 | 1 | R. Vlna |
| Bardejov | 107.1 | 10 | Europa 2 |
| Levice | 107.1 | 4 | Fun R. |
| Poprad | 107.3 | 2 | R. Anténa Rock |
| Prievidza | 107.5 | 1 | R. Expres |
| Bratislava | 107.6 | 10 | R. Expres |
| Stará Lubovna | 107.7 | 1 | R. Jemné |

+ over 60 relays of less than 1kW

**DIGITAL RADIO (DAB+)**
**Towercom** on Blocks: **12A** Zilina (5kW), Banská Bystrica (2kW); **12B** Košice (2kW); **12C** Bratislava (4kW), Dunajská Streda (1kW) with various Slovensky Rozhlas and private stns.
**AVIS** on Blocks: **10B** Banská Bystrica (3kW); **10C** Nitra (20kW), Banská Bystrica (20kW), Levice (2kW); **11C** Levice (2kW) with various Slovensky Rozhlas and private stns.

## SLOVENIA

**L.T:** UTC +1h (31 Mar – 27 Oct: +2h) — **Pop:** 2.1 million — **Pr.L:** Slovenian — **E.C:** 50Hz, 230V — **ITU:** SVN

**AGENCIJA ZA KOMUNIKACIJSKA OMREZJA IN STORITVE (AKOS)**
✉ Stegne 7, p.p. 418, 1000 Ljubljana ☎+386 1 5836300 ▤+386 1 5111101 **W:** srdf.si akos-rs.si **E:** info.box@akos-rs.si

**RADIOTELEVIZIJA SLOVENIJA (Pub.)**
✉ Kolodvorska ulica 2, SI-1550 Ljubljana / Tavcarjeva ul. 17, SI-1550 Ljubljana ☎+386 1 4752151 ▤ +386 1 4752150 **W:** rtvslo.si **E:** pr@ rtvslo.si **LP:** DG: Igor Kadunc.

| MW | kHz | kW | Prgr. | MW | kHz | kW | Prgr. |
|---|---|---|---|---|---|---|---|
| Beli Kriz | 549 | 15 | 1/K | B. Kriz | 1170 | 15 | C |
| Nemcavci | 558 | 15 | 1/MMR | | | | |

**C**=R. Capodistria in Italian, **K**=R. Koper in Slovenian, **MMR**=Muravideki Magyar R. in Hungarian.

| FM (MHz) | Slo 1 | Slo 2 | Slo 3 | Reg. | kW |
|---|---|---|---|---|---|
| Beli Kriz | 92.0 | 94.1 | 96.1 | 104.3k/97.7c | 5 |
| | - | - | - | 102.0si | 1 |
| Blejska Dobrava | - | - | - | 100.4si | 1 |
| Boc | - | - | - | 90.4m | 2 |
| Golnik | - | - | - | 89.0si | 1 |
| Koper | 92.2 | - | - | 104.1k | 1 |
| Krim | 88.0 | 93.5 | 96.5 | - | 5 |
| Krvavec | 91.8 | 98.9 | 102.0 | - | 100 |
| Kuk | 90.8 | 87.8 | 96.4 | 100.6k | 5 |
| Kum | 94.1 | 99.9 | 103.9 | - | 30 |
| Ljubljana-Šance | - | - | - | 100.8si | 1 |
| Nanos | 92.9 | 95.3 | 105.7 | 88.6k | 50/50/50/25 |
| | - | - | - | 103.1c | 100 |
| Pec | 100.1 | 104.0 | 106.0 | - | 1 |
| Pecarovci | - | - | - | 87.6h | 5 |
| Plešivec | 90.0 | 92.4 | 101.4 | - | 10 |
| Pohorje | 88.5 | 96.9 | 105.3 | 93.1m/102.8si | 30/20/50/20/50 |
| Skalnica | - | - | - | 100.3k | 2 |
| Tinjan | 89.3 | 98.9 | 98.1 | 107.6k/103.6c | 6/6/6/6/5 |
| | - | - | - | 94.6si | 6 |
| Trdinov Vrh | 90.9 | 97.6 | 100.6 | - | 7.5/10/11 |
| Trstelj | 92.7 | 94.3 | 102.2 | 96.7si | 5 |

**Reg. stns:** c=R. Capodistria in Italian, h=MMR in Hungarian, k=R. Koper, m=R. Maribor, si=R. Slovenija Int.
**R. Slovenija 1 "Prvi program":** 24h – **R. Slovenija 2 "Val 202":** 0500-2305. Other times relay R. Slovenija Int. Pop + entertainment – **R. Slovenija 3 "Program ARS":** 24h. Serious music, educational – **R. SI, R. Slovenija International**, Ilichova ulica 33, SI-2106 Maribor. **W:** radiosi.eu . Slovene music and information channel 24h in English, German and Slovenian on **FM** ("si").

## RADIO KOPER – CAPODISTRIA (Pub.)
✉ ulica OF 15, SI-6000 Koper-Capodistria ☎+386 5 6685050 ▤ +386 (5) 6684500 (Slovenian Dept.) ☎+386 (5)6685440 (Italian Dept.) **W:** rtvslo.si/radiokoper rtvslo.si/radiocapodistria **E:** radio.koper@rtvslo.si radio.capodistria@rtvslo.si **R. Koper in Slovenian:** 0400-2300 on 549kHz + FM ("k"). Other times rel. Slovenija 1 – **R. Capodistria in Italian:** 24h on 1170kHz + FM ("c").

## RADIO MARIBOR (Pub.)
✉ Ilichova ulica 33, SI-2000 Maribor ☎+386 2 4299111 **W:** rtvslo.si/radiomaribor **E:** radio.maribor@rtvslo.si **FM:** ("m"). **D.Prgr:** Mon-Sat 0440-2100, Sun 0600-2100. At other times rel. Slovenia 1.

## MURAVIDEKI MAGYAR RADIO (Pub.)
✉ Kranjceva ulica 10, SI-9220 Lendava ☎+386 2 4299700 ▤+386 2 4299712 **W:** rtvslo.si/mmr **E:** mmr@rtvslo.si
**MW** 558kHz + **FM:** ("h"). **D.Prgr:** 0445-2300. At other times rel. Slovenia 1 on MW and R. SI on FM.

## OTHER STATIONS:
| MW | kHz | kW | Station | Location |
|---|---|---|---|---|
| A) | 648 | 10 | R. Murski Val | Nemcavci |

**A)** Ul. Arhitekta Novaka 13, SI-9000 Murska Sobota **W:** murskival.si **D.Prgr:** 24h. A joint night prgr. of Koroski R., Murski val, R. Celje, R. Kranj, R. Ptuj, R. Slovenske Gorice, R. Sora, R. Triglav, R. Univox and R. Velenje is broadcast.

| FM | MHz | kW | Station | Location |
|---|---|---|---|---|
| 1) | 87.6 | 1 | R. Bob | Ljubljana-Šance |
| 2) | 87.8 | 1 | R. Salomon | Blejska Dobrava |
| 3) | 88.3 | 1 | R. 1 Portoroz | Malija |
| 3) | 88.4 | 2 | R. 1 Kranj | Krvavec |
| 5) | 89.3 | 1 | R. Student | Ljubljana-Šance |
| 18) | 89.8 | 1 | R. Ptuj | Majšperg |
| 6) | 90.0 | 5 | R. Maxi | Ljutomer |
| 3) | 90.1 | 1 | R. 1 Primorska | Nova Gorica |
| 7) | 90.2 | 1 | R. Hit | Vrhnika |
| 3) | 90.6 | 1 | R. 1 Krim | Krim |
| 30) | 91.0 | 5 | R. Ognjišče | Tinjan |
| 8) | 91.7 | 1 | R. Capris | Markovec |
| 9) | 92.6 | 1 | R. 2 | Ljubljana-Šance |
| 25) | 93.1 | 1 | R. Zeleni Val | Polzevo |
| 30) | 93.2 | 1 | R. Ognjišče | Tomaj |
| 10) | 93.7 | 2 | Štajerski Val | Boc |
| 26) | 93.8 | 1 | Hitradio Center | Markovec |
| 40) | 94.6 | 5 | Murski Val | Pecarovci |
| 43) | 94.6 | 1 | R. Sraka | Trdinov Vrh |
| 11) | 94.9 | 1 | R. Veseljak | Ljubljana-Šance |
| 41) | 95.1 | 2 | R. Celje | Boc |

| FM | MHz | kW | Station | Location |
|---|---|---|---|---|
| 7) | 95.6 | 3 | R. Hit | Dobeno |
| 6) | 95.7 | 1 | R. Maxi | Pecarovci |
| 12) | 95.9 | 1 | R. MARŠ | Maribor |
| 13) | 96.0 | 1 | R. Triglav | Ravni Valvazor |
| 14) | 97.2 | 1 | Koroški R. | Plešivec |
| 3) | 97.3 | 1 | R. 1 Primorska | Hrvatini |
| 15) | 97.3 | 1 | R. Kranj | Smarjetna Gora |
| 3) | 97.4 | 1 | R. 1 Štajerska | Ljubicna |
| 21) | 98.1 | 1 | R. Aktual Kum | Kum |
| 17) | 98.2 | 1 | R. 94 | Postojna |
| 18) | 98.2 | 1 | R. Ptuj | Ptuj |
| 3) | 99.1 | 5 | R. 1 Primorska | Trstelj |
| 3) | 99.3 | 1 | R. 1 Celjski val | Celje |
| 20) | 99.5 | 1 | R. Robin | Nova Gorica |
| 21) | 99.5 | 1 | R. City | Ljubljana-Šance |
| 30) | 99.7 | 1 | R. Ognjišče | Beli Kriz |
| 20) | 100.0 | 1 | R. Robin | Trstelj |
| 21) | 100.2 | 5 | R. Aktual | Krim |
| 22) | 100.2 | 1 | Net FM | Maribor |
| 23) | 100.6 | 1 | R. City | Maribor |
| 23) | 100.8 | 1 | R. City | Topolšica |
| 21) | 101.2 | 1 | R. Aktual | Ljubljana-Šance |
| 19) | 101.3 | 1 | R. Pohorje | Maribor |
| 2) | 101.6 | 1 | R. Salomon | Ljubljana-Šance |
| 24) | 101.9 | 1 | R. Rogla | Konjiška Gora |
| 3) | 102.1 | 4 | R. 1 Pomurje | M.Sobota/ Bogojina |
| 26) | 102.4 | 1 | Hitradio Center | Ljubljana-Šance |
| 21) | 102.4 | 5 | R. Aktual Obala | Hrvatini |
| 21) | 102.8 | 1 | R. Aktual Obala | Portoroz/Šentanje |
| 21) | 103.0 | 5 | R. Aktual Studio D | Trdinov Vrh |
| 26) | 103.2 | 1 | Hitradio Center | Rahtelov Vrh |
| 26) | 103.7 | 1 | Hitradio Center | Maribor |
| 42) | 103.7 | 1 | Primorski Val/R. Odmev | Javornik |
| 17) | 104.1 | 1 | R. 94 | Ilirska Bistrica |
| 30) | 104.5 | 100 | R. Ognjišče | Krvavec |
| 21) | 104.8 | 2 | R. Aktual | Boc |
| 26) | 104.9 | 1 | Hitradio Center | Nova Gorica |
| 3) | 105.0 | 1 | R. 1 Dolenjska | Krško |
| 8) | 105.1 | 5 | R. Capris | Slavnik |
| 32) | 105.1 | 1 | Primorski Val/Alpski Val | Kobariški Stol |
| 33) | 105.2 | 1 | R. Laser | Rahtelov Vrh |
| 34) | 105.2 | 1 | R. Antena | Ljubljana-Šance |
| 40) | 105.7 | 2 | Murski Val | Zlatolicje |
| 30) | 105.9 | 5 | R. Ognjišče | Kum |
| 26) | 106.4 | 6 | Hitradio Center | Tinjan |
| 35) | 106.4 | 4 | R. Ekspres | Krim |
| 36) | 106.6 | 15 | R. Krka | Trdinov Vrh |
| 27) | 106.8 | 1 | R. Brezje | Maribor |
| 37) | 107.0 | 1 | Moj R. | Topolšica |
| 7) | 107.0 | 1 | R. Hit | Markovec |
| 38) | 107.1 | 1 | R. 94 / R. NTR | Rovte |
| 30) | 107.3 | 2 | R. Ognjišče | Boc |
| 37) | 107.5 | 2 | R. Ognjišče | Skalnica |
| 8) | 107.9 | 1 | R. Capris | Portoroz |
| 3) | 107.9 | 1 | R. 1 Štajerska | Maribor |
| 3) | 107.9 | 1 | R. 1 Ljubljana | Ljubljana-Šance |

**NB:** Txs 1kW or higher are listed.
**Addresses:** 1) Stegne 11B, 1000 Ljubljana **W:** radiobob.si – 2) Papirniški trg 17, 1260 Ljubljana-Polje. **W:** radiosalomon.si – 3) Stegne 11B, 1000 Ljubljana **W:** radio1.si Loc.Prgr. 0100-0400 – 5) Cesta 27. aprila 31, 1000 Ljubljana. **W:** radiostudent.si – 6) Prešernova ul. 3, 9240 Ljutomer. **W:** radiomaxi.si – 7) Ljubljanska Cesta 36, 1230 Domzale. **W:** radiohit.si – 8) ul. 15.maja 10B, 6000 Koper. **W:** radiocapris.si – 9) Stegne 11b, 1000 Ljubljana. **W:** radio2.si – 10) Drofenikova 1, 3230 Šentjur. **W:** stajerskival.si – 11) Papirniški trg 17, 1260 Ljubljana-Polje. **W:** veseljak.si – 12) Tkalski prehod 4, 2000 Maribor. **W:** radiomars.si – 13) Trg Toneta Cufarja 4, 4270 Jesenice. **W:** radiotriglav.si – 14) Meškova 21, 2380 Slovenj Gradec. **W:** koroski-radio.si – 15) Stritarjeva 6, 4000 Kranj. **W:** radio-kranj.si – 17) Kazarje 10, 6230 Postojna. **W:** radio94.si – 18) Osojnikova cesta 3, 2250 Ptuj. **W:** radio-ptuj.si – 19) Partizanska cesta 24, 2000 Maribor. **W:** radiopohorje.si – 20) Kromberk, Industrijska cesta 5, 5000 Nova Gorica. **W:** robin.si – 21) Papirniški trg 17, 1260 Ljubljana-Polje. **W:** radioaktual.si – 22) Partizanska cesta 24, 2000 Maribor. **W:** radionet.si – 23) Slovenska ul. 35, 2000 Maribor. **W:** radiocity.si – 24) Škalska 7, 3210 Slovenske Konjice. **W:** radiorogla. si – 25) Taborska cesta 38d, 1290 Grosuplje. **W:** zelenival.com – 26) Zelezna cesta 14, 1000 Ljubljana. **W:** radiocenter.si – 27) ul. Radeckega 1B, 2000 Maribor. **W:** radiobrezje.si – 30) Trg Brolo Št 11, 6000 Koper. **W:** radio.ognjisce.si – 32) Poljubinj 89F, p.p.46, 5220 Tolmin **W:** primorskival.si **D.Prgr:** 1500-1900 Alpski Val. 1900-1500 Primorski Val (a

joint programme of Alpski Val and R. Odmev) – **33) Legen** 101A, 2380 Slovenj Gradec. **W:** laserr.si – **34)** Cesta na Brdo 27, 1000 Ljubljana. **W:** radioantena.si – **35)** Stegne 21C, 1000 Ljubljana. **W:** radioekspres.si – **36)** Ljubljanska Cesta 26, 8000 Novo Mesto. **W:** radiokrka.com – **37)** Kidriceva 2B, 3320 Velenje **W:** mojradio.com – **38)** Trzaška 148, 1370 Logatec. D.Prgr: 2300-0500, other times r. R. 94 – **40) W:** primorskival. si D.Prgr: 1500-1900 R. Odmev & 1900-1500 Primorski Val (a joint programme of Alpski Val and R. Odmev) – **41)** Prešernova 19, 3000 Celje. **W:** radiocelje.com – **42)** see A) – **43)** Valanticevo 17, 8000 Novo Mesto. **W:** radiosraka.com

**DAB:** Krim, Krivavec, Nanos, Plešivec, Pohorje, Tinjan, Trdinov vrh on 215.072 MHz (channel 10D): Slo1, Slo2, Slo3, R. SI, R. Ognjišce, R. Antena, R. Center, Rock R. Štajerska, R. 1 DAB, R. 2, A R. , R. Bob, Glasbeni R.

## SOLOMON ISLANDS

**L.T:** UTC +11h — **Pop:** 611,500 — **Pr.L:** Pijin, English — **E.C:** 50Hz, 220V — **ITU:** SLM

**TELECOMMUNICATIONS COMMISSION OF THE SOLOMON ISLANDS (TCSI)**
✉ 2nd Floor, Alvaro Building, Honiara ☎+677 23850 **W:** tcsi.org.sb **E:** ictpolicy@tcsi.org.sb
Regulator of broadcasting in the Solomon Islands

**SOLOMON ISLANDS BROADCASTING CORP.**
**(Statutory Authority, Comm.)**
✉ **Honiara**, P.O. Box 654, Honiara ☎ +677 20051 🖷 +677 23159. **W:** sibconline.com.sb **E:** sibcnews@solomon.com.sb **L.P:** GM: R. Buaoka. Wantok FM ☎ +677 29600 🖷 +677 29600 ✉ **Gizo:** P. O. Box 78, Gizo, Western Province ☎ +677 60160 ✉ **Lata:** P. O. Box 46, Lata, Santa Cruz ☎ +677 53047
**SW** relays SIBC MW. **Schedule:** 5020kHz 0500v-1200, 1900-2200, 9545kHz 2200-0500v. **FM format:** Common urban breakout 0600 for Wantok FM network otherwise relay SIBC 1035 AM//5020 SW. **D.Prgr:** local 1900-0000, BBC 1300-1900 **N. in English:** 2000, 2200 (R. Australia), 0130W, 0200 (R. Australia), 0500, 0600 (BBC), 0730, 1000 (R. Australia), 1100 **Ann:** "This is the SIBC". **IS:** Drum and Bamboo Pipes **V.** by QSL-card

| MW | kHz | kW | Station |
|---|---|---|---|
| Honiara, Guadalcanal | 1035 | 6 | SIBC |
| SW | kHz | kW | Station |
| Honiara, Guadalcanal | 5020 | 10 | SIBC |
| Honiara, Guadalcanal | 9545 | 10 | SIBC |
| FM | MHz | kW | Station |
| Gizo, Gizo Isl | 96.3 | *1 | Gizo FM, SIBC |
| Honiara, Guadalcanal | 96.3 | - | Wantok FM, SIBC |
| Kirakira, Makiri Isl | 96.3 | *0.5 | - |
| Lata, Nendo Isl | 96.3 | *0.5 | Lata FM, SIBC |

**NB: F.pl.** power increase (*), and other provincial FM stations.

**Other stations:**

| FM | MHz | kW | Station |
|---|---|---|---|
| 2) Gold Ridge, Guadalcanal | 88.0 | - | Gold Ridge FM |
| 3) Honiara, Guadalcanal | 88.1 | - | Hope FM |
| 4) Honiara, Guadalcanal | 88.3 | - | Gud Nius FM |
| 5) Tetere, Guadalcanal | 89.9 | 0.06 | R. Bosco |
| 10) Honiara, Guadalcanal | 93.5 | - | Laef FM |
| 10) Munda, New Georgia | 93.5 | 0.5 | Laef FM |
| 6) Honiara, Guadalcanal | 97.7 | - | Paoa FM |
| 7) Honiara, Guadalcanal | 100.0 | - | ZFM |
| 6) Honiara, Guadalcanal | 101.7 | - | Paoa FM |
| 10) Auki, Malaita | 103.9 | - | Laef FM |
| 8) Honiara, Guadalcanal | 105.6 | - | BBC |
| 9) Honiara, Guadalcanal | 107.0 | - | R. Australia |

**Addresses & other information**
**2)** community radio funded through Gold Ridge Mining Ltd **Prgr:** 1900-1100 – **3)** Kukum SDA church, Honiara. Solomon Islands Mission Office, PO Box R145, Honiara ☎ +677 39267/39269/39281 **F:** +677 38862 **W:** facebook.com/hopefm88.1 **E:** hopefm88.1@sim.adventist.org.sb – **4)** UCB Pacific Partners, P.O. Box 1415, Honiara **W:** pacificpartners.org/christianradiointhesolomonislands **E:** solomons@pacificpartners.org **L.P:** Tina Lemozi SM **F.PI:** FM relay at Gizo and Malaita – **5)** Don Bosco Rural Training Centre, Tetere, Guadalcanal. **E:** ambrose@donbosco. org.sb – **6)** PO Box R331, Panatina Plaza, Prince Philip Hwy, Honiara ☎+677 38984 🖷+677 38980 **W:** solomonstarnews.com & facebook. com/paoafm **E:** paoafm@solomon.com.sb or paoafm.news@gmail. com **L.P:** GM Joel Lamani, News Editor: Uriel Matangani **Other:** Pacific Star newspaper – **7)** P.O. Box 100, Honiara ☎+677 21100 🖷

+677 21100 **L.P:** Sammy 'Sharzy' Saeni **E:** zfm@solomon.com.sb – **8)** 24/7 Pacific stream via satellite from London – **9)** 24/7 Pacific stream via satellite from Melbourne – **10)** Ebenezer House, Vura, Honiara. Low power outlet on 107.5 at Gizo. **FPI:** Additional stn at Kira Kira, Makira/Ulawa Province.

## SOMALIA

**L.T:** UTC +3h — **Pop:** 11 million — **Pr.L:** Somali, Rahanwein (Maay), Arabic, English — **E.C:** 50Hz, 220V — **ITU:** SOM

**MINISTRY OF INFORMATION, CULTURE & TOURISM**
✉ Mogadishu ☎ +252 612777736
**W:** moi.gov.so **E:** media@moi.gov.so

**RADIO MOGADISHU (Gov.)**
✉ Mogadishu ☎ +252 851013
**W:** radomuqdisho.net **E:** radiomogadishu@gmail.com
**FM:** Dhusomareb 87.7, Adado/Guricel 88.5, Baledweyn/Galkacyo 88.8, Abudwaq/Mogadishu 90.0, Baidoa 99.9MHz.
**D.Prgr:** 24h in Somali, incl. limited English segments. Also rel. VOA Somali.
**Ann:** "Raadiyo Muqdisho, Codka Jamhuuriyadda Soomaaliya"

**WARSAN RADIO**
✉ Baidoa **W:** warsanradio.com **E:** warsanradiobaidoa@gmail.com
**L.P:** Dir: Mr. Hilal Sheikh.
**SW:** 7750kHz AM/U 0.1kW. **FM:** 88.2MHz. **D.Prgr:** 0300-1930.

**RADIO ANDALUS**
✉ Jilib **W:** radioandalus24.com
**SW:** 7700kHz (irr.). **FM:** 88.8MHz. **D.Prgr:** 0300-0600v, 1530-1930v.

**Other stations:**
**Dalsan R:** Mogadishu 91.5MHz. **W:** dalsanradio.com
**Goal R,** Mogadishu: 99.0MHz.
**Mogadishu City R,** Mogadishu: 102.8MHz.
**Mustaqbal R:** Mogadishu 97.7MHz. **W:** mustaqbalradio.com
**R. Al Furqaan:** Mogadishu 106.5MHz. **W:** radioalfurqaan.com
**R. Banadir:** Mogadishu 103.5MHz. **W:** radiobanadir.com
**R. Danan:** Mogadishu 94.0MHz. **W:** radiodanan.net
**R. Dhusamareb:** Dhusamareb 88.5MHz.
**R. Jubba:** Mogadishu 99.5MHz. **W:** jubaradio.net
**R. Kulmiye:** Mogadishu 88.0MHz. **W:** kulmiyenews.com
**R. Manta:** Mogadishu 95.5MHz.
**R. Risaala:** Mogadishu 102.2MHz. Also rel. BBC. **W:** risaala.net
**R. Simba:** Mogadishu 95.0MHz 1kW. **W:** simbanews.com
**Star FM,** Mogadishu: 97.0MHz. See main entry under Kenya.
**STN R,** Mogadishu: 98.5MHz.
**Vo Democracy (R. Xamar):** Mogadishu: 93.5MHz **W:** xamarradio.com
**Xurmo R:** Mogadishu 96.0MHz. **W:** xurmo.net

### SOMALILAND
(self-declared autonomous state in northwest Somalia)

**RADIO HARGEISA**
✉ Nala soo xidhiidh, Head Quarter, Near SLNTV, Hargeisa. **E:** radiohargeisa@yahoo.com **L.P:** Dir: Said Adam Ege.
Hargeisa: **SW:** 7120kHz 100kW (irr.) **FM:** 89.7/98.0MHz 1kW.
**D.Prgr in Somali/Amharic/English:** 0330-2100, SW 0330-0500, 0900-1400, 1500-1900. **N.** in E: 1300, 1930.
**Ann:** "Halkani wa Radio Hargeysa, codka jamhuriyada Somaliland".

**Other Stations:**
**Koran R:** Hargeisa 88.6MHz 0.3kW.
**BBC African Sce:** Beledweyne 88.4, Burco 88.8, Baki 89.0, Kismayo 90.5, Baydhabo 90.8, Mogadishu 91.0, Marka 95.1, Jawhar 96.1, Galkacyo 96.6, Hargeisa 98.0MHz.
**VOA Africa:** Hargeisa 88.0 1kW, Mogadishu 99.9MHz.

### PUNTLAND
(self-declared autonomous state in northeast Somalia)

**PUNTLAND RADIO**
✉ Garowe. **W:** puntlandtvradio.net **E:** puntlandradio1@gmail.com
**SW:** 13800kHz 0330-0600v, 1000-1600v. 10kW AM/U (inactive).

**Other Stations:**
**Al-Xikma R:** Bacadweyn/Burtinle/Gaalkacyo/Garowe/Qardho 90.0MHz, Bosaso 92.0MHz. **W:** alxigma.piczo.com
**Horseed R:** Bosaso 89.2MHz 1kW. **W:** horseedmedia.net

**One Nation R:** Garowe 88.8MHz, Bosaso 89.5MHz.**W:** 1nationradio.com
**R. Daljir:** Burtinle/Garowe 88.0MHz, Bosaso/Buuhoodle/Cabudwaq/Qardho 88.8MHz, Galkacyo 89.1MHz **W:** radiodaljir.com
**R. Gaalkacyo:** Gaalkacyo 88.2MHz, Garowe 89.0MHz.**W:** radiogaalkacyo.net
**R. Garowe:** Eyl 88.8MHz, Garowe 89.5MHz. **W:** garoweonline.com
**R. Hobyo:** Gaalkacyo 87.5MHz. **W:** hobyoradio.com
**R. Midnimo:** Bosaso 97.5MHz.
**R. SBC:** Garowe 88.5, Qardho 88.7, Bosaso 89.9MHz. **W:** allsbc.com
**R. Voice of Mudug:** Gaalkacyo 89.5MHz **W:** codkamudug.com
**R. Voice of Peace:** Gaalkacyo 88.8MHz, Bosaso 89.5MHz
**Somali Public R:** Dhahar, fq. not known. **W:** spr.fm

## SOUTH AFRICA

**L.T**: UTC +2h — **Pop**: 58 million — **Pr.L**: English, Afrikaans, isiNdebele, isiXhosa, isiZulu, Sepedi, Sesotho, Setswana, siSwati, Tshivenda, xiTsonga, !Xu, Khwe — **E.C**: 50Hz, 230V — **ITU**: AFS

### INDEPENDENT COMMUNICATIONS AUTHORITY OF SOUTH AFRICA (ICASA)

✉ Private Bag X10002, Sandton 2146 ☎ +27 11 566 3000 **E:** info@icasa.org.za **W:** icasa.org.za
The ICASA is the regulator of telecommunications and the broadcasting sectors. It issues licences for commercial and community stns.

### SOUTH AFRICAN BROADCASTING CORPORATION (SABC) (Pub)

✉ Private Bag X1, Auckland Park 2006 ☎ +27 11 714 9111 🖷 +27 11 714 9744 **W:** sabc.co.za **Regional offices:** PO Box 2551, Cape Town 8000 – PO Box 1588, Durban 4000 – PO Box 563, Bloemfontein 9300 – PO Box 1040, Port Elizabeth 6000 – PO Box 395, Polokwane 0700 – Private Bag X11301, Nelspruit 1200 – PO Box 1008, Kimberley 8300 – Private Bag X2158, Mafikeng 2735 – PO Box 1198, Hatfield (Pretoria) 0001. **L.P.**: Chmn: Bongumusa Makhatini Group CEO: Madoda Mxakwe COO: Chris Maroleng.
**NB:** All txs belong to SENTECH (the common carrier for broadcasting in South Africa), ✉ Private Bag X06, Honeydew 2040

### MW HOME SERVICES (Comm.)

| Location | Station | kHz | kW |
|---|---|---|---|
| Komga | Umhlobo Wenene FM | 846 | 50 (irr.) |

### COUNTRYWIDE FM (Comm.)

| Limpopo FM (MHz) | R. Sonder Grense | SAfm | R. 2000 | 5 FM | R. Metro |
|---|---|---|---|---|---|
| Blouberg | 102.3 | 105.9 | - | - | - |
| Hoedspruit | 102.0 | 105.6 | 98.5 | - | - |
| Louis Trichardt | 100.7 | 104.3 | 97.2 | - | - |
| Modimolle | 102.9 | 106.5 | - | - | - |
| Mokopane | 101.4 | 105.0 | 97.9 | 91.4 | 106.7 |
| Thabazimbi | 101.9 | 105.5 | 98.4 | - | - |
| Tzaneen | 102.6 | 106.2 | 107.7 | - | - |

| NW Province FM (MHz) | R. Sonder Grense | SAfm | R. 2000 | 5 FM | R. Metro |
|---|---|---|---|---|---|
| Christiana | 103.6 | 107.2 | - | - | - |
| Groot Marico | 102.3 | 105.9 | - | - | - |
| Klerksdorp | 101.2 | 104.8 | 97.7 | - | - |
| Piet Plessis | 102.8 | 106.4 | - | - | - |
| Pomfret | 101.1 | 104.7 | - | - | - |
| Rustenburg | 100.7 | 104.3 | 97.2 | - | - |
| Schweizer-Reneke | 103.1 | 106.7 | 99.6 | - | - |
| Zeerust | 102.6 | 106.2 | 99.1 | - | - |

| Gauteng FM (MHz) | R. Sonder Grense | SAfm | R. 2000 | 5 FM | R. Metro |
|---|---|---|---|---|---|
| Heidelberg | 100.8 | 104.4 | 97.3 | - | - |
| Helderkruin | - | - | - | 104.0 | - |
| Johannesburg | 101.5 | 105.1 | 99.7 | 98.0 | 96.4 |
| Menlo Park | 102.1 | 105.7 | 98.6 | - | - |
| Pretoria | 101.0 | 104.6 | 97.5 | 89.9 | 92.4 |
| Sunnyside | - | - | - | 103.6 | - |
| Welverdiend | 102.0 | 105.6 | 104.1 | 107.3 | - |

| Mpumalanga FM (MHz) | R. Sonder Grense | SAfm | R. 2000 | 5 FM | R. Metro |
|---|---|---|---|---|---|
| Carolina | 103.0 | 106.6 | - | - | - |
| Davel | 103.5 | 107.1 | 100.0 | 90.4 | - |
| Dullstroom | 100.8 | 104.4 | - | - | - |
| Lydenburg | 102.8 | 106.4 | - | - | - |
| eMalahleni | 101.8 | 105.4 | 98.3 | 97.0 | 100.3 |
| Nelspruit | 102.5 | 106.1 | 99.0 | 91.1 | - |
| Piet Retief | 102.1 | 105.7 | - | - | - |
| Sabie | 104.2 | 107.9 | - | - | - |
| Volksrust | 102.6 | 106.2 | - | - | - |

| Northern Cape FM (MHz) | R. Sonder Grense | SAfm | R. 2000 | 5 FM | R. Metro |
|---|---|---|---|---|---|
| Alexander Bay | 102.2# | 105.8# | 98.7 | 92.2 | - |
| Calvinia | 101.5 | 105.1 | - | - | - |
| Carnavon | 102.5 | 106.1 | - | - | - |
| Colesberg | 103.8 | 107.5 | - | - | - |
| De Aar | 102.0 | 105.6 | - | - | - |
| Douglas | 102.9 | 106.5 | - | - | - |
| Faans Grove | 103.0 | 106.6 | - | - | - |
| Garies | 100.7# | 104.3# | - | - | - |
| Kimberley | 101.0 | 104.6 | 97.5 | 91.0 | - |
| Kuruman Hills | 102.4 | 106.0 | - | - | - |
| Pofadder | 102.8 | 106.4 | - | - | - |
| Prieska | 100.8 | 104.4 | - | - | - |
| Sringbok | 101.6 | 105.2 | - | - | - |
| Upington | 101.7 | 105.3 | - | - | - |
| Victoria West | 101.1 | 104.7 | - | - | - |
| Williston | 103.2 | - | - | - | - |

| Free State FM (MHz) | R. Sonder Grense | SAfm | R. 2000 | 5 FM | R. Metro |
|---|---|---|---|---|---|
| Bethlehem | 101.9 | 105.5 | 98.4 | - | - |
| Bloemfontein | 103.0 | 106.6 | 99.5 | 91.6 | 98.1 |
| Boesmanskop | 101.2 | 104.8 | - | - | - |
| Ficksburg | 103.7 | 107.3 | - | - | - |
| Kroonstad | 103.4 | 107.0 | 99.9 | 93.4 | - |
| Ladybrand | 102.1 | 105.7 | - | - | - |
| Petrus Steyn | 102.3 | 105.9 | 98.8 | - | - |
| Senekal | 101.1 | 104.7 | 97.6 | - | - |
| Springfontein | 102.6 | 106.2 | 99.1 | - | - |
| Theunissen | 102.5 | 106.1 | 99.0 | 92.5 | - |
| Witsieshoek | 101.3 | 104.9 | - | - | - |

| Kwazulu Natal FM (MHz) | R. Sonder Grense | SAfm | R. 2000 | 5 FM | R. Metro |
|---|---|---|---|---|---|
| Donnybrook | 102.7 | 106.3 | 99.2 | - | - |
| Durban | 100.8 | 104.4 | 97.3 | 89.9 | 93.0 |
| Durban North | 102.5 | 106.1 | 99.0 | 103.8 | 107.9 |
| Eshowe | 103.4 | 107.0 | 99.9 | - | 90.3 |
| Glencoe | 103.1 | 106.7 | 99.6 | - | - |
| Greytown | 101.7 | 105.3 | 98.2 | - | - |
| Kokstad | 101.0 | 104.6 | - | - | - |
| Ladysmith | 101.0 | 104.6 | 97.5 | - | - |
| Matatiele | 101.5 | 105.1 | - | - | - |
| Mooi River | 102.2 | 105.8 | 98.7 | - | - |
| Nongoma | 102.9 | 106.5 | 99.4 | - | 89.8 |
| Pietermaritzburg | 101.4 | 105.0 | 97.9 | 100.3 | - |
| Port Shepstone | 101.3 | 104.9 | 97.8 | - | - |
| The Bluff | 102.0 | 105.6 | 98.5 | 107.4 | - |
| Ubombo | 102.4 | 106.0 | 98.9 | - | - |
| Vryheid | 101.2 | 104.8 | 97.7 | - | - |

| Western Cape FM (MHz) | R. Sonder Grense | SAfm | R. 2000 | 5 FM | R. Metro |
|---|---|---|---|---|---|
| Beaufort West | 100.7@ | 104.3@ | - | - | - |
| Constantiaberg | 102.1 | 105.7 | 98.6 | 89.0 | - |
| Ceres | 103.7 | 107.3 | - | - | - |
| Franschhoek | 100.7 | 104.3 | 97.2 | - | - |
| George | 101.7 | 105.3 | 98.2 | 91.7 | - |
| Grabouw | 101.7 | 105.3 | - | - | - |
| Hermanus | 100.8 | 104.4 | - | - | - |
| Hex River | 102.0 | 105.6 | - | - | - |
| Hout Bay | 100.9 | 104.5 | 97.4 | 87.8 | - |
| Kleinmond | 104.2 | 107.9 | - | - | - |
| Knysna | 102.2 | 105.8 | 98.7 | 92.2 | - |
| Ladysmith | 101.4 | 105.0 | - | - | - |
| Matjiesfontein | 102.8 | 106.4 | - | - | - |
| Montagu | 102.4 | 107.9 | - | - | - |
| Napier | 102.4 | 106.0 | - | - | - |
| Oudtshoorn | 102.6 | 106.2 | 99.1 | 92.6 | - |
| Paarl | 101.6 | 105.2 | 98.1 | 88.5 | - |
| Piketberg | 101.1 | 104.7 | 97.6 | - | - |
| Plettenberg | 100.8 | 104.4 | - | - | - |
| Riversdale | 100.9 | 104.5 | - | - | - |
| Sea Point | 103.5 | 107.1 | 100.0 | 90.4 | 91.7 |
| Simonstown | 100.7 | 104.3 | 97.2 | 87.6 | - |
| Stellenbosch | 100.9 | 104.5 | 97.4 | 87.8 | - |
| Table Mountain | 102.6 | 106.2 | 99.1 | 89.9 | 88.6 |
| Tygerberg | 103.0 | 106.6 | 99.5 | 88.2 | 93.0 |
| Uniondale | 103.4 | 107.0 | - | - | - |
| Vanrhynsdorp | 103.4 | 107.0 | - | - | - |
| Villiersdorp | 103.3 | 106.9 | 99.8 | - | - |

| Eastern Cape FM (MHz) | R. Sonder Grense | SAfm | R. 2000 | 5 FM | R. Metro |
|---|---|---|---|---|---|
| Aliwal North | 101.7 | 105.3 | - | - | - |
| Andrieskraal | 103.2 | 106.8 | - | - | - |

| Eastern Cape FM (MHz) | R. Sonder Grense | SAfm | R. 2000 | 5 FM | R. Metro |
|---|---|---|---|---|---|
| Barkly East | 100.9 | 104.5 | - | - | - |
| Bedford | 100.8 | 104.4 | - | - | - |
| Burgersdorp | 103.9 | 107.6 | - | - | - |
| Butterworth | 101.1 | 104.7 | 97.6 | - | - |
| Cala | 103.4 | 107.0 | - | - | - |
| Cradock | 102.7 | 106.3 | - | - | - |
| East London | 101.6 | 105.2 | 98.1 | 88.5 | 107.7 |
| Elliot | 101.4 | 105.0 | - | - | - |
| Graaff-Reinet | 103.3 | 106.9 | - | - | - |
| Grahamstown | 103.5 | 107.1 | 100.0 | 90.4 | - |
| Hankey | 101.0 | 104.6 | - | - | - |
| Kareedouw | 102.9 | 106.5 | - | - | - |
| King Williams Tn | 103.0 | 106.6 | - | - | - |
| Mount Ayliff | 103.2 | 106.8 | 99.7 | - | - |
| Noupoort | 101.4 | 105.0 | - | - | - |
| Patensie | 101.5 | 105.0 | - | - | - |
| Parsons Hill (PE) | 101.0 | 104.6 | 97.5 | - | 87.9 |
| Paul Sauer Dam | 103.6 | 107.2 | - | - | - |
| Port Elizabeth | 102.3 | 105.9 | 98.8 | 89.2 | 100.5 |
| Port St.Johns | 103.7 | 107.3 | 100.2 | - | - |
| Queenstown | 102.2 | 105.8 | 98.7 | - | - |
| Suurberg | 101.8 | 105.4 | - | - | - |
| Ugie | 102.6 | 106.2 | - | - | - |
| Umtata | 102.0 | 105.6 | 98.5 | - | - |
| Willowmore | 101.2 | 104.8 | - | - | - |

\# = mono – no RDS @ = mono RDS

**NATIONAL SW SERVICES:** Meyerton (G.C: 26S35 028E08): 4 x 100kW txs + 1 standby tx

| kHz | Sce | H of tr |
|---|---|---|
| 3320 | RSG | 1700(1800*)-0600(0500*) |
| 7285 | RSG | 0500(0600*)-0800 (0700*), 1500(1600*)-1700(1800*) |
| 7330 | RSG | 0800*-1600* |
| 9650 | RSG | 0700-1500 |

* = from 28 Oct 2018 to 30 Mar 2019
RSG=R. Sonder Grense (tr for Northern Cape region) – details below.

**SABC PUBLIC BROADCASTING SERVICES (PBS) (Comm.)**
**Ikwekwezi FM** (isiNdebele): ✉ P.O.Box 11620, Hatfield 0028 **W:** ikwekwezifm.co.za ☎+27 12 431 5477 ✆+27 12 431 5312 - **FM**(MHz): Middelburg 91.8/Pretoria 96.8/Dullstroom 107.7/Johannesburg 106.3/Davel 94.5 + 4 rel. – **Lesedi FM** (Sesotho): ✉ PO Box 20707, Bloemfontein 9300 **W:** lesedifm.co.za ☎+27 51 503 3090 ✆+27 51 503 3269 - **FM**(MHz): Bloemfontein 89.9/Durban 106.6/Johannesburg 88.4/Kroonstad 90.3MHz + 13 rel. – **Ligwalagwala FM** (siSwati): ✉ Private Bag X11301, Nelspruit 1200 **W:** ligwalagwalafm.co.za ☎+27 13 759 6611 ✆+27 13 755 3865 - **FM**(MHz): Nelspruit 92.5/Pretoria 89.3MHz + 9 FM rel. – **Lotus FM** ✉ PO Box 1588, Durban 4000 **W:** lotusfm co.za ☎ +27 31 362 5444 - **FM**(MHz): Durban 87.7/Johannesburg 106.8/Pretoria 100.6 + 8 rel. – **Motsweding FM** (Setswana): ✉ Private Bag X2150, Mmabatho 2735 **W:** motswedingfm.co.za ☎+27 18 389 7111 ✆+27 18 389 7326 - **FM**(MHz): Mmabatho 88.7/Johannesburg 89.6/Bloemfontein 93.0/Pretoria 91.0/Rustenburg 87.6MHz + 23 rel. – **Munghana Lonene FM** (xiTsonga): ✉ PO Box 395, Polokwane 0700 **W:** munghanalonenefm.co.za ☎+27 15 290 0262 ✆+27 15 290 0171 - **FM**(MHz): Johannesburg 103.2/Pretoria 95.6/Tzaneen 92.6/Nelspruit 89.4MHz + 4 rel. – **Phalaphala FM** (Tshivenda): ✉ PO Box 985, Polokwane 0700 **W:** phalaphalafm.co.za ☎+27 15 290 0260 ✆+27 15 290 0170 - **FM**(MHz): Johannesburg 107.8/Pretoria 100.1/Tzaneen 99.1MHz + 11 rel. – **Radio Sonder Grense** (National service in Afrikaans): ✉ PO Box 91312, Auckland Park 2006 **W:** rsg.co.za ☎+27 11 714 2702 ✆+27 11 714 3472 - on FM and SW as above – **Radio X-K FM** (in !Xu and Khwe languages for Khoi San communities in N.Cape): ✉ PO Box 1008, Kimberley 8300 ☎+27 53 831 8131 ✆+27 53 831 8127 - **FM**(MHz): Schmidtsdrift 99.4/Kimberley 107.9 – **R.2000** ✉ Private Bag X1, Auckland Park 2006 **W:** radio2000.co.za ☎+27 11 714 4085 - **FM:** (as above) – **SAfm** (Nat. sce in English): ✉ PO Box 91162, Auckland Park 2006 **W:** safm.co.za ☎ +27 11 714 4442 ✆+27 11 714 5829 - **FM:** (as above) – **Thobela FM** (Sepedi): ✉ PO Box 395, Polokwane 0700 **W:** thobelafm.co.za ☎+27 15 290 0264 ✆+27 15 290 0172 - **FM**(MHz): Johannesburg 90.1/Pretoria 87.9/Tzaneen 89.5MHz + 9 rel. – **TruFM** (isiXhosa & English): ✉ Private Bag X0037, Bhisho 5605 **W:** trufm.co.za ☎+27 40 609 1800 ✆+27 40 636 4112 - **FM**(MHz): East London 104.1/Bhisho 100.0 + 2 rel. – **Ukhozi FM** (isiZulu): ✉ PO Box 1588, Durban 4000 **W:** ukhozifm.co.za ☎+27 31 362 5111 ✆+27 31 362 5203 - **FM**(MHz): Durban 90.8, 92.0, 92.5/Johannesburg 91.5/Pretoria 102.4MHz + 21 rel. – **Umhlobo Wenene FM** (isiXhosa): ✉ PO Box 1040, Port

Elizabeth 6000 **W:** umhlobowenene.co.za ☎+27 41 391 1911 ✆+27 41 374 3708 - **FM**(MHz): Port Elizabeth 92.3/King Williams Town 93.0/Durban 96.2/Johannesburg 93.2/Cape Town 92.1MHz + 47 FM rel.

**SABC COMMERCIAL BROADCASTING SERVICES (CBS) (Comm.)**
**Good Hope FM** ✉ PO Box 2551, Cape Town 8000 ☎ +27 21 430 8276 ✆ +27 21 434 3392 **W:** goodhopefm.co.za - **FM:** Cape Town 95.3MHz + 7 rel – **R. Metro FM** ✉ PO Box 91136, Auckland Park 2006 **W:** metrofm.co.za ☎ +27 89 110 3377 ✆ +27 11 714 4166 - **FM:** (as above) – **5 FM** ✉ PO Box 91555, Auckland Park 2006 ☎+27 11 714 2905 ✆+27 11 714 5714 **W:** 5fm.co.za - **FM:** (as above)

**EXTERNAL SERVICE: Channel Africa:** See Int. Broadcasting Section

**PRIVATE STATIONS (Comm.)**

| MW | kHz | kW | Station | Location |
|---|---|---|---|---|
| 1) | 567 | 25 | Cape Talk | Kliphuewel (Cape Town) |
| 20) | 702 | 50 | LM R. | Springs |
| 21) | 828 | 25 | Magic 828 AM | Kliphuewel (Cape Town) |

| FM | MHz | kW | Station | Location |
|---|---|---|---|---|
| 15) | 88.1 | - | Heart FM | Overberg |
| 12) | 88.6 | 10 | Gagasi FM | Greytown |
| 15) | 88.8 | - | Heart FM | Overstrand |
| 2) | 89.0 | 8.9 | Rise FM | Piet Retief |
| 12) | 89.1 | 10 | Gagasi FM | Mooi River |
| 2) | 89.7 | 0.01 | Rise FM | Mashishing |
| 3) | 89.8 | 4 | North West FM | Rustenburg |
| 4) | 89.9 | - | Capricorn FM | Thohoyandou |
| 18) | 90.4 | 10 | Smile FM | Cape Town |
| 7) | 91.5 | - | KFM | Camps Bay |
| 4) | 91.7 | - | Capricorn FM | Pankop |
| 3) | 91.8 | 10 | North West FM | Mmabatho |
| 3) | 91.9 | 5 | North West FM | Taung |
| 5) | 92.7 | 3.5 | Talk R. 702 | Johannesburg |
| 3) | 93.5 | 11 | North West FM | Zeerust |
| 6) | 93.7 | 0.5 | OFM | Sasolburg |
| 7) | 93.9 | 10 | KFM | Beaufort West |
| 7) | 93.9 | 3 | KFM | Garies |
| 8) | 93.9 | 4 | R. Jacaranda | Rustenburg |
| 8) | 93.9 | 15 | R. Jacaranda | Louis Trichardt |
| 9) | 94.0 | 0.04 | Algoa FM | Plettenberg Bay |
| 9) | 94.0 | 5 | Algoa FM | Bedford |
| 8) | 94.0 | 10 | R. Jacaranda | Dullstroom |
| 6) | 94.0 | 9 | OFM | Prieska |
| 6) | 94.0 | 0.65 | OFM | Potchefstroom |
| 10) | 94.0 | 25 | East Coast R. | Durban |
| 11) | 94.0 | 0.1 | Highveld Stereo | Heidelberg |
| 7) | 94.0 | 0.1 | KFM | Hermanus |
| 7) | 94.1 | 13 | KFM | Riversdale |
| 8) | 94.2 | 110 | R. Jacaranda | Pretoria |
| 9) | 94.2 | 0.01 | Algoa FM | Hankey |
| 10) | 94.2 | 0.05 | Kokstad | East Coast R. |
| 10) | 94.2 | 0.1 | East Coast R. | Ladysmith |
| 6) | 94.3 | 10 | OFM | Kimberley |
| 6) | 94.3 | 10 | OFM | Senekal |
| 7) | 94.3 | 10 | KFM | Piketberg |
| 2) | 94.3 | 12 | Rise FM | Nelspruit |
| 9) | 94.3 | 0.2 | Algoa FM | Knysna |
| 10) | 94.4 | 10 | East Coast R. | Vryheid |
| 6) | 94.4 | 22 | OFM | Bosmanskop |
| 6) | 94.4 | 10 | OFM | Klerksdorp |
| 10) | 94.5 | 10 | East Coast R. | Port Shepstone |
| 7) | 94.5 | 1.3 | KFM | Tygerberg |
| 7) | 94.6 | 2.5 | KFM | Ladismith |
| 8) | 94.6 | 10 | R. Jacaranda | Mokopane |
| 10) | 94.6 | 0.3 | East Coast R. | Pietermaritzburg |
| 9) | 94.6 | 10 | Algoa FM | Noupoort |
| 12) | 94.7 | 30 | Gagasi FM | Ulundi |
| 12) | 94.7 | - | Gagasi FM | Richards Bay |
| 10) | 94.7 | 12 | East Coast R. | Matatiele |
| 11) | 94.7 | 38 | Highveld Stereo | Johannesburg |
| 7) | 94.7 | 10 | KFM | Calvinia |
| 7) | 94.8 | 10 | KFM | Springbok |
| 2) | 94.8 | 8.9 | Rise FM | Carolina |
| 8) | 94.8 | 0.3 | R. Jacaranda | Enzelberg |
| 9) | 94.8 | 10 | Algoa FM | East London |
| 9) | 94.8 | 0.01 | Algoa FM | Patensie |
| 7) | 94.9 | 0.01 | KFM | Grabow |
| 7) | 94.9 | 10 | KFM | George |
| 6) | 94.9 | 8 | OFM | Upington |
| 10) | 94.9 | 10 | East Coast R. | Greytown |
| 9) | 94.9 | 10 | Algoa FM | Aliwal North |

| FM | MHz | kW | Station | Location |
|---|---|---|---|---|
| 9) | 94.9 | - | Algoa FM | Barkley East |
| 9) | 95.0 | - | Algoa FM | Somerset East |
| 9) | 95.0 | 11 | Algoa FM | Port Elizabeth |
| 8) | 95.0 | 11 | R. Jacaranda | Middelburg |
| 6) | 95.1 | 10 | OFM | Bethlehem |
| 8) | 95.1 | 11 | R. Jacaranda | Thabazimbi |
| 8) | 95.2 | 18 | R. Jacaranda | Hoedspruit |
| 7) | 95.2 | 0.2 | KFM | Hex River |
| 11) | 95.2 | 20 | Highveld Stereo | Welverdiend |
| 10) | 95.2 | 0.1 | East Coast R. | The Bluff |
| 8) | 95.3 | 0.04 | R. Jacaranda | Menlo Park |
| 8) | 95.3 | 9 | R. Jacaranda | Piet Retief |
| 6) | 95.3 | 10 | OFM | Ladybrand |
| 9) | 95.4 | 12 | Algoa FM | Queenstown |
| 10) | 95.4 | 10 | East Coast R. | Mooi River |
| 7) | 95.4 | 0.05 | KFM | Alexander Bay |
| 7) | 95.4 | 0.2 | KFM | Knysna |
| 8) | 95.5 | 0.13 | R. Jacaranda | Groot Marico |
| 8) | 95.5 | 0.2 | R. Jacaranda | Blouberg |
| 6) | 95.5 | 11 | OFM | Petrus Steyn |
| 9) | 95.5 | - | Algoa FM | Jeffreys Bay |
| 9) | 95.5 | 16 | Algoa FM | Port Elizabeth |
| 10) | 95.6 | 15 | East Coast R. | Ubombo |
| 6) | 95.6 | 11 | OFM | Kuruman Hills |
| 7) | 95.6 | 3 | KFM | Napier |
| 7) | 95.6 | 2.5 | KFM | Ladismith |
| 10) | 95.7 | 6 | East Coast R. | Durban North |
| 8) | 95.7 | 12 | R. Jacaranda | Nelspruit |
| 6) | 95.7 | 10 | OFM | Theunissen |
| 7) | 95.7 | 10 | KFM | Carnarvon |
| 7) | 95.8 | 9 | KFM | Oudtshoorn |
| 8) | 95.8 | 10 | R. Jacaranda | Volksrust |
| 8) | 95.8 | 11 | R. Jacaranda | Zeerust |
| 8) | 95.8 | 12 | R. Jacaranda | Tzaneen |
| 6) | 95.8 | - | OFM | Colesberg |
| 10) | 95.9 | 10 | East Coast R. | Donnybrook |
| 9) | 95.9 | 12 | Algoa FM | Cradock |
| 13) | 95.9 | 35 | Kaya FM | Johannesburg |
| 8) | 96.0 | 0.01 | R. Jacaranda | Lydenburg |
| 9) | 96.0 | - | Algoa FM | Albertinia |
| 9) | 96.0 | 10 | Algoa FM | George |
| 4) | 96.0 | 10 | Capricorn FM | Mokopane |
| 7) | 96.0 | 10 | KFM | Matjiesfontein |
| 7) | 96.0 | 5 | KFM | Pofadder |
| 6) | 96.1 | 9 | OFM | Douglas |
| 8) | 96.1 | 0.2 | R. Jacaranda | Modimole |
| 10) | 96.1 | 10 | East Coast R. | Nongoma |
| 9) | 96.1 | 6 | Algoa FM | Kareedouw |
| 9) | 96.2 | 10 | Algoa FM | King Williams Town |
| 6) | 96.2 | 10 | OFM | Bloemfontein |
| 8) | 96.2 | 9 | R. Jacaranda | Carolina |
| 10) | 96.3 | 10 | East Coast R. | Glencoe |
| 6) | 96.3 | 10 | OFM | Schweitzer-Reineke |
| 9) | 96.4 | 0.01 | Algoa FM | Andrieskraal |
| 9) | 96.5 | 10 | Algoa FM | Graaf-Reinet |
| 7) | 96.5 | 10 | KFM | Villiersdorp |
| 7) | 96.6 | 17 | KFM | Vanrhynsdorp |
| 10) | 96.6 | 10 | East Coast R. | Eshowe |
| 6) | 96.6 | 10 | OFM | Kroonstad |
| 9) | 96.7 | - | Algoa FM | Port Elizabeth |
| 9) | 96.7 | - | Algoa FM | Port Alfred |
| 9) | 96.7 | 10 | Algoa FM | Grahamstown |
| 8) | 96.7 | 10 | R. Jacaranda | Davel |
| 6) | 96.8 | 11 | OFM | Christiana |
| 10) | 96.9 | 1 | East Coast R. | Newcastle |
| 7) | 96.9 | 20 | KFM | Ceres |
| 6) | 96.9 | 0.01 | OFM | Ficksburg |
| 3) | 97.0 | 10 | North West FM | Klerksdorp |
| 8) | 97.1 | 0.02 | R. Jacaranda | Sabie |
| 7) | 97.1 | 0.08 | KFM | Kleinmond |
| 7) | 97.1 | 0.02 | KFM | Montagu |
| 3) | 97.3 | 10- | North West FM | Schweitzer Reneke |
| 4) | 97.6 | 12 | Capricorn FM | Tzaneen |
| 4) | 98.0 | 18 | Capricorn FM | Hoedspruit |
| 12) | 98.5 | 0.1 | Gagasi FM | Pietermaritzburg |
| 17) | 98.7 | 11 | Power FM | Johannesburg |
| 14) | 99.2 | 35 | Y-FM | Johannesburg |
| 3) | 99.4 | - | North West FM | Potchefstroom |
| 12) | 99.5 | 25 | Gagasi FM | Durban |
| 15) | 100.0 | 0.02 | Heart FM | Fishhoek |
| 12) | 100.1 | 6 | Gagasi FM | Durban North |
| 7) | 100.1 | - | KFM | Hout Bay |

| FM | MHz | kW | Station | Location |
|---|---|---|---|---|
| 2) | 101.6 | 10 | Rise FM | Dullstroom |
| 15) | 102.7 | 0.1 | Heart FM | Paarl |
| 16) | 102.7 | 35 | Classic FM | Durban |
| 19) | 103.0 | 5 | Vuma FM | Umhlanga |
| 12) | 103.5 | 10 | Gagasi FM | Port Shepstone |
| 3) | 103.9 | 8 | North West FM | Garankuwa |
| 15) | 104.9 | 0.25 | Heart FM | Tygerberg |
| 4) | 105.4 | 15 | Capricorn FM | Makhado |
| 2) | 105.8 | 10 | Rise FM | Davel |
| 5) | 106.0 | 33 | Talk R. 702 | Pretoria |
| 15) | 106.3 | - | Heart FM | West Coast |
| 2) | 106.4 | 11 | Rise FM | eMalahleni |
| 15) | 107.0 | 0.02 | Heart FM | Hout Bay |
| 7) | 107.2 | - | KFM | Stellenbosch |
| 15) | 107.8 | 0.01 | Heart FM | Grabow |
| 12) | 107.9 | - | Gagasi FM | Newcastle |

**Addresses & other information:**

**1)** Private Bag 567, Vlaeberg 8018 ☎ +27 21 446 4700 ▤ +27 21 446 4800 **W:** capetalk.co.za **E:** ChanelP@capetalk.co.za – **2)** Shop 38, The Grove Shopping Centre, Cnr. R40 & George St., Riverside Park, Nelspruit, 1201 ☎ +27 13 757 0263 **LP:** Mark Schormann **W:** risefm.co.za **E:** info@risefm.co.za – **3)** 17 Kgwebo Ave., Unit 1 Delta Place, Mabe Business Park, Rustenburg 0300 ☎ +27 14 594 8960 ▤ +27 14 597 3345 **LP:** Lawrence Tlhabane **W:** northwestfm.co.za **E:** admin@northwestfm.co.za – **4)** Postnet Suite 93, Private Bag X9676, Polokwane, 0700 ☎ +27 15 590 0900 **LP:** Simphiwe Mdlalose **W:** capricornfm.co.za **E:** info@capricornfm.co.za – **5)** PO Box 5572, Rivonia 2128. ☎ +27 (11) 506 3663 **W:** 702.co.za **E:** comment@702.co.za – **6)** PO Box 7117, Bloemfontein 9300 ☎ +27 51 505 0900 ▤ +27 51 505 0905 **LP:** Gary Stroebel **W:** ofm.co.za **E:** info@ofm.co.za – **7)** Private Bag X945, Cape Town, 8000 ☎ +27 21 446 4700 **W:** kfm.co.za **E:** kfm@kfm.co.za – **8)** PO Box 11961, Centurion 0046 ☎ +27 11 063 5700 **LP:** Alan Khan **W:** jacarandafm.com **E:** enquiries@jacarandafm.com – **9)** PO Box 5973, Walmer, 6065 ☎ +27 41 505 9497 **LP:** Dave Tiltmann **W:** algoafm.co.za **E:** info@algoafm.co.za – **10)** P.O. Box 25095, Gateway, Umhlanga Rocks 4321 ☎ +27 31 570 9495 ▤ +27 86 679 4951. **LP:** Trish Taylor **W:** ecr.co.za **E:** auntyhazel@ecr.co.za – **11)** PO Box 3438, Rivonia 2128 ☎ +27 11 506 3947 ▤ +27 86 501 2014 **LP:** Tery Volkwyn **W:** 947.co.za **E:** webmaster947@947.co.za – **12)** 6 Zenith Drive, Solstice, Umhlanga New Town Centre 4319 ☎ +27 31 580 5300 ▤ +27 31 566 3403 **LP:** Pearl Sokhulu **W:** gagasifm.co.za **E:** management@gagasifm.co.za – **13)** PO Box 395, Parklands, 2121 **W:** kayafm.co.za ☎ +27 11 634 9500 **LP:** Charlene Deacon **E:** pr@kayafm.co.za – **14)** Dunkeld Cresc., 4 Albury Rd., Hyde Park, 2183 ☎ +27 11 772 0800 ▤ +27 11 280 0421 **LP:** Kanthan Pillay **W:** yworld.co.za **E:** digital@yfm.co.za – **15)** Second Floor, Media Centre, Greenpoint 8051 ☎ +27 21 406 8900 **LP:** Gavin Meiring **W:** 1049.fm **E:** info@1049.fm – **16)** PO Box 782, Auckland Park 2006 ☎ +27 11 403 1027 **LP:** Mike Ford **W:** classicfm.co.za **E:** info@classicfm.co.za – **17)** PO Box 3187, Houghton 2041 **W:** powerfm.co.za **E:** info@powerfm.co.za **LP:** Dawn Klatzko ☎ +27 11 014 9000 – **18)** PO Box 50194, Waterfront, 8002 ☎+27 21 818 8904 ▤+27 21 818 8810 **W:** smile904.fm **E:** lois@smile904.fm – **19)** 6th Floor, Centenary Building, Cnr. Equinox & Zenith Dr., Umhlanga New Town Centre, Unhlanga Rocks, 4319 ☎+27 31 833 3000 **W:** vumafm.co.za **E:** info@vumafm.co.za – **20)** Genesis House, 18 Wessel Road, Rivonia ☎+27 11 234 2691 **W:** lmradio.co.za **E:** sales@lmradio.net - **21)** DBN Gardens, Golf Park, 45 Raapenberg Rd., Mowbray, 7700 ☎+27 21 001 828 **W:** magic828.am **E:** info@magic828.am

## COMMUNITY AND RELIGIOUS STATIONS

Numerous licences issued by ICASA with about 150 stns currently on the air, mainly on FM, most of them low power.

| MW | kHz | kW | Station | Location |
|---|---|---|---|---|
| 1) | 576 | 50 | R. Veritas | Meyerton |
| 2) | 657 | 50 | R. Pulpit/R.Kansel | Meyerton |
| 7) | 729 | 25 | Cape Pulpit | Cape Town |
| 3) | 1269 | 2 | Arrowline Chinese R. | Edenvale |
| 9) | 1368 | 0.6 | Eden R. | Edenvale |
| 4) | 1422 | 1 | Hellenic R. | Bedfordview |
| 5) | 1485 | 1 | R. Today | Honeydew |
| 6) | 1548 | 10 | R. Islam | Lenasia |
| 8) | 1584 | 0.25 | R. 1584 | Laudium (Pretoria) |

**Addresses & other information:**

**1)** PO Box 4599, Edenvale 1610 **W:** radioveritas.co.za ☎ +27 11 663 4700 ▤ +27 11 452 7625 **LP:** Fr. Emil Blaser OP – **2)** 42 Jakobus Street, Kilner Park, 0186 **W:** radiokansel.co.za or radiopulpit.co.za **E:** gospel@radiopulpit.co.za ☎ +27 12 334 1200 ▤ +27 86 663 0766 Relig. prgrs in English, Afrikaans and other African languages, 24h – **3)** PO Box 2241, Edenvale 1610 **W:** arrowline.co.za **E:** info@arrowline.co.za ☎ +27 11 454 5808 ▤ +27 86 242 5838 prgrs in Chinese, 0400-2200 – **4)** PO

Box 4077, Edenvale 1610 ☎ +27 11 453 3786 🖷 +27 11 453 3778 **W:** hellenicradio.org.za **E:** info@hellenicradio.org.za **LP:** Tulla Critsotakis, Prgrs in Greek and English 24h – **5)** 3rd floor, Bellairs Shopping Centre, Cor. Bellairs & Malibongwe Rds., Northriding, 2162**W:** radiotoday.co.za ☎ +27 87 985 0297 🖷 +27 86 601 2950 **E:** daryl@radiotoday.co.za **LP:** Daryl Peel, Prgrs in English for over 50s, rel. BBCWS 2300-0500, 24h – **6)** PO Box 2580, Lenasia, 1820 **W:** radioislam.org.za **E:** isv@radioislam.co.za ☎ +27 11 854 7022 🖷 +27 11 854 7024 Prgrs in English, 24h – **7)** 2nd floor, Santyger Building, Willie van Schoor Drive, Bellville, 7535 ☎+27 21 917 7000 🖷+27 21 914 1351 **W:** capepulpit.co.za **E:** gospel@capepulpit.co.za, relig. prgrs in English, Afrikaans, Zulu and Xhoza, 24h – **8)** 330 Carmine St., Laudium, 0037 ☎+27 12 374 1584 🖷+27 12 374 2488 **W:** radio1584.co.za **E:** islamic1584@gmail.com, prgrs of Institute for Islamic Services, 24h – **9)** Park Meadows Shopping Centre, Cor. Cumberland & Allum Rds., Bedfordview, 2416 ☎ +27 83 324 1143 **W:** edenradio.co.za **E:** studio@edenradio.co.za **LP:** Roarke Lessing, Stn.Manager, 24h

## SOUTH SUDAN

**L.T:** UTC +3h — **Pop:** 13 million — **Pr.L:** English (official), Dinka, Juba Arabic — **E.C:** 50Hz, 230V — **ITU:** SSD

**SOUTH SUDAN MEDIA AUTHORITY**
🖃 Juba ☎+211 955 010 147 **L.P:** MD: Elijah Alier Kuai.

**SOUTH SUDAN BROADCASTING CORPORATION (SSBC, Gov.)**
🖃 P.O. Box 126, Juba ☎+211 912 452275 **L.P:** DG: Mr. Arop Bagat. Dir. of Eng: Kamil Ramadan.
**MW:** Juba 693kHz 40kW (inactive). **FM:** Bentiu 99.0MHz, Juba 105.0MHz, Kwajok 99.0MHz, Rumbek 98.0MHz. **D.Prgr:** 693kHz: 0300-0700 & 1300-1830.
**Vo Eastern Equatoria State:** Torit/Kapoeta 97.5MHz.
**Yambio FM,** Western Equatoria State: 90.0MHz 1kW.
**F.PI:** 693 kHz transmitter to be repaired.

**RADIO MIRAYA** (operated by UN Mission in South Sudan)
**N.B:** operation suspended in early 2018 by South Sudan Media Authority.
🖃 c/o UNMISS, Tongping, Juba, Central Equatoria State ☎+211 912 062616 **W:** radio-miraya.org facebook.com/radiomiraya **E:** mirayafm@un.org **LP:** Chief of Op: Ratomir Petrovic. Head of Tech. Op: Sonam Tobgyal.
**FM:** Bor/Juba/Malakal/Rumbek/Wau 5kW, Aweil/Bentiu/Bunj/Ezo/Melut/Naseer/Pibor/Turalei 1kW, all on 101.0MHz, Kuajok/Torit/Yambio/Yei 101.5 1kW, Ar-Rank/Raja/Gok-Machar 101.0 250W, Kapoeta/Maridi/Mundri 101.5 250W. 24h in Arabic and English.

**EYE RADIO** (joint project of Internews and Eye Media)
🖃 P.O. Box 425, Plot 48, Block 1 Korok, Juba ☎ +211 924 486980 **W:** eyeradio.org **LP:** CEO: Stephen Omiri.
**FM:** Juba 98.6 2kW, Aweil/Bor/Rumbek/Wau 88.6,Kuajok 88.8, Torit 98.8, Yambio 89.0, all 500W.

**CATHOLIC RADIO NETWORK (Rlg.)**
🖃 P.O. Box 258, Hai Jerusalem, Juba ☎ +211 924 217188 **W:** catholicradionetwork.org **E:** crn.director@gmail.com **LP:** Dir: Enrica Valentini. **Stations: Bakhita R,** Juba: 91.0 – **Easter R,** Yei: 94.0 1kW – **Good News R,** Rumbek: 89.0 2.5kW – **R. Anisa,** Yambio: 92.0 – **R. Don Bosco,** Tonj: 91.0 2kW – **R. Emmanuel,** Torit: 89.0 – **Vo Hope,** Wau: 98.65 – **Vo Love,** Malakal: 93.6 2kW – **Vo Peace,** Gidel: 107.9.

**INTERNEWS** stations: **Akol Yam,** Aweil 91.0 – **JamJang FM,** Ajuong Thok 89.4 600W – **Kondial FM,** Bentiu 97.2 600W – **Mayardit FM,** Turalei 90.7 1kW – **Mingkaman 100 FM,** Mingkaman: 100.0 MHz – **Nile FM,** Malakal: 98.0 600W – **Nhomlaau FM,** Malualkon 88.0 1kW – **Singaita FM,** Kapoeta 88.0 1.5kW **W:** internews.org – **Vo Freedom,** Magwi: 93.0 **W:** facebook.com/93fm-Voice-of-Freedom-Magwi-741739775952307

**Other Stations (FM** MHz**):**
**Capital FM,** Juba: 89.0 **W:** capitalfmjuba.com – **City FM,** Juba: 88.4 **W:** facebook.com/88.4CityFmJuba – **Dream FM,** Juba: 90.6 **W:** facebook.com/pages/Dream-FM-906-Juba/765092860188519 – **Malakal FM,** Malakal: 105.0 – **Nehemiah Trumpet Call R,** Nimule: 97.3 350W **W:** operationsnehemiah.org/#!nehemiah-gospel-radio-973-fm/cis7 – **Malakal FM,** Malakal: 105.0 – **R. Jonglei,** Bor: 95.9 **W:** facebook.com/RadioJonglei959Fm – **R. Magwi,** Magwi: 92.5 – **R. One,** Juba: 87.9 **W:** facebook.com/RadioOneSouthSudan – **Raja FM,** Raja: 95.0 – **Spirit FM,** Yei: 99.9 – **Wau FM,** Wau: 88.6

**BBC World Sce:** Juba 88.2 (English), Juba/Malakal/Wau 90.0 (Arabic).
**R.France Int/Monte-Carlo Doualiya:** Juba 90.4MHz.
**VOA Africa:** Juba 93.5MHz

## SPAIN

**L.T:** UTC +1h (31 Mar-27 Oct: +2h) — **Pop:** 40.5 million — **Pr.L:** Castilian, Catalan, Galician, Basque — **E.C:** 50Hz, 230V — **ITU:** E

**MINISTERIO DE FOMENTO**
Secretaría General de Comunicaciones
🖃 Paseo de la Castellana, 67, Palacio de Comunicaciones, 28071 Madrid **W:** fomento.gob.es **E:** fomento@fomento.es

**COMISIÓN NACIONAL DE LOS MERCADOS Y LA COMPETENCIA**
🖃 Directorate for Telecommunications and Audiovisual, Carrer de Bolívia 56, 08018 Barcelona ☎ +34 93 6036126 **E:** internacional-dtysa@cnmc.es **W:** www.cnmc.es **LP:** Dir (Directorate for Telecommunications and Audiovisual): Alejandra de Iturriaga

**RADIO NACIONAL DE ESPAÑA (RNE) (Pub)**
🖃 Casa de la Radio, Avenida de la Radio y la Televisión, 4, Prado del Rey, 28223 Pozuelo de Alarcón
☎ +34 91 581 70 00 🖷 +34 91 346 1769 **W:** rne.es **E:** rtve.dircom@rtve.es
**RNE1** (R. Nacional) and **RNE5** (R. 5 Todo Noticias)

| MW | kHz | kW | Net | Rg | Location |
|---|---|---|---|---|---|
| AS01 | 531 | 20 | RNE5 | AS | Oviedo ° |
| AN02 | 531 | 10 | RNE5 | AN | Córdoba |
| GA02 | 531 | 10 | RNE5 | GA | Pontevedra |
| NA01 | 531 | 10 | RNE5 | NA | Pamplona ° |
| VA01 | 558 | 50 | RNE5 | VA | València ° |
| GA01 | 558 | 20 | RNE5 | GA | A Coruña ° |
| EU02 | 558 | 20 | RNE5 | EU | Donosti-San Sebastián |
| MU01 | 567 | 50 | RNE5 | MU | Murcia ° |
| CA01 | 576 | 100 | RNE5 | CA | Barcelona ° |
| MA01 | 585 | 600 | RNE1 | MA | Madrid ° |
| AN01 | 603 | 50 | RNE1 | AN | Sevilla ° |
| CL02 | 603 | 10 | RNE1 | CL | Palencia |
| CA02 | 612 | 10 | RNE1 | CA | Lleida (relay) |
| EU01 | 612 | 10 | RNE1 | EU | Vitoria-Gasteiz ° |
| AN04 | 621 | 10 | RNE1 | AN | Jaén (relay) |
| BA01 | 621 | 10 | RNE1 | BA | Palma de Mallorca ° |
| CL03 | 621 | 10 | RNE1 | CL | Avila (relay) |
| GA01 | 639 | 300 | RNE1 | GA | A Coruña ° |
| AR01 | 639 | 50 | RNE1 | AR | Zaragoza ° |
| EU03 | 639 | 50 | RNE1 | EU | Bilbo-Bilbao (relay) |
| AN05 | 639 | 20 | RNE1 | AN | Almería (relay) |
| CM03 | 639 | 10 | RNE1 | CM | Albacete (relay) |
| EX02 | 648 | 10 | RNE1 | EX | Badajoz (relay) |
| MA01 | 657 | 50 | RNE5 | MA | Madrid ° |
| AN01 | 684 | 600 | RNE1 | AN | Sevilla ° |
| AS01 | 693 | 5 | RNE1 | AS | Boal (rel. of Oviedo) |
| CM01 | 693 | 20 | RNE1 | CM | Toledo ° |
| CA03 | 693 | 10 | RNE1 | CA | Tortosa (rel.of Catalunya) |
| AS01 | 729 | 100 | RNE1 | AS | Oviedo ° |
| AN06 | 729 | 20 | RNE1 | AN | Málaga |
| RI01 | 729 | 20 | RNE1 | RI | Logroño ° |
| CL01 | 729 | 10 | RNE1 | CL | Valladolid ° |
| CM04 | 729 | 10 | RNE1 | CM | Cuenca |
| VA02 | 729 | 10 | RNE1 | VA | Alacant-Alicante (relay) |
| CA01 | 738 | 600 | RNE1 | CA | Barcelona ° |
| AN07 | 747 | 10 | RNE5 | AN | Cádiz |
| VA01 | 774 | 100 | RNE1 | VA | València ° |
| EX01 | 774 | 60 | RNE1 | EX | Cáceres ° |
| EU02 | 774 | 50 | RNE1 | EU | Donosti-San Sebastián |
| GA03 | 774 | 10 | RNE1 | GA | Ourense (relay) |
| AN08 | 774 | 10 | RNE1 | AN | Granada (relay) |
| AN09 | 774 | 10 | RNE1 | AN | La Línea (relay) |
| CL04 | 774 | 10 | RNE1 | CL | León (relay) |
| CL05 | 774 | 10 | RNE1 | CL | Soria (relay) |
| CM05 | 801 | 25 | RNE1 | CM | Ciudad Real (relay) |
| GA04 | 801 | 10 | RNE1 | GA | Lugo (relay) |
| CA04 | 801 | 10 | RNE1 | CA | Girona (relay) |
| CL06 | 801 | 10 | RNE1 | CL | Burgos |
| CL07 | 801 | 10 | RNE1 | CL | Zamora |
| VA03 | 801 | 10 | RNE1 | VA | Castelló (relay) |
| MU01 | 855 | 300 | RNE1 | MU | Murcia ° |
| CT01 | 855 | 50 | RNE1 | CT | Santander ° |
| CA03 | 855 | 20 | RNE1 | CA | Tarragona (relay) |
| GA02 | 855 | 20 | RNE1 | GA | Pontevedra (relay) |

| MW | kHz | kW | Net | Rg | Location |
|---|---|---|---|---|---|
| AN10) | 855 | 10 | RNE1 | AN | Huelva (relay) |
| AR02) | 855 | 10 | RNE1 | AR | Teruel (relay) |
| CL08) | 855 | 10 | RNE1 | CL | Ponferrada (relay) |
| CL09) | 855 | 10 | RNE1 | CL | Salamanca (relay) |
| NA01) | 855 | 10 | RNE1 | NA | Pamplona-Iruñea ° |
| AN03) | 855 | 5 | RNE1 | AN | Marbella (relay) |
| CM02) | 864 | 10 | RNE1 | CM | Socuellamos (rel.of Toledo) |
| BA01) | 909 | 5 | RNE5 | BA | Palma de Mallorca ° |
| AR01) | 936 | 20 | RNE5 | AR | Zaragoza ° |
| CL01) | 936 | 20 | RNE5 | CL | Valladolid ° |
| VA02) | 936 | 10 | RNE5 | VA | Alacant-Alicante |
| AN11) | 972 | 5 | RNE1 | AN | Cabra (rel.of Sevilla) |
| GA05) | 972 | 2 | RNE1 | GA | Monforte de Lemos (relay) |
| AN08) | 1017 | 10 | RNE5 | AN | Granada |
| CL06) | 1017 | 10 | RNE5 | CL | Burgos° |
| AN05) | 1098 | 25 | RNE5 | AN | Almería |
| GA04) | 1098 | 20 | RNE5 | GA | Lugo |
| CL03) | 1098 | 10 | RNE5 | CL | Avila |
| AN10) | 1098 | 5 | RNE5 | AN | Huelva |
| RI01) | 1107 | 25 | RNE5 | RI | Logroño ° |
| CT01) | 1107 | 20 | RNE5 | CT | Santander ° |
| EX01) | 1107 | 20 | RNE5 | EX | Cáceres ° |
| AR02) | 1107 | 10 | RNE5 | AR | Teruel (rel.of zaragoza) |
| CL08) | 1107 | 10 | RNE5 | CL | Ponferrada (rel.of León) |
| CL05) | 1125 | 10 | RNE5 | CL | Soria |
| CM01) | 1125 | 10 | RNE5 | CM | Toledo ° |
| EU01) | 1125 | 10 | RNE5 | EU | Vitoria-Gasteiz ° |
| VA03) | 1125 | 10 | RNE5 | VA | Castelló |
| EX02) | 1125 | 5 | RNE5 | EX | Badajoz |
| AN06) | 1152 | 10 | RNE5 | AN | Málaga |
| CA02) | 1152 | 10 | RNE5 | CA | Lleida |
| CL07) | 1152 | 10 | RNE5 | CL | Zamora |
| CM03) | 1152 | 10 | RNE5 | CM | Albacete |
| MU02) | 1152 | 10 | RNE5 | MU | Cartagena |
| GA03) | 1305 | 25 | RNE5 | GA | Ourense |
| CM05) | 1305 | 20 | RNE5 | CM | Ciudad Real |
| EU03) | 1305 | 20 | RNE5 | EU | Bilbo-Bilbao |
| CL04) | 1305 | 10 | RNE5 | CL | León |
| CM04) | 1314 | 20 | RNE5 | CM | Cuenca |
| CA03) | 1314 | 10 | RNE5 | CA | Tarragona |
| CL09) | 1314 | 10 | RNE5 | CL | Salamanca |
| GA06) | 1413 | 20 | RNE5 | GA | Vigo |
| AN04) | 1413 | 10 | RNE5 | AN | Jaén |
| CA04) | 1413 | 5 | RNE5 | CA | Girona |
| AN09) | 1503 | 5 | RNE5 | AN | La Linea (rel.of Cádiz) |
| GA05) | 1503 | 2 | RNE5 | GA | Monforte de Lemos (rel.of. Lugo) |

° = regional key stn

| FM | Location | RNE1 | RNE2 | RNE3 | RNE4 | RNE5 | kW |
|---|---|---|---|---|---|---|---|
| **Andalucía** | | | | | | | |
| AN08) | Baza | 92.6 | 97.3 | - | - | - | 5 |
| AN02) | Cabra | 95.1 | 89.5 | 103.8 | - | 88.0 | 1 |
| AN02) | Córdoba | - | - | - | - | 99.8 | 2 |
| AN08) | Granada | 104.2 | 96.4 | 94.4 | - | 98.5 | 1 |
| AN01) | Guadalcanal | - | 90.6 | - | - | - | 5 |
| AN07) | Jerez | 103.5 | 94.5 | 96.7 | - | 106.3 | 80 |
| AN02) | Lagar de la Cruz | 92.2 | 97.5 | 98.6 | - | - | 10 |
| AN06) | Málaga | - | 99.2 | 104.0 | - | 92.5 | 1 |
| AN03) | Marbella | - | - | - | - | 87.6 | 1 |
| AN06) | Mijas | 106.6 | 98.1 | 99.8 | - | 88.0 | 10 |
| AN08) | Parapanda | 103.0 | 91.1 | 93.9 | - | - | 5 |
| AN05) | Pechina | 100.9 | 92.4 | 94.9 | - | 106.7 | 70 |
| AN10) | Punta Umbria | 95.2 | 92.6 | 99.0 | - | 88.8 | 5 |
| AN06) | Ronda | 106.1 | 99.3 | 91.6 | - | 102.3 | 1 |
| AN04) | Sierra Almadén | 105.4 | 90.0 | 96.0 | - | - | 10 |
| AN08) | Sierra Lújar | 96.7 | 90.4 | 94.2 | - | - | 5 |
| AN07) | Tajo | 105.0 | 94.0 | 103.1 | - | - | 5 |
| AN01) | Valencina | 91.2 | 93.7 | 98.8 | - | 90.0 | 5 |
| **Aragon** | | | | | | | |
| AR02) | Alcañiz | 89.5 | - | - | - | 99.3 | 1 |
| AR03) | Arguis | 100.9 | 94.4 | 103.7 | - | 92.8 | 5 |
| AR03) | Barbastro | 89.6 | 97.4 | 105.1 | - | 100.2 | 1 |
| AR01) | Caspe | 90.2 | 99.0 | - | - | 103.7 | 1 |
| AR01) | Ejea de los C. | 94.8 | 98.9 | 106.4 | - | 91.2 | |
| AR03) | Fraga | 95.0 | 96.3 | 102.2 | - | 98.8 | 1 |
| AR01) | Inogés | 89.4 | 92.4 | 99.7 | - | 105.0 | 5 |
| AR03) | Jaca | 103.7 | 94.4 | 100.3 | - | 98.7 | 1 |
| AR02) | Javalambre | - | 90.0 | 93.9 | - | - | 1 |
| AR01) | La Muela | 94.5 | 90.9 | 96.3 | - | 103.6 | 10 |
| AR02) | Montalban | 90.5 | 92.7 | 96.4 | - | 105.1 | |
| AR02) | Peracense | 88.3 | 98.1 | 100.6 | - | 106.1 | |
| AR02) | Teruel | 104.7 | 89.2 | 94.5 | - | 95.6 | 1 |

| FM | Location | RNE1 | RNE2 | RNE3 | RNE4 | RNE5 | kW |
|---|---|---|---|---|---|---|---|
| **Asturias** | | | | | | | |
| AS01) | Avilés | 100.0 | 87.9 | 95.6 | - | 102.9 | 1 |
| AS01) | Boal | 93.2 | 97.8 | 88.2 | - | 90.5 | 1 |
| AS01) | Cangas Narcea | 97.2 | 99.0 | 87.7 | - | 90.9 | 1 |
| AS01) | Cangas Onis | 88.8 | 92.5 | 104.0 | - | 100.3 | 1 |
| AS01) | Gamoniteiro | 102.5 | 92.2 | 94.4 | - | 104.4 | 10 |
| AS01) | Gijón | 99.2 | 98.5 | 102.0 | - | 89.9 | 5 |
| AS01) | Ibias | 95.8 | 98.7 | 102.9 | - | 105.1 | 1 |
| AS01) | Llanes | 106.1 | - | - | - | 97.3 | 1 |
| AS01) | Los Oscos | 89.7 | 104.0 | 105.7 | - | 96.1 | 1 |
| AS01) | Luarca | 96.8 | 93.8 | 100.3 | - | - | 1 |
| AS01) | Mieres | - | - | - | - | 101.8 | 1 |
| AS01) | Oviedo | 89.4 | 96.0 | 90.3 | - | 99.6 | 1 |
| AS01) | Peñamelleras | 93.9 | 96.4 | 100.7 | - | 104.6 | |
| AS01) | San Martín | 88.3 | 96.7 | 100.2 | - | 93.3 | 1 |
| **Baleares** | | | | | | | |
| BA01) | Alfabia | 90.1 | 87.9 | 92.3 | - | 104.5 | 10 |
| BA01) | Ibiza | 101.6 | 104.0 | 105.7 | - | 94.9 | 1 |
| BA01) | Menorca | 94.6 | 97.1 | 105.8 | - | 100.4 | 1 |
| BA01) | Pollensa | 93.2 | 95.4 | 97.4 | - | 99.7 | 1 |
| **Cantabria** | | | | | | | |
| CT03) | Embalse Ebro | 89.0 | 94.0 | 98.2 | - | 101.9 | 1 |
| CT01) | Liérganes | 96.9 | 93.0 | 102.9 | - | 105.0 | 10 |
| CT02) | Torrelavega | 99.5 | 97.9 | 103.4 | - | 89.4 | 1 |
| **Catalunya** | | | | | | | |
| CA02) | Alpicat | 94.6 | 89.2 | 97.8 | 87.9 | - | 10 |
| CA02) | Baquéira | 92.2 | 87.7 | 89.0 | 93.3 | - | 1 |
| CA02) | Bossost | 94.4 | 100.5 | 105.2 | 102.3 | - | 1 |
| CA01) | Collserola | 88.3 | 93.0 | 98.6 | 100.8 | 99.0 | 20 |
| CA01) | Collsuspina | 99.2 | 97.9 | 103.1 | 104.7 | - | 1 |
| CA01) | Igualada | 89.4 | 90.9 | 105.1 | 106.9 | - | 1 |
| CA03) | Monte Caro | 104.3 | 96.6 | 99.6 | 90.7 | - | 5 |
| CA01) | Montserrat | 94.3 | 99.6 | - | 103.8 | 98.8 | 2 |
| CA03) | Musara | 106.5 | 91.5 | 94.5 | 88.8 | 94.0 | 5 |
| CA01) | Sant Pere Ribes | 89.4 | 95.2 | 97.5 | 106.3 | 101.3 | 1 |
| CA04) | Rocacorba | 93.3 | 91.1 | 95.9 | 106.2 | 94.0 | 5 |
| CA02) | Soriguera | 99.9 | 103.6 | 106.4 | 90.6 | 97.2 | 1 |
| CA03) | Ulldecona | 95.0 | - | - | - | - | 5 |
| CA02) | Viella | 90.0 | 96.2 | 104.4 | 102.6 | - | 1 |
| CA04) | Olot | 93.8 | 106.6 | - | - | - | |
| CA02) | Pont de Suert | 88.2 | 94.9 | 96.8 | 104.9 | - | |
| **Castilla-León** | | | | | | | |
| CL06) | Aranda Duero | 90.0 | 92.7 | 101.6 | - | 106.2 | 1 |
| CL03) | Arenas Pedro | 102.4 | 90.3 | - | - | - | 1 |
| CL03) | Avila | 87.6 | 92.0 | 97.8 | - | 102.4 | 1 |
| CL07) | Béjar | 99.9 | 101.6 | 104.7 | - | - | 1 |
| CL05) | Burgo Osma | 96.1 | 98.4 | 88.7 | - | 102.8 | 1 |
| CL06) | Burgos | 93.6 | 90.3 | 91.2 | - | 106.6 | 1 |
| CL04) | Castropodame | 103.3 | 93.0 | 99.9 | - | 105.9 | 5 |
| CL02) | Cervera | 88.6 | 94.8 | 97.3 | - | 100.4 | 1 |
| CL09) | El Cabaco | 102.9 | 92.4 | 95.4 | - | - | 5 |
| CL02) | Guardo | 89.8 | 105.6 | - | - | 104.0 | 1 |
| CL04) | León | 97.1 | 91.1 | 89.3 | - | 102.2 | 1 |
| CL02) | Palencia | 91.8 | 101.0 | 97.6 | - | 88.0 | 1 |
| CL06) | Pancorbo | 89.7 | 92.0 | 101.7 | - | 104.5 | 1 |
| CL07) | Pbla Samabria | 93.6 | 103.5 | 100.3 | - | 91.9 | 1 |
| CL09) | Salamanca | 94.5 | 88.1 | 91.4 | - | 102.2 | 1 |
| CL10) | Segovia | 97.0 | - | - | - | 91.5 | 1 |
| CL05) | Soria | 89.7 | 91.5 | 94.3 | - | 104.7 | 2 |
| CL01) | Valladolid | 97.3 | 93.1 | 92.2 | - | 95.1 | 5 |
| CL04) | Villablino | 98.1 | 89.0 | 91.4 | - | 99.4 | 1 |
| CL06) | Villadiego | - | 102.3 | 103.3 | - | - | 1 |
| CL04) | Villafranca | 90.9 | 89.7 | 97.5 | - | 104.1 | 1 |
| CL07) | Zamora | 101.8 | 96.7 | 98.5 | - | 88.8 | 5 |
| **Castilla La Mancha** | | | | | | | |
| CM03) | Almansa | 91.2 | 98.6 | 95.6 | - | 94.4 | 1 |
| CM03) | Chinchila | 91.8 | 93.6 | 99.6 | - | 106.3 | 5 |
| CM05) | Ciudad Real | 95.7 | 92.0 | 94.1 | - | 88.8 | 1 |
| CM04) | Cuenca | 105.6 | 93.0 | 92.0 | - | 96.1 | 1 |
| CM06) | Guadalajara | 103.7 | 93.5 | 96.9 | - | 102.1 | 1 |
| CM05) | La Mancha | 101.0 | 89.8 | 94.5 | - | 106.8 | 10 |
| CM05) | Puertollano | 93.1 | 99.1 | 91.8 | - | 101.8 | 5 |
| CM05) | Socuéllamos | 94.0 | - | - | - | - | 1 |
| CM01) | Talavera | 97.8 | 105.5 | 94.7 | - | 89.4 | 5 |
| CM01) | Toledo | 102.0 | 103.9 | 106.4 | - | 99.9 | 1 |
| CM05) | Valdepeñas | 92.6 | 95.5 | 97.3 | - | 102.1 | |
| **Euskadi** | | | | | | | |
| EU03) | Archanda | 100.7 | 90.6 | 99.2 | - | 96.3 | 5 |
| EU02) | Azcoitia | 88.7 | 104.9 | 106.9 | - | - | 1 |
| EU02) | Beasain | 100.2 | 98.4 | 94.9 | - | - | 1 |
| EU02) | Eibar | 92.9 | 98.7 | 95.9 | - | - | 1 |

| FM Location | RNE1 | RNE2 | RNE3 | RNE4 | RNE5 | kW |
|---|---|---|---|---|---|---|
| EU02) Jaizquibel | 104.7 | 90.0 | 92.1 | - | - | 10 |
| EU02) Monte Igueldo | 87.6 | 99.5 | 98.9 | - | 93.3 | 1 |
| EU03) Oiz | 106.4 | 105.3 | 102.1 | - | - | 5 |
| EU01) San León | - | - | - | - | 93.3 | 1 |
| EU03) Sollube | 105.9 | 93.9 | 95.4 | - | - | 5 |
| EU02) Tolosa | 101.9 | 98.8 | 96.0 | - | - | 1 |
| EU02) Vitoria-Gasteiz | 92.5 | 96.9 | 99.5 | - | 89.4 | 1 |
| **Extremadura** | | | | | | |
| EX02) Badajoz | 94.9 | 90.1 | 92.2 | - | 106.0 | 1 |
| EX01) Cáceres | 95.1 | 101.7 | 93.7 | - | 88.2 | 1 |
| EX02) Mérida | - | - | - | - | 101.3 | 1 |
| EX01) Montánchez | 105.3 | 97.7 | 99.3 | - | - | 5 |
| EX01) Plasencia | 88.6 | - | 99.3 | - | 104.4 | 1 |
| **Galicia** | | | | | | |
| GA03) Barco | 94.7 | 96.4 | 100.3 | - | 104.6 | |
| GA02) Domayo | 90.1 | 92.1 | 97.4 | - | - | 5 |
| GA04) Monforte | - | - | - | - | 88.8 | 1 |
| GA03) Monte Meda | 102.8 | 91.2 | 94.3 | - | 106.8 | 5 |
| GA03) Monte Xalo | 100.4 | 91.6 | 94.5 | - | 95.8 | 10 |
| GA03) Ourense | 100.6 | 97.2 | 99.4 | - | 95.1 | 5 |
| GA04) Páramo | 101.7 | 88.2 | 99.6 | - | 92.8 | 5 |
| GA02) Piedrafita | 89.4 | 92.6 | 105.3 | - | 95.2 | |
| GA02) Pontevedra | - | 88.3 | - | - | - | 1 |
| GA07) Santiago | 103.1 | 98.1 | 99.0 | - | 93.7 | 5 |
| GA03) Verin | 90.7 | 98.4 | 106.4 | - | 94.1 | 1 |
| GA06) Vigo | - | - | - | - | 96.0 | 5 |
| GA04) Xistral | 89.5 | 96.3 | 104.2 | - | 106.6 | 1 |
| **Madrid** | | | | | | |
| MA01) Navacerrada | 104.9 | 98.8 | 95.8 | - | - | 30 |
| MA01) Torrespaña | 88.2 | 96.5 | 93.2 | - | 90.3 | 10 |
| **Murcia** | | | | | | |
| MU01) Carrascoy | 101.7 | 98.2 | 96.0 | - | 92.1 | 5 |
| MU02) Cartagena | 102.9 | 94.5 | 97.5 | - | 103.5 | 1 |
| MU01) Cieza | 91.0 | 93.7 | 99.0 | - | 96.9 | |
| MU01) Jumilla | 89.1 | 93.1 | 100.1 | - | - | 1 |
| MU01) Yecla | 88.8 | 93.4 | 103.7 | - | - | 1 |
| **Navarra** | | | | | | |
| NA01) Estella | 89.0 | 101.2 | 100.6 | - | 90.9 | 1 |
| NA01) Gorramendi | 88.3 | 99.0 | 100.6 | - | 95.3 | 1 |
| NA01) Ibañeta | 89.6 | 93.8 | 103.4 | - | 101.9 | 1 |
| NA01) Isaba | 90.3 | 95.1 | 103.0 | - | 91.8 | 1 |
| NA01) Leire | 88.9 | 101.0 | 99.6 | - | 90.5 | 1 |
| NA01) Lesaka | 90.6 | 94.8 | 97.0 | - | 102.2 | 1 |
| NA01) Monreal | 106.1 | 97.5 | 93.0 | - | 95.7 | 5 |
| NA01) Pamplona | 104.8 | 97.1 | 102.3 | - | 103.7 | |
| NA01) San Miguel | 96.7 | 100.0 | 90.3 | - | 102.7 | 1 |
| NA01) Tudela | 100.9 | 102.2 | 91.3 | - | 88.3 | 1 |
| **La Rioja** | | | | | | |
| RI01) Logroño | 95.4 | 88.1 | 89.9 | - | 97.2 | 1 |
| RI01) Moncalvillo | 102.0 | 88.5 | 94.6 | - | 103.3 | 40 |
| RI01) Monte Yerga | 87.6 | 106.8 | 96.5 | - | 105.4 | 1 |
| **Comunitat Valenciana** | | | | | | |
| VA01) Aitana | 104.8 | 88.6 | 99.7 | - | - | 10 |
| VA02) Alcoi | 95.8 | 92.3 | 91.1 | - | 105.9 | 1 |
| VA02) Alicante | 105.2 | 99.4 | 97.1 | - | 103.6 | |
| VA03) Benicasim | 89.3 | 90.3 | 92.8 | - | 95.5 | 5 |
| VA02) Benidorm | 87.6 | 97.8 | 102.1 | - | - | |
| VA02) Elda | 93.9 | 88.1 | 97.6 | - | - | 1 |
| VA01) Monduber | 97.4 | 99.3 | 100.1 | - | - | 5 |
| VA02) Monte Picayo | 89.8 | 106.6 | 95.1 | - | 88.2 | 10 |
| VA02) Ontinyent | 100.7 | 96.7 | 102.4 | - | - | 1 |
| VA02) Santa Pola | 92.5 | 100.1 | 94.3 | - | 104.2 | 5 |
| VA02) Santa Pola | - | - | - | - | 105.8 | 5 |
| VA02) Utiel | 98.1 | 96.6 | 89.1 | - | 87.9 | 1 |
| VA02) Villena | 90.7 | 97.1 | 101.1 | - | - | 1 |

**RNE1 R. Nacional:** (MW and FM): 24h. **N:** On the h. Regional prgrs from key stn of each region: Mon-Fri UTC Summer (+1 in winter) Regional 0545-0600 RNE1 and RNE5; - Reg/Local 0630-0700 RNE5 (*); - Reg. 1025-1030, RNE5; - Reg. 1110-1200 RNE1 and RNE5; - Reg. 1304-1308 RNE5; - Reg. 1710-1730 RNE1 and RNE5; Sa-Su: 0705-0715 RNE5 1130-1200 RNE1 and RNE5. (*) Each region determines programming: Castilla y León local 0630-0650 and regional 0650-0700, Extremadura all regional. – **RNE2:** R.Clasica: (FM): Classical music & cultural prgrs: 24h. – **RNE3:** (FM): Young people's music prgr: 24h. – **RNE4:** (FM): Regional network in Catalunya: 24h. in Catalán. – **RNE5:** (MW and FM): Informacion. 24h. RNE1/RNE5 simulcasting times (local time): 0000-0900 (except 0725-0730 for local news on RNE5), 1300-1500, 1945-2100 and 2200-2400.

**Addresses for RNE regional key stns:**
**AN Andalucia:** Edif.RTVE, Parque del Alamillo, Isla de la Cartuja,41092 Sevilla – **AR Aragón:** José Luís Albareda 1-3, 50004 Zaragoza – **AS**

**Asturias:** Calle San Esteban de las Cruces 92, 33195 Oviedo – **BA Balears:** Aragó 26, 07006 Palma de Mallorca – **CA Catalunya:** C. Roc Boronat 127, 08018 Barcelona – **CL Castilla y León:** García Morato 27-29, 47007 Valladolid – **CM Castilla La Mancha:** Plaza de San Cristóbal s/n, 45002 Toledo – **CT Cantabria:** Polígono de Raos s/n, 39609 Camargo (Santander) – **EU Euskadi:** Plaza de Simón Bolívar 13, 01003 Vitoria-Gasteiz – **EX Extremadura:** Av. Ruta de la Plata 10, 10001 Cáceres – **GA Galicia:** Paseo Méndez Nuñez 12, 15006 A Coruña – **MA Madrid:** Casa de la Radio, Prado del Rey, 28223 Pozuelo de Alarcón – **MU Murcia:** La Olma 27-29, 30005 Murcia – **NA Navarra:** Calle Aoiz, 31004 Pamplona-Iruñea – **RI La Rioja:** Vara de Rey 42, 26002 Logroño – **VA Comunitat Valenciana:** Av.Colóm 13, 46004 València

### OTHER STATIONS
Only stns with MW broadcasts and FM networks are listed. A number of other stns are heard irr. There are approx. 2,400 FM stns.

### NATIONAL NETWORKS:
**(COPE) CADENA DE ONDAS POPULARES ESPAÑOLAS (Comm)**
Alfonso XI Nº 4, 28014 Madrid ☎ +34 91-3090000 🖷 +34 91-5317517 **W:** cope.es **E:** programas.madrid@cadenacope.net
Local and regional prgr on AM and FM stns: Mon-Fri 0555, 0624, 0650, 0724, 1809-1859, generally at xx27 and xx57 0757-1700, 1930, 2030, 2130, 2230, 2255, 2357. Sat xx27 and xx57 0757-1400, 1557, 1657, 1810, 1840, 1910, 1940, 2040, 2257, 2330. Sun xx27 and xx57 0957-1300, xx10 and xx40 1510-1840, 2157, 2330 **(C100)Cadena 100** (music on FM only) **W:** cadena100.es **E:** jplane@cadena100.es **W: stns list:** cadena100.es/emisoras.php **Gestiona Radio** (business prgr on FM only) **W:** gestionaradio.com **(MEGA) MegaStar FM** (music on FM only) **W:** megastar.fm

**(D) CADENA DIAL (Comm)** Part of Grupo Prisa
Gran Vía 32, 28013 Madrid ☎ +34 91-3470880 🖷 +34 91-5211753 **W:** cadenadial.com **E:** ccampillo@cadenadial.com. List of stations: **W:** cadenadial.com/nosotros/emisoras

**(EFM) EUROPA FM (Comm)** Part of Grupo Antena 3
Fuerteventura 12, 28703 San Sebastian de los Reyes ☎+34 91-4366400 🖷+34 91-4366116 **W:** europafm.com. List of stations: **W:** europafm.com/frecuencias

**(ES) esRADIO (Comm)**
C/ Juan Esplandiú 13, 28007 Madrid ☎+34 91-4094766 🖷+34 91-4094899 **W:** esradio.fm. List of_stns: **W:** esradio.fm/escuchenos.html

**(LOCA) LOCA RADIO ESPAÑA (Comm)** Part of RTL Group France
C/ Enrique Larreta 12 bajo izq., 28036 Madrid ☎+34 90-2302024 **W:** locafm.com **E:** contacto@locaradio.com

**(HFM) Hit FM (Comm)** Part of Grupo KISS Media
José Isbert 6, Ciudad de la Imagen, 28223 Pozuelo de Alarcón **W:** hitfm.es

**(IE) INTERECONOMÍA (Comm)**
Modesto Lafuente 42, 28003 Madrid.☎+34 90-2996556 🖷+34 91-5771314 **W:** intereconomia.com **E:** redaccion@intereconomia.com

**(KFM) KISS FM (Comm)**
José Isbert 6, Ciudad de la Imagen - 28223 Pozuelo de Alarcón ☎+34 91-4440490 🖷+34 91-8379189 **W:** kissfm.es **E:** kissfm@kissfm.es. List of stns: **W:** kissfm.es/contacta-kiss

**(L40) Los 40 Principales (Comm)** Part of Grupo Prisa
Gran Vía 32, 7ª planta, 28013 Madrid. ☎ +34 91-3477700 🖷 +34 91-5228693 **W:** los40.com **E:** los40@los40.com

**(MFM) MAXIMA FM (Comm)** Part of Grupo Prisa
C/ Gran Vía 32, 7ª planta, 28013 Madrid ☎ +34 91-3477624 🖷+34 91-5325808 **W:** maxima.fm **E:** ADSanchez@prisaradio.com. **LP:** Dir.: Toni Sánchez

**(M80) M-80 RADIO (Comm)** Part of Grupo Prisa
Gran Vía 32, 7ª planta, 28013 Madrid ☎ +34 91-3477700 🖷 +34 91-5228693 **W:** m80radio.com **E:** aalvarez@m80radio.com. **LP:** Dir.: Angel Alvarez. List of stns: **W:** m80radio.com/emisoras/ciudad/

**(OCR) ONDA CERO RADIO (Comm)**
C/ Fuerteventura 12, 28703 San Sebastián de los Reyes, Madrid ☎ +34 91-4366400 🖷 +34 91-5386332 **W:** ondacero.es **E:** ondacero@ondacero.es. List of stns: **W:** ondacero.es/frecuencias Prgrs:.Onda Melodia. Local and regional programming on AM stations: Mon-Fri 0527, 0555, 0620, 0655, 0720, 0827, 0855, 0927, 0955, 1025, 1130, 1400, 1527, 1557, 1627, 1657, 1727, 1757, 1800, 2030, 2130, 2230, 2257, 2340, 0030. Sat-Sun 0527, 0727, 0757, 0827, 0857, 0927, 0957, 1027, 1227, 1457, 1850, 2255, 2320, 2340. Times vary.

**(RA) RADIO TELEVISION AMISTAD (Rlg)**
Apartado 269, 08211 Castellar del Vallés (Barcelona) ☎+34 93-7242380 **W:** rtvamistad.net **E:** info@rtvamistad.tv

**(RKM) RKM RADIO (Rlg)**
Carretera de Ajalvir a Daganzo km 1.7, Ajalvir, 28864 Madrid ☎ +34 91- 8844180 **W:** rkmradio.com **E:** madrid@rkmradio.com

**(RM) RADIO MARÌA (Rlg)**
⊡ Paseo de Lanceros 2 (Centro Comercial), Planta 1ª, 28024 Madrid ☎+34 90-2500518 🖷 +34 91-7057727 **W:** radiomaria.es **E:** radiomaria@radiomaria.es
**(RMA) RADIO MARCA (Comm)**
⊡AvenidadeSanLuís25,28033Madrid☎+34 90 2996111 **W:** marca.com **E:** radiomarca@radiomarca.com **LP:** Dir.: Francisco Garcia Caridad
**(RO) Radiolé (Comm)** Part of Grupo Prisa
⊡ Gran Vía 32, 7ª planta, 28013 Madrid ☎ +34 91-3477740 🖷 +34 91-5324769 **W:** radiole.com **E:** direccion@radiole.com **LP:** Dir.: Miguel Ángel Corral Salas. List of Stns: **W:** radiole.com/emisoras
**(ROCK) ROCK FM (Comm)** Part of Grupo COPE
⊡ Alfonso XI N° 4, 28014 Madrid ☎ +34 91-5951210 🖷 +34 91 3090721 **W:** rockfm.fm. List of Stns: **W:** rockfm.fm/noticia.php5?id=641
**(SER) SOCIEDAD ESPANOLA DE RADIODIFUSION (Comm)** Part of Grupo Prisa
⊡ Gran Vía 32, 7ª planta, 28013 Madrid ☎ +34 91-3477700 🖷 +34 91-3470779 **W:** cadenaser.com **E:** redaccion@cadenaser.com. List of Stns: cadenaser.com/emisoras **FM stns:** Local and regional prgr **AM stns:** Mon-Fri 0550, 0620, 0650, 0720, 0827, 0855, 0930, 0957, 1003, 1030, 1057, 1120, 1410, 1530, 1630, 1720, 1810-1855, 1925, 2157, 2255, 2330, 0000, 0030, 0159, 0259. Sat-Sun 0750, 0855, 0955, 1055, 1105 and xx23 or xx53 in the evening. Times vary

**REGIONAL NETWORKS:**
**(AR) ARAGON RADIO**
⊡ María Zambrano 2, 50018 Zaragoza. ☎ +34 876-256500 🖷 +34 876-256519 **W:** aragonradio.es **E:** jmartinez@cartv.es **LP:** Dir. Mktg: Javier Martinez López
**(CR) CORPORACIO CATALANA DE MITJANS AUDIOVISUALS**
⊡ Av. Diagonal 614-616, 08021 Barcelona ☎ +34 93-3069200 🖷 +34 93-3069201 **W:** catradio.cat **E:** correu@catradio.com **Prgrs:** Catalunya Ràdio; Catalunya Informació; Catalunya Música; Icat FM
**(CER) CANAL EXTREMADURA RADIO**
⊡ Av. de las Américas 1, 1º, 06800 Mérida (Badajoz) ☎ +34 924-382000 **W:** radio.canalextremadura.es **E:** cexma@canalextremadura.es
**(CLR) CASTILLA LEON RADIO**
⊡ Calle Manuel Canesi Acevedo 1, ES-47016 Valladolid ☎ +34 98 3131313 🖷 +34 98 3131314 **W:** puntoradiocyl.com **E:** puntoradiocyl@edigrup.es
**(CSR) CANAL SUR RADIO**
⊡ Carretera Edificio Canal Sur. Avda. José Gálvez 1, 41092 Isla de la Cartuja, Sevilla ☎ +34 95-5054600 🖷 +34 95- 5054740 **W:** canalsur.es **E:** comunicacion@rtva.es **Prgrs:** Canal Fiesta: (Int. music and Spanish pop and rock music); Canal Sur Radio: (Andalucian and Spanish music, news and sports); Radio Andalucía Información.
**(EI) EUSKA IRRATI TELEBISTA – RADIO TELEVISIÓN VASCA**
⊡ EiTB Donostia: Paseo Miramon 172, 20014 Donostia-San Sebastián ☎ +34 94-30116 00 🖷 +34 94-301 1995 – ⊡ EiTB Bilbao: Capuchinos de Basurto 2, 48013 Bilbo-Bilbao ☎ +34 94-6563000 🖷 +34 94-6563095 – ⊡ EiTB Vitoria: Domingo Martinez de Aragón, 5-7 bajo, 01006 Vitoria-Gasteiz ☎ +34 94-5012500 🖷 +34 94-5012695 – ⊡ EiTB Iruña: Calle Tomás Caballero 2, 31005 Pamplona-Iruña ☎ +34 94-8012200 🖷 +34 94-8153485. **Prgrs:** Euskadi Irratia (AM + FM), R. Euskadi (AM + FM), R. Vitoria (AM + FM), EiTB Músika (FM), Gaztea Irratia (FM) **W:** eitb.com **E :** info@eitb.com
**(GR) GRUP FLAIX (Comm)**
⊡ Passeig de Gràcia 55, novena planta, 08007 Barcelona ☎ +34 93-5055555 🖷 +34 93-4880776 **W:** flaixfm.cat and radioflaixbac.com **E:** flaixfm@grupflaix.cat & flaixbac@grupflaix.cat **Prgs:** Flaix FM and Flaixbac
**(IB3) IB3 RADIO** ⊡ C/ Manuel Azaña 7-A, 07006 Palma de Mallorca ☎ +34 971-139931 🖷 +34 971-139930 **W:** ib3tv.com **E :** info@eprtvib.com
**(OC) ONA CATALANA (Comm)** Part of Grupo Prisa
⊡ C/ Casp 6, 08010 Barcelona ☎ +34 93-3441400 **W:** ona-fm.cat **E :** ona@onafm.cat
**(OM) ONDA MADRID**
⊡ Paseo del Príncipe 3, 28223 Pozuelo de Alarcón (Madrid) ☎ +34 91-5128200 🖷 +34 91-5128300 **W:** ondamadrid.es **E :** ondamadrid@ondamadrid.es
**(ORM) ONDA REGIONAL MURCIA**
⊡ Avda. Libertad 6, 30009 Murcia ☎+34 968-200000 🖷+34 968-272665 **W:** orm.es **E :** info@orm.es
**(RAC) RAC (Comm)** Belongs to Grupo Godò
Av. Diagonal 477, Planta 15, 08036 Barcelona ☎+34 93-2704400 🖷+34 93-2704464 **W:** rac1.cat and rac105.cat **E :** rac1@rac1.net and rac105@rac105.net. **Prgrs:** RAC1 and RAC 105
**(RCM) RADIO CASTILLA-LA MANCHA**
⊡ Edificio RTVCM, C/ Río Alberche s/n, Polígono Santa María de

Benquerencia, 45007 Toledo. ☎ +34 925-288600 🖷 +34 925-288607 **W:** rtvsm.es **E:** comercial@rtvcm.es
**(RCL) RADIO CASTILLA Y LEÓN**
Edificio Promecal Burgos, Avenida Castilla y León 62-64, 09006 Burgos ☎ +34 947-266868 🖷 +34 947-202752 **W:** rtvcyl.es **E :** burgos@rtvcyl.es
**(RE) RADIO ESTEL (Rlg)**
⊡ Comtes de Bell-lloc 67-69, 08014 Barcelona ☎ +34 93-4092770 🖷 +34 93-4092775 **W:** radioestel.com **E :** estudis@radioestel.com Dir.: Jaume Aymar
**(RG) RADIO GALEGA – COMPAÑÍA DE RADIO TELEVISION DE GALICIA**
⊡ Casa da Radio, Edificio de Usos Múltiples San Marcos, 15820 Santiago de Compostela ☎ +34 981-540640 🖷 +34 981-540949 **W:** crtvg.es/rg **E :** info@crtvg.es
**(RP) RADIO POPULAR - HERRI IRRATIA**
⊡Alameda Mazarredo 47, 48009 Bilbo-Bilbao ☎+34 94-4239200 🖷+34 94-4234703 **W:** radiopopular.com **E:** direccion@radiopopular.com
**(RPA) RADIO DEL PRINCIPADO DE ASTURIAS**
⊡ Camino de las Clarisas 263, 33203 Gijón ☎+34 985-185900 🖷+34 985-185939 **W:** rtpa.es/radio **E :** comunicacion@rtpa.es
**(RTT) RADIO TELE TAXI (Comm)**
⊡ C/ Sant Carles 40, 08922 Sta Coloma de Gramenet (Barcelona) ☎+34 93-4665656 🖷 +34 93-4661534 **W:** radioteletaxi.com **E:** radioteletaxi@radioteletaxi.com
**(RV) RADIO VOZ**
⊡ Av. De la Prensa 84-85, Arteixo, 15142 A Coruña ☎ +34 981-180600 🖷+34 981-180477 **W:** radiovoz.com **E:** director@radiovoz.com
**(XAR) LA XARXA (Comm)**
⊡ Travessera de les Corts 131-159, 08028 Barcelona ☎ +34 93-5080600 **W:** xarxaradio.cat **E:** laxarxa@laxarxa.com

| MW | kHz | kW | Net | Rg | Station, location | FM (MHz) |
|---|---|---|---|---|---|---|
| CA07 | 540 | 50 | OCR | CA | Onda Cero Catal., Barcelona | 93.5 |
| CA08 | 666 | 50 | SER | CA | R. Barcelona, Barcelona | 93.9 |
| MU05 | 711 | 5 | COPE | MU | COPE, Murcia | 89.7 |
| CA09 | 783 | 50 | COPE | CA | COPE Catalunya i Andorra, Barcelona | |
| AN15 | 792 | 50 | SER | AN | R. Sevilla, Sevilla | 97.1 |
| MA05 | 810 | 20 | SER | MA | R. Madrid, Madrid | 93.9 |
| CA13 | 828 | 5 | HFM | CA | HIT FM Catalunya, Terrassa | |
| AN16 | 837 | 10 | COPE | AN | COPE, Sevilla | 99.6 |
| CL15 | 837 | 10 | COPE | CL | COPE, Burgos | 95.5 |
| GA09 | 837 | 5 | COPE | GA | COPE, El Ferrol | 88.7 |
| AR05 | 873 | 25 | SER | AR | R. Zaragoza, Zaragoza | 95.3 |
| GA10 | 873 | 10 | SER | GA | R. Galicia, Stgo de Comp. | 90.0 |
| VA07 | 882 | 5 | COPE | VA | COPE, Alacant-Alicante | 95.6 |
| AN17 | 882 | 5 | COPE | AN | COPE, Málaga | 89.4 |
| AS05 | 882 | 5 | COPE | AS | COPE, Gijón | 103.6 |
| CL16 | 882 | 5 | COPE | CL | COPE, Valladolid | 88.5 |
| EU10 | 900 | 10 | RP | EU | R. Popular, Bilbo-Bilbao | 97.8 |
| AN18 | 900 | 5 | COPE | AN | COPE, Granada | 88.2 |
| GA11 | 900 | 5 | COPE | GA | COPE, Vigo | 87.8 |
| MA06 | †918 | 20 | IE | MA | R. Inter, Madrid | 95.1 |
| MA13 | 954 | 50 | OCR | MA | Onda Cero R., Madrid | 98.0 |
| EU11 | 990 | 10 | SER | EU | R. Bilbao, Bilbo-Bilbao | 89.5 |
| AN19 | 990 | 5 | SER | AN | R. Cádiz, Cádiz | 89.4 |
| MA08 | 999 | 50 | COPE | MA | COPE, Madrid | 99.5 |
| CA11 | 1008 | 10 | SER | CA | R. Girona, Girona | 98.5 |
| EX06 | 1008 | 5 | SER | EX | R. Extremadura, Badajoz | 96.9 |
| VA08 | 1008 | 5 | SER | VA | R. Alacant, Alacant-Alicante | 91.0 |
| CA12 | 1026 | 10 | SER | CA | R. Reus, Reus | 97.7 |
| AS06 | 1026 | 5 | SER | AS | R. Asturias, Oviedo | 97.5 |
| GA12 | 1026 | 5 | SER | GA | R. Vigo, Vigo | 99.4 |
| AN20 | 1026 | 5 | SER | AN | R. Jaén, Jaén | 96.9 |
| AN21 | 1026 | 5 | SER | AN | R. Jerez, J. de la Frontera | 97.8 |
| CL17 | 1026 | 5 | SER | CL | R. Salamanca, Salamanca | 96.9 |
| EU12 | 1044 | 10 | SER | EU | R. San Sebastián, Donosti-S Se | 97.2 |
| CL18 | 1044 | 5 | SER | CL | R. Valladolid, Valladolid | 90.9 |
| AR06 | 1053 | 25 | COPE | AR | COPE, Zaragoza | 88.5 |
| VA09 | 1053 | 5 | COPE | VA | COPE, Vila-Real | 91.7 |
| AN22 | 1080 | 10 | SER | AN | R. Granada, Granada | 95.4 |
| AR07 | 1080 | 10 | SER | AR | R. Huesca, Huesca | 96.9 |
| BA06 | 1080 | 5 | SER | BA | R. Mallorca, P. de Mallorca | 94.1 |
| CM11 | 1080 | 5 | OCR | CM | Onda Cero R., Toledo | 100.8 |
| GA13 | 1080 | 5 | SER | GA | R. Coruña, A Coruña | 91.0 |
| CM12 | 1116 | 5 | SER | CM | R. Albacete, Albacete | 89.6 |
| GA14 | 1116 | 5 | SER | GA | R. Pontevedra, Pontevedra | 95.5 |
| CL19 | 1134 | 10 | COPE | CL | COPE, Salamanca | 90.0 |
| AN23 | 1134 | 5 | COPE | AN | COPE, Jerez de la Frontera | 92.4 |
| NA05 | 1134 | 5 | COPE | NA | COPE, Pamplona-Iruñea | 87.9 |
| AN24 | 1143 | 5 | COPE | AN | COPE, Jaén | 88.8 |
| GA15 | 1143 | 5 | COPE | GA | COPE, Ourense | 92.4 |

| MW | kHz | kW | Net | Rg | Station, location | FM (MHz) |
|---|---|---|---|---|---|---|
| VA10) | 1179 | 50 | SER | VA | R. València, València | 94.2 |
| RI05) | 1179 | 2 | SER | RI | R. Rioja, Logroño | 91.7 |
| AN25) | 1215 | 5 | COPE | AN | COPE, Córdoba | 87.6 |
| CL21) | 1215 | 5 | COPE | CL | COPE, León | 97.7 |
| CT05) | 1215 | 5 | COPE | CT | COPE Cantabria, Santander | 88.4 |
| MU06) | 1215 | 5 | COPE | MU | COPE, Lorca | 89.2 |
| AN26) | 1224 | 5 | COPE | AN | COPE, Huelva | 91.9 |
| AN27) | 1224 | 5 | COPE | AN | COPE, Almería | 97.1 |
| BA08) | 1224 | 5 | COPE | BA | COPE, Palma de Mallorca | 97.6 |
| CA15) | 1224 | 5 | COPE | CA | COPE, Lleida | 97.4 |
| AN28) | 1260 | 5 | SER | AN | R. Algeciras, Algeciras | 95.7 |
| MU07) | 1260 | 5 | SER | MU | R. Murcia, Murcia | 91.3 |
| CL22) | 1269 | 5 | COPE | CL | COPE, Zamora | 94.9 |
| EX07) | 1269 | 5 | COPE | EX | COPE, Badajoz | 89.1 |
| CA17) | 1287 | 10 | SER | CL | R. Lleida, Lleida | 93.4 |
| CL23) | 1287 | 5 | SER | CL | R. Castilla, Burgos | 89.1 |
| GA17) | 1287 | 5 | SER | GA | R. Lugo, Lugo | 91.8 |
| VA11) | 1296 | 50 | COPE | VA | COPE, València | 99.0 |
| AN29) | 1341 | 10 | OCR | AN | Onda Cero R., Almería | 93.8 |
| CL24) | 1341 | 5 | SER | CL | R. León, León | 88.2 |
| CM16) | 1341 | 5 | OCR | CM | Onda Cero R., Ciudad Real | 92.1 |
| CL25) | 1485 | 10 | SER | CL | R. Zamora, Zamora | 89.8 |
| CT06) | 1485 | 10 | SER | CT | R. Santander, Santander | 90.9 |
| VA12) | 1485 | 5 | SER | VA | R. Alcoi, Alcoi | 96.3 |
| VA13) | 1521 | 5 | SER | VA | R. Castelló, Castelló | 94.8 |
| VA14) | 1539 | 6 | SER | VA | R. Elche - R. Elx, Elx | 99.1 |
| CA19) | 1539 | 5 | SER | CA | R. Manresa, Manresa | 95.8 |
| NA06) | 1575 | 10 | SER | NA | R. Pamplona, Pamplona | 92.2 |
| AN31) | 1575 | 5 | SER | AN | R. Córdoba, Córdoba | 96.6 |
| GA18) | 1584 | 5 | SER | GA | R. Ourense, Ourense | 87.6 |
| VA15) | 1584 | 5 | SER | VA | R. Gandia, Gandia | 96.5 |
| AN32) | 1602 | 5 | SER | AN | R. Linares, Linares | 94.9 |
| CL26) | 1602 | 5 | SER | CL | R. Segovia, Segovia | 93.6 |
| MU08) | 1602 | 5 | SER | MU | R. Cartagena, Cartagena | 102.3 |
| VA16) | 1602 | 5 | SER | VA | R. Ontinyent, Ontinyent | 95.3 |

† = irregular

| FM | MHz | kW | Net | Rg | Station, location |
|---|---|---|---|---|---|
| AN41) | 87.6 | 5 | CSR | AN | Canal Sur R., Santo Pitar,Málaga |
| CL20) | 87.6 | | CL | | COPE Astorga |
| CA25) | 87.6 | | CR | CA | Icat FM, L'Estartit, Girona |
| CA25) | 87.6 | | CR | CA | Icat FM, Camprodón, Girona |
| CA25) | 87.6 | | CR | CA | Catalunya Informació, Soriguera, Lleida |
| CA25) | 87.6 | | CR | CA | Catalunya Música, Portbou, Girona |
| AN35) | 87.7 | 6 | HIT | AN | HIT FM, Jerez de Frontera |
| CA34) | 87.7 | 20 | RAC | CA | RAC1, Barcelona Collserola |
| CA25) | 87.7 | | CR | CA | Icat FM, El Vendrell, Tarragona |
| CA25) | 87.7 | | CR | CA | Catalunya Música, El Vendrell, Tarragona |
| CA25) | 87.8 | | CR | CA | Catalunya Música, Calonge, Girona |
| CA09) | 87.8 | | ROCK | CA | ROCK FM, Figueres, Girona |
| AN36) | 87.9 | 5 | SER | AN | R. Morón, Morón de la Frontera ,Sevilla |
| CA25) | 87.9 | | CR | CA | IcatFM, Igualada, Barcelona |
| CA25) | 87.9 | | CR | CA | IcatFM, Collsuspina, Barcelona |
| CA37) | 88.0 | 25 | CR | CA | Icat FM, La Mussara, Tarragona |
| EU25) | 88.0 | 5 | | EU | R. Nervión, Bilbao |
| CA25) | 88.0 | | CR | CA | Catalunya R., Arenys de Munt, Barcelona |
| CA25) | 88.1 | 10 | SER | CA | LOS 40, Rocacorba, Girona |
| CA25) | 88.2 | | CR | CA | IcatFM, Puigdevall, Lleida |
| AN37) | 88.3 | 5 | CSR | AN | Canal Fiesta R., Algeciras |
| CA25) | 88.3 | | CR | CA | Catalunya R., Ponts, Lleida |
| CA25) | 88.4 | 5 | CR | CA | Catalunya R., Montcaro, Tortosa |
| CA25) | 88.4 | | CR | CA | Catalunya R., Cabra del Camp, Tarragona |
| CA25) | 88.4 | | CR | CA | Catalunya Música, La Molina, Girona |
| CA25) | 88.5 | | CR | CA | Catalunya R., Olot, Girona |
| CA25) | 88.5 | | CR | CA | Catalunya R., Arbucies, Girona |
| CA25) | 88.6 | | CR | CA | Catalunya Informació, Boí, Lleida |
| CA25) | 88.6 | 20 | CR | CA | Catalunya R., Soriguera, Lleida |
| CA25) | 88.6 | | CR | CA | Icat FM, Guardiola Berguedá, Barcelona |
| CA35) | 88.7 | 10 | | CA | R. RM, Barcelona Collserola |
| CA25) | 88.7 | | CR | CA | Catalunya R., Cubells, Lleida |
| AN70) | 88.8 | 40 | | AN | Stereo Vision, Sevilla |
| CA25) | 88.8 | | CR | CA | Catalunya Informació, Ripoll, Girona |
| CA25) | 88.8 | | CR | BA | Catalunya Música, Alfábia, Mallorca |
| CA38) | 88.9 | 25 | CR | CA | Icat FM, Rocacorba, Girona |
| CA25) | 88.9 | | CR | CA | Catalunya R., Almacelles, Lleida |
| EU07) | 88.9 | 20 | EI | EU | Euskadi Irratia, Bilbao-Bilbao |
| MU17) | 88.9 | 5 | RMA | MU | R. Marca, Murcia |
| MA05) | 89.0 | 20 | M80 | MA | M80, Madrid |
| CA25) | 89.0 | | CR | CA | Icat FM, Vilaller, Lleida |
| CA25) | 89.0 | | CR | CA | Icat FM, Portillo, Val D'Aran |
| CA07) | 89.1 | 8 | RMA | CA | R.Marca,, Barcelona Collserola |
| EU10) | 89.2 | 5 | ROCK | EU | ROCKFM. Bilbo-Bilbao |
| EU26) | 89.2 | 5 | | EU | Segura Irratia, Segura, Vitoria |
| GA29) | 89.2 | 8 | RMA | GA | R. Marca, A Coruña |
| VA21) | 89.2 | | KFM | VA | Kiss FM, Alacant-Alicante |
| NA11) | 89.3 | 6 | KFM | NA | Kiss FM, Pamplona |
| CA25) | 89.3 | | CR | CA | Icat FM, Bellmunt |
| GA28) | 89.4 | 6 | RA | GA | Ondas de Vida, R. Amistad, Vigo |
| MU14) | 89.4 | 6 | COPE | MU | COPE, Cartagena |
| CA25) | 89.4 | | CR | CA | Catalunya Informació, Falset, Tarragona |
| CA09) | 89.4 | 10 | COPE | CA | Cadena 100, Rocacorba, Girona |
| AN42) | 89.5 | 20 | CSR | AN | Canal Fiesta R., Huelva |
| BA11) | 89.5 | 8 | KFM | BA | Kiss FM, Palma de Mallorca |
| EX11) | 89.5 | 6 | KFM | EX | Kiss FM, Cáceres |
| CA25) | 89.5 | | CR | CA | Catalunya R., La Figuerassa, Barcelona |
| CA25) | 89.5 | | CR | CA | Catalunya R., Artesa de Segre, Lleida |
| CA25) | 89.5 | | CR | CA | Catalunya R., Vielha, Val D'Arán |
| CA25) | 89.5 | | CR | CA | Catalunya Informació, Arenys de Munt, Barcelona |
| BA07) | 89.6 | | COPE | BA | COPE Menorca |
| AR13) | 89.7 | 40 | ROCK | AR | ROCKFM.Zaragoza |
| CA25) | 89.7 | | CR | CA | Icat FM, Sant Carles, Tarragona |
| CA25) | 89.7 | | CR | CA | Catalunya R., Almenar, Lleida |
| CA25) | 89.7 | | CR | CA | Catalunya Música, Solsona, Lleida |
| AN43) | 89.8 | 8 | CSR | AN | RAI R.Andalucía Informacion, Granada |
| CA09) | 89.8 | 10 | ROCK | CA | ROCKFM., Barcelona Collserola |
| AS03) | 89.8 | 8 | RPA | AS | RPA, R.Principado Asturias, Gijón |
| CA36) | 89.9 | 6 | ROCK | CA | ROCKFM., Rocacorba, Girona |
| CA09) | 89.9 | 10 | COPE | CA | COPE Catalunya, Rocacorba, Girona |
| VA08) | 90.0 | 8 | MFM | VA | Maxima FM, Alicante |
| CA25) | 90.0 | | CR | CA | Catalunya R., Pont de Suert, Lleida |
| CA25) | 90.0 | | CR | CA | Catalunya R., Ulldemolins, Tarragona |
| CA25) | 90.0 | | CR | CA | Catalunya Informació, Flix, Tarragona |
| AN38) | 90.1 | 8 | KFM | AN | Kiss FM, Málaga |
| VA30) | 90.1 | 5 | | VA | Peque R., Valencia |
| CA25) | 90.1 | | CR | CA | Catalunya R., Guardiola, Barcelona |
| CA25) | 90.1 | | CR | CA | Catalunya Informació, Ribes de Freser |
| CA25) | 90.2 | 10 | CR | CA | Icat FM, Sant Celoni, Barcelona |
| CA25) | 90.2 | | CR | CA | IcatFM, Oliana, Lleida |
| AN35) | 90.3 | 6 | OCR | AN | Onda Cero R., Jerez de la Frontera |
| EX12) | 90.4 | 5 | OCR | EX | Onda Cero Melodía, Mérida |
| AN57) | 90.5 | 70 | CSR | AN | RAI R.Andalucía Informacion, Almería |
| CA08) | 90.5 | 8 | M80 | CA | M80, Barcelona Collserola |
| CL31) | 90.5 | 5 | SER | CL | SER R. Miranda, Miranda de Ebro Burgos |
| CA25) | 90.5 | | CR | CA | IlcatFM, Montblanc, Tarragona |
| CA25) | 90.7 | | CR | CA | Catalunya R., Calella, Barcelona |
| CA25) | 90.7 | | CR | CA | Catalunya R., Sant Hilari, Girona |
| AN39) | 90.8 | 5 | SER | AN | SER R. Puerto, El Puerto de S.M., Cadiz |
| AN38) | 90.8 | 10 | OCR | AN | Onda Cero R., Málaga |
| AN59) | 90.8 | 64 | CSR | AN | RAI R.Andalucía Informacion, Sevilla |
| GA29) | 90.8 | 5 | RG | GA | R. Galega Música, Vigo |
| CA25) | 90.8 | | CR | CA | Catalunya Música, Maçanet, Girona |
| EU09) | 90.9 | 20 | EI | EU | R. Euskadi, Vitoria |
| CA25) | 90.9 | | CR | CA | Catalunya Informació, Ponts, Lleida |
| MA11) | 91.0 | 100 | EFM | MA | Europa FM, Madrid |
| AS06) | 91.1 | 6 | D | AS | Cadena Dial Asturias, Oviedo |
| RI02) | 91.1 | 6 | COPE | RI | COPE Rioja, Logroño |
| CA25) | 91.1 | | CR | CA | Catalunya R., Puigdevall, Lleida |
| EU07) | 91.2 | 20 | EI | EU | Euskadi Gaztea, Bilbo-Bilbao |
| CM08) | 91.3 | 5 | RCM | CM | R. Castilla-La Mancha, Guadalajara |
| CA25) | 91.3 | | CR | CA | Catalunya Música, La Figuerassa, Barcelona |
| AR04) | 91.4 | 40 | HIT | AR | HIT FM, Zaragoza |
| EX13) | 91.4 | 10 | SER | EX | Los 40, Plasencia |
| AN40) | 91.4 | 8 | EFM | AN | Europa FM, Córdoba |
| CA25) | 91.4 | | CR | CA | IcatFM, Ripoll, Girona |
| CA25) | 91.4 | | CR | CA | Catalunya Informació, Cogulló, Lleida |
| CL27) | 91.5 | 8 | KFM | CL | Kiss FM, Astorga |
| EU21) | 91.5 | 8 | KFM | EU | Kiss FM, Donosti-San Sebastián |
| CA25) | 91.5 | | CR | CA | Catalunya R., Montagut, Girona |
| CA25) | 91.5 | | CR | CA | Catalunya Música, Pont de Suert, Lleida |
| EX05) | 91.6 | 6 | COPE | EX | COPE, Cáceres |
| VA17) | 91.6 | 10 | EFM | VA | Europa FM, La RIbera València |
| CA25) | 91.6 | | CR | CA | Catalunya Informació, Cadaqués, Girona |
| EU07) | 91.7 | 20 | EI | EU | R. Euskadi, Bilbo-Bilbao |
| MA05) | 91.7 | 100 | D | MA | Cadena Dial, Madrid |
| CL40) | 91.7 | 5 | KFM | CL | Kiss FM, Salamanca |
| VA08) | 91.7 | 8 | SER | VA | SER R. Alicante, Alicante |
| CA25) | 91.7 | | CR | CA | Catalunya R., Cabrils, Barcelona |
| CA25) | 91.9 | 15 | CR | CA | Catalunya Música, Alpicat, Lleida |
| CA25) | 91.9 | | CR | C | Catalunya Música, Sant Pere de Ribes, Barcelona |
| CA34) | 91.9 | 10 | RAC | CA | RAC105, Rocacorba, Girona |
| CM08) | 91.9 | 5 | RCM | CM | R. Castilla-La Mancha, Toledo |
| CT11) | 91.9 | 6 | OCR | CT | Onda Cero R., Santander |

| FM | MHz | kW | Net | Rg | Station, location |
|---|---|---|---|---|---|
| AR05) | 92.0 | 40 | MFM | AR | Máxima FM, Zaragoza |
| CA25) | 92.0 | 100 | CR | CA | Catalunya Informació, Barcelona Collserola |
| CA25) | 92.0 | | CR | CA | Catalunya Informació, Sant Carles, Tarragona |
| CA25) | 92.0 | | CR | CA | Catalunya R., Senterada, Lleida |
| VA29) | 92.0 | 10 | MEGA | VA | MegaStar FM, València |
| EU10) | 92.2 | 24 | RP | EU | Popular Irratia Bilbo-Bilbao |
| CA25) | 92.2 | | CR | C | Catalunya Música, Falset, Tarragona |
| CA25) | 92.3 | | CR | CA | Catalunya Informació, L'Estartit, Girona |
| MA05) | 92.4 | 14 | SER | MA | Radiolé, Madrid |
| CA25) | 92.5 | 100 | CR | CA | Icat FM. Barcelona Collserola |
| CA25) | 92.5 | | CR | CA | Catalunya R., Calonge, Girona |
| EX08) | 92.6 | 6 | SER | EX | Los 40, Cáceres |
| GA21) | 92.6 | 8 | RV | GA | R. Voz, A Coruña |
| CA25) | 92.6 | | CR | C | Catalunya R., Camprodón, Girona |
| CM21) | 92.7 | 6 | KFM | CM | Kiss FM, Albacete |
| CA25) | 92.7 | | CR | CA | Catalunya R., Portbou, Girona |
| AN22) | 92.8 | 8 | D | AN | Cadena Dial, Granada |
| VA18) | 92.8 | 6 | EFM | VA | Europa FM, Elx-Elche |
| CA25) | 92.8 | | CR | CA | Catalunya Música, Baqueira, Val D'Arán |
| CL34) | 92.9 | 6 | CLR | CL | Castilla Leon R ., Burgos |
| CA25) | 92.9 | | CR | CA | Catalunya R., Palafrugell, Girona |
| CA25) | 93.0 | | CR | CA | IcatFM, Boí, Lleida |
| CA25) | 93.0 | | CR | CA | IcatFM, Ponts, Lleida |
| CA25) | 93.0 | | CR | CA | Catalunya R., Sant Feliu de Guixols, Girona |
| AN43) | 93.1 | 5 | CSR | AN | Canal Fiesta R. Baza, Granada |
| AN72) | 93.1 | 8 | D | AN | Cadena Dial, Málaga |
| EU18) | 93.1 | 8 | | EU | R.Gorbea, Vitoria-Gasteiz |
| GA22) | 93.1 | 5 | RV | GA | R. Voz,. Pontevedra |
| CA25) | 93.1 | | CR | CA | IcatFM, Pujalt, Tarragona |
| CA25) | 93.1 | | CR | CA | IcatFM, Solsona, Lleida |
| VA11) | 93.1 | 5 | ROCK | VA | ROCK FM, València |
| AN73) | 93.2 | 5 | ROCK | AN | ROCKFM , Sevilla |
| VA08) | 93.2 | 8 | D | VA | Cadena Dial, Alicante |
| CA25) | 93.2 | | CR | CA | IcatFM, Mur, Lleida |
| CA25) | 93.3 | 5 | CR | BA | Catalunya R., Alfabia, Palma M. |
| CA25) | 93.3 | | CR | CA | IcatFM, Sant Pere de Ribes, Barcelona |
| CA25) | 93.3 | | CR | CA | Catalunya Música, Guardiola, Barcelona |
| GA13) | 93.4 | 8 | SER | GA | SER R. Coruña, A Coruña |
| CA30) | 93.4 | 5 | SER | CA | SER, R. LLeida |
| AR05) | 93.5 | 8 | SER | AR | R. Zaragoza 2, Zaragoza |
| CA25) | 93.5 | 20 | OCR | CA | Onda Cero R., Collserola Barcelona |
| CA14) | 93.5 | | COPE | CA | COPE Reus |
| CM15) | 93.6 | | COPE | CM | COPE Ciudad Real |
| CA25) | 93.6 | | CR | CA | Catalunya Informació, Senterada, Lleida |
| CA25) | 93.7 | | CR | CA | IcatFM, Sant Hilari, Girona |
| CA25) | 93.7 | | CR | CA | Catalunya Música, Cadaqués, Girona |
| CA25) | 93.7 | | CR | CA | Catalunya Música, Sant Carles, Tarragona |
| CA25) | 93.7 | | CR | CA | Catalunya Música, Almacelles, Lleida |
| AN47) | 93.8 | 5 | EFM | AN | Europa FM, Almería |
| AN72) | 93.8 | 5 | RO | AN | Radiolé, Málaga |
| CA25) | 93.8 | | CR | CA | Catalunya R., Falset, Tarragona |
| CA25) | 93.8 | | CR | CA | Catalunya Informació, Pujalt |
| CA25) | 93.8 | | CR | CA | Catalunya Música, Artesa de Segre, Lleida |
| CA25) | 93.9 | | CR | CA | Catalunya Informació, Montblanc, Tarragona |
| MA05) | 93.9 | 100 | SER | MA | Los 40, Madrid |
| CA08) | 93.9 | 8 | SER | CA | Los 40, Collserola Barcelona |
| AN42) | 94.0 | 10 | CSR | AN | Canal Sur R., Huelva |
| GA23) | 94.0 | 6 | OCR | GA | Kiss FM, Vigo |
| GA07) | 94.1 | 20 | RG | GA | R. Galega, Santiago de Compostela |
| CA25) | 94.1 | | CR | CA | Catalunya Informació, Calonge, Girona |
| AN12) | 94.2 | 5 | ROCK | AN | ROCKFM, Jaén |
| CT03) | 94.2 | 6 | RMA | CT | R. Marca, Santander |
| CA25) | 94.2 | | CR | CA | Catalunya Informació, Sant Celoni, Barcelona |
| AN59) | 94.3 | 20 | CSR | AN | RAI R.Andalucía Informacion., Sevilla |
| AN55) | 94.3 | 10 | CSR | AN | Canal Sur R., Córdoba |
| CL23) | 94.3 | 6 | D | CL | Cadena Dial, Burgos |
| CA25) | 94.3 | | CR | CA | Catalunya R., Flix, Tarragona |
| CA11) | 94.4 | 10 | MFM | CA | Maxima FM,. Girona, Rocacorba |
| CL39) | 94.4 | 8 | EFM | CL | Europa FM, Valladolid |
| EU08) | 94.4 | 20 | EI | EU | Euskadi Irratia,Donosti-S Sebastián |
| EX08) | 94.4 | 6 | SER | EX | SER, Cáceres |
| CA25) | 94.5 | 5 | CR | CA | Catalunya Informació, Collsuspina Barcelona |
| AN43) | 94.6 | 5 | CSR | AN | Canal Fiesta R., Loja,Granada |
| CA25) | 94.6 | | CR | CA | Catalunya Informació, Guardiola, Barcelona |
| EU07) | 94.7 | 20 | EI | EU | Euskadi Gaztea, Bilbo-Bilbao |
| CA25) | 94.7 | | CR | CA | IcatFM, Arbucies, Girona |
| CA25) | 94.7 | | CR | CA | Catalunya R., Tossa de Mar, Girona |
| CA25) | 94.7 | | CR | CA | Catalunya Informació, Sant Pere de Ribes, Barcelona |
| CA25) | 94.7 | | CR | CA | Catalunya Información, Sant Pere de Ribes |
| AN15) | 94.8 | 40 | M80 | AN | M80, Sevilla |
| CA25) | 94.8 | | CR | CA | Catalunya Informació, La Molina, Girona |
| AN41) | 94.9 | 60 | CSR | AN | RAI R.Andalucía Informacion. Málaga |
| CA07) | 94.9 | 20 | EFM | CA | Europa FM, Collserola Barcelona |
| CM10) | 95.0 | 6 | | CM | R. Surco, Albacete |
| EU09) | 95.0 | 20 | EI | EU | Euskadi Irratia, Vitoria-Gasteiz |
| CA25) | 95.0 | | CR | CA | Catalunya Informació, Vielha, Val D'Arán |
| CA25) | 95.0 | | CR | CA | Catalunya Música, Cabra del Camp, Tarragona |
| AN43) | 95.1 | 5 | CSR | AN | Canal Sur R., Granada |
| CA11) | 95.1 | 10 | D | MA | Cadena Dial Girona, Rocacorba |
| MA17) | 95.1 | 100 | IE | MA | R. Inter, Madrid |
| CA25) | 95.1 | | CR | CA | Catalunya Música, Ponts, Lleida |
| CA08) | 95.1 | 10 | SER | CA | Cadena Dial, Rocacorba, Girona |
| AS08) | 95.2 | 6 | OCR | AS | Onda Cero R., Oviedo |
| CA25) | 95.2 | | CR | BA | Catalunya R., Monte Toro, Menorca |
| AR05) | 95.3 | 13 | SER | AR | Los 40, Zaragoza |
| CA31) | 95.3 | 5 | OCR | CA | Onda Cero R., Tarragona |
| CA25) | 95.3 | | CR | CA | Catalunya R., Ripoll, Girona |
| AS03) | 95.4 | 10 | RPA | AS | RPA,R.Principado Asturias, Boal |
| AN44) | 95.4 | 8 | KFM | AN | Kiss FM, Cádiz |
| CM14) | 95.4 | | COPE | CM | COPE Albacete |
| CA25) | 95.4 | | CR | CA | Catalunya R., Soriguera, Lleida |
| CA25) | 95.4 | | CR | CA | Catalunya R., Boí, Lleida |
| CA25) | 95.5 | | CR | BA | Catalunya R., S.Llorenç, Eivissa i Formentera |
| CA25) | 95.5 | | CR | CA | Catalunya Informació, Ulldemolins, Tarragona |
| AN52) | 95.6 | 8 | KFM | AN | Kiss FM, Córdoba |
| CA25) | 95.6 | | CR | CA | Catalunya R., Sant Pere de Ribes, Barcelona |
| CA25) | 95.6 | | CR | CA | Catalunya Informació, Puigdevall, Lleida |
| CA25) | 95.7 | | CR | CA | Catalunya Informació, Artesa de Segre, Lleida |
| BA02) | 95.8 | 5 | | BA | Insel R., Mallorca |
| CA28) | 95.8 | 20 | KFM | CA | Kiss FM, Barcelona |
| AN45) | 95.9 | 40 | OCR | AN | Onda Cero R., Sevilla |
| CA32) | 95.9 | 5 | RTT | VA | R. Tele Taxi, Benicassim, Valencia |
| CA08) | 96.0 | 20 | RO | CA | Radiolé, Collserola Barcelona |
| MA02) | 96.0 | 20 | FUN | MA | FUN R. Madrid |
| RI03) | 96.0 | 6 | KFM | RI | Kiss FM, Logroño |
| EU04) | 96.1 | 20 | EI | EU | Euskadi Gaztea, Zaldiaran |
| VA10) | 96.1 | 10 | M80 | VA | M80, València |
| CA25) | 96.1 | | CR | CA | Catalunya R., Solsona, Lleida |
| CL32) | 96.2 | 6 | OCR | CL | Europa FM, Salamanca |
| AN67) | 96.2 | 6 | D | AN | Cadena Dial Almería, Almería |
| CA25) | 96.2 | | CR | CA | Catalunya R., Bellmunt, Lleida |
| AN33) | 96.3 | 8 | OCR | AN | Onda Melodia, Malaga |
| MU03) | 96.3 | 5 | AMC | MU | R. 5, Cartagena |
| CM12) | 96.4 | 6 | RO | CM | Radiolé, Albacete |
| CA25) | 96.4 | | CR | BA | Catalunya R., Alcúdia, Balears |
| CA25) | 96.4 | | CR | CA | Catalunya Música, Cabrils, Barcelona |
| EU08) | 96.5 | 20 | EI | EU | R. Euskadi, Donosti-San Sebastián |
| AS09) | 96.5 | 8 | SER | AS | R. Gijón, Gijón |
| VA22) | 96.5 | 8 | R9 | VA | R. Nou, Alacant-Alicante |
| CL35) | 96.5 | | KFM | CL | Kiss FM, León |
| CA25) | 96.5 | 10 | CR | CA | IcatFM, Montserrat, Barcelona |
| AN43) | 96.6 | 5 | CSR | AN | Canal Sur R., Loja, Granada |
| GA08) | 96.6 | 6 | RG | GA | R. Galega Música, Friol |
| CA25) | 96.7 | 25 | CR | CA | Catalunya Música, Girona, Rocacorba |
| CA25) | 96.7 | | CR | CA | IcatFM, Ribes de Fresser, Girona |
| MU11) | 96.7 | 6 | KFM | MU | Kiss FM, Cartagena |
| AN22) | 96.8 | 3 | RO | AN | Radiolé, Granada |
| VA25) | 96.9 | 20 | KFM | VA | Kiss FM, València |
| CA08) | 96.9 | 8 | SER | CA | R. Barcelona 2, Collserola Barcelona |
| MA16) | 96.9 | 20 | RM | MA | R. María España, Madrid |
| CA25) | 96.9 | | CR | CA | Catalunya R., Oliana, Lleida |
| EX08) | 97.0 | 6 | D | EX | Cadena Dial, Cáceres |
| CA25) | 97.0 | | CR | CA | IcatFM, Palafrugell, Girona |
| CA25) | 97.0 | | CR | CA | Catalunya Informació, Alpicat, Lleida |
| AN15) | 97.1 | 40 | SER | AN | Los 40, . Sevilla |
| AN43) | 97.1 | 30 | CSR | AN | Canal Fiesta R., Granada |
| AR05) | 97.1 | 40 | D | AR | CadenaDial Zaragoza, Zaragoza |
| CL23) | 97.1 | 6 | SER | CL | R. Castilla, Burgos |
| MU04) | 97.1 | 5 | | MU | Onda Mediterranea R., Cartagena |
| CA25) | 97.1 | | CR | CA | Catalunya Música, Sant Feliu de Guixols, Girona |
| CA25) | 97.1 | | CR | CA | Catalunya Música, Olot, Girona |

| FM | MHz | kW | Net | Rg | Station, location |
|---|---|---|---|---|---|
| CA25) | 97.1 | | CR | CA | Catalunya Música, Sant Hilari, Girona |
| MA07) | 97.2 | 100 | | MA | Top R. Latina , Madrid |
| CA25) | 97.2 | | CR | CA | Catalunya R., Sant Celoni, Barcelona |
| CA25) | 97.2 | | CR | CA | Catalunya Informació, Calella, Barcelona |
| CA25) | 97.3 | 10 | CR | CA | Catalunya R., Montserrat Barcelona |
| CA25) | 97.3 | | CR | CA | Catalunya Música, Flix, Tarragona |
| EU05 | 97.3 | 8 | C100 | EU | Cadena 100, Vitoria-Gasteiz |
| EU06) | 97.3 | 5 | | EU | Fórmula Hit, Portugalete, Gipuzcoa |
| VA 05) | 97.3 | 8 | OCR | VA | Onda Melodía, Altea.Alicante |
| CA11) | 97.4 | 10 | ONA | CA | FM, Figueres, Girona |
| CA25) | 97.4 | | CR | CA | Catalunya R., Sant Carles, Tarragona |
| CA25) | 97.4 | | CR | CA | Catalunya Música, Mur, Lleida |
| CA25) | 97.4 | 10 | SER | CA | SER Catalunya, Rocacorba, Girona |
| AR06) | 97.5 | 40 | COPE | AR | COPE, Zaragoza |
| CM13) | 97.5 | | COPE | CM | COPE Puertollano |
| CA25) | 97.5 | | CR | CA | IcatFM, Artesa de Segre, Lleida |
| CA25) | 97.5 | | CR | CA | IcatFM, Senterada, Lleida |
| CA25) | 97.5 | | CR | CA | Catalunya R., Montblanc, Tarragona |
| GA13) | 97.6 | 8 | M80 | GA | M80, A Coruña |
| MA18) | 97.6 | 4 | OCR | MA | Onda Cero R., Alcalá de Henares, Madrid |
| CL32) | 97.6 | 6 | OCR | CL | Onda Cero R., Zaragoza |
| CA25) | 97.6 | | CR | CA | IcatFM, Portbou, Girona |
| CA25) | 97.6 | | CR | CA | Catalunya R., Baqueira, Val D'Arán |
| CA32) | 97.7 | 20 | RTT | CA | R. Tele Taxi, Collserola Barcelona |
| VA27) | 97.7 | 20 | VA | LA | 97 Punto 7, València |
| AN48) | 97.9 | 30 | CSR | AN | Canal Fiesta R., Jaén |
| AR06) | 97.9 | 40 | C100 | AR | Cadena 100, Zaragoza |
| CA25) | 97.9 | | CR | CA | Catalunya R., Pujalt, Tarragona |
| CA25) | 97.9 | | CR | CA | Catalunya Informació, Ponts, Lleida |
| CA25) | 97.9 | | CR | CA | Catalunya Informació, Tossa de Mar, Girona |
| AN13) | 98.0 | 30 | COPE | AN | COPE, Alanis, Sevilla |
| EU13) | 98.0 | 8 | MEGA | EU | MegaStar FM, Donosti-San Sebastián |
| EU15) | 98.0 | 8 | | EU | R. Álava,Onda Vasca, Vitoria-Gasteiz |
| MA13) | 98.0 | 100 | OCR | MA | Onda Cero R., Madrid |
| CA14) | 98.0 | | COPE | CA | COPE Tortosa |
| CA25) | 98.0 | | CR | CA | Catalunya Informació, Vilaller, Lleida |
| CA25) | 98.0 | | CR | CA | Catalunya Informació, Portilló, Val D'Arán |
| AN49) | 98.1 | 5 | SER | AN | R. Huelva, Huelva |
| CL18) | 98.1 | 8 | MFM | CL | Maxima FM, Valladolid |
| EX03) | 98.1 | 1 | CER | EX | Canal Extremadura R., Zafra, Badajoz |
| VA07) | 98.1 | 10 | ROCK | VA | ROCK FM, Alicante |
| CA25) | 98.1 | | CR | CA | Catalunya Informació, Cabra del Camp |
| RI04) | 98.2 | 6 | MEGA | RI | MegaStar FM, Logroño |
| CA25) | 98.2 | | CR | CA | Catalunya R., El Vendrell, Tarragona |
| CA25) | 98.2 | | CR | CA | Catalunya Informació, Lloret, Girona |
| CA25) | 98.3 | 10 | CR | CA | Catalunya Informació, Montserrat, Barcelona |
| CM25) | 98.3 | 5 | KFM | CM | Kiss FM, Toledo |
| NA02) | 98.3 | 6 | | NA | 98.3 R., Pamplona |
| BA06) | 98.4 | 5 | MFM | BA | Maxima FM, Alfábia, Palma M. |
| VA10) | 98.4 | 20 | D | VA | Cadena Dial Mediterraneo, València |
| CA25) | 98.4 | | CR | CA | Catalunya Música, Baqueira, Val D'Arán |
| CA25) | 98.4 | | CR | CA | Catalunya Informació, Àrenys de Munt, Barcelona |
| CA25) | 98.5 | 5 | CR | CA | Catalunya Informació, Montcaro, Tortosa |
| CA40) | 98.5 | 10 | SER | CA | SER, Girona |
| CT11) | 98.5 | 5 | KFM | CT | Kiss FM, Santander |
| CM22) | 98.5 | 5 | OCR | CM | Onda Cero R., Talavera de la Reina, Toledo |
| AR05) | 98.6 | 40 | M80 | AR | M80, Zaragoza |
| CL36) | 98.6 | 8 | | CL | R. Arlanzón, Burgos |
| CM08) | 98.6 | 5 | RCM | CM | R. Castilla-La Mancha, Valdepeñas, Ciudad Real |
| EU11) | 98.8 | 5 | M80 | EU | M80, Bilbao |
| MU17) | 98.8 | 6 | RMA | MU | Solo R. R., Marca , Cartagena |
| BA16) | 98.8 | 5 | ROCK | BA | ROCK FM, Ultima Hora., Palma de Mallorca |
| CA25) | 98.8 | | CR | CA | Catalunya Música, Camprodón, Girona |
| CA22) | 98.9 | 10 | OCR | CA | Onda Cero R., Rocacorba Girona |
| VA26) | 98.9 | 5 | COPE | VA | COPE, R.Sirena, Benidorm |
| CA25) | 98.9 | | CR | CA | Catalunya Música, Oliana, Lleida |
| CA25) | 98.9 | | CR | CA | Catalunya Música, Cubells-Balaguer, Lleida |
| VA11) | 99.0 | 40 | C100 | VA | Cadena 100, València |
| CA25) | 99.0 | | CR | CA | Catalunya Música, Almenar, Lleida |
| CA25) | 99.0 | | CR | CA | Catalunya Música, Arbúcies, Girona |
| CL42) | 99.1 | 5 | KFM | CL | Kiss FM, Zamora |
| EU04) | 99.1 | 5 | | EU | Euskadi Gaztea Vitoria-Gasteiz |
| MA03) | 99.1 | 10 | ES | MA | esRadio, Madrid |
| CA25) | 99.1 | | CR | CA | Catalunya Música, Calella, Barcelona |
| CA25) | 99.2 | | CR | CA | IcatFM, Calonge, Girona |
| CA25) | 99.2 | | CR | CA | IcatFM, Montagut, Girona |
| CA25) | 99.2 | | CR | CA | Catalunya R., Igualada, Barcelona |
| CL17) | 99.3 | 6 | D | CL | Cadena Dial, Salamanca |
| MU09) | 99.3 | 8 | KFM | MU | Kiss FM, Murcia |
| AN74) | 99.4 | 30 | CSR | AN | RAI R. Andalucía Informacion., Cádiz |
| AN55) | 99.4 | 60 | CSR | AN | RAI R. Andalucía Informacion., Córdoba |
| AR12) | 99.4 | 40 | OCR | AR | Onda Cero R., Zaragoza |
| CA08) | 99.4 | 10 | D | CA | Cadena Dial Barcelona, Barcelona |
| CL33) | 99.4 | 8 | KFM | CL | Kiss FM, Valladolid |
| CA25) | 99.4 | | CR | CA | Catalunya Informació, Maçanet, Girona |
| AN51) | 99.5 | 8 | EFM | AN | Europa FM, Granada |
| MA08) | 99.5 | 100 | C100 | MA | Cadena 100, Madrid |
| CA05) | 99.6 | 10 | GR | CA | Flaix FM, Girona, Rocacorba |
| CA25) | 99.7 | 5 | CR | CA | Catalunya R., Collsuspina, Barcelona |
| CA25) | 99.7 | | CR | CA | IcatFM, Arenys de Munt, Barcelona |
| CA25) | 99.7 | | CR | CA | Catalunya Informació, El Vendrell, Tarragona |
| MA04) | 99.8 | 10 | | MA | R. Sol XXI, Madrid |
| CA25) | 99.8 | | CR | CA | IcatFM, Ulldemolins, Tarragona |
| CA25) | 99.8 | | CR | CA | IcatFM, Tossa de Mar, Girona |
| AN19) | 99.9 | 8 | D | AN | Cadena Dial Bahía, Cádiz |
| BA18) | 99.9 | 8 | RM | BA | R. Maria, Palma de Mallorca |
| AS03) | 100.0 | 8 | RPA | AS | R.Principado Asturias, Los Oscos |
| CA09) | 100.0 | 20 | C100 | CA | Cadena 100, Collserola Barcelona |
| CA25) | 100.0 | | CR | CA | Icat FM, Vielha, Val D'Aran |
| CA25) | 100.1 | 10 | CR | CA | Catalunya R., Girona, Rocacorba |
| CA34) | 100.1 | 10 | RAC | CA | RAC 1, Rocacorba, Girona |
| EU07) | 100.1 | 20 | EI | EU | EITB IrratiaMusika, Bilbo-Bilbao |
| CA25) | 100.2 | 35 | CR | CA | Catalunya R., La Mussara,Tarragona |
| GA08) | 100.2 | 5 | RG | GA | R. Galega Música, Xistral |
| AN58) | 100.3 | 40 | KFM | AN | Kiss FM, Sevilla |
| CM12) | 100.3 | 5 | SER | CM | SER Albacete |
| AN72) | 100.4 | 6 | SER | AN | SER, Málaga |
| CL18) | 100.4 | 8 | D | CL | Cadena Dial, Valladolid |
| EU22) | 100.4 | 5 | SER | EU | Los 40, Vitoria-Gasteiz |
| MA09) | 100.4 | 5 | | MA | R. Círculo, Madrid |
| VA10) | 100.4 | 20 | SER | VA | R. Valencia 2, Valencia |
| CA25) | 100.4 | | CR | CA | Icat FM, La Molina, Girona |
| CA25) | 100.4 | | CR | CA | Catalunya Música, Palafrugell, Girona |
| AR12) | 100.5 | 10 | EFM | AR | Europa FM, Zaragoza |
| AS03) | 100.5 | 20 | RPA | AS | R.Principado Asturias, Gijón |
| CA25) | 100.5 | 5 | CR | CA | Catalunya Música, Collsuspina, Barcelona |
| CA25) | 100.5 | | CR | CA | Catalunya Informació, Mur, Lleida |
| CM08) | 100.5 | 5 | RCM | CM | R. Castilla-La Mancha, Guadalajara |
| CM23) | 100.5 | 5 | | CM | R. Santa María, Toledo |
| GA12) | 100.6 | 8 | SER | GA | SER. Vigo 2, Vigo |
| AN48) | 100.6 | 30 | CSR | AN | Canal Sur R., Jaén |
| BA16) | 100.6 | 5 | GR | BA | Flaix FM, Mallorca |
| GA08) | 100.6 | 5 | RG | GA | R. Galega Música, Monte Páramo |
| CA25) | 100.7 | 80 | CR | CA | Catalunya R., Alpicat, Lleida |
| CA05) | 100.7 | 10 | GR | CA | Flaixbac FM, Girona, Rocacorba |
| MA08) | 100.7 | 20 | MEGA | MA | MegaStar FM, Madrid |
| AN55) | 100.8 | 5 | CSR | AN | Canal Sur R., Córdoba |
| EX03) | 100.8 | 5 | CER | EX | Canal Extremadura R., Badajoz |
| VA19) | 100.8 | 6 | COPE | VA | COPE,Elche |
| GA24) | 100.9 | 30 | RG | GA | R. Galega, Xesteiras, Pontevedra |
| BA11) | 101.0 | 5 | OCR | BA | Onda Melodía Mallorca |
| CA34) | 101.0 | 5 | RAC | CA | Catalunya R., Mont Caro, Tortosa |
| CA25) | 101.0 | | CR | CA | Icat FM, Cogulló, Lleida |
| EU05) | 101.0 | 8 | COPE | EU | COPE, Vitoria |
| AN72) | 101.1 | 10 | M80 | AN | M80, Málaga |
| CT06) | 101.1 | 6 | M80 | CT | M80, Santander |
| CA25) | 101.1 | | CR | CA | Icat FM, La Figuerassa, Barcelona |
| VA23) | 101.2 | 20 | OCR | VA | Onda Cero R., València |
| AN56) | 101.2 | 5 | OCR | AN | Onda Cero R., Huelva |
| GA12) | 101.2 | 6 | M80 | GA | M80, Vigo |
| CA25) | 101.2 | | CR | CA | Icat FM, Lloret, Girona |
| CA25) | 101.2 | | CR | CA | Catalunya Música, Vilaller, Lleida |
| CA25) | 101.2 | | CR | CA | Catalunya Música, Portilló, Val D'Arán |
| MA14) | 101.3 | 100 | | MA | Onda Madrid, Madrid |
| AN55) | 101.3 | 30 | CSR | AN | Canal Fiesta R., Córdoba |
| AN43) | 101.3 | 5 | CSR | AN | RAI R. Andalucía Informacion Loja, Granada |
| CA25) | 101.3 | | CR | CA | Catalunya Informació, Solsona, Lleida |
| AS03) | 101.4 | 10 | RPA | AS | R. Principado Asturias, Avilés |
| RI02) | 101.4 | 6 | COPE | RI | Cadena 100, Logroño |
| CA25) | 101.4 | | CR | CA | Catalunya R., Ribes de Freser, Girona |
| CA25) | 101.4 | | CR | CA | Catalunya Informació, Sant Feliu de Guíxols, Girona |
| AN15) | 101.5 | 40 | SER | AN | Radiolé, Sevilla |
| CA25) | 101.5 | 8 | CR | CA | Catalunya Música, Collserola Barcelona |
| EU07) | 101.5 | 24 | OCR | EU | Onda Cero R., Bilbo-Bilbao |
| AN53) | 101.6 | 5 | EFM | AN | Europa FM Costa del Sol, Mijas, Malaga |
| CM08) | 101.6 | 5 | CLR | CM | Castilla Leon R, Cuenca |
| CA38) | 101.7 | 25 | CR | CA | Catalunya Informació, Girona, Rocacorba |

| FM | MHz | kW | Net | Rg | Station, location |
|---|---|---|---|---|---|
| CA25) | 101.7 | | CR | CA | Catalunya Informació, Almacelles, Lleida |
| AN67) | 101.8 | 6 | SER | AN | Los 40, Almería |
| CA06) | 101.8 | 5 | GR | CA | Flaix FM, Tarragona |
| AN59) | 101.9 | 60 | CSR | AN | Canal Fiesta R., Sevilla |
| EU04) | 101.9 | 8 | EI | EU | Euskadi Irratia, Amurrio,Alava |
| GA30) | 101.9 | 6 | RMA | GA | R. Marca, Vigo |
| CA25) | 101.9 | | CR | CA | Catalunya Informació, Cubells-Balaguer, Lleida |
| AN14) | 102.0 | 8 | COPE | AN | COPE, Cádiz |
| CA09) | 102.0 | 20 | COPE | CA | COPE, Barcelona |
| CA25) | 102.0 | | CR | CA | Catalunya R., Cogulló, Lleida |
| CA25) | 102.0 | | CR | CA | Catalunya Música, Bellmunt |
| CA25) | 102.0 | | CR | CA | Catalunya R., Senterada, Lleida |
| CA25) | 102.0 | | CR | CA | Catalunya Música, Ulldemolins, Tarragona |
| CA25) | 102.2 | 25 | CR | CA | Catalunya R, Girona, Rocacorba |
| AN42) | 102.2 | 30 | CSR | AN | Canal Fiesta R., Huelva |
| CA25) | 102.2 | | CR | CA | Catalunya Música, Igualada, Barcelona |
| BA06) | 102.3 | 4 | M80 | BA | M80 Mallorca, Palma de Mallorca |
| CA42) | 102.3 | 10 | FUN | CA | FUN R., Barcelona |
| GA25) | 102.3 | 40 | RG | GA | R. Galega, Domaio |
| AN68) | 102.4 | 40 | D | AN | Cadena Dial Sevilla, Sevilla |
| CA25) | 102.4 | 10 | CR | CA | Catalunya Música, Montserrat, Barcelona |
| CT06) | 102.4 | 6 | SER | CT | SER, Liérganes, Santander |
| EU28) | 102.4 | 6 | OCR | EU | Onda Cero R., Vitoria |
| AN57) | 102.5 | 70 | CSR | AN | Canal Fiesta R., Almería, Pechina |
| CA25) | 102.5 | 10 | CR | CA | Catalunya Música, Mont Caro, Tortosa |
| CM08) | 102.5 | 12 | RCM | CM | R. Castilla-La Mancha, Ciudad Real |
| EU29) | 102.5 | 8 | OCR | EU | Onda Cero R., Donosti-San Sebastián |
| AN22) | 102.5 | 8 | D | AN | Cadena Dial, Granada |
| EX03) | 102.6 | 60 | CER | EX | Canal Extremadura R., Montánchez |
| EU23) | 102.6 | 15 | COPE | EU | Bizkaia Irratia, Bilbo-Bilbao |
| CA25) | 102.6 | | CR | CA | Icat FM, Olot, Girona |
| CA25) | 102.6 | | CR | CA | Catalunya Música, L'Estartit, Girona |
| MA13) | 102.7 | 100 | KFM | MA | Kiss FM, Madrid |
| GA26) | 102.7 | 8 | ES | GA | esRADIO.,A Coruña |
| AN72) | 102.8 | 8 | SER | AN | Los 40,, Mijas, Málaga |
| CA25) | 102.8 | 100 | CR | CA | Catalunya R. Collserola Barcelona |
| CA25) | 102.8 | | CR | CA | IcatFM, Maçanet, Girona |
| CL43) | 102.8 | 8 | CLR | CL | Castilla Leon R., Valladolid |
| BA15) | 102.8 | 5 | SER | BA | SER Ibiza, Ibiza |
| VA32) | 102.8 | 90 | R9 | VA | Sí R., Benicassim |
| CA25) | 102.9 | | CR | CA | Catalunya Informació, Pont de Suert, Lleida |
| CA25) | 103.0 | | CR | CA | Icat FM, Almenar, Lleida |
| CA25) | 103.0 | | CR | CA | Catalunya R., Mur, Lleida |
| CA25) | 103.0 | | CR | CA | Catalunya Música, Cogulló, Lleida |
| AN71) | 103.1 | 5 | | AN | R. Pinomar, Málaga |
| CA25) | 103.1 | | CR | CA | Catalunya Informació, Cabrils, Barcelona |
| AN15) | 103.2 | 28 | SER | AN | SER Sevilla 2, Sevilla |
| EU07) | 103.2 | 20 | EI | EU | R. Euskadi, Bilbo-Bilbao |
| MA22) | 103.2 | 5 | | MA | RTC - Radio TV Cristiana, Madrid |
| VA23) | 103.2 | 10 | EFM | VA | Europa FM, València |
| CA25) | 103.2 | | CR | CA | IcatFM,Almacelles, Lleida |
| CA25) | 103.2 | | CR | CA | Catalunya Informació, Montagut, Lleida |
| AN22) | 103.3 | 8 | MFM | AN | Maxima FM, Granada |
| CA25) | 103.3 | | CR | CA | Icat FM, Cubells-Balaguer, Lleida |
| CA29) | 103.4 | 10 | RE | CA | R. Estel, Girona, Rocacorba |
| CL37) | 103.4 | 6 | CLR | CL | Castilla Leon R, Salamanca |
| CM08) | 103.4 | 5 | RCM | CM | R. Castilla-La Mancha, Puertollano, Ciudad Real |
| EU09) | 103.4 | 20 | EI | EU | EITB Musika, Vitoria-Gasteiz |
| BA19) | 103.4 | | COPE | BA | COPE Ibiza – Eivissa |
| CA25) | 103.4 | | CR | CA | Icat FM, Baqueira, Val D'Aran |
| AN43) | 103.5 | 60 | CSR | AN | Canal Sur R., Sierra de Lújar, Córdoba |
| CA08) | 103.5 | 20 | SER | CA | Ona FM, ., Collserola Barcelona |
| EU08) | 103.5 | 20 | EI | EU | Euskadi Gaztea,Donosti-S. Sebastián |
| CA25) | 103.5 | | CR | CA | Catalunya Informació, Camprodón, Girona |
| AN55) | 103 6 | 30 | CSR | AN | Canal Sur R., Córdoba |
| EU30) | 103.7 | 24 | ROCK | EU | ROCK FM , Bilbo-Bilbao |
| GA08) | 103.7 | 70 | RG | GA | R.Galega, Monte Páramo |
| GA30) | 103.8 | 6 | RV | GA | R. Voz, Vigo |
| CA25) | 103.8 | | CR | CA | Catalunya Informació, Bellmunt |
| AN59) | 103.9 | 30 | CSR | AN | Canal Fiesta R., Sevilla, Valencina |
| GA25) | 103.9 | 40 | RG | GA | R. Galega, Monte Faro |
| MA05) | 103.9 | 30 | | MA | Ke Buena FM, Madrid |
| MU07) | 103.9 | 8 | D | MU | Cadena Dial, Murcia, Murcia |
| CA25) | 103.9 | | CR | CA | Icat FM, Calella, Barcelona |
| CA25) | 103.9 | | CR | CA | Catalunya Música, Sant Celoni, Barcelona |
| CM08) | 104.0 | 10 | RCM | CM | R. Castilla-La Mancha, Chinchilla, Albacete |
| EX03) | 104.0 | 5 | CER | EX | Canal Extremadura R., Cáceres |
| CA25) | 104.0 | | CR | VA | Catalunya R., Ontinyent, Valencia |
| CA25) | 104.0 | | CR | CA | Catalunya Informació, Oliana, Lleida |
| CA25) | 104.0 | | CR | CA | Catalunya Música, Igualada, Barcelona |
| AN24) | 104.1 | 5 | ROCK | AN | ROCK FM, Córdoba |
| AN63) | 104.1 | 6 | KFM | AN | Kiss FM, Almería |
| CA25) | 104.1 | | CR | CA | Icat FM, Sant Feliu de Guixols, Girona |
| CA25) | 104.1 | | CR | CA | Catalunya R., Cadaqués, Girona |
| EU09) | 104.1 | 20 | EI | EU | R. Vitoria/Gasteiz Irratia, Vitoria-Gasteiz |
| AN43) | 104.2 | 8 | CSR | AN | Canal Sur R., Granada |
| AS11) | 104.2 | 5 | | AS | R. Amistad, Hevia-Siero, Gijón |
| CA08) | 104.2 | 20 | SER | CA | Máxima FM, Collserola Barcelona |
| GA31) | 104.2 | 5 | RG | GA | R. Galega Música, Santiago de Compostela |
| MA05) | 104.3 | 37 | MFM | MA | Máxima FM, Madrid |
| CA25) | 104.3 | | CR | CA | Catalunya Música, Ribes de Freser, Girona |
| AN42) | 104.4 | 30 | CSR | AN | Canal Sur R., Huelva |
| EU07) | 104.4 | 20 | EI | EU | Euskadi Irratia, Bilbo-Bilbao |
| CA25) | 104.4 | | CR | CA | Catalunya Informació, Arbúcies, Girona |
| CA25) | 104.5 | 2 | CR | CA | Catalunya Informació, La Mussara, Tarragona |
| AN41) | 104.6 | 30 | CSR | AN | Canal Sur R., Málaga |
| AN59) | 104.6 | 60 | CSR | AN | RAI R.Andalucía Informacion, Sevilla |
| MU16) | 104.6 | 6 | ORM | MU | Onda Regional Murcia, Cartagena |
| CA25) | 104.6 | | CR | CA | Catalunya R., Lloret, Girona |
| VA20) | 104.7 | 5 | LOCA | VA | LOCA R., Elx |
| GA12) | 104.7 | 6 | MFM | GA | Máxima FM, Vigo |
| CA25) | 104.7 | | CR | CA | Catalunya R., Vilaller, Lleida |
| CA25) | 104.7 | | CR | CA | Catalunya R., Portilló, Val D'Arán |
| AN37) | 104.8 | 30 | CSR | AN | Canal Sur R., Jerez de la Frontera |
| AN57) | 104.8 | 20 | CSR | AN | Canal Sur R., Almería |
| AR14) | 104.8 | 10 | RKM | AR | RKM, Zaragoza |
| EU31) | 104.8 | 5 | RKM | EU | RKM, Vitoria-Gasteiz |
| GA25) | 104.8 | 40 | RG | GA | R. Galega, Monte Meda |
| CA25) | 104.8 | | CR | CA | Catalunya Informació, Palafrugell, Girona |
| CA25) | 104.8 | | CR | CA | Catalunya Música, Montagut, Girona |
| AN43) | 104.9 | 30 | CSR | AN | Canal Sur R., Granada |
| EU23) | 104.9 | 8 | EI | EU | Euskadi Gaztea, Amurrio |
| CA25) | 104.9 | | CR | CA | Icat FM, Cabra del Camp, Tarragona |
| CA25) | 104.9 | | CR | CA | Icat FM, Montcaro, Tarragona |
| CA25) | 104.9 | | CR | CA | Icat FM, Falset, Tarragona |
| CA34) | 105.0 | 20 | RAC | CA | RAC105, Collserola Barcelona |
| CA25) | 105.0 | | CR | CA | Catalunya Informació, Almenar, Lleida |
| AN59) | 105.1 | 30 | CSR | AN | Canal Sur R., Sevilla |
| CA32) | 105.1 | 10 | RTT | CA | R. Tele Taxi, Girona, Rocacorba |
| MA10) | 105.1 | 5 | | MA | Super Q FM , Madrid |
| CA25) | 105.1 | | CR | CA | Catalunya Música, Pujalt, Tarragona |
| CA25) | 105.2 | | CR | CA | Catalunya Música, Lloret, Girona |
| BA18) | 105.2 | 30 | RM | BA | R. Maria, Alfabia, Palma M. |
| CL39) | 105.2 | 8 | OCR | CL | Onda Cero R., Valladolid |
| MU16) | 105.3 | 60 | ORM | MU | Onda Regional, Murcia |
| CA25) | 105.3 | | CR | CA | Catalunya R., La Molina, Girona |
| AS03) | 105.4 | 8 | RPA | AS | R.Principado Asturias, Oviedo |
| CA25) | 105.4 | 20 | CR | CA | Catalunya Música, La Mussara, Tarragona |
| CA25) | 105.4 | | CR | CA | Icat FM, Cabrils, Barcelona |
| MA05) | 105.4 | 100 | SER | MA | SER Madrid 2, Madrid |
| AN55) | 105.5 | 6 | CSR | AN | Canal Fiesta R. Cabra, Cordoba |
| CL38) | 105.5 | 6 | KFM | CL | Kiss FM, Burgos |
| CA25) | 105.5 | | CR | CA | Icat FM, Soriguera, Lleida |
| CA25) | 105.5 | | CR | CA | Catalunya R., Maçanet, Girona |
| CA25) | 105.5 | | CR | CA | Catalunya Informació, Sant Hilari, Girona |
| CA25) | 105.5 | | CR | CA | Catalunya Música, Boí, Lleida |
| CA25) | 105.5 | | CR | CA | Catalunya Música, Vielha, Val D'Arán |
| AN60) | 105.6 | 16 | CSR | AN | Canal Sur R., Algeciras |
| EU32) | 105.6 | 8 | C100 | EU | Cadena 100,, Vitoria-Gasteiz |
| CA25) | 105.6 | | CR | CA | Catalunya Música, Puigdevall, Lleida |
| CA41) | 105.7 | 8 | GR | CA | Flaix FM, Collserola Barcelona |
| CA25) | 105.7 | | CR | CA | Icat FM, Cadaques, Girona |
| AR12) | 105.8 | 40 | KFM | AR | Kiss FM, Zaragoza |
| AN41) | 105.8 | 30 | CSR | AN | Canal Fiesta R., Málaga |
| CA25) | 105.8 | | CR | CA | Catalunya R., L'Estartit, Girona |
| CA25) | 105.8 | | CR | CA | Catalunya Informació, Portbou, Girona |
| CA25) | 105.8 | | CR | CA | Catalunya Música, Ripoll, Girona |
| CA25) | 105.9 | | CR | CA | Icat FM, Pont de Suert, Leida |
| MA14) | 106.0 | 30 | | MA | Onda Madrid R., Madrid |
| AN55) | 106.1 | 6 | CSR | AN | RAI R. Andalucía Información, Cabra, Cordoba |
| BA06) | 106.1 | 8 | D | BA | Cadena Dial, Palma de Mallorca |
| CA41) | 106.1 | 20 | GR | CA | Faixbac FM, Collserola Barcelona |
| GA27) | 106.1 | 8 | RV | GA | R. Voz, Santiago de Compostela |
| CA25) | 106.1 | | CR | CA | Icat FM, Alpicat, Lleida |
| EU33) | 106.2 | 8 | C100 | EU | CADENA100,, Donosti-San Sebastián |
| MA08) | 106.3 | 10 | COPE | MA | COPE , Madrid |
| CA25) | 106.3 | | CR | CA | Icat FM, Flix, Tarragona |
| CA25) | 106.3 | | CR | VA | Catalunya R., Perentxissa, Valencia |
| AS03) | 106.4 | 60 | RPA | AS | R.Principado Asturias, Gamoniteiro |

| FM | MHz | kW | Net | Rg | Station, location |
|---|---|---|---|---|---|
| CA25) | 106.4 | | CR | CA | Catalunya Informació, La Figuerassa, Barcelona |
| CA25) | 106.4 | | CR | CA | Catalunya Música, Montblanc, Tarragona |
| CA25) | 106.4 | | CR | CA | Catalunya Música, Tossa de Mar, Girona |
| VA28) | 106.5 | 5 | OCR | VA | Onda Cero Alicante, Alicante |
| AN76) | 106.9 | 20 | RMA | AN | R. Marca, Sevilla |
| CA29) | 106.6 | 20 | RE | CA | R. Estel, Collserola Barcelona |
| EU34) | 106.7 | 8 | KFM | EU | Kiss FM, Vitoria-Gasteiz |
| CA25) | 106.7 | | CR | VA | Catalunya R., Bartolo, Castellón |
| BA09) | 106.8 | 100 | IB3 | BA | IB3, Alfábia, Palma M. |
| CA04) | 106.8 | 10 | EFM | CA | Europa FM, Girona, Rocacorba |
| CA25) | 106.8 | | CR | VA | Catalunya R., Carrasqueta, Alicante |
| CA43) | 106.9 | 5 | | CA | RKB, R. Kanal Barcelona |
| MU18) | 106.9 | 8 | ROCK | MU | ROCK FM , Murcia |
| MA27) | 107.0 | 2 | | MA | Libertad FM., Madrid |
| AN65) | 107.1 | 5 | | AN | R. Guadalete, Bornos, Jerez de la F. |
| MA20) | 107.2 | 15 | | MA | Fiesta FM, Madrid |
| CA25) | 107.9 | 15 | RA | CA | R. Amistad,Barcelona.Turó d'en Fotjà |

**NB:** stns less than 2kW omitted

**DAB:** 18 DAB stations and 1 DAB+ station, only in Barcelona and Madrid (20% population). **Ch. 8A:** SER Digital, Onda Cero, Kiss FM, R.María, Cadena 100, Melodía FM, and R. María DAB+ – **Ch. 9D:** Madrid and Onda Barcelona: RNE1, RNE5, COPE Digital, Intereconomía DAB, R.Marca, El Mundo – **Ch. 11B:** RNE1, R.Clásica RNE, RNE3, REE Europa, Megastar, M80 Digital.

**Addresses & other information:**

**AN00) ANDALUCIA**
**AN01)** Edif.RTVE, Parque del Alamillo, 41092 Sevilla. – **AN02)** Góngora 3, 14002 Córdoba. – **AN03)** Av.Ricardo Soriano 11, 29600 Marbella. – **AN04)** Av.de Granada 57, P1, 23001 Jaén. – **AN05)** Hermanos Machado 23, 04004 Almería. – **AN06)** Av.de la Aurora 40, 29006 Málaga. – **AN07)** Av.de Andalucía 61, 11007 Cádiz. – **AN08)** Plaza Carretas 5, 18009 Granada. – **AN09)** Plaza de Europa s/n, 11300 La Línea de la Concepción. – **AN10)** La Fuente 4, 21004 Huelva. – **AN11)** Cervantes 11, 14940 Cabra. – **AN12)** C/ Bartolomé 32 bajo, 23001 Jaén. – **AN13)** C/ Triana 8, 41380 Alanis. – **AN14)** C/ Algeciras 1, 2º módulo 8 "Edificio Fenicia", 11011 Cádiz. – **AN15)** Rafael González Abreu 6, 41001 Sevilla. **E:** radiosevilla@cadenaser.com – **AN16)** Rioja 4, 41001 Sevilla. **E:** sevilla@cadenacope.net – **AN17)** Linaje 2, 29001 Málaga **E:** malaga@cadenacope.net – **AN18)** Gran Vía de Colón 28, 18001 Granada. **E:** granada@cadenacope.net – **AN19)** Paseo Marítimo 1, Edif.Reina Victoria, 11010 Cádiz **E:** sercadiz@cadenaser.com – **AN20)** Obispo Aguilar 1, 23001 Jaén. **W:** radiojaen.es – **AN21)** Guadalete 12, 11403 Jerez de la Frontera. **W:** radiojerez.com – **AN22)** Santa Paula 2 (or: Ap.158), 18001 Granada **W:** radiogranada.es – **AN23)** San Agustín 11 (or: Ap.364), 11403 Jerez de la Frontera **E:** jerez@cadenacope.net – **AN24)** Federico Mendizábal 10, 23001 Jaén **E:** jaen@cadenacope.net – **AN25)** Plaza Cardenal Toledo 4, 14001 Córdoba **E:** cordoba@cadenacope.net – **AN26)** José María Amoz 2, 21001 Huelva **E:** huelva@cadenacope.net – **AN27)** Padre Luque 11, 04001 Almería. **E:** almeria@cadenacope.net – **AN28)** General Castaños 2, 11201 Algeciras. **E:** radioalgeciras@unionradio.es – **AN29)** Av.Federico García Lorca 105, 04005 Almería. – **AN30)** San Agustín 4, 29600 Antequera. – **AN31)** García Lovera 3, 14002 Córdoba. **W:** radiocordoba.com –**AN32)** Plaza Ramón y Cajal 8, 23700 Linares **E:** radiolinares@unionradio.es – **AN33)** C/ Peregrinos 3 "Edif. Galaxia 2º" Puerta 7, 29002 Málaga **AN35)** Gaitan 10, 11402 Jerez de la Frontera. – **AN36)** Pozo Nuevo 40 bajo, 41530 Morón de la Frontera. – **AN37)** C/ Carpinteros de Ribera 2, 11007-Cádiz. – **AN38)** C/ Peregrino 3 "Edif. Galaxia 2º" Puerta 7, 29002 Málaga. – **AN39)** Misericordia 10, 11500 Puerto de Santa María. – **AN40)** C/ Doctor Manuel Ruiz Maya 8,5º, 14004 Córdoba **AN41)** Avenida Velazquez 307, 29004 Malaga – **AN42)** Carretera Huelva-San Juan del Puerto, km. 6,36. 21007 Huelva. – **AN43)** Urb. Bola de Oro, C/ Laguna de Aguas Verdes 11, 18008 Granada. – **AN44)** C/ Dr. Manuel Ruíz Maya 8, 11004 Cádiz. – **AN45)** Pabellón Once, Isla de Cartuja, 41092 Sevilla. – **AN46)** Plaza de España 15, 11006 Cádiz. – **AN47)** Avenida Federico García Lorca 105, 04005 Almería. – **AN48)** Prolongación Av. De Granada s/n, Recinto Institución ferial, 23009 Jaén. – **AN49)** Mendez Nuñez 15-5-6, 21001 Huelva. – **AN50)** Corredera 53, 11402 Jerez de la Frontera. – **AN51)** Recogidas 37, 18005 Granada. – **AN52)** Barroso 4-2, 14003 Córdoba. – **AN53)** C/ Ramón Gómez de la Serna 22 "Edificio King Edward II", 29600 Marbella. –**AN55)** Glorieta de Guadalhorce s/n, "Antigua Estación de RENFE", 14008 Córdoba. – **AN56)** Arquitecto Pérez Carasa 14-16, 21001 Huelva. – **AN57)** Centro Residencial Oliveros, C/ Maestro Serrano 9, 2º-B, 04004 Almería. – **AN58)** Sevilla. – **AN59)** Edificio Canal Sur, Av. José Gálvez 1, 41092 Isla de la Cartuja (Sevilla). – **AN60)** C/ Patriaca Pérez Rodríguez 36, 11201 Algeciras. – **AN61)** Placentines 2, 41004 Sevilla. – **AN62)** Av.de la Borbolla 47, 41013 Sevilla. – **AN63)** Almería. – **AN65)** San Jerónimo 7, 11640 Bornos. –**AN67)** Av. Mediterráneo 159, 2º "Edificio Laura", 04007 Almería– **AN68)** Rafael Gonzáles Abreu 6, 41001 Sevilla. – **AN69)** C/ San Agustín 4, 29200 Antequera. –**AN70)** Pasaje Comercial, Gran Plaza Letra F, 41005 Sevilla **W:** ministerioselshaddaisevilla.net – **AN71)** CL. Coín Parcela 1273, 29130 Alhaurín de la Torre (Málaga). – **AN72)** C/ Dr. Manuel Domínguez "Ed. Bulevar 2", 29001 Málaga. – **AN73)** Edificio de Oficinas del Estadio Olímpico, Isla de la Cartuja, 41092 Sevilla. – **AN74)** C/ Capinteros de Ribera 2, 11002 Cádiz.– **AN76)** Av. República Argentina 25-9º-B, 41011 Sevilla.

**AR00) ARAGON**
**AR01)** José Luís Albareda 1-3, 50004 Zaragoza. – **AR02)** Nueva 1, 44001 Teruel. – **AR03)** José Gil Caves 1, 22005 Huesca. **AR04)** Zaragoza. **W:** hitfm.es – **AR05)** Paseo de la Constitución 21, 50001 Zaragoza **E:** radiozaragoza@unionradio.es – **AR06)** Paseo de Sagasta 50 (or: Ap.42), 50006 Zaragoza. **E:** programas.zaragoza@cadenacope. net – **AR07)** Calle Alcalde Carderera 1, 22080 Huesca. **W:** radiohuesca. com – **AR11)** Coso 46, 50004 Zaragoza. – **AR12)** Zaragoza. – **AR13)** Calle Bilbao, 2, 1ª planta, 50004 Zaragoza. – **AR14)** REMAR, Av. Cataluña 225, 50003 Zaragoza.

**AS00) ASTURIAS**
**AS01)** C/ San Esteban de las Cruces 92, 33195 Oviedo. – **AS02)** Plaza del Instituto 3, 33201 Gijón. – **AS03)** Camino de las Clarisas 263, 33203 Gijón. –**AS05)** Carr.de la Costa 87 (or: Ap.235), 33205 Gijón. – **AS06)** Asturias 19, Bajo, 33004 Oviedo. **W:** radioasturias.com – **AS07)** Prado Picón 16, 33008 Oviedo. **W:** copeasturias.com **E:** c-oviedo@arrakis. es – **AS08)** C/ Cervantes 27, 5º,33003 Oviedo. – **AS09)** Jovellanos 1, 33202 Gijón. – **AS11)** C/ Lugar Orial 16, 33187 Hevia-Siero

**BA00) BALEARES**
**BA01)** Aragó 26, 07006 Palma de Mallorca. – **BA02)** Paseo Marítimo 26, 07014 Palma de Mallorca**. – BA03)** C/ Font i Monteros 21, 07003 Palma de Mallorca**. – BA05)** Felip II Nº 28, 07800 Eivissa **E:** ibiza@cadenacope.net – **BA06)** Rector Bertomeu Martorell 35, Son Xigala, 07013 Palma de Mallorca **E:** informativos.mallorca@cadenaser. com – **BA07)** Av.Capità Negrete 2-3N,07760 Ciutadella Menorca **E:** menorca@cope.es – **BA08)** Av.Jaume III Nº 18, 07012 Palma de Mallorca **E:** mallorca@cadenacope.net – **BA09)** C/ Manuel Azaña 7-A, 07006 Palma de Mallorca. – **BA11)** Forners 7, Edif.Once, 07002 Palma de Mallorca.– **BA13)** Menacor 171, 07007 Palma de Mallorca. – **BA15)** Avenida Sant Jordi s/n, 07800 Figueretes (Ibiza). – **BA16)** C/ Gremi Selleters i Basters 14, "Polígon Son Castelló", 07009 Palma de Mallorca. – **BA18)** Mallorca. – **BA19)** Felipe II, 18 - 2ª, 07800 Ibiza-Eivissa **E:** informativos.ibiza@cadenacope.net

**CA00) CATALUNYA**
**CA01)** C. Roc Boronat 127, 08018 Barcelona. – **CA02)** Carrer Lluis Companys 15 2303 Lleida. – **CA03)** Rambla Nova 23, 43003 Tarragona. – **CA04)** Gran Vía Jaume I Nº 60, 17001 Girona. E-mail: emisora.girne@ rtve.es – **CA05)** Av. Jaume I 76, 17002 Girona. – **CA06)** Plaça del Pati 2, entlo, 43800 Valls – **CA07)** Av. Diagonal 460, 3º, 08006-Barcelona **W:** radiomarcabarcelona.com **E:** info@radiomarcabarcelona.com – **CA08)** Casp 6, 08010 Barcelona. **E:** radiobarcelona@unionradio.es – **CA09)** Diputació 238, 08013 Barcelona **W:** fm/copebarcelona **E:** barcelona@cadenacope.net – **CA10)** Travessera de les Corts 131-159, Recinte Martenitat, Pavello Cambo, 08028 Barcelona **W:** comradio.com – **CA11)** Placa Josep Pla 2, 17001 Girona. **E:** radiogirona@unionradio.es – **CA12)** Tomàs Bergadà 3, 43204 Reus **E:** radioreus@unionradio.es – **CA13)** Carrer de Aragón 390-394, 2a planta, 08013 Barcelona – **CA14)** Llovera 54-56, 43201 Reus **E:** tarragona@cope.es – **CA15)** Acàdèmia 14, 25002 Lleida. **W:** copelleida.com **E:** lerida@cadenaser.com – **CA16)** Sèquia 3, 17001 Girona **E:** girona@cadenacope.net – **CA17)** Vila Antònia 5, 25007 Lleida **E:** lleida@cadenaser.com – **CA18)** Relay Onda Rambla Barcelona (Local adress: Rambla Nova 69, 43003 Tarragona) – **CA19)** Calle Nou 47, 08240 Manresa **E:** informatius@els40.com – **CA20)** Apartado 269, 08211 Castellar del Vallès – **CA21)** Avda. Diagonal 441, 1º, 08006-Barcelona – **CA22)**Avda. Jaume I, 37, 7è 2a, 17001 Girona – **CA25)** El Palau Nou, Ramblas 88-94, 4ª, 08002-Barcelona **CA25)** Av Diagonal 614-616, 08021 Barcelona. **E:** info@catradio.cat – **W:** catradio.cat – **CA27)** Bulidor s/n, Polígnon Industrial 1, 08960 St Just D (Barcelona) – **CA28)** Aragó 390-394, P2, 08013 Barcelona. **E:** onamusica@onacataluna.com – **CA29)** C/ Comtes de Bell-lloc 67-69, 08014 Barcelona **E:** radioestel@radioestel.com – **CA30)** Del Riu 6, 25007 Lleida. – **CA31)** Rambla Nova 38, 43004 Tarragona – **CA32)** C/ Sant Carles 40, 08922 Sta Coloma de Gramenet (Barcelona). – **CA34)** Av. Diagonal 477, 15ª, 08006 Barcelona. – **CA35)** Camí Real 551, 1º, 08302 Mataró. – **CA36)** Rambla de la Llibertat 6, 17004 Girona. – **CA37)** C/ Ramón y Cajal 36, 3º, 43001 Tarragona. – **CA38)** Carretera de Barcelona 33, 4º, 17001 Girona. – **CA39)** Rambla d'Arago 43, 1º, 25003 Lleida.- **CA40)** Gran via de Jaume I 29-2º, 17001 Girona. – **CA41)** Paseo de Gràcia 55-57, 9º, 08007 Girona. – **CA42)** Barcelona. **W:** facebook. com/Locafuncatalunya – **CA43)** Gran vía de les Corts Catalanes 645, 2º-1, 08007 Barcelona.

### CL00) CASTILLA Y LEÓN

**CL01)** García Morato 27-29, 47007 Valladolid. – **CL02)** Becerro de Bengoa 9, 34002 Palencia. – **CL03)** Santa Clara 2, 05001 Avila. – **CL04)** Ordoño II N° 28, 24001 León. – **CL05)** Campo 5, 42001 Soria. **CL06)** Calle Barrio Gimeno 11, 09004 Burgos. – **CL07)** Av.de Requejo 21, 49012 Zamora. – **CL08)** Ave María 11, (or Apartado de Correos 105, 24480 Ponferrada) 24400 Ponferrada. **CL09)** Plaza de Colón 4, 37001 Salamanca. – **CL10)** Paseo Ezequiel Gonzales 24, 40002 Segovia. – **CL15)** Av.del Cid 8, 09005 Burgos **E:** informativos.burgos@ cadenacope.net **CL16)** Duque de la Victoria 23, 47001 Valladolid **E:** direccion.valladolid@cadenacope.net – **CL17)** C/ Veracruz 2 bajo, 37008 Salamanca **W:** radiosalamanca.com – **CL18)** C/ La Estación 3, 47004 Valladolid **E:** radiovalladolid@cadenaser.com – **CL19)** Sol Oriente 11-15, 37002 Salamanca **E:** salamanca@cadenacope.net – **CL20)** Hermanos La Salle 2, 24700 Astorga **E:** astorga@cadenacope. net – **CL21)** Lope de Vega 1, 24002 León **W:** copeleon.com **E:** leon@cadenacope.net – **CL22)** Plaza Fernández Duró 3 (or: Ap.42), 49001 Zamora **E:** zamora@cadenacope.net – **CL23)** Plaza de España 3, 09005 Burgos **E:** radiocastilla.redaccion@unionradio.es – **CL24)** Villafranca 6, 24001 León **W:** radioleon.com **E:** radioleon@radioleon. com – **CL25)** Calle Santa Ana 6, 49006 Zamora **E:** radioz@teleline. es – **CL26)** Plaza Cirilo Rodríguez 2, 40001 Segovia **W:** radiosegovia. com – **CL27)** Astorga. – **CL31)** Vitoria 24, 09200 Miranda de Ebro.– **CL32)** Bermejeros 14, 37001 Salamanca. – **CL33)** Rastrojo 5, 47014 Valladolid. – **CL34)** Plaza de Aragón 5, 09001 Burgos. – **CL35)** Julio del Campo 4-6, 24002 León. – **CL36)** Plaza de los Vadillos 5, 09005 Burgos. **W:** radioarlanzon.com – **CL37)** Aliso 2 bajo, 37004 Salamanca. – **CL38)** Burgos. – **CL39)** Edif.Promecal, c/los Astros s/n, 47009 Valladolid. **CL40)** Salamanca. – **CL41)** Valladolid. – **CL42)** Zamora. – **CL43)** C/ Manuel Canesi Acevedo 1, 4706 Valladolid.

### CM00) CASTILLA-LA MANCHA

**CM01)** Paseo de San Cristóbal s/n, 45002 Toledo. – **CM02)** Ramiro Ledesma 8, 13630 Socuéllamos. – **CM03)** Nuestra. Sra. De Araceli 1, Edif.Las Torres, 02002 Albacete. – **CM04)** Radio Nacional de España 2 (or: Ap.18), 16003 Cuenca. – **CM05)** Ronda del Carmen s/n (or: Ap.150), 13002 Ciudad Real **E:** emisora.cr.rne@rtve.es – **CM06)** Plaza de Consejo, Centro Civico, 19001 Guadalajara. – **CM07)** Ronda del Canillo 35, 45600 Talavera de la Reina. – **CM08)** Polígono Santa María de Benquerencia, C/ Río Alberche s/n, 45007 Toledo. – **CM10)** C/ Gaona 8 , 4°-B, 02001 Albacete. **W:** radiosurco.es – **CM12)** Avenida de la Estación 5, 02001 Albacete. **E:** radioalbacete@unionradio.es – **CM13)** Alejandro Prieto 2, 13500 Puertollano **E:** puertollano@cadenacope.net – **CM14)** Tesifonte Gallego 9, 02002 Albacete **E:** albacete@cadenacope. net – **CM15)** Pasaje San Isidro 3, 13001 Ciudad Real **E:** ciudadreal@ cadenacope.net – **CM21)** Av.de la Estación 5, 02001 Albacete. – **CM22)** C/ Joaquina Santander 13, 1°, 45600 Talavera de la Reina. – **CM23)** Calle Trinidad 12, 45002 Toledo. **W:** rtvd.org/radio.htm **E:** rtvdiocesana@planalfa.es – **CM24)** 02001 Albacete. – **CM25)** Toledo.

### CT00) CANTABRIA

**CT01)** Polígono de Raos s/n, 39609 Camargo (Santander) – **CT02)** Av.del Besaya 1 (or: Ap.46), 39300 Torrelavega – **CT03)** C/ José María Pereda 23, 39100 Santa Cruz de Bezana. – **CT05)** Rualasal 5, 39001 Santander **E:** santander@cadenaser.com – **CT06)** Pasaje de la Peña 2, int 7, Edif.Simeon 39008 Santander **W:** radiosantander.com **E:** informativos@radiosantander.com – **CT11)** Fernandez de Isla 14,2°, 39008 Santander.

### EU00) EUSKADI

**EU01)** Plaza de Simón Bolívar 13, 01003 Vitoria-Gasteiz – **EU02)** Paseo de los Fueros 2, 20006 Donosti-San Sebastián **E:** emisora. ss.rne@the.es – **EU03)** Licenciado Poza 55, 48013 Bilbo-Bilbao. – C/ Polorínviejo 4, 01003 Vitoria-Gasteiz. – **EU04)** C/ Domingo Martínez de Aragón 5-9, 01006 Vitoria-Gasteiz. **W:** eitb.com/eu/gaztea – **EU05)** C/ San Antonio 2 bajo, 01005 Vitoria-Gasteiz. – **EU06)** C/ Alonso Allende 21, Lonja izquierda, 48920 Portugalete. – **EU07)** Capuchinos de Basurto 2, Edificio Bami, 48013 Bilbo-Bilbao **E:** radio_euskadi@ eitb.com – **EU08)** Miramón 172, 20004 Donostia-San Sebastián **W:** www. eitb.com/euskara/ – **EU09)** C/ Domingo Martínez de Aragón 5-9, 01006 Vitoria-Gasteiz **W:** eitb.com/radiovitoria – **EU10)** Calle Alameda Mazarredo 47,7°, 48009 Bilbo-Bilbao **W:** radiopopular.com – **EU11)** C/ Epalza 8, 48007 Bilbo-Bilbao **E:** radiobilbao@unionradio. es – **EU12)** Paseo Portuetxe 51, Edificio ACB, 20018 Donostia-San Sebastián **E:** radiosansebastian@cadenaser.com – **EU13)** Miracruz 9, 20001 Donostia-San Sebastián –**EU15)** C/Portal de Gamarra, 23. Pabellón A, 01002 Vitoria-Gasteiz . **W:** ondavasca.com –**EU17)** Vitoria-Gasteiz. – **EU20)** Bulevar de Beurko 4, local 2, 48902-Barakaldo. **EU18)** C/ La Habana s/n, 01012 Vitoria **W:** radiogorbea.com **EU21)** Av.de la Libertad 17, 20004 -Donosti-San Sebastián **EU22)** General Alava 10-6 Depto 9, 01005 Vitoria-Gasteiz **EU23)** Fontecha y Salazar 9-5, 48007 Bilbo-Bilbao – **EU24)** Eziago Polígonoa 10B, 20120 Hernani. – **EU25)** C. Hurtado de Amezaga 27,17piso, 48008 Bilbo-Bilbao. – **EU26)** C/ Esteban Zurbano 20, 20214 Segura (Guipúzcoa). – **EU27)** Gordóniz 44,

12°, 48002 Bilbao. – **EU28)** C/ San Prudencio 8-A,, 5°, 01005 Vitoria-Gasteiz.– **EU29)** Paseo Federico García Lorca 10, 4°, Puerta 1-2, 20014 Donosti-San Sebastián. – **EU30)** Ribera de Elorrieta 7, 48015 Bilbo-Bilbao. – **EU31)** C/ José Lejarreta 11, 01003 Vitoria-Gasteiz. – **EU32)** C/ Portal de Legutiano 6, 01002 Vitoria-Gasteiz . – **EU33)** Parque Empresarial Zuazu, Ed. Ulía 8, 20018 Donosti-San Sebastián. – **EU34)** Vitoria-Gasteiz.

### EX00) EXTREMADURA

**EX01)** Av.Ruta de la Plata 10, 10001 Cáceres – **EX02)** Plaza de España 5, 06002 Badajoz. – **EX03)** Avenida de las Américas 1, 1°, 06800 Mérida.– **EX05)** C/ Comandante Sánchez Herrero 2, 1°, 10004 Cáceres **E:** caceres@cadenacope.net – **EX06)** Ramón Albarrán 2, 06002 Badajoz **E:** radioextremadura@unionradio.es – **EX07)** Menacho 12, 06001 Badajoz **E:** badajoz@cadenacope.net – **EX08)** C/ Profesor Rodríguez Moñino 1, 8°-A, 10003 Cáceres. – **EX11)** Av.de España 9-6, 10004 Cáceres – **EX12)** Av.de Portugal s/n, Ctro Comercial El Foro, 06800 Mérida – **EX13)** Santa Isabel 4, 10600 Plasencia – **EX16)** Luis Alvarez Lancero 8, 10001 Cáceres.

### GA00) GALICIA

**GA01)** Paseo Méndes Nuñez 12, (or: Ap.199), 15006 A Coruña – **GA02)** Lepanto 7, 36001 Pontevedra – **GA03)** Rua de Progreso 115 (or: Ap.268), 32003 Ourense – **GA04)** Ourense 59-63 (or: Ap.73), 27004 Lugo – **GA05)** Plaza de España 4, 27400 Monforte de Lemos – **GA06)** Av.García Barbón 36, 36201 Vigo – **GA07)** San Marcos s/n, Edif.TVE, 15780 Santiago de Compostela. – **GA08)** Rúa Pascual Veiga 12-14 baixo dereita, 27002 Lugo. – **GA09)** Plaza de España 5-6, 15403 El Ferrol **E:** ferrol@cadenacope.net – **GA10)** San Pedro de Mezonzo 3 (or: Ap 469), 15701 Santiago de Compostela **E:** radiogalicia@unionradio. es – **GA11)** Principe 57, 36202 Vigo **E:** vigo@cadenacope.net – **GA12)** Areal 6-8, 36201 Vigo **W:** radiovigo.es – **GA13)** Plaza de Ourense 3, 15004 A Coruña **W:** radiocoruna.com – **GA14)** Castelao 3 B, 36001 Pontevedra **E:** ser@radiopontevedra.com – **GA15)** Rua de Progreso 89, 32003 Ourense **E:** orense@cadenacope.net – **GA16)** Rua de Valiño s/n, 27002 Lugo **E:** lugo@cadenacope.net – **GA17)** Plaza de Santo Domingo 3, 27001 Lugo **W:** radiolugo.com – **GA18)** Rua do Paseo 30 (or: Ap.1017), 32003 Ourense **W:** radioourense.com **E:** cadenaser@ radioourense.com – **GA21)** Ronda de Outeiro, N°1 y 3 Bajo, 15006 A Coruña– **GA22)** Salvador Moreno 30, 36001 Pontevedra – **GA23)** Av.García Barbón 104, 36201 Vigo – **GA24)** Rúa Benito Corbal 14, 2°, 36001 Pontevedra – **GA25)** Casa de la Radio, San Marcos, 15820 Santiago de Compostela – **GA26)** . **W:** esradio.fm – **GA27)** Salguiriños de Arriba 44, bajo, 15890 Santiago de Compostela. – **GA28)** Apartado de Correos 3114, 36208 Vigo. **W :** ondasdevida.org - **GA29)** C/ Torreiro 13-15, 3°-E, 15005 A Coruña – **GA30)** Av. García Barbón 28, 36201 Vigo. – **GA31)** Rúa Costa Rica 6, 7°, 15005 A Coruña.

### MA00) MADRID

**MA01)** Casa de la Radio, Prado del Rey, 28223 Pozuelo de Alarcón – **MA02)** C/ Enrique Larreta 12, 28036 Madrid. – **MA03)** C/ Juan Esplandiú 15, 2°, 28007 Madrid. – **MA04)** C/ San Bernardo 20, 3°, Centro, 28015 Madrid – **MA05)** Gran Vía 32, 28013 Madrid **E:** redaccion@cadenaser.com – **MA06)** Modesto Lafuente 42, 28003 Madrid **W:** radiointer.com **E:** radiointer@radiointer.com – **MA07)** C/ Juan Esplandiú 15, 2ª, 28007 Madrid – **MA08)** Alfonso XI N° 4, 28014 Madrid **W:** cope.es **E:** programas.madrid@cadenacope.net – **MA09)** Círculo de Bellas Artes, C/ Alcalá 42, 5 planta, 28014 Madrid.- **MA10)** **W:** superqfm.es - **MA11)** Bueso Pineda 7, 28043 Madrid – **MA13)** José Isbert 6, Ciudad de la Imagen - 28223 Pozuelo de Alarcón **W:** kissfm.es **E:** kissfm@kissfm.es – **MA14)** Pso del Principe 3, Cd.de la Imagen, 28223 Pozuelo de Alarcón **W:** telemadrid.com – **MA16)** Av.de los Árqueros n, 28024 Madrid **E:** radiomaria@arsenet.com – **MA17)** Paseo de la Castellana 36-38, 28046 Madrid **W:** intereconomia.com – **MA18)** Sta Clara 7, 28801 Alcalá de Henares – **MA20)** C/ Juan Esparol 47, local bajo, 28026 Madrid. **W:** fiestafm.net - **MA21)** C. Francisco Silvela 122 bajo, 28002 Madrid. – **MA22)** Calle de Secoya 29, Planta 3 Puerta 1, 28054 Madrid – **MA24)** C/ Orense 18, piso 8, of 9, 28020 Madrid. **W:** rtcespana.es – **MA26)** Juan Ignacio Luca de Tena 7, 28027 Madrid.– **MA27)** Paseo de la Castellana 129, 1°-C, 28046-Madrid

### MU00) MURCIA

**MU01)** La Olma 27-29, 30005 Murcia **E:** emisora.mu.rne@rtve.es – **MU02)** Paseo Alfonso XIII N° 51, 30203 Cartagena. – **MU03)** C/ Bucarest 29, 30391 Cartagena. – **MU04)** C/ Carmen Conde 46, 1°, 30203 Cartagena. – **MU05)** Arco de Santo Domingo 2-3, Edif.Fontanar, 30001 Murcia **E:** murcia@cadenacope.net – **MU06)** Av.Juan Carlos I N° 63, 30800 Lorca **E:** lorca@cadenacope.net – **MU07)** Calle Radio Murcia 4, 30001 Murcia **E:** radiomurcia@unionradio.es – **MU08)** Real 70, 30201 Cartagena **E:** informativos.cartagena@cadenaser. com – **MU09)** Murcia – **MU11)** Edif.Mediterráneo, Puerta Murcia 11, 30201 Cartagena – **MU12)** C/ Carmen 51, 1° A, 30201 Cartagena – **MU13)** Madre de Dios 15, 30004 Murcia – **MU14)** Mayor 31, 30280 Cartagena – **MU16)** Av.Libertad 6, bajo, 30009 Murcia. – **MU17)** Pza de los Apóstoles 7, 30001 Murcia. – **MU18)** Ed.del Periódico La Verdad,

Camino Viejo de Monteagudo s/n, 30160 Murcia.

**NA00) NAVARRA**
**NA01)** Emilio Arrieta 8, P8, 31002 Pamplona-Iruñea – **NA02)** Aoiz 17, 31004 Pamplona-Iruñea. – **NA03)** Ed. Ciencias Sociales, Universidad de Navarra, Campus Universitario s/n, 31080 Pamplona.-Iruñea **W:** unav.es/98.3 – **NA05)** Amaya 2-B, 31002 Pamplona-Iruñea **E:** pamplona@cadenacope.net – **NA06)** Polígono Plazaola, Manzana F, 2° A, 31195 Aizoain (or Apartado de Correos 71, 31080 Pamplona) **E:** informativosnavarra@cadenaser.com – **NA11)** Plaza del Castillo 43, 31001 Pamplona-Iruñea – **NA12)** Cortes de Navarra 1, 31002 Pamplona-Iruñea.

**RI00) LA RIOJA**
**RI01)** Vara de Rey 42, (or: Ap.247), 26002 Logroño – **RI02)** Residencia Universitaria Francisco Jordán, Av. Madre de Dios 17, 26001 Logroño – **RI03)** C/ Estambrera 36, 1°, 26006 Logroño. – **RI04)** C/ General Vara del Rey 74, 26002 Logroño. – **RI05)** Av.de Portugal 12 (or: Ap.149), 26001 Logroño **W:** radiorioja.com – **RI11)** Logroño – **RI12)** Miguel Villanueva 2, Ofc.5, 26001 Logroño.

**VA00) CUMUNITAT VALENCIANA**
**VA01)** Av Colóm 13, 46004 València – **VA02)** Angel Lozano 18, 03001 Alacant-Alicante – **VA03)** Passeig de la Ribalta 5, 12001 Castelló – **VA04)** Juan Carlos I 37, 03202 Elx. – **VA05)** Plaça dels Sports 7-8, Ed. Sabater, 03590 Altea – **VA07)** Rambla de Méndez Nuñez 45, 03002 Alacant-Alicante **E:** alicante@cadenacope.net – **VA08)** Calderón de la Barca 26, 03004 Alacant-Alicante **E:** alicante@cadenaser.com – **VA09)** Av.Francisco Tàrrega 69, 12540 Vila-Real **E:** castellon@cadenacope.net – **VA10)** Don Juan de Austria 3, 46002 València **E:** valencia@cadenaser.com – **VA11)** Passatge Dr.Sierra 2, 46004 València **W:** cope.es/valencia – **VA12)** Doctor Sempere 16B y C, Bajos, 03803 Alcoi **E:** radioalcoy@radioalcoy.com – **VA13)** Moyano 5, 12002 Castelló **W:** radiocastellon.comdc – **VA14)** Dr.Caro 43, 03201 Elx **W:** radioelche.com – **VA15)** Calle Loreto 32, 46700 Gandia **E:** ser@radiogandia.net **W:** radiogandia.net – **VA16)** Ereta 2A (or: Ap.84), 46870 Ontinyent **W:** radioontinyent.com – **VA 17)** C/ Hort dels Frares 12, 46600 Alzira. – **VA18)** C/ Doctor Caro 18 entresuelo derecha, 03201 Elx. – **VA19)** C/ La Fira 10, 03202 Elx. – **VA20)** C/ Almorida 2, 4° derecha, 03201 Elx. – **VA21)** Alacant-Alicante. **E** : alicante@kissfm.es – **VA23)** C/ San Vicente 16, entreplanta 1°, 46001 València – **VA24)** Av.Blasco Ibañez 136, 46022 València – **VA25)** València – **VA26)** Vía Emilia Ortuño 5, 3°, 03500 Benidorm – **VA27)** Edificio Levante. Polígono Vara de Quart. Calle Traginers, 7 46014 València **W:** la977.com – **VA28)** Paseo Explanada de España 26, 03001 Alicante – **VA29)** C/ Els Gremis 1, Polígono Vara de Quart, 46014 Valencia **W:** abc.es/radio/valencia – **VA30)** C.C. Alfafar, Pl. Alquería de la Culla 4, Planta1, of.01, 46910 Alfafar,Valencia. **W:** pequeradio.es – **VA32)** Av. Blasco Ibáñez 134, 46022 València. – **VA33)** Av. Aragón 30, 46031 Valéncia.
**For more information see W:** lalistadelafm.com

**AMERICAN FORCES RADIO & TV SERVICE (Mil.)**
**AFN** Rota 102.5MHz, Rota. ✉ FPO AE 09645 0019 Base Naval, Rota (Cadiz) **D.Prgr:** 24h

## SRI LANKA

**L.T:** UTC +5½h — **Pop:** 21 million — **Pr.L:** Sinhala, Tamil, English — **E.C:** 50Hz, 230V — **ITU:** CLN

**TELECOMMUNICATIONS REGULATORY COMMISSION OF SRI LANKA**
✉ 276, Elvitigala Mawatha, Colombo 08 ☎ +94 11 2689345 🖷 +94 11 2689341 **E:** dgtsl@trc.gov.lk **W:** www.trc.gov.lk
**L.P:** Chmn: Austin Fernando

**SRI LANKA BROADCASTING CORPORATION (Pub)**
✉ P.O. Box 574, Independence Square, Colombo 7 ☎ +94 11 2697491 🖷 +94 11 2691568 **E:** ddge@slbc.lk **W:** slbc.lk
**L.P:** Act. Chairman: Dr. Somaratne Dissanayake, DG: Erananda Hettiarachchi, Dir Eng.: M.G.W. Priyadarshana

| FM (MHz) | A | B | C | D | E | F |
|---|---|---|---|---|---|---|
| Colombo | 91.7 | 94.3 | 102.1 | 104.7 | 97.4 | 89.6 |
| Deniyaya | 91.7 | 94.3 | 102.1 | 104.7 | 97.4 | 89.6 |
| Haputale | 91.9 | 94.5 | 102.3 | 104.9 | 90.1 | 89.8 |
| Hunasgiriya | 91.7 | 94.3 | 102.1 | 104.7 | 97.4 | 89.6 |
| Jaffna | - | - | - | 104.7 | - | - |
| Karagahatenna | 91.7 | 94.3 | 102.1 | 104.7 | 97.4 | 89.6 |
| Kovavil | - | - | 107.5 | 104.9 | - | 89.8 |
| Radella | 91.7 | 94.3 | 102.1 | 104.7 | 97.4 | 89.6 |
| Yatiyantota | 91.9 | 94.5 | 102.3 | 104.9 | 97.6 | 89.8 |

**A** = Sinhala National Sce 2300-1600., **B** = Sinhala Commercial Sce 24h, **C** = Tamil National Sce 2300-1715, **D** = Tamil Commercial Sce

2300-1700, **E** = English Sce 0000-1700 (includes rel. of BBC World Sce), **F** = City FM 24h.
**Sports Sce:** operates irr. on FM freqs of Vidula Sce and YAL FM.
**Vidula** (Children's channel): Colombo 107.3MHz,Yatiyantota 107.5MHz: 0000-1630 in Sinhala, Tamil and English.
**Regional services:**
**FM**(MHz): **Akkaraipattu:** Haputale 102.1 (Thirayi Sevaya) – **Anuradhapura:** Anuradhapura 90.1, Karaghatenna 107.3 (Rajarata Sevaya) – **Batticaloa:** Karaghatenna 102.3 (Pirai FM in Tamil) – **Jaffna:** Jaffna 90.1, Palali 102.1 (Palali Sevaya/YAL FM in Tamil & Sinhala) – **Kandy:** Hanthana 90.1, Hunasgiriya 107.5, Radella/Nuwara Eliya 107.3 (Kandurata Sevaya) – **Kurunegala:** Karaghatenna 90.1 (Wayamba Handa) – **Matara:** Haputale 107.5, Deniyaya 107.3 5kW (Ruhunu Sevaya).
Regional Sce operates 2300-0230 & 1000-1530.
**Community Stations:** Badulla 97.6 (Uva Com, R.), Girandurukotte 97.6 (Dambana R.), Mawathura 97.6 0.3kW (Kothmale FM)
**Ann: A:** "Me Sri Lanka Guwan Viduli Sansthave Welanda Sevaya".
**B:** "Me Sri Lanka Guwan Viduli Sansthava Swadeshiya Sevaya". **C:** "Illangar Oliparappu Kootuthapanam Tamil Sevai". **E:** "This is the Sri Lanka Broadcasting Corporation"

**EXTERNAL SERVICE: SLBC** see International Broadcasting section

**MAJOR COMMERCIAL NETWORKS (FM** MHz):

**ASIA BROADCASTING CORPORATION (Pvt) Ltd**
✉ 35th Floor, East Tower, World Trade Center, Colombo 1 ☎ +94 11 2337555 **E:** md@abcradio.lk **W:** abcradio.lk **Stns: Gold FM** in English: Colombo/Kandy/Matale/Matara 93.0, Badulla/Jaffna/Nuwara Eliya/Ratnapura 93.2 – **Hiru FM** in Sinhala: Colombo/Kandy/Matale/Matara 96.1, Badulla/Jaffna/Nuwara Eliya 96.3 – **Shaa FM** in Sinhala: Colombo/Kandy/Matale/Matara 90.9, Badulla/Jaffna/Nuwara Eliya/Ratnapura 91.1 – **Sooriyan FM** in Tamil: Badulla/Jaffna/Mannar/ Nuwara Eliya/Trincomalee/Vauniya 103.4, Colombo/Kandy/Matale/Matara 103.6 – **Sun FM** in English: Badulla/Kilinochchi/Nuwara Eliya/Ratnapura 98.7, Colombo/Jaffna/Kandy/Matale/Matara 98.9

**ASSET RADIO BROADCASTING (Pvt) Ltd**
✉ 09C Ocean Tower Building, Station Road, Bambalapitya, Colombo 4 ☎+94 11 2507080 🖷 +94 11 5342434 **E:** eng@nethfm.com **W:** nethfm.com **Stn: Neth FM** (Sinhala): Bandarawela/Kandy/Kegalla/ 94.8, Colombo/Kandy/Matale/Matara/Ratnapura 95.0. **Fox Fm** (English): Kandy & Colombo 91.4.

**COLOMBO COMMUNICATIONS (Pvt) Ltd**
✉ 686 Galle Road, Colombo 3 ☎+94 11 5577777 🖷 +94 11 2505796 **E:** info@efm.lk **W:** efm.lk **Stns: E! FM** (English): Colombo/Kandy/Matara 88.3 – **RANONE FM** (Sinhala): Kegalle/Matale/Matara 88.1, Bandarawela/Colombo//Ratnapura 100.5 – **Shree FM** (Sinhala): Bandarawela/Colombo/Kandy/Ratnapura 100.0, Kegalle/Matale/Matara 100.2

**INDEPENDENT TELEVISION NETWORK**
✉ Wickramasinghepura, Battaramulla 10120 ☎+94 11 2774424 🖷+94 11 2774591 **E:** itn@slt.lk **W:** itn.lk **L.P:** Chmn.: Rosmand Senarathna, Gen Mgr: W Wijesinghe. **Stns: ITN FM** (Sinhala): Bandarawela/Kandy/Kegalla/Kokavil 93.5, Colombo/Matale/Matara 93.7 – **Vasantham** (Tamil): Bandarawela/Kegalla/Kokavil 102.6, Colombo/Jaffna/Matale/Uda 102.8

**MBC NETWORKS (Pvt) Ltd**
✉ PO Box 25, 36 Araliya Uyana, Depanama, Pannipitiya ☎+94 11 2851371 🖷+94 11 2851373 **W:** www.mbc.lk **Stns: Shakthi FM** (Tamil): ✉ 7 Braybrooke Place, Colombo. Bandarawela/Kalutara/Kandy/Kilinochchi/ Nuwara Eliya/Trincomalee/Vavuniya 103.9, Colombo/Jaffna/Kandy/Mannar/Matale/Matara 104.1 – **Sirasa FM** (Sinhala) ✉ PO Box 25, Araliya Uyana: **E:** radio@sirasafm.maharaja.lk Bandarawela/Kandy/Kurunegala/Magalkanda/Matale/Matara 106.5, Bandarawela/Kalutara/Kandy/Nuwara Eliya/Ratnapura 106.7 – **Y FM** (Sinhala) ✉ 7 Braybrooke Place, Colombo: Bandarawela/Colombo/Jaffna/Kalutara/Kandy/Kurunegala/Matale/Matara/Ratnapura 92.7– **Yes FM** (English) ✉ as MBC Networks: Nuwara Eliya 100.8, Colombo/Jaffna/Kandy/Kurunegala/Matara101.0

**TNL RADIO NETWORK Pvt Ltd**
✉ No.52, 5th Lane, Colombo 3 ☎+94 11 7669966 **W:** www.tnlradio.com **Stns: Lite 87** (English): Nuwara Eliya 87.6, Colombo/Kandy/Matara 87.8 – **Rhythm World** (Sinhala): Colombo/Kandy/Matale/Matara 95.6, Nuwara Eliya 95.8 – **TNL Radio** (English): Colombo/Kandy 99.2, Colombo 101.8.

**Other Stations:**
**Trans World Radio India MW:** Puttalam 882kHz 400kW Broadcasts. for Sri Lanka and southern India.
**SLBC** tx stn Puttalam 1125kHz 50kW Available for hire by Int. broadc.
**SLBC** tx stn Trincomalee 1548kHz 400kW and 250kW SW facility available for hire by Int. broadc.

## ST BARTHÉLEMY (France)

**L.T:** UTC -4h — **Pop:** 7,200 — **Pr. L:** French, Creole, English — **E.C:** 50Hz, 230V — **ITU:** BLM

### GUADELOUPE PREMIÈRE (Pub)
✉ c/o Morne Bernard-Destrellan, B.P. 180, 97122 Baie-Mahault, Guadeloupe. ☎+590 590 939696 🖷 +590 590939682.
**FM:** 88.6MHz 0.3kW

### RADIO SAINT-BARTH
✉ BP 1113, 97014 St Barthélemy. ☎+590 590 27 74 74 & +590 690 242874 (Admin). **W:** radiostbarth.com **E:** radio@radiostbarth.com
**L.P:** Président: Bruno Magras
**FM:** 98.7MHz 0.3kW, 100.7MHz 0.3kW, 103.7MHz 0.3kW.

**R. France Internationale**: via R. St. Barth 100.7MHz

## ST EUSTATIUS (Netherlands)

**L.T:** UTC -4h — **Pop:** 3,200 — **Pr.L:** Dutch (official), English — **E.C:** 60Hz, 110V — **ITU:** BES

### AGENTSCHAP TELECOM Bonaire, St Eustatius, Saba
✉ Kaya Grandi 69, P.O. Box 791, Bonaire ☎ + 599 717 3140 🖷 +599 717 3554 **W:** agentschaptelecom.nl **E:** bes@agentschaptelecom.nl

### PJB-50 RADIO STATIA
**Sint Eustatius Broadcasting Foundation**
✉ Statia Mall, Chaple Piece ☎ +599 318 2722 🖷 +599 318 2168 **L.P:** Dir.: Ivan Rivers; English prgrs **W:** radiostatia.com **E:** radio_statia@yahoo.com
**FM:** PJB50 92.3MHz 0.5kW 24h

## ST HELENA (UK)

**L.T:** UTC — **Pop:** 4,500 — **Pr. L:** English — **E.C:** 50Hz, 240V — **ITU:** SHN

### SOUTH ATLANTIC MEDIA SERVICES LTD (SAMS) (Gov)
✉ The Media Centre, Castle Gardens, Jamestown, St Helena STHL 1ZZ ☎+290 22727 **L.P:** CEO: Richard Wallis, SM: [vacant]
**E:** news@sams.sh **W:** sams.sh (live audio stream)
**FM**(MHz): **SAMS Radio 1**: High Knoll Fort 90.5, Jamestown 102.7, Levelwood 105.1, Blue Hill 105.3 **SAMS Radio 2** (rel. BBC World Service): High Knoll Fort 88.1, Jamestown 100.7. **D.Prgr.:** 24h.

### Saint FM Community Radio
✉ Association Hall, Main St, Jamestown, St Helena STHL 1ZZ. ☎+290 22660 **E:** admin.fm@helanta.co.sh **W:** saint.fm (live audio stream) **L.P:** Chair: [vacant], Dir: Liz Johnson, SM: Tammy Williams
**FM**(MHz): Half Tree Hollow 93.1 0.25kW, Deadwood Plain 95.1 0.05kW, Jamestown 106.7 0.05kW
**F.PI:** Sandy Bay or Blue Hill 91.1MHz 0.05kW.

## ST KITTS & NEVIS

**L.T:** UTC -4h — **Pop:** 56,000 — **Pr.L:** English — **E.C:** 60Hz, 230V — **ITU:** SCN

### NATIONAL BROADCASTING CORPORATION OF ST. KITTS & NEVIS (Gov. Comm.)
✉ PO Box 331, Springfield, Basseterre, St. Kitts ☎ +1 869 465 2621 🖷 +1 869 466 2159 **L.P:** GM: Clement O'Garro **E:** info@zizonline.com **W:** zizonline.com
**FM: Radio ZIZ** 95.9/96.1/96.9MHz – **Big Wave 96.7 FM** 96.7MHz

### SON POWER RADIO (Rlg.)
✉ Flowing Streams, PO Box 690069, Vero Beach FL 32969-0069, USA ☎ +1 772 569 8880 **W:** sonpowerradio.com **L.P:** Doc Burkhart
**MW:** Conaree, St. Kitts ‡820kHz 10kW (Inactive)
**F.pl.** Projected back on the air early 2019

### VOICE OF NEVIS (Comm.)
✉ Bath Plains, PO Box 195, Charlestown, Nevis ☎ +1 869 469

1616/1700 🖷 +1 869 469 5329 **W:** vonradio.com
**L.P:** GM: Evered Herbert
**MW:** 860kHz 10kW **D.Prgr:** 24h **Ann:** "This is VON Radio on 860 AM"

**OTHER STATIONS (in MHz):**
**CSS Caribbean Superstation**. FM 93.1 (Relay Trinidad) – **Dominion Radio**, PO Box 513, Basseterre ☎ +1 869 465 1597 **W:** dominionradioskn.com FM 91.5. Format: Rlg. – **Freedom FM**, The Cable Bldg., Suite 2, Cayon St., Basseterre ☎ +1 869 465 6474 **W:** freedomskn.com L.P: CEO Clement Juni Liburd. FM 106.5 – **Kyss FM The Love FM**, Unit 6, The Sands Complex, Bay Rd, Basseterra ☎ +1 869 466 5978 **E:** info@kyssonline.com **W:** kyssonline.com FM 102.3/102.5 – **Praise FM**, Hamilton Estate, 00265 Charlestown, Nevis ☎ +1 869 663 6491 **W:** praisefmnevis.com L.P: Steve Huggins. FM 99.3. Format: Gospel – **Radio St. Kitts Nevis**, Victoria Rd, Basseterre and Reef Broadcasting, #79 Castle Coakley, Christiansted, VI 99820, USA ☎ +1 869 465 7528 **W:** reefbroadcasting.com FM 90.7 (relays WAXJ 103.5, US Virgin Isl.) – **Sugar City FM**, 8 Green Land's Park, Basseterre ☎ +1 869 466 1113 **W:** sugarcityfm.com FM 90.3 – **Winn FM**, Unit C24, The Sands Complex, Bay Rd, Basseterre, St. Kitts ☎ +1 869 466 9586 **E:** info@winnfm.com **W:** winnfm.com FM 98.9

## ST LUCIA

**L.T:** UTC -4h — **Pop:** 180,000 — **Pr.L:** English, Creole — **E.C:** 50Hz, 240V — **ITU:** LCA

### MINISTRY OF TOURISM INFORMATION AND BROADCASTING
✉ 3rd Floor, Sir Stanislaus James Building, Waterfront, Castries ☎ +1 758 4684629 🖷 +1 758 4517414 **E:** psmot@gosl.gov.lc **W:** tourism.govt.lc **L.P:** Minister: Dominic Fedee

### CATHOLIC TV BROADCASTING SERVICE, Micoud Str, Castries
☎ +1 758 452 7050 FM 87.75 (TV sound of EWTN, USA) – **HOT FM/KISS FM**, Old Victoria Rd, Morne Fortune, PO Box MF 7096, Castries ☎ +1 758 452 6040 🖷 +1 758 458 1462 **W:** caribbeanhotfm.com & caribbeankissfm.com **L.P:** CEO: Patrick Smith. Mgr.: Sandra Recai. Stns: **HOT FM:** 96.1(South)/105.3(North), **KISS FM:** 105.5 (South) /105.9 (North) – **IBAS RADIO**, Darling Rd, Castries ☎ +1 758 4599 0645. FM 104.5/106.7 – **JOY FM**, PO Box MF 7149, Castries ☎ +1 758 453 6962 FM 90.1 (North)/96.9 (South). Format: Rlg – **KAIRI FM**, Morne Du Don, PO Box 1730 Castries ☎ +1 758 451 1079. FM 93.1/107.9 – **LOVE-FM**, Beanefield, PO Box 520, Vieux-Fort ☎ +1 758 454 5683 **W:** lovefmslu.webs.com. FM 103.9(South)/94.9(North)/91.9(West) – **PRAYZ FM RADIO**, Sir John Compton Highway, Sans Soucis, PO Box CP6141, Castries ☎ +1 758 452 1022 **W:** prayzfm.org FM 92.5/98.5 Format: Rlg., Adventist – **RADIO CARIBBEAN INTERNATIONAL**, 11 Mongiraud St., PO Box 121, Castries ☎ +1 758 452 2636 🖷 +1 758 452 2637 **W:** rcistlucia.com L.P: GM: Mr. Antonius Secra Gibson. SM: Peter Ephraim. FM 99.1(South)/101.1(North) – **RADIO 100 HELEN FM**, Morne Fortune, PO Box 621, Castries ☎ +1 758 452 4982 🖷 +1 758 453 1737. FM 100.1(Castries)/100.3(North)/103.5(South) – **REAL 91.3 FM,** PO Box CP 6279, Castries ☎ +1 758 453 7458. **W:** realfm.com. FM 91.3/91.5 – **RADIO FREE IYANOLA (RFI)**, 22 Delieu St, Soufriere ☎ +1 758 489 1021 **W:** rfi1021fm.webs.com FM 102.1. Format: Reggae – **RHYTHM FM/BLAZIN FM INC.,** Julian Charles Rd., PO Box 384, Castries ☎ +1 758 450 9494 🖷 +1 758 451 6217 **W:** rhythmfm.net & blazinfm.com **L.P:** MD Dwayne Mendes. PD: Irvin 'Ace' Loctar. Stns: Rhythm FM 95.5, Blazin FM 99.3 – **RIZZEN 102FM,** McVane Drive, Sans Souci, Castries ☎ +1 758 451 3057 **W:** rizzen102.com FM 99.7/102.5/102.9. Format: Rlg. – **SOUFRIERE FM,** Sulphur Springs Park, PO Box 272, Soufriere ☎ +1 758 459 7885/7889 🖷 +1 758 457 1071 **W:** 885soufrierefm.com FM 88.5 (local community stn) – **THE WAVE,** Karlione Court, Rodney Bay, Castries ☎+1 758 451 6400 **W:** thewavestlucia.com L.P: GM: Sue Monplaisir. PD: Michael Rogers. FM 93.7 (South) /94.5 (North) – **UNITY FM,** Castries PO ☎ +1 758 717 6769. W: unityfmstlucia.com FM 90.5.

## ST MAARTEN (Netherlands)

**L.T:** UTC -4h — **Pop:** 41,485 — **Pr.L:** Dutch (official), English — **E.C:** 60Hz, 120V — **ITU:** SXM

### BUREAU TELECOMMUNICATIONS AND POST
✉ Kannegieter Street 15 – Unit 5.1, Philipsburg, St. Maarten ☎ +1 721 542 5557 🖷 +1 721 542 4817 **W:** sxmregulator.sx **E:** info@sxmregulator.sx

| MW Call | kHz | kW | Station, location |
|---|---|---|---|
| 1) PJD-2 | 1300 | 1 | The Voice of St. Maarten, Philipsburg |

| FM | MHz | kW | Station, location |
|---|---|---|---|
| 4) | 91.9 | 1 | Island 92, Simpson Bay |
| 4) | 94.7 | 1 | Mix 94.7, Philipsburg |
| 6) | 96.3 | 1 | Oasis 96.3, Philipsburg |
| 8) | 98.1 | 1 | Pearl FM, Philipsburg |
| 6) | 101.1 | 1 | Laser 101 FM |
| 1) | 102.7 | 3.5 | PJD3, The V of St. Maarten/Power 102.7, Philipsburg |
| 7) | 104.3 | 1.5 | PJM1, X 104.3, Philipsburg |
| 4) | 105.1 | 1 | Z105.1 FM, Simpson Bay |
| 6) | 105.5 | 1 | Tropixx 105.5, Philipsburg |
| 5) | 106.3 | | Inspire 106.3 FM, Philipsburg |
| 2) | 107.9 | 1 | Gov. R., Philipsburg |

**Addresses & other information:**
**1) 187** Back Street, P.O. Box 366, Philipsburg ☎ +1 721 542 2580, +1 721 542 2764, +1 721 542 2141 🖷 +1 721 542 2356 **E:** info@pjd2radio.com **W:** pjd2radio.com – **2)** PO Box 943, Clem Lebaga Square, Philipsburg ☎+1 721 542 2233 –**4)** Welfare Road # 64, 2ⁿᵈ Floor, Federal Express Building, Simpson Bay ☎ +1 721 544 3377; Island 92: 24 hours in Eng : Classic Rock, Blues and Good Time Music; Z105.1 : 24 hours in Eng: Classic Hits; Director: Jeffrey "Dr. Soc"Sochrin, **E:** info@island92.com **W:** island92.com **W:**z1051.com – **5) W:** radio-inspire.fm – **6)** A.Th. Illidge Road 106 Philipsburg ☎+1 721 543 2200 🖷 +1 721 543 2200; Oasis, Laser and Mix: 24h in English; Tropixx: 24h in English, Papiamentu and Spanish; Laser,Tropixx and Mix: Dir: Gary Euton; Oasis: Dir: Phyllis Meit Mix 94.7: **E:** marketing@philbroad.com **W:** oasis963.fm **E:** request@oasis963.fm **W:** laser101.fm **E:** request@laser101.fm **W:** tropixx.fm **E:** request@tropixx.fm – **7)** Media One Corporation, #9, Walter Nisbeth Road, Suite B, Philipsburg ☎+1 721 543 8104 Studio Line: + 1 721 543 9104 🖷 +1 721 543 8104 24h in English, Dir. Mr E. Brown, **E:** info@x1043.com and info@mediaoneco.com **W:** x1043.com – **8)** Fort Belair Road 3, Philipsburg ☎+1 721 5430 462 **E:** pearlstudio@caribserve.net

## ST MARTIN (France)

**L.T:** UTC -4h — **Pop:** 36,000 — **Pr. L:** French, Creole, English, Dutch — **E.C:** 60Hz, 220V — **ITU:** MAF

### GUADELOUPE PREMIÈRE (Pub)
🖃 Quartier Bellevue-Marigot, 97100 Saint Martin ☎+590 590291716
**FM:** St. Martin 88.9MHz 0.3kW

### RADIO SAINT MARTIN (Comm.)
🖃 Port de Marigot, 97150 Saint Martin **L.P.:** Mgr: H. Cocks.
**FM:** 101.5MHz 0.3kW **D.Prgr:** 1000-0500(Sun -0400) in French & English exc. Spanish: 2000-2100W.

### RADIO CALYPSO
🖃 10, rue du Général de Gaule, 97150 Saint Martin
☎+590 590 522222 🖷 +590 590 52 22 23 **W:** radiocalypso.net **E:** calypsopub@powerantilles.com **FM:** 102.1MHz 1kW

**Other Stations FM:**
**R. Laser Îles du Nord** 89.9MHz 1kW – **Youth R.** 92.5MHz 1kW – **R.** 94.3MHz 1kW – **R. Music FM** 95.1MHz 1kW – **R. SOS** 95.9MHz 1kW – **R. Maranatha** 100.3MHz 1kW – **R. Tropik FM** 104.7MHz 1kW – **Sun FM Music** 107.1MHz 1kW

## ST PIERRE ET MIQUELON (France)

**L.T:** UTC -3h (10 Mar-3 Nov: -2h) — **Pop:** 7,000 — **Pr.L:** French — **E.C:** 50Hz, 230V — **ITU:** SPM

### RADIO ST PIERRE ET MIQUELON PREMIÈRE (Pub)
🖃 B.P. 4227-97500 St. Pierre et Miquelon ☎+508 508411111 **W:** la1ere.francetvinfo.fr/saintpierremiquelon/radio
**L.P:** Dir: vacant, Tech. Dir: Etienne Grisel, Head of N.: Frederic Lahiton
**FM:** Miquelon 98.9 500W, St. Pierre 99.9 100W
**D.Prgr:** 0930-0230. **Rel. France-Inter:** 0230-0930. **N (local):** 1000, 1530, 2200. **Rel. France-Inter N:** 1100, 1200, 1300, 1400, 1800, 1900 **Ann:** "Ici Radio Saint-Pierre et Miquelon Première."

**R. Atlantique** 🖃 B.P. 1282-97500 ☎+508 508412493 **W:** www.radioatlantique.fr **FM:** 94.5 1kW, 102.1 1kW (also rel. R. France Int.)

## ST VINCENT & THE GRENADINES

**L.T:** UTC -4h — **Pop:** 110,000 — **Pr.L:** English — **E.C:** 50Hz, 230V — **ITU:** VCT

**NATIONAL BROADCASTING CORPORATION RADIO ST. VINCENT AND THE GRENADINES – NBCSVG (Gov. Comm.)**
🖃 Richmond Hill, PO Box 705, Kingstown ☎ +1 784 457 1111 🖷 +1 784 456 2749 **W:** nbcsvg.com **E:** nbcsvgadmin@vincysurf.com
**L.P:** GM: Corletha Ollivierre. Dep. GM: Raphael King
**FM:** 90.7MHz 1kW, 107.5MHz 1kW
**D.Prgr:** 24h. Relays BBC 0400-0930. **N:** 1130, 1630, 2230 – Su 1230 only. **Ann:** "NBC Radio"

**OTHER STATIONS (FM in MHz):**
**ADORATION FM**, North Union, Charlotte. **E:** adoration88@gmail.com **W:** adoration88.com FM 88.9. Format: Rlg – **BOOM SVG**, Prospect, PO Box 592, Kingstown ☎ +1 784 451 1069 FM 92.5/106.9 – **CHRISTLIKE RADIO,**, PO Box 701, Kingstown ☎ +1 784 526 4057 E: christlikeradiosvg@gmail.com FM 88.1 Format: Rlg – **HOT 97.1FM**, 1 Melville Street, PO Box 1716, Kingstown ☎ +1 784 452 9797 **W:** hot97svg.com FM 93.1/97.1. Format: Urban Caribbean – **JEM RADIO**, Hopewell Rd, PO Box 1419, Kingstown ☎ +1 784 454 0891 **W:** jemradio.com FM 89.1. Format: Rlg. – **MAGIC 103.7,** St Vincent Broadcasting Corp., Dorsetshire Hill, P.O. Box 617, Kingstown ☎ +1 784 451 1037 **W:** magic1037.com FM 91.5/103.7. Format: Urban Caribbean – **NICE RADIO**, BDS Company Ltd., Dorsetshire Hill, PO Box 324, Kingstown ☎ +1 784 458 1013 🖷 +1 784 456 5556 **W:** niceradio.info L.P: Mgr: Douglas Defreitas. FM 90.3/96.7/101.3 – **PRAISE FM**, Sion Hill, PO Box 324, Kingstown ☎ +1 784 456 1057 **W:** praisefmsvg.com L.P: PD Donny Daniel. FM 95.7/105.7 Format: Rlg – **STAR FM**, Murray's Rd, McKies Hill, PO Box 1651, Kingstown ☎ +1 784 453 7827 🖷 +1 784 485 7827 **W:** star983fm.com FM 98.3/104.7 – **WEFM**, Windy Point, Lower Questelles, PO Box 1346, Kingstown ☎ +1 784 457 9994 🖷 +1 784 457 7123 **E:** wefm@vincysurf.com **W:** 999wefm.com FM 99.9 – **XTREME 104.3,** Vigie Highway, Kingstown ☎ +1 784 456 1043 **W:** x104fm.com FM 88.5/104.3 Format: Urban

## SUDAN

**L.T:** UTC +2h — **Pop:** 42 million — **Pr.L:** Arabic (official), English (official), Nubian, Beja — **E.C:** 50Hz, 230V — **ITU:** SDN

**MINISTRY OF INFORMATION & COMMUNICATION**
**L.P:** Minister: Al-Zahawi Ibrahim Malek

**SUDAN RADIO & TV CORPORATION - SUDAN RADIO (Gov.)**
🖃 P.O. Box 1094, Mulazmin, Omdurman ☎+249 1 87572956 🖷 +249 1 87556006. **W:** sudanradio.sd **E:** web form
**L.P:** Dep. Dir: Mr. Abdul Azim Awad. DG Eng. & Tech. Sces: Abbas Sidig.

| MW | kHz | kW | Prgr. | MW | kHz | kW | Prgr. |
|---|---|---|---|---|---|---|---|
| Nyala | 540 | 50 | R | Wadi Halfa | 873 | 5 | R |
| Al-Ubayyid | 639 | 10 | R | Singa | 891 | 5 | R |
| Kassala | 666 | 10 | R | Al-Foula | 945 | 5 | R |
| Khartoum | 747 | 10 | R | Khartoum Soba | 963 | 100 | S/G/Q |
| Port Sudan | 747 | 5 | R | Al-Damazin | 1026 | 5 | R |
| Khartoum Soba | 765 | 50 | G | Reiba (Sennar) | ‡1296 | 600 | G |
| Atbara | 783 | 5 | R | Al Qadarif | 1485 | 12 | R |
| Al-Fashir | 801 | 5 | R | Kosti | 1584 | 5 | R |
| Dongola | 819 | 10 | R | Kadugli | 1602 | 5 | R |
| Wad Madani | 873 | 10 | R | | | | |

**SW:** Omdurman (Al-Fatihab) 100kW: General prgr: 7205kHz 0230-2100 (irreg.)
**FM:** Khartoum: 88.6MHz (W), 90.0MHz (S/Q), 93.0MHz (Y), 95.0MHz (G), 98.0MHz (E/U), 100.0MHz (N), 105.0MHz (Q).
Prgr. S: Khartoum 90.0MHz & Darfur: Al-Fashir/Al-Junayna 95.0MHz, Nyala 98.0MHz.
**Regional stations:** Al-Gadarif/Dongola/El Obeid/Kassala/Nyala/Sinja 98.0MHz, Port Sudan 105.0MHz, Khartoum 107.0MHz.
**F.P.I:** 4 FM stations in Darfur.
**Prgrs: G=General Prgr** (incl. **National Unity R.** 1000-1200) in Arabic: 24h. 963kHz 0200-2100. **H=Quran R:** 0200-1000. **K=Khartoum State R:** 0300-0700, 1300-1900. **N="Sudan Home Radio":** 24h. **S=R. As-Salam** (Peace): 0530-0830, 1300-2100 on 90.0MHz & 963kHz. **U="Nation's Memory Radio":** 1100-1500, 1900-2300. **E=European prgr.** in English/French: 1500-1900. **W:** Wadi al-Nil (Nile Valley R.). **Y=Youth & Sports R.**
**R=Regional stations.D.Prgr:** mostly 0300-2100. Also relay **G** prgr.
**VO the Armed Forces,** Khartoum: 97.0MHz. **W:** mod.gov.sd
**VO the Police,** Khartoum: 99.6MHz.
**Ann:** "Huna Omdurman, Idha'atu-I-Gumhuriya as-Sudan"
**IS:** Sudanese music.

**Other Stations (FM MHz):**
**Al-Basirah R**, Khartoum 96.3, Al-Jazirah 96.6 **W:** elbasiera.net – **Al-Furqan R** (rlg.), Khartoum 99.0 **W:** furqan.org – **Al-Kawthar R.**(rlg.), Khartoum 92.0 **W:** kawther.sd – **Al-Rabiyah FM,** Khartoum 94.0. Owned by Channel 4, UAE **W:** alrabaafm.com – **Al-Tibbiyah FM,** Khartoum 99.3. **W:** altbia.fm – **BNFM** (tv audio), Khartoum: 91.0 **W:** bnile.tv – **Bokra FM,** Khartoum: 104.6. **W:** facebook.com/BokraFm1046 – **Capital R,** Khartoum: 91.6. **W:** capitalfmsudan.com – **Hala FM,** Khartoum: 96.0 **W:** hala96.fm – **Hawa al-Sudan,** Khartoum: 88.3MHz – **Khartoum FM,** Khartoum: 89.0. **W:** kfm89.net – **Life and Health R,** Khartoum: 106.0 – **Mango FM,** Khartoum/Port Sudan/Wad Madani: 96.0. **W:** mango96.com Also rel. BBC – **OUS R,** Khartoum: 89.5. **W:** ousmedia.net – **R. Darfur:** 90.3 **W:** darfurfm.net – **R. Tonight,** Khartoum: 101.0 – **Sports FM,** Khartoum: 104.0. **W:** sporttsfm104.net – **Tayba FM** (rlg.), Khartoum: 103.0. **W:** tayba.fm – **Vision FM,** Khartoum: 101.3. **W:** facebook.com/vision1013FM – **VO Community,** Kauda: 88.0 300W **W:** internews.org

**BBC Arabic Sce:** El Obeid/Port Sudan 91.0MHz.
**R. Sawa,** Khartoum: 97.5MHz.
**UNAMID R,** Darfur region **W:** unamid.unmissions.org/audio . Broadcasting some programmes via Khartoum 98.0MHz, Al-Fatihab 7205kHz and Al-Fashir 801kHz & 95.0Mhz

## SURINAME

**L.T:** UTC -3h — **Pop:** 552 000 — **Pr.L:** Dutch, English, Sranang Tongo, Sarnami Hindi, Javanese — **E.C:** 60Hz, 110/115/127/220V — **ITU:** SUR – **Int. dialling code:** 597

**TELECOMMUNICATE BEDRIJF SURINAME (TELESUR) (Gov)**
✉ P.O. Box 1839, Paramaribo ☎ 474242/473944 🖷 404800 **W:** telesur.sr **E:** telesur@sr.net

**STICHTING RADIO-OMROEP SURINAME (SRS)**
✉ P.O. Box 271, Paramaribo ☎ 498115 🖷 498116 **W:** radiosrs.com **E:** adm@radiosrs.com
**FM:** Paramaribo 96.3MHz 1kW, Coronie, Nickerie, Moengo, Brokopando all 94.7MHz 0.1kW, Wageningen 95.6 MHz, Albina 105.7MHz 0.1kW **D.Prgr:** 0900-0700

**PRIVATE COMMERCIAL STATIONS:**
**SW: 8) R. Apintie,** Paramaribo 4990kHz 1kW (irregular)
**FM** (Mhz): **1) R. 10** 88.1, 88.7 & 103.7 – **2) Radika** 98.3 – **3) R. Garuda** 97.5, 103.4 & 105.7 – **4) Sky R.** 94.1 & 102.7 – **5) R. Katoilica** 93.1 – **6) R. Trishul** 94.5 – **7) R. Zon** 107.5 – **8) R. Apintie** 97.1 – **9) R. Ishara** 100.7 – **10) R. Noer** 92.1 – **11) R. Paramaribo Rapar "The Hot-One"** 89.7 – **12) RP Acme** 91.3 – **13) RTV Mustika** 106.5 – **14) Sangeetmala R.** 99.3 & 100.1 – **15) R. Shalom** 94.5 – **16) R. Pertjajah** 95.3 – **17) R. Koyeba** 104.9 – **18) Rasonic R.** 102.3 & 105.3 – **19) Kara´s Broadcasting Corp.** 101.1 & 103.1 – **20) R. ABC** 101.7

**Addresses & other information:**
**1)** Stadionlaan 3 (P.O.Box 110), Paramaribo ☎ 410881 🖷 422294 **W:** radio10.sr **E:** info@radio10.sr – **2)** Indira Gandhiweg 165, Paramariba ☎ 482800 – **3)** Goudstraat 20 Maretrait 4, Paramaribo 454 926 **W:** rtvgaruda.com **E:** info@rtv-garuda.com – **4)** Ormosiastraat 2 (P.O.Box 1597), Paramaribo ☎ 530015 **W:** skyradioasuriname.com **E:** info@skyradio.sr – **5)** Paramaribo – **6)** Flocislaan 4, Boyen ☎ 439500 **W:** trishul.sr **E:**info@trishul.sr – **7)** Burenstraat No 60, Paramaribo ☎475261 🖷 420233 **W:** radiozon.com **E:**admin@radiozon.com – **8)** verl. Gemenelandsweg 37, Paramaribo ☎ 400455 🖷 400684 **W:** apintie.sr **E:** apintie@sr.net – **9)** 109 Fredericiweg, Nickerie ☎231244 **W:** isharafm.com **W:** @isharafm.com – **10)** Zwartenhovenbrugstraat 154, Paramaribo **W:** dbsuriname.com/radionoer.php **E:** radionoer@gmail.com – **11)** 18) Coppenamstraat 34 (P.O. Box 975), Paramaribo ☎ 497774 Paramaribo **W:** dbsuriname.com/radiorptthehotone.php **E:** rpthehot1@gmail.com – **12)** Zwartenhovenbrugstraat 154, Paramaribo **W:** dbsuriname.com/radiorptthehotone.php – **13)** Paramaribo **W:** rtvmustika.net **E:** rtvmustikacontact@gmail.com – **14)** Indira Gandhiweg No 40, Wanicxa ☎ 482392 **W:** sgmsuriname.com **E:** info@sgmsuriname.com – **15)** Malebatrumstraat 10-12 BV, Paramaribo ☎ 422630 🖷 422737 **W:** shalomsuriname.com **E:** shalom@sr.net – **16)** Gemenlandsweg/Daneil Coutinhostraat 31, Paramaribo ☎ 401919 **W:** twitter.com/#!/PertjajahLuhur – **17)** Van`t Hogerhuystraat 88 ☎ 403115 **W:**radiokoyebasuriname.com **E:** odjahh@yahoo.com – **18)** Bataviastraat 25, NW. Nickerie ☎ 231447 **W:** rasonictv.com – **19)** Verlengde Gemenelandsweg 177, Paramaribo ☎ 4300666 – **20)** Maystraat 57, Paramaribo ☎ 465092 **W:** abcsuriname.com **E:** info@abcsuriname.com

See ESWATINI

## SWEDEN

**L.T:** UTC +2h (31 Mar-27 Oct: +3h) — **Pop:** 10 million — **Pr.L:** Swedish — **E.C:** 230V/50Hz — **ITU:** S

**MYNDIGHETEN FÖR PRESS, RADIO OCH TV (MPRT) (Swedish Press and Broadcasting Authority)**
✉ P.O.Box 33, 12125 Stockholm ☎ +46 8 58007000 🖷 +46 8 7410870 **E:** registrator@mprt.se **W:** www.mprt.se
**L.P:** DG: Charlotte Ingvar-Nilsson

**POST- OCH TELESTYRELSEN (PTS)**
✉ P.O.Box 5398, 10249 Stockholm ☎ +46 8 6785500 🖷 +46 8 6785505 **E:** pts@pts.se **W:** pts.se **L.P:** DG: Dan Sjöblom
**NB:** PTS is the Swedish telecommunication regulatory authority.

**SVERIGES RADIO AB (SR) (Pub)**
✉ Radiohuset, Oxenstiernsgatan 20, 10510 Stockholm ☎ +46 8 7845000 **E:** lyssnarservice@sverigesradio.se **W:** sverigesradio.se
**L.P:** CEO: Cilla Benkö

**FM** (MHz)

| Location | 1 | 2$ | 3 | 4° | L° | kW |
|---|---|---|---|---|---|---|
| Arvidsjaur | 89.4 | 94.2 | 97.1 | 100.6m | - | 60 |
| Bollnäs | 88.4 | 91.7 | 96.0 | 103.8d | - | 60 |
| Borlänge | 89.4 | 93.0 | 97.7 | 101.3b | - | 60 |
| Borås | 88.5 | 94.6 | 97.9 | 102.9n | - | 10 |
| Bäckefors | 92.7 | 96.8 | 99.1 | 102.2t | - | 60 |
| Emmaboda | 93.0 | 96.7 | 99.7 | 101.8k | - | 60 |
| Emmaboda | - | - | - | 95.6i | - | 60 |
| Enköping | - | - | - | 95.2r | - | 5 |
| Eskilstuna | - | - | - | 100.1q | - | 6 |
| Filipstad | 88.5 | 90.1 | 98.8 | 103.2s | - | 3 |
| Finnveden* | 90.1 | 94.2 | 99.9 | 103.4h | - | 30 |
| Färjestaden | - | - | - | 107.8i | - | 1 |
| Gällivare | 88.3 | 94.9 | 98.5 | 100.9m | - | 60 |
| Gävle | 88.1 | 97.4 | 99.8 | 102.0d | - | 60 |
| Göteborg | 89.3 | 96.3 | 99.4 | 101.9e | - | 60 |
| Halmstad | 87.7 | 91.2 | 95.4 | 97.3f | - | 60 |
| Halmstad | - | - | - | 102.6j | - | 3 |
| Helsingborg | 89.8 | 95.7 | 98.4 | 103.2l | - | 30 |
| Hudiksvall | 87.6 | 90.2 | 93.8 | 100.7d | - | 60 |
| Härnösand | 88.8 | 91.1 | 95.1 | 100.5v | - | 1.5 |
| Hörby | 88.8 | 92.4 | 97.0 | 89.5l | - | 3x60/5 |
| Hörby | - | - | - | 101.4j | - | 60 |
| Jönköping | 91.6 | 93.7 | 97.1 | 100.8h | - | 5 |
| Kalix | 91.3 | 93.6 | 97.9 | 102.2m | - | 60 |
| Karlshamn | 90.3 | 93.4 | 98.3 | 100.4a | - | 15 |
| Karlskrona | 89.1 | 95.0 | 97.7 | 100.7a | - | 10 |
| Karlstad | 90.5 | 94.2 | 96.5 | 103.5s | - | 15 |
| Kiruna | 89.1 | 92.7 | 96.4 | 102.7m | - | 60 |
| Kisa | 90.5 | 92.5 | 96.9 | 103.6y | - | 30 |
| Kramfors | 88.3 | 92.4 | 97.2 | 102.4v | - | 1.2 |
| Kungsbacka | - | - | - | 101.3f | - | 1 |
| Lycksele | 92.9 | 95.4 | 98.7 | 103.3u | - | 60 |
| Malmö | 87.9 | 93.3 | 98.0 | 102.0l | 100.6l[1] | 6 |
| Markaryd | - | - | - | 99.5k | - | 3 |
| Mora | 92.2 | 96.7 | 99.0 | 101.0b | - | 60 |
| Motala | 91.1 | 94.0 | 98.2 | 101.2y | - | 20 |
| Norrköping | 90.0 | 93.5 | 98.7 | 94.8y | - | 60 |
| Norrköping | - | - | - | 103.2q | - | 60 |
| Nässjö | 89.6 | 92.1 | 99.0 | 102.1h | - | 60 |
| Pajala | 90.8 | 93.0 | 95.9 | 100.2m | . | 60 |
| Skellefteå | 93.8 | 96.3 | 100.0 | 103.9u | - | 60 |
| Skövde | 88.9 | 95.1 | 97.5 | 100.3o | - | 60 |
| Sollefteå | 89.3 | 93.5 | 98.1 | 101.2v | - | 60 |
| Stockholm | 92.4 | 96.2& | 99.3 | 103.3p | 93.8p[2] | 4x60/1.5 |
| Stockholm | - | - | - | - | 89.6p[3] | 0.9 |
| Storuman | 87.6 | 91.2 | 99.0 | 102.5u | - | 60 |
| Strängnäs | - | - | - | 96.9q | - | 4 |
| Sundsvall | 92.7 | 96.9 | 99.2 | 102.8v | - | 60 |
| Sunne | 90.9 | 94.5 | 98.5 | 101.8o | - | 60 |
| Sveg | 90.6 | 94.9 | 97.9 | 102.2g | - | 60 |
| Södertälje | - | - | - | - | 97.6p[2] | 3 |
| Södertälje | - | - | - | - | 102.7p[3] | 0.1 |
| Trollhättan | 91.9 | 95.7 | 99.8 | 103.7t | - | 3 |
| Tåsjö** | 88.9 | 94.7 | 97.5 | 100.8g | - | 60 |
| Tåsjö** | - | - | - | 88.2u | - | 60 |
| Törntorp | - | - | - | 89.8x | - | 3 |
| Uddevalla | 89.9 | 93.1 | 97.2 | 103.3t | - | 8 |
| Uppsala | 90.3 | 93.3 | 96.6 | 102.5r | - | 20 |

| Location | 1 | 2$ | 3 | 4° | L° | kW |
|---|---|---|---|---|---|---|
| Varberg | 90.4 | 93.6 | 98.8 | 103.8f | - | 10 |
| Visby | 87.6 | 94.1 | 97.2 | 100.2c | - | 60 |
| Vislanda | 88.0 | 90.6 | 94.7 | 101.0k | - | 30 |
| Väddö | - | - | - | 94.7p | - | 3 |
| Vännäs | 88.5 | 92.1 | 95.8 | 103.6u | - | 60 |
| Västervik | 88.3 | 91.8 | 96.0 | 102.7i | - | 60 |
| Västerås | 90.7 | 95.8 | 98.0 | 100.5w | - | 60 |
| Ånge | 93.2 | 95.6 | 99.6 | 103.1v | - | 60 |
| Ånge | - | - | - | 94.5g | - | 60 |
| Älvsbyn | 90.6 | 94.5 | 99.4 | 102.9m | - | 60 |
| Ängelholm | - | - | - | 103.6j | - | 1 |
| Örebro | 87.9 | 91.5 | 99.6 | 102.8s | - | 60 |
| Örnsköldsvik | 90.8 | 94.4 | 97.8 | 100.1v | - | 60 |
| Östersund | 87.9 | 91.5 | 94.0 | 100.4g | - | 60 |
| Östhammar | 89.1 | 92.8 | 95.5 | 101.6r | - | 60 |
| Överkalix | 88.9 | 91.7 | 95.0 | 103.2m | - | 15 |

+ sites with txs below 1kW *) Bredaryd **) Hoting $) P2 Språk & musik
&) P2 (see below) °) Regional studios a-y: see below L = Local outlets
(see below) ¹) P3 Din Gata ²) P5 STHLM ³) P6

**D.Prgrs: Prgr 1 (P1):** 24h – **Prgr 2 (P2):** 24h on Stockholm 96.2MHz.
**P2 Språk & musik:** 24h (as P2, plus prgrs for ethnic minorities and immigrants in Swedish, Arabic, English, Finnish, Romany, Sami) via P2 FM txs exc. Stockholm 96.2MHz – **Prgr 3 (P3):** 24h – **Prgr 4 (P4):** 24h. Reg. prgrs MF 0459-1635; SS 0730-0733, 0830-0833, 0930-0933, 1130-1133 & 1230-1233 (studios see below); national prgr at other times– **Local outlets: P3 Din Gata:** 24h. **P5 STHLM:** 24h. **P6** 24h in Swedish, Arabic, English, Finnish, Romany, Sami. Rel. BBC World Service (English) MF 1730-0500 (Sat -0600), SS 1800-0600 (Mon -0500) – **SR Sameradion:** (✉Österleden 21, 98138 Kiruna) (for Sami ethnic minority) 24h in Sami, Swedish via webcast; selected prgrs are relayed via P2 Språk & musik, P4, P6 – **SR Sisuradio:** (for Finnish ethnic minority) 24h in Finnish, Meänkieli dialects, Swedish via DAB & webcast; selected prgrs are relayed via P2 Språk & musik, P4, P6.

### SR Regional Studios
**a)** SR Blekinge, P.O.Box 305, 37125 Karlskrona **E:** p4blekinge@sverigesradio.se – **b)** SR Dalarna, P.O.Box 123, 79123 Falun **E:** p4dalarna@sverigesradio.se – **c)** SR Gotland, P.O.Box 1324, 62124 Visby **E:** p4kristianstad@sverigesradio.se – **d)** SR Gävleborg, P.O.Box 311, 80104 Gävle **E:** p4gavleborg@sverigesradio.se – **e)** SR Göteborg, Pumpgatan 2, 40513 Göteborg **E:** p4goteborg@sverigesradio.se – **f)** SR Halland, P.O.Box 133, 30104 Halmstad **E:** p4halland@sverigesradio.se – **g)** SR Jämtland, P.O.Box 476, 83126 Östersund **E:** p4jamtland@sverigesradio.se – **h)** SR Jönköping, Barnarpsgatan 35D, 55192 Jönköping **E:** p4jonkoping@sverigesradio.se – **i)** SR Kalmar, Norra vägen 22, 39183 Kalmar **E:** p4kalmar@sverigesradio.se – **j)** SR Kristianstad, P.O.Box 505, 29125 Kristianstad **E:** p4kristianstad@sverigesradio.se – **k)** SR Kronoberg, P.O.Box 62, 35103 Växjö **E:** p4kronoberg@sverigesradio.se – **l)** SR Malmöhus, Baltzarsgatan 16, 211 01 Malmö **E:** p4malmohus@sverigesradio.se – **m)** SR Norrbotten, Nygatan 3, 97191 Luleå **E:** p4norrbotten@sverigesradio.se – **n)** SR Sjuhärad, P.O.Box 27, 50330 Borås **E:** p4sjuharad@sverigesradio.se – **o)** SR Skaraborg, Norra Bergvägen 4, 54124 Skövde **E:** p4.skaraborg@sverigesradio.se – **p)** SR Stockholm, Oxenstiernsgatan 20, 10510 Stockholm **E:** p4stockholm@sverigesradio.se – **q)** SR Sörmland, P.O.Box 641, 63108 Eskilstuna **E:** p4sormland@sverigesradio.se – **r)** SR Uppland, P.O.Box 1552, 75145 Uppsala **E:** p4uppland@sverigesradio.se – **s)** SR Värmland, P.O.Box 98, 65103 Karlstad **E:** p4varmland@sverigesradio.se – **t)** SR Väst, P.O.Box 654, 45124 Uddevalla **E:** p4vastmanland@sverigesradio.se – **u)** SR Västerbotten, Mariehemsvägen 4, 90615 Umeå **E:** p4vasterbotten@sverigesradio.se – **v)** SR Västernorrland, Krönvägen 18, 85179 Sundsvall **E:** p4vasternorrland@sverigesradio.se – **w)** SR Västmanland, P.O.Box 850, 72122 Västerås **E:** p4vastmanland@sverigesradio.se – **x)** SR Örebro, Västra Bangatan 15, 70180 Örebro **E:** p4orebro@sverigesradio.se – **y)** SR Östergötland, P.O.Box 500, 60107 Norrköping **E:** p4ostergotland@sverigesradio.se.

### NÄRRADIONS RIKSORGANISATION (NRO)
✉ c/o Lars-Erik Backström, Myntgatan 29, 93148 Skellefteå ☎ +46 72 5175607 **W:** www.nro.se **LP:** Chmn: Lars Erik Backström

### OTHER STATIONS

| FM | MHz | kW | Location | Station |
|---|---|---|---|---|
| 1A) | 87.6 | 12 | Karlstad | RIX FM |
| 2B) | 88.1 | 2 | Skövde | NRJ |
| 2A) | 88.6 | 1 | Emmaboda | Mix Megapol |
| 1A) | 88.7 | 1.5 | Enköping | RIX FM |
| 2B) | 88.7 | 3 | Västerås | NRJ |
| 1E) | 89.0 | 1 | Bollnäs | Star FM |
| 16) | 89.2 | 1.5 | Malmö | Malmökanalen 89,2 |
| 1A) | 89.3 | 2 | Arvika | RIX FM |
| 2A) | 89.4 | 2 | Oskarshamn | Mix Megapol |
| 2A) | 89.5 | 1 | Norrköping | Mix Megapol |

| FM | MHz | kW | Location | Station |
|---|---|---|---|---|
| 7) | 89.7 | 1 | Skellefteå | R. Skellefteå |
| 2B) | 90.3 | 1 | Normaling | NRJ |
| 2B) | 90.4 | 1 | Lindesberg | NRJ |
| 2B) | 90.8 | 1 | Aneby | NRJ |
| 2C) | 90.8 | 1 | Bollnäs | Vinyl FM |
| 1E) | 90.9 | 1 | Karlskrona | Star FM |
| 1E) | 90.9 | 2 | Skellefteå | Star FM |
| 1A) | 91.0 | 3 | Trollhättan | RIX FM |
| 2B) | 91.2 | 2 | Trelleborg | NRJ |
| 1E) | 91.3 | 2.5 | Örnsköldsvik | Star FM |
| 15) | 91.6 | 1 | Kristianstad | Kristianstad närradio |
| 1A) | 91.7 | 1 | Älmhult | RIX FM |
| 4) | 91.7 | 1 | Vellinge | Retro FM |
| 1E) | 91.9 | 1 | Piteå | Star FM |
| 1A) | 92.1 | 4 | Uppsala | RIX FM |
| 13) | 92.2 | 1 | Karlstad | R. Solsta 92,2 |
| 2B) | 92.2 | 1.5 | Färjestaden | NRJ |
| 1A) | 92.2 | 1.5 | Skellefteå | RIX FM |
| 5) | 92.5 | 1 | Borås | Borås närradio |
| 2B) | 92.6 | 5 | Karlskrona | NRJ |
| 2D) | 92.7 | 1 | Mora | Rockklassiker |
| 2B) | 92.8 | 1 | Habo | NRJ |
| 2B) | 93.4 | 5 | Alingsås | NRJ |
| 23) | 93.7 | 2 | Kiruna | R. Kiruna |
| 25) | 94.1 | 1 | Mora | R. Siljan |
| 4) | 94.5 | 2 | Landskrona | Retro FM |
| 2A) | 94.9 | 1 | Filipstad | Mix Megapol |
| 10) | 95.3 | 4 | Svedala | Fun Radio 95.3 |
| 18) | 95.4 | 1 | Kungälv | Pirate Rock |
| 2C) | 95.4 | 1 | Borlänge | Vinyl FM |
| 2D) | 95.5 | 2 | Karlstad | Rockklassiker |
| 4) | 95.9 | 1 | Kävlinge | Retro FM |
| 1A) | 96.0 | 2 | Karlskrona | RIX FM |
| 1A) | 96.3 | 6 | Sundsbruk | RIX FM |
| 1E) | 96.3 | 1 | Gävle | Star FM |
| 11) | 96.4 | 1 | Alvesta | Gold FM |
| 1A) | 97.1 | 1 | Katrineholm | RIX FM |
| 2A) | 97.6 | 1 | Älmhult | Mix Megapol |
| 2D) | 97.6 | 1 | Hudiksvall | Rockklassiker |
| 2A) | 98.3 | 1 | Trelleborg | Mix Megapol |
| 2B) | 98.3 | 1 | Vännäs | NRJ |
| 17) | 98.7 | 1 | Revsund | Mittradion |
| 1A) | 98.8 | 1 | Karlshamn | RIX FM |
| 12) | 99.2 | 3 | Helsingborg | Helsingborgs närradio |
| 2A) | 99.3 | 1 | Avesta | Mix Megapol |
| 2A) | 99.4 | 2 | Vimmerby | Mix Megapol |
| 1A) | 99.5 | 5 | Jönköping | RIX FM |
| 3) | 99.7 | 1 | Skurup | Guldkanalen |
| 1A) | 99.8 | 1 | Älvsbyn | RIX FM |
| 2A) | 99.9 | 1 | Ludvika | Mix Megapol |
| 2B) | 100.0 | 1 | Vimmerby | NRJ |
| 2B) | 100.1 | 1 | Uddevalla | NRJ |
| 14) | 100.6 | 1.5 | Sunne | R. Fryksdalen |
| 2A) | 100.8 | 3 | Södertälje | Mix Megapol |
| 9) | 100.9 | 1 | Norrköping | East FM |
| 19A) | 101.1 | 1.6 | Lycksele | Pop och Rock |
| 2D) | 101.3 | 1 | Färjestaden | Rockklassiker |
| 1E) | 101.5 | 1 | Hudiksvall | Star FM |
| 2A) | 101.6 | 2 | Västervik | Mix Megapol |
| 2A) | 101.7 | 2 | Ängelholm | Mix Megapol |
| 2B) | 101.8 | 1 | Gällivare | NRJ |
| 1A) | 101.9 | 2 | Sundsvall | RIX FM |
| 1C) | 101.9 | 3 | Stockholm | Bandit Rock |
| 2D) | 102.1 | 2 | Örnsköldsvik | Rockklassiker |
| 19B) | 102.3 | 2 | Umeå | Rockstar |
| 1A) | 102.3 | 2 | Borås | RIX FM |
| 2A) | 102.4 | 1 | Ystad | NRJ |
| 1A) | 102.5 | 2.5 | Habo | RIX FM |
| 2B) | 102.6 | 1 | Borlänge | NRJ |
| 22) | 102.7 | 1 | Gävle | R. Gävle |
| 19A) | 103.0 | 2 | Vännäs | Pop och Rock |
| 2B) | 103.0 | 1 | Arvika | NRJ |
| 1A) | 103.1 | 7 | Växjö | RIX FM |
| 8) | 103.8 | 1.5 | Degerfors | Cityradion |
| 2B) | 103.9 | 4 | Södertälje | NRJ |
| 2B) | 104.0 | 3 | Färjestaden | NRJ |
| 2B) | 104.0 | 3 | Östersund | NRJ |
| 2D) | 104.0 | 1 | Ludvika | Rockklassiker |
| 2A) | 104.2 | 10 | Halmstad | Mix Megapol |
| 2A) | 104.2 | 2 | Uddevalla | Mix Megapol |
| 2A) | 104.2 | 5 | Umeå | Mix Megapol |
| 2A) | 104.2 | 1 | Adolfsford | NRJ |
| 1A) | 104.3 | 6 | Linköping | RIX FM |
| 1A) | 104.3 | 5 | Växjö | RIX FM |
| 2A) | 104.3 | 16 | Kalix | Mix Megapol |

| FM | MHz | kW | Location | Station | FM | MHz | kW | Location | Station |
|---|---|---|---|---|---|---|---|---|---|
| 2A) | 104.3 | 3 | Stockholm | Mix Megapol | 2B) | 106.9 | 2.5 | Luleå | NRJ |
| 1A) | 104.4 | 25 | Visby | RIX FM | 2B) | 106.9 | 5 | Västerås | NRJ |
| 2B) | 104.4 | 13 | Karlstad | NRJ | 2A) | 107.0 | 2 | Kiruna | Mix Megapol |
| 2B) | 104.4 | 1 | Kiruna | NRJ | 2B) | 107.0 | 10 | Hudiksvall | NRJ |
| 1A) | 104.5 | 10 | Eskilstuna | RIX FM | 2B) | 107.0 | 3 | Umeå | NRJ |
| 2B) | 104.5 | 5 | Vindeln | NRJ | 4) | 107.0 | 1 | Lund | Retro FM |
| 1A) | 104.6 | 1 | Älvsbyn | RIX FM | 1E) | 107.1 | 1 | Borlänge | Star FM |
| 2A) | 104.6 | 3 | Gnosjö | Mix Megapol | 1E) | 107.1 | 1 | Stockholm | Star FM |
| 2B) | 104.6 | 5 | Mora | NRJ | 2B) | 107.1 | 6.3 | Borås | NRJ |
| 1B) | 104.7 | 1 | Stockholm | Lugna Favoriter | 2B) | 107.1 | 10 | Örnsköldsvik | NRJ |
| 2A) | 104.7 | 6 | Örebro | Mix Megapol | 1A) | 107.2 | 1 | Halmstad | RIX FM |
| 3) | 104.7 | 2 | Karlebo* | Guldkanalen | 1A) | 107.2 | 3 | Östersund | RIX FM |
| 1E) | 104.8 | 1 | Göteborg | Star FM | 1A) | 107.3 | 1 | Kristianstad | RIX FM |
| 2A) | 104.8 | 10 | Örnsköldsvik | Mix Megapol | 2A) | 107.3 | 3 | Eskilstuna | Mix Megapol |
| 2A) | 104.8 | 1 | Vetlanda | Mix Megapol | 2A) | 107.3 | 2 | Göteborg | Mix Megapol |
| 1B) | 104.9 | 1 | Norrköping | Lugna Favoriter | 2B) | 107.3 | 1 | Borgholm | NRJ |
| 2A) | 104.9 | 5 | Gävle | Mix Megapol | 2D) | 107.3 | 1 | Söderhamn | Rockklassiker |
| 1A) | 105.0 | 3 | Överkalix | RIX FM | 2A) | 107.4 | 2 | Kristinehamn | Mix Megapol |
| 1A) | 105.0 | 1 | Piteå | RIX FM | 2A) | 107.4 | 1 | Nässjö | Mix Megapol |
| 2B) | 105.0 | 5 | Robertsfors | NRJ | 2B) | 107.4 | 5 | Sundsvall | NRJ |
| 2B) | 105.0 | 3 | Trollhättan | NRJ | 1D) | 107.5 | 3 | Stockholm | Power Hit R. |
| 2A) | 105.1 | 3 | Hudiksvall | Mix Megapol | 21) | 107.5 | 1 | Lysekil | R. Bohuslän |
| 2A) | 105.1 | 5 | Jönköping | Mix Megapol | 2A) | 107.5 | 2 | Växjö | Mix Megapol |
| 2F) | 105.1 | 3 | Stockholm | Cherie FM | 1A) | 107.6 | 4.4 | Helsingborg | RIX FM |
| 2A) | 105.2 | 10 | Gällivare | Mix Megapol | 1A) | 107.6 | 5 | Skövde | RIX FM |
| 2B) | 105.2 | 5 | Malmö | NRJ | 1A) | 107.7 | 10 | Nyköping | RIX FM |
| 2B) | 105.2 | 6 | Örebro | NRJ | 20) | 107.7 | 1 | Svenstavik | R. Berg |
| 1A) | 105.3 | 7 | Göteborg | RIX FM | 1E) | 107.8 | 3 | Göteborg | Star FM |
| 2A) | 105.3 | 4 | Uppsala | Mix Megapol | 24) | 107.8 | 1.2 | Norrtälje | R. Roslagen |
| 1A) | 105.4 | 1 | Hässleholm | RIX FM | 2A) | 107.8 | 1 | Arvika | Mix Megapol |
| 2A) | 105.4 | 3 | Färjestaden | Mix Megapol | | | | | |
| 2A) | 105.4 | 9 | Karlstad | Mix Megapol | | | | | |
| 2A) | 105.4 | 2 | Skellefteå | Mix Megapol | | | | | |
| 1A) | 105.5 | 5 | Helsingborg | RIX FM | | | | | |
| 2A) | 105.5 | 1.9 | Borås | Mix Megapol | | | | | |
| 2A) | 105.5 | 5 | Borlänge | Mix Megapol | | | | | |
| 2A) | 105.5 | 5 | Sundsvall | Mix Megapol | | | | | |
| 2B) | 105.5 | 1 | Stockholm | NRJ | | | | | |
| 1A) | 105.6 | 5 | Luleå | RIX FM | | | | | |
| 2B) | 105.6 | 1 | Västervik | NRJ | | | | | |
| 1A) | 105.7 | 10 | Uddevalla | RIX FM | | | | | |
| 1B) | 105.7 | 4 | Nyköping | Lugna Favoriter | | | | | |
| 2A) | 105.8 | 7 | Växjö | Mix Megapol | | | | | |
| 2B) | 105.8 | 1.4 | Sunne | NRJ | | | | | |
| 1A) | 105.9 | 1 | Härnösand | RIX FM | | | | | |
| 1A) | 105.9 | 3 | Kristianstad | RIX FM | | | | | |
| 2B) | 105.9 | 1 | Åsele | NRJ | | | | | |
| 2B) | 105.9 | 6 | Göteborg | NRJ | | | | | |
| 4) | 105.9 | 5 | Stockholm | Retro FM | | | | | |
| 1A) | 106.0 | 1 | Kristinehamn | RIX FM | | | | | |
| 2A) | 106.0 | 1.9 | Helsingborg | Mix Megapol | | | | | |
| 2B) | 106.0 | 10 | Jönköping | NRJ | | | | | |
| 2B) | 106.0 | 1 | Örnsköldsvik | NRJ | | | | | |
| 2A) | 106.1 | 3 | Västerås | Mix Megapol | | | | | |
| 2A) | 106.1 | 6 | Visby | Mix Megapol | | | | | |
| 2D) | 106.1 | 2.5 | Malmö | Rockklassiker | | | | | |
| 1A) | 106.2 | 5 | Umeå | RIX FM | | | | | |
| 1E) | 106.2 | 1 | Trollhättan | Star FM | | | | | |
| 2D) | 106.2 | 1 | Gävle | Rockklassiker | | | | | |
| 1E) | 106.3 | 1 | Mora | Star FM | | | | | |
| 2A) | 106.3 | 5 | Luleå | Mix Megapol | | | | | |
| 2B) | 106.3 | 6 | Örebro | NRJ | | | | | |
| 2D) | 106.3 | 1.25 | Värnamo | Rockklassiker | | | | | |
| 6) | 106.3 | 1 | Stockholm | Bra Radio | | | | | |
| 1A) | 106.4 | 1 | Torsby | RIX FM | | | | | |
| 1E) | 106.4 | 1 | Söderhamn | Star FM | | | | | |
| 2A) | 106.4 | 3 | Skövde | Mix Megapol | | | | | |
| 2B) | 106.4 | 5 | Karlshamn | NRJ | | | | | |
| 1A) | 106.5 | 3 | Norrköping | RIX FM | | | | | |
| 1A) | 106.5 | 4 | Uppsala | RIX FM | | | | | |
| 2A) | 106.5 | 1 | Varberg | Mix Megapol | | | | | |
| 2B) | 106.5 | 1 | Gällivare | NRJ | | | | | |
| 3) | 106.5 | 1 | Höör | Guldkanalen | | | | | |
| 1E) | 106.6 | 5 | Sundsvall | Star FM | | | | | |
| 2B) | 106.6 | 5 | Kalix | NRJ | | | | | |
| 1A) | 106.7 | 1 | Adolfsford | RIX FM | | | | | |
| 1A) | 106.7 | 5 | Malmö | RIX FM | | | | | |
| 1A) | 106.7 | 3 | Stockholm | RIX FM | | | | | |
| 2B) | 106.7 | 5 | Gävle | NRJ | | | | | |
| 2B) | 106.7 | 3.7 | Skellefteå | NRJ | | | | | |
| 2A) | 106.8 | 7.4 | Mora | Mix Megapol | | | | | |
| 2B) | 106.8 | 2 | Finnveden | NRJ | | | | | |
| 2A) | 106.9 | 7 | Linköping | Mix Megapol | | | | | |
| 2A) | 106.9 | 10 | Trollhättan | Mix Megapol | | | | | |

+ txs below 1kW *) Located in Denmark

**Addresses & other information:**
1A-E) Nordic Entertainment Group, Ringvägen 52, 11867 Stockholm W: nentardio.se; www.ilikeradio.se – 2A-F) Bauer Media, Gjörwellsg. 30, 11260 Stockholm W: bauermedia.se; www.radioplay.se – 3) Klågerupsvägen 16, 24544 Staffanstorp E: reklam@dbmedia.se – 4) Hyllie stationsväg 2, 21532 Malmö E: studion@retrofm.se – 5) Kungsgatan 58, 50335 Borås E: info@borasnarradio.se – 6) Lundagatan 49, 11728 Stockholm E: info@smtradio.se – 7) Åsgatan 24A, 93141 Skellefteå E: info@goldtown.se – 8) P.O.Box 147, 69123 Karlskoga E: info@cityradion.se – 9) Stohagsgatan 4, 60229 Norrköping E: studion@eastfm.se – 10) Tornavägen 13, 22363 Lund E: info@funradio.se – 11) Klostergatan 2, 352 30 Växjö – 12) Árlevägen 4, 25284 Helsingborg E: h.n.f@telia.com – 13) Verkstadsgatan 1, 65219 Karlstad – 14) Svetsarevägen 2, 68633 Sunne E: info@radiofryksdalen.se – 15) P.O.Box 81, 29121 Kristianstad – 16) P.O.Box 30079, 20061 Limhamn E: info@malmokanalen.se – 17) Riksvägen 1, 84060 Bräcke E: mittradion@gmail.com – 18) Olvonvägen 9, 44277 Romelanda E: info@piraterock.se – 19A,B) Bölevägen 38, 90431 Umeå E: redaktion@poporock.se – 20) Industrivägen 27, 84531 Svenstavik E: radioberg.berg@gmail.com – 21) P.O.Box 535, 45121 Uddevalla E: info@radiobo-huslan.se – 22) Södra Centralgatan 10, 80250 Gävle – 23) Gruvvägen 1, 98131 Kiruna E: info@radiokiruna.se – 24) Stora Brogatan 6, 76130 Norrtälje E: info@radioroslagen.se – 25) P.O.Box 131, 79222 Mora E: info@radiosiljan.com.

**Community Radio (Närradio) & Special Event Radio**
There are about 150 community radio stations on FM, most of them with a power below 1kW. Each tx is licensed by MPRT & PTS to a local community radio association (närradioförening); the airtime is usually shared by a variety of different non-profit associations and religious organisations (ca 800) that are individually licensed by MPRT and are transmitting their prgrs under their own names. **Närradio stations in Greater Stockholm area:** (MHz) 88.0 (Stockholm närradio 88.0), 88.2 (R. Sigtuna), 88.4 (Sveriges Kristna Radio), 88.9 (R. Sydväst), 90.2 (Skärgårdsradion 90.2), 90.5 (Västerort närradio), 91.1 (Järva närradio), 91.4 (R. Tyresö), 91.6 (R. Botkyrka), 94.2 (Järfälla R.), 94.6 (Sollentuna R.), 95.3 (Stockholm närradio 95.3), 97.3 (Solna/Sundbyberg närradio), 97.8 (R. Lidingö), 98.3 (R. Nord), 98.5 (R. Haninge Direkt), 99.9 (R. Nacka), 101.1 (Stockholm närradio 101.1), 101.4 (R. Viking), 103.7 (R. Österåker 103.7 MHz), 107.8 (R. Roslagen), 107.9 (Dixie R.). – **Special Event Radio:** MPRT & PTS are issuing short-term licenses for low power txs on FM, MW or SW for the duration of special events (up to 2 weeks).

**DAB Transmitters**
**Tx Operator:** Teracom **Mux 1 (SR):** SR P1, SR P2 Klassikt sommar, SR P3 Star, SR Klassiskt, SR Knattekanalen, SR Världen, SR P7 Sisuradio **Mux 2 (Teracom Trial):** SR P2, SR P3, SR P4 Stockholm, Bandit, Rockklassiker, Vinyl, Lugna Favoriter, NRJ, Mix Megapol, Skärgårdsradion **Mux 3 (Bauer Media):** Mix Megapol, NRJ, Rockklassiker, Svensk Pop, Vinyl FM **Mux DR (Danmarks Radio relay; beamed towards Denmark)** DR P1-3, P4 Bornholm, P4 Fyn, P4 København, P4 Sjælland, P4 Syd, P5, P6 Beat, P7

Mix, P8 Jazz, Radio 24syv.

| Bl | kW | Location | Mux | Bl | kW | Location | Mux |
|----|----|----------|-----|----|----|----------|-----|
| 11C | 1 | Helsingborg | DR | 12C | - | Stockholm (SFN) | 1 |
| 12A | - | Stockholm (SFN) | 2 | 12C | 2 | Södertälje | 1 |
| 12B | 2 | Enköping | 1 | 12C | 6 | Älvsbyn | 1 |
| 12B | 2 | Göteborg | 1 | 12D | - | Stockholm | 3 |
| 12B | 2 | Malmö (SFN) | 1 | 13C | 20 | Uppsala | 2 |
| 12B | 2 | Uppsala | 1 | 13F | 20 | Gävle | 2 |

**NB: Bl**=Block. Detailed info on FM & DAB txs in Sweden can be found on the following websites **W:** teracom.se, onair.nu, radioguiden.se

## SWITZERLAND

**L.T:** UTC +1h (31 Mar-27 Oct: +2h) — **Pop:** 8.5 million — **Pr.L:** Swiss (Alemannic) German, German, French, Italian, Rumantsch — **E.C:** 230V/50Hz — **ITU:** SUI

### BUNDESAMT FÜR KOMMUNIKATION (BAKOM)
(Federal Office of Communications)
Zukunftstrasse 44, 2501 Biel ☎+41 32 3275511 📠+41 32 3275555
**E:** info@bakom.admin.ch **W:** www.bakom.admin.ch
**L.P:** Dir: Philipp Metzger

### SRG SSR (Pub)
Giacomettistrasse 1, 3000 Bern 31 ☎+41 31 3509111 **E:** info@srgssr.ch **W:** srgssr.ch
**L.P:** Pres: Jean-Michel Cina; DG: Gilles Marchand
**NB:** SRG SSR is the administrative holding for the regional branches Schweizer Radio und Fernsehen (SRF), Radiotelevisiun Svizra Rumantscha (RTR), Radio Télévision Suisse (RTS) and Radiotelevisione svizzera (RSI).

### Schweizer Radio und Fernsehen (SRF)
Fernsehstrasse 1-4, 8052 Zürich ☎+41 44 3056611 **E:** srf@srf.ch
**W:** srf.ch **L.P:** Dir: Rudolf Matter (until end of 2018)
Radio studios: Brunnenhofstrasse 22, 8057 Zürich (exc. R. SRF 2 Kultur); Novarastrasse 2, 4002 Basel (R. SRF 2 Kultur), subreg. studios.

| FM (MHz) | 1 | 2 | 3 | kW |
|----------|---|---|---|-----|
| Arth (Rigi-Kulm) | 90.9 | 96.6 | 103.8 | 20 |
| Beatenberg (Niederhorn) | 93.6 | 97.2 | 105.8 | 4 |
| Bettingen (St. Chrischona) | 90.6 | 99.0 | 103.6 | 32 |
| Bolligen (Bantiger) | 88.2 | 93.2 | 99.3 | 5 |
| Bregenz (Pfänder)** | 96.3 | 97.7 | 107.5 | 2 |
| Carona (Monte San Salvatore) | 96.3 | - | - | 20 |
| Castel San Pietro (Caviano) | 93.0 | - | - | 10 |
| Celerina (Laret) | 91.9 | 100.3 | 106.3 | 2 |
| Evilard (Hohmatt) | 96.0 | 99.7 | 91.7 | 0.1/1/0.1 |
| Feschel (Wilerzälg) | 88.2 | 90.3 | 101.5 | 1.6 |
| Gerra (Lutri) | 95.4 | - | - | 1.3 |
| Haute-Nendaz (La Crête) | 92.0 | - | - | 2 |
| Ins (Schaltenrain) | 90.7 | - | - | 1 |
| Lostorf (Froburg) | 96.0 | 98.7 | 91.3 | 1.3 |
| Martigny (Ravoire) | 107.7 | - | - | 2 |
| Mt. Salève* | 87.8 | - | - | 2 |
| Nods (Chasseral) | 103.0 | - | 105.3 | 20 |
| Oberdorf (Nesselboden) | 89.7 | - | - | 1.6 |
| Pianezzo (Monti di Paudo) | 96.9 | - | - | 2.5 |
| Port Valais (Chalavornaire) | 93.6 | - | - | 1 |
| Schattenhalb (Geissholzli) | 95.4 | 98.4 | 105.6 | 2 |
| Tarasp (Sparsels) | 101.3 | 103.9 | 95.1 | 1.3 |
| Thollon (Leucel)* | 88.1 | - | - | 6.3 |
| Valzeina (Mittagplatte) | 93.8 | 102.5 | 104.3 | 1.6 |
| Visperterminen (Gebidem) | 89.4 | 93.9 | 103.9 | 2.5 |
| Widen (Gugelholz) | 98.3 | - | - | 1 |
| Wildhaus (Säntis) | 101.5 | 95.4 | 105.6 | 63 |
| Zürich (Uetliberg) | 94.6 | 99.6 | 105.8 | 2/0.6/2 |

+ sites with only txs below 1kW. *) Located in France **) Located in Austria
**D.Prgr** (in Swiss German, exc. news/traffic info and *= in German): **Prgr 1 (R. SRF 1):** 24h. Subregional prgrs: 0532-0537 (MF), 0632-0637 (MF), 0732-0737 (MF), 1103-1110 (MF), 1630-1640 (Sat), 1630-1700 (Sun-Fri), 1655-1700 (Sat; Graubünden only) — **Prgr 2 (R. SRF 2 Kultur)*:** 24h — **Prgr 3 (R. SRF 3):** 24h — **Prgr 4 (R. SRF 4 News)*:** 24h — **Prgr 5 (R. SRF Musikwelle):** 24h — **Prgr 6 (SRF Virus):** 24h.

### Radiotelevisiun Svizra Rumantscha (RTR)
Via da Masans 2, 7002 Cuira ☎+41 81 2557575 **E:** esther.bigliel@rtr.ch **W:** rtr.ch **L.P:** Dir: Ladina Heimgartner

| FM | MHz | kW | FM | MHz | kW |
|----|-----|----|-----|-----|-----|
| Celerina (Laret) | 89.1 | 2 | Tarasp (Sparsels) | 98.7 | 1.3 |
| Valzeina (Mittagplatte) | 90.3 | 1.6 | + txs below 1kW. | | |

**D.Prgr** (in Rumantsch): **R. Rumantsch:** 24h. Incl. relay of selected R.SRF prgrs in Swiss German/German.

### Radio Télévision Suisse (RTS)
Administration/studios: Quai Ernest-Ansermet 20, 1211 Genève 8
☎+41 58 2367444 **W:** rts.ch **L.P:** Dir: Pascal Crittin
Radio studios: Avenue du Temple 40, 1010 Lausanne.

| FM (MHz) | 1 | 2 | 3 | 4 | kW |
|----------|---|---|---|---|-----|
| Abbaye (Pont-Agouillons) | 99.5 | 87.6 | 101.4 | - | 1 |
| Bolligen (Bantiger) | 95.1 | - | - | - | 5 |
| Bourrignon (Ordons) | 94.2 | 99.6 | 104.8 | - | 10 |
| Carona (Monte San Salvatore) | 104.0 | - | - | - | 20 |
| Castel San Pietro (Caviano) | 87.8 | - | - | - | 10 |
| Chardonne (Mt. Pèlerin) | 91.6 | 101.5 | 90.6 | - | 1.6 |
| Chaux-de-Fonds (Cornu) | 92.3 | 96.3 | 103.4 | - | 1.3 |
| Cudrefin (Tremblex) | 91.3 | 92.0 | 89.1 | - | 4 |
| Feschel (Wilerzälg) | 91.4 | 96.1 | 107.4 | - | 1.6 |
| Gerra (Lutri) | 93.2 | - | - | - | 1.6 |
| Gingins (Barillette) | 91.2 | 100.1 | 105.6 | - | 20 |
| Haute-Nendaz (La Crête) | 94.4 | 96.5 | 106.0 | - | 2 |
| Ins (Schaltenrain) | 96.9 | - | - | - | 1 |
| Martigny (Ravoire) | 93.2 | 106.9 | 100.5 | - | 2 |
| Mt. Salève* | 94.9 | 100.7 | 104.4 | 90.8 | 1 |
| Nods (Chasseral) | 102.3 | 100.3 | 104.2 | - | 20 |
| Ollon (Chamossaire) | 98.1 | 95.0 | 88.6 | - | 1 |
| Ollon (Chamossaire) | 105.1 | - | - | - | 0.3 |
| Pianezzo (Monti di Paudo) | 105.3 | - | - | - | 2.5 |
| Premier (Buclards) | 94.7 | 100.8 | 104.7 | - | 10 |
| Saint-Sulpice (Haut de la Vy) | 102.0 | 95.3 | 104.5 | - | 1 |
| Sorens (Gibloux) | 91.0 | 92.5 | 88.6 | - | 1 |
| Thollon (Leucel)* | 102.6 | 96.2 | 98.5 | - | 6.3 |
| Visperterminen (Gebidem) | 90.8 | - | - | - | 2.5 |
| Wildhaus (Säntis) | 99.9 | - | - | - | 63 |

+ sites with only txs below 1kW.. *) Located in France
**D.Prgr** (in French): **Prgr 1 (La 1ère):** 24h — **Prgr 2 (Espace 2):** 24h **Prgr 3 (Couleur 3):** 24h — **Prgr 4 (Option Musique):** 24h.

### Radiotelevisione svizzera (RSI)
Via Canevascini 5, 6900 Lugano ☎+41 91 8035111 **E:** info@rsi.ch **W:** rsi.ch **L.P:** Dir: Maurizio Canetta

| FM (MHz) | 1 | 2 | 3 | kW |
|----------|---|---|---|-----|
| Arth (Rigi-Kulm) | 106.2 | - | - | 20 |
| Carona (Monte San Salvatore) | 88.1 | 91.5 | 106.0 | 20 |
| Castel San Pietro (Caviano) | 88.8 | 98.8 | 104.5 | 10 |
| Celerina (Laret) | 104.3 | - | - | 2 |
| Gerra (Lutri) | 92.5 | 94.1 | 99.2 | 1.3 |
| Mt. Salève* | 97.1 | - | - | 2 |
| Nods (Chasseral) | 107.3 | - | - | 20 |
| Pianezzo (Monti di Paudo) | 89.4 | 93.5 | 107.4 | 2.5 |
| Thollon (Leucel)* | 97.8 | - | - | 6.3 |
| Valzeina (Mittagplatte) | 95.8 | - | - | 1.6 |
| Visperterminen (Gebidem) | 96.7 | - | - | 2.5 |
| Wildhaus (Säntis) | 107.8 | - | - | 63 |

+ sites with only txs below 1kW. *) Located in France
**D.Prgr** (in Italian): **Prgr 1 (Rete Uno):** 24h — **Prgr 2 (Rete Due):** 24h **Prgr 3 (Rete Tre):** 24h.

### OTHER STATIONS

| FM | MHz | kW | Location | Station |
|----|-----|----|----------|---------|
| 16B) | 87.6 | 2 | Stockeren | R. Freiburg |
| 24) | 88.0 | 2.8 | Rooterberg | R. Sunshine |
| 7) | 88.4 | 2 | Mt. Salève* | LFM |
| 24) | 88.1 | 1 | Schüepenloch | R. Sunshine |
| 24) | 88.8 | 2 | Gugelholz | R. Sunshine |
| 3) | 88.9 | 4 | Dornegg | R. 32 |
| 10) | 89.2 | 1 | Utzenstorf | R. Bern1 |
| 15) | 89.3 | 1 | Rorschacherberg | R. FM1 |
| 16A) | 89.4 | 1.75 | Gibloux | R. Fribourg |
| 19) | 89.8 | 1 | Lenzerheide | R. Südostschweiz |
| 25) | 90.0 | 1 | St. Gallen | R. Top |
| 11) | 90.5 | 1 | Rigi-Kulm | R. Central |
| 14) | 90.6 | 1 | Monti di Paudo | R. Fiume Ticino |
| 8) | 91.6 | 2 | Gugelholz | R. Argovia |
| 18) | 91.8 | 2 | Mt. Salève* | R. Lac |
| 2) | 92.1 | 1 | Honegg | R. 24 |
| 13) | 92.2 | 1 | Mt. Salève* | R. Cité Genève |
| 18) | 92.3 | 4 | Champs Maître | R. Lac |
| 12) | 92.6 | 1 | Giettes | R. Chablais |
| 15) | 92.7 | 3 | Mittagplatte | R. FM1 |
| 27A) | 92.8 | 1 | Elemoos | Canal 3 |
| 14) | 93.0 | 1 | Monte Laura | R. Fiume Ticino |
| 24) | 93.2 | 1 | Rigi-Kulm | R. Sunshine |
| 27B) | 93.9 | 1 | Elemoos | Canal 3 |
| 18) | 94.0 | 1 | Champs Lequet | R. Lac |
| 18) | 95.6 | 6 | Leucel* | R. Lac |
| 21) | 95.7 | 1 | Rigi-Kulm | R. Pilatus |
| 29) | 96.3 | 1 | Ins | RJB |

| FM | MHz | kW | Location | Station |
|---|---|---|---|---|
| 4) | 96.5 | 4 | Alpe del Tiglio | R. 3i |
| 1) | 97.0 | 1 | Champs Lequet | One FM |
| 12) | 97.1 | 1 | Chamossaire | R. Chablais |
| 7) | 97.4 | 4 | Champs Maître | LFM |
| 30) | 97.5 | 1 | Uetliberg | R. LoRa |
| 23) | 97.5 | 1 | Ins | R. RTN |
| 20) | 97.6 | 2 | Mt. Salève* | Rouge FM |
| 10) | 97.7 | 1 | Bantiger | R. Bern1 |
| 11) | 99.2 | 1.5 | Rooterberg | R. Central |
| 1) | 99.3 | 2 | Grand Devin | One FM |
| 24) | 99.6 | 1.5 | Alpnach | R. Sunshine |
| 19) | 99.7 | 1.2 | Davos | R. Südostschweiz |
| 14) | 100.0 | 4 | Monte San Salvatore | R. Fiume Ticino |
| 11) | 100.1 | 1 | Sonnenberg | R. Central |
| 17) | 100.6 | 1 | Loge | RFJ |
| 6) | 100.6 | 1 | Schaltenrain | GRRIF |
| 17) | 100.8 | 4.6 | Ordons | RFJ |
| 5C) | 100.9 | 1 | Uetliberg | Energy Zürich |
| 5B) | 101.0 | 1 | Utzenstorf | Energy Bern |
| 23) | 101.7 | 1 | Loge | R. RTN |
| 5A) | 101.7 | 4 | St.Chrischona | Energy Basel |
| 5B) | 101.7 | 1 | Bantiger | Energy Bern |
| 28) | 101.9 | 4 | Tresillet | Rouge FM |
| 21) | 102.1 | 1.5 | Rooterberg | R. Pilatus |
| 22) | 102.2 | 1.5 | Gebidem | R. Rottu Oberwallis |
| 11) | 102.6 | 2 | Urmiberg | R. Central |
| 2) | 102.8 | 1 | Uetliberg | R. 24 |
| 11) | 103.0 | 1.5 | Alpnach | R. Central |
| 7) | 103.3 | 6 | Leucel* | LFM |
| 28) | 104.3 | 1.2 | Martigny | Rhône FM |
| 21) | 104.9 | 1 | Sonnenberg | R. Pilatus |
| 20) | 106.5 | 6 | Leucel* | Rouge FM |
| 4) | 106.5 | 10 | Caviano | R. 3i |
| 26) | 106.7 | 1 | Uetliberg | R. Zürisee |
| 4) | 106.8 | 2.6 | Monte San Salvatore | R. 3i |
| 1) | 107.0 | 2 | Mt. Salève* | One FM |
| 19) | 107.0 | 3 | Mittagplatte | R. Südostschweiz |
| 14) | 107.1 | 4 | Lutri | R. Fiume Ticino |
| 1) | 107.2 | 3 | Publier* | One FM |
| 23) | 107.6 | 1 | Montela | R. RTN |
| 9) | 107.6 | 4 | St. Chrischona | R. Basilisk |
| 1) | 107.9 | 4 | Champs Maître | One FM |

+ sites with onlt txs below 1kW. *) Located in France

**Addresses & other information:**
**NB**. Stns broadcast in Swiss German/German exc. where indicated otherwise. **1)** Rue des Bains 33, 1205 Genève. In French. – **2)** Limmatstrasse 264, 8005 Zürich – **3)** Zuchwilerstrasse 21, 4501 Solothurn – **4)** Via Carona 15, 6815 Melide. In Italian. – **5A)** Münchensteinerstrasse 43, 4052 Basel, **5B)** Optingenstrasse 56, 3001 Bern **5C)** Dufourstrasse 23, 8008 Zürich – **6)** Rue du Marché 3, 2800 Delémont. In French. – **7)** Chemin de Mornex 1 Bis, 1003 Lausanne. In French. – **8)** Bahnhofstrasse 41, 5001 Aarau – **9)** Marktgasse 8, 4001 Basel – **10)** Dammweg 9, 3001 Bern – **11)** Postfach 464, 6440 Brunnen – **12)** Rue des Fours 11A, 1870 Monthey 1. In French. – **13)** Rue du Pré-de-la-Fontaine 2, 1217 Meyrin 2. In French. – **14)** Via Varenna 18, 6600 Locarno. In Italian. – **15)** Bionstrasse 4, 9001 St.Gallen – **16A,B)** Rue de Romont 35, 1701 Fribourg. 16A) in French. – **17)** Rue du 23-Juin 20, 2800 Delémont. In French. – **18)** Rue des Bains 35, 1205 Genève. In French. – **19)** Sommeraustrasse 32, 7007 Chur – **20)** En Budron A6, 1052 Le-Mont-sur-Lausanne. In French. – **21)** Zürichstr. 5, 6004 Luzern – **22)** Treichweg 1, 3930 Visp – **23)** Champs-Montants 16a, 2074 Marin. In French. – **24)** Erlenstrasse 2, 6343 Rotkreuz – **25)** Bürglistrasse 31a, 8401 Winterthur – **26)** Bahnhofplatz 1, 8640 Rapperswil – **27A,B)** Robert-Walser-Platz 7, 2501 Biel. 27B) in French. – **28)** Chemin Saint-Hubert 5, 1950 Sion. In French. – **29)** L'Orgerie 9, 2710 Tavannes. In French. – **30)** Militärstrasse 85a, 8004 Zürich.

**DAB Transmitters** (DAB+)
**Licensee:** SRG SSR **M1:** R. SRF 1 (incl. subreg), R. SRF 2 Kultur, R. SRF 3, R. SRF 4 News, R. SRF Musikwelle, SRF Virus, Swiss Pop, RTS La 1ère, RTS Couleur 3, RSI Rete Uno, RSI Rete Tre, RTR R. Rumantsch **M2:** RTS La 1ère, RTS Espace 2, RTS Couleur 3, RTS Option Musique, Swiss Pop, Swiss Classic, Swiss Jazz, R. SRF 1 (incl. subreg), R. SRF 3, R. SRF Musikwelle, R. SRF 4 News, SRF Virus, RSI Rete Uno, RSI Rete Tre, RTR R. Rumantsch **M3:** RSI Rete Uno, RSI Rete Due, RSI Rete Tre, Swiss Pop, Swiss Classic, Swiss Jazz, R. SRF 1, R. SRF 3, R. SRF 4 News, R. SRF Musikwelle, RTS La 1ère, RTS Couleur 3, RTS Option Musique, RTR R. Rumantsch, R. F Ticino, R. 3i **M4:** R. SRF 1 (incl. subreg), R. SRF 2 Kultur, R. SRF 3, R. SRF 4 News, R. SRF Musikwelle, SRF Virus, Swiss Pop, Swiss Classic, Swiss Jazz, RTS La 1ère, RTS Couleur 3, RSI Rete Uno, RSI Rete Tre, RTR R. Rumantsch – **Licensee:** SwissMediaCast AG **M5:** R. Central, Energy Basel, Energy Bern, Energy Zürich, ERF Plus, Eviva, R. FM1, Luna R., Life Channel, R. Pilatus, R.

Argovia, R. 24, R. Inside, R. Maria, R. Top, R. Zürisee, RSI Rete Tre **M6a-d: Regional muxes** (on all muxes: Swiss Classic, Swiss Jazz, R. Gloria); 6c includes R. L (Liechtenstein) – **Licensee:** Romandie Médias SA **M7:** BNJ-RJB, BNJ-RTN, BNJ-RFJ, GRIFF, LFM, One FM, R. Chablais, R. Fribourg, R. Fribourg Music, R. Lac, R. Maria, Rhône FM, Rouge FM, Vertical, SRF Virus, RSI Rete Tre – **Licensee:** Digris AG **M: Local muxes** in key agglomerations (not shown).

| Bl | Location | Mux | Bl | Location | Mux |
|---|---|---|---|---|---|
| 7A | SFN (Nordschweiz) | 6a | 11C | SFN (Oberwallis) | 6d |
| 7D | SFN (Deutschschweiz) | 5 | 12A | SFN (Romandie) | 2 |
| 8B | SFN (Mittelland) | 6b | 12A | SFN (Ticino) | 3 |
| 9B | SFN (Ostschweiz) | 6c | 12C | SFN (Deutschschweiz[1]) | 1 |
| 10B | SFN (Romandie) | 7 | 12D | SFN (Graubünden) | 4 |

**Bl**=Block [1]) exc. Graubünden

**L.T:** UTC +2h (29 Mar-25 Oct: +3h) — **Pop:** 19 million — **Pr.L:** Arabic — **E.C:** 50Hz, 220V — **ITU:** SYR

**MINISTRY OF INFORMATION**
Mezzeh Autostrad, Dar al Ba'th Building, Damascus ☎+963 11 6664681 📠 +963 11 6664681 **W:** moi.gov.sy **E:** info@moi.gov.sy **L.P:** Talib Qadi Amin, Asst. Minister.

**SYRIAN RADIO AND TV (Gov.)**
Radio & TV Directorate, Ommayad Square, Damascus ☎+963 11 2720700 📠 +963 11 2234930 **W:** en.ortas.gov.sy **E:** editor@rtv. gov.sy **L.P:** DG: Fayez Al Sayegh. Dir. Eng: Adnan Salhah. Dir. Radio: Mahmoud Al Joma'at.

| MW | kHz | kW | Prgr | MW | kHz | kW | Prgr |
|---|---|---|---|---|---|---|---|
| Damascus | 567 | 300 | 1 | Homs | 936 | 100 | 1 |
| Damascus | 666 | 100 | Y | Tartus | 1071 | 100 | * |
| Tartus | 783 | 300 | 1/E | *relays R. Al-Nour, LBN | | | |

| FM | 1 | 2/M | Y | kW |
|---|---|---|---|---|
| Abu Kamal | - | | 92.6 | |
| Afrin | 93.0 | 90.3 | 96.6 | |
| Al-Hassake | 89.9 | 93.0 | 99.5 | |
| Aleppo | 96.1 | 99.4 | 89.9 | 10 |
| Ayn al-Arab | 89.4 | | 105.1 | |
| Bloudan | 93.5 | | 96.7 | |
| Damascus | 95.5 | 98.3 | 88.7 | |
| Deir ez-Zor | 90.0 | 94.1 | 87.8 | 150/1 |
| Homs | - | | 99.3 | |
| Maliqiyah | 89.4 | 92.1 | 99.0 | |
| Nabi Saleh | 89.0 | 93.0 | 98.8 | |
| Raqqah | 103.7 | 96.9 | 93.7 | |
| Slenfe | 94.9 | 91.7 | 88.6 | 150 |
| Suwayda | 92.6 | 87.8 | 100.9 | 150 |
| Tartus | - | | 95.5 | |
| Yabrud | - | | 93.0 | |

**General Prgr "Radio Dimashk" (1):** 24h. **Voice of Youth (Y)** 24h.
**Other stations** (**W:** ortas.gov.sy/index.php?d=100461):
**Amwaj FM,** Latakia 98.2, Tartus 105.3MHz. **W:** facebook.com/Amwaj.Latakia – **Al-Karma FM,** Suwayda: 88.5/104.5MHz. **W:** facebook.com/al-karma.fm – **Syriana FM** (news prgr.), Damascus 88.3MHz, Tartus 90MHz – **Zenobia FM,** Homs: 98.0MHz
**Ann:** 1: "Idha'at Dimashq". 2: "Huna Idha'at Sowt as-Sha'ab min Dimashq". Y: "Huna Sowt as-Shabab".

**External service:** see International Radio section.

**Other stations:**
**Al Aan FM:** Al Bab 104.4MHz, Aleppo 96.6MHz, Atme 99.7MHz, Damascus 96.9MHz, Daraa 98.2/99.4MHz, Homs 97.6MHz, Latakia 96.3MHz **W:** alaan.fm – **Al Madina FM:** Slenfe 100.5MHz, Aleppo/Damascus 101.5MHz.**W:** almadinafm.com – **Alwan FM:** Idlib 93.3MHz **W:** alwan.fm – **Arabesque FM:** Aleppo/Damascus 102.3MHz, Slenfe 106.9MHz **W:** arabesque.fm – **ARTA FM:** Deir ez-Zor 97.0, Aamouda 99.5 **W:** artafm.com – **Fann FM:** Aleppo/Damascus 89.0MHz, Slenfe 106.1MHz **W:** fann-fm.com – **Farah FM:** Aleppo/Damascus 97.3MHz **W:** farah.fm – **Hala FM:** 99.9/103.8MHz **W:** 7la.fm – **R. Al-Kul** (opposition) Aleppo: 95.5MHz **W:** radioalkul.com – **R. Gecko (UN)** Camp Faouar, Golan: 103.8MHz **W:** radio-gecko.com – **Melody FM:** Aleppo/Damascus 97.9MHz **W:** melodysyria.com – **Mix FM,** Damascus: 105.7MHz **W:** mixfmsyria.com – **Ninar FM:** Aleppo 88.3MHz, Slenfe 89.6MHz, Damascus 93.8MHz **W:** ninarweb.com – **R. Nasaem Syria:** Aleppo 98.5MHz **W:** nasaem-syria.fm – **Rotana Style FM:** Slenfe 103.3MHz, Aleppo/Damascus 105.0MHz **W:** rotanastyle.com – **Sawt el-Ghad,** Damascus: 99.9MHz **W:** sawtelghad.com (see main entry

under Lebanon) – **Shahba FM,** Aleppo 94.0MHz **W:** shahbafm.com – **Sham FM:** Damascus 92.3MHz, Aleppo 95.3MHz, Slenfe 101.8MHz **W:** shamfm.fm – **Syria Al-Ghad FM:** Damascus 104.2MHz, Aleppo 104.4MHz, Slenfe 107.4MHz **W:** syriaalghad.com – **Watan FM:** Aleppo 90.2MHz, Idlib 90.3MHz, Damascus 102.8MHz **W:** watan.fm – **Version FM:** Damascus 94.4MHz **W:** versionfm.com
**R. Al-Nour:** Aleppo 98.7, Damascus 91.3/91.5, Homs/Tartus 92.3 **W:** alnour.com.lb/radio (See main entry under Lebanon)
**Orient Radio** (studios in Turkey): Homs/Idlib 94.6, Deraa 99.2, Antakya (TUR) 94.4, Reyhanli (TUR) 95.8. **W:** orient-radio.net
**NB:** Many stns and txs rep. off the air or operating irregularly. Many unlicensed stns operate without licence.

## TAIWAN (Rep. of China)

**L.T:** UTC +8h — **Pop:** 23.5 million — **Pr.L:** Mandarin (Chinese), Taiwanese (Amoy), Hakka — **E.C:** 60Hz, 110V — **ITU:** CHN (**WRTH:** TWN)

### NATIONAL COMMUNICATIONS COMMISSION (NCC)
RenAi Rd. Office: ✉ No. 50, Sec. 1, RenAi Rd., Taipei 10052 ☎ +886 800 177177 🖷 +886 2 2343 3994 **W:** ncc.gov.tw **E:** po2@ncc.gov.tw
**L.P:** Chairperson: Chan, Ting-I

### CHUNGKUO KUANGPO KUNGSSU (Broadcasting Corporation of China - BCC) (Priv. Comm.)
✉ 375 Sungchiang Rd, Chungshan Ward, Taipei 104 ☎ +886 2 2501 9688 🖷 +886 2 2501 8834 **W:** bcc.com.tw **E:** pr@bcc.com.tw
**L.P:** Chairman: Chao Shao Kang
**Call:** BE followed by the callsign below

| MW | Call | Location | kHz | kW | Netw. |
|---|---|---|---|---|---|
| 1) | D57 | Taipei (Tucheng) | 531 | 10 | L |
| 9) | D65 | Ilan* | 630 | 10 | N |
| 3) | D34 | Taipei (Tucheng) | 648 | 20 | N |
| 6) | D92 | Tainan | 711 | 10 | C |
| 4) | D28 | Taichung | 720 | 10 | N |
| 10) | D18 | Taitung* | 819 | 10 | N |
| 8) | D27 | Hualien | 855 | 4.6 | N |
| 7) | D25 | Kaohsiung | 864 | 10 | N |
| 2) | G77 | Hsinchu | 882 | 10 | N |
| 6) | D24 | Tainan | 891 | 10 | L |
| 4) | D43 | Taichung | 927 | 10 | C |
| 1) | D55 | Taipei (Tucheng) | 963 | 20 | C |
| 10) | D88 | Taitung* | 1008 | 10 | C |
| 2) | D53 | Hsinchu | 1017 | 10 | C |
| 5) | D26 | Chia-i | 1035 | 10 | C |
| 4) | D23 | Taichung | 1062 | 10 | L |
| 11) | D72 | Yuli* | 1116 | 3.5 | N |
| 12) | D68 | Puli* | 1152 | 1 | C |
| 9) | D86 | Ilan* | 1161 | 10 | C |
| 3) | D89 | Miaoli | 1161 | 10 | C |
| 8) | D32 | Hualien | 1188 | 5 | C |
| 7) | D52 | Kaohsiung | 1224 | 10 | C |
| 6) | D47 | Tainan | 1296 | 10 | N |
| 5) | D63 | Chia-i | 1350 | 10 | N |
| 11) | D74 | Yuli* | 1386 | 3.5 | N |
| 3) | D54 | Miaoli | 1413 | 10 | N |
| 12) | D67 | Puli* | 1413 | 1 | N |

N=News Netw, C=Country Netw, L=local , *) relay stn

| FM | Location | P | kW | FM | Location | P | kW |
|---|---|---|---|---|---|---|---|
| 1) | Taipei | 103.3 | 35 | 9) | Ilan* | 102.1 | 2.5 |
| 3) | Huoyenshan | 102.9 | 10 | 10) | Taitung* | 102.1 | 5 |
| 4) | Taichung | 102.1 | 35 | 11) | Yuli* | 103.3 | 1 |
| 5) | Chentoushan | 103.1 | 10 | 12) | Puli* | 107.3 | 1 |
| 7) | Kaohsiung | 103.3 | 35 | 13) | Kinmen* | 96.3 | 10 |
| 8) | Hualien | 102.1 | 5 | | | | |

P=Pop Netw, *) relay stn

**D.Prgr: News Network:** 24h in Mandarin – **Country Network:** 24h in Taiwanese – **Taipei Local R. (i go 531):** 24h mainly in Mandarin – **Pop Network (i like radio):** 24h in Mandarin
**Addresses of local stations:**
**2)** 125-1, Chingpu Rd, Chiingpu, Hsinfeng Village, Hsinchu 304 – **3)** 78, Lane 1008, Chungshan Rd, Kaomiao Li, Miaoli 360 – **4)** 35th Flr, 758 Chungming So. Rd, Taichung 402 – **5)** 121 Wufeng So. Rd, Chia-i 600 – **6)** 5, 19th Flr, 248, Sec. 2, Yunghua Rd, Anping, Tainan 708 – **7)** 1, 24th Flr, 91 Chungshan 2nd Rd, Chienchen, Kaohsiung 806 – **8)** 2nd Flr. 108, Fu'an Rd, Hualien 970 – **9)** Ilan (relay st.) – **10)** Taitung (relay st.) – **11)** Yuli (relay st.) – **12)** Puli (relay st.) – **13)** Kinmen (relay st.), relays also News Netw at certain times
**Ann:** Mandarin: "Chungkuo Kuangpo Kungssu" or "Chungkuo Kuangpo Kungssu, (location) Kuangpo Tientai", Amoy: "Tiyon Gok Kon Po Kon

Sih, (location) Kon Po Den Tai"
**Notes:** Two networks, Formosa Network and Music Network, both ceased FM broadcasting on 14 April,2017. Of these Former Music Network only continues to broadcast via internet as "I Radio"

### EXTERNAL SERVICES: Radio Taiwan International
see International Broadcasting section

### HAN SHENG KUANGPO TIENTAI (Voice of Han Broadcasting Network) (Gov)
(operated by General Political Warfare Bureau, Ministry of National Defense)
✉ B, 5th Flr, 3, Sec. 1, Hsin-i Rd, Chungcheng Ward, Taipei 10048 ☎ +886 2 2321 5191 🖷 +886 2 2396 2657 **W:** voh.com.tw

| MW | Call | Location | kHz | kW |
|---|---|---|---|---|
| 1) | C22 | Taipei | 684 | 10 |
| 1b) | C25 | Taoyuan | 693 | 10 |
| 2b) | C32 | Tainan | 693 | 8 |
| 4) | C33 | Hualien | 792 | 10 |
| 2c) | C38 | Penghu | 846 | 10 |
| 1b) | | Taoyuan | 936 | 5 |
| 1) | C22 | Taipei | 1116 | 10 |
| 4b) | C30 | Ilan | 1116 | 10 |
| 2) | | Kaohsiung | 1251 | 10 |
| 2c) | C44 | Penghu | 1269 | 10 |
| 3) | C27 | Taichung | 1287 | 10 |
| 2) | C36 | Kaohsiung | 1332 | 10 |
| 4) | C40 | Hualien | 1359 | 5 |
| 3b) | C31 | Yunlin | 1377 | 10 |

| FM | Call | Location | MHz | kW |
|---|---|---|---|---|
| 2b) | C28 | Tainan (Chentoushan) | 101.3 | 35 |
| 1) | C26 | Miaoli (Huoyenshan) | 104.5 | 35 |
| 4) | C35 | Hualien | 104.5 | 3 |
| 4c) | C39 | Taitung | 105.3 | 3 |
| 4d) | | Kuanshan | 105.3 | 3 |
| 1) | C24 | Taipei | 106.5 | 35 |
| 4b) | | Ilan | 106.5 | |
| 2) | C34 | Kaohsiung | 107.3 | 35 |
| 1c) | | Kinmen | 107.3 | 0.1 |

**D.Prgr:** 24h on MW & FM. Same prgr broadcasts at certain times. – **1b)** Taoyuan **1c)** Kinmen (relay Taipei) – **2)** 40 Mingte New Village, Tsoying, Kaohsiung 813 – 2b) Tainan 2c) 1 Makong, Penghu (relay Kaohsiung) – **3)** 178 Chenhsing Rd, East Ward, Taichung 401 – 3b) Yunlin (relay Taichung) – 4) 643 Chungcheng Rd, Hualien 970 – 4b) Ilan 4c) Taitng 4d) Kuanshan (relay Hualien)

### BROADCASTS TO MAINLAND:
### KUANGHUA CHIH SHENG (Voice of Kuanghua) (Gov)
✉ P.O.Box 1700, Taipei ☎ +886 2 2603 0429 🖷 +886 2 2603 0433 **W:** khmusic.com.tw

| MW location | kHz | kW | Location | kHz | kW |
|---|---|---|---|---|---|
| Hsinfeng | 711 | 250 | Kuanyin | 846 | 250 |
| Kuanyin | 801 | 250 | Hsinfeng | 981 | 250 |

**D.Prgr:** 0755-0005

| SW Location | kHz | kW |
|---|---|---|
| Kuanyin | ‡9745 | 250 | ‡ inactive

**D.Prgr:** 0755-0005 **Ann:** "Kuanghua chih Sheng"

### FU HSING KUANGPO TIENTAI (Fu Hsing Broadcasting Station) (Gov)
(operated by Ministry of National Defense)
✉ 5, Lane 280, Sec. 5, Chungshan No. Rd, Shihlin Ward, Taipei 111 ☎ +886 2 2882 3450 🖷 +886 2 2881 8218 **W:** fhbs.com.tw

| MW | Call | Location | kHz | kW |
|---|---|---|---|---|
| 1) | H2 | Taipei 1 | 594 | 10 |
| 2) | H38 | Taichung 1 | 594 | 5 |
| 3) | H44 | Kaohsiung 1 | 594 | 10 |

| SW | Call | Location | kHz | kW |
|---|---|---|---|---|
| 1) | | Kuanyin 2 | 9410 | 10 |

| FM | Call | Location | MHz | kW |
|---|---|---|---|---|
| 2) | I44 | Taichung 1 | 107.8 | 10 |

**D.Prgr: 1st Netw.** on 594kHz, **2nd Netw.** on. 2300-0100, 0400-0600, 0800-1000, 1100-1300 for China Mainland. 3 frequencies including 9774, 15375kHz are announced, however only 9410kHz audible occasionally.
**Local (relay) Stations: 2)** 81 Chungtai Rd, Chunshe Li, Nantun, Taichung 408. – **3)** 819 Chengching Rd, Niaosung Village, Kaohsiung 833. **Ann:** "Fu Hsing Kuangpo Tientai."

### OTHER PUBLIC & COMMERCIAL STATIONS (Call: BE_)

| MW | Call | Station | Location | kHz | kW |
|---|---|---|---|---|---|
| 6a) | | Taiwan | Tahsi | 621 | 1 |

| MW | Call | Station | Location | kHz | kW |
|---|---|---|---|---|---|
| 6c) | | Taiwan | Sungling | 630 | 10 |
| 7b) | V59 | Cheng Sheng | Taichung 2 | 657 | 20 |
| 7c) | | Cheng Sheng | Peikang | 675 | 5 |
| 8) | E43 | Shih Hsin | Taipei | 729 | 0.5 |
| 3) | L2 | Yuyeh | Penghu | 738 | 100 |
| 9) | | Sheng Li | Makung | 756 | 1 |
| 6b) | V94 | Taiwan | Taichung | 774 | 20 |
| 10) | V88 | Hsien Sheng | Taoyuan | 774 | 20 |
| 9) | V56 | Sheng Li | Tainan 1 | 774 | 1 |
| 11) | V79 | Keelung | Keelung | 792 | 1 |
| 12) | | Chien kuo | Hsinhua | 801 | 1 |
| 13) | V54 | Kuo Sheng | Changhua | 810 | 10 |
| 7) | V35 | Cheng Sheng | Taipei | 819 | 5 |
| 7a) | V72 | Cheng Sheng | Chia-i | 855 | 1 |
| 14) | V24 | Min Pen | Taipei 2 | 855 | 1 |
| 15) | | Feng Ming | Penghu | 882 | 1 |
| 16) | V98 | Cheng Kung | Kaohsiung | 936 | 1 |
| 12) | V85 | Chien Kuo | Hsinying | 954 | 10 |
| 6c) | V84 | Taiwan | Chunghsing | 963 | 10 |
| 15) | V68 | Feng Ming | Kaohsiung 2 | 981 | 2 |
| 27b) | V58 | Cheng Sheng | Taichung 1 | 990 | 20 |
| 17) | V92 | Tien Nan | Taipei | 999 | 1 |
| 7f) | V60 | Cheng Sheng | Kaohsiung | 1008 | 1 |
| 18) | | Tien Sheng | Yuanli | 1026 | 1 |
| 19) | V51 | Chung Hua | Sanchung 2 | 1026 | 1 |
| 20) | V64 | Yen Sheng | Hualien 1 | 1044 | 5 |
| 7d) | V82 | Cheng Sheng | Ilan | 1062 | 1 |
| 21) | V74 | Min Li | Pingtung | 1062 | 5 |
| 6a) | | Taiwan | Kuanhsi | 1062 | 1 |
| 22) | V96 | Tien Sheng | Tainan | 1071 | 1 |
| 5) | G28 | Kaohsiung | Kaohsiung | 1089 | 10 |
| 7c) | V36 | Cheng Sheng | Yunlin | 1125 | 5 |
| 4) | G26 | Taipei | Taipei | 1134 | 10 |
| 3) | L3 | Yuyeh | Penghu | 1143 | 100 |
| 23) | V70 | Hua Sheng | Taipei 1 | 1152 | 5 |
| 15) | V67 | Feng Ming | Kaohsiung 1 | 1161 | 1.2 |
| 13) | | Kuo Sheng | Erhlin | 1179 | 2.5 |
| 6) | V46 | Taiwan | Taipei 2 | 1188 | 1 |
| 9) | V57 | Sheng Li | Tainan 2 | 1188 | 1 |
| 6a) | V62 | Taiwan | Hsinchu | 1206 | 10 |
| 18) | | Tien Sheng | Pengshan | 1215 | 1 |
| 23) | V71 | Hua Sheng | Taipei 2 | 1224 | 1 |
| 19) | | Chung Hua | Juifang | 1233 | 1 |
| 20) | | Yen Sheng | Hualien 2 | 1242 | 1 |
| 7a) | | Cheng Sheng | Taipao | 1260 | 1 |
| 7e) | V37 | Cheng Sheng | Taitung | 1269 | 1 |
| 24) | | Fuhsingkang | Peitou | 1278 | 1 |
| 21) | | Min Li | Fangliao | 1287 | 1 |
| 14) | V23 | Min Pen | Taipei 1 | 1296 | 1 |
| 1c) | P33 | Ching Cha | Tainan | 1314 | 1 |
| 18) | V76 | Tien Sheng | Chunan | 1314 | 10 |
| 6) | V45 | Taiwan | Taipei 1 | 1323 | 1 |
| 6c) | | Taiwan | Puli | 1332 | 1 |
| 19) | V50 | Chung Hua | Sanchung 1 | 1350 | 2.5 |
| 7f) | | Cheng Sheng | Tafa | 1395 | 1 |
| 25) | V78 | Yi Shih | Keelung | 1404 | 10 |
| 12) | | Chien Kuo | Kuanyin | 1422 | 1 |
| 2) | E32 | Chiao Yu | Taipei | 1494 | 10 |
| 2a) | E34 | Chiao Yu | Changhua | 1494 | 5 |
| 1a) | | Ching Cha | Hsinchu | 1512 | 10 |
| 3a) | | Yuyeh | Ilan | 1593 | 1 |

| FM | Call | MHz | kW | FM | Call | MHz | kW | FM | Call | MHz | kW |
|---|---|---|---|---|---|---|---|---|---|---|---|
| 8) | | 88.1 | | 44) | | 93.9 | 3 | 52) | | 97.3 | 3 |
| 2f) | | 88.9 | 1 | 1) | P41 | 94.3 | 10 | 54) | N74 | 97.5 | 1 |
| 2l) | | 88.9 | 1 | 1f) | P44 | 94.3 | 3 | 55) | | 97.5 | 3 |
| 2n) | | 91.5 | | 1g) | P45 | 94.3 | 3 | 56) | | 97.7 | 3 |
| 32) | | 92.1 | 3 | 1i) | | 94.3 | 1 | 57) | | 97.7 | 3 |
| 33) | | 92.1 | 3 | 5) | G29 | 94.3 | 16 | 58) | | 97.9 | 3 |
| 34) | | 92.3 | 3 | 1b) | P43 | 94.5 | 30 | 59) | | 97.9 | 3 |
| 35) | | 92.7 | 3 | 97) | | 96.3 | 15 | 2i) | | 98.1 | 3 |
| 36) | | 92.9 | 3 | 97a) | | 96.3 | 30 | 60) | M23 | 98.1 | 3 |
| 37) | | 92.9 | 3 | 97b) | | 96.3 | 3 | 61) | | 98.3 | 3 |
| 1d) | P42 | 93.1 | 25 | 97c) | | 96.3 | 3 | 62) | | 98.3 | 3 |
| 1h) | | 93.1 | 1 | 46) | | 96.7 | 3 | 63) | | 98.3 | 3 |
| 1j) | | 93.1 | 2 | 45) | | 96.7 | 3 | 64) | | 98.5 | 3 |
| 4) | G25 | 93.1 | 10 | 47) | | 96.9 | 3 | 65) | | 98.5 | 3 |
| 38) | | 93.3 | 3 | 48) | | 96.9 | 3 | 66) | | 98.7 | 3 |
| 39) | | 93.5 | 3 | 49) | N61 | 97.1 | 3 | 67) | | 98.7 | 3 |
| 40) | | 93.5 | 3 | 50) | | 97.1 | 3 | 68) | | 98.7 | 3 |
| 41) | | 93.7 | 3 | 51) | | 97.1 | 3 | 69) | M31 | 98.9 | 3 |
| 42) | | 93.7 | 3 | 53) | | 97.3 | 3 | 70) | | 98.9 | 3 |
| 43) | | 93.7 | 3 | 2c) | | 97.3 | 3 | 2k) | | 99.1 | 4 |

| FM | Call | MHz | kW | FM | Call | MHz | kW | FM | Call | MHz | kW |
|---|---|---|---|---|---|---|---|---|---|---|---|
| 71) | | 99.1 | 3 | 82) | | 101.1 | 3 | 1d) | P32 | 104.9 | 12 |
| 72) | | 99.1 | 3 | 1f) | P35 | 101.3 | 1.5 | 1j) | | 104.9 | 2 |
| 2m) | | 99.3 | 3 | 1e) | P39 | 101.3 | 1 | 1b) | P30 | 105.1 | 35 |
| 73) | | 99.3 | 3 | 1g) | P37 | 101.3 | 1.5 | 2k) | | 105.3 | 3 |
| 74) | M24 | 99.5 | 3 | 2) | E33 | 101.7 | 30 | 86) | | 105.5 | 3 |
| 75) | N77 | 99.5 | 3 | 2b) | E36 | 101.7 | 30 | 87) | | 105.5 | 3 |
| 76) | | 99.5 | 3 | 83) | | 102.3 | 3 | 88) | | 105.7 | 3 |
| 77) | | 99.7 | 3 | 84) | M27 | 102.5 | 3 | 98) | | 105.9 | 30 |
| 78) | | 99.7 | 3 | 2d) | E38 | 102.9 | 5 | 98a) | | 105.9 | 30 |
| 79) | M30 | 99.9 | 3 | 2g) | E35 | 103.5 | 30 | 89) | M29 | 106.1 | 3 |
| 2e) | | 100.1 | 3 | 2a) | E40 | 103.5 | 10 | 1f) | P36 | 106.5 | 1.5 |
| 31b) | | 100.1 | 13 | 2c) | E37 | 103.7 | 5 | 90) | | 106.5 | 3 |
| 2f) | E39 | 100.3 | 1 | 2h) | E41 | 103.9 | 3 | 91) | | 106.7 | 3 |
| 80) | | 100.3 | 3 | 85) | | 103.9 | 3 | 92) | M28 | 106.9 | 3 |
| 2d) | | 100.5 | 3 | 7) | M22 | 104.1 | 3 | 93) | | 107.1 | 3 |
| 81) | M26 | 100.7 | 3 | 1) | P29 | 104.9 | 35 | 94) | | 107.3 | 3 |
| 31) | M3 | 100.7 | 30 | 1) | | 104.9 | 2 | 95) | | 107.7 | 3 |
| 31a) | | 100.7 | 27 | 1) | | 104.9 | 2 | 2j) | | 107.7 | 3 |
| 31c) | | 100.8 | | 1c) | P31 | 104.9 | 8 | 96) | M25 | 107.7 | 3 |

**NB:** + more than 80 low-powered community FM stns

**Addresses & other information:** under 30) AM or AM/FM stns, above 30) only FM stns
**1)** Chingcha Kuangpo Tientai (Police Broadcasting Service), 17 Kuangchou Str, Chungcheng, Taipei 10066. Three networks in 24h: AM Reg. Public Security Traffic Netw. (ARS), FM Nat. Public Security Traffic Netw. (FNS) and FM Reg. Public Security Traffic Netw. (FRS). FNS on 104.9MHz(2 relay stations on same freq) ,FRS on 94.3MHz – **1a)** 389 Sec.2, Hsinglung Rd, Chupei City, Hsinchu 302. ARS on 1512kHz – **1b)** 99 Po-ai Str, Nantun, Taichung 408. FNS on 105.1MHz, FRS on 94.5MHz – **1c)** 85-21, Nanshih, Nanshih Li, Matou, Tainan 721. ARS on 1314kHz, FNS on 104.9MHz – **1d)** 455 Po-ai 4th Rd, Tsoying Ward, Kaohsiung 813. FNS on 104.9MHz, FRS on 93.1MHz – **1e)** 89 Sec. 2, Minchuan Rd. Ilan 26049. FRS on 101.3MHz – **1f)** 21-2 Fuchien Rd, Hualien 970. , FNS on 101.3, 106.5MHz, FRS on 94.3MHz – **1g)** 289, Chungshan Rd. Taitung 950. FRS on 101.3MHz, FRS on 94.3MHz – **1h)** Peililungshan (relay Kaohsing FRS) – **1i)** Senyung (relay Taitung FRS) **W:** pbs.gov.tw – 1j) Hengchun (relay Kaohsing FNS on 104.9MHz, FRS on 93.1MHz) – **2)** Chiao Yu Broadc. System (National Education R.), 41 Nanhai Rd, Taipei 10066. On MW, FM both 24h *Ann:* "Chiao Yu chih Sheng, Chiao Yu Kuangpo Tientai" – **2a)** 5-1 Hukang Rd, Changhua 50080 – **2b)** 380 Kuangtung 3rd Rd, Chienchen Ward, Kaohsiung 80656 – **2c)** 457 Tunghsing Rd, Hualien 97063. 1st prgr on 103.7MHz, 2nd prgr on 97.3MHz – **2d)** 135, Ma Hengheng Rd, Taitung 95047. 1st prgr on 102.9MHz, 2nd prgr on 100.5MHz –**2e)** Keelung relay Taipei – **2f)** Yuli (1st prgr on 100.3MHz, 2nd prgr on 88.9MHz) relay Hualien – **2g)** Ilan relay Taipei – **2h)** Miaoli relay Changhua – **2i)** Nantou relay Changhua – **2j)** Chia-I relay Kaohsiung – **2k)** Penghu (1st prgr on 99.1MHz relay Taipei FM, 2nd prgr on 105.3MHz relay Taipei AM) – **2l)** Kinmen relay Taipei – **2m)** Hengchun relay Kaohsiung – **2n)** Matzu relay Taipei **W:** eradio.ner.gov.tw – **3)** Yüyeh Broadc. St (Fishery R. Station), 5 Yukang No. 2nd Rd, Chienchen Ward, Kaohsiung 806. 24h Weather rpt. at every h. 1520-1600 in English & Indonesian. Sun-Thu 2130-2200 in Vietnamese, 2230-2300 in Indonesian. Sat 1020-1100 in Mandarin & Indonesian. *Ann:* "Hi-giap Kong-po'-tian-tai"– **3a)** Ilan (relay stn) **W:** frs.gov.tw – **4)** Taipei Broadc. St, 4th Flr, Sec.2, Sec. 3, Chungshan No. Rd, Taipei 10452 (operated by Taipei City Council). AM "Ho Hi Yan" Ch. on 1134kHz, 2300-1600. FM "City Info" Ch. on 93.1MHz, 24h. Rel: BBC-WS: MF1400-1500, Sun-Thu2200-2300 on FM. **W:** radio.gov. taipei . – **5)** Kaohsiung Broadc. St, 90 Hsinchiang Rd, Kushan, Kaohsiung 80472 (operated by Kaohsiung City Council). Two prgr. on 1089kHz, 24h 2000-1800 **W:** kbs.gov.tw – **6)** Taiwan Broadc. Co, 9th Flr, 2, Sec 2, Jen-ai Rd, Chungcheng, Taipei 100. 1st prgr on 1323kHz, 24h 2nd prgr on 1188kHz, 24h **W:** taiwanradio.com.tw – **6a)** 2, Lane 506, Kaofeng Rd, Hsinchu 300. 24h – **6b)** 25th Flr, 787, Chungming So. Rd, Taichung. 24h – **6c)** 258-1 Fentsao Rd, Tsaotun Town, Nantou 542. 24h – **7 )** Cheng Sheng Broadc. Corp., 7th Flr, 1, Lane 66, Sec. 1, Chungching So. Rd, Taipei 10045. 819kHz, 104.1MHz both 24h – **7a)** 17,Chuiyang Rd. Chia-i 60043. 24h – **7b)** 760, Sec. 2, Chunghsing Rd, Tali Ward, Taichung 41244. 1st prgr on 990kHz, 2nd prgr on 657kHz, both 24h. – **7c)** 3rd Flr 32, Lane 416, 1 Sec. Linsen Rd, Huwei Town, Yunlin 63243 – **7d)** Chienchun Rd, Ilan 26051. 24h – **7e)** 21, Lane 380, Hsinsheng Rd, Taitung 95052. 24h – **7f)** 838 Chengching Rd, Niaosung , Kaohsiung 83347. Kaohsiung St. on 1008kHz, Tafa St. on 1395kHz, both 24h **W:** csbc.com.tw – **8)** Shih Hsin Radio St, 1, Lane 17, Sec. 1, Mushan Rd, Wenshan Ward, Taipei 11604. AM: and FM both 2255-1605(Sun 1303) **W:** shrs.shu.edu.tw – **9)** Shengli chih Sheng (Voice of Victory) Broadc. Co, 22, Sec. 1, Chienkang Rd, Chunghsi Ward, Tainan 700. 1st Prgr. on 774kHz, 24h 2nd Prgr. on 1188kHz, 24h Makung St. on 756kHz, 24h *Ann:* "Tainan Sheng Li chih Sheng Kuangpo Tientai" **W:** e-go.org.tw/

victor/ – **10)** Hsien Sheng Broadc. Co, 1, 16th Flr, Lane 505, Chungshan Rd, Taoyuan Ward, Taoyuan 330. 24h – **11)** Keelung Broadc. St, 12th Flr, 13 Chungsu Rd, Keelung 200. 24h **W**: am 792.com.tw – **12)** Chien Kuo Broadc. St, 78 Chienkuo Rd, Hsinying , Tainan 730. 24h– **13)** Kuo Sheng Broadc. Co, 35 Wenchuan Rd, Pakuashan, Changhua 500. 24h – **13a)** 2 Taiping Rd, Erhlin Town, Changhua 526 – **14)** Min Pen Broadc. Co, 6th Flr, 325, Sec. 3, Huanho So. Rd, Wanhua Ward, Taipei 108. 1st Prgr on 1296kHz, 2nd Prgr on 855kHz, both 24h **W**: mingpen.com.tw – **15)** Feng Ming Broadc. Co, 492 Chiuju 2nd Rd, Sanmin Ward, Kaohsiung 807. 1st Prgr on 1161kHz, 2nd Prgr on 981kHz, both 24h **W**: fengmin.com.tw – **15a)** Chentieh Hsien, Li 38, Makung, Penghu – **16)** Chengkung Broadc. St, 63 Chunghua 3rd Rd, Kaohsiung 801. 24h (exc. Sun 1600-2100). – **17)** Tien Nan Broadc. St, 7th Flr. 235, Sec. 4, Chengte Rd, Shihlin Ward, Taipei 111. 24h **W**: tnbcam999. myweb. hinet.net– **18)** T'ien Sheng Broadc. St, 285 Kungyi Rd, Chunan Town, Miaoli 350. 24h – **18a)** 8, Chuchung Rd, Yuanli Town, Miaoli 358. Yuanli St. on 1026kHz, Pengshan St. on 1215kHz, both 24h – **19)** Chung Hwa (China) Broadc. Co, 6th Flr, 238 Hopien No. Str, Sanchung, New Taipei 241. 1st Prgr on 1350kHz, 2nd prgr on 1026kHz, both 24h **Ann**: "Chung Hua Kuangpo Tientai Ti I/Erh Tai". Juifang St., relays 2nd prgr on 1233kHz, 24h **W**: chbc. wunme.com – **20)** Yen Sheng Broadc. St, 31, Sec. 1, Nanpin Rd, Tungchang, Chi-an Village, Hualien 973. On 1044, 1242kHz, both 24h **W**: ysbc.myweb. hinet. net – **21)** Min Li Broadc. St, 57-20 Minsheng Rd, Pingtung 900. 24h – **22)** Tien Sheng Broadc. St, 11, 15th Flr, 149, Sec. 1, Linsen Rd, Ea. Ward Tainan 701. 24h (exc. Sun 1600-2055) **W**: am1071.com.tw – **23)** Hua Sheng Broadc. Co, 18 Huasheng Str, Shihlin Ward, Taipei 111. 1st Prgr on 1152kHz, 2nd Prgr on 1224kHz, both 24h **W**: hsradio.com.tw – **24)** Fuhsingkang Broadac. Stn. 70, Sec .2, Chungyang Rd, Peitou, Taipei 112 – **25)** Yi Shih Broadc. St, 75 Paisan Str, Chitu Ward, Keelung 206. 24h **Ann**: "Keelung Yi Shih Kuangpo Tientai" **W**: yishih.ehosting.com. tw **31)** International Community R. Taipei (ICRT), 19-5F, No.5 Sec 3, New Taipei Rd, Hsinchuang Ward, New Taipei 24250. 24h in English Rel. BBC News Sun-Thu 2200-2230 – **31a)** Kaohsiung – **31b)** Taichung – **31c)** Chia-i **W**: icrt.com.tw – **32)** Fei Tieh (UFO) Broadc. Co (UFO Netw), 25th Flr, 102, Sec. 2, Lossufou Rd, Chungcheng Ward, Taipei 100. 24h **W**: uforadio.com.tw UFO Netw: Miaoli 91.3MHz, Taichung 89.9MHz, Yunlin & Chia-i district 90.5MHz, Kaohusing 103.9MHz, Ilan 89.9MHz, Hualien 91.3MHz, Taitung 91.3MHz, Penghu 89.7MHz – **33)** Chin Sheng Broadc. St, 25th Flr, 206 Kuanghua 1st Rd, Lingya, Kaohsiung 802. 24h – **34)** Chia Le Broadc St, 1, 16th Flr, 193, Hsiaoya Rd, East Ward, Chia-i 600. – **35)** Yachou (Asia) Broadc. St (Asia FM Netw), 2, 22nd Flr, 102 Chungping Rd, Taoyuan Ward, Taoyuan 330. 24h **W**: asiafm.com.tw – **36)** Cheng Shih Broadc. St, 28th Flr, 758 Chungming So. Rd, So. Ward, Taichung 402 **W**: goldfm.com.tw – Other Gold FM Netw st: Taipei 90.1MHz, Miaoli 98.3MHz, Tainan 97.1MHz – **37)** Taiwu chih Chun Broadc.(Yes R.) St. 9, Lane 240, Sec. 1, Poyu Rd, Panglin, Chinning, Kinmen 893 – **38)** Yun Chia Broadc. St, 9th Flr, 617 Chungshan Rd, Chia-i 600. 24h **W**: fm933.com.tw – **39)** Hsin Kechia Broadc. St, 16th Flr, 411 Huannan Rd, Pingchen Ward, Taoyuan 324. 24h – **40)** Lien Hua Broadc. St. (Best 935) 3, 8th Flr. 65, Kuolienssu Rd, Hualien 970 – **41)** Pao Tao Kechia Broadc. St, (Formosa Hakka R. Stn.) 2, 17th Flr, 91, Sec. 2, Loushan Rd, Ta'an Ward, Taipei 10646. 24h **W**: formosahakka.org.tw – **42)** Sheng Tu Broadc. Co, 233 Fentsao Rd, Tsaotun Town, Nantou 542. 24h **W**: fm937.com.tw – **43)** Ling Hsiu Broadc. St., – 10, 20th Flr. 149, Sec. 1, Linsen Rd. Tainan 701 – **44)** Ta Ti chih Sheng Broadc. St. 10, Chengpei Village, Huhsi, Makung, Penghu 880 – **45)** Huan Yu Broadc. Co (Uni R.), 3, 6th Flr, 675, Sec. 1, Chingkuo Rd, Hsinchu 300. 24h **W**: turc967.com.tw – **46)** Penghu Broadc. St. 2nd Flr. 1-204, I-lin Shihchuan-li, Makung, Penghu 880 – **47)** Tien Tien (Sky) Broadc. St, 42nd Flr, 760 Chungming So. Rd, So. Ward, Taichung 402. 24h **W**: tw.myblog.yahoo.com/sky9692004 – **48)** Chu Jen Broadc. St (Boss Radio), 17th Flr, 155, Fujen Rd, Linyang Ward, Kaohsiung 80288. 24h – **49)** Ta Han chih Yin (Voice of Hakka) Broadc. St, 1 Hsintung Rd, Toufen Town, Miaoli 351. 24h **W**: fm971. com.tw – **50)** Tainan chih Yin Broadc. St, 1-134 Chunghua Rd, Yongkang, Tainan 710 – **51)** Chung Shan Broadc. Co, 2nd Flr, 151, Sec 2, Chungshan Rd, Ilan 260. 24h – **52)** Green Peace Broadc. St, 1, 14th Flr, 97, Sec. 4, Chunghsing Rd, Sanchung New Taipei 241. 24h **W**: greenpeace.com.tw – **53)** Ai Yu chih Sheng Broadc. St, 7, Lane 828, Sec. 3, Chinma Rd, Changhua 500. 24h **W**: tw.myblog.yahoo.com/ fm973-fm973 – **54)** IC chih Yin, IC Broadc. Co. Ltd., 2, 11th Flr, 287, Sec. 2, Kuangfu Rd, Hsinchu 30071. 24h **W**: ic975.com – **55)** Kuai Le (Happy) Broadc. St, 1st Flr, 70, Ling-an Rd, Lingya, Kaohsiung 802. 24h Happy. R. Netw: Taipei 89.3MHz, Taichung 89.5MHz, Chia-i 92.3MHz, Hualien 98.3MHz, Penghu 91.3MHz & 96.7MHz – **56)** Taiwan Sheng Yin Broadc. St. 9th Flr. 76, Sec. 1, Minchuan Rd. Chungshan Ward, Taipei, 104. 24h – **57)** Hao Chia Ting Broadc. Co (Family 977 Broadc. Network), 37th Flr, 789 Chungming So. Rd, So. Ward, Taichung 402. 24h **W**: family977.com.tw – **58)** Tainan Kaihsuan Broadc. St, 2, 21th Flr, 425 Chunghua Rd, Yungkang, Tainan 710 – Other Smile Netw sts:

Ilan on 97.9 MHz, Hsinchu on 90.3 MHz, Nantou on105.5 MHz, Chia-I on 107.1 MHz, Kaohsiung on 90.5 MHz, Pingtung on 90.9/91.3/92.5MHz – **59)** Ka Ma Lan Broadc. St, 46, Lane 455, Kungyuan Rd, Ilan 260 – **60)** Taiwan National Broadc. Com. (News 98), 26th Flr, 100, Sec. 2, Lossufu Rd, Chungcheng Ward, Taipei 100. 24h – **61)** Ta Miaoli FM Broadc. St, 3, 16th Flr, 1 Chanchien, Shangmiao Li, Miaoli 360. – **62)** Kang Tu Broadc. St (Best R.), 1, 34th Flr, 80 Mintsu 1st Rd, Sanmin Ward, Kaohsiung 807. 24h **W**: bestradio.com.tw Haoshih (Best) Netw: Taipei 98.9MHz, Taichung 90.3MHz, Hualien 93.5MHz – **63)** Hualien (Huan Le Broadc St), 3rd Flr, 196, Linsen Rd, Hualien 970 – **64)** Pao Tao Hsin Sheng (Super FM 98.5) Broadc. St, 7th Flr. 56, Sec 1, Hsinsheng So. Rd, Chungcheng Ward, Taipei 100. 24h **W**: superfm98-5.com.tw – **65)** Feifanyin Broadc. St (Libra R.), 40, Lane 40, Sec. 2, Shuangshih Rd. No. Ward, Taichung 40455. 24h **W**: libraradio.com.tw – **66)** Mei Jih Broadc. Co (Sakura R.), 1, 7th Flr, 1-67 Wuchuan Rd, We. Ward, Taichung 403. 24h **W**: fm987.com.tw – **67)** Ching Chun Broadc. St, 15-2, 53, Sec. 2, Lin'an Rd, No. Ward, Tainan 704. – **68)** Tung Min Broadc. St. 156, Fuyu Rd. Chihpen, Taitung 950. – **69)** Jen Jen Broadc. St (Best 989), 2nd Flr, 142, Sec. 3, Minchuan East Rd, Chungshan Ward, Taipei 104. 24h – **70)** Cheng Kang Broadc. St. 2, 4th Flr. 73, Teming Rd. Chia-i, 600 – **71)** Ta Chien Broadc. St (Super 99.1), 2,22nd Flr. 309 Sec. 2, Taiwan Tatao, We. Ward, Taichung 403 **W**: superfm99-1.com.tw – **72)** Yang Kuang Broadc. St, 6, 21st Flr, 3, Tzuchiang 3rd Rd, Lingya, Kaohsiung 802. – **73)** Hsin Sheng FM Broadc. St, 1, 19th Flr, 37 Chianchung 1st Rd, Hsinchu 300 **W**: ss-radio. com.tw – **74)** Sen Nong (Farmer R.) Broadc. St., 10th Flr, 234 Peiping Rd, Huwei Town, Yunlin 632.24h **W**: fm995.com.tw – **75)** Tung Fang Broadc. St, 13rd Flr, 168, Sec. 3, Chunching Rd, Lotung Town, Ilan 265. 24h – **76)** Lan Yu Broadc. St, 147, Yujen, Hongtou, Lanyu Village, Taitung 95241.24h **W**: lanan.org.tw/radeo.htm – **77)** Taipei Ai Yue Broadc. Co, 7th Flr, 47 Tunghsing Rd, Hsin-i, Taipei 110. 24h **W**: e-classical.com.tw – **78)** Nantou Broadc. St, 1, 12th Flr, 1-67 Wuchuan Rd, We. Ward, Taichung 403. – **79)** Ta Chung Broadc. Co (Kiss R.), 2, 34th Flr, 6 Minchuan 2nd Rd, Chienchen Ward, Kaohsiung 806. 24h **W**: kiss.com.tw – Kiss R. Netw: Nantou 99.7MHz. – **80)** Pao Tao Broadc. St. 1, 12th Flr. 287, Wenya St. Chia-i 600. – **81)** Taichung Broadc.Co, 21st Flr, 489, Sec. 2, Taiwan Tatao, We. Ward, Taichung 40309. 24h **W**: fm1007lucky.com – **82)** Ching Shan Broadc. St. A-12-7, 20, Talung Rd. We. Ward, Taichung 403 – **83)** Ai Miao Broadc. St, 78, Huatung Str, Chunan Town, Miaoli 350. 24h – **84)** Ku Tu Broadc. Co, 1, 15th Flr, 77, Sec. 2, Chunghua East Rd, Tainan 701. 24h **W**: fm1025.com.tw – **85)** Nan Taiwan chih Sheng (Voice of South Taiwan), 38th Flr, 38, Hsinkuang Rd, Lingya Ward, Kaohsiung 802. – **86)** Huanhsi chih Sheng (Happy R.) Broadc. St, 37th Flr, 760 Chungming So. Rd, So. Ward, Taichung. 24h – **87)** Tung Shan He FM Broadc. St, 13th Flr, 162-5, Sec. 3, Chunching Rd, Lotung Town, Ilan 265 – **88)** Tzumei (Sister R.) Broadc. St, 4th Flr, 32, Lane 416, Sec. 1, Linsen Rd, Huwei Town, Yunlin 632. 24h **W**: sister-radio.com.tw – **89)** Chuan Kuo Broadc. Co, 1, 8th Flr, 659, Sec.2, Taiwan Tatao, Hsitun Ward, Taichung 40759. 24h **W**: mradio.com.tw – **90)** Chih Nan Broadc. St,15th Flr, 53, Sec.2, Lin-an Rd, No. Ward, Tainan 704 – **91)** Kao Ping Hsi Broadc. St, 17th Flr, 161-53 Chiuta Rd, Chiuchu, TashuWard, Kaohsiung 842 – **92)** Taoyuan Broadc. St (TBC R.), 9th Flr, 859, Sec. 1, Chunghua Rd, Chungli, Taoyuan 320. 24h **W**: tbcradio.com.tw – **93)** Chia-i Huanchiu Broadc. St, 1, 19th Flr, 25 Pingtien, Chianghsi Village, Fanlu, Chia-i 600 – **94)** Lan Yang FM Broadc. St, 12th Flr, 186, Sec. 3, Chungcheng Rd, Wuchie Village, Ilan 268. 24h – **95)** Taipei chih Yin Broadc. Co, (Hito R.) 15-1, Sec. 1, Hanchou So. Rd, Chungcheng Ward, Taipei 10050. 24h Hit FM Netw: Taichung 91.5MHz Kaohsiung 90.1MHz Ilan 97.1MHz Hualien 107.7 MHz **W**: hitoradio.com – **96)** Tung Taiwan Broadc. St. 31, Sec. 1, Nanpin Rd, Tungchang, Chi-an Village, Hualien 973. – **97)** Alian Radio, 5th Flr, 120, Chungyang Rd, Nankang Ward, Taipei 11573. 24h **W**: alian963.ipcf.org.tw – **97a)** Kaohsiung – **97b)** Hualien – **97c)** Taitung – **98)** Hakka Radio, 18th Flr of North Tower, 439, Chungping Rd, Hsinchuang Ward, New Taipei 24220. 24h **W**: hakkaradio.org. tw– **98a)** Kaohsiung

## TAJIKISTAN

**L.T**: UTC +5h — **Pop**: 8.9 million — **Pr.L**: Tajik, Uzbek — **E.C**: 220V/50Hz — **ITU**: TJK

### KUMITAI TELEVIZION VA RADIOI
**(State Committee for TV & Radio)**

✉ k. Sheroz 31, 734025 Dushanbe ☎ +992 37 2277497
**E**: info@ktr.tj; radiotoj@mail.ru **W**: ktr.tj; radiotoj.tj
**L.P**: Chmn: Asadulloi Rahmon

**NB**: In addition to being a state broadcaster, the committee is also responsible for issuing licenses to private radio stations in Tajikistan.

| MW | kHz | kW | Prgr | MW | kHz | kW | Prgr |
|---|---|---|---|---|---|---|---|
| Dushanbe° | 549 | 40 | 2 | Orzu° | 702 | 150 | 1 |

| MW | kHz | kW | Prgr | MW | kHz | kW | Prgr |
|---|---|---|---|---|---|---|---|
| Khujand° | 819 | 15 | 1 | Orzu° | 1161 | 40 | 2 |
| Dushanbe (a) | 1143 | 150 | F | Dushanbe° | 1323 | 7 | 1 |

(a) Yangiyul F=International Service °) Status uncertain

| SW | kHz | kW | Prgr |
|---|---|---|---|
| Dushanbe (Yangiyul) | 4765 | 100 | 1 |

| FM (MHz) | 1 | 2 | 3 | kW |
|---|---|---|---|---|
| Ayvanj | - | 107.8 | - | - |
| Dushanbe | 104.7 | 102.2 | 106.5 | 2x4/- |
| Khorugh* | 104.5 | 104.0 | 103.0 | - |
| Khujand | 102.7 | - | 106.1 | 4 |
| Panj | - | 100.3 | - | - |
| Qurghonteppa | 101.7 | - | - | 4 |

+ low power txs. *) Located in Kuhistan-Badakhshan (autonomous province)

**D.Prgr: Prgr 1 (Radioi Tojikiston):** 24h. – **Prgr 2 (Sadoi Dushanbe):** 24h. For ethnic minorities: 0600-0900 (Russian). – **Prgr 3 (Radioi Farhang):** 24h. – **Regional Stations: R. Badakhshon (Khorugh)** planned. **R. Khatlon (Qurghonteppa)** on Qurghonteppa 101.3MHz, **R. Sughd (Khujand)** on Khujand 101.1MHz.
**International Service (Ovozi Tojik):** see International Radio section. On FM: Dushanbe 105.5MHz.

**OTHER STATIONS**

| FM | MHz | kW | Location | Station |
|---|---|---|---|---|
| 16) | 88.8 | 1 | Khujand | Love R. |
| 1) | 92.2 | 1 | Istaravshan | Dunyo FM |
| 15) | 93.3 | 1 | Buston | R. Salom |
| 12) | 95.5 | 1 | Isfara | R. Diyor |
| 17) | 97.7 | 1 | Khujand | R. Shahri Man |
| A) | 100.3 | 1 | Dushanbe | R. Sputnik relay |
| 14) | 100.6 | 1 | Khujand | R. Payvand |
| 9) | 101.5 | 1 | Dushanbe | FM Khovar |
| 10) | 101.5 | 1 | Panjakent | Sadoi Panjakent |
| 2) | 102.4 | 1 | Qurghonteppa | R. Vatan |
| 7A) | 103.0 | 1 | Dushanbe | R. Rusii Oriyono |
| 7B) | 103.0 | 1 | Khujand | R. Imruz |
| 2) | 103.3 | 1 | Khujand | R. Vatan |
| 5) | 104.0 | 1 | Dushanbe | AFM |
| 3B) | 104.4 | 1 | Khujand | R. Aziya Plus |
| 3A) | 104.5 | 1 | Dushanbe | R. Aziya FM |
| 2) | 105.0 | 1 | Khorugh* | R. Vatan |
| 11) | 105.2 | 1 | Isfara | R. Isfara |
| 12) | 105.5 | 1 | Asht | R. Diyor |
| 13) | 105.7 | 1 | Khujand | Sadoi Khujand |
| 4) | 105.9 | 1 | Isfara | R. Mavji ozod |
| 2) | 106.0 | 1 | Dushanbe | R. Vatan |
| 6) | 106.1 | 1 | Istaravshan | R. AVIS-Plus |
| 18) | 106.8 | 1 | Tursunzade | Sadoi Osiyo |
| 3B) | 107.0 | 1 | Dushanbe | R. Aziya Plus |
| 3B) | 107.0 | 1 | Qurghonteppa | R. Aziya Plus |
| B) | 107.1 | 1 | Khujand | R. Sputnik relay |
| 7B) | 107.4 | 1 | Dushanbe | R. Imruz |
| 7B) | 107.4 | 1 | Kulob | R. Imruz |
| 7B) | 107.4 | 1 | Qurghonteppa | R. Imruz |
| 8) | 107.5 | 1 | Ghafurov | R. Jahonoro |

+ txs below 1kW *) Located in Kuhistan-Badakhshan (autonomous province)

**Addresses & other information:**
**1)** 1. Mikrorayon 6-65, 735000 Tursunzade – **2)** pr. S.Sherozi 16, 734018 Dushanbe **E:** info@vatan.tj – **3A,B)** pr. S.Sherozi 16, 734018 Dushanbe **E:** radio@asiaplus.tj – **4)** k. Umari Hazom 18, 735330 Vose – **5)** pr. S.Ayni 27/17, 734000 Dushanbe **E:** info@afm.tj – **6)** k. A.Mirrajabov 10, 735610 Istaravshan **E:** avis@avis.tj – **7A,B)** pr. Rudaki 100, 734001 Dushanbe **E:** info@orionomedia.tj. 7A) rel. Russkoye R. (Russia) – **8)** k. Lenin 22, 735690 Ghafurov – **9)** Dushanbe. **E:** sadrshamsi67@mail.ru – **10)** k. Bobodajarov 7a, 735500 Panjakent **E:** simo-tv@mail.ru – **11)** k. Markazi 40, 735920 Isfara **E:** sahbon@mail.ru – **12)** k. I.Somoni 91a, Shaydon **E:** info@diyorfm.com – **13)** 735700 Khujand – **14)** k. Lenin 303a, 735700 Khujand **E:** akram_urunov@mail.ru – **15)** 735730 Chkalov **E:** radiosalom@mail.ru – **16)** 735700 Khujand – **17)** k. Tanburi 9, 735700 Khujand **E:** shahriman.97.70@gmail.com – **17)** k. Lenin 134, 735000 Tursunzade – **A)** Rel. R. Sputnik (Russia).

**Int. relays on MW:** (Upon demand; txs operated by Teleradiokom) Dushanbe (Yangiyul) 1251kHz 100kW, Orzu 927kHz 300kW; operated on behalf of IBB (USA): Orzu 972kHz 800kW. See Int. Radio section

## TANZANIA

**L.T:** UTC +3h — **Pop:** 57 million — **Pr.L:** Swahili, English — **E.C:** 50Hz, 230V — **ITU:** TZA

---

**TANZANIA COMMUNICATIONS REGULATORY AUTHORITY (TCRA)**
⌨ Mawasiliano House, Plot 304, Ali Hassan Mwinyi/Nkomo Rd, P.O Box 474, Dar es Salaam ☎+255 22 2118947 🖷 +255 22 2116664 **W:** tcra.go.tz **E:** dg@tcra.go.tz
**LP:** DG: John Nkoma. Dir. Broadc. Affairs: Habbi Gunze.

**TANZANIA BROADCASTING CORPORATION (TBC, Gov)**
⌨ P. O. Box 9191, Nyerere Rd, Dar es Salaam ☎+255 22 2860760 🖷 +255 22 2866383 **W:** tbc.go.tz **E:** info@tbc.go.tz
**LP:** DG: Dunstan Tido Mhando. Dir. Radio: Ms. Edah Sanga. TD: Harold Limo. Dir. News: Ms. Susan Mungi. Dir. PR: Ngalimecha Ngayoma.

| MW | kHz | kW | MW | kHz | kW |
|---|---|---|---|---|---|
| Dodoma | 603 | 100/10 | Mwanza | 720 | 50/10 |
| Mbeya | 621 | 50/10 | Kunduchi | 837 | 1 |
| Kigoma | 711 | 100/10 | Arusha | 1215 | 50/10 |

**FM (MHz):** Arusha 91.6, Dar es Salaam 89.9/92.35, Dodoma 87.7, Kigoma 88.4, Lindi 93.5, Mbeya/Masasi/Nachingwea 92.3, Mwanza 89.2, Songea 98.7, Dar es Salaam 94.6/95.3MHz.
**TBC Taifa in Swahili on MW:** 0200-2100 on 675/711/837kHz, others 24h. N. on the hour. Relayed also from Zanzibar at 1600. **TBC FM in Swahili:** 24h. MW & FM channels may opt out at times to carry regional prgrs. **TBC International in English:** Dar es-Salaam 95.3MHz. Also relays RFI.

**PRIVATE STATIONS**
**RADIO ONE,** P.O. Box 4374, Dar es Salaam. **W:** radio1.co.tz **MW:** Moshi 1323kHz 10kW (Swahili 24h), Dar es Salaam 1440kW 10kW (English, but rep. inactive). **FM** (all 5kW): Dar es Salaam 89.7MHz, Mwanza 102.5MHz, Dodoma 100.8MHz, Arusha 95.3MHz.
**RADIO FREE AFRICA,** P.O. Box 1732, Post Road, Mwanza. **W:** radiofreeafricatz.com **E:** info@radiofreeafricatz.com Swahili Sce: **MW:** Mwanza 1377kHz 50kW (irr.). **FM:** Katavi 87.9, Himo/Shinyanga 88.2MHz, Singida 88.3, Geita 88.4, Mbeya 88.8, Iringa/Simiu 88.9, Arusha/Bukoba/Dodoma/Kigoma/Mtwara 89.0, Sumbawanga 89.1, Manyara/Songea 89.6, Mwanza 89.8, Njoluma 89.9, Kagera/Tabora 90.0, Musoma 93.5, Morogoro 93.8, Lindi 96.7, Dar es-Salaam/Pwanii/Zanzibar 98.6, Pemba/Tanga 99.3.
English sce: **Kiss FM:** Mbeya 88.2, Mwanza 88.7, Iringa 89.2, Dodoma/Sindiga 89.4, Arusha/Manyara/Kilimanjaro 89.9, Morogoro 90.2, Tanga 92.7, Bugako/Kagera 94.1, Dar es Salaam/Pwani/Zanzibar 98.9MHz.

**Other Stations:**
**Capital R,** Plot No.130, Mikocheni, Light Industrial Area, P.O. Box 4374 Dar Es Salaam. **W:** capitalradio.co.tz - Morogoro 88.9, Bukoba 95.3, Mbeya 96.4, Dodoma 97.3, Dar es Salaam 103.3, Mwanza 101.2, Arusha 102.1, Moshi 103.3 – **Clouds FM,** P.O. Box 31513, Dar es Salaam - Dar es Salaam 88.4MHz 2kW, Arusha 98.6MHz, Mwanza 99.4MHz – **Dodoma FM,** Dodoma: 98.4MHz **W:** dodomafmtz.com – **East Africa R,** P.O.Box 4374, Dar es Salaam - Dar es Salaam 87.8, Bukoba 89.8, Moshi 93.4, Arusha 93.6, Tanga 97.8, Dodoma 99.6, Mbeya 100.0, Morogoro 102.8, Tabora 105.2. (also relayed on FM in Kampala, Uganda, & Nairobi, Kenya) **W:** eastafricaradio.com – **Moshi FM,** P.O. Box 933, Moshi: 90.2MHz. **W:** facebook.com/90.2mhz – **R. Five;** P.O. Box 11843, Arusha: 105.7MHz. **E:** impala@cybernet.co.tz – **R. Imaan** (Rlg.): Morogoro 96.0MHz, Zanzibar 104.5MHz – **R. Kheri** (Rlg.) Dar es Salaam 104.1MHz – **R. Kwizera,** P.O. Box 154, Ngara Field Office, Ngara. **W:** jrs.net/countries/eaf.php?lang=en - 97.9MHz (in Swahili, also rel. RFI Afrique in English) – **R. Kili FM,** Soweto, Moshi, Kilimanjaro 0000 - Moshi 87.5MHz. **W:** radiokilifm.com – **R. Maria Tanzania,** P.O. Box 34573, Dar es Salaam - Songea 89.1MHz, Iringa 90.4MHz, Mbeya 91.9MHz, Morogoro 102.0MHz, Unguja/Pemba 103.5MHz, Mwanza 106.0MHz, Arusha 106,7MHz. Arusha 2kW, Pemba 0.5kW, others 1kW. **W:** radiomariatanzania.co.tz – **R. Sauti ya Injili** (Rlg.), Lutheran R. Centre, P.O. Box 777, Moshi **W:** sautiyainjili.org - Moshi 92.2, Tanga 96.0, Arusha 96.2, Rombo 96.4, Tanga 96.5, Morogoro 99.9, Same 100.4, Usambara 102.6, Kibaya 102.9MHz – **R. Sauti ya Quran** (Rlg.) Dar es Salaam: 102.0MHz – **R. Tumaini Int:** P.O. Box 9916, Dar es Salaam - Dar es Salaam 96.3/105.9MHz, Kibahe 91.4MHz.

### ZANZIBAR
**(semi-autonomous archipelago)**

**ZANZIBAR BROADCASTING CORPORATION (Pub.)**
⌨ P.O. Box 314, Zanzibar, Tanzania ☎+255 24 2330000 🖷 +255 24 233000 **W:** zbc.co.tz **E:** zanzibarbroadcasting@zbc.co.tz **LP:** DG: Hassan Abdallah Massawi; Dir (Radio): Rafi Haji Makame.
**MW:** Chumbuni 585kHz 50kW.
**SW:** Dole: 6015 & 11735kHz 50kW.

**FM:** Zanzibar 97.7MHz, Pemba 90.5MHz.
**D.Prgr in Swahili:** 0900-2100 on 585kHz. **FM** ("Spice FM"): 0300-2100. **N:** Local bulletins at 0400, 1200, 1600, 1800, 1900. Rel. R.Tanzania from Dar es Salaam at 1700, 1900. **In English:** irr. 1800. **Relays on shortwave:** see International Radio section.

**Other stations:**
**Al-Noor FM** (Rlg.), Zanzibar: 93.3MHz 2kW. **W:** alnoorcharity.org
**Assalam FM** (Rlg.), Zanzibar: 92.1MHz.
**Bomba FM,** Zanzibar: 87.5MHz **W:** facebook.com/bombafmzanzibar
**Chuchu FM,** Zanzibar: 90.9MHz. **W:** chuchufm.com
**Coconut FM,** Zanzibar: 88.9MHz **W:** facebook.com/CoconutFm88.9
**Hits FM,** Zanzibar: 92.5MHz
**Mwenze FM,** Zanzibar: 95.4MHz
**R. Adhana** (Rlg.). Zanzibar: 104.9MHz. **W:** facebook.com/Adhana-fm-1487495931462046
**R. Maria Tanzania** (Rlg.) Pemba: 103.5MHz.
**Swahiba FM,** Zanzibar: 102.9MHz **W:** facebook.com/swahibafm
**Zenji FM,** Zanzibar: 96.9MHz **W:** facebook.com/ZenjiFMRadio
**BBC African Sce:** Zanzibar 94.1MHz, Pemba 93.5MHz, both 4kW.
**RFI Afrique:** Dar es Salaam 94.6MHz in F/E/Swahili

## THAILAND

**L.T:** UTC +7h — **Pop:** 69 million — **Pr. L:** Thai — **E.C:** 50Hz, 220V — **ITU:** THA

### NATIONAL BROADCASTING AND TELECOMMUNICATIONS COMMISSION (NBTC)
⊡ 87 Phahonyotin Rd. Soi 8 (Soi Silom), Samsen Nai, Phayathai Bangkok 10400 ☎ +66 2670 8888 🖶 +66 2290-5240 **W:** nbtc.go.th
**L.P:** Acting Chmn: Gen. Sukit Khamasundara. Sec. Gen.: Mr Takorn Tantasith.
The NBTC controls administrative, legal, technical and programming aspects of broadcasting in Thailand.

### GOVERNMENT PUBLIC RELATIONS DEPT. (Gov.)
⊡ Soi Aree Samphan, Rama VI Road, Bangkok 10400
☎ +66 2618-2323 🖶 +66 2618-2364/2399 **W:** thailand.prd.go.th (general info in English). This body operates the NBT radio & TV services (R. Thailand & Television Thailand).
**L.P:** Acting DG: Lt. Gen Sansern Kaewkamnerd.

### THE NATIONAL BROADCASTING SERVICES OF THAILAND (NBT) – RADIO THAILAND (Sathani Witthayu Krachaisiang Haeng Prathet Thai, Sor. Wor. Thor.) (Gov.)
⊡ 236 Vibhavadi Rangsit Superhighway, Din Daeng, Huay Khwang, Bangkok 10320 ☎ +66 2277-1966 🖶 +66 2277-2809
**W:** nbt.prd.go.th
**L.P:** Exec. Dir. R. Thailand: Mr Kittisak Hankla.

**MW STATIONS:**

| kHz | kW | Location +) | kHz | kW | Location +) |
|---|---|---|---|---|---|
| 531 | 25 | Maha Sarakham | 981 | 25 | Yala |
| 549 | 10 | Mukdahan | 1026 | 25 | Phitsanulok |
| 558 | 10 | Kanchanaburi | 1026 | 10 | Betong (Yala) |
| 639 | 10 | Chiang Mai$ | 1062 | 10 | Phuket |
| 639 | 20 | ‡N. Si Thammarat | 1098 | 10 | Mae Sot |
| 648 | 25 | Khon Kaen | 1116 | 10 | Takua Pa (Phang Nga) |
| 720 | 5/10 | ‡Krabi | 1125 | 25 | Chanthaburi |
| 729 | 25 | N. Ratchasima | 1134 | 10 | Lampang |
| 783 | 10 | Ranong | 1215 | 25 | Surat Thani |
| 810 | 20 | Nong Khai | 1260 | 25 | Chiang Mai |
| 810 | 10 | Sangkhlaburi% | 1296 | ‡10 | Pattani |
| 819 | 10 | Pathum Thani# | 1341 | 20 | Loei |
| 837 | 10 | Pathum Thani# | 1341 | 10 | U. Ratchathani |
| 846 | 10 | Phetchabun | 1341 | 10 | Phangnga |
| 864 | 10 | Tak | 1368 | 25 | Nan |
| 864 | 10 | Si Sa Ket | 1368 | 10 | Buri Ram |
| 891 | 1000 | Sara Buri# | 1377 | 10 | Chumphon |
| 909 | 10 | Dansai (Loei) | 1404 | 25 | Songkhla |
| 909 | 25 | Surin | 1422 | 10 | Amnat Charoen |
| 918 | 10 | Pathum Thani# | 1476 | 50 | Chiang Mai $ |
| 981 | 25 | Mae Hong Son | 1557 | 10 | Trat |
| 981 | 20 | N. Phanom | 1593 | 10 | Ratchaburi |

‡) r. inactive at editorial deadline +) N.=Nakhon, U.=Ubon. %) Kanchanaburi Prov. #) Bangkok area $) tr. loc. in Lamphun Prov.
**D.Prgr:** Main sce: 2200-1700 on 891kHz (tx site: Nong Khae, Sara Buri), 819kHz (tx site: Rangsit, Pathum Thani) & 92.5MHz (Bangkok 10kW) and in full or in part on many RT regional AM stns. **N:** On the h – AM 837: 2300-1700 on 837kHz (tx site: Bang Phun, Pathum Thani).– AM

918 (tx site: Rangsit, Pathum Thani): 2200-1700 ASEAN languages sce. in English & Thai exc. Malay: 0600-0730, Chinese: 0730-0900, Lao: 0910-1000, Burmese: 1010-1100, Khmer: 1110-1200, on 918kHz, also in part on some RT regional FM stns inc. Chiang Mai 98MHz, Phuket 90.5MHz, Samui 96.75MHz, Songkhla 102.25MHz – Bangkok FM prgrs: 88.0MHz Foreign Lang Prgr in English (10kW),, 93.5MHz 'Digital FM HD One' (10kW), 95.5MHz 'Virgin Hitz'in English (10 kW), 97.0MHz (10kW) 'Quality News Station', 105.0MHz (10kW) 'Smile Thailand' prgr for young people and families.

**Selected Reg. Stations:** ⊡ 49 Prachasamphan Rd., Tambon Chang Khlan, Mueang Dist., Chiang Mai 50100 **FM:** 93.25 & 98.0MHz; 1476 kHz: Prgr in Thai and minority langs for hill tribes 2200-1600 ⊡ Kasikon Thungsang Rd, Mueang Dist., Khon Kaen 40000 **FM:** 98.5 & 99.5MHz. ⊡ Soi Sathaban Ratchaphat Phuket, Thepkasatri Rd, Tambon Ratsada, Mueang Dist., Phuket 83000 **FM:** 90.5MHz 'Blue Wave' & 96.75MHz 'Sunshine R.' ⊡ 439 Mu 2, Songkhla - Ko Yo Road, Tambon Phawong, Mueang Dist., Songkhla 90100 **FM:** 89.5, 90.5 & 102.25MHz

**Addresses of other regional stations:** Most stns can be reached by quoting 'Sathani Witthayu Sor. Wor. Thor.' or 'Radio Thailand' and the location given in the freq. list. **D.Prgr** of reg. sts: generally 2200-1700

**EXTERNAL SERVICE: Radio Thailand**
see International Broadcasting section

### NATIONAL EDUCATION RADIO (Sathani Witthayu Krachaisiang Haeng Prathet Thai Phuea Kan Sueksa, Sor. Wor. Sor.)
⊡ Soi Aree Samphan, Rama VI Rd, Samsen, Phaya Thai, Bangkok 10400 ☎ +66 2271-3448 🖶 +66 2245-7083 **W:** edu.prd.go.th
**D.Prgr:** 2200-1700 on 1467kHz in the Bangkok area. Regional stns carry own prgrs and relay Bangkok.
**MW:**

| kHz | kW | Location | kHz | kW | Location |
|---|---|---|---|---|---|
| 549 | 100 | Lampang | ‡936 | 50 | Nakhon Sawan |
| ‡558 | 50 | Songkhla | 963 | 25 | Krabi |
| 621 | 100 | Khon Kaen | ‡1242 | 50 | Surat Thani |
| 711 | 20 | Ubon Ratchathani | 1467 | 100 | Pathum Thani |
| ‡927 | 20 | Chanthaburi | | | |

‡) inactive at editorial deadline

**OTHER STATIONS:**

| MW kHz | kW | Province +) | MW kHz | kW | Province +) |
|---|---|---|---|---|---|
| 39) 540 | 5 | Bangkok | 16) 873 | 5 | Bangkok |
| 24) 567 | 5 | Chaiyaphum | 30) 918 | 10 | Chiang Mai |
| 17) 576 | 5 | Bangkok | 8) 936 | 10 | Pattani |
| 7) 585 | 5 | Phrae | 12) 945 | 10 | Bangkok |
| 32) 585 | 5 | Chumphon | 6) 945 | 10 | Kalasin |
| 9) 594 | 5 | Bangkok | 12) 954 | 10 | Phitsanulok |
| 32) 603 | 5 | Khon Kaen | 12) 954 | 10 | Chanthaburi |
| 10) 612 | 5 | Lop Buri | 18) 963 | 10 | Bangkok |
| 25) 612 | 5 | Chiang Mai | 34) 972 | 10 | Phetchabun |
| 1) 630 | 5 | Bangkok | 38) 981 | 10 | Pathum Thani# |
| 24) 657 | 5 | Bangkok | 30) 990 | 10 | N. Ratchasima |
| 7) ‡666 | 5 | Tak | 7) 999 | 10 | Chiang Rai |
| 6) 666 | 5 | Surin | 33) 999 | 10 | Bangkok |
| 29) 675 | 5 | Bangkok | 12) 1008 | 10 | N. Ratchasima |
| 8) 684 | 5 | N. Si Thammarat | 12) 1017 | 10 | Prachuap KK |
| 39) 684 | 5 | Udon Thani | 31) 1035 | 10 | Bangkok |
| 11) 693 | 5 | Saraburi | 35) 1044 | 10 | Khon Kaen |
| 19) 711 | 5 | Chiang Rai | 8) 1044 | 10 | N. Si Thammarat |
| 10) 711 | 5 | Lop Buri | 1) 1053 | 10 | Bangkok |
| 29) 720 | 5 | Chon Buri | 12) 1062 | 10 | Udon Thani |
| 32) 738 | 5 | Chiang Mai | 4) 1071 | 10 | Bangkok |
| 32) 738 | 5 | Songkhla | 32) 1080 | 10 | Chiang Mai |
| 37) 747 | 5 | Bangkok | 32) 1080 | 10 | N. Sawan |
| 6) 747 | 5 | Udon Thani | 32) 1080 | 10 | Yala |
| 34) 756 | 5 | Narathiwat | 32) 1098 | 10 | Songkhla |
| 35) 756 | 5 | Surin | 25) 1107 | 10 | Samut Sakhon# |
| 31) 765 | 5 | Lampang | 6) 1107 | 10 | Khon Kaen |
| 12) 765 | 5 | Lop Buri | 7) 1116 | 10 | Phitsanulok |
| 18) 774 | 5 | Rayong | 6) 1134 | 10 | N. Ratchasima |
| 36) 774 | 5 | Udon Thani | 27) 1143 | 10 | Bangkok |
| 7) 783 | 5 | Kamphaeng Phet | 37) 1152 | 10 | Chiang Mai |
| 19) 792 | 5 | Bangkok | 37) 1152 | 10 | Khon Kaen |
| 3) 801 | 5 | N. Sawan | 20) 1161 | 20 | Bangkok |
| 12) 801 | 5 | Chiang Rai | 29) 1161 | 10 | U. Ratchathani |
| 12) 801 | 5 | U. Ratchathani | 29) 1170 | 10 | Chanthaburi |
| 32) 828 | 5 | N. Si Thammarat | 29) 1170 | 10 | Phitsanulok |
| 7) 828 | 5 | Sukhothai | 36) 1179 | 10 | Bangkok |
| 34) 837 | 5 | Sakon Nakhon | 34) 1179 | 10 | Chiang Rai |
| 2) 855 | 5 | Prachin Buri | 35) 1188 | 10 | Sakon Nakhon |

| MW kHz | kW | Province +) |
|---|---|---|
| 7) 1188 | 10 | Phitsanulok |
| 5) 1188 | 10 | Sa Kaeo |
| 26) 1197 | 10 | Lop Buri |
| 5) 1206 | 10 | Prachuap KK |
| 35) 1215 | 10 | Phrae |
| 6) 1215 | 10 | U. Ratchathani |
| 12) 1224 | 10 | Chiang Rai |
| 12) 1224 | 10 | N. Sawan |
| 12) 1233 | 10 | Bangkok |
| 32) 1233 | 10 | Udon Thani |
| 7) 1242 | 10 | Phetchabun |
| 24) 1251 | 10 | Roi Et |
| 12) 1251 | 5 | Bangkok |
| 25) 1269 | 10 | Songkhla |
| 15) 1269 | 10 | Bangkok |
| 28) 1287 | 10 | Samut Prakan# |
| 32) 1287 | 10 | U. Ratchathani |
| 7) 1287 | 10 | Uttaradit |
| 39) 1305 | 10 | Sara Buri |
| 25) 1314 | 10 | Khon Kaen |
| 12) 1323 | 10 | Chiang Mai |
| 12) 1323 | 10 | Surat Thani |
| 14) 1332 | 10 | Bangkok |
| 12) 1332 | 10 | Maha Sarakham |
| 32) 1350 | 10 | Trang |
| 33) 1350 | 10 | Bangkok |
| 6) 1359 | 10 | Sakhon Nakhon |

| MW kHz | kW | Province +) |
|---|---|---|
| 12) 1368 | 10 | N. Pathom |
| 22) 1377 | 10 | Phitsanulok |
| 13)‡1386 | 10 | Pathum Thani# |
| 34) 1395 | 10 | Chiang Rai |
| 24) 1404 | 10 | Yasothon |
| 5) 1404 | 10 | Suphan Buri |
| 33) 1422 | 10 | Bangkok |
| 30) 1422 | 10 | Phitsanulok |
| 12) 1431 | 10 | N. Ratchasima |
| 29) 1431 | 5 | Songkhla |
| 6) 1440 | 10 | N. Phanom |
| 32) 1440 | 10 | Samut Sakhon |
| 7) 1449 | 10 | Phichit |
| 10) 1449 | 10 | Chumphon |
| 24) 1458 | 10 | Si Sa Ket |
| 29) 1458 | 10 | Phuket |
| 27) 1494 | 10 | Bangkok |
| 24) 1503 | 10 | Surat Thani |
| 35) 1512 | 10 | Phayao |
| 12) 1512 | 10 | Songkhla |
| 34) 1521 | 10 | Bangkok |
| 32) 1530 | 10 | Uttaradit |
| 5) 1530 | 10 | Chanthaburi |
| 23) 1539 | 10 | Kanchanaburi |
| 11) 1557 | 10 | Phetchabun |
| —) 15751000 | | Ayutthaya |

‡) r. inactive. +) N.=Nakhon, U.=Ubon, KK=Khiri Khan. #) Bangkok area

**GENERAL NOTES:** News: Stns are generally required to relay N. from R. Thailand at 0000 & 1200 daily, each 30 mins, and to relay time signal and national anthem at 0000 and 1100. **Station IDs:** Both short names, e.g. Wor. Por. Tho, and long names may serve as stn identifications, usually preceded by 'Thini' ('This is'), 'Thini Sathani Witthayu (Krachaisiang)' ('This is R. St.') or 'Khun kamlang rap fang' ('You are listening to'). Changwat=province. Amphoe=district (dt.). Prgrs are often supplied by separate production companies. The Thai name for Bangkok is 'Krung Thep' or 'Krung Thep Mahanakhon'. **Thai numerals:** 0 = sun, 1 = nueng (et), 2 = song, 3 = sam, 4 = si, 5 = ha, 6 = hok, 7 = chet, 8 = paet, 9 = kao, 10 = sip, 20 = yi sip, 100 = roi, 1000 = phan; thi = number, jut = decimal point

**1) Mor. Thor. Bor. Sip Et** (Monthon Thahan Bok Thi Sip Et, 11th Military Circle) ☞ 145 Rama V Rd, Dusit Region, Bangkok 10300 Ann: 'Suan Mitsakawan' – **2) Mor. Thor. Bor. Sip Song** (Monthon Thahan Bok Thi Sip Song, 'Siang Khai Chakkrapong', 12th Military Circle, 'Voice of Chakkrapong Camp') Chakkrapong Camp, Dong Phra Ram, Prachin Buri 25000 – **3) Mor. Thor. Bor. Thi Sam Sip Et** (Monthon Thahan Bok Thi Sam Sip Et, 31st Military Circle). ☞ Jiraprawat Camp, Nakhon Sawan 60000 – **4) Sathani Witthayu Rattasapha** (Parliament R. Station). ☞ Parliament House, Uthong Nai Rd, Dusit Region, Bangkok 10300 – **5) Thor. Phor. Nueng** (Kongthap Phak Thi Nueng, 1st Army Area). HQ: ☞ Headquarters of the 1st Army Area, Suan Mitsakawan, Rajchadamnern Nok Ave, Dusit Region, Bangkok 10300. **Regional stns:** 9 Mu 4, Bang Kacha, Chanthaburi 22000 – Phairirayodet Camp, Suwansri Rd, Tha Kasem, Sa Kaeo 27000 – Kao Kuat, Kraw Plub Pla, Ratchaburi 70000 – Ban Sam Liam, Mu 4, Don Pho Thong, Suphan Buri 72000 – **6) Thor. Phor. Song** (Kongthap Phak Thi Song, 2nd Army Area). HQ: ☞ Suranari Camp, Ratchadamnoen Rd, Nong Phailom, Nakhon Ratchasima 30000. **Regional stns:** Aphai Rd, Nai Mueang, Kalasin 46000 – Si Phatcharin Camp, Sila, Khon Kaen 40000 – Phra Yot Mueang Khwang Camp, Nakhon Phanom-Sakon Nakhon Rd, Khurukhu, Nakhon Phanom 48000 – Krit Siwara Camp, That Naveng, Sakon Nakhon 47000 – Wirawatyothin Camp, Phakdichumphon Rd, Nok Mueang, Surin 32000 – Sapphasiti Prasong Camp, Warin Chamrap District, Ubon Ratchathani 34190 – Yutthasin Prasit Camp, Non Sung Rd, Udon Thani 41330 – **7) Thor. Phor. Sam** (Kongthap Phak Thi Sam, 3rd Army Area). ☞ Headquarters of the 3rd Army Area, Somdet Phra Ekathosarot Camp, Aranyik, Phitsanulok 65000. **Regional stns:** Mengrai Maharat Camp, Chiang Mai 57000 – 236/5 Mu 3, Nakhon Sawan - Kamphaeng Phet Rd, Nakhon Chum, Kamphaeng Phet 62000 – Khalang Nakhon Camp, Nong Krating, Lampang 52000 – Phokun Pha Mueang Camp, 166/1 Mu 1, Wat Pa, Lom Sak District, Phetchabun 67110 – 104/1 Mu 5, Ban Krot Ngam, Ban Na, Wachirabarami District, Phichit 66140 – Ban Mai, Ratsadon Uthit Rd, Nai Wiang, Phrae 54000 – Bypass Road, Pak Khwae, Sukhothai 64000 – Charot Withithong Rd, Nam Ruem, Tak 63000 – 109 Mu 8, Tha Sao, Uttaradit 53000 – **8) Thor. Phor. Si** (Kongthap Phak Thi Si, 4th Army Area). HQ: ☞ Wachirawut Camp, Ratchadamnoen-Pak Nun Rd, Nakhon Si Thammarat 80000. **Regional stns:** Senanarong Camp, Kho Hong, Hat Yai District, Songkhla 90110 – Ban Na San District, Surat Thani 84120 – Charoen Pradit Rd, Rusamilae, Pattani 94000 – **9) Phon Por. Thor. Or.** (Kong

Phon Thahan Puen Yai Tosue Akart Yan, Anti-Aircraft Artillery Division), ☞ Kiak Kay Junction, Thahan Road, Bangsue, Dusit Region, Bangkok 10300 – **10) Wor. Sor. Por.** (Witthayu Sun Kan Thahan Puen Yai, Artillery Centre R. St.). ☞ 301 Phahonyothin Camp, Artillery Centre, Khao Phra Ngam, Lop Buri 15160. Regional st: Khet Udomsak Camp, Wang Mai, Chumphon 86000 – **11) Siang Adison** (Sun Kan Thahan Ma, Cavalry Centre, 'Voice of Adison'). ☞ Saraburi Cavalry Centre, Adison Camp, Mitraphap Rd, Pak Phrieo, Saraburi 18000. Regional st: Saraburi-Lom Sak Rd, Nong Khwai, Lom Sak District, Phetchabun 67110 – **12) Thor. Or.** (Thahan Akart, Royal Thai Airforce). ☞ Tor. Or. 01, 1233kHz, Don Mueang: 171 Mu 2, Phahonyothin Rd, Khlong Thanon, Sai Mai, Bangkok 10220. Tor. Or. 01, 945kHz, Min Buri: 74 Mu 2, Nimit Mai, Sai Kong Tin, Min Buri, Bangkok 10510. Tor. Or. 06, 1251kHz: The Empress Hotel, 1091/343 Phetchaburi Tat Mai Road, Charurat, Makassan, Ratcha Thewi, Bangkok 10400. **Regional stns:** Thor. Or. 02: 301 Wing 2, 1st Air Division, Khao Phra Ngam Rd, Lop Buri 15160 – Thor. Or. 03: Wing 1, Mu 3, Nong Phai Lom, Nakhon Ratchasima 30000 – Thor. Or. 04: 305 Mu 4, Wing 4, 3rd Air Division, Takhli District, Nakhon Sawan 60140 – Thor. Or. 05: Wing 53, 4th Air Division, Ko Lak, Prachuap Khiri Khan 77000 – Thor. Or. 7: Surat Thani Airport Entrance, Huatoey, Phunphin District, Surat Thani 84130 – Thor. Or. 08: 38 Mu 14, Ban Nongphai, Chayangkun Rd, Khamyai, Ubon Ratchathani 34000 – Thor. Or. 09: 549 Mu 9, Wing 23, Thahan Rd, Makkhaeng, Udon Thani 41000 – Thor. Or. 10: Wing 46, 3rd Air Division, Yaek Khok Matum, Phitsanulok - Wangthong Rd, Na – **13) Sathani Witthayu Phuea Kan Kaset** (Agricultural R. St.). ☞ Agricultural Radio Section, 2143/1 Phahonyothin Road, Lat Yao, Bang Khen Region, Bangkok 10900 – **14) Or. Sor.** (Sathani Witthayu Amphon Sathan, Phraratchawang Dusit, Amphon Sathan Throne Radio Station). ☞ Dusit Palace, Ratchawithi Rd, Chitralada, Dusit Region, Bangkok 10303 – **15) Kho. Sor. Thor. Bor.** (Kromkan Khon Song Thahan Bok, Army Transportation Dept.). ☞ Army Transportation Broadcasting Station, Transport School Compound, Thahan Road, Dusit Region, Bangkok 10300 – **16) Wor. Kor. Thor. Mor.** (Sathani Witthayu Krung Thep Mahanakhon, Bangkok Radio Station), ☞ 192 Sarasin Rd, Lumphini Park, Pathum Wan Region, Bangkok 10330 – **17) Tor. Chor. Dor.** (Tamruat Trawen Chaidaen, Border Patrol Police). ☞ Bang Khen Police Dept. Club, Vibhavadi-Rangsit Rd, Bang Khen Bangkok 10210 – **18) Phon Mor. Song** (Sathani Witthayu Kong Phan Thahan Ma Thi Song, 2nd Cavalry Division). ☞ Samsen Rd, Bang Krabue, Dusit Region, Bangkok 10300 Bangkok. Regional st: Rayong-Ban Khai Rd, Nam Khok, Rayong 21000 – **19) Wor. Phor. Thor.** (Witthayu Kromkan Phalang Ngan Thahan, Defence Energy Dept. R. St.). ☞ New Building, Sukhumvit 24, Phra Khanong, Bangkok 10250. Regional st: 141/3 Mu 4, Don Kaeo Rd, Chotana, Mae Rim District, Chiang Mai 50180 – **20) Wor. Sor. Sor.** (Witthayu Sueksa, Educational Radio). ☞ Educational Technology Centre, Si Ayutthaya Rd, Ratcha Thewi, Bangkok 10400 – **22) Wor. Phon Si** (Witthayu Kong Phon Thi Si, 4th Infantry Division). ☞ Headquarters of the 4th Infantry Division, Somdet Phra Naresuan Maharat Camp, Phitsanulok 65000 – **23) Phon Ror. Kao** (Kong Phon Thahan Rap Thi Kao, 9th Infantry Division). ☞ Surasi Camp, Kanchanaburi 71190 – **24) Jor. Sor.** (Krom Chaye Thahan Suesarn, Army Signals Department). ☞ Jor. Sor. 1, Rama V Rd, Saphan Daeng, Bangkok. Regional stns: Bangkok 10300. **Regional stns:** Jor. Sor. 2, Tharathibodi Rd, Thakham, Phunphin District, Surat Thani 84130 – Jor. Sor. 3, Prasert Songkhram Camp, Kongphon Si Rd, Nuea, Roi Et 45000 – Jor. Sor. 4, 104 Thetsaban 1 Rd, Nai Mueang, Yasothon 35000 – Jor. Sor. 5, 5 Mu 2 Ban Lao, Ban Lao, Chaiyaphum 36000 – Jor. Sor. 6, 1543/23 Srisumang Rd, Mueang Tai, Si Sa Ket 33000 – **25) Mor. Kor.** (Mahawitthayalai Kasetsat, Kasetsart University). HQ: ☞ 50 Phahonyothin Rd, Bang Khen, Chatuchak, Bangkok 10900. Bangkok. Tr. located at Nongkhaem in Samut Sakhon province. **Regional stns:** 301/1 Mu 5, Paphai, Sansai District, Chiang Mai 50210 – 86/8 Maliwan Rd, Mueang Kao, Sitan, Khon Kaen 40000 – 424 Mu 3, Kanchanawanit Rd, Phawong, Songkhla 90100 – **26) Jor. Tor. Lor.** (Changwat Thahan Bok Lop Buri, Lop Buri Army Province). ☞ 13th Military Circle, Narai Maharat Rd, Lop Buri 15000 – **27) Or. Sor. Mor. Thor.** (Ongkan Suesan Muanchon Haeng Prathet Thai, Mass Communications Org. of Thailand, MCOT Radio Network). ☞ 63/1 Rama IX Rd, Huay Khwang, Bangkok 10320 – **28) Sor. Or. Thor.** (Sathani Witthayu Krom Utiniyom Witthayu, Meteorological Department R. St.). ☞ 4353 Sukhumvit Rd, Bangna, Bangkok 10260 – **29) Sor. Thor. Ror.** (Siang Chak Thahan Ruea, Voice of the Navy). ☞ Sor. Thor. Ror. 2: Phutianan Stadium, Phra Khanong, Bangna District, Bangkok 10260. **Regional stns:** Sor. Thor. Ror. 3: 99/1 Mu 1, Phuket 83000 – Sor. Thor. Ror. 4: 9/9 Thetsaban-Phatthana Rd, Wat Mai, Chanthaburi 22000 – Sor. Thor. Ror. 5: 652 Mu 2, Sattahip District, Chon Buri 20180 – Sor. Thor. Ror. 6: Songkhla Naval Station, Thale Luang Rd, Bo Yang, Songkhla 90000 – Sor. Thor. Ror. 7: Mae Klang River Operation Unit, Nakhon Phanom 48000 – Sor. Thor. Ror. 8: Ban Khlong Mek, Tha Chang, Phrom Phiram District, Phitsanulok 65150 – Sor. Thor. Ror. 9: Ban Thung Sawang, Ubon-Takan Rd, Rai Noi, Ubon Ratchathani 34000 – **30) Sor. Wor. Phor.** (Sathani Witthayu

Phitaksantirat, Police R. St.). ☞ Radio Broadcasting Section, 2nd Communication Division, Directorate of Police Communications, Police Department, Bang Khen Region, Bangkok 10900. **Regional stns:** 40 Mu 1, Chotana Rd, Maesa, Mae Rim District, Chiang Mai 50180 – Sor. Wor. Phor. 2, Suranarai Rd, Cho Ho, Nakhon Ratchasima 30310 – Sor. Wor. Phor. 3, Banphru, Hat Yai District, Songkhla 90250 – Sor. Wor. Phor. 4, Pracha Uthit Rd, Nai Mueang, Phitsanulok – **31) Nueng. Por. Nor.** (Krom Praisani Thoralek, Post & Telegraph Dept.) ☞ Chaengwattana-Thungsonghong Rd, Don Mueang, Bangkok 10210. **Regional stns:** 219 Mu 4, Lampang-Hang Chat Rd, Pong Yang Khok, Hang Chat District, Lampang 52190 – Ban Nong Bu, Rop Mueang Rd, Samphrao, Udon Thani 41000 – **32) Wor. Por. Tho.** (Witthayu Pracham Thin, Local R, Communications Division, Signals Dept, Royal Thai Army) ☞ Wor. Por. Tho. 8: Kamphaeng Phet Akkharayothin Camp, Suan Luang, Krathum Baen District, Samut Sakhon 74110. **Regional stns:** Wor. Por. Tho. 2: Kawila Camp, Kongsai, Wat Ket, Chiang Mai 50000 – Wor. Por. Tho. 3: 001 Na Khai Suranari, Phanibut Rd, Pho Klang, Nakhon Ratchasima 30000 – Wor. Por. Tho. 4: Thep Sattri Si Sunthon Camp, Kabang, Thung Song District, Nakhon Si Thammarat 80310 – Wor. Por. Tho. 5: 5 Kanchanawanit Rd, Hat Yai District, Songkhla 90110 – Wor. Por. Tho. 6: Sapphasiti Prasong Camp, Warin Chamrap District, Ubon Ratchathani 34190 – Wor. Por. Tho. 7: Khai Prachak Sinlaprakhom, Thahan Rd, Mak Khaeng, Udon Thani 41000 – Wor. Por. Tho. 9: Chiraprawat Camp, Na Khai Chiraprawat Rd, Nakhon Sawan 60000 – Wor. Por. Tho. 10: Mengrai Maharat Barracks, Chiang Rai 57000 – Wor. Por. Tho. 12: 140 Kasikonthungsang Rd, Sila, Khon Kaen 40000 – Wor. Por. Tho. 14: Phichai Dap Hak Camp, 13/7 Prachanimit Rd, Tha It, Uttaradit 5 – **33) Phon Nueng Ror. Or.** (Kong Phon Thi Nueng Raksa Phra Ong, 1st Infantry Division, Royal Guard). ☞ Phitsanulok Rd, Dusit Region, Bangkok 10300 – **34) Nor. Thor. Phor.** (Nuai Bannachakan Thahan Phatthana, Armed Forces Development Command AFDC, Royal Thai Armed Forces HQ). ☞ Sathani Witthayu 919, Phitsanulok Rd, Dusit Region, Bangkok 10300. **Regional Stns:** Sathani Witthayu 914, Suan Sak Kieo Tap Yong, Ban Pong O, Mae Chan, Mae Chan District, Chiang Mai 57110. 1395kHz in Thai, 1179kHz prgr in Thai and minority langs for hilltribes – Sathani Witthayu 912, 13 Chan Uthit Rd, Bang Nak, Narathiwat 96000 in Thai and Malay – Sathani Witthayu 921, 114 Mu 1, Na Saeng, Lom Kao District, Phetchabun 67120 – Sathani Witthayu 909, Ban Rung Phatthana, Sakon Nakhon-Nakhon Phanom Rd, That Naweng, Sakon Nakhon 47000 – **35) Kor. Wor. Sor.** (Kitkan Witthayu Krachaisiang, Radio & TV Division, Army Signals Dept). HQ: ☞ Radio Broadcasting & Television Division, Signals Department, Royal Thai Army, Rama V Rd, Saphan Daeng, Bangsue, Dusit Region, Bangkok 10300. **Regional stns:** Kor. Wor. Sor. 1, Surin-Prasat Rd, Nok Mueang, Surin 32000 – Kor. Wor. Sor. 2, Yantarakit Sokon Rd, Sung Men District, Phrae 54130 – Kor. Wor. Sor. 3, 1879 Mu 14, That Choeng Chum, Sakon Nakhon 47000 – Kor. Wor. Sor. 4, 383 Super Highway, Ban Dom, Phayao 56000 – Kor. Wor. Sor. 5, 252 Mitraphap Rd, Ban Phai District, Khon Kaen 40110 – **36) Sor. Sor. Sor.** (Siang Sam Yot, Crime Suppression Division, Royal Thai Police). ☞ Section 1, Superintendency 2, Command Division, Crime Suppression Division, Phahonyothin Rd, Bangkok 10900. **Regional st:** 195 Mu 8, Udon-Nong Samrong Rd, Mumon, Udon Thani 41000 – **37) Ror. Dor.** (Kromkan Raksa Dindaen, Territorial Defence Dept.). HQ: ☞ 2 Charoen Krung Rd, Suan Chaochet, Phra Nakhon Region, Bangkok 10200. **Regional stns:** Nong Ho, Chotana Rd, Chang Phueak, Chiang Mai 50000 – Sri Phatcharin Camp, Rat Khanueng Rd, Nai Mueang, Khon Kaen 40000 – **38) Mahawitthayalai Thammasat** (Thammasat University). ☞ Faculty of Journalism and Mass Communications, Thammasat University, Prachan Rd, Phra Nakhon Region, Bangkok 10200 D.Prgr: Mon-Fri 0300-1400 – **39) Yan Kraw** (4th Cavalry Battalion, Armoured Unit, Royal Guard). HQ: ☞ Military Armoured Car School, 1156 Samsen Road, Bangkabrue, Dusit Region, Bangkok 10300. **Regional stns:** Saraburi Cavalry Centre, Adison Camp, Mitraphap Rd, Pak Phrieo, Saraburi 18000 Mitraphap Rd, Nong Bua Udon Thani 41000.

**FM STATIONS IN SELECTED CITIES** (MHz) (exc. R. Thailand, commercial, institutional and community radio stns):
**Bangkok:** 87.5 Sathani Witthayu Ratthasapha (Parliament R. St.) – 88.5 Sor. Thor. Ror. 1, 'EDS Everyday Station' – 89.0 Yan Kraw, 'Gift FM' – 89.5 Rajamangala University of Technology 'Sweet FM' – 90.0 Phon Nueng Ror. Or. 'Lukthung Rak Thai' – 90.5 Wor. Phor. Thor. – 91.0 Sor. Wor. Phor. 'Traffic Pro' – 91.5 Yan Kraw, 'Mono Fresh' – 92.0 Wor. Sor. Sor. – 93.0 Sor. Thor. Ror. 1, 'Cool Fahrenheit' – 94.0 Thor. Thor. 'Eazy FM' – 94.5 Jor. Sor, 'Lukthung Network' – 95.0 Or. Sor. Mor. Thor 'LTM Lukthung Mahanakhon' – 96.0 Thor. Thor. 'Sport R.' – 96.5 Or. Sor. Mor. Thor, 'Khluen Khwam Khit, Thinking Radio' – 97.5 Or. Sor. Mor. Thor. 'Mellow 97.5' – 98.0 Phon Nueng Ror. Or. 'Isan FM' – 98.5 Nueng Por. Nor, 'Goodtime R.' – 99.0 Or. Sor. Mor. Thor, 'Active R.' – 99.5 Sathani Witthayu 9-1-9, 'Traffic Radio Society (TRS)' – 100.0 Jor.

Sor. Roi – 100.5 Or. Sor. Mor. Thor. 'Modern R. News Network' – 101.0 Sathani Witthayu Kong Banchakan Thahan Sungsut (Royal Thai Armed Forces Command HQ) 'Radio Report One' – 101.5 Sathani Witthayu Chula or 'Witthayu Chula' or 'CU FM' (Chulalongkorn Univ.) – 102.0 Khor. Sor. Thor. Bor. 'Khluen Khon Tham Ngan' – 102.5 Thor. Or, 'Get 102.5' – 103.0 Jor. Sor 'Like FM' – 103.5 Thor. Thor. Bor, 'FM One' – 104.0 Or. Sor. – 104.5 Phon Por. Thor. Or. (Kong Phon Thahan Puen Yai Tosue Akat Yan, Anti-Aircraft Artillery Division), 'EFM' – 105.5 Or. Sor. Mor. Thor 'Eazy FM' – 106.0 Sor. Thor. Ror. 1, 'Fast 106' – 106.5 Nueng Por. Nor, 'Green Wave' – 107.0 Or. Sor. Mor. Thor, 'Met 107'.
**Chiang Mai:** 88.0 Sor. Thor. Ror. – 100.0 Mor. Chor. (Chiang Mai Univ.) – 100.75 Or. Sor. Mor. Thor. – 101.5 Thor.Phor. Sam – 102.5 Thor. Or 013 'Get 102.5' – 105.75 Sor. Sor. Sor. – 106.75 Sathani Witthayu Ratthasapha (Parliament R. St.)
**Khon Kaen:** 88.25 Thor. Phor. Song 'KCS Radio' – 90.75 Or. Sor. Mor. Thor. – 103.0 Mor. Khor. (Khon Kaen Univ.) – 104.5 Sor. Wor. Phor. – 107.0 Thor Or. 020
**Phuket:** 88.0 Sor. Thor. Ror. 'Nice Peak FM' – 89.0 Nueng Por. Nor 'Power Zone FM'– 95.0 Sor. Sor. Sor, 'Kiss FM' – 99.25 Sathani Witthayu Ratthasapha (Parliament R. St.) – 101.5 Or. Sor. Mor. Thor. – 102.5 Por. Dor. – 107.25 Sor. Or. Thor. 'Smart R.'
**Songkhla/Hat Yai:** 88.0 Mor. Or. (Prince of Songkhla Univ.), Hat Yai – 94.5 Sor. Thor. Ror. 6 – 96.5 Or. Sor. Mor. Thor., Hat Yai – 103.25 Sathani Witthayu Ratthasapha (Parliament R. Stn). – 104.0 Tor. Thor. Dor., Hat Yai – 107.0 Thor. Or. 011, Khlong Hoi Khong – 107.75 Thor. Phor. Si, Hat Yai 'Smart R.'

**OTHER FM STATIONS:** FM stns belonging to R. Thailand and other operators are on air throughout Thailand. A large number of local commercial, institutional and community radio stns are also operating, with transmitter powers up to 500 watts.

**International Relays:** See International radio section

## TIMOR-LESTE

**L.T:** UTC +9h — **Pop:** 1.3 million — **Pr. L:** Tetun, Portuguese, Indonesian — **E.C:** 50 Hz, 220V — **ITU:** TLS

### AUTORIDADE NACIONAL DE COMUNICAÇÕES (ANC)
☞ Ground Floor, Telecom Building, Av. Bispo de Medeiros 8, Caicoli, Díli ☎ +670 3339330 **W:** anc.tl **L.P:** Exec. Pres: António Brígido Correia

### RÁDIO TELEVISAUN TIMOR-LESTE (RTTL) (Pub.)
☞ Edifício da Rádio e Televisão, Estrada Mercado Municipal, Caixa Postal 114, Díli ☎ +670 73960050 **W:** rttlep.tl **E:** info@rttlep.tl **L.P:** Dir: Milena Soares Abrantes. RTTL administers R. Timor-Leste (RTL) and TV Timor-Leste (TVTL)

### RÁDIO TIMOR-LESTE (RTL) (Pub.)
☞ Estrada Mercado Municipal, Caixa Postal 114, Díli ☎ +670 73960050 **W:** rttlep.tl **E:** info@rttlep.tl; radiotimorleste@gmail.com **L.P:** Dir: Rosário Maia Martins. PD: Martinho Tavares

| FM(MHz) | kW | Location | FM(MHz) | kW | Location |
|---|---|---|---|---|---|
| 88.9 | 0.5 | Maliana | 95.0 | 0.3 | Manatuto |
| 90.3 | 0.3 | Aileu | 96.8 | 0.5 | Lospalos |
| 90.6 | | Ermera | 97.0 | 1 | Same |
| 90.9 | | Ainaro | 98.9 | 0.3 | Viqueque |
| 91.7 | 4 | Díli | 99.1 | | Liquisa |
| 92.1 | 0.3 | Oecussi | 105.4 | 1 | Baucau |
| 93.3 | 0.3 | Suai | | | |

**D.Prgr** in Tetun, Portuguese and Indonesian: 2100-1500.
**N.** in **Tetun/Portuguese/Indonesian:** 2200-2300, 0330-0430, 1100-1200

### RÁDIO MAUBERE (Operated by Fretilin Party)
☞ Avenida dos Mártires da Pátria, Lurumata, Díli ☎ +670 3322599 **W:** facebook.com/radiomaubere **E:** radio-maubere@live.com
**FM (MHz):** Manatuto 93.8, Viqueque 94.8. Baucau 96.0, Oecusse 96.2, Ermera 96.4, Suai 96.5, Aileu & Ainaro 97.9, Liquisa 97.9, Lospalos 98.0, Same 98.2, Maliana 99.5, Díli 99.9

### TIMOR-LESTE ASSOCIATION OF COMMUNITY RADIO STNS (Asosiasaun Radio Komunidade Timor-Leste) (ARKTL)
☞ National Press Centre, Rua Martires da Patria, Fatuhada, Dili ☎ +670 77239945 **W:** facebook.com/ARKTL **E:** arktl.info@gmail.com **L.P:** Pres: Prezado Ximenes. ARKTL's main role is as advocate for all community and independent stns. Member stns: 5, 8, 9, 10, 11, 13, 15, 17, 19, 20, 21, 25, 26, 27, 28 and 31.
**COMMUNITY RADIO CENTRE (Centru Radio Comunidade) (CRC)**
☞ CNE Building, Rua Bispo de Medeiros, Kintal Ki'ik, PO Box 160,

Santa Cruz, Díli ☎ +670 3310127 or +670 77237890 **W:** facebook. com/crctl **E:** info@crc-tl.org **LP:** Mgr: Luis Evaristo dos Santos. CRC supports stns 5, 8, 9, 10, 11, 13, 14, 15, 17, 19, 20, 21, 24, 26, 27 and 31.

## COMMUNITY AND INDEPENDENT STATIONS

| FM | MHz | kW | Station |
|---|---|---|---|
| 1) | 88.2 | | R. Gardamor, Díli |
| 2) | 88.5 | | R. Na'i Feto, Laleia |
| 3) | 88.8 | 0.15 | M3 R., Díli |
| 4) | 89.5 | 1 | Voz FM, Díli |
| 5) | 89.7 | | R. Comunidade Maubisse Mau-Loko, Maubisse |
| 6) | 90.0 | | R. Akademika, Díli |
| 7) | 91.2 | | R. Lalenok Ba Ema Hotu (Labeh), Díli |
| 8) | 91.7 | 0.2 | R. Comunidade Maliana, Maliana |
| 9) | 92.3 | 0.1 | R. Comunidade Café Ermera, Gleno |
| 10) | 92.3 | 0.1 | R. Comunidade Tokodede, Liquisa |
| 11) | 93.3 | 0.1 | R. Comunidade Atoni Lifau, Oecussi |
| 12) | 94.1 | | R. Comunidade Comoro, Díli |
| 13) | 94.1 | 0.1 | R. Comunidade Cova Taroman, Suai |
| 14) | 94.7 | 0.3 | R. Metro, Díli |
| 15) | 95.1 | 0.1 | R. Comunidade 1912 Dom Boaventura, Same |
| 16) | 95.8 | | R. Liberdade, Díli |
| 17) | 96.1 | 0.1 | R. Comunidade Ili Uai, Manatuto |
| 18) | 97.0 | | R. Suara Timor Lorosae (STL), Díli |
| 19) | 97.1 | 0.1 | R. Comunidade Rai Husar, Aileu |
| 20) | 97.9 | 0.8 | R. Povo Viqueque, Viqueque |
| 21) | 98.1 | 0.1 | R. Comunidade Lian Tatamailau, Ainaro |
| 22) | 98.5 | 0.1 | R. Timor Kmanek, Díli |
| 23) | 98.9 | | R. Kolejiu Fatumaka, Fatumaka |
| 24) | 99.0 | | R. Comunidade Lian Manu-Koko, Vila |
| 25) | 99.5 | 0.16 | R. Rakambia, Díli |
| 26) | 99.9 | 0.1 | R. Comunidade Lian Matebian, Baucau |
| 27) | 100.1 | 0.3 | R. Comunidade Lospalos (Vox Populi), Lospalos |
| 28) | 100.5 | 0.1 | R. Lorico Lian, Díli |
| 29) | 101.1 | | R. Nacional, Díli |
| 30) | 102.0 | | R. Klibur, Díli |
| 31) | 102.5 | 0.15 | R. Popular Kolele Mai, Bukoli |
| 32) | 107.9 | | R. Fini Lorosae, Baucau |

**Addresses & other information:**
**1)** 2nd Floor, Gardamor Building, Fatuhada, Díli **W:** facebook.com/gardamor **E:** rtvgardamor@gmail.com – **2)** Paróquia de Laleia, Laleia, Munisipiu Manatuto **W:** facebook.com/paroquiadelaleia **E:** paroquiadelaleia@gmail.com – **3)** Rua da Guiné, Palapaso, Díli **W:** facebook.com/M3Radio **E:** m3radiodili@gmail.com – **4)** Rua Mundo Perdido II 28 (Caixa Postal 153), Delta, Díli **E:** roei@ucbap.org (Repeater stations at Ainaro, Baucau, Lospalos, Maliana, Manatuto, Oecussi, Suai, Viqueque all on 89.5MHz 0.015 kW and at Same on 100.5MHz 0.015 kW)– **5)** Maubisse, Munisipiu Ainaro – **6)** Universidade Nacional de Timor-Leste, Dili – **7)** Rua 30 de Agosto depan SDN 05, Malinamoc, Comoro, Díli **W:** labeh.org **E:** info@labeh.org – **8)** Maliana, Munisipiu Bobonaro – **9)** Traseiras do Campo de Futebol, Gleno, Munisipiu Ermera – **10)** Liquisa, Munisipiu Liquisa – **11)** Rua de Santa Rosa, Oecussi, Munisipiu Oecussi-Ambeno – **12)** Avenida Presidente Nicolau Lobato, Comoro, Díli **W:** facebook.com/radiocomunidadecomoro – **13)** Suai, Munisipiu Covalima – **14)** Díli **W:** facebook.com/dilimetrofm – **15)** Rua Pousada, Same, Munisipiu Manufahi – **16)** Avenida Hudi Laran, Usindo, Díli **W:** radioliberdadedili.com **E:** info@radioliberdadedili.com – **17)** Manatuto, Munisipiu Manatuto – **18)** STL Park, Surik Mas, Díli **W:** suara-timor-lorosae.com **E:** stl@redaksi.yahoo.com – **19)** Aileu, Munisipiu Aileu – **20)** Rua Central, Viqueque, Munisipiu Viqueque – **21)** Ainaro, Munisipiu Ainaro – **22)** Rua Foho Nain Feto, Ailok Laran (Caixa Postal 354), Maloa, Díli **W:** rtk.tl **E:** radio.rtk@gmail.com – **23)** Kolejiu Don Bosco Fatumaka, Fatumaka, Munisipiu Baucau – **24)** Rua Vila Mau-Meta, Vila, Atauro – **25)** Rua Kampung Alor, Díli **E:** radiorakambia@gmail.com – **26)** Campus Universitário, Kota Baru, Baucau, Munisipiu Baucau – **27)** Rua Central, Lospalos, Munisipiu Lautém – **28)** Rua Governador Serpa Rosa, Farol, Díli **W:** radiolorico.com **E:** radiolorico@gmail.com – **29)** Rua D. Boaventura 8, Díli **W:** gmntv.tl **E:** comercial@gmntv.tl – **30)** Rua Pertamina, Praia dos Coqueiros, Pantai Kelapa, Díli **E:** radiokliburfm@yahoo.com – **31)** Bukoli, Munisipiu Baucau – **32)** Diocese de Baucau, Baucau, Munisipiu Baucau.

**Relays of International Stations:**
**RTP Antena 1**, Díli 103.1MHz - **RDP Internacional**, Díli 105.3MHz 1KW - **BBC World Service**, Díli 95.3MHz - **Radio Australia**, Díli 106.4MHz

## TOGO

**L.T:** UTC — **Pop:** 7.7 million — **Pr.L:** French, Ewé, Kabyè, Kotokoli, Mina — **E.C:** 50Hz, 127(Lomé)/220V — **ITU:** TGO

## HAUTE AUTORITÉ DE L'AUDIOVISUEL ET DE LA COMMUNICATION (HAAC)
📧 Lomé. **L.P:** Pres: Philippe Evegno, Vice Pres: Wiyao Dadja Pouwi

### RADIODIFFUSION-TÉLÉVISION TOGOLAISE (Gov.)
**RADIO LOMÉ** 📧 B.P. 434, Lomé ☎+228 2221 2493 📠 +228 2221 3673 **W:** radiolome.tg **E:** radiolome@radiolome.tg
**L.P:** Dir: Bawa Semedo. CE: Dodzi Soares.
**FM:** Agou 88.3MHz, Alédjo 92.7MHz, Dapaong 88.3MHz, Badou 99.3MHz, Lomé 99.5MHz.
**D.Prgr:** French/Ethnic: 24h. **English:** 1940. **Ann:** "Radio Lomé". **IS:** Soft tempo chime.

### RADIO KARA (Regional station)
📧 B.P. 21, Kara **W:** radiokara.tg **E:** radiokara14@yahoo.fr
**FM:** Dapaong/Kara 91.5MHz, Agou 94.7MHz, Pya Kadjika 96.7MHz, Alédjo 99.2MHz, Lomé 101.5MHz.
**D.Prgr:** 24h. **Ann:** "Radiodiffusion Kara".

### Other Stations (FM MHz):
**Hit R**, Lomé: 104.7 **W:** hitradio.ma – **R. Avenir**, 76 Blvd. de la Kara, Quartier Doumassessé, B.P. 20183, Lomé: 104.3 – **R. de L'Evangile**, Lomé: 100.3. – **R. Delta Santé**, Aneho: 106.1. (Also rel. RFI) – **R. Evangile Jésus Vous Aime**, Bretelle de Klimamé, B.P. 2313, Lomé. **FM:** Lomé 100.2, Agou 104.1 – **R. Maria Togo**, n°155 de la rue 158, Hédzranawoé, B.P. 30162, Lomé **W:** radiomaria.org **E:** rmariatg@ids.tg **FM:** Dapaong 88.5 0.25kW, Lomé 98.8, Kara 101.5, Kpalimé/Sokodé 104.5 – **R. Missionnaire**, Quartier Tomdé Kara, B.P. 170, Kara: 106.3. **E:** emc_kara@yahoo.com – **R. Nana FM**, Angle Rues Tanou et Djossi, B.P. 6035, Lomé: 95.5. **E:** petdog2@yahoo.fr – **Océan FM**, Aneho: 93.1 – **R. Rurale:** Pagouda 88.9, Notsè 100.1, Dapaong 102.5 – **Sport FM**, Tokoin Habitat, B.P. 8675, Lomé: 91.9 **W:** radiosportfm.com – **R. Tropik FM**, Quartier Wuiti, B.P. 2276, Lomé: 93.1. **E:** tropikfm@nomade. fr – **Zephyr FM**, B.P. 20017, Lomé. **W:** zephyr.tg **E:** zephyr@zephyr.tg **FM:** Lomé 92.3, Kara 95.5, Atakpamé 102.9 – **R. Zion**, Adidogomé, B.P. 13853, Lomé. **FM:** Lomé 94.3, Kpalimé 102.5.
**BBC African Sce** in English/French: Lomé 97.5MHz.
**RFI Afrique:** Lomé 91.5, Kara/Kpalimé 98.3MHz

## TOKELAU (New Zealand)

**L.T:** UTC +11h — **Pop:** 1,300 — **Pr.L:** Tokelauan, English — **E.C:** 50Hz, 240V — **ITU:** TOK

### TOKELAU COMMUNITY RADIO
📧 National Public Service - Tokelau Office, PO Box 3298 Apia, Samoa **LP:** Acting GM: Seiuli Aleta ☎ +685 20822 **W:** tokelau.org.nz
**Prgr:** local community news and information, educational talks, weather reports and music. Each stn operates independently, with studios on each atoll.

| FM | MHz | kW | Station |
|---|---|---|---|
| Atafu Atoll | ‡107.5 | 0.005 | R. Atafu FM |
| Fakaofo Atoll | ‡107.5 | 0.005 | R. Fakaofo FM |
| Nukunonu Atoll | ‡107.5 | 0.005 | R. Nukunonu FM |

**NB:** ‡ Tokelau Community Radio and transmitters currently inactive. Discussions since 2017 about reactivation.

## TONGA

**L.T:** UTC +13h — **Pop:** 109,000 — **Pr.L:** Tongan, English — **E.C:** 50Hz, 240V — **ITU:** TON

### MINISTRY OF INFORMATION & COMMUNICATIONS
📧 P.O. Box 1380, Nuku'alofa ☎ +676 28170 📠 +676 24861 **W:** mic. gov.to **E:** enquiries@mic.gov.to **CEO:** Paula Ma'u
**MIC** is the government ministry responsible for broadcasting policy and radio spectrum administration.

### TONGA BROADCASTING COMMISSION
**(Independent Statutory Board, part-Comm.)**
📧 P.O. Box 36, Nuku'alofa, Tongatapu ☎+676 23295 📠+676 24417. 📧 Fangatongo, Neiafu, Vava'u ☎+676 70827, 70843 **W:** tonga-broadcasting.net **E:** tbc_news@tonga-broadcasting.net **LP:** GM: 'Elenoa' Amanaki Chief Prgr Officer: Viola Ulakai C.E: Solomone Finau

| MW | Location | KHz | kW | Station |
|---|---|---|---|---|
| 1) | Nuku'alofa | 1017 | 10 | A3Z |

| FM | Location | MHz | kW | Station |
|---|---|---|---|---|
| 1) | Neiafu, Vava'u | 90.0 | | Vava'u Kool FM |
| 1) | Nuku'alofa | 90.0 | 0.5 | Kool FM |
| 1) | Neiafu, Vava'u | 97.2 | | A3Z R. 1 |
| 1) | Nuku'alofa | 101.7 | | A3Z R. 1 |

**R. Tonga** "The Call of the Friendly Isles" 1017kHz **D.Prgr:** 1900-1110(SS-1200). **N. in English:** 1800 (BBC), 1900 (ABC), 0000 (ABC or RNZI), 0700 (local), 0715 (ABC), 1100. **Kool FM** "Kool 90FM" & "Vava'u Kool 90FM" **N:** local and RNZI **D.Prgr:** 24h

**OTHER STATIONS:**

| FM | Location | MHz | kW | Station |
|----|----------|-----|----|---------|
| 6) | Nuku'alofa | 87.5 | | FM87.5 Tonga Daily News |
| 6) | Neiafu, Vava'u | 87.9 | | 89.5FM |
| 2) | Vaipoa | 88.0 | | A3NTT R. Niuatoputapu |
| 3) | Nuku'alofa | 88.1 | | FM88 |
| 4) | Nuku'alofa | 88.6 | 1 | R. Nuku'alofa |
| 5) | Neiafu, Vava'u | 88.6 | | R. Waves of Vava'u |
| 8) | Neiafu, Vava'u | 89.0 | | Letio Faka-Kalistiane 89FM |
| 9) | Nuku'alofa | 89.1 | | A3V Tonga R. Magic 89.1 |
| 10) | Neiafu, Vava'u | 89.3 | | PIG FM |
| 6) | Nuku'alofa | 89.5 | | R. Tonga Vake-Tali-Folau |
| -) | Unknown | 91.5 | | R. FM 91.5 |
| 14) | Nuku'alofa | 92.1 | | China R. International |
| 11) | Nuku'alofa | 93.1 | 0.2 | A3R Letio Faka-Kalistane 93FM |
| 12) | Nuku'alofa | 98.0 | 0.1 | Le'o'oe Kakai |
| 13) | Nuku'alofa | 103.0 | | R. Australia |

**Addresses and other information**

**2)** Old Catholic Priests residence, Vaipoa, Niuatoputapu, Northern Tonga – **3)** Taimi Media Network, Vaiola Motu'a, Nuku'alofa ☎ +676 25133/27477 **W:** taimi-online.com **E:** kalafim@yahoo.com. au **LP:** CEO Kalafi Moala **Prgr:** news/talk/talkback – **4)** Teufaiva, Nuku'alofa ☎ +676 26262 **W:** facebook.com/radionukualofa/ **Prgr:** 24/7 – **5)** ☎ +676 71128 – **6)** Broadcom Ltd, Ngeieia, Nuku'alofa. ☎ +676 22296 **W:** facebook.com/875fm **LP:** MD Katalina Tohi, C.Ops Mgr Siaosi Lavaka **Prgr:** 24/7 in Tongan/English **Other:** affiliated and shares Tongan language religious programs with R.Tama Ohi network in NZ **W:** tamaohi.org and Radio Tonga Vake-Tali-Folau in San Francisco **W:** radiotongavtfusa.com with internet audio also targeted at Australia and Europe – **8)** UCB Pacific Partners, PO Box 95, Neiafu **W:** pacificpartners.org **LP:** Stn M: Willy Florian **Prgr:** 24/7 Tongan religious – **9)** 13 Vaha'akolo Road, Kaipongipongi, Nuku'alofa ☎ +676 25891 ▤ +676 25600 **W:** tongaradio.com **E:** a3v@tongaradio.com or magic@tongaradio.com **LP:** Mgr Phillip Vea – **10)** **T:** +676 71479 **W:** facebook.com/pigfm-893 **LP:** Greg Carlson **Prgr:** eclectic 'Radio that Rocks the South Pacific' – **11)** UCB Pacific Partners, PO Box 478, Nuku'alofa **W:** pacificpartners.org **E:** tonga@pacificpartners.org **Prgr:** 24/7 Tongan religious – **12)** Voice of the People, Ma'a Fafine moe Famili Inc, Community Media Centre, Fasi, Nuku'alofa. **E:** 98fm.mff@gmail.com **LP:** Bale Huni **Prgr:** community radio – **13)** 24/7 relay of ABC R. in English via satellite from Melbourne – **14)** 24/7 in English & Chinese via satellite from Beijing.

## TRINIDAD & TOBAGO

**LT:** UTC -4h — **Pop:** 1.37 million — **Pr.L:** English — **E.C:** 60Hz, 115V — **ITU:** TRD

### TTT LTD. (Gov. Comm.)
☑ 11A Maraval Rd, Port of Spain ☎ +1 868 622 4141 ▤ +1 868 622 6228 **W:** ctvtt.com, talkcity91fm.com, next99fm.com & sweet100fm. com **LP:** Chairman: Lisa Agard
**FM: Talk City** 91.1MHz – **Next** 99.1MHz – **Sweet** 100.1MHz

### TRINIDAD BROADCASTING COMPANY – TBC RADIO NETWORK (Comm.)
☑ Second Floor, Guardian Building, 22-24 St. Vincent St, P.O. Box 716, Port of Spain ☎ +1 868 623 3802-5 ▤ +1 868 625 1782 **W:** tbcradionetwork.co.tt **LP:** GM: Steve Dipnarine
**FM: 951 Remix:** 95.1MHz (Rock) – **Sky:** 99.5MHz (Rlg.) – **Slam:** 100.5MHz (Caribbean) – **The Vibe CT 105:** 105.1MHz (Local music + sport) – **Sangeet:** 106.1MHz (East Indian) – **Aakash Vani:** 106.5MHz (Easy Listening). TBC also runs Mix90.1FM in Guyana

### ONE CARIBBEAN MEDIA (Comm.)
☑ 5 Rosalina St, Woodbrook, & 47 Tragarete Rd, Port of Spain ☎ +1 868 625 8426 ▤ +1 868 624 3234 **LP:** CEO: Dawn Thomas. PD: Ayne LeBlanc. **W:** onecaribbeanmedia.net
**FM: Taj92.3 FM:** 92.3MHz (East Indian) – **Hott 93:** 93.1MHz (Tobago), 93.5MHz (Port of Spain) – **i95.5 FM:** 95.5MHz (News, talk, current affairs) – **Red 96.7:** 96.7MHz (Urban) – **W107.1 The Word:** 107.1MHz 'Gospel) – **Caribbean SuperStation (CSS):** Txs in nine territories in the Caribbean. Also runs The Wave in St.Lucia

### CARIBBEAN LIFESTYLE COMMUNICATIONS (Comm.)
☑ #4 Herbert St, St. Clair, Port of Spain ☎ +1 868 622 4124 ▤ +1 868 622 6693 **W:** clcommunications.com

**FM: Radio 90.5:** 90.5MHz (East Indian Stn) – **Music Radio 9-7:** 97.1/97.9MHz (East Listening) – **Platinium Hits:** 103.5MHz (AC) – **Heartbeat:** 104.1MHz (For women)

### TRINIDAD & TOBAGO RADIO NETWORK (Comm.)
☑ 153 Tragarete Rd, Newtown, Port of Spain ☎ +1 868 628 9336 **L.P:** MD: Tony Chow Lin On. SM: Robert Dash. PD: Paul Richards
**FM: Star 947:** 94.7MHz (Rock) – **WEFM:** 96.1MHz (Urban Caribbean) – **Music for Life:** 107.7 (Soul)

### RADIO VISION LIMITED (Comm.)
☑ 88-90 Abercromby St., Port of Spain ☎ +1 868 627 6937 **W:** loud. boomchampionstt.com & power102fm.com **LP:** CEP: O'Brian Haynes. MD Brian Knight **FM: Boom Champions** 94.1MHz – **Power 102:** 102.1/102.5

### OTHER STATIONS (FM in MHz):
**BBC:** Port-of-Spain & Scarborough **FM:** 98.7 – **HERITAGE RADIO,** 104 Woodford St, New Town, Port of Spain ☎+1 868 622 3312 ▤+1 868 657 9248 **W:** heritageradiott.com **FM:** 101.7 (Multicultural/rlg.) – **ISAAC 98.1**, Family Focus Broadcasting Network,105a Woodford Street, Newtown, Port of Spain ☎+1 868 622 8981 **W:** isaac981. com **LP:** CEO Margaret Elcock. **FM:** 98.1 (Gospel) – **MORE FM,** 177 Tragarete Rd., Woodbrook, Port of Spain ☎ +1 868 628 9595 **FM:** 104.7 (Top 40) – **103FM,** Level 4, Long Circular Mall, Long Circular Road, St. James ☎ +1 868 628 9222/23/24 **W:** 103fm.net **FM:** 103.1 (East Indian) – **PARLIAMENT OF THE REPUBLIC OF TRINIDAD & TOBAGO,** Abercromby St, Port of Spain. **FM:** 105.5 – **PULSE 89.5,** 65-67 Lambeau Signal Hill Rd, Signal Hill, Tobago ☎+1 868 635 1005 **W:** pulse895fm.com **FM:** 89.5 – **RADIO JAAGRITI,** Corner Pasea Main Road Ext and Churchill Roosevelt Highway, Tunapuna ☎+1 868 663 8743 ▤+1 868 645 0613 **W:** jaagriti.com **LP:** MD: Sat Maharaj. **FM:** 102.7. (Rlg., hindu) – **RADIO TAMBRIN,** 3 Picton Street, Scarborough, Tobago ☎+1 868 639 3437 ▤+1 868 660 7351 **E:** tambrin@tstt.net.tt **W:** tambrintobago.com **LP:** GM: George Leacock. **FM:** 92.7 – **RADIO TOCO,** Galera Road, Toco ☎+1 868 670 0068 **LP:** CEO: Michael Als. **FM:** 106.7 1.2kW, Community Radio for NE Trinidad – **THE STREET,** 8 Pro de Verteuil, Arima ☎ +1 868 628 1158 **FM:** 91.9 (Soca) – **U97.5 HOT LIKE PEPPER,** Couva ☎ +1 868 720 5858 **FM:** 97.5 (Asian) – **WACK FM,** 129C Coffee Street, San Fernando ☎ +1 868 652 4901 **W:** wackradio901fm.com **L.P:** CEO: Kenny Phillips. **FM:** 90.1

## TRISTAN DA CUNHA (UK)

**LT:** UTC — **Pop:** 260 — **Pr.L:** English — **E.C:** 50Hz, 220V — **ITU:** TRC

### TRISTAN BROADCASTING SERVICE (Gov.)
☑ The Administrator, Tristan da Cunha, So. Atlantic via Cape Town, South Africa. **E:** tristan.radio@yahoo.co.uk **L.P:** Head of Telecommunications: Andy Repetto.
**FM: Atlantic FM,** 93.5MHz 25W **D.Prgr:** Sun 1000-1200

**Other stations:**
Satellite relay of **BFBS 1** probably rebroadcast on 93.5MHz

## TUNISIA

**LT:** UTC +1h — **Pop:** 11 million — **Pr.L:** Arabic, French — **E.C:** 50Hz, 230V — **ITU:** TUN

### HAUTE AUTORITÉ INDÉPENDANTE DE LA COMMUNICATION AUDIOVISUELLE (HAICA)
☑ 50 Ave de l'Indépendance, Le Bardo 2000 ☎+216 7166 0177 **W:** haica.tn **E:** contact@haica.tn

### OFFICE NATIONAL DE LA TÉLEDIFFUSION (ONT)- RADIO TUNISIENNE (Gov.)
☑ Cité Ennassim 1 Montplaisir, B.P. 399, Tunis-Cedex-Tunisie ☎+216 71 188000 ▤+216 71 9042923 **W:** www.telediffusion.net.tn **E:** Ont@ telediffusion.net.tn

| MW | kHz | kW | Prgr. | Times |
|----|-----|----|-------|-------|
| Gafsa | 585 | 350 | N | 0400-2400 |
| Tunis | 630 | 300 | N | 24h |
| Medenine | 684 | 10 | N | 0400-2400 |
| Tunis | 963 | 100 | I | 24h |

| FM (MHz) | N | C | I | Y | kW |
|----------|---|---|---|---|-----|
| Ain Draham | 90.3 | 103.4 | 93.4 | 96.6 | 6 |
| Beni Khiar | 93.9 | 101.1 | 98.5 | 102.0 | 0.5 |
| Gabes | 95.5 | 93.3 | - | 90.2 | 1 |
| Gafsa (Biadha) | 104.6 | 105.4 | 101.8 | 95.0 | 50 |
| Gorrâa | 89.1 | 98.7 | 95.4 | 89.1 | 4 |

| FM (MHz) | N | C | I | Y | kW |
|---|---|---|---|---|---|
| Harkoussia | - | - | - | 92.5 | |
| Kasserine | 94.6 | 102.7 | 99.2 | 89.6 | 49 |
| Kchabta | 102.6 | 89.5 | 93.8 | 97.0 | |
| Kef Errand | 89.8 | 96.1 | 88.2 | 99.4 | |
| Ksour-Essaf | 102.0 | 103.7 | - | 92.5 | 1 |
| Remada | 88.9 | 99.9 | 93.4 | 90.3 | 80 |
| Sfax (Ghraba) | 93.0 | 103.0 | 99.5 | 93.0 | 60 |
| Souk Jomaa | 104.9 | 101.3 | 88.2 | 91.3 | 1 |
| Tataouine | 106.4 | 101.2 | - | 97.7 | 1 |
| Tozeur | 94.6 | 105.9 | - | 97.3 | 1 |
| Trozza | 105.9 | 87.7 | - | 90.8 | |
| Tunis | 105.3 | 101.1 | 98.2 | 88.6 | 1 |
| Zaghouan | 94.3 | 101.1 | 92.0 | 96.5 | 20 |
| Zarzis | 106.1 | 90.7 | 97.2 | 93.9 | 72 |

**National Channel (N)** in Arabic on MW & FM: 24h. **N.** on the h MW: radionationale.tn – **Cultural channel (C)** in Arabic: 1100-2400 on FM **W:** radionationale.tn – **R. Tunis Chaîne Internationale (RTCI) (I):** on 963kHz & FM: **French** 24h except English 1303-1330, Italian 1330-1400, Spanish 1903-1930, German 1930-2000 **W:** rtci.tn – **R. Jeunes** (Youth R.) **(Y):** 24h on FM **W:** radiojeunes.tn

**Regional stations (FM MHz): R. Gafsa,** Av. Habib Bourguiba, 2100 Gafsa **W:** radiogafsa.tn **FM:** Tozeur 89.2, Gafsa 91.8 40kW, Chambi 92.7 50kW, Sidi Bouzid 102.7 – **R. El Kef,** Rue Mongi Slim, 7100 El Kef **W:** radiokef.tn **FM:** Souk-Jomaa 90.0, 92.2 50kW, Ain Draham 90.3, Ghardimaou 94.1, Sidi Youssef 95.8, Sidi Salem 96.2, Le Kef 96.8, Nefta 99.6, Nebeur 100.1, Goraa 102.2, Siliana 103.1, Tabarka 106.7 – **R. Monastir,** Rue Farhat Hached, 5019 Monastir **W:**radiomonastir. tn **FM:** Harkoussia 95.7 2kW, Trozza 97.3 2kW, Beni Khiar 98.5 0.5kW, Sousse 99.0 1kW, Zaghouan 104.7 2kW, Monastir 106.1 1kW – **R. Panorama:** Tunis 92.5MHz **W:** facebook.com/RadioPanoramaTunisie – **R. Sfax,** Route de Menzel Chaker Road, 3058 Sfax **W:** radiosfax. tn **FM:** Djerba/Skhira 89.0, Ksour-Essaf 100.2, Trozza 100.8, Sfax 105.2 3kW, El Ghraba 106.6 – **R. Tataouine,** Cité 7 Novembre, 3263 Tataouine **W:** radiotataouine.tn **FM:** Zarzis 87.6 70kW, Tataouine 88.1 70kW, Techout 89.5, Medenine 95.8, Remda 96.6 80kW, Ghomrassen 102.6, Gabes 103.3, Djerba 105.7.
**Ann:** National Channel: "Huna Tunis, Idha'atu-I-Wataniya at-Tunisi-ya". Cultural Channel: "Huna idha'at-Tunis at-thakafiya". F: "Ici Radio Tunisie Internationale".

**Other stations, main networks (FM** MHz**):**
**Cap FM:** Kef-Errand 91.5, Sidi Abdessalem 95.2, Hammamet 105.6 **W:** capradio.tn – **I FM:** Sousse 93.4, Gafsa 96.8, El Kef 97.6, Tunis 100.6, Bizerte 107.3 **W:** ifm.tn – **Knooz FM:** Sousse/Hammamet/Zaghouan105.1,Mahdia/Monastir,98.0 **W:** knoozfm.net – **Nejma FM:** Zeramdine 88.4, 88.9 Sousse 95.9 **W:** nejmafm.com – **Oasis FM:** Gabès 96.5, Medenine 94.4 **W:** oasisfm.tn – **Ulysse FM:** Djerba 92.1, Zarzis 104.3 **W:** ulysse-fm.com – **R. Express FM:**Sousse 91.1, Bizerte 100.2, Tunis 103.6, Sfax 104.0, Monastir 104.5, Cap Bon 106.0. **W:** radioexpressfm.com – **R. Jawhara FM:** Kairouan 89.4, Tunis 90.7, Cap Bon 103.2, Chambi 104.4, Sousse 107.3 1kW. **W:** jawharafm.net – **R. Med:** Tunis 93.5, Zaghouan 100.0, Cap Bon 104.1 **W:** radiomed.tn – **R. MFM:** Sousse 94.7/105.5 **W:**facebook.com/RadioMfmTunisie – **R. Mosaïque FM:** Gafsa 88.2,Hammamet 88.9, Médenine 89.2, Sousse 90.1, Sidi Bou Said 90.3 0.1kW, Kasserine 91.1, Tozeur 92.3, Nabul 92.9, Tunis 94.9 5kW, Sfax 95.3, Nefta 101.4, Béja 105.8, Bizerte 106.8, Ain Deraham/Tataouine 107.0, Mehdia 107.5 **W:** mosaiquefm. net – **R. Oxygene FM:** Bizerte 90.0/104.5 **W:** oxygene.fm – **R. Sabra FM:** Kairouan 89.0, Monastir 98.8 **W:** radiosabrafm.net – **Shems FM:** Gafsa 88.7, Monastir 90.6, Sousse 93.7, Sfax 95.7, Sfax 96.2, Tunis 101.7, Cap Bon 106.5, Kairoun 107.0 **W:** shemsfm.net – **Zitouna FM:** Zaghouan 88.0 80kW, El Ghraba/Sfax 89.9 60kW, Nefta 91.4 1kW, Gorraa 92.2 3kW, Trozza 94.0 5kW, Tataouine 94.4 1kW, Ksour-Essaf 96.9, Zaghouan 97.6 80kW, Souk-Jomaa 97.8, Biadha 35 3 35 kW, Bizerte 99.1 5kW, Medenine 99.3, Gabes 99.8 1kW, Ain Draham 100.4 5kW, Zarzi 100.7 63kW, Kef Errand 100.9, Tozeur 102.3 1kW, Nabeul 102.9 7kW, Remada 103.4 80kW, Chambi 106.3, Sidi Bou Said 106.9 **W:** zitounafm.net

## TURKEY

**L.T:** UTC +3h — **Pop:** 80 million — **Pr.L:** Turkish — **E.C:** 50Hz, 220V — **ITU:** TUR

### SUPREME BOARD OF RADIO AND TELEVISION(RTÜK)
⊡ Bilkent Plaza B2 Blok, 06530 Bilkent/Ankara ☎+90 312 2975000 **W:** rtuk.gov.tr **E:** rtuk@rtuk.gov.tr **L.P:** Pres: Ilhan Yerlikaya.

### TÜRKIYE RADYO-TELEVIZYON KURUMU (TRT) (Pub) (Turkish Radio-Television Corporation)
⊡ TRT Genel Mudurlugu, Turan Günes Bulvarı, 06109 OR-AN, Ankara

☎+90 312 4634343 🖷 +90 312 4632335
**W:** radyo.trt.net.tr **E:** rdb@trt.net.tr
**L.P:** DG: Ibrahim Eren. Dep. DG (Eng.): Zeki Ciftci. Dep. DG (Admin): Erkan Durdu. Dep. DG (Broadc.): Tuncay Yürekli. Head of TV Dept: Osman Urgun. Head of Radio Dept: Ahmet Akçakaya. Head of Transmitters Dept: Yusuf Tashdemir.

| MW | kHz | kW | N | MW | kHz | kW | N |
|---|---|---|---|---|---|---|---|
| Mersin | 630 | 300 | 1/R/4 | Izmir | 927 | 200 | 1 |
| Çatalca* | ‡702 | 600 | 1 | Trabzon | 954 | 300 | 1/R |
| Antalya | 891 | 300 | 1/R | Diyarbakir | 1062 | 300 | K/A |

*) Istanbul (inactive). 1=TRT1, R=reg. prgr, K=Kurdish, A=Arabic: 1100-1500, 1700-1900 on 630kHz & 1500-1900 on 1062kHz.

| FM | TRT1 | TRT2 | TRT3 | TRT4 | Türkü | Nagme | kW |
|---|---|---|---|---|---|---|---|
| Adana (c) | 96.7 | 92.5 | 89.2 | 105.1 | 93.3 | | 30 |
| Adiyaman (d) | 88.8 | 94.4 | | 103.3 | 90.8 | | 30 |
| Afyon | 88.4 | 89.5 | | 94.0 | 107.7 | | 5/30 |
| Agri (e) | 88.2 | 92.2 | | 101.8 | 95.2 | | 30 |
| Amasya | 97.3 | 93.9 | 99.6 | 107.3 | | 98.9 | 30 |
| Ankara | 93.3 | 88.0 | 91.2 | 103.7 | 98.6 | 102.8 | 30 |
| Antalya (a) | 100.6 | 95.6 | 91.6 | | 88.4 | 92.1 | 30/1 |
| Antalya-Alanya (a) | 90.3 | 92.7 | | 94.4 | | | 5 |
| Antalya-Kas (a) | 88.1 | 90.5 | | 97.1 | | | 1/5 |
| Aydin | 88.8 | 92.0 | 97.6 | | 102.2 | 96.6 | 30/5 |
| Aydin-Kusadasi | 98.7 | 90.2 | 93.5 | 103.8 | | | 30 |
| Balikesir | 88.4 | 96.2 | | 101.7 | 106.5 | | 30 |
| Balikesir-Ayvalik | 88.4 | 90.4 | 95.4 | 103.5 | | | 5 |
| Bilecik | 97.1 | 99.1 | | 101.1 | 103.5 | | 5 |
| Bingöl (d) | 89.3 | 92.5 | | 97.6 | 99.6 | | 30 |
| Bitlis (d) | 98.0 | 94.2 | | 100.0 | 102.6 | | 5 |
| Bolu | 89.6 | 92.6 | 94.8 | 98.9 | | | 30/5 |
| Burdur (a) | 101.5 | 91.1 | | 90.1 | 105.8 | | 5 |
| Bursa | 87.9 | 98.9 | 91.1 | 95.2 | 95.5 | 99.5 | 30/5 |
| Çanakkale | 96.5 | 89.5 | | 106.3 | 101.1 | | 30 |
| Çankiri | 98.1 | 100.5 | | 103.0 | 106.3 | | 30 |
| Çorum | 105.7 | 103.7 | | 101.2 | 98.2 | | 5 |
| Denizli | 95.2 | 93.2 | 90.0 | 101.5 | | | 30/5 |
| Diyarbakir (d) | 98.4 | 95.5 | | 107.3 | 105.0 | | 30 |
| Edirne | 97.4 | 99.4 | | 103.7 | 105.8 | | 1/30 |
| Elazig (d) | 100.7 | 105.7 | | 102.2 | 107.5 | 91.1 | 30 |
| Erzincan (e) | 88.0 | 93.2 | 104.5 | 91.2 | | | 30 |
| Erzurum (e) | 90.8 | 98.8 | 96.8 | 102.6 | | | 30/5 |
| Erzurum-Oltu (e) | 95.6 | 93.6 | 99.9 | 101.9 | | | 5 |
| Eskisehir | 89.0 | 96.8 | 94.4 | 101.3 | | | 30 |
| Eskisehir-Sivrihisar | 90.2 | 98.4 | 96.2 | 104.4 | | | 30 |
| Gaziantep (c) | 92.0 | 97.6 | 95.2 | 101.9 | 96.3 | | 30 |
| Gümüshane (t) | 98.0 | 96.0 | 90.0 | 100.2 | | | |
| Hatay (c) | 90.1 | 92.5 | 95.3 | 89.6 | 87.6 | | 30/5 |
| Isparta (a) | 95.1 | 97.3 | 92.7 | 105.5 | 99.9 | 94.3 | 30 |
| Istanbul | 95.6 | 91.4 | 88.2 | 103.4 | | 101.6 | 100 |
| Izmir | 94.7 | 91.2 | 88.0 | 100.5 | | | 100/5 |
| Izmir-Ödemis | 92.9 | 97.9 | | | 87.8 | 95.8 | 5 |
| Izmir-Karaburun | 90.8 | 93.8 | 99.1 | | 101.6 | 88.7 | 100/5 |
| K.Maras (c) | 99.8 | 105.8 | | 87.8 | | 107.9 | 5 |
| K.Maras-Elbistan(c) | 91.4 | 96.4 | | 98.5 | 94.0 | | 30 |
| Karaman (c) | 96.4 | 98.6 | | | 90.8 | 106.5 | 30 |
| Kars (e) | 100.8 | 89.5 | | 91.3 | 103.3 | | 30 |
| Kastamonu | 104.0 | 91.5 | | 101.9 | 97.9 | | 30/5 |
| Kastamonu-Bozkurt | 101.5 | 97.5 | | | 103.5 | | 30 |
| Kayseri | 89.4 | 97.2 | 99.2 | 93.3 | 107.0 | 103.2 | 30 |
| Kilis (c) | 94.4 | 90.8 | | 98.3 | | 88.8 | 5 |
| Kirklareli | 94.5 | 90.0 | 103.4 | 92.0 | 105.6 | 98.5 | 110/30 |
| Kirklareli-Demirköy | 94.5 | 90.0 | 103.4 | 92.0 | 105.6 | | 30 |
| Kirsehir | 97.6 | 92.0 | | | 88.8 | 102.5 | 30 |
| Kocaeli-Gebze | 105.5 | 100.9 | 103.3 | 89.7 | | | 30 |
| Kocaeli-Izmit | 90.5 | 96.0 | 93.6 | 100.5 | | | 30/100 |
| Konya (c) | 103.2 | 90.5 | | 92.9 | 107.6 | | 30/5 |
| Konya-Aksehir | 89.2 | 95.8 | | | 92.4 | 101.0 | 5 |
| Kütahya | 90.2 | 95.4 | 92.1 | 88.1 | | | 30 |
| Malatya (d) | 101.3 | 103.7 | | 107.7 | 105.9 | 98.6 | 30 |
| Manisa | 92.1 | 93.1 | 98.9 | 103.7 | | | 30 |
| Mardin (d) | 91.4 | 104.5 | | 92.8 | 105.3 | | 5 |
| Mardin-Nusaybin(d) | 96.8 | 93.4 | 89.0 | 91.0 | | | 30 |
| Mersin-Icel (c) | 92.0 | 90.0 | 95.8 | 93.1 | 104.3 | 102.1 | 5 |
| Mersin-Silifke (c) | 97.0 | 88.8 | 94.4 | 90.8 | 102.2 | | 30/5 |
| Mugla-Bodrum | 94.6 | 99.3 | 89.4 | 100.3 | | 97.4 | 5 |
| Mugla-Datça | 95.8 | 107.1 | 102.9 | 92.6 | | | 5 |
| Mugla-Fethiye | 97.7 | 94.5 | 89.3 | 103.1 | | 93.7 | 5 |
| Mugla-Köycegiz | 105.1 | 99.8 | 95.4 | 92.8 | | | 30 |
| Mugla-Marmaris | 98.2 | 90.9 | 95.0 | 101.0 | | | 5 |
| Mugla-Yatagan | 88.8 | 92.0 | | 102.2 | | 96.6 | 30 |
| Mus (d) | 90.9 | 98.7 | | 105.9 | 102.7 | | 5 |
| Nevsehir-Avanos | 99.6 | 95.0 | 93.7 | 103.0 | 105.1 | | 5 |
| Nigde (c) | 90.0 | 95.6 | | 105.7 | 93.2 | | 30 |

| FM | TRT1 | TRT2 | TRT3 | TRT4 | Türkü | Nagme | kW |
|---|---|---|---|---|---|---|---|
| Ordu-Persembe (t) | 99.9 | 95.6 | 91.5 | 97.6 | | | 30 |
| Samsun (t) | 95.2 | 92.8 | 93.2 | 96.8 | | | 30 |
| Sanliurfa (d) | 98.1 | 102.5 | | 107.3 | 104.9 | | 5/30 |
| Sanliurfa-Suruc (d) | 97.1 | 100.3 | 90.0 | 105.5 | | | 30 |
| Siirt-Kurtalan (d) | 99.6 | 105.6 | | 101.6 | | | 30 |
| Sirnak (d) | 101.6 | | | | | | 30 |
| Sirnak-Cizre (d) | 101.9 | 97.7 | | 103.8 | | | 30 |
| Sivas | 93.6 | 98.3 | 90.4 | 100.9 | | | 30 |
| Trabzon (t) | 105.7 | 107.7 | | 90.0 | 103.7 | | 30 |
| Tunceli (d) | 91.5 | 93.7 | | 96.7 | 99.5 | 102.6 | 30 |
| Usak | 105.5 | 101.9 | | 95.7 | 98.7 | 98.5 | 30 |
| Van (d) | 94.8 | 89.3 | 92.8 | 100.3 | 93.8 | | 30/5 |
| Van-Özalp (d) | 93.2 | 91.2 | | 101.2 | 97.6 | | 5 |
| Yozgat | 98.0 | 96.0 | | 89.8 | 104.0 | | 5 |
| Zonguldak | 88.8 | 97.2 | 99.2 | 93.4 | 102.1 | | 5/30 |

+about 400 transmitters 1kW or less.

**1=Radyo Bir** (spoken word): 24h on FM. **MW:** 0300-1015 on 630/891/927/954kHz – **2=(TRT-FM)** (popular music): 24h in Turkish – **3=Radyo Üc** (classical music): 24h in Turkish exc. N. in English/French/German (3 min's each): 0403, 0703, 0903, 1203, 1403, 1703. Tourist Prgrs (3 min's each on Saturdays): English: 1615; French: 1415; German: 1915 – **4=Radyo Dört** (art & folk music): 24h on FM – **TRT Türkü** (Turkish folk music channel): 24h on FM (& 0300-2200 on 702 kHz) – **TRT Kurdî in Kurdish:** 0300-1500 on 1062kHz & 24h on **FM:** Adiyaman 88.4, Bingöl 90.2, Bitlis 90.6, Diyarbakir 88.4, Mardin 102.1, Mus 90.2, Siirt 103.6, Sirnak 94.5 & Van 102.3MHz – **TRT Radyo Haber:** news channel 24h in Ankara on 95.0MHz – **TRT Nagme** (Turkish Art Music Channel): 24h – **Regional prgrs** (Bölgesel R): via FM1 on txs near Antalya (a), Çukurova (c), Diyarbakir (d), Erzurum (e) and Trabzon (t) and on MW 630/891/954kHz inside TRT1 segment – **TRT Kent Radyo** (City R.): Izmir 99.1MHz, Ankara 105.6MHz & Istanbul 106.6MHz. 24h, r. TRT FM 2200-0400 – **Armenian Sce** on 106.3MHz: 0430-0500 & 1500-1530 **Ann:** TRT-1: "Burasi TRT Radyo Bir", TRT-4: "Burasi TRT Radyo Dört". Reg.: e.g. Antalya: "Burasi TRT Antalya Radyosu."

**EXTERNAL SERVICE: Voice of Turkey**
See International Radio section.

**Other stations; main networks:**

| FM (MHz) | 1) | 2) | 3) | 4) | 5) | 6) | 7) | 8) | 9) | 10) |
|---|---|---|---|---|---|---|---|---|---|---|
| Adana | 105.4 | 89.6 | 102.9 | 103.8 | 96.0 | 88.6 | 106.3 | 101.9 | 92.0 | 98.7 |
| Adiyaman | | | | | 92.0 | | | 100.5 | | 91.2 |
| Afyon | | 101.2 | | 90.4 | | 95.2 | | 96.2 | | 102.4 |
| Agri | | | | | | 100.4 | | 96.2 | | 104.7 |
| Aksaray | | 100.0 | | | 90.5 | 97.2 | 105.0 | | 107.3 |
| Aksehir | | | | | 104.5 | 105.0 | | | |
| Alanya | | | 100.0 | 89.3 | | 89.9 | 93.5 | | |
| Amasya | | 92.8 | | | | 101.6 | | | 89.1 |
| Ankara | 102.4 | 88.8 | 100.0 | 105.3 | 97.2 | 94.5 | 89.8 | 107.4 | 90.8 | 94.6 |
| Antalya | 90.2 | 89.7 | 100.0 | 89.3 | 102.6 | 90.9 | 101.2 | 95.3 | 94.2 | 95.8 |
| Ardahan | | | | | 95.5 | 98.0 | 99.0 | | 103.7 |
| Artvin | | | | | 100.4 | | 106.8 |
| Aydin | | | 92.3 | | 95.8 | | 91.1 | | 93.2 |
| Ayvalik | | | 98.3 | 93.6 | | | | |
| Balikesir | 98.7 | 88.8 | 100.0 | 90.7 | 93.6 | 94.3 | 97.2 | 88.5 | 100.8 | 99.6 |
| Bandirma | | 89.3 | | 107.7 | 106.2 | 107.0 | | 87.8 |
| Bartin | | | 95.5 | 98.4 | 100.0 | | 105.7 |
| Batman | | | | 95.0 | | 102.8 |
| Bayburt | | | 91.5 | | 95.0 | | 107.0 |
| Bilecik | | | | | 102.5 | | 96.0 |
| Bingöl | | | | | 103.3 | | 102.5 |
| Bitlis | | | | | 101.0 | | 106.3 |
| Bodrum | 104.8 | 103.5 | 89.2 | | | |
| Bolu | | 88.9 | 100.0 | 94.3 | 97.1 | 102.7 | 104.8 | 93.4 |
| Boyabat | | | | | 100.0 | | |
| Bucak | | | | | 100.0 | | |
| Burdur | | 93.5 | 92.0 | | 88.0 | 104.5 | | 93.8 |
| Bursa | 92.0 | 89.8 | 100.0 | 89.2 | 97.2 | 101.6 | 104.6 | 107.6 | 90.8 | 97.9 |
| Ceyhan | | | | | 107.7 | 88.9 | | |
| Çanakkale | | 88.0 | 89.3 | 99.5 | 105.3 | 101.0 | | 106.7 |
| Çankiri | | | 90.1 | | 92.8 | | 97.0 |
| Çesme | 89.6 | 89.3 | | | |
| Çorlu | | 100.0 | | | 91.3 | | 107.5 |
| Çorum | | | | 91.3 | 89.5 | | 90.7 |
| Demirci | | | | 104.6 | | |
| Denizli | | 88.0 | 100.0 | 89.3 | 96.0 | 107.7 | 96.8 | 90.8 | 90.5 |
| Develi | | | | | 102.0 | 99.0 |
| Diyarbakir | 92.0 | 89.8 | 100.3 | 92.3 | 91.2 | 90.4 | 98.0 | 101.0 | 97.5 | 88.0 |
| Düzce | 92.0 | | 96.3 | | 107.6 | | 93.4 |
| Edirne | | | 101.3 | 102.6 | 90.5 | 103.0 | 91.3 | 98.4 | 93.4 |

| FM (MHz) | 1) | 2) | 3) | 4) | 5) | 6) | 7) | 8) | 9) | 10) |
|---|---|---|---|---|---|---|---|---|---|---|
| Edremit | 89.7 | | | | | 90.7 | | 96.0 | | |
| Elazig | 89.9 | | | | | 104.4 | 92.4 | 94.1 | | 101.2 |
| Erzincan | | | | | | 89.5 | | 93.8 | | 107.2 |
| Erzurum | 91.8 | 90.4 | 100.7 | 89.3 | 103.5 | 94.6 | 91.5 | 94.0 | | 89.6 |
| Eskisehir | 88.6 | 100.0 | 100.5 | 89.3 | 97.2 | 92.6 | 106.3 | 106.6 | 98.6 | 89.6 |
| Fethiye | 102.0 | 88.2 | 100.3 | 96.7 | | | 99.0 | 98.5 | | |
| Gaziantep | 107.5 | 92.4 | 104.6 | 102.5 | 103.7 | 96.6 | 107.0 | 103.0 | 99.3 | 88.0 |
| Gerede | | | | | | 94.5 | 102.7 | 107.4 | | 90.5 |
| Giresun | 89.1 | | | | | 91.1 | | 93.0 | | 106.3 |
| Gümüshane | | | | | | 92.0 | | 102.5 | | 101.8 |
| Hakkari | | | | | | 98.0 | | 90.0 | | 91.8 |
| Hatay | | 105.5 | | | | 88.5 | 106.7 | 101.0 | | 99.5 |
| Igdir | | | | | | 95.5 | | 99.5 | | 89.8 |
| Iskenderun | | 101.3 | | | | | 94.6 | 95.6 | | 107.6 |
| Isparta | | 92.5 | | 91.8 | | 96.0 | | 100.0 | | 87.7 |
| Istanbul | 92.0 | 89.8 | 100.0 | 89.2 | 97.2 | 94.1 | 104.6 | 107.6 | 90.8 | 102.6 |
| Izmir | 96.2 | 89.6 | 100.0 | 89.3 | 97.2 | 96.7 | 101.3 | 96.9 | 90.8 | 98.8 |
| K.Maras | | 89.8 | | 89.0 | | 98.2 | | 94.0 | | 102.3 |
| Karaman | | | | | | | 103.9 | | | 96.1 |
| Kars | | 102.0 | | | | 90.6 | 104.6 | 102.7 | | 100.4 |
| Kastamonu | | | | | | 104.6 | 101.0 | | | 104.3 |
| Kayseri | 93.9 | 105.0 | 100.0 | 88.7 | 98.9 | | 100.2 | 88.5 | 96.2 | 106.7 |
| Kirikkale | | | | | | 105.5 | | 105.0 | | 94.0 |
| Kirklareli | | | | | | 89.8 | 107.6 | | | 100.3 |
| Kirsehir | | | | | | | 94.4 | | | 91.3 |
| Kocaeli | 92.0 | 89.8 | 100.0 | 89.2 | 100.7 | 90.7 | 104.6 | 107.6 | 90.8 | 99.5 |
| Konya | 95.1 | 89.9 | | 89.3 | 101.7 | 98.0 | 92.1 | 102.0 | 93.4 | 96.1 |
| Kusadasi | 104.5 | | 100.0 | 89.3 | | | | | | |
| Kütahya | | | | 91.3 | 97.2 | | 107.0 | 93.8 | 90.8 | 100.8 |
| Malatya | | 89.9 | 103.3 | 97.8 | 88.4 | 91.7 | 104.6 | 105.5 | 94.5 | 91.3 |
| Manisa | | 104.1 | | 89.1 | | | 101.3 | 103.3 | 105.4 | 94.3 |
| Mardin | | 89.0 | | | | | 104.0 | 95.0 | | 87.7 |
| Marmaris | 103.6 | 105.5 | 100.0 | 89.3 | | | | 93.0 | | |
| Mersin | | 93.5 | 105.0 | 90.3 | 94.0 | 94.5 | 103.0 | 105.3 | 97.4 | 103.5 |
| Mugla | 104.8 | | 100.3 | 89.3 | | 104.6 | 102.6 | 90.1 | 106.8 |
| Mus | | | | | | | | 102.0 | | 104.2 |
| Nevsehir | | | | | | | | 102.0 | | 91.3 |
| Nigde | 91.7 | | | | | 94.5 | | 103.0 | | 97.3 |
| Ordu | | | | | | | | 92.5 | | 96.5 |
| Osmaniye | | 89.6 | | | | 98.4 | 99.9 | 101.7 | 100.5 | 89.4 |
| Rize | | | | | | | | 102.5 | | 105.3 |
| Sakarya | 101.3 | 88.0 | 100.7 | 101.8 | 91.2 | | 104.6 | 107.8 | 97.8 | 91.5 |
| Samsun | 99.7 | 106.2 | 100.0 | 88.0 | | | 94.1 | 103.0 | 96.3 | 105.8 |
| Sanliurfa | | 104.4 | | | | 92.0 | 93.5 | 105.4 | 103.6 |
| Siirt | | | | | | | 91.0 | | | 102.8 |
| Sinop | | | | | 94.3 | | 99.0 | | | 107.4 |
| Sivas | 96.2 | | | | | 91.0 | 100.1 | | | 92.3 |
| Sivrihisar | | | | | | 97.5 | | 94.9 | | 89.3 |
| Tekirdag | 96.2 | 90.1 | | 90.3 | 96.0 | | 104.6 | 105.4 | 91.8 | 95.2 |
| Tokat | | | | | | | 98.0 | 96.0 | | 97.7 |
| Trabzon | | 100.4 | | 89.3 | | 94.6 | 93.0 | 102.8 | 90.3 | 92.5 |
| Tunceli | | | | | | 94.5 | | 104.0 | | 106.2 |
| Usak | | | | | | 106.0 | | 99.0 | | 107.5 |
| Van | | 97.5 | | | | 104.6 | 96.0 | | 103.3 |
| Yalova | | | | | 94.1 | | | | 102.6 |
| Yozgat | | | | | | | 102.0 | 100.4 | | 106.6 |
| Zile | | | | | | | 98.0 | 96.4 | | |
| Zonguldak | 96.0 | | 90.0 | | | 104.6 | 107.0 | 91.0 | 94.1 |

**Addresses & other information:**
**1) Kral FM** ✉ Ahi Evran Cad. No 3, 34398 Maslak-Sisli-Istanbul ☎+90 212 3350000 **W:** kralfm.com.tr – **2) Show R.** ✉ Ust Zeren Sokak No 40, Levent-Besiktas-Istanbul ☎+90 212 3850000 **W:** show-radyo.com.tr – **3) Power FM** ✉ Gumusyolu Cad. Kusbakisi Sk. No 43, Altunizade-Uskudar-Istanbul ☎+90 216 5540400 **W:** powerfm.com. tr – **4) Alem FM** ✉ Ayazaga Mah. Kemerburgaz Yolu Cendere Mevkii No 29, Sisli-Istanbul ☎+90 212 3318888 **W:** alemfm.com – **5) Metro FM** ✉ Büyükdere Cad. No 23, CEM Is Merkezi Kat. 4, Istanbul ☎+90 212 3686200 **W:** metrofm.com.tr – **6) Polis Radyosu** ✉ Necatibey Caddesi No. 108, Anittepe-Ankara ☎+90 312 2306181 **W:** polis-radyosu.net – **7) Radyo 7** ✉ Defterdar Mah. Otakcilar Cad. No 78, Eyup-Istanbul ☎+90 212 4378585 **W:** radyo7.com – **8) Akra FM** ✉ Barbaros Mah. Mutevelli Cesme Cad. No 21, Uskudar-Istanbul ☎+90 216 3252265 **W:** akradyo.net – **9) Super FM** ✉ Büyükdere Cad. Cem Is Merkezi No:23,Sisli/Istanbul ☎+90 212 3686200 **W:** superfm.com. tr – **10) Diyanet Radyo** (Gov.) ✉ Üniversiteler Mah. Dumlupınar Bulv. No : 147/A 06800 Çankaya/Ankara ☎+90 2957443 **W:** diyanetradyo. com - **Diyanet Kuran R.: W:** diyanetkuranradio.com **FM:** Ankara 88.2, Istanbul 97.4, Izmir 90.3, Adana 106.6, Gaziantep 99.7 & Konya 88.2 + 76 more transmitters - **Diyanet Risalet R.: W:** risaletradyo.com **E:** bilgi@risaletradyo.com **FM:** Ankara 94.0, Istanbul 95.1, Izmir 104.5,

Konya 94.6, Sivas 102.8, Manisa 107.8, Gaziantep 107.8, Tekirdag 106.7, Trabzon 96.7, Canlıurfa 95.9, Samsun 101.3, Eskisehir 102.9, Malatya 100.2, Diyarbakır 101.9, Adana 107.0, Balıkesir 104.7, Antalya 107.8, Aydin 104.8, Bolu 101.8, Bursa 97.4, Canakkale 105.0, Denizli 101.2, Edirne 98.8, Elazig 103.2, Erzurum 106.5, Hatay 103.7, K.Maras 98.7, Kayseri 107.7, Kocaeli 107.9, Mardin 94.3, Mersin 105.9, Mugla 88.5, Ordu 104.8, Sakarya 87.8, Van 99.4.

**CRI Türk FM:** on FM in 11 metropolitan centres. **W:** criturk.fm
In addition there are about 30 national, 100 regional and 1000 local stations in operation on FM.

### AFN INCIRLIK AIR BASE BROADCASTING STN (Mil.)
☎+90 322 3166421 **W:** incirlik.afneurope.net **E:** 39abw.pa@incirlik. af.mil **MW:** 1593kHz 5W. **FM:** 107.1MHz on cable

## TURKMENISTAN

**L.T:** UTC +5h — **Pop:** 5.5 million — **Pr.L:** Turkmen — **E.C:** 220V/50Hz — **ITU:** TKM

### TELEWIDENIÝE, RADIOGEPLESIKLER WE KINE-MATOGRAFIÝA BARADAKY DÖWLET KOMITETI
**(State Committee for TV, Radio and Cinematography)**
⌨ Magtymguly kôçesi 89, 744000 Asgabat ☎ +993 12 351515 🖷 +993 12 394470 **L.P:** Chmn: A. Kakaýewi

| LW/MW | kHz | kW | Prgr | | kHz | kW | Prgr |
|-------|-----|-----|------|---|-----|-----|------|
| Asgabat° | 279 | 150 | 1 | Serhetabat° | 1080 | 5 | 1 |
| Asgabat° | 576 | 150 | 2/3 | Asgabat° | 1125 | 20 | 1 |
| Türkmenbasy° | 675 | 10 | 2/3 | Syrtagta° | 1233 | 40 | 1 |
| Etrek° | 720 | 1 | 1 | Dasoguz° | 1233 | 5 | 1 |
| Ýokarça° | 720 | 1 | 1 | Türkmenbasy° | 1476 | 10 | 1 |
| Türkmenabat° | 927 | 50 | 1 | °) Status uncertain | | | |

| FM (MHz) | 1 | 2/3 | 4 | kW |
|----------|-----|------|-----|-----|
| Arçabyl | 102.3 | - | 100.3 | 4 |
| Asgabat | 103.2 | 104.4 | 101.3 | 4 |
| Atamyrat | 102.8 | - | 100.3 | 4 |
| Baharly | 101.6 | 104.1 | - | 4 |
| Balkanabat | 100.4 | 101.9 | 103.9 | 1 |
| Boldumsaz | 105.6 | 106.9 | 104.0 | 4 |
| Dasoguz | 100.7 | 103.0 | 100.1 | 1 |
| Magdanly | 104.2 | 106.7 | 102.2 | 4 |
| Mary | 103.2 | 104.4 | 102.3 | 4 |
| Türkmenabat | 104.4 | 106.0 | 100.8 | 4 |
| Türkmenbasy | 100.2 | 101.7 | 100.8 | 10 |
| Uly Balkan Gersi | - | - | 103.0 | 4 |

+ translators

**D.Prgr: Prgr 1 (Watan):** 24h — **Prgr 2 (Çar tarapdan):** 0200-0400, 0700-0900, 1400-1700 — **Prgr 3 (Miras):** 0400-0700, 0900-1400, 1700-2300. — **Prgr 4 (Owaz):** 24h. N. in English 0000, Turkmen 0100, Russian 0200; continues in 3h cycles.

**DAB Transmitters** (DAB+)
**Tx Operator:** Ministry of Communications **M:** Watan, Çar tarapdan, Miras, Owaz **Txs:** Block 7B & 13B (Asgabat 3.1kW)

## TURKS & CAICOS ISLANDS (UK)

**L.T:** UTC -5h (10 Mar–3 Nov: -4h) — **Pop:** 36,000 — **Pr.L:** English — **E.C:** 60Hz, 110/220/440V — **ITU:** TCA

### RADIO TURKS & CAICOS (Gov. Comm.)
⌨ Unit 8, Pond Breeze Plaza, Good St., Grand Turk ☎ +1 649 946 2455 🖷 +1 649 946 1600 **W:** rtc89fm.com **L.P:** Dir. Christopher Jarret **FM:** 89.1MHz
**D.Prgr:** 24h Local prgr: 1100-0300; at other times relays country satellite stn.
**Ann:** "This is Radio Turks & Caicos on Grand Turk, Turks & Caicos Islands"
**F.pl.:** New channel - Radio 2

### WIV FM RADIO LTD (Comm.)
⌨ WIV Building, Leeward Highway, Box 324, Providenciales ☎ +1 649 333 4487 **FM: PraiseHim FM** 90.5MHz (Gospel) – **Island FM** 93.9MHz (Island music) – **KISS FM** 102.5MHz (Light rock) – **Power 92** 92.5MHz (Hit music)

### CONNOLLY PRODUCTIONS (Comm.)
⌨ Tropicana Plaza, Leeward Highway, PO Box 63, Providenciales ☎ +1 649 941 7264 **W:** 88jamz.com
**FM: Jamz** 88.7MHz – **Smooth FM** 88.1MHz

### OTHER STATIONS (FM in MHz):
**FAITH FM – ROCK OF JESUS NETWORK**, Safe Heaven, Five Cays,

---

Providenciales ☎ +1 649 941 5451. FM 98.9 – **RADIO EXAMPLE OF CHRIST**, Bottle Creek, PO Box 1095, Five Cays, Providenciales ☎ +1 649 941 7532 **W:** radioexampleofchrist.org FM 95.1 – **TROPICAL VIBES**, Leeward Highway, Stubbs Rd, Providenciales ☎ +1 649 243 0101 FM 103.5/105.5 (0.5kW) – **RADIO VHTC**, Box 262, Providenciales. W: radiovhtc.com FM 91.5 (0.25kW) Relays Radio Vision 2000, Haiti, at night – **ZVIC (Victory In Christ)**, Butterfield, PO Box 32, Providenciales. FM 96.7.

## TUVALU

**L.T:** UTC +12h — **Pop:** 10,024 — **Pr.L:** Tuvaluan, English — **E.C:** 50Hz, 240V (Funafuti only) — **ITU:** TUV

### TUVALU MEDIA DEPARTMENT (Gov.)
⌨ Private Mail Bag, Vaiaku, Funafuti ☎ +688 20139 🖷 + 688 20732 **L.P:** GM Melali Taape **Prgr Prod:** Ms Afasene Pese, Head of Tech. Sces: John Sammons
**E:** meltaape@govt.tv, apese@govt.tv
**MW: Radio Tuvalu AM:** 621kHz 5kW Funafuti (24h nationwide)
**FM:** Funafuti (local coverage) 100.1MHz 0.02kW
**D.Prgr:** 1830-2000, 2325-0100, 0625-1000 daily. **N. in English:** 1910, 0710 **Ann:** "This is Radio Tuvalu" **V.** by letter
**BBC Pacific stream** via satellite from London at other times: 2000-2325, 0100-0625, 1000-1830

## UGANDA

**L.T:** UTC +3h — **Pop:** 42 million — **Pr.L:** Luganda, Swahili, English — **E.C:** 50Hz, 240V — **ITU:** UGA

### UGANDA COMMUNICATIONS COMMISSION (UCC)
⌨ 12th Floor, Communications House, Plot 1, Colville Street, P. O. Box 7376, Kampala ☎+256 41 4339000 🖷 +256 41 4348832
**W:** ucc.co.ug **E:** ucc@ucc.co.ug

### UGANDA BROADCASTING CORPORATION(UBC, Pub.)
⌨ P.O. Box 2038, Plot 17-19, Nile Ave, Kampala ☎+256 41 4257034 🖷 + 256 41 4257252 **W:** ubc.ug **E:** customerservice@ubc. ug **L.P:** Chmn: Chris B. Katuramu. Man. Dir: Musinguzi Mugasa. Commissioners: Radio Broadc: Jack Turyamwijuka. Ag. Contr. of Prgrs (Radio): Charles Byekwaso. Ag. Principal Eng. (Radio): Yona Hamala.

| MW | kHz | kW | Ch. |
|-----|-----|-----|-----|
| Mityana | 576 | 100 | UBC West/Star FM |
| Kampala | ‡909 | 20 | West Nile FM (inactive) |
| Kabale | ‡999 | 100 | UBC R. (inactive) |

| FM (MHz) | UBC R. | West | Butebo | Star FM | Magic |
|----------|--------|------|--------|---------|-------|
| Fort Portal | - | 98.8 | - | - | - |
| Hoima | - | 99.1 | - | - | - |
| Jinja | - | - | - | 95.7 | - |
| Kabale | - | 93.7 | - | - | - |
| Kampala | 98.0 | 107.5 | 107.3 | 87.5 | 100.0 |
| Kisoro | - | 97.7 | - | - | - |
| Lira | 100.0 | - | - | - | - |
| Masaka | - | 99.5 | - | 96.9 | - |
| Mbale | - | - | 96.9 | - | - |
| Mbarara | - | 97.4 | - | - | - |
| Masindi | - | 105.0 | - | - | - |
| Soroti | - | - | 96.7 | - | - |

**UBC R.** in English, Swahili, Luo and Nubian: 24h – **UBC West** in 5 ethnic languages: 0300-2105 – **Butebo Channel** in 11 ethnic languages – **Star FM** in Luganda. **Magic FM** in English.
**Buruli FM** in 5 ethnic languages: Nakasongola 107.0MHz.
**Mega FM** in Luo/others: Gulu 102.1, Moro 103.1MHz 2kW.
**Ngeya FM** in 5 languages: Kasese 101.5MHz.
**Vo Bundibugyo:** Bundibugyo 93.3MHz.
**West Nile FM:** Arua 94.1MHz.

### Other stations (FM MHz):
**African R,** Kampala: 104.5 – **All Karamoja FM,** Moroto: 94.7 – **Arua One FM,** Arua: 88.7 2kW – **Bamboo FM,** Jinja: 107.6 – **Basoga Bainho,** Jinja: 87.7 – **Beat FM,** Kampala: 96.3 – **Bob FM,** Kampala: 92.7 **W:** facebook.com/927BobFM – **Buddu BS,** Masaka: 98.8 – **Bukedde FM:** Kampala 100.5, Masaka 106.8 **W:** bukedde. co.ug – **Bunyoro BS,** Masindi: 98.2 – **Busiro FM,** Kakiri: 107.5 – **Busoga FM,** Jinja: 96.0 – **Campus FM,** Kampala: 106.6 – **Capital FM:** Kampala 91.3, Mbale 90.9, Mbarara 88.7 – **City FM,** Kampala: 98.1 – **Continental FM,** Kumi: 94.7 – **Dembe FM,** Kampala: 90.4 – **Dunamis FM,** Kampala: 103.0 – **East Africa R,** Kampala: 99 (of Tanzania) – **Eastern Voice,** Bugiri: 102.3 – **Elgon FM,** Kapchorwa

89.2 – **Etop R,** Soroti: 99.4 – **Eye FM,** Iganga: 98.8 – **Impact & Alpha FM:** Mbale 98.5, Masaka 101.5 1kW, Kampala 102.1 4kW. **W:** victoryuganda.org – **Juice FM,** Kampala: 103.4 **W:** facebook.com/1034-JUICE-FM-Sports-542359682519594 – **Kaboozi R. Two,** Kampala: 87.9 **W:** akaboozi.fm – **Kibaale Community R:** 91.7 – **Kiira FM,** Jinja: 88.6 – **Kings R,** Masindi 88.2 – **Liberty FM,** Hoima 89.0 – **Maranatha FM,** Jinja: 104.7 – **Mbale FM:** 90.1 – **Nile BS,** Jinja: 89.4 – **Open Gate FM,** Mbale: 103.2 – **Power FM,** Kampala: 104.1 – **Prime R,** Kampala: 91.9 – **R FM,** Iganga: 91.1 **W:** rfm.co.ug – **R. Apac,** Apac 92.9 0.4kW, Odokomit 106.5 0.1kW **W:** radioapac.tripod.com – **R. KFM,** Kampala: 93.3 **W:** kfm.co.ug – **R. Kitara,** Masindi: 101.8 – **Kyoga Veritas R,** Soroti: 91.5 1kW. **W:** facebook.com – **R. Lira,** Lira: 95.3 – **R. Mama,** Kampala: 101.7. **W:** interconnection.org/umwa/community_radio.html – **R. Maria Uganda,** Masaka 94 40W, Masindi 93.4 40W, Fort Portal 104.6, Mbarara 105.4. **W:** radiomaria.org – **R. One,** Kampala: 90.0 – **R. Pacis,** Arua: 90.9/94.5 1kW. **W:** radiopacis.org – **R. Paidha,** Nebbi: 87.8 – **R. Rukungiri:** 96.9 – **R. Rupiny:** Kampala 95.7, Lira 98.1 **W:** visiongroup.co.ug – **R. Sapientia,** Kampala: 94.4 5kW. **W:** radiosapientia.com – **R. Simba,** Kampala: 97.3 **W:** simba.fm – **R. Skynet,** Mityana: 96.9 – **R. Unity,** Lira: 97.7 – **R. Wa,** Lira: 89.4 – **R. West FM:** Mbarara 102.2, Tooro 91.0, Kabale & Masak – **Rhino FM,** Lira: 96.1 – **Rock Mamba FM,** Tororo 106.8 – **Safari FM,** Mayuge 103.9 – **Sanyu FM,** Kampala 88.2 – **Speak FM,** Gulu 89.5 **W:** fowode. org – **Spirit FM,** Mukono: 96.6 – **Ssuubi FM,** Kampala 104.9, Masaka 88.1. **W:** ssuubifmradio.com – **Star FM,** Kampala: 100.0 – **Step FM,** Mbale: 99.8 – **Super FM,** Kampala: 88.5 – **Truth FM,** Mbale: 105.3 – **VO Africa:** Kampala 92.3 – **VO Kigezi,** Kabale 89.5 – **VO Life,** Arua: 100.9 **W:** vol-radio.net – **VO Teso,** Soroti: 88.4 – **Top R,** Kampala: 89.6 – **VO Toro,** Kampala 100.5, Fort Portal 101.0, Mbarara 95.0, Mubende 97.5 – **Touch FM,** Kampala: 95.9 1kW. **W:** touch.fm – **X FM:** Kampala: 94.8, Mbarara 96.6 **W:** xfm.co.ug .

**BBC African Sce:** Arua 99.4, Kampala 101.3, Mbale/Mbarara 107.3MHz in English/Swahili/Kinyarwanda.
**RFI Afrique:** Kampala 93.7MHz in French/English/Swahili.

## UKRAINE

**L.T:** UTC +2h (31 Mar-27 Oct: +3h); Crimea and Donets Basin (de facto): UTC +3h — **Pop:** 44.4 million — **Pr.L:** Ukrainian, Russian — **E.C:** 230V/50Hz — **ITU:** UKR

### NATSIONALNA RADA UKRAINY Z PYTAN TELEBACHENNIA I RADIOMOVLENNIA
**(National Council of Television and Radio Broadcasting in Ukraine)**
✉ vul. Prorizna 2, 01001 Kyiv ☎ +380 44 2787575 🖷 +380 44 2787575 **E:** presa@nrada.gov.ua **W:** nrada.gov.ua
**L.P:** Chmn: Yurii Artemenko

### DERZHAVNYI KOMITET TELEBACHENNIA I RADIOMOVLENNIA UKRAINY (DERZHTELERADIO)
✉ vul. Prorizna 2, 01001 Kyiv ☎ +380 44 2785349 🖷 +380 44 2791170 **E:** pr@comin.gov.ua **W:** comin.kmu.gov.ua
**L.P:** Chmn: Oleh Nalyvaiko

### NATSIONALNA SUSPILNA TELERADIOKOMPANIIA UKRAINY (NSTU) (Pub)
✉ vul. Khreshchatyk 26, 01001 Kyiv ☎ +380 44 2396224 **E:** press@suspilne.media **W:** suspilne.media; nrcu.gov.ua **L.P:** Chmn: Zurabi Alasaniia

| MW | kHz | kW | Prgr | MW | kHz | kW | Prgr |
|---|---|---|---|---|---|---|---|
| Mykolaiv (Luch) | 549 | 400 | 1 | Chasiv Yar | 873 | 25 | 1 |

| FM (MHz) | 1* | 2 | 3 | kW |
|---|---|---|---|---|
| Andriivka | 103.4v | 71.90 | - | 5/1 |
| Antopil | 87.8q | 67.46 | 66.52 | 1 |
| Bakhmutivka | 92.4l | - | - | 1 |
| Bershad | 105.1t | - | 71.93 | 1 |
| Cherkasy | 91.4b | 70.64 | - | 1 |
| Chernivtsi | 91.8c | 67.19 | - | 0.25/1 |
| Dnipro | 87.5d | - | 66.74 | 0.5/1 |
| Dubovyi Hai | 104.2v | - | - | 1 |
| Horokhiv | 106.5u | - | - | 1 |
| Ivano-Frankivsk | 71.24g | - | - | 1 |
| Izium | 102.5g | - | 70.46 | 0.25/1 |
| Kharkiv | 67.13h | 67.91 | 91.6 | 2x1/0.1 |
| Kherson | 100.6i | - | 70.01 | 5/1 |
| Khmelnytskyi | 104.6k | 70.46 | - | 1 |
| Kholmy | 106.1a | 68.27 | - | 0.5/1 |
| Khust | 101.2w | 71.90 | - | 0.1/1 |
| Kostianynivka | 90.0d | - | - | 1 |
| Krasnohorivka | 106.3p | 68.60 | - | 3/4 |

| FM (MHz) | 1* | 2 | 3 | kW |
|---|---|---|---|---|
| Kropyvnytskyi | 91.2j | 68.84 | - | 0.25/1 |
| Kryvyi Rih | 90.4e | - | 69.56 | 0.1/1 |
| Kulchiivtsi | 70.76k | 72.89 | - | 1 |
| Kyiv | 105.0 | 71.30 | °72.98 | 5/5/4 |
| Lozova | 87.7s | 71.75 | - | 0.25/1 |
| Lviv | 103.3m | 68.99 | 67.04 | 0.5/2x1 |
| Liubeshiv | 107.8u | - | 105.2 | 0.1/1 |
| Lutsk | 88.3u | 72.08 | 101.9 | 0.5/0.1/1 |
| Mariupol | 107.3g | - | 69.44 | 0.25/1 |
| Melitopol | 107.7x | - | 66.14 | 0.25/1 |
| Mykolaiv | 92.0n | - | 71.78 | 0.5/1 |
| Odesa | 70.52o | - | 72.14 | 2/1 |
| Olevsk | 100.2v | 69.80 | - | 1 |
| Ovruch | 104.2v | - | - | 2 |
| Pervomaisk | 105.9n | - | 68.03 | 0.1/1 |
| Petrovirivka | 68.99o | - | - | 1 |
| Pidhorivka | 71.66l | - | - | 1 |
| Podilsk | 103.6o | - | 69.35 | 0.5/1 |
| Poltava | 101.8p | 73.88 | - | 1/0.1 |
| Shatsk | 101.5u | - | - | 1 |
| Shostka | 107.8r | 67.49 | - | 1 |
| Shykoryi | 106.9l | - | - | 1 |
| Trostianets | 104.1r | 69.92 | - | 0.5/1 |
| Uzhhorod | 103.0w | 71.54 | - | 0.5/1 |
| Vasylivka | 105.8i | - | - | 5 |
| Vinnytsia | 88.6t | 68.57 | 71.69 | 0.5/1/3 |
| Volnovakha | 88.7d | - | - | 1 |
| Volochysk | 68.72k | - | - | 4 |
| Zaporizhia | 103.7x | - | - | 1 |
| Zarichne | 103.5w | - | - | 1 |

+ sites with only txs below 1kW. * Incl. reg prgrs (a-x, see below) °) Also carries reg. prgr "Holos Kyieva" (vul. Melnikova 42, 04119 Kyiv. **E:** 1kdrtvk@ukr.net)

**D.Prgr: Prgr 1 (Pershyi kanal):** 24h. – **Prgr 2 (Promin):** 24h. – **Prgr 3 (Kultura):** 24h.
**International Service (R. Ukraine Int.):** see Intern. Radio section.

**NSTU Regional Services**
**D.Prgr:** 0510-0600, 1010-1100, 1510-1600, 1810-1850 on FM freqs of Prgr 1 (exc. f - see below). **a) Chernihivska obl.:** pr. Peremohy 62, 14000 Chernihiv **E:** tvodtrk@ukr.net. Reg: "R. Siver-Tsentr"/"Chernihivska khvylia" – **b) Cherkaska obl.:** vul. B.Vishnevetskoho 35/1, 18022 Cherkasy **E:** rosradio@ua.fm. Reg: "R. Ros" – **c) Chernivetska obl.:** vul. Holovna 91, 58001 Chernivtsi **E:** bukdtrk-net@ukr.net. Reg: "R. Bukovyna" – **d+e) Dnipropetrovska obl.: d)** vul. Televiziina 3, 49010 Dnipro **E:** dodtrk@email.ua. Reg: "Dnipropetrovske oblasne R." **e)** vul. Annenka 2, 50099 Kryvyi Rih **E:** kdt@kdtro.com. ua. Reg: "Kryvorizhia" – **f) Donetska obl.:** vul. Shkadinova 48, 84313 Kramatorsk. **E:** dogtrk3@gmail.com. Reg "Holos Donbasu" 24h on (MHz) 87.9 (Bakhmut 0.3kW), 88.0 (Bakhmutivka 0.3kW & Mariupol 0.2kW), 90.4 (Kramatorsk 0.2kW), 95.3 (Yelizavetivka 0.1kW), 95.7 (Avdiivka 0.1kW), 100.3 (Volnovakha 0.1kW) – **g) Ivano-Frankivsk obl.:** vul. Sichovykh striltsiv 30a, 76000 Ivano-Frankivsk **E:** ifodtrk@gmail.com. Reg: "Ivano-Frankivske Oblase R."/"Karpaty FM" – **h) Kharkivska obl.:** vul. Chernyshevska 22, 61002 Kharkiv. **E:** oblradio_kharkiv@ukr. net. Reg: "Hovoryt Kharkiv" – **i) Khersonska obl.:** vul. Perekopska 10, 73000 Kherson **E:** kbersonodtrk@skifiya.ks.ua. Reg: "R. Tavria"/"R. Skifia" – **j) Kirovohradska obl.:** pl. Heroiv Maidanu 1, 25022 Kropyvnytskyi **E:** tvkirovograd@gmail.com. Reg: "R. Skifia-Tsentr" – **k) Khmelnytska obl.:** vul. Volodymyrska 92, 29000 Khmelnytskyi **E:** office@odtrk.km.ua. Reg: "Hovoryt Khmelnytskyi"/"R. Podillia-Tsentr" – **l) Luhanska obl.:** vul. Vilesova 1v, 93400 Severodonetsk. **E:** lgtrk@ukrpost.ua. Reg 1: "Luhanske Oblasne R." on NSTU Prgr 1 freqs; Reg 2: "Puls FM" 0400-2000 on (MHz) 89.3 (Stantsia Luhanska 0.2kW), 95.8 (Bakhmutivka 0.25kW), 99.5 (Shyrokyi 0.5kW), 100.1 (Zorynivka 0.1kW), 100.6 (Pidhorivka 1kW), 101.9 (Bilolutsk 0.1kW), 102.1 (Troitske 0.25kW & Bilovodsk 0.25kW), 102.9 (Markivka 0.25kW), 103.5 (Sosnovyi 0.25kW), 105.9 (Lysychansk 1kW) – **m) Lvivska obl.:** vul. Vysokyi Zamok 4, 79008 Lviv **E:** lodtrk12@gmail.com. Reg: "Lvivske oblasne R." – **n) Mykolaivska obl.:** pr. Tsentralyi 24-b, 54029 Mykolaiv **E:** mksuspilne@gmail.com. Reg: "R. Mykolaiv" – **o) Odeska obl.:** Fontanska doroha 3, 65963 Odesa **E:** odt@ukr.net. Reg: "Odeske Oblasne Derzhave R." – **p) Poltavska obl.:** vul. R.Kyrychenko 1, 36014 Poltava **E:** info@ltava.poltava.ua. Reg: "R. Ltava" – **q) Rivnenska obl.:** vul. Kotliarevskoho 20-a, 33028 Rivne **E:** rodtrk@ukr.net. Reg: "Rivne FM" – **r) Sumska obl.:** vul. Petropavlivska 125, 40030 Sumy **E:** trksumy@ukr. net. Reg: "Sloboda-FM"/"R. Sumy"/"R. Sumshchyny" – **s) Ternopilska obl.:** bul. T.Shevchenka 17, 46021 Ternopil **E:** todtrk@poshta.te.ua. Reg: "R. Lad"/"Ternopilske Oblasne R." – **t) Vinnytska obl.:** vul. Teatralna 15, 21100 Vinnytsia **E:** trk_vintera@ukr.net. Reg: "Hovoryt Vinnytsia" – **u) Volynska obl.:** vul. Slovatskoho 9, 43025 Lutsk **E:** voltv.lutsk@gmail.com. Reg: "R. Lutsk" – **v) Zhytomyrska obl.:** vul. Liubarska 1a,

10014 Zhytomyr **E:** 103fm@ukr.net. Reg: "Zhytomyrska khvylia" – **w)**
**Zakarpatska obl.:** Kyivska nab. 18, 88018 Uzhhorod **E:** tisafm@gmail.com. Reg: "Tysa FM" – **x) Zaporizka obl.:** vul. Matrosova 24, 69057 Zaporizhia **E:** zdtrk@zp.ukrtel.net. Reg: "R. Zaporizhia".

## ARMIIA FM (Mil)

✉ vul. Hrushevskoho 30, 01021 Kyiv ☎ +380 50 3049407 **E:** army-fm@ukr.net **W:** www.armyfm.com.ua **L.P:** Dir: Yana Kholodna

| FM | MHz | kW | FM | MHz | kW |
|---|---|---|---|---|---|
| Bakhmutivka | 90.8 | 1 | Chonhar | 103.0 | 1 |

+ txs below 1kW.
**D.Prgr:** 24h.

## OTHER STATIONS

| FM | MHz | kW | Location | Station |
|---|---|---|---|---|
| 30) | 67.82 | 1 | Lviv | R. Emmanuil |
| 55) | 68.24 | 4 | Antopil | R. Maria |
| 56) | 68.36 | 5 | Odesa | R. M |
| 18) | 69.02 | 1 | Kyiv | Yaskave R. |
| 55) | 69.68 | 1 | Kyiv | R. Maria |
| 30) | 69.92 | 1 | Zaporizhia | R. Emmanuil |
| 27) | 70.40 | 4 | Kyiv | Hromadske R. |
| 55) | 70.91 | 2 | Vinnytsia | R. Maria |
| 18) | 72.47 | 4 | Vinnytsia | Yaskave R. |
| 41) | 87.5 | 1 | Odesa | Pershe R. FM1 |
| 3) | 87.9 | 1 | Odesa | R. NV |
| 19) | 88.0 | 1 | Kharkiv | Russkoye R. Ukraina |
| 17) | 88.5 | 1 | Dnipro | Relax FM |
| 1B) | 88.5 | 1 | Odesa | Retro FM |
| 7) | 89.0 | 1 | Ternopil | Kiss FM |
| 10) | 89.7 | 1 | Odesa | Europa Plus |
| 14) | 90.2 | 1 | Odesa | R. Roks Ukraina |
| 1C) | 90.3 | 1 | Sumy | Nashe R. |
| 3) | 90.9 | 1 | Sumy | R. NV |
| 4) | 90.9 | 1 | Dnipro | Stilnoye R. "Perets FM" |
| 17) | 91.0 | 1 | Cherkasy | Relax FM |
| 5) | 91.0 | 1 | Odesa | Kraina FM |
| 19) | 91.1 | 1 | Lviv | Russkoye R. Ukraina |
| 1A) | 91.1 | 1 | Kryvyi Rih | Avtoradio-Ukraina |
| 34) | 91.2 | 2 | Kharkiv | M-FM |
| 1B) | 91.3 | 1 | Sumy | Retro FM |
| 9) | 91.3 | 1 | Vinnytsia | Power FM |
| 1D) | 91.4 | 2 | Odesa | NRJ |
| 1B) | 91.5 | 1 | Berdiansk | Retro FM |
| 8) | 91.6 | 1 | Kryvyi Rih | Lux FM |
| 1B) | 92.4 | 1 | Kyiv | Retro FM |
| 1D) | 92.8 | 2 | Kyiv | NRJ |
| 24) | 93.8 | 1 | Kyiv | Biznes-R. |
| 12) | 94.2 | 1 | Kyiv | Maximum FM |
| 13) | 95.2 | 1.5 | Kyiv | Melodia FM |
| 1G) | 95.6 | 2 | Kyiv | Dzhem FM |
| 3) | 96.0 | 2 | Kyiv | R. NV |
| 5) | 96.2 | 1 | Bakhmutivka | Kraina FM |
| 6) | 96.4 | 2 | Kyiv | Hit FM Ukraina |
| 57) | 96.5 | 1 | Volnovakha | FM Halychyna |
| 2) | 96.8 | 2 | Kyiv | DJ FM |
| 19) | 97.0 | 2 | Volnovakha | Russkoye R. Ukraina |
| 45) | 98.0 | 1 | Kyiv | R. Kyiv |
| 19) | 98.5 | 2 | Kyiv | Russkoye R. Ukraina |
| 4) | 98.5 | 1 | Shchastia | Stilnoye R. "Perets FM" |
| 3) | 98.9 | 1 | Nikopol | R. NV |
| 38) | 99.0 | 2 | Kyiv | R. Nostalgie |
| 1B) | 99.1 | 1 | Melitopol | Retro FM |
| 1B) | 99.1 | 1 | Poltava | Retro FM |
| 1F) | 99.4 | 1.5 | Kyiv | Lounge FM |
| 8) | 99.4 | 1 | Kherson | Lux FM |
| 5) | 100.0 | 4 | Kyiv | Kraina FM |
| 41) | 100.2 | 2 | Kamianske | Pershe R. FM1 |
| 5) | 100.2 | 1 | Kryvyi Rih | Kraina FM |
| 5) | 100.3 | 1 | Zaporizhia | Kraina FM |
| 29) | 100.4 | 1 | Odesa | Avtoradio-Odesa |
| 62) | 100.5 | 2 | Kyiv | R. Miami |
| 8) | 100.5 | 1 | Dnipro | Lux FM |
| 1A) | 100.6 | 1 | Chernihiv | Avtoradio-Ukraina |
| 33) | 100.6 | 2 | Korosten | Rekord FM |
| 1C) | 100.7 | 1 | Antopil | Nashe R. |
| 14) | 100.8 | 1 | Mykolaiv | R. Roks Ukraina |
| 14) | 100.8 | 1 | Zaporizhia | R. Roks Ukraina |
| 32) | 100.8 | 1 | Lviv | Lvivska khvylia |
| 6) | 100.8 | 1 | Mariupol | Hit FM Ukraina |
| 1B) | 100.9 | 1 | Kremenchuk | Retro FM |
| 12) | 101.0 | 1 | Cherkasy | Maximum FM |
| 15) | 101.0 | 1 | Kryvyi Rih | R. Shanson |
| 3) | 101.0 | 1 | Kramatorsk | R. NV |
| 51) | 101.0 | 1 | Horbkiv | R. Sokal |

| FM | MHz | kW | Location | Station |
|---|---|---|---|---|
| 6) | 101.0 | 1 | Odesa | Hit FM Ukraina |
| 19) | 101.1 | 1 | Dnipro | Russkoye R. Ukraina |
| 1D) | 101.1 | 1 | Kharkiv | NRJ |
| 1E) | 101.1 | 3 | Kyiv | R. Piatnytsia |
| 3) | 101.2 | 1 | Melitopol | R. NV |
| 7) | 101.2 | 1 | Kherson | Kiss FM |
| 8) | 101.2 | 1 | Khmelnytskyi | Lux FM |
| 17) | 101.3 | 1 | Zhytomyr | Relax FM |
| 4) | 101.3 | 1 | Poltava | Stilnoye R. "Perets FM" |
| 13) | 101.4 | 1 | Sumy | Melodia FM |
| 17) | 101.4 | 1 | Antopil | Relax FM |
| 1E) | 101.4 | 1 | Odesa | R. Piatnytsia |
| 4) | 101.4 | 1 | Kryvyi Rih | Stilnoye R. "Perets FM" |
| 58) | 101.4 | 5 | Chonhar | R. Meidan |
| 17) | 101.5 | 4 | Kyiv | Relax FM |
| 19) | 101.5 | 1 | Krasnohorivka | Russkoye R. Ukraina |
| 1B) | 101.5 | 1 | Kropyvnytskyi | Retro FM |
| 1E) | 101.5 | 1 | Dnipro | R. Piatnytsia |
| 4) | 101.5 | 1 | Kharkiv | Stilnoye R. "Perets FM" |
| 1D) | 101.6 | 1 | Cherkasy | NRJ |
| 54) | 101.6 | 1 | Kholmtsi | R. Versia |
| 14) | 101.7 | 1 | Kramatorsk | R. Roks Ukraina |
| 19) | 101.7 | 1 | Khmelnytskyi | Russkoye R. Ukraina |
| 19) | 101.7 | 1 | Zhytomyr | Russkoye R. Ukraina |
| 7) | 101.7 | 1 | Mariupol | Kiss FM |
| 7) | 101.8 | 3 | Odesa | Kiss FM |
| 15) | 101.9 | 4 | Kyiv | R. Shanson |
| 4) | 101.9 | 1 | Kherson | Stilnoye R. "Perets FM" |
| 28) | 102.0 | 1 | Pryluky | Halaktyka plius |
| 6) | 102.0 | 2 | Dnipro | Hit FM Ukraina |
| 12) | 102.1 | 1 | Lviv | Maximum FM |
| 7) | 102.1 | 1 | Mykolaiv | Kiss FM |
| 43) | 102.2 | 2 | Odesa | R. Fil |
| 6) | 102.3 | 1 | Poltava | Hit FM Ukraina |
| 14) | 102.4 | 1 | Cherkasy | R. Roks Ukraina |
| 5) | 102.4 | 1 | Kholmtsi | Kraina FM |
| 7) | 102.4 | 1 | Kharkiv | Kiss FM |
| 8) | 102.4 | 1 | Chernivtsi | Lux FM |
| 11A) | 102.5 | 2 | Kyiv | Prosto R. |
| 13) | 102.5 | 1 | Tokmak | Melodia FM |
| 17) | 102.5 | 1 | Khmelnytskyi | Relax FM |
| 6) | 102.5 | 1 | Kherson | Hit FM Ukraina |
| 1B) | 102.6 | 1 | Lubny | Retro FM |
| 36) | 102.6 | 1 | Kamianske | Hrad FM |
| 6) | 102.6 | 1 | Vinnytsia | Hit FM Ukraina |
| 61) | 102.6 | 1 | Chonhar | R. Khaiat |
| 17) | 102.7 | 1 | Kovel | Relax FM |
| 1C) | 102.7 | 4 | Kryvyi Rih | Nashe R. |
| 1C) | 102.7 | 1 | Zhytomyr | Nashe R. |
| 1C) | 102.8 | 1 | Mykolaiv | Nashe R. |
| 23) | 102.8 | 1 | Mariupol | Best FM |
| 48) | 102.8 | 1 | Pryluky | R. Planeta |
| 1C) | 102.9 | 3 | Dnipro | Nashe R. |
| 1E) | 103.0 | 1 | Kharkiv | R. Piatnytsia |
| 9) | 103.0 | 1 | Ivano-Frankivsk | Power FM |
| 1C) | 103.1 | 1 | Khmelnytskyi | Nashe R. |
| 2) | 103.1 | 1 | Kherson | DJ FM |
| 7) | 103.1 | 1 | Zaporizhia | Kiss FM |
| 8) | 103.1 | 5 | Kyiv | Lux FM |
| 1D) | 103.2 | 1 | Kryvyi Rih | NRJ |
| 1E) | 103.2 | 1 | Melitopol | R. Piatnytsia |
| 37) | 103.2 | 2 | Odesa | Narodnoye R. |
| 2) | 103.3 | 1.2 | Dnipro | DJ FM |
| 3) | 103.3 | 1 | Cherkasy | R. NV |
| 12) | 103.4 | 1 | Dniprorudne | Maximum FM |
| 36) | 103.4 | 2 | Petrovirivka | Hrad FM |
| 6) | 103.4 | 1 | Sumy | Hit FM Ukraina |
| 13) | 103.5 | 1 | Kremenchuk | Melodia FM |
| 14) | 103.5 | 1 | Ternopil | R. Roks Ukraina |
| 14) | 103.6 | 1 | Kyiv | R. Roks Ukraina |
| 7) | 103.6 | 1 | Khmelnytskyi | Kiss FM |
| 9) | 103.6 | 2 | Kryvyi Rih | Power FM |
| 19) | 103.7 | 1 | Cherkasy | Russkoye R. Ukraina |
| 3) | 103.7 | 1 | Kherson | R. NV |
| 52) | 103.7 | 1 | Vinnytsia | R. TAKT |
| 6) | 103.7 | 1 | Antopil | Hit FM Ukraina |
| 19) | 103.8 | 1 | Kropyvnytskyi | Russkoye R. Ukraina |
| 1C) | 103.8 | 1 | Poltava | Nashe R. |
| 36) | 103.8 | 3 | Odesa | Hrad FM |
| 4) | 103.8 | 1 | Bila Tserkva | Stilnoye R. "Perets FM" |
| 8) | 103.8 | 1 | Ivano-Frankivsk | Lux FM |
| 19) | 103.9 | 1 | Kremenchuk | Russkoye R. Ukraina |
| 1D) | 103.9 | 1 | Lviv | NRJ |
| 21) | 103.9 | 1 | Kramatorsk | Klasne R. |
| 3) | 103.9 | 1 | Zhytomyr | R. NV |

| FM | MHz | kW | Location | Station |
|---|---|---|---|---|
| 12) | 104.0 | 2 | Kharkiv | Maximum FM |
| 1A) | 104.0 | 1 | Mariupol | Avtoradio-Ukraina |
| 9) | 104.0 | 1 | Dnipro | Power FM |
| 9) | 104.0 | 4 | Kyiv | Power FM |
| 19) | 104.1 | 1 | Vinnytsia | Russkoye R. Ukraina |
| 3) | 104.1 | 1 | Honchar | R. NV |
| 4) | 104.1 | 1 | Mykolaiv | Stilnoye R. "Perets FM" |
| 13) | 104.3 | 1 | Polohy | Melodia FM |
| 1C) | 104.3 | 1 | Chernihiv | Nashe R. |
| 20) | 104.3 | 1 | Bila Tserkva | Radio.Net |
| 59) | 104.3 | 1 | Lviv | Duzhe R. |
| 8) | 104.3 | 2 | Odesa | Lux FM |
| 1E) | 104.4 | 1 | Kherson | R. Piatnytsia |
| 35) | 104.4 | 1 | Kamianske | Micomp R. |
| 47) | 104.4 | 1 | Novovolynsk | R. Nova |
| 13) | 104.5 | 1 | Cherkasy | Melodia FM |
| 15) | 104.5 | 1 | Zaporizhia | R. Shanson |
| 19) | 104.5 | 1 | Poltava | Russkoye R. Ukraina |
| 1C) | 104.5 | 1 | Kharkiv | Nashe R. |
| 8) | 104.5 | 1 | Ternopil | Lux FM |
| 3) | 104.6 | 1 | Kropyvnytskyi | R. NV |
| 15) | 104.7 | 1 | Melitopol | R. Shanson |
| 17) | 104.7 | 1 | Kryvyi Rih | Relax FM |
| 6) | 104.7 | 1 | Chernihiv | Hit FM Ukraina |
| 8) | 104.7 | 1 | Lviv | Lux FM |
| 19) | 104.8 | 1 | Kherson | Russkoye R. Ukraina |
| 19) | 104.8 | 5 | Shyrokyi | Russkoye R. Ukraina |
| 1C) | 104.8 | 1 | Lutsk | Nashe R. |
| 11A) | 104.9 | 1 | Zhytomyr | Prosto R. |
| 15) | 105.0 | 1 | Poltava | R. Shanson |
| 17) | 105.1 | 1 | Sumy | Relax FM |
| 1E) | 105.1 | 1 | Mykolaiv | R. Piatnytsia |
| 9) | 105.1 | 1 | Zaporizhia | Power FM |
| 1B) | 105.2 | 1 | Krasnohorivka | Retro FM |
| 8) | 105.2 | 1 | Kharkiv | Lux FM |
| 8) | 105.2 | 1 | Uzhhorod | Lux FM |
| 11B) | 105.3 | 4 | Odesa | Prosto R. Odesa |
| 15) | 105.3 | 2 | Dnipro | R. Shanson |
| 19) | 105.3 | 1 | Mariupol | Russkoye R. Ukraina |
| 1B) | 105.3 | 1 | Shostka | Retro FM |
| 31) | 105.3 | 1 | Severodonetsk | STV |
| 6) | 105.3 | 1 | Kropyvnytskyi | Hit FM Ukraina |
| 40) | 105.4 | 1 | Khmelnytskyi | OK FM |
| 8) | 105.4 | 1 | Chernihiv | Lux FM |
| 17) | 105.5 | 1 | Lutsk | Relax FM |
| 4) | 105.5 | 2 | Kyiv | Stilnoye R. "Perets FM" |
| 57) | 105.5 | 1 | Sosnovyi | FM Halychyna |
| 19) | 105.6 | 1 | Sumy | Russkoye R. Ukraina |
| 1C) | 105.6 | 1 | Zaporizhia | Nashe R. |
| 6) | 105.6 | 1 | Krasnohorivka | Hit FM Ukraina |
| 6) | 105.6 | 1 | Ternopil | Hit FM Ukraina |
| 1C) | 105.7 | 1 | Kharkiv | Power FM |
| 11A) | 105.8 | 1 | Dnipro | Prosto R. |
| 13) | 105.8 | 1 | Poltava | Melodia FM |
| 17) | 105.8 | 1 | Kropyvnytskyi | Relax FM |
| 4) | 105.8 | 1 | Mariupol | Stilnoye R. "Perets FM" |
| 49) | 105.8 | 1 | Petrovirivka | R. Shliager |
| 19) | 105.9 | 1 | Kryvyi Rih | Russkoye R. Ukraina |
| 60) | 105.9 | 5 | Chonhar | Krym.Realii |
| 1C) | 106.0 | 1 | Lviv | Nashe R. |
| 1H) | 106.0 | 1 | Kyiv | Holos Stolitsi |
| 22) | 106.0 | 1 | Berdiansk | Azovska Khvylia |
| 39) | 106.0 | 1 | Odesa | Odesa-Mama |
| 13) | 106.1 | 1 | Ternopil | Melodia FM |
| 8) | 106.1 | 1 | Cherkasy | Lux FM |
| 1B) | 106.2 | 1 | Bila Tserkva | Retro FM |
| 1C) | 106.2 | 1 | Kherson | Nashe R. |
| 4) | 106.2 | 1 | Kropyvnytskyi | Stilnoye R. "Perets FM" |
| 49) | 106.2 | 1 | Podilsk | R. Shliager |
| 13) | 106.3 | 1 | Melitopol | Melodia FM |
| 1A) | 106.4 | 1 | Ivano-Frankivsk | Avtoradio-Ukraina |
| 1C) | 106.4 | 1 | Vinnytsia | Nashe R. |
| 53) | 106.4 | 2 | Antopil | R. Trek |
| 1C) | 106.5 | 1 | Mariupol | Nashe R. |
| 57) | 106.5 | 1 | Skyrokyi | FM Halychyna |
| 7) | 106.5 | 2 | Kyiv | Kiss FM |
| 25) | 106.6 | 1 | Chernivtsi | Blysk FM |
| 44) | 106.6 | 2 | Odesa | R. Hlas |
| 6) | 106.6 | 1 | Zaporizhia | Hit FM Ukraina |
| 15) | 106.7 | 1 | Kropyvnytskyi | R. Shanson |
| 1B) | 106.7 | 1 | Kherson | Retro FM |
| 6) | 106.7 | 1 | Chernihiv | Hit FM Ukraina |
| 50) | 106.8 | 1 | Debeslavtsi | R. Siaivo |
| 7) | 106.8 | 3 | Dnipro | Kiss FM |
| 6) | 106.9 | 1 | Kryvyi Rih | Hit FM Ukraina |

| FM | MHz | kW | Location | Station |
|---|---|---|---|---|
| 8) | 106.9 | 1 | Lutsk | Lux FM |
| 10) | 107.0 | 1 | Kyiv | Europa Plus |
| 1B) | 107.0 | 1 | Zaporizhia | Retro FM |
| 26) | 107.0 | 1 | Sumy | Diva-R. |
| 3) | 107.0 | 1 | Kharkiv | R. NV |
| 49) | 107.0 | 1 | Odesa | R. Shliager |
| 7) | 107.0 | 1 | Kramatorsk | Kiss FM |
| 49) | 107.1 | 1 | Izmail | R. Shliager |
| 8) | 107.1 | 1 | Mykolaiv | Lux FM |
| 9) | 107.1 | 1 | Cherkasy | Power FM |
| 19) | 107.2 | 1 | Chernihiv | Russkoye R. Ukraina |
| 42) | 107.2 | 1 | Lviv | R. Vrolos |
| 46) | 107.3 | 1 | Dnipro | Informator FM |
| 12) | 107.4 | 1 | Odesa | Maximum FM |
| 3) | 107.4 | 1 | Kryvyi Rih | R. NV |
| 5) | 107.4 | 1 | Kharkiv | Kraina FM |
| 13) | 107.5 | 1 | Zaporizhia | Melodia FM |
| 4) | 107.5 | 1 | Dubrovytsia | Stilnoye R. "Perets FM" |
| 14) | 107.6 | 2 | Kherson | R. Roks Ukraina |
| 14) | 107.7 | 1 | Chernihiv | R. Roks Ukraina |
| 16) | 107.7 | 1 | Dnipro | R. Vesti |
| 8) | 107.7 | 1 | Zhytomyr | Lux FM |
| 3) | 107.8 | 1.2 | Mykolaiv | R. NV |
| 17) | 107.9 | 1 | Zaporizhia | Relax FM |
| 1A) | 107.9 | 1 | Sumy | Avtoradio-Ukraina |
| 1C) | 107.9 | 1 | Kropyvnytskyi | Nashe R. |
| 1C) | 107.9 | 5 | Kyiv | Nashe R. |
| 1C) | 107.9 | 1 | Odesa | Nashe R. |

+ txs below 1kW.

### Addresses & other information:

**1A-H)** vul. Kyrylivska 108a, 04080 Kyiv – **2)** b-r T.Shevchenka 54/1, 01032 Kyiv – **3)** pr-t Povitrianoflotskyi 54, 03151 Kyiv – **4)** vul. Dovzhenka 14, 03057 Kyiv – **5)** vul. Saksahanskoho 91, 01032 Kyiv – **6)** vul. V.Khvoiky 15/15, 04655 Kyiv – **7)** vul. V.Khvoiky 15/15, 04655 Kyiv – **8)** vul. Volodymyrska 61/11, 01033 Kyiv – **9)** b-r T.Shevchenka 54/1, 01032 Kyiv – **10)** vul. Ivana Kudri 26, 01042 Kyiv – **11A,B)** 11A) vul. O.Shmidta 6, 04107 Kyiv, 11B) vul. Fontanska doroha 3, 65063 Odesa – **12)** pl. Halytska 15, 79008 Lviv – **13)** vul. V.Khvoiky 15/15, 04655 Kyiv – **14)** vul. V.Khvoiky 15/15, 04655 Kyiv – **15)** b-r T.Shevchenka 54/1, 01032 Kyiv – **16)** vul. O.Shmidta 6, 04107 Kyiv – **17)** vul. V.Khvoiky 15/15, 04655 Kyiv – **18)** b-r L. Ukrayinky 3, 01133 Kyiv – **19)** vul. V.Khvoiky 15/15, 04655 Kyiv – **20)** b-r B.Khmelnytskoho 5, 09100 Bila Tserkva – **21)** vul. Soborna 56a, 64309 Izium – **22)** Melitopolske shose 20, 77108 Berdiansk – **23)** vul. Chernyshevskoho 15, 61057 Kharkiv – **24)** b-r T.Shevchenka 54/1, 01032 Kyiv – **25)** vul. Eminesku 2, 58000 Chernivtsi – **26)** vul. Kharkivska 5, 40024 Sumy – **27)** vul. Holosiivska 7, 03039 Kyiv – **28)** vul. Piriatynska 129, 17500 Pryluky – **29)** vul. Kanatna 83, 65107 Odesa – **30)** vul. Velyka Vasylivska 131a, 03150 Kyiv – **31)** vul. Haharina 93, 93400 Severodonetsk – **32)** vul. Hutsulska 9a, 79000 Lviv – **33)** vul. Rylskoho 9, 10014 Zhytomyr – **34)** vul. Petrovskoho 3, 61002 Kharkiv – **35)** vul. Vasylia Stusa 15b, 51900 Kamianske – **36)** vul. Balkivska 120/1, 65005 Odesa – **37)** vul. O.Shmidta 6, 04107 Kyiv – **38)** vul. Y.Konovaltsiia 32a, 01133 Kyiv – **39)** vul. Zaslavskoho 10/12, 65004 Odesa – **40)** pr-t Miru 69, 29000 Khmelnytskyi – **41)** vul. Balkivska 120/1, 65005 Odesa – **42)** vul. Pidvalna 3, 79008 Lviv – **43)** vul. Troitska 50, 65045 Odesa – **44)** vul. Kanatna 83, 65107 Odesa – **45)** vul. Khreshchatyk 44, 01044 Kyiv – **46)** vul. Koltsova 8, 49000 Dnipro – **47)** pr-t Druzhby 27, 45400 Novovolynsk – **48)** vul. Piriatynska 129, 17500 Pryluky – **49)** vul. Tereshkovoi 15, 65078 Odesa – **50)** vul. Sichovykh striltsiv 23, 78200 Kolomyia – **51)** vul. Sichovykh striltsiv 18, 80000 Sokal – **52)** vul. Soborna 59, 21050 Vinnytsia – **53)** vul. Kavkazka 2, 33013 Rivne – **54)** vul. Erdeli 1, 88018 Uzhhorod – **55)** vul. Sribnokilska 8, 02095 Kyiv – **56)** vul. Marshala Vasylevskoho 14-5, 84116 Sloviansk – **57)** pl. Soborna 12/5, 79009 Lviv – **58)** vul. Syretska 33b, 04073 Kyiv – **59)** vul. Horbachevskoho 16, 79000 Lviv – **60)** vul. Cheliabinska 9, 02002 Kyiv – **61)** vul. Mykhailivska 2, 01001 Kyiv – **62)** vul. O.Shmidta 6, 04107 Kyiv.

### DAB Transmitters (Trial) (DAB+)

**Tx Operator:** Concern RRT **M:** Pershyi kanal, Promin, Kultura, R. Meidan, R. Maria, Old Fashioned R., Zemlia, Hype R., Kraina FM, Armia FM **Txs:** Block 1D (Kyiv SFN).

### DONETS BASIN

(Self-proclaimed "Donetsk People"s Rep." and "Luhansk People's Rep.")

### Territory controlled by "Donetsk People's Republic" (DPR)

**RADIO RESPUBLIKA (Gov)** (Run by the "DPR" administration) ▭ vul. Kuibysheva 61, 83016 Donetsk (mail: via Russia) ☎ +380 62 3028245 **E:** dnr.tv@yandex.ru **W:** republic-tv.ru
**FM:** Donetsk 99.0MHz (0.5kW).
**D.Prgr: R. Respublika** 24h in Russian, incl. rel. Vesti FM (Russia).

## OTHER STATIONS

| FM | MHz | kW | Location | Station |
|---|---|---|---|---|
| | 99.4 | 1 | Donetsk | Relax FM* |
| | 100.0 | 1 | Donetsk | R. Sputnik relay* |
| | 101.2 | 1 | Donetsk | R. 7* |
| | 104.7 | 1 | Donetsk | Avtoradio* |
| | 105.1 | 2 | Donetsk | DFM* |
| | 106.8 | 3 | Donetsk | R. Novorossiya - Roks |

+ txs below 1kW. *) Relays from Russia

### Territory controlled by "Luhansk People's Republic" (LPR)

**GTRK LNR (Gov)** (Run by the "LPR" administration)
✉ vul. Demokhina 25, 91016 Luhansk (mail: via Russia) ☎ +380 642 585552 **E:** gtrk.lnr@mail.gtrklnr.com **W:** gtrklnr.com
**FM (MHz)**

| | 1 | 2 | 3 | 4 | kW |
|---|---|---|---|---|---|
| Luhansk | 106.9 | 103.6 | 104.8 | 107.9 | 1 |

+ sites with txs below 1kW.
**D.Prgr: Prgr 1 (R. Pobyeda)** 24h in Russian – **Prgr 2 (Svoye R.)** 24h in Russian – **Prgr 3 (R. Respublika):** 24h in Russian – **Prgr 4 (Vesti Plyus):** 24h in Russian, incl. rel. Vesti FM (Russia)

## OTHER STATIONS

| FM | MHz | kW | Location | Station |
|---|---|---|---|---|
| | 106.5 | 1 | Luhansk | R. Sputnik relay* |

+ txs below 1kW. *) Relay from Russia

### CRIMEA
(under Russian administration)

**L.T:** UTC +3h — **Pop:** 2.4 million — **Pr.L:** Russian, Ukrainian, Crimean Tatar

### UPRAVLENIYE ROSKOMNADZORA PO RESPUBLIKE KRYM I G. SEVASTOPOL
✉ 295034 Simferopol, ul. Moskovskaya 12 ☎ +7 3652 669293 **E:** rsrokanc82@rkn.gov.ru **W:** 82.rkn.gov.ru
**L.P:** Head: Dmitriy V. Mikhaylov

### VSEROSSIYSKAYA GOSUDARSTVENNAYA TELEVIZIONNAYA I RADIOVESHCHATELNAYA KOMPANIYA (VGTRK) (Gov)
✉ Contact details see under "Russia"

| FM (VFM) | | MHz | kW | FM (VFM) | | MHz | kW |
|---|---|---|---|---|---|---|---|
| Simferopol | | 87.5 | 1 | Kerch | | 91.6 | 1 |
| Sevastopol | | 90.8 | 1 | Krasnoperekopsk | | 102.6 | 1 |

+ txs below 1kW.
**D.Prgr: Vesti FM (VFM):** see under "Russia".

### TELERADIOKOMPANIYA "KRYM" (Gov)
✉ 295001 Simferopol, ul. Studencheskaya 14 ☎ +7 3652 788444 **E:** tv@tv.crimea.ru **W:** 1tvcrimea.ru **L.P:** DG: Yekaterina Kozyr

| FM (MHz) | | kW | FM | | 1 | 2 | kW |
|---|---|---|---|---|---|---|---|
| Dzhankoy | - | 105.9 | 1 | Sevastopol | 91.3 | 90.4 | 1/0.5 |
| Kerch | | 88.5 | 100.3 | 1/0.5 | Simferopol | 100.1 100.6 | 0.05/1 |

+ sites with only txs below 1kW.
**D.Prgr: Prgr 1 ("R. Krym")** 24h, **Prgr 2 ("R. Morye")** 24h.

### OBSHCHESTVENNAYA KRYMSKOTATARSKAYA TELERADIOKOMPANIYA (OKTT) (Pub)
✉ 295011 Simferopol, ul. Kozlova 45a ☎ +7 978 9809009 **E:** ok_trk@mail.ru **W:** trkmillet.ru **L.P:** DG: Ervin Musayev

| FM | | MHz | kW |
|---|---|---|---|
| Simferopol | | 99.5 | 1 |

+ txs below 1kW.
**D.Prgr: "Vatan Sedasi"** 24h in Crimean Tatar, Russian.

## OTHER STATIONS

| FM | MHz | kW | Location | Station |
|---|---|---|---|---|
| 21) | 88.3 | 1 | Sevstopol | R. Zvezda |
| 21) | 89.2 | 1 | Kerch | R. Zvezda |
| 21) | 98.3 | 1 | Simferopol | R. Zvezda |
| 4) | 101.4 | 1 | Kerch | Europa Plus |
| X) | 102.0 | 1 | Sevastopol | Sevastopol FM |
| 16) | 102.2 | 1 | Kerch | Retro FM |
| | 102.3 | 1 | Simferopol | R. Sputnik |
| | 105.6 | 1 | Sevastopol | R. Sputnik |
| 10) | 107.0 | 1 | Sevastopol | R. 7 |

+ txs below 1kW.
**Addresses & other information:**
Contact details see "Other Stations" chart under "Russia" (stn numbers refer to that chart) **X)** 299011 Sevastopol, ul. 4-ya Bastionnaya 1.

**Radio via DTT:** see National TV section

---

**L.T:** UTC +4h — **Pop:** 9.4 million — **Pr.L:** Arabic — **E.C:** 50Hz, 220V — **ITU:** UAE

### NATIONAL MEDIA COUNCIL
✉ P.O. Box 17, Abu Dhabi ☎ +971 2 4453000 🖷 +971 2 4452504 **W:** uaeinteract.com **L.P:** Chmn: Saqr Ghubash Saeed Ghubash.

### ABU DHABI MEDIA COMPANY (Pub.)
✉ 4th St, Sector 18, Zone 1, Abu Dhabi ☎+971 2 4144000 🖷 +971 2 4144001 **W:** adradio.ae **L.P:** CEO: Ahmed Ali Mohamed Al Bloushi. Dir. Radio: Jaber Obaid. Head R&TV Eng: Mahmood Al-Redha.
**Abu Dhabi R.** in Arabic on FM(MHz): Ras al-Khaimah 89.7, Abu Dhabi 90.0, Jabal Al-Dhanna 97.3, Dubai 98.4, Habshan 100.1, Liwa 103.7, Fujairah 106.0.
**FM (MHz): Classic FM** (in English): Dubai 87.9. Abu Dhabi 91.6, Al Ain 105.2 – **Emarat FM:** 24h on FM (MHz): Ras al-Khaimah 88.5, Jabal al-Dhanna 92.4, Al-Ain 94.9, Abu Dhabi 95.8, Liwa 95.6, Dubai 97.1, Habshan 98.4, Fujairah 103.9 – **Holy Quran R:** 24h on FM (MHz) Jabel Dhana 87.7, Dubai 88.2, Al-Ain 88.6, Habshan 98.8, Liwa 89.3, Fujairah 97.6, Abu Dhabi 98.1MHz, Ras al-Khaimah 105.2 – **R. Mirchi** (in English): Dubai/Sharjah 88.8MHz, Al-Ain 95.6MHz, Abu Dhabi 97.3MHz – **Star FM:** Abu Dhabi 92.4MHz, Dubai 99.9MHz. Al-Ain 100.1MHz – **R. 1** (in English): Abu Dhabi 100.5MHz, Dubai 104.1MHz – **R. 2** (in English): Abu Dhabi 106.1MHz, Dubai 99.3MHz

### PRAVASI BHARATHI
✉ P.O. Box 77914, Two Four 54, Media Zone Authority, Abu Dhabi ☎+971 2 3043 818 **W:** pravasibharathi.com **L.P:** GM: K. Chandrasenan.
**MW:** Maqta 810kHz. **D.Prgr** in Malayalam: 0100-2010 200 kW AM & 2010-0100 50 kW DRM.

### RAS AL-KHAIMAH BROADCASTING STATION
✉ RAK Media, P.O. Box 141, Ras al Khaimah ☎+971 7 851151 🖷 +971 7 353441
**MW:** 1152kHz 200kW. **FM:** 95.3MHz (Arabic).
MW rel. VO Kerala (**W:** radiovok.com ) 0100v-2100v in Malayalam (Also rel. 1900-2000 SIP Radio in Indonesian: **W:** facebook.com/sipradioindonesia)

### GULF NEWS BROADCASTING
✉ P.O. Box 6519, Dubai ☎+971 4 3446366 🖷+971 4 3448185 **W:** gnbroadcasting.com
**FM: Hayat FM** (Arabic): Umm al-Quwain 95.6MHz – **Josh FM** (English): Umm al-Quwain 95.6MHz

### SHARJAH MEDIA CORPORATION
✉ P.O. Box 111, Sharjah ☎+971 6 566 1111 🖷 +971 6 566 9999 **W:** smc.ae **E:** info@smc.ae
**Pulse FM** in English: Sharjah 95.0MHz **W:** pulse95radio.com
**R. Sharjah** in Arabic: Sharjah 94.4MHz, Abu Dhabi 96.3, Khor Fakkan 107.6MHz, Kalba 107.7MHz. **Quran R:** Sharjah 102.7MHz.

### UMM AL QUWAIN BROADCASTING STATION
✉ Shamal Media Services, P.O. Box 1106, Umm al Quwain ☎+971 6 5657106 🖷 +971 6 5651806
**MW:** Holy Quran R: 846kHz 20kW 24h.
**FM: UAQ FM:** 97.8MHz in Arabic. **W:** uaqfm.com – **Hum FM:** 106.2MHz in Hindi/Urdu. **W:** humfm.com

### ASIANET RADIO
✉ Asianet Global FZ LLC, P.O. Box 62787, Boutique No. 10, Dubai Media City ☎+971 4 3914150 🖷 +971 4 3918045 **W:** asianetradio.me
**MW:** Al-Dhabbiya 657kHz 100kW (irregularly also on 1539kHz).
**D.Prgr:** 24h in Malayalam.

### RADIO ASIA NETWORK
✉ Dolphin Recording Studio, P.O. Box 4300, Dubai ☎+971 4 4534950 🖷 +971 4 3421387 **L.P:** GM: Brij Bhalla. PD: Vettoor G. Sreedharan. **W:** radioasiauae.com **E:** am@radioasiauae.com
**MW: Radioasia:** Ras al Khaimah 1269kHz 200kW. **D.Prgr:** 24h in Malayalam.
**FM: Red:** Ras al-Khaimah 94.7MHz 20kW in Malayalam/Tamil. **W:** red947.com – **Suno FM:** 102.4MHz in Hindi/Urdu. **W:** suno1024.com
**Ann:** "Radio Asia 1269 AM".

### ARABIAN RADIO NETWORK (ARN)
✉ P.O. Box 502255, CNN Bldg, Media City 103, Dubai ☎+971 4

3912000 🖳 +971 4 3912007 **W:** arn.ae **E:** amghrteam@arabmedia-group.ae **LP:** GM: Mahmoud Al-Rasheed. COO: Steve Smith.
**FM: Tag 91.1:** 91.1MHz in Filipino – **Dubai 92:** 92.0MHz 5kW in English – **R. Shoma:** 93.4MHz in Farsi – **Hit FM:** 96.7MHz 5kW in Malayalam – **Al-Arabiya:** 99.0MHz 10kW in Arabic – **Al-Khaleejiya:** 100.9MHz 5kW in Arabic – **City FM:** 101.6MHz 5kW in Hindi – **Dubai Eye:** 103.8MHz 5kW in English – **Virgin R:** Dubai 104.4MHz 30kW.

## DUBAI MEDIA INCORPORATED (DMI)
**W:** dmi.ae **Dubai FM:** 93.0MHz. **Noor Dubai:** 93.9MHz 5kW.

## CHANNEL 4 RADIO NETWORK
🖳 P.O. Box 442, Ajman ☎+971 6 746 1444 **LP:** MD: Mohammad Murad. Prgr. Controller: Peter Gowers. **W:** ch4network.com
**FM:** all in Ajman. **R. 4 FM:** 89.1MHz in English/Hindi – **Channel 4 FM:** 104.8 & 106.5MHz 1kW in English – **Gold FM:** 101.3MHz in Hindi – **Al Rabia FM:** 107.8MHz 1kW in Arabic.

## FUJAIRAH MEDIA GROUP
🖳 Fujairah ☎971 9 2244100 🖳 +971 9 2244101 **W:** fmg.ae
**FM: Fujairah FM:** 92.6MHz 2kW (Arabic) – **R. Hello:** 89.5MHz in Telugu. – **R. Spice FM:** 105.4MHz 3kW (English/Hindi/Tamil) – **Rock R:** 90.7MHz 2kW – **Europa Plus:** 96.2MHz 2kW (Russian) – **Zayed R. for Quran:** 97.6MHz 2kW.

## MALAR GLOBAL MEDIA
**R. Me:** Dubai 100.3MHz in Malayalam. **W:** radiomeonline.com – **R. Salaam,** 106.5MHz in Tamil. **W:** salaam.fm – **Wow FM,** 107.0MHz in Flipino. **W:** wowfm.ae

## MBC FM & PANORAMA FM
🖳 P.O. Box 75335, MBC Building, Media City, Dubai ☎+971 4 3919713 🖳 +971 4 3916683 **W:** mbc.net/ar/panorama-fm **E:** contactus@mbc.ae
**LP:** Dir: Hassan Muawad. **FM:** Txs in Bahrain, Iraq, Jordan, Kuwait, Qatar, Saudi Arabia, Sudan and Palestine West Bank.

**Autoradio,** Dubai: 103.2MHz **W:** autoradio.ae
**Jio FM,** Umm al Quwain: 100.3MHz **W:** jio.fm
**Pearl FM,** Abu Dhabi 102.0MHz **W:** pearlfm.ae
**Sky News Arabia,** Abu Dhabi 90.3MHz. **W:** skynewsarabia.com
**Sowt al-Khaleej,** Abu Dhabi 105.2MHz. See Qatar for main entry.
**R. Sawa:** Dubai 90.5MHz 5kW, Abu Dhabi 98.7MHz 10kW and **R. Farda:** Al-Dhabbiya 1575kHz 800kW 24h. For further details see Int. radio section under USA.
**Monte Carlo Doualiya:** Ras al-Khaimah 95.3MHz

## UNITED KINGDOM

**L.T:** UTC (31 Mar-27 Oct: +1h) — **Pop:** 65 million — **Pr.L:** English Welsh — **E.C:** 50Hz, 230V — **ITU:** G — **Int.Dialling Code:** +44

**CROWN DEPENDENCIES: The Channel Islands** and the **Isle of Man** are dependencies of the British Crown and are not part of the United Kingdom. They are included here for editorial convenience.

## OFFICE OF COMMUNICATIONS (Ofcom)
(Regulatory Authority)
🖳 Riverside House, 2A Southwark Bridge Rd, London SE1 9HA ☎20 7981 3040 🖳20 7981 3333 **W:** ofcom.org.uk **LP:** CEO: Sharon White

## BRITISH BROADCASTING CORPORATION (Pub)
The BBC is an independent body created by Royal Charter and operates under licence.
🖳 Broadcasting House, Portland Place, London W1A 1AA ☎ 20 7580 4468 **W:** bbc.co.uk **LP:** DG: Tony Hall; CEO BBC Studios: Tim Davie; Dir Content: Charlotte Moore; Dir Radio & Education: James Purnell; Dir News & Current Affairs: Fran Unsworth; Chair, BBC Board: Sir David Clementi

**LW/MW:**

| Radio 4 | kHz | kW | Radio 4 | kHz | kW |
|---|---|---|---|---|---|
| Burghead | 198 | 50 | Crystal Palace | 720 | 0.8 |
| Westerglen | 198 | 50 | Redruth | 756 | 2 |
| Droitwich | 198 | 500 | Enniskillen | 774 | 1 |
| Newcastle | 603 | 2 | Plymouth | 774 | 1 |
| Londonderry | 720 | 0.3 | Redmoss | 1449 | 2 |
| Lisnagarvey | 720 | 10 | Carlisle | 1485 | 1 |

| Radio 5 Live | kHz | kW | Radio 5 Live | kHz | kW |
|---|---|---|---|---|---|
| Barrow | 693 | 1 | Bexhill | 693 | 1 |
| Brighton | 693 | 1 | Clevedon | 909 | 50 |
| Burghead | 693 | 25 | Exeter | 909 | 1 |
| Droitwich | 693 | 150.0 | Fareham | 909 | 1 |
| Enniskillen | 693 | 1.0 | Lisnagarvey | 909 | 10.0 |
| Folkestone | 693 | 1.0 | Londonderry | 909 | 1 |
| Postwick | 693 | 10.0 | Moorside Edge | 909 | 200.0 |
| Redmoss | 693 | 1.0 | Redruth | 909 | 2.0 |
| Stagshaw | 693 | 50.0 | Tywyn | 990 | 1 |
| Start Point | 693 | 50.0 | Westerglen | 909 | 50.0 |
| Bournemouth | 909 | 0.3 | Whitehaven | 909 | 1 |
| Brookmans Park | 909 | 150.0 | | | |

**England, Isle of Man, Channel Is FM** (all stereo)

| FM | R1 | R2 | R3 | R4 | kW |
|---|---|---|---|---|---|
| Barnstaple | 98.1 | 88.5 | 90.7 | 92.9 | 1 |
| Beacon Hill | 98.4 | 88.7 | 90.9 | 93.1 | 1 |
| Belmont | 98.3 | 88.8 | 90.9 | 93.1 | 16 |
| Bilsdale | 98.6 | 89.0 | 91.2 | 93.4 | 5 |
| Bow Brickhill | 98.2 | 88.6 | 90.8 | 93.0 | 10 |
| Bristol | 98.9 | 89.3 | 91.5 | 93.7 | 1.3 |
| Chatton | 99.7 | 90.1 | 92.3 | 94.5 | 5.6 |
| Crystal Palace | 98.5 | 88.8 | 91.0 | 93.2 | 4 |
| Douglas (I.O.M.) | 98.0 | 88.4 | 90.6 | 92.8 | 11 |
| Guildford | 97.7 | 88.1 | 90.3 | 92.5 | 3 |
| Caversham | 99.4 | 89.8 | 92.0 | 94.2 | 1 |
| Holme Moss | 98.9 | 89.3 | 91.5 | 93.7 | 250 |
| Keighley | 98.5 | 88.9 | 91.1 | 93.3 | 1 |
| Les Platons (C.I.) | 97.1 | 89.6 | 91.1 | 94.8 | 16 |
| Manningtree | 97.7 | 88.1 | 90.3 | 92.5 | 5 |
| Morecambe Bay | 99.6 | 90.0 | 92.2 | 94.4 | 10 |
| North Hessary Tor | 99.7 | 88.1 | 90.3 | 92.5 | 160 |
| Oxford | 99.1 | 89.5 | 91.7 | 93.9 | 46 |
| Pendle Forest | 97.8 | 90.2 | 92.6 | 94.6 | 1 |
| Peterborough | 99.7 | 90.1 | 92.3 | 94.5 | 40 |
| Pontop Pike | 98.1 | 88.5 | 90.7 | 92.9 | 134 |
| Redruth | 99.3 | 89.7 | 91.9 | 94.1 | 25 |
| Ridge Hill | 98.2 | 88.6 | 90.8 | 93.0 | 10 |
| Rowridge | 98.2 | 88.5 | 90.7 | 92.9 | 250 |
| Sandale | 97.7 | 88.1 | 90.3 | 92.5 | 250 |
| Stanton Moor | 99.4 | 89.8 | 92.0 | 94.2 | 1.2 |
| Sutton Coldfield | 97.9 | 88.3 | 90.5 | 92.7 | 250 |
| Swingate (Dover) | 99.5 | 90.0 | 92.4 | 94.4 | 11 |
| Tacolneston | 99.3 | 89.7 | 91.9 | 94.1 | 250 |
| Winter Hill | 98.2 | 88.6 | 90.8 | 93.0 | 4 |
| Woolmoor | 99.6 | 90.2 | 92.2 | 94.4 | 5 |
| Wrotham | *98.8 | 89.1 | 91.3 | 93.5 | 125*/250 |

+ 74 low power txs less than 1kW

**STATIONS: Radio 1:** New music for youth audience 24h **N:** Newsbeat M-F 1245, 1745 – **Radio 1Xtra** (digital only) – **Radio 2:** Adult contemporary and specialist music: 24h **N:** on the h – **Radio 3:** Classical music, jazz, world music, arts: 24h **N:** 0700, 0800, 0900(SS), 1300, 1700(MF), 1800(MF) – **Radio 4:** News, documentaries, drama, entertainment, and cricket on LW/MW in season: 0520-0100; relays BBCWS 0100-0520 **N:** 0530, then on the h (not 1000 Sun, 1100 Sun, 1500 Sat) – **Radio 4Extra** (digital only) – **Radio 5 Live:** News & sport: 24h **N:** on the h and half h – **Radio 6 Music:** New and archive music: 24h (digital only)

**BBC LOCAL RADIO**

| MW | Station | Location | kHz | kW |
|---|---|---|---|---|
| 1) | Three Counties R. | Luton | 630 | 0.2 |
| 6) | R. Cornwall | Redruth | 630 | 2 |
| 6) | R. Cornwall | Bodmin | 657 | 0.5 |
| 37) | R. York | Fulford | 666 | 0.5 |
| 11) | Essex | Manningtree | 729 | 0.2 |
| 15) | Hereford & Worcs | Worcester | 738 | 0.037 |
| 8) | R. Cumbria | Carlisle | 756 | 1 |
| 11) | Essex | Chelmsford | 765 | 0.5 |
| 20) | R. Leeds | Farnley | 774 | 0.5 |
| 10) | R. Devon | Barnstaple | 801 | 2 |
| 8) | R. Cumbria | Barrow | 837 | 1 |
| 19) | R. Lancashire | Preston | 855 | 1 |
| 26) | R. Norfolk | Postwick | 855 | 1.5 |
| 26) | R. Norfolk | West Lynn | 873 | 0.3 |
| 10) | R. Devon | Exeter | 990 | 1 |
| 33) | R. Solent | Fareham | 999 | 1 |
| 4) | R. Cambridgeshire | Chesterton Fen | 1026 | 0.5 |
| 17) | R. Jersey | Trinity | 1026 | 1 |
| 31) | R. Sheffield | Sheffield | 1035 | 1 |
| 9) | R. Derby | Burnaston Lane | 1116 | 1 |
| 14) | R. Guernsey | Rohais | 1116 | 0.5 |
| 1) | Three Counties R. | Bedford | 1161 | 0.1 |

| MW | Station | Location | kHz | kW |
|---|---|---|---|---|
| 37) | R. York | Scarborough | 1260 | 0.5 |
| 33) | R. Solent for Dorset | Bournemouth | 1359 | 0.85 |
| 12) | R. Gloucestershire | Berkeley Heath | 1413 | 0.5 |
| 12) | R. Gloucestershire | Bourton-on-the-Water | 1413 | 0.5 |
| 8) | R. Cumbria | Whitehaven | 1458 | 0.5 |
| 25) | Newcastle | Wrekenton | 1458 | 2 |
| 23) | R. Merseyside | Wallasey | 1485 | 2 |
| 34) | R. Stoke | Sideway | 1503 | 1 |
| 3) | Somerset & R. Bristol | Taunton | 1566 | 1 |
| 15) | Hereford & Worcs. | Woofferton | 1584 | 0.3 |

| FM | Station | Location | MHz | kW |
|---|---|---|---|---|
| 31) | R. Sheffield | Sheffield | 88.6 | 0.3 |
| 17) | R. Jersey | Les Platons | 88.8 | 3.8 |
| 1) | Three Counties R. | Epping Green | 90.4 | 0.1 |
| 20) | R. Leeds | Holme Moss | 92.4 | 5.6 |
| 14) | R. Guernsey | Les Touillets | 93.2 | 1 |
| 34) | R. Stoke | Alsagers Bank | 94.6 | 6.1 |
| 2) | R. Berkshire | Henley | 94.6 | 0.25 |
| 15) | Hereford & Worcester | Ridge Hill | 94.7 | 2 |
| 1) | Three Counties R. | Aylesbury | 94.7 | 0.2 |
| 31) | R. Sheffield | Chesterfield | 94.7 | 0.4 |
| 7) | Coventry & Warwicks. | Meriden | 94.8 | 2.2 |
| 10) | R. Devon | Huntshaw Cross | 94.8 | 0.675 |
| 24) | R. London | Crystal Palace | 94.9 | 4 |
| 3) | R. Bristol | Dundry Lane | 94.9 | 0.5 |
| 22) | R. Lincolnshire | Belmont | 94.9 | 6 |
| 30) | Sussex | Newhaven | 95.0 | 0.1 |
| 5) | Tees | Bilsdale | 95.0 | 10 |
| 12) | R. Gloucestershire | Stroud | 95.0 | 0.1 |
| 13) | R. Manchester | Holme Moss | 95.1 | 5.6 |
| 28) | R. Nottingham | Newark | 95.1 | 0.2 |
| 26) | R. Norfolk | Stoke Holy Cross | 95.1 | 4 |
| 6) | R. Cornwall | Caradon Hill | 95.2 | 4.3 |
| 8) | R. Cumbria | Kendal | 95.2 | 0.1 |
| 29) | R. Oxford | Beckley | 95.2 | 5.8 |
| 11) | Essex | South Benfleet | 95.3 | 1.2 |
| 30) | Sussex | Brighton | 95.3 | 1.2 |
| 9) | R. Derby | Stanton Moor | 95.3 | 1.2 |
| 20) | R. Leeds | Luddenden | 95.3 | 0.083 |
| 2) | R. Berkshire | Windsor | 95.4 | 0.5 |
| 25) | Newcastle | Pontop Pike | 95.4 | 10 |
| 1) | Three Counties R. | Sandy Heath | 95.5 | 1 |
| 3) | Somerset & R. Bristol | Mendip | 95.5 | 9 |
| 19) | R. Lancashire | Hameldon Hill | 95.5 | 1.6 |
| 28) | R. Nottingham | Mansfield | 95.5 | 2 |
| 35) | R. Suffolk | Lowestoft | 95.5 | 2 |
| 37) | R. York | Olivers Mount | 95.5 | 0.25 |
| 26) | R. Norfolk | West Runton | 95.6 | 2 |
| 8) | R. Cumbria | Sandale | 95.6 | 15 |
| 38) | WM (West Midlands) | Sutton Coldfield | 95.6 | 11 |
| 4) | R. Cambridgeshire | Peterborough | 95.7 | 5.1 |
| 10) | R. Devon | Plymouth | 95.7 | 1 |
| 23) | R. Merseyside | Allerton Park | 95.8 | 8 |
| 5) | Tees | Whitby | 95.8 | 0.1 |
| 10) | R. Devon | Exeter | 95.8 | 0.4 |
| 35) | R. Suffolk | Aldeburgh | 95.9 | 2 |
| 16) | R. Humberside | High Hunsley | 95.9 | 9.6 |
| 4) | R. Cambridgeshire | Cambridge | 96.0 | 1 |
| 9) | R. Derby | Buxton | 96.0 | 1.5 |
| 32) | R. Shropshire | The Wrekin | 96.0 | 4.8 |
| 25) | Newcastle | Chatton | 96.0 | 5.6 |
| 8) | R. Cumbria | Morecambe Bay | 96.1 | 3.2 |
| 33) | R. Solent | Rowridge | 96.1 | 10 |
| 18) | R. Kent | Wrotham | 96.7 | 8.7 |
| 18) | R. Kent | Folkestone | 97.6 | 0.1 |
| 1) | Three Counties R. | High Wycombe | 98.0 | 0.2 |
| 20) | R. Leeds | Keighley | 102.7 | 0.5 |
| 10) | R. Devon | North Hessary Tor | 103.4 | 15 |
| 11) | Essex | Great Braxted | 103.5 | 12 |
| 36) | Wiltshire | Salisbury | 103.5 | 1 |
| 3) | R. Bristol | Weston-S-Mare | 103.6 | 0.1 |
| 36) | Wiltshire | Swindon | 103.6 | 0.5 |
| 27) | R. Northampton | Geddington | 103.6 | 0.8 |
| 7) | Coventry & Warwicks. | Lark Stoke | 103.7 | 1.4 |
| 37) | R. York | Acklam Wold | 103.7 | 2 |
| 25) | Newcastle | Hexham | 103.7 | 0.1 |
| 1) | Three Counties R. | Zouches Farm | 103.8 | 0.5 |
| 28) | R. Nottingham | Mapperley Ridge | 103.8 | 1 |
| 33) | R. Solent (Dorset) | Bincombe Hill | 103.8 | 0.5 |
| 6) | R. Cornwall | Redruth | 103.9 | 18 |
| 19) | R. Lancashire | Winter Hill | 103.9 | 2 |
| 20) | R. Leeds | Beecroft Hill | 103.9 | 0.1 |

| MW | Station | Location | kHz | kW |
|---|---|---|---|---|
| 35) | R. Suffolk | Manningtree | 103.9 | 5 |
| 15) | Hereford & Worcester | Great Malvern | 104.0 | 2 |
| 30a) | Surrey | Reigate | 104.0 | 3.8 |
| 8) | R. Cumbria | Whitehaven | 104.1 | 1 |
| 31) | R. Sheffield | Holme Moss | 104.1 | 4.4 |
| 34) | R. Stoke | Stafford | 104.1 | 0.075 |
| 2) | R. Berkshire | Hannington | 104.1 | 3 |
| 18) | R. Kent | Swingate | 104.2 | 10 |
| 27) | R. Northampton | Northampton | 104.2 | 4 |
| 36) | Wiltshire | Naish Hill | 104.3 | 0.6 |
| 10) | R. Devon | Beacon Hill | 104.3 | 1 |
| 37) | R. York | Woolmoor | 104.3 | 0.5 |
| 2) | R. Berkshire | Reading | 104.4 | 1 |
| 26) | R. Norfolk | Great Massingham | 104.4 | 4.2 |
| 15) | Hereford & Worcester | Redditch | 104.4 | 0.1 |
| 30) | Sussex | Heathfield | 104.5 | 10 |
| 1) | Three Counties R. | Bow Brickhill | 104.5 | 2.2 |
| 9) | R. Derby | Drum Hill | 104.5 | 5.4 |
| 19) | R. Lancashire | Lancaster | 104.5 | 2 |
| 13) | R. Manchester | Saddleworth | 104.6 | 0.1 |
| 15) | Hereford & Worcester | Kidderminster | 104.6 | 0.5 |
| 30a) | Surrey | Guildford | 104.6 | 3 |
| 3) | R. Bristol | Bath | 104.6 | 0.082 |
| 35) | R. Suffolk | Great Barton | 104.6 | 2 |
| 12) | R. Gloucestershire | Churchdown Hill | 104.7 | 2 |
| 30) | Sussex | Burton Down | 104.8 | 2 |
| 21) | R. Leicester | Copt Oak | 104.9 | 8 |
| 36) | Wiltshire | Marlborough | 104.9 | 0.1 |

+ 15 low power txs less than 0.1kW

**Addresses and other information:**

1) Unit 4 Grove Park, Court Drive, Dunstable LU5 4GP ☎1582 636900 E: threecounties@bbc.co.uk – 2) Caversham Park, Peppard Rd, Reading RG4 8TZ ☎118 9464200 E: radio.berkshire.news@bbc.co.uk – 3) Whiteladies Rd, Bristol BS8 2LR ☎117 9741111 E: radio.bristol@bbc.co.uk; BBC Somerset, Broadcasting House, Park Street, Taunton TA1 4DA ☎1823 323956 E: somerset@bbc.co.uk – 4) Cambridge Business Park, Cowley Rd, Cambridge CB4 0WZ ☎1223 259696 E: cambs@bbc.co.uk– 5) Broadcasting House, Newport Rd, Middlesbrough TS 5JA ☎1642 225211 E: tees@bbc.co.uk– 6) Phoenix Wharf, Truro TR1 1UA ☎1872 275421 E: radio.cornwall@bbc.co.uk – 7) Priory Place Coventry CV1 5SQ ☎24 76551000 E: coventry.warwickshire@bbc.co.uk– 8) Annetwell Street, Carlisle CA3 8BB ☎1228 592444 E: radio.cumbria@bbc.co.uk – 9) 56 St Helen's Street, Derby DE1 3HY ☎1332 361111 E: radio.derby@bbc.co.uk – 10) Seymour Rd., Plymouth PL3 5BD ☎1752 260323 E: radio.devon@bbc.co.uk – 11) PO Box 765 Chelmsford CM2 9XB ☎1245 616000 E: essex@bbc.co.uk– 12) London Rd, Gloucester GL1 1SW ☎1452 308585 E: radio.gloucestershire@ bbc.co.uk – 13) Quay House, BBC Media City UK, Salford M50 2QH ☎161 335 6000 E: radio.manchester@bbc.co.uk – 14) Bulwer Ave, St Sampson, Guernsey GY2 4LA ☎1481 200600 E: bbcguernsey@ bbc.co.uk – 15) Hylton Rd, Worcester WR2 5WW ☎1905 748485 E: bbchw@bbc.co.uk and 43 Broad Street, Hereford HR4 9HH ☎1432 355255 – 16) Queens Court, Queens Gardens, Hull HU1 3RH ☎1482 323232 E: radio.humberside@bbc.co.uk – 17) 18-21 Parade Rd, St Helier, Jersey JE2 3PL ☎1534 870000 E: radiojersey@bbc.co.uk – 18) The Great Hall, Mount Pleasant Rd, Tunbridge Wells TN1 1QQ ☎1892 670000 E: radio.kent@bbc.co.uk – 19) 20-26 Darwen Street, Blackburn BB2 2EA ☎1254 262411 E: radio.lancashire@bbc.co.uk – 20) 2 St Peters Square, Leeds LS9 8AH ☎113 244 2131 E: radioleeds@bbc. co.uk – 21) 9 St Nicholas Place, Leicester LE1 5LB ☎116 251 6688 E: radioleicester@bbc.co.uk – 22) Radion Buildings, Newport, Lincoln LN1 3XY ☎1522 511411 E: radio.lincolnshire@bbc.co.uk – 23) 31 College Lane, Liverpool L1 3DS ☎151 708 6161 E: radio.merseyside@ bbc.co.uk – 24) Egton Wing, Broadcasting House, Portland Place, London W1A 1AA ☎20 8743 8000 E: yourlondon@bbc.co.uk – 25) Broadcasting Centre, Barrack Rd, Newcastle-Upon-Tyne NE99 1RN ☎191 222 4141 E: bbcnewcastle@bbc.co.uk – 26) The Forum, Millennium Plain, Norwich NR2 1BH ☎1603 619331 E: norfolk@bbc. co.uk – 27) Broadcasting House, Abington Street, Northampton NN1 2BH ☎1604 239100 E: northamptonshire@bbc.co.uk – 28) London Rd, Nottingham NG2 4UU ☎115 955 0500 E: radio.nottingham@bbc.co.uk – 29) 269 Banbury Rd, Oxford OX2 7DW ☎8459 311444 E: oxford@ bbc.co.uk – 30) Broadcasting House, 40-42 Queen's Rd, Brighton BN1 3XB E: sussex@bbc.co.uk – 30a) Broadcasting Centre, Guildford GU2 7AP ☎1483 306306 E: surrey@bbc.co.uk – 31) 54 Shoreham Street, Sheffield S1 4RS ☎114 2731177 E: radio.sheffield@bbc. co.uk – 32) 2-4 Boscobel Drive, Shrewsbury SY1 3TT ☎1743 248484 E: shropshire@bbc.co.uk – 33) Broadcasting House, 10 Havelock Rd, Southampton SO14 7PW ☎23 8063 1311 E: radio.solent@bbc.co.uk – 34) Cheapside, Hanley, Stoke-on-Trent ST1 1JJ ☎01782 08080 E.

radio.stoke@bbc.co.uk– **35)** Broadcasting House, St. Matthew's Street, Ipswich IP1 3EP ☎1473 250000 **E:** radiosuffolk@bbc.co.uk– **36)** 56-58 Prospect Place, Swindon SN1 3RW ☎ 1793 513626 **E:** wiltshire@bbc.co.uk – **37)** 20 Bootham Row, York Y030 7BR ☎1904 641 351 **E:** northyorkshire.news@bbc.co.uk – **38)** The Mailbox, Wharfside Street, Birmingham B1 1AY ☎121 567 6767 **E:** radio.wm@bbc.co.uk.
**D.Prgr:** Stns generally carry local or regional prgrs from 0600-0100, then BBC Radio 5 Live overnight

## BBC SCOTLAND
🖳 40 Pacific Quay, Glasgow G51 1DA ☎ 141 422 6000
**W:** bbc.co.uk/radioscotland
**MW: R. Scotland:** Burghead 810kHz 100kW, Westerglen 810kHz 100kW, Redmoss 810kHz 5kW, Dumfries 585kHz 2kW

| FM stereo | R1 | R2 | R3 | R4 | RS/L | kW |
|---|---|---|---|---|---|---|
| Ashkirk | 98.7 | 89.1 | 91.3 | 103.9 | 93.5f | 50 |
| Ben Gullipen | 98.3 | 88.7 | 90.9 | 104.9 | 93.1 | 1 |
| Black Hill | 99.5 | 89.9 | 92.1 | *95.8 | 94.3 | 250/200 |
| Bressay | 97.9 | 88.3 | 90.5 | 94.9 | 92.7ac | 43 |
| Clettraval | 97.7 | 88.1 | 90.3 | 95.1 | 92.5d | 2 |
| Daliburgh | 98.9 | 89.3 | 91.5 | 95.9 | 93.7d | 1 |
| Darvel | 99.1 | 89.5 | 91.7 | 104.3 | 93.9 | 10 |
| Durris | 99.0 | 89.4 | 91.6 | 95.9 | 93.8a | 2.1 |
| Eitshal | 99.4 | 89.8 | 92.0 | 95.1 | 94.2d | 2 |
| Forfar | 97.9 | 88.3 | 90.5 | 94.9 | 92.7 | 17 |
| Fort William | 98.9 | 89.3 | 91.5 | 95.9 | 93.7d | 3 |
| Glengorm | 99.1 | 89.5 | 91.7 | 96.1 | 93.9d | 5 |
| Keelylang Hill | 98.9 | 89.3 | 91.5 | 96.0 | 93.7ab | 41 |
| Kirkton Mailer | 98.6 | 89.0 | 91.2 | 94.6 | 93.4 | 1 |
| Meldrum | 98.3 | 88.7 | 90.9 | 95.3 | 93.1a | 150 |
| Melvaig | 98.7 | 89.1 | 91.3 | 95.7 | 93.5d | 50 |
| Oban | 98.5 | 88.9 | 91.1 | 95.3 | 93.3d | 3.6 |
| Rosemarkie | 99.2 | 89.6 | 91.8 | 103.6 | 94.0d | 20 |
| Rumster Forest | 99.7 | 90.1 | 92.3 | 95.6 | 94.5d | 10 |
| Sandale | 97.7 | 88.1 | 90.3 | 92.5 | 94.7e | 250 |
| Skriaig | 98.1 | 88.5 | 90.7 | 94.8 | 92.9d | 30 |
| So. Knapdale | 98.9 | 89.3 | 91.5 | 95.6 | 93.7 | 2.2 |

+ 32 low power txs less than 1kW
RS/L=R. Scotland + local news – a) RS: Aberdeen – b) RS: Orkney – c) RS: Shetland – d) RS: Inverness – e) RS: Dumfries – f) RS: Selkirk.
**D.Prgr: R.Scotland** 0600-0100. Rel. BBC R. 5 overnight

### Local Services (FM only). Freqs as above.
**a)** Beechgrove Terrace, Aberdeen AB15 5ZT. M-F: 0630, 0730, 0830, 1230, 1630, 1730. **W:** bbc.co.uk/northeastscotland – **b)** Castle Str, Kirkwall, Orkney KW15 1DF: M-F 0730-0800, Fri 1810-1900 – **c)** Pitt Lane, Lerwick, Shetland ZE1 0DW: M-F 1730-1800, Fri 1810-1900 – **d)** 7 Culduthel Rd, Inverness IV2 4AD M-F: 0630, 0730, 0830, 1230, 1630, 1730 – **e)** Elmbank, Lovers Walk, Dumfries DG1 1NZ: M-F: 0630, 0730, 0830, 1230, 1630, 1730. **W:** bbc.co.uk/southscotland – **f)** Ettrick Riverside, Dunsdale Rd, Selkirk TD7 5EB M-F 0630, 0730, 0830, 1230, 1630, 1730

## BBC RADIO NAN GAIDHEAL
🖳 54 Seaforth Rd., Stornoway HS1 2SD ☎ 1851 705000 **E:** stornoway@bbc.co.uk **W:** bbc.co.uk/radionangaidheal

| FM | MHz | kW | FM | MHz | kW |
|---|---|---|---|---|---|
| Glengorm | 103.5 | 5 | Meldrum | 104.2 | 150 |
| Clettraval | 103.7 | 2 | Eitshal | 104.3 | 2 |
| So. Knapdale | 103.7 | 2.2 | Kirkton Mailer | 104.5 | 1 |
| Forfar | 103.7 | 1 | Rumster Forest | 104.5 | 10 |
| Melvaig | 103.9 | 50 | Oban | 104.6 | 3.6 |
| Craigkelly | 104.1 | 5 | Black Hill | 104.7 | 10 |
| Daliburgh | 104.2 | 1 | Skriaig | 104.7 | 30 |
| Fort William | 104.2 | 3 | Rosemarkie | 104.9 | 20 |

+ 16 low power txs less than 1kW
**D.Prgr:** Own prgrs in Gaelic and relays of BBC R. Scotland

## BBC CYMRU WALES
🖳 Broadcasting House, Llantrisant Rd, Llandaff, Cardiff CF5 2YQ ☎ 29 2032 2000 🗎 29 2055 5960
**E:** radiowales@bbc.co.uk **W:** bbc.co.uk/radiowales

| FM stereo | R1 | R2 | R3 | R4 | kW |
|---|---|---|---|---|---|
| Blaenplwyf | 98.3 | 88.7 | 90.9 | 104.0 | 250 |
| Carmel | 98.0 | 88.4 | 90.6 | 92.8 | 2.5 |
| Haverfordwest | 98.9 | 89.3 | 91.5 | 104.9 | 20 |
| Kilvey Hill | 99.1 | 89.5 | 91.7 | 94.6 | 1 |
| Llanddona | 99.4 | 89.8 | 92.0 | 103.6 | 21 |
| Llandrindod Wells | 98.7 | 89.1 | - | 103.8 | 2.8 |
| Llangollen | 98.5 | 88.9 | - | 93.3 | 15.6 |
| Wenvoe | 99.5 | 89.9 | 92.1 | 94.3 | 250 |

## BBC CYMRU WALES (continued)

| FM stereo | R. Wales | R.Cymru | kW |
|---|---|---|---|
| Blaenplwyf | 95.3 | 93.1 | 250/120 |
| Carmel | 95.1 | 104.6 | 3/3.2 |
| Haverfordwest | 95.9 | 93.7 | 20 |
| Kilvey Hill | 93.9 | 104.2 | 1 |
| Llanddona | 94.8 | 94.2 | 21/10 |
| Llandrindod Wells | 91.3 | 93.5 | 2.8 |
| Llangollen | 91.9 | 104.3 | 15.6 |
| Wenvoe | 103.9 | | 40 |
| Wenvoe | | 96.8 | 250 |

+ 42 low power txs less than 1kW
**MW R. Wales:** Forden 882kHz 1kW, Llandrindod Wells 1125kHz 1kW, Penmon 882kHz 10kW, Tywyn 882kHz 5kW, Washford 882kHz 100kW, Wrexham 657kHz 2kW
**D.Prgr: R. Wales:** 0500-0100. Rel. BBC WS overnight. **R. Cymru:** 0530-0000. Rel. BBC Radio 5 overnight

## BBC NORTHERN IRELAND
🖳 Broadcasting House, 25-27 Ormeau Avenue, Belfast BT2 8HQ ☎ 28 9033 8000 🗎 28 9032 6453 **W:** bbc.co.uk/radioulster
**MW:** Enniskillen 873kHz 1kW, Lisnagarvey 1341kHz 100kW

| FM stereo | R1 | R2 | R3 | R4 | R. Ulster | kW |
|---|---|---|---|---|---|---|
| Brougher Mntn | 99.0 | 89.4 | 91.6 | 95.6 | 93.8 | 9.8 |
| Camlough | 98.3 | 88.7 | 90.9 | 104.6 | 93.1 | 4 |
| Divis | 99.7 | 90.1 | 92.3 | 96.0 | 94.5 | 250/125 |
| Limavady | 99.2 | 89.6 | 91.8 | 94.0 | 95.4 | 3.4 |
| Londonderry | 98.3 | 88.7 | 90.9 | 94.9 | 93.1h | 31/10 |

+ 5 low power txs of less than 1kW – h) **R. Foyle** (see below)
**R. Ulster:** Enniskillen 873kHz 1kW, Lisnagarvey 1341kHz 100kW.
**D.Prgr:** MF 0630(SaSu0700)-0000. Other times rel. BBC R5

## BBC RADIO FOYLE
🖳 8 Northland Rd, Londonderry BT48 7GD ☎ 28 7137 8600 **W:** bbc.co.uk/radiofoyle
**E:** radio.foyle@bbc.co.uk
**MW:** Londonderry 792kHz 1kW **FM:** 93.1MHz 31kW
**D.Prgr:** 24h. Own prgs and relay BBC R. Ulster. Local N. M-F hourly 0700-1700

## BBC ASIAN NETWORK
🖳 New Broadcasting House, London W1A 1AA **E:** asiannetworknews@bbc.co.uk **W:** bbc.co.uk/asiannetwork

| MW | kHz | kW | MW | kHz | kW |
|---|---|---|---|---|---|
| Sedgley | 828 | 0.2 | Gunthorpe | 1449 | 0.15 |
| Freemen's Common | 837 | 0.5 | Langley Mill | 1458 | 5 |

**D.Prgr:** 0600-0100, mainly in English. Relays BBC R. 1Xtra overnight
### BBC Asian Network relays

| MW | kHz | kW | MW | kHz | kW |
|---|---|---|---|---|---|
| R. Leeds | 774a | 0.7 | R. Sheffield | 1035b | 1 |

**Key:** a) Mon-Fri 1900-0100, b) Mon-Fri 1600-0100. Local Asian prog. also carried on some BBC local radio stns at various times.

## EXTERNAL SERVICE: BBC World Service
See International Broadcasting section

## ARQIVA
🖳 Crawley Court, Winchester SO21 2QA ☎1962 823434
**W:** arqiva.com Operates most BBC domestic and many commercial radio tx sites.

**DIGITAL RADIO (DAB/some DAB+):** DAB trs are on Band 3. **National Multiplexes: BBC Digital Radio:** BBC Radios 1, 1Xtra, 2, 3, 4, 4 Extra, 5 Live, 5 Live Sports Extra, 6 Music, Asian Network and World Service. On 225.648MHz, Block 12B. **Digital One (DAB):** 🖳 UK House, 4th Floor, 2-5 Great Titchfield Str, London W1W 8BB **W:** ukdigitalradio. com. Prgrs includes: Absolute, Absolute 90s, Capital UK, Capital Xtra, Classic FM, Heart Extra, Heart 80s, Kiss, LBC, Magic, Radio X, Smooth Extra, TalkSport, UCB 1. In England, Wales & Northern Ireland on 222.064MHz, Block 11D; in Scotland on 223.936MHz, Block 12A. **Sound Digital (Digital Two) (DAB/DAB+):** **W:** sounddigital.co.uk Prgrs includes: Absolute 80s, Forces Radio BFBS, Fun Kids UK, Heat, Jazz FM, Jack 3, Kisstory, Magic Chilled, Mellow Magic, Panjab, Planet Rock, Premier Christian, Premier Praise, Sunrise, TalkRadio, TalkSport 2, UCB 2, Union Jack, Virgin. On 216.928MHz, Block 11A.
**Local Multiplexes:** Aberdeen (11C), Ayr (11B), Birmingham (11C), Bournemouth (11B), Bradford & Huddersfield (11B), Bristol & Bath (11B), Cambridge (11C), Cardiff & Newport (12C), Central Lancashire (12A), Central Scotland (11D), Cornwall (11B), Coventry (12D), Derbyshire (10B), Dundee & Perth (11B), Edinburgh (12D), Exeter & Torbay (11C), Glasgow (11C), Gloucestershire (10C), Greater London I (12C), Greater

London II (12A), Greater London III (12B), Hereford & Worcester (12A), Herts, Beds & Bucks (10D), Humberside (10D), Inverness (11B), Kent (11C), Leeds (12D), Leicester (11B), Lincolnshire (12A), Liverpool (10C), Manchester (12C), Mid & W Wales (12D), NE Wales & W Cheshire (10D), Northampton (10C), North Devon (12C), North Yorkshire (12D), Northern Ireland (12D), Norwich (10B), Nottingham (12C), Oxford (10B), Peterborough (12D), Plymouth (12D), Reading & Basingstoke (12D), Somerset (10B), Southend & Chelmsford (12D), South Hampshire (11C), South Yorkshire (11C), Stoke-on-Trent (12D), Suffolk (10C), Surrey (10C), Sussex (10C), Swansea (12A), Swindon (11C), Teesside (11B), Tyne & Wear (11C), West Wiltshire (10D), Wolverhampton/Shrewsbury & Telford (11B), **Small scale test multiplexes (Minimux Trials) (DAB/DAB+):** Aldershot (8A), Birmingham (9A), Brighton (9A), Bristol (9A), Cambridge (7D), Glasgow (10B), London (9A), Manchester (10B), Norwich (9A), Portsmouth (7D).

## RADIOCENTRE
🖳 6th Floor, 55 New Oxford St. London W1A 1BS ☎20 7010 0600 **W:** radiocentre.org - Radiocentre represents commercial radio to Government, Ofcom, Copyright Societies and other organisations concerned with radio.

## NATIONAL COMMERCIAL STATIONS:
### ABSOLUTE RADIO
🖳 1 Golden Square, London W1F 9DJ ☎20 7434 1215 📠20 7434 1197 **W:** absoluteradio.co.uk

| MW | kHz | kW | MW | kHz | kW |
|---|---|---|---|---|---|
| Bournemouth | 1197 | 0.25 | Norwich | 1215 | 1.2 |
| Brighton | 1197 | 1.1 | Washford | 1215 | 50 |
| Trowell | 1197 | 0.5 | Westerglen | 1215 | 50 |
| Gloucester | 1197 | 0.3 | Wrekenton | 1215 | 2.2 |
| Oxford | 1197 | 0.25 | Kings Heath | 1233 | 0.5 |
| Brookmans Park | 1215 | 62.5 | Manningtree | 1233 | 0.5 |
| Dartford Tunnel | 1215 | 0.004 | Boston | 1242 | 2 |
| Droitwich | 1215 | 52.5 | Sideway | 1242 | 0.5 |
| Fareham | 1215 | 1 | Stockton | 1242 | 1 |
| Lisnagarvey | 1215 | 16 | Lydd | 1260 | 1 |
| Moorside Edge | 1215 | 50 | | | |

**D.Prgr:** 24h (rock & contemporary music). **N:** on the h
**FM:** West Midlands (Sutton Coldfield) 105.2 MHz, 11kW; London (Crystal Palace) 105.8MHz 4kW

### CAPITAL FM
🖳 30 Leicester Square, London WC2H 7LA ☎ 20 7054 8000 **W:** capitalfm.com

| FM | MHz | kW | Location | FM | MHz | kW | Location |
|---|---|---|---|---|---|---|---|
| 33) | 95.8 | 4 | London | 49) | 105.1 | 3.1 | Emley Moor |
| 69) | 96.2 | 1 | Nottingham | 36) | 105.3 | 8.4 | Burnhope |
| 100) | 96.3 | 1.25 | Llandudno | 69) | 105.4 | 5 | Leicester |
| 100) | 97.1 | 1 | Wirral | 49) | 105.6 | 0.5 | Bradford |
| 42) | 97.4 | 0.5 | Newport | 49) | 105.6 | 0.5 | Sheffield |
| 45) | 102.0 | 0.5 | Manchester | 122) | 105.7 | 10 | Edinburgh |
| 9) | 102.2 | 1 | Birmingham | 36) | 105.8 | 0.2 | Hexham |
| 69) | 102.8 | 0.9 | Derby | 49) | 105.8 | 9.6 | Hull |
| 100) | 103.0 | 5 | Caernarfon | 122) | 106.1 | 20 | Glasgow |
| 42) | 103.2 | 2 | Cardiff | 36) | 106.4 | 10 | Bilsdale |
| 43) | 103.2 | 2 | Southampton | 41) | 107.2 | 0.2 | Brighton |
| 100) | 103.4 | 1.4 | Wrexham | 17) | 107.6 | 0.4 | Liverpool |

### CLASSIC FM
🖳 30 Leicester Square, London WC2H 7LA ☎ 20 7343 9000 **W:** classicfm.com

| FM | MHz | kW | FM | MHz | kW |
|---|---|---|---|---|---|
| Cumbria | 99.9 | 250 | Selkirk | 100.9 | 10 |
| No.Hessary Tor | 100.0 | 160 | Wrotham | 100.9 | 250 |
| Angus | 100.1 | 10 | Fenham | 101.0 | 0.1 |
| Sutton Coldfield | 100.1 | 250 | Blaen Plwyf | 101.1 | 10 |
| Bath | 100.2 | 0.2 | Holme Moss | 101.1 | 250 |
| Douglas I.O.M. | 100.2 | 1 | Darvel | 101.3 | 8 |
| Rowridge | 100.3 | 250 | Oxford | 101.3 | 46 |
| Bradford | 100.3 | 0.5 | Swansea | 101.3 | 1 |
| Pontop Pike | 100.3 | 130 | Bristol | 101.4 | 0.2 |
| Milton Keynes | 100.4 | 10 | Inverness | 101.4 | 11 |
| Ridge Hill | 100.4 | 5 | Tacolneston | 101.5 | 250 |
| Belmont | 100.5 | 6 | Redruth | 101.5 | 10 |
| Londonderry | 100.5 | 31 | Gt. Ormes Hd | 101.6 | 2.5 |
| Meldrum | 100.5 | 150 | Bilsdale | 101.6 | 2 |
| Preseli | 100.5 | 7 | Leeds | 101.6 | 0.5 |
| Crystal Pal. | 100.6 | 2 | Black Hill | 101.7 | 250 |
| Arfon | 100.7 | 19 | Sheffield | 101.7 | 0.5 |
| Swindon | 100.8 | 0.7 | Wenvoe | 101.7 | 250 |

| FM | MHz | kW | FM | MHz | kW |
|---|---|---|---|---|---|
| Dover | 101.8 | 5 | Brighton | 101.9 | 0.4 |
| Morecambe Bay | 101.8 | 6 | Divis | 101.9 | 250 |
| Reading | 101.8 | 0.5 | Peterborough | 101.9 | 35 |

**D.Prgr:** 24h **N:** on the h

### HEART
🖳 30 Leicester Square, London WC2H 7LA ☎20 7766 6000 **W:** heart.co.uk

| FM | MHz | kW | Location | FM | MHz | kW | Location |
|---|---|---|---|---|---|---|---|
| 100) | 88.0 | 1.4 | Wrexham | 42) | 102.3 | 0.5 | Pontypridd |
| 40) | 95.9 | 0.3 | Thanet | 43) | 102.3 | 2 | Bournemouth |
| 40) | 96.1 | 0.2 | Ashford | 41) | 102.4 | 8.2 | Eastbourne |
| 92) | 96.1 | 0.5 | Colchester | 76) | 102.4 | 2 | Gloucester |
| 82) | 96.2 | 2.5 | N. Devon | 104) | 102.4 | 3.3 | Norwich |
| 86) | 96.3 | 2 | Bristol | 92) | 102.6 | 2 | Chelmsford |
| 92) | 96.3 | 1 | Southend | 89) | 102.6 | 9 | Oxford |
| 82) | 96.4 | 1.6 | Torbay | 86) | 102.6 | 4 | Mendip |
| 104) | 96.4 | 2 | Bury St.Eds | 41) | 102.7 | 3.6 | Reigate |
| 86) | 96.5 | 0.1 | Taunton | 88) | 102.7 | 4 | Peterborough |
| 72) | 96.6 | 4 | Northampton | 40) | 102.8 | 1 | Dunkirk |
| 16) | 96.6 | 0.5 | Watford | 100) | 102.8 | 0.2 | Long Mountain |
| 43) | 96.7 | 0.5 | Winchester | 89) | 102.9 | 3.4 | Hannington |
| 72) | 96.9 | 0.8 | Bedford | 88) | 103.0 | 1 | Cambridge |
| 41) | 96.9 | 0.1 | Newhaven | 82) | 103.0 | 1 | Stockland Hl |
| 109) | 96.9 | 3.2 | Morecambe | 76) | 103.0 | 0.1 | Stroud |
| 40) | 97.0 | 0.5 | Dover | 86) | 103.0 | 0.1 | Weston-S-Mare |
| 82) | 97.0 | 1 | Exeter | 40) | 103.1 | 4 | Maidstone |
| 89) | 97.0 | 1 | Reading | 109) | 103.2 | 0.1 | Kendal |
| 82) | 97.0 | 2 | Plymouth | 122) | 103.3 | 0.5 | Penicuik |
| 86) | 97.1 | 0.2 | W. Somerset | 72) | 103.3 | 2 | Milton Keynes |
| 104) | 97.1 | 3.4 | Ipswich | 89) | 103.4 | 0.1 | Henley-on-Th |
| 87) | 97.2 | 0.7 | Swindon | 41) | 103.5 | 1 | Brighton |
| 82) | 97.3 | 0.1 | Ilfracombe | 85) | 105.1 | 2.5 | E.Cornwall |
| 89) | 97.4 | 0.3 | Banbury | 42) | 105.2 | 3 | Carmel |
| 43) | 97.5 | 0.85 | Portsmouth | 45) | 105.4 | 5 | Winter Hill |
| 92) | 97.5 | 0.1 | Southend | 42) | 105.4 | 5 | Cardiff |
| 72) | 97.6 | 1 | Luton | 42) | 105.7 | 9.4 | Preseli |
| 122) | 100.3 | 20 | Black Hill | 100) | 105.7 | 1.25 | Llandudno |
| 82) | 100.5 | 0.3 | Totnes | 42) | 105.9 | 1 | Newport |
| 34) | 100.7 | 11 | Birmingham | 42) | 106.0 | 1 | Swansea |
| 36) | 100.7 | 10 | Bilsdale | 49) | 106.2 | 3.1 | Emley Moor |
| 82) | 100.8 | 0.1 | Dartmouth | 42) | 106.2 | 0.5 | Fishguard |
| 122) | 101.1 | 10 | Edinburgh | 33) | 106.2 | 4 | London |
| 122) | 101.1 | 0.2 | Rosneath | 100) | 106.9 | 0.44 | Meol-y-Parc |
| 36) | 101.2 | 0.2 | Hexham | 85) | 107.0 | 11 | W. Cornwall |
| 82) | 101.2 | 1.25 | Kingsbridge | 100) | 107.2 | 3.1 | Arfon |
| 92) | 101.7 | 0.1 | Harlow | 100) | 107.3 | 0.15 | Bargoed |
| 36) | 101.8 | 8.5 | Burnhope | 49) | 107.6 | 0.2 | Bradford |
| 82) | 101.9 | 0.5 | Ivybridge | 100) | 107.7 | 10.25 | Blaenplwyf |
| 41) | 102.0 | 0.2 | Hastings | 49) | 107.7 | 0.2 | Sheffield |
| 87) | 102.2 | 0.5 | W. Wiltshire | | | | |

**D.Prgr:** 24h **N:** on the h (No. refer to local studio address - see list)

### SMOOTH RADIO
🖳 30 Leicester Square, London WC2H 7LA ☎20 7766 6000 **W:** smoothradio.com

| MW | kHz | kW | Location | MW | kHz | kW | Location |
|---|---|---|---|---|---|---|---|
| 40) | 603 | 0.7 | Littlebourne | 40) | 1242 | 0.32 | Maidstone |
| 76) | 774 | 0.14 | Gloucester | 104) | 1251 | 0.76 | Bury St.Eds. |
| 72) | 792 | 0.28 | Bedford | 100) | 1260 | 0.64 | Wrexham |
| 43) | 828 | 0.27 | Bournemouth | 42) | 1305 | 0.2 | Newport |
| 72) | 828 | 0.2 | Luton | 41) | 1323 | 0.5 | Brighton |
| 87) | 936 | 0.18 | Naish Hill | 88) | 1332 | 0.6 | Peterborough |
| 41) | 945 | 0.7 | Bexhill | 42) | 1359 | 0.2 | Cardiff |
| 104) | 1152 | 0.83 | Norwich | 92) | 1359 | 0.28 | Chelmsford |
| 82) | 1152 | 0.32 | Plymouth | 92) | 1431 | 0.35 | S'thend-on-Sea |
| 87) | 1161 | 0.16 | Swindon | 72) | 1557 | 0.76 | Northampton |
| 104) | 1170 | 0.28 | Ipswich | 43) | 1557 | 0.5 | Southampton |
| 43) | 1170 | 0.12 | Portsmouth | | | | |

| FM | | MHz | kW | FM | | MHz | kW |
|---|---|---|---|---|---|---|---|
| 36) | Newton | 96.4 | 0.2 | 101) | Keswick | 101.4 | 0.1 |
| 36) | Burnhope | 97.5 | 9 | 33) | Croydon | 102.2 | 4 |
| 101) | Kendal | 100.1 | 0.2 | 122) | Glasgow | 105.2 | 30 |
| 37) | Winter Hill | 100.4 | 5 | 9) | Sutton Cldfld | 105.7 | 11 |
| 101) | Windermere | 100.8 | 0.12 | 69) | Waltham | 106.6 | 10.8 |
| 69) | Derby | 101.4 | 0.2 | 36) | Eston Nab | 107.7 | 5 |

**D.Prgr:** 24h (Numbers refer to local studio address - see list below)

### TALKSPORT
🖳 18 Hatfields, London SE1 8DJ ☎20 7959 7800 📠20 7959 7808 **W:** talksport.com

| MW | kHz | kW | MW | kHz | kW |
|---|---|---|---|---|---|
| Bournemouth | 1053 | 1 | Brookmans Pk | 1089 | 400.0 |
| Brighton | 1053 | 2 | Dartford Tunnel | 1089 | 0.0 |
| Droitwich | 1053 | 500 | Lisnagarvey | 1089 | 13.0 |
| Dumfries | 1053 | 10.0 | Moorside Edge | 1089 | 100.0 |
| Dundee | 1053 | 1 | Redmoss | 1089 | 2 |
| Exeter | 1053 | 1 | Redruth | 1089 | 2 |
| Hull | 1053 | 1.0 | Washford | 1089 | 80 |
| Inverness | 1053 | 1 | Westerglen | 1089 | 125.0 |
| Londonderry | 1053 | 1.0 | Boston | 1107 | 1 |
| Plymouth | 1053 | 1.0 | Fareham | 1107 | 1.0 |
| Postwick | 1053 | 1.0 | Lydd | 1107 | 2 |
| Stockton | 1053 | 18.0 | Reigate/Crawley | 1107 | 1 |
| Tonbridge | 1053 | 4 | Torbay | 1107 | 1 |
| Clipstone | 1071 | 1.0 | Wallasey | 1107 | 1 |
| Newcastle | 1071 | 1.0 | | | |

**D.Prgr: 24h**

| MW | kHz | kW | Station or Slogan | Location |
|---|---|---|---|---|
| 156) | 1584 | 0.21 | Tay 2 | Perth |
| 11) | 1584 | 0.2 | Panjab R. | N.London |
| 83) | 1602 | 0.07 | Desi R.* | Southall |
| 29) | 1602 | 0.07 | Heritage R*# | Manchester |
| -) | 1602 | 0.001 | occasional RSLs | |

*community radio stns   # moving to FM in late 2018

## LOCAL RADIO STATIONS:

| MW | kHz | kW | Station or Slogan | Location |
|---|---|---|---|---|
| 120) | 558 | 1 | Love Sport R. | London |
| 12) | 648 | 1 | R. Caroline * | Orford Ness |
| 56) | 828 | 0.12 | R. Aire 2 | Leeds |
| 128) | 855 | 0.15 | Sunshine R. | Ludlow |
| 7) | 936 | 0.15 | Dales R* | Hawes |
| 69) | 945 | 0.2 | Gold | Derby |
| 1) | 963 | 0.95 | Sunrise R. | E. London |
| 93) | 963 | 0.2 | Asian Sound R. | Haslingden |
| 1) | 972 | 1 | Sunrise R. | W. London |
| 34) | 990 | 0.09 | Free R. 80s | Wolverhampton |
| 53) | 990 | 0.25 | Hallam 2 | Doncaster |
| 60) | 999 | 0.8 | Rock 2 | Preston |
| 69) | 999 | 0.25 | Nottingham Gold | |
| 34) | 1017 | 0.63 | Free R. 80s | Shrewsbury |
| 153) | 1026 | 1.7 | Downtown R. | Belfast |
| 160) | 1035 | 0.32 | West Sound | Ayr |
| 167) | 1035 | 2.5 | Lyca Dilse | London |
| 161) | 1107 | 1.5 | MFR 2 | Inverness |
| -) | 1134 | 0.001 | LPAMs | |
| 33) | 1152 | 23.5 | LBC | London |
| 158) | 1152 | 3.6 | Clyde 2 | Glasgow |
| 34) | 1152 | 3 | Free R. 80s | Birmingham |
| 51) | 1152 | 1.5 | Key R. | Manchester |
| 61) | 1152 | 1.8 | Metro 2 | Newcastle |
| 54) | 1161 | 0.35 | Viking 2 | Hull |
| 156) | 1161 | 1.4 | Tay 2 | Dundee |
| 127) | 1170 | 0.58 | Swansea Sound | Swansea |
| 59) | 1170 | 0.32 | TFM 2 | Stockton |
| 35) | 1170 | 0.2 | Signal 2 | Stoke-on-Trent |
| -) | 1251 | 0.001 | LPAMs | |
| 151) | 1260 | 0.29 | Sabras R. | Leicester |
| 106) | 1278 | 0.43 | Pulse 2 | Bradford |
| -) | 1278 | 0.001 | LPAMs/RSLs | |
| -) | 1287 | 0.001 | LPAMs | |
| 131) | 1287 | 0.004 | R. Glan Clwyd* | Bodelwyddan |
| 148) | 1296 | 10 | R. XL | Birmingham |
| 53) | 1305 | 0.15 | Hallam 2 | Barnsley |
| 98) | 1305 | 0.5 | Premier Christian R. | Epsom |
| 98) | 1305 | 0.5 | Premier Christian R. | Chingford |
| 78) | 1323 | 0.002 | Akash R* | Leeds |
| 98) | 1332 | 1 | Premier Christian R. | London |
| 149) | 1332 | 0.1 | R. Warrington* | Warrington |
| -) | 1350 | 0.001 | LPAMs | |
| 34) | 1359 | 0.27 | Free R. 80s | Coventry |
| 93) | 1377 | 0.08 | Asian Sound R. | Ashton Moss |
| -) | 1386 | 0.001 | LPAMs | |
| 98) | 1413 | 0.5 | Premier Christian R. | Heathrow |
| 98) | 1413 | 0.5 | Premier Christian R. | Dartford Marshes |
| 44) | 1413 | 0.04 | Bradford Asian R.* | Bradford |
| -) | 1431 | 0.001 | LPAMs | |
| -) | 1449 | 0.001 | LPAMs | |
| 167) | 1458 | 125 | Lyca R. | W. London |
| 45) | 1458 | 5 | Gold | Manchester |
| 81) | 1503 | 0.1 | Betar Bangla* | E. London |
| 137) | 1521 | 0.07 | Flame CCR* | Wirral |
| 117) | 1521 | 0.04 | R. Panj* | Coventry |
| 106) | 1530 | 0.74 | Pulse 2 | Huddersfield |
| 33) | 1548 | 97.5 | Gold | London |
| 53) | 1548 | 0.74 | Hallam 2 | Sheffield |
| 52) | 1548 | 1 | R. City Talk | Liverpool |
| 159) | 1548 | 2.2 | Forth 2 | Edinburgh |
| 98) | 1566 | 0.8 | Premier Christian R. | Guildford |
| -) | 1575 | 0.001 | LPAMs | |

| FM | MHz | kW | Name or Slogan | Location |
|---|---|---|---|---|
| -) | 87.7 | - | RSLs/LPFMs | |
| -) | 87.9 | - | RSLs | |
| 100) | 88.0 | 1.4 | Heart - N Wales | Wrexham |
| 173) | 93.6 | 0.1 | R. Tyneside* | Newcastle |
| 91) | 95.2 | 0.2 | Kingdom FM | Dunfermline |
| 118) | 96.0 | 0.125 | Wessex FM | Bridport |
| 91) | 96.1 | 0.5 | Kingdom FM | Glenrothes |
| 108) | 96.1 | 0.2 | Rother FM | Rotherham |
| 124) | 96.2 | 4 | SIBC | Shetland |
| 63) | 96.2 | 0.2 | KMFM | Tonbridge |
| 99) | 96.2 | - | Mix 96 | Aylesbury |
| 50) | 96.2 | 2.6 | North Norfolk R. | Stody |
| 138) | 96.2 | 0.1 | Revolution | Oldham |
| 145) | 96.2 | 0.625 | Yorkshire Coast R. | Scarborough |
| 116) | 96.2 | 0.1 | Touch FM | Coventry |
| 56) | 96.3 | 2.5 | R. Aire | Leeds |
| 15) | 96.3 | 0.1 | 2BR | Chorley |
| 67) | 96.3 | 4 | Nation R. | Glasgow |
| 153) | 96.4 | 2 | Downtown R. | Limavady |
| 34) | 96.4 | 10 | Free R, | Birmingham |
| 127) | 96.4 | 1.5 | The Wave | Swansea |
| 154) | 96.4 | 3 | Eagle R. | Guildford |
| 156) | 96.4 | 0.8 | Tay FM | Perth |
| 35) | 96.4 | 0.25 | Signal 1 | Congleton |
| 163) | 96.4 | 3 | CFM | Carlisle |
| 63) | 96.4 | 0.2 | KMFM | Folkestone |
| 112) | 96.4 | 0.1 | Compass FM | Grimsby |
| 47) | 96.5 | 0.4 | R. Wave | Blackpool |
| 157) | 96.5 | 0.12 | West Sound | Stranraer |
| 153) | 96.6 | 8.2 | Downtown R. | Brougher Mountain |
| 79) | 96.6 | 0.1 | The Breeze | Blandford |
| 26) | 96.6 | 0.2 | R North Angus | Arbroath |
| 59) | 96.6 | 10 | TFM R. | Bilsdale |
| 31) | 96.6 | 0.4 | R. Ceredigion | Lampeter |
| 142) | 96.6 | 0.3 | Nevis R.* | Fort William |
| 161) | 96.6 | 0.45 | MFR | Cairngorm |
| 25) | 96.6 | 0.4 | Spirit FM | Chichester |
| 160) | 96.7 | 2.2 | West FM | Ayr |
| 52) | 96.7 | 8 | R. City | Liverpool |
| 135) | 96.7 | 0.55 | Q R. | Belfast |
| 115) | 96.7 | 3 | KL.FM | King's Lynn |
| 96) | 96.7 | 0.2 | Ashbourne R. | Ashbourne |
| 70) | 96.7 | 0.1 | Free R. | Kidderminster |
| 161) | 96.7 | 0.1 | MFR | Fraserburgh |
| 162) | 96.8 | 5 | R. Borders | Selkirk |
| 125) | 96.8 | 0.5 | Lochbroom FM | Polbain |
| 54) | 96.9 | 9.4 | Viking FM | Hull |
| 155) | 96.9 | 10.4 | Northsound 1 | Aberdeen |
| 35) | 96.9 | 0.2 | Signal 1 | Stafford |
| 157) | 97.0 | 1 | West Sound | Dumfries |
| 34) | 97.0 | 1.8 | Free R. | Coventry |
| 61) | 97.1 | 10 | Metro R. | Newcastle |
| 107) | 97.1 | 0.275 | The Breeze | Haslemere |
| 153) | 97.1 | 0.08 | Downtown R. | Larne |
| 66) | 97.1 | 3 | R. Carmarthenshire | Carmel |
| 136) | 97.2 | 0.12 | Connect FM | Wellingborough |
| 34) | 97.2 | 2 | Free R. | Wolverhampton |
| 58) | 97.2 | 0.3 | Kiss | Bristol |
| 135) | 97.2 | 0.31 | Q R. | Coleraine |
| 118) | 97.2 | 0.7 | Wessex FM | Dorchester/Weymouth |
| 147) | 97.2 | 1 | Stray FM | Harrogate |
| 33) | 97.3 | 4 | LBC | London |
| 159) | 97.3 | 9.8 | Forth 1 | Edinburgh |
| 161) | 97.4 | 6.25 | MFR | Inverness |
| 60) | 97.4 | 2 | Rock FM | Preston/Blackpool |
| 153) | 97.4 | 3.2 | Cool FM | Belfast |
| 53) | 97.4 | 0.4 | Hallam FM | Sheffield |
| 31) | 97.4 | 0.4 | R. Ceredigion | Penwaun |
| 79) | 97.4 | 0.125 | The Breeze | Shaftesbury |
| 50) | 97.4 | 0.24 | The Beach | Southwold |
| 106) | 97.5 | 0.5 | Pulse 1 | Bradford |
| 28) | 97.5 | 0.4 | Heartland FM | Pitlochry |
| 160) | 97.5 | 0.15 | West FM | Girvan |
| 66) | 97.5 | 0.2 | R. Carmarthenshire | Llanelli |

| FM | MHz | kW | Name or Slogan | Location | FM | MHz | kW | Name or Slogan | Location |
|---|---|---|---|---|---|---|---|---|---|
| 70) | 97.6 | 0.8 | Free R. | Hereford | 158) | 103.3 | 0.1 | Clyde 1 | Rosneath |
| 159) | 97.6 | 0.1 | Forth 1 | Edinburgh | 6) | 103.3 | 0.4 | Oban FM | Oban |
| 33) | 97.7 | 1 | R. X | Manchester | 53) | 103.4 | 1.6 | Hallam FM | Doncaster |
| 15) | 99.8 | 0.75 | 2BR | Burnley | 153) | 103.4 | 0.2 | Downtown R. | Newcastle |
| 68) | 99.8 | 0.75 | KCFM | Hull | 162) | 103.4 | 0.5 | R. Borders | Eyemouth |
| 50) | 99.9 | 0.5 | R. Norwich | Stoke Holy Cross | 39) | 103.4 | 0.3 | Sun FM | Sunderland |
| 58) | 100.0 | 4 | Kiss | London | 163) | 103.4 | 0.4 | CFM | Whitehaven |
| 105) | 100.2 | 2 | Dream 100 | Clacton-on-Sea | 50) | 103.4 | 2 | The Beach | Lowestoft |
| 63) | 100.4 | 0.3 | KMFM | Hoo St.Werburgh | 141) | 103.5 | 0.2 | Minster FM | Northallerton |
| 135) | 100.5 | 1 | Q R. | Newry | 21) | 103.7 | 4 | Channel 103 FM | Jersey |
| 79) | 100.8 | 0.13 | The Breeze | Porlock | 141) | 104.7 | 2.5 | Minster FM | York |
| 58) | 101.0 | 40 | Kiss | Mendip | 5) | 104.7 | 1.25 | Island FM | Guernsey |
| 135) | 101.1 | 0.4 | Q R. | Kilkeel | 140) | 104.9 | 0.64 | Imagine FM | Stockport |
| 135) | 101.1 | 0.125 | Q R. | Newcastle | 33) | 104.9 | 2.9 | R. X | London |
| 64) | 101.2 | 1.37 | Waves R. | Peterhead | 95) | 105.1 | 0.5 | R. Essex | Southend-on-Sea |
| 135) | 101.2 | 6.26 | Q R. | Brougher Mountain | 58) | 105.2 | 11 | Absolute R. | Sutton Coldfield |
| 172) | 101.4 | 0.1 | Flex FM * | SW London | 164) | 105.2 | 10 | Wave 105 | Solent |
| 107) | 101.6 | 0.1 | The Breeze | Alton | 57) | 105.2 | 0.8 | An R.* | Benbecula |
| 63) | 101.6 | 0.4 | KMFM | Wrotham | 91) | 105.4 | 0.1 | Kingdom FM | Fife |
| 107) | 101.8 | 0.11 | The Breeze | Petersfield | 58) | 105.4 | 4 | Magic 105.4 | Croydon |
| 2) | 102.0 | 1 | Ipswich 102 | Ipswich | 111) | 105.5 | 1.6 | The Breeze | Torbay |
| 108) | 102.0 | 0.45 | Dearne FM | Barnsley | 58) | 105.6 | 1 | Kiss | Cambridge |
| 130) | 102.0 | 0.1 | Peak FM | Matlock | 79) | 105.6 | 0.4 | The Breeze | Yeovil |
| 146) | 102.0 | 1.25 | Spire FM | Salisbury | 63) | 105.6 | 0.15 | KMFM | Maidstone |
| 107) | 102.0 | 0.1 | The Breeze | Alton | 133) | 105.6 | 0.1 | The Breeze | Newbury |
| 116) | 102.0 | 2.6 | Touch FM | Stratford upon Avon | 10) | 105.8 | 1.9 | U105 | Belfast |
| 73) | 102.0 | 0.2 | Wave FM | Dundee | 164) | 105.8 | 0.625 | Wave 105 | Poole |
| 8) | 102.1 | 1.2 | Swansea Bay R. | Swansea | 52) | 105.9 | 7.5 | R. City 2 | Liverpool |
| 159) | 102.2 | 0.5 | Forth 1 | Penicuik | 128) | 105.9 | 1 | Sunshine R. | Woofferton |
| 112) | 102.2 | 6.4 | Lincs FM | Belmont | 107) | 106.0 | 4 | Sam FM | Solent |
| 165) | 102.2 | 2.5 | Pirate FM | Caradon Hill | 38) | 106.0 | 8 | Gem 106 | Copt Oak |
| 163) | 102.2 | 0.815 | CFM | Workington | 135) | 106.0 | 0.6 | Q R. | Cookstown |
| 125) | 102.2 | 0.7 | Lochbroom FM | Ullapool | 63) | 106.0 | 0.1 | KMFM | Canterbury |
| 141) | 102.3 | 0.1 | Minster FM | Thirsk | 75) | 106.0 | 0.6 | Two Lochs R. | Gairloch |
| 158) | 102.3 | 0.6 | Clyde 1 | Rothesay | 58) | 106.1 | 4 | Kiss | Stoke Holy Cross |
| 25) | 102.3 | 0.5 | Spirit FM | Littlehampton | 37) | 106.1 | 1 | XS | Manchester |
| 153) | 102.3 | 0.5 | Downtown R. | Ballymena | 121) | 106.1 | 0.2 | R Newquay * | Newquay |
| 142) | 102.3 | 0.8 | Nevis R.* | Fort William | 103) | 106.2 | 1.5 | Sunshine R. | Hereford |
| 4) | 102.4 | 0.1 | Touch FM | Burton | 91) | 106.3 | 0.15 | Kingdom FM | Fife |
| 84) | 102.4 | 4 | The Breeze | Minehead | 30) | 106.3 | 0.9 | Bridge FM | Bridgend |
| 153) | 102.4 | 10 | Downtown R. | Londonderry | 19) | 106.3 | 0.175 | Original 106 | Peterhead |
| 158) | 102.4 | 0.6 | Clyde 1 | Rosneath | 27) | 106.3 | 0.2 | Dee | Chester |
| 145) | 102.4 | 0.1 | Yorkshire Coast R. | Bridlington | 58) | 106.4 | 20 | Kiss | Mendelsham |
| 22) | 102.4 | 0.1 | Wish FM | Wigan | 55) | 106.4 | 0.4 | More R. | Haywards Heath |
| 142) | 102.4 | 0.5 | Nevis R.* | Glenachulish | 74) | 106.4 | 0.25 | High Peak R.(2 txs) | Buxton/Glossop |
| 158) | 102.5 | 24.5 | Clyde 1 | Glasgow | 133) | 106.4 | 1 | The Breeze | Andover |
| 106) | 102.5 | 2 | Pulse 1 | Halifax | 13) | 106.5 | 0.5 | Argyll FM | Campbeltown |
| 161a) | 102.5 | 1.2 | MFR / Caithness* | Thurso | 3) | 106.5 | 0.5 | Signal 107 | Shrewsbury |
| 102) | 102.5 | 20 | R. Pembrokeshire | Haverfordwest | 84) | 106.5 | 1 | Sam FM | Bristol |
| 163) | 102.5 | 0.1 | CFM | Penrith | 15) | 106.5 | 0.1 | 2BR | Preston |
| 144) | 102.5 | 0.2 | Mon FM* | Anglesey | 107) | 106.6 | 0.3 | Sam FM | Poole |
| 35) | 102.6 | 4 | Signal 1 | Stoke-on-Trent | 79) | 106.6 | 0.25 | The Breeze | Chard |
| 61) | 102.6 | 0.125 | Metro R. | Alnwick | 75) | 106.6 | 2 | Two Lochs R. | Loch Ewe |
| 150) | 102.6 | 0.1 | Rathergood R. | Richmond | 25) | 106.6 | 0.4 | Spirit FM | Midhurst |
| 62) | 102.7 | 9 | Cuillin FM | Isle of Skye | 73) | 106.6 | 0.25 | Wave FM | Perth |
| 150) | 102.8 | 0.33 | Rathergood R. | Sacriston | 168) | 106.6 | 0.2 | BCB* | Bradford |
| 70) | 102.8 | 1 | Free R. | Worcester | 23) | 106.7 | 0.1 | Bob FM | Stevenage |
| 156) | 102.8 | 5 | Tay FM | Dundee | 160) | 106.7 | 0.6 | West FM | Rothesay |
| 165) | 102.8 | 10 | Pirate FM | Redruth | 18) | 106.7 | 0.62 | R. Plymouth | Ft Staddon |
| 147) | 102.8 | 1 | Stray FM | Skipton | 8) | 106.8 | 4 | Nation R. | Cardiff |
| 161) | 102.8 | 1 | MFR | Keith | 55) | 106.8 | 0.1 | More R. | Lewes |
| 8) | 102.9 | 3.2 | Nation R. | Carmel | 63) | 106.8 | 0.1 | KMFM | Dover |
| 53) | 102.9 | 0.45 | Hallam FM | Barnsley | 136) | 106.8 | 0.2 | Connect FM | Peterborough |
| 135) | 102.9 | 3.14 | Q R. | Londonderry | 108) | 106.8 | 0.5 | Ridings FM | Wakefield |
| 51) | 103.0 | 4 | Hits R. | Manchester | 65) | 106.8 | 0.3 | Jack FM | Oxford |
| 143) | 103.0 | 3.6 | Isles FM | Stornoway | 19) | 106.8 | 19 | Original FM | Aberdeen |
| 155) | 103.0 | 0.174 | Northsound 1 | Peterhead | 134) | 106.8 | 0.05 | Rinse FM* | C London |
| 166) | 103.0 | 0.1 | Your R. | Dumbarton | 23) | 106.9 | 0.28 | Bob FM | Hertford |
| 157) | 103.0 | 0.7 | West Sound | Kirkcudbright | 152) | 106.9 | 0.3 | Silk FM | Macclesfield |
| 7) | 103.0 | 0.1 | Dales R.* | Ingleton | 166) | 106.9 | 0.2 | Your R. | Helensburgh |
| 34) | 103.1 | 2.7 | Free R. | Shrewsbury | 24) | 107.0 | 0.1 | Fosse 107 | Loughborough |
| 14) | 103.1 | 0.5 | Central FM | Stirling | 15) | 107.0 | 0.5 | 2BR | Blackburn |
| 153) | 103.1 | 1.8 | Downtown R. | Newry | 113) | 107.0 | 0.1 | Isle of Wight R. | Chillerton Down |
| 50) | 103.2 | 0.25 | North Norfolk R. (2 txs) | N. Norfolk | 133) | 107.0 | 0.2 | The Breeze | Reading |
| 32) | 103.2 | 0.1 | Mansfield 103.2 | Mansfield | 135) | 107.0 | 0.62 | Q R. | Ballymena |
| 123) | 103.2 | 0.5 | Sunrise FM | Bradford | 103) | 107.0 | 1 | Sunshine R. | Monmouth |
| 150) | 103.2 | 0.365 | Rathergood R. | Darlington | 33) | 107.1 | 0.13 | Capital Xtra | N. London |
| 61) | 103.2 | 0.12 | Metro R. | Hexham | 8) | 107.1 | 2.5 | Nation R. | Preseli |
| 74) | 103.3 | 0.17 | High Peak R. | Buxworth | 108) | 107.1 | 0.5 | Trax FM | Doncaster |
| 74) | 103.3 | 0.1 | High Peak R. | Hope Valley | 48) | 107.1 | 0.14 | Speysound R.* | Aviemore |
| 114) | 103.3 | 0.1 | London Greek R. | London | 46) | 107.1 | 0.12 | Star R. | Ely |
| 31) | 103.3 | 5.8 | R. Ceredigion | Blaenplwyf | 147) | 107.1 | 0.1 | Stray FM | Ilkley & Pateley Br. |

| FM | MHz | kW | Name or Slogan | Location |
|---|---|---|---|---|
| 13) | 107.1 | 0.625 | Argyll FM | Ballygroggan |
| 116) | 107.1 | 0.1 | Rugby FM | Rugby |
| 3) | 107.1 | 0.1 | Signal 107 | Oswestry |
| 57) | 107.2 | 0.6 | An R.* | Daliburgh |
| 135) | 107.2 | 0.25 | Q R. | Dungannon |
| 107) | 107.2 | 0.2 | The Breeze | Winchester |
| 22) | 107.2 | 0.18 | Wire FM | Warrington |
| 110) | 107.2 | 0.2 | Rutland R. | Oakham |
| 63) | 107.2 | 0.1 | KMFM | Thanet |
| 84) | 107.2 | 0.66 | The Breeze | Bristol |
| 3) | 107.2 | 0.2 | Signal 107 | Kidderminster |
| 119) | 107.3 | 1 | R. Exe | Exeter |
| 116) | 107.3 | 0.2 | Touch FM | Warwick |
| 8) | 107.3 | 1.25 | Nation R. | Swansea |
| 77) | 107.3 | 0.18 | Reprezent* | S. London |
| 136) | 107.4 | 0.2 | Connect FM | Kettering |
| 84) | 107.4 | 0.1 | The Breeze | Bridgwater |
| 130) | 107.4 | 0.1 | Peak FM | Chesterfield |
| 3) | 107.4 | 0.1 | Signal 107 | Telford |
| 22) | 107.4 | 0.18 | Tower FM | Bolton |
| 107) | 107.4 | 0.2 | The Breeze | Portsmouth |
| 102) | 107.5 | 0.1 | R. Pembrokeshire | Fishguard |
| 80) | 107.5 | 0.1 | The Breeze | Cheltenham |
| 126) | 107.5 | 0.4 | Time | Romford |
| 55) | 107.5 | 0.15 | More R. | Eastbourne |
| 84) | 107.5 | 0.1 | The Breeze | Warminster |
| 133) | 107.6 | 0.1 | The Breeze | Basingstoke |
| 90) | 107.6 | 0.2 | Vibe* | Watford |
| 107) | 107.6 | 1 | Fire R. | Bournemouth |
| 116) | 107.6 | 0.1 | Banbury Sound | Banbury |
| 63) | 107.6 | 0.5 | KMFM | Ashford, Kent |
| 136) | 107.6 | 0.15 | Q R. | Larne |
| 129) | 107.6 | 0.85 | KCR* | Keith |
| 2) | 107.7 | 0.2 | Sam FM | Swindon |
| 84) | 107.7 | 0.1 | The Breeze | Weston Super Mare |
| 95) | 107.7 | 0.1 | R. Essex | Chelmsford |
| 58) | 107.7 | 0.1 | Kiss | Peterborough |
| 55) | 107.7 | 0.1 | More R. | Worthing |
| 3) | 107.7 | 0.17 | Signal 107 | Wolverhampton |
| 13) | 107.7 | 0.5 | Argyll FM | South Knapdale |
| 55) | 107.8 | 0.1 | More R. | Hastings |
| 139) | 107.8 | 0.8 | R. Jackie | SW London |
| 107) | 107.8 | 0.5 | The Breeze | Southampton |
| 171) | 107.8 | 0.2 | The Voice * | Bideford |
| 147) | 107.8 | 1 | Stray FM | Skipton |
| 108) | 107.9 | 0.1 | Trax FM | Worksop |
| 198) | 107.9 | 0.1 | Star R. | Cambridge |
| 24) | 107.9 | 0.2 | Fosse 107 | Hinckley |
| 84) | 107.9 | 0.2 | The Breeze | Bath |
| 65) | 107.9 | 0.2 | Jack 2 | Oxford |
| 63) | 107.9 | 0.5 | KMFM | Rochester |
| 170) | 107.9 | 0.1 | R. Scilly* | St Mary's |
| 94) | 107.9 | 0.1 | GTFM* | Pontypridd |
| 169) | 107.9 | 0.1 | The Cat* | Crewe |

+approx 250 stns of less than 0.1kW *community radio stns

**H. of tr:** Most stns operate 24h Some stns carry automated prgrs outside peak hours

## MAJOR COMMERCIAL RADIO GROUPS:

**CELADOR RADIO** ⌨ Roman Landing, 35-37 St Marys Place, Southampton SO14 1BN ☎ 23 8038 4138 **W:** celador.co.uk

**COMMUNICORP UK** ⌨ Level 7, XYZ Building, Hardman Blvd., Manchester M3 3AQ ☎ 161 886 8800 **W:** communicorpuk.com/radio

**BAUER RADIO LTD** ⌨ 1 Golden Square, London W1W 9DJ ☎ 20 7434 1215 **W:** bauermedia.co.uk

**GLOBAL** ⌨ 30 Leicester Square, London WC2H 7LA ☎ 20 7766 6000 ☐ 20 7766 6111 **W:** global.com/radio

**LINCS FM GROUP** ⌨ Witham Park, Waterside South, Lincoln LN5 7JN ☎ 1522 549900 ☐ 1522 549911 **W:** lincsfmgroup.co.uk

**UKRD GROUP Ltd** ⌨ Unit 10, Barncoose Ind. Est, Wilson Way, Redruth TR15 3RQ ☎ 1209 310435 ☐ 1209 310406 **W:** ukrd.com

**WIRELESS GROUP** ⌨ 1 London Bridge St., London SE1 9GF ☎ 20 7782 6000 **W:** wirelessgroup.co.uk

## Addresses & other information:

**1)** Unit 2, 694-712 London Rd., Hounslow TW3 1PG ☎ 20 8574 6666 **W:** sunriseradio.com – **2)** ☎ 1793 858222 **W:** ipswich102radio.com – **3)** 2nd Floor, Mander House, Wolverhampton WV1 3NB ☎ 1902 571070 **W:** signal107.co.uk – **4)** addr as 116 **W:** 101touchfm.co.uk – **5)** 12 Westerbrook, St Sampsons, Guernsey GY2 4QQ ☎ 1481 242000 **W:** islandfm.com – **6)** 132 George Street, Oban PA34 5NT ☎ 1631 570057 **W:** obanfm.com – **7)** Colvend, Hebden Rd., Grassington, BD23 5LB **W:** dalesradio.co – **8)** St Hilary Transmitter, St Hilary, Cowbridge, CF71 1DP ☎ 1792 716200 **W:** nationradio.wales swanseabayradio. wales– **9)** Eleven Brindley Place, 2 Brunswick Square, Birmingham B1 2LP ☎ 121 695 0000 – **10)** Level 7, City Quays 2, Clarendon Rd., Belfast BT1 3BG ☎ 28 9033 3105 **W:** u105.com – **11)** Springfield Rd, Hayes UB4 0TH ☎ 20 8848 8877 **W:** panjabradio.co.uk – **12)** PO Box 12524, Maldon, Essex CM9 9EX ☎ 208 340 3831 **W:** radiocaroline. co.uk – **13)** 27-29 Longrow, Campbeltown PA28 6ER ☎ 1586 551800 **W:** argyllfm.com – **14)** 9 Munroe Rd., Stirling FK7 7UU ☎ 1324 611164 **W:** centralfm.co.uk – **15)** 2A Petre Court, Petre Rd, Clayton-le-Moors, Accrington BB5 5HH ☎ 1282 690000 **W:** 2br.co.uk – **16)** Unit 5 Metro Centre, Dwight Rd, Watford WD18 9UD ☎ 1923 205480 **W:** heart.co.uk/watfordhemel – **17)** 33-39 Strand Str., Liverpool L1 8LT ☎ 151 550 5800 – **18)** 3 Crescent Ave. Mews, Plymouth PL1 3AP ☎ 1752 389532 **W:** radioplymouth.com – **19)** Craigshaw Rd, Aberdeen AB12 3AR ☎ 1224 294860 **W:** originalfm.com – **20)** 5-6 Aldergate, Tamworth, B79 7DJ ☎ 1827 318000 **W:** touchfm.co.uk – **21)** 6 Tunnell Street, St Helier, Jersey JE2 4LU ☎ 1534 888103 **W:** channel103.com – **22)** Orrell Lodge, Orrell Rd, Wigan WN5 8HJ ☎ 1942 761024 **W:** wishfm.net towerfm.co.uk wirefm.co.uk – **23)** The Pumphouse, Knebworth Park SG3 6HQ ☎ 1438 810900 **W:** bobfm.co.uk – **24)** Graphic House, Druid Str., Hinckley LE10 1QH **W:** fosse107.co.uk – **25)** 9/10 Dukes Court, Bognor Rd, Chichester PO19 8FX ☎ 1243 773600 **W:** spiritfm.net – **26)** Arbroath Infirmary, Rosemount Rd, Arbroath DD11 2AT ☎ 1241 879660 **W:** radionorthangus.co.uk – **27)** 2 Chantry Court, Chester CH1 4QN ☎ 1244 391000 **W:** dee1063.com – **28)** 23 Atholl Rd., Pitlochry PH16 5BX ☎ 1796 474040 **W:** heartlandfm.org – **29)** British Muslim Heritage Centre, College Rd., Manchester M16 8BP ☎161 883 2266 **W:** heritageradio.org.uk – **30)** PO Box 1063, Bridgend CF35 6WY ☎ 1656 838620 **W:** bridgefm.wales – **31)** Merlin House, Parc Merlin, Glan Yr Afon Ind. Est., Aberystwyth SY23 3FF ☎1970 229110 **W:** ceredigionradio.wales – **32)** Unit 4, Brunts Business Centre, Samuel Brunts Way, Mansfield NG18 2AH ☎ 1623 646666 **W:** mansfield103.co.uk – **33)** 30 Leicester Square, London WC2H 7LA ☎ 20 7766 6000 **W:** capitalfm.com Capital Xtra: capitalxtra.com Gold: mygoldmusic.co.uk LBC: lbc.co.uk R.X: radiox. co.uk – **34)** 9 Brindleyplace, 4 Oozells Square, Birmingham B1 2DJ ☎ 121 566 5200 **W:** planetradio.co.uk/free, planetradio.co.uk/free-80s – **35)** 67-73 Stoke Rd, Stoke-on-Trent ST4 2SR ☎ 1782 441 300 **W:** signal1.co.uk – **36)** 36 Gallowgate, Newcastle upon Tyne NE1 4TD ☎ 191 444 2500 – **37)** XYZ Building, 2 Hardman Blvd., Manchester M3 3AQ ☎ 161 662 4602 **W:** smoothradio.com xsmanchester.co.uk – **38)** City Link, Nottingham NG2 4NG ☎ 115 910 6100 **W:** planetradio. co.uk/gem-106 – **39)** Business & Innovation Centre, Sunderland Enterprise Park, Sunderland SR5 2TA ☎ 191 548 1034 **W:** sun-fm.com – **40)** Radio House, John Wilson Business Park, Whitstable CT5 3QX ☎ 1227 772004 – **41)** Radio House, Franklin Rd., Brighton BN41 1AF ☎ 1273 316900 – **42)** Red Dragon Centre, Hemingway Rd., Cardiff CF10 4JY ☎ 29 2031 5100 – **43)** Apple Ind. Estate, Whittle Ave, Fareham PO15 5SX ☎ 1489 587600 – **44)** 8th Floor, West Riding Business Centre, 41 Cheapside, Bradford BD1 4HR ☎ 1274 306677 **W:** bradfordasianradio.co.uk – **45)** XYZ Building, 2 Hardman Str., Manchester M3 3AQ ☎ 161 662 4700 **W:** mygoldmusic.co.uk – **46)** 20 Mercers Row, Cambridge CB5 8HY ☎ 1223 305107 **W:** starradioonline.com – **47)** Mowbray Drive, Blackpool FY3 7UN ☎ 1253 650300 **W:** wave965.com – **48)** Suite 5, Aviemore Shopping Centre, Grampian Rd., Aviemore PH22 1RH ☎ 1479 811888 **W:** speysound.com – **49)** 2a Joseph's Well, Hanover Walk, Leeds LS3 1AB ☎ 113 308 5100 – **50)** 29 Yarmouth Rd, Norwich NR7 0EE ☎ 845 345 1035 **W:** radionorwich.radio, northnorfolkradio.com, thebeach.co.uk – **51)** Castle Quay, Castlefield, Manchester M15 4PR ☎ 161 288 5000 **W:** planetradio.co.uk/hits-radio; planetradio.co.uk/key-radio – **52)** St Johns Beacon, 1 Houghton Street, Liverpool L1 1RL ☎ 151 472 6800 **W:** radiocity.co.uk radiocity2.co.uk – **53)** 900 Herries Rd, Sheffield S6 1RH ☎ 114 2091000 **W:** planetradio.co.uk/hallam – **54)** The Boathouse, Commercial Rd, Hull HU1 2SG ☎ 1482 325141 **W:** planetradio.co.uk/viking – **55)** Guildbourne Centre, Worthing BN11 1LZ ☎1903 233271 **W:** moreradio.online – **56)** PO Box 2000, 51 Burley Rd, Leeds LS3 1LR ☎ 113 283 5500 **W:** radioaire.co – **57)** Room 29, East Camp, Balivanich, Isle of Benbecula HS7 5LA **W:** anradio.scot – **58)** 1 Golden Square, London W1F 9DJ ☎ 20 7434 1215 **W:** Magic: planetradio.co.uk/magic Kiss: planetradio.co.uk/kissf Absolute: absoluteradio.co.uk – **59)** addr as 61 **W:** planetradio.co.uk/ tfm – **60)** St Paul's Square, Preston PR1 1XA ☎ 1772 477700 **W:** planetradio.co.uk/rock-fm – **61)** 55 Degrees North, Pilgrim St., Newcastle upon Tyne NE1 6BF ☎ 191 230 6100 **W:** planetradio. co.uk/metro radio.co.uk/metro/metro-2 – **62)** Stormyhill Rd, Portree IV51 9DT ☎ 1478 611796– **W:** cuillinfm.co.uk – **63)** Medway House, Sir Thomas Longley Rd, , Medway City Estate, Rochester ME2 4DU ☎

1634 711079 **W:** kmfm.co.uk – **64)** 7 Blackhouse Circle, Blackhouse Industrial Estate, Peterhead AB42 1BN ☎ 1779 491012 **W:** wavesfm.com – **65)** 270 Woodstock Rd, Oxford OX2 7NW ☎ 1865 315980 **W:** jackfm.co.uk – **66)** Parc y Scarlets, Llanelli SA14 9UZ ☎ 1267 679250 **W:** radiocarmarthenshire.wales– **67)** 272 Bath Str., Glasgow, G2 4JR ☎ 141 811 0470 **W:** nationradio.scot – **68)** Unit 3, Maritime House, Livingstone Rd., Hessle, HU13 0EG ☎ 1482 333999 **W:** kcfm.co.uk – **69)** Chapel Quarter, Maid Marian Way, Nottingham NG1 6HQ ☎ 115 986 1066 **W:** capitalfm.com; mygoldmusic.co.uk – **70)** Kirkham House, John Comyn Drive, Worcester WR3 7NS ☎ 1905 545510 **W:** planetradio.co.uk/free – **71)** 5 Abbey Court, Fraser Rd, Bedford, MK44 3WH ☎ 1234 235010 – **72)** 412 Midsummer Blvd, Milton Keynes MK9 2EA ☎ 1582 676200 – **73)** 11 Buchanan Str., Dundee, DD4 6SD ☎ 1382 901000 **W:** wavefmradio.co.uk – **74)** Smithbrook Close, Chapel-en-le-Frith, High Peak SK23 0QD ☎ 1298 813144 **W:** highpeakradio.co.uk – **75)** Mansegate, Gairloch IV21 2LR ☎ 870 712106 **W:** 2lr.co.uk – **76)** Bridge Studios, Eastgate Centre, Gloucester GL1 1SS ☎ 1452 572400 – **77)** Pop Brixton, 49 Brixton Station Rd., London SW9 8PQ ☎ 20 7639 8512 **W:** reprezent.org.uk – **78)** 122 Potternewton Lane, Leeds, LS7 2EG ☎ 113 217 4906 **W:** akashradioleeds.co.uk – **79)** Innovation Centre, Copse Rd., Yeovil BA22 8RN ☎ 1935 848488 **W:** thebreeze.com – **80)** Normandy House, 309 High Str., Cheltenham GL50 3HW ☎ 1242 227559 **W:** thebreeze.com – **81)** 4-8 Sutton St., London E1 0BB ☎ 20 7790 7970 **W:** betarbangla1503.net – **82)** Hawthorn Hse., Exeter Business Park, Exeter EX1 3QS ☎ 1392 444444 – **83)** Panjabi Centre, 30 Sussex Rd, Southall UB2 5EG ☎ 20 8574 9591 **W:** desiradio.org.uk – **84)** County Gates, Ashton Rd, Bristol BS3 2JH ☎ 117 966 6107 **W:** thebreeze.com samfm.co.uk/bristol samfm.co.uk/swindon – **85)** 10 Wheal Kitty Workshops, St Agnes TR5 0RD ☎ 1872 554400 – **86)** 1 Passage Str., Bristol BS2 0JF ☎ 117 984 3200 – **87)** Chiseldon House, Stonehill Green, Westlea, Swindon SN5 7HB ☎ 1793 663000 – **88)** 2 Enterprise House, Chivers Way, Histon, Cambridge CB24 9ZR ☎ 1233 623800 – **89)** The Chase, Calcot, Reading RG31 7RB ☎ 118 9454400 – **90)** 59 Clarendon Rd, Watford WD17 1LA ☎ 1923 888650 **W:** vibe1076.co.uk – **91)** Elizabeth House, Barclay Court, Mitchelston Ind. Est., Kirkcaldy KY1 3WE ☎ 1592 753753 **W:** kingdomfm.co.uk – **92)** 31 Glebe Rd, Chelmsford CM1 1QG ☎ 1254 524500 – **93)** 42 Southall Str, Manchester M3 1LQ ☎ 161 288 1000 **W:** asiansoundradio.co.uk – **94)** Pinewood Studios, Pinewood Ave, Rhydyfelin, Pontypridd CF37 5EA ☎ 1443 406111 **W:** gtfm.co.uk – **95)** Icon Bldg., Western Esplanade, Southend-on-Sea SS1 1EE ☎ 1702 455070 **W:** radioessex.com – **96)** St Monicas House, Windmill Lane, Ashbourne DE6 1EY ☎ 1335 346967 **W:** ashbourneradio.co.uk – **97)** The Stanley Centre, Kelvin Way, Crawley RH10 9SE ☎ 1293 636000 **W:** mercuryfm.co.uk – **98)** 22 Chapter Street, London SW1P 4NP ☎ 20 7316 1300 **W:** premierchristianradio.com – **99)** Friars Square Studios, 11 Bourbon Street, Aylesbury HP20 2PZ ☎ 1296 399396 **W:** mix96.co.uk – **100)** The Studios, Mold Rd, Wrexham LL11 4AF ☎ 1978 722200 – **101)** Lakeland Food Park, Crook Rd, Kendal LA8 8QJ ☎ 1539 872000– **102)** Unit 14, Old School Estate, Station Rd, Narberth SA67 7DU ☎ 1834 887160 **W:** radiopembrokeshire.wales – **103)** Suite 5, Penn House, Broad Str. Hereford HR4 9AP ☎ 1432 360246 **W:** sunshineradio.co.uk – **104)** St George's Plain, 47-49 Colegate, Norwich NR3 1DB ☎ 1603 671100 – **105)** Unit 12 Alpha Business Park, White House Rd., Ipswich IP1 5LT ☎ 473 836102 **W:** dream100.com – **106)** New Augustus Str., Bradford BD1 5LL ☎ 1274 203040 **W:** pulse.co.uk, pulse2.net – **107)** Roman Landing, Kingsway, Southampton SO14 1BN ☎ 845 466 1107 **W:** samfm.co.uk/southcoast/ fireradio.co.uk – **108)** 5 Sidings Court, Doncaster DN4 5NU ☎ 1302 341166 **W:** dearnefm.co.uk ridingsfm.co.uk rotherfm.co.uk traxfm.co.uk – **109)** PO Box 969, 26 St George's Quay, Lancaster LA1 3LD ☎ 1524 895000 – **110)** 40 Melton Rd, Oakham LE15 6AY ☎ 1572 757868 **W:** rutlandradio.co.uk – **111)** Marble Court, Lymington Rd, Torquay TQ1 4FB ☎ 1803 321055 **W:** thebreeze.com/southdevon– **112)** Witham Park, Waterside South, Lincoln LN5 7JN ☎ 1472 362964 **W:** lincsfm.co.uk compassfm.co.uk – **113)** Dodnor Park, Newport, Isle of Wight PO30 5XE ☎ 1983 822557 **W:** iwradio.co.uk – **114)** LGR house, 437 High Rd, London N12 0AP ☎ 20 8349 6950 **W:** lgr.co.uk – **115)** 18 Blackfriars Street, Kings Lynn PE30 1NN ☎ 1553 772777 **W:** klfmradio.co.uk – **116)** Holly Farm Business Park, Honily, Kenilworth CV8 1NP ☎ 1788 220140 **W:** touchfm.co.uk rugbyfm.co.uk banburysound.co.uk – **117)** 6 Longford Rd, Coventry CV6 6DX ☎ 24 7668 1521 **W:** radiopanj.com – **118)** Poundbury House, Poundbury West Ind. Est., Dorchester DT1 2PG ☎ 1305 250333 **W:** wessexfm.co.uk – **119)** 6a Cranmere Court, Lustleigh Close, Exeter EX2 8PW ☎ 1392 823557 **W:** radioexe.co.uk – **120)** 115 Southwark St., London SE1 0JF **W:** lovesportradio.com – **121)** Prow Park, Newquay TR7 2SX ☎ 16377 806111 **W:** radionewquay.com – **122)** 8th Floor, 1 Regent Str. West, Glasgow G2 1RW ☎ 141 781 1011 – **123)** 55 Leeds Rd, Bradford BD1 5AF ☎ 1274 735043 **W:** sunriseradio.fm – **124)** Market Street, Lerwick, Shetland ZE1 0JN ☎

1595 695299 **W:** sibc.co.uk – **125)** Mill Street Industrial Estate, Ullapool IV26 2UN ☎ 1854 613131 **W:** lochbroomfm.com – **126)** Laurie Walk, The Liberty Centre, Romford RM1 3RT ☎ 1708 766375 **W:** time1075.net – **127)** Victoria Rd, Gowerton, Swansea SA4 3AB ☎ 1792 511964 **W:** swanseasound.co.uk thewave.co.uk – **128)** Unit 11, Burway Trading Estate, Ludlow SY8 1EN ☎ 1584 873795 **W:** sunshineradio.co.uk – **129)** 59a Land Street, Keith AB55 5AN ☎ 1542 866080 **W:** kcr.fm – **130)** Radio House, Foxwood Rd, Chesterfield S41 9RF ☎ 1246 269107 **W:** peakfm.co.uk – **131)** Glan Clwyd Hospital, Bodelwyddan, Rhyl LL18 5UJ ☎ 1745 584229 **W:** radioglanclwyd.co.uk – **133)** Suite 2, Paddington House, Festival Place, Basingstoke RG21 7LJ ☎ 1256 694000 **W:** thebreeze.com – **134)** Old Truman Brewery, 91 Brick Lane, London E1 6QL ☎ 20 7247 7252 **W:** rinse.fm – **135)** Fountain Centre, College Str., Belfast, BT1 6ET ☎ 28 9023 4967 **W:** goqradio.com – **136)** 55 Headlands, Kettering NN15 7EY ☎ 1536 513664 **W:** connectfm.com – **137)** St Pauls Road Mission Church, Birkenhead CH42 3UZ ☎ 151 643 1696 **W:** flameradio.org – **138)** Sarah Moor Studios, Henshaw St., Oldham OL1 3EN ☎ 161 621 6500 **W:** revolutionon962.com – **139)** 110 Tolworth Broadway, Surbiton KT6 7JD ☎ 20 8288 1300 **W:** radiojackie.com – **140)** 1 Waterloo Place, Watson Square, Stockport SK1 3AZ ☎ 161 476 7340 **W:** imaginefm.net – **141)** PO Box 123, Dunnington, York YO19 5ZX ☎ 1904 488888 **W:** minsterfm.com – **142)** Unit 4A, Ben Nevis Estate, Claggan, Fort William PH33 6PR ☎ 1397 700007 **W:** nevisradio.co.uk – **143)** 50 Seaforth Rd, Stornoway, Isle of Lewis HS1 2SH ☎ 1851 703333 **W:** isles.fm – **144)** 12 Ffordd yr Efail, Llangefni, Anglesey LL77 7ER ☎ 1248 722224 **W:** monfm.net – **145)** PO Box 962, Scarborough YO11 3ZP ☎ 1723 581700 **W:** yorkshirecoastradio.com – **146)** City Hall Studios, Malthouse Lane, Salisbury SP2 7QQ ☎ 1722 416644 **W:** spirefm.co.uk – **147)** The Hamlet, Hornbeam Park Avenue, Harrogate HG2 8RE ☎ 1423 522972 **W:** strayfm.com – **148)** KMS House, Bradford Street, Birmingham B12 0JD ☎ 121 753 5353 **W:** radioxl.net – **149)** Unit 54, Warrington Temporary Market, Academy St., Warrington WA1 2LH ☎ 1925 555110 **W:** radiowarrington.co.uk – **150)** Radio House, 11 Woodland Rd, Darlington DL3 7BJ ☎ 1325 341801 **W:** rathergoodradio.com – **151)** Radio House, 63 Melton Rd, Leicester LE4 6PN ☎ 116 261 0666 **W:** sabrasradio.com – **152)** Adelaide House, Aldelaide Str., Macclesfield SK10 2QS ☎ 1625 268000 **W:** silk1069.com – **153)** Kiltonga Ind. Estate, Newtownards, Co Down BT23 4ES ☎ 28 9181 5555 **W:** planteradio.co.uk/downtown, planetradio.co.uk/cool-fm – **154)** Guildford College, Stoke Rd., Guildford GU1 1EZ ☎ 1483 468700 **W:** 964eagle.co.uk – **155)** Abbottswell Rd, West Tullos, Aberdeen AB12 3AJ ☎ 1224 337000 **W:** planetradio.co.uk/northsound – **156)** 6 North Isla Street, Dundee DD3 7JQ ☎ 1382 200800 **W:** planetradio.co.uk/tay – **157)** Unit 40, Loreburn Centre, High Street, Dumfries DG1 2BD ☎ 1387 250999 **W:** planetradio.co.uk/westsound-fm – **158)** Clydebank Business Park, Clydebank, Glasgow G81 2RX ☎ 141 565 2200 **W:** planetradio.co.uk/clyde – **159)** Forth House, Forth Street, Edinburgh EH1 3LE ☎ 131 556 9255 **W:** planetradio.co.uk/forth – **160)** Ladykirk House, Skye Rd, Prestwick KA9 2TA ☎ 1292 283662 **W:** planetradio.co.uk/west – **161)** Scorguie Place, Inverness IV3 8UJ ☎ 1463 224433 **W:** planetradio.co.uk/mfr – **162a)** Neil Gunn Drive, Thurso KW14 7QU ☎ 1847 890000 **W:** caithnessfm.co.uk – **162)** Tweedside Park, Galashiels TD1 3TD ☎ 1896 759444 **W:** radioborders.com – **163)** Atlantic House, Fletcher Way, Parkhouse, Carlisle CA3 0LJ ☎ 1228 818964 **W:** planetradio.co.uk/cfm – **164)** 5 Manor Court, Barnes Wallis Rd, Segensworth East, Fareham PO15 5TH ☎ 1489 481050 **W:** planetradio.co.uk/wave-105 – **165)** Barncoose Ind. Estate, Wilson Way, Redruth TR15 3XX ☎ 1209 314400 **W:** piratefm.co.uk – **166)** 15 Meadowbank Str., Dumbarton G82 1ST ☎ 1389 887111 **W:** yourradio.scot – **167)** Wallbrook Bldg., 195 Marsh Wall, London E14 9SG ☎ 20 7132 1458 **W:** lycadilse.com, lycaradio.com – **168)** 11 Rawson Rd, Bradford BD1 3SH ☎ 1274 771677 **W:** bcbradio.co.uk – **169)** C206 South Cheshire College, Danebank Ave., Crewe CW2 8AB ☎ 1270 654686 **W:** thisisthecat.com – **170)** Porthmellon, St Mary's, Isles of Scilly TR21 0JY ☎ 1720 423417 **W:** scillytoday.com **171)** Belle Meadow Court, Albert Lane, Barnstaple EX32 8RJ ☎ 1271 323010 **W:** thevoicefm.co.uk – **172)** Office D, Unit 14, 193 Garth Rd., Morden SM4 4LZ ☎ 208 330 4455 **W:** flexfm.co.uk – **173)** 3 North Terrace, Newcastle-upon-Tyne NE2 4AD ☎ 191 222 0789 **W:** radiotyneside.co.uk

## MANX RADIO (Comm.)

⬚ Broadcasting House, Douglas Head, Douglas, Isle of Man IM1 5BW ☎ 1624 682600 **W:** manxradio.com **E:** reception@manxradio.com **L.P:** MD: Anthony Pugh, PC Alex Brindley
**MW:** 1368kHz Foxdale 20kW **FM:** 89.0MHz Snaefell 4kW / 97.2MHz Carnane 11kW / 103.7MHz Jurby 4kW
**D.Prgr:** 24h Separate prgrs on MW at various times & during Manx TT motorcycle events

## ENERGY FM (Comm.)

PO Box 986, Douglas, Isle of Man IM99 2TB ☎ 1624 611936
**W:** energyfm.net **FM:** 91.2MHz Snaefell 1.2kW, 93.4MHz Jurby 1kW, 98.6MHz Carnane 2kW, 102.4 Beary Park 0.33kW (+ relays on 98.4/105.2) **D.Prgr:** 24h

## 3FM (Comm.)

Skanco Court, Cooil Rd., Douglas, Isle of Man IM2 2SR ☎ 1624 616333 🖷 1624 614333 **W:** three.fm
**FM:** 104.2MHz (Ramsey & Mull Hill), 105MHz (Carnane 2kW), 106.6MHz (Snaefell), 106.2MHz (Peel) **D.Prgr:** 24h

## BRITISH FORCES BROADCASTING SERVICE

(a division of Services Sound & Vision Corp.)
SSVC, Narcot Lane, Gerrards Cross SL9 8TN ☎ 1494 878354 🖷 1494 878552 **E:** adminofficer@bfbs.com **W:** forces.net/radio/
**LP:** Dir. Forces Broadcasting: Nicky Ness

## FORCES RADIO BFBS

in English **FM:** 89.3MHz Blandford, 98.5MHz Edinburgh, 100.6MHz Lisburn, 101MHz Belfast, 102.5MHz Aldershot, 106.1 Brize Norton, 106.5MHz Antrim, 106.8MHz Salisbury, 106.9MHz Catterick, 107MHz Colchester. **MW:** Low power relay on 1287kHz (Bovington). **DAB:** Digital One (National) & Oxfordshire (local).
**BFBS GURKHA RADIO** in Nepali, news hourly in English. **MW:** Low power sce on 1134kHz (Bramcote, Catterick, Sandhurst), 1251kHz (York), 1278kHz (Folkestone-main studio & Stafford), 1287kHz (Aldershot, Blandford, Brecon, Gloucester, Maidstone)
See Afghanistan, Bosnia, Ascension Island, Belgium, British Indian Ocean Territory, Brunei, Canada, Cyprus, Falkland Islands, Germany, Gibraltar, Nepal, Netherlands for other BFBS sces.

## RSL (Restricted Service Licences)

Licences are granted for low power special event stns operating for up to 28 days (occ. longer) usually on FM (occ. on MW)
**LPAM (Low Power AM stations)** There are currently 38 stns on the air (including BFBS relays - see above) with txs of 0.001kW e.r.p. Freqs used: 1134, 1251, 1278, 1287, 1350, 1386, 1431, 1449, 1575kHz
**LPFM (Low Power VHF/FM stations)** There are currently 22 stns on the air, most on 87.7MHz, with txs of typically 50mW

## COMMUNITY RADIO

Small-scale, low-power, non-profit community radio sces to serve a particular neighbourhood. Most on FM with 25 - 100W. approx 270 stns on air as of October 2018. MW community radio sces and FM sces above 100W are included in the main frequency lists above. For updated listing of short-term RSLs, long-term RSLs (LPAMs) and Community Radio see Radio Broadcast Licensing at **W:** ofcom.org.uk

## Community Audio Distribution Systems (CADS)

licence-exempt service for religious and community events using 27MHz Citizens Band.

# UNITED STATES OF AMERICA

**L.T:** See World Time Table (DST where applicable: 10 Mar-3 Nov) —
**Pop:** 325 million — **Pr.L:** English — **E.C:** 120V/60Hz — **ITU:** USA

## FEDERAL COMMUNICATIONS COMMISSION (FCC)
(Independent U.S. Govt. agency)

455 12th St SW, Washington, DC 20554 ☎ +1 888 2255322 🖷 +1 888 4180232 **E:** fccinfo@fcc.gov **W:** fcc.gov
**LP:** Chmn: Ajit Pai; Commissioners: Brandan Carr, Michael O'Rielly, Jessica Rosenworcel
The FCC regulates communications by radio, television, wire, satellite, and cable in all 50 U.S. states, the District of Columbia and U.S. territories.

## NATIONAL ASSOCIATION OF BROADCASTERS (NAB)

1771 N St NW, Washington DC 20036 ☎ +1 202 4295300 **E:** nab@nab.org **W:** nab.org **LP:** Pres/CEO: Gordon H. Smith
The NAB is a trade association for broadcasters that advances the interests of its members (more than 8,300 local radio & TV stns, as well as networks) in federal government, industry and public affairs.

## NATIONAL ASSOCIATION OF SHORTWAVE
BROADCASTERS, Inc (NSAB)

10400 NW 240th St, Okeechobee, FL 34972 ☎ +1 305 5599764 🖷 +1 863 4670185 **E:** nasbshortwave@gmail.com **W:** shortwave.org
**LP:** Pres: Charles Caudill, Vice Pres: John D. Tayloe
The NASB represents the privately-owned shortwave radio stations in the United States and promotes shortwave broadcasting in the U.S. and around the world.

## NATIONAL FEDERATION OF COMMUNITY
BROADCASTERS (NFCB)

P.O. Box 11270, Denver, CO 80211 ☎ +1 970 2793411
**E:** membership@nfcb.org **W:** nfcb.org **LP:** Pres: Sonya Green

## NATIONAL RELIGIOUS BROADCASTERS (NRB)

1 Massachusetts Ave NW, Suite 333, Washington, DC 20001 ☎ +1 202 5430073 🖷 +1 202 5432649 **E:** info@nrb.org **W:** nrb.org
**LP:** Pres/CEO: Jerry A. Johnson

## MAJOR PRODUCERS/DISTRIBUTORS OF NETWORK
PROGRAMMING FOR LOCAL STATIONS

## ABC RADIO (ABC, Inc - a division of The Walt Disney Co)

47 West 66th St, New York, NY 10023 ☎ +1 212 4565101 **W:** abcradio.com **LP:** Vice Pres/GM: Steve Jones

## AMERICAN PUBLIC MEDIA GROUP (Non-Comm)

480 Cedar St, St. Paul, MN 55101 ☎ +1 651 2901373 🖷 +1 651 2901415 **W:** americanpublicmedia.org **LP:** Pres/CEO: Jon McTaggart

## AMERICAN URBAN RADIO NETWORKS (AURN)
(ACCESS.1 COMMUNICATIONS CORP)

960 Penn Ave, 4th floor, Pittsburgh, PA 15222-3811 ☎ +1 412 4564000 🖷 +1 412 4564040 **W:** aurn.com
**LP:** CEO (Access.1 Communications Corp): Chesley Maddox-Dorsey

## BIBLE BROADCASTING NETWORK, Inc (Rlg)

11530 Carmel Commons Blvd, Charlotte, NC 28226 ☎ +1 704 5235555 **W:** bbnradio.org

## BOTT RADIO NETWORK
(BOTT COMMUNICATIONS, Inc) (Rlg)

10550 Barkley St, Suite 100, Overland Park, KS 66212 ☎ +1 913 6427770 🖷 +1 913 6421319 **E:** comments@bottradionetwork.com **W:** bottradionetwork.com **LP:** Chmn: Dick Bott

## CBS RADIO, Inc (Division of CBS Corporation)

1271 Avenue of the Americas, 44th floor, New York, NY 10020 ☎ +1 212 6499600 **W:** cbsradio.com **LP:** Pres: Andre J. Fernandez

## COMPASS MEDIA NETWORKS, LLC

150 Purchase St, Suite 11, Rye, NY 10580 ☎ +1 914 6005099 🖷 +1 914 8404137 **E:** info@compassmedianetworks.com **W:** compassmedianetworks.com **LP:** CEO: Peter Kosann

## CUMULUS MEDIA, Inc

3280 Peachtree Rd NW, Suite 2300, Atlanta, GA 30305 ☎ +1 404 9490700 🖷 +1 404 9490740 **W:** cumulus.com
**LP:** Pres/CEO: Mary G. Berner

## ESPN RADIO (ESPN, Inc)

ESPN Plaza, 935 Middle St., Bristol, CT 06010 ☎ +1 860 7662000 **W:** www.espn.com/espnradio; espnmediazone.com
**LP:** Pres (ESPN): Jimmy Pitaro

## FAMILY LIFE NETWORK
(FAMILY LIFE MINISTRIES, Inc) (Rlg)

7634 Campbell Creek Rd, Bath, NY 14810 ☎ +1 607 7764151 🖷 +1 607 7766929 **W:** fln.org
**LP:** Pres/CEO (Family Life Ministries): Rick Snavely

## FAMILY LIFE RADIO
(FAMILY LIFE COMMUNICATIONS, Inc) (Rlg)

7355 N. Oracle Rd, Tucson, AZ 85704 ☎ +1 520 7426976 🖷 +1 520 7426979 **E:** correspondence@flc.org **W:** myflr.org
**LP:** Pres (Family Life Communications): Randy Carlson

## FOX NEWS RADIO (FOX NEWS NETWORK, LLC - a
subsidiary of 21st Century Fox, Inc)

1211 Avenue of the Americas, 18th floor, New York, NY 10036 ☎ +1 212 3015439 **E:** foxnewsradio@foxnews.com **W:** radio.foxnews.com **LP:** CEO (Fox News Network): Suzanne Scott

## GENESIS COMMUNICATIONS NETWORK, Inc (GCN)

190 Cobblestone Lane, Burnsville, MN 55337 ☎ +1 877 9964327 **W:** gcnlive.com **LP:** Pres/CEO: Ted Anderson

## IHEARTMEDIA, Inc

200 E. Basse Rd, San Antonio, TX 78209-8328 ☎ +1 210 8222828 🖷 +1 210 8222299 **W:** iheartmedia.com **LP:** Chmn/CEO: Bob Pittman

## NATIONAL PUBLIC RADIO, Inc (Non-Comm)
635 Massachusetts Avenue NW, Washington, DC 20001 ☎ +1 202 5133232 🖷 +1 202 5133329 **W:** npr.org **L.P:** Pres/CEO: Jarl Mohn

## PREMIERE NETWORKS, Inc
### (Subsidiary of iHeartMedia, Inc)
15260 Ventura Boulevard, Suite 400, Sherman Oaks, CA 91403 ☎ +1 818 3775300 🖷 +1 818 4615490 **E:** feedback@premierenetworks.com **W:** premierenetworks.com **L.P:** Pres: Richard J. Bressler

## RADIO 74 (RADIO 74 INTERNATIONALE) (Rlg)
1209 West Robert Avenue, Ridgecrest, CA 93556-0716 ☎ +1 760 3752355 **E:** contact@radio74.net **W:** radio74.net
**L.P:** Pres: Everet W. Witzel

## RELEVANT RADIO
### (IMMACULATE HEART MEDIA, Inc) (Rlg)
1496 Bellevue St, Suite 202, Green Bay, WI 54311 ☎ +1 920 8841460 🖷 +1 920 4659986 **E:** info@relevantradio.com
**W:** relevantradio.com
**L.P:** Exec. Dir: Francis J. Hoffman

## SALEM RADIO NETWORK (SALEM MEDIA GROUP, Inc)
4880 Santa Rosa Rd, Camarillo, CA 93012 ☎ +1 805 9870400 **W:** salemmedia.com **L.P:** CEO (Salem Media Group): Edward G. Atsinger

## UNIVISION RADIO (UNIVISION COMMUNICATIONS, Inc)
605 Third Avenue, 33rd Floor, New York, NY 10158 ☎ +1 212 4555200 **W:** univision.com
**L.P:** CEO (Univision Communications): Vincent L. Sadusky
Univision Radio is a Spanish language network.

## USA RADIO NETWORKS (ANTHEM BROADCASTING, LLC - a subsidiary of Liftable Media, Inc)
819 W. Hargett St, Raleigh, NC 27603 ☎ +1 844 5000812 **E:** info@usaradio.com **W:** usaradio.com
**L.P:** CEO (Anthem Broadcasting): Fred Weinberg

## WESTWOOD ONE, LLC (Subsidiary of Cumulus Media, Inc)
220 West 42nd St, Candler Tower, New York, NY 10036 ☎ +1 212 9672888 **W:** westwoodone.com **L.P:** Pres: Suzanne M. Grimes

## LOCAL STATIONS
There are more than 17,000 local stns operating on AM and FM. As of 30 Sep, 2018: AM stns: 4,626 - FM (Full Power) Commercial stns: 6,737 - FM (Full power) Educational stns: 4,130 - FM Low power stns (LPFM): 2,175. There are also 7,848 FM translators and boosters.

**Call Letter Assigments:** For broadcasting stns in the U.S., callsigns consist of four letters, beginning with K or W, to which "-FM" or "-LP" may be added for FM stns. Calls with leading K are assigned to stns west of the Mississippi River (incl. Guam and No. Mariana Is), while a leading W is assigned to broadcast stns east of the Mississippi (incl. Puerto Rico). Exceptions: a few stns east of the Mississippi using a "K" callsign and stns west of the Mississippi using a "W" callsign will be noted. These are old callsigns that were assigned for various reasons (e.g. reflecting the initial geographic division in the early days of U.S. radio, or were requested by the stn owner) and are retained by special permission. Similarly some very old callsigns using only three letters may be retained by the stns that were once assigned these callsigns.

**Program Formats:** Especially in multi-station markets, **commercial radio stns** concentrate their prgrs to appeal to a given segment of the population or a given listening taste. Many stns devote their entire broadcast day to news and/or talk prgrs, or sports coverage. Others specialize in various types of music: Hit music (e.g. Contemporary Hit Radio), Country music, Classic Hits or Oldies, African American music (e.g. Urban Contemporary), Latin music (e.g. Mexican Regional), Classical music, etc. The number of Spanish language stns targeting the Hispanic audience has increased considerably in recent years. Some stns address other ethnic communities (e.g. African, Asian, European), incl. relays of foreign radio prgrs. Many stns change to a new format from time to time. **Non-commercial Educational radio stns** include public radio, religious radio, community radio, college radio, high school radio, etc.
**Local radio stns** make extensive use of programming produced and/or distributed by network providers (typically fed by satellite), and many may have only one local identification per hour, usually on top of the hour.
**AM Stations:** In the U.S. the AM band 540-1600kHz & expanded band 1610-1700kHz is divided into "clear", "regional" and "local"

channels, and the AM stns are divided into domestic classes A, B, C, D. "Clear channel" stns in the highest class A today have a protected area extending to 750 miles (c. 1200 km). Outside this area, the frequencies are also used by other stns. In order to combat interference from neighbouring countries, a few stns have been granted temporary licenses for increased powers, and many daytime stns may now operate after local sunset, using low or very low powers. 530kHz is reserved for very low power Travelers' Information Stations (TIS). Also 1610kHz was initially reserved for TIS, but is now available for regular stns (Class C&D), although so far no stn (exc. TIS) has been licensed on this frequency.

**Developments:** With the large decrease in AM listening in favour of FM, an increasing number of AM stns go off the air for a longer or shorter period due to economic difficulties. After a silent period of 12 consecutive months, the license expires. Stns on the so-called "regional channels", previously limited to 5kW power, may now apply for up to 50kW (1610-1700kHz: up to 10kW), limited only by the required protection of other stns. Relaxed ownership rules have allowed groups of co-owned stns to form in larger markets with the group stns often broadcasting from a common studio address

**Travelers' Information Stations (TIS):** State and local governments or institutions may create local stns or networks to provide non-commercial travel- or emergency-related public safety information using LPFM stations, or AM stns of up to 10 Watts primarily on 530kHz, or on any other available AM freq up to 1700kHz.

**Low Power FM Stations (LPFM):** This type of FM license is open to non-commercial educational entities and public safety/travelers' information entities, but not individuals or commercial operations.

**Digital Broadcasting:** An increasing number of stns is transmitting additional digital audio in the FM band, using the IBOC system, while the number of hybrid AM stns still remains relatively small. With the hybrid IBOC system digital signals are emitted on both sides of a transmitter's analogue signal, so that both analogue and digital receivers can recover the audio. Analogue listeners may experience the IBOC signal as an increased noise level on freqs adjacent to the nominal channel of the emitting transmitter. While in the AM band the IBOC signal is limited to one digital audio channel, IBOC in the FM band offers the option for multicasting on several digital subchannels. Most stns are using this possibility to transmit various additional programme feeds. A directory of stns carrying IBOC transmissions and the content of their subchannels can be found on **W:** hdradio.com/stations, a list of AM stns with IBOC trs on **W:** topazdesigns.com/iboc/station-list.html.

## MEDIUMWAVE (AM)
**Call:** Station call letters. All stns are required to announce their actual call letters and city of licence once per hour as close as possible to the top of the hour.
**Ant:** Use of antenna (CH=Critical Hours; ND=Non-directional). **U** = Unlimited time operation (typically 24h): **U1** ND at all hours, **U2** with directional antenna at night only, **U3** with directional antenna at all hours (same pattern day & night), **U4** as U3, but with different patterns day and night, **U5** with directional antenna daytime, ND at night, **U6** with directional antenna at night & during CH, **U7** as U3, but with three different patterns day, CH and night, **U8** as U7 but ND daytime, **U9** with directional antenna day & night (different patterns), but non-directional during CH (usually on reduced power), **U10** with directional antenna during CH, **U11** with directional antenna with separate patterns for daytime & CH, ND at night, **U12** ND daytime & CH, directional antenna at night, **U13** with directional antenna (same pattern day & CH, different pattern at night), **U14** with directional antenna day and night (different patterns), ND during CH. **D** = Daytime operation (between local sunrise and local sunset): **D1** with non-directional antenna, **D2** with directional antenna during CH only, **D3** with directional antenna, **D4** with directional antenna (different patterns during critical and non-critical hours), **D5** with directional antenna except CH. **L** = Limited time operation (usually based upon sunrise or sunset at the dominant station's location on a Clear Channel): **L1** with ND antenna, **L3** with directional antenna. **N** = Nighttime operation (between local sunset and local sunrise): **N1** with ND antenna, **N3** with directional antenna.
**D:** Daytime power in kW. **N:** Nighttime power in kW.
**City of License and Sta:** City (or Community) and State that the license has been issued to: **NB:** Hawaii (HI) and Alaska (AK) are listed under separate country headings.
**Scope:** Due to the large number of stns in operation, the listing has been limited to stns operating at 2.5kW or more during day- or nighttime. Stations on 530 (TIS), and on the "local channels" 1230, 1240,

1340, 1400, 1450, 1490 kHz have been omitted due to their low power.

**STATES:** AL Alabama, AR Arkansas, AZ Arizona, CA California, CO Colorado, CT Connecticut, DE Delaware, FL Florida, GA Georgia, IA Iowa, ID Idaho, IL Illinois, IN Indiana, KS Kansas, KY Kentucky, LA Louisiana, MA Massachusetts, MD Maryland, ME Maine, MI Michigan, MN Minnesota, MO Missouri, MS Mississippi, MT Montana, NC North Carolina, ND North Dakota, NE Nebraska, NH New Hampshire, NJ New Jersey, NM New Mexico, NV Nevada, NY New York, OH Ohio, OK Oklahoma, OR Oregon, PA Pennsylvania, RI Rhode Island, SC South Carolina, SD South Dakota, TN Tennessee, TX Texas, UT Utah, VA Virginia, VT Vermont, WA Washington, WI Wisconsin, WV West Virginia, WY Wyoming. **Federal District:** DC (District of Columbia).

**NB:** **#**=Stns reported transmitting IBOC signals (regularly or intermittently) at day- and/or nighttime. **‡**=inactive at editorial deadline. *=WNZK uses diff. frqs for daytime (690kHz) and nighttime (680kHz).

| MW | Call | kHz | Ant. | D | N | Sta | City of License |
|----|------|-----|------|---|---|-----|-----------------|
| | | **530** | Various stns of 0.01kW or less (TIS only) | | | | |
| 1 | WASG | **540** | U1 | 2.5 | 0.01 | AL | Daphne |
| 2 | KRXA | 540 | U4 | 10 | 0.5 | CA | Carmel Valley |
| 3 | KVIP | 540 | U1 | 2.5 | 0.01 | CA | Redding |
| 4 | WFLF | 540 | U4 | 50 | 46 | FL | Pine Hills |
| 5 | WDAK | 540 | U1 | 4 | 0.03 | GA | Columbus |
| 6 | KWMT | 540 | U4 | 5 | 0.17 | IA | Fort Dodge |
| 7 | KMLB | 540 | U1 | 4 | 0.02 | LA | Monroe |
| 8 | WRGC | 540 | U1 | 5 | 0.14 | NC | Sylva |
| 9 | WETC | 540 | U4 | 4 | 0.5 | NC | Wendell-Zebulon |
| 10 | KNMX | 540 | U4 | 5 | 0.02 | NM | Las Vegas |
| 11 | WLIE | 540 | U4 | 10 | 0.22 | NY | Islip |
| 12 | WWCS | 540 | U4 | 5 | 0.5 | PA | Canonsburg |
| 13 | WKFN | 540 | U1 | 4 | 0.05 | TN | Clarksville |
| 14 | KFYI | **#550** | U1 | 5 | 1 | AZ | Phoenix |
| 15 | KUZZ | 550 | U4 | 5 | 5 | CA | Bakersfield |
| 16 | KRAI | 550 | U2 | 5 | 0.5 | CO | Craig |
| 17 | WAYR | 550 | U4 | 5 | 0.5 | FL | Fleming Island |
| 18 | WDUN | 550 | U4 | 10 | 2.5 | GA | Gainesville |
| 19 | KFRM | 550 | U4 | 5 | 0.11 | KS | Salina |
| 20 | KTRS | 550 | U2 | 5 | 5 | MO | Saint Louis |
| 21 | KBOW | 550 | U2 | 5 | 1 | MT | Butte |
| 22 | KFYR | 550 | U2 | 5 | 5 | ND | Bismarck |
| 23 | WGR | 550 | U4 | 5 | 5 | NY | Buffalo |
| 24 | WKRC | 550 | U2 | 5 | 1 | OH | Cincinnati |
| 25 | KOAC | 550 | U4 | 5 | 5 | OR | Corvallis |
| 26 | KCRS | 550 | U4 | 5 | 1 | TX | Midland |
| 27 | KTSA | 550 | U2 | 5 | 5 | TX | San Antonio |
| 28 | WSVA | 550 | U2 | 5 | 1 | VA | Harrisonburg |
| 29 | WDEV | 550 | U4 | 5 | 1 | VT | Waterbury |
| 30 | KARI | 550 | U4 | 5 | 2.5 | WA | Blaine |
| 31 | WSAU | 550 | U4 | 15 | 20 | WI | Wausau |
| 32 | WOOF | **560** | U1 | 5 | 0.11 | AL | Dothan |
| 33 | KSFO | 560 | U4 | 5 | 5 | CA | San Francisco |
| 34 | KLZ | **#560** | U3 | 5 | 5 | CO | Denver |
| 35 | WQAM | 560 | U1 | 5 | 1 | FL | Miami |
| 36 | WIND | 560 | U4 | 5 | 5 | IL | Chicago |
| 37 | WMIK | 560 | U1 | 2.5 | 0.08 | KY | Middlesboro |
| 38 | WHYN | 560 | U4 | 5 | 1 | MA | Springfield |
| 39 | WFRB | 560 | U1 | 5 | 0.05 | MD | Frostburg |
| 40 | WGAN | 560 | U4 | 5 | 5 | ME | Portland |
| 41 | WEBC | 560 | U4 | 5 | 5 | MN | Duluth |
| 42 | KWTO | 560 | U4 | 5 | 4 | MO | Springfield |
| 43 | KMON | 560 | U2 | 5 | 5 | MT | Great Falls |
| 44 | WFIL | 560 | U4 | 5 | 5 | PA | Philadelphia |
| 45 | WVOC | 560 | U2 | 5 | 5 | SC | Columbia |
| 46 | WNSR | 560 | U4 | 4.5 | 0.07 | TN | Brentwood |
| 47 | WHBQ | 560 | U4 | 5 | 1 | TN | Memphis |
| 48 | KLVI | 560 | U2 | 5 | 5 | TX | Beaumont |
| 49 | KPQ | 560 | U4 | 5 | 5 | WA | Wenatchee |
| 50 | WJLS | 560 | U2 | 4.5 | 0.47 | WV | Beckley |
| 51 | WAAX | **570** | U2 | 5 | 0.5 | AL | Gadsden |
| 52 | KCFJ | 570 | U1 | 5 | 0.04 | CA | Alturas |
| 53 | KLAC | 570 | U4 | 5 | 5 | CA | Los Angeles |
| 54 | WTBN | 570 | U4 | 5 | 5 | FL | Pinellas Park |
| 55 | WWRC | 570 | U4 | 5 | 1 | MD | Bethesda |
| 56 | WWNC | 570 | U2 | 5 | 5 | NC | Asheville |
| 57 | KWML | 570 | U1 | 5 | 0.15 | NM | Las Cruces |
| 58 | WMCA | 570 | U3 | 5 | 5 | NY | New York |
| 59 | WSYR | 570 | U4 | 5 | 5 | NY | Syracuse |
| 60 | WKBN | 570 | U2 | 5 | 5 | OH | Youngstown |
| 61 | WNAX | 570 | U2 | 5 | 5 | SD | Yankton |
| 62 | KLIF | 570 | U4 | 5 | 5 | TX | Dallas |
| 63 | KNRS | 570 | U3 | 5 | 5 | UT | Salt Lake City |
| 64 | KVI | 570 | U1 | 5 | 5 | WA | Seattle |
| 65 | KSAZ | **580** | U2 | 5 | 0.39 | AZ | Marana |
| 66 | KMJ | 580 | U3 | 50 | 50 | CA | Fresno |
| 67 | KUBC | 580 | U2 | 5 | 1 | CO | Montrose |
| 68 | WDBO | 580 | U2 | 5 | 5 | FL | Orlando |
| 69 | WGAC | **#580** | U2 | 5 | 0.84 | GA | Augusta |
| 70 | KIDO | 580 | U2 | 5 | 5 | ID | Nampa |
| 71 | WILL | 580 | U4 | 5 | 0.1 | IL | Urbana |
| 72 | WIBW | 580 | U2 | 5 | 5 | KS | Topeka |
| 73 | KJMJ | 580 | U2 | 5 | 1 | LA | Alexandria |
| 74 | WTAG | 580 | U4 | 5 | 5 | MA | Worcester |
| 75 | WTCM | 580 | U4 | 50 | 1.1 | MI | Traverse City |
| 76 | WKSK | 580 | U1 | 5 | 0.03 | NC | West Jefferson |
| 77 | WHP | 580 | U2 | 5 | 5 | PA | Harrisburg |
| 78 | WYHM | 580 | U1 | 5 | 0.04 | TN | Rockwood |
| 79 | WKTY | 580 | U4 | 5 | 0.74 | WI | La Crosse |
| 80 | WCHS | 580 | U2 | 5 | 5 | WV | Charleston |
| 81 | KTIE | **590** | U4 | 2.5 | 0.96 | CA | San Bernardino |
| 82 | KTHO | 590 | U2 | 2.5 | 0.5 | CA | South Lake Tahoe |
| 83 | WDIZ | 590 | U2 | 1.7 | 2.5 | FL | Panama City |
| 84 | WDWD | 590 | U4 | 12 | 4.5 | GA | Atlanta |
| 85 | KID | 590 | U2 | 5 | 1 | ID | Idaho Falls |
| 86 | WVLK | 590 | U4 | 5 | 1 | KY | Lexington |
| 87 | WEZE | 590 | U3 | 5 | 5 | MA | Boston |
| 88 | WJMS | 590 | U2 | 5 | 1 | MI | Ironwood |
| 89 | WKZO | 590 | U2 | 5 | 5 | MI | Kalamazoo |
| 90 | KXSP | 590 | U1 | 5 | 5 | NE | Omaha |
| 91 | WROW | 590 | U4 | 5 | 1 | NY | Albany |
| 92 | KUGN | 590 | U2 | 5 | 5 | OR | Eugene |
| 93 | KLBJ | 590 | U2 | 5 | 1 | TX | Austin |
| 94 | KSUB | 590 | U2 | 5 | 1 | UT | Cedar City |
| 95 | KQNT | 590 | U1 | 5 | 5 | WA | Spokane |
| 96 | KOGO | **#600** | U4 | 5 | 5 | CA | San Diego |
| 97 | KCOL | 600 | U4 | 5 | 0.5 | CO | Wellington |
| 98 | WBOB | 600 | U2 | 50 | 9.7 | FL | Jacksonville |
| 99 | WMT | 600 | U2 | 5 | 5 | IA | Cedar Rapids |
| 100 | WKYH | 600 | U1 | 5 | 0.04 | KY | Paintsville |
| 101 | WCAO | **#600** | U3 | 5 | 5 | MD | Baltimore |
| 102 | WFST | 600 | U1 | 5 | 0.12 | ME | Caribou |
| 103 | KGEZ | 600 | U4 | 5 | 1 | MT | Kalispell |
| 104 | WSJS | 600 | U4 | 5 | 5 | NC | Winston-Salem |

| MW | Call | kHz | Ant. | D | N | Sta | City of License |
|---|---|---|---|---|---|---|---|
| 105 | KSJB | 600 | U3 | 5 | 5 | ND | Jamestown |
| 106 | WREC | 600 | U4 | 5 | 5 | TN | Memphis |
| 107 | KROD | 600 | U2 | 5 | 5 | TX | El Paso |
| 108 | KTBB | 600 | U4 | 5 | 2.5 | TX | Tyler |
| 109 | WAGG | 610 | U1 | 5 | 0.61 | AL | Birmingham |
| 110 | KAVL | 610 | U4 | 4.9 | 4 | CA | Lancaster |
| 111 | KEAR | 610 | U1 | 5 | 5 | CA | San Francisco |
| 112 | WIOD | 610 | U4 | 5 | 5 | FL | Miami |
| 113 | KDAL | 610 | U2 | 5 | 5 | MN | Duluth |
| 114 | KCSP | 610 | U1 | 5 | 5 | MO | Kansas City |
| 115 | WFNZ | #610 | U4 | 5 | 1 | NC | Charlotte |
| 116 | WGIR | 610 | U4 | 5 | 1 | NH | Manchester |
| 117 | KNML | 610 | U2 | 5 | 5 | NM | Albuquerque |
| 118 | WTVN | 610 | U2 | 5 | 5 | OH | Columbus |
| 119 | KRTA | 610 | U4 | 2.5 | 5 | OR | Medford |
| 120 | WTEL | 610 | U3 | 5 | 5 | PA | Philadelphia |
| 121 | KILT | 610 | U4 | 5 | 5 | TX | Houston |
| 122 | KVNU | 610 | U2 | 10 | 1 | UT | Logan |
| 123 | WPLY | 610 | U4 | 5 | 1 | VA | Roanoke |
| 124 | KONA | 610 | U4 | 5 | 5 | WA | Kennewick-Richland-Pasco |
| 125 | KTAR | #620 | U4 | 5 | 5 | AZ | Phoenix |
| 126 | KJOL | 620 | U1 | 5 | 0.07 | CO | Grand Junction |
| 127 | WDAE | 620 | U2 | 5.6 | 5.5 | FL | Saint Petersburg |
| 128 | WTRP | 620 | U1 | 2.5 | 0.12 | GA | La Grange |
| 129 | WZON | 620 | U2 | 5 | 5 | ME | Bangor |
| 130 | WJDX | 620 | U2 | 5 | 1 | MS | Jackson |
| 131 | WSNR | 620 | U4 | 3 | 7.6 | NJ | Jersey City |
| 132 | WHEN | 620 | U2 | 5 | 1 | NY | Syracuse |
| 133 | KPOJ | 620 | U2 | 25 | 10 | OR | Portland |
| 134 | WKHB | 620 | U1 | 5.5 | 0.05 | PA | Irwin |
| 135 | WGCV | 620 | U1 | 2.5 | 0.12 | SC | Cayce |
| 136 | WRJZ | 620 | U2 | 5 | 5 | TN | Knoxville |
| 137 | KEXB | 620 | U4 | 5 | 4.5 | TX | Plano |
| 138 | WVMT | 620 | U4 | 5 | 5 | VT | Burlington |
| 139 | WTMJ | 620 | U4 | 50 | 10 | WI | Milwaukee |
| 140 | WWNR | 620 | U1 | 5 | 0.02 | WV | Beckley |
| 141 | KHOW | 630 | U4 | 5 | 5 | CO | Denver |
| 142 | WMAL | 630 | U4 | 10 | 2.7 | DC | Washington |
| 143 | WBMQ | 630 | U4 | 4.8 | 0.04 | GA | Savannah |
| 144 | WNEG | 630 | U1 | 5 | 0.04 | GA | Toccoa |
| 145 | KFXD | 630 | U4 | 5 | 5 | ID | Boise |
| 146 | WLAP | 630 | U4 | 5 | 1 | KY | Lexington |
| 147 | WREY | 630 | U4 | 3 | 2.4 | MN | Saint Paul |
| 148 | KYFI | 630 | U4 | 5 | 5 | MO | Saint Louis |
| 149 | KPLY | 630 | U2 | 5 | 1 | NV | Reno |
| 150 | KWRO | 630 | U1 | 5 | 0.04 | OR | Coquille |
| 151 | WPRO | 630 | U2 | 5 | 5 | RI | Providence |
| 152 | KSLR | 630 | U4 | 5 | 4.3 | TX | San Antonio |
| 153 | KCIS | 630 | U2 | 5 | 5 | WA | Edmonds |
| 154 | KFI | 640 | U1 | 50 | 50 | CA | Los Angeles |
| 155 | WMEN | 640 | U4 | 7.5 | 0.46 | FL | Royal Palm Beach |
| 156 | WGST | 640 | U4 | 50 | 1 | GA | Atlanta |
| 157 | WOI | 640 | U2 | 5 | 1 | IA | Ames |
| 158 | WMFN | 640 | U4 | 4.4 | 1.6 | IL | Peotone |
| 159 | KTIB | 640 | U4 | 5 | 1 | LA | Thibodaux |
| 160 | WNNZ | 640 | U4 | 50 | 1 | MA | Westfield |
| 161 | WFNC | 640 | U1 | 10 | 1 | NC | Fayetteville |
| 162 | WWJZ | 640 | U4 | 50 | 0.95 | NJ | Mount Holly |
| 163 | WHLO | 640 | U4 | 5 | 0.5 | OH | Akron |
| 164 | KWPN | #640 | U4 | 5 | 1 | OK | Moore |
| 165 | WXSM | 640 | U2 | 10 | 0.81 | TN | Blountville |
| 166 | WCRV | 640 | U2 | 50 | 0.48 | TN | Collierville |
| 167 | KSTE | 650 | U4 | 21.4 | 0.92 | CA | Rancho Cordova |
| 168 | WNMT | 650 | U2 | 10 | 1 | MN | Nashwauk |
| 169 | WSM | 650 | U1 | 50 | 50 | TN | Nashville |
| 170 | KMTI | 650 | U4 | 10 | 0.9 | UT | Manti |
| 171 | KGAB | 650 | U2 | 8.5 | 0.5 | WY | Orchard Valley |
| 172 | WXQW | 660 | U2 | 10 | 0.85 | AL | Fairhope |
| 173 | KTNN | 660 | U2 | 50 | 50 | AZ | Window Rock |
| 174 | KGSV | 660 | U4 | 8 | 6 | CA | Oildale |
| 175 | WORL | 660 | U4 | 3.5 | 1 | FL | Altamonte Springs |
| 176 | WBHR | 660 | U4 | 10 | 0.5 | MN | Sauk Rapids |
| 177 | KEYZ | 660 | U4 | 5 | 5 | ND | Williston |
| 178 | WFAN | 660 | U1 | 50 | 50 | NY | New York |
| 179 | KXOR | 660 | U1 | 10 | 0.07 | OR | Junction City |
| 180 | WLFJ | 660 | D1 | 50 | | SC | Greenville |
| 181 | KSKY | 660 | U4 | 20 | 0.7 | TX | Balch Springs |
| 182 | KAPS | 660 | U4 | 10 | 1 | WA | Mount Vernon |
| 183 | WYLS | 670 | D1 | 4.8 | | AL | York |
| 184 | KHGZ | 670 | D1 | 5 | | AR | Glenwood |
| 185 | KIRN | 670 | U4 | 5 | 3 | CA | Simi Valley |
| 186 | KLTT | #670 | U4 | 50 | 1.4 | CO | Commerce City |
| 187 | WWFE | 670 | U4 | 50 | 1 | FL | Miami |
| 188 | KBOI | 670 | U2 | 50 | 50 | ID | Boise |
| 189 | WSCR | #670 | U1 | 50 | 50 | IL | Chicago |
| 190 | KMZQ | 670 | U4 | 25 | 0.6 | NV | Las Vegas |
| 191 | WLUI | 670 | D1 | 5.4 | | PA | Lewistown |
| 192 | WRJR | 670 | U4 | 20 | 0.003 | VA | Claremont |
| 193 | KNBR | 680 | U1 | 50 | 50 | CA | San Francisco |
| 194 | WCNN | 680 | U4 | 50 | 10 | GA | North Atlanta |
| 195 | WRKO | 680 | U4 | 50 | 50 | MA | Boston |
| 196 | WCBM | 680 | U4 | 50 | 20 | MD | Baltimore |
| 197 | WNZKn | 680 | N2 | - | 2.5 | MI | Dearborn Heights |
| 198 | WDBC | 680 | U4 | 10 | 1 | MI | Escanaba |
| 199 | KFEQ | 680 | U4 | 5 | 5 | MO | Saint Joseph |
| 200 | KKGR | 680 | D1 | 5 | | MT | East Helena |
| 201 | WPTF | 680 | U2 | 50 | 50 | NC | Raleigh |
| 202 | WINR | 680 | U4 | 5 | 0.5 | NY | Binghamton |
| 203 | WMFS | 680 | U2 | 8 | 5 | TN | Memphis |
| 204 | KKYX | 680 | U2 | 50 | 10 | TX | San Antonio |
| 205 | KOMW | 680 | D1 | 5 | | WA | Omak |
| 206 | WOGO | 680 | U4 | 2.5 | 0.5 | WI | Hallie |
| 207 | WKAZ | 680 | U2 | 10 | 0.22 | WV | Charleston |
| 208 | WJOX | 690 | U2 | 50 | 0.5 | AL | Birmingham |
| 209 | WADS | 690 | D3 | 3.2 | | CT | Ansonia |
| 210 | WOKV | 690 | U2 | 50 | 25 | FL | Jacksonville |
| 211 | KGGF | 690 | U4 | 10 | 5 | KS | Coffeyville |
| 212 | WQNO | 690 | U2 | 9.1 | 2.1 | LA | New Orleans |
| 197 | WNZK | 690 | D3 | 2.5 | - | MI | Dearborn Heights |
| 214 | KTSM | 690 | U4 | 10 | 10 | TX | El Paso |
| 215 | WZAP | 690 | U1 | 10 | 0.01 | VA | Bristol |
| 216 | WELD | 690 | U1 | 3 | 0.01 | WV | Fisher |
| 217 | KMBX | 700 | U1 | 2.5 | 0.7 | CA | Soledad |
| 218 | WFAT | 700 | D1 | 2.5 | | MA | Orange-Athol |
| 219 | WDMV | 700 | D3 | 5 | | MD | Walkersville |
| 220 | WLW | 700 | U1 | 50 | 50 | OH | Cincinnati |
| 221 | KGRV | 700 | U1 | 23 | 0.47 | OR | Winston |
| 222 | KSEV | 700 | U4 | 15 | 1 | TX | Tomball |
| 223 | KALL | 700 | U4 | 50 | 10 | UT | North Salt Lake City |
| 224 | KXLX | 700 | U2 | 10 | 0.6 | WA | Airway Heights |
| 225 | KBMB | 710 | U4 | 22 | 3.9 | AZ | Black Canyon City |
| 226 | KFIA | 710 | U4 | 25 | 1 | CA | Carmichael |
| 227 | KSPN | 710 | U2 | 50 | 10 | CA | Los Angeles |
| 228 | KNUS | 710 | U3 | 5 | 5 | CO | Denver |
| 229 | WAQI | 710 | U4 | 50 | 50 | FL | Miami |
| 230 | WUFF | 710 | D1 | 2.5 | | GA | Eastman |
| 231 | WEKC | 710 | D1 | 4.2 | | KY | Williamsburg |
| 232 | KEEL | 710 | U4 | 50 | 5 | LA | Shreveport |
| 233 | KCMO | 710 | U4 | 10 | 5 | MO | Kansas City |
| 234 | WEGG | 710 | D1 | 2.5 | | NC | Rose Hill |
| 235 | KXMR | 710 | U7 | 50 | 4 | ND | Bismarck |
| 236 | WOR | 710 | U4 | 50 | 50 | NY | New York |
| 237 | KGNC | 710 | U4 | 10 | 10 | TX | Amarillo |
| 238 | WFNR | 710 | D3 | 10 | | VA | Blacksburg |
| 239 | KIRO | 710 | U2 | 50 | 50 | WA | Seattle |
| 240 | WDSM | 710 | U2 | 50 | 5 | WI | Superior |
| 241 | WRZN | 720 | U2 | 10 | 0.25 | FL | Hernando |
| 242 | WVCC | 720 | D1 | 7.97 | | GA | Hogansville |
| 243 | WGN | 720 | U1 | 50 | 50 | IL | Chicago |
| 244 | WGCR | 720 | U1 | 50 | | NC | Pisgah Forest |
| 245 | KDWN | #720 | U2 | 50 | 50 | NV | Las Vegas |
| 246 | KFIR | 720 | U1 | 10 | 0.14 | OR | Sweet Home |
| 247 | KSAH | 720 | U4 | 10 | 0.89 | TX | Universal City |
| 248 | WSTT | 730 | U1 | 5 | 0.02 | GA | Thomasville |
| 249 | KDBI | 730 | U4 | 15 | 0.5 | ID | Boise |
| 250 | WACE | 730 | U1 | 5 | 0.008 | MA | Chicopee |
| 251 | KYYA | 730 | U1 | 5 | 0.23 | MT | Billings |
| 252 | WZGV | 730 | U1 | 10 | 0.16 | NC | Cramerton |
| 253 | WPIT | 730 | U1 | 5 | 0.02 | PA | Pittsburgh |
| 254 | WLTQ | 730 | U1 | 5 | 0.1 | SC | Charleston |
| 255 | WTNT | 730 | U1 | 8 | 0.02 | VA | Alexandria |
| 256 | WMSP | 740 | U4 | 10 | 0.23 | AL | Montgomery |
| 257 | KBRT | #740 | U4 | 50 | 0.19 | CA | Costa Mesa |
| 258 | KCBS | 740 | U4 | 50 | 50 | CA | San Francisco |
| 259 | KVOR | #740 | U4 | 3.3 | 1.5 | CO | Colorado Springs |
| 260 | WSBR | 740 | U4 | 2.5 | 0.94 | FL | Boca Raton |
| 261 | WYGM | 740 | U4 | 50 | 50 | FL | Orlando |
| 262 | WNOP | 740 | U4 | 2.5 | 0.03 | KY | Newport |
| 263 | WPAQ | 740 | U1 | 10 | 0.007 | NC | Mount Airy |
| 264 | KNFL | 740 | U7 | 50 | 0.94 | ND | Fargo |
| 265 | WNYH | 740 | U4 | 25 | 0.04 | NY | Huntington |
| 266 | KRMG | 740 | U4 | 50 | 25 | OK | Tulsa |
| 267 | KTRH | 740 | U4 | 50 | 50 | TX | Houston |
| 268 | WDGY | 740 | D3 | 5 | | WI | Hudson |

| MW | Call | kHz | Ant. | D | N | Sta | City of License | MW | Call | kHz | Ant. | D | N | Sta | City of License |
|---|---|---|---|---|---|---|---|---|---|---|---|---|---|---|---|
| 269 | WSB | 750 | U1 | 50 | 50 | GA | Atlanta | 351 | WWOS | 810 | D1 | 5 | | SC | Walterboro |
| 270 | WNDZ | 750 | D3 | 15 | | IN | Portage | 352 | KBHB | 810 | U1 | 25 | 0.06 | SD | Sturgis |
| 271 | KBNN | 750 | D1 | 5 | | MO | Lebanon | 353 | WMGC | 810 | U1 | 5 | 0.006 | TN | Murfreesboro |
| 272 | KERR | 750 | U2 | 50 | 1 | MT | Polson | 354 | WPIN | 810 | D1 | 4.2 | | VA | Dublin |
| 273 | KMMJ | 750 | L3 | 10.5 | | NE | Grand Island | 355 | KTBI | 810 | D1 | 50 | | WA | Ephrata |
| 274 | KXTG | 750 | U4 | 50 | 20 | OR | Portland | 356 | WWBA | 820 | U4 | 50 | 1 | FL | Largo |
| 275 | KAMA | 750 | U4 | 10 | 1 | TX | El Paso | 357 | WCPT | 820 | U2 | 5.8 | 1.5 | IL | Willow Springs |
| 276 | KOAL | #750 | U2 | 10 | 6.8 | UT | Price | 358 | WWFD | 820 | U2 | 4.3 | 0.43 | MD | Frederick |
| 277 | KMTL | ‡760 | D1 | 10 | | AR | Sherwood | 359 | WBKK | 820 | U4 | 10 | 0.75 | MN | Wilton |
| 278 | KFMB | 760 | U2 | 5 | 50 | CA | San Diego | 360 | WWLZ | 820 | U2 | 4.1 | 0.85 | NY | Horseheads |
| 279 | KDSP | 760 | U4 | 50 | 1 | CO | Thornton | 361 | WNYC | 820 | U4 | 10 | 1 | NY | New York |
| 280 | WLCC | 760 | U4 | 10 | 1 | FL | Brandon | 362 | WVSG | #820 | U2 | 6.5 | 0.79 | OH | Columbus |
| 281 | WEFL | 760 | U4 | 3 | 1.5 | FL | Tequesta | 363 | WBAP | 820 | U1 | 50 | 50 | TX | Fort Worth |
| 282 | KCCV | 760 | U4 | 6 | 0.2 | KS | Overland Park | 364 | KUTR | #820 | U8 | 50 | 2.5 | UT | Taylorsville |
| 283 | WVNE | 760 | D1 | 25 | | MA | Leicester | 365 | WNTW | 820 | U4 | 10 | 1 | VA | Chester |
| 284 | WJR | 760 | U1 | 50 | 50 | MI | Detroit | 366 | KGNW | 820 | U4 | 50 | 5 | WA | Burien-Seattle |
| 285 | WCIS | 760 | D1 | 3.5 | | NC | Morganton | 367 | KFLT | 830 | U2 | 50 | 1 | AZ | Tucson |
| 286 | WCHP | 760 | U4 | 35 | 0.01 | NY | Champlain | 368 | KNCO | 830 | U2 | 5 | 5 | CA | Grass Valley |
| 287 | KTKR | 760 | U2 | 50 | 1 | TX | San Antonio | 369 | KLAA | 830 | U4 | 50 | 20 | CA | Orange |
| 288 | WVNN | 770 | U2 | 7 | 0.25 | AL | Athens | 370 | WFNO | 830 | U4 | 5 | 0.75 | LA | Norco |
| 289 | KCBC | #770 | U4 | 50 | 4.1 | CA | Manteca | 371 | WCRN | 830 | U4 | 50 | 50 | MA | Worcester |
| 290 | WJBX | 770 | U4 | 10 | 0.63 | FL | North Fort Myers | 372 | WCCO | 830 | U1 | 50 | 50 | MN | Minneapolis |
| 291 | KUOM | 770 | D1 | 5 | | MN | Minneapolis | 373 | WTRU | 830 | U4 | 50 | 10 | NC | Kernersville |
| 292 | KATL | 770 | U2 | 10 | 1 | MT | Miles City | 374 | WEEU | 830 | U4 | 20 | 6 | PA | Reading |
| 293 | WLWL | 770 | D1 | 5 | | NC | Rockingham | 375 | WUMY | 830 | D1 | 3 | | TN | Memphis |
| 294 | KKOB | 770 | U2 | 50 | 50 | NM | Albuquerque | 376 | KUYO | 830 | D1 | 25 | | WY | Evansville |
| 295 | WABC | 770 | U1 | 50 | 50 | NY | New York | 377 | WBHY | 840 | D1 | 10 | | AL | Mobile |
| 296 | WTOR | 770 | D3 | 13 | | NY | Youngstown | 378 | KMPH | 840 | U4 | 5 | 5 | CA | Modesto |
| 297 | KAAM | 770 | U4 | 10 | 1 | TX | Garland | 379 | WHGH | 840 | D1 | 10 | | GA | Thomasville |
| 298 | WYRV | 770 | D1 | 5 | | VA | Cedar Bluff | 380 | WHAS | 840 | U1 | 50 | 50 | KY | Louisville |
| 299 | KTTH | 770 | U4 | 50 | 5 | WA | Seattle | 381 | KWDF | 840 | D1 | 8 | | LA | Ball |
| 300 | KAZM | 780 | U2 | 5 | 0.25 | AZ | Sedona | 382 | KTIC | 840 | D1 | 5 | | NE | West Point |
| 301 | WBBM | #780 | U1 | 50 | 50 | IL | Chicago | 383 | KXNT | #840 | U4 | 50 | 25 | NV | North Las Vegas |
| 302 | WXME | 780 | U1 | 5 | 0.06 | ME | Monticello | 384 | WCEO | 840 | D3 | 50 | | SC | Columbia |
| 303 | WIIN | 780 | D1 | 4.4 | | MS | Ridgeland | 385 | KVJY | 840 | U4 | 5 | 1 | TX | Pharr |
| 304 | WCKB | 780 | U1 | 7 | 0.001 | NC | Dunn | 386 | WKTR | 840 | D3 | 8.2 | | VA | Earlysville |
| 305 | WWOL | 780 | D1 | 10 | | NC | Forest City | 387 | KMAX | 840 | U1 | 10 | 0.28 | WA | Colfax |
| 306 | KKOH | 780 | U2 | 50 | 50 | NV | Reno | 388 | WXJC | 850 | U4 | 50 | 1 | AL | Birmingham |
| 307 | WAVA | 780 | D1 | 12 | | VA | Arlington | 389 | KOA | 850 | U1 | 50 | 50 | CO | Denver |
| 308 | WTSK | 790 | U1 | 5 | 0.03 | AL | Tuscaloosa | 390 | WAXB | 850 | D1 | 2.5 | | CT | Ridgefield |
| 309 | KURM | 790 | U2 | 5 | 0.5 | AR | Rogers | 391 | WRUF | 850 | U2 | 5 | 5 | FL | Gainesville |
| 310 | KNST | 790 | U4 | 5 | 0.5 | AZ | Tucson | 392 | WFTL | 850 | U4 | 50 | 20 | FL | West Palm Beach |
| 311 | KFPT | 790 | U4 | 5 | 2.5 | CA | Clovis | 393 | WAIT | 850 | D3 | 2.5 | | IL | Crystal Lake |
| 312 | KEJY | 790 | U4 | 5 | 0.11 | CA | Eureka | 394 | WEEI | 850 | U4 | 50 | 50 | MA | Boston |
| 313 | KABC | #790 | U2 | 6.6 | 7.9 | CA | Los Angeles | 395 | WQRM | 850 | D1 | 50 | | MN | Duluth |
| 314 | WLBE | 790 | U2 | 5 | 1 | FL | Leesburg-Eustis | 396 | KFUO | #850 | D1 | 5 | | MO | Clayton |
| 315 | WAXY | 790 | U4 | 5 | 5 | FL | South Miami | 397 | WPTK | 850 | U2 | 10 | 5 | NC | Raleigh |
| 316 | WQXI | 790 | U2 | 28 | 1 | GA | Atlanta | 398 | WKNR | 850 | U4 | 50 | 4.7 | OH | Cleveland |
| 317 | KXXX | 790 | U1 | 5 | 0.02 | KS | Colby | 399 | WKGE | 850 | U3 | 10 | 10 | PA | Johnstown |
| 318 | WKRD | 790 | U4 | 5 | 1 | KY | Louisville | 400 | WKVL | 850 | D3 | 50 | | TN | Knoxville |
| 319 | WSGW | 790 | U4 | 5 | 1 | MI | Saginaw | 401 | KJON | 850 | D3 | 5 | | TX | Carrollton |
| 320 | KGHL | 790 | U1 | 5 | 1.8 | MT | Billings | 402 | KEYH | 850 | U4 | 10 | 0.18 | TX | Houston |
| 321 | WBLO | 790 | U1 | 10 | 0.02 | NC | Thomasville | 403 | WTAR | 850 | U4 | 50 | 25 | VA | Norfolk |
| 322 | KFGO | 790 | U2 | 5 | 5 | ND | Fargo | 404 | KHHO | 850 | U4 | 10 | 1 | WA | Tacoma |
| 323 | WAEB | 790 | U4 | 3.6 | 1.5 | PA | Allentown | 405 | KTRB | 860 | U2 | 50 | 50 | CA | San Francisco |
| 324 | WPRV | 790 | U2 | 5 | 5 | RI | Providence | 406 | WGUL | 860 | U4 | 5 | 1.5 | FL | Dunedin |
| 325 | WETB | 790 | U1 | 5 | 0.07 | TN | Johnson City | 407 | WAEC | 860 | U1 | 5 | 0.5 | GA | Atlanta |
| 326 | WMC | 790 | U2 | 5 | 5 | TN | Memphis | 408 | WDMG | 860 | U12 | 5 | 5 | GA | Douglas |
| 327 | KBME | 790 | U4 | 5 | 5 | TX | Houston | 409 | KKOW | 860 | U2 | 10 | 5 | KS | Pittsburg |
| 328 | KFYO | 790 | U4 | 5 | 1 | TX | Lubbock | 410 | WSBS | 860 | U1 | 2.7 | 0.004 | MA | Great Barrington |
| 329 | WNIS | 790 | U3 | 5 | 5 | VA | Norfolk | 411 | WFSI | 860 | U4 | 2.5 | 0.06 | MD | Baltimore |
| 330 | KGMI | 790 | U2 | 5 | 1 | WA | Bellingham | 412 | KPAM | 860 | U2 | 50 | 15 | OR | Troutdale |
| 331 | KJRB | 790 | U4 | 5 | 3.8 | WA | Spokane | 413 | WWDB | 860 | D3 | 10 | | PA | Philadelphia |
| 332 | WAYY | 790 | U2 | 5 | 0.12 | WI | Eau Claire | 414 | KONO | 860 | U2 | 5 | 0.9 | TX | San Antonio |
| 333 | KBRV | 800 | U1 | 10 | 0.15 | ID | Soda Springs | 415 | KKAT | 860 | U1 | 10 | 0.19 | UT | Salt Lake City |
| 334 | WNNW | 800 | U1 | 3 | 0.24 | MA | Lawrence | 416 | WOAY | 860 | U1 | 10 | 0.01 | WV | Oak Hill |
| 335 | WVAL | 800 | U4 | 2.6 | 0.85 | MN | Sauk Rapids | 417 | WQRX | 870 | D1 | 10 | | AL | Valley Head |
| 336 | WTMR | 800 | U4 | 5 | 0.5 | NJ | Camden | 418 | KRLA | 870 | U4 | 50 | 3 | CA | Glendale |
| 337 | KQCV | 800 | U4 | 2.5 | 1 | OK | Oklahoma City | 419 | WWL | 870 | U3 | 50 | 50 | LA | New Orleans |
| 338 | WSVS | 800 | U1 | 10 | 0.27 | VA | Crewe | 420 | WLVP | 870 | U1 | 10 | 1 | ME | Gorham |
| 339 | WDUX | 800 | U4 | 5 | 0.5 | WI | Waupaca | 421 | WKAR | 870 | D3 | 10 | | MI | East Lansing |
| 340 | WVHU | 800 | U1 | 5 | 0.18 | WV | Huntington | 422 | KPRM | 870 | U4 | 50 | 2.5 | MN | Park Rapids |
| 341 | WCKA | 810 | U4 | 50 | 0.5 | AL | Jacksonville | 423 | WTCG | 870 | D1 | 5 | | NC | Mount Holly |
| 342 | KGO | 810 | U3 | 50 | 50 | CA | San Francisco | 424 | KLSQ | 870 | U2 | 5 | 0.43 | NV | Whitney |
| 343 | WRSO | 810 | U4 | 20 | 0.4 | FL | Orlovista | 425 | WHCU | 870 | U2 | 5 | 1 | NY | Ithaca |
| 344 | WZYN | 810 | D1 | 2.5 | | GA | Hahira | 426 | WPWT | 870 | D1 | 10 | | TN | Colonial Heights |
| 345 | WEKG | 810 | D1 | 5 | | KY | Jackson | 427 | KFLD | 870 | U1 | 10 | 0.25 | WA | Pasco |
| 346 | WMJH | 810 | D1 | 3.6 | | MI | Rockford | 428 | KLRG | 880 | U2 | 50 | 0.22 | AR | Sheridan |
| 347 | WHB | 810 | U2 | 50 | 5 | MO | Kansas City | 429 | KKMC | 880 | U4 | 10 | 10 | CA | Gonzales |
| 348 | WSJC | 810 | U2 | 50 | 0.5 | MS | Magee | 430 | WZAB | 880 | U4 | 4 | 5 | FL | Sweetwater |
| 349 | KSWV | 810 | U1 | 5 | 0.01 | NM | Santa Fe | 431 | KJJR | 880 | U1 | 10 | 0.5 | MT | Whitefish |
| 350 | WGY | #810 | U1 | 50 | 50 | NY | Schenectady | 432 | WPEK | 880 | D1 | 5 | | NC | Fairview |

| MW | Call | kHz | Ant. | D | N | Sta | City of License |
|---|---|---|---|---|---|---|---|
| 433 | KRVN | 880 | U2 | 50 | 50 | NE | Lexington |
| 434 | KHAC | 880 | U1 | 10 | 0.43 | NM | Tse Bonito |
| 435 | WCBS | #880 | U1 | 50 | 50 | NY | New York |
| 436 | WRFD | 880 | D1 | 23 | | OH | Columbus-Worthington |
| 437 | KWIP | 880 | U1 | 5 | 1 | OR | Dallas |
| 438 | WMDB | 880 | U1 | 2.5 | 0.002 | TN | Nashville |
| 439 | KJOZ | 880 | U4 | 10 | 1 | TX | Conroe |
| 440 | KIXI | 880 | U4 | 50 | 10 | WA | Mercer Island-Seattle |
| 441 | WMEQ | 880 | U2 | 10 | 0.21 | WI | Menomonie |
| 442 | WYAM | **890** | D1 | 2.5 | | AL | Hartselle |
| 443 | KIHC | 890 | U4 | 5 | 5 | CA | Arroyo Grande |
| 444 | KVMX | 890 | U4 | 10 | 0.48 | CA | Olivehurst |
| 445 | KJME | 890 | U4 | 5 | 0.58 | CO | Fountain |
| 446 | WJTP | 890 | D1 | 5 | | GA | Lithia Springs |
| 447 | KYWN | 890 | U2 | 50 | 0.25 | ID | Meridian |
| 448 | WLS | 890 | U1 | 50 | 50 | IL | Chicago |
| 449 | WAMG | 890 | U4 | 25 | 6 | MA | Dedham |
| 450 | WHJA | 890 | D1 | 10 | | MS | Laurel |
| 451 | WBAJ | 890 | D1 | 50 | | SC | Blythewood |
| 452 | KVOZ | 890 | U2 | 10 | 1 | TX | Del Mar Hills |
| 453 | KTXV | 890 | U4 | 20 | 0.25 | TX | Mabank |
| 454 | KDXU | 890 | U2 | 10 | 10 | UT | Saint George |
| 455 | WKNV | 890 | D3 | 10 | | VA | Fairlawn |
| 456 | KALI | **900** | U4 | 5 | 0.15 | CA | West Covina |
| 457 | WMOP | 900 | U1 | 2.7 | 0.02 | FL | Ocala |
| 458 | WJLG | 900 | U1 | 4.35 | 0.15 | GA | Savannah |
| 459 | WLSI | 900 | U1 | 3.5 | 0.12 | KY | Pikeville |
| 460 | KTIS | 900 | U4 | 50 | 0.5 | MN | Minneapolis |
| 461 | WYCV | 900 | U1 | 2.5 | 0.25 | NC | Granite Falls |
| 462 | WCPA | 900 | U4 | 2.5 | 0.5 | PA | Clearfield |
| 463 | WKDA | 900 | U1 | 5 | 0.13 | TN | Lebanon |
| 464 | KREH | 900 | U4 | 5 | 0.01 | TX | Pecan Grove |
| 465 | WKDW | 900 | U1 | 2.5 | 0.12 | VA | Staunton |
| 466 | KLCN | **‡910** | U1 | 5 | 0.08 | AR | Blytheville |
| 467 | KGME | #910 | U2 | 5 | 5 | AZ | Phoenix |
| 468 | KECR | 910 | U4 | 5 | 5 | CA | El Cajon |
| 469 | KKSF | 910 | U2 | 20 | 5 | CA | Oakland |
| 470 | KOXR | 910 | U4 | 5 | 1 | CA | Oxnard |
| 471 | KPOF | #910 | U1 | 5 | 1 | CO | Denver |
| 472 | WLAT | 910 | U2 | 5 | 2.8 | CT | New Britain |
| 473 | WTWD | 910 | U3 | 5 | 5 | FL | Plant City |
| 474 | WRFV | 910 | U1 | 5 | 5 | GA | Valdosta |
| 475 | WSUI | 910 | U2 | 5 | 4 | IA | Iowa City |
| 476 | WABK | 910 | U2 | 5 | 5 | ME | Bangor |
| 477 | WFDF | #910 | U4 | 50 | 25 | MI | Farmington Hills |
| 478 | WALT | 910 | U1 | 5 | 1 | MS | Meridian |
| 479 | WSRP | 910 | U2 | 5 | 5 | NC | Jacksonville |
| 480 | KCJB | 910 | U4 | 5 | 5 | ND | Minot |
| 481 | KKBE | 910 | U2 | 5 | 0.5 | NM | Roswell |
| 482 | WLTP | 910 | U5 | 5 | 0.04 | OH | Marietta |
| 483 | WAVL | 910 | U4 | 5 | 0.06 | PA | Apollo |
| 484 | WSBA | 910 | U4 | 5 | 1 | PA | York |
| 485 | WOLI | 910 | U4 | 3.6 | 0.89 | SC | Spartanburg |
| 486 | WJCW | 910 | U2 | 5 | 1 | TN | Johnson City |
| 487 | WEPG | 910 | U1 | 5 | 0.09 | TN | South Pittsburg |
| 488 | KRIO | 910 | U4 | 5 | 5 | TX | McAllen |
| 489 | WRNL | 910 | U2 | 5 | 1.5 | VA | Richmond |
| 490 | KMTT | 910 | U4 | 3.3 | 4.3 | WA | Vancouver |
| 491 | WCBN | 910 | U1 | 5 | 0.07 | WI | Hayward |
| 492 | KARN | **920** | U2 | 5 | 5 | AR | Little Rock |
| 493 | KVIN | 920 | U4 | 0.5 | 2.5 | CA | Ceres |
| 494 | KKGX | 920 | U4 | 5 | 1 | CA | Palm Springs |
| 495 | KLMR | 920 | U2 | 5 | 0.5 | CO | Lamar |
| 496 | WDMC | 920 | U4 | 8 | 4 | FL | Melbourne |
| 497 | WGKA | 920 | U1 | 14 | 0.49 | GA | Atlanta |
| 498 | KYFR | 920 | U4 | 5 | 2.5 | IA | Shenandoah |
| 499 | WBAA | #920 | U2 | 5 | 1 | IN | West Lafayette |
| 500 | WTCW | 920 | U1 | 4.2 | 0.04 | KY | Whitesburg |
| 501 | KDHL | 920 | U4 | 5 | 5 | MN | Faribault |
| 502 | WPCM | 920 | U4 | 5 | 0.05 | NC | Burlington-Graham |
| 503 | KBAD | 920 | U2 | 5 | 0.5 | NV | Las Vegas |
| 504 | KIHM | 920 | U2 | 4.8 | 0.05 | NV | Reno |
| 505 | WHJJ | 920 | U2 | 5 | 5 | RI | Providence |
| 506 | KKLS | 920 | U4 | 5 | 0.11 | SD | Rapid City |
| 507 | KYST | 920 | U4 | 5 | 1 | TX | Texas City |
| 508 | KVEL | 920 | U2 | 5 | 1 | UT | Vernal |
| 509 | WURA | 920 | U4 | 7 | 0.07 | VA | Quantico |
| 510 | KGTK | 920 | U1 | 3 | 0.007 | WA | Olympia |
| 511 | KXLY | 920 | U1 | 20 | 5 | WA | Spokane |
| 512 | WOKY | 920 | U4 | 5 | 1 | WI | Milwaukee |
| 513 | WMMN | 920 | U2 | 5 | 0.2 | WV | Fairmont |
| 514 | WGAD | **930** | U2 | 5 | 0.5 | AL | Rainbow City |
| 515 | KAPR | 930 | U1 | 2.5 | 0.07 | AZ | Douglas |
| 516 | KAFF | 930 | U1 | 5 | 0.03 | AZ | Flagstaff |
| 517 | KHJ | 930 | U2 | 5 | 5 | CA | Los Angeles |
| 518 | KIUP | 930 | U1 | 5 | 0.1 | CO | Durango |
| 519 | KRKY | 930 | U1 | 4.5 | 0.12 | CO | Granby |
| 520 | WFXJ | #930 | U2 | 5 | 5 | FL | Jacksonville |
| 521 | WLSS | 930 | U4 | 5 | 3 | FL | Sarasota |
| 522 | WMGR | 930 | U2 | 5 | 0.5 | GA | Bainbridge |
| 523 | KSEI | 930 | U2 | 5 | 5 | ID | Pocatello |
| 524 | WTAD | 930 | U2 | 5 | 1 | IL | Quincy |
| 525 | WKBM | 930 | U4 | 2.5 | 4.2 | IL | Sandwich |
| 526 | WKCT | 930 | U2 | 5 | 0.5 | KY | Bowling Green |
| 527 | WFMD | 930 | U2 | 5 | 2.5 | MD | Frederick |
| 528 | WTOU | 930 | U4 | 5 | 1 | MI | Battle Creek |
| 529 | KAIN | 930 | U1 | 2.5 | 0.36 | MN | Aitkin |
| 530 | KWOC | 930 | U1 | 5 | 0.5 | MO | Poplar Bluff |
| 531 | WSFZ | 930 | U1 | 3.7 | 0.06 | MS | Jackson |
| 532 | KMPT | 930 | U2 | 5 | 1 | MT | East Missoula |
| 533 | WYFQ | 930 | U2 | 5 | 1 | NC | Charlotte |
| 534 | WDLX | 930 | U2 | 5 | 1 | NC | Washington |
| 535 | WPKX | 930 | U2 | 5 | 5 | NH | Rochester |
| 536 | WPAT | 930 | U4 | 5 | 5 | NJ | Paterson |
| 537 | WBEN | 930 | U2 | 5 | 5 | NY | Buffalo |
| 538 | WKY | 930 | U1 | 5 | 0.51 | OK | Oklahoma City |
| 539 | KAGI | 930 | U1 | 5 | 0.12 | OR | Grants Pass |
| 540 | KSDN | 930 | U4 | 5 | 1 | SD | Aberdeen |
| 541 | WSEV | 930 | U1 | 5 | 0.14 | TN | Sevierville |
| 542 | KLUP | 930 | U2 | 5 | 1 | TX | Terrell Hills |
| 543 | WLLL | 930 | U1 | 9 | 0.04 | VA | Lynchburg |
| 544 | KYAK | 930 | U1 | 10 | 0.12 | WA | Yakima |
| 545 | WLBL | #930 | U1 | 5 | 0.07 | WI | Auburndale |
| 546 | WRVC | 930 | U2 | 5 | 1 | WV | Huntington |
| 547 | KROE | 930 | U1 | 5 | 0.11 | WY | Sheridan |
| 548 | KFIG | **940** | U4 | 50 | 50 | CA | Fresno |
| 549 | WINZ | 940 | U2 | 50 | 10 | FL | Miami |
| 550 | WMAC | 940 | U2 | 50 | 10 | GA | Macon |
| 551 | KPSZ | 940 | U4 | 10 | 5 | IA | Des Moines |
| 552 | WMIX | 940 | U4 | 5 | 1.5 | IL | Mount Vernon |
| 553 | WYLD | 940 | U2 | 10 | 0.5 | LA | New Orleans |
| 554 | WIDG | 940 | U1 | 5 | 0.004 | MI | Saint Ignace |
| 555 | WCPC | 940 | U2 | 31 | 0.007 | MS | Houston |
| 556 | WKYK | 940 | U2 | 4.6 | 0.25 | NC | Burnsville |
| 557 | KVSH | 940 | U1 | 5 | 0.01 | NE | Valentine |
| 558 | KCOE | ‡940 | U4 | 10 | 0.06 | OR | Bend |
| 559 | WECO | 940 | U1 | 5 | 0.01 | TN | Wartburg |
| 560 | KIXZ | 940 | U4 | 5 | 1 | TX | Amarillo |
| 561 | KTFS | 940 | U1 | 2.5 | 0.01 | TX | Texarkana |
| 562 | WNRG | 940 | U1 | 5 | 0.01 | VA | Grundy |
| 563 | WKGM | 940 | U2 | 10 | 3.1 | VA | Smithfield |
| 564 | KXJK | **950** | U1 | 5 | 0.08 | AR | Forrest City |
| 565 | KAHI | 950 | U4 | 5 | 5 | CA | Auburn |
| 566 | KKSE | 950 | U3 | 5 | 5 | CO | Parker |
| 567 | WTLN | 950 | U2 | 12 | 5 | FL | Orlando |
| 568 | WGUN | 950 | U1 | 3.5 | 0.06 | GA | Valdosta |
| 569 | KOEL | 950 | U4 | 5 | 0.5 | IA | Oelwein |
| 570 | KMHR | 950 | U1 | 3.5 | 0.03 | ID | Boise |
| 571 | KOZE | 950 | U4 | 5 | 1 | ID | Lewiston |
| 572 | WNTD | 950 | U2 | 1 | 5 | IL | Chicago |
| 573 | WROL | 950 | U1 | 5 | 0.09 | MA | Boston |
| 574 | WCTN | 950 | U4 | 2.5 | 0.35 | MD | Potomac-Cabin John |
| 575 | WWJ | #950 | U4 | 50 | 50 | MI | Detroit |
| 576 | KWOS | 950 | U2 | 5 | 0.5 | MO | Jefferson City |
| 577 | WHSY | 950 | U1 | 5 | 0.06 | MS | Hattiesburg |
| 578 | KCAP | #950 | U2 | 5 | 5 | MT | Helena |
| 579 | KNFT | 950 | U1 | 5 | 0.22 | NM | Bayard |
| 580 | KDCE | 950 | U1 | 4.2 | 0.08 | NM | Española |
| 581 | WIBX | 950 | U3 | 5 | 5 | NY | Utica |
| 582 | KTBR | 950 | U1 | 3.4 | 0.02 | OR | Roseburg |
| 583 | WKDN | 950 | U4 | 43 | 21 | PA | Philadelphia |
| 584 | WJKB | 950 | U1 | 10 | 6 | SC | Moncks Corner |
| 585 | WORD | 950 | U2 | 5 | 5 | SC | Spartanburg |
| 586 | WAKM | 950 | U1 | 5 | 0.07 | TN | Franklin |
| 587 | KPRC | 950 | U2 | 5 | 5 | TX | Houston |
| 588 | KJTV | 950 | U4 | 5 | 0.5 | TX | Lubbock |
| 589 | WXGI | 950 | U1 | 3.9 | 0.04 | VA | Richmond |
| 590 | KJR | 950 | U4 | 50 | 50 | WA | Seattle |
| 591 | WBES | 950 | U1 | 5 | 1 | WV | Charleston |
| 592 | WERC | **960** | U2 | 5 | 5 | AL | Birmingham |
| 593 | WLPR | 960 | U1 | 6 | 0.03 | AL | Prichard |
| 594 | KCGS | 960 | U1 | 5 | 0.04 | AR | Marshall |
| 595 | KKNT | 960 | U2 | 5 | 5 | AZ | Phoenix |
| 596 | KIXW | 960 | U1 | 5 | 0.02 | CA | Apple Valley |

| MW | Call | kHz | Ant. | D | N | Sta | City of License |
|----|------|-----|------|---|---|-----|-----------------|
| 597 | KNEW | 960 | U3 | 5 | 5 | CA | Oakland |
| 598 | WELI | #960 | U2 | 5 | 5 | CT | New Haven |
| 599 | WJYZ | 960 | U4 | 5 | 0.39 | GA | Albany |
| 600 | WRFC | 960 | U2 | 5 | 2.5 | GA | Athens |
| 601 | KMA | 960 | U2 | 5 | 5 | IA | Shenandoah |
| 602 | WSBT | 960 | U4 | 5 | 5 | IN | South Bend |
| 603 | WPRT | 960 | U1 | 3.8 | 0.01 | KY | Prestonsburg |
| 604 | WFGL | 960 | U4 | 2.5 | 1 | MA | Fitchburg |
| 605 | WTGM | 960 | U4 | 5 | 5 | MD | Salisbury |
| 606 | WHAK | 960 | U1 | 5 | 0.13 | MI | Rogers City |
| 607 | KLTF | 960 | U1 | 5 | 0.03 | MN | Little Falls |
| 608 | KZIM | 960 | U2 | 5 | 0.5 | MO | Cape Girardeau |
| 609 | KFLN | 960 | U1 | 5 | 0.09 | MT | Baker |
| 610 | WCRU | 960 | U4 | 10 | 0.5 | NC | Dallas |
| 611 | WRNS | 960 | U2 | 5 | 1 | NC | Kinston |
| 612 | KNEB | 960 | U4 | 5 | 0.35 | NE | Scottsbluff |
| 613 | KNDN | 960 | U1 | 5 | 0.16 | NM | Farmington |
| 614 | WEAV | 960 | U4 | 5 | 5 | NY | Plattsburgh |
| 615 | KLAD | 960 | U2 | 5 | 5 | OR | Klamath Falls |
| 616 | WHYL | 960 | U4 | 5 | 0.02 | PA | Carlisle |
| 617 | WATS | 960 | U1 | 5 | 0.05 | PA | Sayre |
| 618 | KGKL | 960 | U2 | 5 | 1 | TX | San Angelo |
| 619 | KOVO | 960 | U1 | 5 | 0.14 | UT | Provo |
| 620 | WFIR | 960 | U2 | 10 | 5 | VA | Roanoke |
| 621 | KALE | 960 | U2 | 5 | 1 | WA | Richland |
| 622 | WTBF | **970** | U1 | 5 | 0.04 | AL | Troy |
| 623 | KVWM | 970 | U4 | 5 | 0.19 | AZ | Show Low |
| 624 | KHTY | 970 | U1 | 1 | 5 | CA | Bakersfield |
| 625 | KNWZ | 970 | U4 | 5 | 0.36 | CA | Coachella |
| 626 | KFEL | 970 | U1 | 3.2 | 0.18 | CO | Pueblo |
| 627 | WFLA | 970 | U4 | 25 | 11 | FL | Tampa |
| 628 | WNIV | 970 | U1 | 5 | 0.03 | GA | Atlanta |
| 629 | WVOP | 970 | U1 | 4 | 0.06 | GA | Vidalia |
| 630 | KXTA | 970 | U2 | 2.5 | 0.9 | ID | Rupert |
| 631 | WFSR | 970 | U1 | 5 | 0.02 | KY | Harlan |
| 632 | WGTK | 970 | U4 | 5 | 5 | KY | Louisville |
| 633 | WZAN | 970 | U2 | 5 | 5 | ME | Portland |
| 634 | WZAM | 970 | U1 | 5 | 0.06 | MI | Ishpeming |
| 635 | KQAQ | 970 | U1 | 5 | 0.5 | MN | Austin |
| 636 | KBUL | 970 | U2 | 5 | 5 | MT | Billings |
| 637 | WYSE | 970 | U1 | 5 | 0.03 | NC | Canton |
| 638 | WDAY | 970 | U4 | 10 | 10 | ND | Fargo |
| 639 | KJLT | 970 | U1 | 5 | 0.05 | NE | North Platte |
| 640 | WNYM | 970 | U4 | 50 | 5 | NJ | Hackensack |
| 641 | KNIH | 970 | U4 | 5 | 0.5 | NV | Paradise |
| 642 | WDCZ | 970 | U3 | 5 | 5 | NY | Buffalo |
| 643 | WFUN | 970 | U4 | 5 | 1 | OH | Ashtabula |
| 644 | KCFO | 970 | U4 | 2.5 | 1 | OK | Tulsa |
| 645 | KUFO | 970 | U2 | 5 | 5 | OR | Portland |
| 646 | WBGG | 970 | U4 | 5 | 5 | PA | Pittsburgh |
| 647 | WWRK | 970 | U1 | 10 | 0.03 | SC | Florence |
| 648 | WKCI | 970 | U4 | 5 | 1 | VA | Waynesboro |
| 649 | KTTO | 970 | U2 | 5.3 | 0.75 | WA | Spokane |
| 650 | WHA | #970 | U1 | 5 | 0.05 | WI | Madison |
| 651 | KCAB | **980** | U1 | 5 | 0.03 | AR | Dardanelle |
| 652 | KWSW | 980 | U2 | 5 | 0.5 | CA | Eureka |
| 653 | KFWB | #980 | U1 | 5 | 5 | CA | Los Angeles |
| 654 | KDBV | 980 | U4 | 10 | 10 | CA | Salinas |
| 655 | WTEM | 980 | U4 | 50 | 5 | DC | Washington |
| 656 | WDVH | 980 | U1 | 5 | 0.16 | FL | Gainesville |
| 657 | WRNE | 980 | U2 | 4 | 1 | FL | Gulf Breeze |
| 658 | WHSR | 980 | U4 | 5 | 2.2 | FL | Pompano Beach |
| 659 | WDDO | 980 | U1 | 2.6 | 0.08 | GA | Perry |
| 660 | KSPZ | 980 | U4 | 5 | 1 | ID | Ammon |
| 661 | KOKA | 980 | U1 | 5 | 0.07 | LA | Shreveport |
| 662 | WCAP | 980 | U4 | 5 | 5 | MA | Lowell |
| 663 | KKMS | 980 | U3 | 5 | 5 | MN | Richfield |
| 664 | KMBZ | 980 | U2 | 9 | 5 | MO | Kansas City |
| 665 | WAAV | 980 | U2 | 5 | 5 | NC | Leland |
| 666 | KMIN | 980 | U1 | 5 | 0.23 | NM | Grants |
| 667 | KVLV | 980 | D1 | 5 | | NV | Fallon |
| 668 | WOFX | #980 | U2 | 5 | 5 | NY | Troy |
| 669 | WONE | #980 | U2 | 5 | 5 | OH | Dayton |
| 670 | WILK | 980 | U2 | 5 | 1 | PA | Wilkes-Barre |
| 671 | WULR | 980 | U4 | 3 | 0.16 | SC | York |
| 672 | KDSJ | 980 | U2 | 5 | 1 | SD | Deadwood |
| 673 | WYFN | 980 | U2 | 5 | 5 | TN | Nashville |
| 674 | KQUE | 980 | U4 | 5 | 4 | TX | Rosenberg-Richmond |
| 675 | KSVC | 980 | U2 | 10 | 1 | UT | Richfield |
| 676 | WWTB | 980 | U2 | 5 | 1 | VA | Bristol |
| 677 | KTCR | 980 | U4 | 5 | 0.5 | WA | Selah |
| 678 | WCUB | 980 | U4 | 5 | 5 | WI | Two Rivers |
| 679 | WHAW | 980 | U1 | 25 | 0.04 | WV | Lost Creek |
| 680 | KTKT | **990** | U4 | 10 | 0.49 | AZ | Tucson |
| 681 | KATD | 990 | U4 | 10 | 5 | CA | Pittsburg |
| 682 | KTMS | 990 | U4 | 5 | 0.5 | CA | Santa Barbara |
| 683 | KRKS | 990 | U2 | 6.5 | 0.39 | CO | Denver |
| 684 | WNTY | 990 | U4 | 2.5 | 0.08 | CT | Southington |
| 685 | WMYM | 990 | U4 | 7.5 | 5 | FL | Kendall |
| 686 | WDYZ | 990 | U4 | 50 | 14 | FL | Orlando |
| 687 | WISK | 990 | D1 | 2.5 | | GA | Lawrenceville |
| 688 | WDEO | 990 | U4 | 9.2 | 0.25 | MI | Ypsilanti |
| 689 | KRMO | 990 | U1 | 2.5 | 0.04 | MO | Cassville |
| 690 | WEEB | 990 | U1 | 10 | 0.03 | NC | Southern Pines |
| 691 | WDCX | #990 | U4 | 5 | 2.5 | NY | Rochester |
| 692 | WNTP | 990 | U4 | 50 | 10 | PA | Philadelphia |
| 693 | WNTI | 990 | U4 | 10 | 0.1 | PA | Somerset |
| 694 | WNML | 990 | U2 | 10 | 10 | TN | Knoxville |
| 695 | KWAM | 990 | U4 | 10 | 0.45 | TN | Memphis |
| 696 | KFCD | 990 | U4 | 7 | 0.92 | TX | Farmersville |
| 697 | WNRV | 990 | U1 | 5 | 0.01 | VA | Narrows-Pearisburg |
| 698 | KCEO | **1000** | U4 | 10.53 | 0.97 | CA | Vista |
| 699 | WYBT | 1000 | D1 | 5 | | FL | Blountstown |
| 700 | WMVP | 1000 | U4 | 50 | 50 | IL | Chicago |
| 701 | WXTN | 1000 | D1 | 5 | | MS | Benton |
| 702 | KKIM | 1000 | U1 | 10 | 0.05 | NM | Albuquerque |
| 703 | WLNL | 1000 | D1 | 5 | | NY | Horseheads |
| 704 | KTOK | 1000 | U4 | 5.8 | 5.8 | OK | Oklahoma City |
| 705 | KSOO | 1000 | U4 | 10 | 0.1 | SD | Sioux Falls |
| 706 | WRQR | 1000 | D4 | 5 | | TN | Paris |
| 707 | KOMO | 1000 | U2 | 50 | 50 | WA | Seattle |
| 708 | KXXT | **1010** | U5 | 15 | 0.25 | AZ | Tolleson |
| 709 | KCHJ | 1010 | U4 | 5 | 1 | CA | Delano |
| 710 | KIQI | 1010 | U4 | 10 | 0.5 | CA | San Francisco |
| 711 | KXPS | 1010 | U4 | 3.6 | 0.4 | CA | Thousand Palms |
| 712 | KSIR | 1010 | U4 | 25 | 0.28 | CO | Brush |
| 713 | WJXL | 1010 | U4 | 50 | 30 | FL | Jacksonville Beach |
| 714 | WHFS | 1010 | U4 | 50 | 5 | FL | Seffner |
| 715 | WTZA | 1010 | U1 | 50 | 0.07 | GA | Atlanta |
| 716 | KXEN | 1010 | U4 | 50 | 0.5 | MO | Saint Louis |
| 717 | WMOX | 1010 | U4 | 10 | 1 | MS | Meridian |
| 718 | WKJW | 1010 | U10 | 47 | 0.09 | NC | Black Mountain |
| 719 | WCNL | 1010 | U1 | 10 | 0.03 | NH | Newport |
| 720 | WINS | #1010 | U3 | 50 | 50 | NY | New York |
| 721 | KOOR | 1010 | D1 | 4.5 | | OR | Milwaukie |
| 722 | WHIN | 1010 | U1 | 5 | 0.04 | TN | Gallatin |
| 723 | KTNZ | 1010 | U4 | 5 | 0.5 | TX | Amarillo |
| 724 | KLAT | 1010 | U4 | 5 | 3.6 | TX | Houston |
| 725 | KBBW | 1010 | U4 | 10 | 2.5 | TX | Waco |
| 726 | KIHU | 1010 | U13 | 50 | 0.19 | UT | Tooele |
| 727 | WPMH | 1010 | U4 | 5 | 0.44 | VA | Portsmouth |
| 728 | KTNQ | **1020** | U4 | 50 | 50 | CA | Los Angeles |
| 729 | WHDD | 1020 | D1 | 2.5 | | CT | Sharon |
| 730 | WLVJ | 1020 | U4 | 4.7 | 1.5 | FL | Boynton Beach |
| 731 | KMMQ | 1020 | U4 | 50 | 1.4 | NE | Plattsmouth |
| 732 | KCKN | ‡1020 | U4 | 50 | 50 | NM | Roswell |
| 733 | KDKA | 1020 | U1 | 50 | 50 | PA | Pittsburgh |
| 734 | WRIX | 1020 | D1 | 10 | | SC | Homeland Park |
| 735 | KDYK | 1020 | U5 | 4 | 0.4 | WA | Union Gap |
| 736 | KFAY | **1030** | U4 | 6 | 1 | AR | Farmington |
| 737 | KVOI | 1030 | U4 | 10 | 1 | AZ | Cortaro |
| 738 | KJDJ | 1030 | U1 | 2.5 | 0.7 | CA | San Luis Obispo |
| 739 | WONQ | 1030 | U2 | 45 | 1.7 | FL | Oviedo |
| 740 | WEBS | 1030 | U1 | 5 | 0.003 | GA | Calhoun |
| 741 | WNVR | 1030 | U7 | 10 | 0.12 | IL | Vernon Hills |
| 742 | KBUF | 1030 | U2 | 2.5 | 1.2 | KS | Holcomb |
| 743 | WBZ | #1030 | U3 | 50 | 50 | MA | Boston |
| 744 | WWGB | 1030 | D3 | 50 | | MD | Indian Head |
| 745 | WUFL | 1030 | D3 | 5 | | MI | Sterling Heights |
| 746 | WCTS | 1030 | U4 | 50 | 4 | MN | Maplewood |
| 747 | KCWJ | 1030 | U4 | 5 | 0.5 | MO | Blue Springs |
| 748 | WDRU | 1030 | D3 | 50 | | NC | Creedmoor |
| 749 | WNOW | 1030 | D3 | 9.4 | | NC | Mint Hill |
| 750 | KDUN | 1030 | U1 | 50 | 0.63 | OR | Reedsport |
| 751 | WGSF | 1030 | U12 | 50 | 1 | TN | Memphis |
| 752 | KCTA | 1030 | L1 | 50 | | TX | Corpus Christi |
| 753 | KMAS | 1030 | U1 | 10 | 1 | WA | Shelton |
| 754 | WTHQ | 1030 | D5 | 10 | | WV | Point Pleasant |
| 755 | KTWO | 1030 | U2 | 50 | 50 | WY | Casper |
| 756 | KCBR | **#1040** | D1 | 15 | | CO | Monument |
| 757 | WURN | 1040 | U4 | 50 | 5 | FL | Miami |
| 758 | WPBS | 1040 | U2 | 3.6 | 0.42 | FL | Pinellas Park |
| 759 | WPBS | 1040 | D1 | 50 | | GA | Conyers |
| 760 | WHO | 1040 | U1 | 50 | 50 | IA | Des Moines |

| MW | Call | kHz | Ant. | D | N | Sta | City of License | MW | Call | kHz | Ant. | D | N | Sta | City of License |
|----|------|-----|------|---|---|-----|-----------------|----|------|-----|------|---|---|-----|-----------------|
| 761 | WSGH | 1040 | U4 | 9.1 | 0.18 | NC | Lewisville | 843 | KMXA | #1090 | U4 | 50 | 0.5 | CO | Aurora |
| 762 | WCHR | 1040 | U7 | 15 | 1.5 | NJ | Flemington | 844 | WFCV | 1090 | D4 | 2.5 | | IN | Fort Wayne |
| 763 | WYSL | 1040 | U7 | 20 | 0.5 | NY | Avon | 845 | WILD | 1090 | D1 | 4.8 | | MA | Boston |
| 764 | WZSK | 1040 | D1 | 2.5 | | PA | Everett | 846 | WBAL | 1090 | U2 | 50 | 50 | MD | Baltimore |
| 765 | WJBE | 1040 | D1 | 10 | | TN | Powell | 847 | KEXS | 1090 | D4 | 10 | | MO | Excelsior Springs |
| 766 | KGGR | 1040 | D1 | 3.3 | | TX | Dallas | 848 | KBOZ | ‡1090 | U2 | 5 | 5 | MT | Bozeman |
| 767 | KJPG | 1050 | D3 | 10 | | CA | Frazier Park | 849 | WTSB | 1090 | D1 | 9 | | NC | Selma |
| 768 | KTCT | 1050 | U4 | 50 | 10 | CA | San Mateo | 850 | WCZZ | 1090 | D1 | 5 | | SC | Greenwood |
| 769 | WJSB | 1050 | D1 | 3.1 | | FL | Crestview | 851 | WHGG | 1090 | D1 | 10 | | TN | Kingsport |
| 770 | WROS | 1050 | U4 | 5 | 0.01 | FL | Jacksonville | 852 | KVOP | ‡1090 | U4 | 5 | 0.5 | TX | Plainview |
| 771 | WFAM | 1050 | U1 | 5 | 0.08 | GA | Augusta | 853 | KFNQ | 1090 | U4 | 50 | 50 | WA | Seattle |
| 772 | WBQH | 1050 | U1 | 10 | 0.04 | MD | Silver Spring | 854 | WAQE | 1090 | D1 | 5 | | WI | Rice Lake |
| 773 | WTKA | 1050 | U4 | 10 | 0.5 | MI | Ann Arbor | 855 | KFNX | 1100 | U4 | 50 | 1 | AZ | Cave Creek |
| 774 | KLOH | 1050 | U4 | 9.38 | 0.43 | MN | Pipestone | 856 | KAFY | 1100 | U2 | 4.2 | 0.8 | CA | Bakersfield |
| 775 | KMTA | 1050 | U1 | 10 | 0.13 | MT | Miles City | 857 | KFAX | 1100 | U3 | 50 | 50 | CA | San Francisco |
| 776 | WFSC | 1050 | U1 | 5 | 0.15 | NC | Franklin | 858 | KNZZ | 1100 | U12 | 50 | 10 | CO | Grand Junction |
| 777 | WBVG | 1050 | U4 | 2.5 | 0.01 | NY | Baldwinsville | 859 | WWWE | 1100 | D1 | 5 | | GA | Hapeville |
| 778 | WEPN | 1050 | U4 | 50 | 50 | NY | New York | 860 | WCGA | 1100 | D1 | 10 | | GA | Woodbine |
| 779 | KORE | 1050 | U1 | 5 | 0.1 | OR | Springfield-Eugene | 861 | WZFG | 1100 | U2 | 50 | 0.44 | MN | Dilworth |
| 780 | WRWM | 1050 | U4 | 5 | 0.47 | SC | Conway | 862 | KKLL | 1100 | D1 | 5 | | MO | Webb City |
| 781 | WBRG | 1050 | U1 | 3.8 | 0.09 | VA | Lynchburg | 863 | KWWN | 1100 | U4 | 22 | 2 | NV | Las Vegas |
| 782 | WVXX | 1050 | U4 | 5 | 0.35 | VA | Norfolk | 864 | WHLI | 1100 | D3 | 10 | | NY | Hempstead |
| 783 | KFIO | 1050 | U1 | 25 | 0.26 | WA | Dishman | 865 | WTAM | 1100 | U1 | 50 | 50 | OH | Cleveland |
| 784 | KBLE | 1050 | U1 | 5 | 0.44 | WA | Seattle | 866 | KDRY | 1100 | U2 | 11 | 1 | TX | Alamo Heights |
| 785 | WLYQ | 1050 | U1 | 5 | 0.14 | WV | Parkersburg | 867 | WTWN | 1100 | D1 | 5 | | VT | Wells River |
| 786 | KDUS | **1060** | U2 | 5 | 0.5 | AZ | Tempe | 868 | WISS | 1100 | D1 | 2.5 | | WI | Berlin |
| 787 | KTNS | 1060 | U1 | 5 | 0.02 | CA | Oakhurst | 869 | WTOF | **1110** | D1 | 10 | | AL | Bay Minette |
| 788 | KRCN | 1060 | U1 | 50 | 0.11 | CO | Longmont | 870 | KGFL | 1110 | D1 | 5 | | AR | Clinton |
| 789 | WIXC | 1060 | U7 | 50 | 5 | FL | Titusville | 871 | KRDC | 1110 | U4 | 50 | 20 | CA | Pasadena |
| 790 | WKNG | 1060 | D1 | 50 | | GA | Tallapoosa | 872 | KLIB | 1110 | U4 | 5 | 0.5 | CA | Roseville |
| 791 | KBGN | 1060 | D1 | 10 | | ID | Caldwell | 873 | WTIS | 1110 | D1 | 10 | | FL | Tampa |
| 792 | WMCL | 1060 | U5 | 2.5 | 0.002 | IL | McLeansboro | 874 | WMBI | 1110 | D1 | 4.2 | | IL | Chicago |
| 793 | WLNO | 1060 | U4 | 50 | 5 | LA | New Orleans | 875 | WUPE | 1110 | D3 | 5 | | MA | Pittsfield |
| 794 | WQOM | 1060 | U4 | 50 | 2.5 | MA | Natick | 876 | WJML | 1110 | U4 | 10 | 0.01 | MI | Petoskey |
| 795 | WHFB | 1060 | U1 | 5 | 0.001 | MI | Benton Harbor-St.Joseph | 877 | WBT | 1110 | U2 | 50 | 50 | NC | Charlotte |
| 796 | WXNC | 1060 | D1 | 4 | | NC | Monroe | 878 | KFAB | 1110 | U2 | 50 | 50 | NE | Omaha |
| 797 | KKVV | 1060 | U1 | 5 | 0.04 | NV | Las Vegas | 879 | WMVX | 1110 | D3 | 5 | | NH | Salem |
| 798 | KFOY | 1060 | U2 | 5 | 0.5 | NV | Sparks | 880 | KEJL | 1110 | D1 | 5 | | NM | Humble City |
| 799 | WILB | 1060 | D4 | 15 | | OH | Canton | 881 | WGNZ | 1110 | U7 | 5 | 0.002 | OH | Fairborn |
| 800 | KYW | #1060 | U3 | 50 | 50 | PA | Philadelphia | 882 | KBND | 1110 | U2 | 10 | 5 | OR | Bend |
| 801 | KGFX | 1060 | U4 | 10 | 1 | SD | Pierre | 883 | WNAP | 1110 | D5 | 4.8 | | PA | Norristown |
| 802 | KXPL | 1060 | D1 | 10 | | TX | El Paso | 884 | WPMZ | 1110 | D3 | 5 | | RI | East Providence |
| 803 | KIJN | 1060 | D3 | 10 | | TX | Farwell | 885 | WSLV | 1110 | D1 | 2.5 | | TN | Ardmore |
| 804 | KDYL | 1060 | U1 | 10 | 0.14 | UT | South Salt Lake | 886 | KTEK | 1110 | D3 | 2.5 | | TX | Alvin |
| 805 | WAPI | **1070** | U2 | 50 | 5 | AL | Birmingham | 887 | KVTT | 1110 | D4 | 50 | | TX | Mineral Wells |
| 806 | KNX | #1070 | U1 | 50 | 50 | CA | Los Angeles | 888 | WKQA | 1110 | D1 | 5 | | VA | Norfolk |
| 807 | WNVY | 1070 | U1 | 15 | 0.02 | FL | Cantonment | 889 | KZSJ | **1120** | U1 | 5 | 0.15 | CA | San Martin |
| 808 | WFRF | 1070 | D1 | 10 | | FL | Tallahassee | 890 | WUST | 1120 | D5 | 50 | | DC | Washington |
| 809 | WFNI | #1070 | U4 | 50 | 10 | IN | Indianapolis | 891 | WBNW | 1120 | U4 | 5 | 1 | MA | Concord |
| 810 | KFTI | 1070 | U2 | 10 | 1 | KS | Wichita | 892 | KMOX | #1120 | U1 | 50 | 50 | MO | Saint Louis |
| 811 | KSKK | 1070 | U2 | 10 | 5 | MN | Verndale | 893 | WTWZ | 1120 | D1 | 10 | | MS | Clinton |
| 812 | KHMO | 1070 | U4 | 5 | 1 | MO | Hannibal | 894 | WSME | 1120 | D1 | 6 | | NC | Camp Lejeune |
| 813 | KATQ | 1070 | U1 | 5 | 0.05 | MT | Plentywood | 895 | WKAJ | 1120 | U4 | 10 | 0.4 | NY | Saint Johnsville |
| 814 | WNCT | 1070 | U4 | 50 | 10 | NC | Greenville | 896 | KETU | 1120 | D4 | 10 | | OK | Catoosa |
| 815 | WPLB | 1070 | D1 | 5 | | NY | Plattsburgh | 897 | KPNW | 1120 | U3 | 50 | 50 | OR | Eugene |
| 816 | WZUN | 1070 | D1 | 2.5 | | NY | Sandy Creek-Pulaski | 898 | KTXW | 1120 | U4 | 5.6 | 0.15 | TX | Manor |
| 817 | WKOK | 1070 | U2 | 10 | 1 | PA | Sunbury | 899 | KANN | 1120 | U4 | 10 | 1.1 | UT | Roy |
| 818 | WCSZ | 1070 | U4 | 50 | 1.5 | SC | Sans Souci | 900 | WALQ | ‡1130 | D1 | 25 | | AL | Carrville |
| 819 | WFLI | 1070 | U4 | 50 | 2.5 | TN | Lookout Mountain | 901 | KRDU | 1130 | U4 | 5 | 6.2 | CA | Dinuba |
| 820 | WDIA | 1070 | U4 | 50 | 5 | TN | Memphis | 902 | KSDO | 1130 | U4 | 10 | 10 | CA | San Diego |
| 821 | KNTH | 1070 | U4 | 10 | 5 | TX | Houston | 903 | WWBF | 1130 | U2 | 2.5 | 0.5 | FL | Bartow |
| 822 | KWEL | 1070 | D1 | 2.5 | | TX | Midland | 904 | WLBA | 1130 | D1 | 10 | | GA | Gainesville |
| 823 | WINA | 1070 | U2 | 5 | 5 | VA | Charlottesville | 905 | KWKH | 1130 | U2 | 50 | 50 | LA | Shreveport |
| 824 | WTSO | 1070 | U4 | 10 | 5 | WI | Madison | 906 | WDFN | 1130 | U2 | 50 | 10 | MI | Detroit |
| 825 | WBKW | 1070 | D1 | 10 | | WV | Beckley | 907 | KTLK | 1130 | U4 | 50 | 25 | MN | Minneapolis |
| 826 | WKAC | **1080** | D1 | 5 | | AL | Athens | 908 | WPYB | 1130 | D1 | 6.5 | | NC | Benson |
| 827 | KSCO | 1080 | U2 | 10 | 5 | CA | Santa Cruz | 909 | KBMR | 1130 | U1 | 10 | 0.02 | ND | Bismarck |
| 828 | WTIC | #1080 | U2 | 50 | 50 | CT | Hartford | 910 | WBBR | 1130 | U2 | 50 | 50 | NY | New York |
| 829 | WKAT | 1080 | U4 | 50 | 10 | FL | Coral Gables | 911 | KXET | 1130 | U4 | 25 | 0.49 | OR | Mount Angel |
| 830 | WHOO | 1080 | U7 | 19 | 0.19 | FL | Kissimmee | 912 | WEAF | 1130 | U1 | 5 | 0.007 | SC | Camden |
| 831 | WFTD | 1080 | D4 | 50 | | GA | Marietta | 913 | KTMR | 1130 | D3 | 25 | | TX | Converse |
| 832 | KVNI | 1080 | U2 | 10 | 1 | ID | Coeur d' Alene | 914 | WISN | 1130 | U4 | 50 | 10 | WI | Milwaukee |
| 833 | WNWI | 1080 | U2 | 5 | 2.6 | IL | Oak Lawn | 915 | WBXR | **1140** | D4 | 15 | | AL | Hazel Green |
| 834 | WKJK | 1080 | U4 | 10 | 1 | KY | Louisville | 916 | KLTK | 1140 | D1 | 5 | | AR | Centerton |
| 835 | WKGX | 1080 | D1 | 5 | | NC | Lenoir | 917 | KNWQ | 1140 | U4 | 10 | 2.5 | CA | Palm Springs |
| 836 | KFXX | 1080 | U4 | 50 | 9 | OR | Portland | 918 | KHTK | #1140 | U4 | 50 | 50 | CA | Sacramento |
| 837 | WWNL | 1080 | D4 | 50 | | PA | Pittsburgh | 919 | WNWF | 1140 | U1 | 3 | 0.01 | FL | Destin |
| 838 | WALD | 1080 | D1 | 9 | | SC | Johnsonville | 920 | WQBA | 1140 | U4 | 50 | 10 | FL | Miami |
| 839 | KRLD | #1080 | U2 | 50 | 50 | TX | Dallas | 921 | WURF | 1140 | U2 | 5 | 0.008 | FL | Orlando |
| 840 | KSLL | 1080 | D1 | 10 | | UT | Price | 922 | KGEM | 1140 | U2 | 10 | 10 | ID | Boise |
| 841 | KAAY | **1090** | U2 | 50 | 50 | AR | Little Rock | 923 | WVEL | 1140 | D1 | 5 | | IL | Pekin |
| 842 | KNCR | 1090 | D1 | 10 | | CA | Fortuna | 924 | WVHF | 1140 | D3 | 5 | | MI | Kentwood |

| MW | Call | kHz | Ant. | D | N | Sta | City of License |
|----|------|-----|------|---|---|-----|-----------------|
| 925 | KCXL | 1140 | U1 | 4 | 0.006 | MO | Liberty |
| 926 | KXST | 1140 | U2 | 10 | 2.5 | NV | North Las Vegas |
| 927 | WCJW | 1140 | D4 | 8 | | NY | Warsaw |
| 928 | KXRB | 1140 | U2 | 10 | 5 | SD | Sioux Falls |
| 929 | KHFX | 1140 | U4 | 5 | 0.71 | TX | Cleburne |
| 930 | KYOK | 1140 | D3 | 5 | | TX | Conroe |
| 931 | WRVA #1140 | 1140 | U3 | 50 | 50 | VA | Richmond |
| 932 | WXLZ | 1140 | D1 | 2.5 | | VA | Saint Paul |
| 933 | KZMQ | 1140 | D1 | 10 | | WY | Greybull |
| 934 | WJRD | **1150** | U2 | 20 | 1 | AL | Tuscaloosa |
| 935 | KCKY | 1150 | U4 | 5 | 1 | AZ | Coolidge |
| 936 | KEIB | 1150 | U4 | 50 | 44 | CA | Los Angeles |
| 937 | KNRV | 1150 | U4 | 10 | 1 | CO | Englewood |
| 938 | WMRD | 1150 | U1 | 2.5 | 0.04 | CT | Middletown |
| 939 | WDEL | 1150 | U4 | 5 | 5 | DE | Wilmington |
| 940 | WTMP | 1150 | U4 | 10 | 0.5 | FL | Egypt Lake |
| 941 | WJEM | 1150 | U4 | 5 | 0.1 | GA | Valdosta |
| 942 | KWKY | 1150 | U4 | 2.5 | 1 | IA | Des Moines |
| 943 | WGGH | 1150 | U4 | 5 | 0.04 | IL | Marion |
| 944 | KSAL | 1150 | U2 | 5 | 5 | KS | Salina |
| 945 | WMST | 1150 | U1 | 2.5 | 0.05 | KY | Mount Sterling |
| 946 | WJBO | 1150 | U4 | 15 | 5 | LA | Baton Rouge |
| 947 | WWDJ | 1150 | U4 | 5 | 5 | MA | Boston |
| 948 | KSEN | 1150 | U4 | 10 | 5 | MT | Shelby |
| 949 | WGBR | 1150 | U4 | 5 | 0.8 | NC | Goldsboro |
| 950 | WCUE | 1150 | U4 | 5 | 0.5 | OH | Cuyahoga Falls |
| 951 | KAGO | 1150 | U2 | 5 | 1 | OR | Klamath Falls |
| 952 | KGDD | 1150 | U1 | 5 | 0.01 | OR | Portland |
| 953 | WHUN | 1150 | U1 | 5 | 0.03 | PA | Huntingdon |
| 954 | WAVO | 1150 | U1 | 5 | 0.05 | SC | Rock Hill |
| 955 | WSNW | 1150 | U1 | 5 | 0.05 | SC | Walhalla |
| 956 | KIMM | 1150 | U1 | 5 | 0.03 | SD | Rapid City |
| 957 | WGOW | 1150 | U2 | 5 | 1 | TN | Chattanooga |
| 958 | WCRK | 1150 | U2 | 5 | 0.5 | TN | Morristown |
| 959 | KHRO | 1150 | U1 | 5 | 0.38 | TX | El Paso |
| 960 | WNLR | 1150 | U1 | 2.5 | 0.03 | VA | Churchville |
| 961 | KQQQ | 1150 | U1 | 11 | 0.02 | WA | Pullman |
| 962 | KKNW | 1150 | U2 | 10 | 6 | WA | Seattle |
| 963 | WEAQ | 1150 | U4 | 5 | 0.04 | WI | Chippewa Falls |
| 964 | WHBY | 1150 | U4 | 20 | 25 | WI | Kimberly |
| 965 | WELC | 1150 | D1 | 5 | | WV | Welch |
| 966 | WEWC | **1160** | U5 | 5 | 0.25 | FL | Callahan |
| 967 | WIWA | 1160 | U4 | 2.5 | 0.5 | FL | Saint Cloud |
| 968 | WCFO | 1160 | U4 | 50 | 0.16 | GA | East Point |
| 969 | WYLL | 1160 | U4 | 50 | 50 | IL | Chicago |
| 970 | WCVX | 1160 | U4 | 5 | 0.99 | KY | Florence |
| 971 | WKCM | 1160 | U1 | 5 | 0.05 | KY | Hawesville |
| 972 | WMET | 1160 | U4 | 50 | 1.5 | MD | Gaithersburg |
| 973 | WSKW | 1160 | U1 | 10 | 0.73 | ME | Skowhegan |
| 974 | KCTO | 1160 | U4 | 5 | 0.23 | MO | Cleveland |
| 975 | WYDU | 1160 | U1 | 5 | 0.25 | NC | Red Springs |
| 976 | WWQT | 1160 | U2 | 25 | 0.5 | NC | Tryon |
| 977 | WOBM | 1160 | U4 | 5 | 8.9 | NJ | Lakewood Township |
| 978 | WVNJ | 1160 | U4 | 20 | 2.5 | NJ | Oakland |
| 979 | WAIX ‡1160 | 1160 | U1 | 5 | 0.57 | NY | Mechanicville |
| 980 | WPIE | 1160 | U4 | 5 | 0.31 | NY | Trumansburg |
| 981 | WCCS | 1160 | U4 | 10 | 1 | PA | Homer City |
| 982 | WBYN ‡1160 | 1160 | U4 | 4 | 1 | PA | Lehighton |
| 983 | WCRT | 1160 | U2 | 50 | 1 | TN | Donelson |
| 984 | KBDT | 1160 | U4 | 35 | 1 | TX | Highland Park |
| 985 | KRDY | 1160 | U4 | 10 | 1 | TX | San Antonio |
| 986 | KSL #1160 | 1160 | U1 | 50 | 50 | UT | Salt Lake City |
| 987 | WODY | 1160 | U2 | 5 | 0.25 | VA | Fieldale |
| 988 | KYET | **1170** | U1 | 6 | 0.001 | AZ | Golden Valley |
| 989 | KCBQ | 1170 | U4 | 50 | 2.9 | CA | San Diego |
| 990 | KLOK #1170 | 1170 | U4 | 50 | 9 | CA | San Jose |
| 991 | WAVS | 1170 | U2 | 5 | 0.25 | FL | Davie |
| 992 | WLBH | 1170 | D3 | 5 | | IL | Mattoon |
| 993 | KOWZ | 1170 | U1 | 2.5 | 0.005 | MN | Waseca |
| 994 | WCXN | 1170 | D1 | 7.7 | | NC | Claremont |
| 995 | WCLN | 1170 | D1 | 5 | | NC | Clinton |
| 996 | KFAQ | 1170 | U2 | 50 | 50 | OK | Tulsa |
| 997 | WDEK | 1170 | D1 | 10 | | SC | Lexington |
| 998 | KPUG | 1170 | U2 | 10 | 5 | WA | Bellingham |
| 999 | WWVA | 1170 | U2 | 50 | 50 | WV | Wheeling |
| 1000 | WGUE | **1180** | U7 | 5 | 0.02 | AR | Turrell |
| 1001 | KERN | 1180 | U4 | 10 | 10 | CA | Wasco-Greenacres |
| 1002 | - | 1180 | U3 | 100 | 100 | FL | Marathon (R. Marti) |
| 1003 | WZQZ | 1180 | D1 | 5 | | GA | Trion |
| 1004 | WXLA | 1180 | D4 | 10 | | MI | Dimondale |
| 1005 | KYES | 1180 | U7 | 50 | 5 | MN | Rockville |
| 1006 | WJNT | 1180 | U12 | 50 | 0.5 | MS | Pearl |
| 1007 | KOFI | 1180 | U2 | 50 | 10 | MT | Kalispell |
| 1008 | WLTT | 1180 | D3 | 10 | | NC | Carolina Beach |
| 1009 | KZOT | 1180 | U4 | 25 | 1 | NE | Bellevue |
| 1010 | KCKQ | 1180 | U2 | 4 | 0.19 | NV | Sparks |
| 1011 | WHAM | 1180 | U1 | 50 | 50 | NY | Rochester |
| 1012 | WFGN | 1180 | D1 | 2.5 | | SC | Gaffney |
| 1013 | WVLZ | 1180 | D1 | 10 | | TN | Knoxville |
| 1014 | KGOL | 1180 | U4 | 50 | 3 | TX | Humble |
| 1015 | KLPF | 1180 | U1 | 25 | 0.21 | TX | Midland |
| 1016 | KLAY | 1180 | U2 | 5 | 1 | WA | Lakewood |
| 1017 | WEUV | **1190** | D1 | 2.5 | | AL | Moulton |
| 1018 | KREB | 1190 | D1 | 5 | | AR | Bentonville-Bella Vista |
| 1019 | KJJI | 1190 | U2 | 25 | 0.35 | AR | White Hall |
| 1020 | KNUV | 1190 | U4 | 5 | 0.25 | AZ | Tolleson |
| 1021 | KGBN | 1190 | U4 | 20 | 1.3 | CA | Anaheim |
| 1022 | KDYA | 1190 | D3 | 3 | | CA | Vallejo |
| 1023 | KVCU | 1190 | U1 | 6.8 | 0.11 | CO | Boulder |
| 1024 | WAMT | 1190 | U2 | 4.7 | 0.23 | FL | Pine Castle-Sky Lake |
| 1025 | WAFS | 1190 | D1 | 25 | | GA | Atlanta |
| 1026 | KQQZ | 1190 | U4 | 10 | 0.65 | IL | Fairview Heights |
| 1027 | WOWO #1190 | 1190 | U2 | 50 | 9.8 | IN | Fort Wayne |
| 1028 | KKOJ | 1190 | D3 | 5 | | MN | Jackson |
| 1029 | KDMR | 1190 | U2 | 5 | 0.5 | MO | Kansas City |
| 1030 | WMEJ | 1190 | D1 | 5 | | MS | Bay Saint Louis |
| 1031 | WIXE | 1190 | U1 | 5 | 0.07 | NC | Monroe |
| 1032 | KXKS | 1190 | U1 | 10 | 0.02 | NM | Albuquerque |
| 1033 | WLIB | 1190 | U4 | 10 | 30 | NY | New York |
| 1034 | KEX | 1190 | U2 | 50 | 50 | OR | Portland |
| 1035 | WSDQ | 1190 | D1 | 5 | | TN | Dunlap |
| 1036 | KFXR | 1190 | U4 | 50 | 5 | TX | Dallas |
| 1037 | WCRW | 1190 | U4 | 50 | 1.2 | VA | Leesburg |
| 1038 | WNWC | 1190 | U4 | 4.8 | 0.02 | WI | Sun Prairie |
| 1039 | WVUS | 1190 | U1 | 4.5 | 0.02 | WV | Grafton |
| 1040 | KPSF | **1200** | U4 | 5 | 1.3 | CA | Cathedral City |
| 1041 | KYAA | 1200 | U2 | 25 | 10 | CA | Soquel |
| 1042 | WAXA | 1200 | U4 | 5 | 1 | FL | Pine Island Center |
| 1043 | WRTO | 1200 | U4 | 20 | 4.5 | IL | Chicago |
| 1044 | WXKS | 1200 | U4 | 50 | 50 | MA | Newton |
| 1045 | WMUZ | 1200 | U4 | 50 | 15 | MI | Taylor |
| 1046 | WXIT | 1200 | D1 | 4.2 | | NC | Blowing Rock |
| 1047 | WSML | 1200 | U2 | 10 | 1 | NC | Graham |
| 1048 | KFNW | 1200 | U4 | 50 | 13 | ND | West Fargo |
| 1049 | WRKK | 1200 | U4 | 10 | 0.25 | PA | Hughesville |
| 1050 | WKST | 1200 | U2 | 5 | 1 | PA | New Castle |
| 1051 | WJXY | 1200 | U1 | 6.5 | 0.01 | SC | Atlantic Beach |
| 1052 | WFCN | 1200 | D1 | 10 | | TN | Nashville |
| 1053 | WOAI #1200 | 1200 | U1 | 50 | 50 | TX | San Antonio |
| 1054 | WYSN | 1200 | U1 | 5 | 0.009 | WV | Huntington |
| 1055 | WTXK | **1210** | U1 | 10 | 0.003 | AL | Pike Road |
| 1056 | KEVT | 1210 | U2 | 10 | 1 | AZ | Sahuarita |
| 1057 | KQEQ | 1210 | U5 | 5 | 0.37 | CA | Fowler |
| 1058 | KRPU | 1210 | U5 | 5 | 0.5 | CA | Rocklin |
| 1059 | KPRZ | 1210 | U4 | 20 | 10 | CA | San Marcos |
| 1060 | WNMA | 1210 | U4 | 47 | 2.5 | FL | Miami Springs |
| 1061 | WDGR ‡1210 | 1210 | D1 | 10 | | GA | Dahlonega |
| 1062 | WILY | 1210 | U11 | 10 | 0.003 | IL | Centralia |
| 1063 | WJNL | 1210 | D1 | 50 | | MI | Kingsley |
| 1064 | KGYN | 1210 | U2 | 10 | 10 | OK | Guymon |
| 1065 | WPHT | 1210 | U1 | 50 | 50 | PA | Philadelphia |
| 1066 | WANB | 1210 | D1 | 5 | | PA | Waynesburg |
| 1067 | KOKK | 1210 | U4 | 5 | 0.87 | SD | Huron |
| 1068 | WMPS | 1210 | U4 | 10 | 0.25 | TN | Bartlett |
| 1069 | WSBI | 1210 | D1 | 10 | | TN | Static |
| 1070 | KUBR | 1210 | U4 | 10 | 5 | TX | San Juan |
| 1071 | KHKR | 1210 | U1 | 10 | 0.23 | UT | Washington |
| 1072 | KMIA | 1210 | U4 | 27.5 | 10 | WA | Auburn-Federal Way |
| 1073 | KRSV | 1210 | U1 | 5 | 0.25 | WY | Afton |
| 1074 | KHAT | 1210 | U2 | 10 | 1 | WY | Laramie |
| 1075 | KDOW | **1220** | U1 | 5 | 0.14 | CA | Palo Alto |
| 1076 | WSLM | 1220 | U4 | 5 | 0.08 | IN | Salem |
| 1077 | KLBB ‡1220 | 1220 | U1 | 5 | 0.25 | MN | Stillwater |
| 1078 | WDYT | 1220 | U5 | 25 | 0.1 | NC | Kings Mountain |
| 1079 | WENC | 1220 | U1 | 5 | 0.15 | NC | Whiteville |
| 1080 | WGNY | 1220 | U4 | 10 | 0.18 | NY | Newburgh |
| 1081 | WHKW | 1220 | U3 | 50 | 50 | OH | Cleveland |
| 1082 | WFAX | 1220 | U1 | 5 | 0.04 | VA | Falls Church |
| | | **1230** | | Various stns of 1kW or less | | | |
| | | **1240** | | Various stns of 1kW or less | | | |
| 1083 | WZOB | **1250** | U1 | 5 | 0.12 | AL | Fort Payne |
| 1084 | WRBZ | 1250 | U1 | 5 | 0.08 | AL | Wetumpka |
| 1085 | KHIL | 1250 | U1 | 5 | 0.19 | AZ | Willcox |
| 1086 | KZER | 1250 | U4 | 2.5 | 1 | CA | Santa Barbara |

| MW | Call | kHz | Ant. | D | N | Sta | City of License |
|----|------|-----|------|---|---|-----|-----------------|
| 1087 | KLLK | 1250 | U4 | 5 | 2.5 | CA | Willits |
| 1088 | WHNZ | #1250 | U4 | 25 | 5.9 | FL | Tampa |
| 1089 | KYYS | 1250 | U4 | 25 | 3.7 | KS | Kansas City |
| 1090 | WARE | 1250 | U4 | 5 | 2.5 | MA | Ware |
| 1091 | WJMK | 1250 | U4 | 5 | 1.1 | MI | Bridgeport |
| 1092 | KBRF | 1250 | U2 | 5 | 2.2 | MN | Fergus Falls |
| 1093 | KIKC | 1250 | U1 | 5 | 0.13 | MT | Forsyth |
| 1094 | WGHB | 1250 | U4 | 5 | 2.5 | NC | Farmville |
| 1095 | WBRM | 1250 | U1 | 5 | 0.05 | NC | Marion |
| 1096 | WGAM | 1250 | U4 | 5 | 5 | NH | Manchester |
| 1097 | WMTR | 1250 | U4 | 5 | 7 | NJ | Morristown |
| 1098 | WLEM | 1250 | U1 | 2.5 | 0.03 | PA | Emporium |
| 1099 | WPGP | 1250 | U2 | 5 | 5 | PA | Pittsburgh |
| 1100 | WTMA | 1250 | U2 | 5 | 1 | SC | Charleston |
| 1101 | KDEI | 1250 | U2 | 5 | 1 | TX | Port Arthur |
| 1102 | KZDC | 1250 | U4 | 25 | 0.92 | TX | San Antonio |
| 1103 | KNEU | 1250 | U1 | 5 | 0.12 | UT | Roosevelt |
| 1104 | WDVA | 1250 | U2 | 5 | 5 | VA | Danville |
| 1105 | WRCW | 1250 | U4 | 3 | 0.12 | VA | Warrenton |
| 1106 | KWSU | #1250 | U1 | 5 | 2.5 | WA | Pullman |
| 1107 | KKDZ | 1250 | U2 | 5 | 5 | WA | Seattle |
| 1108 | WSSP | 1250 | U4 | 5 | 5 | WI | Milwaukee |
| 1109 | WYKM | 1250 | | 5 | | WV | Rupert |
| 1110 | WYDE | 1260 | U1 | 5 | 0.04 | AL | Birmingham |
| 1111 | KBSZ | 1260 | U1 | 4.5 | 0.05 | AZ | Apache Junction |
| 1112 | KSUR | 1260 | U4 | 20 | 7.5 | CA | Beverly Hills |
| 1113 | KSFB | 1260 | U1 | 5 | 1 | CA | San Francisco |
| 1114 | WSPZ | 1260 | U4 | 35 | 5 | DC | Washington |
| 1115 | WFTW | 1260 | U1 | 2.5 | 0.13 | FL | Fort Walton Beach |
| 1116 | WSUA | 1260 | U4 | 50 | 20 | FL | Miami |
| 1117 | WUFE | 1260 | D1 | 5 | | GA | Baxley |
| 1118 | WMDG | 1260 | U1 | 5.1 | 0.05 | GA | East Point |
| 1119 | KDLF | 1260 | U5 | 5 | 0.03 | IA | Boone |
| 1120 | KNBL | 1260 | U1 | 5 | 0.06 | ID | Idaho Falls |
| 1121 | KWEI | 1260 | U1 | 8.4 | 0.03 | ID | Weiser |
| 1122 | WSDZ | 1260 | U4 | 20 | 5 | IL | Belleville |
| 1123 | WNDE | #1260 | U2 | 5 | 5 | IN | Indianapolis |
| 1124 | KBRH | 1260 | U1 | 5 | 0.12 | LA | Baton Rouge |
| 1125 | WBIX | 1260 | U2 | 5 | 5 | MA | Boston |
| 1126 | WPNW | 1260 | U4 | 10 | 1 | MI | Zeeland |
| 1127 | KSGF | 1260 | U2 | 5 | 5 | MO | Springfield |
| 1128 | WKXR | 1260 | U4 | 5 | 0.5 | NC | Asheboro |
| 1129 | WFJS | 1260 | U4 | 5.9 | 2.5 | NJ | Trenton |
| 1130 | KTRC | 1260 | U1 | 5 | 1 | NM | Santa Fe |
| 1131 | WSKO | 1260 | U2 | 5 | 5 | NY | Syracuse |
| 1132 | WCCR | #1260 | U4 | 10 | 5 | OH | Cleveland |
| 1133 | WNXT | 1260 | U4 | 5 | 1 | OH | Portsmouth |
| 1134 | WRIE | 1260 | U4 | 5 | 5 | PA | Erie |
| 1135 | WPHB | 1260 | U1 | 5 | 0.03 | PA | Philipsburg |
| 1136 | WPJF | 1260 | U1 | 5 | 0.01 | SC | Greenville |
| 1137 | WHYM | 1260 | U1 | 5 | 0.05 | SC | Lake City |
| 1138 | KWYR | 1260 | U1 | 5 | 0.14 | SD | Winner |
| 1139 | WNOO | 1260 | U1 | 5 | 0.02 | TN | Chattanooga |
| 1140 | WDKN | 1260 | U1 | 5 | 0.01 | TN | Dickson |
| 1141 | KSML | 1260 | U1 | 4.5 | 5 | TX | Diboll |
| 1142 | WCHV | 1260 | U4 | 5 | 2.5 | VA | Charlottesville |
| 1143 | WWVT | #1260 | U1 | 5 | 0.02 | VA | Christiansburg |
| 1144 | WXCE | 1260 | U4 | 5 | 5 | WI | Amery |
| 1145 | KPOW | 1260 | U2 | 5 | 1 | WY | Powell |
| 1146 | WIJD | 1270 | U1 | 5 | 0.1 | AL | Prichard |
| 1147 | KDJI | 1270 | U1 | 5 | 0.13 | AZ | Holbrook |
| 1148 | KVGH | 1270 | U4 | 5 | 0.75 | CA | Thousand Palms |
| 1149 | KVMI | 1270 | U2 | 5 | 1 | CA | Tulare |
| 1150 | WRLZ | 1270 | U4 | 25 | 5 | FL | Eatonville |
| 1151 | WNOG | 1270 | U4 | 5 | 5 | FL | Naples |
| 1152 | WTLY | 1270 | U1 | 5 | 0.11 | FL | Tallahassee |
| 1153 | WBOJ | 1270 | U1 | 5 | 0.23 | GA | Columbus |
| 1154 | WJJC | 1270 | U1 | 5 | 0.17 | GA | Commerce |
| 1155 | KTFI | 1270 | U1 | 5 | 0.86 | ID | Twin Falls |
| 1156 | WKBF | 1270 | U2 | 5 | 5 | IL | Rock Island |
| 1157 | WCMR | 1270 | U4 | 5 | 1 | IN | Elkhart |
| 1158 | KSCB | 1270 | U1 | 5 | 0.02 | KS | Liberal |
| 1159 | WACM | 1270 | U1 | 5 | 1 | MA | Springfield |
| 1160 | WCBC | 1270 | U1 | 5 | 1 | MD | Cumberland |
| 1161 | WMKT | 1270 | U2 | 27 | 5 | MI | Charlevoix |
| 1162 | WXYT | #1270 | U4 | 50 | 50 | MI | Detroit |
| 1163 | WWWI | 1270 | U2 | 5 | 5 | MN | Baxter |
| 1164 | KFAN | 1270 | U4 | 5 | 5 | MN | Rochester |
| 1165 | WCGC | 1270 | U4 | 10 | 0.5 | NC | Belmont |
| 1166 | WMPM | 1270 | U1 | 5 | 0.14 | NC | Smithfield |
| 1167 | WTSN | 1270 | U4 | 5 | 5 | NH | Dover |
| 1168 | KZTQ | 1270 | U2 | 13 | 5 | NV | Sparks |
| 1169 | WHLD | 1270 | U4 | 5 | 1 | NY | Niagara Falls |
| 1170 | WDLA | 1270 | U1 | 5 | 0.08 | NY | Walton |
| 1171 | KRXO | 1270 | U4 | 5 | 1 | OK | Claremore |
| 1172 | KAJO | 1270 | U1 | 10 | 0.04 | OR | Grants Pass |
| 1173 | WLBR | 1270 | U4 | 5 | 1 | PA | Lebanon |
| 1174 | WHGS | ‡1270 | U1 | 10 | 0.21 | SC | Hampton |
| 1175 | KNWC | 1270 | U4 | 5 | 2.3 | SD | Sioux Falls |
| 1176 | WLIK | 1270 | U2 | 5 | 0.5 | TN | Newport |
| 1177 | KFLC | #1270 | U4 | 50 | 5 | TX | Benbrook |
| 1178 | WHEO | 1270 | D1 | 5 | | VA | Stuart |
| 1179 | KBAM | 1270 | U1 | 5 | 0.08 | WA | Longview |
| 1180 | KIML | 1270 | U2 | 5 | 1 | WY | Gillette |
| 1181 | WMXB | 1280 | U2 | 5 | 0.5 | AL | Tuscaloosa |
| 1182 | KXEG | 1280 | U1 | 2.5 | 0.04 | AZ | Phoenix |
| 1183 | KXTK | 1280 | U4 | 10 | 2.5 | CA | Arroyo Grande |
| 1184 | KBNO | 1280 | U1 | 5 | 5 | CO | Denver |
| 1185 | WDSP | 1280 | U1 | 5 | 0.04 | FL | De Funiak Springs |
| 1186 | WIHB | 1280 | U1 | 5 | 0.09 | GA | Macon |
| 1187 | WGBF | 1280 | U2 | 5 | 1 | IN | Evansville |
| 1188 | WODT | 1280 | U3 | 5 | 5 | LA | New Orleans |
| 1189 | WPKZ | 1280 | U4 | 5 | 1 | MA | Fitchburg |
| 1190 | WJYE | 1280 | U1 | 5 | 0.04 | ME | Gardiner |
| 1191 | WWTC | 1280 | U2 | 5 | 5 | MN | Minneapolis |
| 1192 | KVXR | 1280 | U4 | 5 | 1 | MN | Moorhead |
| 1193 | WYAL | 1280 | D1 | 5 | | NC | Scotland Neck |
| 1194 | KRZE | 1280 | U1 | 5 | 0.1 | NM | Farmington |
| 1195 | KQLL | 1280 | U1 | 5 | 0.02 | NV | Henderson |
| 1196 | WADO | 1280 | U4 | 50 | 7.2 | NY | New York |
| 1197 | WHTK | 1280 | U2 | 5 | 5 | NY | Rochester |
| 1198 | KRVM | 1280 | U4 | 5 | 1.5 | OR | Eugene |
| 1199 | WHVR | 1280 | U4 | 5 | 0.5 | PA | Hanover |
| 1200 | WUZZ | 1280 | U2 | 4.9 | 1 | PA | New Castle |
| 1201 | WANS | 1280 | U2 | 5 | 1 | SC | Anderson |
| 1202 | WJAY | 1280 | U1 | 4.2 | 0.27 | SC | Mullins |
| 1203 | WMCP | 1280 | U4 | 5 | 0.5 | TN | Columbia |
| 1204 | KZNS | 1280 | U4 | 50 | 0.67 | UT | Salt Lake City |
| 1205 | WYVE | 1280 | U1 | 2.5 | 0.16 | VA | Wytheville |
| 1206 | KZFS | 1280 | U4 | 5 | 0.12 | WA | Spokane |
| 1207 | KIT | 1280 | U4 | 5 | 1 | WA | Yakima |
| 1208 | WNAM | 1280 | U4 | 5 | 5 | WI | Neenah-Menasha |
| 1209 | WOPP | 1290 | U4 | 2.5 | 0.5 | AL | Opp |
| 1210 | KUOA | 1290 | U1 | 5 | 0.03 | AR | Siloam Springs |
| 1211 | KPAY | 1290 | U2 | 5 | 5 | CA | Chico |
| 1212 | KAZA | 1290 | U4 | 5 | 0.08 | CA | Gilroy |
| 1213 | KKDD | 1290 | U4 | 5 | 5 | CA | San Bernardino |
| 1214 | WWTX | #1290 | U1 | 2.5 | 0.03 | DE | Wilmington |
| 1215 | WJNO | 1290 | U4 | 10 | 4.9 | FL | West Palm Beach |
| 1216 | WCHK | 1290 | U2 | 10 | 0.5 | GA | Canton |
| 1217 | WTKS | 1290 | U2 | 5.3 | 5 | GA | Savannah |
| 1218 | KOUU | 1290 | U5 | 50 | 0.02 | ID | Pocatello |
| 1219 | WIRL | 1290 | U4 | 5 | 5 | IL | Peoria |
| 1220 | KMMM | 1290 | U4 | 5 | 0.5 | KS | Pratt |
| 1221 | WCBL | 1290 | U1 | 5 | 0.05 | KY | Benton |
| 1222 | WKLB | 1290 | U1 | 5 | 0.03 | KY | Manchester |
| 1223 | KGVO | 1290 | U2 | 5 | 5 | MT | Missoula |
| 1224 | WHKY | 1290 | U4 | 50 | 1 | NC | Hickory |
| 1225 | WJCV | 1290 | U1 | 5 | 0.04 | NC | Jacksonville |
| 1226 | KOIL | 1290 | U2 | 5 | 5 | NE | Omaha |
| 1227 | WKBK | 1290 | U3 | 5 | 5 | NH | Keene |
| 1228 | WNBF | 1290 | U2 | 9.3 | 5 | NY | Binghamton |
| 1229 | WHIO | 1290 | U2 | 5 | 5 | OH | Dayton |
| 1230 | KUMA | 1290 | U2 | 5 | 5 | OR | Pendleton |
| 1231 | WFBG | 1290 | U2 | 5 | 1 | PA | Altoona |
| 1232 | WRPA | 1290 | U4 | 10 | 10 | RI | Providence |
| 1233 | KIVY | 1290 | U1 | 2.5 | 0.17 | TX | Crockett |
| 1234 | KRGE | 1290 | U2 | 5 | 5 | TX | Weslaco |
| 1235 | KWFS | 1290 | U1 | 5 | 0.07 | TX | Wichita Falls |
| 1236 | WDZY | 1290 | U1 | 25 | 0.04 | VA | Colonial Heights |
| 1237 | WZTI | 1290 | U4 | 5 | 5 | WI | Greenfield |
| 1238 | WKLJ | 1290 | U1 | 5 | 0.05 | WI | Sparta |
| 1239 | WVOW | 1290 | U2 | 5 | 1 | WV | Logan |
| 1240 | KOWB | 1290 | U4 | 5 | 1 | WY | Laramie |
| 1241 | KSMD | 1300 | D1 | 5 | | AR | Searcy |
| 1242 | KWRU | 1300 | U2 | 5 | 1 | CA | Fresno |
| 1243 | KPMO | #1300 | U1 | 5 | 0.07 | CA | Mendocino |
| 1244 | KAZN | 1300 | U4 | 23 | 4.2 | CA | Pasadena |
| 1245 | KCSF | #1300 | U1 | 5 | 1 | CO | Colorado Springs |
| 1246 | WKQK | 1300 | U1 | 5 | 1 | FL | Cocoa Beach |
| 1247 | WFFG | ‡1300 | U3 | 2.5 | 2.5 | FL | Marathon |
| 1248 | WQBN | 1300 | U5 | 5 | 0.16 | FL | Temple Terrace |
| 1249 | WMTM | 1300 | U1 | 5 | 0.06 | GA | Moultrie |
| 1250 | KGLO | 1300 | U4 | 5 | 5 | IA | Mason City |

| MW | Call | kHz | Ant. | D | N | Sta | City of License |
|---|---|---|---|---|---|---|---|
| 1251 | KLER | 1300 | U2 | 5 | 1 | ID | Orofino |
| 1252 | WRDZ | 1300 | U4 | 4.5 | 4 | IL | La Grange |
| 1253 | WLXG | 1300 | U2 | 2.5 | 1 | KY | Lexington |
| 1254 | WIBR | 1300 | U4 | 5 | 1 | LA | Baton Rouge |
| 1255 | KSYB | 1300 | U1 | 5 | 0.03 | LA | Shreveport |
| 1256 | WJZ | 1300 | U4 | 5 | 5 | MD | Baltimore |
| 1257 | WOOD | 1300 | U3 | 20 | 20 | MI | Grand Rapids |
| 1258 | KPMI | 1300 | U2 | 2.5 | 0.6 | MN | Bemidji |
| 1259 | WOAD | 1300 | U1 | 3.6 | 0.73 | MS | Jackson |
| 1260 | WSYD | 1300 | U2 | 5 | 1 | NC | Mount Airy |
| 1261 | KBRL | 1300 | U4 | 5 | 0.13 | NE | McCook |
| 1262 | WPNH | 1300 | U1 | 5 | 0.08 | NH | Plymouth |
| 1263 | WIMG | 1300 | U4 | 3.2 | 1.3 | NJ | Ewing |
| 1264 | KCMY | 1300 | U1 | 5 | 0.12 | NV | Carson City |
| 1265 | WXRL | 1300 | U4 | 5 | 2.5 | NY | Lancaster |
| 1266 | WGDJ | 1300 | U4 | 10 | 8 | NY | Rensselaer |
| 1267 | WJMO | 1300 | U3 | 5 | 5 | OH | Cleveland |
| 1268 | KAKC | 1300 | U4 | 5 | 1 | OK | Tulsa |
| 1269 | KAPL | 1300 | U2 | 20 | 5 | OR | Phoenix |
| 1270 | WKZN | 1300 | U4 | 5 | 0.5 | PA | West Hazleton |
| 1271 | KOLY | 1300 | U1 | 5 | 0.11 | SD | Mobridge |
| 1272 | WMTN | 1300 | U1 | 5 | 0.09 | TN | Morristown |
| 1273 | WNQM | 1300 | U2 | 50 | 5 | TN | Nashville |
| 1274 | KVET | 1300 | U4 | 5 | 1 | TX | Austin |
| 1275 | WKCY | 1300 | U1 | 6.4 | 0.005 | VA | Harrisonburg |
| 1276 | KKOL | ‡1300 | U4 | 50 | 47 | WA | Seattle |
| 1277 | WCLG | 1300 | U1 | 2.5 | 0.04 | WV | Morgantown |
| 1278 | WHEP | **1310** | U1 | 2.5 | 0.04 | AL | Foley |
| 1279 | WJUS | 1310 | U1 | 5 | 0.03 | AL | Marion |
| 1280 | KIHP | 1310 | U1 | 3.4 | 0.26 | AZ | Mesa |
| 1281 | KIQQ | ‡1310 | U4 | 5 | 0.11 | CA | Barstow |
| 1282 | KMKY | 1310 | U3 | 5 | 5 | CA | Oakland |
| 1283 | KFKA | 1310 | U2 | 5 | 1 | CO | Greeley |
| 1284 | WICH | 1310 | U4 | 5 | 5 | CT | Norwich |
| 1285 | WYND | 1310 | U1 | 10.4 | 0.11 | FL | DeLand |
| 1286 | WAUC | 1310 | U4 | 5 | 0.5 | FL | Wauchula |
| 1287 | WJZA | 1310 | U1 | 2.5 | 0.03 | GA | Decatur |
| 1288 | WOKA | 1310 | U1 | 3.9 | 0.03 | GA | Douglas |
| 1289 | KLIX | 1310 | U2 | 5 | 2.5 | ID | Twin Falls |
| 1290 | WTLC | 1310 | U2 | 5 | 1 | IN | Indianapolis |
| 1291 | WDOC | 1310 | U1 | 5 | 0.02 | KY | Prestonsburg |
| 1292 | KMBS | 1310 | U1 | 5 | 0.04 | LA | West Monroe |
| 1293 | WORC | 1310 | U4 | 5 | 1 | MA | Worcester |
| 1294 | WLOB | 1310 | U4 | 5 | 5 | ME | Portland |
| 1295 | WDTW | 1310 | U4 | 5 | 5 | MI | Dearborn |
| 1296 | WCCW | 1310 | U4 | 15 | 7.5 | MI | Traverse City |
| 1297 | KGLB | 1310 | U4 | 5 | 0.27 | MN | Glencoe |
| 1298 | KZRG | 1310 | U4 | 5 | 1 | MO | Joplin |
| 1299 | KEIN | 1310 | U1 | 5 | 1 | MT | Great Falls |
| 1300 | WISE | 1310 | U2 | 5 | 1 | NC | Asheville |
| 1301 | WGSP | 1310 | U2 | 5 | 0.24 | NC | Charlotte |
| 1302 | WTIK | 1310 | U4 | 5 | 1 | NC | Durham |
| 1303 | KNOX | 1310 | U2 | 5 | 5 | ND | Grand Forks |
| 1304 | WADB | 1310 | U4 | 2.5 | 1 | NJ | Asbury Park |
| 1305 | KKNS | 1310 | U1 | 5 | 0.08 | NM | Corrales |
| 1306 | WRVP | 1310 | U4 | 5 | 0.03 | NY | Mount Kisco |
| 1307 | WTLB | 1310 | U4 | 5 | 0.5 | NY | Utica |
| 1308 | KNPT | 1310 | U2 | 5 | 1 | OR | Newport |
| 1309 | WBFD | 1310 | U1 | 2.5 | 0.08 | PA | Bedford |
| 1310 | WNAE | 1310 | U1 | 5 | 0.09 | PA | Warren |
| 1311 | WDKD | 1310 | U1 | 5 | 0.06 | SC | Kingstree |
| 1312 | WDXI | 1310 | U2 | 5 | 1 | TN | Jackson |
| 1313 | KTCK | 1310 | U4 | 25 | 5 | TX | Dallas |
| 1314 | KAHL | 1310 | U4 | 5 | 0.23 | TX | San Antonio |
| 1315 | WDCT | 1310 | U4 | 5 | 0.5 | VA | Fairfax |
| 1316 | WGH | 1310 | U4 | 20 | 5 | VA | Newport News |
| 1317 | KZXR | 1310 | U1 | 5 | 0.06 | WA | Prosser |
| 1318 | WIBA | 1310 | U2 | 5 | 5 | WI | Madison |
| 1319 | WSLW | 1310 | D1 | 5 |  | WV | White Sulphur Springs |
| 1320 | WENN | **1320** | U1 | 5 | 0.11 | AL | Birmingham |
| 1321 | KWHN | 1320 | U2 | 5 | 5 | AR | Fort Smith |
| 1322 | KIFM | 1320 | U4 | 5 | 5 | CA | West Sacramento |
| 1323 | WATR | 1320 | U4 | 5 | 1 | CT | Waterbury |
| 1324 | WLQY | 1320 | U4 | 5 | 5 | FL | Hollywood |
| 1325 | WJNJ | 1320 | U2 | 50 | 5 | FL | Jacksonville |
| 1326 | WDDV | 1320 | U4 | 5 | 1 | FL | Venice |
| 1327 | WHIE | 1320 | U1 | 5 | 0.08 | GA | Griffin |
| 1328 | KNCB | 1320 | U1 | 5 | 0.05 | LA | Vivian |
| 1329 | WARA | 1320 | U4 | 5 | 5 | MA | Attleboro |
| 1330 | WILS | 1320 | U4 | 25 | 1.9 | MI | Lansing |
| 1331 | WDMJ | 1320 | U1 | 5 | 0.13 | MI | Marquette |
| 1332 | KOZY | 1320 | U2 | 5 | 5 | MN | Grand Rapids |
| 1333 | KSIV | 1320 | U2 | 4.6 | 0.27 | MO | Clayton |
| 1334 | WRJW | 1320 | U1 | 5 | 0.07 | MS | Picayune |
| 1335 | WCOG | 1320 | U4 | 5 | 5 | NC | Greensboro |
| 1336 | WKRK | 1320 | U1 | 5 | 0.06 | NC | Murphy |
| 1337 | KHRT | 1320 | U1 | 2.5 | 0.31 | ND | Minot |
| 1338 | KOLT | 1320 | U2 | 5 | 1 | NE | Scottsbluff |
| 1339 | WDER | 1320 | U4 | 10 | 1 | NH | Derry |
| 1340 | WJAS | 1320 | U4 | 7 | 3.3 | PA | Pittsburgh |
| 1341 | WISW | 1320 | U2 | 5 | 2.5 | SC | Columbia |
| 1342 | KELO | 1320 | U2 | 5 | 5 | SD | Sioux Falls |
| 1343 | WGOC | 1320 | U2 | 5 | 0.5 | TN | Kingsport |
| 1344 | WMSR | 1320 | U1 | 5 | 0.07 | TN | Manchester |
| 1345 | KXYZ | 1320 | U4 | 10 | 5 | TX | Houston |
| 1346 | KNIT | 1320 | U3 | 5 | 5 | UT | Salt Lake City |
| 1347 | WVNZ | 1320 | U4 | 5 | 0.008 | VA | Richmond |
| 1348 | KXRO | 1320 | U2 | 5 | 1 | WA | Aberdeen |
| 1349 | WFHR | 1320 | U2 | 5 | 0.5 | WI | Wisconsin Rapids |
| 1350 | WZCT | **1330** | U1 | 5 | 0.03 | AL | Scottsboro |
| 1351 | KWFM | 1330 | U2 | 2 | 5 | AZ | South Tucson |
| 1352 | KWKW | 1330 | U2 | 5 | 5 | CA | Los Angeles |
| 1353 | KLBS | 1330 | U2 | 0.42 | 5 | CA | Los Banos |
| 1354 | WJNX | 1330 | U4 | 5 | 1 | FL | Fort Pierce |
| 1355 | WEBY | 1330 | U5 | 25 | 0.07 | FL | Milton |
| 1356 | WCVC | 1330 | D1 | 5 |  | FL | Tallahassee |
| 1357 | KPTY | 1330 | U4 | 5 | 5 | IA | Waterloo |
| 1358 | WKTA | 1330 | U4 | 5 | 0.11 | IL | Evanston |
| 1359 | WBGW | 1330 | U2 | 5 | 1 | IN | Evansville |
| 1360 | KNSS | 1330 | U2 | 5 | 5 | KS | Wichita |
| 1361 | WKDP | 1330 | U4 | 5 | 0.01 | KY | Corbin |
| 1362 | KVOL | 1330 | U2 | 5 | 1 | LA | Lafayette |
| 1363 | WRCA | 1330 | U4 | 25 | 17 | MA | Watertown |
| 1364 | WHGM | 1330 | U2 | 5 | 0.5 | MD | Havre de Grace |
| 1365 | WTRX | 1330 | U4 | 5 | 1 | MI | Flint |
| 1366 | WLOL | 1330 | U4 | 9.7 | 5.1 | MN | Minneapolis |
| 1367 | WNIX | 1330 | U1 | 3.8 | 0.05 | MS | Greenville |
| 1368 | KGAK | 1330 | U2 | 5 | 1 | NM | Gallup |
| 1369 | WWRV | 1330 | U4 | 10 | 5 | NY | New York |
| 1370 | WEBO | 1330 | U1 | 5 | 0.03 | NY | Owego |
| 1371 | KKPZ | #1330 | U3 | 5 | 5 | OR | Portland |
| 1372 | WFNN | 1330 | U4 | 5 | 5 | PA | Erie |
| 1373 | WPJS | 1330 | U1 | 3.2 | 0.02 | SC | Conway |
| 1374 | WYRD | 1330 | U2 | 5 | 5 | SC | Greenville |
| 1375 | KCKM | 1330 | U2 | 12 | 1 | TX | Monahans |
| 1376 | WBTM | 1330 | U2 | 5 | 1 | VA | Danville |
| 1377 | WSNQ | 1330 | U1 | 5 | 0.03 | VA | Marion |
| 1378 | WESR | 1330 | U1 | 5 | 0.05 | VA | Onley-Onancock |
| 1379 | KYOZ | 1330 | U1 | 5 | 0.02 | WA | Spokane |
| 1380 | WHBL | 1330 | U4 | 5 | 1 | WI | Sheboygan |
| 1381 | KOVE | 1330 | U1 | 5 | 0.25 | WY | Lander |
|  |  | **1340** | Various stns of 1kW or less | | | | |
| 1382 | WTDR | **1350** | U2 | 5 | 1 | AL | Gadsden |
| 1383 | KZTD | 1350 | U1 | 2.5 | 0.07 | AR | Cabot |
| 1384 | KPWK | 1350 | U4 | 5 | 0.6 | CA | San Bernardino |
| 1385 | KSRO | 1350 | U2 | 5 | 5 | CA | Santa Rosa |
| 1386 | WINY | 1350 | U1 | 5 | 0.07 | CT | Putnam |
| 1387 | WFNS | 1350 | U1 | 2.5 | 0.11 | GA | Blackshear |
| 1388 | WBML | 1350 | U2 | 15 | 0.5 | GA | Warner Robins |
| 1389 | KRNT | 1350 | U2 | 5 | 5 | IA | Des Moines |
| 1390 | KRLC | 1350 | U1 | 5 | 0.15 | ID | Lewiston |
| 1391 | KTIK | 1350 | U2 | 5 | 0.6 | ID | Nampa |
| 1392 | WIOU | 1350 | U4 | 5 | 1 | IN | Kokomo |
| 1393 | WWWL | 1350 | U2 | 5 | 5 | LA | New Orleans |
| 1394 | WQGM | 1350 | U1 | 10 | 0.05 | NC | Black Mountain |
| 1395 | WEZS | 1350 | U1 | 5 | 0.11 | NH | Laconia |
| 1396 | WHWH | 1350 | U4 | 5 | 5 | NJ | Princeton |
| 1397 | KABQ | 1350 | U2 | 5 | 0.5 | NM | Albuquerque |
| 1398 | WARF | #1350 | U3 | 5 | 5 | OH | Akron |
| 1399 | WOYK | 1350 | U2 | 5 | 1 | PA | York |
| 1400 | KCOX | 1350 | U1 | 5 | 0.03 | TX | Jasper |
| 1401 | KCOR | 1350 | U2 | 5 | 5 | TX | San Antonio |
| 1402 | WBLT | 1350 | U1 | 5 | 0.04 | VA | Bedford |
| 1403 | WNVA | 1350 | U1 | 5 | 0.03 | VA | Norton |
| 1404 | WGPL | 1350 | U4 | 5 | 5 | VA | Portsmouth |
| 1405 | WIXI | **1360** | U2 | 12 | 0.04 | AL | Jasper |
| 1406 | WMOB | 1360 | U4 | 9 | 0.2 | AL | Mobile |
| 1407 | KPXQ | 1360 | U2 | 50 | 1 | AZ | Glendale |
| 1408 | KFIV | 1360 | U4 | 4 | 0.95 | CA | Modesto |
| 1409 | KLSD | 1360 | U1 | 5 | 1 | CA | San Diego |
| 1410 | KHNC | 1360 | U2 | 10 | 1 | CO | Johnstown |
| 1411 | WDRC | 1360 | U2 | 5 | 5 | CT | Hartford |
| 1412 | WHNR | 1360 | U4 | 5 | 2.5 | FL | Cypress Gardens |
| 1413 | WCGL | 1360 | U1 | 5 | 0.08 | FL | Jacksonville |

| MW | Call | kHz | Ant. | D | N | Sta | City of License |
|---|---|---|---|---|---|---|---|
| 1414 | WQVN | 1360 | U1 | 9.3 | 0.4 | FL | North Miami |
| 1415 | KSCJ | 1360 | U2 | 5 | 5 | IA | Sioux City |
| 1416 | WKMI | 1360 | U2 | 5 | 1 | MI | Kalamazoo |
| 1417 | KKBJ | 1360 | U2 | 5 | 2.5 | MN | Bemidji |
| 1418 | WCHL | 1360 | U2 | 5 | 1 | NC | Chapel Hill |
| 1419 | WNJC | 1360 | U4 | 5 | 0.8 | NJ | Washington Twnshp |
| 1420 | KBUY | 1360 | U1 | 5 | 0.2 | NM | Ruidoso |
| 1421 | WYOS | 1360 | U4 | 5 | 0.5 | NY | Binghamton |
| 1422 | WSAI | 1360 | U2 | 5 | 5 | OH | Cincinnati |
| 1423 | WWOW | 1360 | U1 | 5 | 0.03 | OH | Conneaut |
| 1424 | KOHU | 1360 | U2 | 4.3 | 0.5 | OR | Hermiston |
| 1425 | KUIK | ‡1360 | U2 | 5 | 5 | OR | Hillsboro |
| 1426 | WGBN | 1360 | U2 | 5 | 1 | PA | McKeesport |
| 1427 | WPPA | 1360 | U4 | 5 | 0.5 | PA | Pottsville |
| 1428 | WELP | 1360 | U1 | 5 | 0.03 | SC | Easley |
| 1429 | KDJW | 1360 | U4 | 6 | 0.32 | TX | Amarillo |
| 1430 | KWWJ | 1360 | U4 | 5 | 1 | TX | Baytown |
| 1431 | KMNY | 1360 | U4 | 50 | 0.89 | TX | Hurst |
| 1432 | WCGX | 1360 | U1 | 5 | 0.03 | VA | Galax |
| 1433 | WHBG | 1360 | U1 | 5 | 0.009 | VA | Harrisonburg |
| 1434 | KKMO | 1360 | U1 | 5 | 5 | WA | Tacoma |
| 1435 | WTAQ | 1360 | U4 | 10 | 5 | WI | Green Bay |
| 1436 | WMOV | 1360 | D1 | 5 | | WV | Ravenswood |
| 1437 | KRKK | 1360 | U2 | 5 | 1 | WY | Rock Springs |
| 1438 | KWRM | 1370 | U4 | 5 | 2.5 | CA | Corona |
| 1439 | KRAC | 1370 | U4 | 4 | 0.2 | CA | Red Bluff |
| 1440 | KZSF | 1370 | U3 | 5 | 5 | CA | San Jose |
| 1441 | WOCA | 1370 | U1 | 5 | 0.03 | FL | Ocala |
| 1442 | WCOA | 1370 | U2 | 5 | 5 | FL | Pensacola |
| 1443 | WLOP | 1370 | U1 | 5 | 0.03 | GA | Jesup |
| 1444 | KDTH | 1370 | U2 | 5 | 5 | IA | Dubuque |
| 1445 | WGCL | 1370 | U4 | 5 | 0.5 | IN | Bloomington |
| 1446 | KGNO | 1370 | U1 | 5 | 0.23 | KS | Dodge City |
| 1447 | WGOH | 1370 | U1 | 5 | 0.02 | KY | Grayson |
| 1448 | WQLL | 1370 | U4 | 50 | 24 | MD | Pikesville |
| 1449 | WDEA | 1370 | U4 | 5 | 5 | ME | Ellsworth |
| 1450 | WLJW | 1370 | U4 | 5 | 1 | MI | Cadillac |
| 1451 | KXTL | 1370 | U1 | 5 | 5 | MT | Butte |
| 1452 | WLLN | 1370 | U4 | 5 | 0.04 | NC | Lillington |
| 1453 | WGIV | 1370 | U1 | 16 | 0.04 | NC | Pineville |
| 1454 | WTAB | 1370 | U1 | 5 | 0.1 | NC | Tabor City |
| 1455 | KWTL | 1370 | U1 | 12 | 0.27 | ND | Grand Forks |
| 1456 | WFEA | 1370 | U4 | 5 | 5 | NH | Manchester |
| 1457 | WJIP | 1370 | D1 | 5 | | NY | Ellenville |
| 1458 | WXXI | 1370 | U2 | 5 | 5 | NY | Rochester |
| 1459 | WSPD | 1370 | U2 | 5 | 5 | OH | Toledo |
| 1460 | WKMC | 1370 | U4 | 5 | 0.03 | PA | Roaring Spring |
| 1461 | WXCT | 1370 | U2 | 5 | 5 | TN | Chattanooga |
| 1462 | KJCE | 1370 | U4 | 5 | 0.5 | TX | Rollingwood |
| 1463 | KSOP | 1370 | U2 | 5 | 0.5 | UT | South Salt Lake |
| 1464 | WHEE | 1370 | D1 | 5 | | VA | Martinsville |
| 1465 | WSHV | 1370 | U1 | 4.2 | 0.41 | VA | South Hill |
| 1466 | WCCN | 1370 | U1 | 5 | 0.04 | WI | Neillsville |
| 1467 | WVMR | 1370 | D1 | 5 | | WV | Frost |
| 1468 | WVLY | 1370 | U1 | 5 | 0.02 | WV | Moundsville |
| 1469 | WVSA | 1380 | U1 | 5 | 0.03 | AL | Vernon |
| 1470 | KZTS | 1380 | U4 | 5 | 2.5 | AR | North Little Rock |
| 1471 | KLPZ | 1380 | U1 | 2.5 | 0.05 | AZ | Parker |
| 1472 | KTKZ | 1380 | U4 | 5 | 5 | CA | Sacramento |
| 1473 | WFNW | 1380 | U4 | 3.5 | 0.35 | CT | Naugatuck |
| 1474 | WELE | 1380 | U4 | 5 | 2.5 | FL | Ormond Beach |
| 1475 | WWMI | 1380 | U2 | 9.8 | 6.5 | FL | Saint Petersburg |
| 1476 | WAOK | 1380 | U2 | 25 | 4.2 | GA | Atlanta |
| 1477 | WBEL | 1380 | U2 | 5 | 5 | IL | South Beloit |
| 1478 | WKJG | 1380 | U4 | 5 | 5 | IN | Fort Wayne |
| 1479 | KCNW | 1380 | U1 | 2.5 | 0.02 | KS | Fairway |
| 1480 | WMJR | 1380 | U1 | 5 | 0.03 | KY | Nicholasville |
| 1481 | WPYR | 1380 | U4 | 5 | 0.06 | LA | Baton Rouge |
| 1482 | WPHM | 1380 | U4 | 5 | 5 | MI | Port Huron |
| 1483 | KLIZ | 1380 | U2 | 5 | 5 | MN | Brainerd |
| 1484 | KXFN | 1380 | U4 | 5 | 1 | MO | Saint Louis |
| 1485 | WKJV | 1380 | U2 | 25 | 1 | NC | Asheville |
| 1486 | WWNT | ‡1380 | U4 | 5 | 2.5 | NC | Winston-Salem |
| 1487 | WABH | 1380 | U4 | 10 | 0.45 | NY | Bath |
| 1488 | WKDM | 1380 | U4 | 5 | 13 | NY | New York |
| 1489 | KMUS | 1380 | U4 | 7 | 0.25 | OK | Sperry |
| 1490 | KKOO | 1380 | U1 | 5 | 0.02 | OR | Ontario |
| 1491 | WNRI | 1380 | U1 | 2.5 | 0.01 | RI | Woonsocket |
| 1492 | WNRR | 1380 | U1 | 4 | 0.07 | SC | North Augusta |
| 1493 | KOTA | 1380 | U2 | 5 | 5 | SD | Rapid City |
| 1494 | WHEW | 1380 | D1 | 2.8 | | TN | Franklin |
| 1495 | WLRM | 1380 | U4 | 2.5 | 1 | TN | Millington |
| 1496 | KHEY | 1380 | U1 | 5 | 0.5 | TX | El Paso |
| 1497 | KWMF | 1380 | U5 | 4 | 0.16 | TX | Pleasanton |
| 1498 | KRCM | 1380 | U4 | 22 | 0.05 | TX | Shenandoah |
| 1499 | WBTK | 1380 | U4 | 5 | 5 | VA | Richmond |
| 1500 | WSYB | 1380 | U2 | 5 | 1 | VT | Rutland |
| 1501 | KRKO | 1380 | U2 | 50 | 50 | WA | Everett |
| 1502 | WOTE | 1380 | U4 | 3.9 | 1.8 | WI | Clintonville |
| 1503 | WHMA | 1390 | U2 | 5 | 1 | AL | Anniston |
| 1504 | KFFK | 1390 | U1 | 5 | 0.03 | AR | Rogers |
| 1505 | KLTX | 1390 | U4 | 5 | 3.6 | CA | Long Beach |
| 1506 | KLOC | 1390 | U4 | 5 | 5 | CA | Turlock |
| 1507 | KGNU | 1390 | U1 | 5 | 0.13 | CO | Denver |
| 1508 | WAJD | 1390 | U1 | 5 | 0.05 | FL | Gainesville |
| 1509 | WGRB | #1390 | U4 | 5 | 5 | IL | Chicago |
| 1510 | WZQQ | 1390 | D1 | 5 | | KY | Hazard |
| 1511 | WPLM | ‡1390 | U4 | 5 | 5 | MA | Plymouth |
| 1512 | WZHF | 1390 | U4 | 9 | 1 | MD | Capitol Heights |
| 1513 | WEGP | 1390 | U4 | 25 | 10 | ME | Presque Isle |
| 1514 | WLCM | 1390 | U4 | 5 | 4.5 | MI | Holt |
| 1515 | KXSS | 1390 | U4 | 2.5 | 1 | MN | Waite Park |
| 1516 | KJPW | 1390 | U1 | 5 | 0.11 | MO | Waynesville |
| 1517 | WROA | 1390 | U4 | 5 | 5 | MS | Gulfport |
| 1518 | WMER | 1390 | U1 | 5 | 0.1 | MS | Meridian |
| 1519 | WEED | 1390 | U1 | 5 | 0.03 | NC | Rocky Mount |
| 1520 | KRRZ | 1390 | U1 | 5 | 1 | ND | Minot |
| 1521 | KENN | 1390 | U2 | 5 | 1.3 | NM | Farmington |
| 1522 | KHOB | 1390 | U2 | 5 | 0.5 | NM | Hobbs |
| 1523 | WEOK | 1390 | U1 | 5 | 0.1 | NY | Poughkeepsie |
| 1524 | WFBL | 1390 | U4 | 5 | 5 | NY | Syracuse |
| 1525 | WMPO | 1390 | U1 | 5 | 0.12 | OH | Middleport-Pomeroy |
| 1526 | WNIO | #1390 | U2 | 9.5 | 4.8 | OH | Youngstown |
| 1527 | KZGD | 1390 | U1 | 5 | 0.69 | OR | Salem |
| 1528 | WSPO | 1390 | U2 | 5 | 5 | SC | Charleston |
| 1529 | WYXI | 1390 | U1 | 2.5 | 0.06 | TN | Athens |
| 1530 | WLLI | 1390 | U2 | 5 | 1 | TN | Jackson |
| 1531 | KLGN | 1390 | U2 | 5 | 0.5 | UT | Logan |
| 1532 | WKPA | 1390 | U1 | 4.7 | 0.03 | VA | Lynchburg |
| 1533 | WCAT | 1390 | U2 | 5 | 5 | VT | Burlington |
| 1534 | KBBO | 1390 | U4 | 5 | 0.39 | WA | Yakima |
| 1535 | WRIG | 1390 | U4 | 10 | 7.2 | WI | Schofield |
| | **1400** | | Various stns of 1kW or less | | | | |
| 1536 | WNGL | 1410 | U2 | 5 | 4.6 | AL | Mobile |
| 1537 | WIQR | ‡1410 | U4 | 5 | 1 | AL | Prattville |
| 1538 | KMYC | 1410 | U4 | 5 | 1 | CA | Marysville |
| 1539 | KCAL | 1410 | U4 | 5 | 4 | CA | Redlands |
| 1540 | WPOP | 1410 | U4 | 5 | 5 | CT | Hartford |
| 1541 | WDOV | 1410 | U4 | 5 | 5 | DE | Dover |
| 1542 | WMYR | 1410 | U2 | 5 | 5 | FL | Fort Myers |
| 1543 | WQBQ | 1410 | U1 | 5 | 0.08 | FL | Leesburg |
| 1544 | WHBT | 1410 | U1 | 5 | 0.01 | FL | Tallahassee |
| 1545 | WKKP | 1410 | U1 | 2.5 | 0.05 | GA | McDonough |
| 1546 | KKLO | 1410 | U4 | 5 | 0.5 | KS | Leavenworth |
| 1547 | KGSO | 1410 | U4 | 5 | 1 | KS | Wichita |
| 1548 | WHLN | 1410 | U1 | 5 | 0.04 | KY | Harlan |
| 1549 | WRJD | 1410 | U4 | 5 | 0.29 | NC | Durham |
| 1550 | KOOQ | 1410 | U2 | 5 | 0.5 | NE | North Platte |
| 1551 | WELM | 1410 | U2 | 5 | 1 | NY | Elmira |
| 1552 | WNER | 1410 | U1 | 3.5 | 0.05 | NY | Watertown |
| 1553 | WING | 1410 | U2 | 5 | 5 | OH | Dayton |
| 1554 | KBNP | 1410 | U1 | 5 | 0.009 | OR | Portland |
| 1555 | WLSH | 1410 | D3 | 5 | | PA | Lansford |
| 1556 | KQV | ‡1410 | U4 | 5 | 5 | PA | Pittsburgh |
| 1557 | WRTZ | 1410 | U1 | 5 | 0.07 | VA | Roanoke |
| 1558 | WIZM | 1410 | U1 | 5 | 5 | WI | La Crosse |
| 1559 | WSCW | 1410 | D1 | 5 | | WV | South Charleston |
| 1560 | KWYO | 1410 | U1 | 5 | 0.35 | WY | Sheridan |
| 1561 | WACT | 1420 | U1 | 5 | 0.1 | AL | Tuscaloosa |
| 1562 | KBHS | 1420 | U1 | 5 | 0.08 | AR | Hot Springs |
| 1563 | KMOG | 1420 | U2 | 2.5 | 0.5 | AZ | Payson |
| 1564 | KSTN | 1420 | U4 | 5 | 1 | CA | Stockton |
| 1565 | WLIS | 1420 | U1 | 5 | 0.5 | CT | Old Saybrook |
| 1566 | WDJA | 1420 | U4 | 5 | 0.5 | FL | Delray Beach |
| 1567 | WBRD | 1420 | U4 | 2.5 | 1 | FL | Palmetto |
| 1568 | WRCG | 1420 | U1 | 5 | 0.08 | GA | Columbus |
| 1569 | WKWN | 1420 | U1 | 2.5 | 0.11 | GA | Trenton |
| 1570 | WOC | 1420 | U4 | 5 | 5 | IA | Davenport |
| 1571 | KIGO | 1420 | U1 | 32 | 0.01 | ID | Saint Anthony |
| 1572 | WIMS | 1420 | U1 | 5 | 5 | IN | Michigan City |
| 1573 | WBSM | 1420 | U1 | 5 | 1 | MA | New Bedford |
| 1574 | KTOE | 1420 | U2 | 5 | 5 | MN | Mankato |
| 1575 | WASR | 1420 | U1 | 5 | 0.13 | NH | Wolfeboro |
| 1576 | WACK | 1420 | U4 | 5 | 0.5 | NY | Newark |

| MW | Call | kHz | Ant. | D | N | Sta | City of License |
|---|---|---|---|---|---|---|---|
| 1577 | WLNA | 1420 | U4 | 5 | 1 | NY | Peekskill |
| 1578 | WHK | 1420 | U1 | 5 | 5 | OH | Cleveland |
| 1579 | WCOJ | 1420 | U2 | 5 | 5 | PA | Coatesville |
| 1580 | WCED | 1420 | U1 | 4.2 | 0.005 | PA | Du Bois |
| 1581 | WEMB | 1420 | U1 | 5 | 0.02 | TN | Erwin |
| 1582 | WKCW | 1420 | U4 | 22 | 0.06 | VA | Warrenton |
| 1583 | KITI | 1420 | U4 | 5 | 5 | WA | Centralia - Chehalis |
| 1584 | KUJ | 1420 | U1 | 5 | 0.9 | WA | Walla Walla |
| 1585 | WTCR | 1420 | U2 | 5 | 0.5 | WV | Kenova |
| 1586 | WFHK | **1430** | D1 | 5 | | AL | Pell City |
| 1587 | KYNO | 1430 | U3 | 5 | 5 | CA | Fresno |
| 1588 | KMRB | 1430 | U4 | 50 | 9.8 | CA | San Gabriel |
| 1589 | KVVN | 1430 | U4 | 1 | 2.5 | CA | Santa Clara |
| 1590 | KEZW | 1430 | U2 | 10 | 5 | CO | Aurora |
| 1591 | WTMN | 1430 | U1 | 10 | 0.04 | FL | Gainesville |
| 1592 | WOIR | 1430 | U2 | 5 | 0.5 | FL | Homestead |
| 1593 | WLKF | 1430 | U1 | 5 | 1 | FL | Lakeland |
| 1594 | WLTG | 1430 | U4 | 5 | 5 | FL | Panama City |
| 1595 | WGFS | 1430 | U1 | 3.9 | 0.21 | GA | Covington |
| 1596 | WDAL | 1430 | U1 | 2.5 | 0.07 | GA | Dalton |
| 1597 | WXNT | 1430 | U2 | 5 | 5 | IN | Indianapolis |
| 1598 | WCWC | 1430 | U1 | 4.6 | 0.03 | KY | Williamsburg |
| 1599 | WKOX | 1430 | U2 | 5 | 1 | MA | Everett |
| 1600 | WNAV | 1430 | U2 | 5 | 1 | MD | Annapolis |
| 1601 | WION | 1430 | U2 | 4.7 | 0.33 | MI | Ionia |
| 1602 | KZQZ | 1430 | U4 | 50 | 5 | MO | Saint Louis |
| 1603 | WDEX | 1430 | U4 | 2.5 | 2.5 | NC | Monroe |
| 1604 | WMNC | 1430 | U1 | 2.7 | 0.04 | NC | Morganton |
| 1605 | WDJS | 1430 | U4 | 10 | 5 | NC | Mount Olive |
| 1606 | KRGI | 1430 | U2 | 5 | 1 | NE | Grand Island |
| 1607 | WNSW | 1430 | U4 | 10 | 7 | NJ | Newark |
| 1608 | WENE | 1430 | U2 | 5 | 5 | NY | Endicott |
| 1609 | KTBZ | 1430 | U4 | 25 | 5 | OK | Tulsa |
| 1610 | KYKN | 1430 | U2 | 5 | 5 | OR | Keizer |
| 1611 | WVAM | 1430 | U2 | 5 | 1 | PA | Altoona |
| 1612 | WBLR | 1430 | U1 | 5 | 0.16 | SC | Batesburg |
| 1613 | WOWW | 1430 | U2 | 2.5 | 2.5 | TN | Germantown |
| 1614 | WPLN | 1430 | U2 | 15 | 1 | TN | Madison |
| 1615 | KEES | 1430 | U2 | 5 | 1 | TX | Gladewater |
| 1616 | KSHJ | 1430 | U4 | 5 | 1 | TX | Houston |
| 1617 | KLO | 1430 | U4 | 25 | 5 | UT | Ogden |
| 1618 | WDIC | 1430 | U1 | 5 | 0.05 | VA | Clinchco |
| 1619 | KCLK | 1430 | U4 | 5 | 1 | WA | Asotin |
| 1620 | KBRC | 1430 | U1 | 5 | 1 | WA | Mount Vernon |
| 1621 | WLWI | **1440** | U2 | 5 | 1 | AL | Montgomery |
| 1622 | KTUV | 1440 | U2 | 5 | 0.24 | AR | Little Rock |
| 1623 | KAZG | 1440 | U1 | 5 | 0.05 | AZ | Scottsdale |
| 1624 | KVON | 1440 | U4 | 5 | 1 | CA | Napa |
| 1625 | KUHL | 1440 | U2 | 5 | 1 | CA | Santa Maria |
| 1626 | KRDZ | 1440 | U1 | 5 | 0.21 | CO | Wray |
| 1627 | WWCL | 1440 | U4 | 5 | 1 | FL | Lehigh Acres |
| 1628 | WPRD | 1440 | U2 | 5 | 1 | FL | Winter Park |
| 1629 | WGMI | 1440 | U1 | 2.5 | 0.06 | GA | Bremen |
| 1630 | WGIG | 1440 | U2 | 5 | 1 | GA | Brunswick |
| 1631 | KPTO | 1440 | U4 | 2.5 | 0.35 | ID | Pocatello |
| 1632 | WGEM | 1440 | U4 | 5 | 1 | IL | Quincy |
| 1633 | WROK | 1440 | U5 | 5 | 0.27 | IL | Rockford |
| 1634 | KMAJ | 1440 | U4 | 5 | 1 | KS | Topeka |
| 1635 | WVEI | 1440 | U2 | 5 | 5 | MA | Worcester |
| 1636 | WRED | 1440 | U2 | 5 | 5 | ME | Westbrook |
| 1637 | WMAX | 1440 | U4 | 5 | 2.5 | MI | Bay City |
| 1638 | WKPR | 1440 | U1 | 2.7 | 0.02 | MI | Kalamazoo |
| 1639 | KYCR | 1440 | U2 | 5 | 0.5 | MN | Golden Valley |
| 1640 | WVGG | 1440 | D1 | 5 | | MS | Lucedale |
| 1641 | WBLA | 1440 | U1 | 5 | 0.19 | NC | Elizabethtown |
| 1642 | WLXN | 1440 | U2 | 5.3 | 1 | NC | Lexington |
| 1643 | WFNY | 1440 | U2 | 5 | 0.5 | NY | Gloversville |
| 1644 | WHKZ | 1440 | U4 | 5 | 5 | OH | Warren |
| 1645 | KMED | 1440 | U1 | 5 | 1 | OR | Medford |
| 1646 | WCDL | 1440 | U1 | 5 | 0.03 | PA | Carbondale |
| 1647 | WNPV | 1440 | U4 | 2.5 | 0.5 | PA | Lansdale |
| 1648 | WGVL | 1440 | U2 | 5 | 5 | SC | Greenville |
| 1649 | WZYX | 1440 | U1 | 5 | 0.06 | TN | Cowan |
| 1650 | KPUR | 1440 | U2 | 5 | 1 | TX | Amarillo |
| 1651 | KETX | 1440 | U1 | 5 | 0.09 | TX | Livingston |
| 1652 | KTNO | 1440 | U4 | 50 | 0.35 | TX | University Park |
| 1653 | WKLV | 1440 | U1 | 5 | 0.07 | VA | Blackstone |
| 1654 | WNFL | 1440 | U4 | 5 | 0.5 | WI | Green Bay |
| 1655 | WHIS | 1440 | U1 | 5 | 0.5 | WV | Bluefield |
| 1656 | WAJR | 1440 | U4 | 5 | 5 | WV | Morgantown |
| | | **1450** | | Various stns of 1kW or less | | | |
| 1657 | WMCJ | **1460** | U2 | 5 | 0.5 | AL | Cullman |
| 1658 | WGSY | 1460 | U1 | 4 | 0.14 | AL | Phenix City |
| 1659 | KTYM | 1460 | U4 | 5 | 0.5 | CA | Inglewood |
| 1660 | KION | 1460 | U3 | 10 | 10 | CA | Salinas |
| 1661 | KZNT | 1460 | U2 | 5 | 0.54 | CO | Colorado Springs |
| 1662 | WQXM | 1460 | U5 | 10 | 0.15 | FL | Bartow |
| 1663 | WZEP | 1460 | U1 | 10 | 0.18 | FL | Defuniak Springs |
| 1664 | WNPL | 1460 | U4 | 7 | 2 | FL | Golden Gate |
| 1665 | WQOP | 1460 | U2 | 15 | 5 | FL | Jacksonville |
| 1666 | WXEM | 1460 | U1 | 5 | 0.19 | GA | Buford |
| 1667 | KXNO | #1460 | U2 | 5 | 5 | IA | Des Moines |
| 1668 | WKAM | 1460 | U2 | 2.5 | 0.5 | IN | Goshen |
| 1669 | WEKB | 1460 | U1 | 5 | 0.11 | KY | Elkhorn City |
| 1670 | WXOK | 1460 | U1 | 4.7 | 0.29 | LA | Port Allen |
| 1671 | WATD | ‡1460 | U2 | 5 | 1 | MA | Brockton |
| 1672 | WBRN | 1460 | U2 | 5 | 2.5 | MI | Big Rapids |
| 1673 | KKAQ | 1460 | U1 | 2.5 | 0.15 | MN | Thief River Falls |
| 1674 | KHOJ | 1460 | U4 | 12 | 0.21 | MO | Saint Charles |
| 1675 | WEWO | 1460 | U4 | 5 | 5 | NC | Laurinburg |
| 1676 | WHBK | 1460 | U1 | 5 | 0.13 | NC | Marshall |
| 1677 | KLTC | 1460 | U1 | 5 | 0.77 | ND | Dickinson |
| 1678 | KXPN | 1460 | U1 | 5 | 0.05 | NE | Kearney |
| 1679 | WIFI | 1460 | U4 | 5 | 0.5 | NJ | Florence |
| 1680 | KENO | 1460 | U4 | 10 | 0.62 | NV | Las Vegas |
| 1681 | WOPG | 1460 | U2 | 5 | 5 | NY | Albany |
| 1682 | WHIC | 1460 | U2 | 3.7 | 5 | NY | Rochester |
| 1683 | WBNS | 1460 | U2 | 5 | 1 | OH | Columbus |
| 1684 | WTKT | 1460 | U4 | 5 | 4.2 | PA | Harrisburg |
| 1685 | WZMF | 1460 | U4 | 5 | 1 | PA | Tunkhannock |
| 1686 | KCLE | 1460 | U4 | 11 | 0.7 | TX | Burleson |
| 1687 | KBRZ | 1460 | U1 | 5 | 0.12 | TX | Missouri City |
| 1688 | WKDV | 1460 | U4 | 5 | 5 | VA | Manassas |
| 1689 | WRAD | 1460 | U1 | 5 | 0.03 | VA | Radford |
| 1690 | KARR | 1460 | U4 | 5 | 2.5 | WA | Kirkland |
| 1691 | KUTI | 1460 | U2 | 5 | 3.7 | WA | Yakima |
| 1692 | WBUC | 1460 | U1 | 5.5 | 0.02 | WV | Buckhannon |
| 1693 | KVSL | **1470** | U2 | 5 | 0.08 | AZ | Show Low |
| 1694 | KNXN | 1470 | U1 | 2.5 | 0.03 | AZ | Sierra Vista |
| 1695 | KUTY | 1470 | U4 | 5 | 5 | CA | Palmdale |
| 1696 | KIID | 1470 | U4 | 5 | 1 | CA | Sacramento |
| 1697 | WMMW | 1470 | U4 | 2.5 | 2.5 | CT | Meriden |
| 1698 | WMGG | 1470 | U4 | 2.8 | 0.8 | FL | Egypt Lake |
| 1699 | WWNN | 1470 | U4 | 50 | 2.5 | FL | Pompano Beach |
| 1700 | WRGA | 1470 | U2 | 5 | 5 | GA | Rome |
| 1701 | WMBD | 1470 | U4 | 5 | 5 | IL | Peoria |
| 1702 | WBFC | 1470 | U1 | 2.5 | 0.02 | KY | Stanton |
| 1703 | KLCL | 1470 | U1 | 5 | 0.5 | LA | Lake Charles |
| 1704 | WAZN | 1470 | U4 | 1.4 | 3.4 | MA | Watertown |
| 1705 | WJDY | 1470 | U1 | 5 | 0.04 | MD | Salisbury |
| 1706 | WLAM | 1470 | U3 | 5 | 5 | ME | Lewiston |
| 1707 | WFNT | 1470 | U4 | 5 | 1 | MI | Flint |
| 1708 | KMNQ | 1470 | U4 | 5 | 5 | MN | Brooklyn Park |
| 1709 | WNAU | 1470 | U2 | 2.5 | 0.5 | MS | New Albany |
| 1710 | WWBG | ‡1470 | U4 | 10 | 5 | NC | Greensboro |
| 1711 | WTOE | 1470 | U1 | 5 | 0.1 | NC | Spruce Pine |
| 1712 | WNYY | 1470 | U2 | 5 | 1 | NY | Ithaca |
| 1713 | WSAN | #1470 | U2 | 5 | 5 | PA | Allentown |
| 1714 | WQXL | 1470 | U1 | 11 | 0.1 | SC | Columbia |
| 1715 | WVOL | 1470 | U1 | 5 | 1 | TN | Berry Hill |
| 1716 | KYYW | 1470 | U1 | 5 | 0.11 | TX | Abilene |
| 1717 | KWRD | 1470 | D1 | 5 | | TX | Henderson |
| 1718 | WBTX | 1470 | U1 | 5 | 0.03 | VA | Broadway-Timberville |
| 1719 | WTZE | 1470 | D1 | 5 | | VA | Tazewell |
| 1720 | KELA | 1470 | U1 | 5 | 1 | WA | Centralia-Chehalis |
| 1721 | KBSN | 1470 | U4 | 5 | 1 | WA | Moses Lake |
| 1722 | WIBD | 1470 | U4 | 2.5 | 2.5 | WI | West Bend |
| 1723 | WMMA | **1480** | U1 | 5 | 0.02 | AL | Irondale |
| 1724 | WABF | 1480 | U2 | 5 | 4.4 | AL | Mobile |
| 1725 | KTHS | 1480 | U1 | 5 | 0.06 | AR | Green Forest |
| 1726 | KPHX | 1480 | U2 | 5 | 0.5 | AZ | Phoenix |
| 1727 | KGOE | 1480 | U1 | 5 | 1 | CA | Eureka |
| 1728 | KYOS | 1480 | U2 | 5 | 5 | CA | Merced |
| 1729 | KVNR | 1480 | U4 | 5 | 5 | CA | Santa Ana |
| 1730 | WKGC | 1480 | U1 | 5 | 0.03 | FL | Southport |
| 1731 | WYZE | 1480 | U1 | 10 | 0.04 | GA | Atlanta |
| 1732 | KRXR | 1480 | U1 | 5 | 0.09 | ID | Gooding |
| 1733 | WPFR | 1480 | U4 | 5 | 1 | IN | Terre Haute |
| 1734 | KQAM | 1480 | U4 | 5 | 1 | KS | Wichita |
| 1735 | WNKW | 1480 | D1 | 5 | | KY | Neon |
| 1736 | WSAR | 1480 | U3 | 5 | 5 | MA | Fall River |
| 1737 | WGVU | #1480 | U2 | 2 | 5 | MI | Kentwood |
| 1738 | WSDS | 1480 | U4 | 0.75 | 3.8 | MI | Salem Township |
| 1739 | KKCQ | 1480 | U1 | 5 | 0.09 | MN | Fosston |

| MW | Call | kHz | Ant. | D | N | Sta | City of License |
|---|---|---|---|---|---|---|---|
| 1740 | WGFY | 1480 | U4 | 4.4 | | 5 | NC | Charlotte |
| 1741 | WQTM | 1480 | U1 | 10 | 0.04 | | NC | Fair Bluff |
| 1742 | WPFJ | 1480 | U1 | 5 | 0.01 | | NC | Franklin |
| 1743 | WLEA | 1480 | U1 | 2.5 | 0.01 | | NY | Hornell |
| 1744 | WZRC | 1480 | U4 | 5 | | 5 | NY | New York |
| 1745 | WRCK | ‡1480 | D1 | 5 | | | NY | Remsen |
| 1746 | WHBC | 1480 | U4 | 15 | | 5 | OH | Canton |
| 1747 | WDJO | 1480 | U4 | 4.5 | 0.3 | | OH | Cincinnati |
| 1748 | WDAS | 1480 | U4 | 5 | | 1 | PA | Philadelphia |
| 1749 | WBBP | 1480 | U1 | 5 | 0.04 | | TN | Memphis |
| 1750 | KBXD | 1480 | U4 | 50 | 1.9 | | TX | Dallas |
| 1751 | KLVL | 1480 | U4 | 5 | 0.5 | | TX | Pasadena |
| 1752 | KCHL | 1480 | U4 | 2.5 | 0.09 | | TX | San Antonio |
| 1753 | WPWC | 1480 | U4 | 5 | 0.5 | | VA | Dumfries-Triangle |
| 1754 | WTOX | 1480 | U4 | 6.3 | 1.5 | | VA | Glen Allen |
| 1755 | WTOY | 1480 | U1 | 5 | 0.02 | | VA | Salem |
| 1756 | WCFR | 1480 | U1 | 5 | 0.02 | | VT | Springfield |
| 1757 | KBMS | 1480 | U2 | 1 | | 2.5 | WA | Vancouver |
| 1758 | WLMV | 1480 | U4 | 5 | | 5 | WI | Madison |
| | | **1490** | Various stns of 1kW or less | | | | | |
| 1759 | KSJX | 1500 | U4 | 10 | | 5 | CA | San Jose |
| 1760 | WFIF | 1500 | D3 | 5 | | | CT | Milford |
| 1761 | WFED | 1500 | U4 | 50 | | 50 | DC | Washington |
| 1762 | WQNY | 1500 | D4 | 5 | | | GA | Dallas |
| 1763 | WBRI | 1500 | D3 | 5 | | | IN | Indianapolis |
| 1764 | WLQV | 1500 | U4 | 50 | | 10 | MI | Detroit |
| 1765 | KSTP | 1500 | U2 | 50 | | 50 | MN | Saint Paul |
| 1766 | KFNN | 1510 | U4 | 22 | 0.1 | | AZ | Mesa |
| 1767 | KIRV | 1510 | D3 | 10 | | | CA | Fresno |
| 1768 | KSPA | 1510 | U4 | 10 | | 1 | CA | Ontario |
| 1769 | KSFN | 1510 | U4 | 8 | 2.4 | | CA | Piedmont |
| 1770 | KCKK | 1510 | U4 | 10 | | 25 | CO | Littleton |
| 1771 | WWBC | 1510 | D4 | 50 | | | FL | Cocoa |
| 1772 | WMEX | 1510 | U7 | 50 | | 50 | MA | Boston |
| 1773 | KCTE | 1510 | D3 | 10 | | | MO | Independence |
| 1774 | KMRF | 1510 | D4 | 5 | | | MO | Marshfield |
| 1775 | WFAI | 1510 | D3 | 2.5 | | | NJ | Salem |
| 1776 | KOAZ | 1510 | U1 | 5 | 0.02 | | NM | Isleta |
| 1777 | WWSM | 1510 | D3 | 5 | | | PA | Annville-Cleona |
| 1778 | WPGR | 1510 | U11 | 5 | 0.001 | | PA | Monroeville |
| 1779 | KMSD | 1510 | U1 | 5 | 0.01 | | SD | Milbank |
| 1780 | WLAC | 1510 | U2 | 50 | | 50 | TN | Nashville |
| 1781 | KBED | 1510 | D3 | 5 | | | TX | Nederland |
| 1782 | KGA | 1510 | U4 | 50 | | 15 | WA | Spokane |
| 1783 | WRRD | 1510 | D4 | 23 | | | WI | Waukesha |
| 1784 | KMPG | **1520** | D4 | 5 | | | CA | Hollister |
| 1785 | KKZZ | 1520 | U4 | 10 | | 1 | CA | Port Hueneme |
| 1786 | WBZW | 1520 | U4 | 5 | 0.35 | | FL | Apopka |
| 1787 | WEXY | 1520 | U2 | 5 | 0.8 | | FL | Wilton Manors |
| 1788 | WDCY | 1520 | D1 | 2.5 | | | GA | Douglasville |
| 1789 | WHOW | 1520 | D1 | 5 | | | IL | Clinton |
| 1790 | KFXZ | 1520 | U6 | 10 | 0.5 | | LA | Lafayette |
| 1791 | WIZZ | 1520 | D3 | 10 | | | MA | Greenfield |
| 1792 | WTRI | 1520 | D3 | 17 | | | MD | Brunswick |
| 1793 | KOLM | 1520 | U8 | 10 | 0.8 | | MN | Rochester |
| 1794 | KRHW | 1520 | U7 | 5 | 1.6 | | MO | Sikeston |
| 1795 | WDSL | 1520 | D1 | 5 | | | NC | Mocksville |
| 1796 | WARR | 1520 | D1 | 5 | | | NC | Warrenton |
| 1797 | WWKB | 1520 | U3 | 50 | | 50 | NY | Buffalo |
| 1798 | KOKC | 1520 | U2 | 50 | | 50 | OK | Oklahoma City |
| 1799 | KQRR | 1520 | U4 | 50 | | 15 | OR | Oregon City |
| 1800 | KYND | 1520 | D4 | 25 | | | TX | Cypress |
| 1801 | KQQB | 1520 | D3 | 2.5 | | | TX | Stockdale |
| 1802 | KKXA | ‡1520 | U2 | 50 | | 50 | WA | Snohomish |
| 1803 | KVDW | **1530** | D1 | 2.5 | | | AR | England |
| 1804 | KFBK | 1530 | U4 | 50 | | 50 | CA | Sacramento |
| 1805 | KQSC | 1530 | U1 | 15 | 0.01 | | CO | Colorado Springs |
| 1806 | WYMM | 1530 | D3 | 50 | | | FL | Jacksonville |
| 1807 | WTTI | 1530 | D4 | 10 | | | GA | Dalton |
| 1808 | WVBF | 1530 | U14 | 5 | 0.004 | | MA | Middleborough Center |
| 1809 | WLCO | 1530 | D3 | 5 | | | MI | Lapeer |
| 1810 | KGPO | 1530 | U4 | 8.6 | 0.01 | | MN | Shakopee |
| 1811 | WLLQ | 1530 | D3 | 10 | | | NC | Chapel Hill |
| 1812 | WCKY | ‡1530 | U2 | 50 | | 50 | OH | Cincinnati |
| 1813 | KXTD | 1530 | D3 | 5 | | | OK | Wagoner |
| 1814 | KZNX | 1530 | U7 | 10 | 0.22 | | TX | Creedmoor |
| 1815 | KGBT | 1530 | U8 | 50 | | 10 | TX | Harlingen |
| 1816 | KLBW | 1530 | D1 | 2.5 | | | TX | New Boston |
| 1817 | KASA | **1540** | U4 | 10 | 0.01 | | AZ | Phoenix |
| 1818 | KMPC | 1540 | U4 | 50 | | 37 | CA | Los Angeles |
| 1819 | WKVQ | 1540 | D1 | 10 | | | GA | Eatonton |
| 1820 | KXEL | 1540 | U2 | 50 | | 50 | IA | Waterloo |

| MW | Call | kHz | Ant. | D | N | Sta | City of License |
|---|---|---|---|---|---|---|---|
| 1821 | WACA | 1540 | D1 | 5 | | | MD | Wheaton |
| 1822 | WYNC | 1540 | D1 | 2.5 | | | NC | Yanceyville |
| 1823 | WXEX | 1540 | U1 | 5 | 0.003 | | NH | Exeter |
| 1824 | WDCD | 1540 | U3 | 50 | | 50 | NY | Albany |
| 1825 | WNWR | ‡1540 | U4 | 50 | 0.25 | | PA | Philadelphia |
| 1826 | WECZ | 1540 | D1 | 5 | | | PA | Punxsutawney |
| 1827 | WTBI | 1540 | D1 | 10 | | | SC | Pickens |
| 1828 | KGBC | 1540 | U4 | 2.5 | 0.25 | | TX | Galveston |
| 1829 | KEDA | 1540 | U4 | 5 | | 1 | TX | San Antonio |
| 1830 | KZMP | 1540 | U4 | 32 | 0.75 | | TX | University Park |
| 1831 | WBTL | 1540 | U4 | 10 | 0.007 | | VA | Richmond |
| 1832 | KXPA | 1540 | U2 | 5 | | 5 | WA | Bellevue |
| 1833 | WLOR | **1550** | U4 | 50 | 0.04 | | AL | Huntsville |
| 1834 | KUAZ | 1550 | D1 | 50 | | | AZ | Tucson |
| 1835 | KWRN | 1550 | U2 | 5 | 0.5 | | CA | Apple Valley |
| 1836 | KXEX | 1550 | U4 | 5 | 2.5 | | CA | Fresno |
| 1837 | KGMZ | 1550 | U4 | 10 | | 10 | CA | San Francisco |
| 1838 | WSDK | 1550 | U4 | 5 | 2.4 | | CT | Bloomfield |
| 1839 | WNZF | 1550 | U1 | 5.5 | 0.05 | | FL | Bunnell |
| 1840 | WRHC | 1550 | U4 | 10 | 0.5 | | FL | Coral Gables |
| 1841 | WAMA | 1550 | U1 | 10 | 0.13 | | FL | Tampa |
| 1842 | WTHB | 1550 | U1 | 5 | 0.01 | | GA | Augusta |
| 1843 | WAZX | 1550 | U4 | 50 | 0.01 | | GA | Smyrna |
| 1844 | WKTF | 1550 | U1 | 10 | 0.02 | | GA | Vienna |
| 1845 | WPFC | 1550 | U1 | 5 | 0.04 | | LA | Baton Rouge |
| 1846 | WNTN | 1550 | U1 | 10 | 0.003 | | MA | Newton |
| 1847 | KAPE | 1550 | U4 | 5 | 0.04 | | MO | Cape Girardeau |
| 1848 | KESJ | 1550 | U2 | 2.5 | 0.5 | | MO | Saint Joseph |
| 1849 | KRZD | 1550 | U1 | 5 | 0.02 | | MO | Springfield |
| 1850 | KQNM | 1550 | U1 | 10 | 0.02 | | NM | Albuquerque |
| 1851 | KXTO | 1550 | U1 | 2.5 | 0.09 | | NV | Reno |
| 1852 | KYAL | 1550 | U4 | 2.5 | 0.04 | | OK | Sapulpa |
| 1853 | WITK | 1550 | U4 | 10 | 0.5 | | PA | Pittston |
| 1854 | WIGN | 1550 | U1 | 35 | 0.006 | | TN | Bristol |
| 1855 | KMRI | 1550 | U1 | 10 | 0.34 | | UT | West Valley City |
| 1856 | WKBA | 1550 | D3 | 10 | | | VA | Vinton |
| 1857 | WVAB | 1550 | U1 | 5 | 0.009 | | VA | Virginia Beach |
| 1858 | KRPI | 1550 | U4 | 50 | | 10 | WA | Ferndale |
| 1859 | KKOV | 1550 | U2 | 50 | | 12 | WA | Vancouver |
| 1860 | WHIT | 1550 | D3 | 5 | | | WI | Madison |
| 1861 | WMRE | 1550 | U1 | 5 | 0.006 | | WV | Charles Town |
| 1862 | KNZR | **1560** | U2 | 25 | | 10 | CA | Bakersfield |
| 1863 | WLZR | 1560 | D1 | 5 | | | FL | Melbourne |
| 1864 | KLNG | 1560 | D1 | 10 | | | IA | Council Bluffs |
| 1865 | WNWN | 1560 | D3 | 4.1 | | | MI | Portage |
| 1866 | WYZD | 1560 | D1 | 4.2 | | | NC | Dobson |
| 1867 | WFME | 1560 | U4 | 50 | | 50 | NY | New York |
| 1868 | WCNW | 1560 | D4 | 5 | | | OH | Fairfield |
| 1869 | KKAA | 1560 | U4 | 10 | | 10 | SD | Aberdeen |
| 1870 | KGOW | 1560 | U4 | 46 | | 15 | TX | Bellaire |
| 1871 | KTXZ | 1560 | U4 | 2.5 | 2.5 | | TX | West Lake Hills |
| 1872 | WSBV | 1560 | D1 | 2.5 | | | VA | South Boston |
| 1873 | KVAN | 1560 | U4 | 10 | 0.7 | | WA | Burbank |
| 1874 | KZIZ | 1560 | U12 | 5 | 0.9 | | WA | Pacific |
| 1875 | WCRL | **1570** | U1 | 2.5 | 0.06 | | AL | Oneonta |
| 1876 | KCVR | ‡1570 | U4 | 5 | 0.5 | | CA | Lodi |
| 1877 | KPRO | 1570 | U4 | 5 | 0.19 | | CA | Riverside |
| 1878 | KTGE | 1570 | U4 | 5 | 0.5 | | CA | Salinas |
| 1879 | WTWB | 1570 | U1 | 5 | 0.01 | | FL | Auburndale |
| 1880 | WVOJ | 1570 | U1 | 10 | 0.03 | | FL | Fernandina Beach |
| 1881 | WIGO | 1570 | U1 | 5 | 0.05 | | GA | Morrow |
| 1882 | WFRL | 1570 | U4 | 5 | 0.5 | | IL | Freeport |
| 1883 | WUBG | 1570 | U1 | 44 | 0.14 | | MA | Methuen |
| 1884 | WNST | 1570 | U1 | 5 | 0.23 | | MD | Towson |
| 1885 | KDIZ | 1570 | U1 | 3.8 | 0.23 | | MN | Golden Valley |
| 1886 | KAKK | 1570 | U1 | 9.5 | 0.25 | | MN | Walker |
| 1887 | KBCV | 1570 | U4 | 5 | | 3 | MO | Hollister |
| 1888 | WIZK | 1570 | D1 | 3.2 | | | MS | Bay Springs |
| 1889 | WNCA | 1570 | U1 | 5 | 0.28 | | NC | Siler City |
| 1890 | WECU | 1570 | U1 | 8 | 0.2 | | NC | Winterville |
| 1891 | WFLR | 1570 | U1 | 5 | 0.44 | | NY | Dundee |
| 1892 | WPGM | 1570 | U1 | 2.5 | 0.22 | | PA | Danville |
| 1893 | WISP | 1570 | U4 | 5 | 0.9 | | PA | Doylestown |
| 1894 | WCLE | 1570 | U1 | 5 | 0.08 | | TN | Cleveland |
| 1895 | WYTI | 1570 | U1 | 2.5 | 0.22 | | VA | Rocky Mount |
| 1896 | WLKD | 1570 | U1 | 5 | 0.5 | | WI | Minocqua |
| 1897 | WVOK | **1580** | U1 | 2.5 | 0.02 | | AL | Oxford |
| 1898 | KQFN | 1580 | U2 | 50 | | 50 | AZ | Tempe |
| 1899 | KBLA | 1580 | U4 | 50 | | 50 | CA | Santa Monica |
| 1900 | KFCS | 1580 | U1 | 10 | 0.14 | | CO | Colorado Springs |
| 1901 | WNTF | 1580 | D3 | 10 | | | FL | Bithlo |
| 1902 | WTCL | 1580 | D1 | 10 | | | FL | Chattahoochee |

| MW | Call | kHz | Ant. | D | N | Sta | City of License |
|---|---|---|---|---|---|---|---|
| 1903 | WSRF | 1580 | U4 | 10 | 1.5 | FL | Fort Lauderdale |
| 1904 | WWTF | 1580 | U4 | 10 | 0.04 | KY | Georgetown |
| 1905 | WJFK | 1580 | U4 | 50 | 0.27 | MD | Morningside |
| 1906 | WPMO | 1580 | U4 | 5 | 0.05 | MS | Pascagoula-Moss Point |
| 1907 | WLIM | 1580 | U2 | 10 | 0.5 | NY | Patchogue |
| 1908 | WVKO | 1580 | U4 | 3.2 | 0.29 | OH | Columbus |
| 1909 | KGAL | 1580 | U2 | 5 | 1 | OR | Lebanon |
| 1910 | WDAB | 1580 | U1 | 5 | 0.01 | SC | Travelers Rest |
| 1911 | WNPZ | 1580 | D1 | 5 | | TN | Knoxville |
| 1912 | WLIJ | 1580 | U1 | 5 | 0.01 | TN | Shelbyville |
| 1913 | WTTN | 1580 | U15 | 5 | 0.004 | WI | Columbus |
| 1914 | **WVNA** | **1590** | U2 | 5 | 1 | AL | Tuscumbia |
| 1915 | KBJT | 1590 | U1 | 4.7 | 0.03 | AR | Fordyce |
| 1916 | KYNG | 1590 | U1 | 2.5 | 0.05 | AR | Springdale |
| 1917 | KLIV | 1590 | U2 | 5 | 5 | CA | San Jose |
| 1918 | KVTA | 1590 | U4 | 5 | 5 | CA | Ventura |
| 1919 | WPSL | 1590 | U1 | 5 | 0.06 | FL | Port Saint Lucie |
| 1920 | WRXB | 1590 | U4 | 5 | 1 | FL | Saint Pete Beach |
| 1921 | WALG | 1590 | U1 | 3.3 | 0.04 | GA | Albany |
| 1922 | WQCH | 1590 | D1 | 5 | | GA | Lafayette |
| 1923 | WXRS | 1590 | U1 | 2.5 | 0.02 | GA | Swainsboro |
| 1924 | WCGO | 1590 | U2 | 10 | 2.5 | IL | Evanston |
| 1925 | WAIK | 1590 | U4 | 5 | 0.05 | IL | Galesburg |
| 1926 | WNTS | 1590 | U4 | 5 | 0.5 | IN | Beech Grove |
| 1927 | KVGB | 1590 | U2 | 5 | 5 | KS | Great Bend |
| 1928 | WHGT | 1590 | U4 | 15 | 0.05 | MD | Maugansville |
| 1929 | WTVB | 1590 | U2 | 5 | 1 | MI | Coldwater |
| 1930 | KGFK | 1590 | U4 | 5 | 1 | MN | East Grand Forks |
| 1931 | WCSL | 1590 | U1 | 10 | 0.03 | NC | Cherryville |
| 1932 | WHPY | 1590 | U4 | 5 | 0.02 | NC | Clayton |
| 1933 | KCTY | 1590 | U4 | 2.5 | 0.04 | NE | Wayne |
| 1934 | WSMN | 1590 | U3 | 5 | 5 | NH | Nashua |
| 1935 | WGGO | 1590 | U1 | 5 | 0.01 | NY | Salamanca |
| 1936 | WAKR | 1590 | U2 | 5 | 5 | OH | Akron |
| 1937 | KTIL | 1590 | U2 | 5 | 1 | OR | Netarts |
| 1938 | WPWA | 1590 | U2 | 2.5 | 1 | PA | Chester |
| 1939 | WPSN | 1590 | U1 | 2.5 | 0.01 | PA | Honesdale |
| 1940 | WARV | 1590 | U4 | 8 | 5 | RI | Warwick |
| 1941 | WKTP | 1590 | U3 | 5 | 5 | TN | Jonesborough |
| 1942 | KGAS | 1590 | U1 | 2.5 | 0.12 | TX | Carthage |
| 1943 | KELP | 1590 | U4 | 5 | 0.8 | TX | El Paso |
| 1944 | KMIC | 1590 | U2 | 5 | 5 | TX | Houston |
| 1945 | KLRK | 1590 | U4 | 2.5 | 0.06 | TX | Mexia |
| 1946 | WFTH | 1590 | U1 | 5 | 0.01 | VA | Richmond |
| 1947 | KLFE | 1590 | U4 | 20 | 5 | WA | Seattle |
| 1948 | WGBW | 1590 | U4 | 10 | 0.5 | WI | Denmark |
| 1949 | WIXK | 1590 | U1 | 5 | 0.09 | WI | New Richmond |
| 1950 | **WHIY** | **1600** | U2 | 5 | 0.5 | AL | Huntsville |
| 1951 | WXVI | 1600 | U4 | 5 | 1 | AL | Montgomery |
| 1952 | KGST | 1600 | U2 | 5 | 5 | CA | Fresno |
| 1953 | KAHZ | 1600 | U2 | 5 | 5 | CA | Pomona |
| 1954 | KUBA | 1600 | U2 | 5 | 2.5 | CA | Yuba City |
| 1955 | KEPN | 1600 | U2 | 5 | 5 | CO | Lakewood |
| 1956 | WZNZ | 1600 | U1 | 5 | 0.08 | FL | Atlantic Beach |
| 1957 | WPOM | 1600 | U4 | 5 | 4.7 | FL | Riviera Beach |
| 1958 | WAOS | 1600 | U1 | 20 | 0.06 | GA | Austell |
| 1959 | KGYM | 1600 | U2 | 5 | 5 | IA | Cedar Rapids |
| 1960 | KLEB | 1600 | U4 | 5 | 0.25 | LA | Golden Meadow |
| 1961 | WUNR | 1600 | U3 | 20 | 20 | MA | Brookline |
| 1962 | WLZX | 1600 | D1 | 2.5 | | MA | East Longmeadow |
| 1963 | WAAM | 1600 | U4 | 5 | 5 | MI | Ann Arbor |
| 1964 | KPNP | 1600 | U3 | 5 | 5 | MN | Watertown |
| 1965 | KATZ | 1600 | U2 | 6 | 3.5 | MO | Saint Louis |
| 1966 | WIDU | 1600 | U4 | 5 | 0.14 | NC | Fayetteville |
| 1967 | WTZQ | 1600 | U1 | 5 | 0.03 | NC | Hendersonville |
| 1968 | KIVA | 1600 | U1 | 10 | 0.17 | NM | Albuquerque |
| 1969 | WEHH | 1600 | U4 | 5 | 0.17 | NY | Elmira Heights-Horseheads |
| 1970 | WWRL | 1600 | U4 | 25 | 5 | NY | New York |
| 1971 | KUSH | 1600 | U1 | 5 | 0.07 | OK | Cushing |
| 1972 | KOPB | 1600 | U2 | 5 | 1 | OR | Eugene |
| 1973 | WAYC | 1600 | U1 | 2.7 | 0.01 | PA | Bedford |
| 1974 | WKZK | 1600 | U1 | 4 | 0.02 | SC | North Augusta |
| 1975 | WUCT | 1600 | U1 | 2.5 | 0.02 | TN | Algood |
| 1976 | WMQM | 1600 | U1 | 50 | 0.03 | TN | Lakeland |
| 1977 | KRVA | 1600 | U4 | 25 | 0.93 | TX | Cockrell Hill |
| 1978 | KOKE | 1600 | U4 | 5 | 0.7 | TX | Pflugerville |
| 1979 | KTUB | 1600 | U2 | 5 | 1 | UT | Centerville |
| 1980 | WCPK | 1600 | U1 | 4.2 | 0.02 | VA | Chesapeake |
| 1981 | KVRI | 1600 | U4 | 50 | 10 | WA | Blaine |
| 1982 | WRPN | 1600 | U4 | 5 | 5 | WI | Ripon |
| 1983 | WZZW | 1600 | U1 | 5 | 0.02 | WV | Milton |
| 1984 | WKKX | 1600 | U1 | 5 | 0.03 | WV | Wheeling |

| MW | Call | kHz | Ant. | D | N | Sta | City of License |
|---|---|---|---|---|---|---|---|
| | | **1610** | | Currently TIS only (0.01kW or less) | | | |
| 1985 | KSMH | **1620** | U1 | 10 | 1 | CA | West Sacramento |
| 1986 | WNRP | 1620 | U1 | 10 | 1 | FL | Gulf Breeze |
| 1987 | WDND | ‡1620 | U1 | 10 | 1 | IN | South Bend |
| 1988 | KOZN | 1620 | U1 | 10 | 1 | NE | Bellevue |
| 1989 | WTAW | #1620 | U1 | 10 | 1 | TX | College Station |
| 1990 | KYIZ | 1620 | U1 | 10 | 1 | WA | Renton |
| 1991 | WRDW | **#1630** | U1 | 10 | 1 | GA | Augusta |
| 1992 | KCJJ | 1630 | U1 | 10 | 1 | IA | Iowa City |
| 1993 | KKGM | 1630 | U1 | 10 | 1 | TX | Fort Worth |
| 1994 | KRND | 1630 | U1 | 10 | 1 | WY | Fox Farm |
| 1995 | KDIA | **1640** | U2 | 10 | 10 | CA | Vallejo |
| 1996 | WTNI | 1640 | U1 | 10 | 1 | MS | Biloxi |
| 1997 | KZLS | 1640 | U4 | 10 | 1 | OK | Enid |
| 1998 | KDZR | #1640 | U1 | 10 | 1 | OR | Lake Oswego |
| 1999 | KBJA | 1640 | U1 | 10 | 1 | UT | Sandy |
| 2000 | WSJP | 1640 | U1 | 10 | 1 | WI | Sussex |
| 2001 | KFSW | **1650** | U1 | 10 | 1 | AR | Fort Smith |
| 2002 | KFOX | 1650 | U1 | 10 | 0.49 | CA | Torrance |
| 2003 | KBJD | 1650 | U1 | 10 | 1 | CO | Denver |
| 2004 | KCNZ | 1650 | U1 | 10 | 1 | IA | Cedar Falls |
| 2005 | KSVE | 1650 | U1 | 8.5 | 0.85 | TX | El Paso |
| 2006 | WHKT | 1650 | U1 | 10 | 1 | VA | Portsmouth |
| 2007 | KBRE | **1660** | U1 | 10 | 1 | CA | Merced |
| 2008 | WCNZ | 1660 | U1 | 10 | 1 | FL | Marco Island |
| 2009 | KWOD | 1660 | U1 | 10 | 1 | KS | Kansas City |
| 2010 | WQLR | 1660 | U1 | 10 | 1 | MI | Kalamazoo |
| 2011 | WBCN | #1660 | U1 | 10 | 1 | NC | Charlotte |
| 2012 | KQWB | 1660 | U1 | 10 | 1 | ND | West Fargo |
| 2013 | WWRU | 1660 | U4 | 10 | 10 | NJ | Jersey City |
| 2014 | KRZI | 1660 | U1 | 10 | 1 | TX | Waco |
| 2015 | KHPY | **1670** | U1 | 10 | 9 | CA | Moreno Valley |
| 2016 | KQMS | 1670 | U1 | 10 | 1 | CA | Redding |
| 2017 | WMGE | 1670 | U1 | 10 | 1 | GA | Dry Branch |
| 2018 | WOZN | 1670 | U1 | 10 | 1 | WI | Madison |
| 2019 | KGED | **1680** | U1 | 10 | 1 | CA | Fresno |
| 2020 | WOKB | 1680 | U1 | 10 | 1 | FL | Winter Garden |
| 2021 | KRJO | 1680 | U1 | 10 | 1 | LA | Monroe |
| 2022 | WPRR | 1680 | U1 | 10 | 0.68 | MI | Ada |
| 2023 | WTTM | 1680 | U1 | 10 | 1 | NJ | Lindenwold |
| 2024 | KNTS | 1680 | U1 | 10 | 1 | WA | Seattle |
| 2025 | KFSG | **1690** | U1 | 10 | 1 | CA | Roseville |
| 2026 | KDMT | 1690 | U1 | 10 | 1 | CO | Arvada |
| 2027 | WMLB | 1690 | U1 | 10 | 1 | GA | Avondale Estates |
| 2028 | WVON | 1690 | U1 | 10 | 1 | IL | Berwyn |
| 2029 | WPTX | 1690 | U1 | 10 | 1 | MD | Lexington Park |
| 2030 | WEUP | **1700** | U1 | 10 | 1 | AL | Huntsville |
| 2031 | WJCC | 1700 | U1 | 10 | 1 | FL | Miami Springs |
| 2032 | KBGG | 1700 | U1 | 10 | 1 | IA | Des Moines |
| 2033 | WRCR | ‡1700 | U1 | 10 | 1 | NY | Ramapo |
| 2034 | KVNS | 1700 | U1 | 8.8 | 0.88 | TX | Brownsville |
| 2035 | KKLF | 1700 | U1 | 5 | 1 | TX | Richardson |

**Addresses:**
**1)** 3929 Airport Blvd #2-403, Mobile, AL 36609 – **2)** 20720 Marilla St, Chatsworth, CA 91311-4407 – **3)** 1139 Hartnell Ave, Redding, CA 96002-2113 – **4)** 2500 Maitland Center Pkwy #401, Maitland, FL 32751-4122 – **5)** 1501 13th Ave, Columbus, GA 31901-1908 – **6)** 200 N 10th St, Fort Dodge, IA 50501-3925 – **7)** 1109 Hudson Lane, Monroe, LA 71201-6003 – **8)** 1846 Skyland Dr, Sylva, NC 28779-8008 – **9)** 2411 E. Millbrook Rd, #114, Raleigh, NC 27604 – **10)** 304 S Grand Ave, Las Vegas, NM 87701-3873 – **11)** 2395 Ocean Ave #3, Ronkonkoma, NY 11779-5670 – **12)** 32500 Parklane St,  Garden City, MI 48135-1572 – **13)** 1640 Old Russellville Pike, Clarksville, TN 37043-1709 – **14)** 4686 E Van Buren St #300, Phoenix, AZ 85008-6967 – **15)** 3223 Sillect Ave, Bakersfield, CA 93308-6329 – **16)** 1111 W Victory Way, Craig, CO 81625-2950 – **17)** 2500 Russell Rd, Green Cove Springs, FL 32043-9492 – **18)** 1102 Thompson Bridge Rd, Gainesville, GA 30501-1706 – **19)** 1815 Meadowlark Rd, Clay Center, KS 67432-8201 – **20)** 638 West Port Plaza, Saint Louis, MO 63146-3106 – **21)** 660 Dewey Blvd, Butte, MT 59701-2318 – **22)** 3500 E Rosser Ave, Bismarck, ND 58501-3398 – **23)** 500 Corporate Parkway #200, Buffalo, NY 14226-1263 – **24)** 8044 Montgomery Rd #650, Cincinnati, OH 45236-2959 – **25)** 7140 SW Macadam Ave, Portland, OR 97219-3013 – **26)** 1330 E 8th St #207, Odessa, TX 79761-4731 – **27)** 4050 Eisenhauer Rd, San Antonio, TX 78218-3409 – **28)** 1820 Heritage Center Way, Harrisonburg, VA 22801-8451 – **29)** 9 Stowe St, Waterbury, VT 05670-1820 – **30)** 4840 Lincoln Rd, Blaine, WA 98230-9602 or PO Box 75150 RPO White Rock, White Rock, BC V4A 5L3 – **31)** 557 Scott St, Wausau, WI 54403-4829 – **32)** 2518 Columbia Hwy, Dothan, AL 36303-5402 – **33)** 55 Hawthorne St #1000, San Francisco, CA 94105-3966 – **34)** 2821 S Parker Rd #1205,

Aurora, CO 80014-2708 – **35)** 194 NW 187th St, Miami, FL 33169-4050 – **36)** 25 NW Point Blvd #400, Elk Grove, IL 60007-1030 – **37)** PO Box 608, Middlesboro, KY 40965-0608 – **38)** 1331 Main St, Springfield, MA 01103-1669 – **39)** 350 Byrd Ave, Cumberland, MD 21502-3219 – **40)** 420 Western Ave, South Portland, ME 04106-1704 – **41)** 14 E Central Entrance, Duluth, MN 55811-5508 – **42)** 3000 Chestnut Expressway, Springfield, MO 65802-2528 – **43)** 20 3rd St N #231, Great Falls, MT 59401-3188 – **44)** 117 Ridge Pike, Lafayette Hill, PA 19444-1900 – **45)** 316 Greystone Blvd, Columbia, SC 29210-8007 – **46)** 1815 Division St #110, Nashville, TN 37203-2753 – **47)** 6080 Mount Moriah Rd Ext, Memphis, TN 38115-2698 – **48)** 2885 Interstate 10 E, Beaumont, TX 77702-1001 – **49)** 231 N Wenatchee Ave, Wenatchee, WA 98801-2009 – **50)** 102 N Kanawha St, Beckley, WV 25801-4715 – **51)** 6510 Whorton Bend Rd, Gadsden, AL 35901-8873 – **52)** PO Box 580, Alturas, CA 96101-0580 – **53)** 3400 Olive Ave #550, Burbank, CA 91505-5544 – **54)** 5211 W Laurel St #101, Tampa, FL 33607-1725 – **55)** 1801 Rockville Pike #405, Rockville, MD 20852-5604 – **56)** 13 Summerlin Rd, Asheville, NC 28806-2800 – **57)** 1355 California Ave, Las Cruces, NM 88001-4130 – **58)** 111 Broadway #302, New York, NY 10006-1901 – **59)** 500 Plum St #100, Syracuse, NY 13204-1427 – **60)** 7461 South Ave, Youngstown, OH 44512-5789 – **61)** WNAX Bldg - 1609 E Hwy 50, Yankton, SD 57078-6406 – **62)** 3090 Olive St #400, Dallas, TX 75219-7640 – **63)** 2801 Decker Lake Dr, West Valley City, UT 84119-2330 – **64)** 140 4th Ave N #340, Seattle, WA 98109-4932 – **65)** 1110 S Park Ave, Tucson, AZ 85719-6745 – **66)** 1071 W Shaw St, Fresno, CA 93771-3702 – **67)** 106 Rose Lane, Montrose, CO 81401-3823 – **68)** 4192 N John Young Pkwy, Orlando, FL 32804-2696 – **69)** 4051 Jimmie Dyess Pkwy, Augusta, GA 30909-9469 – **70)** 827 Park Blvd #1001, Boise, ID 83712-7781 – **71)** Campbell Hall - 300 N Goodwin Ave, Urbana, IL 61801-2316 – **72)** 1200 SW Executive Dr, Topeka, KS 66615-3850 – **73)** 601 Washington St, Alexandria, LA 71301-8028 – **74)** 96 Stereo Lane, Paxton, MA 01612-1376 – **75)** 314 E Front St, Traverse City, MI 49684-2528 – **76)** 240 Radio Road, West Jefferson, NC 28694-ND – **77)** 600 Corporate Cir #100, Harrisburg, PA 17110-9787 – **78)** 319 W Rockwood St, Rockwood, TN 37854-2245 – **79)** 201 State St, La Crosse, WI 54601-3246 – **80)** 1111 Virginia St E, Charleston, WV 25301-2406 – **81)** 701 N Brand Blvd #550, Glendale, CA 91203-1235 – **82)** 1001 Heavenly Village Way #36A, South Lake Tahoe, CA 96150-6985 – **83)** 1834 Lisenby Ave, Panama City, FL 32405-3713 – **84)** 900 Circle 75 Pkwy SE #1320, Atlanta, GA 30339-3095 – **85)** 1406 Commerce Way, Idaho Falls, ID 83401-1233 – **86)** 300 W Vine St 3rd Flr, Lexington, KY 40507-1807 – **87)** 500 Victory Rd #2, Quincy, MA 02171-3132 – **88)** 222 S Lawrence St, Ironwood, MI 49938-2524 – **89)** 4200 W Main St, Kalamazoo, MI 49006-2766 – **90)** 10714 Mockingbird Dr, Omaha, NE 68127-1942 – **91)** 6 Johnson Rd, Latham, NY 12110-5638 – **92)** 1200 Executive Pkwy #440, Eugene, OR 97401-2169 – **93)** 8309 N Interstate 35, Austin, TX 78753-5771 – **94)** 750 Ridgeview Dr #204, St. George, UT 84770-2697 – **95)** 808 E Sprague Ave, Spokane, WA 99202-2126 – **96)** 9660 Granite Ridge Dr, San Diego, CA 92123-2657 – **97)** 4270 Byrd Dr, Loveland, CO 80538-7074 – **98)** 4190 Belfort Rd #450, Jacksonville, FL 32216-1405 – **99)** 600 Old Marion Rd NE, Cedar Rapids, IA 52402-2152 – **100)** 330 2nd Ave, Paintsville, KY 41240-1034 – **101)** 711 W 40th St #350, Baltimore, MD 21211-2190 – **102)** 670 Sweden St, Caribou, ME 04736-3419 – **103)** 2995 US Highway 93 S, Kalispell, MT 59901-8640 – **104)** 875 W 5th St, Winston-Salem, NC 27101-2505 – **105)** 2400 8th Ave SW #D1, Jamestown, ND 58401-6623 – **106)** 2650 Thousand Oaks Blvd #4100, Memphis, TN 38118-2451 – **107)** 4180 N Mesa St, El Paso, TX 79902-1420 – **108)** 1001 E Southeast Loop 323 #455, Tyler, TX 75701-9600 – **109)** 2700 Corporate Dr #115, Birmingham, AL 35242-2735 – **110)** 352 "E" Ave #K4, Lancaster, CA 93535-4505 – **111)** 260 Hegenberger Rd, Oakland, CA 94621-1491 – **112)** 7601 Riviera Blvd, Miramar, FL 33023-6574 – **113)** 11 E Superior St #380, Duluth, MN 55802-3016 – **114)** 7000 Squibb Rd, Mission, KS 66202-3233 – **115)** 1520 South Blvd #300, Charlotte, NC 28203-3701 – **116)** 195 McGregor St #810, Manchester, NH 03102-3755 – **117)** 500 4th St NW, Albuquerque, NM 87102-5324 – **118)** 2323 W 5th Ave #200, Columbus, OH 43204-4988 – **119)** 511 Rossanley Dr, Medford, OR 97501-1771 – **120)** 555 E City Ave #330, Bala Cynwyd, PA 19004-1137 – **121)** 24 E Greenway Plaza #1900, Houston, TX 77046-2428 – **122)** 810 W 200 N, Logan, UT 84321-3726 – **123)** 3934 Electric Rd, Roanoke, VA 24018-4513 – **124)** 2823 W Lewis St, Pasco, WA 99301-6700 – **125)** 7740 N 16th St #200, Phoenix, AZ 85020-4482 – **126)** 1354 E Sherwood Dr, Grand Junction, CO 81501-7546 – **127)** 4002 W Gandy Blvd, Tampa, FL 33611-3410 – **128)** 806 New Franklin Rd, La Grange, GA 30240-1859 – **129)** 861 Broadway, Bangor, ME 04401-2916 – **130)** 1375 Beasley Rd, Jackson, MS 39206-2018 – **131)** 2508 Coney Island Ave 2nd Flr, Brooklyn, NY 11223-5026 – **132)** 500 Plum St #100, Syracuse, NY 13204-1427 – **133)** 13333 SW 68th Pkwy, Tigard, OR 97223-8304 – **134)** 1918 Lincoln Hwy, North Versailles, PA 15137-2706 or PO Box 990, Greensburg, PA 15601-0990 – **135)** 2440 Millwood Ave, Columbia, SC 29205-1128 or PO Box 2355, West Columbia, SC 29171-2355 – **136)** 1621 E Magnolia Ave, Knoxville,

TN 37917-7825 – **137)** 13725 Montfort Dr, Dallas, TX 75240-4455 – **138)** 118 Malletts Bay Ave, Colchester, VT 05446-2009 – **139)** 720 E Capitol Dr, Milwaukee, WI 53212-1308 – **140)** 306 S Kanawha St, Beckley, WV 25801-5619 – **141)** 4695 S Monaco St, Denver, CO 80237-3403 – **142)** 4400 Jenifer St NW #400, Washington, DC 20015-2183 – **143)** 214 Television Circle, Savannah, GA 31406-4519 – **144)** 145 N Alexander St, Toccoa, GA 30577-2371 – **145)** 827 Park Blvd #100, Boise, ID 83712-7782 – **146)** 2601 Nicholasville Rd, Lexington, KY 40503-3307 – **147)** 205 Cesar Chavez St, Saint Paul, MN 55107-2309 – **148)** 10845 Olive Blvd #160, Saint Louis, MO 63141-7792 or PO Box 7300, Charlotte, NC 28241-7300 – **149)** 2900 Sutro St, Reno, NV 89512-1616 – **150)** 320 Central Ave #519, Coos Bay, OR 97420-2272 – **151)** 1502 Wampanoag Trail, Riverside, RI 02915-1075 – **152)** 9601 McAllister Freeway #1200, San Antonio, TX 78216-4686 – **153)** 19319 Fremont Ave N, Shoreline, WA 98133-3800 – **154)** 3400 Olive Ave #500, Burbank, CA 91505-5544 – **155)** 2100 Park Central Blvd #100, Pompano Beach, FL 33064-2219 – **156)** 1819 Peachtree Rd NE #700, Atlanta, GA 30309-1849 – **157)** 1013 WOI Rd, Ames, IA 50011-1067 – **158)** 21700 Northwestern Hwy.Tower 14 #1190, Southfield, MI 48075 – **159)** 108 Green St, Thibodaux, LA 70301-3144 – **160)** 131 County Circle, Amherst, MA 01003-9257 – **161)** 1009 Drayton Rd, Fayetteville, NC 28303-3887 – **162)** 501 Office Center Dr #190, Fort Washington, PA 19034-3268 – **163)** 7755 Freedom Ave NW, North Canton, OH 44720-6905 – **164)** 4045 NW 64th St #600, Oklahoma City, OK 73116-2615 – **165)** 162 Free Hill Rd, Gray, TN 37615-3144 – **166)** 6401 Poplar Ave #640, Memphis, TN 38119-4808 – **167)** 1545 River Park Dr #500, Sacramento, CA 95815-4693 – **168)** 800 W 37th St, Hibbing, MN 55746-2856 – **169)** 2644 McGavock Pike, Nashville, TN 37214-1202 – **170)** 1600 W 500 N, Manti, UT 84642-5503 – **171)** 1912 Capitol Ave #300, Cheyenne, WY 82001-3659 – **172)** 2800 Dauphin St #104, Mobile, AL 36606-2400 – **173)** PO Box 2569, Window Rock, AZ 86515-2569 – **174)** 3000 W MacArthur Blvd #500, Santa Ana, CA 92704-7947 – **175)** 1188 Lake View Dr, Altamonte Springs, FL 32714-2713 – **176)** 1010 2nd St N, Sauk Rapids, MN 56379-2527 – **177)** 410 E 6th St, Williston, ND 58801-5552 – **178)** 345 Hudson St Fl10, New York, NY 10014-4502 – **179)** 2911 Tennyson Ave, #400, Eugene, OR 7408-4811 or PO Box 40231, Downey, CA 90239-1231 – **180)** 2420 Wade Hampton Blvd, Greenville, SC 29615-1107 – **181)** 6400 N Belt Line Rd #110, Irving, TX 75063-6065 – **182)** 2029 Freeway Dr, Mount Vernon, WA 98273-5470 – **183)** 11474 US Hwy 11, York, AL 36925-9764 – **184)** 108 Highway 70 E #11, Glenwood, AR 71943-8800 – **185)** 3301 Barham Blvd #300, Los Angeles, CA 90068-1477 – **186)** 2821 S Parker Rd #1205, Aurora, CO 80014-2708 – **187)** 330 SW 27th Ave #207, Miami, FL 33135-2957 – **188)** 1419 W Bannock St, Boise, ID 83702-5234 – **189)** 180 N Stetson St #1250, Chicago, IL 60601-6732 – **190)** 3999 Las Vegas Blvd S #K, Las Vegas, NV 89119-1097 – **191)** 12½ E Market St, Lewistown, PA 17044-2123 – **192)** 6223 Old Mendenhall Rd, High Point, NC 27263-3940 – **193)** 55 Hawthorne St #1100, San Francisco, CA 94105-3932 – **194)** 780 Johnson Ferry Rd NE #500, Atlanta, GA 30342-1436 – **195)** 20 Guest St 3rd Flr, Brighton, MA 02135-2040 – **196)** 1726 Reisterstown Rd #117, Pikesville, MD 21208-2986 – **197)** Tower 14-21700 Northwestern Hwy #1190, Southfield, MI 48075-4923 – **198)** 604 Ludington St, Escanaba, MI 49829-3830 – **199)** 4104 Country Lane, Saint Joseph, MO 64506-4921 – **200)** 1400 11th Ave #3, Helena, MT 59601-7996 – **201)** 3012 Highwoods Blvd #201, Raleigh, NC 27604-1031 – **202)** 320 N Jensen Rd, Vestal, NY 13850-2111 – **203)** 1835 Moriah Woods Blvd, Memphis, TN 38117-7122 – **204)** 8122 Datapoint Dr #600, San Antonio, TX 78229-3446 – **205)** 320 Emery Dr, Omak, WA 98841-9237 – **206)** 2396 Hallie Rd, Chippewa Falls, WI 54729-7519 – **207)** 1111 Virginia St E, Charleston, WV 25301-2406 – **208)** 241 Goodwin Crest Dr #300, Birmingham, AL 35209-3700 – **209)** 261 Portsea St, New Haven, CT 06519-2104 – **210)** 8000 Belfort Parkway #100, Jacksonville, FL 32256-6971 – **211)** 306 W 8th St, Coffeyville, KS 67337-5829 – **212)** 8230 Summa Ave, Baton Rouge, LA 70809-3421 – **214)** 4005 N Mesa St, El Paso, TX 79902-1526 – **215)** 11373 Wallace Pike, Bristol, VA 24202-2743 – **216)** 126 Kessel Rd, Fisher, WV 26818-4012 – **217)** 67 Garden Court, Monterey, CA 93940-5302 – **218)** 30 How St, Haverhill, MA 01830-6131 – **219)** 615 S Frederick Ave #900, Gaithersburg, MD 20877-1243 or PO Box 2195, Manassas, VA 20108-2195 – **220)** 8044 Montgomery Rd #650, Cincinnati, OH 45236-2959 – **221)** 196 Main St, Winston, OR 97496-ND – **222)** 11451 Katy Freeway #125, Houston, TX 77079-2004 – **223)** 50 W Broadway #200, Salt Lake City, UT 84101-2024 – **224)** 500 W Boone Ave, Spokane, WA 99201-2404 – **225)** 501 N 44th St #425, Phoenix, AZ 85008-6587 – **226)** 1425 River Park Dr #520, Sacramento, CA 95815-4524 – **227)** 800 W Olympic Blvd #A-200, Los Angeles, CA 90015-1360 – **228)** 3131 S Vaughn Way #601, Aurora, CO 80014-3516 – **229)** 8551 NM 30th Ter, Miami, FL 33122 – **230)** 855 College St, Eastman, GA 31023-6771 – **231)** 402 Main St, Williamsburg, KY 40769-1126 – **232)** 6341 W Port Ave, Shreveport, LA 71129-2415 – **233)** 5800 Foxridge Dr #600, Mission, KS 66202-2347 – **234)** 3228 S US Hwy 117, Rose Hill, NC 28458-8498 –

**235)** 3500 E Rosser Ave, Bismarck, ND 58501-3398 – **236)** 32 Ave of the Americas 3 Floor, New York, NY 10013-2473 – **237)** 3505 Olsen Blvd #117, Amarillo, TX 79109-3096 – **238)** 7080 Lee Highway, Fairlawn, VA 24141-8416 – **239)** 1820 Eastlake Ave S, Seattle, WA 98102-3711 – **240)** 11 E Superior St #380, Duluth, MN 55802-3016 – **241)** 100 NW 76th Dr #2, Gainesville, FL 32607-6659 – **242)** 154 Boone Dr, Newman, GA 30263-2801 – **243)** 435 N Michigan Ave, Chicago, IL 60611-4076 – **244)** 3232 Hendersonville Hwy, Pisgah Forest, NC 28768-7806 – **245)** 2920 S Durango Dr, Las Vegas, NV 89117-4412 – **246)** 28041 Pleasant Valley Rd, Sweet Home, OR 97386-9599 – **247)** 4050 Eisenhauer Rd, San Antonio, TX 78218-3409 – **248)** 2194 US Hwy 319 S, Thomasville, GA 31792-1417 – **249)** 5660 E Franklin Rd # 200, Nampa, ID 83687-5133 – **250)** PO Box 1, Springfield, MA 01101-0001 – **251)** 2075 Central Ave, Billings, MT 59102-4956 – **252)** 201 West Morehead St #200, Charlotte, NC 28202 – **253)** 7 Parkway Center #625, Pittsburgh, PA 15220-3707 – **254)** 2 Beeco Rd, Greer, SC 29650-1004 – **255)** 11240 Waples Mill Rd #405, Fairfax, VA 22030-6078 – **256)** 1 Commerce St #300, Montgomery, AL 36104-3542 – **257)** 3183 Airway Ave #D, Costa Mesa, CA 92626-4611 – **258)** 865 Battery St, San Francisco, CA 94111-1503 – **259)** 6805 Corporate Dr #130, Colorado Springs, CO 80919-5903 – **260)** 1650 S Dixie Hwy, Boca Raton, FL 33432-7462 – **261)** 2500 Maitland Center Pkwy #401, Maitland, FL 32751-4179 – **262)** 5440 Moeller Ave, Cincinnati, OH 45212-1211 – **263)** 2147 Springs Rd, Mount Airy, NC 27030-2447 – **264)** 1020 S 25th St, Fargo, ND 58103-2312 – **265)** PO Box 2000012, Brooklyn, NY 11220-0012 – **266)** 7136 S Yale Ave #500, Tulsa, OK 74136-6325 – **267)** 2000 West Loop S #300, Houston, TX 77027-3510 – **268)** 300 St Croix Trail S, Lakeland, MN 55043-ND or PO Box 25130, Saint Paul, MN 55125-0130 – **269)** 1601 W Peachtree St NE, Atlanta, GA 30309-2663 – **270)** 5625 N Milwaukee Ave, Chicago, IL 60646-6221 – **271)** 18553 Gentry Rd, Lebanon, MO 65536-5748 – **272)** 36581 N Reservoir Rd, Polson, MT 59860-8677 – **273)** 128 S 4th St, O'Neill, NE 68763-1814 or PO Box 8, Aurora, NE 68818-0008 – **274)** 1211 SW 5th Ave 6 Flr, Portland, OR 97204-3735 – **275)** 2211 E Missiouri Ave # S-300, El Paso, TX 79903-3831 – **276)** 1899 Carbonville Rd, Helper, UT 84526-ND or PO Box 875, Price, UT 84501-0875 – **277)** 301 Brookswood Rd #208, Sherwood, AR 72120-4200 – **278)** 7677 Engineer Rd, San Diego, CA 92111-1582 – **279)** 4695 S Monaco St, Denver, CO 80237-3408 – **280)** 5211 W Laurel St #101, Tampa, FL 33607-1725 – **281)** 2090 Palm Beach Lake Blvd #801, West Palm Beach, FL 33409-6508 – **282)** 10550 Barkley St, Overland Park, KS 66212-1824 – **283)** 8 Lawrence Rd , Derry, NH 03038-4191 – **284)** 3011 W Grand Blvd #800, Detroit, MI 48202-3086 – **285)** 2828 NC 126, Morganton, NC 28655-8264 – **286)** 137 Rapids Rd, Champlain, NY 12919-4945 – **287)** 6222 West Interstate 10, San Antonio, TX 78201-2097 – **288)** 1717 US Hwy 72 E, Athens, AL 35611-4413 – **289)** 10948 Cleveland Ave, Oakdale, CA 95361-9709 – **290)** 20125 S Tamiami Trail, Estero, FL 33928-2117 – **291)** 330 21st Ave S #610, Minneapolis, MN 55455-4550 – **292)** 818 Main St, Miles City, MT 59301-3221 – **293)** 275 River Rd, Rockingham, NC 28380-1536 – **294)** 500 4th St NW, Albuquerque, NM 87102-2102 – **295)** 2 Penn Plaza #1700, New York, NY 10121-0085 – **296)** 904 Center St, Lewiston, NY 14092-1737 or 600 The East Mall #400, Toronto, ON M9B 4B1 – **297)** 3201 Royalty Row, Irving, TX 75062-4961 – **298)** 504 Middle Creek Rd, Cedar Bluff, VA 24609-ND – **299)** 1820 Eastlake Ave E, Seattle, WA 98102-3711 – **300)** 3400 W Highway 89a, Sedona, AZ 86336-4914 – **301)** 180 N Stetson St #1100, Chicago, IL 60601-6723 – **302)** 274 Britton Rd, Monticello, ME 04760-3110 – **303)** 265 Highpoint Dr, Ridgeland, MS 39157-6018 – **304)** 17336 US Highway 421 S, Dunn, NC 28334-5580 – **305)** 1381 W Main St, Forest City, NC 28043-2525 – **306)** 595 E Plumb Lane, Reno, NV 89502-3503 – **307)** 1735 North Lynn St, Arlington, VA 22209 – **308)** 142 Skyland Blvd E, Tuscaloosa, AL 35405-4096 – **309)** 113 E New Hope Rd, Rogers, AR 72758-6058 – **310)** 3202 N Oracle Rd, Tucson, AZ 85705-3820 – **311)** 1415 Fulton St, Fresno, CA 93721-1609 – **312)** 1101 Marsh Rd, Eureka, CA 95501-1574 – **313)** 8965 Lindblade St, Culver City, CA 90232 – **314)** 32900 Radio Road, Leesburg, FL 34788-3903 – **315)** 20450 NW 2nd Ave, Miami, FL 33169-2505 – **316)** 210 Interstate North Cir SE #100, Atlanta, GA 30339-2206 – **317)** 1065 S Range Ave, Colby, KS 67701-3505 – **318)** 4000 Radio Drive #1, Louisville, KY 40218-4568 – **319)** 1795 Tittabawassee Rd, Saginaw, MI 48604-9431 – **320)** 600 First Ave N, Billings, MT 59101-2654 – **321)** 4801 E Independence Blvd #815, Charlotte, NC 28212-5490 – **322)** 1020 S 25th St, Fargo, ND 58103-3212 – **323)** 1541 Alta Dr #400, Whitehall, PA 18052-5632 – **324)** 1502 Wampanoag Trail, Riverside, RI 02915-1075 – **325)** 231 Brandonwood Dr, Johnson City, TN 37604-2156 – **326)** 1835 Moriah Woods Blvd, Memphis, TN 38117-7122 – **327)** 2000 West Loop S #300, Houston, TX 77027-3510 – **328)** 4413 82nd St #300, Lubbock, TX 79424-3395 – **329)** 500 Dominion Tower - 999 Waterside Dr, Norfolk, VA 23510-3300 – **330)** 2219 Yew St Rd, Bellingham, WA 98229-8898 – **331)** 1601 E 57th Ave, Spokane, WA 99223-6623 – **332)** 944 Harlem St, Altoona, WI 54720-1127 – **333)** 213 E 2nd St, Soda Springs, ID 83276-1411 – **334)** 462 Merrimack St, Methuen, MA 01844-5804 – **335)** 1010 2nd St N,

Sauk Rapids, MN 56379-2527 – **336)** 2775 Mt Ephraim Ave, Camden, NJ 08104-3295 – **337)** 1919 N Broadway Ave, Oklahoma City, OK 73103-4499 – **338)** 1032 Melody Lane, Crewe, VA 23930-ND – **339)** 200 Tower Rd, Waupaca, WI 54981-1699 – **340)** 134 4th Ave, Huntington, WV 25701-1253 – **341)** 188 John Turner Broadcast Blvd, Jacksonville, AL 36265-6659 or PO Box 8, Anniston, AL 36202-0008 – **342)** 750 Battery Street, 2nd Floor, San Francisco, CA 94111 – **343)** 999 Douglas Ave #3318, Altamonte Springs, FL 32714-5213 – **344)** 4198 Rebecca Circle, Valdosta, GA 31606-2201 – **345)** 1501 Hargis Lane, Jackson, KY 41339-1102 – **346)** 2422 Burton St SE, Grand Rapids, MI 49546-4806 – **347)** 6721 W 121st St, Overland Park, KS 66209-2003 – **348)** 1115 Honeysuckle Dr, Keene, TX 76059-2101 – **349)** 102 Taos St, Santa Fe, NM 87505-3832 – **350)** 1203 Troy-Schenectady Rd #201, Latham, NY 12110-1046 – **351)** 2 Beeco Rd, Greer, SC 29650-1004 – **352)** 1612 Junction Ave #1, Sturgis, SD 57785-2166 – **353)** 2514 Eugenia Ave, Nashville, TN 37211-2117 – **354)** 145 Jackson St NE, Blacksburg, VA 24060-3931 – **355)** 55 Alder St NW #3, Ephrata, WA 98823-1663 – **356)** 800 8th Ave SE, Largo, FL 33771-2162 – **357)** 5475 N Milwaukee Ave, Chicago, IL 60630-1249 – **358)** 3400 Idaho Ave NW #200, Washington, DC 20016-3000 – **359)** 17487 Driftwood Ln, Park Rapids, MN 56470-2739 – **360)** 2205 College Ave #3, Elmira, NY 14903-1223 – **361)** 160 Varick St, New York, NY 10013-1220 – **362)** 4673 Winterset Dr, Columbus, OH 43220-8113 – **363)** 3090 Olive St #400, Dallas, TX 75219-7640 – **364)** 460 West Century Dr, Salt Lake City, UT 84123-2534 – **365)** 4301 W Hundred Rd, Chester, VA 23831-1737 – **366)** 2201 6th Ave #1500, Seattle, WA 98121-1840 – **367)** 7355 N Orcale Rd #102, Tucson, AZ 85704-6353 – **368)** 1255 E Main St #A, Grass Valley, CA 95945-5711 – **369)** 2000 E Gene Autry Way, Anaheim, CA 92806-6143 – **370)** 3500 N Causeway Blvd #830, Metairie, LA 70002-3561 – **371)** 276 Turnpike Rd, Westborough, MA 01581 – **372)** 625 2nd Ave S #200, Minneapolis, MN 55402-1961 – **373)** 4405 Providence Lane #D, Winston-Salem, NC 27106-3226 – **374)** 34 N 4th St, Reading, PA 19601-3996 – **375)** 230-2 Goodman Rd E #202, Southaven, MS 38671-5151 – **376)** 1233 S Beverly St, Casper, WY 82609-4131 – **377)** 6530 Spanish Fort Blvd #B, Spanish Fort, AL 36527-5014 or PO Box 1328, Mobile, AL 36633-1328 – **378)** 3256 Penryn Rd #100, Loomis, CA 95650-8052 – **379)** 221 Pall Bearer Rd, Thomasville, GA 31792-1101 – **380)** 4000 Radio Drive #1, Louisville, KY 40218-4568 – **381)** 3735 Rigolette Rd, Pineville, LA 71360-7365 – **382)** 1011 N Lincoln St, West Point, NE 68788-1003 – **383)** 7255 S Tenaya Way #100, Las Vegas, NV 89113-1900 – **384)** 4801 E Independence Blvd #815, Charlotte, NC 28212-5490 – **385)** 1201 N Jackson Ave #900, McAllen, TX 78501-5764 – **386)** PO Box 7111, Charlottesville, VA 22906-7111 – **387)** 1114 N Almon St, Moscow, ID 83843-8507 – **388)** 120 Summit Pkwy #200, Birmingham, AL 35209-4741 – **389)** 4695 S Monaco St, Denver, CO 80237-3403 – **390)** 98 Mill Plain Rd, Danbury, CT 06811-6101 – **391)** 1200 Weimer Hall, Gainesville, FL 32611 – **392)** 2100 Park Central Blvd #100, Pompano Beach, FL 33064-2219 – **393)** 5625 N Milwaukee Ave, Chicago, IL 60646-6221 – **394)** 20 Guest St 3rd Flr, Brighton, MA 02135-2040 – **395)** 3434 W Kilbourn Ave, Milwaukee, MN 53208-3313 – **396)** 1333 S Kirkwood Rd St, Saint Louis, MO 63122-7266 – **397)** 3012 Highwoods Blvd #201, Raleigh, NC 27604-1031 – **398)** 1301 E 9th St #252, Cleveland, OH 44114-1800 – **399)** 104 S Center St #401, Ebensburg, PA 15931-1656 – **400)** 261 Hannum St, Alcoa, TN 37701-2451 – **401)** 8828 N Stemmons Fwy #106, Dallas, TX 75247-3720 – **402)** 3000 Bering Dr, Houston, TX 77057-5708 – **403)** 500 Dominion Tower - 999 Waterside Dr, Norfolk, VA 23510-3300 – **404)** 645 Elliott Ave W #400, Seattle, WA 98119-3911 – **405)** 300 Broadway #8, San Francisco, CA 94133-4545 – **406)** 5211 W Laurel St #101, Tampa, FL 33607-1725 – **407)** 1465 Northside Dr NW #218, Atlanta, GA 30318-4239 – **408)** 601 W Roanoke Dr, Fitzgerald, GA 31750-3633 – **409)** 1162 E Hwy 126, Pittsburg, KS 66762-8712 – **410)** 425 Stockbridge Rd, Great Barrington, MA 01230-1223 – **411)** 260 Hegenberger Rd, Oakland, CA 94621-1491 – **412)** 6605 SE Lake Rd, Portland, OR 97222-2161 – **413)** 555 E City Ave #330, Bala Cynwyd, PA 19004-1137 – **414)** 8122 Datapoint Dr #600, San Antonio, TX 78229-3446 – **415)** 434 Bearcat Dr, Salt Lake City, UT 84115-2520 – **416)** 240 Central Ave, Oak Hill, WV 25901-3006 – **417)** 2278 Wortham Lane, Grovetown, GA 30813-5103 – **418)** 701 N Brand Blvd #550, Glendale, CA 91203-1235 – **419)** 400 Poydras St #800, New Orleans, LA 70130-3245 – **420)** PO Box 308, Bath, ME 04530-0308 – **421)** MSU - 404 Wilson Road Room 212, East Lansing, MI 48824-1212 – **422)** PO Box 49, Park Rapids, MN 56470-0049 – **423)** 1115 Honeysuckle Dr, Keene, TX 76059-2101 – **424)** 6767 W Tropicana Ave #102, Las Vegas, NV 89103-4755 – **425)** 1751 Hanshaw Rd, Ithaca, NY 14850-9105 – **426)** 340 Martin Luther King Blvd, Bristol, TN 37620-3996 – **427)** 2621 West A St, Pasco, WA 99301-4702 – **428)** 2360 NE Coachman Rd, Clearwater, FL 33765-2216 – **429)** 30 E San Joaquin St #105, Salinas, CA 93901-2946 – **430)** 2828 W Flagler St, Miami, FL 33135-1337 – **431)** 2432 US Hwy 2 E, Kalispell, MT 59901-2310 – **432)** 13 Summerlin Rd, Asheville, NC 28806-2800 – **433)** 1007 Plum Creek Parkway , Lexington, NE 68850-2621 – **434)** PO

Box 9090, Window Rock, AZ 86515-9090 – **435)** 345 Hudson St Flr 11, New York, NY 10014-4502 – **436)** 8101 N High St #360, Columbus, OH 43235-1442 – **437)** 1405 E Ellendale Ave, Dallas, OR 97338-1709 – **438)** 3715 N Natchez Ct, Nashville, TN 37211-3421 – **439)** 1600 Pasadena Blvd, Pasadena, TX 77502-2402 – **440)** 3650 131st SE #550, Bellevue, WA 98006-1334 – **441)** 619 Cameron St, Eau Claire, WI 54703-4700 – **442)** 1301 Central Pkwy SW, Decatur, AL 35601-4817 – **443)** 560 Higuera St #G, San Luis Obispo, CA 93401-3850 – **444)** 1442 Ethan Way #101, Sacramento, CA 95825-2232 – **445)** 965 S Irving St, Denver, CO 80219-3422 – **446)** 2800 Shallowford Rd NE, Atlanta, GA 30341-5217 – **447)** PO Box 490, Cauldwell, ID 83606-0490 – **448)** 455 N Cityfront Plaza Dr, Chicago, IL 60611 – **449)** 122 Green St #2L, Worcester, MA 01604-4138 – **450)** 37 Ellisville Blvd, Laurel, MS 39440-4523 – **451)** 243 Riverchase Way #A, Lexington, SC 29072-9470 – **452)** 4501 N McColl Rd, McAllen, TX 78504-2431 – **453)** 10613 Bellaire Blvd #900, Houston, TX 77072-5221 – **454)** 750 Ridgeview Dr #204, Saint George, UT 84770-2665 – **455)** 145 Jackson St NE, Blacksburg, VA 24060-3931 – **456)** 747 E Green St #101, Pasadena, CA 91101 – **457)** 2320 NE 2nd St #5, Ocala, FL 34470-6992 – **458)** 214 Television Circle, Savannah, GA 31406-4519 – **459)** 1240 Radio Drive, Pikeville, KY 41501-4779 – **460)** 3003 Snelling Ave N, Saint Paul, MN 55113-1599 – **461)** 398 S Main St, Granite Falls, NC 28630-8535 – **462)** 801 E DuBois Ave, DuBois, PA 15801-3643 – **463)** 2514 Eugenia Ave, Nashville, TN 37211-2117 – **464)** 10613 Bellaire Blvd #900, Houston, TX 77072-5221 – **465)** 207 University Blvd #200, Harrisonburg, VA 22801-3752 – **466)** 125 S 2nd St, Blytheville, AR 72315-3413 – **467)** 4686 E Van Buren St #300, Phoenix, AZ 85008-6967 – **468)** 260 Hegenberger Rd, Oakland, CA 94621-1491 – **469)** 340 Townsend St #4, San Francisco, CA 94107-1698 – **470)** 200 S A St #400, Oxnard, CA 93030-5717 – **471)** 3455 W 83rd Ave, Westminster, CO 80030-4005 – **472)** 135 Burnside Ave, East Hartford, CT 06108-3466 – **473)** 5211 W Laurel St, Tampa, FL 33607-1736 – **474)** 3765 N John Young Parkway, Orlando, FL 32804-3213 – **475)** 710 S Clinton St, Iowa City, IA 52242-4214 – **476)** 184 Target Industrial Circle #207, Bangor, ME 04401-5718 – **477)** 20733 W 10 Mile Rd, Southfield, MI 48075-1086 – **478)** 3436 Highway 45N, Meridian, MS 39301 – **479)** PO Box 15400, Durham, NC 27704-0400 – **480)** 1000 20th Ave SW, Minot, ND 58701-6447 – **481)** 1301 N Main St, Roswell, NM 88201-5013 – **482)** 6006 Grand Central Ave, Parkersburg, WV 26105-9125 or PO Box 5559, Vienna, WV 26105-5559 – **483)** 114 S Jefferson St, Kittanning, PA 16201-2408 – **484)** 5989 Susquehanna Plaza Dr, Hellam, PA 17406-8910 – **485)** 225 S Pleasantburg Dr #3B, Greenville, SC 29607-2533 – **486)** 162 Freehill Rd, Gray, TN 37615-3144 – **487)** 105 N Ash Ave, South Pittsburg, TN 37380-1565 – **488)** 4300 S US Highway 281, Edinburg, TX 78539-9650 – **489)** 3245 Basie Rd, Richmond, VA 23228-3404 – **490)** 0700 SW Bancroft St, Portland, OR 97239-4226 – **491)** 16880 W US Highway 63, Hayward, WI 54843-7186 – **492)** 700 Wellington Hills Rd, Little Rock, AR 72211-2026 – **493)** 961 N Emerald Ave #A, Modesto, CA 95351-1556 – **494)** 2100 E Tahquitz Canyon Way, Palm Springs, CA 92262-7046 – **495)** 7350 US Hwy 50, Lamar, CO 81052-9563 – **496)** 1800 Turtle Mound Rd, Melbourne, FL 32934-8105 – **497)** 2970 Peachtree Rd NW #700, Atlanta, GA 30305-4919 – **498)** 290 Hegenberger Rd, Oakland, CA 94621-1436 – **499)** 712 3rd St, West Lafayette, IN 47907-2005 – **500)** PO Box 228, Mayking, KY 41837-0228 – **501)** 601 Central Ave N, Faribault, MN 55021-1307 – **502)** 1109 Tower Dr, Burlington, NC 27215-4425 – **503)** 8755 W Flamingo Rd, Las Vegas, NV 89147-8667 – **504)** 3256 Penryn Rd #100, Loomis, CA 95650-8052 – **505)** 75 Oxford St, Providence, RI 02905-4722 – **506)** 660 Flormann St #100, Rapid City, SD 57701-4679 – **507)** 7322 Southwest Frwy #500, Houston, TX 77074-2084 – **508)** 2495 N Vernal Ave, Vernal, UT 84078-ND – **509)** 1770 Van Buren Dr, Dumfries, VA 22025-2036 – **510)** 1700 SE Mile Hill Dr #243, Port Orchard, WA 98366-3507 – **511)** 500 W Boone Ave, Spokane, WA 99201-2497 – **512)** 12100 W Howard Ave, Greenfield, WI 53228-1851 – **513)** 450 Leonard Ave Extension, Fairmont, WV 26554-3878 – **514)** 1913 Barry St, Oxford, AL 36203-2319 – **515)** PO Box 1179, Douglas, AZ 85608-1179 – **516)** 1117 W Route 66, Flagstaff, AZ 86001-6213 – **517)** 1845 W Empire Ave, Burbank, CA 91504-3402 – **518)** 190 Turner Dr #G, Durango, CO 81303-8231 – **519)** PO Box 7069, Breckenridge, CO 80424-7069 – **520)** 11700 Central Pkwy, Jacksonville, FL 32224-2600 – **521)** 5211 W Laurel St, Tampa, FL 33607-1736 – **522)** 521 S Scott St, Bainbridge, GA 39819-4101 – **523)** 544 N Arthur Ave, Pocatello, ID 83204-3002 – **524)** 329 Maine St, Quincy, IL 62301-3928 – **525)** 1496 Bellevue St #202, Green Bay, WI 54311-4205 – **526)** 804 College St, Bowling Green, KY 42101-2133 – **527)** 5966 Grove Hill Rd, Frederick, MD 21703-6012 – **528)** 390 Golden Ave, Battle Creek, MI 49015-4598 – **529)** 37208 US Hwy 169, Aitkin, MN 56431-4195 – **530)** 1015 W Pine St, Poplar Bluff, MO 63901-4839 – **531)** 4908 Ridgewood Rd, Jackson, MS 39211-5422 – **532)** 3250 S Reserve St #200, Missoula, MT 59801-8236 – **533)** 11530 Carmel Commons Blvd, Charlotte, NC 28226-3976 – **534)** 525 Evans St, Greenville, NC 27858-2311 – **535)** 815 Lafayette Rd, Portsmouth, NH 03801-5406 – **536)** 27 William St 11th Flr, New York, NY 10005-2718 – **537)** 500 Corporate Parkway #200, Buffalo, NY 14226-1263 – **538)** 4045 NW 64th St #600, Oklahoma City, OK 73116-2615 – **539)** 1250 Siskiyou Blvd, Ashland, OR 97520-5010 – **540)** 3304 S Highway 281, Aberdeen, SD 57401-8792 – **541)** 430 State Highway 165 #C, Branson, MO 65616-3541 – **542)** 9601 McAllister Freeway #1200, San Antonio, TX 78216-4686 – **543)** 100 Whitehall Rd, Lynchburg, VA 24501-6706 – **544)** PO Box 31000, Spokane, WA 99223-3016 – **545)** 821 University Ave, Madison, WI 53706-1412 – **546)** 401 11th St #200, Huntington, WV 25701-2235 – **547)** 1716 KROE Lane, Sheridan, WY 82801-9681 – **548)** 1415 Fulton St, Fresno, CA 93721-1609 – **549)** 7601 Riviera Blvd, Miramar, FL 33023-6574 – **550)** 544 Mulberry St #500, Macon, GA 31201-8258 – **551)** 1416 Locust St, Des Moines, IA 50309-3014 – **552)** 3501 Broadway St, Mount Vernon, IL 62864-2202 – **553)** 929 Howard Ave, New Orleans, LA 70113-1148 – **554)** 7119 W M-68, Indian River, MI 49749-9472 – **555)** 1189 N Jackson St, Houston, MS 38851-8273 – **556)** 401 Saw Mill Hollow Rd, Burnsville, NC 28714-9789 – **557)** 126 W 3rd St, Valentine, NE 69201-1826 – **558)** 345 SW Cyber Dr #100, Bend, OR 97702-1045 – **559)** 305 N Church St, Wartburg, TN 37887-3164 – **560)** 6214 W 34th Ave, Amarillo, TX 79109-4006 – **561)** 615 Olive St, Texarkana, TX 75501-5512 – **562)** 1011 Radio Drive, Grundy, VA 24614-6157 – **563)** 13379 Great Springs Rd, Smithfield, VA 23430-6930 – **564)** 501 E Broadway St, Forrest City, AR 72335-3801 – **565)** 985 Lincoln Way #103, Auburn, CA 95603-5255 – **566)** 7800 E Orchard Rd #400, Greenwood Village, CO 80111-2599 – **567)** 1188 Lake View Dr, Altamonte Springs, FL 32714-2713 – **568)** 2973 US Hwy 84 W, Valdosta, GA 31601 – **569)** 2502 S Frederick Ave, Oelwein, IA 50662-3116 – **570)** 624 3rd St S, Nampa, ID 83651-3840 – **571)** 2560 Snake River Ave, Lewiston, ID 83501-9685 – **572)** 1496 Bellevue St #202, Green Bay, WI 54311-4205 – **573)** 500 Victory Rd #2, Quincy, MA 02171-3132 – **574)** 7825 Tuckerman Ln #217, Potomac, MD 20854-3241 – **575)** 26495 American Dr, Southfield, MI 48034-6114 – **576)** 3109 S 10 Mile Dr, Jefferson City, MO 65109-1012 – **577)** 63 Braswell Rd, Hattiesburg, MS 39401-9730 – **578)** 100 W Lyndale Ave #B, Helena, MT 59601-2999 – **579)** 1560 N Corbin St, Silver City, NM 88061-6526 – **580)** 403 W Pueblo Dr, Española, NM 87532-2530 – **581)** 9418 River Rd, Marcy, NY 13403-2071 – **582)** 1250 Siskiyou Blvd, Ashland, OR 97520-5010 – **583)** 260 Hegenberger Rd, Oakland, PA 94621-1491 – **584)** 60 Markfield Dr #4, Charleston, SC 29407-7907 – **585)** 25 Garlington Rd, Greenville, SC 29615-4613 – **586)** 222 Mallory Station Rd, Franklin, TN 37067-0201 – **587)** 2000 West Loop S #300, Houston, TX 77027-3150 – **588)** 9800 University Ave, Lubbock, TX 79423-5302 – **589)** 701 German School Rd, Richmond, VA 23225-5357 – **590)** 351 Elliott Ave W #400, Seattle, WA 98119-3911 – **591)** 817 Suncrest Place, Charleston, WV 25303-2302 – **592)** 600 Beacon Parkway W #400, Birmingham, AL 35209-3118 – **593)** 6530 Spanish Fort Blvd #B, Spanish Fort, AL 36527-5014 or PO Box 1328, Mobile, AL 36633-1328 – **594)** 260 Battle St, Marshall, AR 72650-9440 – **595)** 2425 E Camelback Rd #570, Phoenix, AZ 85016-4250 – **596)** 12370 Hesperia Rd #16, Victorville, CA 92392-5808 – **597)** 340 Townsend St #4, San Francisco, CA 94107-1698 – **598)** 495 Benham St, Hamden, CT 06514-2009 – **599)** 809 S Westover Blvd, Albany, GA 31707-4953 – **600)** 1010 Tower Place, Bogart, GA 30622-3052 – **601)** 209 N Elm St, Shenandoah, IA 51601-1139 – **602)** 1301 E Douglas Rd, Mishawaka, IN 46545-1732 – **603)** 1240 Radio Drive, Pikeville, KY 41501-4779 – **604)** 356 Broad St, Fitchburg, MA 01420-3030 – **605)** 351 Tilghman Rd, Salisbury, MD 21804-1920 – **606)** PO Box 432, Elk Rapids, MI 46629 – **607)** 16405 Haven Rd, Little Falls, MN 56345-6400 – **608)** 324 Broadway St, Cape Girardeau, MO 63701-7331 – **609)** 3600 Highway 7 N, Baker, MT 59313-ND – **610)** 4405 Providence Lane #D, Winston-Salem, NC 27106-3226 – **611)** 1361 Colony Dr, New Bern, NC 28562-4129 – **612)** 1928 E Portal Place, Scottsbluff, NE 69361-2727 – **613)** 1515 W Main St, Farmington, NM 87401-3896 – **614)** 265 Hegeman Ave, Colchester, VT 05446-3174 – **615)** 404 Main St #4, Klamath Falls, OR 97601-6021 – **616)** 1703 Walnut Bottom Rd, Carlisle, PA 17015-9151 – **617)** 193 S Keystone Ave, Sayre, PA 18840-1330 – **618)** 1301 S Abe St, San Angelo, TX 76903-7245 – **619)** 50 W Broadway #200, Salt Lake City, UT 84101-2024 – **620)** 3934 Electric Rd, Roanoke, VA 24018-4513 – **621)** 4304 W 24th Ave Suite 200, Kennewick, WA 99338 – **622)** 67 W Court Square, Troy, AL 36081-2611 – **623)** 1838 Commerce Dr #A, Lakeside, AZ 85929-7007 – **624)** 1100 Mohawk St #280, Bakersfield, CA 93309-7417 – **625)** 1231 N Gene Autry Trail, Palm Springs, CA 92262-5473 – **626)** 201 N Industrial Park Rd, Excelsior Springs, MO 64024-1736 – **627)** 4002 W Gandy Blvd #A, Tampa, FL 33611-3410 – **628)** 2970 Peachtree Rd NW #700, Atlanta, GA 30305-4919 – **629)** 1501 Mount Vernon Rd, Vidalia, GA 30474-3031 – **630)** 3219 Laurelwood Dr, Twin Falls, ID 83301-8106 – **631)** 125 S Main St, Harlan, KY 40831-2109 – **632)** 9960 Corporate Campus Dr #3600, Louisville, KY 40223-4070 – **633)** 420 Western Ave, South Portland, ME 04106-1704 – **634)** 121 N Front St, Marquette, MI 49855-4300 – **635)** 109 E Clark St, Albert Lea, MN 56007-2420 – **636)** 27 N 27th St, Billings, MT 59101-2357 – **637)** 1190 Patton Ave, Asheville, NC 28806-2706 – **638)** 301 8th St S, Fargo, ND 58103-1826

– **639)** 201 S Bailey Ave, North Platte, NE 69101-5406 – **640)** 111 Broadway, New York, NJ 10006-1901 – **641)** 3256 Penryn Rd #100, Loomis, CA 95650-8052 – **642)** 625 Delaware Ave #308, Buffalo, NY 14202-1007 – **643)** 3226 Jefferson Rd, Ashtabula, OH 44004-9112 – **644)** 5800 E Skelly Dr #150, Tulsa, OK 74135-6416 – **645)** 1211 SW 5th Ave 6th Fl, Portland, OR 97204-3735 – **646)** 200 Fleet St 4th Flr, Pittsburgh, PA 15220-2910 – **647)** 181 E Evans St #311, Florence, SC 29506-2512 – **648)** 207 University Blvd #200, Harrisonburg, VA 22801-3752 – **649)** PO Box 2482, Kirkland, WA 98083-2482 – **650)** 821 University Ave, Madison, WI 53706-1412 – **651)** 2705 E Parkway Dr, Russellville, AR 72802-2006 – **652)** 1101 Marsh Rd, Eureka, CA 95501-1574 – **653)** 5670 Wilshire Blvd #200, Los Angeles, CA 90036-5611 – **654)** 229 Pajaro St #205, Salinas, CA 93901-3499 – **655)** 1801 Rockville Pike #405, Rockville, MD 20852-5604 – **656)** 100 NW 76th Dr #2, Gainesville, FL 32607-6659 – **657)** 312 E Nine Mile Rd #29D, Pensacola, FL 32514-1475 – **658)** 1650 S Dixie Hwy, Boca Raton, FL 33432-7462 – **659)** 1691 Forsyth St, Macon, GA 31201-1407 – **660)** 854 Lindsay Blvd, Idaho Falls, ID 83402-1820 – **661)** 208 N Thomas Dr, Shreveport, LA 71107-6520 – **662)** 243 Central St, Lowell, MA 01852-2214 – **663)** 2110 Cliff Rd, St Paul, MN 55122-3522 – **664)** 7000 Squibb Rd, Mission, KS 66202-3233 – **665)** 3233 Burnt Mill Dr #4, Wilmington, NC 28403-2676 – **666)** 733 E Roosevelt Ave, Grants, NM 87020-2113 – **667)** 1155 Gummow Dr, Fallon, NV 89406-9453 – **668)** 1203 Troy-Schenectady Rd #201, Latham, NY 12110-1046 – **669)** 101 Pine St, Dayton, OH 45402-2925 – **670)** 305 Hwy 315, Pittston, PA 18640-3987 – **671)** 6223 Old Mendenhall Rd, High Point, NC 27263-3940 – **672)** 745 Main St, Deadwood, SD 57732-1015 – **673)** 11530 Carmel Commons Blvd, Charlotte, NC 28226-3976 – **674)** 1600 Pasadena Blvd, Pasadena, TX 77502-2404 – **675)** 390 E Annabella Rd, Richfield, UT 84701-2692 – **676)** 901 E Valley Dr, Bristol, VA 24201-4903 – **677)** 1200 Chesterly Dr #160, Yakima, WA 98902-7345 – **678)** 1915 Mirro Dr, Manitowoc, WI 54220-6715 – **679)** 300 Harrison Ave, Weston, WV 26452-2100 – **680)** 3871 N Commerce Dr, Tucson, AZ 85705-2983 – **681)** 44 Gough St #301, San Francisco, CA 94103-5424 – **682)** 414 E Cota St, Santa Barbara, CA 93101-1624 – **683)** 3131 S Vaughn Way #601, Aurora, CO 80014-3516 – **684)** 758 Colonel Ledyard Hwy, Ledyard, CT 06339 – **685)** 2150 W 68th St #202, Hialeah, FL 33016-1802 – **686)** 610 Sycamore St #220, Celebration, FL 34747-4996 – **687)** 239 Ezzard St, Lawrenceville, GA 30046-5396 – **688)** 24 Frank Lloyd Wright Dr, Ann Arbor, MI 48105-9755 – **689)** 1569 N Central Ave, Monett, MO 65708-1104 – **690)** 1650 Midland Rd, Southern Pines, NC 28387-2111 – **691)** 625 Delaware Ave #308, Buffalo, NY 14202-1007 – **692)** 117 Ridge Pike, Lafayette Hill, PA 19444-1900 – **693)** 109 Plaza Dr #2, Johnstown, PA 15905-1212 – **694)** 4711 Old Kingston Pike, Knoxville, TN 37919-5207 – **695)** 5495 Murray Rd, Memphis, TN 38119-3703 – **696)** 12900 Preston Rd #200, Dallas, TX 75230-1380 – **697)** 1535 Narrows Rd, Narrows, VA 24124-ND – **698)** 3256 Penryn Rd #100, Loomis, CA 95650-8052 – **699)** 20872 NE Kelley Ave, Blountstown, FL 32424-1115 – **700)** 190 N State St, Chicago, IL 60601-3302 – **701)** PO Box 1336, Yazoo, MS 39194-1336 – **702)** 309 Renard Place SE #206, Albuquerque, NM 87107-4848 – **703)** 3134 Lake Rd, Horseheads, NY 14845-3103 – **704)** 1900 NW Expressway St #1000, Oklahoma City, OK 73118-1854 – **705)** 5100 S Tennis Lane, Sioux Falls, SD 57108-2212 – **706)** 110 India Rd, Paris, TN 38242-7565 – **707)** 140 4th Ave N #340, Seattle, WA 98109-4932 – **708)** 2800 N 44th St #100, Phoenix, AZ 85008-1560 – **709)** 5100 Commerce Dr, Bakersfield, CA 93309-0684 – **710)** 44 Gough St #301, San Francisco, CA 94103-5424 – **711)** 75153 Merle Dr #D, Palm Desert, CA 92211-5197 – **712)** 220 State St #106, Fort Morgan, CO 80701-2116 – **713)** 9090 Hogan Rd, Jacksonville, FL 32216-4648 – **714)** 9721 Executive Center Dr N #200, St Petersburg, FL 33702-2439 – **715)** 1570 Northside Dr NW Bldg 200, Atlanta, GA 30318-4204 – **716)** 5615 Pershing Ave #12, Saint Louis, MO 63112-1757 – **717)** 451 Highway 11 & 80, Meridian, MS 39301-2779 – **718)** 70 Adams Hill Rd, Asheville, NC 28806-3841 or PO Box 159, Black Mountain, NC 28711-0159 – **719)** 103 Hanover St, Newport, NH 03766-1098 or PO Box 2295, New London, NH 03257-2295 – **720)** 345 Hudson St Fl 11, New York, NY 10014-4502 – **721)** 5110 SE Stark St, Portland, OR 97215-1751 – **722)** 1625 Hwy 109 N, Gallatin, TN 37066-8135 – **723)** 3639 Wolfin Ave, Amarillo, TX 79102-2119 – **724)** 5100 Southwest Freeway, Houston, TX 77056-7308 – **725)** 1019 Washington Ave, Waco, TX 76701-1256 – **726)** 3256 Penryn Rd #100, Loomis, CA 95650-8052 – **727)** 2202 Jolliff Rd, Chesapeake, VA 23321-1416 – **728)** 5999 Center Dr, Los Angeles, CA 90045-8901 – **729)** 67 Main St, Sharon, CT 06069-2018 – **730)** 2555 Ponce De Leon Blvd #225, Coarl Gables, FL 33134-6033 – **731)** 5011 Capitol Ave, Omaha, NE 68132-2921 – **732)** 419 Broadway, Paterson, NM 07501-2104 – **733)** Foster Plaza 5, 651 Holiday Dr, Pittsburgh, PA 15220-2740 – **734)** 100 E Shockley Ferry Rd, Anderson, SC 29624-3746 – **735)** 706 Butterfield Rd, Yakima, WA 98901-2021 – **736)** 4209 N Frontage Rd, Fayetteville, AR 72703-5002 – **737)** 3222 S Richey Ave, Tucson, AZ 85704-7738 – **738)** 121 W Alvin Ave, Santa Maria, CA 93458-3002 – **739)** 1355 E Altamonte Dr, Altamonte Springs, FL 32701-

5011 – **740)** 427 S Wall Sreet, Calhoun, GA 30701-2431 – **741)** 3656 W Belmont Ave, Chicago, IL 60618-5328 – **742)** 1402 E Kansas Ave, Garden City, KS 67846-5806 – **743)** 1170 Soldiers Field Rd, Allston, MA 02134-1092 – **744)** 6710 Oxon Hill Rd #100, Oxon Hill, MD 20745-1158 – **745)** 7355 N Orcale Rd #102, Tucson, AZ 85704-6353 – **746)** 900 Forestview Lane N, Plymouth, MN 55441-5934 – **747)** 18920 E Valley View Pkwy #C, Independence, MO 64055-7020 – **748)** 4405 Providence Lane #D, Winston-Salem, NC 27106-3226 – **749)** 4321 Stuart Andrew Blvd #E, Charlotte, NC 28217-1588 – **750)** 136 N 7th St, Reedsport, OR 97467-1503 – **751)** 3654 Park Ave, Memphis, TN 38111-5626 – **752)** 1602 S Brownlee Blvd, Corpus Christi, TX 78404-3134 – **753)** 210 W Cota St, Shelton, WA 98584-2264 – **754)** 303 8th St, Point Pleasant, WV 25550-1209 – **755)** 150 Nichols Ave, Casper, WY 82601-1816 – **756)** 5050 Edison Ave #218, Colorado Springs, CO 80915-3450 – **757)** 2555 Ponce De Leon Blvd #225, Coral Gables, FL 33134-6033 – **758)** 800 8th Ave SE, Largo, FL 33771-2162 – **759)** 3200 Steve Reynolds Blvd #219, Duluth, GA 30096-8833 – **760)** 2141 Grand Ave, Des Moines, IA 50312-5303 – **761)** 4321 Stuart Andrew Blvd #E, Charlotte, NC 28217-1588 – **762)** 619 Alexander Rd Fl 3, Princeton, NJ 08540-6000 – **763)** 5620 S Lima Rd, Avon, NY 14414-9791 – **764)** 151 E 1st Ave, Everett, PA 15537-1351 – **765)** 2340 Martin Luther King Jr Ave, Knoxville, TN 37915-1625 – **766)** 5787 S Hampton Rd #285, Dallas, TX 75232-2290 – **767)** 3256 Penryn Rd #100, Loomis, CA 95650-8052 – **768)** 55 Hawthorne St #1100, San Francisco, CA 94105-3914 – **769)** 506 W 1st Ave, Crestview, FL 32536-2420 – **770)** 5590 Rio Grande Ave, Jacksonville, FL 32254-1354 – **771)** 552 Laney-Walker Extension, Augusta, GA 30901-3014 – **772)** 3400 Idaho Ave NW #200, Washington, DC 20016-3000 – **773)** 1100 Victors Way #100, Ann Arbor, MI 48108-5220 – **774)** 608 State Highway 30, Pipestone, MN 56164-1458 – **775)** 508 Main St, Miles City, MT 59301-3047 – **776)** 180 Radio Hill Road, Franklin, NC 28734-6927 – **777)** 8456 Smokey Hollow Rd, Baldwinsville, NY 13027-8222 – **778)** 125 West End Ave 6th Flr, New York, NY 10023-6387 – **779)** 2080 Laura St, Springfield, OR 97477-2197 – **780)** 11640 Highway 17 Bypass, Murrells Inlet, SC 29576-9332 – **781)** 539 Ragland Rd, Madison Heights, VA 24572-ND or PO Box 1079, Lynchburg, VA 24505-1079 – **782)** 700 Monticello Ave #301, Norfolk, VA 23510-2538 – **783)** PO Box 31000, Spokane, WA 99223-3016 – **784)** PO Box 2482, Kirkland, WA 98083-2482 – **785)** 5 Rosemar Circle, Parkersburg, WV 26104-1203 – **786)** 1900 W Carmen St, Guadalupe, AZ 85283-2559 – **787)** 40356 Oak Park Way, Oakhurst, CA 93612-8872 – **788)** 614 Kimbark St, Longmont, CO 80501-4911 – **789)** 800 8th Ave SE, Largo, FL 33771-2162 – **790)** 1546 Golf Course Road, Tallapoosa, GA 30176 – **791)** 3303 E Chicago St, Caldwell, ID 83605-6904 – **792)** PO Box 818, Benton, IL 62812-0818 – **793)** 401 Whitney Ave #160, Gretna, LA 70056-2573 – **794)** 350 Mass Ave #145, Arlington, MA 02474-6713 – **795)** 2100 Fairplain Ave, Benton Harbor, MI 49022-6828 – **796)** 4801 E Independence Blvd #815, Charlotte, NC 28212-5490 – **797)** 3185 S Highland Dr #13, Las Vegas, NV 89109-1029 – **798)** 2900 Sutro St, Reno, NV 89512-1616 – **799)** 4365 Fulton Dr NW, Canton, OH 44718-2823 – **800)** 1555 Hamilton St Fl 6, Philadelphia, PA 19130-4085 – **801)** 214 W Pleasant Dr, Pierre, SD 57501-2472 – **802)** 1200 Trawood Dr, El Paso, TX 79935-3301 – **803)** 205 9th St, Farwell, TX 79325-ND – **804)** 3606 S 500 W, Salt Lake City, UT 84115-4208 – **805)** 244 Goodwin Crest Dr #300, Birmingham, AL 35209-3700 – **806)** 5670 Wilshire Blvd #200, Los Angeles, CA 90036-5611 – **807)** 2070 N Palafox St, Pensacola, FL 32501-2145 – **808)** 4015 N Monroe St, Tallahassee, FL 32303-2139 – **809)** 40 Monument Circle #600, Indianapolis, IN 46204-3011 – **810)** 4200 N Old Lawrence Rd, Wichita, KS 67219-3211 – **811)** 11 Bryant Ave SE, Wadena, MN 56482-1543 – **812)** 119 N 3rd St, Hannibal, MO 63401-0711 – **813)** 112 E 3rd Ave, Plentywood, MT 59254-2223 – **814)** 2929 Radio Station Road, Greenville, NC 27834-0864 – **815)** 372 S Dorset St, South Burlington, VT 05403-6363 – **816)** 235 Walton St, Syracuse, NY 13202-1533 – **817)** 1227 County Line Rd, Selinsgrove, PA 17870-8188 or PO Box 1070, Sunbury, PA 17801-0870 – **818)** 6304 White Horse Rd #B-5, Greenville, SC 29611-3203 – **819)** 621 O'Grady Dr, Chattanooga, TN 37419-1305 – **820)** 2650 Thousand Oaks Blvd #4100, Memphis, TN 38118-2451 – **821)** 6161 Savoy Dr #1200, Houston, TX 77036-3363 – **822)** 310 W Wall St #104, Midland, TX 79701-5123 – **823)** 1140 Rose Hill Dr, Charlottesville, VA 22903-5128 – **824)** 2651 S Fish Hatchery Rd, Fitchburg, WI 53711-5410 – **825)** 306 S Kanawha St, Beckley, WV 25801-5619 – **826)** 19245 Hwy 127, Athens, AL 35614-6805 – **827)** 2300 Portola Dr, Santa Cruz, CA 95062-4203 – **828)** 10 Executive Dr, Farmington, CT 06032-2841 – **829)** 2828 W Flagler St, Miami, FL 33135-1337 – **830)** 4300 W Cypress St, #1040, Tampa, FL 33607 4185 – **831)** 3490 Shallowford Rd NE #302, Atlanta, GA 30341-2934 – **832)** 500 W Boone Ave, Spokane, WA 99201-2404 – **833)** 934 W 138th St, Riverdale, IL 60827-1673 – **834)** 4000 Radio Drive #1, Louisville, KY 40218-1568 – **835)** 827 Fairview Dr SW, Lenoir, NC 28645-6023 – **836)** 0700 SW Bancroft St, Portland, OR 97239-4226 – **837)** 2652 Library Rd #3, Pittsburgh, PA 15234-3127 – **838)** 2440 Millwood Ave, Columbia, SC 29205-1128 – **839)** 4131 N Central

Expressway #1000, Dallas, TX 75204-2121 – **840)** 6 E Main St, Price, UT 84501-3032 – **841)** 700 Wellington Hills Rd, Little Rock, AR 72211-2026 – **842)** 2200 Smith Lane, Fortuna, CA 95540-2771 or PO Box 109, Eureka, CA 95502-0109 – **843)** 1907 Mile High Stadium West Cir, Denver, CO 80204-1908 – **844)** 3737 Lake Ave, Fort Wayne, IN 46805-5554 – **845)** 500 Victory Rd, Quincy, MA 02171-3139 – **846)** 3800 Hooper Ave, Baltimore, MD 21211-1313 – **847)** 201 Industrial Park Rd, Excelsior Springs, MO 64024-1736 – **848)** 5445 Johnson Rd, Bozeman, MT 59718-8333 – **849)** PO Box 90, Smithfield, NC 27577-0090 – **850)** 210 Montague Ave, Greenwood, SC 29649-1935 – **851)** 340 Martin Luther King Blvd, Bristol, TN 37620-2313 – **852)** 3218 Quincy St, Plainview, TX 79072-1906 – **853)** 1000 Dexter Ave N #100, Seattle, WA 98109-3582 – **854)** 1859 21st Ave, Rice Lake, WI 54868-9502 – **855)** 2001 N 3rd St #102, Phoenix, AZ 85004-1439 – **856)** 4043 Geer Rd, Hughson, CA 95326-9715 – **857)** 39650 Liberty Street, Fremont, CA 94538 – **858)** 1360 E Sherwood Dr, Grand Junction, CO 81501-7546 – **859)** 1465 Northside Dr NW #218, Atlanta, GA 30318-4220 – **860)** 714 Narrow Way, Saint Simons Island, GA 31522-9712 – **861)** 3301 University Dr S, Fargo, ND 58104-6289 – **862)** 1411 Locust St, Saint Louis, MO 63103-2332 – **863)** 8755 W Flamingo Rd, Las Vegas, NV 89147-8667 – **864)** 234 Airport Plaza Blvd #5, Farmingdale, NY 11735-3938 – **865)** 6200 Oak Tree Blvd 4th Flr, Independence, OH 44131-2510 – **866)** 16414 San Pedro Ave #575, San Antonio, TX 78232-2277 – **867)** 1047 Route 302, Wells River, VT 05081-9742 – **868)** 112 N Pearl St, Berlin, WI 54923-1570 – **869)** 2500 Battleship Pkwy, Mobile, AL 36602-8003 – **870)** 360 Main St, Clinton, AR 72031-6622 – **871)** 3800 W Alameda Ave, Burbank, CA 91505-4300 – **872)** 3463 Ramona Ave #15, Sacramento, CA 95826-3827 – **873)** 311 112th Ave NE, St Petersburg, FL 33716-3394 – **874)** 820 N LaSalle St, Chicago, IL 60610-3214 – **875)** 211 Jason St, Pittsfield, MA 01201-5998 – **876)** 120 West State St, Traverse City, MI 49684 – **877)** 1 Julian Price Place, Charlotte, NC 28208-5211 – **878)** 5010 Underwood Ave, Omaha, NE 68132-2297 – **879)** 462 Merrimack St, Methuen, MA 01844-5804 – **880)** 619 N Turner St, Hobbs, NM 88240-8232 – **881)** 8010 N Main St, Dayton, OH 45405-2249 – **882)** 63088 NE 18th St #200, Bend, OR 97701-7102 – **883)** 2311 Old Arch Rd, Norristown, PA 19401-2013 – **884)** 1270 Mineral Spring Ave, North Providence, RI 02904-4637 – **885)** 26321 Stateline Rd W, Ardmore, TN 38449-3083 – **886)** 6161 Savoy Dr #1200, Houston, TX 77036-3363 – **887)** 6545 Crown Forest Dr, Plano, TX 75024-7489 or PO Box 1629, Cleburne, TX 76033-1628 – **888)** 700 Monticello Ave #311, Norfolk, VA 23510-2523 – **889)** 1630 Oakland Rd #A109, San Jose, CA 95131-2450 – **890)** 2131 Crimmins Lane, Falls Church, VA 22043-1962 – **891)** 144 Gould St #155, Needham Heights, MA 02494-2338 – **892)** 1220 Olive St, 3rd Floor, Saint Louis, MO 63103-2324 – **893)** 4611 Terry Rd #C, Jackson, MS 39212-5646 – **894)** 410 New Bridge St #3B, Jacksonville, NC 28540-4759 – **895)** 1250 Riverfront Center, Saint Johnsville, NY 12010-4602 – **896)** 7700 S Lewis Ave, Tulsa, OK 74136-7701 – **897)** 1500 Valley River Dr #350, Eugene, OR 97401-2163 – **898)** 314 E Highland Mall Blvd #250, Austin, TX 78752-3725 – **899)** 2201 S 6th St, Las Vegas, NV 89104-2999 – **900)** 320 Barnett Blvd, Tallassee, AL 36078-1506 – **901)** 83 E Shaw Ave #150, Fresno, CA 93710-7622 – **902)** 136 S Oak Knoll Ave #300, Pasadena, CA 91101-2624 – **903)** 1130 Radio Road, Bartow, FL 33830-7600 – **904)** 5815 Westside Rd, Austell, GA 30106-3179 – **905)** 6341 W Port Ave, Shreveport, LA 71129-2415 – **906)** 27675 Halsted Rd, Farmington Hills, MI 48331-3511 – **907)** 1600 Utica Ave S #400, Minneapolis, MN 55416-1480 – **908)** 2234 Hodges Chapel Rd, Benson, NC 27504 – **909)** 3500 E Rosser Ave, Bismarck, ND 58501-3398 – **910)** 731 Lexington Ave, New York, NY 10022-1331 – **911)** 5110 SE Stark St, Portland, OR 97215-1751 – **912)** 2440 Millwood Ave, Columbia, SC 29205-1128 – **913)** 1302 N Shepherd Dr, Houston, TX 77008-3752 – **914)** 12100 W Howard Ave, Milwaukee, WI 53228-1851 – **915)** 2926 Huntsville Hwy #D, Fayetteville, TN 37334-6687 – **916)** 305 N 2nd St, Rogers, AR 72756 – **917)** 1321 N Gene Autry Trail, Palm Springs, CA 92262-5473 – **918)** 5244 Madison Ave, Sacramento, CA 95841-3004 – **919)** 641 Bayou Blvd, Pensacola, FL 32503-6329 – **920)** 8551 NW 30th Ter, Miami, 33122-1908 – **921)** 1355 E Altamonte Dr, Altamonte Springs, FL 32701-5011 – **922)** 5601 Cassia St, Boise, ID 83705-1836 – **923)** 120 Eaton St, Peoria, IL 61603-4217 – **924)** 2504 Ardmore St SE, Grand Rapids, MI 49506-4901 – **925)** 310 South Lafrenz Dr, Liberty, MO 64068-7944 – **926)** 7255 S Tenaya Way #100, Las Vegas, NV 89113-1900 – **927)** 3258 Merchant Rd, Warsaw, NY 14569-9320 – **928)** 5100 S Tennis Lane, Sioux Falls, SD 57108-2212 – **929)** 1302 N Shepherd Dr, Houston, TX 77008-3752 – **930)** 4638 Decker Dr, Baytown, TX 77520-1418 – **931)** 3245 Basie Rd, Richmond, VA 23228-3404 – **932)** PO Box 1299, Lebanon, VA 24266-1299 – **933)** 1949 Mountain View Dr, Cody, WY 82414-4932 – **934)** 5455 Jug Factory Rd, Tuscaloosa, AL 35405-4213 – **935)** 1445 W Baseline Rd, Phoenix, AZ 85041-7010 – **936)** 3400 Olive Ave #550, Burbank, CA 91505-5544 – **937)** 1582 S Parker Rd #204, Denver, CO 80231-2716 – **938)** 777 River Rd, Middletown, CT 06457-3922 – **939)** 2727 Shipley Rd, Wilmington, DE 19810-3299 – **940)** 407 N Howard Ave #200, Tampa, FL 33606-1575

– **941)** 118 N Patterson St, Valdosta, GA 31601-5570 – **942)** 6626 Dubuque Trail, Norwalk, IA 50211-9645 or PO Box 838, Des Moines, IA 50304-0838 – **943)** 1801 E Main St, Marion, IL 62959-5115 – **944)** 131 N Santa Fe Ave, Salina, KS 67401-2615 – **945)** 22 W Main St, Mount Sterling, KY 40353-1314 – **946)** 5555 Hilton Ave #500, Baton Rouge, LA 70808-2564 – **947)** 500 Victory Rd #2, Quincy, MA 02171-3132 – **948)** 830 Oilfield Ave, Shelby, MT 59474-1641 – **949)** 2581 US Hwy 70 W, Goldsboro, NC 27530-9553 – **950)** 290 Hegenberger Rd, Oakland, CA 94621-1436 – **951)** 404 Main St, Klamath Falls, OR 97601-6021 – **952)** 5110 SE Stark St, Portland, OR 97215-1751 – **953)** 1 Forever Dr, Holidaysburg, PA 16648-3029 – **954)** 5732 N Tryon St, Charlotte, NC 28213-6802 – **955)** 103 Ram Cat Alley, Seneca, SC 29678-3243 – **956)** 11 Main St, Rapid City, SD 57701-2831 – **957)** 821 Pineville Rd, Chattanooga, TN 37405-2633 – **958)** 510 W Economy Rd, Morristown, TN 37814-3223 – **959)** 5426 N Mesa St, El Paso, TX 79912-5421 – **960)** 35 Eagle Rock Lane, Churchville, VA 24421 – **961)** 801 Old Wawawai Rd, Pullman, WA 99163-9002 – **962)** 3650 131st Ave #550, Bellevue, WA 98006-1334 – **963)** 944 Harlem St, Altoona, WI 54720-1127 – **964)** 2800 E College Ave, Appleton, WI 54915-3255 – **965)** 494 Blue Prince Rd, Bluefield, WV 24701-9577 – **966)** 9831 Beach Blvd #7, Jacksonville, FL 32207-7229 – **967)** PO Box 593642, Orlando, FL 32859-3642 – **968)** 1100 Spring St #610, Atlanta, GA 30309-2828 – **969)** 25 NW Point Blvd #400, Elk Grove Village, IL 60007-1030 – **970)** 635 W 7th St #400, Cincinnati, OH 45203-1549 – **971)** 1115 Tamarack Rd #500, Owensboro, KY 42301-6988 – **972)** 8121 Georgia Ave #806, Silver Spring, MD 20910-4945 – **973)** 208 Middle Rd, Skowhegan, ME 04976-5023 – **974)** 310 S La Frenz Rd, Liberty, MO 66105-2003 – **975)** 1338 Bragg Blvd, Fayetteville, NC 28301-4202 – **976)** PO Box 52, Greenville, SC 29602-0052 – **977)** 8 Robbins St #201, Toms River, NJ 08753-7668 – **978)** 1086 Teaneck Rd #4F, Teaneck, NJ 07666-4858 – **979)** 100 Saratoga Village Blvd #21, Malta, NY 12020-3703 – **980)** 3100 N Triphammer Rd #100, Lansing, NY 14882-8906 – **981)** 840 Philadelphia St #100, Indiana, PA 15701-3922 – **982)** 619 Alexander Rd, Princeton, NJ 08540-6000 – **983)** 15 Century Blvd #101, Nashville, TN 37214-3692 – **984)** 13725 Montfort Dr, Dallas, TX 75240-4455 – **985)** 9601 McAllister Fwy #1200, San Antonio, TX 78216-4695 – **986)** 55 N 300 W, Salt Lake City, UT 84180-1109 – **987)** 1675 Grandview Rd, Martinsville, VA 24112-2319 – **988)** 812 E Beale St, Kingman, AZ 86401-5925 – **989)** 9255 Towne Centre Dr #535, San Diego, CA 92121-3038 – **990)** 2905 King St, San Jose, CA 95122-1518 – **991)** 6360 SW 41st Place, Davie, FL 33314-3412 – **992)** PO Box 1848, Mattoon, IL 61938-1848 – **993)** 255 Cedardale Dr SE, Owatonna, MN 55060-4425 – **994)** 4321 Stuart Andrew Blvd #E, Charlotte, NC 28217-1588 – **995)** 118 E Main St, Clinton, NC 28328-4029 – **996)** 4590 E 29th St, Tulsa, OK 74114-6208 – **997)** 109 Old Chapin Rd #Q, Lexington, SC 29072-2065 – **998)** 2219 Yew St Rd, Bellingham, WA 98229-8855 – **999)** 1015 Main St, Wheeling, WV 26003-2782 – **1000)** 230 Goodman Rd E #202, Southaven, TN 38671-5151 – **1001)** 1400 Eon Dr #144B, Bakersfield, CA 93309-9404 – **1002)** VOA - 330 Independence Ave SW, Washington, DC 20547-0003 – **1003)** 10143 Commerce St, Summerville, GA 30747-1356 – **1004)** 600 W Cavanaugh Rd, Lansing, MI 48910-5254 – **1005)** 1926 W Division St, St Cloud, MN 56301 – **1006)** 731 S Pear Orchard Rd #27, Ridgeland, MS 39157-4839 – **1007)** 317 First Ave E, Kalispell, MT 59901-9601 – **1008)** 122 Cinema Dr, Wilmington, NC 28403-1490 – **1009)** 5011 Capitol Ave, Omaha, NE 68132-2921 – **1010)** 2900 Sutro St, Reno, NV 89512-1616 – **1011)** 100 Chestnut St #1700, Rochester, NY 14604-2418 – **1012)** 470 Leadmine Rd, Gaffney, SC 29340-4037 – **1013)** 9400 Executive Dr #303, Knoxville, TN 37923-4639 – **1014)** 5353 W Alabama St #450, Houston, TX 77056-5922 – **1015)** 1903 S Lamesa Rd, Midland, TX 79701-1706 – **1016)** 10025 Lakewood Dr SW #B, Tacoma, WA 98499-3897 – **1017)** 2609 Jordan Lane NW, Huntsville, AL 35816-1030 – **1018)** 1780 W Holly St, Fayetteville, AR 72703-1307 – **1019)** 5183 N 35th St, Milwaukee, WI 53209-5399 – **1020)** 1601 N 7th St #310, Phoenix, AZ 85006-2481 – **1021)** 621 S Virgil Ave #400, Los Angeles, CA 90005-4043 – **1022)** 3260 Blume Dr #520 Plaza II, Richmond, CA 94806-5715 – **1023)** UMC Campus Box 207, Boulder, CO 80309-1001 – **1024)** 4300 W Cypress St #1040, Tampa, FL 33607 4185 – **1025)** 2970 Peachtree Rd NW #700, Atlanta, GA 30305-4919 – **1026)** 6500 W Main St #315, Belleville, IL 62223-3700 – **1027)** 2915 Maples Rd, Fort Wayne, IN 46816-3199 – **1028)** 71991 US Hwy 71 S, Jackson, MN 56143-ND – **1029)** 201 Industrial Park Rd, Kansas City, MO 64024-1736 – **1030)** 1190 Hollywood Blvd, Bay Saint Louis, MS 39520-1662 – **1031)** 1700 Buena Vista Dr, Monroe, NC 28112-6306 – **1032)** 2000 Randolph Rd SE #103, Albuquerque, NM 87106-2146 – **1033)** 395 Hudson St Fl 7, New York, NY 10014-7452 – **1034)** 13333 SW 68th Pkwy, Tigard, OR 97223-8304 – **1035)** 105 Ash Ave, South Pittsburg, TN 37380-1513 – **1036)** 14001 Dallas Pkwy #300, Dallas, TX 75240-7369 – **1037)** 2131 Crimmins Lane, Falls Church, VA 22043-1962 – **1038)** 5606 Medical Circle, Madison, WI 53719-1232 – **1039)** 132 Carubia Dr, Core, WV 26541-7137 – **1040)** 75-153 Merle Dr #D, Palm Desert, CA 92211-5197 – **1041)** 3256 Penryn Rd #100, Loomis, CA 95650-8052 – **1042)** 2824

# NATIONAL RADIO — United States of America

Palm Beach Blvd, Fort Myers, FL 33916-1503 — **1043)** 625 N Michigan Ave #390, Chicago, IL 60611-3163 — **1044)** 10 Cabot Rd #302, Medford, MA 02155-5173 — **1045)** 3250 Franklin St, Detroit, MI 48207-4219 — **1046)** 738 Blowing Rock Rd, Boone, NC 28607-4840 — **1047)** 875 W 5th St, Winston-Salem, NC 27101-2505 — **1048)** 5702 52nd Ave S, Fargo, ND 58104-5605 — **1049)** 1559 W 4th St, Williamsport, PA 17701-5650 — **1050)** 219 Savannah-Gardner Rd, New Castle, PA 16101-5546 — **1051)** 4337 Big Barn Dr, Little River, SC 29566-6802 — **1052)** 2514 Eugenia Ave, Nashville, TN 37211-2117 — **1053)** 6222 West Interstate 10, San Antonio, TX 78201-2097 — **1054)** 703 3rd Ave, Huntington, WV 25701-1421 — **1055)** 1359 Carmichael Way, Montgomery, AL 36106-3629 — **1056)** 2919 E Broadway Blvd #235, Tucson, AZ 85716-5301 — **1057)** 139 W Olive Ave, Fresno, CA 93728-3035 — **1058)** 4135 Northgate Blvd #1, Sacramento, CA 95834-1226 — **1059)** 9255 Towne Centre Dr #535, San Diego, CA 92121-3038 — **1060)** 350 NW 71st St, Miami, FL 33138-5530 — **1061)** PO Box 2964, Duluth, GA 30096-2964 — **1062)** 302 S Poplar St, Centralia, IL 62801-3900 — **1063)** 120 West State St, Traverse City, MI 49684 — **1064)** 2300 N Lelia St, Guymon, OK 73942-2840 — **1065)** 400 Market St Fl 10, Philadelphia, PA 19106-2530 — **1066)** 369 Tower Rd, Waynesburg, PA 15370-3663 or PO Box 990, Greensburg, PA 15601-0990 — **1067)** 1726 Dakota Ave S, Huron, SD 57350-4024 — **1068)** 6080 Mt Moriah Rd Ext, Memphis, TN 38115-2645 — **1069)** 1079 E Trinity Lane, Nashville, TN 37216-3043 — **1070)** 4501 N McColl Rd, McAllen, TX 78504-2431 — **1071)** 750 Ridgeview Dr #204, Saint George, UT 84770-2665 — **1072)** 1400 W Main St, Auburn, WA 98001-5230 — **1073)** 10399 State Hwy 238, Afton, WY 83110-ND — **1074)** 302 S 2nd St #204, Laramie, WY 82070-3650 — **1075)** 39138 Fremont Blvd 3rd Flr, Fremont, CA 94538-1305 — **1076)** 1308 E Hwy 56, Salem, IN 47167-9690 — **1077)** 104 Main St N, Stillwater, MN 55082-5076 — **1078)** 6223 Old Mendenhall Rd, High Point, NC 27263-3940 — **1079)** 108 Radio Station Rd, Whiteville, NC 28472-4906 — **1080)** 661 Little Britain Rd, Newburgh, NY 12553-6150 — **1081)** 4 Summit Park Dr #150, Independence, OH 44131-6921 — **1082)** 161 Hillwood Ave #B, Falls Church, VA 22046-2983 — **1083)** PO Box 680748, Fort Payne, AL 35968-1608 — **1084)** 2821 US Highway 231, Wetumpka, AL 36093-1222 — **1085)** 900 Patte Rd, Willcox, AZ 85643-3408 — **1086)** 200 South "A" St #400, Oxnard, CA 93030-5717 — **1087)** 140 N Main, Lakeport, CA 95453-4815 — **1088)** 4002 W Gandy Blvd, Tampa, FL 33611-3410 — **1089)** 1701 S 55th St, Kansas City, KS 66106-2241 — **1090)** 3 Converse St #101, Palmer, MA 01069-1538 — **1091)** PO Box 504, Ann Arbor, MI 48106-0504 — **1092)** 728 Western Ave, Fergus Falls, MN 56537-1095 — **1093)** 210 W Front St, Forsyth, MT 59327-ND — **1094)** 525 Evans St, Greenville, NC 27858-2311 — **1095)** 147 N Garden St, Marion, NC 28752-3709 — **1096)** 149 Main St #210, Nashua, NH 03060-2725 — **1097)** 55 Horsehill Rd, Cedar Knolls, NJ 07927-2003 — **1098)** 241 W 4th St, Emporium, PA 15834-1047 — **1099)** 7 Parkway Center #625, Pittsburgh, PA 15221-3019 — **1100)** 4230 Faber Place Dr #100, North Charleston, SC 29405-8512 — **1101)** 601 Washington St, Alexandria, LA 71301-8028 — **1102)** 4050 Eisenhauer Rd, San Antonio, TX 78218-3409 — **1103)** 2242 E 1000 S, Roosevelt, UT 84066-4554 — **1104)** 1 Radio Lane, Danville, VA 24541-5235 — **1105)** 1901 N Moore St #200, Arlington, VA 22209-1746 — **1106)** Murrow Comm Cntr - WSU, Pullman, WA 99163-ND — **1107)** 200 1st Ave W #104, Seattle, WA 98119-4291 — **1108)** 11800 W Grange Ave, Hales Corners, WI 53130-1099 — **1109)** 714 Nicholas St, Rupert, WV 25984 — **1110)** 120 Summit Pkwy #200, Birmingham, AL 35209-4719 — **1111)** 4501 Broadway, Miami, AZ 85539-3800 — **1112)** 1500 Cotner Ave, Los Angeles, CA 90025-3303 — **1113)** 3256 Penryn Rd #100, Loomis, CA 95650-8052 — **1114)** 1901 N Moore St #200, Arlington, VA 22209-1706 — **1115)** 225 Hollywood Blvd NW, Fort Walton Beach, FL 32548-4725 — **1116)** 2100 Coral Way #200, Coral Gables, FL 33145-2639 — **1117)** 4005 Golden Isle W, Baxley, GA 31513-7972 — **1118)** 1410 Hwy 411 NE, Cartersville, GA 30121-5115 — **1119)** 1541 E Grand Ave, Des Moines, IA 50316-3542 — **1120)** 400 W Sunnyside Rd, Idaho Falls, ID 83402-4613 — **1121)** 1156 N Orchard St, Boise, ID 83706-2234 — **1122)** 1978 Interbelt Business Center Dr, Saint Louis, MO 63114-5760 — **1123)** 6161 Fall Creek Rd, Indianapolis, IN 46220-5032 — **1124)** 2825 Government St, Baton Rouge, LA 70806-5412 — **1125)** 309 Waverly Oaks Rd #103, Waltham, MA 02452-8403 — **1126)** 425 Centerstone Ct #1, Zeeland, MI 49464-2249 — **1127)** 2330 W Grand St, Springfield, MO 65802-4900 — **1128)** 1119 Eastview Dr, Asheboro, NC 27203-4576 — **1129)** PO Box 7509, Trenton, NJ 08628-0509 — **1130)** 2502 Camino Entrada #C, Santa Fe, NM 87507-4911 — **1131)** 1046 James St, Syracuse, NY 13203-2704 — **1132)** 175 Ken Mar Industrial Pkwy, Broadview Heights, OH 44147-2950 — **1133)** 604 Chillicothe St #405, Portsmouth, OH 45662-4024 — **1134)** 471 Robison Rd W, Erie, PA 16509-5425 — **1135)** 315 S Atherton St, State College, PA 16801-4476 — **1136)** 6223 Old Mendenhall Rd, High Point, NC 27263-3940 — **1137)** 51 Commerce St, Sumter, SC 29150-5014 or PO Box 6344, Florence, SC 29501-6344 — **1138)** 346 S Main St, Winner, SD 57580-1832 — **1139)** 1108 Hendricks St, Chattanooga, TN 37406-3159 — **1140)** 108 W College St, Dickson, TN 37055-1936 — **1141)** 121 S Cotton Square,

Lufkin, TX 75904-2933 — **1142)** 1150 Pepsi Place #300, Charlottesville, VA 22901-2865 — **1143)** 3520 Kingsbury Cir, Roanoke, VA 24014-1356 — **1144)** 328 100th St, Amery, WI 54001-4024 — **1145)** 912 Lane 11½, Powell, WY 82435-9222 — **1146)** 273 Azalea Rd #403, Mobile, AL 36609-1970 — **1147)** 1838 Commerce Dr #A, Lakeside, AZ 85929-7007 — **1148)** 1321 N Gene Autry Trail, Palm Springs, CA 92262-5473 — **1149)** 700 E Mineral King Ave, Visalia, CA 93292-6923 — **1150)** 6106 Hoffner Ave, Orlando, FL 32822-4906 — **1151)** 2824 Palm Beach Blvd, Ft Myers, FL 33916-1503 — **1152)** 325 John Knox Rd #G, Tallahassee, FL 32303-4161 — **1153)** 1501 13th Ave, Columbus, GA 31901-1908 — **1154)** 1801 N Elm St, Commerce, GA 30529-2347 — **1155)** 630 Falls Ave, Twin Falls, ID 83301-3300 — **1156)** 1035 Lincoln Rd #205, Bettendorf, IA 52722-4149 — **1157)** 25802 County Road 26, Elkhart, IN 46517-9132 — **1158)** 1410 N Western Ave, Liberal, KS 67901-2212 — **1159)** 758 Colonel Ledyard Hwy, Ledyard, CT 06339 — **1160)** 35 Baltimore St, Cumberland, MD 21502-3024 — **1161)** 2095 S US Highway 131, Petoskey, MI 49770-9216 — **1162)** 26455 American Dr, Southfield, MI 48034-6114 — **1163)** 305 W Washington St, Brainerd, MN 56401-2923 — **1164)** 1530 Greenview Dr SW #200, Rochester, MN 55902-1080 — **1165)** 5732 N Tryon St, Charlotte, NC 28607-4835 — **1166)** 1270 Buffalo Rd, Smithfield, NC 27577-7443 — **1167)** 101 Back Rd, Dover, NH 03820-5012 — **1168)** 961 Matley Lane #120, Reno, NV 89502-2119 — **1169)** 50 James E Casey Dr, Buffalo, NY 14206-2367 — **1170)** 34 Chestnut St, Oneonta, NY 13820-2466 — **1171)** 5101 S Shields Blvd, Oklahoma City, OK 73129-3217 — **1172)** 888 Rogue River Highway, Grants Pass, OR 97527-5209 — **1173)** 440 Rebecca Lane, Lebanon, PA 17046-1734 — **1174)** 1816 Savannah Hwy, Hampton, SC 29924-6545 — **1175)** 6300 S Tallgrass Ave, Sioux Falls, SD 57108-8184 — **1176)** 640 W Hwy 25/70, Newport, TN 37821-8068 — **1177)** 7700 Carpenter Freeway Fl2, Dallas, TX 75247-4829 — **1178)** 3824 Wayside Rd, Stuart, VA 24171-2506 — **1179)** 1130 14th Ave, Longview, WA 98632-3017 — **1180)** 2810 Southern Dr, Gillette, WY 82718-9369 — **1181)** 601 Greensboro Ave #507, Tuscaloosa, AL 35401-1795 — **1182)** 2800 N 44th St #100, Phoenix, AZ 85008-1559 — **1183)** 880 Via Esteban #C, San Luis Obispo, CA 93420-2462 — **1184)** 600 Grant St #600, Denver, CO 80203-3540 — **1185)** 500 Grand Ave #210, Destin, FL 32541-1410 — **1186)** 7080 Industrial Way, Macon, GA 31206-7538 — **1187)** 117 SE 5th St, Evansville, IN 47708-1639 — **1188)** 929 Howard Ave, New Orleans, LA 70113-1148 — **1189)** 762 Water St, Fitchburg, MA 01420-6481 — **1190)** PO Box 308, Bath, ME 04530-0308 — **1191)** 2110 Cliff Rd, Saint Paul, MN 55122-2347 — **1192)** 216 Belmont Rd, Grand Forks, ND 58201-4620 — **1193)** 25539 NC Hwy 125, Scotland Neck, NC 27874-ND — **1194)** 204 E Broadway, Farmington, NM 87401-6418 — **1195)** 150 Spectrum Blvd, Las Vegas, NV 89101-4860 — **1196)** 500 Frank W. Burr Buld #19, Teaneck, NY 07666 — **1197)** 100 Chestnut St #1700, Rochester, NY 14604-2418 — **1198)** 1574 Coburg Rd PMB 237, Eugene, OR 97401-4802 — **1199)** 275 Radio Road, Hanover, PA 17331-1140 — **1200)** 219 Savannah-Gardner Rd, New Castle, PA 16101-5546 — **1201)** 106 Assembly Dr, Piedmont, SC 29673 — **1202)** 3004 E Highway 76, Mullins, SC 29574-7396 or PO Box 1020, Marion, SC 29571-1020 — **1203)** 886 Mt Olivet Rd, Columbia, TN 38401-8031 — **1204)** 301 W South Temple, Salt Lake City, UT 84101-1216 — **1205)** 110 W Spiller Ave, Wytheville, VA 24382-1953 — **1206)** 808 E Sprague Ave, Spokane, WA 99202-2126 — **1207)** 4010 Summitview Ave, Yakima, WA 98908-2966 — **1208)** 491 S Washburn St #400, Oshkosh, WI 54904-6733 — **1209)** 1101 Cameron Rd, Opp, AL 36467-2407 — **1210)** 2250 W Sunset Ave #3, Springdale, AR 72762-5187 — **1211)** 2664 Cramer Lane, Chico, CA 95928-8838 — **1212)** 765 Story Rd, San Jose, CA 95122 — **1213)** 2030 Iowa Ave #A, Riverside, CA 92507-7412 — **1214)** 920 W Basin Rd #400, New Castle, DE 19720-1013 — **1215)** 3071 Continental Dr, West Palm Beach, FL 33407-3274 — **1216)** 1176 Satellite Blvd NW #200, Suwanee, GA 30024-2868 — **1217)** 245 Alfred St, Savannah, GA 31408-3205 — **1218)** 436 N Main St, Pocatello, ID 83204-3018 — **1219)** 331 Fulton St #1200, Peoria, IL 61602-1475 — **1220)** 30129 E US Hwy 54, Pratt, KS 67124-8304 — **1221)** 1039 Eggners Ferry Rd, Benton, KY 42025-8070 — **1222)** 219 Main St, Manchester, KY 40962-1259 — **1223)** 3250 S Reserve St #200, Missoula, MT 59801-8236 — **1224)** 526 Main Ave SE, Hickory, NC 28602-1103 — **1225)** 907 Lejeune Blvd, Jacksonville, NC 28540-5916 — **1226)** 5011 Capitol Ave, Omaha, NE 68132-2921 — **1227)** 69 Stanhope Ave, Keene, NH 03431-1577 — **1228)** 59 Court St #100, Binghamton, NY 13901-3293 — **1229)** 1611 S Main St, Dayton, OH 45409-2547 — **1230)** 2003 NW 56th St, Pendleton, OR 97801-4593 — **1231)** 1 Forever Dr, Holidaysburg, PA 16648-3029 — **1232)** 1246 Cranston St, Cranston, RI 02920-7318 — **1233)** 102 S 5th St, Crockett, TX 75835-2037 — **1234)** 2720 Highway 83, Weslaco, TX 78596-1225 — **1235)** 2525 Kell Blvd #200, Wichita Falls, TX 76308-1008 — **1236)** 2602 Whitehouse Rd #E, South Chesterfield, VA 23834-5398 — **1237)** N72 W12922 Good Hope Rd, Menomonee Falls, WI 53051-4441 — **1238)** 113 W Oak St, Sparta, WI 54656-1712 — **1239)** 204 Main St #201, Logan, WV 25601-3943 — **1240)** 3525 Soldier Springs Rd, Laramie, WY 82070-8903 — **1241)** 111 N Spring St, Searcy, AR 72143-7712 — **1242)** 44 Gough St #301, San Francisco, CA 94103-5424 — **1243)** 1250 Siskiyou

Blvd, Ashland, OR 97520-5010 – **1244)** 747 E Green St #101, Pasadena, CA 91101 – **1245)** 6805 Corporate Dr #130, Colorado Springs, CO 80919-1977 – **1246)** 2355 Pluckebaum Rd, Cocoa, FL 32926-5179 – **1247)** 1 Boot Key, Marathon, FL 33050 – **1248)** PO Box 151300, Tampa, FL 33684-1300 – **1249)** 100 WMTM Road, Moultrie, GA 31788-4104 – **1250)** 341 S Yorktown Pike, Mason City, IA 50401-4533 – **1251)** 3110 Upper Fords Creek Rd, Orofino, ID 83544-9629 – **1252)** 401 N Michigan Ave #2010, Chicago, IL 60611-4206 – **1253)** 401 W Main St #301, Lexington, KY 40507-1646 – **1254)** 631 Main St, Baton Rouge, LA 70801-1911 – **1255)** 1526 Corporate Dr, Shreveport, LA 71107-6338 – **1256)** 1423 Clarkview Rd, Baltimore, MD 21209-2134 – **1257)** 77 Monroe Center NW #1000, Grand Rapids, MI 49503-2912 – **1258)** 2115 Washington Ave S, Bemidji, MN 56601-8918 – **1259)** 731 S Pear Orchard Rd #27, Ridgeland, MS 39157-4839 – **1260)** 2147 Springs Rd, Mount Airy, NC 27030-ND – **1261)** 1811 W O St, McCook, NE 69001-4264 – **1262)** 110 Babbitt Rd, Franklin, NH 03235-2105 – **1263)** 1842 S Broad St, Trenton, NJ 08610-6002 – **1264)** 1960 Idaho St, Carson City, NV 89701-5324 – **1265)** 5426 William St, Lancaster, NY 14086-9320 – **1266)** 51 S Pearl St, Albany, NY 12207-1500 – **1267)** 6555 Carnegie Ave #100, Cleveland, OH 44103-4619 – **1268)** 7136 S. Yale #500, Tulsa, OK 74136 – **1269)** 7590 Highway 238, Jacksonville, OR 97530-9728 – **1270)** 305 Hwy 315, Pittston, PA 18460-3987 – **1271)** 118 E 3rd St E, Mobridge, SD 57601-2511 – **1272)** 510 W Economy Rd, Morristown, TN 37814-3223 – **1273)** 1300 WWCR Ave, Nashville, TN 37218-3800 – **1274)** 3601 S Congress Ave #F, Austin, TX 78704-7280 – **1275)** 207 University Blvd #200 , Harrisonburg, VA 22801-3752 – **1276)** 2201 6th Ave #1500, Seattle, WA 98121-1840 – **1277)** 343 High St, Morgantown, WV 26505-5515 – **1278)** PO Box 1747, Foley, AL 36536-1747 – **1279)** 16 Martin Luther King St, Selma, AL 36703-3109 – **1280)** 3256 Penryn Rd #100, Loomis, CA 95650-8052 – **1281)** 650 S E St #H, San Bernadino, CA 92408-1946 – **1282)** 900 Front St, San Francisco, CA 94111-1427 – **1283)** 820 11th Ave, Greeley, CO 80631-3246 – **1284)** 40 Cuprak Rd, Norwich, CT 06360-2008 – **1285)** 316 E Taylor Rd, DeLand, FL 32724-7817 – **1286)** 1310 S Florida Ave, Wauchula, FL 33873-9479 – **1287)** 2215 Perimeter Park Dr, Atlanta, GA 30341-1307 – **1288)** 1310 Walker St W, Douglas, GA 31533-7952 – **1289)** 415 Park Ave, Twin Falls, ID 83301-7752 – **1290)** 21 E St Joseph St, Indianapolis, IN 46204-1025 – **1291)** 95 Jackson St, Prestonsburg, KY 41653-1010 – **1292)** 613 N 5th St, West Monroe, LA 71291-1726 – **1293)** 122 Green St #2L, Worcester, MA 01604-4138 – **1294)** 779 Warren Ave, Portland, ME 04103-1176 – **1295)** 23300 Goddard Rd, Taylor, MI 48180-4131 – **1296)** 300 E Front St #450, Traverse City, MI 49684-5720 – **1297)** 20132 Highway 15, Glencoe, MN 55350-5643 – **1298)** 2702 E 32nd St, Joplin, MO 64804-4307 – **1299)** 3313 15th St #F, Great Falls, MT 59405-ND – **1300)** 1190 Patton Ave, Asheville, NC 28806-2706 – **1301)** 4801 E Independence Blvd #815, Charlotte, NC 28212-5497 – **1302)** 707 Leon St, Durham, NC 27704-4125 – **1303)** 1185 9th St NE, Thompson, ND 58278-9343 – **1304)** 8 Robbins St #201, Toms River, NJ 08753-7668 – **1305)** 1606 Central Ave SE #104, Albuquerque, NM 87106-4478 – **1306)** 419 Broadway, Paterson, NJ 07501-2104 – **1307)** 39 Kellogg Rd, New Hartford, NY 13413-2849 – **1308)** 906 SW Alder St, Newport, OR 97365-4712 – **1309)** 134 E Pitt St, Bedford, PA 15522-1311 – **1310)** 310 2nd Ave, Warren, PA 16365-2407 – **1311)** 51 Commerce St, Florence, SC 29501-6344 or PO Box 6344, Sumter, SC 29151-1269 – **1312)** 1 WDXI Drive, Jackson, TN 38305-4124 – **1313)** 3090 Olive St #400, Dallas, TX 75219-7640 – **1314)** 8023 Vantage Dr #840, San Antonio, TX 78230-4771 – **1315)** 3231 Old Lee Highway #506, Fairfax, VA 22030-1504 – **1316)** 5589 Greenwich Rd #200, Virginia Beach, VA 23462-6565 – **1317)** 150121 W County Road 12, Prosser, WA 99350-7265 – **1318)** 2651 S Fish Hatchery Rd, Madison, WI 53711-5400 – **1319)** 276 Seneca Trail, Ronceverte, WV 24970-1343 – **1320)** 2700 Corporate Dr #115, Birmingham, AL 35242-2735 – **1321)** 311 Lexington Ave, Fort Smith, AR 72901-3842 – **1322)** 5435 Madison Ave, Sacramento, CA 95841-3141 – **1323)** 1 Broadcast Ln, Waterbury, CT 06706 – **1324)** 1055 NE 125th St, North Miami, FL 33161-5804 – **1325)** 2360 St Johns Bluff Rd S #2, Jacksonville, FL 32246-2310 – **1326)** 1779 Independence Blvd, Sarasota, FL 34234-2106 – **1327)** 1000 Memorial Dr, Griffin, GA 30223-4446 – **1328)** 17525 Highway 1, Vivian, LA 71082-9526 – **1329)** 42 Union St, Attleboro, MA 02703 – **1330)** 600 W Cavanaugh Rd, Lansing, MI 48910-5254 – **1331)** 1009 W Ridge St #A, Marquette, MI 49855-3963 – **1332)** 507 SE 11th St, Grand Rapids, MN 55744-3950 – **1333)** 1750 S Brentwood Blvd #811, Saint Louis, MO 63144-1344 – **1334)** 2438 Highway 43 S, Picayune, MS 39466-7486 – **1335)** 875 W 5th St, Winston Salem, NC 27101-2505 – **1336)** 50 Tennessee St #B, Murphy, NC 28906-2958 – **1337)** 3600 County Road 19 S, Minot, ND 58701-ND – **1338)** 2002 Char Ave, Scottsbluff, NE 69361-2255 – **1339)** 8 Lawrence Rd , Derry, NH 03038-4191 – **1340)** 900 Parish St 3rd FLR, Pittsburgh, PA 15220-3407 – **1341)** 1801 Charleston Hwy #J, Cayce, SC 29033-2019 or PO Box 5106, Columbia, SC 29250-0626 – **1342)** 500 S Phillips Ave, Sioux Falls, SD 57104-6825 – **1343)** 162 Free Hill Rd, Gray, TN 37615-3144 – **1344)** 1030 Oakdale St, Manchester, TN 37355-5618

– **1345)** 1782 W Sam Houston Pkwy N, Houston, TX 77043-2723 – **1346)** 434 Bearcat Dr, Salt Lake City, UT 84115-2520 – **1347)** 306 W Broad St, Richmond, VA 23220-4219 – **1348)** 1308 Coolidge Rd, Aberdeen, WA 98520-6317 – **1349)** 645 25th Ave N, Wisconsin Rapids, WI 54495-3294 – **1350)** 1111 E Willow St, Scottsboro, AL 35768-2210 – **1351)** 4433 E Broadway Blvd #210, Tucson, AZ 85711-3536 – **1352)** 3301 Barham Blvd #201, Los Angeles, CA 90068-1477 – **1353)** 401 Pacheco Blvd, Los Banos, CA 93635-4227 – **1354)** 4100 Metzgar Rd, Fort Pierce, FL 34947-1712 – **1355)** 7179 Printers Alley, Milton, FL 32583-5347 – **1356)** PO Box 866, Pensacola, FL 32591-0866 – **1357)** 514 Jefferson St, Waterloo, IA 50701-5422 – **1358)** 4320 Dundee Rd, Northbrook, IL 60062-1703 – **1359)** 2207 E Morgan Ave #J, Evansville, IN 47711-4355 – **1360)** 2120 N Woodlawn St #352, Wichita, KS 67208-1881 – **1361)** 821 Adams Rd, Corbin, KY 40701-4708 – **1362)** PO Box 159, Carencro, LA 70520-0159 – **1363)** 552 Massachusetts Ave #201, Cambridge, MA 02139-4088 – **1364)** 13321 New Hampshire Ave #207, Silver Spring, MD 20904-3450 – **1365)** 6317 Taylor Dr, Flint, MI 48507-4683 – **1366)** 1496 Bellevue St #202, Green Bay, WI 54311-4205 – **1367)** 1399 E Reed Rd, Greenville, MS 38703-7234 – **1368)** 401 E Coal Ave, Gallup, NM 87301-6099 – **1369)** 419 Broadway, Paterson, NJ 07501-2104 – **1370)** 60 North Ave, Owego, NY 13827-1325 – **1371)** 9700 SE Eastview Dr, Happy Valley, OR 97086-6975 – **1372)** 1 Boston Store Place, Erie, PA 16501-2312 – **1373)** 1516 4th Ave #B, Conway, SC 29526-5032 – **1374)** 25 Garlington Rd, Greenville, SC 29615-4613 – **1375)** 1200 S Stockton Ave, Monahans, TX 79756-4060 – **1376)** 710 Grove St, Danville, VA 24541-1704 – **1377)** 2340 Martin Luther King Jr Ave, Knoxville, TN 37915-1625 – **1378)** 22479 Front St, Accomac, VA 23301-1641 or PO Box 460, Onley, VA 23418-0460 – **1379)** 5408 S Freya St, Spokane, WA 99223-7114 – **1380)** 2100 Washington Ave, Sheboygan, WI 53081-7042 – **1381)** 1530 Main St, Lander, WY 82520-2658 – **1382)** 1913 Barry St, Oxford, AL 36203-2319 or PO Box 1350, Gadsden, AL 35902-1350 – **1383)** 2222 Main St, North Little Rock, AR 72114-2302 – **1384)** 2030 Iowa Ave #A, Riverside, CA 92507-7412 – **1385)** 1410 Neotomas Ave #200, Santa Rosa, CA 95405-7533 – **1386)** 45 Pomfret St, Putnam, CT 06260-1827 – **1387)** 436 Mall Blvd, Brunswick, GA 31525-1819 – **1388)** 6174 GA Hwy 57, Macon, GA 31217-3405 or PO Box 2127, Warner Robins, GA 31099-2127 – **1389)** 1416 Locust St, Des Moines, IA 50309-3014 – **1390)** 805 Stewart Ave, Lewiston, ID 83501-4709 – **1391)** 1419 W Bannock St, Boise, ID 83702-5234 – **1392)** 671 E County Road 400 S, Kokomo, IN 46902-8101 – **1393)** 400 Poydras St #800, New Orleans, LA 70130-3245 – **1394)** 46 Haywood St #352, Asheville, NC 28801-2749 – **1395)** 277 Union Ave #205, Laconia, NH 03246-3114 – **1396)** 27 Wiliam St 11th Flr, New York, NY 10005-2718 – **1397)** 5411 Jefferson St NE #100, Albuquerque, NM 87109-3485 – **1398)** 7755 Freedom Ave NW, North Canton, OH 44720-6905 – **1399)** 5 Brooks Robinson Way, York, PA 17401-2401 – **1400)** 1408 E Gibson St, Jasper, TX 75951-6123 – **1401)** 12451 Network Blvd #140, San Antonio, TX 78249-3445 – **1402)** 1035 Avalon Dr, Forest, VA 24551-2970 – **1403)** 214 Walnut Dr SE, Wise, VA 24293-ND – **1404)** 645 Church St #400, Norfolk, VA 23510-1712 – **1405)** PO Box 19123, Birmingham, AL 35219-9123 or PO Box 622, Jasper, AL 35502-0622 – **1406)** 316 East Taylor Rd., Deland, FL 32724 or PO Pox 63, Mobile, AL 36601-0063 – **1407)** 2425 E Camelback Rd #570, Phoenix, AZ 85016-4250 – **1408)** 2121 Lancey Dr, Modesto, CA 95355-3000 – **1409)** 9660 Granite Ridge Dr, San Diego, CA 92123-2657 – **1410)** 2 S Parish Ave, Johnstown, CO 80534-7800 – **1411)** 869 Blue Hills Ave, Bloomfield, CT 06002-3710 – **1412)** 1505 Dundee Rd, Winter Haven, FL 33884-1013 – **1413)** 3890 Dunn Ave #804, Jacksonville, FL 32218-6429 – **1414)** 2828 W Flagler St, Miami, FL 33135-1337 – **1415)** 2000 Indian Hills Dr, Sioux City, IA 51104-1602 – **1416)** 4154 Jennings Dr, Kalamazoo, MI 49048-1087 – **1417)** 2115 Washington Ave S, Bemidji, MN 56601-8918 – **1418)** 88 Vilcom Center Dr #130, Chapel Hill, NC 27514-1660 – **1419)** 123 Egg Harbor Rd #302, Sewell, NJ 08080-9406 – **1420)** 1096 Mechem Dr #G3, Ruidoso, NM 88345-7057 – **1421)** 59 Court St #100, Binghamton, NY 13901-3293 – **1422)** 8044 Montgomery Rd #650, Cincinnati, OH 45236-2959 – **1423)** 229 Broad St, Conneaut, OH 44030-2616 – **1424)** 80404 Cooney Lane, Hermiston, OR 97838-6613 – **1425)** 3355 NE Cornell Rd, Hillsboro, OR 97124-5018 – **1426)** 560 7th St, New Kensington, PA 15068-6527 – **1427)** 212 S Centre St, Pottsville, PA 17901-3532 – **1428)** 100 Cross Hill Way, Easley, SC 29640-8854 – **1429)** 701 S Pierce St #101, Amarillo, TX 79101-2428 – **1430)** 4638 Decker Dr, Baytown, TX 77520-1418 – **1431)** 5801 Marvin D Love Freeway #409, Dallas, TX 75237-2319 – **1432)** 325 Poplar Knob Rd, Galax, VA 24333-4106 – **1433)** 1820 Heritage Center Way, Harrisonburg, VA 22801-8451 – **1434)** 1040 S Henderson St, Seattle, WA 98108-4720 – **1435)** 1420 Bellevue St, Green Bay, WI 54311-5649 – **1436)** 527 Gibbs St, Ravenswood, WV 26164-1011 – **1437)** 2717 Yellowstone Rd, Rock Springs, WY 82901-2813 – **1438)** 210 Radio Road, Corona, CA 92879-1722 – **1439)** PO Box 669, Marysville, CA 95901-0018 – **1440)** 2347 Bering Dr, San Jose, CA 95131-1125 – **1441)** 1515 E Silver Springs Blvd #134, Ocala, FL 34470-6830 – **1442)** 6565 North W St #270, Pensacola,

FL 32505-1797 – **1443)** 2420 Waycross Highway, Jesup, GA 31545-2332 – **1444)** 346 W 8th St, Dubuque, IA 52001-4649 – **1445)** 120 W 7th St #400, Bloomington, IN 47404-3869 – **1446)** 2601 Central Ave #C, Dodge City, KS 67801-6212 – **1447)** PO Box 487, Grayson, KY 41143-0487 – **1448)** 1726 Reisterstown Rd #117, Pikesville, MD 21208-2986 – **1449)** 49 Acme Rd, Brewer, ME 04412-1545 – **1450)** 1101 S Cass St, Traverse City, MI 49684-3235 – **1451)** 750 Dewey Blvd #1, Butte, MT 59701-3200 – **1452)** 910 E McNeill St, Lillington, NC 27546-7483 – **1453)** 9349 China Grove Church Rd, Pineville, NC 28134-8531 – **1454)** PO Box 127, Tabor City, NC 28463-0127 – **1455)** 216 Belmont Rd, Grand Forks, ND 58201-4620 – **1456)** 500 N Commercial St, Manchester, NH 03101-1151 – **1457)** 20 Tucker Dr, Poughkeepsie, NY 12603-1644 – **1458)** 280 State St, Rochester, NY 14614-1033 – **1459)** 125 S Superior St, Toledo, OH 43602-1790 – **1460)** 2513 6th Ave, Altoona, PA 16602-2129 – **1461)** 2615 Broad St, Chattanooga, TN 37408-3100 – **1462)** 4301 Westbank Dr #301, Austin, TX 78746-4400 – **1463)** 1285 W 2320 S, Salt Lake City, UT 84119-1448 – **1464)** 1129 Chatham Heights, Martinsville, VA 24112-2149 – **1465)** 26256 Highway 47, South Hill, VA 23970-ND – **1466)** 1201 E Division St, Neillsville, WI 54456-2123 – **1467)** RR1 Box 139, Dunmore, WV 24934-9712 – **1468)** 1201 Main St, Moundsville, WV 26003-2844 – **1469)** PO Box 630, Vernon, AL 35592-0630 – **1470)** PO Box 55450, North Little Rock, AR 72215-5450 – **1471)** 816 W 6th St, Parker, AZ 85344-4599 – **1472)** 1425 River Park Dr #520, Sacramento, CA 95815-4524 – **1473)** 175 Church St, Naugatuck, CT 06770-4180 – **1474)** 432 S Nova Rd, Ormond Beach, FL 32174-6121 – **1475)** 11300 4th St N #143, Saint Petersburg, FL 33716-2939 – **1476)** 1201 Peachtree Street, NE #800, Atlanta, GA 30361 – **1477)** 1 Parker Place #485, Janesville, WI 53545-4078 – **1478)** 2915 Maples Rd, Fort Wayne, IN 46816-3199 – **1479)** 4535 Metropolitan Ave, Kansas City, KS 66106-2599 – **1480)** 110 Dennis Dr, Lexington, KY 40503-2917 – **1481)** 8230 Summa Ave, Baton Rouge, LA 70809-3421 – **1482)** 808 Huron Ave, Port Huron, MI 48060-3705 – **1483)** 13225 Dogwood Dr, Baxter, MN 56425-8669 – **1484)** 12250 Weber Hill Rd #25, Saint Louis, MO 63127-1552 – **1485)** 70 Adams Hill Rd, Asheville, NC 28806-3841 – **1486)** 3720 Reynolda Rd, Winston-Salem, NC 27106-2232 – **1487)** 7035 E Washington St Ext, Bath, NY 14810 – **1488)** 27 Wiliam St 11th Flr, New York, NY 10005-2718 – **1489)** 1232 E 2nd St, Tulsa, OK 74120-2010 – **1490)** 1725 N Oregon St, Ontario, OR 97914-1541 – **1491)** 786 Diamond Hill Rd, Woonsocket, RI 02895-1499 – **1492)** 445 Carolina Springs Rd, North Augusta, SC 29841-8801 – **1493)** 518 St Joseph St, Rapid City, SD 57701-2717 – **1494)** 1811 Carters Creek Pike, Franklin, TN 37064-6823 – **1495)** 3704 Whittier Rd, Millington, TN 38108-2649 – **1496)** 4045 N Mesa St, El Paso, TX 79902-1526 – **1497)** 3308 Broadway St #401, San Antonio, TX 78209-6550 – **1498)** 1600 Pasadena Blvd, Pasadena, TX 77502-2404 – **1499)** 2809 Emerywood Pkwy #540, Henrico, VA 23294-3745 – **1500)** 67 Merchants Row, Rutland, VT 05701-5910 – **1501)** 2707 Colby Ave #1380, Everett, WA 98201-3568 – **1502)** 1456 E Green Bay St, Shawano, WI 54166-2258 – **1503)** 801 Noble St #30, Anniston, AL 36201-5698 – **1504)** 1780 W Holly St, Fayetteville, AR 72703-1307 – **1505)** 136 S Oak Knoll Ave #300, Pasadena, CA 91101-2624 – **1506)** 4043 Geer Rd, Hughson, CA 95326-9715 – **1507)** 4700 Walnut St, Boulder, CO 80301-2548 – **1508)** 7120 SW 24th Ave, Gainesville, FL 32607-3705 – **1509)** 233 N Michigan Ave #2800, Chicago, IL 60601-5519 – **1510)** 516 Main St, Hazard, KY 41701-1775 – **1511)** 17 Columbus Rd, Plymouth, MA 02360-4810 – **1512)** 1325 G Street #750, Washington, DC 20005-3104 – **1513)** 28 Houlton Rd, Presque Isle, ME 04769-5206 – **1514)** 1613 Lawrence Hwy Charlotte, MI 48813-8844 – **1515)** 640 Lincoln Ave SE, Saint Cloud, MN 56304-1024 – **1516)** 313 Old Route 66, Saint Robert, MO 65584-ND or PO Box D, Waynesville, MO 65583-0480 – **1517)** 10250 Lorraine Rd, Gulfport, MS 39503-6005 – **1518)** 315 A Street, Meridian, MS 39301-4512 – **1519)** 115 N Church St, Rocky Mount, NC 27804-5402 – **1520)** 1000 20th Ave SW, Minot, ND 58701-6447 – **1521)** 212 W Apache St, Farmington, NM 87401-6235 – **1522)** 1304 W Broadway Pl, Hobbs, NM 88240-5508 – **1523)** 2 Pendell Rd, Poughkeepsie, NY 12601-1500 – **1524)** 8456 Smokey Hollow Rd, Baldwinsville, NY 13027-8222 – **1525)** 39540 Bradbury Rd, Middleport, OH 45760-9703 – **1526)** 7461 South Ave, Youngstown, OH 44512-5789 – **1527)** 285 Liberty St NE #365, Salem, OR 97301-0034 – **1528)** 2294 Clements Ferry Rd, Charleston, SC 29492-7729 – **1529)** 104 Cherry St, Athens, TN 37303-ND – **1530)** 122 Radio Road, Jackson, TN 38301-3465 – **1531)** 810 W 200 N, Logan, UT 84321-3726 – **1532)** 2043 10th St NE, Roanoke, VA 24012-5309 – **1533)** 372 Dorset St, South Burlington, VT 05403-6212 – **1534)** 17 N. 3rd Street #103, Yakima, WA 98901 – **1535)** 557 Scott St, Wausau, WI 54403-4829 – **1536)** 366 S Section St, Fairhope, AL 36532-ND – **1537)** 800 County Road 4 E, Prattville, AL 36067-6610 – **1538)** 1605 Simpson Lane, Marysville, CA 95901-9747 – **1539)** 1950 S Sunwest Lane #302, San Bernadino, Ca 92408-3227 – **1540)** 10 Columbus Blvd #24, Hartford, CT 06106-1973 – **1541)** 1575 McKee Rd #206, Dover, DE 19904-1382 – **1542)** 1061 Collier Center Way #9, Naples, FL 34110-8403 – **1543)** 3765 N John Young Pkwy, Orlando, FL 32804-3213 –

**1544)** 3411 W Tharpe St, Tallahassee, FL 32303-1139 – **1545)** 940 Brownlee Rd, Jackson, GA 30233-2418 – **1546)** 1411 Locust St, Saint Louis, MO 63103-2332 – **1547)** 1632 S Maize Rd, Wichita, KS 67209-3912 – **1548)** 100 Eversole St #1 , Harlan, KY 40831-2346 – **1549)** 707 Leon St, Durham, NC 27704-4125 – **1550)** 1301 E 4th St, North Platte, NE 69101-4302 – **1551)** 1705 Lake St, Elmira, NY 14901-1299 – **1552)** 134 Mullin St, Watertown, NY 13601-3616 – **1553)** 717 E David Rd, Dayton, OH 45429-5218 – **1554)** 278 SW Arthur St, Portland, OR 97201-4745 – **1555)** 2147 Market St, Nesquehoning, PA 18240-1422 or PO Box D, Lansford, PA 18232-0801 – **1556)** Centre City Towers - 650 Smithfield St #620, Pittsburgh, PA 15222-3913 – **1557)** 219 Luckett St NW, Roanoke, VA 24017-6812 – **1558)** 201 State St, La Crosse, WI 54601-3246 – **1559)** 100 Kanawha Terrace, Saint Albans, WV 25177-2771 – **1560)** 1716 KROE Lane, Sheridan, WY 82801-9681 – **1561)** 3900 11th Ave, Tuscaloosa, AL 35401-7056 – **1562)** 208 Buena Vista Rd, Hot Springs, AR 71913-8208 – **1563)** 500 E Tyler Pkwy, Payson, AZ 85541-3276 – **1564)** 2171 Ralph Ave, Stockton, CA 95206-3699 – **1565)** 777 River Rd, Middletown, CT 06457-3922 – **1566)** 2710 W Atlantic Ave, Delray Beach, FL 33445-4431 – **1567)** 1800 Northgate Blvd #A10, Sarasota, FL 34234-2157 – **1568)** 1820 Wynnton Rd, Columbus, GA 31906-2930 – **1569)** 12544 N Main St, Trenton, GA 30752-2227 – **1570)** 3535 E Kimberly Rd, Davenport, IA 52807-2583 – **1571)** PO Box 84, Jerome, ID 83338-0084 – **1572)** 685 E 1675 N, Michigan City, IN 46360-9503 – **1573)** 22 Sconticut Neck Rd, Fairhaven, MA 02719-1930 – **1574)** 59346 Madison Ave, Mankato, MN 56001-8518 – **1575)** 73 Varney Rd #A, Wolfeboro, NH 03894-ND – **1576)** 187 Vienna Rd, Newark, NY 14513-9124 – **1577)** 715 Route 52, Beacon, NY 12508-1047 – **1578)** 4 Summit Park Dr #150, Independence, OH 44131-6921 – **1579)** 40 Rickert Rd, Doylestown, PA 18901-2326 – **1580)** 12 W Long Ave, Du Bois, PA 15801-2100 – **1581)** 101 Riverview Rd, Erwin, TN 37650-8722 – **1582)** 7351 Hunton St, Warrenton, VA 20187-2222 – **1583)** 1133 Kresky Ave, Centralia, WA 98531-3789 – **1584)** 45 Campbell Rd, Walla Walla, WA 99362-9597 – **1585)** 114 4th Ave, Huntington, WV 25701-1220 – **1586)** 22 Cogswell Ave, Pell City, AL 35125-2438 – **1587)** 1415 Fulton St, Fresno, CA 93721-1609 – **1588)** 747 E Green St #101, Pasadena, CA 91101 – **1589)** 342 Day St, San Francisco, CA 94131-2313 – **1590)** 4700 S Syracuse St #1050, Denver, CO 80237-2713 – **1591)** 100 NW 76th Dr #2, Gainesville, FL 32607-6659 – **1592)** 13085 SW 133rd Ct, Miami, FL 33186-5850 – **1593)** 404 W Lime St, Lakeland, FL 33815-4651 – **1594)** 3100 E 15th St, Panama City, FL 32405-7421 – **1595)** PO Box 2419, Covington, GA 30015-7419 – **1596)** 613 Silver Circle, Dalton, GA 30721-4551 – **1597)** 9245 N Meridian St #300, Indianapolis, IN 46260-1832 – **1598)** 116 N 4th St, Williamsburg, KY 40769-1115 – **1599)** 10 Cabot Rd #302, Medford, MA 02155-5173 – **1600)** 236 Admiral Dr, Annapolis, MD 21401-3123 – **1601)** 1150 Haynor Rd, Ionia, MI 48846-8532 – **1602)** 6500 W Main St #315, Belleville, IL 62223-3700 – **1603)** 3216 Griffith Rd, Monroe, NC 28110 – **1604)** 1103 N Green St, Morganton, NC 28655-9003 – **1605)** 990 N Center St Extension, Mount Olive, NC 28365-2704 – **1606)** 3205 W North Front St, Grand Island, NE 68803-4024 – **1607)** 1496 Bellevue St #202, Green Bay, WI 54311-4205 – **1608)** 320 N Jensen Rd, Vestel, NY 13850-2111 – **1609)** 2625 S Memorial Dr, Tulsa, OK 74129-2600 – **1610)** 4205 Cherry Ave NE, Keizer, OR 97303-4856 or PO Box 1430, Salem, OR 97308-1430 – **1611)** 1 Forever St, Holidaysburg, PA 16648-3029 – **1612)** 2278 Wortham Lane, Grovetown, GA 30813-5103 or PO Box 510, Appling, GA 30802-0510 – **1613)** 230 Goodman Rd E #202, Southaven, MS 38671-5151 – **1614)** 630 Mainstream Dr, Nashville, TN 37228-1204 – **1615)** 4638 Decker Dr, Baytown, TX 77520-1418 – **1616)** 3308 Broadway St #401, San Antonio, TX 78209-6550 – **1617)** 257 E 200 S #400, Salt Lake City, UT 84111-2073 – **1618)** 2298 Rose Ridge, Clintwood, VA 24228-7738 – **1619)** 403 Capital St, Lewiston, ID 83501-1815 – **1620)** 2029 Freeway Dr, Mount Vernon, WA 98273-5470 – **1621)** 1 Commerce St #300, Montgomery, AL 36104-3549 – **1622)** 8211 Geyer Springs Rd #P6, Little Rock, AR 72209-4909 – **1623)** 1100 N. 52nd St, Phoenix, AZ 85008 – **1624)** 1124 Foster Rd, Napa, CA 94558-6520 – **1625)** 1101 S Broadway #C, Santa Maria, CA 93454-6660 – **1626)** 32992 US Highway 34, Wray, CO 80758-9161 – **1627)** 419 Broadway, Paterson, NJ 07501-2104 – **1628)** 222 Hazard St, Orlando, FL 32804-3030 – **1629)** 613 Tallapoosa St W, Bremen, GA 30110-1838 – **1630)** 3833 US Highway 82, Brunswick, GA 31523-7735 – **1631)** 1192 E Draper Pkwy #462, Draper, UT 84020-9356 – **1632)** 513 Hampshire St, Quincy, IL 62301-2928 – **1633)** 3901 Brendenwood Rd, Rockford, IL 61107-2200 – **1634)** 825 S Kansas Ave #100, Topeka, KS 66612-1233 – **1635)** 1350 Main St #1206, Springfield, MA 01103-1667 – **1636)** 779 Warren Ave, Portland, ME 04103-1007 – **1637)** 24 Frank Lloyd Wright Dr, Ann Arbor, MI 48105-9755 – **1638)** 2244 Ravine Rd, Kalamazoo, MI 49004-3506 – **1639)** 1300 Godward St NE #1440, Minneapolis, MN 55413-3089 – **1640)** PO Box 1369, Pascagoula, MS 39568-1369 – **1641)** 512 Peanut Rd, Elizabethtown, NC 28337-8811 – **1642)** 200 Radio Drive, Lexington, NC 27292-8010 – **1643)** 101 S Main St, Gloversville, NY 12078-3820 – **1644)** 4 Summit Park Dr #150, Independence, OH

44131-6921 – **1645)** 3624 Avion Dr, Medford, OR 97504-4011 – **1646)** 1049 N Sekol Ave, Scranton, PA 18504-1098 – **1647)** 1210 Snyder Rd, Lansdale, PA 19446-4614 – **1648)** 101 N. Main St #1000, Greenville, SC 29601-4852 – **1649)** 540 Cumberland St W, Cowan, TN 37318-3115 – **1650)** 301 S Polk St #100, Amarillo, TX 79101-1404 – **1651)** 115 Radio Road, Livingston, TX 77351-7702 – **1652)** 6400 N Belt Line Rd #110, Irving, TX 75063-6065 or QSL's to CE Mortenson Broadcasting Co 3270 Blazer Pkwy #101, Lexington, KY 40509-1847 – **1653)** 950 Kenbridge Rd, Blackstone, VA 23824-3105 – **1654)** 1420 Bellevue St, Green Bay, WI 54311-5649 – **1655)** 900 Bluefield Ave, Bluefield, WV 24701-2760 – **1656)** 1251 Earl L Core Rd, Morgantown, WV 26505-5881 – **1657)** 1707 Warnke Rd NW, Cullman, AL 35055-2231 – **1658)** 1501 13th Ave, Columbus, GA 31901-1908 – **1659)** 6803 West Blvd, Inglewood, CA 90302-1895 – **1660)** 903 N Main St, Salinas, CA 93906-3912 – **1661)** 7150 Campus Dr #150, Colorado Springs, CO 80920-3157 – **1662)** 1355 N Maple Ave, Bartow, FL 33830-3024 or PO Box 452905, Miami, FL 33245-2905 – **1663)** 449 N 12th St, Defuniak Springs, FL 32433-0411 – **1664)** 2824 Palm Beach Blvd, Fort Myers, FL 33916-1503 – **1665)** 1611 Atlantic Blvd, Atlantic Beach, FL 32233-2516 or PO Box 51585, Jacksonville Beach, FL 32240-1585 – **1666)** 5815 Westside Rd, Austell, GA 30106-3179 – **1667)** 2141 Grand Ave, Des Moines, IA 50312-5303 – **1668)** 930 E Lincoln Ave, Goshen, IN 46528-3504 – **1669)** 1240 Radio Drive, Pikeville, KY 41501-4779 – **1670)** 631 Main St, Baton Rouge, LA 70801-1911 – **1671)** 130 Enterprise Dr, Marshfield, MA 02050-2110 – **1672)** 18720 16 Mile Road, Big Rapids, MI 49307-9303 – **1673)** 1433 Main Ave N, Thief River Falls, MN 56701-1141 – **1674)** 4424 Hampton Ave, Saint Louis, MO 63109-2232 – **1675)** 1338 Bragg Blvd, Fayetteville, NC 28301-4202 – **1676)** 1055 Skyway Dr, Marshall, NC 28753-3809 – **1677)** 11291 39th St SW, Dickinson, ND 58601-9206 – **1678)** 403 E 25th St, Kearney, NE 68847-5515 – **1679)** 123 Egg Harbor Rd #302, Sewell, NJ 08080-9406 – **1680)** 8755 W Flamingo Rd, Las Vegas, NV 89147-8667 – **1681)** 105 Kenwood Ave, Bethlehem, NY 12148-ND or PO Box 89, Rexford, NY 12148-0089 – **1682)** 6325 Sheridan Dr, Williamsville, NY 14221-4801 – **1683)** 605 S Front St #300, Columbus, OH 43215-5626 – **1684)** 600 Corporate Cir #100, Harrisburg, PA 17110-9787 – **1685)** PO Box 701, Tunkhannock, PA 18657-0701 – **1686)** 919 N Main St, Cleburne, TX 76033-3853 – **1687)** 10614 Rockley Rd, Houston, TX 77099-3514 – **1688)** 11240 Waples Mill Rd #405, Fairfax, VA 22030-6078 – **1689)** 7080 Lee Highway , Fairlawn, VA 24141-8416 – **1690)** 290 Hegenberger Rd, Oakland, CA 94621-1436 – **1691)** 4010 Summitview Ave, Yakima, WA 98908-2966 – **1692)** 1065 Radio Park Dr, Mt. Clare, WV 26408-9516 – **1693)** 1838 Commerce Dr #A, Lakeside, AZ 85929-7007 – **1694)** 3222 S Richey Ave, Tucson, AZ 85713-5453 – **1695)** 570 E Avenue Q9, Palmdale, CA 93550-2354 – **1696)** 8265 Sierra College Blvd #312, Roseville, CA 95661-9403 – **1697)** 869 Blue Hills Ave, Bloomfield, CT 06002-3789 – **1698)** 800 8th Ave SE, Largo, FL 33771-2162 – **1699)** 1650 S Dixie Hwy, Boca Raton, FL 33432-7462 – **1700)** 20 John Davenport Dr NW, Rome, GA 30165-2536 – **1701)** 331 Fulton St #1200, Peoria, IL 61602-1475 – **1702)** 2401 Paint Creek Rd, Stanton, KY 40380-9272 – **1703)** 900 N Lake Shore Dr, Lake Charles, LA 70601-2120 – **1704)** 500 W Cummings Park #2600, Woburn, MA 01801-6503 – **1705)** 351 Tilghman Rd, Salisbury, MD 21804-1920 – **1706)** PO Box 30, Bath, ME 04530-0308 – **1707)** 3338 E Bristol Rd, Burton, MI 48529-1408 – **1708)** 3003 27th Ave S #400, Minneapolis, MN 55406-1914 – **1709)** 240 Moss Hill Dr, New Albany, MS 38652-3400 – **1710)** 4321 Stuart Andrew Blvd #E, Charlotte, NC 28217-1588 – **1711)** 401 Saw Mill Hollow Rd, Burnsville, NC 28714-9789 – **1712)** 7151 Hanshaw Rd, Ithaca, NY 14850-9105 – **1713)** 1541 Alta Dr #400, Whitehall, PA 18052-5622 – **1714)** 2440 Millwood Ave, Columbia, SC 29205-1128 – **1715)** 1320 Brick Church Pike, Nashville, TN 37207-5038 – **1716)** 3911 S 1st St, Abilene, TX 79605-1639 – **1717)** 1101 Kilgore St, Henderson, TX 75652-5129 – **1718)** 166 N Main St, Broadway, VA 22815-9702 – **1719)** 100 Bluefield Ave #3, Bluefield, WV 24701-2884 – **1720)** 1635 S Gold St, Centralia, WA 98531-8997 – **1721)** 2241 W Main St, Moses Lake, WA 98837-2826 – **1722)** 2410 S Main St #A, West Bend, WI 53095-5270 – **1723)** 40 Park Rd #B, Pleasant Grove, AL 35127-1910 – **1724)** 9 North Church St #C, Fairhope, AL 36532-2427 – **1725)** 1 Radio Drive, Berryville, AR 72616-ND – **1726)** 824 E Washington St, Phoenix, AZ 85034-1088 – **1727)** 5640 S Broadway St, Eureka, CA 95503-6997 – **1728)** 514 W. 19th St, Merced, CA 95340 – **1729)** 13749 Beach Blvd, Westminster, CA 92683-3204 – **1730)** 5230 W Highway 98, Panama City, FL 32401-1058 – **1731)** 1111 Boulevard SE, Atlanta, GA 30312-3895 – **1732)** PO Box 786, Jerome, ID 83338-5483 – **1733)** 3775 W Dugger Ave W, Terre Haute, IN 47885-9794 – **1734)** 1632 S Maize Rd, Wichita, KS 67209-3912 – **1735)** 486 Lakeside Dr, Jenkins, KY 41537-8917 – **1736)** 1 Home St, Somerset, MA 02720-5229 – **1737)** 301 Fulton St W, Grand Rapids, MI 49404-6492 – **1738)** 28084 Van Born Rd, Westland, MI 48186-5159 – **1739)** 35006 US Highway 2 E, Fosston, MN 56542-9268 – **1740)** 1100 S Tryon St #210, Charlotte, NC 28203-4297 – **1741)** 804 Perryman St, Fair Bluff, NC 36401-1902 – **1742)** 292

Old Clarkesville Rd, Toccoa Falls, NC 30577-ND – **1743)** 5942 County Route 64, Hornell, NY 14843-9730 – **1744)** 27 Wiliam St 11th Flr, New York, NY 10005-2718 – **1745)** 185 Genesee St #1501, Utica, NY 13501-2109 – **1746)** 550 Market Ave S, Canton, OH 44702-2103 – **1747)** 635 W 7th St #201A, Cincinnati, OH 45203-1513 – **1748)** 111 Presidential Blvd #100, Bala Cynwyd, PA 19004-1009 – **1749)** 369 E GE Patterson Ave, Memphis, TN 38126-3301 – **1750)** 12900 Preston Rd #201, Dallas, TX 75230-1380 – **1751)** 6161 Savoy Dr #1140, Houston, TX 77036-3323 – **1752)** 1211 W Hein Rd, San Antonio, TX 78220-3301 – **1753)** 4415 39th Place, Brentwood, MD 20772-1106 – **1754)** 306 W Broad St, Richmond, VA 23220-4219 – **1755)** 504 23rd St NW, Roanoke, VA 24017-5414 – **1756)** 10 Clinton St #10, Springfield, VT 05156-3310 – **1757)** 601 Main St #400, Vancouver, WA 98660-3404 – **1758)** 730 Ray O Vac Lane, Madison, WI 53711-2472 – **1759)** 44 Gough St #301, San Francisco, CA 94103-5424 – **1760)** 90 Kay Ave, Milford, CT 06460-5495 – **1761)** 3400 Idaho Ave NW #200, Washington, DC 20016-3000 – **1762)** 8451 S Cherokee Blvd #B, Douglasville, GA 30134-8520 – **1763)** 4802 E 62nd St, Indianapolis, IN 46220-5296 – **1764)** 2 Radio Plaza St, Ferndale, MI 48220-2129 – **1765)** 3415 University Ave SE, Minneapolis, MN 55114-3327 – **1766)** 8145 E Evans Rd #8, Scottsdale, AZ 85260-3645 – **1767)** PO Box 6326, Santa Maria, CA 93456-6326 – **1768)** 8229 9th St #110, Rancho Cucamonga, CA 91730-4312 – **1769)** 2600 El Camino Real #224, Palo Alto, CA 94306-1721 – **1770)** 1032 S Union Blvd #100, Lakewood, CO 80228-3374 – **1771)** 1150 W King St, Cocoa, FL 32922-8618 – **1772)** 308 Victory Rd, Quincy, MA 02171-3129 – **1773)** 6721 W 121st St, Overland Park, KS 66209-2003 – **1774)** 1411 Locust St, Saint Louis, MO 63103-2332 – **1775)** 704 N King St #604, Wilmington, DE 19801-3535 – **1776)** 1213 San Pedro Dr NE, Albuquerque, NM 87110-6725 – **1777)** 277 Gravel Hill Rd, Palmyra, PA 17078-8535 – **1778)** 3660 Route 30 #D, Latrobe, PA 15650-4309 – **1779)** 15096 South Dakota Highway 15 , Milbank, SD 57252-5954 – **1780)** 55 Music Square W, Nashville, TN 37203-3207 – **1781)** 755 S 11th St #102, Beaumont, TX 77701-3723 – **1782)** 1601 E 57th Ave, Spokane, WA 99223-6623 – **1783)** 1224 E. Brady Street, Milwaukee, WI 53202 – **1784)** PO Box 2245, Watsonville, CA 95077-2245 – **1785)** 2284 S Victoria Ave #2-G, Ventura, CA 93003-6626 – **1786)** 1188 Lake View Dr, Altamonte Springs, FL 32714-2713 – **1787)** 412 W Oakland Park Blvd, Wilton Manors, FL 33311-1712 – **1788)** 8451 S Cherokee Blvd #B, Douglasville, GA 30134-8520 – **1789)** 2980 US Highway 51, Clinton, IL 61727-9479 – **1790)** PO Box 159, Carencro, LA 70520-0159 – **1791)** 369 Shelburne Rd, Greenfield, MA 01301-9653 – **1792)** 10 Radio Lane, Brunswick, ME 21788-1645 – **1793)** 122 4th Ave SW, Rochester, MN 55902-3339 – **1794)** 125 S Kingshighway St, Sikeston, MO 63801-2943 – **1795)** 431 Eaton Rd, Mocksville, NC 27028-8653 – **1796)** 824 US Hwy 158 W Bypass, Warrenton, NC 27589-9796 – **1797)** 500 Corporate Parkway #200, Buffalo, NY 14226-1265 – **1798)** 400 E Britton Rd, Oklahoma City, OK 73114-7507 – **1799)** 5110 SE Stark St, Portland, OR 97215-1751 – **1800)** 6161 Savoy Dr #1140, Houston, TX 77036-3323 – **1801)** 1211 W. Hein Rd, San Antonio, TX 78220 – **1802)** 2707 Colby Ave #1380, Snohomish, WA 98201-3568 – **1803)** 4317 E Broadway St, North Little Rock, AR 72117-4124 – **1804)** 1545 River Park Dr #500, Sacramento, CA 95815-4693 – **1805)** 6455 N. Union Dr. #200, Colorado Springs, CO 80918-5844 – **1806)** 5900 Pickettville Rd, Jacksonville, FL 32254-1172 – **1807)** PO Box 216, Dalton, GA 30722-0216 – **1808)** 123 Broadway, Taunton, MA 02780-2507 or PO Box 329, Middleborough Center, MA 02346-2329 – **1809)** 3338 E Bristol Rd, Burton, MI 48529-1408 – **1810)** 919 Lilac Dr N, Golden Valley, MN 55422-4615 – **1811)** 3025 Waughtown St #G, Winston-Salem, NC 27107-1634 – **1812)** 8044 Montgomery Rd #650, Cincinnati, OH 45236-2959 – **1813)** 5807 S Garnett St #K, Tulsa, OK 74146-6847 – **1814)** 5079 Pan American Dr, El Paso, TX 79927-2001 – **1815)** 200 S 10th #600, McAllen, TX 78501-4869 – **1816)** 1190 Daniels Chapel Rd, New Boston, TX 75570-ND – **1817)** 1445 W Baseline Rd, Phoenix, AZ 85041-7010 – **1818)** 3700 Wilshire Blvd #600, Los Angeles, CA 90010-3013 – **1819)** 869 Church St, Eatonton, GA 31024-6452 – **1820)** 514 Jefferson St, Waterloo, IA 50701-5422 – **1821)** 2730 University Blvd W #200, Wheaton, MD 20902-4658 – **1822)** 545 Fire Tower Rd, Yanceyville, NC 27379-ND – **1823)** PO Box 1540, Exeter, NH 03833-1540 – **1824)** 4243 Albany St, Albany, NY 12205-4609 – **1825)** 200 Monument Rd #6, Bala Cynwyd, PA 19004-1726 – **1826)** 904 N Main St, Punxsutawney, PA 15767-2641 – **1827)** 3931 Whitehorse Rd, Greenville, SC 29611-5599 – **1828)** 6161 Savoy Dr #1140, Houston, TX 77036-3323 – **1829)** 1246 W Laurel #200, San Antonio, TX 78201-6431 – **1830)** 400 Las Colinas Blvd E #1033, Irving, TX 75039-5599 – **1831)** 306 W Broad St, Richmond, VA 23220-4219 – **1832)** 114 Lakeside Ave, Seattle, WA 98122-6542 – **1833)** 1550 The Boardwalk #1, Huntsville, AL 35816-ND – **1834)** Univ of Arizona, Tucson, AZ 85721-0067 – **1835)** 15165 7th St #D, Victorville, CA 92392-3816 – **1836)** 139 W Olive Ave, Fresno, CA 93728-3035 – **1837)** 40931 Freemont Blvd, Freemont, CA 94538-4307 – **1838)** 8 Lawrence Rd , Derry, NH 03038-4191 – **1839)** 2405 E Moody

Blvd #402, Bunnell, FL 32110-5994 – **1840)** 330 SW 27th Ave #207, Miami, FL 33135-2957 – **1841)** 4107 W Spruce St #250, Tampa, FL 33607-2327 – **1842)** 411 Radio Station Road, North Augusta, SC 29841-9411 – **1843)** 2460 Atlanta Rd, Smyrna, GA 30080 – **1844)** 7120 US Highway 41, Vienna, GA 31092-4605 – **1845)** 6943 Titian Dr, Baton Rouge, LA 70806-2767 – **1846)** 143 Rumford Ave, Auburndale, MA 02466-1311 – **1847)** 901 S Kingshighway, Cape Girardeau, MO 63703-8003 – **1848)** 4104 Country Lane, Saint Joseph, MO 64506-4921 – **1849)** 430-C State Highway 165 S, Branson, MO 65616-3541 – **1850)** 1213 San Pedro Dr NE, Albuquerque, NM 87110-6725 – **1851)** 5166 Meadowood Mall Circle, Reno, NV 89502-6502 – **1852)** 2448 E 81st St #5500, Tulsa, OK 74137-4201 – **1853)** 944 Exeter Ave, Exeter, PA 18643-1215 – **1854)** 101 Lee St, Bristol, VA 24201-4355 – **1855)** 314 S Redwood Rd, Salt Lake City, UT 84104-3536 – **1856)** 2043 10th St NE, Roanoke, VA 24012-5309 – **1857)** 2202 Jolliff Rd, Chesapeake, VA 23321-1416 – **1858)** PO Box 3213, Ferndale, WA 98248-3213 – **1859)** 6605 SE Lake Rd, Portland, OR 97222-2161 – **1860)** 730 Ray O Vac Lane, Madison, WI 53711-2472 – **1861)** 510 Pegasus Court, Winchester, VA 22602-4596 – **1862)** 3561 Pegasus Dr #107, Bakersfield, CA 93308-0658 – **1863)** 1800 W Hibiscus Blvd #138, Melbourne, FL 32901-2624 – **1864)** 120 S 35th St #2, Council Bluffs, IA 51501-3203 – **1865)** 4200 W Main St, Kalamazoo, MI 49006-2766 – **1866)** 121 W Atkins St, Dobson, NC 27017-8709 – **1867)** 290 Hegenberger Rd, Oakland, CA 94621-1436 – **1868)** 8686 Michael Lane, Fairfield, OH 45014-3096 – **1869)** 1111 Westrac Dr #104, Fargo, ND 58103 – **1870)** 5353 W Alabama #415, Houston, TX 77056 – **1871)** 9434 Parkfield Dr, Austin, TX 78758-6227 – **1872)** PO Box 778, South Boston, VA 24592-0778 – **1873)** 9834 17th Ave SW, Seattle, WA 98106-2713 – **1874)** 2600 S Jackson St, Seattle, WA 98144-2499 – **1875)** 215 3rd Street S, Oneonta, AL 35121-2184 – **1876)** 6820 Pacific Ave #3A, Stockton, CA 95207-2604 – **1877)** 7351 Lincoln Ave, Riverside, CA 92504-4618 – **1878)** 548 E Alisal St, Salinas, CA 93905-2760 – **1879)** 127 Glenn Rd, Auburndale, FL 33823-2401 – **1880)** 9831 Beach Blvd #7, Jacksonville, FL 32246-4703 – **1881)** 2424 Old Rex Morrow Rd, Ellenwood, GA 30294-3901 – **1882)** 834 N Tower Rd, Freeport, IL 61032-8650 – **1883)** 462 Merrimack St, Methuen, MA 01844-5804 – **1884)** 1550 Hart Rd, Towson, MD 21286-1697 – **1885)** 2110 Cliff Rd, Eagan, MN 55122-2347 – **1886)** PO Box 49, Park Rapids, MN 56470-0049 – **1887)** 1111 S Glenstone Ave #3-102,, Springfield, MO 65804 – **1888)** PO Box 1071, Bay Springs, MS 39422-1071 – **1889)** 17890 US Hwy 64 W, Siler City, NC 27344-1631 – **1890)** 3105 Evans St #E, Greenville, NC 27834-8498 – **1891)** 3568 Lenox Rd, Geneva, NY 14456-2058 – **1892)** 28 E Market St, Danville, PA 17821-1940 – **1893)** 40 Rickert Rd, Doylestown, PA 18901-2326 – **1894)** 1860 Executive Park NW #E, Cleveland, TN 37312-2743 – **1895)** 275 Glenwood Dr, Rocky Mount, VA 24151-2136 – **1896)** 3616 State Highway 47, Rhinelander, WI 54501-8819 – **1897)** 1215 Church St, Oxford, AL 36203-1639 – **1898)** 8145 E. Evans Road, #8, Scottsdale, AZ 85260 – **1899)** 747 E Green St #101, Pasadena, CA 91101 – **1900)** 5050 E Edison Ave #218, Colorado Springs, CO 80915-3540 – **1901)** 3765 N John Young Parkway, Orlando, FL 32804-3213 – **1902)** PO Box 2312, Quincy, FL 32353-2312 – **1903)** 1510 NE 162nd St, North Miami Beach, FL 33162-4716 – **1904)** 2601 Nicholasville Rd, Lexington, KY 40503-3307 – **1905)** 4200 Parliament Place #300, Lanham, MD 20706-1881 – **1906)** 5115 Telephone Rd, Pascagoula, MS 39567-1130 – **1907)** 41 Pennsylvania Ave, Medford, NY 11763-3717 – **1908)** 3360 E Livingston Ave #2A, Columbus, OH 43227-1961 – **1909)** 36991 KGAL Drive, Lebanon, OR 97355-9666 – **1910)** 830 Old Buncombe Rd, Travelers Rest, SC 29690-9467 – **1911)** 4284 Memorial Dr Ste B, Decatur, GA 30032-1220 – **1912)** 236 Woodland Dr, Shelbyville, TN 37160-6759 – **1913)** 100 Stoddart St, Beaver Dam, WI 53916-1306 – **1914)** 509 N Main St, Tuscumbia, AL 35674-2048 – **1915)** 303 N Spring St, Fordyce, AR 71742-3317 – **1916)** 4209 N Frontage Rd, Fayetteville, AR 72703-5002 – **1917)** 750 Story Rd, San Jose, CA 95122-2604 – **1918)** 2284 Victoria Ave #2-G, Ventura, CA 93003-6626 – **1919)** 4100 Metzger Rd, Fort Pierce, FL 34947-1712 – **1920)** 3551 42nd Ave S #B106, Saint Petersburg, FL 33711-4369 – **1921)** 1104 W Broad Ave, Albany, GA 31707-4340 – **1922)** PO Box 746, Lafayette, GA 30728-0746 – **1923)** 2 Radio Loop, Swainsboro, GA 30401-5673 – **1924)** 2100 Lee St, Evanston, IL 60202-1539 – **1925)** 55 Public Square, Monmouth, IL 61462-1755 – **1926)** 1800 N Meridian St #603, Indianapolis, IN 46202-1433 – **1927)** 1200 Baker Ave, Great Bend, KS 67530-4523 – **1928)** 16221 National Pike, Hagerstown, MD 21740-2150 – **1929)** 182 N Angola Rd, Coldwater, MI 49036-9554 – **1930)** 1185 9th St NE, Thompson, ND 58278-9343 or PO Box 13638, Grand Forks, ND 58208-3638 – **1931)** 1416 Shelby Highway, Cherryville, NC 28021-8356 – **1932)** 911 W Main St, Clayton, NC 27520-1620 – **1933)** 85592 574th Ave, Wayne, NE 68787-7043 – **1934)** 149 Main St #210, Nashua, NH 03060-2725 – **1935)** 231 N Union St, Olean, NY 14760-2663 – **1936)** 1795 W Market St, Akron, OH 44313-7001 – **1937)** 170 3rd St, Netarts, OR 97141-9489 – **1938)** 12 Kent Rd, Aston, PA 19014-1498 – **1939)** 575 Grove St, Honesdale, PA 18431-1041 – **1940)** 19 Luther Ave, Warwick, RI 02886-4615 – **1941)** 222 Commerce St, Kingsport, TN 37660-4319 – **1942)** 215 S Market St, Carthage, TX 75633-2623 – **1943)** 6900 Commerce Ave, El Paso, TX 79915-1102 – **1944)** 1600 Pasadena Blvd, Pasadena, TX 77502-2404 – **1945)** 5501 Bagby Ave, Waco, TX 76711-2300 – **1946)** 227 E Belt Blvd, Richmond, VA 23224-1205 – **1947)** 2201 6th Ave #1500, Seattle, WA 98121-1840 – **1948)** 1414 16th St, Two Rivers, WI 54241-3031 or PO Box 100, Denmark, WI 54208-0100 – **1949)** 125 E 3rd St, New Richmond, WI 54017-1800 – **1950)** 2609 Jordan Lane NW, Huntsville, AL 35816-1030 – **1951)** 912 S Perry St, Montgomery, AL 36104-5002 – **1952)** 1110 E Olive Ave, Fresno, CA 93728-3535 – **1953)** 747 E Green St #101, Pasadena, CA 91101 – **1954)** 1479 Sanborn Rd, Yuba City, CA 95993-6042 – **1955)** 7800 E Orchard Rd #400, Greenwood Village, CO 80111-2599 – **1956)** 4190 Belfort Rd #450, Jacksonville, FL 32233-2516 – **1957)** 2475 Mercer Ave #104, West Palm Beach, FL 33401-7447 – **1958)** 5815 Westside Rd SW , Austell, GA 30106-3179 – **1959)** 1110 26th Ave SW, Cedar Rapids, IA 52404-3430 – **1960)** 11603 Highway 308, Larose, LA 70373 – **1961)** 60 Temple Pl #200, Boston, MA 02111-1324 – **1962)** 15 Hampton Ave, Northampton, MA 01060-3809 – **1963)** 4230 Packard Rd, Ann Arbor, MI 48108-1597 – **1964)** 6500 Brooklyn Blvd, Brooklyn Center, MN 55429-1754 – **1965)** 1001 Highlands Plaza Dr W #100, Saint Louis, MO 63110-1339 – **1966)** 1338 Bragg Blvd, Fayetteville, NC 28301-4202 – **1967)** 418 Duncan Rd, Flat Rock, NC 28731-4712 or PO Box 462, Hendersonville, NC 28793-0462 – **1968)** 1213 San Pedro Dr NE, Albuquerque, NM 87110-6725 – **1969)** 1705 Lake St, Elmira, NY 14901-1299 – **1970)** 333 7th Ave #1401, New York, NY 10001-5021 – **1971)** 3818 E Main St, Cushing, OK 74023 – **1972)** 7140 SW Macadam Ave, Portland, OR 97219-3013 – **1973)** 134 E Pitt St, Bedford, PA 15522-1311 – **1974)** 2 Milledge Rd, Augusta, GA 30904-3063 – **1975)** 259 S Willow Ave #A, Cookeville, TN 38501-3140 – **1976)** 3704 Whittier Rd, Memphis, TN 38108-2649 – **1977)** PO Box 300901, Arlington, TX 76007-0901 – **1978)** 9434 Parkfield Dr, Austin, TX 78758-6227 – **1979)** 2722 S Redwood Rd #1, Salt Lake City, UT 84119-8410 – **1980)** 645 Church St #400, Norfolk, VA 23510-1712 – **1981)** 4840 Lincoln Rd, Blaine, WA 98230-9602 or PO Box 75150 RPO White Rock, White Rock, BC V4B 5L3 – **1982)** N7502 Radio Road, Ripon, WI 54971-9231 – **1983)** 134 4th Ave, Huntington, WV 25701-1253 – **1984)** 1201 Main St, Wheeling, WV 26003-2844 – **1985)** 3256 Penryn Rd #100, Loomis, CA 95650-8052 – **1986)** 7251 Plantation Rd, Pensacola, FL 32504-6334 – **1987)** 3371 W Cleveland Rd Ext #300, South Bend, IN 46628-9780 – **1988)** 5011 Capitol Ave, Omaha, NE 68132-2921 – **1989)** 2700 Earl Rudder Freeway S #5000, College Station, TX 77845-5011 – **1990)** 2600 S Jackson St, Seattle, WA 98144-2499 – **1991)** 4051 Jimmie Dyess Pkwy, Augusta, GA 30909-9469 – **1992)** 4404 Napoleon Street SE, Iowa City, IA 52240-8143 – **1993)** 5787 S Hampton Rd #108, Dallas, TX 75232-6377 or QSL's to CE Mortenson Broadcasting Co 3270 Blazer Pkwy #101, Lexington, KY 40509-1847 – **1994)** PO Box 1531, Broomfield, CO 80038-1531 – **1995)** 3260 Blume Dr #520 Plaza II, Richmond, CA 94806-5715 – **1996)** 1909 East Pass Rd #D11, Gulfport, MS 39507-3778 – **1997)** 4045 NW 64th St #306, Oklahoma City, OK 73116-2616 – **1998)** 3030 SW Moody Ave #210, Portland, OR 97201-4868 – **1999)** 10348 South Redwood Rd, South Jordan, UT 84095 – **2000)** 1496 Bellevue St #202, Green Bay, WI 54311-4205 – **2001)** 333 S Kerr Blvd, Sallisaw, OK 74955-7212 – **2002)** 4525 Wilshire Blvd 3rd Flr, Los Angeles, CA 90010-3845 – **2003)** 3131 S Vaughn Way #601, Aurora, CO 80014-3516 – **2004)** 721 Shirley St, Cedar Falls, IA 50613-1513 – **2005)** 5426 N Mesa St, El Paso, TX 79912-5442 – **2006)** 2202 Mt Jolliff Rd, Chesapeake, VA 23321-1416 – **2007)** 1020 W Main St, Merced, CA 95340-4521 – **2008)** 1496 Bellevue St #202, Green Bay, FL 54311-4205 – **2009)** 7000 Squibb Rd, Mission, KS 66202-3233 – **2010)** 4200 W Main St, Kalamazoo, MI 49006-2749 – **2011)** 1520 South Blvd #300, Charlotte, NC 28203-3701 – **2012)** 2720 S 7th Ave SW, Fargo, ND 58103-8710 – **2013)** 27 Wiliam St 11th Flr, New York, NY 10005-2718 – **2014)** 5501 Bagby Ave, Waco, TX 76711-2300 – **2015)** 20720 Marilla St, Chatsworth, CA 91311-4407 – **2016)** 3360 Alta Mesa Dr, Redding, CA 96002-2831 – **2017)** 7080 Industrial Way, Macon, GA 31216-7538 – **2018)** 730 Ray O Vac Lane, Madison, WI 53711-2472 – **2019)** 139 W Olive Ave, Fresno, CA 93728-3035 – **2020)** 3765 N John Young Parkway, Orlando, FL 32804-3213 – **2021)** 1109 Hudson Lane, Monroe, LA 71201-6003 – **2022)** 3777 44th St SE, Grand Rapids, MI 49512-3945 – **2023)** 27 William St Fl 11, New York, NY 19125-4347 – **2024)** 705 5th Ave S #350, Seattle, WA 98104-4425 – **2025)** 3463 Ramona Ave #15, Sacramento, CA 95826-3827 – **2026)** 12136 Bayaud Ave #125, Lakewood, CO 80228-2115 – **2027)** 1100 Spring St #610, Atlanta, GA 30309-2828 – **2028)** 1000 E 87th St, Chicago, IL 60619-6397 – **2029)** 28095 Three Notch Rd #2B, Mechanicsville, MD 20659-3373 – **2030)** 2609 Jordan Lane NW, Huntsville, AL 35816-1030 – **2031)** 75 NW 167th St, North Miami Beach, FL 33169-6017 – **2032)** 4143 109th St, Urbandale, IA 50322-7925 – **2033)** 5 Provident Bank Park Dr, Pomona, NY 10970-3540 –

**2034)** 901 E Pike Blvd, Weslaco, TX 78596-4937 – **2035)** 11737 Nelon Dr, Corpus Christi, TX 78410-3028

## FM STATIONS IN MAJOR METROPOLITAN AREAS

**Scope:** The listing shows FM stations (87.9-107.9MHz) with a City of License (CL) in the respective Metropolitan Statistical Area (MSA), plus other stations (marked °) - incl. fringe stations - with a CL in adjacent MSA's that may also be audible in the defining city/cities of each metro area (e.g. Atlanta in the Atlanta Metro Area or Houston and/ or Galveston in the Houston-Galveston Metro Area etc) and beyond.

**Atlanta Metro Area** (Atlanta–Sandy Springs–Roswell, GA MSA)

| MHz | kW | Sta | City of License | Station |
|---|---|---|---|---|
| 88.1 | 0.019 | GA | Buford | W201CC (KAWZ) |
| # 88.1 | 100 | GA | Warm Springs | WJSP-FM |
| 88.1 | 0.009 | GA | Woodstock | W201DM (KAWZ) |
| # 88.5 | 100 | GA | Atlanta | WRAS |
| 88.7 | 0.115 | GA | Tallapoosa | WEYY |
| # 89.1 | 0.84 | GA | Gainesville | WBCX |
| 89.3 | 65 | GA | Atlanta | WRFG |
| 89.5 | 6 | GA | Winder | WYFW |
| 89.7 | 0.01 | GA | Atlanta | W209CD (WLOG) |
| 89.7 | 0.01 | GA | Tallapoosa | W209CG (WCLK) |
| # 90.1 | 100 | GA | Atlanta | WABE |
| 90.5 | 0.01 | GA | Snellville | W213BE (KAWZ) |
| # 90.7 | 0.43 | GA | Carrollton | WUWG |
| 90.7 | 18 | GA | Griffin | WMVV |
| # 91.1 | 100 | GA | Atlanta | WREK |
| 91.5 | 8.9 | GA | Cumming | WWEV-FM |
| 91.7 | 7.3 | GA | Cartersville | WCCV |
| 91.7 | 13 | GA | Peachtree City | WMVW |
| # 91.9 | 6 | GA | Atlanta | WCLK |
| 91.9 | 0.008 | GA | Gainesville | W220EH (KAWZ) |
| 92.1 | 1.65 | GA | Carrollton | WBTR-FM |
| 92.1 | 5.5 | GA | Jackson | WJGA-FM |
| 92.1 | 0.01 | GA | North Canton | W221AW (WCCV) |
| 92.3 | 0.099 | GA | Marietta | W222AF (WSRV-HD3) |
| 92.5 | 0.25 | GA | Lilburn | W223CQ (WLKQ-FM) (sp) |
| 92.5 | 0.12 | GA | Lithia Springs | W223BP (WUBL-HD2) |
| 92.5 | 12 | GA | Zebulon | WEKS |
| # 92.9 | 66 | GA | Atlanta | WZGC |
| 93.3 | 57 | GA | Greenville | WVFJ-FM |
| 93.5 | 0.23 | GA | Suwanee | W228CA (WSRV-HD2) |
| 93.7 | 0.25 | GA | Atlanta | W229AG (WCNN) |
| 93.7 | 0.25 | GA | Tallapoosa | W229CI (WKNG) |
| # 94.1 | 100 | GA | Smyrna | WSTR |
| 94.5 | 0.185 | GA | Atlanta | W233BF (WSTR-HD3) |
| 94.5 | 0.25 | GA | Gainesville | W233CO (WGGA) |
| 94.5 | 0.022 | GA | Suwanee | WAOO-LP |
| # 94.9 | 78 | GA | Atlanta | WUBL |
| # 95.5 | 40 | GA | Doraville | WSBB-FM |
| # 96.1 | 97 | GA | Atlanta | WWPW |
| 96.5 | 0.1 | GA | Norcross | WWXR-LP |
| # 96.7 | 2.1 | GA | Union City | WRDG |
| 96.9 | 0.055 | GA | Griffin | W245CN (WYFK) |
| # 97.1 | 100 | GA | Gainesville | WSRV |
| 97.3 | 0.25 | GA | Manchester | W247CJ (WFDR) |
| ‡ 97.5 | 0.09 | GA | Cumming | W248BV (WRDA) |
| # 97.5 | 8.5 | GA | Fayetteville | WUMJ |
| 97.7 | 0.075 | GA | Duluth | W249CK (WSRV-FM) |
| 97.9 | 0.25 | GA | Atlanta | W250BC (WWWQ-HD3) |
| 98.1 | 0.022 | GA | Duluth | WNRE-LP |
| 98.1 | 0.06 | GA | Snellville | WWSV-LP |
| # 98.5 | 100 | GA | Atlanta | WSB-FM |
| 98.9 | 0.25 | GA | Atlanta | W255CJ (WWWQ-HD2) |
| 98.9 | 1.85 | GA | Tallapoosa | WWGA |
| 99.1 | 0.03 | GA | Marietta | WIEH-LP (sp) |
| 99.1 | 0.02 | GA | Newnan | WQEE-LP |
| 99.1 | 0.1 | GA | Riverdale | WRGU-LP |
| ‡ 99.3 | 0.012 | GA | Atlanta | W257DF (WCLK) |
| 99.3 | 100 | GA | Cornelia° | WCON-FM |
| # 99.7 | 100 | GA | Atlanta | WWWQ |
| 100.1 | 0.0415 | GA | Marietta | WNIZ-LP |
| 100.1 | 0.005 | GA | Morrow | W261BG (WCCV) |
| 100.3 | 0.25 | GA | Cartersville | W262CD (WBHF) |
| 100.3 | 0.15 | GA | Gainesville | W262AL (WCON-FM) |
| #100.5 | 13.5 | GA | College Park | WNNX |
| 100.9 | 0.105 | GA | Woodstock | W265AV (WUBL-HD3) |
| #101.1 | 21.5 | GA | Ellijay° | WLJA-FM |
| 101.1 | 0.25 | GA | Winder | W266BW (WJZA) |
| #101.5 | 100 | GA | Marietta | WKHX-FM |
| 101.9 | 0.1 | GA | Atlanta | WATB-LP (ch) |
| 101.9 | 0.01 | GA | Carrollton | W270AS (WVFJ-FM) |
| 102.1 | 0.1 | GA | Fayetteville | WGAF-LP |
| 102.1 | 0.1 | GA | Kennesaw | WEZM-LP |

| MHz | kW | Sta | City of License | Station |
|---|---|---|---|---|
| 102.3 | 8.2 | GA | Buford | WLKQ-FM (sp) |
| 102.3 | 0.25 | GA | Griffin | W272DM (WKEU) |
| 102.5 | 0.25 | GA | Canton | W273CT (WYYZ) |
| #102.5 | 3 | GA | Mableton | WPZE |
| 102.7 | 0.029 | GA | Lawrenceville | WLWV-LP |
| 102.9 | 0.015 | GA | Canton | WPCG-LP |
| 102.9 | 0.115 | GA | Decatur | W275BK (WUMJ-HD2) |
| 103.1 | 0.25 | GA | Atlanta Junction | W276CL (WROM) |
| #103.3 | 100 | GA | Atlanta | WVEE |
| 103.7 | 0.099 | GA | Atlanta | W279CZ (WIFN) |
| 103.7 | 0.02 | GA | Atlanta | WRUX-LP |
| 103.9 | 0.25 | GA | Lawrenceville | W280EZ (WISK) (sp) |
| #104.1 | 100 | GA | Palmetto | WALR-FM |
| 104.5 | 0.1 | GA | Cartersville | WHLB-LP |
| 104.5 | 0.18 | GA | Douglasville | W283CT (WXJO) |
| 104.5 | 0.032 | GA | Newnan | WVJR-LP (sp) |
| #104.7 | 24 | GA | Athens° | WFSH-FM |
| #105.3 | 61 | GA | Bowdon | WBZY (sp) |
| #105.7 | 20 | GA | Canton | WRDA |
| 105.9 | 4.9 | GA | Milner | WFAL |
| 106.1 | 100 | GA | Arcade | WNGC |
| 106.3 | 0.19 | GA | Carrollton | W292EW (WLBB) |
| 106.3 | 0.25 | GA | Marietta | W292EV (WFOM) |
| #106.7 | 77 | GA | Gainesville | WYAY |
| 107.1 | 100 | GA | Aragon | WTSH-FM |
| 107.1 | 0.25 | GA | Jonesboro | W296BB (WSB-FM) |
| 107.1 | 0.25 | GA | Winder | W296CX (WJBB) |
| #107.5 | 33 | GA | Roswell | WAMJ |
| 107.9 | 0.1 | GA | Gainesville | WJPV-LP |
| 107.9 | 35 | GA | Hampton | WHTA |

**Baltimore Metro Area** (Baltimore–Columbia–Towson, MD MSA)

| MHz | kW | Sta | City of License | Station |
|---|---|---|---|---|
| # 88.1 | 15.5 | MD | Baltimore | WYPR |
| # 88.5 | 50 | DC | Washington° | WAMU |
| # 88.7 | 7 | PA | Middletown° | WXPH |
| 88.9 | 12.5 | MD | Baltimore | WEAA |
| 89.3 | 50 | DC | Washington° | WPFW |
| # 89.7 | 10 | MD | Towson | WTMD |
| # 90.1 | 36 | DC | Washington° | WCSP-FM |
| 90.5 | 17.5 | MD | Worton° | WKHS |
| # 90.9 | 75 | DC | Washington° | WETA |
| 91.1 | 1.1 | MD | Bel Air | WHFC |
| # 91.5 | 50 | MD | Baltimore | WBJC |
| # 91.9 | 23.5 | MD | Takoma Park° | WGTS |
| # 92.3 | 37 | MD | Baltimore | WERQ-FM |
| 92.5 | 22 | VA | Winchester° | WINC-FM |
| 92.7 | 0.006 | MD | Baltimore | WVTO-LP |
| 92.7 | 2.85 | MD | Prince Frederick° | WDCJ |
| # 93.1 | 16 | MD | Baltimore | WPOC |
| 93.5 | 0.004 | MD | Baltimore | WTTZ-LP |
| # 93.9 | 24.5 | DC | Washington° | WKYS |
| 94.3 | 0.004 | MD | Baltimore | W232CL (WRBS) |
| # 94.5 | 19 | PA | Lancaster° | WDAC |
| # 94.7 | 20.5 | MD | Bethesda° | WIAD |
| # 94.7 | 50 | DE | Dover° | WDSD |
| 95.1 | 50 | MD | Baltimore | WRBS-FM |
| # 95.5 | 50 | MD | Morningside° | WPGC-FM |
| # 95.9 | 3 | MD | Glen Burnie | WWIN-FM |
| # 96.1 | 13.5 | PA | Red Lion° | WSOX |
| # 96.3 | 16.5 | DC | Washington° | WHUR-FM |
| 96.7 | 0.08 | MD | Baltimore | W244DA (WZBA) |
| 96.7 | 12.5 | MD | Easton° | WCEI-FM |
| 96.9 | 50 | PA | Lancaster° | WLAN-FM |
| # 97.1 | 17.5 | DC | Washington° | WASH |
| 97.5 | 0.25 | MD | Baltimore | W248AO (WLIF-HD4) |
| # 97.9 | 13.5 | MD | Baltimore | WIYY |
| 98.3 | 0.005 | MD | Edgemere | W252BR (WCTR) |
| 98.5 | 10.5 | PA | York-Hanover° | WYCR |
| # 98.7 | 50 | DC | Washington° | WMZQ-FM |
| 99.1 | 45 | MD | Bowie° | WDCH-FM |
| 99.5 | 22 | DC | Washington° | WIHT |
| 99.9 | 0.22 | MD | Aberdeen | W260BV (WQLL) |
| 99.9 | 0.013 | MD | Annapolis | W260BM (WNAV) |
| 99.9 | 8.4 | MD | Frederick° | WFRE |
| 100.1 | 0.002 | MD | Baltimore | W261CD (WZBA) |
| #100.3 | 50 | DC | Washington° | WBIG-FM |
| 100.7 | 25 | MD | Westminster | WZBA |
| #101.1 | 22.5 | DC | Washington° | WWDC |
| #101.3 | 7.4 | PA | Lancaster° | WROZ |
| ‡101.5 | 0.25 | MD | Baltimore | W268DA (WWIN) |
| #101.9 | 13.5 | MD | Baltimore | WLIF |
| #102.3 | 2.9 | MD | Bethesda° | WMMJ |
| 102.3 | 0.205 | MD | Westminster | W272CX (WTTR) |
| #102.7 | 50 | MD | Baltimore | WQSR |
| 103.1 | 6 | MD | Grasonville | WRNR-FM |
| #103.3 | 6.4 | PA | York° | WARM-FM |

| MHz | kW | Sta | City of License | Station |
|---|---|---|---|---|
| #103.5 | 44 | DC | Washington° | WTOP-FM |
| 103.7 | 39 | MD | Havre de Grace | WXCY |
| #104.1 | 20 | MD | Waldorf° | WPRS-FM |
| #104.3 | 13 | MD | Baltimore | WZFT |
| 104.7 | 0.057 | MD | Annapolis | WYZT-LP |
| 104.7 | 8.3 | MD | Hagerstown° | WAYZ |
| 104.7 | 0.25 | MD | Havre de Grace | W284BE (WHGM) |
| 104.9 | 0.01 | MD | White Marsh | W285EJ (WLIF) |
| #105.1 | 33 | VA | Arlington° | WAVA-FM |
| 105.1 | 25 | PA | Ephrata° | WIOV-FM |
| #105.7 | 50 | MD | Catonsville | WJZ-FM |
| 105.7 | 25 | PA | York° | WQXA-FM |
| #105.9 | 28 | VA | Woodbridge° | WMAL-FM |
| 106.1 | 0.25 | MD | Baltimore | W291BA (WLIF-HD2) |
| #106.5 | 11 | MD | Baltimore | WWMX |
| #106.7 | 20 | VA | Manassas° | WJFK-FM |
| #106.9 | 16.5 | MD | Myersville° | WWEG |
| 107.3 | 19.5 | DC | Washington° | WRQX |
| 107.5 | 0.25 | MD | Bel Air | W298CG (WHGM) |
| 107.7 | 16 | PA | Gettysburg° | WGTY |
| #107.9 | 49 | MD | College Park° | WLZL (sp) |
| **Boston Metro Area** (Boston-Cambridge-Newton, MA-NH MSA) | | | | |
| 88.1 | 0.72 | MA | Cambridge | WMBR |
| 88.3 | 0.66 | MA | Boxford | WBMT |
| 88.3 | 0.1 | MA | Concord | WIQH |
| 88.3 | 0.175 | MA | Franklin | WGAO |
| 88.3 | 0.105 | MA | Rockland | WRPS |
| 88.5 | 2.7 | MA | Rockport | WWRN |
| # 88.9 | 4 | MA | Boston | WERS |
| 89.1 | 0.008 | MA | Acton | WHAB |
| 89.3 | 0.014 | MA | Lynn | WCDV-LP |
| 89.3 | 7 | RI | Newport° | WNPN |
| # 89.7 | 100 | MA | Boston | WGBH |
| 90.3 | 1 | MA | Newton | WZBC |
| 90.5 | 7.7 | MA | Scituate | WSMA |
| # 90.9 | 8.6 | MA | Boston | WBUR-FM |
| 91.3 | 0.1 | MA | Framingham | WDJM-FM |
| 91.5 | 0.18 | MA | Bridgewater | WBIM-FM |
| 91.5 | 1.4 | MA | Lowell | WUML |
| 91.5 | 0.125 | MA | Medford | WMFO |
| 91.5 | 0.17 | MA | Milton | WMLN-FM |
| 91.5 | 0.007 | MA | Wellesley | WZLY |
| 91.7 | 1.1 | MA | Marshfield | WUMT |
| 91.7 | 0.5 | MA | Maynard | WAVM |
| 91.7 | 0.13 | MA | Salem | WMWM |
| 91.7 | 0.5 | MA | Stow | WUMG |
| # 91.9 | 0.16 | MA | Boston | WUMB-FM |
| 92.3 | 39 | RI | Providence° | WPRO-FM |
| # 92.5 | 25 | MA | Andover | WXRV |
| 92.5 | 1.2 | MA | Boston | WXRV-FM4 |
| 92.5 | 0.24 | MA | Boston | WXRV-FM5 |
| 92.5 | 0.099 | MA | Framingham | WXRV-FM1 |
| 92.5 | 0.099 | MA | Newton | WXRV-FM3 |
| # 92.9 | 18.5 | MA | Brookline | WBOS |
| # 93.3 | 31 | MA | Taunton° | WSNE-FM |
| # 93.7 | 34 | MA | Lawrence | WEEI-FM |
| 94.1 | 50 | RI | Providence° | WHJY |
| # 94.5 | 9.2 | MA | Boston | WJMN |
| 94.8 | 0.027 | MA | Dedham | W235CS (WAMG) |
| 94.9 | 0.021 | MA | Acton | WAEM-LP |
| 94.9 | 0.07 | MA | East Boston | $ WZMR-LP |
| 94.9 | 0.07 | MA | East Boston | $ WZMW-LP |
| 95.1 | 0.07 | MA | Lowell | W236CU (WLLH) |
| 95.3 | 1.45 | MA | Cambridge | WHRB |
| 95.5 | 18.5 | RI | Providence° | WLVO |
| # 95.7 | 14.5 | MA | Manchester° | WZID |
| 95.9 | 1.6 | MA | Marshfield | WATD-FM |
| 96.1 | 0.015 | NH | Portsmouth | WBUB-LP |
| # 96.1 | 16.5 | MA | Worcester° | WSRS |
| 96.3 | 0.005 | MA | Beacon Hill | W242AA (WCRB) |
| 96.5 | 0.19 | MA | Needham | W243DC (WXRV-FM) |
| 96.7 | 0.01 | MA | Plymouth | W244CF (WRYP) |
| # 96.9 | 22.5 | MA | Boston | WBQT |
| 97.3 | 50 | MA | New Bedford° | WJFD-FM |
| 97.5 | 50 | NH | Dover° | WOKQ |
| 97.7 | 2.05 | MA | Brockton | WKAF |
| 97.7 | 0.004 | MA | Sudbury | WYAJ |
| 98.1 | 0.006 | MA | Lawrence | WGUA-LP (Sp) |
| # 98.1 | 0.13 | MA | Medford | W251CR (WZBR) |
| # 98.1 | 44 | MA | New Bedford° | WCTK |
| # 98.5 | 9 | MA | Boston | WBZ-FM |
| 99.1 | 50 | MA | Plymouth | WPLM-FM |
| # 99.5 | 27 | MA | Lowell | WCRB |
| 99.9 | 50 | MA | Barnstable° | WQRC |
| 99.9 | 0.017 | MA | Holliston | WHHB |

| MHz | kW | Sta | City of License | Station |
|---|---|---|---|---|
| 99.9 | 0.01 | MA | Lawrence | W260AS (WMSJ) |
| 99.9 | 0.1 | MA | Winchester | WQEB-LP |
| 99.9 | 0.25 | RI | Woonsocket° | W260CD (WNRI) |
| 100.1 | 0.21 | MA | Quincy | W261DX (WJDA) |
| 100.1 | 2.85 | MA | Southbridge° | WWFX |
| 100.1 | 0.025 | MA | Waltham | WBRS |
| 100.3 | 0.04 | MA | Boston | W262CV (WROL) |
| #100.3 | 50 | NH | Portsmouth | WHEB |
| #100.7 | 21.5 | MA | Boston | WZLX |
| 101.1 | 11.5 | MA | Manchester° | WGIR-FM |
| 101.3 | 0.25 | MA | Cambridge | W267CE (WJIB) |
| 101.3 | 0.15 | MA | Milford° | W267CD (WMRC) |
| 101.5 | 0.038 | MA | Gloucester | W268AM (WERS) |
| 101.7 | 13.5 | MA | Lynn | WBWL |
| 102.1 | 0.25 | MA | Framingham | W271CU (WSRO) |
| 102.1 | 3 | NH | Hampton | WSAK |
| 102.1 | 0.01 | MA | Quincy | W271CG (WRYP) |
| #102.5 | 14 | MA | Waltham | WKLB-FM |
| 102.9 | 0.1 | MA | Auburndale | WLAS-LP |
| 102.9 | 0.014 | MA | Boston | WBCA-LP |
| 102.9 | 0.082 | MA | Concord | W275CM (WBNW) |
| 102.9 | 0.1 | MA | Dorchester | WBPG-LP |
| 102.9 | 0.008 | MA | Framingham | WBNU-LP (sp) |
| 102.9 | 0.019 | MA | Franklin | WFPR-LP |
| 102.9 | 0.097 | MA | Lawrence | W275BH (WNNW) |
| #103.3 | 8.7 | MA | Boston | WODS |
| 103.7 | 0.01 | MA | Boston | W279BQ (WWRN-FM) |
| 103.7 | 37 | RI | Westerly° | WVEI-FM |
| 103.9 | 0.25 | NH | Portsmouth | W280DG (WEVO) |
| #104.1 | 21 | MA | Boston | WBMX |
| 104.5 | 37 | MA | Fitchburg° | WXLO |
| 104.9 | 0.019 | MA | Boston | WRBB |
| 104.9 | 6 | MA | Gloucester | WBOQ |
| #105.1 | 50 | RI | Providence° | WWLI |
| 105.3 | 0.25 | MA | Methuen | W287CW (WUBG) |
| #105.7 | 23 | MA | Framingham | WROR-FM |
| 106.1 | 0.099 | MA | Boston | W291CZ (WRCA) |
| 106.1 | 50 | MA | Hyannis° | WCOD-FM |
| 106.1 | 0.1 | NH | Portsmouth | WSCA-LP |
| 106.3 | 6 | NH | Nashua° | WFNQ |
| #106.3 | 1.15 | RI | Woonsocket° | WWKX |
| #106.7 | 21.5 | MA | Boston | WMJX |
| #107.3 | 9.6 | MA | Westborough° | WAAF |
| #107.9 | 20.5 | MA | Medford | WXKS-FM |
| **Charlotte Metro Area** (Charlotte-Concord-Gastonia, NC-SC MSA) | | | | |
| 88.1 | 26.5 | NC | Hickory° | WJYJ |
| 88.1 | 0.17 | NC | Monroe | W201DI (WOTJ) |
| 88.3 | 50 | NC | Boiling Springs° | WLXK |
| 88.3 | 0.01 | NC | Harrisburg | W202BW (WOGR-FM) |
| # 88.5 | 60 | NC | Winston-Salem° | WFDD |
| 88.9 | 100 | SC | Rock Hill | WNSC |
| 89.3 | 50 | SC | Chesterfield | WRFE |
| 89.9 | 100 | NC | Davidson | WDAV |
| 90.3 | 7.5 | SC | Richburg | WRBK |
| # 90.7 | 100 | NC | Charlotte | WFAE |
| 91.1 | 100 | SC | Gaffney° | WYFG |
| 91.3 | 98 | SC | Columbia° | WLTR |
| 91.3 | 0.25 | NC | Harrisburg | W217AX (WEND) |
| 91.5 | 0.14 | SC | Ft. Mill | WRFJ |
| 91.7 | 7.5 | SC | Dallas | WSGE |
| 91.7 | 0.01 | SC | Lowrys | W219CH (WRBK) |
| 91.9 | 0.038 | NC | Statesville | W220DL (WHPE-FM) |
| # 91.9 | 30 | NC | Wingate | WRCM |
| 92.3 | 100 | NC | Asheboro° | WKRR |
| # 92.5 | 95 | SC | Greenville° | WESC-FM |
| # 92.7 | 10.5 | NC | Harrisburg | WQNC |
| 92.9 | 0.25 | NC | Statesville | W225BD (WAME) |
| 93.1 | 0.18 | NC | Monroe | W226CD (WIXE) |
| 93.1 | 0.035 | SC | Rock Hill | WRHJ-LP |
| 93.3 | 93 | NC | Forest City° | WTPT |
| 93.3 | 0.01 | NC | Salisbury | WOGR-FM |
| 93.5 | 8.7 | NC | Wadesboro° | WYFQ-FM |
| 93.7 | 0.095 | NC | Charlotte | W229CF (WYFQ) |
| # 93.7 | 100 | SC | Greenville° | WFBC-FM |
| 93.9 | 8.9 | NC | Winnsboro° | WSCZ |
| 94.1 | 100 | NC | Lexington° | WWLV |
| 94.3 | 0.019 | NC | Monroe | W232DI (WXRC) |
| 94.3 | 0.054 | SC | Rock Hill | W232AX (WRHM-FM) |
| # 94.5 | 100 | SC | Greenville° | WGTK-FM |
| 94.7 | 0.25 | NC | Charlotte | W234BY (WXRC) |
| 94.7 | 0.1 | NC | Mooresville | WLYT-LP |
| # 95.1 | 100 | NC | Charlotte | WNKS |
| 95.5 | 100 | NC | High Point° | WHPE-FM |
| 95.7 | 100 | NC | Hickory° | WXRC |
| 96.1 | 98 | NC | Shelby° | WHQC |

| MHz | kW | Sta | City of License | Station | | MHz | kW | Sta | City of License | Station |
|---|---|---|---|---|---|---|---|---|---|---|
| 96.5 | 0.25 | NC | Charlotte | W243BY (WOSF) | | 89.1 | 0.025 | IL | DeKalb | W206CE (KLOV) |
| # 96.9 | 100 | NC | Statesville | WKKT | | 89.1 | 1.1 | IN | Lowell | WLPR-FM |
| 97.3 | 0.25 | NC | Monroe | W247CV (WXNC) (sp) | | ‡ 89.1 | 0.12 | IL | Mount Prospect | W206BL (KGBV) |
| 97.3 | 100 | NC | No. Wilkesboro° | WKBC-FM | | 89.1 | 1.5 | IL | Naperville | WONC |
| 97.5 | 0.25 | NC | Charlotte | W248CO (WZGV) | | 89.1 | 0.55 | IL | Round Lake Beach | WOKL |
| # 97.5 | 100 | SC | Columbia° | WCOS-FM | | # 89.3 | 0.28 | IL | Chicago | WKKC |
| # 97.9 | 95 | NC | Concord | WPEG | | 89.3 | 7.2 | IL | Evanston | WNUR-FM |
| 98.3 | 0.25 | NC | Concord | W252DI (WTIX) | | 89.3 | 1.35 | IL | Morris | WUON |
| 98.3 | 0.25 | NC | Dallas | W252BU (WOSF) | | ‡ 89.3 | 0.013 | IL | University Park | W207BI (WWGN) |
| 98.5 | 0.24 | NC | Indian Trail | W253BA (WEND) | | # 89.5 | 4 | IN | Chesterton | WBEW |
| 98.5 | 0.088 | SC | Rock Hill | WYTX-LP | | # 89.5 | 50 | IL | DeKalb | WNIJ |
| 98.7 | 0.18 | NC | Belmont | W254AZ (WRFX) | | # 89.7 | 35 | IL | Kankakee° | WONU |
| # 98.7 | 100 | NC | Greensboro° | WSMW | | # 90.1 | 100 | IL | Chicago | WMBI-FM |
| # 98.9 | 100 | SC | Spartanburg° | WSPA-FM | | 90.5 | 3.1 | IN | Crown Point | WRTW |
| 99.1 | 0.25 | NC | Charlotte | W256BP (WNCW) | | 90.5 | 0.008 | IL | Park Ridge | WMTH |
| 99.1 | 0.067 | NC | Monroe | WDZD-LP | | 90.7 | 50 | MI | Berrien Springs° | WAUS |
| 99.1 | 0.08 | NC | Statesville | WASQ-LP | | # 90.7 | 0.006 | IL | Chicago | WRTE |
| # 99.3 | 7.7 | SC | Chester | WBT-FM | | 90.7 | 1.45 | IL | Morris | WBEQ |
| # 99.5 | 100 | NC | High Point° | WMAG | | # 90.9 | 5 | IL | Glen Ellyn | WDCB |
| # 99.7 | 84 | NC | Kannapolis | WRFX | | 91.1 | 0.099 | IL | Chicago | W216CL (WBEZ) |
| 100.1 | 0.25 | NC | Huntersville | W261BZ (WHQC) | | # 91.5 | 5.7 | IL | Chicago | WBEZ |
| 100.1 | 0.085 | SC | Rock Hill | W261CY (WRHI) | | 91.7 | 0.01 | IL | Elgin | W219CD (WWTG) |
| 100.3 | 0.25 | NC | Charlotte | W262BM (WHQC) | | 91.7 | 6.5 | IL | Woodstock | WZKL |
| 100.3 | 100 | NC | High Point° | WMKS | | 91.9 | 50 | IL | Joliet | WJCH |
| #100.5 | 100 | SC | Gray Court° | WSSL-FM | | # 92.3 | 50 | IN | Hammond | WPWX |
| 100.7 | 0.25 | NC | Statesville | W264CU (WSIC) | | 92.5 | 20 | IL | DeKalb | WCPT-FM |
| #100.9 | 6 | NC | Indian Trail | WPZS | | 92.5 | 0.065 | IL | Zion | W223CN (WPJX) (sp) |
| 101.1 | 0.22 | NC | Gastonia | W266DC (WGNC) | | 92.7 | 1.8 | IL | Arlington Heights | WCPY |
| 101.3 | 0.08 | NC | Charlotte | W267BZ (WNCW) | | 92.7 | 0.055 | IN | Gary | W224EA (WLTH) |
| 101.3 | 0.038 | NC | Salisbury | W267AG (WBFJ-FM) | | # 93.1 | 6.7 | IL | Chicago | WXRT |
| 101.3 | 100 | SC | Sumter° | WWDM | | 93.5 | 3.5 | IL | Lemont | WVIV-FM |
| 101.5 | 0.1 | NC | Belmont | WBAC-LP | | ‡ 93.5 | 0.051 | IN | Valparaiso | WITW-LP |
| #101.9 | 99 | NC | Gastonia | WBAV-FM | | # 93.9 | 4 | IL | Chicago | WLIT-FM |
| 102.5 | 2.55 | NC | Pageland | WGSP-FM (sp) | | 94.3 | 0.099 | IL | Cicero | WJKL-FM2 |
| 102.5 | 0.2 | NC | Charlotte | W273DA (WLNK) | | 94.3 | 0.012 | IN | Gary | W232CK (WFRN-FM) |
| 102.5 | 0.027 | NC | Statesville | WWRO-LP | | 94.3 | 3.5 | IL | Glendale Heights | WJKL |
| #102.9 | 30.5 | NC | Hickory° | WLKO | | # 94.7 | 4.4 | IL | Chicago | WLS-FM |
| 103.3 | 0.25 | NC | Charlotte | W277CB (WGIV) | | 94.9 | 3 | IL | DeKalb | WDKB |
| 103.3 | 0.25 | NC | Salisbury | W277DD (WSAT) | | 95.1 | 0.06 | IL | Chicago | W236CF (WLEY-FM-HD2) |
| #103.7 | 100 | NC | Charlotte | WSOC-FM | | # 95.1 | 50 | WI | Union Grove° | WIIL |
| 104.1 | 0.25 | SC | Ft. Mill | W281BE (WRHM) | | 95.1 | 0.031 | IN | Valparaiso | WVUR-FM |
| #104.1 | 99 | NC | Winston-Salem° | WTQR | | # 95.5 | 5.3 | IL | Chicago | WEBG |
| 104.3 | 0.25 | NC | Charlotte | W282BP (WHVN) | | # 95.9 | 2.85 | IL | Aurora | WERV-FM |
| #104.7 | 96 | NC | Charlotte | WKQC | | 95.9 | 0.01 | IN | Crown Point | W240BJ (WHLP) |
| #105.3 | 51 | SC | Gaffney° | WOSF | | 95.9 | 0.08 | IL | Evanston | W240DE (WKTA) |
| 105.7 | 0.25 | NC | Pineville | W289BO (WCRU) | | 95.9 | 3 | IN | Michigan City° | WEFM |
| 105.9 | 0.25 | NC | Mooresville | W290DK (WSIC) | | # 96.3 | 3.3 | IL | Chicago | WBBM-FM |
| #106.1 | 21 | NC | Waxhaw | WOLS (sp) | | 96.7 | 0.1 | IL | Elgin | W244EJ (WRMN) |
| #106.5 | 84 | NC | Salisbury | WEND | | # 96.7 | 3.1 | IL | Joliet | WSSR |
| #106.9 | 36 | NC | Black Mountain° | WMIT | | 96.7 | 0.099 | IL | Park Ridge | W244BQ (WLEY-FM ) (sp) |
| #107.1 | 2.4 | SC | Lancaster | WRHM | | 96.9 | 0.25 | IL | Morris | W245CE (WCSJ) |
| 107.1 | 0.035 | NC | Salisbury | WLJZ-LP | | # 96.9 | 50 | IL | Zion | WWDV |
| 107.3 | 4.5 | SC | Chesterfield | WVSZ | | # 97.1 | 8.3 | IL | Chicago | WDRV |
| 107.5 | 0.25 | NC | Charlotte | W298CF (WGSP) (sp) | | 97.5 | 0.25 | IL | Chicago | W248BB (WLIT-HD2) (sp) |
| #107.9 | 100 | NC | Charlotte | WLNK | | 97.5 | 0.01 | IN | Gary | WGHU-LP |
| **Chicago Metro Area** (Chicago-Naperville-Elgin, IL-IN-WI MSA) | | | | | | # 97.9 | 4 | IL | Chicago | WCKL-FM |
| 88.1 | 2 | IL | Carpentersville | WWTG | | ‡ 98.3 | 0.09 | IL | Chicago | W252AW (WMBI-FM) (sp) |
| 88.1 | 0.1 | IL | Chicago | WCRX | | 98.3 | 0.1 | IL | Chicago | WGHC-LP |
| 88.1 | 0.09 | IL | Crete | WBMF | | 98.3 | 0.1 | IL | Chicago | WQEG-LP (ch) |
| 88.1 | 0.18 | IL | La Grange | WLTL | | 98.3 | 3 | IL | Crest Hill | WCCQ |
| 88.1 | 0.15 | IL | Lincolnshire | WAES | | 98.3 | 0.096 | IL | Round Lake Hts | WRLR-LP |
| 88.1 | 0.14 | IL | Lockport | WLRA | | # 98.7 | 6 | IL | Chicago | WFMT |
| 88.1 | 0.3 | IL | Rosemont | WTZI | | 98.9 | 0.25 | IL | DeKalb | W255BN (WLBK) |
| 88.1 | 0.25 | IL | Wheaton | WAIW | | 99.1 | 0.1 | IL | Cicero | WZQC-LP |
| 88.1 | 0.1 | IL | Winnetka | WNTH | | 99.1 | 0.01 | IL | Joliet | W256CA (WJKL) |
| 88.3 | 0.4 | IN | Chesterton | WDSO | | 99.1 | 0.1 | IL | Park Forest | W256CL (WLIT-FM) |
| 88.3 | 0.15 | IL | Chicago | WXAV | | 99.3 | 1.15 | IL | Zion | WXFM-FM |
| 88.3 | 0.1 | IL | Chicago | WZRD | | # 99.5 | 5.7 | IL | Chicago | WUSN |
| 88.3 | 0.25 | IL | Downers Grove | WDGC-FM | | 99.9 | 50 | IL | Park Forest | WYHI |
| 88.3 | 0.1 | IL | Palatine | WHCM | | 99.9 | 0.01 | IL | Waukegan | W260BL (WLGS-LP) |
| 88.5 | 0.16 | IL | Chicago | WHPK | | #100.3 | 5.7 | IL | Chicago | WSHE-FM |
| 88.5 | 1.5 | IL | Flossmoor | WHFH | | 100.5 | 0.25 | IL | DeKalb | W263BM (WSQR) |
| 88.5 | 0.185 | IL | Glenview | WGBK | | 100.7 | 2.45 | IL | Coal City | WRXQ |
| 88.5 | 0.125 | IL | Hinsdale | WHSD | | 100.7 | 0.006 | IL | Englewood | W264BF (WILV) |
| 88.7 | 0.1 | IL | Chicago | WLUW | | #100.7 | 50 | WI | Racine° | WKKV-FM |
| 88.7 | 0.32 | IL | Elmhurst | WRSE | | #101.1 | 5.7 | IL | Chicago | WKQX |
| 88.7 | 2.1 | IN | Gary | WGVE-FM | | 101.5 | 0.032 | IL | Huntley | WHRU-LP |
| 88.7 | 0.1 | IL | Joliet | WCSF | | 101.5 | 0.1 | IL | Lake Villa | WLGS-LP |
| 88.7 | 0.6 | IL | Sugar Grove | WSRI | | 101.5 | 0.25 | IL | Seward Township | W268AY (WMBI) |
| 88.9 | 0.017 | IL | Chicago | WIIT | | #101.9 | 4.2 | IL | Skokie | WTMX |
| 88.9 | 0.74 | IL | Elgin | WEPS | | 102.3 | 0.099 | IL | Chicago | W272DQ (WCKG) |
| 88.9 | 0.295 | IL | Lake Forest | WMXM | | #102.3 | 1.05 | IL | Crete | WYCA |
| 88.9 | 0.1 | IL | Monee | WGEN-FM | | 102.3 | 0.027 | IN | Portage | W272BZ (WFRN-FM) |
| 88.9 | 0.1 | IL | River Grove | WRRG | | 102.3 | 3 | IL | Waukegan | WXLC |
| 88.9 | 0.5 | IL | Summit | WARG | | #102.7 | 3.8 | IL | Oak Park | WVAZ |

| MHz | kW | Sta | City of License | Station |
|---|---|---|---|---|
| 103.1 | 6 | IL | Highland Park | WPNA-FM (pol) |
| 103.1 | 6 | IL | Morris | WCSJ-FM |
| 103.1 | 0.25 | IL | Park Forest | W276BM (WRDZ) (pol) |
| 103.1 | 0.01 | IL | Tinley Park | W276BM (WRDZ) (pol) |
| 103.1 | 0.1 | IN | Valparaiso | WVLP-LP |
| #103.5 | 4.3 | IL | Chicago | WKSC-FM |
| 103.9 | 0.1 | IL | Channahon | WLMM-LP |
| 103.9 | 0.17 | IL | Chicago | W280EM (WTMX-HD2) |
| 103.9 | 1.35 | IN | Crown Point | WXRD |
| 103.9 | 2.55 | IL | Dundee | WFXF |
| #104.3 | 4.1 | IL | Chicago | WBMX |
| 104.7 | 0.099 | IL | Chicago | W284DA (WRDZ) |
| 104.7 | 0.25 | IN | Hammond | W284CY (WJOB) |
| 104.7 | 50 | IL | Morris | WCFL |
| #105.1 | 5.7 | IL | Evanston | WOJO (sp) |
| 105.3 | 0.027 | IL | DeKalb | W287AU (WILV) |
| 105.5 | 0.075 | IL | Aurora | W288EA (WBIG) |
| 105.5 | 0.017 | IL | Chicago | WLPN-LP |
| #105.5 | 1.6 | IL | Woodstock | WZSR |
| #105.9 | 4.1 | IL | Elmwood Park | WCFS-FM |
| 106.3 | 3.8 | IL | Genoa | WYRB |
| #106.3 | 4.1 | IL | Lansing | WSRB |
| 106.7 | 50 | IL | Des Plaines | WPPN (sp) |
| 106.7 | 0.25 | IN | Valparaiso | W294BA (WIMS) |
| 106.9 | 0.25 | IL | Lake Bluff | W295CG (WPPN) (sp) |
| 107.1 | 0.018 | IL | Chicago | WCPX-LP |
| 107.1 | 2.65 | IN | Lowell | WZVN |
| 107.1 | 3.1 | IL | Plano | WSPY-FM |
| 107.1 | 0.07 | IL | Vernon Hills | W296DA (WNVR) (pol) |
| #107.5 | 3.7 | IL | Chicago | WGCI-FM |
| 107.9 | 21 | IL | Aurora | WLEY-FM (sp) |
| 107.9 | 0.099 | IL | Chicago | WLEY-FM4 (sp) |
| 107.9 | 0.099 | IL | Chicago | WLEY-FM3 (sp) |
| 107.9 | 0.099 | IL | Cicero | WLEY-FM1 (sp) |
| 107.9 | 0.099 | IL | Cicero | WLEY-FM2 (sp) |
| ‡107.9 | 0.25 | IN | Valparaiso | W300DM (WAKE) |

**Dallas - Fort Worth Metro Area** (Dallas-Ft. Worth-Arlington, TX MSA)

| MHz | kW | Sta | City of License | Station |
|---|---|---|---|---|
| 88.1 | 100 | TX | McKinney | KNTU |
| 88.3 | 9.4 | TX | Keene | KJRN |
| # 88.5 | 61 | TX | Mesquite | KEOM |
| 88.5 | 3.5 | TX | Weatherford | KMQX |
| 88.7 | 10 | TX | Ft. Worth | KTCU-FM |
| 88.9 | 100 | TX | Commerce | KETR |
| 89.1 | 47 | TX | Springtown | KSGX |
| 89.1 | 1.2 | TX | Stephenville° | KQXS |
| # 89.3 | 55 | TX | Dallas | KNON |
| 89.3 | 0.34 | TX | Mineral Wells | KYQX |
| 89.7 | 65 | TX | Sanger | KAWA |
| 90.1 | 29.7 | TX | Dallas | KERA |
| 90.5 | 38 | TX | Greenville | KTXG |
| 90.5 | 0.25 | TX | Mineral Wells | K213CS (KCZO) (sp) |
| 90.5 | 4.7 | TX | Stephenville° | KTRL |
| 90.9 | 98 | TX | Dallas | KCBI |
| 91.3 | 0.35 | TX | Commerce | KYJC |
| 91.3 | 100 | TX | Decatur | KDKR |
| 91.5 | 0.25 | TX | Greenville | K218EB (WYFQ-FM) |
| # 91.7 | 19.29 | TX | Dallas | KKXT |
| 92.1 | 0.1 | TX | Dallas | KPVC-LP (sp) |
| 92.1 | 0.015 | TX | Denton | KXDE-LP (sp) |
| 92.1 | 1.65 | TX | Farmersville | KXEZ |
| 92.1 | 25 | TX | Glen Rose | KTFW-FM |
| # 92.5 | 99 | TX | Dallas | KZPS |
| ‡ 92.9 | 0.099 | TX | Dallas | K225CM (KBFB) |
| 92.9 | 0.067 | TX | Denton | KUZU-LP |
| 92.9 | 0.25 | TX | Ft. Worth | K225BR (KBFB) |
| 92.9 | 0.07 | TX | Garland | KYYE-LP (sp) |
| 93.3 | 50 | TX | Haltom City | KLIF-FM |
| 93.7 | 43 | TX | Krum | KNOR (sp) |
| # 94.1 | 98 | TX | Ft. Worth | KLNO (sp) |
| # 94.5 | 100 | TX | Gainesville° | KZMJ |
| 94.9 | 99 | TX | Arlington | KLTY |
| 95.3 | 17 | TX | Howe° | KHYI |
| 95.3 | 11 | TX | Meridian° | KOME-FM |
| 95.5 | 0.058 | TX | Arlington | KRQP-LP |
| 95.5 | 0.25 | TX | Dallas | K238CC (KVTT) (as) |
| 95.5 | 0.07 | TX | Dallas | KVWR-LP |
| 95.5 | 0.027 | TX | Seagoville | KSGV-LP |
| 95.7 | 0.25 | TX | Burleson | K239CC (KCLE) |
| 95.9 | 0.115 | TX | Garland | K240DS (KYFA-FM) (sp) |
| 95.9 | 100 | TX | Jacksboro° | KFWR |
| 96.3 | 99 | TX | Ft. Worth | KSCS |
| 96.7 | 90 | TX | Flower Mound | KTCK-FM |
| 96.7 | 0.01 | TX | Greenville | KCCG-LP |
| # 97.1 | 97 | TX | Ft. Worth | KEGL |

| MHz | kW | Sta | City of License | Station |
|---|---|---|---|---|
| 97.5 | 0.05 | TX | Dallas | K248BC (KDKR) |
| # 97.5 | 32 | TX | Tom Bean° | KLAK |
| 97.5 | 0.043 | TX | Weatherford | K248BY (KYGX) |
| # 97.9 | 99 | TX | Dallas | KBFB |
| 98.3 | 93 | TX | Bridgeport | KBOC (sp) |
| # 98.7 | 99 | TX | Dallas | KLUV |
| 99.1 | 0.25 | TX | Waxahachie | K256DE (KBEC) |
| # 99.1 | 100 | TX | Denton | KFZO (Sp) |
| # 99.5 | 100 | TX | Ft. Worth | KPLX |
| 99.9 | 0.1 | TX | Balch Springs | KYBS-LP |
| 99.9 | 0.064 | TX | Denton | KDVP-LP (sp) |
| 99.9 | 0.25 | TX | Irving | K260BP (KDKR) |
| 99.9 | 0.25 | TX | McKinney | K260CX (KFCD) (sp) |
| 99.9 | 90 | TX | Waco° | WACO-FM |
| #100.3 | 97 | TX | Dallas | KJKK |
| 100.7 | 98 | TX | Highland Village | KWRD-FM |
| #101.1 | 100 | TX | Dallas | WRR |
| 101.5 | 0.25 | TX | Garland | K268CL (KGPF) |
| 101.5 | 0.1 | TX | Greenville | KYLP-LP (sp) |
| 101.7 | 92 | TX | Azle | KYDA |
| 102.1 | 100 | TX | Ft. Worth-Dallas | KDGE |
| 102.5 | 0.25 | TX | Dallas | K273BJ (KTNO) (sp) |
| 102.5 | 0.029 | TX | Denton | KOCQ-LP |
| 102.5 | 0.25 | TX | Ft. Worth | K273CS (KFJZ) (sp) |
| 102.5 | 0.01 | TX | Ft. Worth | KEFW-LP (sp) |
| 102.5 | 100 | TX | Hillsboro° | KBRQ |
| 102.5 | 0.02 | TX | Weatherford | K273CP (KYGX) |
| 102.5 | 18 | TX | Whitesboro° | KMAD-FM |
| #102.9 | 100 | TX | Dallas | KDMX |
| 103.3 | 98 | TX | Allen | KESN |
| #103.7 | 99 | TX | Highland Park-Dallas | KVIL |
| 104.1 | 0.1 | TX | Dallas | KEJC-LP (sp) |
| 104.1 | 0.1 | TX | Ft. Worth | KLEJ-LP (sp) |
| 104.1 | 0.1 | TX | Mansfield | KYRE-LP |
| 104.1 | 0.25 | TX | McKinney | K281CS (KHSE) (sp) |
| 104.5 | 99 | TX | Dallas | KKDA-FM |
| 104.9 | 20.15 | TX | Pilot Point | KZMP-FM |
| #105.3 | 97 | TX | Dallas | KRLD-FM |
| 105.7 | 93 | TX | Decatur | KRNB |
| 105.9 | 0.25 | TX | Commerce | K290AP (KGVL) |
| #106.1 | 97 | TX | Denton | KHKS |
| 106.5 | 0.1 | TX | Dallas | K293CM (KBFB-HD3) |
| 106.7 | 75 | TX | Muenster° | KZZA (sp) |
| 106.9 | 0.14 | TX | Royse City | K295BF (KYLP-LP) (sp) |
| #107.1 | 74 | TX | Benbrook | KESS-FM (sp) |
| 107.1 | 0.013 | TX | Garland | KYEB-LP (sp) |
| #107.5 | 16.5 | TX | Ft. Worth | KMVK (sp) |
| #107.9 | 100 | TX | Lewisville | KDXX (sp) |

**Denver Metro Area** (Denver-Aurora-Lakewood, CO MSA)

| MHz | kW | Sta | City of License | Station |
|---|---|---|---|---|
| 88.1 | 1.2 | CO | Lakewood | KVOD |
| # 88.5 | 4 | CO | Boulder° | KGNU-FM |
| # 88.7 | 8.9 | CO | Manitou Springs° | KCME |
| 88.9 | 0.099 | CO | Plainview | K205FV (KLDV) |
| # 89.3 | 12 | CO | Denver | KUVO |
| 89.7 | 80 | CO | Loveland° | KXGR |
| # 90.1 | 50 | CO | Denver | KCFR-FM |
| # 90.5 | 20 | CO | Colorado Springs° | KTLF |
| 90.5 | 0.18 | CO | Golden | K213FH (KRKY-FM) |
| 90.5 | 0.003 | CO | Littleton | K213EG (KTSG) |
| 90.7 | 0.9 | CO | Longmont° | KGUD |
| 90.9 | 0.09 | CO | Pleasant View | K215FI (KZET) |
| 91.1 | 100 | CO | Morrison | KLDV-FM |
| # 91.5 | 36 | CO | Greeley° | KUNC |
| 91.7 | 0.026 | CO | Idaho Springs | K219LF (KUNC) |
| 92.1 | 42 | CO | Castle Rock | KJMN (sp) |
| # 92.5 | 57 | CO | Broomfield | KWOF |
| 92.9 | 60 | CO | Colorado Springs° | KKPK |
| # 93.3 | 71 | CO | Wheat Ridge | KTCL |
| 93.7 | 0.099 | CO | Lakewood | K229BS (KCKK) |
| 93.9 | 0.1 | CO | Aurora | KETO-LP |
| 93.9 | 0.58 | CO | Loveland° | KCWA |
| 94.1 | 0.25 | CO | Golden | K231BQ (KBCO-HD3) |
| 94.3 | 0.25 | CO | Brighton° | K232FK (KLVZ) |
| 94.3 | 59.2 | CO | Colorado Springs° | KILO |
| 94.7 | 100 | CO | Lafayette° | KRKS-FM |
| 95.1 | 58 | CO | Colorado Springs° | KATC-FM |
| 95.1 | 0.25 | CO | Commerce City | K236CQ (KLTT) |
| 95.3 | 0.065 | CO | Denver | K237GG (KLDC) |
| # 95.7 | 100 | CO | Denver | KPTT |
| 96.1 | 0.099 | CO | Englewood | K241CP (KNRV) |
| # 96.1 | 100 | CO | Greeley° | KSME |
| 96.5 | 100 | CO | Evergreen | KXPK |
| 96.9 | 0.001 | CO | Golden | K245CM (KKLC) |
| # 96.9 | 58 | CO | Pueblo° | KCCY-FM |
| # 97.3 | 94 | CO | Boulder° | KBCO |

| MHz | kW | Sta | City of License | Station |
|---|---|---|---|---|
| 97.7 | 0.25 | CO | Denver | K249EX (KBNO) |
| 97.7 | 50 | CO | Strassburg | KSJL |
| # 97.9 | 100 | WY | Cheyenne° | KXBG |
| 98.1 | 71 | CO | Colorado Springs° | KKFM |
| 98.5 | 96 | CO | Denver | KYGO-FM |
| # 98.9 | 57 | CO | Pueblo° | KKMG |
| 99.1 | 100 | CO | Windsor° | KUAD-FM |
| # 99.5 | 74 | CO | Denver | KQMT |
| # 99.9 | 57 | CO | Pueblo° | KVUU |
| #100.3 | 98.6 | CO | Denver | KIMN |
| 100.7 | 0.099 | CO | Denver | K264BO (KLZ) |
| 100.7 | 77 | CO | Pueblo° | KGFT |
| #101.1 | 74 | CO | Denver | KOSI |
| 101.5 | 20 | CO | Commerce City | KJHM-FM1 |
| 101.5 | 97 | CO | Watkins | KJHM |
| 101.7 | 0.035 | CO | Evergreen | K269CL (KPTT) (sp) |
| 101.9 | 9.5 | CO | Centennial | KXWA |
| 102.1 | 6 | CO | Estes Park° | KGRE-FM |
| 102.3 | 1 | CO | Greenwood Vlg | KVOQ-FM |
| 102.5 | 17 | CO | Loveland° | KTRR |
| 102.7 | 0.1 | CO | Idaho Springs | KYGT-LP |
| 102.7 | 57 | CO | Manitou Springs° | KBIQ |
| 103.1 | 0.25 | CO | Denver | K276FK (KYGO-HD2) |
| #103.5 | 100 | CO | Denver | KRFX |
| 103.9 | 0.03 | CO | Pleasant View | K280GB (KLDV) |
| 103.9 | 1.75 | CO | Pueblo West° | KRXP |
| 103.9 | 16.5 | CO | Severance° | KRKA |
| #104.3 | 91 | CO | Longmont° | KKFN |
| 104.7 | 0.1 | CO | Denver | KOMF-LP |
| 104.7 | 0.14 | CO | Denver | K284CI (KDCO) |
| #105.1 | 98.5 | CO | Denver | KXKL-FM |
| #105.5 | 50 | CO | Timnath° | KJAC |
| #105.9 | 96 | CO | Denver | KALC |
| 106.3 | 0.099 | CO | Denver | K292FM (KYGO-FM) |
| 106.3 | 1.6 | CO | Widefield° | KKLI |
| #106.7 | 100 | CO | Denver | KBPI |
| 107.1 | 20 | CO | Aurora | KFCO-FM3 |
| 107.1 | 97 | CO | Bennett | KFCO |
| #107.5 | 91 | CO | Lakewood | KQKS |
| 107.9 | 0.25 | CO | Denver | K300CP (KPTT-HD2) |
| #107.9 | 100 | CO | Ft. Collins° | KBPI |
| #107.9 | 32 | CO | Pueblo° | KBPL |

**Detroit Metro Area** (Detroit-Warren-Dearborn, MI MSA)

| MHz | kW | Sta | City of License | Station |
|---|---|---|---|---|
| 88.1 | 0.36 | MI | Bloomfield Hills | WBFH |
| 88.1 | 0.044 | MI | Highland Park | WHPR-FM |
| 88.1 | 0.2 | MI | Plymouth | WSDP |
| 88.3 | 0.11 | MI | Auburn Hills | WXOU |
| 88.3 | 5.5 | MI | Grosse Pte Shores | WDTE |
| 88.3 | 1.3 | MI | Port Huron | WNFA |
| 88.3 | 0.105 | MI | Southfield | WSHJ |
| 88.9 | 7.4 | MI | Imlay City | WDTR |
| 89.1 | 0.1 | MI | Warren | WPHS |
| # 89.1 | 15.5 | MI | Ypsilanti° | WEMU |
| 89.3 | 0.27 | MI | Dearborn | WHFR |
| 89.3 | 0.044 | MI | Orchard Lake | WBLD |
| 89.5 | 2.4 | MI | Auburn Hills | WAHS |
| 89.5 | 0.1 | MI | Novi | WOVI |
| 90.1 | 50 | MI | Huron Township | WDTP |
| 90.3 | 0.037 | MI | Rochester Hills | KDTI |
| 90.5 | 85 | MI | East Lansing° | WKAR-FM |
| # 90.9 | 22.5 | MI | Detroit | WRCJ-FM |
| 91.3 | 0.12 | MI | Port Huron | WRSX |
| 91.5 | 1.05 | MI | China Township | WVMV |
| # 91.7 | 93 | MI | Ann Arbor° | WUOM |
| 91.9 | 0.18 | MI | Port Huron | WORW |
| # 92.3 | 45 | MI | Detroit | WMXD |
| 92.3 | 0.01 | MI | New Baltimore | W222AP (WESA) |
| 92.7 | 0.099 | MI | Detroit | W224CC (WLQV) |
| # 93.1 | 26.5 | MI | Detroit | WDRQ |
| 93.5 | 0.099 | MI | Detroit | W228CJ (WDMK-HD2) |
| 93.5 | 5.2 | MI | Howell | WHMI-FM |
| 93.5 | 0.2 | MI | New Baltimore | W228DE (WNIC) |
| 93.5 | 0.25 | MI | Riverview | W228CU (WDMK-HD2) |
| 94.1 | 0.21 | MI | Holly | W231CV (WUFL) |
| 94.3 | 0.099 | MI | Detroit | W232CA (WUFL) |
| # 94.7 | 13.5 | MI | Birmingham | WCSX |
| # 95.5 | 100 | MI | Detroit | WKQI |
| # 96.3 | 20 | MI | Detroit | WDVD |
| 96.7 | 0.058 | MI | Detroit | WNUC-LP |
| 96.7 | 0.099 | MI | Detroit | W244DL (WEXL) |
| # 97.1 | 15 | MI | Detroit | WXYT-FM |
| 97.5 | 0.25 | MI | Ecorse | W248CC (WDTP) |
| # 97.9 | 50 | MI | Detroit | WJLB |
| 98.3 | 0.115 | MI | Detroit | W252BX (WMXD-HD2) |
| 98.3 | 0.13 | MI | Holly | W252CP (WAKL) |

| MHz | kW | Sta | City of License | Station |
|---|---|---|---|---|
| # 98.7 | 50 | MI | Detroit | WDZH |
| # 99.5 | 17.5 | MI | Detroit | WYCD |
| 99.9 | 0.25 | MI | Detroit | W260CB (WDMK-HD2) |
| #100.3 | 32 | MI | Dearborn | WNIC |
| 100.7 | 0.1 | MI | Ferndale | WFCB-LP |
| #101.1 | 27 | MI | Detroit | WRIF |
| 101.5 | 0.099 | MI | Detroit | W268CN (WDTK) |
| #101.9 | 48 | MI | Detroit | WDET-FM |
| 102.3 | 3 | MI | Port Huron | WGRT |
| #102.7 | 36 | MI | Mount Clemens | WDKL |
| 102.9 | 50 | MI | Ann Arbor° | WWWW-FM |
| 103.1 | 2.6 | MI | Lapeer | WQUS |
| 103.1 | 0.25 | MI | Rochester Hills | W276DB (WUFL) |
| #103.5 | 50 | MI | Detroit | WMUZ-FM |
| 103.9 | 0.099 | MI | Yates° | W280EL (WRCJ-FM) |
| #104.3 | 190 | MI | Detroit | WOMC |
| 104.7 | 0.25 | MI | Detroit | W284BQ (WUFL) |
| #105.1 | 50 | MI | Detroit | WMGC-FM |
| 105.5 | 0.038 | MI | Rochester Hills | W288BK (WMXD-HD2) |
| #105.9 | 20 | MI | Detroit | WDMK |
| 106.3 | 0.099 | MI | Westland | W292DK (WMXD-HD2) |
| #106.7 | 61 | MI | Detroit | WDTW-FM |
| 107.1 | 3 | MI | Ann Arbor° | WQKL |
| ‡107.1 | 0.099 | MI | Detroit | W296DY (WRDT) |
| 107.1 | 0.25 | MI | Detroit | W296CG (WMXD-HD3) |
| 107.1 | 6 | MI | Port Huron | WSAQ |
| #107.5 | 50 | MI | Detroit | WGPR |
| 107.9 | 0.085 | MI | Dearborn | W300DI (WDTW-FM) |
| #107.9 | 50 | MI | Flint° | WCRZ |

**Houston - Galveston Metro Area** (Houston-The Woodlands-Sugar Land, TX MSA)

| MHz | kW | Sta | City of License | Station |
|---|---|---|---|---|
| 88.1 | 0.05 | TX | Freeport | K201FA (KCZO) (sp) |
| 88.1 | 0.2 | TX | Galveston | K201DZ (KFTG) (sp) |
| 88.1 | 0.25 | TX | Houston | K201IY (KJIC) (sp) |
| 88.1 | 0.25 | TX | Katy | K201EU (KFTG) |
| 88.1 | 0.7 | TX | Pasadena | KFTG (sp) |
| 88.3 | 100 | TX | Willis | KAFR |
| # 88.7 | 100 | TX | Houston | KUHF |
| # 89.3 | 100 | TX | Humble | KSBJ |
| 89.5 | 0.25 | TX | Galveston | K208DG (KPFT) |
| 89.7 | 5.6 | TX | Alvin | KACC |
| # 90.1 | 100 | TX | Houston | KPFT |
| 90.5 | 36 | TX | Santa Fe | KJIC-FM |
| 90.7 | 0.1 | TX | Hardin | KGBV |
| 90.9 | 18.5 | TX | Houston | KTSU |
| 91.1 | 17.5 | TX | Lake Jackson | KYBJ |
| 91.3 | 0.099 | TX | Houston | K217GB (KXNG) |
| # 91.3 | 31 | TX | Prairie View | KPVU |
| 91.5 | 0.099 | TX | Houston | K218EJ (KJIC) |
| # 91.7 | 50 | TX | Houston | KXNG |
| # 92.1 | 21.36 | TX | Seabrook | KROI |
| 92.3 | 0.25 | TX | Houston | K222CX (KYOK) |
| 92.3 | 32 | TX | Livingston° | KETX-FM |
| 92.5 | 0.032 | TX | Houston | KHGF-LP (sp) |
| 92.5 | 0.03 | TX | Houston | K223CW (KCOH) (sp) |
| 92.5 | 0.1 | TX | South Houston | KJJG-LP (sp) |
| # 92.9 | 93.7 | TX | Pasadena | KKBQ-FM |
| 93.3 | 97 | TX | Port Arthur° | KQBU-FM |
| # 93.7 | 100 | TX | Houston | KQBT |
| 94.1 | 50 | TX | Hempstead | KLTR |
| 94.1 | 0.1 | TX | Houston | KBIH-LP (sp) |
| 94.1 | 0.099 | TX | Houston | K231CN (KGOW) (viet) |
| # 94.5 | 97 | TX | Houston | KTBZ-FM |
| 94.9 | 0.042 | TX | Conroe | KKFH-LP (sp) |
| 94.9 | 100 | TX | Ganado° | KHTZ |
| 94.9 | 0.25 | TX | Houston | K235CS (KLVL) |
| 94.9 | 0.1 | TX | Houston | KRUT-LP (sp) |
| 94.9 | 0.1 | TX | Pasadena | KPFG-LP |
| 95.1 | 0.099 | TX | Missouri City | K236AR (KFTG) |
| 95.3 | 0.064 | TX | Cleveland | KORG-LP |
| 95.3 | 0.075 | TX | Conroe | K237FS (KHJK) |
| 95.3 | 0.088 | TX | Friendswood | KEPH-LP |
| 95.3 | 0.057 | TX | Houston | KZLD-LP (sp) |
| 95.3 | 0.1 | TX | Houston | KCDE-LP (sp) |
| # 95.7 | 95 | TX | Houston | KKHH |
| 96.1 | 0.041 | TX | Houston | KBLT-LP |
| 96.1 | 0.25 | TX | Houston | K241CO (KSHJ) (sp) |
| 96.1 | 0.25 | TX | Houston | K241CM (KTEK) |
| 96.1 | 0.017 | TX | Sugar Land | KIRP-LP (sp) |
| # 96.5 | 97 | TX | Houston | KHMX |
| # 96.9 | 100 | TX | El Campo° | KXBJ |
| 96.9 | 0.03 | TX | Houston | K245CQ (KWWJ) |
| # 97.1 | 100 | TX | Cleveland | KTHT |
| 97.3 | 0.25 | TX | Houston | K247CP (KODA) |
| # 97.5 | 100 | TX | Mont Belvieu | KFNC |

| MHz | kW | Sta | City of License | Station |
|---|---|---|---|---|
| # 97.9 | 95 | TX | Houston | KBXX |
| 98.3 | 0.03 | TX | Houston | K252FR (KMIC) (sp) |
| # 98.5 | 100 | TX | Port Arthur° | KTJM (sp) |
| 98.7 | 0.2 | TX | Houston | K254BZ (KBXX) (sp) |
| # 99.1 | 96 | TX | Houston | KODA |
| 99.5 | 0.08 | TX | Houston | K258DA (KFNC) |
| # 99.5 | 0.25 | TX | Humble | K258DI (KJOZ) (sp) |
| 99.5 | 0.025 | TX | La Marque | KHEA-LP |
| 99.5 | 0.1 | TX | Pasadena | KPSR-LP |
| 99.5 | 0.099 | TX | Sugar Land | K258BZ (KSBJ) |
| 99.7 | 0.1 | TX | Galveston | KLHG-LP (sp) |
| 99.7 | 0.1 | TX | Houston | KHGV-LP |
| 99.7 | 0.01 | TX | Houston | K259DC (KREH) (viet) |
| 99.7 | 0.1 | TX | Houston | KOYM-LP (sp) |
| 99.9 | 0.1 | TX | Houston | KNJC-LP (sp) |
| 99.9 | 26 | TX | Liberty | KSHN |
| #100.3 | 95 | TX | Houston | KILT-FM |
| 100.7 | 100 | TX | Lumberton | KKHT-FM |
| 100.7 | 0.1 | TX | Richmond | K264CN (KQUE) (sp) |
| #101.1 | 96 | TX | Houston | KLOL (sp) |
| 101.5 | 0.09 | TX | Cleveland | KZCL-LP |
| 101.5 | 0.1 | TX | Cypress | KOER-LP |
| 101.5 | 0.25 | TX | Houston | K268CW (KHCB) (sp) |
| ‡101.5 | 0.1 | TX | Houston | KHSX-LP |
| 101.5 | 0.083 | TX | Liberty | KXAQ-LP |
| #101.7 | 35 | TX | Bay City° | KNTE (sp) |
| 101.7 | 0.1 | TX | Houston | KQEU-LP (ch) |
| 101.7 | 0.25 | TX | Houston | K269GS (KGBC) |
| 101.7 | 0.25 | TX | Humble | K269GT (KBXX) |
| #102.1 | 100 | TX | Houston | KMJQ |
| 102.5 | 50 | TX | Beaumont° | KTCX |
| 102.5 | 0.099 | TX | Houston | K273AL (KJOZ) (sp) |
| 102.5 | 0.001 | TX | Houston | KMAZ-LP |
| #102.9 | 99.5 | TX | Houston | KLTN (sp) |
| 103.3 | 0.01 | TX | Conroe | KIAA-LP |
| 103.3 | 100 | TX | Freeport | KJOJ (sp) |
| 103.3 | 0.25 | TX | Houston | K277DE (KNTH) |
| 103.5 | 0.022 | TX | Cypress | KCYB-LP |
| 103.5 | 0.085 | TX | Houston | K278CR (KBRZ) (hindi) |
| #103.7 | 99 | TX | La Porte | KHJK |
| 104.1 | 92.18 | TX | Houston | KRBE |
| 104.5 | 0.008 | TX | Conroe | KZCW-LP |
| 104.5 | 0.099 | TX | Houston | K283CH (KTBZ-FM-HD2) |
| #104.5 | 100 | TX | Orange° | KKMY |
| #104.9 | 10.5 | TX | Deer Park | KAMA-FM |
| 105.3 | 0.099 | TX | Houston | K287BQ (KODA) |
| #105.3 | 50 | TX | Winnie | KXXF |
| 105.7 | 100 | TX | Houston | KHCB-FM |
| 106.1 | 0.007 | TX | Conroe | KZCC-LP |
| 106.1 | 100 | TX | Orange° | KIOC |
| 106.1 | 0.19 | TX | Sugar Land | K291CE (KGLK) |
| 106.5 | 98 | TX | Galveston | KOVE-FM (sp) |
| #106.9 | 91.6 | TX | Conroe | KHPT |
| #107.5 | 98 | TX | Lake Jackson | KGLK |
| #107.9 | 90 | TX | Beaumont° | KQQK (sp) |
| **Los Angeles Metro Area** (Los Angeles-Long Beach-Anaheim, CA MSA) | | | | |
| # 88.1 | 30 | CA | Long Beach | KKJZ |
| # 88.3 | 3.2 | CA | Thousand Oaks° | KCLU-FM |
| # 88.5 | 0.37 | CA | Northridge | KCSN |
| 88.5 | 0.8 | CA | West Los Angeles | KCSN-FM1 |
| 88.7 | 0.2 | CA | Avalon | KISL |
| 88.7 | 0.4 | CA | Claremont | KSPC |
| # 88.7 | 12 | CA | Santa Barbara° | KDRW |
| 88.9 | 0.2 | CA | Irvine | KUCI |
| 88.9 | 5.8 | CA | Lancaster | KTLW |
| 88.9 | 2.9 | CA | Los Angeles | KXLU |
| 88.9 | 0.01 | CA | Santa Clarita | K205EP (KTLW) |
| 89.1 | 0.04 | CA | Laguna Beach | K206AA (KSBR) |
| # 89.3 | 0.6 | CA | Pasadena | KPCC |
| 89.3 | 0.003 | CA | Santa Clarita | KPCC-FM1 |
| 89.3 | 0.35 | CA | West Los Angeles | KPCC-FM2 |
| 89.3 | 0.7 | CA | West Los Angeles | KPCC-FM3 |
| 89.5 | 0.075 | CA | Newport Beach | K208AM (KSBR) |
| 89.5 | 0.097 | CA | Ojai° | KJAI |
| 89.7 | 2.75 | CA | Riverside° | KSGN |
| # 89.9 | 6.9 | CA | Santa Monica | KCRW |
| 90.1 | 0.019 | CA | Buena Park | KBPK |
| 90.1 | 0.01 | CA | Palmdale | K211EY (KHMS) |
| 90.1 | 0.01 | CA | Santa Ana | K211DK (KMRO) (sp) |
| 90.1 | 0.0017 | CA | Walnut | KSAK |
| 90.3 | 10.5 | CA | Camarillo° | KMRO (sp) |
| 90.3 | 0.09 | CA | Fountain Valley | KLIE-LP |
| 90.3 | 0.01 | CA | Temple City | K212FA (KHRI) |
| 90.7 | 110 | CA | Los Angeles | KPFK |
| 90.7 | 1.5 | CA | Malibu | KPFK-FM1 |
| 91.1 | 0.02 | CA | Arcadia | K216EM (KYLA) |
| 91.1 | 0.01 | CA | Quartz Hill | K216FA (KAWZ) |
| # 91.1 | 7.4 | CA | Thousand Oaks° | KDSC |
| 91.1 | 0.25 | CA | Valley Village | K216FM (KTLW) |
| # 91.5 | 39 | CA | Los Angeles | KUSC |
| 91.5 | 0.2 | CA | Santa Clarita | KUSC-FM1 |
| # 91.9 | 3.8 | CA | San Bernardino° | KVCR |
| 91.9 | 0.01 | CA | Simi Valley° | K220FR (KYRA) |
| 91.9 | 0.01 | CA | Studio City | K220HC (KTLW) |
| # 92.3 | 42 | CA | Los Angeles | KRRL |
| 92.3 | 0.32 | CA | Santa Clarita | KRRL-FM1 |
| 92.7 | 0.69 | CA | Fountain Valley | KYLA |
| 92.7 | 0.045 | CA | Malibu Vista | KYRA-FM1 |
| 92.7 | 1.4 | CA | Thousand Oaks° | KYRA |
| # 93.1 | 27.5 | CA | Los Angeles | KCBS-FM |
| 93.5 | 0.01 | CA | Laguna Beach | KXRN-LP-FM1 |
| 93.5 | 0.1 | CA | Laguna Niguel | KXRN-LP |
| 93.5 | 5 | CA | Ontario° | KDEY-FM |
| 93.5 | 4.2 | CA | Redondo Beach | KDAY |
| 93.5 | 6 | CA | Rosamond° | KQAV |
| 93.7 | 12.5 | CA | Santa Barbara° | KDB |
| # 93.9 | 18.5 | CA | Los Angeles | KXOS (sp) |
| 93.9 | 0.25 | CA | Santa Clarita | KXOS-FM1 (sp) |
| 94.3 | 6 | CA | Garden Grove | KEBN (sp) |
| 94.3 | 6 | CA | San Fernando | KBUA (sp) |
| 94.3 | 0.046 | CA | Valencia & Newhall | KBUA-FM1 (sp) |
| # 94.7 | 52 | CA | Los Angeles | KTWV |
| 95.1 | 0.01 | CA | Lancaster | K236AW (KOST) |
| # 95.1 | 50 | CA | San Bernardino° | KFRG |
| 95.1 | 12.5 | CA | Ventura° | KBBY-FM |
| # 95.5 | 61 | CA | Los Angeles | KLOS |
| 95.9 | 1.2 | CA | Camarillo° | KCAQ |
| 95.9 | 6 | CA | La Mirada | KFSH-FM |
| ‡ 96.1 | 0.01 | CA | Palmdale | K241AJ (KEBR) |
| 96.3 | 6.6 | CA | Los Angeles | KXOL-FM (sp) |
| 96.3 | 0.01 | CA | Palmdale | K242CR (KMRO) (sp) |
| 96.7 | 1.75 | CA | Redlands° | KCAL |
| # 96.7 | 6 | CA | Santa Ana | KWIZ (sp) |
| 96.7 | 0.28 | CA | Santa Paula° | KLJR-FM |
| 96.9 | 0.25 | CA | Lancaster | K245CL (KUTY) (sp) |
| # 97.1 | 21 | CA | Los Angeles | KAMP-FM |
| # 97.5 | 0.1 | CA | Castaic | KHUG-LP |
| # 97.5 | 16 | CA | Goleta° | KLSB |
| # 97.5 | 72 | CA | Riverside° | KLYY (sp) |
| # 97.9 | 33 | CA | East Los Angeles | KLAX-FM (sp) |
| 98.1 | 0.1 | CA | Santa Clarita | K251CF (KHTS) |
| 98.3 | 0.08 | CA | Culver City | K252FK (KOCP) |
| 98.3 | 0.1 | CA | Lancaster | KFXM-LP |
| 98.3 | 0.1 | CA | Los Angeles | K252FO (KSUR) |
| 98.3 | 1.5 | CA | Oxnard° | KDAR |
| # 98.3 | 6 | CA | West Covina | KRCV (sp) |
| # 98.7 | 75 | CA | Los Angeles | KYSR |
| 99.1 | 0.006 | CA | Chatsworth | KWSV-LP-FM1 |
| 99.1 | 0.003 | CA | Los Angeles | KZUT-LP |
| 99.1 | 0.1 | CA | Los Angeles | KFEP-LP |
| 99.1 | 0.1 | CA | Los Angeles | KLDB-LP |
| 99.1 | 0.071 | CA | Malibu | KBUU-LP |
| 99.1 | 0.01 | CA | Palmdale | K256BS (KODV) (sp) |
| 99.1 | 0.25 | CA | Pasadena | K256CX (KRDC) |
| # 99.1 | 2.55 | CA | Riverside° | KGGI |
| 99.1 | 0.1 | CA | Simi Valley° | KWSV-LP |
| 99.1 | 0.05 | CA | Venice | KTPC-LP |
| 99.5 | 10 | CA | Los Angeles | KKLA-FM |
| 99.9 | 29.5 | CA | San Bernardino° | KOLA |
| 99.9 | 34 | CA | Santa Barbara° | KTYD |
| #100.3 | 5.4 | CA | Los Angeles | KKLQ |
| 100.3 | 0.1 | CA | Santa Clarita | KKLQ-FM2 |
| 100.7 | 0.25 | CA | Guasti° | K264AF (KRLD-FM) |
| 100.7 | 0.06 | CA | Los Angeles | K264CQ (KWKW) (sp) |
| 100.7 | 0.01 | CA | Palmdale | K264BQ (KTQX) (sp) |
| ‡100.7 | 0.02 | CA | Santa Ana | KPPH-LP |
| 100.7 | 39 | CA | Ventura° | KHAY |
| #101.1 | 51 | CA | Los Angeles | KRTH |
| 101.5 | 0.1 | CA | El Monte | KQSG-LP |
| 101.5 | 0.185 | CA | Lake Los Angeles | K268CO (KTLW) |
| 101.5 | 0.024 | CA | Los Angeles | K268DD (KTYM) |
| 101.5 | 0.05 | CA | Los Angeles | KQBH-LP |
| 101.5 | 0.025 | CA | Los Angeles | KZKA-LP |
| 101.5 | 0.042 | CA | Newport Beach | KOCI-LP |
| 101.5 | 0.1 | CA | Pasadena | KHBG-LP (sp) |
| 101.5 | 0.1 | CA | Santa Clarita | KZNQ-LP |
| #101.9 | 4.8 | CA | Glendale | KSCA (sp) |
| 101.9 | 0.09 | CA | Santa Clarita | KSCA-FM1 (sp) |
| 102.3 | 5.6 | CA | Compton | KJLH |
| 102.3 | 0.008 | CA | Lancaster | K272FI (KOSS) |

| MHz | kW | Sta | City of License | Station |
|---|---|---|---|---|
| #102.7 | 8 | CA | Los Angeles | KIIS-FM |
| 102.7 | 0.21 | CA | Santa Clarita | KIIS-FM1 |
| 102.9 | 5.5 | CA | Oxnard° | KXLM |
| 103.1 | 0.3 | CA | Newport Beach | KDLE (sp) |
| #103.1 | 3.7 | CA | Santa Monica | KDLD (sp) |
| 103.3 | 105 | CA | Santa Barbara° | KVYB |
| #103.5 | 12.5 | CA | Los Angeles | KOST |
| 103.5 | 0.5 | CA | Santa Clarita | KOST-FM1 |
| 103.7 | 0.95 | CA | El Rio° | KMLA |
| #103.9 | 4.1 | CA | Inglewood | KRCD (sp) |
| #104.3 | 65 | CA | Los Angeles | KBIG |
| 104.3 | 0.38 | CA | Santa Clarita | KBIG-FM1 |
| 104.7 | 0.25 | CA | Calabasas | KOCP-FM3 |
| 104.7 | 1.9 | CA | Granada Hills | KOCP-FM4 |
| 104.7 | 2.3 | CA | Las Flores Canyon | KOCP-FM5 |
| 104.7 | 18 | CA | Oxnard° | KOCP |
| 104.7 | 0.007 | CA | Quartz Hill | K284CD (KODV) (sp) |
| 104.7 | 0.05 | CA | Santa Ana | $ KSXA-LP |
| 104.7 | 0.05 | CA | Santa Ana | $ KRQL-LP |
| 104.7 | 0.048 | CA | Walnut | KQEV-LP (ch) |
| #105.1 | 18 | CA | Los Angeles | KKGO |
| 105.1 | 0.06 | CA | Santa Clarita | KKGO-FM1 |
| 105.5 | 6 | CA | Hemet° | KXRS (sp) |
| 105.5 | 3 | CA | Long Beach | KBUE (sp) |
| 105.5 | 0.31 | CA | Ojai° | KFYV |
| 105.5 | 6 | CA | Rosamond° | KVVS |
| #105.9 | 25 | CA | Los Angeles | KPWR |
| 106.3 | 3 | CA | Lancaster | KGMX |
| 106.3 | 0.96 | CA | Oak View° | KRUZ |
| 106.3 | 6 | CA | Santa Ana | KALI-FM |
| 106.7 | 0.18 | CA | Lancaster | K294DA (KAVL) |
| 106.7 | 5.5 | CA | Pasadena | KROQ-FM |
| 106.7 | 0.05 | CA | Santa Clarita | KROQ-FM1 |
| #107.1 | 6 | CA | Arcadia | KSSE (sp) |
| 107.1 | 0.1 | CA | Lancaster | K296GX (KOSS) |
| 107.1 | 0.02 | CA | San Fernando | KSSE-FM1 (sp) |
| 107.1 | 0.37 | CA | Ventura° | KSSC |
| #107.5 | 29.5 | CA | Los Angeles | KLVE |
| 107.5 | 0.1 | CA | Santa Clarita | KLVE-FM1 |
| 107.9 | 0.08 | CA | Lancaster | K300CZ (KJPG) |
| 107.9 | 0.02 | CA | San Clemente | KWVE-FM4 |
| #107.9 | 0.53 | CA | San Clemente | KWVE-FM |
| 107.9 | 0.05 | CA | Santa Clarita | KQRU-LP |

**Miami - Fort Lauderdale Metro Area** (Miami-Fort Lauderdale-West Palm Beach, FL MSA)

| MHz | kW | Sta | City of License | Station |
|---|---|---|---|---|
| 88.1 | 0.165 | FL | Homestead | WRGP |
| 88.1 | 50 | FL | West Palm Beach | WAYF |
| 88.3 | 6 | FL | Pennsuco | WGNK (sp) |
| 88.5 | 7.7 | FL | Florida City | WMFL |
| 88.5 | 3 | FL | Sunrise | WKPX |
| # 88.9 | 7.4 | FL | Miami | WDNA |
| 89.3 | 100 | FL | Boynton Beach | WRMB |
| 89.7 | 100 | FL | Miami | WMLV |
| 90.3 | 8 | FL | Ft. Lauderdale | WYBP |
| 90.3 | 0.2 | FL | West Palm Beach | W212CG (WAYF) |
| 90.5 | 5.9 | FL | Coral Gables | WVUM |
| # 90.7 | 38 | FL | West Palm Beach | WFLV |
| 90.9 | 100 | FL | Cutler Bay | WLFE |
| # 91.3 | 47 | FL | Miami | WLRN-FM |
| 91.9 | 50 | FL | Hammocks | WMKL |
| # 92.1 | 7.2 | FL | West Palm Beach | WRLX (sp) |
| 92.3 | 31 | FL | Hialeah | WCMQ-FM (sp) |
| 92.5 | 0.25 | FL | Belle Glade | W223AJ (WAFC) |
| 92.5 | 0.24 | FL | West Palm Beach | W223CJ (WSVU) |
| 92.7 | 0.022 | FL | Ft. Lauderdale | WZOP-LP |
| 92.7 | 0.057 | FL | Miami | WIBE-LP |
| 92.7 | 0.1 | FL | Miami | WMXR-LP |
| # 93.1 | 98 | FL | Miami | WFEZ |
| 93.5 | 15.5 | FL | Belle Glade | WBGF |
| 93.5 | 0.179 | FL | Ft. Lauderdale | W228BV (WHYI-FM) |
| 93.5 | 50 | FL | Islamorada° | WZFL |
| 93.5 | 0.25 | FL | Miami | W228BY (WZFL) |
| # 93.9 | 98 | FL | Miami Beach | WMIA-FM |
| 94.3 | 0.05 | FL | Boca Raton | WRIZ-LP |
| 94.3 | 0.055 | FL | Miami | WMIV-LP |
| 94.3 | 0.045 | FL | Miami | WQPN-LP |
| # 94.3 | 50 | FL | Riviera Beach | WZZR |
| 94.5 | 0.031 | FL | Key Biscayne | WSQF-LP |
| 94.5 | 0.1 | FL | Miami | WVGK-LP (sp) |
| 94.5 | 0.099 | FL | Oakland Park | W233AP (WZTU) |
| 94.7 | 0.099 | FL | West Palm Beach | W234DA (WWRF) (sp) |
| # 94.9 | 98 | FL | Miami Beach | WTZU (sp) |
| 95.3 | 0.25 | FL | Boca Raton | W237BD (WWNN) (sp) |
| 95.3 | 0.031 | FL | Miami | WJEW-LP (sp) |
| 95.3 | 0.07 | FL | Miami | W237CP (WMLV) |

| MHz | kW | Sta | City of License | Station |
|---|---|---|---|---|
| 95.3 | 0.049 | FL | Miami Beach | WLJM-LP |
| # 95.5 | 100 | FL | Juno Beach | WLDI |
| # 95.7 | 40 | FL | No. Miami Beach | WRMA (sp) |
| 96.1 | 0.25 | FL | Boca Raton | W241AX (WPBR) (ha) |
| 96.1 | 0.048 | FL | Hollywood | WZPP-LP |
| 96.3 | 0.201 | FL | Jupiter | W242CI (WMBX) |
| # 96.5 | 98 | FL | Miami | WPOW |
| 96.9 | 0.25 | FL | Ft. Lauderdale | W245BC (WSBR) |
| 96.9 | 0.25 | FL | Lauderdale Lakes | W245BC (WSBR) |
| 96.9 | 0.095 | FL | Miami | WWWO-LP |
| 96.9 | 0.099 | FL | North Miami | W245BF (WRGP) |
| # 97.3 | 98 | FL | Miami | WFLC |
| 97.7 | 0.02 | FL | Homestead | WWPP-LP |
| 97.7 | 0.25 | FL | Miami | W249DM (WKAT) (sp) |
| # 97.9 | 100 | FL | Palm Beach | WRMF |
| # 98.3 | 100 | FL | Goulds | WRTO-FM (sp) |
| 98.3 | 0.054 | FL | Palm Beach | WPBV-LP |
| 98.3 | 0.045 | FL | West Palm Beach | WPBE-LP (sp) |
| 98.7 | 0.014 | FL | Miami | WPSI-LP |
| # 98.7 | 100 | FL | Wellington | WKGR |
| # 99.1 | 100 | FL | Miami | WEDR |
| 99.5 | 0.094 | FL | Hialeah Gardens | WHIM-LP (sp) |
| 99.5 | 0.084 | FL | Miami Shores | WBUJ-LP |
| 99.5 | 6 | FL | Palm Beach Gardens | WLLY-FM (sp) |
| # 99.9 | 98.4 | FL | Boca Raton | WKIS |
| 100.3 | 4 | FL | Lake Park | WLML |
| ‡100.3 | 0.47 | FL | Miami | WQNB-LP |
| #100.7 | 98 | FL | Ft. Lauderdale | WHYI-FM |
| 101.1 | 0.05 | FL | Boca Raton | WRIZ-LP |
| 101.1 | 0.1 | FL | Hollywood | WDKK-LP |
| 101.1 | 0.05 | FL | Miami | WDVS-LP |
| 101.1 | 0.097 | FL | West Palm Beach | WDZP-LP (cr) |
| #101.5 | 100 | FL | Miami | WLYF |
| 101.9 | 0.25 | FL | Miami | W270CV (WOCN) |
| 101.9 | 0.08 | FL | Oakland Park | WOIB-LP |
| 101.9 | 0.25 | FL | West Palm Beach | W270AD (WFLV-HD2) |
| 102.1 | 0.08 | FL | Ft. Lauderdale | WNGK-LP |
| ‡102.3 | 0.07 | FL | Hallandale | WEXI-LP |
| #102.3 | 100 | FL | Jensen Beach° | WMBX |
| 102.3 | 0.01 | FL | Miami | W267BW (WKAT) (sp) |
| #102.7 | 98 | FL | Pompano Beach | WMXJ |
| #103.1 | 90 | FL | Indiantown | WIRK |
| 103.1 | 0.045 | FL | Miramar | WUGR-LP |
| #103.5 | 98 | FL | Ft. Lauderdale | WMIB |
| 103.7 | 0.013 | FL | West Palm Beach | W279DG (WPSP) (sp) |
| 103.9 | 0.25 | FL | Boca Raton | W280DU (WSBR) |
| 103.9 | 0.02 | FL | Jupiter | WJUP-LP |
| 104.1 | 0.25 | FL | West Palm Beach | W279DG (WCNO) |
| #104.3 | 100 | FL | Miramar | WSFS |
| 104.7 | 0.031 | FL | Coconut Creek | WYUN-LP |
| 104.7 | 0.054 | FL | Miami | WAYG-LP |
| 104.7 | 0.099 | FL | Miami | W284CS (WMIA-FM) |
| 104.7 | 0.25 | FL | West Palm Beach | W284CR (WFLV-HD3) |
| #105.1 | 98 | FL | Coral Gables | WHQT |
| #105.5 | 50 | FL | Hobe Sound° | WOLL |
| 105.5 | 0.93 | FL | Islamorada° | WWWK |
| 105.5 | 0.085 | FL | Tamarac | W288DD (WLOG) |
| #105.9 | 100 | FL | Ft. Lauderdale | WBGG-FM |
| #106.3 | 19 | FL | Jupiter | WUUB |
| 106.3 | 50 | FL | Leisure City | WRAZ-FM (sp) |
| 106.3 | 6 | FL | Miramar Beach | WSBZ |
| #106.7 | 100 | FL | Ft. Lauderdale | WXDJ (sp) |
| 106.9 | 0.19 | FL | Jupiter | W295BJ (WSVU) |
| #107.1 | 50 | FL | Key Largo | WURN-FM (sp) |
| 107.1 | 0.1 | FL | Pompano Beach | WAFG-LP |
| #107.5 | 95 | FL | Miami | WAMR-FM (sp) |
| 107.9 | 0.1 | FL | Key Largo | WORZ-LP |
| 107.9 | 0.099 | FL | No. Miami Beach | W300DF (WAVS) |
| #107.90 | 100 | FL | West Palm Beach | WEAT |

**Minneapolis - St. Paul Metro Area** (Minneapolis-St. Paul-Bloomington, MN-WI MSA)

| MHz | kW | Sta | City of License | Station |
|---|---|---|---|---|
| 88.1 | 5.52 | MN | Newport | WAJC |
| # 88.3 | 70 | WI | Menomonie° | WHWC |
| 88.3 | 11 | MN | Waconia | KJGT |
| 88.5 | 2.9 | MN | Minneapolis | KBEM-FM |
| 88.7 | 0.1 | MN | Cambridge | WUSG-LP |
| 88.7 | 3 | WI | River Falls | WRFW |
| 88.9 | 0.095 | MN | St. Louis Park | KPPS-LP |
| # 89.3 | 97.6 | MN | Northfield° | KCMP |
| 89.7 | 40 | MN | Princeton | KPCS |
| # 89.9 | 6.2 | MN | Minneapolis | KMOJ |
| # 90.1 | 100 | MN | Collegeville° | KSJR |
| 90.3 | 0.9 | MN | Minneapolis | KFAI |
| 90.3 | 15 | MN | North Branch | KMKL |
| # 90.5 | 75 | MN | St. Peter° | KNGA |

| MHz | kW | Sta | City of License | Station |
|---|---|---|---|---|
| 90.7 | 0.099 | MN | Golden Valley | K214DF (KTIS-FM) |
| # 91.1 | 100 | MN | Minneapolis | KNOW-FM |
| 91.5 | 0.216 | MN | Bloomington | K218DK (KJLY) |
| ‡ 91.7 | 0.25 | MN | North Branch | W219DT (WAJC) |
| # 91.7 | 94 | MN | Rochester° | KZSE |
| 91.7 | 0.005 | MN | St. Paul | WMCN |
| 91.9 | 0.025 | MN | Minneapolis | K220JP (KSJN) |
| 92.1 | 0.25 | MN | Albertville | K221ES (KHRI) |
| 92.1 | 0.06 | MN | St. Paul | W221BS (WDGY) |
| # 92.5 | 100 | MN | Golden Valley | KQRS-FM |
| 92.9 | 0.17 | MN | St. Paul | W225AP (KTCZ-HD2) |
| 93.3 | 0.099 | MN | Shoreview | W227BF (KQQL-HD2) |
| # 93.7 | 100 | MN | Minneapolis | KXXR |
| 94.1 | 0.1 | MN | St. Paul | WFNU-LP |
| # 94.5 | 95 | MN | St. Paul | KSTP-FM |
| 94.9 | 0.25 | MN | St. Paul | W235CT (WREY) (sp) |
| 95.3 | 0.9 | MN | St. Paul | KZGO |
| 95.5 | 25 | MN | Mora° | KBEK |
| 95.5 | 6 | MN | New Prague | KCHK-FM |
| 95.7 | 4 | WI | Baldwin | WDMO |
| 95.7 | 0.25 | MN | St. Paul | K239CJ (KMNV) (sp) |
| 95.9 | 3 | MN | Faribault° | KQCL |
| 95.9 | 3 | MN | Forest Lake | WLKX-FM |
| # 96.3 | 19 | MN | Edina | KQGO |
| 96.7 | 0.17 | MN | Calhoun Beach | K244FE (KFXN-FM) |
| # 97.1 | 100 | MN | Minneapolis | KTCZ-FM |
| 97.5 | 0.25 | MN | Minneapolis | W248CU (KTIS) |
| 97.5 | 100 | MN | Rochester° | KNXR |
| 97.7 | 0.25 | MN | Albertville | K249ED (KTCZ-FM) |
| 97.9 | 0.1 | MN | Lakeville | KEFE-LP (sp) |
| 97.9 | 0.09 | MN | St. Paul | KQEP-LP (ch) |
| 98.1 | 97 | MN | St. Cloud° | WWJO |
| 98.1 | 0.1 | MN | St. Paul | KENL-LP (sp) |
| 98.5 | 100 | MN | Minneapolis | KTIS-FM |
| 98.9 | 0.1 | MN | Minneapolis | KRSM-LP |
| 99.1 | 0.1 | MN | Maple Grove | KPJT-LP |
| # 99.5 | 100 | MN | Minneapolis | KSJN |
| 99.9 | 0.25 | MN | Coon Rapids | K260BA (KFXN-FM-HD3) |
| #100.3 | 98 | MN | Minneapolis | KFXN-FM |
| 100.7 | 0.099 | MN | Falcon Heights | W264BR (KUOM) |
| 100.9 | 100 | MN | Blooming Prairie° | KOWZ-FM |
| #101.3 | 100 | MN | Richfield | KDWB-FM |
| 101.7 | 0.1 | MN | Minneapolis | KALY-LP |
| #102.1 | 100 | MN | St. Paul | KEEY-FM |
| 102.5 | 0.25 | MN | Fridley | K273BH (KTCZ-FM-HD3) |
| #102.9 | 100 | MN | Minneapolis | KMNB |
| 103.3 | 0.25 | WI | New Richmond | W277CW (WIXK) (hm) |
| 103.5 | 0.175 | MN | Cottage Grove | K278BP (KTLK) |
| 103.5 | 100 | MN | Mankato° | KYSM-FM |
| 103.7 | 0.25 | WI | Hudson | W279DD (WDGY) |
| #104.1 | 100 | MN | St. Louis Park | KZJK |
| 104.5 | 0.099 | MN | Minneapolis | K283BG (KUOM) |
| 104.7 | 100 | MN | St. Cloud° | KCLD-FM |
| 104.7 | 0.1 | MN | St. Paul | WEQY-LP |
| 104.9 | 0.25 | MN | St. Paul | K285CQ (KFXN) (hm) |
| 105.1 | 2.6 | MN | Lakeville | WGVX |
| 105.3 | 25 | MN | Cambridge | WLUP |
| 105.5 | 0.25 | MN | Bayport | K288GR (KFXN-FM-HD3) |
| 105.7 | 0.95 | MN | Eden Prarie | WWWM-FM |
| 105.9 | 12 | MN | Red Wing° | KWNG |
| #106.1 | 9.1 | MN | Elk River | KLCI |
| 106.3 | 6 | WI | River Falls | WEVR-FM |
| 106.5 | 0.196 | MN | Elko | K293BA (KJLY) |
| 106.5 | 0.01 | MN | St. Louis Park | KUOM-FM |
| 106.7 | 0.17 | MN | St. Paul | K294AM (KFAI) |
| 106.7 | 0.17 | MN | West St. Paul | K294AM (KFAI) |
| #107.1 | 22 | MN | Coon Rapids | KTMY |
| 107.5 | 48 | MN | Faribault° | KBGY |
| 107.5 | 0.25 | MN | Minneapolis | K298CO (WWTC) |
| #107.9 | 96 | MN | Anoka | KQQL |

**New York Metro Area** (New York-Newark-Jersey City, NY-NJ-PA MSA)

| MHz | kW | Sta | City of License | Station |
|---|---|---|---|---|
| 88.1 | 0.78 | NJ | Asbury Park° | WYGG |
| 88.1 | 0.18 | NY | Brentwood | WXBA |
| 88.1 | 0.1 | NY | Brookville | WCWP |
| 88.1 | 0.5 | NJ | Hopatcong | WDNJ (sp) |
| 88.1 | 0.042 | NY | Valhalla | WARY |
| # 88.3 | 2.5 | NJ | Newark | WBGO |
| 88.5 | 0.125 | NY | Plainview | WPOB |
| 88.5 | 2 | CT | Stamford° | WEDW-FM |
| 88.5 | 0.45 | NJ | Sussex | WNJP |
| 88.5 | 0.125 | NY | Syosset | WKWZ |
| 88.7 | 0.47 | NY | Hempstead | WRHU |
| 88.7 | 1.35 | NJ | New Brunswick° | WRSU-FM |
| 88.7 | 0.01 | NY | Nyack | WNYK |
| 88.7 | 0.2 | NJ | Wayne | WPSC-FM |
| # 88.9 | 0.2 | NY | Mt Kisco | WWES |
| 88.9 | 1.5 | NY | Smithtown | WFRS |
| 88.9 | 0.011 | NY | Staten Island | WSIA |
| 88.9 | 1 | NJ | West Long Branch | WMCX |
| 89.1 | 8.3 | NY | New York | WNYU-FM |
| 89.1 | 0.005 | NY | New York | WNYU-FM1 |
| # 89.1 | 3 | NJ | Teaneck | WFDU |
| 89.3 | 0.11 | NY | Copiague | WGSS |
| 89.3 | 15 | NJ | Freehold | WFJS-FM |
| 89.3 | 1.6 | NY | Monroe | WLJP |
| 89.3 | 0.52 | NJ | Netcong | WNJY |
| 89.5 | 10 | CT | Bridgeport° | WPKN |
| # 89.5 | 2.4 | NJ | South Orange | WSOU |
| 89.7 | 1.6 | NJ | Freehold Township | WRDR |
| 89.7 | 0.038 | NY | Mt Kisco | W209CJ (WMNR) |
| 89.9 | 0.25 | NJ | Manahawkin | WNJM |
| 89.9 | 1.35 | NY | New York | WKCR-FM |
| 90.1 | 3.6 | NY | Stony Brook | WUSB |
| 90.3 | 0.01 | NY | Brooklyn | WKRB |
| # 90.3 | 0.5 | NY | Garden City | WHPC |
| 90.3 | 0.1 | NJ | Mahwah | WRPR |
| 90.3 | 0.008 | NY | New York | WHCR-FM |
| 90.3 | 0.25 | NY | Ossining | WQXW |
| 90.3 | 0.1 | NJ | Piscataway | WVPH |
| 90.3 | 0.009 | NJ | Union Township | WKNJ-FM |
| 90.3 | 0.001 | NJ | Upper Montclair | WMSC |
| # 90.5 | 0.9 | NJ | Lincroft | WBJB-FM |
| 90.5 | 0.125 | NJ | Morristown | WJSV |
| # 90.7 | 15 | NY | Manahawkin | WYRS |
| # 90.7 | 46 | NY | New York | WFUV |
| 90.7 | 2.5 | NY | New York | WFUV-FM3 |
| 91.1 | 1.25 | NJ | East Orange | WFMU |
| # 91.1 | 20 | CT | Fairfield° | WSHU-FM |
| 91.1 | 0.015 | NY | Ossining | WOSS |
| 91.3 | 0.25 | NY | Huntington Stn | W217AF (WSHU-FM) |
| 91.3 | 3.7 | NY | Poughkeepsie° | WVKR-FM |
| # 91.5 | 2 | NY | New York | WNYE |
| 91.7 | 0.82 | NY | Pomona | WLFR |
| # 91.9 | 5.4 | NJ | Hackettstown° | WXPJ |
| 91.9 | 6 | NY | Lake Ronkonkoma | WSHR |
| 91.9 | 0.01 | NY | New City | W220EG (WMFU) |
| 91.9 | 0.01 | NJ | Parlin | W220AA (WRDR) |
| 91.9 | 0.01 | NJ | Weehawken | W220EJ (WFMU) |
| # 92.3 | 6 | NY | New York | WNYL |
| 92.7 | 1.2 | NY | Brooklyn | WQBU-FM2 (sp) |
| 92.7 | 0.105 | NJ | Franklin Township | W224CW (WPRB) (as) |
| # 92.7 | 2 | NY | Garden City | WQBU-FM (sp) |
| 92.7 | 6 | NY | Middletown° | WRRV |
| 92.7 | 0.08 | NY | New York | WQBU-FM1 (sp) |
| 92.9 | 3.1 | NY | Manorville | WEHM |
| 92.9 | 0.08 | NY | Pomona | W225BV (WYRS) |
| # 93.1 | 5.4 | NJ | Paterson | WPAT-FM (sp) |
| # 93.5 | 1.75 | NY | New Rochelle | WVIP |
| 93.5 | 0.25 | NY | Warwick | W228CG (WTBQ) |
| 93.7 | 0.1 | NY | Westbrookville | WQPU-LP |
| # 93.9 | 5.2 | NY | New York | WNYC-FM |
| 94.1 | 0.25 | NY | Chester | W231BP (WLJP) |
| # 94.3 | 1.3 | NJ | Asbury Park° | WJLK |
| 94.3 | 0.055 | NY | Pomona | W232AL (WPLJ-HD2) |
| 94.3 | 2.6 | NY | Smithtown | WWSK |
| 94.3 | 0.058 | NJ | Wood Ridge | WSBP-LP |
| 94.5 | 50 | NJ | Trenton° | WPST |
| # 94.7 | 23.5 | NY | Newark | WNSH |
| 94.9 | 0.01 | NY | Hauppauge | W235BB (WKLV) |
| # 95.1 | 30 | PA | Bethlehem° | WZZO |
| 95.1 | 29.5 | CT | Brookfield° | WRKI |
| 95.1 | 0.027 | NY | Ft. Greene | W236CH (WNSH) |
| # 95.5 | 6.7 | NY | New York | WPLJ |
| 95.9 | 0.06 | NJ | Dover | W240EE (WTOC) |
| 95.9 | 0.19 | NY | Freeport | W240DF (WGBB) |
| 95.9 | 0.039 | NJ | Maplewood | WZYE-LP |
| 95.9 | 0.01 | NY | Peekskill | W240CR (WAMC) |
| # 95.9 | 1.45 | NJ | Point Pleasant | WRAT |
| 95.9 | 3 | CT | Southport° | WFOX |
| 95.9 | 0.027 | NJ | Wayne | WYNE-LP |
| 96.3 | 6 | NY | New York | WXNY-FM (sp) |
| 96.7 | 0.05 | NJ | Parsippany | W232CY (WXMC) (as) |
| # 96.7 | 3.1 | NY | Port Chester | WKLV-FM |
| 96.9 | 0.01 | NY | Manorville | W245BA (WLIR-LP) |
| # 97.1 | 6.7 | NY | New York | WQHT |
| 97.5 | 0.11 | NJ | Jersey City | W248CG (WVIP-HD4) |
| 97.5 | 0.063 | NJ | Newton | WRSK-LP |
| # 97.5 | 39 | NY | Patchogue | WALK-FM |
| # 97.9 | 6 | NY | New York | WSKQ-FM (sp) |
| 98.1 | 0.25 | NY | Patchogue | W251BY (WPTY-HD2) |

| MHz | kW | Sta | City of License | Station |
|---|---|---|---|---|
| 98.3 | 0.01 | NY | Brooklyn | W252CS (WVIP) |
| 98.3 | 3 | NY | Hempstead | WKJY |
| # 98.3 | 1.2 | NJ | New Brunswick° | WMGQ |
| # 98.7 | 6 | NY | New York | WEPN-FM |
| # 99.1 | 15 | CT | New Haven° | WPLR |
| # 99.1 | 28 | NJ | Zarephath | WAWZ |
| 99.5 | 4.3 | NY | New York | WBAI |
| 99.9 | 27.5 | CT | Bridgeport° | WEZN-FM |
| # 99.9 | 50 | PA | Easton° | WODE-FM |
| #100.1 | 1.7 | NJ | Manahawkin | WJRZ-FM |
| #100.3 | 6 | NJ | Newark | WHTZ |
| 100.7 | 0.125 | NJ | Eatontown | W264DH (WHTG) |
| 100.7 | 0.2 | NJ | Edison | W264BT (WWTR) |
| 100.7 | 50 | NY | Peekskill | WHUD |
| 100.9 | 0.25 | NJ | Manahawkin | W265CS (WSJO) |
| #101.1 | 6.7 | NY | New York | WCBS-FM |
| #101.3 | 12 | CT | Hamden° | WKCI-FM |
| 101.5 | 0.013 | NJ | Plainview | W268AN (WVIP-HD3) |
| 101.5 | 0.038 | NJ | Queens | W268BY (WVIP) |
| #101.5 | 15.5 | NJ | Trenton° | WKXW |
| #101.9 | 6.2 | NY | New York | WFAN-FM |
| 102.3 | 0.1 | NY | Arrowhead Vlg | WUPC-LP (sp) |
| #102.3 | 6 | NJ | Babylon | WBAB |
| 102.3 | 0.01 | NY | Brooklyn | WBQE-LP |
| 102.3 | 0.59 | NJ | Franklin | WSUS |
| #102.7 | 6 | NY | New York | WNEW |
| 103.1 | 1.55 | NY | Bay Shore | WBZO |
| 103.1 | 0.095 | NJ | Ft. Lee | W276AQ (WRDR) |
| #103.3 | 14 | NJ | Princetown° | WPRB |
| #103.5 | 6 | NY | Lake Success | WKTU |
| 103.7 | 0.01 | NJ | Hazlet | WPDI (sp) |
| 103.7 | 2.3 | NJ | Newton | WNNJ |
| #103.9 | 0.98 | NY | Bronxville | WNBM |
| #104.3 | 6 | NY | New York | WAXQ |
| 104.5 | 0.01 | NY | Selden | W283BA (WLIR-FM) |
| 104.7 | 0.2 | NJ | Franklin Township | W264BT (WQHT-HD2) |
| 104.7 | 0.25 | NY | Hempstead | W284DG (WHLI) |
| 104.7 | 0.17 | NY | New York | W284BW(WPAT-FM-HD2)(sp) |
| 104.7 | 7.4 | NY | Poughkeepsie° | WSPK |
| #105.1 | 6 | NY | New York | WWPR-FM |
| #105.5 | 1 | NY | Dover | WDHA-FM |
| 105.5 | 0.019 | NY | Flushing | $+ WQEQ-LP |
| 105.5 | 0.019 | NY | Queens | $+ WDMB-LP |
| 105.7 | 12 | NY | Manahawkin | WCHR-FM |
| 105.7 | 0.25 | NY | Selden | W289AD (WSUF) |
| #105.9 | 0.61 | NJ | Newark | WQXR-FM |
| #106.1 | 49 | NY | Patchogue | WBLI |
| 106.3 | 1.1 | NJ | Eatontown | WKMK |
| 106.3 | 0.98 | NY | Mt Kisco | WFME |
| 106.3 | 0.099 | NY | New York | W292DV (WVIP-HD2) |
| #106.7 | 6 | NY | New York | WLTW |
| 107.1 | 1.9 | NY | Briarcliff Manor | WXPK |
| 107.1 | 5 | NJ | Long Branch | WWZY |
| 107.1 | 0.14 | NY | Melville | W296CQ (WBZO) |
| 107.1 | 0.01 | NY | Warwick | W296BD (WAMC-FM) |
| 107.3 | 0.006 | NY | Stony Brook | W297BM (WUSB) |
| #107.5 | 4.2 | NY | New York | WBLS |
| 107.9 | 0.004 | NY | Dover | WCFT-LP |
| 107.9 | 0.1 | NJ | Lakewood | WMDI-LP |
| 107.9 | 0.25 | NJ | Manahawkin | W300AO (WJRZ-HD2) |

**Orlando Metro Area** (Orlando-Kissimmee-Sanford, FL MSA)

| MHz | kW | Sta | City of License | Station |
|---|---|---|---|---|
| # 88.3 | 98.4 | FL | Orlando | WPOZ |
| # 88.7 | 35 | FL | Clermont | WMYZ |
| 88.9 | 25 | FL | Edgewater° | WKTO |
| 89.1 | 5.2 | FL | Kissimmee | WLAZ (sp) |
| 89.3 | 7.1 | FL | Titusville° | WPIO |
| 89.5 | 22 | FL | Cedar Creek° | WMFV |
| # 89.7 | 69 | FL | Tampa° | WUSF |
| # 89.9 | 5.6 | FL | Orlando | WUCF-FM |
| 90.3 | 9.4 | FL | Eustis | WIGW |
| 90.3 | 0.75 | FL | Haines City° | WLVF |
| # 90.7 | 100 | FL | Orlando | WMFE-FM |
| 91.1 | 100 | FL | Lakeland° | WKES |
| ‡ 91.5 | 0.9 | FL | Winter Park | WPRK |
| 91.9 | 25 | FL | Lakeland° | WYFO |
| # 92.3 | 99 | FL | Orlando | WWKA |
| 92.7 | 0.028 | FL | Kissimmee | WKIE-LP (sp) |
| 92.7 | 0.027 | FL | Winter Garden | W224CQ (WYFO) |
| 92.7 | 0.027 | FL | Winter Park | WRXW-LP |
| 92.9 | 50 | FL | Ocala° | WMFQ |
| 93.1 | 0.25 | FL | Orlando | W226BT (WFLF) |
| 93.3 | 0.25 | FL | Sanford | W227CP (WPOZ-HD3) |
| # 93.3 | 97 | FL | Tampa° | WFLZ-FM |
| 93.5 | 0.01 | FL | Orlando | W228DF (WOTW) |
| 93.5 | 0.038 | FL | Union Park | W228BK (WYFO) |
| 93.7 | 0.051 | FL | Kissimmee | WNKQ-LP (sp) |
| 93.7 | 100 | FL | Ocala° | WOGK |
| 93.9 | 0.085 | FL | Orlando | WWRT-LP (sp) |
| # 94.1 | 100 | FL | Lakeland° | WLLD |
| 94.1 | 0.25 | FL | Orlando | W231CT (WOTW-HD2) |
| 94.8 | 0.225 | FL | Orlando | W235CR (WTLN) |
| 94.9 | 97.3 | FL | Tampa° | WWRM |
| # 95.3 | 12 | FL | Maitland | WYPO |
| 95.7 | 0.1 | FL | Christmas | WLPM-LP |
| ‡ 95.7 | 0.054 | FL | Kissimmee | WLJJ-LP |
| 95.7 | 48 | FL | Ormond-by-the-Sea° | WHOG-FM |
| 95.9 | 0.099 | FL | Orlando | W240BV (WPOZ-HD2) |
| 96.1 | 0.019 | FL | Kissimmee | W241BP (WYFO) |
| 96.1 | 0.068 | FL | Orlando | WWID-LP (sp) |
| # 96.5 | 99 | FL | Orlando | WDBO-FM |
| 97.1 | 0.14 | FL | Clermont | W246BT (WRUM) (sp) |
| 97.1 | 0.25 | FL | Kissimmee | W246CK (WRUM-HD2)(sp) |
| 97.1 | 0.1 | FL | Mount Dora | WVGT-LP |
| # 97.9 | 100 | FL | Clearwater° | WXTB |
| 97.9 | 0.25 | FL | Kissimmee | W250CE (WRSO) (sp) |
| # 98.1 | 50 | FL | Deltona° | WNUE-FM (sp) |
| # 98.3 | 27 | FL | Ft. Meade° | WWRZ |
| 98.5 | 0.018 | FL | Orlando | WHPB-LP |
| # 98.9 | 44 | FL | Orlando | WMMO |
| # 99.3 | 54 | FL | Cocoa° | WLRQ-FM |
| 99.5 | 0.25 | FL | Orlando | W258DD (WONQ) (sp) |
| 99.7 | 0.016 | FL | Kissimmee | WBVL-LP (sp) |
| 99.7 | 0.1 | FL | Mary Lake | WWRG-LP |
| 99.7 | 0.012 | FL | Winter Garden | WIDT-LP (sp) |
| 99.9 | 0.067 | FL | Apopka | WPKA-LP |
| 99.9 | 0.048 | FL | Orlando | WOGJ-LP (ha) |
| 99.9 | 0.1 | FL | Orlando | WIME-LP (sp) |
| ‡ 99.9 | 0.019 | FL | Winter Garden | WDDT-LP (sp) |
| #100.3 | 95 | FL | Orlando | WRUM (sp) |
| 100.7 | 0.01 | FL | Orlando | WUOH-LP |
| #100.7 | 96 | FL | Tampa° | WMTX |
| #101.1 | 95 | FL | Cocoa Beach° | WJRR |
| 101.5 | 0.225 | FL | Orlando | W268CT (WDYZ) (sp) |
| #101.5 | 97.1 | FL | St. Petersburg° | WPOI |
| 101.9 | 90 | FL | Daytona Beach° | WQMP |
| 102.3 | 0.08 | FL | Kissimmee | WMQV-LP (sp) |
| 102.5 | 0.25 | FL | Orlando | W273CA (WFLF) |
| 102.7 | 50 | FL | Rockledge° | WHKR |
| 103.1 | 22 | FL | Windermere | WOTW |
| 103.5 | 0.25 | FL | Eatonville | W278CN (WURF) |
| #103.5 | 66 | FL | Gulfport° | WFUS |
| 103.7 | 0.18 | FL | Clermont | W279CT (WPOZ-HD4) |
| 103.7 | 0.191 | FL | Kissimmee | W279DI (WRMQ) (sp) |
| #104.1 | 94 | FL | Cocoa Beach° | WTKS-FM |
| 104.5 | 0.221 | FL | Altamonte Springs | W283AN (WTKS-HD2) |
| #105.1 | 94 | FL | Orlando | WOMX |
| 105.5 | 0.08 | FL | Kissimmee | WTMS-LP (sp) |
| 105.5 | 0.25 | FL | Oviedo | W288CJ (WORL) |
| #105.9 | 96 | FL | DeLand° | WOCL |
| 106.3 | 13.5 | FL | Melbourne° | WCIF |
| 106.3 | 0.215 | FL | Orlando | W292DZ (WPOZ-HD3) |
| #106.7 | 100 | FL | Tavares | WXXL |
| 107.1 | 100 | FL | Melbourne° | WAOA-FM |
| 107.3 | 0.25 | FL | Orlando | W297BB (WCFB) |
| 107.5 | 98 | FL | Mount Dora | WMGF |

**Philadelphia Metro Area** (Philadelphia-Camden-Wilmington, PA-NJ-DE-MD MSA)

| MHz | kW | Sta | City of License | Station |
|---|---|---|---|---|
| 88.1 | 0.08 | NJ | Berlin | WNJS-FM |
| 88.1 | 0.01 | PA | Philadelphia | WPEB |
| 88.1 | 0.088 | DE | Pike Creek | WMHS |
| 88.1 | 0.11 | NJ | Trenton° | WNJT-FM |
| 88.1 | 0.43 | PA | Warwick | WZZD |
| # 88.5 | 2.65 | PA | Philadelphia | WXPN |
| 88.9 | 0.9 | PA | Sellersville | WBYO |
| 89.1 | 1.2 | DE | Christiana | WXHL-FM |
| 89.1 | 0.7 | PA | Radnor Township | WYBF |
| # 89.1 | 1.15 | NJ | Trenton° | WWFM |
| 89.1 | 0.1 | PA | Villanova | WXVU |
| 89.3 | 2.5 | NJ | Bridgeton° | WNJB-FM |
| 89.3 | 0.46 | PA | Coatesville | WRTJ |
| 89.3 | 1.6 | PA | Warminster | WRDV |
| # 89.5 | 1.9 | NJ | Cherry Hill | WYPA |
| 89.7 | 3.8 | NJ | Delaware Township° | WDVR |
| 89.7 | 0.75 | NJ | Glassboro | WGLS-FM |
| # 90.1 | 7.7 | PA | Philadelphia | WRTI |
| # 90.5 | 21 | NJ | Medford Lakes° | WWBV |

| MHz | kW | Sta | City of License | Station |
|---|---|---|---|---|
| # 90.9 | 13.5 | PA | Philadelphia | WHYY-FM |
| # 91.3 | 6.8 | DE | Newark | WVUD |
| # 91.3 | 13.5 | NJ | Ocean City° | WRTQ |
| 91.3 | 1.5 | NJ | Trenton° | WTSR |
| 91.5 | 0.1 | NJ | Blackwood | WDBK |
| 91.5 | 0.11 | PA | Swarthmore | WSRN-FM |
| 91.7 | 0.1 | PA | Bristol | WLBS |
| 91.7 | 0.8 | PA | Philadelphia | WKDU |
| 91.7 | 0.5 | PA | Telford | WBMR |
| 91.7 | 0.1 | PA | West Chester | WCUR |
| 91.7 | 0.1 | DE | Wilmington | WMPH |
| 92.1 | 0.016 | PA | Horsham | WEMQ-LP |
| 92.1 | 6 | NJ | Vineland° | WVLT |
| # 92.5 | 15 | PA | Philadelphia | WXTU |
| 92.9 | 0.1 | PA | Philadelphia | WOOM-LP |
| 92.9 | 0.015 | PA | Philadelphia | $ WRLG-LP |
| 92.9 | 0.015 | PA | Philadelphia | $ WRGU-LP |
| 92.9 | 0.015 | PA | Philadelphia | $ WGGT-LP |
| # 93.3 | 16.5 | PA | Philadelphia | WMMR |
| # 93.7 | 47.1 | DE | Wilmington | WSTW |
| # 94.1 | 9.6 | PA | Philadelphia | WIP-FM |
| 94.5 | 19 | PA | Lancaster° | WDAC |
| 94.5 | 50 | NJ | Trenton° | WPST |
| # 94.7 | 50 | DE | Dover° | WDSD |
| 94.9 | 0.004 | PA | Coatesville | W235AT (WVBV) |
| 94.9 | 0.014 | PA | Folsom | WRSD |
| 94.9 | 0.022 | NJ | Marlton° | W235BZ (WVBV) |
| 94.9 | 0.074 | PA | Philadelphia | W235CE (WVBV) |
| 95.1 | 50 | NJ | Atlantic City° | WAYV |
| 95.1 | 30 | PA | Bethlehem° | WZZO |
| 95.1 | 0.007 | PA | Philadelphia | W236CL (WPEB) |
| 95.3 | 0.25 | NJ | Pennsauken | W237EH (WSTW-HD2) |
| 95.3 | 0.084 | PA | Radnor | W235AP (WBYO) |
| 95.3 | 0.05 | DE | Wilmington | WHGE-LP |
| # 95.7 | 8.9 | PA | Philadelphia | WBEN-FM |
| 96.1 | 50 | PA | Easton° | WCTO |
| 96.1 | 0.25 | PA | Philadelphia | W241CH (WURD) |
| # 96.5 | 9.6 | PA | Philadelphia | WTDY-FM |
| 96.9 | 50 | NJ | Atlantic City° | WFPG |
| 96.9 | 0.026 | PA | Glenside | W245AG (WBYO) |
| 96.9 | 0.25 | DE | Wilmington | W245CJ (WJBR-HD3) (sp) |
| 97.1 | 0.074 | PA | Bensalem | W246AR (WDVR) |
| 97.1 | 0.01 | NJ | Collingswood | W246AQ (WXHL-FM ) |
| 97.1 | 0.25 | PA | Colmar | W246CN (WPAZ) |
| 97.3 | 0.018 | PA | Glen Mills | WZZE |
| 97.3 | 50 | PA | Millville° | WENJ |
| # 97.5 | 26 | NJ | Burlington° | WPEN |
| 98.1 | 9.6 | PA | Philadelphia | WOGL |
| 98.5 | 0.1 | PA | No. Philadelphia | WJYN-LP |
| 98.5 | 0.077 | PA | Philadelphia | WQEW-LP (ch) |
| 98.5 | 0.1 | DE | Wilmington | W253CQ (WTMC) |
| # 98.9 | 27 | PA | Philadelphia | WUSL |
| # 99.1 | 28 | NJ | Zarephath° | WAWZ |
| # 99.5 | 50 | DE | Wilmington | WJBR-FM |
| # 99.9 | 50 | PA | Easton° | WODE-FM |
| 99.9 | 0.0095 | PA | Havertown | WHHS |
| 99.9 | 0.085 | DE | Newark | WIZU-LP |
| 99.9 | 0.05 | PA | Philadelphia | W260CZ (WHAT) |
| #100.3 | 17 | PA | Media | WRNB |
| #100.7 | 11.5 | PA | Allentown° | WLEV |
| †100.7 | 0.099 | NJ | Mount Holly | W264BH (WKVP) |
| #101.1 | 14 | PA | Philadelphia | WBEB |
| #101.5 | 15.5 | NJ | Trenton° | WKXW |
| 101.7 | 3.3 | NJ | Canton° | WDEL-FM |
| 101.7 | 0.003 | PA | Coatesville | W269BL (WBYO) |
| 101.7 | 0.015 | PA | Pottstown | W269BT (WVBV) |
| #102.1 | 27 | PA | Philadelphia | WIOQ |
| 102.5 | 0.099 | PA | Philadelphia | W273DO (WDAS) |
| 102.5 | 10 | PA | Reading° | WRFY-FM |
| #102.9 | 8.9 | PA | Philadelphia | WMGK |
| #103.3 | 14 | NJ | Princeton° | WPRB |
| 103.5 | 0.2 | PA | Pottstown | W278BR (WPAZ) |
| 103.5 | 0.08 | PA | Village Green | W278AK (WXHL) |
| 103.7 | 50 | NJ | Atlantic City° | WMGM |
| 103.7 | 0.09 | NJ | Cherry Hill | W279CN (WXHL-FM) |
| 103.7 | 39 | MD | Havre de Grace° | WXCY |
| 103.9 | 0.27 | PA | Jenkintown | WPHI-FM |
| 103.9 | 0.005 | PA | Wagontown | W280CP (WDAC) |
| #104.1 | 50 | PA | Allentown° | WAEB-FM |
| #104.5 | 11.5 | PA | Philadelphia | WRFF |
| #104.9 | 10 | NJ | Egg Harbor City° | WSJO |
| 104.9 | 0.25 | PA | Lansdale | W285EW (WNPV) |
| †104.9 | 0.099 | PA | Philadelphia | W285FF (WWDB) |

| MHz | kW | Sta | City of License | Station |
|---|---|---|---|---|
| 105.1 | 25 | PA | Ephrata° | WIOV-FM |
| #105.3 | 16.5 | PA | Philadelphia | WDAS-FM |
| 105.7 | 0.25 | NJ | Camden | W289AZ (WEMG) (sp) |
| 105.7 | 12 | NJ | Manahawkin° | WCHR-FM |
| 105.7 | 0.024 | PA | Plymouth° | WEMZ-LP |
| #106.1 | 22.5 | PA | Philadelphia | WISX |
| 106.5 | 0.007 | PA | Eagleville | WRDY-LP |
| 106.5 | 0.09 | PA | Philadelphia | WPPM-LP |
| 106.5 | 0.016 | PA | Warminster | WHII-LP |
| #106.9 | 38 | NJ | Camden | WKVP |
| 107.3 | 0.02 | PA | Philadelphia | W297AD (WRDV) |
| 107.5 | 30 | PA | Boyertown° | WBYN-FM |
| 107.7 | 0.25 | DE | Marshallton | W299BH (WRTI) |
| 107.9 | 0.78 | NJ | Pennsauken | WPPZ-FM |

**Phoenix Metro Area** (Phoenix-Mesa-Scottsdale, AZ MSA)

| MHz | kW | Sta | City of License | Station |
|---|---|---|---|---|
| 88.3 | 22.5 | AZ | Phoenix | $ KNAI |
| 88.3 | 22.5 | AZ | Phoenix | $ KPHF |
| 88.7 | 15 | AZ | Chandler | KPNG |
| 88.9 | 0.01 | AZ | Phoenix | K205CI (KEBR-FM) |
| 89.1 | 30 | AZ | Fountain Hills | KLVK |
| # 89.5 | 29.7 | AZ | Phoenix | KBAQ |
| 89.7 | 0.01 | AZ | Scottsdale | K209DV (KBAQ-FM) |
| 89.9 | 45 | AZ | Superior | KZAI |
| 90.3 | 100 | AZ | Phoenix | KLRF-FM |
| 90.7 | 2 | AZ | Apache Junction | KVIT |
| 90.9 | 58 | AZ | Prescott° | KLVH |
| 91.1 | 0.075 | AZ | Cave Creek | K216GN (KRKY-FM) |
| 91.1 | 0.075 | AZ | Guadalupe | K216FO (KNOG-FM) (sp) |
| 91.1 | 0.25 | AZ | Wickenburg | K216GP (KLVK) |
| # 91.5 | 100 | AZ | Phoenix | KJZZ |
| 91.7 | 0.01 | AZ | Rio Verde | K219DZ (KJZZ) |
| 92.1 | 0.01 | AZ | Wickenburg | K221GE (KNLB) |
| # 92.3 | 98 | AZ | Glendale | KTAR-FM |
| 92.7 | 0.25 | AZ | Phoenix | K224CJ (KAZG) |
| 92.9 | 0.1 | AZ | Desert Ridge | KDWR-LP |
| # 93.3 | 100 | AZ | Mesa | KDKB |
| 93.7 | 0.25 | AZ | Phoenix | K229DB (KOY) (sp) |
| 93.9 | 0.002 | AZ | Scottsdale | KWSS-LP |
| 94.1 | 4.7 | AZ | San Carlos° | KRDE |
| # 94.5 | 95.6 | AZ | Phoenix | KOOL-FM |
| 94.9 | 0.25 | AZ | Chandler | K235CB (KOAI) |
| 95.1 | 41 | AZ | Sun City West | KOAI |
| # 95.5 | 96 | AZ | Phoenix | KYOT-FM |
| 95.9 | 0.25 | AZ | Buckeye | K240DC (KESZ) |
| 95.9 | 21 | AZ | Cottonwood° | KKLD |
| 95.9 | 0.25 | AZ | Tempe | K240EU (KQFN) |
| 96.1 | 0.14 | AZ | Ft. McDowell | K241BQ (KZON) |
| 96.1 | 0.25 | AZ | Phoenix | K241CS (KXEG) |
| 96.3 | 5.3 | AZ | Wickenburg | KSWG |
| 96.5 | 0.25 | AZ | Laveen | K243BN (KLVK) |
| # 96.9 | 98 | AZ | Phoenix | KMXP |
| 97.3 | 0.04 | AZ | Goodyear | K247BH (KFLR-FM) |
| 97.3 | 0.25 | AZ | Payson° | K247CF (KZON) |
| # 97.5 | 42 | AZ | Dewey-Humboldt° | KMVA |
| # 97.9 | 96 | AZ | Tempe | KUPD |
| 98.3 | 41 | AZ | Mayer° | KKFR |
| # 98.7 | 97 | AZ | Phoenix | KMVP-FM |
| 99.3 | 17 | AZ | Payson° | KEMP |
| 99.3 | 0.25 | AZ | Phoenix | K257CD (KQFN) |
| ‡ 99.5 | 0.625 | AZ | Wittman | KRPH-FM1 (sp) |
| # 99.9 | 99 | AZ | Phoenix | KESZ |
| #100.3 | 90 | AZ | Globe° | KQMR |
| #100.7 | 100 | AZ | Scottsdale | KSLX-FM |
| 101.1 | 40 | AZ | Cordes Lakes° | KNRJ |
| 101.1 | 0.05 | AZ | Florence | KOHF-LP |
| #101.5 | 100 | AZ | Phoenix | KALV-FM |
| 101.9 | 0.25 | AZ | Phoenix | K270BZ (KNAI) (sp) |
| #102.1 | 25.5 | AZ | Spring Valley° | KAHM |
| #102.5 | 98 | AZ | Phoenix | KNIX-FM |
| 102.9 | 0.1 | AZ | Phoenix | KDIF-LP |
| 102.9 | 0.19 | AZ | Phoenix | K275CP (KIHP) |
| 103.1 | 42 | AZ | Florence | KCDX |
| 103.1 | 0.1 | AZ | Sun City West | KSCW-LP |
| #103.5 | 48 | AZ | Glendale | KLNZ (sp) |
| #103.9 | 99.59 | AZ | Gilbert | KZON |
| #104.3 | 40 | AZ | Camp Verde° | KAJM |
| #104.7 | 100 | AZ | Mesa | KZZP |
| 105.1 | 46 | AZ | Wickenburg | KHOV-FM (sp) |
| 105.3 | 0.42 | AZ | Constellation° | KHOV-FM1 (sp) |
| 105.3 | 0.25 | AZ | Mesa | K287BX (KFNN) |
| 105.5 | 0.8 | AZ | Avondale | KLVA |
| #105.9 | 7 | AZ | Glendale | KHOT-FM1 (sp) |
| 105.9 | 36 | AZ | Paradise Valley | KHOT-FM (sp) |

| MHz | kW | Sta | City of License | Station |
|---|---|---|---|---|
| #106.3 | 23 | AZ | Sun City | KOMR |
| 106.5 | 0.86 | AZ | Arizona City | KKMR |
| 106.5 | 0.25 | AZ | Phoenix | K283CO (KSUN) (sp) |
| 106.7 | 0.25 | AZ | Phoenix | K294CW (KASA) |
| 106.7 | 3.7 | AZ | Prescott Valley° | KPPV |
| 106.9 | 6 | AZ | Buckeye | KDVA |
| #107.1 | 17 | AZ | Apache Junction | KVVA-FM (sp) |
| ‡107.3 | 50 | AZ | Aguilla | KAZV |
| 107.5 | 0.25 | AZ | Phoenix | K298CK (KNUV) (sp) |
| #107.9 | 96 | AZ | Chandler | KMLE |

**Riverside - San Bernadino Metro Area** (Riverside-San Bernardino-Ontario, CA MSA)

| MHz | kW | Sta | City of License | Station |
|---|---|---|---|---|
| 88.1 | 0.15 | CA | Banning | KRTM |
| 88.1 | 0.01 | CA | Victorville | K201CD (KVCR) |
| 88.3 | 0.01 | CA | Barstow | K202DM (KHMS) |
| 88.3 | 0.15 | CA | Riverside | KUCR |
| # 88.5 | 1.6 | CA | Palm Springs | KPSC |
| 88.5 | 0.2 | CA | Victorville | KHMS |
| ‡ 88.7 | 0.014 | CA | Banning | K204GG (KSGN) |
| 88.7 | 0.4 | CA | Claremont° | KSPC |
| 88.9 | 0.006 | CA | Indio | K205DT (KAWZ) |
| 88.9 | 0.27 | CA | Temecula | KSDW |
| 88.9 | 0.01 | CA | Yucca Valley | K205DK (KODV) |
| 89.1 | 5.8 | CA | Barstow | KODV (sp) |
| # 89.1 | 0.35 | CA | Redlands | KUOR-FM |
| # 89.3 | 3.2 | CA | Indio | KCRI |
| 89.3 | 0.6 | CA | Pasadena° | KPCC |
| 89.5 | 1.2 | CA | Victorville | KLXD |
| ‡ 89.7 | 0.009 | CA | Palm Springs | K209AK (KSGN) |
| 89.7 | 2.75 | CA | Riverside | KSGN |
| 89.9 | 0.01 | CA | Apple Valley | K210DL (KEFX) |
| # 89.9 | 6.9 | CA | Santa Monica° | KCRW |
| 90.1 | 0.59 | CA | Yucaipa | KLRD |
| 90.3 | 0.006 | CA | Barstow | K212BD (KAWZ) |
| # 90.3 | 0.34 | CA | Coachella | KVLA-FM |
| 90.3 | 0.01 | CA | Victorville | K212EK (KAWZ) |
| 90.5 | 0.01 | CA | Palm Springs | K213AB (KLOV) |
| 90.5 | 3.5 | CA | Yucca Valley | KNLM |
| 90.7 | 110 | CA | Los Angeles° | KPFK |
| 90.9 | 0.01 | CA | Barstow | K215ET (KNLB) |
| 90.9 | 0.01 | CA | Beaumont | K215BA (KCRW) |
| 90.9 | 0.23 | CA | Coachella | KPSH |
| 91.1 | 0.285 | CA | Perris | KKLP |
| 91.1 | 0.056 | CA | Yucca Valley | K216CX (KAWZ) |
| 91.3 | 1.55 | CA | Barstow | KWTH |
| 91.3 | 0.01 | CA | Coachella | K217EZ (KMRO) (sp) |
| # 91.5 | 39 | CA | Los Angeles° | KUSC |
| 91.7 | 0.01 | CA | Victorville | K219DK (KMRO) (sp) |
| # 91.9 | 3.8 | CA | San Bernardino | KVCR |
| 92.1 | 0.027 | CA | Barstow | K221GB (KLXD) |
| 92.3 | 0.06 | CA | Cathedral City | K222DA (KWXY) |
| 92.3 | 42 | CA | Los Angeles° | KRRL |
| 92.5 | 0.1 | CA | Yucaipa | KQLH-LP |
| 92.7 | 0.285 | CA | Adelanto | KYZA |
| 92.7 | 0.005 | CA | Fontana | K224DK (KLRD) |
| # 92.7 | 4.2 | CA | Indio | KKUU |
| # 92.9 | 6 | CA | Menifee | KXFG |
| ‡ 93.1 | 0.039 | CA | Indio | K226BT (KVGH) |
| # 93.1 | 27.5 | CA | Los Angeles° | KCBS-FM |
| 93.3 | 0.01 | CA | Palm Springs | K227BX (KVLA-FM) |
| 93.5 | 0.006 | CA | Barstow | K228CO (KODV) |
| 93.5 | 5 | CA | Ontario | KDEY-FM |
| 93.7 | 26.5 | CA | Coachella | KCLB-FM |
| # 93.7 | 6 | CA | Newberry Springs | KIQQ-FM |
| 93.9 | 0.01 | CA | Barstow | K230AO (KNLB) |
| # 93.9 | 18.5 | CA | Los Angeles° | KXOS |
| 94.3 | 4.6 | CA | Barstow | KDUC |
| 94.3 | 0.1 | CA | Redlands | KHSH-LP |
| 94.3 | 0.1 | CA | San Bernardino | KJVA-LP (sp) |
| 94.5 | 0.099 | CA | Big Bear Lake | KVBB-LP |
| 94.5 | 0.54 | CA | Temecula | KMYT |
| # 94.7 | 52 | CA | Los Angeles° | KTWV |
| 95.1 | 0.05 | CA | Coachella | KWXZ-LP |
| # 95.1 | 50 | CA | San Bernardino | KFRG |
| # 95.5 | 61 | CA | Los Angeles° | KLOS |
| 95.5 | 0.01 | CA | Palm Springs | K238BB (KMRO) |
| 95.9 | 8.9 | CA | Barstow | KXXZ (sp) |
| 95.9 | 6 | CA | La Mirada ° | KFSH-FM |
| 96.1 | 1.4 | CA | San Jacinto | KRQB (sp) |
| 96.3 | 0.01 | CA | Indio | K242BR (KMRO) |
| 96.3 | 6.6 | CA | Los Angeles° | KXOL-FM (sp) |
| 96.3 | 0.13 | CA | Victorville | K242CS (KATJ-FM) |
| 96.7 | 1.75 | CA | Redlands | KCAL-FM |

| MHz | kW | Sta | City of License | Station |
|---|---|---|---|---|
| 96.9 | 0.05 | CA | Temecula | KPTL-LP |
| 97.1 | 0.01 | CA | Apple Valley | K246CL (KLXD) |
| # 97.1 | 21 | CA | Los Angeles° | KAMP-FM |
| 97.3 | 0.034 | CA | Indio | K247CL (KLXB) (sp) |
| 97.5 | 72 | CA | Riverside | KLYY |
| 97.9 | 33 | CA | East Los Angeles° | KLAX-FM (sp) |
| 98.1 | 0.01 | CA | Beaumont | K251CC (KMET) (sp) |
| 98.1 | 0.008 | CA | Grand Terrace | K251AH (KMRO) (sp) |
| 98.1 | 0.158 | CA | Indio | K251BX (KRCK-FM) |
| 98.1 | 1.55 | CA | Yermo | KRXV |
| 98.3 | 0.03 | CA | Temecula | K252BF (KSSD) |
| # 98.3 | 6 | CA | West Covina° | KRCV (sp) |
| # 98.5 | 38 | CA | Cathedral City | KDES-FM |
| # 98.7 | 75 | CA | Los Angeles° | KYSR |
| 98.7 | 0.001 | CA | Victorville | KNVU-LP (sp) |
| 99.1 | 0.054 | CA | Palm Springs | K256CU (KKGX) |
| # 99.1 | 2.55 | CA | Riverside | KGGI |
| 99.5 | 0.19 | CA | Apple Valley | K258DE (KWRN) |
| 99.5 | 0.01 | CA | Barstow | K258CK (KTQX) (sp) |
| 99.5 | 10 | CA | Los Angeles° | KKLA-FM |
| 99.5 | 3 | CA | Rancho Mirage | KMRJ |
| 99.9 | 29.5 | CA | San Bernardino | KOLA |
| 100.1 | 0.003 | CA | Rancho Mirage | KRAQ-LP (sp) |
| #100.3 | 5.4 | CA | Los Angeles° | KKLQ |
| 100.5 | 25 | CA | Palm Springs | KPSI-FM |
| 100.7 | 0.013 | CA | Corona | K264CI (KBRT) |
| #100.7 | 0.26 | CA | George | KATJ-FM |
| 100.7 | 0.25 | CA | Guasti | K264AF (KLRD) |
| 100.9 | 1.5 | CA | Beaumont | KAEH (sp) |
| 100.9 | 0.19 | CA | Cathedral City | K265FH (KPSF) |
| #101.1 | 51 | CA | Los Angeles° | KRTH |
| ‡101.3 | 2.25 | CA | Barstow | KWIE |
| 101.3 | 1.55 | CA | Idyllwild | KATY-FM |
| 101.3 | 0.5 | CA | Menifee | KATY-FM1 |
| 101.5 | 0.1 | CA | Corona | KORM-LP (sp) |
| 101.5 | 0.25 | CA | Palm Springs | K268AH (KJJZ-HD2) |
| 101.7 | 0.3 | CA | Big Bear Lake | KXSB |
| 101.9 | 0.095 | CA | Cathedral City | K270AI (KLOV) |
| #101.9 | 4.8 | CA | Glendale° | KSCA (sp) |
| 102.3 | 6 | CA | Apple Valley | KZXY-FM |
| 102.3 | 2.6 | CA | Indio | KRHQ |
| 102.3 | 0.05 | CA | Riverside | K272FQ (KCAA) |
| 102.5 | 4.3 | CA | Hemet | KGGN |
| #102.7 | 8 | CA | Los Angeles° | KIIS-FM |
| 103.1 | 0.01 | CA | Muscoy | K276EF (KAWZ) |
| 103.1 | 0.3 | CA | Newport Beach° | KDLE |
| 103.1 | 0.25 | CA | Victorville | KVFG |
| 103.3 | 1.25 | CA | Temecula | KTMQ |
| 103.5 | 1.9 | CA | Coachella | KPST-FM |
| #103.5 | 12.5 | CA | Los Angeles° | KOST |
| 103.7 | 0.25 | CA | Yucca Valley | K279CO (KNWH) |
| 103.9 | 0.25 | CA | Cathedral City | K280CV (KKUU-HD2) |
| 103.9 | 0.022 | CA | Coachella | K280FO (KYRM) |
| 103.9 | 0.18 | CA | Lake Arrowhead | KHTI |
| 104.1 | 4.1 | CA | Murrieta | KKLM |
| #104.3 | 65 | CA | Los Angeles° | KBIG |
| 104.7 | 0.175 | CA | Palm Springs | K284CR (KNWZ) |
| 104.7 | 1.35 | CA | Redlands | KQIE |
| #105.1 | 18 | CA | Los Angeles° | KKGO |
| 105.5 | 0.008 | CA | Big Bear Lake | KWBB-LP |
| 105.5 | 0.059 | CA | Corona | KGIC-LP (sp) |
| 105.5 | 6 | CA | Hemet | KXRS (sp) |
| 105.5 | 3 | CA | Long Beach° | KBUE |
| 105.5 | 0.01 | CA | Victorville | K288DJ (KFSG) |
| #105.9 | 25 | CA | Los Angeles° | KPWR |
| 106.1 | 50 | CA | Palm Springs | KPLM |
| 106.1 | 0.25 | CA | San Jacinto | KPLM-FM2 |
| 106.1 | 0.003 | CA | Victorville | K291CM (KVTR) |
| ‡106.3 | 0.07 | CA | San Bernardino | K292GN (KJVA-LP) (sp) |
| 106.3 | 6 | CA | Santa Ana° | KALI-FM |
| 106.5 | 0.56 | CA | Lucerne Valley | KIXA |
| 106.5 | 0.04 | CA | Moreno Valley | K293CF (KCCA) |
| #106.7 | 5.5 | CA | Pasadena° | KROQ-FM |
| 106.9 | 0.007 | CA | Muscoy | K295AI (KMRO) (sp) |
| 106.9 | 4 | CA | Yucca Valley | KDGL |
| 107.1 | 0.1 | CA | Adelanto | KPTG-LP |
| #107.1 | 6 | CA | Arcadia° | KSSE (sp) |
| 107.3 | 0.25 | CA | Palm Springs | K297BO (KDES-HD2) |
| 107.3 | 0.1 | CA | Redlands | KWRS-LP |
| #107.5 | 29.5 | CA | Los Angeles° | KLVE |
| 107.9 | 0.05 | CA | Indio | K300CW (KLRD) (sp) |
| 107.9 | 0.53 | CA | San Clemente° | KWVE-FM |

**San Diego Metro Area** (San Diego-Carlsbad, CA MSA)

| MHz | kW | Sta | City of License | Station |
|---|---|---|---|---|
| # 88.3 | 22 | CA | San Diego | KSDS |
| 88.9 | 0.27 | CA | Temecula° | KSDW |
| 89.1 | 0.33 | CA | Descanso | KNSJ |
| 89.1 | 0.004 | CA | San Diego | K206AC (KPBS-FM) |
| # 89.5 | 25.7 | CA | San Diego | KPBS-FM |
| 89.9 | 0.001 | CA | Lemon Grove | K210CL (KCRW) |
| 90.7 | 110 | CA | Los Angeles° | KPFK |
| 91.3 | 0.19 | CA | Borrego Springs | KKJD |
| 91.3 | 0.1 | CA | Pala | KPRI |
| 91.9 | 0.05 | CA | Borrego Springs | K220GJ (KAWZ) |
| # 92.1 | 0.47 | CA | Escondido | KYDQ |
| # 92.3 | 42 | CA | Los Angeles° | KRRL |
| 92.9 | 0.05 | CA | Borrego Springs | K225BA (KCRI) |
| # 92.9 | 6 | CA | Menifee° | KXFG |
| # 93.3 | 50 | CA | El Cajon | KHTS-FM |
| 93.7 | 0.01 | CA | Rancho Bernardo | K229BO (KPFK) |
| 93.7 | 0.05 | CA | San Diego | KCZP-LP |
| # 94.1 | 77 | CA | San Diego | KMYI |
| 94.5 | 0.54 | CA | Temecula° | KMYT |
| 94.7 | 52 | CA | Los Angeles° | KTWV |
| # 94.9 | 26.5 | CA | San Diego | KBZT |
| # 95.1 | 50 | CA | San Bernadino° | KFRG |
| # 95.5 | 61 | CA | Los Angeles° | KLOS |
| 95.7 | 0.004 | CA | Borrego Springs | K239CE (KKJD) |
| # 95.7 | 28 | CA | Carlsbad | KSSX |
| 96.1 | 25 | CA | Campo | KYDO |
| 96.1 | 0.25 | CA | Oceanside | K241CT (KCBQ) |
| ‡ 96.1 | 0.011 | CA | San Diego | K241CH (KSDW) |
| 96.1 | 0.7 | CA | Santee | KYDO-FM1 |
| # 96.5 | 26.5 | CA | San Diego | KYXY |
| 96.9 | 0.25 | CA | San Pasqual | K245AI (KSDW) |
| # 97.3 | 50 | CA | San Diego | KWFN |
| 97.5 | 72 | CA | Riverside° | KLYY |
| # 98.1 | 26.5 | CA | San Diego | KXSN |
| 98.5 | 0.25 | CA | Oceanside | K253AD (KSSX-HD2) |
| 99.5 | 0.05 | CA | Fallbrook | KXFB-LP |
| 99.9 | 29.5 | CA | San Bernadino° | KOLA |
| 100.1 | 0.11 | CA | Julian | KKLJ |
| 100.7 | 30 | CA | San Diego | KFMB-FM |
| 101.1 | 0.019 | CA | El Cajon | KRSA-LP |
| #101.1 | 51 | CA | Los Angeles | KRTH |
| #101.5 | 50 | CA | San Diego | KGB-FM |
| 102.1 | 30 | CA | Encinitas | KLVJ |
| #102.9 | 30 | CA | San Diego | KLQV (sp) |
| 103.3 | 0.05 | CA | San Diego | K277DI (KOGO) |
| 103.3 | 0.015 | CA | San Diego | K277DG (KNSN) |
| 103.3 | 0.25 | CA | San Diego | K277DH (KLSD) |
| 103.3 | 1.25 | CA | Temecula° | KTMQ |
| #103.7 | 26.5 | CA | San Diego | KSON |
| 104.1 | 4.1 | CA | Murrieta° | KKLM |
| #104.3 | 65 | CA | Los Angeles° | KBIG |
| #105.3 | 26 | CA | San Diego | KIOZ |
| 105.3 | 0.01 | CA | San Diego | KIOZ-FM1 |
| 106.1 | 0.25 | CA | Encinitas | K291CR (KPRZ) |
| 106.1 | 50 | CA | Palm Springs° | KPLM |
| #106.5 | 50 | CA | San Diego | KLNV (sp) |
| ‡106.7 | 0.001 | CA | Fallbrook | K294CS (KRTM) |
| 107.1 | 3 | CA | Fallbrook | KSSD (sp) |
| 107.9 | 0.004 | CA | Alpine | KRLY-LP |
| #107.9 | 0.53 | CA | San Clemente° | KWVE-FM |

**San Francisco Metro Area** (San Francisco-Oakland-Hayward, CA MSA)

| MHz | kW | Sta | City of License | Station |
|---|---|---|---|---|
| 88.1 | 0.017 | CA | El Cerrito | KECG |
| 88.1 | 8.4 | CA | Sacramento° | KEBR |
| 88.1 | 0.007 | CA | San Rafael | KSRH |
| # 88.5 | 110 | CA | San Francisco | KQED-FM |
| 88.9 | 0.25 | CA | Oakland | K205BM (KLVS) |
| # 88.9 | 50 | CA | Sacramento° | KXPR |
| 89.1 | 0.1 | CA | Atherton | KCEA |
| 89.1 | 0.42 | CA | Calistoga° | KBBF |
| 89.3 | 0.46 | CA | Berkeley | KPFB |
| 89.3 | 0.01 | CA | Concord | K207EP (KYCC) |
| 89.3 | 0.145 | CA | Fremont | KOHL |
| 89.3 | 0.043 | CA | Moss Beach | KMVS |
| 89.3 | 0.1 | CA | Pescadero | KPDO |
| 89.5 | 0.8 | CA | Moraga | KSMC |
| 89.5 | 0.27 | CA | San Francisco | KPOO |
| 89.7 | 0.11 | CA | Los Altos° | KFJC |
| 89.9 | 0.8 | CA | Angwin° | KOSC |
| 89.9 | 0.01 | CA | Bolinas | K210EH (KWMR) |
| 89.9 | 0.018 | CA | Hayward | KCRH |
| 90.1 | 0.01 | CA | Livermore | K211EZ (KYCC) |
| 90.1 | 0.5 | CA | Stanford° | KZSU |
| 90.3 | 0.2 | CA | Dublin | K212BJ (KYCC) |

| MHz | kW | Sta | City of License | Station |
|---|---|---|---|---|
| 90.3 | 1 | CA | San Francisco | KDFC |
| 90.5 | 0.41 | CA | Concord | KVHS |
| 90.5 | 0.004 | CA | Inverness Park | KWMR-FM2 |
| 90.5 | 0.235 | CA | Point Reyes Stn | KWMR |
| 90.5 | 1.5 | CA | San Jose° | KSJS |
| 90.7 | 0.5 | CA | Berkeley | KALX |
| # 91.1 | 11 | CA | San Mateo | KCSM |
| ‡ 91.5 | 0.01 | CA | Marshall | KXCF |
| # 91.7 | 1.9 | CA | San Francisco | KALW |
| 91.9 | 0.01 | CA | Byron | K220JV (KAWZ) |
| 92.1 | 0.253 | CA | Martinez | KKDV-FM3 |
| 92.1 | 3 | CA | Walnut Creek | KKDV |
| # 92.3 | 32 | CA | San Jose | KSJO |
| 92.7 | 6 | CA | Alameda | KREV |
| 92.9 | 2.3 | CA | Healdsburg° | KFGY |
| 92.9 | 0.058 | CA | Oakley | KLSN-LP |
| 93.3 | 0.19 | CA | Pleasanton | KRZZ-FM1 |
| 93.3 | 6 | CA | San Francisco | KRZZ (sp) |
| 93.5 | 0.01 | CA | Vacaville° | K228DM (KYCC) |
| 93.7 | 0.41 | CA | Felton° | KXZM (sp) |
| 93.7 | 0.099 | CA | San Francisco | K267BO (KVTO) (ch) |
| 94.1 | 59 | CA | Berkeley | KPFA |
| 94.1 | 0.045 | CA | Oakley | KPFA-FM3 |
| 94.5 | 44 | CA | Gilroy | KBAY |
| 94.9 | 0.186 | CA | Pleasanton | KYLD-FM1 |
| # 94.9 | 30 | CA | San Francisco | KYLD |
| 95.3 | 0.87 | CA | Los Gatos° | KRTY |
| 95.3 | 0.49 | CA | Vacaville° | KUIC |
| # 95.7 | 6.9 | CA | San Francisco | KGMZ-FM |
| 95.7 | 0.186 | CA | Walnut Creek | KGMZ-FM1 |
| 96.1 | 0.1 | CA | Alameda | $ KJTZ-LP |
| 96.1 | 0.1 | CA | Alameda | $ KACR-LP |
| 96.1 | 0.008 | CA | Millbrae | KQEM-LP |
| 96.1 | 4.7 | CA | Morgan Hill° | KSQQ (por) |
| 96.1 | 0.1 | CA | Oakland | KEXU-LP |
| ‡ 96.1 | 0.05 | CA | San Francisco | KPEA-LP |
| 96.5 | 3.3 | CA | Martinez | KOIT-FM3 |
| # 96.5 | 24 | CA | San Francisco | KOIT |
| 96.9 | 0.1 | CA | Hayward | KEPT-LP |
| ‡ 96.9 | 0.1 | CA | Oakland | KGPC-LP |
| 96.9 | 0.001 | CA | San Francisco | KQEA-LP (ch) |
| 96.9 | 0.003 | CA | San Francisco | KQEB-LP (ch) |
| 97.3 | 4.8 | CA | Pleasanton | KLLC-FM2 |
| # 97.3 | 82 | CA | San Francisco | KLLC |
| # 97.7 | 4 | CA | Los Altos° | KFFG |
| 97.7 | 2.05 | CA | Monte Rio° | KVRV |
| 97.7 | 0.01 | CA | San Pablo | K249DJ (KECG) |
| 97.7 | 0.1 | CA | Walnut Creek | KQWA-LP (ch) |
| 98.1 | 1 | CA | Concord | KISQ-FM3 |
| 98.1 | 10 | CA | Pleasanton | KISQ-FM2 |
| # 98.1 | 75 | CA | San Francisco | KISQ |
| 98.5 | 0.15 | CA | Pleasanton | KUFX-FM3 |
| # 98.5 | 10 | CA | San Jose° | KUFX |
| 98.9 | 0.185 | CA | Pleasanton | KSOL-FM3 (sp) |
| # 98.9 | 6.1 | CA | San Francisco | KSOL (sp) |
| 98.9 | 0.15 | CA | Sausalito | KSOL-FM2 (sp) |
| # 99.1 | 1.1 | CA | Santa Cruz° | KSQL (sp) |
| 99.3 | 0.01 | CA | Los Gatos° | K257BE (KLVS) |
| 99.3 | 0.05 | CA | Muir Beach | KGXY-LP |
| 99.3 | 0.099 | CA | San Francisco | K257GE (KGMZ) |
| 99.3 | 6 | CA | St. Helena° | KVYN |
| # 99.7 | 40 | CA | San Francisco | KMVQ-FM |
| 99.7 | 0.185 | CA | Walnut Creek | KMVQ-FM3 |
| 100.1 | 6 | CA | Santa Rosa° | KZST |
| #100.3 | 14.5 | CA | San Jose° | KBRG (sp) |
| 100.7 | 6 | CA | San Rafael | KVVZ |
| 100.9 | 0.008 | CA | Fremont | K265CV (KLVR) |
| 100.9 | 0.08 | CA | Sausalito | K265DI (KVVZ) (sp) |
| #101.3 | 0.9 | CA | Pleasanton | KIOI-FM2 |
| #101.3 | 125 | CA | San Francisco | KIOI |
| 101.3 | 0.15 | CA | Walnut Creek | KIOI-FM1 |
| 101.7 | 0.46 | CA | Hayward | KKIQ-FM1 |
| 101.7 | 4.1 | CA | Livermore | KKIQ |
| 101.7 | 0.075 | CA | San Francisco | K269FB (KSFB) |
| 101.7 | 2.2 | CA | Santa Rosa° | KHTH |
| 102.1 | 1 | CA | San Francisco | KRBQ-FM2 |
| #102.1 | 33 | CA | San Francisco | KRBQ |
| #102.5 | 15 | CA | Salinas° | KDON-FM |
| 102.5 | 0.002 | CA | San Francisco | KXSF-LP |
| #102.9 | 7.2 | CA | Berkeley | KBLX-FM |
| 102.9 | 0.185 | CA | Pleasanton | KBLX-FM2 |
| 103.3 | 0.01 | CA | San Francisco | K277CH (KLVS) |
| 103.7 | 0.185 | CA | Pleasanton | KOSF-FM1 |

| MHz | kW | Sta | City of License | Station |
|---|---|---|---|---|
| #103.7 | 6.4 | CA | San Francisco | KOSF |
| 104.1 | 0.08 | CA | San Francisco | K281BU (KLVS) |
| 104.5 | 0.185 | CA | Pleasanton | KFOG-FM3 |
| #104.5 | 7.1 | CA | San Francisco | KFOG |
| 104.9 | 2.3 | CA | Rohnert Park° | KDHT |
| #105.1 | 50 | CA | Sacramento° | KNCI |
| 105.3 | 0.33 | CA | Antioch | KITS-FM4 |
| 105.3 | 0.044 | CA | Pleasanton | KITS-FM2 |
| #105.3 | 15 | CA | San Francisco | KITS |
| 105.3 | 0.61 | CA | Walnut Creek | KITS-FM1 |
| #105.7 | 50 | CA | Santa Clara° | KVVF |
| #106.1 | 69 | CA | San Francisco | KMEL |
| 106.1 | 6.5 | CA | Walnut Creek | KMEL-FM2 |
| 106.5 | 42 | CA | San Jose° | KEZR |
| 106.9 | 4.8 | CA | Pleasanton | KFRC-FM1 |
| #106.9 | 80 | CA | San Francisco | KFRC-FM |
| #107.3 | 4.1 | CA | Livermore | KLVS |
| 107.7 | 0.185 | CA | Pleasanton | KSAN-FM1 |
| #107.7 | 8.9 | CA | San Mateo | KSAN |

**Seattle - Tacoma Metro Area** (Seattle-Tacoma-Bellevue, WA MSA)

| MHz | kW | Sta | City of License | Station |
|---|---|---|---|---|
| 88.1 | 0.005 | WA | Everett | K201EN (KWAO) |
| 88.1 | 65 | WA | Vashon | KWAO |
| # 88.5 | 64 | WA | Tacoma | KNKX |
| 88.9 | 0.002 | WA | Enumclaw | K205DF (KAWZ) |
| 88.9 | 0.03 | WA | Mercer Island | KMIH |
| 89.1 | 0.013 | WA | Bremerton° | K206DM (KAWZ) |
| 89.1 | 0.01 | WA | Granite Falls | K206DL (KAWZ) |
| 89.1 | 0.009 | WA | Issaquah | K206CJ (KQXI) |
| 89.3 | 0.0325 | WA | Gig Harbor | K207AZ (KGHP) |
| # 89.3 | 1.25 | WA | Olympia° | KAOS |
| 89.3 | 0.07 | WA | Sumner&Lake Tapps | K207AP (KGRG-FM) |
| # 89.5 | 8.5 | WA | Seattle | KNHC |
| 89.7 | 1 | WA | Roy | KWFJ |
| # 89.9 | 0.23 | WA | Auburn | KGRG-FM |
| 89.9 | 0.06 | WA | Bellevue | KASB |
| 89.9 | 1.35 | WA | Gig Harbor | KGHP |
| 90.1 | 0.1 | WA | Tacoma | KUPS |
| # 90.3 | 4.7 | WA | Seattle | KEXP-FM |
| 90.7 | 5.8 | WA | Everett | KSER |
| 90.9 | 51 | WA | Tacoma | KVTI |
| 91.1 | 1.15 | WA | Port Townsend° | KROH |
| # 91.3 | 8 | WA | Bellevue | KBCS |
| 91.5 | 1.6 | WA | Granite Falls | KQXI |
| # 91.7 | 23 | WA | Tacoma | KYFQ |
| 91.9 | 1.15 | WA | Port Townsend° | KROH |
| ‡ 92.1 | 0.15 | WA | Tacoma | K221FJ (KNTB) (sp) |
| 92.1 | 0.25 | WA | West Seattle | K221FR (KNKX) |
| # 92.5 | 56.8 | WA | Bellevue | KQMV |
| # 92.9 | 50 | WA | Bellingham° | KISM |
| 92.9 | 0.25 | WA | Olympia° | K225BY (KRXY) |
| 92.9 | 0.05 | WA | Waller | KNLI-LP |
| 93.1 | 0.25 | WA | Montesano° | K226AN (KJET) |
| # 93.3 | 98 | WA | Seattle | KPWK |
| 93.7 | 28 | WA | Montesano° | KLSY (sp) |
| # 94.1 | 69 | WA | Seattle | KSWD |
| 94.5 | 0.099 | WA | Seattle | K233BU (KTTH) |
| # 94.5 | 0.83 | WA | Shelton° | KRXY |
| # 94.9 | 100 | WA | Seattle | KUOW-FM |
| 95.3 | 0.12 | WA | Everett | K237GN (KRKO) |
| 95.3 | 0.099 | WA | Kent | K263BJ (KZIZ) |
| 95.3 | 0.003 | WA | Seattle | KDXB-LP |
| ‡ 95.3 | 0.019 | WA | Tacoma | KTQA-LP |
| 95.3 | 0.22 | WA | Tumwater° | K237FR (KYYO) |
| # 95.7 | 98 | WA | Seattle | KJR-FM |
| 96.1 | 37 | WA | Olympia° | KXXO |
| # 96.5 | 49 | WA | Seattle | KJAQ |
| # 96.9 | 11 | WA | McCleary° | KYYO |
| 96.9 | 0.038 | WA | Seattle | KODX-LP |
| # 97.3 | 52 | WA | Tacoma | KIRO-FM |
| 97.7 | 69 | WA | Oakville° | KOMO-FM |
| 97.7 | 0.03 | WA | Redmond | K249DX (KOMO-FM) |
| # 98.1 | 66 | WA | Seattle | KING-FM |
| 98.5 | 1.6 | WA | Central Park° | KNBQ |
| 98.5 | 0.25 | WA | Redmond | K253CG (KARR) |
| # 98.9 | 63.9 | WA | Seattle | KNUC |
| 99.3 | 64 | WA | Elma° | KDDS-FM (sp) |
| 99.3 | 1 | WA | Kent | KDDS-FM4 (sp) |
| 99.3 | 0.5 | WA | Seattle | KDDS-FM1 (sp) |
| ‡ 99.5 | 0.005 | WA | Everett | K258BJ (KEJI) (sp) |
| # 99.9 | 67 | WA | Seattle | KISW |
| 100.3 | 0.041 | WA | Kent | KUCP-LP |
| 100.3 | 0.14 | WA | Olympia° | K225BY (KRXY-HD3) |
| 100.3 | 0.25 | WA | Shoreline | K262CX (KBLE) |

| MHz | kW | Sta | City of License | Station |
|---|---|---|---|---|
| 100.3 | 0.01 | WA | Tacoma | K262CI (KLSW) |
| #100.7 | 67 | WA | Seattle | KKWF |
| 101.1 | 0.12 | WA | Everett | K266CJ (KKXA) |
| 101.1 | 0.46 | WA | Magnuson Park | KMGP-LP |
| 101.1 | 0.25 | WA | Olympia° | K266BM (KGTK) |
| 101.5 | 99 | WA | Seattle | KPLZ-FM |
| 101.9 | 0.076 | WA | Bellevue | KQES-LP (ch) |
| 101.9 | 0.016 | WA | Tacoma | KTAH-LP |
| 101.9 | 0.007 | WA | Vashon | KVSH-LP |
| 102.1 | 0.1 | WA | Auburn | K271BS (KOMO-FM) |
| 102.1 | 0.007 | WA | Seattle | KXSU-LP |
| #102.5 | 68 | WA | Seattle | KZOK-FM |
| #102.9 | 60 | WA | Opportunity° | KFOO-FM |
| 103.1 | 0.1 | WA | Duvall | KAPY-LP |
| 103.3 | 1.4 | WA | Oak Harbor° | KZNW |
| 103.3 | 0.25 | WA | Seattle | K277AE (KHTP) |
| 103.3 | 0.25 | WA | Shelton° | K277CZ (KMAS) |
| #103.7 | 67 | WA | Tacoma | KHTP |
| #104.1 | 60 | WA | Bellingham° | KAFE |
| 104.1 | 0.06 | WA | Lakewood | K281CI (KGHO-LP) |
| 104.1 | 0.099 | WA | Seattle | K281CQ (KGNW) |
| #104.3 | 2.35 | WA | Chehalis° | KMNT |
| 104.5 | 6.7 | WA | Covington | KLSW |
| 104.9 | 0.1 | WA | Duvall | KAPY-LP |
| #104.9 | 17 | WA | Eatonville | KTDD |
| 104.9 | 0.015 | WA | Seattle | KHUH-LP |
| #105.3 | 54 | WA | Edmonds | KCMS |
| 105.7 | 0.06 | WA | Gig Harbor | K289BZ (KGHP) |
| 105.7 | 0.009 | WA | Orting | K289AK (KAWZ) |
| 105.7 | 0.1 | WA | Seattle | KVRU-LP |
| #106.1 | 68 | WA | Tacoma | KBKS-FM |
| 106.5 | 0.01 | WA | Enumclaw | K293AY (KRQZ) |
| #106.5 | 63 | WA | Lynden° | KWPZ |
| #106.9 | 49 | WA | Bremerton° | KRWM |
| 107.3 | 0.006 | WA | Greenwater | K297BD (KAWZ) |
| 107.3 | 0.009 | WA | Seattle | KBFG-LP |
| #107.7 | 67 | WA | Seattle | KNDD |

**St. Louis Metro Area** (St. Louis, MO–IL MSA)

| MHz | kW | Sta | City of License | Station |
|---|---|---|---|---|
| # 88.1 | 42 | MO | St. Louis | KDHX |
| 88.7 | 50 | IL | Edwardsville | WSIE |
| # 88.9 | 20 | MO | Ste. Genevieve° | KSEF |
| 89.1 | 0.08 | IL | Carlinville | W206AN (WYFG) |
| # 89.1 | 50 | IL | St. Charles | KCLC |
| 89.3 | 25 | MO | Festus | KTBJ |
| 89.5 | 0.068 | MO | Cedar Hill | KNLH |
| 89.5 | 0.1 | MO | Ferguson | KCFV |
| 89.5 | 0.3 | IL | Greenville | WGRN |
| 89.7 | 0.12 | MO | Ballwin | KGNX |
| 89.7 | 0.25 | IL | East St. Louis | WCBW-FM |
| 89.9 | 0.084 | MO | Arnold | KGNA-FM |
| # 89.9 | 1.5 | IL | Godfrey | WLCA |
| 89.9 | 1 | MO | Washington | KGNV |
| 90.1 | 5 | IL | Carlinville | WLLM-FM |
| 90.1 | 0.06 | IL | Granite City | W211AD (WBGL) |
| 90.1 | 0.05 | MO | Gray Summit | K211GB (WMSH) |
| 90.1 | 0.01 | MO | Overland | KRHS |
| 90.3 | 0.009 | MO | Clayton | KWUR |
| 90.3 | 5.2 | IL | Sparta° | WMSH |
| # 90.7 | 100 | MO | St. Louis | KWMU |
| 91.1 | 50 | IL | Carlinville | WIBI |
| 91.5 | 85 | MO | St. Louis | KSIV-FM |
| 91.9 | 0.17 | IL | Carlyle | W220EN (WOLG) |
| 91.9 | 0.099 | MO | St. Louis | K220HT (KAWZ) |
| # 92.3 | 99 | MO | St. Louis | WIL-FM |
| 92.7 | 0.25 | IL | Caseyville | W224DC (WRYT) |
| 92.7 | 0.089 | MO | Fenton | KFTN-LP |
| 92.9 | 0.25 | IL | Staunton | W225CX (WSMI) |
| 92.9 | 0.036 | MO | Webster Groves | KWRH-LP |
| 93.1 | 36 | MO | Perryville° | KBDZ |
| 93.3 | 50 | MO | Hermann° | KLUQ |
| # 93.7 | 74 | MO | St. Louis | KSD |
| 94.3 | 0.25 | IL | Alton | W232CR (WBGZ) |
| # 94.7 | 100 | MO | Crestwood | KSHE |
| 95.1 | 0.25 | MO | Warrenton | K236CK (KWRE) |
| # 95.5 | 24.5 | IL | Bethalto | WFUN-FM |
| 95.7 | 0.25 | IL | Crestwood | K244FO (KHOJ) |
| 95.9 | 6 | IL | Carlinville | WOLG |
| 95.9 | 0.099 | MO | St. Louis | K240ES (KSIV) |
| # 96.3 | 92 | MO | St. Louis | KNOU |
| 96.7 | 2.1 | IL | Carlyle | WCXO |
| # 97.1 | 100 | MO | Florissant | KFTK-FM |
| 97.5 | 2.5 | IL | Breese | WDJL |
| 97.5 | 0.25 | MO | Florissant | KWAP-LP |

| MHz | kW | Sta | City of License | Station |
|---|---|---|---|---|
| 97.7 | 26.5 | MO | Potosi° | KHZR |
| # 98.1 | 90 | MO | St. Louis | KYKY |
| 98.5 | 100 | MO | Farmington° | KTJJ |
| 98.7 | 0.25 | MO | St. Louis | K254CR (KFTK-FM) |
| # 99.1 | 100 | MO | Clayton | KLJY |
| 99.5 | 0.008 | MO | St. Louis | KTGP-LP |
| 99.7 | 50 | IL | Hillsboro° | WXAJ |
| 99.9 | 0.1 | IL | Freeburg | WZJM-LP |
| 99.9 | 10.5 | MO | Warrenton | KFAV |
| 100.1 | 2 | MO | De Soto | KDJR |
| #100.3 | 17 | MO | Bridgeton | KATZ-FM |
| 100.7 | 6 | MO | Troy | KFNS-FM |
| #101.1 | 100 | IL | East St. Louis | WXOS |
| 101.5 | 0.099 | MO | St. Louis | K268CT (WHHL) |
| 101.7 | 3.1 | MO | Elsberry | KWUL |
| 101.7 | 6 | IL | Greenville | WGEL |
| 101.9 | 0.25 | MO | Bellefontaine° | K270BW (KSD) |
| #102.5 | 100 | MO | St. Louis | KEZK-FM |
| 102.7 | 0.25 | IL | Greenville | W274CE (WPMB) |
| 102.9 | 0.25 | MO | St. Charles | K275CI (KHOJ) |
| 102.9 | 0.075 | MO | Washington | K275BU (WMSH) |
| #103.3 | 90 | MO | St. Louis | KLOU |
| 103.7 | 0.25 | IL | Mascoutah | W279AQ (KATZ-HD2) |
| 103.9 | 0.25 | IL | Greenville | W280DR (WGEL) |
| #104.1 | 50 | MO | Hazelwood | WHHL |
| 104.5 | 0.099 | MO | St. Louis | K283CI (KXEN) |
| 104.5 | 3 | MO | Washington | KSLQ-FM |
| #104.9 | 8.4 | IL | Columbia | KLLT |
| 105.1 | 0.016 | MO | Washington | K286BG (KFAV) |
| 105.3 | 0.099 | MO | St. Louis | K287BY (KXFN) |
| 105.3 | 6 | IL | Staunton | WAOX |
| #105.7 | 53.14 | IL | Collinsville | KPNT |
| 106.1 | 50 | IL | Litchfield | WSMI-FM |
| #106.5 | 90 | IL | Granite City | WARH |
| 106.9 | 0.099 | MO | St. Louis | K295CQ (WGNU) |
| 107.1 | 0.25 | MO | Washington | K296HA (KRAP) |
| 107.3 | 0.25 | MO | St. Louis | K297BI (KNOU-HD2) |
| #107.7 | 100 | MO | St. Louis | KSLZ |

**Tampa - St. Petersburg Metro Area** (Tampa–St. Petersburg–Clearwater, FL MSA)

| MHz | kW | Sta | City of License | Station |
|---|---|---|---|---|
| # 88.1 | 100 | FL | Bradenton° | WJIS |
| # 88.5 | 6.65 | FL | Tampa | WMNF |
| 88.9 | 60 | FL | Tarpon Springs | WYFE |
| 89.1 | 54 | FL | Sarasota° | WSMR |
| 89.3 | 3.9 | FL | St. Catherine° | WKFA |
| # 89.7 | 69 | FL | Tampa | WUSF |
| 90.1 | 0.023 | FL | Brandon | WYPW-LP |
| # 90.1 | 21 | FL | Inverness° | WJUF |
| # 90.5 | 77 | FL | Tampa | WBVM |
| 90.9 | 0.07 | FL | Tampa | W215CJ (WKES) |
| 91.1 | 100 | FL | Lakeland° | WKES |
| # 91.5 | 75 | FL | New Port Richey | WCIE |
| 91.9 | 25 | FL | Lakeland° | WYFO |
| 91.9 | 0.03 | FL | Oldsmar | W220EK (WCIE) |
| 92.1 | 0.099 | FL | Tampa | W221DW (WHFS) |
| # 92.1 | 11.5 | FL | Venice° | WCTQ |
| 92.3 | 0.25 | FL | Brooksville | W222CI (WWJB) |
| # 92.5 | 50 | FL | Safety Harbor | WYUU (sp) |
| 92.9 | 100 | FL | Port Charlotte° | WIKX |
| 92.9 | 0.25 | FL | Tampa | W246BY (WGES) (sp) |
| # 93.3 | 97 | FL | Tampa | WFLZ-FM |
| 93.7 | 0.23 | FL | Riverview | W229BM (WBTP) |
| # 94.1 | 100 | FL | Lakeland° | WLLD |
| 94.5 | 0.25 | FL | Brandon | W233CV (WHBO) |
| 94.5 | 0.25 | FL | Gulfport | W233AV (WMTX-HD2) |
| # 94.9 | 97.3 | FL | Tampa | WWRM |
| 95.3 | 0.25 | FL | Pinellas Park | W237CW (WBTP) |
| # 95.7 | 100 | FL | Clearwater | WBTP |
| 96.1 | 2.8 | FL | Dade City | WTMP-FM |
| 96.3 | 0.024 | FL | Clearwater | WPCQ-LP |
| 96.3 | 0.089 | FL | St. Petersburg | WBPU-LP |
| 96.3 | 0.091 | FL | Sun City Center | WSCQ-LP |
| ‡ 96.3 | 0.1 | FL | Tampa | WURK-LP |
| 96.7 | 0.087 | FL | Brandon | W244BE (WFLA) |
| 96.7 | 0.1 | FL | Dade City | WZPH-LP |
| 96.7 | 0.026 | FL | St. Petersburg | WMTB-LP |
| 96.7 | 0.099 | FL | Tampa | W244EG (WWBA) |
| 96.9 | 98 | FL | Ft. Myers° | WINK-FM |
| # 97.1 | 11.5 | FL | Holiday | WSUN |
| 97.1 | 1.3 | FL | Pinellas Park | WSUN-FM4 |
| 97.1 | 0.8 | FL | St. Petersburg | WSUN-FM3 |
| 97.5 | 0.25 | FL | St. Petersburg | W248CA (WTMP) |
| 97.5 | 100 | FL | Winter Haven° | WPCV |

| MHz | kW | Sta | City of License | Station |
|---|---|---|---|---|
| # 97.9 | 100 | FL | Clearwater | WXTB |
| # 98.1 | 27 | FL | Ft. Meade° | WWRZ |
| 98.3 | 0.25 | FL | Largo | W252DF (WWBA) |
| # 98.7 | 50 | FL | Holmes Beach° | WPBB |
| 99.1 | 0.25 | FL | Bayonet Point | W256CT (WMTX) |
| 99.1 | 0.06 | FL | Seffner | WVVD-LP |
| 99.1 | 0.457 | FL | St. Petersburg | WUJM-LP |
| # 99.5 | 99 | FL | St. Petersburg | WQYK-FM |
| 99.9 | 9.2 | FL | Homosassa° | WXJB |
| 100.1 | 0.1 | FL | Sun City Center | WGGF-LP |
| 100.1 | 0.08 | FL | Town 'n' Country | WVF-LP |
| 100.3 | 0.25 | FL | Bayonet Point | W262CP (WFUS) |
| 100.5 | 0.1 | FL | St. Petersburg | WUBP-LP |
| #100.7 | 96 | FL | Tampa | WMTX |
| 101.1 | 0.235 | FL | Tampa | W266CW (WTIS) |
| #101.5 | 97.2 | FL | St. Petersburg | WPOI |
| 101.9 | 0.1 | FL | Brandon | WSDX-LP |
| 101.9 | 0.25 | FL | New Port Richey | W270DH (WPSO) |
| 101.9 | 0.1 | FL | Ruskin | WPHX-LP |
| 102.1 | 0.011 | FL | Land O' Lakes | WWFH-LP |
| 102.1 | 0.015 | FL | St. Petersburg | WPBW-LP |
| 102.3 | 0.25 | FL | Dade City | W272EH (WDCF) |
| 102.5 | 0.25 | FL | New Port Richey | W273CP (WSUN) |
| #102.5 | 100 | FL | Sarasota° | WHPT |
| 102.9 | 0.25 | FL | Oldsmar | W275AZ (WFLA) |
| 103.1 | 0.25 | FL | New Port Richey | W276CX (WRBQ-FM) |
| 103.1 | 22 | FL | Windermere° | WOTW |
| #103.5 | 66 | FL | Gulfport | WFUS |
| 103.9 | 0.25 | FL | Largo | W280FD (WXYB) |
| 103.9 | 0.25 | FL | Spring Hill | W280DK (WWJB) |
| 103.9 | 0.25 | FL | Tampa | W280DW (WUSF) |
| 104.1 | 0.1 | FL | Palm Harbor | WZIG-LP |
| 104.3 | 25 | FL | Sarasota° | WKZM |
| 104.3 | 0.25 | FL | Tampa | W282CI (WLCC) (sp) |
| #104.7 | 99 | FL | Tampa | WRBQ-FM |
| 105.1 | 0.25 | FL | Sarasota° | W286CQ (WRUB) (sp) |
| 105.1 | 0.048 | FL | Tampa | WWZT-LP |
| #105.5 | 33 | FL | New Port Richey | WDUV |
| 105.9 | 0.25 | FL | West Tampa | W290BJ (WMTX-HD2) |
| 106.1 | 0.25 | FL | Clearwater | W291CW (WTAN) |
| 106.3 | 25 | FL | Spring Hill | WGHR |
| #106.5 | 13 | FL | Sarasota° | WRUB |
| 106.7 | 0.25 | FL | Tampa | W294CR (WQBN) (sp) |
| #106.7 | 100 | FL | Tavares° | WXXL |
| 106.9 | 0.25 | FL | Clearwater | W295CF (WYUU-HD2) (sp) |
| #107.3 | 100 | FL | St. Petersburg | WXGL |
| 107.7 | 0.25 | FL | Tampa | W299CI (WAMA) (sp) |
| #107.9 | 47 | FL | Coral Cove° | WSRZ-FM |
| 107.9 | 0.1 | FL | Spring Hill | WPHC-LP |

**Washington (DC) Metro Area** (Washington-Arlington-Alexandria, DC-VA-MD-WV MSA)

| MHz | kW | Sta | City of License | Station |
|---|---|---|---|---|
| # 88.1 | 15.5 | MD | Baltimore° | WYPR |
| 88.1 | 0.01 | MD | College Park | WMUC-FM |
| 88.1 | 1 | MD | Frederick | WYPF |
| # 88.5 | 50 | DC | Washington | WAMU |
| 88.7 | 0.027 | VA | Fredericksburg | W204CH (WYFJ) |
| # 88.9 | 12.5 | MD | Baltimore° | WEAA |
| 88.9 | 0.2 | MD | Frederick | W205BL (WETA) |
| 89.3 | 50 | DC | Washington | WPFW |
| # 89.7 | 7.4 | MD | Towson° | WTMD |
| 89.7 | 0.008 | VA | Woodbridge | W209BY (WRVL) |
| # 89.9 | 41 | VA | Culpeper | WPIR |
| # 90.1 | 36 | DC | Washington | WCSP-FM |
| 90.5 | 47 | VA | Fredericksburg | WPER |
| # 90.9 | 75 | DC | Washington | WETA |
| 91.1 | 0.006 | MD | Frederick | W216CM (WCRH) |
| 91.3 | 13.5 | VA | Culpeper | WARN |
| # 91.5 | 50 | MD | Baltimore° | WBJC |
| 91.5 | 0.019 | VA | Fredericksburg | W218CV (KAWZ) |
| # 91.9 | 23.5 | MD | Takoma Park | WGTS |
| # 92.3 | 37 | MD | Baltimore° | WERQ-FM |
| 92.5 | 22 | VA | Winchester° | WINC-FM |
| 92.7 | 2.3 | MD | Prince Frederick | WDCJ |
| # 93.1 | 16 | MD | Baltimore° | WPOC |
| # 93.3 | 50 | VA | Fredericksburg | WFLS-FM |
| 93.5 | 0.15 | MD | Frederick | W228AM (WWEG) |
| 93.5 | 0.13 | MD | Silver Spring | W228DI (WBQH) (sp) |
| # 93.9 | 24.5 | DC | Washington | WKYS |
| 94.1 | 0.01 | VA | Fredericksburg | W231BJ (WLMP-LP) |
| 94.3 | 2 | VA | Buckland | WLZV |
| 94.3 | 0.16 | MD | Frederick | W232WG (WWFD) |
| 94.3 | 0.02 | MD | Takoma Park | WOWD-LP |
| # 94.7 | 20.5 | MD | Bethesda | WIAD |

| MHz | kW | Sta | City of License | Station |
|---|---|---|---|---|
| 94.9 | 0.08 | VA | Fredericksburg | W235BT (WQIQ) |
| # 95.1 | 50 | MD | Baltimore° | WRBS-FM |
| 95.3 | 0.178 | VA | Culpeper | W237CA (WCVA) |
| # 95.5 | 50 | MD | Morningside | WPGC-FM |
| # 95.9 | 3 | MD | Glen Burnie° | WWIN-FM |
| 95.9 | 0.25 | DC | Washington | W240DJ (WOL) |
| # 96.3 | 16.5 | DC | Washington | WHUR-FM |
| 96.5 | 0.25 | VA | Fredericksburg | W243BS (WFLS-HD2) |
| 96.7 | 0.021 | VA | Arlington° | WERA-LP |
| 96.7 | 12.5 | MD | Easton° | WCEI-FM |
| 96.7 | 0.18 | MD | Rockville | WQER-LP |
| # 97.1 | 17.5 | DC | Washington | WASH |
| 97.5 | 0.25 | VA | Alexandria | W248BN (WMMJ) (sp) |
| 97.5 | 0.25 | MD | Baltimore° | W248AO (WLIF-HD4) |
| 97.5 | 11.4 | WV | Martinsburg° | WKMZ-FM |
| 97.7 | 0.05 | VA | Reston | W249DX (WKDV) |
| # 97.9 | 13.5 | MD | Baltimore° | WIYY |
| 98.1 | 0.25 | VA | Manassas | W251CH (WURA) |
| 98.3 | 3 | MD | Mechanicsville° | WSMD-FM |
| 98.3 | 0.2 | VA | Reston | W252DC (WAMU) |
| # 98.7 | 50 | DC | Washington | WMZQ-FM |
| 99.1 | 45 | MD | Bowie | WDCH-FM |
| # 99.5 | 22 | DC | Washington | WIHT |
| 99.9 | 7.6 | MD | Frederick | WFRE |
| #100.3 | 50 | DC | Washington | WBIG-FM |
| 100.7 | 0.1 | VA | Falls Church | W264DB (WFAX) |
| 100.7 | 25 | MD | Westminster° | WZBA |
| #101.1 | 22.5 | DC | Washington | WWDC |
| 101.3 | 0.25 | VA | Winchester° | W267AK (WYFT) |
| 101.5 | 50 | VA | Fredericksburg | WBQB |
| #101.9 | 13.5 | MD | Baltimore° | WLIF |
| 102.1 | 0.082 | MD | Prince Frederick | WMJS-LP |
| #102.3 | 2.9 | MD | Bethesda | WMMJ |
| #102.7 | 50 | MD | Baltimore° | WQSR |
| 102.7 | 0.014 | VA | Fredericksburg | WLMP-LP |
| 102.9 | 4 | MD | California° | WKIK-FM |
| 102.9 | 0.05 | VA | Reston | W275BO (WWWT-FM-HD2) |
| 103.1 | 6 | VA | Culpeper | WJMA |
| 103.1 | 6 | MD | Grasonville° | WRNR-FM |
| 103.1 | 1 | MD | Middletown | WAFY |
| #103.5 | 44 | DC | Washington | WTOP-FM |
| #103.9 | 0.35 | MD | Braddock Heights | WTLP |
| #104.1 | 20 | MD | Waldorf | WPRS-FM |
| #104.3 | 13 | MD | Baltimore° | WZFT |
| 104.7 | 8.3 | MD | Hagerstown° | WAYZ |
| 104.7 | 0.099 | DC | Washington | W284CQ (WWDC-HD2) |
| #105.1 | 33 | VA | Arlington° | WAVA-FM |
| 105.5 | 0.099 | VA | Reston | W288BS (WKYS-HD3) |
| #105.7 | 50 | MD | Catonsville° | WJZ-FM |
| 105.9 | 28 | VA | Woodbridge | WMAL-FM |
| 106.1 | 0.23 | MD | Baltimore° | W291BA (WLIF-HD2) |
| 106.3 | 0.075 | VA | Fredericksburg | W292EF (WJYJ-FM) |
| #106.5 | 10.3 | MD | Baltimore° | WWMX |
| #106.7 | 20 | VA | Manassas | WJFK-FM |
| #106.9 | 15.5 | MD | Myersville | WWEG |
| #107.3 | 20 | DC | Washington | WRQX |
| #107.7 | 29 | VA | Manassas | WWWT-FM |
| #107.9 | 49 | MD | College Park | WLZL |

**NB:** #) HD Radio (hybrid trs) ‡) Temporarily inactive at time of publication (FCC authorized "Silent STA" status) $) Time-shared allocation (shared tx) $+) as $ but with different CLs.
Languages other than English: as) Asian languages, ch) Chinese, cr) Creole, ha) Haitian, hm) Hmong, pol) Polish, por) Portuguese, sp) Spanish, viet) Vietnamese.

## URUGUAY

**L.T:** UTC -3h — **Pop:** 3.45 million — **Pr.L:** Spanish — **E.C:** 50Hz, 230V — **ITU:** URG — **Int. dialling code:** +598

### DIRECCION NACIONAL DE TELECOMUNICACIONES Y SERVICIOS DE COMUNICACIÓN AUDIOVISUAL
Ministerio de Industria, Energía y Minería
✉ Av. Uruguay 988 (Casilla de Correo 927), 11100 Montevideo Edificio Ciudadela Sarandí 690 D, 2° entrepiso ☎2915 0856 **E:** info@dinatel.miem.gub.uy **W:** dinatel.gub.uy

### UNIDAD REGULADORA DE SERVICIOS DE COMUNICACIONES (URSEC)
✉ Av. Uruguay 988 (Casilla de Correo 927), 11100 Montevideo ☎ 2902 8082, 2900 5708 **E:** radiodifusion@ursec.gub.uy **W:** ursec.gub.uy **L.P:** Ing. Gabriel Lombide

### ASOCIACION NACIONAL DE BROADCASTERS URUGUAYOS (ANDEBU)
✉ Carlos Quijano 1264, 11100 Montevideo ☎ 2902 1525, 2908 0037 🖷 2902 1540 **E:** andebu@adinet.com.uy **W:** andebu.org

### COOPERATIVA DE RADIO EMISORAS DEL INTERIOR (CORI)
✉ Av. 18 de Julio 948, Oficina 603, 11000 Montevideo ☎ 2902 9047 **W:** cori.com.uy **E:** coriamfm@adinet.com.uy

### RADIOS AM DEL INTERIOR (RAMI)
✉ Nueva York 1618, 11800 Montevideo ☎ 29246722 / 9241310 🖷29247279 **E:** rami@adinet.com.uy **W:** rami.com.uy
**W:** ramiradiosdelinterior.com **E:** rami@adinet.com.uy

### RED ORO
✉ Rio Negro 1337, Esc. 209, 11100 Montevideo ☎ 2903 1678 🖷2 900 3916 **E:** redoro@adinet.com.uy

### ASOCIACION MUNDIAL DE RADIOS COMUNITARIAS (AMARC URUGUAY)
✉ Germán Barbato 1480, 11000, Montevideo ☎ 29021236 **W:** sitio. amarcuruguay.org **E:** mesanacional@amarcuruguay.org

### RADIODIFUSIÓN NACIONAL DEL URUGUAY (RNU) (Gov)
✉ Sarandí 450, 11000 Montevideo ☎ 2 1768 2 915 5378 **W:** rnu. com.uy **E:** organizacion@rnu.uy **L.P:** Dir:. Pedro Ramela Tech. Dir: José Cuello **E:** departamentotecnico@rnu.uy

| MW Call | | kHz | kW | Station, location, h. of tr. |
|---|---|---|---|---|
| CO01) | CW1 | 550 | 25 | R. Colonia, Colonia: 24h |
| MO01) | CX58 | 580 | 2 | R. Clarín, Montevideo: 24h |
| MO02) | CX4 | 610 | 50 | R. Rural, Montevideo: 24h |
| MO03a) | CX6 | 650 | 25 | R. Clásica, (Rdif. Nal. del Uruguay, Montevideo: 24h |
| RN01) | CW68 | 680 | 1 | R. Young, Young |
| MO04) | CX8 | 690 | 25 | R. Sarandí, Montevideo: 24h |
| MO05) | CX10 | 730 | 5/2.5 | R. Continente, Montevideo: 24h |
| SA01) | CW27 | 740 | 5 | R. Tabaré, Salto: 0900-0300 |
| MO06) | CX12 | 770 | 100 | R. Oriental, Montevideo: 24h |
| MO07) | CX14 | 810 | 50/25 | R. El Espectador, Montevideo: 0800-0500 |
| SA02) | CW23 | ‡820 | 1 | R. Cultural, Salto |
| MO08) | CX16 | 850 | 50 | R. Carve, Montevideo: 0825-0300 |
| MO09) | CX18 | 890 | 50/10 | R. Sport 890, Montevideo: 0900-0300 SS 24h |
| AR01) | CW17 | 900 | 3 | R. Frontera, Artigas |
| MO10) | CX20 | 930 | 50 | R. Monte Carlo, "la Super R.", Montevideo: 24h |
| DU01) | CW96 | 960 | 2 | R. Yi, Durazno |
| MO11) | CX22 | 970 | 20/3 | R. Universal, Montevideo: 0815-0330 |
| MO12) | CX24 | 1010 | 25 | R. 1010, Montevideo: 0900-0500 |
| SA03) | CW102 | 1020 | 0.1 | R. Libertadores, Salto: 0700-0300 |
| MO03b) | CX26 | 1050 | 50 | R. Uruguay (Rdif. Nal. del Uruguay, Montevideo: 24h |
| MO14) | CX28 | 1090 | 15 | R. Imparcial, Montevideo: 24h |
| TA01) | CX111 | 1110 | 3 | R. Paso de los Toros, Paso de los Toros: 1000-0300 |
| SA04) | CW31 | 1120 | 10 | R. Salto, Salto |
| MO15) | CX30 | 1130 | 20 | R. Nacional, Montevideo: 24h |
| FL02) | CW116 | 1160 | 2/1 | R. Agraria del Uruguay, Cerro Chato: 0800-0100 |
| MO16) | CX32 | 1170 | 10 | Radiomundo, Montevideo: 1100-0300 |
| AR02) | CX118 | 1180 | 10 | LV de Artigas, Artigas: 0900-0300 |
| FL01) | CW33 | 1200 | 1 | La Nueva R., Florida |
| SO01) | CX121 | 1210 | 2/1 | Difusora Soriano, Mercedes: 24h |
| MA01) | CV121 | 1210 | 2/1 | Em. RBC del Este, Piriápolis: 24h |
| TT02) | CW121 | 1210 | 0.25 | R. El Libertador, Vergara: 1045-0300 |
| RI05) | CX122 | 1220 | 1/0.5 | R. Reconquista, Rivera: 1000-0300 |
| PA01) | CW35 | 1240 | 5 | R. Paysandú, Paysandú |
| MO17) | CX36 | 1250 | 3 | R. Centenario, Montevideo:24h |
| AR03) | CW125 | 1250 | 3 | R. Bella Unión, Bella Unión: 24h |
| RO01) | CW37 | 1260 | 3 | Dif. Rochense, Rocha: 24h |
| AR04) | CV127 | 1280 | 4/2 | R. Cuareim, Artigas: 0900-0300 |
| TA02) | CW64 | 1280 | 3/1 | R. Tacuarembó, Tacuarembó: 0750-0230 Sun: 1000-0200 |
| MO03c) | CX38 | 1290 | 10 | Radiodifusión Nacional del Uruguay "Em. del Sur". Montevideo: 24h |
| PA02) | CW39 | 1320 | 1 | R. LV de Paysandú, Paysandú |
| RO02) | CW132 | 1320 | 1/0.5 | R. Fortaleza, Rocha: 1000-0200 |
| MO19) | CX40 | 1330 | 5 | R. Fénix, Montevideo: 0900-0400 Sat/Sun: 1000-0600 |
| CL01) | CW53 | 1340 | 10/1 | LV de Melo, Melo: 0800-0300 |
| CL02) | CW136 | 1360 | 1 | R. Río Branco, Río Branco: 1055-0200 |
| SJ01) | CW41 | 1360 | 2.5 | R. 41, San José: 24h |
| MO20) | CX42 | 1370 | 5.3/2.5 | Em. Ciudad de Montevideo: 1100-0300 |

| MW Call | kHz | kW | Station, location, h. of tr. |
|---|---|---|---|
| RI01) CV137A | 1370 | 0.5 | R. Real, Minas de Corrales: 0930-0130 |
| RN02) CW137 | 1370 | 1 | R. San Javier, San Javier: 0900-0100 |
| TT03) CW45 | ±1390 | 5 | Dif. Treinta y Tres, Treinta y Tres: 0800-0300 |
| TA03) CX140 | 1400 | 25 | R. Zorrilla de San Martín, Tacuarembó: 0900-0300 |
| MO21) CX44 | 1410 | 10/5 | La Catorce 10, Montevideo: 24h |
| SA05) CW141 | 1410 | 2/0.5 | R. Turística, Salto: 0900-0300 |
| LA01) CW43 | 1420 | 5 | R. Lavalleja, Minas: 0900-0300 |
| PA03) CX142 | 1420 | 1/0.5 | R. Felicidad, Paysandú: 0830-0130 |
| DU02) CW25 | 1430 | 20/5 | R. Durazno, Durazno: 0830-0300 |
| RI02) CX144 | 1440 | 3/0.5 | R. Rivera, Rivera: 0830(Su: 1000)-0300) |
| MO22) CX46 | 1450 | 10/5 | R. América, Montevideo: (0930-0630) |
| SA06) CW145 | 1450 | 1/0.25 | R. Arapey, Salto: 24h |
| CO02) CX146 | 1460 | 1 | R. Carmelo, Carmelo: 0930-0030 (Su: 1000-0100) |
| LA02) CV146 | 1460 | 0.25 | R. José Batlle y Ordóñez, José Batlle y Ordóñez |
| CA01) CX147 | 1470 | 2 | R. Cristal del Uruguay,Las Piedras: 24h |
| CL03) CW147 | 1470 | 1 | R. Maria, Melo: 24h |
| RO04) CW148 | 1480 | 3 | R. Universo, Castillos: 0900-0300 |
| RI03) CW43B | 1480 | 3/0.5 | R. Internacional, Rivera |
| RN03) CX148 | 1480 | 1 | Difusora Rio Negro, Young:0900-0300 |
| AR05) CV149 | 1490 | 1/0.25 | R. del Centro, Baltasar Brum: 0900-0100 (Su: 1000-0200) |
| CO03) CX149 | 1490 | 5 | R. del Oeste, Nueva Helvecia |
| RN04) CX151 | 1510 | 5 | R. Rincón, Fray Bentos: 0915-0230 |
| MA02) CW57 | 1510 | 2/0.5 | R. San Carlos, San Carlos: 0800-0400 |
| TA04) CW151 | 1510 | 0.5 | R. Ibirapitá, San Gregorio de Polanco: 1000-0200 |
| CL04) CX152 | 1520 | 2 | R. Acuarela, Melo: 0900-0300 |
| PA05) CV152 | 1520 | 1/0.5 | R. Paz, "La Nueva R.", Guichón: 1000-0300 |
| CO04) CW153 | 1530 | 0.25 | Em. Cono Sur, Nueva Palmira: 0925-0100 |
| PA04) CW154 | 1540 | 0.1 | R. Charrúa, Paysandú: 1000-0300 |
| TT04) CX154 | 1540 | 1 | R. Patria, Treinta y Tres: 0800-0300 |
| SO02) CW154 | 1540 | 1 | R. Centro, Cardona: 0900-0300 |
| SO04) CV155 | 1550 | 0.25 | R. Agraciada, Mercedes: 24h |
| DU03) CW155 | 1550 | 2/0.5 | R. Sarandí del Yí, Sarandí del Yí: 1030-0130 |
| FO01) CW156 | 1560 | 2/0.5 | Dif. Americana, Trinidad: 0930-0130 |
| RI04) CV156 | 1560 | 1 | R. Vichadero: 1000-0200 |
| CA02) CX157 | 1570 | 2/0.5 | R. Canelones: 0830-0300 |
| AR06) CW157A | 1570 | 0..25 | Em. Celeste, Tomás Gomensoro: 0830-0100 |
| LA03) CW54 | 1580 | 2/0.5 | Em. del Este, Minas: 0800-0200 |
| SO05) CW158 | 1580 | 1/0.5 | R. San Salvador, Dolores: 24h |
| RO05) CW159 | 1590 | 1/0.25 | R. Nueva R. Lascano, Lascano |
| CO06) CX159 | 1590 | 1 | R. Real, Colonia: 0930-0300 |
| SA07) CV159 | 1590 | 0.25 | R. Regional, Constitución |
| CA03) CV160 | 1600 | 1 | R. Continental, Pando: 0915-0300 |
| RN05) CX160 | 1600 | 1 | R. Litoral, Fray Bentos: 0900-0300 |

| SW Call | kHz | kW | Station, location |
|---|---|---|---|
| MO03) CXA4 | ‡6125 | 0.3 | Radiodifusión Nacional del Uruguay, "R. Uruguay", Montevideo: 24h |

‡ = inactive, ± = varying freq,

## Addresses & other information:

**AR00) ARTIGAS**
**AR01)** Av Lecueder 803, 55000 Artigas ☎477 22433 **W:** radiofronterafm.blogspot.com **E:** emisorafronter@hotmail.com – **FM:** 88.3MHz "Frontera FM" – **AR02)** Av Lecueder 483, 55000 Artigas ☎4772 2447 🖹4772 4744 **W:** radioartigas.com **E:** radioartigas118@gmail.com - **FM:** 90.7MHz "Amatista FM" – **AR03)** Enrique Ferreira 1550, 55100 Bella Unión ☎4779 2058 **W:** radiobellaunion.com **E:** radiobellaunion@gmail.com or informativoradiobu@gmail.com - **FM:** 105.5MHz "Stereo Norte FM" – **AR04)** Av Lecueder 167, 55000 Artigas ☎🖹4772 2867 **W:** radiocuareim.com **E:** racua@adinet.com.uy – **AR05)** Batlle y Ordóñez y 25 de Agosto, 55001 Baltasar Brum, Artigas ☎4776 2109 **W:** radiodelcentro.com **E:** radiodelcentro_95@hotmail.com – **AR06)** 18 de Julio y 19 de Abril, 55002 Tomás Gomensoro ☎4777 2157 🖹4777 3059 **W:** radioceleste1570.com **E:** radioceleste@hotmail.com

**CA00) CANELONES**
**CA01)** Av Artigas 781, 90200 Las Piedras, Canelones ☎4236 44775 🖹4236 44814 **W:** radiocristaldeluruguay.com.uy **E:** cx147cristal@adinet.com.uy – **CA02)** Gral. Fructuoso Rivera 216, 90000 Canelones ☎4332 1570 🖹4332 2589 **W:** radiocanelones.com.uy **E:** 1570amsrl@gmail.com – **CA03)** Av Artigas 977, 91000 Pando ☎2292 2512 🖹2292 4440 **W:** radiocontinental.com.uy **E:** administracion@radiocontinental.com.uy or programación@radiocontinental.com.uy

**CL00) CERRO LARGO**
**CL01)** Remigio Castellanos 721, 37000 Melo ☎4642 2397 **W:** lavozdemelo.com **E:** director@lavozdemelo.com – **CL02)** Virrey Arredondo 986, 37100 Rio Branco ☎🖹4675 2009 **E:** am1360@adinet.com.uy – **CL03)** Treinta y Tres 949, 37000 Melo ☎4642 2387

**W:** radiomaria.org.uy **E:** info.ury@radiomaria.org – **CL04)** José Pedro Varela 750, Melo ☎4642 2051 **W:** radioacuarela.blogspot.com **E:** acuarelaradio@yahoo.com

**CO00) COLONIA**
**CO01)** Rivadavia 383, 70000 Colonia ☎4522 2006 🖹4522 2961 **W:** radio-colonia.com.ar **E:** cw1@adinet.com.uy - **FM:** 93.5MHz "FM Mágica" – **CO02)** 19 de Abril 444, 70100 Carmelo ☎4542 3558 **W:** radiocarmelo.com **E:** radiocarmelo@adinet.com.uy – **CO03)** Calle Berna 1375, 70201 Nueva Helvecia ☎4554 4217 🖹4554 4409 **W:** ro.com.uy **E:**1490@ro.com.uy - **FM:** 90.7MHz "Reflejos" – **CO04)** Chile 1162 y Gral Artigas, 70101 Nueva Palmira ☎4544 6053 **W:**emisoraconosur1530.com **E:** emisoraconosur@gmail.com / emisoraconosurventas@gmail.com – **CO06)** Av Gral Flores 472, 70000 Colonia ☎4522 2030 **E:** radioreal@adinet.com .uy

**DU00) DURAZNO**
**DU01)** Zorrilla de San Martín 875, 97000 Durazno ☎4362 2701 **W:** am960.com.uy **E:** multimyi@adinet.com.uy - **FM:** 90.1MHz Yi FM – **DU02)** Br. Gral. Fructuoso Rivera 501, 97000 Durazno ☎4362 2015 🖹4362 2058 **W:** radiodurazno.com **E:** info@radiodurazno or com director@radiodurazno.com - **FM:** 95.1MHz "Radio City" – **DU03)** Calle Sarandí del Yí 428, 97100 Sarandí del Yí ☎4367 9155 **E:** norasan@adinet.com.uy - **FM:** 89.5MHz "Scala FM"

**FL00) FLORIDA**
**FL01)** Antonio Maria Fernández 800, 94000 Florida ☎4352 2026 **W:** cw33florida.com.uy **E:** cw33@adinet.com.uy - **FM:** 88.7MHz "Claridad" – **FL02)** Juan Muñoz (RN-7) s/n, 30204 Cerro Chato ☎4466 2200 **W:** radioagraria.com **E:** radioagraria@hotmail.com Rpts. to: cx2ua@hotmail.com

**FO00) FLORES**
**FO01)** Herrera 435, 85000 Trinidad ☎4364 2229 **W:** agenda.org.uy/difusoraamericana **E:** am1560@hotmail.com

**LA00) LAVALLEJA**
**LA01)** José E Rodó 530, 30000 Minas ☎4442 2304 – **W:** radiolavalleja.jimdo.com **E:** cw43radiolavalleja@gmail.com – **LA02)** Camino Nacional s/n - [RN-7, Km 205], 30200 José Batlle y Ordóñez ☎4469 2132 **E:** contacto@fmnicoperez.com - **FM:** 96.5 MHz – **LA03)** Treinta y Tres 632, 30000 Minas ☎4442 3092 **W:** cw54emisoradeleste.com **E:** federalfm@federalfm.com.uy - **FM:** 107.3MHz "Federal FM"

**MA00) MALDONADO**
**MA01)** Chacabuco y Moreno, PA, 20200 Piriápolis ☎4432 2771 **W:** radiorbc.com **E:** radiorbc@adinet com.uy – **MA02)** Calle Sarandí 775, entre 18 de Julio y Treinta y Tres, 20400 San Carlos ☎426 6426 64050 🖹426 69575 **E:** rscaudio@adinet.com.uy

**MO00) MONTEVIDEO**
**MO01)** Av. 18 de Julio 1516, P.9, Esc 7, 11200 Montevideo ☎240 06877 🖹240 15841 **W:** radioclarin.com **E:** clarinam580@adinet.com.uy – **MO02)** Joaquín Suarez 3409, 11700 Montevideo ☎233 60610 **W:** radiorural.com **E:** rural@cx4radiorural.com – **MO03)** Sarandí 430, 1° piso, 11000 Montevideo ☎2902 5640 **W:** radionacional.com.uy **E:** info@radionacional.com.uy– Rpt. to: Cas, 7011, 11000 Montevideo. **E:** lmoreira@montevideo.com.uy – **MO03a)** R. Clásica **W:** radioclasica.com.uy **E:** clasic@rnu.com.uy – **MO03b)** R. Uruguay **W:** radiouruguay.com.uy **E:** direccionradiouruguay@rnu.com.uy – **MO03c)** Em. Del Sur **W:** emisoradelsur.com.uy **E:** emisoradelsur947@gmail.com - **FM** (MHz): 103.9 Colonia, 100.1 Bella Unión, 98.7 Artigas, 104.3 Salto, 103.5 Paysandú, 92.1 & 94.7 Montevideo, 107.7 Rocha, 93.5 Chuy, 106.9 Melo, 93.9 Rivera, 97.1 Montevideo, 100.9 Maldonado, 92.1 Mercedes, 102.9 Fray Bentos, 92.7 Treinta y Tres, 105.1 Durazno, 103.7 Tacuarembó, 106.1 Minas – **MO04)** Enriqueta Compte y Riquet 1250, 11800 Montevideo ☎2208 2612 🖹2208 5617 **W:** sarandi690.com.uy **E:** direccion@sarandi690.com.uy – **MO05)** Germán Barbato 1472, 11100 Montevideo ☎2902 4038 🖹2902 4038 **E:** cx10.730.continente@adinet.com.uy – **MO06)** Cerrito 475, 11000 Montevideo ☎2916 1130 **W:** oriental.com.uy **E:** programacion@oriental.com.uy – **MO07)** Río Branco 1481, 11100 Montevideo ☎2902 3531 **W:** espectador.com **E:** am810@espectador.com.uy – **MO08)** Mercedes 973, 11100 Montevideo ☎2902 6162 🖹2902 6712 **W:** carve850.com.uy **E:** matiasreyesroque@gmail.com (Matías Reyes Roque, stn mgr) prensacarve@gmail.com – **MO09)** Enriqueta Compte y Riquet 1250, 11800 Montevideo ☎sport890.com.uy ☎ sport890@sport890.com.uy – Rpt. to: fgopar34@gmail.com – **MO10)** Av 18 de Julio 1224, 1° piso, 11100 Montevideo ☎2901 4433 29010509 **W:** radiomontecarlo.com.uy **E:** cx20@radiomontecarlo.com.uy – **MO11)** Av 18 de Julio, 1220, 3° piso, 11100 Montevideo ☎290 26022 🖹290 26050 **W:** 970universal.com **E:** administracion@970universal.com / cx22@adinet.com.uy – **MO12)** Mercedes 973, 11100 Montevideo **W:** radio1010.uy **E:** ☎2902 6162 🖹2902 6712 **W:** radio1010.uy **E:** programacion@sadrep.com.uy – **MO14)** Av del Libertador Brig Gral. Lavalleja 1708, ap 101, Edificio Carioca, 11800 Montevideo ☎2924 2828 **W:** radioimparcial.com **E:** radioimparcial@adinet.

uy – **M015)** Plaza Independencia 846, EP, 11100 Montevideo ☎2902 5640 📠2908 1295 **W:** radionacional.com.uy **E:** prensa@radionacional. com.uy – **M016)** Rambla Armenia 1647, 11300 Montevideo ☎2628 9240 📠2628 9239 – **M017)** Av 18 de Julio 1357, Apto. 202, 11200 Montevideo ☎2903 0302 📠2903 0307 **E:** radio36@gmail. com **W:** radio36.com.uy – **M019)** Canelones 1969, 11200 Montevideo ☎📠240 83292 **W:** cx40radiofenix.com **E:** radiofenix@adinet.com. uy – **M020)** Arenal Grande 2093, 11800 Montevideo ☎2929 1370 📠2924 0700 **W:** emisoraciudaddemontevideo.com.uy **E:** CX42@ emisoraciudaddemontevideo.com.uy – **M021)** Garibaldi 2579, 11600 Montevideo ☎2487 3565 **W:** lacatorce10.com.uy **E:** dcomercial@ lacatorce10.com – **M022)** Emilio Frugoni 1312, Montevideo ☎2409 0094 📠2408 9314 **W:** cx46.com.uy **E:** correo@cx46.com

**PA00) PAYSANDÚ**
**PA01)** Av España 1629, 60000 Paysandú ☎4722 3617 **W:** radiopaysandu.com.uy **E:** am1240@adinet.com.uy or correo@ radiocw39.com – **PA02)** 18 de Julio 614, 60000 Paysandú ☎4722 2267 **W:** radiocw39.com **E:** correo@radiocw39.com – **PA03)** 33 Orientales 946,1° piso, Apt 1, 60000 Paysandú ☎4722 4020 **W:** paysandu.com/ radiofelicidad **E:** radiofelicidad@adinet.com.uy – **PA04)** Ruta Nacional N° 3 y Capitán Francisco Bicudo, 60000 Paysandú ☎ 4722 4856 **W:** charruaradio.com **E:** cw154@adinet.com.uy – **PA05)** Luis Alberto de Herrera 346, 60008 Guichón ☎4742 2053 **W:** guichon.com.uy/ radiolanuevapaz **E:** lanuevapaz@adinet.com.uy

**RI00) RIVERA**
**RI01)** Dr Dávison s/n, 40002 Minas de Corrales ☎4658 2073 **W:** radioreal.com.uy **E:** eduardo.andina@gmail.com – **RI02)** Dr Gabriel Anolles 441, 40000 Rivera ☎4622 3230 **W:** radiorivera.com.uy **E:** radiorivera@gmail.com – **RI03)** Av Sarandí 792, 40000 Rivera ☎4622 3259 **W:** internacionalamyfm.com **E:** internac@gmail.com – **FM:** 94.5MHz – **RI04)** Buld. Gral. José Gervasio Artigas 160, 40003 Vichadero ☎4654 2018 **W:** radiovichadero.com **E:** radiosamfm@ hotmail.com or radiovichadero@gmail.com – **RI05)** Francisco Acuña de Figueroa 887, 40000 Rivera ☎📠462 25893 **W:** multimediadelnorte. com/reconquista **E:** reconquista1220@hotmail.com - **FM:** 90.6MHz

**RN00) RIO NEGRO**
**RN01)** Rincón 1689, 65100 Young ☎4567 2071 **W:** radioyoung680. listen2myradio.com (streaming audio) **E:** am680@adinet.com.uy – **FM:** 93.3MHz FM Luna – **RN02)** 27 de Julio s/n y Basilio Lubkov, San Javier ☎4569 2005 **W:** 1370am.com.uy/ **E:** radiosanjavier@hotmail.com – **RN03)** Rincón 1811, 65100 Young ☎4567 3125 **E:** imagenfm@adinet. com.uy - **FM:** 89.1MHz "Imágen FM" – **RN04)** 25 de Mayo 3164 al 3168, 65000 Fray Bentos ☎4562 2022 **W:** agenda.org.uy/radiorincon **E:** rinconprensa@gmail.com or rinconamfm@adinet.com.uy - **FM:** 107.7 MHz Rincón FM – **RN05)** 18 de Julio y 25 de Agosto, 65000 Fray Bentos ☎4562 3100 📠4562 3528 **E:** litoral@adinet.com.uy

**RO00) ROCHA**
**RO01)** Ramírez 127, 27000 Rocha ☎4472 2250 📠447 2 **W:** difusorarochense.com.uy **E:** difusorarochense@gmail.com - **FM:** 91.5MHz & 106.3MHz – **RO02)** Zorrilla de San Martin 200, 27000 Rocha ☎4472 1198 **E:** fortaleza1320@gmail.com – **RO04)** 18 de Julio 1322, 27200 Castillos ☎4475 8755 **W:** radiouniverso.com.uy **E:** am1440@adinet.com.uy (radio) grupouniverso@adinet.com.uy – **RO05)** Nicolás Corbo 1152, 27300 Lascano **W:** nuevaradiolascano.com.uy **E:** lanuevaradio@adinet.com.uy ☎4456 9280 & 4456 4380

**SA00) SALTO**
**SA01)** Lavalleja 22, 50000 Salto ☎4734 0298 **W:** radiotabare. com.uy **E:** info@radiotabare.com.uy or amtabare@adinet.com.uy – **SA02)** Lavalleja 48, 50000 Salto ☎4732 4330 - **FM:** 106.5MHz "Emisora del Éxodo" – **SA03)** Uruguay 1416, 50000 Salto ☎📠732 6272 **W:** amlibertadores.com **E:** amlibertadores@adinet.com.uy - **FM:** 101.5MHz "Siglo XXI" – **SA04)** Brasil 715, 50000 Salto ☎4733 2615 ☎4733 3414 **W:** agenda.org.uy/radiosalto **E:** cw31salt@adinet. com.uy & radiosalto@adinet.com.uy - **FM:** 88.3MHz "Emisora del Lago" – **SA05)** Av. Armando Barbieri , 50000 Salto ☎473 42186 **W:** 1410salto.com – **SA06)** Treinta y Tres 73, 50000 Salto ☎4732 6264 **W:** 10minutos.com.uy **E:** amarapey@adinet.com.uy - **FM:** 90.9 MHz FM Impacto

**SJ00) SAN JOSÉ**
**SJ01)** Evaristo Ciganda 511, 80000 San José de Mayo ☎4342 6444 **W:** radio41.com.uy **E:** 1360am@radio41.com.uy

**S000) SORIANO**
**S001)** De Castro y Careaga 568, 75000 Mercedes ☎453 23430 📠453 22977 **W:** difusorasoriano.com **E:** difusorasoriano@adinet.com.uy - **FM:** 89.3 MHz – **S002)** Calle Joaquín Suárez al final, 75200 Cardona ☎4536 9315 **W:** radiocentrocardona.blogspot.com **E:** radiocentro@ adinet.com.uy – **S004)** Colón 319 Planta Alta, 75000 Mercedes ☎4532 8536 **W:** enterarte.info/agraciadanueva/noticias.php **E:** radioagraciada1550@hotmail.com - **FM:** 100.3MHz "Galicia" – **S005)** Av Asencio 1695, 75100 Dolores ☎📠4534 2110 **W:** radiosansalvador. com.uy **E:** administracion@radiosansalvador.com.uy - **FM:** 89.7MHz

"Skorpio" – **SA07)** Av.Gral. Artigas y Av. Domingo Pérez, 50002 Constitución ☎4764 2051 **E:** cw159@adinet.com.uy
**TA00) TACUAREMBÓ**
**TA01)** 18 de Julio 743, 45100 Paso de los Toros ☎4664 2333 **W:** am.pasodelostoros.com **E:** am1110@adinet.com.uy or radiopasodelostoros@pasodelostoros.com - **FM:** 91.9MHz "Toros FM" – **TA02)** Ituzaingó 246, 45000 Tacuarembó ☎463 22898 **W:** emisorastacuarembo.com **E:** radiotboclientes@hotmail.com - **FM:** 92.5MHz – **TA03)** 18 de Julio 302, 45000 Tacuarembó ☎463 32605 📠462 32779 – **W:** radiozorrilla.com **E:** zorrillaprensa@hotmail.com - **FM:** 88.9MHz "Em de la Música" – **TA04)** Arturo J. Mollo 141, 42500 San Gregorio de Polanco, Tacuarembó ☎4639 4547 **W:** radioibirapita1510am.blogspot.com **E:**radioibirapita1510am@yahoo.com
**TT00) TREINTA Y TRES**
**TT02)** Marcelo Barreto s/n, Villa Vergara, 33002 Vergara ☎4458 2917 **W:** ellibertador.com.uy **E:** ellibertador@adinet.com.uy – **TT03)** Pablo Zufriátegui 1076, 33000 Treinta y Tres ☎4452 22476 **W:** difusoratreintaytres.com.uy **E:** cw45@adinet.com.uy – **TT04)** Celedonio Rojas 1392, 33000 Treinta y Tres ☎4452 3532 **W:** radiopatria.com.uy **E:** radiopatria@gmail.com

**FM in Montevideo (MHz):** all stns 10-100kW. 89.1 Uni-Radio (LP stn) – **M021)** 89.7 La Catorce 10 – **M022)** 90.3 FM Oldies – 91.1 R.Futura – 91.5 ZOE Gospel Music – **M004)** 91.9 R.Disney – **M07)** 92.5 Urbana FM - 93.9 Océano – **M003)** 94.7 Emisora del Sur (SODRE) – 95.5 Em. Del Plata – 96.3 Alfa FM – **M003a)** 97.1 Babel (R.Clasica) – 97.9 M24 – 98.7 Diamante FM – 99.5 Em. del Sol – 100.3 Aire FM – 101.3 Nuevo Tiempo – 101.9 Azul FM – 103.7 Latina FM – **M010)** 104.3 Radio Cero – 105.9 Galaxia FM – 106.7 La Ley FM.
**NB:** In the rest of the country there are 165 FM outlets. There are also 156 authorised Community LPFM stns

## UZBEKISTAN

**L.T:** UTC +5h — **Pop:** 30.7 million — **Pr.L:** Uzbek — **E.C:** 220V/50Hz — **ITU:** UZB

**O'ZBEKISTON RESPUBLIKASI AXBOROT TEXNOLOGIYALARI VA KOMMUNIKATSIYALARINI RIVOJLANTIRISH VAZIRLIGI**
**(Ministry for Information Technology & Communications)**
📧 Amir Temur sho ko'chasi 4, 100047 Toshkent ☎ +998 71 2384107 📠 +998 71 2398782 **E:** info@mitc.uz **W:** mitc.uz
**L.P:** Minister: Shukhrat Sadikov
**NB:** The ministry issues broadcasting licenses.

**O'ZBEKISTON MILLY TELERADIOKOMPANIYASI (Gov)**
📧 A. Navoiy ko'chasi 69, 100011 Toshkent ☎ +998 71 2141250 **E:** info@mtrk.uz **W:** mtrk.uz
📻 Radio studios: Xorazm ko'chasi 49, 100047 Toshkent
**L.P:** Pres: Alisher Xadjayev

| FM | 1* | 2 | 3 | kW |
|---|---|---|---|---|
| Andijon | | 105.2 | - | 1 |
| Buxoro | 102.0c | 103.9 | 105.4 | 2 |
| Namangan | | 105.2 | - | 2 |
| Navoi | 106.6g | 104.0 | 105.8 | 2 |
| Nukus** | 103.1f | 104.6 | - | 2 |
| Qarshi | 102.3e | 103.1 | 105.6 | 1 |
| Toshkent | 103.1 | 104.0 | 107.8 | 4 |
| Samarqand | 105.2i | 101.9 | - | 1 |
| Urganch | 103.5l | 101.5 | - | 4 |

+ translators  *) incl. reg prgrs (see below) **) Located in Karakalpakstan (autonomous province)
**D.Prgr:** **Prgr 1 (O'zbekiston):** 0000-2200. For ethnic minorities: 1515-1545. – **Prgr 2 (Yoshlar):** 2300-2100 – **Prgr 3 (Mahalla):** 0000-2200 – **Local Station: "Toshkent"** on Toshkent 87.9 (4kW): 0000-2200 in Uzbek, Russian.

**O'zbekiston MTRK Regional Services**
**D.Prgr:** via Prgr 1 txs. Some branches also transmit on exclusive freqs (see below). **a) Andijon TRK:** Istiqlol ko'chasi 9, 170120 Andijon **E:** andijon@mtrk.uz – **b) Buxoro TRK:** Eshanov ko'chasi 20, 200120 Buxoro **E:** buxorotv@mtrk.uz – **c) Farg'ona TRK:** 150100 Farg'ona **E:** fargona@mtrk.uz – **d) Jizzax TRK:** Rashidov maydon, 130100 Jizzax **E:** jizzaxtvr@mtrk.uz. "R. Sanzar" on 105.4MHz: 24h. – **e) Qashqadaryo TRK:** 180100 Qarshi **E:** qashqadaryo_trk@mtrk.uz – **f) Qoraqalpog'iston TRK:** Dustnazarov ko'chasi 20, 230100 Nukus – **g) Navoi TRK:** Xalklar Do'stligi ko'chasi 32, 210100 Navoiy **E:** ntrk. nazorat@mtrk.uz – **h) Namangan TRK:** Holhonov ko'chasi 1, 160136 Namangan **E:** namangan@mtrk.uz – **i) Samarqand TRK:** 140100 Samarqand. "R. Jahon" on 105.2MHz: 24h. – **j) Sirdaryo TRK:** 120100

Guliston **E:** svtrk@mtrk.uz – **k) Surxondaryo TRK:** 190100 Termiz. – **I) Xorazm TRK:** 220100 Urganch. **E:** xorazmtvr@mtrk.uz.

### OTHER STATIONS

| FM | MHz | kW | Location | Station |
|---|---|---|---|---|
| 8) | 88.4 | 1 | Toshkent | Navro'z FM |
| 9) | 100.4 | 2 | Nukus* | Nukus-FM |
| 1B) | 100.5 | 2 | Toshkent | Oriat FM |
| 10) | 100.5 | 1 | Farg'ona | Ruxsor FM |
| 3) | 101.0 | 1 | Toshkent¹ | O'zbegim taronasi |
| 2) | 101.5 | 1 | Toshkent | R. Grand |
| 5) | 102.0 | 2 | Toshkent | Avtoradio Hamroh |
| 6) | 102.7 | 1 | Toshkent¹ | Vodiy sadosi |
| 4A) | 103.5 | 1 | Toshkent | R. Poytaxt |
| 4A) | 104.5 | 1 | Samarqand | R. Poytaxt |
| 1A) | 106.5 | 4 | Toshkent | Oriat Dono |
| 6) | 106.9 | 1 | Angren¹ | Vodiy sadosi |
| 4B) | 107.2 | 1 | Toshkent | R. Poytaxt-Inform |
| 7) | 107.2 | 1 | Samarqand | STV Radio |

+ txs below 1kW. *) Located in Karakalpakstan (autonomous province) ¹) + txs in other towns on same freq. (synchr. network)

**Addresses & other information:**
**1A,B)** Istikbol ko'chasi 6, 100000 Toshkent. 1A) in Uzbek **E:** radio@oriatdono.uz; 1B) in Russian **E:** fm@oriat.uz – **2)** Bunyodkor ko'chasi 15, 100043 Toshkent **E:** radio@grand.uz – **3)** Shaxrisabz ko'chasi 16a, 100000 Toshkent **E:** ut101@mail.ru – **4A,B)** Movaraunnahr ko'chasi 14, 100000 Toshkent **E:** radio1072@rambler.ru 9B) in Russian. – **5)** Shayxontohur ko'chasi 36, 100007 Toshkent **E:** hamroh@mail.ru – **6)** Mirobod ko'chasi 39/1A, 100000 Toshkent **E:** mtrk@intal.uz – **7)** Firdavskiy ko'chasi 1, 140100 Samarqand **E:** info@stv.uz – **8)** Muqumiy ko'chasi 178, 100096 Toshkent **E:** info@navruzfm.uz – **9)** Nukus – **10)** Marg'ilon ko'chasi 76, 150100 Farg'ona **E:** 100_5@inbox.ru

## VANUATU

**I.T.** UTC + 11h — **Pop:** 282,000 — **Pr.L:** Bislama, English, French — **E.C:** 50Hz, 220V — **ITU:** VUT

### TELECOMMUNICATIONS AND RADIOCOMMUNICATIONS REGULATOR (TRR)
PO Box 3547, Port Vila, Efate ☎ + 678 27621 **W:** www.trr.vu

### VANUATU BROADCASTING AND TELEVISION CORPORATION (VBTC)
PMB 9049, Port Vila ☎ +678 23615/22999 Ext 127/128 +678 22026 **L.P:** AGM: Fred Vurobaravu, Mgr Radio: Samuel Seiragi, Mgr-Tech. Srvcs: Warren Robert **W:** vbtc.vu **E:** technical@vbtc.com.vu

| MW | kHz | kW | Station |
|---|---|---|---|
| Emten Lagoon, Efate | 1125 | 10 | R. Vanuatu |

| SW | kHz | kW | Station |
|---|---|---|---|
| Emten Lagoon, Efate | 3945 | 1.5-2 | R. Vanuatu |
| Emten Lagoon, Efate | 7260 | 1.5-2 | R. Vanuatu |

| FM | MHz | kW | Station |
|---|---|---|---|
| Port Vila, Efate | 98.0 | 0.2 | Paradise FM |
| Tanna | 98.0 | 0.2 | Paradise FM |
| Luganville, Espiritu Santo | 100.0 | | R. Vanuatu |
| Port Vila, Efate | 100.0 | 1 | R. Vanuatu |

**National Radio Service: Radio Vanuatu D.Prgr:** Mon-Sat 1815-0030, Sun 1815-1030 other times relay Paradise FM **Schedule:** 3945kHz [overnight] 0400-2200 7260 [daytime] 2200-0400 [**NB:** SW schedule may vary depending on technical requirements and rebuilding after cyclone damage] **MW:** 24/7 including relay Paradise FM **FM:** Halo FM Luganville **Paradise FM** Port Vila **Prgr:** commercial 24/7 **NB:** VBTC operations have been under review because of systemic failures in operations and management. VBTC was given an ultimatum by the government Aug 2017 to correct failures within 6 months. MW and SW frequencies shown as active on their website and 3945 has been heard regularly.

### Other Stations:

| FM | MHz | kW | Station |
|---|---|---|---|
| 2) Port Vila, Efate | 96.0 | | BUZZ FM |
| 3) Luganville, Espiritu Santo | 99.0 | 0.25 | BBC |
| 3) Port Vila, Efate | 99.0 | 0.25 | BBC |
| 5) Luganville, Espiritu Santo | 102.0 | | China R. Int. |
| 5) Port Vila, Efate | 102.0 | | China R. Int. |
| 6) Port Vila, Efate | 103.0 | 0.2 | R. Australia |
| 6) Luganville, Espiritu Santo | 103.0 | | R. Australia |
| 4) Luganville, Espiritu Santo | 105.0 | | R. France Int |
| 4) Port Vila, Efate | 105.0 | 0.2 | R. France Int |
| 5) Lakatoro, Malakula | 106.0 | | China R. Int. |
| 1) Port Vila | 107.0 | | Capital FM107 |

| FM | MHz | kW | Station |
|---|---|---|---|
| 1) Santo | 107.0 | | Capital FM107 |
| 1) Tanna | 107.0 | | Capital FM107 |
| 1) Outer Islands | 107.0 | | Capital FM107 |

**Addresses & other information:**
**1)** Capital FM Lugana Building, PO Box 258, Port Vila Vanuatu ☎ +678 23847 **E:** salesinfo@gmail.com – **2)** Port Vila ☎ +678 23224 **L.P:** Marc Neil-Jones **W:** fm96.vu/ **E:** advertising@fm96.vu **ID:** Today's Best Music & News **Prgr:** 24/7 **Other:** associated with Vanuatu Daily Post. – **3)** 24/7 Pacific stream via satellite from London – **4)** 24/7 French language stream via satellite from Paris – **5)** 24/7 English language stream via satellite from Beijing – **6)** 24/7 English and French languages stream via satellite from Melbourne
**NB:** Several other LP FM stns in Port Vila region rep. including 24/7 rel. of RNZI which recently sustained major cyclone damage. Status of FM community stn for Saratamata, Penama province currently unknown.

## VATICAN CITY STATE

**L.T:** UTC +1h (31 Mar-27 Oct: +2h) — **Pop:** 900 — **E.C:** 50Hz, 230V — **ITU:** CVA

### RADIO VATICANA (Rlg.)
Vatican Radio, 00120 Vatican City ☎ +39 06 6988 3551 Int. Rel: ☎ +39 06 6988 3551 +39 06 6988 4565 **W:** radiovaticana.va **E:** promo@vatiradio.va
**L.P:** TD: Paolo Ruffini; CE: Maurizio Venuti; Head of Int. Rel: Giacomo Ghisani; Vatican Radio Museum, guided visiting tour c/o Palazzo Pio XII, Piazza Pia 3 ☎ +39 06 6988 3995 **E:** visitemuseorv@vatiradio.va **W:** radiovaticana.org/museo_tecnico/it/index.asp
**FM:** 105.0MHz 10kW
**Progr: RV Italia** 105.0MHz 24h
**DAB+: Channel 7B (Roma) Channel 13E (Milano)**
**Ann:** Before all transmissions: Latin: "Laudetur Jesus Christus" (Praised be Jesus Christ), repeated in the language of the broadcast, then stn identification. **IS:** "Christus Vincit". **V.** by QSL-card

**EXTERNAL SERVICE:** Vatican Radio see International Radio section

## VENEZUELA

**L.T:** UTC -4h — **Pop:** 32 million — **Pr.L:** Spanish — **E.C:** 60Hz, 120V — **ITU:** VEN

### COMISION NACIONAL DE TELECOMUNICACIONES (CONATEL)
Avenida Veracruz con Calle Cali, Edificio CONATEL, Urb. Las Mercedes, Caracas 1060 +58 212 993 8801 **W:** conatel.gob.ve **E:** conatel@conatel.gob.ve

### CAMARA VENEZOLANA DE LA INDUSTRIA DE RADIODIFUSION
Ap. 3955, Caracas 1060 ☎ +58 212 2634855, 2634528 +58 212 2614783.

**Hrs of tr:** 24h unless shown. **Call:** YV—, ‡=inactive, (r)=repeater, ±=variable frequency. **NB:** Due to crisis, many stations operate irregularly or on lower power.

| MW | Call | kHz | kW | Station, location, h. of tr. |
|---|---|---|---|---|
| AM01) | | 540 | 10 | LV de Manapiare, San Juan de Manapiare |
| ZU01) | OY | 540 | 50/25 | R. Perijá, La Villa del Rosario: 0900-0400 |
| DC01) | KE | 550 | 50 | R. Mundial, Caracas |
| DC02) | RH | 560 | 50 | RNV El Informativo, Pto.Ordaz: 1000-0400 |
| BA01) | SW | 600 | 15 | R. Alto Llano, Sta Bárbara de Barinas |
| AN01) | XY | 610 | 10 | R. Centro, Cantaura |
| LA01) | SE | 610 | 10 | R. Cristal, Barquisimeto |
| AP01) | ZC | 620 | 50/25 | R. Fe y Alegría,Guasdualito 0900-0400 |
| ZU03) | NO | 620 | 10 | R. Libertad, Cabimas: 0900-0400 |
| DC02) | KA | 630 | 50/25 | RNV El Informativo, Caracas: 1000-0400 |
| AN02) | QO | ‡640 | 30 | Deportes Unión R., Puerto La Cruz |
| LA02) | MU | 640 | 10/5 | R. Carora, Carora: 1000-0400 |
| DC02) | | 650 | | RNV El Informativo, Güigüe |
| DC03) | LL | 670 | 100 | R. Rumbos, Caracas (also r. LV de la Lib.) |
| SU02) | QR | 690 | 10 | R. Continente, Cumaná: 1000-0500 |
| DC05) | KY | 710 | 50/20 | R. Capital, Caracas: 1000-0600 |
| AP02) | XE | 720 | 10 | R. Elorza, Elorza |
| DC06) | KS | 750 | 100 | RCR 750 Radio Caracas Radio, Caracas |
| TR01) | SO | 760 | 10 | R. Simpática 760, Trujillo |
| DC02) | KK | ‡770 | 50/20 | RNV El Informativo, Valencia |
| FA02) | MN | 780 | 15 | R. Coro, Coro |
| TA03) | OD | 780 | 50/20 | Ecos del Torbes, San Cristóbal: |

| MW | Call | kHz | kW | Station, location, h. of tr. |
|---|---|---|---|---|
| DC02) | | 790 | | RNV El Informativo, Cd. Bolívar |
| DC07) | KC | 790 | 10 | R. Venezuela, Caracas |
| LA05) | XM | 790 | 50 | R. Minuto, Barquisimeto |
| DC08) | LT | 830 | 25 | R. Sensación, Caracas(also r.LV de la Lib.) |
| GU01) | YE | 860 | 20/10 | Enlace 8-60, Valle de la Pascua |
| TA05) | OL | 860 | 10 | R. Mundial, San Cristóbal: 0900-0500 |
| LA11) | MP | 870 | 10 | Unión R. Notícias, Barquisimeto: 1000-0400 |
| ZU07) | MD | 900 | 25 | R. Venezuela Mara Ritmo, Maracaibo |
| DC10) | RQ | 910 | 50/20 | RQ 910 AM Center, Caracas |
| CO01) | QU | 920 | 10/5 | R. San Carlos, San Carlos |
| NE02) | QX | 920 | 20 | R. Nueva Esparta, Porlamar: 1000-0400 |
| AR02) | LJ | 930 | 10 | R. Maracay, Maracay: 1000-0600 |
| AN08) | LU | 940 | 10 | R. Fe y Alegría, El Tigre: 0900-0300 |
| TA06) | SS | 960 | 10 | R. San Sebastián, San Cristóbal: 1000-0500 |
| AR03) | LR | 970 | 10 | R. Continente 970, Maracay: 0900-0400 |
| TR02) | SD | 970 | 15 | R. Turismo, Valera: 0900-0400 |
| DC12) | RT | 990 | 20 | R. Tropical, Caracas(r. LV de la Liberación) |
| CA04) | NM | 1000 | 10 | R. Caribeña Mil AM (Continente), Morón: |
| TA11) | OA | 1000 | 10 | Deportes Unión R, San Cristóbal:1000-0400 |
| AR04) | PC | 1010 | 10 | R. Aragua, Cagua: 0900-0400 |
| YA01) | TW | 1020 | 25 | R. Alegría 1020 AM Stereo, Chivacoa |
| CA05) | LB | 1040 | 10 | LV de Carabobo, Valencia: 0900-0400 |
| ME01) | ON | 1040 | 20/10 | R. Mundial Los Andes, Mérida |
| GU02) | LN | 1060 | 10 | R. Guárico, San Juan de los Morros |
| TA07) | OE | 1060 | 10 | Unión R. Noticias, San Cristóbal |
| AP03) | | 1070 | 10 | Superior 1070 Biruaca, S. Fernando de Apure |
| AR05) | NR | 1080 | 10 | Mundial/R. Venezuela 1080, Maracay |
| DC13) | SZ | 1090 | 20 | Deportes Unión R., Caracas |
| YA02) | PB | 1090 | 10 | R. Yaracuy "Operadora 1090 AM", S. Felipe |
| CA06) | RX | 1110 | 10 | Deportes Unión R., Valencia |
| SU03) | QT | 1110 | 10 | R. Carúpano, Carúpano: 0900-0400 |
| AP04) | SK | 1120 | 20/10 | R. Dif.del Sur, San Fernando de Apure |
| LA07) | KQ | 1130 | 10 | R. Popular, Barquisimeto: 0900-0400 |
| DC16) | RL | 1130 | 20/10 | R. Ideal, Maiquetía |
| B007) | QD | 1150 | 10 | Ecos del Orinoco, Cd.Bolívar |
| VA01) | KW | 1170 | 10 | R. Bolivariana "R. 1070", Maiquetía |
| AR06) | LQ | 1180 | 10 | Super Suave 11-80, La Victoria |
| B008) | PF | 1190 | 20/10 | Ondas de Libertad, San Felix: 0900-0300 |
| TA09) | ZD | ‡1190 | 10 | La Cultural del Táchira, San Cristóbal |
| DC14) | OZ | 1200 | 10 | R. Tiempo, Caracas |
| AP05) | RD | 1220 | 10 | LV de Apure, San Fernando de Apure |
| CA07) | VM | 1220 | 10/5 | Valencia 1220 - R. Venezuela, Valencia |
| TR03) | OH | 1230 | 10 | R. Valera, Valera: 0900-0400 |
| DC15) | RM | 1260 | 10 | BBN R, Caracas |
| ME04) | OU | 1270 | 10 | R. Ondas Panamericanas, El Vigía |
| GU03) | QS | 1280 | 10/5 | R. Zaraza, Zaraza: 1000-0300 |
| TR04) | OF | 1280 | 10 | R. Trujillo, Trujillo |
| CA08) | LF | 1290 | 10 | R. Puerto Cabello, Puerto Cabello |
| DC10) | KH | 1300 | 10 | Deportiva 1300 AM Stereo, Caracas |
| DC02) | SL | 1310 | 1 | RNV El Informativo, Guri: 1000-0400 |
| DC02) | | 1310 | | RNV El Informativo, Sta. Elena: 1000-0400 |
| TR05) | TS | 1310 | 5 | R. Andina "Sonido 13-10", Isnotú: 0900-0500 |
| AR07) | WP | 1320 | 10/5 | R. Apolo, Turmero |
| LA08) | SG | 1320 | 10 | R. Colonial, El Tocuyo |
| DC02) | | 1330 | | RNV El Informativo, La Paragua |
| DC17) | NE | 1340 | 10 | R. Uno, Caracas |
| MI04) | TZ | ‡1360 | 5 | R. Armonía, Charallave: 1000-0300 |
| ME05) | JI | 1370 | 10 | R. Continente Cumbre, Mérida: 1000-0400 |
| PO05) | SV | 1370 | 5 | RNV Portuguesa, Acarigua: 1000-0400 |
| CA09) | NG | 1380 | 10 | Ondas del Mar, Puerto Cabello: 0900-0400 |
| DC18) | ZA | 1390 | 20 | R. Fe y Alegría, Caracas |
| ZU20) | ZO | 1390 | 10 | R. Lumen, Maracaibo: 1000-0500 |
| TR01) | SP | ‡1410 | 10 | R. Simpatía, Valera |
| DC21) | | 1420 | 5 | R. Sintonía, Caracas |
| LA10) | RW | 1420 | 10/5 | R. Cardenal, Carora: 1000-0400 |
| CA10) | NB | 1430 | 10 | Unión Radio, Guacara |
| PO07) | ZI | ‡1440 | 10 | R. Estelar 14-40, Guanare: 0900-0400 |
| B012) | XC | 1450 | 10/5 | R. Mega Visión, San Felix |
| VA02) | KJ | 1450 | 10/8 | R. María, Caracas |
| CA11) | JW | ‡1470 | 10 | Union R. Cultural, Valencia |
| FA08) | | 1480 | | R. Cumarebo, Cumarebo |
| DC19) | XD | 1490 | 10 | R. Dinámica, Caracas |
| ME06) | SQ | 1490 | 1 | R. Mérida 14-90, Mérida |
| SU05) | RZ | 1500 | 10/5 | R. 2000, Cumaná: 1000-0400 |
| DC02) | | 1510 | | RNV Musical, Güigüe |
| YA04) | NP | ‡1530 | 10 | R. San Felipe el Fuerte, San Felipe |
| DC02) | LZ | 1560 | 10/5 | RNV El Informativo, Mérida |
| DC20) | UD | 1590 | 10 | R. Deporte, Caracas |

**Networks:**

**CNB - CIRCUITO NACIONAL BELFORT**
⊡ Quinta CNB, Av.Los Naranjos, La Florida, Caracas **W:** cnb.com.ve

## CIRCUITO AM CENTER
⊡ CentroComercialConcresa, Nivel 1, Circuito Center, Prados del Este, Caracas 1080, Edo.Miranda ☎ +58 212 976-2013
**E:** feloespinosa@cantv.et.
## CIRCUITO RADIAL ALFA OMEGA
⊡ Calle 25, Con Calle 67, Sector El Paraíso, frente Al Colegio La Epifanía, Maracaibo, Edo.Zulia ☎ +58 261 783-2524
## CIRCUITO POPULAR
⊡ Boulevard de Sabana Grande, Torre Provincial, P10, Sabana Grande, Caracas 1050 ☎ +58 212 762 5052
## CIRCUITO RADIO CARACAS RADIO
⊡ Av.Páez, Quinta RCR, El Paraíso, Caracas 1021 ☎ +58 212 481-3590
## CIRCUITO RADIAL CONTINENTE
⊡ Calle La Joya, Edif.Cosmos, PH, Chacao, Caracas 1060, Edo. Miranda ☎ +58 212 267-3132 🖷 +58 212 267-1223 **W:** radiocontinente.jimdo.com **E:** produccion@radiocontinente zzn.com
## CIRCUITO RADIO VENEZUELA
⊡ Av.Rómulo Gallegos, Edif.KLM, P12, Ofcs CyD, Los Palos Grandes, Caracas 1062, Edo.Miranda ☎ +58 212 286-8492 **W:** radiovenezuela.com.ve **E:** radiovenezuela@hotmail.com
## CIRCUITO SATELITAL RUMBOS
⊡ Av.Francisco de Miranda, Multicentro Empresarial del Este, Edif. Libertador, Núcleo A, P7, Chacao, Caracas 1060, Edo.Miranda ☎ +58 212 263-3236 🖷 +58 212 263-2212 **E:** radiorumbos@ip-net.work.net
## CIRCUITO UNION RADIO
⊡ Av.Mohedano, Entre Calle Los Granados y 1ª transversal, Edif. Splendor, La Castellana, Caracas 1060, Edo.Miranda ☎ +58 212 263-5133 **W:** unionradio.net
## GRUPO RADIAL DE ORIENTE
⊡ Urb.Tricentenaria, Centro ComercialTricentenaria, P2, Ofcs 03y09, Barcelona 6001, Edo.Anzoátegui ☎ +58 281 277-1743 🖷 +58 281 277-1776 **E:** radioanzoategui@hotmail.com
## SISTEMA RADIO MUNDIAL
⊡ Calle Nueva York, Edif.Manzanillo, P2, Las Mercedes, Caracas 1060, Edo.Miranda ☎ +58 212 993-9391 **W:** radiomundial.com.ve **E:** prensayvke@cantv.net

**State abbreviations:** AM = Amazonas, AN = Anzoátegui, AP = Apure, AR = Aragua, BA = Barinas, BO = Bolívar, CA = Carabobo, CO = Cojedes, DA = Delta Amacuro, DC = Distrito Capital, FA = Falcón, GU = Guárico, LA = Lara, ME = Mérida, MI = Miranda, MO = Monagas, NE = Nueva Esparta, PO = Portuguesa, SU = Sucre, TA = Táchira, TR = Trujillo, VA = Vargas, YA = Yaracuy, ZU = Zulia.
**N.B.** These abbreviations are not officially recognized by the Venezuelan Post Office. Letters should therefore carry the full name.

**Addresses & other information:**
**AM00) AMAZONAS**
**AM01)** San Juan de Manapiare.
**AAN00) ANZOÁTEGUI**
**AN01)** Av Hospital cruce con Calle Freites, Edif.Radio Centro, Cantaura 6007 **W:** rc610am.radio12345.com – **AN02)** Av 5 de Julio, Edif Los Angeles, Sotanos 1y2, Puerto La Cruz 6023. **W:** unionradio. net/deportes – **AN08)** Av.Simon Rodríguez con 8va Calle Norte, Complejo Cultural Simón Rodríguez, El Tigre 6034 **W:** feyalegria.org
**AP00) APURE**
**AP01)** Carr Nacional, Vía Elorza La Arenosa, Edif. Fe y Alegría, Guasdualito 5063. **W:** feyalegria.org – **AP02)** Calle 9 con Cra 4, Municipio Rómulo Gallegos, Elorza 7007 – **AP03)** Av.Fuerzas Armadas, Edif.Superior, P1, San Fernando de Apure 7001 0930-0400 – **AP04)** Calle Carlos Rodríguez Rincones, Gobernación del Estado Apure, San Fernando de Apure 7001 – **AP05)** Av Miranda, Edif.Don António Cestari, San Fernando de Apure 7001.
**AR00) ARAGUA**
**AR01)** See DC02 – **AR02)** Calle Boyacá, Edif Centro, P9, Ofc 1, Maracay 2101 – **AR03)** Av Miranda Oeste N° 149, Entre Carabobo y Pinhincha, Edif.Canaobre, PH, Maracay 2101 **W:** radiocontinente. jimdo.com – **AR04)** Calle Sucre, Edificio Comercial y Profesional Sucre, Piso 2, Oficina #3, Cagua 2122 **W:** radioaragua.com – **AR05)** Urb.Calicanto, Calle Coromoto, Norte 6, Detrás de la Maestranza Cesar Girón, Maracay 2101 **W:** radiovenezuela.com.ve – **AR06)** Edif Veliz, Calle Aldao, frente a la Plaza Rivas, La Víctoria 2126 – **AR07)** Av.Bermúdez, Torre Apolo, PB, entre Mariño y Bolívar, Turmero 2115 **W:** apolo1320am.venesur.com
**BA00) BARINAS**
**BA01)** Cra 3 N° 7-39, entre Calles 7 y 8, Santa Bárbara de Barinas 5210
**BO00) BOLÍVAR**
**BO07)** Paseo Meneses, Centro Comercial Meneses, PA, Locales 11 y 12, Cd Bolívar 8001 – **BO08)** Calle México, Parcela El Roble, Detrás de la Estación de Servicio Volfo, Sector La Antena, San Félix 8024 –

**B012)** Av.Della Costa, Edif.Flor Motors, PB, San Felix 8024.

**CA00) CARABOBO**

**CA04)** Carr.Panamericana, Edif.Radio Mil, Morón – **CA05)** Av Rosarito, Torre Trebol, P1, Ofc 13, Urb Lomas del Este, Valencia 2001 – **CA06)** Av.Bolívar Norte, Torre Banavén, P12, Ofc.12-9, Valencia 2001 **W:** deportesunionradio.net – **CA07)** Av.Rosario, Edif.El Parque, PB Local 2, Urb.Lomas del Este, Valencia 2001 **W:** radiovenezuela.com.ve – **CA08)** Av.Marina, Edif.Diproca, PB, Local 3, Puerto Cabello 2024. **W:** radio-puertocabello.com – **CA09)** Av Bolívar, Edif Sabatino, P1, Urb.Rancho Grande, Puerto Cabello 2024 – **CA10)** Final de La Calle Jacinto con Calles Ricaurte y Girardot, Edif.Radio Satélite, Guacara 2015 – **CA11)** Av.Montes de Oca, Edif.Don Pelayo, P12, Valencia 2001 **W:** unionradio. net/cultural - **FM:** 99.1MHz.

**C000) COJEDES**

**CO01)** Av.Sucre, Edif.General Manuel Manrique, P3, Local 46, San Carlos 2201 - 0955-0400 **W:** unionradio.net

**DC00) DISTRITO CAPITAL**

**DC01)** Calle Nueva York Cruce con Av.Rio de Janeiro, Edif YVKE Mundial, P1, Las Mercedes, Caracas 1060, Edo.Miranda **W:** radiomundial.com.ve – **DC02)** Final Calle Las Marías, Edif. Radio Nacional de Venezuela, entre Chapellín y Country Club, La Frorida, Caracas 1050, Edo. Miranda **W:** rnv.gob.ve **E:** infornv@gmail.com – **DC03)** Av.Francisco de Miranda, Multicentro Empresarial del Este, Edif. Libertador, P7, Núcleo A Chacao, Caracas 1060, Edo Miranda – **DC05)** Av.Francisco de Miranda, Centro Comercial Los Ruices, P3, Los Ruices, Caracas 1071, Edo Miranda – **DC06)** Av José A Paez, Quinta RCR, El Paraiso, Caracas 1021, Distrito Capital – **DC07)** Av.Rómulo Gallegos, Edif.KLM, P12, Ofc CyD, Los Palos Grandes, Caracas 1062, Edo Miranda. **W:** radiovenezuela.com.ve – **DC08)** Av Santiago de Chile, Quinta Radio Sensación, Los Caobos, Caracas 1050 – **DC10)** Centro Comercial Concresa, Nivel 1, Circuito Center, Prados del Este, Caracas 1080, Edo.Miranda. **W:** deportiva.com.ve – **DC12)** Puente Nuevo a Puerto Escondido, Edif.Torre del Oeste, P1, El Silencio, Caracas 1010, Distrito Capital (or Ap.3674, Caracas 1010-A) **W:** ipdave.com.ve facebook.com/La-Voz-De-La-Liberacion-Venezuela-1513240865583338 – **DC13)** Av.Mohedano, Entre Calle Los Granados y 1ª transversal, Edif. Splendor, La Castellana, Caracas 1060, Edo.Miranda **W:** unionradio. net/deportes – **DC14)** Av Los Mangos N° 49, Qta.Radio Tiempo, La Florida, Caracas 1050-A, Edo.Miranda **W:** radiotiempo.com.ve – **DC15)** Av Los Mangos con Av.Valencia Parpacén, Qta. Marisabel (BBN), La Florida, Caracas 1050, Edo.Miranda **W:** bbnradio.org/wcm4/spanish/Radio/Emisoras/tabid/646/StationID/236/Default.aspx – **DC16)** Centro Comercial Uslar, P15, Ofc 152, Montalbán, Caracas 1021, Distrito Capital **W:** radioideal.com.ve – **DC17)** Edif Mundial, Av Tamanaco, El Rosal, Caracas 1060. **W:** radiouno.com.ve – **DC18)** Calle 3B, Edif.C-207, P2, (detrás del McDonald's), La Urbina, Caracas 1070, Edo.Miranda **W:** feyalegria.org comunicamundi.net/live/irfa. html – **DC19)** Av.Boulevard Brasil N° 74, de Santa Ana a Providencia La Pastora, Caracas 1010, Distrito Capital. **W:** radiodinamica.com – **DC20)** Av Circunvalación del Sol, Centro Profesional Sta Paula, Torre A, P5 Ofc 51, Caracas 1061, Edo.Miranda. **W:** radiodeporte.com – **DC21)** Calle La Joya, Torre Cosmos, P9, Ofc 9A, Chacao, Caracas 1060, Edo.Miranda (or Centro Comercial El Pichacho, P8, San António de los Altos 1204). **W:** radiosintonia1420.com.ve

**FA00) FALCÓN**

**FA02)** Avenida Manaure esquina Maparari, Edificio Pepelupe, Coro 4101. **W:** radiocoro.com – **FA08)** Centro Ciudad Comercial Tamanaco (CCCT), Torre B, P7, Ofc 704, Chuao, Caracas 1060, Edo Miranda

**GU00) GUÁRICO**

**GU01)** Av RómuloGallegos, Edif.Flor de Pascua, Loc 2, Valle de la Pascua 2307. **W:** enlace860am.tk – **GU02)** Av Principal La Moreras, Edif.Ghersy N° 28, San Juan de los Morros 2301 – **GU03)** Calle Concordia, Qta Puerto Arturo N° 35, Zaraza 2332

**LA00) LARA**

**LA01)** Av Venezuela con Calles 13 y 14, Edif.Radio Cristal, Barquisimeto 3001 – **LA02)** Calle Sucre Entre Cras 7 y 8, La Casita, Carora 3040 - **FM:** 100.5MHz – **LA05)** Av.Pedro León Torres, Centro Comercial Venrol, locales 29 y 30, Barquisimeto 3001. **W:** radiominuto.net – **LA07)** Calle 29, Entre Calles 18 y 19, Casa N° 18-74, Barquisimeto 3001 – **LA08)** Calle 10 cruce con Calle 9, Casa S/N, El Tocuyo 3018 – **LA10)** Av Bolívar, Edif Guillermo, Locales 2 y 3, Carora 3040 – **LA11)** Av Los Leones, Centro Empresarial Caracas, P5, Ofc 5-2, Barquisimeto 3002 **W:** unionradio.net

**ME00) MÉRIDA**

**ME01)** Calle 44 N° 3-57, Diagonal al Colegio de Médicos, Mérida 5101 **W:** radiomundial.com.ve – **ME04)** Av Bolívar, Esquina Calle 11, N° 10-87, El Vigía 5145 – **ME05)** Av.Andrés Bello, Centro Comercial Las Tapias, P3, Ofc.40-41, Mérida 5101 **W:** radiocontinente.jimdo.com – **ME06)** Av 3, Esquina con Calle 22, Mérida 5101

**MI00) MIRANDA**

**MI04)** Final Av.Tosta Gracía, Resd.Boal, Mezz.2, Charallave 1200.

**NE00) NUEVA ESPARTA**

**NE02)** Av Miranda, Edif.Best, P2, Porlamar 6301

**P000) PORTUGUESA**

**PO05)** Av. 28 entre calles 26 y 27 del sector Campo Lindo del Municipio Páez, Acarigua – **PO07)** Av Los Próceres, Urb.Francisco de Miranda, Edif.Radial, Guanare 3310

**SU00) SUCRE**

**SU02)** Av.Gran Mariscal Sucre N° 30, Cumaná 6101 **W:** circuito-radiocontinente.com – **SU03)** Calle Independencia con Calle Páez, Multinacional, P5, Radio Venezuela, Carúpano 6124 **W:** radiocarupanoam.com.ve – **SU05)** Av Santa Rosa 18, Sector La Copita, frente a la Iglesia Santa Rosa de Lima, Cumaná 6101 **W:** radio2000.com.ve

**TA00) TÁCHIRA**

**TA03)** Calle 9 N° 8-16, San Cristóbal 5001 **W:** ecosdeltorbes. net – **TA05)** Av Las Lomas, Edif.Primo Centro, Locales 3-12 y 3-13, San Cristóbal 5001 – **TA06)** Av 19 de Abril, Qta.Circuito Lider, San Cristóbal 5001 – **TA07)** Pasaje Acueducto N° 24-60, Barrio Obrero, San Cristóbal 5001 **W:** unionradio.net – **TA09)** Av 19 de Abril con Av 8, La Concordia, San Cristóbal 5001 **W:** laculturalfm.com.ve – **TA11)** Cra 9 cruce con Calle 9, Edif.El Ciclón, P4, San Cristóbal 5001.

**TR00) TRUJILLO**

**TR01)** Av 11, entre Calles 12y13 N° 12-56, Valera 3101 – 1045-0400 **W:** radiosimpatia.com.ve – **TR02)** Av Bolívar con Calle 15, Edif. Grasso, P1, Valera 3101 – **TR03)** Av 10 entre Calles 9y10, Edif.Radio Valera, Local 9-31, Valera 3101 – **TR04)** Calle Independencia N° 10-11, Trujillo 3102 – **TR05)** Calle Iglesia, José Gregorio Hernández, Isnotu 3109.

**VA00) VARGAS**

**VA01)** Av Soublette, Edif Las Américas B, P16, Maiquetía 1161 – **VA02)** 3era Norte Av Guaicaipuro, Quinta Mirna, Caracas **W:** radiomaria.org.ve

**YA00) YARACUY**

**YA01)** Av 10, Entre Calles 7y8, Edif.Alegría, Chivacoa 3202 – **YA02)** Prolongación 5ta Av.Urb.Andrés Eloy Blanco, Sector la Aduana, San Felipe 3201 – **YA04)** Av.Cartagena, entre Calles 19 y 20, Edif.Radio San Felipe, San Felipe 3201.

**ZU00) ZULIA**

**ZU01)** Calle Central, Edif.Radio Perijá, P2, La Villa del Rosario 4047 – **ZU03)** Av El Muelle N° 1, Edif.Radio Libertad, frente a la Plaza Bolívar, Cabimas 4013 – **ZU07)** Calle 67 cruce con Av 27, detrás del Colegio La Epifanía, Sector Santa María, Maracaibo 4005 **W:** radiovenezuela. com.ve – **ZU20)** Iglesia de María en Pentecostés, Urb. San Jacinto, primera entrada, vía El Moján, Maracaibo 4005

**FM in Caracas (MHz):** 88.1 Imagen – 88.9 Romántica – 89.7 X FM – 90.3 Unión Noti– 91.1 RNV Clásica – 91.9 Candela Pura Estrella – 92.9 Tu FM – 93.5 Melodía Stereo – 94.1 Hot 94 – 94.9 Clásicos FM – 95.5 Jazz – 96.3 Alba Ciudad – 96.9 X FM – 97.7 Em.Cultural – 98.5 La Radio del Sur – 99.1 La Nueva Mágica – 99.9 Éxitos – 100.7 Ateneo – 101.5 Kys – 101.9 Tiuna – 102.3 AN Radio, La Voz de la Asamblea Nacional – 102.7 Original – 103.3 Radiorama Stereo – 103.9 RNV Activa/Canal Juvenil – 104.5 Rumbera – 105.3 Planeta – 105.9 Sonera – 106.5 Fiesta 106 – 106.9 Playa 107 – 107.3 La Mega Estación107 – 107.9 Onda

## VIETNAM

**L.T:** UTC +7h — **Pop:** 96 million — **Pr.L:** Vietnamese, ethnic — **E.C:** 50Hz, 220V — **ITU:** VTN

### AUTHORITY OF BROADCASTING AND ELECTRONIC INFORMATION

✉ 9th Floor, 115 Tran Duy Hung, Cau Giay, Hanoi ☎ +84 24 39448034 🖷 +84 24 39448036 **E:** vanthucucqlptth@mic.gov.vn **W:** mic.gov.vn **L.P:** DG: Nguyen Thanh Lam

### DÀI TIÉNG NÓI VIÊT NAM
### (VOV, RADIO THE VOICE OF VIETNAM) (Gov)

✉ 58 Quan Su Str, Hanoi ☎ +84 24 8255694 🖷 +84 24 8265875 **W:** vov.vn **E:** qhqt.vov@hn.vnn.vn

**L.P:** Pres: Mr Nguyen The Ky. Dir Editorial Sce: Uong Ngoc Dau. Dir Tech Sce: Nguyen Xuan Huy

| MW | kHz | Net | kW | Station, location, h of tr |
|---|---|---|---|---|
| 1) | 549 | 2 | 200 | Hung Yen, (Site: My Hao): 2145-1700 |
| 2) | 576 | 2,P | 50 | Khanh Hoa, Nha Trang: 2145-1700 |
| 1) | 594 | 1 | 50 | Danang, (Site: An Hai): 2145-1700 |
| 3) | 610 | H | 200 | Ho Chi Minh City, Tang Nhon Phu: 2100-1700 |
| 1) | 630 | 1 | 200 | Quang Binh, Dong Hoi: 2145-1700 |
| 1) | 648 | 1 | 50 | Binh Dinh, Quy Nhon, (Site: An Nhon): 2145-1700 |
| 1) | 657 | 1,C | 100 | Ho Chi Minh C., Quan Tre: 2145-1700 |
| 1) | 666 | 1 | 50 | Khanh Hoa, Nha Trang: 2145-1700 |

| MW | kHz | Net | kW | Station, location, h of tr |
|---|---|---|---|---|
| 1) | 675 | 1 | 500 | Hung Yen, (Site: My Hao): 2145-1700 |
| 4) | 702 | 2,Q,D | 50 | Danang, (Site: An Hai): 2145-1700 |
| 1) | 711 | 1 | 500 | Can Tho, Thoi Long: 2145-1700 |
| 1) | 729 | 2 | 200 | Quang Binh, Dong Hoi: 2145-1700 |
| 5) | 740 | 2,P | 50 | Binh Dinh, Quy Nhon, (Site: An Nhon): 2145-1700 |
| 6) | 756 | P | 10 | Long An, Tan An: 2200-1100§ |
| 1) | 783 | 2 | 500 | Can Tho, Thoi Long: 2145-1700 |
| 1) | 819 | 2 | 20 | Dac Lac, Buon Ma Thuot: 2145-1700 |
| 7) | 828 | P | 50 | Son La: 2200-1400§ |
| 8) | 846 | P | 10 | Thanh Hoa: 0400-1030§ |
| 1) | 873 | 1,3,4 | 500 | Can Tho, Thoi Long: 2155-1700§ |
| 9) | ±900 | P | 10 | Ha Tinh: 2200-1200§ |
| 10) | 909 | P | 10 | Ca Mau: 2200-1330§ |
| 11) | ‡1035 | P | 10 | Hoa Binh: 2215-1100§ |
| 12) | ‡1089 | P | 10 | Cao Bang |
| 13) | 1098 | P | 10 | Thua Thien Hue, Hue: 2145-1145/1310§ |
| 1) | 1242 | E | 500 | Can Tho, Thoi Long: 1300-1600 |

‡) r. inactive ±) variable fq. §) split schedule, see Reg. stns for details

| SW | kHz | Net | kW | Location, h. of tr |
|---|---|---|---|---|
| 1) | 6020 | 4 | 20 | Buon Ma Thuot: 2200-1600 |
| 1) | 6165 | 4 | 50 | Xuan Mai: 2200-2300, 2330-2400, 1130-1400 |
| 1) | 7210 | 1 | 20 | Buon Ma Thuot: 2145-1700 |
| 1) | ±9635 | 1 | 100 | Son Tay: 24h+ |
| 1) | 9850 | 4 | 50 | Xuan Mai: 0400-0600 |
| 1) | 11720 | 1 | 50 | Xuan Mai: 1030-1500v |

**SW Stations:** Xuan Mai (also known as CK2) 50kW (GC: 105.36E 20.53N). Buon Me Thuot 2x20kW (G.C: 108.03E 12.41N). Son Tay (see Int Radio section)
**Netw.: 1/2/3:** Voice of Vietnam 1st/2nd/3rd national prgr – **4:** Voice of Vietnam minorities network – **C:** VOV Thanh Pho Ho Chi Minh **D:** Radio & TV Danang – **E:** Voice of Vietnam external sces – **H:** Voice of the People of Ho Chi Minh City – **P:** Provincial sce – **Q:** Radio & TV Quang Nam (Hoi An, Quang Nam Province).

**FM:** All FM powers shown are TRP.
**Prgrs. from Hanoi**
**VOV1, news & current affairs:** 2145-1700. **FM:** A Luoi 102.7MHz, Ba Thuoc 93.1MHz, Bach Long Vi 103.0MHz, Ca Mau 95.9MHz, Cao Bang 94.0MHz, Cat Ba 95.8MHz, Con Dao 101.0MHz, Da Nang 100.0MHz, Dac Lac 104.5MHz, Dao Ly Son 89.9MHz, Dien Bien Phu 96.3MHz, Dong Van 101.0MHz, Ha Giang 100.0MHz, Ha Long 104.0MHz, Ham Rong 105.1MHz, Hanoi (Tam Dao) 100.0MHz 10kW, Ho Chi Minh C. 94.0MHz 10kW, Huang Su Phi 94.0MHz, Kon Tum 91.5MHz, Lai Chau 95.0MHz, Lao Bao 101.0MHz, Lao Cai 94.0MHz, Meo Vac 100.0MHz, Mong Cai 96.6MHz, Muong Nhe 95.0MHz, Muong Te 101.5MHz, Nguyen Binh 97.0MHz, Phu Quoc 95.0MHz, Quan Ba 95.0MHz, Quang Ngai 95.5MHz, Quy Hop 101.5MHz, Phu Quoc 95.0MHz, Son La 93.5MHz, Sop Cop 99.0MHz, Thai Binh 97.0MHz, Tra Vinh 102.5MHz, Truong Sa 100.0MHz, Tuy Hoa 102.7MHz, Van Don 94.0MHz, and also relayed in part by many regional sts. **N:** 2205, 2300, 0100, 0300, 0500, Mon-Sat 0630, 0700, Mon-Sat 0730, 0800, Mon-Sat 1000, 1100, 1230, MF 1330, 1430. SW freqs marked + relay VOV3 1700-2145
**VOV2, economic, social, cultural & education prgrs:** 2145-1700. **FM:** Bac Kan 99.5MHz, Buon Ma Thuot 102.7MHz 5kW, Cao Bang 103.5MHz, Da Nang 89.0MHz, Hanoi (Tam Dao) 96.5MHz 10kW, Ho Chi Minh C. 96.5MHz 10kW, Huang Su Phi 99.5MHz, Kon Tum 92.5MHz, Lai Chau 100.5MHz, Lang Son (Mau Son) 93.5MHz, Moc Chau 92.5MHz, Muong Nhe 96.5MHz, Phu Quoc 103.5MHz, Quan Ba 96.5MHz,Son La (Deo Pha Din) 93.5MHz 20kW, Phu Yen 102.7MHz 5kW, Tuong Duong 104,0MHz, Van Don 99.5MHz, Yen Bai 97.5MHz. **LL:** English 0600, French 0615, Chinese/Japanese/Vietnamese through English 0630 (repeated Mon-Sat 1600-1645)
**VOV3, news & music prgrs:** 24h on FM (freqs in MHz) An Giang (Nui Cam) 102.7MHz, Dac Nong (Gia Nghia) 96.6 5kW, Da Nang (Ba Na) 102.5 10kW, Hanoi (Tam Dao) 102.7 20kW, Ho Chi Minh C. (Quan Tre) 104.5 10kW, Hue 106.1 10kW, Quang Binh 96.1 5kW, Qui Nhon 103.1 10kW, Son La 101.0, Thanh Hoa 94.9, Vinh (Thien Tung) 102.7. Inc.
**One Radio:** Mon-Sat 2300-0200, 0900-1600, Sun 0600-1600.
**VOV4, prgrs for ethnic minorities: Bana, Ede, Giarai, Hmong, K'Hor (Koho), Sedang, Thai, M'Nong:** 2200-1600 on 819kHz, 6020kHz, Bing Thuan (Phan Thiet) 102.0MHz 5kW, Dac Lac (Buon Ma Thuot) 100.0MHz 5kW, Da Lat 101.0MHz, Dac Nong (Gia Nghia) 101.5MHz 5kW, Ninh Thuan 102.7MHz, Phu Yen (Tuy Hoa) 96.0 2.5kW, for Central Highlands. **Dao, H'Mong (Ho Mong), Thai:** 2150-2300, 0000-0030, 1145-1400 on 6165kHz, 0400-0530 on 9850kHz for Northern Vietnam, also in whole or in part on Bac Kan 97.8MHz, Cao Bang (Phan Thanh) 97.0MHz 10kW, Ba Thuoc 94.9MHz, Dien Bien Phu 98.0MHz 2kW, Ha Giang (Quan Ba) 103.2MHz 10kW, Huang Su Phi 97.0MHz, Lai Chau (Muong Te) 101.5MHz 2kW, Lang Son (Mau Son) 101.0MHz

10kW, Lao Cai 99.1MHz, Muong Nhe 97.5MHz, Quan Ba 90.5MHz, Son La (Deo Pha Din) 104.3MHz 10kW. **Co Tu:** 2330-2400, 0420-0450, 1230-1300 on Danang (Ba Na) 100.0MHz 10kW, Dong Giang 99.5MHz. **Cham, Khmer (Kho Me), Vietnamese:** 2155-1330 on 873kHz, Can Tho 88.0MHz, An Giang (Nui Cam) 91.5MHz 20kW, Tay Ninh (Nui Ba Den) 101.0MHz 20kW for the Mekong Delta. **FM:** most freqs relay VOV1, VOV3 and provincial stns at times.
**VOV5, prgrs for foreigners:** Hanoi 105.5MHz, Ha Long 105.7MHz, Ho Chi Minh City (Quan Tre) 105.7MHz: **Cambodian:** 0800-0830. **Chinese:** 0400-0430, 1100-1130. **English:** 0030-0130, 0500-0600, 0900-1030, 1200-1300, 1400-1500, 1600-1730. **French:** 0130-0230, 0600-0700, 1300-1330. **German:** 0000-0030 **Indonesian:** 0730-0800. **Japanese:** 0430-0500, 1330-1400. **Lao:** 0700-0730. **Russian:** 0230-0300, 0830-0900. **Spanish:** 1030-1100. **Thai:** 1130-1200. **Vietnamese:** 0300-0400, 1500-1600
**VOV Traffic Channel (VOV Giao Thông):** 2230-1800. **FM:** Hanoi (Me Tri) 91.0MHz 5kW, Ho Chi Minh C. (Quan Tre) 91.0MHz 5kW, Quang Tri 88.5MHz, Binh Dinh/Dak Lak/Da Nang (Son Tra)/Ha Tinh/ Mong Cai/Nha Trang 91.0MHz, Dong Hoi/Ha Long/Lang Son/Lao Cai/ Ninh Thuan/Phan Thiet/Phu Yen/Quang Ngai/Thanh Hoa 91.5MHz
**Mekong FM:** 24h regional prgrs and relay VOV Traffic Channel in Vietnamese. **FM:** Can Tho 90.0MHz
**Xone FM:** 24h music prgrs for young people ✉ 4th Floor, 100 Nguyen Luong Bang, District 7, Ho Chi Minh City. **FM:** Hanoi 96.0MHz, Ho Chi Minh C. 87.7MHz.
**VOV 24/7:** 24h in **English. FM:** Can Tho/Da Nang/ Ha Long/Hanoi/Ho Chi Minh C./Nha Trang 104.0MHz, Hue/Phu Quoc 104.5MHz
**VOV89:** 2300-1600 health, environment and food safety prgrs in Vietnamese. **FM:** Can Tho/Da Nang (Son Tra)/Hanoi/Ho Chi Minh C. 89.0MHz
**Joy FM:** 2300-1700 health and lifestyle prgrs in Vietnamese. **FM:** Hanoi 98.9MHz, Bing Duong (Thu Dau Mot area) 101.7MHz
**VOV Thanh Pho Ho Chi Minh (TPHCM):** opt-out programming in Vietnamese & Cham for Ho Chi Minh C. area on 657kHz: 2330-2400, 0330-0500, 0930-1100 (times vary).
**Ann:** 'Dây là Tiếng Nói Việt Nam, phát thanh từ Hà Nội, thu đô nuớc Công Hòa Xá Hội Chu Nghia Việt Nam'. Khmer: 'Thini Vithayu Samlang Vietnam'.

**Regional stations**
**General remarks:** Schedules shown are for provincial services on MW. Stns may also relay VOV1,at times, but relays of VOV as a rule are not included in the schedules below. Several hundred FM stns are operated by local gvnts of county-level admin. divisions (huyen or counties, thi xa or county-level towns, and quan or urban districts). These generally transmit with powers in the 50-500W range and with limited hours, and in many cases relay the provincial stn or Hanoi at times. **Ann:** Provincial sces usually identify as 'Radio & TV (name of province)", in Vietnamese: 'Dài Phất Thanh Truyện Hình (name)'

**Addresses & other information:**
**1)** National freqs. See above for details – **2)** 70 Tran Phu, Nha Trang. 2230-2200, 0430-0500, 1030-1100 - **FM:** 103.3MHz 0.1kW/106.5MHz 2kW + relays – **3)** 3 Nguyen Dinh Chieu, Dist. 1, Ho Chi Minh City. H: 2100-1700 in Vietnamese/Khmer – **FM:** 95.6 20kW/99.9MHz 20kW. Districts: Hoc Mon 93.0MHz, Nha Be 96.5MHz, Binh Chanh 103.4MHz, Can Gio 105.0MHz, Cu Chi 106.5MHz – **4)** Q: Tran Phu Road, Tan Thanh Ward, Tam Ky Town, Quang Nam: 2220-2245, 0400-0430, 1145-1215 – **FM:** 97.6MHz 2kW. D: 33 Le Loi, Hai Chau Ward, Da Nang. 2245-2300, 0430-0445, 1215-1315(SS 1400) - **FM:** 96.3MHz 5kW – **5)** 23 Mai Xuan Thuong, Quy Nhon City. 2230-2300, 0430-0500, 1145-1230 - **FM:** 97.0MHz 5kW, (Huai Nhon) 99.9MHz 1kW – **6)** 125 National Road 1A, Ward 4, Tan An City. 2200-0030(Sat 0100, Sun 0315), 0430-0530, 1000-1110/1210 - **FM:** 96.9MHz 3kW – **7)** Group 12, Quyet Thang Ward, Son La Town. 2200-2400, 0400-0600, 1200-1400 in Vietnamese/ Hmong - **FM:** 96.0MHz 2kW + relays – **8)** 8 Hai Thuong St, Thanh Hoa City. 2200-2300, 0250-0600, 0930-1045 – **9)** 28 Phan Dinh Phung, Ha Tinh Town. 2200-2330, 0400-0600, 1100-1200 - **FM:** 93.6MHz 0.05kW – **10)** 413 Nguyen Trai, Phuoong 9, Ca Mau. - **FM:** 94.6MHz 5kW – **11)** 115 Tran Hung Dao St, Phuoong Lam Ward, Hoa Binh City - **FM:** 97.5MHz 0.2kW – **12)** 87 Be Van Dan Rd, Cao Bang Town. 2200-2300, 0300-0500, 1200-1400 - **FM:** 99.0MHz 5kW – **13)** 58 Huong Vong St, Hue. 2230-2300, 0400-0500, 0955-1100, occ. 1145-1310 – **FM:** 93.0MHz 2kW & 96.0MHz 0.02kW

**Provincial sces operating on FM only (MHz):**
An Giang (Long Xuyen) 90.1MHz; Bac Giang 98.4 5kW; Bac Kan 99.3 2kW; Bac Lieu 93.8 2kW; Bac Ninh 92.1 2kW; Ba Ria Vung Tau (Nui Nho) 92.0 5kW; Ben Tre 97.9 2kW; Bing Duong (Thu Dau Mot) 92.5 10kW; Binh Phuoc (Dong Xoai) 89.4 2kW; Binh Thuan (Phan Thiet) 92.3MHz 5kW; Dac Lac (Buon Ma Thuot) 94.7 5kW; Ca Mau 94.6MHz 5kW; Can Tho 97.3MHz 5kW; Dac Nong (Gia Nghia) 88.8 2kW, (Dak Mil) 95.5 2kW;

Dien Bien (Dien Bien Phu) 96.3 1kW; Dong Nai 97.5 5kW; Gia Lai (Pleiku) 93.7 2kW + relays; Ha Giang 92.0 2kW + relays; Hai Duong 104.5 5kW; Hai Phong 93.7 3kW; Ha Nam (Phu Ly) 93.3 2kW; Hanoi 90.0 10kW (+ 5 Huynh Thuc Khang, Dong Da District, Hanoi) + 96.0 2kW (Prgr 2, tr. In Ha Dong), Hau Giang 89.6 3kW; Hung Yen 92.7 2kW; Kien Giang (Rach Gia_ 99.4MHz 5kW; Kon Tum 95.1MHz 3kW; Lam Dong (Da Lat) 97.0 2kW + relays; Lang Son 88.2MHz 1kW, (Mau Son) 101.0MHz 10kW; Lao Cai 91.0 5kW, 95.2 1kW & 97.0 10kW; Nam Dinh 95.1 2kW; Nghe An (Vinh) 99.6 10kW + relays; Ninh Binh 98.1 2kW; Ninh Thuan (Phan Rang Thap Cham) 95.0 5kW & 99.6 2kW; Phu Tho (Viet Tri) 106.0 5kW; Phu Yen 96.0 2.5kW; Quang Binh (Dong Hoi) 94.1 1kW; Quang Ngai 102.9MHz 5kW; Quang Ninh (Ha Long) 97.8 10kW; Quang Tri (Dong Ha) 92.5 5kW;Soc Trang 100.4 2kW; Tay Ninh 103.1MHz 5kW; Thai Binh 91.7 3.3kW; Tieng Giang (My Tho) 96.2 2kW; Thai Nguyen 106.5MHz 1kW; Tra Vinh 92.7 2kW; Tuyen Quang 95.6 2kW;Vinh Long 90.2 1kW; Vinh Phuc 102.7 2kW; Yen Bai 92.1 2kW + relays

## VIRGIN ISLANDS (AMERICAN) (USA)

**LT:** UTC -4h — **Pop:** 105,000 — **Pr.L:** English, Spanish, Creole — **E.C:** 60Hz, 110V — **ITU:** VIR

### FEDERAL COMMUNICATIONS COMMISSION (FCC)
see USA for details

| MW | Call | kHz | kW | MW | Call | kHz | kW |
|----|------|-----|-----|----|------|-----|-----|
| 1) | WSTX | 970 | 5/1 | 4) | WSTA | 1340 | 1 |
| 2) | WVWI | 1000 | 5/1 | 5) | WDHP | 1620 | 10/1 |
| 3) | WUVI | 1090 | 0.25 | 6) | WIGT | 1690 | 0.9 |
| **FM** | **Call** | **MHz** | **kW** | **FM** | **Call** | **MHz** | **kW** |
| 7) | WIVH | 89.9 | 1.4 | 2) | WVIQ | 99.5 | 32 |
| 8) | WSKX | 90.7 | 10 | 1) | WSTX | 100.3 | 50 |
| 9) | WVSE | 91.9 | 7.4 | 16) | WEVI | 101.3 | 4.6 |
| 10) | WTJX | 93.1 | 1.3 | 2) | WIVI | 102.1 | 1.75 |
| 11) | WVVI | 93.5 | 9.6 | 17) | WIUJ | 102.9 | 1.5 |
| 12) | WJKC | 95.1 | 15 | 2) | WVJZ | 103.1 | 0.17 |
| 13) | WVIY | 95.3 | 50 | 5) | WAXJ | 103.5 | 6 |
| 2) | WWKS | 96.1 | 2.4 | 18) | WZIN | 104.3 | 44 |
| 14) | WTJC | 96.0 | 0.01 | 19) | WMNG | 104.9 | 6 |
| 5) | WUVI | 97.3 | 0.1 | 2) | WVJZ | 105.3 | 30 |
| 6) | WGOD | 97.9 | 50 | 20) | WVIE | 107.3 | 1.7 |
| 15) | WMYP | 98.3 | 1.9 | 21) | WLDV | 107.9 | 3.6 |

**Addresses & other information:**
**1)** Caledonia Communications Corp., 2111 Company St, Suite 3, Christiansted, St. Croix 00820 ☎ +1 340 643-9789 **W:** wstxradio. com Stns: WSTX-AM on 970kHz (news/sport/talk) & WSTX-FM on 100.3MHz (reggae) – **2)** Gark LLC/Ackley Media Group, 13 Crown Bay Fill, PO Box 302179, Charlotte Amalie, St. Thomas 00803 ☎ +1 340 776 1000 **W:** amg.vi Stns: KISS on 96.1 (Urban Adult), Life on 101.3 FM (Rlg.), Pirate Radio on 102.1, 105 JAMZ on 103.1/105.3 (CHR/rythmic ) & Radio One on 1000kHz (News/talk/sport) – **3)** Penha House 3ʳᵈ floor, 2 John Brewer's Bay, St. Thomas 00802 ☎ +1 340 643 1099 **E:** wuviradio@gmail.com **Ann:** "The Voice of the University" (College radio/rlg) – **4)** 121 Sub Base, St. Thomas 00802 ☎ +1 340 774 1340 **W:** lucky13wsta.com **Ann:** Lucky 13 – WSTA (Rlg) – **5)** Reef Broadcasting Inc., 6079A Castle Coakley, Christiansted, St. Croix 00820 ☎ +1 340 719 1620 🖷 +1 340 778 1686 **W:** reefbroadcasting.com Stns: WAXJ 'The Reef' on 103.5MHz (Urban AC/reggae) & WDHP on 1620kHz (Local Information/Music) – **6)** 22A Estate Dorothea, Box 5012, Charlotte Amalie, St. Thomas 00803 ☎ +1 340 774 4498 **W:** wgod98vi.org **Ann:** WGOD - The Word of God in The Caribbean. Relays 3ABN after 0200 – **7)** Global Radio Mission, 5007 Mt. Washington, Christiansted, St. Croix 00820 ☎ +1 340 718 2852 **W:** wivh.org. **Ann:** "WIVH The Voice Of Hope" (Rlg.) – **8)** Better Communications Group, PO Box 6867, Christiansted, St. Croix VI00823 (Educ.) – **9)** Ste. 101 Barren Spot, Village Mall, Christiansted, St. Croix 00823 **W:** radiopapilove.com **Ann:** "Papi Love Radio" (Spanish; Rlg) – **10)** PO Box7879, St. Thomas, VI 00801 & PO Box 808, St. Croix VI00821 ☎ +1 340 774 6255/718 3339 **W:** wtjx.org. **Ann:** National Public Radio – **11)** PO Box 25387, Christiansted, St. Croix 00824 ☎ +1 340 773 5935. **Ann:** "Caribbean Country" – **11)** JKC Communications/Radio 95, 5020 Anchors Way, PO Box 25680, Christiansted, St. Croix 00824 ☎ +1 340 773 0995 **W:** isle95.com Stns: Isle 95 on 95.1MHz (Urban/reggae) & Sunny 99.5 (A/C) – **12)** PO Box 1045, St. Thomas 00804 ☎ +1 340 776 4531 (Rlg.) – **13)** WVIY, Charlotte Amalie (planned) – **14)** PO Box 25387, Christiansted, St. Croix 00824 ☎ +1 340 773 0995. **Ann:** Rumba 98.3 (Spanish/Tropical/Variety) – **16)** Lifeline, 6215 Peter's Rest, Christiansted 00820 ☎ +1 340 227 5644 **W:** liferadiovi.org **Ann:** Life Radio (Rlg.) – **17)** Virgin Isl. Youth Development Radio, PO Box 2477, Charlotte Amalie, St. Thomas 00803 ☎ +1 340 776 1029 (Pub./Educ.) – **18)** PO Box 306117, Charlotte Amalie, St. Thomas 00803 ☎ +1 340 776 1043. **Ann:** "The Buzz" (Rock)

– **19)** Clara Communications Corp., PO Box 25680, Christiansted, St. Croix 00824 ☎ +1 340 713 9666. **Ann:** "The Mongoose" (Classic hits) – **20)** Virgin Islands Radio Entertainment Detroit, 160 Victor St, Highland Park, MI 48203-3130 ☎ +1 313 868 6612 **W:** wviefm1073.com – **21)** 1013 Western Suburbs, Christiansted, St. Croix ☎ +1 340 713 1079 **W:** davybe.com **Ann:** "Da Vybe"

## VIRGIN ISLANDS (BRITISH) (UK)

**LT:** UTC -4h — **Pop:** 32,000 — **Pr.L:** English — **E.C:** 60Hz, 110V — **ITU:** VRG

### VIRGIN ISLANDS BROADCASTING LTD. (Comm.)
🖃 Baughers Bay, P.O. Box 78, Road Town, Tortola, BVI ☎ +1 284 494 2250/2430/6994 🖷 +1 284 494 1139 **E:** zbvi@surfbvi.com **W:** zbviradio.net **L.P:** MD: Meritt Herbert. GM: Harvey Herbert. Ops Mgr: Sandra Warrican. Production Mgr: Iris Jones
**MW:** ZBVI 780kHz 10kW **D.Prgr:** MF 0930-0130, SS 1100-0130.
**Ann:** "This is ZBVI Radio from Tortola"

### CARIBBEAN BROADCAST NETWORK (Comm.)
🖃 2nd Floor Chevelle Center, Road Town, Tortola ☎ +1 284 340 3461 **W:** cbnvirginislands.com
**CBN Radio/Caribbean Super Station:** FM 92.3MHz **CBN Radio/ The Breeze of the Virgin Islands**

### OTHER STATIONS (FM in MHz):
**ZCCR,** Little Dix Hill Rd, East End, PO Box 41, Tortola VG 1110 ☎ +1 284 495 2161 🖷 +1 284 495 1461. FM 94.1 (8.5kW). **Ann:** CCR Your Caribbean Christian Station. Format: Gospel – **ZKING - The Voice of the Virgin Islands,** Christian Broadcasting Network, Horsepath, Road Town, Tortola ☎ +1 284 494 4600 🖷 +1 284 494 8747 FM 100.9. Format: Rlg. – **ZROD,** 19 Flemming St.,P.O. Box 992, Road Town, Tortola ☎ +1 284 494 1037 🖷 +1 284 494 4564 L.P: GM: Rodney Herbert. FM 103.7. Ann.: Z-Rod The Virgin Islands Best Music Mix – **Z.V.C.R.,** Main St., P.O.Box 43, Road Town, Tortola ☎ +1 284 494 6995/7305 **W:** zvcr1069fm.com FM 106.9

## WAKE ISLAND (USA)

**LT:** UTC +12h — **Pop:** 100 — **Pr.L:** English — **E.C:** 60Hz, 110V — **ITU:** WAK

### THE QUAKE
🖃 USAF Detachment 3, 13AF, PACAF/Chugach Federal Solutions Inc. PO Box 187, Wake Island 96898 ☎ +1 808 424 2101 **E:** baseops@ wakeisland.net **L.P:** Comms Mgr: Colin Bradley
**FM:** 104.5MHz **Prgr:** Local prgrs and automated music 24/7 No recent information available
**NB:** Another 4 FM satellite radio prgr feeds are supplied from Armed Forces Radio

## WALLIS & FUTUNA (France)

**LT:** UTC +12h — **Pop:** 13,000 — **Pr.L:** French, Wallisian — **E.C:** 50Hz, 220V — **ITU:** WAL

### WALLIS ET FUTUNA PREMIÈRE (Pub)
🖃 B.P.102, Pointe Matala, 98600 Mata-Utu, Uvea, Iles de Wallis et Futuna (par Nouméa, Nouvelle-Calédonie) ☎ +33 68 1721300 🖷 +33 68 1722346 **W:** la1ere.francetvinfo.fr/wallisfutuna (live streaming)
**D.Prgr:** 24h local and satellite relay from Paris

| FM | MHz | kW | Station |
|----|-----|-----|---------|
| Sigave/ Mt Utulimu, Futuna | 88.0 | 0.3 | W et F la 1ère |
| Sigave/ Nuku, Futuna | 89.0 | 0.1 | W et F la 1ère |
| Mata'Utu, Wallis | 89.0 | | W et F la 1ère |
| Sigave/ Apipi, Futuna | 90.0 | 0.1 | W et F la 1ère |
| Alo/Mont Mamati, Futuna | 91.0 | 0.1 | W et F la 1ère |
| Uvea/Pointe de Matalaa, Wallis | 100.0 | 0.35 | W et F la 1ère |
| Uvea/Mont Loka, Wallis | 101.0 | 0.5 | W et F la 1ère |
| Uvea/Pointe de Matalaa | 103.0 | 0.2 | France Inter |

## YEMEN

**LT:** UTC +3h — **Pop:** 28 million — **Pr.L:** Arabic — **E.C:** 50Hz, 220/230V — **ITU:** YEM

### MINISTRY OF INFORMATION
🖃 P.O. Box 19560, Al-Zubairy St, San'a ☎+967 1 215116/7/8 🖷 +967 1 207716 **W:** yemen-media.gov.ye **E:** yemen-info@y.net.ye

**NB: All transmitters except 97.1, 98.1 and 104.1MHz below, operated by Houthi rebels, are reported inactive.** Radio operation from San'a is under rebel control and Saudi Arabian & UAE backed government radio operates from Aden studio via Saudi Arabian & UAE transmitters, for more details see COTB section.

### YEMEN GENERAL CORPORATION FOR RADIO & TV

| MW | kHz | kW | Netw. | Times |
|---|---|---|---|---|
| San'a | ‡711 | 200 | G | 0700-1700 |
| San'a | ‡837 | 30 | G | 1700-0400 |

**FM (MHz):** Ad-Damigh 99.9 5kW, Al-Ashmur 92.6 5kW, Hudayda, 90.4 (L)/107.0 (G), Ibb 96.0 (G)/98.4 (L), Riam 92.4 5kW, San'a 97.1 (G)/89.9 (L)/96.5 (Y), Taiz 88.1 (G)/89.0 (L).
**G=General prgr.** from San'a: 24h. **Y=Youth prgr.** on 89.9/96.5MHz + 3 other trs. **L=Local prgr.** All r. inactive ‡

**Other (rebel) Stations:**
**Grand FM,** San'a: 93.9MHz **W:** facebook.com/RadioGrandFM
**Voice of the People,** San'a: 97.1/104.1MHz **W:** sawtalshaab.com
**Voice of Yemen R,** San'a: 98.1MHz **W:** yemen-voice-fm.com

### VOICE OF THE REPUBLIC (SOWT AL-JUMHURIYA)
⌨ Hudayda
**MW:** relayed via Dhabbaya, UAE 1170kHz 1300-0300v.
**FM:** Al-Mukha 93.1MHz, Hudayda 104.1MHz
See also COTB section under Target: Yemen.

**Other stations:**
**R. Al-Ghad al-Mashriq,** Aden: 90.9MHz, Hudaydah 88.8MHz **W:** alghadye.com
**R. Bandaraden,** Aden: 99.9MHz **W:** bandaraden.net
**R. Belqees,** Aden: 97.7MHz **W:** belqees.tv
**R. Lana,** Aden: 91.9MHz **W:** lanaradio.fm

## ZAMBIA

**LT:** UTC +2h — **Pop:** 17 million — **Pr.L:** English, Bemba, Lozi, Lunda, Nyanja, Tonga, Chichewa, others — **E.C:** 50Hz, 230V — **ITU:** ZMB

### MINISTRY OF INFORMATION AND BROADCASTING SERVICES (MIBS)
⌨ P.O. Box 51025, 6th Floor, New Government Complex, Nassar Rd, Lusaka ☎+260 211 237150 🖷 +260 211 235410 **W:** www.mibs.gov.zm

### ZAMBIA NATIONAL BROADCASTING CORPORATION (ZNBC, Pub)
⌨ P.O. Box 50015, Mass Media Complex, Alick Nkhata Rd, Lusaka 10101 ☎+260 211 252005 🖷 +260 211 254920 **W:** www.znbc.co.zm **E:** sales2@znbc.co.zm **L.P:** DG: Chibamba Kanyama. Actg. Dir. Tech. Sces: Mr. Malolela Lusambo. PD: Kenneth Maduma. PR Officer: Masuzyo Ndhlovu.

| SW | kHz | kW | Sce | Times |
|---|---|---|---|---|
| Lusaka | 5915 | 100 | R1 | 0245-2205 |

| FM(MHz) | R1 | R2 | N | R4 | kW |
|---|---|---|---|---|---|
| Chipata | 93.3 | 96.5 | 95.7 | - | 1 |
| Choma | - | - | 105.7 | - | 1 |
| Kabwe | - | - | - | 92.1 | 0.5 |
| Kapiri Mposhi | 97.5 | 94.3 | 91.3 | - | 1 |
| Kasama | 88.3 | 92.3 | 91.5 | - | 1 |
| Kitwe | 98.5 | 95.7 | 94.1 | 88.1 | 2 |
| Livingstone | 89.3 | 97.3 | 100.5 | 95.7 | 1/0.5 |
| Lusaka | 102.9 | 95.7 | 92.5 | 88.1 | 2 |
| Mansa | 88.3 | 92.3 | 91.5 | - | 1 |
| Mongu | 94.9 | 91.7 | 98.1 | - | 1 |
| Solwezi | 95.3 | 91.3 | 93.3 | - | 1 |

**R. One in 7 Zambian languages:** 0245-2205 – **R. Two in English:** 0245-2205 – **N=Parliament Radio** (stream on **W:** streamer.parliament.gov.zm:8063/listen.pls – **R. Four (music channel) in English:** 0240-2205
**Ann:** E: "This is Radio Two of ZNBC broadcasting from Lusaka". Chichewa: "Kuno ndi ku Zambia National Broadcasting Corporation wa Lusaka." **IS:** Call of the Fish Eagle.

**Other stations (FM:** MHz):
**Breeze FM:** Chipata 89.3, Petauke 89.7, Katete 98.9. **W:** breezefm-chipata.com – **Chikuni R,** Monze: 91.9 0.5kW. **W:** chikuniradiozm. org – **Explorers R,** Petauke: 88.1 **W:** facebook.com/88.1fmPetauke – **Flava FM,** Kitwe: 87.7 **W:** flavafm.co.zm – **Hone FM,** Lusaka: 94.1

**W:** evelynhone.edu.zm – **Hot FM,** Lusaka: 87.7, Kapiri 88.7, Copper Belt 97.3. **W:** hot877.com – **Joy FM,** Lusaka: 92.1. **W:** facebook.com/JoyfmRadioZambia – **MAZ FM,** Luapula: 95.5/100.9 **W:** facebook.com/mazfm100.9 – **Pan African R,** Lusaka: 105.1 **W:** panafricanfm.com – **Pasme R,** Petauke: 91.3 **W:** facebook.com/pasmeradiostations – **Q. FM:** Lusaka 93.3, Kabwe 88.9, Choma 89.8, Mumbwa 89.1 **W:** www.qfmzambia.com – **R. Christian Voice:** FM: Ndola 98.9, Kapiri 101.5, Kitwe 105.3, Lusaka 106.1. **W:** rcvoice.co.zm – **R. Icengelo:** Kitwe 89.1, Kaloko 102.9 **W:** www.radioicengelo.org – **R. Liseli,** Mongu 105.3 **W:** facebook.com/oblateradioliseli – **R. Lyambai,** Mongu 101.3 **W:** en.unesco.org/radioict/radios/radio-lyambai – **R. Maria Zambia:** FM: Kanjala 88.5 0.3kW, Katete 94.9. **W:** www.radiomaria.org.zm **Yatsani Voice,** Lusaka: 99.3 2kW. **W:** facebook.com/radiomariayatsanivoice – **R. Musi-o-Tunya,** Livingstone: 106.1 **W:** facebook.com/RadioMusiotunya106.1FM – **R. Phoenix:** Lusaka 89.5, Kabwe 100, Kitwe 100.5, Chingola 104, Kapiri/Mposhi 104.5, Ndola/Luanshya 107.6 **W:** radiophoenix.co.zm – **Sky FM:** Lusaka 88.5, Choma 88.8, Zimba 93.8, Monze 95.1, Livingstone 102.4 **W:** facebook.com/skyfm.zambia – **UNZA R,** Lusaka: 91.7 **W:** facebook.com/unzafm – **Yar FM,** Kitwe: 89.9 **W:** yarfm.co.zm – **Zambezi FM,** Livingstone: 94.1/107.7MHz **W:** facebook.com/zambezifm107.7 – **5 FM,** Lusaka: 89.9MHz 0.5kW **W:** 5fm.co.zm

**BBC African Sce:** Kitwe/Lusaka 98.1 2kW.
**RFI Afrique:** Kitwe 92.5, Lusaka 100.5 in English/French/Swahili

## ZIMBABWE

**LT:** UTC +2h — **Pop:** 16 million — **Pr.L:** English, Shona, Ndebele, Chewa — **E.C:** 50Hz, 220V — **ITU:** ZWE

### BROADCASTING AUTHORITY OF ZIMBABWE (BAZ)
⌨ 1 Pennefather , Media Centre, Rainbow Towers Grounds, P.O. Box CY496, Causeway, Harare ☎+263 4 797382-5 🖷 +263 4 797375 **W:** baz.co.zw **E:** baz@comone.co.zw

### ZIMBABWE BROADCASTING CORPORATION (ZBC, Gov)
⌨ P.O. Box HG 444, Broadcasting Centre, Pockets Hill, Highlands, Harare ☎+263 4 498610 **W:** zbc.co.zw **E:** onlinenewszbc@gmail.com

| FM (MHz) | R1 | R2 | R3 | R4 | kW |
|---|---|---|---|---|---|
| Beithbridge | 88.5 | 93.6 | 98.1 | 105.2 | |
| Bulawayo | 90.0 | 96.3 | 99.6 | 103.1 | 10 |
| Chipinge | 94.5 | 97.8 | 101.3 | 104.9 | 10 |
| Chiredzi | 93.3 | 95.5 | 98.8 | 102.3 | 10 |
| Chivhu | 93.3 | 96.5 | 103.3 | 106.8 | |
| Gokwe | 89.9 | 96.8 | 89.6 | 103.5 | |
| Gwanda | 105.8 | 95.4 | 98.7 | 102.2 | 20 |
| Gweru | 90.7 | 93.9 | 97.2 | 100.7 | 5 |
| Harare | 92.8 | 96.0 | 99.3 | 102.8 | 10 |
| Hwange | 91.5 | 98.2 | 94.7 | 101.5 | 10 |
| Kadoma | 88.5 | 94.8 | 98.1 | 101.6 | 10 |
| Karoi | 99.9 | 96.6 | 93.4 | 90.3 | 10 |
| Kenmaur | 90.4 | 93.5 | 97.5 | 103.5 | |
| Masvingo | 106.5 | 92.9 | 99.4 | 102.9 | |
| Mount Darwin | 92.0 | 95.2 | 98.5 | 102.0 | 10 |
| Mutare | 105.3 | 89.1 | 98.7 | 105.8 | 3 |
| Mutorashanga | 104.7 | 94.3 | 91.1 | 101.1 | |
| Nyanga | 105.5 | 91.7 | 94.9 | 101.7 | 3 |
| Rutenga | 101.1 | 88.0 | 91.1 | 94.3 | |
| Victoria Falls | 92.3 | 96.1 | 92.9 | 89.9 | 8 |

**R1) Classic263:** mainly in English: 24h – **R2) R. Zimbabwe:** in Shona/Ndebele/English: 24h – **R3) Power FM:** youth programme in English: 24h – **R4) National FM:** in 14 minority languages: 24h
**Central Radio,** Gweru: 95.8MHz in English, Ndebele, Shona.
**Khulumani FM,** Bulawayo: 95.0MHz.

**Other stations:**
**Breeze FM,** Victoria Falls: 91.2MHz **W:** breezefm.co.zw
**Capitalk,** Harare: 100.4MHz **W:** capitalkfm.com
**Diamond FM,** Mutare: 103.8MHz **W:** diamondfm.co.zw
**Hevoi FM,** Masvingo: 100.2MHz **W:** facebook.com/hevoifm
**Midlands FM,** Gweru: 98.4MHz **W:** facebook.com/Midlands984
**Nyaminyami FM,** Kariba: 94.5MHz **W:** nyaminyamifm.co.zw
**Star FM:** Harare 89.7MHz, Bulawayo 93.1MHz. **W:** starfm.co.zw
**Skyz Metro FM,** Bulawayo: 100.3MHz **W:** skyzmetroradio.co.zw
**Ya FM,** Zvishavane: 91.8MHz **W:** yafm.co.zw
**Zi FM:** Mutare 95.4MHz, Masvingo 96.1MHz, Mutorashanga 97.6MHz, Nyanga 98.2MHz, Beitbridge 101.6MHz, Gweru 104.3MHz, Kadoma 1052.MHz, Harare 106.4MHz, Victoria Falls 106.5MHz, Bulawayo 106.7MHz. **W:** zifmstereo.co.zw

# INTERNATIONAL RADIO

## Section Contents

Initial entries for each letter,
see Main Index for full details.

Features & Reviews

Afghanistan............................ 456
Bahrain .................................. 460
Cameroon.............................. 461
Denmark................................. 468
Ecuador ................................. 468
Finland................................... 469
Germany................................ 470
India...................................... 473
Japan..................................... 478
Korea, North ......................... 479
Laos....................................... 482
Macedonia ............................ 482
Netherlands .......................... 483
Oman..................................... 484
Pakistan................................. 485
Romania ................................ 487
São Tomé.............................. 488
Taiwan .................................. 493
Ukraine ................................. 496
Vatican City State ................. 509
Zambia .................................. 510


Clandestine & OTB................ 511
Religious Broadcasters.......... 520

National Radio

International Radio

Frequency Lists

National Television

**NB:** The copy deadline for this section was 14 November 2018

Reference

## Notes for the International Radio section

Country abbreviation codes are shown after the country name. The three-letter codes after each frequency are transmitter site codes. These, and the Area/Country codes in the Area column, can all be decoded by referring to the tables in the Reference Section.

Where a frequency has an asterisk (*) etc. after it, see the '**KEY**' section at the end of the schedule entry.

The following symbols are used throughout this section:
† = Irregular transmissions/broadcasts;
‡ = Inactive at editorial deadline;
± = variable frequency;
+ = DRM (Digital Radio Mondiale) transmission.
§ = Transmitter not yet on air

Where transmitter details are given for a particular entity, the number of units shown represents the installed capability of the site, but does not reflect any details of txs being coupled/bridged (to increase overall power output), run at reduced power or remaining unused.
Should a site become decommissioned or dismantled it is removed from the table, but if a site is merely dormant/inactive it is marked with the 'inactive' symbol shown above.

If **Webcast** is shown, the letter(s) after indicate the service(s) available: **D**=On Demand audio; **L**=Live audio; **P**=Podcast For international services we have shown, where possible, languages available only via the webcast. We do not include those broadcasters that have a foreign service only available via the internet and are no longer broadcasting via MW/SW radio.

An alphabetical listing of **Religious Broadcasters**, cross-referenced by country, is given at the end of the section.

### AFGHANISTAN (AFG)

**RADIO TELEVISION AFGHANISTAN (RTA) (Gov)**
✉ 13th Street, Wazir Mohammad Akhbar Khan, Kabul, Afghanistan.
☎ +92 20 2310147.
**E:** info@rta.org.af **W:** www.rta.org.af
**Webcast:** L
**L.P:** DG: Zarin Anzor.
**MW:** [KAB] Kabul, Pol-e Charkhi: 1296kHz 400kW; [KHO] Khost, Tani: 621kHz 200kW (Both txs operated on behalf of USAGM (USA)).
**SW:** [KAB] Kabul, Yakatut : 1 x 100kW
**FM/DAB:** FM: 93.0MHz (Kabul).
**kHz:** 6100

| Arabic | Days | Area | kHz |
|---|---|---|---|
| 1630-1700 | daily | ME | 6100kabt |
| **English** | **Days** | **Area** | **kHz** |
| 1530-1600 | daily | SAs | 6100kab |
| **Russian** | **Days** | **Area** | **kHz** |
| 1700-1730 | daily | RUS | 6100kabt |
| **Urdu** | **Days** | **Area** | **kHz** |
| 1600-1630 | daily | SAs | 6100kab |

**Key:** † Irregular.
**Ann:** English: "Radio Afghanistan".
**Notes:** External Service of the state broadcasting company Radio Television Afghanistan (RTA). RTA is also providing relay facilities on MW for IBB (USA).

### ALASKA (ALS)

**KNLS INTERNATIONAL (Rlg)**
✉ P.O. Box 473, Anchor Point, AK 99556, USA. (Transmitting station)
☎ +1 907 2352326. 🖷 +1 907 2352326.
**E:** knls@aol.com **W:** www.knls.org (English); www.knls.net (Russian); www.smzg.org (Chinese)
**Webcast:** D
✉ 605 Bradley Court, Franklin, TN 37067, USA. (World Christian Broadcasting HQ & studios)
☎ +1 615 3718707. 🖷 +1 615 3718791.
**L.P:** SM: Dave Dvorak; WCB Vice Pres of Engineering (Franklin, TN): Kevin Chambers.
**SW:** [NLS] Anchor Point, AK: 2 x 100kW.

**kHz:** 7320, 7340, 7355, 7370, 7560

**Winter Schedule 2018/2019**

| Chinese | Days | Area | kHz |
|---|---|---|---|
| 0800-1000 | daily | EAs | 7355nls |
| 1000-1100 | daily | EAs | 7355nls |
| 1100-1200 | daily | EAs | 7355nls |
| 1300-1400 | daily | EAs | 7320nls |
| 1300-1500 | daily | EAs | 7560nls |
| 1500-1600 | daily | EAs | 7560nls |
| 1600-1800 | daily | EAs | 7340nls |
| **English** | **Days** | **Area** | **kHz** |
| 0800-0900 | daily | EAs | 7370nls |
| 1000-1100 | daily | EAs | 7370nls |
| 1200-1300 | daily | EAs | 7320nls, 7355nls |
| 1400-1500 | daily | EAs | 7320nls |
| **Russian** | **Days** | **Area** | **kHz** |
| 0900-1000 | daily | RUS | 7370nls |
| 1100-1200 | daily | RUS | 7320nls |
| 1500-1600 | daily | RUS | 7320nls |
| 1600-1800 | daily | RUS | 7370nls |

**Ann:** English: "This is Alaska calling. You're listening to station KNLS, Anchor Point, Alaska, United States of America", "This your New Life Station KNLS, Anchor Point, Alaska, broadcasting from the top of the world".
**V:** QSL-card.
**Notes:** On air since 23 July 1983. KNLS is a SW transmitting station owned by World Christian Broadcasting, Inc. (WCB). See under USA for corporate details. The stn retransmits prgrs produced in the U.S. studios of WCB and WCB partner organisations. Further prgrs of WCB's language services in Chinese, English and Russian can be heard via its sister transmitting stn Madagascar World Voice (see under Madagascar for schedules).

### ALBANIA (ALB)

**RADIO TIRANA INTERNATIONAL (Pub)**
✉ Rruga "Ismail Qemali" nr. 11, 1001 Tirana, Albania.
☎ +355 42223650. 🖷 +355 42223650.
**E:** english@rtsh.al **W:** www.rtsh.al
**Webcast:** L (Webcast languages: English, French, German, Greek, Italian, Serbian, Turkish)L (Webcast languages: English, French, German, Greek, Italian, Serbian, Turkish)

**L.P:** DG (RTSH): Thoma Gëllçi.
**SAT:** Eutelsat 16A.
**kHz:** *3985, 5850, 5950, 6005, 9395*

### Winter Schedule 2018/2019

| English | Days | Area | kHz |
|---|---|---|---|
| 0230-0300 | daily | NAm | 5950rmi, 9395rmi |
| 1330-1400 | mtwtfs. | CEu,WEu | 6005kll |
| 2300-2330 | ....f.. | NAm | 5850rmi |
| **French** | **Days** | **Area** | **kHz** |
| 1600-1630 | daily | CEu,WEu | 3985kll* |
| **German** | **Days** | **Area** | **kHz** |
| 2030-2100 | daily | CEu,WEu | 3985kll* |
| **Italian** | **Days** | **Area** | **kHz** |
| 2130-2200 | mtwtf.. | CEu,WEu | 3985kll* |

**Key:** * Relayed via Shortwaveservice (Germany).
**Ann:** English: "This is Radio Tirana"; French: "Ici Tirana".
**V:** QSL-card.
**Notes:** RadioTirana International is the international service of the public broadcaster Radio Televizioni Shqiptar (RTSH). RTSH ended SW & MW transmissions from txs in Albania in March 2017. The rebroadcasts via a 1kW SW tx at Kall (Germany) are an independent, personal initiative of the operator of the German relay platform "Shortwaveservice"; a project that is primarily targeting SWLs/DXers in Europe.

### CHINA RADIO INTERNATIONAL (CRI) RELAY
**SW:** [CER] Cërrik, Shtërmen: 6 x 150kW.
**V:** QSL-card. (Rpt to CRI, in P.R. China)
**Notes:** The Cërrik transmitting stn is owned by Radiotelevizioni Shqiptar (RTSH), and was leased to China Radio International for 15 years in 2003.

## ALGERIA (ALG)

### RADIO ALGÉRIENNE (Pub)
✉ 21 Boulevard des Martyrs, 16000 Algiers, Algeria.
☎ +213 21483790. 🖷 +213 21230823.
**E:** radioalgerie@gmail.com **W:** www.radioalgerie.dz
**Webcast:** L
**L.P:** (EPRS) DG: Chabane Lounakel; Dir, Technical Services: Mohamed Salah Saidi.
**SAT:** Badr 6, Eutelsat 5WA/Hot Bird 13C, Galaxy 19, Nilesat 201, SES 4.
**kHz:** *5940, 6040, 6060, 6105, 6170, 7315, 7375*

### Winter Schedule 2018/2019

| French/Arabic | Days | Area | kHz |
|---|---|---|---|
| 0400-0600 | daily | CAf,WAf | 6060iss |
| 0500-0700 | daily | NAf,WAf | 6105iss |
| 1800-2000 | daily | CAf,WAf | 7375iss |
| 1900-2000 | daily | NAf,WAf | 7315iss |
| 2000-2100 | daily | NAf,WAf | 6170iss |
| 2000-2200 | daily | NAf,CAf | 5940iss |
| 2100-2300 | daily | NAf,WAf | 6040iss |

**Ann:** Arabic: "Huna Al-Djazair".
**V:** QSL-card.
**Notes:** Relays of EPRS (Etablissement Public de Radiodiffusion Sonore) Home Sce 'Koran' prgr and Chaîne 1/3.

### TÉLÉDIFFUSION D'ALGÉRIE (TDA) (Tx Operator)
✉ BP 50, 16340 Alger, Algeria.
☎ +213 23181065. 🖷 +213 23181045.
**E:** contact@tda.dz **W:** www.tda.dz
**L.P:** DG: Abdelmalek Houyou.
**SW:** [BEC] Béchar ‡: 1 x 300kW (under construction); [ORG] Ouargla ‡: 1 x 300kW (under construction). F.pl: SW expansion of the MW site Sidi Hamadouche.
**Notes:** Télédiffusion d'Algérie is the national transmitter network operator.

## ANGOLA (AGL)

### ANGOLAN NATIONAL RADIO ‡ (Pub)
✉ Avenida Comandante Gika, Luanda, Angola.
☎ +244 222323172. 🖷 +244 222324647.
**E:** rnacanalinternacional@gmail.com **W:** www.rna.ao

**L.P:** Chmn (RNA): Henriques Manuel João dos Santos; Dir (Canal Internacional): Cláudia Longa.
**MW:** [MUL] Luanda, Mulenvos: 945kHz 25kW.
**FM/DAB:** FM: 101.4MHz (Luanda, 4kW).
**Key:** ‡ Believed inactive on MW at time of publication.
**Ann:** English: "This is the International Channel of Angola's National Radio, broadcasting from Luanda".
**V:** QSL-card.
**Notes:** The International Channel (Canal Internacional) of the national broadcaster Rádio Nacional de Angola (RNA) was launched in 1979.

## ANGUILLA (AIA)

### CARIBBEAN BEACON (UNIVERSITY NETWORK RELAY) (Rlg)
✉ P.O. Box 690, AI-2640 The Valley, Anguilla.
☎ +1 264 4974340. 🖷 +1 264 4974311.
**E:** beacon@anguillanet.com
✉ Long Road, AI-2640 Long Bay Village, Anguilla.
**L.P:** SM/Chief Engineer: Eddie Sutton.
**MW:** [AIA] The Valley, The Farrington ‡: 1610kHz 50kW.
**SW:** [AIA] The Valley, The Farrington: 1 x 100kW.
**FM/DAB:** FM: 100.1MHz (The Valley, 35kW), 0000-2400.
**Key:** ‡ Inactive at time of publication.
**V:** QSL-card.
**Notes:** Radio station owned by The Caribbean Beacon Ltd., rebroadcasting the "University Network" satellite TV channel audio (see "University Network" under "USA" for schedules). MW/FM may opt-out for separate (local) programming at times.

## ANTARCTICA (ATA)

### RADIO NACIONAL "ARCÁNGEL SAN GABRIEL" (LRA36) (Pub)
✉ Base Esperanza, Antártida Argentina 9411, Argentina.
☎ +54 2974 445304.
**E:** lra36@hotmail.com
**L.P:** Dir: Tenl. Miguel Ángel Vazquez.
**SW:** [LRA] Base Antártica Esperanza: 1 x 10kW (operated at lower power).
**FM/DAB:** FM: 97.6MHz (Esperanza Base)
**kHz:** *15476*

### Winter Schedule 2018/2019

| Spanish | Days | Area | kHz |
|---|---|---|---|
| 1200-1500 | mtwtf.. | SAm | 15476lra† |

**Key:** † Irregular.
**Ann:** Spanish: "Desde Base Esperanza, transmite LRA36, Radio Nacional Arcángel San Gabriel".
**V:** QSL-card/Letter. Rp. (1 IRC)
**Notes:** Local stn of the Argentinian national public service broadcaster Radio Nacional, launched on 20 October 1979. Operated by staff of the Argentinian Army (Comando antártico del Ejército). 24h on FM for the population of the Esperanza base. The SW trs are intended as a link between servicemen/scientists on the base and their families & friends on the Argentinian mainland.

## ARGENTINA (ARG)

### RAE – ARGENTINA AL MUNDO (Pub)
✉ Casilla de Correo 555, Correo Central, C1000WAF Buenos Aires, Argentina.
☎ +54 11 43256368. 🖷 +54 11 43259433.
**E:** rae@radionacional.gov.ar; argentinainternacionalradio@gmail.com (English Sce)
**W:** www.radionacional.com.ar/rae-argentina-al-mundo
**Webcast:** L
**L.P:** Dir: Luis María Barassi.
**SW:** [BUE] Buenos Aires, General Pacheco: 2 x 50, 1 x 100kW.
**kHz:** *5010, 5850, 5950, 6005, 7780, 9395, 9955*

### Winter Schedule 2018/2019

| Chinese | Days | Area | kHz |
|---|---|---|---|
| 0900-1000 | ..twtfs | NAm,EAs | 5850rmi |
| **English** | **Days** | **Area** | **kHz** |
| 0200-0300 | ..twtfs | NAm | 5950rmi, 9395rmi |
| **French** | **Days** | **Area** | **kHz** |
| 2330-0000 | mtwtf.. | NAm,Eu | 7780rmi |

| German | Days | Area | kHz |
|---|---|---|---|
| 0800-0900 | .mtwtf. | D,CEu | 6005kII* |
| 2100-2200 | mtwtf.. | NAm,Eu | 7780rmi |

| Italian | Days | Area | kHz |
|---|---|---|---|
| 2200-2300 | mtwtf.. | NAm,Eu | 7780rmi |

| Japanese | Days | Area | kHz |
|---|---|---|---|
| 0800-0900 | ..twtfs | NAm,EAs | 5850rmi |

| Portuguese | Days | Area | kHz |
|---|---|---|---|
| 1200-1300 | mtwtf.. | LAm | 9955rmi |

| Spanish | Days | Area | kHz |
|---|---|---|---|
| 2200-2300 | mtwtf.. | CAm | 5010rmi |

**Key:** * Relayed via Shortwaveservice (Kall, Germany).
**Ann:** English: "RAE Argentina to the World".
**V:** QSL-card.
**Notes:** External Sce of the national public-service broadcaster Radio y Televisión Argentina (RTA S.E.). The relay via a 1kW SW tx at Kall (Germany) is an independent, personal initiative of the operator of the German relay platform "Shortwaveservice"; a project that is primarily targeting SWLs/DXers in Europe.

## ARMENIA (ARM)

### PUBLIC RADIO OF ARMENIA (Pub)
⌨ A. Manoogian Street 5, 0025 Yerevan, Armenia.
☎ +374 10 558010. 🖹 +374 10 551513.
**E:** info@armradio.am **W:** www.armradio.am; www.armradio.info
**Webcast:** D (www.armradio.info; only excerpts from broadcasts)
**LP:** CEO: Arman Saghatelyan.
**MW/SW:** Via Gavar transmitting station.
**kHz:** *1314, 4810*

**Winter Schedule 2018/2019**

| Arabic | Days | Area | kHz |
|---|---|---|---|
| 1815-1845 | daily | ME | 1314erv, 4810erv |

| Assyrian* | Days | Area | kHz |
|---|---|---|---|
| 1530-1545 | daily | ARM | 1314erv*, 4810erv* |

| Azeri | Days | Area | kHz |
|---|---|---|---|
| 1715-1745 | mtwtf.. | Cau | 1314erv, 4810erv |
| 1730-1745 | .....ss | Cau | 1314erv, 4810erv |

| Farsi | Days | Area | kHz |
|---|---|---|---|
| 1745-1815 | daily | IRN | 1314erv, 4810erv |

| Greek* | Days | Area | kHz |
|---|---|---|---|
| 1545-1600 | daily | ARM | 1314erv*, 4810erv* |

| Kurdish ("Yezidi")* | Days | Area | kHz |
|---|---|---|---|
| 1630-1700 | daily | ARM | 1314erv*, 4810erv* |

| Kurdish* | Days | Area | kHz |
|---|---|---|---|
| 1600-1630 | daily | ARM | 1314erv*, 4810erv* |

| Turkish | Days | Area | kHz |
|---|---|---|---|
| 1700-1715 | mtwtf.. | TUR | 1314erv, 4810erv |
| 1700-1730 | .....ss | TUR | 1314erv, 4810erv |

**Key:** * Broadcast for ethnic minorities in Armenia (All Kurdish prgrs are in the Kurmanji dialect. "Yezidi": is a dialect of Kurmanji for the Yezidi ethnic minority.)
**Ann:** At beginning of each broadcast, in Armenian: "Yerevan kho-sum", followed by ID in the language of the prgr: Arabic: "Huna Idha'at Jumhuriyat al-Yermaniyah min Yerevan", Azeri: "Danisir Iravan", Farsi: "Inja Yerevane", Turkish: "Burasi Erivan".
**IS:** After IS, opens with National Anthem.
**Notes:** The schedule contains both Foreign Service trs and prgrs for ethnic minorities in Armenia.

### AR RADIO INTERCONTINENTAL (Tx Operator)
⌨ A. Manoogian Street 5, 0025 Yerevan, Armenia.
☎ +374 10 551143. 🖹 +374 10 554600.
**E:** aa@arradio.am **W:** www.arradio.am
**LP:** Pres: Armen Amiryan; CEO: Mher Margaryan.
**MW:** [ERV] Gavar, Noratus: 864/1350/1377kHz 1000kW.
**Notes:** AR Radio Intercontinental is the operator of high power MW txs at the Noratus transmitting site.

### RADIO (CLOSED JOINT STOCK COMPANY) (Tx Operator)
⌨ 1213 Noratus, Armenia.
☎ +374 99 706767.
**E:** info@radio-int.am **W:** www.radio-int.am
**LP:** Dir: Gagik Aloyan.

**MW:** [ERV] Gavar, Noratus: 1314kHz 1000kW ‡, 1395kHz 500kW.
**SW:** [ERV] Gavar, Noratus: 3 x 100, 3 x 1000kW
**Notes:** The Closed Joined Stock Company (CJSC) "Radio" is the operator of high power MW&SW txs at the Noratus transmitting site. CJSC "Radio", initially a state-run company, was owned by the (now liquidated) Swiss-registered Europress Group Sàrl until October 2016.

## ASCENSION ISLAND (ASC)

### BBC ATLANTIC RELAY STATION
⌨ English Bay, Ascension Island, ASCN 1ZZ.
☎ +247 64458. 🖹 +247 66117.
**E:** ops.asc@babcock.co.ac
**LP:** Engineering Mgr: Jeff Francis.
**SW:** [ASC] English Bay: 6 x 250kW.
**V:** QSL-letter. (For direct report)
**Notes:** Owned by the BBC and operated by Encompass Digital Media Services Ltd (see under United Kingdom).

## AUSTRALIA (AUS)

### REACH BEYOND AUSTRALIA (Rlg)
⌨ P.O. Box 291, Kilsyth VIC 3137, Australia; 281-283 Colchester Road, Kilsyth VIC 3137, Australia.
☎ +61 3 87208000.
**E:** radio@reachbeyond.org.au **W:** www.reachbeyond.org.au
⌨ Transmitting site: P.O. Box 1339, Kununurra WA 6743, Australia; Lot 579, Packsaddle Road, Kununurra WA 6743, Australia
☎ +61 8 91669000.
**LP:** CEO: Dale Stagg; Frequency Mgr: Ken Lingwood; Media Mgr: Jonas Santos.
**SW:** [KNX] Kununurra: 3 x 100kW.
**kHz:** *7530, 9610, 9740, 11865, 11875, 11905, 11945, 12025, 15410, 15575*

**Winter Schedule 2018/2019**

| Bengali | Days | Area | kHz |
|---|---|---|---|
| 1245-1300 | .....s. | SAs | 11875knx |
| 1300-1330 | ...t... | SAs | 11875knx |
| 1300-1400 | m...... | SAs | 11875knx |
| 1330-1345 | m..t... | SAs | 12025knx |
| 1400-1415 | m..t... | SAs | 9740knx |

| Bhojpuri | Days | Area | kHz |
|---|---|---|---|
| 1345-1400 | .t..s. | SAs | 12025knx |
| 1400-1415 | .....s. | SAs | 9740knx |

| Burmese | Days | Area | kHz |
|---|---|---|---|
| 0030-0045 | mt..... | SEA | 12025knx |
| 0030-0100 | ..wtfss | SEA | 12025knx |
| 1115-1130 | ..w.... | SEA | 11865knx |
| 1115-1200 | .tw.f.. | SEA | 11865knx |
| 1130-1200 | m.....s | SEA | 11865knx |
| 1200-1230 | mt..f.s | SEA | 11945knx |

| Chhattisgarhi | Days | Area | kHz |
|---|---|---|---|
| 1200-1215 | .....ss | SAs | 11865knx |
| 1330-1345 | .....ss | SAs | 12025knx |

| Chin (Matu) | Days | Area | kHz |
|---|---|---|---|
| 1130-1200 | ..w.... | SAs | 11865knx |
| 1200-1230 | ...t... | SAs | 11945knx |

| Dzongkha | Days | Area | kHz |
|---|---|---|---|
| 1230-1245 | ....f.. | SAs | 11875knx |
| 1300-1315 | .....ss | SAs | 11875knx |
| 1315-1330 | .t..... | SAs | 11875knx |

| English | Days | Area | kHz |
|---|---|---|---|
| 1115-1130 | mtw.f.. | SAs | 15575knx |
| 1230-1300 | daily | SAs | 11945knx |
| 1315-1330 | m.w.f.. | SAs | 11865knx |
| 1445-1500 | mtw.... | SAs | 9740knx |
| 1515-1530 | ....f.. | EAs | 7530knx |

| Gujarati | Days | Area | kHz |
|---|---|---|---|
| 1315-1330 | .....s | SAs | 9610knx |
| 1315-1330 | ..w.... | SAs | 9610knx |
| 1330-1345 | ....f.. | SAs | 12025knx |
| 1415-1500 | ....f.. | SAs | 9740knx |

| Himachali | Days | Area | kHz |
|---|---|---|---|
| 1230-1245 | ..w.... | SAs | 11875knx |
| 1330-1345 | ..w.... | SAs | 12025knx |

| Himachali | Days | Area | kHz |
|---|---|---|---|
| 1400-1415 | ..w.... | SAs | 9740knx |
| **Hindi** | **Days** | **Area** | **kHz** |
| 1200-1230 | daily | SAs | 11875knx |
| 1215-1245 | m....s. | SAs | 11865knx |
| 1215-1300 | .twtf.. | SAs | 11865knx |
| 1215-1330 | ......s | SAs | 11865knx |
| 1245-1300 | ......s | SAs | 11875knx |
| 1245-1315 | .tw..s. | SAs | 11875knx |
| 1300-1330 | ....f.. | SAs | 9610knx |
| 1400-1415 | ......s | SAs | 9740knx |
| **Japanese** | **Days** | **Area** | **kHz** |
| 1100-1130 | .....ss | EAs | 11905knx |
| 2230-2300 | mtwt..s | EAs | 15410knx |
| 2230-2300 | ....fs. | EAs | 15410knx |
| **Kannada** | **Days** | **Area** | **kHz** |
| 1200-1215 | mtwtf.. | SAs | 11865knx |
| **Korean** | **Days** | **Area** | **kHz** |
| 1500-1515 | ....f.. | EAs | 7530knx |
| 1500-1530 | mtwt.ss | EAs | 7530knx |
| **Kuruk** | **Days** | **Area** | **kHz** |
| 1230-1245 | .t..... | SAs | 11875knx |
| 1345-1400 | ...t... | SAs | 12025knx |
| 1400-1415 | .t..... | SAs | 9740knx |
| **Malayalam** | **Days** | **Area** | **kHz** |
| 1300-1315 | m.w.... | SAs | 9610knx |
| **Marathi** | **Days** | **Area** | **kHz** |
| 1345-1400 | m...f.. | SAs | 12025knx |
| 1430-1445 | ...t..1 | SAs | 9740knx |
| **Marwari** | **Days** | **Area** | **kHz** |
| 1230-1245 | ......s | SAs | 11875knx |
| 1330-1345 | .t..... | SAs | 12025knx |
| 1400-1415 | ....f.. | SAs | 9740knx |
| **Meitei** | **Days** | **Area** | **kHz** |
| 1415-1430 | .....s. | SAs | 9740knx |
| **Nagamese** | **Days** | **Area** | **kHz** |
| 1200-1230 | ..w..s. | SAs | 11945knx |
| **Nepali** | **Days** | **Area** | **kHz** |
| 1230-1245 | ...t... | SAs | 11875knx |
| 1230-1300 | m...... | SAs | 11875knx |
| 1330-1400 | .twt... | SAs | 11875knx |
| 1415-1430 | ...t..1 | SAs | 9740knx |
| 1415-1445 | .t..... | SAs | 9740knx |
| **Oriya** | **Days** | **Area** | **kHz** |
| 1230-1245 | .....s. | SAs | 11875knx |
| 1315-1400 | ....f.. | SAs | 11875knx |
| 1345-1400 | .....ss | SAs | 11875knx |
| 1430-1500 | .....s. | SAs | 9740knx |
| **Punjabi** | **Days** | **Area** | **kHz** |
| 1245-1300 | ...t... | SAs | 11875knx |
| 1345-1400 | ..w..s | SAs | 12025knx |
| 1415-1445 | m.w.... | SAs | 9740knx |
| **Rohingya** | **Days** | **Area** | **kHz** |
| 0030-0045 | mt..... | SAs | 12025knx |
| 1115-1130 | m....ss | SAs | 11865knx |
| 1445-1500 | ...t..1 | SAs | 9740knx |
| **Saraiki** | **Days** | **Area** | **kHz** |
| 1330-1345 | .....ss | SAs | 11875knx |
| **Tamil** | **Days** | **Area** | **kHz** |
| 1300-1315 | .t.t.s. | SAs | 9610knx |
| 1300-1315 | m.wtf.. | SAs | 11865knx |
| 1315-1330 | .t..s.. | SAs | 11865knx |
| **Telugu** | **Days** | **Area** | **kHz** |
| 1315-1330 | ...t... | SAs | 11865knx |
| 1315-1330 | mt.t.s. | SAs | 9610knx |
| **Tibetan** | **Days** | **Area** | **kHz** |
| 1100-1115 | m.w.... | SAs | 15575knx |
| **Tsangla** | **Days** | **Area** | **kHz** |
| 1315-1330 | .....ss | SAs | 11875knx |
| **Urdu** | **Days** | **Area** | **kHz** |
| 1245-1300 | m....s. | SAs | 11865knx |
| 1315-1330 | ..w.... | SAs | 11875knx |
| **Vietnamese** | **Days** | **Area** | **kHz** |
| 1100-1115 | .t..f.. | SEA | 15575knx |

| Vietnamese | Days | Area | kHz |
|---|---|---|---|
| 1100-1130 | ...t... | SEA | 15575knx |

**Ann:** English: "This is Reach Beyond Australia - Life Changing Radio".
**V:** QSL-card.
**Notes:** Partner organisation of World Radio Missionary Fellowship, Inc (USA) and its media ministry Reach Beyond. Launched 2003 as "HCJB Australia", later rebranded "HCJB Global Australia", and in 2014 "Reach Beyond Australia".

## HOBART RADIO INTERNATIONAL
Based in Lewisham, TAS 7173, Australia.
**E:** hriradio@gmail.com **W:** hriradio.org
**Webcast:** D
**L.P:** Host: Robb Wise.
**SW:** Via 3rd party facilities.
**kHz:** *5985, 7780, 9265, 9955*

| English | Winter Schedule 2018/2019 | | |
|---|---|---|---|
| | **Days** | **Area** | **kHz** |
| 0330-0400 | ...t... | CAm | 5985rmi |
| 1100-1130 | .....s. | NAm | 9265inb |
| 1830-1900 | .....s. | LAm | 9955rmi |
| 2330-2400 | .....s. | NAm,Eu,ME | 7780rmi |

**Ann:** English: "Hobart Radio International".
**V:** e-QSL.
**Notes:** "Hobart Radio International" (HRI) is a radio show produced by the Tasmanian DXer Robb Wise. HRI was founded 2004 and initially transmitted via various European pirate radio stns. Since 2015, HRI began hiring airtime via legal third party providers.

## AUSTRIA (AUT)

### RADIO Ö1 (ORF) (Pub)
Argentinierstrasse 30a, A-1040 Wien, Austria.
☎ +43 1 5010116060. 🖷 +43 1 5010116066.
**E:** roi.service@orf.at **W:** oe1.orf.at
**Webcast:** D/L/P
**L.P:** DG (ORF): Dr. Alexander Wrabetz.
**SW:** Uses txs provided by ORS.
**SAT:** Astra 1N.
**kHz:** *6155*

| German | Winter Schedule 2018/2019 | | |
|---|---|---|---|
| | **Days** | **Area** | **kHz** |
| 0600-0710 | .....ss | Eu,NAf,ME | 6155mos |
| 0600-0720 | mtwtf.. | Eu,NAf,ME | 6155mos |

**V:** QSL-letter.
**Notes:** Ö1 is a domestic radio channel of the public broadcaster ORF. The SW prgr consist of a relay of the "Morgenjournal" news magazine.

### TWR EUROPE AND CAMENA (Rlg)
Postfach 141, A-1235 Wien, Austria.
☎ +43 1 863120. 🖷 +43 1 8631220.
**E:** twre@twr.org **W:** www.twreurope.org
**Webcast:** D
Other European branches: P.O. Box 176, 3780 BD Voorthuizen, The Netherlands; P.O. Box 12, 820 02 Bratislava 22, Slovakia.
**L.P:** Dir: Felix Widme.
**SAT:** Astra 2G. (TWR UK)
**kHz:** *864, 999, 1035, 1233, 1350, 1377, 1467, 1548*

| | Winter Schedule 2018/2019 | | |
|---|---|---|---|
| **Arabic** | **Days** | **Area** | **kHz** |
| 2000-2100 | daily | ME | 1377erv |
| 2025-2155 | daily | RUS | 1233cgr |
| 2145-2245 | daily | NAf,ME | 1467rou |
| **Belarusian** | **Days** | **Area** | **kHz** |
| 2015-2030 | m...... | Eu | 999kch |
| **Bosnian** | **Days** | **Area** | **kHz** |
| 2040-2055 | ......s | Eu | 1548kch |
| **Bulgarian** | **Days** | **Area** | **kHz** |
| 1900-1930 | daily | Eu | 1548kch |
| **Chechen** | **Days** | **Area** | **kHz** |
| 1740-1755 | ...t.s | Cau | 864erv |
| **Dargwa** | **Days** | **Area** | **kHz** |
| 1740-1755 | ..w.... | Cau | 864erv |

| Farsi | Days | Area | kHz |
|---|---|---|---|
| 1815-1830 | mtw..ss | ME | 1377erv |
| 1830-2000 | daily | ME | 1377erv |
| **Gilaki** | **Days** | **Area** | **kHz** |
| 1815-1830 | ...t... | ME | 1377erv |
| **Hebrew** | **Days** | **Area** | **kHz** |
| 1845-1915 | mtwt.ss | ME | 1350erv |
| **Hungarian** | **Days** | **Area** | **kHz** |
| 2015-2040 | .....ss | Eu | 1548kch |
| 2015-2040 | mtwtf.. | Eu | 1548kch |
| **Kabyle** | **Days** | **Area** | **kHz** |
| 2115-2145 | mtwtfs. | NAf | 1467rou |
| **Karakalpak** | **Days** | **Area** | **kHz** |
| 1640-1655 | .....s | CAs | 864erv |
| 1655-1710 | ....s. | CAs | 864erv |
| **Kazakh** | **Days** | **Area** | **kHz** |
| 1500-1530 | daily | CAs | 1467bis |
| 1625-1640 | daily | CAs | 864erv |
| **Kumyk** | **Days** | **Area** | **kHz** |
| 1740-1755 | ....f.. | Cau | 864erv |
| **Kurdish (Kurmanji)** | **Days** | **Area** | **kHz** |
| 1800-1815 | daily | ME | 1350erv |
| **Kurdish (Sorani)** | **Days** | **Area** | **kHz** |
| 1800-1815 | daily | ME | 1377erv |
| **Kyrgyz** | **Days** | **Area** | **kHz** |
| 1715-1730 | .....ss | CAs | 1467bis |
| **Lezgi** | **Days** | **Area** | **kHz** |
| 1740-1755 | .t..... | Cau | 864erv |
| **Polish** | **Days** | **Area** | **kHz** |
| 2045-2115 | mtwtf.s | Eu | 1467rou |
| **Qashqai** | **Days** | **Area** | **kHz** |
| 1850-1830 | ....f.. | ME | 1377erv |
| **Romani (Balkan)** | **Days** | **Area** | **kHz** |
| 1930-1945 | daily | Eu | 1548kch |
| **Romani (Vlax)** | **Days** | **Area** | **kHz** |
| 1945-2015 | mtwtf.. | Eu | 1548kch |
| **Romanian** | **Days** | **Area** | **kHz** |
| 1945-2015 | .....ss | Eu | 1548kch |
| 2030-2100 | daily | Eu | 999kch |
| **Russian** | **Days** | **Area** | **kHz** |
| 0300-0500 | daily | RUS | 1035ttu |
| 1640-1710 | mtwtf.. | CAs | 864erv |
| 1730-1800 | daily | CAs | 1467bis |
| 1800-2000 | daily | RUS | 1035ttu |
| 1845-1915 | ....f.. | RUS | 1350erv |
| 1915-1930 | .....s. | Eu | 999kch |
| 1915-1930 | .....s. | Eu | 999kch |
| 1930-2015 | m...... | Eu | 999kch |
| 1930-2030 | ..wtf.. | Eu | 999kch |
| 2015-2030 | .....s. | Eu | 999kch |
| **Serbian/ Montenegrian** | **Days** | **Area** | **kHz** |
| 2040-2055 | .....s. | Eu | 1548kch |
| **Tabasaran** | **Days** | **Area** | **kHz** |
| 1740-1755 | m...... | Cau | 864erv |
| **Tachelhit** | **Days** | **Area** | **kHz** |
| 2130-2145 | ......s | NAf | 1467rou |
| **Tajik** | **Days** | **Area** | **kHz** |
| 1630-1645 | daily | CAs | 1467bis |
| **Tarifit** | **Days** | **Area** | **kHz** |
| 2115-2130 | ......s | NAf | 1467rou |
| **Tatar** | **Days** | **Area** | **kHz** |
| 1740-1755 | .....s. | Cau | 864erv |
| **Turkish** | **Days** | **Area** | **kHz** |
| 1815-1845 | daily | ME | 1350erv |
| **Turkmen** | **Days** | **Area** | **kHz** |
| 1610-1625 | daily | CAs | 864erv |
| **Ukrainian** | **Days** | **Area** | **kHz** |
| 1900-1915 | .....ss | Eu | 999kch |
| 1900-1930 | mt..... | Eu | 999kch |
| 1900-2000 | ..wtf.. | Eu | 999kch |
| 1930-2000 | .....s. | Eu | 999kch |

| Uyghur | Days | Area | kHz |
|---|---|---|---|
| 1645-1715 | .....ss | CAs | 1467bis |
| **Uzbek** | **Days** | **Area** | **kHz** |
| 1645-1730 | mtwtf.. | CAs | 1467bis |
| 1655-1710 | ......s | CAs | 864erv |
| 1710-1740 | .....s. | CAs | 864erv |

**Ann:** English: "This is Trans World Radio. The following programme is in the ... language".
**V:** QSL-card.
**Notes:** TWR regional division, covering Europe, Russia, and CAMENA (Central Asia, Middle East, North Africa). For corporate details, see under TWR (USA).

## ÖSTERREICHISCHE RUNDFUNKSENDER GMBH & CO KG (ORS) (Tx Operator)

✉ Würzburggasse 30, A-1136 Wien, Austria.
☎ +43 1 87012680. 🖷 +43 1 8704012773.
**E:** office@ors.at **W:** www.ors.at
**LP:** CEO: Michael Wagenhofer, MD: Norbert Grill.
**SW:** [MOS] Moosbrunn: 2 x 100, 2 x 500kW.
**Notes:** ORS is the national transmitter network operator.

## BAHRAIN (BHR)

### RADIO BAHRAIN (Pub)
✉ See National Radio section.
**Webcast:** L (www.bna.bh; www.mia.gov.bh)
**SW:** [ABH] Abu Hayan: 1 x 10, 1 x 60kW.
**SAT:** Badr 4.
**kHz:** 9745

**Winter Schedule 2018/2019**

| Arabic | Days | Area | kHz |
|---|---|---|---|
| 0000-2400 | daily | ME | 9745abh* |

**Key:** * AM/USB (H3E) mode.
**Ann:** Arabic: "Idhaat al-Bahrain".
**V:** eQSL-card.
**Notes:** Relay of General/Home Sce prgrs.

## BANGLADESH (BGD)

### BANGLADESH BETAR (Pub)
✉ 31 Syed Mahbub Morshad Avenue, Shah-e-Bangla Nagar, Dhaka-1207, Bangladesh.
☎ +880 2 9670657. (Ext. Sce); +880 2 44813062. (DG) 🖷 +880 2 44813063. (DG)
**E:** betar.external@yahoo.com (Dir, Ext Sce); dg@betar.gov.bd (DG)
**W:** www.betar.gov.bd
**Webcast:** D/L
✉ 121 Kazi Nazrul Islam Avenue, Shahbagh, Dhaka-1000, Bangladesh.
**LP:** DG: Narayan Chandra Shil; Dir, External Sce: Kamal Ahmed; Senior Engineer, Research & Receiving Centre: Abu Tabib Md. Zia Hasan.
**SW:** [DKA] Dhaka, Kabirpur: 2 x 250kW.
**kHz:** 7250, 9455, 13580, 15105, 15505

**Winter Schedule 2018/2019**

| Arabic | Days | Area | kHz |
|---|---|---|---|
| 1600-1630 | daily | ME | 7250dka |
| **Bengali** | **Days** | **Area** | **kHz** |
| 1630-1730 | daily | ME | 7250dka |
| 1915-2000 | daily | Eu | 13580dka |
| **English** | **Days** | **Area** | **kHz** |
| 1230-1300 | daily | SEA | 15105dka |
| 1745-1900 | daily | Eu | 13580dka |
| **Hindi** | **Days** | **Area** | **kHz** |
| 1515-1545 | daily | SAs | 15505dka |
| **Nepali** | **Days** | **Area** | **kHz** |
| 1315-1345 | daily | SAs | 9455dka |
| **Urdu** | **Days** | **Area** | **kHz** |
| 1400-1430 | daily | SAs | 15505dka |

**Ann:** English: "This is the External Service of Bangladesh Betar".
**IS:** Local composition, played on violin and tanpura.
**V:** QSL-card. (Rpt to Senior Engineer, Research & Receiving Centre. Email rpt to: rrc@dhaka.net)
**Notes:** External service of the national public broadcaster Bangladesh

Betar, launched on 1 Jan 1972. Plans to begin broadcasting in Persian and Chinese.

## BELARUS (BLR)

### RADIO BELARUS INTERNATIONAL (Gov)
☐ Cyrvonaja Street 4, 220807 Minsk, Belarus.
☎ +375 17 2395852. 🖹 +375 17 2848574.
**E:** radio_belarus@tvr.by **W:** radiobelarus.tvr.by
**Webcast:** D/L (Webcast/Satellite/FM languages: Belarusian, English, French, German, Polish, Russian, Spanish)
**L.P:** Dir: Navum Halpiarovic; Vice Dir: Vjacaslaú Lakcjušyn.
**SW:** Via Shortwaveservice (Germany).
**FM/DAB:** FM: See National Radio section.
**kHz:** *6005*

| | Winter Schedule 2018/2019 | | |
|---|---|---|---|
| German | Days | Area | kHz |
| 0900-1100 | daily | D,CEu | 6005kll* |

**Key:** * Relayed via Shortwaveservice (Germany).
**Ann:** German: "Hier ist Radio Belarus International".
**Notes:** International Service of the National State Radio-TV Company of Belarus. Short and mediumwave transmissions ended in spring 2016.The current rebroadcasts of the German webcasts via a 1kW SW tx at Kall (Germany) are an independent, personal initiative of the operator of the German relay platform "Shortwaveservice"; a project that is primarily targeting SWLs/DXers in Europe.

## BELGIUM (BEL)

### RTBF INTERNATIONAL (Pub)
☐ Local 3P09, 52 Bd Reyers, B-1044 Bruxelles, Belgium.
☎ +32 2 7374014. 🖹 +32 2 7373032.
**E:** rtbfi@rtbf.be **W:** www.rtbf.be/rtbfi
**Webcast:** L
**L.P:** Dir/GM (RTBF): Jean-Paul Philippot.
**MW:** [WAV] Wavre: 621kHz 300kW.
**FM/DAB:** FM: 99.2MHz (Kinshasa, Dem. Rep. of Congo).
**SAT:** Eutelsat 5WA.
**kHz:** *621*

| | Winter Schedule 2018/2019 | | |
|---|---|---|---|
| French | Days | Area | kHz |
| 0500-1905 | daily | Eu | 621wav* |

**Key:** * Scheduled to cease operation before end of 2018.
**V:** QSL-card.
**Notes:** Transmissions include relays of RTBF's domestic networks La Prem1ère, VivaCité and Classic 21.

### BROADCAST BELGIUM (CONSULTANTS) (Broker)
☐ P.O. Box 1, B-2310 Rijkevorsel, Belgium.
☎ +32 33 147800.
**E:** info@broadcast.be **W:** www.broadcast.be
**L.P:** MD: Ludo Maes.
**Notes:** Broadcast Belgium is an international radio consultancy which, among other services, provides SW airtime brokerage for radio stns/prgr producers with political, religious, commercial and NGO background, in conjunction with its sister company Alyx & Yeyi (see under USA).

## BENIN (BEN)

### TWR RELAY STATION
☐ B.P. 1039, Parakou, Benin.
☎ +229 23102055.
**E:** 1566@twr.org
**L.P:** SM: Garth Kennedy.
**MW:** [PAR] Parakou: 1566kHz 100kW. F.pl: Additional 200kW MW tx on second freq.
**Notes:** Owned by TWR. For corporate details, see under TWR (USA). For schedule, see TWR Africa (South Africa).

## BONAIRE (BES)

### TWR BONAIRE (Rlg)
☐ P.O. Box 388, Kralendijk, Bonaire, Caribbean Netherlands.
☎ +599 7178800. 🖹 +599 7178808.
**E:** 800am@twr.org **W:** www.twrbonaire.com
**Webcast:** D/L

**L.P:** Dir: Bernard Oosterhoff.
**MW:** [TWB] Belnem: 800kHz 100kW, 800kHz 400kW (run at 440kW).
**FM/DAB:** FM: 89.5MHz (Bonaire) with separate, local schedule.
**kHz:** *800*

| | Winter Schedule 2018/2019 | | |
|---|---|---|---|
| Baniua | Days | Area | kHz |
| 0945-1000 | .....s. | B | 800twb |
| English | Days | Area | kHz |
| 2300-2400 | daily | Car | 800twb |
| Macuxi | Days | Area | kHz |
| 0945-1000 | ......s | B | 800twb |
| Portuguese | Days | Area | kHz |
| 0800-0945 | daily | B | 800twb |
| Spanish | Days | Area | kHz |
| 0000-0300 | daily | CUB | 800twb |
| 0300-0800 | daily | Car | 800twb |
| 1000-1230 | daily | Car | 800twb |
| 2130-2300 | daily | Car | 800twb |

**Ann:** English: "TWR Bonaire, in the Dutch Caribbean".
**V:** QSL-card.
**Notes:** Branch and transmitting station. Owned by TWR, for corporate details, see under USA.

## BOTSWANA (BOT)

### USAGM BOTSWANA TRANSMITTING STATION
☐ Private Bag 38, Selebi-Phikwe, Botswana.
☎ +267 2610932. 🖹 +267 2610185.
**L.P:** SM: George O. Miller.
**MW:** [BOT] Selebi-Phikwe, Moepeng Hill: 909kHz 600kW. (Reserve tx: 50kW).
**SW:** [BOT] Selebi-Phikwe, Moepeng Hill: 4 x 100kW.
**V:** QSL-card. (Email rpt to manager_botswana@bot.usagm.gov)

## BULGARIA (BUL)

### SPACELINE LTD
☐ bul. James Bourchier 71, 6th Floor, 1407 Sofia, Bulgaria.
☎ +359 2 9625962.
**E:** info@spaceline.bg
**W:** www.spaceline.bg; www.facebook.com/shortwave.airtime
**L.P:** GM: Dimitar Todorov.
**V:** eQSL-card (for brokered stns).
**Notes:** Spaceline Ltd manages & brokers the operation of the NURTS-owned SW transmitting center Kostinbrod (see NURTS Bulgaria entry). Spaceline also brokers airtime on the Gavar SW/MW transmitting center in Armenia (see Radio CJSC entry under Armenia).

### NURTS BULGARIA (Tx Operator)
☐ bul. Peyo K. Yavorov 2, 1164 Sofia, Bulgaria.
☎ +359 2 8069300. 🖹 +359 2 8069309.
**E:** office@nurts.bg **W:** www.nurts.bg
**L.P:** CEO's: Emil Atanasov, Svilen Popov.
**SW:** [SOF] Sofia, Kostinbrod: 4 x 50, 3 x 100, 1 x 250kW (incl. 4 DRM capable txs, run at 70kW in DRM mode).
**Notes:** NURTS, a subsidiary of Bulgarian Telecommunications Company EAD, is the Bulgarian national transmitter operator. The operation of the SW transmitting center Kostinbrod is managed and brokered by Spaceline Ltd (see separate entry).

## CAMEROON (CME)

### SAWTU LINJIILA (VOICE OF THE GOSPEL) (Rlg)
☐ B.P. 02, Ngaoundéré, Cameroon.
☎ +237 699875781.
**E:** sawtulinjiila@yahoo.fr
**W:** www.oseelc.org (EELC); nms.no (NMS); www.lutheranworld.org (LWF)
**L.P:** Dir: Rev Yaya Bournang.
**FM/DAB:** FM: Txs in Cameroon, Chad and Central African Republic.
**kHz:** *9800*

| | Winter Schedule 2018/2019 | | |
|---|---|---|---|
| Fulfulde | Days | Area | kHz |
| 1830-1900 | daily | WAf | 9800iss |

**Ann:** Fulfulde: "Sawtu Linjiila".
**V:** QSL-email.

**Notes:** Multimedia ministry for Fulfulde (Fulani) speakers in West Africa. The project is funded by the Evangelical Lutheran Church of Cameroon (EELC), the Norwegian missionary organisation Det Norske Misjonsselskap (NMS) and the Lutheran World Federation (LWF). Launched on 6 November 1966, initially broadcast on shortwave via Trans World Radio.

## CANADA (CAN)

### RADIO CANADA INTERNATIONAL (RCI) (Pub)
✉ 1400, boulevard René-Levesque Est, Montréal QC H2L 2M2, Canada.
☎ +1 514 5977461.
**E:** info@rcinet.ca **W:** www.rcinet.ca
**Webcast:** D/P
**L.P:** Editor-in-Chief: Soleïman Mellali.
**SW:** Via ShortwaveService (Germany).
**kHz:** *3985, 6005*

#### Winter Schedule 2018/2019

| English | Days | Area | kHz |
|---|---|---|---|
| 0800-0900 | ......s | Eu | 6005kll* |
| 1800-1900 | ......s | Eu | 3985kll* |

| French | Days | Area | kHz |
|---|---|---|---|
| 0800-0900 | .....s. | Eu | 6005kll* |
| 1800-1900 | .....s. | Eu | 3985kll* |

**Key:** * Relayed via Shortwaveservice (Germany).
**Notes:** RCI is the External Service of the public service Canadian Broadcasting Corp. RCI ended shortwave transmissions in 2013. The current rebroadcasts of selected RCI webcasts via a 1kW SW tx at Kall (Germany) are an independent, personal initiative of the operator of the German relay platform "Shortwaveservice"; a project that is primarily targeting SWLs/DXers in Europe".

### BIBLE VOICE BROADCASTING (BVB) (Rlg)
✉P.O. Box 95561, Newmarket, ON L3Y 8J8, Canada.
☎ +1 905 8982500.
**E:** mail@bvbroadcasting.org **W:** www.bvbroadcasting.org
**Webcast:** D
✉ 350 Davis Drive, Newmarket, ON L3Y 2N7, Canada. (HAGCM)
☎ +1 905 8985447. 🖷 +1 905 8982500.
**W:** www.hagcm.org
**L.P:** International Ministry Coordinator: Mrs. Marty McLaughlin.
**kHz:** *5900, 5935, 5995, 6030, 6145, 6260, 7220, 7325, 7365, 7435, 9400, 9440, 9450, 9715, 11790, 11875, 11900, 15640, 17650, 21480*

#### Winter Schedule 2018/2019

| Amharic | Days | Area | kHz |
|---|---|---|---|
| 1630-1700 | m...f... | EAf | 11790nau |
| 1630-1730 | .twt... | EAf | 11790nau |
| 1700-1800 | ......s | EAf | 11790nau |

| Arabic | Days | Area | kHz |
|---|---|---|---|
| 0200-0230 | daily | ME | 5900sof |
| 0500-0515 | ...f.. | ME | 9450nau |
| 0500-0530 | ......s | ME | 7325nau |
| 0600-0615 | daily | NAf | 9440nau |
| 1710-1730 | m.w.... | ME | 5995nau |
| 1710-1745 | .t.tf.. | ME | 5995nau |
| 1745-1800 | daily | ME | 5995sof |
| 1800-1830 | .....s. | IRN | 7365nau |
| 1930-1945 | daily | ME | 5900sof |
| 1945-2000 | daily | NAf | 9400sof |

| English | Days | Area | kHz |
|---|---|---|---|
| 0200-0300 | ..wtf... | SAs | 11790mdc |
| 0800-0830 | ......s | Eu | 7220nau |
| 1130-1200 | ......s | CHN | 15640dsb |
| 1200-1230 | .....s. | CHN | 17650mdc |
| 1230-1245 | ......s | INS | 21480mdc |
| 1400-1500 | .....s. | SAs | 11900nau |
| 1800-1815 | ...f.. | ME | 9715nau |
| 1800-1830 | ...t... | ME | 9715nau |
| 1800-2000 | ......s | ME | 9715nau |
| 1830-2000 | .....s. | ME | 9715nau |
| 1900-2000 | ......s | Eu | 6030erv |
| 1915-1930 | ......s | ME | 5935nau |
| 1930-2015 | ......s | ME | 7435mos |

| Farsi | Days | Area | kHz |
|---|---|---|---|
| 1800-1830 | ....f.. | IRN | 7365nau |
| 1800-1900 | ...t... | IRN | 7365nau |
| 1830-1900 | .t...s | IRN | 7365nau |

| Nuer | Days | Area | kHz |
|---|---|---|---|
| 1630-1700 | daily | EAf | 11875nau |

| Oromo | Days | Area | kHz |
|---|---|---|---|
| 1600-1630 | mt....s | EAf | 11790nau |

| Punjabi | Days | Area | kHz |
|---|---|---|---|
| 1200-1300 | ....f.. | PAK | 6260tac |

| Somali | Days | Area | kHz |
|---|---|---|---|
| 1600-1730 | .....s. | EAf | 11790nau |
| 1630-1700 | ......s | EAf | 11790nau |

| Spanish | Days | Area | kHz |
|---|---|---|---|
| 1830-1900 | ......s | Eu | 6145nau |

| Tigrinya | Days | Area | kHz |
|---|---|---|---|
| 1700-1800 | m...... | EAf | 11790nau |

| Urdu | Days | Area | kHz |
|---|---|---|---|
| 1200-1300 | ..w.... | PAK | 6260tac |

**V:** QSL-card.
**Notes:** BVB is a service of High Adventure Gospel Communication Ministries (Canada), in cooperation with Bible Voice (UK) and High Adventure Gospel Communication Ministries, Inc (USA). BVB's SW transmissions consist of religious paid programming, produced by small religious organisations, or individuals. Each prgr has its own brand. The schedule is subject to change without notice.

### RADIO SADAYE ZINDAGI (Rlg)
✉ Based in Canada.
☎ +1 450 3051354.
**E:** info@afghanradio.org **W:** afghanradio.org
**Webcast:** L
✉ P.O.Box 322, Port Colborne, ON L3K SW1, Canada. (Pamir Productions).
☎ +1 289 4781189.
**E:** info@pamirmedia.org **W:** pamirmedia.org
**L.P:** Associate Dir (Pamir Productions): Shoaib Ebadi.
**kHz:** *1467, 5130, 5940*

#### Winter Schedule 2018/2019

| Dari | Days | Area | kHz |
|---|---|---|---|
| 0230-0300 | daily | AFG | 5940dha |
| 1500-1800 | daily | AFG | 5130bis |
| 1530-1600 | daily | AFG | 1467bis |

**V:** eQSL-card.
**Notes:** Sadaye Zindagi ("Sound of Life") is a 24h Internet radio station for listeners in Afghanistan, produced by Pamir Productions. Parts of the programming is distributed on MW/SW with assistance of global religious platforms like TWR (USA) and IBRA Media (Sweden). Pamir Productions is a partner ministry of TWR.

### RED TELECOM (Broker)
✉ 522 Old Orchard Grove, Toronto, ON M5M 2G6, Canada.
☎ +1 416 7311266. 🖷 +1 416 3527539.
**E:** info@red-telecom.com **W:** www.red-telecom.com
✉ 116 Main St., 2nd Floor, Road Town, Tortola, British Virgin Islands.
**L.P:** MD: Daniel Robinson.
**Notes:** Red Telecom Ltd brokers airtime for tx facilities of Teleradiokom in Tajikistan and RRTM in Uzbekistan.

## CHINA (CHN)

### CHINA RADIO INTERNATIONAL (CRI) (Gov)
✉ 16a, Shijingshan Rd, Beijing 100040, P.R. China.
☎ +86 10 68891000, 68891001. 🖷 +86 10 68892738, 68891582.
**E:** aboutcri@cri.com.cn; crieng@cri.com.cn **W:** www.cri.cn; www.cri.com.cn (corporate)
**Webcast:** D/L
**L.P:** GD: Wang Gengnian; CE: Wang Lian; Dir, English Sce: Yang Lei.
**MW/SW:** See SART for tx information.
**SAT:** Apstar 6, Intelsat 14/19/20/21, Superbird C2, Telstar 11N, Yamal 202.
**kHz:** *603, 684, 900, 963, 1017, 1044, 1080, 1188, 1269, 1296, 1323, 1341, 1422, 1521, 5905, 5910, 5915, 5955, 5960, 5965, 5970, 5975, 5980, 5985, 5990, 6010, 6020, 6025, 6040, 6055, 6060, 6065, 6070, 6075, 6080, 6090, 6095, 6100, 6105, 6110, 6115, 6135, 6140, 6145, 6150, 6155, 6160, 6165, 6175, 6180, 6185, 6190, 7205, 7210, 7215,*

7220, 7225, 7235, 7240, 7245, 7250, 7255, 7260, 7265, 7275, 7285, 7290, 7295, 7300, 7305, 7315, 7320, 7325, 7330, 7335, 7340, 7345, 7350, 7360, 7365, 7370, 7380, 7385, 7390, 7395, 7400, 7405, 7410, 7415, 7420, 7425, 7430, 7435, 7440, 7445, 9410, 9415, 9425, 9430, 9435, 9440, 9450, 9455, 9460, 9470, 9490, 9515, 9520, 9525, 9535, 9540, 9550, 9555, 9560, 9565, 9570, 9580, 9585, 9590, 9600, 9610, 9615, 9620, 9630, 9640, 9645, 9655, 9665, 9675, 9685, 9690, 9695, 9705, 9710, 9720, 9730, 9745, 9760, 9765, 9770, 9785, 9795, 9800, 9825, 9855, 9860, 9865, 9870, 9875, 9880, 11610, 11635, 11640, 11650, 11680, 11690, 11700, 11710, 11720, 11725, 11730, 11750, 11760, 11770, 11780, 11785, 11790, 11795, 11805, 11820, 11855, 11860, 11870, 11875, 11880, 11885, 11895, 11900, 11910, 11920, 11945, 11955, 11975, 11980, 11990, 12015, 12035, 12070, 13570, 13580, 13590, 13600, 13610, 13640, 13645, 13650, 13655, 13660, 13665, 13670, 13720, 13730, 13740, 13750, 13770, 13780, 13790, 13800, 13810, 13850, 13855, 15110, 15120, 15125, 15130, 15135, 15145, 15160, 15170, 15185, 15190, 15205, 15210, 15220, 15225, 15250, 15535, 15340, 15350, 15425, 15440, 15435, 15440, 15445, 15465, 15525, 15550, 15560, 15620, 15665, 15700, 17485, 17490, 17510, 17520, 17540, 17560, 17570, 17615, 17640, 17650, 17670, 17680, 17690, 17710, 17720, 17730, 17735, 17740, 17750, 17855

## Winter Schedule 2018/2019

| | Days | Area | kHz |
|---|---|---|---|
| **Albanian** | | | |
| 1900-2000 | daily | Eu | 6020szg, 7385kas |
| **Amoy** | **Days** | **Area** | **kHz** |
| 0100-0200 | daily | SAs | 9610kun |
| 0100-0200 | daily | SEA | 9460kun, 9550kun, 9860jin, 11945kun, 11980kun |
| 0100-0300 | daily | SEA | 15425xia, 17490bei |
| 1200-1300 | daily | SEA | 11910bei |
| 1400-1500 | daily | SEA | 9655kun, 11650kun |
| **Arabic** | **Days** | **Area** | **kHz** |
| 0500-0700 | daily | ME,NAf | 17485kas |
| 0500-0700 | daily | ME | 9590cer |
| 0500-0700 | daily | NAf | 5985cer, 7210cer |
| 1600-1800 | daily | NAf | 9555cer, 11725cer |
| 1600-1800 | daily | ME,NAf | 7300kas |
| 2000-2200 | daily | ME,NAf | 6100xia, 6185cer, 7215cer |
| **Bengali** | **Days** | **Area** | **kHz** |
| 0200-0300 | daily | SAs | 9655kun, 11640kun |
| 1300-1400 | daily | SAs | 1188kun, 9600bji |
| 1300-1500 | daily | SAs | 9490kun, 11610kun |
| 1400-1500 | daily | SAs | 1269xuw |
| 1500-1600 | daily | SAs | 9610kun, 9690kun |
| **Bulgarian** | **Days** | **Area** | **kHz** |
| 1100-1200 | daily | Eu | 7220cer |
| 1830-1900 | daily | Eu | 6020szg, 7265uru, 9695kun |
| 2030-2100 | daily | Eu | 7320kun, 9720uru |
| **Burmese** | **Days** | **Area** | **kHz** |
| 0200-0300 | daily | BRM | 900deh |
| 0700-0800 | daily | BRM | 900deh |
| 1100-1200 | daily | SEA | 1188kun, 9880kun |
| 1300-1400 | daily | SEA | 9880kun |
| 1300-1500 | daily | SEA | 7400kun |
| 1400-1500 | daily | BRM | 900deh |
| **Cantonese** | **Days** | **Area** | **kHz** |
| 0000-0100 | daily | SEA | 11820xia, 17490bei |
| 0400-0500 | daily | NAm | 5910qvc |
| 0400-0600 | daily | EAs | 13655xia, 15160jin |
| 0700-0800 | daily | EAs | 11640jin, 13610xia |
| 1000-1100 | daily | Pac | 15440kun, 17670kun |
| 1100-1200 | daily | Pac | 9540kun, 13580kun |
| 1100-1200 | daily | SEA | 603dof, 7370nnn, 9590kun, 9645bei |
| 1200-1300 | daily | NAm | 9570qvc |
| 1700-1800 | daily | SAf | 7325uru |
| 1700-1800 | daily | EAf | 7220xia |
| 1900-2000 | daily | Eu | 7215bei, 9770kas |
| 2300-2400 | daily | SEA | 6140kun, 6180kun, 7325kun, 9630jin, 11945kun |

| Chaozhou | Days | Area | kHz |
|---|---|---|---|
| 0700-0800 | daily | SEA | 15145xia, 17750xia |
| 1100-1200 | daily | SEA | 9440kun, 11875kun |
| 1800-1900 | daily | Eu | 6010uru, 7285xia |
| **Chinese** | **Days** | **Area** | **kHz** |
| 0000-0100 | daily | EAs | 11780jin, 11900bei |
| 0000-0100 | daily | SEA | 9435kun, 11975kun, 12035xia |
| 0000-0200 | daily | SEA | 13580bei |
| 0000-0400 | daily | EAs | 13655kas |
| 0100-0200 | daily | SEA | 9655nnn, 11640xia, 11770nnn |
| 0100-0200 | daily | SAs | 7250uru, 7300kas |
| 0100-0400 | daily | EAs | 15160jin |
| 0200-0300 | daily | SAm | 7330kas, 11780bei |
| 0200-0300 | daily | SAs | 9825kas |
| 0200-0300 | daily | NAm | 6180qvc |
| 0200-0400 | daily | NAm | 6020cer, 9570cer |
| 0300-0400 | daily | SAs | 9450kas, 17540bei |
| 0300-0600 | daily | EAs | 15130bei |
| 0400-0500 | daily | SAs | 13640kas, 15170kas |
| 0500-0600 | daily | SAs | 15110kas |
| 0500-0700 | daily | EAs | 13570xia, 15120bei |
| 0600-0700 | daily | Eu | 13720kas |
| 0600-0700 | daily | EAs | 13655xia, 15160jin |
| 0600-0800 | daily | SEA | 11710nnn, 13750kas, 17740xia |
| 0700-0800 | daily | SAs | 17520kas |
| 0700-0800 | daily | SEA | 11875nnn |
| 0700-0900 | daily | Eu | 11855cer, 17650kas |
| 0800-0900 | daily | EAs | 9880bei, 11640jin, 13610xia |
| 0800-0900 | daily | SAs | 15550kas |
| 0800-1000 | daily | CAs,Cau | 15560xia, 17560xia |
| 0900-1000 | daily | EAs | 7430jin, 9440xia |
| 0900-1000 | daily | SEA | 11895nnn |
| 0900-1000 | daily | Pac | 15440kun, 17670kun |
| 0900-1100 | daily | SEA | 9460nnn, 11980kun, 13850bei, 15250kun, 15340xia |
| 0900-1100 | daily | EAs | 5965bei |
| 0900-1100 | daily | SAs | 13780kas, 15525uru |
| 1000-1100 | daily | EAs | 7255xia, 9880bei |
| 1000-1200 | daily | Eu | 17650kas |
| 1100-1200 | daily | SAs | 9515kas, 11980kas |
| 1100-1200 | daily | Pac | 11750kas, 15440kun |
| 1100-1200 | daily | EAs | 7435bei |
| 1200-1300 | daily | EAs | 7390bei |
| 1200-1300 | daily | Eu | 13720kas |
| 1200-1300 | daily | SAs | 7205kas, 9655kas |
| 1200-1400 | daily | ME,NAf | 11790kas*, 13810kas* |
| 1200-1400 | daily | SAs | 9540kun |
| 1200-1400 | daily | SEA | 7440nnn, 9855bei |
| 1200-1500 | daily | ME | 9520uru |
| 1300-1400 | daily | Eu | 13855kas |
| 1300-1400 | daily | SEA | 7215xia |
| 1300-1400 | daily | EAs | 7205kas |
| 1400-1500 | daily | Eu | 9430kas, 11785kas |
| 1400-1500 | daily | EAs | 7210bei |
| 1400-1500 | daily | SEA | 6040xia, 7410bei |
| 1400-1500 | daily | SAs | 9730kas |
| 1400-1600 | daily | SAs | 7235kas |
| 1500-1600 | daily | SEA | 5910bei, 9455kun |
| 1500-1600 | daily | SAs | 9560kas |
| 1500-1600 | daily | Eu | 9590kas, 9705kas |
| 1500-1600 | daily | EAs | 7255bei |
| 1730-1830 | daily | Eu | 6150szg, 7445uru |
| 1730-1830 | daily | ME,NAf | 7275uru, 7315kun, 9695kun |
| 2000-2100 | daily | SAf | 7405xia |
| 2000-2100 | daily | Eu | 7335szg, 7440bei |
| 2000-2100 | daily | ME,NAf | 7245kas, 9865kun |
| 2200-2300 | daily | SEA | 6100kun, 6140kun, 6180kun, 7325kun |

| Chinese | Days | Area | kHz |
|---|---|---|---|
| 2200-2300 | daily | SAf | 5975bei, 7430jin |
| 2200-2300 | daily | EAs | 7305bei |
| 2200-2300 | daily | NAf,ME | 7265kun, 7395uru |
| 2300-2400 | daily | EAs | 9555bei |
| 2300-2400 | daily | Eu | 7300uru |

| Croatian | Days | Area | kHz |
|---|---|---|---|
| 1700-1800 | daily | Eu | 7335bei, 9435kas |
| 2100-2200 | daily | Eu | 6135bei, 7225bei |

| Czech | Days | Area | kHz |
|---|---|---|---|
| 1100-1200 | daily | Eu | 15225kas, 17570kas |
| 1900-1930 | daily | Eu | 7325szg |
| 1900-2000 | daily | Eu | 7415uru |

| English | Days | Area | kHz |
|---|---|---|---|
| 0000-0100 | daily | SAs | 7425kas |
| 0000-0100 | daily | EAs | 9425bei |
| 0000-0200 | daily | SEA | 11885xia, 15125bei |
| 0000-0200 | daily | SAs | 6075kas, 6180kas |
| 0000-0200 | daily | NAm | 6020cer, 9570cer |
| 0100-0200 | daily | Eu | 9675kas |
| 0100-0200 | daily | NAm | 9580qvc |
| 0100-0200 | daily | SAs | 7370kas |
| 0200-0300 | daily | SAs | 9610kas |
| 0200-0400 | daily | SAs | 11770kas |
| 0300-0400 | daily | NAm | 5910qvc |
| 0300-0400 | daily | SAs | 13800kas |
| 0300-0500 | daily | EAs | 13570xia, 13590bei, 15120bei |
| 0400-0600 | daily | CAs | 17855bei |
| 0400-0600 | daily | CAs,Eu | 17730xia |
| 0500-0600 | daily | NAf | 7220cer |
| 0500-0700 | daily | ME,NAf | 17510kas |
| 0500-0700 | daily | SAs | 15430kas |
| 0500-0900 | daily | SAs | 11895kas, 15465kas |
| 0500-1100 | daily | SAs | 15350kas |
| 0600-0700 | daily | ME | 11870kas, 15145kas |
| 0600-0700 | daily | NAf | 11750cer |
| 0600-0700 | daily | SEA | 13645xia |
| 0600-0800 | daily | SEA | 11710bei |
| 0700-0800 | daily | SEA | 13660xia |
| 0700-0900 | daily | Eu | 11785cer |
| 0700-0900 | daily | ME,NAf | 17670kas |
| 0700-1000 | daily | SAs | 15185kas |
| 0700-1300 | daily | Eu | 17490kas |
| 0800-1000 | daily | EAs | 9415xia |
| 0900-1000 | daily | Eu | 17570uru, 17650kas |
| 0900-1100 | daily | Pac | 15210kun, 17690jin |
| 1000-1100 | daily | EAs | 5955xia, 7215xia, 11635bei |
| 1000-1100 | daily | SAs | 15190kas |
| 1000-1200 | daily | SEA | 13590bei, 13720xia |
| 1100-1200 | daily | SAs | 11795kas |
| 1100-1200 | daily | SEA | 9730bei |
| 1100-1300 | daily | Eu | 13665cer |
| 1100-1300 | daily | SAs | 7250kas, 11650uru, 12015kas |
| 1100-1300 | daily | SEA | 1269xuw |
| 1100-1600 | daily | EAs | 5955bei |
| 1200-1300 | daily | CAs | 11690xia |
| 1200-1300 | daily | Pac | 9760kun |
| 1200-1300 | daily | SAs | 9460kas |
| 1200-1300 | daily | SEA | 684dof, 1188kun, 9600kun, 9645bei, 9730kun |
| 1200-1400 | daily | Eu | 13790uru |
| 1200-1400 | daily | Pac | 11760kun |
| 1200-1400 | daily | SEA | 1341hdu, 11980kun |
| 1300-1400 | daily | NAm | 9570qvc |
| 1300-1400 | daily | SEA | 9730bei, 11910bei |
| 1300-1400 | daily | Eu | 11640kas |
| 1300-1400 | daily | SAs | 7300kas, 9655kas |
| 1300-1400 | daily | Pac | 11900kun |
| 1300-1500 | daily | CAs,Eu | 9765bji |
| 1300-1600 | daily | SEA | 9870xia |

| English | Days | Area | kHz |
|---|---|---|---|
| 1400-1500 | daily | Eu | 9795uru, 11880kas |
| 1400-1500 | daily | ME | 6100uru |
| 1400-1500 | daily | SAs | 7300uru, 9460uru |
| 1400-1600 | daily | NAm | 15700qvc |
| 1400-1600 | daily | SEA | 6135xia |
| 1500-1600 | daily | NAf,ME | 6095kas, 9720uru |
| 1500-1600 | daily | SAs | 1188kun, 7395uru, 9785jin |
| 1500-1600 | daily | Eu | 9525kas |
| 1500-1600 | daily | SEA | 7325bei |
| 1500-1700 | daily | Eu | 9435kas |
| 1500-1800 | daily | SAs | 1323uru |
| 1500-1800 | daily | SEA | 9880nnn |
| 1600-1700 | daily | Eu | 9875kas |
| 1600-1700 | daily | NAf,ME | 7420uru |
| 1600-1700 | daily | SEA | 6060kun |
| 1600-1800 | daily | Eu | 7255kas |
| 1600-1800 | daily | SAf | 7435jin, 9570bei |
| 1600-1800 | daily | SAs | 7235kas |
| 1600-1800 | daily | SEA | 1080xuw, 6175nnn |
| 1700-1800 | daily | SAs | 6140kas, 7410kas |
| 1700-1800 | daily | SEA | 6090kun, 7420kun |
| 1700-1800 | daily | ME | 6165bei |
| 1700-1900 | daily | Eu | 6100bei |
| 1800-1900 | daily | Eu | 7405bei |
| 1900-2100 | daily | ME,NAf | 7295kas, 9440kun |
| 2000-2100 | daily | SAf | 5985bei |
| 2000-2200 | daily | Eu | 5960cer, 7285cer, 7415kas, 9600kas |
| 2100-2200 | daily | SAf | 7205xia, 7325bei |
| 2200-2300 | daily | EAs | 5915bei |
| 2300-0100 | daily | SEA | 11790xia |
| 2300-0200 | daily | Eu | 7350kas |
| 2300-2400 | daily | SEA | 9535kun |
| 2300-2400 | daily | SAs | 5915kas, 7410kas |
| 2300-2400 | daily | EAs | 6145bei |
| 2300-2400 | daily | NAm,CAm | 5990qvc |

| Esperanto | Days | Area | kHz |
|---|---|---|---|
| 1100-1200 | daily | EAs | 7210uru, 9450uru |
| 1300-1400 | daily | SEA | 9440nnn, 9695bei |
| 1700-1800 | daily | Eu | 7205bei, 7245xia |
| 1930-2030 | daily | Eu | 7265uru, 9745uru |
| 2200-2300 | daily | SAm | 7315kas, 9860kas |

| Filipino | Days | Area | kHz |
|---|---|---|---|
| 1130-1200 | daily | SEA | 1341hdu, 5910bei, 7410jin, 11955kun, 12070xia |
| 1430-1500 | daily | SEA | 1341hdu, 7325bei, 11640bei |

| French | Days | Area | kHz |
|---|---|---|---|
| 0600-0800 | daily | Eu | 15220kas |
| 1200-1400 | daily | Eu | 15205kas |
| 1300-1400 | daily | Eu | 13720kas |
| 1400-1600 | daily | WAf | 11920cer, 13670cer |
| 1600-1800 | daily | Eu | 7350kas |
| 1800-2000 | daily | Eu | 5970cer, 7360cer |
| 1800-2000 | daily | NAf,WAf | 6055cer, 7385cer |
| 1830-2030 | daily | WAf | 7350uru, 9645kun |
| 2030-2230 | daily | Eu | 6115bei, 7350uru |

| German | Days | Area | kHz |
|---|---|---|---|
| 0600-0800 | daily | Eu | 17615uru, 17720kas |
| 1600-1800 | daily | Eu | 5970cer, 7380cer |
| 1800-2000 | daily | Eu | 6160xia, 7395kas, 9615uru |

| Hakka | Days | Area | kHz |
|---|---|---|---|
| 0000-0100 | daily | SEA | 9460kun, 9550kun, 9610kun, 9860jin |
| 0400-0500 | daily | SEA | 17510xia, 17710bei |
| 0400-0500 | daily | SAs | 13740kas, 15350kas |
| 1600-1700 | daily | SAf | 6090xia, 7325uru |

| Hausa | Days | Area | kHz |
|---|---|---|---|
| 1630-1730 | daily | WAf | 9620kas, 9665kun |
| 1730-1830 | daily | WAf | 9450kas, 9685kun |

| Hindi | Days | Area | kHz |
|---|---|---|---|
| 0300-0400 | daily | SAs | 9695kas, 9870kas, 11640kas, 11700kas |
| 1300-1400 | daily | SAs | 1269xuw, 1422kas, 7265uru, 9450kas |
| 1500-1600 | daily | SAs | 7225uru, 7265kas |
| 1600-1700 | daily | SAs | 1188kun, 1422kas, 5915kas, 7395kun |
| 1600-1800 | daily | SAs | 1269xuw |

| Hungarian | Days | Area | kHz |
|---|---|---|---|
| 1000-1100 | daily | Eu | 15220kas, 17570kas |
| 1900-1930 | daily | Eu | 7435xia, 9560uru |
| 2030-2100 | daily | Eu | 7390jin, 9585kas |
| 2130-2200 | daily | Eu | 7445uru |

| Indonesian | Days | Area | kHz |
|---|---|---|---|
| 0830-0930 | daily | SEA | 15135kun, 17735kun |
| 1030-1130 | daily | SEA | 11700kun, 15135kun |
| 1330-1430 | daily | SEA | 11805kun, 11955kun |

| Italian | Days | Area | kHz |
|---|---|---|---|
| 0600-0700 | daily | Eu | 15620kas |
| 1800-1900 | daily | Eu | 7340kas, 7435jin |
| 2030-2130 | daily | Eu | 7265uru, 7345kas |

| Japanese | Days | Area | kHz |
|---|---|---|---|
| 1000-1100 | daily | EAs | 9440xia |
| 1000-1300 | daily | EAs | 7325jin |
| 1100-1300 | daily | EAs | 7260xia |
| 1100-1600 | daily | EAs | 1044hnl |
| 1300-1400 | daily | EAs | 7325xia |
| 1300-1500 | daily | EAs | 7410jin |
| 1400-1500 | daily | EAs | 7395xia |
| 1500-1600 | daily | EAs | 5980xia, 7220jin |
| 2200-2300 | daily | EAs | 5985xia, 7440jin |
| 2300-2400 | daily | EAs | 9695jin, 9720xia |

| Khmer | Days | Area | kHz |
|---|---|---|---|
| 0000-0100 | daily | SEA | 11990nnn |
| 1030-1130 | daily | SEA | 684dof, 15160nnn, 17680kun |
| 1200-1300 | daily | SEA | 9440kun, 11680nnn |
| 1400-1500 | daily | SEA | 684dof, 6055nnn, 9880nnn |
| 2300-0100 | daily | SEA | 684dof, 9765nnn |
| 2300-2400 | daily | SEA | 7430nnn |

| Korean | Days | Area | kHz |
|---|---|---|---|
| 1100-1500 | daily | EAs | 5965xia |
| 1100-1600 | daily | EAs | 1017cah, 1323hdn |
| 2100-2300 | daily | EAs | 1017cah, 1323hdn, 7290xia |

| Lao | Days | Area | kHz |
|---|---|---|---|
| 1230-1330 | daily | SEA | 1080xuw, 7360kun, 9785kun |
| 1430-1530 | daily | SEA | 1080xuw, 7360kun, 9675kun |

| Malay | Days | Area | kHz |
|---|---|---|---|
| 0930-1030 | daily | SEA | 15135kun, 17680kun |
| 1230-1330 | daily | SEA | 11700kun, 11955kun |

| Mongolian | Days | Area | kHz |
|---|---|---|---|
| 0000-0100 | daily | EAs | 7205bei, 9470xia |
| 1100-1200 | daily | EAs | 6100uru, 7390huh |
| 1200-1300 | daily | EAs | 1323uru, 5915huh, 5990huh |
| 1300-1400 | daily | EAs | 6100uru, 7285bei |
| 1400-1500 | daily | EAs | 5915huh, 5990huh |
| 2300-2400 | daily | EAs | 6185xia, 7205xia |

| Nepali | Days | Area | kHz |
|---|---|---|---|
| 0130-0230 | daily | SAs | 11860kun |
| 0130-0330 | daily | SAs | 13780kun |
| 0230-0330 | daily | SAs | 11730kun |
| 1400-1500 | daily | SAs | 1188kun, 7220xia, 7435kun |
| 1500-1600 | daily | SAs | 1269xuw, 7215kun, 9535xia |

| Pashto | Days | Area | kHz |
|---|---|---|---|
| 0200-0230 | daily | WAs | 6065kas, 7350kas, 15435xia |
| 1500-1600 | daily | WAs | 7435kun, 9665kas |
| 1530-1600 | daily | WAs | 6165uru |

| Persian | Days | Area | kHz |
|---|---|---|---|
| 1500-1530 | daily | ME | 6165uru, 9600kas |
| 1800-1900 | daily | ME | 7325bei, 7415xia |

| Polish | Days | Area | kHz |
|---|---|---|---|
| 2000-2100 | daily | Eu | 6020szg, 7305uru |

| Portuguese | Days | Area | kHz |
|---|---|---|---|
| 0000-0100 | daily | SAm | 9710kas |
| 1900-2000 | daily | Eu | 7335jin, 9730kas |
| 1900-2000 | daily | SAf | 5985bei, 7365bei, 7405xia, 9535bji |
| 2200-2300 | daily | Eu | 6175cer, 7260uru |
| 2200-2300 | daily | SAm | 9410kas, 9685kas |
| 2300-0100 | daily | SAm | 6100bei |
| 2300-2400 | daily | SAm | 13650qvc |

| Romanian | Days | Area | kHz |
|---|---|---|---|
| 0900-1000 | daily | Eu | 7285cer, 9460cer |
| 1900-2000 | daily | Eu | 6090uru |
| 1930-2000 | daily | Eu | 7435xia |

| Russian | Days | Area | kHz |
|---|---|---|---|
| 0000-0200 | daily | CAs | 1521uru |
| 0100-0200 | daily | CAs | 5905kas |
| 0100-0200 | daily | CAs,Eu | 9440xia |
| 0200-0300 | daily | CAs | 5915kas |
| 0200-0300 | daily | CAs,Eu | 11980xia |
| 0300-0400 | daily | CAs | 11710uru, 15435xia |
| 0300-0400 | daily | CAs,Eu | 17710jin |
| 0300-0500 | daily | CAs | 7325kas |
| 0400-0500 | daily | CAs | 17640xia |
| 0400-0600 | daily | CAs,Eu | 15445kas, 15665uru |
| 0800-1000 | daily | CAs,Eu | 15335kas, 15665uru |
| 1000-1100 | daily | EAs | 7390huh |
| 1000-1200 | daily | EAs | 5915huh, 7290szg |
| 1100-1200 | daily | CAs | 6080bei |
| 1100-1200 | daily | EAs | 1323uru |
| 1100-1500 | daily | EAs | 1323hei |
| 1100-1600 | daily | EAs | 963hdn |
| 1100-2000 | daily | CAs | 1521uru |
| 1200-1300 | daily | CAs,Eu | 7215xia, 9590szg, 9685uru |
| 1200-1300 | daily | EAs | 6100bei, 7410szg |
| 1200-1700 | daily | CAs | 5905kas |
| 1300-1400 | daily | EAs | 5915huh, 5990huh, 7255szg |
| 1300-1400 | daily | CAs,Eu | 9665xia |
| 1300-1500 | daily | EAs | 1323uru |
| 1400-1500 | daily | EAs | 7435szg |
| 1400-1500 | daily | CAs,Eu | 7330xia |
| 1500-1600 | daily | CAs,Eu | 6025xia, 6105szg, 6180uru |
| 1500-1600 | daily | EAs | 5915huh, 5965bei, 5990huh |
| 1600-1700 | daily | CAs,Eu | 7215szg, 7265bei |
| 1600-1800 | daily | CAs,Eu | 6040uru |
| 1700-1800 | daily | CAs,Eu | 6070xia, 7265uru, 7410szg |
| 1800-1900 | daily | CAs,Eu | 6070bei, 7210uru, 7255szg |
| 1900-2000 | daily | CAs,Eu | 6100bei, 6110xia, 7245bji |
| 2000-2100 | daily | CAs,Eu | 6155bei, 7255bji |
| 2300-0100 | daily | EAs | 5990huh, 7415huh |

| Serbian | Days | Area | kHz |
|---|---|---|---|
| 1200-1300 | daily | Eu | 7345cer |
| 2000-2030 | daily | Eu | 7325xia, 7390xia, 9585kas |
| 2100-2130 | daily | Eu | 7325xia, 7445kun |

| Sinhala | Days | Area | kHz |
|---|---|---|---|
| 1400-1500 | daily | SAs | 7265kas, 9665jin |
| 2330-0030 | daily | SAs | 6100kun, 7260kas |

| Spanish | Days | Area | kHz |
|---|---|---|---|
| 0000-0100 | daily | NAm,CAm | 5990qvc |

| Spanish | Days | Area | kHz |
|---|---|---|---|
| 0000-0100 | daily | SAm | 15120qvc |
| 0100-0300 | daily | SAm | 9710kas |
| 0600-0800 | daily | Eu | 15135kas |
| 2100-2300 | daily | Eu | 6020szg, 9640kas |
| 2200-2300 | daily | SAm | 6100bei |
| 2200-2400 | daily | Eu | 7210cer, 7250uru |
| 2300-0100 | daily | SAm | 9800kas |
| 2300-0300 | daily | SAm | 9590kas |
| 2300-2400 | daily | Eu | 6175cer |
| **Swahili** | **Days** | **Area** | **kHz** |
| 1600-1700 | daily | EAf | 7245xia |
| 1600-1800 | daily | EAf | 5985bei |
| 1700-1800 | daily | EAf | 7400xia |
| **Tamil** | **Days** | **Area** | **kHz** |
| 0200-0300 | daily | SAs | 9800kas, 11870kas |
| 0300-0400 | daily | SAs | 13600kun, 13730kas |
| 1400-1500 | daily | SAs | 5965kas, 9610kas |
| 1500-1600 | daily | SAs | 7360kas, 9490kas |
| **Thai** | **Days** | **Area** | **kHz** |
| 1130-1230 | daily | SEA | 1080xuw, 7360kun, 9785kun |
| 1330-1430 | daily | SEA | 1080xuw, 7360kun, 9785kun |
| **Turkish** | **Days** | **Area** | **kHz** |
| 1500-1600 | daily | ME | 7345cer, 9565cer |
| 1600-1700 | daily | ME | 6165uru, 7325kun |
| 1900-2000 | daily | ME | 7255kun, 9655kun |
| **Urdu** | **Days** | **Area** | **kHz** |
| 0100-0200 | daily | SAs | 7240kas |
| 0100-0300 | daily | SAs | 6020kas |
| 0200-0300 | daily | SAs | 7290kas |
| 1400-1500 | daily | SAs | 7285kun |
| 1400-1600 | daily | SAs | 1422kas, 6075kas |
| 1500-1600 | daily | SAs | 7285kas |
| **Vietnamese** | **Days** | **Area** | **kHz** |
| 0000-0100 | daily | SEA | 11770bei, 13770xia |
| 0400-0600 | daily | SEA | 603dof, 684dof, 11650kun, 17740xia |
| 1100-1200 | daily | SEA | 11785bji, 11990xia |
| 1100-1500 | daily | SEA | 9550bei |
| 1100-1700 | daily | SEA | 1296kun |
| 1200-1300 | daily | SEA | 11640xia, 11720bji |
| 1200-1700 | daily | SEA | 603dof |
| 1300-1400 | daily | SEA | 684dof, 9685xia |
| 1400-1500 | daily | SEA | 9685bji |
| 1500-1600 | daily | SEA | 6190bei |
| 1500-1700 | daily | SEA | 684dof |
| 1600-1700 | daily | SEA | 6010bei, 7315kun |
| 2300-0100 | daily | SEA | 603dof |
| 2300-2400 | daily | SEA | 7220xia, 9415bei |

**Key:** * Relay of CRI News Radio.
**Ann:** Arabic: "Idha'at as-Sin ad-Duwaliyah"; Chinese: "Zhongguo guoji guangbo diantai"; English: "This is China Radio International, broadcasting from Beijing"; French: "Ici Radio Chine Internationale"; German: "Hier ist Radio China International"; Indonesian: "Inilah Radio CRI, China Radio International"; Japanese: "Kochirawa Pekin Hoso, Chugoku Kokusai Hosokyoku desu"; Korean: "Jungguk gukje bangsonggugimnida"; Malay: "Inilah Radio Antarabangsa China, dalam bahasa Melayu"; Mongolian: "Hyatadyn Olon Ulsyn Radio"; Russian: "Govorit Mezhdunarodnoye Radio Kitaya"; Spanish: "Esta es Radio Internacional de China"; Swahili: "Hii ni Radio China kimataifa"; Vietnamese: "Day la dai phatthanh quoc te Trung quoc".
**IS:** First bars of the National Anthem.
**V:** QSL-card.
**Notes:** Founded on 3 Dec 1941. Since March 2018, China Radio International is produced under the umbrella of the state-owned China Media Group.

## CHINA TIBET BROADCASTING (CTB) – HOLY TIBET (Gov)
🖃 41 Beijing Zhonglu, Lhasa, Xizang 85000, P.R. China.
☎ +86 891 6834073.
**E:** holytibetprogram@163.com; newvtibet@yahoo.com.cn (CTB)
**W:** www.vtibet.com
**Webcast:** D

**SW:** See SART for tx information.
**kHz:** *4905, 4920, 6025, 6110, 6130, 6200, 7255, 7385, 9490, 9580*

| **Winter Schedule 2018/2019** | | | |
|---|---|---|---|
| **English** | **Days** | **Area** | **kHz** |
| 0700-0800 | daily | As | 4905lha, 4920lha, 6025lha, 6110lha, 6130lha, 6200lha, 9490lha, 9580lha |
| 1600-1700 | daily | As | 4905lha, 4920lha, 6025lha, 6110lha, 6130lha, 6200lha, 7255lha, 7385lha |

**Ann:** English: "This is Holy Tibet, presented to you by China Tibet Broadcasting".
**Notes:** "Holy Tibet" is a daily one-hour English language prgr produced by the provincial Xizang People's Broadcasting Station a.k.a China Tibet Broadcasting (CTB).

## CRI – VOICE OF THE SOUTH CHINA SEA (Gov)
🖃 See China Radio International for contact details.
**W:** vscs.cri.cn
**Webcast:** L
**FM/DAB:** FM: 89.1MHz (Sanya, 3kW); 96.6MHz (Wuzhishan, 3kW); 96.8MHz (Wenchang, 3kW); 101.0MHz (Sansha*, 3kW); 102.0MHz (Qionghai, 3kW), all in Hainan province (* located in the South China Sea).
**kHz:** *9720, 11955*

| **Winter Schedule 2018/2019** | | | |
|---|---|---|---|
| **Filipino** | **Days** | **Area** | **kHz** |
| 1200-1230 | daily | SEA | 9720xia, 11955kun |

**Notes:** Launched on 9 Apr 2013. The Voice of the South China Sea is a service produced by China Radio International (CRI), aimed at countries around the South China Sea. It is planned to eventually broadcast in 6 languages: Chinese, English, Filipino, Indonesian, Malaysian and Vietnamese.

## VOICE OF GUANGXI BEIBU WAN (BEIBU BAY RADIO) (Gov)
🖃 75 Minzu Dadao, Nanning, Guangxi 530022, P.R.China.
☎ +86 771 5802999. 🖷 +86 771 5802555.
**E:** bbrtv@bbrtv.com
**W:** www.bbrtv.com; www.weibo.com/beibubayradio
**Webcast:** L
**SW:** See SART for tx information.
**FM/DAB:** FM: 96.4MHz (Nan Shan, 10kW)
**kHz:** *5050, 9820*

| **Winter Schedule 2018/2019** | | | |
|---|---|---|---|
| **Cantonese** | **Days** | **Area** | **kHz** |
| 1300-1400 | daily | SEA | 5050nnn, 9820nnn |
| **Chinese** | **Days** | **Area** | **kHz** |
| 1000-1100 | daily | SEA | 5050nnn, 9820nnn |
| **Multilingual** | **Days** | **Area** | **kHz** |
| 1500-1600 | daily | SEA | 5050nnn**, 9820nnn** |
| 2300-2400 | daily | SEA | 5050nnn**, 9820nnn** |
| **Thai** | **Days** | **Area** | **kHz** |
| 0000-0100 | daily | SEA | 5050nnn, 9820nnn |
| 1200-1300 | daily | SEA | 5050nnn, 9820nnn |
| **Vietnamese** | **Days** | **Area** | **kHz** |
| 1100-1200 | daily | SEA | 5050nnn, 9820nnn |
| 1400-1500 | daily | SEA | 5050nnn*, 9820nnn* |

**Key:** * Relay of CRI Vietnamese prgr; ** Burmese/Chinese/English/Thai/Vietnamese.
**Ann:** Chinese: "Guangxi Bei-bu Wan zhi sheng"; English: "Beibu Bay Radio"; Vietnamese: "Tiếng nói Vinh bac bô Quảng Tây".
**V:** QSL-letter.
**Notes:** The Voice of Guangxi Beibu Wan (English brand: "Beibu Bay Radio") is a joint External Service project of the provincial Guangxi People's Broadcasting Station and China Radio International. Beibu Bay in the South China Sea is also known as Gulf of Tonkin.

## YUNNAN RADIO AND TELEVISION INTERNATIONAL – THE VOICE OF SHANGRI–LA ‡ (Gov)
🖃 182 Renmin Xi Lu, Kunming, Yunnan 650031, P.R.China.
☎ +86 871 5310211. 🖷 +86 871 5361744.

**E:** admin@ynradio.com
**Webcast:** L
**SW:** See SART for tx information.
**kHz:** 6035

### Winter Schedule 2018/2019

| Chinese | Days | Area | kHz |
|---|---|---|---|
| 2300-1630 | daily | SEA | 6035sha‡ |

| Vietnamese | Days | Area | kHz |
|---|---|---|---|
| 1630-1700 | daily | SEA | 6035sha‡ |

**Key:** ‡ Inactive on SW at time of publication.
**Ann:** Chinese: "Xianggelila zhi sheng"; English: "Yunnan Radio and Television International, The Voice of Shangri-la".
**V:** QSL-letter.
**Notes:** International Service of the provincial Yunnan People's Broadcasting Station, launched on 1 Oct 1986. Identified as "Yunnan People's Broadcasting Station - The Voice of Shangri-La", until early 2018, when it adopted the current name.

### STATE ADMINISTRATION OF RADIO AND TELEVISION (SART) (Tx Operator)
✉ 2 Fuxingmenwai Street, Xicheng District, Beijing 100866, P.R.China.
☎ +86 10 66093114. 🖷 +86 10 86092437.
**W:** www.sapprft.gov.cn
**L.P:** Minister/Dir: Nie Chenxi.
**MW:** [CAH] Changchun (Jilin prov.): 1017kHz 100kW; [DEH] Mingshi (Dehong pref., Yunnan prov.): 900kHz 50kW; [DOF] Dongfang, (Hainan prov.): 603/684kHz 600kW; [HDN] Huadian (Jilin prov.): 963/1323kHz 600kW; [HDU] Guangzhou, Liantang (Huadu district, Guangdong prov.): 1341kHz 300kW; [HEI] Shuangyashan (Heilongjiang prov.): 1323 kHz 200kW; [HNL] Changzhou, Henglin (Jiangsu prov.) 1044kHz 600kW; [KAS] Kashgar (Kashi), Sayibage (Xinjiang Uighur autonomous region): 1422kHz 600kW; [KUN] Kunming, Anning (Yunnan prov.): 1188/1296kHz 300kW; [URU] Ürümqi (Wurumqi), Hutubi (Xinjiang Uighur autonomous region): 1323/1521kHz 500kW; [XUW] Xuanwei (Yunnan prov.): 1080/1269kHz 600kW.
**SW:** [BEI] Beijing, Doudian: 150/500kW; [BJI] Baoji, Qishan (Shaanxi prov.): 150kW; [HUH] Hohhot, Bikeqi (Nei Menggu autonomous region): 4 x 100kW; [JIN] Jinhua, Lanxi (Zhejiang prov.): 2 x 100, 3 x 500kW; [KAS] Kashgar (Kashi), Sayibage (Xinjiang Uighur autonomous region): 2 x 100, 8 x 500kW; [KUN] Kunming, Anning (Yunnan prov.): 4 x 150, 4 x 500kW; [NNN] Nanning (Guangxi Zhuang autonomous region): 2 x 15; 2 x 100kW; [SHA] Kunming, Shalang (Yunnan prov.): 1 x 50kW; [SZG] Shijiazhuang, Nanpozhuan (Hebei prov.): 2 x 500kW; [URU] Ürümqi (Wurumqi), Hutubi (Xinjiang Uighur autonomous region): 9 x 100, 8 x 500kW; [XIA] Xi'an, Xianyang (Shaanxi prov.): 150/500kW; [XUW] Xuanwei (Yunnan prov.) ‡: 4 x 100kW.
**Notes:** SART is an executive branch under the State Council of the People's Republic of China. SART was formed in 2018 as one of the successors to the former State Administration for Press, Publication, Radio, Film and Television (SAPPRFT).

## CUBA (CUB)

### RADIO HABANA CUBA (RHC) (Gov)
✉ Apartado 6240, La Habana 10600, Cuba.
☎ +53 7 8775524. 🖷 +53 7 8776531.
**E:** inforhc@enet.cu **W:** www.radiohc.cu
**Webcast:** L
**L.P:** DG: Tania Hernández Castellanos; Advisor Consultant to DG: Prof. Arnaldo Coro Antich; Head of International Correspondence Dept: Rosario Latifa Fernandez; Chief Eng: Ing. Luis Pruna Amer.
**SW:** Uses txs operated by Radiocuba.
**FM/DAB:** FM: 91.7MHz (Isla de la Juventud); 102.5MHz (La Habana).
**SAT:** Hispasat 30W-4.
**kHz:** 5040, 6000, 6060, 6100, 6165, 9535, 9640, 9720, 11670, 11700, 11760, 11840, 11950, 13700, 13740, 13780, 15140, 15370, 15730

### Winter Schedule 2018/2019

| Arabic | Days | Area | kHz |
|---|---|---|---|
| 1900-1930 | daily | NAm | 15140hab |
| 2130-2200 | daily | Eu | 15370hab |

| Creole | Days | Area | kHz |
|---|---|---|---|
| 0000-0030 | daily | SAm | 15730hab |
| 0100-0130 | daily | Car | 5040hab |
| 1930-2000 | daily | NAm | 15140hab |

| English | Days | Area | kHz |
|---|---|---|---|
| 0000-0100 | daily | CAm | 5040hab |
| 0200-0800 | daily | NAm | 6000hab, 6165hab |
| 0600-0700 | daily | CAm | 5040hab |
| 0600-0800 | daily | NAm | 6060hab, 6100hab |
| 2000-2100 | daily | NAm | 15140hab |
| 2400-0100 | daily | Af | 9720hab |

| Esperanto | Days | Area | kHz |
|---|---|---|---|
| 0800-0830 | ......s | NAm | 6100hab |
| 1600-1630 | ......s | Am | 11760hab |
| 2330-2400 | ......s | SAm | 15730hab |

| French | Days | Area | kHz |
|---|---|---|---|
| 0100-0130 | daily | SAm | 15730hab |
| 0130-0200 | daily | Car | 5040hab |
| 2030-2100 | daily | Eu | 15370hab |
| 2100-2130 | daily | NAm | 15140hab |
| 2300-2330 | daily | Af | 9720hab |
| 2330-2400 | mtwtfs. | SAm | 15730hab |

| Portuguese | Days | Area | kHz |
|---|---|---|---|
| 0030-0100 | daily | SAm | 15730hab |
| 2100-2130 | daily | Eu | 15370hab |
| 2300-2400 | daily | SAm | 11700hab |
| 2330-2400 | daily | Af | 9720hab |

| Spanish | Days | Area | kHz |
|---|---|---|---|
| 0000-0100 | .twtfs. | NAm | 6000hab*, 11950hab* |
| 0000-0500 | daily | SAm | 11670hab |
| 0000-0600 | daily | SAm | 11700hab |
| 0100-0600 | daily | NAm | 6060hab |
| 0200-0600 | daily | CAm | 5040hab |
| 1200-1400 | daily | NAm | 11950hab |
| 1200-1500 | daily | NAm | 6000hab |
| 1200-1500 | daily | SAm | 13780hab |
| 1200-1600 | daily | Car | 9640hab |
| 1200-1600 | daily | SAm | 15140hab |
| 1200-1600 | daily | CAm | 9535hab |
| 1200-1600 | daily | Am | 11760hab |
| 1400-1600 | daily | NAm | 13700hab |
| 1600-1630 | mtwtfs. | Am | 11760hab |
| 1600-1900 | daily | NAm | 15140hab |
| 1630-1900 | daily | Am | 11760hab |
| 2200-0300 | daily | Am | 11760hab |
| 2200-0500 | daily | Car | 9640hab |
| 2200-0500 | daily | SAm | 13740hab |
| 2200-0600 | daily | CAm | 9535hab |
| 2200-0600 | daily | SAm | 11840hab |
| 2200-2400 | daily | Eu | 15370hab |
| 2200-2400 | daily | CAm | 5040hab |

**Key:** * Mesa Redonda TV talkshow audio (teleSUR).
**Ann:** English: "This is Radio Havana Cuba".
**V:** QSL-card and letter. (Email to: radiohc@enet.cu)
**Notes:** Radio Habana Cuba is the External Sce of the state-owned Instituto Cubano de Radio y Television (ICRT). Frequencies and schedule are variable.

### EMPRESA DE RADIOCOMUNICACIÓN Y DIFUSIÓN DE CUBA (RADIOCUBA) (Tx Operator)
✉ Calle Habana No 406, e/ Obispo y Obrapía, Habana Vieja, La Habana 10100, Cuba.
☎ +53 7 8607181. 🖷 +53 7 8603107.
**E:** atencion.poblacion@radiocuba.cu **W:** www.radiocuba.cu
**L.P:** DG: Justo Moreno García.
**SW:** La Habana, three sites: [BEJ] Bejucal, Casualidad 3 x 50, 1 x 100kW; [HAB] Bauta, Corralillo: 1 x 50, 6 x 100kW; [QVC] Quivicán, San Felipe (Transmitting centre "Titán"): 5 x 250kW.
**Notes:** Radiocuba, a state operated company that forms part of the Ministry of Information and Communications, is the national transmitter network operator.

## CYPRUS (CYP)

### FG RADIO
✉ Based in Nicosia, Cyprus.
☎ +357 22007961.
**E:** broadcast@cytanet.com.cy
✉ P.O.Box 30582, 5344 Famagusta, Cyprus. (Famagusta Gazette)
**L.P:** Producer: Nathan Morley.
**kHz:** 5950, 9955

## Winter Schedule 2018/2019

| English | Days | Area | kHz |
|---|---|---|---|
| 0245-0300 | m...... | LAm | 9955rmi |
| 0245-0300 | ..w.... | LAm | 9955rmi |
| 1015-1030 | ....f.. | NAm | 5950rmi |
| 1330-1345 | ..w.... | NAm | 5950rmi |
| 1345-1400 | .t..... | NAm | 5950rmi |
| 1400-1415 | ..w.... | NAm | 5950rmi |
| 1430-1445 | ..w.... | LAm | 9955rmi |
| 1445-1500 | .t..... | NAm | 5950rmi |
| 1445-1500 | .t..... | LAm | 9955rmi |
| 2100-2115 | ..w.... | NAm | 5950rmi |
| 2245-2300 | ...t... | LAm | 9955rmi |

**IS:** Instrumental Waltz.
**Notes:** Weekly prgr with Europe related news, linked with the (now discontinued) online news portal "Famagusta Gazette".

### BBC EAST MEDITERRANEAN RELAY STATION
✉ P.O. Box 54912, 3729 Limassol, Cyprus.
☎ +357 24332511. 🖷 +357 24332595.
**LP:** Engineering Mgr: Andreas Themistocleous.
**MW:** [ZAK] Zakaki, Lady's Mile (Akrotiri Sovereign Base Area): 639/720kHz 500kW.
**V:** QSL-card. (For direct report)
**Notes:** Owned by the BBC and operated by Encompass Digital Media Services Ltd (see under United Kingdom).

### FMM RELAY STATION
✉ Cape Gkreko, Cyprus.
☎ +357 23831344. 🖷 +357 23831344.
**E:** psardos@aol.com
**LP:** Technical Manager: Philippe Sardos.
**MW:** [CGR] Cape Gkreko: 990kHz 600kW (leased by USAGM (USA)), 1233kHz 1200kW (run at 600kW).
**V:** QSL-letter. (for relayed prgrs)
**Notes:** Transmitting station owned by the French External Services holding company France Médias Monde (FMM), formerly Audiovisuel extérieur de la France (AEF).

## CZECHIA (CZE)

### RADIO PRAGUE (Pub)
✉ Vinohradská 12, 120 99 Praha 2, Czechia.
☎ +420 221552933. 🖷 +420 221552903.
**E:** cr@radio.cz **W:** www.radio.cz
**Webcast:** D/L/P. (Webcast/Satellite languages: Czech, English, French, German, Russian)
**LP:** Editor-in-Chief: Miroslav Krupicka.
**SW:** Leases airtime on WRMI (See under USA).
**SAT:** Astra 3B.
**kHz:** 738, 5010, 5850, 5950, 7780, 9395, 9955

### Winter Schedule 2018/2019

| English | Days | Area | kHz |
|---|---|---|---|
| 0100-0130 | daily | NAm | 5950rmi# |
| 0200-0230 | daily | NAm,Eu | 7780rmi |
| 0300-0330 | daily | NAm | 5950rmi, 9395rmi |
| 0400-0430 | m.....s | LAm | 9955rmi |
| 0930-1000 | daily | NAm | 5950rmi# |
| 1300-1330 | mtwtfs. | LAm | 9955rmi |
| 1530-1600 | daily | NAm | 5950rmi, 5950rmi# |
| 1730-1800 | mtwtf.. | NAm | 5950rmi, 5950rmi# |
| 2330-0000 | ....f.. | NAm | 5850rmi |
| **Russian** | **Days** | **Area** | **kHz** |
| 0000-0030 | ...f... | RUS | 738msk~ |
| 0230-0300 | .....s. | RUS | 738msk~ |
| 0500-0530 | .....s. | RUS | 738msk~ |
| 0700-0730 | ...t... | RUS | 738msk~ |
| 1000-1030 | ...f... | RUS | 738msk~ |
| 1300-1330 | ...t... | RUS | 738msk~ |
| 1530-1600 | .....s. | RUS | 738msk~ |
| 1930-2000 | ..w.... | RUS | 738msk~ |
| 2100-2130 | .....s. | RUS | 738msk~ |
| 2230-2300 | ...t... | RUS | 738msk~ |

| Spanish | Days | Area | kHz |
|---|---|---|---|
| 0300-0330 | daily | LAm | 9955rmi |
| 1130-1200 | daily | CAm | 5010rmi |

**Key:** ~ Relayed via Vsemirnaya radioset (Moscow, Russia); # Unoffical WRN relay via WRMI.
**Ann:** English: "You're listening to Radio Prague, the international service of Czech Radio".
**V:** QSL-card.
**Notes:** R. Prague (Český Rozhlas 7 - R. Praha) is the Int. Sce of the public service broadcaster Ceský Rozhlas. The transmissions on 738kHz (via the local stn Vsemirnaya radioset in Moscow) are part of the Encompass Digital Media (UK) Russian language Satellite/Internet feed (branded "WRN"), and are intended for listeners in Moscow and Moscow region.

## DENMARK (DNK)

### RADIO OZ–VIOLA
✉ Engparken 35, DK-3400 Hillerød, Denmark.
**E:** jansteendk@hotmail.com **W:** www.ozviola.dk
**LP:** Project Coordinator: Jan Sørensen.
**SW:** [HIL] Hillerød: 1 x 0.15kW.
**kHz:** 5800

### Winter Schedule 2018/2019

| English | Days | Area | kHz |
|---|---|---|---|
| 1300-1600 | .....ss | Eu | 5800hil† |

**Key:** † Irregular.

### WORLD MUSIC RADIO (WMR)
✉ P.O.Box 112, DK-8960 Randers SØ, Denmark.
**E:** hartvig@wmr.dk **W:** wmr.dk
**Webcast:** L
**LP:** Dir: Stig Hartvig Nielsen.
**MW:** [CPH] Copenhagen 927kHz 0.3kW.
**SW:** [RND] Randers: 1 x 0.1, 1 x 0.3kW.
**kHz:** 5840

### Winter Schedule 2018/2019

| English | Days | Area | kHz |
|---|---|---|---|
| 0000-2400 | daily | Eu | 5840rnd |

**V:** eQSL-card.
**Notes:** Produced by Hartvig Media (See National R. section). Initially launched as a pirate radio station in 1967, later as a licensed station (on air until 2005).

## DJIBOUTI (DJI)

### USAGM DJIBOUTI TRANSMITTING STATION
✉ Radiodiffusion Télévision de Djibouti, PK 12, Djibouti.
**MW:** [DJI] Djibouti, Dorale: 1431kHz 600kW.
**Notes:** Formally a transmitting centre of the state broadcaster Radiodiffusion Télévision de Djibouti (RTD). The USAGM operations are managed by the USAGM Germany Transmitting Station.

## ECUADOR (EQA)

### VOZANDES MEDIA (Rlg)
✉ Casilla 17-17-691, Quito, Ecuador.
☎ +593 2 5101770.
**E:** vozandes@gmail.com; hcjb@andenstimme.org
**W:** andenstimme.org (in German)
✉ Pasaje Jacinto de la Cuava Oe4-33 y Av. Brasil, Quito, Ecuador.
☎ +593 2 2278831.
**E:** kichwa@hcjb.org (HCJB Quito Qechua section)
**W:** www.facebook.com/hcjbkichwa (HCJB Quito Qechua section)
**LP:** Chmn: Horst Rosiak.
**SW:** [QUI] Quito, Mount Pichincha 1 x 1kW.
**kHz:** 6050

### Winter Schedule 2018/2019

| Cha palaa | Days | Area | kHz |
|---|---|---|---|
| 2130-2200 | mtwtf.. | EQA | 6050qui |
| **Cofan** | **Days** | **Area** | **kHz** |
| 0000-0030 | daily | EQA,CLM | 6050qui |
| **Quechua** | **Days** | **Area** | **kHz** |
| 0100-0230 | .....ss | EQA,PRU | 6050qui |
| 0130-0230 | mtwtf.. | EQA,PRU | 6050qui |
| 0925-1100 | daily | EQA,PRU | 6050qui |

| Shuar | Days | Area | kHz |
|---|---|---|---|
| 2330-2400 | mtwtf.. | EQA,PRU | 6050qui |

| Spanish | Days | Area | kHz |
|---|---|---|---|
| 0100-0130 | mtwtf.. | EQA,CLM,PRU | 6050qui* |
| 1100-1400 | daily | EQA,CLM,PRU | 6050qui* |
| 2100-2130 | mtwtf.. | EQA,CLM,PRU | 6050qui* |
| 2100-2400 | .....ss | EQA,CLM,PRU | 6050qui* |

| Waorani | Days | Area | kHz |
|---|---|---|---|
| 0030-0100 | daily | EQA | 6050qui |

**Key:** * Relay HCJB FM (Quito).
**V:** QSL-card. Rp (1 IRC). Online rpt form available.
**Notes:** The voluntary organisation Asociación Vozandes Media (AVM) was founded in 2009 by staff of the former, Quito-based HCJB German language service, and took over the operation of the former HCJB SW tx site in Quito. The SW service (labeled "Indianerradio" in German) is primarily targeting the indigenous population in Ecuador (as well as in stretches of neighbouring Columbia & Peru). AVM provides the technical and administrative support for these prgrs that are produced by local, 3rd-party partners (in part in cooperation with Radio HCJB, Quito). The SW service also includes some prgrs in Spanish (mostly a rel. Of HCJB FM, Quito). AVM is not part of the HCJB organisation, but is closely cooperating with Radio HCJB - La Voz des los Andes (Ecuador) - a part of the global media ministry Reach Beyond (USA).

## EGYPT (EGY)

### RADIO CAIRO (Gov)
📧 P.O. Box 1186, 11511 Cairo, Egypt.
☎ +20 2 25789461. 📠 +20 2 25789461.
**E:** freqmeg@yahoo.com **W:** www.egradio.eg; dotnet.ertu.org
**Webcast:** D/L (www.egradio.eg)
**LP:** (NMA) Pres: Hussein Zein; Secretary Gen: Amgad Baleigh.
**MW:** [BTR] Batrah: 621kHz 1000kW; [ELA] El Arish: 1008kHz 100kW.
**SW:** [ABS] Abis: 8 x 250, 1 x 500kW; [ABZ] Abu Zaabal: 13 x 100, 1 x 250, 4 x 500kW.
**FM/DAB:** FM: See National Radio section (NMA "European Programme" tx network.)
**kHz:** 1008, 9420, 9480, 9540, 9570, 9590, 9660, 9720, 9880, 9900, 9940, 11880, 12065, 15285, 15290, 15310, 15450, 15630

#### Winter Schedule 2018/2019

| Afar | Days | Area | kHz |
|---|---|---|---|
| 1600-1700 | daily | EAf | 15450abz† |

| Albanian | Days | Area | kHz |
|---|---|---|---|
| 1500-1600 | daily | Eu | 11880abs† |

| Amharic | Days | Area | kHz |
|---|---|---|---|
| 1730-1900 | daily | EAf | 15285abz† |

| Arabic | Days | Area | kHz |
|---|---|---|---|
| 0000-2400 | m.w.f.. | ERI | 9720btr |
| 0600-1500 | daily | ISR | 1008ela |
| 2330-0045 | daily | SAm | 9660abs† |

| Dari | Days | Area | kHz |
|---|---|---|---|
| 1300-1400 | daily | WAs | 15630abs† |

| English | Days | Area | kHz |
|---|---|---|---|
| 1600-1640 | daily | ISR | 1008ela |
| 1900-2030 | daily | WAf | 15290abz† |
| 2115-2245 | daily | Eu | 9900abs† |

| French | Days | Area | kHz |
|---|---|---|---|
| 1640-1700 | daily | ISR | 1008ela |
| 2000-2115 | daily | Eu | 9900abs† |

| German | Days | Area | kHz |
|---|---|---|---|
| 1900-2000 | daily | Eu | 9570abs† |

| Hausa | Days | Area | kHz |
|---|---|---|---|
| 1800-2100 | daily | WAf | 15310abs† |

| Hebrew | Days | Area | kHz |
|---|---|---|---|
| 1700-2200 | daily | ISR | 1008ela |

| Italian | Days | Area | kHz |
|---|---|---|---|
| 1800-1900 | daily | Eu | 9540abs† |

| Pashto | Days | Area | kHz |
|---|---|---|---|
| 1400-1600 | daily | WAs | 12065abs† |

| Portuguese | Days | Area | kHz |
|---|---|---|---|
| 2215-2330 | daily | SAm | 9880abs† |

| Russian | Days | Area | kHz |
|---|---|---|---|
| 1500-1600 | daily | ISR | 1008ela |
| 1900-2000 | daily | Eu | 9590abs† |

| Somali | Days | Area | kHz |
|---|---|---|---|
| 1700-1730 | daily | EAf | 15285abz† |

| Spanish | Days | Area | kHz |
|---|---|---|---|
| 0045-0200 | daily | SAm | 9420abs† |

| Swahili | Days | Area | kHz |
|---|---|---|---|
| 0400-0600 | daily | EAf,CAf | 9480abs† |
| 1600-1800 | daily | EAf | 15310abs† |

| Turkish | Days | Area | kHz |
|---|---|---|---|
| 1700-1900 | daily | ME | 9940abs† |

**Key:** † Irregular; * Voice of Arabs prgr.
**Ann:** English: "You are tuned to Radio Cairo"; Arabic: "Sowt il-Arab min al-Qahira", "Sowt-il Afrikiy min al-Qahira".
**V:** QSL-card. (Send to: P.O. Box 566, 11511 Cairo, Egypt). Email rpt to freqmeg@yahoo.com
**Notes:** Radio Cairo is the External Sce of the National Media Authority (NMA) (previously known as "Egyptian Radio & TV Union (ERTU)").

## ESTONIA (EST)

### TARTU PERERAADIO (Rlg)
📧 See National Radio section.
**Webcast:** D/L (radioeli.ru)
**MW:** [TTU] Tartu, Kavastu: 1035kHz 200kW.
**Notes:** Tartu Pereraadio is an Estonian evangelical broadcaster. Its transmissions include TWR broadcasts, see TWR Europe schedule (under Austria).

## ESWATINI (Formerly SWAZILAND) (SWZ)

### TWR RELAY STATION
📧 P.O. Box 64, Manzini, Eswatini.
☎ +268 25052781. 📠 +268 25055333.
**LP:** Chief Engineer (interim): Klaus Schiller.
**MW:** [MAN] Manzini, Mpangela Ranch: 1170kHz 100kW.
**SW:** [MAN] Manzini, Mpangela Ranch: 3 x 100kW.
**Ann:** English: "This is Trans World Radio, Eswatini".
**V:** eQSL-card.
**Notes:** Owned by TWR. For corporate details, see under USA. For schedule, see TWR Africa, under South Africa.

## ETHIOPIA (ETH)

### ETHIOPIAN BROADCASTING CORPORATION (EBC) (RADIO ETHIOPIA) (Pub)
📧 P.O. Box 654, Addis Ababa, Ethiopia.
☎ +251 11 5524079. 📠 +251 11 5512686.
**E:** ebc@ebc.et **W:** www.ebc.et
**LP:** Head, Foreign Languages Dept: Melesse Edea Beyi.
**SW:** [GJW] Geja: 3 x 100kW (Tx status uncertain); new 50kW & 150kW txs were installed 2007-2012.
**kHz:** 7237

#### Winter Schedule 2018/2019

| Afar | Days | Area | kHz |
|---|---|---|---|
| 1300-1400 | daily | EAf | 7237gjw±,† |

| Arabic | Days | Area | kHz |
|---|---|---|---|
| 1400-1500 | daily | EAf | 7237gjw±,† |

| Somali | Days | Area | kHz |
|---|---|---|---|
| 1200-1300 | daily | EAf | 7237gjw±,† |

**Key:** ± Variable frequency; † Irregular.
**Ann:** English: "This is the External Service of Radio Ethiopia".
**V:** QSL-card.
**Notes:** External Sce of the national public service broadcaster Ethiopian Broadcasting Corporation (EBC).

## FINLAND (FIN)

### SCANDINAVIAN WEEKEND RADIO (SWR)
📧 Hollitie 1025, FI-34930 Liedenpohja, Finland.
☎ +358 3 4755776. (studio, during broadcast only)
**E:** info@swradio.net **W:** www.swradio.net
**Webcast:** L (www.radioverkko.fi, 0800-2200 only)
**LP:** Chief Editor: Esa Saunamäki; QSL Mgr: Tapani Häkkinen.
**MW:** [VIR] Virrat, Liedenpohja: 1602kHz 0.4kW.
**SW:** [VIR] Virrat, Liedenpohja: 2 x 0.1kW.
**FM/DAB:** FM: 94.9MHz (Virrat, Liedenpohja, 0.5kW).

kHz: *1602, 5980, 6170, 11690, 11720*

### Winter Schedule 2018/2019

| English/Finnish | Days | Area | kHz |
|---|---|---|---|
| 0000-0600 | .....s. | Eu | 6170vir* |
| 0000-0800 | .....s. | Eu | 11690vir* |
| 0000-2200 | .....s. | Eu | 1602vir* |
| 0600-0900 | .....s. | Eu | 5980vir* |
| 0800-1400 | .....s. | Eu | 11720vir* |
| 0900-1500 | .....s. | Eu | 6170vir* |
| 1400-1700 | .....s. | Eu | 11690vir* |
| 1500-1900 | .....s. | Eu | 5980vir* |
| 1700-1900 | .....s. | Eu | 11720vir* |
| 1900-2200 | .....s. | Eu | 6170vir*, 11690vir* |
| 2200-2300 | ....f.. | Eu | 11720vir* |
| 2200-2400 | ....f.. | Eu | 1602vir*, 6170vir* |
| 2300-2400 | ....f.. | Eu | 11690vir* |

**Key:** * 1st Sat (local time) of each month.
**Ann:** English: "You are listening to Scandinavian Weekend Radio".
**V:** QSL-card (for rpt sent by mail; rpt form downloadable from website) Rp (2 IRCs/EUR/USD); eQSL-card (for online rpt via website).
**Notes:** On air since 1 July 2000. Leisure time operation by a group of SW enthusiasts and organised with the amateur radio club 'Vaihtoehtoisen radiotoiminnan tukiyhdistys ry' (callsign: OH6SWR). The stn is run as a series of temporary licences for 24h on the first Sat Local Time (Fri 2200-Sat 2200 UTC) for three consecutive months. No transmissions in Jan, May, Sep as required by law, before the club is entitled to a new series of licences.

## FRANCE (F)

### MONTE CARLO DOUALIYA (Pub)
✉ 80 rue Camille Desmoulins, F-92130 Issy-les-Moulineaux, France.
☎ +33 184228484.
**E:** Via website. **W:** www.mc-douealiya.com
**Webcast:** D/L/P
**L.P:** Dir: Souad El Tayeb.
**MW:** via FMM transmitting station Cape Gkreco, Cyprus.
**FM/DAB:** FM: Txs in Bahrain, Djibouti, Iraq, Jordan, Kuwait, Lebanon, Mauritania, Palestinian Territories and Qatar. (See National Radio section)
**SAT:** Astra 1N, Badr 4/6, Eutelsat 5WA/7B, Nilesat 201.
**kHz:** *1233*

### Winter Schedule 2018/2019

| Arabic | Days | Area | kHz |
|---|---|---|---|
| 0330-2020 | daily | NAf,ME | 1233cgr |

**Ann:** Arabic: "Monte Carlo Doualiya".
**V:** QSL-card.
**Notes:** Produced under the umbrella of the External Services holding France Médias Monde (FMM), formerly Audiovisuel extérieur de la France (AEF).

### RADIO FRANCE INTERNATIONALE (RFI) (Pub)
✉ 80 rue Camille Desmoulins, F-92130 Issy-les-Moulineaux, France.
☎ +33 184228484.
**E:** english.service@rfi.fr **W:** www.rfi.fr
**Webcast:** L/P
✉ B.P. 9516, F-75016 Paris Cedex 16, France.
**L.P:** Pres/DG (FMM): Marie-Christine Saragosse; Dir (RFI): Victor Rocaries.
**SW:** Leased from TDF & third-party foreign relays.
**SAT:** Anik F1R/F2/F3, AsiaSat 7, Astra 1N, Badr 4/6, Eutelsat 5WA/7A/7B/9BA/16A/36B/Hot Bird 13C, Galaxy 3C-Intelsat 30, Intelsat 11/18/20/903, Nimiq 6, SES 5/6/7, Superbird C2.
**kHz:** *3965, 5925, 5950, 6040, 7205, 7245, 7380, 7390, 9580, 9635, 9650, 9660, 9665, 9725, 9790, 9805, 9810, 11700, 11760, 11765, 11790, 11995, 13695, 13740, 15275, 15300, 15455, 17620, 17660, 17815, 17850, 21580, 21690*

### Winter Schedule 2018/2019

| English | Days | Area | kHz |
|---|---|---|---|
| 0000-0100 | daily | NAm | 5950rmi# |
| 0600-0700 | daily | NAm | 5950rmi# |
| 1000-1100 | daily | NAm | 5950rmi# |
| 1600-1700 | daily | NAm | 5950rmi# |
| **French** | **Days** | **Area** | **kHz** |
| 0000-2400 | daily | Eu | 3965iss+ |

| French | Days | Area | kHz |
|---|---|---|---|
| 0400-0600 | daily | CAf | 9790iss |
| 0400-0600 | daily | EAf,CAf | 7390iss |
| 0500-0600 | daily | CAf | 6040iss |
| 0600-0700 | daily | NAf,WAf | 5925iss*, 7390iss*, 9790iss** |
| 0600-0800 | daily | WAf,CAf | 11700iss |
| 0600-0900 | daily | WAf,CAf | 13695iss |
| 0700-0800 | daily | NAf,WAf | 9790iss |
| 0700-0900 | daily | Af | 15300iss |
| 0800-0900 | daily | CAf | 17850iss, 21580iss |
| 1200-1300 | daily | WAf,CAf | 17660iss |
| 1200-1300 | daily | CAf | 21580iss, 21690mdc |
| 1200-1300 | daily | NAf,WAf | 17620iss |
| 1700-1800 | daily | CAf | 9660iss*, 13740iss**, 15300iss |
| 1700-1800 | daily | WAf,CAf | 11995iss, 13740iss |
| 1800-1900 | daily | NAf,WAf | 9810iss |
| 1800-1900 | daily | WAf,CAf | 9725iss*, 11765iss*, 11995iss**, 15300iss** |
| 1900-2000 | daily | WAf,CAf | 7245iss, 9580iss, 9635iss, 11995iss |
| 2000-2200 | daily | NAf,WAf | 7205iss, 9790iss |
| **Hausa** | **Days** | **Area** | **kHz** |
| 0600-0630 | daily | WAf,CAf | 7295iss*, 9805iss, 11995iss** |
| 0700-0730 | daily | WAf,CAf | 11760iss, 13740iss |
| 1600-1700 | daily | WAf,CAf | 15300iss |
| 2000-2030 | daily | WAf,CAf | 7380iss |
| **Mandinka** | **Days** | **Area** | **kHz** |
| 0800-0830 | mtwtf.. | WAf | 15455iss |
| 1200-1230 | mtwtf.. | WAf | 15275iss**, 17815iss** |
| **Swahili** | **Days** | **Area** | **kHz** |
| 0430-0500 | daily | EAf,CAf | 9665mdc |
| 0530-0600 | daily | EAf,CAf | 11790mdc |
| 1500-1600 | daily | EAf,CAf | 21690iss |
| **Vietnamese** | **Days** | **Area** | **kHz** |
| 1300-1400 | ......s | SEA | 9650pao |

**Key:** + DRM; * Dec-Jan; ** Feb-Mar; # Unoffical WRN relay via WRMI.
**Ann:** French: "Ici Paris, Radio France Internationale".
**V:** QSL-card.
**Notes:** RFI is produced under the umbrella of the External Services holding France Médias Monde (FMM), formerly Audiovisuel extérieur de la France (AEF). For FMM programming in Arabic, see Monte Carlo Doualiya.

### TDF S.A.S. (Tx Operator)
✉ 106 Avenue Marx Dormoy, 92541 Montrouge Cedex, France.
☎ +33 149651000.
**W:** www.tdf.fr; www.tdf-group.com
**L.P:** (TDF Group) Pres: Olivier Huart; DG: Benoit Mérel.
**SW:** [ISS] Issoudun: 17 x 500kW.
**V:** QSL-card. (For RFI and other broadcaster relays via ISS)
**Notes:** TDF S.A.S., part of the TDF group, is the national French transmitter network operator.

## GERMANY (D)

### DEUTSCHER WETTERDIENST (DWD) (Gov)
✉ DWD Seeschifffahrtsberatung, Bernhard-Nocht-Str. 26, D-20359 Hamburg, Germany.
☎ +49 69 80626201. 📠 +49 69 80626193.
**E:** seeschifffahrt@dwd.de **W:** www.dwd.de
✉ Transmitter site: DWD Wetterfunkstelle, Haidkamp 10, D-25421 Pinneberg, Germany.
**L.P:** Pres: Prof. Dr. Gerhard Adrian.
**SW:** [PIN] Pinneberg: 2 x 10kW.
**kHz:** *5905, 6180*

### Winter Schedule 2018/2019

| German | Days | Area | kHz |
|---|---|---|---|
| 0600-0630 | daily | BaS,NoS | 5905pin, 6180pin |
| 1200-1230 | daily | BaS,NoS | 5905pin, 6180pin |
| 1600-1630 | daily | Med | 5905pin, 6180pin |
| 2000-2030 | daily | BaS,NoS,Med | 5905pin, 6180pin |

**V:** QSL-card.
**Notes:** Shipping forecasts for the Baltic & North Sea, produced by DWD (Germany's National Meteorological Service).

## DEUTSCHE WELLE (DW) (Pub)
✉ Kurt-Schumacher-Str. 3, D-53113 Bonn, Germany.
☎ +49 228 4290. 🖷 +49 228 4293000.
**E:** info@dw.com **W:** www.dw.com
**Webcast:** D/L/P. Webcast-only languages (some of which may also be broadcast on local FM affiliate stns): Arabic, Bengali, Chinese, Dari, Croatian, Greek, Pashto, Persian, Portuguese, Spanish, Turkish, Urdu.
✉ Voltastr. 6, D-13355 Berlin.
☎ +49 30 46460.
**L.P:** DG: Peter Limbourg; PD: Gerda Meuer; MD, Distribution, Marketing and Technology: Guido Baumhauer; Dir, Int Relations: Klaus Bergmann.
**SAT:** Badr 4, Eutelsat 5WA/7B/Hot Bird 13B, Intelsat 20, Nilesat 201, SES 3/5.
**kHz:** 5950, 7220, 9720, 9785, 9830, 11720, 11980, 13780, 15195, 15200, 15275, 15320, 17710, 17800

### Winter Schedule 2018/2019

| Amharic | Days | Area | kHz |
|---|---|---|---|
| 1600-1700 | daily | ETH | 13780dha, 15275iss |
| **Dari** | **Days** | **Area** | **kHz** |
| 1330-1400 | daily | AFG | 9720dha, 11720dha |
| **English** | **Days** | **Area** | **kHz** |
| 0700-0800 | daily | NAm | 5950rmi# |
| 1100-1200 | daily | NAm | 5950rmi# |
| 2200-2300 | daily | NAm | 5950rmi# |
| **Hausa** | **Days** | **Area** | **kHz** |
| 0630-0700 | daily | WAf | 7220sao, 9830iss, 15200mey |
| 1300-1400 | daily | WAf | 9830sao, 11980sao, 17800iss |
| 1425-1630 | .....s. | WAf | 15195iss*, 15320iss* |
| 1800-1900 | daily | WAf | 9785iss, 9830sao, 15200mey |
| **Pashto** | **Days** | **Area** | **kHz** |
| 1400-1430 | daily | AFG | 9720dha, 11720dha |
| **Swahili** | **Days** | **Area** | **kHz** |
| 1000-1100 | daily | EAf | 15275mdc, 17710mey |

**Key:** * Live coverage of German football league (Bundesliga) matches; # Unofficial WRN relay via WRMI.
**V:** QSL-card. (Rpt to DW Customer Service; Email rpt to tb@dw.com)
**Notes:** Deutsche Welle is a public service External broadcaster.

## EVANGELISCHE MISSIONS–GEMEINDEN (Rlg)
✉ Lauenburger Strasse 12, D-51709 Marienheide, Germany.
☎ +49 2264 3625.
**E:** info@missionsbote.de **W:** www.missionsbote.de
**Webcast:** D
**L.P:** Head of missionary society: Andreas Herzog.
**kHz:** 6055

### Winter Schedule 2018/2019

| German | Days | Area | kHz |
|---|---|---|---|
| 1130-1200 | .....ss | Eu | 6055nau |

**V:** QSL-card.
**Notes:** Produced by Missionswerk Evangelische Missions-Gemeinden in Deutschland e.V.

## MISSIONSWERK FRIEDENSSTIMME (Rlg)
✉ Gimborner Str. 20, D-51709 Marienheide, Germany.
☎ +49 2261 60170. 🖷 +49 2261 60173.
**E:** info@friedensstimme.com **W:** www.friedensstimme.com
**kHz:** 6060, 13710

### Winter Schedule 2018/2019

| Russian | Days | Area | kHz |
|---|---|---|---|
| 1200-1230 | .....s. | RUS | 13710nau |
| 1600-1630 | .....s. | RUS | 6060nau |

**V:** QSL-card.
**Notes:** Produced by Missionswerk Friedensstimme der Vereinigung der Evangeliums-Christen-Baptisten e.V.

## RADIO HCJB DEUTSCHLAND (Rlg)
✉ Postfach 8025, D-32736 Detmold, Germany.
☎ +49 5232 7980816. 🖷 +49 30 61090010376.

**E:** info@hcjb.de **W:** www.hcjb.de
**Webcast:** L
**L.P:** Prgr Mgr: Marco Schaa.
**SW:** [WNM] Weenermoor: 2 x 1.5, 1 x 3kW.
**SAT:** Astra 1N.
**kHz:** 3995, 5920, 7365

### Winter Schedule 2018/2019

| English | Days | Area | kHz |
|---|---|---|---|
| 2300-0400 | daily | CEu,WEu | 3995wnm* |
| **German** | **Days** | **Area** | **kHz** |
| 0500-2300 | daily | D,CEu | 3995wnm** |
| 0700-2300 | daily | D,CEu | 5920wnm** |
| 1700-2300 | daily | D,CEu | 7365wnm** |
| **Russian** | **Days** | **Area** | **kHz** |
| 0400-0500 | daily | D,CEu | 3995wnm***, 5920wnm*** |

**Key:** * Relay of LifeFM (Ireland); ** Incl. segment in Low German 1700-1730 (repeated 2000-2030) produced by SW-Radio; *** Segment provided by SW-Radio (various producers, including Radio Studio "Otkroveniye", Russia).
**V:** QSL-card.
**Notes:** Run by Arbeitsgemeinschaft Radio HCJB e.V., a partner organisation of Vozandes Media (Ecuador) and the Reach Beyond media ministry of World Radio Missionary Fellowship, Inc. (USA). Most of the The 24/7 programming is produced by various small religious German prgr producers, e.g. Lutherische Stunde, Missionswerk Heuckelbach, SW-Radio. At night, the stn relays LifeFM (Cork, Ireland) in English. The schedule includes prgrs in Low German and Russian for re-immigrated mennonites of German origin from Russia and Central Asia. The latest detailed schedule can be found on the stn's website. While the satellite&internet feed is aimed at a general audience, the SW txs (installed on private land) are owned and operated by a group of SW enthusiasts and are primarily targeting listeners in the DX/SWL community.

## CHANNEL 292
✉ Eja 2, D-85276 Pfaffenhofen, Germany.
☎ +49 8441 4569988.
**E:** info@channel292.de **W:** www.channel292.de
**L.P:** Project coordinator/CEO (Intermedicom GmbH): Rainer Ebeling (DB8QC).
**SW:** [ROB] Rohrbach, Eja: 2 x 10kW.
**kHz:** 6070, 7440

### Winter Schedule 2018/2019

| German/Various | Days | Area | kHz |
|---|---|---|---|
| 0000-2400 | daily | Eu | 6070rob† |
| 0400-2400 | daily | Eu | 7440rob† |

**Key:** † Irregular (flexible) schedule, depending on airtime bookings (latest schedule with relay details: see www.channel292.de/schedule-for-bookings); on 7440kHz: currently only test transmissions.
**Ann:** English: "Radio Channel 2-9-2".
**V:** eQSL-card. For direct rpts to relayed prgrs: see www.channel292.de/stations-contact-data
**Notes:** Channel 292 (initially launched as R. 6150 in 2012, renamed in 2013) is a leisure time operation, run by a group of SW enthusiasts. Formally licensed to Intermedicom GmbH. The tx is installed on private land. Airtime is leased to third-party prgr producers. Schedule is variable (dependent on airtime bookings). Vacant tr hrs may be filled with rebroadcasts of vintage radio shows from the era of offshore radio.

## DP07 SEEWETTERDIENST ‡
✉ Estedeich 84, D-21129 Hamburg, Germany.
☎ +49 40 23855780. 🖷 +49 40 74134242.
**E:** info@dp07.com **W:** www.dp07.com/unser-service/kurzwellen-funkbetrieb.html
**L.P:** Company owner: Reiner Dietzel.
**SW:** Leases airtime via Shortwave Service.
**Key:** ‡ Inactive during winter seasons.
**V:** QSL-card.
**Notes:** Maritime weather forecasts for Baltic & North Sea, produced by the company Reiner Horst Dietzel - DP07 Seefunk. On the air 1 May - 30 Sep only, during the leisure time boating season.

## EUROPA 24
✉ c/o Interessengemeinschaft Hochfrequenztechnik e.V., Johann-Strauß-Str. 22, D-45711 Datteln, Germany.
☎ +49 2363 731582.

**E:** europa24onshortwave@yahoo.com **W:** radio-marabu.de/word-press/tag/europa-24
✉ Postfach 1166, D-49187 Beim, Germany. (Radio Marabu)
☎ +49 5406 899484. 🖷 +49 5406 899485.
**E:** info@radiomarabu.de **W:** radio-marabu.de
**L.P:** Prgr Coordinator: Bernd Feyock (DG2YID).
**SW:** [DAT] Datteln 1 x 0.25kW.
**kHz:** *6150*

### Winter Schedule 2018/2019

| German | Days | Area | kHz |
|---|---|---|---|
| 0700-1900 | daily | D,CEu | 6150dat* |

**Key:** * Relay of R. Marabu (www.radio-marabu.de)
**Ann:** Dutch: "Dit is Europa 24 (vierentwintig)"; English: "This is Europe 24"; German: "Hier ist Europa 24 (vierundzwanzig)".
**V:** eQSL-card.
**Notes:** On the air since 2014. Leisure time operation by a group of SW enthusiasts (licensed to the registered voluntary association "Interessengemeinschaft Hochfrequenztechnik e.V."). The tx is installed in a residential house. The prgrs consist of a full-time relay of the German Internet radio station Radio Marabu.

## HAMBURGER LOKALRADIO
✉ c/o Kulturzentrum LOLA, Lohbrügger Landstrasse 8, D-21031 Hamburg, Germany.
☎ +49 40 72692422. 🖷 +49 40 72692423.
**E:** redaktion@hamburger-lokalradio.de **W:** www.hhlr.de; www.hamburger-lokalradio.net
✉ Max-Eichholz-Ring 18, D-21031 Hamburg, Germany (Editorial Office).
☎ +49 40 7382417. 🖷 +49 40 7382417.
**L.P:** Editor-in-Chief: Michael Kittner.
**SW:** Via txs of MV Baltic Radio (airtime lease).
**FM/DAB:** FM: Unrelated to SW: time-shared via 96.0MHz (Hamburg, 0.1kW); DAB: 24h via DAB block 11C (Hamburg, 4kW).
**kHz:** *6190, 7265, 9485*

### Winter Schedule 2018/2019

| English | Days | Area | kHz |
|---|---|---|---|
| 0700-0800 | .....s. | CEu,WEu | 6190goh* |
| 1100-1200 | ......s | CEu,WEu | 7265goh* |
| 1200-1400 | .....s. | CEu,WEu | 9485goh* |
| 1500-1600 | .....s. | CEu,WEu | 7265goh* |
| **German** | **Days** | **Area** | **kHz** |
| 0800-1200 | .....s. | CEu,WEu | 6190goh* |
| 1000-1100 | ......s | CEu,WEu | 7265goh* |
| **Spanish** | **Days** | **Area** | **kHz** |
| 1200-1300 | ......s | CEu,WEu | 7265goh* |
| 1400-1500 | .....s. | CEu,WEu | 9485goh* |

**Key:** * AM/USB (H3E) mode.
**Ann:** English: "Coming to you on Hamburger Lokalradio's shortwave service on ... kHz".
**V:** QSL-card. Rpt (1 USD).
**Notes:** Hamburger Lokalradio is a local community radio stn licensed to the registered voluntary association "Anbietergemeinschaft Hamburger Lokalradio e.V.", broadcasting on FM & DAB in the Hamburg region. The weekend SW transmissions are a separate project in cooperation with the operator of the leisure time SW service MV Baltic Radio (Göhren), consisting of selected own productions, as well as relays of third-party prgrs.

## MV BALTIC RADIO ‡
✉ Seestrasse 17, D-19089 Göhren, Germany.
☎ +49 3861 301380. 🖷 +49 3861 3029720.
**E:** info@mvbalticradio.de
**L.P:** Project coordinator/Prgr Host ("MV Baltic Radio" show): Roland Rohde.
**SW:** [GOH] Göhren: 1 x 0.15, 2 x 1kW.
**Key:** ‡ No longer transmits own prgrs.
**Ann:** English: "This is MV Baltic Radio".
**V:** QSL-card (Email rpt to qsl@mvbalticradio.de)
**Notes:** Weekend leisure time operation by a group of SW enthusiasts. The txs are installed in a private home, and are owned & operated by Roland Rohde (R&R Medienservice). Ceased own prgrs, but leases airtime to Hamburger Lokalradio (see separate entry).

## RADIO DARC
✉ Lindenstr. 4, D-34225 Baunatal, Germany.
☎ +49 561 949880.
**E:** radio@darc.de **W:** www.darc.de
**kHz:** *6070*

### Winter Schedule 2018/2019

| German | Days | Area | kHz |
|---|---|---|---|
| 1000-1100 | ......s | Eu | 6070mos |
| 1600-1700 | m...... | D,CEu | 6070rob |
| 2000-2100 | m...... | D,CEu | 6070rob |

**Ann:** German: "Sie hören Radio DARC".
**V:** QSL-card.
**Notes:** Prgr produced by association of German radio amateurs, Deutscher Amateur-Radio-Club e.V. (DARC). On SW since 22 March 2015.

## RADIO JOYSTICK
✉ Postfach 595, D-55529 Bad Kreuznach, Germany.
☎ +49 671 20278967.
**E:** chapri@radiojoystick.de **W:** www.radiojoystick.de; www.facebook.com/radiojoystick
**Webcast:** L (24h rotation of the show)
**L.P:** Presenter: Jens F. Hofstadt. (a.k.a "Charlie Prince")
**kHz:** *7330*

### Winter Schedule 2018/2019

| German | Days | Area | kHz |
|---|---|---|---|
| 1100-1200 | ......s | Eu | 7330mos* |

**Key:** * 1st Sunday of month.
**V:** QSL-card.
**Notes:** Monthly broadcast of the "Charlie-Prince-Show". R. Joystick was launched 1985 as a pirate radio prgr; the show has been relayed on SW via various (pirate and legal) rebroadcasters over the years.

## RADIO ÖÖMRANG
✉ Tanenwai 24, D-25946 Nebel-Westerheide, Germany.
☎ +49 4682 2688. 🖷 +49 4682 2262.
**E:** familie-koelzow@t-online.de
**L.P:** Producer: Gernot Schrader.
**FM/DAB:** FM: 96.7/97.6/98.8/105.2MHz (Via Offener Kanal Westküste).
**kHz:** *15215*

### Winter Schedule 2018/2019

| English/German | Days | Area | kHz |
|---|---|---|---|
| 1600-1700 | ...t... | NAm | 15215iss* |

**Key:** * 21 February 2019 only (tentative schedule, subject to confirmation).
**Ann:** English: "This is Radio Öömrang, the freedom voice of Öömrang".
**V:** Does not verify. Rpt can be sent to Media Broadcast Services GmbH.
**Notes:** The prgr "Radio Öömrang" ("Radio Amrum") is broadcast each year on 21 February, a major North Frisian holiday (Biikebrånen). The prgr was founded by radio amateur Arjan Kölzow on the island of Amrum in North Germany; the first SW broadcast was on 21 February 2006. The broadcast is aimed at the descendants of North Frisian immigrants in North America, and is presented bilingually in Standard German & English, incl. interviews in the North Frisian language (Öömrang dialect).

## SHORTWAVERADIO
**E:** 3975@shortwaveradio.de; 6160@shortwaveradio.de
**W:** shortwaveradio.de
**SW:** [WIS] Winsen an der Aller: 1 x 2.5, 1 x 1kW.
**kHz:** *3975, 6160*

### Winter Schedule 2018/2019

| English | Days | Area | kHz |
|---|---|---|---|
| 0800-1500 | mtwtfs. | CEu,WEu | 6160wis |
| 0800-2300 | mtwtfs. | CEu,WEu | 3975wis |

**Ann:** English: "This is Shortwave 3-9-7-5", "This is Shortwave 6-1-6-0".
**V:** eQSL-card.
**Notes:** On the air since August 2017. Leisure time operation by a group of SW enthusiasts. The txs are installed in a private house.

## SHORTWAVESERVICE
✉ Kuchenheimer Str. 155, D-53881 Euskirchen, Germany.
☎ +49 2251 146085. 🖷 +49 2251 146089.
**E:** info@shortwaveservice.com **W:** www.shortwaveservice.com; classicbroadcast.de (Technical info); radio360.eu (Podcast portal)
**Webcast:** L/P (P: radio360.eu)

**L.P:** Project Coordinator: Christian Milling.
**SW:** [KLL] Kall, Krekel: 4 x 1kW.
**kHz:** *3985, 6005*

### Winter Schedule 2018/2019

| German/Various | Days | Area | kHz |
|---|---|---|---|
| 0800-1800 | daily | CEu,WEu | 6005kII* |
| 1600-2030 | ......s | CEu,WEu | 3985kII* |
| 1600-2100 | .....s. | CEu,WEu | 3985kII* |
| 1600-2200 | mtwtf.. | CEu,WEu | 3985kII* |

**Key:** * Latest schedule with relay details: see www.shortwaveservice.com
**Ann:** German: "Sie hören Shortwaveservice".
**V:** QSL-card (for relayed prgrs). Online rpt form available.
**Notes:** On the air since 24 November 2007. The SW relay service (initially branded "R. 700 Kurzwellendienst") is a leisure time operation by a group of radio enthusiasts, and primarily targeting listeners in the European DX/SWL community. The programming consists of relays of third-party prgrs & nonstop music. Shortwaveservice is transmitted via 1kW txs that are owned & operated by the radio amateur Burkhard Baumgartner (DF5XV), installed at a vintage utility radio site (formerly run by German police forces).

## USAGM GERMANY TRANSMITTING STATION
⌨ Postfach 1145, D- 68601 Lampertheim, Germany.
☎ +49 6206 1590. 🖨 +49 6206 159189.
**E:** hreis@bbg.gov
**L.P:** SM: Michael R. Hardegen; Transmitter Plant Supervisor: Harald Reis.
**SW:** [BIB] Biblis: 11 x 100kW; [LAM] Lampertheim: 9 x 100kW.
**V:** QSL-card.

## MEDIA BROADCAST GMBH (Tx Operator)
⌨ Erna-Scheffler-Str. 1, D-51103 Köln, Germany.
☎ +49 221 71015000.
**E:** info@media-broadcast.com **W:** www.media-broadcast.com
**L.P:** CEO: Wolfgang Breuer; Sales Consultant, Business Unit Radio: Michael Pütz.
**SW:** [NAU] Nauen: 2 x 100, 4 x 500kW.
**V:** QSL-card. (For relayed stns. Email rpts: qsl-shortwave@media-broadcast.com).
**Notes:** Media Broadcast GmbH, a subsidiary of Freenet AG, is a major transmitter network operator in Germany and owner of the SW transmitting centre in Nauen.

## GREECE (GRC)

### VOICE OF GREECE (I FONI TIS ELLADAS) (Pub)
⌨ Mesogeion Ave. 432, Office P 211, 15342 Agia Paraskevi, Greece.
☎ +30 2106066439.
**E:** thevoiceofgreece@ert.gr; ertinternational@ert.gr **W:** int.ert.gr
**Webcast:** L (webradio.ert.gr/i-foni-tis-elladas)
**L.P:** MD (ERT): Lambis Tagmatarchis; Channel Dir (I Foni tis Elladas): Mrs Gianna Triantafilli; Head of Netw. Development & Operation (ERT): Dmitris K.Gazidellis
**SW:** [AVL] Vathy (Avlida municipality), Kalochori-Pantichi: 2 x 100kW, 1 x 250kW.
**kHz:** *9420, 9935*

### Winter Schedule 2018/2019

| Greek | Days | Area | kHz |
|---|---|---|---|
| 2000-0800 | daily | Eu,Am | 9420avl† |
| 2200-0400 | daily | Eu,Am | 9935avl† |

**Key:** † Irregular, times variable.
**Ann:** Greek: "Edo Athina, I Foni tis Elladas".
**V:** eQSL-card. Email rpt to dgazidellis@ert.gr (Dmitris Gazidellis)
**Notes:** International service produced by the Greek public broadcaster ERT, primarily serving the Greek communities abroad. The prgrs include relays of ERT Home Service channels and may include segments in Albanian, English, Polish, Romanian, Russian and Spanish, see webradio.ert.gr/programma-i-foni-tis-elladas for details. SW tr hours are highly variable.

## GUAM (GUM)

### KSDA (AWR ASIA/PACIFIC RELAY STATION)
⌨ P.O. Box 8990, Agat, Guam 96928. (Transmitting station)
☎ +1 671 5652000. 🖨 +1 671 5652983.
**E:** guam@awr.org

⌨ EIS Building B, Unit 1101, 71/15 Soi Pridi Banomyong 37, Sukhumvit 71 Road, Klongton Nua, Vadhana District, Bangkok 10110, Thailand. (AWR Asia/Pacific branch & studios)
☎ +66 223818869.
**W:** www.awr.org
**L.P:** SM: Victor Shepherd; Chief Engineer: Brook Powers.
**SW:** [SDA] Agat, Facpi Point: 5 x 100kW.
**Ann:** English: "This is Adventist World Radio - The Voice of Hope - KDSA, Agat, Guam".
**V:** QSL-card (Rpt to AWR Asia/Pacific Branch in Thailand).
**Notes:** Transmitting station owned by Adventist Broadcasting Service, Inc., see USA for corporate details. For schedules, see AWR Asia/Pacific (Thailand).

### KTWR (TWR RELAY STATION)
⌨ P.O.Box 6095, Merizo, Guam 96916-0395. (Transmitting station)
☎ +1 671 8288637. 🖨 +1 671 8288636.
**E:** ktwrfcd@twr.org **W:** www.twr.asia/about/guam
⌨ 85 Playfair Road #04-01, Tong Yuan Industrial Building, Singapore 368000. (TWR Asia branch & studios)
☎ +65 65015150. 🖨 +65 64443053.
**E:** info@twr.asia **W:** ktwrdrm.blogspot.com (technical blog)
**L.P:** Stn Dir: George Ross; Chief Engineer: Mike Sabin.
**SW:** [TWR] Merizo: 1 x 100, 3 x 250kW.
**Ann:** English: "Welcome to KTWR Agana, Guam".
**IS:** "We've a story to tell the Nations", played on an organ.
**V:** QSL-card. Rp. (3 IRCs)
**Notes:** Transmitting station owned by TWR, Inc. See USA for corporate details. For schedule, see TWR Asia (Singapore).

## INDIA (IND)

### ALL INDIA RADIO (AIR) (Pub)
⌨ External Services Division (ESD), P.O.Box 500, New Delhi 110001, India.
☎ +91 11 23421220. 🖨 +91 11 23421220.
**E:** esd@@prasarbharati.gov.in; adg.esd@@prasarbharati.gov.in (ESD) **W:** www.allindiaradio.gov.in; airworldservice.org
**Webcast:** D/L (airworldservice.org)
⌨ New Broadcasting House, 27 Mahadev Road, New Delhi 110001, India. (Studios)
**E:** esd.gos@@prasarbharati.gov.in; gosesdair@yahoo.co.in (GOS)
**W:** newsonair.nic.in (AIR News Services Division Web Portal); www. hptkhampur.wix.com/airkhampur (AIR Khampur tx centre).
**L.P:** DG: Fayyaz Sheheryar; Additional DG (ESD): Raj Shekhay Vyas; Engineer-in-Chief: Chandra Bhanu Singh.
**MW:** [JAL] Jalandhar: 702kHz 300kW; [KKT] Chinsurah: 594/603kHz 1000kW*; [RAJ] Rajkot 1071/1080kHz 1000kW*; [TUT] Tuticorin: 1053kHz 200kW. *) Reduced power applies to DRM freqs 603 & 1080kHz.
**SW:** [ALG] Aligarh: 4 x 250kW; [BGL] Bengalaru, Doddaballapur: 6 x 500kW; [DEL] Delhi, two sites: Khampur (G.C. 28N49 077E07): 7 x 250kW; Kingsway (G.C. 28N43 077E12): 2 x 100kW; [MUM] Mumbai: 1 x 100kW; [PAN] Panaji: 2 x 250kW.
**FM/DAB:** FM: 103.6MHz (Amritsar, 20kW). Ext. Sce Schedule: Punjabi: 1300-1430; Sarakki: 1230-1300; Urdu: 0025-0130, 0430-0830, 0930-1230, 1430-1830.
**kHz:** *594, 702, 1053, 1071, 4870, 6045, 6140, 7250, 7270, 7340, 7380, 7520, 7550, 7555, 9445, 9575, 9620, 9645, 9690, 9835, 9910, 9950, 11560, 11590, 11620, 11645, 11710, 11740, 11935, 12025, 13605, 13640, 13645, 13695, 13795, 15030, 15185, 15210, 15410, 15770, 17510, 17705, 17870, 17895*

### Winter Schedule 2018/2019

| Arabic | Days | Area | kHz |
|---|---|---|---|
| 0430-0530 | daily | ME | 11560bgl‡, 15210pan |
| 1730-1945 | daily | ME | 9620alg , 11710del†, 13640bgl |
| **Baluchi** | **Days** | **Area** | **kHz** |
| 1500-1600 | daily | SAs | 1071raj, 7340mum, 9620alg |
| **Bengali** | **Days** | **Area** | **kHz** |
| 0025-0830 | daily | SAs | 594kkt* |
| 1000-1730 | daily | SAs | 594kkt* |
| **Burmese** | **Days** | **Area** | **kHz** |
| 1215-1315 | daily | SEA | 9950del‡ |
| **Chinese** | **Days** | **Area** | **kHz** |
| 1145-1315 | daily | EAs | 15030bgl+*, 17705bgl |

| Dari | Days | Area | kHz |
|---|---|---|---|
| 0300-0345 | daily | WAs | 9910delt, 11560bgl‡, 11740pan |
| 1315-1415 | daily | WAs | 11560bgl |
| **English** | **Days** | **Area** | **kHz** |
| 1000-1100 | daily | SEA | 15770pan |
| 1000-1100 | daily | SAs | 1053tut, 7270cni |
| 1000-1100 | daily | EAs | 13605bgl, 15410bgl |
| 1000-1100 | daily | Pac | 13695bgl, 17510bgl, 17895bgl+* |
| 1330-1500 | daily | SEA | 9690bgl‡, 13695bgl |
| 1745-1945 | daily | EAf | 9910bgl, 11935mum, 13695bgl |
| 1745-1945 | daily | Eu | 7550bgl+, 9950del‡ |
| 1745-1945 | daily | NAf,WAf | 9445bgl |
| 2045-2230 | daily | Eu | 7550bgl+, 9445bgl, 9950del‡ |
| 2045-2230 | daily | Pac | 9910bgl, 11740pan |
| 2245-0045 | daily | EAs | 7550bgl+, 9445bgl, 11645del, 11645delt |
| 2245-0045 | daily | SEA | 6045delt |
| **Farsi** | **Days** | **Area** | **kHz** |
| 0400-0430 | daily | ME | 11560bgl‡, 15210pan |
| 1615-1730 | daily | ME | 9620alg , 11710delt, 13640bgl |
| **French** | **Days** | **Area** | **kHz** |
| 1945-2045 | daily | Eu | 7550bgl+ |
| 1945-2045 | daily | NAf,WAf | 9620alg, 11710delt, 13640bgl |
| **Gujarati** | **Days** | **Area** | **kHz** |
| 0415-0430 | daily | EAf | 15185bgl+* |
| 1515-1600 | daily | EAf | 13695bgl |
| **Hindi** | **Days** | **Area** | **kHz** |
| 0315-0415 | daily | EAf | 15185bgl+* |
| 0315-0415 | daily | ME | 13695bgl, 15030bgl |
| 0430-0530 | daily | EAf | 15185bgl+* |
| 1615-1730 | daily | EAf | 9950bgl‡, 13605bgl |
| 1615-1730 | daily | ME | 12025pan |
| 1945-2045 | daily | Eu | 7550bgl+ |
| 1945-2045 | daily | NAf,WAf | 9445bgl |
| 2300-2400 | daily | SEA | 9910bgl, 11590pan , 13795bgl |
| **Indonesian** | **Days** | **Area** | **kHz** |
| 0845-0945 | daily | SEA | 15770pan, 17510bgl, 17870bgl |
| **Kannada** | **Days** | **Area** | **kHz** |
| 0215-0300 | daily | ME | 13695bgl, 15030bgl |
| **Malayalam** | **Days** | **Area** | **kHz** |
| 1730-1830 | daily | ME | 12025pan |
| **Nepali** | **Days** | **Area** | **kHz** |
| 0130-0230 | daily | SAs | 7555del‡, 9950bgl |
| 0700-0800 | daily | SAs | 7520del‡, 9950del‡, 11620del |
| 1330-1430 | daily | SAs | 4870del, 7555del‡, 11620pan |
| **Pashto** | **Days** | **Area** | **kHz** |
| 0215-0300 | daily | WAs | 9910delt, 11560bgl‡, 11740pan |
| 1415-1530 | daily | WAs | 11560bgl |
| **Punjabi** | **Days** | **Area** | **kHz** |
| 0800-0830 | daily | SAs | 702jal |
| 1130-1230 | daily | SAs | 702jal |
| 1300-1430 | daily | SAs | 702jal |
| **Russian** | **Days** | **Area** | **kHz** |
| 1615-1715 | daily | RUS | 11560bgl |
| **Saraiki** | **Days** | **Area** | **kHz** |
| 1230-1300 | daily | SAs | 702jal |
| **Sindhi** | **Days** | **Area** | **kHz** |
| 0100-0200 | daily | SAs | 1071raj, 7380del‡, 9645delt |
| 1230-1500 | daily | SAs | 1071raj, 7340mum, 9620alg |
| **Sinhala** | **Days** | **Area** | **kHz** |
| 0045-0115 | daily | SAs | 1053tut, 7270cni, 11590pan |

| Sinhala | Days | Area | kHz |
|---|---|---|---|
| 1300-1500 | daily | SAs | 1053tut, 7270cni, 11590delt |
| **Swahili** | **Days** | **Area** | **kHz** |
| 1515-1615 | daily | EAf | 9950bgl‡, 13605bgl |
| **Tamil** | **Days** | **Area** | **kHz** |
| 0000-0045 | daily | SAs | 1053tut, 7270cni, 9835del‡ |
| 0000-0045 | daily | SEA | 11590pan , 13795bgl |
| 0115-0330 | daily | SAs | 1053tut |
| 1100-1300 | daily | SAs | 1053tut |
| 1115-1215 | daily | SAs | 7270cni |
| 1115-1215 | daily | SEA | 13695bgl |
| 1500-1530 | daily | SAs | 1053tut |
| **Telugu** | **Days** | **Area** | **kHz** |
| 1215-1245 | daily | SEA | 13695bgl |
| **Thai** | **Days** | **Area** | **kHz** |
| 1115-1200 | daily | SEA | 13645bgl, 15410pan |
| **Tibetan** | **Days** | **Area** | **kHz** |
| 1215-1330 | daily | EAs | 7555del‡, 9575bgl‡, 11620pan , 15030bgl+* |
| **Urdu** | **Days** | **Area** | **kHz** |
| 0025-0100 | daily | SAs | 1071raj |
| 0025-0430 | daily | SAs | 702jal, 6140alg, 7340mum, 7520delt |
| 0200-0430 | daily | SAs | 1071raj |
| 0630-0815 | daily | SAs | 1071raj+ |
| 0830-1130 | daily | SAs | 702jal, 7250del‡, 7340mum, 9620alg, 9950del‡, 11560delt |
| 0830-1230 | daily | SAs | 1071raj |
| 0830-1930 | daily | SAs | 7520delt |
| 1430-1930 | daily | SAs | 702jal |
| 1600-1930 | daily | SAs | 1071raj |

**Key:** † Irregular; ‡ Temporarily off air; + DRM; +* DRM (temporarily on AM mode); * Maitree Channel.

**Ann:** Dari: "Inja Delhi"; English: "This is the General Overseas Service of All India Radio"; Hindi: "Yeh Akashvani ki videsh prasaran sewa hai"; Nepali: "Yo All India Radio ho"; Sinhala: "Me All India Radio videshiya sevayai"; Tamil: "Idi Akashvani videsh sewai".

**V:** QSL-card. Email rpt to spectrum-manager@prasarbharati.gov. in (downloadable rpt form avaiable). Rpt by mail/fax to Director (Spectrum Management & Synergy), All India Radio, Room No. 204, Akashvani Bhawan, New Delhi-110001, India; Fax: +91 11 23421062.

**Notes:** External Sce of All India Radio (the radio division of the national public broadcaster Prasar Bharati Corporation). Established on 1 October 1939. AIR's External Sce in English is branded "General Overseas Service" (GOS). Some services in national languages of India are produced by AIR's regional stations. The services in Gujarati, Hindi, Makayam, Tamil and Telugu are directed at overseas Indians, while those in Bengali, Kannada, Punjabi, Urdu, Saraiki and Sindhi are meant for listeners in the Indian Sub-continent.

## ATHMIK YATRA RADIO ‡ (Rlg)
P.O. Box 12, Manjadi Junction S.O., Tiruvalla taluk, Kerala-689105, India.
☎ +91 469 2630654.
**E:** ayradio4567@gmail.com **W:** www.ayradio.com
**Webcast:** D
P.O.Box 3342, Kathmandu, Nepal. (Atmik Yatra Nepal)
☎ +977 98 56085115. (cellphone)
**E:** atmikyatra@aynepal.com **W:** www.aynepal.com
**LP:** Pres: Dr K.P. Yohannan.
**Key:** ‡Inactive on SW at time of publication.
**Ann:** Malayalam: "Athmeeya Yathra".
**V:** QSL-card.
**Notes:** Athmik Yatra Radio ("AY Radio") is the radio mission of the Believers Church (a network of Pentecostal Churches in India). Successor station to "Gospel For Asia" (GFA). The name of the service originates in the prgr "Athmik Yatra" ("Spiritual Journey"), hosted by K.P. Yohannan, and transmitted for Malalayam speakers in India via Trans World Radio since 1985.

## FEBA INDIA (Rlg)
7 Commissariat Road, Bengaluru 560025, India. (Head Office & Studio)
☎ +91 80 25328191; +91 80 25559063.

**E:** febaindia@vsnl.com **W:** febaindia.org; febaonline.org
✉ A-42-44, Manushri Building, Dr. Mukherji Nagar, New Delhi 110009, India. (Branch Office & Studio)
☎ +91 11 27652426; +91 11 27652084.
**LP:** Dir: Christian Benjamin.
**kHz:** *873, 9540, 11580*

### Winter Schedule 2018/2019

| English | Days | Area | kHz |
|---|---|---|---|
| 1330-1345 | m...... | IND | 11580twr |

| Hindi | Days | Area | kHz |
|---|---|---|---|
| 1430-1500 | ..wtfss | IND | 9540tac |

| Kannada | Days | Area | kHz |
|---|---|---|---|
| 1315-1345 | ......s | IND | 11580twr |
| 1330-1345 | ...tfs. | IND | 11580twr |

| Malayalam | Days | Area | kHz |
|---|---|---|---|
| 1315-1330 | ..wtfs. | IND | 11580twr |

| Tamil | Days | Area | kHz |
|---|---|---|---|
| 0130-0200 | mt...ss | IND | 873put |
| 1330-1345 | .tw.... | IND | 11580twr |

| Telugu | Days | Area | kHz |
|---|---|---|---|
| 1315-1330 | mt..... | IND | 11580twr |

**V:** QSL-email. E-mail rpt to: kenneth@febaindia.org (Kenneth Edward)
**Notes:** Far East Broadcasting Associates of India (FEBA India) is regional partner of Far East Broadcasting Company, Inc (USA) (see USA for FEBC corporate details), targeting the Indian subcontinent.

### TWR INDIA (Rlg)
✉ 1st Floor, 24/46 Aspiran Garden 1st St, Aspiran Garden Colony, Kilpauk, Chennai, Tamil Nadu-600010, India
☎ +91 44 26440161.
**E:** info@twr.in **W:** twr.in; radio882.com
**Webcast:** D/L
**LP:** CEO: George Philip.
**kHz:** *882, 1467, 6240, 7280, 7505, 7535, 7550, 9305, 9910, 9950, 9975, 15360*

### Winter Schedule 2018/2019

| Assamese | Days | Area | kHz |
|---|---|---|---|
| 1215-1245 | mtwtf.. | As | 9910twr |

| Awadhi | Days | Area | kHz |
|---|---|---|---|
| 1345-1400 | m...... | As | 9910erv |

| Bagri | Days | Area | kHz |
|---|---|---|---|
| 1345-1400 | ...f.. | As | 1467bis |

| Banjara | Days | Area | kHz |
|---|---|---|---|
| 1330-1345 | .....s. | As | 882put |

| Bengali | Days | Area | kHz |
|---|---|---|---|
| 1315-1330 | .....s. | As | 9910erv |
| 2230-2300 | daily | As | 882put |

| Bhatri | Days | Area | kHz |
|---|---|---|---|
| 1315-1330 | ......s | As | 9910erv |

| Bhili | Days | Area | kHz |
|---|---|---|---|
| 1430-1445 | m...... | As | 9950kch |

| Bhojpuri | Days | Area | kHz |
|---|---|---|---|
| 1400-1430 | mtwtf.. | As | 9910erv |

| Bondo | Days | Area | kHz |
|---|---|---|---|
| 1330-1345 | ..w.... | As | 9305erv |

| Braj Bhasha | Days | Area | kHz |
|---|---|---|---|
| 1500-1545 | ......s | As | 7550erv |

| Bundelkhandi | Days | Area | kHz |
|---|---|---|---|
| 1330-1345 | .....s. | As | 9910erv |

| Chhattisgarhi | Days | Area | kHz |
|---|---|---|---|
| 1400-1415 | ......s | As | 882put |
| 1500-1530 | mtwtf.. | As | 882put |
| 1615-1630 | ......s | As | 882put |

| Chodhri | Days | Area | kHz |
|---|---|---|---|
| 1345-1400 | .....s. | As | 9950kch |

| Deccani | Days | Area | kHz |
|---|---|---|---|
| 1415-1430 | ......s | As | 882put |
| 1630-1700 | mtwtf.. | As | 882put |

| Dhodiya | Days | Area | kHz |
|---|---|---|---|
| 1415-1430 | ......s | As | 9950kch |

| Dogri | Days | Area | kHz |
|---|---|---|---|
| 1345-1400 | mtwtf.. | As | 9305erv |

| Dzongkha | Days | Area | kHz |
|---|---|---|---|
| 0115-0130 | ..w.... | As | 7280tac |
| 1230-1245 | .....ss | As | 9975twr |

| English | Days | Area | kHz |
|---|---|---|---|
| 1530-1600 | .....ss | As | 7550erv |
| 1535-1540 | mtwtf.. | As | 7550erv |

| Gamit | Days | Area | kHz |
|---|---|---|---|
| 1400-1415 | ......s | As | 9950kch |
| 1400-1430 | .....s. | As | 9950kch |

| Garhwali | Days | Area | kHz |
|---|---|---|---|
| 1400-1415 | mtwtf.. | As | 9305erv |

| Gondi | Days | Area | kHz |
|---|---|---|---|
| 1330-1345 | mtwtf.. | As | 882put |
| 1345-1400 | ......s | As | 882put |

| Gujarati | Days | Area | kHz |
|---|---|---|---|
| 1430-1445 | .t..... | As | 9950kch |
| 1430-1500 | .....s. | As | 882put |
| 1500-1515 | .....s. | As | 882put |
| 1500-1530 | ......s | As | 882put |
| 2330-2400 | mtwt..s | As | 882put |

| Haryanvi | Days | Area | kHz |
|---|---|---|---|
| 1430-1445 | .....s. | As | 9305erv |

| Hindi | Days | Area | kHz |
|---|---|---|---|
| 0045-0115 | mtwtf.. | As | 7280tac |
| 0115-0130 | .t..... | As | 7280tac |
| 1330-1345 | ......s | As | 9910erv |
| 1330-1405 | .....s. | As | 1467bis |
| 1345-1400 | .twtfss | As | 9910erv |
| 1400-1430 | .....s. | As | 9910erv |
| 1400-1430 | ....ss | As | 9305erv |
| 1415-1445 | mtwtf.. | As | 9305erv |
| 1500-1530 | mtwtfs. | As | 7550erv |
| 1530-1535 | mtwtf.. | As | 7550erv |
| 2300-2330 | daily | As | 882put |

| Ho | Days | Area | kHz |
|---|---|---|---|
| 1330-1345 | .....s. | As | 9305erv |

| Kangri | Days | Area | kHz |
|---|---|---|---|
| 1330-1345 | ...f.. | As | 1467bis |

| Kannada | Days | Area | kHz |
|---|---|---|---|
| 1430-1445 | ......s | As | 882put |
| 1430-1500 | mtwtf.. | As | 882put |

| Kashmiri | Days | Area | kHz |
|---|---|---|---|
| 1330-1345 | .....s. | As | 1467bis |
| 1330-1400 | .t..... | As | 1467bis |
| 1345-1400 | .....ss | As | 9305erv |

| Kharia | Days | Area | kHz |
|---|---|---|---|
| 1330-1345 | m...... | As | 9305erv |

| Kokborok | Days | Area | kHz |
|---|---|---|---|
| 1245-1300 | ......s | As | 9910twr |
| 1245-1315 | mtwtf.. | As | 9910twr |

| Konkani | Days | Area | kHz |
|---|---|---|---|
| 1415-1430 | .....s. | As | 882put |

| Koya | Days | Area | kHz |
|---|---|---|---|
| 1400-1415 | .....s. | As | 882put |

| Kui | Days | Area | kHz |
|---|---|---|---|
| 1315-1330 | .....s. | As | 9305erv |

| Kukna | Days | Area | kHz |
|---|---|---|---|
| 2330-2345 | ...f.. | As | 882put |

| Kumaoni | Days | Area | kHz |
|---|---|---|---|
| 1345-1355 | .....s. | As | 1467bis |

| Kurukh | Days | Area | kHz |
|---|---|---|---|
| 1315-1330 | ..wtf.. | As | 9305erv |
| 1345-1400 | ......s | As | 9950kch |

| Kutchi | Days | Area | kHz |
|---|---|---|---|
| 2345-2400 | ...f.. | As | 882put |

| Maghai | Days | Area | kHz |
|---|---|---|---|
| 1330-1345 | ..tf.. | As | 9305erv |

| Maithili | Days | Area | kHz |
|---|---|---|---|
| 1315-1345 | mtwtf.. | As | 9910erv |
| 1330-1345 | ......s | As | 9305erv |

| Malayalam | Days | Area | kHz |
|---|---|---|---|
| 0000-0030 | daily | As | 882put |

| Manipuri | Days | Area | kHz |
|---|---|---|---|
| 1300-1315 | ......s | As | 9910twr |
| **Marathi** | **Days** | **Area** | **kHz** |
| 1600-1630 | mtwtfs. | As | 882put |
| **Marwari** | **Days** | **Area** | **kHz** |
| 1345-1400 | mtw.... | As | 9950kch |
| **Mawchi** | **Days** | **Area** | **kHz** |
| 1345-1400 | ...tf.. | As | 9950kch |
| **Mewadi** | **Days** | **Area** | **kHz** |
| 1430-1445 | ......s | As | 9305erv |
| **Mundari** | **Days** | **Area** | **kHz** |
| 1315-1330 | mt..... | As | 9305erv |
| **Nepali** | **Days** | **Area** | **kHz** |
| 0115-0130 | m...... | As | 7280tac |
| 1300-1315 | .....s. | As | 9910twr |
| **Oriya** | **Days** | **Area** | **kHz** |
| 1515-1530 | .....s. | As | 882put |
| 1530-1600 | mtwtf.. | As | 882put |
| 1600-1615 | ......s | As | 882put |
| **Punjabi** | **Days** | **Area** | **kHz** |
| 1330-1400 | m...... | As | 1467bis |
| 1355-1400 | .....s. | As | 1467bis |
| 1400-1430 | ......s | As | 9910erv |
| 1445-1545 | mtwtf.. | As | 7505tac |
| **Sadri** | **Days** | **Area** | **kHz** |
| 1330-1345 | .t..... | As | 9305erv |
| **Santhali** | **Days** | **Area** | **kHz** |
| 1315-1330 | ......s | As | 9305erv |
| **Sindhi** | **Days** | **Area** | **kHz** |
| 1400-1430 | mtwtf.. | As | 9950kch |
| **Soura** | **Days** | **Area** | **kHz** |
| 1445-1500 | ......s | As | 882put |
| **Surgujia** | **Days** | **Area** | **kHz** |
| 1545-1600 | ......s | As | 7550erv |
| **Tamil** | **Days** | **Area** | **kHz** |
| 0030-0130 | daily | As | 882put |
| **Telugu** | **Days** | **Area** | **kHz** |
| 1345-1400 | ....s. | As | 882put |
| 1400-1430 | mtwtf.. | As | 882put |
| **Tibetan** | **Days** | **Area** | **kHz** |
| 0115-0130 | ...tf.. | As | 7280tac |
| **Tulu** | **Days** | **Area** | **kHz** |
| 1630-1645 | ......s | As | 882put |
| **Urdu** | **Days** | **Area** | **kHz** |
| 1330-1400 | ..wt... | As | 1467bis |
| 1400-1415 | daily | As | 15360man |
| 1600-1630 | daily | As | 7535kch |
| **Uyghur** | **Days** | **Area** | **kHz** |
| 1545-1600 | daily | As | 6240tac |
| **Varli** | **Days** | **Area** | **kHz** |
| 1330-1345 | ......s | As | 882put |
| **Vasavi** | **Days** | **Area** | **kHz** |
| 1430-1445 | ..wtf.. | As | 9950kch |

**V:** QSL-card.
**Notes:** TWR regional division, covering the Indian subcontinent. For corporate details, see under TWR (USA).

## INDONESIA (INS)

**VOICE OF INDONESIA (VOI) (Pub)**
P.O. Box 1157, Jakarta 10110, Indonesia; Jl. Medan Merdeka Barat 4-5, Jakarta 10110, Indonesia.
☎ +62 21 3456811. 🖷 +62 21 3500990.
**E:** voi@voinews.id; english@voinews.id **W:** www.voinews.id
**Webcast:** D/L
**LP:** Dir: Eddy Sukmana.
**SW:** [PGA] Palangkaraya 1 x 10kW.
**kHz:** *3325*

**Winter Schedule 2018/2019**

| Arabic | Days | Area | kHz |
|---|---|---|---|
| 1600-1700 | daily | SEA | 3325pga† |
| **Chinese** | **Days** | **Area** | **kHz** |
| 1100-1200 | daily | SEA | 3325pga† |

| Dutch | Days | Area | kHz |
|---|---|---|---|
| 1500-1600 | daily | SEA | 3325pga† |
| **English** | **Days** | **Area** | **kHz** |
| 1000-1100 | daily | SEA | 3325pga† |
| 1300-1400 | daily | SEA | 3325pga† |
| 1900-2000 | daily | SEA | 3325pga† |
| **French** | **Days** | **Area** | **kHz** |
| 2000-2100 | daily | SEA | 3325pga† |
| **German** | **Days** | **Area** | **kHz** |
| 1800-1900 | daily | SEA | 3325pga† |
| **Indonesian** | **Days** | **Area** | **kHz** |
| 1400-1500 | daily | SEA | 3325pga† |
| **Japanese** | **Days** | **Area** | **kHz** |
| 1200-1300 | daily | SEA | 3325pga† |
| **Spanish** | **Days** | **Area** | **kHz** |
| 1700-1800 | daily | SEA | 3325pga† |

**Key:** † Irregular.
**Ann:** English: "This is the Voice of Indonesia, in Jakarta"; Spanish: "La Voz de Indonesia en Jakarta".
**V:** QSL-card.
**Notes:** The Voice of Indonesia (RRI World Service) is the External Sce of the public service broadcaster Radio Republik Indonesia (RRI)

## IRAN (IRN)

**PARS TODAY (VOICE OF THE ISLAMIC REPUBLIC OF IRAN) (Gov)**
P.O. Box 19395-6767, Tehran, Iran.
☎ +98 21 22013687; +98 21 22162731. 🖷 +98 21 22044287.
**E:** english@parstoday.com **W:** parstoday.com; worldservice.irib.ir
**Webcast:** D/L.
☎ +98 21 22013720.
**LP:** Pres (IRIB): Mohammad Sarafraz; DG, Int. Affairs: Abbas Naseri Taheri.
**MW:** [AHW] Ahwaz, Bandar-e Mahshar: 576/1080kHz 750kW; [BNB] Bonab: 639kHz 400kW; [BNT] Bandar-e Torkaman: 1449kHz 400kW; [CHR] Chabahar: 765kHz 1000kW; [JOL] Jolfa 1323kHz 50kW; [KIA] Bandar-e Kiashahr: 702kHz 500kW; [KIH] Kish Island: 1224kHz 300kW; [QSH] Qasr-e Shirin: 612/1161kHz 600kW; [TYB] Tayebad: 720kHz 400kW; [ZAB] Zabol: 1098kHz 200kW.
**SW:** [AHW] Ahwaz, Bandar-e Mahshar ‡: 2 x 250kW; [SIR] Sirjan: 10 x 500kW; [ZAH] Zahedan: 2 x 500kW.
**SAT:** Eutelsat 3B/Hot Bird 13C, Galaxy 19, Intelsat 20/902.
**kHz:** *576, 612, 639, 702, 720, 765, 1080, 1098, 1161, 1224, 1323, 1395, 1449, 5920, 5925, 5935, 5940, 5950, 5965, 6000, 6025, 6040, 6060, 6075, 6085, 6090, 6110, 6135, 6155, 6190, 7225, 7230, 7260, 7280, 7305, 7310, 7355, 7360, 7370, 7375, 7380, 7390, 7425, 7430, 7435, 9440, 9495, 9510, 9550, 9660, 9755, 9800, 9835, 9850, 9870, 9900, 11780, 11870, 11875, 11880, 12035, 13680, 13710, 13740, 13790, 13820, 15130, 15140, 15200, 15240, 15360, 15440, 17540, 17665*

**Winter Schedule 2018/2019**

| Albanian | Days | Area | kHz |
|---|---|---|---|
| 1820-1920 | daily | Eu | 5925sir, 7305sir |
| **Arabic** | **Days** | **Area** | **kHz** |
| 0000-2400 | daily | ME | 1224kih*** |
| 0130-0320 | daily | ME | 1161qsh |
| 0130-0600 | daily | NAf,ME | 7370sir |
| 0220-1250 | daily | ME | 765chr |
| 0230-0530 | daily | ME | 7380zah* |
| 0320-0420 | daily | ME | 6085sir* |
| 0330-1630 | daily | ME | 576ahw |
| 0420-1530 | daily | ME | 612qsh |
| 0530-0730 | daily | NAf,ME | 13820zah |
| 0600-0830 | daily | ME | 13790sir |
| 0830-1030 | daily | ME | 13820sir |
| 0930-1430 | daily | NAf,ME | 15130sir |
| 1030-1430 | daily | ME | 9440zah |
| 1430-1730 | daily | ME | 9800sir |
| 1430-1730 | daily | NAf,ME | 7310zah |
| 1530-2030 | daily | ME | 1161qsh** |
| 1620-0120 | daily | ME | 765chr** |
| 1700-0330 | daily | ME | 1080ahw**** |
| 1730-0230 | daily | NAf,ME | 6060zah** |

| Armenian | Days | Area | kHz |
|---|---|---|---|
| 1620-1720 | daily | Cau | 7430sir |
| **Azeri** | **Days** | **Area** | **kHz** |
| 0050-0520 | daily | ME | 1323jol |
| 0100-0520 | daily | Cau | 702kia |
| 1420-1650 | daily | ME | 702kia, 1323jol |
| **Azeri (Aran)** | **Days** | **Area** | **kHz** |
| 0530-0930 | daily | Cau | 702kia |
| **Bengali** | **Days** | **Area** | **kHz** |
| 1420-1520 | daily | SAs | 6155sir |
| 1420-1520 | daily | ME | 9870ahw |
| 1620-1650 | daily | SAs | 6155sir, 7375sir |
| **Bosnian** | **Days** | **Area** | **kHz** |
| 1720-1820 | daily | Eu | 6110sir |
| **Dari** | **Days** | **Area** | **kHz** |
| 0300-0630 | daily | ME | 1098zab |
| 0300-1500 | daily | WAs | 720tyb |
| 0550-0820 | daily | WAs | 12035sir |
| 0820-1450 | daily | WAs | 1098zab |
| 0920-1220 | daily | WAs | 9495sir |
| 0920-1250 | daily | WAs | 13740sir |
| **English** | **Days** | **Area** | **kHz** |
| 1020-1120 | daily | ME | 702kia |
| 1520-1620 | daily | SAs,SEA | 5965sir |
| 1920-2020 | daily | Eu | 6040sir |
| 1920-2020 | daily | SAf | 11880sir |
| **French** | **Days** | **Area** | **kHz** |
| 1820-1920 | daily | Eu | 6135sir |
| 2320-0020 | daily | WAf,CAf | 7260sir, 9660sir |
| **German** | **Days** | **Area** | **kHz** |
| 1720-1820 | daily | Eu | 6025sir, 7425sir |
| **Hausa** | **Days** | **Area** | **kHz** |
| 0550-0650 | daily | WAf,CAf | 13710sir, 15360sir |
| 1120-1150 | daily | WAf,CAf | 17665sir |
| 1820-1920 | daily | WAf,CAf | 9850sir |
| 2220-2320 | daily | WAf,CAf | 7225sir, 7280sir |
| **Hebrew** | **Days** | **Area** | **kHz** |
| 0420-0450 | daily | ME | 9755sir, 11780sir |
| 0650-0720 | daily | ME | 15440sir |
| 1150-1220 | daily | ME | 15240sir |
| **Hindi** | **Days** | **Area** | **kHz** |
| 1420-1520 | daily | SAs | 5920sir, 9900sir |
| **Italian** | **Days** | **Area** | **kHz** |
| 1920-1950 | daily | Eu | 6135sir, 6190sir |
| **Kurdish** | **Days** | **Area** | **kHz** |
| 0420-0520 | daily | ME | 639bnb |
| 1320-1420 | daily | ME | 7355sir |
| 1320-1620 | daily | ME | 639bnb |
| **Pashto** | **Days** | **Area** | **kHz** |
| 0220-0320 | daily | WAs | 6075sir, 7390sir |
| 0720-0820 | daily | WAs | 1098zab |
| 1220-1320 | daily | WAs | 7435sir, 9510zah |
| 1250-1320 | daily | WAs | 765chr |
| 1620-1720 | daily | WAs | 5935zah |
| **Russian** | **Days** | **Area** | **kHz** |
| 0320-0420 | daily | Cau,CAs | 9550sir |
| 1320-1420 | daily | Cau,CAs | 1449bnt, 9835sir |
| 1920-2020 | daily | Eu,Cau | 702kia |
| **Spanish** | **Days** | **Area** | **kHz** |
| 0720-0820 | daily | Eu | 15200sir, 17540sir |
| 2020-2120 | daily | Eu | 7360sir, 11870sir |
| 2320-0050 | daily | Eu,LAm | 7230sir |
| 2320-0220 | daily | Eu,LAm | 6090sir |
| 2320-0220 | daily | LAm | 6090sir |
| **Swahili** | **Days** | **Area** | **kHz** |
| 0450-0550 | daily | CAf,EAf | 13680sir, 15140sir |
| **Tajik** | **Days** | **Area** | **kHz** |
| 0050-0220 | daily | CAs | 720tyb, 5950sir, 7360sir |
| 1550-1720 | daily | CAs | 720tyb |
| 1550-1720 | daily | WAs | 1098zab |

| Talysh | Days | Area | kHz |
|---|---|---|---|
| 1720-1820 | daily | ME | 702kia |
| **Turkish** | **Days** | **Area** | **kHz** |
| 0420-0550 | daily | ME | 11875sir |
| 1550-1720 | daily | ME | 5925sir |
| 1820-1920 | daily | ME | 639bnb, 702kia |
| **Turkmen** | **Days** | **Area** | **kHz** |
| 1420-1820 | daily | CAs | 1395grg~, 1449bnt |
| **Urdu** | **Days** | **Area** | **kHz** |
| 0130-0230 | daily | ME | 1098zab |
| 0130-0230 | daily | SAs | 765chr |
| 1250-1420 | daily | SAs | 6000sir |
| 1320-1420 | daily | SAs | 765chr |
| 1520-1620 | daily | SAs | 765chr, 5940sir |

**Key:** * "VO Palestine" prgr (0320-0420); ** VO Palestine (1930-2030); *** Incl. Neda al-Bahrain prgr. 0900-1200 (W: nedaalbahrain.com); **** Incl. Neda al-Bahrain prgr. 1700-2000 (W: nedaalbahrain.com); ~Tentative location: Gorgan, N.E. Iran.

**Ann:** Arabic: "Huna Tahran - Sawt al Jumhuriya al Islamiya fi Iran"; English: "IRIB English Radio", "This is the Voice of the Islamic Republic of Iran"; French: "Ici Tehran, la Voix de la République Islamique de l'Iran"; Russian: "Govorit Tegeran, Golos Islamskoy Respubliki Iran".

**IS:** "Love's Rainfall", by Nasser Cheshmazar.

**V:** QSL-card.

**Notes:** The Voice of the Islamic Republic of Iran is the External Sce of the state broadcaster IRIB. Voice of the Islamic Republic of Iran is currently undergoing rebranding as "Pars Today". There will be a crossover period where either, or both, names may be used. The prgr "Voice of the Palestinian Islamic Revolution" targets listeners in the territories under Palestinian Authority.

## ISRAEL (ISR)

### VOICE OF HOPE – MIDDLE EAST (Rlg)
⌨ Bet Gabriel, Israel. (Studio)
**E:** mail@voiceofhope.com (general); studio@voiceofhope.com (prgr feedback) **W:** www.voiceofhope.com/station_middleeast.html
⌨ 543 Country Club Drive, Simi Valley, CA 93065, USA.
**L.P:** Pres (SCG): John D. Tayloe; Vice Pres, Ops (SCG): Ray Robinson; CEO (Voice of Hope Ltd): Jacob Dayan; SM (VOH - Middle East): Gary Hull.
**MW:** Via own tx installed at Bezeq site (see Bezeq).
**kHz:** *1287*

#### Winter Schedule 2018/2019

| Arabic | Days | Area | kHz |
|---|---|---|---|
| 0000-2000 | ....f.. | ME | 1287she |
| 0000-2400 | mtwt.ss | ME | 1287she |
| 2200-2400 | ....f.. | ME | 1287she |
| **English** | **Days** | **Area** | **kHz** |
| 2000-2200 | ....f.. | ME | 1287she |

**Ann:** Arabic: "Sawt al Amal"; English: "From the shores of the Sea of Galilee, this is the Voice of Hope".

**V:** QSL-card. (Email rpt to: reports@voiceofhope.com)

**Notes:** Produced by Voice of Hope Ltd (Israel), part of the Voice of Hope World Radio Network operated by Strategic Communications Group (SCG), USA (see KVOH - Voice of Hope entry under USA). On the air since 28 March 2017. The station is a re-launch of the original "Voice of Hope" founded by George Otis (High Adventure Ministries) in 1979 and broadcasting from MW & SW transmitters in Southern Lebanon until 2000. F.pl: Arabic & Farsi on SW (from own tx installed at Bezeq's SW site at Yavne).

### BEZEQ (THE ISRAEL TELECOMMUNICATIONS CORP. LTD) (Tx Operator)
⌨ Azrieli Center 2, 61620 Tel Aviv, Israel.
☎ +972 3 6262600. 🖷 +972 3 6262609
**E:** dover@bezeq.co.il **W:** www.bezeq.co.il
**L.P:** Chmn (Bezeq Group): Shaul Elovitch
**MW:** [SHE] She'ar Yashuv: 1287kHz 50kW (tx owned by, and operated on behalf of Strategic Communications Group, USA).
**SW:** [ISR] Yavne: 1 x 100kW ‡ (F.pl) (Tx to be supplied by, and operated on behalf of Strategic Communications Group, USA).
**Key:** ‡ SW equipment currently under construction.
**Notes:** Established in 1984. Bezeq is the national transmitter network operator in Israel.

## ITALY (I)

### IRRS–SHORTWAVE (NEXUS–IBA)
☎ +39 02 2666971.
**E:** info@nexus.org **W:** www.nexus.org (General); www.egradio.org (European Gospel Radio)
**Webcast:** L (mp3.nexus.org)
✉ 34 Temple Hall, Mount Saint Annes, Milltown, Dublin 6, Ireland (Milano Ventures Ltd)
☎ +353 1 9069231.
**E:** info@mv.ie **W:** www.milanoventures.com
**L.P:** Chmn (NEXUS-IBA)/CEO (Milano Ventures Ltd): Alfredo E. Cotroneo
**SW:** Via tx leased from Radiocom (Romania).
**kHz:** 7290, 9510, 15515

### Winter Schedule 2018/2019

| English | Days | Area | kHz |
|---|---|---|---|
| 0900-1000 | ....s. | Eu,ME,NAf | 9510tig |
| 1030-1300 | ......s | Eu,ME,NAf | 9510tig |
| 1900-2000 | ....fss | Eu,ME,NAf | 7290tig |
| **Oromo** | **Days** | **Area** | **kHz** |
| 1500-1530 | .....s. | EAf | 15515tig* |

**Key:** * R. Wara Wangeelaa (Rlg) (W: www.facebook.com/Radiowarrawangeelaa).
**Ann:** English: "This is IRRS Shortwave, the Italian Radio Relay Service in Milano"; "This is NEXUS-IBA in Milano, Italy".
**IS:** S/on: Triumphal Scene from Aida (Verdi); S/off: Prisoners' Chorus (Verdi).
**V:** QSL-card. Rp. (Rpt by email to: reports@nexus.org)
**Notes:** Relay services for prgr producers and broadcasters, via Internet (24/7) and on weekends (Fri-Sun) via leased airtime on a third party SW tx in Bulgaria and/or Romania. Some prgs are relayed by the local MW stn Challenger Radio (Villa Estense, Northern Italy), see National R. section for contact details. Brands used for SW services are "Italian Radio Relay Service", "Irish Radio Relay Service", as well as "European Gospel Radio" (for religious relays). NEXUS-International Broadcasting Association (NEXUS-IBA) was founded 1990 in Italy as a non-commercial broadcasting association. While initially broadcasting via own txs in Milan (Italy), NEXUS-IBA later began to rent airtime from SW providers in several European countries (Bulgaria, Romania, Slovakia). Milano Ventures Ltd (Ireland) was founded 2016 and is the commercial arm of the operations.

### ITALIAN BROADCASTING CORPORATION (IBC)
**E:** ibc@europe.com **W:** ibcradio.webs.com
**Webcast:** L (hr.77400.fm; username: IBC, password: 123456), 1300-1430 (daily) only (1300 Italian, 1400 English).
**MW/SW:** Via 3rd party transmitting facilities.
**kHz:** 5010, 5850, 5900, 5985, 6070, 7730, 7780, 9395, 9955

### Winter Schedule 2018/2019

| English | Days | Area | kHz |
|---|---|---|---|
| 0030-0100 | ......s | NAm,Pac | 7730rmi |
| 0030-0100 | ......s | NAm | 9395rmi |
| 0100-0130 | .t..... | NAm,Eu,ME | 7780rmi |
| 0100-0130 | .t..... | Car | 5010rmi |
| 0130-0200 | .t..... | NAm,As | 5850rmi |
| 0130-0200 | .....s. | NAm,Eu,ME | 7780rmi |
| 0200-0230 | ....f.. | LAm | 9955rmi |
| 0330-0400 | ....f.. | CAm | 5985rmi |
| 2030-2100 | .....s. | NAm | 9395rmi |
| 2100-2130 | ..w.... | Eu | 5900sof |
| **Italian** | **Days** | **Area** | **kHz** |
| 1300-1400 | .....s. | CEu,WEu | 6070rob |
| 1900-2030 | ..w.... | CEu,WEu | 6070rob |
| 2030-2100 | ..w.... | Eu | 5900sof |

**NB:** Last 5 minutes of each broadcast are in the soundcard generated digital mode MFSK32 (AM modulation + digital subcarrier).
**Ann:** English: "IBC - Italian Broadcasting Corporation".
**V:** QSL-card.
**Notes:** Launched on 3 July 1979 as Italy's first SW pirate radio stn. Started to lease airtime on legal relay platforms in mid-2016. Some programme segments are transmitted in quasi-digital modes (AM modulation with digital subcarriers).

## JAPAN (J)

### RADIO JAPAN (NHK WORLD) (Pub)
✉ 2-1, Jinnan 2-chome, Shibuya-ku, Tokyo. 150-8001, Japan.
☎ +81 3 34651111. 🖷 +81 3 34811350.
**E:** nhkworld@nhk.jp **W:** www.nhk.or.jp/nhkworld
**Webcast:** D/L/P
**W:** www.nhkint.or.jp (NHK International, Inc)
**L.P:** DG (NHK International, Inc): Keiichi Imamura; Pres (NHK): Ryoichi Uedai; DG, Broadcasting (NHK): Hiroshi Araki.
**SW:** Leased from KDDI & foreign relays.
**SAT:** Badr 4, Eutelsat Hot Bird 13B, Intelsat 19/20/21.
**kHz:** 738, 927, 1386, 5950, 5985, 6075, 6090, 6105, 6155, 6165, 6190, 6195, 7410, 7450, 7565, 9560, 9580, 9620, 9625, 9670, 9680, 9750, 9765, 9855, 9960, 11665, 11685, 11730, 11740, 11790, 11815, 11825, 11910, 11925, 11945, 13650, 13720, 13725, 13730, 13840, 15130, 15195, 15280, 15290, 15325, 15590, 15720, 17810

### Winter Schedule 2018/2019

| Arabic | Days | Area | kHz |
|---|---|---|---|
| 0600-0630 | daily | ME,NAf | 6165iss |
| **Bengali** | **Days** | **Area** | **kHz** |
| 1300-1345 | daily | SAs | 11685sng |
| **Burmese** | **Days** | **Area** | **kHz** |
| 1030-1100 | daily | SEA | 11740sng |
| 1430-1500 | daily | SEA | 11740sng |
| 1445-1505 | .....ss | SEA | 5985yan* |
| 2340-2400 | daily | SEA | 13650yam |
| **Chinese** | **Days** | **Area** | **kHz** |
| 0430-0500 | daily | EAs | 11825yam |
| 1130-1200 | daily | EAs | 6090yam |
| 1230-1300 | daily | EAs | 6190yam |
| 1330-1400 | daily | EAs | 6190yam |
| 1430-1500 | daily | EAs | 6190yam |
| 2230-2250 | daily | EAs | 9560yam |
| **English** | **Days** | **Area** | **kHz** |
| 0000-0030 | daily | NAm | 5950rmi# |
| 0230-0300 | .twtfs. | NAm | 5950rmi# |
| 0500-0530 | daily | Eu | 6155mos |
| 0500-0530 | daily | SAf | 7410iss |
| 0500-0530 | daily | WAf | 9860smg |
| 1100-1130 | daily | SEA | 11825sng |
| 1200-1230 | daily | NAm | 5950rmi# |
| 1400-1430 | daily | SAs | 6165tac |
| 1400-1430 | daily | SEA | 11925hbn |
| 1500-1530 | mtwtf.. | NAm | 5950rmi# |
| 1540-1600 | ...tf.. | SEA | 5985yan* |
| **French** | **Days** | **Area** | **kHz** |
| 0530-0600 | daily | CAf | 13840mdc |
| 0530-0600 | daily | WAf | 7450iss |
| 2030-2100 | daily | WAf | 9855mdc |
| **Hindi** | **Days** | **Area** | **kHz** |
| 0100-0120 | daily | SAs | 6155tac |
| 1430-1500 | daily | SAs | 15720mdc |
| 1530-1600 | daily | SAs | 7565tac |
| **Indonesian** | **Days** | **Area** | **kHz** |
| 1115-1200 | daily | SEA | 9625hbn |
| 1315-1400 | daily | SEA | 11925hbn |
| 2130-2200 | daily | SEA | 6075yam |
| **Japanese** | **Days** | **Area** | **kHz** |
| 0200-0400 | daily | CAm | 6105iss |
| 0200-0400 | daily | SAs | 15590yam |
| 0200-0500 | daily | SEA | 17810yam |
| 0200-0500 | daily | EAs | 15195yam |
| 0300-0400 | daily | EAs | 11790yam |
| 0300-0500 | daily | ME,NAf | 9620nau |
| 0700-0800 | daily | EAs | 11825yam |
| 0700-0900 | daily | SEA | 15280yam |
| 0800-1000 | daily | WAf | 15290iss |
| 0800-1600 | daily | EAs | 9750yam |
| 0900-1000 | daily | SAs | 15325yam |
| 0900-1500 | daily | SEA | 11815yam |
| 1500-1700 | daily | SAs | 9680yam |
| 1700-1900 | daily | ME,NAf | 9765nau |

| Japanese | Days | Area | kHz |
|---|---|---|---|
| 1700-1900 | daily | SAf | 11945iss |
| 1700-1900 | daily | SAm | 13720yam |
| 1900-2100 | daily | CAf | 15130iss |
| 1900-2100 | daily | ME,NAf | 9670yam |
| 2000-2100 | daily | Pac | 9625yam |
| 2100-2300 | daily | SEA | 11665yam |
| 2100-2400 | daily | EAs | 11910yam |

| Korean | Days | Area | kHz |
|---|---|---|---|
| 0415-0445 | daily | EAs | 13720yam |
| 1100-1130 | daily | EAs | 6090yam |
| 1200-1230 | daily | EAs | 6090yam |
| 1300-1330 | daily | EAs | 6190yam |
| 1400-1430 | daily | EAs | 6190yam |
| 2210-2230 | daily | EAs | 9560yam |

| Persian | Days | Area | kHz |
|---|---|---|---|
| 0400-0430 | daily | ME | 11730tac |
| 1430-1500 | daily | ME | 13725iss |
| 1630-1700 | daily | ME | 927dsb |

| Portuguese | Days | Area | kHz |
|---|---|---|---|
| 0900-0930 | daily | SAm | 6195hri |

| Russian | Days | Area | kHz |
|---|---|---|---|
| 0330-0400 | daily | Eu | 1386vst |
| 0330-0400 | daily | RUS | 738msk~ |
| 0430-0500 | daily | Eu | 6165nau |
| 0530-0600 | daily | RUS | 738msk~ |
| 0530-0600 | daily | EAs | 11790yam |
| 0800-0830 | daily | RUS | 738msk~ |
| 1100-1130 | daily | EAs | 5985yam |
| 1100-1130 | daily | RUS | 738msk~ |
| 1330-1400 | daily | RUS | 738msk~ |
| 1600-1630 | daily | CAs | 927dsb |
| 1600-1630 | daily | RUS | 738msk~ |
| 1730-1800 | daily | Eu | 1386vst |
| 1830-1900 | daily | RUS | 738msk~ |
| 2200-2230 | daily | RUS | 738msk~ |

| Spanish | Days | Area | kHz |
|---|---|---|---|
| 0400-0430 | daily | SAm | 6195hri |
| 0930-1000 | daily | SAm | 6195hri |

| Swahili | Days | Area | kHz |
|---|---|---|---|
| 0315-0400 | daily | EAf | 9560mdc |
| 1730-1800 | daily | EAf | 13730mdc |

| Thai | Days | Area | kHz |
|---|---|---|---|
| 1130-1200 | daily | SEA | 11740sng |
| 1230-1300 | daily | SEA | 11740sng |
| 2300-2320 | daily | SEA | 13650yam |

| Urdu | Days | Area | kHz |
|---|---|---|---|
| 1515-1545 | daily | SAs | 9580dha |
| 1700-1730 | daily | SAs | 927dsb |

| Vietnamese | Days | Area | kHz |
|---|---|---|---|
| 1100-1130 | daily | SEA | 11740sng |
| 2320-2340 | daily | SEA | 13650yam |

**Key:** * via MRTV Yangon (also on 576 & 594kHz); ~ Relayed via Vsemirnaya radioset (Moscow, Russia); # Unoffical WRN relay via WRMI.
**Ann:** Chinese: "Zheli shi riben guoji guangbo diantai, NHK huan-qiu guangbowang"; English: "This is NHK World, Radio Japan in Tokyo"; Indonesian: "Inilah Radio Jepang, NHK World, siaran bahasa Indonesia"; Japanese: "Kochirawa NHK Warudo, Rajio Nippon, NHK no kokusaihoso desu"; Korean: "Yeogineun NHK World, Radio Ilbonimnda".
**IS:** Melody "Kazoe Uta".
**V:** QSL-card.
**Notes:** Radio Japan is the External Sce of the public broadcaster NHK, produced by its subsidiary NHK International, Inc. The Japanese programmes include relays of NHK domestic Radio 1. Radio Japan's foreign language prgr's are also relayed by local stations in the following countries: Arabic, to IRQ: 2000-2030 via R. Dijla (Baghdad 88.3MHz + 4 cities) & to ISR (West Bank & Gaza) via Reehan FM (Ramallah 87.8MHz, Jerico 95.6MHz); Bengali, to BGD: 1500-1545 via Bangladesh Betar (Dhaka 104.0MHz + nationwide FM); Hindi, to IND: 1830-1900 via Big FM (New Delhi 92.7MHz + 4 cities); Indonesian, to INS: 1205-1220 via R. Elshinta (Jakarta 90.0MHz + 7 cities), 1400-1445 via R. Rasita (Simalungun 1170kHz) & via various local FM stns in 43 cities; Persian, to AFG: 1430-1500 via R. Khillid (Kabul & Herat

88.0MHz); Swahili, to TZA: 0315-0400 via R. Uhai (Tabora 94.1MHz), 1730-1800 via Tanzania Broadcasting Corp. (Dar es Salaam 90.0MHz + nationwide FM) & Hits FM (Zanzibar 92.5MHz); Thai, to THA: MF 0100-0130 via Naresuan Univ. R. (Phitsanulokon 107.25MHz), 0530-0545 & 1230-1245 via Maejo Univ. R. (Chiang Mai 95.5MHz), MF 1230-1300 via Thammasat Univ. R. (Bangkok 981kHz 10kW) & via Mahasarakham Univ. R. (Maha Sarakham 102.25MHz), 1230-1300 via Khon Kaen Univ. R. (Khon Kaen 103.0MHz); Vietnamese to VTN: Mon 1300-1320, Tue-Fri 1300-1315, Sat 1330-1345, Sun 1330-1350 via VOV Giao Thong on 91.0MHz (Hanoi, Ho Chi Minh City, Can Tho and Quang Binh).

## KDDI CORPORATION (Tx Operator)
⌨ Garden Air Tower, 10-10, Iidabashi 3-chome, Chiyoda-ku, Tokyo 102-8460, Japan.
☎ +81 3 33470077. 🖷 +81 3 33475845.
**W:** www.kddi.com
**L.P:** Pres: Takashi Tanaka.
**SW:** [YAM] Sakuragawa, Yamato (Ibaraki prefecture): 4 x 100, 7 x 300kW.
**Notes:** KDDI Corporation is a major national telecommunications provider.

## KOREA, North (KRE)

### PYONGYANG BROADCASTING STATION (PYONGYANG PANGSONG) (Gov)
⌨ Pyongyang, Democratic People's Republic of Korea.
**W:** www.gnu.rep.kp
**Webcast:** D
**MW/SW:** Uses txs provided by the Ministry of Post & Telecommunications.
**FM/DAB:** FM: 92.1/93.6MHz (unknown locations)
**kHz:** 621, 657, 801, 855, 873, 3220, 3320, 6400

#### Winter Schedule 2018/2019

| Korean | Days | Area | kHz |
|---|---|---|---|
| 0300-0700 | daily | EAs | 621chj |
| 1300-2000 | daily | EAs | 621chj |
| 1800-2000 | daily | EAs | 873snu, 3220ham |
| 2100-1800 | daily | EAs | 6400kng |
| 2100-1900 | daily | EAs | 801kng, 3320pyo |
| 2100-2000 | daily | EAs | 657kan, 855swo |

**Ann:** Korean: "Pyongyang Pangsong-imnida".
**IS:** Song of General Kim Il Sung. Opening & closing music: National Anthem.
**V:** QSL-card
**Notes:** External Sce of the Radio & TV Broadcasting Committee of the Democratic People's Republic of Korea for Korean listeners in South Korea, Japan and the P.R. China. Jammed in parts of the target area.

### VOICE OF KOREA (VOK) (Gov)
⌨ Pyongyang, Democratic People's Republic of Korea.
☎ +850 2 3816035. 🖷 +850 2 3814416.
**E:** vok@star-co.net.kp **W:** vok.rep.kp
**Webcast:** D
**MW/SW:** Uses txs provided by the Ministry of Post & Telecommunications.
**SAT:** Thaicom 5.
**kHz:** 621, 6070, 6170, 6185, 7210, 7220, 7235, 7570, 7580, 9425, 9435, 9445, 9650, 9730, 9850, 9875, 9890, 11635, 11645, 11710, 11735, 11910, 12015, 13650, 13760, 15105, 15180, 15245

#### Winter Schedule 2018/2019

| Arabic | Days | Area | kHz |
|---|---|---|---|
| 1500-1600 | daily | ME,NAf | 9890kuj, 11645kuj |
| 1700-1800 | daily | ME,NAf | 9890kuj, 11645kuj |

| Chinese | Days | Area | kHz |
|---|---|---|---|
| 0300-0400 | daily | SEA | 13650kuj, 15105kuj |
| 0500-0600 | daily | EAs | 7220kuj, 9445kuj, 9730kuj |
| 0600-0700 | daily | SEA | 13650kuj, 15105kuj |
| 0800-0900 | daily | EAs | 7220kuj, 9445kuj |
| 1100-1200 | daily | EAs | 7220kuj, 9445kuj |
| 1300-1400 | daily | SEA | 6185kuj, 9850kuj |
| 2100-2300 | daily | EAs | 7235kuj, 9445kuj, 9875kuj, 11635kuj |

| English | Days | Area | kHz |
|---|---|---|---|
| 0400-0500 | daily | EAs | 7220kuj, 9445kuj, 9730kuj |
| 0400-0500 | daily | LAm | 11735kuj, 13760kuj, 15180kuj |
| 0500-0600 | daily | SEA | 13650kuj, 15105kuj |
| 0600-0700 | daily | EAs | 7220kuj, 9445kuj, 9730kuj |
| 1000-1100 | daily | LAm | 6170kuj, 9435kuj |
| 1000-1100 | daily | SEA | 6185kuj, 9850kuj |
| 1300-1400 | daily | NAm | 9435kuj, 11710kuj |
| 1300-1400 | daily | Eu | 7570kuj, 12015kuj |
| 1500-1600 | daily | Eu | 7570kuj, 12015kuj |
| 1500-1600 | daily | NAm | 9435kuj, 11710kuj |
| 1600-1700 | daily | ME,NAf | 9890kuj, 11645kuj |
| 1800-1900 | daily | Eu | 7570kuj, 12015kuj |
| 1900-2000 | daily | ME,NAf | 9875kuj, 11635kuj |
| 1900-2000 | daily | SAf | 7210kuj, 11910kuj |
| 2100-2200 | daily | Eu | 7570kuj, 12015kuj |

| French | Days | Area | kHz |
|---|---|---|---|
| 0400-0500 | daily | SEA | 13650kuj, 15105kuj |
| 0600-0700 | daily | LAm | 11735kuj, 13760kuj, 15180kuj |
| 1100-1200 | daily | LAm | 6170kuj, 9435kuj |
| 1100-1200 | daily | SEA | 6185kuj, 9850kuj |
| 1400-1500 | daily | NAm | 9435kuj, 11710kuj |
| 1400-1500 | daily | Eu | 7570kuj, 12015kuj |
| 1600-1700 | daily | Eu | 7570kuj, 12015kuj |
| 1600-1700 | daily | NAm | 9435kuj, 11710kuj |
| 1800-1900 | daily | ME,NAf | 9875kuj, 11635kuj |
| 1800-1900 | daily | SAf | 7210kuj, 11910kuj |
| 2000-2100 | daily | Eu | 7570kuj, 12015kuj |

| German | Days | Area | kHz |
|---|---|---|---|
| 1600-1700 | daily | Eu | 6170kuj, 9425kuj |
| 1800-2000 | daily | Eu | 6170kuj, 9425kuj |

| Japanese | Days | Area | kHz |
|---|---|---|---|
| 0700-1300 | daily | EAs | 621chj, 7580kuj, 9650kuj |
| 0900-1300 | daily | EAs | 6070kng |
| 2100-2350 | daily | EAs | 621chj, 7580kuj, 9650kuj |

| Korean | Days | Area | kHz |
|---|---|---|---|
| 0900-0950 | daily | EAs | 7220kuj, 9445kuj |
| 1200-1250 | daily | LAm | 6170kuj, 9435kuj |
| 1200-1250 | daily | SEA | 6185kuj, 9850kuj |
| 1400-1450 | daily | SEA | 6185kuj, 9850kuj |
| 1700-1750 | daily | Eu | 7570kuj, 12015kuj |
| 1700-1750 | daily | NAm | 9435kuj, 11710kuj |
| 2000-2050 | daily | Eu | 6170kuj, 9425kuj |
| 2000-2050 | daily | ME,NAf | 9875kuj, 11635kuj |
| 2000-2050 | daily | SAf | 7210kuj, 11910kuj |
| 2300-2350 | daily | EAs | 7235kuj, 9445kuj, 9875kuj, 11635kuj |
| 2300-2350 | daily | Eu | 7570kuj, 12015kuj |

| Russian | Days | Area | kHz |
|---|---|---|---|
| 0700-0900 | daily | EAs | 9875kuj, 11735kuj |
| 0700-0900 | daily | Eu | 13760kuj, 15245kuj |
| 1400-1600 | daily | Eu | 6170kuj, 9425kuj |
| 1700-1800 | daily | Eu | 6170kuj, 9425kuj |

| Spanish | Days | Area | kHz |
|---|---|---|---|
| 0300-0400 | daily | LAm | 11735kuj, 13760kuj, 15180kuj |
| 0500-0600 | daily | LAm | 11735kuj, 13760kuj, 15180kuj |
| 1900-2000 | daily | Eu | 7570kuj, 12015kuj |
| 2100-2300 | daily | Eu | 7570kuj, 12015kuj |

**Ann:** Arabic: "Huna Sowt al Koriya"; Chinese: "Chaoxian zhi sheng guangbo diantai"; English: "This is Voice of Korea"; French: "La Voix de la Corée"; German: "Hier ist die Stimme Koreas"; Japanese: "Choson no koe hoso desu"; Korean: "Joson Jung-ang Pangsong-imnida"; Russian: "Govorit Golos Korei"; Spanish: "Aqui la Voz de Corea".
**IS:** Song of General Kim Il Sung. Opening music: National Anthem.
**V:** QSL-card.

**Notes:** Voice of Korea ("R. Pyongyang" until 2002) is the External Sce of the Radio & TV Broadcasting Committee of the Democratic People's Republic of Korea.

## MINISTRY OF POST & TELECOMMUNICATIONS (Tx Operator)

⌨ Oesong-dong, Central District, Pyongyang, Democratic People's Republic of Korea.
☎ +850 2 3813180. 🖷 +850 2 3814418.
**E:** mptird@star-co.net.kp
**L.P:** Minister: Kwang Chol Kim.
**MW:** [CHJ] Chongjin: 621kHz 500kW; [HJU] Haeju: 1053kHz 1000kW; [KAN] Kangnam: 657kHz 1500kW; [KMK] Kimchaek 801kHz 500kW; [SNU] Sinuiju: 873kHz 250kW; [SWO] Sangwon: 855kHz 500kW.
**SW:** [CHJ] Chongjin: 1 x 5kW; [KNG] Kanggye: 1 x 250kW; [KUJ] Kujang: 10 x 200kW; [PYO] Pyongyang: 1 x 100kW. The line-up reflects the situation before the installation of new Chinese-made txs (20/50/100/150kW) in recent years.
**Notes:** The Ministry of Post and Telecommunications owns and operates the transmitter network in the Democratic People's Republic of Korea.

## KOREA, South (KOR)

### KBS WORLD RADIO (Pub)

⌨ 13, Yeouigongwon-ro, Yeongdeungpo-gu, Seoul, 07235, Rep. of Korea.
☎ +82 2 7813885. (English) 🖷 +82 2 7813694.
**E:** rki@kbs.co.kr; english@kbs.co.kr **W:** world.kbs.co.kr
**Webcast:** D/L/P
**L.P:** Pres/CEO (KBS): Ko Dae-Young; Exec. Producer (KBS World Radio): Paek Seung Yeop.
**MW:** [DAN] Dangjin (HLCA): 972kHz 1500kW; [KIM] Gimje (HLSR): 1170kHz 500kW.
**SW:** [KIM] Gimje: 8 x 100, 3 x 250kW; [HWA] Hwaseong: 1 x 100kW.
**kHz:** 738, 972, 1170, 3955, 5910, 5950, 6015, 6040, 6045, 6095, 6155, 7215, 7275, 9515, 9570, 9580, 9605, 9630, 9640, 9645, 9740, 9770, 9805, 11795, 11810, 15160, 15575

### Winter Schedule 2018/2019

| Arabic | Days | Area | kHz |
|---|---|---|---|
| 2000-2100 | daily | ME,NAf | 5910dha |

| Chinese | Days | Area | kHz |
|---|---|---|---|
| 1130-1230 | daily | EAs,SEA | 6095kim, 9770kim |
| 1300-1400 | daily | EAs | 1170kim, 7275kim |
| 2300-2400 | daily | EAs,SEA | 7215kim, 9805kim |

| English | Days | Area | kHz |
|---|---|---|---|
| 0200-0300 | daily | LAm | 9580kim |
| 0300-0400 | daily | NAm | 5950rmi# |
| 0800-1030 | daily | SEA | 9770kim |
| 1300-1400 | daily | NAm | 5950rmi#, 15575kim |
| 1300-1400 | daily | SEA | 9570kim |
| 1500-1700 | daily | Eu | 9515kim |
| 1600-1700 | daily | SEA | 9640kim |
| 1800-2100 | daily | SAs | 9630kim |
| 2100-2200 | daily | NAm | 5950rmi# |
| 2200-2300 | daily | Eu | 11810kim |

| French | Days | Area | kHz |
|---|---|---|---|
| 2000-2100 | daily | Af | 5950iss |
| 2100-2200 | daily | Eu | 3955wof |

| German | Days | Area | kHz |
|---|---|---|---|
| 2000-2100 | daily | Eu | 3955wof |

| Indonesian | Days | Area | kHz |
|---|---|---|---|
| 1200-1300 | daily | SEA | 9570kim |
| 1400-1500 | daily | SEA | 9570kim |
| 1600-1700 | daily | SEA | 9805kim |
| 2200-2300 | daily | SEA | 9805kim |

| Japanese | Days | Area | kHz |
|---|---|---|---|
| 0100-0200 | daily | EAs | 9580kim |
| 0200-0300 | daily | EAs,SAm | 11810kim |
| 0800-0900 | daily | EAs | 7275kim |
| 0800-1000 | daily | EAs | 6155kim |
| 1000-1100 | daily | EAs | 6095kim |
| 1100-1300 | daily | EAs | 1170kim |

| Korean | Days | Area | kHz |
|---|---|---|---|
| 0350-2400 | daily | EAs | 972dan*, 6015hwa* |

| Korean | Days | Area | kHz |
|---|---|---|---|
| 0700-0800 | daily | Eu | 6045wof |
| 0800-1100 | daily | EAs,SEA | 9570kim |
| 0900-1000 | daily | ME,Af | 15160kim |
| 0900-1200 | daily | EAs,SEA | 7275kim |
| 1000-1100 | daily | EAs | 1170km |
| 1400-0400 | daily | EAs | 1170kim** |
| 1400-1500 | daily | NAm | 15575kim |
| 1600-1800 | daily | Eu | 7275kim |
| 1600-1800 | daily | ME,Af | 9740kim |
| 1700-1900 | daily | Eu | 9515kim |
| 2300-2400 | daily | LAm | 11810kim |

| Russian | Days | Area | kHz |
|---|---|---|---|
| 0100-0130 | daily | RUS | 738msk~ |
| 0600-0630 | daily | RUS | 738msk~ |
| 0930-1000 | daily | RUS | 738msk~ |
| 1300-1400 | daily | CAs | 9645kim |
| 1400-1430 | daily | RUS | 738msk~ |
| 1730-1800 | daily | RUS | 738msk~ |
| 1800-1900 | daily | Eu | 6040wof |
| 2000-2030 | daily | RUS | 738msk~ |

| Spanish | Days | Area | kHz |
|---|---|---|---|
| 0100-0200 | daily | LAm | 9605hri, 11810kim |
| 0200-0300 | daily | NAm | 15575kim |
| 1100-1200 | daily | LAm | 11795kim |
| 1800-1900 | daily | Eu | 9740kim |

| Vietnamese | Days | Area | kHz |
|---|---|---|---|
| 1030-1130 | daily | SEA | 9770kim |
| 1500-1600 | daily | SEA | 9640kim |
| 2300-2400 | daily | SEA | 7275kim |

**Key:** * 1st Global Korean Network; ** 2nd Global Korean Network; ~ Relayed via Vsemirnaya radioset, Moscow; # Unoffical WRN relay via WRMI.

**Ann:** Arabic: "Huna KBS World Radio min Si'ul"; Chinese: "Zheli shi Hanguo guoji guangbo diantai, zai Dahanminguo shoudu Shou'er wei nin boyin"; English: "This is KBS World Radio, the overseas service of the Korean Broadcasting System, coming to you from Seoul, the capital of the Republic of Korea"; German: "Hier ist KBS World Radio aus Seoul, der Auslandssender der Republik Korea"; Indonesian: "Inilah siaran bahasa Indonesia, KBS World Radio, yang dipancarkan langsung dari ibu kota Republik Korea, Seoul"; Japanese: "Kochirawa Kankoku Souru kara okurishiteimasu KBS no rajio kokusai hoso, KBS warudo rajio desu"; Korean: "Yeogineun Daehan Minguk Seoul-eseo bonaedeurineun KBS World Radio urimal bangsong-imnida"; Spanish: "Esto es KBS World Radio, emitiendo desde Seúl, Republica de Corea."; Vietnamese: "Day la chuong trinh phat thanh tieng Viet cua dai KBS World Radio phat thanh tu Seoul Han quoc". Global Korean Network 1: "Jungpa Gubaek-chilsib-i (972) kHz, Hanminjok Neteuwokeu Chaeneol, KBS Hanminjok Je-il Bangsong-imnida"; Global Korean Network 2: "Jungpa Cheonbaek-chilsip (1170) kHz, Daehan Mingook Seoureseo Bonae Deurineun Hanminjok Neteuwokeu Chaeneol, KBS Hanminjok Je-I Bangsong-imnida".

**IS:** Korean children's song "Dar-a Dar-a Balgeun Dar-a (Oh, Bright Moon)", played on a glockenspiel. Original music "Dawn" composed by Kim Hee Jyo, with KBS symphony orchestra.

**V:** QSL-card. Online-form available on website.

**Notes:** KBS World Radio is the External Sce of the public broadcaster Korean Broadcasting System (KBS). The KBS Global Korean Network channels are services for ethnic Koreans living outside of the Republic of Korea. KBS World Radio prgrs are also distributed as part of the global WRN Satellite/Internet feeds, some of these are relayed locally on MW/FM: Russian (schedule see above) via the local WRN relay on 738kHz (5kW) in Moscow for listeners in Moscow & Moscow region; Indonesian 1200-1300 via R. Camajaya FM on 102.6MHz in Jakarta & via GISA FM on 107.7MHz in Aceh Utara (Indonesia); and Spanish M-F 1800-1855 via R. Palermo FM on 94.7MHz in Buenos Aires (Argentina).

### FEBC KOREA (Rlg)
📧 P.O. Box 88, Seoul 04067, Republic of Korea.
☎ +82 2 3200431. 📠 +82 2 3200229.
**E:** febcadm@febc.net **W:** www.febc.net (Korean); english.febc.net (English)
**Webcast:** L
📧 Yeongdeungpo-dong 6-ga 8-1, Yeongdeungpo-gu, Seoul 150-036, Republic of Korea.
**L.P:** Pres: Dr Billy Kim; Mgr, Int'l Relations: Chung Soo Kim.
**MW:** [JEJ] Jeju (HLAZ): 1566kHz 250kW; [SEO] Seoul, Siheung (HLKX):

1188kHz 100kW.
**FM/DAB:** FM: See National Radio section.
**kHz:** *1188, 1566*

### Winter Schedule 2018/2019

| Chinese | Days | Area | kHz |
|---|---|---|---|
| 1100-1230 | daily | EAs | 1566jej |
| 1345-1600 | daily | EAs | 1566jej |
| **English** | **Days** | **Area** | **kHz** |
| 1000-1100 | daily | EAs | 1188seo |
| **Japanese** | **Days** | **Area** | **kHz** |
| 1230-1345 | daily | J | 1566jej |
| **Korean** | **Days** | **Area** | **kHz** |
| 1600-1800 | daily | EAs | 1566jej |
| 1900-1900 | daily | EAs | 1188seo, 1566jej |
| **Russian** | **Days** | **Area** | **kHz** |
| 1830-1900 | daily | RUS | 1566jej |

**Ann:** Chinese: "HLKX. Zheli shi zhongpo 1188 (yao yao ba ba) qianhe, Yiyou Diantai di 2 (er) dai.", "HLAZ. Zheli shi zhongbo 1566 (yao wu liu liu) qianhe, Yiyou Diantai di 1 (yi) dai"; English: "It's 8 o'clock and time for daily English segment on HLKX 1188 on your AM radio dial"; Japanese: "Kochirawa kirisutokyo hosokyoku FEBC desu"; Korean: Jungpa Cheonbaek-palsip-pal (1188) kHz, Pyojun FM Paeng-nyuk-jeom-gu (106.9) MHz, Areumdaun Chanyanggwa Gibbeun Sosigeul Jeonhaneun Geukdong Bangsong-imnida", "Jungpa Cheon-o-baeng-nyuk-sim-nyuk (1566) kHz, Pyojun FM Jeju Baek-sa-jeom-chil (104.7) MHz, Seogwipo Baeg-il-jeom-il (101.1) MHz, Daehan Minguk Seongyo Jungsim Jeju Geukdong Bangsong-imnida. HLAZ".

**V:** QSL-card.

**Notes:** FEBC Korea is a regional division of Far East Broadcasting Company, Inc (FEBC) (USA) with a nationwide tx network on MW&FM. FEBC Korea's MW txs also carry prgrs produced by other national studios of FEBC, targeting China, Japan and the Far Eastern part of Russia. The trs may include prgrs provided by small religious prgr producers and broadcast under own labels. Some airtime is leased to non-religious third-party broadcasters.

## KUWAIT (KWT)

### RADIO KUWAIT (Gov)
📧 See National Radio section.
**Webcast:** L (www.media.gov.kw)
**SW:** [KBD] Kuwait, Kabd: 5 x 500kW (3 txs are DRM capable).
**FM/DAB:** FM: See National Radio section.
**SAT:** Arabsat 5C, AsiaSat 5, Badr 4, Eutelsat 8WB/Hot Bird 13B, Galaxy 19, Hispasat 30W-5, Intelsat 19, Nilesat 201.
**kHz:** 5960, 7250, 9750, 11630, 11970, 13650, 15110, 15515, 15530, 15540, 17550, 17760

### Winter Schedule 2018/2019

| Arabic | Days | Area | kHz |
|---|---|---|---|
| 0300-0630 | daily | ME | 5960kbd |
| 0500-0900 | daily | EAs | 15515kbd |
| 0945-1325 | daily | Eu | 15110kbd+ |
| 1000-1600 | daily | CAf | 11630kbd† |
| 1100-1325 | daily | NAf | 9750kbd |
| 1700-2000 | daily | NAm | 13650kbd+ |
| 2000-2400 | daily | NAm | 17550kbd |
| **English** | **Days** | **Area** | **kHz** |
| 0500-0800 | daily | SAs | 11970kbd+ |
| 0500-0800 | daily | Eu | 15530kbd |
| 1800-2100 | daily | Eu | 15540kbd+,† |
| **Filipino** | **Days** | **Area** | **kHz** |
| 1000-1200 | daily | SEA | 17760kbd |
| **Persian** | **Days** | **Area** | **kHz** |
| 0800-1000 | daily | ME | 7250kbd |
| **Urdu** | **Days** | **Area** | **kHz** |
| 1600-1800 | daily | SAs | 15540kbd |

**Key:** + DRM; † Irregular.
**Ann:** Arabic: "Huna al-Kuwait".
**V:** QSL-card. (Email rpt to kwtfreq@media.gov.kw)
**Notes:** Arabic prgrs are relays of Home Sce networks.

### USAGM KUWAIT "GEORGE A. MOORE JR" TRANSMITTING STATION
📧 USAGM Transmitting Station, c/o US Embassy, P.O. Box 77, Safat 13001, Kuwait City, Kuwait.

☎ +965 24562754. 🖹 +965 24562754.
**L.P:** SM: Gaines Johnson.
**MW:** [KWT] Kuwait, Umm Al-Rimam: 1548kHz 600kW; 1593kHz 150kW.
**SW:** [KWT] Kuwait, Umm Al-Rimam: 6 x 250kW.
**V:** QSL-card. (Email to manager_kuwait@kuw.usagm.gov)

## KYRGYZSTAN (KGZ)

**KYRGYZTELECOM (Tx Operator)**
🖃 Chui avenue 96, 720000 Bishkek, Kyrgyzstan.
☎ +996 312 681616. 🖹 +996 312 662424.
**E:** info@kt.kg **W:** www.kt.kg
**L.P:** DG: Salavat Iskakov.
**MW:** [BIS] Bishkek, Krasnaya Rechka: 1287kHz 2x100kW (under construction), 1467kHz 500kW (both operated on behalf of TWR).
**SW:** [BIS] Bishkek, Krasnaya Rechka: 1 x 15kW. (Estimated power)
**Notes:** Kyrgyztelekom is the national tx operator.

## LAOS (LAO)

**LAO NATIONAL RADIO (Gov)**
🖃 See National Radio Section.
**MW:** [VIE] Vientiane 567kHz 200kW.
**SW:** [VIE] Vientiane 1 x 50kW.
**FM/DAB:** FM: See National Radio section.
**kHz:** 567, 6130

### Winter Schedule 2018/2019

| Chinese | Days | Area | kHz |
|---|---|---|---|
| 1400-1430 | daily | SEA | 567vie, 6130vie |
| **English** | **Days** | **Area** | **kHz** |
| 1430-1500 | daily | SEA | 567vie, 6130vie |
| **French** | **Days** | **Area** | **kHz** |
| 1500-1530 | daily | SEA | 567vie, 6130vie |
| **Khmer** | **Days** | **Area** | **kHz** |
| 1330-1400 | daily | SEA | 567vie, 6130vie |
| **Thai** | **Days** | **Area** | **kHz** |
| 1530-1600 | daily | SEA | 567vie, 6130vie |
| **Vietnamese** | **Days** | **Area** | **kHz** |
| 1600-1630 | daily | SEA | 567vie, 6130vie |

**Ann:** English: "This is the Lao National Radio, broadcasting from Vientiane, capital - the Lao People's Democratic Republic".
**V:** QSL-card.
**Notes:** The foreign language trs are part of LNR's "National Channel".

## LITHUANIA (LTU)

**RADIO BALTIC WAVES INTERNATIONAL (RBWI)**
🖃 Algirdo g. 13-9, LT-03219 Vilnius, Lithuania.
☎ +370 699 05074.
**E:** pleikys@tbbr.lt
**L.P:** Dir: Rolandas Stirblys; Project Coordinator: Rimantas Pleikys.
**MW:** Leased from LRTC.
**V:** QSL-email.
**Notes:** RBWI markets air time on MW relay facilities in Lithuania for foreign broadcasters.

**LIETUVOS RADIJO IR TELEVIZIJOS CENTRAS (LRTC) (Tx Operator)**
🖃 Sausio 13-osios g. 10, LT-04347 Vilnius, Lithuania.
☎ +370 5 2040300. 🖹 +370 5 2040325.
**E:** info@telecentras.lt **W:** www.telecentras.lt
**L.P:** GD: Remigijus Šeris.
**MW:** [VST] Anykščiai, Viešintos: 612/1386kHz 300kW (currently run at 75kW).
**Notes:** LRTC is the national transmitter network operator.

## MACEDONIA (MKD)

**RADIO MAKEDONIJA (Pub)**
🖃 blvd. "Goce Delcev" bb, 1000 Skopje, Macedonia.
☎ +389 2 5119874.
**E:** radiomakedonija@mrt.com.mk **W:** mrt.com.mk
**Webcast:** L
**L.P:** Editor: Vangel Borozinovski.
**MW:** Leased from Makedonska Radiodifuzija.
**kHz:** 810

### Winter Schedule 2018/2019

| Albanian | Days | Area | kHz |
|---|---|---|---|
| 2000-2030 | mtwtf.. | Eu | 810sko |
| **Bulgarian** | **Days** | **Area** | **kHz** |
| 1900-1930 | mtwtf.. | Eu | 810sko |
| **Greek** | **Days** | **Area** | **kHz** |
| 1930-2000 | mtwtf.. | Eu | 810sko |
| **Macedonian** | **Days** | **Area** | **kHz** |
| 1830-2100 | .....s. | Eu | 810sko |
| **Music*** | **Days** | **Area** | **kHz** |
| 1830-1900 | mtwtf.. | Eu | 810sko |
| **Serbian** | **Days** | **Area** | **kHz** |
| 2030-2100 | mtwtf.. | Eu | 810sko |

**Key:** * Opening announcement in Macedonian, followed by intro to non-stop music, in English.
**Ann:** English: "This is Macedonian Radio Television - This is Radio Macedonia"; Macedonian: "Radio Makedonija - programa za sdranstvo".
**V:** QSL-letter.
**Notes:** International Sce of the public service broadcaster Makedonska Radio Televizija (MRT), incl. a weekly prgr in Macedonian (on Saturdays). Outside of the R. Makedonija prgr block, the MW tx & Internet stream carries Prgr 1 of MRT (see National Radio section).

## MADAGASCAR (MDG)

**MADAGASCAR WORLD VOICE (Rlg)**
🖃 World Christian Broadcasting, Immeuble Assist, 7ème etage, 101 Antananarivo, Madagascar.
**E:** mwvradio@gmail.com **W:** www.africanpathways.com (English); www.smzg.org (Chinese); www.lavozalegre.com (Spanish); knls.net (Russian)
🖃 605 Bradley Court, Franklin, TN 37067, USA. (World Christian Broadcasting)
☎ +1 615 3718707. (USA)
**E:** info@worldchristian.org **W:** www.worldchristian.org
**L.P:** Pres/CEO (USA): Earl Young; WCB Vice Pres of Engineering (USA): Kevin Chambers; SM (Madagascar): Mahefa Rakotomamonjy.
**SW:** [MWV] Mahajanga II (Belobaka); Amparemahitsy: 2 x 100kW.
**kHz:** 6180, 6190, 9690, 11610, 11790, 11825, 11885, 11965, 13670, 13710, 15510, 17530

### Winter Schedule 2018/2019

| Arabic | Days | Area | kHz |
|---|---|---|---|
| 1900-2000 | daily | NAf,ME | 11965mwv |
| 2000-2100 | daily | NAf,ME | 13710mwv |
| 2200-2300 | daily | NAf,ME | 11790mwv |
| **Chinese** | **Days** | **Area** | **kHz** |
| 0400-0500 | daily | EAs,SEA | 17530mwv |
| 2100-2200 | daily | Eu | 11610mwv |
| 2200-2300 | daily | EAs,SEA | 11965mwv |
| **English** | **Days** | **Area** | **kHz** |
| 0200-0300 | daily | As | 15510mwv |
| 0300-0400 | daily | As | 15510mwv |
| 0400-0500 | daily | Af | 11825mwv |
| 1800-1900 | daily | Af | 13670mwv |
| 2000-2100 | daily | Af | 11965mwv |
| **Portuguese** | **Days** | **Area** | **kHz** |
| 2100-2200 | daily | Af | 11965mwv |
| **Russian** | **Days** | **Area** | **kHz** |
| 1800-1900 | daily | RUS | 11885mwv |
| 1900-2000 | daily | RUS | 9690mwv |
| **Spanish** | **Days** | **Area** | **kHz** |
| 0200-0300 | daily | SAm | 6190mwv |
| 0300-0400 | daily | SAm | 6190mwv |

**Ann:** Arabic: "Radio Fida"; English: "Madagascar World Voice", "From the beautiful region of the Indian Ocean, this is your New Life Station", "African Pathways Radio"; Spanish: "La Voz Alegre".
**IS:** "Chariots of Fire", by Vangelis.
**V:** QSL-card. (rpt to USA address)
**Notes:** Transmitting station owned by World Christian Broadcasting, Inc (WCB). See USA for corporate details. The stn retransmits prgrs produced in the U.S. studios of WCB and WCB partner organisations. Further prgrs of WCB's language services in Chinese, English and Russian can be heard via its sister transmitting stn KNLS (see under

Alaska for schedules).

## MALAGASY GLOBAL BUSINESS S.A. (MGLOB) (Tx Operator)

⌨ P.O.Box 404, 101 Antananarivo, Madagascar.
☎ +261 202242222. 🖷 +261 202243184.
E: talata@mglob.mg
⌨ Lot Bonnet 88, Ivandry, 101 Antananarivo, Madagascar.
L.P: Dir: Ms Flore Ravelojaona; Technical Mgr: Tovonirina Razananaivo; Airtime Sales & Frequency Mgr: Rocus de Joode.
SW: [MDC] Talata Volonondry: 3 x 250kW. Backup tx 1 x 250kW
V: QSL-card (for relayed prgrs). Email rpt to monitoring@mglob.mg
Notes: In 2012, Malagasy Global Business S.A. (MGLOB) took over the operation of the former Radio Netherlands Worldwide Relay Station at Talata Volonondry. The company was founded by former staff of the transmitting station.

## MALI (MLI)

### CHINA RADIO INTERNATIONAL (CRI) RELAY ‡
SW: [BKO] Bamako, Kati: 2 x 100kW.
Key: ‡ Transmissions suspended, pending contract renewal with RTM
V: QSL-card. (Rpt to CRI, in China)
Notes: The shortwave facilities are leased to CRI by Radiodiffusion-Télevision du Mali.

## MOLDOVA Transnistria (MDP)

### PRIDNESTROVSKIY RADIOTELETSENTR (Tx Operator)
⌨ MD-4006 Maiac, Pridnestrovian Moldavian Republic, Moldova.
☎ +373 210 66500.
E: prtc@idknet.com
L.P: DG: Vitaliy Kucherenko; Technical Dir: Sergey Omelchenko.
MW: [KCH] Grigoriopol, Maiac: 999/1413/1548kHz 1000kW.
SW: [KCH] Grigoriopol, Maiac: 5 x 1000kW.
V: eQSL-card. (For relayed stns)
Notes: Pridnestrovskiy Radioteletsentr (owned by RTRN, Russia) provides high power MW & SW transmitting facilities.

## MONACO (MCO)

### MONACO MEDIA DIFFUSION (MMD) (Tx Operator)
⌨ 10-12 quai Antoine 1er, MC-98000 Monte Carlo, Monaco.
☎ +377 97974700. 🖷 +377 97974707.
E: contact@mmd.mc W: www.mmd.mc
L.P: Chmn: Jean Pastorelli; Managing Dir: Pierre Medicin.
MW: [ROU] Roumoules (France): 1467kHz 1000kW.
Notes: MMD (formerly Monte Carlo Radiodiffusion/MCR) is majority-owned by the Principality of Monaco and a joint venture with the French transmitter operator TDF. MMD is the national transmitter network owner in Monaco and also maintains high power transmitting centres in France (at the border to Monaco).

## MONGOLIA (MNG)

### VOICE OF MONGOLIA (Pub)
⌨ P.O. Box 365, Ulaanbaatar 13, Mongolia.
☎ +976 1 1327900. 🖷 +976 1 1323096.
E: vom_english@yahoo.com W: www.vom.mn
Webcast: D (Webcast languages: Chinese (Mandarin), English, Japanese, Mongolian & Russian)
L.P: Dir, Foreign Sce: Mrs Narantuya B; Mail Editor: Bolorchimeg E.
SW: Leased from RTBN.
kHz: 6005, 12015, 12085

### Winter Schedule 2018/2019

| Chinese | Days | Area | kHz |
|---|---|---|---|
| 1000-1030 | daily | EAs | 12085uba |
| 1430-1500 | daily | EAs | 12015uba |

| English | Days | Area | kHz |
|---|---|---|---|
| 0900-0930 | daily | EAs | 12085uba |
| 1300-1330 | mtwtfs. | CEu,WEu | 6005kll* |
| 1530-1600 | daily | EAs | 12015uba |

| Japanese | Days | Area | kHz |
|---|---|---|---|
| 1030-1100 | daily | EAs | 12085uba |
| 1500-1530 | daily | EAs | 12015uba |

| Mongolian | Days | Area | kHz |
|---|---|---|---|
| 0930-1000 | daily | EAs | 12085uba |
| 1400-1430 | daily | EAs | 12015uba |

Key: * Relayed via Shortwaveservice (Kall, Germany).
Ann: English: "Welcome to the Voice of Mongolia, in English".
V: QSL-card. Rp (2 IRCs or 1 USD) appreciated.
Notes: The Voice of Mongolia is the External Sce of the Mongolian National Radio & TV. Launched 1964 as "R. Ulaanbaatar", renamed "Voice of Mongolia" on 1 Jan 1997. The relay via a 1kW SW tx at Kall (Germany) is an independent, personal initiative of the operator of the German relay platform "Shortwaveservice"; a project that is primarily targeting SWLs/DXers in Europe.

### RADIO AND TELEVISION BROADCASTING NETWORK (RTBN) (Tx Operator)
⌨ Bayangol district, 17th subdistrict, Amarsanaagiin St., Ulaanbaatar, Mongolia.
☎ +976 77 003111. 🖷 +976 77 003119.
E: info@rtbn.gov.mn W: rtbn.gov.mn
L.P: CEO: Ch. Oyuünbaatar.
MW: [CHB] Choibalsan 1431kHz 500kW.
SW: [UBA] Ulaanbaatar, Khonkhor: 1 x 250kW.
Notes: RTBN is the national transmitter operator in Mongolia.

## NETHERLANDS (HOL)

### THE MIGHTY KBC
⌨ Argonstraat 6, NL-6718 WT Ede, Netherlands.
☎ +31 318 552491. 🖷 +31 318 437801.
E: themightykbc@gmail.com W: www.kbcradio.eu
Webcast: L
L.P: Producer: Eric van Willegen.
kHz: 5960, 11600

### Winter Schedule 2018/2019

| English | Days | Area | kHz |
|---|---|---|---|
| 0000-0200 | ......s | NAm | 5960nau |
| 1300-1400 | .....s. | Eu | 11600sof |

V: QSL-card. Rp. (2 EUR/2 USD/2 IRCs or equivalent PayPal donation); eQSL-letter (no Rp.)
Notes: Relay of KBC Import/Export-sponsored KBC Radio. Occasionally, the airtime is subleased to third-party prgr producers.

## NEW ZEALAND (NZL)

### RADIO NEW ZEALAND INTERNATIONAL (RNZI) (RNZ PACIFIC) (Pub)
⌨ P.O. Box 123, Wellington, New Zealand.
☎ +64 4 4741437. 🖷 +64 4 4741433.
E: info@rnzi.com W: www.radionz.co.nz/international
Webcast: D/L/P
L.P: Mgr: Linden Clark; Technical Mgr: Adrian Sainsbury; Transmission Engineer: Andy Anderson.
SW: [RAN] Rangitaiki: 1 x 100kW. Backup tx: 1 x 100kW.
kHz: 5950, 5975, 7390, 9700, 9765, 9780, 11725, 13730, 13840, 15720

### Winter Schedule 2018/2019

| English | Days | Area | kHz |
|---|---|---|---|
| 0200-0215 | .twtfss | NAm | 5950rmi# |
| 0400-0700 | daily | Pac | 13730ran |
| 0700-1100 | daily | Pac | 9765ran |
| 0915-0930 | .twtfs. | NAm | 5950rmi# |
| 1100-1300 | daily | Pac | 9700ran |
| 1300-1650 | daily | Pac | 7390ran |
| 1500-1530 | .....s. | NAm | 5950rmi# |
| 1650-1750 | mtwtf.s | Pac | 5975ran+ |
| 1650-1800 | .....s. | Pac | 7390ran |
| 1700-1715 | mtwtf.. | NAm | 5950rmi# |
| 1750-1835 | mtwtf.s | Pac | 9780ran+ |
| 1800-1900 | .....s. | Pac | 9780ran |
| 1835-1950 | mtwtf.s | Pac | 9780ran+ |
| 1900-2000 | .....s. | Pac | 11725ran |
| 1950-2050 | mtwtf.s | Pac | 13840ran+ |
| 2000-2100 | .....s. | Eu | 13840ran |
| 2050-2100 | mtwtf.s | Pac | 15720ran+ |
| 2100-0400 | daily | Pac | 15720ran |

**Key:** + DRM; # Unoffical WRN relay via WRMI.
**Ann:** English: "You are listening to RNZ International"; Maori: "Te reo irirangi o Aotearoa, o te Moana-nui-a-Kiwa".
**IS:** Call of the New Zealand Bellbird.
**V:** eQSL-card for rpt by email or via online form on website. Rpts received by by postal mail are no longer processed.
**Notes:** Radio New Zealand International (RNZI) is the External Sce of the public broadcaster Radio New Zealand. RNZI's online brand was changed to RNZ Pacific in May 2017, but for the time being the traditional RNZI brand continues to be maintained on-air. RNZI's SW transmissions are in English, with news in various Pacific languages. There is a maintenance day at the tx site every 1st Wednesday (UTC) from 2230 to Thursday 0600. During this period there may be interruptions to the transmissions or maintenance tests.

## NIGERIA (NIG)

### RADIO NIGERIA KADUNA (Gov)
See National Radio section.
**kHz:** 7235, 7335, 13840, 17690

#### Winter Schedule 2018/2019

| Hausa | Days | Area | kHz |
|---|---|---|---|
| 0500-0700 | daily | NIG | 7335iss |
| 0700-0900 | daily | NIG | 13840iss |
| 1100-1500 | daily | NIG | 17690iss |
| 2000-2300 | daily | NIG | 7235iss |

**Ann:** Hausa: "Radio Kaduna".
**Notes:** Radio Nigeria Kaduna is a regional station of Federal Radio Corporation of Nigeria (FRCN).

### VOICE OF NIGERIA (VON) (Gov)
6th & 7th Floors, Radio House, Herbert Macaulay Way, Area 10, Garki, 900001 Abuja, Nigeria. (Headquarters)
☎ +234 9 2344016. 📠 +234 9 2346970.
**E:** info@von.gov.ng **W:** von.gov.ng
**Webcast:** L
Broadcasting House, Plot no 345, Ikoyi Rd, 40003 Lagos, Nigeria. (Main studio building)
☎ +234 1 2693076. 📠 +234 1 2691944.
**L.P:** DG: Osita Okechukwu.
**SW:** [AJA] Abuja, Lugbe: 2 x 250kW.
**kHz:** 7255, 15120

#### Winter Schedule 2018/2019

| English | Days | Area | kHz |
|---|---|---|---|
| 0800-0900 | daily | WAf | 7255aja |
| 1800-1930 | daily | WAf | 7255aja* |
| 1800-1930 | daily | Eu | 15120aja+,† |

| French | Days | Area | kHz |
|---|---|---|---|
| 0700-0730 | daily | WAf | 7255aja |

| Fulfulde | Days | Area | kHz |
|---|---|---|---|
| 0730-0800 | daily | WAf | 7255aja |
| 1930-2000 | daily | WAf | 7255aja* |

| Hausa | Days | Area | kHz |
|---|---|---|---|
| 0600-0700 | daily | WAf | 7255aja |
| 2000-2100 | daily | WAf | 7255aja* |

**Key:** * Alternative frequency: 9690kHz; +DRM; † Irregular.
**Ann:** English: "You're listening to the Voice of Nigeria, Abuja".
**V:** QSL-card.
**Notes:** The External Sce The Voice of Nigeria was initially produced by the national broadcaster Federal Radio Corporation of Nigeria (FRCN), but became an autonomous broadcasting entity in 1990.

## NORTHERN MARIANA ISL. (MRA)

### USAGM "ROBERT E. KAMOSA" TRANSMITTING STATION ‡
P.O. Box 504969, Saipan, MP 96950, USA.
☎ +1 670 2331624. 📠 +1 670 2331614.
**L.P:** SM: David Strawman.
**SW:** [SAI] Saipan, Agingan Point ‡: 3 x 100kW; [TIN] Tinian ‡: 2 x 250, 6 x 500kW.
**V:** QSL-card (Email rpt to manager_mariana@mar.usagm.gov)
**Notes:** Both Saipan and Tinian sites have sustained catastrophic damage, caused by Super Typhoon Yutu. Both sites will be off air for at least 6 months, and it maybe as long as 12 months before repairs and infrastructure are completed.

## NORWAY (NOR)

### LKB/LLE BERGEN KRINGKASTER
P.O.Box 100, N-5331 Rong, Norway.
☎ +47 56141270.
**E:** styret@bergenkringkaster.no **W:** www.bergenkringkaster.no; www.la1ask.no; www.facebook.com/groups/bergenkringkaster
Grensedalen 59, N-5306 Erdal, Norway. (Museum Tx site & Studio)
**L.P:** Chmn: Per Dagfinn Green (LA1TNA); Chief Eng: Øystein Ask (LA7CFA); Chief Editor: Svenn Martinsen.
**MW:** [ERD] Bergen, Erdal: 1314kHz 1kW (run on reduced power).
**SW:** [ERD] Bergen, Erdal: 1 x 0.1kW (run on reduced power)
**FM/DAB:** FM: 93.8MHz (Erdal, 0.1kW)
**kHz:** 1314

#### Winter Schedule 2018/2019

| Norwegian/Others | Days | Area | kHz |
|---|---|---|---|
| 1000-1400 | ......s | NEu | 1314erd |
| 1400-2310 | daily | NEu | 1314erd |

**Ann:** English: "You are listening to LKB/LLE Bergen Broadcasting Station"; Norwegian: "Du lytter til LKB LLE Bergen Kringkaster".
**IS:** "MacGyver in Space" by Øyvind Ask.
**V:** QSL-card/letter (Rp: 3 USD) or eQSL-card (Email to report@bergenkringkaster.no)
**Notes:** LKB/LLK Bergen Kringkaster is a stn operated by the voluntary association "Foreningen Bergen Kringkaster" (FBK), a group of enthusiasts with background in amateur radio, and run with vintage and/or amateur radio equipment on the premises of a radio museum. Due to the leisure time nature of the operation, trs may be irregular at times. The programming consist of a mix of own prgrs and a relay of the Internet radio stns R. Northern Star/The Ferry (see separate entry).

### RADIO NORTHERN STAR / THE FERRY
P.O.Box 100, N-5331 Rong, Norway.
☎ +47 56324985.
**E:** 1000@northernstar.no; 2000@theferry.cc **W:** www.northernstar.cc; www.theferry.cc
**Webcast:** L
c/o P7 Kristen Riksradio, Idrettsvegen 10, N-5353 Straume, Norway. (Studio)
**L.P:** MD: Svenn Martinsen.
**MW:** [ERD] Bergen, Erdal: 1611kHz 0.25kW (run on reduced power). F.pl (site tbd): 630kHz 0.01kW.
**SW:** [ERD] Bergen, Erdal: 1 x 1kW (run on reduced power)
**FM/DAB:** FM: 91.8MHz (Erdal, 0.1kW)
**kHz:** 1611, 5895

#### Winter Schedule 2018/2019

| English/Norwegian | Days | Area | kHz |
|---|---|---|---|
| 0000-2400 | daily | NEu | 1611erd* |
| 1400-0005 | daily | Eu | 5895erd* |

**Key:** * AM/USB (H3E) mode.
**Ann:** English: R. Northern Star: "This is Radio Northern Star - Your Radio Heartland of Music"; The Ferry: "You're listening to a test transmission from The Ferry - Your Beautiful Music Connection - theferry.cc".
**IS:** R. Northern Star: "Northern Star" by Ann Reed; The Ferry: "Water Music - Suite in D major - Alla Hornpipe" by Georg Friedrich Händel
**V:** QSL-email or letter. Rp.
**Notes:** R. Northern Star (launched 2013) & The Ferry (launched 2017) are two Internet radio stns produced by Northern Star Media Services AS in a studio leased from the Norwegian Christian radio station P7 Kristen Riksradio. Both prgrs carry religious segments during certain times of the day. The txs are co-located with the txs of Bergen Kringkaster (see separate entry).

## OMAN (OMA)

### RADIO SULTANATE OF OMAN (Pub)
P.O. Box 397, 113 Muscat, Oman.
☎ +968 24603888. 📠 +968 24604629.
**E:** feedback@part.gov.om **W:** part.gov.om
**Webcast:** L
**L.P:** Dir, Foreign Sce: Salim Mohammed Al-Ghammari; Dir, Engineering: Mohammed Salim Al-Marhouby; Frequency Mgr: Salim Al-Nomani.
**SW:** [THU] Thumrait: 1 x 100kW (presumed to be run at 50kW).

**SAT:** Arabsat 5C, AsiaSat 5, Badr 6, Eutelsat 7WA/Hot Bird 13C, Galaxy 19, Hispasat 30W-4, Optus D2.
**kHz:** *9540, 12015, 13600, 15140*

### Winter Schedule 2018/2019

| Arabic | Days | Area | kHz |
|---|---|---|---|
| 0200-0300 | daily | EAf | 9540thu |
| 0400-1000 | daily | EAf | 13600thu |
| 1500-1800 | daily | Eu,ME | 15140thu |
| 2200-0200 | daily | EAf | 12015thu† |

| English | Days | Area | kHz |
|---|---|---|---|
| 0300-0400 | daily | EAf | 9540thu |
| 1400-1500 | daily | Eu,ME | 15140thu |

**Key:** † Irregular.
**Ann:** Arabic: "Idha'atu Saltanat Oman min Muscat"; English: "This is Radio Sultanate of Oman FM".
**V:** QSL-folder.
**Notes:** On air since 30 July 1970. Relays of Home Sce programmes in Arabic and English.

### BBC EASTERN RELAY STATION
✉ P.O. Box 40, 422 Al Ashkarah, Oman.
**E:** opsaseela@yahoo.com
**L.P:** Senior Transmitter Engineer: Khalid Nasser.
**MW:** [SLA] A'Seela: 702/1413kHz 800kW.
**SW:** [SLA] A'Seela: 3 x 250kW.
**V:** QSL-card. (For direct report)
**Notes:** Owned by the BBC and operated by Encompass Digital Media Services Ltd (see under United Kingdom).

## PAKISTAN (PAK)

### FEBA PAKISTAN (Rlg)
✉ P.O.Box 318, Rawalpindi, Pakistan.
☎ +92 51 5166621.
**E:** fctp74@gmail.com **W:** www.febapak.org; www.feba-radio.org
**Webcast:** L
**L.P:** Dir: Saleem Shazaad.
**kHz:** *7320*

### Winter Schedule 2018/2019

| Pashto | Days | Area | kHz |
|---|---|---|---|
| 0230-0300 | ....f.. | PAK | 7320dha |

| Punjabi | Days | Area | kHz |
|---|---|---|---|
| 0215-0230 | m...... | PAK | 7320dha |

| Sindhi | Days | Area | kHz |
|---|---|---|---|
| 0215-0230 | .twt... | PAK | 7320dha |

| Urdu | Days | Area | kHz |
|---|---|---|---|
| 0200-0215 | daily | PAK | 7320dha |
| 0215-0230 | ....fss | PAK | 7320dha |

**Notes:** Produced by the charitable Feba Communications Trust, associated with Far East Broadcasting Company, Inc (USA).

## PALAU (PLW)

### T8WH – WORLD HARVEST RADIO (WHR) (Rlg)
✉ P.O. Box 66, Koror, PW 96940, Republic of Palau.
**Webcast:** L (lesea.com)
✉ 61300 S Ironwood Rd, South Bend, IN 46614, USA (Family Broadcasting Corp.)
**W:** familybroadcastingcorporation.com/whr
**L.P:** Chief Engineer: Gary Shirk.
**SW:** [HBN] Medorm (Babeldaob Island): 3 x 100kW.
**FM/DAB:** FM: 102.5MHz (KRST-FM, Koror, 0.75kW).
**SAT:** Apstar 7, Galaxy 16, Intelsat 19.
**kHz:** *9930, 9965, 11675, 15675*

### Winter Schedule 2018/2019

| English | Days | Area | kHz |
|---|---|---|---|
| 0100-0500 | ......s | SEA | 15675hbn |
| 0800-1000 | daily | EAs | 9930hbn* |
| 1000-1200 | .....s. | SEA | 9965hbn |
| 1000-1500 | .....s. | EAs | 9930hbn* |
| 1000-1600 | ......s | EAs | 9930hbn* |
| 1200-1300 | daily | SEA | 9965hbn |
| 1400-1430 | daily | SEA | 9965hbn |
| 1530-1600 | ......s | SEA | 11675hbn |
| 1630-1700 | daily | SEA | 9965hbn |

**Key:** * May have prgr breaks (if airtime is not booked); includes prgrs in Japanese & Vietnamese.
**Ann:** English: "This is World Harvest Radio - T8WH, Palau".
**V:** QSL-card. (Rpts should be sent to Family Broadcasting Corp. address in USA). Rp (IRC/USD) appreciated.
**Notes:** Transmitting station owned by Family Broadcasting Corp. (USA). Historical callsigns (licensed to previous owners): T8BZ, KHBN. Actual schedule may vary during the course of the season, depending on airtime sales/tx lease. T8WH transmits prgrs of World Harvest Radio (see USA).

## PHILIPPINES (PHL)

### RADYO PILIPINAS OVERSEAS SERVICE (DZRP) (Gov)
✉ 4th floor, Government Media Center Bldg. (PIA), Visayas Ave, Vasra, 1128 Quezon City, Metro Manila, Philippines.
☎ +63 2 7727716.
**E:** dzrp.radyopilipinas@gmail.com **W:** www.pbs.gov.ph
**Webcast:** L
**L.P:** Acting SM: Remigio L. Sampang.
**SW:** Uses facilities provided by USAGM (USA).
**kHz:** *9925, 12120, 15190, 15640, 17700, 17820*

### Winter Schedule 2018/2019

| English | Days | Area | kHz |
|---|---|---|---|
| 0200-0330 | daily | ME | 15640pht, 17700pht, 17820pht |

| Filipino | Days | Area | kHz |
|---|---|---|---|
| 1730-1930 | daily | ME | 9925pht, 12120pht, 15190pht |

**Ann:** English: "This is Radyo Pilipinas, the Overseas Service of the Philippines Broadcasting Service, PBS. Radyo Pilipinas is reaching you from Manila, Philippines."; "Radyo Pilipinas Overseas Service, The Voice of the Philippines".
**V:** QSL-card. Rp (2 IRCs). Rec. acc.
**Notes:** Radyo Pilipinas is the External Sce of the Philippine Broadcasting Service (PBS), organised under the Philippine government Bureau of Broadcast Services (BBS). Broadcasts include relays of PBS's domestic services Radyo ng Bayan and Radyo Magasin.

### FEBC PHILIPPINES (Rlg)
✉ P.O.Box 14205, Ortigas Center Post Office, Pasig City 1605, Philippines.
☎ +63 2 6543322. 🖷 +63 2 6540894.
**E:** info@febc.ph **W:** febc.ph
✉ 46/F One Corporate Centre, Dona Julia Vargas cor. Meralco Avenues, Ortigas Center, Pasig City 1605, Philippines.
**L.P:** Pres: Dan Andrew S. Cura.
**SW:** [BOC] Bocaue (Bulacan prov.): 5 x 100kW; [IBA] Iba (Zambales prov.): 4 x 100kW.
**kHz:** *7410, 9275, 9345, 9400, 9405, 9450, 9465, 9795, 9920, 9940, 11750, 11825, 12055, 12070, 12095, 12120, 15215, 15330, 15435, 15450, 15560, 15580, 15620, 15640*

### Winter Schedule 2018/2019

| Achang | Days | Area | kHz |
|---|---|---|---|
| 1230-1245 | daily | As | 12095boc |

| Akha | Days | Area | kHz |
|---|---|---|---|
| 1215-1230 | daily | As | 12120boc |

| Bahnar | Days | Area | kHz |
|---|---|---|---|
| 1230-1300 | m.w.f... | As | 9920iba |

| Buginese | Days | Area | kHz |
|---|---|---|---|
| 0930-1000 | daily | As | 15580boc |

| Burmese | Days | Area | kHz |
|---|---|---|---|
| 1330-1400 | daily | As | 12120boc |
| 2330-0030 | daily | As | 15640boc |

| Cambodian | Days | Area | kHz |
|---|---|---|---|
| 1100-1300 | daily | As | 7410boc |

| Chin (Daai) | Days | Area | kHz |
|---|---|---|---|
| 1245-1259 | daily | As | 12120boc |

| Chin (Mro) | Days | Area | kHz |
|---|---|---|---|
| 0030-0045 | daily | As | 15640boc |

| Chinese | Days | Area | kHz |
|---|---|---|---|
| 1000-1400 | daily | As | 9400iba |
| 1000-1600 | daily | As | 9275boc |

| Chinese | Days | Area | kHz |
|---|---|---|---|
| 1400-1600 | daily | As | 9345iba |
| 2230-0030 | daily | As | 9405boc |
| 2300-0100 | daily | As | 12070iba |

| Hmong (Black) | Days | Area | kHz |
|---|---|---|---|
| 1300-1330 | daily | As | 12095boc |

| Hmong (Blue/Njua) | Days | Area | kHz |
|---|---|---|---|
| 1100-1130 | .....ss | As | 12095boc |
| 2300-2330 | .....ss | As | 12095boc |

| Hmong (White/Daw) | Days | Area | kHz |
|---|---|---|---|
| 1100-1130 | mtwtf.. | As | 12095boc |
| 2300-2330 | mtwtf.. | As | 12095boc |

| Hre | Days | Area | kHz |
|---|---|---|---|
| 1230-1300 | .t.t.ss | As | 9920iba |

| Hui zu | Days | Area | kHz |
|---|---|---|---|
| 0900-0930 | daily | As | 15450iba |

| Iu Mien | Days | Area | kHz |
|---|---|---|---|
| 1200-1230 | daily | As | 12095boc |
| 2300-2330 | daily | As | 9450boc |

| Jarai | Days | Area | kHz |
|---|---|---|---|
| 1200-1230 | ...tfs. | As | 9920iba |

| Javanese | Days | Area | kHz |
|---|---|---|---|
| 0100-0130 | daily | As | 15560boc |
| 1400-1430 | daily | As | 15620boc |

| Jingpho | Days | Area | kHz |
|---|---|---|---|
| 0045-0100 | daily | As | 15640boc |

| Karen Pa o | Days | Area | kHz |
|---|---|---|---|
| 1145-1200 | daily | As | 15330boc |

| Khmu | Days | Area | kHz |
|---|---|---|---|
| 0000-0015 | daily | As | 9795iba |
| 1330-1400 | daily | As | 12095boc |

| Koho | Days | Area | kHz |
|---|---|---|---|
| 1300-1330 | daily | As | 9920iba |

| Lahu | Days | Area | kHz |
|---|---|---|---|
| 0015-0045 | daily | As | 12055boc |
| 1400-1430 | daily | As | 11750boc |

| Lao | Days | Area | kHz |
|---|---|---|---|
| 1130-1200 | daily | As | 12095boc |
| 2330-2400 | daily | As | 9795iba |

| Lisu | Days | Area | kHz |
|---|---|---|---|
| 1300-1330 | daily | As | 12120boc |

| Lu | Days | Area | kHz |
|---|---|---|---|
| 1030-1100 | daily | As | 12095boc |
| 2345-0015 | daily | As | 12055boc |

| Makassarese | Days | Area | kHz |
|---|---|---|---|
| 0900-0930 | daily | As | 15580boc |

| Minangkabau | Days | Area | kHz |
|---|---|---|---|
| 0930-1000 | daily | As | 15450boc |

| Mon | Days | Area | kHz |
|---|---|---|---|
| 1115-1145 | daily | As | 15330boc |
| 2300-2330 | daily | As | 9795iba |

| Nagamese | Days | Area | kHz |
|---|---|---|---|
| 1230-1245 | daily | As | 12120boc |

| Palaung (Pale) | Days | Area | kHz |
|---|---|---|---|
| 2330-2345 | daily | As | 12055boc |

| Rade | Days | Area | kHz |
|---|---|---|---|
| 1200-1230 | mtw...s | As | 9920iba |

| Rawang | Days | Area | kHz |
|---|---|---|---|
| 1200-1215 | daily | As | 12120boc |

| Russian | Days | Area | kHz |
|---|---|---|---|
| 1500-1600 | daily | RUS | 9920boc |

| Sasak | Days | Area | kHz |
|---|---|---|---|
| 1030-1100 | daily | As | 15580boc |

| Shan | Days | Area | kHz |
|---|---|---|---|
| 0000-0045 | daily | As | 15435boc |

| Sunda | Days | Area | kHz |
|---|---|---|---|
| 1000-1030 | daily | As | 15580boc |

| Tai (Dam) | Days | Area | kHz |
|---|---|---|---|
| 1245-1300 | daily | As | 12095boc |

| Tai (Nua) | Days | Area | kHz |
|---|---|---|---|
| 0045-0100 | daily | As | 15435boc |

| Tibetan | Days | Area | kHz |
|---|---|---|---|
| 1200-1230 | daily | As | 15215dha |

| Tibetan (Khams) | Days | Area | kHz |
|---|---|---|---|
| 1300-1330 | daily | As | 11825boc |

| Uyghur | Days | Area | kHz |
|---|---|---|---|
| 1430-1500 | daily | As | 9940boc |

| Vietnamese | Days | Area | kHz |
|---|---|---|---|
| 1100-1200 | daily | As | 9795iba |

| Wa | Days | Area | kHz |
|---|---|---|---|
| 0045-0100 | daily | As | 12055boc |

| Yunnan | Days | Area | kHz |
|---|---|---|---|
| 1330-1400 | daily | As | 9465boc |

| Zhuang (Northern) | Days | Area | kHz |
|---|---|---|---|
| 0930-1000 | daily | As | 15450iba |

**Ann:** English: "This is FEBC Radio, broadcasting from Manila, Philippines".
**V:** QSL-card. Rp. preferred (3 IRCs)
**Notes:** Far East Broadcasting Company (Philippines), Inc is a regional division of Far East Broadcasting Company, Inc (FEBC) (USA), see USA for corporate details. FEBC Philippines runs a network of local FM/MW stns in the country and operates the SW transmitting stations Bocaue and Iba. The prgrs on SW (targeting Asia and Russia) are produced by FEBC partner organisations around the world and may include broadcasts under their own labels.

### RADIO VERITAS ASIA (Rlg)
☐ Buick St., Fairview Park, Quezon City, Metro Manila 1106, Philippines.
☎ +63 2 9390011. 🖷 +63 2 9390011.
**E:** rvaprogram@rveritas-asia.org **W:** www.rveritas-asia.org
**L.P:** GM: Fr. Carlos S. Lariosa; PD: Rev. Msgr. Gabriel Htun Myint; Technical Dir: Engr. Alex M. Movilla.
**Relayed Via:** 3rd party transmitting facilities.
**kHz:** 9700

| | Winter Schedule 2018/2019 | | |
|---|---|---|---|
| Kachin | Days | Area | kHz |
| 0000-0030 | daily | SEA | 9700smg |

**Ann:** English: "This is Radio Veritas Asia broadcasting from Quezon City, Philippines".
**V:** QSL-card.
**Notes:** Catholic station, on air since 11 April 1969. Owned by the "Philippine Radio Educational and Information Center" (PREIC), composed of Filipino bishops and professionals.

### USAGM PHILIPPINES TRANSMITTING STATION
☐ P.O.Box 151, CPO 1099, 1050 Manila, Philippines.
☎ +63 45 9820254. 🖷 +63 45 9821402.
**L.P:** SM: William Martin.
**SW:** [PHT] Tinang: 12 x 250kW.
**V:** QSL-card. (Email rpt to manager_philippines@usagm.gov)

## POLAND (POL)

### RADIO POLAND (Pub)
☐ Al. Niepodleglosci 77/85, 00-977 Warszawa, Poland.
☎ +48 226453302. 🖷 +48 226453952.
**E:** zagranica@polskieradio.pl; ru@polskieradio.pl (Russian)
**W:** external.polskieradio.pl; www.radiopolsha.pl (Russian); www.radyjo.net (Belarusian)
**Webcast:** D/L/P. Additional languages on Web/DAB/SAT/local FM affiliates: English, Polish, Ukrainian.
**L.P:** Dir: Andrzej Rybalt.
**FM/DAB:** DAB: See National Radio section.
**SAT:** Eutelsat Hot Bird 13C.
**kHz:** 1386, 5950, 6005

| | Winter Schedule 2018/2019 | | |
|---|---|---|---|
| Belarusian | Days | Area | kHz |
| 0400-0500 | daily | BLR | 1386vst |
| English | Days | Area | kHz |
| 0400-0500 | daily | NAm | 5950rmi# |
| 0800-0900 | daily | NAm | 5950rmi# |
| 1900-2000 | daily | NAm | 5950rmi# |
| 2300-2400 | daily | NAm | 5950rmi# |
| German | Days | Area | kHz |
| 1600-1630 | daily | D,CEu | 6005kll* |

## Polish / Russian

| Polish | Days | Area | kHz |
|---|---|---|---|
| 1630-1700 | daily | LTU,BLR,UKR | 1386vst |

| Russian | Days | Area | kHz |
|---|---|---|---|
| 1700-1730 | daily | RUS | 1386vst |

**Key:** * Relayed via Shortwaveservice (Kall, Germany); # Unoffical WRN relay via WRMI.

**Ann:** Belarusian: "Belaruskaja sluzba Polskaha radyjo"; Russian: "Radio Polsha - zarubezhnaya sluzhba Polskogo radio, "V efire Radio Polsha".

**V:** QSL-card.

**Notes:** International Sce of the public broadcaster Polskie Radio. The current SW relay via a 1kW tx at Kall (Germany) is an independent, personal initiative of the operator of the German relay platform "Shortwaveservice"; a project that is primarily targeting SWLs/DXers in Europe.

## ROMANIA (ROU)

### RADIO ROMANIA INTERNATIONAL (RRI) (Pub)

P.O. Box 1-111, 014700 Bucuresti, Romania.
☎ +40 213031357; +40 213031465. 🖶 +40 212232613.
**E:** rri@rri.ro **W:** www.rri.ro
**Webcast:** L/P
**LP:** Secretary General: Eugen Cojocariu.
**SW:** Leased from Radiocom.
**kHz:** 5910, 5920, 5930, 5935, 5940, 5955, 5980, 5990, 6020, 6030, 6040, 6100, 6130, 6145, 6155, 6170, 6180, 7220, 7235, 7310, 7325, 7330, 7340, 7345, 7350, 7360, 7370, 7375, 7410, 9490, 9570, 9585, 9600, 9610, 9620, 9740, 9770, 9800, 9810, 9820, 9870, 9880, 11660, 11780, 11790, 11800, 11820, 11825, 11945, 11960, 11975, 13630, 13730, 15255, 15260, 15380, 15400, 15430, 15450, 15460, 17640, 17780, 17800, 17810, 17850, 21490

#### Winter Schedule 2018/2019

| Arabic | Days | Area | kHz |
|---|---|---|---|
| 0730-0800 | daily | ME | 11960tig, 13630tig |
| 0730-0800 | daily | NAf | 9610gal, 11660gal |
| 1300-1330 | daily | ME | 11945gal, 13630tig |
| 1300-1330 | daily | NAf | 15400tig, 15460gal, 17810tig |
| 1630-1700 | daily | ME | 6100tig, 9585tig |
| 1630-1700 | daily | NAf | 9610gal, 11975gal |

| Aromanian | Days | Area | kHz |
|---|---|---|---|
| 1530-1600 | daily | Eu | 5955tig |
| 1730-1800 | daily | Eu | 5955tig |
| 1930-2000 | daily | Eu | 5955tig |

| Chinese | Days | Area | kHz |
|---|---|---|---|
| 0500-0530 | daily | CHN | 11820tig, 13730tig+ |
| 1330-1400 | daily | CHN | 9610tig, 11825tig |

| English | Days | Area | kHz |
|---|---|---|---|
| 0100-0200 | daily | NAm | 6130gal, 7325gal |
| 0400-0500 | daily | As | 9820tig+, 11790gal |
| 0400-0500 | daily | NAm | 6020gal, 7410tig |
| 0630-0700 | daily | AUS,NZL,Pac | 15450tig+, 17780gal |
| 0630-0700 | daily | Eu | 7345tig, 9770gal+ |
| 1200-1300 | daily | Af | 17800gal, 21490tig |
| 1200-1300 | daily | Eu | 11825tig, 15460tig |
| 1800-1900 | daily | Eu | 5935tig, 7350tig+ |
| 2130-2200 | daily | Eu | 6030gal+, 7375gal |
| 2130-2200 | daily | NAm | 6170tig, 7310tig |
| 2300-2400 | daily | Eu | 5980gal+, 7220gal |
| 2300-2400 | daily | EAs | 7325tig, 9620tig |

| French | Days | Area | kHz |
|---|---|---|---|
| 0200-0300 | daily | NAm | 6130gal, 7410gal |
| 0600-0630 | daily | Eu | 7360gal, 9610gal+ |
| 0600-0630 | daily | Af | 11790tig, 13730tig |
| 1100-1200 | daily | Eu | 11780gal, 15255gal, 15430tig |
| 1100-1200 | daily | NAf | 17640tig |
| 1700-1800 | daily | Eu | 7325tig, 9870tig+ |
| 2100-2130 | daily | Eu | 6030gal, 7375gal |

| German | Days | Area | kHz |
|---|---|---|---|
| 0700-0730 | daily | Eu | 7345tig, 9770tig+ |
| 1500-1600 | daily | Eu | 6040tig, 7330tig |
| 1900-2000 | daily | Eu | 6180tig+, 7235tig |

| Italian | Days | Area | kHz |
|---|---|---|---|
| 1500-1530 | daily | Eu | 5955tig |
| 1700-1730 | daily | Eu | 5955tig |
| 1900-1930 | daily | Eu | 5955tig+ |

| Romanian | Days | Area | kHz |
|---|---|---|---|
| 0100-0300 | daily | NAm | 5910tig, 7340tig |
| 0500-0600 | daily | Eu | 6145gal, 7220gal |
| 0800-0900 | ......s | ME | 11960tig, 13630tig, 15430gal, 17850gal |
| 0900-1000 | ......s | ME | 11960tig, 13630tig |
| 0900-1000 | ......s | NAf | 11780gal, 15380gal |
| 1000-1100 | ......s | Eu | 11780gal, 15260gal |
| 1000-1100 | ......s | NAf | 15430tig, 17640tig |
| 1300-1400 | daily | Eu | 9880tig |
| 1400-1600 | daily | Eu | 9810gal, 11975gal |
| 1700-1800 | daily | ME | 7370gal, 9810gal |
| 1800-2100 | daily | Eu | 5990gal, 7375gal |

| Russian | Days | Area | kHz |
|---|---|---|---|
| 0530-0600 | daily | RUS | 5940tig+, 7330tig |
| 1400-1500 | daily | RUS | 7410tig, 9570tig |
| 1600-1630 | daily | RUS | 6030tig+, 9800tig |

| Serbian | Days | Area | kHz |
|---|---|---|---|
| 1630-1700 | daily | SRB | 5955tig |
| 1830-1900 | daily | SRB | 5955tig |
| 2030-2100 | daily | SRB | 5930tig |

| Spanish | Days | Area | kHz |
|---|---|---|---|
| 0000-0100 | daily | SAm | 5980gal, 7325gal, 9600tig, 11800tig |
| 0300-0400 | daily | CAm | 6155gal, 7410gal |
| 0300-0400 | daily | SAm | 9740tig, 11800tig |
| 2000-2100 | daily | Eu | 7235tig |
| 2000-2100 | daily | NAf | 5920tig |
| 2200-2300 | daily | SAm | 9490tig+, 11800tig |

| Ukrainian | Days | Area | kHz |
|---|---|---|---|
| 1600-1630 | daily | UKR | 5955tig |
| 1800-1830 | daily | UKR | 5955tig |
| 2000-2030 | daily | UKR | 5930tig |

**Key:** + DRM.

**Ann:** English: "This is Radio Romania International".

**V:** QSL-card. (Online reception report form available)

**Notes:** Radio Romania International is the External Sce of the public broadcaster Radio Romania. Romanian language prgrs include relays of Home Sce networks.

### RADIOCOM (Tx Operator)

sos. Oltenitei nr. 103, sector 4, 041303 Bucuresti, Romania.
☎ +40 315003013. 🖶 +40 315003013.
**E:** office@radiocom.ro **W:** www.radiocom.ro
**LP:** DG: Gabriel Grecu.
**SW:** [GAL] Bacau, Galbeni: 2 x 300kW; [TIG] Bucuresti, two sites: Tiganesti (G.C. 44N45 026E06): 3 x 300kW; Saftica (G.C. 44N38 026E05): 1 x 100kW.
**Notes:** Radiocom is the national transmitter network owner.

## RUSSIA (RUS)

### GTRK "ADYGEYA" (Gov)

ul. Zhukovskogo 24, 385000 Maykop, Russia.
☎ +7 8772 522615.
**E:** adigradio@mail.ru **W:** www.adygtv.ru/radio
**Webcast:** D
**LP:** Dir: Vyacheslav Zhachemuk.
**SW:** Leased from RTRN.
**kHz:** 6000

#### Winter Schedule 2018/2019

| Adyghe* | Days | Area | kHz |
|---|---|---|---|
| 1800-1900 | m..f.. | ME | 6000arm* |
| 1900-2000 | ......s | ME | 6000arm* |

**Key:** * Mondays also in Arabic and Turkish.

**Notes:** Prgr for the Circassian communities in the Near East, produced by the state broadcasting company GTRK "Adygeya" (a regional branch of the national broadcasting company VGTRK). Prgrs for domestic audience: See National Radio section.

## VESTI FM (Gov)
📠 Contact details see National Radio Section.
**kHz:** *1413*

### Winter Schedule 2018/2019

| Russian | Days | Area | kHz |
|---|---|---|---|
| 0000-2400 | daily | UKR | 1413kch |

**Notes:** Relay of domestic prgr, produced by the national broadcasting company VGTRK.

## RADIOAGENCY–M (Broker)
📠 123308 Moskva, ul. Demyana Bednogo 24, Russia.
☎ +7 499 1919161. 🖨 +7 499 1918591.
**E:** abat@radioagency.ru
**LP:** Dir: Aleksey A. Titov.
**V:** QSL-card. (For brokered stns)
**Notes:** Radioagency-M brokers air time for SW txs in Moldova (Pridnestrovian Moldavian Republic) and Uzbekistan.

## RUSSIAN TELEVISION AND RADIO BROADCASTING NETWORK (RTRN) (Tx Operator)
📠 ul. Nikolskaya 7, 109012 Moscow, Russia.
☎ +7 495 6480111. 🖨 +7 495 6480111.
**E:** press@rtrn.ru **W:** www.rtrs.ru
**LP:** DG: Andrey Romanchenko.
**MW:** [MSK] Moskva 738kHz 5kW.
**SW:** [ARM] Krasnodar, Tbilisskaya: 1 x 100kW.
**Notes:** RTRN is the national transmitter network operator in Russia. RTRN also owns the transmitting centre Maiac in Moldova (Transnistria).

## SÃO TOMÉ E PRÍNCIPE (STP)

### USAGM SÃO TOMÉ TRANSMITTING STATION
📠 CP 522, São Tomé, São Tomé e Príncipe.
☎ +239 2223406. 🖨 +239 2223406.
**LP:** SM: Kenneth Tripp.
**MW:** [SAO] Pinheira: 1530kHz 100/600kW.
**SW:** [SAO] Pinheira: 5 x 100kW.
**V:** QSL-card. (Email rpt to Secretary of SM, Helena de Menezes: hmenezes@usagm.gov)

## SAUDI ARABIA (ARS)

### SAUDI RADIO INTERNATIONAL (SAUDI BROADCASTING AUTHORITY (SBA)) (Gov)
📠 P.O. Box 60059, Riyadh-11545, Saudi Arabia.
☎ +966 11 4425170. 🖨 +966 11 4041692.
**E:** vinfo@sbc.sa **W:** www.sbc.sa; moci.gov.sa; www.sr.sa; international.sr.sa
**Webcast:** L
**W:** www.moci.gov.sa (Ministry of Culture and Information)
**LP:** Minister, Culture and Information: Dr. Awwad Bin Saleh Al-Awwad; Chmn/Pres (SBA): Dawood Bin Abdulaziz Al-Shiryan.
**SW:** [JED] Jeddah, Al-Khumra: 4 x 250kW (Tx site may be operated directly by the Engineering Dept of the Ministry (MOCI). Exact no of txs unconfirmed; additional txs may be installed); [RIY] Riyadh: 8 x 500kW.
**SAT:** Arabsat 5A/C, AsiaSat 5, Badr 4, Eutelsat Hot Bird 13C, Galaxy 19, Hispasat 30W-4, Nilesat 201.
**kHz:** *7240, 7425, 9555, 9650, 9675, 9695, 9800, 9870, 9885, 11820, 11915, 11930, 11935, 13610, 13710, 13720, 13780, 13785, 15120, 15170, 15205, 15225, 15285, 15380, 15435, 15490, 17560, 17615, 17625, 17660, 17705, 17730, 17740, 17805, 17895, 21505, 21670*

### Winter Schedule 2018/2019

| Arabic | Days | Area | kHz |
|---|---|---|---|
| 0230-0530 | daily | YEM | 9800riy** |
| 0300-0600 | daily | Eu,CAs | 15170riy* |
| 0300-0800 | daily | CAs,EAs | 17895riy* |
| 0600-0900 | daily | Eu | 17740riy** |
| 0600-0900 | daily | ME | 15380riy* |
| 0600-0900 | daily | NAf | 17730riy** |
| 0600-1100 | daily | YEM | 13780riy** |
| 0600-1400 | daily | YEM | 13610riy** |
| 0900-1200 | daily | Eu | 15490riy** |
| 0900-1200 | daily | SAs,SEA | 17615riy* |
| 0900-1200 | daily | ME | 11935riy* |
| 0900-1200 | daily | NAf | 17805riy** |

| Arabic | Days | Area | kHz |
|---|---|---|---|
| 1200-1400 | daily | ME | 15380riy* |
| 1200-1400 | daily | SAs,SEA | 17625riy* |
| 1200-1400 | daily | YEM | 13785riy** |
| 1200-1500 | daily | Eu | 17705riy** |
| 1200-1500 | daily | NAf | 17895riy*, 21505riy** |
| 1300-1600 | daily | SAf | 17615riy* |
| 1400-2100 | daily | YEM | 9650riy** |
| 1500-1800 | daily | Eu | 15435riy** |
| 1500-1800 | daily | NAf | 13710riy*, 15225riy** |
| 1600-1800 | daily | Eu | 15205riy* |
| 1600-1800 | daily | WAf,CAf | 17560riy* |
| 1800-2300 | daily | WAf,CAf | 11930riy* |
| 1800-2300 | daily | Eu | 9870riy**, 11820riy* |
| 1800-2300 | daily | NAf | 9555riy**, 11915riy* |
| 1900-2300 | daily | YEM | 7425riy* |
| **Bengali** | **Days** | **Area** | **kHz** |
| 0900-1200 | daily | SAs | 15120riy |
| **French** | **Days** | **Area** | **kHz** |
| 1400-1600 | daily | WAf | 17660riy |
| **Indonesian** | **Days** | **Area** | **kHz** |
| 0900-1200 | daily | SEA | 21670riy |
| **Pashto** | **Days** | **Area** | **kHz** |
| 1400-1600 | daily | WAs | 9695riy |
| **Persian** | **Days** | **Area** | **kHz** |
| 1200-1800 | daily | ME | 7240riy |
| **Somali** | **Days** | **Area** | **kHz** |
| 0700-0900 | daily | EAf | 13720riy |
| **Swahili** | **Days** | **Area** | **kHz** |
| 0400-0700 | daily | EAf | 15285riy |
| **Turkish** | **Days** | **Area** | **kHz** |
| 1800-2100 | daily | ME | 9675riy |
| **Urdu** | **Days** | **Area** | **kHz** |
| 1200-1500 | daily | SAs | 15120riy |
| **Uzbek/Turkmen** | **Days** | **Area** | **kHz** |
| 1600-1800 | daily | CAs | 9885riy |

**Key:** * Quran prgr; ** General prgr.
**Ann:** Arabic: "Idha'at ar-Riyadh" (General Prgr); "Idha-atu'l-Koran al-Kareem min al-mamlakah al-arabiyah t'il-saudiah"(Quran Prgr).
**IS:** 'Ud' (Oriental Lute). Opens and closes with National Anthem.
**V:** Does not verify reception reports.
**Notes:** The Saudi Broadcasting Authority (SBA) is a government entity operating under the Ministry of Culture and Information (MOCI). The prgrs in Arabic are relays of Home Sce prgrs.

## SINGAPORE (SNG)

### TWR ASIA (Rlg)
📠 85 Playfair Road #04-01, Tong Yuan Industrial Building, Singapore 368000.
☎ +65 65015150. 🖨 +65 64443053.
**E:** info@twr.asia **W:** www.twr.asia
**Webcast:** D
**LP:** Dir: Sebastian Chan.
**SW:** Via TWR Guam relay station (KTWR).
**kHz:** *1467, 7500, 7510, 9910, 9975, 11965, 11995, 12040, 12120*

### Winter Schedule 2018/2019

| Burmese | Days | Area | kHz |
|---|---|---|---|
| 1200-1230 | mtwtfs. | As | 12040twr |
| 1200-1245 | ......s | As | 12040twr |
| **Cantonese** | **Days** | **Area** | **kHz** |
| 1115-1130 | daily | CHN | 9975twr |
| 1350-1430 | mtwtf.. | CHN | 9975twr |
| **Chinese** | **Days** | **Area** | **kHz** |
| 1030-1100 | daily | CHN | 12120twr |
| 1100-1200 | mtwtf.. | CHN | 9910twr |
| 1145-1200 | ......s | CHN | 9910twr |
| 1145-1200 | mtwtf.. | CHN | 9975twr |
| 1200-1215 | mtwtf.s | CHN | 9910twr |
| 1315-1330 | .....s. | CHN | 9975twr |
| 1315-1350 | mtwtf.. | CHN | 9975twr |
| **Dari** | **Days** | **Area** | **kHz** |
| 1445-1500 | .t..... | WAs | 1467bis, 1467bis |
| 1530-1600 | daily | WAs | 1467bis, 1467bis |

| English | Days | Area | kHz |
|---|---|---|---|
| 1000-1025 | mtwtf.. | AUS,NZL,Pac | 11995twr |
| 1000-1030 | ......s | SEA | 11965twr |
| 1000-1045 | .....s. | AUS,NZL,Pac | 11995twr |
| 1100-1125 | m...... | SEA | 11965twr |
| 1100-1130 | ......s | EAs | 9910twr |
| 1100-1140 | .twtf.. | SEA | 11965twr |
| 1100-1200 | ......s | SEA | 11965twr |
| 1130-1145 | ......s | EAs | 9910twr |
| 1130-1200 | .....s. | EAs | 9910twr |
| 1230-1300 | .....s. | EAs | 9910twr |
| 1315-1345 | .....s. | EAs | 7510twr |

| Hakka | Days | Area | kHz |
|---|---|---|---|
| 1130-1145 | daily | EAs | 9975twr |

| Japanese | Days | Area | kHz |
|---|---|---|---|
| 1215-1245 | ......s | EAs | 7500twr |

| Kazakh | Days | Area | kHz |
|---|---|---|---|
| 1215-1230 | mtwtf.. | EAs | 9975twr |

| Korean | Days | Area | kHz |
|---|---|---|---|
| 1315-1345 | mtwtf.. | EAs | 7510twr |
| 1346-1515 | daily | EAs | 7510twr |

| Madurese | Days | Area | kHz |
|---|---|---|---|
| 1000-1030 | mtwtf.. | SEA | 11965twr |

| Mongolian | Days | Area | kHz |
|---|---|---|---|
| 1100-1115 | daily | EAs | 9975twr |

| Pahari (Kangri) | Days | Area | kHz |
|---|---|---|---|
| 1330-1345 | ...f.. | SAs | 1467bis |

| Pashto | Days | Area | kHz |
|---|---|---|---|
| 1430-1500 | m...... | WAs | 1467bis, 1467bis |
| 1600-1630 | daily | WAs | 1467bis, 1467bis |

| Sgaw | Days | Area | kHz |
|---|---|---|---|
| 1230-1300 | mtwtf.. | As | 12040twr |
| 1245-1300 | ......s | As | 12040twr |

| Sundanese | Days | Area | kHz |
|---|---|---|---|
| 0945-1000 | mtwtf.. | SEA | 11965twr |
| 1030-1100 | mtwtf.s | SEA | 11965twr |
| 1045-1100 | .....s. | SEA | 11965twr |

| Uyghur | Days | Area | kHz |
|---|---|---|---|
| 1230-1245 | mtwtf.. | EAs | 9975twr |

| Vietnamese | Days | Area | kHz |
|---|---|---|---|
| 1245-1300 | ......s | SEA | 9975twr |
| 1245-1315 | mtwtf.. | SEA | 9975twr |

| Yi | Days | Area | kHz |
|---|---|---|---|
| 1200-1215 | daily | EAs | 9975twr |

**V:** QSL-card. (Online form on website)
**Notes:** TWR regional branch for Asia. For corporate details, see under TWR (USA).

## BBC FAR EASTERN RELAY STATION
✉ 51 Turut Track, Singapore 718930.
☎ +65 67937511. 🖷 +65 67937834.
**L.P:** Stn Mgr: Cindy Yao; Chief Eng: Tam Lam Soon.
**SW:** [SNG] Singapore: 4 x 100, 5 x 250kW.
**V:** QSL-card. (For direct report)
**Notes:** Owned by the BBC and operated by Encompass Digital Media Services Ltd (see under United Kingdom).

## SLOVAKIA (SVK)

### RADIO SLOVAKIA INTERNATIONAL (Pub)
✉ Mýtna 1, P.O. Box 55, 817 55 Bratislava 15, Slovakia.
☎ +421 2 57273734. 🖷 +421 2 52496282.
**E:** rsi@slovakradio.sk; englishsection@slovakradio.sk **W:** rsi.rtvs.sk
**Webcast:** L. Webcast languages: English, French, German, Russian, Slovak, Spanish.
**L.P:** Chief Script Adviser: Mária Mikušová.
**SW:** Leases airtime on WRMI (See under USA).
**SAT:** Astra 3B.
**kHz:** *738, 3985, 5010, 5850, 5950, 6005, 7780, 9395, 9955*

| | Winter Schedule 2018/2019 | | |
|---|---|---|---|
| **English** | **Days** | **Area** | **kHz** |
| 0030-0100 | daily | NAm | 5850rmi |
| 0030-0100 | daily | Eu,NAm | 7780rmi |

| English | Days | Area | kHz |
|---|---|---|---|
| 0130-0200 | daily | NAm | 5950rmi# |
| 0330-0400 | daily | NAm | 5950rmi, 9395rmi |
| 1200-1230 | daily | Eu | 6005kll* |
| 1230-1300 | daily | NAm | 5950rmi# |
| 1530-1600 | daily | Eu | 6005kll* |
| 1630-1700 | daily | Eu | 6005kll* |
| 2000-2030 | daily | Eu | 3985kll* |
| 2000-2030 | daily | NAm | 5950rmi, 5950rmi# |

| French | Days | Area | kHz |
|---|---|---|---|
| 1230-1300 | daily | Eu | 6005kll* |
| 1430-1500 | daily | Eu | 6005kll* |
| 1630-1700 | daily | Eu | 3985kll* |
| 1930-2000 | daily | Eu | 3985kll* |

| German | Days | Area | kHz |
|---|---|---|---|
| 1100-1130 | daily | Eu | 6005kll* |
| 1400-1430 | daily | Eu | 6005kll* |
| 1900-1930 | daily | Eu | 3985kll* |

| Russian | Days | Area | kHz |
|---|---|---|---|
| 0130-0200 | daily | RUS | 738msk~ |
| 0400-0430 | mtwtf.. | RUS | 738msk~ |
| 0530-0700 | daily | RUS | 738msk~ |
| 1130-1200 | daily | RUS | 738msk~ |
| 1630-1700 | daily | RUS | 738msk~ |
| 1900-1930 | daily | RUS | 738msk~ |
| 2300-2330 | daily | RUS | 738msk~ |

| Slovak | Days | Area | kHz |
|---|---|---|---|
| 0000-0030 | daily | Eu,NAm | 7780rmi |
| 0000-0030 | daily | NAm | 5850rmi |

| Spanish | Days | Area | kHz |
|---|---|---|---|
| 0030-0100 | daily | CAm | 5010rmi |
| 0330-0400 | daily | LAm | 9955rmi |
| 1330-1400 | mtwtf.. | LAm | 9955rmi |
| 1500-1530 | daily | Eu | 6005kll* |

**Key:** ~ Relayed via Vsemirnaya radioset (Moscow, Russia); * Relayed via Shortwaveservice (Kall, Germany); # Unoffical WRN relay via WRMI.
**Ann:** English: "You are listening to Radio Slovakia International".
**V:** QSL-card.
**Notes:** International service of the public service Slovak Radio (Slovenský Rozhlas), launched 1993. The trs on 738kHz (via the local stn Vsemirnaya radioset in Moscow) are part of the Encompass Digital Media (UK) Russian language Satellite/Internet feed (branded "WRN"), and are intended for listeners in Moscow and Moscow region. The relay via a SW 1kW tx at Kall (Germany) is an independent, personal initiative of the operator of the German relay platform "Shortwaveservice"; a project that is primarily targeting SWLs/DXers in Europe.

## SOUTH AFRICA (AFS)

### CHANNEL AFRICA (Pub)
✉ P.O. Box 91313, Auckland Park 2006, South Africa.
☎ +27 11 7142255. 🖷 +27 11 7142072.
**E:** phetoess@sabc.co.za (General Manager); dawetimj@sabc.co.za (Prgr Manager) **W:** www.channelafrica.co.za
**Webcast:** D/L/P
**L.P:** GM: Solly Phetoe; Managing Editor: Moshongwa Matsena; Prgr Mgr: Lungi Daweti.
**SW:** Leased from Sentech.
**SAT:** Intelsat 20.
**kHz:** *3345, 6155, 7230, 7260, 11925, 15235, 17770*

| | Winter Schedule 2018/2019 | | |
|---|---|---|---|
| **English** | **Days** | **Area** | **kHz** |
| 0300-0400 | mtwtf.. | EAf | 6155mey |
| 0300-0500 | mtwtf.. | SAf | 3345mey |
| 0500-1200 | mtwtf.. | SAf | 7230mey |
| 0600-0700 | mtwtf.. | WAf | 11925mey |
| 1500-1600 | mtwtf.. | SAf | 7260mey |
| 1700-1800 | mtwtf.. | WAf | 15235mey |

| French | Days | Area | kHz |
|---|---|---|---|
| 1600-1700 | mtwtf.. | WAf | 15235mey |

| Lozi | Days | Area | kHz |
|---|---|---|---|
| 1300-1400 | mtwtf.. | SAf | 7230mey |

| Nyanja | Days | Area | kHz |
|---|---|---|---|
| 1200-1300 | mtwtf.. | SAf | 7230mey |
| **Portuguese** | **Days** | **Area** | **kHz** |
| 1400-1500 | mtwtf.. | SAf | 7230mey |
| **Swahili** | **Days** | **Area** | **kHz** |
| 1500-1600 | mtwtf.. | EAf | 17770mey |

**Ann:** English: "You are tuned to the English service of Channel Africa, broadcasting to Africa from Johannesburg, South Africa. The Voice of the African Renaissance".
**IS:** Birds chirping and native melody.
**V:** Does not verify. Rpts should be sent to Sentech.
**Notes:** Channel Africa is the External Sce of the public-service South African Broadcasting Corporation (SABC).

### TWR AFRICA (Rlg)
✉ P.O. Box 4232, Kempton Park, 1620, South Africa.
☎ +27 11 9742885. 🖷 +27 11 9749960.
**E:** info@twrafrica.org **W:** www.twrafrica.org
**Webcast:** D/L/P
✉ San Croy Business Park, Die Agora Rd., Kempton Park, 1619, South Africa.
**LP:** Dir: Sphiwe Nxumalo; Dir (Tech Sces) James Burnett.
**MW:** Via TWR Benin relay station.
**SW:** Via TWR Swaziland relay station & leased foreign relays.
**SAT:** Intelsat 20.
**kHz:** *1566, 3200, 3240, 4760, 4775, 6120, 6130, 7245, 7300, 9475, 9500, 9585, 9940, 11660, 11780, 15105, 17680*

**Winter Schedule 2018/2019**

| Afar | Days | Area | kHz |
|---|---|---|---|
| 1300-1315 | ...tfss | EAf | 17680dha |
| **Amharic** | **Days** | **Area** | **kHz** |
| 0330-0345 | m...f.s | EAf | 7245dha |
| 1630-1645 | m...... | EAf | 11660man |
| 1700-1730 | daily | EAf | 11660man |
| 1730-1800 | ......s | EAf | 11660man |
| **Arabic (Juba)** | **Days** | **Area** | **kHz** |
| 1830-1845 | mtwtf.. | EAf | 9500man |
| **Bambara** | **Days** | **Area** | **kHz** |
| 2025-2040 | ....f.. | WAf | 1566par |
| **Bariba** | **Days** | **Area** | **kHz** |
| 2010-2025 | ...t... | WAf | 1566par |
| **Chokwe** | **Days** | **Area** | **kHz** |
| 1850-1905 | .....s. | SAf | 6130man |
| **Dendi** | **Days** | **Area** | **kHz** |
| 2010-2025 | m.....s | WAf | 1566par |
| **English** | **Days** | **Area** | **kHz** |
| 0230-0330 | mtwtf.. | WAf | 1566par |
| 0430-0500 | .....s. | WAf | 1566par |
| 0430-0500 | mtwtf.. | SAf | 3200man, 4775man |
| 0500-0700 | daily | SAf | 4775man, 6120man |
| 0530-0545 | mtwtf.. | WAf | 1566par |
| 1420-1455 | daily | SAf | 7300man |
| 1745-1825 | daily | WAf | 1566par |
| 1800-1830 | mtwtf.. | EAf | 9500man |
| 1800-1900 | .....s. | EAf | 9500man |
| **Ewe** | **Days** | **Area** | **kHz** |
| 0515-0530 | .....s. | WAf | 1566par |
| **Fiote** | **Days** | **Area** | **kHz** |
| 1905-1920 | ....f.. | SAf | 6130man |
| **Fon** | **Days** | **Area** | **kHz** |
| 1940-2010 | mtwtf.. | WAf | 1566par |
| 2010-2025 | .tw.... | WAf | 1566par |
| **Fongbe** | **Days** | **Area** | **kHz** |
| 1725-1745 | daily | WAf | 1566par |
| **French** | **Days** | **Area** | **kHz** |
| 1455-1525 | .....ss | CAf | 9585man |
| 1935-1950 | daily | CAf | 9940man |
| 2040-2215 | daily | WAf | 1566par |
| **Fulfulde** | **Days** | **Area** | **kHz** |
| 1925-1940 | daily | WAf | 1566par |
| 1940-2010 | .....ss | WAf | 1566par |
| **Hadiyya** | **Days** | **Area** | **kHz** |
| 1645-1700 | ....fs. | EAf | 11660man |

| Hausa | Days | Area | kHz |
|---|---|---|---|
| 0330-0430 | mtwtf.. | WAf | 1566par |
| 0345-0430 | .....ss | WAf | 1566par |
| 1855-1910 | mtwtf.. | WAf | 1566par |
| **Ife** | **Days** | **Area** | **kHz** |
| 2010-2025 | ....f.. | WAf | 1566par |
| **Igbo** | **Days** | **Area** | **kHz** |
| 0430-0500 | mtwtf.. | WAf | 1566par |
| 2025-2040 | .....ss | WAf | 1566par |
| **Jula** | **Days** | **Area** | **kHz** |
| 2025-2040 | ..t... | WAf | 1566par |
| **Kambaata** | **Days** | **Area** | **kHz** |
| 1630-1645 | ....fs. | EAf | 11660man |
| **Kanuri** | **Days** | **Area** | **kHz** |
| 1855-1910 | .....ss | WAf | 1566par |
| 1910-1925 | daily | WAf | 1566par |
| **KiKongo** | **Days** | **Area** | **kHz** |
| 1905-1920 | ......s | SAf | 6130man |
| **Kimbundu** | **Days** | **Area** | **kHz** |
| 1950-2005 | mtwtf.. | SAf | 6130man |
| **Kirundi** | **Days** | **Area** | **kHz** |
| 1600-1630 | mtwtf.. | Af | 15105man |
| **Kuanyama** | **Days** | **Area** | **kHz** |
| 1920-1935 | ......s | SAf | 6130man |
| **Kunama** | **Days** | **Area** | **kHz** |
| 1800-1830 | ......s | EAf | 7245kch |
| **Lingala** | **Days** | **Area** | **kHz** |
| 1905-1935 | daily | CAf | 9940man |
| **Lomwe/** | | | |
| **Portuguese** | **Days** | **Area** | **kHz** |
| 1420-1435 | mtwtf.. | SAf | 9585man |
| **Luchazi** | **Days** | **Area** | **kHz** |
| 1905-1920 | .w.... | SAf | 6130man |
| **Luvale** | **Days** | **Area** | **kHz** |
| 1905-1920 | ...t... | SAf | 6130man |
| **Makua** | **Days** | **Area** | **kHz** |
| 1420-1450 | .....s. | SAf | 9585man |
| **Malagasy** | **Days** | **Area** | **kHz** |
| 1455-1525 | mtwtf.. | SAf | 9585man |
| **Moore** | **Days** | **Area** | **kHz** |
| 2025-2040 | mtw.... | WAf | 1566par |
| **Ndau** | **Days** | **Area** | **kHz** |
| 0330-0345 | daily | SAf | 3240man |
| **Oromo** | **Days** | **Area** | **kHz** |
| 0330-0345 | .t..... | EAf | 7245dha |
| 1630-1645 | .t....s | EAf | 11660man |
| 1630-1700 | ..wt... | EAf | 11660man |
| 1730-1800 | mtwtfs. | EAf | 11660man |
| **Oromo/Borana** | **Days** | **Area** | **kHz** |
| 1645-1700 | mt....s | EAf | 11660man |
| **Portuguese** | **Days** | **Area** | **kHz** |
| 1630-1645 | .....s. | SAf | 4760man |
| 1905-1920 | mt..... | SAf | 6130man |
| 1920-1950 | mtwtf.. | SAf | 6130man |
| 1920-2005 | .....s. | SAf | 6130man |
| 1935-2005 | ......s | SAf | 6130man |
| **Shangaan** | **Days** | **Area** | **kHz** |
| 1630-1645 | .t..... | SAf | 4760man |
| **Shona** | **Days** | **Area** | **kHz** |
| 0300-0330 | daily | SAf | 3240man |
| 1455-1525 | daily | SAf | 7300man |
| 1525-1555 | mtwtf.. | SAf | 7300man |
| **Sidamo** | **Days** | **Area** | **kHz** |
| 0330-0345 | ..wt... | EAf | 7245dha |
| **Somali** | **Days** | **Area** | **kHz** |
| 1500-1530 | daily | EAf | 11780man |
| 1530-1545 | ......s | EAf | 11780man |
| 1630-1700 | mtwtfs. | EAf | 15105kch |
| **Songhai** | **Days** | **Area** | **kHz** |
| 2010-2025 | .....s. | WAf | 1566par |
| **Swahili** | **Days** | **Area** | **kHz** |
| 1745-1800 | ......s | EAf | 9475man |
| 1745-1815 | mtwtf.. | EAf | 9475man |

| Swahili | Days | Area | kHz |
|---|---|---|---|
| 1800-1815 | .....s. | EAf | 9475man |
| 1835-1850 | ......s | EAf | 9500man |
| **Tigre** | **Days** | **Area** | **kHz** |
| 1800-1830 | .....s. | EAf | 7245kch |
| **Tigrinya** | **Days** | **Area** | **kHz** |
| 1800-1815 | mtwt... | EAf | 7245kch |
| 1815-1845 | mtwtf.. | EAf | 7245kch |
| 1830-1845 | .....s. | EAf | 7245kch |
| **Turkana** | **Days** | **Area** | **kHz** |
| 1745-1800 | .....s. | EAf | 9475man |
| **Twi** | **Days** | **Area** | **kHz** |
| 0500-0515 | .....s. | WAf | 1566par |
| 0500-0530 | mtwtf.. | WAf | 1566par |
| **Umbundu** | **Days** | **Area** | **kHz** |
| 1820-1850 | mtwtf.. | SAf | 6130man |
| 1850-1905 | mtwtf.s | SAf | 6130man |
| 1905-1920 | .....s. | SAf | 6130man |
| **Yao** | **Days** | **Area** | **kHz** |
| 1700-1730 | daily | SAf | 7300man |
| **Yoruba** | **Days** | **Area** | **kHz** |
| 1825-1855 | daily | WAf | 1566par |

**Ann:** English: "Trans World Radio", "TWR".
**IS:** Last bar of "We've a story to tell the Nations", played on hand bells.
**V:** QSL-folder. Rp. (IRCs appreciated, 3 IRCs for airmail reply)
**Notes:** TWR regional division covering most parts of Africa (except North Africa, which is served by TWR Europe). For corporate details, see under TWR (USA). TWR Africa administrates the TWR transmitting stations in Benin and Swaziland.

## AMATEUR RADIO TODAY
✉ P.O. Box 90438, Garsfontein 0042, South Africa.
☎ +27 11 6752393. 🖷 +27 11 6752793.
**E:** artoday@sarl.org.za
**W:** www.amateurradio.org.za/amateur%20radio%20today.htm
**Webcast:** D/P (P: zs6ro.org/podcast)
**L.P:** Prgr Coordinator/Prgr Host: Hans van de Groenendaal (ZS6AKV).
**SW:** Leased from Sentech.
**kHz:** *4895, 7205, 17760*

### Winter Schedule 2018/2019
| English | Days | Area | kHz |
|---|---|---|---|
| 0800-0900 | ......s | SAf | 7205mey |
| 0800-0900 | ......s | EAf | 17760mey |
| 1630-1730 | m...... | EAf | 4895mey |

**V:** Does not verify, reception rpts should be sent to Sentech (Pty) Ltd, see entry below.
**Notes:** Amateur Radio Today (previously known as Amateur Radio Mirror International) is a weekly prgr about amateur radio, shortwave listening and electronics, produced by the South African Radio League.

## SENTECH (PTY) LTD. (Tx Operator)
✉ Private Bag X06, Honeydew 2040, South Africa.
☎ +27 11 4388883. 🖷 +27 11 6917107.
**E:** support@sentech.co.za **W:** www.sentech.co.za
✉ P.O. Box 234, Meyerton 1960, South Africa. (Transmitter site)
☎ +27 16 3661055. 🖷 +27 16 3660709.
**L.P:** Chmn: Magatho Mello; CEO: Setumo Mohapi; HF Coverage Planning: Sikander Hoosen.
**SW:** [MEY] Meyerton, Bloemendal: 7 x 100, 4 x 250kW.
**V:** QSL-letter (for relayed prgrs). Email rpt to hoosens@sentech.co.za (Sikander Hoosen).
**Notes:** Sentech (Pty) Ltd. is the operator of the transmitter networks in South Africa.

# SPAIN (E)

## RADIO EXTERIOR DE ESPAÑA (REE) (Pub)
✉ Casa de la Radio, Avenida de la Radio y la Televisión 4, Pozuelo de Alarcón, 28223 Madrid, Spain.
☎ +34 91 5817000.
**E:** secretariatecnica.ree@rtve.es **W:** www.rtve.es/radio/radio-exterior
**Webcast:** D/L/P (Webcast languages: Arabic, English, Ladino, Portuguese, Russian, Spanish)
**L.P:** Dir: Antonio Buitrago.

**SW:** [NOB] Noblejas: 4 x 300kW.
**SAT:** Astra 1M, EchoStar 9-Galaxy 23, Eutelsat 5WA.
**kHz:** *738, 9690, 11685, 11940, 12030*

### Winter Schedule 2018/2019
| English | Days | Area | kHz |
|---|---|---|---|
| 2300-2330 | m.w.f.. | NAm | 9690nob |
| 2300-2330 | m.w.f.. | SAm | 11940nob |
| 2300-2330 | m.w.f.. | WAf,Atl | 11685nob |
| 2300-2330 | m.w.f.. | ME,IOc | 12030nob |
| **French** | **Days** | **Area** | **kHz** |
| 2330-2400 | mtwtf.. | ME,IOc | 12030nob |
| 2330-2400 | mtwtf.. | NAm | 9690nob |
| 2330-2400 | mtwtf.. | SAm | 11940nob |
| 2330-2400 | mtwtf.. | WAf,Atl | 11685nob |
| **Portuguese** | **Days** | **Area** | **kHz** |
| 0000-0030 | .twtf.. | SAm | 11940nob |
| 0000-0030 | .twtf.. | NAm | 9690nob |
| **Russian** | **Days** | **Area** | **kHz** |
| 0000-0030 | .t..... | RUS | 738msk~ |
| 0230-0300 | ..w.... | RUS | 738msk~ |
| 0500-0530 | ..w.... | RUS | 738msk~ |
| 0700-0730 | m...... | RUS | 738msk~ |
| 1000-1030 | .t..... | RUS | 738msk~ |
| 1300-1330 | m...... | RUS | 738msk~ |
| 1530-1600 | ..w.... | RUS | 738msk~ |
| 1800-1830 | mtwtf.. | ME,IOc | 12030nob |
| 1800-1830 | mtwtf.. | WAf,Atl | 11685nob |
| 1930-2000 | ......s | RUS | 738msk~ |
| 2100-2130 | ..w.... | RUS | 738msk~ |
| 2230-2300 | m...... | RUS | 738msk~ |
| **Spanish** | **Days** | **Area** | **kHz** |
| 0000-0030 | m...... | NAm | 9690nob |
| 0000-0030 | m...... | SAm | 11940nob |
| 0030-0300 | mtwtf.. | NAm | 9690nob |
| 0030-0300 | mtwtf.. | SAm | 11940nob |
| 1500-2300 | .....ss | WAf,Atl | 11685nob* |
| 1500-2300 | .....ss | ME,IOc | 12030nob* |
| 1500-2300 | .....ss | NAm | 9690nob* |
| 1500-2300 | .....ss | SAm | 11940nob* |
| 1600-1800 | mtwtf.. | ME,IOc | 12030nob |
| 1600-1800 | mtwtf.. | WAf,Atl | 11685nob |
| 1830-2300 | mtwtf.. | ME,IOc | 12030nob |
| 1830-2300 | mtwtf.. | WAf,Atl | 11685nob |
| 1900-2300 | mtwtf.. | NAm | 9690nob |
| 1900-2300 | mtwtf.. | SAm | 11940nob |
| 2300-2330 | .t.t... | WAf,Atl | 11685nob |
| 2300-2330 | .t.t... | ME,IOc | 12030nob |
| 2300-2330 | .t.t... | NAm | 9690nob |
| 2300-2330 | .t.t... | SAm | 11940nob |

**Key:** * Ladino Sun 2230-2300; ~ Relayed via Vsemirnaya radioset (Moscow, Russia)
**V:** QSL-card.
**Notes:** REE is the Int. Sce of the public broadcaster Radio Nacional de España (RNE). The transmissions on 738kHz (via the local stn Vsemirnaya radioset in Moscow) are part of the Babcock (UK) Russian language Satellite/Internet feed (branded "WRN"), and are intended for listeners in Moscow and Moscow region.

## RADIO MI AMIGO INTERNATIONAL
✉ Avda. de Europa 85, Urb.La Marina, 03177 San Fulgencio, Alicante, Spain.
☎ +34 96 6790195.
**E:** studio@radiomiamigo.international **W:** www.radiomiamigo.international
**Webcast:** L
**L.P:** Dir (R. Mi Amigo): Kord Lemkau.
**kHz:** *3985, 6085, 7310*

### Winter Schedule 2018/2019
| English/Dutch/German | Days | Area | kHz |
|---|---|---|---|
| 0800-1800 | daily | CEu,WEu | 6085kll |
| 1100-1500 | .....ss | CEu,WEu | 7310kll |
| 1800-1900 | mtwtf.. | CEu,WEu | 3985kll |

**Ann:** English: "Welcome to Radio Mi Amigo International".
**V:** QSL-card.
**Notes:** Radio Mi Amigo International is a 24/7 Internet channel, produced with support of the German language radio station R. Mi Amigo that broadcasts on FM for listeners along the Costa Blanca coast of Spain. The prgr consists of music shows by German, Dutch and English DJs.

## SRI LANKA (CLN)

### SRI LANKA BROADCASTING CORPORATION (SLBC) (Pub)
✉ P.O. Box 574, Colombo 00700, Sri Lanka; Independence Square, Colombo 00700, Sri Lanka.
☎ +94 11 2697491. 🖷 +94 11 2691568.
**E:** chmnslbc@slbc.lk (Chairman); ddge@slbc.lk (Dir, Engineering) **W:** www.slbc.lk
**Webcast:** L
✉ SLBC Trincomalee Relay Station, Kuchchavali, Trincomalee, Sri Lanka. (Transmitting Station/Airtime Sales)
☎ +94 26 2222699. 🖷 +94 26 2222097.
**E:** sales@slbctrs.com **W:** www.slbctrs.com
**LP:** Chmn: Siddi Mohamed Farook; DG: Erananda Hettiarachchi; Dir, Engineering: M.G.W. Priyadarshana.
**MW:** [PUT] Puttalam: 873/882kHz 400kW, 1125kHz 50kW; [TRM] Trincomalee, Perkara: 1548kHz 400kW.
**SW:** [TRM] Trincomalee, Perkara: 3 x 300kW.
**kHz:** 1125, 9720, 11750, 11835, 11905

#### Winter Schedule 2018/2019

| Bengali | Days | Area | kHz |
|---|---|---|---|
| 0115-0130 | daily | SAs | 11905trm |
| **Hindi** | **Days** | **Area** | **kHz** |
| 0130-0230 | daily | SAs | 11905trm |
| **Hindi/Malayalam/** | | | |
| **Tamil/Telugu** | **Days** | **Area** | **kHz** |
| 1115-1215 | daily | SAs | 9720trm |
| **Sinhala** | **Days** | **Area** | **kHz** |
| 1630-1730 | daily | ME | 11750trm* |
| **Tamil** | **Days** | **Area** | **kHz** |
| 0630-0800 | ....f.. | SAs | 1125put |
| 1700-1800 | daily | ME | 11835trm |

**Key:** * Relay of City FM.
**Ann:** Sinhala: "Sri Lanka Guwan Viduliye Mada Peradiga Sevaya"; Tamil " Sri Lanka Vanoli".
**IS:** Melody on drums.
**V:** QSL-card. Rp.
**Notes:** SLBC's External Service ("Asian Service") for listeners in Asia and expatriates in Asia & the Middle East. SLBC is also leasing airtime on its transmitting facilities to third party customers, both from the Puttalam MW site and the Trincomalee MW/SW site (in 2012, SLBC took over the former Deutsche Welle Relay Station in Trincomalee).

## SUDAN (SDN)

### VOICE OF AFRICA – SUDAN RADIO (Pub)
✉ P.O.Box 572, Omdurman, Sudan.
☎ +249 1 87572956. 🖷 +249 1 87556006.
**E:** voiceofafrica@sudanradio.info **W:** www.sudanradio.info
**E:** info@mininfo.gov.sd (Ministry of Information)
**W:** mininfo.gov.sd (Ministry of Information)
**LP:** DG (Sudan National Public Radio Corp.): Mutasim Fadul.
**SW:** [ALF] Omdurman, Al Fitahab: 1 x 100kW.
**kHz:** 9505

#### Winter Schedule 2018/2019

| English | Days | Area | kHz |
|---|---|---|---|
| 1700-1800 | daily | CAf | 9505alf |
| **French** | **Days** | **Area** | **kHz** |
| 1600-1700 | daily | CAf | 9505alf |
| **Swahili** | **Days** | **Area** | **kHz** |
| 1800-1900 | daily | CAf | 9505alf |

**Ann:** English: "This is the Voice of Africa, broadcasting from Sudan Radio"; French: "La Voix de L'Afrique, Radio National de Soudan".
**Notes:** The Voice of Africa is the External Service of the Sudan National Public Radio Corp. ("Sudan Radio"). First transmissions in October 2012.

## SWEDEN (S)

### IBRA MEDIA (RIg)
✉ P.O.Box 15144, SE-16715 Bromma, Sweden.
☎ +46 8 6089680.
**E:** info@ibra.se **W:** ibra.se (Swedish); ibra.org (English)
✉ P.O. Box 2899, Stoke-on-Trent, ST4 9EL, United Kingdom.
☎ +44 1782 623759.
**E:** info@ibra.co.uk **W:** ibra.uk
**LP:** Mgr, IBRA Media: Pontus Fridolfsson; Public Relations: Birger Thureson.
**kHz:** 6180, 9540, 9635, 9775, 11655, 15260

#### Winter Schedule 2018/2019

| Afar | Days | Area | kHz |
|---|---|---|---|
| 1600-1630 | daily | Af | 11655dha |
| **Amharic** | **Days** | **Area** | **kHz** |
| 1600-1630 | ..wtf.s | Af | 9540erv |
| 1630-1700 | daily | Af | 9540erv |
| **Arabic** | **Days** | **Area** | **kHz** |
| 0800-0830 | daily | Af | 15260mos |
| 1700-1800 | daily | Af | 9775wof |
| 1830-1900 | daily | Af | 9635wof |
| **Beja** | **Days** | **Area** | **kHz** |
| 1730-1800 | daily | Af | 9635wof |
| **Fur** | **Days** | **Area** | **kHz** |
| 1800-1830 | daily | Af | 9635wof |
| **Guragena** | **Days** | **Area** | **kHz** |
| 1600-1630 | mtw.... | Af | 9540erv |
| **Oromo** | **Days** | **Area** | **kHz** |
| 1700-1730 | daily | Af | 9540dha |
| **Somali** | **Days** | **Area** | **kHz** |
| 1700-1800 | daily | Af | 6180dha |
| **Tigrinya** | **Days** | **Area** | **kHz** |
| 1730-1800 | daily | Af | 9540dha |

**V:** QSL-card.
**Notes:** IBRA Media is a multimedia ministry of the Swedish Pentecostal Movement. IBRA radio prgrs (formerly branded "IBRA Radio") are on air since July 1955.

## SWITZERLAND (SUI)

### SRG SSR (SWISS BROADCASTING CORP.) (Pub)
✉ Giacomettistrasse 1, CH-3000 Bern 31, Switzerland.
☎ +41 31 3509111. 🖷 +41 31 3509256.
**E:** info@srgssr.ch **W:** www.srgssr.ch; www.srf.ch
**Webcast:** D/L
**LP:** Pres: Jean-Michel Cina; DG: Gilles Marchand.
**SW:** Via Shortwaveservice (Germany).
**kHz:** 3985, 6005

#### Winter Schedule 2018/2019

| German | Days | Area | kHz |
|---|---|---|---|
| 1230-1300 | mtwtf.. | D,CEu | 6005kII* |
| 1700-1800 | daily | D,CEu | 3985kII*, 6005kII* |
| 2100-2130 | mtwtf.. | D,CEu | 3985kII* |

**Key:** * Relay of R. SRF1.
**Notes:** The Swiss Broadcasting Corp. ended shortwave transmissions in 2004. The current relay via a 1kW SW tx at Kall (Germany) is an independent, personal initiative of the operator of the German relay platform "Shortwaveservice"; a project that is primarily targeting SWLs/DXers in Europe. The prgrs consist of selected relays of R. SRF1 (a domestic channel produced by SRG SSR's German language unit Schweizer Rundfunk und Fernsehen - SRF).

## SYRIA (SYR)

### RADIO DAMASCUS (Gov)
✉ Ommayad Square, Damascus, Syria
☎ +963 11 2720700. 🖷 +963 11 2234930.
**E:** en@rtv.gov.sy; englishradio1@gmail.com
**W:** en.ortas.gov.sy/?f=Radio-Damascus; www.radio-damascus.net (unofficial)
**Webcast:** D (en.ortas.gov.sy/?f=Radio-Damascus; soundcloud.com/ SyrianForeignRadios); L (82.137.248.20:1935/RCham/RChamLive/ playlist.m3u8). Web languages: Arabic, English, French, German,

Hebrew, Spanish, Turkish, Russian)
**MW:** [TTS] Tartus: 783kHz 300kW.
**SAT:** Eutelsat 8WB.
**kHz:** *783*

### Winter Schedule 2018/2019

| English | Days | Area | kHz |
|---|---|---|---|
| 0600-0700 | daily | ME | 783tts |
| **Hebrew** | **Days** | **Area** | **kHz** |
| 0430-0530 | daily | ME | 783tts |
| **Russian** | **Days** | **Area** | **kHz** |
| 0530-0600 | daily | ME | 783tts |

**Key:** † Irregular.
**Ann:** Russian: "Govorit Damask, radioveshchatelnaya stantsiya Siriyskoy Arabskoy Respubliki".
**V:** QSL-card.
**Notes:** Radio Damascus is the International Sce of the state broadcaster General Organization of Radio & TV - Syria (ORTAS). The online stream is distributed under the label "Radio Sham" ("Radio Levant").

## TAIWAN (Rep. of China) (TWN)

### RADIO TAIWAN INTERNATIONAL (RTI) (Gov)
🖃 P.O. Box 123-199, Taipei 11199, Taiwan; 55 Pei An Road, Taipei 10462, Taiwan.
☎ +886 2 28856168. 🖷 +886 2 28862382.
**E:** rti@rti.org.tw **W:** www.rti.org.tw
**Webcast:** D/L/P
**LP:** Chmn: Lu Ping; Pres: Shao Lichung.
**MW:** [KOU] Kouhu: 1098/1557kHz 300kW; [MIN] Minhsiung: 1422kHz 50kW.
**SW:** [KOU] Kouhu: 3 x 100kW; [PAO] Paochung: 3 x 300kW; [TSH] Tanshui: 4 x 300kW.
**kHz:** *1098, 1422, 1557, 5900, 6075, 6105, 6145, 6180, 7220, 7300, 9405, 9415, 9450, 9545, 9590, 9625, 9660, 9680, 9685, 9735, 9900, 11640, 11655, 11915, 11985, 12100, 15270, 15320, 15350, 15465*

### Winter Schedule 2018/2019

| Cantonese | Days | Area | kHz |
|---|---|---|---|
| 0400-0430 | daily | SEA | 15320pao |
| 1000-1030 | daily | SEA | 9735pao, 15270pao |
| 1200-1230 | daily | EAs | 6105kou |
| 1200-1230 | daily | EAs | 9735pao |
| 1500-1530 | daily | SEA | 9545pao |
| **Chinese** | **Days** | **Area** | **kHz** |
| 0400-0600 | daily | EAs | 11640pao |
| 0900-1000 | daily | SEA | 15465pao |
| 0900-1700 | daily | EAs | 1557kou |
| 1000-1100 | daily | EAs | 7300tsh |
| 1000-1200 | daily | EAs | 6105kou |
| 1000-1400 | daily | EAs | 11640pao |
| 1000-1600 | daily | EAs | 6180tsh*, 9405tsh**, 9660kou |
| 1100-1400 | daily | EAs | 9680tsh |
| 1200-1300 | daily | EAs | 11985pao |
| 1300-1400 | daily | EAs | 6105kou |
| 1300-1705 | daily | EAs | 1098kou |
| 1400-1700 | daily | EAs | 6075kou, 6145kou |
| 1500-1705 | daily | EAs | 7300tsh |
| 2200-2400 | daily | EAs | 6075kou, 6105kou, 9450tsh, 9900pao |
| 2300-2400 | daily | EAs | 9685tsh |
| **English** | **Days** | **Area** | **kHz** |
| 0030-0130 | ......s | EAs | 1098kou |
| 0300-0400 | daily | SEA | 15320pao |
| 0945-1000 | ......s | EAs | 1098kou |
| 1120-1140 | daily | SEA | 12100pao |
| 1600-1700 | daily | SAs,Af | 6180tsh |
| **French** | **Days** | **Area** | **kHz** |
| 1900-2000 | ......s | Af | 9680iss |
| **German** | **Days** | **Area** | **kHz** |
| 1900-1930 | daily | Eu | 5900sof |
| **Hakka** | **Days** | **Area** | **kHz** |
| 0430-0500 | daily | SEA | 15320pao |
| 0900-1000 | daily | EAs | 6105kou |
| 1030-1100 | daily | SEA | 9735pao, 15270pao |
| 1230-1300 | daily | EAs | 6105kou, 9735pao |
| **Hakka** | **Days** | **Area** | **kHz** |
| 1530-1600 | daily | SEA | 9545pao |
| **Hokkien** | **Days** | **Area** | **kHz** |
| 1100-1120 | daily | SEA | 12100pao |
| 1200-1300 | daily | EAs | 1098kou |
| **Indonesian** | **Days** | **Area** | **kHz** |
| 0000-0100 | ....f.. | EAs | 1422min |
| 1000-1100 | daily | SEA | 11915pao |
| 1200-1300 | ...t... | EAs | 1422min |
| 1200-1300 | daily | SEA | 11915pao |
| 1400-1500 | daily | SEA | 9735pao |
| **Japanese** | **Days** | **Area** | **kHz** |
| 1100-1200 | daily | EAs | 9735pao |
| **Russian** | **Days** | **Area** | **kHz** |
| 1400-1500 | daily | CAs | 9590tsh |
| 1700-1800 | daily | Eu | 7220iss |
| **Thai** | **Days** | **Area** | **kHz** |
| 0000-0100 | daily | SEA | 9625pao |
| 0100-0200 | ...t... | EAs | 1422min |
| 1300-1400 | ..w.... | EAs | 1422min |
| 1400-1500 | daily | SEA | 9415pao |
| 1500-1600 | daily | SEA | 9625pao |
| **Vietnamese** | **Days** | **Area** | **kHz** |
| 0200-0300 | ..w.... | EAs | 1422min |
| 1100-1200 | .t..... | EAs | 1422min |
| 1100-1200 | daily | SEA | 15350pao |
| 1140-1200 | daily | SEA | 12100pao |
| 1400-1500 | daily | SEA | 9625pao |
| 2300-2400 | daily | SEA | 11655pao |

**Key:** * Dec-Feb; ** Mar.
**Ann:** Chinese: "Cheli shih Chungyang Kuangpo Tientai, Taiwan chih Yin"; English: "This is Radio Taiwan International"; Indonesian: "Inilah Radio Taiwan Internasional"; Japanese: "Kochirawa Taiwan Kokusai Hoso, RTI, Chukaminkoku Chuohosokyoku no nihongobangumi desu".
**V:** QSL-card.
**Notes:** Formed in 1998, when the former Central Broadcasting System (owned by the Ministry of Defense) was joined with the international section of the Broadcasting Corporation of China (Voice of Free China). Schedule includes some CBS networks. Programmes to mainland China are jammed by "China National Radio (CNR)" 1st programme transmissions (usually).

### PCJ RADIO INTERNATIONAL
🖃 8th FL, No. 47, Lane 31, Sec. 1, Sanmin Rd., Banciao Dist., New Taipei 22070, Taiwan.
☎ +886 9 38408592. (cellphone)
**E:** pcjmedia@gmail.com
**LP:** Dir (PCJ Media): Keith Perron.
**kHz:** *5010, 5950*

### Winter Schedule 2018/2019

| English | Days | Area | kHz |
|---|---|---|---|
| 0100-0200 | ..w.... | Car | 5010rmi* |
| 0230-0300 | ......s | NAm | 5950rmi# |
| 1700-1715 | ......s | NAm | 5950rmi# |

**Key:** * Media Network Plus Prgr; # Unoffical WRN relay via WRMI.
**Ann:** English: "This is PCJ Radio International".
**V:** eQSL-card. Email rpt to pcjqsl@pcjmedia.com
**Notes:** Produced by PCJ Media; the programming consists of own and/or third-party radio shows. PCJ Media also provides freq/transmission brokerage.

## TAJIKISTAN (TJK)

### VOICE OF TAJIK (OVOZI TOJIK) (Gov)
🖃 Sheroz St. 31, 734025 Dushanbe, Tajikistan.
☎ +992 37 2277417.
**E:** ovozitojik2016@mail.ru, info@ktr.tj
**W:** ktr.kj; radiotoj.tj; www.facebook.com/safhaimusicol
**Webcast:** L (www.mediabay.tv)
**LP:** Chmn (State Committee for Radio & TV): Asadulloi Rahmon.
**MW/SW:** Leased from Teleradiokom.
**SAT:** Al Yah 1, NSS12.
**kHz:** *1143, 7245*

### Winter Schedule 2018/2019

| Arabic | Days | Area | kHz |
|---|---|---|---|
| 1200-1300 | daily | ME | 1143dsb, 7245dsb |

| Dari | Days | Area | kHz |
|---|---|---|---|
| 0600-0800 | daily | WAs | 1143dsb, 7245dsb |

| English | Days | Area | kHz |
|---|---|---|---|
| 1300-1400 | daily | WAs | 1143dsb, 7245dsb |

| Farsi | Days | Area | kHz |
|---|---|---|---|
| 0400-0600 | daily | ME | 1143dsb, 7245dsb |
| 1600-1800 | daily | ME | 1143dsb, 7245dsb |

| Hindi | Days | Area | kHz |
|---|---|---|---|
| 1100-1200 | daily | SAs | 1143dsb, 7245dsb |

| Russian | Days | Area | kHz |
|---|---|---|---|
| 0800-1000 | daily | CAs | 1143dsb, 7245dsb |

| Tajik | Days | Area | kHz |
|---|---|---|---|
| 0200-0400 | daily | CAs | 1143dsb, 7245dsb |
| 1400-1600 | daily | CAs | 1143dsb, 7245dsb |

| Uzbek | Days | Area | kHz |
|---|---|---|---|
| 1000-1100 | daily | CAs | 1143dsb, 7245dsb |

**V:** eQSL-letter.
**Notes:** External Sce of the State Committee for TV and Radio Broadcasting.

### TELERADIOKOM (Tx Operator)
✉ Safarov St. 85, 734001 Dushanbe, Tajikistan.
☎ +992 37 2210912. 📠 +992 37 2217974.
**E:** info@teleradiocom.tj **W:** www.teleradiocom.tj
**L.P:** DG: Suhrob Aliyev.
**MW:** [DSB] Two sites: Dushanbe, Yangiyul (G.C.: 38N29 068E48): 1143kHz 150kW, 1251kHz 100kW; Orzu (G.C: 37N32 068E48): 927kHz 300kW. Operated on behalf of USAGM (USA): 972kHz 800kW.
**SW:** [DSB] Two sites: Dushanbe, Yangiyul (G.C: 38N29 068E48): 1 x 50, 5 x 100kW; Orzu (G.C: 37N32 068E48): 2 x 1000kW. Operated on behalf of USAGM (USA): 1 x 250, 1 x 500kW.
**Notes:** Teleradiokom, operating under the roof of the State Committee for Radio & Television, is the national transmitter network owner.

## TANZANIA (TZA)

### ZANZIBAR BROADCASTING CORPORATION (Pub)
✉ P.O. Box 314, Zanzibar, Tanzania.
☎ +255 24 2330000. 📠 +255 24 2330000.
**E:** zanzibarbroadcasting@zbc.co.tz **W:** zbc.co.tz
**L.P:** DG: Hassan Abdallah Massawi; Dir (Radio): Rafi Haji Makame.
**SW:** [DOL] Zanzibar City; Dole: 1 x 50kW.
**kHz:** *6015, 11735*

#### Winter Schedule 2018/2019

| English | Days | Area | kHz |
|---|---|---|---|
| 1800-1810 | daily | EAf,ME | 11735dol† |

| Swahili | Days | Area | kHz |
|---|---|---|---|
| 0300-0600 | daily | EAf | 6015dol† |
| 1500-1800 | daily | EAf,ME | 11735dol† |
| 1810-2100 | daily | EAf,ME | 11735dol† |

**Key:** † Irregular.
**Ann:** English: "Zanzibar Broadcasting Corporation"; "ZBC".
**Notes:** Relay of domestic services (see National Radio section), incl. (irreg.) News in English 1800-1810.

## THAILAND (THA)

### RADIO SARANROM (Gov)
✉ 443 Sri Ayudhya Road, Bangkok 10400, Thailand.
☎ +66 26435094. 📠 +66 26435093.
**E:** radio_saranrom@mfa.go.th; information05@mfa.go.th
**W:** saranrom.mfa.go.th
**Webcast:** D
**L.P:** Dir, Broadcasting Division (Information Dept): Jesda Katavetin.
**MW:** Uses tx operated by USAGM (USA).
**kHz:** *1575*

#### Winter Schedule 2018/2019

| English | Days | Area | kHz |
|---|---|---|---|
| 1100-1130 | m...... | SEA | 1575bph |

| Thai | Days | Area | kHz |
|---|---|---|---|
| 1030-1100 | daily | SEA | 1575bph |
| 1100-1130 | .twtf.. | SEA | 1575bph |
| 1200-1230 | mtwtf.. | SEA | 1575bph |
| 1500-1530 | mtwtf.. | SEA | 1575bph |
| 2230-2400 | mtw..s | SEA | 1575bph |

**V:** QSL-card.
**Notes:** Service for Thai's living in South East Asia, produced by the Information Department of the Thai Ministry of Foreign Affairs.

### RADIO THAILAND WORLD SERVICE (HSK9) (Gov)
✉ Public Relations Department, Royal Thai Government, 236 Vibhavadi Rangsit Road, Ding Daeng, Bangkok 10400, Thailand.
☎ +66 22771814. 📠 +66 22776139.
**E:** english@hsk9.org; feedback@hsk9.org **W:** www.hsk9.org; www.facebook.com/RadioThailandWorldService.
**Webcast:** D/L
**L.P:** Dir: Mrs Kasemsiri Pengpis.
**SW:** Uses txs operated by USAGM (USA).
**SAT:** Thaicom 5.
**kHz:** *5875, 7475, 9940, 13745, 17630, 17640*

#### Winter Schedule 2018/2019

| Burmese | Days | Area | kHz |
|---|---|---|---|
| 1145-1200 | daily | SEA | 5875udo |

| Chinese | Days | Area | kHz |
|---|---|---|---|
| 1315-1330 | daily | EAs | 9940udo |

| English | Days | Area | kHz |
|---|---|---|---|
| 0000-0100 | daily | NAm | 13745udo |
| 0200-0230 | daily | NAm | 13745udo |
| 0530-0600 | daily | Eu | 17640udo |
| 1230-1300 | daily | As,Pac | 9940udo |
| 1400-1430 | daily | As,Pac | 9940udo |
| 1900-2000 | daily | Eu | 7475udo |
| 2030-2045 | daily | Eu | 7475udo |

| German | Days | Area | kHz |
|---|---|---|---|
| 2000-2015 | daily | Eu | 7475udo |

| Japanese | Days | Area | kHz |
|---|---|---|---|
| 1130-1145 | daily | EAs | 5875udo |
| 1300-1315 | daily | EAs | 9940udo |

| Khmer | Days | Area | kHz |
|---|---|---|---|
| 1115-1130 | daily | SEA | 5875udo |

| Malay | Days | Area | kHz |
|---|---|---|---|
| 1200-1215 | daily | SEA | 9940udo |

| Thai | Days | Area | kHz |
|---|---|---|---|
| 0100-0200 | daily | NAm | 13745udo |
| 0230-0330 | daily | NAm | 13745udo |
| 1000-1100 | daily | ME | 17630udo |
| 1330-1400 | daily | EAs | 9940udo |
| 1800-1900 | daily | Eu | 7475udo |
| 2045-2115 | daily | Eu | 7475udo |

| Vietnamese | Days | Area | kHz |
|---|---|---|---|
| 1100-1115 | daily | SEA | 5875udo |

**Ann:** English: "Broadcasting from Bangkok, this is Radio Thailand's World Service".
**IS:** Gongs and chimes.
**V:** QSL-card.
**Notes:** Radio Thailand World Service is the External Sce and is produced by the Thai Government Public Relations Department.

### AWR ASIA/PACIFIC (Rlg)
✉ EIS Building B, Unit 1101, 71/15 Soi Pridi Banomyong 37, Sukhumvit 71 Road, Klongton Nua, Vadhana District, Bangkok 10110, Thailand.
☎ +66 23818869.
**E:** asia@awr.org
**L.P:** Dir, Asia/Pacific Region: Surachet Insom.
**kHz:** *5965, 9450, 9460, 9510, 9540, 9580, 9610, 9740, 9765, 9800, 9830, 9855, 9905, 11590, 11610, 11630, 11690, 11730, 11825, 11855, 11870, 11935, 11945, 11955, 11980, 11985, 12035, 12040, 12085, 15180, 15195, 15215, 15250, 15255, 15320, 15360, 15365, 15400, 15430, 15445, 15450, 15500, 15610, 15625, 15680, 15685, 17530, 17540, 17650, 17670, 17730, 17880*

#### Winter Schedule 2018/2019

| Amoy | Days | Area | kHz |
|---|---|---|---|
| 0100-0130 | mtwt..s | CHN | 15625trm, 17650sda |
| 1200-1230 | mtwt..s | CHN | 9450sda, 9610sda, 9800sda, 11630sda |

| Asho | Days | Area | kHz |
|---|---|---|---|
| 1400-1430 | daily | As | 11870sda |

| Asho | Days | Area | kHz |
|---|---|---|---|
| 2330-2400 | daily | As | 17650sda |

| Assamese | Days | Area | kHz |
|---|---|---|---|
| 1330-1400 | ..w...s | As | 11945trm |

| Bengali | Days | Area | kHz |
|---|---|---|---|
| 1230-1300 | mt.t.s. | As | 15430trm |
| 1300-1330 | daily | As | 15255sda |

| Burmese | Days | Area | kHz |
|---|---|---|---|
| 0000-0030 | daily | As | 17650sda |
| 1430-1500 | daily | As | 15215trm |

| Cambodian | Days | Area | kHz |
|---|---|---|---|
| 1300-1330 | daily | SEA | 11590sda |
| 2300-2330 | daily | SEA | 15365sda |

| Cantonese | Days | Area | kHz |
|---|---|---|---|
| 0130-0200 | mtwtf.s | CHN | 15625trm |
| 0130-0200 | mtwt..s | CHN | 17650sda |
| 1230-1300 | mtwt.ss | CHN | 9450sda, 9610sda, 9800sda, 11630sda |

| Chinese | Days | Area | kHz |
|---|---|---|---|
| 0000-0100 | daily | CHN | 17880sda |
| 0100-0130 | ....f.. | CHN | 17650sda |
| 0100-0130 | ...fs. | CHN | 15625trm |
| 0100-0200 | .....s. | CHN | 17650sda |
| 0130-0200 | .....s. | CHN | 15625trm |
| 1000-1100 | daily | CHN | 11690sda, 15450sda |
| 1100-1200 | daily | CHN | 9610sda, 9610sda, 11690sda, 15195sda |
| 1200-1230 | ....fs. | CHN | 9450sda, 9610sda, 9800sda, 11630sda |
| 1230-1300 | ....f.. | CHN | 9450sda, 9610sda, 9800sda, 11630sda |
| 1300-1330 | mtwtf.. | CHN | 11730sof |
| 1300-1400 | daily | CHN | 11935trm |
| 1330-1400 | daily | CHN | 11730sof |
| 1400-1500 | daily | CHN | 9580sda, 11730nau |
| 2100-2200 | daily | CHN | 9540trm |
| 2200-2300 | daily | CHN | 11870sda, 11980sda |
| 2300-2400 | daily | CHN | 15215sda, 15685sda |

| English | Days | Area | kHz |
|---|---|---|---|
| 1530-1600 | mtw..ss | EAs | 11985trm |
| 1600-1630 | daily | As | 17730mdc |
| 2200-2230 | .t.t..s | SEA | 12040sda |

| Gujarati | Days | Area | kHz |
|---|---|---|---|
| 1530-1600 | daily | As | 11945sof |

| Hindi | Days | Area | kHz |
|---|---|---|---|
| 1530-1600 | daily | As | 9830sof, 17730mdc |

| Hmong | Days | Area | kHz |
|---|---|---|---|
| 1330-1400 | ...tf.. | SEA | 11945trm |

| Ilocano | Days | Area | kHz |
|---|---|---|---|
| 1030-1100 | ....f.s | SEA | 17540sda |

| Indonesian | Days | Area | kHz |
|---|---|---|---|
| 1100-1130 | daily | SEA | 15500sda |
| 2200-2300 | daily | SEA | 11955sda |

| Javanese | Days | Area | kHz |
|---|---|---|---|
| 1130-1200 | m.w.f.. | SEA | 15500sda |
| 2230-2300 | daily | SEA | 12040sda |

| Kachin | Days | Area | kHz |
|---|---|---|---|
| 1300-1330 | daily | SEA | 15450sda |

| Kannada | Days | Area | kHz |
|---|---|---|---|
| 1530-1600 | daily | As | 9905erv |

| Karen | Days | Area | kHz |
|---|---|---|---|
| 0030-0100 | daily | SEA | 17530sda |
| 1430-1500 | daily | SEA | 11985sda, 15180trm |

| Kokborok | Days | Area | kHz |
|---|---|---|---|
| 1330-1400 | daily | As | 15255sda |

| Korean | Days | Area | kHz |
|---|---|---|---|
| 1200-1300 | daily | EAs | 9460sda, 11825trm |
| 1300-1400 | daily | EAs | 11855sda |
| 1530-1630 | daily | EAs | 9765sda |
| 2100-2200 | daily | EAs | 5965sda |

| Lao | Days | Area | kHz |
|---|---|---|---|
| 1330-1400 | ...t.s. | SEA | 12085sda |
| 2330-2400 | ...t.s. | SEA | 15365sda |

| Malay | Days | Area | kHz |
|---|---|---|---|
| 1330-1400 | mt...s. | SEA | 11945trm |

| Malayalam | Days | Area | kHz |
|---|---|---|---|
| 1530-1600 | daily | SEA | 15680mdc |

| Marathi | Days | Area | kHz |
|---|---|---|---|
| 1530-1600 | daily | As | 12035trm |

| Meitei | Days | Area | kHz |
|---|---|---|---|
| 1230-1300 | ..w..ss | As | 15430trm |

| Mizo | Days | Area | kHz |
|---|---|---|---|
| 1500-1530 | daily | As | 15250trm |

| Mon | Days | Area | kHz |
|---|---|---|---|
| 1200-1230 | daily | SEA | 15400sda |

| Mongolian | Days | Area | kHz |
|---|---|---|---|
| 1030-1100 | daily | EAs | 15180sda |

| Nepali | Days | Area | kHz |
|---|---|---|---|
| 1300-1330 | daily | EAs | 15430trm |
| 1500-1530 | daily | EAs | 9740trm |

| Oriya | Days | Area | kHz |
|---|---|---|---|
| 1530-1600 | daily | EAs | 9855dsb |

| Shan | Days | Area | kHz |
|---|---|---|---|
| 1130-1200 | daily | SEA | 15610trm |

| Sindhi | Days | Area | kHz |
|---|---|---|---|
| 1630-1700 | .t.t.s. | As | 15360trm |

| Sinhala | Days | Area | kHz |
|---|---|---|---|
| 1400-1430 | daily | SEA | 15255mdc |

| Sundanese | Days | Area | kHz |
|---|---|---|---|
| 1130-1200 | .t.t.s. | INS | 15500sda |
| 2200-2230 | m.w.fs. | INS | 12040sda |

| Tagalog | Days | Area | kHz |
|---|---|---|---|
| 1030-1100 | mtwt.s. | SEA | 17540sda |

| Tamil | Days | Area | kHz |
|---|---|---|---|
| 1500-1530 | daily | As | 11945sof |

| Telugu | Days | Area | kHz |
|---|---|---|---|
| 1500-1530 | daily | As | 11985sof |

| Thai | Days | Area | kHz |
|---|---|---|---|
| 0000-0030 | daily | SEA | 9510trm |
| 1330-1400 | mtw.f.s | SEA | 12085sda |
| 1330-1400 | daily | SEA | 12035sda |
| 2330-2400 | mtw.f.s | SEA | 15365sda |

| Tibetan | Days | Area | kHz |
|---|---|---|---|
| 1530-1600 | ...tf.. | EAs | 11985trm |

| Uyghur | Days | Area | kHz |
|---|---|---|---|
| 1300-1330 | .....ss | EAs | 11730sof |

| Vietnamese | Days | Area | kHz |
|---|---|---|---|
| 0100-0200 | .....s. | SEA | 15445tsh |
| 1300-1400 | daily | SEA | 17670mdc |
| 2200-2300 | daily | SEA | 11610sda |
| 2300-2330 | daily | SEA | 15320sda |

**V:** QSL-card.

**Notes:** Regional branch of Adventist Broadcasting Service, Inc (USA), see USA for corporate details. In 2014, this branch was moved to Thailand after having been based in Indonesia in earlier years. The individual AWR prgrs are produced by a large number of partner studios within the region.

### USAGM THAILAND TRANSMITTING STATION
✉ P.O. Box 99, Amphur Muang, Udon Thani 41000, Thailand.
✉ Bangkok MW Transmitter Plant: Rangsit-Bangpoon Road, Bangkok, Thailand.
**LP:** SM: Dennis G.Brewer.
**MW:** [BPH] Bangkok, Rasom: 1575kHz 1000kW.
**SW:** [UDO] Udon Thani, Ban Dung: 7 x 500kW.
**V:** QSL-card. (Email to manager_thailand@tha.usagm.gov)

## TURKEY (TUR)

### VOICE OF TURKEY (VOT) (Pub)
✉ P.O. Box 333, Yenisehir, Ankara 06443, Turkey; TRT Sitesi, A Blok No: 427, Ankara 06109, Turkey.
☎ +90 312 4909809. 🖷 +90 312 4909845.
**E:** tsrturkce@trt.net.tr (Turkish); englishdesk@trt.net.tr (English)
**W:** trtvotworld.com; www.turkiyeninsesiradyosu.com
**Webcast:** D/L/P
☎ +90 312 4633372. (English Desk)

**L.P:** Head (TRT External Services Department): Süleyman Erdal.
**MW:** [DIY] Diyabakir, Toraman: 1062kHz 300kW, [MER] Mersin: 630kHz 300kW.
**SW:** [EMR] Emirler: 5 x 500kW.
**SAT:** Astra 1N, Eutelsat Hot Bird 13D, Galaxy 19, Optus D2, Türksat 3A/4A.
**kHz:** 630, 1062, 5945, 5960, 5965, 5970, 5980, 6000, 6050, 6070, 6120, 6125, 6185, 7240, 7245, 7295, 9410, 9460, 9495, 9595, 9610, 9620, 9625, 9650, 9700, 9785, 9840, 11660, 11710, 11730, 11795, 11815, 11925, 11955, 11965, 12035, 13630, 13655, 13685, 15235, 15270, 15350, 15360, 15390, 15480, 17530, 17720

## Winter Schedule 2018/2019

| Arabic | Days | Area | kHz |
|---|---|---|---|
| 1000-1100 | daily | ME,NAf | 11955emr |
| 1100-1500 | daily | ME | 630mer |
| 1500-1600 | daily | ME | 7295emr |
| 1500-1600 | daily | NAf | 17720emr |
| 1500-1900 | daily | ME | 1062diy |
| 1700-1900 | daily | ME | 630mer* |

| Azeri | Days | Area | kHz |
|---|---|---|---|
| 0800-0900 | daily | ME | 11710emr |
| 1630-1730 | daily | ME | 5965emr |

| Bulgarian | Days | Area | kHz |
|---|---|---|---|
| 1200-1230 | daily | Eu | 7245emr |

| Chinese | Days | Area | kHz |
|---|---|---|---|
| 1200-1300 | daily | EAs | 13630emr |

| Dari | Days | Area | kHz |
|---|---|---|---|
| 1600-1630 | daily | WAs | 9595emr |

| English | Days | Area | kHz |
|---|---|---|---|
| 0400-0500 | daily | ME,NAf | 6125emr |
| 0400-0500 | daily | Eu,NAm | 7240emr |
| 1330-1430 | daily | Eu | 12035emr |
| 1730-1830 | daily | CAs,SAs | 11730emr |
| 1930-2030 | daily | Eu | 6050emr |
| 2130-2230 | daily | SEA,Pac | 9610emr |
| 2300-2400 | daily | Eu,NAm | 5960emr |

| Farsi | Days | Area | kHz |
|---|---|---|---|
| 0930-1100 | daily | ME | 11795emr |
| 1600-1700 | daily | ME | 6070emr |

| French | Days | Area | kHz |
|---|---|---|---|
| 1830-1930 | daily | CAf | 9620emr |
| 2030-2130 | daily | Eu | 5970emr |
| 2030-2130 | daily | NAf,WAf | 9625emr |

| Georgian | Days | Area | kHz |
|---|---|---|---|
| 1100-1200 | daily | Cau | 9840emr |

| German | Days | Area | kHz |
|---|---|---|---|
| 1230-1330 | daily | Eu | 15270emr |
| 1830-1930 | daily | Eu | 5945emr |

| Hausa | Days | Area | kHz |
|---|---|---|---|
| 0600-0700 | daily | WAf | 15235emr |

| Italian | Days | Area | kHz |
|---|---|---|---|
| 1500-1530 | daily | Eu | 6185emr |

| Kazakh | Days | Area | kHz |
|---|---|---|---|
| 1430-1500 | daily | CAs | 9785emr |

| Malay | Days | Area | kHz |
|---|---|---|---|
| 0500-0600 | daily | SEA | 17530emr |

| Pashto | Days | Area | kHz |
|---|---|---|---|
| 1630-1700 | daily | WAs | 9595emr |

| Russian | Days | Area | kHz |
|---|---|---|---|
| 1400-1500 | daily | RUS | 9410emr |

| Spanish | Days | Area | kHz |
|---|---|---|---|
| 0200-0300 | daily | CAm,Eu | 9650emr |
| 0200-0300 | daily | SAm,Eu | 9410emr |
| 1730-1830 | daily | Eu | 9495emr |

| Swahili | Days | Area | kHz |
|---|---|---|---|
| 0700-0800 | daily | CAf | 15235emr |

| Tatar | Days | Area | kHz |
|---|---|---|---|
| 1100-1130 | daily | Eu,CAs | 15360emr |

| Turkish | Days | Area | kHz |
|---|---|---|---|
| 0100-0300 | daily | CAs | 6000emr |
| 0400-0700 | daily | Eu | 9700emr |
| 0500-0700 | daily | ME | 11660emr |
| 0700-1000 | daily | ME | 11925emr |
| 0700-1300 | daily | ME,NAf | 15480emr |
| 0700-1400 | daily | Eu | 15350emr |
| 1400-1700 | daily | Eu | 11815emr |
| 1700-2200 | daily | Eu | 5980emr |
| 1700-2200 | daily | ME,NAf | 6120emr |

| Turkmen | Days | Area | kHz |
|---|---|---|---|
| 1300-1330 | daily | CAs | 11965emr |

| Urdu | Days | Area | kHz |
|---|---|---|---|
| 1300-1400 | daily | SAs | 15390emr |

| Uyghur | Days | Area | kHz |
|---|---|---|---|
| 0300-0400 | daily | CAs | 9460emr |
| 1330-1430 | daily | CAs | 13685emr |

| Uzbek | Days | Area | kHz |
|---|---|---|---|
| 1130-1200 | daily | CAs | 13655emr |
| 1700-1730 | daily | CAs | 9595emr |

**Key:** * Relay of TRT Al Arabiya TV audio (trtarabic.tv)
**Ann:** English: "This is the Voice of Turkey's English transmission"; German: "Hier ist der Kurzwellensender Die Stimme der Türkei"; Spanish: "Esta es La Voz de Turquia"; Turkish: "Burasi Türkiye'nin Sesi Radyosu".
**V:** QSL-card.
**Notes:** The Voice of Turkey is the External Sce of the public service Turkish Radio-TV Corporation, TRT (Türkiye Radyo Televizyon Kurumu).

## UKRAINE (UKR)

**RADIO UKRAINE INTERNATIONAL (RUI) (Pub)**
✉ vul. Kreshchatyk 26, 01001 Kyiv, Ukraine.
☎ +380 44 2791757.
**E:** inoradio@nrcu.gov.ua **W:** nrcu.gov.ua
**Webcast:** D/L. Webcast/Satellite languages: English, German, Romanian, Russian, Ukrainian.
**L.P:** Dir: Zhanna Mishcherska.
**SAT:** Amos 3.
**kHz:** 7780

### Winter Schedule 2018/2019

| English | Days | Area | kHz |
|---|---|---|---|
| 0230-0300 | .twtfs. | NAm,Eu,NAf | 7780rmi |

**V:** QSL-card.
**Notes:** Produced by the National Public Broadcasting Company of Ukraine.

## UNITED KINGDOM (G)

**BBC WORLD SERVICE (Pub)**
✉ Broadcasting House, Portland Place, London W1A 1AA, United Kingdom.
☎ +44 20 72403456. 📠 +44 20 75571258.
**E:** worldservice.letters@bbc.co.uk
**W:** www.bbc.co.uk/worldserviceradio
**Webcast:** D/L/P. Web-only audio languages (also relayed by local affiliates): Kyrgyz, Vietnamese.
**L.P:** Dir (World Service Group): Francesca Unsworth.
**MW/SW:** Uses txs (domestic and BBC-owned overseas relay stations) operated by Encompass Digital Media Services & third party foreign relays.
**SAT:** AsiaSat 5, Astra 1N/2E, Badr 4, Eutelsat 7A/36B/Hot Bird 13B/13C, Intelsat 19/10-02/20/34/907, Nilesat 201, Palapa D, SES 7, Y1A.
**kHz:** 198, 639, 702, 720, 1251, 1413, 3255, 3915, 3955, 5845, 5855, 5875, 5890, 5895, 5910, 5925, 5930, 5960, 5970, 5975, 5995, 6005, 6010, 6090, 6095, 6100, 6135, 6145, 6180, 6190, 6195, 7265, 7285, 7300, 7305, 7325, 7345, 7355, 7395, 7405, 7430, 7445, 7465, 7485, 9410, 9440, 9445, 9465, 9510, 9540, 9545, 9560, 9580, 9600, 9885, 9900, 9915, 11660, 11700, 11720, 11750, 11810, 11875, 11905, 11945, 11975, 11995, 12015, 12065, 12095, 13660, 13840, 13860, 15310, 15315, 15400, 15420, 15490, 15510, 15620, 17640, 17745, 17780, 17830, 17870, 21470, 21630

### Winter Schedule 2018/2019

| Amharic | Days | Area | kHz |
|---|---|---|---|
| 1730-1750 | mtwtf.. | EAf | 9600sla, 11720dha, 12095mey |
| 1830-1850 | mtwtf.. | EAf | 9600sla, 9885mey |

| Arabic | Days | Area | kHz |
|---|---|---|---|
| 0300-0400 | daily | NAf | 5995dha |

| Arabic | Days | Area | kHz |
|---|---|---|---|
| 0300-0500 | daily | NAf | 5875wof |
| 0300-0700 | daily | ME | 639zak, 720zak |
| 0500-0600 | daily | NAf | 12015dha |
| 0600-0700 | daily | NAf | 15315sla |
| 1500-2100 | daily | ME | 702sla |
| 1700-1900 | daily | NAf | 9580dha |
| 1700-2100 | daily | ME | 720zak |
| 1800-2100 | daily | ME | 639zak |
| 1900-2000 | daily | NAf | 6145dha |
| 2000-2100 | daily | NAf | 6145sla |

| Bengali | Days | Area | kHz |
|---|---|---|---|
| 0130-0200 | daily | SAs | 9560sng, 11995sng |
| 1330-1400 | daily | SAs | 5875tac, 9510sng, 11750sla |

| Burmese | Days | Area | kHz |
|---|---|---|---|
| 0000-0030 | daily | SEA | 7465sng, 11700sng, 15310sng |
| 1330-1400 | daily | SEA | 5855tac, 7485sng, 11995sng |

| Dari | Days | Area | kHz |
|---|---|---|---|
| 0030-0100 | daily | WAs | 1413sla, 5930mos, 7445wof |
| 0130-0200 | daily | WAs | 5930mos, 6195sof, 7445wof |
| 0230-0300 | daily | WAs | 5875erv, 6195sla, 7445wof |
| 0830-0900 | daily | WAs | 13660sla, 15310sla |
| 0930-1000 | daily | WAs | 13660sla, 15310sla |
| 1030-1100 | daily | WAs | 13660sla, 15310sla |
| 1400-1500 | daily | WAs | 5975sla, 7465sng |
| 1600-1630 | daily | WAs | 5975sla, 7465sng |
| 1630-1700 | .....ss | WAs | 5975sla, 7465sng |
| 1700-1800 | daily | WAs | 5910erv, 6090sla, 7465sng |

| English | Days | Area | kHz |
|---|---|---|---|
| 0000-0100 | daily | SAs | 5875wof |
| 0000-0200 | daily | SAs | 5970erv |
| 0100-0200 | daily | SAs | 9410sng |
| 0100-0520 | daily | Eu | 198dro |
| 0130-0230 | daily | SAs | 1413sla |
| 0300-0400 | daily | ME | 6195sla |
| 0300-0500 | daily | ME | 7285sla |
| 0400-0500 | daily | EAf | 9915mdc, 12095dha |
| 0400-0500 | daily | ME | 9410sla |
| 0500-0600 | daily | CAf | 7345wof |
| 0500-0600 | daily | EAf | 9915mey, 12095mdc |
| 0500-0600 | daily | ME | 1413sla |
| 0500-0600 | daily | SAf | 3255mey, 5925asc |
| 0500-0600 | daily | WAf | 5875asc |
| 0500-0700 | daily | WAf | 6005asc |
| 0500-0800 | daily | SAf | 6190mey |
| 0600-0700 | daily | CAf | 7345asc, 12095mey |
| 0600-0700 | daily | Eu | 3955wof+ |
| 0600-0700 | daily | WAf | 7325wof |
| 0600-0800 | daily | EAf | 15420mey, 17640dha |
| 0600-0800 | daily | SAf | 15400dha |
| 0700-0800 | daily | CAf | 9410asc, 15490mey |
| 0700-0800 | daily | WAf | 7325asc, 9915asc |
| 0800-0900 | daily | SAs | 15620sng+ |
| 1000-1030 | .twtfs. | CAs | 1251dsb |
| 1000-1200 | daily | EAs,SEA | 9900sng |
| 1000-1200 | daily | SEA | 6195sng, 12065sng |
| 1200-1300 | daily | EAs | 15510sng |
| 1200-1300 | daily | SAs | 12065sla |
| 1200-1400 | daily | SAs | 9410sla |
| 1300-1330 | daily | CAs | 1251dsb |
| 1300-1400 | daily | SAs | 1413sla, 12065sng |
| 1430-1500 | daily | SAs | 1413sla |
| 1500-1600 | daily | EAf | 12095mdc, 15420mey |
| 1500-1700 | daily | ME | 7405sla |
| 1600-1700 | daily | EAf | 12095mey |
| 1600-1700 | daily | SAf | 15400asc |
| 1600-1800 | daily | CAf | 17830asc |

| English | Days | Area | kHz |
|---|---|---|---|
| 1600-2000 | daily | EAf | 7445mdc |
| 1600-2000 | daily | SAf | 3255mey, 6190mey |
| 1700-1800 | daily | SAs | 1413sla |
| 1700-1800 | daily | CAs | 1251dsb |
| 1700-1800 | daily | EAf | 9410mey |
| 1700-1800 | daily | WAf | 17780asc |
| 1700-1900 | daily | WAf | 15400asc |
| 1700-1900 | daily | ME | 6195sla |
| 1800-1900 | daily | WAf | 9915wof |
| 1800-2000 | daily | EAf | 9410dha |
| 1800-2100 | daily | CAf | 11810asc |
| 1900-2100 | daily | ME | 1413sla |
| 1900-2100 | daily | WAf | 5875wof |
| 2000-2100 | daily | WAf | 12095asc |
| 2100-2200 | mtwtf.. | CAf | 11810asc |
| 2100-2200 | mtwtf.. | WAf | 5875wof, 12095asc |
| 2200-2300 | daily | EAs,SEA | 5960sla |
| 2200-2300 | daily | SEA | 7300dha |
| 2200-2400 | daily | EAs,SEA | 6195sng |
| 2200-2400 | daily | SEA | 3915sng, 5890sng |
| 2300-2400 | daily | SEA | 7445sla |

| Farsi | Days | Area | kHz |
|---|---|---|---|
| 0330-0430 | daily | ME | 6010tac, 6095sla, 7485kch |
| 0330-0430 | daily | CAs | 1251dsb |
| 0330-0500 | daily | ME | 1413sla |
| 0430-0530 | daily | ME | 9440dha, 11905sla, 13860tac |
| 1600-1700 | daily | ME | 1413sla, 5875sof, 6195sla |

| French | Days | Area | kHz |
|---|---|---|---|
| 0600-0630 | daily | CAf | 7305asc |
| 0600-0630 | daily | NAf | 6135wof, 7265wof |
| 0600-0630 | daily | WAf | 5875asc |
| 0700-0730 | daily | CAf | 17830dha |
| 0700-0730 | daily | WAf | 7305asc |
| 1200-1230 | daily | CAf | 17830mey |
| 1200-1230 | daily | NAf | 15490wof |
| 1200-1230 | daily | WAf | 17640asc |
| 1800-1830 | daily | CAf | 12065asc |
| 1800-1830 | daily | NAf | 7265wof |
| 1800-1830 | daily | SAf | 7395mey |
| 1800-1830 | daily | WAf | 11975asc, 15490asc |

| Hausa | Days | Area | kHz |
|---|---|---|---|
| 0530-0600 | daily | WAf | 5975wof, 6135asc, 7305asc |
| 0630-0700 | daily | WAf | 5975asc, 7305asc, 17830dha |
| 1400-1430 | mtwtf.. | WAf | 17640mey, 17780asc, 21630asc |
| 1430-1700 | .....s. | WAf | 17780asc |
| 1930-2000 | daily | WAf | 9545wof, 11660asc, 15490asc |
| 2000-2030 | ....f.. | WAf | 9545wof, 11660asc, 15490asc |

| Hindi | Days | Area | kHz |
|---|---|---|---|
| 0100-0130 | daily | SAs | 1413sla, 5875tac, 6100wof, 7430wof, 11995sng |
| 1400-1430 | daily | SAs | 1413sla, 5875tac, 9510sng, 9540sla, 11995sng |

| Kinyarwanda/ Kirundi | Days | Area | kHz |
|---|---|---|---|
| 0500-0600 | .....s. | EAf | 11945mey, 15490mey |
| 0530-0600 | ......s | EAf | 11945mey, 15490mey |
| 1630-1700 | mtwtf.. | EAf | 15420mdc, 17870mey |

| Korean | Days | Area | kHz |
|---|---|---|---|
| 1530-1600 | daily | EAs | 5845sng, 5895dsb, 7355sng |

| Oromo | Days | Area | kHz |
|---|---|---|---|
| 1750-1810 | mtwtf.. | EAf | 9600sla, 11720dha, 12095mey |

| Oromo | Days | Area | kHz |
|---|---|---|---|
| 1850-1910 | mtwtf.. | EAf | 9600sla, 9885mey |

| Pashto | Days | Area | kHz |
|---|---|---|---|
| 0100-0130 | daily | WAs | 5930mos, 6195sof, 7445wof |
| 0200-0230 | daily | WAs | 5875erv, 6195sla, 7445wof |
| 0300-0330 | daily | WAs | 7300dha, 7445erv, 9410dha |
| 0900-0930 | daily | WAs | 13660sla, 15310sla |
| 1000-1030 | daily | WAs | 13660sla, 15310sla |
| 1000-1030 | m.....s | CAs | 1251dsb |
| 1100-1130 | daily | WAs | 13660sla, 15310sla |
| 1500-1600 | daily | WAs | 5975sla, 7465sng |
| 1630-1700 | mtwtf.. | WAs | 5975sla, 7465sng |
| 1800-1830 | daily | WAs | 1413sla, 5910erv, 6090sla |
| 1830-1900 | daily | CAs | 1251dsb |
| 1830-1900 | daily | WAs | 1413sla |

| Somali | Days | Area | kHz |
|---|---|---|---|
| 0400-0430 | daily | EAf | 11995mdc, 13840dha |
| 1100-1130 | daily | EAf | 15420dha, 17745dha |
| 1400-1500 | daily | EAf | 12095mdc, 17745mey, 21470dha |
| 1500-1700 | .....s. | EAf | 17745mey, 21470asc |
| 1800-1830 | daily | EAf | 6180dha, 9465mey, 11875mey |

| Tajik | Days | Area | kHz |
|---|---|---|---|
| 0200-0230 | daily | CAs | 1251dsb |
| 0930-1000 | daily | CAs | 1251dsb |
| 1400-1500 | daily | CAs | 1251dsb |
| 1800-1830 | daily | CAs | 1251dsb |

| Tigrinya | Days | Area | kHz |
|---|---|---|---|
| 1810-1830 | mtwtf.. | EAf | 9600sla, 11720dha, 12095mey |
| 1910-1930 | mtwtf.. | EAf | 9600sla, 9885mey |

| Urdu | Days | Area | kHz |
|---|---|---|---|
| 1500-1600 | daily | SAs | 1413sla, 7300dha, 7485sng, 9410sng, 9445sof |

| Uzbek | Days | Area | kHz |
|---|---|---|---|
| 1330-1400 | daily | CAs | 1251dsb |

**Key:** + DRM
**Ann:** English: "BBC World Service"; "This is the BBC".
**V:** Does not verify reception reports.
**Notes:** BBC World Service is produced by the Global News division of the British Broadcasting Corp. The English service is available 24/7 on local FM/MW relays in many countries, as well as part-time relayed on national domestic channels, esp. in countries of the British Commonwealth. Many language services are relayed by local affiliates. Transmissions in some Asian languages are jammed.

## AWR AFRICA (Rlg)
☐ 1 Milbanke Court, Milbanke Way, Bracknell, Berkshire RG12 1RP, United Kingdom.
☎ +44 1344 401401. 🖷 +44 1344 401419.
**E:** africa@awr.org
**L.P:** Dir, Africa Region: Ray Allen.
**kHz:** 6045, 6055, 6065, 6120, 7205, 7220, 7225, 7270, 7275, 7310, 7350, 7375, 9515, 9630, 9770, 9780, 9800, 9850, 9895, 11720, 11790, 11800, 11870, 11880, 11955, 11980, 11985, 12035, 15145, 15155, 15160, 15490, 15500, 17570, 17605, 17780

### Winter Schedule 2018/2019

| Afar | Days | Area | kHz |
|---|---|---|---|
| 1430-1500 | daily | EAf | 17605mos |

| Amharic | Days | Area | kHz |
|---|---|---|---|
| 0400-0430 | daily | EAf | 15500trm |
| 1630-1700 | daily | EAf | 12035nau |

| Arabic | Days | Area | kHz |
|---|---|---|---|
| 0500-0600 | daily | NAf,ME | 17780trm |
| 0600-0700 | daily | NAf | 11880mos |
| 0700-0800 | daily | NAf | 11980nau |
| 1800-1900 | daily | NAf | 7225mos |

| Arabic | Days | Area | kHz |
|---|---|---|---|
| 1900-2000 | daily | NAf | 6120nau |
| 1900-2000 | daily | NAf,ME | 11985mdc |

| Dyula | Days | Area | kHz |
|---|---|---|---|
| 2000-2030 | daily | WAf | 7310mos |

| English | Days | Area | kHz |
|---|---|---|---|
| 1600-1630 | daily | WAf | 9770sof |
| 1830-1900 | daily | Af | 15155trm |
| 2100-2130 | daily | WAf | 7270mos |

| French | Days | Area | kHz |
|---|---|---|---|
| 0430-0500 | daily | NAf | 6045nau |
| 0600-0630 | daily | NAf | 7375iss |
| 0600-0630 | daily | WAf | 7220iss |
| 0700-0730 | daily | NAf | 11880iss |
| 0800-0830 | daily | NAf | 15145mos |
| 1930-2000 | daily | CAf | 9780mos |
| 2000-2030 | daily | WAf | 9515mdc, 9780mey |
| 2030-2100 | daily | WAf | 7270mos |

| Fulfulde | Days | Area | kHz |
|---|---|---|---|
| 1930-2000 | daily | Af | 11790mey |

| Hausa | Days | Area | kHz |
|---|---|---|---|
| 0500-0530 | daily | WAf | 9630mos |
| 1900-1930 | daily | WAf | 7275mos |

| Ibo | Days | Area | kHz |
|---|---|---|---|
| 1930-2000 | daily | Af | 9850mey |

| Kabyle | Days | Area | kHz |
|---|---|---|---|
| 0800-0830 | daily | NAf | 15160nau |
| 1730-1800 | daily | NAf | 9800iss |

| Maasai | Days | Area | kHz |
|---|---|---|---|
| 1730-1800 | daily | Af | 15490mey |

| Malagasy | Days | Area | kHz |
|---|---|---|---|
| 0300-0400 | daily | SAf | 6065mdc |
| 1400-1500 | daily | SAf | 6055mdc |

| Mossi | Days | Area | kHz |
|---|---|---|---|
| 2000-2030 | daily | WAf | 17570mdc |

| Oromo | Days | Area | kHz |
|---|---|---|---|
| 0300-0330 | daily | EAf | 15500trm |
| 1730-1800 | daily | EAf | 11870iss |

| Somali | Days | Area | kHz |
|---|---|---|---|
| 1630-1700 | daily | EAf | 15490iss |

| Swahili | Days | Area | kHz |
|---|---|---|---|
| 1700-1730 | daily | EAf | 11720mdc, 11800mey |

| Tachelhit | Days | Area | kHz |
|---|---|---|---|
| 0830-0900 | daily | NAf | 15145nau |
| 1930-2000 | daily | NAf | 7205nau |

| Tigrinya | Days | Area | kHz |
|---|---|---|---|
| 0300-0330 | daily | EAf | 7350nau |
| 1630-1700 | daily | EAf | 11955nau |

| Wolof | Days | Area | kHz |
|---|---|---|---|
| 1900-1930 | daily | Af | 9895nau |

| Yoruba | Days | Area | kHz |
|---|---|---|---|
| 2030-2100 | daily | Af | 9780mey |

**V:** QSL-card.
**Notes:** Regional branch of Adventist Broadcasting Service, Inc (USA), covering Africa. The individual AWR prgrs are produced by a large number of partner studios within the region. Earlier, this branch also managed transmissions to Europe and prgrs in Persian, Punjabi, Turkish, Urdu, they are now administered by the HQ in the USA (see USA entry for schedules and corporate details).

## END TIMES COMING RADIO (Rlg)
☐ c/o Hilton House, 71-73 Chapel Street, Salford M3 5BZ, United Kingdom.
**W:** www.excatholicsforchrist.com
**Webcast:** D/L/P
☐ ETC Ministry, c/o Pennywise, 15a St. Andrews Court, Bolton BL1 1LD, United Kingdom.
**L.P:** Host: G. Patrick Battell.
**kHz:** 9400

### Winter Schedule 2018/2019

| English | Days | Area | kHz |
|---|---|---|---|
| 1900-1930 | daily | Eu | 9400sof |

**Ann:** English: "End Times Coming"; "ETC Radio".
**Notes:** "End Times Coming" is a Bible Study broadcast.

## ENCOMPASS DIGITAL MEDIA SERVICES LTD (Tx Operator)

📧 610 Chiswick High Road, London W4 5RU, United Kingdom.
☎ +44 20 71316131.
**E:** via website. **W:** www.encompass.tv
**W:** World Radio Network (WRN): babcock.media/world-radio-network
**L.P:** Dir: Mathew Lavelle.
**SW:** [WOF] Woofferton: 6 x 250, 4 x 300kW.
**V:** Does not verify. See Encompass Digital Media Services operated BBC Relay Stations (Ascension, Cyprus, Oman and Singapore) for direct QSLs.
**Notes:** After acquiring Babcock Media Services in September 2018, Encompass Digital Media Services Ltd is the new owner and operator of the shortwave transmitting centre Woofferton in the UK; it also operates the BBC overseas relay stations, under a management contract.

## UNITED STATES OF AMERICA (USA)

## OCB – RADIO MARTÍ (Gov)

📧 4201 NW 77th Avenue, Miami, FL 33166, USA.
☎ +1 305 4377000. 🖨 +1 305 4377016.
**E:** info@martinoticias.com **W:** www.martinoticias.com
**Webcast:** L/P
📧 3919 VOA Site B Road, Grimesland, NC 27837, USA (SW tx site - "Edward R. Murrow" Transmitting Station); US Government Rd, Marathon, FL 33050, USA (MW tx site)
**L.P:** Dir: Tomás P. Regalado.
**MW:** [MTH] Marathon, FL: 1180kHz 100kW.
**SW:** Via txs provided by USAGM (USA).
**SAT:** Hispasat 30W-4.
**kHz:** *1180, 5980, 6030, 7355, 7365, 7375, 7435, 9565, 11860, 11930, 13820*

### Winter Schedule 2018/2019

| Spanish | Days | Area | kHz |
|---|---|---|---|
| 0000-1200 | daily | CUB | 6030grv |
| 0000-2400 | daily | CUB | 1180mth |
| 0100-0200 | daily | CUB | 7365grv |
| 0200-0700 | daily | CUB | 7435grv |
| 0600-1300 | daily | CUB | 5980grv |
| 1000-1400 | daily | CUB | 7355grv |
| 1200-1400 | daily | CUB | 7435grv |
| 1300-2200 | daily | CUB | 11930grv |
| 1400-2000 | daily | CUB | 13820grv |
| 1400-2200 | mtwtf.. | CUB | 11860grv |
| 2000-2400 | daily | CUB | 9565grv |
| 2200-2300 | daily | CUB | 7375grv |
| 2300-0100 | daily | CUB | 7435grv |
| 2300-0600 | daily | CUB | 7355grv |

**Ann:** Spanish: "Aquí Radio Martí, servicio de información para Cuba, transmitiendo desde Miami, Estados Unidos".
**V:** QSL-card.
**Notes:** USAGM funded station for listeners in Cuba, launched in May 1985. Produced by Office of Cuba Broadcasting (OCB). Jammed. OCB operates the MW transmitting station Marathon, FL and (since 2014) the SW transmitting station Greenville, NC.

## RADIO FARDA (Gov)

📧 1201 Connecticut Avenue NW, Washington, D.C. 20036, USA.
☎ +1 202 8287220. 🖨 +1 202 8287235.
**E:** comment@radiofarda.com; info@radiofarda.com
**W:** www.radiofarda.com
**Webcast:** D/L/P
📧 Vinohradská 159A, 100 00 Prague 10, Czechia. (Studio)
☎ +420 2 21124113. 🖨 +420 2 21122622.
**L.P:** Dir: Armand Mostofi.
**MW/SW:** Via txs provided by USAGM (USA), plus other relays.
**SAT:** AsiaSat 7, Badr 4, Eutelsat Hot Bird 7A/13B, Nilesat 101, NSS 12, SES 6, Telstar 12, Türksat 3A.
**kHz:** *1575, 5860, 7585, 9990, 11695, 12005, 13765, 15690*

### Winter Schedule 2018/2019

| Farsi | Days | Area | kHz |
|---|---|---|---|
| 0000-2400 | daily | ME | 1575dha* |
| 0230-0830 | daily | ME | 7585kwt |
| 0300-0500 | daily | ME | 5860kwt |
| 0400-0530 | daily | ME | 13765udo |
| 0430-1530 | daily | ME | 15690bib |
| 0530-0730 | daily | ME | 13765lam |
| 0630-1800 | daily | ME | 12005bib |
| 0730-1530 | daily | ME | 13765lam |
| 0830-1330 | daily | ME | 9990kwt |
| 1330-1430 | daily | ME | 9990udo |
| 1430-1630 | daily | ME | 11695lam |
| 1430-2300 | daily | ME | 5860kwt |
| 1730-2130 | daily | ME | 7585udo |
| 2300-0300 | daily | ME | 5860lam |

**Key:** * Jammed.
**Ann:** Farsi: "Radyo Farda".
**V:** QSL-card.
**Notes:** USAGM funded station for listeners in Iran, launched in December 2002. Produced by RFE/RL, Inc. Transmissions on medium wave are jammed.

## RADIO FREE ASIA (RFA) (Gov)

📧 2025 M Street NW, Suite 300, Washington, D.C. 20036, USA.
☎ +1 202 5304900. 🖨 +1 202 5307794.
**E:** contact@rfa.org; info@rfa.org **W:** www.rfa.org
**Webcast:** D/L/P
**L.P:** Chmn (RFA): Kenneth Weinstein; Pres: Libby Liu; Vice Pres, Government Relations & Corporate Communications: John A. Estrella; Dir, Programme & Ops Support: A.J. Janitschek.
**MW/SW:** Via txs provided by USAGM (USA), plus other relays.
**SAT:** NSS 12, Telstar 18.
**kHz:** *1098, 1188, 1566, 5885, 5890, 5970, 6120, 7415, 7470, 7480, 7485, 7520, 7540, 7545, 7565, 7580, 9310, 9315, 9325, 9390, 9410, 9450, 9455, 9510, 9535, 9590, 9670, 9690, 9700, 9720, 9790, 9860, 9900, 9905, 9910, 9985, 11550, 11555, 11590, 11660, 11720, 11775, 11750, 11765, 11775, 11780, 11795, 11800, 11805, 11850, 11885, 11890, 11895, 11950, 11980, 12050, 12055, 12065, 12130, 13610, 13645, 13650, 13675, 13685, 13735, 13795, 13810, 15155, 15340, 15375, 15665, 15745, 17510, 17525, 17660, 17675, 17790, 17795, 17815, 17820, 17830, 17840, 17855, 21480, 21490, 21500, 21510, 21530, 21610, 21620, 21680, 21700*

### Winter Schedule 2018/2019

| Burmese | Days | Area | kHz |
|---|---|---|---|
| 0030-0130 | daily | BRM | 9510bib, 13735tin‡, 17510tin‡ |
| 1230-1330 | daily | BRM | 11795tin‡, 12130tin‡, 13735dha |
| 1330-1400 | daily | BRM | 13735tin‡ |
| 1330-1430 | daily | BRM | 11795kwt, 12130lam |
| **Cantonese** | **Days** | **Area** | **kHz** |
| 1400-1500 | .....s | CHN | 13645tin‡ |
| 1400-1500 | .....s. | CHN | 13610tin‡ |
| 1400-1500 | .t.t... | CHN | 13675tin‡ |
| 1400-1500 | m.w.f.. | CHN | 13810tin‡ |
| **Chinese** | **Days** | **Area** | **kHz** |
| 0300-0400 | daily | CHN | 11980kwt |
| 0300-0700 | daily | CHN | 15340lam, 17660sai‡ |
| 0400-0700 | daily | CHN | 11980dsb |
| 0500-0700 | daily | CHN | 21700tin‡ |
| 1500-1600 | .....ss | CHN | 11590kwt |
| 1500-1600 | .t.t... | CHN | 11725kwt |
| 1500-1600 | daily | CHN | 9790sai‡ |
| 1500-1600 | m.w.f.. | CHN | 11765kwt |
| 1500-1700 | .t.t.ss | CHN | 7520tin‡ |
| 1500-1700 | m.w.f.. | CHN | 7415tin‡ |
| 1600-1700 | m.w.f.. | CHN | 9455sai‡ |
| 1600-1700 | .....ss | CHN | 9905sai‡ |
| 1600-1700 | .t.t... | CHN | 9720sai‡ |
| 1600-1700 | daily | CHN | 6120tin‡ |
| 1700-1900 | daily | CHN | 7415tin‡ |
| 1700-2000 | daily | CHN | 9455bib, 9860sai‡ |
| 1900-2100 | daily | CHN | 5890kwt, 7520lam |
| 1900-2200 | daily | CHN | 1098kou |
| 2000-2100 | daily | CHN | 9410sai‡, 9455sai‡, 9535tin‡ |
| 2100-2200 | daily | CHN | 7520kwt, 9410bib, 9455lam |

| Chinese | Days | Area | kHz |
|---|---|---|---|
| 2300-2400 | daily | CHN | 9860kwt, 9900lam, 11775kwt |

| Khmer | Days | Area | kHz |
|---|---|---|---|
| 1230-1330 | daily | CBG | 9325tin‡, 15155lam |
| 1430-1500 | daily | CBG | 9720tin‡, 11750tin‡ |
| 2230-2330 | daily | CBG | 9390bib, 11850kwt |

| Korean | Days | Area | kHz |
|---|---|---|---|
| 1000-1100 | daily | KRE | 1566jej |
| 1500-1700 | daily | KRE | 9590sai‡ |
| 1500-1900 | daily | KRE | 1188seo, 5885tin‡, 9985tin‡ |
| 2100-2200 | daily | KRE | 7485tin‡, 9860tin‡, 9985tin‡ |

| Lao | Days | Area | kHz |
|---|---|---|---|
| 0000-0100 | daily | LAO | 9910kwt |
| 1100-1200 | daily | LAO | 13685sai‡ |

| Tibetan | Days | Area | kHz |
|---|---|---|---|
| 0100-0200 | daily | CHN | 11895dsb, 13795lam |
| 0100-0300 | daily | CHN | 9670dsb, 11950kwt |
| 0200-0300 | daily | CHN | 9455kwt, 11895kwt, 17525tin‡ |
| 0600-0700 | .t..... | CHN | 21490tin‡ |
| 0600-0700 | daily | CHN | 17675tin‡, 17815dsb, 21680dha |
| 0600-0700 | ..w.... | CHN | 21500tin‡ |
| 0600-0700 | ...t... | CHN | 21510tin‡ |
| 0600-0700 | ....f.. | CHN | 21530tin‡ |
| 0600-0700 | .....s. | CHN | 21610tin‡ |
| 0600-0700 | ......s | CHN | 21620tin‡ |
| 0600-0700 | m...... | CHN | 21480tin‡ |
| 1000-1100 | m...... | CHN | 17830lam |
| 1000-1100 | ......s | CHN | 17855lam |
| 1000-1100 | ....s. | CHN | 17795lam |
| 1000-1100 | ....f.. | CHN | 17840lam |
| 1000-1100 | ...t... | CHN | 17820lam |
| 1000-1100 | ..w.... | CHN | 17815lam |
| 1000-1100 | .t..... | CHN | 17790lam |
| 1000-1100 | daily | CHN | 9690tin‡, 15665lam |
| 1100-1200 | daily | CHN | 11550kwt |
| 1100-1400 | daily | CHN | 9315dsb, 15745dsb |
| 1200-1230 | daily | CHN | 12055lam |
| 1200-1300 | daily | CHN | 11555bib |
| 1200-1400 | daily | CHN | 15375dsb |
| 1230-1300 | daily | CHN | 12055kwt |
| 1300-1400 | daily | CHN | 12050kwt, 13650kwt |
| 1500-1600 | daily | CHN | 7540dsb, 9315tin‡, 11660tin‡, 11805kwt |
| 2200-2300 | daily | CHN | 7480kwt, 9790kwt |
| 2200-2400 | daily | CHN | 7470dsb |
| 2300-2400 | daily | CHN | 5970dha, 7540kwt, 9535kwt |

| Uyghur | Days | Area | kHz |
|---|---|---|---|
| 0100-0200 | daily | CHN | 7580dsb, 9310lam, 9450kwt, 9700kwt, 12065kwt |
| 1600-1700 | m...... | CHN | 11800kwt |
| 1600-1700 | .....s. | CHN | 11890kwt |
| 1600-1700 | ....f.. | CHN | 11885kwt |
| 1600-1700 | ...t... | CHN | 11780kwt |
| 1600-1700 | ..w.... | CHN | 11805kwt |
| 1600-1700 | .t....s | CHN | 11775kwt |
| 1600-1700 | daily | CHN | 7545dsb, 7565kwt, 11720tin‡ |

**Key:** ‡ Due to typhoon damage at the Saipan (sai) and Tinian (tin) sites, they are no longer operational. Broadcasts from these sites will be moved to another site wherever possible.
**Ann:** At the start of each transmission (language) block, in English: "You are listening to Radio Free Asia", followed by ID in the language of the broadcast.
**V:** QSL-card. (Rpt to 'Reception Reports', Radio Free Asia, 2025 M. Street NW, Washington, DC 20036, USA or by email to qsl@rfa.org. Online rpt submission (registration required): techweb.rfa.org)
**Notes:** USAGM funded station for listeners in East & South East Asia. Produced by Radio Free Asia, Inc. Initially launched in 1951 by the "Committee for Free Asia". Burmese and Tibetan language broadcasts

include segments in various local languages/dialects. Transmissions are jammed in parts of the target area. Some freqs may be variable, to avoid jamming.

## RADIO FREE EUROPE/RADIO LIBERTY (RFE/RL) (Gov)

🖃 1201 Connecticut Avenue NW, Washington, D.C. 20036, USA. (Corporate Office)
☎ +1 202 4576900. 🖷 +1 202 4576992.
**E:** levisonj@rferl.org **W:** www.rferl.org
**Webcast:** D/L Web-only languages (some of which may also be broadcast on local FM affiliate stns): Albanian (Kosovo), Armenian, Bosnian, Georgian, Macedonian, Montenegrin, Serbian, Ukrainian.
🖃 Vinohradská 159A, 100 00 Prague 10, Czechia. (HQ/Studios)
☎ +420 2 21121111. 🖷 +420 2 21123013.
**E:** knappj@rferl.org **W:** All language services have own dedicated websites, see www.rferl.org for details.
**L.P:** Chmn (RFE-RL): Kenneth Weinstein; Pres: Thomas Kent; Vice Pres/Editor-in-Chief: Nenad Pejic; Dir of Communications (Prague): Joanna Levison; Deputy Dir of Communications (Washington, D.C.): Martins Zvaners.
**MW/SW:** Via txs provided by USAGM (USA), plus other relays.
**SAT:** AsiaSat 7, Eutelsat Hot Bird 13B, Intelsat 907, NSS 12.
**kHz:** *1386, 6060, 7475, 9470, 9490, 9940, 11965, 12045, 12055*

### Winter Schedule 2018/2019

| Belarusian | Days | Area | kHz |
|---|---|---|---|
| 0300-0330 | daily | BLR | 1386vst |
| 1900-1930 | daily | BLR | 1386vst |

| Russian | Days | Area | kHz |
|---|---|---|---|
| 1800-1900 | daily | EEu | 1386vst |
| 1930-0300 | daily | EEu | 1386vst |

| Tajik | Days | Area | kHz |
|---|---|---|---|
| 1400-1700 | daily | CAs | 7475udo, 9470lam |

| Turkmen | Days | Area | kHz |
|---|---|---|---|
| 1400-1600 | daily | CAs | 6060kwt, 11965bib |

| Uzbek | Days | Area | kHz |
|---|---|---|---|
| 1400-1500 | daily | CAs | 12045lam, 12055lam |
| 1600-1700 | daily | CAs | 9490udo, 9940bib |

**Ann:** English: "This is Radio Free Europe, Radio Liberty, Praha"; Radio Liberty: Belarusian: "Havoryc Radyjo Svaboda"; Russian: "Govorit Radio Svoboda"; Tajik: "Injo Radioi Ozodi"; Turkmen: "Gepleyär Azatlyk Radiosy"; Uzbek: "Ozodlik Radiosidan gapiramiz".
**V:** QSL-card.
**Notes:** USAGM funded station for listeners in Eastern Europe and the successor states to the former USSR. Radio Free Europe (launched 1949, targeting Eastern Europe incl. Prgrs in Baltic languages) and Radio Liberty (launched 1953, targeting the USSR) merged into a single broadcaster, RFE/RL Inc, in 1976. Since the 1990s, the task of RFE/RL has been expanded to produce services targeting Afghanistan, Iran and Pakistan, see Radio Azadi, Radio Farda, Radio Mashaal.

## RADIO MASHAAL (Gov)

🖃 1201 Connecticut Avenue NW, Washington, D.C. 20036, USA.
☎ +1 202 4576900. 🖷 +1 202 4576992.
**W:** www.mashaalradio.com
**Webcast:** L/D/P
🖃 Vinohradská 159A, 100 00 Prague 10, Czechia. (Studio)
☎ +420 2 21121111. 🖷 +420 2 21123013.
**L.P:** Dir: Amanullah Ghilzai.
**MW/SW:** Via txs provided by USAGM (USA), plus other relays.
**FM/DAB:** FM: See National Radio section. (Afghanistan)
**SAT:** Eutelsat Hot Bird 13B.
**kHz:** *621, 12110, 13580, 15760, 17880*

### Winter Schedule 2018/2019

| Pashto | Days | Area | kHz |
|---|---|---|---|
| 0400-0500 | daily | AFG,PAK | 13580udo |
| 0400-1300 | daily | AFG,PAK | 621kho, 12110kwt, 15760udo |
| 0500-1000 | daily | AFG,PAK | 13580kwt |
| 1000-1300 | daily | AFG,PAK | 17880bib |

**Ann:** Pashto: "Daa Mashaal Radyo".
**V:** QSL-card.
**Notes:** Service for Pashto speaking listeners in Pakistan in the Federally Administered Tribal Areas along the border with Afghanistan, launched on 15 January 2010. Produced in the studios of RFE/RL.

## RADIO SAWA (Gov)

⌨ 7600 Boston Boulevard, Springfield, VA 22153, USA.
☎ +1 703 6885200. 🖷 +1 703 6885255.
**E:** comments@alhurra.com **W:** www.radiosawa.com
**Webcast:** L
**L.P:** Pres (MBN): Ambassador Alberto M. Fernandez; Managing Editor: Maha Rabie.
**MW:** Via txs provided by USAGM (USA), plus other relays.
**FM/DAB:** FM: See National Radio section. (Djibouti, Iraq, Jordan, Kuwait, Lebanon, Morocco, Palestinian Territories, Sudan, United Arab Emirates).
**SAT:** Badr 4, Eutelsat Hot Bird 13B, Intelsat 907, Nilesat 201, NSS 12.
**kHz:** *990, 1431, 1548, 1593*

### Winter Schedule 2018/2019

| Arabic | Days | Area | kHz |
|---|---|---|---|
| 0000-0100 | mt.tfss | ME,NAf | 990cgr |
| 0000-2400 | daily | IRQ | 1593kwt |
| 0000-2400 | daily | ARS,YEM | 1548kwt |
| 0100-2200 | daily | ME,NAf | 990cgr |
| 0645-0400 | daily | SDN | 1431dji |
| 2200-2400 | m.wtfss | ME,NAf | 990cgr |

**Ann:** Arabic: "Radio Sawa".
**V:** QSL-card.
**Notes:** Station for young Arab listeners in the Middle East, North & Northeastern Africa, launched on 23 March 2002. Produced by Middle East Broadcasting Networks, Inc. (MBN).

## RFE–RL – RADIO AZADI (Gov)

⌨ 1201 Connecticut Avenue NW, Washington, D.C. 20036, USA.
☎ +1 202 4576900. 🖷 +1 202 4576992.
**E:** azadiweb@rferl.org **W:** www.azadiradio.org; pa.azadiradio.org (Pashto); da.azadiradio.org (Dari)
**Webcast:** L
⌨ Vinohradská 159A, 100 00 Prague 10, Czechia. (Studio)
☎ +420 2 21122370. 🖷 +420 2 21123245.
**L.P:** Dir: Hashem Mohmand.
**FM/DAB:** FM: See National Radio section. (Afghanistan)
**SAT:** Eutelsat Hot Bird 13B.
**kHz:** *1296, 12075, 12140, 13860, 15640, 17690*

### Winter Schedule 2018/2019

| Dari | Days | Area | kHz |
|---|---|---|---|
| 0300-0330 | daily | AFG | 1296kab, 12140udo, 13860udo |
| 0430-0530 | daily | AFG | 1296kab, 12140kwt, 17690kwt |
| 0630-0730 | daily | AFG | 1296kab, 12140kwt, 17690kwt |
| 0830-0930 | daily | AFG | 1296kab, 12140kwt, 15640kwt |
| 1030-1130 | daily | AFG | 1296kab, 12140kwt, 15640kwt |
| 1230-1330 | daily | AFG | 1296kab, 12140kwt, 15640kwt |
| 1400-1430 | daily | AFG | 1296kab, 12075smg, 12140kwt |

| Pashto | Days | Area | kHz |
|---|---|---|---|
| 0230-0300 | daily | AFG | 1296kab, 12140udo, 13860udo |
| 0330-0430 | daily | AFG | 1296kab, 12140kwt, 13860dha |
| 0530-0630 | daily | AFG | 1296kab, 12140kwt, 17690kwt |
| 0730-0830 | daily | AFG | 1296kab, 12140kwt, 17690kwt |
| 0930-1030 | daily | AFG | 1296kab, 12140kwt, 15640kwt |
| 1130-1230 | daily | AFG | 1296kab, 12140kwt, 15640kwt |
| 1330-1400 | daily | AFG | 1296kab, 12140kwt, 15640kwt |

**Ann:** Dari: "Inja Radyoi Azadi"; Pashto: "Da Azadi Radyo".
**V:** QSL-card.
**Notes:** USAGM funded station for listeners in Afghanistan, launched in January 2002 as "R. Free Afghanistan". Produced in the RFE/RL studios in Prague, Czechia.

## U.S. AGENCY FOR GLOBAL MEDIA (USAGM) (EX BROADCASTING BOARD OF GOVERNORS) (Gov)

⌨ 330 Independence Avenue SW, Washington, D.C. 20237, USA.
☎ +1 202 2034400. 🖷 +1 202 2034585.
**W:** usagm.gov
**L.P:** Chmn: Kenneth Weinstein; CEO: John F. Lansing; Dir (Office of Technology, Services & Innovation (TSI)): Terry Balazs.
**Notes:** USAGM (until August 2018: BBG - Broadcasting Board of Governors) is the independent, autonomous agency responsible for all U.S. government and government sponsored, non-military, international broadcasting. USAGM funded services are produced by the following entities: Voice of America (VOA), Office of Cuba Broadcasting (OCB), Middle East Broadcasting Networks Inc (MBN), R. Free Asia Inc (RFA) and RFE/RL Inc (see separate entries for schedules). The USAGM Office of Technology, Services & Innovation (TSI) manages, operates, and maintains the domestic "Robert E. Kamosa" SW transmitting station in the Northern Mariana Islands, and a network of overseas SW and/or MW transmitting stations in Botswana, Djibouti, Germany, Kuwait, Philippines, São Tomé & Príncipe and Thailand.

## VOA ASHNA RADIO (Gov)

⌨ 330 Independence Avenue SW, Washington, D.C. 20237, USA.
☎ +1 202 6193136. (Dari); +1 202 3027619. (Pashto) 🖷 +1 202 3825193. (Dari); +1 202 2125260. (Pashto)
**E:** dari@voanews.com (Dari); pashto@voanews.com (Pashto)
**W:** www.darivoa.com; www.pashtovoa.com
**Webcast:** L/P
**L.P:** Chief (VOA Afghanistan Service): Beth Mendelson.
**MW/SW:** Via txs provided by USAGM (USA), plus other relays.
**FM/DAB:** FM: See National Radio section. (Afghanistan)
**kHz:** *1296, 7290, 7495, 9480, 12075, 12140, 13860*

### Winter Schedule 2018/2019

| Dari | Days | Area | kHz |
|---|---|---|---|
| 0100-0130 | daily | WAs | 1296kab, 7290bib, 7495udo |
| 0200-0230 | daily | WAs | 1296kab, 7495kwt, 12140udo |
| 1500-1530 | daily | WAs | 1296kab, 12075udo, 12140kwt, 13860wof |

| Dari/Pashto | Days | Area | kHz |
|---|---|---|---|
| 1530-1630 | daily | WAs | 1296kab, 12075udo, 12140kwt, 13860wof |

| Pashto | Days | Area | kHz |
|---|---|---|---|
| 0030-0100 | daily | WAs | 1296kab, 7290bib, 7495udo |
| 0130-0200 | daily | WAs | 1296kab, 7495udo, 12140udo |
| 1430-1500 | daily | WAs | 1296kab, 12075smg, 12140kwt, 13860wof |
| 1630-1730 | daily | WAs | 1296kab, 9480lam, 12075udo, 12140kwt |

**Ann:** Dari: "Inja VOA Radyoi Ashna"; Pashto: "Da VOA Ashna Radyo".
**V:** QSL-card.
**Notes:** BBG funded service for listeners in Afghanistan, launched April 2004. Produced in the VOA studios.

## VOA DEEWA RADIO (Gov)

⌨ 330 Independence Avenue SW, Washington, D.C. 20237, USA.
☎ +1 202 2050403. 🖷 +1 202 3825218.
**E:** deewaradio@voanews.com **W:** www.voadeewaradio.com
**Webcast:** L/P
**L.P:** Managing Editor: Nafees Talkar.
**MW/SW:** Via txs provided by USAGM (USA), plus other relays.
**FM/DAB:** FM: See National Radio section. (Afghanistan)
**SAT:** Eutelsat Hot Bird 13B.
**kHz:** *621, 7470, 7495, 7530, 9355, 9370, 9765, 9820, 13590*

### Winter Schedule 2018/2019

| Pashto | Days | Area | kHz |
|---|---|---|---|
| 0100-0400 | daily | AFG,PAK | 621kho, 7470lam, 7530kwt, 9765udo |
| 1300-1500 | daily | AFG,PAK | 13590udo |
| 1300-1600 | daily | AFG,PAK | 7495udo |
| 1300-1700 | daily | AFG,PAK | 9355udo |
| 1300-1900 | daily | AFG,PAK | 621kho, 9370udo |
| 1500-1700 | daily | AFG,PAK | 13590lam |
| 1600-1900 | daily | AFG,PAK | 7495bib |

| Pashto | Days | Area | kHz |
|---|---|---|---|
| 1700-1900 | daily | AFG,PAK | 9355kwt, 9820wof |

**Ann:** Pashto: "Deewa Radio".
**V:** QSL-card.
**Notes:** Service for Pashto speaking listeners in Eastern Afghanistan in areas along the border with Pakistan. Launched 29 September 2006. Produced in the VOA studios.

## VOA RADIO AAP KI DUNYAA (Gov)
330 Independence Avenue SW, Washington, D.C. 20237, USA.
☎ +1 202 6191933. 🖷 +1 202 6190339.
**E:** urdu@voanews.com **W:** www.urduvoa.com
**Webcast:** L/P
**L.P:** Chief (VOA Urdu Service): Faiz Rehman.
**MW:** Via tx operated by Teleradiokom (Tajikistan), on behalf of USAGM (USA).
**kHz:** 972

### Winter Schedule 2018/2019

| Urdu | Days | Area | kHz |
|---|---|---|---|
| 1400-0200 | daily | SAs | 972dsb* |

**Key:** * News in English: 1900-1905, 2000-2005, 2100-2105, 2200-2205, 2300-2305 & 0000-0005. Relay of VOA Deewa R. in Pashto: 2005-2100 & 0005-0100.
**Ann:** Urdu: "Ye Radio Aap Ki Dunyaa".
**V:** QSL-card.
**Notes:** Station for listeners in Pakistan, launched on 10 May 2004. Produced in the VOA studios. News in English: 1900-1905, 2000-2005, 2100-2105, 2200-2205, 2300-2305 & 0000-0005. Relay of VOA Deewa R. in Pashto: 2005-2100 & 0005-0100.

## VOA STUDIO 7 (Gov)
Voice of America, Africa Division, 330 Independence Avenue SW, Washington, D.C. 20237, USA.
☎ +1 202 2059942. (Then select #11) 🖷 +1 202 2034230.
**E:** studio7@voanews.com **W:** www.voazimbabwe.com
**Webcast:** D/P
**L.P:** Dir (Africa Division): Negussie Mengesha.
**MW/SW:** Via txs provided by USAGM (USA).
**kHz:** 909, 4930, 6175, 9825, 13860, 15460

### Winter Schedule 2018/2019

| English/Ndebele/Shona | Days | Area | kHz |
|---|---|---|---|
| 0400-0500 | mtwtf.. | Af | 909bot, 6175bot, 9825sao |
| 1700-1800 | daily | Af | 909bot, 4930bot, 13860sao, 15460sao |
| 1800-1900 | mtwtf.. | Af | 909bot, 4930bot, 13860sao, 15460sao |

**Ann:** English: "You're listening to Studio 7 for Zimbabwe, coming to you live from the Voice of America in Washington".
**V:** QSL-card.
**Notes:** Service for listeners in Zimbabwe, launched on 7 April 2003. Produced in the VOA studios.

## VOICE OF AMERICA (VOA) (Gov)
330 Independence Avenue SW, Washington, D.C. 20237, USA.
☎ +1 202 2034959. (Public Relations) 🖷 +1 202 2034960.
**E:** askvoa@voanews.com
**W:** www.voanews.com; www.insidevoa.com
**Webcast:** D/L/P. Web-only audio languages: Creole, Indonesian, Spanish, Uzbek.
**W:** All language services have own dedicated websites, see www.voanews.com for details.
**L.P:** Dir: Amanda Bennett; Deputy Dir: Sandy Sugawara; Associate Dir, Operations: Mark L. Prahl; Managing Editor: Clara Dominguez.
**MW/SW:** Via txs provided by USAGM (USA), plus other relays.
**SAT:** AsiaSat 7, Eutelsat Hot Bird 13B, Intelsat 20, Nilesat 201, NSS 12, SES 6, Superbird C2, Telstar 12.
**kHz:** 909, 1188, 1431, 1530, 1566, 1575, 4930, 4960, 5840, 5880, 5885, 5890, 6020, 6040, 6080, 6150, 6170, 6195, 7225, 7275, 7445, 7455, 7460, 7465, 7470, 7480, 7485, 7545, 7560, 7580, 9335, 9390, 9480, 9485, 9490, 9510, 9515, 9550, 9585, 9600, 9605, 9620, 9670, 9750, 9760, 9765, 9790, 9800, 9825, 9880, 9885, 9975, 11570, 11610, 11650, 11655, 11660, 11670, 11690, 11695, 11820, 11850, 11870, 11900, 11905, 11910, 11945, 11965, 11975, 12030, 12040, 12045, 12070, 12075, 12120, 12125, 13590, 13630, 13710, 13750, 13765, 13830, 13865, 15110, 15120, 15150, 15160, 15175, 15180, 15260, 15300, 15425, 15450, 15460, 15560, 15580, 15600, 15610, 15620, 15715, 15730, 17585, 17600, 17655, 17680, 17700, 17720, 17790, 17830, 17850, 17865, 17870, 17885, 17895, 21600, 21620, 21760, 21795

### Winter Schedule 2018/2019

| Amharic | Days | Area | kHz |
|---|---|---|---|
| 1600-1630 | mtwtf.. | EAf | 1431dji |
| 1700-1730 | mtwtf.. | EAf | 11690sao, 15580bot |
| 1800-1900 | daily | EAf | 9485wof, 12040mey, 13765kwt |

| Bambara | Days | Area | kHz |
|---|---|---|---|
| 2130-2200 | mtwtf.. | WAf | 5885bot, 9485bot, 12075bot, 15120asc |

| Bengali | Days | Area | kHz |
|---|---|---|---|
| 1600-1700 | daily | SAs | 1575bph |

| Burmese | Days | Area | kHz |
|---|---|---|---|
| 0000-0030 | daily | SEA | 1575bph |
| 0130-0230 | daily | SEA | 9335udo, 11820pht, 15110pht |
| 1200-1230 | daily | SEA | 11965pht, 15560pht, 17680kwt |
| 1430-1500 | daily | SEA | 1575bph |
| 1430-1530 | daily | SEA | 15450pht |
| 1430-1630 | daily | SEA | 9335pht, 11870pht |
| 1500-1530 | .....ss | SEA | 1575bph |
| 1530-1600 | daily | SEA | 1575bph |
| 2330-0030 | daily | SEA | 6150udo, 7480pht, 9335pht |

| Cantonese | Days | Area | kHz |
|---|---|---|---|
| 1300-1500 | daily | EAs | 7545pht |

| Chinese | Days | Area | kHz |
|---|---|---|---|
| 0000-0100 | daily | EAs | 7560udo, 9880udo, 11945pht, 15425pht |
| 0900-1000 | daily | EAs | 17720udo |
| 0900-1100 | daily | EAs | 9790pht, 11650udo, 13710udo |
| 0900-1200 | daily | EAs | 15150udo |
| 1000-1500 | daily | EAs | 9825pht |
| 1100-1200 | daily | EAs | 11660pht, 12045pht |
| 1200-1300 | daily | EAs | 11660udo, 11900pht |
| 1200-1400 | daily | EAs | 7470udo |
| 1300-1400 | daily | EAs | 9585pht, 11660pht |
| 1400-1430 | daily | EAs | 11655pht |
| 1400-1500 | daily | EAs | 9605pht, 12120pht |
| 1430-1500 | daily | EAs | 11655udo |
| 2200-2300 | daily | EAs | 7445udo, 9620pht |

| English | Days | Area | kHz |
|---|---|---|---|
| 0300-0400 | daily | Af | 909bot |
| 0300-0430 | daily | Af | 1530sao |
| 0300-0600 | daily | Af | 4930bot |
| 0300-0700 | daily | Af | 6080sao, 15580bot |
| 0400-0500 | .....ss | Af | 909bot |
| 0400-0500 | daily | Af | 4960sao |
| 0500-0700 | daily | Af | 909bot |
| 0600-0700 | daily | Af | 1530sao, 9550sao |
| 1130-1200 | daily | SEA | 1575bph, 12125udo, 15715udo, 17790pht |
| 1400-1500 | daily | Af | 17885bot |
| 1400-1630 | daily | Af | 15580bot |
| 1400-1700 | daily | Af | 4930bot |
| 1500-1600 | daily | Af | 7455bot, 17895sao |
| 1600-1630 | daily | Af | 6080sao |
| 1600-1700 | daily | Af | 909bot, 1530sao |
| 1600-1800 | daily | Af | 17895bot |
| 1630-1700 | mtwtf.. | Af | 11850mey*, 13865wof*, 15180sao* |
| 1630-1700 | .....ss | Af | 6080sao |
| 1630-1730 | .....ss | Af | 15580bot |
| 1700-1730 | daily | Af | 13590kwt |
| 1700-1800 | daily | Af | 6080sao |
| 1730-1800 | daily | Af | 13590sao |
| 1730-2000 | daily | Af | 15580bot |
| 1800-1900 | .....ss | Af | 909bot, 4930bot |
| 1800-1900 | daily | Af | 13590udo |
| 1900-2000 | daily | Af | 13590sao |
| 1900-2100 | daily | Af | 909bot, 4930bot |
| 2000-2100 | daily | Af | 6195bot, 15580bot |
| 2000-2200 | daily | Af | 1530sao |

| English | Days | Area | kHz |
|---|---|---|---|
| 2030-2100 | .....ss | Af | 4960sao |
| 2100-2200 | daily | Af | 6195sao, 15580grv |
| **French** | **Days** | **Area** | **kHz** |
| 0530-0600 | mtwtf.. | Af | 1530sao |
| 0530-0630 | mtwtf.. | Af | 4960sao, 6020sao, 9885smg, 13830bot |
| 0830-0900 | ..w..s. | Af | 12030sao, 15715smg, 17700bot |
| 1100-1130 | .....s. | Af | 12030sao, 13750bot, 15715bot, 17850smg |
| 1830-1930 | daily | Af | 12075smg, 15730bot |
| 1830-2000 | daily | Af | 1530sao |
| 1900-2000 | daily | Af | 9515sao |
| 1930-2030 | daily | Af | 11900sao, 12075bot, 15730grv |
| 2000-2030 | daily | Af | 9485kwt |
| 2030-2100 | ......s | Af | 11900sao, 11975smg |
| 2030-2100 | .....ss | Af | 9485kwt, 13750sao |
| 2100-2130 | mtwtf.. | Af | 5885bot, 9485kwt, 12075bot |
| **Hausa** | **Days** | **Area** | **kHz** |
| 0500-0530 | daily | WAf | 1530sao, 4960sao, 6020sao, 6170asc |
| 0700-0730 | daily | WAf | 4960sao, 12070sao, 15175bot |
| 1500-1530 | daily | WAf | 9765sao, 11850sao, 17700bot |
| 1530-1600 | mtwtf.. | WAf | 9600sao, 11850sao, 17700bot |
| 2030-2100 | .....s. | WAf | 11900sao, 11975smg |
| 2030-2100 | mtwtf.. | WAf | 4960sao |
| 2030-2100 | mtwtfs. | WAf | 6040sao, 9765wof, 11850bot, 12075sao |
| **Khmer** | **Days** | **Area** | **kHz** |
| 1330-1430 | daily | SEA | 1575bph, 9335pht, 11695pht |
| 2200-2230 | daily | SEA | 1575bph, 5880pht, 7460pht |
| **Kinyarwanda/ Kirundi** | **Days** | **Area** | **kHz** |
| 0330-0430 | daily | CAf | 7275sao, 7460bot, 9885sao |
| 0430-0530 | mtwtf.. | CAf | 7275sao, 7460bot, 9885sao |
| 1400-1500 | .....ss | CAf | 9885sao, 13630bot, 15300smg |
| 1600-1630 | daily | CAf | 11850smg, 13630sao, 15460sao |
| 1830-1900 | mtwtf.. | CAf | 11850bot, 13630sao |
| 1930-2000 | mtwtf.. | CAf | 9885sao, 11850sao, 12040kwt |
| **Korean** | **Days** | **Area** | **kHz** |
| 1100-1500 | daily | EAs | 1188seo |
| 1200-1300 | daily | EAs | 9490pht |
| 1200-1400 | daily | EAs | 11570pht |
| 1200-1500 | daily | EAs | 5840tin‡ |
| 1300-1500 | daily | EAs | 9800pht |
| 1700-1800 | daily | EAs | 1566jej |
| 1900-2100 | daily | EAs | 7465pht, 9800pht, 9975udo |
| **Kurdish** | **Days** | **Area** | **kHz** |
| 1400-1500 | daily | ME | 15600wof, 17870lam |
| 1700-1800 | daily | ME | 7485bib, 9390bib, 9750lam |
| 1900-2000 | daily | ME | 7225bib, 7485lam, 9750bib |
| **Lao** | **Days** | **Area** | **kHz** |
| 1230-1300 | daily | SEA | 1575bph |
| **Oromo** | **Days** | **Area** | **kHz** |
| 1730-1800 | mtwtf.. | EAf | 9485wof, 12040mey, 13765kwt |
| **Portuguese** | **Days** | **Area** | **kHz** |
| 1630-1700 | ...f.. | Af | 13630bot, 17655sao |
| 1700-1800 | daily | Af | 1530sao, 13630bot, 17655grv |
| 1800-1830 | mtwtf.. | Af | 13630bot, 17655grv |

| Somali | Days | Area | kHz |
|---|---|---|---|
| 0330-0400 | daily | EAf | 9480dha, 9510smg, 9825lam |
| 1030-1100 | daily | EAf | 13580kwt, 15620bot, 17600udo |
| 1300-1400 | daily | EAf | 15620smg, 17600bot |
| 1600-1630 | .....ss | EAf | 1431dji |
| 1600-1800 | daily | EAf | 11610wof, 11905lam |
| **Swahili** | **Days** | **Area** | **kHz** |
| 1630-1700 | daily | EAf | 13750kwt, 15260mey, 15460sao |
| **Tibetan** | **Days** | **Area** | **kHz** |
| 0000-0100 | daily | EAs | 5890kwt, 7580kwt, 9670udo |
| 0300-0400 | daily | EAs | 21600pht, 21795pht |
| 0300-0600 | daily | EAs | 17865pht |
| 0400-0500 | daily | EAs | 15610udo, 21620pht |
| 0500-0600 | daily | EAs | 15560udo, 21760pht |
| 1400-1500 | daily | EAs | 11910kwt, 15160kwt, 17585bib, 17830pht |
| 1600-1700 | daily | EAs | 7580pht, 9760udo, 11670pht |
| **Tigrinya** | **Days** | **Area** | **kHz** |
| 1900-1930 | mtwtf.. | EAf | 9485wof, 12040dha, 13765kwt |
| **Vietnamese** | **Days** | **Area** | **kHz** |
| 2130-2200 | daily | SEA | 1575bph |

**Key:** * Special service for Sudan; ‡ Due to typhoon damage at the Saipan (sai) and Tinian (tin) sites, they are no longer operational. Broadcasts from these sites will be moved to another site wherever possible.

**Ann:** English: Before the start of all foreign language programs: "Welcome to the Voice of America in... (language)"; at the end of the transmission period on each frequency before tx s/off: "This program has come to you from the Voice of America, Washington".

**V:** QSL-card. (Email to: letters@voa.gov)

**Notes:** Launched in 1942, under the roof of the U.S. Foreign Information Service (FIS). From 1953-1994, financed by the U.S. Information Agency (USIA). BBG funded since April 1994. Some transmissions in Asian languages are jammed.

## ADVENTIST WORLD RADIO (AWR) (Rlg)

✉ 12501 Old Columbia Pike, Silver Spring, ML 20904-6600, USA.
☎ +1 301 6806304. 🖷 +1 301 6806303.
**E:** info@awr.org **W:** www.awr.org
**Webcast:** D/L/P
**W:** eu.awr.org (European services)
**L.P:** Pres: Duane McKey; Freq Manager: Claudius Dedio.
**kHz:** 5010, 5970, 5975, 6170, 6185, 7380, 9445, 9460, 9610, 9770, 9830, 11955, 11985, 12025, 15150, 15360

**Winter Schedule 2018/2019**

| Bulgarian | Days | Area | kHz |
|---|---|---|---|
| 0400-0430 | daily | Eu | 5975iss |
| 1600-1630 | daily | Eu | 9830nau |
| **Italian** | **Days** | **Area** | **kHz** |
| 1000-1100 | ......s | Eu | 9610nau |
| **Pashto** | **Days** | **Area** | **kHz** |
| 1630-1700 | m.w.f.. | WAs | 15360trm |
| **Persian** | **Days** | **Area** | **kHz** |
| 0330-0400 | daily | WAs | 6170mos |
| 1630-1700 | daily | WAs | 9770mos |
| **Punjabi** | **Days** | **Area** | **kHz** |
| 0230-0300 | daily | As | 5975mos |
| 1500-1530 | daily | As | 15150mdc |
| 1530-1600 | daily | As | 11955mos |
| **Russian** | **Days** | **Area** | **kHz** |
| 1100-1130 | daily | RUS | 9460sda |
| 2000-2030 | daily | RUS | 7380sda |
| **Spanish** | **Days** | **Area** | **kHz** |
| 0000-0030 | daily | CAm | 5010rmi |
| 1100-1130 | daily | CAm | 5010rmi |
| **Turkish** | **Days** | **Area** | **kHz** |
| 0400-0430 | daily | ME | 6185mos |
| 1500-1530 | daily | ME | 11955mos |
| **Urdu** | **Days** | **Area** | **kHz** |
| 0200-0230 | daily | As | 5970mos |

| Urdu | Days | Area | kHz |
|---|---|---|---|
| 1400-1430 | daily | As | 12025mos |
| 1600-1630 | daily | As | 9445mos, 11985trm |

**IS:** Various arrangements of the melody "Lift Up the Trumpet".
**V:** QSL-card.
**Notes:** AWR the international broadcast ministry of the Seventh-day Adventist Church. Produced by Adventist Broadcasting Service, Inc. which also is the owner of the SW transmitting station KSDA in Guam. The schedule contains transmissions of AWR Americas & AWR Europe which are administered by the U.S. headquarters. For schedules of other regional divisions, see AWR Africa (United Kingdom) and AWR Asia/Pacific (Thailand).

## FAMILY RADIO (Rlg)
⌨ 1360 South Loop Rd., Ste. 130, Alameda, CA 94502, USA.
☎ +1 800 5431495.
**E:** info@familyradio.org **W:** www.familyradio.org
**Webcast:** D/L
**L.P:** Pres: Tom Evans.
**kHz:** *5010, 5950, 5985*

### Winter Schedule 2018/2019

| Spanish | Days | Area | kHz |
|---|---|---|---|
| 0200-0300 | daily | NAm | 5950rmi |
| 0430-0500 | m...... | CAm | 5985rmi |
| 2300-2400 | daily | CAm | 5010rmi |

**Ann:** English: "You are listening to Family Radio".
**V:** QSL-card.
**Notes:** Produced by Family Stations, Inc. Launched in 1959, first SW broadcasts in 1973.

## FAR EAST BROADCASTING COMPANY INC (FEBC) (Rlg)
⌨ P.O. Box 1, La Mirada, CA 90637-0001, USA; 15700 Imperial Hwy, La Miranda, CA 90638-2500, USA.
☎ +1 562 9474651. 🖷 +1 562 9430160.
**E:** info@febc.org **W:** www.febc.org; febcintl.org
**Webcast:** D
**L.P:** Chmn/CEO: Ed Cannon.
**V:** QSL-email for transmissions by FEBC branches. Printed QSL-cards are available only directly from the FEBC branches in South Korea and the Philippines.
**Notes:** Far East Broadcasting Company, Inc (FEBC) is a global evangelical media enterprise. For schedules, see India (FEBA India), Pakistan (FEBA Pakistan), Philipines (FEBC Philippines) and South Korea (FEBC Korea). FEBC owns transmitting stations in several countries, incl. the Philippines and South Korea.

## FOLLOW THE BIBLE MINISTRIES (Rlg)
⌨ P.O.Box 1332, Alameda, CA 94501, USA.
☎ +1 510 7480504.
**E:** followthebibleministries@yahoo.com **W:** www.followthebibleministries.com; www.isannihilationtrue.com/ftbm
**Webcast:** D
⌨ 3374 Washington Court, Alameda, CA 94501, USA.
**L.P:** Host: David Hoff.
**kHz:** *7425, 12005, 12030*

### Winter Schedule 2018/2019

| Arabic | Days | Area | kHz |
|---|---|---|---|
| 1830-1900 | ......s | NAf,ME | 7425wof |

| English | Days | Area | kHz |
|---|---|---|---|
| 1900-1930 | ......s | WAf | 12005asc |
| 1900-1930 | ......s | SAf | 12030asc |

**V:** QSL-email.
**Notes:** Bible Study prgr produced by the Christian organisation "Follow The Bible Ministries".

## KVOH – VOICE OF HOPE (Rlg)
⌨ 543 Country Club Drive, Simi Valley, CA 93065, USA.
☎ +1 805 3380075. 🖷 +1 805 2736905.
**E:** mail@voiceofhope.com (general); studio@voiceofhope.com (prgr feedback) **W:** www.voiceofhope.com
**Webcast:** L
**L.P:** Pres (SCG): John D. Tayloe; Vice Pres, Ops (SCG): Ray Robinson; CE (KVOH): Jim Shoffner.
**SW:** [VOH] Rancho Simi, CA: 1 x 50, 1 x 100kW.
**kHz:** *17775*

### Winter Schedule 2018/2019

| English | Days | Area | kHz |
|---|---|---|---|
| 1600-2000 | .....s | CAm,SAm | 17775voh |

| Spanish | Days | Area | kHz |
|---|---|---|---|
| 1400-2100 | mtwtf.. | CAm,SAm | 17775voh |

**Ann:** English: "This is The Voice of Hope - KVOH, Rancho Simi, Los Angeles, The United States of America"; Spanish: "Esta es KVOH, Rancho Simi, California, Estados Unidos de América".
**V:** QSL-card. (Email rpt to: reports@voiceofhope.com)
**Notes:** Owned by the charitable organisation Strategic Communications Group (SCG). Part of the Voice of Hope World Radio Network; sister stations operated by SCG outside of the U.S.: Voice of Hope - Africa (see under Zambia) and Voice of Hope - Middle East (see under Israel). KVOH Initially began broadcasting in November 1986 under the ownership of High Adventures Ministries. The network broadcasts both own and paid religious programming.

## LIVING WATER MINISTRY BROADCASTING (Rlg)
⌨ 308 Shadow Lane, Euless, TX 76039, USA.
☎ +1 817 9836527.
**E:** bill.byers@yahoo.com **W:** www.lwmintl.org
**L.P:** Dir (Living Water Ministries International, Inc): Bill Byers.
**kHz:** *5905*

### Winter Schedule 2018/2019

| Korean | Days | Area | kHz |
|---|---|---|---|
| 1530-1600 | ....f.. | EAs | 5905twr |
| 1530-1630 | .twt... | EAs | 5905twr |

**Ann:** Korean: "Saengmyeong-ui Gang Bangsong".
**Notes:** Produced by Living Water Ministries International, Inc.

## PAN AMERICAN BROADCASTING (Rlg)
⌨ Suite 250, 7011 Koll Center Parkway, Pleasanton CA 94566-3253 USA.
☎ +1 925 4629800.
**E:** info@panambc.com **W:** www.radiopanam.com
**L.P:** Pres: Jeff Bernald.
**kHz:** *11800, 21525*

### Winter Schedule 2018/2019

| English | Days | Area | kHz |
|---|---|---|---|
| 1400-2100 | daily | Af | 21525rmi* |
| 1430-1445 | ......s | ME | 11800iss |

**Key:** * Radio Africa Network.
**V:** QSL-card.
**Notes:** Pan American Broadcasting, Inc. sells air time for religious paid programming, broadcast via international tx providers, and via Radio Miami International ("Radio Africa Network").

## REACH BEYOND (Rlg)
⌨ 1065 Garden of the Gods Road, Colorado Springs, CO 80907, USA.
☎ +1 719 5909800. 🖷 +1 719 5909801.
**E:** info@reachbeyond.org **W:** reachbeyond.org
**Webcast:** P
**L.P:** Pres/CEO: Wayne Pederson; Frequency Mgr: Douglas Weber.
**kHz:** *1251, 7300, 9500, 9530*

### Winter Schedule 2018/2019

| Arabic | Days | Area | kHz |
|---|---|---|---|
| 2115-2145 | daily | NAf | 7300wof |
| **Chechen** | **Days** | **Area** | **kHz** |
| 1600-1630 | .....s. | RUS | 9500mos |
| **Dari** | **Days** | **Area** | **kHz** |
| 1530-1600 | m..tfss | CAs | 1251dsb |
| **Pulaar** | **Days** | **Area** | **kHz** |
| 2145-2215 | mt.tfss | Af | 9530asc |
| **Russian** | **Days** | **Area** | **kHz** |
| 1530-1600 | .....s. | RUS | 9500mos* |
| **Tachelhit** | **Days** | **Area** | **kHz** |
| 2100-2115 | daily | NAf | 7300wof |
| **Turkmen** | **Days** | **Area** | **kHz** |
| 1545-1600 | .tw.... | CAs | 1251dsb |
| 1600-1615 | daily | CAs | 1251dsb |
| **Uzbek** | **Days** | **Area** | **kHz** |
| 1530-1545 | .tw.... | CAs | 1251dsb |

**Key:** * Produced by Radio Studio "Otkroveniye" (Russia), see also R. HCJB Deutschland (Germany).
**V:** QSL-card.

**Notes:** Reach Beyond (previously known as HCJB Global Voice) is the media ministry of World Radio Missionary Fellowship, Inc. See Australia and Germany for shortwave stations run by Reach Beyond partner organisations.

## SUAB XAA MOO ZOO (Rlg)
✉ Hmong District, 12287 Pennsylvania St, Thornton, CO 80241-3113, USA.
☎ +1 303 2521793. 🖷 +1 303 2527911.
**E:** sxmz777@gmail.com **W:** www.facebook.com/sxmzradioministry
**Webcast:** D
**E:** radio@hmongdistrict.org **W:** www.hmongdistrict.org
**L.P:** Head, Radio Ministry (Hmong District): Num Nyaj Hawj.
**kHz:** 7530

### Winter Schedule 2018/2019

| Hmong | Days | Area | kHz |
|---|---|---|---|
| 2230-2300 | daily | SEA | 7530pao |

**V:** QSL-card.
**Notes:** Zuab Xaa Moo Zoo ("The Voice of Good News"), SXMZ Radio, is a Christian missionary programme targeting Hmong listeners, produced by the Hmong District of the Christian & Missionary Alliance.

## THE OVERCOMER MINISTRY (Rlg)
✉ P.O. Box 691, Walterboro, SC 29488-0007, USA.
☎ +1 843 5384202. 🖷 +1 843 5384202.
**E:** lastime@overcomerministry.org **W:** www.overcomerministry.org
**Webcast:** L
✉ 12680 Augusta Hwy, Walterboro, SC 29488-7829, USA.
**L.P:** Owner (Faith Cathedral Fellowship, Inc) & Radio Host: Ralph G. Stair. (a.k.a. "Brother Stair")
**SAT:** Amos 3, Eutelsat 25B/Hot Bird 13B, Galaxy 19, Optus D2, Thaicom 5.
**kHz:** 3215, 5850, 5900, 6000, 7490, 7570, 7730, 7780, 9330, 9350, 9395, 9400, 9455, 11600

### Winter Schedule 2018/2019

| English | Days | Area | kHz |
|---|---|---|---|
| 0000-0100 | ....f.. | NAm | 9455rmi |
| 0000-2400 | daily | NAm | 9330bcq |
| 0100-0400 | daily | NAm | 7730rmi |
| 0200-0500 | daily | NAm | 5850rmi |
| 0400-0500 | ....f.. | NAm | 9455rmi |
| 0400-0500 | mtwtf.. | NAm | 3215wcr |
| 1100-2100 | daily | NAm | 9395rmi |
| 1300-1400 | mtwtf.s | ME,Eu | 11600sof |
| 1405-1455 | daily | ME,Eu | 11600sof |
| 1700-1945 | daily | Eu | 9400sof |
| 1700-2000 | daily | NAm,ME,Eu | 7780rmi |
| 1805-2000 | mtwtf.. | EEu | 6000sof |
| 2005-0300 | daily | Eu,NAm | 5900sof |
| 2100-2300 | .....s. | NAm | 9350wcr |
| 2200-2300 | mtwtf.. | NAm | 7490bcq |
| 2300-0500 | daily | NAm | 7570rmi |

**Key:** * AM/USB (H3E) mode; Times variable and schedule subject to change.
**Ann:** English: "You are listening to The Overcomer radio broadcast".
**V:** QSL-card.
**Notes:** Evangelist, radio based ministry of Ralph G. Stair and his religious organisation Faith Cathedral Fellowship, Inc. Schedule is subject to change without notice.

## TRANS WORLD RADIO (TWR) (Rlg)
✉ P.O. Box 8700, Cary, NC 27512, USA.
☎ +1 919 4603700. 🖷 +1 919 4603702.
**E:** info2@twr.org **W:** www.twr.org; www.twr360.org
**Webcast:** D/L
**L.P:** Chmn: Dr Thomas J. Lowell; Pres/CEO: Lauren Libby.
**V:** QSL-card.
**Notes:** Trans World Radio, Inc (TWR) is a global Christian media enterprise. For TWR's regional divisions and schedules, see under Austria (TWR Europe), India (TWR India), Singapore (TWR Asia) and South Africa (TWR Africa). TWR owns transmitting facilities in Benin, Bonaire, Eswatini and Guam.

## UNIVERSITY NETWORK (Rlg)
✉ P.O. Box 1, Los Angeles, CA 90053-0001, USA.
☎ +1 818 2408151.
**E:** pastor@pastormelissascottvideos.com **W:** www.pastormelissas-cott.com; www.drgenescott.com
**Webcast:** L
**L.P:** Pres/CEO: Melissa Scott.
**MW/SW:** See "Caribbean Beacon", under Anguilla.
**SAT:** Galaxy 19.
**kHz:** 5935, 6090, 11775, 13845

### Winter Schedule 2018/2019

| English | Days | Area | kHz |
|---|---|---|---|
| 0000-1200 | daily | Af | 5935wcr |
| 1000-2200 | daily | NAm | 11775aia† |
| 1200-1500 | .....ss | NAm,Eu | 13845wcr |
| 1500-2400 | mtwtf.. | NAm,Eu | 13845wcr |
| 2200-1000 | daily | NAm | 6090aia† |

**Key:** † Irregular.
**Ann:** English: "You're watching the University Network".
**V:** Does not verify reception reports. For QSLs regarding Caribbean Beacon Relay freqs, see under "Anguilla".
**Notes:** Run by (Pastor) Melissa Scott, who took over the operation in 2005 after the death of her husband, (Pastor) Dr. William Eugene "Gene" Scott. The transmissions are a relay of the "University Network" satellite TV channel audio and consist of sermons by Melissa Scott and archived material from the period of Gene Scott.

## WEWN – EWTN SHORTWAVE RADIO (Rlg)
✉ 5817 Old Leeds Rd, Irondale, AL 35210-2164, USA.
☎ +1 205 2712900. 🖷 +1 205 2712926.
**E:** radio@ewtn.com **W:** www.ewtn.com
**Webcast:** D/L/P
✉ High Rd, Vandiver, AL 35176, USA. (Tx Site)
**L.P:** Chmn/CEO: Michael P. Warsaw; Pres/COO: Doug Keck; Vice Pres, Engineering: Terry L Borders; Freq Mgr: Glen Tapley.
**SW:** [EWN] Vandiver, AL: 4 x 500kW.
**SAT:** Galaxy 15, Intelsat 19/20/21, Sirius FM 5, XM3/4.
**kHz:** 5970, 9470, 11520, 12050, 15610

### Winter Schedule 2018/2019

| English | Days | Area | kHz |
|---|---|---|---|
| 0000-0900 | daily | Af | 11520ewn |
| 0900-1300 | daily | EAs | 9470ewn |
| 1900-2400 | daily | Af | 15610ewn |
| **Spanish** | **Days** | **Area** | **kHz** |
| 0000-1400 | daily | LAm | 5970ewn |
| 1400-2400 | daily | LAm | 12050ewn |

**Ann:** English: "This is EWTN Global Catholic Radio Network - WEWN, Birmingham, Alabama, USA".
**V:** QSL-card. (Online reception rpt form available)
**Notes:** Owned by the Eternal Word Television Network, Inc. Catholic station, began broadcasting on 28 December 1992.

## WHRI – WORLD HARVEST RADIO (WHR) (Rlg)
✉ 61300 Ironwood Rd, South Bend, IN 46614, USA.
☎ +1 574 2918200. 🖷 +1 574 2919043.
**E:** via website. **W:** familybroadcastingcorporation.com/whr
**Webcast:** L
**L.P:** Pres/CEO (Family Broadcasting Corp.): Andrew Sumrall; Dir, Engineering (Shortwave): Larry Vehorn.
**SW:** [HRI] Furman, SC: 1 x 100, 2 x 500kW.
**SAT:** Galaxy 16, Intelsat 19.
**kHz:** 5920, 7315, 7385, 9505, 9830, 9840, 11750, 17815, 21610

### Winter Schedule 2018/2019

| English | Days | Area | kHz |
|---|---|---|---|
| 0000-0400 | daily | NAm,Eu | 5920hri |
| 0200-0400 | daily | SAm | 7315hri |
| 0430-0600 | daily | NAf | 9830hri |
| 0600-0700 | mtwtf.s | SAm | 7315hri |
| 0930-1200 | m.....s | SAm | 7315hri |
| 1000-2000 | daily | NAm | 9840hri |
| 1100-1200 | daily | NAm,Eu | 5920hri |
| 1100-2200 | m.....s | NAm | 7385hri |
| 1400-1900 | daily | Af | 21610hri |
| 1900-2100 | daily | Af | 17815hri |
| 2000-2200 | ......s | NAm,Eu | 11750hri |
| 2200-2400 | ......s | NAm,Eu | 9505hri |
| 2300-0500 | daily | NAm | 7385hri |

| English | Days | Area | kHz |
|---|---|---|---|
| 2300-2400 | daily | SAm | 7315hri |

**V:** QSL-card (Online rpt form available)
**Notes:** World Harvest Radio is a service of Family Broadcasting Corp. (formerly LeSEA Broadcasting Corp.). On air since 25 Dec 1985. Family Broadcasting Corp. owns the shortwave transmitting stations WHRI (Furman, SC) and T8WH (Palau). WHR transmits mainly own and paid religious programming; certain airtime is leased to non-religious broadcasters or prgr producers. Actual schedule may vary during the course of the season, depending on airtime sales.

## WINB (Rlg)
📭 P.O. Box 88, Red Lion, PA 17356, USA; 2900 Windsor Road, Red Lion, PA 17356-8534, USA.
☎ +1 717 2445360. 🖨 +1 717 2460363.
**E:** sally@winb.com **W:** www.winb.com
**Webcast:** D/L
**L.P:** Pres (World International Broadcasters, Inc): John H. Norris; Airtime Sales/Frequency Mgr: Hans Johnson.
**SW:** [INB] Red Lion, PA: 1 x 15, 1 x 50kW.
**kHz:** *7315, 9265, 13690*

### Winter Schedule 2018/2019
| English | Days | Area | kHz |
|---|---|---|---|
| 0700-0900 | mtwtf.. | Eu.NAf | 7315inb+ |
| 0900-1100 | mtwtf.. | Eu.NAf | 9265inb+ |
| 1100-1700 | mtwtf.. | Eu.NAf | 13690inb+ |

| English/Spanish | Days | Area | kHz |
|---|---|---|---|
| 1000-1230 | .....s. | CAm | 9265inb* |
| 1200-2100 | .....s | CAm | 9265inb |
| 1430-2100 | .....s. | CAm | 9265inb |
| 2100-0400 | daily | CAm | 9265inb |

**Key:** + DRM tests; * Relay of Unique Radio (Australia).
**Ann:** English: "This is WINB, Red Lion, Pennsylvania, USA".
**V:** QSL-card.
**Notes:** Owned by World International Broadcasters, Inc. Operational since October 1962. The station transmits religious and other programming. Schedule varies, depending on airtime sales. Transmissions will be one hour (UTC) earlier during DST USA (10 Mar - 3 Nov 2019).

## WJHR RADIO INTERNATIONAL (Rlg)
📭 5920 Oak Manor Drive, Milton, FL 32570, USA.
☎ +1 850 6235405.
**E:** wjhr@usa.com
**L.P:** Owner: George Scott Mock.
**SW:** [JHR] Milton, FL: 1 x 0.25kW (run at 1kW PEP).
**kHz:** *15555*

### Winter Schedule 2018/2019
| English | Days | Area | kHz |
|---|---|---|---|
| 1400-2200 | daily | NAm | 15555jhr* |

**Key:** * USB (J3E) mode.
**Ann:** English: "You're listening to WJHR Radio International. WJHR Radio is located in the city of Milton, Florida".
**V:** QSL-email.
**Notes:** WJHR ("John Hill Radio") is owned by George Scott Mock (dba "Hill Radio International"), and operated by members of the Mt. Calvary Baptist Church. On the air since November 2009.

## WMLK ‡ (Rlg)
📭 P.O. Box C, Bethel, PA 19507, USA; 190 Frantz Rd, Bethel, PA 19507, USA.
☎ +1 717 9334518.
**E:** aoy@wmlkradio.net **W:** www.wmlkradio.net
**L.P:** Operating Engineer: Gary A. McAvin.
**SW:** [MLK] Bethel, PA ‡: 1 x 300kW (under construction).
**Key:** ‡ Inactive on SW at time of publication (due to fire damage in March '17). Plans to return to SW in early 2019.
**Ann:** English: "This is Radio Station WMLK".
**V:** QSL-card. Rp.
**Notes:** Owned by the Assemblies of Yahweh.

## WORLD CHRISTIAN BROADCASTING INC. (Rlg)
📭 605 Bradley Court, Franklin, TN 37067, USA.
☎ +1 615 3718707.
**E:** info@worldchristian.org **W:** www.worldchristian.org
**L.P:** Chmn: Dr. Frank Harrell; Pres: Charles H. Caudill; Vice Pres, Development: Andy Baker; Vice Pres/Dir, Engineering: Kevin K. Chambers.

**Notes:** World Christian Broadcasting, Inc owns and runs the SW transmitting stations KNLS (see under Alaska) and Madagascar World Voice (see under Madagascar).

## WRNO WORLDWIDE (Rlg)
📭 P.O. Box 895, Fort Worth, TX 76101, USA; 777 Main St., Suite 1235, Fort Worth, TX 76102, USA.
☎ +1 817 8509990. 🖨 +1 817 8509994.
**E:** wrnoradio@mailup.net
**W:** www.wrnoworldwide.com; www.wrnoradionetwork.com
**Webcast:** L
📭 3711 Barataria Blvd, Marrero, LA 70072, USA. (Tx Site)
**L.P:** Chmn, Good News World Outreach: Robert E. Mawire.
**SW:** [RNO] New Orleans, LA: 1 x 50kW.
**kHz:** *7505*

### Winter Schedule 2018/2019
| English/Chinese | Days | Area | kHz |
|---|---|---|---|
| 0100-1300 | daily | NAm | 7505rno† |

**Key:** † Irregular (schedule depends on airtime bookings)
**Ann:** English: "You're listening to WRNO Worldwide".
**V:** QSL-card. Rp. (2 IRCs).
**Notes:** Owned by Good News World Outreach. The station transmits religious paid programming.

## WTWW (Rlg)
📭 P.O.Box 102, Lebanon, TN 37088, USA; 2115 Leeville Pike, Lebanon, TN 37090, USA.
☎ +1 615 7245225.
**E:** email@wtww.us **W:** wtww.us
**Webcast:** L
📭 131 Hiwassee Rd, Lebanon, TN 37087, USA (Tx Site); 6611 Ormond Dr, Nashville, TN 37205, USA (Studio).
☎ +1 615 3528682.
**L.P:** Pres (Leap of Faith, Inc): George V. McClintock; Engineer: Ted Randall.
**SW:** [TWW] Lebanon, TN: 1 x 50, 2 x 100kW.
**kHz:** *5085, 5830, 9475, 9930*

### Winter Schedule 2018/2019
| English | Days | Area | kHz |
|---|---|---|---|
| 0000-1100 | daily | LAm | 5085tww |
| 0000-1400 | daily | NAm,Eu,Af | 5830tww |
| 1400-0200 | daily | NAm,Eu | 9475tww |
| 1400-2400 | daily | NAm | 9930tww |

**Ann:** English: "This is WTWW, Lebanon, Tennessee, USA".
**V:** QSL-card.
**Notes:** Owned by Leap of Faith, Inc. Initially licensed as WBWW while under construction; on the air since 19 Feb 2010 (tests from Jan 2010). WTWW ("We Transmit World Wide") transmits mainly paid religious programming, as well as some own productions.

## WWCR SHORTWAVE – WORLD WIDE CHRISTIAN RADIO (Rlg)
📭 1300 WWCR Avenue, Nashville, TN 37218, USA.
☎ +1 615 2551300. 🖨 +1 615 2551311.
**E:** wwcr@wwcr.com **W:** www.wwcr.com
**Webcast:** L
**L.P:** GM: Eric Westenberger; Chief Engineer: Phil Patton; Ops Mgr: Brady Murray; Frequency Mgr: Dr Jerry Plummer.
**SW:** [WCR] Nashville, TN: 4 x 100kW.
**kHz:** *3215, 4840, 5890, 5935, 6115, 7490, 7520, 9350, 9980, 12160, 13845, 15795, 15825*

### Winter Schedule 2018/2019
| English | Days | Area | kHz |
|---|---|---|---|
| 0000-0200 | daily | NAm,Af | 7520wcr |
| 0100-1300 | daily | NAm | 4840wcr |
| 0200-0600 | daily | NAm | 3215wcr |
| 0300-0500 | daily | CAm | 5890wcr |
| 1000-1200 | daily | NAm,Eu,NAf | 15795wcr |
| 1200-2200 | daily | NAm,Eu,NAf | 15825wcr |
| 1300-1600 | daily | Af | 7490wcr |
| 1300-1800 | daily | NAm | 13845wcr |
| 1600-2100 | daily | Af | 12160wcr |
| 2100-2300 | daily | NAM,Af | 9980wcr |
| 2100-2300 | daily | Af | 9350wcr |
| 2300-0100 | daily | Af | 5935wcr |

| English/Spanish | Days | Area | kHz |
|---|---|---|---|
| 2200-0300 | daily | Af | 6115wcr |

**Ann:** English: "This is World Wide Christian Radio-WWCR, Nashville, Tennessee, USA".
**V:** QSL-card. Rp. preferred (1 USD). Email rpt to qsl@wwcr.com
**Notes:** Owned by F.W. Robbert Broadcasting Co., Inc. The station transmits religious paid programming.

## FROM THE ISLE OF MUSIC / UNCLE BILL'S MELTING POT

🖃 5713 N. St. Louis Av, Chicago, IL 60659-4405, USA.
☎ +1 773 2676548.
**E:** tilfordproductions@gmail.com; Bill@tilfordproductions.com
**W:** www.facebook.com/fromtheisleofmusic; www.facebook.com/UncleBillsMeltingPot
**L.P:** Owner (Tilfold Productions)/Host: William "Bill" Tilford
**kHz:** *6070, 7490, 9400*

### Winter Schedule 2018/2019

| English | Days | Area | kHz |
|---|---|---|---|
| 1900-2000 | .t..... | CEu,WEu | 6070rob* |
| 2300-2330 | .....s | NAm | 7490bcq* |

| English/Spanish | Days | Area | kHz |
|---|---|---|---|
| 0100-0200 | .t..... | NAm | 7490bcq |
| 1200-1300 | .....s. | CEu,WEu | 6070rob |
| 1500-1600 | .....s | Eu | 9400sof |

**Key:** * Uncle Bill's Melting Pot
(W: www.facebook.com/UncleBillsMeltingPot)
**Notes:** Weekly music shows, produced by Tilford Productions LLC. "From the Isle of Music" is dedicated to the music of Cuba (aka 'The Isle of Music').

## SHORTWAVE RADIOGRAM

**E:** radiogram@verizon.net **W:** swradiogram.net;
**W:** www.facebook.com/groups/567099476753304 (SW Radiogram group)
**L.P:** Presenter: Dr Kim Andrew Elliott (KD9XB).
**kHz:** *5850, 5950, 7730, 7780, 9400*

### Winter Schedule 2018/2019

| English | Days | Area | kHz |
|---|---|---|---|
| 0800-0830 | m...... | NAm,Pac | 7730rmi |
| 0800-0830 | m...... | NAm,As | 5850rmi |
| 0800-0830 | m...... | LAm | 5950rmi |
| 1400-1430 | .....s. | Eu | 9400sof* |
| 2030-2100 | ....f.. | NAm,Eu,ME | 7780rmi |
| 2030-2100 | ....f.. | LAm | 5950rmi |
| 2330-2400 | ......s | NAm,Eu,ME | 7780rmi |

**Key:** * Text and images are broadcast in various soundcard generated digital modes, such as MFSK32, Olivia and others.
**V:** Eqsl.
**Notes:** Shortwave Radiogram (initially VOA Radiogram 2013-2017) is a weekly prgr for the technical-minded enthusiast, created & produced by Dr Kim Andrew Elliott. It transmits experimental digital test & images via analogue SW txs, using sound card produced digital signals that are superimposed on the audio feed, in modes like Olivia, MFSK, Thor, IKFP and decodable with freeware like Fldigi. SW Radiogram is the successor to VOA Radiogram which Elliot launched in March 2013 while working for Voice of America; it was aired each weekend via the IBB transmitting stn Greenville until his retirement in June 2017.

## VORW RADIO INTERNATIONAL

🖃 Produced in Lynchburg, VA, USA.
**E:** vorwinfo@gmail.com
**W:** www.patreon.com/TheReportOfTheWeek
**Webcast:** D (soundcloud.com/vorw_radio_int)
**kHz:** *5850, 5950, 7570, 7730, 7780, 9395, 9955*

### Winter Schedule 2018/2019

| English | Days | Area | kHz |
|---|---|---|---|
| 0000-0100 | ....f.. | NAm | 5950rmi, 7730rmi, 9395rmi |
| 0100-0200 | ....f.. | NAm,Eu,ME | 7780rmi |
| 0100-0200 | ....f.. | NAm | 5850rmi |
| 0400-0500 | ....f.. | NAm | 7730rmi |
| 1000-1100 | ...t... | NAm | 5950rmi |
| 2000-2100 | ...t... | NAm,Eu,ME | 7780rmi |
| 2000-2100 | ...t... | NAm | 5950rmi |
| 2000-2100 | .....s | NAm | 9395rmi |
| 2200-2300 | .....s | NAm | 7570rmi |
| 2300-2400 | ...t... | NAm | 5950rmi |
| 2300-2400 | ...t... | LAm | 9955rmi |

**V:** eQSL-card.
**Notes:** VORW ("Voice of The Report of the Week") is a weekly radio show hosted by John Jurasek, the author of the (food-related) Youtube channel "The Report of the Week". Sporadically on SW since 2015; regularly since 2016 (via rebroadcasters).

## WBCQ – THE PLANET

🖃 274 Britton Road, Monticello, ME 04760, USA.
☎ +1 207 5389180.
**E:** wbcq@wbcq.com **W:** www.wbcq.com
**Webcast:** D/L
**L.P:** Owner/GM: Allan Weiner; Chief Engineer: Tim Smith.
**SW:** [BCQ] Monticello, ME: 4 x 50kW. Projected: 1 x 500kW.
**kHz:** *5130, 7490, 9330*

### Winter Schedule 2018/2019

| English | Days | Area | kHz |
|---|---|---|---|
| 0000-0500 | daily | NAm,CAm | 5130bcq*,† |
| 0000-2400 | daily | NAm,CAm | 9330bcq*,† |
| 2000-0500 | daily | NAm,CAm | 7490bcq† |

**Key:** † Flexible schedule, depending on booked airtime (may have breaks) * H3E (AM/USB) mode.
**Ann:** English: "You are listening to WBCQ, Monticello, Maine, The United States of America - The Planet".
**V:** QSL-card. (SASE)
**Notes:** Owned by Allan H. Weiner/Becker Broadcast Systems, Inc. Leases air time to religious and non-religious prgr producers. Schedule is subject to daily variation (according to bookings) and start/end times are approximate. On air since 8 September 1998.

## WORLD OF RADIO (WOR)

🖃 P.O. Box 1684, Enid, OK 73702, USA.
**E:** woradio@yahoo.com
**W:** www.worldofradio.com; www.angelfire.com/ok/worldofradio
**Webcast:** D/P
**L.P:** Producer and host: Glenn Hauser.
**SW:** Via WRMI & WBCQ (Both USA); Hamburger Lokalradio (Germany).
**kHz:** *5130, 5950, 6190, 7265, 7490, 7730, 7780, 9265, 9485, 9955*

### Winter Schedule 2018/2019

| English | Days | Area | kHz |
|---|---|---|---|
| 0030-0100 | .t..... | NAm | 7730rmi |
| 0200-0230 | .t..... | LAm | 9955rmi |
| 0230-0300 | m...... | NAm | 5950rmi, 5950rmi# |
| 0400-0430 | m...... | NAm,CAm | 5130bcq* |
| 0430-0500 | m...... | LAm | 9955rmi |
| 0730-0800 | .....s. | CEu,WEu | 6190goh* |
| 1030-1100 | ..w.... | NAm | 5950rmi |
| 1130-1200 | .....s | CEu,WEu | 7265goh* |
| 1200-1230 | .....s. | Eu,NAf | 9265inb+ |
| 1530-1600 | .....s. | CEu,WEu | 9485goh* |
| 1700-1715 | .....s. | NAm | 5950rmi# |
| 1700-1730 | .....s. | NAm | 5950rmi |
| 2030-2100 | .t..... | NAm,Eu,ME | 7780rmi |
| 2130-2200 | .....s | NAm,Eu,ME | 7780rmi |
| 2200-2230 | ..w.... | LAm | 9955rmi |
| 2200-2230 | ..w.... | NAm,CAm | 7490bcq |
| 2230-2300 | .....s | LAm | 9955rmi |

**Key:** Schedule is subject to change without notice (times via WBCQ, WINB & WRMI may change frequently), for latest schedule: see www.w4uvh.net/dxlatest.txt; * AM/USB (H3E) mode; # Unoffical WRN relay via WRMI.+ DRM
**V:** QSL-card (A dedicated WOR QSL-card is only available for bcasts via WRMI, issued by WRMI for direct rpt)
**Notes:** World of Radio is a weekly non-commercial listener-supported, public service program about communications around the world, especially shortwave. Has been on the air since 1982, first via WRNO, and since via several US SW stations. It summarizes extensive DX and other news published each week in DX Listening Digest, incorporating Review of International Broadcasting, freely

available via: http://www.worldofradio.com/dxldmid.html. See website for latest schedule.

## WRMI – RADIO MIAMI INTERNATIONAL
✉ 175 Fontainebleau Blvd., Suite 1N4, Miami, FL 33172, USA.
☎ +1 305 5599764. 🖷 +1 305 5598186.
**E:** info@wrmi.net **W:** www.wrmi.net
**Webcast:** L (only trs on 9955kHz)
**LP:** GM: Jeff White; Dir, Technical: Jose Raul Mena.
**SW:** [RMI] Okeechobee, FL: 1 x 50, 12 x 100kW.
**kHz:** *5010, 5850, 5950, 5985, 7730, 7780, 9395, 9455, 9955, 21525*

### Winter Schedule 2018/2019

| English | Days | Area | kHz |
|---|---|---|---|
| 0000-0015 | .t.t.s. | Car,LAm | 9955rmi |
| 0000-0030 | .t.t..s | NAm | 7730rmi, 9395rmi |
| 0000-0100 | m.w.... | NAm | 7730rmi, 9395rmi |
| 0015-0045 | .....s. | Car,LAm | 9955rmi |
| 0030-0045 | ......s | Car,LAm | 9955rmi |
| 0030-0100 | ...t.s. | NAm | 7730rmi, 9395rmi |
| 0030-0100 | daily | NAm | 5950rmi |
| 0045-0100 | .....s. | Car,LAm | 9955rmi |
| 0100-0115 | .t...ss | Car,LAm | 9955rmi |
| 0100-0115 | .....s. | Car | 5010rmi |
| 0100-0115 | .....s. | NAm,Eu,ME | 7780rmi |
| 0100-0130 | ...t... | Car | 5010rmi |
| 0100-0130 | ..wt... | Car,LAm | 9955rmi |
| 0100-0130 | m...... | NAm | 9395rmi |
| 0100-0130 | m..t... | NAm,Eu,ME | 7780rmi |
| 0100-0145 | ......s | Car | 5010rmi |
| 0100-0200 | ..w..s | NAm,Eu,ME | 7780rmi |
| 0100-0200 | m...... | NAm | 9395rmi |
| 0100-0300 | ...t... | NAm | 9455rmi |
| 0115-0130 | ....fs. | Car,LAm | 9955rmi |
| 0130-0145 | m...... | Car,LAm | 9955rmi |
| 0130-0200 | .t.t... | NAm,Eu,ME | 7780rmi |
| 0130-0230 | daily | NAm | 9395rmi |
| 0200-0230 | m.wt.s. | Car,LAm | 9955rmi |
| 0200-0300 | daily | NAm | 5950rmi |
| 0230-0245 | ......s | NAm,Eu,ME | 7780rmi |
| 0230-0245 | ..wt... | Car,LAm | 9955rmi |
| 0230-0300 | m..t.s. | Car,LAm | 9955rmi |
| 0245-0300 | m.....s | NAm,Eu,ME | 7780rmi |
| 0300-0400 | daily | NAm | 5950rmi |
| 0300-0500 | .....s. | NAm,Eu,ME | 7780rmi |
| 0330-0400 | ....ss | CAm | 5985rmi |
| 0330-0500 | m.....s | NAm,Eu,ME | 7780rmi |
| 0345-0400 | ...tf.. | CAm | 5985rmi |
| 0400-0415 | ...tf.. | Car,LAm | 9955rmi |
| 0400-0500 | mt....s | NAm | 7730rmi |
| 0400-1000 | daily | NAm | 9395rmi |
| 0430-0445 | .....s. | Car,LAm | 9955rmi |
| 0430-0500 | .tw.f.. | Car,LAm | 9955rmi |
| 0445-0500 | .....s. | Car,LAm | 9955rmi |
| 0500-0600 | m...... | CAm | 5985rmi |
| 0700-0800 | m...... | NAm | 7730rmi |
| 0700-0800 | m...... | NAm,As | 5850rmi |
| 0700-0900 | ......s | NAm | 7730rmi |
| 0700-0900 | ......s | NAm,As | 5850rmi |
| 0800-1000 | m.....s | NAm | 5950rmi |
| 0830-0930 | m...... | NAm | 7730rmi |
| 0830-0930 | m...... | NAm,As | 5850rmi |
| 0900-0930 | ......s | NAm | 7730rmi |
| 0900-0930 | ......s | NAm,As | 5850rmi |
| 1000-1030 | .tw...s | NAm | 5950rmi |
| 1000-1100 | .....s. | NAm | 5950rmi |
| 1030-1100 | .t....s | NAm | 5950rmi |
| 1100-1130 | ......s | Car,LAm | 9955rmi |
| 1100-1500 | daily | NAm | 5950rmi |
| 1130-1145 | ......s | Car,LAm | 9955rmi |
| 1200-1215 | ......s | Car,LAm | 9955rmi |
| 1200-1230 | .....s. | Car,LAm | 9955rmi |
| 1200-1230 | ..w.f.s | Car | 5010rmi |
| 1215-1230 | ......s | Car,LAm | 9955rmi |
| 1230-1300 | ....ss | Car,LAm | 9955rmi |
| 1300-1500 | ......s | NAm,Eu,ME | 7780rmi |

| English | Days | Area | kHz |
|---|---|---|---|
| 1330-1345 | .....ss | Car,LAm | 9955rmi |
| 1345-1400 | ......s | Car,LAm | 9955rmi |
| 1400-1415 | m...... | Car,LAm | 9955rmi |
| 1400-1430 | .tw.f.s | Car,LAm | 9955rmi |
| 1415-1445 | m...... | Car,LAm | 9955rmi |
| 1430-1445 | ...tf.. | Car,LAm | 9955rmi |
| 1430-1500 | ....ss | Car,LAm | 9955rmi |
| 1500-1600 | ......s | NAm,Eu,ME | 7780rmi |
| 1500-1700 | ....s. | Car,LAm | 9955rmi |
| 1530-1600 | m...... | Af | 21525rmi |
| 2000-2015 | .....ss | NAm,Eu,ME | 7780rmi |
| 2000-2030 | .t.f.. | NAm,Eu,ME | 7780rmi |
| 2000-2100 | ..w.... | NAm,Eu,ME | 7780rmi |
| 2000-2200 | mtwtf.. | NAm | 9395rmi |
| 2015-2030 | .....s. | NAm,Eu,ME | 7780rmi |
| 2030-2100 | m.....s | NAm,Eu,ME | 7780rmi |
| 2045-2100 | .....s. | NAm,Eu,ME | 7780rmi |
| 2100-2130 | ......s | NAm,Eu,ME | 7780rmi |
| 2100-2200 | .....s. | NAm,Eu,ME | 7780rmi |
| 2100-2200 | ....ss | NAm | 9395rmi |
| 2200-2230 | ......s | Car,LAm | 9955rmi |
| 2200-2300 | ....ss | Car | 5010rmi |
| 2200-2300 | ....ss | NAm | 9395rmi |
| 2200-2300 | ....ss | NAm,Eu,ME | 7780rmi |
| 2230-2300 | ....ss | Car,LAm | 9955rmi |
| 2230-2300 | ....f.. | NAm,As | 5850rmi |
| 2300-2315 | ......s. | Car,LAm | 9955rmi |
| 2300-2315 | .....s. | NAm | 5950rmi |
| 2300-2330 | daily | NAm,Eu,ME | 7780rmi |
| 2300-2330 | m.....s | Car,LAm | 9955rmi |
| 2300-2330 | m.....s | NAm | 5950rmi |
| 2300-2400 | daily | NAm | 9395rmi |
| 2330-2400 | ......s | Car,LAm | 9955rmi |
| 2330-2400 | ......s | NAm | 5950rmi |

| Portuguese | Days | Area | kHz |
|---|---|---|---|
| 2315-2330 | .....s. | NAm | 5950rmi |
| 2315-2330 | .....s. | Car,LAm | 9955rmi |

| Spanish | Days | Area | kHz |
|---|---|---|---|
| 0000-0015 | m...f.. | Car,LAm | 9955rmi |
| 0000-0030 | ......s. | NAm | 7730rmi, 9395rmi |
| 0015-0030 | mtwtf.. | Car,LAm | 9955rmi |
| 0030-0100 | mtwtf.. | Car,LAm | 9955rmi |
| 0100-0115 | m...f.. | Car,LAm | 9955rmi |
| 0100-0200 | m...... | Car | 5010rmi |
| 0115-0130 | ......s. | NAm,Eu,ME | 7780rmi |
| 0115-0130 | mt..... | Car,LAm | 9955rmi |
| 0115-0145 | ......s | Car,LAm | 9955rmi |
| 0130-0200 | .twtf.. | Car,LAm | 9955rmi |
| 0130-0200 | ....s. | Car,LAm | 9955rmi |
| 0145-0200 | m.....s | Car,LAm | 9955rmi |
| 0200-0215 | ......s | Car,LAm | 9955rmi |
| 0200-0230 | .t..... | Car,LAm | 9955rmi |
| 0230-0245 | ....s. | Car,LAm | 9955rmi |
| 0230-0245 | m...... | NAm,Eu,ME | 7780rmi |
| 0230-0300 | .t..... | Car,LAm | 9955rmi |
| 0245-0300 | .t..... | Car,LAm | 9955rmi |
| 0330-0345 | ...tf.. | CAm | 5985rmi |
| 0330-0400 | m...... | CAm | 5985rmi |
| 0400-0415 | ..w.... | Car,LAm | 9955rmi |
| 0400-0500 | ..wt... | NAm | 7730rmi |
| 0415-0430 | .twtfs. | Car,LAm | 9955rmi |
| 0445-0500 | ...t... | Car,LAm | 9955rmi |
| 1000-1015 | ...f.. | NAm | 5950rmi |
| 1000-1100 | m...... | NAm | 5950rmi |
| 1030-1100 | ....f.. | NAm | 5950rmi |
| 1145-1200 | ......s | Car,LAm | 9955rmi |
| 1200-1230 | mt.t... | Car | 5010rmi |
| 1345-1400 | ....s. | Car,LAm | 9955rmi |
| 1400-1430 | ...t... | Car,LAm | 9955rmi |
| 1430-1445 | .t..... | Car,LAm | 9955rmi |
| 1445-1500 | m.wtf.. | Car,LAm | 9955rmi |
| 2000-2030 | m...... | NAm,Eu,ME | 7780rmi |
| 2015-2030 | ......s | NAm,Eu,ME | 7780rmi |
| 2030-2045 | .....s. | NAm,Eu,ME | 7780rmi |

| Spanish | Days | Area | kHz |
|---|---|---|---|
| 2200-2230 | ....f.. | Car,LAm | 9955rmi |
| 2200-2300 | m...... | Car,LAm | 9955rmi |
| 2215-2230 | .t.t..s | Car,LAm | 9955rmi |
| 2230-2300 | ....f.. | Car,LAm | 9955rmi |
| 2245-2300 | .t..... | Car,LAm | 9955rmi |
| 2300-2400 | .t..f.. | Car,LAm | 9955rmi |
| 2300-2400 | .t..f.. | NAm | 5950rmi |
| 2330-2400 | m....s. | NAm | 5950rmi |
| 2330-2400 | m....s. | Car,LAm | 9955rmi |

**Ann:** English: "You're listening to WRMI, Radio Miami International, Okeechobee, Florida, USA".
**V:** QSL-card.
**Notes:** Owned by Radio Miami International, Inc. On air since June 1994. WRMI provides air time for prgrs by various production companies and rebroadcasts international radio stations. Some programme blocks are relays of World Radio Network (WRN). See WRMI web site for detailed schedule. Some prgrs aimed at a Cuban audience are jammed. Detailed schedule: see www.wrmi.net

## WWRB
Airline Transport Communications Inc., Listener Services, P.O. Box 7, Manchester, TN 37349-0007, USA.
☎ +1 931 7286087. ᐧ +1 931 7286087.
**E:** dfrantz@wwrb.org **W:** www.wwrb.org
**Webcast:** L
6755 Shady Grove Road, Morrison, TN 37355, USA. (Tx Site & Studio)
**L.P:** Owner & CE: Dave Frantz.
**SW:** [WRB] Morrison, TN: 1 x 100kW.
**kHz:** *5050*

### Winter Schedule 2018/2019
| English | Days | Area | kHz |
|---|---|---|---|
| 0000-0400 | m....ss | NAm | 5050wrb* |

**Key:** * Other frequencies available: 3185, 3195, 3215.
**Ann:** English: "This is radio station WWRB - Worldwide Radio Broadcasting".
**V:** QSL-card. (Email rpts not accepted)
**Notes:** A subsidiary operation of Airline Transport Communications, Inc. The station transmits religious paid programming. Freq usage/schedule varies, depending on airtime sales.

## ALYX & YEYI (TECHNICAL SERVICE PROVIDER) (Broker)
5201 Blue Lagoon Drive, 8th Floor, Miami, FL 33126, USA.
☎ +1 305 5728070.
**E:** info@alyx-yeyi.com **W:** www.alyx-yeyi.com; www.airtime.org
**L.P:** MD: Ludo Maes.
**Notes:** Alyx & Yeyi, LLC, a sister company of Broadcast Belgium (see under Belgium), is a technical service provider and brokers airtime on shortwave, satellite and Internet for radio stns/prgr producers with political, religious, commercial and NGO background. The latest SW schedule can be found at www.airtime.org/shortwave/schedule.php.

## UZBEKISTAN (UZB)

### RADIOALOQA, RADIOESHITTIRISH VA TELEVIDENIYE MARKAZI (RRTM) (Tx Operator)
Amir Timur Street 109a, 100202 Toshkent, Uzbekistan.
☎ +998 71 2356516. ᐧ +998 71 2344517.
**E:** qabulhona@crrt.uz **W:** www.crrt.uz
**L.P:** GD: Emir R. Gaziyev.
**SW:** [TAC] Toshkent: 11 x 100kW.
**Notes:** RRTM, a division of the State Communications and Information Agency of Uzbekistan, is the national transmitter network operator in Uzbekistan.

## VATICAN CITY STATE (CVA)

### VATICAN RADIO (Rlg)
Piazza Pia 3, I-00120 Vatican City.
☎ +39 06 69883945. ᐧ +39 06 69883463.
**E:** english@vatiradio.va
**W:** www.vaticannews.va; www.radiovaticana.va
**Webcast:** D/L/P
**L.P:** DG (Secretariat for Communication): Paolo Nusiner.
**SW:** [SMG] Santa Maria di Galeria: 4 x 100, 5 x 500kW.

**FM/DAB:** FM: See National Radio section.
**SAT:** Eutelsat 12WB/Hot Bird 13B.
**kHz:** *5950, 6010, 6115, 6145, 6185, 7230, 7235, 7250, 7305, 7360, 7365, 7410, 7435, 7485, 9505, 9560, 9580, 9645, 9695, 9700, 9705, 11620, 11625, 11740, 11900, 11935, 13830, 15595, 17590*

### Winter Schedule 2018/2019
| Amharic | Days | Area | kHz |
|---|---|---|---|
| 1530-1600 | daily | Af | 11620smg, 13830smg |
| **Amharic (Liturgy)** | **Days** | **Area** | **kHz** |
| 0930-1050 | ......s | Af | 15595smg, 17590smg |
| **Arabic** | **Days** | **Area** | **kHz** |
| 0710-0730 | mtwtfs. | NAf,ME | 11935smg |
| 1630-1700 | daily | NAf,ME | 7230smg, 9700smg |
| **Arabic (Liturgy)** | **Days** | **Area** | **kHz** |
| 0930-1050 | ......s | NAf,ME | 15595smg, 17590smg |
| **Armenian** | **Days** | **Area** | **kHz** |
| 1600-1620 | daily | Eu | 6185smg, 7360smg |
| **Armenian (Liturgy)** | **Days** | **Area** | **kHz** |
| 0930-1050 | ......s | Eu | 15595smg, 17590smg |
| **Belarusian** | **Days** | **Area** | **kHz** |
| 1700-1720 | daily | BLR | 6185smg |
| **Chinese** | **Days** | **Area** | **kHz** |
| 1230-1300 | .....s. | As | 6115pht, 7485pht, 9560pht |
| 2200-2230 | daily | As | 6185smg, 7410smg, 9580pht |
| **English** | **Days** | **Area** | **kHz** |
| 0215-0230 | .twtfs. | NAm | 5950rmi# |
| 0900-0915 | daily | NAm | 5950rmi# |
| 0915-0930 | m.....s | NAm | 5950rmi# |
| 1630-1700 | daily | Af | 11625mdc, 13830smg |
| 1715-1730 | daily | NAf,ME | 7230smg |
| 1715-1730 | daily | NAm | 5950rmi# |
| 2000-2030 | daily | Af | 6010smg, 7365smg |
| 2030-2100 | .....s. | NAm | 5950rmi# |
| **English (Liturgy)** | **Days** | **Area** | **kHz** |
| 1130-1200 | ....f.. | NAf | 17590smg |
| 1130-1200 | ....f.. | NAf,ME | 15595smg |
| **French** | **Days** | **Area** | **kHz** |
| 0730-0745 | mtwtfs. | NAf,ME | 11935smg |
| 1700-1715 | daily | Af | 7230smg |
| 1700-1730 | daily | Af | 9705smg, 11625smg |
| 2030-2100 | daily | Af | 6010smg, 7365smg |
| **Hindi** | **Days** | **Area** | **kHz** |
| 1430-1450 | daily | As | 7250pht, 9505pht |
| **Italian** | **Days** | **Area** | **kHz** |
| 0700-0710 | mtwtfs. | NAf,ME | 11935smg |
| **Latin (Liturgy)** | **Days** | **Area** | **kHz** |
| 1940-2000 | daily | Af | 6010smg, 7235smg, 7365smg |
| **Latin (Mass)** | **Days** | **Area** | **kHz** |
| 0620-0700 | daily | NAf,ME | 11935smg |
| **Malayalam** | **Days** | **Area** | **kHz** |
| 1510-1530 | daily | As | 7250pht, 9505pht |
| **Portuguese** | **Days** | **Area** | **kHz** |
| 1800-1830 | daily | Af | 9705smg |
| 2100-2130 | daily | Af | 7365smg |
| **Romanian (Liturgy)** | **Days** | **Area** | **kHz** |
| 0810-0925 | ......s | Eu | 7250smg, 9645smg |
| **Russian** | **Days** | **Area** | **kHz** |
| 1230-1300 | daily | RUS | 6145pht, 7435pht |
| 1620-1640 | daily | RUS | 6185smg, 7360smg |
| **Russian (Liturgy)** | **Days** | **Area** | **kHz** |
| 0930-1050 | ......s | RUS | 15595smg, 17590smg |
| **Somali** | **Days** | **Area** | **kHz** |
| 1615-1630 | .....s. | Af | 11625mdc, 13830smg |
| **Spanish** | **Days** | **Area** | **kHz** |
| 0145-0200 | daily | SAm | 7305grv |
| 1230-1245 | daily | SAm | 9695grv |
| **Swahili** | **Days** | **Area** | **kHz** |
| 1600-1615 | .....s. | Af | 11625mdc, 13830smg |
| 1600-1630 | mtwtf.s | Af | 11625mdc, 13830smg |

| Tamil | Days | Area | kHz |
|---|---|---|---|
| 1450-1510 | daily | As | 7250pht, 9505pht |
| **Tigrinya** | **Days** | **Area** | **kHz** |
| 1730-1800 | daily | Af | 9705smg, 11625mdc |
| **Ukrainian** | **Days** | **Area** | **kHz** |
| 1740-1800 | daily | UKR | 6185smg, 7360smg |
| **Ukrainian** | | | |
| **(Liturgy)** | **Days** | **Area** | **kHz** |
| 0705-0800 | ......s | UKR | 9645smg, 11740smg |
| **Vietnamese** | **Days** | **Area** | **kHz** |
| 2315-2400 | daily | SEA | 9580pht, 11900pht |

**Key:** # Unoffical WRN relay via WRMI.

**Ann:** Before all transmissions: Latin: "Laudetur Jesus Christus" (Praised be Jesus Christ), repeated in the language of the broadcast, then station identification. English: "This is the English program of Vatican Radio".

**V:** QSL-card. Email rpt to qsl.request@spc.va

**Notes:** On air since 12 Feb 1931. Produced by the Vatican Secretariat for Communications. Certain schedule variations apply on Catholic Holy Days.

## VIETNAM (VTN)

### VOICE OF VIETNAM (OVERSEAS SERVICE) (VOV) (Gov)
⌖ 45 Ba Trieu Street, Hanoi, Vietnam.
☎ +84 24 38266809. 🖃 +84 24 38266707..
**E:** vovworld@vov.org.vn **W:** vovworld.vn; tnvn.gov.vn; vov.vn
**Webcast:** D/L
**LP:** Dir (VOV5): Nguyen Tien Long.
**MW:** [OMO] Can Tho, Thoi Hung: 1242kHz 2000kW (assumed to be run at 500kW).
**SW:** [VNI] Son Tay: 11 x 100kW.
**FM/DAB:** FM: 105.5MHz (Hanoi); 105.7MHz (Ho Chi Minh City).
**SAT:** Vinasat 1.
**kHz:** *1242, 7220, 7280, 7285, 7315, 9730, 9840, 12020*

#### Winter Schedule 2018/2019

| Chinese | Days | Area | kHz |
|---|---|---|---|
| 1100-1130 | daily | As | 7220vni |
| 1200-1230 | daily | As | 7220vni |
| 1300-1330 | daily | As | 7220vni |
| 2200-2230 | daily | As | 7220vni |
| 2230-2300 | daily | As | 9840vni, 12020vni |
| **English** | **Days** | **Area** | **kHz** |
| 0000-0030 | daily | NAm | 7315hri |
| 0100-0130 | daily | NAm | 7315hri |
| 1000-1030 | daily | As | 9840vni, 12020vni |
| 1130-1200 | daily | As | 9840vni, 12020vni |
| 1230-1300 | daily | As | 9840vni, 12020vni |
| 1330-1400 | daily | As | 9840vni, 12020vni |
| 1500-1530 | daily | As | 9840vni, 12020vni |
| 1600-1630 | daily | Eu | 7280vni, 9730vni |
| 1600-1630 | daily | ME | 7220vni |
| 1900-1930 | daily | Eu | 7280vni, 9730vni |
| 2030-2100 | daily | ME | 7220vni |
| 2130-2200 | daily | Eu | 7280vni, 9730vni |
| 2330-2400 | daily | As | 9840vni, 12020vni |
| **French** | **Days** | **Area** | **kHz** |
| 1200-1230 | daily | As | 7285vni |
| 1300-1330 | daily | As | 7285vni |
| 1630-1700 | daily | ME | 7220vni |
| 1930-2000 | daily | Eu | 7280vni, 9730vni |
| 2030-2100 | daily | Eu | 7280vni, 9730vni |
| 2100-2130 | daily | ME | 7220vni |
| **German** | **Days** | **Area** | **kHz** |
| 1830-1900 | daily | Eu | 7280vni, 9730vni |
| 2000-2030 | daily | Eu | 7280vni, 9730vni |
| **Indonesian** | **Days** | **Area** | **kHz** |
| 1030-1100 | daily | As | 9840vni, 12020vni |
| 1300-1330 | daily | As | 9840vni, 12020vni |
| 1430-1500 | daily | As | 9840vni, 12020vni |
| 2300-2330 | daily | As | 9840vni, 12020vni |
| **Japanese** | **Days** | **Area** | **kHz** |
| 1100-1130 | daily | As | 9840vni, 12020vni |
| 1200-1230 | daily | As | 9840vni, 12020vni |

| Japanese | Days | Area | kHz |
|---|---|---|---|
| 1400-1430 | daily | As | 9840vni, 12020vni |
| 2200-2230 | daily | As | 9840vni, 12020vni |
| **Khmer** | **Days** | **Area** | **kHz** |
| 1600-1630 | daily | As | 1242omo |
| **Lao** | **Days** | **Area** | **kHz** |
| 1100-1200 | daily | As | 7285vni |
| 1330-1430 | daily | SEA | 1242omo |
| **Russian** | **Days** | **Area** | **kHz** |
| 1130-1200 | daily | As | 7220vni |
| 1230-1300 | daily | As | 7220vni |
| 1630-1700 | daily | Eu | 7280vni, 9730vni |
| **Spanish** | **Days** | **Area** | **kHz** |
| 0030-0100 | daily | LAm | 7315hri |
| 0130-0200 | daily | LAm | 7315hri |
| 1800-1830 | daily | Eu | 7280vni, 9730vni |
| 2100-2130 | daily | Eu | 7280vni, 9730vni |
| **Thai** | **Days** | **Area** | **kHz** |
| 1230-1300 | daily | As | 7285vni |
| 1430-1500 | daily | SEA | 1242omo |
| **Vietnamese** | **Days** | **Area** | **kHz** |
| 1500-1600 | daily | ME | 7220vni |
| 1500-1600 | daily | SEA | 1242omo |
| 1700-1800 | daily | Eu | 7280vni, 9730vni |

**Ann:** English: "This is the Voice of Vietnam".
**V:** QSL-card.
**Notes:** External Sce (also branded VOV5) of the national state broadcaster Đài Tiếng Nói Việt Nam (R. Voice of Vietnam). The Chinese programming includes segments in Cantonese.

## ZAMBIA (ZMB)

### VOICE OF HOPE – AFRICA (Rlg)
⌖ 543 Country Club Drive, Simi Valley, CA 93065, USA. (SCG)
**E:** mail@voiceofhope.com (general); studio@voiceofhope.com (prgr feedback) **W:** www.voiceofhope.com/station_africa.html
**Webcast:** L
**LP:** Pres (SCG): John D. Tayloe; Vice Pres, Operations (SCG); Ray Robinson; Vice Pres (VOH - Africa): Chela Silwamba; CE (VOH - Africa): Fancis Musonda.
**SW:** [LUV] Lusaka, Makeni Ranch: 2 x 100kW.
**kHz:** *6065, 9680, 13680*

#### Winter Schedule 2018/2019

| English | Days | Area | kHz |
|---|---|---|---|
| 0500-0800 | mtwtf.. | Af | 9680luv |
| 1200-1700 | .....ss | Af | 9680luv, 13680luv |
| 1600-1900 | mtwtf.. | Af | 6065luv |
| 1700-1730 | ......s | Af | 9680luv, 13680luv |

**Ann:** English: "With love from Zambia. This is the Voice of Hope broadcasting to all of Africa on frequency ... kHz".
**V:** QSL-card. (Email rpt to: reports@voiceofhope.com)
**Notes:** Run by Strategic Communications Group (SCG), USA. Sister station to KVOH (see under USA) and Voice of Hope - Middle East (see under Israel). FPI: DRM.

# CLANDESTINE AND OTHER TARGET BROADCASTS

**Clandestine Broadcasts** (Clan) are politically-motivated broadcasts produced by groups opposed to the government of the target country.

**Other Target Broadcasts** can be produced by either governmental or non-governmental organisations and are targetted at zones of regional or local conflict.

Most COTBs are transmitted via the facilities of international transmitter operators.

The following symbols are used in this section: † Irregular transmsission; ‡ Inactive at editorial deadline. ± Variable frequency.

Where a station is no longer broadcasting, the inactive symbol (‡) appears next to the station name. If a station has been inactive for the past two seasons and remains inactive, it will be removed from the listing.

---

## Target: CHAD (TCD)

**RADIO NDARASON INTERNATIONAL**
⌨ Based in N'Djamena, Chad.
☎ +235 65078648.
⌨ Johannesburg, South Africa. (Okapi Consulting)
☎ +27 72 3788235. (cell)
**E:** info@okapi.cc **W:** www.okapi.cc
**L.P:** Project Dir (Dir, Okapi Consulting): David Smith.
**kHz:** *5960, 12050, 13810*

**Winter Schedule 2018/2019**

| Kanuri/Kanembu/ French | Days | Area | kHz |
|---|---|---|---|
| 0500-0700 | daily | TCD | 5960asc |
| 0700-0800 | daily | TCD | 13810wof |
| 1800-2100 | daily | TCD | 12050asc |

**Ann:** French: "Radio Internationale".
**Notes:** On SW since 24 Feb 2018. Produced by the Chad branch of Okapi Consulting in partnership with the intergovernmental "Lake Chad Commission". The stn targets the Kanuri and Kanembu speaking populations in areas under influence of Boko Haram in the Chad Basin region (esp. Northern Nigeria and Chad). The Kanuri word "ndarason" translates as "Everywhere You Go" ("This radio station is with you, wherever you go"). Former sister stn and successor project of the Nigeria-based Dandal Kura Radio International.

---

## Target: CHINA (CHN)

**SOUND OF HOPE (XI WANG ZHI SHENG)**
⌨ 6-4, Lane 84, Guotai St, North District, Taichung 404, Taiwan.
**Webcast:** D/L/P
⌨ 333 Kearny St, San Francisco, CA 94108, USA. (HQ)
☎ +1 415 3988009. 🖷 +1 415 2765861.
**E:** soh.soundofhope1990@gmail.com **W:** www.bayvoice.net
**L.P:** Pres (Sound of Hope Radio Network, Inc): Allen Yong Zeng.
**kHz:** *6230, 6280, 6370, 6730, 6870, 6900, 6970, 7210, 7280, 7310, 7460, 7600, 7650, 7730, 7810, 9080, 9120, 9155, 9180, 9200, 9230, 9255, 9280, 9320, 9540, 9635, 9730, 9850, 9920, 9970, 10160, 10820, 10870, 10920, 10960, 11070, 11100, 11120, 11300, 11370, 11410, 11440, 11460, 11500, 11530, 11580, 11600, 11715, 11765, 11775, 11970, 12150, 12170, 12190, 12230, 12345, 12370, 12430, 12500, 12560, 12775, 12800, 12870, 12910, 12950, 12980, 13070, 13130, 13200, 13230, 13270, 13530, 13620, 13640, 13680, 13775, 13820, 13870, 13890, 13920, 13980, 14370, 14430, 14500, 14560, 14600, 14690, 14775, 14800, 14820, 14850, 14870, 14900, 14920, 14980, 15070, 15295, 15340, 15580, 15740, 15775, 15800, 15870, 15920, 15940, 15970, 16100, 16160, 16250, 16300, 16350, 16600, 16680, 16770, 16980, 17080, 17170, 17200, 17400, 17440, 17760, 18180, 18870, 21530, 21800*

**Winter Schedule 2018/2019**

| Chinese | Days | Area | kHz |
|---|---|---|---|
| 0000-2400 | daily | CHN | 6230ust±,*, 6280ust±,*, 6370ust±,*, 6730ust±,*, 6870ust±,*, 6900ust±,*, 6970ust±,*, 7210ust±,*, 7280ust±,* |
| 0100-1600 | daily | CHN | 9320ust±,**, 9635ust±,**, 9730ust±,**, 10960ust±,**, 12430ust±,**, 12910ust±,**, 14430ust±,**, 14800ust±,**, 14900ust±,**, 15340ust±,**, 16300ust±,**, 17440ust±,** |
| 1100-2300 | daily | CHN | 7600ust±,** |
| 2100-1700 | daily | CHN | 7310ust±,*, 7460ust±,*, 7650ust±,*, 7730ust±,*, 7810ust±,*, 9080ust±,*, 9120ust±,*, 9155ust±,*, 9180ust±,*, 9200ust±,*, 9230ust±,*, 9255ust±,*, 9280ust±,*, 9540ust±,*, 9850ust±,*, 9920ust±,*, 9970ust±,*, 10160ust±,*, 10820ust±,*, 10870ust±,*, 10920ust±,*, 11070ust±,*, 11100ust±,*, 11120ust±,*, 11300ust±,*, 11370ust±,*, 11440ust±,* |

| Chinese | Days | Area | kHz |
|---|---|---|---|
| | | | 11460ust±,*, |
| | | | 11500ust±,*, |
| | | | 11530ust±,*, |
| | | | 11580ust±,*, |
| | | | 11600ust±,*, |
| | | | 11715ust±,*, |
| | | | 11765ust±,*, |
| | | | 11775ust±,*, |
| | | | 11970ust±,*, |
| | | | 12150ust±,*, |
| | | | 12170ust±,*, |
| | | | 12190ust±,*, |
| | | | 12230ust±,*, |
| | | | 12345ust±,*, |
| | | | 12370ust±,*, |
| | | | 12430ust±,*, |
| | | | 12500ust±,*, |
| | | | 12560ust±,*, |
| | | | 12775ust±,*, |
| | | | 12800ust±,*, |
| | | | 12870ust±,*, |
| | | | 12910ust±,*, |
| | | | 12950ust±,*, |
| | | | 12980ust±,*, |
| | | | 13070ust±,*, |
| | | | 13130ust±,*, |
| | | | 13200ust±,*, |
| | | | 13230ust±,*, |
| | | | 13270ust±,*, |
| | | | 13530ust±,*, |
| | | | 13620ust±,*, |
| | | | 13640ust±,*, |
| | | | 13680ust±,*, |
| | | | 13775ust±,*, |
| | | | 13820ust±,*, |
| | | | 13870ust±,*, |
| | | | 13890ust±,*, |
| | | | 13920ust±,*, |
| | | | 13980ust±,*, |
| | | | 14370ust±,*, |
| | | | 14500ust±,*, |
| 2300-1100 | daily | CHN | 11410ust±,** |

**Key:** ± Variable frequency; * Includes segments in Cantonese, (times variable); ** Relay of R. Free Asia (RFA), Includes Cantonese 1400-1500 (times variable).
**Ann:** Chinese: "Xiwang zhi sheng guoji guangbo diantai".
**V:** QSL-card. Email rpt to joanna.xia@bayvoice.net

**Notes:** Established on 20 June 2003 in San Francisco, USA. Falun Gong-related Sound of Hope Radio International is the shortwave service of Sound of Hope Radio Network, Inc (USA). The organisation is a provider of Chinese language news and cultural programming for the worldwide Chinese community. Some frequencies are jammed. The site code "ust" refers to "Unknown site in Taiwan". All transmissions are believed to be broadcast from txs with a few kW output. The International Telecommunication Union (ITU) have reported their direction finding revealed 9155, 9360, 10920, 11530, 12430, 12870, 12950, 14560, 14600, 14800, 14820 and 15920kHz to be from Rep. of Korea & 11410, 13980 and 17400kHz from Mongolia.

## VOICE OF TIBET
✉ Stiftelsen Voice of Tibet, Kirkegata 5, N-0153 Oslo, Norway. (Administration)
☎ +47 22111209.
**E:** info@vot.org, editor@vot.org, oystalme@gmail.com
**W:** www.vot.org
**Webcast:** D
✉ Ratoe Chuwar Labrang, Phuntsok Gyatsal House, Session Road, Dharamsala 176215, Distt Kangra H.P., India (Main Editorial Office)
☎ +91 1892 228179; +91 1892 222384. 🖶 +91 1892 224913.
**L.P:** Dir: Øystein Alme; Editor-in-Chief: Tenzin Paldon.
**SAT:** Telstar 18/Apstar 5.
**kHz:** *7488, 9888, 11605, 11651, 11674*

### Winter Schedule 2018/2019

| Chinese | Days | Area | kHz |
|---|---|---|---|
| 1200-1230 | daily | CHN | 11674dsb± |
| 1300-1330 | daily | CHN | 11651dsb± |

| Tibetan | Days | Area | kHz |
|---|---|---|---|
| 1230-1300 | daily | CHN | 11605dsb± |
| 1300-1400 | daily | CHN | 9888dsb± |
| 2300-2400 | daily | CHN | 7488dsb± |

**Key:** ± Variable frequency.
**Ann:** Chinese: "Zheli shi Nuowei Xizang zhi Sheng Guangbo Diantai huayu jiemu"; Tibetan: "Di nor we bod kyi rlung 'phrin khang yin".
**V:** QSL-card.

**Notes:** On the air since 14 May 1996. Produced by the Norwegian foundation "Voice of Tibet". 24/7 on satellite, with half-hourly prgrs (:00 in Chinese, :30 in Tibetan); relayed on SW as per schedule above. SW freqs are often changed to counter jamming. Alternate relay site: TAC, Toshkent (UZB).

## VOICE OF CHINA (Clan)
✉ 27 Agate, Irvine, CA 92614, USA.
**L.P:** Pres: Robert Higgins.
**kHz:** *7270*

### Winter Schedule 2018/2019

| Chinese | Days | Area | kHz |
|---|---|---|---|
| 1400-1500 | daily | CHN | 7270tsh |
| 2300-2400 | daily | CHN | 7270tsh |

**Ann:** Chinese: "Zhongguo zhi yin".
**Notes:** On air since April 1991. Produced by the NGO "Voice of China". Initially funded by the NGO "Foundation for China in the 21st Century" until its dissolution in 2009. Jammed.

---

## Target: CUBA (CUB)

---

## WRMI – RADIO MIAMI INTERNATIONAL
✉ See International Radio section, under "USA".
**SW:** See International Radio section, under USA.

**Notes:** WRMI relays a number of anti-Government broadcasts to Cuba, in Spanish, from various programmme producers. For full programme details, see www.wrmi.net

## RADIO REPÚBLICA (Clan)
✉ P.O. Box 110235, Hialeah, FL 33011-0235, USA.
☎ +1 305 2794416.
**Webcast:** P
✉ 730 NW 107th Ave, Ste 117, Miami, FL 33155, USA (Directorio Democrático Cubano).
☎ +1 305 2202713.
**E:** info@directorio.org **W:** www.directorio.org
**L.P:** National Secretary (Directorio Democrático Cubano): Orlando Gutierrez-Boronat.
**kHz:** *9490*

### Winter Schedule 2018/2019

| Spanish | Days | Area | kHz |
|---|---|---|---|
| 0200-0400 | daily | CUB | 9490iss |

**Ann:** Spanish: "Esta es Radio República, voz del Directorio Democrático Cubano, transmitiendo para Cuba".
**V:** QSL-email. Rpt to Maria Lima (Special Assistant to Program Coordinator) marialima@directorio.org

**Notes:** On air since August 2005. Produced by Directorio Democrático Cubano. Jammed.

---

## Target: ERITREA (ERI)

---

## ALSMOOD (Clan)
**kHz:** *17545*

### Winter Schedule 2018/2019

| Tigrinya | Days | Area | kHz |
|---|---|---|---|
| 1500-1600 | m...fss | ERI | 17545iss |

**Notes:** On SW since November 2018.

## DIMTSI WEGAHTA (VOICE OF THE DAWN) (Clan)
⌕ Based in Mekelle, Ethiopia.
**Webcast:** D
**MW:** [MEK] Mek'ele (Ethiopia) 918kHz 100kW.
**kHz:** *918*

### Winter Schedule 2018/2019

| Arabic/Tigrinya | Days | Area | kHz |
|---|---|---|---|
| 0250-0600 | daily | ERI | 918mek |
| 1400-2000 | daily | ERI | 918mek |

**Ann:** Tigrinya: "Dimtsi Wegahta".

**Notes:** Established on 19 July 2007. Dimtsi Wegahta ("Voice of the Dawn") claims to be produced by the Eritrean oppositional "Charity of Civic Society of Eritrea", but is thought to be run by an Ethiopian government agency. Also referred to as "Radio Wegahta". Successor station to "Eastern Radio" (Izaat Al Sharq), which was transmitted via a tx in Sudan 2006-2007.

## VOICE OF DEMOCRATIC ALLIANCE ‡ (Clan)
⌕ c/o Radio Ethiopia, P.O. Box 1020, Addis Ababa, Ethiopia.
**E:** erit_alliance_2008@yahoo.com **W:** www.erit-alliance.com (EDA)
**SW:** Via txs of the Ethiopian public service broadcaster Ethiopian Broadcasting Corp. (EBC)
**Key:** ‡ Inactive on SW at time of publication.
**Ann:** Arabic: "Sawt al-Tahalufa al-Dimuqrati".
**V:** QSL-letter.

**Notes:** On air since April 2005. Produced by the "Eritrean Democratic Alliance" (EDA), an umbrella organisation for around a dozen opposition political parties and groups.

## VOICE OF PEACE AND DEMOCRACY OF ERITREA ‡ (Clan)
⌕ c/o Radio Ethiopia, P.O. Box 1020, Addis Ababa, Ethiopia.
**SW:** Via tx of the Ethiopian public service broadcaster Ethiopian Broadcasting Corp. (EBC)
**Key:** ‡ Inactive on SW at time of publication.
**Ann:** Tigrinya: "Dimtsi Salaman Demokratia Ertrai".

**Notes:** On air since February 1999. Produced in support of the "National Alliance of Eritrean Forces" (NAEF).

---

## Target: ETHIOPIA (ETH)

## VOICE OF AMARA RADIO (VAR/VOAR)
⌕ P.O. Box 55321, Washington DC 20040-5321, USA.
☎ +1 202 6770094.
**W:** www.facebook.com/www.moreshwegenie.org
**Webcast:** D
⌕ 8221 Georgia Ave, Silver Spring, MD 20919-5727, USA. (MWAO)
**W:** www.moreshwegenie.org (MWAO)
**kHz:** *15360*

### Winter Schedule 2018/2019

| Amharic | Days | Area | kHz |
|---|---|---|---|
| 1700-1800 | m.w..s. | ETH | 15360iss |

**Ann:** Amharic: "Yeh Amara Dimtse Radio".

**Notes:** On the air since 1 October 2016. Produced by the charitable NGO Moresh Wegene Amara Organization, Inc (MWAO).

## GINBOT 7 DIMTS RADIO ‡ (Clan)
⌕ P.O. Box 56281, London, N4 9BH, United Kingdom.
☎ +44 20 32869661.
**E:** g7radio@ginbot7.org; info@ginbot7.org **W:** www.ginbot7.org
**Webcast:** D
**E:** pg7radio@patriotg7.org **W:** www.patriotg7.org
**MW/SW:** Via tx of the Eritrean state broadcaster Voice of the Broad

---

Masses of Eritrea.
**Key:** ‡ Inactive on SW at time of publication.
**Ann:** Amharic: "Yeh Ginbot Sabat Dimtse now".
**V:** QSL-email.
**Notes:** On air since September 2008. Produced by the Ethiopian oppositional party "Ginbot 7 - Movement for Justice, Freedom and Democracy".

## RADIO XORIYO (Clan)
⌕ P.O. Box 27618, Toronto, ON M3A 3B8, Canada.
**E:** raadioxoriyo@yahoo.com
**Webcast:** D
**kHz:** *11970, 17850*

### Winter Schedule 2018/2019

| Somali | Days | Area | kHz |
|---|---|---|---|
| 1600-1630 | m...f.. | ETH | 17850iss |
| 1600-1630 | .t...s. | ETH | 11970iss |

**Ann:** Somali: "Halkani waa Radio Xoriyo, codkii ummadda Ogadenya".
**V:** QSL-email.

**Notes:** Radio Xoriyo (Somali: "Freedom") has been on the air, intermittently, since May 2000. Produced by the "Ogaden National Liberation Front" (ONLF).

## VOICE OF INDEPENDENT OROMIA (RSWO) (Clan)
⌕ P.O.Box 21762, Washington, D.C, 20009, USA.
☎ +1 202 5215653.
**E:** independentoromia@gmail.com; voice.ioromia@gmail.com
**W:** www.independentoromia.org
**Webcast:** D
**W:** www.oromoliberationfront.info (OLF)
**kHz:** *17850*

### Winter Schedule 2018/2019

| Oromo | Days | Area | kHz |
|---|---|---|---|
| 1600-1630 | ......s | ETH | 17850iss |

**Ann:** Oromo: "Raadiyoo Sagalee Walabummaa Oromiyaa".

**Notes:** On air since April 2016. Raadiyoo Sagalee Walabummaa Oromiyaa (RSWO) is produced by the "Oromo Liberation Front" (OLF).

## VOICE OF OROMO LIBERATION (Clan)
⌕ Postfach 510620, D-13366 Berlin, Germany.
☎ +49 30 4943372. ⎙ +49 30 4943372.
**E:** sbo.radio88@gmail.com **W:** www.oromoliberationfront.org/sbo.html
**Webcast:** D
**kHz:** *9610*

### Winter Schedule 2018/2019

| Amharic | Days | Area | kHz |
|---|---|---|---|
| 1730-1800 | ..w.... | ETH | 9610nau |

| Oromo | Days | Area | kHz |
|---|---|---|---|
| 1700-1730 | ..w.f.s | ETH | 9610nau |

**Ann:** Amharic: "Radio Bilisummaa Oromoo"; Oromo: "Kun Sagalee Bilisummaa Oromoo".
**V:** QSL-letter.

**Notes:** On air since 6 July 1988. Produced by the "Oromo Liberation Front" (OLF).

---

## Target: IRAN (IRN)

## RADIO RANGINKAMAN
⌕ Based in Los Angeles, California, USA.
☎ +1 818 6499406.
**E:** radioranginkaman@gmail.com **W:** radioranginkaman.org
**Webcast:** D
**SAT:** Eutelsat Hot Bird 13B. (via Encompass "WRN Persian" Sat-Feed "R. Jahani")
**kHz:** *7560*

### Winter Schedule 2018/2019

| Farsi | Days | Area | kHz |
|---|---|---|---|
| 1730-1800 | daily | IRN | 7560kch |

**Notes:** Prgr targetting the LGBT (lesbian, gay, bisexual and transgender) communities in Iran, Afghanistan and Tajikistan. The name translates in English as 'Radio Rainbow'. On SW since 24 September 2012. Also carried by KIRN Simi Valley, CA 670kHz (USA).

---

## Target: KOREA, North (KRE)

### FURUSATO NO KAZE/ILBON–E BARAM (WIND FROM JAPAN) (Gov)
⌨ Policy Planning Division, Headquarters for the Abduction Issue, Cabinet Secretariat, 6-1 Nagata-cho 1-chome, Chiyoda-ku, Tokyo 100-8968, Japan.
☎ +81 3 52532111. 📠 +81 3 3592 2300, +81 3 3581 6011.
**E:** info@rachi.go.jp **W:** www.rachi.go.jp/jp/shisei/radio; www.rachi.go.jp/en (English)
**Webcast:** D
**kHz:** *6045, 6155, 7290, 7295, 9560, 9690, 9705, 9800, 9960, 9965, 9975*

#### Winter Schedule 2018/2019

| Japanese | Days | Area | kHz |
|---|---|---|---|
| 1330-1400 | daily | KRE | 7295tsh, 9705pao, 9965hbn |
| 1430-1500 | daily | KRE | 7295tsh, 9560pao, 9960hbn |
| 1600-1630 | daily | KRE | 6045tsh, 9690pao, 9975hbn |
| 1700-1730 | daily | KRE | 6155tsh |
| **Korean** | **Days** | **Area** | **kHz** |
| 1300-1330 | daily | KRE | 7295tsh, 9705pao, 9965hbn |
| 1500-1530 | daily | KRE | 9975hbn |
| 1500-1600 | daily | KRE | 7290tsh, 9800pao |
| 1530-1600 | daily | KRE | 9965hbn |
| 1630-1700 | daily | KRE | 6155tsh |

**Ann:** Japanese: "Furusato no Kaze"; Korean: "Ilbon-e Baram".
**V:** QSL-letter.

**Notes:** On the air since 9 July 2007. Produced by the Japanese government agency "Headquarters for the Abduction Issue", targeting Japanese citizens that are believed to have been abducted to North Korea between 1977 and 1983. Jammed. "Furusato no Kaze" (English: "Wind from the Homeland") is the name of the Japanese broadcast; "Ilbon-e Baram" is the name of the Korean broadcast (English: "Wind from Japan", Japanese: "Nippon no Kaze").

### VOICE OF THE MARTYRS KOREA (Rlg)
⌨ Duksung Building 236-1, Mapo-dong, Mapo-gu, Seoul 04176, Rep. of Korea.
☎ +82 2 20650703. 📠 +82 2 20650704.
**E:** tfoley@vomkorea.kr **W:** vomkorea.co.kr
⌨ 1815 SE Bison Rd, Bartlesville, OK 74006, USA. (The Voice of the Martyrs, Inc)
☎ +1 918 3378016.
**E:** thevoice@vom-usa.org **W:** www.persecution.com
**LP:** CEO: Eric Foley.
**kHz:** *7505*

#### Winter Schedule 2018/2019

| Korean | Days | Area | kHz |
|---|---|---|---|
| 1530-1600 | daily | EAs | 7505tac± |

**Key:** ± Variable frequency.
**Ann:** Korean: "I-bangsong-oen Daehan-Minguk Seoul-eseo bonaedeurineun Sungyo sori Tansaeng sori bangsong-imnida" (Translation: "This is a broadcast from the Republic of Korea, Seoul. This is the Voice of Martyrdom - The Voice of Birth").
**V:** QSL-email.

**Notes:** On shortwave since 31 October 2009, initially as "Voice of Freedom". Produced by the South Korean branch of the world-wide operating ministry The Voice of the Martyrs, Inc (USA). Jammed.

### VOICE OF WILDERNESS (Rlg)
⌨ 208, Hannam-dong, Yongsan-gu, Seoul, 04410, Rep. of Korea.
☎ +82 2 7968846. 📠 +82 2 7927567.
**E:** info@vowkorea.com; Cornerstone Ministries: main@cornerstone.or.kr **W:** www.vowkorea.com; Cornerstone Ministries: www.cornerstone.or.kr, uscornerstone.org
**Webcast:** D/L
⌨ Cornerstone Ministries Int., P.O. Box 4002, Tustin, CA 92781, USA.
☎ +1 714 4840042. 📠 +1 714 4840046.
**E:** info@cornerstoneusa.org (USA) **W:** cornerstoneusa.org
**LP:** Principle (Cornerstone Ministries Int.): Isaac Lee.
**kHz:** *7625*

#### Winter Schedule 2018/2019

| Korean | Days | Area | kHz |
|---|---|---|---|
| 1330-1530 | daily | EAs | 7625tac± |

**Key:** ± Variable frequency.
**Ann:** Korean: "Gwangya-e Sori Bangsong-imnida".
**V:** QSL-letter.

**Notes:** Produced by the South Korean branch of Cornerstone Ministries International (USA). On SW since 2 October 1993 (on international religious broadcasting platforms, incl. World Harvest Radio, Bible Voice Broadcasting). VO Wilderness prgrs are also carried on MW/FM by FEBC Korea (South Korea). Jammed.

### NATIONAL UNITY RADIO
⌨ Unification Media Group, 2F, 59, Donggyo-ro, Mapo-gu, Seoul, 04018, Rep. of Korea.
☎ +82 2 63542012. 📠 +82 505 8712012.
**E:** rfchosun@rfchosun.org, umg@uni-media.net
**W:** www.uni-media.net
**Webcast:** D
**LP:** Pres (UMG): Lee Gwang Baek.
**MW:** [CHC] MBC Chuncheon (HLAN): 774kHz 10kW (Local MW station).
**FM/DAB:** FM: 92.3MHz (HLAN-FM Chuncheon, Rep. of Korea, 3kW)
**kHz:** *774, 6045*

#### Winter Schedule 2018/2019

| Korean | Days | Area | kHz |
|---|---|---|---|
| 1100-1300 | daily | KRE | 6045tsh |
| 1800-1900 | daily | KRE | 6045tsh |
| 1800-1955 | daily | KRE | 774chc |

**Ann:** Korean: "Gugmintong-Ilbangsong Ladio Jayujoseon".
**V:** QSL-email.

**Notes:** On air since 10 December 2005, initially launched as "Radio Free Chosun" (RFC). Re-branded "National Unity Radio" on 22 October 2015. A project of the U.S. Congress-funded NGO "Unification Media Group" (UMG), which was co-founded by RFC together with Open R. for North Korea (and two other South Korean media outlets) on 26 November 2014. Jammed on SW. The 1800-200 broadcast on 774kHz is in parallel with 92.3MHz FM. This time slot was previously used by the now defunct Open Radio for North Korea, which merged with National Unity Radio, to become a single station.

### SHIOKAZE (SEA BREEZE)
⌨ c/o COMJAN, Dairoku Matsuya Building 301, 3-8, Koraku 2-chome, Bunkyo-ku, Tokyo 112-0004, Japan.
☎ +81 3 56845058. 📠 +81 3 56845059.
**E:** comjansite2003@chosa-kai.jp **W:** www.chosa-kai.jp/shiokaze
**LP:** Dir, COMJAN & Producer/Editor: Tatsuru Murao.
**kHz:** *6070, 6110, 7245*

#### Winter Schedule 2018/2019

| Chinese | Days | Area | kHz |
|---|---|---|---|
| 1300-1330 | m...... | KRE | 7245yam* |
| 1600-1630 | m...... | KRE | 6110yam** |
| **English** | **Days** | **Area** | **kHz** |
| 1300-1400 | ...t... | KRE | 7245yam* |
| 1600-1700 | ...t... | KRE | 6110yam** |
| **Japanese** | **Days** | **Area** | **kHz** |
| 1300-1330 | .....s. | KRE | 7245yam* |

| Japanese | Days | Area | kHz |
|---|---|---|---|
| 1300-1400 | .t..... | KRE | 7245yam* |
| 1330-1400 | ......s | KRE | 7245yam* |
| 1405-1435 | daily | KRE | 6070yam*** |
| 1600-1630 | .....s. | KRE | 6110yam** |
| 1600-1700 | .t..... | KRE | 6110yam** |
| 1630-1700 | ......s | KRE | 6110yam** |

| Korean | Days | Area | kHz |
|---|---|---|---|
| 1300-1330 | ......s | KRE | 7245yam* |
| 1300-1400 | ..w.f.. | KRE | 7245yam* |
| 1330-1400 | m....s. | KRE | 7245yam* |
| 1600-1630 | .....s | KRE | 6110yam** |
| 1600-1700 | ..w.f.. | KRE | 6110yam** |
| 1630-1700 | m....s. | KRE | 6110yam** |
| 1630-1700 | .....s | KRE | 6110yam** |

**Key:** Alternative frequencies: *5965/6040/7215kHz; ** 6090/6165kHz; *** 6070/6165/7295kHz.
**Ann:** Chinese: "Zheshi Shiokaze, Chaofeng Bosong"; English: "This is JSR Shiokaze, Sea Breeze, from Tokyo, Japan"; Japanese: "Kochirawa Shiokaze desu"; Korean: "Yeogineun Shiokaze, Badatbaramimnida".
**V:** QSL-card. Rp (1 USD).

**Notes:** On SW since 30 October 2005. JSR Shiokaze (JSR = callsign of the prgr) is produced by the private "Investigation Commission on Missing Japanese Probably Related to North Korea" (COMJAN) and is aimed at reaching Japanese citizens believed to have been abducted to North Korea between 1977 and 1983. Jammed. Frequencies subject to change without notice.

## ECHO OF HOPE (VOH) (Clan)
🖃 c/o National Intelligence Service (NIS), Naegok-dong, Seocho-gu, Seoul, 06796, Rep. of Korea.
**W:** www.nis.go.kr (NIS); eng.nis.go.kr (NIS, English)
**L.P:** First Deputy Dir (NIS): Seo Dong Gu.
**SW:** [JNM] Hwaseong, Jeongnam (South Korea); 4 x 100kW; [NWN] Seoul, Taereung (Nowon district in Seoul) (South Korea): 2 x 10, 1 x 100kW (presumed power).
**kHz:** 3985, 4885, 5995, 6250, 6350, 9100

### Winter Schedule 2018/2019
| Korean | Days | Area | kHz |
|---|---|---|---|
| 0700-0100 | daily | KRE | 3985jnm, 4885nwn, 5995nm, 6250nwn, 6350jnm, 9100nwn |

**Ann:** Korean: "Huimang-e meari pangsong-imnida, VOH (vee-oh-aitch)".

**Notes:** Initially launched as "Voice of Reunification", re-named "Echo of Hope" in 1973. Operated by the South Korean National Intelligence Service (NIS), though claiming to be a prgr of the (non-existent) "General Union of Overseas Compatriots". Since 2008, the stn been using the English abbreviation "VOH" (="Voice of Hope") in the ID. Jammed.

## FREE NORTH KOREA RADIO (Clan)
🖃 402, Dongyang Building,181 Garogongwon-ro, Gangseo-gu, Seoul 07718, Rep. of Korea.
☎ +82 2 63965259, +82 2 26990977. 🖷 +82 2 64390968, +82 2 26990978.
**E:** mini6915@hanmail.net **W:** www.fnkradio.com
**Webcast:** D
**L.P:** Pres: Kim Seong Min.
**kHz:** 7610

### Winter Schedule 2018/2019
| Korean | Days | Area | kHz |
|---|---|---|---|
| 1200-1300 | daily | KRE | 7610tac |

**Ann:** Korean: "Daehan Minguk Seoul-eso bonaeneun Jayu Bukhan Bangsong-imnida".
**V:** QSL-letter.

**Notes:** On SW since 15 Dec 2005. Founded on 20 April 2004 as Internet-based radio prgr by Kim Seong Min, a defector from North Korea. Funded by the U.S. foundation "National Endowment for Democracy" (U.S. Congress grants). Jammed.

## FREEDOM FM RADIO (Clan)
🖃 c/o National Intelligence Service (NIS), Naegok-dong, Seocho-gu, Seoul, 06796, Rep. of Korea.
**W:** www.nis.go.kr (NIS); eng.nis.go.kr (NIS, English)
**L.P:** First Deputy Dir (NIS): Seo Dong Gu.
**FM/DAB:** FM: 94.5MHz/97.7MHz/100.6MHz/103.1MHz. Txs are located in South Korea, near the North Korean border.

**Notes:** First heard in May 1999. Operated by the South Korean National Intelligence Service (NIS), though until around 2014 claiming to be a prgr of the (non-existent) "Young Men's Hangyeore Fellowship Association" (Hangyeore Sarang Cheongnyon Moim). On the air 0500-0100. Jammed.

## NORTH KOREA REFORM RADIO (Clan)
🖃 11, Cheonggu-ro 14-gil, Jung-gu (Songwon Buiding) floor 3, Seoul 04613, Republic of Korea.
☎ +82 2 22426512. 🖷 +82 2 22426512.
**E:** nkreform@naver.com **W:** www.nkreform.com; eng.nkreform.com
**Webcast:** D
**L.P:** Pres: Kim Seung Chul.
**kHz:** 7495, 7580

### Winter Schedule 2018/2019
| Korean | Days | Area | kHz |
|---|---|---|---|
| 1430-1530 | daily | KRE | 7580tac |
| 2030-2130 | daily | KRE | 7495tac |

**Ann:** Korean: "Inmini baraneun saeroun sesang-ul hamgge ggumgguneun Joseon Gyaehyeok Bangsong-imnida".
**V:** QSL-card.

**Notes:** On SW since December 2007. Produced by the NGO "North Korea Development Institute" (NKDI), funded by the U.S. foundation "National Endowment for Democracy" (U.S. Congress grants). Jammed.

## RADIO FREE KOREA (Clan)
🖃 c/o National Intelligence Service (NIS), Naegok-dong, Seocho-gu, Seoul, 06796, Rep. of Korea.
**W:** www.nis.go.kr (NIS); eng.nis.go.kr (NIS, English)
**L.P:** First Deputy Dir (NIS): Seo Dong Gu.
**MW:** [GOY] Seoul, Goyang (South Korea): 1143kHz 100kW. (estimated power)
**kHz:** 1143

### Winter Schedule 2018/2019
| Korean | Days | Area | kHz |
|---|---|---|---|
| 0700-0100 | daily | KRE | 1143goy |

**Ann:** Korean: "Jayu Koria Bangsong-imnida. RFK"; ""Koria Mirae Yeondae-eseo bonae deurineun Radio Free Korea, Jayu Koria Bangsong-imnida".

**Notes:** On air since 25 June 2014. Operated by the South Korean National Intelligence Service (NIS), though claiming to be a prgr of the (non-existent) organisation "Korea Future Solidarity". Jammed.

## VOICE OF FREEDOM (Clan)
🖃 c/o Ministry of National Defence (MND), 1, Yongsan-dong 3-ga, Yongsan-gu, Seoul, 04383, Rep. of Korea.
☎ +82 2 7484662.
**W:** www.mnd.go.kr (MND)
**SW:** [JAN] Hwaseong, Jangan (South Korea): 1 x 10kW. (presumed power)
**FM/DAB:** FM: 101.7MHz (Baengnyeongdo Island); 103.1MHz (Ganghwado Island & Mt. Daeamsan); 107.3MHz (Mt. Hwaaksan). Txs are located in South Korea, near the North Korean border.
**kHz:** 6045

### Winter Schedule 2018/2019
| Korean | Days | Area | kHz |
|---|---|---|---|
| 0300-0800 | daily | KRE | 6045jan±,* |
| 0900-1400 | daily | KRE | 6045jan±,* |
| 1500-2000 | daily | KRE | 6045jan±,* |
| 2100-0200 | daily | KRE | 6045jan±,* |

**Key:** ± Variable frequency; * Alternate frequencies: 5920/5940/6020/6135kHz.

**Ann:** Korean: "Yeogineun Daehan Minguk Seoul-eseo bonae deurineun Jayu-ui Sori Bangsong-imnida".

**Notes:** Launched on FM on 24 May 2010 and on SW in August 2014 (tests since May 2014). Operated by the Ministry of National Defense. Jammed. Schedule on FM: as SW.

## VOICE OF THE PEOPLE (Clan)

✉ c/o National Intelligence Service (NIS), Naegok-dong, Seocho-gu, Seoul, 06796, Rep. of Korea.
**W:** www.nis.go.kr (NIS); eng.nis.go.kr (NIS, English)
**LP:** First Deputy Dir (NIS): Seo Dong Gu.
**SW:** [GOY] Seoul, Goyang (South Korea): 6 x 50kW. (presumed power)
**kHz:** 3480, 3910, 3930, 4450, 6520, 6600

### Winter Schedule 2018/2019

| Korean | Days | Area | kHz |
|---|---|---|---|
| 0500-2300 | daily | KRE | 3480goy, 3910goy, 3930goy, 4450goy, 6520goy, 6600goy |

**Ann:** Korean: "Joseon Nodongja Chongdongmaeng-eseo bonae deurineun Inmin-ui Sori pangsong-imnida".

**Notes:** On air since 25 June 1985. Operated by the South Korean National Intelligence Service (NIS), although claiming to be a prgr of the "Korean Workers Union". Jammed.

---

## Target: KOREA, South (KOR)

## ECHO OF UNIFICATION (TONG–IL–E MEARI PANGSONG) (Clan)

✉ Pyongyang, Democratic People's Republic of Korea.
**E:** webmaster@tongilvoice.com **W:** www.tongilvoice.com
**Webcast:** D/P
**SW:** Uses txs provided by the North Korean Ministry of Post & Telecommunications.
**FM/DAB:** FM: 89.4/97.0/97.8MHz (Haeju, North Korea, 10kW).
**kHz:** 3945, 3970, 6250

### Winter Schedule 2018/2019

| Korean | Days | Area | kHz |
|---|---|---|---|
| 0400-0600 | daily | KOR | 3945pyo, 3970chj±,†, 6250pyo |
| 1200-1400 | daily | KOR | 3945pyo, 3970chj±,†, 6250pyo |
| 2200-0000 | daily | KOR | 3945pyo, 3970chj±,†, 6250pyo |

**Key:** ± Variable frequency; † Irregular.
**Ann:** Korean: "Yeogineun Tong-il-e Meari Pangsong-imnida".
**IS:** "We Are One".

**Notes:** On the air since 1 Dec 2012. Produced by the "Committee for the Peaceful Reunification of the Fatherland". The FM txs follow the same schedule as SW. Jammed.

---

## Target: NIGERIA (NIG)

## DANDAL KURA RADIO INTERNATIONAL

✉ 37 Cemetery Road, Maiduguri, Borno State, Nigeria.
☎ +234 809 4818092.
**E:** info@dandalkura.com
**W:** www.dandalkura.com; www.facebook.com/dandalkura
**Webcast:** L
**LP:** MD/CEO: Faruk Dalhatu.
**kHz:** 7315, 7455, 9620, 9770

### Winter Schedule 2018/2019

| Kanuri/English | Days | Area | kHz |
|---|---|---|---|
| 0500-0600 | daily | NIG | 7315nau |
| 0600-0700 | daily | NIG | 9620nau |
| 1800-1900 | daily | NIG | 9770iss |
| 1900-2000 | daily | NIG | 7455iss |

**Notes:** Funded by the USAID and established with support of Freedom Radio (an independent local radio network in Northern Nigeria and VOA affiliate, owned by Film Lab & Production Services Ltd). Target audience is the Kanuri and Hausa speaking population in areas under influence of Boko Haram in and around the Lake Chad Basin (parts of Nigeria, Chad, Niger and Cameroon). On SW since January 2015. Dandal Kura translates as "meeting place".

## RADIO NA GASKIYA (RADIO TRUTH) ‡ (Clan)

✉ Based in Kano state, Nigeria.
**W:** www.facebook.com/Radio-Nigeria-Hausa-service-506033216438570
**W:** www.ipob.org (IPOB)
**LP:** Media & Publicity Secretary (IPOB): Emma Powerful.
**Key:** ‡ Inactive on SW at time of publication.
**Ann:** Hausa: "Radio Na Gaskiya".

**Notes:** On SW since 6 January 2018. Opposition station, produced by the organisation "Indigenous People of Biafra" (IPOB), and targeting the Hausa population in Northern Nigeria. Officially run under the brand "Radio Nigeria Hausa Service", but identifies on-air as "Radio Na Gaskiya" which translates as "Radio (Of) Truth".

---

## Target: PAKISTAN (PAK)

## RADIO SEDAYEE KASHMIR (Clan)

✉ c/o All India Radio (AIR), Akashvani Bhavan, Sansad Marg, New Delhi-110001, India.
**SW:** Via txs of All India Radio (AIR).
**kHz:** 4870, 6030, 6100

### Winter Schedule 2018/2019

| Dogri | Days | Area | kHz |
|---|---|---|---|
| 0310-0330 | daily | PAK | 4870del, 6030del |
| 0810-0830 | daily | PAK | 6100del |
| 1510-1530 | daily | PAK | 4870del, 6030del |
| **Kashmiri** | **Days** | **Area** | **kHz** |
| 0230-0310 | daily | PAK | 4870del, 6030del |
| 0730-0810 | daily | PAK | 6100del |
| 1430-1510 | daily | PAK | 4870del, 6030del |

**Ann:** Urdu: "Ye Radio Sedayee Kashmir".

**Notes:** On air since early 2003. Radio Sedayee Kashmir is a prgr representing the views of the Indian government in the dispute with Pakistan over Kashmir.

---

## Target: RWANDA (RRW)

## RADIO ITAHUKA

✉ Based in Washington D.C., USA.
☎ +1 202 5096774. (Cell)
**E:** radioitahuka@gmail.com
**W:** www.blogtalkradio.com/radioitahuka
**Webcast:** D/P
✉ 1200 G St NW, Suite 800, Washington, DC 20005, USA. (RNC)
☎ +1 508 3358771. (Cell, RNC)
**E:** jpturayishimye@yahoo.com (RNC) **W:** www.rncihuriro.com (RNC)
**kHz:** 15420

### Winter Schedule 2018/2019

| Kinyarwanda | Days | Area | kHz |
|---|---|---|---|
| 1800-1900 | .....s. | RRW | 15420mdc |

**Notes:** Produced by the U.S. based oppositional group "Rwanda National Congress" (RNC). On SW since November 2016.

## Target:SOMALIA (SOM)

**RADIO ERGO**
⌧ P.O.Box 2234, 00621 Nairobi, Kenya.
☎ +254 20 4002102.
**E:** info@radioergo.org **W:** www.radioergo.org
**Webcast:** D/P
⌧ Nørregade 18, DK-1165 København K, Denmark. (IMS)
☎ +45 88327000. ▤ +45 33120099.
**E:** info@mediasupport.org **W:** www.mediasupport.org
**LP:** Prgr Mgr: Louise Tunbridge.
**kHz:** *17845*

| | **Winter Schedule 2018/2019** | | |
|---|---|---|---|
| **Somali** | **Days** | **Area** | **kHz** |
| 1200-1300 | daily | SOM | 17845dha |

**Ann:** Somali: "Halkani waa Radio Ergo".
**V:** QSL-card

**Notes:** Produced by IMS Productions Aps (a branch of IMS - International Media Support). Originally aired under the name "IRIN Radio" by the UN Office for the Coordination of Humanitarian Affairs (OCHA) since 2008. IMS Productions took over the operation on 1 July 2011 and rebranded the service "Radio Ergo".

## Target: SOUTH SUDAN (SSD)

**EYE RADIO**
⌧ P.O. Box 425, Plot 48, Block 1 Korok, Juba, South Sudan.
☎ +211 922486980.
**E:** eyemediahr@eyeradio.org **W:** www.eyeradio.org
**Webcast:** L
**LP:** Chmn (Eye Media): Tombura Michael Renzi; CEO (Eye Media): Stephen Omiri.
**FM/DAB:** FM: See National Radio section (South Sudan).
**kHz:** *11620, 15410*

| | **Winter Schedule 2018/2019** | | |
|---|---|---|---|
| **Arabic/English/ Others** | **Days** | **Area** | **kHz** |
| 0400-0500 | mtwtf.. | SSD | 11620mdc |
| 1500-1600 | mtwtf.. | SSD | 15410smg |
| 1600-1800 | mtwtf.. | SSD | 15410iss |

**Notes:** Eye Radio began in 2010 as "SRS FM", a local FM stn set up in Juba by the U.S.-funded, originally Nairobi-based Sudan Radio Service (SRS). It was re-branded "Eye Radio" in August 2012. Since then it is produced by the U.S.-funded NGO "Eye Media". The stn can be heard 24/7 on FM in large parts of the country; complementing SW trs began in April 2016. The SW broadcasts are in Arabic, Bari, Dinka, Lotuhu, Nuer, Shilluk, Zande, as well as in English.

**RADIO TAMAZUJ**
⌧ c/o Free Press Unlimited, Witte Kruislaan 55, 1217 AM Hilversum, The Netherlands
☎ +31 35 6254340.
**E:** radiotamazuj@gmail.com **W:** radiotamazuj.org
**Webcast:** D
**E:** info@freepressunlimited.org **W:** www.freepressunlimited.org
**LP:** Dir: Hildebrand Bijleveld.
**kHz:** *6020, 7315, 11705, 15550*

| | **Winter Schedule 2018/2019** | | |
|---|---|---|---|
| **Arabic (Juba)** | **Days** | **Area** | **kHz** |
| 0330-0400 | daily | SSD | 6020mdc, 7315smg |
| 1500-1530 | daily | SSD | 11705mdc, 15550smg |

**Key:** ± Variable frequency.
**Ann:** Arabic (Juba): "Radio Tamazuj".
**V:** QSL-card.

**Notes:** Radio Tamazuj (Tamazuj meaning "intermingling" or "mixing" in Arabic) was launched in November 2011 as broadcast within the timeslot of the sister prgr R. Dabanga (which is targeting Sudan); on air as separate prgr since January 2012. Produced by the Dutch foundation "Free Press Unlimited". The prgr targets audiences in South Sudan and the southern states of Sudan, with particular focus on the border areas between both countries. Jammed.

## Target: SUDAN (SDN)

**RADIO DABANGA**
⌧ c/o Free Press Unlimited, Weesperstraat 3, 1018 DN Amsterdam, The Netherlands.
☎ +31 20 8000470.
**E:** radiodabanga@gmail.com **W:** www.dabangasudan.org
**Webcast:** D
**E:** info@freepressunlimited.org **W:** www.freepressunlimited.org
**LP:** Editor-in-chief: Kamal Elsadig.
**kHz:** *7315, 9600, 15350, 15550*

| | **Winter Schedule 2018/2019** | | |
|---|---|---|---|
| **Arabic (Darfuri)** | **Days** | **Area** | **kHz** |
| 0430-0500 | daily | SDN | 7315iss, 9600mey |
| 1530-1600 | daily | SDN | 15350mey, 15550iss |

**Ann:** All languages: "Radio Dabanga".
**V:** QSL-card.

**Notes:** On air since 15 November 2008, produced by the Dutch foundation "Free Press Unlimited". Radio Dabanga is aimed at listeners in the Darfur area in Western Sudan. The broadcasts are in Standard Arabic, Darfuri Arabic, Fur, Masalit and Zaghawa. Occasionally Jammed.

## Target: TURKEY (TUR)

**DENGÊ WELAT**
⌧ Based in Belgium.
☎ +32 53 415717.
**W:** denge-welat.org; radyo-welat.com; radyowelat.com
**Webcast:** D/L
**SAT:** Eutelsat 7WA/Hot Bird 13C.
**kHz:** *9525, 11530*

| | **Winter Schedule 2018/2019** | | |
|---|---|---|---|
| **Kurdish** | **Days** | **Area** | **kHz** |
| 0330-0600 | daily | ME | 9525iss |
| 0600-1500 | daily | ME | 11530kch |
| 1500-1600 | daily | ME | 11530iss |
| 1500-2200 | daily | ME | 9525iss |

**Ann:** Kurdish: "Era Dengê Welat".

**Notes:** Dengê Welat ("Voice of Homeland") replaced Dengê Kurdistanê on 1 Oct 2017. Originally launched as Dengê Mezopotamya on 1 Sep 2012 (on shortwave since 7 Sep). The station broadcasts in various Kurdish dialects and is targeting Kurdish listeners across the Near East & Caucasus (Turkey, Iran, Iraq, Syria, Armenia, Azerbaijan, Georgia).

## Target: UGANDA (UGA)

**RADIO MUNANSI ‡**
⌧ 7035 Laurel Canyon Blvd, #15333, North Hollywood, CA 91615, USA.
☎ +1 818 5348273. (Studio)
**E:** blukandamanda@radiomunansi.com **W:** radiomunansi.com; www. facebook.com/radiomunansi.lukandamanda
**Webcast:** L

**Key:** ‡ Inactive on SW at time of publication.

**Notes:** Internet based opposition radio station, on SW intermittently since May 2016.

---

## Target: VIETNAM (VTN)

**QUÊ ME RADIO ‡**
✉ BP 60063, F-94472 Boissy Saint Léger Cedex, France.
☎ +33 145983085. 🖷 +33 145983261.
**E:** queme.democracy@gmail.com; queme@free.fr
**W:** www.queme.net
**Webcast:** D
**Key:** ‡ Inactive on SW at time of publication.
**V:** QSL-email.

**Notes:** Produced by the non-profit organisation "Action for Democracy in Vietnam" and its international organ "Vietnam Committee on Human Rights".

**RADIO DLSN**
✉ Vietnam Democracy Radio, P.O. Box 612882, San Jose, CA 95161, USA.
☎ +1 408 6639860.
**E:** lienlac.dlsn@gmail.com
**W:** radiodlsn.com; www.facebook.com/radiodlsn
**Webcast:** D
**kHz:** *9670*

| Winter Schedule 2018/2019 | | | |
|---|---|---|---|
| Vietnamese | Days | Area | kHz |
| 1230-1300 | daily | VTN | 9670pao |

**Ann:** Vietnamese: "Đây là dây phát thanh Đáp Lời Sông Núi".

**Notes:** Radio DLSN (Đáp Lời Sông Núi - "Fatherland") was launched on 15 May 2011. Produced by the "Foundation for Democracy in Vietnam".

---

## Target: WESTERN SAHARA (AOE)

**NATIONAL RADIO OF THE SAHRAWI ARAB DEMOCRATIC REPUBLIC**
✉ Based in Rabouni, Algeria.
**W:** rasdradio.info
**Webcast:** D/L
✉ c/o Ambassade du République Arabe Sahraouie Démocratique, 1, Rue Franklin Roosevelt, 16000 Algiers, Algeria.
**L.P:** DG: Mohamed Salem Laabeid.
**MW:** [RBN] Rabouni (Algeria): 1550kHz 100kW (presumed to be run on reduced power).
**kHz:** *1550*

| Winter Schedule 2018/2019 | | | |
|---|---|---|---|
| Arabic | Days | Area | kHz |
| 0700-1300 | daily | NAf | 1550rbn† |
| 1700-2300 | daily | NAf | 1550rbn |

**Key:** † Irregular.
**Ann:** Arabic: "Huna el-estudiohaay al-markaziya al-wataniya, Sowt al-sha'ab a-Sahraui al-mukafa".
**V:** QSL-letter.

**Notes:** On air since 28 December 1975, founded by the "Polisario Front". Operated by the Ministry of Information of the government-in-exile of the Sahrawi Arab Democratic Republic, with approval by the Algerian authorities. Jammed.

---

## Target: YEMEN (YEM)

**RADIO AL–AZM (SAUDI BROADCASTING CORP. – SBC) (Gov)**
✉ See National Radio section (Saudi Arabia).

**MW:** See National Radio section. (Saudi Arabia)
**SW:** Via tx of SBC/Saudi Ministry of Culture & Information (Saudi Arabia). Location presumed to be Jeddah, but not confirmed at time of publication.
**FM/DAB:** FM: See National Radio section. (Saudi Arabia)
**kHz:** *11745*

| Winter Schedule 2018/2019 | | | |
|---|---|---|---|
| Arabic | Days | Area | kHz |
| 0000-2400 | daily | YEM | 11745jed |

**Notes:** On SW since 11 September 2017. Produced by Saudi Broadcasting Corporation - (SBC), for Saudi military personnel serving in Yemen and Southern Saudi Arabia.

**REPUBLIC OF YEMEN RADIO (RADIO SANA'A) (Gov)**
**kHz:** *11860*

| Winter Schedule 2018/2019 | | | |
|---|---|---|---|
| Arabic | Days | Area | kHz |
| 0900-0700 | daily | YEM | 11860jed |

**Notes:** Broadcasts in support of Yemeni president Hadi and the Aden-based provisional government. Appears to be a relocated service, formerly produced by the Yemen General Corp. for Radio&TV in Sana'a (after that the Sana'a broadcasting house came under rebel control). Possibly produced in state radio studios in Aden, or in Saudi Arabia. Assumed to be aired via a transmitter in Saudi Arabia.

**VOICE OF THE REPUBLIC (Clan)**
✉ Reported to be based in Al Mukha, Taizz Governate, Yemen.
**L.P:** Founder: Brig. Gen. Tariq Mohammed Abdullah Saleh.
**FM/DAB:** FM: 93.1MHz (Al Mukha, Taizz)
**Relayed Via:** Abu Dhabi Radio, Al-Dhabbaya, UAE (1170kHz, 800kW)
**kHz:** *1170*

| Winter Schedule 2018/2019 | | | |
|---|---|---|---|
| Arabic | Days | Area | kHz |
| 1500-0300 | daily | YEM | 1170dha* |

**Key:** * Times variable.
**Ann:** Arabic: "Idh'at Sowt-il Jumhuriya".

**Notes:** Broadcasts are in support of National Resistance Forces (RNF).

---

## INTERNATIONAL & CLANDESTINE UPDATES

Pdfs containing updates of the B18 schedules in this edition will be uploaded to *www.wrth.com* in early February 2019.

The A19 schedules will be uploaded in early May 2019, and an A19 update in mid-July 2019.

# Notes

# Religious Broadcasters Cross Reference Table

This table shows the names of religious broadcasters in the International Radio and COTB sections, together with a cross reference to enable the station and/or schedule to be looked up, by country. If a station is shown as not having a schedule under its entry, marked '✘', (because it is a relay station or similar), look in the 'Schedule Location' column, where you will find the name of the broadcaster and country where the schedule can be found (usually a parent broadcaster or station HQ)

| Broadcaster/Station | Broadcaster Country | Has own Schedule? | Schedule Location (if different) | Schedule Country | WRTH Section |
|---|---|---|---|---|---|
| AWR Asia/Pacific | THA | ✓ | | THA | International |
| Adventist World Radio (AWR) | USA | ✓ | | USA | International |
| Athmik Yatra Radio ‡ | IND | ✘ | ‡ No Schedule | — | International |
| AWR Africa | G | ✓ | | G | International |
| AWR Asia/Pacific | THA | ✓ | | THA | International |
| Bible Voice Broadcasting (BVB) | CAN | ✓ | | CAN | International |
| Caribbean Beacon (University Network Relay) | AIA | ✘ | University Network | USA | International |
| End Times Coming Radio | G | ✓ | | G | International |
| Evangelische Missions-Gemeinden | D | ✓ | | D | International |
| Family Radio | USA | ✓ | | USA | International |
| Far East Broadcasting Company Inc (FEBC) | USA | ✘ | HQ, no schedule | — | International |
| FEBA India | IND | ✓ | | IND | International |
| FEBA Pakistan | PAK | ✓ | | PAK | International |
| FEBC Korea | KOR | ✓ | | KOR | International |
| FEBC Philippines | PHL | ✓ | | PHL | International |
| Follow the Bible Ministries | USA | ✓ | | USA | International |
| Ibra Media | S | ✓ | | S | International |
| KNLS International | ALS | ✓ | | ALS | International |
| KSDA (AWR Asia/Pacific Relay Station) | GUM | ✘ | Adventist World R | USA | International |
| KTWR (TWR Relay Station) | GUM | ✘ | TWR Asia/Pacific | USA | International |
| KVOH - Voice of Hope | USA | ✓ | | USA | International |
| Living Water Ministry Broadcasting | USA | ✓ | | USA | International |
| Madagascar World Voice | MDG | ✓ | | MDG | International |
| Missionswerk Friedensstimme | D | ✓ | | D | International |
| Pan American Broadcasting | USA | ✓ | | USA | International |
| Radio HCJB Deutschland | D | ✓ | | D | International |
| Radio Sadaye Zindagi | CAN | ✓ | | CAN | International |
| Radio Veritas Asia | PHL | ✓ | | PHL | International |
| Reach Beyond | USA | ✓ | | USA | International |
| Reach Beyond Australia | AUS | ✓ | | AUS | International |
| Sawtu Linjiila (Voice of the Gospel) | CME | ✓ | | CME | International |
| Suab Xaa Moo Zoo | USA | ✓ | | USA | International |
| T8WH - World Harvest Radio (WHR) | PLW | ✓ | | PLW | International |
| Tartu Pereraadio | EST | ✘ | TWR Europe and CAMENA | AUT | International |
| The Overcomer Ministry | USA | ✓ | | USA | International |
| Trans World Radio (TWR) | USA | ✘ | HQ, no schedule | — | International |
| TWR Africa | AFS | ✓ | | AFS | International |
| TWR Asia | SNG | ✓ | | SNG | International |
| TWR Bonaire | BES | ✓ | | BES | International |
| TWR Europe and CAMENA | AUT | ✓ | | AUT | International |
| TWR India | IND | ✓ | | IND | International |
| TWR Relay Station | BEN | ✘ | TWR Africa | AFS | International |
| TWR Relay Station | SWZ | ✘ | TWR Africa | AFS | International |
| University Network | USA | ✓ | | USA | International |
| Vatican Radio | CVA | ✓ | | CVA | International |
| Voice of Hope - Africa | ZMB | ✓ | | ZMB | International |
| Voice of Hope - Middle East | ISR | ✓ | | ISR | International |
| Voice of the Martyrs Korea | KRE | ✓ | | KRE | C&OTB |
| Voice of Wilderness | KRE | ✓ | | KRE | C&OTB |
| Vozandes Media | EQA | ✓ | | EQA | International |
| WEWN - EWTN Shortwave Radio | USA | ✓ | | USA | International |
| WHRI - World Harvest Radio (WHR) | USA | ✓ | | USA | International |
| WINB | USA | ✓ | | USA | International |
| WJHR Radio International | USA | ✓ | | USA | International |
| WMLK ‡ | USA | ✘ | ‡ No Schedule | — | International |
| World Christian Broadcasting Inc. | USA | ✘ | HQ, no schedule | — | International |
| WRNO Worldwide | USA | ✓ | | USA | International |
| WTWW | USA | ✓ | | USA | International |
| WWCR Shortwave - World Wide Christian R. | USA | ✓ | | USA | International |

© WRTH Publications Ltd - November 2018
**Key:** ‡ Station inactive on MW/SW at time of publication

# FREQUENCY LISTS

## Section Contents

Features & Reviews

MW Listings:

Europe, Africa &
Middle East..........................522
East Asia & Pacific..............530
Central America,
Caribbean & Mexico...........544
South America...................554

SW Listing:

SW Stations of the World...571

International MW & SW
by Language:

Broadcasts in English........592
Broadcasts in French.........598
Broadcasts in German.......600
Broadcasts in Portuguese...600
Broadcasts in Spanish.......601

International DRM.............603

National Radio

International Radio

Frequency Lists

(For country codes and transmitter codes, please see the decode tables in the Reference section)

**Please note** that the North America MW listing has been removed in order to increase the number of MW stations in the main USA listing

National Television

Reference

# EUROPE, AFRICA & MIDDLE EAST

| kHz | kW | Ctry | Station, location |
|---|---|---|---|
| 25 | 300 | BLR | STFT Station, Vileyka (CW) |
| | 900 | RUS | STFT Station, 3 stns (CW) |
| 60 | 15 | G | STFT Station, Anthorn (CW) |
| 66.66 | 10 | RUS | STFT Station, Moscow (AM) |
| 77.5 | 50 | D | STFT Station, Mainflingen (CW/PSK) |
| 153 | | ALG | R. Algérienne 1, Béchar (inactive) |
| | 100 | NOR | NRK P1/Troms og Finnmark, Ingøy |
| | 200 | ROU | Antena Satelor, Brasov |
| 162 | 800 | F | STFT Station, Allouis |
| 171 | 1600 | MRC | Medi 1, Nador |
| 183 | 1500 | D | Europe 1, Felsberg |
| 189 | 150 | ISL | RUV Rás 1/2, Gufuskálar |
| 198 | | ALG | R. Algérienne 1, Ouargla (inactive) |
| | 50 | G | BBC R4, Burghead |
| | 500 | G | BBC R4, Droitwich |
| | 50 | G | BBC R4, Westerglen |
| 207 | 75 | ISL | RUV Rás 1/2, Eidar |
| | 400 | MRC | SNRT National Netw, Azilal (inactive) |
| 216 | 1400/900 | F | RMC Info, Roumoules |
| 225 | 1200/700 | POL | Polskie R. 1, Solec Kujawski |
| 234 | 1500 | LUX | RTL, Beidweiler |
| 243 | 50 | DNK | DR P4 news & weather, Kalundborg |
| 252 | 1500/750 | ALG | R. Algérienne 3, Tipaza |
| | 300/150 | IRL | RTE Radio 1, Summerhill (Clarkstown) |
| 270 | 50 | CZE | CRo 1, Uherské Hradiště (Topolná) |
| 531 | 600 | ALG | R. Algérienne Jil FM, F'Kirina |
| | 10 | ARS | SBA Quran prgr, Bisha |
| | 50 | BOT | R. Botswana, Maun |
| | 10 | E | RNE R. 5, Córdoba |
| | 20 | E | RNE R. 5, Oviedo |
| | 10 | E | RNE R. 5, Pamplona |
| | 10 | E | RNE R. 5, Pontevedra |
| | 10 | FRO | Kringvarp Føroya Útvarpið, Akraberg |
| | 600 | IRN | R. Iran, Iranshahr |
| | 50 | ISR | Kl Reshet Moresheet, Yavne |
| | 15 | ROU | Antena Satelor, Urziceni |
| | 15 | ROU | R. România Actualitati, Petrosani |
| 540 | 50 | E | OCR Catalunya, Barcelona |
| | 1000 | HNG | MR Kossuth R, Solt |
| | 600 | KWT | R. Kuwait Main prgr, Kabd |
| | 600 | MRC | SNRT National Netw./Reg, Sidi Bennour |
| | 10 | MWI | MBC R. 1, Mangochi |
| | 50 | NIG | Sokoto State BC "Rima R. ", Sokoto |
| | 50 | SDN | South Darfur State R, Nyala |
| 549 | 600 | ALG | R. Algérienne Jil FM, Sidi Hamadouche |
| | 1 | ARS | SBA R. Al-Azm, Jizan |
| | 30 | ARS | SBA R. Riyadh, 2 stns |
| | 2000 | ARS | SBA R. Riyadh, Qurayyat |
| | 20 | GAB | RTG 2, Oyem |
| | 25 | IRL | Spirit R, Carrickroe |
| | 400/100 | IRN | R. Iran, Sirjan |
| | 25 | NIG | Broadc. Sce of the Ekiti State, Ado |
| | 1 | RKS | R. Kosova 1, Priština |
| | 15 | SVN | R. Koper, Beli Kriz |
| | 720 | UKR | UR1, Mykolaiv |
| 558 | 10 | ALG | R. Algérienne 1/R. Ouargla, Touggourt |
| | 50 | BOT | R. Botswana, Muchenje |
| | 20 | E | RNE R. 5, A Coruña |
| | 20 | E | RNE R. 5, San Sebastián |
| | 50 | E | RNE R. 5, Valencia |
| | 100 | EGY | Educ./Youth&Sports prgr, Cairo (Abu Zaabal) |
| | 1 | G | Love Sport Radio, London |
| | 150 | IRN | R. Birjand, Bojd |

| kHz | kW | Ctry | Station, location |
|---|---|---|---|
| | 500 | IRN | R. Iran, Azarshahr |
| | 200 | IRN | R. Iran, Bushehr |
| | 50 | IRN | R. Iran, Chabahar |
| | 600 | IRN | R. Iran, Gonbad-e Kavus |
| | 200 | IRN | R. Iran, Habibabad (Isfahan) |
| | 100 | IRN | R. Iran, Hamadan |
| | 100 | IRN | R. Iran, Kiashahr |
| | 200 | IRN | R. Iran, Mashhad |
| | 50 | IRN | R. Iran, Sefiddasht (Shahrekord) |
| | 400 | IRN | R. Iran, Shiraz (Dehnow) |
| | 400 | IRN | R. Iran, Shushtar |
| | 600 | IRN | R. Iran, Tehran (Goldashteh) |
| | 50 | IRN | R. Iran, Yazd |
| | 50 | IRN | R. Iran, Zanjan |
| | 25 | KEN | KBC Western Sce, Kapsimotwa |
| | 10 | MWI | MBC R. 1, Karonga |
| | 500 | OMA | R. Sultanate of Oman, Bidiya |
| | 400 | ROU | R. România Actualitati, Tirgu Jiu |
| | 10 | SVN | MMR/R. Slovenija 1, Nemcavci |
| 567 | 25 | AFS | Cape Talk, Cape Town |
| | 20 | ARS | SBA Quran prgr, Abha/Afif |
| | 200 | ARS | SBA Quran prgr, Jeddah (Bahrah) |
| | 50 | E | RNE R. 5, Murcia |
| | 1 | I | Challenger R, Villa Estense |
| | 50 | KEN | KBC R. Taifa, Garissa |
| | 50 | NIG | Imo BC, Owerri |
| | 50 | NIG | Zamfara State R, Gusau |
| | 100 | ROU | R. România Actualitati, Brasov/Satu Mare |
| | 300 | SYR | Syrian R. 1, Damascus Adra |
| 576 | 50 | AFS | R. Veritas, Meyerton |
| | 400/200 | ALG | R. Algérienne R. Béchar |
| | 20 | ARS | SBA Quran prgr, Jizan |
| | 200 | BUL | Horizont, Vidin Gramada |
| | 20 | CNR | RNE R. Nacional, Las Palmas |
| | 100 | E | RNE R. 5, Barcelona |
| | 50 | IRN | R. Urmia, Maku |
| | 400/150 | IRN | VOIRI, Bandar-e Mahshahr |
| | 25 | NIG | FRCN Ibadan, Moniya |
| | 100 | OMA | R. Sultanate of Oman, Haima |
| | 100 | UGA | UBC West/Star FM, Mityana |
| 585 | 1200 | ARS | SBA R. Riyadh, Riyadh |
| | 600 | E | RNE R. Nacional, Madrid |
| | 2 | G | BBC R. Scotland, Dumfries |
| | 1000 | IRN | R. Farhang, Tehran (Gheslagh) |
| | 350 | TUN | ERTT National prgr, Gafsa |
| | 50 | TZA | Zanzibar BC, Chumbuni |
| 594 | 50 | ARS | SBA Call of Islam, Makkah |
| | 2000 | ARS | SBA R. Riyadh, Duba |
| | 10 | ARS | SBA R. Riyadh, Hofuf |
| | 50 | IRN | R. Iran, Zahedan |
| | 30 | MWI | MBC R. 1, Lilongwe |
| | 200 | NIG | FRCN Kaduna, Jaji |
| 595 | 50 | MRC | SNRT A/R, Oujda (alt. on 594kHz) |
| 603 | 100 | CYP | CyBC 3, Nicosia |
| | 10 | E | RNE R. 5, Palencia |
| | 50 | E | RNE R. 5, Sevilla |
| | 50 | EGY | ERTU Koran prgr, Sohag |
| | 2 | G | BBC R. 4, Newcastle |
| | 0.4 | G | Smooth R, Littlebourne |
| | 10 | IRN | R. Mashhad, Bajgiran |
| | 50 | NIG | Borno R. & TV Corp, Maiduguri |
| | 25 | NIG | Ogun State BC, Abeokuta |
| | 30 | ROU | Antena Satelor, Bucuresti |

| kHz | kW | Ctry | Station, location |
|---|---|---|---|
| | 100 | ROU | R. România Actualitati, Botosani/Oradea |
| | 15 | ROU | R. România Actualitati, Drobeta-T. Severin |
| | 100/10 | TZA | TBC Taifa, Dodoma |
| **612** | 5 | ARS | SBA R. Jeddah, Hail |
| | 15 | ARS | SBA R. Riyadh, Aflaj |
| | 100 | BHR | R. Bahrain Quran prgr, Manama |
| | 10 | E | RNE R. Nacional, Lleida |
| | 10 | E | RNE R. Nacional, Vitoria |
| | 600 | IRN | VOIRI, Qasr-e-Shirin |
| | 100 | JOR | R. Jordan Main prgr, Shobak |
| | 100 | KEN | KBC R. Taifa, Ngong |
| | 300 | MRC | SNRT National Netw, Sebaa-Aioun |
| | 50 | NIG | Kwara State BC, Ilorin |
| | 20 | RUS | R. Radonezh/Narodnoye R, Moskva |
| **621** | 200 | AFG | BBG Deewa R. /R. Mashal, Khost |
| | 300 | BEL | RTBFi, Wavre (expected to close) |
| | 100 | BOT | R. Botswana, Selebi-Phikwe |
| | 100 | CNR | RNE R. Nacional, Santa Cruz de Tenerife |
| | 10 | E | RNE R. Nacional, Avila |
| | 10 | E | RNE R. Nacional, Jaén |
| | 10 | E | RNE R. Nacional, Palma de Mallorca |
| | 1000 | EGY | ERTU Vo Arabs, Batra (Al-Mansura) |
| | 100 | EGY | ERTU Vo Arabs, Tanta |
| | 50 | IRN | R. Khalij e Fars, Bandar Abbas |
| | 150 | MDA | PGTRK R. 1 Plyus, Grigoriopol |
| | 50/10 | TZA | TBC Taifa, Mbeya |
| **630** | 10 | ARS | SBA Quran prgr, Najran |
| | 20 | ARS | SBA R. Jeddah, Jizan |
| | 2 | G | BBC R. Cornwall, Redruth |
| | 0.2 | G | BBC Three Counties R, Luton |
| | 10 | KWT | R. Kuwait Quran prgr, Magwa |
| | 50 | MDG | RNM, Antananarivo (irreg.) |
| | 0.01 | NOR | The Ferry, Bergen (irR.) |
| | 12 | POR | RTP Antena 1, Montemor-o-Velho/ Miranda do D. |
| | 50 | ROU | Antena Satelor, Voinesti |
| | 400 | ROU | R. Timisoara/R. R. Act, Ortisoara |
| | 300 | TUN | ERTT National prgr, Tunis Djedeida |
| | 300 | TUR | TRT 1/4/VOT Arabic, Mersin Kazanli |
| **639** | 500 | CYP | BBC Arabic Sce, Zakaki (Ladies Mile) |
| | 780 | CZE | CRo 2, Praha (Liblice)/Ostrava (Svinov) |
| | 300 | E | RNE R. Nacional, A Coruña |
| | 10 | E | RNE R. Nacional, Albacete |
| | 20 | E | RNE R. Nacional, Almeria |
| | 50 | E | RNE R. Nacional, Bilbao |
| | 50 | E | RNE R. Nacional, Zaragoza |
| | 400 | IRN | VOIRI, Bonab |
| | 50 | KEN | KBC Somali Sce, Garissa |
| | 100 | LSO | LNBS R. Lesotho, Lancer's Gap |
| | 50 | NIG | Kaduna State Media Corp, Katabu |
| | 100 | OMA | R. Sultanate of Oman, Buraimi |
| | 10 | SDN | North Kordofan State R, Al-Ubayyid |
| **648** | 2000 | ARS | SBA R. Riyadh, Jeddah (Khumra) |
| | 50 | BOT | R. Botswana, Mopipi |
| | 10 | E | RNE R. Nacional, Badajoz |
| | 1 | G | R. Caroline, Orfordness |
| | 10 | SVN | R. Murski Val, Nemcavci |
| **657** | 50 | AFS | R. Pulpit/R. Kansel, Meyerton |
| | 20 | ARS | SBA Quran prgr, Rafha |
| | 50 | E | RNE R. 5, Madrid |
| | 0.5 | G | BBC R. Cornwall, Bodmin |
| | 2 | G | BBC R. Wales, Wrexham |
| | 100 | I | RAI Radiouno/Reg, Pisa |
| | 100 | IRN | R. Gilan, Kiashahr |
| | 100 | IRN | R. Zahedan, Zahedan |
| | 100 | ISR | KI Reshet Bet, Yavne |
| | 100 | NIG | FRCN Ibadan, Ibadan |
| | 100 | UAE | Asianet R, Al-Dhabbiya |
| | 25 | UKR | UR1, Chernivtsi (inactive) |
| **666** | 10 | ALG | R. Algérienne 1/R. Tindouf |

| kHz | kW | Ctry | Station, location |
|---|---|---|---|
| | 50 | E | SER R. Barcelona, Barcelona |
| | 0.5 | G | R. York, Fulford |
| | 50 | IRN | R. Fars, Abadeh |
| | 60 | IRN | R. Fars, Darab |
| | 150 | IRN | R. Fars, Lamerd/Lar/Qir |
| | 400 | IRN | R. Fars, Shiraz (Dehnow) |
| | 1 | ISL | RUV Rás 1/2, Reykjavík |
| | 52 | POR | RTP Antena 1, 5 stns |
| | 10 | SDN | Kassala State R, Kassala |
| | 100 | SYR | Syrian R. Vo Youth, Damascus Adra |
| **675** | 25 | ARS | SBA R. Riyadh, Abha/Afif |
| | 0.1 | HOL | Hotradio Classics, Emmeloord |
| | 0.1 | HOL | Hotradio Hits, Bornerbroek |
| | 0.1 | HOL | R. Babylona, Musselkanaal |
| | 0.1 | HOL | Radio Nostalgie, Kollumerzwaag |
| | 0.1 | HOL | Stichting Haags R. Erfgoed, Wassenaar (F.PI.) |
| | 0.05 | HOL | Stichting Middengolf, Utrecht (F.PI.) |
| | 0.1 | HOL | Unique, Wijchen |
| | 50 | KEN | KBC R. Taifa, Marsabit |
| | 100 | LBY | Vo Homeland, Benghazi (inactive) |
| | 50 | MWI | MBC R. 1, Ekwendeni |
| | 600 | QAT | Qatar RTC, Al Arish |
| **684** | 200 | ARS | SBA R. Jeddah, Jeddah (Bahrah) |
| | 10 | ARS | SBA R. Jeddah, Riyadh |
| | 200 | E | RNE R. Nacional, Sevilla |
| | 100 | ETH | R. Ethiopia, Metu |
| | 50 | IRN | R. Mashhad, Kashmar |
| | 100 | IRN | R. Mashhad, Mashhad |
| | 10 | MAU | MBC R. Maurice, Malherbes |
| | 10 | RUS | R. Radonezh, Olgino (Sankt-Peterburg) |
| | 10 | TUN | ERTT National prgr, Medenine |
| **693** | 10 | ALG | R. Algérienne 1/R. Adrar, Reggane |
| | 5 | ALG | R. Algérienne 2, Aboudid (inactive) |
| | 25 | BOT | R. Botswana, Shakawe |
| | 5 | E | RNE R. Nacional, Boal |
| | 20 | E | RNE R. Nacional, Toledo |
| | 10 | E | RNE R. Nacional, Tortosa |
| | 50/1 | G | BBC R. 5 Live, 10 stns |
| | 150 | G | BBC R. 5 Live, Droitwich |
| | | GRC | Diavlos 1, Athína |
| | 100 | IRN | R. Khalij e Fars, Bandar Lengeh |
| | 40 | SSD | South Sudan BC, Juba (inactive) |
| **702** | 50 | AFS | LM Radio, Springs (Johannesburg) |
| | 25 | ALG | R. Algérienne 1/R. Laghouat |
| | 50 | ARS | SBA R. Jeddah, Bisha/Duba |
| | 10 | EGY | ERTU Reg./Koran prgr, Asswan |
| | 10 | EGY | ERTU Reg./Koran prgr, El-Kharga |
| | 500 | IRN | VOIRI, Kiashahr |
| | 800 | OMA | BBC Arabic Service, A'Seela |
| | 5 | SVK | SR R. Patria/Devín, Kosice |
| | 600 | TUR | TRT 1, Istanbul Catalca (inactive) |
| **711** | 25 | E | COPE Murcia |
| | 100 | EGY | ERTU Youth & Sports prgr, Tanta |
| | 600/200 | IRN | R. Ahvaz, Ahvaz |
| | 300 | MRC | SNRT National Netw./R, Laâyoune |
| | 50 | ROU | R. România Actualitati, Sighetul Marmatiei |
| | 100/10 | TZA | TBC Taifa, Kigoma |
| | 200 | YEM | YRTC General prgr, San'a (inactive) |
| **720** | 10 | CNR | RNE R. 5, Santa Cruz de Tenerife |
| | 500 | CYP | BBC Arabic Sce, Zakaki (Ladies Mile) |
| | 10/0.3 | G | BBC R. 4, Lisnagarvey + 2 stns |
| | 750 | IRN | R. Iran, Mahidasht |
| | 400 | IRN | R. Mashhad/VOIRI, Taybad |
| | 40 | POR | RTP Antena 1, 4 stns |
| | 40 | ROU | R. România Actualitati, Isaccea + 2 stns |
| | 50/10 | TZA | TBC Taifa, Mwanza |
| **729** | 25 | AFS | Cape Pulpit/Kaapse Kansel, Cape Town |
| | 10 | E | RNE R. Nacional, Alicante |
| | 10 | E | RNE R. Nacional, Cuenca |
| | 20 | E | RNE R. Nacional, Logroño |

| kHz | kW | Ctry | Station, location |
|-----|-----|------|-------------------|
| | 20 | E | RNE R. Nacional, Málaga |
| | 100 | E | RNE R. Nacional, Oviedo |
| | 10 | E | RNE R. Nacional, Valladolid |
| | 0.2 | G | BBC Essex, Manningtree |
| | 70 | GRC | ERT1, Athína |
| | | GRC | Studio 1, Athína |
| | 50 | NIG | Kano State BC, Jogana |
| 738 | 5 | ALG | R. Algérienne 1/R. Illizi, In Amenas |
| | 600 | E | RNE R. Nacional, Barcelona |
| | 0.04 | G | BBC Hereford & W, Worcester |
| | 50 | IRN | R. Bushehr, Dayyer |
| | 10 | ISR | KI Arabic prgr, Akko |
| | 50 | MOZ | Antena Nacional, Maputo (Joannisse) |
| | 100 | OMA | R. Sultanate of Oman, Salalah |
| | 5 | RUS | WRN Relay, Kurkino (Moskva) |
| 747 | 10 | ARS | SBA R. Al-Azm, Najran |
| | 10 | ARS | SBA R. Jeddah, Buraidah |
| | 25 | CNR | RNE R. 5, Las Palmas (inactive) |
| | 10 | E | RNE R. 5, Cádiz |
| | 0.1 | HOL | Cupra Radio, Emmer-Compascuum |
| | 0.05 | HOL | Different R. 747 AM, Nijkerk |
| | 0.1 | HOL | Groeistad R, Wassenaar |
| | 0.1 | HOL | R. 0511/Seagull, Harlingen |
| | 0.1 | HOL | R. Overland, Maastricht |
| | 0.1 | HOL | Radio 4 Brainport, Waalre |
| | 0.1 | HOL | Salland 747 AM, Deventer |
| | 150 | IRN | R. Kerman, Sirjan |
| | 100 | KEN | KBC Central Sce, Ngong |
| | 60 | NIG | Nagarta R, Kaduna |
| | 10 | SDN | Khartoum State R, Khartoum |
| | 5 | SDN | Red Sea State R, Port Sudan |
| 756 | 10 | EGY | ERTU Reg./Koran prgr, Qena |
| | 2 | G | BBC R 4, Redruth |
| | 1 | G | R. Cumbria, Carlisle |
| | 200/50 | IRN | R. Jahanbin, Shahr-e-Kord |
| | 10 | MWI | MBC R. 1, Blantyre |
| | 100 | NIG | R. Oyo, Ibadan |
| | 2 | POR | RTP Antena 1, Lamego |
| | 400 | ROU | R. România Actualitati, Lugoj (Boldur) |
| 765 | 50 | ARS | SBA Quran prgr, 3 stns |
| | 0.5 | G | BBC Essex, Chelmsford |
| | 600 | IRN | R. Iran/VOIRI, Chabahar |
| | 50 | MOZ | EP de Nampula, Nampula |
| | 50 | SDN | SRTC General prgr, Khartoum Soba |
| | 40 | UKR | R. Maiak, Odesa (inactive) |
| 774 | 40 | E | RNE R. Nacional, 4 stns |
| | 60 | E | RNE R. Nacional, Cáceres |
| | 20 | E | RNE R. Nacional, Ourense |
| | 50 | E | RNE R. Nacional, San Sebastián |
| | 100 | E | RNE R. Nacional, Valencia |
| | 1000 | EGY | ERTU Middle East prgr, Alexandria (Abis) |
| | 1 | G | BBC R4, Enniskillen/Plymouth |
| | 0.5 | G | R. Leeds/BBC Asian Network, Farnley |
| | 0.1 | G | Smooth R, Gloucester |
| | 100 | IRN | R. Markazi, Arak |
| 783 | 5 | ALG | R. Algérienne 1/R. Illizi, Djanet |
| | 10 | ALG | R. Algérienne 1/R. Souf, El Oued |
| | 100 | ARS | SBA Call of Islam, Ras al-Khair |
| | 50 | E | COPE, Barcelona |
| | 150 | IRN | R. Zahedan, Iranshahr |
| | 50 | MTN | R. Mauritanie, Nouakchott (inactive) |
| | 5 | SDN | River Nile State R, Atbara |
| | 300 | SYR | Syrian R. 1, Tartus Besira |
| 792 | 50 | ARS | SBA Quran prgr, Jeddah (An-Nuziah) |
| | 5 | CZE | R. Dechovka, Hradec Králové (Stěžery) |
| | 50 | E | SER R. Sevilla |
| | 1 | G | BBC R. Foyle, Londonderry |
| | 0.3 | G | Smooth R, Bedford |
| | 50 | IRN | R. Zanjan, Sohravard |
| | 20 | IRQ | IMN Republic of Iraq R, Baghdad |

| kHz | kW | Ctry | Station, location |
|-----|-----|------|-------------------|
| 801 | 100 | BHR | R. Bahrain General prgr, Manama |
| | 10 | E | RNE R. Nacional, Burgos |
| | 10 | E | RNE R. Nacional, Castello |
| | 25 | E | RNE R. Nacional, Ciudad Real |
| | 10 | E | RNE R. Nacional, Girona |
| | 20 | E | RNE R. Nacional, Lugo |
| | 10 | E | RNE R. Nacional, Zamora |
| | 100 | ETH | Vo Amhara State, Bahir Dar (Zege) |
| | 2 | G | R. Devon, Barnstaple |
| | 1 | NIG | R. Kebbi, Zuru |
| | 20 | NIG | Yobe BC, Damaturu |
| 810 | 20 | ARS | SBA Quran prgr, Hafar al-Batin |
| | 5 | ARS | SBA R. Jeddah, Abha |
| | 20 | E | SER R. Madrid |
| | 100 | G | BBC R. Scotland, Burghead |
| | 5 | G | BBC R. Scotland, Redmoss |
| | 100 | G | BBC R. Scotland, Westerglen |
| | 100 | IRN | R. Lorestan, Khorramabad |
| | 100 | MKD | MR1/R. Makedonija, Sveti Nikole |
| | 50 | MOZ | EP de Gaza, Xai-Xai |
| | 10 | MWI | MBC R. 1, Bangula |
| | 200/50 | UAE | Pravasi Bharathi, Maqta (AM/DRM) |
| 819 | 1000 | EGY | ERTU General prgr, Batra (Al-Mansura) |
| | 30 | IRN | R. Tabaristan, Sari |
| | 10 | MAU | MBC R. Mauritius, Malherbes |
| | 10 | SDN | Northern State R, Dongola |
| 828 | 25 | AFS | Magic 828, Cape Town (Klipheuwel) |
| | 1 | AZR | RDP Açores, Monte das Cruzes |
| | 5 | E | Hit FM Catalunya, Terrassa |
| | 100 | ETH | R. Ethiopia, Arba Minch |
| | 0.2 | G | BBC Asian Network, Sedgley |
| | 0.1 | G | R. Aire 2, Leeds |
| | 0.3 | G | Smooth R, Bournemouth |
| | 0.2 | G | Smooth R, Luton |
| | | GRC | Studio 54, Athína |
| | 0.1 | HOL | Hotradio Hits, Huissen |
| | 0.05 | HOL | Quality RTV, Utrecht (F.Pl.) |
| | 0.1 | HOL | R. Bontekoe, Hoorn |
| | 0.1 | HOL | R. JND, Best |
| | 0.1 | HOL | Wereldstad Radio, Rotterdam |
| | 1 | I | Z100, Pavia |
| | 50 | IRN | R. Birjand, Tabas |
| | 100 | NIG | FRCN Enugu |
| | 10 | RUS | Rgazeta Slovo/Pravoslavnoye R, Skt-P. |
| 837 | 5 | ALG | R. Algérienne 3, Béchar (inactive) |
| | 10 | CNR | COPE Las Palmas, Gran Canaria (inactive) |
| | 10 | E | COPE, Burgos |
| | 5 | E | COPE, El Ferrol |
| | 10 | E | COPE, Sevilla |
| | 100 | ERI | VO the Broad Masses 2, Asmara (alt. fq 840kHz) |
| | 100 | ETH | R. Oromiya, Robe (Bale) |
| | 0.5 | G | BBC Asian Netw, Freemen's Common |
| | 1 | G | R. Cumbria, Barrow |
| | 300 | IRN | R. Isfahan, Habibabad |
| | 1 | TZA | TBC Taifa, Dar es Salaam |
| | 150 | UKR | UR1,Taranivka (inactive) |
| | 30 | YEM | YRTC General prgr, San'a (inactive) |
| 846 | 50 | AFS | Umhlobo Wenene FM, Komga (irR.) |
| | 20 | ARS | SBA Quran prgr, Buraida |
| | 0.3 | DNK | NB24, København (F.Pl.) |
| | 1 | I | Challenger R, Villa Estense |
| | 3 | IRL | R. North, Redcastle |
| | 50 | IRN | R. Tabriz, Miyaneh |
| | 20 | UAE | Holy Quran R, Umm al Qiwain |
| 855 | 100 | ARS | SBA Quran prgr, Ras al-Khair |
| | 50 | E | RNE R. Nacional, 5 stns |
| | 300 | E | RNE R. Nacional, Murcia |
| | 20 | E | RNE R. Nacional, Pontevedra |
| | 50 | E | RNE R. Nacional, Santander |

| kHz | kW | Ctry | Station, location |
|-----|-----|------|-------------------|
| | 20 | E | RNE R. Nacional, Tarragona |
| | 100 | ETH | R. Ethiopia, Harar |
| | 1 | G | BBC R. Lancashire, Preston |
| | 1.5 | G | BBC R. Norfolk, Postwick |
| | 0.2 | G | Sunshine R, Ludlow |
| | 400 | ROU | R. România Actualitati, Tancabesti |
| **864** | 1000 | ARM | TWR relay, Gavar |
| | 10 | E | RNE R. Nacional, Socuellamos |
| | 400 | EGY | ERTU Koran prgr, Santah |
| | 50 | IRN | R. Kermanshah, Qasr-e Shirin |
| **873** | 10 | ALG | R. Algérienne 1/R. Ghardaïa |
| | 10 | ARS | SBA Quran prgr, Ar-Rass |
| | 50 | BOT | R. Botswana, Gantsi |
| | 10 | E | SER R. Galicia, Stgo. de Compostela |
| | 25 | E | SER R. Zaragoza |
| | 100 | ETH | R. Ethiopia, Addis Ababa |
| | 0.3 | G | BBC R. Norfolk, West Lynn |
| | 1 | G | BBC R. Ulster, Enniskillen |
| | 40 | HNG | Magyar R. 4, Lakihegy/Pécs |
| | 50 | IRN | R. Bojnurd, Bojnurd |
| | 50 | MDA | R. Moldova Actualitati, Chisinau |
| | 50 | MOZ | EP de Sofala, Beira (Dondo) |
| | 10 | SDN | Al-Gezira State R, Wad Madani |
| | 5 | SDN | Northern State R, Wadi Halfa |
| | 25 | UKR | UR1, Chasiv Yar |
| **882** | 100 | ARS | SBA Quran prgr, Dammam |
| | 20 | CNR | COPE Tenerife, La Laguña |
| | 5 | E | COPE, Alicante |
| | 5 | E | COPE, Gijón |
| | 5 | E | COPE, Málaga |
| | 5 | E | COPE, Valladolid |
| | 10 | EGY | ERTU General prgr, Matruh |
| | 10/5/1 | G | BBC Wales, Penmon/Tywyn/Forden |
| | 100 | G | BBC Wales, Washford |
| | 60 | IRN | R. Mahabad, Mahabad |
| | 10 | ISR | KI Reshet Bet, She'ar Yashuv |
| **891** | 600/300 | ALG | R. Algérienne 1, Ouled Fayet (also DRM) |
| | 100 | ETH | R. Ethiopia, Dese |
| | 0.1 | HOL | Euregio Radio, Baexem |
| | 0.1 | HOL | Fidelio Radio, Driebergen-Rijsenburg |
| | 0.05 | HOL | R. City International, Zeeland |
| | 50 | IRN | R. Dena, Dehdasht/Yasouj |
| | 50 | LSO | LNBS Ultimate FM, Lancer's Gap |
| | 2.5 | POR | R. Sim, Vilamoura |
| | 5 | SDN | Sennar State R, Singa |
| | 300 | TUR | TRT 1, Antalya |
| **900** | 1000 | ARS | SBA R. Riyadh, Qurayyat |
| | 5 | E | COPE, Granada |
| | 5 | E | COPE, Vigo |
| | 10 | E | R. Popular, Bilbao |
| | 100/50 | I | RAI Radiouno/Reg, Milano |
| | 600 | IRN | R. Quran, Tehran (Goldasteh) |
| **909** | 10 | ALG | R. Algérienne 1, Tamanrasset |
| | 600 | BOT | VOA, Mopeng Hill (Selebi-Phikwe) |
| | 5 | E | RNE R. 5, Palma de Mallorca |
| | 50/1 | G | BBC R. 5 Live, 9 stns |
| | 150 | G | BBC R. 5 Live, Brookmans Park |
| | 200 | G | BBC R. 5 Live,Moorside Edge |
| | 200 | ROU | R. Cluj, Jucu |
| | 25 | ROU | R. Constanta, Valu lui Traian |
| | 50 | ROU | R. România Actualitati, Timisoara |
| | 20 | UGA | UBC West Nile FM, Kampala (inactive) |
| **917** | 50 | NIG | R. Gotel, Yola |
| **918** | 20 | E | R. Intereconomia, Madrid (irreg.) |
| | 10 | EGY | ERTU General prgr, Bawiti |
| | 100 | ETH | Dimtse Wegahta (Vo the Dawn), Mekele |
| | 50 | IRN | R. Kerman, Jiroft |
| | 50 | NIG | R. Benue, Makurdi |
| **927** | 10 | ALG | R. Algérienne 1/R. Adrar, Timimoun |
| | 20 | ARS | SBA R. Jeddah, Hofuf |

| kHz | kW | Ctry | Station, location |
|-----|-----|------|-------------------|
| | 0.3 | DNK | World Music R, København (F.Pl.) |
| | | GRC | Black & White, Athína |
| | 50 | IRN | R. Lorestan, Dorud |
| | 200 | TUR | TRT 1/4, Izmir |
| **936** | 100 | ARS | SBA Quran prgr, Makkah/Riyadh |
| | 20 | E | RNE R. 5, Alicante |
| | 20 | E | RNE R. 5, Valladolid |
| | 20 | E | RNE R. 5, Zaragoza |
| | 10 | EGY | ERTU General prgr, Salum |
| | 50 | EGY | ERTU Om Kalthoum prgr, Cairo |
| | 0.15 | G | Dales R, Hawes |
| | 0.2 | G | Smooth R, Naish Hill |
| | 10/5 | I | RAI Radiouno/Reg, Venezia |
| | 300 | IRN | R. Urmia, Miandoab |
| | 50 | IRN | R. Urmia, Urmia |
| | 100 | MRC | SNRT A/R, Agadir |
| | 100 | SYR | Syrian R. 1, Homs |
| **945** | 10/2.5 | AFG | R. Talwaza, Sharana |
| | 25 | ANG | RNA N'Gola Yetu/Int. Sce, Mulenvos |
| | 5 | ARS | SBA R. Riyadh, Hail |
| | 25 | BOT | R. Botswana, Mmathethe |
| | 100 | ERI | VO the Broad Masses 1, Asmara |
| | | | (alt. fq 950kHz) |
| | 0.2 | G | Gold, Derby |
| | 0.7 | G | Smooth R, Bexhill |
| | | GRC | R. Galatsi, Athína |
| | 100 | IRN | R. Kordestan, Dehgolan |
| | 10 | NIG | R. Kebbi, Birnin Kebbi |
| | 15 | ROU | R. România Actualitati, Miercurea Ciuc |
| | 5 | SDN | South Kordofan State R, Al-Fulah |
| | 20 | STP | R. Nacional, Pinheira |
| **954** | 250 | CZE | CRo 2, Brno (Dobrochov) + 2 stns |
| | 50 | E | Onda Cero R, Madrid |
| | 3 | ETH | R. Sidama, Yirgalem |
| | 300 | TUR | TRT 1/4, Trabzon |
| **963** | 100 | CYP | CyBC 1, Nicosia |
| | 0.2 | G | Asian Sound R, Haslingden |
| | 1 | G | Sunrise R, East London |
| | 200 | IRN | R. Birjand, Bojd (Birjand) |
| | 20 | KWT | R. Kuwait Multilingual/Main prgr, Magwa |
| | 50 | MOZ | EP de Tete, Tete |
| | 0.1 | POL | R. AM (Twoje R.), Lipsko |
| | 1 | POR | R. Sim, Seixal |
| | 100 | SDN | SRTC Peace R. /Koran prgr, Khartoum Soba |
| | 100 | TUN | ERTT International ch, Tunis Djedeida |
| **972** | | BOT | R. Botswana, Takotokwane |
| | 5 | E | RNE R. Nacional, Cabra |
| | 2 | E | RNE R. Nacional, Monforte de Lemos |
| | 100 | ETH | R. Ethiopia, Robe (Bale) |
| | 1 | G | Sunrise R, West London |
| | 100 | IRN | R. Ilam, Ilam |
| | 5 | MEL | RNE R. Nacional, Mellilla |
| | 25 | NIG | Katsina State R, Katsina |
| | 10 | NIG | R. Kogi, Otite |
| **981** | 100 | ALG | R. Algérienne 2, Ouled Fayet (Algér) |
| | 20 | ARS | SBA Quran prgr, Madinah |
| | 15 | CZE | R. Český Impuls, Praha (Libeznice)/Domamil |
| | 2 | EGY | ERTU General prgr, Abu Simbel/Baris |
| | 10 | EGY | ERTU Reg./Koran prgr, Assiut |
| | 20/10 | I | RAI Reg. "Trst A", Trieste |
| | 1 | IRL | R. Star Country, Emmyvale |
| | 100 | IRN | R. Hamadan, Hamadan |
| | 3 | POR | R. Sim, Coimbra |
| **989** | 1 | ETH | R. Ethiopia FS relay, Addis Ababa |
| **990** | 600 | CYP | R. Sawa, Cape Greco |
| | 10 | E | SER R. Bilbao |
| | 5 | E | SER R. Cádiz |
| | 1 | G | BBC R. 5 Live, Tywyn |
| | 1 | G | BBC R. Devon, Exeter |
| | 0.1 | G | Free R. 80s, Wolverhampton |

| kHz | kW | Ctry | Station, location |
|---|---|---|---|
| | 0.3 | G | Hallam 2, Doncaster |
| | 50 | NIG | Bauchi R. Corp, Bauchi |
| | 10 | NIG | Lagos State BC, Ikeja |
| **999** | 20 | ARS | SBA Quran prgr, Duba |
| | 50 | E | COPE, Madrid |
| | 0.3 | G | Gold, Nottingham |
| | 1 | G | R. Solent, Fareham |
| | 0.8 | G | Rock 2, Preston |
| | 50/10 | I | RAI Radiouno/Reg, Torino |
| | 50 | IRN | R. Sanandaj, Baneh |
| | 20 | IRQ | R. Bilad, Baghdad |
| | 500 | MDA | TWR, Grigoriopol |
| | 5 | MLT | R. Malta, Bizbizja |
| | 100 | UGA | UBC R, Kabale (inactive) |
| **1008** | 10 | CNR | esRadio, Las Palmas (inactive) |
| | 5 | E | SER R. Alicante |
| | 5 | E | SER R. Extremadura, Badajoz |
| | 10 | E | SER R. Girona |
| | 100 | EGY | ERTU Palestine/Hebrew prgr, El Arish |
| | 10 | EGY | ERTU Reg. prgr, El Fayoum |
| | 50 | GRC | ERT1/Reg, Kerkira |
| | 100 | IRN | R. Semnan, Semnan |
| | 20 | IRQ | Sowt al-Fadhila, Najaf |
| | 50 | MOZ | EP de Maputo, Maputo |
| | 10 | NIG | Niger State Media Corp, Kontagora |
| | 10 | NIG | Osun State BC, Iree |
| **1017** | 10 | E | RNE R. 5, Burgos |
| | 10 | E | RNE R. 5, Granada |
| | 0.6 | G | Free R. 80s, Shrewsbury |
| | 50 | IRN | R. Iran, Bandar Abbas |
| | 10 | IRQ | R. Karbala, Karbala |
| **1026** | 10 | ALG | RA 1/R. Ouargla, Hassi Messaoud |
| | 5 | E | SER R. Asturias, Oviedo |
| | 5 | E | SER R. Jaén |
| | 5 | E | SER R. Jerez, J. de la Frontera |
| | 10 | E | SER R. Reus |
| | 5 | E | SER R. Salamanca |
| | 5 | E | SER R. Vigo |
| | 0.5 | G | BBC R. Cambrigeshire, Chesterton Fen |
| | 1 | G | BBC R. Jersey, Trinity |
| | 1.7 | G | Downtown R, Belfast |
| | 200 | IRN | R. Tabriz, Azarshahr |
| | 50 | MOZ | EP de Manica, Chimoio |
| | 25 | NIG | Jigawa BC, Dutse |
| | 5 | SDN | Blue Nile State R, Al-Damazin |
| **1035** | 20 | ARS | SBA R. Jeddah, Rafha |
| | 100/200 | EST | R. Eli/TWR, Tartu |
| | 10 | ETH | R. Oromiya, Adama (Nazret) |
| | 1 | G | BBC R. Sheffield/Asian Netw, Sheffield |
| | 1 | G | Lyca Dilse, London |
| | 0.3 | G | Westsound, Ayr |
| | 0.1 | HOL | Neverland AM, Venlo |
| | 100 | IRN | R. Yazd, Yazd |
| | 20 | JOR | R. Jordan Main prgr, Amman |
| **1044** | 20 | ARS | SBA R. Jeddah, Afif |
| | 10 | E | SER R. San Sebastian, Donostia-S.S. |
| | 5 | E | SER R. Valladolid |
| | 200 | ETH | R. Ethiopia, Mekele |
| | | GRC | Daffy, Athína |
| | 50 | IRN | R. Ilam, Dehloran |
| | 1 | UKR | UR1/Reg, Verkhovyna (inactive) |
| **1053** | 5 | E | COPE, Vila Real |
| | 25 | E | COPE, Zaragoza |
| | 100 | ETH | R. Oromiya, Nekemte |
| | 500 | G | TalkSport, Droitwich + 12 stns |
| | 100 | IRN | R. Iran, Khorramabad |
| | 30 | IRN | R. Zahedan, Saravan |
| | 3 | IRQ | R. As-Salam, Baghdad |
| | 100 | LBY | Vo Homeland, Tripoli (inactive) |
| | 400 | ROU | R. Iasi, Uricani |

| kHz | kW | Ctry | Station, location |
|---|---|---|---|
| | 10 | RUS | R. Mariya, Sankt-Peterburg |
| **1062** | 20/1 | CZE | Country R, Praha (Zbraslav) |
| | 10/6 | I | RAI Radiouno/Reg, Ancona |
| | 60/10 | I | RAI Radiouno/Reg, Cagliari |
| | 20/2 | I | RAI Radiouno/Reg, Catania |
| | 200 | IRN | R. Kerman, Kerman |
| | 0.8 | POL | R. AM (Twoje R.), Cmolas |
| | 300 | TUR | TRT Kurdî/VOT Arabic, Diyarbakir |
| **1071** | 5 | ALG | R. Algérienne 1, Illizi |
| | 50 | ARS | SBA R. Riyadh, Bisha |
| | 25 | BOT | R. Botswana, Jwaneng |
| | 10 | CZE | CRo Plus, České Budějovice/Ostrava |
| | 100 | EGY | ERTU Adults/Wadi al Nil, Cairo (Abu Zaabal) |
| | 20 | F | TDF Smartcast, Brest (DRM, irR.) |
| | 1 | G | TalkSport, Clipstone/Newcastle |
| | | GRC | R. Mesogeia, Athína |
| | 100 | IRN | R. Ma'aref, Qom (Alborz) |
| | 100 | SYR | R. Al-Nour (LBN) relay, Tartus Amrit |
| **1080** | 10 | ARS | SBA R. Jeddah, Najran |
| | 10 | E | Onda Cero R, Toledo |
| | 5 | E | SER R. Coruña, A Coruña |
| | 5 | E | SER R. Granada |
| | 10 | E | SER R. Huesca |
| | 5 | E | SER R. Mallorca, Palma de M. |
| | 20 | EGY | ERTU General prgr, El Minya/Luxor |
| | 3 | ETH | R. Fana, Addis Ababa |
| | 600/400 | IRN | VOIRI, Mahshahr |
| | 50 | ISR | KI Arabic prgr, Yavne |
| **1089** | 10 | ALG | R. Algérienne 1/R. Adrar |
| | 20 | ARS | SBA R. Jeddah, Qurayyat |
| | 400 | G | TalkSport, Brookmans Park |
| | 100 | G | TalkSport, Moorside Edge |
| | 80/1 | G | TalkSport, Washford + 4 stns |
| | 125 | G | TalkSport, Westerglen |
| | 50 | IRN | R. Semnan, Shahrud |
| **1098** | 100 | ARS | SBA R. Jeddah, Dammam |
| | 25 | E | RNE R. 5, Almeria |
| | 10 | E | RNE R. 5, Avila |
| | 5 | E | RNE R. 5, Huelva |
| | 20 | E | RNE R. 5, Lugo |
| | 0.3 | I | Media R. Castellana, Castel San Pietro Terme |
| | 200/100 | IRN | VOIRI, Zabol |
| | 25 | SVK | SR R. Patria/Devín, Nitra |
| **1107** | 400 | AFG | RTV Afghanistan, Pol-e-Charkhi |
| | 20 | E | RNE R. 5, Caceres |
| | 20 | E | RNE R. 5, Camargo |
| | 25 | E | RNE R. 5, Logroño |
| | 10 | E | RNE R. 5, Ponferrada |
| | 10 | E | RNE R. 5, Teruel |
| | 1.5 | G | Moray Firth R. 2, Inverness |
| | 2/0.5 | G | TalkSport, 6 stns |
| | | GRC | R. 322, Athína |
| | 10 | I | RAI Radiouno/Reg, Roma |
| | 50 | IRN | R. Mashhad, Sabzevar |
| | 100 | KEN | KBC R. Taifa, Maralal |
| | 25 | NIG | FRCN Kaduna, Jaji |
| **1116** | 20 | ARS | SBA R. Jeddah, Madinah |
| | 5 | E | SER R. Albacete |
| | 5 | E | SER R. Pontevedra |
| | 1 | G | BBC R Derby/Asian N, Burnaston Lane |
| | 0.5 | G | BBC R. Guernsey, Rohais |
| | 20 | HNG | MR Dankó Rádió, Miskolc/Mosonmagyaróvár |
| | 10 | I | RAI Radiouno/Reg, Palermo |
| | 200 | IRN | R. Iran, Ardakan |
| | 20 | IRQ | R. Dar as-Salam, Baghdad |
| **1125** | 5 | E | RNE R. 5, Badajoz |
| | 10 | E | RNE R. 5, Castelló |
| | 10 | E | RNE R. 5, Soria |
| | 10 | E | RNE R. 5, Toledo |

| kHz | kW | Ctry | Station, location |
|---|---|---|---|
| | 10 | E | RNE R. 5, Vitoria |
| | 1 | G | R. Wales, Llandrindod Wells |
| | | GRC | Mini Watt, Athína |
| | 50 | IRN | R. Qazvin, Qazvin |
| 1134 | 10 | AGL | EP do Bengo, Mulenvos |
| | 5 | E | COPE, Jerez de la Frontera |
| | 5 | E | COPE, Pamplona |
| | 10 | E | COPE, Salamanca |
| | 0.003 | G | BFBS Gurkha R, 3 sites |
| | 0.001 | G | LPAMs |
| | 0.02 | GRC | ERT Open, Chania |
| | 10 | IRN | R. Tabriz, Kaleybar |
| | 100 | KWT | R. Kuwait Main prgr, Kabd |
| | 20 | NIG | Cross River State BC, Ugaga |
| 1143 | 5 | E | COPE, Jaén |
| | 2 | E | COPE, Ourense |
| | 50 | IRN | R. Iran, Yasuj |
| 1152 | 10 | E | RNE R. 5, Albacete |
| | 10 | E | RNE R. 5, Cartagena |
| | 10 | E | RNE R. 5, Lleida |
| | 20 | E | RNE R. 5, Málaga |
| | 10 | E | RNE R. 5, Zamora |
| | 4 | G | Clyde 2, Glasgow |
| | 3 | G | Free R. 80s, Birmingham |
| | 1.5 | G | Key Radio, Manchester |
| | 24 | G | LBC News, London |
| | 2 | G | Metro R. 2, Newcastle |
| | 0.8 | G | Smooth R, Norwich |
| | 0.3 | G | Smooth R, Plymouth |
| | 50 | KEN | KBC R. Taifa, Wajir |
| | 400 | ROU | R. România Actualitati, Cluj (Jucu) |
| | 200 | UAE | Voice of Kerala, Ras al-Khaimah |
| 1161 | 5 | ALG | RA 1/R. Tamanrasset, In Salah |
| | 100 | EGY | ERTU Reg. prgr, Tanta |
| | 0.1 | G | BBC Three Counties R, Bedford |
| | 0.2 | G | Smooth R, Swindon |
| | 1 | G | Tay 2, Dundee |
| | 0.4 | G | Viking 2, Hull |
| | 600 | IRN | VOIRI, Qasr-e Shirin |
| 1170 | 0.2 | G | Signal Two, Stoke-on-Trent |
| | 0.3 | G | Smooth R, Ipswich |
| | 0.1 | G | Smooth R, Portsmouth |
| | 0.6 | G | Swansea Sound, Swansea |
| | 0.3 | G | TFM 2, Stockton |
| | 15 | SVN | R. Capodistria, Beli Kriz |
| | 100 | SWZ | TWR, Mpangela Ranch (Manzini) |
| | 800 | UAE | Vo the Republic of Yemen, Al-Dhabbaya |
| 1179 | 25 | CNR | SER R. Club Tenerife, Santa Cruz |
| | 2 | E | SER R. Rioja, Logroño |
| | 50 | E | SER R. València |
| | 10 | EGY | ERTU General prgr, Qena |
| | 0.05 | G | R. BGWS, Farnborough |
| | 30 | IRQ | R. Voice of Iraq, Baghdad |
| | 50 | MOZ | EP da Zambézia, Quelimane (Namacata) |
| | 400 | ROU | R. România Actualitati, Bacau (Galbeni) |
| | 10 | ROU | R. România Actualitati, Resita |
| | 0.005 | S | Hörby Radioförening, Hörby |
| 1188 | | GRC | R. Nikolaos Elata, Athína |
| | 400 | HNG | Magyar R. 4, Marcali/Szolnok |
| | 300 | IRN | R. Payam, Tehran |
| 1197 | 2.4 | G | Absolute R, 5 stns |
| | 50 | IRN | R. Ardabil, Moghan |
| | 50 | LSO | LNBS Ultimate FM, Lancer's Gap |
| | 15 | ROU | Brasov FM, Brasov |
| 1206 | 20 | ARS | SBA R. Jeddah, Aflaj |
| | 1 | I | Amica Radio Veneta, Vigonza di Padova |
| | 10 | IRN | R. Birjand, Nehbandan |
| | 50 | ISR | KI Reshet Bet, Akko |
| | 50 | MOZ | EP de Inhambane, Inhambane |
| | 1 | ROD | Mauritius BC R. Rodrigues, Citronelle |
| 1215 | 20 | ARS | SBA R. Jeddah, Hafar al-Barin |
| | 20 | ARS | SBA R. Riyadh, Madinah |
| | 50 | BOT | R. Botswana, Mahalapye |
| | 5 | E | COPE, Córdoba |
| | 5 | E | COPE, Léon |
| | 5 | E | COPE, Santander |
| | 285 | G | Absolute R, 10 stns |
| | 60 | IRN | R. Tabaristan, Chalus (Darya) |
| | 10 | TZA | TBC Taifa, Arusha |
| 1224 | 5 | E | COPE, Almería |
| | 5 | E | COPE, Huelva |
| | 5 | E | COPE, Lleida |
| | 5 | E | COPE, Lugo |
| | 5 | E | COPE, Palma de Mallorca |
| | 0.1 | HOL | Extra AM, Amsterdam |
| | 0.1 | HOL | Kilrock 1224 AM, 's-Gravendeel |
| | 0.1 | HOL | Nostalgie AM, Siddeburen (F.Pl.) |
| | 0.05 | HOL | R. Eldorado, Damwâld |
| | 0.1 | HOL | R. Emmeloord, Emmeloord |
| | 0.1 | HOL | R. Overland/R. 1224, Lunteren |
| | 0.1 | HOL | R. T-POT, Gasselternijveen |
| | 0.1 | HOL | United AM, Neede (irreg.) |
| | 50 | IRN | R. Iran, Kerman |
| | 400 | IRN | VOIRI, Kish Island |
| | 50 | MOZ | EP de Cabo Delgado, Pemba |
| | 50 | NIG | Plateau R. & TV Corp, Jos |
| 1233 | 600 | CYP | Monte-Carlo Doualiya/TWR, Cape Greco |
| | 20 | CZE | R. Dechovka, Praha (Líbeznice) + 4 stns |
| | 1 | G | Absolute R, 2 stns |
| | 50 | KEN | KBC Northeastern Sce, Marsabit |
| 1242 | 3.5 | G | Absolute R, 3 stns |
| | 0.3 | G | Smooth R, Maidstone |
| | | GRC | R. Apollon, Athína |
| | 500 | OMA | R. Sultanate of Oman, Barka (Seeb) |
| 1251 | 0.001 | G | BFBS Gurkha R, York |
| | 0.001 | G | LPAMs |
| | 0.8 | G | Smooth R, Bury St. Edmunds |
| | 50 | HNG | MR Dankó Rádió, Nyíregyháza/Szombathely |
| | 0.1 | HOL | Memories AM, Geffen |
| | 2 | POR | R. Sim, Castelo Branco/Chaves |
| 1260 | 500 | ARS | SBA R. Riyadh, Dammam |
| | 5 | E | SER R. Algeciras |
| | 5 | E | SER R. Murcia |
| | 1 | G | Absolute R, Lydd |
| | 0.5 | G | BBC R. York, Scarborough |
| | 0.3 | G | Sabras R, Leicester |
| | 0.6 | G | Smooth R, Wrexham |
| | 10 | IRN | R. Isfahan, Khur |
| | 50 | MOZ | EP do Niassa, Lichinga |
| 1269 | 2 | AFS | Arrowline Chinese R, Edenvale |
| | 5 | E | COPE, Badajoz |
| | 5 | E | COPE, Zamora |
| | | GRC | R. FBI, Athína |
| | 50 | IRN | R. Ardabil, Khalkhal |
| | 100 | KWT | R. Kuwait Classical music, Kabd |
| | 10 | NIG | Taraba State BS, Jalingo |
| | 200 | UAE | R. Asia, Ras al-Khaimah |
| 1278 | 10 | EGY | ERTU General prgr, Asswan |
| | 0.002 | G | BFBS Gurkha R, Folkestone/Stafford |
| | 0.4 | G | Pulse 2, Bradford |
| | 300 | IRN | R. Kermanshah, Kermanshah |
| | 100 | OMA | R. Sultanate of Oman, Bahla |
| | 100 | UKR | UR3 Kultura, Kurisove (inactive) |
| 1287 | 5 | E | SER R. Castilla, Burgos |
| | 10 | E | SER R. Lleida |
| | 5 | E | SER R. Lugo |
| | 0.001 | G | BFBS Gurkha R, 4 sites |
| | 0.002 | G | BFBS UK, 2 sites |
| | 0.001 | G | LPAMs |
| | 0.004 | G | R. Clan Clwyd, Bodelwyddan |

| kHz | kW | Ctry | Station, location |
|---|---|---|---|
| | 50 | ISR | Vo Hope Middle East, She'ar Yashuv |
| | 2 | POR | RTP Antena 1, Portalegre |
| 1290 | 1 | AGL | EP do Zaire, Soyo |
| 1296 | 400 | AFG | Azadi/Ashna R, Pol-e-Charkhi |
| | 50 | E | COPE, Valencia |
| | 10 | G | R. XL, Birmingham |
| | 600 | SDN | SRTC General prgr, Sennar (inactive) |
| 1305 | 10 | AFG | R. Kandahar |
| | 20 | E | RNE R. 5, Bilbao |
| | 20 | E | RNE R. 5, Ciudad Real |
| | 10 | E | RNE R. 5, León |
| | 25 | E | RNE R. 5, Ourense |
| | 10 | EGY | ERTU General prgr, Assiut |
| | 0.2 | G | Hallam 2, Barnsley |
| | 0.5 | G | Premier Christian R, Chingford/Epsom |
| | 0.2 | G | Smooth R, Newport |
| | 1 | GRC | ERT1/Reg, Tripoli |
| | 1 | I | R. Coltano Marconi |
| | 50 | IRN | R. Bushehr, Bushehr |
| | 50 | KEN | KBC Somali Sce, Wajir |
| 1314 | 1000 | ARM | Public R. of Armenia FS, Gavar |
| | 20 | E | RNE R. 5, Cuenca |
| | 10 | E | RNE R. 5, Salamanca |
| | 10 | E | RNE R. 5, Tarragona |
| | 1 | EGY | ERTU General prgr, Nag Hamadi |
| | 1 | EGY | ERTU Reg./Koran prgr, Abu Simbel |
| | 50 | IRN | R. Iran, Ardabil |
| | 1 | NOR | R. Northern Star, Bergen Erdal (irR.) |
| | 50 | ROU | Antena Satelor, Constanta (Valu lui Traian) |
| | 25 | ROU | Antena Satelor, Timisoara |
| | 15 | ROU | R. Oltenia Craiova, Craiova |
| 1323 | 0.02 | G | Akash R, Leeds |
| | 0.5 | G | Smooth R, Brighton |
| | 50 | IRN | VOIRI/R. Tabriz, Jolfa |
| | 15 | ROU | R. Târgu Mures, Târgu Mures |
| | 10 | TZA | R. One Swahili channel, Moshi |
| 1332 | 50 | CZE | CRo2, Moravské Budějovice (Domamil) |
| | 1 | G | Premier Christian R, London |
| | 0.1 | G | R. Warrington |
| | 0.6 | G | Smooth R, Peterborough |
| | 0.05 | HOL | Alfa Radio, Haaksbergen |
| | 0.1 | HOL | Citrus AM, Emst |
| | 0.1 | HOL | Impact AM, Wassenaar |
| | 0.1 | HOL | R. 0511/Seagull, Ternaard |
| | 0.1 | HOL | R. Flandria, Hemelum |
| | 0.1 | HOL | R. Transparant, Creil |
| | 0.1 | HOL | Sterrekijker AM, Elim |
| | 300 | IRN | Tehran Province Radio, Tehran (Goldasteh) |
| | 50 | ROU | R. România Actualitati, Galati |
| 1341 | 10 | E | Onda Cero R, Almeria |
| | 5 | E | Onda Cero R, Ciudad Real |
| | 5 | E | SER R. León |
| | 100 | EGY | ERTU Cult./Songs prgr, Cairo (Abu Zaabal) |
| | 20 | EGY | ERTU General prgr, Idfu/Siwa |
| | 10 | EGY | ERTU Koran/Educ./Sports prgr, Bawiti |
| | 100 | G | BBC R. Ulster, Lisnagarvey |
| | | GRC | Smooth Radio, Athína |
| | 20 | IRN | R. Kerman, Bam |
| | 100 | KWT | R. Kuwait Quran/2nd prgr, Magwa |
| 1350 | 1000 | ARM | TWR relay, Gavar |
| | 50 | BOT | R. Botswana, Tshabong |
| | 10 | EGY | ERTU General prgr, Quseir |
| | 0.001 | G | LPAMs |
| | 30 | GEO | Abkhaz State R, Sokhumi |
| | 5 | HNG | Magyar R. 4, Győr |
| | 5 | I | R. I AM, Milano (weekends) |
| 1359 | 100 | ETH | VO Tigray Revolution, Mekele |
| | 0.8 | G | BBC R. Solent, Bournemouth |
| | 0.3 | G | Free R. 80s, Coventry |
| | 0.2 | G | Smooth R, Cardiff |
| | 0.3 | G | Smooth R, Chelmsford |

| kHz | kW | Ctry | Station, location |
|---|---|---|---|
| 1368 | 10 | EGY | ERTU General prgr, El Kharga |
| | 20 | G | Manx Radio, Foxdale |
| | 150 | IRN | R. Golestan, Gonbad-e Kavus |
| | 10 | SEY | SBC Radio, Victoria |
| 1377 | 1000 | ARM | TWR relay, Gavar |
| | 0.1 | G | Asian Sound R, Ashton Moss |
| | | GRC | Supersonic, Athína |
| | 1 | I | R. One, Pistoia area |
| | 50 | IRN | R. Kermanshah, Paveh |
| | 50 | IRN | R. Zahedan, Chabahar |
| | 50 | TZA | R. Free Africa, Mwanza |
| 1386 | 10 | EGY | ERTU Reg./Koran prgr, Luxor |
| | 0.001 | G | LPAMs |
| | 100 | KEN | KBC Northeastern Sce, Maralal |
| | 75 | LTU | Relays via R. Baltic Waves Int, Viešintos |
| 1395 | 0.05 | HOL | Barkey, Almere Buiten (F.P.I.) |
| | 0.1 | HOL | Cupra Radio, Emmer-Compascuum |
| | 0.1 | HOL | Happy AM, Middelburg |
| | 0.1 | HOL | Loostad Radio, Apeldoorn |
| | 0.1 | HOL | Q AM, Waardenburg |
| | 0.1 | HOL | Radio Seabreeze AM, Grou |
| | 0.1 | HOL | Studio Denakker, Klazienaveen |
| | 0.1 | HOL | Westcoast AM, Katwijk aan Zee |
| | 0.3 | IRL | Energy Power AM, Dublin (wweekends) |
| | 50 | IRN | R. Khalij e-Fars, Hajiabad |
| | 50 | IRN | VOIRI, Gorgan |
| 1404 | 50 | GRC | ERT1/Reg, Komotini |
| | 0.1 | I | R. 106 AM, Chiozza di Scandiano |
| | 10 | IRN | R. Iran, Qir |
| | 10 | MWI | MBC R. 1, Chitipa |
| | 50 | ROU | R. Cluj/R. Sighet, Sighetu Marmatiei |
| | 15 | ROU | R. România Actualitati, Sibiu |
| | 10 | UKR | UR1, Izmail (inactive) |
| 1413 | 5 | E | RNE R. 5, Girona |
| | 10 | E | RNE R. 5, Jaén |
| | 20 | E | RNE R. 5, Vigo |
| | 1 | G | BBC R. Gloucestershire, 2 stns |
| | 0.04 | G | Bradford Asian R, Bradford |
| | 1 | G | Premier Christian R, 2 stns |
| | 10 | IRN | R. Fars, Estahban |
| | 500 | MDA | Vesti FM, Grigoriopol |
| | 800 | OMA | BBC World Sce, A'Seela |
| 1422 | 1 | AFS | Hellenic R, Bedfordview |
| | 50 | ALG | R. Multichaîne, Ouled Fayet (Algér) |
| | 20 | ARS | SBA Call of Islam, Riyadh |
| | 10 | EGY | ERTU Reg./Koran prgr, Salum |
| | 10 | MWI | MBC R. 1, Matiya |
| | 10 | ROU | R. România Actualitati, Olanesti |
| 1431 | 600 | DJI | R. Sawa, Djibouti (Pk 12) |
| | 0.001 | G | LPAMs |
| | 0.35 | G | Smooth R, Southend |
| | 0.35 | GRC | 1431 AM, Thessaloniki |
| | 5/2 | I | RAI Radiouno/Reg, Foggia |
| | 800 | UKR | R. Ukraine Int, Mykolaiv (inactive) |
| 1440 | 1600 | ARS | SBA R. Riyadh, Ras al-Khair |
| | 0.5 | DNK | R. 208, København (F.P.I.) |
| | 10 | NIG | Adamawa BC, Yola |
| | 10 | TZA | R. One English channel, Dar es Salaam |
| 1449 | 200 | ARS | SBA R. Riyadh, Jeddah (Bahrah) |
| | 0.2 | G | BBC Asian Network, Gunthorpe |
| | 2 | G | BBC R. 4, Redmoss |
| | 0.001 | G | LPAMs |
| | 2 | I | RAI Radiouno/Reg, Belluno |
| | 400 | IRN | VOIRI, Bandar Torkaman |
| 1458 | 10 | AGL | EP do Moxico, Luena |
| | 10 | BHR | R. Bahrain General prgr, Manama |
| | 5 | G | BBC Asian Network, Langley Mill |
| | 2 | G | BBC Newcastle, Wrekenton |
| | 0.5 | G | BBC R. Cumbria, Whitehaven |
| | 5 | G | Gold, Manchester |
| | 125 | G | Lyca R. 1458, London |

| kHz | kW | Ctry | Station, location |
|---|---|---|---|
| | 4 | GIB | GBC R. Gibraltar, Wellington Front |
| | 10 | IRN | R. Birjand, Ghayen |
| | 20 | ISR | Kl Reshet Alef, Eilat/She'ar Yashuv |
| | 100 | ROU | R. România Actualitati, Constanta |
| 1467 | 50 | ARS | SBA R. Riyadh, Hafar Al-Batin |
| | 1000 | F | Trans World R, Roumoules |
| | 100 | IRN | R. Qom, Alborz (Qom) |
| 1476 | 10 | EGY | ERTU Reg./Koran prgr, El Minya |
| | | GRC | R. Veteranos, Athína |
| | 0.05 | I | R. Briscola, Lenta |
| | 50 | IRN | R. Kurdistan, Marivan |
| 1485 | 1 | AFS | R. Today, Honeydew |
| | 5 | E | SER R. Alcoi |
| | 10 | E | SER R. Santander |
| | 10 | E | SER R. Zamora |
| | 10 | ETH | R. Ethiopia, Negele Borana |
| | 1 | G | BBC R 4, Carlisle |
| | 2 | G | BBC R. Merseyside, Wallasey |
| | 0.1 | GRC | ERT1/Reg, Volos |
| | 0.001 | HOL | approx. 30 stations |
| | 400/100 | IRN | R. Abadan, Jamshidabad |
| | 10 | IRN | R. Fars, Jahrom |
| | 10 | IRN | R. Iran, Damghan |
| | 10 | IRN | R. Urmia, Khoy |
| | 1.2/2.7 | LVA | R. Merkurs, Riga (planned to close) |
| | 1 | MEL | SER R. Melilla, Melilla |
| | 1 | NOR | NRK P1/Troms og Finnmark, Longyearbyen |
| | 1 | ROU | R. Maria, Rotunda |
| | 3 | ROU | R. Vocea Sperantei, 3 sites |
| | 12 | SDN | Al-Qadarif State R, Al-Qadarif |
| 1494 | 10 | IRN | R. Mashhad, Taybad |
| | 50 | MDA | R. Moldova Actualitati, Cahul/Edinet |
| 1503 | 0.1 | AZR | AFN, Lajes |
| | 1 | BIH | R. 1503 Zavidovici, Zavidovici |
| | 5 | E | RNE R. 5, La Linea |
| | 2 | E | RNE R. 5, Monforte de Lemos |
| | 25 | EGY | ERTU Koran prgr, El Arish |
| | 1 | G | BBC R. Stoke, Sideway |
| | 0.1 | G | Betar Bangla, East London |
| 1512 | 1000 | ARS | SBA Quran prgr, Jeddah (Khumra) |
| | 100 | GRC | ERT1/Reg, Hania |
| | 0.02 | I | Mini Radio, Castano Primo |
| | 50 | IRN | R. Ardabil, Ardabil |
| 1521 | 2000 | ARS | SBA R. Riyadh, Duba (irreg.) |
| | 10 | BHR | Bahrain TV audio, Manama |
| | 5 | E | SER R. Castelló |
| | 0.07 | G | Flame Christian & Community R, Wirral |
| | 0.04 | G | R. Panj, Coventry |
| | 10 | SVK | SR R. Patria/Devín, Rimavská Sobota |
| 1530 | 0.7 | G | Pulse 2, Huddersfield |
| | 3 | MDR | Posto Emissor do Funchal, Poiso |
| | 15 | ROU | R. Constanta, Mahmudia (Nufaru) |
| | 15 | ROU | R. România Actualitati, Radauti |
| | 600 | STP | VOA, Pinheira |
| 1539 | 6 | E | SER R. Elche, Elx |
| | 5 | E | SER R. Manresa (irregular) |
| | | GRC | Voreios Ihos, Thessaloniki |
| | 50 | IRN | R. Golestan, Gorgan |
| | 10 | IRN | R. Iran, Garmsar |
| | 100 | UAE | Asianet R, Al-Dhabbiya (irR.) |
| 1548 | 10 | AFS | R. Islam, Lenasia |
| | 2 | G | Forth 2, Edinburgh |
| | 97 | G | Gold, London |
| | 0.7 | G | Hallam 2, Sheffield |
| | 1 | G | R. City Talk, Liverpool |
| | 10 | IRN | R. Birjand, Ferdows |
| | 15 | IRN | R. Dena, Gachsaran |
| | 70 | IRN | R. Iran, 3 sites |
| | 10 | IRN | R. Mazandaran, Larijan |
| | 600 | KWT | R. Sawa, Kuwait |
| | 500 | MDA | TWR, Grigoriopol |
| 1550 | 50 | ALG | R. Nacional de la RASD, Rabouni |
| 1557 | 0.8 | G | Smooth R, Northampton |
| | 0.5 | G | Smooth R, Southampton |
| | 50 | IRN | R. Iran, Zabol |
| 1566 | 100 | BEN | TWR Africa, Parakou |
| | 0.6 | G | BBC Somerset, Taunton |
| | 0.8 | G | Premier Christian R, Guildford |
| | 1 | HOL | Vahon Hindustani Radio, Haag |
| | 0.1 | I | R. Kolbe, Schio |
| | 50 | IRN | R. Iran, Bam |
| 1575 | 5 | E | SER R. Córdoba |
| | 10 | E | SER R. Pamplona |
| | 10 | EGY | ERTU Koran/Educ./Sports, Quseir |
| | 0.001 | G | LPAMs |
| | 50/30 | I | RAI Radiouno/Reg, Genova |
| | 2 | MAU | BBC WS, Bigara |
| | 1 | ROU | ALT FM, Resita |
| | 800 | UAE | R. Farda, Al-Dhabbiya (jammed) |
| 1584 | 0.25 | AFS | R 1584, Pretoria (Laudium) |
| | 1 | BHR | R. Bahrain English prgr, Manama |
| | 5 | CEU | SER Radiolé, Ceuta |
| | 5 | E | SER R. Gandía |
| | 5 | E | SER R. Ourense |
| | 11 | EGY | ERTU Reg./Koran prgr, Idfu/Baris |
| | 0.3 | G | BBC Hereford & Worcester, Woofferton |
| | 0.2 | G | Panjab R, N. London |
| | 0.2 | G | Tay 2, Perth |
| | 1 | GRC | Ilida R, Kastro |
| | 0.1 | HOL | Antenne Domstad, Utrecht |
| | 1 | I | Free Radio AM, Trieste |
| | 0.5 | I | Regional Radio, Otricoli |
| | 50 | IRN | R. Semnan, Biyarjomand |
| | 10 | IRN | R. Semnan, unk. loc. |
| | 0.1 | POL | R. AM (Twoje R.), Andrychów |
| | 1 | ROU | ALT FM, Timisoara |
| | 4 | ROU | R. Vocea Sperantei, 4 sites |
| | 5 | SDN | White Nile State R, Kosti |
| 1593 | 10 | EGY | ERTU Reg./Koran prgr, Matruh |
| | 5 | F | Bretagne 5, Saint-Gouéno |
| | 150 | KWT | R. Sawa, Kuwait |
| | 10 | ROU | Brasov FM, Sibiu |
| | 15 | ROU | R. Cluj, Oradea |
| | 15 | ROU | R. România Actualitati, Ion Corvin |
| | 15 | ROU | R. Târgu Mures, Miercurea Ciuc |
| | 0.005 | TUR | AFN Incirlik (Adana) |
| 1602 | 5 | E | SER R. Cartagena |
| | 5 | E | SER R. Linares |
| | 5 | E | SER R. Ontinyent |
| | 5 | E | SER R. Segovia |
| | 10/1 | EGY | ERTU Reg./Koran prgr, Nag Hamadi |
| | 10 | EGY | ERTU Reg./Koran/Sports, Siwa |
| | 0.4 | FIN | Scandinavian Weekend R, Virrat |
| | 0.1 | G | Desi R, Southall |
| | 0.001 | G | RSLs |
| | 0.1 | HOL | R. Seagull, Pietersbierum |
| | 0.02 | I | Dot Radio, Spello |
| | 0.02 | I | R. Tre Network, Poggibonsi |
| | 0.02 | I | RTV R. Treviso, Treviso |
| | 1 | IRN | R. Ahvaz, Dezful |
| | 10 | IRN | R. Fars, Kazerun |
| | 1 | IRN | R. Iran, Bahabad |
| | 20 | IRN | R. Semnan, Damghan/Garmsar |
| | 0.8 | POL | R. AM, Kraków |
| | 2 | ROU | ALT FM, Arad/Deva |
| | 1 | ROU | R. Vocea Sperantei, Piatra Neamt |
| | 5 | SDN | South Kordofan State R, Kadugli |
| | 0.5 | SRB | RTS Beograd 1, Sjenica |
| 1611 | 0.1 | NOR | R. Northern Star, Bergen Erdal (irR.) |

# EAST ASIA & PACIFIC

**Abbreviations** peculiar to the E.Asia/Pacific section of MW freq. lists: AF = allocated freq; C. = City; PO = Present operation on; Proj. = Projected station; (t) = translator.
**Australia:** The numeral preceding the call letters indicates the state: 2 = New South Wales. 3 = Victoria. 4 = Queensland. 5 = South Australia. 6 = Western Australia. 7 = Tasmania. 8 = Northern Territory. ACT = Australian Capital Territory. **China, P.R:** If several locations are listed for one frequency, the power listed applies to the first entry. For full details see country section. **Indonesia:** Only RRI stns included. For details of other stns see country section. **Philippines:** Province Abbreviations: Ag Nte = Agusan del Norte; Ag Sur = Agusan del Sur;  Ant = Antique; Boh = Bohol; Bat = Batangas; Buk = Bukidnon; Bul = Bulacan; Cag = Cagayan; Cam Nte = Camarines Norte; Cam Sur = Camarines Sur; Dvo Nte = Davao del Norte; Dvo Sur = Davao del Sur; Isa = Isabela; I.Nte = Ilocos Norte; I.Sur = Ilocos Sur; LU = La Union; Lanao Nte = Lanao del Norte; Lanao Sur = Lanao del Sur; Mag = Maguindanao; Mas = Masbate;  M Octal = Mindoro Occidental; Mind Or = Mindoro Oriental; Mis Octal = Misamis Occidental; Mis Or = Misamis Oriental; Mt Prov = Mountain Province; Neg Occ = Negros Occidental; Neg Or = Negros Oriental; Nva Viz = Nueva Vizcaya;  Pam = Pampanga; Pang = Pangasinan; Que = Quezon; Riz = Rizal; S Cot = South Cotabato; S Leyte = Southern Leyte; S Sur = Surigao del Sur; Sor = Sorsogon; Tar = Tarlac; Z Nte = Zamboanga del Norte; Z Sib = Zamboanga Sibugay; Z Sur = Zamboanga del Sur; Zamb = Zambales.
**Russia:** Regions in the Asian parts of Russia: Sib. = Siberia. FE = Far East.

| kHz | kW | Ctry | Call | Station, location | kHz | kW | Ctry | Call | Station, location |
|---|---|---|---|---|---|---|---|---|---|
| **164** | 500 | MNG | | MRT (1), Ulaanbaatar | | 2 | NZL | | Rhema, Kaitaia |
| **209** | 75 | MNG | | MRT (1), Choibalsan | | 1 | NZL | | TAB Trackside R., Hawkes Bay |
| | 75 | MNG | | MRT (1) + Goviin Dolgion Büsiin Public R., | | 5 | PHL | DXHM | Catholic Media Netw., Madong, Mind Or |
| | | | | Dalanzadgad | | 10 | PHL | DWRB | Philippine Bc. Sce., Naga C, Cam. Sur |
| | 75 | MNG | | MRT (1) + Reg., Ölgii | | 10 | THA | | R. Thailand, Mukdahan |
| **227** | 75 | MNG | | MRT (1) + Govi-Altai Public R., Altai | | 100 | THA | | SoR. WoR. Sor, Lampang |
| **279** | 150 | TKM | | Turkmen Radio (1), Asgabat | | 40 | TJK | | TR (2), Dushanbe |
| **531** | 10 | AUS | 6DL | ABC (L), Dalwallinu | | 200 | VTN | | Hung Yen (2), My Hao |
| | 5 | AUS | 4KZ | Innisfail | **550** | 5 | HWA | KNUI | Kahului, Maui |
| | 5 | AUS | 2PM | Kempsey | | 50 | AUS | 6WA | ABC (L), Wagin |
| | 0.5 | AUS | 5RTI | R. Italiana, Adelaide (HPON) | **558** | 5 | AUS | 4AM | Atherton |
| | 5 | AUS | 3GG | Warragul | | 2 | AUS | 7BU | Burnie |
| | 10 | CHN | | ZJ | | 5 | AUS | 4GY | Gympie |
| | 300 | IND | | AIR, Jodhpur A | | 100 | BGD | | Bangladesh Betar, Khulna |
| | 10 | J | JOQG | NHK (1), Morioka | | 120 | CHN | | XJ + 9 stns |
| | 1 | J | | NHK (1), Nago | | 10 | FJI | | Fiji Bc. Corp. Ltd. (RF1), Suva |
| | 5 | NZL | | 531pi, Auckland | | 100 | IND | | AIR, Mumbai B |
| | 2 | NZL | | More FM, Alexandra | | 20 | J | JOCR | CRK, Kobe |
| | 10 | PHL | DZBR | Allied Bc. Center, Batangas C, Bat. | | 250 | KOR | HLQH | KBS, Daegu (2) |
| | 5 | PHL | DXGH | Pacific Bc. System, Gen. Santos C, S Cot | | 5 | NZL | | R. Sport, Invercargill |
| | 25 | THA | | R. Thailand, Maha Sarakham | | 40 | PHL | DZXL | R. Mindanao Netw., Pasig C, NCR |
| | 10 | TWN | BED57 | BCC (L), Taipei (Tucheng) | | 10 | THA | | R. Thailand, Kanchanaburi |
| **540** | 10 | AUS | 4QL | ABC (L), Longreach | **567** | 10 | AUS | 4JK | ABC (L), Julia Creek |
| | 5 | AUS | 7SD | Scottsdale | | 0.1 | AUS | 6... | ABC (L), W. A., 4 stns |
| | 50 | CHN | | AH (CNR1); LN (CNR1) | | 0.5 | AUS | 2BH | Broken Hill |
| | 10 | CHN | | QH; NM (2 stns) | | 10 | CHN | | JS (CNR1) |
| | 20 | IND | | AIR, Aizawl | | 20 | CHN | | TJ; EN |
| | 10 | INS | | RRI, Bandung (4) | | 10 | GUM | KGUM | Agana |
| | 1 | J | JOSK | NHK (1), Kitakyushu | | 20 | HKG | | RTHK (3), Golden Hill |
| | 1 | J | | NHK (1), Matsumoto | | 300 | IND | | AIR, Dibrugarh |
| | 5 | J | JOMG | NHK (1), Miyazaki | | 100 | J | JOIK | NHK (1), Sapporo |
| | 1 | J | | NHK (1), Nanao/Ishigaki | | 100 | KOR | HLKF | KBS, Jeonju |
| | 5 | J | JOJG | NHK (1), Yamagata | | 200 | LAO | | Lao National Radio (N), Vientiane (kM 49) |
| | 1 | KOR | HLSM | KBS, Jangheung | | 50 | NZL | | RNZ (N), Wellington |
| | 1 | NZL | | Rhema, Christchurch | | 300 | PAK | | PBC, Khuzdar |
| | 2 | NZL | | Rhema, New Plymouth | | 5 | PHL | DXCH | Pacific Bc. System, Cotabato C, Mag. |
| | 5 | NZL | | Rhema/Star, Tauranga | | 5 | THA | | JoR. SoR. 5, Chaiyaphum |
| | 300 | PAK | | PBC (1), Peshawar | **570** | 1 | HWA | KUAI | Eleele, Kauai |
| | 1 | PHL | DYRB | DWRL Radio, Inc., Cebu C | **576** | 50 | AUS | 2RN | ABC (N), Sydney |
| | 10 | PHL | DZWT | Mt. Province BC, Baguio C, Benguet | | 100 | BRM | | Myanma Radio (N), Yangon |
| | 5 | SMO | | National Radio 2AP, Apia (repl.mast) | | 200 | CHN | | YN; ZJ(v); EN; FJ |
| | 5 | THA | | Yaan Kraw, Bangkok | | 200 | IND | | AIR, Alappuzha |
| **549** | 50 | AUS | 2CR | ABC (L), Orange | | 1 | J | JODG | NHK (1), Hamamatsu |
| | 25 | CHN | | EN; NM | | 10 | J | JOHG | NHK (1), Kagoshima |
| | 1200 | CHN | | FJ (CNR5) | | 1 | KOR | | KBS, Suncheon (3) |
| | 100 | IND | | AIR, Ranchi A | | 100 | NPL | | R. Nepal, Surkhet |
| | 10 | J | JOAP | NHK (1), Okinawa | | 2.5 | NZL | | Star, Hamilton |
| | 1 | NZL | | R. Sport, Nelson | | 5 | PHL | DZHR | Cebu Bc. Co., Tuguegarao, Cag. |

| kHz | kW | Ctry | Call | Station, location |
|-----|-----|------|------|-------------------|
| | 10 | PHL | DXMF | People's Bc. Sce., Davao C, Dvo Sur |
| | 10 | PHL | DYMR | Philippine Bc. Sce., Cebu C |
| | 10 | PHL | DZMQ | Philippine Bc. Sce., Dagupan C, Pang. |
| | 5 | THA | | ToR. ChoR. DoR., Bangkok |
| | 150 | TKM | | Turkmen Radio (2/3), Asgabat |
| | 50 | VTN | | Khanh Hoa (2/P), Nha Trang |
| **585** | 10 | AUS | 7RN | ABC (N), Hobart |
| | 10 | AUS | 6PB | ABC (P), Perth |
| | 10 | AUS | 2WEB | Bourke (CRS) |
| | 50 | CHN | | JS + 11 stns |
| | 200 | CHN | | Southeast BC, FJ |
| | 300 | IND | | AIR, Nagpur A |
| | 50 | INS | | RRI, Surabaya (4) |
| | 10 | J | JOPG | NHK (1), Kushiro |
| | 20 | LAO | | Lao National Radio (P), Khantabouly |
| | 2 | NZL | | R. Ngati Porou, Ruatoria |
| | 500 | PAK | | PBC, Islamabad |
| | 5 | PHL | DXCP | Catholic Media Netw., Gen. Santos C, S Cot |
| | 1 | PHL | DYLL | Philippine Bc. Sce., Iloilo C |
| | 2 | PNG | | NBC Gulf, Kerema (r. ‡) |
| | 2 | PNG | | NBC Karai, Vanimo (r. ‡) |
| | 10 | PNG | | NBC National, Port Moresby (r. ‡) |
| | 2 | PNG | | NBC Northern, Popondetta (r. ‡) |
| | 2 | PNG | | NBC Western, Daru (r. ‡) |
| | 5 | THA | | ThoR. PhoR. 3, Phrae |
| | 5 | THA | | WoR. PoR. Tho. 15, Chumphon |
| **590** | 7.5 | HWA | KSSK | Honolulu, Oahu |
| **594** | 50 | AUS | 3WV | ABC (L), Horsham |
| | 200 | BRM | | Myanma Radio (N), Naypyidaw |
| | 300 | CHN | | XZ; SD (2 stns) |
| | 1000 | IND | | AIR, Chinsurah, FS |
| | 300 | J | JOAK | NHK (1), Tokyo |
| | 5 | NZL | | Star, Timaru |
| | 2 | NZL | | Star, Wanagnui |
| | 5 | PHL | DXDB | Catholic Media Netw., Malaybalay, Buk. |
| | 20 | PHL | DZBB | GMA Network, Inc., Quezon C, NCR |
| | 5 | THA | | Phon. PoR. ThoR. OR., Bangkok |
| | 10 | TWN | BEH44 | Fu Hsing BS (1), Kaohsiung |
| | 5 | TWN | BEH38 | Fu Hsing BS (2), Taichung |
| | 10 | TWN | BEH2 | Fu Hsing BS (2), Taipei |
| | 50 | VTN | | Danang (1), An Hai |
| **603** | 10 | AUS | 4CH | ABC (L), Charleville |
| | 2 | AUS | 6PH | ABC (L), Port Hedland |
| | 10 | AUS | 2RN | ABC (N), Nowra |
| | 100 | CHN | | EN + 39 stns |
| | 10 | CHN | | GD (CNR1) |
| | 600 | CHN | | HA (CRI) |
| | 200 | IND | | AIR, Ajmer |
| | 5 | J | JOOG | NHK (1), Obihiro |
| | 5 | J | JOKK | NHK (1), Okayama |
| | 500 | KOR | HLSA | KBS, Namyang (Seoul) |
| | 5 | NZL | | R. Waatea, Auckland |
| | 10 | PHL | DZLL | Bicol Bc. System, Naga C, Cam Sur |
| | 5 | PHL | DZVV | Consolidated Bc. Syst., Inc., Vigan, I. Sur |
| | 5 | THA | | WoR. PoR. Tho. 12, Khon Kaen |
| **610** | 200 | VTN | | Ho Chi Minh C. (H), Tang Nhon Phu |
| **612** | 50 | AUS | 4QR | ABC (L), Brisbane |
| | 10 | AUS | 6RN | ABC (N), Dalwallinu |
| | 100 | CHN | | FJ; GD; LN (2stns); SC (2stns) |
| | 200 | IND | | AIR, Bengaluru A |
| | 100 | J | JOLK | NHK (1), Fukuoka |
| | 150 | KGZ | | Kyrgyz R. (1), Bishkek |
| | 2 | NZL | | Star, Christchurch |
| | 2 | NZL | | Star, Nelson |
| | 5 | NZL | | Star, New Plymouth |
| | 5 | PHL | DWSP | Philippine Bc. Corp., Itogon, Benguet |
| | 10 | PHL | DYHP | R. Mindanao Netw., Cebu C |
| | 5 | THA | | MoR. KoR., Chiang Mai |
| | 5 | THA | | WoR. SoR. PoR., Lop Buri |
| **621** | 50 | AUS | 3RN | ABC (N), Melbourne |
| | 2 | AUS | 6EL | Bunbury |

| kHz | kW | Ctry | Call | Station, location |
|-----|-----|------|------|-------------------|
| | 200 | CHN | | HL; HB; QH; SC; SD |
| | 20 | HKG | | RTHK (P), Golden Hill |
| | 100 | IND | | AIR, Patna A |
| | 3 | J | JOCG | NHK (1), Asahikawa |
| | 1 | J | | NHK (1), Iida/Nobeoka |
| | 10 | KOR | | KBS, Seogwipo |
| | 500 | KRE | | Pyongyang BS/VoK, Chongjin |
| | 2 | NZL | | Rhema, Dunedin |
| | 2 | NZL | | Rhema, Whangarei |
| | 1 | PHL | DZVC | Philippine Bc. Sce., Virac, Catanduanes |
| | 10 | PHL | DXDC | R. Mindanao Netw., Davao C, Dvo Sur |
| | 5 | PHL | DZTG | R. Philippines Netw., Tuguegarao, Cag. |
| | 100 | THA | | SoR. WoR. Sor, Khon Kaen |
| | 5 | TUV | | R. Tuvalu, Funafuti |
| | 1 | TWN | | Taiwan BC, Tahsi |
| **630** | 5 | AUS | 6AL | ABC (L), Albany |
| | 50 | AUS | 4QN | ABC (L), Townsville |
| | 0.4 | AUS | 7RN | ABC (N), Queenstown |
| | 10 | AUS | 2PB | ABC (P), Sydney |
| | 100 | BGD | | Bangladesh Betar (B), Dhaka |
| | 200 | CHN | | JX (CNR2); EN (CNR2) |
| | 2.5 | CKH | | R. Cook Is. AM, Rarotonga |
| | 10 | GUM | KUAM | Agana |
| | 100 | IND | | AIR, Thrissur |
| | 50 | INS | | RRI, Makassar |
| | 10 | KOR | | KBS, Yeosu |
| | 10 | NZL | | RNZ (N), Hawkes Bay |
| | 100 | PAK | | PBC (1), Lahore |
| | 50 | PHL | DZMM | ABS-CBN Bc. Corp., Quezon C, NCR |
| | 10/5 | PHL | DYWB | Consolidated Bc. Syst., Inc., Bacolod C, Neg. Occ. |
| | 5 | THA | | MoR. ThoR. BoR. 11, Bangkok |
| | 10 | TWN | BED65 | BCC (N), Ilan |
| | 10 | TWN | | Taiwan BC, Sungling |
| | 200 | VTN | | Quang Binh (1), Dong Hoi |
| **639** | 1 | AUS | 4MS | ABC (L), Mossman |
| | 10 | AUS | 5CK | ABC (L), Port Pirie |
| | 2 | AUS | 8RN | ABC (N), Katherine |
| | 5 | AUS | 2HC | Coff's Harbour |
| | 400 | BRM | | Thazin Radio (M) |
| | 200/400 | CHN | | BJ (CNR1); SC (CNR1) |
| | 100 | IND | | AIR, Kohima |
| | 5 | J | JOIP | NHK (1), Oita |
| | 10 | J | JOPB | NHK (2), Shizuoka |
| | 5 | J | JOWN | STV, Hakodate |
| | 2 | NZL | | RNZ (N), Alexandra |
| | 100 | PAK | | PBC, Karachi (Landhi) |
| | 5 | PHL | DXKR | R. Mindanao Netw., Koronadal, Cot. Sur |
| | 1 | PHL | DZRL | R. Philippines Netw., Batac, I. Nte |
| | 10 | THA | | R. Thailand, Chiang Mai |
| | 20 | THA | | R. Thailand, N. Si Thammarat (r. ‡) |
| **648** | 2 | AUS | 6GF | ABC (L), Kalgoorlie |
| | 10 | AUS | 2NU | ABC (L), Tamworth |
| | 50 | CHN | | GD + 4 stns |
| | 200 | IND | | AIR, Indore A |
| | 10 | J | | AFN, Okinawa C. |
| | 5 | J | JOIG | NHK (1), Toyama |
| | 100 | NPL | | R. Nepal, Dhankuta |
| | 5 | PHL | DYRC | Manila Bc. Co., Cebu C |
| | 10 | PHL | DWRH | Pacific Bc. System, Santiago C, Isa. |
| | 10 | PHL | DWRM | Philippine Bc. Sce., Pto. Princesa, Palawan |
| | 3 | PHL | DXMB | R. Mindanao Netw., Malaybalay, Buk. |
| | 25 | THA | | R. Thailand, Khon Kaen |
| | 20 | TWN | BED34 | BCC (N), Taipei (Tucheng) |
| | 50 | VTN | | Binh Dinh (1), An Nhon |
| **650** | 10 | HWA | KPRP | Honolulu, Oahu |
| **657** | 10 | AUS | 2BY | ABC (L), Byrock |
| | 2 | AUS | 8RN | ABC (N), Darwin |
| | 2 | AUS | 6RF | Niche R. Netw., Perth (HPON) |
| | 300 | CHN | | EN; JL; ZJ |
| | 5 | CHN | | FJ (CNR1) |

| kHz | kW | Ctry | Call | Station, location |
|---|---|---|---|---|
| | 200 | IND | | AIR, Kolkata A |
| | 50 | KOR | HLKM | KBS, Chuncheon |
| | 1500 | KRE | | Pyongyang BS, Kangnam |
| | 10 | NZL | | RNZ (AM)/Star, Tauranga |
| | 50 | NZL | | RNZ (AM)/Star, Wellington |
| | 5 | PHL | DXDD | Dan-ag sa Dakbayan Bc. Corp., Ozamis C, Mis. Occ. |
| | 1 | PHL | DYES | Philippine Bc. Sce., Borongan, E. Samar |
| | 5 | PHL | DWRN | Philippine R. Corp., Naga C, Cam. Sur |
| | 5 | PHL | DYVR | R. Mindanao Netw., Roxas C, Capiz |
| | 1 | PHL | DZLU | Satellite Bc. Corp., S. Fernando C, LU |
| | 5 | THA | | JoR. SoR. 1, Bangkok |
| | 20 | TWN | BEV59 | Cheng Sheng BC (2), Taichung |
| | 100 | VTN | | Ho Chi Minh C. (1/C), Quan Tre |
| 666 | 5 | AUS | 2CN | ABC (L), Canberra |
| | 2 | AUS | 4CC | Biloela (t) |
| | 1 | AUS | 6LN | Carnarvon |
| | 2 | AUS | 4LM | Mt. Isa |
| | 200 | CHN | | QH + 10 stns |
| | 600 | CHN | | VO Strait, FJ |
| | 100 | IND | | AIR, New Delhi B |
| | 100 | J | JOBK | NHK (1), Osaka |
| | 35 | PHL | DZRH | Manila Bc. Co., Makati C, NCR |
| | 10 | PHL | DXRP | Philippine Bc. Sce., Davao C, Dvo Sur (r. ‡) |
| | 5 | THA | | ThoR. PhoR. 2, Surin |
| | 50 | VTN | | Khanh Hoa (1), Nha Trang |
| 670 | 5 | HWA | KPUA | Hilo, Hawaii |
| 675 | 10 | AUS | 2CO | ABC (L), Albury |
| | 5 | AUS | 6BE | ABC (L), Broome |
| | 200 | CHN | | NM; XJ; YN (2 stns); ZJ |
| | 10 | HKG | | RTHK (6), Peng Chau |
| | 20 | IND | | AIR, Bhadravathi |
| | 20 | IND | | AIR, Chhatarpur |
| | 100 | IND | | AIR, Itanagar |
| | 5 | J | JOVK | NHK (1), Hakodate |
| | 5 | J | JOUG | NHK (1), Yamaguchi |
| | 10 | KOR | | KBS, Jeonju (3) |
| | 10 | NZL | | RNZ (N), Christchurch |
| | 5 | PHL | DYKC | R. Philippines Netw., Mandaue, Cebu |
| | 1 | PHL | DXGD | Sulu Tawi-Tawi Bc. Found., Bongao, Tawi-Tawi |
| | 2 | PNG | | NBC Wewak (r. ‡) |
| | 5 | THA | | SoR. ThoR. RoR. 2, Bangkok |
| | 10 | TKM | | Turkmen R. (2/3), Türkmenbasy |
| | 5 | TWN | | Cheng Sheng BC, Peikang |
| | 500 | VTN | | Hung Yen (1), My Hao |
| 684 | 5 | AUS | 6BS | ABC (L), Busselton |
| | 10 | AUS | 2KP | ABC (L), Kempsey |
| | 1 | AUS | 8RN | ABC (N), Tennant Creek |
| | 1200 | CHN | | FJ (CNR6) |
| | 200 | CHN | | GS + 9 stns |
| | 600 | CHN | | HA (CRI) |
| | 200 | IND | | AIR, Kargil A |
| | 100 | IND | | AIR, Kozhikode A |
| | 100 | IND | | AIR, Port Blair |
| | 5 | J | JODF | IBC, Morioka |
| | 1 | J | JOLO | IBC, Ofunato |
| | 5 | J | JOAG | NHK (1), Nagasaki |
| | 100 | NPL | | R. Nepal, Pokhara |
| | 5 | PHL | DZCV | Filipinas Bc. Netw.,., Tuguegarao, Cag. |
| | 5 | PHL | DWJJ | Kaissar Bc. Netw., Cabanatuan, Nva. Ecija |
| | 10 | PHL | DYEZ | Manila Bc. Co., Bacolod, Neg. Occ. |
| | 5 | THA | | ThoR. PhoR. 4, N. Si Thammarat |
| | 5 | THA | | Yaan Kraw, Udon Thani |
| | 10 | TWN | BEC22 | VO Han Bc. Netw., Taipei |
| 690 | 10 | HWA | KHNR | Honolulu, Oahu |
| 693 | 2 | AUS | 5SY | ABC (L), Streaky Bay |
| | 10/5 | AUS | 4KQ | Brisbane |
| | 1 | AUS | 4LM | Cloncurry (t) |
| | 5 | AUS | 6WR | Kununurra (CRS) |
| | 5 | AUS | 3AW | Melbourne |
| | 0.5 | AUS | 4KZ | Tully (t) |
| | 1000 | BGD | | Bangladesh Betar (A), Dhaka |
| | 300 | CHN | | SN; HL |
| | 500 | J | JOAB | NHK (2), Tokyo |
| | 5 | NZL | | R. Sport, Dunedin |
| | 1 | PHL | DYKX | Manila Bc. Co., Kalibo, Aklan |
| | 10 | PHL | DYPH | Manila Bc. Co., Pto. Princesa, Palawan |
| | 10 | PHL | DXBC | R. Mindanao Netw., Butuan, Ag. Nte |
| | 1 | PHL | DXDX | R. Philippines Netw., Gen. Santos C, S. Cot |
| | 10/5 | PHL | DZTP | Tirad Pass R/TV Bc. Netw., Candon, I. Sur |
| | 5 | THA | | Siang Adison, Saraburi |
| | 8 | TWN | BEC32 | VO Han Bc. Netw., Tainan |
| | 10 | TWN | BEC25 | VO Han Bc. Netw., Taoyuan |
| 702 | 10 | AUS | 6KP | ABC (L), Karratha |
| | 50 | AUS | 2BL | ABC (L), Sydney |
| | | CHN | | GD (CRI DS) |
| | 200 | CHN | | JS + 6 stns |
| | 200 | IND | | AIR, Jalandhar A, FS |
| | 10 | INS | | RRI, Manokwari |
| | 10 | J | JOFB | NHK (2), Hiroshima |
| | 10 | J | JOKD | NHK (2), Kitami |
| | 50 | KRE | | Korean Central BS (C/R), Chongjin |
| | 10 | NZL | | Magic, Auckland |
| | 1 | NZL | | R. Sport, Ashburton |
| | 50 | PHL | DZAS | FEBC, Valenzuela, NCR |
| | 150 | TJK | | TR (1), Orzu |
| | 50 | VTN | | Danang (2/Q/D), An Hai |
| 705 | 10 | LAO | | Lao National Radio (P), Luang Prabang |
| 711 | 10 | AUS | 4QW | ABC (L), Roma/St. George |
| | 10 | CHN | | QH + 7 stns |
| | 200 | IND | | AIR, Siliguri |
| | 500 | KOR | HLKA | KBS, Sorae (Seoul) |
| | 5 | NZL | | TAB Trackside R., Wellington |
| | 100 | PAK | | PBS, Dera Ismail Khan |
| | 5 | PHL | DZVR | Newsounds Bc. Netw., Laoag, I. Nte |
| | 5 | PHL | DXIC | R. Mindanao Netw., Iligan C, Lanao Nte |
| | 5 | PHL | DXRD | Swara Sug Media Corp., Davao C, Dvo. Sur |
| | 5 | PHL | DZYI | Swara Sug Media Corp., Ilagan, Isa. |
| | 20 | THA | | SoR. WoR. Sor, U. Ratchathani |
| | 5 | THA | | WoR. PoR. ThoR., Chiang Mai |
| | 5 | THA | | WoR. SoR. PoR., Lop Buri |
| | 10 | TWN | BED92 | BCC (C), Tainan |
| | 250 | TWN | | VO Kuanghua, Hsinfeng |
| | 500 | VTN | | Can Tho (1), Thoi Long |
| 720 | 0.05 | AUS | 2RN | ABC (N), Armidale |
| | 4 | AUS | 4AT | ABC (L), Atherton |
| | 0.4 | AUS | 2ML | ABC (L), Murwillumbah |
| | 2 | AUS | 3MT | ABC (L), Omeo |
| | 50 | AUS | 6WF | ABC (L), Perth |
| | 200 | CHN | | BJ (CNR16) |
| | 50 | CHN | | FJ (CNR2) (2 stns) |
| | 10 | CHN | | JL(CNR8) |
| | 1 | CHN | | SC; AH (2 stns) |
| | 10 | CHN | | XJ (CNR13) (2 stns) |
| | 200 | IND | | AIR, Chennai A |
| | 10 | INS | | RRI, Ambon |
| | 1 | J | JOIL | KBC, Kitakyushu |
| | 500 | KRE | | Korean Central BS (C/R), Wiwon (Kanggye) |
| | 10 | NZL | | RNZ (N), Invercargill |
| | 5 | PHL | DZJO | Bayanihan Bc. Corp., San Juan, NCR |
| | 1 | PHL | DYOK | Manila Bc. Co., Iloilo C |
| | 5 | PHL | DZSO | Newsounds Bc. Netw., San Fernando, LU |
| | 5 | THA | | SoR. ThoR. RoR. 5, Chon Buri |
| | 1 | TKM | | Turkmen Radio (1), Etrek/Yokarça |
| | 10 | TWN | BED58 | BCC (N), Taichung |
| 729 | 50 | AUS | 5RN | ABC (N), Adelaide |
| | 100 | BRM | | Myanma Radio (Y), Yangon |
| | 200 | CHN | | JX; EN |
| | 100 | IND | | AIR, Guwahati A |
| | 10 | INS | | RRI, Nabire |
| | 50 | J | JOCK | NHK (1), Nagoya |

| kHz | kW | Ctry | Call | Station, location |
|---|---|---|---|---|
| | 0.1 | NZL | | Burn 729AM, Ranfurly |
| | 3 | NZL | | R. Sport, Whangarei |
| | 2.5 | NZL | | RNZ (N), Tokoroa |
| | 10 | PHL | DXIF | Newsounds Bc. Netw., Cagayan de Oro C, Mis. OR. |
| | 5 | PHL | DXOR | Pedro N. Roa Bc., Cagayan de Oro C, Mis. OR. |
| | 5 | PHL | DZGB | People's Bc. Netw., Legaspi C, Albay |
| | 10 | PHL | DWPE | Philippine Bc. Sce., Tuguegarao, Cag. |
| | 5 | PHL | DXMY | R. Mindanao Netw., Cotabato C, Mag. |
| | 25 | THA | | R. Thailand, N. Ratchasima |
| | 0.5 | TWN | BEE43 | Shih Hsin BS, Taipei |
| | 200 | VTN | | Quang Binh (2), Dong Hoi |
| **738** | 50 | AUS | 2NR | ABC (L), Grafton |
| | 5 | AUS | 6MJ | ABC (L), Manjimup |
| | 200 | CHN | | HN + 5 stns |
| | 200 | IND | | AIR, Hyderabad A |
| | 1 | J | | KNB, Takaoka |
| | 5 | J | JOLR | KNB, Toyama |
| | 10 | J | JORR | RBC, Naha, Okinawa |
| | 100 | KOR | HLKG | KBS, Daegu |
| | 5 | NZL | | Magic, Christchurch |
| | 60 | PHL | DZRB | Philippine Bc. Sce., Quezon C, NCR |
| | 5 | THA | | WoR. PoR. Tho. 2, Chiang Mai |
| | 5 | THA | | WoR. PoR. Tho. 5, Songkhla |
| | 100 | TWN | BEL2 | Yuyeh BS, Penghu |
| **740** | 5 | HWA | KCIK | Kihei, Maui |
| | 50 | VTN | | Binh Dinh (2/P), An Nhon |
| **747** | 3.5 | AUS | 7PB | ABC (P), Hobart |
| | 0.2 | AUS | 8JB | ABC (L), Jabiru |
| | 10 | AUS | 4QS | ABC (L), Toowoomba |
| | 5 | AUS | 6SE | Esperance |
| | 10 | CHN | | GD (CNR1/12) |
| | 200 | CHN | | SC + 31 stns |
| | 300 | IND | | AIR, Lucknow A |
| | 10 | INS | | RRI, Bengkulu |
| | 500 | J | JOIB | NHK (2), Sapporo |
| | 100 | KOR | HLKH | KBS, Gwangju |
| | 0.4 | NZL | | NewstalkZB, Rotorua |
| | 10 | PHL | DZJC | Manila Bc. Co., Laoag C, I. Nte |
| | 5 | PHL | DXND | Notre Dame Bc. Corp., Kidapawan, N. Cot. |
| | 10 | PHL | DYHB | R. Mindanao Netw., Bacolod, Neg. Occ. |
| | 5 | SMO | | National Radio 2AP, Apia (repl.mast) |
| | 5 | THA | | RoR. DoR., Bangkok |
| | 5 | THA | | ThoR. PhoR. 2, Udon Thani |
| **750** | 1 | CHN | | SX |
| **756** | 2 | AUS | 2TR | ABC (L), Taree |
| | 10 | AUS | 3RN | ABC (N), Wangaratta |
| | 2 | AUS | 6TZ | Margaret River |
| | 50 | CHN | | GD (CNR1) (3 stns) |
| | 150 | CHN | | HL (CNR1 ) |
| | 100 | IND | | AIR, Jagdalpur |
| | 10 | INS | | RRI, Purwokerto |
| | 10 | J | JOGK | NHK (1), Kumamoto |
| | 0.8 | NZL | | Puketapu R., Palmerston |
| | 10 | NZL | | RNZ (N), Auckland |
| | 150 | PAK | | PBC, Quetta (Yaru) |
| | 10 | PHL | DXBZ | Baganian Bc. Corp., Pagadiani, Z Sur |
| | 1 | PHL | DWHL | Beta Bc. Syst., Olongapo C, Zamb. |
| | 10 | PHL | DWRS | Philippine Bc. Sce., Tayug, Pang. |
| | 2 | PHL | DXJM | R. Corp. of Philippines, Butuan C, Ag. Nte |
| | 5 | THA | | KoR. WoR. SoR. 1, Surin |
| | 5 | THA | | NoR. ThoR. PhoR., Narathiwat |
| | 1 | TWN | | Sheng Li chih Sheng BC, Makung |
| | 5 | VTN | | Long An (P), Tan An |
| **760** | 10 | HWA | KGU | Honolulu, Oahu |
| **765** | 5 | AUS | 2EC | Bega |
| | 0.5 | AUS | 4GC | Hughenden (t) |
| | 0.5 | AUS | 8HOT | Katherine (t) |
| | 5 | AUS | 5CC | Port Lincoln |
| | 10 | CHN | | EN + 4 stns |

| kHz | kW | Ctry | Call | Station, location |
|---|---|---|---|---|
| | 600 | CHN | | FJ (CNR5) |
| | 200 | IND | | AIR, Dharwad A |
| | 1 | INS | | RRI, Tual |
| | 5 | J | JOPF | KRY, Shunan |
| | 5 | J | JOJF | YBS, Kofu |
| | 10 | KOR | HLCQ | MBC, Daejeon |
| | 2.5 | NZL | | R. Kahungungu, Hawkes Bay |
| | 5 | PHL | DXGS | DWRL Radio, Inc., Gen. Santos C, S. Cot. |
| | 10 | PHL | DYAP | Palawan Bc. Corp., Pto. Princesa, Palawan |
| | 5 | PHL | DYAR | Swara Sug Media Corp., Cebu C |
| | 5 | PHL | DZYT | Swara Sug Media Corp., Tuguegarao, Cag. |
| | 5 | RUS | | R. Vostok Rossii, Chegdomin, FE + 7 stns |
| | 20 | RUS | | R. Vostok Rossii, Khabarovsk, FE + 1 stn |
| | 5 | THA | | Neung. PoR. NoR., Lampang |
| | 5 | THA | | ThoR. OR. 2, Lop Buri |
| **774** | 50 | AUS | 3LO | ABC (L), Melbourne |
| | 10 | CHN | | BJ (Bejing Int.) |
| | 200 | CHN | | HB; LN; SX; XJ |
| | 100 | IND | | AIR, Shimla |
| | | INS | | RRI, Fak-Fak |
| | 500 | J | JOUB | NHK (2), Akita |
| | 10 | KOR | HLAN | MBC, Chuncheon |
| | 10 | KOR | HLAJ | MBC, Jeju |
| | 5 | NZL | | R. Sport, New Plymouth |
| | 25 | PHL | DWWW | Interactive Bc. Media, Inc., Quezon C, NCR |
| | 10 | PHL | DXSM | Philippine Bc. Sce., Jolo, Sulu |
| | 10 | PHL | DXSO | Philippine Bc. Sce., Marawi C, Lanao Sur |
| | 10 | PHL | DYRI | R. Mindanao Netw., Iloilo C |
| | 5 | THA | | Phon. MoR. 2, Rayong |
| | 5 | THA | | SoR. SoR. SoR., Udon Thani |
| | 20 | TWN | BEV88 | Hsien Sheng BC, Taoyuan |
| | 1 | TWN | BEV56 | Sheng Li chih Sheng BC (1), Tainan |
| | 20 | TWN | BEV94 | Taiwan BC, Taichung |
| **783** | 2 | AUS | 8AL | ABC (L), Alice Springs |
| | 2 | AUS | 6VA | Albany |
| | 100 | CHN | | EB (4 stns); GD |
| | 600 | CHN | | VO Strait, FJ |
| | 20 | HKG | | RTHK (5), Golden Hill |
| | 10 | INS | | RRI, Ende |
| | 5 | PHL | DYME | Masbate Comm. Bc. Co., Masbate C |
| | 5 | PHL | DZNL | Philippine Bc. Corp., San Fernando, LU |
| | 10 | PHL | DXRA | RMC Bc. Co., Inc., Davao C, Dvo Sur |
| | 10 | THA | | R. Thailand, Ranong |
| | 5 | THA | | ThoR. PhoR. 3, Kamphaeng Phet |
| | 500 | VTN | | |
| **790** | 5 | HWA | KKON | Kealakekua, Hawaii |
| **792** | 25 | AUS | 4RN | ABC (N), Brisbane |
| | 200 | CHN | | GX + 6 stns |
| | 100 | IND | | AIR, Pune A |
| | 1 | J | | NHK (1), Takada/Naze |
| | 1 | J | | NHK (1), Takayama/Enbetsu |
| | 50 | KOR | HLSQ | Seoul Bc. System, Goyang (Seoul) |
| | 100 | NPL | | R. Nepal, Kathmandu |
| | 5 | NZL | | R. Sport, Hamilton |
| | 5 | PHL | DWGV | GV Bc. System, Angeles C, Pampanga |
| | 5 | PHL | DYRR | Ormoc Bc. Co., Ormoc C, Leyte |
| | 5 | PHL | DXPD | People's Bc. Sce., Pagadian, Z. Sur |
| | 10 | PHL | DXBN | Philippine Bc. Sce., Butuan, Ag. Nte |
| | 5 | PHL | DWES | Rolin Bc. Enterprises, Narra, Palawan |
| | 5 | THA | | WoR. PoR. ThoR., Bangkok |
| | 1 | TWN | BEV79 | Keelung BS, Keelung |
| | 10 | TWN | BEC33 | VO Han Bc. Netw., Hualien |
| **801** | 2 | AUS | 4QY | ABC (L), Cairns |
| | 2 | AUS | 5RM | Berri |
| | 5 | AUS | 2RF | Niche R. Netw., Gosford (HPON) |
| | 50 | CHN | | GD + 28 stns |
| | 10 | GUM | KTWG | Agana |
| | 200 | IND | | AIR, Jabalpur |
| | 10 | INS | | RRI, Semarang |
| | 500 | KRE | | Pyongyang BS, Kimchaek |
| | 1.5 | NZL | | Rhema, Nelson |

| kHz | kW | Ctry | Call | Station, location |
|---|---|---|---|---|
| | 5 | PHL | DYKA | Catholic Media Netw., San José, Ant. |
| | 5 | PHL | DXES | Consolidated Bc. Syst., Inc., Gen. Santos C, S. Cot. |
| | 5 | PHL | DYWC | Franciscan Bc. Corp., Dumaguete, Neg. OR. |
| | 10 | PHL | DZNC | Newsounds Bc. Netw., Cauayan, Isa. |
| | 1 | PHL | DXBL | Swara Sug Media Corp., Bislig, Surigao S. |
| | 5 | THA | | MoR. ThoR. BoR. No. 31, N. Sawan |
| | 5 | THA | | ThoR. OR. 15, Chiang Rai |
| | 5 | THA | | ThoR. OR. 8, U. Ratchathani |
| | 1 | TWN | | Chien Kuo BS, Hsinhua |
| | 250 | TWN | | VO Kuanghua, Kuanyin |
| 810 | 10 | AUS | 2BA | ABC (L), Bega |
| | 20 | AUS | 6RN | ABC (N), Perth |
| | 200 | CHN | | ZJ + 6 stns |
| | 300 | IND | | AIR, Rajkot A |
| | 7.5 | INS | | RRI, Merauke |
| | 50 | J | | AFN, Tokyo |
| | 20 | KOR | HLCT | MBC, Daegu |
| | 50 | KRE | | Korean Central BS (C/R), Kaesong |
| | 10 | NPL | | R. Nepal, Dipayal |
| | 2 | NZL | | BBC WS NZ, Auckland |
| | 10 | NZL | | RNZ (N), Dunedin |
| | 1 | PHL | DXRG | Philippine Bc. Sce., Gingoog C, Mis. OR. |
| | 10 | PHL | DZRJ | Rajah Bc. Netw., Manila, NCR |
| | 10 | PNG | | NBC Morobe, Lae (r. ‡) |
| | 2 | PNG | | NBC Rabaul (r. ‡) |
| | 20 | THA | | R. Thailand, Nong Khai |
| | 10 | THA | | R. Thailand, Sangkhlaburi |
| | 10 | TWN | BEV54 | Kuo Sheng BC, Changhua |
| 819 | 10 | AUS | 2GL | ABC (L), Glen Innes |
| | 5 | AUS | 6KW | ABC (L), Kununurra |
| | 100 | BGD | | Bangladesh Betar, Dhaka |
| | 200 | CHN | | SX; SD; XJ(2 stns) |
| | 200 | IND | | AIR, New Delhi A |
| | 5 | J | JONK | NHK (1), Nagano |
| | 20 | KOR | HLCN | MBC, Gwangju |
| | 500 | KRE | | Korean Central BS (C), Pyongyang |
| | 10 | NZL | | RNZ (N), Tauranga |
| | 10 | PHL | DYVL | Manila Bc. Co., Tacloban, Leyte |
| | 5 | PHL | DWAR | Swara Sug Media Corp., Laoag C, I. Nte |
| | 10 | PHL | DXUM | Univ. of Mindanao Bc. Netwk, Davao C, Dvo Sur |
| | 1 | PHL | DWMG | Vanguard R. Netw., Solano, Nva Viz |
| | 10 | THA | | R. Thailand, Bangkok (Pathum Thani) |
| | 15 | TJK | | TR (1), Khujand |
| | 10 | TWN | BED28 | BCC (N), Taitung |
| | 5 | TWN | BEV35 | Cheng Sheng BC, Taipei |
| | 20 | VTN | | Dac Lac (2), Buon Ma Tuhot |
| 828 | 10 | AUS | 6GN | ABC (L), Geraldton |
| | 10 | AUS | 3GI | ABC (L), Sale |
| | 1 | AUS | 4GC | Charters Towers |
| | 50 | CHN | | BJ + 7 stns |
| | 10 | CHN | | HL (CNR2) |
| | 20 | IND | | AIR, Panaji B |
| | 20 | IND | | AIR, Silchar |
| | 300 | J | JOBB | NHK (2), Osaka |
| | 2 | NZL | | TAB Trackside R., Palmerston N. |
| | 1 | PHL | DZTC | Govt of Tarlac Prov., Tarlac C |
| | 5 | PHL | DWZR | Hypersonic Bc. Center, Legaspi C, Albay |
| | 10 | PHL | DXCC | R. Mindanao Netw., Cagayan de Oro C, Mis. OR. |
| | 5 | THA | | ThoR. PhoR. 3, Sukhothai |
| | 5 | THA | | WoR. PoR. Tho. 4, N. Si Thammarat |
| | 50 | VTN | | Son La (P) |
| 830 | 10 | HWA | KHVH | Honolulu, Oahu |
| 837 | 1 | AUS | 6ED | ABC (L), Esperance |
| | 10 | AUS | 4RK | ABC (L), Rockhampton |
| | 1000 | CHN | | FJ (CNR5) |
| | 50 | CHN | | HL + 5 stns |
| | 100 | IND | | AIR, Vijayawada A |

| kHz | kW | Ctry | Call | Station, location |
|---|---|---|---|---|
| | 1 | J | | NHK (1), Nayoro |
| | 10 | J | JOQK | NHK (1), Niigata |
| | 50 | KOR | HLKY | CBS, Seoul |
| | 2 | NZL | | RNZ (N), Kaitaia |
| | 2.5 | NZL | | RNZ (N), Whangarei |
| | 10 | PHL | DYFM | Consolidated Bc. Syst., Inc., Iloilo C |
| | 10 | PHL | DXJS | Philippine Bc. Sce., Tandag, S Sur |
| | 5 | PHL | DXRE | Swara Sug Media Corp., Gen. Santos C, S. Cotab. |
| | 5 | THA | | NoR. ThoR. PhoR., Sakon Nakhon |
| | 10 | THA | | R. Thailand, Bangkok (Pathum Thani) |
| 846 | 2.5 | AUS | 6CA | ABC (L), Carnarvon |
| | 10 | AUS | 2RN | ABC (N), Canberra |
| | 5 | AUS | 4EL | Cairns |
| | 100 | BGD | | Bangladesh Betar, Rajshahi (Bogra) |
| | 10 | CHN | | BJ (CRI DS4) |
| | 30 | CHN | | HB + 29 stns |
| | 200 | IND | | AIR, Ahmedabad A |
| | 5 | J | | NHK (1), Koriyama |
| | 1 | J | | NHK (1), Uwajima/Hitoyoshi |
| | | KIR | | R. Kiribati, Kiritimati Is |
| | 10 | KOR | HLAU | MBC, Ulsan |
| | 2 | NZL | | NewstalkZB, Masterton |
| | 50 | PHL | DZRV | R. Veritas, Quezon C, NCR |
| | 10 | THA | | R. Thailand, Phetchabun |
| | 10 | TWN | BEC38 | VO Han Bc. Netw., Penghu |
| | 250 | TWN | | VO Kuanghua, Kuanyin |
| | 10 | VTN | | Thanh Hoa (P) |
| 850 | 5 | HWA | KHLO | Hilo, Hawaii |
| 855 | 10 | AUS | 4QO | ABC (L), Eidsvold |
| | 10 | AUS | 4QB | ABC (L), Pialba |
| | 2 | AUS | 3CR | Melbourne (CRS) |
| | 50 | CHN | | YN (CNR2); XJ (CNR13); NM |
| | 10 | INS | | RRI, Mataram |
| | 10 | KOR | HLCX | MBC, Jeonju |
| | 500 | KRE | | Pyongyang BS, Sangwon |
| | 2 | NZL | | Rhema, Hamilton |
| | 5 | PHL | DXZH | Cebu Bc. Co., Zamboanga C, Z. Sur |
| | 10 | PHL | DZGE | Filipinas Bc. Netw,., Naga C, Cam. Sur |
| | 5 | PHL | DXGO | Pacific Bc. System, Davao C, Dvo Sur |
| | 5 | THA | | MoR. ThoR. BoR. 12, Prachin Buri |
| | 4.6 | TWN | BED27 | BCC (N), Hualien |
| | 1 | TWN | BEV72 | Cheng Sheng BC, Chia-i |
| | 1 | TWN | BEV24 | Min Pen BC (2), Taipei |
| 864 | 2 | AUS | 7RPH | Hobart (CRS) |
| | 2 | AUS | 6AM | Northam |
| | 2 | AUS | 4GR | Toowoomba |
| | 50 | CHN | | AH; EB; EN; SD; ZJ (2 stns) |
| | 10 | HKG | | Hong Kong Comm. Bc. Co., Peng Chau |
| | 100 | IND | | AIR, Shillong |
| | 10 | INS | | RRI, Cirebon |
| | 1 | J | JOXN | CRT, Nasu |
| | 5 | J | JOPR | FBC, Fukui |
| | 3 | J | JOHE | HBC, Asahikawa |
| | 1 | J | | HBC, Enbetsu |
| | 3 | J | JOQF | HBC, Muroran |
| | 10 | J | JOXR | KOR, Naha, Okinawa |
| | 1 | J | JOSO | SBC, Matsumoto |
| | 100 | KOR | HLKR | KBS, Gangneung |
| | 10 | NZL | | NewstalkZB, Invercargill |
| | 5 | PHL | DZWM | Alaminos City Bc. Corp., Alaminos, Pang. |
| | 10 | PHL | DYHH | Philippine Air Force, Bogo, Cebu |
| | 10 | PHL | DZIP | R. Palaweño, Pto. Princesa, Palawan |
| | 5 | PHL | DZSP | Swara Sug Media Corp., San Pablo C, Laguna |
| | 5 | PHL | DWSI | Swara Sug Media Corp., Santiago, Isa. |
| | 2 | PNG | | NBC Madang (r. ‡) |
| | 10 | THA | | R. Thailand, Si Sa Ket |
| | 10 | THA | | R. Thailand, Tak |
| | 10 | TWN | BED25 | BCC (N), Kaohsiung |

| kHz | kW | Ctry | Call | Station, location |
|---|---|---|---|---|
| 873 | 2 | AUS | 6DB | ABC (L), Derby |
| | 2 | AUS | 4AY | Innisfail (HPON) |
| | 6 | AUS | 2GB | Sydney |
| | 100 | BGD | | Bangladesh Betar, Chittagong |
| | 200 | CHN | | China Huayi BC, FJ |
| | 100 | CHN | | HL + 7 stns |
| | 300 | IND | | AIR, Jalandhar B |
| | 500 | J | JOGB | NHK (2), Kumamoto |
| | 250 | KRE | | Pyongyang BS (C/R), Sinuiju |
| | 1 | NZL | | Newstalk ZB, Ashburton |
| | 1 | NZL | | TAB Trackside R., Tauranga |
| | 5 | PHL | DZPA | Abra Comm. Bc. Corp., Bangued, Abra |
| | 5 | PHL | DZRC | Filipinas Bc. Netw.,. Legasci C, Albay |
| | 5 | PHL | DXRB | Swara Sug Media Corp., Butuan C, Ag. Nte |
| | 5 | PHL | DYUP | Univ. of the Philippines in the Visyas, Miagao, Iloilo |
| | 5 | THA | | WoR. KoR. ThoR. MoR., Bangkok |
| | 500 | VTN | | Can Tho (1/3/4), Thoi Long |
| 880 | 2 | HWA | KHCM | Honolulu, Oahu |
| 882 | 5 | AUS | 4BH | Brisbane |
| | 10 | AUS | 6PR | Perth |
| | 2 | AUS | 3RPH | Warrnambool (CRS) |
| | 200 | CHN | | FJ (3 stns) + 10 stns |
| | 400 | CLN | | TWR relay, Puttalam |
| | 300 | IND | | AIR, Imphal |
| | 10 | J | JOPK | NHK (1), Shizuoka |
| | 1 | J | | STV, Esashi |
| | 3 | J | JOWS | STV, Kushiro |
| | 20 | KOR | HLKI | KBS, Daejeon |
| | 75 | MNG | | MRT (1), Mörön |
| | 10 | NZL | | RNZ (AM)/Star, Auckland |
| | 50 | PHL | DWIZ | Aliw Bc. Corp., Navotas, NCR |
| | 10 | PHL | DXMS | Notre Dame Bc. Corp., Cotabato C, Mag. |
| | 10 | PHL | DYOG | Philippine Bc. Sce., Calbayog, W. Samar |
| | 10 | TWN | BEG77 | BCC (N), Hsinchu |
| | 1 | TWN | | Feng Ming BC, Penghu |
| 891 | 50 | AUS | 5AN | ABC (L), Adelaide |
| | 5 | AUS | 4TAB | R. TAB, Townsville (HPON) |
| | 200 | CHN | | NX; LN; NM; SD; XJ |
| | 20 | IND | | AIR, Rampur |
| | 10 | INS | | RRI Ternate |
| | 10 | INS | | RRI, Malang (4) |
| | 20 | J | JOHK | NHK (1), Sendai |
| | 250 | KOR | HLKB | KBS, Busan |
| | 5 | NZL | | Magic, Wellington |
| | 5 | PHL | DZGR | People's Bc. Sce., Tuguegarao, Cag. |
| | 1000 | THA | | R. Thailand, Bangkok (Sara Buri) |
| | 10 | TWN | BED24 | BCC (L), Tainan |
| 900 | 2 | AUS | 8HA | Alice Springs |
| | 2 | AUS | 6BY | Bridgetown |
| | 2 | AUS | 7AD | Devonport |
| | 5 | AUS | 2LM | Lismore |
| | 5 | AUS | 2LT | Lithgow |
| | | CHN | | BJ (CRI DS5) |
| | 10 | CHN | | QH (CNR2) |
| | 100 | CHN | | YN (CRI) |
| | 100 | CHN | | YN + 42 stns |
| | 5 | HWA | KMVI | Kahului, Maui |
| | 100 | IND | | AIR, Kadapa |
| | 5 | J | JOHF | BSS, Yonago |
| | 5 | J | JOHO | HBC, Hakodate |
| | 5 | J | JOZR | RKC, Kochi |
| | 50 | KOR | HLKV | MBC, Seoul |
| | 2.5 | NZL | | Coast, Whangarei |
| | 6 | NZL | | RNZ (AM)/Star, Dunedin |
| | 5 | PHL | DYOW | Consolidated Bc. Syst., Inc., Roxas, Capiz |
| | 5 | PHL | DWNE | Nueva Ecija Prov. Gov., Cabanatuan C, Nva Viz. |
| | 5 | PHL | DXRZ | R. Mindanao Netw., Zamboanga C, Z . Sur |
| | 2 | PNG | | NBC Eastern Highlands, Goroka (r. ‡) |

| kHz | kW | Ctry | Call | Station, location |
|---|---|---|---|---|
| | 10 | PNG | | NBC Kimbe (r. ‡) |
| | 10 | VTN | | Ha Tinh (v) (P) |
| 909 | 300 | CHN | | FJ (CNR6) |
| | 50 | CHN | | SC + 6 stns |
| | 100 | IND | | AIR, Gorakhpur |
| | 10 | INS | | RRI, Sorong |
| | 10 | J | JOCB | NHK (2), Nagoya |
| | 5 | J | JOVX | STV, Abashiri |
| | 5 | NZL | | RNZ (AM)/Star, Hawkes Bay |
| | 5 | PHL | DZEA | Catholic Media Netw., Laoag C, I. Nte |
| | 5 | PHL | DYSP | Republic Bc. System, Pto. Princesa, Palawan |
| | 5 | PHL | DYLA | Visayas Mindanao C. of TU, Cebu C |
| | 10 | THA | | R. Thailand, Dansai (Loei) |
| | 25 | THA | | R. Thailand, Surin |
| | 10 | VTN | | Ca Mau (P) |
| 918 | 2/2.5 | AUS | 4VL | Charleville |
| | 2 | AUS | 2XL | Cooma |
| | 2 | AUS | 6NA | Narrogin |
| | 600 | CBG | | Nat. Radio of Kampuchea, Phnom Penh (Kandal Steung) |
| | 200 | CHN | | SD; GX |
| | 300 | IND | | AIR, Suratgarh |
| | 1 | J | JOPN | KRY, Iwakuni |
| | 1 | J | JOPM | KRY, Shimonoseki |
| | 1 | J | | YBC, Tsuruoka/Yonezawa/Shinjo |
| | 5 | J | JOEF | YBC, Yamagata |
| | 2.5 | NZL | | RNZ (N), New Plymouth |
| | 2.5 | NZL | | RNZ (N), Timaru |
| | 50 | PHL | DZSR | Philippine Bc. Sce., Quezon C, NCR |
| | 5 | PHL | DXRS | R. Mindanao Netw., Surigao C, S. Nte |
| | 10 | THA | | R. Thailand, Bangkok (Pathum Thani) |
| | 10 | THA | | SoR. WoR. PhoR. 1, Chiang Mai |
| 927 | 5 | AUS | 4CC | Gladstone |
| | 5 | AUS | 3UZ | Melbourne |
| | 100 | CHN | | FJ (CNR6) |
| | 200 | CHN | | GZ + 25 stns |
| | 100 | IND | | AIR, Visakhapatnam |
| | 25 | INS | | RRI, Pekanbaru (4) |
| | 5 | J | JOFG | NHK (1), Fukui |
| | 5 | J | JOKG | NHK (1), Kofu |
| | 1 | J | | NHK (1), Wakkanai/Tsuyama |
| | 2 | NZL | | NewstalkZB, Palmerston N. |
| | 5 | PHL | DXDA | Office of Governor, San Francisco, Ag. Sur |
| | 5 | PHL | DZLG | People's Bc. Sce., Legaspi, Albay |
| | 5 | PHL | DXMD | R. Mindanao Netw., Gen. Santos C, S. Cot. |
| | 5 | PHL | DWRS | Solidnorth Bc.Syst., Vigan, I. Sur |
| | 5 | PHL | DXMM | Sulu Tawi-Tawi Bc. Found., Jolo,Sulu |
| | 20 | THA | | SoR. WoR. Sor, Chanthaburi (r. ‡) |
| | 300 | TJK | | Relays |
| | 50 | TKM | | Turkmen Radio (1), Türkmenabat |
| | 10 | TWN | BED43 | BCC (C), Taichung |
| 930 | | CHN | | ZJ |
| 936 | 10 | AUS | 4PB | ABC (P), Brisbane |
| | 10 | AUS | 7ZR | ABC (L), Hobart |
| | 5 | AUS | 6FX | Fitzroy Crossing (CRS) |
| | 200 | CHN | | AH |
| | 100 | IND | | AIR, Tiruchirapalli A |
| | 5 | J | JOTR | ABS, Akita |
| | 1 | J | | MRT, 4 stns |
| | 5 | J | JONF | MRT, Miyazaki |
| | 10 | KOR | | KBS, Changwon (3) |
| | 1 | NZL | | AM936 Chinese R., Auckland |
| | 5 | PHL | DWIM | Insular Bc. System, Calapan, Mind. OR. |
| | 10 | PHL | DXIM | Philippine Bc. Sce. Cagayan de Oro C, Mis. OR. |
| | 1 | PHL | DZXT | R. Corp. of the Philippines, Tarlac C |
| | 1 | PHL | DYCC | R. Mindanao Netw., Calbayog C, W. Samar |
| | 1 | PHL | DYKW | R. Philippines Netw., Binalbagan, Neg. Occ. |
| | 5 | PHL | DXDN | Univ. of Mindanao, Tagum C, Dvo Nte |
| | 50 | THA | | SoR. WoR. Sor, N. Sawan (r. ‡) |

| kHz | kW | Ctry | Call | Station, location |
|---|---|---|---|---|
| | 10 | THA | | ThoR. PhoR. 4, Pattani |
| | 1 | TWN | BEV98 | Cheng Kung BS, Kaohsiung |
| | 5 | TWN | | VO Han Bc. Netw., Taoyuan |
| 940 | 10 | HWA | KKNE | Honolulu, Oahu |
| 945 | 1 | AUS | 4HI | Dysart (t) |
| | 2 | AUS | 3UZ | RSN, Bendigo (HPON) |
| | 50 | CHN | | HL (2 stns); HB (2 stns); NM (3 stns) |
| | 400 | CHN | | JL (CNR 1) |
| | 10 | CHN | | XJ (CNR13) (2 stns) |
| | 100 | IND | | AIR, Sambalpur |
| | 1 | J | | NHK (1), Fukue |
| | 1 | J | JOQP | NHK (1), Hikone |
| | 3 | J | JOIQ | NHK (1), Muroran |
| | 5 | J | JOXK | NHK (1), Tokushima |
| | 2 | NZL | | NewstalkZB, Gisborne |
| | 5 | PHL | DXRO | Swara Sug Media Corp., Cotabato C, Mag. |
| | 10 | PHL | DXDV | Vismin R. & TV Bc. Net, Butuan C, Ag. Nte |
| | 10 | THA | | ThoR. OR. 1, Bangkok |
| | 10 | THA | | ThoR. OR. 2, Kalasin |
| 954 | 0.35 | AUS | 4EL | Gordonvale (t) |
| | 5 | AUS | 2UE | Sydney |
| | 50 | CHN | | NM (2 stns) + 7 stns |
| | 200 | IND | | AIR, Najibabad |
| | 10 | INS | | RRI, Kendari |
| | 100 | J | JOKR | TBS Radio, Tokyo |
| | 1 | NZL | | Coast, Dunedin |
| | 2 | NZL | | TAB Trackside R., Hamilton |
| | 40 | PHL | DZEM | Christian Era Bc. Sce., Quezon City, NCR |
| | 10 | PHL | DWFB | Philippine Bc. Sce., Laoag C, I. Nte |
| | 1 | PHL | DXJT | Philippine Bc. Sce., Tanguб C, Mis Octal |
| | 10 | THA | | ThoR. OR. 10, Phitsanulok |
| | 10 | THA | | ThoR. OR. 16, Chantaburi |
| | 10 | TWN | BEV85 | Chien Kuo BS, Hsinying |
| 963 | 2 | AUS | 6TZ | Bunbury |
| | 5 | AUS | 2RG | Griffith |
| | 5 | AUS | 5SE | Mt. Gambier |
| | 5 | AUS | 4WK | Warwick |
| | 20 | BGD | | Bangladesh Betar, Sylhet |
| | 600 | CHN | | JL (CRI) |
| | 50 | CHN | | LN; EB; HB; XJ (2 stns) |
| | 20 | IND | | AIR, Jalgaon |
| | 10 | INS | | RRI, Jember (r. ‡) |
| | 5 | J | JOTG | NHK (1), Aomori |
| | 5 | J | JOZK | NHK (1), Matsuyama |
| | 1 | J | JOSP | NHK (1), Saga |
| | 1 | J | | NHK (1), Yonago/Hagi |
| | 10 | KOR | HLCR | KBS, Andong |
| | 10 | KOR | HLKS | KBS, Jeju |
| | 10 | NZL | | RNZ (AM)/Star, Christchurch |
| | 5 | PHL | DZNS | Archdiocese of Nueva Segovia, Vigan, I. Sur |
| | 10 | PHL | DXOM | Notre Dame Bc. Corp., Koronadal C, S. Cot. |
| | 10 | PHL | DYMF | People's Bc. Sce., Cebu C |
| | 5 | PHL | DXYZ | Swara Sug Media Corp., Zamboanga C, Z. Sur |
| | 10 | THA | | Phon MoR. 2, Bangkok |
| | 25 | THA | | SoR. WoR. Sor, Krabi |
| | 20 | TWN | BED55 | BCC (C), Taipei (Tucheng) |
| | 10 | TWN | BEV84 | Taiwan BC, Chunghsing |
| 972 | 2 | AUS | 5PB | ABC (P), Adelaide |
| | 0.3 | AUS | 2DU | Cobar (t) |
| | 5 | AUS | 2MW | Murwillumbah |
| | 150 | CHN | | EN; HL; XJ |
| | 300 | IND | | AIR, Cuttack A |
| | 50 | INS | | RRI, Surakarta |
| | 1500 | KOR | HLCA | KBS, Dangjin |
| | 5 | NZL | | Rhema, Wellington |
| | 5 | PHL | DXKH | Cebu Bc. Co., Cagayan de Oro C, Mis. OR. |
| | 1 | PHL | DYSM | Cebu Bc. Co., Catarman, N. Samar |
| | 5 | PHL | DWTI | Katigbak Enterprises, Lucena C, Que. |
| | 5 | PHL | DWFR | Philippine Bc. Sce., Bontoc, Mt. Prov. |

| kHz | kW | Ctry | Call | Station, location |
|---|---|---|---|---|
| | 10 | THA | | NoR. ThoR. PhoR., Phetchabun |
| | 800 | TJK | | VOA R. Aap ki Dunyaa relay, Orzu |
| 981 | 2 | AUS | 3HA | Hamilton |
| | 2 | AUS | 6KG | Kalgoorlie |
| | 5 | AUS | 2NM | Muswellbrook |
| | 200 | CHN | | JL (CNR1); JX (CNR1); GD (CNR1) (3 stns) |
| | 5 | CHN | | SD |
| | 100 | IND | | AIR, Raipur |
| | 1 | J | | NHK (1), Kisofukushima/Sasebo |
| | 2 | NZL | | RNZ (N), Kaikohe |
| | 100 | PAK | | PBC, Turbat |
| | 10 | PHL | DXBR | Consolidated Bc. Syst., Inc., Butuan C, Ag. Nte |
| | 10 | PHL | DYBQ | Intercontinental Bc. Corp., Iloilo C |
| | 5 | PHL | DWMT | Philippine Bc. Corp., Naga C, Cam. Sur |
| | 5 | PHL | DXDR | R. Mindanao Netw., Dipolog, Z. Nte |
| | 10 | PHL | DXOW | R. Pilipino Corp., Davao C, Dvo Sur |
| | 5 | PHL | DZRD | Swara Sug Media Corp., Dagupan C, Pang. |
| | 10 | THA | | Mahaawittayalai Thammasat, Pathum Thani |
| | 25 | THA | | R. Thailand, Mae Hong Son |
| | 20 | THA | | R. Thailand, Nakhon Phanom |
| | 25 | THA | | R. Thailand, Yala |
| | 2 | TWN | BEV68 | Feng Ming BC (2), Kaohsiung |
| | 250 | TWN | | VO Kuanghua, Hsinfeng |
| 990 | 0.5 | AUS | 3RN | ABC (N), Albury-Wodonga |
| | 0.5 | AUS | 8GO | ABC (L), Nhulunbuy |
| | 5 | AUS | 6RPH | Perth (CRS) (‡?) |
| | 5 | AUS | 4RO | Rockhampton |
| | 100 | CHN | | SH; EB; NM (2 stns); YN (2 stns) |
| | 10 | FJI | | Fiji Bc. Corp. Ltd. (RFGold), Suva |
| | 5 | HWA | KIKI | Honolulu, Oahu |
| | 300 | IND | | AIR, Jammu A |
| | 10 | J | JORK | NHK (1), Kochi |
| | 10 | KOR | HLAP | MBC, Changwon |
| | 1 | NZL | | Apna 990, Auckland |
| | 1 | NZL | | TAB Trackside R., Nelson |
| | 5 | PHL | DZMT | Pacific Bc. System, Laoag, I. Nte |
| | 5 | PHL | DYTH | Pacific Bc. System, Tacloban C, Leyte |
| | 5 | PHL | DXBM | Republic Bc. System, Cotabato C, Mag. |
| | 10 | PHL | DZIQ | Trans-Radio Bc. Corp., Makati C, NCR |
| | 10 | THA | | SoR. WoR. PhoR. 2, N. Ratchasima |
| | 20 | TWN | BEV58 | Cheng Sheng BC (1), Taichung |
| 999 | 2 | AUS | 2NB | ABC (L), Broken Hill |
| | 5 | AUS | 2ST | Nowra |
| | 10 | BGD | | Bangladesh Betar, Thakurgaon |
| | 200 | CHN | | LN + 9 stns |
| | 1 | FSM | V6AF | Baptist R. Pohnpei, Kolonia |
| | 1 | IND | | AIR, Almora |
| | 20 | IND | | AIR, Coimbatore |
| | 150 | INS | | RRI, Jakarta (3) |
| | 1 | J | | NHK (1), Fukuyama/Hachinoe |
| | 1 | J | | NHK (1), Nakamura |
| | 10 | KOR | HLCL | CBS, Gwangju |
| | 1.5 | NZL | | Access Manawatu R., Palmerston N. |
| | 5 | PHL | DWMI | Katigbak Enterprises, Calapan, Mind. OR. |
| | 5 | PHL | DZEQ | Philippine Bc. Sce., Baguio C, Benguet |
| | 1 | PHL | DXPT | Philippine Bc. Sce., Bongao, Tawi-Tawi |
| | 1 | PHL | DXHP | R. Mindanao Netw., Bislig, S. Sur |
| | 5 | PHL | DYSS | Republic Bc. System, Cebu C |
| | 10 | THA | | Phon. Neung RoR. OR., Bangkok |
| | 10 | THA | | ThoR. PhoR. 3, Chiang Rai |
| | 1 | TWN | BEV92 | Tien Nan BS, Taipei |
| 1008 | 10 | AUS | 4TAB | Brisbane |
| | 5 | AUS | 7TAB | R. TAB, Launceston (HPON) |
| | 0.3 | AUS | 2TAB | Sky Sports R., Canberra (HPON) |
| | 2 | AUS | 6TAB | TAB R., Geraldton (HPON) |
| | 1 | CHN | | BJ (CNR DS3) |
| | 50 | CHN | | TJ + 24 stns |
| | 3 | CHN | | XJ (CNR DS) |
| | 200 | CHN | | YN (CNR1) |
| | 100 | IND | | AIR, Kolkata B |

| kHz | kW | Ctry | Call | Station, location |
|---|---|---|---|---|
| | 10 | INS | | RRI, Gorontalo |
| | 10 | INS | | RRI, Madiun |
| | 50 | J | JONR | ABC, Osaka |
| | 50 | KOR | | KBS, Gangneung (3) |
| | 10 | NZL | | NewstalkZB, Tauranga |
| | 120 | PAK | | PBC (city), Hyderabad |
| | 5 | PHL | DWBS | Catholic Media Netw., Sto. Domingo, Albay |
| | 10 | PHL | DXXX | R. Philippines Netw., Zamboanga C, Z. Sur (v) |
| | 5 | PHL | DWGO | Subic Bc. Corp., Olongapo C, Zamb. |
| | 10 | THA | | WoR. PoR. Tho 3, N. Ratchasima |
| | 10 | TWN | BED88 | BCC (C), Taitung |
| | 1 | TWN | BEV60 | Cheng Sheng BC, Kaohsiung |
| **1017** | 0.5 | AUS | 6WH | ABC (L), Wyndham |
| | 5 | AUS | 2KY | Sydney |
| | 1 | AUS | 6TAB | Vision ChR. R., Bunbury (HPON) |
| | 50 | CHN | | GD (2 stns); EB; QH |
| | 600 | CHN | | JL (CNR8/CRI) |
| | 1 | CHN | | ZJ (CNR1) |
| | 20 | IND | | AIR, Chennai B |
| | 50 | J | JOLB | NHK (2), Fukuoka |
| | 10 | KOR | HLAW | MBC, Andong |
| | 10 | NZL | | NewstalkZB, Christchurch |
| | 10 | PHL | DWDC | Intercontinental Bc. Corp., Dagupan C, Pang. |
| | 10 | PHL | DXRR | Kalayaan Bc. System, Davao C, Dvo Sur |
| | 10 | PHL | DWLC | Philippine Bc. Sce., Lucena C, Que. |
| | 5 | PHL | DXSN | Silangan Bc. Corp., Surigao C, S. Nte |
| | 10 | THA | | ThoR. OR. 5, Prachuap KK |
| | 10 | TON | A3Z | Tonga Bc. Comm., Nuku'alofa |
| | 10 | TWN | BED53 | BCC (C), Hsinchu |
| **1026** | 14.5 | AUS | 3PB | ABC (P), Melbourne |
| | 5 | AUS | 4AA | Mackay |
| | 200 | CHN | | GZ; BJ + 4 stns |
| | 20 | IND | | AIR, Allahabad A |
| | 5 | INS | | RRI, Serui |
| | 2 | NZL | | Newstalk ZB, Kaitaia/Whangarei |
| | 2.5 | NZL | | Star, Invercargill |
| | 5 | PHL | DXMC | People's Bc. Sce., Koronadal, S. Cot. |
| | 10 | PHL | DZAR | Swara Sug Media Corp., Quezon C, NCR |
| | 10 | THA | | R. Thailand, Betong (Yala) |
| | 25 | THA | | R. Thailand, Phitsanulok |
| | 1 | TWN | BEV51 | Chung Hua BC (2), Sanchung |
| | 1 | TWN | | Tien Sheng BS, Yuanli |
| **1035** | 2 | AUS | 2EA | Wollongong (SBS) |
| | 50 | CHN | | HB (CNR1); LN (CNR1) |
| | 20 | IND | | AIR, Guwahati B |
| | 5 | INS | | RRI, Bandar Lampung |
| | | INS | | RRI, Palu |
| | 1 | J | JOHD | NHK (2), Takamatsu |
| | 1 | J | JOIC | NHK (2), Toyama |
| | 1 | J | | NHK (2), Tsuruoka |
| | 10 | KOR | HLCP | KBS, Pohang |
| | 20 | NZL | | Newstalk ZB, Wellington |
| | 100 | PAK | | PBC, Multan |
| | 5 | PHL | DZWX | Consolidated Bc. Syst., Inc., Baguio C, Benguet |
| | 10 | PHL | DYRL | R. Pilipino Corp., Bacolod C, Neg. Occ. |
| | 5/1 | PHL | DXUZ | Univ. de Zamboanga, Ipil, Z. Sib (v) |
| | 6 | SLM | | SIBC, Honiara |
| | 10 | THA | | Phaak Phiset, Bangkok |
| | 10 | TWN | BED26 | BCC (C), Chia-i |
| **1040** | 10 | HWA | KLHT | Honolulu, Oahu |
| **1044** | 1 | AUS | 6BR | ABC (L), Bridgetown |
| | 2 | AUS | 2UH | ABC (L), Muswellbrook |
| | 0.5 | AUS | 4WP | ABC (L), Weipa |
| | 2 | AUS | 5AU | Port Pirie (t) |
| | 600 | CHN | | JS (CRI) |
| | 10 | CHN | | XJ (2 stns); YN |
| | 10 | HKG | | Metro Bc. Corp., Peng Chau |
| | 100 | IND | | AIR, Mumbai A |
| | 2 | INS | | RRI, Biak |
| | 10 | INS | | RRI, Sibolga |
| | 1 | KOR | | AFNK, Chuncheon |
| | 10 | NZL | | NewstalkZB, Dunedin |
| | 5 | PHL | DYMS | Cebu Bc. Co., Catbalogan, W. Samar (v) |
| | 10 | PHL | DZNG | Newsounds Bc. Netw., Naga C, Cam. Sur (v) |
| | 5 | PHL | DXCO | R. Pilipino Corp., Cayagan de Oro, Mis. OR. |
| | 5 | PHL | DXLL | R. T. Bc. Specialists Phil., Zamboanga C, Z. Sur |
| | 10 | THA | | KoR. WoR. SoR. 5, Khon Kaen |
| | 10 | THA | | ThoR. PhoR. 4, N. Si Thammarat |
| | 5 | TWN | BEV64 | Yen Sheng BS (1), Hualien |
| **1050** | | CHN | | ZJ |
| **1053** | 5 | AUS | 2CA | Canberra, ACT |
| | 0.5 | AUS | 4RF | R. Rhythm, Brisbane (HPON) |
| | 10 | BGD | | Bangladesh Betar, Rangpur |
| | 10 | CHN | | BJ (CNR 10) |
| | 50 | CHN | | LN + 15 stns |
| | 20 | IND | | AIR, Leh |
| | 200 | IND | | AIR, Tuticorin, FS |
| | 50 | J | JOAR | CBC, Nagoya |
| | 2 | NZL | | NewstalkZB, New Plymouth |
| | 100 | PAK | | PBC, Larkana |
| | 10 | PHL | DXKD | R. Philippines Netw., Dipolog, Z. Nte |
| | 5 | PHL | DYSA | Univ. of San Agustin, Iloilo C |
| | 10 | THA | | MoR. ThoR. BoR. 11, Bangkok |
| **1060** | 5 | HWA | KIPA | Hilo, Hawaii |
| **1062** | 2 | AUS | 5MV | ABC (L), Renmark/Loxton |
| | 2 | AUS | 4TI | ABC (L), Thursday Isl. |
| | 150 | CHN | | Zhujiang EBS, GD; GD;HL |
| | 100 | IND | | AIR, Passighat |
| | 50 | KOR | HLKQ | KBS, Cheongju |
| | 1 | NZL | | R. Sport, Wanganui |
| | 40 | PHL | DZEC | Eagle Bc. Corp., Quezon C, NRC |
| | 5 | PHL | DXKI | FEBC, Koronadal C, S. Cot. |
| | 10/5 | PHL | DYEC | Puerto Princesa Bc.Co., Pto Princesa C, Palawan |
| | 10 | THA | | R. Thailand, Phuket |
| | 10 | THA | | ThoR. OR. 9, Udon Thani |
| | 10 | TWN | BED23 | BCC (L), Taichung |
| | 1 | TWN | BEV82 | Cheng Sheng BC, Ilan |
| | 5 | TWN | BEV74 | Min Li BS, Pingtung |
| | 1 | TWN | | Taiwan BC, Kuanhsi |
| **1071** | 2 | AUS | 6WB | Katanning |
| | 2 | AUS | 4SB | Kingaroy |
| | 5 | AUS | 3EL | Maryborough |
| | 100 | CHN | | XJ + 8 stns |
| | 1000 | IND | | AIR, Rajkot, FS |
| | 20 | J | JOFK | NHK (1), Hiroshima |
| | 5 | J | JOWM | STV, Obihiro |
| | 100 | KAZ | | Shygyz Qazaqstan OTRK, Ösqemen |
| | 2.5 | NZL | | RNZ (N), Masterton |
| | 1 | NZL | | TAB Trackside R., Ashburton |
| | 5 | PHL | DXKT | R. Philippines Netw., Davao C, Dvo Sur |
| | 1 | PHL | DZSL | S. O. L. Telebc. Station, Talisay, Cam Nte |
| | 1 | PHL | DYXT | Universal Bc. System, Tagbilaran C, Bohol |
| | 10 | THA | | SW Rattasapha, Bangkok |
| | 1 | TWN | BEV96 | Tien Sheng BS, Tainan |
| **1080** | 2 | AUS | 2MO | Gunnedah |
| | 2 | AUS | 6IX | Perth |
| | 5 | AUS | 7TAB | R. TAB, Hobart (HPON) |
| | 10 | BGD | | Bangladesh Betar, Rajshahi |
| | 10 | CHN | | JS + 4 stns |
| | 600 | CHN | | YN (CRI) |
| | 5 | HWA | KWAI | Honolulu, Oahu |
| | 10 | INS | | RRI, Singaraja |
| | 10 | KOR | HLAT | MBC, Yeosu |
| | 1.1 | MRA | KCNM | Choice Bc. Comp., Chalan Kiya, Saipan |
| | 10 | NZL | | NewstalkZB, Auckland |
| | 5 | PHL | DWRL | DWRL Radio, Inc., Legaspi C, Albay |
| | 5 | PHL | DWIN | Eagle Bc. Corp., Dagupan C, Pang. |

| kHz | kW | Ctry | Call | Station, location |
|---|---|---|---|---|
| | 5 | PHL | DYBH | Pacific Bc. System, Bacolod C, Neg Occ |
| | 1 | PHL | DXKS | R. Philippines Netw., Surigao, S. Nte |
| | 10 | THA | | WoR. PoR. Tho. 10, Chiang Rai |
| | 10 | THA | | WoR. PoR. Tho. 16, Yala |
| | 10 | THA | | WoR. PoR. Tho. 9, N. Sawan |
| | 5 | TKM | | Turkmen Radio (1), Serhetabat |
| 1089 | 5 | AUS | 3WM | Horsham |
| | 5 | AUS | 2EL | Orange |
| | 600 | CHN | | FJ (CNR6) |
| | 200 | CHN | | LN; HN |
| | 20 | IND | | AIR, Naushera |
| | 20 | IND | | AIR, Udipi |
| | 10 | J | JOHB | NHK (2), Sendai |
| | 2.5 | NZL | | R. Sport, Palmerston N. |
| | 10 | PHL | DXCM | Univ. of Mindanao, Cotabato C, Mag. |
| | 10 | TWN | BEG28 | Kaohsiung BS, Kaohsiung |
| | 10 | VTN | | Cao Bang (P) (r. ‡) |
| 1098 | 0.2 | AUS | 2RN | ABC (N), Goulburn |
| | 2 | AUS | 4LG | Longreach |
| | 2 | AUS | 6MD | Merredin |
| | 1000 | CHN | | QH (CNR1/11) |
| | 50 | CHN | | TJ + 22 stns |
| | 10 | INS | | RRI, Jambi |
| | 10 | INS | | RRI, Sumenep |
| | 1 | J | JOMF | NBC, Sasebo |
| | 5 | J | JOGF | OBS, Oita |
| | 5 | J | JOWO | RFC, Koriyama |
| | 1 | J | JOSW | SBC, Iida |
| | 5 | J | JOSR | SBC, Nagano |
| | 20 | KOR | HLCJ | KBS, Jinju |
| | 25 | MHL | V7AB | R. Marshall Islands, Majuro |
| | 5 | NZL | | NewstalkZB, Christchurch |
| | 10 | PHL | DWAD | Crusaders Bc. System, Mandaluyong C, NCR |
| | 5 | PHL | DXCL | Swara Sug Media Corp., Cagayan de Oro C, Mis. OR. |
| | 10 | THA | | R. Thailand, Mae Sot |
| | 10 | THA | | SoR. WoR. PhoR. 3, Songkhla |
| | 300 | TWN | | RTI, Kouhu |
| | 10 | VTN | | Thua Tien Hue (P), Hue |
| 1107 | 5 | AUS | 2EA | Sydney (SBS) |
| | 100 | CHN | | XJ + 7 stns |
| | 20 | IND | | AIR, Kalaburgi |
| | 5 | INS | | RRI, Kupang |
| | 10 | INS | | RRI, Yogyakarta (4) |
| | 1 | J | | MBC, Akune/Oguchi/Sendai |
| | 20 | J | JOCF | MBC, Kagoshima |
| | 5 | J | JOMR | MRO, Kanazawa |
| | 1 | J | | MRO, Nanao |
| | 10 | KOR | HLAV | MBC, Pohang |
| | 1 | NZL | | R. Live, Tauranga/Rotorua |
| | 1 | PHL | DZOM | Ben Viduya, Calapan C, Mind. OR. |
| | 5 | PHL | DYIN | Inter-Island Broadc. Corp., Kalibo, Aklan |
| | 10 | PHL | DWDY | Northeastern Bc. Sce., Cauayan, Isa. |
| | 5 | PHL | DXBB | Sarangani Bc. Network, Gen. Santos C, S. Cot. |
| | 10 | PNG | | NBC Alotau (r. ‡) |
| | 10 | THA | | MoR. KoR., Bangkok (Samut Sakhon) |
| | 10 | THA | | ThoR. PhoR. 2, Khon Kaen |
| 1110 | 5 | HWA | KAOI | Kihei, Maui |
| 1116 | 6.3/17 | AUS | 4BC | Brisbane |
| | 2 | AUS | 6MM | Mandurah |
| | 5 | AUS | 3AK | Melbourne |
| | 600 | CHN | | FJ (CNR5) |
| | 120 | CHN | | HL (CNR2) |
| | 200 | CHN | | SC; AH; HA; SD |
| | 300 | IND | | AIR, Srinagar A |
| | 5 | J | JODR | BSN, Niigata |
| | 5 | J | JOAF | RNB, Matsuyama |
| | 1 | J | JOAL | RNB, Niihama |
| | 1 | J | JOAM | RNB, Uwajima |

| kHz | kW | Ctry | Call | Station, location |
|---|---|---|---|---|
| | 2.5 | NZL | | RNZ (N), Nelson |
| | 5 | PHL | DYAG | Cadiz R. And TV Netw., Cadiz C, Neg. Occ. |
| | 5 | PHL | DXAS | FEBC, Zamboanga C, Z. Sur |
| | 10 | PHL | DYTR | Tagbilaran Bc. Corp., Tagbilaran C, Bohol |
| | 5 | PHL | DZLB | Univ. of the Philippines, Los Banos, Laguna |
| | 10 | THA | | R. Thailand, Takua Pa (Phang Nga) |
| | 10 | THA | | ThoR. PhoR. 3, Phitsanulok |
| | 3.5 | TWN | BED72 | BCC (N), Yuli |
| | 10 | TWN | BEC30 | VO Han Bc. Netw., Ilan |
| | 10 | TWN | BEC22 | VO Han Bc. Netw., Taipei |
| 1125 | 2 | AUS | 1RPH | Canberra (CRS) |
| | 5 | AUS | 5MU | Murray Bridge |
| | 50 | CHN | | HB (2 stns); EB |
| | 50 | CLN | | WRN relay, Puttalam |
| | 20 | IND | | AIR, Tezpur |
| | 20 | IND | | AIR, Udaipur |
| | 1 | J | | NHK (2), Hagi/Nayoro |
| | 1 | J | JOIZ | NHK (2), Muroran |
| | 10 | J | JOAD | NHK (2), Naha, Okinawa |
| | 1 | J | JOOC | NHK (2), Obihiro |
| | 1 | J | | NHK (2), Takayama |
| | 1 | J | JOLC | NHK (2), Tottori |
| | | NZL | | R. Hauraki, Dunedin |
| | 1 | NZL | | R. Sport, Hawkes Bay |
| | 10 | PHL | DZWN | Consolidated Bc. Syst., Inc., Dagupan C, Pang. |
| | 10 | PHL | DXGL | PEC Bc. Corp., Butuan C, Ag. Nte |
| | 5 | PHL | DXGM | Republic Bc. System, Davao C, Dvo. Sur |
| | 25 | THA | | R. Thailand, Chanthaburi |
| | 20 | TKM | | Turkmen Radio (1), Asgabat |
| | 5 | TWN | BEV36 | Cheng Sheng BC, Yunlin |
| | 10 | VUT | | R. Vanuatu (VBTC), Efate |
| 1130 | 1 | HWA | KPHI | Honolulu, Oahu |
| 1134 | 2 | AUS | 2AD | Armidale |
| | 5 | AUS | 3CS | Colac |
| | 2 | AUS | 6TZ | Collie(t) |
| | 10 | CHN | | SN; GS; XJ; ZJ |
| | 1000 | IND | | AIR, Chinsurah (Mogra) |
| | 100 | J | JOQR | NCB, Tokyo |
| | 500 | KOR | HLKC | KBS, Hwaseong |
| | 2 | NZL | | RNZ (N), Queenstown |
| | 100 | PAK | | PBC (city), Quetta |
| | 10 | PHL | DWDD | Dept. of Nat. Defence, Quezon C, NCR |
| | 1 | PHL | DWBT | Philippine Bc. Sce., Basco, Batanes |
| | 1 | PHL | DYRM | Philippine R. Corp., Dumaguete, Neg. OR. (v) |
| | 10 | PHL | DXOS | Publ.Affairs Service, AFP, Basilan Isl., Basilan |
| | 5 | PHL | DWJS | Rolin Bc. Enterprises, Roxas, Palawan |
| | 5 | PHL | DXMV | Univ. of Mindanao, Valencia, Buk. |
| | 10 | THA | | R. Thailand, Lampang |
| | 10 | THA | | ThoR. PhoR. 2, N. Ratchasima |
| | 10 | TWN | BEG26 | Taipei BS, Taipei |
| 1143 | 5 | AUS | 4HI | Emerald |
| | 2 | AUS | 2HD | Newcastle |
| | 10 | CHN | | BJ (CNR8) |
| | 50 | CHN | | EN + 34 stns |
| | 20 | IND | | AIR, Ratnagiri |
| | 20 | IND | | AIR, Rohtak |
| | 20 | J | JOBR | KBS, Kyoto |
| | 100 | KOR | | R. Free Korea, Gyeonggi-do |
| | 10 | NPL | | R. Nepal, Bardibas |
| | 2.5 | NZL | | RNZ (N), Hamilton |
| | 10 | PHL | DYAF | Diocese of Bacolod, Bacolod, Neg. Occ. |
| | 10 | PHL | DZMR | FEBC, Santiago C, Isa |
| | 10 | THA | | OR. SoR. MoR. ThoR., Bangkok |
| | 150 | TJK | | TR (FS), Yangiyul |
| | 100 | TWN | BEL3 | Yuyeh BS, Penghu |
| 1152 | 10 | AUS | 6PB | ABC (P), Busselton |
| | 2 | AUS | 2WG | Wagga Wagga |
| | 150 | CHN | | HN; LN; NM (2 stns) |

| kHz | kW | Ctry | Call | Station, location |
|---|---|---|---|---|
| | 10 | IND | | AIR, Kavaratti |
| | 10 | J | JORB | NHK (2), Kochi |
| | 10 | J | JOPC | NHK (2), Kushiro |
| | 10 | KOR | HLCW | KBS, Wonju |
| | 2 | NZL | | Newstalk ZB, Timaru |
| | 100 | PAK | | PBC, Rawalpindi |
| | 5 | PHL | DYCM | Masbate Comm. Bc. Co., Bogo, Cebu |
| | 10 | THA | | RoR. DoR., Chiang Mai |
| | 10 | THA | | RoR. DoR., Khon Kaen |
| | 1 | TWN | BED68 | BCC (C), Puli |
| | 5 | TWN | BEV70 | Hua Sheng BC (1), Taipei |
| 1161 | 1 | AUS | 7FG | ABC (L), Fingal |
| | 10 | AUS | 5PA | ABC (L), Naracoorte |
| | 2 | AUS | 4FC | Maryborough |
| | 10 | BGD | | Bangladesh Betar, Rangamati |
| | | CHN | | CNR1 |
| | 10 | CHN | | SD + 4 stns |
| | 20 | IND | | AIR, Trivandrum |
| | 0.25 | KOR | | AFNK, Uijeongbu |
| | 20 | KOR | HLKU | MBC, Busan |
| | 5 | NZL | | Te Upoko o te Ika, Wellington |
| | 5 | PHL | DYRD | Bohol Chronicle R. Corp., Tagbilaran C, Bohol |
| | 5 | PHL | DZMD | People's Bc. Netw., Daet, Cam. Nte |
| | 10 | PHL | DWCM | Philippine Bc. Corp., Dagupan C, Pang. |
| | 5 | PHL | DYKR | R. Mindanao Netw., Kalibo, Aklan |
| | 1 | PHL | DXDS | Univ. of Mindanao, Davao C, Dvo. Sur |
| | 10 | THA | | SoR. ThoR. RoR. 9, U. Ratchathani |
| | 20 | THA | | WoR. SoR. SoR., Bangkok |
| | 40 | TJK | | TR (2), Orzu |
| | 10 | TWN | BED86 | BCC (C), Ilan |
| | 10 | TWN | BED89 | BCC (C), Miaoli |
| | 1.2 | TWN | BEV67 | Feng Ming BC (1), Kaohsiung |
| 1170 | 5 | AUS | 2CH | Sydney |
| | 20 | BGD | | Bangladesh Betar (C), Dhaka |
| | 600 | CHN | | JX (CNR1); GD (CNR1) |
| | 10 | CHN | | NM (5 stns) + 10 stns |
| | 1 | IND | | AIR, Hyderabad (stand-by) |
| | 500 | KOR | HLSR | KBS, Gimje |
| | 5 | MHL | | Eagle Christian Radio, Majuro (r. ‡) |
| | 100 | PAK | | PBS (3), Peshawar |
| | 10 | PHL | DYSL | FEBC, Sogod, S Leyte |
| | 10 | PHL | DXMR | Philippine Bc. Sce., Zamboanga C, Z. Sur |
| | 10 | THA | | SoR. ThoR. RoR. 4, Chantaburi |
| | 10 | THA | | SoR. ThoR. RoR. 8, Phitsanulok |
| 1179 | 5 | AUS | 3RPH | Melbourne (CRS) |
| | 100 | CHN | | HB; HL; JS; XJ |
| | 20 | IND | | AIR, Rewa |
| | 10 | INS | | RRI, Padang |
| | 50 | J | JOOR | MBS, Osaka |
| | 5 | NZL | | Ake, Auckland |
| | 10 | PHL | DWET | End-Time Mission Bc.Sce., Santiago C, Isa. |
| | 5 | PHL | DYSB | GMA Netw., Inc., Bacolod C, Neg. Occ |
| | 5 | PHL | DYCX | Newsounds Bc. Netw., S. J. de Buenavista, Antique |
| | 1 | PHL | DZRS | R. Sorsogon Netw., Inc., Sorsogon C |
| | 5 | PHL | DXYK | Republic Bc. System, Butuan C, Ag. Nte |
| | 5 | THA | | NoR. ThoR. Phor, Chiang Rai |
| | 10 | THA | | SoR. SoR. SoR., Bangkok |
| | 2.5 | TWN | | Kuo Sheng BC, Erhlin |
| | 10 | VUT | | R. Vanuatu (VBTC), Espiritu Santo (r. silent) |
| 1188 | 2 | AUS | 6XM | ABC (L), Exmouth |
| | 2 | AUS | 2NZ | Inverell |
| | 10 | CHN | | EB(2 stns); JL |
| | 300 | CHN | | YN (CRI) |
| | 50 | IND | | AIR, Mumbai C |
| | 10 | INS | | RRI, Manado (4) |
| | 10 | J | JOKP | NHK (1), Kitami |
| | 100 | KOR | HLKX | FEBC, Seoul |
| | 0.4 | NZL | | RNZ (N), Rotorua |

| kHz | kW | Ctry | Call | Station, location |
|---|---|---|---|---|
| | 5 | PHL | DXLX | Consolidated Bc. Syst., Inc., Iligan, Lanao Nte |
| | 5 | PHL | DZLT | R. Corp. of the Philippines, Lucena C, Que. |
| | 5 | PHL | DZXO | Vanguard R. Netw., Cabanatuan, Nva. Ecija |
| | 10 | THA | | KoR. WoR. SoR. 3, Sakon Nakhon |
| | 10 | THA | | ThoR. PhoR. 1, Sa Kaeo |
| | 10 | THA | | ThoR. PhoR. 3, Phitsanulok |
| | 5 | TWN | BED32 | BCC (C), Hualien |
| | 1 | TWN | BEV57 | Sheng Li chih Sheng BC (2), Tainan |
| | 1 | TWN | BEV46 | Taiwan BC (2), Taipei |
| 1197 | 2 | AUS | 5RPH | Adelaide (CRS) |
| | 0.5 | AUS | 4YB | Brisbane (CRS) |
| | 10 | CHN | | HL; FJ; SD; SH; YN |
| | 1 | IND | | AIR, Shillong (stand-by) |
| | 20 | IND | | AIR, Tirunelveli |
| | 10 | INS | | RRI, Palangkaraya |
| | 5 | J | JOYF | IBS, Mito |
| | 1 | J | JOFO | RKB, Kitakyushu |
| | 1 | J | | RKC, Nakamura |
| | 1 | J | | RKK, 3 stns |
| | 10 | J | JOBF | RKK, Kumamoto |
| | 1 | J | | STV, 3 stns |
| | 3 | J | JOWL | STV, Asahikawa |
| | 1 | KOR | | AFNK, Dongducheon |
| | 2 | NZL | | NewstalkZB, Wanganui |
| | 5 | PHL | DXFE | FEBC, Davao C, Dvo Sur |
| | 5 | PHL | DWBA | Satellite Bc. Corp., Banguea, Abra |
| | 10 | THA | | JoR. ToR. Lor, Lop Buri |
| 1206 | 5/5 | AUS | 2CC | Canberra |
| | 5 | AUS | 2GF | Grafton |
| | 2 | AUS | 6TAB | TAB R., Perth (HPON) |
| | 200 | CHN | | JL + 11 stns |
| | 10 | CNH | | FJ (CNR2) |
| | 200 | IND | | AIR, Bhawanipatna |
| | 10 | INS | | RRI, Denpasar |
| | 2 | NZL | | TAB Trackside R., Dunedin |
| | 10 | THA | | ThoR. PhoR. 1, Prachuap KK |
| | 100 | TWN | | RTI, Minxiong |
| | 10 | TWN | BEV62 | Taiwan BC, Hsinchu |
| 1210 | 1 | HWA | KZOO | Honolulu, Oahu |
| 1215 | 0.5 | AUS | 6NM | ABC (L), Northam |
| | 0.25 | AUS | 4HI | Moranbah (t) |
| | 50 | CHN | | GD (CNR7) |
| | 50 | CHN | | HL; HB (2 stns) |
| | 20 | CHN | | LN (CNR2) |
| | 20 | IND | | AIR, New Delhi (Kingsway) N |
| | 20 | IND | | AIR, Puducherri |
| | | INS | | RRI, Bandung (3) |
| | 10 | INS | | RRI, Samarinda |
| | 1 | J | JOBW | KBS, Hikone |
| | 2 | J | JOBO | KBS, Maizuru |
| | 10 | KOR | HLAK | MBC, Jinju |
| | 2 | NZL | | NewstalkZB, Kaikohe |
| | 10 | PHL | DYRF | Word Bc. Corp., Cebu C |
| | 10 | THA | | KoR. WoR. SoR. 2, Phrae |
| | 25 | THA | | R. Thailand, Surat Thani |
| | 10 | THA | | ThoR. PhoR. 2, U. Ratchathani |
| | 1 | TWN | | Tien Sheng BS, Pengshan |
| 1224 | 5 | AUS | 3EA | Melbourne (SBS) |
| | 5 | AUS | 2RPH | Sydney (CRS) |
| | 100 | CHN | | FJ (CNR6) |
| | 100 | CHN | | GX; JS; NM |
| | 10 | IND | | AIR Srinagar C |
| | 10 | J | JOJK | NHK (1), Kanazawa |
| | 20 | KOR | | KBS, Gwangju (3) |
| | 2 | NZL | | TAB Trackside R., Invercargill |
| | 10 | PHL | DXED | Eagle Bc. Corp., Davao C, Dvo Sur |
| | 5 | PHL | DWSR | Manila Bc. Co., Lucena, Que. |
| | 10 | PHL | DZAG | Philippine Bc. Sce., Agoo, LU |
| | 10 | THA | | ThoR. OR. 15, Chiang Rai |

| kHz | kW | Ctry | Call | Station, location |
|---|---|---|---|---|
| | 10 | THA | | ThoR. OR. 4, N. Sawan |
| | 10 | TWN | BED52 | BCC (C), Kaohsiung |
| | 1 | TWN | BEV71 | Hua Sheng BC (2), Taipei |
| 1233 | 10 | AUS | 2NC | ABC (L), Newcastle |
| | 120 | CHN | | XJ (3 stns); HN (2 stns); JS |
| | 20 | IND | | AIR, Tura |
| | 5 | INS | | RRI, Pontianak |
| | 5 | J | JOUR | NBC, Nagasaki |
| | 5 | J | JOGR | RAB, Aomori |
| | 2 | NZL | | R. Live, Wellington |
| | 5 | PHL | DYVS | FEBC, Bacolod, Neg. Occ. |
| | 5 | PHL | DWRV | R. Veritas, Bayombong, Nva Viz. |
| | 10 | THA | | ThoR. OR. 1, Bangkok |
| | 10 | THA | | WoR. PoR. Tho. 7, Udon Thani |
| | 5 | TKM | | Turkmen Radio (1), Dasoguz |
| | 40 | TKM | | Turkmen Radio (1), Syrtagta |
| | 1 | TWN | | Chung Hua BC, Juifang |
| 1240 | 5 | HWA | KEWE | Wailuku, Maui |
| 1242 | 2 | AUS | 5AU | Port Augusta |
| | 2 | AUS | 8TAB | R. TAB, Darwin (HPON) |
| | 5 | AUS | 3GV | Sale |
| | 2 | AUS | 4AK | Toowoomba |
| | 100 | CHN | | YN + 4 stns |
| | 100 | IND | | AIR, Varanasi |
| | 10 | INS | | RRI, Bogor |
| | 100 | J | JOLF | NBS, Tokyo |
| | 10 | KOR | HLSB | MBC, Wonju |
| | 2 | NZL | | One Double X, Whakatane |
| | 1 | NZL | | TAB Trackside R., Timaru |
| | 5 | PHL | DXZB | DXZB/TV13 Coop., Inc., Zamboanga C, Z. Sur |
| | 20 | PHL | DWBL | FBS R. Netw., Pasig C, NCR |
| | 5 | PHL | DXSY | Times Bc. Corp., Ozamis C, Mis. Occ. |
| | 10 | THA | | ThoR. PhoR. 3, Phetchabun |
| | 1 | TWN | | Yen Sheng BS (2), Hualien |
| | 500 | VTN | | Can Tho (E), Thoi Long |
| 1250 | 1 | CHN | | ZJ |
| 1251 | 2 | AUS | 2DU | Dubbo |
| | | CHN | | BJ (CRI DS1) |
| | 200 | CHN | | QH + 27 stns |
| | 20 | IND | | AIR, Sangli |
| | 10 | INS | | RRI, Banda Aceh (4) |
| | 10 | KOR | HLKT | CBS, Daegu |
| | 5 | NZL | | Rhema, Auckland |
| | 10 | PAK | | PBC, Loralai |
| | 1 | PHL | DYRG | Intercontinental Bc. Corp., Kalibo, Aklan |
| | 2.5 | PHL | DZMS | People's Bc. Netw., Sorsogon C |
| | 10 | THA | | JoR. SoR. 3, Roi Et |
| | 5 | THA | | ThoR. OR. 6, Bangkok |
| | 100 | TJK | | Various relays, Yangiyul |
| | 10 | TWN | | VO Han Bc. Netw., Kaohsiung |
| 1260 | 2 | AUS | 3SR | Shepparton |
| | 2 | AUS | 4MW | Thursday Island (CRS) |
| | 10 | CHN | | LN; HN; XZ |
| | 1 | FSM | V6AG | Joy Family R., Colonia, Yap |
| | 20 | IND | | AIR, Ambikapur |
| | 20 | J | JOIR | TBC, Sendai |
| | 2 | NZL | | TAB Trackside R., Christchurch |
| | 400 | PAK | | PBS (2), Quetta |
| | 5 | PHL | DZEL | Eagle Bc. Corp., Lucena C, Que. |
| | 5 | PHL | DWMC | Magiliw Comm. Bc. Co., Rosales, Pang. |
| | 5 | PHL | DXRF | Manila Bc. Co., Davao C, Dvo Sur |
| | 10 | PHL | DYDD | Siam Bc. Netw. Corp., Lapu-Lapu C, Cebu |
| | 25 | THA | | R. Thailand, Chiang Rai |
| | 1 | TWN | | Cheng Sheng BC, Taipao |
| 1269 | 5 | AUS | 6RN | ABC (N), Busselton |
| | 5 | AUS | 2SM | Sydney |
| | 10 | CHN | | SX (2 stns); JL; JS |
| | 600 | CHN | | YN (CRI) |
| | 20 | IND | | AIR, Agartala |
| | 20 | IND | | AIR, Madurai |

| kHz | kW | Ctry | Call | Station, location |
|---|---|---|---|---|
| | 1 | J | JOFM | HBC, Esashi |
| | 5 | J | JOHW | HBC, Obihiro |
| | 1 | J | | JRT, Ikeda |
| | 5 | J | JOJR | JRT, Tokushima |
| | | NZL | | The Hits, Takaka |
| | 10 | PHL | DWRC | Republic Bc. System, San Nicolas, I. Nte |
| | 10 | THA | | Kho. SoR. ThoR. BoR., Bangkok |
| | 10 | THA | | MoR. Kor, Songkhla |
| | 1 | TWN | BEV37 | Cheng Sheng BC, Taitung |
| | 10 | TWN | BEC44 | VO Han Bc. Netw., Penghu |
| 1270 | 5 | HWA | KNDI | Honolulu, Oahu |
| 1278 | 5 | AUS | 3EE | Melbourne |
| | 100 | CHN | | EB (2 stns); FJ; HL; JX |
| | 50 | J | JOFR | RKB, Fukuoka |
| | 1 | KOR | | KBS, Hapcheon |
| | 2 | NZL | | Newstalk ZB, Napier-Hastings |
| | 10 | PHL | DZRM | Philippine Bc. Sce., Quezon C, NCR |
| | 1 | TWN | | Fuhsingkang BS, Peitou |
| 1287 | 2 | AUS | 2TM | Tamworth |
| | 10 | BGD | | Bangladesh Betar, Barishal |
| | 10 | CHN | | FJ (CNR1) |
| | 25 | CHN | | GD + 8 stns |
| | 100 | IND | | AIR, Panaji A |
| | 25 | INS | | RRI, Palembang |
| | 50 | J | JOHR | HBC, Sapporo |
| | 10 | KOR | HLAX | MBC, Cheongju |
| | 10 | KOR | HLAF | MBC, Gangneung |
| | 2 | NZL | | Newstalk ZB, Westport |
| | 5 | PHL | DZZH | Manila Bc. Co., Sorsogon C |
| | 10 | THA | | SoR. OR. ThoR., Bangkok (Samut Prakan) |
| | 10 | THA | | ThoR. PhoR. 3, Uttaradit |
| | 10 | THA | | WoR. PoR. Tho. 6, U. Ratchathani |
| | 1 | TWN | BEC27 | VO Han Bc. Netw., Taichung |
| 1296 | 10 | AUS | 6RN | ABC (N), Wagin |
| | 5 | AUS | 4RPH | Brisbane (CRS) |
| | 25 | CHN | | SH + 5 stns |
| | 300 | CHN | | YN (CRI) |
| | 10 | IND | | AIR, Darbhanga |
| | 10 | J | JOTK | NHK (1), Matsue |
| | 2.5 | NZL | | NewstalkZB, Hamilton |
| | 10 | PHL | DXAB | ABS-CBN Bc. Corp., Davao C, Dvo Sur |
| | 5 | PHL | DYJJ | Intercontinental Bc. Corp., Roxas C, Capiz |
| | 5 | PHL | DWPR | Multipoint Broadc. Netwk., Dagupan C, Pang. |
| | 10 | TWN | BED47 | BCC (N), Tainan |
| | 1 | TWN | BEV23 | Min Pen BC (1), Taipei |
| 1305 | 2 | AUS | 5RN | ABC (N), Renmark/Loxton |
| | 10 | CHN | | QH (CNR2) |
| | 10 | CHN | | SD; NM |
| | 20 | IND | | AIR, Parbhani |
| | 2.5 | NZL | | R. Dunedin |
| | 10 | THA | | Yaan Kraw, Sara Buri |
| 1314 | 5 | AUS | 3BT | Ballarat |
| | 5 | AUS | 2TAB | Sky Sports R., Wollongong (HPON) |
| | 10 | BGD | | Bangladesh Betar, Cox's Bazar |
| | 50 | CHN | | CQ + 6 stns |
| | 20 | IND | | AIR, Bhuj |
| | 50 | J | JOUF | OBC, Osaka |
| | 10 | KOR | HLCM | CBS, Jeonbuk |
| | 6 | NZL | | RNZ (AM)/Star, Invercargill |
| | 2 | NZL | | RNZ (N), Gisborne |
| | 10 | PHL | DWXI | Delta Bc. System, Parañaque, NCR |
| | 10 | THA | | MoR. KoR., Khon Kaen |
| | 1 | TWN | BEP33 | Ching Cha BS, Tainan |
| | 10 | TWN | BEV76 | Tien Sheng BS, Chunan |
| 1322 | 5 | PHL | DXAD | Mindanao DMPC, Marawi, Lanao Sur (v) |
| 1323 | 3.3 | AUS | 5DN | Adelaide |
| | 0.4 | AUS | 1-- | Star AM, Canberra (HPON) |
| | 200 | CHN | | HL(CRI) |

| kHz | kW | Ctry | Call | Station, location |
|-----|-----|------|------|-------------------|
| | 600 | CHN | | JL (CRI) |
| | 500 | CHN | | XJ (CRI) |
| | 10 | CHN | | ZJ + 5 stns |
| | 20 | IND | | AIR, Kolkata C |
| | 1 | J | JOFP | NHK (1), Fukushima |
| | 1 | J | | NHK (1), Yamada |
| | 3 | NZL | | Coast, Hawera |
| | 10 | PHL | DXHR | Gateway UHF Bc., Butuan C, Ag. Nte. (v) |
| | 10 | PHL | DYSI | GMA Netw., Inc., Iloilo C |
| | 10 | PHL | DZRK | Philippine Bc. Sce., Tabuk, Kalinga |
| | 10 | THA | | ThoR. OR. 13, Chiang Mai |
| | 10 | THA | | ThoR. OR. 7, Surat Thani |
| | 7 | TJK | | Tajik R1, Dushanbe |
| | 1 | TWN | BEV45 | Taiwan BC (1), Taipei |
| **1332** | 5 | AUS | 4BU | Bundaberg |
| | 2 | AUS | 3SH | Swan Hill |
| | 10 | CHN | | EN (4 stns) + 4 stns |
| | 10 | IND | | AIR, Tezu |
| | 10 | INS | | RRI, Jakarta (4) |
| | 50 | J | JOSF | Tokai R., Nagoya |
| | 10 | KOR | HLAO | MBC, Chungju |
| | 10 | NZL | | R. Sport, Auckland |
| | 100 | PAK | | PBC (city), Lahore |
| | 1 | PHL | DZKI | R. Philippines Netw., Iriga C, Cam. Sur |
| | 5 | PHL | DWAY | Swara Sug Media Corp., Cabanatuan, Nva. Ecija |
| | 10 | THA | | OR. SoR., Bangkok |
| | 10 | THA | | ThoR. OR. 14, Maha Sarakham |
| | 1 | TWN | | Taiwan BC, Puli |
| | 10 | TWN | BEC36 | VO Han Bc. Netw., Kaohsiung |
| **1341** | 5 | AUS | 3CW | 3CW 1341, Geelong (HPON) |
| | 5 | AUS | 2TAB | Sky Sports R., Newcastle (HPON) |
| | 300 | CHN | | GD (CRI/CNR 1) |
| | 100 | CHN | | HL + 6 stns |
| | 1 | IND | | AIR, Kohima |
| | 1 | J | | NHK (1), Iwaki/Minamata |
| | 25 | KAZ | | Qazaq Radiosy, Aqtaý |
| | 2 | NZL | | NewstalkZB, Nelson |
| | 10 | PAK | | PBC, Bhawalpur |
| | 20 | THA | | R. Thailand, Loei |
| | 10 | THA | | R. Thailand, Phangnga |
| | 25 | THA | | R. Thailand, Ubon Ratchathani |
| **1350** | 5 | AUS | 2LF | Young |
| | 50 | CHN | | YN + 6 stns |
| | 1 | FSM | V6A | Baptist Mid-Missions, Weno, Chuuk (r. ‡) |
| | 0.09 | GUM | KUSG | Agana |
| | 20 | IND | | AIR, Kupwara |
| | 10 | INS | | RRI, Tarakan |
| | 20 | J | JOER | RCC, Hiroshima |
| | 10 | KOR | HLAQ | MBC, Samcheok |
| | 1 | NZL | | R. Sport, Rotorua |
| | 50 | PHL | DWUN | Prog.Bc.Corp., Quezon, C, NCR |
| | 10 | THA | | Phon. Neung RoR. OR., Bangkok |
| | 10 | THA | | WoR. PoR. Tho. 17, Trang |
| | 10 | TWN | BED63 | BCC (N), Chia-i |
| | 2.5 | TWN | BEV50 | Chung Hua BC (1), Sanchung |
| **1359** | 0.2 | AUS | 3UZ | RSN, Mildura (HPON) |
| | | CHN | | FJ / JS (CNR1) |
| | 2.5 | NZL | | Coast, New Plymouth |
| | 1 | NZL | | More FM, Queenstown |
| | 1 | PHL | DYSJ | Inter-Island Broadc. Corp., S. J. de Buenavista, Antique |
| | 5 | PHL | DZYR | Philippine R. Corp., S. Fernando, LU |
| | 10 | THA | | ThoR. PhoR. 2, Sakhon Nakhon |
| | 600 | TWN | | RTI, Fangliao |
| | 5 | TWN | BEC40 | VO Han Bc. Netw., Hualien |
| **1368** | 2 | AUS | 2GN | Goulburn |
| | 10 | CHN | | HL; FJ (v); HB (2 stns) |
| | 1 | J | JOTS | HBC, Wakkanai |
| | 5 | J | JOHP | NHK (1), Takamatsu |

| kHz | kW | Ctry | Call | Station, location |
|-----|-----|------|------|-------------------|
| | 1 | J | JOLG | NHK (1), Tottori |
| | 1 | J | | NHK (1), Tsuruoka |
| | 2 | KRE | | Korean Central BS (E), Pyongyang |
| | 1 | NZL | | R. Live, Hawkes Bay |
| | 0.8/0.1 | NZL | | Village R., Tauranga |
| | 1 | PHL | DZRA | Catanduanes State College, Virac, Catanduanes |
| | 2.5 | PHL | DZBS | R. Philippines Netw., Baguio C, Benguet |
| | 10 | PHL | DXKO | R. Philippines Netw., Cagayan de Oro C, Mis. OR. |
| | 10 | THA | | R. Thailand, Buri Ram |
| | 25 | THA | | R. Thailand, Nan |
| | 10 | THA | | ThoR. OR. 12, N. Pathom |
| **1370** | 6.2 | HWA | KUPA | Pearl City, Oahu |
| **1377** | 5 | AUS | 3MP | Melbourne |
| | 600 | CHN | | EN (CNR1) |
| | 100 | CHN | | XZ + 5 stns |
| | 20 | IND | | AIR, Hyderabad B |
| | 10 | INS | | RRI, Tolitoli |
| | 1 | J | | NHK (2), Hachinohe |
| | 1 | J | JOAC | NHK (2), Nagasaki |
| | 5 | J | JOUC | NHK (2), Yamaguchi |
| | 2 | NZL | | R. Sport, Levin/Kapiti |
| | 2 | NZL | | Star, Dunedin |
| | 10 | PHL | DXKP | R. Philippines Netw., Pagadian C, Z. Sur |
| | 10 | THA | | R. Thailand, Chumphon |
| | 10 | THA | | WoR. Phon 4, Phitsanulok |
| | 10 | TWN | BEC31 | VO Han Bc. Netw., Yunlin |
| **1386** | 50 | CHN | | TJ + 6 stns |
| | 20 | IND | | AIR, Gwalior |
| | 10 | J | JOHC | NHK (2), Kagoshima |
| | 10 | J | JOJB | NHK (2), Kanazawa |
| | 10 | J | JOQC | NHK (2), Morioka |
| | 5 | J | JOKB | NHK (2), Okayama |
| | 10 | KOR | HLAM | MBC, Mokpo |
| | 10 | NZL | | R. Tarana, Auckland |
| | 5 | PHL | DYVW | Catholic Media Netw., Borongan, E. Samar |
| | 10 | PHL | DXCR | Mt. View College, Valencia, Buk. |
| | 10 | THA | | SW Pheua Kaan Kaset, Bangkok (P. Thani) (r. ‡) |
| | 3.5 | TWN | BED74 | BCC (C), Yuli |
| **1395** | 0.2 | AUS | 2LG | ABC (L), Lithgow |
| | 5 | AUS | 5AA | Adelaide |
| | 50 | CHN | | AH (3 stns) + 3 stns |
| | 20 | IND | | AIR, Bikaner |
| | 1 | INS | | RRI, Wamena |
| | 1 | J | JOCE | CRK, Toyooka |
| | 1 | J | JOWE | RFC, Wakamatsu |
| | 2 | NZL | | NewstalkZB, Oamaru |
| | 5 | PHL | DZVT | Apostolic Vicariate of S. J., San Jose, Min. Occ. |
| | 10 | PHL | DYCH | Cebu Bc. Co., Talisay C, Cebu |
| | 10 | THA | | NoR. ThoR. PhoR., Chiang Rai |
| | 1 | TWN | | Cheng Sheng BC, Tafa |
| **1404** | 2 | AUS | 2PK | Parkes/Forbes |
| | 4 | AUS | 6TAB | TAB R., Busselton (HPON) |
| | 50 | CHN | | FJ (2 stns); HB (3 stns); LN |
| | 20 | IND | | AIR, Gangtok |
| | 5 | J | JOQL | HBC, Kushiro |
| | 1 | J | JOVO | SBS, Hamamatsu |
| | 10 | J | JOVR | SBS, Shizuoka |
| | 7 | KGZ | | KGR (1), Aydarken/Naryn |
| | 1 | KGZ | | KGR (1), Cholponata |
| | 20 | KGZ | | KGR (1), Dödömöl |
| | | KGZ | | KGR (1), Orgochor |
| | 10 | KOR | HLKP | CBS, Busan |
| | 5 | NZL | | Rhema, Invercargill |
| | | PHL | DXAQ | End Time Mission, Lucena C, Que (r. ‡) |
| | 1 | PHL | DYKB | R. Philippines Netw., Bacolod, Neg. Occ. |
| | 10 | THA | | JoR. SoR. 4, Yasothon |

| kHz | kW | Ctry | Call | Station, location |
|---|---|---|---|---|
| | 25 | THA | | R. Thailand, Songkhla |
| | 10 | THA | | ThoR. PhoR. 1, Suphan Buri |
| | 10 | TWN | BEV78 | Yi Shih BS, Keelung |
| **1413** | 5 | AUS | 2EA | Newcastle (SBS) |
| | 0.5 | AUS | 3UCB | Vison ChR. R., Shepparton (HPON) |
| | 10 | BGD | | Bangladesh Betar, Comilla |
| | 10 | CHN | | XJ + 8 stns |
| | 20 | IND | | AIR, Kota |
| | 5 | INS | | RRI, Sungai Liat |
| | 50 | J | JOIF | KBC, Fukuoka |
| | 2 | NZL | | NewstalkZB, Tokoroa |
| | 1 | NZL | | R. Ferrymead, Christchurch |
| | 5 | PHL | DYXW | Filipinas Bc. Netw.,. Tacloban C, Leyte |
| | 5 | PHL | DWRA | Republic Bc. System, Bauio C, Benguet |
| | 10 | TWN | BED54 | BCC (N), Miaoli |
| | 1 | TWN | BED67 | BCC (N), Puli |
| **1420** | 5 | HWA | KKEA | Honolulu, Oahu |
| **1422** | 1 | AUS | 4AM | Port Douglas (t) |
| | 2 | AUS | 6GS | R. Great Southern, Wagin (HPON) |
| | 5 | AUS | 3XY | R. Hellas, Melbourne (HPON) |
| | 20 | CHN | | SH; SX (2 stns); SC |
| | 600 | CHN | | XJ (CNR1/8/13/CRI) |
| | 0.5 | CHR | 6ABCRN | ABC Radio National, Phosphate Hill |
| | 50 | J | JORF | RF, Yokohama |
| | 10 | THA | | Phon. Neung RoR. OR., Bangkok |
| | 10 | THA | | R. Thailand, Amnat Charoen |
| | 10 | THA | | SoR. WoR. PhoR. 4, Phitsanulok |
| | 1 | TWN | | Chien Kuo BS, Kuanyin |
| | 50 | TWN | | RTI, Minxiong |
| **1431** | 2 | AUS | 2RN | ABC (N), Wollongong |
| | 2 | AUS | | Vision ChR. R., Kalgoorlie (HPON) |
| | 10 | BGD | | Bangladesh Betar, Bandorban |
| | 10 | CHN | | EB + 6 stns |
| | 1 | J | | BSS, Izumo |
| | 1 | J | JOHL | BSS, Tottori |
| | 5 | J | JOZF | GBS, Gifu |
| | 1 | J | | NBC, Fukue |
| | 1 | J | JOWW | RFC, Iwaki |
| | 5 | J | JOVF | WBS, Wakayama |
| | 40 | KGZ | | KGR1, Jalalabat |
| | 500 | MNG | | Relays, Choibalsan |
| | 2 | NZL | | R. Kidnappers, Hawkes Bay |
| | 5 | THA | | SoR. ThoR. RoR. 6, Songkhla |
| | 10 | THA | | ThoR. OR. 3, N. Ratchasima |
| **1440** | 2 | AUS | 1EA | Canberra (SBS) |
| | 10 | CHN | | FJ (CNR1) |
| | 50 | CHN | | GC; LN; NM |
| | 3 | J | | STV, Muroran |
| | 50 | J | JOWF | STV, Sapporo |
| | 1 | J | | STV, Tomakomai |
| | 10 | KIR | | R. Kiribati, Bairiki, Tarawa Is |
| | 1 | KOR | | AFNK, Gunsan |
| | 5 | KOR | | AFNK, Pyeongtak/Waegwan |
| | 1.1 | MRA | KKMP | Blue Continent Comm., Saipan |
| | 0.2 | NZL | | Moana Radio, Tauranga |
| | 10 | PHL | DWDH | Manila Bc. Co., Dagupan C, Pang. |
| | 0.01 | PHL | DXSI | So. Inst. of Tech., Cagayan de Oro C, Mis. OR. |
| | 10 | THA | | ThoR. PhoR. 2, N. Phanom |
| | 10 | THA | | WoR. PoR. Tho. 8, Samut Sakhon |
| **1449** | 5 | AUS | 2MG | Mudgee |
| | 2 | AUS | 6TAB | TAB R., Mandurah (HPON) |
| | 20 | CHN | | JX; FJ; SD(2 stns) |
| | 10 | FSM | V6AH | FSMBS R. Pohnpei, Kolonia |
| | 5 | J | JOQM | HBC, Abashiri |
| | 1 | J | | RNC, Marugame |
| | 5 | J | JOKF | RNC, Takamatsu |
| | 10 | KOR | HLQB | KBS, Ulsan |
| | 10 | MLD | | Divehi Raajjeyge Adu, Thilafushi |
| | 2 | NZL | | RNZ (N), Palmerston N. |
| | 10 | PAK | | PBC, Zhob |
| | 5 | PHL | DXSA | Mindanao Bc. Co., Inc., Marawi C, Lanao Sur |
| | 10 | THA | | ThoR. PhoR. 3, Phichit |
| | 10 | THA | | WoR. SoR. PoR., Chumphon |
| **1458** | 2 | AUS | 2PB | ABC (P), Newcastle |
| | 200 | CHN | | NM; EN; JS; LN |
| | 20 | IND | | AIR, Barmer |
| | 20 | IND | | AIR, Bhagalpur |
| | 1 | J | | IBS, Sekijo |
| | 1 | J | JOYL | IBS, Tsuchiura |
| | 1 | J | JOUO | NBC, Saga |
| | 1 | J | | RCC, Shobara |
| | 1 | J | JOWR | RFC, Fukushima |
| | 2.5 | NZL | | RNZ (N), Westport |
| | 10 | PHL | DYZZ | Siam Bc. Netw. Corp., Gihulngan, Neg. Occ. |
| | 10 | PHL | DZJV | ZOE Bc. Netw., Calamba, Laguna |
| | 10 | THA | | JoR. SoR. 6, Si Sa Ket |
| | 10 | THA | | SoR. ThoR. RoR. 3, Phuket |
| **1460** | 5 | HWA | KHRA | Honolulu, Oahu |
| **1467** | 2 | AUS | 3ML | Mildura |
| | 10 | CHN | | EB; FJ; JX; SD |
| | 100 | IND | | AIR, Jeypore |
| | 1 | J | JOVB | NHK (2), Hakodate |
| | 1 | J | JOMC | NHK (2), Miyazaki |
| | 1 | J | JONB | NHK (2), Nagano |
| | 1 | J | JOID | NHK (2), Oita |
| | 1 | J | | NHK (2), Wakkanai |
| | 500 | KGZ | | TWR relay, Bishkek |
| | 50 | KOR | HLKN | KBS, Mokpo |
| | 1 | PHL | DWVR | R. Veritas, San Jose C, Nva Ecija |
| | 5 | PHL | DXVP | RCA-ZBN, Zamboanga C, Z. Sur |
| | 100 | THA | | SoR. WoR. Sor, Pathum Thani |
| **1476** | 1 | AUS | 5MG | ABC (L), Mt. Gambier |
| | 2 | AUS | 4ZR | Roma |
| | 50 | CHN | | HL (3 stns) + 7 stns |
| | 1 | J | | NHK (2), Iida |
| | 5 | NZL | | TAB Trackside R., Auckland |
| | 10 | PAK | | PBC, Faisalabad |
| | 1 | PHL | DZYA | R. Pilipino Corp., Angeles C, Pamp. |
| | 10 | PHL | DXRJ | Rajah Bc. Netw., Iligan C, Lanao Nte |
| | 1 | PHL | DWRB | Ribbon Bc. Netw., Lipa C, Bat |
| | 50 | THA | | R. Thailand, Chiang Mai |
| | 10 | TKM | | Turkmen R. (1), Türkmenbasy |
| **1485** | 0.05-0.2 | AUS | | ABC (L), 2 stns |
| | 0.1 | AUS | 2RN | ABC (N), Wilcannia |
| | 0.15 | AUS | 2EA | Wollongong (SBS) |
| | 10 | CHN | | HB + 16 stns |
| | 1 | IND | | AIR, 10 stns |
| | 1 | J | JOPL | KRY, Hagi |
| | 1 | J | JOGO | RAB, Hachinohe |
| | 1 | NZL | | TAB Trackside R., Gisborne |
| | 5 | PHL | DYDH | Pacific Bc. System, Iloilo C |
| **1494** | 2 | AUS | 2AY | Albury |
| | 1 | CHN | | XJ (2stns) + 4 stns |
| | 5 | FSM | V6AI | FSMBS R. Yap, Colonia |
| | 1 | J | JOTL | HBC, Nayoro |
| | 1 | J | | RSK, 5 stns |
| | 10 | J | JOYR | RSK, Okayama |
| | 2.5 | NZL | | R. Sport, Timaru |
| | 3 | NZL | | RNZ (AM)/Star, Hamilton |
| | 5 | PHL | DXOC | DWRL Radio, Inc., Ozamis C, Mis. Occ. |
| | 10 | PHL | DWSS | Supreme Bc. Systems DWSS, Pasig C, NCR |
| | 10 | PNG | | NBC National, Wabag (r. ‡) |
| | 10 | THA | | OR. SoR. MoR. ThoR., Bangkok |
| | 5 | TWN | BEE34 | Chiao Yu Bc. System, Changhua |
| | 10 | TWN | BEE32 | Chiao Yu Bc. System, Taipei |
| **1500** | 5 | HWA | KHKA | Honolulu, Oahu |
| **1503** | 0.11/5 | AUS | 2BS | Bathurst |
| | 5 | AUS | 3KND | Melbourne (CRS) |

| kHz | kW | Ctry | Call | Station, location |
|---|---|---|---|---|
| | 10 | CHN | | HN; AH; SX (2 stns) |
| | 1 | FSM | V6AJ | FSMBS R. Kosrae, Tofol |
| | 10 | J | JOUK | NHK (1), Akita |
| | 1 | J | | NHK (1), Aso |
| | 2.5 | NZL | | R. Sport, Christchurch |
| | 5 | NZL | | R. Sport, Wellington |
| | 10 | THA | | JoR. SoR. 2, Surat Thani |
| | 600 | TWN | | RTI, Fangliao |
| 1512 | 10 | AUS | 2RN | ABC (N), Newcastle |
| | 5 | AUS | 6BAY | Morawa (t) |
| | 10 | CHN | | GS; SD |
| | 20 | IND | | AIR, Kokrajhar |
| | 10 | INS | | RRI, Bukittinggi |
| | 1 | J | | NHK (2), Koriyama/Matsumoto |
| | 5 | J | JOZB | NHK (2), Matsuyama |
| | 0.25 | KOR | | AFNK, Pohang/Jinhae |
| | 10 | PAK | | PBC, Gilgit |
| | 10 | PHL | DYAB | ABS-CBN Bc. Corp., Cebu C |
| | 10 | PHL | DZAT | End Time Mission, Lucena C, Que |
| | 10 | THA | | KoR. WoR. SoR. 4, Phayao |
| | 10 | THA | | ThoR. OR. 11, Songkhla |
| | 10 | TWN | | Ching Cha BS, Hsinchu |
| 1521 | 2 | AUS | 2QN | Deniliquin |
| | 25 | CHN | | EB (2 stns) + 22 stns |
| | 500 | CHN | | XJ (CRI) |
| | 20 | IND | | AIR, Tawang |
| | 1 | J | JOTC | NHK (2), Aomori |
| | 1 | J | JOFC | NHK (2), Fukui |
| | 1 | J | JODC | NHK (2), Hamamatsu |
| | 1 | J | | NHK (2), Ishigaki/Nakamura |
| | 1 | J | JOJC | NHK (2), Yamagata |
| | 1 | J | | NHK (2), Yonago |
| | 1 | NZL | | R. Sport, Tauranga |
| | 10 | THA | | NoR. ThoR. Phor, Bangkok |
| 1530 | 2 | AUS | 2VM | Moree |
| | 50 | CHN | | ZJ; JL; SX |
| | 0.25 | GUM | KVOG | Agana |
| | 20 | IND | | AIR, Agra |
| | 1 | J | JODO | BSN, Joetsu |
| | 5 | J | JOXF | CRT, Utsunomiya |
| | 1 | J | JOEO | RCC, Fukuyama |
| | 1 | J | | RCC, Mihara |
| | 1 | NZL | | The Wireless Station, Hawkes Bay |
| | 25 | PHL | DZME | Capitol Bc. Center, Quezon C, NCR |
| | 10 | THA | | ThoR. PhoR. 1, Chanthaburi |
| | 10 | THA | | WoR. PoR. Tho. 14, Uttaradit |
| 1539 | 1 | AUS | 2RF | Niche R. Netw., Sydney (HPON) |
| | 5 | AUS | 5TAB | R. TAB, Adelaide (HPON) |
| | 100 | CHN | | QH (CNR1); ZJ |
| | 5 | PHL | DZYM | Philippine R. Corp., San José, Mind. Occ. |
| | 10 | THA | | Phon RoR. Kao, Kanchanaburi |
| 1540 | 5 | HWA | KREA | Honolulu, Oahu |
| 1548 | 50 | AUS | 4QD | ABC (L), Emerald |
| | 200 | CHN | | SD |
| | 400 | CLN | | Gospel for Asia, Trincomalee |
| | 1 | NZL | | Coast, Palmerston N. |
| | 0.9 | NZL | | TAB Trackside R., Rotorua |
| | 5 | PHL | DYDM | Catholic Media Netw., Maasin C, So. Leyte |
| | 10 | PHL | DZSD | GMA Netw., Inc., Dagupan C, Pang. |
| 1557 | 0.5 | AUS | 5TAB | KIX Country, Renmark/Loxton (HPON) |
| | 2 | AUS | 2RE | Taree |
| | 25 | CHN | | EB (2 stns) |
| | | KAZ | | Qazaq Radiosy, Lepsi |
| | 2 | NZL | | Hokonui R., Hawera |
| | 10 | PAK | | PBC, Skardu |
| | 10 | THA | | R. Thailand, Trat |
| | 10 | THA | | Siang Adison, Phetchabun |
| | 300 | TWN | | RTI, Kouhu |
| 1566 | 0.2 | AUS | 4GM | ABC (L), Gympie |

| kHz | kW | Ctry | Call | Station, location |
|---|---|---|---|---|
| | 5 | AUS | 3NE | Wangaratta |
| | 10 | CHN | | EB + 5 stns |
| | 1000 | IND | | AIR, Nagpur (Buttibori) N |
| | 250 | KOR | HLAZ | FEBC, Jeju |
| | 0.1 | NFK | VL2NI | R. Norfolk |
| | 10 | PHL | DXID | Ass. of Islamic Dev. Coop., Pagadian C, Z. Sur |
| 1570 | 15 | HWA | KUAU | Haiku, Maui |
| 1575 | 5 | AUS | 2RF | Niche R. Netw., Wollongong (HPON) |
| | 2 | CHN | | LN; GX; JL |
| | 1 | J | | AFN, Iwakuni |
| | 1 | J | | AFN, Misawa |
| | 0.3 | J | | AFN, Sasebo |
| | 2.5 | NZL | | OAR 105.4 FM, Dunedin |
| | 10 | PHL | DXJR | Cagayan de Oro Media Corp., Manolo Fortich, Buk. |
| | 1000 | THA | | R. Saranrom/BBG, Ayutthaya |
| 1584 | 0.05-0.1 | AUS | | ABC (L), 3 stns |
| | 0.2 | AUS | 4VL | Cunnamulla (t) |
| | 0.2 | AUS | 2EC | Narooma (t) |
| | 0.5 | AUS | 4CC | Rockhampton (t) |
| | 10 | CHN | | SX (3 stns) + 9 stns |
| | 0.1 | HKG | | RTHK (3), Chung Hom Kok |
| | 1 | IND | | AIR, 10 stns |
| | 1 | NZL | | R. Hauraki, Hawkes Bay |
| | 0.25 | PAK | | PBC, Chitral/Sibi |
| | 1 | PHL | DWBR | Dawnbreaker's Found., Talavera, Nva Ecija |
| 1593 | 5 | AUS | 3RG | Niche R. Netw., Melbourne (HPON) |
| | 0.2 | AUS | 2TAB | Sky Sports R., Murwillumbah (HPON) |
| | 10 | CHN | | HL; XJ |
| | 600 | CHN | | JS (CNR1) |
| | 5 | FSM | V6AK | FSMBS R. Chuuk, Weno |
| | 10 | IND | | AIR, Bhopal A |
| | 10 | J | JOTB | NHK (2), Matsue |
| | 10 | J | JOQB | NHK (2), Niigata |
| | 2.5 | NZL | | Coast, Christchurch |
| | 5 | NZL | | R. Samoa, Auckland |
| | 10 | PHL | DXSK | Ranao Radio & TV Bc. Sys. Corp, Marawi C, Lanao Sur |
| | 10 | PNG | | NBC Vanimo (r. ‡) |
| | 10 | THA | | R. Thailand, Ratchaburi |
| | 1 | TWN | | Yuyeh BS, Ilan |
| 1602 | 0.2-0.4 | AUS | | ABC (L), 3 stns |
| | 1 | CHN | | JS |
| | 1 | IND | | AIR, 9 stns |
| | 1 | J | | NHK (2), 6 stns |
| | 1 | J | JOCC | NHK (2), Asahikawa |
| | 1 | J | JOFD | NHK (2), Fukushima |
| | 1 | J | JOSB | NHK (2), Kitakyushu |
| | 1 | J | JOKC | NHK (2), Kofu |
| | 2.5 | NZL | | R. Reading Service, Levin |
| | 0.25 | PAK | | PBC, Abbotabad |
| | 1 | PHL | DZUP | Univ. of the Philippines, Quzon C, NCR |
| 1611 | 0.05-0.4 | AUS | | 24 stns (MFNAS) |
| | 10 | PHL | DWNX | R. Mindanao Netw., Naga C, Cam Sur |
| 1620 | 0.4 | AUS | | 10 stns (MFNAS) |
| 1629 | 0.1-0.4 | AUS | | 10 stns (MFNAS) |
| 1638 | 0.4 | AUS | | 2 stns (MFNAS) |
| | 0.6 | PHL | DWGI | Guzman Inst. Of Tech., Manila, NCR |
| 1647 | 0.4 | AUS | 4--- | Vision ChR. R., Mackay (MFNAS) |
| 1656 | 0.4 | AUS | | 3 stns (MFNAS) |
| 1665 | 0.4 | AUS | | 2MM, Sydney (MFNAS) |
| 1674 | 0.4 | AUS | | R. Hanji, Melbourne (MFNAS) |
| | 1 | PHL | DZBF | Mun. of Marikina, Marikina C, NCR |
| 1683 | 0.4 | AUS | | 2 stns (MFNAS) |
| 1692 | 0.06-0.4 | AUS | | 4 stns (MFNAS) |
| 1701 | 0.1-0.4 | AUS | | 4 stns (MFNAS) |

# NORTH AMERICA

The North American MW frequency listing has been moved into each respective country: Alaska, Canada and the United States. This change allowed for the addition of over 1000 extra US MW stations in the National Radio section.

# CENTRAL AMERICA, CARIBBEAN, & MEXICO

**Abbreviations:** Broadc.=Broadcasting, Corp.=Corporation, Em=Emisora, LV=La Voz, Nal=Nacional, Nat=National, Sce=Service.
**Call signs:** Costa Rica TI_, Cuba CM_, Dominican Republic HI_, El Salvador YS_, Guatemala TG_, Honduras HR_, Mexico XE_, Nicaragua YN_, Panama HO_

| kHz | kW | Ctry | Call | Station, location | kHz | kW | Ctry | Call | Station, location |
|---|---|---|---|---|---|---|---|---|---|
| 530 | 10 | CUB | BQ | R. Enciclopedia, Villa María, CH | | 10/5 | DOM | B22 | R. Cristal, Santo Domingo |
| | | CUB | BA | R. Rebelde, Caribe, IJ | | 1 | GTM | PA | R. Palmeras, Escuintla |
| | 1 | CUB | BA | R. Rebelde, Guantánamo-R. Reloj, GU | | 5/2 | MEX | BJB | BJB Regional Mexicana, Monterrey |
| 540 | 1 | CUB | BA | R. Rebelde, Sancti Spíritus-Progreso, SS | | 2/1.7 | MEX | LQ | Candela, Morelia |
| | 10 | CUB | BA | R. Rebelde, Santa Rita, Maisí, GU | | 5/2.5 | MEX | OA | La Mexicana, Oaxaca |
| | 5 | DOM | B20 | R. ABC, Santo Domingo | | 5/1 | MEX | TD | R. Red, Tecuala |
| | 20/2.5 | MEX | WF | La Bestia Grupera, Tlalmanalco | | 5/1 | MEX | VJP | R. Xicotepec, Xicotepec de Juárez |
| | 5/2.5 | MEX | HS | La Mejor, Los Mochis | | 5 | NCG | A2RQ | R. Stereo Veritas, Chinandega |
| | 4/1 | MEX | TX | La Ranchera de Paquimé, Nuevo Casas Grandes | 580 | 2.5 | CUB | BA | R. Rebelde, Mabujabo, GU |
| | | | | | | 5 | GTM | Y | R. Progreso, Guatemala |
| | 1. 5/1 | MEX | WA | Los 40, Monterrey | | 3 | HND | ZQ | R. Cadena Voces, Tegucigalpa |
| | 150 | MEX | WA | Los 40, San Luis Potosí | | 3 | HND | EO | Super Estrella de Occidente, Sta Rosa de Copán |
| | 5/1 | MEX | MIT | R. IMER, LV de Balún Canán, Comitán | | | | | |
| | 0.1 | MEX | SURF | R. Zion, Tijuana | | 10/1 | MEX | AV | Canal 58, Guadalajara |
| | 25 | NCG | A30W | R. Corporación, Managua | | 5/0.7 | MEX | FI | Fiesta Mexicana, Chihuahua |
| | 5 | SLV | HV | La Estación de la Palabra, San Salvador | | 5/2.5 | MEX | LRDA | La Rancherita del Aire, Piedras Negras |
| 550 | 5 | CTR | SCL | R. Santa Clara, Cd. Quesada | | 1/0.25 | MEX | YI | Mix FM, Cancún |
| | 12 | CUB | BA | R. Rebelde, Pinar del Río-San Juan, PR | | 10 | NCG | A3LP | R. 580, Managua |
| | 1 | HND | XT | ABC R., Tegucigalpa | | 10 | PNR | H4 | RPC R., David |
| | 0.5 | HND | XD | R. Manantial, San Marcos | | 4.5 | PTR | WKAQ | R. KAQ, San Juan |
| | 5/0.15 | MEX | PL | La Super Estación, Cd. Cuauhtémoc | 590 | 25 | CUB | BF | R. Musical Nacional, La Julia, MB |
| | 2.5/0.15 | MEX | GNAY | R. Aztlán, Tepic | | 10 | CUB | BA | R. Rebelde, Guantánamo-Burenes, GU |
| | | PNR | | R. Estéreo Universidad, Santiago | | 10/5 | DOM | B24 | R. Santa María, La Vega |
| | 5 | PTR | WPAB | WPAB 550, Ponce | | 5 | GTM | RQ | R. Quiché, Sta Cruz del Quiché |
| 560 | 10 | CUB | BA | R. Rebelde, Ciego de Avila-Rebelde/Reloj, CA | | | HND | RE | Catacamas |
| | | | | | | 10 | HND | LP3 | R. América, San Pedro Sula |
| | 1 | GTM | | R. Quetzal, Malacatán | | 1 | HND | | R. América, Tela |
| | 1 | HND | KL | R. Reloj, San Pedro Sula | | 10/0.25 | MEX | GTO | Hits 95.5, León |
| | 1.4/0.25 | MEX | GIK | La Acerera, Monclova | | 5/0.5 | MEX | FD | La Mejor, Reynosa |
| | 10/1 | MEX | SRD | La Tremenda, Santiago Papasquiaro | | 1 | MEX | E | R. Fórmula Durango, Durango |
| | 1.5/0.5 | MEX | OC | R. Chapultepec, México | | 21/2 | MEX | PH | Sabrosita 590, México |
| | 10/1 | MEX | MZA | Sol FM, Manzanillo | | 10 | PNR | H3 | RPC R., Chitré |
| | 3 | PNR | H2 | RPC R., Colón | 600 | 50 | CUB | BA | R. Rebelde, San Germán, HO |
| 570 | 5 | CTR | ELR | R. Libertad, San José | | | DOM | C85 | Celestial 600, Santo Domingo |
| | 1 | CUB | BA | R. Rebelde, Pilón-Siguanea, GR | | 10/0.5 | MEX | OCH | K'in R., Ocosingo |
| | 25 | CUB | BD | R. Reloj, Santa Clara-Reloj, VC | | 5/1 | MEX | BB | La Comadre, Puros Éxitos, Acapulco |

| kHz | kW | Ctry | Call | Station, location |
|-----|-----|------|------|-------------------|
|  | 5/1 | MEX | HW | La Mejor, Chametla |
|  | 1/0.5 | MEX | MN | La Regiomontana, Monterrey |
|  | 10 | NCG | A3MD | La Nueva R. Ya, Managua |
|  | 5 | PTR | WYEL | Mayagüez |
|  | 3 | SLV | NK | R. Alabanza, San Salvador |
| 610 | 10 | CUB | BA | R. Rebelde, Bueycito, GR |
|  | 1 | CUB | BA | R. Rebelde, Cienfuegos-Malecón, CI |
|  | 10 | CUB | BA | R. Rebelde, Guane, PR |
|  | 1 | CUB | BD | R. Reloj, Trinidad- R. Trinidad, SS |
|  | 5 | GTM | GA | R. Alianza, Guatemala |
|  | 1 | HND |  | R. América, Gracias |
|  | 3 | HND | LP4 | R. América, Santa Rosa de Copán |
|  | 10 | HND | LD | R. América, Tegucigalpa |
|  | 6/1 | MEX | GS | Chavez R. GS, Guasave |
|  | 10/0.2 | MEX | UM | La Nueva Candela, Valladolid |
|  | 5/1 | MEX | UF | La Z, Uruapan |
|  | 1 | MEX | SORN | Viva Saltillo, Saltillo |
|  | 10 | PNR | HM | RPC R., Panamá |
|  | 1/0.25 | PTR | WEXS | X-61, Patillas |
| 620 | 25 | CUB | BA | R. Rebelde, Colón, MA |
|  | 10 | DOM | B28 | R. Santo Domingo, Santo Domingo |
|  | 5 | GTM | PQ | R. 6-20, San Cristóbal |
|  | 1 | HND | LP | R. América, Juticalpa |
|  | 10 | HND |  | R. América, Siguatepeque |
|  | 2.5 | MEX | GMSR | 620 AM, La R. Que Se Ve, Villahermosa |
|  | 5 | MEX | SS | ESPN Deportes, Ensenada |
|  | 1/0.25 | MEX | GH | La Lupe, Río Bravo |
|  | 50/5 | MEX | NK | R. 6-20, México |
|  | 50 | NCG | N | R. Nicaragua, Managua |
| 630 | 5 | CUB | BC | R. Progreso, Camagüey-Isabel Hortensia, CM |
|  |  | GTM | EL | R. Cultural Porvenir, Sta Elena |
|  | 3.5 | HND | LP | R. América, Choluteca |
|  | 5 | HND | LP7 | R. América, La Ceiba |
|  | 1/0.25 | MEX | FX | Amor 101, Guaymas |
|  | 10/0.5 | MEX | PBGJ | Jalisco R., Guadalajara |
|  | 10 | MEX | FB | La F-B 6-30, Monterrey |
|  | 10/0.75 | MEX | FU | La Nueva Voz, Cosamaloapan |
|  | 0.5 | MEX | CCQ | La Z, Cancún |
|  | 1/0.15 | MEX | ERO | R. Tamaulipas, Esteros |
|  | 2 | PNR | J35 | R. Provincias, Chitré |
|  | 5 | PTR | WUNO | NotiUno 6-30, San Juan |
|  | 10 | SLV | LN | R. Santa Sion, San Salvador |
| 640 | 20 | CTR | ALY | R. Rica, San José |
|  | 50 | CUB | BC | R. Progreso, Guanabacoa-Progreso, CH |
|  | 10 | CUB | BC | R. Progreso, Las Tunas-Progreso, LT |
|  | 5/1 | MEX | TAM | Ke Buena, Cd.Victoria |
|  | 5 | MEX | JUA | La Caliente, Cd.Juárez |
|  | 50/25 | MEX | NQ | La NQ, Tulancingo |
|  | 2.5 | PNR | K22 | CPR, Colón |
|  | 2.5 | PNR |  | R. Panamá, La Palma |
| 650 | 10 | CUB | BC | R. Progreso, Ciego de Avila-Surco/ Progreso, CA |
|  | 5 | CUB | BA | R. Rebelde, Santiago de Cuba-Eide, SC |
|  | 15/5 | DOM | B31 | R. Universal, Santo Domingo |
|  | 1 | HND | LP | R. América, Danlí |
|  | 2.5 | HND |  | R. América, Olanchito |
|  | 1 | HND |  | R. América, Tocoa |
|  | 2.5 | HND | VS | R. Católica de Olancho, Juticalpa |
|  | 1 | MEX | HEEP | Acustik R., Hermosillo |
|  | 5/0.25 | MEX | CHH | Capital Máxima, Chilpancingo |
|  | 5/1 | MEX | TNT | Chavez R. 65, Los Mochis |
|  | 10 | MEX | EJ | La Patrona, Puerto Vallarta |
|  | 5/0.2 | MEX | PX | LV de Ángel, Puerto Ángel |
|  | 2.5/0.02 | MEX | VG | R. Fórmula, Primera Cad, Mérida |
|  | 5 | PNR | S22 | R. Mía, Panamá |
| 660 | 12 | CUB | BC | R. Progreso, Jovellanos, MA |
|  | 3 | DOM | B32 | R. Visión Cristiana, Santiago |
|  | 3 | GTM | Q | LV de Quetzaltenango |
|  | 3 | HND | NN18 | LV de Honduras, La Ceiba |
|  | 5 | HTI |  | R. Lumière, Port-au-Prince |
|  | 10/1 | MEX | FZ | ABC R., Monterrey |
|  | 1 | MEX | DGEP | Acustik R., Durango |
|  | 2.5/0.25 | MEX | SJC | KVOZ, San José del Cabo |
|  | 50/10 | MEX | EY | La Kaliente, Aguascalientes |
|  | 30 | MEX | CPR | R. Chan Santa Cruz, Felipe Carrillo Puerto |
|  | 50 | MEX | DTL | R. Ciudadana, México |
|  | 5 | PNR |  | La Nueva Exitosa, Sabana Grande |
|  | 1 | PNR | H5 | RPC R., Bocas del Toro |
|  | 10 | SLV | UES | R. Universitaria, San Salvador |
| 670 | 10 | CTR | TNT | R. Managua, San José |
|  | 1 | CUB | BQ | R. Enciclopedia, Cárdenas-2, MA |
|  | 50 | CUB | BA | R. Rebelde, Arroyo Arenas, CH |
|  | 5 | CUB | BA | R. Rebelde, Bahía Honda, AR |
|  | 10 | CUB | BA | R. Rebelde, Camagüey-Villa Rosita, CM |
|  |  | CUB | BA | R. Rebelde, Caribe, IJ |
|  | 10 | CUB | BA | R. Rebelde, Central Brasil, Jaronú, CM |
|  | 10 | CUB | UES | R. Rebelde, El Coco, HO |
|  | 10 | CUB | BA | R. Rebelde, Las Tunas-Rebelde1180, LT |
|  | 1 | CUB | BA | R. Rebelde, Los Palacios, PR |
|  | 5 | CUB | BA | R. Rebelde, Matanzas-Circunvalación, MA |
|  |  | CUB | BA | R. Rebelde, Mayarí, HO |
|  | 5 | CUB | BA | R. Rebelde, Morón, CA |
|  | 1 | CUB | BA | R. Rebelde, Pinar del Río-Coloma, PR |
|  | 50 | CUB | BA | R. Rebelde, Santa Clara-Rebelde670, VC |
|  | 1 | CUB | BA | R. Rebelde, Santa Lucía, PR |
|  | 5 | DOM | B33 | R. Dial, San Pedro de Macorís |
|  | 1 | HND | NN20 | LV de Honduras, Sta Rosa de Copán |
|  | 10 | HND | NN | LV de Honduras, Tegucigalpa |
|  | 5 | PNR | LY | R. Hogar, Panamá |
| 680 | 3 | DOM | B38 | R. Zamba, San Ignacio de Sabaneta |
|  | 10 | GTM | VP | R. Norte, Cobán |
|  | 1 | HND | NN7 | LV de Honduras, Danlí |
|  | 1 | HND | NN10 | LV de Honduras, Juticalpa |
|  | 10 | HND | NN8 | LV de Honduras, San Pedro Sula |
|  | 10 | HND | NN2 | LV de Honduras, Siguatepeque |
|  | 50/1 | MEX | FCSM | R. María, Mérida |
|  | 5/2.5 | MEX | CHG | Súper 107.1, Chilpancingo |
|  | 10/2 | NCG | AM | R. La Primerísima, Managua |
|  | 5 | PNR | F32 | Bendición R., David |
|  | 5 | PNR |  | Voz sin Fronteras, Metetí |
|  | 10 | PTR | WAPA | Cadena WAPA R., San Juan |
| 690 | 10 | CUB | BC | R. Progreso, Santa Clara-Progreso, VC |
|  | 5 | CUB | BC | R. Progreso, Santiago de Cuba-Sta. María, SC |
|  | 1 | GTM | VB | R. Tamazulapa, Jutiapa |
|  | 1 | HND | NN3 | LV de Honduras, Choluteca |
|  | 78/50 | MEX | WW | La 690, Tijuana |
|  | 50/2 | MEX | MA | La Mejor Zacatecas, Fresnillo |
|  | 50/5 | MEX | N | R. Centro y El Fonógrafo, México |
|  | 10/1 | MEX | RG | RG La Deportiva, Monterrey |
|  | 10/5 | NCG | RH | R. Hermanos, Matagalpa |
|  | 5 | PNR |  | R. Evangelio Vivo, Panamá |
| 700 | 10 | CTR | JC | R. Sonora, San José |
|  | 1 | GTM | AJ | R. Inspiración, Escuintla |
|  | 15 | GTM | HR | R. Mundial, Guatemala |
|  | 5 | MEX | ETCH | LV de los Tres Ríos, Etchojoa |
|  | 5 | MEX | XPUJ | LV del Corazón de la Selva, X'pujil |
|  | 10/0.15 | MEX | DKR | R. Red, Guadalajara |
|  | 5 | MEX | LX | R. Zitácuaro, Zitácuaro |
|  | 12 | SLV | JW | R. Cadena Mi Gente, San Salvador |

| kHz | kW | Ctry | Call | Station, location |
|-----|-----|------|------|-------------------|
| 710 | 10 | CUB | AM | R. Guamá, La Palma, PR |
| | 50 | CUB | BA | R. Rebelde, Cacocúm, HO |
| | 25 | CUB | BA | R. Rebelde, Camagüey-Tagarro, CM |
| | 200 | CUB | BA | R. Rebelde, Chambas-Centro 6, CA |
| | 50 | CUB | BA | R. Rebelde, La Julia, MB |
| | 50 | CUB | BA | R. Rebelde, Martí-Centro 5, MA |
| | 50 | CUB | BA | R. Rebelde, Santa Clara-Reloj, VC |
| | 1 | CUB | BA | R. Rebelde, Yaguajay, SS |
| | | DOM | B41 | Ondas del Caribe, San Cristóbal |
| | | DOM | | Red Nacional Cristiana, Santo Domingo |
| | 1 | GTM | XL | R. Tecún Umán, Quetzaltenango |
| | 2.5 | HND | SG | R. LV de la Libertad, Catacamas |
| | 5/0.5 | MEX | OAEP | Acustik R., Oaxaca |
| | 1/0.25 | MEX | SLEP | Acustik R., San Luis Potosì |
| | 5/0.25 | MEX | BL | La Ke Buena, Culiacán |
| | 10 | MEX | MP | R. 710, México |
| | 1 | MEX | MAR | R. Disney, Acapulco |
| | 10 | PNR | Q51 | KW R. Continente, Panamá |
| | 5 | PNR | B52 | Ondas del Caribe, Bocas del Toro |
| | 10/0.75 | PTR | WKJB | KJb, Mayagüez |
| 720 | 2.5 | CUB | BC | R. Progreso, Mabujabo, GU |
| | 5 | DOM | B48 | R. Cayacoa, Higüey |
| | 1.5 | DOM | B42 | R. Norte, Santiago |
| | 1 | HND | NN3 | R. Caribe, La Ceiba |
| | 1 | HTI | | R. Lumière, Petite Riviere |
| | 1 | MEX | JCC | El Fonógrafo, Cd. Juárez |
| | 2 | MEX | JAGC | La Bonita del Norte, Juan Aldama |
| | 8/0.25 | MEX | DE | La Kaliente, Saltillo |
| | 5 | MEX | KN | La Ke Buena, Huetamo |
| | | NCG | | R. Asunción, Juigalpa |
| | 25 | NCG | A3RC | R. Católica, Managua |
| | 10 | PNR | B50 | R. República, Chitré |
| | 1 | SLV | RA | Radio Qué Buena, San Salvador |
| 730 | 1 | CTR | | R. Pacífico, Puntarenas |
| | 10 | CUB | BC | R. Progreso, La Fe-Progreso, IJ |
| | 1 | HND | NN4 | R. Centro, Tegucigalpa |
| | 5/1 | MEX | GDL | @FM, Guadalajara |
| | 2.5 | MEX | LBC | La Giganta, Loreto |
| | 50/1 | MEX | HB | La Mexicana, Hidalgo del Parral |
| | 2/0.3 | MEX | SOS | La Ranchera, Agua Prieta |
| | 10 | MEX | PET | LV de los Mayas, Peto |
| | 100 | MEX | X | W Deportes, México |
| 740 | 10 | CUB | KO | R. Angulo, Sagua de Tánamo, HO |
| | 5 | HND | IH | La Super Grande, Juticalpa |
| | 2.5 | HND | VC | LV Evangélica, Olanchito |
| | 1 | HND | QQ | R. Intibucá, La Esperanza |
| | 1 | HND | TG2 | R. Satélite, San Pedro Sula |
| | 1 | HTI | | R. Lumière, Pignon |
| | 1 | MEX | VAY | Amor, Puerto Vallarta |
| | 10/1 | MEX | KV | EXA FM, Villahermosa |
| | 20/10 | MEX | CAQ | R. Fórmula QR Cancún, Cancún |
| | 10/1 | MEX | QN | R. Fórmula, Torreón |
| | 5/1 | MEX | POR | T-Prende, Putla de Guerrero |
| | 50 | NCG | A3LS | La Sandino, Managua |
| | 2.6 | PNR | R44 | La Exitosa, La Chorrera |
| | 5 | PNR | N26 | R. Cristal, David |
| | 0.5/0.1 | PTR | WIAC | WIAC La Original, Ponce |
| | 10 | PTR | WIAC | WIAC La Original, San Juan |
| 750 | 10 | CUB | BC | R. Progreso, Palmira, CI |
| | 5 | DOM | B44 | R. Jesús, Santiago |
| | 10 | MEX | UORN | Acustik Michoacán, Uruapan |
| | 5 | MEX | ACEP | Acustik R., Acapulco |
| | 10 | MEX | JMN | LV de los Cuatro Pueblos, Jesús María |
| | 5/0.25 | MEX | CSI | Romántica, Culiacán |
| | 5 | PNR | | R. Inolvidable, Chitré |
| 760 | 5 | CTR | LX | R. Columbia, San José |

| kHz | kW | Ctry | Call | Station, location |
|-----|-----|------|------|-------------------|
| | 10 | CUB | BC | R. Progreso, Guane, PR |
| | | CUB | BC | R. Progreso, Mayarí Arriba-II Frente1, SC |
| | | GTM | | R. 760, Guatemala |
| | 2.5 | HND | XW | R. Comayagüela, Tegucigalpa |
| | 2 | HTI | | R. Lumière, Les Cayes |
| | 70/10 | MEX | ABC | ABC R., México |
| | 5/0.5 | MEX | DGO | La Mejor, Durango |
| | 5/1 | MEX | EB | La Zeta, Cd.Obregón |
| | 5/1 | MEX | ZZ | R. Gallito, Guadalajara |
| | 5/0.5 | MEX | RA | R. Uno, San Cristóbal las Casas |
| | 5/0.1 | MEX | NY | R. Xeny, Nogales |
| | 5 | PNR | XO | LV del Istmo, Panamá |
| | 5 | PTR | WORA | NotiUno, Mayagüez |
| | 5 | SLV | KL | YSKL La Poderosa, San Miguel |
| | 1 | SLV | KL | YSKL La Poderosa, Sonsonate |
| | | SLV | KL | YSKL La Poderosa, Zacateluca |
| 770 | 10 | CUB | CW | R. Artemisa, La Salud, AR |
| | 10 | CUB | BA | R. Rebelde, Las Tunas-Victoria, LT |
| | 1 | HND | RD | R. Majestad, Juticalpa |
| | 5/1.5 | MEX | ML | La Ranchera, Apatzingán |
| | 10 | MEX | ANT | LV de las Huastecas, Tancanhuitz de Santos |
| | 2.5/1 | MEX | ACH | R. Fórmula Monterrey, Monterrey |
| | 2.5/1 | MEX | FRTM | XEFRTM, Zacatecas |
| | 10 | PNR | L83 | R. Nacional, Chitré |
| | 10 | SLV | KL | YSKL La Poderosa, San Salvador |
| 780 | 10 | CTR | RA | R. América, San José |
| | 0.5 | DOM | B47 | R. Constanza, Constanza |
| | 1 | GTM | CK | Sultana La Cristiana, Zacapa |
| | 1/0.25 | MEX | TMEP | Acustik R., Tampico |
| | 5/1 | MEX | ZN | Exa FM, Celaya |
| | 10/0.25 | MEX | WGR | Exa FM, Monclova |
| | 2. 5/1 | MEX | XY | La Poderosa Voz del Balsas, Cd.Altamirano |
| | 5/1 | MEX | SFT | La Poderosa, San Fernando |
| | 10 | MEX | GLO | LV de la Sierra Juárez, Guelatao de Juárez |
| | 5/0.5 | MEX | LD | R. Costa, Autlán |
| | 5 | PNR | | MQV R., Panamá |
| | 1 | SLV | KL | YSKL La Poderosa, Sta Ana |
| | 1 | SLV | KL | YSKL La Poderosa, Usulután |
| | 10 | VRG | | ZVBI R., Tortola |
| 790 | 10 | CUB | BD | R. Reloj, Holguín, HO |
| | 25 | CUB | BD | R. Reloj, Pinar del Río-Politécnico, PR |
| | 50/1 | MEX | RC | Formato 21, México |
| | 0.25 | MEX | GAJ | Grupo Fórmula Jalisco 7-90 AM, Guadalajara |
| | 1/0.25 | MEX | SU | La Dinámica, Mexicali |
| | 1/0.5 | MEX | FE | La R. de Nuevo Laredo, Nuevo Laredo |
| | 5/0.75 | MEX | NT | R. La Paz/R. Fórmula, La Paz |
| | 6 | PNR | | R. Panamá, Santiago |
| 800 | 440 | BES | PJB | Trans World R., Kralendijk |
| | 3 | CTR | SD | R. La Gigante, San José |
| | 1 | DOM | B50 | R. Bonao Bendición, Bonao |
| | 1 | HND | DL | R. Corporación, Comayagua |
| | 3 | HND | XS2 | R. Moderna, San Pedro Sula |
| | 0.5/0.25 | MEX | SPN | Cadena 800, Tijuana |
| | 1 | MEX | QT | La Poderosa, Veracruz |
| | 5 | MEX | ZV | LV de la Montaña, Tlapa de Comonfort |
| | 50 | MEX | ROK | R. Cañón/Onda Cristiana, Cd.Juárez |
| | 10/2.5 | MEX | DD | RG La Deportiva, Montemorelos |
| | 50 | NCG | A3RO | R. Cadena 800, Managua |
| | 3 | PNR | | Tropical 800, Los Santos |
| | 12 | SLV | AX | R. María El Salvador, San Salvador |
| 810 | 10 | BAH | | ZNS-3 Gospel, Freeport |
| | 10 | CUB | BC | R. Progreso, Guantánamo-Burenes, GU |

| kHz | kW | Ctry | Call | Station, location |
|---|---|---|---|---|
| | 5 | DOM | B52 | R. Salvación Internacional, Baní |
| | | GTM | | R. Circuito San Juan, San Juan |
| | | GTM | END | R. Constelación, Guatemala |
| | | GTM | | R. Moapán, Sta Elena |
| | 6 | HND | VC | LV Evangélica, La Ceiba |
| | 3 | HND | LP24 | R. Valle, Choluteca |
| | 50/1 | MEX | FW | Hits FM 106.3, Tampico |
| | 7/0.6 | MEX | AGR | R. Fórmula, Acapulco |
| | 5/1 | MEX | HT | R. Huamantla, Huamantla |
| | 1/0.5 | MEX | EMM | R. La Salmantina, Salamanca |
| | 1/0.1 | MEX | RI | R. Rey, Reynosa |
| | 2.5/0.25 | MEX | RB | Sol Estéreo, Cozumel |
| | 5 | MEX | RSV | Tribuna R., Cd. Obregón |
| | 1 | PNR | G | R. 10, Panamá |
| | 25 | PTR | WKVM | R. Paz 810, San Juan |
| | 1.5 | SLV | DA | R. Imperial, Sonsonate |
| | 2 | SLV | FA | R. Lorenzana, San Vicente |
| **820** | 2.5 | CTR | GC | R. Tigre, San José |
| | 10 | CUB | BU | R. Ciudad Habana, Arroyo Arenas, CH |
| | 1 | CUB | BC | R. Progreso, Moa-Rolo Monterrey, HO |
| | 10 | CUB | BD | R. Reloj, Ciego de Ávila-Rebelde/Reloj, CA |
| | 5 | HND | LP16 | R. Moderna, Tegucigalpa |
| | 7/3 | HND | KW | R. Sultana, Sta Rosa de Copán |
| | 3.5/0.5 | MEX | ABCA | ABC R. /R. Frontera, Mexicali |
| | 10/1 | MEX | BM | Ke Buena, San Luis Potosí |
| | 10/1 | MEX | BA | La Consentida, Guadalajara |
| | 1 | MEX | GRC | RTG R, Coyuca de Catalán |
| | 3 | PNR | F28 | R. Ritmo Chiriquí, David |
| | 10 | SCN | | Son Power R., Conaree, St Kitts |
| **830** | | CUB | J | CMKC R. Revolucion, Mayarí Arriba-II Frente2, SC |
| | 10 | DOM | B54 | Emisora HIJB, Santo Domingo |
| | 5 | GTM | AV | R. Satélite, Mazatenango |
| | 1 | HND | JB | Cadena Radial Impacto, Comayagua |
| | 1 | HND | RU | R. Uno, San Pedro Sula |
| | 5/0.25 | MEX | LN | La Caliente, Linares |
| | 1/0.5 | MEX | TLX | La Poderosa, Tlaxiaco |
| | 8 | MEX | PUR | LV de los P'urhepechas, Cheran |
| | 10/5 | MEX | ITE | R. Capital, México |
| | 5 | PNR | R56 | R. Península, Macaracas |
| **840** | 1 | CUB | J | CMKC R. Revolución, Palma Soriano, SC |
| | 10 | CUB | E | R. CMHW, Santa Clara-CMHW, VC |
| | | GTM | | Idea Radio, Jutiapa |
| | 2.5 | GTM | | R. Luz, San Pedro Carchá |
| | 3 | HND | QW | LV Evangélica, Tela |
| | 10 | HTI | | R. 4VEH, Cap Haitien |
| | 5/1 | MEX | XXX | Fiesta Mexicana, Tamazula |
| | 2.5/0.1 | MEX | PV | La Fiera Grupera, Papantla |
| | 1 | MEX | MY | La Jefa, Cd.Mante |
| | 1/0.25 | MEX | TEY | R. Sensación, Tepic |
| | 5 | NCG | A3NT | R. Fe 840, Managua |
| | 10 | PNR | L80 | R. Nacional, Panamá |
| | 5/1 | PTR | WXEW | R. Victoria, Yabucoa |
| | 10 | SLV | FB | R. Santa Biblia, San Salvador |
| **850** | 2 | CTR | RDR | R. Cartago, Cartago |
| | 1 | CUB | BC | R. Progreso, Trinidad-Tetraplexer, SS |
| | 1 | CUB | BD | R. Reloj, Nueva Gerona, IJ |
| | 0.25 | MEX | ZF | Buenísima, Mexicali |
| | 1/0.1 | MEX | JAQ | La Ke Buena, Jalpan |
| | 1 | MEX | ZI | Maxistar, Zacapu |
| | 3/1 | MEX | MIA | R. Disney, Guadalajara |
| | 5 | PNR | T61 | La Exitosa de Chiriquí, David |
| | 1 | PNR | | La Exitosa, Colón |
| | 5/1 | PTR | WABA | WABA, Aguadilla |
| **860** | | CUB | BD | R. Reloj, Bolondrón, MA |

| kHz | kW | Ctry | Call | Station, location |
|---|---|---|---|---|
| | 10 | CUW | PJZ-86 | Z-86 R. Curom, Willemstad |
| | 1.5 | HND | BV | R. Piedra Blanca, Catacamas |
| | 0.5 | HND | | R. Río de Dios, Olanchito |
| | 10/7.5 | MEX | MO | 8-60 La Poderosa/Uniradio, Tijuana |
| | 1/0.25 | MEX | NW | Máxima 103, Culiacán |
| | 10/1 | MEX | CTL | R. Chetumal, Chetumal |
| | 5/0.1 | MEX | AL | R. Fórmula, Manzanillo |
| | 1/0.5 | MEX | ZOL | R. Noticias 860, Cd.Juárez |
| | 5/1.5 | MEX | NL | R. Recuerdo, Monterrey |
| | 4.5/10 | MEX | UN | R. UNAM, México |
| | 10 | PNR | L55 | R. Reforma, Chitré |
| | 10 | SCN | | Voice of Nevis, Nevis |
| **870** | 10 | CTR | UCR | R. 870 UCR, San Pedro Montes de Oca |
| | 10 | CUB | BD | R. Reloj, Baracoa-Van Van, GU |
| | 10 | CUB | BD | R. Reloj, Bueycito, GR |
| | 1 | CUB | BD | R. Reloj, Sancti Spíritus-Reloj, SS |
| | 4 | DOM | B59 | R. La Vega, La Vega |
| | 0.5 | GTM | L | R. Victoria, Mazatenango |
| | 10 | MEX | TAR | LV de la Sierra Tarahumara, Guachochi |
| | 10/0.25 | MEX | ACC | LV del Puerto, Pto. Escondido |
| | 1 | MEX | GRO | RTG R, Chilpancingo |
| | 10 | NCG | CD | R. Centro, Juigalpa |
| | 5.5 | PNR | HO | R. Libre, Panamá |
| | 1.25 | PTR | WQBS | WQBS R., San Juan |
| | 2 | SLV | AR | R. Renacer, San Salvador |
| **880** | 12 | CUB | BC | R. Progreso, Pinar del Río-San Juan, PR |
| | 10 | HND | H | R. Nacional de Honduras, Tegucigalpa |
| | 5/1 | MEX | EM | La M Mexicana, Río Verde |
| | 20/1 | MEX | AAA | R. Mujer, Guadalajara |
| | 5/0.25 | MEX | CHEP | XECHEP, Chihuahua |
| | 10 | NCG | A3EP | R. El Pensamiento, Managua |
| | 2.5 | PNR | | R. Panamá, Bocas del Toro |
| | 2.5 | PNR | | R. Panamá, Chiriquí |
| | 1 | PNR | B51 | R. Visión Panamá, Colón |
| | 1/0.5 | PTR | WYKO | La Poderosa 880, Sabana Grande |
| **890** | | CUB | J | CMKC R. Revolución, Santiago de Cuba, SC |
| | 200 | CUB | BC | R. Progreso, Chambas-Centro 6, CA |
| | 3 | DOM | | Consentida, Mao |
| | 1 | GTM | HU | R. Escuintla, Escuintla |
| | 5/0.5 | MEX | AK | La Mejor, Acámbaro |
| | 10/0.5 | MEX | NZ | La Sinaloense, Culiacán |
| | 5 | PNR | Q62 | R. Ritmo Stereo, Chitré |
| | 0.25 | PTR | WFAB | R. Unidad Cristiana, Ceiba |
| | 3 | SLV | LA | R. Elohim, Santa Ana |
| **900** | 5 | BRB | | FM 94.7, St Michael |
| | 50 | CUB | BC | R. Progreso, San Germán, HO |
| | 1 | GTM | MA | R. Amatique, Puerto Barrios |
| | 1 | HND | UP6 | R. Satélite, La Ceiba |
| | 10/2.5 | MEX | OK | La OK, Monterrey |
| | 100 | MEX | W | W R., México |
| | 10 | PNR | HA | CD R., Panamá |
| | 2 | SLV | QJ | R. Tiempo, San Salvador |
| **910** | 10 | CTR | UM | BBN, San José/San Carlos |
| | 25 | CUB | HA | R. Cadena Agramonte, Camagüey-Tagarro, CM |
| | 5 | CUB | BL | R. Metropolitana, Villa María, CH |
| | 5 | CUB | BD | R. Reloj, Bolondrón, MA |
| | 10 | GTM | KL | R. Fe y Esperanza, Guatemala |
| | 10 | HND | VS | La Voz de Suyapa, Tegucigalpa |
| | 5/0.1 | MEX | LNEP | Acustik R., León |
| | 0.25 | MEX | AO | R. Mexicana, Mexicali |
| | 5 | NCG | | R. Jinotega, Jinotega |
| | 4.4 | PTR | WPRP | NotiUno, Ponce |
| **920** | 1 | CUB | BC | R. Progreso, Pilón-Siguanea, GR |
| | 0.2 | GTM | RS | R. Cultural, Escuintla |

| kHz | kW | Ctry | Call | Station, location |
|---|---|---|---|---|
| | 5 | HND | SK | R. Catacamas, Catacamas |
| | 1 | HND | RM | R. Sistema, Comayagua |
| | 1 | HND | ZV | Una Voz Que Clama en el Desierto, S. P. S. |
| | 1 | MEX | ZAR | @FM, Puebla |
| | 5/1 | MEX | RE | La Comadre, Puros Éxitos, Celaya |
| | 5/2.5 | MEX | LCM | La Poderosa, Cd.Lázaro Cárdenas |
| | 5/0.2 | MEX | RCA | Planeta, Torreón |
| | 10/1 | MEX | LT | R. María, Tlaquepaque |
| | 1.5/0.5 | MEX | STRC | Voces, Campeche |
| | 10 | NCG | W | R. Mundial, Managua |
| | 5 | PNR | S56 | R. Mía, Los Santos |
| **930** | 5 | CTR | RCR | R. Costa Rica, Guadalupe |
| | 1 | CUB | BD | R. Reloj, Cienfuegos-Malecón, CI |
| | 1 | CUB | BD | R. Reloj, La Jaiba, MA |
| | 1 | CUB | BD | R. Reloj, Stgo de Cuba-Sta.María, SC |
| | 4 | HND | CQ | Cadena Radial Samaritano, La Ceiba |
| | 5 | MEX | TLA | LV de la Mixteca, Tlaxiaco |
| | 1 | MEX | SAME | XESAME, Saltillo |
| | 10 | PNR | R46 | La Exitosa, Panamá |
| | 2 | PNR | K85 | R. Mi Preferida,Pto Armuelles |
| | 2.5 | PTR | WYAC | WIAC La Original, Cabo Rojo |
| | 3 | SLV | TG | R. San José, San Salvador |
| **940** | 1 | CUB | BC | R. Progreso, Sancti Spíritus-Progreso, SS |
| | 10 | GTM | LV | Eventos Católicos R., S. Pedro Sacatepéquez, Guatemala |
| | 1 | HND | CR | DCR, Tegucigalpa |
| | 1/0.1 | MEX | MMM | 940 AM Oldies, Mexicali |
| | 50 | MEX | Q | Ke Buena 9-40, México |
| | 1 | MEX | HE | Ke Buena, Atotonilco |
| | 10/0.1 | MEX | YJ | La Fiera Musical, Nueva Rosita |
| | 10/1 | MEX | RLA | R. Surcalifornia, Santa Rosalía |
| | 1 | MEX | RKS | Romántica, Reynosa |
| | 10/2.5 | PTR | WIPR | Máxima 940 AM, San Juan |
| **950** | 1 | CUB | KC | R. R. Reloj, Mayarí Arriba-II Frente1, SC |
| | 10 | CUB | BD | R. Reloj, Arroyo Arenas, HA |
| | 10 | CUB | BD | R. Reloj, Camagüey-Isabel Hortensia, CM |
| | 10 | DOM | B68 | R. Popular, Santo Domingo |
| | 1 | GTM | AF | R. Indiana, Mazatenango |
| | 5 | HND | QL | R. Centro de Honduras, Siguatepeque |
| | 10/0.1 | MEX | PB | Grupera 93.1, Hermosillo |
| | 5/0.5 | MEX | MEX | La Mexicana, Cd.Guzmán |
| | 1/0.5 | MEX | FA | La Poderosa, Chihuahua |
| | 10 | MEX | OJN | LV de la Chinantla, San Lucas Ojitlán |
| | 20/5 | MEX | KAM | R. Fórmula Californias, Tijuana |
| | 5/1 | MEX | ACA | R. Fórmula, Acapulco |
| | 5/1 | MEX | RN | R. Naranjera, Monterrey |
| | 3/0.9 | MEX | MAB | Retro FM, Cd. del Carmen |
| | 1 | SLV | HG | R. Chaparrastique, San Miguel |
| **960** | 10 | CUB | BD | R. Reloj, Guantánamo-La Piña, GU |
| | 1. 5/1 | MEX | XC | ABC R. 960, Taxco |
| | 1 | MEX | CZ | ABC R., San Luis Potosí |
| | 1/0.25 | MEX | OZ | Amor, Xalapa |
| | 10/2.5 | MEX | HK | HK 9-60, LV de Guadalajara, Guadalajara |
| | 5/1 | MEX | K | La Estación Grande, Nuevo Laredo |
| | 5 | MEX | TPH | Las Tres Voces de Durango, Santa María de Ocotán |
| | 1/0.5 | MEX | IQ | Toño, Cd.Obregón |
| | 2.5 | NCG | ACTH | R. Trópico Húmedo, San Carlos |
| | 1 | PNR | M33 | AM Tropical, David |
| | 1 | PNR | | R. Capital, Panamá |
| | 1/1.7 | PTR | WDNO | Cima Norte, Quebradillas |
| **970** | 5 | CUB | AM | R. Guamá, Los Palacios, PR |
| | 1 | CUB | BA | R. Rebelde, Trinidad-Tetraplexer, SS |
| | 5/1 | DOM | B72 | R. Barahona, Barahona |
| | 6 | DOM | B71 | R. Olímpica, La Vega |
| | 5 | GTM | AX | R. Continental, Guatemala |

| kHz | kW | Ctry | Call | Station, location |
|---|---|---|---|---|
| | 2 | HND | LY | R. Millenium, Tegucigalpa |
| | 5/0.5 | MEX | MH | Candela FM, Mérida |
| | 5/0.4 | MEX | VOX | Fiesta Mexicana, Mazatlán |
| | 50/4 | MEX | RFR | Grupo Fórmula 970, México |
| | 5/0.25 | MEX | EZ | La Mejor, Caborca |
| | 1/0.25 | MEX | CJ | Los 40, Apatzingán |
| | 1 | MEX | O | NotiGAPE, Matamoros |
| | 1/0.5 | MEX | SW | R. Madera, Cd. Madera |
| | 5 | MEX | J | R. México Noticias, Cd.Juárez |
| | 1 | MEX | UG | R. Universidad de Guanajuato, Guanajuato |
| | 3 | PNR | S97 | Ondas Centrales, Santiago |
| | 5/1 | VIR | WSTX | WSTX R., St Croix |
| **980** | 2.5 | CUB | B | R. COCO, El Sapo, CH |
| | 1 | CUB | BD | R. Reloj, Moa-Rolo Monterrey, HO |
| | 5 | HND | VC | LV Evangélica, Comayagua |
| | 2 | HND | ZC | R. Rhema, San Pedro Sula |
| | 1 | HND | AO | R. Tocoa, Tocoa |
| | 2.5/0.5 | MEX | FQ | La FQ, Cananea |
| | 5/0.2 | MEX | LC | R. Pía, La Piedad |
| | 5 | MEX | FS | XELFFS, Izúcar de Matamoros |
| **990** | 25 | CUB | AM | R. Guamá, Pinar del Río-Politécnico, PR |
| | 5/1 | DOM | C84 | R. Eternidad, Sto Domingo |
| | 1 | GTM | AL | R. Perla de Oriente, Chiquimula |
| | 3.5 | HND | PR | R. Paz, Choluteca |
| | 1/0.1 | MEX | BC | BC R., Cd.Guzmán |
| | 20/1 | MEX | TG | Extremo, Tuxtla Gutiérrez |
| | 1.4/3 | MEX | CL | La Rocola 9-90, Mexicali |
| | 50 | MEX | T | La T Grande, Monterrey |
| | 2. 5/1 | MEX | IU | Stereo Cristal, Oaxaca |
| | 5 | PNR | | COC R., Panamá |
| | 0.91 | PTR | WPRA | La Primera, Mayagüez |
| **1000** | 1 | CTR | MIL | R. 2 Rock, San José |
| | 10 | CUB | CW | R. Artemisa, Artemisa, AR |
| | 5 | CUB | NM | R. Granma, Media Luna, GR |
| | | GTM | | R. Cultural y Educativa, Patzún |
| | | GTM | | R. Revelación y Verdad, Guatemala |
| | 1 | HND | XZ | HCH Radio, Tegucigalpa |
| | 3 | HND | CY | R. Congolón, Gracias |
| | 10/1 | MEX | TAC | Exa FM, Tapachula |
| | 1 | MEX | MMS | La Ke Buena, Mazatlán |
| | 1 | MEX | FV | La Rancherita, Cd.Juárez |
| | 50/20 | MEX | OY | Mil AM, México |
| | 1/0.1 | MEX | NLT | R. Fórmula Nuevo Laredo, Nuevo Laredo |
| | 5/0.35 | MEX | MYL | So Good, Mérida |
| | 10 | NCG | FF | R. Hosanna, Managua |
| | 10 | PNR | K36 | R. Poderosa, Aguadulce |
| | 5/1 | VIR | WVWI | WVWI R., St Thomas |
| **1010** | 1 | GTM | | R. Caribe, Izabal |
| | 1 | GTM | XI | R. Ixil, Nebaj |
| | 1 | HND | CD | R. Constelación. Juticalpa |
| | 1 | HND | LL | R. Visión Cristiana, Tocoa |
| | 1 | MEX | HGO | Hidalgo R, Huejutla |
| | 20/2 | MEX | PA | Ke Buena, Puebla |
| | 5 | MEX | TUX | LV de la Sierra Oriente, Tuxpan |
| | 0.5/0.2 | MEX | XN | R. Ures, Ures |
| | 50/5 | MEX | HL | W Deportes, Guadalajara |
| | 5 | NCG | FAVP | R. LV del Pinar, Ocotal |
| **1020** | | CTR | | R. Metrópoli, Cartago |
| | 10 | CUB | M | CMKS R. Trinchera Antiimp., Baracoa-Van Van, GU |
| | 5 | CUB | CW | R. Artemisa, Bahía Honda AR |
| | 1 | CUB | AM | R. Guamá, Santa Lucía, PR |
| | 10 | CUB | BD | R. Reloj, Las Tunas-Progreso, LT |
| | 5 | GTM | CM | R. Frontera, Pajapita |
| | 3 | HND | PN | R. Visión Cristiana Internacional, |

| kHz | kW | Ctry | Call | Station, location |
|---|---|---|---|---|
| | | | | Marcovia |
| | 1 | MEX | COEP | Acustik R., Colima |
| | 5/0.5 | MEX | PR | Éxtasis Digital, Poza Rica |
| | 1/0.25 | MEX | WO | Sol Stereo, Chetumal |
| | 5 | PNR | | R. Ancón, Panamá |
| | 1/0.3 | PTR | WOQI | R. Casa Pueblo, Adjuntas |
| | 5 | SLV | CA | R. Máxima, San Salvador |
| 1030 | 10 | GTM | UX | R. Panamericana, Guatemala |
| | | HTI | | R. Ginen, Port-au-Prince |
| | 1/0.25 | MEX | BCC | La Mejor, Cd. del Carmen |
| | 1/0.5 | MEX | PAV | La Picuda, Tampico |
| | 5 | MEX | SDD | La Tremenda, Ensenada |
| | 10/0.25 | MEX | VFS | LV de la Frontera Sur, Las Margaritas |
| | 5 | MEX | FEL | LV del Gran Pueblo, Felipe Carrillo Puerto |
| | 50/5 | MEX | QR | R. Centro, México |
| | 5/1 | MEX | IE | Stereo 1030, Matehuala |
| | 10/1 | MEX | ROPJ | XEROPJ, Lagos de Moreno |
| | 0.3/0.3 | PTR | WOSO | San Juan |
| | 1 | SLV | RM | R. Frontera, Ahuachapán |
| 1040 | 10 | CUB | CL | R. Mayabeque, Güines, MB |
| | 1 | GTM | JP | R. Oriental, Jalapa |
| | 1 | HND | VC | LV Evangélica, Danlí |
| | 5 | HND | VC | LV Evangélica, Juticalpa |
| | 10/1 | MEX | BBB | ESNE R, Guadalajara |
| | 5/0.75 | MEX | CH | Pirata FM 89.3, Toluca |
| | 5/0.25 | MEX | SAG | R. Lobo Bajío, Irapuato |
| | 5/0.5 | MEX | PLE | R. Palanque, Palenque |
| | 2.5 | PNR | J2 | Canajagua AM Stereo, Las Tablas |
| | 9/0.25 | PTR | WNVI | R. Nueva Vida, Moca |
| 1050 | 10 | CUB | LL | R. Victoria, Las Tunas-Victoria, LT |
| | 1.5 | DOM | B80 | R. Hispaniola, Santiago |
| | 5/1 | GTM | SL | LV de los Cuchumatanes, Huehuetenango |
| | 10 | MEX | D | La Gran D, Mexicali |
| | 1 | MEX | IP | La Poderosa, Uruapán |
| | 10/1 | MEX | BCS | La R. de Sudcalifornia, La Paz |
| | 100 | MEX | G | La Ranchera 1050, Monterrey |
| | 5 | MEX | JF | R. Max, Tierra Blanca |
| | 10 | SLV | U | R. Evangélica Sinaí, San Salvador |
| 1060 | 25 | CUB | DL | CMGW R. 26, Jovellanos, MA |
| | | HND | KT | R. La Catracha, Tegucigalpa |
| | 7/2.5 | MEX | RDO | La Raza 1060, Reynosa |
| | 100/20 | MEX | EP | R. Educación, México |
| | 10 | PNR | WK | R. Metrópolis, Panamá |
| | 5/0.5 | PTR | WCGB | Rock R. Network, Juana Díaz |
| 1070 | 10 | CUB | M | CMKS R. Trinchera Antiimp., Guant.-Burenes, GU |
| | 10 | CUB | AM | R. Guamá, Guane, PR |
| | 5/1 | DOM | B83 | HIBI Radio, San Francisco de Macorís |
| | 3/2 | GTM | D | LV de Occidente, Quetzaltenango |
| | 1 | HND | LE | R. Unica, San Pedro Sula |
| | 3 | HND | BB | R. Unidad Evangélica, Catacamas |
| | 1/0.2 | MEX | AGS | Amor, Acapulco |
| | 1/0.25 | MEX | IT | Exa FM, Cd. del Carmen |
| | 10/1 | MEX | SP | Rock & Soul, Guadalajara |
| | 3 | PNR | | R. Estéreo Mi Favorita, Penonomé |
| | 0.5/2.5 | PTR | WMIA | Cadena WAPA R., Arecibo |
| 1080 | 1 | CTR | FC | Faro del Caribe AM, San José |
| | 5 | CUB | CH | R. Cadena Habana, Villa María, CH |
| | 10 | CUB | IP | R. Surco, Ciego de Ávila-Surco/Progreso, CA |
| | 1 | DOM | B84 | R. RPQ Sport, Santo Domingo |
| | 1 | GTM | LU | R. Novedad, Zacapa |
| | 3 | HND | IE | R. Senda de Vida, San Lorenzo |
| | 5 | MEX | PBPV | Jalisco R., Puerto Vallarta |
| | 1/0.13 | MEX | UU | La Mejor, Colima |
| | 0.5/0.25 | MEX | PAB | R. Celebridad, La Paz |

| kHz | kW | Ctry | Call | Station, location |
|---|---|---|---|---|
| | 5/0.25 | MEX | TUL | R. Mexiquense Valle de México, Tultitlán |
| | 5 | PNR | J24 | R. Mundo Internacional, Panamá |
| | 0.25 | PTR | WLEY | R. Ley, Cayey |
| | 6 | SLV | ME | R. Cadena CRET, San Salvador |
| 1090 | 1 | CUB | LL | R. Victoria, Amancio, LT |
| | 2.5 | DOM | B85 | R. Amistad, Santiago |
| | 10 | HND | CQ | Cadena Radial Samaritano, Tegucigalpa |
| | 10 | MEX | MCA | La Grande de las Huastecas, Pánuco |
| | 1 | MEX | HR | La HR, Puebla |
| | 1 | MEX | WL | La Romántica, Nuevo Laredo |
| | 5/0.5 | MEX | AU | Milenio R, Monterrey |
| | 50 | MEX | PRS | XX Sports 1090 AM/Mighty 1090, Rosarito |
| | 0.2/0.7 | PTR | WSOL | R. Sol, San Germán |
| | 3 | SLV | MG | R. Cadena CRET, Atiquizaya |
| | 0.25 | VIR | WUVI | WUVI R., St Thomas |
| 1100 | 5 | CTR | SCR | R. Chorotega, Santa Cruz |
| | 1 | CUB | KO | R. Angulo, Mayarí, HO |
| | 1 | DOM | B86 | Aliento FM, San Pedro de Macorís |
| | 1 | GTM | SR | R. Superior, Coatepeque |
| | 1.5 | HND | ND | R. La Esperanza, La Esperanza |
| | 1 | HND | VA | R. Tiempo, San Pedro Sula |
| | 1 | HND | AJ | Radio Gualaco, Gualaco |
| | 5 | MEX | BV | R. Alegría, Moroleón |
| | 1 | MEX | BAC | R. Asunción/R. Sur California, Bahía Asunción |
| | 5/0.5 | MEX | TGO | R. Cañón, Tlaltenango |
| | 1 | MEX | GRM | RTG R, Ometepec |
| | 5 | PNR | M92 | LV de la Liberación, Panamá |
| | 6 | SLV | RF | R. Cristo Viene, San Salvador |
| 1110 | 10 | CUB | KO | R. Angulo, Holguín, HO |
| | 1/0.5 | DOM | B91 | R. Marién, Dajabón |
| | 1 | GTM | MK | R. Verapaz, Cobán |
| | 1/0.5 | MEX | WR | Cristo Rey R., Ciudad Juarez |
| | 1/0.2 | MEX | PVJ | Fiesta Mexicana, Puerto Vallarta |
| | 0.25 | MEX | PU | La P-U, Monclova |
| | 1/0.25 | MEX | VS | Maxima 96-3, Hermosillo |
| | 1 | MEX | OQ | NotiGAPE, Reynosa |
| | 100 | MEX | RED | R. RED y Formato 21, México |
| | 25/0.5 | PTR | WVJP | Z101 Digital, Caguas |
| 1120 | 1 | CTR | ACE | R. Alajuela, Alajuela |
| | 0.5 | GTM | C | R. Poderosa, Guatemala |
| | 2 | HND | TL | R. Fiesta, Tegucigalpa |
| | 5 | MEX | POP | Fórmula 11-20 AM, Puebla |
| | 5/0.5 | MEX | TQE | La R. de Tabasco, Tenosique |
| | 0.4/0.1 | MEX | MX | Noticias 1120, Mexicali |
| | 1 | MEX | RUY | R. Universidad, Mérida |
| | 0.5 | MEX | UNO | R. Uno La Popular , Guadalajara |
| | 5 | NCG | A3CP | R. CEPAD, Managua |
| | 5 | PNR | M21 | R. Sonora, Panamá |
| | 2.6/5 | PTR | WMSW | R. Once, Hatillo |
| | 3 | SLV | LR | R. Elohim, San Salvador |
| 1130 | | CUB | BA | R. Rebelde, Imías, GU |
| | 1 | GTM | VR | Em. Unidas LV de la Costa Sur, Retalhuleu |
| | 2 | HND | HP | Estéreo Pinares, Siguatepeque |
| | 1 | HND | BT | Ritmo 1130, Juticalpa |
| | 1/0.1 | MEX | FN | Candela, Uruapan |
| | 10/2.5 | MEX | YZ | La Poderosa, Aguascalientes |
| | 5 | MEX | CHAP | R. Chapingo, Chapingo |
| | 1 | MEX | LUP | R. Lupita, Las Varas |
| | 1 | MEX | HN | Toño, Nogales |
| | 2.5 | PNR | U80 | Vox MN, Aguadulce |
| | 0.2/0.7 | PTR | WOIZ | R. Antillas, Guayanilla |
| | 1 | SLV | AJ | R. Moderna, Sta Ana |
| 1140 | 5 | CTR | DKN | R. Nueva, Guápiles |

| kHz | kW | Ctry | Call | Station, location |
|---|---|---|---|---|
| | 1 | CUB | NL | R. Bayamo, Media Luna, GR |
| | 1 | CUB | BQ | R. Camagüey, Camagüey-Isabel Hortensia,CM |
| | 1 | CUB | DP | R. Ciudad Bandera, Cárdenas-2, MA |
| | | CUB | FL | R. Ciudad del Mar, Cienfuegos-Malecón, CI |
| | 25 | CUB | CL | R. Mayabeque, La Salud, MB |
| | 10 | CUB | BF | R. Musical Nacional, Santa Clara-Progreso, VC |
| | 10 | CUB | BA | R. Rebelde, Aguada, CI |
| | | CUB | BA | R. Rebelde, Caribe, IJ |
| | | CUB | BA | R. Rebelde, Guantánamo-La Piña, GU |
| | 5 | CUB | BA | R. Rebelde, Matanzas-Circunvalación, MA |
| | 25 | CUB | IP | R. Surco, Morón, CA |
| | 3 | HND | VC | LV Evangélica, Choluteca |
| | 1 | HND | UL | R. Pico Bonito, La Ceiba |
| | 5 | MEX | TE | 106.3 FM, Tehuacán |
| | 50 | MEX | MR | R. Esperanza, Monterrey |
| | 1/0.5 | MEX | TEC | R. Tecpatán, Tecpatán |
| | 1 | MEX | PEC | Sonoarmonía, San Bartolo Tutotepec |
| | 5 | PNR | B49 | R. Panamericana, Panamá |
| | 10 | PTR | WQII | Once Q Cadena Nac., San Juan |
| 1150 | 10 | CUB | NL | R. Bayamo, Entronque Bueycito, GR |
| | 5 | DOM | B96 | Onda Musical, Sto Domingo |
| | 10 | GTM | T | R. Sonora, Guatemala |
| | 1 | HND | LP12 | R. Universal, Tegucigalpa |
| | 1.5/0.5 | MEX | TVR | Azul 106.9, Tuxpan |
| | 50/10 | MEX | JP | El Fonógrafo, México |
| | 10/1 | MEX | XP | La Mejor, Tuxtepec |
| | 1 | MEX | RM | R. Fórmula, Mexicali |
| | 50/1 | MEX | AD | R. Metrópoli, Guadalajara |
| | 10/0.15 | MEX | UAS | R. UAS, Culiacán |
| | | | NCG | R. Darío, León |
| | 1 | SLV | CF | R. Elohim, San Miguel |
| 1160 | 10 | ATG | | Caribbean R., Lighthouse, St John's |
| | 1 | CUB | NL | R. Bayamo, Pilón-Siguanea, GR |
| | 1 | GTM | RI | R. Izabal, Morales |
| | 1 | HND | VZ | R. Juan Pablo II, Siguatepeque |
| | | HND | | R. Nueva Palestina, Nueva Palestina |
| | 5 | HND | FJ | R. País, Progreso |
| | 10 | MEX | QIN | LV del Valle, San Quintín |
| | 5 | PNR | C20 | Ondas Chiricanas, David |
| | 5/2.5 | PTR | WBQN | R. Borinquén, Barceloneta-Manatí |
| 1170 | 10 | CUB | M | CMKS R. Trinchera Antiimp., Sta. Rita, Maisí, GU |
| | 5 | GTM | RL | R. Cadena Landívar, Quetzaltenango |
| | 2 | HND | AF | La Campeonísima, Choluteca |
| | 5 | MEX | RT | Ke Buena, Reynosa |
| | 10/2.5 | MEX | CD | La Romántica, Puebla |
| | 5/0.1 | MEX | FEM | R. Disney, Hermosillo |
| | 2. 5/1 | MEX | ZS | R. Hit, Coatzacoalcos |
| | 1/0.25 | MEX | RLK | Super Stereo Miled, Atlacomulco |
| | 0.2 | PTR | WLEO | R. Leo, Ponce |
| 1180 | 5 | CTR | PJ | R. Victoria, Heredia |
| | 1 | CUB | DX | CMDX R. Baracoa, Mabujabo, GU |
| | 10 | CUB | BA | R. Rebelde, Arroyo Arenas, CH |
| | 10 | CUB | BA | R. Rebelde, Artemisa, AR |
| | 5 | CUB | BA | R. Rebelde, Bahía Honda, AR |
| | 1 | CUB | BA | R. Rebelde, Banes, HO |
| | | CUB | BA | R. Rebelde, Bolondrón, MA |
| | 50 | CUB | BA | R. Rebelde, Cacocúm, HO |
| | 50 | CUB | BA | R. Rebelde, Camagüey-Villa Rosita, CM |
| | 5 | CUB | BA | R. Rebelde, Cárdenas-1, MA |
| | 10 | CUB | BA | R. Rebelde, Central Brasil, Jaronú CM |
| | 50 | CUB | BA | R. Rebelde, Chambas-Centro 6, CA |

| kHz | kW | Ctry | Call | Station, location |
|---|---|---|---|---|
| | 1 | CUB | BA | R. Rebelde, Ciego de Avila-Rebelde/Reloj, CA |
| | 5 | CUB | BA | R. Rebelde, Cienfuegos-1ra Tulipán, CI |
| | 25 | CUB | BA | R. Rebelde, Colón, MA |
| | | CUB | BA | R. Rebelde, Corralillo, VC |
| | | CUB | BA | R. Rebelde, Guáimaro, CM |
| | 50 | CUB | BA | R. Rebelde, Guanabacoa, CH |
| | 1 | CUB | BA | R. Rebelde, Guantánamo-Radio Reloj, GU |
| | 10 | CUB | BA | R. Rebelde, Güines, MB |
| | | CUB | BA | R. Rebelde, Hectométrico, MB |
| | 10 | CUB | BA | R. Rebelde, La Palma, PR |
| | 10 | CUB | BA | R. Rebelde, Las Tunas-Rebelde1180, LT |
| | 10 | CUB | BA | R. Rebelde, Los Palacios, PR |
| | 200 | CUB | BA | R. Rebelde, Martí-Centro 5, MA |
| | 5 | CUB | BA | R. Rebelde, Matanzas-La Jaiba, MA |
| | 1 | CUB | BA | R. Rebelde, Mayarí Arriba-II Frente1, SC |
| | 1 | CUB | BA | R. Rebelde, Moa-Rolo Monterrey, HO |
| | 5 | CUB | BA | R. Rebelde, Nueva Gerona, IJ |
| | | CUB | BA | R. Rebelde, Pinar del Río-Coloma, PR |
| | 1 | CUB | BA | R. Rebelde, Puerto Padre, LT |
| | 5 | CUB | BA | R. Rebelde, Sagua de Tánamo, HO |
| | 10 | CUB | BA | R. Rebelde, Sagua la Grande, VC |
| | 1 | CUB | BA | R. Rebelde, San Cristóbal, PR |
| | 1 | CUB | BA | R. Rebelde, Sancti Spíritus-Progreso, SS |
| | 10 | CUB | BA | R. Rebelde, Santa Catalina, CH |
| | 10 | CUB | BA | R. Rebelde, Santa Clara-CMHW, VC |
| | 1 | CUB | BA | R. Rebelde, Santa Lucía, PR |
| | | CUB | BQ | R. Rebelde, Santiago de Cuba-Eide, SC |
| | 10 | CUB | BA | R. Rebelde, Sta Cruz del Norte-La Sierrita, MB |
| | 1 | HND | AZ | R. El Tigre, Tegucigalpa |
| | 1 | HND | | R. Río de Dios, Belén |
| | 5/1.5 | MEX | DCH | Ke Buena, Cd. Delicias |
| | 10/5 | MEX | FR | R. Felicidad, México |
| | 10 | MEX | UBS | R. Universidad Autonoma de Baja California Sur, La Paz |
| | 10 | PNR | U | AM Original, Santiago |
| | 10 | PNR | | R. Chinavisión, Panamá |
| | 5 | SLV | VG | R. VEA, San Salvador |
| 1190 | 10 | CUB | JD | R. Coral/R. Revolución, Chivirico, SC |
| | 1 | CUB | GL | R. Sancti Spíritus, Trinidad-Tetraplexer, SS |
| | 5 | HND | VW3 | R. Cadena Voces, El Progreso |
| | 5 | MEX | JOEP | Acustik R., Jojutla |
| | 0.25/0.1 | MEX | MBC | Cadena 1190 AM, Mexicali |
| | 10/0.1 | MEX | CT | Contacto 11-90, Monterrey |
| | 5 | MEX | PP | La Comadre, Orizaba |
| | 1/0.1 | MEX | PZ | R. Centro, Cd.Juárez |
| | 2.5/1 | MEX | XQ | R. Universidad, San Luís Potosí |
| | 50/10 | MEX | WK | W R. /W Guadalajara, Guadalajara |
| | 1 | NCG | A6RB | R. Bendición, Cayanlipe |
| | 10/5 | PTR | WBMJ | Rock R. Netw., San Juan |
| 1200 | 5 | CTR | TQ | R. Cucu, San José |
| | 1 | CUB | GL | R. Sancti Spíritus, Yaguajay, SS |
| | | DOM | C23 | R. VEN, Sto Domingo |
| | 12 | GTM | RJ | R. Unción, Jutiapa |
| | 1 | HND | SI | R. Impacto, Tela |
| | 5 | MEX | QJAL | R. Jalpan, Jalpan |
| | 1 | MEX | PAS | R. Punta Abreojos, Punta Abreojos |
| | 2.5 | MEX | QY | Retro FM, Toluca |
| | 0.25/1 | PTR | WGDL | La Mejor AM, Lares |
| 1210 | | CUB | BA | R. Rebelde, Las Tunas-Progreso, LT |
| | 10 | CUB | GL | R. Sancti Spíritus, Sancti Spíritus-Reloj, SS |
| | 5 | DOM | | R. Merengue, San Francisco de Macorís |
| | 10/5 | GTM | MX | R. Palabra Miel, Guatemala |

| kHz | kW | Ctry | Call | Station, location |
|---|---|---|---|---|
| | 5 | MEX | COPA | LV de los Vientos, Copainalá |
| | 5/1 | MEX | PUE | Pasion FM, Puebla |
| | 1 | PNR | E91 | R. Diez, Panamá |
| | 5 | PTR | WHOY | R. Hoy, Salinas |
| | 1 | SLV | CG | R. Salem, Zacatecoluca |
| 1220 | 1 | CTR | Q | R. Fe y Poder, Limón |
| | 10 | CUB | BY | R. Caribe, La Fe-Progreso, IJ |
| | 1 | HND | OP | R. Costeña Ebenezer, San Pedro Sula |
| | 1 | HND | | R. Destellos de Luz, Sabá |
| | 3 | HND | SD | R. Destellos de Luz, Sabá |
| | 1 | HND | YS | R. Suari, Marcala |
| | 100 | MEX | B | La B Grande, México |
| | 4.5 | MEX | SAL | R. Universidad Agraria, Saltillo |
| 1230 | | CUB | BC | R. Progreso, Bayamo, GR |
| | | GTM | | R. América, Cuyotenango |
| | 1 | GTM | AT | R. Atlántida, Puerto Barrios |
| | 3 | HND | CQ | Cad. R. Samaritano, San Marcos de Colón |
| | 10 | MEX | CSEP | Acustik R., Culiacán |
| | 0.5 | MEX | DKN | Fórmula Jalisco 12-30 AM, Guadalajara |
| | 20/1 | MEX | TVH | La R. de Tabasco, Villahermosa |
| | 10/1 | MEX | IZ | R. Fórmula Monterrey 1230, Monterrey |
| | 5 | NCG | MNG | R. Manantial, Nueva Guinea |
| | 1 | PTR | WNIK | Única R., Arecibo |
| 1240 | 1 | DOM | C26 | R. María de la Altagracia, Santo Domingo |
| | 1 | DOM | | Red Nacional Cristiana, Puerto Plata |
| | 1 | HND | ZC | R. Vanguardia, Tegucigalpa |
| | 25 | MEX | MEFM | Acustik Michoacán, Morelia |
| | 1 | MEX | CG | Arroba FM, Nogales |
| | 1 | MEX | WG | Bengala 12-40, Cd.Juárez |
| | 1 | MEX | RD | La Comadre, Pachuca |
| | 5 | NCG | A3RR | R. Vida, Managua |
| | 3 | PNR | M56 | Ondas de Vida, David |
| | 1 | PNR | | R. Infantil, Panamá |
| | 1/5 | PTR | WALO | Walo R., Humacao |
| | 1 | SLV | QN | R. Norteña, San Miguel |
| 1250 | 1 | CUB | M | CMKS R. Trinchera Antimperialista, Imías, GU |
| | 1 | GTM | | LV Cristiana, Totonicapán |
| | 1 | GTM | PY | R. Payakí, Esquipulas |
| | 1 | HND | KF | R. Garzel, Juticalpa |
| | 1 | HND | YF | R. Renacimiento, Comayagua |
| | 1 | MEX | VREP | Acustik R., Veracruz |
| | 10/1 | MEX | DK | DK 12-50, Guadalajara |
| | 5/0.5 | MEX | ZT | La Mejor, Puebla |
| | 1/0.25 | MEX | TEJ | R. Mexiquense, Tejupilco |
| | 5 | PNR | LY | R. Hogar, Penonomé |
| | 0.25/1 | PTR | WJIT | R. Hit, Sabana |
| 1260 | 5 | CTR | DIO | R. Emaús, San Vito de Coto Brus |
| | 2.5 | CUB | BC | R. Progreso, Media Luna, GR |
| | 1 | HND | FP | R. Amistad, San Marcos de Colón |
| | 20/10 | MEX | L | La Comadre, México |
| | 1/0.25 | MEX | ZH | La Estación que se Escucha, Salamanca |
| | 5/1 | MEX | JY | La Mejor, Autlán |
| | 10 | MEX | JAM | LV de la Costa Chica, Santiago Jamiltepec |
| | 1 | MEX | MTV | R. Lobo de Mina, Minatitlán |
| | 1/0.25 | MEX | MW | Río Digital 93.9, San Luis Río Colorado |
| | 2.5/2 | PTR | WISO | Cadena WAPA R, Ponce |
| | 12 | SLV | AA | R. Abba, San Salvador |
| 1270 | 1 | DOM | C32 | R. Ambiente, Baní |
| | 2.5 | GTM | CQ | R. Exclusiva, Guatemala |
| | 1/0.25 | MEX | RRR | La Huasteca, Papantla |
| | 10/0.15 | MEX | RPL | La Poderosa RPL, León |
| | 1/0.5 | MEX | GL | La Verdad R., Navojoa |

| kHz | kW | Ctry | Call | Station, location |
|---|---|---|---|---|
| | 0.5 | MEX | AZ | La Z, Tijuana |
| | 10 | MEX | TGME | XETGME, Torreón |
| | 3 | PNR | J22 | R. Tipy Q, Panamá |
| | 3.5 | SLV | QZ | R. Visión, San Miguel |
| 1280 | | CUB | BQ | R. Enciclopedia, Trinidad-RadioTrinidad, SC |
| | 1 | CUB | JN | R. Mambí, Santiago de Cuba-Sta.María, SC |
| | 1 | HND | OW | LV de la Victoria, Juticalpa |
| | 1 | HND | BN | R. San Miguel, Marcala |
| | 1/0.5 | MEX | EG | ABC R., Puebla |
| | 10/1 | MEX | AW | AW, Involvidable, Monterrey |
| | 0.5/0.25 | MEX | BON | R. Fórmula Jalisco, Guadalajara |
| | 2. 5/1 | MEX | SQ | R. San Miguel, S. M. de Allende |
| | 1 | MEX | TUT | R. Tamaulipas, Tula |
| | 5/1 | PTR | WCMN | NotiUno, Arecibo |
| | 1 | SLV | MQ | R. Emaús, San Vicente |
| 1290 | | GTM | | R. Miramundo, Zacapa |
| | 1/0.5 | MEX | IX | La Pantera, Sahuayo |
| | 5/0.5 | MEX | FAC | La Poderosa, Salvatierra |
| | 1/0.25 | MEX | AP | Romántica, Cd.Obregón |
| | 3 | PNR | S23 | R. Única, Chiriqui |
| | 5.5 | PNR | | R. Única, Los Santos |
| | 5 | PNR | | R. Única, Panamá |
| | 1 | SLV | MA | R. Chalatenango, Chalatenango |
| 1300 | 1 | CTR | GL | R. La Fuente Musical, Cartago |
| | | CUB | JB | R. Titán, Palma Soriano, SC |
| | 5 | HND | IV | CCI Radio, Tegucigalpa |
| | 5 | HND | LR | Estéreo Emaus, Santa Rosa de Copán |
| | 1/0.25 | MEX | AWL | El Corazón de la Sierra,Jacala |
| | 38/0.2 | MEX | P | Fiesta Mexicana, Cd.Juárez |
| | 1/0.1 | MEX | XW | La Bestia Grupera, Nogales |
| | 10/0.75 | MEX | XV | La Z, León |
| | 1 | NCG | A2CC | Canal 130 AM, Managua |
| | 5 | PNR | I417 | R. Bahá'ís, Boca del Monte |
| | 1 | PTR | WTIL | Cadena WAPA R., Mayagüez |
| | | SLV | KG | R. Llanera, San Miguel |
| | 1 | SXM | PJD-2 | The Voice of St. Maarten, Philipsburg |
| 1310 | 1 | CUB | BQ | R. Enciclopedia, Nueva Gerona, IJ |
| | 1 | DOM | C36 | R. Real AM, La Vega |
| | 1 | GTM | AN | R. LV de los Altos, Quetzaltenango |
| | 2.5 | HND | VC | LV Evangélica, San Pedro Sula |
| | 5 | HND | CM | R. Universidad de Agricultura, Catacamas |
| | 1/0.25 | MEX | AM | La Mandona, Matamoros |
| | 5/0.25 | MEX | VB | R. 13, Monterrey |
| | 1 | MEX | RAM | R. Amanecer, LV Indígena, Betania |
| | 1 | MEX | C | R. Enciso, Tijuana |
| | 5/1 | MEX | HIT | R. Felicidad, Puebla |
| | 10/1 | MEX | TIA | R. Vital, Guadalajara |
| | 1 | MEX | GRT | RTG R, Taxco |
| | 5 | MEX | QRMD | XEQRMD, Querétaro |
| 1320 | 1 | CUB | DL | CMGW R. 26, Matanzas-La Jaiba, MA |
| | | CUB | KA | Ecos de Sagua, Sagua de Tánamo, HO |
| | | CUB | CW | R. Artemisa, San Cristóbal, AR |
| | 0.5 | GTM | ME | R. Quezada, Jutiapa |
| | 10 | MEX | PNME | XEPNME, Piedras Negras |
| | 5/2.3 | PTR | WSKN | R. Isla 1320, San Juan |
| 1330 | 3 | DOM | C38 | R. Visión Cristiana, Santo Domingo |
| | 5 | GTM | MU | Unión R, Guatemala |
| | 5 | PNR | | Stereo Fe, Panamá |
| | 1.5 | PTR | WENA | La Buena 1330, Yauco |
| | | SLV | FG | R. Cristo Te Llama, San Salvador |
| 1340 | 5 | CTR | HR | R. Sideral, San Ramón |
| | 10 | CUB | FL | R. Ciudad del Mar, Palmira, CI |
| | 0.25 | CUB | | Talk R., Guantánamo Bay |
| | 5 | HND | CQ | Cadena Radial Samaritano, Comayagua |

| kHz | kW | Ctry | Call | Station, location |
|---|---|---|---|---|
| | 10 | HND | TQ | R. Adventista Maranatha, San Pedro Sula |
| | 1 | MEX | APM | Candela, Apatzingán |
| | 10/5 | MEX | LU | Ke Buena Puebla, Cd. Serdán |
| | 1 | MEX | BK | La Raza, Nuevo Laredo |
| | 1 | MEX | CR | La Zeta, Morelia |
| | 0.6 | MEX | MT | R. Diamante, Matamoros |
| | | MEX | AA | R. Variedades, Mexicali |
| | 5/1 | MEX | DKT | Radiorama 13-40, Frecuencia Deportiva, Guadalajara |
| | 1 | MEX | NV | Romántica 1340, Monterrey |
| | 1 | MEX | QB | Super Stereo Miled, Tulancingo |
| | 2.5 | PNR | | Tipikal 13-40, Las Tablas |
| | 0.95 | PTR | WWNA | R. Una 1340, Aguadilla |
| | 1 | VIR | WSTA | WSTA R., St Thomas |
| 1350 | 10 | CUB | FL | R. Ciudad del Mar, Aguada, CI |
| | 1 | CUB | LM | R. Libertad, Puerto Padre, LT |
| | 1 | DOM | C41 | Ondas del Yuna, Bonao |
| | 1 | GTM | MC | R. Monja Blanca, Cobán |
| | 0.25 | MEX | ZD | La Mandona, Camargo |
| | 5/1 | MEX | CAH | La Popular, LV de Soconusco, Cacahoatán |
| | 10 | MEX | CTZ | LV de la Sierra Norte, Cuetzalán |
| | 8 | MEX | LBL | R. Centro, San Luis Río Colorado |
| | 5/0.5 | MEX | TB | R. Laguna, Torreón |
| | 5/1 | MEX | QK | Tropicalísima 13-50, México |
| | 5 | PNR | Z38 | BBN R., Panamá |
| | 2.5 | PTR | WEGA | Candelita 7, Vega Baja |
| 1360 | 10 | GTM | LK | R. Tic Tac, Guatemala |
| | 1 | HND | BS | R. San Pedro, Tegucigalpa |
| | 1/0.4 | MEX | DI | @FM, Chihuahua |
| | - | MEX | IGEP | Acustik R., Iguala |
| | 10 | MEX | ZON | LV de la Sierra, Zongolica |
| 1370 | 1 | CUB | MA | R. Playita, Imías, GU |
| | 1 | GTM | AC | LV de Colomba, Colomba |
| | 5 | HND | UN | LVC Radio, Catacamas |
| | 5/0.5 | MEX | GNK | La La Ranchera Norteña, Nuevo Laredo |
| | 1/0.25 | MEX | RPU | La Z, Durango |
| | 10/0.4 | MEX | MON | R. Fórmula, Monterrey |
| | 5 | MEX | HF | R. Fórmula, Nogales |
| | 5/0.5 | MEX | SV | R. Nicolaita, Morelia |
| | 10/1 | MEX | PJ | R. Ranchito, Guadalajara |
| | 0.5 | MEX | HG | Vida 13-70, Mexicali |
| | 5/1.2 | PTR | WIVV | Rock R. Network,Vieques Island |
| | 1 | SLV | KO | R. Lluvias de Bendición, San Miguel |
| 1380 | 1 | CTR | MS | R. Guanacaste, Liberia |
| | 1 | CUB | KO | R. Angulo, Banes, HO |
| | | DOM | | Antena 13-80, Santo Domingo |
| | 1 | DOM | C47 | R. Nacional, Santiago |
| | 0.5 | GTM | EB | R. Momostenango Educativa, Momostenango |
| | 50/5 | MEX | CO | Romántica 13-80, México |
| | 10/1 | MEX | TP | Sensación FM, Xalapa |
| | 10 | PNR | | Bendición R., Panamá |
| | 1 | PTR | WOLA | R. Prócer, Barranquitas |
| 1390 | 1 | HND | VC | LV Evangélica, Sata Rosa de Copán |
| | 10/5 | HND | VC | LV Evangélica, Tegucigalpa |
| | 10/2.5 | MEX | TY | @FM, Tecomán |
| | 1 | MEX | CTAM | La R. de Morelos, Cuautla |
| | 5/1 | MEX | XO | La Super Buena, Cd.Mante |
| | 1 | MEX | OR | NotiGAPE, Reynosa |
| | 10/2.5 | MEX | ZG | R. Mezquital, Ixmiquilpan |
| | 5 | PNR | | R. Mundo Internacional, Colón |
| | 1 | PTR | WISA | WIAC La Original, Isabela |
| | 1 | SLV | JU | R. Getsemani, La Unión |
| | | SLV | | R. LV de la Palabra Que Cambia, Chalchuapa |

| kHz | kW | Ctry | Call | Station, location |
|---|---|---|---|---|
| | 1 | SLV | JS | Sinaí R, Soyapango |
| 1400 | 1 | CUB | ES | R. Sagua, Sagua La Grande, VC |
| | 5 | GRD | | Harbour Light of the Windwards, Carriacou |
| | 1 | HND | UV | R. El Patrón, Catacamas |
| | 1 | HND | YT | R. Estrella de Oro, San Pedro Sula |
| | 2. 5/1 | MEX | XI | Capital Máxima, Ixtapan de la Sal |
| | 51 | MEX | SH | R. Sabinas, Cd.Sabinas |
| | 1 | MEX | UBJ | R. Universidad, Oaxaca |
| | 10 | PNR | T40 | Digital R. Luz, La Chorrera |
| | 1 | PTR | WIDA | Cadena R. Vida, Carolina |
| | 1 | SLV | JI | LV del Litoral, Usulután |
| 1410 | 1 | DOM | C50 | R. Tricolor, Santo Domingo |
| | 5 | GTM | GH | Nueva R. Xelajú, Quetzaltenango |
| | 2.5/1 | MEX | BS | Bandolera 14-10, México |
| | 21/2 | MEX | KB | Canal 14-10, Guadalajara |
| | 1/0.25 | MEX | AS | Fiesta Mexicana, Nuevo Laredo |
| | 1/0.25 | MEX | CUA | R. Universidad, Campeche |
| | 5 | PNR | H779 | R. Mensabé, Las Tablas |
| | 1 | PTR | WRSS | R. Progreso, San Sebastián |
| 1420 | 1 | CTR | RPN | R. Pampa, Liberia |
| | | GTM | | R. Capital, Guatemala |
| | 5/0.5 | MEX | F | Activa 14-20, Cd.Juárez |
| | 5/0.4 | MEX | H | La H, Antología Vallenata, Monterrey |
| | 10/2 | MEX | XX | Vida, Tijuana |
| | 1 | MEX | EW | W1420/LV del Bajo Bravo, Matamoros |
| | 1 | PTR | WUKQ | Ponce |
| 1430 | 3 | CTR | RDVC | R. San Carlos, Cd. Quesada |
| | 5 | DOM | C54 | R. Emanuel, Santiago |
| | 1.2 | GTM | AG | LV de Huehuetenango |
| | 1 | HND | FO | LV Evangélica, Puerto Cortés |
| | 1 | HND | VM | R. Maranatha, La Paz |
| | 5/1 | MEX | TT | R. Tlaxcala, La Doble T, Tlaxcala |
| | 5/0.15 | MEX | WD | R. X, Cd. Miguel Alemán |
| | 7.5 | PNR | | R. Kids, Panamá |
| | 5 | PTR | WNEL | R. Tiempo, Caguas |
| 1440 | 5 | DOM | C55 | R. Impactante, Sto Domingo |
| | 0.5 | GTM | MS | R. Nacional, Mazatenango |
| | 5 | HND | RD | R. Belén, La Ceiba |
| | 10/1 | MEX | ABCJ | ABC R., Guadalajara |
| | 25/5 | MEX | EST | Quiéreme 14-40, México |
| | 25 | NCG | A3MR | R. Maranatha, Managua |
| 1450 | 1 | CUB | LN | R. Maboas, Amancio Rodríguez, LT |
| | 1 | CUB | CL | R. Mayabeque, Sta. Cruz del Norte-La Sierrita, MB |
| | 1 | GTM | LG | R. Hosanna, Guatemala |
| | 1 | MEX | PREP | Acustik R., Poza Rica |
| | 2/1 | MEX | RY | La Poderosa Voz del Sur, Arcelia |
| | 0.5 | MEX | DJ | R. Clave, Magdalena de Kino |
| | 1 | MEX | RNB | R. Impacto, Sahuayo y Jiquilpan |
| | 5/1 | MEX | JM | U ERRE R., Monterrey |
| | 5 | PNR | | R. Melodía, Panamá |
| | 1 | PTR | WCPR | Coamomall R., Coamo |
| | 1 | SLV | KR | R. Restauración, San Miguel |
| 1460 | | CUB | JL | R. 8SF, Mayarí Arriba-II Frente2, SC |
| | 2.5 | GTM | RN | R. Petén, Flores |
| | 2.5 | HND | GC | R. Reino, San Pedro Sula |
| | 5/0.5 | MEX | KC | Planeta, Oaxaca |
| | 1 | MEX | YC | R. Fórmula, Cd.Juárez |
| | 10/0.25 | MEX | CB | R. Ranchito, San Luis Río Colorado |
| | 1 | MEX | GRA | RTG R., Acapulco |
| | 0.5 | PNR | D42 | LV de Almirante, Bocas del Toro |
| | 0.5/0.3 | PTR | WRRE | Maranatha R. Ministries, Juncos |
| | 0.5 | PTR | WLRP | R. Raíces, San Sebastián |
| 1470 | 1 | CUB | LB | R. Chaparra, Puerto Padre, LT |
| | | DOM | | R. Barahona, Duvergé |

| kHz | kW | Ctry | Call | Station, location |
|---|---|---|---|---|
| | 1 | DOM | C60 | Red Nal. Cristiana, San Francisco de Macorís |
| | 50/5 | MEX | AI | Grupo Fórmula 1470, México |
| | 1/0.5 | MEX | IND | Hidalgo R., Tlanchinol |
| | 10/0.25 | MEX | HI | La Consentida, Ciudad Miguel Alemán |
| | 2.5/0.5 | MEX | BAL | R. Voz Maya de México, Bécal |
| | 10/5 | MEX | RCN | RCN/Uniradio 14-70, Tijuana |
| | 1/0.1 | MEX | ACE | Trión, Mazatlán |
| | 1 | NCG | RY | R. Yarrince, Boaco |
| | 5 | PNR | | La Primerísima, Panamá |
| | 2/4 | PTR | WKUM | Cumbre, Orocovis |
| **1480** | 5 | GTM | HB | R. Horizontes, Guatemala |
| | 1 | HND | EZ | R. Misiones Int., Comayagüela |
| | 10/1 | MEX | TKR | La TKR, Rancherita y Regional, Monterrey |
| | 5 | MEX | CARH | LV del Pueblo Hña-hñu, Cárdonal |
| | 5/0.15 | MEX | VIC | R. Tamaulipas, Cd.Victoria |
| | 20/1 | MEX | ZJ | Simplemente Supérate, Guadalajara |
| | 1/0.25 | MEX | NS | Z107.1, Navojoa |
| | 5 | PTR | WMDD | El 14-80, Fajardo |
| **1490** | 1 | CUB | KN | R. Mayarí, Mayarí, HO |
| | 1 | GTM | RE | R. Modelo, Retalhuleu |
| | 1 | HND | HY | R. Boquerón, Juticalpa |
| | 1 | MEX | MS | R. Mexicana, Matamoros |
| | 1 | MEX | CJC | R. Net, Cd.Juárez |
| | 1 | MEX | YTM | R. Teocelo, Teocelo |
| | 3 | PNR | | Asamblea Nacional, Cocle |
| | 5/1 | PTR | WDEP | R. Isla, Ponce |
| **1500** | 1 | CTR | RC | R. Cima, Ciudad Quesada |
| | 50 | MEX | DF | Grupo Fórmula 1500, México |
| | 1/0.5 | MEX | FL | La FL, Guanajuato |
| | 1/0.25 | PTR | WMNT | R. Atenas, Manatí |
| | 1 | SLV | DA | R. Peniel, San Salvador |
| | 1 | SLV | CS | R. Pentecostal Bethel, Usulután |
| **1510** | 10/3 | DOM | C67 | R. Pueblo, Sto Domingo |
| | | GTM | DX | R. Centroamericana, Guatemala |
| | 1 | HND | EM | R. Emmanuel, Nueva Ocotepeque |
| | 10 | MEX | QI | Opus 1510 R. Nuevo León, Monterrey |
| | 0.25 | MEX | HUI | R. Huichapan, Huichapan |
| | 5 | PNR | A95 | Hosanna R., Panamá |
| | 1 | PTR | WBSG | R. Voz, Lajas |
| **1520** | | CUB | KZ | R. Baraguá,Palma Soriano, SC |
| | | GTM | | R. Taysal, Sta Elena de la Cruz |
| | 5 | HND | MQ | R. Manantial de Vida Eterna, Juticalpa |
| | 1 | HND | DF | R. Ríos de Agua Viva, Siguatepeque |
| | 1 | MEX | VO | La Mega, San Rafael |
| | 1 | MEX | VUC | La Norteñita, Allende |
| | 1 | MEX | EH | La Primera, San Luis Río Colorado |
| | 1/0.25 | MEX | ATL | R. Mexiquense, Atlacomulco |
| | 25 | PTR | WRSJ | IBC News Network, San Juan |
| **1530** | 50/1 | MEX | UR | Éxtasis Digital, México |
| | 10/0.1 | MEX | SD | La Lupe, Silao |
| | 0.5 | NCG | A4TS | R. LV de Teresa, Santa Teresa |
| | 10 | PNR | | R. Avivamiento, Panamá |
| | 1/0.25 | PTR | WUPR | Exitos 1530, Utuado |
| **1540** | 50 | BAH | | ZNS-1 National Voice of Bahamas, Nassau |
| | 5 | MEX | HOS | La Invasora, Hermosillo |
| | 5/0.5 | MEX | STN | R. Red, Monterrey |
| | 4 | PNR | | Festival 1540 AM, Santiago |
| | 1 | PTR | WIBS | Caribe 1540 AM, Guayama |
| **1550** | | CUB | BC | R. Progreso, La Palma, PR |
| | 1 | CUB | BA | R. Progreso, Sagua La Grande, VC |
| | 5 | CUB | BA | R. Rebelde, Cárdenas-2, MA |
| | 5 | CUB | BA | R. Rebelde, Cienfuegos-1ra Tulipán, CI |
| | | CUB | BA | R. Rebelde, Corralillo, VC |
| | | CUB | BA | R. Rebelde, Guáimaro, CM |
| | 1 | CUB | BA | R. Rebelde, Guantánamo-La Piña, GU |
| | | CUB | BA | R. Rebelde, Hectométrico, MB |
| | | CUB | BA | R. Rebelde, Jayamá, CM |
| | 5 | CUB | BA | R. Rebelde, Matanzas-Circunvalación, MA |
| | | CUB | BA | R. Rebelde, San Cristóbal, AR |
| | 10 | CUB | BA | R. Rebelde, Santa Catalina, CH |
| | 10 | CUB | BA | R. Rebelde, Santa Clara-Rebelde 670, VC |
| | 1 | CUB | BA | R. Rebelde, Yaguajay, SS |
| | 1 | HND | | R. Miel, Sabá |
| | 1 | MEX | BG | Cadena 1550 AM, Tijuana |
| | 1 | MEX | REL | La R. del Sistema, Morelia |
| | 5/0.25 | MEX | NU | La Rancherita, Nuevo Laredo |
| | 10 | MEX | RUV | R. Universidad Veracruzana, Xalapa |
| | 0.25 | PTR | WKFE | R. Café Dinámica, Yauco |
| | 5 | SLV | CZ | R. Sanidad Divina, San Salvador |
| **1560** | 5 | CTR | OAR | R. Nicoya, Nicoya |
| | | GTM | | R. Inspiración, Quetzaltenango |
| | 50/10 | MEX | INFO | Aire Libre R., México |
| | 5/1 | MEX | LAC | Azul FM, Cd.Lázaro Cárdenas |
| | 1/0.25 | MEX | MAS | La Estación Familiar, Salamanca |
| | 1 | MEX | JPV | R. Deportiva 15-60, Cd. Juárez |
| | 20/0.15 | MEX | CHZ | R. Lagarto, Chiapa de Corzo |
| | 10 | PNR | | Cadena Radial Adventista, Panamá |
| | 5/0.75 | PTR | WBYM | La Mas Z R., Bayamón |
| **1570** | 10 | GTM | VE | R. VEA-Voz Evengélica de América, Guatemala |
| | 100 | MEX | RF | La Poderosa, Cd. Acuña |
| | 1/0.1 | PTR | WPPC | R. Felicidad, Peñuelas |
| **1580** | 1 | DOM | C76 | R. Neyba, Neyba |
| | 10 | MEX | DM | Mix, Hermosillo |
| | 1 | PNR | | Hosanna Manantial, Panamá |
| | 5/2 | PTR | WVOZ | Cadena WAPA R, Morovis |
| **1590** | 1.5 | CTR | LGJ | R. 16, Grecia |
| | 1 | GTM | XC | R. Triunfadora, Chimaltenango |
| | 5 | HND | BX | R. Perla, El Progreso |
| | 20/10 | MEX | VOZ | Arroba 15-90, México |
| | 1/0.25 | MEX | BZ | Éxtasis Digital, Cd.Delicias |
| | 1 | PTR | WXRF | Cadena WAPA R, Guayama |
| **1600** | 2.5 | CTR | CC | R. Buenísima, Puerto Golfito |
| | 1.5 | CTR | MQ | R. Pococí, Guápiles |
| | 5 | DOM | C78 | R. Revelación en América, Santo Domingo |
| | 5 | MEX | GEM | R. Mexiquense, Metepec |
| | 1 | MEX | TPA | RTG R, Tlapa de Comonfort |
| | 5 | PTR | WCMA | Cima 103.7, Bayamón |
| | | SLV | MV | R. Maya Visión, San Salvador |
| **1610** | 50 | AIA | | Caribbean Beacon, The Valley |
| **1620** | | CUB | NL | R. Bayamo, Bayamo GR |
| | | CUB | BA | R. Rebelde, Amancio Rodríguez, LT |
| | | CUB | BA | R. Rebelde, El Coco, HO |
| | | CUB | BA | R. Rebelde, El Sapo, CH |
| | 1 | CUB | BA | R. Rebelde, Guantánamo-R. Reloj, GU |
| | 10/1 | VIR | WDHP | WDHP R., St Croix |
| **1630** | 10/1 | MEX | UT | UABC R., Mexicali |
| | | SLV | | R. Elohim, San Salvador |
| **1640** | 1/0.5 | DOM | C80 | R. Juventus Don Bosco, Santo Domingo |
| **1650** | 5 | MEX | ARZ | ZER R. 16-50, México |
| **1660** | 10/1 | PTR | WGIT | Faro de Santidad, Canóvanas |
| **1670** | 3 | DOM | C81 | LV del Yuna, Bonao |
| | 1 | MEX | ANAH | R. Anáhuac, Huixquilucan |
| **1680** | 1 | DOM | C82 | R. Senda, San Pedro de Macorís |
| **1690** | 0.9 | VIR | WIGT | WIGT R., St Thomas |
| **1700** | 10 | MEX | PE | ESPN R., Tecate |

# SOUTH AMERICA

## (excluding Brazil)

**NB:** Brazil has been excluded to save space – see country entry for frequencies

**Abbreviations:** Dif=Difusora, Em=Emisora, LV=La Voz, Nal=Nacional, SF=Santafé.

| khz | kW | Ctry | Call | Station, location |
|---|---|---|---|---|
| 530 | 1/0.25 | ARG | | Somos R. 530, Buenos Aires |
| | 15 | FLK | | Falklands R., Stanley |
| 540 | 5 | ARG | LU17 | R. Golfo Nuevo, Pto. Madryn |
| | | ARG | | R. Italia, Villa Martelli |
| | 25/1 | ARG | LRA14 | R. Nacional, Santa Fé |
| | 10 | ARG | LRA25 | R. Nacional,Tartagal |
| | | ARG | | R. Pasión, Buenos Aires |
| | 25/5 | ARG | | Ushuaia |
| | | BOL | | Radiodifusora Victoria, La Paz |
| | 1 | CHL | CB54 | R. Ignacio Serrano, Melipilla |
| | 10 | CLM | KA | R. Auténtica Básica, Bogotá |
| | 25 | EQA | FA2 | R. Santiago, Guayaquil |
| | 10 | PRU | OBX4E | R. Inca del Perú, Lima |
| | 1 | PRU | OCX2D | R. San Antonio, El Porvenir |
| | 10 | VEN | | LV de Manapiare, San Juan de Manapiare |
| | 50/25 | VEN | OY | R. Perijá, La Villa del Rosario |
| 550 | 5/0.5 | ARG | LRG206 | AM 550 La Primera, Neuquen |
| | 2 | CHL | CC55 | R. Corporación, Concepción |
| | 1 | CHL | CD55 | R. Voz de la Tierra, Angol |
| | 30 | CLM | R36 | Cadena Radial Vida, Mitú |
| | 50 | CLM | HF | R. Nac. de Colombia, Medellín |
| | 20/12 | PRG | ZP16 | R. Parque, Ciudad del Este |
| | 1 | PRU | OBU6W | R. Bacan Sat // 750, Pocollay |
| | 25 | URG | CW1 | R. Colonia, Colonia |
| | 50 | VEN | KE | R. Mundial, Caracas |
| 560 | 25/5 | ARG | LV1 | R. Colón, San Juan |
| | 10/3 | ARG | LT15 | R. del Litoral, Concordia |
| | 25/5 | ARG | LRA13 | R. Nacional, Bahia Blanca |
| | 25/1 | ARG | LRA9 | R. Nacional, Esquel |
| | 25/1 | ARG | LRA16 | R. Nacional, La Quiaca |
| | 15 | BOL | | R. El Mundo, La Paz |
| | 25/10 | CLM | PF | LV de la Pampa, Maicao |
| | 10 | CLM | GS | R. Nac. de Colombia, Tunja |
| | 10 | EQA | AK2 | CRE Satelital, Guayaquil |
| | 10 | GUY | | Nat. Comm. Network, Georgetown |
| | 1 | PRU | OBU4M | R. Bacan Sat, Sicaya |
| | 5 | PRU | OBZ4L | R. Oriente, Lima |
| | 5 | PRU | OBX1H | Radiomar, Chiclayo |
| | 50 | VEN | RH | RNV El Informativo, Pto.Ordaz |
| 570 | 5 | ARG | | R. Argentina, Buenos Aires |
| | | CHL | CB57 | R. Salud 570, Santiago |
| | 30 | CLM | C61 | Cadena Radial Vida, Puerto Carreño |
| | 100 | CLM | ND | R. Nac. de Colombia, Bogotá |
| | 1 | EQA | CE1 | R. El Sol, Quito |
| | 1 | PRG | ZP15 | R. LV del Amambay, Pedro Juan Caballero |
| | 3 | PRU | OAM2M | R. Antena 9, Huamachuco |
| | 1 | PRU | OAM5I | R. OAM5I, Salas |
| | 3 | PRU | OAU1M | R. Univ. Nal. Pedro Ruiz Gallo, Lambayeque |
| 580 | 3 | ARG | | R. Andina, San Rafael |
| | 20 | ARG | LU20 | R. Chubut, Trelew |
| | 25/5 | ARG | LW1 | R. Univ. Nal. de Córdoba, Córdoba |
| | 10 | BOL | | R. Panamericana, La Paz |
| | 50/10 | CLM | HP | R. Nac. de Colombia, Cali |
| | 10 | EQA | FC2 | R. Uno, Guayaquil |
| | 1 | PRU | OCY2L | R. El Sol, La Esperanza |
| | 10 | PRU | OAX2E | R. Marañón, Jaén |
| | 12 | PRU | OAX4M | R. Maria, Lima |

| khz | kW | Ctry | Call | Station, location |
|---|---|---|---|---|
| | 1 | PRU | OAM7N | R. Publica, Puno |
| | 2 | URG | CX58 | R. Clarín, Montevideo |
| 590 | 50 | ARG | LS4 | R. Continental, Buenos Aires |
| | 5 | ARG | LV12 | R. Independencia, San Miguel de Tucumán |
| | 25/1 | ARG | LRA30 | R. Nacional, San Carlos de Bariloche |
| | 1 | CHL | CC59 | CARACOL 590, Concepción |
| | 10 | CHL | CD59 | R. Pingüino, Punta Arenas |
| | 50 | CLM | CR | Volvamos a Dios R., Medellín |
| | 5 | EQA | RF1 | R. Super K800, Quito |
| | 5 | PRG | ZP32 | R. Ycuámandyyú, San Pedro |
| | 1 | PRU | OCX6V | NSE R., Arequipa |
| | 1 | PRU | OAM5E | R. Sembrador, Chincha |
| 600 | 25/1 | ARG | LU5 | R. Neuquén, Neuquén |
| | 10 | BOL | | R. ACLO, Sucre |
| | | BOL | | R. Familiar, Santa Cruz |
| | 1 | BOL | | Radioemisoras del Recobro, La Paz |
| | 10 | CHL | CB60 | R. Vida Nueva, Santiago |
| | 1 | CLM | Z95 | LV de los Awas, Ricaurte el Diviso |
| | 50 | CLM | HJ | R. Libertad, Barranquilla |
| | 40 | EQA | XY2 | R. Ciudadana, Guayaquil |
| | 10 | PRU | OBZ4W | R. Cora, Lima |
| | 1 | PRU | OCU1K | R. Frias, Frias |
| | 1 | PRU | OCU6S | R. OCU6S, Marsical Nieto |
| | 1 | PRU | OBX2B | R. Onda de Paz, Trujillo |
| | 15 | VEN | SW | R. Alto Llano, Sta Bárbara de Barinas |
| 610 | 5 | ARG | | R. General, San Martin |
| | 2 | ARG | LRK201 | R. Solidaridad, Añatuya |
| | 30 | CLM | KL | La Cariñosa, Bogotá |
| | 50 | CLM | D90 | R. Nac. de Colombia, Riohacha |
| | 10 | EQA | MJ1 | R. Caravana, Quito |
| | 50 | PRG | ZP30 | LV del Chaco Paraguayo, Filadelfia |
| | 1 | PRU | OAM7M | R. Continental, Ayaviri |
| | 1 | PRU | OBU6V | R. OBU6V, Pocollay |
| | 6 | PRU | OCY2I | R. Santa Monica, Chota |
| | 50 | URG | CX4 | R. Rural, Montevideo |
| | 10 | VEN | XY | R. Centro, Cantaura |
| | 10 | VEN | SE | R. Cristal, Barquisimeto |
| 620 | 25/5 | ARG | LRA28 | R. Nacional, La Rioja |
| | 25/5 | ARG | LRA18 | R. Nacional, Río Turbio |
| | 25/5 | ARG | LV4 | R. Nacional, San Rafael |
| | 25 | ARG | LRA26 | R. Nacional. Resistencia |
| | 25/5 | ARG | LT17 | R. Provincia de Misiones, Posadas |
| | 10 | BOL | | R. San Gabriel, El Alto |
| | 10 | CHL | CC62 | R. Bío-Bío, Concepción |
| | 1 | CHL | CA62 | R. Norte Verde, Ovalle |
| | 50/20 | CLM | EL | Colmundo R., Cali |
| | 10 | CLM | VP | Colmundo R., Cartagena |
| | 7 | EQA | XY3 | R. Ciudadana, Loja |
| | 5 | PRG | ZP40 | R. Ñasaindý, San Estanislao |
| | 0.4 | PRU | OAX2M | R. Chepen, Chepen |
| | 1 | PRU | OCX6K | R. Maria, Uchumayo, Aqp |
| | 10 | PRU | OBU4B | R. Ovación, San Isidro |
| | 50/25 | VEN | ZC | R. Fe y Alegría,Guasdualito |
| | 10 | VEN | NO | R. Libertad, Cabimas |
| 630 | 10/5 | ARG | LRF201 | R. Nacional Patagonia,Comodoro Rivadavia |
| | 50 | ARG | LS5 | R. Rivadavia, Buenos Aires |

| kHz | kW | Ctry | Call | Station, location |
|---|---|---|---|---|
| | 25/5 | ARG | LW8 | R. San Salvador de Jujuy |
| | 10 | CHL | CB63 | R. Stela Maris, Valparaíso |
| | 10 | CLM | FD | R. Manizales, Manizales |
| | 1 | PRU | OBU7I | Chaski R., Urubamba |
| | 18 | PRU | OBX1U | R. Cutivalú, Castilla |
| | 50/25 | VEN | KA | RNV El Informativo, Caracas |
| **640** | 10 | ARG | LU18 | R. El Valle, General Roca |
| | 25/5 | ARG | LRA24 | R. Nacional, Río Grande |
| | 10/5 | ARG | LV15 | R. Villa Mercedes |
| | | BOL | | R. ACLO, Tarija |
| | 1 | CHL | CD64 | R. Cooperativa, Temuco |
| | 0.25 | CHL | CC64 | R. Portales, Curico |
| | 10 | CLM | BJ | RCN, Santa Marta |
| | 10 | EQA | BI2 | R. Morena, Guayaquil |
| | 15 | PRG | ZP19 | R. Caaguazú, Coronel Oviedo |
| | 10 | PRU | OAZ4K | R. Del Pacífico, Lima |
| | 3 | PRU | OAU1Y | R. La Luz, José Leonardo Ortiz |
| | 10 | PRU | OBX7B | R. Onda Azul, Puno |
| | 30 | VEN | QO | Deportes Unión R., Puerto La Cruz |
| | 10/5 | VEN | MU | R. Carora, Carora |
| **650** | 3 | ARG | | Belgrano AM 650, Buenos Aires |
| | 15 | BOL | | R. Dif. Integración, El Alto |
| | 50 | CLM | KH | RCN Antena 2, Bogotá |
| | 5 | EQA | FD4 | R. Visión, Manta |
| | 50 | PRG | ZP4 | R. Uno, Asunción |
| | 1.5 | PRU | OBU2P | R. Bendición Cristiana, Huambos |
| | | PRU | OAU9D | R. Kampagkis, Nieva |
| | 1 | PRU | OBM7C | R. OBM7C, Sandia |
| | 1 | PRU | OCU5Q | R. OCU5Q, Pueblo Nuevo |
| | 1 | PRU | OCU6L | R. OCU6L, Alto de la Alianza |
| | 1 | PRU | OAX2N | R. Regional del Norte, Trujillo |
| | 25 | URG | CX6 | R. Clásica, Montevideo |
| | | VEN | | RNV El Informativo, Güigüe |
| **660** | 1 | ARG | | Amplitud 660, Ciudad Evita |
| | 1/0.5 | ARG | LT41 | R. LV del Sur Entrerriano, Gualeguaychú |
| | 1 | BOL | | R. ABC, Santa Cruz |
| | | BOL | | R. Taller de Historia Oral Andina, La Paz |
| | 50 | CHL | CB66 | R. UC, Santiago |
| | 25 | CLM | QS | Colmundo R., Cúcuta |
| | 10 | CLM | EZ | R. Auténtica, Cali |
| | 5 | PRG | ZP26 | R. Itapirú, Cd. del Este |
| | 10 | PRG | ZP74 | R. Regional, Concepción |
| | 3 | PRU | OCX1U | R. J.H.C., Chiclayo |
| | 10 | PRU | OCX4R | R. La Inolvidable, Lima |
| | 3 | PRU | OAZ7J | R. Santa Monica, Wanshaq |
| **670** | 1 | ARG | LT4 | R. LT4 Digital, Posadas |
| | 25/5 | ARG | LRI209 | R. Mar del Plata, Mar del Plata |
| | 10 | ARG | LRA52 | R. Nacional, Chos Malal |
| | 25/5 | ARG | LRA11 | R. Nacional, Comodoro Rivadavia |
| | 4 | ARG | | R. Republica, Ciudad Evita |
| | 5/1 | ARG | | R. Universidad, La Rioja |
| | | BOL | | R. Comunitaria Cadena Provincial, Jihuacuta |
| | 50 | CLM | PL | RCN Antena 2, Medellín |
| | 10 | CLM | R33 | UIS AM, Bucaramanga |
| | 10 | EQA | FF1 | R. Jesus del Gran Poder, Quito |
| | 10 | PRU | OAX7H | R. Nal. del Perú, Puno |
| | 100 | VEN | LL | R. Rumbos, Caracas |
| **680** | 5 | ARG | LT3 | R. Cerealista, Rosario |
| | 2 | ARG | | R. Magna, Villa Martelli |
| | 15 | ARG | LV6 | R. Nihuil, Mendoza |
| | 1 | ARG | | R. Popular, Claypole |
| | 25/5 | ARG | LU12 | R. Río Gallegos, Río Gallegos |
| | | BOL | | R. ACLO, Potosi |
| | 5 | BOL | | R. Andina, La Paz |
| | 10 | BOL | | R. Jallalla Coca, Chulumani |
| | 10 | CHL | CC68 | R. Cooperativa, Concepción |
| | 50 | CLM | ZO | R. Nac. de Colombia, Barranquilla |
| | 10 | EQA | VP2 | R. Atalaya, Guayaquil |

| kHz | kW | Ctry | Call | Station, location |
|---|---|---|---|---|
| | 50 | PRG | ZP11 | R. Caritas, Asunción |
| | 5 | PRU | OAX5E | Emisora del Pacifico, Ica |
| | 0.5 | PRU | OBX2L | R. Amauta, Chócope |
| | | PRU | OCU6Q | R. Americana, Moquegua |
| | 5 | PRU | OAM4B | R. OAM4B, Chaupimarca |
| | 20 | PRU | OBX4A | R. RBC, San Isidro |
| | 5 | PRU | OCY2Y | R. San Luis, Jaén |
| | 1 | PRU | OBU7G | R. Vida, Cusco |
| | 1 | URG | CW68 | R. Young, Young |
| | 10 | VEN | QR | R. Continente, Cumaná |
| **690** | 2 | ARG | | K-24 en R., Virrey del Pino |
| | 10/5 | ARG | LU19 | R. LV de Comahue, Cipolletti |
| | 25/5 | ARG | LRA4 | R. Nacional. Salta |
| | 10 | CHL | CD69 | R. Estrella del Mar, Ancud |
| | 10 | CHL | CB69 | R. Santiago, Santiago |
| | 1 | CLM | Z73 | Em. Embera Chami y Zenu de laPalma, Apartado |
| | 35 | CLM | CZ | W R., Bogotá |
| | 1 | PRU | OAM7C | R. Altiva, Yanaoca |
| | 25 | URG | CX8 | R. Sarandí, Montevideo |
| **700** | 25/5 | ARG | LV3 | Cadena 3 - R. Córdoba |
| | | BOL | | R. Pacha Kamasa, El Alto |
| | 1 | CHL | CD70 | Nueva R. Valdivia, Valdivia |
| | 5 | CHL | CD70A | R. Magallanes, Punta Arenas |
| | 30 | CLM | CX | W R., Cali |
| | 50 | EQA | RS2 | R. Sucre, Guayaquil |
| | 12 | PRG | ZP12 | R. Carlos Antonio López, Pilar |
| | 25 | PRU | OBZ4H | R. Integridad, San Miguel |
| | 3 | PRU | OBU4J | R. La Luz, El Tambo |
| | 1 | PRU | OBU7K | R. La Salle, Maras |
| | 10 | PRU | OAU9A | R. Maria, Moyobamba |
| | 1 | PRU | OBU2T | R. Sausal Superior, Ascope |
| **710** | 50 | ARG | LRL202 | R. Diez, Buenos Aires |
| | 25/5 | ARG | LRA19 | R. Nacional, Pto. Iguazú |
| | 25/1 | ARG | LRA17 | R. Nacional, Zapala |
| | 10 | BOL | | R. Pío XII, Siglo Veinte |
| | 1 | CLM | YD | R. La Paz, Paipa |
| | 10 | CLM | NX | R. Red RCN, Medellín |
| | 1 | PRU | OAU6L | R. Amor, Socabaya, Aqp |
| | 10 | PRU | OCX7I | R. Nacional del Peru, Puerto Maldonado |
| | 5 | PRU | OBX5Q | R. Programas del Perú, Ica |
| | 5 | PRU | OCU2X | R. TurboMix, Cajamarcal |
| | 50/20 | VEN | KY | R. Capital, Caracas |
| **720** | 50/5 | ARG | LV10 | LV Diez, Mendoza |
| | 1 | ARG | LRA59 | R. Nacional, Gobernador Gregores |
| | 10 | BOL | | R. La Cruz del Sur, La Paz |
| | 1 | CHL | CC72 | R. Interamericana, Concepción |
| | 1 | CHL | CA72 | R. Portales, Iquique |
| | 30 | CLM | AN | Emisoras Unidas, Barranquilla |
| | 25 | CLM | VO | Transmisora Quindío, Armenia |
| | 5 | EQA | GB4 | LV de Portoviejo, Portoviejo |
| | 5 | EQA | IC1 | R. Municipal, Quito |
| | 10 | EQA | PR2 | R. Única, Machala |
| | 50 | PRG | ZP17 | R. Pai Puku, Teniente Irala Fernández |
| | 3 | PRU | OBU7D | NSE R., Santiago |
| | 0.5 | PRU | OAU1O | R. Frecuencia Oceánica, San José |
| | 25 | PRU | OAX2J | R. Nal.. del Perú, Trujillo |
| | 2 | PRU | OCU7J | R. Noticias, Puno |
| | 10 | PRU | OAU4E | R. Sideral, La Oroya |
| | 10 | VEN | XE | R. Elorza, Elorza |
| **730** | 10/5 | ARG | | R. Concepto |
| | 25/1 | ARG | LU23 | R. Lago Argentino - R. Nal., El Calafate |
| | 25/5 | ARG | LRA27 | R. Nacional, Catamarca |
| | 20/5 | ARG | LRA3 | R. Nacional, Santa Rosa |
| | 2.5 | BOL | | R. Yungas, Chulumani |
| | 1 | CHL | CD73 | R. Angelina, Los Angeles |
| | 10 | CHL | CB73 | R. Cooperativa AM, Valparaíso |
| | 10 | CLM | CU | Melodía Estéreo, Bogotá |
| | 15 | CLM | TJ | R. Uno, Montería |

| kHz | kW | Ctry | Call | Station, location |
|---|---|---|---|---|
| | 50 | PRG | ZP7 | R. ABC Cardinal, Lambaré |
| | 1 | PRU | OAM7X | R. Altura, Macusani |
| | 10 | PRU | OAX1D | R. del Pacifico, Piura |
| | 2.5 | PRU | OBU2Q | R. Maria, Cajamarca |
| | 1 | PRU | OCU6G | R. OCU6G, Tacna |
| | 50 | PRU | OAX4G | R. Programas del Perú, San Isidro |
| | 5/2.5 | URG | CX10 | R. Continente, Montevideo |
| 740 | 10 | ARG | | AM 740 La Carretera, Allen |
| | 10/1 | ARG | LRI200 | R. Municipal, Puerto Deseado |
| | 1 | ARG | LRA55 | R. Nacional, Alto Río Senguer |
| | 25/5 | ARG | LRH251 | R. Provincia del Chaco, Resistencia |
| | | ARG | | R. Rebelde, Buenos Aires |
| | | BOL | | R. Pueblo de Dios, La Paz |
| | 10 | CLM | HB | Ecos de Pasto, Pasto |
| | 50 | CLM | NS | R. Guatapurí, Valledupar |
| | 10 | EQA | GC1 | R. Melodía, Quito |
| | 1/0.5 | PRG | ZP38 | R. Hechizo, Caazapá |
| | 10 | PRU | OAX6C | R. Continental, Paucarpat Aqp |
| | 1 | PRU | OCX2X | R. El Puerto, Pascamayo |
| | 5 | PRU | OBX2U | R. Ilucan, Cutervo |
| | 1 | PRU | OAM7R | R. Publica, Juliaca |
| | 1 | PRU | OBU7C | R. Rede, Cusco |
| | 3 | PRU | OCU4X | R. Vision, Huancayo |
| | 5 | URG | CW27 | R. Tabaré, Salto |
| 750 | 1/0.25 | ARG | LRL203 | R. AM 7-50, Lomas de Zamora |
| | 100/10 | ARG | LRA7 | R. Nacional, Córdoba |
| | 50 | CLM | DK | Caracol R., Medellín |
| | 5 | CLM | LH | LV de Yopal, Yopal |
| | 30 | EQA | RC2 | R. Caravana, Guayaquil |
| | 5 | PRG | ZP42 | R. LV de la Policía Nacional, Asunción |
| | 1 | PRU | OBU6I | R. Bacan Sat, Pocollay |
| | 10 | PRU | OCX4X | R. Los Andes, Cerro de Pasco |
| | 1 | PRU | OAM5D | R. OAM5D, Chincha |
| | 5 | PRU | OAU9G | R. OAU9G, Bellavista |
| | 1 | PRU | OCU7Q | R. Tupac Anaru/FM, Yanaoca Canas |
| | 100 | VEN | KS | RCR 750 R. Caracas R., Caracas |
| 760 | 18/4 | ARG | LU6 | Emisora Atlántica, Mar del Plata |
| | 50 | BOL | | R. Fides, La Paz |
| | 50 | CHL | CB76 | R. Cooperativa, Santiago |
| | 25 | CLM | AJ | RCN La R., Barranquilla |
| | 10 | EQA | QE1 | R. Quito, Quito |
| | 25/10 | PRG | ZP80 | R. Encarnación, Encarnación |
| | 0.5 | PRU | OBX2K | R. Andino, Otuzco |
| | 1 | PRU | OAM7Q | R. Azángaro, Azángaro |
| | 10 | PRU | OCU4G | R. Bienstar, Chorillos //1360 |
| | | PRU | OCX7V | R. Cadena Los Andes, Chaski |
| | 1 | PRU | OBU5B | R. Municipal, Chincheros |
| | 1 | PRU | OBM7K | R. OBM7K, Mazuku |
| | 10 | VEN | SO | R. Simpática 760, Trujillo |
| 770 | 5/1 | ARG | | R. Cooperativa, Valentín Alsina |
| | 5 | BOL | | R. Cosmos, Cochabamba |
| | 5 | CHL | CD127 | R. Agricultura, Temuco |
| | 1 | CHL | CD77 | R. Cooperativa, Castro |
| | 100 | CLM | JX | RCN La R., Bogotá |
| | 25/12 | EQA | MF2 | R. Revolución, Guayaquil |
| | 2.5 | PRU | OAU7D | R. Allinccapac, Macusani |
| | 2.5 | PRU | OBX6H | R. La Inolvidable, Caiama, Aqp |
| | 1 | PRU | OCU7K | R. LV Evangelica, Urcos |
| | 3 | PRU | OCX1T | R. Vision, José Leonardo Ortiz |
| | 100 | URG | CX12 | R. Oriental, Montevideo |
| | 50/20 | VEN | KK | RNV El Informativo, Valencia |
| 780 | 25/5 | ARG | LV8 | R. Libertador |
| | 25/5 | ARG | LRA12 | R. Nacional, Santo Tomé |
| | 25/1 | ARG | LRA10 | R. Nacionall, Ushuaía |
| | 10/5 | ARG | LRF210 | R. Tres, Trelew |
| | 10 | CHL | CD78 | R. Sago, Osorno |
| | 10 | CLM | C21 | Antena del Río, Barrancabermeja |
| | 10 | CLM | ZG | LV del Valle, Cali |
| | 5 | CLM | FV | R. Viva, Pasto |
| | 30 | PRG | ZP70 | R. Primero de Marzo, Asunción |
| | 1 | PRU | OBU2N | R. Coremarca, Bambamarca |
| | 10 | PRU | OAX1K | R. Nal. del Perú, Tumbes |
| | 10 | PRU | OAZ7S | R. Nuevo Tiempo, Juliaca |
| | 2 | PRU | OCU5L | R. OCU5L, Ayacucho |
| | 3 | PRU | OAX4X | R. Victoria,Lima |
| | 50/20 | VEN | OD | Ecos del Torbes, San Cristóbal |
| | 15 | VEN | MN | R. Coro, Coro |
| 790 | 10 | ARG | LV19 | R. Malargüe |
| | 25/5 | ARG | LR6 | R. Mitre, Buenos Aires |
| | 25/5 | ARG | LRA22 | R. Nacional, San Salvador de Jujuy |
| | 1 | CLM | NC | Ecos del Combeima, Ibagué |
| | 15 | CLM | DC | Múnera Eastman R, Medellín |
| | 3 | PRU | OAZ7H | R. La Luz, Cusco |
| | 10 | PRU | OAX2I | R. Programas del Perú, Trujillo |
| | 2.5 | PRU | OBU6D | R. Uno, Tacna |
| | 50 | VEN | XM | R. Minuto, Barquisimeto |
| | 10 | VEN | KC | R. Venezuela, Caracas |
| | | VEN | | RNV El Informativo, Cd. Bolívar |
| 800 | 1/0.25 | ARG | LV23 | R. Andina General Alvear |
| | 5 | ARG | LT43 | R. Mocoví, Charata |
| | 25/2 | ARG | LU15 | R. Viedma |
| | 5 | BOL | | R. Play, La Paz |
| | 5/1 | CHL | CB80 | R. Maria, Viña del Mar |
| | 1 | CLM | JH | R. Ciudad Milagro, Armenia |
| | 100 | CLM | BW | RCN, Bucaramanga |
| | 10 | EQA | ML2 | R. Super K800, Guayaquil |
| | 5 | PRG | ZP23 | La Union R800, Asunción |
| | 5/3 | PRG | ZP27 | R. Mbaracayú, Salto del Guairá |
| | 0.3 | PRU | OBX6A | Contacto Sur, Cerro Colorado, Aqp |
| | 0.5 | PRU | OAU4H | R. La Luz, Huaral |
| | 0.5 | PRU | OBX5B | R. Sur, Ica |
| | 1 | PRU | OBU4D | R. Vida, Huancayo |
| | 3 | PRU | OCU2Y | R. Vision, Cajamarca |
| | 1 | PRU | OCX1P | Telecom del Norte, Piura |
| 810 | | ARG | | R. Federal, CF Buenos Aires |
| | 10/1 | ARG | | R. Mitre AM 810, Córdoba |
| | 60 | CLM | CY | Caracol R., Bogotá |
| | 1.5 | PRU | OBU5E | ABC R. TV, Huamanga |
| | 1 | PRU | OAU2G | R. Apocali, Trujillo |
| | 3 | PRU | OCU5Z | R. Asociación Cultural Tintaya, Cotabambas |
| | 5 | PRU | OAM7E | R. Jerusalen, Cusco |
| | 1 | PRU | OCU2V | R. Nor Andina, Jaen |
| | 1 | PRU | OCU6R | R. OCU6R, General Sanchec |
| | 10 | PRU | OAX7T | R. Programas del Perú, Juliaca |
| | 2 | PRU | OCU6Q | R. R. Santa Cruz, Moquegua |
| | 50/25 | URG | CX14 | R. El Espectador, Montevideo |
| 820 | 2/0.5 | ARG | LRI208 | Estacion 820, Lomas de Zamora |
| | 25/5 | ARG | LRA8 | R. Nacional, Formosa |
| | 5/1 | ARG | LU24 | R. Tres Arroyos |
| | 10 | BOL | | R. Altiplano Advenir, La Paz |
| | | CHL | CB82 | R. Carabineros, Santiago |
| | 1 | CHL | CD82 | R. Concordia, La Unión |
| | 10/1 | CHL | CA82B | R. Portales, La Serena |
| | 1 | CHL | CC82 | R. UCSC, Concepción |
| | 50 | CLM | ED | Caracol R., Cali |
| | 10 | CLM | AD | R. Vigía, Cartagena |
| | 5 | EQA | VI5 | R. LV de Ingapirca, Cañar |
| | 20 | PRU | OAX4O | R. Libertad, Lima |
| | 0.5 | PRU | OBX2J | R. Nuevo Continente, Cajamarca |
| | | PRU | OBU1X | R. Vision, Piura |
| | 2 | URG | CW23 | R. Cultural, Salto |
| 830 | 5 | ARG | | R. Del Pueblo, Villa Forito |
| | 1/0.5 | ARG | LT21 | R. Municipal, Alvear |
| | 25/5 | ARG | LV18 | R. Municipal, San Rafael |
| | 25 | ARG | LU14 | R. Provincia de Santa Cruz,Río Gallegos |
| | 10/5 | ARG | LT8 | R. Rosario, Rosario |
| | 15 | CLM | DM | Q'hubo R. AM/R. Reloj, Medellín |

| kHz | kW | Ctry | Call | Station, location |
|---|---|---|---|---|
| | 10 | EQA | RM2 | R. Huancavilca, Guayaquil |
| | 10 | PRU | OAU4C | R. Capital, El Tambo |
| | 5 | PRU | OAM2A | R. Educacion, Trujillo |
| | 1 | PRU | OAZ7U | R. Inti Raymi, Santiago |
| | 10 | PRU | OAX6D | R. Nacional del Perú, Tacna |
| | 1 | PRU | OAM7W | R. OAM7W, Macusani |
| | 1 | PRU | OCU2M | R. Universo, Bambamarca |
| | 25 | VEN | LT | R. Sensación, Caracas |
| 840 | 25/5 | ARG | LU2 | R. Bahía Blanca, Bahía Blanca |
| | 5 | ARG | | R. General Belgrano, Buenos Aires |
| | 10/5 | ARG | LT12 | R. General Madariaga, Paso de los Libres |
| | 25/5 | ARG | LV9 | R. Salta AM 840, Salta |
| | 3 | BOL | | R. Atipiri, El Alto |
| | 10 | CHL | CB84 | R. Portales, Valparaíso |
| | 10 | CHL | CD84 | R. Santa María, Coyhaique |
| | 30 | CLM | KK | HJKK Sistema INRAI, Neiva |
| | 10 | CLM | BI | Ondas del Caribe, Santa Marta |
| | 5 | CLM | NA | R. Robledo |
| | 25 | EQA | PN1 | R. Vigía, Quito |
| | 5 | PRG | ZP6 | R. Guairá, Villarrica |
| | 1 | PRU | OBX6Y | R. Azul, Cayama Aqp |
| | 1 | PRU | OCU1C | R. Campesina de Ayabaca, Ayabaca |
| | | PRU | | R. Campesina, Huari |
| | 1 | PRU | OAU2E | R. Nuevo Continente, San Ignacio |
| | 1 | PRU | OCU5N | R. OCU5N, Abancay |
| | 1 | PRU | OCU7I | R. Santa Cruz, Kunturkanki |
| | 1 | PRU | OAU3Q | R. Vision, Casma |
| 850 | 1 | ARG | | R. La Gauchita, Morón |
| | 5 | BOL | | R. María, Montero |
| | 35 | CLM | KC | Candela, Bogotá |
| | 20 | EQA | YS2 | R. San Francisco, Guayaquil |
| | 5 | PRU | OAM7I | R. Lorena, San Sebastian |
| | 1 | PRU | OBU1M | R. Nal. del Peru, Ayabaca |
| | 40 | PRU | OAX4A | R. Nal. del Perú, Lima |
| | | PRU | OAU6S | R. Nal. del Peru, Tarata |
| | 1 | PRU | OAM5L | R. OAM5L, Acori |
| | 1 | PRU | OBU3B | R. OBU3B. Cerro Jactay |
| | 1 | PRU | OBX9W | R. OBX9W, Chachapoyas |
| | 1 | PRU | OCU1Y | R. OCU1Y, Chiclayo |
| | | PRU | OBU7Z | R. Pachamama, Puno |
| | 50 | URG | CX16 | R. Carve, Montevideo |
| 860 | 0.5 | ARG | | R. Digital, Lanus |
| | 1 | ARG | LRA56 | R. Nacional, Perito Moreno |
| | | BOL | | R. FM Colores, Cochabamba |
| | 10 | BOL | | R. Nueva America, La Paz |
| | 10 | CHL | CC86 | R. Inés de Suárez, Concepción |
| | 50 | CLM | NJ | LV del Cañaguate/W R., Valledupar |
| | 10 | CLM | DV | Voces de Occidente, Buga |
| | 10 | EQA | PC1 | R. Positiva, Quito |
| | 1 | PRG | ZP28 | LV de la Cordillera, Caacupé |
| | 3 | PRU | OCX1M | R. Nuevo Norte, Sullana |
| | | PRU | OBM7B | R. OBM7B, Sandia |
| | 20/10 | VEN | YE | Enlace 8-60, Valle de la Pascua |
| | 10 | VEN | OL | R. Mundial, San Cristóbal |
| 870 | 100 | ARG | LRA1 | R. Nacional, Buenos Aires |
| | 5 | CLM | ZH | Cadena Radial Vida, Medellín |
| | 1 | CLM | GD | Em. Reina de Colombia, Chiquinquirá |
| | 10 | CLM | LA | LV del Tolima, Ibagué |
| | 16 | EQA | LY2 | R. Cristal, Guayaquil |
| | 0.5 | EQA | GS6 | R. Píllaro, Píllaro |
| | 2.5 | PRU | OCX4D | R. Huancayo, El Tambo |
| | 2.5 | PRU | OCX6F | R. Impacto Universal, Uchumayo Aqp |
| | 5 | PRU | OAU7O | R. Libertad, Puno |
| | 1 | PRU | OCX7R | R. Mundo, Wanchaq |
| | 10 | PRU | OBX1F | R. Programas del Perú, Chiclayo |
| | 10 | VEN | MP | Unión R. Notícias, Barquisimeto |
| 880 | | ARG | | R. Democracia, Longchamps |
| | 5/3 | ARG | LU14 | R. Provincia de Santa Cruz, Las Heras |
| | 1/0.25 | ARG | | R. Provincial de Sierra Colorada, Sierra |

| kHz | kW | Ctry | Call | Station, location |
|---|---|---|---|---|
| | | | | Colorada |
| | | BOL | | R. Inca, El Alto |
| | | BOL | | Rdif. Oriente, Santa Cruz |
| | 10 | CHL | CB88 | R. Colo Colo, Santiago |
| | 20 | CLM | GE | Caracol R., Bucaramanga |
| | 10 | CLM | FH | R. Regional Independiente, Anserma |
| | 10 | EQA | FJ1 | R. Católica Nacional, Quito |
| | 5 | PRU | OCU4S | R. Cumbre, Chaupimarca |
| | 1 | PRU | OBU5W | R. OBU5W, |
| | 2 | PRU | OAX2P | R. Sintonia, Trujillo |
| | 50 | PRU | OBZ4N | R. Union, Lima |
| 890 | 25/5 | ARG | LV11 | Em. Santiago del Estero, Santiago del Estero |
| | 25/1 | ARG | LU33 | Emisora Pampeana, Santa Rosa |
| | 10 | ARG | | R. Libre, Villa Caraza |
| | 10 | CLM | CE | Cadena Radial Unida, Bogotá |
| | 20 | CLM | PM | Caracol R., Santa Marta |
| | 5/0.5 | PRG | ZP33 | R. Tres de Febrero, Itá |
| | 3 | PRU | OBX7S | R. Bahá´í del Lago Titicaca, Chiucuito |
| | 1 | PRU | OCU5J | R. Cielo, San Pedro de Cachora |
| | 1 | PRU | OCU7C | R. Laramani, Espinar |
| | 1 | PRU | OAU2N | R. Nor Andina, Celendin |
| | 1 | PRU | OCU5W | R. OCU5W, Ica |
| | 50/10 | URG | CX18 | R. Sport 890, Montevideo |
| 900 | 1 | ARG | | R. Municipal, 25 de Mayo |
| | 25/2.5 | ARG | LT7 | R. Provincia de Corrientes, Corrientes |
| | 5/0.1 | BOL | | La Popular, La Paz |
| | 1 | BOL | | R. Central Misionera, Cochabamba |
| | | BOL | | R. Dios es Amor Universal, Potosi |
| | 0.25 | BOL | | R. LV Nacional, Tarija |
| | | BOL | | R. Tomina la Frontera, Villa Tomina |
| | 1 | CHL | CD90 | R. LV de la Costa, Osorno |
| | 1 | CHL | CC90 | R. Nuble, Chillán |
| | 1 | CHL | CB90 | R. Portales, Viña del Mar |
| | 10 | CLM | EY | LV de Cali, Cali |
| | 10 | CLM | DD | RCN Fiesta, Cúcuta |
| | 10 | EQA | VA1 | R. Sucre, Quito |
| | 10 | PRU | OBX4X | R. Felicidad, Lima |
| | 1 | PRU | OCU1P | R. Huarmaca, Huarmaca |
| | 3 | PRU | OBX6K | R. Nevada, Uchumayo, Aqp |
| | | PRU | OAX3E | R. Ribereña, Aucaycu |
| | 3 | URG | CW17 | R. Frontera, Artigas |
| | 25 | VEN | MD | R. Venezuela Mara Ritmo, Maracaibo |
| 910 | 150 | ARG | LR5 | R. La Red, Ituzaingó |
| | 25/5 | ARG | LRA23 | R. Nacional,San Juan |
| | 1 | CHL | CC91 | R. Tropical Latina,Talca |
| | 20 | CLM | C84 | Cadena Radial Vida, Puerto Inírida |
| | 15 | CLM | S52 | Colombia Estereo, Florencia |
| | 10 | CLM | DO | LV del Río Grande, Medellín |
| | 1 | CLM | TT | Ondas del Porvenir, Samacá |
| | 30 | CLM | MY | RCN, San Andrés |
| | 10 | EQA | BO2 | La R. Redonda, Guayaquil |
| | 1 | PRU | OAU5M | R. Estacion Wari, Ayacucho |
| | 1 | PRU | OAU7G | R. Frontera, Juliaca |
| | 1 | PRU | OAU7M | R. Regional - R. Quechua, Sicuani |
| | 50/20 | VEN | RQ | RQ 910 AM Center, Caracas |
| 920 | | BOL | | R. Bartolina Sisa, El Alto |
| | | BOL | | R. Dios es Amor Universal, Cochabamba |
| | 3 | BOL | | R. Encuentro, Sucre |
| | 1 | BOL | | R. San Andres de Topohoco, Topohoco |
| | 1 | CHL | CD92 | R. 920, Temuco |
| | 10 | CLM | SJ | Colmundo R., Ibagué |
| | 10 | CLM | AA | Em. Fuentes, Cartagena |
| | 10 | CLM | JN | HSB R., Pasto |
| | 10 | EQA | RU3 | CRO, Machala |
| | 10 | EQA | AB1 | R. Democracia, Quito |
| | 20/100 | PRG | ZP1 | R. Nal del Paraguay, Chaco-i |
| | 1 | PRU | OAM7H | CVC La Voz, Cusco |
| | | PRU | | R. Campesina, Juli |

| kHz | kW | Ctry | Call | Station, location |
|---|---|---|---|---|
| | 1 | PRU | OAX9V | R. Marginal, Tocache |
| | 1 | PRU | OCU7W | R. OCU7W, Tambopata |
| | 1 | PRU | OBX2S | R. Ollantay, Virú |
| | 10 | PRU | OBX1J | R. Programas del Perú, Piura |
| | 1 | PRU | OCX5C | R. Stelar, Chinca Alta |
| | 2.5 | PRU | OBU6M | R. Uno, Tacna |
| | 3 | PRU | OAM2G | R. Vision, Samangay |
| | 20 | VEN | QX | R. Nueva Esparta, Porlamar |
| | 10/5 | VEN | QU | R. San Carlos, San Carlos |
| 930 | 5 | ARG | | R. Nativa, Ciudad Evita |
| | 25/5 | ARG | LV7 | R. Tucumán, San Miguel de Tucumán |
| | 5/0.5 | ARG | LV28 | R. Villa María, Villa María |
| | 10 | CHL | CB93 | R. Nuevo Mundo, Santiago |
| | 10 | CHL | CD93 | R. Reloncaví, Puerto Montt |
| | 5 | CLM | IA | Bésame, Manizales |
| | 10 | CLM | CS | LV de Bogotá, Bogotá |
| | 5 | EQA | BA6 | R. Ambato, Ambato |
| | 5 | PRU | OAX4E | Moderna - R. Papa, Lima |
| | 3 | PRU | OBU7T | R. Cadena Colca, Juliaca |
| | 1 | PRU | OAM7J | R. Cadena Sur, Espinar |
| | 1 | PRU | OCX2V | R. Inti, Chepén |
| | 3 | PRU | OCU1O | R. Nor Andina, Olmos |
| | 1 | PRU | OBU5S | R. OBU5S, Pucar del Sara Sara |
| | 5 | PRU | OBX9V | R. OBX9V, Huambo |
| | 5 | PRU | OBX6T | R. Yaravi, Cerro Colorado, Aqp. |
| | 50 | URG | CX20 | R. Monte Carlo, Montevideo |
| | 10 | VEN | LJ | R. Maracay, Maracay |
| 940 | 3/5 | ARG | LRH200 | R. Chajarí, Chajarí |
| | 20/5 | ARG | LRJ241 | R. Dimensión, San Luís |
| | 1.5 | ARG | | R. Excelsior, Monte Grande |
| | 1 | BOL | | R. Chuquisaca XXI, Sucre |
| | | BOL | | R. Metropolitana, La Paz |
| | | BOL | | R. Pan de Vida, Santa Cruz |
| | 1 | CHL | CB94 | R. Valentín Letelier, Valparaíso |
| | 5 | CLM | A76 | Frecuencia U, Medellín |
| | 10 | CLM | GB | R. Calima, Cali |
| | 25 | CLM | TL | RCN, Cúcuta |
| | 3 | EQA | CP5 | R. Caravana, Cuenca |
| | 10 | EQA | BZ1 | R. CCE, Quito |
| | | PRU | OBX2G | R. Cutervo, Cutervo |
| | 1.5 | PRU | OBX7P | R. Las Vegas - W R., Wanchaq |
| | 1 | PRU | OBU4E | R. Luz, Jauja |
| | 1 | PRU | OBU6G | R. OBU6G, Cotahuasi |
| | 1 | PRU | OBU1Y | R. Studio Satelite, Tambo Grande |
| | 10 | VEN | LU | R. Fe y Alegría, El Tigre |
| 950 | 25/5 | ARG | LR3 | R. Belgrano, Buenos Aires |
| | 25/5 | ARG | LT16 | RSP , Roque Saénz Peña |
| | 5 | CLM | UJ | Armonias Boyacenses, Tunja |
| | 15 | CLM | FN | Caracol R., Pereira |
| | 3 | EQA | UE5 | LV de AIIECH, Colta |
| | 3 | EQA | AV1 | R. Chaskis del Norte, Ibarra |
| | 1.5 | PRU | OAM2H | Onda Popular, Bambamarca |
| | | PRU | | R. Campesina, Tarata |
| | 1 | PRU | OAM7S | R. OAM7S, Juliaca |
| | 1 | PRU | OBU5N | R. OBU5N, Paucar del Sara Sara |
| | 1 | PRU | OBU5R | R. OBU5R, Cotabambas |
| | 1 | PRU | OBX3S | R. Programas del Perú, Chimbote |
| 960 | 25/5 | ARG | LRA6 | R. Nacionall, Guaymallén |
| | 10/1 | ARG | LU13 | R. Necochea, Necochea |
| | 10 | BOL | | R. Fe y Alegria, Santa Cruz |
| | 1 | BOL | | R. Huayna Potosí, Milluni |
| | 1 | BOL | | R. Kollasuyo, Potosí |
| | 10 | CHL | CB96 | R. Carrera, Santiago |
| | 10 | CHL | CD96 | R. Polar, Punta Arenas |
| | 5 | CLM | HX | Bluradio, Bucaramanga |
| | 15 | CLM | R31 | Candela, San Andrés: |
| | 10 | CLM | HN | Caracol R., Maganngué |
| | 1 | EQA | JX6 | LV del Santuario, Baños |
| | 1.5 | EQA | SA5 | R. Sonoonda Internacional, Cuenca |
| | 1 | PRU | OBU7P | R. Concierto Santa Monica, Espinar |
| | 18 | PRU | OBX6S | R. El Pueblo 960, Mariano Melgar, Aqp |
| | 1 | PRU | OCY4V | R. Manantial, Chilca |
| | 10 | PRU | OAX4D | R. Panamericana, Lima |
| | 3 | PRU | OBX1Y | R. WSP, Chiclayo |
| | 2/1 | URG | CW96 | R. Yi, Durazno |
| | 10 | VEN | SS | R. San Sebastián, San Cristóbal |
| 970 | 3 | ARG | | R. Génesis, Valentin Alsina |
| | 1/0.25 | ARG | LT25 | R. Guaraní, Curuzú Cuatiá |
| | 25 | ARG | LRA43 | R. Nacional, Neuquén |
| | 1 | CHL | CD97 | R. Austral, Valdivia |
| | 1 | CHL | CC97 | R. Lautaro, Talca |
| | 1 | CHL | CD97A | R. Patagonia Chilena, Coyhaique |
| | 15 | CLM | VK | Armonias del Caquetá, Florencia |
| | 10 | CLM | CI | R. Red RCN, Bogotá |
| | 1 | EQA | MB1 | R. Imperio, Ibarra |
| | 80 | PRG | ZP9 | R. 9-70, Asunción |
| | 1 | PRU | OBX5A | R. Comericial Sonora, Ica |
| | 1.5 | PRU | OBX1V | R. La Capullana, Sullana |
| | 1 | PRU | OAU2K | R. Lider del Norte, Cajamarca |
| | 5 | PRU | OAU7A | R. Tropicana, Wanchaq |
| | 1 | PRU | OBU7B | R. Union Qollasuyo, Juliaca |
| | 20/3 | URG | CX22 | R. Universal, Montevideo |
| | 10 | VEN | LR | R. Continente 970, Maracay |
| | 15 | VEN | SD | R. Turismo, Valera |
| 980 | 3/1 | ARG | LU37 | R. General, Pico |
| | 1 | ARG | | R. Luján, Valcheta |
| | 5 | ARG | LT39 | R. Victoria, Victoria |
| | 25/5 | ARG | | Rio Gallegos |
| | 5/1 | ARG | | San Salvador de Jujuy |
| | | BOL | | R. dif. Concordia, Oruro |
| | 3 | BOL | | R. Esperanza, Aiquile |
| | | BOL | | R. La Bohemia, Sucre |
| | 2.5 | BOL | | R. Mar, La Paz |
| | 1 | CHL | CA98 | La Serena |
| | 5 | CHL | CB98 | Valparaíso |
| | 15 | CLM | JV | Bésame, Cúcuta |
| | 100 | CLM | ES | RCN, Cali |
| | 1 | EQA | JI5 | R. El Prado, Riobamba |
| | 5 | PRG | ZP31 | R. Mburucuyá, Pedro Juan Caballero |
| | 1 | PRU | OCX2R | Andina R., Chota |
| | 1 | PRU | OCU7X | R. Caden Sur, Sicuani |
| | 1 | PRU | OBU1N | R. Campesina, Huancabamba |
| | | PRU | | R. Comercial Cosmos, La Peca |
| | 1 | PRU | OBU5K | R. LV de Huamanga, Huamanga |
| | 1 | PRU | OBU4H | R. OBU4H, Huancayo |
| | 1 | PRU | OAU1N | R. Primavera, Lambayeque |
| | 1.5 | PRU | OAU6F | R. Universidad, Arequipa |
| 990 | 25/5 | ARG | LRH203 | R. AM 990, Formosa |
| | 1 | ARG | LRJ201 | R. Calingasta, Tamberías |
| | 25/5 | ARG | LR4 | R. Splendid AM 990, Villa Domínico |
| | | BOL | | R. Municipal de Colcha |
| | 5 | CLM | HI | LV de Garagoa, Garagoa |
| | 50 | CLM | CH | RCN, Medellín |
| | 3 | PRU | OCU1H | R. Bendicion Cristiana, Piura |
| | 10 | PRU | OAX6K | R. Continental, Tacna |
| | 0.5 | PRU | OBX2M | R. Contumaza, Contumaza |
| | 12 | PRU | OBX4J | R. Latina, Miraflores |
| | 2.5 | PRU | OCU7T | R. Milagros, Juliaca |
| | | PRU | OCU4A | R. Oro, Huayllay |
| | | PRU | OBX3L | R. Peruana, Chimbote |
| | 20 | VEN | RT | R. Tropical, Caracas |
| 1000 | 51 | ARG | | Comodoro Rivadavia |
| | 10/1 | ARG | | La Rioja |
| | 5 | ARG | LT42 | R. Del Iberá, Mercedes |
| | 3 | ARG | LU16 | R. Río Negro, Villa Regina |
| | 1 | ARG | | R. Sintonia, José C.Paz |
| | | BOL | | FM Unica, Cochabamba |
| | | BOL | | R. LV del Arrebatamiento, Guaqui |

| kHz | kW | Ctry | Call | Station, location |
|---|---|---|---|---|
| | 1 | BOL | | R. Taypi, La Paz |
| | 1 | BOL | | Rdif. del Oriente, Santa Cruz |
| | 10 | CHL | CB100 | BBN R., Santiago |
| | 10 | CLM | JG | R. Nac. de Colombia, Manizales |
| | 15 | CLM | AQ | RCN, Cartagena |
| | 20 | CLM | Q98 | Vida, San José del Guaviare |
| | 5/0.5 | PRG | ZP36 | R. Mil, San Antonio |
| | 2.5 | PRU | OBX6R | R. Edesa, Cerro Colorado, Aqp |
| | 1 | PRU | OBX3V | R. Huanuco |
| | 1 | PRU | OBX5W | R. Lircay, Lircay |
| | 1 | PRU | OAM4N | R. OAM4N, Barranca |
| | 1 | PRU | OBU4Z | R. OBU4Z, Pariahuanaca |
| | 7 | PRU | OCU1N | R. OCU1N, San José |
| | 2 | PRU | OAZ7P | R. Prensa al Dia, Cusco |
| | 10 | VEN | OA | Deportes Unión R., San Cristóbal |
| | 10 | VEN | NM | R. Caribeña Mil AM |
| 1010 | 0.25 | ARG | LW2 | R. Emis. Tartagal |
| | 4 | ARG | | R. Onda Latina, Valentin Alsina |
| | 20/10 | ARG | LV16 | R. Rio Cuarto, Rio Cuarto |
| | 10 | BOL | | R. Bahá'í de Bolivia, Oruro |
| | 10 | CHL | CD101 | R. Nielol, Temuco |
| | 10 | CLM | CC | Acuario Estéreo, Bogotá |
| | 15 | CLM | JR | Caracol R., Neiva |
| | 10/5 | CLM | BN | LV del Galeras, Pasto |
| | 15 | CLM | ZD | R. Panzenú, Montería |
| | 10 | CLM | IX | R. Yarima, Barrancabermeja |
| | 10 | CLM | OP | Sistema Cardenal, Barranquilla |
| | 10 | EQA | NR6 | R. Líder TSB, Ambato |
| | 1 | PRU | OBU1L | LV de las Huaringas, Huancabamba |
| | | PRU | | R. Cajamarca, Cajamarca |
| | 10 | PRU | OAX4U | R. Cielo, Lima |
| | 1 | PRU | OBX9T | R. Fé, Bagua Grande |
| | 1 | PRU | OCU7P | R. Nac. del Peru, Juli |
| | 1 | PRU | OBU5T | R. OBU5T, Cotabambas |
| | 1 | PRU | OBU6L | R. Orcopampa, Orcopampa |
| | 1.5 | PRU | OBX2P | R. San Francisco, Cajamarca |
| | 1 | PRU | OBZ1C | R. Sonora, Tumbes |
| | 25 | URG | CX24 | R. 1010, Montevideo |
| | 10 | VEN | PC | R. Aragua, Cagua |
| 1020 | 25/2.5 | ARG | LRJ214 | AM Mil 20, San Juan |
| | 5 | ARG | LRA58 | R. Nacional, Río Mayo |
| | 10/5 | ARG | LT10 | R. Univ. Nal. del Litoral, Santa Fé |
| | | BOL | | R. Illimani - R. Patria Nueva, Azurduy |
| | | BOL | | R. Illimani - R. Patria Nueva, Bermejo |
| | | BOL | | R. Illimani - R. Patria Nueva, Camiri |
| | | BOL | | R. Illimani - R. Patria Nueva, Caracolla |
| | | BOL | | R. Illimani - R. Patria Nueva, Caranavi |
| | | BOL | | R. Illimani - R. Patria Nueva, Catavi |
| | | BOL | | R. Illimani - R. Patria Nueva, Challapata |
| | | BOL | | R. Illimani - R. Patria Nueva, Chapare |
| | | BOL | | R. Illimani - R. Patria Nueva, Chulumani |
| | | BOL | | R. Illimani - R. Patria Nueva, Cobija |
| | | BOL | | R. Illimani - R. Patria Nueva, Cochabamba |
| | | BOL | | R. Illimani - R. Patria Nueva, Colomi |
| | | BOL | | R. Illimani - R. Patria Nueva, Copacabana |
| | | BOL | | R. Illimani - R. Patria Nueva, Coro Coro |
| | | BOL | | R. Illimani - R. Patria Nueva, Desaguadero |
| | | BOL | | R. Illimani - R. Patria Nueva, Entre Rios |
| | | BOL | | R. Illimani - R. Patria Nueva, Escoma |
| | | BOL | | R. Illimani - R. Patria Nueva, Guaqui |
| | | BOL | | R. Illimani - R. Patria Nueva, Huanuni |
| | | BOL | | R. Illimani - R. Patria Nueva, Ichoca-Quime |
| | | BOL | | R. Illimani - R. Patria Nueva, Independencia |
| | | BOL | | R. Illimani - R. Patria Nueva, Kami |
| | | BOL | | R. Illimani - R. Patria Nueva, La Asunta |
| | 10 | BOL | | R. Illimani - R. Patria Nueva, La Paz |
| | | BOL | | R. Illimani - R. Patria Nueva, Llica |
| | | BOL | | R. Illimani - R. Patria Nueva, Machareti |
| | | BOL | | R. Illimani - R. Patria Nueva, Oruro |
| | | BOL | | R. Illimani - R. Patria Nueva, Potosi |
| | | BOL | | R. Illimani - R. Patria Nueva, Pucarani |
| | | BOL | | R. Illimani - R. Patria Nueva, Puerto Quijarro |
| | | BOL | | R. Illimani - R. Patria Nueva, Qhurpa |
| | | BOL | | R. Illimani - R. Patria Nueva, Riberalta |
| | | BOL | | R. Illimani - R. Patria Nueva, San Borja |
| | | BOL | | R. Illimani - R. Patria Nueva, Santa Cruz |
| | | BOL | | R. Illimani - R. Patria Nueva, Sopachuy |
| | | BOL | | R. Illimani - R. Patria Nueva, Sucre |
| | | BOL | | R. Illimani - R. Patria Nueva, Tapichullo |
| | | BOL | | R. Illimani - R. Patria Nueva, Taraco |
| | | BOL | | R. Illimani - R. Patria Nueva, Tarija |
| | | BOL | | R. Illimani - R. Patria Nueva, Tiawanaku |
| | | BOL | | R. Illimani - R. Patria Nueva, Tirague |
| | | BOL | | R. Illimani - R. Patria Nueva, Topohoco |
| | | BOL | | R. Illimani - R. Patria Nueva, Trinidad |
| | | BOL | | R. Illimani - R. Patria Nueva, Tupiza |
| | | BOL | | R. Illimani - R. Patria Nueva, Unica |
| | | BOL | | R. Illimani - R. Patria Nueva, Uyuni |
| | | BOL | | R. Illimani - R. Patria Nueva, Valle Alto |
| | | BOL | | R. Illimani - R. Patria Nueva, Vallegrande |
| | | BOL | | R. Illimani - R. Patria Nueva, Vilaque |
| | | BOL | | R. Illimani - R. Patria Nueva, Villamontes |
| | | BOL | | R. Illimani - R. Patria Nueva, Villazon |
| | | BOL | | R. Illimani - R. Patria Nueva, Yacuiba |
| | | BOL | | R. Illimani - R. Patria Nueva, Yapacani |
| | | BOL | | R. Illimani - R. Patria Nueva. Tarata |
| | 5 | CHL | CC102 | R. Amiga,Talca |
| | 10 | CLM | DQ | Emisora Claridad, Medellín |
| | 10 | CLM | KS | La Cariñosa/LV del Llano, Villavicencio |
| | 10 | CLM | FT | La FM, Ibagué |
| | 15 | CLM | DZ | R. Primavera, Bucaramanga |
| | 10 | CLM | FQ | RCN, Pereira |
| | 5 | EQA | GO3 | R. Estelar, Santa Rosa |
| | 25 | PRG | ZP14 | R. Ñandutí, Asunción |
| | 0.5 | PRU | OBU5M | R. AM Vida, Huamanga |
| | 2 | PRU | OAU2P | R. Bambamarca, Bambamarca |
| | 1 | PRU | OBU4F | R. Cristo Vive, Huancayo |
| | 1 | PRU | OBU7O | R. Informes, Sicuani |
| | 1 | PRU | OAU6J | R. Internacional, Tacna |
| | 5 | PRU | OAM7Y | R. Kinsachata Tintaya, Espinar |
| | 1 | PRU | OBU1D | R. La Luz, Piura |
| | 1 | PRU | OCU1M | R. OCU1M, José Leonardo Ortiz |
| | 0.1 | URG | CW102 | R. Libertadores, Salto |
| | 25 | VEN | TW | R. Alegría 1020 AM Stereo, Chivacoa |
| 1030 | 25/5 | ARG | LS10 | R. del Plata, Buenos Aires |
| | | BOL | | R. 24 de Junio, Totora |
| | 3 | BOL | | R. Comunitaria Riberalte, Riberalta |
| | 3 | BOL | | R. de los Pueblos Originarios, Orinaca |
| | | BOL | | R. Illimani - R. Patria Nueva, Camargo |
| | | BOL | | R. Illimani - R. Patria Nueva, Coripata |
| | | BOL | | R. Illimani - R. Patria Nueva, Coroico |
| | | BOL | | R. Illimani - R. Patria Nueva, San Pablo de Lipez |
| | 3 | BOL | | R. Independencia, Independencia |
| | | BOL | | R. Mojocoya AM, Mojocoya |
| | 10 | CHL | CC103 | R. Chilena, Concepción |
| | 1 | CHL | CD103 | R. Chiloé, Castro |
| | 1 | CHL | CD103A | R. Payne AM, Puerto Natales |
| | 1 | CHL | CB103 | R. Progreso, Talagante |
| | 10 | CLM | DJ | La Cariñosa, Duitama |
| | 15 | CLM | RF | Ondas del Cesar, Aguachica |
| | 5 | CLM | | Ondas del Vaupés, Mitú |
| | 30 | CLM | DT | RCN Antena 2, Cali |
| | 1 | CLM | GX | RPC R., Lorica |
| | 5 | EQA | RF2 | R. Ecuantena, Guayaquil |

| kHz | kW | Ctry | Call | Station, location |
|---|---|---|---|---|
| | 1 | PRU | OCX6L | R. Cumbia, Arequipa |
| | 1 | PRU | OCX7O | R. HG-AM, Cusco |
| | 5 | PRU | OAM2E | R. La Beta Cajamarca |
| | 5 | PRU | OAU2U | R. Los Andes, Huamachuco |
| | 1 | PRU | OAX7N | R. LV del Altiplano, Puno |
| | 1 | PRU | OBX9Z | R. OBX9Z, San Ramon |
| 1040 | 10/1 | ARG | LRG203 | R. Capital, Santa Rosa |
| | | ARG | | R. Revolution, Luján |
| | | BOL | | R. 12 de Marzo, Tarabuco |
| | 0.25 | BOL | | R. Atlántida, Oruro |
| | 1 | BOL | | R. Bolivianíssima, La Paz |
| | | BOL | | R. San Julián, San Julián |
| | 15 | CLM | CJ | Colmundo R., Bogotá |
| | 15 | CLM | UB | Colmundo R., Pasto |
| | 15 | CLM | FM | LV de Armenia, Armenia |
| | 15 | CLM | BF | LV del Norte/Blu R., Cúcuta |
| | 10 | CLM | SY | R. 1040, Popayán |
| | 15 | CLM | AI | R. Tropical, Barranquilla |
| | 1 | EQA | GB6 | R. Colosal, Ambato |
| | 10 | EQA | EV5 | R. Splendid, Cuenca |
| | 5 | PRG | ZP43 | R. Arapysandú, San Ignacio |
| | 1 | PRU | OBX5U | R. La Luz, Ica |
| | 1 | PRU | OAU7H | R. Los Andes, Espinar |
| | 10 | PRU | OBX4O | R. Metropolitiana, Miraflores |
| | 1 | PRU | OAU3P | R. Nueva Vida, Chimbote |
| | 1 | PRU | OAM2L | R. OAM2L, Pomahuaca |
| | 1 | PRU | OAZ1D | R. Vecinal, Piura |
| | 20 | VEN | LB | LV de Carabobo, Valencia |
| | 20/10 | VEN | ON | R. Mundial Los Andes, Mérida |
| 1050 | 1.3 | ARG | | R. General Güemes, Villa Lynch |
| | 10 | ARG | LV27 | R. San Francisco, San Francisco |
| | | BOL | | R. Caiza D, Caiza D |
| | | BOL | | R. Comunitaria, Huacaya |
| | 3 | BOL | | R. Sabaya, Sabaya |
| | 15 | CLM | S62 | Cusiana R., Yopal |
| | 10 | CLM | FZ | La Cariñosa del Centro, Espinal |
| | 5 | CLM | IO | LV de la Conquista, Granada |
| | 10 | CLM | E73 | LV del Cinaruco/Caracol, Arauca |
| | 10 | CLM | GU | R. Bucarica, Bucaramanga |
| | 5 | CLM | NG | R. Palmira, Palmira |
| | 10 | CLM | AW | RCN La R., Montería |
| | 10 | CLM | BB | Sistema Cardenal, Valledupar |
| | 10 | CLM | DR | Vida, Medellín |
| | 5 | EQA | RQ2 | R. Águila, Guayaquil |
| | 1 | PRU | OBZ4J | Bethel R., Huancayo |
| | 3 | PRU | OBX6B | Bethel R., Uchumayo, Aqp |
| | 3 | PRU | OCU1E | R. Bendición Cristiana, Chiclayo |
| | 1 | PRU | OAZ7Q | R. Noticias, Juliaca |
| | 1 | PRU | OCX2B | R. San Sebastian, Chepen |
| | 1 | PRU | OAZ1C | R. Superior, Chulucanas |
| | | PRU | | R. Tigre, Rejopampa, Sorochuco |
| | 50 | URG | CX26 | R. Uruguay, Montevideo |
| 1060 | | ARG | | R. La Más Santiagueña, Gregorio de Laferrere |
| | 1 | BOL | | R. Dif. Colosal, Sucre |
| | 1.5 | BOL | | R. Noticias, Oruro |
| | | BOL | | R. Qhana Amazonía, Caranavi |
| | 100 | CHL | CB106 | R. Maria, Santiago |
| | 1 | CLM | YX | R. Caracolí, Sincelejo |
| | 10 | CLM | LY | R. Delfín, Riohacha |
| | 10 | CLM | MV | R. Furatena, Chiquinquirá |
| | 1 | CLM | MG | R. Litoral, Turbo |
| | 15 | CLM | OV | R. Surcolombiana, Neiva |
| | 15 | CLM | FJ | RCN, Manizales |
| | 1.5 | EQA | MG6 | R. Ecos del Pueblo, Saquisilí |
| | 3 | EQA | CH2 | R. Fiesta, Machala |
| | 1 | PRU | OAU5P | Estacion Wari, Huamanga |
| | 1 | PRU | OAU7U | R. Estudio 1060, Cusco |
| | 1 | PRU | OCY4D | R. Exito, Lima |

| kHz | kW | Ctry | Call | Station, location |
|---|---|---|---|---|
| | 1 | PRU | OBU6O | R. Municipilidad, Omate |
| | 2 | PRU | OCU1V | R. OCU1V, Tumbes |
| | 3 | PRU | OAU3S | R. R. Cielo, Chimbote |
| | 2 | PRU | OBU5Q | R. Restauracion, Andahuaylas |
| | | PRU | OBU1F | R. Studio 1060. Piura |
| | 5 | PRU | OCY2O | R. Sudamerica, Cutervo |
| | 1 | PRU | OCU7V | Tambopata |
| | 10 | VEN | LN | R. Guárico, San Juan de los Morros |
| | 10 | VEN | OE | Unión R. Noticias, San Cristóbal |
| 1070 | 25/1 | ARG | | Paseo de Indios |
| | 25/5 | ARG | LR1 | R. El Mundo, Buenos Aires |
| | 20 | CLM | AH | Em. Atlántico, Barranquilla |
| | 15 | CLM | VR | Nueva R. Super, Popayán |
| | 30 | CLM | CG | R. Santa Fe, Bogotá |
| | 5 | EQA | CJ5 | LV del Tomebamba, Cuenca |
| | 3 | PRU | OBX9J | R. Andes, Tarapoto |
| | 1 | PRU | OAM5K | R. OAM5K, Huancavelica |
| | 1 | PRU | OAU3N | R. OAU3N, Huánuco |
| | 0.2 | PRU | OAX5A | R. San Juan, San Juan de Marcona |
| | 1 | PRU | OAU6K | R. Trinidad, Paucarpata, Aqp. |
| | 1 | PRU | OAU1J | R. Vida, José Leonardo Ortiz |
| | 1 | PRU | OBX4G | R. Visión, San Ramón |
| | 10 | VEN | | Superior 1070 Biruaca, S. Fernando de Apure |
| 1080 | 25/5 | ARG | LU3 | Ondas del Sur, Bahía Blanca |
| | 10/1 | ARG | | Paso de los Libres |
| | 0.25 | ARG | LW4 | R. Orán/R. Maria, Argentina |
| | | BOL | | R. Comunitaria, Juana Azurduy |
| | | BOL | | R. Comunitaria, Sopachuy |
| | | BOL | | R. Comunitario Carama, Machareti |
| | | BOL | | R. Comunitario Carama, Sucre |
| | | BOL | | R. Espiritu Santo, La Paz |
| | 1 | CHL | CD108 | R. Los Confines, Angol |
| | 1 | CHL | CA108 | Vicuña |
| | 10 | CLM | AX | LV de Antioquia, Medellín |
| | 10 | CLM | AW | LV de Montería, Montería |
| | 10 | CLM | KT | R. Autentica, Villavicencio |
| | 10 | CLM | MH | R. Melodía, Bucaramanga |
| | 15 | CLM | JS | R. Uno, La Dorada |
| | 10 | CLM | JF | Vida, Cali |
| | 1 | EQA | AB4 | R. Contacto, Manta |
| | 10 | EQA | BH6 | R. Latacunga AM, Latacunga |
| | 10 | EQA | KD2 | Sistema 2, Guayaquil |
| | 10 | PRG | ZP25 | R. Monumental, Caco-i |
| | 10 | PRU | OAU4I | R. La Luz, Lima |
| | 1.5 | PRU | OBX1D | R. La Luz, Piura |
| | 1 | PRU | OBU6H | R. LV del Sur, Moquegua |
| | 5 | PRU | OCU4O | R. Mineria, Chaupimarca |
| | 1 | PRU | OCU7O | R. Nacional, Ayaviri |
| | 1 | PRU | OAU2L | R. Nueva Vida, Cajamarca |
| | 1 | PRU | OBU4W | R. OBU4W, Huancayo |
| | 2.2 | PRU | OAX7S | R. Salkantay, Cusco |
| | 10 | VEN | NR | Mundial/R. Venezuela 1080, Maracay |
| 1090 | 1 | ARG | | Libertad AM 1100, Rosario |
| | 3 | ARG | | R. Décadas, José León Suárez |
| | 2 | ARG | | R. Popular, Valentín Alsina |
| | | BOL | | R. Comunitaria Pachakuti, Achocalla |
| | 5 | CHL | CD109 | Castro |
| | 5/1 | CHL | CC109 | R. Chilena del Maule, Talca |
| | 5 | CLM | OM | Bluradio, Cartagena |
| | 15 | CLM | BC | Caracol R., Cúcuta |
| | 8 | CLM | IH | Caracol R., Sogamoso |
| | 10 | CLM | JB | Click R. /Blu R., Guamo |
| | 10 | CLM | IG | R. Autentica, Florencia |
| | 10 | CLM | IA | W R., Manizales |
| | 3 | EQA | VC1 | R. Irfeyal, Quito |
| | 1 | PRU | OBX6X | R. Amistad, Arequipa |
| | 1 | PRU | OAU5F | R. Inti Andina, Aucara |
| | 15 | URG | CX28 | R. Imparcial, Montevideo |

| kHz | kW | Ctry | Call | Station, location |
|---|---|---|---|---|
| | 20 | VEN | SZ | Deportes Unión R., Caracas |
| | 10 | VEN | PB | R. Yaracuy, S. Felipe |
| 1100 | 1 | ARG | | R. Estilo, Glew |
| | 10/0.5 | ARG | | R. Mitre, Corrientes |
| | 1 | ARG | | Red Pampeana, General Pico |
| | | BOL | | R. Chaka, Pucarani |
| | 1 | BOL | | R. Universidad de Oruro |
| | | BOL | | Universal M. Concienia, El Alto |
| | 10 | CHL | CB110 | BBN R. Viña del Mar |
| | 10 | CLM | CN | BBN R, Bogotá |
| | 15 | CLM | AT | Caracol R., Barranquilla |
| | 5 | CLM | MK | Emisora Ideal, Planeta Rica |
| | 1 | CLM | GI | LV de Colombia, Socorro |
| | 15 | CLM | YZ | R. Uno, Neiva |
| | 5 | CLM | GQ | Transmisora Surandes, Andes |
| | 1 | EQA | GR6 | R. Novedades, Latacunga |
| | 1 | EQA | LE7 | R. Oriental, Tena |
| | 5 | PRG | ZP71 | R. Ñú Verá, Capitán Bado |
| | | PRU | OCU2E | R. 1000, Julcan |
| | 1 | PRU | OBX7Z | R. LTC, Juliaca |
| | 1 | PRU | OCU4N | R. OCU4N, Cañete |
| | 1 | PRU | OBX1L | R. Ondas de Paz, Chiclayo |
| | 1 | PRU | OAZ4W | R. Programas del Peru, Barranca |
| | 1 | PRU | OCY4G | Sonorama R., Huancayo |
| 1110 | 25/5 | ARG | LS1 | R. de la Ciudad, Dique Luján |
| | | BOL | | R. Raqaypampa, Raqaypampa |
| | 10 | CHL | CD111 | R. La Frontera, Temuco |
| | 5 | CLM | GP | LV del Río Arauca, Arauca |
| | 9 | CLM | DI | R. Bolivariana, Medellín |
| | 15 | CLM | ZE | R. Piragua, Sincelejo |
| | 10 | CLM | JP | RCN, Villavicencio |
| | 10 | CLM | EW | Tropicana FM, Cali |
| | 7 | EQA | JR1 | R. Arpeggio, Quito |
| | 5 | EQA | FC5 | R. Ondas Azuayas, Cuenca |
| | 1 | PRU | OBU6F | R. Austral, Ilo |
| | 0.5 | PRU | OCX1R | R. Centro Popular, La Union |
| | 3 | PRU | OAU3R | R. Cielo, Huánuco |
| | 1 | PRU | OAU4J | R. Feliz, Lima |
| | 1 | PRU | OCX2U | R. Jaén, Jaén |
| | 5 | PRU | OCX7T | R. Machupicchu, Cusco |
| | 3 | URG | CX111 | R. Paso de los Toros, Paso de los Toros |
| | 10 | VEN | RX | Deportes Unión R., Valencia |
| | 10 | VEN | QT | R. Carúpano, Carúpano |
| 1120 | 2 | ARG | | AM Tango, Villa Dominico |
| | 1 | ARG | | Em. Santiago y Copla, Ciudad Evita |
| | 1/0.5 | ARG | LRK204 | R. 21, Yerba Buena |
| | 25/5 | ARG | LV5 | R. Sarmiento, San Juan |
| | 1 | ARG | | R. Sudamericana, San Martin |
| | | BOL | | R. Celestial el Milagro, El Alto |
| | | BOL | | R. El Porvenir, Tiquipaya |
| | | BOL | | R. Illimani - R. Patria Nueva, Huarina |
| | | BOL | | R. Wiñay Khantatt, Tiawuanaku |
| | 15 | CLM | GH | 24 Horas R., Bucaramanga |
| | 5 | CLM | JC | Cadena Radial Vida, Pereira |
| | 10 | CLM | KQ | Caracol R., Tunja |
| | 5 | CLM | Q92 | Colombia Mía, Yopal, CS |
| | 10 | CLM | TI | Vox Dei, Cúcuta |
| | 10 | PRG | ZP24 | La Deportiva, San Lorenzo |
| | 1 | PRU | OCU4E | R. Bendición, Barranca |
| | 1.5 | PRU | OBX2I | R. Dinamica, Trujillo |
| | 0.5 | PRU | OAU5W | R. Huayllahuara |
| | 1 | PRU | OCX6U | R. Municipal, Cerro Colorado, Aqp |
| | 5 | PRU | OAX8A | R. Nacional, Iquitos |
| | 3 | PRU | OAM2F | R. Paz, Chota |
| | 1 | PRU | OAU5H | R. Quispillaccta, Ayacucho |
| | | PRU | | R. San Bartolome, Junin |
| | 10 | URG | CW31 | R. Salto, Salto |
| | 20/10 | VEN | SK | R. Dif.del Sur, San Fernando de Apure |
| 1125 | 1 | PRU | OBX8R | R. Nuevo Tiempo, Campoverde |

| kHz | kW | Ctry | Call | Station, location |
|---|---|---|---|---|
| 1130 | 25/5 | ARG | LRA21 | R. Nacional, Santiago del Estero |
| | 5 | ARG | | R. Show, Francisco Alvarez |
| | | BOL | | R. Illimani - R. Patria Nueva, Montero |
| | 10 | CLM | QQ | Bésame, Pasto |
| | 15 | CLM | VA | Cadena Radial Vida, Bogotá |
| | 10 | CLM | AC | Em. Riomar, Barranquilla |
| | 3 | EQA | PV6 | R. Centro, Ambato |
| | 1 | EQA | CC3 | R. Romántica, Machala |
| | 2.6 | PRU | OAX4N | R. Bacán Sat., Lima |
| | 1.2 | PRU | OAX2V | R. Los Andes, Cjamarca |
| | | PRU | OAM4K | R. OAM4K, Junin |
| | 3 | PRU | OBU6Q | R. OBU6Q, Moquegua |
| | 1 | PRU | OCU1R | R. OCU1R, Huarmaca |
| | 1 | PRU | OCU6I | R. OCU6I, Camaná |
| | 1 | PRU | OAU7B | R. Onda Popular, Juliaca |
| | 5 | PRU | OAM7F | R. Ondas de Paz, Cuzco |
| | 20 | URG | CX30 | R. Nacional, Montevideo |
| | 20/10 | VEN | RL | R. Ideal, Maiquetía |
| | 10 | VEN | KQ | R. Popular, Barquisimeto |
| 1140 | 1 | ARG | | R. La Luna, El Palomar |
| | 10/1 | ARG | LU22 | R. Tandil, Tandil |
| | | BOL | | R. San Isidro, Colomi |
| | | BOL | | R. Sol Poder de Dios, Huancane |
| | | BOL | | R. Sol Poder de Dios, La Paz |
| | 100 | CHL | CB114 | R. Nal., Santiago |
| | 10 | CLM | E67 | Caracol R., Villavicencio |
| | 10 | CLM | KO | R. Esperanza, Cartagena |
| | 10 | CLM | DL | R. Paisa La Cariñosa, Medellín |
| | 10 | CLM | CL | R. Panamericana, Girardot |
| | | CLM | | R. Piendamo, Piendamo |
| | 10 | CLM | RN | RCN, Barbosa |
| | 1 | EQA | AZ5 | R. Alpha Musical, Cuenca |
| | 3 | EQA | IR1 | R. Raíz, Quito |
| | 5/2 | PRG | CP22 | R. Central de Notícias, Atyrá |
| | | PRU | OCU2D | Chami R., Otuzco |
| | 1 | PRU | OAU3C | R. Bahia, Chimbote |
| | 1 | PRU | OAX6L | R. Capital, Cerro Colorado, Aqp |
| | 0.5 | PRU | OAX5W | R. Chinchaysuyo, Chinca Alta |
| | 5 | PRU | OAU1T | R. Fraternal, Ferreñafe |
| | 5 | PRU | OAM2O | R. Maria, Chota |
| | 1.5 | PRU | OBX1W | R. Piura, Piura |
| | 1 | PRU | OCY4C | R. Programas del Perú, Pilcomayo |
| 1150 | 10/1 | ARG | LT9 | R. Brigadier López, Santa Fé |
| | 5 | ARG | LRA51 | R. Nacional, Jáchal |
| | 25 | ARG | LRA2 | R. Nacional, Viedma |
| | 0.1 | ARG | | R. Sagrada Familia |
| | 50 | ARG | LRH202 | R. Tupá Mbaé, Posadas |
| | 0.3 | BOL | | R. Guaqui, Puerto de Guaqui |
| | 15 | CLM | FI | Caracol R., Armenia |
| | 10 | CLM | BT | Catatumbo R. /Blu R., Ocaña |
| | 10 | CLM | FP | RCN, Neiva |
| | 1 | CLM | GJ | W R., Duitama |
| | 0.5 | PRU | OCY2E | R. Chasquillacta, Pedro Galvez |
| | 2.5 | PRU | OAU7X | R. La Sureña, Juliaca |
| | 5 | PRU | OBU4K | R. Mineria, Cerro de Pasco |
| | 2.5 | PRU | OCX7Q | R. Universal, Wanchaq |
| | 10 | VEN | QD | Ecos del Orinoco, Cd.Bolívar |
| 1160 | 5/0.5 | ARG | LRH253 | R. Cataratas, Pto. Iguazú |
| | 10/2.5 | ARG | LU32 | R. Coronel Olavarría, Olavarría |
| | 1 | ARG | | R. Independencia, Remedios de Escalada |
| | 5/1 | ARG | LRA57 | R. Nacional, El Bolsón |
| | 5/1 | ARG | | Salta |
| | 5 | BOL | | R. Centenario, Sta. Cruz |
| | 10 | BOL | | R. Continental, La Paz |
| | 1 | BOL | | R. Nuevo Mundo, Sucre |
| | 3/1 | BOL | | R. RTC Deportiva, Cochabamba |
| | 1 | CHL | CC116 | R. Ancoa, Linares |
| | 1 | CHL | CD116A | R. Baha'i, Temuco |
| | 10 | CLM | S31 | Colombia Mía, Barrancabermeja |

| kHz | kW | Ctry | Call | Station, location |
|---|---|---|---|---|
| | 5 | CLM | AZ | Frecuencia Bolivariana, Montería |
| | 15 | CLM | OC | Fuego AM, Bogotá |
| | 15 | CLM | AU | Ondas del Orteguaza, Florencia |
| | 10 | CLM | BL | R. Aeropuerto, Barranquilla |
| | 10 | CLM | EV | R. Eco, Cali |
| | 10 | CLM | EC | R. San José de Cúcuta, Cúcuta |
| | 5 | CLM | ZV | RCN R. Las Lajas, Ipiales |
| | 3 | EQA | CY5 | LV del Pueblo, Azogues |
| | 1 | EQA | UR6 | R. Runatacuyac, Latacunga |
| | 1 | EQA | VR3 | R. Vía, Machala |
| | 10 | PRG | ZP72 | R. Antena Dos, Asunción |
| | 5 | PRU | OAX4C | R. 1160/R. Onda Cero Lima |
| | 1 | PRU | OCX7Z | R. del Sur, Tambopata |
| | 1 | PRU | OBX50 | R. Huanta 2000, Huanta |
| | 0.3 | PRU | OAX2C | R. Libertad Mundo, Trujillo |
| | 1 | PRU | OCU1Q | R. LV Campesino, Huarmaca |
| | 1 | PRU | OCU4V | R. Maranatha, Huancayo |
| | 1 | PRU | OBX6G | R. Nac. del Perú, Moquegua |
| | 1 | PRU | OCX1S | Radiales Nor Oriental del Marañon, Chiclayo |
| | 2/1 | URG | CW116 | R. Agraria del Uruguay, Cerro Chato |
| 1170 | 1 | ARG | | R. Luz del Mundo, Rafael Calzada |
| | 5 | ARG | | R. Mi País, Hurlingham |
| | 10 | ARG | LRA29 | R. Nacional, San Luis |
| | 5 | CHL | CD117 | R. Natales, Puerto Natales |
| | 10 | CLM | GA | Cadena Radial Vida, Tunja |
| | 10 | CLM | NW | Caracol R., Cartagena |
| | 10 | CLM | E74 | Meridiano 70, Arauca |
| | 10 | CLM | BX | Ondas del Meta, Villavicencio |
| | 10 | CLM | FW | R. Nutibara, Medellín |
| | 1 | CLM | JE | RCN, Tuluá |
| | 5 | EQA | RV2 | R. Filadelfia, Guayaquil |
| | 1 | PRU | OBU7F | Bethel R., Cusco |
| | 0.5 | PRU | OCX7Y | R. Constelación, Puno |
| | 1 | PRU | OAM4I | R. COSAT, Satipo |
| | 1 | PRU | OAU4N | R. Horizonte La Voz del Agro, Pueblo Nuevo |
| | 1 | PRU | OAU2M | R. Jerusalen, Cajamarca |
| | 1 | PRU | OAZ3K | R. Nor Peruana Chimbote |
| | 1 | PRU | OAM7A | R. OAM4E, Paramonga |
| | 2 | PRU | OAM5B | R. OAM5B, Acobamba |
| | 10 | PRU | OBX6L | R. Programas del Perú, Uchumayo, Aqp |
| | 10 | URG | CX32 | Radiomundo, Montevideo |
| | 10 | VEN | KW | R. Bolivariana, Maiquetía |
| 1180 | 0.25 | ARG | | AM San Ponciano, Abasto |
| | 1/0.5 | ARG | LRI230 | R. de la Sierra, Tandil |
| | 1 | BOL | | R. Ingavi, Viacha |
| | | BOL | | R. Sajama Estero, Oruro |
| | 50 | CHL | CB118 | R. Portales, Santiago |
| | 15 | CLM | FX | Caracol R., Manizales |
| | | CLM | | Em. Coorprubá, Apartadó |
| | 20 | CLM | GK | La Cariñosa, Bucaramanga |
| | 5 | CLM | WA | LV del Guaviare, San José del Guaviare |
| | 10/5 | CLM | JT | RCN, Ibagué |
| | 2 | EQA | DP5 | R. Cuenca, Cuenca |
| | 5/1 | PRG | ZP52 | R. Coronel Oviedo, Coronel Oviedo |
| | 1 | PRU | OAM2K | Municipalidad Provincial de Jaen, Jaen |
| | 10 | PRU | OCU4K | NSE R., Lima |
| | 1 | PRU | OCU6N | R. Bacan Sat 2, Pocollay |
| | 1 | PRU | OCY4Z | R. Libertad , Junin |
| | 1 | PRU | OAU2T | R. Siglo 21, Chota |
| | 2.5 | PRU | OAZ1H | R. Vencinal, Piura |
| | 10 | URG | CX118 | LV de Artigas, Artigas |
| | 10 | VEN | LQ | Super Suave 11-80, La Victoria |
| 1190 | 100/10 | ARG | LR9 | Buenos Aires |
| | 25 | ARG | LRA15 | R. Nacional, San Miguel de Tucumán |
| | | BOL | | R. Comunitaria, Guaqui |
| | 1 | CLM | CT | LV de la Costa, Barranquilla |
| | 10 | CLM | CV | R. Cordillera, Bogotá |

| kHz | kW | Ctry | Call | Station, location |
|---|---|---|---|---|
| | 10 | CLM | KG | R. Mira, Tumaco |
| | 1 | EQA | RF6 | R. Nueva Sol, Pujilí |
| | 2 | EQA | DE2 | UCSG R., Guayaquil |
| | 5 | PRG | ZP45 | LV de la Libertad, Henendarias |
| | 10 | PRU | OAX1E | Bravasa R., Chiclayo |
| | 5 | PRU | OBX3D | R. Ancash, Huaraz |
| | 1 | PRU | OCX6G | R. Central de Noticias, Miraflores Aqp |
| | 3 | PRU | OAM7V | R. Cielo, Tambopata |
| | 3 | PRU | OCU1S | R. Cielo. Tumbes |
| | 2 | PRU | OBU5U | R. OBU5U, Huamanga |
| | 2 | PRU | OAX7B | R. Tawantinsuyo, Cusco |
| | 10 | VEN | ZD | La Cultural del Táchira, San Cristóbal |
| | 20/10 | VEN | PF | Ondas de Libertad, San Felix |
| 1195 | | CLM | | Ondas delRanchería, Barrancas |
| 1200 | | ARG | | AM 1200 La R. del Chamamé, Morón |
| | 10/1 | ARG | LRF203 | R. 3 AndinA, Ejido |
| | 1 | ARG | LT6 | R. Goya, Goya |
| | 25/5 | ARG | | Rio Grande |
| | | BOL | | Cuarzo Comunicaciones, La Paz |
| | 0.25 | BOL | | R. 24 de Noviembre, Valle Alto |
| | | BOL | | R. Capital, Oruro |
| | 5 | BOL | | R. Oriental, Santa Cruz |
| | 10 | CHL | CD120 | R. Agricultura, Los Angeles |
| | 10 | CLM | CD | Em. Nueva Epoca, Fusagasugá |
| | 15 | CLM | IJ | LV de la Raza, Medellín |
| | 10 | CLM | BZ | Ondas del Riohacha, Riohacha |
| | 10 | CLM | NF | R. Red RCN, Cali |
| | 10 | CLM | GC | RCN R., Sogamoso |
| | 2 | EQA | RM5 | R. El Mercurio, Cuenca |
| | 3 | EQA | CS1 | R. Super K 1200, Sangolquí |
| | 10 | PRG | ZP44 | R. Libre, Fernando de la Mora |
| | 3 | PRU | OAX4B | Cadena R. 1200, Lima |
| | 1 | PRU | OAU2A | LV de Cumbe, Cajamarca |
| | 3 | PRU | OAU4G | R. Andes, Huancayo |
| | 1 | PRU | OBX5X | R. Comercial, Abancay |
| | | PRU | OCX7S | R. Continental, Juliaca |
| | 1 | PRU | OCU1A | R. Fe, Piura |
| | 3 | PRU | OAU6P | R. La Luz, Tacna |
| | | PRU | | R. Master Mix, Huancavelica |
| | 1 | PRU | OAM7O | R. Universidad, Puno |
| | 1 | URG | CW33 | La Nueva R., Florida |
| | 10 | VEN | OZ | R. Tiempo, Caracas |
| 1210 | | ARG | | R. del Promesero, José C. Paz |
| | 1/0.5 | ARG | LRI229 | R. Las Flores, Las Flores |
| | 1.5 | ARG | | R. Mailin, Gregorio de Laferrere |
| | 1 | CHL | CD121 | Puerto Montt |
| | 1 | CHL | CC121 | R. Universidad de Talca, Talca |
| | | CHL | CB121 | R. Valparaiso, Valparaiso |
| | 10 | CLM | FR | Bésame, Neiva |
| | 10 | CLM | E65 | La Cariñosa, Cúcuta |
| | 10 | CLM | BQ | La Cariñosa, Pereira |
| | 10 | EQA | VC3 | La Hechichera, Loja |
| | 10 | EQA | BJ2 | R. El Mundo, Guayaquil |
| | 1 | EQA | JM6 | R. SIRA, Ambato |
| | 1 | PRU | OCY4T | R. Galaxia, Satipo |
| | 1 | PRU | OBU3D | R. OBU3D, Chimbote |
| | 1 | PRU | OCU2W | R. OCU2W, Querocoto |
| | 1 | PRU | OBX3X | R. Ondas de Paz, Huanuco |
| | 1 | PRU | OCU7B | R. Qorilazo, Chumbivilcas |
| | 1 | PRU | OAX7M | R. Quillabamba, Quillabamba |
| | 1 | PRU | OAX2Q | R. Universo, Trujillo |
| | 2/1 | URG | CX121 | Difusora Soriano, Mercedes |
| | 2/1 | URG | CV121 | Em. RBC del Este, Piriápolis |
| | 0.25 | URG | CW121 | R. El Libertador, Vergara |
| 1220 | 5/1 | ARG | | Eco R. AM 1210, Buenos Aires |
| | 1 | ARG | | LRC R., Pres. Roque Sanez Peña |
| | 10/5 | ARG | LRI224 | R. Onda Marina, Mar del Plata |
| | 1 | BOL | | R. Batallión Topátar, Oruro 1055-0100 |
| | | BOL | | R. La Asunta, Asunta |

| kHz | kW | Ctry | Call | Station, location |
|-----|-----|------|------|-------------------|
| | | BOL | | R. La Voz Cristiana, Achachi |
| | 1 | BOL | | R. Nueva Splendid, La Paz |
| | | BOL | | R. Progreso La Luz del Alba, Cochabamba |
| | 10 | CHL | CD122 | R. Maria, Temuco |
| | 10 | CLM | KR | R. María, Bogotá |
| | 10 | CLM | AV | R. Uno, Montería |
| | 10 | CLM | NM | R. Viva Cultural Bolívar, Ipiales |
| | 10 | CLM | MT | RCN La R., San Gil |
| | 5 | EQA | PA1 | R. Marañón, Quito |
| | | PRU | OBU5I | R. Bethel, San Clemente |
| | 1.5 | PRU | OCU4W | R. Cora, Huancayo |
| | | PRU | OCU4H | R. Fe, Lima |
| | 3 | PRU | OCX1X | R. Libertad, Chiclayo |
| | 10 | PRU | OAX6X | R. Melodia, Hunter, Aqp |
| | 1 | PRU | OAU7N | R. Universidad de San Antonio Abad, Cusco |
| | 1/0.5 | URG | CX122 | R. Reconquista, Rivera |
| | 10 | VEN | RD | LV de Apure, San Fernando de Apure |
| | 10/5 | VEN | VM | Valencia 1220 - R. Venezuela, Valencia |
| **1230** | | ARG | | R. Claridad, Monte Grande |
| | 1 | ARG | | R. Creativa, Lanus |
| | 25/5 | ARG | LT2 | R. Gen. San Martín, Rosario |
| | 5/1 | ARG | LW5 | R. Libertador, General San Martin |
| | 1 | ARG | | R. Litoral, Isidro Casanova |
| | 15 | CLM | EH | Colmundo R., Bucaramanga |
| | 6 | CLM | BR | Emisora R. Recuerdos, Tunja |
| | 10 | CLM | IL | Minuto de Dios, Medellín |
| | 10 | CLM | LK | R. Calidad, Cali |
| | 1 | CLM | TP | R. Colina Caracol, Girardot |
| | 1.5 | EQA | RI1 | CRI, Ibarra |
| | 5 | EQA | FV2 | R. Galáctica, Guayaquil |
| | 1 | PRU | OAM2B | R. Fé, Cajamarca |
| | | PRU | | R. Frecuencia Amistad, Juliaca |
| | | PRU | OCU4C | R. La Luz, Huacho |
| | 1 | PRU | OBX4Z | R. LV de Oxapampa, Oxapampa |
| | 1 | PRU | OBU6T | R. OBU6T, Moquequa |
| | 1 | PRU | OBZ4Y | R. Selecciones,Tarma |
| | 1 | PRU | OAU7V | R. Surupana, Caminca |
| | 2.5 | PRU | OAM7T | R. Tambopata, Tambopata |
| | 10 | VEN | OH | R. Valera, Valera |
| **1240** | 1 | ARG | | R. Cadena Uno, Paso del Rey |
| | 1 | ARG | LRI218 | R. Universidad Nal. del Sur, Bahia Blanca |
| | | BOL | | R. Lider Zárate Willka, La Paz |
| | 2 | BOL | | R. Los Andes, Tarija |
| | | BOL | | R. Nueva Generación, Qhurpa |
| | 0.25 | CHL | CA124 | R. Club Chuquicamate, Calma |
| | 25 | CHL | CB124 | R. Universidad de Santiago, Santiago |
| | 5 | CLM | GN | R. Barrancabermeja, Barrancabermeja |
| | 3 | CLM | JA | R. Buenaventura, Buenaventura |
| | 10 | CLM | FG | RCN, Calarcá |
| | 1 | EQA | PA1 | R. Metropolitana, Yaruquí |
| | 1 | PRU | OAU9B | R. Bagua Grande, Chachapoyas |
| | | PRU | OCX1C | R. Campesina, Ayaviri |
| | 12 | PRU | OAU4V | R. Cumbre, Huancayo |
| | 1 | PRU | OAU5U | R. Eco, Ica |
| | 1 | PRU | OAZ1A | R. Ferreñafe, Ferrañafe |
| | 1 | PRU | OAU3L | R. La Luz, Chimbote |
| | 15 | PRU | OAU6D | R. Lider, Socabaya, Aqp |
| | 1 | PRU | OAU2Y | R. Nor Andino, Santiago de Chuco |
| | 5 | PRU | OCU7Z | R. Pachatusán, Sicuani |
| | 1 | PRU | OCX1C | R. Sechura, Sechura |
| | 5 | URG | CW35 | R. Paysandú, Paysandú |
| **1250** | 25/5 | ARG | | Puerto Madryn |
| | 10 | ARG | | R. Estirpe Nacional., San Justo |
| | | BOL | | R. Amboro, Santa Cruz |
| | | BOL | | R. Comunitaria Compi, Capilaya |
| | | BOL | | R. Indoamerica, Potosi |
| | 2.5 | BOL | | R. La Plata, Sucre |
| | | BOL | | R. Sararenda, Camiri |

| kHz | kW | Ctry | Call | Station, location |
|-----|-----|------|------|-------------------|
| | | BOL | | Rdif. Achocalla, Achocalla |
| | 10 | CHL | CD125 | R. Pilmaiquen, Valdivia |
| | 10 | CLM | CA | Capital R., Bogotá |
| | 10 | CLM | OK | Em. ABC, Barranquilla |
| | 1 | CLM | EM | LV de Corozal, Corozal |
| | 15 | CLM | HS | W R., Cúcuta |
| | 2 | EQA | EM1 | R. Ondas Carchenses, Tulcán |
| | 5 | PRG | ZP3 | R. Asunción, Asunción |
| | 1 | PRU | OAX9C | R. Americana, Nueva Cajamarca |
| | 1 | PRU | OAU6I | R. Campesina, Omate |
| | 3 | PRU | OBX8S | R. Cielo, Calleria |
| | 5 | PRU | OAX4L | R. Cora, Lima |
| | 1.5 | PRU | OBZ1B | R. Dif. BNS, Talara Alta |
| | 1 | PRU | OAU2V | R. HGV, Santa Cruz |
| | 3 | PRU | OBX7A | R. Solar, Cusco |
| | 5 | URG | CW125 | R. Bella Unión, Bella Unión |
| | 3 | URG | CX36 | R. Centenario, Montevideo |
| **1260** | 2 | ARG | | R. Amor, Villa Tesel |
| | 10/5 | ARG | LT14 | R. General Urquiza, Paraná |
| | 9 | ARG | | R. Oliva, General Rodriguez |
| | | ARG | | R. y Television del Neuquén, Neuquén |
| | | BOL | | R. Dios es Amor Universal, Tarija |
| | | BOL | | R. LV de la Esperanca, Quillacollo |
| | 10 | BOL | | R. Nacional de Huanuni, Hunanuni |
| | | BOL | | R. SERVIR, Caranavi |
| | | BOL | | Red de Com. Nueva Imagen Para Bolivia |
| | 1 | CHL | CC126 | R. Condell, Curicó |
| | 10 | CHL | CD126 | R. Maria, Punta Arenas |
| | 5 | CLM | CO | Caracol R., Ibagué |
| | 1 | CLM | HU | Caracol R., San Andrés |
| | 5 | CLM | LX | Minuto de Dios Eco Llanero, Villavicencio |
| | 2 | CLM | OU | Ondas del Amazonas, Leticia |
| | 5 | CLM | DA | R. Auténtica, Medellín |
| | 5 | CLM | ET | R. María, Cali |
| | 5 | CLM | TM | R. Sonar, Ocaña |
| | 5 | CLM | OH | RCN Cesar, Valledupar |
| | 5 | CLM | NO | Torre Fuerte R., Duitama |
| | 1 | EQA | RO6 | R. Calidad, Ambato |
| | 2 | EQA | CL3 | R. Contacto XG, Cuenca |
| | 5 | PRG | ZP34 | R. Panambi Vera, Villarrica |
| | | PRU | | R. Cielo, Trujillo |
| | 1 | PRU | OCU4F | R. Corazón Andino, El Tambo |
| | 3 | PRU | OAU3G | R. El Pregonero, Chimbote |
| | 1 | PRU | OAU3F | R. La Luz, Huanuco |
| | 3 | PRU | OCU4B | R. La Luz, San Vicente de Cañete |
| | 1 | PRU | OBX6D | R. Manahaim, Uchumayo Aqp |
| | 0.3 | PRU | OBX5S | R. Nac. del Perú, Ayacucho |
| | 1 | PRU | OCX10 | R. Nova, Chiclayo |
| | | PRU | OBX2C | R. Otuzco, Otuzco |
| | 3 | URG | CW37 | Dif. Rochense, Rocha |
| | 10 | VEN | RM | BBN R, Caracas |
| **1270** | 25/5 | ARG | LRA20 | R. Nacional, Las Lomitas |
| | 100 | ARG | LS11 | R. Provincia de Buenos Aires, La Plata |
| | 5 | CHL | CB127 | R. Festival, Viña del Mar |
| | 1 | CLM | XQ | Cadena Radial Vida, Ubaté |
| | 1 | CLM | IM | Colmundo R., Pereira |
| | 5 | CLM | Q99 | Colombia Mía, San José del Guaviare |
| | 2 | CLM | AR | La Cariñosa, Cartagena |
| | 1.5 | CLM | KJ | LV de Curumaní, Curumaní |
| | 1 | CLM | SV | LV de Orito, Orito |
| | 5 | CLM | BM | R. Internacional, Honda |
| | 5 | CLM | TX | W R., Bucaramanga |
| | 2 | EQA | LD4 | R. Junín, Junín |
| | 10 | EQA | UM2 | R. Universal, Guayaquil |
| | 1 | PRU | OCX2Z | R. Estacion Latina, Cepén |
| | 2 | PRU | OAU7S | R. Horizonte - LV de Agro, Cusco |
| | 0.4 | PRU | OAZ4H | R. Huacho, Huacho |
| | 0.4 | PRU | OBZ4T | R. La Merced, Chanchamayo |
| | 1 | PRU | OAU1S | R. Nor Peru, Paita |

| kHz | kW | Ctry | Call | Station, location |
|---|---|---|---|---|
| | 2 | PRU | OAM5A | R. OAM5A, Huancavelica |
| | 3 | PRU | OBU6N | R. OBU6N, Tacna |
| | 1 | PRU | OBU6P | R. San Antonio, Callalli |
| | 4/2 | URG | CV127 | R. Cuareim, Artigas |
| | 10 | VEN | OU | R. Ondas Panamericanas, El Vigía |
| **1280** | | ARG | | AM 1280, Gregorio de Laferrere |
| | 6 | ARG | | R. Cadena Eco, CA Buenos Aires |
| | 1 | ARG | | R. Provinciana, San Miguel |
| | 10/5 | ARG | LU11 | R. Trenque Lauquén, TR. Lauquén |
| | | BOL | | R. Altar de Dios, Achacachi |
| | | BOL | | R. Comunitaria del Sur, Cochabamba |
| | | BOL | | R. Comunitaria Ondas del Titicaca, Huarina |
| | | BOL | | R. Fronera, Yacuiba |
| | 1 | CHL | CD128 | R. la Palabra, Osorno |
| | 5 | CLM | KN | Aviva2, Bogotá |
| | 5 | CLM | LR | Caracol R., Pasto |
| | 5 | CLM | RP | Ecos de Tibú, Tibú |
| | 5 | CLM | CM | HJKK Sistema INRAI, Pitalito |
| | 5 | CLM | HO | Impacto Popular, San Juan del Cesar |
| | 1 | CLM | NQ | LV del Río Suárez, Barbosa |
| | 5 | CLM | SO | R. Playa Mendoza, Barranquilla |
| | 5 | CLM | MB | R. Suroeste, Concordia |
| | 1 | EQA | | R. Universitaria, Quito |
| | 10/0.25 | PRG | ZP53 | LV del Este, Cd. del Este |
| | | PRU | | R. Bethel, Chaquimarca |
| | 1 | PRU | OAU1R | R. Bethel, San Jose |
| | 2.5 | PRU | OCU7S | R. Continental, Macusani |
| | | PRU | OBX3C | R. El Puerto, Chimbote |
| | 1 | PRU | OCU7R | R. Fé, Sicuani |
| | 0.5 | PRU | OBX6P | R. Fénix, Camaná |
| | 1 | PRU | OAX3Y | R. La Selva, Rupa-Rupa |
| | 1 | PRU | OBX2F | R. Moderna, Cajamarca |
| | 3 | PRU | OBU5J | Yeshua R., Chinca Alta |
| | 3/1 | URG | CW64 | R. Tacuarembó, Tacuarembó |
| | 10 | VEN | OF | R. Trujillo, Trujillo |
| | 10/5 | VEN | QS | R. Zaraza, Zaraza |
| **1290** | 1/0.5 | ARG | LRI371 | R. Amanecer, Reconquista |
| | 1 | ARG | | R. Interactiva, Ciudad Madero |
| | 5/1 | ARG | LRJ212 | R. Murialdo, Villa Nueva de Guaymallén |
| | | BOL | | R. Comunitaria Alaxpacha, Canaviri |
| | | BOL | | R. Tomas Katari de America, Ocuri |
| | 1 | BOL | | Radiodifusoras Minería, Oruro |
| | 0.25 | CHL | CA129 | R. Coya, Los Angeles |
| | 5 | CLM | SZ | Colombia Mía, Saravena, AR |
| | 5 | CLM | OI | ConecZión R., Sampués |
| | 5 | CLM | TH | LV de las Estrellas, Medellín |
| | 5 | CLM | NE | LV del Ariari, Granada |
| | 5 | CLM | EB | LV del Turismo, Santa Marta |
| | 5 | CLM | MC | R. Viva 12-90, Cali |
| | 5 | CLM | KY | RCN, Girardot |
| | 3 | EQA | JA5 | LV del Río Tarqui, Cuenca |
| | 1 | EQA | NS1 | R. Popular, Atuntaqui |
| | 5 | PRU | OCX6B | R. Cielo, Cerro Colorado Aqp |
| | 1 | PRU | OAM2C | R. Estelar, Chota |
| | 1 | PRU | OBU4S | R. Exito, La Oroya |
| | 1 | PRU | OBU5V | R. OBU5V, Ayacucho |
| | 1 | PRU | OCX1Q | R. Programas del Perú, Tumbes |
| | 1 | PRU | OBU2D | R. Sonorama, Trujillo |
| | 1 | PRU | OBU4Q | S & RD, Hualmay |
| | 1 | PRU | OCU4P | San Vicente de Cañete |
| | 10 | URG | CX38 | Radiodifusión Nac. del Uruguay, Montevideo |
| | 10 | VEN | LF | R. Puerto Cabello, Puerto Cabello |
| **1300** | 2 | ARG | | R. La Salada - RLS, Buenos Aires |
| | 10/1 | ARG | LRA5 | R. Nacional, Rosario |
| | 5 | BOL | | R. Bandera Beniana, Trinidad |
| | 1 | BOL | | R. Fuerzas Armadas, Sta. Cruz |
| | 2.5 | BOL | | R. Loyola, Sucre |

| kHz | kW | Ctry | Call | Station, location |
|---|---|---|---|---|
| | | BOL | | R. San Simón, Cochabamba |
| | 15/6 | BOL | | R. Sol Poder de Diós, El Alto |
| | | BOL | | Sistem de Comuncacion, Oruro |
| | 1 | CHL | CB130 | R. Conexiones, Santiago |
| | 5 | CLM | OG | Aviva2, Cartagena |
| | 5 | CLM | LD | Bésame, Pereira |
| | 5 | CLM | RB | CRB Cadena Radial Boyacense, Tunja |
| | 5 | CLM | NB | Onda 5, Bucaramanga |
| | 5 | CLM | IN | R. Eucha, Belalcázar |
| | 5 | CLM | EA | R. Lumbí, Mariquita |
| | 2.5 | EQA | RU1 | R. Festival, Sto Domingo de los Colorados |
| | 3.5 | EQA | AK6 | R. La Paz, Guaranda |
| | 5 | PRG | ZP53 | R. Fe y Alegria, Villa Hayes |
| | 3 | PRU | OBU6X | R. Candarave, Ilabaya |
| | | PRU | | R. Chumpiwilkas, Santo Tomas Chumbivilcas |
| | 5 | PRU | OAX4S | R. Comas, Comas |
| | 1 | PRU | OAU1U | R. Frecuencia Lider, Morro |
| | 0.5 | PRU | OAX3O | R. Huascarán, Independencia |
| | 0.35 | PRU | OAX7X | R. La Decana - R. Juliaca, Juliaca |
| | 1 | PRU | OBX9P | R. La Luz, Tarapoto |
| | 1 | PRU | OAZ8B | R. Nuevo Mundo, Pucallpa |
| | 2.5 | PRU | OCU4R | R. OCU4R, Ahuac |
| | 5 | PRU | OAX7P | R. Onda Imperial, Cusco |
| | 1 | PRU | OAU2I | R. Paraiso, Cajabamba |
| | 10 | VEN | KH | Deportiva 1300 AM Stereo, Caracas |
| **1310** | 0.8 | ARG | | AM Renacer, Moreno |
| | 0.25 | ARG | | Gesell R., Villa Gesell |
| | 1 | ARG | | R. dif. Antártida Argentina, Buenos Aires |
| | 0.5 | ARG | | R. DR. Gregorio Alvarez, Piedra del Aguila |
| | 10 | ARG | LRA42 | R. Nacional, Gualeguaychú |
| | 5 | CLM | DG | Caracol R., Monteria |
| | 5 | CLM | TQ | G12 R., Cúcuta |
| | 5 | CLM | AK | LV de la Patria Celestial, Barranquilla |
| | 5 | CLM | WD | Micrófono Civico, Palermo |
| | 5 | CLM | JZ | R. 3:16, Bogotá |
| | 5 | CLM | LM | R. Santa Bárbara |
| | 5 | CLM | IR | RCN Urabá, Apartadó |
| | 0.5 | EQA | AI5 | Eco de los Andes, Cumanda |
| | 0.5 | EQA | CP3 | LV de El Oro, Pasaje |
| | 3 | EQA | CI5 | R. Internacional TVO, Biblián |
| | 10/0.25 | PRG | ZP53 | LV del Este, Cd. del Este |
| | 3 | PRU | OBU5X | Ayacucho |
| | 3 | PRU | OCU1D | Bethel R., Piura |
| | 1 | PRU | OBX2D | R. Chota, Chota |
| | 1 | PRU | OBX4L | R. Irvisa, Huacho |
| | 6 | PRU | OAU6N | R. Libertad, Alto Selva Alegre Aqp |
| | 5 | PRU | OAU3T | R. OAU3T, Rupa Rupa |
| | 12 | PRU | OBX8L | R. Vision Amazonia, Iquitos |
| | 5 | VEN | TS | R. Andina, Isnotú |
| | 1 | VEN | SL | RNV El Informativo, Guri |
| | | VEN | | RNV El Informativo, Sta. Elena |
| **1320** | | ARG | | Plus R., Lanús |
| | 0.25 | ARG | LV24 | R. Andina, Tunuyán |
| | | ARG | | R. Area Uno, Caseros |
| | 10 | ARG | LU10 | R. Azul, Azul |
| | 1 | ARG | | R. Máster, Luján |
| | 3 | BOL | | R. Comunitaria La Lumbrera, La Paz |
| | | BOL | | R. Comunitaria Tawantinsuyo, Taraco |
| | | BOL | | R. Em. Septima Voz, Achocalla |
| | 10 | BOL | | R. San Rafael, Cochabamba |
| | | BOL | | R. Sucre, Sucre |
| | 1 | CHL | CD132 | R. Lincoyan, Mulchén |
| | 5 | CLM | MS | La Cariñosa, Barrancabarmeja |
| | 5 | CLM | NV | La Cariñosa, Girardot |
| | 5 | CLM | HT | R. Guateque, Guateque |
| | 1 | CLM | NK | R. Luna, Palmira |
| | 5 | CLM | TA | R. María, Medellín |
| | 5 | CLM | LV | R. Onda Fantastica, Fundación |

| kHz | kW | Ctry | Call | Station, location |
|---|---|---|---|---|
| | 1 | EQA | VO4 | R. Carrizal, Calceta |
| | 3 | EQA | JD6 | R. Continental, Ambato |
| | 1 | EQA | FR2 | R. Guayaquil, Babahoyo |
| | 1 | PRU | OBU5L | La Luz del Mundo, Pueblo Nuevo |
| | 2.5 | PRU | OCU4T | R. Bacan Sat., Huancayo |
| | 5 | PRU | OCU5V | R. Cultural Tintaya, Cotabambas |
| | 1 | PRU | OBU1S | R. Frecuencia Popular, Olmos |
| | | PRU | OAX4I | R. La Cronica, Lima |
| | 0.5 | PRU | OBU6B | R. Majes |
| | 5 | PRU | OAU3W | R. OAU3W, La Caleta |
| | 1 | PRU | OBU6A | R. OBU6A, Tacna |
| | 3 | PRU | OAU7W | R. TV Peru, Juliaca |
| | 1/0.5 | URG | CW132 | R. Fortaleza, Rocha |
| | 1 | URG | CW39 | R. LV de Paysandú, Paysandú |
| | 10/5 | VEN | WP | R. Apolo, Turmero |
| | 10 | VEN | SG | R. Colonial, El Tocuyo |
| 1330 | 1/0.25 | ARG | | AM Rosario, Rosario |
| | 3 | CHL | CB133 | R. La Perla del Dial, Santiago |
| | 3/1.5 | CHL | CD133 | R. Vicente Pérez Rosales, Puerto Montt |
| | 5 | CLM | FE | Antena 2, Pereira |
| | 5 | CLM | LS | Caracol R., Popayán |
| | 5 | CLM | NR | La Caliente 13-30, San Gil |
| | 1 | CLM | MP | LV de Aguachica/R. María, Aguachica |
| | 5 | CLM | AP | R. Auténtica, Cartagena |
| | 1 | CLM | RD | R. Fénix de Oriente 1330 AM, El Peñol |
| | 2 | EQA | RV3 | R. Nacional El Oro, Machala |
| | 10 | PRG | ZP13 | R. Chaco Boreal, Asunción |
| | 1 | PRU | OVX6E | Frecuencia 1330, Arequipa |
| | 1 | PRU | OAU1A | R. Amistad, Chiclayo |
| | 0.5 | PRU | OBU5P | R. Bethel, Huamanga |
| | 1 | PRU | OAM2D | R. Fé, La Esperanza |
| | 1 | PRU | OBX9Y | R. Fé, Tarapoto |
| | 1 | PRU | OCU1J | R. Frecuencia Ideal, Frias |
| | 2 | PRU | OAM4L | R. OAM4L, Tarma |
| | 1 | PRU | OCX7K | R. San Miguel, Wanchaq |
| | 5 | URG | CX40 | R. Fénix, Montevideo |
| | | VEN | | RNV El Informativo, La Paragua |
| 1340 | 1/0.25 | ARG | | Goya |
| | | ARG | | R. Imagen, Castelar |
| | 1 | ARG | | R. Mediterránea, Rosario del Tala |
| | | ARG | | R. Tradicional Conurbano Norte, Florida |
| | 0.5 | BOL | | R. Comunitaria Jach'a Suyu, Corocoro |
| | | BOL | | R. Comunitaria La Voz de Valle, Sococoni |
| | 0.5 | BOL | | R. Copacabana, Copacabana |
| | | BOL | | R. La Mision, La Paz |
| | | BOL | | TV Sist. de Comunicacione Mundial, Cochabama |
| | 10 | CHL | CB134 | R. Colo Colo, Valparaíso |
| | 1 | CHL | CC134 | R. La Discusión, Chillán |
| | 1 | CHL | CD134 | R. Vida Nueva, Panguipulli |
| | 5 | CLM | FB | Años Maravillosos, Bogotá |
| | 0.5 | CLM | VL | Brisas del Catatumbo, Tibú |
| | 5 | CLM | KD | La Cariñosa, Neiva |
| | 5 | CLM | FA | R. Alegre, Barranquilla |
| | 1 | CLM | NP | R. Comunal, Nariño |
| | 5 | CLM | IS | R. El Sol, Buenaventura |
| | 5 | CLM | PY | R. Lemas, Cúcuta |
| | 4 | CLM | NY | R. Unica, Bucaramanga |
| | 5 | CLM | HA | RCN Nariño, Pasto |
| | 5 | CLM | HY | RCN Sucre, Sincelejo |
| | 5 | EQA | CO4 | LV de su Amigo, Esmeraldas |
| | 1 | EQA | RG3 | Ondas de Esperanza, Loja |
| | 10 | PRU | OAU4Q | R. Alegria, Pucasana |
| | 0.5 | PRU | OAX5D | R. Chincha, Chincha Alta |
| | | PRU | | R. Choque, Chumbivilcas |
| | 1 | PRU | OAU4N | R. Jauja, Jauja |
| | 1 | PRU | OBU3C | R. OBU3C, Casma |
| | 1 | PRU | OBX1K | R. San Francisco, Piura |
| | 1 | PRU | OAU2S | R. Shalom, Cajamarca |

| kHz | kW | Ctry | Call | Station, location |
|---|---|---|---|---|
| | 1 | PRU | OBU7V | R. Sudamericana, Juliaca |
| | 10/1 | URG | CW53 | LV de Melo, Melo |
| | 10 | VEN | NE | R. Uno, Caracas |
| 1350 | 1/0.25 | ARG | | Juan José Castelli, Chaco |
| | 10/5 | ARG | LS6 | R. Buenos Aires, Burzaco |
| | 5/1 | ARG | LRJ747 | R. Sucesos, Villa Carlos Paz |
| | | BOL | | R. America, Sucre |
| | | BOL | | R. Comunitario Inti, Contorno/Viacha |
| | | BOL | | R. Llacxa, Achocalla |
| | | BOL | | R. TV Salesiana, Yapacani |
| | 0.02 | CHL | CD135 | Puerto Montt |
| | 1 | CHL | CA135 | R. Riquelme, Coquimbo |
| | 5 | CLM | HL | Bésame, Ibagué |
| | 5 | CLM | LO | La Cariñosa, Caucasia |
| | 5 | CLM | DS | Ondas de la Montaña, Medellín |
| | 5 | CLM | EN | R. Armonía, Cali |
| | 1 | CLM | MN | R. Perijá, Codazzi |
| | 5 | CLM | OA | R. Uno, Santa Marta |
| | 1 | EQA | SF5 | San Fernando R., San Fernando |
| | 3 | EQA | VR2 | Teleradio 1350 AM , Guayaquil |
| | 1 | PRU | OBU5O | R. Atlantis, Huamanga |
| | 1 | PRU | OCU1I | R. Fé, Tumbes |
| | 3 | PRU | OCU6D | R. Municipal, Ichuña |
| | 1 | PRU | OAU3X | R. OAU3X, Pillco Marca |
| | 1 | PRU | OAM4H | R. Paraiso, Huacho |
| | | PRU | OBX8D | R. Super, Pucallpa |
| | 1 | PRU | OAU1H | R. Vision, Chiclayo |
| 1355 | 0.25 | BOL | | R. Armonía, Cliza (n.f. |
| 1360 | 1 | ARG | | AM 1360 R. Cooperativa Estirpe Entrerriana, Maria Grande |
| | 0.4 | ARG | | R. Itatí, Morón |
| | | BOL | | R. 24 de Septiembre, Santa Cruz |
| | 2.5 | BOL | | R. Cochabamba, Cochabamba |
| | | BOL | | R. La Cruz del Sur, Potosi |
| | 5 | CHL | CC136 | R. Universidad Bio Bio, Concepcion |
| | 5 | CLM | RA | Ecos 1360 R. /R. María, Pereira |
| | 10/5 | CLM | PK | LV de Abejorral, Abejorral |
| | 5 | CLM | MI | R. Auténtica, Melgar |
| | 1 | CLM | KV | R. Láser, Zapatoca |
| | 0.5 | CLM | | R. Segovia, Segovia |
| | 5 | CLM | UO | Sistema Cardenal, Cartagena |
| | 1 | PRG | ZP37 | R. Yby Ya'u, Ybu Ya'u |
| | 10 | PRU | OCU4I | R. Bienestar, Lima |
| | 1 | PRU | OBZ5Z | R. Cruz del Sur, Palpa |
| | 1 | PRU | OBZ1A | R. del Norte, Sullana |
| | 1 | PRU | OAU3A | R. Intercontinental, Yungay |
| | 2 | PRU | OCU2Z | R. Las Palmas, Querocotillo |
| | 7.5 | PRU | OCX6T | R. Popular, Mariano Melgar |
| | 2.5 | PRU | OAX7R | R. Sicuani, Sicuani |
| | 1 | PRU | OAU4O | R. Sudamericana, Tarma |
| | 2.5 | URG | CW41 | R. 41, San José |
| | 1 | URG | CW136 | R. Río Branco, Río Branco |
| | 5 | VEN | TZ | R. Armonía, Charallave |
| 1370 | 1/0.25 | ARG | | AM Pilar - Aire de Santa Fe, Potencia |
| | 3 | ARG | | AM Trece-70, González Catan |
| | | ARG | | Junin |
| | 10 | ARG | LRA54 | R. Nacional, Ingeniero Jacobacci |
| | | BOL | | R. Coral, Oruro |
| | 0.15 | BOL | | R. Libertad, Cliza |
| | 1 | CHL | CD137 | R. Vida Nueva, Temuco |
| | 5 | CLM | BO | Minuto de Dios, Barranquilla |
| | 1 | CLM | BD | R. Guaimaral, Cúcuta |
| | 5 | CLM | KI | R. Mundial/Auténtica, Bogotá |
| | 1 | CLM | NI | R. Sabanas/Blu R., Sincelejo |
| | 5 | CLM | EQ | RCN Cauca, Popayán: 24h |
| | 2.5 | CLM | NU | RCN, Rionegro |
| | 5 | EQA | VO2 | LV de Milagro, Milagro |
| | 7 | EQA | AO5 | R. El Rocio, Biblián |
| | 1 | PRU | OCX5A | Inti R., Abanacy |

| kHz | kW | Ctry | Call | Station, location |
|---|---|---|---|---|
| | 2.5 | PRU | OUA7L | R. Andina, Juliaca |
| | 3 | PRU | OCU5Y | R. Chalhuahuacho, Chalhuahuacho |
| | 10 | PRU | OCU4U | R. Los Andes, Cerro de Pasco |
| | | PRU | OAX6T | R. Moquegua, Moquegua |
| | 5 | PRU | OAU9E | R. OAU9E, Moyobamba |
| | 1 | PRU | OBU6Y | R. OBU6Y, Viraco |
| | 3 | PRU | OAM7G | R. Qosqo Wayra, Cusco |
| | 5.3/2.5 | URG | CX42 | Em. Ciudad de Montevideo |
| | 0.5 | URG | CV137A | R. Real, Minas de Corrales |
| | 1/0.5 | URG | CW137 | R. San Javier, San Javier |
| | 10 | VEN | JI | R. Continente Cumbre, Mérida |
| | 5 | VEN | SV | RNV Portuguesa, Acarigua |
| **1380** | 5/1 | ARG | LRI231 | LV del Sudeste, Necochea |
| | 0.5 | ARG | | R. AM Súper Sport, Temperley |
| | 2 | ARG | | R. Buenas Nuevas, Merlo |
| | | BOL | | LV del Espiritu Santo, El Alto |
| | 1.5 | BOL | | R. Bandera Tricolor, Cochabamba |
| | | BOL | | R. Em. Tunupa, Tianawaku |
| | | BOL | | R. Global, Sucre |
| | | BOL | | R. Horizontes, Huanuni |
| | 0.5 | BOL | | R. Luis de Fuentes, Tarija |
| | | BOL | | R. Maria, La Paz |
| | | BOL | | R. Maria, Santa Cruz |
| | | BOL | | R. TV Minera Matilde, Carabuco |
| | 50 | CHL | CB138 | R. Corporación, Santiago |
| | 1 | CLM | EJ | Armonías del Palmar, Palmira |
| | 5 | CLM | MM | Cadena Radial Vida, Valledupar |
| | 3 | CLM | LG | LV de La Dorada, La Dorada |
| | 3 | CLM | JD | NSE R., Medellín |
| | 5 | CLM | ID | R. Potencia Latina, La Plata |
| | 5 | CLM | EE | RCN, Tunja |
| | 5 | EQA | CV1 | R. Cristal, Quito |
| | 1 | EQA | JR6 | R. Mera, Ambato |
| | 1 | PRG | ZP8 | R. Concepción, Concepción |
| | 1 | PRU | OAX2W | R. Atahualpa, Cajamarca |
| | 1 | PRU | OAU2H | R. Campesina, Cajamarca |
| | | PRU | OBU4L | R. Chilca,Chilca |
| | 1 | PRU | OCY4U | R. Nuevo Tiempo, Lima |
| | 1 | PRU | OAM5E | R. OAM5E, Salas |
| | 1 | PRU | OCU7U | R. OCU7U, Tambopata |
| | 1 | PRU | OBX3I | R. Pilco Mozo, Huanuco |
| | 1 | PRU | OAU3U | R. R. dif San Juan, Chimbote |
| | 3 | PRU | OAX6O | R. San Martin, Arequipa |
| | 1 | PRU | OBZ1D | RB - R. Bellavista, Bellavista |
| | 10 | VEN | NG | Ondas del Mar, Puerto Cabello |
| **1390** | | ARG | | La Rocha Azul AM 1390, Libertad |
| | | ARG | | R. General Paz, José C. Paz |
| | 10 | ARG | LR11 | R. Univ. Nacional, La Plata |
| | | BOL | | R. Andina, Pongo Khasa |
| | 5 | CLM | FO | LV de los Andes, Manizales |
| | 5 | CLM | FY | Olímpica, Espinal |
| | 5 | CLM | YW | R. Auténtica, Pacho |
| | 1 | CLM | ZY | R. María, Bucaramanga |
| | 1.5 | EQA | EA5 | R. Tropicana, Cuenca |
| | 0.5 | PRU | OBU2U | Frecuencia del Norte, Santa Cruz |
| | 2.5 | PRU | OCU5C | R. Cielo, Ayacucho |
| | 1 | PRU | OAU7T | R. Enlace, Kunturkanki |
| | 3 | PRU | OAM7A | R. Exitosa, Sicuani |
| | | PRU | OCU1G | R. Fe, Pimentel |
| | 3 | PRU | OAU2Z | R. La Luz, Trujillo |
| | 5 | URG | CW45 | Dif. Treinta y Tres, Treinta y Tres |
| | 20 | VEN | ZA | R. Fe y Alegría, Caracas |
| | 10 | VEN | ZO | R. Lumen, Maracaibo |
| **1400** | | ARG | | AM 1400, Luján |
| | 1/0.25 | ARG | LRH207 | AM del NEA, Charata |
| | | ARG | | R. Carandá, Gregorio de Laferrerè |
| | 5/1 | ARG | LRG202 | R. Cumbre, Neuquén |
| | 0.25 | ARG | | Red 24, Rosario |
| | | BOL | | R. Antena 2000, Sucre |

| kHz | kW | Ctry | Call | Station, location |
|---|---|---|---|---|
| | 5 | BOL | | R. Nacional de Bolivia, La Paz |
| | 5 | CHL | CD140 | R. La Amistad, Los Angeles |
| | 5 | CHL | CD140A | R. Maria, Puerto Montt |
| | 0.25 | CLM | | Brisas del Sinú, Tierralta |
| | 1 | CLM | ER | Ecos del Atrato/W R., Quibdó |
| | 5 | CLM | KM | Em. Mariana, Bogotá |
| | 5 | CLM | HM | La Cariñosa de Armenia, Calarcá |
| | 1 | CLM | D31 | LV de Cimitarra, Cimitarra |
| | 1 | CLM | BK | LV de la Gran Colombia, Cúcuta |
| | 1 | CLM | WY | LV de los Samanes: Quilichao |
| | 1.5 | CLM | | LV de Samaniego, Samaniego |
| | 0.45 | CLM | | R. Cañaveral, Morales |
| | 1 | CLM | JJ | R. Ipiales, Ipiales |
| | 5 | CLM | AS | RCN Antena 2, Barranquilla |
| | 1 | CLM | LL | RCN Antena 2, Santa Bárbara |
| | 3 | EQA | FL2 | R. Z Uno, Guayaquil |
| | 1 | PRU | OAU2H | R. Agricultura, Cajamarca |
| | 1 | PRU | OCU6F | R. Candaravena, Candaravna |
| | 2.5 | PRU | OBX4W | R. Ecco, Lima |
| | 1 | PRU | OAX7I | R. La Hora, Cuzco |
| | 1 | PRU | OBX4H | R. Luz, Tarma |
| | 1 | PRU | OAM5G | R. OAM5G, Ica |
| | 1 | PRU | OBU3E | R. OBU3E, Chimbote |
| | 1 | PRU | OCU5S | R. OCU5S, Preov |
| | 25 | URG | CX140 | R. Zorrilla de San Martín, Tacuarembó |
| **1410** | 1 | ARG | | Godoy Cruz - |
| | 1 | ARG | | La Mil 410, Chivilcoy |
| | 5/1 | ARG | | R. Folclorismo, Moreno |
| | 0.5 | ARG | | R. Fundacion, Rafael Calzada |
| | 1 | ARG | | R. Lider, Mendoza |
| | 0.5 | ARG | | R. María de La Paz, Villa Mercedes |
| | 0.25 | BOL | | R. Atlantida, Oruro |
| | 5 | CHL | CB141 | R. Amor, Viña del Mar |
| | 1 | CHL | CD141 | R. Loncoche, Loncoche |
| | 5 | CLM | DU | Em. Cultural Univ. de Antioquia, Medellín |
| | 1 | CLM | TY | LV del Carare, Vélez |
| | 2 | CLM | P79 | R. Evangélica, Uribia |
| | 5 | CLM | EI | R. Minuto de Dios, Buga |
| | 1 | EQA | FB4 | LV de Quinindé, Quinindé |
| | 1 | EQA | KD5 | R. Centro Gualaceo, Gualaceo |
| | 1 | EQA | VE1 | R. El Tiempo, Quito |
| | 1 | EQA | CQ2 | R. San Francisco, Milagro |
| | 1 | PRU | OBX8I | Dif. Comercial, Pucallpa |
| | 1 | PRU | OBZ4V | R. Bethel, Huacho |
| | 1 | PRU | OBU7A | R. Corporacion Wayra, Juliaca |
| | 3 | PRU | OCU5G | R. Genesis, Huanta |
| | 1 | PRU | OCU2Q | R. Huracana, Pedro Galvez |
| | 1 | PRU | OAU3Y | R. Ke Buena, Paucarbambilia |
| | 3 | PRU | OBU1H | R. La Luz, Tumbes |
| | 1 | PRU | OBU1G | R. Olmos, Olomos |
| | 10/5 | URG | CX44 | La Catorce 10, Montevideo |
| | 2/0.5 | URG | CW141 | R. Turistica, Salto |
| | 10 | VEN | SP | R. Simpatía, Valera |
| **1420** | 1/0.5 | ARG | LRK221 | R. Ciudad Perico, Perico |
| | 1/0.5 | ARG | LRI220 | R. Dime, Villa Martelli |
| | 1 | ARG | | R. Génesis 2000, General Conesa |
| | 1 | BOL | | R. Centro, Cochabamba |
| | | BOL | | R. Comunitaria, José Ballivian |
| | | BOL | | R. Creo en Milagros, Murillo |
| | 1.5 | BOL | | R. Guadalquivir, Tarija |
| | | BOL | | R. Luz del Mundo, Santa Cruz |
| | | BOL | | R. Omasuyos Andina, Achacachi |
| | 1 | BOL | | R. Real Audiencia, Sucre |
| | 1 | CHL | CB142 | R. Panamericana, Santiago |
| | 5 | CLM | HK | Cadena Radial Vida, Manizales |
| | 1 | CLM | D23 | Ecos de Frontino, Frontino |
| | 1 | CLM | LE | La Cariñosa, Ibagué |
| | 2 | CLM | SN | R. Lenguerque, Zapatoca |
| | 5 | CLM | BH | R. Magdalena, Santa Marta |

| kHz | kW | Ctry | Call | Station, location |
|---|---|---|---|---|
| | 2 | EQA | MJ7 | LV del Napo, Tena |
| | 2 | EQA | IM3 | R. Corazón, Machala |
| | 5 | PRG | ZP42 | R. Güyrá Campana, Horqueta |
| | 1 | PRU | OBU6C | R. Fe, Arequipa |
| | 0.5 | PRU | OBU5H | R. la Luz, Salas |
| | 5 | PRU | OAM2P | R. La Positiva, Bambamarca |
| | 2 | PRU | OCU1F | R. OCU1F, Tambo Grande |
| | 1 | PRU | OBZ4G | R. San Isidro, Lima |
| | 1.5 | PRU | OAM7K | R. San Luis, Pallpata |
| | 1/0.5 | URG | CX142 | R. Felicidad, Paysandú |
| | 5 | URG | CW43 | R. Lavalleja, Minas |
| | 10/5 | VEN | RW | R. Cardenal, Carora |
| | 5 | VEN | | R. Sintonía, Caracas |
| 1430 | 0.25 | ARG | LRI235 | R. Balcarce, Balcarce |
| | 1 | ARG | | R. Cunumi Guazú, Rafael Castillo |
| | 1/0.25 | ARG | LV26 | R. Rio Terceo, Río Tercero |
| | 1/0.25 | ARG | LT24 | R. San Nicolas, San Nicolás |
| | | ARG | | San Fernando del Valle |
| | 1 | CHL | CC143 | Rancagua |
| | 5 | CLM | PW | Colmundo R., Barranquilla |
| | 5 | CLM | MF | La Ribereña, Puerto Berrío |
| | 0.25 | CLM | X61 | La U FM Estéreo, Armenia |
| | 0.5 | CLM | G42 | R. Alejandría, Alejandría |
| | 2 | CLM | BP | R. Cariongo, Pamplona |
| | 5 | CLM | QX | R. Majagual, Sincelejo |
| | 1 | CLM | CK | R. Sensación, Yarumal |
| | 5 | CLM | KU | Uniminuto R., Bogotá |
| | 3.5 | EQA | GF1 | R. Futura, Quito |
| | 2 | PRG | ZP35 | R. Mangore, S. Juan Bautista |
| | 1 | PRU | OCU4L | Chilca, Cañete |
| | 1 | PRU | OAZ3H | R. Chavin, Chimbote |
| | 1 | PRU | OAU6M | R. Lider, Tacna |
| | 1 | PRU | OAZ7M | R. OAZ7M, Cusco |
| | 3 | PRU | OBU7U | R. Red Andina, Juliaca |
| | 0.5 | PRU | OAZ4V | R. Universal, El Tambo |
| | 1 | PRU | OBX9H | R. Utcubamba, Bagua Grande |
| | 1 | PRU | OCU2U | R. Vision, Jaén |
| | 20/5 | URG | CW25 | R. Durazno, Durazno |
| | 10 | VEN | NB | Unión R., Guacara |
| 1440 | | ARG | | AM 1440 R. FEDETUR, Mar de Ajó |
| | 1 | ARG | LU36 | R. Coronel Suárez, Coronel Suárez |
| | 0.25 | ARG | | R. Cristo Viene, Mar del Plata |
| | 5/1 | ARG | LRI221 | R. General Obligado, Avellaneda |
| | 2 | ARG | | R. Impacto, Ciudad Madero |
| | 1/0.25 | ARG | LV20 | R. Laboulaye, Laboulaye |
| | 5 | ARG | LRA53 | R. Nacional, San Martín de los Andes |
| | 5/1 | ARG | | Santiago del Estero |
| | 0.25 | ARG | | Villa Gesell |
| | | BOL | | LV de Juno, Tiraque |
| | 1 | BOL | | R. Batallón Colorados, La Paz |
| | 0.25 | BOL | | R. Bolivia, Cochabamba |
| | | BOL | | R. Comunitaria Eco Saywani, Carabuco |
| | | BOL | | R. Dif. Tropico, Trinidad |
| | 2/1 | BOL | | R. Yaguary, Vallegrande |
| | | BOL | | Sistema de Comunicaciones Horizontes, Sucre |
| | 1 | CHL | C144A | R. Coquimbo Stereo, La Serene |
| | 1 | CHL | CC144 | R. El Sembrador, Chillán |
| | 5 | CLM | EK | Caracol R., Tuluá |
| | 5 | CLM | NZ | Colmundo R., Medellín |
| | 5 | CLM | IB | R. Uno, Florencia |
| | 5 | CLM | GM | RCN Antena 2, Sogamoso |
| | 2 | EQA | OV5 | Ondas del Volante, Azogues |
| | 1 | EQA | BA1 | R. Panorama, Ibarra |
| | 3 | PRU | OCU5P | R. Cielo, Ica |
| | 2 | PRU | OBX1T | R. Cooperativa Tumán, , Tumán |
| | 2 | PRU | OAU2O | R. Frecuencia VH, Celendin |
| | 1 | PRU | OAX4K | R. Imperial 2, Lima |
| | 1 | PRU | OBU1Z | R. OBU1Z, Vice |

| kHz | kW | Ctry | Call | Station, location |
|---|---|---|---|---|
| | 2.5 | PRU | OCU5K | R. OCU5K, Ayacucho |
| | 2.5 | PRU | OAX6R | R. Santa Monica, Hunter, Aqp |
| | 3 | PRU | OAM7L | R. Solar, Espinar |
| | 3/0.5 | URG | CX144 | R. Rivera, Rivera |
| | 10 | VEN | ZI | R. Estelar 14-40, Guanare |
| 1450 | 1/0.5 | ARG | | General Acha |
| | 5 | ARG | | R. Banderas, Moreno |
| | 1.32 | ARG | LRI213 | R. El Sol, Porción Quilmes |
| | 5/1 | ARG | | R. Epoca, Corrientes |
| | 1/0.25 | ARG | LRI211 | R. Las 40, Villa Aberastain |
| | 1 | BOL | | R. Em. Bolivia, Oruro |
| | 0.5 | BOL | | R. Magnal, Capinota |
| | 4 | CHL | CC145 | R. Tropical Latina, Curicó |
| | 1 | CHL | CB145 | R. Universidad Técnica, Valparaíso |
| | 5 | CLM | NL | La Cariñosa, Manizales |
| | 0.5 | CLM | | LV del Cauca, El Bordo |
| | 5 | CLM | BY | Olímpica, Flandes |
| | 5 | CLM | HH | R. Católica Metropolitana, Bucaramanga |
| | 1 | CLM | E20 | R. María, Urrao |
| | 1 | EQA | SC1 | AS La R., Tabacundo |
| | 1 | EQA | SE2 | R. Santa Elena, Santa Elena |
| | 5 | PRG | ZP29 | R. Vallemi, Vallemi |
| | 1 | PRU | OBX4K | R. Fortaleza, Barranca |
| | 1 | PRU | OBU4Y | R. La Nueva Andina, Huancayo |
| | | PRU | | R. Libertad, Bambamarca |
| | | PRU | OAU2W | R. Manantial de Vida, Cajamarca |
| | 1 | PRU | OBU6K | R. OBU6K, Chivay |
| | 1 | PRU | OCX2J | R. San Juan, Trujillo |
| | | PRU | OCU6E | R. Santa Cruz, Ichuña |
| | 1 | PRU | OAM4A | R. Vida, Tinyahuarco |
| | 10/5 | URG | CX46 | R. América, Montevideo |
| | 1/0.25 | URG | CW145 | R. Arapey, Salto |
| | 10/8 | VEN | KJ | R. María, Caracas |
| | 10/5 | VEN | XC | R. Mega Visión, San Felix |
| 1460 | 1 | ARG | | R. Contacto, San Antonio de Padua |
| | 0,25 | ARG | | R. Jerusalén, Monte Grande |
| | 0.25 | ARG | LU30 | R. Maipú, Maipú |
| | 0.1 | ARG | LU34 | R. Pigüé, Pigüé |
| | 1/0.25 | ARG | LT29 | R. Venado Tuerto, Venado Tuerto |
| | | BOL | | R. Canal de Television Quillacollo |
| | | BOL | | R. Jiwasa, Carabuco |
| | | BOL | | R. Plenitud de Vida, El Alto |
| | 1 | CHL | CC146 | R. Armonía, Talcahuano |
| | 1 | CHL | CB146 | R. Palabra Viva, Santiago |
| | 1 | CLM | FL | Agustiniana Minuto de Dios, San Agustín |
| | 5 | CLM | JW | ENC R. |
| | 5 | CLM | ZU | La Cariñosa, Pasto |
| | 1 | CLM | MU | LV de Amalfi "La Primera", Amalfi |
| | 1 | CLM | E26 | R. Capiro, La Ceja |
| | 5 | CLM | TN | R. María, Turbo |
| | 1 | CLM | IW | R. Monumental, Cúcuta |
| | 1 | CLM | AL | R. Sincelejo, Sincelejo |
| | 5 | CLM | VH | R. Uno, Barranquilla |
| | 3 | EQA | IC6 | R. Nuevos Horizontes, Latacunga |
| | 1 | PRU | OBU6R | R. Bahia, Mollendo |
| | 0.5 | PRU | OCY4I | R. Imperial, Junin |
| | 1 | PRU | OAZ4F | R. La Oroya, La Oroya |
| | 2.5 | PRU | OAU3V | R. Municipal, Cabana |
| | | PRU | OBU7M | R. OBU7M, Marcapata |
| | 10 | PRU | OAX7W | R. Sol de los Andes, Juliaca |
| | 1 | PRU | OAX1V | R. Sullana, Sullana |
| | 1 | PRU | OCU4Y | R. Voz Cristiana, Chongo Bajo |
| | 1 | PRU | OAM5C | Rdif. Disaga, Pueblo Nuevo |
| | 1 | URG | CX146 | R. Carmelo, Carmelo |
| | 0.25 | URG | CV146 | R. José Batlle y Ordóñez, José Batlle y Ordóñez |
| 1470 | 0.7 | ARG | | Cadena 1470, Remedios de Escalada |
| | 0.25 | ARG | LU26 | La Dorrego AM 1470, Coronel Dorrego |
| | 1/0.25 | ARG | LT20 | R. Junín, Junin |

| kHz | kW | Ctry | Call | Station, location |
|---|---|---|---|---|
| | | ARG | | R. Lider, Mariano Acosta |
| | 1 | ARG | | R. Municipal, Luis Beltrán |
| | 1/0.25 | ARG | LT26 | R. Nuevo Mundo, Colón |
| | 1/0.25 | ARG | LT28 | R. Rafaela, Rafaela |
| | | BOL | | R. Em. Ayni, Corapata |
| | 1 | BOL | | R. Integración, Padilla |
| | 1 | CHL | CB147 | R. Sargento Aldea, San Antonio |
| | 5 | CLM | ll | Aviva2, Medellín |
| | 5 | CLM | TB | Ondas de Ibagué/R. María, Ibagué |
| | 5 | CLM | HQ | R. Futurama, Pacho |
| | 5 | CLM | NT | R. Huellas, Cali |
| | 1.5 | EQA | LD2 | R. Ecos de Naranjito, Naranjito |
| | 1 | EQA | ED1 | Rdif. Ecos de Cayambe, Cayambe |
| | 1 | PRU | OAU1P | R. California, Lambayeque |
| | 20 | PRU | OAU4B | R. Capital, Lima |
| | 1 | PRU | OAX7G | R. Cusco, Cusco |
| | 1 | PRU | OCY2G | R. Oliversa, Quiruvilca |
| | 0.8 | PRU | OAX6M | R. Tacna, Tacna |
| | 2.5 | PRU | OAU6E | R. Victoria, Alto Selva Alegre Aqp |
| | 1 | PRU | OCU4Y | R. Voz Cristiana, Chongo Bajo |
| | 2 | URG | CX147 | R. Cristal del Uruguay,Las Piedras |
| | 1 | URG | CW147 | R. Maria, Melo |
| | 10 | VEN | JW | Union R. Cultural, Valencia |
| 1480 | 1 | ARG | | R. Sensaciones, Tapiales |
| | | BOL | | LV de los Andes, Carabuco |
| | | BOL | | R. Amor de Diós, El Alto |
| | | BOL | | R. Bendita Trinidad y Espirito Santo, Cobija |
| | | BOL | | R. Bendita Trinidad y Espirito Santo, Cochabamba |
| | | BOL | | R. Bendita Trinidad y Espirito Santo, Santa Cruz |
| | 0.1 | BOL | | R. Cadena Sur, Potosi |
| | | BOL | | R. Charcas-Mundial, Sucre |
| | 1/0.8 | BOL | | R. Chiwalakii, Vacas |
| | | BOL | | R. Comunitaria Waley, Desaguadero |
| | | BOL | | R. Domingo Savio, Independencia |
| | 1 | CHL | CA148 | R. Comunicativa, Ovalle |
| | 1 | CHL | CC148 | R. La Amistad de Tomé, Tomé |
| | 5 | CLM | OD | R. Rodadero, Santa Marta |
| | 1 | CLM | TC | R. Sonsón, Sonsón |
| | 5 | CLM | FC | R. Única, Pereira |
| | 5 | CLM | TZ | RCN Antena 2, Bucaramanga |
| | 1 | EQA | HV4 | R. LV de Jipijapa, Jipijapa |
| | 5 | PRG | ZP20 | R. América, Ñemby |
| | 1 | PRG | ZP23 | R. Dos Fronteras, Bella Vista Norte |
| | 0.6 | PRU | OCX2C | R. Comercial San Pedro, Virú |
| | 1 | PRU | OAZ7G | R. Espinar, Yauri |
| | 1 | PRU | OAU4A | R. Mineria, Santa Rosa de Sacco |
| | 1 | PRU | OAM4F | R. OAM4F, Barranca |
| | | PRU | OBM7F | R. OBM7F, Tambopata |
| | 0.2 | PRU | OBU2H | R. Santa Ana, Cutervo |
| | 1 | URG | CX148 | Difusora Rio Negro, Young |
| | 3/0.5 | URG | CW43B | R. Internacional, Rivera |
| | 3 | URG | CW148 | R. Universo, Castillos |
| | | VEN | | R. Cumarebo, Cumarebo |
| 1490 | | ARG | | R. Ciudad de Caá Cati, José C. Paz |
| | | ARG | | R. Dif. Emanuel, Partido de Ezieza |
| | 1.5 | ARG | | R. Gama, Lanús |
| | 1/0.25 | ARG | LV22 | R. Huinca Renancó, Huinca Renancó |
| | | ARG | | R. Vida, Córdoba |
| | | ARG | | R. Vida, Mar del Plata |
| | 1/0.25 | ARG | | Rivadavia |
| | 1 | BOL | | R. San José, San José, Oruro |
| | 0.25 | CHL | CB149 | Hola R., San Bernardo |
| | 1 | CHL | CA149 | R. Alicanto, El Salvador |
| | 4 | CLM | BS | Em. Punto Cinco, Bogotá |
| | 1 | CLM | JO | LV de San Marcos, San Marcos |
| | 1 | CLM | E62 | R. Garzón, Garzón |

| kHz | kW | Ctry | Call | Station, location |
|---|---|---|---|---|
| | 5 | CLM | AY | R. Vida Nueva, Barranquilla |
| | 5 | CLM | ZB | Robles 14-90, La Nueva, Tuluá |
| | 1 | EQA | VY2 | R. Dinámica, Guayaquil |
| | 3 | EQA | MV1 | R. La Poderosa, Quito |
| | 2 | EQA | AM5 | R. Santa María, Azogues |
| | 2.5 | PRU | OCU7Y | Cadena Sur del Peru, Cusco |
| | 1 | PRU | OAX8F | R. Atlántiada, Iquitos |
| | 1.3 | PRU | OAX6Q | R. Fidelidad, Cerro Colorado, Aqp |
| | 1 | PRU | OAX1L | R. Imperio, Chiclayo |
| | 0.5 | PRU | OCX4P | R. La Luz, Cerro de Pasco |
| | 1 | PRU | OAX5N | R. Nazca, Nazca |
| | 1 | PRU | OAM7P | R. OAM7P, Capachica |
| | | PRU | | R. Patron Santiago, Challhuacho |
| | 2.5 | PRU | OBU5C | Radiodifusora los Chankas, Andahuaylas |
| | 1/0.25 | URG | CV149 | R. del Centro, Baltasar Brum |
| | 5 | URG | CX149 | R. del Oeste, Nueva Helvecia |
| | 10 | VEN | XD | R. Dinámica, Caracas |
| | 1 | VEN | SQ | R. Mérida 14-90, Mérida |
| 1500 | | ARG | | AM Entre Mares, San Clemente del Tuyú |
| | 5/1 | ARG | | Mendoza |
| | 2 | ARG | LRI214 | R. Bonaerense, Lavallol |
| | 0.25 | ARG | LT34 | R. Nuclear, Zárate |
| | 0.25 | ARG | | R. Olivera, General Rodriguez |
| | | ARG | | R. Vida, Río Cuarto |
| | 2 | BOL | | R. Comunitaria Tawantinsuyo, Laja |
| | | BOL | | R. Litoral, Cochabamba |
| | 1 | BOL | | R. Sagrado Corazón, Mineros |
| | | BOL | | R. Universidad Juan Misael Saracho, Villamontes |
| | 1 | CHL | CC150 | R. Centenario |
| | 1 | CHL | CD150 | R. Tierra del Fuego, Porvenir |
| | 1 | CHL | CB150 | R. Trasandina, Los Andes |
| | 5 | CLM | TW | Kirios R, Fusagasugá |
| | 5 | CLM | UW | R. María, Manizales |
| | 5 | CLM | LJ | Sonora AM, Cali |
| | 1 | PRU | OAU6B | R. Bulevar, Tacna |
| | 0.5 | PRU | OBX2X | R. Comercial, Trujillo |
| | 1 | PRU | OBX3J | R. Luz y Sonido, Huanuco |
| | 2 | PRU | OBU2J | R. San Pablo, San Pablo |
| | 18 | PRU | OBX4I | R. Santa Rosa, Lima |
| | 1 | PRU | OCU4Q | R. Scala de Oro, Huancayo |
| | 1 | PRU | OAM7B | R. TV Cristiana, Sicuani |
| | 10/5 | VEN | RZ | R. 2000, Cumaná |
| 1510 | | ARG | | LV del Oeste,Libertad |
| | 5/1 | ARG | | R. Alabanza, Guernica |
| | 1/0.25 | ARG | LRI253 | R. Belgrano, Suardi |
| | 2 | ARG | | R. Nueva Bolivia, La Paz |
| | 1 | ARG | | R. RBN, Banfield Oeste |
| | | ARG | | Villa Angela |
| | | BOL | | R. Wiñay Jatha, El Alto |
| | 1/0.5 | CHL | CA151 | R. Luís Alvarez Sierra, Illapel |
| | 1 | CHL | CC151 | R. Poder Pentecostal, Rancagua |
| | 1 | CLM | HX | Candela AM, Bucaramanga |
| | 5 | CLM | D24 | LV de La Unión, La Unión |
| | 1 | CLM | A22 | LV de San Luis, San Luis de Gaceno |
| | 1 | CLM | ZA | R. Cristal, Armenia |
| | 2 | EQA | MC5 | LV de la Juventud, Cañar |
| | 3 | EQA | BD1 | R. Monumental, Quito |
| | 0.5 | EQA | I02 | R. Naval, Guayaquil |
| | 1 | EQA | RY6 | R. Runacunapac Yachana, Simiátug |
| | 3 | PRU | OCX6Q | R. Alegria, Mariano Melgar, Aqp |
| | 1 | PRU | OBX8K | R. Centro de los Medios, Sepahua |
| | 1 | PRU | OBX7P | R. Las Vegas, Wanchaq |
| | 1 | PRU | OCU4M | R. OCU4M, San Vicente de Cañete |
| | 1 | PRU | OBU1B | R. Super Real, Olmos |
| | 1 | PRU | OCX4J | R. Tarma, Tarma |
| | 1 | PRU | OCX1V | R. Tumbes, Tumbes |
| | 0.5 | URG | CW151 | R. Ibirapitá, San Gregorio de Polanco |
| | 1/0.5 | URG | CX151 | R. Rincón, Fray Bentos |

| kHz | kW | Ctry | Call | Station, location |
|---|---|---|---|---|
| | 2/0.5 | URG | CW57 | R. San Carlos, San Carlos |
| | | VEN | | RNV Musical, Güigüe |
| **1516** | 1 | PRU | OAM2Q | R. Charles, Bambamarca |
| **1520** | 2 | ARG | | LV del Sur, Luis Guillón |
| | 5/1 | ARG | | R. Chascomus, Chascomús |
| | 3 | ARG | | R. Cielo Nuevo, Isidro Casanova |
| | 0.25 | ARG | LT38 | R. Gualeguay, Gualeguay |
| | 1 | ARG | | R. Metropolitana, Ciudadela |
| | 2 | ARG | | R. Norteña, Los Polvorines |
| | 1 | BOL | | R. la Chiwana, Cochabamba |
| | | BOL | | R. La Luz del Tiempo, El Alto |
| | | BOL | | R. Rural, Tarata |
| | | BOL | | R. San Pedro, Tiawuanaku |
| | | BOL | | R. Universidad Juan Misael Saracho, Sucre |
| | 1 | CHL | CB152 | R. Integración, San Antonio |
| | 1 | CHL | CC152 | R. Soberanía, Linares |
| | 1 | CLM | RL | Antena de los Andes, Sta Rosa de Cabal |
| | 0.3 | CLM | | Brisas del Palmar, Caucasia |
| | 0.25 | CLM | T21 | Colombia Mía, Tierralta, CO |
| | 1 | CLM | MZ | Ecos de la Sierra Flor, Sincelejo |
| | 1 | CLM | J98 | Em. Una Voz de la Frontera, Puerto Santander |
| | 5 | CLM | LQ | La R. del Príncipe de Paz, Barranquilla |
| | 1 | CLM | MA | LV de Suroeste, Jericó |
| | 1 | CLM | AM | R. Altamizal, Dolores |
| | | CLM | | Sonoradio 1520 AM, Viterbo |
| | 5 | CLM | LI | Su Presencia R., Bogotá |
| | 0.5 | EQA | RI5 | LV de Guamote, Guamote |
| | | PRU | | R. Andina, Lampa |
| | 1 | PRU | OBU7X | R. Avance - Voz Evangelica, Espinar |
| | 1 | PRU | OAX1C | R. Cristal, Chiclayo |
| | 1 | PRU | OCU1T | R. LV del Campesino, Ayabacha |
| | 3 | PRU | OBU5Z | R. Municipal, Castrovirreyna |
| | | PRU | OAM4C | R. OAM4C, San Juan |
| | 6 | PRU | OBU6Z | R. OBU6Z, Mascal Nieto |
| | 2 | PRU | OCU5F | R. OCU5F, Huanta |
| | 2 | URG | CX152 | R. Acuarela, Melo |
| | 1/0.5 | URG | CV152 | R. Paz, Guichón |
| **1530** | | ARG | | Am. Siloé, Gregorio de Laferrere |
| | 5 | ARG | | LV del Futuro, Merlo |
| | 0.25 | ARG | LRJ200 | R. Centro Morteros, Morteros |
| | 1.5 | ARG | | R. Esencia, San Miguel Oeste |
| | 0.25 | BOL | | R. Litoral, Llica |
| | | BOL | | R. Salesiana, Kami |
| | 1 | CHL | CB153 | R. Nexo, Quillota |
| | 1 | CHL | CA153 | R. Vida Nueva, Copiapó |
| | 1 | CLM | HKV82 | Alcaraván R., Puerto Lleras |
| | 1 | CLM | EU | Caracol Sevilla, Sevilla |
| | 5 | CLM | OZ | LV de la Prov. de Padilla, San Juan del Cesar |
| | | CLM | | R. Integración, Morales |
| | 5 | CLM | DN | Yeshu'a LV de Jesucristo, Medellín |
| | 5 | EQA | MP2 | LV de la Península, La Libertad |
| | 1 | EQA | VP5 | LV de Pallatanga, Pallatanga |
| | 5 | EQA | CC5 | Ondas Cañaris AM, Azogues |
| | 3 | EQA | MZ6 | R. Dorado Deportes, Pelileo |
| | 1 | PRU | OBZ4S | R. 15-50, Huancayo |
| | 1 | PRU | OAM2Q | R. Charles, Bambamarca |
| | | PRU | | R. La Jefa, Sullana |
| | 10 | PRU | OBU4C | R. Milenia, Lima |
| | 1 | PRU | OBU7N | R. Ondas del Sur Oriente, Quillabamba |
| | 3 | PRU | OBX2R | R. Oriental, Jaén |
| | 1 | PRU | OAU5R | R. Universidad San Juan Bautista, Subtanjalla |
| | 0.5 | PRU | OAZ7F | Rdif. Espinar, Yauri |
| | 0.25 | URG | CW153 | Em. Cono Sur, Nueva Palmira |
| | 10 | VEN | NP | R. San Felipe el Fuerte, San Felipe |
| **1540** | | ARG | | Cadena D, Monte Chingolo |

| kHz | kW | Ctry | Call | Station, location |
|---|---|---|---|---|
| | 1 | ARG | | R. AM Lider, Benavidez |
| | 0.25 | ARG | LT35 | R. Mon, Pergamino |
| | 0.25 | ARG | LU28 | R. Tuyú |
| | | ARG | | R. Zorobabel, 9 de Abril |
| | | ARG | | Rio Gallegos |
| | | BOL | | R. Bendita Trinidad y Espiritu Santo, El Alto |
| | | BOL | | R. Comunitaria Rio Chico, Sucre |
| | | BOL | | R. Comunitario Tutuka, Vilaque |
| | 0.8 | BOL | | R. Sariri, Escoma |
| | 1 | CHL | CC154 | R. Portales, Chillán |
| | 1 | CHL | CD154 | R. San José de Alcudia, Río Bueno |
| | | CHL | CB144 | R. Sud America, Santiago |
| | 1 | CLM | A26 | Em. Brisas del Río Chico, Belmira |
| | 1 | CLM | HD | LV del Petróleo, Barrancabermeja |
| | 2 | CLM | RQ | R. Austral, Túquerres |
| | 5 | CLM | ZF | R. Cóndor, Manizales |
| | 3 | EQA | FM2 | R. Cristal de Ventanas, Babahoyo |
| | 1 | PRU | OAM4G | R. Angie@Net, Barranca |
| | 0.3 | PRU | OBX4N | R. Corporacion, Cerro de Pasco |
| | 1 | PRU | OCX7V | R. Los Andes, Cusco |
| | 1 | PRU | OBX1B | R. LV de la Frontera, Tumbes |
| | 1 | PRU | OAU6A | R. Milenio Universal, Alto Selva Alegre |
| | 2 | PRU | OBU2A | R. Mundial, Trujillo |
| | 1 | PRU | OCU6H | R. OCU6H, Pocollay |
| | 1 | URG | CV154 | R. Centro, Cardona |
| | 0.1 | URG | CW154 | R. Charrúa, Paysandú |
| | 1 | URG | CX154 | R. Patria, Treinta y Tres |
| **1550** | | ARG | | Estacion Quince Cincuenta, Villa Florito |
| | 0.25 | ARG | LT32 | R. Chivilcoy, Chivilcoy |
| | | ARG | | R. Esperanza, Gregorio de Laferrere |
| | | ARG | | R. La Amistad, José C. Paz |
| | 1 | ARG | LT40 | R. LV de la Paz, La Paz |
| | | ARG | | R. Popular, José León Suárez |
| | 5/0.25 | ARG | LT23 | R. Regional, San Jenaro Norte |
| | 10 | BOL | | R. Caranavi, Caranavi |
| | 1 | CHL | CC155 | R. Manuel Rodríguez, San Fernando |
| | 1 | CHL | CB155 | R. Provincial AM, Putaendo |
| | 5 | CLM | QD | Cadena Radial Vida, Calarcá |
| | 5 | CLM | LT | Em. Revivir en Cristo, Cali |
| | 5 | CLM | ZI | G12 R., Bogotá |
| | 5 | CLM | CB | R. El Sol "La Cariñosa", Barranquilla |
| | 1 | EQA | AD2 | LV de El Triunfo, El Triunfo |
| | 1 | EQA | AD5 | R. Chaguarurco, Santa Isabel |
| | 1 | PRU | OAU3D | R. Cruz, Chimbote |
| | 5 | PRU | OBX4P | R. Independencia, Independencia |
| | | PRU | | R. Integracion, Cutervo |
| | 1 | PRU | OCU1B | R. La Clave, Castilla |
| | 3 | PRU | OAU5Z | R. La Luz del Mundo, Subtanjalla |
| | 1 | PRU | OBX5J | R. Maria, Huamanaga |
| | 1 | PRU | OCU1W | R. OCU1W, Monsefú |
| | 1 | PRU | OAM7D | R. San Sebastian, Livitaca |
| | 0.25 | URG | CV155 | R. Agraciada, Mercedes |
| | 2/0.5 | URG | CW155 | R. Sarandí del Yí, Sarandí del Yí |
| **1560** | 0.5/0.25 | ARG | | AM 1560, Tandil |
| | 0.25 | ARG | LT33 | Cadena Nueve, 9 de Julio |
| | 1/0.25 | ARG | | Mendoza |
| | 1 | ARG | | R. Antena, Lobos |
| | 1.5 | ARG | | R. Castañares, Ituzaingó |
| | 2.5/1.5 | ARG | LT11 | R. Gral. Francisco Ramírez, Concepción del Uruguay |
| | | ARG | | R. Restauración, Llavallol |
| | 15 | BOL | | R. Luz del Mundo, La Paz |
| | 1 | BOL | | R. Occidental, Oruro |
| | 0.5 | BOL | | R. Urkupiña, Quillacollo |
| | 1 | CHL | CB156 | R. Manantial, Talagante |
| | 5/3 | CHL | CA156 | R. Parinacota, Putre |
| | 1 | CHL | CD156 | R. Parque, Villarrica |
| | 5 | CLM | LP | La Cariñosa, Tuluá |

| kHz | kW | Ctry | Call | Station, location |
|---|---|---|---|---|
| | 5 | CLM | XZ | Santa María de la Paz R., Medellín |
| | 5 | CLM | HE | Voces Rovirenses, Málaga |
| | 1.5 | EQA | ZD1 | R. Ecos Culturales de Urcuquí, Urcuquí |
| | 1 | PRU | OAZ7N | R. Maria, Wanchaq |
| | 1 | PRU | OCU6K | R. OCU6K, Alto de la Alianza |
| | 1 | PRU | OAM2I | R. R. Antena Norte, Cajabamba |
| | 2.5 | PRU | OCU4Z | R. R. Rumba, Hualhuas |
| | 1 | PRU | OCX6N | R. Sabor, Arequipa |
| | 2/0.5 | URG | CX156 | Dif. Americana, Trinidad |
| | 1 | URG | CV156 | R. Vichadero |
| | 10/5 | VEN | LZ | RNV El Informativo, Mérida |
| **1570** | 5/1 | ARG | LRI223 | Lomas de Zamora |
| | | ARG | | R. Alegría Regional, Luis Palacio |
| | 1 | ARG | | R. AM Rocha, Tolosa |
| | 0.5 | ARG | | R. Eben-Ezer, Ezeiza |
| | | ARG | | R. La Morena de Itati, Grand Bourg |
| | 2.5 | ARG | | R. Melody, Remedios de Escalada |
| | | BOL | | R. Pedro Ignacio Muiba |
| | 1 | CHL | CC157 | R. Cristo Llama Al Pecador, Rancagua |
| | 1 | CHL | CC157A | R. Familia del Maule, Talca |
| | 1 | CLM | E96 | Colombia Mía, Palmira, VA |
| | 1 | CLM | E70 | R. Auténtica, Manizales |
| | 1 | CLM | TG | R. María, Machetá |
| | 0.5 | EQA | CC4 | R. La Voz, Manta |
| | 25 | PRU | OCU4J | R. Bethel, Lima |
| | 1 | PRU | OAU7Z | R. Carraviz, Juliaca |
| | | PRU | OBU2L | R. Colonial, Contumaza |
| | 1 | PRU | OCX1Z | R. La Nueva Esperanza, Tambo Grande |
| | 2.5 | PRU | OCU5O | R. Musuq Chaski R., Huamanga |
| | 1 | PRU | OAM5H | R. OAM5H, Chinca Alta |
| | 1 | PRU | OBU3A | R. OBU3A. Cerro Jactay |
| | 1 | PRU | OCU7L | R. Vilcanota, Sicuani |
| | 1 | PRU | OCU2C | Rdif. Julcan, Otuzco |
| | 0..25 | URG | CW157A | Em. Celeste, Tomás Gomensoro |
| | 2/0.5 | URG | CX157 | R. Canelones |
| **1580** | | ARG | | Charata |
| | 1 | ARG | | R. 26. de Julio, Longchamps |
| | 0.25 | ARG | LT36 | R. Chacabuco, Chacabuco |
| | | ARG | | R. Cóndor, Moreno |
| | 1 | ARG | | R. La Cueva, 25 de Mayo |
| | 1 | ARG | LT27 | R. LV del Montiel, Villaguay |
| | | ARG | | R. Provincial de Sierra Colorada, Sierra Colorada |
| | 2 | ARG | | R. Tradición, San Martín |
| | | BOL | | LV del Valle, Valle Alto |
| | 1 | BOL | | R. Adonai, Santa Cruz |
| | 3 | BOL | | R. Bermejo, Bermejo |
| | | BOL | | R. Comunitaria Jacinto Rodrìguez, Caracolla |
| | | BOL | | R. Contacto, Sucre |
| | | BOL | | R. El Fuego del Espíritu Santo, El Alto |
| | | BOL | | R. Magazine Tarija, Tarija |
| | 1 | CHL | CC158 | R. Colchagua, Santa Cruz |
| | 1 | CLM | LC | LV del Banco, El Banco |
| | 1 | CLM | E66 | LV del Café, Rovira |
| | 5 | CLM | QZ | R. María, Barranquilla |
| | 5 | CLM | RM | Sistema Cardenal, Sincelejo |
| | 5 | CLM | QT | Wepa Salsa/Verdad R., Bogotá |
| | 1 | EQA | LF1 | R. Orellana, Machachi |
| | | PRU | OAM4O | R. Andina, Huachoa |
| | | PRU | OCU6M | R. Bacan Sat., Tacna |
| | 1 | PRU | OBX1M | R. Naylamp, Lambayeque |
| | | PRU | OAM2R | R. OAM2R, Jaen |
| | 1 | PRU | OBU6S | R. OBU6S, Orcopampa |
| | 1 | PRU | OAU4P | R. San Juan, Tarma |
| | 1 | PRU | OAU5J | R. Virgen del Carmen, Huancavelica |
| | 2/0.5 | URG | CW54 | Em. del Este, Minas |
| | 1/0.5 | URG | CW158 | R. San Salvador, Dolores |
| **1590** | 1 | ARG | | R. Dolores, Dolores |

| kHz | kW | Ctry | Call | Station, location |
|---|---|---|---|---|
| | 1 | ARG | | R. Guabiyú, Gregorio de Laferrere |
| | | ARG | | R. Serodino, Serodino |
| | 1 | ARG | | R. Sin Fronteras, Merlo |
| | | ARG | | R. Stentor, Buenos Aires |
| | | BOL | | R. Kollasuyo Marka, Tiawanaku |
| | 1 | BOL | | R. Wayana Songo, Pongo K´asa |
| | 0.1 | CHL | CC159A | Parral |
| | 1 | CHL | CB159 | R. Aconcagua, San Felipe |
| | 5 | CLM | IP | BBN 15-90 R., Envigado |
| | 5 | CLM | WB | R. María/Em. Nuestra Sra, Socorro |
| | 1 | EQA | RZ1 | R. Mensaje, Cayambe |
| | 1 | EQA | QT6 | R. Panamericana, Quero |
| | 1 | PRU | OAU7C | R. Asillo, Azangaro |
| | 1 | PRU | OBU2C | R. Bendicion, Trujillo |
| | 1 | PRU | OCX6S | R. Mundo, Arequipa |
| | | PRU | OAM2S | R. Municipal, San Marcos |
| | 3 | PRU | OAM5J | R. OAM5J, Ica |
| | 1 | PRU | OBU5F | R. OBU5F, Lucanas |
| | 1.5 | PRU | OAZ4Z | R. Vida, Lima |
| | 1/0.25 | URG | CW159 | R. Nueva R. Lascano, Lascano |
| | 1 | URG | CX159 | R. Real, Colonia |
| | 0.25 | URG | CV159 | R. Regional, Constitución |
| | 10 | VEN | UD | R. Deporte, Caracas |
| **1600** | 1 | ARG | | R. Armonia, Caseros |
| | 0.25 | ARG | | R. EME Centro, Montes de Oca |
| | | BOL | | LV del Campesino, Cochabamba |
| | 0.5 | BOL | | R. P.C.A., Valle Alto |
| | 0.25 | CHL | CD160 | R. Alternativa, Temuco |
| | 0.25 | CHL | CC160 | R. Llacolén, Concepción |
| | 0.25 | CHL | CB160 | R. Nuevo Tiempo, Santiago |
| | 0.25 | CHL | CB160A | R. Positiva, Viña del Mar |
| | 5 | CLM | HV | Emisora Armoniaz, Zipaquirá |
| | 0.25 | CLM | F33 | R. Restauración, Cali |
| | 2.5 | PRU | OBU4R | R. Nuevo Tiempo, Huancayo |
| | 3 | PRU | OBM7A | R. OBM7A, Wanchaq |
| | 3 | PRU | OCU6C | R. OCU6C Moquegua |
| | 1 | URG | CV160 | R. Continental, Pando |
| | 1 | URG | CX160 | R. Litoral, Fray Bentos |
| **1610** | 0.5 | ARG | | R. Comunitaria Regional, Laboulaye |
| | 0.5 | ARG | | R. Santa Fe, Canning |
| | 0.5 | PRU | OAU6O | R. El Sol, Arequipa |
| | | PRU | | R. Inka, Acora |
| **1620** | 10/1 | ARG | | AM 16-20 La R., Mar del Plata |
| | | ARG | | R. Mitre, Cañada de Gómez//R. Mitre 790 |
| | | ARG | | R. Sentires,Merlo |
| | 2 | ARG | | R. Vida, Monte Grande |
| | | PRU | | R. Choquechamaca, Chamaca |
| **1630** | 1/0.25 | ARG | | R. America, San José |
| | 1 | ARG | | R. Restauración, Hurlingham |
| | 1 | ARG | | R. Unidad, Alejandro Korn |
| **1640** | | ARG | | General Madariaga |
| | 1 | ARG | | R. Hosanna 1640, Isidro Casanova |
| **1650** | 1/0.5 | ARG | LRI227 | Antares AM 1650 |
| | | ARG | | R. El Mensajero, Rafael Castillo |
| | | ARG | | R. Estrellas, Longchamps |
| | | PRU | | R. Santa Roas, San Ignacio, Otuzco |
| **1660** | | ARG | | Junin |
| | 1/0.25 | ARG | | Paso de los Libres |
| | 5/0.25 | ARG | LRI232 | R. Ciudad de Nogoyá Nogoyá |
| | 1 | ARG | | R. Revivir, Gregorio de la Ferrere |
| **1680** | | ARG | | R. Bethel, Banfield |
| **1690** | 1 | ARG | | R. Cristo la Solucuión, San Justo |
| **1700** | 5/1 | ARG | LRI236 | R. Fantastico, Jose |
| | | ARG | | R. Juventud, Florencia Varela |
| **1710** | | ARG | | AM Selva, Paretido de La Matanza |

# SHORTWAVE STATIONS OF THE WORLD

**November 2018 - © Copyright WRTH Publications Ltd**

For country and site codes, see relevant tables in the reference section. Stations marked as '*dom*' in the site column are domestic/national broadcasts. Stations marked with '**STF**' in the site column are Standard Time/Frequency transmissions. The column '**N**' indicates Notes. Symbols used in the '**N**' column are '**+**', indicating DRM transmissions; '**±**' which indicates variable frequency; '**†**' for irregular transmissions and **‡** for frequencies that were inactive at the editorial deadline. The '**Ctry**' column shows the location of the transmitter site. The country code shown after international entries denotes the country the station is listed under in the International or COTB sections of WRTH.

| kHz | N kW | Ctry | Site | Station, location | kHz | N kW | Ctry | Site | Station, location |
|---|---|---|---|---|---|---|---|---|---|
| 2350 | 5 | AUS | dom | Ozy Radio, Alice Springs | 3970 | ±† 5 | KRE | chj | Echo of Unification, KOR |
| 2500 | 10 | CHN | STF | BPM, Pucheng | 3975 | 1 | D | wis | Shortwaveradio, D |
| | 5 | HWA | STF | WWVH, Kekaha (HI) | 3985 | 100 | CHN | dom | CNR2 Business R., Golmud |
| | 2.5 | USA | STF | WWV, Fort Collins (CO) | | 1 | D | kll | R. Canada International (RCI), CAN |
| 2850 | 50 | KRE | dom | KCBS, Pyongyang | | 1 | D | kll | R. Mi Amigo Int., E |
| 3200 | 50 | SWZ | man | TWR Africa, AFS | | 1 | D | kll | R. Slovakia Int., SVK |
| 3205 | ‡ 10 | PNG | dom | NBC Sandaun, Vanimo | | 1 | D | kll | R.Tirana Int., ALB |
| 3210 | 1 | AUS | dom | Radio DX, Bundaberg | | 1 | D | kll | SRG SSR Swiss B'casting Corp., SUI |
| | 1 | AUS | dom | Station X, Wee Waa | | 1 | D | kll | SWService, D |
| 3215 | 100 | USA | wcr | The Overcomer Ministry, USA | | 100 | KOR | jnm | Echo of Hope (VOH), KRE |
| | 100 | USA | wcr | WWCR, USA | 3990 | † 15 | CHN | dom | Gannan PBS, Hezuo |
| 3220 | 5 | KRE | dom | KCBS/Reg., Hamhung | | 100 | CHN | dom | Xinjiang PBS, Urumqi |
| | 5 | KRE | ham | Pyongyang Broadcasting Stn., KRE | 3995 | 1.5 | D | wnm | R.HCJB Deutschland, D |
| 3235 | ‡ 10 | PNG | dom | NBC West New Britain, Kimbe | 4010 | 100 | KGZ | dom | KGR1, Bishkek |
| 3240 | 50 | SWZ | man | TWR Africa, AFS | 4055 | † 0.7 | GTM | dom | R. Verdad, Chiquimula |
| 3250 | ‡ 1 | HND | dom | R. Luz y Vida, San Luís | 4450 | 50 | KOR | goy | Voice of the People, KRE |
| 3255 | 100 | AFS | mey | BBC World Service, G | 4500 | 50 | CHN | dom | Xinjiang PBS, Urumqi |
| 3260 | ‡ 4 | PNG | dom | NBC Madang, Madang | 4748 | ± 0.5 | PRU | dom | R. Huanta 2000, Huanta |
| 3275 | ‡ 10 | PNG | dom | NBC Sthn Highlands, Mendi | 4750 | † 100 | BGD | dom | Bangladesh Betar, Savar |
| 3290 | ‡ 10 | PNG | dom | NBC Central, Port Moresby | | 100 | CHN | dom | CNR1 VO China, Hailar |
| 3305 | ‡ 10 | PNG | dom | NBC Western, Daru | | ‡ 50 | INS | dom | RRI, Makassar |
| 3310 | 10 | BOL | dom | R. Mosoj Chaski, Cochabamba | 4760 | ‡ 10 | IND | dom | AIR, Leh |
| 3315 | ‡ 10 | PNG | dom | NBC Manus, Lorengau | | 8 | IND | dom | AIR, Port Blair |
| 3320 | 100 | AFS | dom | R. Sonder Grense, Meyerton | | ‡ 1 | LBR | dom | ELWA R., Monrovia |
| | 50 | KRE | pyo | Pyongyang Broadcasting Stn., KRE | | 50 | SWZ | man | TWR Africa, AFS |
| 3325 | † 10 | INS | pga | Voice of Indonesia, INS | 4765 | 50 | CUB | dom | R. Progreso, Bejucal |
| | † 10 | PNG | dom | NBC Bougainville, Buka | | 50 | TJK | dom | Tajik R., Yangiyul |
| 3330 | 3 | CAN | STF | CHU, Ottawa | 4775 | † 1 | B | dom | R. Congonhas, Congonhas |
| 3340 | ‡ 2 | HND | dom | R. Misiones Int., Comayagüela | | † 1 | PRU | dom | R. Tarma Internacional, Tarma |
| 3345 | 100 | AFS | mey | Channel Africa, AFS | | 50 | SWZ | man | TWR Africa, AFS |
| | † 10 | INS | dom | RRI, Ternate | 4800 | 100 | CHN | dom | CNR1 VO China, Golmud |
| | ‡ 10 | PNG | dom | NBC Northern, Popondetta | | † 50 | IND | dom | AIR, Hyderabad |
| 3365 | † 1 | B | dom | R. Cultura, Araraquara | 4805 | † 5 | B | dom | R. Dif. do Amazonas, Manaus |
| | ‡ 10 | PNG | dom | NBC Milne Bay, Alotau | 4810 | 100 | ARM | erv | Public R. of Armenia, ARM |
| 3375 | † 1 | B | dom | R. Municipal, São Gabriel Cach. | | 50 | IND | dom | AIR, Bhopal |
| 3385 | ‡ 10 | PNG | dom | NBC E. New Britain, Rabaul | | 1 | PRU | dom | R. Logos, Chazuta |
| 3480 | 50 | KOR | goy | Voice of the People, KRE | 4820 | 100 | CHN | dom | Xizang PBS, Lhasa |
| 3900 | 5 | CHN | dom | Hulun Buir PBS, Hailar | | † 15 | KGZ | dom | KGR2, Bishkek |
| 3910 | 50 | KOR | goy | Voice of the People, KRE | 4824 | 10 | PRU | dom | LV de la Selva, Iquitos |
| 3915 | 100 | SNG | sng | BBC World Service, G | 4830 | † 10 | MNG | dom | Mongolian R., Altay |
| 3920 | † 5 | KRE | dom | KCBS/Reg., Hyesan | 4835 | † 0.5 | AUS | dom | Ozy Radio, Sydney |
| 3925 | 10 | J | dom | R. Nikkei 1, Sapporo | | † 10 | IND | dom | AIR, Gangtok |
| 3930 | 50 | KOR | goy | Voice of the People, KRE | 4840 | 100 | USA | wcr | WWCR, USA |
| 3945 | 10 | J | dom | R. Nikkei 2, Tokyo | 4845 | 10 | B | dom | R. Cultura, Manaus |
| | 100 | KRE | pyo | Echo of Unification, KOR | | † 1 | B | dom | R. Met. Paulista, Ibitinga |
| 3950 | 100 | CHN | dom | Xinjiang PBS, Urumqi | 4850 | 100 | CHN | dom | Xinjiang PBS, Urumqi |
| 3955 | + 250 | G | wof | BBC World Service, G | 4862 | ± 5 | B | dom | R. Alvorada, Londrina |
| | 250 | G | wof | KBS World R., KOR | 4870 | 100 | IND | del | All India R. (AIR), IND |
| 3959 | † 5 | KRE | dom | KCBS/Reg., Kanggye | | 100 | IND | del | R. Sedayee Kashmir, PAK |
| 3965 | + 1 | F | iss | R. France Int. (RFI), F | | ‡ 5 | INS | dom | RRI, Wamena |

| kHz | N kW | Ctry | Site | Station, location | kHz | N kW | Ctry | Site | Station, location |
|---|---|---|---|---|---|---|---|---|---|
| 4875 | 10 | B | dom | R. Roraima, Boa Vista | 5055 | 1 | AUS | dom | 4KZ, Innisfail Qld |
| 4885 | 2 | B | dom | R. Clube do Pará, Belém | | 1 | AUS | dom | Station X, Wee Waa |
| † | 5 | B | dom | Rdif. Acreana, Rio Branco | 5060 | 100 | CHN | dom | Xinjiang PBS, Urumqi |
| | 100 | KOR | nwn | Echo of Hope (VOH), KRE | 5066 | ‡ 1 | COD | dom | R. Télé Candip, Bunia |
| 4895 | 100 | AFS | mey | Amateur R. Today, AFS | 5085 | 100 | USA | tww | WTWW, USA |
| † | 5 | B | dom | R. Novo Tempo, Campo Grande | 5130 | 15 | KGZ | bis | R. Sadaye Zindagi, CAN |
| ‡ | 50 | IND | dom | AIR, Kurseong | † | 50 | USA | bcq | WBCQ, USA |
| † | 10 | MNG | dom | Mongolian R. 3, Mörön | | 50 | USA | bcq | World of Radio, USA |
| 4900 | 50 | CHN | dom | VO Strait Dialect Sce, Fuzhou | 5800 | † 0.15 | DNK | hil | R. Oz-Viola, DNK |
| 4905 | 5 | B | dom | R. Relógio, Rio de Janeiro | 5825 | 0.1 | CHL | dom | R. Triunfal Evangélica, Talagante |
| | 50 | CHN | lha | CTB - Holy Tibet, CHN | 5830 | 100 | USA | tww | WTWW, USA |
| | 100 | CHN | dom | Xizang PBS, Lhasa | 5840 | 0.3 | DNK | rnd | World Music Radio (WMR), DNK |
| 4910 | 50 | IND | dom | AIR, Jaipur | | ‡ 250 | MRA | tin | VO America (VOA), USA |
| 4920 | 50 | CHN | lha | CTB - Holy Tibet, CHN | 5845 | 250 | SNG | sng | BBC World Service, G |
| | 100 | CHN | dom | Xizang PBS, Lhasa | 5850 | 100 | USA | rmi | Italian Broadcasting Corp., I |
| | 50 | IND | dom | AIR, Chennai | | 100 | USA | rmi | R. Prague, CZE |
| † | 1 | PRU | dom | R. LV del Pueblo, Santiago de Chuco | | 100 | USA | rmi | R. Slovakia Int., SVK |
| 4925 | 5 | B | dom | R. Educação Rural, Tefé | | 100 | USA | rmi | R.Tirana Int., ALB |
| 4930 | 100 | BOT | bot | VO America (VOA), USA | | 100 | USA | rmi | RAE - Argentina Al Mundo, ARG |
| | 100 | BOT | bot | VOA Studio 7, USA | | 100 | USA | rmi | Shortwave Radiogram, USA |
| 4940 | 50 | CHN | dom | VO Strait News Ch, Fuzhou | | 100 | USA | rmi | The Overcomer Ministry, USA |
| † | 1 | PRU | dom | R. San Antonio, Villa Atalaya | | 100 | USA | rmi | VORW R. International, USA |
| 4950 | † 25 | AGL | dom | R. Nal de Angola, Mulenvos | | 100 | USA | rmi | WRMI - R. Miami Int., USA |
| † | 50 | IND | dom | AIR, Kashmir, Srinagar | 5855 | 100 | UZB | tac | BBC World Service, G |
| 4955 | † 5 | PRU | dom | R. Cultural Amauta, Huanta | 5860 | 100 | D | lam | R. Farda, USA |
| 4960 | 100 | STP | sao | VO America (VOA), USA | | 250 | KWT | kwt | R. Farda, USA |
| 4965 | 5 | B | dom | R. Alvorada, Parintins | 5875 | 300 | ARM | erv | BBC World Service, G |
| 4970 | 50 | IND | dom | AIR, Shillong | | 250 | ASC | asc | BBC World Service, G |
| 4975 | 10 | CHN | dom | Fujian PBS, Fuzhou | | 250 | BUL | sof | BBC World Service, G |
| 4980 | 100 | CHN | dom | Xinjiang PBS, Urumqi | | 250 | G | wof | BBC World Service, G |
| 4985 | 10 | B | dom | R. Brasil Central, Goiânia | | 250 | THA | udo | R. Thailand World Service, THA |
| 4990 | 10 | CHN | dom | Hunan PBS, Xiangtan | | 100 | UZB | tac | BBC World Service, G |
| † | 1 | SUR | dom | R. Apintie, Paramaribo | 5880 | 250 | PHL | pht | VO America (VOA), USA |
| 4996 | 10 | RUS | STF | RWM, Taldom | 5885 | 100 | BOT | bot | VO America (VOA), USA |
| 4998 | 1 | E | STF | EBC, San Fernando | | ‡ 250 | MRA | tin | R. Free Asia (RFA), USA |
| 5000 | 20 | CHN | STF | BPM, Pucheng | 5890 | 250 | KWT | kwt | R. Free Asia (RFA), USA |
| | 10 | HWA | STF | WWVH, Kekaha (HI) | | 250 | KWT | kwt | VO America (VOA), USA |
| | 2 | KOR | STF | HLA, Daejeon | | 250 | SNG | sng | BBC World Service, G |
| | 10 | USA | STF | WWV, Fort Collins (CO) | | 100 | USA | wcr | WWCR, USA |
| 5005 | † 50 | GNE | dom | Rdif Guinea Ecuatorial, Bata | 5895 | 0.05 | NOR | erd | R. Nthrn Star/The Ferry, NOR |
| | 1 | NPL | dom | R. Nepal, Khumaltar | | 250 | TJK | dsb | BBC World Service, G |
| 5010 | 50 | IND | dom | AIR, Thiruvananthapuram | 5900 | 100 | BUL | sof | Bible Voice Broadcasting (BVB), CAN |
| | †± 10 | MDG | dom | R. Nal Malagasy, Ambohidrano | | 100 | BUL | sof | Italian Broadcasting Corp., I |
| | 100 | USA | rmi | Adventist World R. (AWR), USA | | 250 | BUL | sof | R. Taiwan International, TWN |
| | 100 | USA | rmi | Family R., USA | | 100 | BUL | sof | The Overcomer Ministry, USA |
| | 100 | USA | rmi | Italian Broadcasting Corp., I | 5905 | 100 | CHN | kas | China R. Int. (CRI), CHN |
| | 100 | USA | rmi | PCJ R. International, TWN | | 10 | D | pin | Deutscher Wetterdienst (DWD), D |
| | 100 | USA | rmi | R. Prague, CZE | | 100 | GUM | twr | Living Water Ministry, USA |
| | 100 | USA | rmi | R. Slovakia Int., SVK | 5910 | 100 | ARM | erv | BBC World Service, G |
| | 100 | USA | rmi | RAE - Argentina Al Mundo, ARG | | 500 | CHN | bei | China R. Int. (CRI), CHN |
| | 100 | USA | rmi | WRMI - R. Miami Int., USA | † | 5 | CLM | dom | Alcaraván R., Puerto Lleras |
| 5020 | 5 | SLM | dom | Solomon Islands BC, Honiara | | 250 | CUB | qvc | China R. Int. (CRI), CHN |
| 5025 | 100 | CUB | dom | R. Rebelde, Bauta | | 300 | ROU | tig | R. Romania International, ROU |
| | 5 | PRU | dom | R. Quillabamba, Quillabamba | | 250 | UAE | dha | KBS World R., KOR |
| 5035 | ‡ 5 | B | dom | R. Educação Rural, Coari | 5915 | 50 | BRM | dom | Myanma R., Naypyitaw |
| 5040 | 100 | CUB | hab | R. Habana Cuba, CUB | | 500 | CHN | bei | China R. Int. (CRI), CHN |
| | 50 | IND | dom | AIR, Jeypore | | 100 | CHN | huh | China R. Int. (CRI), CHN |
| 5045 | 1 | AUS | dom | Radio DX, Bundaberg | | 100 | CHN | kas | China R. Int. (CRI), CHN |
| | 0.05 | AUS | dom | Unique Radio, Gunnedah | † | 35 | ZMB | dom | ZNBC R. One, Lusaka |
| 5050 | 5 | AUS | dom | Ozy Radio, Alice Springs | 5920 | 1.5 | D | wnm | R.HCJB Deutschland, D |
| | 50 | CHN | nnn | Beibu Bay R., CHN | | 500 | IRN | sir | Pars Today (VOIRI), IRN |
| | ‡ 10 | IND | dom | AIR, Aizawl | | 300 | ROU | tig | R. Romania International, ROU |
| | 100 | USA | wrb | WWRB, USA | | 250 | USA | hri | WHRI - World Harvest R., USA |

| kHz | N | kW | Ctry | Site | Station, location |
|---|---|---|---|---|---|
| 5925 | | 250 | ASC | asc | BBC World Service, G |
| | | 100 | CHN | dom | CNR5 Vo Zhonghua, Beijing |
| | | 500 | F | iss | R. France Int. (RFI), F |
| | | 500 | IRN | sir | Pars Today (VOIRI), IRN |
| | | 50 | VTN | dom | VO Vietnam 2, Xuan Mai |
| 5930 | | 300 | AUT | mos | BBC World Service, G |
| | | 100 | ROU | tig | R. Romania International, ROU |
| 5935 | | 1 | BOL | dom | R. Yatun Ayllu Yura, Yura |
| | | 100 | CHN | dom | Xizang PBS, Lhasa |
| | | 100 | D | nau | Bible Voice Broadcasting (BVB), CAN |
| | | 500 | IRN | zah | Pars Today (VOIRI), IRN |
| | | 300 | ROU | tig | R. Romania International, ROU |
| | | 100 | USA | wcr | University Network, USA |
| | | 100 | USA | wcr | WWCR, USA |
| 5940 | | 10 | B | dom | Voz Missionária, Camboriú |
| | | 50 | ETH | dom | Ethiopian Somal Reg. State R., Jigjiga |
| | | 500 | F | iss | R. Algeriénnne, ALG |
| | | 500 | IRN | sir | Pars Today (VOIRI), IRN |
| | + | 90 | ROU | tig | R. Romania International, ROU |
| | | 250 | UAE | dha | R. Sadaye Zindagi, CAN |
| 5945 | | 100 | CHN | dom | CNR1 VO China, Beijing |
| | | 250 | TUR | emr | Voice of Turkey (VOT), TUR |
| 5950 | | 100 | ETH | dom | VO Tigray Revolution, Geja |
| | | 250 | F | iss | KBS World R., KOR |
| | | 500 | IRN | sir | Pars Today (VOIRI), IRN |
| | | 100 | USA | rmi | Deutsche Welle, D |
| | | 100 | USA | rmi | Family R., USA |
| | | 100 | USA | rmi | FG R., CYP |
| | | 100 | USA | rmi | KBS World R., KOR |
| | | 100 | USA | rmi | PCJ R. International, TWN |
| | | 100 | USA | rmi | R. France Int. (RFI), F |
| | | 100 | USA | rmi | R. Japan (NHK World), J |
| | | 100 | USA | rmi | R. Poland, POL |
| | | 100 | USA | rmi | R. Prague, CZE |
| | | 100 | USA | rmi | R. Slovakia Int., SVK |
| | | 100 | USA | rmi | R.Tirana Int., ALB |
| | | 100 | USA | rmi | RAE - Argentina Al Mundo, ARG |
| | | 100 | USA | rmi | RNZI (RNZ Pacific), NZL |
| | | 100 | USA | rmi | Shortwave Radiogram, USA |
| | | 100 | USA | rmi | Vatican R., CVA |
| | | 100 | USA | rmi | VORW R. International, USA |
| | | 100 | USA | rmi | World of Radio, USA |
| | | 100 | USA | rmi | WRMI - R. Miami Int., USA |
| 5952 | | 5 | BOL | dom | R. Pío XII, Siglo Veinte |
| 5955 | | 150 | CHN | bei | China R. Int. (CRI), CHN |
| | | 500 | CHN | xia | China R. Int. (CRI), CHN |
| | | 100 | ROU | tig | R. Romania International, ROU |
| | + | 40 | ROU | tig | R. Romania International, ROU |
| | | 75 | ROU | tig | R. Romania International, ROU |
| 5960 | | 150 | ALB | cer | China R. Int. (CRI), CHN |
| | | 250 | ASC | asc | R. Ndarason Int., TCD |
| | | 100 | CHN | dom | Xinjiang PBS, Urumqi |
| | | 125 | D | nau | The Mighty KBC, HOL |
| | | 250 | KWT | kbd | R.Kuwait, KWT |
| | | 250 | OMA | sla | BBC World Service, G |
| | | 500 | TUR | emr | Voice of Turkey (VOT), TUR |
| 5965 | | 500 | CHN | bei | China R. Int. (CRI), CHN |
| | | 100 | CHN | kas | China R. Int. (CRI), CHN |
| | | 500 | CHN | xia | China R. Int. (CRI), CHN |
| | | 100 | GUM | sda | AWR Asia/Pacific, THA |
| | | 500 | IRN | sir | Pars Today (VOIRI), IRN |
| | | 500 | TUR | emr | Voice of Turkey (VOT), TUR |
| 5970 | | 150 | ALB | cer | China R. Int. (CRI), CHN |

| kHz | N | kW | Ctry | Site | Station, location |
|---|---|---|---|---|---|
| | | 300 | ARM | erv | BBC World Service, G |
| | | 300 | AUT | mos | Adventist World R. (AWR), USA |
| | | 15 | CHN | dom | Gannan PBS, Hezuo |
| | | 500 | TUR | emr | Voice of Turkey (VOT), TUR |
| | | 500 | UAE | dha | R. Free Asia (RFA), USA |
| | | 100 | USA | ewn | WEWN - EWTN Shortwave, USA |
| 5975 | | 250 | ASC | asc | BBC World Service, G |
| | | 300 | AUT | mos | Adventist World R. (AWR), USA |
| | | 500 | CHN | bei | China R. Int. (CRI), CHN |
| | | 100 | CHN | dom | CNR8, Beijing |
| | | 125 | F | iss | Adventist World R. (AWR), USA |
| | | 250 | G | wof | BBC World Service, G |
| | + | 50 | NZL | ran | RNZI (RNZ Pacific), NZL |
| | | 250 | OMA | sla | BBC World Service, G |
| | | 50 | VTN | dom | VO Vietnam 1, Hanoi |
| 5980 | | 500 | CHN | xia | China R. Int. (CRI), CHN |
| | | 0.1 | FIN | vir | Scandinavian Weekend R., FIN |
| | | 1 | PRU | dom | R. Chaski, Urubamba |
| | | 300 | ROU | gal | R. Romania International, ROU |
| | + | 300 | ROU | gal | R. Romania International, ROU |
| | | 500 | TUR | emr | Voice of Turkey (VOT), TUR |
| | | 250 | USA | grv | R. Martí, USA |
| 5985 | | 150 | ALB | cer | China R. Int. (CRI), CHN |
| | | 50 | BRM | dom | Myanmar R., Yangon |
| | | 50 | BRM | yan | R. Japan (NHK World), J |
| | | 500 | CHN | bei | China R. Int. (CRI), CHN |
| | | 500 | CHN | xia | China R. Int. (CRI), CHN |
| | | 300 | J | yam | R. Japan (NHK World), J |
| | | 100 | USA | rmi | Family R., USA |
| | | 100 | USA | rmi | Hobart R. International, AUS |
| | | 100 | USA | rmi | Italian Broadcasting Corp., I |
| | | 100 | USA | rmi | WRMI - R. Miami Int., USA |
| 5990 | | 100 | CHN | huh | China R. Int. (CRI), CHN |
| † | | 50 | CHN | dom | Qinghai PBS, Xining |
| | | 250 | CUB | qvc | China R. Int. (CRI), CHN |
| | | 300 | ROU | gal | R. Romania International, ROU |
| 5995 | | 100 | BUL | sof | Bible Voice Broadcasting (BVB), CAN |
| | | 100 | D | nau | Bible Voice Broadcasting (BVB), CAN |
| | | 100 | KOR | jnm | Echo of Hope (VOH), KRE |
| | | 50 | MLI | dom | R. Mali, Bamako (Kati) |
| | | 250 | UAE | dha | BBC World Service, G |
| 6000 | | 50 | BUL | sof | The Overcomer Ministry, USA |
| | | 100 | CHN | dom | CNR1 VO China, Beijing |
| | | 250 | CUB | hab | R. Habana Cuba, CUB |
| | | 10 | IND | dom | AIR, Leh |
| | | 500 | IRN | sir | Pars Today (VOIRI), IRN |
| | | 100 | RUS | arm | GTRK "Adygeya", RUS |
| | | 500 | TUR | emr | Voice of Turkey (VOT), TUR |
| 6005 | | 250 | ASC | asc | BBC World Service, G |
| | | 1 | D | kll | R. Belarus Int., BLR |
| | | 1 | D | kll | R. Canada International (RCI), CAN |
| | | 1 | D | kll | R. Poland, POL |
| | | 1 | D | kll | R. Slovakia Int., SVK |
| | | 1 | D | kll | R.Tirana Int., ALB |
| | | 1 | D | kll | RAE - Argentina Al Mundo, ARG |
| | | 1 | D | kll | SRG SSR Swiss B'casting Corp., SUI |
| | | 1 | D | kll | SWService, D |
| | | 1 | D | kll | Voice of Mongolia, MNG |
| 6010 | † | 5 | B | dom | R. Inconfidência, Belo Horizonte |
| | | 500 | CHN | bei | China R. Int. (CRI), CHN |
| | | 500 | CHN | uru | China R. Int. (CRI), CHN |
| | | 100 | CHN | dom | CNR11 Tibetan Sce, Xi'an |
| † | | 5 | CLM | dom | LV Conciencia, Puerto Lleras |

| kHz | N kW | Ctry | Site | Station, location |
|---|---|---|---|---|
| | 100 | CVA | smg | Vatican R., CVA |
| | 250 | CVA | smg | Vatican R., CVA |
| | 100 | UZB | tac | BBC World Service, G |
| **6015** | 100 | CHN | dom | Xinjiang PBS, Urumqi |
| | 100 | KOR | hwa | KBS World R., KOR |
| † | 50 | TZA | dol | Zanzibar Broadcasting Corp., TZA |
| **6020** | 300 | ALB | cer | China R. Int. (CRI), CHN |
| | 100 | CHN | kas | China R. Int. (CRI), CHN |
| | 500 | CHN | szg | China R. Int. (CRI), CHN |
| | 250 | MDG | mdc | R. Tamazuj, SSD |
| | 300 | ROU | gal | R. Romania International, ROU |
| | 100 | STP | sao | VO America (VOA), USA |
| | 20 | VTN | dom | VO Vietnam 1, Buôn Ma Thuôt |
| **6025** | 10 | BOL | dom | Red Patria Nueva, La Paz |
| | 500 | CHN | xia | China R. Int. (CRI), CHN |
| | 100 | CHN | lha | CTB - Holy Tibet, CHN |
| | 100 | CHN | dom | Xizang PBS, Lhasa |
| ‡ | 1 | DOM | dom | R. Amanecer Int., Sto Domingo |
| | 500 | IRN | sir | Pars Today (VOIRI), IRN |
| **6030** | 100 | ARM | erv | Bible Voice Broadcasting (BVB), CAN |
| | 1 | CAF | dom | R. Ndeke Luka, Boali |
| | 1 | CAF | dom | Water for Good R., Boali |
| † | 0.1 | CAN | dom | CFVP Calgary, AB |
| | 30 | CHN | dom | CNR1 VO China, Beijing |
| | 100 | ETH | dom | R. Oromiya, Geja |
| | 250 | IND | dom | AIR, Delhi |
| | 250 | IND | del | R. Sedayee Kashmir, PAK |
| | 90 | ROU | gal | R. Romania International, ROU |
| + | 90 | ROU | gal | R. Romania International, ROU |
| + | 90 | ROU | tig | R. Romania International, ROU |
| | 250 | USA | grv | R. Martí, USA |
| **6035** † | 30 | BTN | dom | Bhutan BS, Thimpu |
| ‡ | 50 | CHN | sha | Yunnan RTV Int., CHN |
| **6040** † | 7.5 | B | dom | R. Evangelizar, Curitiba |
| | 500 | CHN | uru | China R. Int. (CRI), CHN |
| | 500 | CHN | xia | China R. Int. (CRI), CHN |
| | 150 | CHN | dom | CNR2 Business R., Beijing |
| | 50 | CHN | dom | Nei Menggu-Mo, Hohhot |
| | 500 | F | iss | R. Algeriénnne, ALG |
| | 500 | F | iss | R. France Int. (RFI), F |
| | 250 | G | wof | KBS World R., KOR |
| | 500 | IRN | sir | Pars Today (VOIRI), IRN |
| | 300 | ROU | tig | R. Romania International, ROU |
| | 100 | STP | sao | VO America (VOA), USA |
| **6045** | 100 | D | nau | AWR Africa, G |
| | 300 | G | wof | KBS World R., KOR |
| † | 250 | IND | del | All India R. (AIR), IND |
| ± | 10 | KOR | jan | Voice of Freedom, KRE |
| ‡ | 0.45 | MEX | dom | R. Universidad, San Luis Potosí |
| | 300 | TWN | tsh | Furusato no Kaze/Ilbon-e Baram, KRE |
| | 200 | TWN | tsh | National Unity R., KRE |
| **6050** | 100 | CHN | dom | Xizang PBS, Lhasa |
| | 1 | EQU | qui | Vozandes Media, EQA |
| | 1 | LBR | dom | ELWA R., Monrovia |
| ‡ | 50 | MLA | dom | RTM Asyik FM, Kajang |
| | 250 | TUR | emr | Voice of Turkey (VOT), TUR |
| **6055** | 150 | ALB | cer | China R. Int. (CRI), CHN |
| | 100 | CHN | nnn | China R. Int. (CRI), CHN |
| | 125 | D | nau | Ev. Missions-Gemeinden, D |
| | 50 | J | dom | R. Nikkei 1, Tokyo |
| | 100 | MDG | mdc | AWR Africa, G |
| **6060** | 10 | B | dom | Super R. Deus é Amor, Curitiba |
| | 150 | CHN | kun | China R. Int. (CRI), CHN |

| kHz | N kW | Ctry | Site | Station, location |
|---|---|---|---|---|
| | 15 | CHN | dom | Sichuan PBS, Xichang |
| | 100 | CUB | hab | R. Habana Cuba, CUB |
| | 250 | D | nau | Missionswerk Friedensstimme, D |
| | 500 | F | iss | R. Algeriénnne, ALG |
| | 500 | IRN | zah | Pars Today (VOIRI), IRN |
| | 250 | KWT | kwt | RFE/RL, USA |
| **6065** | 100 | CHN | kas | China R. Int. (CRI), CHN |
| | 150 | CHN | dom | CNR2 Business R., Beijing |
| | 100 | MDG | mdc | AWR Africa, G |
| | 100 | ZMB | luv | Voice of Hope - Africa, ZMB |
| **6070** | 100 | AUT | mos | R. DARC, D |
| † | 1 | CAN | dom | CFRX Toronto, ON |
| | 500 | CHN | bei | China R. Int. (CRI), CHN |
| | 500 | CHN | xia | China R. Int. (CRI), CHN |
| † | 5 | D | rob | Channel 292, D |
| | 1 | D | rob | Isle of Music/Melting Pot, USA |
| | 5 | D | rob | Italian Broadcasting Corp., I |
| | 1 | D | rob | R. DARC, D |
| | 300 | J | yam | Shiokaze, KRE |
| | 200 | KRE | kng | Voice of Korea, KRE |
| | 500 | TUR | emr | Voice of Turkey (VOT), TUR |
| **6075** | 100 | CHN | kas | China R. Int. (CRI), CHN |
| | 500 | IRN | sir | Pars Today (VOIRI), IRN |
| | 300 | J | yam | R. Japan (NHK World), J |
| | 100 | TWN | kou | R. Taiwan International, TWN |
| **6080** | 10 | B | dom | R. Marumby, Curitiba |
| | 500 | CHN | bei | China R. Int. (CRI), CHN |
| | 100 | CHN | dom | CNR1 VO China, Golmud |
| | 7 | CHN | dom | Hulun Buir PBS, Hailar |
| | 100 | STP | sao | VO America (VOA), USA |
| **6085** | 1 | D | kll | R. Mi Amigo Int., E |
| † | 10 | IND | dom | AIR, Gangtok |
| | 500 | IRN | sir | Pars Today (VOIRI), IRN |
| **6090** † | 100 | AIA | aia | University Network, USA |
| | 150 | CHN | kun | China R. Int. (CRI), CHN |
| | 500 | CHN | uru | China R. Int. (CRI), CHN |
| | 500 | CHN | xia | China R. Int. (CRI), CHN |
| | 100 | CHN | dom | CNR2 Business R., Golmud |
| | 100 | ETH | dom | Amhara R., Geja |
| | 500 | IRN | sir | Pars Today (VOIRI), IRN |
| | 300 | J | yam | R. Japan (NHK World), J |
| † | 10 | NIG | dom | FRCN, Kaduna |
| | 250 | OMA | sla | BBC World Service, G |
| **6095** | 500 | CHN | kas | China R. Int. (CRI), CHN |
| | 100 | KOR | kim | KBS World R., KOR |
| | 250 | KOR | kim | KBS World R., KOR |
| | 250 | OMA | sla | BBC World Service, G |
| **6100** † | 100 | AFG | kab | R.Television Afghanistan (RTA), AFG |
| | 100 | AFG | kab | R.Television Afghanistan (RTA), AFG |
| | 500 | CHN | bei | China R. Int. (CRI), CHN |
| | 150 | CHN | kun | China R. Int. (CRI), CHN |
| | 100 | CHN | uru | China R. Int. (CRI), CHN |
| | 500 | CHN | uru | China R. Int. (CRI), CHN |
| | 500 | CHN | xia | China R. Int. (CRI), CHN |
| | 100 | CUB | hab | R. Habana Cuba, CUB |
| | 300 | G | wof | BBC World Service, G |
| | 250 | IND | dom | AIR, Delhi |
| | 250 | IND | del | R. Sedayee Kashmir, PAK |
| | 125 | KRE | dom | KCBS, Kanggye |
| | 300 | ROU | tig | R. Romania International, ROU |
| **6105** † | 10 | BOL | dom | R. Panamericana, La Paz |
| | 500 | CHN | szg | China R. Int. (CRI), CHN |
| | 500 | F | iss | R. Algeriénnne, ALG |

| kHz | N kW | Ctry | Site | Station, location |
|---|---|---|---|---|
| | 500 | F | iss | R. Japan (NHK World), J |
| | ‡ 0.25 | MEX | dom | Candela FM, Mérida |
| | 100 | TWN | kou | R. Taiwan International, TWN |
| | 50 | TWN | kou | R. Taiwan International, TWN |
| 6110 | 500 | CHN | xia | China R. Int. (CRI), CHN |
| | 100 | CHN | lha | CTB - Holy Tibet, CHN |
| | 100 | CHN | dom | Xizang PBS, Lhasa |
| | 100 | ETH | dom | R. Fana, Geja |
| | ‡ 50 | IND | dom | AIR, Kashmir, Srinagar |
| | 500 | IRN | sir | Pars Today (VOIRI), IRN |
| | 300 | J | yam | Shiokaze, KRE |
| 6115 | 500 | CHN | bei | China R. Int. (CRI), CHN |
| | † 50 | COG | dom | R. Congo, Brazzaville |
| | 50 | J | dom | R. Nikkei 2, Tokyo |
| | 250 | PHL | pht | Vatican R., CVA |
| | 100 | USA | wcr | WWCR, USA |
| 6120 | ‡ 10 | B | dom | Super R. Deus é Amor, São Paulo |
| | 100 | CHN | dom | Xinjiang PBS, Urumqi |
| | 100 | D | nau | AWR Africa, G |
| | ‡ 250 | MRA | tin | R. Free Asia (RFA), USA |
| | 50 | SWZ | man | TWR Africa, AFS |
| | 500 | TUR | emr | Voice of Turkey (VOT), TUR |
| 6125 | 100 | CHN | dom | CNR1 VO China, Beijing |
| | 100 | CHN | dom | CNR1 VO China, Shijiazhuang |
| | ‡ 10 | INS | dom | RRI, Nabire |
| | 500 | TUR | emr | Voice of Turkey (VOT), TUR |
| 6130 | 100 | CHN | lha | CTB - Holy Tibet, CHN |
| | 100 | CHN | dom | Xizang PBS, Lhasa |
| | 50 | LAO | vie | Lao National R., LAO |
| | 50 | LAO | dom | R. Nationale Lao, Vientiane |
| | 300 | ROU | gal | R. Romania International, ROU |
| | 100 | SWZ | man | TWR Africa, AFS |
| 6135 | 250 | ASC | asc | BBC World Service, G |
| | 10 | BOL | dom | R. Santa Cruz, Santa Cruz |
| | 500 | CHN | bei | China R. Int. (CRI), CHN |
| | 100 | CHN | xia | China R. Int. (CRI), CHN |
| | 250 | G | wof | BBC World Service, G |
| | 500 | IRN | sir | Pars Today (VOIRI), IRN |
| | † 30 | MDG | dom | R. Nal Malagasy, Ambohidrano |
| 6140 | 100 | CHN | kas | China R. Int. (CRI), CHN |
| | 100 | CHN | kun | China R. Int. (CRI), CHN |
| | 250 | IND | alg | All India R. (AIR), IND |
| 6145 | 150 | CHN | bei | China R. Int. (CRI), CHN |
| | 100 | CHN | dom | CNR17 Kazakh Sce, Lingshi |
| | † 50 | CHN | dom | Qinghai PBS, Xining |
| | 100 | D | nau | Bible Voice Broadcasting (BVB), CAN |
| | 250 | OMA | sla | BBC World Service, G |
| | 250 | PHL | pht | Vatican R., CVA |
| | 300 | ROU | gal | R. Romania International, ROU |
| | 100 | TWN | kou | R. Taiwan International, TWN |
| | 250 | UAE | dha | BBC World Service, G |
| 6150 | 500 | CHN | szg | China R. Int. (CRI), CHN |
| | 0.25 | D | dat | Europa 24, D |
| | 250 | THA | udo | VO America (VOA), USA |
| 6155 | 250 | AFS | mey | Channel Africa, AFS |
| | 300 | AUT | mos | R. Japan (NHK World), J |
| | 300 | AUT | mos | R. Ö1 (ORF), AUT |
| | 500 | CHN | bei | China R. Int. (CRI), CHN |
| | 150 | CHN | dom | CNR2 Business R., Beijing |
| | 500 | IRN | sir | Pars Today (VOIRI), IRN |
| | 100 | KOR | kim | KBS World R., KOR |
| | 300 | ROU | gal | R. Romania International, ROU |
| | 300 | TWN | tsh | Furusato no Kaze/Ilbon-e Baram, KRE |

| kHz | N kW | Ctry | Site | Station, location |
|---|---|---|---|---|
| | 100 | UZB | tac | R. Japan (NHK World), J |
| 6160 | † 10 | B | dom | R. Boa Vontade, Porto Alegre |
| | 500 | CHN | xia | China R. Int. (CRI), CHN |
| | 1 | D | wis | Shortwaveradio, D |
| 6165 | 50 | BRM | dom | Thazin R., Pyin U Lwin |
| | 250 | CHN | bei | China R. Int. (CRI), CHN |
| | 500 | CHN | uru | China R. Int. (CRI), CHN |
| | 100 | CHN | dom | CNR6 VO Shenzhou, Beijing |
| | 100 | CUB | hab | R. Habana Cuba, CUB |
| | 125 | D | nau | R. Japan (NHK World), J |
| | 500 | F | iss | R. Japan (NHK World), J |
| | ‡ 100 | TCD | dom | ONRTV, N'Djamena-Gredia |
| | 100 | UZB | tac | R. Japan (NHK World), J |
| | 50 | VTN | dom | VO Vietnam Min, Xuan Mai |
| 6170 | 250 | ASC | asc | VO America (VOA), USA |
| | 300 | AUT | mos | Adventist World R. (AWR), USA |
| | 500 | F | iss | R. Algeriénnne, ALG |
| | 0.1 | FIN | vir | Scandinavian Weekend R., FIN |
| | 200 | KRE | kuj | Voice of Korea, KRE |
| | 300 | ROU | tig | R. Romania International, ROU |
| 6174 | 1 | PRU | dom | R. Tawantinsuyo, Cusco |
| 6175 | 150 | ALB | cer | China R. Int. (CRI), CHN |
| | 100 | BOT | bot | VOA Studio 7, USA |
| | 100 | CHN | nnn | China R. Int. (CRI), CHN |
| | 100 | CHN | dom | CNR1 VO China, Beijing |
| 6180 | ‡ 25 | B | dom | R. Nac. da Amazônia, Brasília |
| | 100 | CHN | kas | China R. Int. (CRI), CHN |
| | 100 | CHN | kun | China R. Int. (CRI), CHN |
| | 150 | CHN | kun | China R. Int. (CRI), CHN |
| | 500 | CHN | uru | China R. Int. (CRI), CHN |
| | 100 | CHN | dom | CNR17 Kazakh Sce, Lingshi |
| | 250 | CUB | qvc | China R. Int. (CRI), CHN |
| | 10 | D | pin | Deutscher Wetterdienst (DWD), D |
| | 100 | MDG | mwv | Madagascar World Voice, MDG |
| | + 90 | ROU | tig | R. Romania International, ROU |
| | 300 | TWN | tsh | R. Taiwan International, TWN |
| | 250 | UAE | dha | BBC World Service, G |
| | 250 | UAE | dha | IBRA Media, S |
| 6185 | 150 | ALB | cer | China R. Int. (CRI), CHN |
| | 300 | AUT | mos | Adventist World R. (AWR), USA |
| | 15 | CHN | dom | China Huayi BC, Fuzhou |
| | 500 | CHN | xia | China R. Int. (CRI), CHN |
| | 100 | CVA | smg | Vatican R., CVA |
| | 250 | CVA | smg | Vatican R., CVA |
| | 200 | KRE | kuj | Voice of Korea, KRE |
| | 10 | MEX | dom | Señal Cultura México, México |
| | 500 | TUR | emr | Voice of Turkey (VOT), TUR |
| 6190 | 100 | AFS | mey | BBC World Service, G |
| | 500 | CHN | bei | China R. Int. (CRI), CHN |
| | 100 | CHN | dom | CNR2 Business R., Golmud |
| | 50 | CHN | dom | Xinjiang PBS, Urumqi |
| | 1 | D | goh | Hamburger LokalR., D |
| | 1 | D | goh | World of Radio, USA |
| | 500 | IRN | sir | Pars Today (VOIRI), IRN |
| | 300 | J | yam | R. Japan (NHK World), J |
| | 100 | MDG | mwv | Madagascar World Voice, MDG |
| 6195 | 100 | BOT | bot | VO America (VOA), USA |
| | 250 | BUL | sof | BBC World Service, G |
| | 250 | OMA | sla | BBC World Service, G |
| | 250 | SNG | sng | BBC World Service, G |
| | 100 | STP | sao | VO America (VOA), USA |
| | 250 | USA | hri | R. Japan (NHK World), J |
| 6200 | 100 | CHN | lha | CTB - Holy Tibet, CHN |

| kHz | N | kW | Ctry | Site | Station, location |
|---|---|---|---|---|---|
| | | 50 | CHN | dom | VO Jinling, Nanjing |
| | | 100 | CHN | dom | Xizang PBS, Lhasa |
| 6210 | † | 1 | COD | dom | R. Kahuzi, Bukavu |
| 6230 | ± | 1 | TWN | ust | Sound of Hope, CHN |
| 6240 | | 100 | UZB | tac | TWR India, IND |
| 6250 | ‡ | 20 | GNE | dom | Rdif Guinea Ecuatorial, Malabo |
| | | 10 | KOR | nwn | Echo of Hope (VOH), KRE |
| | | 100 | KRE | pyo | Echo of Unification, KOR |
| 6260 | | 100 | UZB | tac | Bible Voice Broadcasting (BVB), CAN |
| 6280 | ± | 1 | TWN | ust | Sound of Hope, CHN |
| 6350 | | 100 | KOR | jnm | Echo of Hope (VOH), KRE |
| 6370 | ± | 1 | TWN | ust | Sound of Hope, CHN |
| 6400 | | 50 | KRE | kng | Pyongyang Broadcasting Stn., KRE |
| 6520 | | 50 | KOR | goy | Voice of the People, KRE |
| 6600 | | 50 | KOR | goy | Voice of the People, KRE |
| 6730 | ± | 1 | TWN | ust | Sound of Hope, CHN |
| 6870 | ± | 1 | TWN | ust | Sound of Hope, CHN |
| 6900 | ± | 1 | TWN | ust | Sound of Hope, CHN |
| 6970 | ± | 1 | TWN | ust | Sound of Hope, CHN |
| 7120 | † | 100 | SOM | dom | R. Hargeisa |
| 7140 | † | 100 | ERI | dom | VO Broad Masses 1, Asmara |
| 7180 | † | 100 | ERI | dom | VO Broad Masses 2, Asmara |
| 7200 | | 50 | BRM | dom | Myanma R., Yangon |
| 7205 | | 100 | AFS | mey | Amateur R. Today, AFS |
| | | 150 | CHN | bei | China R. Int. (CRI), CHN |
| | | 500 | CHN | bei | China R. Int. (CRI), CHN |
| | | 100 | CHN | kas | China R. Int. (CRI), CHN |
| | | 500 | CHN | xia | China R. Int. (CRI), CHN |
| | | 100 | CHN | dom | Xinjiang PBS, Urumqi |
| | | 100 | D | nau | AWR Africa, G |
| | | 500 | F | iss | R. France Int. (RFI), F |
| | † | 100 | SDN | dom | SRTC, Khartoum |
| 7210 | | 150 | ALB | cer | China R. Int. (CRI), CHN |
| | | 150 | CHN | bei | China R. Int. (CRI), CHN |
| | | 100 | CHN | uru | China R. Int. (CRI), CHN |
| | | 500 | CHN | uru | China R. Int. (CRI), CHN |
| | | 20 | CHN | dom | Yunnan PBS, Kunming |
| | | 200 | KRE | kuj | Voice of Korea, KRE |
| | ± | 1 | TWN | ust | Sound of Hope, CHN |
| | | 20 | VTN | dom | VO Vietnam 1, Buôn Ma Thuôt |
| 7215 | | 150 | ALB | cer | China R. Int. (CRI), CHN |
| | | 500 | CHN | bei | China R. Int. (CRI), CHN |
| | | 500 | CHN | kun | China R. Int. (CRI), CHN |
| | | 500 | CHN | szg | China R. Int. (CRI), CHN |
| | | 500 | CHN | xia | China R. Int. (CRI), CHN |
| | | 100 | CHN | dom | CNR1 VO China, Shijiazhuang |
| | | 250 | KOR | kim | KBS World R., KOR |
| 7220 | | 150 | ALB | cer | China R. Int. (CRI), CHN |
| | | 10 | CAF | dom | R. Centrafrique, Bangui |
| | | 500 | CHN | jin | China R. Int. (CRI), CHN |
| | | 500 | CHN | xia | China R. Int. (CRI), CHN |
| | | 100 | CHN | dom | CNR2 Business R., Golmud |
| | | 100 | D | nau | Bible Voice Broadcasting (BVB), CAN |
| | | 250 | F | iss | AWR Africa, G |
| | | 500 | F | iss | R. Taiwan International, TWN |
| | | 200 | KRE | kuj | Voice of Korea, KRE |
| | | 300 | ROU | gal | R. Romania International, ROU |
| | | 100 | STP | sao | Deutsche Welle, D |
| | | 100 | VTN | vni | Voice of Vietnam (VOV), VTN |
| 7225 | | 300 | AUT | mos | AWR Africa, G |
| | | 500 | CHN | bei | China R. Int. (CRI), CHN |
| | | 500 | CHN | uru | China R. Int. (CRI), CHN |
| | | 10 | CHN | dom | Sichuan PBS, Chengdu |
| | | 100 | D | bib | VO America (VOA), USA |
| | | 500 | IRN | sir | Pars Today (VOIRI), IRN |
| 7230 | | 100 | AFS | mey | Channel Africa, AFS |
| | | 100 | CHN | dom | CNR1 VO China, Xi'an |
| | | 50 | CHN | dom | Xinjiang PBS, Urumqi |
| | | 100 | CVA | smg | Vatican R., CVA |
| | ‡ | 50 | IND | dom | AIR, Kurseong |
| | | 500 | IRN | sir | Pars Today (VOIRI), IRN |
| 7235 | | 100 | CHN | kas | China R. Int. (CRI), CHN |
| | | 500 | CHN | kas | China R. Int. (CRI), CHN |
| | | 250 | CVA | smg | Vatican R., CVA |
| | | 150 | F | iss | R. Nigeria Kaduna, NIG |
| | | 200 | KRE | kuj | Voice of Korea, KRE |
| | | 300 | ROU | tig | R. Romania International, ROU |
| 7237 | ±† | 100 | ETH | gjw | R. Ethiopia (EBC), ETH |
| 7240 | | 500 | ARS | riy | Saudi R. Int. (SBA), ARS |
| | | 100 | CHN | kas | China R. Int. (CRI), CHN |
| | | 100 | CHN | dom | Xizang PBS, Lhasa |
| | | 500 | TUR | emr | Voice of Turkey (VOT), TUR |
| 7245 | | 150 | CHN | bji | China R. Int. (CRI), CHN |
| | | 500 | CHN | kas | China R. Int. (CRI), CHN |
| | | 500 | CHN | xia | China R. Int. (CRI), CHN |
| | | 150 | CHN | dom | CNR2 Business R., Beijing |
| | | 500 | F | iss | R. France Int. (RFI), F |
| | | 300 | J | yam | Shiokaze, KRE |
| | | 300 | MDA | kch | TWR Africa, AFS |
| | | 100 | TJK | dsb | Voice of Tajik (Ovozi Tojik), TJK |
| | | 250 | TUR | emr | Voice of Turkey (VOT), TUR |
| | | 250 | UAE | dha | TWR Africa, AFS |
| 7250 | | 250 | BGD | dka | Bangladesh Betar, BGD |
| | | 100 | CHN | kas | China R. Int. (CRI), CHN |
| | | 500 | CHN | uru | China R. Int. (CRI), CHN |
| | | 250 | CVA | smg | Vatican R., CVA |
| | | 100 | IND | dom | AIR, Delhi |
| | ‡ | 100 | IND | del | All India R. (AIR), IND |
| | | 250 | KWT | kbd | R.Kuwait, KWT |
| | | 250 | PHL | pht | Vatican R., CVA |
| 7255 | | 150 | CHN | bei | China R. Int. (CRI), CHN |
| | | 150 | CHN | bji | China R. Int. (CRI), CHN |
| | | 500 | CHN | kas | China R. Int. (CRI), CHN |
| | | 500 | CHN | kun | China R. Int. (CRI), CHN |
| | | 500 | CHN | szg | China R. Int. (CRI), CHN |
| | | 500 | CHN | xia | China R. Int. (CRI), CHN |
| | | 100 | CHN | dom | CNR2 Business R., Baoji |
| | | 100 | CHN | lha | CTB - Holy Tibet, CHN |
| | | 100 | CHN | dom | Xizang PBS, Lhasa |
| | | 250 | NIG | aja | Voice of Nigeria, NIG |
| 7260 | | 100 | AFS | mey | Channel Africa, AFS |
| | | 100 | CHN | kas | China R. Int. (CRI), CHN |
| | | 500 | CHN | uru | China R. Int. (CRI), CHN |
| | | 500 | CHN | xia | China R. Int. (CRI), CHN |
| | | 100 | CHN | dom | Xinjiang PBS, Urumqi |
| | | 500 | IRN | sir | Pars Today (VOIRI), IRN |
| | † | 50 | MNG | dom | Mongolian R. 3, Ulaanbaatar |
| | ‡ | 1 | VUT | dom | R. Vanuatu, Port Vila |
| 7265 | | 500 | CHN | bei | China R. Int. (CRI), CHN |
| | | 100 | CHN | kas | China R. Int. (CRI), CHN |
| | | 500 | CHN | kun | China R. Int. (CRI), CHN |
| | | 500 | CHN | uru | China R. Int. (CRI), CHN |
| | † | 100 | CHN | dom | CNR2 Business R., Baoji |
| | | 1 | D | goh | Hamburger LokalR., D |
| | | 1 | D | goh | World of Radio, USA |
| | | 250 | G | wof | BBC World Service, G |

| kHz | N | kW | Ctry | Site | Station, location |
|---|---|---|---|---|---|
| | | 300 | G | wof | BBC World Service, G |
| | ‡ | 100 | PAK | dom | Azad Kashmir R., Islamabad |
| 7270 | | 300 | AUT | mos | AWR Africa, G |
| | | 50 | CHN | dom | Nei Menggu-Mo, Hohhot |
| | | 100 | IND | dom | AIR FM Gold, Chennai |
| | | 100 | IND | cni | All India R. (AIR), IND |
| | | 100 | TWN | tsh | Voice of China, CHN |
| | | 300 | TWN | tsh | Voice of China, CHN |
| 7275 | | 300 | AUT | mos | AWR Africa, G |
| | | 500 | CHN | uru | China R. Int. (CRI), CHN |
| | | 100 | CHN | dom | CNR1 VO China, Beijing |
| | | 7 | CHN | dom | Guizhou PBS, Guiyang |
| | | 100 | CHN | dom | Xinjiang PBS, Urumqi |
| | | 100 | KOR | kim | KBS World R., KOR |
| | | 250 | KOR | kim | KBS World R., KOR |
| | | 100 | STP | sao | VO America (VOA), USA |
| 7280 | | 500 | IRN | sir | Pars Today (VOIRI), IRN |
| | ± | 1 | TWN | ust | Sound of Hope, CHN |
| | | 100 | UZB | tac | TWR India, IND |
| | | 100 | VTN | vni | Voice of Vietnam (VOV), VTN |
| 7285 | | 100 | AFS | dom | R. Sonder Grense, Meyerton |
| | | 150 | ALB | cer | China R. Int. (CRI), CHN |
| | | 500 | CHN | bei | China R. Int. (CRI), CHN |
| | | 100 | CHN | kas | China R. Int. (CRI), CHN |
| | | 500 | CHN | kun | China R. Int. (CRI), CHN |
| | | 500 | CHN | xia | China R. Int. (CRI), CHN |
| | | 250 | OMA | sla | BBC World Service, G |
| | | 100 | VTN | vni | Voice of Vietnam (VOV), VTN |
| 7290 | | 100 | CHN | kas | China R. Int. (CRI), CHN |
| | | 500 | CHN | szg | China R. Int. (CRI), CHN |
| | | 500 | CHN | xia | China R. Int. (CRI), CHN |
| | | 100 | CHN | dom | CNR1 VO China, Beijing |
| | | 100 | D | bib | VOA Ashna R., USA |
| | | 50 | IND | dom | AIR, Thiruvananthapuram |
| | † | 10 | INS | dom | RRI, Nabire |
| | | 100 | ROU | tig | IRRS Shortwave, I |
| | | 300 | TWN | tsh | Furusato no Kaze/Ilbon-e Baram, KRE |
| 7295 | | 500 | CHN | kas | China R. Int. (CRI), CHN |
| | | 100 | CHN | dom | Xinjiang PBS, Urumqi |
| | | 500 | F | iss | R. France Int. (RFI), F |
| | ‡ | 10 | IND | dom | AIR, Aizawl |
| | | 250 | TUR | emr | Voice of Turkey (VOT), TUR |
| | | 300 | TWN | tsh | Furusato no Kaze/Ilbon-e Baram, KRE |
| 7300 | | 100 | CHN | kas | China R. Int. (CRI), CHN |
| | | 500 | CHN | kas | China R. Int. (CRI), CHN |
| | | 500 | CHN | uru | China R. Int. (CRI), CHN |
| | | 250 | G | wof | Reach Beyond, USA |
| | | 100 | SWZ | man | TWR Africa, AFS |
| | | 50 | SWZ | man | TWR Africa, AFS |
| | | 200 | TWN | tsh | R. Taiwan International, TWN |
| | | 300 | TWN | tsh | R. Taiwan International, TWN |
| | | 250 | UAE | dha | BBC World Service, G |
| 7305 | | 250 | ASC | asc | BBC World Service, G |
| | | 150 | CHN | bei | China R. Int. (CRI), CHN |
| | | 500 | CHN | uru | China R. Int. (CRI), CHN |
| | | 100 | CHN | dom | CNR1 VO China, Shijiazhuang |
| | | 500 | IRN | sir | Pars Today (VOIRI), IRN |
| | | 250 | USA | grv | Vatican R., CVA |
| 7310 | | 300 | AUT | mos | AWR Africa, G |
| | | 100 | CHN | dom | Xinjiang PBS, Urumqi |
| | | 1 | D | kll | R. Mi Amigo Int., E |
| | | 500 | IRN | zah | Pars Today (VOIRI), IRN |
| | | 300 | ROU | tig | R. Romania International, ROU |

| kHz | N | kW | Ctry | Site | Station, location |
|---|---|---|---|---|---|
| | ± | 1 | TWN | ust | Sound of Hope, CHN |
| 7315 | | 500 | CHN | kas | China R. Int. (CRI), CHN |
| | | 100 | CHN | kun | China R. Int. (CRI), CHN |
| | | 500 | CHN | kun | China R. Int. (CRI), CHN |
| | | 150 | CHN | dom | CNR2 Business R., Xi'an |
| | | 250 | CVA | smg | R. Tamazuj, SSD |
| | | 125 | D | nau | Dandal Kura R. Int., NIG |
| | | 500 | F | iss | R. Algeriénnne, ALG |
| | | 250 | F | iss | R. Dabanga, SDN |
| | | 50 | IND | dom | AIR, Shillong |
| | | 250 | USA | hri | Voice of Vietnam (VOV), VTN |
| | | 250 | USA | hri | WHRI - World Harvest R., USA |
| | + | 15 | USA | inb | WINB, USA |
| 7320 | | 100 | ALS | nls | KNLS International, ALS |
| | | 500 | CHN | kun | China R. Int. (CRI), CHN |
| | | 250 | UAE | dha | FEBA Pakistan, PAK |
| 7325 | | 125 | ASC | asc | BBC World Service, G |
| | | 500 | CHN | bei | China R. Int. (CRI), CHN |
| | | 500 | CHN | jin | China R. Int. (CRI), CHN |
| | | 100 | CHN | kas | China R. Int. (CRI), CHN |
| | | 150 | CHN | kun | China R. Int. (CRI), CHN |
| | | 500 | CHN | kun | China R. Int. (CRI), CHN |
| | | 500 | CHN | szg | China R. Int. (CRI), CHN |
| | | 500 | CHN | uru | China R. Int. (CRI), CHN |
| | | 500 | CHN | xia | China R. Int. (CRI), CHN |
| | | 100 | D | nau | Bible Voice Broadcasting (BVB), CAN |
| | | 200 | G | wof | BBC World Service, G |
| | | 50 | IND | dom | AIR, Jaipur |
| | | 1 | PNG | dom | Wantok R. Light, Port Moresby |
| | | 300 | ROU | gal | R. Romania International, ROU |
| | | 300 | ROU | tig | R. Romania International, ROU |
| 7330 | | 100 | AUT | mos | R. Joystick, D |
| | | 500 | CHN | kas | China R. Int. (CRI), CHN |
| | | 500 | CHN | xia | China R. Int. (CRI), CHN |
| | | 300 | ROU | tig | R. Romania International, ROU |
| 7335 | | 500 | CHN | bei | China R. Int. (CRI), CHN |
| | | 500 | CHN | jin | China R. Int. (CRI), CHN |
| | | 500 | CHN | szg | China R. Int. (CRI), CHN |
| | | 100 | CHN | dom | CNR2 Business R., Baoji |
| | | 150 | F | iss | R. Nigeria Kaduna, NIG |
| 7340 | | 100 | ALS | nls | KNLS International, ALS |
| | | 500 | CHN | kas | China R. Int. (CRI), CHN |
| | | 100 | CHN | dom | Xinjiang PBS, Urumqi |
| | | 100 | IND | dom | AIR, Mumbai |
| | | 100 | IND | mum | All India R. (AIR), IND |
| | | 300 | ROU | tig | R. Romania International, ROU |
| 7345 | | 150 | ALB | cer | China R. Int. (CRI), CHN |
| | | 125 | ASC | asc | BBC World Service, G |
| | | 50 | BRM | dom | Thazin R., Pyin U Lwin |
| | | 500 | CHN | kas | China R. Int. (CRI), CHN |
| | | 100 | CHN | dom | CNR1 VO China, Beijing |
| | | 250 | G | wof | BBC World Service, G |
| | | 300 | ROU | tig | R. Romania International, ROU |
| 7350 | | 100 | CHN | kas | China R. Int. (CRI), CHN |
| | | 500 | CHN | kas | China R. Int. (CRI), CHN |
| | | 500 | CHN | uru | China R. Int. (CRI), CHN |
| | | 100 | CHN | dom | CNR11 Tibetan Sce, Xi'an |
| | | 250 | D | nau | AWR Africa, G |
| | + | 300 | ROU | tig | R. Romania International, ROU |
| 7355 | | 100 | ALS | nls | KNLS International, ALS |
| | | 500 | IRN | sir | Pars Today (VOIRI), IRN |
| | | 250 | SNG | sng | BBC World Service, G |
| | | 250 | USA | grv | R. Martí, USA |

# SW Stations of the World · FREQUENCY LISTS

| kHz | N | kW | Ctry | Site | Station, location |
|---|---|---|---|---|---|
| 7360 | | 150 | ALB | cer | China R. Int. (CRI), CHN |
| | | 100 | CHN | kas | China R. Int. (CRI), CHN |
| | | 100 | CHN | kun | China R. Int. (CRI), CHN |
| | | 100 | CHN | dom | CNR11 Tibetan Sce, Xi'an |
| | | 100 | CVA | smg | Vatican R., CVA |
| | | 250 | CVA | smg | Vatican R., CVA |
| | | 500 | IRN | sir | Pars Today (VOIRI), IRN |
| | | 300 | ROU | gal | R. Romania International, ROU |
| 7365 | | 500 | CHN | bei | China R. Int. (CRI), CHN |
| | | 100 | CHN | dom | CNR1 VO China, Shijiazhuang |
| | | 100 | CVA | smg | Vatican R., CVA |
| | | 250 | CVA | smg | Vatican R., CVA |
| | | 100 | D | nau | Bible Voice Broadcasting (BVB), CAN |
| | | 3 | D | wnm | R.HCJB Deutschland, D |
| | | 250 | USA | grv | R. Martí, USA |
| 7370 | | 100 | ALS | nls | KNLS International, ALS |
| | | 100 | CHN | kas | China R. Int. (CRI), CHN |
| | | 100 | CHN | nnn | China R. Int. (CRI), CHN |
| | | 150 | CHN | dom | CNR2 Business R., Beijing |
| | | 500 | IRN | sir | Pars Today (VOIRI), IRN |
| | | 300 | ROU | gal | R. Romania International, ROU |
| 7375 | | 150 | CHN | dom | CNR2 Business R., Beijing |
| | | 250 | F | iss | AWR Africa, G |
| | | 500 | F | iss | R. Algeriénnne, ALG |
| | | 500 | IRN | sir | Pars Today (VOIRI), IRN |
| | | 300 | ROU | gal | R. Romania International, ROU |
| | | 250 | USA | grv | R. Martí, USA |
| 7380 | | 150 | ALB | cer | China R. Int. (CRI), CHN |
| | | 500 | F | iss | R. France Int. (RFI), F |
| | | 100 | GUM | sda | Adventist World R. (AWR), USA |
| | | 50 | IND | dom | AIR, Chennai |
| ‡ | | 100 | IND | del | All India R. (AIR), IND |
| | | 500 | IRN | zah | Pars Today (VOIRI), IRN |
| 7385 | | 150 | ALB | cer | China R. Int. (CRI), CHN |
| | | 500 | CHN | kas | China R. Int. (CRI), CHN |
| | | 100 | CHN | dom | CNR5 Vo Zhonghua, Beijing |
| | | 100 | CHN | lha | CTB - Holy Tibet, CHN |
| | | 100 | CHN | dom | Xizang PBS, Lhasa |
| | | 100 | USA | hri | WHRI - World Harvest R., USA |
| 7390 | | 150 | CHN | bei | China R. Int. (CRI), CHN |
| | | 100 | CHN | huh | China R. Int. (CRI), CHN |
| | | 500 | CHN | jin | China R. Int. (CRI), CHN |
| | | 500 | CHN | xia | China R. Int. (CRI), CHN |
| | | 500 | F | iss | R. France Int. (RFI), F |
| | | 8 | IND | dom | AIR, Port Blair |
| | | 500 | IRN | sir | Pars Today (VOIRI), IRN |
| | | 50 | NZL | ran | RNZI (RNZ Pacific), NZL |
| 7395 | | 250 | AFS | mey | BBC World Service, G |
| | | 500 | CHN | kas | China R. Int. (CRI), CHN |
| | | 500 | CHN | kun | China R. Int. (CRI), CHN |
| | | 500 | CHN | uru | China R. Int. (CRI), CHN |
| | | 500 | CHN | xia | China R. Int. (CRI), CHN |
| | | 150 | CHN | dom | CNR2 Business R., Xianyang |
| 7400 | | 100 | CHN | kun | China R. Int. (CRI), CHN |
| | | 500 | CHN | xia | China R. Int. (CRI), CHN |
| 7405 | | 500 | CHN | bei | China R. Int. (CRI), CHN |
| | | 500 | CHN | kun | China R. Int. (CRI), CHN |
| | | 250 | OMA | sla | BBC World Service, G |
| 7410 | | 500 | CHN | bei | China R. Int. (CRI), CHN |
| | | 500 | CHN | jin | China R. Int. (CRI), CHN |
| | | 100 | CHN | kas | China R. Int. (CRI), CHN |
| | | 500 | CHN | szg | China R. Int. (CRI), CHN |
| | | 250 | CVA | smg | Vatican R., CVA |

| kHz | N | kW | Ctry | Site | Station, location |
|---|---|---|---|---|---|
| | | 500 | F | iss | R. Japan (NHK World), J |
| | | 100 | PHL | boc | FEBC Philippines, PHL |
| | | 300 | ROU | gal | R. Romania International, ROU |
| | | 300 | ROU | tig | R. Romania International, ROU |
| 7415 | | 100 | CHN | huh | China R. Int. (CRI), CHN |
| | | 500 | CHN | kas | China R. Int. (CRI), CHN |
| | | 500 | CHN | uru | China R. Int. (CRI), CHN |
| | | 500 | CHN | xia | China R. Int. (CRI), CHN |
| ‡ | | 250 | MRA | tin | R. Free Asia (RFA), USA |
| 7420 | | 150 | CHN | kun | China R. Int. (CRI), CHN |
| | | 500 | CHN | uru | China R. Int. (CRI), CHN |
| | | 100 | CHN | dom | Nei Menggu-Ch, Hohhot |
| | | 50 | IND | dom | AIR, Hyderabad |
| 7425 | | 100 | ARS | riy | Saudi R. Int. (SBA), ARS |
| | | 100 | CHN | kas | China R. Int. (CRI), CHN |
| | | 150 | CHN | dom | CNR2 Business R., Xianyang |
| | | 300 | G | wof | Follow The Bible Ministries, USA |
| | | 500 | IRN | sir | Pars Today (VOIRI), IRN |
| 7430 | | 500 | CHN | jin | China R. Int. (CRI), CHN |
| | | 100 | CHN | nnn | China R. Int. (CRI), CHN |
| | | 300 | G | wof | BBC World Service, G |
| | | 50 | IND | dom | AIR, Bhopal |
| | | 500 | IRN | sir | Pars Today (VOIRI), IRN |
| 7435 | | 100 | AUT | mos | Bible Voice Broadcasting (BVB), CAN |
| | | 500 | CHN | bei | China R. Int. (CRI), CHN |
| | | 500 | CHN | jin | China R. Int. (CRI), CHN |
| | | 500 | CHN | kun | China R. Int. (CRI), CHN |
| | | 500 | CHN | szg | China R. Int. (CRI), CHN |
| | | 500 | CHN | xia | China R. Int. (CRI), CHN |
| | | 500 | IRN | sir | Pars Today (VOIRI), IRN |
| | | 250 | PHL | pht | Vatican R., CVA |
| | | 250 | USA | grv | R. Martí, USA |
| 7440 | | 500 | CHN | bei | China R. Int. (CRI), CHN |
| | | 500 | CHN | jin | China R. Int. (CRI), CHN |
| | | 100 | CHN | nnn | China R. Int. (CRI), CHN |
| † | | 5 | D | rob | Channel 292, D |
| 7445 | | 300 | ARM | erv | BBC World Service, G |
| | | 500 | CHN | kun | China R. Int. (CRI), CHN |
| | | 500 | CHN | uru | China R. Int. (CRI), CHN |
| | | 250 | G | wof | BBC World Service, G |
| | | 250 | MDG | mdc | BBC World Service, G |
| | | 250 | OMA | sla | BBC World Service, G |
| | | 250 | THA | udo | VO America (VOA), USA |
| 7450 | | 100 | CHN | dom | Xizang PBS, Lhasa |
| | | 500 | F | iss | R. Japan (NHK World), J |
| 7455 | | 100 | BOT | bot | VO America (VOA), USA |
| | | 100 | F | iss | Dandal Kura R. Int., NIG |
| 7460 | | 100 | BOT | bot | VO America (VOA), USA |
| | | 250 | PHL | pht | VO America (VOA), USA |
| ± | | 1 | TWN | ust | Sound of Hope, CHN |
| 7465 | | 250 | PHL | pht | VO America (VOA), USA |
| | | 250 | SNG | sng | BBC World Service, G |
| 7470 | | 100 | D | lam | VOA Deewa R., USA |
| | | 250 | THA | udo | VO America (VOA), USA |
| | | 250 | TJK | dsb | R. Free Asia (RFA), USA |
| 7475 | | 250 | THA | udo | R. Thailand World Service, THA |
| | | 250 | THA | udo | RFE/RL, USA |
| 7480 | | 250 | KWT | kwt | R. Free Asia (RFA), USA |
| | | 250 | PHL | pht | VO America (VOA), USA |
| 7485 | | 100 | D | bib | VO America (VOA), USA |
| | | 100 | D | lam | VO America (VOA), USA |
| | | 300 | MDA | kch | BBC World Service, G |
| ‡ | | 250 | MRA | tin | R. Free Asia (RFA), USA |

| kHz | N kW | Ctry | Site | Station, location |
|---|---|---|---|---|
| | 250 | PHL | pht | Vatican R., CVA |
| | 250 | SNG | sng | BBC World Service, G |
| 7488 | ± 100 | TJK | dsb | Voice of Tibet, CHN |
| 7490 | 50 | USA | bcq | Isle of Music/Melting Pot, USA |
| | 50 | USA | bcq | The Overcomer Ministry, USA |
| | † 50 | USA | bcq | WBCQ, USA |
| | 50 | USA | bcq | World of Radio, USA |
| | 100 | USA | wcr | WWCR, USA |
| 7495 | 100 | D | bib | VOA Deewa R., USA |
| | 250 | KWT | kwt | VOA Ashna R., USA |
| | 250 | THA | udo | VOA Ashna R., USA |
| | 250 | THA | udo | VOA Deewa R., USA |
| | 100 | UZB | tac | North Korea Reform R., KRE |
| 7500 | 200 | GUM | twr | TWR Asia, SNG |
| 7505 | 100 | IND | dom | AIR, Delhi |
| | † 50 | USA | rno | WRNO Worldwide, USA |
| | 100 | UZB | tac | TWR India, IND |
| | ± 100 | UZB | tac | VO the Martyrs Korea, KRE |
| 7510 | 100 | GUM | twr | TWR Asia, SNG |
| | 200 | GUM | twr | TWR Asia, SNG |
| 7520 | 100 | D | lam | R. Free Asia (RFA), USA |
| | † 250 | IND | del | All India R. (AIR), IND |
| | 250 | KWT | kwt | R. Free Asia (RFA), USA |
| | ‡ 250 | MRA | tin | R. Free Asia (RFA), USA |
| | 100 | USA | wcr | WWCR, USA |
| 7530 | 100 | AUS | knx | Reach Beyond Australia, AUS |
| | 250 | KWT | kwt | VOA Deewa R., USA |
| | 100 | TWN | pao | Suab Xaa Moo Zoo, USA |
| 7535 | 300 | MDA | kch | TWR India, IND |
| 7540 | 250 | KWT | kwt | R. Free Asia (RFA), USA |
| | 200 | TJK | dsb | R. Free Asia (RFA), USA |
| 7545 | 250 | PHL | pht | VO America (VOA), USA |
| | 200 | TJK | dsb | R. Free Asia (RFA), USA |
| 7550 | 300 | ARM | erv | TWR India, IND |
| | + 500 | IND | bgl | All India R. (AIR), IND |
| 7555 | 100 | IND | dom | AIR, Delhi |
| | ‡ 100 | IND | del | All India R. (AIR), IND |
| 7560 | 100 | ALS | nls | KNLS International, ALS |
| | 500 | MDA | kch | R. Ranginkaman, IRN |
| | 250 | THA | udo | VO America (VOA), USA |
| 7565 | 250 | KWT | kwt | R. Free Asia (RFA), USA |
| | 100 | UZB | tac | R. Japan (NHK World), J |
| 7570 | 200 | KRE | kuj | Voice of Korea, KRE |
| | 100 | USA | rmi | The Overcomer Ministry, USA |
| | 100 | USA | rmi | VORW R. International, USA |
| 7580 | 200 | KRE | kuj | Voice of Korea, KRE |
| | 250 | KWT | kwt | VO America (VOA), USA |
| | 250 | PHL | pht | VO America (VOA), USA |
| | 200 | TJK | dsb | R. Free Asia (RFA), USA |
| | 100 | UZB | tac | North Korea Reform R., KRE |
| 7585 | 250 | KWT | kwt | R. Farda, USA |
| | 250 | THA | udo | R. Farda, USA |
| 7600 | ± 1 | TWN | ust | Sound of Hope, CHN |
| 7610 | 100 | UZB | tac | Free North Korea R., KRE |
| 7625 | ± 100 | UZB | tac | Voice of Wilderness, KRE |
| 7650 | ± 1 | TWN | ust | Sound of Hope, CHN |
| 7700 | † 0.1 | SOM | dom | R. Andalus, Jilib |
| 7730 | ± 1 | TWN | ust | Sound of Hope, CHN |
| | 100 | USA | rmi | Italian Broadcasting Corp., I |
| | 100 | USA | rmi | Shortwave Radiogram, USA |
| | 100 | USA | rmi | The Overcomer Ministry, USA |
| | 100 | USA | rmi | VORW R. International, USA |
| | 100 | USA | rmi | World of Radio, USA |

| kHz | N kW | Ctry | Site | Station, location |
|---|---|---|---|---|
| | 100 | USA | rmi | WRMI - R. Miami Int., USA |
| 7750 | 0.1 | SOM | dom | Warsan Radio, Baidoa |
| 7780 | 100 | USA | rmi | Hobart R. International, AUS |
| | 100 | USA | rmi | Italian Broadcasting Corp., I |
| | 100 | USA | rmi | R. Prague, CZE |
| | 100 | USA | rmi | R. Slovakia Int., SVK |
| | 100 | USA | rmi | R. Ukraine Int. (RUI), UKR |
| | 100 | USA | rmi | RAE - Argentina Al Mundo, ARG |
| | 100 | USA | rmi | Shortwave Radiogram, USA |
| | 100 | USA | rmi | The Overcomer Ministry, USA |
| | 100 | USA | rmi | VORW R. International, USA |
| | 100 | USA | rmi | World of Radio, USA |
| | 100 | USA | rmi | WRMI - R. Miami Int., USA |
| 7810 | ± 1 | TWN | ust | Sound of Hope, CHN |
| 7850 | 5 | CAN | STF | CHU, Ottawa |
| 9080 | ± 1 | TWN | ust | Sound of Hope, CHN |
| 9100 | 10 | KOR | nwn | Echo of Hope (VOH), KRE |
| 9120 | ± 1 | TWN | ust | Sound of Hope, CHN |
| 9155 | ± 1 | TWN | ust | Sound of Hope, CHN |
| 9180 | ± 1 | TWN | ust | Sound of Hope, CHN |
| 9200 | ± 1 | TWN | ust | Sound of Hope, CHN |
| 9230 | ± 1 | TWN | ust | Sound of Hope, CHN |
| 9255 | ± 1 | TWN | ust | Sound of Hope, CHN |
| 9265 | 50 | USA | inb | Hobart R. International, AUS |
| | + 15 | USA | inb | WINB, USA |
| | 50 | USA | inb | WINB, USA |
| | + 15 | USA | inb | World of Radio, USA |
| 9275 | 100 | PHL | boc | FEBC Philippines, PHL |
| 9280 | ± 1 | TWN | ust | Sound of Hope, CHN |
| 9305 | 300 | ARM | erv | TWR India, IND |
| 9310 | 100 | D | lam | R. Free Asia (RFA), USA |
| 9315 | ‡ 250 | MRA | tin | R. Free Asia (RFA), USA |
| | 200 | TJK | dsb | R. Free Asia (RFA), USA |
| 9320 | ± 1 | TWN | ust | Sound of Hope, CHN |
| 9325 | ‡ 250 | MRA | tin | R. Free Asia (RFA), USA |
| 9330 | 50 | USA | bcq | The Overcomer Ministry, USA |
| | † 50 | USA | bcq | WBCQ, USA |
| 9335 | 250 | PHL | pht | VO America (VOA), USA |
| | 250 | THA | udo | VO America (VOA), USA |
| 9345 | 100 | PHL | iba | FEBC Philippines, PHL |
| 9350 | 100 | USA | wcr | The Overcomer Ministry, USA |
| | 100 | USA | wcr | WWCR, USA |
| 9355 | 250 | KWT | kwt | VOA Deewa R., USA |
| | 250 | THA | udo | VOA Deewa R., USA |
| 9370 | 250 | THA | udo | VOA Deewa R., USA |
| 9380 | 250 | IND | dom | AIR Vividh Bharati, Aligarh |
| 9390 | 100 | D | bib | R. Free Asia (RFA), USA |
| | 100 | D | bib | VO America (VOA), USA |
| 9395 | 100 | USA | rmi | Italian Broadcasting Corp., I |
| | 100 | USA | rmi | R. Prague, CZE |
| | 100 | USA | rmi | R. Slovakia Int., SVK |
| | 100 | USA | rmi | R.Tirana Int., ALB |
| | 100 | USA | rmi | RAE - Argentina Al Mundo, ARG |
| | 100 | USA | rmi | The Overcomer Ministry, USA |
| | 100 | USA | rmi | VORW R. International, USA |
| | 100 | USA | rmi | WRMI - R. Miami Int., USA |
| 9400 | 100 | BUL | sof | Bible Voice Broadcasting (BVB), CAN |
| | 100 | BUL | sof | ETC R., G |
| | 100 | BUL | sof | Isle of Music/Melting Pot, USA |
| | 100 | BUL | sof | Shortwave Radiogram, USA |
| | 100 | BUL | sof | The Overcomer Ministry, USA |
| | 100 | PHL | iba | FEBC Philippines, PHL |
| 9405 | 100 | PHL | boc | FEBC Philippines, PHL |

| kHz | N kW | Ctry | Site | Station, location |
|---|---|---|---|---|
| | 300 | TWN | tsh | R. Taiwan International, TWN |
| 9410 | 100 | AFS | mey | BBC World Service, G |
| | 125 | ASC | asc | BBC World Service, G |
| | 500 | CHN | kas | China R. Int. (CRI), CHN |
| | 100 | D | bib | R. Free Asia (RFA), USA |
| ‡ | 100 | MRA | sai | R. Free Asia (RFA), USA |
| | 250 | OMA | sla | BBC World Service, G |
| | 250 | SNG | sng | BBC World Service, G |
| | 500 | TUR | emr | Voice of Turkey (VOT), TUR |
| † | 10 | TWN | dom | Fu Hsing BS, Kuanyin |
| | 250 | UAE | dha | BBC World Service, G |
| 9415 | 500 | CHN | bei | China R. Int. (CRI), CHN |
| | 500 | CHN | xia | China R. Int. (CRI), CHN |
| | 300 | TWN | pao | R. Taiwan International, TWN |
| 9420 | 100 | CHN | dom | CNR13 Uyghur Sce, Lingshi |
| | 100 | CHN | dom | CNR6 VO Shenzhou, Beijing |
| † | 100 | EGY | abs | R. Cairo, EGY |
| † | 170 | GRC | avl | Voice of Greece, GRC |
| 9425 | 150 | CHN | bei | China R. Int. (CRI), CHN |
| | 200 | KRE | kuj | Voice of Korea, KRE |
| 9430 | 500 | CHN | kas | China R. Int. (CRI), CHN |
| 9435 | 500 | CHN | kas | China R. Int. (CRI), CHN |
| | 100 | CHN | kun | China R. Int. (CRI), CHN |
| | 200 | KRE | kuj | Voice of Korea, KRE |
| 9440 | 150 | CHN | kun | China R. Int. (CRI), CHN |
| | 500 | CHN | kun | China R. Int. (CRI), CHN |
| | 100 | CHN | nnn | China R. Int. (CRI), CHN |
| | 500 | CHN | xia | China R. Int. (CRI), CHN |
| | 100 | D | nau | Bible Voice Broadcasting (BVB), CAN |
| | 500 | IRN | zah | Pars Today (VOIRI), IRN |
| | 250 | UAE | dha | BBC World Service, G |
| 9445 | 300 | AUT | mos | Adventist World R. (AWR), USA |
| | 250 | BUL | sof | BBC World Service, G |
| | 500 | IND | bgl | All India R. (AIR), IND |
| | 200 | KRE | kuj | Voice of Korea, KRE |
| 9450 | 100 | CHN | kas | China R. Int. (CRI), CHN |
| | 500 | CHN | kas | China R. Int. (CRI), CHN |
| | 100 | CHN | uru | China R. Int. (CRI), CHN |
| | 100 | D | nau | Bible Voice Broadcasting (BVB), CAN |
| | 100 | GUM | sda | AWR Asia/Pacific, THA |
| | 250 | KWT | kwt | R. Free Asia (RFA), USA |
| | 100 | PHL | boc | FEBC Philippines, PHL |
| | 300 | TWN | tsh | R. Taiwan International, TWN |
| 9455 | 250 | BGD | dka | Bangladesh Betar, BGD |
| | 150 | CHN | kun | China R. Int. (CRI), CHN |
| | 100 | CHN | dom | CNR1 VO China, Lingshi |
| | 100 | D | bib | R. Free Asia (RFA), USA |
| | 100 | D | lam | R. Free Asia (RFA), USA |
| | 250 | KWT | kwt | R. Free Asia (RFA), USA |
| ‡ | 100 | MRA | sai | R. Free Asia (RFA), USA |
| | 100 | USA | rmi | The Overcomer Ministry, USA |
| | 100 | USA | rmi | WRMI - R. Miami Int., USA |
| 9460 | 150 | ALB | cer | China R. Int. (CRI), CHN |
| | 100 | CHN | kas | China R. Int. (CRI), CHN |
| | 150 | CHN | kun | China R. Int. (CRI), CHN |
| | 100 | CHN | nnn | China R. Int. (CRI), CHN |
| | 500 | CHN | uru | China R. Int. (CRI), CHN |
| | 100 | GUM | sda | Adventist World R. (AWR), USA |
| | 100 | GUM | sda | AWR Asia/Pacific, THA |
| | 500 | TUR | emr | Voice of Turkey (VOT), TUR |
| 9465 | 250 | AFS | mey | BBC World Service, G |
| | 100 | PHL | boc | FEBC Philippines, PHL |
| 9470 | 100 | CHN | xia | China R. Int. (CRI), CHN |

| kHz | N kW | Ctry | Site | Station, location |
|---|---|---|---|---|
| | 100 | CHN | dom | CNR1 VO China, Beijing |
| | 100 | CHN | dom | Xinjiang PBS, Urumqi |
| | 100 | D | lam | RFE/RL, USA |
| | 250 | USA | ewn | WEWN - EWTN Shortwave, USA |
| 9475 | 100 | SWZ | man | TWR Africa, AFS |
| | 100 | USA | tww | WTWW, USA |
| 9480 | 100 | CHN | dom | CNR11 Tibetan Sce, Xi'an |
| | 100 | D | lam | VOA Ashna R., USA |
| † | 250 | EGY | abs | R. Cairo, EGY |
| | 250 | UAE | dha | VO America (VOA), USA |
| 9485 | 100 | BOT | bot | VO America (VOA), USA |
| | 1 | D | goh | Hamburger LokalR., D |
| | 1 | D | goh | World of Radio, USA |
| | 300 | G | wof | VO America (VOA), USA |
| | 250 | KWT | kwt | VO America (VOA), USA |
| 9490 | 100 | CHN | kas | China R. Int. (CRI), CHN |
| | 150 | CHN | kun | China R. Int. (CRI), CHN |
| | 100 | CHN | lha | CTB - Holy Tibet, CHN |
| | 100 | CHN | dom | Xizang PBS, Lhasa |
| | 150 | F | iss | R. República, CUB |
| | 250 | PHL | pht | VO America (VOA), USA |
| + | 90 | ROU | tig | R. Romania International, ROU |
| | 250 | THA | udo | RFE/RL, USA |
| 9495 | 500 | IRN | sir | Pars Today (VOIRI), IRN |
| | 250 | TUR | emr | Voice of Turkey (VOT), TUR |
| 9500 | 100 | AUT | mos | Reach Beyond, USA |
| | 100 | CHN | dom | CNR1 VO China, Shijiazhuang |
| | 100 | SWZ | man | TWR Africa, AFS |
| 9505 | 250 | PHL | pht | Vatican R., CVA |
| | 100 | SDN | alf | VO Africa - Sudan R., SDN |
| | 250 | USA | hri | WHRI - World Harvest R., USA |
| 9510 | 50 | CHN | dom | Xinjiang PBS, Urumqi |
| | 125 | CLN | trm | AWR Asia/Pacific, THA |
| | 250 | CVA | smg | VO America (VOA), USA |
| | 100 | D | bib | R. Free Asia (RFA), USA |
| | 250 | IRN | zah | Pars Today (VOIRI), IRN |
| | 100 | ROU | tig | IRRS Shortwave, I |
| | 250 | SNG | sng | BBC World Service, G |
| 9515 | 10 | B | dom | R. Marumby, Curitiba |
| | 100 | CHN | kas | China R. Int. (CRI), CHN |
| | 150 | CHN | dom | CNR2 Business R., Beijing |
| | 100 | KOR | kim | KBS World R., KOR |
| | 250 | KOR | kim | KBS World R., KOR |
| | 125 | MDG | mdc | AWR Africa, G |
| | 100 | STP | sao | VO America (VOA), USA |
| 9520 | 500 | CHN | uru | China R. Int. (CRI), CHN |
| | 50 | CHN | dom | Nei Menggu-Ch, Hohhot |
| 9525 | 500 | CHN | kas | China R. Int. (CRI), CHN |
| | 250 | F | iss | Dengê Welat, TUR |
| 9530 | 250 | ASC | asc | Reach Beyond, USA |
| | 100 | CHN | dom | CNR11 Tibetan Sce, Xi'an |
| | 50 | VTN | dom | VO Vietnam 1, Xuan Mai |
| 9535 | 150 | CHN | bji | China R. Int. (CRI), CHN |
| | 100 | CHN | kun | China R. Int. (CRI), CHN |
| | 500 | CHN | xia | China R. Int. (CRI), CHN |
| | 100 | CUB | hab | R. Habana Cuba, CUB |
| | 250 | KWT | kwt | R. Free Asia (RFA), USA |
| ‡ | 250 | MRA | tin | R. Free Asia (RFA), USA |
| 9540 | 300 | ARM | erv | IBRA Media, S |
| | 500 | CHN | bei | China R. Int. (CRI), CHN |
| | 500 | CHN | kun | China R. Int. (CRI), CHN |
| | 125 | CLN | trm | AWR Asia/Pacific, THA |
| † | 125 | EGY | abs | R. Cairo, EGY |

| kHz | N | kW | Ctry | Site | Station, location |
|---|---|---|---|---|---|
| | | 250 | OMA | sla | BBC World Service, G |
| | | 50 | OMA | thu | R. Sultanate of Oman, OMA |
| | ± | 1 | TWN | ust | Sound of Hope, CHN |
| | | 250 | UAE | dha | IBRA Media, S |
| | | 100 | UZB | tac | FEBA India, IND |
| 9545 | | 300 | G | wof | BBC World Service, G |
| | | 300 | TWN | pao | R. Taiwan International, TWN |
| 9550 | | 10 | B | dom | R. Boa Vontade, Porto Alegre |
| | | 500 | CHN | bei | China R. Int. (CRI), CHN |
| | | 150 | CHN | kun | China R. Int. (CRI), CHN |
| | | 500 | IRN | sir | Pars Today (VOIRI), IRN |
| | | 100 | STP | sao | VO America (VOA), USA |
| 9555 | | 150 | ALB | cer | China R. Int. (CRI), CHN |
| | | 500 | ARS | riy | Saudi R. Int. (SBA), ARS |
| | | 150 | CHN | bei | China R. Int. (CRI), CHN |
| 9560 | | 100 | CHN | kas | China R. Int. (CRI), CHN |
| | | 500 | CHN | uru | China R. Int. (CRI), CHN |
| | | 100 | CHN | dom | Xinjiang PBS, Urumqi |
| | | 300 | J | yam | R. Japan (NHK World), J |
| | | 250 | MDG | mdc | R. Japan (NHK World), J |
| | | 250 | PHL | pht | Vatican R., CVA |
| | | 250 | SNG | sng | BBC World Service, G |
| | | 300 | TWN | pao | Furusato no Kaze/Ilbon-e Baram, KRE |
| 9565 | | 150 | ALB | cer | China R. Int. (CRI), CHN |
| | | 20 | B | dom | Super R. Deus é Amor, Curitiba |
| | | 250 | USA | grv | R. Martí, USA |
| 9570 | | 300 | ALB | cer | China R. Int. (CRI), CHN |
| | | 500 | CHN | bei | China R. Int. (CRI), CHN |
| | | 100 | CHN | dom | CNR2 Business R., Golmud |
| | | 250 | CUB | qvc | China R. Int. (CRI), CHN |
| | † | 125 | EGY | abs | R. Cairo, EGY |
| | | 100 | KOR | kim | KBS World R., KOR |
| | | 300 | ROU | tig | R. Romania International, ROU |
| 9575 | ‡ | 500 | IND | bgl | All India R. (AIR), IND |
| 9580 | | 100 | CHN | lha | CTB - Holy Tibet, CHN |
| | | 100 | CHN | dom | Xizang PBS, Lhasa |
| | | 250 | CUB | qvc | China R. Int. (CRI), CHN |
| | | 500 | F | iss | R. France Int. (RFI), F |
| | | 100 | GUM | sda | AWR Asia/Pacific, THA |
| | | 250 | KOR | kim | KBS World R., KOR |
| | | 250 | PHL | pht | Vatican R., CVA |
| | | 250 | UAE | dha | BBC World Service, G |
| | | 250 | UAE | dha | R. Japan (NHK World), J |
| 9585 | | 500 | CHN | kas | China R. Int. (CRI), CHN |
| | | 250 | PHL | pht | VO America (VOA), USA |
| | | 300 | ROU | tig | R. Romania International, ROU |
| | | 100 | SWZ | man | TWR Africa, AFS |
| 9590 | | 150 | ALB | cer | China R. Int. (CRI), CHN |
| | | 50 | BRM | dom | Thazin R., Pyin U Lwin |
| | | 500 | CHN | kas | China R. Int. (CRI), CHN |
| | | 150 | CHN | kun | China R. Int. (CRI), CHN |
| | | 500 | CHN | szg | China R. Int. (CRI), CHN |
| | † | 125 | EGY | abs | R. Cairo, EGY |
| | ‡ | 100 | MRA | sai | R. Free Asia (RFA), USA |
| | | 300 | TWN | tsh | R. Taiwan International, TWN |
| 9595 | | 250 | TUR | emr | Voice of Turkey (VOT), TUR |
| 9600 | | 250 | AFS | mey | R. Dabanga, SDN |
| | | 150 | CHN | bji | China R. Int. (CRI), CHN |
| | | 500 | CHN | kas | China R. Int. (CRI), CHN |
| | | 150 | CHN | kun | China R. Int. (CRI), CHN |
| | | 250 | OMA | sla | BBC World Service, G |
| | | 300 | ROU | tig | R. Romania International, ROU |
| | | 100 | STP | sao | VO America (VOA), USA |

| kHz | N | kW | Ctry | Site | Station, location |
|---|---|---|---|---|---|
| 9605 | | 250 | PHL | pht | VO America (VOA), USA |
| | | 250 | USA | hri | KBS World R., KOR |
| 9610 | | 100 | AUS | knx | Reach Beyond Australia, AUS |
| | | 100 | CHN | kas | China R. Int. (CRI), CHN |
| | | 100 | CHN | kun | China R. Int. (CRI), CHN |
| | | 150 | CHN | kun | China R. Int. (CRI), CHN |
| | | 100 | CHN | dom | CNR8, Beijing |
| | | 100 | D | nau | Adventist World R. (AWR), USA |
| | | 100 | D | nau | Voice of Oromo Liberation, ETH |
| | | 100 | GUM | sda | AWR Asia/Pacific, THA |
| | + | 300 | ROU | gal | R. Romania International, ROU |
| | | 300 | ROU | gal | R. Romania International, ROU |
| | | 300 | ROU | tig | R. Romania International, ROU |
| | | 500 | TUR | emr | Voice of Turkey (VOT), TUR |
| 9615 | | 500 | CHN | uru | China R. Int. (CRI), CHN |
| 9620 | | 500 | CHN | kas | China R. Int. (CRI), CHN |
| | | 150 | CHN | dom | CNR2 Business R., Beijing |
| | | 125 | D | nau | Dandal Kura R. Int., NIG |
| | | 250 | D | nau | R. Japan (NHK World), J |
| | | 250 | IND | alg | All India R. (AIR), IND |
| | | 250 | PHL | pht | VO America (VOA), USA |
| | | 300 | ROU | tig | R. Romania International, ROU |
| | | 500 | TUR | emr | Voice of Turkey (VOT), TUR |
| 9625 | | 300 | J | yam | R. Japan (NHK World), J |
| | | 100 | PLW | hbn | R. Japan (NHK World), J |
| | | 500 | TUR | emr | Voice of Turkey (VOT), TUR |
| | | 300 | TWN | pao | R. Taiwan International, TWN |
| 9630 | | 300 | AUT | mos | AWR Africa, G |
| | | 500 | CHN | jin | China R. Int. (CRI), CHN |
| | | 100 | CHN | dom | CNR1 VO China, Golmud |
| | | 100 | CHN | dom | CNR17 Kazakh Sce, Lingshi |
| | | 100 | KOR | kim | KBS World R., KOR |
| 9635 | | 500 | F | iss | R. France Int. (RFI), F |
| | | 250 | G | wof | IBRA Media, S |
| | | 50 | MLI | dom | R. Mali, Bamako (Kati) |
| | ± | 1 | TWN | ust | Sound of Hope, CHN |
| 9636 | ± | 100 | VTN | dom | VO Vietnam 1, Son Tay |
| 9640 | | 500 | CHN | kas | China R. Int. (CRI), CHN |
| | | 50 | CUB | hab | R. Habana Cuba, CUB |
| | | 100 | KOR | kim | KBS World R., KOR |
| 9645 | | 500 | CHN | bei | China R. Int. (CRI), CHN |
| | | 500 | CHN | kun | China R. Int. (CRI), CHN |
| | | 100 | CHN | dom | CNR1 VO China, Beijing |
| | | 250 | CVA | smg | Vatican R., CVA |
| | † | 250 | IND | del | All India R. (AIR), IND |
| | | 100 | KOR | kim | KBS World R., KOR |
| 9650 | | 100 | AFS | dom | R. Sonder Grense, Meyerton |
| | | 100 | ARS | riy | Saudi R. Int. (SBA), ARS |
| | † | 50 | GUI | dom | RTG, Conakry |
| | | 200 | KRE | kuj | Voice of Korea, KRE |
| | | 500 | TUR | emr | Voice of Turkey (VOT), TUR |
| | | 300 | TWN | pao | R. France Int. (RFI), F |
| 9655 | | 100 | CHN | kas | China R. Int. (CRI), CHN |
| | | 100 | CHN | kun | China R. Int. (CRI), CHN |
| | | 150 | CHN | kun | China R. Int. (CRI), CHN |
| | | 500 | CHN | kun | China R. Int. (CRI), CHN |
| | | 100 | CHN | nnn | China R. Int. (CRI), CHN |
| 9660 | † | 100 | EGY | abs | R. Cairo, EGY |
| | | 500 | F | iss | R. France Int. (RFI), F |
| | | 500 | IRN | sir | Pars Today (VOIRI), IRN |
| | | 100 | TWN | kou | R. Taiwan International, TWN |
| 9665 | | 10 | B | dom | Voz Missionária, Camboriú |
| | | 500 | CHN | jin | China R. Int. (CRI), CHN |

| kHz | N kW | Ctry | Site | Station, location |
|---|---|---|---|---|
| | 100 | CHN | kas | China R. Int. (CRI), CHN |
| | 500 | CHN | kun | China R. Int. (CRI), CHN |
| | 500 | CHN | xia | China R. Int. (CRI), CHN |
| | 100 | CHN | dom | CNR5 Vo Zhonghua, Beijing |
| | 50 | KRE | dom | KCBS, Pyongyang |
| | 250 | MDG | mdc | R. France Int. (RFI), F |
| 9670 | 300 | J | yam | R. Japan (NHK World), J |
| | 250 | THA | udo | VO America (VOA), USA |
| | 250 | TJK | dsb | R. Free Asia (RFA), USA |
| | 300 | TWN | pao | R. DLSN, VTN |
| 9675 | 500 | ARS | riy | Saudi R. Int. (SBA), ARS |
| | 10 | B | dom | R Canção Nova, Cachoeira Paulista |
| | 500 | CHN | kas | China R. Int. (CRI), CHN |
| | 150 | CHN | kun | China R. Int. (CRI), CHN |
| | 100 | CHN | dom | CNR1 VO China, Beijing |
| 9680 | 500 | F | iss | R. Taiwan International, TWN |
| | 300 | J | yam | R. Japan (NHK World), J |
| | 300 | TWN | tsh | R. Taiwan International, TWN |
| | 100 | ZMB | luv | Voice of Hope - Africa, ZMB |
| 9685 | 150 | CHN | bji | China R. Int. (CRI), CHN |
| | 500 | CHN | kas | China R. Int. (CRI), CHN |
| | 500 | CHN | kun | China R. Int. (CRI), CHN |
| | 500 | CHN | uru | China R. Int. (CRI), CHN |
| | 500 | CHN | xia | China R. Int. (CRI), CHN |
| | 100 | CHN | dom | CNR5 Vo Zhonghua, Beijing |
| | 300 | TWN | tsh | R. Taiwan International, TWN |
| 9690 | 150 | CHN | kun | China R. Int. (CRI), CHN |
| | 100 | E | nob | R. Exterior de España (REE), E |
| ‡ | 500 | IND | bgl | All India R. (AIR), IND |
| | 100 | MDG | mwv | Madagascar World Voice, MDG |
| ‡ | 250 | MRA | tin | R. Free Asia (RFA), USA |
| | 300 | TWN | pao | Furusato no Kaze/Ilbon-e Baram, KRE |
| 9695 | 500 | ARS | riy | Saudi R. Int. (SBA), ARS |
| | 500 | CHN | bei | China R. Int. (CRI), CHN |
| | 500 | CHN | jin | China R. Int. (CRI), CHN |
| | 100 | CHN | kas | China R. Int. (CRI), CHN |
| | 500 | CHN | kun | China R. Int. (CRI), CHN |
| | 250 | USA | grv | Vatican R., CVA |
| 9700 | 250 | CVA | smg | R. Veritas Asia, PHL |
| | 100 | CVA | smg | Vatican R., CVA |
| | 250 | KWT | kwt | R. Free Asia (RFA), USA |
| | 50 | NZL | ran | RNZI (RNZ Pacific), NZL |
| | 500 | TUR | emr | Voice of Turkey (VOT), TUR |
| 9705 | 500 | CHN | kas | China R. Int. (CRI), CHN |
| | 100 | CHN | dom | Xinjiang PBS, Urumqi |
| | 250 | CVA | smg | Vatican R., CVA |
| | 300 | TWN | pao | Furusato no Kaze/Ilbon-e Baram, KRE |
| 9710 | 500 | CHN | kas | China R. Int. (CRI), CHN |
| | 100 | CHN | dom | CNR1 VO China, Shijiazhuang |
| 9715 | 100 | D | nau | Bible Voice Broadcasting (BVB), CAN |
| 9720 | 50 | BUL | sof | R. Erena, ERI |
| | 500 | CHN | uru | China R. Int. (CRI), CHN |
| | 500 | CHN | xia | China R. Int. (CRI), CHN |
| | 150 | CHN | dom | CNR2 Business R., Baoji |
| | 500 | CHN | xia | CRI - VO South China Sea, CHN |
| | 125 | CLN | trm | Sri Lanka Broadcasting Corp., CLN |
| | 100 | CUB | hab | R. Habana Cuba, CUB |
| | 50 | EGY | btr | R. Cairo, EGY |
| ‡ | 100 | MRA | sai | R. Free Asia (RFA), USA |
| ‡ | 250 | MRA | tin | R. Free Asia (RFA), USA |
| | 250 | UAE | dha | Deutsche Welle, D |
| 9725 † | 10 | B | dom | R. Evangelizar, Curitiba |
| | 500 | F | iss | R. France Int. (RFI), F |

| kHz | N kW | Ctry | Site | Station, location |
|---|---|---|---|---|
| 9730 | 50 | BRM | dom | Myanmar R., Yangon |
| | 500 | CHN | bei | China R. Int. (CRI), CHN |
| | 100 | CHN | kas | China R. Int. (CRI), CHN |
| | 500 | CHN | kas | China R. Int. (CRI), CHN |
| | 100 | CHN | kun | China R. Int. (CRI), CHN |
| | 200 | KRE | kuj | Voice of Korea, KRE |
| ± | 1 | TWN | ust | Sound of Hope, CHN |
| | 100 | VTN | vni | Voice of Vietnam (VOV), VTN |
| 9735 | 300 | TWN | pao | R. Taiwan International, TWN |
| 9740 | 100 | AUS | knx | Reach Beyond Australia, AUS |
| | 125 | CLN | trm | AWR Asia/Pacific, THA |
| | 250 | KOR | kim | KBS World R., KOR |
| | 300 | ROU | tig | R. Romania International, ROU |
| 9745 | 10 | BHR | abh | R. Bahrain, BHR |
| | 500 | CHN | uru | China R. Int. (CRI), CHN |
| 9750 | 50 | CHN | dom | Nei Menggu-Mo, Hohhot |
| | 100 | D | bib | VO America (VOA), USA |
| | 100 | D | lam | VO America (VOA), USA |
| | 300 | J | yam | R. Japan (NHK World), J |
| | 250 | KWT | kbd | R.Kuwait, KWT |
| 9755 | 100 | CHN | dom | CNR2 Business R., Baoji |
| | 500 | IRN | sir | Pars Today (VOIRI), IRN |
| 9760 | 500 | CHN | kun | China R. Int. (CRI), CHN |
| | 250 | THA | udo | VO America (VOA), USA |
| 9765 | 150 | CHN | bji | China R. Int. (CRI), CHN |
| | 100 | CHN | nnn | China R. Int. (CRI), CHN |
| | 250 | D | nau | R. Japan (NHK World), J |
| | 250 | G | wof | VO America (VOA), USA |
| | 100 | GUM | sda | AWR Asia/Pacific, THA |
| | 50 | NZL | ran | RNZI (RNZ Pacific), NZL |
| | 100 | STP | sao | VO America (VOA), USA |
| | 250 | THA | udo | VOA Deewa R., USA |
| 9770 | 300 | AUT | mos | Adventist World R. (AWR), USA |
| | 250 | BUL | sof | AWR Africa, G |
| | 500 | CHN | kas | China R. Int. (CRI), CHN |
| | 100 | F | iss | Dandal Kura R. Int., NIG |
| | 100 | KOR | kim | KBS World R., KOR |
| + | 90 | ROU | gal | R. Romania International, ROU |
| + | 300 | ROU | tig | R. Romania International, ROU |
| 9774 † | 10 | TWN | dom | Fu Hsing BS, Kuanyin |
| 9775 | 150 | CHN | dom | CNR2 Business R., Beijing |
| | 250 | G | wof | IBRA Media, S |
| 9780 | 250 | AFS | mey | AWR Africa, G |
| | 300 | AUT | mos | AWR Africa, G |
| † | 50 | CHN | dom | Qinghai PBS, Xining |
| + | 50 | NZL | ran | RNZI (RNZ Pacific), NZL |
| | 50 | NZL | ran | RNZI (RNZ Pacific), NZL |
| 9785 | 500 | CHN | jin | China R. Int. (CRI), CHN |
| | 150 | CHN | kun | China R. Int. (CRI), CHN |
| | 100 | CHN | dom | CNR8, Beijing |
| | 500 | F | iss | Deutsche Welle, D |
| | 500 | TUR | emr | Voice of Turkey (VOT), TUR |
| 9790 | 500 | F | iss | R. France Int. (RFI), F |
| | 250 | KWT | kwt | R. Free Asia (RFA), USA |
| ‡ | 100 | MRA | sai | R. Free Asia (RFA), USA |
| | 250 | PHL | pht | VO America (VOA), USA |
| 9795 | 500 | CHN | uru | China R. Int. (CRI), CHN |
| | 100 | PHL | iba | FEBC Philippines, PHL |
| 9800 | 100 | ARS | riy | Saudi R. Int. (SBA), ARS |
| | 100 | CHN | kas | China R. Int. (CRI), CHN |
| | 500 | CHN | kas | China R. Int. (CRI), CHN |
| | 125 | F | iss | AWR Africa, G |
| | 250 | F | iss | Sawtu Linjiila, CME |

| kHz | N | kW | Ctry | Site | Station, location |
|---|---|---|---|---|---|
| | | 100 | GUM | sda | AWR Asia/Pacific, THA |
| | | 500 | IRN | sir | Pars Today (VOIRI), IRN |
| | | 250 | PHL | pht | VO America (VOA), USA |
| | | 300 | ROU | tig | R. Romania International, ROU |
| | | 300 | TWN | pao | Furusato no Kaze/Ilbon-e Baram, KRE |
| 9805 | | 500 | F | iss | R. France Int. (RFI), F |
| | | 100 | KOR | kim | KBS World R., KOR |
| 9810 | | 100 | CHN | *dom* | CNR1 VO China, Nanning |
| | | 100 | CHN | *dom* | CNR2 Business R., Baoji |
| | | 500 | F | iss | R. France Int. (RFI), F |
| | | 300 | ROU | gal | R. Romania International, ROU |
| 9820 | | 10 | B | *dom* | R. Nove de Julho, São Paulo |
| | | 15 | CHN | nnn | Beibu Bay R., CHN |
| | | 150 | CHN | *dom* | CNR2 Business R., Xianyang |
| | | 300 | G | wof | VOA Deewa R., USA |
| | + | 90 | ROU | tig | R. Romania International, ROU |
| 9825 | | 100 | CHN | kas | China R. Int. (CRI), CHN |
| | | 100 | D | lam | VO America (VOA), USA |
| | | 250 | PHL | pht | VO America (VOA), USA |
| | | 100 | STP | sao | VOA Studio 7, USA |
| 9830 | | 250 | BUL | sof | AWR Asia/Pacific, THA |
| | | 100 | CHN | *dom* | CNR1 VO China, Beijing |
| | | 100 | D | nau | Adventist World R. (AWR), USA |
| | | 500 | F | iss | Deutsche Welle, D |
| | | 100 | STP | sao | Deutsche Welle, D |
| | | 250 | USA | hri | WHRI - World Harvest R., USA |
| 9835 | | 100 | CHN | *dom* | Xinjiang PBS, Urumqi |
| | ‡ | 100 | IND | del | All India R. (AIR), IND |
| | | 500 | IRN | sir | Pars Today (VOIRI), IRN |
| | † | 100 | MLA | *dom* | RTM Sarawak FM, Kajang |
| 9840 | | 250 | TUR | emr | Voice of Turkey (VOT), TUR |
| | | 250 | USA | hri | WHRI - World Harvest R., USA |
| | | 100 | VTN | vni | Voice of Vietnam (VOV), VTN |
| 9845 | | 100 | CHN | *dom* | CNR1 VO China, Beijing |
| 9850 | | 250 | AFS | mey | AWR Africa, G |
| | † | 50 | CHN | *dom* | Qinghai PBS, Xining |
| | | 500 | IRN | sir | Pars Today (VOIRI), IRN |
| | | 200 | KRE | kuj | Voice of Korea, KRE |
| | ± | 1 | TWN | ust | Sound of Hope, CHN |
| | | 100 | VTN | *dom* | VO Vietnam Min, Xuan Mai |
| 9855 | | 500 | CHN | bei | China R. Int. (CRI), CHN |
| | | 250 | MDG | mdc | R. Japan (NHK World), J |
| | | 100 | TJK | dsb | AWR Asia/Pacific, THA |
| 9860 | | 500 | CHN | jin | China R. Int. (CRI), CHN |
| | | 500 | CHN | kas | China R. Int. (CRI), CHN |
| | | 100 | CHN | *dom* | CNR1 VO China, Beijing |
| | | 250 | CVA | smg | R. Japan (NHK World), J |
| | | 250 | KWT | kwt | R. Free Asia (RFA), USA |
| | ‡ | 100 | MRA | sai | R. Free Asia (RFA), USA |
| | ‡ | 250 | MRA | tin | R. Free Asia (RFA), USA |
| 9865 | | 500 | CHN | kun | China R. Int. (CRI), CHN |
| | | 500 | IND | *dom* | AIR Vividh Bharati, Bengaluru |
| 9870 | | 500 | ARS | riy | Saudi R. Int. (SBA), ARS |
| | | 100 | CHN | kas | China R. Int. (CRI), CHN |
| | | 500 | CHN | xia | China R. Int. (CRI), CHN |
| | | 500 | IRN | ahw | Pars Today (VOIRI), IRN |
| | + | 90 | ROU | tig | R. Romania International, ROU |
| 9875 | | 500 | CHN | kas | China R. Int. (CRI), CHN |
| | | 200 | KRE | kuj | Voice of Korea, KRE |
| 9880 | | 500 | CHN | bei | China R. Int. (CRI), CHN |
| | | 100 | CHN | kun | China R. Int. (CRI), CHN |
| | | 100 | CHN | nnn | China R. Int. (CRI), CHN |
| | † | 100 | EGY | abs | R. Cairo, EGY |
| | | 100 | ROU | tig | R. Romania International, ROU |
| | | 250 | THA | udo | VO America (VOA), USA |
| 9885 | | 100 | AFS | mey | BBC World Service, G |
| | | 250 | AFS | mey | BBC World Service, G |
| | | 500 | ARS | riy | Saudi R. Int. (SBA), ARS |
| | | 100 | BOT | bot | VO America (VOA), USA |
| | | 250 | CVA | smg | VO America (VOA), USA |
| | | 100 | STP | sao | VO America (VOA), USA |
| 9888 | ± | 100 | TJK | dsb | Voice of Tibet, CHN |
| 9890 | | 100 | CHN | *dom* | CNR13 Uyghur Sce, Lingshi |
| | | 200 | KRE | kuj | Voice of Korea, KRE |
| 9895 | | 250 | D | nau | AWR Africa, G |
| 9900 | | 100 | D | lam | R. Free Asia (RFA), USA |
| | † | 125 | EGY | abs | R. Cairo, EGY |
| | | 500 | IRN | sir | Pars Today (VOIRI), IRN |
| | | 250 | SNG | sng | BBC World Service, G |
| | | 300 | TWN | pao | R. Taiwan International, TWN |
| 9905 | | 100 | ARM | erv | AWR Asia/Pacific, THA |
| | ‡ | 100 | MRA | sai | R. Free Asia (RFA), USA |
| 9910 | | 300 | ARM | erv | TWR India, IND |
| | | 200 | GUM | twr | TWR Asia, SNG |
| | | 250 | GUM | twr | TWR Asia, SNG |
| | | 250 | GUM | twr | TWR India, IND |
| | | 500 | IND | bgl | All India R. (AIR), IND |
| | † | 250 | IND | del | All India R. (AIR), IND |
| | | 250 | KWT | kwt | R. Free Asia (RFA), USA |
| 9915 | | 250 | AFS | mey | BBC World Service, G |
| | | 125 | ASC | asc | BBC World Service, G |
| | | 200 | G | wof | BBC World Service, G |
| | | 250 | MDG | mdc | BBC World Service, G |
| 9920 | | 100 | PHL | boc | FEBC Philippines, PHL |
| | | 100 | PHL | iba | FEBC Philippines, PHL |
| | ± | 1 | TWN | ust | Sound of Hope, CHN |
| 9925 | | 250 | PHL | pht | R. Pilipinas (DZRP), PHL |
| 9930 | | 100 | PLW | hbn | T8WH - World Harvest R. Int, PLW |
| | | 100 | USA | tww | WTWW, USA |
| 9935 | † | 100 | GRC | avl | Voice of Greece, GRC |
| 9940 | | 100 | D | bib | RFE/RL, USA |
| | † | 125 | EGY | abs | R. Cairo, EGY |
| | | 100 | PHL | boc | FEBC Philippines, PHL |
| | | 100 | SWZ | man | TWR Africa, AFS |
| | | 250 | THA | udo | R. Thailand World Service, THA |
| 9950 | | 100 | IND | *dom* | AIR, Delhi |
| | | 500 | IND | bgl | All India R. (AIR), IND |
| | ‡ | 500 | IND | bgl | All India R. (AIR), IND |
| | ‡ | 100 | IND | del | All India R. (AIR), IND |
| | ‡ | 250 | IND | del | All India R. (AIR), IND |
| | | 300 | MDA | kch | TWR India, IND |
| 9955 | | 100 | USA | rmi | FG R., CYP |
| | | 100 | USA | rmi | Hobart R. International, AUS |
| | | 100 | USA | rmi | Italian Broadcasting Corp., I |
| | | 100 | USA | rmi | R. Prague, CZE |
| | | 100 | USA | rmi | R. Slovakia Int., SVK |
| | | 100 | USA | rmi | RAE - Argentina Al Mundo, ARG |
| | | 100 | USA | rmi | VORW R. International, USA |
| | | 100 | USA | rmi | World of Radio, USA |
| | | 100 | USA | rmi | WRMI - R. Miami Int., USA |
| 9960 | | 100 | PLW | hbn | Furusato no Kaze/Ilbon-e Baram, KRE |
| 9965 | | 100 | PLW | hbn | Furusato no Kaze/Ilbon-e Baram, KRE |
| | | 100 | PLW | hbn | T8WH - World Harvest R. Int, PLW |
| 9970 | ± | 1 | TWN | ust | Sound of Hope, CHN |
| 9975 | | 100 | GUM | twr | TWR Asia, SNG |
| | | 200 | GUM | twr | TWR Asia, SNG |

| kHz | N | kW | Ctry | Site | Station, location |
|---|---|---|---|---|---|
|  |  | 200 | GUM | twr | TWR India, IND |
|  |  | 100 | PLW | hbn | Furusato no Kaze/Ilbon-e Baram, KRE |
|  |  | 250 | THA | udo | VO America (VOA), USA |
| 9980 |  | 100 | USA | wcr | WWCR, USA |
| 9985 | ‡ | 250 | MRA | tin | R. Free Asia (RFA), USA |
| 9990 |  | 250 | KWT | kwt | R. Farda, USA |
|  |  | 250 | THA | udo | R. Farda, USA |
| 9996 |  | 10 | RUS | STF | RWM, Taldom |
| 10000 |  | 2 | ARG | STF | LOL, Buenos Aires |
|  |  | 1 | B | STF | PPE, Rio de Janeiro |
|  |  | 20 | CHN | STF | BPM, Pucheng |
|  |  | 10 | HWA | STF | WWVH, Kekaha (HI) |
|  |  | 10 | USA | STF | WWV, Fort Collins (CO) |
| 10160 ± |  | 1 | TWN | ust | Sound of Hope, CHN |
| 10820 ± |  | 1 | TWN | ust | Sound of Hope, CHN |
| 10870 ± |  | 1 | TWN | ust | Sound of Hope, CHN |
| 10920 ± |  | 1 | TWN | ust | Sound of Hope, CHN |
| 10960 ± |  | 1 | TWN | ust | Sound of Hope, CHN |
| 11070 ± |  | 1 | TWN | ust | Sound of Hope, CHN |
| 11100 ± |  | 1 | TWN | ust | Sound of Hope, CHN |
| 11120 ± |  | 1 | TWN | ust | Sound of Hope, CHN |
| 11300 ± |  | 1 | TWN | ust | Sound of Hope, CHN |
| 11370 ± |  | 1 | TWN | ust | Sound of Hope, CHN |
| 11410 ± |  | 1 | TWN | ust | Sound of Hope, CHN |
| 11440 ± |  | 1 | TWN | ust | Sound of Hope, CHN |
| 11460 ± |  | 1 | TWN | ust | Sound of Hope, CHN |
| 11500 ± |  | 1 | TWN | ust | Sound of Hope, CHN |
| 11520 |  | 250 | USA | ewn | WEWN - EWTN Shortwave, USA |
| 11530 |  | 250 | F | iss | Dengê Welat, TUR |
|  |  | 300 | MDA | kch | Dengê Welat, TUR |
|  | ± | 1 | TWN | ust | Sound of Hope, CHN |
| 11550 |  | 250 | KWT | kwt | R. Free Asia (RFA), USA |
| 11555 |  | 100 | D | bib | R. Free Asia (RFA), USA |
| 11560 |  | 500 | IND | bgl | All India R. (AIR), IND |
|  | ‡ | 500 | IND | bgl | All India R. (AIR), IND |
|  | † | 250 | IND | del | All India R. (AIR), IND |
| 11570 |  | 250 | PHL | pht | VO America (VOA), USA |
| 11580 |  | 200 | GUM | twr | FEBA India, IND |
|  | ± | 1 | TWN | ust | Sound of Hope, CHN |
| 11590 |  | 100 | GUM | sda | AWR Asia/Pacific, THA |
|  | † | 250 | IND | del | All India R. (AIR), IND |
|  |  | 250 | IND | pan | All India R. (AIR), IND |
|  |  | 250 | KWT | kwt | R. Free Asia (RFA), USA |
| 11600 |  | 100 | BUL | sof | The Mighty KBC, HOL |
|  |  | 100 | BUL | sof | The Overcomer Ministry, USA |
|  | ± | 1 | TWN | ust | Sound of Hope, CHN |
| 11605 ± |  | 100 | TJK | dsb | Voice of Tibet, CHN |
| 11610 |  | 150 | CHN | kun | China R. Int. (CRI), CHN |
|  |  | 150 | CHN | dom | CNR2 Business R., Beijing |
|  |  | 250 | G | wof | VO America (VOA), USA |
|  |  | 100 | GUM | sda | AWR Asia/Pacific, THA |
|  |  | 100 | MDG | mwv | Madagascar World Voice, MDG |
| 11620 |  | 100 | CHN | dom | CNR5 Vo Zhonghua, Beijing |
|  |  | 250 | CVA | smg | Vatican R., CVA |
|  |  | 100 | IND | del | All India R. (AIR), IND |
|  |  | 250 | IND | pan | All India R. (AIR), IND |
|  |  | 250 | MDG | mdc | Eye R., SSD |
| 11625 |  | 250 | CVA | smg | Vatican R., CVA |
|  |  | 250 | MDG | mdc | Vatican R., CVA |
| 11630 |  | 100 | CHN | dom | CNR17 Kazakh Sce, Lingshi |
|  |  | 100 | GUM | sda | AWR Asia/Pacific, THA |
|  | † | 250 | KWT | kbd | R.Kuwait, KWT |
| 11635 |  | 500 | CHN | bei | China R. Int. (CRI), CHN |
|  |  | 200 | KRE | kuj | Voice of Korea, KRE |
| 11640 |  | 500 | CHN | bei | China R. Int. (CRI), CHN |
|  |  | 500 | CHN | jin | China R. Int. (CRI), CHN |
|  |  | 100 | CHN | kas | China R. Int. (CRI), CHN |
|  |  | 500 | CHN | kas | China R. Int. (CRI), CHN |
|  |  | 150 | CHN | kun | China R. Int. (CRI), CHN |
|  |  | 500 | CHN | xia | China R. Int. (CRI), CHN |
|  |  | 100 | TWN | pao | R. Taiwan International, TWN |
| 11645 |  | 250 | IND | del | All India R. (AIR), IND |
|  | † | 250 | IND | del | All India R. (AIR), IND |
|  |  | 200 | KRE | kuj | Voice of Korea, KRE |
| 11650 |  | 100 | CHN | kun | China R. Int. (CRI), CHN |
|  |  | 150 | CHN | kun | China R. Int. (CRI), CHN |
|  |  | 500 | CHN | uru | China R. Int. (CRI), CHN |
|  |  | 250 | THA | udo | VO America (VOA), USA |
| 11651 ± |  | 100 | TJK | dsb | Voice of Tibet, CHN |
| 11655 |  | 250 | PHL | pht | VO America (VOA), USA |
|  |  | 250 | THA | udo | VO America (VOA), USA |
|  |  | 100 | TWN | pao | R. Taiwan International, TWN |
|  |  | 250 | UAE | dha | IBRA Media, S |
| 11660 |  | 250 | ASC | asc | BBC World Service, G |
|  |  | 150 | CHN | dom | CNR2 Business R., Xi'an |
|  | ‡ | 250 | MRA | tin | R. Free Asia (RFA), USA |
|  |  | 250 | PHL | pht | VO America (VOA), USA |
|  |  | 300 | ROU | gal | R. Romania International, ROU |
|  |  | 100 | SWZ | man | TWR Africa, AFS |
|  |  | 250 | THA | udo | VO America (VOA), USA |
|  |  | 250 | TUR | emr | Voice of Turkey (VOT), TUR |
| 11665 |  | 300 | J | yam | R. Japan (NHK World), J |
|  | † | 100 | MLA | dom | RTM Wai FM, Kajang |
| 11670 |  | 150 | CHN | dom | CNR2 Business R., Beijing |
|  |  | 100 | CUB | hab | R. Habana Cuba, CUB |
|  |  | 250 | PHL | pht | VO America (VOA), USA |
| 11674 ± |  | 100 | TJK | dsb | Voice of Tibet, CHN |
| 11675 |  | 100 | PLW | hbn | T8WH - World Harvest R. Int, PLW |
| 11680 |  | 100 | CHN | nnn | China R. Int. (CRI), CHN |
|  |  | 100 | KRE | dom | KCBS, Kanggye |
| 11685 |  | 100 | CHN | dom | CNR11 Tibetan Sce, Xi'an |
|  |  | 100 | E | nob | R. Exterior de España (REE), E |
|  |  | 250 | SNG | sng | R. Japan (NHK World), J |
| 11690 |  | 500 | CHN | xia | China R. Int. (CRI), CHN |
|  |  | 0.1 | FIN | vir | Scandinavian Weekend R., FIN |
|  |  | 100 | GUM | sda | AWR Asia/Pacific, THA |
|  |  | 100 | STP | sao | VO America (VOA), USA |
| 11695 + |  | 30 | CHN | dom | CNR1 VO China, Dongfang |
|  |  | 100 | D | lam | R. Farda, USA |
|  |  | 250 | PHL | pht | VO America (VOA), USA |
| 11700 |  | 100 | CHN | kas | China R. Int. (CRI), CHN |
|  |  | 100 | CHN | kun | China R. Int. (CRI), CHN |
|  |  | 150 | CHN | kun | China R. Int. (CRI), CHN |
|  |  | 250 | CUB | hab | R. Habana Cuba, CUB |
|  |  | 500 | F | iss | R. France Int. (RFI), F |
|  |  | 250 | SNG | sng | BBC World Service, G |
| 11705 |  | 250 | MDG | mdc | R. Tamazuj, SSD |
| 11710 |  | 100 | CHN | nnn | China R. Int. (CRI), CHN |
|  |  | 500 | CHN | uru | China R. Int. (CRI), CHN |
|  |  | 100 | CHN | dom | CNR1 VO China, Beijing |
|  | † | 250 | IND | del | All India R. (AIR), IND |
|  |  | 200 | KRE | kuj | Voice of Korea, KRE |
|  |  | 250 | TUR | emr | Voice of Turkey (VOT), TUR |
| 11715 ± |  | 1 | TWN | ust | Sound of Hope, CHN |
| 11720 |  | 150 | CHN | bji | China R. Int. (CRI), CHN |
|  |  | 100 | CHN | dom | CNR1 VO China, Shijiazhuang |

| kHz | N kW | Ctry | Site | Station, location |
|---|---|---|---|---|
| | 0.1 | FIN | vir | Scandinavian Weekend R., FIN |
| | 250 | MDG | mdc | AWR Africa, G |
| | ‡ 250 | MRA | tin | R. Free Asia (RFA), USA |
| | 250 | UAE | dha | BBC World Service, G |
| | 250 | UAE | dha | Deutsche Welle, D |
| | 100 | VTN | dom | VO Vietnam 1, Xuan Mai |
| 11725 | 150 | ALB | cer | China R. Int. (CRI), CHN |
| | 250 | KWT | kwt | R. Free Asia (RFA), USA |
| | 50 | NZL | ran | RNZI (RNZ Pacific), NZL |
| 11730 | 250 | BUL | sof | AWR Asia/Pacific, THA |
| | 500 | CHN | kun | China R. Int. (CRI), CHN |
| | 250 | D | nau | AWR Asia/Pacific, THA |
| | 500 | TUR | emr | Voice of Turkey (VOT), TUR |
| | 100 | UZB | tac | R. Japan (NHK World), J |
| 11735 | 200 | KRE | kuj | Voice of Korea, KRE |
| | † 50 | TZA | dol | Zanzibar Broadcasting Corp., TZA |
| 11740 | 100 | CHN | dom | CNR2 Business R., Lingshi |
| | 250 | CVA | smg | Vatican R., CVA |
| | 250 | IND | pan | All India R. (AIR), IND |
| | 250 | SNG | sng | R. Japan (NHK World), J |
| 11745 | 250 | ARS | jed | R. Al-Azm, YEM |
| 11750 | 150 | ALB | cer | China R. Int. (CRI), CHN |
| | 500 | CHN | bei | China R. Int. (CRI), CHN |
| | 100 | CHN | dom | CNR1 VO China, Shijiazhuang |
| | 125 | CLN | trm | Sri Lanka Broadcasting Corp., CLN |
| | ‡ 250 | MRA | tin | R. Free Asia (RFA), USA |
| | 250 | OMA | sla | BBC World Service, G |
| | 100 | PHL | boc | FEBC Philippines, PHL |
| | 250 | USA | hri | WHRI - World Harvest R., USA |
| 11760 | 500 | CHN | kun | China R. Int. (CRI), CHN |
| | 100 | CHN | dom | CNR1 VO China, Shijiazhuang |
| | 100 | CUB | hab | R. Habana Cuba, CUB |
| | 500 | F | iss | R. France Int. (RFI), F |
| 11765 | 20 | B | dom | Super R. Deus é Amor, Curitiba |
| | 500 | F | iss | R. France Int. (RFI), F |
| | 250 | KWT | kwt | R. Free Asia (RFA), USA |
| | ± 1 | TWN | ust | Sound of Hope, CHN |
| 11770 | 500 | CHN | bei | China R. Int. (CRI), CHN |
| | 100 | CHN | kas | China R. Int. (CRI), CHN |
| | 100 | CHN | nnn | China R. Int. (CRI), CHN |
| | 100 | CHN | dom | Xinjiang PBS, Urumqi |
| 11775 † | 100 | AIA | aia | University Network, USA |
| | 250 | KWT | kwt | R. Free Asia (RFA), USA |
| | ± 1 | TWN | ust | Sound of Hope, CHN |
| 11780 † | 25 | B | dom | R. Nac. da Amazônia, Brasília |
| | 500 | CHN | bei | China R. Int. (CRI), CHN |
| | 500 | CHN | jin | China R. Int. (CRI), CHN |
| | 500 | IRN | sir | Pars Today (VOIRI), IRN |
| | 250 | KWT | kwt | R. Free Asia (RFA), USA |
| | 300 | ROU | gal | R. Romania International, ROU |
| | 100 | SWZ | man | TWR Africa, AFS |
| 11785 | 150 | ALB | cer | China R. Int. (CRI), CHN |
| | 150 | CHN | bji | China R. Int. (CRI), CHN |
| | 500 | CHN | kas | China R. Int. (CRI), CHN |
| 11790 | 250 | AFS | mey | AWR Africa, G |
| | 100 | CHN | kas | China R. Int. (CRI), CHN |
| | 500 | CHN | xia | China R. Int. (CRI), CHN |
| | 100 | D | nau | Bible Voice Broadcasting (BVB), CAN |
| | 300 | J | yam | R. Japan (NHK World), J |
| | 125 | MDG | mdc | Bible Voice Broadcasting (BVB), CAN |
| | 100 | MDG | mwv | Madagascar World Voice, MDG |
| | 250 | MDG | mdc | R. France Int. (RFI), F |
| | 300 | ROU | gal | R. Romania International, ROU |

| kHz | N kW | Ctry | Site | Station, location |
|---|---|---|---|---|
| | 300 | ROU | tig | R. Romania International, ROU |
| 11795 | 100 | CHN | kas | China R. Int. (CRI), CHN |
| | 250 | KOR | kim | KBS World R., KOR |
| | 250 | KWT | kwt | R. Free Asia (RFA), USA |
| | ‡ 250 | MRA | tin | R. Free Asia (RFA), USA |
| | 500 | TUR | emr | Voice of Turkey (VOT), TUR |
| 11800 | 250 | AFS | mey | AWR Africa, G |
| | 150 | CHN | dom | CNR2 Business R., Beijing |
| | 250 | F | iss | Pan American Broadcasting, USA |
| | 250 | KWT | kwt | R. Free Asia (RFA), USA |
| | 300 | ROU | tig | R. Romania International, ROU |
| 11805 | 100 | CHN | kun | China R. Int. (CRI), CHN |
| | 250 | KWT | kwt | R. Free Asia (RFA), USA |
| 11810 | 125 | ASC | asc | BBC World Service, G |
| | 250 | ASC | asc | BBC World Service, G |
| | 100 | CHN | dom | CNR8, Beijing |
| | 250 | KOR | kim | KBS World R., KOR |
| 11815 † | 10 | B | dom | R. Brasil Central, Goiânia |
| | 300 | J | yam | R. Japan (NHK World), J |
| | 250 | TUR | emr | Voice of Turkey (VOT), TUR |
| 11820 | 500 | ARS | riy | Saudi R. Int. (SBA), ARS |
| | 500 | CHN | xia | China R. Int. (CRI), CHN |
| | 250 | PHL | pht | VO America (VOA), USA |
| | 300 | ROU | tig | R. Romania International, ROU |
| 11825 | 125 | CLN | trm | AWR Asia/Pacific, THA |
| | 300 | J | yam | R. Japan (NHK World), J |
| | 100 | MDG | mwv | Madagascar World Voice, MDG |
| | 100 | PHL | boc | FEBC Philippines, PHL |
| | 300 | ROU | tig | R. Romania International, ROU |
| | 250 | SNG | sng | R. Japan (NHK World), J |
| 11835 | 150 | CHN | dom | CNR2 Business R., Xianyang |
| | 125 | CLN | trm | Sri Lanka Broadcasting Corp., CLN |
| 11840 | 250 | CUB | hab | R. Habana Cuba, CUB |
| 11845 | 150 | CHN | dom | CNR2 Business R., Xianyang |
| 11850 | 100 | AFS | mey | VO America (VOA), USA |
| | 100 | BOT | bot | VO America (VOA), USA |
| | 250 | CVA | smg | VO America (VOA), USA |
| | 125 | KWT | kwt | R. Free Asia (RFA), USA |
| | 100 | STP | sao | VO America (VOA), USA |
| 11855 | 150 | ALB | cer | China R. Int. (CRI), CHN |
| | 100 | GUM | sda | AWR Asia/Pacific, THA |
| 11860 | 250 | ARS | jed | Rep. of Yemen R. (R. Sana'a), YEM |
| | 500 | CHN | kun | China R. Int. (CRI), CHN |
| | 100 | CHN | dom | Xizang PBS, Lhasa |
| | 250 | USA | grv | R. Martí, USA |
| 11865 | 100 | AUS | knx | Reach Beyond Australia, AUS |
| 11870 | 100 | CHN | kas | China R. Int. (CRI), CHN |
| | 250 | F | iss | AWR Africa, G |
| | 100 | GUM | sda | AWR Asia/Pacific, THA |
| | 500 | IRN | sir | Pars Today (VOIRI), IRN |
| | 250 | PHL | pht | VO America (VOA), USA |
| 11875 | 100 | AFS | mey | BBC World Service, G |
| | 100 | AUS | knx | Reach Beyond Australia, AUS |
| | 500 | CHN | kun | China R. Int. (CRI), CHN |
| | 100 | CHN | nnn | China R. Int. (CRI), CHN |
| | 100 | D | nau | Bible Voice Broadcasting (BVB), CAN |
| | 500 | IRN | sir | Pars Today (VOIRI), IRN |
| 11880 | 300 | AUT | mos | AWR Africa, G |
| | 500 | CHN | kas | China R. Int. (CRI), CHN |
| | † 125 | EGY | abs | R. Cairo, EGY |
| | 250 | F | iss | AWR Africa, G |
| | 500 | IRN | sir | Pars Today (VOIRI), IRN |
| 11885 | 500 | CHN | xia | China R. Int. (CRI), CHN |

| kHz | N kW | Ctry | Site | Station, location |
|-----|------|------|------|-------------------|
| | 100 | CHN | dom | Xinjiang PBS, Urumqi |
| | 250 | KWT | kwt | R. Free Asia (RFA), USA |
| | 250 | MDG | mwv | Madagascar World Voice, MDG |
| 11890 | 250 | KWT | kwt | R. Free Asia (RFA), USA |
| 11895 | 10 | B | dom | R. Boa Vontade, Porto Alegre |
| | 100 | CHN | kas | China R. Int. (CRI), CHN |
| | 100 | CHN | nnn | China R. Int. (CRI), CHN |
| | 250 | KWT | kwt | R. Free Asia (RFA), USA |
| | 200 | TJK | dsb | R. Free Asia (RFA), USA |
| 11900 | 500 | CHN | bei | China R. Int. (CRI), CHN |
| | 150 | CHN | kun | China R. Int. (CRI), CHN |
| | 100 | D | nau | Bible Voice Broadcasting (BVB), CAN |
| | 250 | PHL | pht | Vatican R., CVA |
| | 250 | PHL | pht | VO America (VOA), USA |
| | 100 | STP | sao | VO America (VOA), USA |
| 11905 | 100 | AUS | knx | Reach Beyond Australia, AUS |
| | 100 | CHN | dom | CNR6 VO Shenzhou, Beijing |
| | 125 | CLN | trm | Sri Lanka Broadcasting Corp., CLN |
| | 100 | D | lam | VO America (VOA), USA |
| | 250 | OMA | sla | BBC World Service, G |
| 11910 | 500 | CHN | bei | China R. Int. (CRI), CHN |
| | 300 | J | yam | R. Japan (NHK World), J |
| | 200 | KRE | kuj | Voice of Korea, KRE |
| | 250 | KWT | kwt | VO America (VOA), USA |
| 11915 | 500 | ARS | riy | Saudi R. Int. (SBA), ARS |
| | 10 | B | dom | R. Gaucha, Porto Alegre |
| | 100 | CHN | dom | CNR2 Business R., Baoji |
| | 300 | TWN | pao | R. Taiwan International, TWN |
| 11920 | 150 | ALB | cer | China R. Int. (CRI), CHN |
| 11925 | 250 | AFS | mey | Channel Africa, AFS |
| | 100 | CHN | dom | CNR1 VO China, Lingshi |
| | 100 | PLW | hbn | R. Japan (NHK World), J |
| | 500 | TUR | emr | Voice of Turkey (VOT), TUR |
| 11930 | 500 | ARS | riy | Saudi R. Int. (SBA), ARS |
| | 250 | USA | grv | R. Martí, USA |
| 11935 | 500 | ARS | riy | Saudi R. Int. (SBA), ARS |
| | 10 | B | dom | R. Evangelizar, Curitiba |
| | 100 | CHN | dom | CNR5 Vo Zhonghua, Beijing |
| | 125 | CLN | trm | AWR Asia/Pacific, THA |
| | 250 | CVA | smg | Vatican R., CVA |
| | 100 | IND | mum | All India R. (AIR), IND |
| 11940 | 100 | E | nob | R. Exterior de España (REE), E |
| 11945 | 250 | AFS | mey | BBC World Service, G |
| | 100 | AUS | knx | Reach Beyond Australia, AUS |
| | 250 | BUL | sof | AWR Asia/Pacific, THA |
| | 100 | CHN | kun | China R. Int. (CRI), CHN |
| | 150 | CHN | kun | China R. Int. (CRI), CHN |
| | 125 | CLN | trm | AWR Asia/Pacific, THA |
| | 500 | F | iss | R. Japan (NHK World), J |
| | 250 | PHL | pht | VO America (VOA), USA |
| | 300 | ROU | gal | R. Romania International, ROU |
| 11950 | 100 | CHN | dom | Xizang PBS, Lhasa |
| | 100 | CUB | hab | R. Habana Cuba, CUB |
| | 250 | KWT | kwt | R. Free Asia (RFA), USA |
| 11955 | 300 | AUT | mos | Adventist World R. (AWR), USA |
| | 100 | CHN | kun | China R. Int. (CRI), CHN |
| | 500 | CHN | kun | China R. Int. (CRI), CHN |
| | 100 | CHN | kun | CRI - VO South China Sea, CHN |
| | 250 | D | nau | AWR Africa, G |
| | 100 | GUM | sda | AWR Asia/Pacific, THA |
| | 500 | TUR | emr | Voice of Turkey (VOT), TUR |
| 11960 | 100 | CHN | dom | CNR1 VO China, Beijing |
| | 300 | ROU | tig | R. Romania International, ROU |
| 11965 | 100 | D | bib | RFE/RL, USA |

| kHz | N kW | Ctry | Site | Station, location |
|-----|------|------|------|-------------------|
| | 100 | GUM | twr | TWR Asia, SNG |
| | 100 | MDG | mwv | Madagascar World Voice, MDG |
| | 250 | PHL | pht | VO America (VOA), USA |
| | 250 | TUR | emr | Voice of Turkey (VOT), TUR |
| 11970 | 500 | F | iss | R. Xoriyo, ETH |
| + | 200 | KWT | kbd | R.Kuwait, KWT |
| ± | 1 | TWN | ust | Sound of Hope, CHN |
| 11975 | 250 | ASC | asc | BBC World Service, G |
| | 500 | CHN | kun | China R. Int. (CRI), CHN |
| | 100 | CHN | dom | Xinjiang PBS, Urumqi |
| | 250 | CVA | smg | VO America (VOA), USA |
| | 300 | ROU | gal | R. Romania International, ROU |
| 11980 | 100 | CHN | kas | China R. Int. (CRI), CHN |
| | 100 | CHN | kun | China R. Int. (CRI), CHN |
| | 150 | CHN | kun | China R. Int. (CRI), CHN |
| | 500 | CHN | xia | China R. Int. (CRI), CHN |
| | 100 | D | nau | AWR Africa, G |
| | 100 | GUM | sda | AWR Asia/Pacific, THA |
| | 250 | KWT | kwt | R. Free Asia (RFA), USA |
| | 100 | STP | sao | Deutsche Welle, D |
| | 200 | TJK | dsb | R. Free Asia (RFA), USA |
| 11985 | 250 | BUL | sof | AWR Asia/Pacific, THA |
| | 125 | CLN | trm | Adventist World R. (AWR), USA |
| | 125 | CLN | trm | AWR Asia/Pacific, THA |
| | 100 | GUM | sda | AWR Asia/Pacific, THA |
| | 250 | MDG | mdc | AWR Africa, G |
| | 300 | TWN | pao | R. Taiwan International, TWN |
| 11990 | 100 | CHN | nnn | China R. Int. (CRI), CHN |
| | 500 | CHN | xia | China R. Int. (CRI), CHN |
| 11995 | 500 | F | iss | R. France Int. (RFI), F |
| | 100 | GUM | twr | TWR Asia, SNG |
| | 250 | MDG | mdc | BBC World Service, G |
| | 250 | SNG | sng | BBC World Service, G |
| 12005 | 250 | ASC | asc | Follow The Bible Ministries, USA |
| | 100 | D | bib | R. Farda, USA |
| 12015 | 100 | CHN | kas | China R. Int. (CRI), CHN |
| | 200 | KRE | kuj | Voice of Korea, KRE |
| | 250 | MNG | uba | Voice of Mongolia, MNG |
| † | 50 | OMA | thu | R. Sultanate of Oman, OMA |
| | 250 | UAE | dha | BBC World Service, G |
| 12020 | 100 | VTN | vni | Voice of Vietnam (VOV), VTN |
| 12025 | 100 | AUS | knx | Reach Beyond Australia, AUS |
| | 300 | AUT | mos | Adventist World R. (AWR), USA |
| | 250 | IND | pan | All India R. (AIR), IND |
| 12030 | 250 | ASC | asc | Follow The Bible Ministries, USA |
| | 100 | E | nob | R. Exterior de España (REE), E |
| | 100 | STP | sao | VO America (VOA), USA |
| 12035 | 500 | CHN | xia | China R. Int. (CRI), CHN |
| | 125 | CLN | trm | AWR Asia/Pacific, THA |
| | 250 | D | nau | AWR Africa, G |
| | 100 | GUM | sda | AWR Asia/Pacific, THA |
| | 500 | IRN | sir | Pars Today (VOIRI), IRN |
| | 500 | TUR | emr | Voice of Turkey (VOT), TUR |
| 12040 | 100 | AFS | mey | VO America (VOA), USA |
| | 100 | GUM | sda | AWR Asia/Pacific, THA |
| | 100 | GUM | twr | TWR Asia, SNG |
| | 250 | KWT | kwt | VO America (VOA), USA |
| | 250 | UAE | dha | VO America (VOA), USA |
| 12045 | 100 | CHN | dom | CNR1 VO China, Beijing |
| | 100 | D | lam | RFE/RL, USA |
| | 250 | PHL | pht | VO America (VOA), USA |
| 12050 | 250 | ASC | asc | R. Ndarason Int., TCD |
| | 250 | KWT | kwt | R. Free Asia (RFA), USA |
| | 100 | USA | ewn | WEWN - EWTN Shortwave, USA |

| kHz | N kW | Ctry | Site | Station, location |
|---|---|---|---|---|
| 12055 | 100 | CHN | dom | CNR17 Kazakh Sce, Lingshi |
| | 100 | D | lam | R. Free Asia (RFA), USA |
| | 100 | D | lam | RFE/RL, USA |
| | 250 | KWT | kwt | R. Free Asia (RFA), USA |
| | 100 | PHL | boc | FEBC Philippines, PHL |
| 12065 | 250 | ASC | asc | BBC World Service, G |
| | † 125 | EGY | abs | R. Cairo, EGY |
| | 250 | KWT | kwt | R. Free Asia (RFA), USA |
| | 250 | OMA | sla | BBC World Service, G |
| | 250 | SNG | sng | BBC World Service, G |
| 12070 | 500 | CHN | xia | China R. Int. (CRI), CHN |
| | 100 | PHL | iba | FEBC Philippines, PHL |
| | 100 | STP | sao | VO America (VOA), USA |
| 12075 | 100 | BOT | bot | VO America (VOA), USA |
| | 250 | CVA | smg | R. Azadi, USA |
| | 250 | CVA | smg | VO America (VOA), USA |
| | 250 | CVA | smg | VOA Ashna R., USA |
| | 100 | STP | sao | VO America (VOA), USA |
| | 250 | THA | udo | VOA Ashna R., USA |
| 12080 | 100 | CHN | dom | CNR2 Business R., Baoji |
| 12085 | 100 | GUM | sda | AWR Asia/Pacific, THA |
| | 250 | MNG | uba | Voice of Mongolia, MNG |
| 12095 | 100 | AFS | mey | BBC World Service, G |
| | 250 | AFS | mey | BBC World Service, G |
| | 125 | ASC | asc | BBC World Service, G |
| | 250 | MDG | mdc | BBC World Service, G |
| | 100 | PHL | boc | FEBC Philippines, PHL |
| | 250 | UAE | dha | BBC World Service, G |
| 12100 | 300 | TWN | pao | R. Taiwan International, TWN |
| 12110 | 250 | KWT | kwt | R. Mashaal, USA |
| 12120 | 200 | GUM | twr | TWR Asia, SNG |
| | 100 | PHL | boc | FEBC Philippines, PHL |
| | 250 | PHL | pht | R. Pilipinas (DZRP), PHL |
| | 250 | PHL | pht | VO America (VOA), USA |
| 12125 | 250 | THA | udo | VO America (VOA), USA |
| 12130 | 100 | D | lam | R. Free Asia (RFA), USA |
| | ‡ 250 | MRA | tin | R. Free Asia (RFA), USA |
| 12140 | 250 | KWT | kwt | R. Azadi, USA |
| | 250 | KWT | kwt | VOA Ashna R., USA |
| | 250 | THA | udo | R. Azadi, USA |
| | 250 | THA | udo | VOA Ashna R., USA |
| 12150 ± | 1 | TWN | ust | Sound of Hope, CHN |
| 12160 | 100 | USA | wcr | WWCR, USA |
| 12170 ± | 1 | TWN | ust | Sound of Hope, CHN |
| 12190 ± | 1 | TWN | ust | Sound of Hope, CHN |
| 12230 ± | 1 | TWN | ust | Sound of Hope, CHN |
| 12345 ± | 1 | TWN | ust | Sound of Hope, CHN |
| 12370 ± | 1 | TWN | ust | Sound of Hope, CHN |
| 12430 ± | 1 | TWN | ust | Sound of Hope, CHN |
| 12500 ± | 1 | TWN | ust | Sound of Hope, CHN |
| 12560 ± | 1 | TWN | ust | Sound of Hope, CHN |
| 12775 ± | 1 | TWN | ust | Sound of Hope, CHN |
| 12800 ± | 1 | TWN | ust | Sound of Hope, CHN |
| 12870 ± | 1 | TWN | ust | Sound of Hope, CHN |
| 12910 ± | 1 | TWN | ust | Sound of Hope, CHN |
| 12950 ± | 1 | TWN | ust | Sound of Hope, CHN |
| 12980 ± | 1 | TWN | ust | Sound of Hope, CHN |
| 13070 ± | 1 | TWN | ust | Sound of Hope, CHN |
| 13130 ± | 1 | TWN | ust | Sound of Hope, CHN |
| 13200 ± | 1 | TWN | ust | Sound of Hope, CHN |
| 13230 ± | 1 | TWN | ust | Sound of Hope, CHN |
| 13270 ± | 1 | TWN | ust | Sound of Hope, CHN |
| 13530 ± | 1 | TWN | ust | Sound of Hope, CHN |
| 13570 | 500 | CHN | xia | China R. Int. (CRI), CHN |

| kHz | N kW | Ctry | Site | Station, location |
|---|---|---|---|---|
| 13580 | 250 | BGD | dka | Bangladesh Betar, BGD |
| | 500 | CHN | bei | China R. Int. (CRI), CHN |
| | 500 | CHN | kun | China R. Int. (CRI), CHN |
| | 250 | KWT | kwt | R. Mashaal, USA |
| | 250 | KWT | kwt | VO America (VOA), USA |
| | 250 | THA | udo | R. Mashaal, USA |
| 13590 | 500 | CHN | bei | China R. Int. (CRI), CHN |
| | 100 | D | lam | VOA Deewa R., USA |
| | 250 | KWT | kwt | VO America (VOA), USA |
| | 100 | STP | sao | VO America (VOA), USA |
| | 250 | THA | udo | VO America (VOA), USA |
| | 250 | THA | udo | VOA Deewa R., USA |
| 13600 | 150 | CHN | kun | China R. Int. (CRI), CHN |
| | 50 | OMA | thu | R. Sultanate of Oman, OMA |
| 13605 | 500 | IND | bgl | All India R. (AIR), IND |
| 13610 | 100 | ARS | riy | Saudi R. Int. (SBA), ARS |
| | 500 | CHN | xia | China R. Int. (CRI), CHN |
| | 100 | CHN | dom | CNR1 VO China, Nanning |
| | ‡ 250 | MRA | tin | R. Free Asia (RFA), USA |
| 13620 ± | 1 | TWN | ust | Sound of Hope, CHN |
| 13630 | 100 | BOT | bot | VO America (VOA), USA |
| | 300 | ROU | tig | R. Romania International, ROU |
| | 100 | STP | sao | VO America (VOA), USA |
| | 500 | TUR | emr | Voice of Turkey (VOT), TUR |
| 13640 | 100 | CHN | kas | China R. Int. (CRI), CHN |
| | 500 | IND | bgl | All India R. (AIR), IND |
| ± | 1 | TWN | ust | Sound of Hope, CHN |
| 13645 | 500 | CHN | xia | China R. Int. (CRI), CHN |
| | 500 | IND | bgl | All India R. (AIR), IND |
| | ‡ 250 | MRA | tin | R. Free Asia (RFA), USA |
| 13650 | 250 | CUB | qvc | China R. Int. (CRI), CHN |
| | 300 | J | yam | R. Japan (NHK World), J |
| | 200 | KRE | kuj | Voice of Korea, KRE |
| | 250 | KWT | kwt | R. Free Asia (RFA), USA |
| | ± 250 | KWT | kbd | R.Kuwait, KWT |
| 13655 | 500 | CHN | xia | China R. Int. (CRI), CHN |
| | 500 | TUR | emr | Voice of Turkey (VOT), TUR |
| 13660 | 500 | CHN | xia | China R. Int. (CRI), CHN |
| | 250 | OMA | sla | BBC World Service, G |
| 13665 | 150 | ALB | cer | China R. Int. (CRI), CHN |
| 13670 | 150 | ALB | cer | China R. Int. (CRI), CHN |
| | 100 | CHN | dom | Xinjiang PBS, Urumqi |
| | 100 | MDG | mwv | Madagascar World Voice, MDG |
| 13675 ‡ | 250 | MRA | tin | R. Free Asia (RFA), USA |
| 13680 | 500 | IRN | sir | Pars Today (VOIRI), IRN |
| ± | 1 | TWN | ust | Sound of Hope, CHN |
| | 100 | ZMB | luv | Voice of Hope - Africa, ZMB |
| 13685 ‡ | 100 | MRA | sai | R. Free Asia (RFA), USA |
| | 500 | TUR | emr | Voice of Turkey (VOT), TUR |
| 13690 + | 15 | USA | inb | WINB, USA |
| 13695 | 500 | F | iss | R. France Int. (RFI), F |
| | 500 | IND | bgl | All India R. (AIR), IND |
| 13700 | 100 | CHN | dom | CNR13 Uyghur Sce, Lingshi |
| | 100 | CUB | hab | R. Habana Cuba, CUB |
| 13710 | 500 | ARS | riy | Saudi R. Int. (SBA), ARS |
| | 250 | D | nau | Missionswerk Friedensstimme, D |
| | 500 | IRN | sir | Pars Today (VOIRI), IRN |
| | 100 | MDG | mwv | Madagascar World Voice, MDG |
| | 250 | THA | udo | VO America (VOA), USA |
| 13720 | 500 | ARS | riy | Saudi R. Int. (SBA), ARS |
| | 500 | CHN | kas | China R. Int. (CRI), CHN |
| | 500 | CHN | xia | China R. Int. (CRI), CHN |
| | 300 | J | yam | R. Japan (NHK World), J |
| 13725 | 500 | F | iss | R. Japan (NHK World), J |

| kHz | N kW | Ctry | Site | Station, location |
|---|---|---|---|---|
| 13730 | 100 | CHN | kas | China R. Int. (CRI), CHN |
| | 250 | MDG | mdc | R. Japan (NHK World), J |
| | 50 | NZL | ran | RNZI (RNZ Pacific), NZL |
| | 300 | ROU | tig | R. Romania International, ROU |
| + | 90 | ROU | tig | R. Romania International, ROU |
| 13735 ‡ | 250 | MRA | tin | R. Free Asia (RFA), USA |
| | 500 | UAE | dha | R. Free Asia (RFA), USA |
| 13740 | 100 | CHN | kas | China R. Int. (CRI), CHN |
| | 100 | CUB | hab | R. Habana Cuba, CUB |
| | 500 | F | iss | R. France Int. (RFI), F |
| | 500 | IRN | sir | Pars Today (VOIRI), IRN |
| 13745 | 250 | THA | udo | R. Thailand World Service, THA |
| 13750 | 100 | BOT | bot | VO America (VOA), USA |
| | 500 | CHN | kun | China R. Int. (CRI), CHN |
| | 250 | KWT | kwt | VO America (VOA), USA |
| | 100 | STP | sao | VO America (VOA), USA |
| 13760 | 200 | KRE | kuj | Voice of Korea, KRE |
| 13765 | 100 | D | lam | R. Farda, USA |
| | 250 | KWT | kwt | VO America (VOA), USA |
| | 250 | THA | udo | R. Farda, USA |
| 13770 | 500 | CHN | xia | China R. Int. (CRI), CHN |
| 13775 ± | 1 | TWN | ust | Sound of Hope, CHN |
| 13780 | 100 | ARS | riy | Saudi R. Int. (SBA), ARS |
| | 100 | CHN | kas | China R. Int. (CRI), CHN |
| | 500 | CHN | kun | China R. Int. (CRI), CHN |
| | 100 | CUB | hab | R. Habana Cuba, CUB |
| | 250 | UAE | dha | Deutsche Welle, D |
| 13785 | 100 | ARS | riy | Saudi R. Int. (SBA), ARS |
| 13790 | 500 | CHN | uru | China R. Int. (CRI), CHN |
| | 500 | IRN | sir | Pars Today (VOIRI), IRN |
| 13795 | 100 | D | lam | R. Free Asia (RFA), USA |
| | 500 | IND | bgl | All India R. (AIR), IND |
| 13800 | 100 | CHN | kas | China R. Int. (CRI), CHN |
| † | 10 | SOM | *dom* | Puntland R., Garowe |
| 13810 | 100 | CHN | kas | China R. Int. (CRI), CHN |
| | 250 | G | wof | R. Ndarason Int., TCD |
| ‡ | 250 | MRA | tin | R. Free Asia (RFA), USA |
| 13820 | 500 | IRN | sir | Pars Today (VOIRI), IRN |
| | 500 | IRN | zah | Pars Today (VOIRI), IRN |
| ± | 1 | TWN | ust | Sound of Hope, CHN |
| | 250 | USA | grv | R. Martí, USA |
| 13830 | 100 | BOT | bot | VO America (VOA), USA |
| | 250 | CVA | smg | Vatican R., CVA |
| 13840 | 150 | F | iss | R. Nigeria Kaduna, NIG |
| | 250 | MDG | mdc | R. Japan (NHK World), J |
| + | 50 | NZL | ran | RNZI (RNZ Pacific), NZL |
| | 50 | NZL | ran | RNZI (RNZ Pacific), NZL |
| | 250 | UAE | dha | BBC World Service, G |
| 13845 | 100 | USA | wcr | University Network, USA |
| | 100 | USA | wcr | WWCR, USA |
| 13850 | 500 | CHN | bei | China R. Int. (CRI), CHN |
| 13855 | 500 | CHN | kas | China R. Int. (CRI), CHN |
| 13860 | 300 | G | wof | VOA Ashna R., USA |
| | 100 | STP | sao | VOA Studio 7, USA |
| | 250 | THA | udo | R. Azadi, USA |
| | 250 | UAE | dha | R. Azadi, USA |
| | 100 | UZB | tac | BBC World Service, G |
| 13865 | 300 | G | wof | VO America (VOA), USA |
| 13870 | 100 | CHN | *dom* | Xizang PBS, Lhasa |
| ± | 1 | TWN | ust | Sound of Hope, CHN |
| 13890 ± | 1 | TWN | ust | Sound of Hope, CHN |
| 13920 ± | 1 | TWN | ust | Sound of Hope, CHN |
| 13980 ± | 1 | TWN | ust | Sound of Hope, CHN |
| 14370 ± | 1 | TWN | ust | Sound of Hope, CHN |
| 14430 ± | 1 | TWN | ust | Sound of Hope, CHN |

| kHz | N kW | Ctry | Site | Station, location |
|---|---|---|---|---|
| 14500 ± | 1 | TWN | ust | Sound of Hope, CHN |
| 14560 ± | 1 | TWN | ust | Sound of Hope, CHN |
| 14600 ± | 1 | TWN | ust | Sound of Hope, CHN |
| 14670 | 3 | CAN | STF | CHU, Ottawa |
| 14690 ± | 1 | TWN | ust | Sound of Hope, CHN |
| 14775 ± | 1 | TWN | ust | Sound of Hope, CHN |
| 14800 ± | 1 | TWN | ust | Sound of Hope, CHN |
| 14820 ± | 1 | TWN | ust | Sound of Hope, CHN |
| 14850 ± | 1 | TWN | ust | Sound of Hope, CHN |
| 14870 ± | 1 | TWN | ust | Sound of Hope, CHN |
| 14900 ± | 1 | TWN | ust | Sound of Hope, CHN |
| 14920 ± | 1 | TWN | ust | Sound of Hope, CHN |
| 14980 ± | 1 | TWN | ust | Sound of Hope, CHN |
| 14996 | 10 | RUS | STF | RWM, Taldom |
| 15000 | 20 | CHN | STF | BPM, Pucheng |
| | 10 | HWA | STF | WWVH, Kekaha (HI) |
| | 10 | USA | STF | WWV, Fort Collins (CO) |
| 15006 | 1 | E | STF | EBC, San Fernando |
| 15030 ± | 500 | IND | bgl | All India R. (AIR), IND |
| | 500 | IND | bgl | All India R. (AIR), IND |
| 15070 ± | 1 | TWN | ust | Sound of Hope, CHN |
| 15105 | 250 | BGD | dka | Bangladesh Betar, BGD |
| | 200 | KRE | kuj | Voice of Korea, KRE |
| | 300 | MDA | kch | TWR Africa, AFS |
| | 100 | SWZ | man | TWR Africa, AFS |
| 15110 | 100 | CHN | kas | China R. Int. (CRI), CHN |
| + | 250 | KWT | kbd | R.Kuwait, KWT |
| | 250 | PHL | pht | VO America (VOA), USA |
| 15120 | 500 | ARS | riy | Saudi R. Int. (SBA), ARS |
| | 250 | ASC | asc | VO America (VOA), USA |
| | 500 | CHN | bei | China R. Int. (CRI), CHN |
| | 250 | CUB | qvc | China R. Int. (CRI), CHN |
| +† | 250 | NIG | aja | Voice of Nigeria, NIG |
| 15125 | 500 | CHN | bei | China R. Int. (CRI), CHN |
| 15130 | 150 | CHN | bei | China R. Int. (CRI), CHN |
| | 500 | F | iss | R. Japan (NHK World), J |
| | 500 | IRN | sir | Pars Today (VOIRI), IRN |
| 15135 | 500 | CHN | kas | China R. Int. (CRI), CHN |
| | 100 | CHN | kun | China R. Int. (CRI), CHN |
| | 500 | CHN | kun | China R. Int. (CRI), CHN |
| 15140 | 100 | CUB | hab | R. Habana Cuba, CUB |
| | 250 | CUB | hab | R. Habana Cuba, CUB |
| | 500 | IRN | sir | Pars Today (VOIRI), IRN |
| | 50 | OMA | thu | R. Sultanate of Oman, OMA |
| 15145 | 300 | AUT | mos | AWR Africa, G |
| | 100 | CHN | kas | China R. Int. (CRI), CHN |
| | 500 | CHN | xia | China R. Int. (CRI), CHN |
| | 100 | D | nau | AWR Africa, G |
| 15150 | 250 | MDG | mdc | Adventist World R. (AWR), USA |
| | 250 | THA | udo | VO America (VOA), USA |
| 15155 | 125 | CLN | trm | AWR Africa, G |
| | 100 | D | lam | R. Free Asia (RFA), USA |
| 15160 | 500 | CHN | jin | China R. Int. (CRI), CHN |
| | 100 | CHN | nnn | China R. Int. (CRI), CHN |
| | 250 | D | nau | AWR Africa, G |
| | 250 | KOR | kim | KBS World R., KOR |
| | 250 | KWT | kwt | VO America (VOA), USA |
| 15170 | 500 | ARS | riy | Saudi R. Int. (SBA), ARS |
| | 100 | CHN | kas | China R. Int. (CRI), CHN |
| 15175 | 100 | BOT | bot | VO America (VOA), USA |
| 15180 | 125 | CLN | trm | AWR Asia/Pacific, THA |
| | 100 | GUM | sda | AWR Asia/Pacific, THA |
| | 200 | KRE | kuj | Voice of Korea, KRE |
| | 100 | STP | sao | VO America (VOA), USA |
| 15185 | 100 | CHN | kas | China R. Int. (CRI), CHN |

| kHz | N | kW | Ctry | Site | Station, location |
|---|---|---|---|---|---|
| | + | 500 | IND | bgl | All India R. (AIR), IND |
| 15190 | † | 5 | B | *dom* | R. Inconfidência, Belo Horizonte |
| | | 500 | CHN | kas | China R. Int. (CRI), CHN |
| | | 250 | PHL | pht | R. Pilipinas (DZRP), PHL |
| 15195 | | 500 | F | iss | Deutsche Welle, D |
| | | 100 | GUM | sda | AWR Asia/Pacific, THA |
| | | 300 | J | yam | R. Japan (NHK World), J |
| 15200 | | 250 | AFS | mey | Deutsche Welle, D |
| | | 500 | IRN | sir | Pars Today (VOIRI), IRN |
| 15205 | | 500 | ARS | riy | Saudi R. Int. (SBA), ARS |
| | | 500 | CHN | kas | China R. Int. (CRI), CHN |
| 15210 | | 500 | CHN | kun | China R. Int. (CRI), CHN |
| | | 250 | IND | pan | All India R. (AIR), IND |
| 15215 | | 125 | CLN | trm | AWR Asia/Pacific, THA |
| | | 500 | F | iss | R. Öömrang, D |
| | | 100 | GUM | sda | AWR Asia/Pacific, THA |
| | | 250 | UAE | dha | FEBC Philippines, PHL |
| 15220 | | 500 | CHN | kas | China R. Int. (CRI), CHN |
| 15225 | | 500 | ARS | riy | Saudi R. Int. (SBA), ARS |
| | | 500 | CHN | kas | China R. Int. (CRI), CHN |
| 15235 | | 250 | AFS | mey | Channel Africa, AFS |
| | | 500 | TUR | emr | Voice of Turkey (VOT), TUR |
| 15240 | | 500 | IRN | sir | Pars Today (VOIRI), IRN |
| 15245 | | 200 | KRE | kuj | Voice of Korea, KRE |
| 15250 | | 100 | CHN | kun | China R. Int. (CRI), CHN |
| | | 125 | CLN | trm | AWR Asia/Pacific, THA |
| 15255 | | 100 | GUM | sda | AWR Asia/Pacific, THA |
| | | 250 | MDG | mdc | AWR Asia/Pacific, THA |
| | | 300 | ROU | gal | R. Romania International, ROU |
| 15260 | | 250 | AFS | mey | VO America (VOA), USA |
| | | 250 | AUT | mos | IBRA Media, S |
| | | 300 | ROU | gal | R. Romania International, ROU |
| 15270 | | 150 | CHN | *dom* | CNR2 Business R., Beijing |
| | | 500 | TUR | emr | Voice of Turkey (VOT), TUR |
| | | 100 | TWN | pao | R. Taiwan International, TWN |
| 15275 | | 500 | F | iss | Deutsche Welle, D |
| | | 500 | F | iss | R. France Int. (RFI), F |
| | | 250 | MDG | mdc | Deutsche Welle, D |
| 15280 | | 300 | J | yam | R. Japan (NHK World), J |
| 15285 | | 500 | ARS | riy | Saudi R. Int. (SBA), ARS |
| | † | 100 | EGY | abz | R. Cairo, EGY |
| 15290 | † | 100 | EGY | abz | R. Cairo, EGY |
| | | 250 | F | iss | R. Japan (NHK World), J |
| 15295 | ± | 1 | TWN | ust | Sound of Hope, CHN |
| 15300 | | 250 | CVA | smg | VO America (VOA), USA |
| | | 500 | F | iss | R. France Int. (RFI), F |
| 15310 | † | 100 | EGY | abs | R. Cairo, EGY |
| | † | 125 | EGY | abs | R. Cairo, EGY |
| | | 250 | OMA | sla | BBC World Service, G |
| | | 250 | SNG | sng | BBC World Service, G |
| 15315 | | 250 | OMA | sla | BBC World Service, G |
| 15320 | | 500 | F | iss | Deutsche Welle, D |
| | | 100 | GUM | sda | AWR Asia/Pacific, THA |
| | | 300 | TWN | pao | R. Taiwan International, TWN |
| 15325 | | 300 | J | yam | R. Japan (NHK World), J |
| 15330 | | 100 | PHL | boc | FEBC Philippines, PHL |
| 15335 | | 500 | CHN | kas | China R. Int. (CRI), CHN |
| 15340 | | 500 | CHN | xia | China R. Int. (CRI), CHN |
| | | 100 | D | lam | R. Free Asia (RFA), USA |
| | ± | 1 | TWN | ust | Sound of Hope, CHN |
| 15350 | | 250 | AFS | mey | R. Dabanga, SDN |
| | | 100 | CHN | kas | China R. Int. (CRI), CHN |
| | | 500 | TUR | emr | Voice of Turkey (VOT), TUR |
| | | 300 | TWN | pao | R. Taiwan International, TWN |
| 15360 | | 125 | CLN | trm | Adventist World R. (AWR), USA |

| kHz | N | kW | Ctry | Site | Station, location |
|---|---|---|---|---|---|
| | | 125 | CLN | trm | AWR Asia/Pacific, THA |
| | | 250 | F | iss | VO Amara Radio, ETH |
| | | 500 | IRN | sir | Pars Today (VOIRI), IRN |
| | | 100 | SWZ | man | TWR India, IND |
| | | 500 | TUR | emr | Voice of Turkey (VOT), TUR |
| 15365 | | 100 | GUM | sda | AWR Asia/Pacific, THA |
| 15370 | | 100 | CHN | *dom* | CNR1 VO China, Shijiazhuang |
| | | 100 | CUB | hab | R. Habana Cuba, CUB |
| 15375 | | 250 | TJK | dsb | R. Free Asia (RFA), USA |
| 15380 | | 500 | ARS | riy | Saudi R. Int. (SBA), ARS |
| | | 100 | CHN | *dom* | CNR1 VO China, Beijing |
| | | 300 | ROU | gal | R. Romania International, ROU |
| 15390 | | 100 | CHN | *dom* | CNR13 Uyghur Sce, Lingshi |
| | | 500 | TUR | emr | Voice of Turkey (VOT), TUR |
| 15400 | | 125 | ASC | asc | BBC World Service, G |
| | | 125 | CLN | trm | AWR Asia/Pacific, THA |
| | | 250 | MDG | mdc | BBC World Service, G |
| | | 300 | ROU | tig | R. Romania International, ROU |
| 15410 | | 75 | AUS | knx | Reach Beyond Australia, AUS |
| | | 250 | CVA | smg | Eye R., SSD |
| | | 250 | F | iss | Eye R., SSD |
| | | 500 | IND | bgl | All India R. (AIR), IND |
| | | 250 | IND | pan | All India R. (AIR), IND |
| 15420 | | 100 | AFS | mey | BBC World Service, G |
| | | 250 | MDG | mdc | BBC World Service, G |
| | | 250 | MDG | mdc | R. Itahuka, RRW |
| | | 250 | UAE | dha | BBC World Service, G |
| 15425 | | 500 | CHN | xia | China R. Int. (CRI), CHN |
| | | 250 | PHL | pht | VO America (VOA), USA |
| 15430 | | 100 | CHN | kas | China R. Int. (CRI), CHN |
| | | 125 | CLN | trm | AWR Asia/Pacific, THA |
| | | 300 | ROU | gal | R. Romania International, ROU |
| | | 300 | ROU | tig | R. Romania International, ROU |
| 15435 | | 500 | ARS | riy | Saudi R. Int. (SBA), ARS |
| | | 500 | CHN | xia | China R. Int. (CRI), CHN |
| | | 100 | PHL | boc | FEBC Philippines, PHL |
| 15440 | | 500 | CHN | kun | China R. Int. (CRI), CHN |
| | | 500 | IRN | sir | Pars Today (VOIRI), IRN |
| 15445 | | 500 | CHN | kas | China R. Int. (CRI), CHN |
| | | 100 | TWN | tsh | AWR Asia/Pacific, THA |
| 15450 | † | 100 | EGY | abz | R. Cairo, EGY |
| | | 100 | GUM | sda | AWR Asia/Pacific, THA |
| | | 100 | PHL | boc | FEBC Philippines, PHL |
| | | 100 | PHL | iba | FEBC Philippines, PHL |
| | | 250 | PHL | pht | VO America (VOA), USA |
| | + | 90 | ROU | tig | R. Romania International, ROU |
| 15455 | | 500 | F | iss | R. France Int. (RFI), F |
| 15460 | | 300 | ROU | gal | R. Romania International, ROU |
| | | 90 | ROU | tig | R. Romania International, ROU |
| | | 100 | STP | sao | VO America (VOA), USA |
| | | 100 | STP | sao | VOA Studio 7, USA |
| 15465 | | 100 | CHN | kas | China R. Int. (CRI), CHN |
| | | 100 | TWN | pao | R. Taiwan International, TWN |
| 15476 | † | 2 | ATA | lra | RN Arcángel S.Gabriel (LRA36), ATA |
| 15480 | | 100 | CHN | *dom* | CNR1 VO China, Beijing |
| | | 500 | TUR | emr | Voice of Turkey (VOT), TUR |
| 15490 | | 250 | AFS | mey | AWR Africa, G |
| | | 250 | AFS | mey | BBC World Service, G |
| | | 500 | ARS | riy | Saudi R. Int. (SBA), ARS |
| | | 250 | ASC | asc | BBC World Service, G |
| | | 250 | F | iss | AWR Africa, G |
| | | 250 | G | wof | BBC World Service, G |
| 15500 | | 150 | CHN | *dom* | CNR2 Business R., Beijing |
| | | 125 | CLN | trm | AWR Africa, G |
| | | 100 | GUM | sda | AWR Asia/Pacific, THA |

| kHz | N | kW | Ctry | Site | Station, location |
|---|---|---|---|---|---|
| 15505 | | 250 | BGD | dka | Bangladesh Betar, BGD |
| 15510 | | 100 | MDG | mwv | Madagascar World Voice, MDG |
| | | 250 | SNG | sng | BBC World Service, G |
| 15515 | | 250 | KWT | kbd | R.Kuwait, KWT |
| | | 100 | ROU | tig | IRRS Shortwave, I |
| 15525 | | 500 | CHN | uru | China R. Int. (CRI), CHN |
| 15530 | | 250 | KWT | kbd | R.Kuwait, KWT |
| 15540 | | 100 | CHN | dom | CNR2 Business R., Lingshi |
| | | 250 | KWT | kbd | R.Kuwait, KWT |
| | + | 250 | KWT | kbd | R.Kuwait, KWT |
| 15550 | | 100 | CHN | kas | China R. Int. (CRI), CHN |
| | | 100 | CHN | dom | CNR1 VO China, Beijing |
| | | 250 | CVA | smg | R. Tamazuj, SSD |
| | | 250 | F | iss | R. Dabanga, SDN |
| 15555 | | 1 | USA | jhr | WJHR R. International, USA |
| 15560 | | 500 | CHN | xia | China R. Int. (CRI), CHN |
| | | 100 | PHL | boc | FEBC Philippines, PHL |
| | | 250 | PHL | pht | VO America (VOA), USA |
| | | 250 | THA | udo | VO America (VOA), USA |
| 15570 | | 100 | CHN | dom | CNR11 Tibetan Sce, Xi'an |
| 15575 | | 100 | AUS | knx | Reach Beyond Australia, AUS |
| | | 250 | KOR | kim | KBS World R., KOR |
| 15580 | | 100 | BOT | bot | VO America (VOA), USA |
| | + | 30 | CHN | dom | CNR1 VO China, Dongfang |
| | | 100 | PHL | boc | FEBC Philippines, PHL |
| | ± | 1 | TWN | ust | Sound of Hope, CHN |
| | | 250 | USA | grv | VO America (VOA), USA |
| 15590 | | 300 | J | yam | R. Japan (NHK World), J |
| 15595 | | 100 | CVA | smg | Vatican R., CVA |
| | | 250 | CVA | smg | Vatican R., CVA |
| 15600 | | 250 | G | wof | VO America (VOA), USA |
| 15610 | | 125 | CLN | trm | AWR Asia/Pacific, THA |
| | | 250 | THA | udo | VO America (VOA), USA |
| | | 250 | USA | ewn | WEWN - EWTN Shortwave, USA |
| 15620 | | 100 | BOT | bot | VO America (VOA), USA |
| | | 500 | CHN | kas | China R. Int. (CRI), CHN |
| | | 250 | CVA | smg | VO America (VOA), USA |
| | | 100 | PHL | boc | FEBC Philippines, PHL |
| | + | 100 | SNG | sng | BBC World Service, G |
| 15625 | | 125 | CLN | trm | AWR Asia/Pacific, THA |
| 15630 | † | 100 | EGY | abs | R. Cairo, EGY |
| 15640 | | 250 | KWT | kwt | R. Azadi, USA |
| | | 100 | PHL | boc | FEBC Philippines, PHL |
| | | 250 | PHL | pht | R. Pilipinas (DZRP), PHL |
| | | 100 | TJK | dsb | Bible Voice Broadcasting (BVB), CAN |
| 15665 | | 500 | CHN | uru | China R. Int. (CRI), CHN |
| | | 100 | D | lam | R. Free Asia (RFA), USA |
| 15675 | | 100 | PLW | hbn | T8WH - World Harvest R. Int, PLW |
| 15680 | | 100 | CHN | dom | Xizang PBS, Lhasa |
| | | 250 | MDG | mdc | AWR Asia/Pacific, THA |
| 15685 | | 100 | GUM | sda | AWR Asia/Pacific, THA |
| 15690 | | 100 | D | bib | R. Farda, USA |
| 15700 | | 250 | CUB | qvc | China R. Int. (CRI), CHN |
| 15710 | | 100 | CHN | dom | CNR6 VO Shenzhou, Beijing |
| 15715 | | 100 | BOT | bot | VO America (VOA), USA |
| | | 250 | CVA | smg | VO America (VOA), USA |
| | | 250 | THA | udo | VO America (VOA), USA |
| 15720 | | 250 | MDG | mdc | R. Japan (NHK World), J |
| | | 50 | NZL | ran | RNZI (RNZ Pacific), NZL |
| 15730 | | 100 | BOT | bot | VO America (VOA), USA |
| | | 50 | CUB | hab | R. Habana Cuba, CUB |
| | | 250 | USA | grv | VO America (VOA), USA |
| 15740 | ± | 1 | TWN | ust | Sound of Hope, CHN |
| 15745 | | 200 | TJK | dsb | R. Free Asia (RFA), USA |
| 15760 | | 250 | THA | udo | R. Mashaal, USA |
| 15770 | | 250 | IND | pan | All India R. (AIR), IND |
| 15775 | ± | 1 | TWN | ust | Sound of Hope, CHN |
| 15785 | + | 0.1 | D | dom | Funklust, Erlangen |
| 15795 | | 100 | USA | wcr | WWCR, USA |
| 15800 | ± | 1 | TWN | ust | Sound of Hope, CHN |
| 15825 | | 100 | USA | wcr | WWCR, USA |
| 15840 | ± | 1 | TWN | ust | Sound of Hope, CHN |
| 15870 | ± | 1 | TWN | ust | Sound of Hope, CHN |
| 15920 | ± | 1 | TWN | ust | Sound of Hope, CHN |
| 15940 | ± | 1 | TWN | ust | Sound of Hope, CHN |
| 15970 | ± | 1 | TWN | ust | Sound of Hope, CHN |
| 16100 | ± | 1 | TWN | ust | Sound of Hope, CHN |
| 16160 | ± | 1 | TWN | ust | Sound of Hope, CHN |
| 16250 | ± | 1 | TWN | ust | Sound of Hope, CHN |
| 16300 | ± | 1 | TWN | ust | Sound of Hope, CHN |
| 16350 | ± | 1 | TWN | ust | Sound of Hope, CHN |
| 16600 | ± | 1 | TWN | ust | Sound of Hope, CHN |
| 16680 | ± | 1 | TWN | ust | Sound of Hope, CHN |
| 16770 | ± | 1 | TWN | ust | Sound of Hope, CHN |
| 16980 | ± | 1 | TWN | ust | Sound of Hope, CHN |
| 17080 | ± | 1 | TWN | ust | Sound of Hope, CHN |
| 17170 | ± | 1 | TWN | ust | Sound of Hope, CHN |
| 17200 | ± | 1 | TWN | ust | Sound of Hope, CHN |
| 17400 | ± | 1 | TWN | ust | Sound of Hope, CHN |
| 17440 | ± | 1 | TWN | ust | Sound of Hope, CHN |
| 17485 | | 500 | CHN | kas | China R. Int. (CRI), CHN |
| 17490 | | 500 | CHN | bei | China R. Int. (CRI), CHN |
| | | 500 | CHN | kas | China R. Int. (CRI), CHN |
| 17510 | | 500 | CHN | kas | China R. Int. (CRI), CHN |
| | | 500 | CHN | xia | China R. Int. (CRI), CHN |
| | | 500 | IND | bgl | All India R. (AIR), IND |
| | ‡ | 250 | MRA | tin | R. Free Asia (RFA), USA |
| 17520 | | 100 | CHN | kas | China R. Int. (CRI), CHN |
| 17525 | ‡ | 250 | MRA | tin | R. Free Asia (RFA), USA |
| 17530 | | 100 | GUM | sda | AWR Asia/Pacific, THA |
| | | 100 | MDG | mwv | Madagascar World Voice, MDG |
| | | 500 | TUR | emr | Voice of Turkey (VOT), TUR |
| 17540 | | 500 | CHN | bei | China R. Int. (CRI), CHN |
| | | 100 | GUM | sda | AWR Asia/Pacific, THA |
| | | 500 | IRN | sir | Pars Today (VOIRI), IRN |
| 17545 | | 150 | F | iss | Alsmood, ERI |
| 17550 | | 100 | CHN | dom | CNR1 VO China, Beijing |
| | | 250 | KWT | kbd | R.Kuwait, KWT |
| 17560 | | 500 | ARS | riy | Saudi R. Int. (SBA), ARS |
| | | 500 | CHN | xia | China R. Int. (CRI), CHN |
| 17565 | | 100 | CHN | dom | CNR1 VO China, Beijing |
| 17570 | | 500 | CHN | kas | China R. Int. (CRI), CHN |
| | | 500 | CHN | uru | China R. Int. (CRI), CHN |
| | | 250 | MDG | mdc | AWR Africa, G |
| 17580 | | 100 | CHN | dom | CNR1 VO China, Lingshi |
| 17585 | | 100 | D | bib | VO America (VOA), USA |
| 17590 | | 100 | CVA | smg | Vatican R., CVA |
| | | 250 | CVA | smg | Vatican R., CVA |
| 17595 | | 100 | CHN | dom | CNR1 VO China, Shijiazhuang |
| 17600 | | 100 | BOT | bot | VO America (VOA), USA |
| | | 250 | THA | udo | VO America (VOA), USA |
| 17605 | | 300 | AUT | mos | AWR Africa, G |
| | | 100 | CHN | dom | CNR1 VO China, Beijing |
| 17615 | | 500 | ARS | riy | Saudi R. Int. (SBA), ARS |
| | | 500 | CHN | uru | China R. Int. (CRI), CHN |
| 17620 | | 500 | F | iss | R. France Int. (RFI), F |
| 17625 | | 500 | ARS | riy | Saudi R. Int. (SBA), ARS |
| | | 150 | CHN | dom | CNR2 Business R., Beijing |

| kHz | N | kW | Ctry | Site | Station, location |
|---|---|---|---|---|---|
| 17630 | | 250 | THA | udo | R. Thailand World Service, THA |
| 17640 | | 250 | AFS | mey | BBC World Service, G |
| | | 250 | ASC | asc | BBC World Service, G |
| | | 500 | CHN | xia | China R. Int. (CRI), CHN |
| | | 300 | ROU | tig | R. Romania International, ROU |
| | | 250 | THA | udo | R. Thailand World Service, THA |
| | | 250 | UAE | dha | BBC World Service, G |
| 17650 | | 500 | CHN | kas | China R. Int. (CRI), CHN |
| | | 100 | GUM | sda | AWR Asia/Pacific, THA |
| | | 125 | MDG | mdc | Bible Voice Broadcasting (BVB), CAN |
| 17655 | | 100 | STP | sao | VO America (VOA), USA |
| | | 250 | USA | grv | VO America (VOA), USA |
| 17660 | | 500 | ARS | riy | Saudi R. Int. (SBA), ARS |
| | | 500 | F | iss | R. France Int. (RFI), F |
| | ‡ | 100 | MRA | sai | R. Free Asia (RFA), USA |
| 17665 | | 500 | IRN | sir | Pars Today (VOIRI), IRN |
| 17670 | | 500 | CHN | kas | China R. Int. (CRI), CHN |
| | | 500 | CHN | kun | China R. Int. (CRI), CHN |
| | | 250 | MDG | mdc | AWR Asia/Pacific, THA |
| 17675 | ‡ | 250 | MRA | tin | R. Free Asia (RFA), USA |
| 17680 | | 100 | CHN | kun | China R. Int. (CRI), CHN |
| | | 150 | CHN | kun | China R. Int. (CRI), CHN |
| | | 250 | KWT | kwt | VO America (VOA), USA |
| | | 250 | UAE | dha | TWR Africa, AFS |
| 17690 | | 500 | CHN | jin | China R. Int. (CRI), CHN |
| | | 100 | CHN | dom | CNR1 VO China, Nanning |
| | | 100 | F | iss | R. Nigeria Kaduna, NIG |
| | | 250 | KWT | kwt | R. Azadi, USA |
| 17700 | | 100 | BOT | bot | VO America (VOA), USA |
| | | 250 | PHL | pht | R. Pilipinas (DZRP), PHL |
| 17705 | | 500 | ARS | riy | Saudi R. Int. (SBA), ARS |
| | | 500 | IND | bgl | All India R. (AIR), IND |
| 17710 | | 250 | AFS | mey | Deutsche Welle, D |
| | | 500 | CHN | bei | China R. Int. (CRI), CHN |
| | | 500 | CHN | jin | China R. Int. (CRI), CHN |
| 17720 | | 500 | CHN | kas | China R. Int. (CRI), CHN |
| | | 250 | THA | udo | VO America (VOA), USA |
| | | 500 | TUR | emr | Voice of Turkey (VOT), TUR |
| 17730 | | 500 | ARS | riy | Saudi R. Int. (SBA), ARS |
| | | 500 | CHN | xia | China R. Int. (CRI), CHN |
| | | 250 | MDG | mdc | AWR Asia/Pacific, THA |
| 17735 | | 100 | CHN | kun | China R. Int. (CRI), CHN |
| 17740 | | 500 | ARS | riy | Saudi R. Int. (SBA), ARS |
| | | 500 | CHN | xia | China R. Int. (CRI), CHN |
| 17745 | | 250 | AFS | mey | BBC World Service, G |
| | | 250 | UAE | dha | BBC World Service, G |
| 17750 | | 500 | CHN | xia | China R. Int. (CRI), CHN |
| 17760 | | 250 | AFS | mey | Amateur R. Today, AFS |
| | | 250 | KWT | kbd | R.Kuwait, KWT |
| | ± | 1 | TWN | ust | Sound of Hope, CHN |
| 17770 | | 250 | AFS | mey | Channel Africa, AFS |
| 17775 | | 50 | USA | voh | KVOH - Voice of Hope, USA |
| 17780 | | 125 | ASC | asc | BBC World Service, G |
| | | 250 | ASC | asc | BBC World Service, G |
| | | 250 | CLN | trm | AWR Africa, G |
| | | 300 | ROU | gal | R. Romania International, ROU |
| 17790 | | 100 | D | lam | R. Free Asia (RFA), USA |
| | | 250 | PHL | pht | VO America (VOA), USA |
| 17795 | | 100 | D | lam | R. Free Asia (RFA), USA |
| 17800 | | 500 | F | iss | Deutsche Welle, D |
| | | 300 | ROU | gal | R. Romania International, ROU |
| 17805 | | 500 | ARS | riy | Saudi R. Int. (SBA), ARS |
| 17810 | | 300 | J | yam | R. Japan (NHK World), J |
| | | 300 | ROU | tig | R. Romania International, ROU |
| 17815 | | 100 | D | lam | R. Free Asia (RFA), USA |

| kHz | N | kW | Ctry | Site | Station, location |
|---|---|---|---|---|---|
| | | 500 | F | iss | R. France Int. (RFI), F |
| | | 200 | TJK | dsb | R. Free Asia (RFA), USA |
| | | 250 | USA | hri | WHRI - World Harvest R., USA |
| 17820 | | 100 | D | lam | R. Free Asia (RFA), USA |
| | | 250 | PHL | pht | R. Pilipinas (DZRP), PHL |
| 17830 | | 250 | AFS | mey | BBC World Service, G |
| | | 125 | ASC | asc | BBC World Service, G |
| | | 100 | D | lam | R. Free Asia (RFA), USA |
| | | 250 | PHL | pht | VO America (VOA), USA |
| | | 250 | UAE | dha | BBC World Service, G |
| 17840 | | 100 | D | lam | R. Free Asia (RFA), USA |
| 17845 | | 100 | CHN | dom | CNR1 VO China, Shijiazhuang |
| | | 250 | UAE | dha | R. Ergo, SOM |
| 17850 | | 250 | CVA | smg | VO America (VOA), USA |
| | | 500 | F | iss | R. France Int. (RFI), F |
| | | 250 | F | iss | R. Xoriyo, ETH |
| | | 250 | F | iss | VO Independent Oromia, ETH |
| | | 300 | ROU | gal | R. Romania International, ROU |
| 17855 | | 500 | CHN | bei | China R. Int. (CRI), CHN |
| | | 100 | D | lam | R. Free Asia (RFA), USA |
| 17865 | | 250 | PHL | pht | VO America (VOA), USA |
| 17870 | | 250 | AFS | mey | BBC World Service, G |
| | | 100 | D | lam | VO America (VOA), USA |
| | | 500 | IND | bgl | All India R. (AIR), IND |
| 17880 | | 100 | D | bib | R. Mashaal, USA |
| | | 100 | GUM | sda | AWR Asia/Pacific, THA |
| 17885 | | 100 | BOT | bot | VO America (VOA), USA |
| 17890 | | 100 | CHN | dom | CNR1 VO China, Beijing |
| 17895 | | 500 | ARS | riy | Saudi R. Int. (SBA), ARS |
| | | 100 | BOT | bot | VO America (VOA), USA |
| | + | 500 | IND | bgl | All India R. (AIR), IND |
| | | 100 | STP | sao | VO America (VOA), USA |
| 18180 | ± | 1 | TWN | ust | Sound of Hope, CHN |
| 18870 | ± | 1 | TWN | ust | Sound of Hope, CHN |
| 20000 | | 2.5 | USA | STF | WWV, Fort Collins (CO) |
| 21470 | | 250 | ASC | asc | BBC World Service, G |
| | | 250 | UAE | dha | BBC World Service, G |
| 21480 | | 125 | MDG | mdc | Bible Voice Broadcasting (BVB), CAN |
| | ‡ | 250 | MRA | tin | R. Free Asia (RFA), USA |
| 21490 | ‡ | 250 | MRA | tin | R. Free Asia (RFA), USA |
| | | 300 | ROU | tig | R. Romania International, ROU |
| 21500 | ‡ | 250 | MRA | tin | R. Free Asia (RFA), USA |
| 21505 | | 500 | ARS | riy | Saudi R. Int. (SBA), ARS |
| 21510 | ‡ | 250 | MRA | tin | R. Free Asia (RFA), USA |
| 21525 | | 100 | USA | rmi | Pan American Broadcasting, USA |
| | | 100 | USA | rmi | WRMI - R. Miami Int., USA |
| 21530 | ‡ | 250 | MRA | tin | R. Free Asia (RFA), USA |
| | ± | 1 | TWN | ust | Sound of Hope, CHN |
| 21580 | | 500 | F | iss | R. France Int. (RFI), F |
| 21600 | | 250 | PHL | pht | VO America (VOA), USA |
| 21610 | ‡ | 250 | MRA | tin | R. Free Asia (RFA), USA |
| | | 250 | USA | hri | WHRI - World Harvest R., USA |
| 21620 | ‡ | 250 | MRA | tin | R. Free Asia (RFA), USA |
| | | 250 | PHL | pht | VO America (VOA), USA |
| 21630 | | 250 | ASC | asc | BBC World Service, G |
| 21670 | | 500 | ARS | riy | Saudi R. Int. (SBA), ARS |
| 21680 | | 500 | UAE | dha | R. Free Asia (RFA), USA |
| 21690 | | 500 | F | iss | R. France Int. (RFI), F |
| | | 250 | MDG | mdc | R. France Int. (RFI), F |
| 21700 | ‡ | 250 | MRA | tin | R. Free Asia (RFA), USA |
| 21760 | | 250 | PHL | pht | VO America (VOA), USA |
| 21795 | | 250 | PHL | pht | VO America (VOA), USA |
| 21800 | ± | 1 | TWN | ust | Sound of Hope, CHN |
| 25000 | | 2.5 | USA | STF | WWV, Fort Collins (CO) |

# International Broadcasts in English, French, German, Portuguese and Spanish

## English

| 0000 | English | Area | kHz |
|---|---|---|---|
| 0000-0015 | WRMI | Car,LAm | 9955rmi |
| 0000-0030 | R. Japan | NAm | 5950rmi^ |
| 0000-0030 | VO Vietnam | NAm | 7315hri |
| 0000-0030 | WRMI | NAm | 7730rmi, 9395rmi |
| 0000-0100 | BBC World Sce | SAs | 5875wof |
| 0000-0100 | CRI | SAs | 7425kas |
| 0000-0100 | CRI | EAs | 9425bei |
| 0000-0100 | RFI | NAm | 5950rmi^ |
| 0000-0100 | R. Habana Cuba | CAm | 5040hab |
| 0000-0100 | R. Thailand WS | NAm | 13745udo |
| 0000-0100 | Overcomer Min. | NAm | 9455rmi |
| 0000-0100 | VORW R. Int | NAm | 5950rmi, 7730rmi, 9395rmi |
| 0000-0100 | WRMI | NAm | 7730rmi, 9395rmi |
| 0000-0200 | BBC World Sce | SAs | 5970erv |
| 0000-0200 | CRI | SEA | 11885xia, 15125bei |
| 0000-0200 | CRI | NAm | 6020cer, 9570cer |
| 0000-0200 | CRI | SAs | 6075kas, 6180kas |
| 0000-0200 | The Mighty KBC | NAm | 5960nau |
| 0000-0200 | WWCR | NAm,Af | 7520wcr |
| 0000-0400 | WHRI | NAm,Eu | 5920hri |
| 0000-0400 | WWRB | NAm | 5050wrb |
| 0000-0500 | WBCQ | NAm,CAm | 5130bcq*,† |
| 0000-0900 | WEWN | Af | 11520ewn |
| 0000-1100 | WTWW | LAm | 5085tww |
| 0000-1200 | University Net. | Af | 5935wcr |
| 0000-1400 | WTWW | NAm,Eu,Af | 5830tww |
| 0000-2400 | Overcomer Min. | NAm | 9330bcq |
| 0000-2400 | WBCQ | NAm,CAm | 9330bcq*,† |
| 0000-2400 | World Music R. | Eu | 5840rnd |
| 0015-0045 | WRMI | Car,LAm | 9955rmi |
| 0030-0045 | WRMI | Car,LAm | 9955rmi |
| 0030-0100 | IBC | NAm,Pac | 7730rmi |
| 0030-0100 | IBC | NAm | 9395rmi |
| 0030-0100 | R. Slovakia Int | NAm | 5850rmi |
| 0030-0100 | R. Slovakia Int | Eu,NAm | 7780rmi |
| 0030-0100 | World of Radio | NAm | 7730rmi |
| 0030-0100 | WRMI | NAm | 5950rmi |
| 0030-0100 | WRMI | NAm | 7730rmi, 9395rmi |
| 0030-0130 | R.Taiwan Int. | EAs | 1098kou |
| 0045-0100 | WRMI | Car,LAm | 9955rmi |
| **0100** | **English** | | |
| 0100-0115 | WRMI | Car | 5010rmi |
| 0100-0115 | WRMI | NAm,Eu,ME | 7780rmi |
| 0100-0115 | WRMI | Car,LAm | 9955rmi |

| 0100 | English | Area | kHz |
|---|---|---|---|
| 0100-0130 | IBC | Car | 5010rmi |
| 0100-0130 | IBC | NAm,Eu,ME | 7780rmi |
| 0100-0130 | R. Prague | NAm | 5950rmi^ |
| 0100-0130 | VO Vietnam | NAm | 7315hri |
| 0100-0130 | WRMI | Car | 5010rmi |
| 0100-0130 | WRMI | NAm,Eu,ME | 7780rmi |
| 0100-0130 | WRMI | NAm | 9395rmi |
| 0100-0130 | WRMI | Car,LAm | 9955rmi |
| 0100-0145 | WRMI | Car | 5010rmi |
| 0100-0200 | BBC World Sce | SAs | 9410sng |
| 0100-0200 | CRI | SAs | 7370kas |
| 0100-0200 | CRI | NAm | 9580qvc |
| 0100-0200 | CRI | Eu | 9675kas |
| 0100-0200 | PCJ R. Int. | Car | 5010rmi* |
| 0100-0200 | R.Romania Int | NAm | 6130gal, 7325gal |
| 0100-0200 | VORW R. Int | NAm | 5850rmi |
| 0100-0200 | VORW R. Int | NAm,Eu,ME | 7780rmi |
| 0100-0200 | WRMI | NAm,Eu,ME | 7780rmi |
| 0100-0200 | WRMI | NAm | 9395rmi |
| 0100-0300 | WRMI | NAm | 9455rmi |
| 0100-0400 | Overcomer Min. | NAm | 7730rmi |
| 0100-0500 | T8WH - WHR Int | SEA | 15675hbn |
| 0100-0520 | BBC World Sce | Eu | 198dro |
| 0100-1300 | WWCR | NAm | 4840wcr |
| 0115-0130 | WRMI | Car,LAm | 9955rmi |
| 0130-0145 | WRMI | Car,LAm | 9955rmi |
| 0130-0200 | IBC | NAm,As | 5850rmi |
| 0130-0200 | IBC | NAm,Eu,ME | 7780rmi |
| 0130-0200 | R. Slovakia Int | NAm | 5950rmi^ |
| 0130-0200 | WRMI | NAm,Eu,ME | 7780rmi |
| 0130-0230 | BBC World Sce | SAs | 1413sla |
| 0130-0230 | WRMI | NAm | 9395rmi |
| **0200** | **English** | | |
| 0200-0215 | RNZI (RNZ Pac.) | NAm | 5950rmi^ |
| 0200-0230 | IBC | LAm | 9955rmi |
| 0200-0230 | R. Prague | NAm,Eu | 7780rmi |
| 0200-0230 | R. Thailand WS | NAm | 13745udo |
| 0200-0230 | World of Radio | LAm | 9955rmi |
| 0200-0230 | WRMI | Car,LAm | 9955rmi |
| 0200-0300 | BVB | SAs | 11790mdc |
| 0200-0300 | CRI | SAs | 9610kas |
| 0200-0300 | KBS World R. | LAm | 9580kim |
| 0200-0300 | Madagascar W.V. | As | 15510mwv |
| 0200-0300 | RAE | NAm | 5950rmi, 9395rmi |
| 0200-0300 | WRMI | NAm | 5950rmi |
| 0200-0330 | R. Pilipinas | ME | 15640pht, 17700pht, 17820pht |
| 0200-0400 | CRI | SAs | 11770kas |

| 0200 | English | Area | kHz |
|------|---------|------|-----|
| 0200-0400 | WHRI | SAm | 7315hri |
| 0200-0500 | Overcomer Min. | NAm | 5850rmi |
| 0200-0600 | WWCR | NAm | 3215wcr |
| 0200-0800 | R. Habana Cuba | NAm | 6000hab, 6165hab |
| 0215-0230 | Vatican R. | NAm | 5950rmi^ |
| 0230-0245 | WRMI | NAm,Eu,ME | 7780rmi |
| 0230-0245 | WRMI | Car,LAm | 9955rmi |
| 0230-0300 | PCJ R. Int. | NAm | 5950rmi^ |
| 0230-0300 | R. Japan | NAm | 5950rmi^ |
| 0230-0300 | R. Tirana Int | NAm | 5950rmi, 9395rmi |
| 0230-0300 | R. Ukraine Int. | NAm,Eu,NAf | 7780rmi |
| 0230-0300 | World of Radio | NAm | 5950rmi, 5950rmi^ |
| 0230-0300 | WRMI | Car,LAm | 9955rmi |
| 0230-0330 | TWR Africa | WAf | 1566par |
| 0245-0300 | FG R. | LAm | 9955rmi |
| 0245-0300 | WRMI | NAm,Eu,ME | 7780rmi |
| **0300** | **English** | | |
| 0300-0330 | R. Prague | NAm | 5950rmi, 9395rmi |
| 0300-0400 | BBC World Sce | ME | 6195sla |
| 0300-0400 | Channel Africa | EAf | 6155mey |
| 0300-0400 | CRI | SAs | 13800kas |
| 0300-0400 | CRI | SAs | 5910qvc |
| 0300-0400 | KBS World R. | NAm | 5950rmi^ |
| 0300-0400 | Madagascar W.V. | As | 15510mwv |
| 0300-0400 | R. Sult.of Oman | EAf | 9540thu |
| 0300-0400 | R.Taiwan Int. | SEA | 15320pao |
| 0300-0400 | VOA | Af | 909bot |
| 0300-0400 | WRMI | NAm | 5950rmi |
| 0300-0430 | VOA | Af | 1530sao |
| 0300-0500 | BBC World Sce | ME | 7285sla |
| 0300-0500 | Channel Africa | SAf | 3345mey |
| 0300-0500 | CRI | EAs | 13570xia, 13590bei, 15120bei |
| 0300-0500 | WRMI | NAm,Eu,ME | 7780rmi |
| 0300-0500 | WWCR | CAm | 5890wcr |
| 0300-0600 | VOA | Af | 4930bot |
| 0300-0700 | VOA | Af | 6080sao, 15580bot |
| 0330-0400 | Hobart R. Int. | CAm | 5985rmi |
| 0330-0400 | IBC | CAm | 5985rmi |
| 0330-0400 | R. Slovakia Int | NAm | 5950rmi, 9395rmi |
| 0330-0400 | WRMI | CAm | 5985rmi |
| 0330-0500 | WRMI | NAm,Eu,ME | 7780rmi |
| 0345-0400 | WRMI | CAm | 5985rmi |
| **0400** | **English** | | |
| 0400-0415 | WRMI | Car,LAm | 9955rmi |
| 0400-0430 | R. Prague | LAm | 9955rmi |
| 0400-0430 | World of Radio | NAm,CAm | 5130bcq* |
| 0400-0500 | BBC World Sce | ME | 9410sla |
| 0400-0500 | BBC World Sce | EAf | 9915mdc, 12095dha |
| 0400-0500 | Madagascar W.V. | Af | 11825mwv |
| 0400-0500 | R. Poland | NAm | 5950rmi^ |
| 0400-0500 | R.Romania Int | NAm | 6020gal, 7410tig |
| 0400-0500 | R.Romania Int | As | 9820tig+, 11790gal |
| 0400-0500 | Overcomer Min. | NAm | 3215wcr |
| 0400-0500 | Overcomer Min. | NAm | 9455rmi |
| 0400-0500 | VOA | Af | 4960sao |
| 0400-0500 | VOA | Af | 909bot |
| 0400-0500 | VO Korea | LAm | 11735kuj, 13760kuj, 15180kuj |
| 0400-0500 | VO Korea | EAs | 7220kuj, 9445kuj, 9730kuj |
| 0400-0500 | VO Turkey | ME,NAf | 6125emr |

| 0400 | English | Area | kHz |
|------|---------|------|-----|
| 0400-0500 | VO Turkey | Eu,NAm | 7240emr |
| 0400-0500 | VORW R. Int | NAm | 7730rmi |
| 0400-0500 | WRMI | NAm | 7730rmi |
| 0400-0600 | CRI | CAs,Eu | 17730xia |
| 0400-0600 | CRI | CAs | 17855bei |
| 0400-0700 | RNZI (RNZ Pac.) | Pac | 13730ran |
| 0400-1000 | WRMI | NAm | 9395rmi |
| 0430-0445 | WRMI | Car,LAm | 9955rmi |
| 0430-0500 | TWR Africa | WAf | 1566par |
| 0430-0500 | TWR Africa | SAf | 3200man, 4775man |
| 0430-0500 | World of Radio | LAm | 9955rmi |
| 0430-0500 | WRMI | Car,LAm | 9955rmi |
| 0430-0600 | WHRI | NAf | 9830hri |
| 0445-0500 | WRMI | Car,LAm | 9955rmi |
| **0500** | **English** | | |
| 0500-0530 | R. Japan | Eu | 6155mos |
| 0500-0530 | R. Japan | SAf | 7410iss |
| 0500-0530 | R. Japan | WAf | 9860smg |
| 0500-0600 | BBC World Sce | ME | 1413sla |
| 0500-0600 | BBC World Sce | SAf | 3255mey, 5925asc |
| 0500-0600 | BBC World Sce | WAf | 5875asc |
| 0500-0600 | BBC World Sce | CAf | 7345wof |
| 0500-0600 | BBC World Sce | EAf | 9915mey, 12095mdc |
| 0500-0600 | CRI | NAf | 7220cer |
| 0500-0600 | VO Korea | SEA | 13650kuj, 15105kuj |
| 0500-0600 | WRMI | CAm | 5985rmi |
| 0500-0700 | BBC World Sce | WAf | 6005asc |
| 0500-0700 | CRI | SAs | 15430kas |
| 0500-0700 | CRI | ME,NAf | 17510kas |
| 0500-0700 | TWR Africa | SAf | 4775man, 6120man |
| 0500-0700 | VOA | Af | 909bot |
| 0500-0800 | BBC World Sce | SAf | 6190mey |
| 0500-0800 | R. Kuwait | SAs | 11970kbd+ |
| 0500-0800 | R. Kuwait | Eu | 15530kbd |
| 0500-0800 | VOH - Africa | Af | 9680luv |
| 0500-0900 | CRI | SAs | 11895kas, 15465kas |
| 0500-1100 | CRI | SAs | 15350kas |
| 0500-1200 | Channel Africa | SAf | 7230mey |
| 0530-0545 | TWR Africa | WAf | 1566par |
| 0530-0600 | R. Thailand WS | Eu | 17640udo |
| **0600** | **English** | | |
| 0600-0700 | BBC World Sce | Eu | 3955wof+ |
| 0600-0700 | BBC World Sce | WAf | 7325wof |
| 0600-0700 | BBC World Sce | CAf | 7345asc, 12095mey |
| 0600-0700 | Channel Africa | WAf | 11925mey |
| 0600-0700 | CRI | NAf | 11750cer |
| 0600-0700 | CRI | ME | 11870kas, 15145kas |
| 0600-0700 | CRI | SEA | 13645xia |
| 0600-0700 | R .Damascus | ME | 783tts |
| 0600-0700 | RFI | NAm | 5950rmi^ |
| 0600-0700 | R. Habana Cuba | CAm | 5040hab |
| 0600-0700 | VOA | Af | 1530sao, 9550sao |
| 0600-0700 | VO Korea | EAs | 7220kuj, 9445kuj, 9730kuj |
| 0600-0700 | WHRI | SAm | 7315hri |
| 0600-0800 | BBC World Sce | SAf | 15400mdc |
| 0600-0800 | BBC World Sce | EAf | 15420mey, 17640dha |
| 0600-0800 | CRI | SEA | 17710bei |
| 0600-0800 | R. Habana Cuba | NAm | 6060hab, 6100hab |
| 0630-0700 | R.Romania Int | AUS,NZL,Pac | 15450tig+, 17780gal |
| 0630-0700 | R.Romania Int | Eu | 7345tig, 9770gal+ |

# Broadcasts in English

| 0700 | English | Area | kHz |
|------|---------|------|-----|
| 0700-0800 | BBC World Sce | WAf | 7325asc, 9915asc |
| 0700-0800 | BBC World Sce | CAf | 9410asc, 15490mey |
| 0700-0800 | CRI | SEA | 13660xia |
| 0700-0800 | CTB-Holy Tibet | As | 4905lha, 4920lha, 6025lha, 6110lha, 6130lha, 6200lha, 9490lha, 9580lha |
| 0700-0800 | Deutsche Welle | NAm | 5950rmi^ |
| 0700-0800 | Hamburger LR | CEu,WEu | 6190goh* |
| 0700-0800 | WRMI | NAm,As | 5850rmi |
| 0700-0800 | WRMI | NAm | 7730rmi |
| 0700-0900 | CRI | Eu | 11785cer |
| 0700-0900 | CRI | ME,NAf | 17670kas |
| 0700-0900 | WINB | Eu.NAf | 7315inb+ |
| 0700-0900 | WRMI | NAm,As | 5850rmi |
| 0700-0900 | WRMI | NAm | 7730rmi |
| 0700-1000 | CRI | SAs | 15185kas |
| 0700-1100 | RNZI (RNZ Pac.) | Pac | 9765ran |
| 0700-1300 | CRI | Eu | 17490kas |
| 0730-0800 | World of Radio | CEu,WEu | 6190goh* |
| **0800** | **English** | | |
| 0800-0830 | BVB | Eu | 7220nau |
| 0800-0830 | SW Radiogram | NAm,As | 5850rmi |
| 0800-0830 | SW Radiogram | LAm | 5950rmi |
| 0800-0830 | SW Radiogram | NAm,Pac | 7730rmi |
| 0800-0900 | Amateur R.Today | EAf | 17760mey |
| 0800-0900 | Amateur R.Today | SAf | 7205mey |
| 0800-0900 | BBC World Sce | SAs | 15620sng+ |
| 0800-0900 | KNLS Int. | EAs | 7370nls |
| 0800-0900 | RCI | Eu | 6005kll |
| 0800-0900 | R. Poland | NAm | 5950rmi^ |
| 0800-0900 | VO Nigeria | WAf | 7255aja |
| 0800-1000 | CRI | EAs | 9415xia |
| 0800-1000 | T8WH - WHR Int | EAs | 9930hbn* |
| 0800-1000 | WRMI | NAm | 5950rmi |
| 0800-1030 | KBS World R. | SEA | 9770kim |
| 0800-1500 | SWradio | CEu,WEu | 6160wis |
| 0800-2300 | SWradio | CEu,WEu | 3975wis |
| 0830-0930 | WRMI | NAm,As | 5850rmi |
| 0830-0930 | WRMI | NAm | 7730rmi |
| **0900** | **English** | | |
| 0900-0915 | Vatican R. | NAm | 5950rmi^ |
| 0900-0930 | VO Mongolia | EAs | 12085uba |
| 0900-0930 | WRMI | NAm,As | 5850rmi |
| 0900-0930 | WRMI | NAm | 7730rmi |
| 0900-1000 | CRI | Eu | 17570uru, 17650kas |
| 0900-1000 | IRRS Shortwave | Eu,ME,NAf | 9510tig |
| 0900-1100 | CRI | Pac | 15210kun, 17690jin |
| 0900-1100 | WINB | Eu.NAf | 9265inb+ |
| 0900-1300 | WEWN | EAs | 9470ewn |
| 0915-0930 | RNZI (RNZ Pac.) | NAm | 5950rmi^ |
| 0915-0930 | Vatican R. | NAm | 5950rmi^ |
| 0930-1000 | R. Prague | NAm | 5950rmi^ |
| 0930-1200 | WHRI | SAm | 7315hri |
| 0945-1000 | R.Taiwan Int. | EAs | 1098kou |
| **1000** | **English** | | |
| 1000-1025 | TWR Asia | AUS,NZL,Pac | 11995twr |
| 1000-1030 | BBC World Sce | CAs | 1251dsb |
| 1000-1030 | TWR Asia | SEA | 11965twr |
| 1000-1030 | VO Vietnam | As | 9840vni, 12020vni |
| 1000-1030 | WRMI | NAm | 5950rmi |
| 1000-1045 | TWR Asia | AUS,NZL,Pac | 11995twr |
| 1000-1100 | All India R. | SAs | 1053tut, 7270cni |

| 1000 | English | Area | kHz |
|------|---------|------|-----|
| 1000-1100 | All India R. | EAs | 13605bgl, 15410bgl |
| 1000-1100 | All India R. | Pac | 13695bgl, 17510bgl, 17895bgl+* |
| 1000-1100 | All India R. | SEA | 15770pan |
| 1000-1100 | CRI | SAs | 15190kas |
| 1000-1100 | CRI | EAs | 5955xia, 7215xia, 11635bei |
| 1000-1100 | FEBC Korea | EAs | 1188seo |
| 1000-1100 | KNLS Int. | EAs | 7370nls |
| 1000-1100 | RFI | NAm | 5950rmi^ |
| 1000-1100 | VO Indonesia | SEA | 3325pgat |
| 1000-1100 | VO Korea | LAm | 6170kuj, 9435kuj |
| 1000-1100 | VO Korea | SEA | 6185kuj, 9850kuj |
| 1000-1100 | VORW R. Int | NAm | 5950rmi |
| 1000-1100 | WRMI | NAm | 5950rmi |
| 1000-1200 | BBC World Sce | SEA | 6195sng, 12065sng |
| 1000-1200 | BBC World Sce | EAs,SEA | 9900sng |
| 1000-1200 | CRI | SEA | 13590bei, 13720xia |
| 1000-1200 | T8WH - WHR Int | SEA | 9965hbn |
| 1000-1200 | WWCR | NAm,Eu,NAf | 15795wcr |
| 1000-1500 | T8WH - WHR Int | EAs | 9930hbn* |
| 1000-1600 | T8WH - WHR Int | EAs | 9930hbn* |
| 1000-2000 | WHRI | NAm | 9840hri |
| 1000-2200 | University Net. | NAm | 11775aiat |
| 1015-1030 | FG R. | NAm | 5950rmi |
| 1020-1120 | Pars Today | ME | 702kia |
| 1030-1100 | World of Radio | NAm | 5950rmi |
| 1030-1100 | WRMI | NAm | 5950rmi |
| 1030-1300 | IRRS Shortwave | Eu,ME,NAf | 9510tig |
| **1100** | **English** | | |
| 1100-1125 | TWR Asia | SEA | 11965twr |
| 1100-1130 | Hobart R. Int. | NAm | 9265inb |
| 1100-1130 | R. Japan | SEA | 11825sng |
| 1100-1130 | R. Saranrom | SEA | 1575bph |
| 1100-1130 | TWR Asia | EAs | 9910twr |
| 1100-1130 | WRMI | Car,LAm | 9955rmi |
| 1100-1140 | TWR Asia | SEA | 11965twr |
| 1100-1200 | CRI | SAs | 11795kas |
| 1100-1200 | CRI | SEA | 9730bei |
| 1100-1200 | Deutsche Welle | NAm | 5950rmi^ |
| 1100-1200 | Hamburger LR | CEu,WEu | 7265goh* |
| 1100-1200 | TWR Asia | SEA | 11965twr |
| 1100-1200 | WHRI | NAm,Eu | 5920hri |
| 1100-1300 | CRI | SEA | 1269xuw |
| 1100-1300 | CRI | Eu | 13665cer |
| 1100-1300 | CRI | SAs | 7250kas, 11650uru, 12015kas |
| 1100-1300 | RNZI (RNZ Pac.) | Pac | 9700ran |
| 1100-1500 | WRMI | NAm | 5950rmi |
| 1100-1600 | CRI | EAs | 5955bei |
| 1100-1700 | WINB | Eu.NAf | 13690inb+ |
| 1100-2100 | Overcomer Min. | NAm | 9395rmi |
| 1100-2200 | WHRI | NAm | 7385hri |
| 1115-1130 | RchBeyondAUS | SAs | 15575knx |
| 1120-1140 | R.Taiwan Int. | SEA | 12100pao |
| 1130-1145 | TWR Asia | EAs | 9910twr |
| 1130-1145 | WRMI | Car,LAm | 9955rmi |
| 1130-1200 | BVB | CHN | 15640dsb |
| 1130-1200 | TWR Asia | EAs | 9910twr |
| 1130-1200 | VOA | SEA | 1575bph, 12125udo, 15715udo, 17790pht |
| 1130-1200 | VO Vietnam | As | 9840vni, 12020vni |
| 1130-1200 | World of Radio | CEu,WEu | 7265goh* |

| 1200 | English | Area | kHz |
|------|---------|------|-----|
| 1200-1215 | WRMI | Car,LAm | 9955rmi |
| 1200-1230 | BVB | CHN | 17650mdc |
| 1200-1230 | R. Japan | NAm | 5950rmi^ |
| 1200-1230 | R. Slovakia Int | Eu | 6005kll* |
| 1200-1230 | World of Radio | Eu,NAf | 9265inb+ |
| 1200-1230 | WRMI | Car | 5010rmi |
| 1200-1230 | WRMI | Car,LAm | 9955rmi |
| 1200-1300 | BBC World Sce | SAs | 12065sla |
| 1200-1300 | BBC World Sce | EAs | 15510sng |
| 1200-1300 | CRI | CAs | 11690xia |
| 1200-1300 | CRI | SEA | 684dof, 1188kun, 9600kun, 9645bei, 9730kun |
| 1200-1300 | CRI | SAs | 9460kas |
| 1200-1300 | CRI | Pac | 9760kun |
| 1200-1300 | KNLS Int. | EAs | 7320nls, 7355nls |
| 1200-1300 | R.Romania Int | Eu | 11825tig, 15460tig |
| 1200-1300 | R.Romania Int | Af | 17800gal, 21490tig |
| 1200-1300 | T8WH - WHR Int | SEA | 9965hbn |
| 1200-1400 | BBC World Sce | SAs | 9410sla |
| 1200-1400 | CRI | Pac | 11760kun |
| 1200-1400 | CRI | SEA | 1341hdu, 11980kun |
| 1200-1400 | CRI | Eu | 13790uru |
| 1200-1400 | Hamburger LR | CEu,WEu | 9485goh* |
| 1200-1500 | University Net. | NAm,Eu | 13845wcr |
| 1200-1700 | VOH - Africa | Af | 9680luv, 13680luv |
| 1200-2200 | WWCR | NAm,Eu,NAf | 15825wcr |
| 1215-1230 | WRMI | Car,LAm | 9955rmi |
| 1230-1245 | BVB | INS | 21480mdc |
| 1230-1300 | Bangladesh Bet. | SEA | 15105dka |
| 1230-1300 | R. Slovakia Int | NAm | 5950rmi^ |
| 1230-1300 | R. Thailand WS | As,Pac | 9940udo |
| 1230-1300 | RchBeyondAUS | SAs | 11945knx |
| 1230-1300 | TWR Asia | EAs | 9910twr |
| 1230-1300 | VO Vietnam | As | 9840vni, 12020vni |
| 1230-1300 | WRMI | Car,LAm | 9955rmi |
| **1300** | **English** | | |
| 1300-1330 | BBC World Sce | CAs | 1251dsb |
| 1300-1330 | R. Prague | LAm | 9955rmi |
| 1300-1330 | VO Mongolia | CEu,WEu | 6005kll* |
| 1300-1400 | BBC World Sce | SAs | 1413sla, 12065sng |
| 1300-1400 | CRI | Eu | 11640kas |
| 1300-1400 | CRI | Pac | 11900kun |
| 1300-1400 | CRI | SAs | 7300kas, 9655kas |
| 1300-1400 | CRI | NAm | 9570qvc |
| 1300-1400 | CRI | SEA | 9730bei, 11910bei |
| 1300-1400 | KBS World R. | NAm | 5950rmi^, 15575kim |
| 1300-1400 | KBS World R. | SEA | 9570kim |
| 1300-1400 | Shiokaze | KRE | 7245yam* |
| 1300-1400 | The Mighty KBC | Eu | 11600sof |
| 1300-1400 | Overcomer Min. | ME,Eu | 11600sof |
| 1300-1400 | VO Indonesia | SEA | 3325pga† |
| 1300-1400 | VO Korea | Eu | 7570kuj, 12015kuj |
| 1300-1400 | VO Korea | NAm | 9435kuj, 11710kuj |
| 1300-1400 | VO Tajik | WAs | 1143dsb, 7245dsb |
| 1300-1500 | CRI | CAs,Eu | 9765bji |
| 1300-1500 | WRMI | NAm,Eu,ME | 7780rmi |
| 1300-1600 | CRI | SEA | 9870xia |
| 1300-1600 | R. Oz-Viola | Eu | 5800hil† |
| 1300-1600 | WWCR | Af | 7490wcr |
| 1300-1650 | RNZI (RNZ Pac.) | Pac | 7390ran |
| 1300-1800 | WWCR | NAm | 13845wcr |
| 1315-1330 | RchBeyondAUS | SAs | 11865knx |

| 1300 | English | Area | kHz |
|------|---------|------|-----|
| 1315-1345 | TWR Asia | EAs | 7510twr |
| 1330-1345 | FEBA India | IND | 11580twr |
| 1330-1345 | FG R. | NAm | 5950rmi |
| 1330-1345 | WRMI | Car,LAm | 9955rmi |
| 1330-1400 | R. Tirana Int | CEu,WEu | 6005kll |
| 1330-1400 | VO Vietnam | As | 9840vni, 12020vni |
| 1330-1430 | VO Turkey | Eu | 12035emr |
| 1330-1500 | All India R. | SEA | 9690bgl‡, 13695bgl |
| 1345-1400 | FG R. | NAm | 5950rmi |
| 1345-1400 | WRMI | Car,LAm | 9955rmi |
| **1400** | **English** | | |
| 1400-0200 | WTWW | NAm,Eu | 9475tww |
| 1400-1415 | FG R. | NAm | 5950rmi |
| 1400-1415 | WRMI | Car,LAm | 9955rmi |
| 1400-1430 | R. Japan | SEA | 11925hbn |
| 1400-1430 | R. Japan | SAs | 6165tac |
| 1400-1430 | R. Thailand WS | As,Pac | 9940udo |
| 1400-1430 | SW Radiogram | Eu | 9400sof* |
| 1400-1430 | T8WH - WHR Int | SEA | 9965hbn |
| 1400-1430 | WRMI | Car,LAm | 9955rmi |
| 1400-1500 | BVB | SAs | 11900nau |
| 1400-1500 | CRI | ME | 6100uru |
| 1400-1500 | CRI | SAs | 7300uru, 9460uru |
| 1400-1500 | CRI | Eu | 9795uru, 11880kas |
| 1400-1500 | KNLS Int. | EAs | 7320nls |
| 1400-1500 | R. Sult.of Oman | Eu,ME | 15140thu |
| 1400-1500 | VOA | Af | 17885bot |
| 1400-1600 | CRI | NAm | 15700qvc |
| 1400-1600 | CRI | SEA | 6135xia |
| 1400-1630 | VOA | Af | 15580bot |
| 1400-1700 | VOA | Af | 4930bot |
| 1400-1900 | WHRI | Af | 21610hri |
| 1400-2100 | PanAm Bc | Af | 21525rmi* |
| 1400-2200 | WJHR | NAm | 15555jhr* |
| 1400-2400 | WTWW | NAm | 9930tww |
| 1405-1455 | Overcomer Min. | ME,Eu | 11600sof |
| 1415-1445 | WRMI | Car,LAm | 9955rmi |
| 1420-1455 | TWR Africa | SAf | 7300man |
| 1430-1445 | FG R. | LAm | 9955rmi |
| 1430-1445 | PanAm Bc | ME | 11800iss |
| 1430-1445 | WRMI | Car,LAm | 9955rmi |
| 1430-1500 | BBC World Sce | SAs | 1413sla |
| 1430-1500 | Lao National R. | SEA | 567vie, 6130vie |
| 1430-1500 | WRMI | Car,LAm | 9955rmi |
| 1445-1500 | FG R. | NAm | 5950rmi |
| 1445-1500 | FG R. | LAm | 9955rmi |
| 1445-1500 | RchBeyondAUS | SAs | 9740knx |
| **1500** | **English** | | |
| 1500-1530 | R. Japan | NAm | 5950rmi^ |
| 1500-1530 | RNZI (RNZ Pac.) | NAm | 5950rmi^ |
| 1500-1530 | VO Vietnam | As | 9840vni, 12020vni |
| 1500-1600 | BBC World Sce | EAf | 12095mdc, 15420mey |
| 1500-1600 | Channel Africa | SAf | 7260mey |
| 1500-1600 | CRI | SAs | 1188kun, 7395uru, 9785jin |
| 1500-1600 | CRI | NAf,ME | 6095kas, 9720uru |
| 1500-1600 | CRI | SEA | 7325bei |
| 1500-1600 | CRI | Eu | 9525kas |
| 1500-1600 | Hamburger LR | CEu,WEu | 7265goh* |
| 1500-1600 | VOA | Af | 7455bot, 17895sao |
| 1500-1600 | VO Korea | Eu | 7570kuj, 12015kuj |
| 1500-1600 | VO Korea | NAm | 9435kuj, 11710kuj |
| 1500-1600 | WRMI | NAm,Eu,ME | 7780rmi |

| 1500 | English | Area | kHz |
|---|---|---|---|
| 1500-1700 | BBC World Sce | ME | 7405sla |
| 1500-1700 | CRI | Eu | 9435kas |
| 1500-1700 | KBS World R. | Eu | 9515kim |
| 1500-1700 | WRMI | Car,LAm | 9955rmi |
| 1500-1800 | CRI | SAs | 1323uru |
| 1500-1800 | CRI | SEA | 9880nnn |
| 1500-2400 | University Net. | NAm,Eu | 13845wcr |
| 1515-1530 | RchBeyondAUS | EAs | 7530knx |
| 1520-1620 | Pars Today | SAs,SEA | 5965sir |
| 1530-1600 | AWR As/Pacific | EAs | 11985trm |
| 1530-1600 | R. Prague | NAm | 5950rmi, 5950rmi^ |
| 1530-1600 | R. Slovakia Int | Eu | 6005kll* |
| 1530-1600 | RTV Afghanistan | SAs | 6100kab |
| 1530-1600 | T8WH - WHR Int | SEA | 11675hbn |
| 1530-1600 | TWR India | As | 7550erv |
| 1530-1600 | VO Mongolia | EAs | 12015uba |
| 1530-1600 | World of Radio | CEu,WEu | 9485goh* |
| 1530-1600 | WRMI | Af | 21525rmi |
| 1535-1540 | TWR India | As | 7550erv |
| 1540-1600 | R. Japan | SEA | 5985yan* |
| **1600** | **English** | | |
| 1600-1630 | AWR Africa | WAf | 9770sof |
| 1600-1630 | AWR As/Pacific | As | 17730mdc |
| 1600-1630 | VOA | Af | 6080sao |
| 1600-1630 | VO Vietnam | ME | 7220vni |
| 1600-1630 | VO Vietnam | Eu | 7280vni, 9730vni |
| 1600-1640 | R. Cairo | ISR | 1008ela |
| 1600-1700 | BBC World Sce | EAf | 12095mey |
| 1600-1700 | BBC World Sce | SAf | 15400asc |
| 1600-1700 | CRI | SEA | 6060kun |
| 1600-1700 | CRI | NAf,ME | 7420uru |
| 1600-1700 | CRI | Eu | 9875kas |
| 1600-1700 | CTB-Holy Tibet | As | 4905lha, 4920lha, 6025lha, 6110lha, 6130lha, 6200lha, 7255lha, 7385lha |
| 1600-1700 | KBS World R. | SEA | 9640kim |
| 1600-1700 | RFI | NAm | 5950rmi^ |
| 1600-1700 | R.Taiwan Int. | SAs,Af | 6180tsh |
| 1600-1700 | Shiokaze | KRE | 6110yam** |
| 1600-1700 | VOA | Af | 909bot, 1530sao |
| 1600-1700 | VO Korea | ME,NAf | 9890kuj, 11645kuj |
| 1600-1800 | BBC World Sce | CAf | 17830asc |
| 1600-1800 | CRI | SEA | 1080xuw, 6175nnn |
| 1600-1800 | CRI | SAs | 7235kas |
| 1600-1800 | CRI | Eu | 7255kas |
| 1600-1800 | CRI | SAf | 7435jin, 9570bei |
| 1600-1800 | VOA | Af | 17895bot |
| 1600-1900 | VOH - Africa | Af | 6065luv |
| 1600-2000 | BBC World Sce | SAf | 3255mey, 6190mey |
| 1600-2000 | BBC World Sce | EAf | 7445mdc |
| 1600-2000 | KVOH | CAm,SAm | 17775voh |
| 1600-2100 | WWCR | Af | 12160wcr |
| 1630-1700 | R. Slovakia Int | Eu | 6005kll* |
| 1630-1700 | T8WH - WHR Int | SEA | 9965hbn |
| 1630-1700 | Vatican R. | Af | 11625mdc, 13830smg |
| 1630-1700 | VOA | Af | 11850mey*, 13865wof*, 15180sao* |
| 1630-1700 | VOA | Af | 6080sao |
| 1630-1730 | Amateur R.Today | EAf | 4895mey |
| 1630-1730 | VOA | Af | 15580bot |
| 1650-1750 | RNZI (RNZ Pac.) | Pac | 5975ran+ |

| 1600 | English | Area | kHz |
|---|---|---|---|
| 1650-1800 | RNZI (RNZ Pac.) | Pac | 7390ran |
| **1700** | **English** | | |
| 1700-1715 | PCJ R. Int. | NAm | 5950rmi^ |
| 1700-1715 | RNZI (RNZ Pac.) | NAm | 5950rmi^ |
| 1700-1715 | World of Radio | NAm | 5950rmi^ |
| 1700-1730 | VOA | Af | 13590kwt |
| 1700-1730 | VOH - Africa | Af | 9680luv, 13680luv |
| 1700-1730 | World of Radio | NAm | 5950rmi |
| 1700-1800 | BBC World Sce | CAs | 1251dsb |
| 1700-1800 | BBC World Sce | SAs | 1413sla |
| 1700-1800 | BBC World Sce | WAf | 17780asc |
| 1700-1800 | BBC World Sce | EAf | 9410mey |
| 1700-1800 | Channel Africa | WAf | 15235mey |
| 1700-1800 | CRI | SEA | 6090kun, 7420kun |
| 1700-1800 | CRI | SAs | 6140kas, 7410kas |
| 1700-1800 | CRI | ME | 6165bei |
| 1700-1800 | CAf | 9505alf | |
| 1700-1800 | VOA | Af | 6080sao |
| 1700-1900 | BBC World Sce | WAf | 15400asc |
| 1700-1900 | BBC World Sce | ME | 6195sla |
| 1700-1900 | CRI | Eu | 6100bei |
| 1700-1945 | Overcomer Min. | Eu | 9400sof |
| 1700-2000 | Overcomer Min. | NAm,ME,Eu | 7780rmi |
| 1715-1730 | Vatican R. | NAm | 5950rmi^ |
| 1715-1730 | Vatican R. | NAf,ME | 7230smg |
| 1730-1800 | R. Prague | NAm | 5950rmi, 5950rmi^ |
| 1730-1800 | VOA | Af | 13590sao |
| 1730-1830 | VO Turkey | CAs,SAs | 11730emr |
| 1730-2000 | VOA | Af | 15580bot |
| 1745-1825 | TWR Africa | WAf | 1566par |
| 1745-1900 | Bangladesh Bet. | Eu | 13580dka |
| 1745-1945 | All India R. | Eu | 7550bgl+, 9950del‡ |
| 1745-1945 | All India R. | NAf,WAf | 9445bgl |
| 1745-1945 | All India R. | EAf | 9910bgl, 11935mum, 13695bgl |
| 1750-1835 | RNZI (RNZ Pac.) | Pac | 9780ran+ |
| **1800** | **English** | | |
| 1800-1810 | Zanzibar BC | EAf,ME | 11735dol† |
| 1800-1815 | BVB | ME | 9715nau |
| 1800-1830 | BVB | ME | 9715nau |
| 1800-1830 | TWR Africa | EAf | 9500man |
| 1800-1900 | BBC World Sce | WAf | 9915wof |
| 1800-1900 | CRI | Eu | 7405bei |
| 1800-1900 | Madagascar W.V. | Af | 13670mwv |
| 1800-1900 | RCI | Eu | 3985kll |
| 1800-1900 | RNZI (RNZ Pac.) | Pac | 9780ran |
| 1800-1900 | R.Romania Int | Eu | 5935tig, 7350tig+ |
| 1800-1900 | TWR Africa | EAf | 9500man |
| 1800-1900 | VOA | Af | 13590udo |
| 1800-1900 | VOA | Af | 909bot, 4930bot |
| 1800-1900 | VO Korea | Eu | 7570kuj, 12015kuj |
| 1800-1930 | VO Nigeria | Eu | 15120aja+,† |
| 1800-1930 | VO Nigeria | WAf | 7255aja* |
| 1800-2000 | BBC World Sce | EAf | 9410dha |
| 1800-2000 | BVB | ME | 9715nau |
| 1800-2100 | BBC World Sce | CAf | 11810asc |
| 1800-2100 | KBS World R. | SAs | 9630kim |
| 1800-2100 | R. Kuwait | Eu | 15540kbd+,† |
| 1805-2000 | Overcomer Min. | EEu | 6000sof |
| 1830-1900 | AWR Africa | Af | 15155trm |
| 1830-1900 | Hobart R. Int. | LAm | 9955rmi |
| 1830-2000 | BVB | ME | 9715nau |
| 1835-1950 | RNZI (RNZ Pac.) | Pac | 9780ran+ |

| 1900 | English | Area | kHz |
|---|---|---|---|
| 1900-1930 | ETC R. | Eu | 9400sof |
| 1900-1930 | FollowTheBible | WAf | 12005asc |
| 1900-1930 | FollowTheBible | SAf | 12030asc |
| 1900-1930 | VO Vietnam | Eu | 7280vni, 9730vni |
| 1900-2000 | BVB | Eu | 6030erv |
| 1900-2000 | IsleOfM/MeltPot | CEu,WEu | 6070rob* |
| 1900-2000 | IRRS Shortwave | Eu,ME,NAf | 7290tig |
| 1900-2000 | RNZI (RNZ Pac.) | Pac | 11725ran |
| 1900-2000 | R. Poland | NAm | 5950rmi^ |
| 1900-2000 | R. Thailand WS | Eu | 7475udo |
| 1900-2000 | VOA | Af | 13590sao |
| 1900-2000 | VO Indonesia | SEA | 3325pga† |
| 1900-2000 | VO Korea | SAf | 7210kuj, 11910kuj |
| 1900-2000 | VO Korea | ME,NAf | 9875kuj, 11635kuj |
| 1900-2030 | R. Cairo | WAf | 15290abz† |
| 1900-2100 | BBC World Sce | ME | 1413sla |
| 1900-2100 | BBC World Sce | WAf | 5875wof |
| 1900-2100 | CRI | ME,NAf | 7295kas, 9440kun |
| 1900-2100 | VOA | Af | 909bot, 4930bot |
| 1900-2100 | WHRI | Af | 17815hri |
| 1900-2400 | WEWN | Af | 15610ewn |
| 1915-1930 | BVB | ME | 5935nau |
| 1920-2020 | Pars Today | SAf | 11880sir |
| 1920-2020 | Pars Today | Eu | 6040sir |
| 1930-2015 | BVB | ME | 7435mos |
| 1930-2030 | VO Turkey | Eu | 6050emr |
| 1950-2050 | RNZI (RNZ Pac.) | Pac | 13840ran+ |
| **2000** | **English** | | |
| 2000-0500 | WBCQ | NAm,CAm | 7490bcq† |
| 2000-2015 | WRMI | NAm,Eu,ME | 7780rmi |
| 2000-2030 | R. Slovakia Int | Eu | 3985kll* |
| 2000-2030 | R. Slovakia Int | NAm | 5950rmi, 5950rmi^ |
| 2000-2030 | Vatican R. | Af | 6010smg, 7365smg |
| 2000-2030 | WRMI | NAm,Eu,ME | 7780rmi |
| 2000-2100 | BBC World Sce | WAf | 12095asc |
| 2000-2100 | CRI | SAf | 5985bei |
| 2000-2100 | Madagascar W.V. | Af | 11965mwv |
| 2000-2100 | R. Habana Cuba | NAm | 15140hab |
| 2000-2100 | RNZI (RNZ Pac.) | Pac | 13840ran |
| 2000-2100 | VOA | Af | 6195bot, 15580bot |
| 2000-2100 | VORW R. Int | NAm | 5950rmi |
| 2000-2100 | VORW R. Int | NAm,Eu,ME | 7780rmi |
| 2000-2100 | VORW R. Int | NAm | 9395rmi |
| 2000-2100 | WRMI | NAm,Eu,ME | 7780rmi |
| 2000-2200 | CRI | Eu | 5960cer, 7285cer, 7415kas, 9600kas |
| 2000-2200 | VOA | Af | 1530sao |
| 2000-2200 | WHRI | NAm,Eu | 11750hri |
| 2000-2200 | WRMI | NAm | 9395rmi |
| 2005-0300 | Overcomer Min. | Eu,NAm | 5900sof |
| 2015-2030 | WRMI | NAm,Eu,ME | 7780rmi |
| 2030-2045 | R. Thailand WS | Eu | 7475udo |
| 2030-2100 | IBC | NAm | 9395rmi |
| 2030-2100 | SW Radiogram | LAm | 5950rmi |
| 2030-2100 | SW Radiogram | NAm,Eu,ME | 7780rmi |
| 2030-2100 | Vatican R. | NAm | 5950rmi^ |
| 2030-2100 | VOA | Af | 4960sao |
| 2030-2100 | VO Vietnam | ME | 7220vni |
| 2030-2100 | World of Radio | NAm,Eu,ME | 7780rmi |
| 2030-2100 | WRMI | NAm,Eu,ME | 7780rmi |
| 2045-2100 | WRMI | NAm,Eu,ME | 7780rmi |
| 2045-2230 | All India R. | Eu | 7550bgl+, 9445bgl, 9950del‡ |

| 2000 | English | Area | kHz |
|---|---|---|---|
| 2045-2230 | All India R. | Pac | 9910bgl, 11740pan |
| 2050-2100 | RNZI (RNZ Pac.) | Pac | 15720ran |
| **2100** | **English** | | |
| 2100-0400 | RNZI (RNZ Pac.) | Pac | 15720ran |
| 2100-2115 | FG R. | NAm | 5950rmi |
| 2100-2130 | AWR Africa | WAf | 7270mos |
| 2100-2130 | IBC | Eu | 5900sof |
| 2100-2130 | WRMI | NAm,Eu,ME | 7780rmi |
| 2100-2200 | BBC World Sce | CAf | 11810asc |
| 2100-2200 | BBC World Sce | WAf | 5875wof, 12095asc |
| 2100-2200 | CRI | SAf | 7205xia, 7325bei |
| 2100-2200 | KBS World R. | NAm | 5950rmi^ |
| 2100-2200 | VOA | Af | 6195sao, 15580grv |
| 2100-2200 | VO Korea | Eu | 7570kuj, 12015kuj |
| 2100-2200 | WRMI | NAm,Eu,ME | 7780rmi |
| 2100-2200 | WRMI | NAm | 9395rmi |
| 2100-2300 | Overcomer Min. | NAm | 9350wcr |
| 2100-2300 | WWCR | Af | 9350wcr |
| 2100-2300 | WWCR | NAM,Af | 9980wcr |
| 2115-2245 | R. Cairo | Eu | 9900abs† |
| 2130-2200 | R.Romania Int | Eu | 6030gal+, 7375gal |
| 2130-2200 | R.Romania Int | NAm | 6170tig, 7310tig |
| 2130-2200 | VO Vietnam | Eu | 7280vni, 9730vni |
| 2130-2200 | World of Radio | NAm,Eu,ME | 7780rmi |
| 2130-2230 | VO Turkey | SEA,Pac | 9610emr |
| **2200** | **English** | | |
| 2200-1000 | University Net. | NAm | 6090aia† |
| 2200-2230 | AWR As/Pacific | SEA | 12040sda |
| 2200-2230 | World of Radio | NAm,CAm | 7490bcq |
| 2200-2230 | World of Radio | LAm | 9955rmi |
| 2200-2230 | WRMI | Car,LAm | 9955rmi |
| 2200-2300 | BBC World Sce | EAs,SEA | 5960sla |
| 2200-2300 | BBC World Sce | SEA | 7300dha |
| 2200-2300 | CRI | EAs | 5915bei |
| 2200-2300 | Deutsche Welle | NAm | 5950rmi^ |
| 2200-2300 | KBS World R. | Eu | 11810kim |
| 2200-2300 | Overcomer Min. | NAm | 7490bcq |
| 2200-2300 | VORW R. Int | NAm | 7570rmi |
| 2200-2300 | WRMI | Car | 5010rmi |
| 2200-2300 | WRMI | NAm,Eu,ME | 7780rmi |
| 2200-2300 | WRMI | NAm | 9395rmi |
| 2200-2400 | BBC World Sce | SEA | 3915sng, 5890sng |
| 2200-2400 | BBC World Sce | EAs,SEA | 6195sng |
| 2200-2400 | WHRI | NAm,Eu | 9505hri |
| 2230-2300 | World of Radio | LAm | 9955rmi |
| 2230-2300 | WRMI | NAm,As | 5850rmi |
| 2230-2300 | WRMI | Car,LAm | 9955rmi |
| 2245-0045 | All India R. | SEA | 6045del† |
| 2245-0045 | All India R. | EAs | 7550bgl+, 9445bgl, 11645del, 11645del† |
| 2245-2300 | FG R. | LAm | 9955rmi |
| **2300** | **English** | | |
| 2300-0100 | CRI | SEA | 11790xia |
| 2300-0100 | WWCR | Af | 5935wcr |
| 2300-0200 | CRI | Eu | 7350kas |
| 2300-0400 | R.HCJB DeuLand | CEu,WEu | 3995wnm* |
| 2300-0500 | Overcomer Min. | NAm | 7570rmi |
| 2300-0500 | WHRI | NAm | 7385hri |
| 2300-2315 | WRMI | NAm | 5950rmi |
| 2300-2315 | WRMI | Car,LAm | 9955rmi |
| 2300-2330 | IsleOfM/MeltPot | NAm | 7490bcq* |
| 2300-2330 | REE | WAf,Atl | 11685nob |
| 2300-2330 | REE | SAm | 11940nob |

| 2300 | English | Area | kHz |
|---|---|---|---|
| 2300-2330 | REE | ME,IOc | 12030nob |
| 2300-2330 | REE | NAm | 9690nob |
| 2300-2330 | R. Tirana Int | NAm | 5850rmi |
| 2300-2330 | WRMI | NAm | 5950rmi |
| 2300-2330 | WRMI | NAm,Eu,ME | 7780rmi |
| 2300-2330 | WRMI | Car,LAm | 9955rmi |
| 2300-2400 | BBC World Sce | SEA | 7445sla |
| 2300-2400 | CRI | SAs | 5915kas, 7410kas |
| 2300-2400 | CRI | NAm,CAm | 5990qvc |
| 2300-2400 | CRI | EAs | 6145bei |
| 2300-2400 | CRI | SEA | 9535kun |
| 2300-2400 | R. Poland | NAm | 5950rmi^ |
| 2300-2400 | R.Romania Int | Eu | 5980gal+, 7220gal |
| 2300-2400 | R.Romania Int | EAs | 7325tig, 9620tig |
| 2300-2400 | TWR Bonaire | Car | 800twb |
| 2300-2400 | VO Turkey | Eu,NAm | 5960emr |
| 2300-2400 | VORW R. Int | NAm | 5950rmi |
| 2300-2400 | VORW R. Int | LAm | 9955rmi |
| 2300-2400 | WHRI | SAm | 7315hri |
| 2300-2400 | WRMI | NAm | 9395rmi |
| 2330-0000 | R. Prague | NAm | 5850rmi |
| 2330-2400 | Hobart R. Int. | NAm,Eu,ME | 7780rmi |
| 2330-2400 | SW Radiogram | NAm,Eu,ME | 7780rmi |
| 2330-2400 | VO Vietnam | As | 9840vni, 12020vni |
| 2330-2400 | WRMI | NAm | 5950rmi |
| 2330-2400 | WRMI | Car,LAm | 9955rmi |
| **2400** | **English** | | |
| 2400-0100 | R. Habana Cuba | Af | 9720hab |

## ENGLISH/OTHERS

| 1100 | English (Liturgy) | Area | kHz |
|---|---|---|---|
| 1130-1200 | Vatican R. | NAf,ME | 15595smg |
| 1130-1200 | Vatican R. | NAf | 17590smg |
| **0100** | **English/Chinese** | | |
| 0100-1300 | WRNO | NAm | 7505rno† |
| **0800** | **English/Dutch/German** | | |
| 0800-1800 | R. Mi Amigo Int | CEu,WEu | 6085kll |
| **1100** | **English/Dutch/German** | | |
| 1100-1500 | R. Mi Amigo Int | CEu,WEu | 7310kll |
| **1800** | **English/Dutch/German** | | |
| 1800-1900 | R. Mi Amigo Int | CEu,WEu | 3985kll |
| **0000** | **English/Finnish** | | |
| 0000-0600 | Scan.Weekend R. | Eu | 6170vir* |
| 0000-0800 | Scan.Weekend R. | Eu | 11690vir* |
| 0000-2200 | Scan.Weekend R. | Eu | 1602vir* |
| **0600** | **English/Finnish** | | |
| 0600-0900 | Scan.Weekend R. | Eu | 5980vir* |
| **0800** | **English/Finnish** | | |
| 0800-1400 | Scan.Weekend R. | Eu | 11720vir* |
| **0900** | **English/Finnish** | | |
| 0900-1500 | Scan.Weekend R. | Eu | 6170vir* |
| **1400** | **English/Finnish** | | |
| 1400-1700 | Scan.Weekend R. | Eu | 11690vir* |
| **1500** | **English/Finnish** | | |
| 1500-1900 | Scan.Weekend R. | Eu | 5980vir* |
| **1700** | **English/Finnish** | | |
| 1700-1900 | Scan.Weekend R. | Eu | 11720vir* |
| **1900** | **English/Finnish** | | |
| 1900-2200 | Scan.Weekend R. | Eu | 6170vir*, 11690vir* |
| **2200** | **English/Finnish** | | |
| 2200-2300 | Scan.Weekend R. | Eu | 11720vir* |

| 2200 | Eng/Finnish | Area | kHz |
|---|---|---|---|
| 2200-2400 | Scan.Weekend R. | Eu | 1602vir*, 6170vir* |
| **2300** | **English/Finnish** | | |
| 2300-2400 | Scan.Weekend R. | Eu | 11690vir* |
| **1600** | **English/German** | | |
| 1600-1700 | R. Öömrang | NAm | 15215iss* |
| **0400** | **English/Ndebele/Shona** | | |
| 0400-0500 | VOA Studio7 | Af | 909bot, 6175bot, 9825sao |
| **1700** | **English/Ndebele/Shona** | | |
| 1700-1800 | VOA Studio7 | Af | 909bot, 4930bot, 13860sao, 15460sao |
| **1800** | **English/Ndebele/Shona** | | |
| 1800-1900 | VOA Studio7 | Af | 909bot, 4930bot, 13860sao, 15460sao |
| **0000** | **English/Norwegian** | | |
| 0000-2400 | R. N.Star/Ferry | NEu | 1611erd* |
| **1400** | **English/Norwegian** | | |
| 1400-0005 | R. N.Star/Ferry | Eu | 5895erd* |
| **0100** | **English/Spanish** | | |
| 0100-0200 | IsleOfM/MeltPot | NAm | 7490bcq |
| **1000** | **English/Spanish** | | |
| 1000-1230 | WINB | CAm | 9265inb* |
| **1200** | **English/Spanish** | | |
| 1200-1300 | IsleOfM/MeltPot | CEu,WEu | 6070rob |
| 1200-2100 | WINB | CAm | 9265inb |
| **1400** | **English/Spanish** | | |
| 1430-2100 | WINB | CAm | 9265inb |
| **1500** | **English/Spanish** | | |
| 1500-1600 | IsleOfM/MeltPot | Eu | 9400sof |
| **2100** | **English/Spanish** | | |
| 2100-0400 | WINB | CAm | 9265inb |
| **2200** | **English/Spanish** | | |
| 2200-0300 | WWCR | Af | 6115wcr |

## FRENCH

| 0000 | French | Area | kHz |
|---|---|---|---|
| 0000-2400 | RFI | Eu | 3965iss+ |
| **0100** | **French** | | |
| 0100-0130 | R. Habana Cuba | SAm | 15730hab |
| 0130-0200 | R. Habana Cuba | Car | 5040hab |
| **0200** | **French** | | |
| 0200-0300 | R.Romania Int | NAm | 6130gal, 7410gal |
| **0400** | **French** | | |
| 0400-0500 | VO Korea | SEA | 13650kuj, 15105kuj |
| 0400-0600 | RFI | EAf,CAf | 7390iss |
| 0400-0600 | RFI | CAf | 9790iss |
| 0430-0500 | AWR Africa | NAf | 6045nau |
| **0500** | **French** | | |
| 0500-0600 | RFI | CAf | 6040iss |
| 0500-1905 | RTBF Int. | Eu | 621wav* |
| 0530-0600 | R. Japan | CAf | 13840mdc |
| 0530-0600 | R. Japan | WAf | 7450iss |
| 0530-0600 | VOA | Af | 1530sao |
| 0530-0630 | VOA | Af | 4960sao, 6020sao, 9885smg, 13830bot |
| **0600** | **French** | | |
| 0600-0630 | AWR Africa | WAf | 7220iss |
| 0600-0630 | AWR Africa | NAf | 7375iss |
| 0600-0630 | BBC World Sce | WAf | 5875asc |
| 0600-0630 | BBC World Sce | NAf | 6135wof, 7265wof |
| 0600-0630 | BBC World Sce | CAf | 7305asc |

| 0600 | French | Area | kHz |
|------|--------|------|-----|
| 0600-0630 | R.Romania Int | Af | 11790tig, 13730tig |
| 0600-0630 | R.Romania Int | Eu | 7360gal, 9610gal+ |
| 0600-0700 | RFI | NAf,WAf | 5925iss*, 7390iss*, 9790iss** |
| 0600-0700 | VO Korea | LAm | 11735kuj, 13760kuj, 15180kuj |
| 0600-0800 | CRI | Eu | 15220kas |
| 0600-0800 | RFI | WAf,CAf | 11700iss |
| 0600-0900 | RFI | WAf,CAf | 13695iss |
| **0700** | **French** | | |
| 0700-0730 | AWR Africa | NAf | 11880iss |
| 0700-0730 | BBC World Sce | CAf | 17830dha |
| 0700-0730 | BBC World Sce | WAf | 7305asc |
| 0700-0730 | VO Nigeria | WAf | 7255aja |
| 0700-0800 | RFI | NAf,WAf | 9790iss |
| 0700-0900 | RFI | Af | 15300iss |
| 0730-0745 | Vatican R. | NAf,ME | 11935smg |
| **0800** | **French** | | |
| 0800-0830 | AWR Africa | NAf | 15145mos |
| 0800-0900 | RCI | Eu | 6005kll |
| 0800-0900 | RFI | CAf | 17850iss, 21580iss |
| 0830-0900 | VOA | Af | 12030sao, 15715smg, 17700bot |
| **1100** | **French** | | |
| 1100-1130 | VOA | Af | 12030sao, 13750bot, 15715bot, 17850smg |
| 1100-1200 | R.Romania Int | Eu | 11780gal, 15255gal, 15430tig |
| 1100-1200 | R.Romania Int | NAf | 17640tig |
| 1100-1200 | VO Korea | LAm | 6170kuj, 9435kuj |
| 1100-1200 | VO Korea | SEA | 6185kuj, 9850kuj |
| **1200** | **French** | | |
| 1200-1230 | BBC World Sce | NAf | 15490wof |
| 1200-1230 | BBC World Sce | WAf | 17640asc |
| 1200-1230 | BBC World Sce | CAf | 17830mey |
| 1200-1230 | VO Vietnam | As | 7285vni |
| 1200-1300 | RFI | NAf,WAf | 17620iss |
| 1200-1300 | RFI | WAf,CAf | 17660iss |
| 1200-1300 | RFI | CAf | 21580iss, 21690mdc |
| 1200-1400 | CRI | Eu | 15205kas |
| 1230-1300 | R. Slovakia Int | Eu | 6005kll* |
| **1300** | **French** | | |
| 1300-1330 | VO Vietnam | As | 7285vni |
| 1300-1400 | CRI | Eu | 13720kas |
| **1400** | **French** | | |
| 1400-1500 | VO Korea | Eu | 7570kuj, 12015kuj |
| 1400-1500 | VO Korea | NAm | 9435kuj, 11710kuj |
| 1400-1600 | CRI | WAf | 11920cer, 13670cer |
| 1400-1600 | Saudi R. Int. | WAf | 17660riy |
| 1430-1500 | R. Slovakia Int | Eu | 6005kll* |
| 1455-1525 | TWR Africa | CAf | 9585man |
| **1500** | **French** | | |
| 1500-1530 | Lao National R. | SEA | 567vie, 6130vie |
| **1600** | **French** | | |
| 1600-1630 | R. Tirana Int | CEu,WEu | 3985kll |
| 1600-1700 | Channel Africa | WAf | 15235mey |
| 1600-1700 | CAf | 9505alf | |
| 1600-1700 | VO Korea | Eu | 7570kuj, 12015kuj |
| 1600-1700 | VO Korea | NAm | 9435kuj, 11710kuj |
| 1600-1800 | CRI | Eu | 7350kas |
| 1630-1700 | R. Slovakia Int | Eu | 3985kll* |
| 1630-1700 | VO Vietnam | ME | 7220vni |
| 1640-1700 | R. Cairo | ISR | 1008ela |

| 1700 | French | Area | kHz |
|------|--------|------|-----|
| 1700-1715 | Vatican R. | Af | 7230smg |
| 1700-1730 | Vatican R. | Af | 9705smg, 11625smg |
| 1700-1800 | RFI | WAf,CAf | 11995iss, 13740iss |
| 1700-1800 | RFI | CAf | 9660iss*, 13740iss**, 15300iss |
| 1700-1800 | R.Romania Int | Eu | 7325tig, 9870tig+ |
| **1800** | **French** | | |
| 1800-1830 | BBC World Sce | WAf | 11975asc, 15490asc |
| 1800-1830 | BBC World Sce | CAf | 12065asc |
| 1800-1830 | BBC World Sce | NAf | 7265wof |
| 1800-1830 | BBC World Sce | SAf | 7395mey |
| 1800-1900 | RCI | Eu | 3985kll |
| 1800-1900 | RFI | WAf,CAf | 9725iss*, 11765iss*, 11995iss**, 15300iss** |
| 1800-1900 | RFI | NAf,WAf | 9810iss |
| 1800-1900 | VO Korea | SAf | 7210kuj, 11910kuj |
| 1800-1900 | VO Korea | ME,NAf | 9875kuj, 11635kuj |
| 1800-2000 | CRI | Eu | 5970cer, 7360cer |
| 1800-2000 | CRI | NAf,WAf | 6055cer, 7385cer |
| 1820-1920 | Pars Today | Eu | 6135sir |
| 1830-1930 | VOA | Af | 12075smg, 15730bot |
| 1830-1930 | VO Turkey | CAf | 9620emr |
| 1830-2000 | VOA | Af | 1530sao |
| 1830-2030 | CRI | WAf | 7350uru, 9645kun |
| **1900** | **French** | | |
| 1900-2000 | RFI | WAf,CAf | 7245iss, 9580iss, 9635iss, 11995iss |
| 1900-2000 | R.Taiwan Int. | Af | 9680iss |
| 1900-2000 | VOA | Af | 9515sao |
| 1930-2000 | AWR Africa | CAf | 9780mos |
| 1930-2000 | R. Slovakia Int | Eu | 3985kll* |
| 1930-2000 | VO Vietnam | Eu | 7280vni, 9730vni |
| 1930-2030 | VOA | Af | 11900sao, 12075bot, 15730grv |
| 1935-1950 | TWR Africa | CAf | 9940man |
| 1945-2045 | All India R. | Eu | 7550bgl+ |
| 1945-2045 | All India R. | NAf,WAf | 9620alg, 11710delt, 13640bgl |
| **2000** | **French** | | |
| 2000-2030 | AWR Africa | WAf | 9515mdc, 9780mey |
| 2000-2030 | VOA | Af | 9485kwt |
| 2000-2100 | KBS World R. | Af | 5950iss |
| 2000-2100 | VO Indonesia | SEA | 3325pgat |
| 2000-2100 | VO Korea | Eu | 7570kuj, 12015kuj |
| 2000-2115 | R. Cairo | Eu | 9900abst |
| 2000-2200 | RFI | NAf,WAf | 7205iss, 9790iss |
| 2030-2100 | AWR Africa | WAf | 7270mos |
| 2030-2100 | R. Habana Cuba | Eu | 15370hab |
| 2030-2100 | R. Japan | WAf | 9855mdc |
| 2030-2100 | Vatican R. | Af | 6010smg, 7365smg |
| 2030-2100 | VOA | Af | 11900sao, 11975smg |
| 2030-2100 | VOA | Af | 9485kwt, 13750sao |
| 2030-2100 | VO Vietnam | Eu | 7280vni, 9730vni |
| 2030-2130 | VO Turkey | Eu | 5970emr |
| 2030-2130 | VO Turkey | NAf,WAf | 9625emr |
| 2030-2230 | CRI | Eu | 6115bei, 7350uru |
| 2040-2215 | TWR Africa | WAf | 1566par |
| **2100** | **French** | | |
| 2100-2130 | R. Habana Cuba | NAm | 15140hab |
| 2100-2130 | R.Romania Int | Eu | 6030gal, 7375gal |
| 2100-2130 | VOA | Af | 5885bot, 9485kwt, 12075bot |

| 2100 | French | Area | kHz |
|------|--------|------|-----|
| 2100-2130 | VO Vietnam | ME | 7220vni |
| 2100-2200 | KBS World R. | Eu | 3955wof |
| **2300** | **French** | | |
| 2300-2330 | R. Habana Cuba | Af | 9720hab |
| 2320-0020 | Pars Today | WAf,CAf | 7260sir, 9660sir |
| 2330-0000 | RAE | NAm,Eu | 7780rmi |
| 2330-2400 | REE | WAf,Atl | 11685nob |
| 2330-2400 | REE | SAm | 11940nob |
| 2330-2400 | REE | ME,IOc | 12030nob |
| 2330-2400 | REE | NAm | 9690nob |
| 2330-2400 | R. Habana Cuba | SAm | 15730hab |

## FRENCH/OTHERS

| 0400 | French/Arabic | Area | kHz |
|------|---------------|------|-----|
| 0400-0600 | R. Algeriénnne | CAf,WAf | 6060iss |
| **0500** | **French/Arabic** | | |
| 0500-0700 | R. Algeriénnne | NAf,WAf | 6105iss |
| **1800** | **French/Arabic** | | |
| 1800-2000 | R. Algeriénnne | CAf,WAf | 7375iss |
| **1900** | **French/Arabic** | | |
| 1900-2000 | R. Algeriénnne | NAf,WAf | 7315iss |
| **2000** | **French/Arabic** | | |
| 2000-2100 | R. Algeriénnne | NAf,WAf | 6170iss |
| 2000-2200 | R. Algeriénnne | NAf,CAf | 5940iss |
| **2100** | **French/Arabic** | | |
| 2100-2300 | R. Algeriénnne | NAf,WAf | 6040iss |

## GERMAN

| 0500 | German | Area | kHz |
|------|--------|------|-----|
| 0500-2300 | R.HCJB DeuLand | D,CEu | 3995wnm** |
| **0600** | **German** | | |
| 0600-0630 | DWD | BaS,NoS | 5905pin, 6180pin |
| 0600-0710 | R. Ö1 (ORF) | Eu,NAf,ME | 6155mos |
| 0600-0720 | R. Ö1 (ORF) | Eu,NAf,ME | 6155mos |
| 0600-0800 | CRI | Eu | 17615uru, 17720kas |
| **0700** | **German** | | |
| 0700-0730 | R.Romania Int | Eu | 7345tig, 9770tig+ |
| 0700-1900 | Europa 24 | D,CEu | 6150dat* |
| 0700-2300 | R.HCJB DeuLand | D,CEu | 5920wnm** |
| **0800** | **German** | | |
| 0800-0900 | RAE | D,CEu | 6005kll |
| 0800-1200 | Hamburger LR | CEu,WEu | 6190goh* |
| **0900** | **German** | | |
| 0900-1100 | R. Belarus Int. | D,CEu | 6005kll |
| **1000** | **German** | | |
| 1000-1100 | Hamburger LR | CEu,WEu | 7265goh* |
| 1000-1100 | R. DARC | Eu | 6070mos |
| **1100** | **German** | | |
| 1100-1130 | R. Slovakia Int | Eu | 6005kll* |
| 1100-1200 | R. Joystick | Eu | 7330mos* |
| 1130-1200 | Ev.MissionsGem | Eu | 6055nau |
| **1200** | **German** | | |
| 1200-1230 | DWD | BaS,NoS | 5905pin, 6180pin |
| 1230-1300 | SRG - SSR | D,CEu | 6005kll* |
| 1230-1330 | VO Turkey | Eu | 15270emr |
| **1400** | **German** | | |
| 1400-1430 | R. Slovakia Int | Eu | 6005kll* |
| **1500** | **German** | | |
| 1500-1600 | R.Romania Int | Eu | 6040tig, 7330tig |

| 1600 | German | Area | kHz |
|------|--------|------|-----|
| 1600-1630 | DWD | Med | 5905pin, 6180pin |
| 1600-1630 | R. Poland | D,CEu | 6005kll* |
| 1600-1700 | R. DARC | D,CEu | 6070rob |
| 1600-1700 | VO Korea | Eu | 6170kuj, 9425kuj |
| 1600-1800 | CRI | Eu | 5970cer, 7380cer |
| **1700** | **German** | | |
| 1700-1800 | SRG - SSR | D,CEu | 3985kll*, 6005kll* |
| 1700-2300 | R.HCJB DeuLand | D,CEu | 7365wnm** |
| 1720-1820 | Pars Today | Eu | 6025sir, 7425sir |
| **1800** | **German** | | |
| 1800-1900 | VO Indonesia | SEA | 3325pga† |
| 1800-2000 | CRI | Eu | 6160xia, 7395kas, 9615uru |
| 1800-2000 | VO Korea | Eu | 6170kuj, 9425kuj |
| 1830-1900 | VO Vietnam | Eu | 7280vni, 9730vni |
| 1830-1930 | VO Turkey | Eu | 5945emr |
| **1900** | **German** | | |
| 1900-1930 | R. Slovakia Int | Eu | 3985kll* |
| 1900-1930 | R.Taiwan Int. | Eu | 5900sof |
| 1900-2000 | R. Cairo | Eu | 9570abs† |
| 1900-2000 | R.Romania Int | Eu | 6180tig+, 7235tig |
| **2000** | **German** | | |
| 2000-2015 | R. Thailand WS | Eu | 7475udo |
| 2000-2030 | DWD | BaS,NoS,Med | 5905pin, 6180pin |
| 2000-2030 | VO Vietnam | Eu | 7280vni, 9730vni |
| 2000-2100 | KBS World R. | Eu | 3955wof |
| 2000-2100 | R. DARC | D,CEu | 6070rob |
| 2030-2100 | R. Tirana Int | CEu,WEu | 3985kll |
| **2100** | **German** | | |
| 2100-2130 | SRG - SSR | D,CEu | 3985kll* |
| 2100-2200 | RAE | NAm,Eu | 7780rmi |

## GERMAN/OTHERS

| 0000 | German/Various | Area | kHz |
|------|----------------|------|-----|
| 0000-2400 | Channel 292 | Eu | 6070rob† |
| **0400** | **German/Various** | | |
| 0400-2400 | Channel 292 | Eu | 7440rob† |
| **0800** | **German/Various** | | |
| 0800-1800 | SWService | CEu,WEu | 6005kll* |
| **1600** | **German/Various** | | |
| 1600-2030 | SWService | CEu,WEu | 3985kll* |
| 1600-2100 | SWService | CEu,WEu | 3985kll* |
| 1600-2200 | SWService | CEu,WEu | 3985kll* |

## PORTUGUESE

| 0000 | Portuguese | Area | kHz |
|------|-----------|------|-----|
| 0000-0030 | REE | SAm | 11940nob |
| 0000-0030 | REE | NAm | 9690nob |
| 0000-0100 | CRI | SAm | 9710kas |
| 0030-0100 | R. Habana Cuba | SAm | 15730hab |
| **0800** | **Portuguese** | | |
| 0800-0945 | TWR Bonaire | B | 800twb |
| **0900** | **Portuguese** | | |
| 0900-0930 | R. Japan | SAm | 6195hri |
| **1200** | **Portuguese** | | |
| 1200-1300 | RAE | LAm | 9955rmi |
| **1400** | **Portuguese** | | |
| 1400-1500 | Channel Africa | SAf | 7230mey |
| **1600** | **Portuguese** | | |
| 1630-1645 | TWR Africa | SAf | 4760man |

| 1600 | **Portuguese** | **Area** | **kHz** |
|---|---|---|---|
| 1630-1700 | VOA | Af | 13630bot, 17655sao |
| **1700** | **Portuguese** | | |
| 1700-1800 | VOA | Af | 1530sao, 13630bot, 17655grv |
| **1800** | **Portuguese** | | |
| 1800-1830 | Vatican R. | Af | 9705smg |
| 1800-1830 | VOA | Af | 13630bot, 17655grv |
| **1900** | **Portuguese** | | |
| 1900-2000 | CRI | SAf | 5985bei, 7365bei, 7405xia, 9535bji |
| 1900-2000 | CRI | Eu | 7335jin, 9730kas |
| 1905-1920 | TWR Africa | SAf | 6130man |
| 1920-1950 | TWR Africa | SAf | 6130man |
| 1920-2005 | TWR Africa | SAf | 6130man |
| 1935-2005 | TWR Africa | SAf | 6130man |
| **2100** | **Portuguese** | | |
| 2100-2130 | R. Habana Cuba | Eu | 15370hab |
| 2100-2130 | Vatican R. | Af | 7365smg |
| 2100-2200 | Madagascar W.V. | Af | 11965mwv |
| **2200** | **Portuguese** | | |
| 2200-2300 | CRI | Eu | 6175cer, 7260uru |
| 2200-2300 | CRI | SAm | 9410kas, 9685kas |
| 2215-2330 | R. Cairo | SAm | 9880abs† |
| **2300** | **Portuguese** | | |
| 2300-0100 | CRI | SAm | 6100bei |
| 2300-2400 | CRI | SAm | 13650qvc |
| 2300-2400 | R. Habana Cuba | SAm | 11700hab |
| 2315-2330 | WRMI | NAm | 5950rmi |
| 2315-2330 | WRMI | Car,LAm | 9955rmi |
| 2330-2400 | R. Habana Cuba | Af | 9720hab |

## SPANISH

| 0000 | **Spanish** | **Area** | **kHz** |
|---|---|---|---|
| 0000-0015 | WRMI | Car,LAm | 9955rmi |
| 0000-0030 | AWR | CAm | 5010rmi |
| 0000-0030 | REE | SAm | 11940nob |
| 0000-0030 | REE | NAm | 9690nob |
| 0000-0030 | WRMI | NAm | 7730rmi, 9395rmi |
| 0000-0100 | CRI | SAm | 15120qvc |
| 0000-0100 | CRI | NAm,CAm | 5990qvc |
| 0000-0100 | R. Habana Cuba | NAm | 6000hab*, 11950hab* |
| 0000-0100 | R.Romania Int | SAm | 5980gal, 7325gal, 9600tig, 11800tig |
| 0000-0300 | TWR Bonaire | CUB | 800twb |
| 0000-0500 | R. Habana Cuba | SAm | 11670hab |
| 0000-0600 | R. Habana Cuba | SAm | 11700hab |
| 0000-1200 | R.Martí | CUB | 6030grv |
| 0000-1400 | WEWN | LAm | 5970ewn |
| 0000-2400 | R.Martí | CUB | 1180mth |
| 0015-0030 | WRMI | Car,LAm | 9955rmi |
| 0030-0100 | R. Slovakia Int | CAm | 5010rmi |
| 0030-0100 | VO Vietnam | LAm | 7315hri |
| 0030-0100 | WRMI | Car,LAm | 9955rmi |
| 0030-0300 | REE | SAm | 11940nob |
| 0030-0300 | REE | NAm | 9690nob |
| 0045-0200 | R. Cairo | SAm | 9420abs† |
| **0100** | **Spanish** | | |
| 0100-0115 | WRMI | Car,LAm | 9955rmi |
| 0100-0130 | Vozandes Media | EQA,CLM,PRU | 6050qui* |
| 0100-0200 | KBS World R. | LAm | 9605hri, 11810kim |
| 0100-0200 | R.Martí | CUB | 7365grv |

| 0100 | **Spanish** | **Area** | **kHz** |
|---|---|---|---|
| 0100-0200 | WRMI | Car | 5010rmi |
| 0100-0300 | CRI | SAm | 9710kas |
| 0100-0600 | R. Habana Cuba | NAm | 6060hab |
| 0115-0130 | WRMI | NAm,Eu,ME | 7780rmi |
| 0115-0130 | WRMI | Car,LAm | 9955rmi |
| 0115-0145 | WRMI | Car,LAm | 9955rmi |
| 0130-0200 | VO Vietnam | LAm | 7315hri |
| 0130-0200 | WRMI | Car,LAm | 9955rmi |
| 0145-0200 | Vatican R. | SAm | 7305grv |
| 0145-0200 | WRMI | Car,LAm | 9955rmi |
| **0200** | **Spanish** | | |
| 0200-0215 | WRMI | Car,LAm | 9955rmi |
| 0200-0230 | WRMI | Car,LAm | 9955rmi |
| 0200-0300 | Family R. | NAm | 5950rmi |
| 0200-0300 | KBS World R. | NAm | 15575kim |
| 0200-0300 | Madagascar W.V. | SAm | 6190mwv |
| 0200-0300 | VO Turkey | SAm,Eu | 9410emr |
| 0200-0300 | VO Turkey | CAm,Eu | 9650emr |
| 0200-0400 | R. República | CUB | 9490iss |
| 0200-0600 | R. Habana Cuba | CAm | 5040hab |
| 0200-0700 | R.Martí | CUB | 7435grv |
| 0230-0245 | WRMI | NAm,Eu,ME | 7780rmi |
| 0230-0245 | WRMI | Car,LAm | 9955rmi |
| 0230-0300 | WRMI | Car,LAm | 9955rmi |
| 0245-0300 | WRMI | Car,LAm | 9955rmi |
| **0300** | **Spanish** | | |
| 0300-0330 | R. Prague | LAm | 9955rmi |
| 0300-0400 | Madagascar W.V. | SAm | 6180mwv |
| 0300-0400 | R.Romania Int | CAm | 6155gal, 7410gal |
| 0300-0400 | R.Romania Int | SAm | 9740tig, 11800tig |
| 0300-0400 | VO Korea | LAm | 11735kuj, 13760kuj, 15180kuj |
| 0300-0800 | TWR Bonaire | Car | 800twb |
| 0330-0345 | WRMI | CAm | 5985rmi |
| 0330-0400 | R. Slovakia Int | LAm | 9955rmi |
| 0330-0400 | WRMI | CAm | 5985rmi |
| **0400** | **Spanish** | | |
| 0400-0415 | WRMI | Car,LAm | 9955rmi |
| 0400-0430 | R. Japan | SAm | 6195hri |
| 0400-0500 | WRMI | NAm | 7730rmi |
| 0415-0430 | WRMI | Car,LAm | 9955rmi |
| 0430-0500 | Family R. | CAm | 5985rmi |
| 0445-0500 | WRMI | Car,LAm | 9955rmi |
| **0500** | **Spanish** | | |
| 0500-0600 | VO Korea | LAm | 11735kuj, 13760kuj, 15180kuj |
| **0600** | **Spanish** | | |
| 0600-0800 | CRI | Eu | 15135kas |
| 0600-1300 | R.Martí | CUB | 5980grv |
| **0700** | **Spanish** | | |
| 0720-0820 | Pars Today | Eu | 15200sir, 17540sir |
| **0900** | **Spanish** | | |
| 0930-1000 | R. Japan | SAm | 6195hri |
| **1000** | **Spanish** | | |
| 1000-1015 | WRMI | NAm | 5950rmi |
| 1000-1100 | WRMI | NAm | 5950rmi |
| 1000-1230 | TWR Bonaire | Car | 800twb |
| 1000-1400 | R.Martí | CUB | 7355grv |
| 1030-1100 | WRMI | NAm | 5950rmi |
| **1100** | **Spanish** | | |
| 1100-1130 | AWR | CAm | 5010rmi |
| 1100-1200 | KBS World R. | LAm | 11795kim |
| 1100-1400 | Vozandes Media | EQA,CLM,PRU | 6050qui* |

| 1100 | Spanish | Area | kHz |
|---|---|---|---|
| 1130-1200 | R. Prague | CAm | 5010rmi |
| 1145-1200 | WRMI | Car,LAm | 9955rmi |
| **1200** | **Spanish** | | |
| 1200-1230 | WRMI | Car | 5010rmi |
| 1200-1300 | Hamburger LR | CEu,WEu | 7265goh* |
| 1200-1400 | R.Martí | CUB | 7435grv |
| 1200-1400 | R. Habana Cuba | NAm | 11950hab |
| 1200-1500 | R. Habana Cuba | SAm | 13780hab |
| 1200-1500 | R. Habana Cuba | NAm | 6000hab |
| 1200-1500 | RNASG (LRA36) | SAm | 15476lra† |
| 1200-1600 | R. Habana Cuba | Am | 11760hab |
| 1200-1600 | R. Habana Cuba | SAm | 15140hab |
| 1200-1600 | R. Habana Cuba | CAm | 9535hab |
| 1200-1600 | R. Habana Cuba | Car | 9640hab |
| 1230-1245 | Vatican R. | SAm | 9695grv |
| **1300** | **Spanish** | | |
| 1300-2200 | R.Martí | CUB | 11930grv |
| 1330-1400 | R. Slovakia Int | LAm | 9955rmi |
| 1345-1400 | WRMI | Car,LAm | 9955rmi |
| **1400** | **Spanish** | | |
| 1400-1430 | WRMI | Car,LAm | 9955rmi |
| 1400-1500 | Hamburger LR | CEu,WEu | 9485goh* |
| 1400-1600 | R. Habana Cuba | NAm | 13700hab |
| 1400-2000 | R.Martí | CUB | 13820grv |
| 1400-2100 | KVOH | CAm,SAm | 17775voh |
| 1400-2200 | R.Martí | CUB | 11860grv |
| 1400-2400 | WEWN | LAm | 12050ewn |
| 1430-1445 | WRMI | Car,LAm | 9955rmi |
| 1445-1500 | WRMI | Car,LAm | 9955rmi |
| **1500** | **Spanish** | | |
| 1500-1530 | R. Slovakia Int | Eu | 6005kll* |
| 1500-2300 | REE | WAf,Atl | 11685nob* |
| 1500-2300 | REE | SAm | 11940nob* |
| 1500-2300 | REE | ME,IOc | 12030nob* |
| 1500-2300 | REE | NAm | 9690nob* |
| **1600** | **Spanish** | | |
| 1600-1630 | R. Habana Cuba | Am | 11760hab |
| 1600-1800 | REE | WAf,Atl | 11685nob |
| 1600-1800 | REE | ME,IOc | 12030nob |
| 1600-1900 | R. Habana Cuba | NAm | 15140hab |
| 1630-1900 | R. Habana Cuba | Am | 11760hab |
| **1700** | **Spanish** | | |
| 1700-1800 | VO Indonesia | SEA | 3325pga† |
| 1730-1830 | VO Turkey | Eu | 9495emr |
| **1800** | **Spanish** | | |
| 1800-1830 | VO Vietnam | Eu | 7280vni, 9730vni |
| 1800-1900 | KBS World R. | Eu | 9740kim |
| 1830-1900 | BVB | Eu | 6145nau |
| 1830-2300 | REE | WAf,Atl | 11685nob |
| 1830-2300 | REE | ME,IOc | 12030nob |
| **1900** | **Spanish** | | |
| 1900-2000 | VO Korea | Eu | 7570kuj, 12015kuj |
| 1900-2300 | REE | SAm | 11940nob |
| 1900-2300 | REE | NAm | 9690nob |
| **2000** | **Spanish** | | |
| 2000-2030 | WRMI | NAm,Eu,ME | 7780rmi |
| 2000-2100 | R.Romania Int | NAf | 5920tig |
| 2000-2100 | R.Romania Int | Eu | 7235tig |
| 2000-2400 | R.Martí | CUB | 9565grv |
| 2015-2030 | WRMI | NAm,Eu,ME | 7780rmi |
| 2020-2120 | Pars Today | Eu | 7360sir, 11870sir |
| 2030-2045 | WRMI | NAm,Eu,ME | 7780rmi |

| 2100 | Spanish | Area | kHz |
|---|---|---|---|
| 2100-2130 | VO Vietnam | Eu | 7280vni, 9730vni |
| 2100-2130 | Vozandes Media | EQA,CLM,PRU | 6050qui* |
| 2100-2300 | CRI | Eu | 6020szg, 9640kas |
| 2100-2300 | VO Korea | Eu | 7570kuj, 12015kuj |
| 2100-2400 | Vozandes Media | EQA,CLM,PRU | 6050qui* |
| 2130-2300 | TWR Bonaire | Car | 800twb |
| **2200** | **Spanish** | | |
| 2200-0300 | R. Habana Cuba | Am | 11760hab |
| 2200-0500 | R. Habana Cuba | SAm | 13740hab |
| 2200-0500 | R. Habana Cuba | Car | 9640hab |
| 2200-0600 | R. Habana Cuba | SAm | 11840hab |
| 2200-0600 | R. Habana Cuba | CAm | 9535hab |
| 2200-2230 | WRMI | Car,LAm | 9955rmi |
| 2200-2300 | CRI | SAm | 6100bei |
| 2200-2300 | R.Martí | CUB | 7375grv |
| 2200-2300 | R.Romania Int | SAm | 9490tig+, 11800tig |
| 2200-2300 | RAE | CAm | 5010rmi |
| 2200-2300 | WRMI | Car,LAm | 9955rmi |
| 2200-2400 | CRI | Eu | 7210cer, 7250uru |
| 2200-2400 | R. Habana Cuba | Eu | 15370hab |
| 2200-2400 | R. Habana Cuba | CAm | 5040hab |
| 2215-2230 | WRMI | Car,LAm | 9955rmi |
| 2230-2300 | WRMI | Car,LAm | 9955rmi |
| 2245-2300 | WRMI | Car,LAm | 9955rmi |
| **2300** | **Spanish** | | |
| 2300-0100 | CRI | SAm | 9800kas |
| 2300-0100 | R.Martí | CUB | 7435grv |
| 2300-0300 | CRI | SAm | 9590kas |
| 2300-0600 | R.Martí | CUB | 7355grv |
| 2300-2330 | REE | WAf,Atl | 11685nob |
| 2300-2330 | REE | SAm | 11940nob |
| 2300-2330 | REE | ME,IOc | 12030nob |
| 2300-2330 | REE | NAm | 9690nob |
| 2300-2400 | CRI | Eu | 6175cer |
| 2300-2400 | Family R. | CAm | 5010rmi |
| 2300-2400 | WRMI | NAm | 5950rmi |
| 2300-2400 | WRMI | Car,LAm | 9955rmi |
| 2320-0050 | Pars Today | Eu,LAm | 7230sir |
| 2320-0220 | Pars Today | Eu,LAm | 6090sir |
| 2320-0220 | Pars Today | LAm | 6090sir |
| 2330-2400 | WRMI | NAm | 5950rmi |
| 2330-2400 | WRMI | Car,LAm | 9955rmi |

**NB:** not all broadcasts are daily, please check main schedules under the appropriate country for full details. Language combinations are only shown for broadcasts where English, French, German, Portuguese or Spanish is listed as the first language in the combination. English etc. may appear in parts of other language combinations not shown here, (see full schedule under main station entries).

For *, ** and *** please see '**Key**' under the individual entry for that station in the International Radio section

**Key:** + = DRM broadcast; † = irregular; ‡ = inactive at time of publication; .± = variable frequency

© WRTH Publications Ltd, November 2018

# DRM International Broadcasts

| 0000 | Language | Area | Station | kHz, site | | 2000 | Language | Area | Station | kHz, site |
|------|----------|------|---------|-----------|---|------|----------|------|---------|-----------|
| 0000-2400 | French | Eu | RFI | 3965iss+ | | 2045-2230 | English | Eu | All India R. | 7550bgl+ |
| **0300** | | | | | | **2100** | | | | |
| 0315-0415 | Hindi | EAf | All India R. | 15185bgl+* | | 2130-2200 | English | Eu | R.Romania Int | 6030gal+ |
| **0400** | | | | | | **2200** | | | | |
| 0400-0500 | English | As | R.Romania Int | 9820tig+ | | 2245-0045 | English | EAs | All India R. | 7550bgl+ |
| 0415-0430 | Gujarati | EAf | All India R. | 15185bgl+* | | 2200-2300 | Spanish | SAm | R.Romania Int | 9490tig+ |
| 0430-0530 | Hindi | EAf | All India R. | 15185bgl+* | | **2300** | | | | |
| **0500** | | | | | | 2300-2400 | English | Eu | R.Romania Int | 5980gal+ |
| 0500-0530 | Chinese | CHN | R.Romania Int | 13730tig+ | | | | | | |
| 0500-0800 | English | SAs | R. Kuwait | 11970kbd+ | | | | | | |
| 0530-0600 | Russian | RUS | R.Romania Int | 5940tig+ | | | | | | |
| **0600** | | | | | | | | | | |

**Key:**
† Irregular.
+ DRM (Digital Radio Mondiale)
+* DRM Simulcast (Hindi (Vividh Bharati) on 2nd channel)
# and NZL,Pac

**NB:** Not all broadcasts are daily. Please refer to individual schedules under the main station entry in the International radio section for full details.

Some DRM transmissions may be test broadcasts and subject to change or interruption during the broadcast.

Further information on DRM broadcasts, including details of low power test transmissions, can be found online.

© WRTH Publications Ltd, November 2018

| 0000 | Language | Area | Station | kHz, site |
|------|----------|------|---------|-----------|
| 0600-0700 | English | Eu | BBC World Sce | 3955wof+ |
| 0630-0700 | English | AUS# | R.Romania Int | 15450tig+ |
| 0630-0700 | English | Eu | R.Romania Int | 9770gal+ |
| 0600-0630 | French | Eu | R.Romania Int | 9610gal+ |
| 0630-0815 | Urdu | SAs | All India R. | 1071raj+ |
| **0700** | | | | |
| 0700-0900 | English | Eu.NAf | WINB | 7315inb+ |
| 0700-0730 | German | Eu | R.Romania Int | 9770tig+ |
| **0800** | | | | |
| 0800-0900 | English | SAs | BBC World Sce | 15620sng+ |
| **0900** | | | | |
| 0945-1325 | Arabic | Eu | R. Kuwait | 15110kbd+ |
| 0900-1100 | English | Eu.NAf | WINB | 9265inb+ |
| **1000** | | | | |
| 1000-1100 | English | Pac | All India R. | 17895bgl+* |
| **1100** | | | | |
| 1145-1315 | Chinese | EAs | All India R. | 15030bgl+* |
| 1100-1700 | English | Eu.NAf | WINB | 13690inb+ |
| **1200** | | | | |
| 1200-1230 | English | Eu,NAf | World of Radio | 9265inb+ |
| 1215-1330 | Tibetan | EAs | All India R. | 15030bgl+* |
| **1600** | | | | |
| 1650-1750 | English | Pac | RNZI (RNZ Pac.) | 5975ran+ |
| 1600-1630 | Russian | RUS | R.Romania Int | 6030tig+ |
| **1700** | | | | |
| 1700-2000 | Arabic | NAm | R. Kuwait | 13650kbd+ |
| 1745-1945 | English | Eu | All India R. | 7550bgl+ |
| 1750-1835 | English | Pac | RNZI (RNZ Pac.) | 9780ran+ |
| 1700-1800 | French | Eu | R.Romania Int | 9870tig+ |
| **1800** | | | | |
| 1800-2100 | English | Eu | R. Kuwait | 15540kbd+,† |
| 1835-1950 | English | Pac | RNZI (RNZ Pac.) | 9780ran+ |
| 1800-1930 | English | Eu | VO Nigeria | 15120aja+,† |
| 1800-1900 | English | Eu | R.Romania Int | 7350tig+ |
| **1900** | | | | |
| 1950-2050 | English | Pac | RNZI (RNZ Pac.) | 13840ran+ |
| 1945-2045 | French | Eu | All India R. | 7550bgl+ |
| 1900-2000 | German | Eu | R.Romania Int | 6180tig+ |
| 1945-2045 | Hindi | Eu | All India R. | 7550bgl+ |
| 1900-1930 | Italian | Eu | R.Romania Int | 5955tig+ |

# Notes

# NATIONAL TELEVISION

## Section Contents

Initial entries for each letter,
see Main Index for full details

TV Systems .................... 606

Afghanistan.................... 608
Bahamas ...................... 610
Cabo Verde .................. 613
Denmark....................... 617
Easter Island ................ 618
Falkland Islands ............ 619
Gabon.......................... 621
Haiti ............................. 624
Iceland.......................... 625
Jamaica ........................ 627
Kazakhstan................... 628
Laos............................. 629
Macau.......................... 631
Namibia ....................... 634
Oman........................... 636
Pakistan....................... 636
Qatar........................... 639
Réunion ....................... 639
Saba ........................... 640
Taiwan......................... 645
Uganda ........................ 647
Vanuatu ....................... 653
Wake Island................. 654
Yemen ......................... 654
Zambia......................... 654

Features & Reviews

National Radio

International Radio

Frequency Lists

National Television
(incl. Radio via DTT)

Reference

## CHARACTERISTICS OF ANALOGUE TELEVISION SYSTEMS
(Recommendation ITU-R BT.470-6, Revision 2005)

| System | Number of lines | Channel width MHz. | Vision band-width MHz. | Vision/Sound separation MHz. | Vestigial side-band MHz. | Vision mod. | Sound mod. |
|---|---|---|---|---|---|---|---|
| B | 625 | 7 | 5 | +5.5 | 0.75 | Neg. | FM |
| B1 | 625 | 8 | 5 | +5.5 | 0.75 | Neg. | FM |
| D | 625 | 8 | 6 | +6.5 | 0.75 | Neg. | FM |
| D1 | 625 | 8 | 5 | +6.5 | 0.75 | Neg. | FM |
| G | 625 | 8 | 5 | +5.5 | 0.75 | Neg. | FM |
| H | 625 | 8 | 5 | +5.5 | 1.25 | Neg. | FM |
| I | 625 | 8 | 5.5 | +5.996 | 1.25 | Neg. | FM |
| I1 | 625 | 8 | 5.5 | +5.996 | 1.25 | Neg. | FM |
| K | 625 | 8 | 6 | +6.5 | 0.75 | Neg. | FM |
| K1 | 625 | 8 | 5 | +6.5 | 0.75 | Neg. | FM |
| L | 625 | 8 | 6 | +6.5 | 1.25 | Pos. | AM |
| M | 525 | 6 | 4.2 | +4.5 | 0.75 | Neg. | FM |
| N | 625 | 6 | 4.2 | +4.5 | 0.75 | Neg. | FM |

## DIGITAL TERRESTRIAL TELEVISION SYSTEMS (DTT)

**ATSC** (**A**dvanced **T**elevision **S**ystems **C**ommittee)
(North America, parts of Central America & Asia))

**DTMB** (**D**igital **T**errestrial **M**ultimedia **B**roadcast) i
(P.R. China, Cuba, Laos)

**DVB-T/DVB-T2** (**D**igital **V**ideo **B**roadcasting - **T**errestrial)
(Europe, Africa, parts of Asia, Pacific)

**ISDB-T/ISDB-TB** (**I**ntegrated **S**ervices **D**igital **B**roadcasting - **T**errestrial)
(ISDB-T: Japan, parts of Asia; ISDB-TB: Parts of So. America, Botswana)

## DIGITAL/ANALOGUE CHANNEL INFORMATION
**Digital:** Centre carrier frequencies in MHz
**Analogue:** Vision carrier frequencies in MHz
(**NB:** Not all assigned channels are in use)

## VHF CHANNELS

**[A] Channels (Digital & Analogue)**
(Americas, parts of Asia & Pacific)

| | Dig | Analg | | Dig | Analg | | Dig | Analg |
|---|---|---|---|---|---|---|---|---|
| A2 = | 57 | 55.25 | A6 = | 85 | 83.25 | A10 = | 195 | 193.25 |
| A3 = | 63 | 61.75 | A7 = | 177 | 175.25 | A11 = | 201 | 199.25 |
| A4 = | 69 | 67.25 | A8 = | 183 | 181.25 | A12 = | 207 | 205.25 |
| A5 = | 79 | 77.25 | A9 = | 189 | 187.25 | A13 = | 213 | 211.25 |

**[E] Channels (Digital & Analogue)**
(Most of Europe, Greenland, Africa, most of Asia & Pacific)

| | Dig | Analg | | Dig | Analg | | Dig | Analg |
|---|---|---|---|---|---|---|---|---|
| E2 = | (*) | 48.25 | E6 = | 184.5 | 182.25 | A10 = | 212.5 | 210.25 |
| E3 = | (*) | 55.75 | E7 = | 191.5 | 189.25 | A11 = | 219.5 | 217.25 |
| E4 = | (*) | 62.25 | E8 = | 198.5 | 196.25 | E12 = | 226.5 | 224.25 |
| E5 = | 177.5 | 175.25 | E9 = | 205.5 | 203.25 | | | |

*) Analogue only

**[K] Channels (Analogue only)**
(Parts of Africa)

| | | | | | | | |
|---|---|---|---|---|---|---|---|
| K4 | = | 175.25 | K7 | = | 199.25 | K10 | = 223.25 |
| K5 | = | 183.25 | K8 | = | 207.25 | | |
| K6 | = | 191.25 | K9 | = | 215.25 | | |

**[R] Channels (Analogue only)**
(Parts of Europe, Russia, parts of Asia)

| | | | | | | | | |
|---|---|---|---|---|---|---|---|---|
| R1 | = | 49.75 | R5 | = | 93.25 | R9 | = | 199.25 |
| R2 | = | 59.25 | R6 | = | 175.25 | R10 | = | 207.25 |
| R3 | = | 77.25 | R7 | = | 183.25 | R11 | = | 215.25 |
| R4 | = | 85.25 | R8 | = | 191.25 | R12 | = | 223.25 |

### Specific National Parameters:

**South Africa & Namibia (Analogue only)**

| | | | | | | | | |
|---|---|---|---|---|---|---|---|---|
| SA4 | = | 175.25 | SA7 | = | 199.25 | SA10 | = | 223.25 |
| SA5 | = | 183.25 | SA8 | = | 207.25 | SA11 | = | 231.25 |
| SA6 | = | 191.25 | SA9 | = | 215.25 | SA13 | = | 247.43 |

**China (P.R.) (Analogue only)**

| | | | | | | | | |
|---|---|---|---|---|---|---|---|---|
| DS1 | = | 49.75 | DS5 | = | 85.25 | DS9 | = | 192.25 |
| DS2 | = | 57.75 | DS6 | = | 168.25 | DS10 | = | 200.25 |
| DS3 | = | 65.75 | DS7 | = | 176.25 | DS11 | = | 208.25 |
| DS4 | = | 77.25 | DS8 | = | 184.25 | DS12 | = | 216.25 |

**Australia & parts of Pacific (Digital & Analogue)**

| | | Dig | Analg | | | Dig | Analg |
|---|---|---|---|---|---|---|---|
| AU0 | = | 48.5 | 46.25 | AU7 | = | 184.5 | 182.25 |
| AU1 | = | 59.5 | 57.25 | AU8 | = | 191.5 | 189.25 |
| AU2 | = | 66.5 | 64.25 | AU9 | = | 198.5 | 196.25 |
| AU3 | = | 88.5 | 86.25 | AU9A | = | 205.5 | 203.25 |
| AU4 | = | 97.5 | 95.25 | AU10 | = | 212.5 | 209.25 |
| AU5 | = | 104.5 | 102.25 | AU11 | = | 219.5 | 216.25 |
| AU5A | = | 140.5 | 138.25 | AU12 | = | 226.5 | 224.25 |
| AU6 | = | 177.5 | 175.25 | | | | |

## UHF CHANNELS

### [A] Channels (Digital & Analogue)
(Americas, parts of Asia & Pacific)

| Dig | Analg | Dig | Analg | Dig | Analg |
|---|---|---|---|---|---|
| 14 = 473 | 471.25 | 33 = 587 | 585.25 | 52 = 701 | 699.25 |
| 15 = 479 | 477.25 | 34 = 593 | 591.25 | 53 = 707 | 705.25 |
| 16 = 485 | 483.25 | 35 = 599 | 597.25 | 54 = 713 | 711.25 |
| 17 = 491 | 489.25 | 36 = 605 | 603.25 | 55 = 720 | 717.25 |
| 18 = 497 | 495.25 | 37 = 611 | 609.25 | 56 = 725 | 723.25 |
| 19 = 503 | 501.25 | 38 = 617 | 615.25 | 57 = 731 | 729.25 |
| 20 = 509 | 507.25 | 39 = 623 | 621.25 | 58 = 737 | 735.25 |
| 21 = 515 | 513.25 | 40 = 629 | 627.25 | 59 = 743 | 741.25 |
| 22 = 521 | 519.25 | 41 = 635 | 633.25 | 60 = 749 | 747.25 |
| 23 = 527 | 525.25 | 42 = 641 | 639.25 | 61 = 755 | 753.25 |
| 24 = 533 | 531.25 | 43 = 647 | 645.25 | 62 = 761 | 759.25 |
| 25 = 539 | 537.25 | 44 = 653 | 651.25 | 63 = 767 | 765.25 |
| 26 = 545 | 543.25 | 45 = 659 | 657.25 | 64 = 773 | 771.25 |
| 27 = 551 | 549.25 | 46 = 665 | 663.25 | 65 = 779 | 777.25 |
| 28 = 557 | 555.25 | 47 = 671 | 669.25 | 66 = 785 | 783.25 |
| 29 = 563 | 561.25 | 48 = 677 | 675.25 | 67 = 791 | 789.25 |
| 30 = 569 | 567.25 | 49 = 683 | 681.25 | 68 = 797 | 795.25 |
| 31 = 575 | 573.25 | 50 = 689 | 687.25 | 69 = 803 | 801.25 |
| 32 = 581 | 579.25 | 51 = 695 | 693.25 | | |

### [E] Channels (Digital & Analogue), [R] Channels (Analogue)
(Europe, Greenland, Russia, Africa, most of Asia & Oceania)

| Dig | Analg | Dig | Analg | Dig | Analg |
|---|---|---|---|---|---|
| 21 = 474 | 474.25 | 38 = 610 | 607.25 | 55 = 746 | 743.25 |
| 22 = 482 | 479.25 | 39 = 618 | 615.25 | 56 = 754 | 751.25 |
| 23 = 490 | 487.25 | 40 = 626 | 623.25 | 57 = 762 | 759.25 |
| 24 = 498 | 495.25 | 41 = 634 | 631.25 | 58 = 770 | 767.25 |
| 25 = 506 | 503.25 | 42 = 642 | 639.25 | 59 = 778 | 775.25 |
| 26 = 514 | 511.25 | 43 = 650 | 647.25 | 60 = 786 | 783.25 |
| 27 = 522 | 519.25 | 44 = 658 | 655.25 | 61 = 794 | 791.25 |
| 28 = 530 | 527.25 | 45 = 666 | 663.25 | 62 = 802 | 799.25 |
| 29 = 538 | 535.25 | 46 = 674 | 671.25 | 63 = 810 | 807.25 |
| 30 = 546 | 543.25 | 47 = 682 | 679.25 | 64 = 818 | 815.25 |
| 31 = 554 | 551.25 | 48 = 690 | 687.25 | 65 = 826 | 823.25 |
| 32 = 562 | 559.25 | 49 = 698 | 695.25 | 66 = 834 | 831.25 |
| 33 = 570 | 567.25 | 50 = 706 | 703.25 | 67 = 842 | 839.25 |
| 34 = 578 | 575.25 | 51 = 714 | 711.25 | 68 = 850 | 847.25 |
| 35 = 586 | 583.25 | 52 = 722 | 719.25 | 69 = 858 | 855.25 |
| 36 = 594 | 591.25 | 53 = 730 | 727.25 | | |
| 37 = 602 | 599.25 | 54 = 738 | 735.25 | | |

### [DS] Channels (Digital & Analogue)
(China, P.R., exc. SAR Macau, SAR Hong Kong)

| Dig | Analg | Dig | Analg | Dig | Analg |
|---|---|---|---|---|---|
| 13 = 474 | 471.25 | 28 = 634 | 631.25 | 43 = 754 | 751.25 |
| 14 = 482 | 479.25 | 29 = 642 | 645.25 | 44 = 762 | 759.25 |
| 15 = 490 | 487.25 | 30 = 650 | 647.25 | 45 = 770 | 767.25 |
| 16 = 498 | 493.25 | 31 = 658 | 655.25 | 46 = 778 | 775.25 |
| 17 = 503 | 503.25 | 32 = 666 | 663.25 | 47 = 786 | 783.25 |
| 18 = 514 | 517.25 | 33 = 674 | 671.25 | 48 = 794 | 791.25 |
| 19 = 522 | 519.25 | 34 = 682 | 679.25 | 49 = 802 | 799.25 |
| 20 = 530 | 527.25 | 35 = 690 | 687.25 | 50 = 810 | 807.25 |
| 21 = 538 | 535.25 | 36 = 698 | 695.25 | 51 = 818 | 815.25 |
| 22 = 549 | 546.25 | 37 = 706 | 703.25 | 52 = 826 | 823.25 |
| 23 = 554 | 551.25 | 38 = 714 | 711.25 | 53 = 834 | 831.25 |
| 24 = 562 | 559.25 | 39 = 722 | 719.25 | 54 = 842 | 839.25 |
| 25 = 610 | 607.25 | 40 = 730 | 727.25 | 55 = 850 | 847.25 |
| 26 = 618 | 615.25 | 41 = 738 | 735.25 | 56 = 856 | 855.25 |
| 27 = 626 | 623.25 | 42 = 746 | 743.25 | 57 = 866 | 863.25 |

### [J] Channels (Digital only)
(Japan)

| | | | | | |
|---|---|---|---|---|---|
| 13 = 473 | 30 = 575 | 47 = 677 |
| 14 = 479 | 31 = 581 | 48 = 683 |
| 15 = 485 | 32 = 587 | 49 = 689 |
| 16 = 491 | 33 = 593 | 50 = 695 |
| 17 = 497 | 34 = 599 | 51 = 701 |
| 18 = 503 | 35 = 605 | 52 = 707 |
| 19 = 509 | 36 = 611 | 53 = 713 |
| 20 = 515 | 37 = 617 | 54 = 720 |
| 21 = 521 | 38 = 623 | 55 = 725 |
| 22 = 527 | 39 = 629 | 56 = 731 |
| 23 = 533 | 40 = 635 | 57 = 737 |
| 24 = 539 | 41 = 641 | 58 = 743 |
| 25 = 545 | 42 = 647 | 59 = 749 |
| 26 = 551 | 43 = 653 | 60 = 755 |
| 27 = 557 | 44 = 659 | 61 = 761 |
| 28 = 563 | 45 = 665 | 62 = 767 |
| 29 = 569 | 46 = 671 | |

### [AU] Channels (Digital only)
(Australia & parts of Oceania)

| | | | | | |
|---|---|---|---|---|---|
| 28 = 529.5 | 42 = 627.5 | 56 = 732.5 |
| 29 = 536.5 | 43 = 641.5 | 57 = 739.5 |
| 30 = 543.5 | 44 = 648.5 | 58 = 746.5 |
| 31 = 550.5 | 45 = 655.5 | 60 = 753.5 |
| 32 = 557.5 | 46 = 662.5 | 61 = 760.5 |
| 33 = 565.5 | 47 = 669.5 | 62 = 767.5 |
| 34 = 571.5 | 48 = 676.5 | 63 = 774.5 |
| 35 = 578.5 | 49 = 683.5 | 64 = 781.5 |
| 36 = 585.5 | 50 = 690.5 | 65 = 788.5 |
| 37 = 592.5 | 51 = 697.5 | 66 = 795.5 |
| 38 = 599.5 | 52 = 704.5 | 67 = 802.5 |
| 39 = 606.5 | 53 = 711.5 | 68 = 809.5 |
| 40 = 613.5 | 54 = 718.5 | 69 = 816.5 |
| 41 = 620.5 | 55 = 725.5 | |

### [NZ] Channels (Digital only)
(New Zealand & parts of Oceania)

| | | | | | |
|---|---|---|---|---|---|
| 25 = 506 | 34 = 578 | 43 = 650 |
| 26 = 514 | 35 = 586 | 44 = 658 |
| 27 = 522 | 36 = 594 | 45 = 666 |
| 28 = 530 | 37 = 602 | 46 = 674 |
| 29 = 538 | 38 = 610 | 47 = 682 |
| 30 = 546 | 39 = 618 | 48 = 690 |
| 31 = 554 | 40 = 626 | 49 = 698 |
| 32 = 562 | 41 = 634 | |
| 33 = 570 | 42 = 642 | |

# INTRODUCTION

The TV section contains information about terrestrial TV stations (and ✶ radio prgrs via DTT), in a compact format. If applicable, each country entry is devided into subsections: "National Stations", "Regional Stations", "Local Stations", "Foreign TV Relays", "Foreign Military Stations". The subsection "DTT Tx Networks" contains details of DTT transmitter operators or licensees, and DTT transmitters. Contact info for domestic prgrs included in the DTT multiplexes is found in the subsections mentioned above.
Keys: "Systems" : # = txs to be phased out, § = analogue or digital txs are being phased out (tx details no longer listed) ⬇=analogue shutdown date; [A], [DS], [E], [J], [K], [R], [AU], [NZ], [SA] refer to the channel characteristics as shown in the "Channel Information" table. Tx networks for national stations are listed either with main txs (power limit applied) or with key tx(s). Local Stations (if included) are listed in full; if no tx location is given, the site refers to the city of the station's headquarters. (-) = tx details not received at editorial deadline.

## AFGHANISTAN

Systems: # PAL-B/G [E]; DVB-T2 (MPEG4) [E]

National Stations (ᵃ=analogue)
RTA TV (Gov) 🖃 Street #13, Wazir Mohammad Akbar Khan, Kabul ☎ +93 20 2102487 📠 +93 20 2101086 E: info@rta.org.af W: www. rta.org.af LP: DG (RTA): Zarin Anzor Chs: RTA, RTA News Txs: RTA: Kabul ᵃch11 (2kW) & relay txs. NB: Local stations in Herat, Kandahar, Khost. – AFGHAN TV (Comm)🖃 Kabul ☎ +93 777 555566 📠 +93 798 555566 LP: DG: Ahmed Shah Afghanzai Txs: Kabul ᵃch24 & relay txs. – ARIANA TELEVISION NETWORK (ATN) (Comm) 🖃 318, Darulaman Rd, Kabul ☎ +93 700 111113 E: marketing@arianatelevision.com W: arianatelevision.com LP: MD: Arral Azizullah Txs: Kabul ᵃch4 & relay txs. – TOLO TV (Comm)🖃 P.O.Box 225, Kabul E: info@tolo.tv W: www.tolo.tv LP: Dir: Saad Mohseni Txs: Kabul ᵃch9 & relay txs.

Local Stations not shown.

DTT Tx Network
Tx Operator: Oqaab W: www.oqaab.af M1-4✪: 1TV, 3 Sport, AAA Family, AAA Music, Afghan TV, Al Jazeera Arabic, Al Jazeera English, Anaar TV, Aria TV, ARY TV, ATV, BBC Persian, BBC World News, CCTV, CNBC Europe, CNNi, DD News, DD Urdu, Dubai Sport 3, DW TV, Emrooz TV, Family 1, France 24, GEM Bollywood, GEM Junior, GEM Life, GEM Travel, GEM TV, Hum TV, iMovie, IRINN, Jahonnamo, Kabul News, Khawar, Khurshid, Maiwand, Manoto 1, MBC 2, MBC 3 Cartoon, MBC 4, MBC Action, MBC Ballywood, MBC Max, Mitra, My Cartoon, Onyx, Parliament, Pashto 1, Peace TV HD, Persian Movie, Persian Music, Pigham TV, Press TV HD, Quran TV, Rah-e Farda, River TV, RTA, RTA News, Rubix, Russia Today English, Shamshad, Sunnah TV, Tamadoon, TV Bokhoristan, TV Safina, TVT 1 Tajikistan, VOA Persian, Watan, Yas Sport, Zhowandoon Txs: (Kabul); nationwide netw. planned.

## ALASKA (USA)

System: ATSC [A]

Local Stations (Full power licenses; LP licenses not listed)
KAKM (Pub) 3877 University Dr, Anchorage, AK 99508-4676. Tx: Anchorage ch8 (50kW). KATN (Comm): 516 2nd Ave Ste 400, Fairbanks, AK 99701-4729. Tx: ch18 (16kW). KDMD (Comm): 1310 E 66th Ave, Anchorage, AK 99518-1915. Tx: ch33 (17.2kW). KFXF (Comm): 3650 Braddock St Ste 2, Fairbanks, AK 99701-7617. Tx: ch7 (6.1kW). KJNP-TV (Rlg): 2501 Mission Rd, North Pole, AK 99705-6361. Tx: ch20 (30.9kW). KJUD (Comm) 175 S Franklin St, Juneau, AK 99801-1384. Tx: ch11 (0.14kW). KTBY (Comm): 440 E Benson Blvd Ste 1, Anchorage, AK 99503-4121. Tx: ch20 (234.4kW). KTNL-TV (Comm): 520 Lake St, Sitka, AK 99835-7403. Tx: ch7 (0.35kW). KTOO-TV (Pub): 360 Egan Dr, Juneau, AK 99801-1748. Tx: ch10 (1kW). KTUU-TV (Comm): 701 E Tudor Rd Ste 220, Anchorage, AK 99503-7488. Tx: ch10 (21kW). KTVA (Comm): 1007 W 32nd Ave, Anchorage, AK 99503-3728. Tx: ch28 (28.9kW). KTVF (Comm): 3528 International Way, Fairbanks, AK 99701-7382. Tx: ch26 (12kW). KUAC-TV (Pub): 312 Tanana Dr, Fairbanks, AK 99775-2004. Tx: ch9 (30kW). KUTB (Comm) 2417 Tongass Ave, Ketchikan, AK 99901 Tx: ch13 (1.5kW). KYES-TV (Comm) 3700 Woodland Dr Ste 800, Anchorage, AK 99517-2588. Tx: ch5 (15kW).

## ALBANIA

Systems: DVB-T (MPEG4); DVB-T2 (MPEG4) [E]

National Stations
RADIOTELEVISIONI SHQIPTAR (RTSH) (Pub) 🖃 Rr. Ismail Qemali nr. 11, 1001 Tiranë ☎ +355 42230842 E: marketing@rtsh.al W: www.rtsh.al LP: DG: Thoma Gëllçi Chs: TVSH1, TVSH2. – TOP CHANNEL (Comm) 🖃 Rr. 5 Dëshmorët nr. 20, Mëzez, 1050 Tiranë ☎ +355 42253177 E: info@top-channel.tv W: top-channel.tv – TV KLAN (Comm) 🖃 Rr. Aleksandër Moisiu nr. 97, 1007 Tiranë ☎ +355 42347805 E: info@tvklan.al W: tvklan.al.

Local Stations not shown.

DTT Tx Networks (DVB-T exc. where noted)
Licensee: RTSH Mux (DVB-T2): RTSH 1 HD, RTSH 2 HD, RTSH 3, RTSH Sport HD, RTSH Film, RTSH Shqip, RTSH Muzike, RTSH Kuvend, RTSH Fëmije, RTSH Plus, RTSH 24, RTK1 Txs: MFN – Licensee: DigitALB W: www.digitalb.al M1✪(exc.*): Top News*, Top Channel, Bang Bang, Çufo, Junior TV, My Music, Serial Stinët, EXP Histori, EXP Natyra, EXP Shkencë M2✪(exc.*): BCTV Europe*, Film Aksion, Film Autor, Film Drame, Film Hits, Film Komedi, Film Thriller, Film Gold, Dorcel TV, Stars XXX TV M3✪: RTSH1, TV Klan, ABC News, News 24, IN TV, Supersport 1-5 M4✪: Report TV, Alpha TV, Music Al, T, Mega, Rai Uno, Rai Due, Italia 1, Canale 5, BBC World News, CNN int., Euronews, Fashion TV, Supersport 6 M5✪(exc.*): Ndihma e Klientit*, City TV, IN TV, Baby TV, Family HD, Film Nje HD, Film Dy HD, Supersport 1-4 HD, Travel Channel HD Txs: M1: ch62 (SFN), M2: ch64 (SFN), M3: ch67 (SFN), M4: ch69 (SFN). M5 (DVB-T2): ch29 (Dajt) – Licensee: Tring Digital W: www.tring.al M1✪(exc.*): RTV 21, Fax News*, National Geographic Channel, Tip TV, Tring Tring, Tring Kids, Tring Fantasy, Rai Uno, Italia 1, Canale 5, Ant1 Europe, Tring Jolly HD M2✪(exc.*): Vision+*, Living HD, Tring Super, Tring Comedy, Tring Planet, Tring Life, Tring Action, Tring Shqip, Tring World, 3 Plus, Folk+ M3✪: Fox, Fox Life, Fox Crime, Smile TV, Tring Sport News HD, Tring Sport 1-4 HD, Desire Txs: M1: ch47 (Dajt) M2: ch59 (Dajt) M3: ch56 (Dajt).
Local Licensees not shown.

## ALGERIA

Systems: DVB-T (MPEG4) [E]. Sahrawi Refugee Camps: PAL-B [E]

EPTV TÉLÉVISION ALGÉRIENNE (Pub)🖃 21, Boulevard des Martyrs, Alger ☎ +213 21 602300 📠 +213 21 230914 E: alger-contact@entv.dz W: www.entv.dz LP: DG (EPTV): Toufik Kheladi Chs: EPTV, Canal Algérie, Algérie 3, Algérie 4 (Tamazight), Algérie 5 (Kannat el-Coraän), Regional stns.

DTT Tx Network
Tx Operator: Télédiffusion d'Algérienne (TDA) 🖃 BP 50, 16340 Bouzareah ☎ +213 21 901717 📠 +213 21 902424 E: tnt@tda.dz W: www.tda.dz M: EPTV, Canal Algérie, Algérie 3, Algérie 4 (Tamazight), Algérie 5 (Kannat el-Coraän), Regional stns ✶ Chaîne I, II, III

| Location | ch | kW | Location | ch | kW |
|---|---|---|---|---|---|
| Adrar | 21 | 1.5 | Bouzaréah | 32 | 1.5 |
| Tamanrasset | 21 | 1.5 | Zerga | 32 | 1.5 |
| Filfila | 22 | 1.2 | Akfadou | 33 | 2 |
| Timimoun | 22 | 1.5 | Antar | 35 | 1.5 |
| Ain Salah | 22 | 1.5 | Bechar | 37 | 1.5 |
| Doukhane | 22 | 1.5 | Meghress | 41 | 1.5 |
| El Oued | 22 | 1.5 | Ain N'sour | 41 | 1.5 |
| DJ Khar | 23 | 1.5 | M'Cid | 42 | 1.5 |
| Hassi R'Mel | 23 | 1.5 | Hassi Messaoud | 42 | 1.5 |
| Ouargla | 23 | 1.5 | Chrea | 43 | 1.2 |
| Bordj El Bahri | 24 | 1.5 | Tessala | 43 | 1.2 |
| Dirah | 25 | 1.5 | Mahouna | 44 | 1.5 |
| Nador | 25 | 1.5 | Bouzizi | 45 | 1.5 |
| Mezghitane | 27 | 1.5 | Sbaa Mokrane | 49 | 1.2 |
| Kef lekhel | 28 | 1.5 | | | |

+ txs below 1kW.

### Sahrawi Refugee Camps

RASD TV (Gov) 🖃 BP 470, 37000 Tindouf ☎ +213 49 923525 W: www.rasd-tv.com Tx: Rabouni ᵃch22 (10kW). Rel. Al Aoula (Morocco) & own prgrs (ᵃ=analogue)

## ANDORRA

**System:** DVB-T (MPEG2) [E]

**RÀDIO I TELEVISIÓ D'ANDORRA (Pub)**⌨ Baixada del Molí 24, AD500 Andorra la Vella ☎ +376 873777 **E:** rtva@rtva.ad **W:** www. andorradifusio.ad **L.P:** DG: Xavier Mujal Closa **Ch:** ATV.

**DTT Tx Networks**
**Licensee:** Andorra Telecom ⌨ Mossèn LLuís Pujol 8-14, AD500 Santa Coloma ☎ +376 875274 **E:** comunicacio@andorratelecom.ad **W:** www.andorratelecom.ad **M1:** Direct8, Teledeporte, TVI Internacional, 8TV **M2:** Arte, BBC World News, RTPi, Telecinco, 3/24 **M3:** CNN Int., Cuatro, La Sexta, NRJ12, SIC **M4:** ATV, La 2, M6, TF1, TV3 **M5:** Antena 3, France 2, France 3, La 1, Super3/33 **M6:** Esport3, Euronews, Pirineus TV, TV5 Monde

| Location | M1 | M2 | M3 | M4 | M5 | M6 |
|---|---|---|---|---|---|---|
| SFN | 25 | 28 | 36 | 42 | 45 | 57 |

## ANGOLA

**Systems:** ISDB-TB [E]; § PAL-I [E]

**TELEVISÃO PÚBLICA DE ANGOLA (Pub)** ⌨ CP 2604, Luanda ☎ +244 222 320326 🖷 +244 222 323622 **W:** tpa.sapo.ao **L.P:** Pres: Hélder Manuel Bárber Dias dos Santos **Chs:** TPA1, TPA2

**Local Station**
**TV Zimbo:** Avenida de Talatona, Luanda Sul.

**DTT Tx Networks**
**Tx Operator:** TPA **M:** TPA1, TPA2, TV Zimbo **Txs:** ch31 (Luanda) & nationwide MFN under construction

## ANGUILLA (UK)

**System:** NTSC-M [A]

**KREATIVE COMMUNICATIONS NETWORK (KCN) (Comm)**⌨ P.O.Box 154, The Valley ☎ +1 264 5843519 🖷 +1 264 4973367 **E:** kcn@ caribcable.com **W:** www.facebook.com/Kreative-Communications-Network-Television-Channel-4-265275133505349 **L.P:** CEO: Carlton Pickering **Stns:** ZJF-TV3 ch3 (0.003kW), ZJF-TV9 ch9 (0.03kW).

## ANTARCTICA

**NB:** No terrestrial TV station.

## ANTIGUA & BARBUDA

**System:** NTSC-M [A]

**ABS-TV (Gov)** ⌨ Cross St., St. John's, Antigua ☎ +1 268 4620010 🖷 +1 268 4624442 **E:** abstvradio@ab.gov.ag **W:** www.abstvradio.com **L.P:** SM: Trevor Parker. **Tx:** ch10V (5kW).

## ARGENTINA

**Systems:** ISDB-TB [A]; # PAL-N [A] ⇩2019

**National Stations** (ª=analogue)
**TV PÚBLICA (Pub)** ⌨Avenida Figueroa Alcorta 2977, 1425 Buenos Aires ☎+54 11 8026001 **W:** www.tvpublica.com.ar **Txs:** ªch7 (212kW) & relay txs. – **EL NUEVE (Comm)**⌨ Av. Dorrego 1708, 1414 Buenos Aires ☎ +54 11 50936838 **W:** www.elnueve.com.ar **Txs:** ªch9 (62kW) & relay txs. – **EL TRECE (Comm)**⌨ Lima 1261, Constitucion, Capital Federal ☎ +54 11 3050013 🖷 +54 11 3318559 **W:** www.eltrecetv.com.ar **Txs:** ªch13 (116kW) & relay txs. – **TELEFE (Comm)**⌨ Pavón 2495, 1248 Buenos Aires ☎ +54 11 43080145 🖷 +54 11 4301522 **W:** telefe.com **Txs:** ªch11 (180kW) & relay txs. **NB:** all tx sites above = Buenos Aires.

**Local Stations** not shown.

**DTT Tx Networks**
**Licensee:** Radio y Televisión Argentina **Mux 1:** Encuentro, Encuentro Movil, Paka Paka, TaTeTi **Txs:** ch22 (Buenos Aires) & MFN. **Mux 2:** TV Pública HD, TV Pública Movil, Construir TV **Txs:** ch23 (Buenos Aires) & MFN. **Mux 3:** Gol TV, Go TV Movil, V!vra, Suri TV, Video Éxito **Txs:** ch24 (Buenos Aires) & MFN. **Mux 4:** CN23, C5N, Telesur, 360 TV **Txs:**

ch25 (Buenos Aires) & MFN. – **Licensee:** Telefe **M:** Telefe, Telefe HD **Tx:** ch34 (Buenos Aires) & MFN. – **Licensee:** El Trece **M:** El Trece **Tx:** ch33 (Buenos Aires) & MFN. – **Licensee:** El Nueve **M:** El Nueve, El Nueve HD, El Nueve Movil **Txs:** ch35 (Buenos Aires) & MFN.
**Local licensees** not shown.

## ARMENIA

**System:** DVB-T (MPEG4) [E]

**National Stations**
**ARMENIAN PUBLIC TELEVISION (Pub)**⌨ 26, G. Hovsepyan St., Nork 47, 0047 Yerevan ☎ +374 10 650015 **E:** International@ armtv.com **W:** www.1tv.am **L.P:** CEO: Margarita Grigoryan **Ch:** H1 – **ARMENIA TV (Comm)**⌨ 1, Yeghvard Highway, 0054 Yerevan ☎ +374 10 369344 🖷 +374 10 366852 **E:** info@armeniatv.am **W:** www. armeniatv.am – **H2 (Comm)**⌨ 3/1, Quarter # G-3, 0088 Yerevan ☎ +374 10 398831 🖷 +374 10 395640 **E:** Iraber@tv.am **W:** www.tv.am **L.P:** DG: Samvel Mayrapetyan.

**Local Stations** not shown.

**DTT Tx Network**
**Tx Operator:** Television and Radio Broadcasting Network of Armenia **W:** tna.am **M1:** H1, H2, Shant TV, Kentron TV, Shoghakat TV, Armenia TV, Yerkir Media, RTR Planeta **M2:** Mir TV Armenia, AR TV, Arm News, Dari 21, ATV, Ararat, H3, CNN International, Pervyy kanal, Rossiya K **M3:** Local stns

| Location | M1 | M2 | M3 | M4 |
|---|---|---|---|---|
| Yerevan | 23 | 28 | 35 | 43 |

+ nationwide MFN

## ARUBA (Netherlands)

**Systems:** # NTSC-M [A]; DVB-T (MPEG2) planned

**ARUBA BROADCASTING CO. N.V. (ATV) (Comm)**⌨ P.O.Box 5040, Oranjestad ☎+297 5838150 🖷 +297 5838110 **Tx:** Oranjestad ch15. – **CANAL 22 (Comm)** ⌨ Oranjestad. ☎+297 5859500 **W:** www.facebook. com/Canal22aruba **Tx:** Oranjestad ch22. – **TELEARUBA (Comm)**⌨ P.O.Box 392, Oranjestad ☎ +297 5857302 🖷 + 297 5851683 **E:** info@ telearuba.aw **W:** www.telearuba.aw. **Tx:** Oranjestad ch13 (3kW H).

## ASCENSION ISLAND (UK)

**System:** PAL-I [E]

**BFBS-TV Relay (Serving British Mil)**⌨ Chalfont Grove, Narcot Lane, Chalfont St Peter, Buckinghamshire, SL9 8TN, United Kingdom. **Txs: BBC One:** Travellers Hill ch64, Cross Hill ch50 & ch61 **ITV:** Travellers Hill ch64, Cross Hill ch46.

## AUSTRALIA

**System:** DVB-T (MPEG2) [AU]

**National Stations**
**AUSTRALIAN BROADCASTING CORPORATION (ABC) (Pub)**⌨ ABC Ultimo Centre, 700 Harris St, Ultimo, NSW 2007 ☎ +61 2 83331500 **E:** comments@your.abc.net.au **W:** www.abc.net.au **L.P:** MD: Michelle Guthrie **Chs (terr.):** ABC1, ABC2, ABC Me, ABC Kids, ABC News 24 – **SPECIAL BROADCASTING SERVICE (SBS) (Pub)**⌨ Locked bag 028, Crows Nest, NSW 1585 ☎ +61 2 94302828 **E:** comments@sbs.com.au **W:** www.sbs.com.au **L.P:** MD: Michael Ebeid – **NATIONAL INDIGIOUS TELEVISION (NITV) (Pub)**⌨ 5 Parsons Street, Alice Springs, NT 0870 ☎ +61 8 89534763 **E:** admin@ nitv.org.au **W:** www.nitv.org.au – **SEVEN NETWORK (Comm)**⌨ Television Centre, Mobbs Lane, Epping, NSW 2121 ☎ +61 2 8587777 **W:** www.sevenwestmedia.com.au **L.P:** CEO: Tim Worner – **NINE NETWORK (Comm)**⌨ P.O.Box 27, Willoughby, NSW 2068 ☎ +61 2 99069999 **W:** www.nine.com.au **L.P:** CEO: Hugh Marks – **TEN NETWORK (Comm)**⌨ P.O. Box 10, Lane Cove, NSW 2066 ☎ +61 2 8870222 **W:** tenplay.com.au **L.P:** CEO: Paul Anderson

**Regional Stations**
**IMPARJA TELEVISION (Pub)**⌨ P.O.Box 2924, Alice Springs, NT 0871 ☎ +61 89 523744 **W:** www.imparja.com.au – **PRIME TELEVISION (Comm)**⌨ PO Box 878, Dickson, ACT 2602 ☎ +61 2 62423700 **W:** au.prime7.yahoo.com – **SOUTHERN CROSS TELEVISION (Comm)**⌨ 70 Park Street, South Melbourne, VIC

3205 ☎ +61 3 92432100 **W:** www.southerncrosstelevision.com. au – **WIN TELEVISION (Comm)**⬚ Television Ave, Mt St Thomas, Wollongong, NSW 2500 ☎ +61 2 42234199 **W:** www.wintv.com.au.
**Local Stations** not shown.

**DTT Tx Networks** (National Stations)
**Licensee:** ABC **M:** ABC, ABC HD, ABC2/ABC Kids, ABC Me, ABC News 24 ❋ ABC Double J, ABC Jazz – **Licensee:** Seven Network **M:** Seven, 7HD, 7mate, 7Two, 7flix, Racing.com – **Licensee:** Nine Network **M:** Nine, 9HD, 9Gem, 9Go!, 9Life, Extra – **Licensee:** Ten Network **M:** Ten, Ten HD, Eleven, One, TVSN, Spree TV – **Licensee:** SBS **M:** SBS, SBS HD, SBS Viceland, SBS Viceland HD, Food Network, NITV ❋ SBS Radio 1-3, SBS Arabic24.

| Location | ABC | 7N | 9N | 10N | SBS | kW |
|---|---|---|---|---|---|---|
| Sydney | 12 | 6 | 8 | 11 | 34 | 50 |
| + nationwide tx MFN | | | | | | |

## AUSTRIA

**Systems:** DVB-T (MPEG2), DVB-T2 (MPEG4) [E]

**National Stations**
**ÖSTERREICHISCHER RUNDFUNK (ORF) (Pub)**⬚ Würzburggasse 30, 1136 Wien ☎ +43 1 878780 **E:** presse@orf.at **W:** orf.at **L.P:** DG: Alexander Wrabetz **Chs:** ORF eins, ORF2 incl. reg. stns: a) ORF Burgenland (Buchgraben 51, 7000 Eisenstadt), b) ORF Kärnten (Sponheimer Straße 13, 9020 Klagenfurt), c) ORF Niederösterreich (Radioplatz 1, 3109 St.Pölten), d) ORF Oberösterreich (Europaplatz 3, 4010 Linz), e) ORF Salzburg (Nonntaler Hauptstraße 49d, 5020 Salzburg), f) ORF Steiermark (Marburgerstr. 20, 8042 Graz), g) ORF Tirol (Rennweg 14, 6010 Innsbruck), h) ORF Vorarlberg (Höchsterstraße 38, 6850 Dornbirn), i) ORF Wien (Argentinierstr. 30a, 1040 Wien), ORF III – **ATV (Comm)**⬚ Aspernbrückengasse 2, 1020 Wien ☎ +43 1 213640 **E:** atv@atv.at **W:** atv.at **L.P:** MD: Thomas Gruber – **PULS 4 (Comm)** ⬚ Maria Jacobi Gasse 1, 1030 Wien ☎ +43 1 999880 **W:** www.puls4.com **L.P:** CEO: Markus Breitenecker – **SERVUS TV (Comm)** ⬚ Ludwig-Bieringer-Platz 1, 5073 Wals-Himmelreich ☎ +43 662 84224428181 **E:** kontakt@servustv.at **W:** www.servus.com **L.P:** CEO: Ferdinand Wegscheider.
**Local Stations** not shown (via Mux 3 txs).

**DTT Tx Networks (DVB-T2 exc. where stated)**
**Tx Operator:** Österreichische Sender GmbH & Co KG (ORS) **W:** www.ors.at **M1✪(exc.\*)** ORF 1\*, ORF 1 HD, ORF2 Wien\*, ORF2 HD incl. reg. prgrs, ORF III HD, ORF Sport+ HD ❋ Ö1, Ö3, FM4 **M2✪(exc.\*):** 3sat HD, ATV HD, ATV II SD\*, Puls 4 SD, RTL HD, Servus TV HD/Red Bull TV HD, SRF1 SD, SRF Zwei HD **M3: Version A (DVB-T2/Licensee: ORS) ✪:** Comedy Central/VIVA, gotv, OKTO, Hope Channel, Kabel eins Doku, Schau TV, oe24.TV, w24, ProSieben Maxx, Welt, ZDF Info **Version B (DVB-T/Regional or Local licensees)**. **M4✪:** Arte, BR HD, DMAX, Nickelodeon, n-tv, Phoenix, RTL NITRO, Sat1 Gold, Super RTL **M5✪:** Das Erste HD, ZDF HD, KiKa, ZDFneo HD, Eurosport 1, Kabel eins, RTL 2, Sixx, Sport 1, Playboy TV **M6✪:** ATV, CNN, Sat.1 HD, ProSieben HD, Vox HD, Deluxe Music, Disney Channel, Puls 4 HD ❋ Kronehit, R. Maria, R. OE24.

| Location | M1 | M2 | M3 | M4 | M5 | M6 | kW |
|---|---|---|---|---|---|---|---|
| Bregenz (Pfänder\*) | 24 | 21 | 55 | 31 | 59 | 42 | 2x56/20/3x50 |
| Bruck a.d.M. (Mugel) | 41 | 25 | - | - | - | - | 45/56 |
| Graz (Schöckl) | 26 | 23 | - | 47 | 39 | 50 | 2x48/2/3x25 |
| Innsbruck (Patscherkofel\*) | 23 | 27 | 36 | 37 | 24 | 22 | 63 |
| Klagenfurt (Dobratsch) | 24 | 23 | - | 48 | 30 | 51 | (\*\*) |
| Linz (Lichtenberg) | 43 | 37 | 51 | 41 | 45 | 24 | 2x50/6.3/2x50 |
| Mattersburg (Heuberg) | 52V | 30V | - | 36V | 60V | 53V | 20 |
| Rechnitz (Hirschenstein) | 43V | 23V | - | - | - | 25 | |
| Salzburg (Gaisberg) | 32 | 29 | 55 | 47 | 59 | 55 | 2x40/25/32/3x25 |
| St.Pölten (Jauerling) | 31 | 21 | - | 38 | 55 | 58 | 2x50/3x40 |
| Schärding (Schardenberg) | 43 | - | - | - | - | 16 | |
| Schladming (Hauser Kaibling) | 34 | 39 | 48 | - | - | - | 30/25/3 |
| Viktring (Stifterkogel) | 24 | 23 | - | 48 | 30 | 51 | 15/4x14.5 |
| Waidhofen/Ybbs (Sonntagbg.) | 43 | - | - | - | - | 12 | |
| Weitra (Wachberg) | 31 | - | - | - | - | 14 | |
| Wien (Kahlenberg\*) | 24 | 34 | 41V | 36 | 60 | 53 | 2x63/5/3x63 |
| + sites with txs below 10kW. \*) + SFN \*\*) 80/66/50/66/50/63/50 | | | | | | | |

## AZERBAIJAN

**System:** DVB-T2 (MPEG4) [E]

**National Stations**
**AZƏRBAYCAN TELEVIZIYA VƏ RADIO VERISLƏRI (Gov)**⬚ Mehdi Hüseyn St. 1, AZ 1011 Baki ☎ +994 12 4984720 ⬚ +994

12 4972020 **E:** info@aztv.az **W:** www.aztv.az **L.P:** Chmn: Arif Alisanov **Chs:** AzTV, Idman Azärbaycan, Mädäniyyät TV. – **ICTIMAI TELEVIZIYA (ITV) (Pub)**⬚ Särifzadä St. 241, AZ 1012 Baki ☎ +994 12 4335525 ⬚ +994 12 4302958 **E:** info@itv.az **W:** www.itv.az **L.P:** Dir: Cämil Quliyev – **AZAD AZƏRBAYCAN TV (ATV) (Comm)** ⬚Särifzadä St. 10, AZ 1012 Baki ☎ +994 12 4977274 ⬚ +994 12 4989498 **E:** info@atv.az **W:** news.atv.az – **LIDER TV (Comm)** ⬚ Ä.Äläkbärov St. 83/23, AZ 1141 Baki ☎ +994 12 4978899 ⬚ +994 12 4978898 **E:** mail@lidermedia.az **W:** www.lidertv.com – **SPACE TV (Comm)** ⬚ Hüseyn Cavid ave. 8, AZ 1073 Baki ☎ +994 12 4921256 ⬚ +994 12 4927665 **E:** info@spacetv.az **W:** www.spacetv.az.

**Local Stations** not shown.

**DTT Tx Network**
**Tx Operator:** RITN Teleradio IB **W:** www.teleradio.az **M1:** AzTV, Idman Azärbaycan, Mädäniyyät TV, Lider TV, Space TV, ATV, Xäzär TV, TRT1, local stns **Local licensees** not shown.

| Location | M | kW |
|---|---|---|
| Baki | 37 | 1.2 |
| + nationwide MFN. | | |

### MOUNTAINOUS KARABAGH

**LERNAYIN GHARABAGH HANRAYIN HERUSTARADIOYIN KERUTYUN** ⬚ Tigran Mets St. 23a, Stepanakert (mail via Armenia) ☎ +374 47 945261 **E:** artv_or@ktsurf.net **W:** www.artsakh.tv **L.P:** Chmn: Norek A. Gasparyan

**DTT Tx Networks**
**Tx Operator Mux 1:** Television and Radio Broadcasting Network of Armenia **W:** tna.am **M:** H1, H2, Shant TV, Kentron TV, Shoghakat TV, Armenia TV, Yerkir Media, RTR Planeta **Txs:**(-) – **Tx Operator Mux 2:** Arsakh TV **M:** Artsakh TV **Txs:**(-)

## AZORES (Portugal)

**System:** DVB-T (MPEG4) [E]

**RTP AÇORES (Pub)**⬚ Rua Ernesto do Canto 40, 9500-312 Ponta Delgada ☎ +351 296202700 **E:** rtpa@rtp.pt **W:** www.rtp.pt/acores **L.P:** Dir: Lorina Bernardo.

**DTT Tx Network**
**Licensee:** Portugal Telecom **M:** RTP1, RTP2, RTP3/RTP Açores, RTP Memória, SIC, TVI, ARTV **Txs:** ch47 (São Jorge), ch48 (S.Miguel, Graciosa), ch49 (Faial), ch54 (Terceira, S.Maria, Flores, Corvo), ch56 (Pico).

## BAHAMAS

**System:** ATSC [A]

**ZNS TV (Pub)**⬚ P.O.Box N-1347, Nassau ☎ +1 242 5023800 ⬚ +1 242 3226598 **E:** info@znsbahamas.com **W:** znsbahamas.com **L.P:** Chmn (Broadcasting Corp, of the Bahamas): Mike Smith **Tx:** Nassau ch13 (50kW).

## BAHRAIN

**Systems:** DVB-T2 (MPEG4) [E]; § PAL-B/G [E]

**BAHRAIN TELEVISION (BTV) (Pub)**⬚ P.O.Box 1075, Bahrain ☎ +973 17686000 ⬚ +973 17681544 **L.P:** Dir: Yousef Mohammed **Chs:** BTV Arabic, BTV English, BTV Sports Channel 1, BTV Sports Channel 2, BTV Quran Channel, BTV International

**DTT Tx Network**
**Tx Operator:** BTV **M:** BTV Arabic, BTV English, BTV Sports Channel 1, BTV Sports Channel 2, BTV Quran Channel, BTV International, BBC World Service News **Txs:** (-)

## BANGLADESH

**Systems:** DVB-T2 (MPEG4) [E]; # PAL-B [E]

**SANGSAD BANGLADESH TV (Gov)**⬚ Dhaka **W:** www.facebook. com/Sangsad-Bangladesh-Television-642062122595783; www.parliament.gov.bd **Tx:** Dhaka °ch6 (20kW) – **BANGLADESH TELEVISION (BTV) (Pub)**⬚ TV Bhaban, Rampura, Dhaka 1219 ☎ +880 2 8618606

+880 2 8312927 **W**: www.btv.gov.bd **L.P**: DG: Haroon-or-Rashid. **Txs**: Dhaka ªch9 (20kW) & netw. (ª=analogue)

**DTT Tx Networks** (under construction)
**Tx Operator**: BTV **M**: BTV, BTV World, Sangsad Bangladesh TV **Txs**: ch(-) Dhaka, Chittagong, Khulna (3.5kW)

## BARBADOS

**System**: NTSC-M [A]

**CARIBBEAN BROADCASTING CORP. (CBC-TV) (Pub)** P.O. Box 900, Pine Hill, Bridgetown ☎ +1 246 4675400 🖷 +1 246 4294795 **W**: www.cbc.bb **L.P**: GM: Doug Hoyte **Txs**: Bridgetown ch8 (60kW).

## BELARUS

**Systems**: DVB-T (MPEG4), DVB-T2 (MPEG4) [E]

**National Stations**
**BELARUSKAJE TELEBACANNE (BT) (Gov)** Makaionka St. 9, 220807 Minsk ☎ +375 17 2634301 **E**: pr@tvr.by **W**: www.tvr.by **Chs (terr.)**: Belarus 1 (incl. reg prgrs), Belarus 2, Belarus 3, Belarus 4 (Regional Stns), Belarus 5 – **OBSHCHENATSIONALNOYE TELEVIDENIYE (ONT) (Gov)** Kamunistycny St. 6, 220029 Minsk ☎ +375 17 2170424 **E**: w@ont.by **W**: ont.by **L.P**: Pres: Grigoriy L. Kisel. – **STOLICHNOYE TV (STV) (Gov)** Kamunistycny St. 6, 220029 Minsk ☎ +375 17 2906272 **E**: reklama@ctv.by **W**: www.ctv.by **L.P**: DG: Yuriy Koziyatko.

**DTT Tx Networks** (DVB-T2 exc. where noted)
**Licensee Mux 1**: Belteleradyjo **M1 (DVB-T)**: Belarus 1 (incl. reg prgrs), Belarus 2, Belarus 3, Belarus 4, ONT, STV, NTV-Belarus, RTR-Belarus, TV Mir ✳Belaruskaje R. 1, 2, R. Stalica, Radyus FM – **Licensee Mux 2+3**: Beltelekom **M2✪(exc.*)** Belarus 5*, 8 Kanal, Russkiy Illusion, Detskiy Mir/Teleklub, Kinomiks, VTV, Lubimoe Kino, TV 3 Belarus, TNT International, RU TV Belarus, Karusel, Shanson TV, Moya Planeta, Rossiya K, Okhota i Rybalka, Usadba Telekanal, Setanta Sport, KHL **M3✪**: Soyuz TV, Sovershenno Sekretno TV, Kukhnya TV, BelMuz, RTVi, Muzhskoe Kino, Kinosemya, Tiji, Gulli Girl, Detskiy, Multimania TV, TV 1000, TV 1000 Action, TV 1000 Russkoe Kino, Kinohit, Rodnoye Kino, Virtualniy Kinozal.

| Location | 1 | 2 | 3 | kW | Location | 1 | 2 | 3 | kW |
|---|---|---|---|---|---|---|---|---|---|
| Asipovicy | 49 | 51 | 38 | 2 | Masty | 21 | 25 | 36 | 1 |
| Astryna | 42 | 37 | 51 | 1 | Mazyr | 48 | 41 | 31 | 1 |
| Asveja | 33 | 30 | 42 | 1 | Miadziel | 44 | 51 | 34 | 2 |
| Aziareck | 25 | 36 | 38 | 1 | Minsk | 48 | 32 | 57 | 1 |
| Babrujsk | 47 | 52 | 40 | 2 | Mscislaul | 49 | 56 | 33 | 2 |
| Baranavicy | 39 | 26 | 31 | 2 | Myta | 49 | 29 | 33 | 2 |
| Barisau | 48 | 23 | 57 | 1 | Navaselle | 48 | 32 | 57 | 1 |
| Berazino | 41 | 46 | 58 | 2 | Pinsk | 56 | 50 | 52 | 2 |
| Biahoml | 40 | 47 | 50 | 1 | Radaškovicy | 48 | 32 | 57 | 1 |
| Biarecca | 43 | 58 | 35 | 1 | Rakitnica | 51 | 53 | 47 | 2 |
| Brahin | 43 | 39 | 21 | 2 | Salihorsk | 34 | 43 | 47 | 2 |
| Braslau | 43 | 53 | 21 | 1 | Saltanoú | 51 | 30 | 38 | 1 |
| Ciachcin | 43 | 46 | 58 | 2 | Sianno | 25 | 36 | 38 | 2 |
| Drahicyn | 57 | 58 | 35 | 2 | Sinkevicy | 58 | 35 | 37 | 2 |
| Drycyn | 44 | 51 | 38 | 2 | Slauharad | 50 | 59 | 39 | 2 |
| Hara | 33 | 30 | 42 | 2 | Slonim | 41 | 36 | 31 | 2 |
| Heraniony | 49 | 29 | 33 | 2 | Smiatanicy | 46 | 41 | 31 | 1 |
| Homiel | 51 | 30 | 38 | 2 | St. Darohi | 44 | 51 | 38 | 2 |
| Hrodna | 42 | 37 | 51 | 1 | Stoubcy | 34 | 43 | 47 | 1 |
| Ivanava Slabada | 42 | 35 | 37 | 2 | Strelcukcy | 59 | 25 | 23 | 1 |
| Kapyl | 34 | 43 | 47 | 1 | Sviclac | 21 | 25 | 36 | 2 |
| Kašaliou | 41 | 26 | 31 | 1 | Ušacy | 40 | 47 | 50 | 1 |
| Kastjukovicy | 50 | 51 | 39 | 2 | V. Cucavicy | 56 | 50 | 33 | 1 |
| Kreva | 59 | 25 | 23 | 1 | Valosavicy | 46 | 41 | 31 | 2 |
| Krupski | 41 | 46 | 58 | 2 | Viciebsk | 43 | 31 | 48 | 1 |
| Krycau | 50 | 59 | 39 | 1 | Vorša | 25 | 36 | 38 | 1 |
| Kuplin | 51 | 53 | 47 | 2 | Zaščobje | 43 | 39 | 31 | 1 |
| Ljuban | 44 | 51 | 34 | 1 | Zitkovicy | 42 | 35 | 37 | 2 |
| Luki | 41 | 26 | 31 | 1 | Zlobin | 57 | 52 | 40 | 2 |
| Mahilioú | 49 | 56 | 33 | 2 | + sites with txs below 1kW | | | | |

**Local licensee**: Kosmos TV **W**: cosmostv.com **M✪(exc.*) (DVB-T)**: TLC, Discovery Channel, Animal Planet, Eurosport, Belarus 5, Karusel, Shanson TV, Ohota i Rybalka, TNT International, National Geographic, Usadba, Bestseller +, Muzhskoe Kino, Kinokomedia, Kinohit, Nashe Novoe Kino, Kinomiks, 2x2, RU TV Belarus, Cosmos TV Cinema* **Tx**: ch29 (Minsk 1kW).

## BELGIUM

**Systems**: DVB-T (MPEG2) [E], DVB-T2 (MPEG4) [E]

### Flanders

**National Station**
**VLAAMSE RADIO EN TELEVISIEOMROEP (VRT) (Pub)** A. Reyerslaan 52, 1043 Brussel ☎ +32 2 7413111 **E**: info@vrt.be **W**: www.vrt.be **L.P**: CEO: Paul Lembrechts **Chs (terr.)**: (in Flemish) Één, Canvas, Ketnet.

**DTT Tx Network (DVB-T2)**
**Licensee**: TV Vlaanderen **M1✪**: Één, Canvas, Ketnet, CAZ, Q2, Penthouse, VIER, Vijf, Vitaya, VTM, Zes **M2✪**: Club-RTL, Kadet, NPO1, NPO2, NPO3, Plug RTL, RTL-TVi, VTM Kzoom/Kanaal Z

| Location | M1 | M2 | kW | Location | M1 | M2 | kW |
|---|---|---|---|---|---|---|---|
| Antwerpen | 44V | 47V | 10 | St.Pieters-Leew | 43V | 46V | 20 |
| Brussel | 43 | 46 | 10 | Schoten | 44V | 47V | 20 |
| Egem | 43V | 46V | 20 | Veltem | 43V | 46V | |
| Genk | 44 | 47 | 20 | | | | |

+ txs below 10kW

### Wallonia

**National Stations**
**RADIO TÉLÉVISION BELGE DE LA COMMUNAUTÉ FRANÇAISE (RTBF) (Pub)** Boulevard Reyers 52, 1044 Bruxelles ☎ +32 2 7372111 **W**: www.rtbf.be **L.P**: CEO: Jean-Paul Philippot **Chs**: (in French) La une, La deux, La troix – **BELGISCHER RUNDFUNK (BRF) (Pub)** Kehrweg 11, 4700 Eupen ☎ +32 87 591111 **E**: info@brf.be **W**: brf.be **L.P**: Dir: Toni Wimmer. **Ch**: (News-magazine in German) Blickpunkt.

**DTT Tx Network (DVB-T)**
**Tx Operator**: RTBF **M**: La Une, La Deux, La Troix, Euronews (via Liège tx: Euronews/BRF Blickpunkt) ✳ RTBF La Première, VivaCité, Musiq3, Classic 21, Pure FM, BRF1.

| Location | Ch | kW | Location | Ch | kW |
|---|---|---|---|---|---|
| Liège | 45 | 100 | Wavre | 56 | 80 |
| Anderlues | 56 | 80 | Léglise | 57 | 100 |
| Profondville | 56 | 50 | Marche-en-Famene | 57 | 13 |
| Tournai | 56V | 40 | | | |

+ txs below 10kW
**Local Licensees**: BX1 rue Gabrielle Petit 32/34, 1080 Bruxelles ☎ +32 2 4212121 **E**: pv@bx1.be **W**: bx1.be **M**: BX1 **Tx**: ch55V (Bruxelles 8kW).

## BELIZE

**Systems**: NTSC-M [A]. BFBS-TV: DVB-T (MPEG4) [E]

**BELIZE BROADCASTING NETWORK (Comm)** Belize City ☎ +501 2232008 **E**: ramon@bbn9.com **W**: www.bbn9.com **L.P**: Chmn/CEO: Ramon Vasquez **Tx**: ch9. – **CHANNEL 5 (Comm)** P.O.Box 679, Belize City ☎ +501 2277781 🖷 +501 2274936 **E**: gbtz@btl.net **W**: edition.channel5belize.com **Tx**: ch5. – **CHANNEL 7 (Comm)** P.O.Box 89, Belize City ☎ +501 2277246 🖷 +501 2275040 **E**: tvseven@btl.net **W**: www.7newsbelize.com **Tx**: ch7. – **TBN (Rlg)** Belize City **Tx**: ch13.

**Foreign Military Station**
**BFBS-TV Relay (Serving British Mil)** BFBS Belize, Airport Camp, BFPO 12, United Kingdom. **M✪**: BBC One*, BBC Two/CBBC*, ITV*, BFBS Extra/Cbeebies*, BFBS Sport, Sky News, Sky Sports 1, Sky Sports 2, Nepali TV* (*=time-shifted) ✳ BFBS R. (Belize), BFBS R.2, BFBS Gurkha R. **Tx**: ch27 (Price Barracks).

## BENIN

**System**: DVB-T2 (MPEG4) [E]

**National Stations**
**OFFICE DE RADIODIFFUSION ET TÉLÉVISION DU BÉNIN (ORTB) (Gov)** BP 366, Cotonou ☎+229 21301096 🖷 +229 21301437 **E**: ortb@intnet.bj **W**: www.ortb.bj **L.P**: Dir: Georges Amlon – **LC2 (Comm)** 05 BP 427 Cotonou. ☎+229 21334749 🖷 +229 21334675 **E**: lc2@intnet.bj

**Local Stations**
**Canal 3**: 02 BP 371, Cotonou **Carrefour TV**: 01BP 440 Bohicon **Golfe TV**: 06 BP 1624, Cotonou **Imalè Africa**: Puerto-Novo

**DTT Tx Network**
**Licensee:** Startimes **M1+2(partly○):** multiprgr **Txs:** MFN

## BERMUDA (UK)

**System:** DVB-T (MPEG4) [A]

**BERMUDA BROADCASTING CO. LTD (Comm)** P.O.Box HM 452, Hamilton HMBX ☎ +1 441 2952828 🖹 +1 441 2954282 **E:** contactus@bermudabroadcasting.com **W:** bermudabroadcasting.com **Chs:** ZFB-TV (ABC affiliate), ZBM-TV (CBS affiliate).

**DTT Tx Networks**
**Licensee:** Bermuda Broadcasting Co. Ltd **M:** ZFB-TV, ZBM-TV **Tx:** ch20 (Hamilton) – **Licensee:** The World in Wireless Ltd 🖳 Church Street, Washington Mall Phase II, Hamilton HM 12 ☎ +1 441 2921969 🖹 +1 441 2921979 **E:** info@wow.bm **W:** www.facebook.com/wowbermuda **M○:** multiprgr **Txs:** (-).

## BHUTAN

**Systems:** DVB-T2 (MPEG4) [E]; § PAL-B/G [E] ⇩ 2020

**BHUTAN BROADCASTING SERVICE (BBS) (Pub)** P.O.Box 101, Thimphu ☎ +975 2 323580 🖹 +975 2 323073 **E:** md@bbs.bt **W:** www.bbs.bt **L.P:** CEO: Pema Choden **Chs:** BBS 1, BBS 2 **Txs:** **BBS 1:** Thimpu ªch5 (1kW) & relay txs. **BBS 2:** Thimpu ªch7. (ª=analogue)

**DTT Tx Network**
**Tx Operator:** BBS **M:** BBS 1, BBS 2 **Txs:** MFN

## BOLIVIA

**Systems:** ISDB-TB [A]; § NTSC-M [A] ⇩ 2019

**National Stations** (ª=analogue)
**BOLIVIA TV (BTV) (Gov)** Av. Camacho 1485, Ed. La Urbana, La Paz ☎ +591 2 2203404 🖹 +591 2 2203015 **W:** www.boliviatv.bo **Txs:** **BTV:** La Paz ch7 & relay txs; **BTV HD:** La Paz ch16. – **TELEVISIÓN UNIVERSITARIA (Educ)** Av. 6 de Agosto No. 2170, 13383 La Paz ☎ +591 2 359297 🖹 +591 2 359491 **E:** canal13@umsa.bo **W:** www.tyu.umsa.bo. **Txs:** La Paz ªch13 (10kW) & relay txs – **ATB (ASOCIACIÓN TELEVISIÓN BOLIVIANO) (Comm)** Av. Argentina 2057, La Paz ☎ +591 2 2229922 🖹 +591 2 227935 **E:** atbcbb@atb.com.bo **W:** www.atb.com.bo **Tx:** La Paz ªch9 & relay txs. – **BOLIVISIÓN (Comm)** Av Santa Cruz esq, Tres pasos al frente, Santa Cruz ☎ +591 3 3524544 🖹 +591 3 3530707 **W:** www.redbolivision.tv.bo **Tx:** La Paz ªch5 & relay txs. – **RED UNO DE BOLIVIA (Comm)** Romecin Campos 592, Sopocachi, 14976 La Paz ☎ +591 2 2421111 🖹 +591 2 2415101 **E:** notivision@reduno.com.bo **W:** www.reduno.com.bo **Tx:** La Paz ªch11 & relay txs. – **UNITEL (UNIVERSAL DE TELEVISIÓN) (Comm)** A83 La Paz ☎ +591 2 359297 🖹 +591 2 359491 **W:** www.unitel.tv. **Txs:** La Paz ªch2 (10kW) & relay txs.

**Local Stations** not shown.

## BONAIRE (Netherlands)

**System:** DVB-T (MPEG2) [E]

**TELECURAÇAO RELAY (Curaçao):** ch(-).

## BOSNIA & HERZEGOVINA

**Systems:** DVB-T2 (MPEG4) [E]; § PAL-B/G [E]

**National (Federal) Station**
**RADIO TELEVIZIJA BOSNE I HERCEGOVINE (BHRT) (Pub)** Bulevar Meše Selimovica 12, 71000 Sarajevo ☎ +387 33 455124 **E:** sptrgov@bhrt.ba **W:** www.bhrt.ba **L.P:** DG: Belmin Karamehmedovic **Ch:** BHT1.

### Federacija Bosna i Hercegovina

**National Station**
**FTV (Pub)** Bulevar Meše Selimovica 12, 71000 Sarajevo ☎ +387 33 461539 **E:** press@rtvfbih.ba **W:** www.rtvbih.ba **L.P:** DG (RTVFBiH): Džemal Šabic.

---

**Local Stations** not shown.

**DTT Tx Network** (under construction)
**Licensee:** BHRT **M:** BHT1, FTV, RTRS, TV K5

| Location | ch | Location | ch |
|---|---|---|---|
| Bjelašnica | 30 | Tušenica | 38 |
| Majevica | 25 | Velez | 26 |
| Plješevica | 24 | Vlašic | 22 |
| Trovrh | 38 | | |

### Republika Srpska

**National Station**
**RADIO TELEVIZIJA REPUBLIKE SRPSKE (RTRS) (Pub)** ul. Kralja Petra I Karadjordjevica 129, 78000 Banja Luka ☎ +387 51 301660 **E:** tv@rtrs.tv **W:** www.rtrs.tv **L.P:** DG: Draško Milinovic.

**Local Stations** not shown.

**DTT Tx Network** (under construction)
**Licensee:** BHRT **M:** BHT1, FTV, RTRS

| Location | ch | Location | ch |
|---|---|---|---|
| Kozara | 32 | Leotar | 46 |

*) not on the air

## BOTSWANA

**Systems:** ISDB-TB [E]; § PAL-I [E]

**BOTSWANA TV (BTV) (Gov)** P.O.Box 0060, Gaborone ☎ +267 3658000 🖹 +267 3900051 **E:** marketing@btv.gov.bw **W:** www.btv.gov.bw **L.P:** GM: Bontle Mogotllwana – **E-BOTSWANA (Comm)** P.O.Box 921, Gaborone **E:** info@ebotswana.co.bw **W:** www.ebotswana.co.bw **L.P:** GM: David Coles.

**DTT Tx Network**
**Licensee:** Startimes **M(partly○):** multiprgr **Txs:** MFN

## BRAZIL

**System:** ISDB-TB [A]

**National Stations**
**TV BRAZIL (Pub)** An. Gomes Freire 474, Centro, 20231-010 Rio de Janeiro, RJ ☎ +55 21 21176208 **W:** tvbrasil.ebc.com.br – **TV CULTURA (Pub)** Rua Vladimir Herzog 75, Agua Branca, SP 05036-900 São Paulo ☎ +55 11 38743122 🖹 +55 11 36112014 **E:** dirprog@tvcultura.com.br **W:** tvcultura.cmais.com.br – **CENTRAL NACIONAL DE TELEVISÃO (CNT) (Comm)** Rua Francisco Caron 29, Pilarzinho, 82120-200 Curitiba, PR ☎ +55 41 3383377 🖹 +55 41 3384878 **E:** cnt@cnt.com.br **W:** www.cnt.com.br – **REDE BRASIL DE TELEVISÃO (RBTV) (Comm)** Alameda dos Uapés, 313 - Saúde, 04067-030 São Paulo, SP **W:** rbtv.com.br – **REDE GLOBO (Comm)** Rua Lopes Quintas 303, Jardim Botanico, 22460-010 Rio de Janeiro, RJ ☎ +55 21 25402000 🖹 +55 21 22942092 **E:** wm@redeglobo.com.br **W:** redeglobo.globo.com – **REDE RECORD (Comm)** Rua da Várzea 240, 01140-080 São Paulo, SP ☎ +55 11 36604761 🖹 +55 11 36604756 **E:** tvrecord@rederecord.com.br **W:** rederecord.r7.com – **SISTEMA BRASILEIRO DE TELEVISÃO (SBT) (Comm)** Av. das Comunicações 4, Vila Jaraguá, 06278-905 Osasco, SP ☎ +55 11 70873000 🖹 +55 11 70873509 **E:** marketing@sbt.com.br **W:** www.sbt.com.br.

**Local Stations** not shown.

**DTT Tx Networks**
Nationwide & local multiprgr MFNs.

## BRITISH INDIAN OCEAN TERRITORY

**Systems:** BFBS-TV: DVB-T (MPEG4) [E]; AFN-TV: NTSC [A]

### Diego Garcia

**BFBS-TV Relay (Serving British Mil)** BFBS Diego Garcia **M:** BBC One*, BBC Two/CBBC*, ITV*, BFBS Extra/Cbeebies*, Sky News, Nepali TV* (*=time-shifted) ❸ BFBS R., BFBS R.2, BFBS Gurkha R. **Tx:** ch27.

**Foreign Military Station**
**AFN-TV Relay (U.S. Mil)** AFN Diego Garcia, APO, AP 96595-0014, USA **Chs:** AFN Pacific line-up **Txs:** Diego Garcia ch6/8/10/12 (0.2kW)

## BRUNEI

**Systems:** DVB-T (MPEG4), DVB-T2 (MPEG4) [E]

**RADIO TELEVISYEN BRUNEI (RTB) (Gov)** ☑ Bandar Seri Begawan, BS8610, Negara ☎ +673 2243111 🖹 +673 2220884 **E:** rtbdir@rtb.gov.bn **W:** www.rtb.gov.bn **L.P:** Dir: Hj Muhd. Suffian Bin Hj. Bungsu **Chs:** RTB1, RTB2, RTB3, RTB4, RTB5.

**DTT Tx Network** (DVB-T2 exc. *=DVB-T)
**Tx Operator:** RTB **Mux:** RTB1, RTB2, RTB3, RTB4, RTB5 **Txs:** ch28* (Bt. Subok), ch30 (Bt. Subok 5kW, Bt. Andulau 5kW).

## BULGARIA

**System:** DVB-T (MPEG4) [E]

**BALGARSKA NATSIONALNA TELEVIZIA (BNT) (Pub)** ☑ ul. San Stefano 29, 1504 Sofia ☎ +359 2 9661149 5 **E:** press@bnt.bg **W:** www.bnt.bg **L.P:** DG: Vyara Ankova **Chs (terr.):** BNT1, BNT2, BNT3 & reg. studios. – **BTV (Comm)** ☑ Natsionalen Dvorets na Kulturata, 1463 Sofia ☎ +359 2 9176800 **E:** pr@btv.bg **W:** www.btv.bg **L.P:** DG (bTV Media Group): Florian Skala – **BULGARIA ON AIR (Comm)** ☑ bul. Bryuksel 1, 1540 Sofia ☎ +359 2 4484070 **E:** office@bulgarionair. bg **W:** bgonair.bg **L.P:** DG (Bulgaria On Air Media Group): Viktoria Mitkova – **FOLKLOR TV (Comm)** ☑ ul. Gyueshevo 85, 1330 Sofia ☎ +359 2 9201640 **E:** office@folklor-tv.bg **W:** folklor-tv.bg – **NOVA TELEVIZIA (Comm)** ☑ bul. Hristofor Kolumb 41, 1592 Sofia ☎ +359 2 805000 **E:** office@novatv.bg **W:** novatv.bg **L.P:** CEO: Didier Stoessel – **TV EVROPA (Comm)** ☑ bul. Tsarigradsko shose 101, 1113 Sofia ☎ +359 2 9797044 **E:** office@tvevropa.com **W:** www.tvevropa.com **L.P:** CEO: Emil Stoyanov.

**DTT Tx Networks**
**Licensee Mux 1+2:** NURTS Digital **W:** www.nurts.bg **M1:** Kanal 3, Bulgaria On Air, The Voice, TV Evropa, Fan Folk TV, Folklor TV **M2:** BNT1 & reg. prgrs, BNT2, BNT3, bTV, Bulgaria On Air, Nova Televizia.

| Location | M1 | M2 | kW | Location | M1 | M2 | kW |
|---|---|---|---|---|---|---|---|
| Belogradchik | 32 | 49 | 5 | Smolyan | 34 | 49 | 5 |
| Dobrich | 22 | 29 | 5 | Sofia | 23 | 40 | 5 |
| Gotse Delchev | 31 | 29 | 5 | St. Zagora | 22 | 37 | 5 |
| Kardzhali | 26 | 42 | 5 | Shumen | 28 | 40 | 5 |
| Plovdiv | 25 | 35 | 5 | Varna | 22 | 29 | 5 |
| Ruse | 26 | 49 | 5 | Vidin | 32 | 49 | 2 |
| Sliven | 22 | 37 | 5 | | | | |

+ sites with txs below 2kW.
**NB.** Local muxes not shown.

## BURKINA FASO

**System:** DVB-T2 (MPEG4) [E]

**National Station**
**RADIODIFFUSION TÉLÉVISION DU BURKINA (RTB) (Gov)** ☑ 01 BP 2530, Ouagadougou 01 ☎ +226 50318353 🖹 +226 50318393 **E:** television@rtb.bf **W:** www.rtb.bf **L.P:** Dir: Yacouba Bonkoungou **Chs:** RTB, RTB2 (Regional).

**Local Stations** not shown.

**DTT Tx Network**
**Tx Operator:** RTB **M:** RTB, RTB2 (Regional) **Txs:** nationwide MFN.

## BURUNDI

**Systems:** DVB-T2 (MPEG4) [E]

**National Station**
**RADIO TÉLÉVISION NATIONALE DU BURUNDI (Gov)** ☑ BP 1900, Bujumbura ☎ +257 22224760 🖹 +257 22244877 **E:** rtnb@cbinf.com **W:** www.rtnb.bi **L.P:** DG: Salvator Nizigiyimana.

**Local stations**
**Héritage TV:** BP 4251, Bujumbura. **Rema TV:** 29, Rue de la Mission, Bujumbara. **Télé Renaissance:** BP 2986, Bujumbura. **TV Salama:** BP 2607, Bujumbura.

**DTT Tx Network**
**Tx Operator:** Startimes **M(partly☉):** multiprgr **Txs:** MFN.

## CABO VERDE

**System:** DVB-T2 (MPEG2) [E]

**TELEVISÃO DE CABO VERDE (TCV) (Pub)** ☑ Rua 13 de Janeiro, 1-A, Achada Santo António, Praia ☎ +238 2605200 🖹 +238 2605256 **E:** tcv@rtc.cv **W:** www.rtc.cv **L.P:** Dir (TV): Júlio Rodrigues.

**DTT Tx Network**
**Licensee:** CV Telecom **W:** www.cvtelecom.cv **M:** Televisão de Cabo Verde, SIC Noticias, TV Record, Rai Uno, BBC World, TV5, TV Galicia, Infinito, Fox Life, Fashion TV, Euronews, Eurosport, Extreme Sport, TVE Internacional, CNBC, MCM, RTP África, Lusomundo Premium, Lusomundo Gallery, Playboy, SportTv, RTP1, RTP2, SIC, TVI. **Txs:** (-)

## CAMBODIA

**Systems:** DVB-T (MPEG4) [E]; § PAL-B [E] ⇩2020

**National Stations**
**TV KHMER (TVK) (Gov)** ☑ 62 Preah Monivong Boulevard, Sangkat Sras Chork, Khan Daun Penh, Phnom Penh 12202 ☎ +855 23 430827 🖹 +855 23 430752 **E:** info@tvk.gov.kh **W:** www.tvk.gov.kh **L.P:** DG: Khim Vuthy – **BAYON TV (Comm)** ☑ National Road No 1, Boeung Snoa, Chbar Ampeou, Phnon Penh 12357 ☎ +855 23 363695 🖹 +855 23 726619 **E:** bayontv@camnet.gov.kh **W:** bayontv.com.kh – **CAMBODIAN TV NETWORK (CTN) (Comm)** ☑ National Highway 5, Phum Krol Ko, Sangkat Kilomet 6, Khan Russei Keo, Phnom Penh 12104 ☎ +855 12 800800 🖹 +855 12 801801 **E:** wmaster@ctncambodia.com **W:** www.ctn.com.kh **Chs:** CTN, MyTV. – **TV FARK (Mil)** ☑ rue 169, Borei Keila, Phnom Penh 12253 ☎ +855 23 366061 🖹 +855 23 366063.

**Local Stations** not shown.

**DTT Tx Network**
**Licensee:** PPCTV **W:** www.ppctv.com.kh **M(partly☉):** multiprgr **Txs:** MFN.

## CAMEROON

**System:** DVB-T2 (MPEG4) [E]

**National Stations**
**CAMEROON RADIO AND TELEVISION (CRTV) (Gov)** ☑ BP 1634, Yaoundé ☎ +237 2214088 🖹 +237 2204340 **E:** infps@crtv.cm **W:** crtv.cm **L.P:** DG: Charles Ndongo – **SPECTRUM TELEVISION (STV) (Comm)** ☑ BP 4883, Douala ☎ +237 3433045 🖹 +237 3433048 **E:** spectrum1@camnet.com **Chs:** STV1, STV2.

**Local Stations** (all Comm)
**Equinoxe Télévision (E.TV):** BP 15333, Douala. **RTV Lumière:** Yaoundé. **TV Max:** BP 4527, Douala.

**DTT Tx Network**
**Tx Operator:** Startimes **M(partly☉):** multiprgr **Txs:** MFN

## CANADA

**Systems:** ATSC [A]; § NTSC-M [A] (small markets only)

**National Networks** (ᵃ=analogue; O&O = owned-and-operated)
**CANADIAN BROADCASTING CORP. (CBC/RADIO-CANADA) (Pub)** ☑ 181 Queen St, Box 3220 Stn C, Ottawa ON K1Y 1E4 ☎ +1 613 2886000 **W:** www.cbc.ca **L.P:** Pres/CEO: Hubert T. Lacroix. **Networks:** CBC Television (English), ICI Radio-Canada Télé (French). **CBC Television:** ☑ 250 Front St W, Box 500 Stn A, Toronto ON M5W 1E6 ☎ +1 416 2053311 **W:** www.cbc.radio-canada.ca **L.P:** Exec. Vice Pres. (English Networks): Heather Conway **O&O Stations:** CBAT-DT Fredericton NB ch31 (7.4kW), CBCT-DT Charlottetown PE ch13 (13kW), CBET-DT Windsor ON ch9 (26kW), CBHT-DT Halifax NS ch39 (157.5kW), CBKT-DT Regina SK ch9 (60kW), CBLT-DT Toronto ON ch20 (106.9kW), CBMT-DT Montréal QC ch21 (107kW), CBNT-DT St. John's NF ch8 (14.5kW), CBOT-DT Ottawa ON ch25 (165kW), CBRT-DT Calgary AB ch21 (23.5kW), CBUT-DT Vancouver BC ch43 (103.3kW), CBWT-DT Winnipeg MB ch27 (42kW), CBXT-DT Edmonton AB ch42 (131.7kW), CFYK-DT Yellowknife NT ch8 (2.4kW) & translators. **ICI Radio-Canada Télé:** ☑ 1400 René-Lévesque Boul. E, Box 6000, Montréal QC H3C 3A8 ☎ +1 514 5976000 **W:** ici.radio-canada.ca **L.P:** Exec. Vice Pres. (French Networks): Louis Lalande. **O&O Stations:** CBAFT-DT Moncton

NB ch11 (17.7kW), CBFT-DT Montréal QC ch19 (250kW), CBKFT-DT Regina SK ch13 (27.1kW), CBLFT-DT Toronto ON ch25 (106.2kW), CBOFT-DT Ottawa ON ch9 (3.5kW), CBUFT-DT Vancouver BC ch26 (27.5kW), CBVT-DT Québec QC ch25 (2.5kW), CBWFT-DT Winnipeg MB ch51 (7.6kW), CBXFT-DT Edmonton AB ch47 (15.2kW), CJBR-DT Rimouski QC ch45 (167.5kW), CKSH-DT Sherbrooke QC ch9 (36.3kW), CKTM-DT Trois-Rivières QC ch28 (38.9kW), CKTV-DT Saguenay QC ch12 (7.4kW) & translators. Affiliates: 2. – **CTV INC. (Comm)** (Div. of Bell Media Inc) ✉ 9 Channel Nine Court, Scarborough ON M1S 4B5 ☎ +1 416 3325000 **E:** bellmediapr@bellmedia.ca **W:** www.ctv.ca **LP:** Pres (Bell Media): Randy Lennox. **Networks:** CTV, CTV Two **O&O Stations: CTV:** CFCF-DT Montréal QC ch12 (10.6kW), CFCN-DT Calgary AB ch29 (220kW), CFCN-DT-5 Lethbridge AB ch13 (139kW), CFQC-DT Saskatoon SK ch8 (13kW), CFRN-DT Edmonton AB ch12 (25kW), CFRN-TV-6 Red Deer AB ch12 (25kW), CFTO-DT Toronto ON ch9 (10.2kW), CHBX-TV Sault Ste. Marie ON [a]ch2 (100kW), CICC-TV Yorkton SK [a]ch10 (56kW), CICI-TV Sudbury ON [a]ch5 (100kW), CIPA-TV Prince Albert SK [a]ch9 (325kW), CITO-TV Timmins ON [a]ch3 (100kW), CIVT-DT Vancouver BC ch32 (33kW), CJCB-TV Sydney NS [a]ch4 (180kW), CJCH-DT Halifax NS ch48 (400kW), CJOH-DT Ottawa ON ch13 (19kW), CKCK-DT Regina SK ch8 (23kW), CKCO-DT Kitchener ON ch13 (12kW), CKCW-DT Moncton NB ch29 (390kW), CKLT-DT St. John NB ch9 (7.6kW), CKNY-TV North Bay ON [a]ch10 (132.6kW), CKY-DT Winnipeg MB ch7 (24kW) & translators. Affiliates: 5. **CTV Two:** CFPL-DT London ON ch10 (45kW), CFTK-TV Terrace/Kitimat BC [a]ch3 (13.8kW), CHRO-DT-43 Ottawa ON ch43 (60kW), CHRO-TV Pembroke ON [a]ch5 (100kW), CHWI-DT Windsor ON ch16 (3.4kW), CIVI-DT Victoria BC ch23 (1.5kW), CJDC-TV Dawson Creek BC [a]ch5 (9.5kW), CKVR-DT Barrie ON ch10 (11kW) & translators. – **GLOBAL TV NETWORK INC. (Comm)** (Div. of Corus Entertainment Inc) ✉ 81 Barber Greene Road, Toronto, ON M3C 2A2 ☎+1 416 4465311 **W:** www.globaltv.com **LP:** Pres/CEO (Corus Entertainment): Doug Murphy **Network:** Global. **O&O Stations:** CFRE-DT Regina SK ch11 (17.3kW), CFSK-DT Saskatoon SK ch42 (30kW), CHAN-DT Vancouver BC ch22 (40kW), CHBC-DT Kelowna BC ch27 (32.6kW), CHNB-DT St. John NB ch12 (6kW), CICT-DT Calgary AB ch41 (50kW), CIHF-DT Halifax NS ch8 (1kW), CIII-DT Toronto ON ch41 (100kW), CISA-DT Lethbridge AB ch7 (19.7kW), CITV-DT Edmonton AB ch13 (25kW), CKMI-DT Québec QC ch20 (18kW), CKND-DT Winnipeg MB ch40 (25.1kW) & translators. Affiliates: 2

**Major Regional Networks** ([a]=analogue)
**ONTARIO EDUCATIONAL COMMUNICATIONS AUTHORITY (Pub)** ✉ 2180 Yonge Street, Toronto, ON M4S 2B9 ☎ +1 416 4842600 **W:** tvo.org **LP:** Chmn (TVO): Peter O'Brian **Network:** TVOntario (TVO). **O&O Stations:** CICA-DT Toronto ch19 (106.5kW) & translators (ON). – **SOCIÉTÉ DE TÉLÉDIFFUSION DU QUEBEC (Pub)** ✉ 1000 rue Fullum, Montréal QC H2K 3L7 ☎ +1 514 5212424 **W:** www.telequebec.tv **LP:** Pres/CEO: Marie Collin **Network:** Télé-Québec (French). **O&O Stations:** CIVA-DT Val-d'Or QC ch12 (22kW), CIVB-DT Rimouski QC ch22 (136kW), CIVC-DT Trois-Rivières QC ch45 (290kW), CIVF-DT Baie-Trinité QC ch12 (46kW), CIVG-DT Sept-Îles QC ch9 (19kW), CIVK-DT Carleton QC ch15 (140kW), CIVM-DT Montréal QC ch26 (269kW), CIVO-DT Gatineau QC ch30 (300kW), CIVP-DT Chapeau QC ch23 (0.76kW), CIVQ-DT Québec QC ch15 (194kW), CIVS-DT Sherbrooke QC ch24 (31kW), CIVV-DT Saguenay QC ch8 (84.9kW) & translators (QC). – **2190015 ONTARIO INC. (Comm)** ✉Box 6143 Stn A, Toronto ON M5W 1P6 ☎ +1 416 4921595 **W:** www.chz.com; www.chch.com **LP:** Chmn/CEO: Romen Podzyhun. **Network:** Channel Zero. **O&O Stations:** CHCH-DT Hamilton ON ch15 (132kW) & translators (ON). – **GROUPE TVA INC. (Comm)** (Div. of Québecor Media Inc) ✉ 1600 boul. de Maisonneuve Est, Montréal QC H2L 4P2 ☎ +1 514 5269251 **W:** tva.canoe.com **LP:** Pres/CEO (Québecor Media): France Lauzière **Network:** TVA (French). **O&O Stations:** CFCM-DT Québec QC ch17 (210kW), CFER-DT Rimouski QC ch11 (3.3kW), CFTM-DT Montréal QC ch10 (11kW), CHEM-DT Trois-Rivières QC ch8 (11.5kW), CHLT-DT Sherbrooke QC ch7 (40kW), CJPM-DT Saguenay QC ch46 (200kW). Affiliates: 4 – **GROUPE V MÉDIA INC. (Comm)** (Div. of Groupe Remstar Inc) ✉ 85 Rue Saint-Paul Ouest, Montréal QC H2Y 3V4 ☎ +1 514 3906035 **W:** www.vmedia.ca; noovo.ca **LP:** Pres/CEO: Maxime Rémillard **Network:** V (French). **O&O Stations:** CFAB-DT Québec QC ch39 (98kW), CFJP-DT Montréal QC ch35 (13.9kW), CFRS-DT Saguenay QC ch38 (4.3kW), CFKS-DT Sherbrooke QC ch30 (4.6kW), CFKM-DT Trois-Rivières QC ch34 (9.4kW). Affiliates: 4 (QC). – **JIM PATTISON BROADCAST GROUP LP (Comm)** ✉ 460 Pemberton Terrace, Kamloops BC V2C 1T5 ☎ +1 250 3723322 **W:** jpbroadcast.com **LP:** Pres/GM: Rod Schween **O&O Stations (City Affiliates):** CFJC-TV Kamloops BC [a]ch4 (3.7kW), CHAT-TV Medicine Hat AB [a]ch6 (58kW), CKPG-TV Prince George BC [a]ch2 (8.3kW) & translators (AB & BC). – **ROGERS MEDIA INC. (Comm)** (Div. of Rogers Communications Inc) ✉ 333 Bloor St. E, 7th flr, Toronto ON M4W 1G9 ☎ +1 416 9358200 **W:** www.rogersmedia.com; www.citytv.com; www.omnitv.ca **LP:** Pres/CEO: Joseph Natale **Networks:** City, OMNI Television (OMNI 1, OMNI 2). **O&O Stations: City:** CHMI-DT Portage la Prairie MB ch13 (8.3kW),

CITY-DT Toronto ON ch44 (15kW), CJNT-DT Montréal QC ch49 (4kW), CKAL-DT Calgary AB ch49 (100kW), CKEM-DT Edmonton AB ch17 (107kW), CKVU-DT Vancouver BC ch33 (8.3kW) & translators. Affiliates: 3 (see Jim Pattison Broadcast Group) **OMNI 1:** CFMT-DT Toronto ON ch47 (22.2kW), CHNM-DT Vancouver BC ch20 (8.3kW), CJCO-DT Calgary AB ch38 (25kW), CJEO-DT Edmonton QC ch44 (58kW) & translators. **OMNI 2:** CJMT-DT Toronto ON ch40 (18.1kW) & translators.

**Other Regional Networks & Local Stations** not shown.

## CANARY ISLANDS (Spain)

**System:** DVB-T (MPEG2, MPEG4) [E]

**National (Regional) Stations**
**TELEVISION ESPAÑOLA EN CANARIAS (TVE) (Pub)** ✉ Plazoleta de Milton 1, 35005 Las Palmas de Gran Canaria ☎ +34 928 293096. – **RADIOTELEVISIÓN CANARIA (RTCV) (Pub)** ✉Mariucha 2, 35012 Las Palmas de Gran Canaria ☎ +34 928 280188 **W:** www.rtvc.es. **Ch:** TV Canaria.

**Local Stations** not shown.

**DTT Tx Networks**
**Operator:** n/a **National Muxes 1-7:** see Spain; **Regional Mux (R):** TV Canaria, TV Canaria HD ✵ Canarias R., R. Ecca

| Location | M1 | M2 | M3 | M4 | M5 | M6 | M7 | R |
|---|---|---|---|---|---|---|---|---|
| Fuerteventura | 52 | 36 | 35 | 32 | 34 | 31 | 55 | 49 |
| Lanzarote | 52 | 36 | 35 | 32 | 34 | 31 | 56 | 30 |
| Las Palmas (SFN) | 28 | 36 | 35 | 32 | 38 | 50 | 25 | 22 |
| Tenerife (SFN) | 27 | 48 | 23 | 29 | 26 | 41 | 43 | 59 |

**Local muxes** not shown.

## CAYMAN ISLANDS (UK)

**System:** NTSC-M [A]

**CAYMAN INTERNATIONAL TV NETWORK (CITN) (Comm)** ✉ P.O. Box 30563 SMB, Grand Cayman ☎ +1 345 9452739 ▤ +1 345 9490021 **E:** citn@cayman27.com.ky **W:** cayman27.com.ky **Tx:** ch27. – **CAYMAN TELEVISION SERVICE (CTS) (Comm)** ✉ P.O.Box 3117 SMB, Grand Cayman. **Tx:** ch24. – **CAYMAN ADVENTIST TELEVISION NETWORK (CATN) (Rlg)** ✉ P.O.Box 515 GT, Grand Cayman. **E:** mission@candw.ky **Tx:** ch30. Rel. 3ABN (USA). – **CAYMAN CHRISTIAN TELEVISION (CCT) (Rlg)** ✉ Grand Cayman. **Tx:** ch21. Rel. TBN (USA).

## CENTRAL AFRICAN REPUBLIC

**Systems:** DVB-T2 (MPEG4) [E]; § SECAM-K1 [VHF=K]

**National Stations**
**TÉLÉVISION CENTRAFRICAINE (TVCA) (Gov)** ✉ BP 940, Bangui ☎ +236 75501412 ▤ +236 21615985 – **VISION 4TV-RCA (Comm)** ✉ Bangui.

**DTT Tx Network**
**Tx Operator:** Startimes **M(partly♲):** multiprgr **Txs:** MFN

## CHAD

**Systems:** DVB-T2 (HEVC) [E]; § SECAM-K1 [VHF=K, UHF=E]

**TÉLÉ TCHAD (Gov)** ✉ BP 5123, N'Djamena ☎ +235 22522923 ▤ +235 22525163 **E:** tele.tchad@intnet.td **W:** www.onrtv.org **LP:** DG (ONRTV): Doubaï Kletouin

**DTT Tx Network**
**Tx Operator:** Startimes **M(partly♲):** multiprgr **Txs:** MFN

## CHILE

**Systems:** ISDB-TB [A]; § NTSC-M [A] ⇩2019

**National Stations** ([a]=analogue)
**TVN CHILE (Pub)** ✉ Bellavista 0990, Providencia, Santiago ☎ +56 2 7077130 **E:** tvngprog@tvn.cl **W:** www.tvchile.cl **Txs:** Santiago [a]ch7/ch33 & relay txs. – **CANAL 13 (Rlg, Comm)** ✉ Inés Matte Urrejola 0825, Providencia, Santiago ☎ +56 2 6302356 **E:** mailbag@13.cl **W:** www.13.cl **Txs:** Santiago [a]ch13/ch24 & relay txs. – **CHILEVISIÓN**

**(CHV) (Comm)** ✉ Inés Matte Urrejola 0890, Providencia, Santiago ☎ +56 2 4615100 **E:** rcarmi@chilevision.cl **W:** www.chilevision.cl. **Txs:** Santiago ªch11 (60kW)/ch30 & relays txs. – **MEGA (Comm)** ✉ Av. Vicuña Mackenna 1348, Santiago ☎ +56 2 8108000 **E:** mega@mega.cl **W:** www.mega.cl **Txs:** Santiago ªch9/ch27 & relays. – **RED TV (Comm)** ✉ Avenida Quilín 3750, Macul, Santiago ☎ +56 2 23854000 **E:** lared@lared.cl **W:** lared.cl **Txs:** Santiago ªch4 & relay txs. – **TELECANAL (Comm)** ✉ Nueva Tajamar 481, Oficina 201, Torre Central, Las Condes, Santiago ☎ +56 2 4115600 **E:** telecanal@telecanal.cl **W:** www.telecanal.cl **Tx:** Santiago ªch2 & relays txs – **UCV TV (Comm)** ✉ Av. 11 Septiembre 2155 Of. 1402, Edificio Panorámico Torre A, Santiago ☎ +56 2 5864350 **E:** direccion@ucv.cl **W:** www.ucvmedios.cl **Txs:** Santiago ªch5/ch26 & relay txs.

**Local Stations** not shown.

## CHINA (People's Rep. of)

**Systems:** DTMB [DS]; § PAL-D [DS]

**National Stations**
**CHINA MEDIA GROUP (Gov)** ✉ 11 Fuxing Lu, Haidian Qu, Beijing 100859 ☎ +86 10 68500114 🖹 +86 10 68508743 **L.P:** Pres: Shen Haixiong **Networks:** China Central Television (CCTV) **W:** www.cctv.cn; China Global Television Network (CGTN) ✉ 13rd Ring North Road, Chaoyang Qu, Beijing 100020) **W:** www.cgtn.com – **CHINA EDUCATION TELEVISION (CETV)** ✉ 160 Fuxingmennei Dajie, Xicheng Qu, Beijing 100031 ☎ +86 10 66419055 🖹 +86 10 66084298 **L.P:** Pres: Yuan Xiaoping **W:** www.centv.cn.

**Provincial Stations** (all Gov)
**AH)** Anhui TV: 666 Longtu Lu, Hefei, Anhui 230071 **W:** www.ahrtv.cn **BJ)** Beijing TV: 98 A Jianguo Lu, Chaoyang Qu, Beijing 100022 **W:** www.btime.com **CQ)** Chongqing TV: 333 Longshan Dadao, Chongqing 401147 **W:** www.cbg.cn **EB)** Hebei TV: 100 Jianshe Dajie, Shijiazhuang, Hebei 050021 **W:** www.hebtv.com **EN)** Henan TV: 18 Zhenghua Lu, Zhengzhou, Henan 450008 **W:** www.hntv.tv **FJ)** Fujian TV: 128 Xihuan Nanlu, Fuzhou, Fujian 350004 **W:** www.fjtv.net **GD)** Guangdong TV: 686 Renmin Beilu, Guangzhou, Guangdong 510012 **W:** www.gdtv.cn **GS)** Gansu TV: 561 Zhangsutan, Chengguan Qu, Lanzhou, Gansu 730010 **W:** www.gstv.com.cn **GX)** Guangxi TV: 73 Minzu Dadao, Nanning, Guangxi 530022 **W:** www.gxtv.cn **GZ)** Guizhou TV: 25 Ruijin Nanlu, Guiyang, Guizhou 550001 **W:** www.gzstv.com **HA)** Hainan TV: 61 Nansha Lu, Haikou, Hainan 570206 **W:** www.hnntv.cn **HB)** Hubei TV: 1 Zhongbei Lu, Liangdao Jie,Wuchang Qu, Wuhan, Hubei 430071 **W:** news.hbtv.com.cn **HL)** Heilongjiang TV: 333 Hanshui Lu, Harbin, Heilongjiang 150090 **W:** www.hljtv.com.cn **HN)** Hunan TV: Liuyang He Daqiao Dong, Changsha, Hunan 410003 **W:** zixun.hunantv.com **JL)** Jilin TV: 2066 Weixing Lu, Changchun, Jilin 130033 **W:** www.jilintv.cn **JS)** Jiangsu TV: 48 Xi Citang Xiang, Zhongshan Donglu, Nanjing, Jiangsu 210002 **W:** www.jstv.com **JX)** Jiangxi TV: 207 Hongdu Zhong Dadao, Nanchang, Jiangxi 330046 **W:** www.jxntv.cn **LN)** Liaoning TV: 79 Wenhua Lu, Heping Qu, Shenyang, Liaoning 110003 **W:** www.lntv.com.cn **NM)** Nei Menggu TV: 71 Xinhua Dajie, Hohhot, Nei Menggu 010058 **W:** www.nmtv.cn **NX)** Ningxia TV: 66 Beijing Zhonglu, Jinfeng Qu, Yinchuan, Ningxia 75000135 **W:** www.nxtv.cn **QH)** Qinghai TV: 81 Xiguan Dajie, Xining, Qinghai 810008 **W:** www.qhbtv.com **SD)** Shandong TV: 81 Jingshi Lu, Jinan, Shandong 250062 **W:** www.sdtv.cn **SC)** Sichuan TV: 66 Shiji Cheng Lu, Chengdu, Sichuan 610041 **W:** www.sctv.com **SH)** Shanghai TV: 298 Weihai Lu, Shanghai 200041 **W:** www.smg.cn **SN)** Shaanxi TV: 336 Chang'an Nanlu, Xi'an, Shaanxi 710061 **W:** www.sxtvs.com **SX)** Shanxi TV: 318 Yingze Dajie, Taiyuan, Shanxi 030001 **W:** www.sxrtv.com **TJ)** Tianjin TV: 143 Weijin Lu, Heping Qu, Tianjin 300071 **W:** tjtv.enorth.com.cn **XJ)** Xinjiang TV: 830 Tuanjie Lu, Urumqi, Xinjiang 830044 **W:** www.xjtvs.com.cn **XZ)** Xizang TV: 8 Linkuo Xilu, Lhasa, Xizang 850000 **W:** www.vtibet.com/ds **YN)** Yunnan TV: 182 Renmin Xilu, Kunming, Yunnan 650031 **W:** www.yntv.cn **ZJ)** Zhejiang TV: 111 Moganshan Lu, Hangzhou, Zhejiang 310005 **W:** www.cztv.com. **NB:** Keys to regional codes - see National radio section.

**DTT Tx Networks**
**Tx Operator:** SART **M1:** CCTV1, CCTV2, CCTV4, CCTV10, CCTV12, CCTV13, CCTV14, CCTV15 **M2:** CCTV1 HD, CCTV7, CCTV9, CCTV11, CGTN, CETV3 **R1+R2:** various provincial/local stations

| Location | M1 | M2 | R1 | R2 |
|----------|----|----|----|----|
| Beijing | 45 | 46 | 22 | 40 |

+ nationwide MFN
**Local muxes** not shown.

## CHRISTMAS ISLAND (Australia)

**NB:** No terrestrial TV station.

## COCOS (Keeling) ISLANDS (Australia)

**NB:** No terrestrial TV station.

## COLOMBIA

**Systems:** DVB-T2 (MPEG4) [A]; § NTSC-M [A] ⤓2019

**National Stations**
**RADIO TELEVISIÓN NACIONAL DE COLOMBIA (RTVC) (Pub)** ✉ Avenida El Dorado No. 46 - 76, Bogotá ☎+57 1 2200700 🖹 +57 1 2222765 **E:** info@rtvc.gov.co **W:** www.rtvc.gov.co **Chs:** Canal Uno, Canal Institucional, Canal 13 – **CARACOL TELEVISIÓN (Comm)** ✉ Calle 103 #69 B 43, Bogota ☎ +57 1 6430430 🖹 +57 1 6430444 **E:** servieiocliente@caracol.com.co **W:** www.caracoltv.com **Chs:** Caracol HD, Caracol HD2, Novelas Caracol, La Kalle, Época – **RCN TELEVISIÓN (Comm)** ✉ Av Americas 65-82, Bogotá ☎ +57 1 4269292 🖹 +57 1 4140412 **W:** www.canalrcn.com **Chs:** NTN24, RCN HD, RCN HD2, Tacho Pistacho, Win Sports, RCN Nuestra Tele, RCN Novelas.

**Local Stations** not shown.

**DTT Tx Networks**
| Location | RTVC* | Caracol** | RCN*** |
|----------|-------|-----------|--------|
| Bogotá | 16 | 14 | 15 |

+ nationwide netw. under construction
*) **M:** Canal Uno, Canal Institucional, Canal 13 **) **M:** Caracol HD, Caracol HD2, Novelas Caracol, La Kalle, Época ***) **M:** NTN24, RCN HD, RCN HD2, Tacho Pistacho, Win Sports, RCN Nuestra Tele, RCN Novelas
**Local muxes** not shown.

## COMOROS

**Systems:** DTMB [E]; § SECAM-K1 [VHF=K]

**National Station**
**OFFICE DE RADIO ET TÉLÉVISION DES COMORES (ORTC) (Pub)** ✉ BP 250, Moroni ☎ +269 7744045 🖹 +269 7731079 **W:** www.ortc.fr **L.P:** DG: Msa Ali Djamal.

**Local Stations** (all Comm)
**Djabal TV:** Iconi. **Kartala RTV:** Moroni. **TV-Sha:** Moroni. **MTV:** Moroni. **RTV Anjouanaise (RTA):** Mbouyoujou-Ouani, Ile Autonome d'Anjouan.

**DTT Tx Network**
**Tx Operator:** n/a **M:** multiprgr **Txs:** nationwide MFN under constr.

## CONGO (Dem. Rep.)

**System:** DVB-T2 (MPEG4) [E]

**National Station**
**RADIOTÉLÉVISION NATIONALE CONGOLAISE (RTNC) (Pub)** ✉ BP 3164, Gombe, Kinshasa ☎ +243 1 5260601 🖹 +243 1 5220655 **E:** ica@ic.cd **W:** www.rtnc.cd **Chs:** RTNC1, RTNC2, RTNC3.

**Local Stations** not shown.

**DTT Tx Network**
**Tx Operator:** Startimes **M (partly☉):** RTNC3, Tropicana TV, La chaîne du Sénat, Télé 50, Raga TV, B-Ones **Txs:** ch26 (Kinshasa 0.5kW) & netw. under constr. – **Local Tx Operators** not shown.

## CONGO (Rep.)

**System:** DVB-T2 (MPEG4) [E]]

**TÉLÉ CONGO (Gov)** ✉ BP 1046, Brazzaville ☎ +242 222810116 🖹 +242 222814128 **W:** telecongo.cg **L.P:** DG: Jean Obambi – **DRTV (Comm)** ✉ BP 1974, Brazzaville **W:** www.facebook.com/DRTV-International-230828793639419.

**DTT Tx Network**
**Tx Operator:** Startimes **M(partly☉):** multiprgr **Txs:** MFN

## COOK ISLANDS

**System:** PAL-B [NZ]

**COOK ISLANDS TV (CITV) (Comm)** ⌨ P.O.Box 126, Avarua, Rarotonga ☎ +682 29460 🖷 +682 21907 **E:** watchus@citv.co.ck **W:** www.citv.co.ck **LP:** CEO: Jeane Matenga **Txs:** Airport ch4, Works Depot, TV studio, Mauke ch5, Matavera ch6, Titikaveka ch7, Aitutaki & Rarotonga ch9, Tu Papa ch10, Hospital & Ngatangiia ch11.

## COSTA RICA

**Systems:** ISDB-TB [A]; § NTSC-M [A] ⇩2019

**National Stations**
**SISTEMA NACIONAL DE RADIO Y TELEVISIÓN (SINART) (Pub)** ⌨ Apt 7-1908-1000, San José ☎ +506 22313333 **E:** canal13@sinart. go.cr **W:** www.sinart.go.cr **LP:** Pres: Mario Alfaro Rodríguez **Txs:** San José ch13 & relay txs. – **REPRETEL (Comm)** ⌨ Apartado 2860, 1000 San José ☎ +506 22906665 **E:** info@repretel.com **W:** www.repretel. com **Chs:** Canal 4, 6, 11. **Txs:** San José ch26. – **TELETICA (Comm)** ⌨Sabana Oeste, San José ☎ +506 22101201 🖷 +506 22321107 **E:** info@teletica.com **W:** www.teletica.com **Tx:** San José ch14.

**Local Stations** not shown.

## CÔTE D'IVOIRE

**System:** DVB-T2 (MPEG4) [E]

**RADIODIFFUSION TÉLÉVISION IVOIRIENNE (Pub)** ⌨ 08 BP 883, Abidjan 08 ☎ +225 22449039 🖷 +225 22447339 **E:** dgrti@aviso.ci **W:** www.rti.ci **LP:** DG: Ahmadou Bakayoko **Chs:** RTI1, RTI2.

**DTT Tx Network**
**Tx Operator:** Startimes **M(partly☼):** multiprgr **Txs:** MFN

## CROATIA

**System:** DVB-T (MPEG2); DVB-T2 (HEVC) planned

**National Stations**
**HRVATSKA RADIO-TELEVIZIJA (HRT) (Pub)** ⌨ Prisavlje 3, 10000 Zagreb. ☎ + 385 1 6163366 **W:** www.hrt.hr **LP:** DG: Kazimir Bacic. **Chs:** HRT1, HRT2, HRT3, HRT4 – **NOVA TV (Comm)** ⌨ Remetinecka cesta 139, 10000 Zagreb ☎ +385 1 6008300 **E:** novatv@novatv.hr **W:** novatv.dnevnik.hr **LP:** DG: Dražen Mavric **Chs:** Nova TV, Doma TV. – **RTL TELEVIZIJA (Comm)** ⌨ Krapinska 45, 10000 Zagreb ☎ +385 1 3660000 **E:** rtl@rtl.hr **W:** www.rtl.hr **LP:** Pres/CEO: Henning Tewes. **Chs (terr.):** RTL, RTL2.

**Local Stations** (via Mux 4, DTT regions: a-i)
**Gradska TV:** Molatska bb, 23000 Zadar (g) **Kanal RI:** Trg Rijecke rezolucije 3, 51000 Rijeka (e). **Nezavisna Istarska Televizija (NIT):** Trg pod lipom 1, 52000 Pazin (e). **RI-TV:** Užarska 17/3, 51000 Rijeka (e). **Slavonskobrodska Televizija:** Mile Budaka 1/IV, 35 000 Slavonski Brod (b). **TV Cakovec:** Kralja Tomislava 6, 40000 Cakovec (f). **TV Jadran:** Split (h). **TV Nova:** M. Laginje 5, 52100 Pula (e). **TV Slavonije i Baranje:** Hrvatske republike 20, 31000 Osijek (a). **Varaždinska Televizija (VTV):** Kralja P. Kresimira IV 6a, 42000 Varaždin (c). **Vinkovacka Televizija (VKTV):** Trg dr.F.Tudjmana 2, Vinkovci (a).

**DTT Tx Networks**
**Tx Operator:** OIV **W:** www.oiv.hr **M1:** HRT1, HRT2, RTL, Nova TV **M2:** HRT3, HRT4, RTL2, Doma TV **M4:** Local stns.

| Location | M1 | M2 | M4* |
|---|---|---|---|
| Belje | 38 | 44 | 21a |
| Biokovo | 33 | 53 | 34h |
| Borinci | 38 | 44 | 21a |
| Brac | 33 | 53 | 53h |
| Celevac | 51 | 59 | 31g |
| Drenovci | 36 | - | - |
| Gruda | 51 | 59 | - |
| Ivanšcica | 44V | 48V | 36Vc |
| Kalnik | 44 | 48 | - |
| Krk | 28 | 53 | 45 |
| Labinštica | 33 | 53 | 34h |
| Lastovo | 33 | - | - |
| Licka Plješevica | 30 | 44 | 54 |
| Mali Losinj | 28 | 53 | - |
| Mirkovica | 30 | 44 | 54 |

| Location | M1 | M2 | M4* |
|---|---|---|---|
| Moslavacka Gora | 23 | 39 | - |
| Pag | 51 | 59 | - |
| Papuk | 23 | 39 | 58 |
| Petrova Gora | 25 | 48 | - |
| Promina | 51 | 59 | 31g |
| Psunj | 23 | 39 | 58 |
| Pula | 28 | 53 | 45e |
| Razromir | 28 | 53 | - |
| Rota | 33 | 53 | - |
| Sljeme | 25 | 48 | 42d |
| Srdj | 51 | 59 | 28i |
| Stipanov Gric | 30 | 44 | 54 |
| Sveta Gera | 25 | 48 | - |
| Sveta Nedjelja | 25 | 48 | 42 |
| Šibenik | 51 | 59 | 31g |
| Ucka | 28 | 53 | 29e |
| Ugljan | 51 | 59 | 31g |
| Uljenje | 51 | 59 | - |
| Zagreb (HRT HQ) | 25 | 48 | - |

+ repeaters. *) DTT regions a-i, see under "Local Stations".

## CUBA

**Systems:** DTMB [A]; § NTSC-M [A] ⇩2024

**National Station** (ᵃ=analogue)
**INSTITUTO CUBANO DE RADIO Y TELEVISIÓN (ICRT) (Gov)** ⌨ Televisión Cubana, Calle 23 #258 e/L y M, Vedado, La Habana 10400 ☎ +53 7 8309705 🖷 +53 7 8309705 **E:** tvcubana@icrt.cu **W:** www. tvcubana.icrt.cu **LP:** Pres: Alfonso Noya **Chs:** Canal Educativo, Canal Educativo 2, Cubavisión, Tele Rebelde, Multivisión, Canal Clave, Canal Infantil, Regional stns. **Txs: Canal Educativo:** La Habana ᵃch4 (309kW) & netw.; **Canal Educativo 2:** La Habana ᵃch15 (631kW) & netw.; **Cubavisión:** La Habana ᵃch6 (129kW) & netw.; **Tele Rebelde:** La Habana ᵃch2 (132kW) & netw. **Multivisión:** La Habana ᵃch21 (3.2kW) & netw.

**Local Stations** not shown.

**DTT Tx Network** (under construction)
**Tx Operator:** Radiocuba **M1:** Canal Educativo, Canal Educativo 2, Cubavisión, Cubavisión Internacional, Multivisión, Tele Rebelde, Canal Clave, Canal Infantil ⌘ R.Rebelde, R.Progreso, R.Taíno, R. Enciclopedia, R. CMBF, R.Reloj **M2:** HD-mux **R:** Regional stns

| Location | M1 | M2 | R | kW |
|---|---|---|---|---|
| Baracoa | 38 | - | - | 12.6 |
| Bartolome Maso | 51 | - | - | 63 |
| Ciego de Avila | 33 | - | - | 12.6 |
| Cienfuegos | 27 | 42 | - | 4/10 |
| Isla de la Juventud | 41 | - | - | 12.6 |
| Jacan | 45 | 51 | 20 | 200/4/200 |
| La Capitana | 39 | - | - | 12.6 |
| La Habana | 38 | 36 | - | 79.4/39.8 |
| La Palma | 28 | - | - | 20 |
| Las Tunas | 33 | - | - | 12.6 |
| Matanzas | 31 | - | - | 15.8 |
| Moa | 43 | - | - | 12.6 |
| Pinar del Rio | 36 | - | - | 50 |
| San Pedro de Alamar | 51 | - | - | 12.6 |
| Sancti Spiritus | 29 | - | - | 40 |
| Santa Clara | 13 | 32 | - | 100/40 |
| Santiago de Cuba | 33 | - | - | 1000 |
| Tabacal | 29 | - | - | 15.8 |
| Trinidad | 46 | - | - | 12.6 |

+ sites with txs below 10kW.

## CURAÇAO (Netherlands)

**System:** DVB-T (MPEG2) [E]

**TELECURAÇAO (Gov)** ⌨ Berg Ararat zn., Willemstad ☎ +599 9 7771688 🖷 +599 9 4614138 **E:** info@telecuracao.com **W:** www. telecuracao.com **M:** TeleCuraçao ⌘ TCFM 93.3 **Txs:** ch26 (SFN).

## CYPRUS

**System:** DVB-T (MPEG4) [E]

**National Stations**
**CYPRUS BROADCASTING CORP. (CYBC) (Pub)** ⌨ P.O.Box 24824, 1397 Lefkosia ☎ +357 22862000 **E:** rik@cybc.com.cy **W:**

www.riknews.com.cy **L.P:** DG (acting): Costas Nikolaides **Chs:** RIK1, RIK 2 – **ANT1 (Comm)** ⌨ P.O.Box 20923, 1665 Lefkosia ☎+357 22200200 **W:** www.ant1iwo.com – **CAPITAL TV (Comm)** ⌨ P.O.Box 55633, 3781 Limassol ☎ +357 25577577 **W:** www. capitaltv.com.cy – **EXTRA TV (Comm)** ⌨ P.O.Box 70651, 3801 Limassol ☎ +357 25715111 **W:** www.facebook.com/Extra-Tv-Cyprus-Channel-192069144189665 – **PLUS TV (Comm)** ⌨ Neas Engomis St. 8, 2409 Lefkosia ☎ +357 22600600 **W:** www.facebook.com/PlusChannelCy – **SIGMA TV (Comm)** ⌨ P.O.Box 21836, 1513 Lefkosia ☎ +357 22580100 **E:** info@sigmatv.com **W:** www.sigmatv.com – **TV ONE (Comm)** ⌨ P.O.Box 27400, 1644 Lefkosia ☎ +357 22477777 **E:** newsdpt@megatv.com **W:** www.megatv.com.

**Local stations** not shown.

**DTT Tx Networks**
**Tx Operator Mux 1:** CYBC **M1:** RIK1, RIK2, RIK HD, ERT World, Euronews ⌘ RIK1-4 **Tx Operator Mux 2+3:** Velister **W:** www.velister.com.cy **M2:** ANT1, Sigma TV, Plus TV, TVOne, Extra TV, Capital TV **M3:** Prime Tel, Alpha TV, Smile TV, CBC TV Mall.

| Location | M1 | M2 | M3 |
|---|---|---|---|
| SFN1 | 49 | 50 | 54 |
| SFN2 | 39 | 41 | 30 |

### NORTHERN CYPRUS

**National Station**
**BAYRAK RADIO TELEVISYON KURUMU (BRTK) (Gov)** ⌨ Dr. Fazil Küçük Bulvari, BRT Sitesi, Lefkosa (mail: via Mersin 10, Turkey) ☎ +90 392 2254577 ▤ +90 392 2254577 **E:** info@brtk.net **W:** www.brtk.net **L.P:** Chmn: Hüseyin Çobanoglu **Chs:** BRT1, BRT2.

**Local Stations** not shown.

**DTT Tx Networks**
**Tx Operator:** BRTK **M1:** BRT1, BRT1 HD, BRT2, Kanal T, KTV (Kibris TV), Kibris Genç TV, Kanal SIM, Ada, Diyalog TV **M2:** currently duplicates M1 **Txs: M1:** ch41 (SFN) **M2:** ch33 (SFN).

### AKROTIRI & DHEKELIA (UK)

**System:** DVB-T (MPEG2) [E]

**BFBS-TV Relay (Serving British Military)** ⌨ BFPO 57, Dhekelia Mil 381 ☎ +357 24748518 **Mux⟳:** BBC One, BBC Two/CBBC, ITV, BFBS Extra/Cbeebies, BFBS Sport, BFBS Movies, Sky News, Sky Sports 1, Sky Sports 2, Sky Sports 3, Nepali TV ⌘ BFBS R. (Cyprus), BFBS R.2, BFBS Gurkha R. **Txs:** ch27 (SFN).

## CZECHIA

**Systems**: DVB-T2 (HEVC); § DVB-T (MPEG2, MPEG4)

**National Stations**
**CESKÁ TELEVIZE (CT) (Pub)** ⌨ Kavcí Hory, 14070 Praha 4 ☎ +420 261131111 **E:** info@ceskatelevize.cz **W:** www.ceskatelevize.cz **L.P:** DG: Petr Dvorák **Chs:** CT1, CT2, Reg prgrs, CT24, CT Art/Décko, CT Sport – **PRIMA TV (Comm)** ⌨ Na Zertvách 24, 18000 Praha 8 ☎ +420 266700111 **E:** informace@iprima.cz **W:** www.iprima.cz **Chs:** TV Prima, Prima COOL, Prima Love, Prima Zoom, Prima Krimi – **TV NOVA (Comm)** ⌨ Kríženeckého nám. 5, 15252 Praha 5 ☎ +420 233100111 **E:** info@nova.cz **W:** tv.nova.cz **L.P:** DG: Christoph Mainusch **Chs:** Nova, Nova 2, Nova Action, Nova Cinema, Nova Gold – **TV BARRANDOV (Comm)** ⌨ Kríženeckého nám. 322, 15200 Praha 5 **W:** www.barrandov.tv **Chs:** TV Barrandov, Barrandov Family, Barrandov Kino, Barrandov Plus – **TV ÓCKO (Comm)** ⌨ Vrchlického 29, 15000 Praha ☎ +420 257222256 **E:** ocko@ocko.tv **W:** ocko.tv **Chs:** Ócko, Ócko Gold.

**Regional & Local Stations** not shown (via DTT regional muxes)

**DTT Tx Networks** (DVB-T2)
**Tx Operator:** Ceské Radiokomunikace a.s. **W:** www.radiokomunikace.cz **M1:** CT1 HD, CT2 HD (incl. reg prgrs), CT24, CT Sport HD, CT Art/Décko **M2:** Nova Cinema, Prima Family, Nova, Prima Cool, Prima Love, Ócko, Prima Zoom, Šlágr TV, Ócko Gold, TV Noe, Barrandov Kino, Barrandov Plus, Prima MAX, Seznam.cz, TV Barrandov, Barrandov Family, Prima Krimi **M3:** Nova Cinema, Nova, Relax, Rebel, Kino Svet, Východoceská televize, Polar TV, Prima Comedy Central, JOJ Family, Nova 2, Nova Gold, Nova Action. **DVB-T Networks/Licensees** not shown. All existing DVB-T txs will be gradually switched off 2019-2021.

| Location | M1 | M2 | M3 | kW |
|---|---|---|---|---|
| Brno (Barvicova) | 26V | 28V | 31V | 10 |
| Brno (Jihlavská) | - | - | 43 | 10 |
| Brno (Kojál) | 26 | 28 | - | 100 |

| Location | M1 | M2 | M3 | kW |
|---|---|---|---|---|
| Brno (Hády) | 26 | 28 | - | 10 |
| C.Budejovice (Klet') | 50 | - | 32 | 10/63 |
| Cheb (Zelená hora) | 26 | 31 | - | 20 |
| Chomutov (Jedlova hora) | 50 | 31 | - | 32 |
| Domazlice (Vraní vrch) | 26 | 31 | - | 10 |
| Frýdek (Lysá hora) | 26 | 28 | - | 25 |
| Hlubocec (Hurka) | - | - | 31 | 40 |
| Hradec Králové (Chlum) | - | - | 24 | 10 |
| Hronov (Jírová hora) | 48 | 29 | - | 10 |
| Jeseník (Zlaté hory) | - | 28 | - | 19 |
| Jeseník (Praded) | 26 | 28 | - | 100/50 |
| Jihlava (Javorice) | 26 | 28 | - | 100 |
| Jihlava (Vetrny Jenikov) | - | - | 24 | 10 |
| Karlovy Vary (Tri Kríže) | - | 31 | - | 25 |
| Klínovec | - | 31 | - | 50 |
| Liberec (Ješted) | - | 31 | - | 50 |
| Mariánské Lázne (Dylen) | - | - | 28 | 16 |
| Mikolov (Devín) | 26 | 28 | - | 25 |
| Olomouc (Slavonín) | - | - | 24 | 10 |
| Ostrava (Hošťálkovice) | 26 | 28 | - | 100 |
| Ostrava (Lanová) | - | - | 31 | 10 |
| Pardubice (vrch Krásný) | 26 | 28 | - | 100 |
| Pardubice (Slatinany) | - | - | 24 | 20 |
| Plzen | - | - | 24 | 32 |
| Plzen (Krašov) | 26 | 31 | - | 100 |
| Praha (Cukrák) | 26 | - | - | 100 |
| Praha (Ládví) | - | - | 24 | 20 |
| Praha (Mahlerovy sady) | - | 31 | - | 32 |
| Praha (Novodvorská) | - | - | 24 | 10 |
| Praha (Olšanská) | - | - | 24 | 10 |
| Rakovník (Louštín) | - | - | 24 | 63 |
| Sušice (Svatobor) | 26 | 31 | - | 100 |
| Teplice | - | - | 28 | 10 |
| Trutnov (Cerná hora) | 26 | 28 | - | 100 |
| Uherské Hradište (Rovnina) | - | - | 43 | 10 |
| Ústí n.L. (Buková hora) | 50 | 31 | - | 100/40 |
| Ústí n.L. (Vanov) | - | 31 | - | 10 |
| Ústí n.L. (Krušnohorská) | - | - | 28 | 10 |
| Ústí n. Orlicí | - | - | 24 | 10 |
| Valašské Klobouky | 26 | 22 | - | 25 |
| Vimperk | 50 | - | - | 20 |
| Votice (Mezivrata) | 26 | - | - | 32 |
| Zlín (Jizní svahy) | - | - | 31 | 10 |
| Zlín (Tlustá hora) | 26 | 22 | - | 10 |
| Znojmo (Deblínek) | - | - | 22 | 10 |

+ sites with txs below 10kW.

## DENMARK

**Systems:** DVB-T (MPEG4), DVB-T2 (MPEG4) [E]

**National Stations**
**DR (Pub)** ⌨ TV Byen, Emil Holms Kanal 20, 0999 København C ☎ +45 35203040 **E:** presse@dr.dk **W:** www.dr.dk **L.P:** DG: Maria Rørbye Rønn **Chs:** DR1, DR2, DR3, DR K, DR Ramasjang, DR Ultra. – **TV2 DANMARK (Pub)** ⌨ Rugaardsvej 25, 5100 Odense C ☎ +45 65919191 **E:** tv2@tv2.dk **W:** tv2.dk **L.P:** CEO: Merete Eldrup. Regional stns (**W:** www.tv2regionerne.dk): a) TV2/Bornholm (Brovangen 1, 3720 Aakirkeby), b) TV2/Fyn (Olfert Fischers Vej 31, 5220 Odense SØ), c) TV2/Lorry (Allégade 7-9, 2000 Frederiksberg), d) TV/Midt-Vest (Søvej 2, 7500 Holstebro), e) TV2/Nord (Søparken 4, 9440 Aabybro), f) TV Syd (Media Park 1, 6000 Kolding), g) TV2 Øst (Kildemarksvej 7, 4760 Vordingborg), h) TV2/Østjylland (Skejbyparken 1, 8200 Århus N) **Chs (terr.):** TV2, TV2 Regional Stations, TV2 Charlie, TV2 Fri, TV2 NEWS, TV2 Sport, TV2 Zulu – **Nordic Entertainment Group (Comm)** ⌨ Strandlodsvej 30, 2300 København S ☎ +45 77305500 **W:** nentgroup.dk **L.P:** CEO: Kim Poder **Chs (terr.):** TV3, TV3+, TV3 Puls, TV3 Sport 1&2.

**Local Stations** (via Mux 1, see below)
**a) Øens TV:** Åbogade 9, 3760 Gudhjem; **b) Fynboen TV:** Sendesamvirke FYN 2014-19, Banevænget 24, Odense, 5270 Odense N; **c) Kanal Hovedstaden:** Helgolandsgade 10, 1653 København V; **d) Kanal Midt-Vest:** FKG, Gl. Kirkevej 33, 7400 Herning; **e) Kanal Nord:** Sendesamvirke Kanal Nord, Søparken 2, 9440 Aabybro; **f) Kanal Syd:** Sendesamvirke Syd, c/o Gunnar Thomsen, Østerbrogade 30, 6000 Kolding; **g) Lokalkanalen:** NFMK (Nykøbing Falster Multimedie Klub), Voldgade 1, 4800 Nykøbing F; **h) Kanal Østjylland:** Sendesamvirke Kanal Østjylland, c/o Aarhus Global Media, Bjørnholms Allé 6, 8260 Viby J.

**DTT Tx Networks** (DVB-T exc. where indicated)
**Licensee Mux 1+2:** DIGI-TV I/S **W:** www.digi-tv.dk **M1:** DR1, DR2, TV2 Regional stns, Local stns **M2:** DR3, DR K, DR Ramasjang, DR Ultra, Folketinget. – **Licensee Mux 3-6:** Boxer TV A/S **W:** www.

boxertv.dk **M3✪:** Kanal 5, TV2 (incl. reg. prgrs), TV3, TV3 Puls **M4✪:** DK4, Kanal 4, SVT1, TV2 Charlie, TV2 NEWS, TV2 Sport **M5✪ (DVB-T2):** 6'eren, Comedy Central, Disney Channel, Disney Jr, History Channel, ID Discovery, MTV, Nickelodeon/VH1 Classic, NRK1, TLC, TV3+, TV3 Sport, ZDF **M6✪ (DVB-T2):** Animal Planet, Canal 9, Discovery, Eurosport 1+2, TV2 Fri, TV2 Zulu, TV3 MAX.

| Location | M1* | M2 | M3* | M4 | M5 | M6 | kW |
|---|---|---|---|---|---|---|---|
| Hadsten | 26h | 44 | 24h | 56 | 55 | 36 | 50 |
| Hedensted | 30f | 44 | 46f | 33 | 55 | 36 | 50 |
| Jyderup | 58g | 51 | 42g | 31 | 48 | 23 | 50 |
| København (1) | 53c | 51 | 54c | 31 | 59 | 23 | 50 |
| København (2) | 53c | 51 | 54c | 31 | 59 | 23 | 10 |
| Nakskov | 58g | 34 | 42g | 38 | 48 | 60 | 10 |
| Nibe | 29e | 57 | 50e | 37 | 35 | 39 | 50 |
| Rø | 59a | 56 | 31a | 39 | 51 | 32 | 25 |
| Svendborg | 25b | 43 | 27b | 22 | 49 | 41 | 25 |
| Thisted | 31dV | 42V | 21dV | 43V | 22V | 49V | 25 |
| Tolne | 29e | 57 | 50e | 37 | 35 | 39 | 10 |
| Tommerup | 25b | 43 | 27b | 22 | 49 | 41 | 50 |
| Varde | 30f | 54 | 46f | 33 | 53 | 28 | 50 |
| Viborg | 40d | 59 | 21d | 56 | 52 | 45 | 50 |
| Videbæk | 40d | 59 | 34d | 48 | 52 | 28 | 50 |
| Vordingborg | 58g | 34 | 42g | 38 | 48 | 60 | 50 |
| Abenrå | 37f | 50 | 32f | 22 | 49 | 41 | 50 |

+ sites with txs below 10kW. (1) Søborg (2) Gladsaxe *) incl. Local stns (Mux 1 a-h) & TV 2 Reg stns (Mux 1+3 a-h)

**Systems:** DVB-T2 (MPEG4); § SECAM-B [E]

**RADIODIFFUSION TÉLÉVISION DJIBOUTI (RTD) (Gov)** ⌹ BP 97, Djibouti ☎ +253 21352294 ▤ +253 21356502 **E:** rtd@intnet.dj **W:** www.rtd.dj **L.P:** DG: Abdoulkader Ahmed Idriss **Ch:** Télé Djibouti 1.

**DTT Tx Network**
**Tx Operator:** Djibouti Télécom **M:** Télé Djibouti 1 **Txs:** MFN.

**NB:** No terrestrial TV stations.

**System:** ATSC [A]

**National Station**
**CORPORACIÓN ESTATAL DE RADIO Y TV (CERTV) (Pub)** ⌹ Av. Dr. Tejeda Florentino 8, Sto. Domingo ☎ +1 809 6892121 **E:** info@certv.gob.do **W:** www.certv.gob.do **L.P:** DG: Ramón Tejeda Read. **Txs:** ch4 (SFN).

**Local Stations** not shown.

**System:** NTSC-M [A]

**TV RAPA NUI** ⌹ Hanga Roa, Isla de Pascua. **Tx:** ch13.

**Systems:** ISDB-TB [A]; § NTSC-M [A] ⇩2023

**National Stations**
**SISTEMA ECUATORIANA DE RADIO Y TELEVISIÓN (Pub)**⌹ San Salvador E6-49 y Eloy Alfaro, Edificio Medias Públicos, Quito. **W:** www.rtvecuador.ec; www.tctelevision.com; www.gamatv.com.ec **Chs:** Ecuador TV, TC Televisión, Gama TV. **Txs: TC Televisión:** Quito ch36 & relay txs, **Gama TV:** Quito ch30 & relay txs, **Ecuador TV:** Quito ch26 & relay txs. – **CANAL UNO (Comm)** ⌹ Av. del Bosque Mz 112, Ciudadela Kennedy Norte, Guayaquil ☎ +593 4 2680200 ▤ +593 4 2680185 **E:** relad_sa@canal1tv.com **W:** www.canal1tv.com **Txs:** Quito ch12 & relay txs. – **ECUAVISA (Comm)** ⌹ Bosmediano 447, José Carb, Quito 1 ☎ +593 2 2995300 ▤ +593 2 2445488 **W:** www.ecuavisa.com. **Txs:** Quito ch36 & relay txs. – **RTS (RED TELESISTEMA) (Comm)** ⌹ Av. de los Shyris y Suecia, Edificio Renazzo Plaza #202, Quito ☎ +593 2 2272086 ▤ +593 2 2272086 **E:** rts@rts.com.ec **W:** www.rts.com.ec. **Txs:** Quito ch34 & relay txs. – **RTU (RADIO Y TELEVISIÓN UNIDAS) (Comm)** ⌹

Carrión E5-55 y Juan León Mera, Quito. **E:** noticias@rtunoticias.com **W:** www.rtunoticias.com **Txs:** Quito ch46 & relay txs. – **TELEAMAZONAS (Comm)** ⌹ Av. A. Granda C. 529 y Av. Brasil, Quito ☎ +593 2 2430350 ▤ +593 2 2441620 **E:** contactenos@teleamazonas.com **W:** www.teleamazonas.com. **Txs:** Quito ch32 & relay txs.

**Local Stations** not shown.

**Systems:** DVB-T2 (MPEG4) [E]; # PAL-B/G [E] ⇩2020

**NATIONAL MEDIA AUTHORITY (Gov)** ⌹ TV Bldg, Corniche El Nil, Cairo 11511 ☎ +20 2 25757155 ▤ +20 2 25746989 **E:** tvinfo@ertu.org **W:** ertu.org **L.P:** Chmn: Hussein Zein **Chs (terr.):** Channel 1 & Channel 2 (National), Regional stns, Nile TV, Nile Comedy, Nile Culture, Nile Drama, Nile Family, Nile Life, Nile News, Nile Sport, Maspero Zaman

| Location | 1 | 2 | kW | Location | 1 | 2 | kW |
|---|---|---|---|---|---|---|---|
| Abu Znima | 26 | 29 | 15.5 | Halayeb | 9V | 11V | 31.6 |
| Alexandria | 6 | 11 | 110 | Hassana | 34 | 31 | 35.5 |
| Aswan | 5 | 9 | 67 | Hurghada | 5V | 7V | 89 |
| Asyut | 10 | 6 | 60 | Idfu | 8 | 11 | 165 |
| Baris | 7V | 5V | 10 | Ismailia | 11V | 9V | 260 |
| Barnis | 24 | 29 | 830 | Kom Ombo | 10 | 7 | 40 |
| Beni Ali | 6V | 9V | 5 | Luxor | 11 | 7 | 19 |
| Beni Suef | 11V | 7V | 110 | Matruh | 10 | 8 | 39.2 |
| Cairo | 5 | 9 | 200 | Nag Hammadi | 5 | 8 | 17 |
| Dahab | 6V | 8V | 9.3 | Natron | 41 | 44 | 36.4 |
| Dumyat | 58 | 61 | 15.2 | Port Said | 5V | 7V | 200 |
| El Amain | 46 | 48 | 126 | Qena | 9 | 6 | 30 |
| El Arish | 6V | 10V | 182 | Rafah | 45 | 48 | 350 |
| El Bawiti | 10 | 8 | 22.4 | Ras El Hekma | 32 | 35 | 31.6 |
| El Dakhla | 8 | 6 | 23 | Ras Gharib | 9 | 11 | 66 |
| El Farafra | 5V | 7V | 10 | Ras Sedr | 58 | 61 | 66.2 |
| El Hammam | 39 | 42 | 69.2 | Safaga | 11V | 9V | 50 |
| El Kharga | 10V | 8V | 40 | Sallum | 9 | 11 | 6 |
| El Mahalla | 8 | 10 | 1600 | Sharm El Sheikh | 27 | 33 | 8.9 |
| El Minya | 8V | 5V | 165 | Sidy Barany | 49 | 52 | 74 |
| El Negila | 22 | 25 | 74 | Siwa | 6V | 8V | 10 |
| El Quseyr | 7 | 5 | 50 | Sohag | 7 | 11 | 52 |
| El Tur | 10 | 8 | 33 | Suez | 7 | 5 | 200 |
| Esna | 6 | 9 | 18 | Taba | 32 | 37 | 25.7 |

+ sites with txs below 5kW. 1/2=Channel 1, Channel 2
**El Mahrousa Regional Services**
**Aswan:** Aswan ch21 (67.6kW), Luxor ch22 (69.2kW), Sohag ch27 (340kW), Kom Ombo ch29 (33.9kW), Qena ch30 (85.1kW), Nag Hammadi ch32 (77.6kW), Idfu ch40 (66kW), Isna ch49 (70.9kW). **Alexandria:** Matruh ch5 (11kW), Siwa ch7V (11kW), Negila ch28 (74kW), Alexandria ch36 (678kW), Ras Hekma ch39 (31.6kW). Hammam ch51 (69kW), Sidi Barany ch55 (74kW). **Cairo:** Cairo ch7 (200kW). **El Minya:** Beni Ali ch22V (13.2kW), El Minya ch39V (56kW), Asyut ch48 (117kW), Beni Suef ch51V (43kW), Fayoum ch55 (107kW). **Ismailia:** Negila ch28 (74kW), Suez ch30 (20.3kW), Ismailia ch33V (79.4kW), Port Said ch42V (20.3kW), Zagazig ch52 (158kW). **Tanta:** Mahalla ch49 (321kW).
**Nile Television Network (NTN)**
**Nile TV:** Sharm El Sheikh ch31 (79.4kW), Cairo ch46 (282kW) **Nile Cinema:** Alexandria ch21 (74kW), Sohag ch23 (340kW), Aswan ch24 (67.6kW), Luxor ch25 (69.2kW), Cairo ch28 (282kW), Ismailia ch31 (20.7kW) **Nile Comedy:** Cairo ch30 (282kW) **Nile Culture:** Cairo ch43 (91kW) **Nile Drama:** Cairo ch34 (282kW) **Nile Family:** Cairo ch40 (89kW) **Nile Life:** Cairo ch22 (282kW) **Nile News:** Alexandria ch24 (74kW); Cairo ch26 (282kW), Barnis ch26 (79.4kW), Sohag ch29 (79.4kW), Ismailia ch29V (79.4kW), Nag Hammadi ch35 (79.4kW), Qena ch36 (79.4kW), Quseir ch40 (79.4kW), Suez ch42 (79.4kW), Asyut ch43 (79.4kW), Tanta ch45 (79.4kW), Ras Sedr ch46 (79.4kW), Port Said ch54V (79.4kW) **Nile Sports:** Suez ch21 (79.4kW), Sohag ch23 (340kW), Luxor ch25 (69.2kW), Sharm El Sheikh ch29 (79.4kW), Hurghada ch32V (79.4kW), Qena ch33 (88.1kW), Cairo ch38 (316kW), Port Said ch38V (79.4kW), Ismailia ch35V (79.4kW), El Minya ch42V (56kW), Beni Suef ch53V (43kW0. Asyut ch51 (115kW).
**Maspero Zaman:** Cairo ch24 (282kW).
(+ txs below 5kW; Pol=H exc. where indicated)

**DTT Tx Networks** (under construction)
**Tx Operator:** ERTU **M1:** multiprgr **Tx:** ch32 (Cairo 50kW) + MFN **M2:** multiprgr **Tx:** ch36 (Cairo 30kW) + MFN

**Systems:** ISDB-T [A]; § NTSC-M [A]

**National Stations**
**TELEVISION EL SALVADOR (TVES) (CANAL 10) (Pub)** ✉ Ap. Postal No. 104, Neuva San Salvador ☎ +503 2280499 ▤ +503 2280973 **E:** tydiez@es.com.sv **W:** www.tencanal10.tv **Txs:** ch10 (SFN). – **CANAL 12 (Comm)** ✉ Carretera Panaméricana #12, Antiguo Custatlan, La Libertad, San Salvador ☎ +503 25601212 ▤ +503 25101222 **E:** canal12@canal12.com.sv **W:** www.canal12.com.sv **Txs:** ch12 (SFN). – **TELECORPORACIÓN SALVADOREÑA (TCS) (Comm)** ✉ Alameda Manuel Enrique Araújo, Edifício Canales 2, 4 y 6, San Salvador ☎ +503 22092000 ▤ +503 22092065 **W:** www.esmitv.com **L.P:** CEO: Boris Eserski. **Chs:** Teledos, Canal Cuatro, Canal Seis. **Txs:** Teledos ch2 (SFN), Canal Cuatro ch4 (SFN), Canal Seis ch6 (SFN). – **AGAPE TV (CANAL 8) (Rlg)** ✉ Calle Gerardo Barrios No. 1511, Col. Cucumacayán, Santa Salvador ☎ +503 22812828 ▤ +503 22110799 **E:** info@agapetv8.com **W:** www.agapetv8.com **Txs:** ch8 (SFN).

**Local Stations** not shown.

## EQUATORIAL GUINEA

**Systems:** DVB-T2 (MPEG4); § PAL-B/G [E]

**TELEVISIÓN GUINEA ECUATORIAL (TVGE) (Pub)** ✉ Calle 3 Augusto, Malabo ☎ +240 222515335 **E:** info@rtvge.tv **W:** www.rtvge.tv **L.P:** DG: Luis Ndong Ovono – **ASONGA TELEVISIÓN (Comm)** ✉ Bata **W:** www.facebook.com/radiotelevisionasonga.

**DTT Tx Network**
**Tx Operator:** Startimes **M(partly⊘):** multiprgr **Txs:** MFN

## ERITREA

**System:** PAL-B/G [E]

**ERITREA TELEVISION (ERI-TV) (Gov)** ✉ Asmara ☎ +291 1 116033 ▤ +291 1 124847 **E:** aslmelashe@yahoo.com **W:** www.eri.tv **L.P:** DG: Asmelash Abraha **Chs:** ERI-TV1, ERI-TV2, ERI-TV3 **Txs:** ERI-TV1: (Pol.=H) Asmara ch5 (5kW), Assab ch11 (5kW) & relay txs. **ERI-TV2:** (-). **ERI-TV3:** (-).

## ESTONIA

**Systems:** DVB-T (MPEG4), DVB-T2 (MPEG4) [E]

**EESTI TELEVISIOON (ETV) (Pub)** ✉ Faehlmanni 12, 15029 Tallinn ☎ +372 6284133 **E:** etv@etv.ee **W:** etv.err.ee **L.P:** Chmn (ERR): Margus Allikmaa. **Chs:** ETV, ETV2, ETV+ – **TALLINNA TV (TTV) (Municipal)** ✉ Rävala pst 12, 10143 Tallinn ☎ +372 6005523 **E:** info@tallinnatv.eu **W:** www.tallinnatv.eu **L.P:** Chmn: Allan Alaküla – **ALL MEDIA EESTI (Comm)** ✉ Peterburi tee 81, 11415 Tallinn ☎ +372 6220200 **L.P:** CEO: Priit Leito **Chs:** TV3, TV6 – **EESTI MEEDIA (Comm)** ✉ Maakri 23a, 10145 Tallinn ☎ +372 6662350 **E:** eesti-meedia@eestimeedia.ee **W:** www.eestimeedia.ee **L.P:** CEO: Sven Nuutmanni **Chs:** Kanal 2, Kanal 11, Kanal 12, MyHits.

**DTT Tx Networks** (DVB-T except where indicated)
**Tx Operator:** Levira AS **W:** www.levira.ee **M1:** ETV, ETV2, ETV+, Kanal 2⊘, Tallinna TV **M2⊘:** Kanal 12, TV6, Sony TV, Sony Turbo, Discovery, Animal Planet, History, Kidzone TV, Eurosport, Setana Sports, TV3+, PBK Estonia, NTV Mir **M3⊘:** Kanal 11, Euronews, Fox Life, Fox, Filmzone, Filmzone+, ID Xtra, National Geographic, Pingviniukas, Eurosport 2, MyHits, TLC, Hustler TV **M6:** France 24, RTL Television⊘, Travel⊘, RTR Planeta⊘, REN TV, Estonia TV3⊘ **M7 (DVB-T2):** ETV HD, ETV2 HD, Tallinna TV HD.

| Location | M1 | M2 | M3 | M6 | M7 | kW |
|---|---|---|---|---|---|---|
| Ellamaa | 28 | - | - | - | - | 8.8 |
| Koeru | 39 | 27 | 43 | 44 | 41 | 5/2x1.6/6/2.5 |
| Kohtla-Nõmme | 33 | 34 | 31 | 29 | 48 | 15/4x2 |
| Pehka | 28V | - | - | - | - | 6.6 |
| Pärnu | 26 | 34 | 36 | 32 | 24 | 18/2x20/19/7 |
| Tallinn (TV-tower) | 28 | 25 | 45 | 30 | 42 | 19/2x15/20/8.5 |
| Valgjärve | 23 | 40 | 43 | 44 | 35 | 20/2x14/19.5/8 |

+ sites with txs below 5kW **NB:** Mux 4&5 currently not assigned.

## ESWATINI

**System:** DVB-T2 (MPEG4) [E]

**ESWATINI TELEVISION AUTHORITY (ETVA) (Pub)** ✉ Private Bag A146, Mbabane ☎ +268 24043036 ▤ +268 24042093 **E:** info@swazitv.co.sz **W:** www.swazitv.co.sz **L.P:** Chair: Nozizwe Mulela.

**DTT Tx Network**
**Tx Operator:** Multichoice Eswatini **M(partly⊘):** multiprgr **Txs:** MFN

## ETHIOPIA

**Systems:** DVB-T2 (MPEG4) [E]; § PAL-B/G [E] ⇩2020

**National Station**
**ETHIOPIAN BROADCASTING CORP. (EBC) (Pub)** ✉ P.O.Box 5544, Addis Ababa ☎ +251 11 5505483 ▤ +251 11 5505174 **W:** www.ebc.et **L.P:** GM: Berhane Kidanemariam **Chs (terr.):** EBC1, EBC2, EBC3, reg. stns.

**Local Stations**
**Dire TV:** Dire Dawa **Harari TV:** Harar. **Oromia Radio & TV (ORTV):** P.O.Box 2919, Adama **Somali TV:** Jijiga.

**DTT Tx Network**
**Tx Operator:** EBC **Mux:** EBC1, EBC2, EBC3, EBC4 **Txs:** ch42 (Addis Ababa 10kW) & MFN.

## FALKLAND ISLANDS (UK)

**Systems:** DVB-T (MPEG4) [E]

**BFBS-TV Relay (Serving British Military)** ✉ BFBS Falkland Islands, Mt. Pleasant, BFPO 655 ☎ +500 32179 ▤ +500 32193 **E:** falklands@bfbs.com **M:** BBC One*, BBC Two/CBBC*, ITV*, BFBS Extra/Cbeebies*, Sky News, Nepali TV* (*=time-shifted) ⌘ BFBS R. (Falkland Islands), BFBS R.2, BFBS Gurkha R. **Txs:** ch27 (SFN).

## FAROE ISLANDS (Denmark)

**System:** DVB-T (MPEG4) [E]

**KRINGVARP FØROYA - SJÓNVARP (KVF) (Pub)** ✉ P.O.Box 1299, 110 Tórshavn ☎ +298 347500 **E:** kringvarp@kvf.fo **W:** kvf.fo **L.P:** CEO: Ivan Hentze Niclasen – **IKTUS (Rlg)** ✉ c/o Anja Hansen, Landsvegur 9, 511 Gøtugjógv **E:** iktus@iktus.fo **W:** iktus.fo.

**DTT Tx Networks**
**Licensee Mux 1-4:** Televarpið ✉ P.O.Box 3128, 110 Tórshavn ☎ +298 340340 **E:** televarp@televarp.fo **W:** tv.fo **M1⊘:** DR Ultra, TV3 HD, Kanal 4, Kanal 5, Visjon Norge, National Geographic, BBC Brit, BBC World News **M2(⊘exc.*):** KVF*, DR1 HD, DR2, DR3, NRK1, TV3, TV3 Puls, TV2 Charlie **M3⊘:** RUV, DR Ramasjang/Viasat Film Family, Viasat Film Action, Viasat Series, Discovery, MTV, Nickelodeon/VH1 **M4(⊘exc.*):** Rás 1*, TV2 HD, TV3 Sport, TV3 Max, Disney Channel, Animal Planet, Europort 1. **Licensee Mux 5:** R2 Net ✉ Søldarfjarðarvefur 11, 660 Søldarfjørður ☎ +298 559997 **E:** r2net@r2net.fo **W:** r2net.fo **M5:** 10'arin, IKTUS.

| Location | M1 | M2 | M3 | M4 | M5 | kW |
|---|---|---|---|---|---|---|
| Klakkur | 22 | 24 | 26 | 28 | 31 | 0.25 |
| Knúkur | 37 | 39 | 41 | 43 | 31 | 0.04 |
| Stongin | 52 | 50 | 48 | 46 | 34 | 0.04 |
| Støðlafjall | 52 | 50 | 48 | 46 | - | 0.04 |
| Velbastaður | 52V | 50V | 48V | 46V | - | 0.04 |

+ repeaters.

## FIJI

**Systems:** DVB-T2 (MPEG4) [E]; § PAL-B [NZ] ⇩2019

**National Stations**
**FIJI BROADCASTING CORP. (FBC) (Pub)** ✉ 69 Gladstone Rd, Suva ☎ +679 3314333 ▤ +679 3220990 **E:** infocenter@fbc.com.fj **W:** www.fbc.com.fj **L.P:** CEO: Riyaz Sayed-Khaiyum. **Ch:** FBC TV – **FIJI TV (Comm)** ✉ 20 Gorrie Street, Suva ☎ +679 3305100 ▤ +679 3304630 **E:** fijitv@is.com.fj **W:** fijione.tv **L.P:** CEO (Fiji TV Ltd): Karen Lobendahn. – **MAI TV (Comm)** ✉ Grantham Rd, Suva ☎ +679 3275051 **E:** info@tv.com.fj **W:** www.facebook.com/maitvfiji **L.P:** CEO: Richard Broadbridge.

**Local Stations** not shown.

**DTT Tx Network**
**Tx Operator:** Walesi Ltd **M:** FBC TV, Fiji TV, Mai TV; Sky Pacific channels⊘**Txs:** MFN

## FINLAND

**Systems:** DVB-T2 (MPEG4) [E]; § DVB-T (MPEG2)

**National Stations**
**YLEISRADIO OY (Pub)** ✉ Uutiskatu 5, 00240 Helsinki ☎ +358 9 14801 **W:** www.yle.fi **LP:** CEO: Merja Ylä-Anttila **Chs:** Yle TV1, Yle TV2, Yle Teema & Fem – **ALFA TV (Comm)** ✉ Jäspilänkatu 2B, 04250 Kerava ☎ +358 10 3273000 **E:** info@alfatv.fi **W:** www.alfatv. fi **LP:** Chmn/CEO: Hannu Haukka – **CANAL DIGITAL (Comm)** ✉ P.O.Box 2, 00381 Helsinki ☎ +358 9 54264200 ▤ +358 9 54264270 **E:** asiakaspalvelu@canaldigital.fi **W:** www.canaldigital.fi – **MTV OY (Comm)** ✉ Ilmalankatu 2, 00033 MTV ☎ +358 10 300300 **W:** www. mtv3.fi **LP:** CEO (MTV3 Media): Jarkko Nordlund **Chs (terr.):** MTV3, MTV3 Max, MTV3 Sport, AVA, Jim, Sub – **NELONEN (Comm)** ✉ Töölönlahdenkatu 2, 00100 Helsinki ☎ +358 9 4545414 **W:** www. nelonen.fi **LP:** Pres (Nelonen Media): Kari Laakso. **Chs (terr.):** Nelonen, Liv, Ruutu+ Urheilu, Ruutu+ Dokkarit, Ruutu+ Lapset, Ruutu+ Leffat ja Sarjat – **DISCOVERY NETWORKS FINLAND OY (Comm)** ✉ Tallberginkatu 1C, 00180 Helsinki ☎ +358 20 7870850 **E:** info_ dnf@discovery.com **W:** discoverynetworks.fi **Chs:** TV5, Kutonen, Frii.

**DTT Tx Networks** (DVB-T2 except where noted)
**Licensee: Mux 1-3,5+6** Digita Oy **W:** www.digita.fi **M1 (DVB-T):** Yle TV1, Yle TV2, Yle Teema & Fem, AVA, MTV3, Nelonen, 0700 1 1111 deitti, Estradi **M2✪:** Animal Planet, C More First, C More Series, C More Hits, Investigation Discovery, Viasat History, Discovery, Nick Jr, MTV, Ruutu+ Dokkarit **M3 (DVB-T):** TLC, National Geographic, Fox, Frii, Aito Iskelmä Harju & Pöntinen, Kutonen, TV5, Viacom Channel **M5 (DVB-T):** Sub, Liv, Hero, AlfaTV, Jim **M6✪:** Viasat Sport, Viasat Hockey, Viasat Golf, Viasat Urheilu, Viasat NHL Xtra 8, Nat Geo Wild, C More Sport 2, Eurosport 2, Disney XD, Disney Jr, Ruutu+ Urheilu 1, C More Juniori, C More MAX, C More Sport 1, Eurosport, Ruutu+ Lapset, Hustler, Blue Hustler, Viasat Film Premiere, Ruutu+ Urheilu 3-7, Viasat NHL Xtra 1-7, Ruutu+ Urheilu 2, Viasat Jalkapallo, Viasat Jääkiekko, Disney Channel, Ruutu+ Leffat ja Sarjat. – **Licensee Mux 7-9:** DNA Oy **W:** www.dna.fi **M7:** Yle TV1 HD, Yle TV2 HD, Yle Teema & Fem HD, MTV3 HD **M8✪:** MTV MAX HD, MTV Sport 1 HD, MTV Sport 2 HD, Ruutu+ Urheilu 1 HD, Ruutu+ Urheilu 2 HD **M9✪:** C More First HD, Viasat Film Comedy HD, Viasat Golf HD, Viasat Sport Finland HD, Viasat Sport HD.

| Location | M1 | M2 | M3 | M5 | M6 | M7 | M8 | M9 | kW |
|---|---|---|---|---|---|---|---|---|---|
| Anjalankoski | 22 | 44 | 26 | 39 | 41 | - | - | - | 50 |
| Espoo | 32 | 43 | 46 | 26 | 39 | 6 | 8 | 5 | 5x50/3x1.9 |
| Eurajoki | 38 | 36 | 42 | 37 | 33 | 9 | 7 | 6 | 5x50/3x1.9 |
| Fiskars | 32 | - | 46 | 23 | - | - | - | - | 10 |
| Haapavesi | 34 | - | 44 | 24 | - | - | - | - | 50 |
| Iisalmi | 26 | - | - | 38 | - | - | - | - | 30 |
| Inari | 48 | - | - | - | - | - | - | - | 12 |
| Joutseno | 47 | 44 | 36 | 32 | 41 | - | - | - | 50 |
| Jyväskylä | 30 | 27 | 28 | 22 | 41 | 11 | 9 | 5 | 5x50/3x3.5 |
| Kerimäki | 30 | - | 33 | 37 | - | - | - | - | 50 |
| Kiihtelysvaara | 26 | - | - | - | - | - | - | - | 30 |
| Koli | 25 | 40 | 47 | - | - | - | - | - | 60 |
| Kruunupyy | 30 | 40 | 41 | 28 | 25 | - | - | - | 50 |
| Kuopio | 24 | 32 | 39 | 46 | 41 | 6 | 7 | 8 | 5x50/3x3.5 |
| Lahti | 33 | 37 | 40 | 48 | 42 | 7 | 9 | 5 | 5x50/2x3/2 |
| Lapua | 38 | 40 | 33 | 48 | 25 | 7 | 9 | 5 | 5x50/2x3/2 |
| Mikkeli | 29 | - | 25 | 38 | - | 10 | 9 | 12 | 3x50/3x3.4 |
| Oulu | 41 | 25 | 28 | 37 | 33 | - | - | - | 50 |
| Pernaja | 23 | - | - | 36 | - | - | - | - | 10 |
| Pihtipudas | 23 | - | 43 | 45 | - | - | - | - | 80 |
| Posio | 31 | - | - | - | - | - | - | - | 14 |
| Pyhätunturi | 24 | - | 41 | - | - | - | - | - | 16 |
| Pyhävuori | 28 | - | 35 | - | - | - | - | - | 50 |
| Rovaniemi | 43 | - | 46 | - | - | - | - | - | 10 |
| Ruka | 33 | - | 28 | - | - | - | - | - | 10 |
| Taivalkoski | 32 | - | 38 | - | - | - | - | - | 14 |
| Tammela | 22 | 31 | 25 | 30 | 35 | - | - | - | 60 |
| Tampere | 34 | 43 | 44 | 46 | 24 | - | - | - | 50 |
| Tervola | 40 | - | 44 | - | - | - | - | - | 18 |
| Turku | 29 | 36 | 47 | 41 | 33 | - | - | - | 5x100/50 |
| Vaasa | 38 | - | 48 | - | 11 | 7 | 5 | - | 2x10/3x4.4 |
| Vuokatti | 30 | - | 27 | 35 | - | - | - | - | 80 |
| Ylläs | 30 | - | 36 | - | - | - | - | - | 14 |
| Ähtäri | 26 | - | - | - | - | - | - | - | 50 |

+ sites with txs below 10kW.
**Licensee Local Mux:** Anvia (Elisa) **W:** elisa.fi/anvia **Mux✪:** SVT1, SVT2, SVTB/SVT24, SVT Kunskapskanalen, TV3, TV4, När-TV, Krs-TV **Txs:** ch31 (Vaasa 3.5kW + SFN), ch33 (SFN), ch35 (SFN).

### Åland
**ÅLANDS RADIO/TV AB (Pub)** ✉ Ålandsvägen 24, 22101 Mariehamn ☎ +358 18 26060 ▤ +358 18 26520 **E:** info@radiotv.ax **W:** www.radiotv.ax **LP:** Editor-in-Chief: Camilla Karlsson-Henderson **Ch:** Ålandskanalen.

**DTT Tx Network (DVB-T exc. where stated))**
**Licensee:** Ålands Radio/TV AB **M1:** SVT1, SVT2, SVTB/SVT24, SVT Kunskapskanalen, Ålandskanalen **M2:** Yle TV1, Yle TV2, Yle Teema & Fem, TV4 **M3:** SVT1 HD, SVT2 HD, Yle 1 HD, Yle 2 HD, Yle Teema & Fem HD TV1. **Txs: M1:** ch25 (Smedsböle 30kW) **M2:** ch35 (Smedsböle 30kW) **M3 (DVB-T2):** ch28 (Smedsböle 30kW).

## FRANCE

**System:** DVB-T (MPEG4) [E]

**National Stations**
**ARTE (Pub)** ✉ 8 rue Marceau, 92785 Issy-les-Moulineaux CEDEX 9 ☎ +33 155007777 **W:** www.arte.tv **LP:** Pres: Véronique Cayla – **FRANCE 24 (Pub)** ✉ 80 rue Camille Desmoulins, 92130 Issy-les-Moulineaux ☎ +33 184228484 **W:** www.france24.com **LP:** Chair/CEO (France Médias Monde): Marie-Christine Saragosse **NB:** Terrestrially available via Mux 15 in Paris and in all French overseas territories. – **FRANCE TÉLÉVISIONS (Pub)** ✉ (HQ/France 2-4/Franceinfo) 7 esplanade Henri-de-France, 75907 Paris CEDEX 15 ☎ +33 156226000 **W:** www.francetelevisions.fr; www. france.tv; france3-regions.francetvinfo.fr (France 3 regional stns); www. la1ere.fr (La 1ère) **LP:** CEO: Delphine Ernotte Cunci **Chs:** France 2-5, France 3 regional stns, France Ô, Franceinfo, La 1ère (for French overseas territories) **France 5:** ✉ 10 rue Horace Vernet, 92123 Issy-les-Moulineaux CEDEX 9 ☎ +33 156229191. **France Ô/La 1ère:** ✉ 35-37 rue Danton, 92240 Malakoff ☎ +33 155227100 – **LA CHAÎNE PARLEMENTAIRE - ASSEMBLÉE NATIONALE (LCP-AN) (Pub)** ✉ 106 rue de l'Université, 75007 Paris ☎ +33 140639050 **W:** www.lcp.fr/le-direct **LP:** Pres: Bertrand Delais – **PUBLIC SÉNAT (Pub)** ✉ 92 boulevard Raspail, 75006 Paris ☎ +33 142344400 **W:** www.publicsenat.fr/direct **LP:** Chmn/ CEO: Emmanuel Kessler – **GROUPE CANAL+ (C8/CANAL+*/CNEWS/ CSTAR/PLANETE+) (Comm)** ✉ 1 place du spectacle, 92863 Issy-les-Moulineaux CEDEX 9 ☎ +33 171353535 **LP:** Chmn: Jean-Christophe Thiery **W:** www.vivendi.com/activites/canal-groupe; www.canalplus.fr; www.c8.fr; www.cnews.fr; www.cstar.fr; www.planeteplus.com (*=Chs (terr.): Canal+, Canal+ Cinéma, Canal+ Sport) – **GROUPE M6 (6TER/ M6/PARIS PREMIÈRE/W9) (Comm)** ✉ 89-91 avenue Charles de Gaulle, 92200 Neuilly-sur-Seine CEDEX ☎ +33 141926666 **W:** www. groupem6.fr; www.6play.fr **LP:** Chmn: Nicolas de Tavernost – **GROUPE NEXTRADIOTV (BFM TV/RMC DÉCOUVERTE/RMC STORY) (Comm)** ✉ 12 rue d'Oradour-sur-Glane, 75740 Paris CEDEX 15 ☎ +33 171191181 **W:** www.nextradiotv.com; www.bfmtv.com; rmcdecouverte.bfmtv.com; www.rmcstory.fr **LP:** Chmn: Alain Weill – **GROUPE NRJ (CHERIE 25/ NRJ12) (Comm)** ✉ 46-50 avenue Théophile Gautier, 75016 Paris ☎ +33 140713929 **W:** www.nrjgroup.fr; www.nrj-play.fr **LP:** COO: Guillaume Perrier – **GROUPE TF1 (HD1/LCI/TF1/TFX/TMC) (Comm)** ✉ 1 quai du Point-du-Jour, 92656 Boulogne-Billancourt CEDEX ☎ +33 141411234 **W:** www.groupe-tf1.fr; www.tf1.fr; www.lci.fr **LP:** Chmn/CEO: Gilles Pélisson – **GULLI (Comm)** ✉ 28 rue François 1er, 75008 Paris ☎ +33 156365555 **W:** www.gulli.fr **LP:** CEO: Caroline Cochaux – **L'ÉQUIPE (Comm)** ✉ 4 cours de l'Île Seguin, 92102 Boulogne-Billancourt CEDEX ☎ +33 140932020 **W:** www.lequipe.fr/lachainelequipe.

**Local/Regional Stations** (~ =time-shared on Paris ch28)
Txs: (a-u) or (-) = via txs of Mux 1 ("a-u" via txs of 10kW & above, see main tx table; "-" via txs below 10kW, txs not shown); (15) = via txs of Regional Mux 15 (see main tx table; only txs at main sites shown).
**Alsace 20** (a): 333A avenue de Colmar, 67100 Strasbourg. **Angers Télé** (-): 3 rue de la Rame, 49100 Angers. **Azur TV** (q) / **Province Azur** (s) / **Var Azur** (t): 16 avenue Edouard Grinda, 06200 Nice. **BDM TV** (15²-): 51 avenue de Flandre, 75019 Paris. **BFM Paris** (n): 12 rue d'Oradour-sur-Glane, 75015 Paris CEDEX 15. **BIP TV** (-): Rue des Noués Chaudes, 36100 Issoudun. **Canal 32** (15³): 7 rue Raymond Aron, 10120 Saint-André-les-Verger. **D!CI TV** (-): ZA La Grande Île Nord, 05230 Chorges. **Demain IDF** (15²): 11 rue Erard, 75012 Paris. **Grand Lille TV** (-)/ **Grand Littoral TV** (r): 9 rue Archimède, 59200 Villeneuve-d'Ascq. **IDF1** (15²-): 7 rue des Bretons, 93210 La Plaine Saint-Denis. **LCN (La Chaîne Normande)** (b): 4 passage de la Luciline, Le Vauban - Immeuble A, 76000 Rouen. **LDVTV (Léonard De Vinci Télévision)** (-): Lycée Léonard de Vinci, Le Mazel, 43120 Monistrol-sur-Loire. **LMTV Sarthe** (c): 21-25 rue Pasteur, 72000 Le Mans. **Matélé** (o): Espace Créatis, 6 avenue Archimède, 02100 Saint-Quentin. **Mirabelle TV** (d): 2 rue Saint-Vincent, 57140 Woippy. **Tébéo** (f): 19 rue Jean Macé, 29200 Brest. **TébéSud** (j): 8 rue Auguste Nayel, 56100 Lorient. **Télénantes** (e): 10 rue Voltaire, 44000 Nantes. **Télé Bocal** (15²-): 10B rue Bisson, 75020 Paris. **TéléGrenoble** (-): Le

Palladium, 5 rue Eugène Faure, 38000 Grenoble. **Télé Paese** (-): 36 chemin de Palazzi, 20220 Sant-Reparata-di-Balagn. **TLC (Télévision Locale du Choletais)** (15¹): ZI la Bergerie, rue Ampère, 49280 La Séguinière. **TLM (Télé Lyon Métropole)** (-): 227 cours Lafayette, 69006 Lyon CEDEX 7. **TL7 (Télévision Loire 7)** (-): Rue Jules Verne, 42530 Saint-Genest-Lerpt. **TV Sud Camargue-Cévennes** (-) / **TV Sud Montpellier** (p) / **TV Sud PO** (-)/ **TV Sud Toulouse** (-): 14 allée du Piot, 30660 Gallargues-le-Montueux. **TV Tours Val de Loire** (h): 232 avenue de Grammont, 37019 Tours CEDEX. **TV Vendée** (15¹): ZI le Séjour, 13 rue Thomas Edison, 85170 Dompierre-sur-Yon. **TVPI** (m): 1 rue Contresta, 64210 Bidart. **TV7 Bordeaux** (i): 73 avenue Thiers, 33100 Bordeaux. **TV8 Mont-Blanc** (-): 170 rue des Lys, 74330 Epagny-Metz-Tess. **TVR** (g): 19 rue de la Quintaine, 35000 Rennes. **Via Grand Paris** (15²): 4, rue de la Prairie, 95000 Cergy. **Vosges Télévision Images Plus** (k): 2 rue de la Chipotte, 88007 Epinal **Wéo Nord Pas de Calais** (l) / **Wéo Picardie** (u): 8 place du Général de Gaulle, 59023 Lille CEDEX.

**DTT Tx Networks** (HD except where noted)
**Licensee Mux 1:** Société de gestion du réseau R1 ⌧ 7 esplanade Henri-de-France, 75015 Paris ☎ +33 156226000 **M:** France 2, France 3 incl. reg prgrs, France 4, France Ô (SD), Franceinfo (SD), local/regional stns (SD) – **Licensee Mux 2:** Nouvelles télévisions numériques ⌧ 1 place du Spectacle, 92130 Issy-les-Moulineaux ☎ +33 171354839 **M:** BFM TV, C8, CNEWS, CStar, Gulli – **Licensee Mux 3:** Compagnie du numérique hertzien ⌧1 place du Spectacle, 92863 Issy-les-Moulineaux ☎ +33 171350151 **M✪:** Canal+, Canal+ Cinéma, Canal+ Sport, LCI (SD), Paris Première (SD), Planète+ – **Licensee Mux 4:** Multi 4 ⌧ 89 avenue Charles de Gaulle, 92200 Neuilly-sur-Seine ☎ +33 141926664 **M:** 6ter, Arte, France 5, M6, W9 – **Licensee Mux 6:** SMR6 ⌧ 1 quai du Point-du-Jour, 92100 Boulogne-Billancourt ☎ +33 141411234 **M:** LCP-AN/Public Sénat, NRJ12, NT1, TF1, TMC – **Licensee Mux 7:** MHD7 ⌧1 quai du Point-du-Jour, 92100 Boulogne-Billancourt ☎ +33 141411234 **M:** Chérie 25, HD1, L'Équipe, RMC Découverte, RMC Story – **Licensees Mux 15 (Local/Regional):** various local/regional licensees **M:** various local/regional stns (SD) (depending on region, cf. chapter "Local/Regional Stations" 15¹²³).

| Location | 1 | 2 | 3 | 4 | 6 | 7 | 15 kW |
|---|---|---|---|---|---|---|---|
| Abbeville | 57u | 25 | 28 | 55 | 39 | 22 | - 79 |
| Ajaccio | 21 | 37 | 34 | 44 | 31 | 24 | - 65 |
| Amiens | 41u | 60 | 49 | 47 | 44 | 59 | - 40 |
| Aurillac | 54 | 45 | 43 | 51 | 48 | 39 | - 40 |
| Autun | 48 | 42 | 32 | 35 | 37 | 39 | - 40 |
| Auxerre | 55 | 60 | 49 | 31 | 44 | 23 | - 40 |
| Avignon | 45 | 36 | 33 | 47 | 42 | 39 | - 50/32/4x50 |
| Bar-le-Duc | 48 | 30 | 44 | 22 | 35 | 34 | - 13 |
| Bastia | 21 | 37 | 34 | 44 | 31 | 24 | - 32/2x36/32/36/32 |
| Bayonne | 42m | 46 | 45 | 39 | 30 | 43 | 33⁶ 6x25/1 |
| Bergerac | 33 | 41 | 56 | 31 | 58 | 59 | - 40 |
| Besançon (Lomont) | 43 | 44 | 41 | 23 | 47 | 26 | - 50 |
| Besançon (Montf.) | 43 | 44 | 41 | 23 | 47 | 26 | - 25 |
| Bordeaux | 23i | 37 | 45 | 39 | 30 | 26 | - 63/36/4x63 |
| Bourges | 56 | 46 | 43 | 24 | 36 | 33 | - 63 |
| Brest | 43f | 58 | 35 | 39 | 34 | 46 | - 191/145/107/141/145/100 |
| Caen | 25 | 42 | 22 | 29 | 28 | 30 | - 100/50/100/94/2x100 |
| Carcassonne | 32 | 31 | 43 | 42 | 46 | 41 | - 50/28/6x50 |
| Chambéry | 47 | 29 | 27 | 25 | 26 | 39 | - 13 |
| Charleville-Méz. | 44 | 36 | 26 | 34 | 23 | 40 | - 100/27/50/54/2x50 |
| Chartres | 47 | 21 | 49 | 40 | 44 | 55 | - 25 |
| Cherbourg-Octev. | 35 | 34 | 59 | 37 | 36 | 30 | - 10/7/3x11/10 |
| Clermont-Ferrand | 25 | 47 | 22 | 30 | 28 | 29 | - 50 |
| Corte | 21 | 37 | 34 | 44 | 31 | 24 | - 10/6/4x10 |
| Dijon | 29 | 21 | 27 | 33 | 37 | 39 | - 32 |
| Dunkerque | 42r | 52 | 27 | 45 | 21 | 25 | - 13/6/4x13 |
| Gex | 45 | 21 | 27 | 55 | 24 | 53 | - 63 |
| Hirson | 48o | 32 | 27 | 55 | 54 | 39 | - 80/2x22/3x80 |
| Laval | 33 | 58 | 43 | 57 | 51 | 35 | - 9/14/3x10/8 |
| Le Havre | 43 | 44 | 57 | 32 | 46 | 47 | - 20/16/6/2x20/13 |
| Le Mans | 26c | 34 | 22 | 59 | 36 | 35 | - 3x79/66/79/32 |
| Lille | 24l | 23 | 27 | 26 | 21 | 30 | - 79/20/79/14/2x79 |
| Limoges | 49 | 47 | 50 | 34 | 29 | 46 | - 100/69/4x100 |
| Longwy | 25d | 31 | 47 | 22 | 33 | 39 | - 20/10/5/3x10 |
| Lyon | 43 | 44 | 41 | 40 | 46 | 23 | - 126 |
| Marseille | 23s | 38 | 30 | 35 | 26 | 29 | - 2x100/32/3x100 |
| Metz | 36d | 31 | 47 | 22 | 29 | 34 | - 100/87/79/2x85/65 |
| Montpellier | 40p | 52 | 50 | 53 | 56 | 41 | - 100/32/4x100 |
| Mulhouse | 24a | 21 | 41 | 37 | 27 | 45 | - 100 |
| Nancy | 28 | 26 | 43 | 22 | 33 | 34 | - 50/31/4x50 |
| Nantes | 47e | 23 | 30 | 45 | 29 | 32 | 38¹ 98/2x65/83/2x65/30 |
| Niort | 25 | 27 | 22 | 40 | 36 | 43 | - 71 |
| Paris | 35n | 25 | 22 | 30 | 32 | 42 | 28² 50/51/50/51/2x50/5 |
| Parthenay | 48 | 31 | 33 | 21 | 39 | 43 | - 13 |
| Reims | 29 | 36 | 43 | 46 | 45 | 40 | - 79 |
| Rennes | 21g | 40 | 27 | 49 | 24 | 46 | - 79 |
| Rouen | 26b | 34 | 33 | 40 | 23 | 37 | - 40/26/10/3x40 |

| Location | 1 | 2 | 3 | 4 | 6 | 7 | 15 kW |
|---|---|---|---|---|---|---|---|
| Saint-Raphaël | 39q | 54 | 28 | 25 | 48 | 45 | - 63 |
| Sarrebourg | 23d | 26 | 47 | 22 | 25 | 34 | - 50/47/4x50 |
| Sens | 47 | 50 | 49 | 31 | 44 | 23 | 59* 5x10/0.65 |
| Strasbourg | 48a | 26 | 47 | 22 | 25 | 43 | - 50/2x20/10/2x20 |
| Toulon | 43t | 22 | 28 | 25 | 48 | 29 | - 10 |
| Toulouse | 21 | 38 | 24 | 27 | 36 | 34 | - 50 |
| Tours | 42h | 23 | 45 | 24 | 29 | 58 | - 50/42/4x50 |
| Troyes | 41 | 21 | 28 | 24 | 25 | 23 | 27³ 6x100/2 |
| Ussel | 23 | 27 | 24 | 55 | 36 | 40 | - 10 |
| Vannes | 57j | 25 | 53 | 48 | 50 | 28 | - 20/23/2x20/22/20 |
| Verdun | 25d | 31 | 47 | 22 | 33 | 39 | - 100/4x65/100 |
| Vittel | 42k | 39 | 29 | 37 | 27 | 45 | - 2x10/7/3x10 |

+ sites with txs below 10kW; 1-7=National Muxes 1-4/6/7; °=rel. Euskal Telebista (ETB) Spain (ETB1-3, ETB SAT) *) France 3 Ile de France
**NB:** In preparation for the re-assignment of the 700MHz band to mobile services, txs on chs 49-60 will gradually move to lower chs until 30 June 2019 – **DVB-T2 (HEVC) technical trial:** ch26 (Paris/Tour Eiffel 1kW) (Licensee: TDF).

## FRENCH GUIANA

**System:** DVB-T (MPEG4) [E]

**GUYANE LA 1ÈRE (Pub)** ⌧ Boulevard du docteur Lama, F-97354 Rémire-Montjoly ☎ +594 594256700 **W:** guyane.la1ere.fr **LP:** Dir: Marie-Laure Phinera-Hort – **ANTENNE TÉLÉ GUYANE (ATV) (Comm)** ⌧ Boute de la Madeleine, Immeuble Verriers, F-97300 Cayenne ☎ +594 594256940 **W:** www.myatg.tv **LP:** Pres: Marc Ho-Ha-Chuck.– **KVT (Comm)** ⌧ 100, avenue Boudinot, F-97310 Kourou ☎ +594 594321541 **E:** ktv.tnt@gmail.com **LP:** Pres: Emmanuel Toko.

**DTT Tx Networks**
**Tx Operator:** TDF **Mux:** Guyane la 1ère, France 2-5, France Ô, France 24, Arte, ATV, KVT **Txs:** MFN.

## FRENCH POLYNESIA

**System:** DVB-T (MPEG4) [E]

**POLYNÉSIE LA 1ÈRE (Pub)** ⌧ BP 60125, F-98702 Faa'a ☎ +33 689861616 **W:** polynesie.la1ere.fr **LP:** Dir: Gérald Prufer – **TAHITI NUI TV (TNTV) (Comm)** ⌧ BP 348, F-98713 Papeete ☎ +33 689473636 **E:** tntv@tntv.pf **W:** www.tntv.pf **DG:** Mateata Maamaatuaiahutapu.

**DTT Tx Networks**
**Tx Operator:** TDF **Mux:** Polynésie la 1ère, France 2-5, France Ô, France 24, Arte, TNTV **Txs:** MFN.

## FRENCH SO. & ANTARTIC LANDS

**NB:** No terrestrial TV station.

## GABON

**Systems:** DVB-T2 (MPEG4); § SECAM-K1 [VHF=K]

**GABON TÉLÉVISION (Gov)** ⌧ BP 10150, Libreville ☎ +241 1732152 ▤ +241 1732153 **E:** ggabontelevisions@gmail.com **Chs:** RTG1, RTG2. – **TV+ CHAÎNE 3 (Comm)** ⌧BP 8344, Libreville ☎ +241 1775740 ▤ +241 1729204.

**DTT Tx Networks**
**Tx Operator:** Startimes **Mux(partly ✪):** multiprgr **Txs:** MFN

## GALAPAGOS ISLANDS (Ecuador)

**System:** NTSC-M [A]

**CANAL MUNICIPAL (Pub)** ⌧ San Cristóbal **Tx:** ch7. – **TELE INSULAR (Comm)** ⌧ San Cristóbal **Tx:** ch9. – **TELE GALÁPAGOS (Rlg)** ⌧ Misión Franciscana, Puerto Baquerizo Moreno, Isla San Cristóbal, Galapagos, Ecuador ☎ +593 5 2520144 **Tx:** ch13.

## GAMBIA

**System:** DVB-T2 (MPEG4) [E]

**GAMBIA RADIO & TELEVISION SERVICES (GRTS) (Gov)** ⌧ P.O.Box 2380, Serekunda ☎ +220 4374251 ▤ +220 4374242 **E:** grts@gamtel.gm **W:** www.grts.gm **LP:** DG: Abdou MK Touray

**DTT Tx Network**
**Tx Operator:** Startimes **Mux(partly ✪):** multiprgr **Txs:** MFN

**Systems:** DVB-T2 (MPEG4) [E]

**National Stations**
**GEORGIAN PUBLIC BROADCASTER (Pub)** ✉ M. Kostava St. 68, 0171 Tbilisi ☎ +995 32 2362294 🖷 +995 32 2368665 **E:** info@gpb. ge **W:** www.gpb.ge **L.P:** DG:Vasil Maghlaperidze **Chs:** GPB TV1, GPB TV2. **Regional Station:** Ajara Radio & TV, Memed Abashidze Ave. 41, 6000 Batumi – **IMEDI TV (Comm)** ✉ Lubliana St. 5, 0159 Tbilisi ☎+995 32 2463041 **E:** contact@imedi.ge **W:** www.imedi.ge **Chs:** Imedi TV, GDS TV – **KOMEDIA TV (Comm)** ✉ Tbilisi – **RUSTAVI 2 (Comm)** ✉ Sandro Euli St.. Sa, 0186 Tbilisi ☎ +995 32 2201111 🖷 +995 32 2200012 **E:** tv@rustavi2.com **W:** rustavi2.com.

**Local Stations** not shown.

**DTT Tx Networks**
**Licensee Mux 1:** Georgian Teleradio Center **W:** www.tvrcenter.ge **M1:** GPB TV1 HD, GPB TV2, GPB Ajara TV **Licensee Mux 2-4** Stereo+ Ltd **M2:** Imedi TV HD, Rustavi 2, Marao Arkhi, Komedi Arkhi, GDS HD, Pirveli TV HD, Obiektivi TV, Iberia TV, Palitra News **M3:** Maestro TV, Stereo+ HD, Ertsulovneba, Silk, Kartuli Arkhi, Pirveli Gasartobi TV, Starvision, Ragbi TV, Saperavi TV, Enki Benki✪, Mult✪, Nauka 2.0✪ **M4✪:** Pervyy Kanal, RTR Planeta, TV 3, Ren TV, STS, TNT, Pyatnitsa!, Perec, Ru TV, Telekanal Oruzhe, Okhota i Rybalka, Cinema, Kinopremiera, Kinosemya, Kinohit, FOX, Setanta Sports, Setanta Sports+, Euronews 2, VH1, Baby TV, Nickelodeon, Discovery Channel, National Geographi, Nat Geo Wild, Russkaya Nots, Euronews, BBC World News **Txs: M1:** ch36 (Tbilisi) & MFN. **M2-4:** ch(-) (Tbilisi) & nationwide MFN. **Local licensees/muxes** not shown.

**ABKHAZIA**

**APSUA XÖYNTKARRATÄ TELERADIOKOMPANIA** ✉ V.Ardzinba St. 16, Sokhumi (mail via Russia) ☎ +7 840 2266144 🖷 +7 840 2266144 **E:** info@apsua.tv **W:** www.apsua.tv **L.P:** Dir: Alxas Colokwua

**DTT Tx Network**
**Licensee:** Ekran ABK **M1:** Apsua TV, Abaza TV, Pervyy Kanal, Rossiya 1, NTV, TV Tsentr, 5 Kanal, TV Zvezda, Rossiya K, Rossiya 24, Kuban 24V: **M2✪:** STS, TNT, Match!, Karusel, Che, Kinopokaz, Ohotnik i Rybolov, Teleputeshestviya, Match!Boets, Discovery Channel, Kanal Disney, HD Life **M3✪:** Sport 1, Ren TV, TV 3, Domashniy, RU TV, National Geographic, Nat Geo Wild.

**SOUTH OSSETIA**

**PTRK "IR"** ✉ Geroev St. 48, Tskhinvali (mail via Russia) ☎ +7 9974 451218 **E:** radio-ir@yandex.ru **L.P:** Dir: Robert Kulumbegov

**DTT Tx Network**
**Licensee:** RTRS **M1:** Rossiya 1, Rossiya 24, Rossiya K, Karusel, Match TV, Pervyy kanal, NTV, OTR, 5-kanal, TV Tsentr **M2:** Domashniy, TV Zvezda, Mir TV, Muz-TV, Pyatnitsa, REN TV, Spas, STS, TNT, TV-3 **M3:** PTRK "Ir" **Txs:**(-).

**System:** DVB-T (MPEG2), DVB-T2 (HEVC) [E]

**National Stations**
**ARBEITSGEMEINSCHAFT DER ÖFFENTLICH-RECHTLICHEN RUNDFUNKANSTALTEN DEUTSCHLANDS (ARD) (Pub)** ✉ Arnulfstrasse 42, 80335 München ☎ +49 89 590001 **L.P:** Chair: Ulrich Wilhelm **W:** www.ard.de, www.daserste.de **Chs (terr.):** Das Erste, regional stns, tagesschau24, One, Phoenix, KIKA (KIKA is produced jointly with ZDF). **NB.** ARD is the head organisation for the regional public service broadcasters: **Bayerischer Rundfunk (BR)**: Rundfunkplatz 1, 80335 München ☎ +49 89 59002433 **W:** www.br.de **Hessischer Rundfunk (HR)**: Bertramstrasse 8, 60320 Frankfurt ☎ + 49 69 1551 **W:** www.hr-online.de **Mitteldeutscher Rundfunk (MDR)**, Kantstrasse 71-73, 04275 Leipzig ☎ +49 341 22760 **W:** www. mdr.de **Norddeutscher Rundfunk (NDR)**, Rothenbaumchaussee 132, 20149 Hamburg ☎ +49 40 4131 **W:** www.ndr.de **Rundfunk Berlin-Brandenburg (RBB)** Masurenallee 8-14, 14057 Berlin ☎ +49 30 9799330141 **W:** www.rbb-online.de **Radio Bremen**

**Fernsehen (RB)**, Diepenau 10, 28195 Bremen ☎ +49 421 2460 **W:** www.radiobremen.de **Saarländischer Rundfunk (SR)**, Funkhaus Halberg, 66100 Saarbrücken ☎ +49 681 6020 **W:** www.sr.de **Südwestrundfunk (SWR)**, Neckarstrasse 230, 70190 Stuttgart ☎ +49 711 92910001 **W:** www.swr.de **Westdeutscher Rundfunk (WDR)**, Appellhoffplatz 1, 50667 Köln ☎ +49 221 2202100 **W:** www.wdr.de – **ZWEITES DEUTSCHES FERNSEHEN (ZDF) (Pub)** ✉ Postfach 4040, 55030 Mainz ☎ +49 6131 701 **E:** info@zdf.de **W:** www.zdf.de **L.P:** DG: Thomas Bellut **Chs (terr.):** ZDF, ZDF_neo, ZDFinfo, 3sat (3sat is produced jointly with ARD) – **MEDIENGRUPPE RTL DEUTSCHLAND GMBH (Comm)** ✉ Picassoplatz 1, 50679 Köln ☎ +49 221 45600 **E:** info@mediengruppe-rtl.de **W:** www.medi-engruppe-rtl.de **L.P:** CEO: Anke Schäferkordt **Chs (terr.):** RTL, RTL II, SuperRTL, RTL NITRO, Vox, n-tv. – **PROSIEBENSAT.1 MEDIA SE (Comm)** ✉ Medienallee 7, 85774 Unterföhring ☎ +49 89 950710 **W:** www.prosiebensat1.com **L.P:** CEO: Max Conze **Chs (terr.):** ProSieben, ProSieben Maxx, Sat1, Sat1 Gold, Kabel eins, Sixx – **TELE 5** ✉ Bavariafilmplatz 7, 82031 Grünwald ☎ +49 89 6495680 **E:** info@ tele5.de **W:** www.tele5.de **L.P:** CEO: Herbert G. Kloiber, Kai Blasberg – **WELT (Comm)** ✉ Axel-Springer-Straße 65, 10888 Berlin ☎ +49 30 20902400 **E:** info@n24.de **W:** www.welt.de **L.P:** Editor-in-Chief: Ulf Poschard.

**Local Stations** not shown.

**DTT Tx Networks** (DVB-T2; all in HD)
**Licensee M1+2:** ARD **M1:** Das Erste, arte, Phoenix, One, Tagesschau24 **M3:** Regional public service stns – **Licensee M3:** ZDF **M3:** ZDF , 3Sat, ZDFinfo, ZDF_neo, KIKA – **Licensee M4-6:** Freenet **W:** www.freen-et-group.de **M4✪:** RTL, RTL II, Vox, SuperRTL, RTL NITRO, n-tv, Tele 5 **M5✪:** Sat1, ProSieben, Kabel eins, Sixx, ProSieben Maxx. Sat1 Gold, Sport 1 **M6 (✪exc.*):** Disney Channel, Welt, DMAX, Eurosport 1, Nickelodeon, 1.2.3.TV*, QVC*, HSE24*, Bibel TV*.
**NB:** The content of the muxes is licensed individually by each federal state and may vary in certain cases. Not shown are txs of the obsolete DVB-T network (being closed down).

| RE | Location | M1 | M2 | M3 | M4 | M5 | M6 | kW |
|---|---|---|---|---|---|---|---|---|
| NW | Aachen (SFN) | 26V | 35V | 29V | 40V | 43V | 36V | (-) |
| BW | Aalen | 32 | 28 | 23 | - | - | - | 50 |
| BY | Amberg | 23 | 47 | 37 | - | - | - | 50 |
| BY | Augsburg | 41 | 22 | 44 | 33 | 39 | 25 | 50 |
| NI | Aurich | 29 | 43 | 35 | - | - | - | 79 |
| BW | Baden-Baden | 36 | 39 | 33 | 35 | 44 | 29 | 50 |
| BY | Bamberg | 40 | 30 | 37 | - | - | - | 50 |
| BE | Berlin (SFN)[1] | 25 | 40 | 33 | 27 | 31 | 42 | (-) |
| NW | Bonn | 26V | 35V | 29V | 40V | 43V | 36V | 20 |
| NI | Braunschweig (SFN)[1] | 23V | 40V | 36V | 44V | 21V | 47V | (-) |
| SH | Bredstedt | 26 | 24 | 31 | - | - | - | 25 |
| | Bregenz* | 45 | 46 | - | - | - | - | 10 |
| HB | Bremen | 29 | 46 | 35 | 42 | 48 | 22 | 20/10/32/3x50 |
| HB | Bremen | - | 30 | - | - | - | - | 20 |
| ST | Brocken | 45V | 34V | 37V | - | - | - | 50 |
| BY | Brotjacklriegel | 28V | 40V | - | - | - | - | 100 |
| SH | Bungsberg | 47V | 39V | 21V | - | - | - | 2x100/50 |
| BY | Büttelberg | 42 | 29 | - | - | - | - | 50 |
| BB | Cottbus | 22 | 44 | 36 | - | - | - | 100 |
| NS | Dannenberg | 32 | 43 | - | - | - | - | 10 |
| HE | Darmstadt | 42V | 34V | 22V | 31V | 25V | 47V | 10 |
| BY | Dillberg | 42V | 29V | 34V | - | - | - | 50 |
| BW | Donaueschingen | 43 | 47 | 37 | - | - | - | 50 |
| RP | Donnersberg | 30 | 46 | - | - | - | - | 50 |
| NW | Dortmund | 25V | 35V | 29V | 40V | 43V | 48V | 50 |
| SN | Dresden | 34V | 39V | 36V | 46V | 29V | 42V | 3x100/3x50 |
| NW | Düsseldorf | 46V | 35V | 29V | 40V | 43V | 48V | 50 |
| NW | Essen | 25V | 35V | 29V | 40V | 43V | 48V | 20/5x50 |
| SL | Felsberg | 32V | - | - | - | - | - | 20 |
| SH | Flensburg | 47V | 39V | 21V | - | - | - | 79 |
| HE | Frankfurt/M. | 42V | 34V | 22V | 31V | 25V | 47V | 50 |
| BB | Frankfurt/O. | 25V | 40V | 33V | - | - | - | 50 |
| BW | Freiburg | 36 | 39 | 33 | 28 | 42 | 29 | 50 |
| MV | Garz | 36 | 29 | 46 | - | - | - | 2x40/20 |
| BY | Gelbelsee | 41 | 22 | 44 | - | - | - | 50 |
| SL | Göttelborner Höhe | 32V | 42V | 55V | - | - | - | 50 |
| NI | Göttingen (SFN)[1] | 23 | 40 | 35 | - | - | - | (-) |
| HE | Großer Feldberg | 42V | 34V | 22V | 31V | 25V | 47V | 50 |
| BY | Grünten | 45 | 46 | 40 | - | - | - | 100 |
| HE | Habichtswald | 46 | 29 | 35 | 28 | 25 | 48 | 20 |
| NW | Hagen | 25V | 35V | 29V | 40V | 43V | 48V | 10 |
| ST | Halle | 38V | 24V | 49V | 43V | 28V | 26V | 50 |
| HH | Hamburg (SFN)[1] | 23 | 41 | 33 | 27 | 28 | 45 | (-) |
| NI | Hannover | 23 | 40 | 36 | 44 | 21 | 47 | 40/5x50 |
| SH | Heide | 26 | 24 | 31 | - | - | - | 32 |
| BW | Heidelberg | 27 | 21 | 41 | 35 | 44 | 24 | 50 |
| BY | Heidelstein | - | - | 26 | - | - | - | 50 |

| RE | Location | M1 | M2 | M3 | M4 | M5 | M6 | kW |
|----|----------|-----|-----|-----|-----|-----|-----|-----|
| MV | Helpterberg | 36 | 22 | 23 | - | - | - | 20 |
| NI | Hildesheim | 23V | 40V | 36V | - | - | - | 40/50/40 |
| BY | Hohe Linie | 27V | 21V | 36V | - | - | - | 100 |
| HE | Hohe Wurzel | 42V | 34V | 22V | 31V | 25V | 47V | 100 |
| BY | Hohenpeissenberg | 45 | 46 | 40 | - | - | - | 50 |
| BY | Hoher Bogen | 28V | 21V | - | - | - | - | 100 |
| HE | Hoher Meißner | 46 | 29 | 35 | - | - | - | 50 |
| TH | Inselsberg | 27V | 39V | 41V | - | - | - | 50 |
| TH | Jena | 39V | 56V | 41V | 44V | 33V | 47V | 2x10/5/3x10 |
| RP | Kaiserslautern | 30 | 46 | 37 | 35 | 44 | 40 | 20 |
| BW | Karlsruhe | 27V | 21V | 41V | 35V | 44V | 24V | 10 |
| HE | Kassel | 46V | 29V | 35V | 28V | 25V | 48V | 10 |
| SH | Kiel | 47 | 39 | 21 | 27 | 28 | 45 | 3x50/3x20 |
| RP | Koblenz | 23 | 33 | 28 | 31 | 25 | 47 | 3x50/3x20 |
| NW | Köln | 26V | 35V | 29V | 40V | 43V | 36V | 20 |
| BY | Kreuzberg | 36 | 43 | - | - | - | - | 100 |
| BY | Landshut | 28 | 40 | 46 | - | - | - | 50 |
| NW | Langenberg | 25V | 35V | 29V | 40V | 43V | 48V | 50 |
| BW | Langenbrand | 27 | 21 | 33 | 35 | 44 | 29 | 50 |
| SN | Leipzig | 35V | 24V | 49V | 43V | 28V | 26V | 3x100/3x50 |
| SN | Löbau | 34V | 39V | 36V | - | - | - | 50 |
| SH | Lübeck (SFN)[1] | 23 | 40 | 33 | 27 | 28 | 45 | (-) |
| ST | Magdeburg | 45V | 34V | 37V | 46V | 29V | 48V | 2x100/4x50 |
| BY | München | 31V | 30V | 34V | 35V | 26V | 48V | 100 |
| BY | Nürnberg | 42V | 47V | 34V | 35V | 24V | 25V | 50 |
| BY | Ochsenkopf | 40 | 30 | 37 | - | - | - | 100 |
| BY | Pfaffenberg | 36 | 43 | 26 | - | - | - | 50 |
| BY | Pfarrkirchen | 28 | 40 | 46 | - | - | - | 50 |
| BY | Pfaffenhofen | 41 | 22 | 44 | - | - | - | 2x5/50 |
| HE | Rimberg | 42 | 29 | 22 | - | - | - | 50 |
| BW | Ravensburg | 43 | 47 | 37 | - | - | - | 50 |
| MV | Rostock | 36V | 29V | 46V | 44V | 24V | 26V | 40 |
| SL | Saarbrücken | 32V | 46V | 37V | 35V | 44V | 45V | 10 |
| RP | Scharteberg | 30 | 46 | 37 | - | - | - | 50 |
| NI | Schiffdorf | 29 | 30 | 35 | 42 | 48 | 22 | 2x10/5/3x20 |
| NI | Schiffdorf | - | 46 | - | - | - | - | 2 |
| SH | Schleswig | 47V | 39V | 21V | - | - | - | 10 |
| MV | Schwerin | 36 | 29 | 46 | 44 | 24 | 26 | 32 |
| SL | Spiesen | 32V | - | - | - | - | - | 25 |
| NI | Steinkimmen | 29 | 30 | 35 | - | - | - | 2x79/5 |
| NI | Steinkimmen | - | 46 | - | - | - | - | 4 |
| BW | Stuttgart | 32 | 28 | 23 | 42 | 25 | 45 | 50 |
| NI | Torfhaus | 23V | 40V | - | - | - | - | 32 |
| RP | Trier | 30 | 46 | 37 | 35 | 44 | 40 | 10 |
| NS | Visselhövede | 32 | 43 | 25 | - | - | - | 50 |
| BW | Ulm | 43 | 47 | 37 | - | - | - | 50 |
| BW | Waldenburg | 32 | 28 | 23 | - | - | - | 50 |
| SH | Wedel | 23 | 40 | - | - | - | - | 10 |
| BY | Wendelstein | 31V | 30V | 34V | 35V | 26V | 48V | 100 |
| NW | Wesel | 46V | 35V | 29V | 40V | 43V | 48V | 50 |
| ST | Wittenberg | 38V | 24V | 37V | - | - | - | 50 |
| NI | Wolfsburg | 22V | 42V | 36V | - | - | - | 25 |
| NW | Wuppertal | 46 | 35 | 29 | 40 | 43 | 48 | 20 |
| HE | Würzburg | 48 | 34 | 41 | - | - | - | 50 |
| BY | Würzburg | 36 | 43 | 26 | - | - | - | 50 |

+ sites with txs below 10kW. *) Located in Austria [1] SFN txs have H or V polarisation

**Regional & Local Licensees (DVB-T)** not shown.

**RE) Region codes (federal states):** BB=Brandenburg, BE=Berlin, BW=Baden-Württemberg, BY=Bayern, HB=Bremen, HE=Hessen, HH=Hamburg, MV=Mecklenburg-Vorpommern, NI=Niedersachsen, NW=Nordrhein-Westfalen, RP=Rheinland-Pfalz, SH=Schleswig-Holstein, SL=Saarland, ST=Sachsen-Anhalt, SN=Sachsen, TH=Thüringen.

## GHANA

**System:** DVB-T2 (MPEG4) [E]

**GHANA BROADCASTING CORP. (GBC) (Gov)** ▣ P.O. Box 1633, Accra ☎ +233 30 2221161 🖷 +233 30 2773240 **E:** info@gbcghana. comh **W:** www.gbcghana.com **L.P:** CEO: Albert Don-Chebe. **Chs:** GTV, GBC 24, GBC Life, GTV Sports+ – **E.TV GHANA (Comm)** ▣ P.O.Box CT 5976, Accra ☎ +233 30 2912071 **E:** info@etvghana. com **W:** etvghana.com – **METRO TV (Semi-Gov, Comm)** 59 Josiah Tongogara Street, Labone, Accra 🖷 +233 30 2765701 🖷 +233 30 2765703 **W:** www.facebook.com/metrotvgh **L.P:** CEO: Talal Fattal – **TV3 (Comm)** ▣ Box M83, Accra ☎ +233 30 2763458 🖷 +233 30 2763450 **E:** info@tv3network.com **W:** 3news.com **L.P:** CEO: Santokh Singh.

## DTT Tx Networks

**Tx Operator:** Startimes **M1:** GTV, GBC 24, GBC Life, GTV Sports+,TV3, Kwese Free Sports, NET2, BBC World News, God TV, FOX Entertainment✪, Showtime✪, Hi Nolly✪, Homebase✪, Setanta Africa✪, Kiss✪, KidsCo✪ **M2:** Skyy One, Music World, Channel D, Sports24, Cinimax, Heaven, Planet Kidz, Fiesta, Skyy World, e.TV Ghana ⌘ Skyy Power FM, Citi FM **Txs:** (-).

## GIBRALTAR (UK)

**Systems:** DVB-T (MPEG2), DVB-T2 (MPEG4) [E]

**GBC TELEVISION (Pub)** ▣ Broadcasting House, 18 So. Barrack Rd, Gibraltar ☎ +350 20048990 **E:** television@gbc.gi **W:** www.gbc.gi **L.P:** CEO (Gibraltar Broadcasting Corp): Gerard Teuma.

## DTT Tx Networks

**Tx Operator:** Arqiva **M1:** GBC TV ⌘ R. Gibraltar 1 **M2:** GBC TV HD, Al Jazeera **Txs: M1 (DVB-T):** ch56 (Upper Rock) **M2 (DVB-T2):** ch30 (Upper Rock).

## GREECE

**System:** DVB-T (MPEG4) [E]

**National Stations**
**ELLINIKI RADIOFONIA TILEORASI A.E. (ERT) (Pub)** ▣ TV studios: Leoforos Mesogeion 136, 11527 Athina ☎+30 2106066000 **E:** info@ert.gr **W:** www.ert.gr **L.P:** MD: Christos Leontis **Chs:** ERT1, ERT2, ERT3, ERT HD – **VOULI TILEORASI (Pub)** ▣ Leoforos Vasilisis Sofias 11, 10671 Athina ☎ +30 2103735320 **E:** kanali@parliament. gr **W:** www.hellenicparliament.gr/Enimerosi/Vouli-Tileorasi – **ALPHA TV (Comm)** ▣ Ambelakion, Biomichaniko Parko, 15351 Pallini ☎ +30 2122124000 **E:** pr@alphatv.gr **W:** www.alphatv.gr **L.P:** Pres/CEO: Dimitris Kontominas – **ANTENNA TV (ANT1) (Comm)** ▣ Leoforos Kifisias 10-12, 15125 Marousi ☎ +30 2106886100 **E:** pr@antenna. gr **W:** www.antenna.gr **L.P:** CEO: Tasos Michalakis – **MAKEDONIA TV (m.) (Comm)** ▣ 26is Oktovriou 90, 54627 Thessaloniki ☎ +30 2310504300 **E:** info@maktv.gr **W:** www.maktv.gr **L.P:** GM: Georgios Zois – **OPEN BEYOND TV (Comm)** ▣ 2o chlm Leoforos Paianias-Markopoulou, 19400 Koropi ☎ +30 2112122000 **E:** info@tvopen.gr **W:** www.tvopen.gr **L.P:** CEO: Dimitris Michalelis – **SKAI TV (Comm)** ▣ Ethnarchou Makariou & Falireos 2, 18547 Neo Faliro ☎ +30 2104800170 **E:** technicaltv@skai.gr **W:** www.skai.gr **L.P:** CEO (Skai Group): Giannis Alafouzos – **STAR CHANNEL (Comm)** ▣ Viltanioti 36, 14564 Kifisia ☎ +30 2111891000 **E:** info@star.gr **W:** www.star. gr **L.P:** GM: Karolos Alkalai.

**Regional & Local Stations** not shown.

## DTT Tx Networks

**Licencee M1+4:** ERT **M1:** ERT1, ERT2, ERT3, ERT HD, Vouli ⌘ ERA Radio 1-3, ERA Sport, Kosmos, I Foni tis Elladas **M4:** BBC World News, DW-TV, RIK Sat, TV5 Monde Europe – **Licensee M2+3,5+6,** **R1-R3:** Digea **W:** www.digea.gr **M2:** Alpha TV, ANT1, Open Beyond TV **M3:** m. (Makedonia TV), Skai TV, Star Channel **M5:** ANT1 HD, Star Channel HD, Skai HD, m.HD **M6:** Alpha TV HD, Open Beyond TV HD **Muxes R1-3:** Regional muxes with various regional/local stns **Additional muxes (+):** Transitional: [1] Euro TV, Gnomi TV [2] Egnatia TV, Pella TV, Time TV; Digea: [3] Ena Channel, Epsilon TV, Star Kentrikis Elladas

| Location | M1 | M2 | M3 | M4 | M5 | M6 | R1 | R2 | R3 | (+) | kW |
|----------|-----|-----|-----|-----|-----|-----|-----|-----|-----|-----|-----|
| Achendrias | 24 | 25 | 37 | - | - | - | 55 | - | - | - | 3.2 |
| Aigina | 21 | 22 | 27 | 28 | 30 | 40 | 45 | 52 | 54 | - | 6.3 |
| Ainos | 21 | 22 | 33 | 36 | - | - | 59 | 60 | 52 | - | 10 |
| Ainos | - | - | - | - | - | - | - | - | 56 | - | 10 |
| Akarnanika | 23 | 27 | 28 | 32 | - | - | 46 | 51 | - | - | 25 |
| Aroi | 24 | 25 | 31 | 34 | 35 | 42 | 44 | 53 | - | - | 6.3 |
| Avlonas | 21 | 22 | 27 | 28 | 30 | 40 | 45 | 52 | 54 | - | 3.2 |
| Axonas | 39 | 24 | 26 | 32 | - | - | 41 | - | - | - | 1.6 |
| Chlomo | 39 | 33 | 35 | - | - | - | 53 | - | - | - | 6.3 |
| Chortiatis | 24 | 27 | 30 | 36 | 43 | 48 | 55 | 56 | - | 50[1] | 25 |
| Chortiatis | - | - | - | - | - | - | - | - | - | 51[2] | 25 |
| Doliana | 21 | 23 | 24 | - | 42 | 45 | 50 | 60 | - | - | 6.3 |
| Dovroutsi | 22 | 35 | 38 | 40 | 42 | 45 | 52 | - | - | - | 6.3 |
| Kelli | 44 | 26 | 32 | - | - | - | 47 | 52 | - | - | 3.2 |
| Kleisoura | 44 | 26 | 32 | - | - | - | 47 | 52 | - | - | 1.6 |
| Lichada | 46 | 33 | 35 | - | - | - | 53 | - | - | - | 3.2 |
| Ligkiades | 24 | 25 | 30 | 31 | - | 42 | 52 | 54 | - | - | 6.3 |
| Malaxa | 21 | 31 | 34 | - | - | - | 54 | - | - | - | 6.3 |
| Metaxas | 41 | 28 | 29 | - | - | - | 50 | 54 | - | - | 3.2 |

| Location | M1 | M2 | M3 | M4 | M5 | M6 | R1 | R2 | R3 | (+) | kW |
|---|---|---|---|---|---|---|---|---|---|---|---|
| Monte Smith | 21 | 24 | 26 | 32 | - | - | 41 | - | - | - | 1.6 |
| Monte Smith | 39 | - | - | - | - | - | - | - | - | - | 1.6 |
| Osios Patapios | 26 | 29 | 41 | - | - | - | 51 | 56 | - | - | 1.6 |
| Pantokratoras | 37 | 30 | 34 | - | - | - | 54 | 56 | - | - | 6.3 |
| Parnitha | 21 | 22 | 27 | 28 | 30 | 40 | 45 | 52 | 54 | 53³ | 16 |
| Paros | 42 | 33 | 39 | - | - | - | 53 | - | - | - | 6.3 |
| Petalidi | 29 | 31 | 32 | 37 | 43 | 44 | 48 | 51 | - | - | 6.3 |
| Pilio | 21 | 26 | 29 | 37 | - | - | 47 | - | - | - | 16 |
| Plaka | 24 | 27 | 30 | 31 | 33 | 36 | 43 | 48 | - | - | 6.3 |
| Polygyros | 25 | 31 | 34 | 38 | 46 | 49 | 50 | 54 | - | - | 1.6 |
| Pythio | 25 | 32 | 35 | 46 | 47 | 50 | 51 | 56 | - | - | 3.2 |
| Rogdia | 39 | 25 | 37 | - | - | - | 55 | - | - | - | 6.3 |
| Soros | 21 | 26 | 29 | 37 | - | - | 47 | - | - | - | 1.6 |
| Soros | 44 | - | - | - | - | - | - | - | - | - | 1.6 |
| Styra | 23 | 24 | 31 | 32 | 34 | 36 | 38 | 49 | 50 | - | 6.3 |
| Syros | 46 | 29 | 37 | - | - | - | 48 | - | - | - | 3.2 |
| Thasos | 22 | 23 | 37 | 39 | 41 | 44 | 47 | 51 | - | - | 16 |
| Xylokastro | 26 | 29 | 41 | 43 | 47 | 48 | 51 | 56 | - | - | 3.2 |
| Ymittos | 21 | 22 | 27 | 28 | 30 | 40 | 45 | 52 | 54 | - | 32 |

+ sites with txs below 1kW.

## GREENLAND (Denmark)

**System:** DVB-T (MPEG2, MPEG4) [E]

**National Station**
**KNR-TV (Pub)** ▣ P.O.Box 1007, 3900 Nuuk ☎ +299 361500 ▤ +299 325042 **E:** knr@knr.gl **W:** knr.gl **L.P:** Dir (KNR): Karl Henrik Simonsen **Chs:** KNR1, KNR2.

**DTT Tx Networks**
**Tx Operator:** TELE Greenland **M (MPEG4):** KNR1, KNR2, DR1+4, DR2+4, DR Ultra+4 ✳ KNR Radio, DR P1, DR P2, DR P3 **Txs:** MFN –
**Local Licencees:** not shown.

## GRENADA

**System:** NTSC-M [A]

**GBN-TV (Gov)** ▣ P.O.Box 535, St. George's ☎ +1 473 4445521 **E:** grenadabroadcastingnetwork@gmail.com **W:** www.gbn.gd **Txs:** North/East ch7 (4kW), St. George's ch11 (5kW) – **MEANINGFUL TELEVISION (MTV) (Comm)** ▣ Lagoon Road, St. George ☎ +1 473 4408442 **E:** mtvgrenada@gmail.com **W:** www.facebook.com/ MTVNEWSGRENADA **Txs:** Saint George's ch9 & netw. – **GFN-TV (Rlg)** ▣ P.O.Box 2747, St. Paul's, St. George ☎ +1 473 4354297 **W:** www.globalfamilynetwork.net **L.P:** Project Dir: John Bartels **Tx:** St. George's ch4.

## GUADELOUPE (France)

**System:** DVB-T (MPEG4) [E]

**GUADELOUPE LA 1ÈRE (Pub)** ▣ BP 180, F-97122 Baie-Mahault ☎ +590 590939696 **E:** secretariaguadir@francetv.fr **W:** guadeloupe. la1ere.fr **L.P:** Dir: Sylvie Gengoul – **ALIZES TV (Comm)** ▣ Tour Sécid, Place de la Rénovation, F-97110 Pointe-à-Pitre ☎ +590 590572600 **E:** contact@alizes.com **W:** www.alizes.com – **CANAL 10 (Comm)** ▣ 21, Bd Marquisart De Houelbourg, F-97122 Baie-Mahault ☎ +590 590267303 **E:** contact@canal10-tv.com **W:** www. canal10-tv.com **L.P:** Pres: Lisa Rodriguez – **ÉCLAIR TV (ETV) (Comm)** ▣ 12, rue Alfred Lumière, Bureau n° 6, F-97122 Baie-Mahaut. ☎ +590 590328080 3 **W:** www.efm-etv.com **L.P:** Pres: Mario Constant Moradel.

**DTT Tx Networks**
**Tx Operator:** TDF **M:** Guadeloupe la 1ère, France 2-5, France Ô, France 24, Arte, Canal 10 **Txs:** MFN. **Local Mux:** Alizes TV HD, ETV HD **Txs:** MFN.

## GUAM (USA)

**System:** ATSC [A]

**Local Stations** (Full power licenses; LP licenses not listed)
**KGTF (Pub):** P.O.Box 21449, GMF, Agana, GU 96921. Tx: Agana ch12 (54.7kW). **KTGM (Comm):** 692 N Marine Dr, Tamuning, GU 96913-4454. Tx: Tamuning ch14 (12.5kW). **KUAM-TV (Comm):** 600 Harmon Loop Rd, #102, Dededo, GU 96912-2536. Tx: Agana ch8 (3.5kW).

## GUATEMALA

**Systems:** ISDB-TB [A]; # NTSC-M [A] ⇩2022

**National Stations** (ᵃ=analogue)
**GUATEVISIÓN (Pub)** ▣ Calzada Roosevelt 22-43, Zona 11, Edificio Tikal Futura, Torre Sol 4o, Nivel, Guatemala ☎ +502 23286000 **E:** info@guatevjsion.com **W:** www.guatevision.com **Txs:** ᵃch25 – **RADIO Y TELEVISIÓN DE GUATEMALA (Comm)** ▣ 30, Av. 3-40, Zona 11, 01011 Guatemala ☎ +502 25945320 **Chs:** Canal 3, Canal 7, Teleonce, Trecevisión **W:** www.chapintv.com **Txs: Canal 3:** ᵃch3 (240kW); **Canal 7:** ᵃch7 (180kW), **Teleonce:** ch11 (316kW); **Trecevisión:** ᵃch13 (25kW) – **AZTECA GUATEMALA (Comm)** ▣ 12 Avenida 1-96, Zona 2 de Mixco, Colonia Alvarado, Guatemala ☎ +502 24111140 ▤ +502 24111200 **E:** festrada@tvaguatemala.tv **W:** www.azteca. com.gt Tx: ᵃch31 – **MAZATELEVISIÓN (Comm)** ▣ Suchitepequez. **Tx:** ᵃch58 – **TV USAC (Educ)** ▣ Guatemala **W:** www.usac.edu.gt **Tx:** ᵃch33 – **CANAL 27 (Rlg)** ▣ Carretera Vieja a Antigua 2 Calle 23-70, Zona 1 de Mixco, Guatemala ☎ +502 24213434 **E:** canal27@ motivacioncristiana.org **W:** www.canal27.org **Tx:** ᵃch27 – **CANAL 63 (Rlg)** ▣ Guatemala **W:** www.canalcatolico.tv **Tx:** ᵃch63 – **CANAL 65 (Rlg)** ▣ Guatemala **Tx:** ᵃch65. Rel. ETWN (USA) – **ENLACE CANAL 21 (Rlg)** ▣ Guatemala **Tx:** ᵃch21. Rel. TBN (USA).

**Local Stations** not shown.

## GUINEA

**Systems:** DVB-T2 (MPEG4) [E]; § PAL-K1 [VHF=K, UHF=E] ⇩2019

**RADIO TÉLÉVISION GUINÉENNE (RTG) (Pub)** ▣ BP 391, Conakry. ☎ +224 30452786 ▤ +224 30451408 **W:** rtgkoloma.info **L.P:** DG: Sékouba Savané **Chs:** RTG1, RTG2

**DTT Tx Network**
**Tx Operator:** Startimes **M(partly↻):** multiprgr **Txs:** MFN.

## GUINEA-BISSAU

**System:** DVB-T2 (MPEG4) [E]

**TELEVISÃO DA GUINÉ-BISSAU (TGB) (Gov)** ▣ CP 178, Bissau **W:** www.facebook.com/Televis%C3%A3o-da-Guine-Bissau-170013679766466 **L.P:** DG: Daniel Barros.

**DTT Tx Network**
**Tx Operator:** Startimes **M(partly↻):** multiprgr **Txs:** MFN.

## GUYANA

**Systems:** # NTSC-M [A]; ATSC [A] planned

**National Station**
**NATIONAL COMMUNICATIONS NETWORK (NCN) (Gov)** ▣ Homestretch Ave, Durban Backland, Georgetown ☎ +592 2235162 ▤ +592 2235163 **E:** ceo@ncnguyana.com **W:** ncnguyana.com **Tx:** ch11.

**Local Stations** not shown.

## HAITI

**System:** NTSC-M [A]

**National Station**
**RADIO TÉLÉVISION NATIONALE D'HAÏTI (RTNH) (Pub)** ▣ BP 13400, Delmas 33, Port-au-Prince ☎ +509 2460200 ▤ +509 2463889 **W:** www.rtnh.ht **L.P:** DG: Gamal Augustin **Txs:** Port-au-Prince ch8 (0.3kW) & nationwide network.

**Local Stations** not shown.

## HAWAII (USA)

**System:** ATSC [A]

**Local Stations** (Full power licenses; LP licenses not listed)
**KAAH-TV (Rlg):** 1152 Smith St, Honolulu, HI 96817-5101. Tx: ch27 (262kW). **KAII-TV (Comm):** satellite of KHON-TV. Tx: Wailuku ch7 (7.2kW). **KALO (Rlg):** 875 Waimanu St, Ste 110, Honolulu, HI 96813-5271. Tx: ch38 (155kW). **KBFD (Comm):** 1188 Bishop St PH-1, Honolulu,

HI 96813-3300. Tx: ch33 (108kW). **KFVE (Comm):** 150-B Puuhale Rd, Honolulu, HI 96819-2233. Tx: ch22 (40kW). **KGMB (Comm):** 1534 Kapiolani Blvd, Honolulu, HI 96814-3715. Tx: ch23 (23kW). **KGMD-TV (Comm):** satellite of KGMB. Tx: Hilo ch9 (40kW). **KGMV (Comm):** satellite of KGMB. Tx: Wailuku ch24 (72.4kW). **KHAW-TV (Comm):** satellite of KHON-TV. Tx: Hilo ch11 (7.2kW). **KHBC-TV (Comm):** satellite of KHNL. Tx: Hilo ch22 (8kW). **KHET (Pub):** 2350 Dole St, Honolulu, HI 96822-2410. Tx: ch11 (15.7kW). **KHNL (Comm):** 150-B Puuhale Rd, Honolulu, HI 96819-2233. Tx: ch35 (5.9kW). **KHON-TV (Comm):** 88 Piikoi St, Honolulu, HI 96814-4245. Tx: ch8 (7.2kW). **KHVO (Comm):** satellite of KITV. Tx: Hilo ch13 (85kW). **KIKU (Comm):** 737 Bishop St Ste 1430, Honolulu, HI 96813-3204. Tx: ch19 (60.7kW). **KITV (Comm):** 801 S King St, Honolulu, HI 96813-3013. Tx: ch40 (85kW). **KKAI (Rlg):** 875 Waimanu St, Ste 110, Honolulu, HI 96813-5271. Tx: ch50 (12kW). **KLEI (Comm):** satellite of KPXO. Tx: Kailua-Kona ch25 (700kW). **KMAU (Comm):** satellite of KITV. Tx: Wailuku ch12 (85kW). **KMEB (Pub):** satellite of KHET. Tx: Wailuku ch10 (21.2kW). **KOGG (Comm):** satellite of KHNL. Tx: Wailuku ch16 (50kW). **KPXO (Comm):** 875 Waimanu St Ste 630, Honolulu, HI 96813-5267. Tx: Kane'ohe ch41 (34kW). **KUPU (Rlg):** 1188 Bishop St Ste 502, Honolulu, HI 96813-3302. Tx: Waimanalo ch15 (12kW). **KWBN (Rlg):** 3901 S Hwy 121 S, Bedford, TX 76021-2066. Tx: ch43 (6.46kW). **KWHD (Rlg):** satellite of KWHE. Tx: Hilo ch23 (14.9kW). **KWHE (Rlg):** 1188 Bishop St Ste 502, Honolulu, HI 96813-3302. Tx: ch31 (20.1kW). **KWHM (Rlg):** satellite of KWHE. Tx: Wailuku 21 (23.5kW). **NB:** Tx sites are Honolulu unless mentioned otherwise.

## HONDURAS

**Systems:** ISDB-TB [A]; § NTSC-M [A]

**National Stations** (ª=analogue)
**TELEVISIÓN NACIONAL DE HONDURAS (TNH) (Gov)** ⌨Edificio Ejecutivo #2 - 4 nivel Frente Casa Presidencial Tegucigalpa, M.D.C., Tegucigalpa **E:** info@tnh.gob.hn **W:** tnh.gob.hn **L.P:** Chmn: Víctor G. Hémela **Txs:** Tegucigalpa ªch20 & relays. – **CANAL 6 (Comm)** ⌨ 5ta CII, 26 y 27 Ave., Bo. Río de Piedras, San Pedro Sula ☎ +504 25505009 🖷 +504 25531810 **W:** canal6.com.hn **Tx:** Tegucigalpa ªch6 & relays. – **CANAL 11 (Comm)** ⌨ 5ta CII, 26 y 27 Ave., Bo. Río de Piedras, San Pedro Sula **W:** canal11.hn **Tx:** San Pedro Sula ªch11 & relays. – **HONDURED (Comm)** ⌨ Casilla 3424, Tegucigalpa. **W:** www.hondured.tv **Txs:** Tegucigalpa ªch13 & relays. – **TELEPROGRESO (Comm)** ⌨ 9 Ave 12 St. N, Edificio Turiplaza, El Progreso 23201 ☎ +504 26482222 **E:** micanal@teleprogreso.tv **W:** www.teleprogreso.tv **Txs:** Tegucigalpa ªch48 & relays – **TELEVICENTRO (TVC) (Comm)** ⌨ Boulevard Suyapa, Tegucigalpa ☎ +504 22327835 🖷 +504 2320097 **W:** televicentro.hn **Chs:** Canal Cinco, Canal 3, Cadena 7/4 **Txs:** Tegucigalpa ªch3 (Canal 3), Tegucigalpa ªch5 (Canal Cinco), Tegucigalpa ªch7 (Cadena 7/4) & relays.– **VTV (Comm)** ⌨ 9 CII. 10 Ave, N.O. Bo. Guamalito, San Pedro Sula **W:** www.vtv.com.hn **Txs:** Tegucigalpa ªch9 & relays.

**Local Stations** not shown.

## HONG KONG (China, SAR)

**Systems:** DTMB [E]; § PAL-I [E] ⬇2020

**RADIO TELEVISION HONG KONG (RTHK) (Pub)** ⌨ 30 Broadcast Drive, Kowloon, Hong Kong ☎ +852 23396330 🖷 +852 3380279 **E:** ccu@rthk.hk **W:** www.rthk.hk **L.P:** Dir of Broadcasting: Ka-wing Leung. **Chs:** RTHK TV31, RTHK TV32, RTHK TV33 – **HK TELEVISION ENTERTAINMENT CO. LTD (HKTE) (Comm)** ⌨ 39/F, PCCW Tower, Taikoo Place, 979 King's Road, Quarry Bay, Hong Kong ☎ +852 22398899 **E:** enquiry@viu.tv **Chs:** ViuTVsix, ViuTV – **TELEVISION BROADCASTS LTD. (TVB) (Comm)** ⌨ TVB City, 77 Chun Choi Street, Tseung Kwan O Industrial Estate, Kowloon, Hong Kong ☎ +852 23359123 🖷+852 23581300 **E:** tvbpr@tvb.com.hk **W:** www.tvb.com **L.P:** Chmn: Kwok Keung Chan **Chs:** Jade, J2, TVB News, Pearl, TVB Finance & Information.

**DTT Tx Networks**
**Licensee M1:** RTHK **M:** RTHK TV31, RTHK TV32, RTHK TV33
**Licensee M2:** TVB **M:** Jade, J2, TVB News, Pearl, TVB Finance & Information – **Licensee M3:** HKTE **M:** ViuTVsix, ViuTV.

| Location | M1 | M2 | M3 |
|---|---|---|---|
| SFN | 62 | 35 | (MFN) |

## HUNGARY

**System:** DVB-T (MPEG4) [E]

---

**National Stations**
**DUNA MÉDIASZOLGÁLTATÓ NONPROFIT ZRT. (DMN) (Pub)** ⌨ Naphegy tér 8, 1016 Budapest ☎ +36 1 7595050 **E:** **E:** international@dunamsz.hu **W:** www.dunamsz.hu **L.P:** DG: Menyhert Dobos. Studios: ⌨ Szabadság tér 17, 1810 Budapest 5; Mészáros u. 48-54, 1016 Budapest (Duna). **Chs:** M1, M2, M2 Petöfi, M3 Anno, M4 Sport, M5, reg. prgrs: a) Budapesti stúdió, b) Debreceni stúdió, c) Miskolci stúdió, d) Pécsi stúdió, e) Soproni stúdió, f) Szegedi stúdió; Duna, Duna World – **RTL KLUB (Comm)** ⌨ Nagytétényi út 29, 1222 Budapest ☎ +36 1 3828283 **E:** rtlklub@rtl.hu **W:** rtl.hu **L.P:** CEO: Gabriella Vidus. – **TV2 (Comm)** ⌨ Róna u. 174, 1145 Budapest ☎ +36 1 4676400 **E:** info@tv2.hu **W:** tv2.hu **L.P:** CEO: Dirk Gerkens.

**Local Stations** not shown.

**DTT Tx Networks**
**Tx Operator:** Antenna Hungária **W:** ahrt.hu **M1:** M1 HD (incl. reg prgrs), M4 Sport HD, Duna World, Duna HD ✡ Kossuth R., Petöfi R., Bartók R., Dankó R. **M2(♻exc.\*):** AXN, Viasat 3, RTL+, PRIME, Da Vinci Learning, Comedy Central, Nickelodeon, Cartoon Network, National Geographic, Filmbox, Mozi+, Izaura TV\*, Zenebutik\*, FEM3\*, Spektrum Home\* **M3(♻exc.\*):** M2 HD\*, M3 Anno, M5 HD\*, RTL Klub\*, TV2\*, ATV, HírTV **M4♻:** Film+, Film4, Spiler TV, RTL2, Super TV2, Kiwi TV, Disney Channel, AMC, Paramount Channel, Discovery Channel, Humor+, Viasat 6, Cool, Ozone Network, TV4, Sport 1, TV Paprika **M5(♻exc.\*):** Echo TV, TLC, RTL Fold, Fishing & Hunting, Brazzers TV, Animal Planet, Discovery Science, NatGeo Wild, Viasat History, Filmbox Premium, Story 4, Sláger TV\*, Pax TV, Bonum TV, Chili TV, SuperOne, RTL Spike, Heti TV, FIX TV, D1 TV.

| Location | M1 | M2 | M3 | M4 | M5 | kW |
|---|---|---|---|---|---|---|
| Aggtelek | 45c | 31 | 28 | 48 | 35 | 39/4x50 |
| Budapest | 38a | 55 | 58 | 41 | 24 | 100/39/100/58/42 |
| Csávoly | 45f | 25 | 28 | 42 | 27 | 76/66/50/69/49 |
| Csengöd | 45f | 25 | 28 | 42 | 27 | 42/38/43/42/35 |
| Debrecen | 46b | 51 | 49 | 32 | 29 | 2x13/12/13.5/14 |
| Fehérgyarmat | 58b | 24 | 38 | 41 | - | 85/26/15.5/76 |
| Gerecse | 26e | 29 | 59 | 41 | - | 15/16/42/11 |
| Györ | 42e | 35 | 22 | 46 | 51 | 32/29.5/27.5/36/33 |
| Kabhegy | 57e | 35 | 22 | 46 | 51 | 2x100/83/98/83 |
| Kékes | 53c | 39 | 44 | 36 | 56 | 89/79/16/74/91 |
| Komádi | 46b | 51 | 49 | 32 | 29 | 79/87/71/51/50 |
| Nagykanizsa | 24e | 55 | 54 | 60 | 31 | 2x50/53/52.5/60 |
| Pécs | 52d | 37 | 47 | 32 | 50 | 72/18/78/60/78 |
| Salgótarján | 38e | 55 | 46 | 36 | 24 | 17/15/18/14/13.5 |
| Sopron | 42e | 40 | 49 | 32 | 33 | 83/81/83/72/74 |
| Szeged | 23f | 26 | 60 | 57 | 22 | 3x20/18/20 |
| Szentes | 23f | 26 | 60 | 57 | 22 | 83/87/2x100/83 |
| Szolnok | 53c | 30 | 59 | 36 | 56 | 24.5/19/24.5/18/- |
| Szombathely | 38e | 58 | 49 | 32 | 33 | 14.5/17/14/13/- |
| Tokaj | 43c | 31 | 43 | 26 | 35 | 43/13/18/65/66 |
| Uzd | 52d | 37 | 47 | 32 | 50 | 56/50/3x55 |
| Vásvár | 38e | 58 | 49 | 32 | 33 | 98/85/79/68/69 |

+ site with txs below 10kW. °) incl. reg prgrs (a-f), see above
**Local licensees** not shown.

## ICELAND

**Systems:** DVB-T (MPEG4), DVB-T2 (MPEG4) [E]

**National Stations**
**RÚV (Pub)** ⌨ Efstaleiti 1, 150 Reykjavík ☎ +354 5153000 **E:** istv@ruv.is **W:** www.ruv.is **L.P:** DG: Magnús Geir Þórðarsson **Chs:** RÚV, RÚV2 – **SIMINN HF (Comm)** ⌨ Ármúla 25, 108 Reykjavík ☎ +354 5956000 **W:** www.siminn.is **Ch:** Sjónvarp Símans, Símanum Sport – **SYN HF (Comm)** ⌨ Suðurlandsbraut 8, 108 Reykjavík ☎ +354 599900 **E:** syn@syn.is **W:** syn.is **L.P:** CEO: Stefán Sigurðsson **Chs (terr.):** Stöð 2, Stöð 3, Bíóstöðin, Krakkastöðin, Stöð 2 Sport 1-4, Golfstöðin.

**Local Stations**
**Omega Kristniboðskirkja (Rlg) (DVB-T2):** Grensásvegi 8, 108 Reykjavík; ch41 (Vatnssendi 0.3kW), Mosfellsbaer 0.05kW, Straumsvik 0.05kW, Kópavogur 0.01kW). **SkjáVarp (Comm):** Litlubrú 1, 780 Höfn; ch31 (0.05 kW).

**DTT Tx Networks** (DVB-T exc. where noted)
**Licensee: Sýn hf W:** syn.is **M1♻(exc.\*):** RÚV\*, Stöð 3, Stöð 2 Sport 1, Stöð 2 Sport 2, Bíóstöðin, Krakkastöðin ✡ RÚV Rás 1\*, Rás 2\*, Rondó\* **M2♻(exc.\*) (DVB-T2):** RÚV HD\*, RÚV2 HD\*, N4\*, Hringbraut\*, Sjónvarp Símans, DR1, BBC Brit, Discovery Channel, Animal Planet, National Geographic, Food Network, JimJam, CNNi, Sky News **M3♻:** Golfstöðin, Símanum Sport, Stöð 2 Sport 3, Stöð 2 Sport 4, Cartoon Network, E!, Hustler TV.

| Location | M1 | M2 | M3 | kW |
|----------|----|----|----|----|
| Gagnheiði | 26 | 28 | - | 1 |
| Skálafell | 34 | 35 | - | 1 |
| Stykkishólmur | 22 | 21 | - | 1 |

+ sites with txs below 1kW (M3=only txs below 1kW)

## INDIA

**Systems:** DVB-T2 (MPEG4) [E]; § PAL-B/G [E] ⇓2023

**DOORDARSHAN (DD) (Pub)** ⌨ Doordarshan Bhawan, Copernicus Marg, New Delhi-110001 ☎ +91 11 23386055 **E:** dgdd@doordarshan.gov.in **W:** www.ddindia.gov.in **L.P:** DG: Supriya Sahu **Chs (terr.):** DD-National, DD-News, DD-Sports, DD-Bharati, DD-Kendra (Regional Channels).

**DTT Tx Networks** (under construction)
**Tx Operator:** Doordarshan **M1:** DD-National, DD-News, DD-Sports, DD-Bharati, DD-Regional ✇ FM Rainbow, FM Gold **M2:** multiprgr.

| Location | M1 | M2 | kW | Location | M1 | M2 | kW |
|----------|----|----|----|----------|----|----|----|
| Ahmedabad | 32 | - | 6 | Kolkata | 22 | - | 6 |
| Aurangabad | 23 | - | 6 | Lucknow | 32 | - | 6 |
| Bangalore | 24 | - | 6 | Mumbai | 21 | 27 | 6 |
| Bhopal | 23 | - | -6 | New Delhi | 34 | 26 | 6 |
| Chennai | 29 | - | 6 | Patna | 24 | - | 6 |
| Cuttack | 29 | - | 6 | Raipur | 23 | - | 6 |
| Guwahati | 29 | - | 6 | Ranchi | 23 | - | 6 |
| Hyderabad | 24 | - | 6 | Srinagar | 24 | - | 6 |
| Indore | 26 | - | 6 | Thiruvananthapuram | 28 | - | 6 |
| Jalandhar | 33 | - | 6 | | | | |

+ nationwide MFN under construction

## INDONESIA

**Systems:** DVB-T2 (MPEG4) [E]; § PAL-B/G [E] ⇓2023

**National Stations** (ᵃ=analogue)
**TELEVISI REPUBLIK INDONESIA (TVRI) (Gov)** ⌨ Jalan Gerbang Pemuda, Senayan, Jakarta 10270 ☎ +62 21 3846740 ▤ +62 21 5737152 **E:** wmaster@tvri.co.id **W:** tvri.co.id **L.P:** MD: Farhat Syukri **Chs:** TVRI Nasional, TVRI Sumut. **Txs:** TVRI1: Jakarta ᵃch6 (5kW) & netw.; TVRI2: Jakarta ᵃch9. – **TELEVISIE EDUKASIE (TVE) (Gov)** ⌨ Jl. RE. Martadinata Km. 5.5 Ciputat, Tangerang 15411. ☎ +62 21 7418808 **W:** tve.kemdikbud.go.id **Chs:** Channel 1, Channel 2 **Txs:** via DTT & relays in provinces. – **ANTV (PT CAKRAWALA ANDALAS TELEVISI) (Comm)** ⌨ Mulia Center Building, 19th Floor, Jl. HR Rasuna Said Kav. X-6 No.8, Jakarta 12940 ☎ +62 21 5222084 ▤ +62 62 215222087 **E:** sales@anteve.co.id **W:** www.antvklik.com **Txs:** Jakarta ᵃch47 (40kW) & netw. – **GTV (PT GLOBAL INFORMASI BERMUTU) (Comm)** ⌨Wisma Indovision Lantai 17, Jalan Raya Panjang J/III, Green Garden, Jakarta 11520 ☎ +62 21 5828555 ▤ +62 21 5823636 **E:** globaltv@globaltv.co.id **W:** www.globaltv.co.id **Txs:** Jakarta ᵃch51 (120kW) & netw. – **INDOSIAR (PT. INDOSIAR VISUAL MANDIRI) (Comm)** ⌨ Jl. Damai No 11, Daan Mogot, Jakarta 11510 ☎ +62 21 5672222 ▤ +62 21 5652221 **E:** program@indosiar.com **W:** www.indosiar.com **Txs:** Jakarta ᵃch41 (120kW) & netw. – **METRO TV (PT MEDIA TELEVISI INDONESIA) (Comm)** ⌨ Jl. Pilar Mas Raya Kav. A-D., Kedoya, Kebon Jeruk, Jakarta 11520 ☎ +62 21 58300077 ▤ +62 21 5816365 **E:** info@metrotvnews.com **W:** www.metrotvnews.com **Txs:** Jakarta ᵃch57 & netw. – **MNC TV (PT MEDIA NUSANTARA CITRA TV) (Comm)** ⌨ Jalan Pintu II, Taman Mini Indonesia Indah, Pondok Gede, Jakarta Timur 13810 ☎ +62 21 8412473 ▤ +62 21 8412471 **E:** info@mnctv.com **W:** www.mnctv.com **Txs:** Jakarta ᵃch37 (80kW) & netw. **RCTI (PT RAJAWALI CITRA TELEVISI INDONESIA) (Comm)** ⌨ Jl. Raya Perjuangan No. 3, kb. Jeruk, Jakarta 11000 ☎ +62 21 5303540 ▤ +62 21 5493852 **E:** pr@rcti.tv **W:** www.rcti.tv **Txs:** Jakarta ᵃch43 & netw. – **SCTV (PT SURYA CITRA TELEVISI) (Comm)** ⌨ Graha SCTV 2nd floor, Jl. Gatot Subroto Kav 21, Jakarta 12930 ☎ +62 21 5225555 ▤ +62 21 5224777 **E:** pr@sctv.co.id **W:** www.sctv.co.id **Txs:** Jakarta ᵃch45 (120kW) & netw. – **TRANS TV (PT TELEVISI TRANSFORMASI INDONESIA) (Comm)** ⌨ Jl. Kapten Tendean Kav. 12-14A, Jakarta 12790 ☎ +62 21 7944240 ▤ +62 21 7992600 **E:** wmaster@transtv.co.id **W:** www.transtv.co.id **Txs:** Jakarta ᵃch29 (80kW) & netw. – **TRANS 7 (PT DUTA VISUAL NUSANTARA TIVI TUJUH) (Comm)** ⌨ Menara Bank Mega Lt. 20, Jl. Kapt. P. Tendean Kav.12-14A, Jakarta 12790 ☎ +62 21 79177000 ▤ +62 21 79184684 **E:** info@trans7.co.id **W:** www.trans7.co.id **Txs:** Jakarta ᵃch49 (60kW) & network. – **TVONE (PT LATIVI MEDIA KARYA (Comm)** ⌨ Kawasan Industri Pulo Gadung, Jl Rawa Teratai II No 2, Jakarta Timur 13260 ☎ +62 21 4613545 ▤ +62 21 4616255 **E:**

info@tvone.co.id **W:** www.tvonenews.tv **Txs:** Jakarta ᵃch53 & netw.

**Local Stations** not shown.

**DTT Tx Networks** (under construction)
**Licensee:** TVRI/PT Telekom **Mux 1:** TVRI Nasional, TVRI Sumut, TV Edukasi, MNC TV/GTV – **Licensee:** Televisi Digital Indonesie **W:** tvdigital.kominfo.go.id **Mux 2:** SCTV, ANTV, tvOne, Trans TV, Trans7, Metro TV

| Location | M1 | M2 | kW |
|----------|----|----|----|
| Jakarta | 42 | 46 | 1.5/5 |

+ nationwide MFN under construction

## IRAN

**Systems:** DVB-T2 (MPEG4) [E]; § PAL-B/G [E]

**ISLAMIC REPUBLIC OF IRAN BROADCASTING (IRIB) (Gov)** ⌨ P.O.Box 19395-3333, 19395 Tehran ☎ +98 21 22041093 ▤ +98 21 22014802 **E:** tv@irib.ir **W:** www.iribtv.ir **L.P:** Pres: Abdolali Ali Asgari **Chs (terr.):** IRIB TV1-TV5, IRIB Provincial stations, Amoozesh, IFilm, Iran Kala, IRINN, Mostanad, Namayesh, Nasim, Ofogh, Omid, Pooya/Nahal, Quran, Salamat, Shoma, Tamasha, Varzesh, Al-Alam, Al-Khawtar, Press TV.

**DTT Tx Network**
**Tx Operator:** IRIB **M1:** IRIB TV1-TV5, Amoozesh, IRINN, Nasim, Quran, Salamat ✇ IRIB radio channels **M2:** IFilm, Mostanad HD, Namayesh, Ofogh, Pooya/Nahal, Press TV, Varzesh, IRIB Provincial stations, Al-Alam, Al-Khawtar ✇ IRIB radio channels **M3:** IRIB TV3 HD, IFilm HD, Iran Kala, Omid, Press TV HD, Shoma, Tamasha HD ✇ IRIB radio channels.

| Location | M1 | M2 | M3 |
|----------|----|----|----|
| Tehran (Jamaran) | 37 | 43 | 34 |

+ nationwide MFN

## IRAQ

**Systems:** PAL-B/G [E]; DVB-T (MPEG4) [E]

**National Station**
**IRAQI MEDIA NETWORK (IMN) (Pub)** ⌨ Salhiya, Baghdad ☎ +964 1 8844412 ▤ +964 1 5410480 **W:** imn.iq **L.P:** DG: Mujahid Abu al-Hill **Chs (terr.):** Al-Iraqiya TV, Al-Riyadiya TV, Al-Turkmenia TV. **Txs:** **Al-Iraqiya TV:** Baghdad ch9 & netw. **Al-Riyadiya TV:** Baghdad ch7 & netw. **Al-Turkmenia TV:** Baghdad ch37 & netw.

**Local Stations & Foreign TV Relays** not shown.

### Iraqi Kurdistan

**DTT Tx Network**
**Tx Operator:** Mix Media ⌨ House No 635, Italian City Compound, Erbil ☎ +964 750 6421919 **E:** info@mixmedia.tv **W:** www.mixmedia.tv **Mux:** Ala TV, Amozhgary, Ankawa TV, Asman TV, Aso Sports TV, Astera TV, Babylon TV, Bangawaz TV, Best HD, Biaban Family, Biaban Movies, Biaban Music, Biaban Sport, BMC TV, Chare TV, Cihan TV, Dahen TV, Duhok TV, Effect HD, Esta, Falcon Eye, Falcon Family, GK Sulejmania, GK Hawler, GK Satellite, GK Sport, I Movies, I Baby, Jamawar, Jojo Mama TV, Judi TV, K24 TV, Kanal 6, Key House, Khak TV, Khezan TV, KNN TV, Komall TV, Kurdistan Sport, Kurdistan TV, Kurdmax, Kurdmax Pepule, Kurdsat TV, Kurdsat News TV, Law TV, Max TV, Mnara TV, Net TV, New Life TV, New Art HD, Niga Family, Niga Kids, Niga Movies, NRT, NRT 2, One World TV, Parwarda TV, Payam TV, Pelistank TV, Qellat TV, Rasan TV, Rudaw, Speda TV, Sport HD, Srusht, Suly, U2 HD, UTV Suleymania, X FM TV, Xezan TV, Zagros **Txs:** MFN.

## IRELAND

**System:** DVB-T (MPEG4) [E]

**RTÉ (Pub)** ⌨ Donnybrook, Dublin 4 ☎ +353 1 2083111 **E:** info@rte.ie **W:** www.rte.ie **L.P:** DG: Dee Forbes **Chs:** RTÉ One, RTÉ2, RTÉ News Now, RTÉjr. – **TG4 (Pub)** ⌨ Baile na hAbhann, Co. Galway H91 X4TO ☎ +353 91 505050 **E:** info@tg4.ie **W:** www.tg4.ie **L.P:** DG: Alan Esslemont – **VIRGIN MEDIA (Comm)** ⌨ Building P2, EastPoint Business Park, Clontarf, Dublin 3 ☎ +353 1 2458000 **W:** www.virginmedia.ie **L.P:** CEO: Tony Hanway **Chs:** Virgin Media One, Two, Three

**DTT Tx Networks**

**Tx Operator:** RTÉ Network Ltd (2RN) **M1:** RTÉ2 HD, RTÉ News Now/ Euronews HD, TG4, Tithe an Oireachtais, Virgin Media One, Virgin Media Two, Virgin Media Three ⌘ RTÉ R. 1, R. 1 Extra, 2FM, Lyric FM, Raidió na Gaeltachta, Pulse, 2XM, Choice, Gold, Chill/Junior **M2:** RTÉ One HD, RTÉ One +1, RTÉjr.

| Location | M1 | M2 | kW | Location | M1 | M2 | kW |
|---|---|---|---|---|---|---|---|
| Cairn Hill | 47 | 44 | 160 | Mount Leinster | 23 | 26 | 160 |
| Clermont Carn | 52V | 56V | 160 | Mullaghanish | 21 | 24 | 200 |
| Dungarvan | 55 | 59 | 10 | Spur Hill | 45 | 49 | 50 |
| Holywell Hill | 30 | 33 | 20 | Three Rock | 30 | 33 | 126 |
| Kippure | 54 | 58 | 63 | Truskmore | 53 | 57 | 160 |
| Maghera | 48 | 55 | 160 | Woodcock Hill | 47 | 44 | 10 |

+ sites with txs below 10kW.

## ISRAEL

**Systems:** DVB-T2 (MPEG4), § DVB-T (MPEG4) [E]

**ISRAELI PUBLIC BROADCASTING CORP. (IPBC) (Pub)** ▣161 Jaffa Road, Jerusalem 91280 **E:** info@kan.org.il **W:** www.kan.org. il **L.P:** CEO: Eldad Koblenz **Chs:** KAN 11, KAN Educational, MAKAN 33 (in Arabic) **KAN 11** ▣ P.O.Box 7139, Jerusalem 91071 ☎ +972 2 5301333 **MAKAN 33** ▣ P.O.Box 13172, Jerusalem 91131 ☎ +972 2 5013800 – **THE SECOND AUTHORITY FOR TELEVISION AND RADIO (SATR) (Pub)** ▣ P.O.Box 3445, Jerusalem ☎+972 2 6556222 **E:** rashut@rashut2.org.il **W:** www.rashut2.org.il **L.P:** Chmn: Eva Madjiboj. **NB:** SATR supervises the commercial TV channels Channel 10, Keshet 12 and Reshet 13. **Channel 10 (Comm)** ▣53 Derech Hashalom St., Givatayim 53454 ☎ +972 3 7331000 **W:** www. nana10.co.il **L.P:** CEO: Yossi Varshavsky **Chs:** Channel 10, Channel 14; **Keshet 12 (Comm)** ▣Ramat HaHayal, Tel Aviv **W:** www.mako. co.il/tv; **Reshet 13 (Comm)** ▣Ramat HaHayal, Tel Aviv **W:** reshet.tv/ general/channel13 – **CHANNEL 20 (Comm)** ▣ Tel Aviv **E:** news20@ ch-20.tv **W:** www.20il.co.il – **CHANNEL 99 (KNESSET CHANNEL) (Gov)** ▣ Kiryat Ben-Gurion, Jerusalem 91950 ☎ +972 2 6541636 **E:** feedback@knesset.gov.il **W:** www.knesset.gov.il.

**DTT Tx Networks**
**Tx Operator:** Bezeq **W:** www.bezeq.co.il **Mux:** KAN 11, KAN 11 HD, KAN Educational, MAKAN 33, MAKAN 33 HD, Channel 10, Channel 99, Keshet 12, Reshet 13, Channel 14, Channel 20, Music 24 **Txs:** ch26 (DVB-T)/ch28 (DVB-T) (SFN, Central Israel), ch29 (DVB-T)/ch32 (DVB-T2) (SFN, Northern/Southern Israel).

**WEST BANK & GAZA STRIP
(Palestinian Authority/State of Palestine)**

**Systems:** # PAL-B/G [E]; DVB-T2 (MPEG4) [E]

**National Station**
**PALESTINE PUBLIC BROADCASTING CORP.** ▣ P.O.Box 984, Ramallah Albereih, West Bank ☎ +970 2 2987903 ▤ +970 2 29879031 **E:** pbcinfo@pbc.ps **W:** www.pbc.ps **L.P:** Chmn: Riyad Al-Hassan **Txs:** Nablus ch5, Khan Yunis ch21, Ariha (Jericho) ch21, Kasser-Elhakim (Gaza) ch23, Ramallah ch25, Halhul ch30, Jenin ch31, Betjala ch34.

**Local Stations** not shown.

**DTT Tx Network**
**Tx Operator:** Starcom for Media Services **M:** multiprgr **Tx:** ch34 (Gaza)

## ITALY

**Systems:** DVB-T (MPEG2), DVB-T2 (MPEG4) [E]

**National Stations**
**RADIOTELEVISIONE ITALIANA (RAI) (Pub)** ▣ Direzione Centrale TV, Viale Mazzini 14, 00195 Roma (RM) ☎ +39 06 36864046 **E:** portale@rai.it **W:** www.rai.it **L.P:** DG: Antonio Campo Dall'Orto **Chs (terr.):** Rai 1-5, Rai News 24, Rai Sport, Rai Movie, Rai Gulp, Rai YoYo, Rai Scuola, Rai Storia – **LA 7 (Comm)** ▣ Via della Pineta Sacchetti 229, 00166 Roma (RM) ☎ +39 06 35584 **E:** la7@la7.tv **W:** www. la7.tv – **MEDIASET (Comm)** ▣ Viale Europa 48, Palazzo dei Cigni, 20093 Cologno Monzese (MI) ☎ +39 02 21021 **W:** www.mediaset.it.

**Local Stations** not shown.

**DTT Tx Networks** (DVB-T except where noted)
**Licensee:** Rai **M1:** Rai 1, Rai 2, Rai 3 + regional prgrs, Rai News 24

⌘ Rai R.1-3 **M2:** Rai 5, Rai Storia, Rai Sport, Rai Scuola ⌘ Rai R.Tutta Italiana, Rai R.Classica, Rai R. Techetè, Rai R.Live, Rai R.Kids, Rai Rai Isoradio, Rai GrParlamento, Rai R.1 Sport, Rai R,2 Indie **M3:** Rai 4, Rai Movie, Rai Premium, Rai Gulp, Rai YoYo, Rai 1 HD **M4:** Rai 2 HD, Rai 3 HD, Rai Sport+ HD **M5 (DVB-T2):** Rai 4 HD, Rai Premium HD.

| Location | M1 | M2 | M3 | M4 | M5 |
|---|---|---|---|---|---|
| SFN | (MFN) | 30 | 26 | 40 | (MFN) |
| SFN (Sardegna 1) | (MFN) | 49 | 43 | 41 | 45 |
| SFN (Sardegna 2) | (MFN) | 49 | 43 | 47 | 45 |

**Licensee:** Mediaset **M1✪:** Premium Action, Premium Crime, Premium Joi, Premium Stories, Sky Sport 24 HD, Sky Sport Serie A HD, Sky Sport Serie A, Sky Sport **M2:** 20 Mediaset, QVC, Food Network, Mediaset Extra, Focus, TOPcrime, Boing, Cartoonito **M3✪:** Premium Comedy, Premium Sport HD, Premium Sport 2 HD, Eurosport, Eurosport 2 **M4:** Rete4, Canale5, Italia1, Iris, La 5, TGCOM24 **M5✪:** Sky Uno, Sky Atlantic, Fox, National Geographic, Sky Sport Uno HD, Sky Sport 24.

| Location | M1 | M2 | M3 | M4 | M5 |
|---|---|---|---|---|---|
| SFN | 52 | 36 | 38 | 49 | 56 |
| SFN (Sardegna) | 50 | 46 | 29 | 52 | 42 |
| SFN (Sicilia) | 52 | 36 | 24 | 49 | 54 |

**Licensee:** Persidera **W:** www.persidera.it **M1:** Real Time, RTL 102.5 TV, HSE24. Giallo, Super!, DMAX, Radiofreccia, RTL 102.5 TV HD, Radiofreccia HD, Zeta Italiana ⌘ R.Capital, R.Deejay, R.m2o, RTL 102.5 **M2:** TV2000, Alpha, ibox65. ibox.it, Alice, Marcopolo, Casedesignstili, PopEconomy HD ⌘ R.Vaticana HD, K2, frisbee, Pop, Spike, Supertennis, VH1, RadioItaliaTV, TV8 ⌘ R.Italia SMI **M4:** Nove, Cielo, Paramount Channel, Sky TG24, Cine Sony, Motor Trend, Zelig Sport, Deejay TV ⌘ R. Maria **M5:** Life 120 Channel, Fight Network, Italia Channel, Gold TV Italia, La 4 Italia, Channel 24, Rete Italia, Lineagem, Juwelo, Vero, Air Italia, Linea Italia, Orler TV, Fire TV, Mondo Calcio, Canale 162, Mediatext.it, ILike.tv, Canale 232, Canale 237, Pianeta TV.

| Location | M1 | M2 | M3 | M4 | M5 |
|---|---|---|---|---|---|
| SFN | 47 | 55 | 48[1] | 44 | 33[2] |
| SFN (Sardegna) | 56 | 55 | 26 | 32 | 27 |

[1] Lazio (Viterbo), Liguria, Toscana, Umbria: ch42; [2]Abruzzo, Basilicata, Calabria, Marche Sud, Molise, Puglia, Sicilia: ch42; Emilia-Romagna, Friuli Venezia Giulia, Marche Nord, Veneto: ch54.

**Licensee:** Dfree **W:** www.dfree.tv **M1✪(exc.*):** Sportitalia*, Padre Pio TV*, Zelig243*, R. Zeta*, Premium Cinema, Premium Energy, Premium Emotion, Premium Comedy **Txs:** ch50 (SFN), exc. ch38 (Sardegna SFN) – **Licensee:** H3G **W:** www.tre.it **M:** Mediaset Canale Due, R101 TV, Rete 4 HD, Italia 1 HD, 20 Mediaset HD ⌘ R. R101, R. 105, Virgin R. **Txs:** ch37 (SFN), exc. ch22 (Sardegna SFN. – **Licensee:** Cairo Communication **W:** www.cairocommunication.it **M:** La7, La7 HD, La7d, La7d HD **Txs:** ch25 (SFN), ch59 (SFN2) – **Licensee:** Canale Italia **W:** www.canaleitalia.it **M1:** Italia 53/83/84/121/126 /127/134/135/136/141/142/150/156/159/160, Arte Italia 124/125, Cantando Ballando, Italia TV 2, Italia TV 1-3 ⌘ R.Padania **Txs:** Roma ch39 & MFN. **M2:** Italia 53/143/154/155, Canale Italia, Canale Italia 4/6/7/83/84, Galaxy TV2, Shopping Italia, France 24, Show TV ⌘ R.Canale Italia, Volami Nel Cuore **Txs:** Roma ch22 & MFN.

**Regional licensees** not shown (except below).

**South Tyrol**

**Regional Licensee:** Rundfunk-Anstalt Südtirol (RAS) ▣ Europallee 164A, 39100 Bozen ☎ +39 0471 546666 **E:** info@ras.bz.it **W:** www. ras.bz.it **M1:** ORF eins, ORF2, Das Erste, ZDF, 3Sat, ORF III **M2:** SRF1, SRF2, BR, Kika, Arte, RSI LA1, **M3*:** ZDF HD, SRF1 HD, SRF2 HD **M4*:** ORF eins HD, ORF2 HD, Das Erste HD **Txs: M1:** ch34 (SFN), **M2:** ch51 (SFN) **M3:** ch27 (SFN) **M4:** ch59 (SFN). (*=MPEG4)

## JAMAICA

**Systems:** ATSC [A]; # NTSC-M [A] ⇩2020

**PUBLIC BROADCASTING CORP. OF JAMAICA (Pub)** ▣ 5-9 South Odeon Avenue, Kingston ☎ +1 876 7549123 ▤ +1 876 9060435 **E:** info@pbcjamaica.org **W:** www.pbcjamaica.org **Txs:** (-) – **CVM TELEVISION LTD (Comm)** ▣ 69 Constant Spring Rd, Kingston 10 ☎ +1 876 9319400 ▤ +1 876 9311573 **E:** customerservice@cvmtv. com **W:** www.cvmtv.com **L.P:** CEO: Andre McGlone **Txs:** Kingston ch4 (3.2kW) & Netw. – **TELEVISION JAMAICA LTD (TVJ) (Comm)** ▣ P.O.Box 100, Kingston 10. ☎ +1 876 9265620 ▤ +1 876 9291029 **E:** tvjadmin@cwjamaica.com **W:** www.televisionjamaica.com **L.P:** GM: Claire C. Grant **Txs:** Kingston [a] ch11 (3.2kW) & netw. – **LOVE TV (Rlg)** ▣ 12 Carlton crescent, Kingston ☎ +1 876 9689596 ▤ +1 876 9685379 **L.P:** GM: Moya Thomas **Txs:** Kingston [a] ch6 (2.5kW) & netw. ([a]=analogue)

## JAPAN

**System:** ISDB-T [J]

**National Stations**
**NIPPON HOSO KYOKAI (NHK) (Pub)** ✉ 2-1, Jinnan 2-chome, Shibuya-ku, Tokyo 150-8001 ☎ +81 3 34651111 **W:** www.nhk.or.jp **Chs:** NHK General TV, NHK Educational TV **L.P:** Pres: Ryoichi Ueda – **ALL-NIPPON NEWS NETWORK (ANN) (Comm)** ✉ 9-1, Roppongi 6-chome, Minato-ku, Tokyo 106-8001 ☎ +81 3 64061111 **W:** www. tv-asahi.co.jp **L.P:** Chmn/CEO: Hiroshi Hayakawa – **FUJI TELEVISION NETWORK (FTN) (Comm)** ✉ 4-8, Daiba 2-chome, Minato-ku, Tokyo 137-8088 ☎ +81 3 55008888 **W:** www.fujitv.co.jp; www.fnn-news. com **L.P:** Chmn: Shuji Kanoh. – **JAPAN NEWS NETWORK (JNN) (Comm)** ✉ 3-6, Akasaka 5-chome, Minato-ku, Tokyo 107-8006. ☎ +81 3 37461111 **W:** www.tbs.co.jp **L.P:** Chmn: Shinji Takeda – **NIPPON NEWS NETWORK (NNN) (Comm)** ✉ 6-1, Higashi Shimbashi 1-chome, Minato-ku, Tokyo 105-7444 ☎ +81 3 62154444 **W:** www.ntv.co.jp; www.news24.jp **L.P:** Pres: Yoshio Okubo – **TV TOKYO NETWORK (TXN) (Comm)** ✉ 3-12, Toranomon 4-chome, Minato-ku, Tokyo 105-8012 ☎ +81 3 54707777 **W:** www.tv-tokyo. co.jp **L.P:** Chmn: Yuichi Takamashi.
**NB.** Commercial stns are relayed nationwide via local affiliates.

**Local Stations** not shown.

**DTT Tx Networks** (National Stations)

| Location | NHK[1] | NHK[2] | ANN | FTN | JNN | NNN | TXN |
|---|---|---|---|---|---|---|---|
| Tokyo (Tokyo Skytree) | 27 | 26 | 24 | 21 | 22 | 25 | 23 |

+ nationwide tx networks [1]) NHK General TV [2]) NHK Educational TV

## JORDAN

**System:** DVB-T2 (MPEG4) [E]

**JORDAN RADIO & TELEVISION (JRTV) (Pub)** ✉ P.O.Box 1041, 11118 Amman ☎ +962 6 4749171 🖷 +962 6 4778578 **E:** tv@jrtv.gov. jo **W:** www.jrtv.jo **L.P:** DG: Mohammad Tarawneh **Chs:** Jordan TV.

**DTT Tx Network**
**Tx Operator:** JRTV **Mux:** Jordan TV **Txs:** MFN

## KAZAKHSTAN

**Systems:** DVB-T2 (MPEG4) [E]; § SECAM-D/K [R], § PAL-D/K [R] ⇩2021

**National Stations**
**QAZAQSTAN RTRK (Gov)** ✉ Qonaev k. 4, 010000 Astana ☎ +7 7172 757161 **W:** kaztrk.kz **Chs:** Qazaqstan, Qazsport, Balapan, Regional stations. – **HABAR (Gov)** ✉ Jeltoqsan k. 185, 050013 Almaty ☎ +7 727 2700001 🖷 +7 727 2627805 **E:** khabar@khabar. kz **W:** khabar.kz **Chs:** Habar, Habar 24, Kazakh TV – **KTK (Comm)** ✉ Respýblika alany 13, 050013 Almaty ☎ +7 727 2583657 🖷 +7 727 2583693 **E:** ktk@ktk.kz **L.P:** DG: Arman Shuraev. – **NTK (Comm)** ✉ Respýblika alany 13, 050013 Almaty ☎ +7 727 2672750 🖷 +7 727 2721154 **E:** office@ntk.kz **W:** ntk.kz **L.P:** GD: Saida Igenbek – **31 ARNA (Comm)** ✉ Tajibaev k. 155, 050060 Almaty ☎ +7 727 3153131.

**Local Stations** not shown.

**DTT Tx Networks** (under construction)
**Tx Operator:** Kazteleradio **M1:** Pervyy kanal Eurasia, Qazaqstan, Balapan, Qazsport, Habar, Habar 24, Kazakh TV, 7 Kanal, KTK, 31 Arna, Astana TV, Mir **M2:** Asyl Arna, NTK, ON! Pyatnitsa, Almaty TV, STV Kazakhstan, Qazaqstan RTRK Regional stns, Novoe Televidenye, Tvoye TV, TDK 42, Gakku TV, Muzzone, Muzlife, Local stns **Txs: M1:** ch47 (Almaty) + MFN under construction. **M2:** ch33 (Almaty) + MFN under construction.

## KENYA

**System:** DVB-T2 (MPEG4) [E]

**National Stations**
**KENYA BROADCASTING CORP. (Gov)** ✉ P.O.Box 30456, Harry Thuku Road, 00100 Nairobi ☎ +254 20 334567 🖷 +254 20 220675 **E:** kbctv@swiftkenya.com **W:** www.kbc.co.ke **L.P:** Chmn: Victor Kyalo **Chs:** Channel 1, Heritage TV. – **CITIZEN TV (Comm)** ✉ P.O.Box 7468, 00300 Nairobi ☎ +254 20 2721415 🖷 +254 20 2724220 **E:** news@royalmedia.co.ke **W:** citizentv.co.ke – **KENYA TELEVISION NETWORK (KTN) (Comm)** ✉ P.O.Box 56985, 00100 Nairobi ☎ +254 20 227122 🖷 +254 20 214467 **E:** admin@ktnkenya.com **W:** www.standardmedia.co.ke **L.P:** Chmn: Mwakio Sio. – **K24 (Comm)** ✉ 3rd Floor, Longonot Place, Kijabe St., 00100 Nairobi. ☎ +254 21 248000 **W:** www.news24.co.ke – **NATION TV (NTV) (Comm)** ✉ P.O.Box 49010, Nairobi 00100 GPO ☎ +254 20 3208000 **E:** views@ ntv.co.ke **W:** www.ntv.co.ke – **OXYGEN TV (Comm)** ✉ P.O.Box 48445, 00100 Nairobi. **E:** info@odtv.co.ke **L.P:** MD: Kass Khimji. – **STELLAVISION (STV) (Comm)** ✉ P.O. Box 20190, Nairobi ☎ +254 20 2712982 🖷 +254 20 2713146.– **FAMILY TV (Rlg)** ✉ P.O.Box 2330 KNH, Nairobi ☎ +254 20 4200000 🖷 +254 20 4200100 **E:** info@ familykenya.com **W:** familymedia.tv

**Local Stations** not shown.

**DTT Tx Networks**
**Licensee:** Signet Ltd (KBC) **M:** KBC Channel One, Heritage TV, NTV, KTN, CNBC Africa, K24, STV, EATN, EATV, Oxygen TV, Family TV, God TV, Kiss TV, Classic TV, Citizen TV, GBS ✳ KBC English Service, KBC Idha FM, Metro FM, Coro FM **Txs:** ch57 (Nairobi 2.5kW) & nationwide MFN. – **Licensee:** Pan-Africa Network Group Co. Ltd ✉ P.O.Box 29538, 00100 Nairobi **E:** info@pang.co.ke **W:** www.pang. co.ke **Mux✿:** multiprgr **Txs:** MFN – **Licensee:** Startimes **M✿:** multiprgr **Txs:** MFN.

## KIRIBATI

**NB:** No terrestrial TV station.

## KOREA, North

**Systems:** #PAL-D/K [R], NTSC-M [R]; DTT planned

**RADIO AND TELEVISION BROADCASTING COMMITTEE (Gov)** ✉ Jonsung-dong, Moranbong District, Pyongyang ☎ +850 2 816035 🖷 +850 2 812100 **L.P:** Chmn: Yong Bo Hwang **Chs:** Korean Central Television (KCTV), Mansudae Television (MTV), Ryongnamsan Television (RTV), Sports Television (STV).
**Txs: KCTV:**

| Location | ch | kW | Location | ch | kW |
|---|---|---|---|---|---|
| Sangmasan | 1 | 10 | Ripbong | 8 | 10 |
| Chayubong | 2 | 30 | Chaedoksan | 9 | 10 |
| Suryongsan | 2 | 30 | Sepo | 9 | 70 |
| Hamhung | 3 | 70 | Sinyang | 9 | 30 |
| Pagaebong | 3 | 30 | Unjubong | 9 | 70 |
| Chaedoksan | 4 | 30 | Wangjaesan | 9 | 30 |
| Songjinsan | 4 | 20 | Wonsan | 10 | 70 |
| Wonsan | 4 | 10 | Chonchon | 11 | 10 |
| Chajiryong | 5 | 30 | Haeju | 11 | 70 |
| Paekam | 5 | 10 | Sambongsan | 11 | 10 |
| Kangtyong | 5 | 30 | Chajiryong | 12 | 30 |
| Kumgangsan | 5 | 30 | Chonchon | 12 | 10 |
| Sambongsan | 5 | 10 | Chongjin | 12 | 70 |
| Tokusan | 5 | 20 | Haksongsan | 12 | 20 |
| Chongjin | 6 | 70 | Kaesong | 12 | 70 |
| Hyangsan | 6 | 10 | Pyongyang | 12 | 70 |
| Sepo | 6 | 70 | Ripbong | 12 | 10 |
| Sinuiju | 6 | 70 | Sobaeksan | 12 | 30 |
| Sariwon | 7 | 30 | Songsan | 12 | 10 |
| Chayubong | 8 | 30 | Tokusan | 12 | 10 |
| Haksongsan | 8 | 20 | Wangjaesan | 12 | 30 |
| Kanggye | 8 | 70 | + relay txs below 10kW | | |

**MTV:** Pyongyang ch5 (350kW); **RTV/STV:** Kaesong ch9* (30kW), Pyongyang ch9 (140kW) **NB:** * Directed towards So. Korea (NTSC-M); equals So. Korean channel A11. UHF in Pyongyang: ch25 & 31 (prgrs unconfirmed).

**DTT Tx Network** (planned)
**Tx Operator:** Ministry of Post and Telecommunication **M:** KCTV, MTV, RTV, STV **Txs:** Nationwide MFN planned.

## KOREA, South

**System:** ATSC [A]

**National Stations**
**EDUCATIONAL BROADCASTING SYSTEM (EBS) (Pub)** ✉ 35, Baumoe-ro 1-gil, Seocho-gu, Seoul 06762 ☎ +82 2 5211586

**W:** www.ebs.co.kr **L.P:** Pres/CEO: Chang Hae-rang. **Chs:** EBS1, EBS2 – **KOREAN BROADCASTING SYSTEM (KBS) (Pub)** ▣ 113, Yeouigongwon-ro, Yeoungdeungpo-gu, Seoul 07235 ☎ +82 2 7812001 **W:** www.kbs.co.kr **L.P:** Pres: Yang Sung-Dong **Chs:** KBS1, KBS2. – **MUNHWA BROADCASTING CORP. (MBC) (Comm)** ▣ 267, Seongam-ro, Mapo-gu, Seoul 03925 ☎ +82 2 7890011 **W:** www.imbc.com **L.P:** Pres/CEO: Choi Seung-Ho – **SEOUL BROADCASTING SYSTEM (SBS) (Comm)** ▣ 161, Mokdongseo-ro, Yangcheon-gu, Seoul 07996 ☎ +82 2 20610006 **W:** www.sbs.co.kr **L.P:** Pres: Park Jung-Hoon.

**Local Stations**
**O Broadcasting System (OBS):** 233, Ojeong-ro, Bucheon-si, Gyeonggi-do 14442; Seoul ch36. **CJB** (Cheongju), **G1** (Chuncheon), **JIBS** (Jeju), **JTV** (Jeonju), **KBC** (Gwangju), **KNN** (Busan), **TBC** (Daegu), **TJB** (Daejeon), **UBC (Ulsan)** are SBS affiliates and carry the SBS network outside of local programming (txs see below).

**DTT Tx Networks** (National Stations)

| Location | E* | E*[1] | K1 | K1[1] | K2 | K2[1] | M | M[1] | S/L° | S[1] | LOCAL |
|---|---|---|---|---|---|---|---|---|---|---|---|
| Andong | 36 | - | 32 | - | 34 | - | 22 | - | 24 | - | (TBC) |
| Busan | 18 | - | 14 | - | 16 | - | 17 | - | 15 | - | (KNN) |
| Changwon | 32 | - | 22 | - | 25 | - | 26 | - | 33 | - | (KNN) |
| Cheongju | 35 | - | 23 | - | 34 | - | 20 | - | 23 | - | (CJB) |
| Chuncheon | 48 | - | 32 | - | 41 | - | 33 | - | 40 | - | (G1) |
| Chungju | 49 | - | 39 | - | 47 | - | 40 | - | 43 | - | (CJB) |
| Daegu | 18 | - | 14 | - | 16 | - | 17 | - | 15 | - | (TBC) |
| Daejeon | 38 | - | 26 | - | 32 | - | 17 | - | 15 | - | (TJB) |
| Gangneung | 18 | - | 15 | - | 17 | - | 14 | - | 16 | - | (G1) |
| Gwangju | 32 | - | 17 | - | 18 | - | 14 | - | 15 | - | (KBC) |
| Jeju | 35 | - | 27 | - | 29 | - | 31 | - | 33 | - | (JIBS) |
| Jeonju | 46 | - | 27 | - | 44 | - | 41 | - | 33 | - | (JTV) |
| Jinju | 31 | - | 20 | - | 23 | - | 21 | - | 19 | - | (KNN) |
| Mokpo | 38 | - | 44 | - | 46 | - | 37 | - | 16 | - | (KBC) |
| Pohang | 51 | - | 42 | - | 50 | - | 46 | - | 41 | - | (TBC) |
| Seoul | 18 | 54 | 15 | 52 | 17 | 56 | 14 | 55 | 16 | 53 | (SBS) |
| Suncheon | 24 | - | 44 | - | 46 | - | 16 | - | 38 | - | (KBC) |
| Ulsan | 48 | - | 28 | - | 40 | - | 34 | - | 30 | - | (UBC) |
| Wonju | 51 | - | 44 | - | 45 | - | 46 | - | 40 | - | (G1) |

+ translators E=EBS, K1=KBS1, K2=KBS2, M=MBC, S=SBS L=Local *) Multiplex includes EBS1, EBS2 °) Local stns (SBS affiliates) [1]) UHD (nationwide netw. under construction)
**NB:** T-DMB (VHF) networks with radio & TV services for mobile devices not shown (see National Radio section).

**Systems:** DVB-T (MPEG4), DVB-T2 (MPEG4); § PAL-B/G [E]

**National Stations**
**RADIOTELEVIZIONI I KOSOVËS (RTK) (Pub)** ▣ Rr. Xhemail Prishtina nr. 12, 10000 Prishtinë ☎+383 38 230102 **E:** post@rtklive.com **W:** www.rtklive.com **L.P:** Chmn: Ismet Bexheti **Chs (terr.):** RTK1-4, RTK HD – **KOHAVISION TV (KTV) (Comm)** ▣ Rr. Nene Tereza, 10000 Prishtinë ☎ +381 38 248014 **E:** kohavision@koha.net **W:** www.kohavision.net – **RTV 21 (Comm)** ▣ Pallati i Mediave, Aneks II, 10000 Prishtinë ☎ +381 38 241526 ▤ +381 38 241526 **E:** lajmet@rtv21.tv **W:** rtv21.tv.

**Local Stations** (ª=analogue)
**TV Ballkan:** Rr. Adem Jashari 8, 20000 Prizereni; ªch53. **TV Besa:** Rr. Kater Kullat n.n., 20000 Prizereni; ªch30. **TV Dukagjini:** Rr. Fehmi Agani 16, 30000 Pejë; ªch36. **TV Festina:** Rr. Deshmoret e Kombit n.n., Ferizaj; ªch40. **TV Herc:** 73000 Shterpcë; ch35. **TV Iliria:** Rr. Hoxhë Jonuzi n.n., 61000 Viti; ªch28. **TV Liria:** Rr. Reçak n.n., Ferizaj; ªch29. **TV Mir:** Rr. Vojske Jugoslavije n.n., Leposaviq; ªch23. **TV Mitrovica:** 40000 Mitrovicë; ªch42. **TV Most:** Rr. Nemanjica 14, Zveqan; ªch61. **TV Opinion:** Rr. Marin Barleti, n.n, Zym; ªch28. **TV Prizren:** Rr. Papa Gjon Pali II 1A, 20000 Prizereni; ªch60. **TV Puls:** Shillovë; 60000 Gjilan ªch36. **TV Syri Vision:** Rr. Sadik Pozhegu 28, 50000 Gjakovë; ªch33. **TV Tema:** Rr. Sadik Bega n.n., Ferizaj; ch50. **TV Vali:** Pasjak; 60000 Gjilan ªch39. **TV Zoom:** Kuvcë e Epërme; ªch43.

**DTT Tx Networks** (DVB-T2 exc. where noted)
**Licensee Mux 1:** RTK **M (DVB-T):** RTK1-4, RTK HD, RTSH1, Klan Kosova HD, Rrokum HD – **Licensee Mux 2:** RTV 21 Media **M:** TV 21 HD, RTV 21 Plus HD, RTV 21 Mix HD, RTV 21 Popullore HD, RTV 21 Junior HD, RTV 21 NewsBiz HD, RTV 21 Maqedoni HD, Klan Kosova – **Licensee Mux 3:** Kohavision **M:** KTV HD, Arta HD. **Txs:** nationwide MFN under construction.

**Systems:** DVB-T2 (MPEG4) [E]. BFBS-TV: DVB-T (MPEG4) [E]

**KUWAIT TELEVISION (Gov)** ▣ P.O. Box 621, 13007 Safat ☎ +965 22415300 ▤ +965 22454233 **W:** www.media.gov.kw **Chs:** KTV1, KTV2, KTV3, KTV4.

**DTT Tx Network**
**Tx Operator:** Ministry of Information **M:** KTV1-4 **Txs:** SFN.

**Foreign Military Station**
**BFBS-TV Relay (Serving British Mil)** ▣ Chalfont Grove, Narcot Lane, Chalfont St Peter, Buckinghamshire, SL9 8TN, United Kingdom. **Mux✪:** BBC One, BBC Two/CBBC, ITV, BFBS Extra/Cbeebies, BFBS Sport, BFBS Movies, Sky News, Sky Sports 1, Sky Sports 2, Sky Sports 3, Nepali TV ⌘ BFBS R., BFBS R.2, BFBS Gurkha R. **Tx:** ch27 (Camp Beuhring)

**System:** DVB-T2 (MPEG4) [E]

**National Stations**
**KOOMDUK TELERADIO BERÜÜ KORPORATSIYASY (KTRK)** ▣ Jash Gvardiya blvd. 59, 720010 Bishkek ☎ +996 312 392059 **E:** public@ktrk.kg **W:** www.ktrk.kg **L.P:** DG: Ilim Karypbekov **Ch:** Kyrgyzstan, Balastan, Madaniyat, Muzyka, Sport – **ELTR (Pub)** ▣ blvd. Erkindik 122, 720040 Bishkek ☎ +996 312 906144 **L.P:** Dir: Shayyrbek Abdrakhmanov **E:** eltr@ktnet.kg **W:** www.eltr-tv.kg – **5 KANAL (Pub)** ▣ Ibraimov St 24, 720000 Bishkek ☎ +996 312 592066 **E:** koordinator@5tv.kg **W:** 5tv.kg.

**Local Stations** not shown.

**DTT Tx Networks**
**Tx Operator:** Kyrgyztelecom **W:** www.kt.kg **M1:** KTRK, Madaniyat, Balastan, KTRK Muzyka, KTRK Sport, Ala-Too 24, 5 Kanal, Piramida, ELTR, ELTR Ilim Jana Bilim, Mir, Pervyy kanal, Rossiya 24, Intimak TV, Local stns **M2:** Mir 24, TNT Kyrgyzstan, Domashniy Telekanal, Sanat TV, Kyrgyz TV, Tumar TV, 312 Kino, 312 Muzika, Semieyniy, NTS HD, Lyubimiy TV, TV1.KG, Aziya TV, Umut TV, Prime TV, Bilim TV, Osh TV, Saltanat **M3:** RTR Planeta, Ren TV Kyrgyzstan, NTV Kyrgyzstan, Kyrgyzstan TV, ON 1, NTS Sport HD, Nur TV, Osh Pirim, Keremet TV, Anten TV **M4:** Pyatnitsa, NBT, Ayan TV, Eho Manasa, Ya!, Next TV, 24 TV, RTR Rossiya, 7 Kanal, 8 Kanal, RTV. **Txs:** M1: ch25 (Bishkek) & nationwide netw. **M2-4:** MFN

**Systems:** DTMB [E]; § PAL-B [E] ⬇2020

**National Station**
**LAO NATIONAL TELEVISION (LNTV) (Gov)** ▣ P.O.Box 5635, Vientiane ☎ +856 21 710643 ▤ +856 21 710182 **E:** laotv1@gmail.com **W:** www.tnl.gov.la **L.P:** DG: Bounchao Phichit **Chs:** TV1, TV3, Provincial stns.

**DTT Tx Networks**
**Licensee:** Lao Digital TV Co. Ltd **Mux 1-3(partly✪):** multiprgr **Txs:** **M1:** ch21 (Savannakhet 2.5kW) & MFN **M2:** ch23 (Savannakhet 2.5kW) & MFN **M3:** ch25 (Savannakhet 2.5kW) & MFN

**System:** DVB-T (MPEG4) [E]

**National Stations**
**LATVIJAS TELEVIZIJA (LTV) (Pub)** ▣ Zakusalas krastmala 3, 1509 Riga ☎ +371 67200316 **E:** ltv@ltv.lv **W:** ltv.lsm.lv **L.P:** Chmn: Ivars Belte **Chs:** Kanals 2, LNT, TV3, TV6, 3+ – **LATVIJAS REGIONU TELEVIZIJA (RE:TV) (Comm)** ▣ Purva iela 12a, 4201 Valmiera ☎ +371 64219043 **E:** redakcija@retv.lv **W:** www.retv.lv **L.P:** Dir: Aiva Logina – **LATVIJAS SLAGERKANALS (Comm)** ▣ Elizabetes iela 57a-22, 1050 Riga ☎ +371 67296345 **E:** info@slageris.lv **W:** slageris.lv – **RIGA TV24 (Comm)** ▣ Blaumana iela 32, 1011 Riga ☎ +371 67630301 **E:** reklama@rigatv24.lv **W:** rigatv24.lv **L.P:** Dir: Klavs Kalninš.

*(– ALL MEDIA LATVIA (Comm) ▣ Dzelzavas iela 120g, 1021 Riga ☎ +371 67479100 **E:** pasts@skaties.lv. **W:** skaties.lv **L.P:** CEO: Pierre Danon **Chs:** Kanals 2, LNT, TV3, TV6, LTV1, LTV7)*

**Local Station**
**Vidusdaugavas Televizija (Comm):** Brivibas iela 2d, 5201 Jekabpils; ch55 (0.5 kW).

**DTT Tx Networks**
**Licensee:** Lattelecom SIA **W:** www.lattelecom.lv **M1:** LTV1, LTV7, RE:TV, Riga TV24, Sportacentrs.com **M2✪:** 3+, Eurosport 1, LNT, National Geographic, PBK, REN TV Baltija, RTR Planeta, S.TV, TV1000, TV3, TV6 **M3✪:** 360 TV, Comedy TV 1000, Dom Kino Premium, Euronews, Kanals 2, Latvijas Šlagerkanals, MTV Music 24, Nickelodeon, NTV Mir, Ohotnik i Ribolov, PBMK **M4✪:** Animal Planet, BBC Earth, CNN International, Discovery Channel, Discovery Science, DTX, ID Extra, MTV Europe, Nick Jr, TLC, Travel Channel **M5✪:** AMC, CTC Baltics, Dom Kino, FilmZone, Fox, Fox Life, Hustler TV, Sony Channel, Sony Turbo, THT, VH-1 Europe **M6✪:** Best4Sport, Disney Channel, Disney Jr, , Disney XD, Eurosport 2, Jim Jam, KHL, KidZone, Motors TV, NBA TV, Setanta Sports **M7✪:** Discovery HD Showcase, Eurosport HD, MTV HD.

| Location | M1 | M2 | M3 | M4 | M5 | M6 | M7 | kW |
|---|---|---|---|---|---|---|---|---|
| Cesvaine | 22 | 46 | 41 | 58 | 30 | 24 | - | 75/2x120/110/2x100 |
| Daugavpils | 27 | 51 | 56 | 47 | 39 | 40 | - | 65/80/65/100/2x80 |
| Dundaga | 30 | - | - | - | - | - | - | 15 |
| Kuldiga | 30 | 40 | 47 | 52 | 25 | 35 | - | 65/5x80 |
| Liepaja | 21 | 23 | 39 | 26 | 33 | 35 | - | 50 |
| Rezekne | 44 | 50 | 56 | 27 | 39 | 37 | - | 5x100/5 |
| Riga | 28 | 31 | 43 | 45 | 48 | 44 | 59 | 5x85/74/80 |
| Valmiera | 21 | 51 | 54 | 50 | 33 | 37 | - | 65/3x80/65/25 |
| Viesite | 38 | 46 | 60 | 53 | 26 | 23 | - | 16 |
| Vitrupe | 21 | - | - | - | - | - | - | 13 |

+ sites with txs below 10kW.

**Systems:** # PAL-B/G [E]; DVB-T2 (MPEG4) [E] planned

**TÉLÉ-LIBAN (Pub)** ✉ Tallet El Khayat, Corniche canal 7, P.O.Box 4848, Beirut ☎ +961 1 786930 🖷 +961 1 786931 **W:** www.teleliban.com.lb **LP:** CEO: Talal El Makdessi **Chs:** Channel 1, Channel 2 **Txs: Channel 1:** Beirut ch7 (50kW) & netw., **Channel 2:** Beirut ch9 & netw. – **AL-JADEED TV (Comm)** ✉ BP 110, 5958 Beirut ☎ +961 1 303300 🖷 +961 1 303300 **E:** info@aljadeed.tv **W:** www.aljadeed.tv **Txs:** (-). – **AL-MANAR TV** ✉ BP 354/25, Beirut ☎ +961 1 276000 🖷 +961 1 823794 **E:** info@almanar.com.lb **W:** www.almanar.com.lb **Txs:** (-). – **FUTURE TELEVISION (Comm)** ✉ BP 13-6052, Sanayeh, Beirut ☎ +961 1 355355 🖷 +961 1 753232 **W:** www.futuretvnetwork.com **Txs:** (-). – **LEBANESE BROADCASTING CORP. (LBC) (Comm)** ✉ BP 165853, Zouk 111, Beirut ☎ +961 9 850850 🖷 +961 9 850916 **E:** info@lbcgroup.tv **W:** www.lbcgroup.tv **LP:** SM: Pierre Al Daher. **Txs:**(-). – **MURR TELEVISION (MTV) (Comm)** ✉ Ashrafieh Fouad Chehab Street, RML Building, Beirut ☎ +961 1 841025 🖷 +961 1 841029 **W:** www.mtv.com.lb **LP:** Chmn/CEO: Michel El Murr. **Txs:** (-). – **NATIONAL BROADCASTING NETWORK (NBN) (Comm)** ✉ BP 13-6633 Chouran, Beirut ☎ +961 1 841020 🖷 +961 1 841029 **E:** info@nbn.com.lb **W:** www.nbn.com.lb **Txs:** (-).

**System:** DVB-T2 (MPEG4) [E]

**LESOTHO TELEVISION (LTV) (Gov)** ✉ P.O.Box 552, Maseru 0100 ☎ +266 22323808 🖷 +266 22323808 **L.P:** DG: Dada Lebohang Moqasa.

**DTT Tx Network**
**Tx Operator:** Startimes **M(partly✪):** multiprgr **Txs:** MFN

**System:** DVB-T2 (MPEG4) [E]

**LIBERIA BROADCASTING SYSTEM (Pub)** ✉ P.O.Box 594, Paynesville ☎ +231 88 6669808 **E:** lbs@yahoo.com **W:** elbcradio.com **LP:** DG: Darryl Ambrose Nmah – **CLAR TV (Comm)** ✉ Pegasus Building, Mechlin St. 231, Monrovia **E:** royalcommedia@yahoo.com **W:** www.facebook.com/ClarTv **LP:** SM: Ahmed Pabai – **DCTV (Comm)** ✉ P.O.Box 1312, Monrovia. – **POWER TV (Comm)** ✉ Broad & Gurley St., Monrovia ☎ +231 6514343 – **REAL TV (Comm)** ✉ Ashmun St., Monrovia ☎ +231 6518418 **E:** abkollie2002@yahoo.com **LP:** SM: Aaron Kollie.

**DTT Tx Network**

**Tx Operator:** Startimes **M(partly✪):** multiprgr **Txs:** MFN

**Systems:** PAL-B/G [E] ; DVB-T2 (MPEG4) [E] planned

**National Station**
**LIBYA NATIONAL CHANNEL (LNC) (Gov)** ✉ P.O.Box 80237, Tripoli ☎ +218 21 3402153 🖷 +218 21 3403458 **W:** www.ltv.ly **Txs:** (pol.H) Tripoli ch6 (20kW) & network.

**Local Stations** not shown.

**NB:** No terrestrial TV station.

**System:** DVB-T (MPEG4) [E]

**National Stations**
**LIETUVOS NACIONALINIS RADIJAS IR TELEVIZIJA (LRT) (Pub)** ✉ Konarskio g. 49, 03123 Vilnius ☎ +370 5 2363100 **E:** lrt@lrt.lt **W:** www.lrt.lt **L.P:** DG: Monika Garbaciauskaite-Budriene. **Chs (terr.):** LRT Televizija, LRT Plius – **LIETUVOS RYTAS TV (Comm)** ✉ Gedimino pr. 12 A, 01103 Vilnius ☎ +370 5 2743718 **E:** tv@lrytas.lt **W:** tv.lrytas.lt **L.P:** Dir: Linas Ryškus – **ALL MEDIA LITHUANIA (Comm)** ✉ Kalvariju g. 143, 08221 Vilnius ☎ +370 5 2030101 **E:** info@@tv3.lt **W:** www.tv3.lt **L.P:** CEO: Laura Blaževiciute. **Chs:** TV3, TV6, TV8 – **UAB LAISVAS IR NEPRIKLAUSOMAS KANALAS (Comm)** ✉ Šeškines g. 20, 07156 Vilnius ☎ +370 5 2431058 **E:** lnk@lnk.lt **W:** lnk.lt **L.P:** DG: Zita Sarakiene **Chs**: LNK, TV1, Info TV, BTV, Liuks!

**Local Stations** (all Comm)
**Dzukijos televizija:** Pramones g. 9, 62175 Alytus; ch55 (3.2kW).
**FMT TV:** Vilniaus g. 31, 01402 Vilnius; Papliauškos ch24 (1kW). **LN Televizija:** A. Vaišvilos g. 30-1, 90127 Plunge; ch40 (0.9kW). **Marijampoles televizija:** Gedimino g. 11, 68307 Marijampole; ch41 (1kW). **Pukas-TV:** Ringuvos g. 45, 45242 Kaunas; ch54 (Juragiai 0.8kW). **Roventos TV:** Draugystes g. 18-1, 89168 Mažeikiai; ch58 (Mažeikiai 1.6kW). **Siauliu televizija:** Liejyklos g. 10, 78147 Siauliai; ch30 (Bubai 0.9kW). **TV7:** Chemiku g. 138a, 55218 Jonava; ch40 (0.3kW). **Ventos regionine televizija:** Ventos g. 32a, Venta, 85316 Akmenes r.; ch37 (Venta 2kW).

**DTT Tx Networks**
**Tx Operator:** Lietuvos radijo ir televizijos centras (LRTC) **W:** www.telecentras.lt **M1:** LRT Televizija HD, LRT Plius HD, LRT Televizija, LRT Plius **M2:** LNK, TV3, BTV, TV6, TV8, Info TV, Lietuvos rytas TV, Liuks!, Current Time (RFE/RL) **Regional Mux (R):** TVP Info, TVP Historia, TVP Polonia, Nuta TV, Power TV.

| Location | M1 | M2 | R | kW |
|---|---|---|---|---|
| Bubiai | 34 | 22 | - | 32/21 |
| Druskininkai | 40 | 47 | - | 7.6/3.5 |
| Giruliai | 29 | 60 | - | 30/19 |
| Ignalina | 35 | 28 | - | 5.1/4.7 |
| Juragiai | 21 | 44 | - | 37/19 |
| Moletai | 48 | 57 | - | 7/3.6 |
| Nida | 29 | 60 | - | 5 |
| Pažagieniai | 32 | 29 | - | 25/9 |
| Rokiškis | 32 | 49 | - | 8/2 |
| Švekšna | 29 | 60 | - | 10/1 |
| Švencionys | 35 | 28 | 33 | 8/6/1 |
| Taurage | 29 | 60 | - | 35/40 |
| Utena | 35 | 28 | - | 11/6 |
| Varena | 40 | 47 | - | 7/4 |
| Viešintos | 32 | 49 | - | 7 |
| Vilnius | 48 | 57 | 31 | 120/32/5 |
| Visaginas | 35 | 28 | - | 5.1/4.7 |

+ sites with txs below 5kW

**NB:** No terrestrial TV station.

**System:** DVB-T (MPEG2) [E]

**Tx Operator:** Startimes **M(partly✪):** multiprgr **Txs:** MFN

**RTL GROUP (Comm)** ✉ 45, blvd Pierre Frieden, 1543 Luxembourg ☎ +352 24865200 **W:** www.rtlgroup.com; www.rtl.lu **LP:** CEO (RTL Group): Bert Habets. **NB:** RTL Group is the company holding for several radio & TV enterprises. Prgrs distributed terrestrially via txs in Luxembourg: **RTL Télé Lëtzebuerg, den 2ten RTL** (in Luxembourgish); **RTL4, RTL5, RTL7, RTL8** (in Dutch, for viewers in the Netherlands); **Club RTL** (in Flemish, for viewers in Belgium); **Plug RTL, RTL TVI** (in French, for viewers in Belgium); **M6** (in French, for viewers in France).

**DTT Tx Networks**
**Tx Operator:** BCE **W:** www.bce.lu **M1:** Club RTL, Plug RTL, RTL TVI, RTL4, RTL5, RTL7 **Tx:** ch24 (Dudelange 40kW) **M2:** RTL Télé Lëtzebuerg, RTL Télé Lëtzebuerg HD, den 2ten RTL, den 2ten RTL HD **Tx:** ch27 (Dudelange 145kW) **M3:** RTL8, Luxe.TV ⌘ RTL France **Tx:** ch21 (Dudelange 200kW).

## MACAU (China, SAR)

**Systems:** DTMB [E]; § PAL-I [E] ⇩2020

**TELEDIFUSÃO DE MACAU S.A. (TDM) (Pub)** ✉ CP 446, Macau ☎ +853 28520206 📠 +853 28520208 **E:** tdmadm@tdm.com.mo **W:** www.tdm.com.mo **L.P:** Chmn: Manuel Pires

**DTT Tx Networks**
**Tx Operator:** TDM **M1:** Canal Macau, TDM Ou Mun, TDM Informação **M2:** CCTV-9, CCTV-13, CGTN, CGTN Documentary, Fujian TV, Hunan TV, Guangdong TV **M3:** TDM HD, TDM Desporto

| Location | M1 | M2 | M3 |
|---|---|---|---|
| SFN | 24 | 43 | 48 |

## MACEDONIA

**System:** DVB-T (MPEG4) [E]

**National Stations**
**MAKEDONSKA RADIO-TELEVIZIJA (MRT) (Pub)** ✉ bul. Goce Delcev bb, 1000 Skopje ☎ +389 2 5119899 **W:** www.mtv.com.mk **Chs:** MRT1, MRT2, Sobraniski kanal. – **ALFA (Comm)** ✉ Gradski stadion, 1000 Skopje ☎ +389 2 3217170 **W:** www.alfa.mk – **ALSAT-M (Comm)** ✉ ul. Krste Misirkov 7, DTC Mavrovka lom. C kat 9, 1000 Skopje ☎ +389 2 3290364 **W:** alsat.mk – **KANAL 5 (Comm)** ✉ ul. Skupi bb, 1000 Skopje ☎ +389 2 3091551 **E:** kanal5@kanal5.com.mk **W:** kanal5.com.mk – **TV SITEL (Comm)** ✉ ul. Gradski stadion bb, 1000 Skopje ☎ +389 2 3116566 **E:** marketing@sitel.com.mk **W:** sitel.com.mk – **TV TELMA (Comm)** ✉ ul. Nikola Parapunov bb, 1000 Skopje ☎ +389 2 3076677 **E:** telma@telma.com.mk **W:** telma.com.mk.

**Local Stations** not shown.

**DTT Tx Networks**
**Licensee M1-3+6:** one.Vip **W:** www.vip.mk **M1✪(exc.*):** MRT 1*, MRT 2*, MRT Sobraniski kanal*, Sitel 3, Kanal 5 Plus, Nasha TV, DM Sat, Cine Star Premiere 2, Cine Star Action TV, Sport Klub 3, Da Vinci Learning, Baby TV, HBO, HBO 2, Shenja TV, Viasat Explore **M2✪:** TV 24, N1 Srbija, Sport Klub, Sport Klub 4, Viasat History, Viasat Nature HD/Viasat History HD, National Geographic, 24 Kitchen, Cine Star TV, FOX Life, FOX Crime, Pikaboo, Magic TV, Dorcel TV, Cinemania, TV 1000 **M3✪:** TV Nova, RTV 21 Maqedoni, Grand TV, Cine Star Premiere 1, Sport Klub 2, Sport Klub 5, FOX, FOX Movies, HBO 3, E!, Cartoon Network, Boomerang, VH 1 Adria, Hustler TV, Private TV **M6:** Alfa, Alsat-M, Kanal 5, TV Telma, TV Sitel, Local stns – **Licensee M4+5:** MRT **M4:** MRT1, MRT2, Sobraniski kanal **M5:** MRT1 HD, MRT 2 HD.

| Location | M1 | M2 | M3 | M4 | M5 | M6 |
|---|---|---|---|---|---|---|
| Boskija | 21 | 37 | 49 | 34 | 41 | 50 |
| Crn Vrv | 26 | 28 | 30 | 23 | 52 | 40 |
| Mali Vlaj | 32 | 39 | 41 | 26 | 36 | 44 |
| Pelister | 25 | 29 | 33 | 22 | 37 | 38 |
| Popova Šapka | 24 | 34 | 38 | 27 | 36 | 41 |
| Stracin | 21 | 41 | 46 | 37 | 42 | 50 |
| Turtel | 22 | 32 | 43 | 24 | 39 | 38 |
| + translators | | | | | | |

## MADAGASCAR

**Systems:** DVB-T2 (MPEG4) [E]; § SECAM-K1 [VHF=K]

**National Station**
**TELEVISIONA MALAGASY (TVM) (Pub)** ✉ BP 271, 101 Antananarivo ☎ +261 20 2221784 📠 +261 20 2232815 **E:** webtvmalagasy@gmail.com **W:** www.facebook.com/tvmalagasyofficiel.

**Local Stations** not shown.

**DTT Tx Network**
**Licensee:** Startimes **M(partly✪):** multiprgr **Txs:** MFN.

## MADEIRA (Portugal)

**System:** DVB-T (MPEG4) [E]

**RTP MADEIRA (Pub)** ✉ Rua Caminho de Santo António 145, 9020-002 Funchal ☎ +351 291709100 **E:** martim.santos@rtp.pt **W:** www.rtp.pt/rtpmadeira **L.P:** Dir: Martim Santos.

**DTT Tx Network**
**Licensee:** Portugal Telecom **Mux:** RTP1, RTP2, RTP3/RTP Madeira, RTP Memória, SIC, TVI, ARTV **Txs:** ch54 (SFN).

## MALAWI

**System:** DVB-T2 (MPEG4) [E]

**National Station**
**MALAWI BROADCASTING CORP. (Pub)** ✉ P.O.Box 30133, Chichiri, Blantyre 3 ☎ +265 1871971 📠 +265 1871257 **E:** tvmalawi@malawi.net **W:** www.mbc.mw **L.P:** DG: Aubrey Edward Sumbuleta.

**Local Stations** not shown.

**DTT Tx Network**
**Licensee:** Multichoice Malawi **M(partly✪):** MBC TV, Luso, God News Broadcasting Services (GBS), Timveni, Luntha, Channel for All Africa (CAN), Calvary (CFC), Times, Hope, Zodiak, Joy, Matindi, Ufulu, Beta, Ufulu, Angaliba, African Bible College (ABC), Laura TV **Txs:** MFN.

## MALAYSIA

**Systems:** DVB-T2 (MPEG4) [E]; § PAL-B/G [E] ⇩2019

**RADIO TELEVISYEN MALAYSIA (RTM) (Gov)** ✉ Dept. of Broadc, Angkasapuri, Kuala Lumpur 50614 ☎ +60 3 22825333 📠 +60 3 22825103 **E:** aduan@rtm.gov.my **W:** www.rtm.gov.my **L.P:** DG: Datuk Abu Bakar Ab Rahim **Chs:** TV1, TV2, TVi, regional stns – **METROPOLITAN TV (8TV)** ✉ Metropolitan TV sdn bhd, Sri Pentas, 3 Persiaran Bandar Utama, 47800 Petaling Jaya, Selangor Darul Ehsan ☎ +60 3 77288282 📠 +60 3 77268282 **E:** info@8tv.com.my **W:** www.8tv.com.my – **NTV7 (Comm)** ✉ 7, Jalan Jurubina U1/18, Hicom-Glenmarie Industrial Park, 40000 Shah Alam, Selangor Darul Ehsan ☎ +60 3 55691777 📠 +60 3 55692515 **E:** feedback@ntv7.com.my **W:** www.ntv7.com.my – **SYSTEM TV MALAYSIA BERHAD (TV3)** ✉ Sri Pentas (Ground Floor, South Wing) No. 3, Persiaran Banjar Utama, 47800 Petaling Jaya Selangor Darul Ehsan ☎ +60 3 7166333 📠 +60 3 77278455 **E:** query@tv3.com.my **W:** www.tv3.com.my – **TV9 (Comm)** ✉ Lot 31, Jalan Pelukis U1/46, Temasya Industrial Park, 40150 Shah Alam, Selangor Darul Ehsan ☎ +60 3 55685999 **W:** www.tv9.com.my

**DTT Tx Networks**
**Licensee:** RTM **Mux:** TV1, TV2, TVi, regional stns **Txs:** ch44 (Kuala Lumpur) & nationwide MFN. – **Licensee:** U Television ✉ 3rd Floor, KL Plaza, 179 Jalan Bukit Bintang, 55100 Kuala Lumpur **Mux✪:** multiprgr. **Txs:** MFN.

## MALDIVES

**Systems:** ISDB-T [E]; § PAL-B [E] ⇩2019

**PUBLIC SERVICE MEDIA (PSM)** ✉ Radio Building, Ameenee Magu, Malé, 20331 ☎ +960 3000300 📠 +960 3317273 **E:** info@psm.mv **W:** www.psm.mv; psmnews.mv **L.P:** Chmn: Ibrahim Umar Manik **Chs:** TV Maldives, Yes TV.

**DTT Tx Network**
**Licensee:** PSM **Mux:** multiprgr **Txs:** (-)

## MALI

**Systems:** DVB-T2 (MPEG2) [E]; § SECAM-B/G [VHF=K, UHF=E]

**RADIODIFFUSION TÉLÉVISION DU MALI (ORTM) (Pub)** ✉ BP 171, Bamako ☎ +223 20210737 🖷 +223 20214205 **E:** info@ortm.ml **W:** ortm.ml **L.P:** Dir (TV): Youssouf Touré **Chs:** ORTM, TM2

**DTT Tx Network**
**Tx Operator:** Société Malienne de Transmission et de Diffusion (SMDT-SA) **M:** ORTM, TM2, TV5 Monde **Txs:** MFN.

## MALTA

**System:** DVB-T (MPEG4) [E]

**PUBLIC BROADCASTING SERVICES LTD (PBS) (Pub)** ✉ 75, Triq San Luqa, Gwardamangia, Pieta', PTA 1022 ☎ +356 21225051 **E:** info@tvm.com.mt **W:** www.tvm.com.mt **L.P:** CEO: Charles Dalli. **Chs:** TVM, TVM2, Parlament ta'Malta TV – **F LIVING CHANNEL (Comm)** ✉ BME Studios, Gudja Road, Luqa, LQA 2022 ☎ +356 21664566 **E:** flivingchannel@gmail.com **W:** fliving.tv **L.P:** Dir's (Bonaci Media Entertainment): Karl & Romina Bonaci – **NET TV (Comm)** ✉ Media.Link Communications, Dar Centrali, Triq Herbert Ganado, Pieta', PTA 1450 ☎ +356 21243641 **E:** news@media.link.com.mt **W:** www.nettv.com.mt **L.P:** Chmn: Joe Saliba – **ONE TV (Comm)** ✉ ONE Productions Ltd., A28b, Qasam Industrijali, Marsa, MRS 3000 ☎ +356 25682568 9 **E:** info@one.com.mt **W:** www.one.com. mt **L.P:** Chmn: Jason Micallef – **SMASH TV (Comm)** ✉ Smash Communications Ltd., 4, Triq Tax-Xewk, Paola, PLA 1341 ☎ +356 21697829 0 **E:** info@smashmalta.com **W:** www.smash.com.mt **L.P:** Dir: Joseph Baldacchino – **XEJK TV (Comm)** ✉ 28, New Street in Valletta Road, Luqa, LQA 6000 ☎ +356 21578022 **E:** info@xejkmalta. com **W:** www.xejkmalta.com.

**DTT Tx Networks**
**Licensee:** PBS **M:** TVM HD, TVM2 HD ✂ Magic Malta, R.4, Radju Malta, Radju Malta 2 **Tx:** ch5 (Gharghur) – **Licensee:** GO PLC **W:** www.go.com.mt **M1✪:** BBC Entertainment, FOX, myZen.TV, TV 2000, MTV Europe, VH1 Europe, Nickelodeon, GO Sports 3 **M2✪:** Boomerang, Discovery Channel, Discovery Science, Discovery Family, National Geographic, TLC, GO Sports 5 **M3✪:** La 5, Travel Channel, BBC World News, Sky News, Bloomberg, History Channel, Lifetime, Trace Urban **M4✪:** Mediaset Italia, AMC, FOX Life, Animal Planet, Cartoonito, Jim Jam, Eurosport 2, Chelsea TV **M5✪:** ITV Choice, CBS Reality, Food Network, Nat Geo Wild, H2, Cartoon Network, GO Stars, GO Sports 4 **M6✪:** Rai 1, Rai 2, Rai 3, Crime+Investigation, Disney Channel, Nick Jr., GO Sports 6 **M7✪:** Italia 1, Rete 4, Canale 5, FLN, E!, Baby TV, GO Sports 1 **M8✪:** Weather & Info Channel, CNBC Europe, Euronews, CNN International, TCM, Eurosport 1, GO Sports 2 **M9:** TVM, TVM 2, One TV, Net TV, Smash TV, F Living, Xejk TV, Parlament ta'Malta TV

| Location | M1 | M2 | M3 | M4 | M5 | M6 | M7 | M8 | M9 |
|---|---|---|---|---|---|---|---|---|---|
| SFN | 35 | 28 | 31 | 38 | 45 | 56 | 58 | 60 | 43 |

## MARSHALL ISLANDS (USA associated)

**NB:** No terrestrial TV station.

## MARTINIQUE (France)

**System:** DVB-T (MPEG4) [E]

**MARTINIQUE LA 1ÈRE (Pub)** ✉ BP 662, F-97263 Fort-de-France CEDEX ☎ +596 596595200 **W:** martinique.la1ere.fr **L.P:** Dir: Augustin Hoareau – **ANTILLES TÉLÉVISION (ATV) (Comm)** ✉ 2 Habitation la Trompeuse, F-97232 Le Lamentin ☎ +596 596754444 **E:** accueil@atv. mq **W:** atv.mq **L.P:** DG: Patrick Jean-Pierre – **KANAL MARTINIQUE TÉLÉVISION (KMT) (Comm)** ✉ Voie n° 7, Renéville, F-97200 Fort-de-France ☎ +596 596718604 **E:** webmaster@kmttelevision.com **W:** kmttelevision.com **L.P:** Pres: Roland Laouchez – **ZOUK TV (Comm)** ✉ Rue de la Pointe Simon, F-97200 Fort-de-France ☎ +596 596712727 **E:** contact@zouktv.com **W:** zouktv.com **L.P:** Pres: Emmanuel Granier.

**DTT Tx Network**
**Tx Operator:** TDF **M:** Martinique la 1ère, France 2-5, France Ô, France 24, Arte, ATV, KMT **Txs:** MFN. **Local Mux:** Zouk TV **Txs:** MFN

## MAURITANIA

**Systems:** DVB-T2 (MPEG4) [E]; § SECAM-B [E] ⬇2020

**TÉLÉDIFFUSION DE MAURITANIE (TDM) (Pub)** ✉ Ilot A lot Nr 627/TV-Zeina, BP 5176, Nouakchott ☎ +222 45255548 🖷 +222 45255547 **E:** tdm@tdm.mr **W:** www.tdm.mr **L.P:** DG: Mohamed Dieh Ould Sidaty **Chs:** TVM1 TVM Plus **Txs:** **TVM:** Nouakchott ᵃch5 (2kW H) & relay txs; **TVM Plus:** (-). (ᵃ=analogue)

**DTT Tx Network**
**Tx Operator:** TDM **M:** TVM1, TVM Plus **Txs:** MFN

## MAURITIUS

**System:** DVB-T (MPEG2) [E]

**MAURITIUS BROADCASTING CORP. (MBC) (Pub)** ✉ BP 48, Curepipe ☎ +230 6755001 🖷 +230 6757332 **E:** dirgen@mbc.intnet. mu **W:** www.mbcradio.tv **L.P:** DG: Mekraj Baldowa.
**DTT Tx Networks**
**Licensee:** Multi Carrier Mauritius Ltd ✉ Clement Charoux Street, Malherbes, Curepipe ☎ +230 6753234 🖷 +230 6746547 **E:** mcml@ multi-carrier.net **W:** www.multi-carrier.net **M1:** MBC1, MBC2, MBC3, MBC Digital 4, Cine 12, TV5 Monde, Zoom TV ✂ RM1, RM2, Kool FM **M2:** Sports 11, CCTV-9, France 24, MBC Knowledge, Bhojpuri Channel, BBC World News **M3:** Senn Kreol, DD Podhigai, DD Sahyadri, DD Saptagiri, DD Urdu Channel ✂ Best FM **Txs:** MFN

## MAYOTTE (France)

**System:** DVB-T (MPEG4) [E]

**MAYOTTE LA 1ÈRE (Pub)** ✉ BP 660, F-97600 Kaweni, Ile de Mayotte ☎ +262 269601017 **W:** mayotte.la1ere.fr **L.P:** Dir: Gérard Hoarau – **KWEZI TÉLÉVISION (KTV) (Comm)** ✉ F-97610 Dzaoudzi, Ile de Mayotte **E:** tv@kwezi.fr **W:** www.linfokwezi.fr **L.P:** Patrick Millan – **TÉLÉMANTE (Comm)** ✉ 1, Bahoni Ld Pamandzi, F-97615 Dzaoudzi, Ile de Mayotte ☎ +262 639694792 **E:** telemante@gmail. com **L.P:** Pres: Thierry Mac-Luckie.

**DTT Tx Network**
**Tx Operator:** TDF **Mux:** Mayotte la 1ère, France 2-5, France Ô, France 24, Arte, KTV, Télémante **Txs:** MFN.

## MEXICO

**System:** ATSC [A]

**National Stations**
**AZTECA, SA DE C.V. (Comm)** ✉ Periférico Sur 4121, Col. Fuentes del Pedregal, México, D.F. 14140 ☎ +52 55 30991313 🖷 +52 55 30991418 **E:** webtv@tvazteca.com **W:** www.tvazteca.com **L.P:** CEO: Benjamin Salinas Sada. **Chs:** Azteca 7, Azteca Trece. **Txs:** **Azteca 7:** XHIMT-TDT Ciudad de México ch24 (464kW) & relay txs; **Azteca Trece:** XHDF-TDT Ciudad de México ch25 (468kW) & relay txs. – **CADENA TRES I, SA DE C.V. (Comm)** ✉ Mariano Escobedo #700, Col. Anzures, Delegación Miguel Hidalgo, Ciudad de México, D.F. 11590 ☎ +52 55 51283000 **W:** www.imagentv.com **Ch:** Imagen Televisión **Txs:** XHCTMX-TDT Ciudad de México ch29 (295kW) & relay txs. – **TELEVISA, SA DE C.V. (Comm)** ✉ 2000 Avenida Vasco De Quiroga Santa Fe, México, D.F. 01210 ☎ +52 55 52612000 🖷 +52 55 52612494 **W:** www.televisa.com. **Chs:** Las Estrellas, Canal 5, Galavisión, FOROtv. **Txs:** **Las Estrellas:** XEW-TDT Ciudad de México ch32 (270kW) & relay txs; **Canal 5:** XHGC-TDT Ciudad de México ch31 (270kW) & relay txs; **FOROtv:** XHTV-TDT Ciudad de México ch49 (270kW) & relay txs; **Galavisión:** XEQ-TDT Ciudad de México ch22 (270kW) & relay txs.

**Regional/Local Stations** not shown.

## MICRONESIA (USA associated)

**System:** NTSC-M [A]

**WAAB-TV (Gov)** ✉ Department of Youth and Civic Affairs, P.O.Box 30, Colonia, Yap, FM 96943 ☎ +1 691 3502502 **Tx:** ch7 (1kW) – **KPON-TV (Comm)** ✉ Central Micronesia Communications, P.O.Box 460, Kolonia, Pohnpei, FM 96941. **Tx:** Pohnpei ch7 (1kW) – **TTTK-TV (Comm)** ✉ Chuuk, FM 96942. **Tx:** Moen ch7 (0.1kW).

## MOLDOVA

**Systems:** DVB-T2 (MPEG4) [E]; § SECAM-D/K [R], § PAL-D/K

**National Stations**
**TELERADIO-MOLDOVA (Pub)** ☑ str. Hâncesti nr. 64, 2018 Chisinau ☎ +373 22 723380 🖻 +373 22 723329 **E:** tvdir@trm.md **W:** www.trm.md **L.P:** Pres: Olga Bordeianu **Ch:** Moldova 1, Moldova 2 – **CANAL 2 (Comm)** ☑ bd. D.Cantemir nr. 1/1, 2001 Chisinau ☎+373 22 809112 🖻 +373 22 809110 **W:** www.canal2.md – **CANAL 3 (Comm)** ☑ Str. Banulescu-Bodoni nr. 57/1, 2102 Chisinau ☎ +373 22 854615 **E:** info@mediaproduction.md **W:** www.canal3.md – **JURNAL TV (Comm)** ☑ str. Vlaicu Pârcalab 63, 2012 Chisinau ☎ +373 22 235008 🖻 +373 22 234230 **E:** contact@jurnaltv.md **W:** jurnaltv.md – **N4 (Comm)** ☑ str. Mihai Eminescu, 41/1, 2012 Chisinau ☎ +373 22 821801 **E:** office@n4.md **W:** n4.md – **PRIME (Comm)** ☑str. Banulescu-Bodoni nr. 57/1, 2005 Chisinau ☎ +373 22 244746 🖻 +373 22 244746 **E:** info@prime.md **W:** www.prime.md – **PUBLICA TV (Comm)** ☑str. Ghioceilor nr. 1, 2071 Chisinau ☎+373 22 815555 🖻: +373 22 221722 **W:** www.publika.md.

**Local Stations** (all analogue)
**Drochia TV:** str. Sorocii nr. 44, ap. 7, 5201 Drochia; ch28 (0.3kW). **Elita TV:** str. 1 mai nr. 2, 5400 Rezina; Rezina ch21 (0.3kW), Soldanesti ch45 (0.4kW). **Media TV:** str. Stefan cel Mare nr. 14, 4101 Cimislia; ch43 (0.4kW). **Sor-TV:** str. Banulescu-Bodoni nr. 2, 3000 Soroca; ch43 (0.3kW). **Studio-L:** bd. M. Eminescu nr. 23, 4301 Causeni; ch35 (0.2kW). **TV Prim:** str. Suveranitatii nr. 5, of. 94, 4901 Glodeni; ch35 (0.4kW). **TV6:** str. 31 August nr. 20-B, 3121 Balti; ch26 (0.3kW).

**DTT Tx Networks**
**Tx Operator:** Radiocomunicatii **W:** www.radiocom.md **M1:** Moldova-1, TVR Moldova, Publika TV, Canal 2, Canal 3, Prime **M2:** tbd

| Location | M1 | M2* | Location | M1 | M2* |
|----------|-----|-----|----------|-----|-----|
| Cahul | 36 | 28 | Mindesti Noi | 22 | 24 |
| Causeni | 21 | 29 | Straseni | 31 | 26 |
| Chisinau | 56 | 58 | Trifesti | 28 | 36 |
| Cimislia | 36 | 28 | Ungheni | 22 | 24 |
| Edinet | 30 | 37 | + translators *) not on air | | |

### Gagauzia

**GRT (Pub):** str. Lenin nr. 134, 3802 Comrat; Vulcanesti ch24 (0.2kW), Comrat ch36 (0.2kW), Copceac ch47 (0.03kW) – **ATV:** str. Tretiacov nr. 4, of. 36, 3801 Comrat; ch40 (0.2kW).

### TRANSNISTRIA

**PRIDNESTROVSKAYA GTRK (PGTRK)** ☑ per. Khristoforovo 5, 3300 Tiraspol ☎ +373 533 25708 **W:** tv.pgtrk.ru **L.P:** Dir: Irina Dementyeva **Ch:** Pervyy Pridnestrovskiy.

**Local Stations** not shown.

**DTT Tx Networks**
**Licensee M1+2:** Interdnestrkom **W:** idc.md **M1:** Pervyy Pridnestrovskiy, TSV, Pershyi Natsionalnyi, Pervyy Kanal, Rossiya 1, NTV, Rossiya 24, Ren TV, STS, TNT, TV Tsentr, TV Zvezda, Karusel, Mult, Disney Channel **M2✪:** Inter, STB, Pyatnitsa!, Match TV, Match! Igra, Match! Futbol 1, Kinohit, Kino Plus, Nashe Lubimoye Kino, La Minor, Ohota i Rybalka, Animal Planet, Discovery Science, MTV Hits, BBC World News.

| Location | M1 | M2 |
|----------|-----|-----|
| SFN | 59 | 61 |

**Local muxes** not shown.

## MONACO

**System:** DVB-T (MPEG2) [E]

**TÉLÉ MONTE-CARLO (TMC) (Comm)** ☑ 6 Quai Antoine 1ᵉʳ, 98000 Monaco ☎ +377 93151415 **E:** tmc@fr.multithematiques.com **W:** www.tf1.fr/tmc **L.P:** Pres (TF1 Group): Jean Pastorelli.

**DTT Tx Networks**
**Tx Operator:** Monaco Telecom ☑ 25 Boulevard de Suisse, 98000 Monaco ☎ +377 99663497 **E:** a.segala@monaco-telecom.mc **W:** www.monaco-telecom.mc **M:** TMC, Monaco Info, TF1, France 2-5, M6, Arte, Canal+ (unencrypted sequences), BFM TV, CNEWS, Euronews, RAI 1-3, Canale 5, CNBC **Tx:** ch10 (Mont Agel). – **Tx Operator:** Monaco Media Diffusion **M:** multiprgr **Tx:** (-).

## MONGOLIA

**System:** DVB-T2 (MPEG4) [E]

**MONGOLYN ÜNDESNII OLON NIITIYN RADIO TELEVIZ (MÜONRT) (Pub)** ☑ Bayangol district, 11th subdistrict, Khuvisgalyn Rd. 3, Ulaanbaatar ☎ +976 1 1325802 🖻 +976 1 1328334 **E:** info@mnb.mn **W:** www.mnb.mn **L.P:** DG: Ninjjamts Luvsandash.

**Local Stations** not shown.

**DTT Tx Networks**
**Tx Operator:** MRTBN **Mux 1-3 (partly✪):** multiprgr **Local Muxes L1-L4 (Ulaanbaatar) (partly✪):** multiprgr.

| Location | M1 | M2 | M3 | L1 | L2 | L3 | L4 |
|----------|-----|-----|-----|-----|-----|-----|-----|
| Ulaanbaatar | 39 | 49 | 51 | 31 | 33 | 35 | 37 |

+ nationwide MFN

## MONTENEGRO

**System:** DVB-T2 (MPEG4) [E]

**National Stations**
**RADIO I TELEVIZIJA CRNE GORE (RTCG) (Pub)** ☑ Bul. Džordža Vašingtona bb, 81000 Podgorica ☎ +382 20 225999 **E:** kontakt@rtcg.me **W:** www.rtcg.me **L.P:** DG: Božidar Šundic, **Chs (terr.):** TVCG1, TVCG2 – **TV PINK M (Comm)** ☑ Bul. Ivana Crnojevica 97, 81000 Podgorica ☎ +382 20 403505 **E:** kabinet@pinkm.co.me **W:** www.pinkm.me **L.P:** Dir: Goran Radenovic – **TV PRVA (Comm)** ☑ Bul. Džordža Vašingtona 56/6, 81000 Podgorica ☎ +382 20 234840 **E:** info@prvatv.me **W:** www.prvatv.me **L.P:** Dir: Aleksandar Boškovic – **TV VIJESTI (Comm)** ☑ Trg Republike bb, 81000 Podgorica ☎ +382 20 404601 **E:** desk@vijesti.me **W:** www.vijesti.me **L.P:** Dir: Slavoljub Šcekic.

**Local Stations** (via Mux L1)
**TV Boin:** Dušici bb, 81206 Tuzi; (a) + ch39. **TV Budva:** 13. jula bb, 85310 Budva; ch46. **TV Glas Plava:** Caršijska bb, 84325 Plav; ch38. **TV Nikšic:** Novice Cerovica 30a, 81400 Nikšic; ch23 (SFN). **TV Pljevlja:** Zekerijaha Cinare bb, 84210 Pljevlja (b). **TV Sun:** Partizanska 9, 84000 Bijelo Polje; ch40. **TV Teuta:** Totoši bb, 85360 Ulcinj; ch39.

**DTT Tx Networks**
**Tx Operator:** Radio-difuzni centar d.o.o. **W:** www.rdc.co.me **M1✪(exc.*):** TVCG1*, TVCG2*, TV Prva*, TV Vijesti*, TV Pink M*, Nat. Geographic, 24 Kitchen, Pink 2, Nickelodeon, Arenasport 1, RTS1, RTS Sat, Happy TV, Studio B, DM Sat, Hayat Plus, Al Jazeera Balkans ⌘ R. Crne Gore*, R. 98* **M2✪(exc.*):** Fox Crime, Fox Movies, Fox Life, Arenasport 2-5, Nick Jr, Pink Film, Pink Kids, Pink Music, Elta*, DW-TV, RTV1, O2.TV, Fashion TV **L1:** Local stns

| Location | M1 | M2 | L1* | kW | Location | M1 | M2 | L1* | kW |
|----------|-----|-----|-----|-----|----------|-----|-----|-----|-----|
| Bjelasica | 43 | 25 | - | 78 | Tovic | 35 | 27 | - | 11.5 |
| Lovcen | 35 | 27 | - | 100 | Tvrdaš | 49 | 22 | 26b | 2.9 |
| Sjenica | 24 | 27 | 21a | 17.5 | | | | | |

+ sites with txs below 2kW. *) Local stns a+b: see above

## MONTSERRAT (UK)

**System:** NTSC-M [A]

**ZJB-TV (Gov)** ☑ Sweeney's, Montserrat. ☎ +1 664 4912885 🖻 +1 664 4919250 **E:** zjb@gov.ms **W:** zjb.gov.ms **Tx:** Chance Pic ch13. – **ANTILLES TV LTD (Comm)** ☑ P.O. Box 342, Plymouth, Montserrat ☎ +1 664 4912226 🖻 +1 664 4914511 **Tx:** Chance Pic ch7 (48kW).

## MOROCCO

**System:** DVB-T (MPEG2) [E]

**SOCIÉTÉ NATIONALE DE RADIODIFFUSION ET DE TÉLÉVISION (SNRT) (Pub)** ☑ BP 1042, Rabat ☎ +212 537700319 🖻 +212 537722047 **W:** www.srnt.ma **L.P:** DG: Faiçal Laraichi, **Chs (terr.):** Al Aoula, Arriyadia, Arrabia, Assadissa, Aflam, Tamazight, Laayoune TV – **TÉLÉVISION 2M (Semi-Gov, Comm)** ☑ Km 7,3 route de Rabat Ain Sebaa, Casablanca 20250 ☎+212 522354444 🖻 +212 522343390 **W:** www.2m.ma **L.P:** DG: Salim Cheikh – **MEDI 1 TV (Comm)** ☑ Zone Franche de Tanger, Lot 31BP, Tangier 90100 ☎ +212 539399800 🖻 +212 539394507 **W:** www.medi1tv.com

**DTT Tx Networks**
**Tx Operator:** SNRT **M1:** Al Aoula, 2M, Arriyadia, Arrabia, Assadissa,

Aflam **M2**: Aflam, Medi 1 TV, Tamazight, Laayoune TV

| Location | M1 | M2 |
|---|---|---|
| Rabat | 30 | 23 |

+ nationwide MFN

### CEUTA (Spain)

**System:** DVB-T (MPEG2, MPEG4) [E]

**Local Stations**
**Radio Televisión de Ceuta (RTVCE) (Pub)**: Alcalde Sanchez Prados nº 5, 51001 Ceuta. **Ceuta Televisión (Comm)**: Avenida Alcalde Sánchez Prado 6, 3ª planta Puerta 5-6, 51001 Ceuta.

**DTT Tx Networks**
**Operator:** n/a **National Muxes 1-7:** see Spain; **Local Mux Ceuta (L):** RTVCE, Ceuta TV, Canal Sur ✹ Radio Ceuta.

| Location | M1 | M2 | M3 | M4 | M5 | M6 | M7 | L |
|---|---|---|---|---|---|---|---|---|
| Ceuta | 52 | 55 | 53 | 44 | 49 | 35 | 25 | 37 |

### MELILLA (Spain)

**System:** DVB-T (MPEG2, MPEG4) [E]

**Local Stations**
**TV Melilla (TVM) (Pub)**: Miguel Zazo, 31, 2º 52004 Pontevedra. **Melilla Televisión (Comm)**: Los Castaños, Urb Los Balandros nº 33, Aguadulce, 04720 Roquetas de Mar.

**DTT Tx Networks**
**Operator:** n/a **National Muxes 1-7:** see Spain; **Local Mux Melilla (L):** TV Melilla, Popular TV, Canal Sur, Canal Sur 2.

| Location | M1 | M2 | M3 | M4 | M5 | M6 | M7 | L |
|---|---|---|---|---|---|---|---|---|
| Melilla | 27 | 24 | 21 | 41 | 45 | 38 | 36 | 43 |

## MOZAMBIQUE

**System:** DVB-T2 (MPEG4) [E]

**TELEVISÃO DE MOÇAMBIQUE (TVM) (Pub)** ☑ CP 2675, Maputo ☎ +258 21 308117 🖷 +258 21 308122 **E:** tvm@tvm.co.mz **W:** www. tvm.co.mz **L.P:** Chmn: Jaime Alfredo Cuambe **Chs:** TVM, TVM2 – **KTV (Comm)** ☑ Av. Julius Nyerere 390, Maputo ☎ +258 21 491744 🖷 +258 21 491745 **E:** comercialktv@sapo.mz **L.P:** DG: Izilda Kayroniss Mussa – **SOICO TELEVISÃO (STV) (Comm)** ☑ Rua de Timor Leste 108, Maputo ☎ +258 21 315117 🖷 +258 21 301865 **E:** stv@soico. co.mz **W:** stv.co.mz **L.P:** DG: Daniel David. – **TELEVISÃO MIRAMAR (Comm)** ☑ Av. Orlando Mendes 213, R/C, Sommerchield. ☎ +258 21 498440 **E:** comercial@miramar.co.mz **W** miramar.co.mz.

**DTT Tx Networks**
**Licensee:** TVM **M:** TVM, TVM2, RTP África **Txs:** MFN – **Licensee:** Multichoice Moçambique SA ☑ Av. Vladimir Lenine 3071, Maputo ☎+258 21 416130 **M✿:** multiprgr **Txs:** MFN – **Licensee:** Startimes ☑ Av. Alberth Lithuli 934, Maputo ☎ +258 21 342400 **W:** www. startimes.co.mz **M✿:** multiprgr. **Txs:** MFN.

## MYANMAR

**Systems:** DVB-T2 (MPEG4) [E]; § NTSC-M [A] ⬇2020

**MYANMA RADIO AND TELEVISION (MRTV) (Gov)** ☑ Naypyidaw ☎ +95 67 79483 **E:** mrtv@mptmail.net.mm **W:** www.mrtv.gov.mm **Chs:** MRTV, MRTV Entertainment, MRTV-4, Channel7, Readers Channel, Farmer Channel, Hluttaw Channel, MITV, MNTV – **MYAWADY TV (Mil)** ☑ Yangon **W:** www.myanmartvchannel.com **Chs:** MWD1, MWD2, MWD3, MWD4.

**DTT Tx Networks**
**Licensee:** MRTV **M:** MRTV, MRTV Entertainment, MRTV-4, Channel7, Readers Channel, Farmer Channel, Hluttaw Channel, MITV, MNTV **Txs:** Nationwide MFN. – **Licensee:** Myawady TV **M:** MWD1, MWD2, MWD3, MWD4 **Tx:** Nationwide MFN.

## NAMIBIA

**System:** DVB-T2 (MPEG4) [E]

**NAMIBIAN BROADCASTING CORP. (NBC) (Pub)** ☑ P.O.Box 321, Windhoek 9000 ☎ +264 61 2913111 🖷 +264 61 216209 **E:** pr@

nbc.na **W:** www.nbc.na **L.P:** DG: Stanley Similo **Chs:** NBC1, NBC2, NBC3, Edu-TV – **ONE AFRICA TV (Comm)** ☑ Storch House, Storch St., Windhoek ☎ +264 61 253190 🖷 +264 61 220410 **E:** paul@mac. com.na **W:** www.oneafrica.tv **L.P:** MD: Paul van Schalkwyk – **THIS TV (Rlg)** ☑ Windhoek **W:** www.facebook.com/thistvnamibia – **TBN NAMIBIA (Rlg)** ☑ P.O.Box 1587, Swakopmund ☎ +264 64 401100 🖷 +264 64 403752 **E:** comments@tbnnamibia.tv **W:** www. tbnnamibia.tv.

**DTT Tx Networks**
**Licensee:** NBC **M:** NBC1, NBC2, NBC3, One Africa TV, TBN, Edu-TV, This TV, ✹ 10 NBC Radio prgrs **Txs:** MFN – **Licensee:** MultiChoice Namibia Pty. ☑ P.O.Box 2662, Windhoek ☎ +264 61 2705111 🖷 +264 61 2705247 **M✿:** M-Net, SuperSport 1, SABC Africa, Discovery, Channel O. **Txs:** MFN.

## NAURU

**System:** PAL-B [NZ]

**NAURU TELEVISION (NTV) (Gov)** ☑ Government Offices, Yaren District ☎ +674 4443113 🖷 +674 4443153 **Txs:** Command Ridge ch4 (0.1kW), NTV studio building ch10 (0.01kW).

## NEPAL

**System:** DVB-T2 (MPEG4) [E]

**National Stations**
**NEPAL TELEVISION (Pub)** ☑ P.O.Box 3826, Singha Durbar, Kathmandu ☎ +977 1 4200348 🖷 +977 1 4200212 **E:** info@ntv.org.np **W:** ntv.org.np **L.P:** GM: Gobinda Rokka **Chs:** NTV, NTV Plus, NTV News – **KANTIPUR TELEVISION (Comm)** ☑ P.O.Box 7368, Subidhanagar, Kathmandu ☎ +977 1 4466300 🖷 +977 1 4466321 **E:** info@kantipurtv. com **W:** kantipurtv.com **L.P:** MD: Kailash Sirohiya.

**Local Stations** not shown.

**DTT Tx Network**
**Tx Operator:** Prabhu TV **M:** multiprgr **Txs:** MFN.

## NETHERLANDS

**System:** DVB-T (MPEG2) [E]

**National Stations**
**NEDERLANDSE PUBLIEKE OMROEP (NPO) (Pub)** ☑ P.O.Box 26444, 1202 JJ Hilversum ☎ +31 35 6779222 **E:** voorlichting@ npo.nl **W:** www.npo.nl **L.P:** Chmn: Shula Rijxman. **Chs (terr.):** NPO 1, NPO 2, NPO 3. Prgrs for the NPO are provided by **Nederlandse Omroep Stichting (NOS):** Sumatralaan 45, 1217 GP Hilversum; **NTR:** P.O.Box 29000, 1202 MA Hilversum; and the following broadcasting organizations: **AVROTROS:** P.O.Box 2, 1200 JA Hilversum; **BNNVARA:** P.O.Box 175 1200 AD Hilversum; **EO:** P.O.Box 21000, 1202 BB Hilversum; **Human:** P.O.Box 135, 1200 AC Hilversum; **KRO-NCRV:** P.O.Box 200, 1200 AE Hilversum; **MAX:** P.O.Box 554, 2700 AM Hilversum; **PowNed:** P.O.Box 92109, 1090 AC Amsterdam; **VPRO:** P.O.Box 11, 1200 JC Hilversum; **WNL:** P.O.Box 23620, 1100 EC Amsterdam – **RTL NEDERLAND (Comm)** ☑ P.O.Box 15016, 1200 TV Hilversum ☎ +31 35 6718718 **E:** info@rtl.nl **W:** www.rtl.nl **Chs (terr.):** RTL4, RTL5, RTL7, RTL8 – **TALPA TV (Comm)** ☑ P.O.Box 18179, 1001 ZB Amsterdam ☎ +31 20 8007000 **E:** mediasolutions@ talpanetwork.com **W:** tv.talpanetwork.com **Chs (terr.):** NET5, SBS6, Veronica TV.

**Regional Stations (Pub)** (via DTT Mux 1)
**a) L1TV:** P.O.Box 31, 6200 AA Maastricht; **b) Omroep Brabant TV:** Postbus 108, 5600 AC Eindhoven; **c) Omroep Fryslân:** P.O.Box 7600, 8903 JP Leeuwarden; **d) Omroep Zeeland TV:** P.O.Box 1090, 4388 ZH Oost-Souburg; **e) RTV Utrecht:** P.O.Box 9043, 3506 GA Utrecht; **f) RTV Drenthe:** P.O.Box 999, 9400 AZ Assen; **g) Omroep Flevoland:** P.O.Box 567, 8200 AN Lelystad; **h) Omroep Gelderland:** P.O.Box 747, 6800 AS Arnhem; **i) TV Noord:** P.O.Box 30101, 9701 BH Groningen; **j) RTV Noord Holland:** P.O.Box 9823, 1006 AM Amsterdam; **k) TV Oost:** P.O.Box 1000, 7550 BA Hengelo; **l) TV Rijmond:** P.O.Box 350, 3000 AJ Rotterdam; **m) TV West:** P.O.Box 24012, 2490 AA Den Haag.

**Local Stations**
**AT5:** P.O.Box 3976, 1001 AT Amsterdam; via DTT Mux 3. **Haarlem 105:** P.O.Box 3355, 2001 DJ Haarlem; ch46V (0.025kW).

**DTT Tx Networks**
**Licensee:** KPN **W:** www.kpn.com **M1:** NPO 1, NPO 2, NPO 3, Public Regional Stations (a-m) ✂ NPO R.1, 2, 3FM, 4, 5, 6, FunX, Public reg. radio stns **M2✪:** RTL4, RTL5, RTL7, NET5, SBS6 ✂ Classic FM, R. 10, Q-Music, R.Veronica, Sky R. 101 FM, Slam!FM, 100%NL **M3✪:** BBC One, BBC Two, MTV, NGC, TLC, FOX Sports Eredivisie Live 1/FOX Sports 3, ONS/Cartoon Netw./AT5, 24Kitchen ✂ Arrow Classic Rock, BNR Nieuwsradio, R.538 **M4✪:** Één, Canvas, Discovery Channel, Eurosport, Comedy Central, RTL8, Veronica TV/Disney HD, Meiden van Holland Hard **M5✪:** CNN, Nickelodeon/Spike, Xite, FOX, Investigation Discovery, RTL Z, Ketnet/OP12 ✂ BBC Radio 1-4, SubLime FM, VRT R.1, R.2, Klara, Studio Brussel, MNM.

| Location | M1* | M2 | M3 | M4 | M5 | kW |
|---|---|---|---|---|---|---|
| Alkmar | 39j | 45 | 34 | 35 | 44 | 20 |
| Alphen a.d.R. | 52m | 49 | 57 | 24 | 27 | 10/15/3x2 |
| Amsterdam | 39j | 49 | 57 | 24 | 27 | 10 |
| Apeldoorn | 42h | 36 | 58 | 53 | 28 | 20 |
| Arnhem | 42h | 36 | 58 | 53 | 28 | 20/2x40/2x20 |
| Breda | 30b | 60 | 31 | 32 | 33 | 2x20/3x15 |
| Den Bosch | 30b | 60 | 31 | 56 | 33 | 2x10/5/10/5 |
| Den Haag | 52m | 49 | 57 | 24 | 27 | 10 |
| Den Haag (Zichtenb.) | 52m | 49 | 57 | 24 | 27 | 10 |
| Deventer | 22k | 36 | 23 | 47 | 28 | 10 |
| Doetinchem | 42h | 36 | 58 | 53 | 28 | 20/100/2x20 |
| Eindhoven (Tongelre) | 30b | 60 | 31 | 56 | 33 | 15/10/3x15 |
| Eindhoven (Croy) | 30b | 60 | 31 | 56 | 33 | 4x10/5 |
| Enschede | 22k | 36 | 23 | 47 | 28 | 10/4x20 |
| Goes | 54d | 48 | 29 | 32 | 35 | 10 |
| Groningen | 46i | 30 | 54 | 33 | 25 | 20 |
| Haarlem | 39j | 49 | 57 | 24 | 27 | 20 |
| Heerlen | 54a | 34 | 51 | 51 | 27 | 40/20/2x40/20 |
| Helmond | 30b | 60 | 31 | 56 | 33 | 20 |
| Hengelo | 22k | 36 | 23 | 47 | 28 | 3x40/2x20 |
| Hilversum | 39j | 49 | 57 | 24 | 27 | 15 |
| Ijsselstein | 50e | 49 | 57 | 24 | 27 | 3x15/10 |
| Krimpen a.d.IJ. | 21l | 49 | 57 | 24 | 27 | 10 |
| Leeuwarden | 32c | 55 | 34 | 21 | 44 | 20 |
| Lelystad | 26g | 36 | 23 | 47 | 44 | 2x20/10/2x20 |
| Leusden | 50e | 49 | 57 | 24 | 27 | 10/2x2.5/3 |
| Loon op Zand | 30b | 60 | 31 | 56 | 33 | 15 |
| Maarssen | 50e | 49 | 57 | 24 | 27 | 10 |
| Maastricht | 54a | 34 | 51 | 51 | 27 | 20/2x10/15/10 |
| Nijmegen | 42h | 60 | 31 | 56 | 33 | 10/20/10/20/15 |
| Oegstgeest | 52m | 49 | 57 | 24 | 27 | 15 |
| Oss | 42h | 60 | 31 | 56 | 33 | 20/4x10 |
| Oss | 30b | - | - | - | - | 10 |
| Roermond | 54a | 34 | 24 | 51 | 27 | 20 |
| Rosendaal | 30b | 48 | 29 | 32 | 35 | 20 |
| Rotterdam (Waalhaven) | 21l | 49 | 57 | 24 | 27 | 10 |
| Sittard | 54a | 34 | 24 | 51 | 27 | 20 |
| Sliedrecht | 21l | 49 | 57 | 24 | 27 | 10 |
| Smilde | 60f | 30 | 54 | 33 | 25 | 3x40/30/40 |
| Utrecht | 50e | 49 | 57 | 24 | 27 | 10/5/3x4 |
| Veenendal | 50e | 36 | 58 | 53 | 28 | 20 |
| Veenendal | 42h | - | - | - | - | 20 |
| Venlo | 54a | 34 | 31 | 56 | 27 | 20/40/20/40/20 |
| Zoetermeer | 52m | 49 | 57 | 24 | 27 | 10 |
| Zwolle | 22k | 36 | 23 | 47 | 28 | 20 |

+ sites with txs below 10kW. Pol=V. *) incl. regional stns (see above).

**System:** DVB-T (MPEG4) [E]

**NOUVELLE CALEDONIE LA 1ÈRE (Pub)** ✉ 1, rue Maréchal Leclerc, F-98848 Nouméa CEDEX ☎ +687 687274327 🖷 +687 687281252 **W:** nouvellecaledonie.la1ere.fr **L.P:** Dir: Jean-Philippe Pascal – **NCTV (Comm)** ✉ Centre d'affaires de Paiamboue, 683, Avenue de Téari, Lotissement Les Cassis, F-98860 Koné **E:** nctv@nctv.nc **W:** www.nctv. nc **L.P:** DG: Laurent Le Brun.

**DTT Tx Networks**
**Tx Operator:** TDF **Mux:** Nouvelle Caledonie la 1ère, France 2-5, France Ô, France 24, Arte, NCTV **Txs:** MFN

**System:** DVB-T (MPEG4) [NZ]

**National Stations**
**MAORI TELEVISION (Pub)** ✉ P.O.Box 113-017, Newmarket,

Auckland 1149 ☎ +64 9 5397000 **W:** www.maoritelevision.com – **TELEVISION NEW ZEALAND (TVNZ) (Pub)** ✉ P.O.Box 3819, Auckland ☎ +64 9 9167000 **W:** tvnz.co.nz **L.P:** CEO: Kevin Kenrick **Chs:** TV One, TV One Plus 1, TV2, TV2 +1, TNVZ Pop-up – **MEDIAWORKS TV (Comm)** ✉ P.O.Box 92624, Symonds St., Auckland 1150 ☎ +64 9 9289000 **E:** replies@mediaworks.co.nz **W:** www.mediaworks. co.nz **Chs:** TV3, TV3+, Four, C4, The Edge TV – **PRIME TELEVISION (Comm)** ✉ 1 John Glenn Ave., North Harbour, Auckland ☎ +64 9 4140700 **E:** info@primetv.co.nz **W:** www.primetv.co.nz.

**Local Stations** not shown.

**DTT Tx Networks**
**Licensee M1:** TVNZ **M:** TV One, TV One Plus 1, TV2, TV2 +1, TVNZ Pop-up – **Licensee M2:** MediaWorks **M:** TV3, TV3+, C4, Four, The Edge TV – **Licensee M3:** Kordia ✉ P.O.Box 2495, Auckland ☎ +64 9 9166400 🖷 +64 9 9166403 **W:** kordiasolutions.com **M:** Parliament TV, Maori Television, CTV8, Prime, TV29, Apnia, Choice TV ✂ R. NZ National, R. NZ Concert, BaseFM.

| Location | M1 | M2 | M3 |
|---|---|---|---|
| Auckland (Waiatarua) | 29 | 33 | 45 |

+ nationwide MFN

**Systems:** # NTSC-M [A]; ISDB-TB [A]

**National Stations** (ᵃ=analogue)
**CANAL 6 (Comm)** ✉ 3 1/2 Carretera Sur Contig o Shell, Managua ☎ +505 22660118 🖷 +505 22666522 **E:** info@canal6.com.ni **W:** www. canal6.com.ni **Tx:** Managua ᵃch6 (25kW). – **CANAL 10 (Comm)** ✉ Hotel Mansión Teodolinda, 2c, Abajo ☎ +505 22227788 **W:** canal10.com.ni **Tx:** Managua ᵃch10. – **100% NOTICIAS (CANAL 15) (Comm)** ✉ Lomas de Tiscapa, frente al Hospital Militar, Managua ☎ +505 22669086 **E:** info@canal15.com.ni **W:** 100noticias.com.ni **Tx:** Managua ᵃch15. – **CANAL DE NOTICIAS DE NICARAGUA (CDNN) (Comm)** ✉ Carretera a Masaya Km. 4½, Motorama ½c al Su, Managua ☎ +505 22670170 **W:** www.cdnn23.com **Tx:** Managua ᵃch23. – **MULTINOTICIAS (CANAL 4)** ✉ Del Montoya, 1c al Sur, 1c al Este, Managua ☎ +505 22663420 **W:** www.canal4.com.ni **Tx:** Managua ᵃch4. – **NICAVISIÓN (CANAL 12) (Comm)** ✉ Apdo 2766, Managua ☎ +505 22660691 🖷 +505 22661424 **W:** www.canal12.com.ni **Tx:** ᵃch12. – **TELENICA (CANAL 8) (Comm)** ✉ Apdo Postal 3611, Hotel Mansión Teodolinda 1c al Sur, y ½ Abajo ☎ +505 22665021 🖷 +505 22665024 **W:** www.tn8. tv **Tx:** Managua ᵃch8. – **TELEVICENTRO (CANAL 2) (Comm)** ✉ Apdo Postal 688, Managua ☎ +505 22682222 **E:** canal2@canal2. com.ni **W:** www.canal2.com.ni **Tx:** Managua ᵃch2 (25kW). – **ENLACE NICARAGUA (CANAL 21) (Rlg)** ✉ 12 Avenida SO, Distrito II, Managua ☎ +505 22512000 **E:** nicaragua@enlace.org **W:** www. enlace.org/nicaragua **Tx:** Managua ᵃch21. Rel. TBN (USA).

**Local Stations** not shown.

**System:** DVB-T2 (MPEG4)

**OFFICE DE RADIODIFFUSION TELEVISION DU NIGER (ORTN) (Gov)** ✉ BP 309, Niamey ☎ +227 20723686 🖷 +227 20723153 **E:** ortny@intnet.net **W:** www.ortn.ne **L.P:** DG: Loïc Crespin. **Chs:** Télé-Sahel, Tal-TV. – **TÉNÉRÉ TV (Comm)** ✉ BP 13600, Niamey ☎ +227 20736576 🖷 +227 20737775 **E:** tenerefm@intnet.net.

**DTT Tx Network)**
**Tx Operator:** n/a **M:** Télé-Sahel, Tal-TV, Ténéré TV **Txs:** MFN.

**Systems:** DVB-T2 (MPEG4) [E]; § PAL-B [E]

**National Station**
**NIGERIAN TELEVISION AUTHORITY (NTA) (Pub)** ✉ P.M.B 113, Garki, Abuja ☎ +234 9 2346907 🖷 +234 9 2345914 **E:** info@nta.ng **W:** www.nta.ng **L.P:** DG: Yakubu Ibn Mohammed **Chs:** NTA, NTA2, reg. stns.

**Local Stations**
**DBN Television (Comm):** The Dream Centre, Durosinmi etti Drive, Lekki Phase 1, Lagos. **Galaxy TV (Comm):** Lagos. **Lagos TV (Comm)**

Lagos. **Minaj Broadcast International (MBI) (Comm):** P.O.Box 3975, Mushin, Lagos.

**DTT Tx Network**
**Tx Operator:** Startimes **M(partly✪):** multiprgr **Txs:** MFN.

## NIUE

**Systems:** # PAL-B [NZ]; DTT planned

**TV NIUE (Gov)** ▣ P.O.Box 68, Alofi ☎ +683 4026 ▤ +683 4217 **E:** gm.bcn@mail.gov.nu **W:** www.facebook.com/tvniue **L.P:** GM: Trever Tiakia **Txs:** Makefu ch4 (0.01kW), Alofi ch6 (0.75kW), Mutulau ch8 (0.04kW).

## NORFOLK ISLAND (Australia)

**System:** DVB-T (MPEG2) [NZ]

**TV NORFOLK ISLAND (TVNI)** ▣ Taylors Road, Norfolk Island 2899, Australia ☎ +672 3 52500 **Txs: TVNI:** ch10 (Mt. Pitt); **Rel. Hope Channel (USA):** ch7V (Mt. Pitt 0.02kW).

**DTT Tx Network**
**Tx Operator:** Norfolk Telecom **M1:** ABC, ABC2, ABC News 24 ✖ ABC Jazz R., ABC Double J. **M2:** Seven, Imparja, SBS One, SBS Two **Txs: M1:** ch25 (Mt. Pitt 0.02kW), **M2:** ch32 (Mt. Pitt 0.02kW)

## NO. MARIANA IS (USA associated)

**NB:** No terrestrial TV station.

## NORWAY

**System:** DVB-T (MPEG4) [E]

**National Stations**
**NORSK RIKSKRINGKASTING (NRK) (Pub)** ▣ 0340 Oslo ☎ +47 23047000 **E:** info@nrk.no **W:** www.nrk.no **L.P:** DG: Thor Gjermund Eriksen. **Chs:** NRK1 (incl. regional prgrs), NRK2, NRK3/NRK Super – **CANAL DIGITAL (Comm)** ▣4896 Grimstad ☎ +47 81559600 **E:** kundeservice@canaldigital.no **W:** www.canaldigital.no – **DISCOVERY NETWORKS NORWAY (Comm)** ▣ Postboks 4800, 0422 Oslo ☎ +47 21022000 **E:** resepsjon@discovery.com **W:** www.discovery.no – **TV2 (Comm)** ▣ Postboks 7222, 5020 Bergen ☎ +47 55908070 **E:** info@ tv2.no **W:** www.tv2.no **L.P:** CEO: Olav T. Sandnes.

**Local Stations** (all Comm) (via Mux 3)
**a) TKTV:** P.O.Box 8, 6501 Kristiansund; **b) TV Haugaland:** P.O.Box 408, 5501 Haugesund; **c) TV Nord:** P.O.Box 1193, 9504 Alta; **d) TV Telemark:** P.O.Box 2833, 3702 Skien; **e) TV Vest:** Lervigsveien 16, 4095 Stavanger; **f) TV Vestfold:** Bjellandveien 24, 3172, Tønsberg; **g) TV Øst:** Hjellumveien 89, 2322 Ridabu.

**DTT Tx Networks**
**Licensee:** Norges televisjon AS **W:** www.ntv.no **M1:** NRK1 (incl. reg prgrs), NRK2, NRK3/NRK Super ✖ NRK P1, P1+, P3, P13, mP3, Super, Alltid Nyheter, Jazz, Klassisk, Folkemusikk, Sport, Sámi R. **M2** (✪exc.*): TV2*, TV2 Livsstil, TV2 Nyhetskanalen, TV2 Sportskanalen, TV2 Sport Premium, TV2 Sport Premium 3 **M3** (✪exc.*): BBC World News, Comedy Central, Discovery Channel, Eurosport 1, FEM, FOX, Frikanalen/Local Stations*, Matkanalen, National Geographic, Viasat 4, TV Norge ✖ Kiss R., P4 Norge, R. Norge **M4✪:** Animal Planet, C More First, C More Series, Disney Channel, MAX, TLC, TV3, Viasat 4, Viasport 1 **M5✪:** BBC Brit, Disney Junior, Disney XD, Eurosport Norge, History, SVT1, TV2 Sport Premium 2, TV2 Zebra HD, Viasport+, Visjon Norge, VOX.

| Location | M1 | M2 | M3* | M4 | M5 | kW |
|---|---|---|---|---|---|---|
| Bagn | 32 | 39 | 42g | 22 | 59 | 50 |
| Bergen | 33 | 49 | 39 | 43 | 53 | 50 |
| Bjerkreim | 23 | 26 | 30e | 27 | 34 | 50 |
| Bokn | 36 | 54 | 57b | 44 | 35 | 50 |
| Bremager | 25 | 28 | 31 | 46 | 52 | 50 |
| Førde | 35 | 45 | 48 | 22 | 32 | 10 |
| Gamlemsveten | 37 | 38 | 54a | 24 | 34 | 50 |
| Gausta | 25 | 27 | 35 | 32 | 42 | 10 |
| Greipstad | 51 | 54 | 47 | 36 | 60 | 50 |
| Grong | 21 | 31 | 35 | 24 | 34 | 50 |
| Gulen | 37 | 42 | 26 | 29 | 23 | 50 |

| Location | M1 | M2 | M3* | M4 | M5 | kW |
|---|---|---|---|---|---|---|
| Hadsel | 45 | 48 | 58 | 25 | 38 | 50 |
| Halden | 32 | 42 | 31 | 38 | 45 | 60 |
| Hammerfest | 33 | 37 | 48c | 41 | 26 | 50 |
| Hemnes | 42 | 45 | 48 | 29 | 39 | 50 |
| Hovdefjell | 41 | 52 | 48 | 55 | 58 | 40 |
| Jetta | 45 | 48 | 58g | 41 | 51 | 50 |
| Kistefjell | 26 | 46 | 43 | 23 | 36 | 50 |
| Kongsberg | 60 | 34 | 51 | 43 | 44 | 50 |
| Kongsvinger | 24 | 48 | 55 | 28 | 41 | 50 |
| Kopparen | 26 | 40 | 45 | 23 | 36 | 50 |
| Lyngdal | 25 | 53 | 47 | 32 | 33 | 50 |
| Lønahorgi | 31 | 41 | 44 | 46 | 54 | 50 |
| Melhus | 55 | 28 | 25 | 30 | 33 | 50 |
| Mosvik | 44 | 47 | 46 | 37 | 41 | 50 |
| Narvik | 21 | 27 | 37 | 24 | 34 | 50 |
| Nordfjordeid | 40 | 44 | 33 | 27 | 30 | 10 |
| Nordhue | 33 | 43 | 56g | 27 | 31 | 50 |
| Nordkapp | 30 | 40 | 43c | 23 | 53 | 50 |
| Oslo | 52 | 58 | 46 | 30 | 40 | 50 |
| Reinsfjell | 39 | 42 | 35a | 25 | 53 | 50 |
| Salten | 50 | 43 | 60 | 30 | 33 | 50 |
| Skien | 60 | 34 | 54d | 24 | 44 | 50 |
| Sogndal | 21 | 24 | 34 | 38 | 57 | 50 |
| Steigen | 31 | 41 | 44 | 47 | 55 | 50 |
| Stord | 55 | 58 | 60b | 47 | 50 | 50 |
| Trolltind | 27 | 39 | 42 | 34 | 22 | 50 |
| Tron | 26 | 34 | 49g | 23 | 40 | 50 |
| Varanger | 28 | 33 | 50c | 35 | 41 | 50 |
| Vega | 25 | 32 | 37 | 22 | 28 | 50 |

+ sites with txs below 10kW. *) incl. local stns (see above)

## OMAN

**Systems:** DVB-T2 (MPEG4); § PAL-B/G [E]

**PUBLIC AUTHORITY FOR RADIO TV (PART)** ▣ P.O.Box 1130, 113 Madinat Al Ilam, Oman ☎ +968 24603888 ▤ +968 24604629 **E:** feedback@part.gov.om **W:** www.part.gov.om **L.P:** DG (TV): Abdullah Said AL-Shaili.

**DTT Tx Network**
**Tx Operator:** Ministry of Transport and Communications **M:** multiprgr **Txs:** MFN

## PAKISTAN

**System:** PAL-B/G [E]

**PAKISTAN TELEVISION CORP. LTD (PTV) (Gov)** ▣ P.O.Box 1221, Islamabad 44000 ☎ +92 51 9208651 ▤ +92 51 9203406 **E:** ptvhq@ hotmail.com **W:** www.ptv.com.pk **Chs (terr.):** PTV Home, PTV News, regional stns, PTV Bolan, AJK TV **Txs: PTV Home:** Islamabad ch6 (50kW) & network; **PTV News:** (-) – **ATV (Comm)** ▣ 11 -F, Model Town, Lahore ☎ +92 42 5853669 ▤ +92 42 5853668 **E:** info@atv.com. pk **W:** atv.com.pk **Txs:** (-).

## PALAU (USA associated)

**NB:** No terrestrial TV station.

## PANAMA

**System:** DVB-T (MPEG2) [A]

**National Stations**
**SYSTEMA ESTATAL DE RADIO Y TELEVISIÓN (SERT) (Pub)** ▣ Apt. 0843-0256, Curundu, diagonal al Ministerio de Obras Públicas, Panamá ☎ +507 5071500 ▤ +507 2362987 **E:** administracion@sertv. gob.pa **W:** www.sertv.gob.pa **Chs:** SERTV – **FETV (Educ)** ▣Ave Ricardo J. Alfaro Contiguo al Gimnasio de la USMA, Apdo.6-7295, El Dorado, Panamá ☎ +507 2308888 ▤ +507 2301955 **W:** www. fetv.org **L.P:** DG: Manuel Santiago Blanquer i Planells – **COMPAÑIA DIGITAL DE TELEVISIÓN, S.A (NEXT TV) (Comm)** ▣ Via Espana Sector de Carrasquilla, Apdo. postal 87-1989, Zona 7, Panamá **W:** nextvpanama.com – **RPC TELEVISIÓN (Comm)** ▣Ave 12 de Octubre, Apartado 1-1425, Panamá 8 ☎ +507 2104104 **W:** www.rpctv.com –

**TELEMETRO (TLM) (Comm)** ✉ Ave 12 de Octubre, Apartado 0827-00116, Panamá ☎ +507 2106845 🖷 +507 2106929 **W:** www.telemetro.com **L.P:** Pres: Fernando Eleta Almarán – **TELEVISORA NACIONAL S.A (TVN) (Comm)** ✉ Apt. 0819-07129, El Dorado, Panamá ☎ +507 2793700 🖷 +507 2362987 **E:** tvn@tvn-2.com **W:** www.tvn-2.com **L.P:** DG: Agustin De La Guardia **Chs:** TVN, TVMAX.

**Local Stations** not shown.

**DTT Tx Networks**
**Tx Operator:** n/a **M1:** Tu Canal TV **M2:** Enlace, Enlace Juvenil **M3:** SERTV ✺ R. Nacional, Crisol FM **M4:** RPC HD, TLM HD, Mall TV **M5:** TVN HD, TVN+, TVMAX HD **M6:** Hosanna Vision HD ✺ Hosanna R. **M7:** FETV **M8:** NEXT TV, +23 ✺ RCM R. **M9:** ATV

| Location | M1 | M2 | M3 | M4 | M5 | M6 | M7 | M8 | M9 |
|---|---|---|---|---|---|---|---|---|---|
| SFN | 26 | 30 | 41 | 42 | 45 | 47 | 48 | 49 | 51 |

## PAPUA NEW GUINEA

**Systems:** DVB-T2 (MPEG4) [E]; § PAL-B/G [NZ]

**EMTV (Comm)** ✉ P.O.Box 443, Boroko NCD 111 ☎ +675 3257322 🖷 +675 3254450 **E:** online@emtv.com.pg **W:** www.emtv.com.pg **L.P:** CEO (Media Niugini Ltd): Ken Clark.

**DTT Tx Network**
**Tx Operator:** Digicel **M:** EMTV **Txs:** MFN

## PARAGUAY

**Systems:** ISDB-TB [A]; # PAL-N [A] ⬇2022

**National Stations** (ᵃ=analogue)
**TV PÚBLICA PARAGUAY (Pub)** ✉ Avda. Alberdi 633 c/Gral Díaz, Asunción ☎ +595 21 494000 **E:** info@tvpublica.com.py **W:** www.tvpublica.com.py **Txs:** Asunción ᵃch14/ch15 – **LATELE (Comm)** ✉ Av. Eusebio Ayala 2995, Esq. Pasaje Tembetary, Asunción ☎ +595 21 4157400 **E:** info@latele.com.py **W:** www.latele.com.py **Txs:** Asunción ᵃch11 (40kW) & relays. – **PARAVISIÓN (Comm)** ✉ Av. Mariscal López esq. Bélgica, Asunción ☎ +595 21 664380 **E:** info@paravision.com.py **W:** www.paravision.com.py **Txs:** Asunción ᵃch5 (20kW) & relays – **RED GUARANI (Comm)** ✉ Gral. Santos 1024 c/Concordia, Asunción ☎ +595 21 205444 **E:** info@redguarani.com.py **W:** www.redguarani.com.py **Txs:** Asunción ᵃch2 (20kW) & relays. – **RED PARAGUAYA DE COMUNICACIÓN (RPC) (Comm)** ✉ Calles Comendador Nicolás Bó y Guaranies, Lambaré, Asunción ☎ +595 21 332823 🖷 +595 21 331695 **E:** commercial@rpc.com.py **W:** rpc.com.py **Txs:** Asunción ᵃch13 (40kW) & relays. – **SISTEMA NACIONAL DE TELEVISIÓN (SNT) (Comm)** ✉ Av. Carlos Antonio Lopez 572, Asunción ☎ +595 21 424222 🖷 +595 21 480230 **E:** snt@snt.com.py **W:** www.snt.com.py **Txs:** Asunción ᵃch9 (40kW) & relays. – **TELEFUTURO (Comm)** ✉ Andrade c/ O'Higgins, Villa Morra, Asunción ☎ +595 21 608756 **W:** telefuturo.com.py **Txs:** Asunción ᵃch4 (60kW) & relays.

**Local Stations** not shown.

## PERU

**Systems:** ISDB-TB [A]; # NTSC-M [A] ⬇2020

**National Stations** (ᵃ=analogue)
**TV PERU (Pub)** ✉ Av. Jose Galvez 1040, Santa Beatriz, Lima ☎ +51 1 6190707 🖷 +51 1 6190711 **W:** www.tvperu.gob.pe **Txs:** Lima ᵃch7 (10kW)/ch16 (0.24kW) & relays txs. – **AMÉRICA TELEVISIÓN (Comm)** ✉ Montero Rosas 1099, Santa Beatriz, Lima ☎ +51 1 2657361 🖷 +51 1 2656976 **E:** americanoticias@americatv.com.pe **W:** www.americatv.com.pe **L.P:** CEO: Eric Jurgensen **Txs:** Lima ᵃch4 (2kW)/ch24 (0.24kW) & relay txs. – **ATV (ANDINA DE RADIODIFUSIÓN) (Comm)** ✉ Arequipa 3570, San Isidro, Apartado 270077, Lima ☎ +51 1 2212261 🖷 +51 1 4217263 **W:** www.atv.pe **Txs:** Lima ᵃch9 (315kW)/ch18 (1kW) & relay txs. – **FRECUENCIA LATINA (Comm)** ✉ Av. San Felipe 968, Jesús Mariá, Lima 11 ☎ +51 1 4707272 🖷 +51 1 4712688 **E:** info@latina.pe **W:** www.latina.pe **Txs:** Lima ᵃch2 (22.5kW)/ch20 (0.24kW) & relays txs. – **PANAMERICANA TELEVISION (Comm)** ✉ Av. Arequipa 1110, Lima ☎ +51 1 4113200 🖷 +51 1 4113309 **W:** www.panamericana.pe **Txs:** Lima ᵃch5 (290kW)/ch26 (0.24kW)& relay txs. – **RBC TELEVISIÓN (Comm)** ✉ Manco Capac 333, La Victoria, Lima ☎ +51 1 4337674 🖷 +51 1 4331237 **Txs:** Lima ᵃch11 (30kW)/ch38 (0.24kW) & relays.

**Local Stations** not shown.

**Systems:** ISDB-TB [A]; § NTSC-M [A] ⬇2023

**National Stations**
**INTERCONTINENTAL BROADCASTING CORP. (IBC) (Gov)** ✉ Broadcast City, Capitol Hills, Diliman, Quezon City ☎ +63 2 9318781 🖷 +63 2 9324611 **L.P:** Pres/CEO: Manolito Ocampo-Cruz. **Txs:** DZTV-TV Manila ch26 & relay stns. **NB:** IBC is due to be privatized. – **PEOPLE'S TELEVISION NETWORK, INC (PTV) (Gov)** ✉ Broadcast Complex, Visayas Ave, Quezon City 1100 ☎ +63 2 9206521 🖷 +63 2 9204342 **W:** ptv.ph **L.P:** GM: Dino Apolonio. **Txs:** DGWT-TV Manila ch42 & relay stns – **PROGRESSIVE BROADCASTING CORP. (UNTV) (Pub)** ✉ #907 ESDA Philam, Quezon City. **W:** www.untvweb.com **L.P:** Pres: Alfredo L. Henares. **Txs:** DWAO-TV Manila ch38 & relay stns. – **ABC DEVELOPMENT CORP. (TV5) (Comm)** ✉ AMPC Bldg., 136 Amorsolo cor. Gamboa Sts., Legaspi Village, Makati City ☎ +63 2 8923801 🖷 +63 2 8154314 **W:** www.tv5.com.ph **L.P:** Chmn: Manny V. Pangilinan. **Txs:** DWET-TV Manila ch51 & relay stns – **ABS-CBN BROADCASTING CORP. (Comm)** ✉ Eugenio Lopez Jnr St, Quezon C. ☎ +63 2 4111166 🖷 +63 2 4152272 **W:** www.abs-cbn.com **L.P:** Chmn/CEO: Eugenio Lopez III. **Txs:** DWWX-TV Manila ch43 & relay stns. – **BROADCAST ENTERPRISES AND AFFILIATED MEDIA, INC (Comm)** ✉ 3/F The Globe Plaza 1, Pioneer Highlands South Condominiun Corp., Pioner St, Metro Manila ☎ +63 2 5864747 **W:** www.beam.com.ph **L.P:** Chmn: Steve Macion. **Txs:** DWKC-TV Manila ch32 & relay stns – **GMA NETWORK, INC (Comm)** ✉ EDSA, Diliman, Quezon City, Metro Manila ☎ +63 2 9285041 🖷 +63 2 9285041 **W:** www.gmanetwork.com **L.P:** Chmn/CEO: Filipe Gozon. **Txs:** DZBB-TV Manila ch27 & relay stns. – **NINE MEDIA CORP, INC. (Comm)** ✉ Broadcast City, Capitol Hills, Quezon City ☎ +63 2 9315080 🖷 +63 2 9321470 **L.P:** Pres/CEO: Reggie Galura **Txs:** DZKB-TV Manila ch19 & relay stns – **RAJAH BROADCASTING NETWORK, INC. (2ND AVENUE) (Comm)** ✉ 3/F Save-A-Lot Mall, 2284 Pasong Tamo Ext., Makati City ☎ +63 2 8933404 🖷 +63 2 8932360 **E:** rjofc@compass.com.ph **W:** www.rjplanet.com **L.P:** Owner: Ramon Jacinto **Txs:** DZRJ-TV Manila ch30 & relay stns – **SOUTHERN BROADCASTING NETWORK, INC. (ETC) (Comm)** ✉ Suite 2901 Jollibee Plaza, Emerald Ave., Ortigas Center, Pasig City ☎ +63 2 6363286 🖷 +63 2 6363288 **E:** genceo@sbnphilippines.net **W:** www.solarentertainmentcorp.com **L.P:** Pres/CEO: Teofilo A. Henson **Txs:** DWCP-TV Manila ch22 & relay stns. – **GATEWAY UHF BROADCASTING (3ABN) (Rlg)** ✉ Sumulong Highway, Block 5, Brgy. Sta. Cruz, Antipolo City **Txs:** DWVN-TV Manila ch44 & relay stns – **SONSHINE MEDIA NETWORK INTERNATIONAL (SMNI) (Rlg)** ✉ Suite 3102 31/F Jollibee Plaza, F. Ortigas Jr. Road, Ortigas Center, Pasig City, 1600 ☎ +63 2 6830772 🖷 +63 2 6830775 **E:** sonshine@sonshinemedia.com **W:** www.smni.com **Txs:** DWBP-TV Manila ch40 & relay stns – **ZOE BROADCASTING NETWORK, INC. (LIGHT NETWORK) (Rlg)** ✉ 22F Strata 2000 Bldg., F. Ortigas Road, Ortigas Ctr, Pasig City ☎ +63 6383469 **W:** www.lightnetwork.ph **L.P:** Chmn: Eddie Villanueva. **Txs:** DZOZ-TV Manila ch33 & relay stns.

**Local Stations** not shown.

**System:** PAL-G [E]

**Foreign TV Relay**
**Hope Channel (USA):** ch29 (0.0035kW).

**System:** DVB-T (MPEG4)

**National Stations**
**TELEWIZJA POLSKA S.A. (TVP) (Pub)** ✉ ul. Woronicza 17, 00-999 Warszawa ☎ +48 225478000 **E:** tvp@tvp.pl **W:** www.tvp.pl **L.P:** Pres: Jacek Kurski **Chs (terr.):** TVP1, TVP2, TVP3 + regional stns, TVP INFO, TVP ABC, TVP Historia, TVP Kultura, TVP Polonia, TVP Rozrywka, TVP Seriale, TVP Sport – **TVN S.A. (Comm)** ✉ ul. Wiertnicza 166, 02-952 Warszawa ☎ +48 228566060 **E:** widzowie@tvn.pl **W:** www.tvn.pl **L.P:** Chmn: Piotr Korycki – **TELEVIZJA POLSAT SP.Z.O.O. (Comm)** ✉ ul. Ostrobramska 77, 04-175 Warszawa ☎ +48 225145533 **E:** poczta@polsat.pl **W:** www.polsat.pl **L.P:** Chmn: Miroslaw Blaszczyk. **Chs (terr.):** TV Polsat, TV4, Polsat Cafe, Polsat Film, Polsat News, Polsat Play, Polsat Sport – **TV PULS (Comm)** ✉ ul. Chelmska 21, 00-724 Warszawa ☎ +48 225597300 **E:** recepcja@pulstv.pl **W:** tvpuls.pl **L.P:** Chmn: Dariusz Dabski.

**Local Stations** (all Comm)
**Echo24:** Dwa Swiaty 1, 55-040 Bielany Wroclawskie **M:** TVN HD, Polsat HD, Eska TV Extra, STARS.TV, 4fun.tv, Mango, Tele5; ch24 (Wroclaw 2kW, Swidnica 1kW). **NTL:** ul. 11-go Listopada 2, 97-500 Radomsko **M:** NTL, 4fun.tv, 4fun Gold Hits, Eska TV Extra, STARS.TV; ch36 (Kamiensk 1.5kW, Lodz 0.79kW, Czestochowa 0.36kW, Tomaszów Maz. 0.01kW). **TV Luzyce:** ul. Zgorzelecka 12, 59-700 Boleslawiec **M:** TV Luzyce, Eska TV Extra, STARS.TV, Wspólna TV; ch38 (Gryfów Sl. 5kW, Chojnów 1kW, Jelenia Góra 1kW). **TVL:** ul. Tysiaclecia 2, 59-300 Lubin **M:** Tele5; ch43 (Glogów 1kW, Lubin 1kW). **TVT:** Rynek 1, 44-200 Rybnik **M:** TVT, Polsat Viasat History, Epic Drama, Eska TV Extra, STARS. TV, TVN HD, TVN7 HD; ch47 (Ornontowice 1.5kW, Rybnik 1kW).

**DTT Tx Networks** (DVB-T exc. where indicated)
**Tx Operator:** EmiTel **W:** www.emitel.pl **M1:** TVP ABC, TV Trwam, Stopklatka TV, Fokus TV, TTV, ATM Rozrywka, Eska TV, Polo TV **M2:** Polsat, TVN, TV4, TV Puls, TVN7, Super Polsat, TV 6, TV Puls 2 **M3:** TVP1 HD, TVP2 HD, TVP3 (Regional stations), TVP INFO, TVP Kultura, TVP Historia, TVP Sport **M4↻ (DVB-H):** Polsat Sport, Polsat Sport Extra, Polsat News, Polsat Play, Polsat Film, Polsat Cafe, TVN Style, TVP Seriale, Kino Polska, Comedy Central, Comedy Central Family, Nickelodeon ✖ R.RMF FM, R.RMF MAXXX, R.ZET, Antyradio, R.Plus, TOK FM, Złote Przeboje, Eska Rock, R. MUZO FM, R. VOX FM, Rock R. **M8:** Nowa TV, Metro, WP, ZOOM TV.

| Location | M1 | M2 | M3 | M4 | M8 | kW |
|---|---|---|---|---|---|---|
| Bialogard (Slawoborze) | 45 | 50 | 60 | - | 7 | 3x50/25 |
| Bialystok (Krynice) | 46 | 49 | 22 | 30 | 8 | 58/63/100/5/24 |
| Bydgoszcz (Trzeciewiec) | 41 | 32 | 36 | - | 8 | 3x100/20 |
| Ciechanów | 25 | 57 | 39 | - | 12V | 2x5/10/16 |
| Czestochowa (Wreczyna) | 35 | 39 | 41 | - | 9V | 2x100/80/7.9 |
| Elblag (Jagodnik) | 43 | 25 | 26 | - | 6 | 3x10/2.8 |
| Gdansk (Chwaszczyno) | 37 | 35 | 48 | - | 6V | 3x100/20 |
| Gizycko (Milki) | 43 | 48 | 50 | - | 7V | 2x100/90/2 |
| Golancz (Chojna) | 42 | 43 | 31 | - | 9V | 2x20/23/40 |
| Gorlice | 45 | 36 | 34 | - | 7 | 3x20/0.5 |
| Ilawa (Kisielice) | 38 | 24 | 48 | - | 8 | 2x100/50/8.3 |
| Jelenia Gora (Sniezne Kotly) | 30 | 35 | 49 | - | 6V | 3x100/7.9 |
| Kalisz (Mikstat) | 38 | 44 | 31 | - | 7V | 3x100/5 |
| Katowice (Kosztowy) | 55 | 49 | 41 | - | 6 | 25/63/100/20 |
| Kielce (Swiety Krzyz) | 30 | 37 | 47 | - | 8V | 2x100/150/10 |
| Klodzko (Czarna Góra) | 55 | 58 | 25 | - | 6V | 3x50/0.5 |
| Kobyla Góra | - | - | - | 8 | 15 | |
| Konin (Zolwieniec) | 55 | 45 | 27 | - | 7V | 2x100/15/14 |
| Konin (Zolwieniec) | - | 36 | - | - | 40 | |
| Koronowo (Okole) | - | - | - | 39V | - | 10 |
| Koszalin (Gologóra) | 44 | 47 | 23 | - | 7 | 3x100/15 |
| Kraków (Choragwica) | 25 | 23 | 50 | - | 7V | 3x100/10 |
| Kraków (Choragwica) | - | - | 47 | - | 35 | |
| Krosno (Sucha Góra) | 52 | 32 | 29 | - | 6V | 3x100/18 |
| Lebork (Skórowo Nowe) | 37 | 25 | 23 | - | 8V | 3x10/7.1 |
| Lezajsk (Giedlarowa) | 43 | 59 | 26 | - | 6V | 2x100/70/20 |
| Lódz | 46 | 24 | 43 | - | 9 | 2x100/170/25 |
| Luban (Nowa Karczma) | - | - | 49 | - | - | 20 |
| Lublin (Piaski) | 33 | 21 | 23 | - | 12 | 3x100/35 |
| Lublin (Bozy Dar) | | | 12 | | 30 | |
| Olsztyn (Komin MPEC) | - | - | - | 53V | - | 10 |
| Olsztyn (Pieczewo) | 28 | 33 | 26 | - | 9 | 3x100/60 |
| Opole (Chrzelice) | 46 | 23 | 34 | - | 6 | 3x100/10 |
| Ostroleka (Lawy) | 40 | 41 | 42 | - | - | 60 |
| Ostroleka (Kopernika) | | | | 12V | 11 | |
| Plock (Rachocin) | 25 | 57 | 39 | - | 12V | 3x100/10 |
| Plock (Komin... | | | | 12V | 25 | |
| Poznan (Komin EC Karolin | - | - | - | 36V | - | 10 |
| Poznan (Srem) | 23 | 39 | 27 | - | 7 | 2x100/110/22 |
| Przemysl (Tatarska Góra) | 43 | 59 | 26 | - | 6V | 3x20/7.9 |
| Przysucha (Kozlowiec) | 30 | 37 | 26 | - | 8V | 2x50/10/15 |
| Rabka (G. Lubon Wielki) | 43 | 36 | 34 | - | 7V | 2x10/9.8/0.2 |
| Radom (Wacyn) | - | - | 42 | - | 8V | 50/8.5 |
| Ryki (Janiszewska) | 22 | 24 | 52 | - | 7V | 3x20/7.9 |
| Siedlce (Losice) | 36 | 43 | 52 | - | 9V | 20/50/100/10 |
| Sokolów Podlaski | 36 | - | 56 | - | 9V | 5/10/7.1 |
| Solina (Góra Jawor) | 52 | 32 | 29 | - | 6V | 3x20/1.1 |
| Suwalki (G. Krzemianucha) | 43 | 29 | 58 | - | 7V | 3x20/9.5 |
| Swinoujscie (Chrobrego) | 58 | 34 | - | - | 10 | |
| Szczawnica (Góra Prehyba) | 45 | 36 | 34 | - | 7V | 2x20/22/1.6 |
| Szczecin (Kolowo) | 41 | 54 | 48 | - | 6 | 3x100/20 |
| Szczecin | - | - | 55V | - | 10 | |
| Tarnobrzeg | 43 | - | 26 | | 8 | 5/30/15 |
| Tarnów (G. Sw.Marcina) | 45 | 23 | 50 | - | 7 | 3x50/3 |
| Tarnów (Góra Wal) | - | - | - | 55V | - | 10 |

| Location | M1 | M2 | M3 | M4 | M8 | kW |
|---|---|---|---|---|---|---|
| Torun (Komin Cergia) | - | - | 36 | 34V | 8 | 12/2.5/15 |
| Walcz (Rusinowo) | 42 | 43 | 31 | - | 9V | 3x100/40 |
| Warszawa (PKiN) | 58 | 48 | 27 | 37V | 7V | 2x3/10/2.2/2 |
| Warszawa (Raszyn) | 58 | 48 | 55 | - | - | 2x100/130 |
| Wisla (G. Skrzyczne) | 55 | 58 | 41 | - | 7V | 2x100/60/1.5 |
| Wroclaw (G. Sleza) | 55 | 58 | 25 | - | 6V | 3x100/16 |
| Zagan (Wichów) | 45 | 41 | 32 | - | 8V | 3x50/20 |
| Zakopane (G. Gubalówka) | 43 | 36 | 34 | - | 7V | 3x20/0.5 |
| Zamosc (Tarnawatka) | 50 | 53 | 36 | - | 12 | 3x50/40 |
| Zielona Góra (G. Wilkanowska) | - | - | 48V | - | - | 10 |
| Zielona Góra (Jemiolów) | 45 | 46 | 32 | - | 8V | 2x80/100/22 |

+ sites with txs below 10kW. Pol.=H exc. where stated otherwise

**System:** DVB-T (MPEG4) [E]

**RÁDIO E TELEVISÃO DE PORTUGAL, S.A. (RTP) (Pub)** ✉
Av. Marechal Gomes da Costa 37, 1849-030 Lisboa ☎ +351 217947000 **E:** rtp@rtp.pt **W:** www.rtp.pt **L.P:** Pres: Gonçalo Reis **Chs (terr.):** RTP1, RTP2, RTP3, RTP Memória, RTP Açores and RTP Madeira (see Azores, Madeira), RTP África (see Cape Verde, Guinea-Bissau, Mozambique, São Tomé e Príncipe). – **SOCIEDADE INDEPENDENTE DE COMUNICAÇÃO, S.A. (SIC) (Comm)** ✉ Estrada da Outurela 119, 2794-052 Carnaxide ☎ +351 214179550 **E:** contacto@siconline.pt **W:** sic.sapo.pt **L.P:** Pres: Francisco Pedro Balsemão – **TELEVISÃO INDEPENDENTE, S.A. (TVI) (Comm)** ✉ R. Mário Castelhano, 40, Queluz de Baixo, 2749-502 Barcarena ☎ +351 214347500 **E:** relacoes.exteriores@tvi.pt **W:** www.tvi.iol.pt **L.P:** DG: Bruno Santos. – **ARTV (CANAL PARLAMENTO)** ✉ Palácio de S. Bento, 1249-068 Lisboa ☎ +351 213919663 **E:** canal.parlamento@ar.parlamento.pt **W:** www.canal.parlamento.pt

**DTT Tx Networks**
**Licensee:** Portugal Telecom ✉ Av. Fontes Pereira de Melo 40, 1069-300 Lisboa ☎ +351 215002000 **E:** contact@telecom.pt **W:** www.telecom.pt **Mux:** RTP1, RTP2, RTP3, RTP Memória, SIC, TVI, ARTV **Txs:** ch56 (SFN), exc. ch40 (Mendro), ch42 (Monte da Virgem), ch45 (Palmela), ch46 (Lousã, Boa Viagem), ch48 (São Mamede), ch48 (Marofa), ch49 (Montejunto).

**System:** ATSC [A]

**Local Stations** (Full power licenses; LP licenses not shown)
**WAPA-TV (Comm):** Carr 19 Kilometro 0.5, Guaynabo, PR 00966. Tx: ch27 (1000kW). **WCCV-TV (Rlg):** Carr No 2 K92.6, Camuy, PR 00627-2348. Tx: Arecibo ch46 (50kW). **WDWL (Rlg):** Ave Sabana Seca Section 5, Toa Baja, PR 00949. Tx: Bayamon ch30 (50kW). **WECN (Rlg):** Carr 167 KM 18.9, Bayamon, PR 00957. Tx: Naranjito ch18 (23kW). **WELU (Rlg):** Carr #2 Km162.8, Hormigueros, PR 00660. Tx: ch34 (250kW). **WIDP (Rlg):** Loma Verde San Jose 1820, Rio Piedras, PR 00926. Tx: ch45 (50.1kW). **WIPM-TV (Pub):** satellite of WIPR-TV. Tx: Mayagüez ch35 (620kW). **WIPR-TV (Pub):** 570 Ave.Hostos U.Baldrich, Hato Rey, PR 00918. Tx: ch43 (790kW). **WIRS (Comm):** Carr ch11 (48kW). **WMEI (Comm):** 1095 Avenida Wilson, Edificio Puerta del Condado, Suite 2, San Juan, PR 00907. Tx: Arecibo ch14 (50kW). **WMTJ (Pub):** Isodoro Colon Estatal176, San Juan, PR 00928-1345. Tx: ch16 (140kW). **WNJX-TV (Comm):** satellite of WAPA-TV. Tx: Mayagüez ch23 (400kW). **WOLE-DT (Comm):** Carr 111 Bario Palmar, Aguadilla, PR 00603-5125. Repeater for WKAQ-TV. Tx: Aguadilla ch12 (47kW). **WORA-TV (Comm):** satellite of WLII. Tx: Mayagüez ch29 (550kW). **WORO-DT (Rlg):** Ave Iturreguy/ Baldorioti, Carolina, PR 00902. Tx: ch13 (38kW). **WOST (Comm):** Edificio Chevere, Pda. 22, 328 De Diego, Esq. Ponce de Leon, Suite #304, Santurce,PR 00910. Tx: Mayagüez ch22 (15kW). **WQHA (Rlg):** satellite of WUJA. Tx: Aguada ch50 (50kW). **WQTO (Pub):** satellite of WMTJ. Tx: Ponce ch25 (200kW). **WRFB (Comm):** #21Clle B Sabana Abajo Ind, Carolina, PR 00982. Tx: ch51 (16kW). **WRUA (Rlg):** satellite of WECN. Tx: Fajardo ch33 (37kW). **WSJN-CA (Rlg):** Carr 861 KM 4.4, Toa Alta, PR 00953. Tx: ch15 (38.8kW). **WSJU-TV (Comm):** 1508 Calle Bori Urb Antonsant, San Juan, PR 00927-6116. Tx: ch31 (66kW). **WSTE-DT (Comm):** Calle Carazo 64, Guaynabo, PR 00969. Tx: Ponce ch7 (25kW). Boosters in San Juan

(WSTE-DT2), Mayagüez (WSTE-DT3), Arecibo (WSTE-DT4). **WSUR-DT (Comm):** satellite of WLII. Tx: Ponce ch9 (21.6kW). **WTCV (Comm):** Calle Bori # 1554, San Juan, PR 00927-6113. Tx: ch32 (50kW). **WTIN (Comm):** satellite of WAPA-TV. Tx: Ponce ch15 (380.2kW). **WUJA (Rlg):** Calle B #24 Urb Ind, Sabana Abajo Carolina, PR 00984-4039. Tx: Caguas ch48 (2.5kW). **WVEO (Comm):** satellite of WTCV. Tx: Aguadilla ch17 (42kW). **WVOZ-TV (Comm):** satellite of WTCV. Tx: Ponce ch47 (50.1kW). **WVSN (Rlg):** Satellite of WCCV-TV. Tx: Humaco ch49 (46kW).

**NB:** Tx sites are San Juan, unless indicated otherwise. Following hurricane damage in 2017 and lack of electricity, some txs are still off the air as of October 2018.

## QATAR

**System:** DVB-T2 (MPEG4) [E]

**QATAR MEDIA CORP. (Pub)** ✉ P.O.Box 1944, Doha ☎ +974 44894444 🖷 +974 44864611 **E:** contact@qna.org.qa **W:** www.qtv.qa **Chs:** Qatar TV, Al Rayan TV, Al Dawri/Al Kass, Jeem TV, Baraem TV, Al Bidda TV.

### DTT Tx Networks
**Tx Operator:** Qatar Media Corp. **M:** Qatar TV, Al Rayan TV, Al Dawri/Al Kass, Jeem TV, Baraem TV, Al Bidda TV **Txs:** ch53 (Doha) & nationwide MFN. – **Local Licensees** not shown.

## RÉUNION (France)

**System:** DVB-T (MPEG4) [E]

**RÉUNION LA 1ÈRE (Pub)** ✉ 12 rue René Demarne F-97490 Saint Denis ☎ +262 262406767 **W:** reunion.1ere.fr **LP:** Dir: Eric Barraud – **ANTENNE RÉUNION (Comm)** ✉ BP 80001, F-97801 Saint-Denis CEDEX 009 ☎ +262 262482828 **W:** www.antennereunion.fr **LP:** DG: Christophe Ducasse.

### DTT Tx Network
**Tx Operator:** TDF **Mux:** Réunion la 1ère, France 2-5, France Ô, France 24, Arte, Antenne Réunion **Txs:** MFN.

## ROMANIA

**System:** DVB-T2 (MPEG4) [E]

### National Station
**TELEVIZIUNEA ROMÂNA (TVR) (Pub)** ✉ Calea Dorobantilor nr. 191, sector 1, 010565 Bucuresti ☎ +40 21 3199112 **E:** office@tvr.ro **W:** www.tvr.ro **LP:** DG: Doina Gradea. **Chs (terr.):** TVR1, TVR2, TVR3, TVR HD, TVR Cultural, TVR News, Regional stns.

**Local/Regional Stations** not shown.

### DTT Tx Network
**Tx Operator:** Radiocom **W:** www.radiocom.ro **M:** TVR1, TVR2, TVR3, TVR HD, TVR Cultural, TVR News, ProTV HD, Sport.ro HD, National TV, Realitatea TV, Antena 1, Antena 3, B1 TV, Kanal D, Prima TV, Transilvania Look, Nasul TV, Music Channel, Money.ro

| Location | ch | kW | Location | ch | kW |
|---|---|---|---|---|---|
| Arad (Siria) | 21 | 90 | Iasi (Pietraria) | 43 | 70 |
| Bacau | 39 | 60 | Magura Boiu | 21 | 65 |
| Baia Mare (Mogosa) | 21 | 32 | Magura Odobesti | 38 | 75 |
| Balota | 40 | 55 | Nasaud (Dej) | 30 | 10 |
| Baneasa (Calarasi) | 36 | 62 | Negresti-Oas | 21 | 11 |
| Bârlad | 39 | 50 | Oltenita (Hotarele) | 30 | 20 |
| Bihor | 30 | 60 | Oradea | 44 | 70 |
| Bistrita (Heniu) | 40 | 80 | Parang | 29 | 20 |
| Botosani (Saveni) | 31 | 30 | Piatra Neamt | 26 | 17 |
| Brasov (Tampa) | 34 | 20 | Pitesti | 27 | 11 |
| Bucegi (Costila) | 22 | 150 | Rarau | 38 | 805 |
| Bucuresti (CNCR) | 30 | 10 | Semenic | 44 | 800 |
| Bucuresti (Herastrau) | 30 | 60 | Sibiu (Paltenis) | 37 | 95 |
| Buzau (Istrita) | 28 | 13 | Suceava | 38 | 50 |
| Calafat (Plenita) | 21 | 10 | Târgu Mures | 24 | 12 |
| Cerbu (Novaci) | 29 | 130 | Timisoara (Urseni) | 21 | 160 |
| Cluj (Feleac) | 26 | 40 | Toplita (Borsec) | 32 | 15 |
| Comanesti | 40 | 85 | Topolog | 38 | 60 |
| Constanta | 30 | 55 | Tulcea | 38 | 10 |
| Cozia | 27 | 30 | Varatec | 32 | 42 |
| Craiova (Simnic) | 28 | 11 | Vaslui | 39 | 45 |
| Galati (Vacareni) | 24 | 70 | Zarna | 30 | 15 |
| Hargita | 32 | 80 | + site with txs below 10kW | | |

**Local/Regional muxes** not shown.

## RUSSIA

**System:** DVB-T2 (MPEG4) [E]

### National Stations
**VSEROSSIYSKAYA GOSUDARSTVENNAYA TELEVIZIONNAYA I RADIOVESHCHATELNAYA KOMPANIYA (VGTRK) (Gov)** ✉ 125040 Moskva, 5-ya Yamskogo Polya ul. 19/21 ☎ +7 495 2326333 **W:** www.vgtrk.com **LP:** DG: Oleg B. Dobrodeyev. ✉ Studios: Rossiya 1, Rossiya 24, Match TV: 15162 Moskva, ul. Shabolovka 37; Rossiya K: 119902 Moskva, ul. Zubovskiy bul. 4; Karusel: 127427 Moskva, ul. Ak. Korolyova 19. **Chs:** Rossiya 1, Rossiya K, Rossiya 24, Karusel, Match TV; Regional Stations (see chapter below).

**VGTRK Regional Services: AD)** GTRK "Adygeya": 385000 Maykop, ul. Zhukovskogo 24. **AK)** GTRK "Altay": 656045 Barnaul, Zmeinogorskiy trakt 27a. **AM)** GTRK "Amur": 675000 Blagoveshchensk, per. Svyatitelya Innokentiya 15. **AR)** GTRK "Pomorye": 163061 Arkhangelsk, ul. Popova 2. **AS)** GTRK "Lotos": 414000 Astrakhan, ul. Molodoy Gvardii 17. **BA)** GTRK "Bashkortostan": 450076 Ufa, ul. Gafuri 9/1. **BE)** GTRK "Belgorod": 308000 Belgorod, pr. Slavy 60. **BR)** GTRK "Bryansk": 241033 Bryansk, ul. Stanke Dimitrova 77. **BU)** GTRK "Buryatiya": 670000 Ulan-Ude, ul. Erbanova 7. **CB)** GTRK "Yuzhnyy Ural": 454000 Chelyabinsk, ul. Ordzhonikidze 54b. **CC)** GTRK "Vaynakh": 364000 Groznyy, ul. B.Khmelnitskogo 147, korpus 5. **CK)** GTRK "Chukotka": 686710 Anadyr, ul. Lenina 18. **CV)** GTRK "Chuvashiya": 428003 Cheboksary, ul. Nikolayeva 4. **DA)** GTRK "Dagestan": 367032 Makhachkala, ul. Magomeda Gadzhieva 182. **IN)** GTRK "Ingushetiya": 366720 Nazran, pr. Bazorkina 72. **IR)** GTRK "Irkutsk": 664003 Irkutsk, ul. Gorkogo 15. **IV)** GTRK "Ivteleradio": 153647 Ivanovo, ul. Teatralnaya 31. **KA)** GTRK "Kaliningrad": 236016 Kaliningrad, ul. Klinicheskaya 19. **KB)** GTRK "Kabardino-Balkariya": 360000 Nalchik, pr. Lenina 3. **KC)** GTRK "Karachayevo-Cherkesiya": 357100 Cherkessk, ul. Krasnoarmeyskaya 51. **KD)** GTRK "Kuban": 350038 Krasnodar, ul. Radio 5. **KE)** GTRK "Kuzbass": 650099 Kemerovo, ul. Krasnoarmeyskaya 137a. **KG)** GTRK "Kurgan": 640018 Kurgan, ul. Sovetskaya 105. **KH)** GTRK "Dalnevostochnaya": 682632 Khabarovsk, ul. Lenina 4. **KL)** GTRK "Kaluga": 248021 Kaluga, Pole Svobody 40a. **KM)** GTRK "Kamchatka": 683000 Petropavlovsk-Kamchatskiy, ul. Sovetskaya 62. **KN)** GTRK "Krasnoyarsk": 660028 Krasnoyarsk, ul. Mechnikova 44a. **KO)** GTRK "Komi Gor": 167610 Syktyvkar, Oktyabrskiy pr. 164. **KS)** GTRK "Kostroma": 156005 Kostroma, ul. Nikitskaya 10. **KT)** GTRK "Kareliya": 185630 Petrozavodsk, ul. Pirogova 2. **KU)** GTRK "Kursk": 305016 Kursk, ul. Sovetskaya 32. **KV)** GTRK "Vyatka": 610002 Kirov, ul. Uritskogo 34. **KX)** GTRK "Kalmykiya": 358000 Elista, ul. M. Gorkogo 34. **KY)** GTRK "Yugoriya": 626200 Khanty-Mansiysk, ul. Mira 7. **LI)** GTRK "Lipetsk": 398050 Lipetsk, pl. Plekhanova 1. **MA)** GTRK "Magadan": 685024 Magadan, ul. Kommuny 8/12. **MD)** GTRK "Mordoviya": 430000 Saransk, ul. Dokuchayeva 29. **ME)** GTRK "Mariy-El": 424014 Yoshkar-Ola, ul. Osipenko 50. **MU)** GTRK "Murman": 183032 Murmansk, per. Rusanova 7. **NE)** Territorialnoye otdeleniya GTRK "Pomorye", 164700 Naryan-Mar, ul. Smidovicha 19. **NN)** GTRK "Nizhniy Novgorod": 603600 Nizhniy Novgorod, ul. Belinskogo 9a. **NO)** GTRK "Slaviya": 173620 Velikiy Novgorod, ul. B.Moskovskaya 106. **NS)** GTRK "Novosibirsk": 630048 Novosibirsk, ul. Rimskogo-Korsakova 9. **OB)** GTRK "Orenburg": 460024 Orenburg, per. Televizionnyy 3. **OL)** GTRK "Oryol": 302028 Oryol, ul. 7 Noyabrya 43. **OM)** GTRK "Irtysh": 644050 Omsk, pr. Mira 2. **PM)** GTRK "Vladivostok": 690091 Vladivostok, ul. Uborevicha 20a. **PR)** GTRK "Perm": 614070 Perm, ul. Tekhnicheskaya 7. **PS)** GTRK "Pskov": 180000 Pskov, ul. Nekrasova 50. **PZ)** GTRK "Penza": 440602 Penza, ul. Lermontova 39. **RA)** GTRK "Gornyy Altay": 659700 Gorno-Altaysk, ul. Choros-Gurkina 38. **RK)** GTRK "Khakasiya": 660000 Abakan, ul. Vyatkina 12. **RO)** GTRK "Don-TR": 344101 Rostov-na-Donu, ul. 1-ya Barrikadnaya 18. **RS)** GTRK "Sakha": 677007 Yakutsk, ul. Ordzhonikidze 48. **RT)** GTRK "Tyva": 667003 Kyzyl, ul. Gornaya 31. **RY)** GTRK "Oka": 390006 Ryazan, ul. Skomoroshinskaya 20. **SA)** GTRK "Samara": 443011 Samara, ul. Sovetskoy Armii 205. **SL)** GTRK "Sakhalin": 693000 Yuzhno-Sakhalinsk, ul. Komsomolskaya 209. **SM)** GTRK "Smolensk": 214025 Smolensk, ul. Nakhimova 1. **SO)** GTRK "Alaniya": 362007 Vladikavkaz, Osetinskaya gorka 2. **SP)** GTRK "Sankt-Peterburg": 197022 St.Peterburg, nab. reki Karpovki 43. **SR)** GTRK "Saratov": 410004 Saratov, 2-ya Sadovaya ul. 7. **ST)** GTRK "Stavropolye": 355000 Stavropol, ul. Artema 35a. **SV)** GTRK "Ural": 620026 Yekaterinburg, ul. Lunacharskogo 212. **TA)** GTRK "Tambov": 392720 Tambov, ul. Michurinskaya 8a. **TL)** GTRK "Tula": 300600 Tula, Staronikitskaya ul. 13. **TO)** GTRK "Tomsk": 634050 Tomsk, ul. Pushkina 19. **TS)** GTRK "Tatarstan": 420015 Kazan, ul. M. Gorkogo 15. **TV)** GTRK "Tver": 170000 Tver, ul. Vagzhanova 9. **TY)** GTRK "Region-Tyumen": 625013 Tyumen, ul. Permyakova 6. **UD)** GTRK "Udmurtiya": 426004 Izhevsk, ul. Komunarov 216. **UL)** GTRK "Volga": 432030 Ulyanovsk, ul. Sovetskaya 5. **VG)** GTRK "Volgograd-TRV": 400066 Volgograd, ul. Mira 9. **VL)** GTRK "Vladimir": 600000 Vladimir, ul. Bol. Moskovskaya 62. **VN)** GTRK "Voronezh": 394625 Voronezh, ul. Karl

Marksa 114. **VO)** GTRK "Vologda": 160000 Vologda, ul. Predtecheskaya 32. **YA)** GTRK "Yaroslaviya": 150014 Yaroslavl, ul. Bogdanovicha 20. **YN)** GTRK "Yamal": 626600 Salekhard, ul. Lambinykh 3. **YV)** GTRK "Bira": 679016 Birobidzhan, ul. Oktyabrskaya 15. **ZB)** GTRK "Chita": 672090 Chita, ul. Kostyushko-Grigorovicha 27. **NB:** Keys to region codes: see National Radio section. — **MIR TV (Gov)** 107076 Moskva, ul. Krasnobogatyrskaya 44 +7 495 6480792 **E:** mir24@mirtv.ru **W:** mirtv.ru **LP:** Chmn: Radik Batyrshin – **TV ZVEZDA (Mil)** 129110 Moskva, Suvorovskaya pl. 2 +7 495 6316883 **E:** info@tvzvezda.ru **W:** tvzvezda.ru **LP:** DG: Aleksey Pimanov – **PERVYY KANAL (Semi-Gov)** 127000 Moskva, ul. Ak. Korolyova 12 +7 495 2179838 +7 495 2151976. **E:** dip@1tv.ru **W:** www.1tv.ru **LP:** DG: Konstantin Ernst – **TV TSENTR (Municipal)** 115184 Moskva, ul. Bolshaya Tatarskaya 33-1 +7 495 9593900 **E:** press@tvc.ru **W:** www.tvc.ru **LP:** DG: Yuliya Bystritskaya – **OBSHCHESTVENNOYE TELEVIDENIYE ROSSII (OTR) (Pub)** 127427 Moskva, ul. Ak. Korolyova 19 **E:** press@otr-on-line.ru **W:** otr-online.ru **LP:** DG: Anatoliy Lysenko – **5 KANAL (Comm)** 197376 St.Peterburg, ul. Chapygina 6 +7 812 3351560 +7 812 2343846 **E:** trk@spbtv.ru **W:** www.5-tv.ru **LP:** DG: Yuriy Shapimov – **DOMASHNIY (Comm)** 125124 Moskva, ul. Pravdy 15a +7 495 7856333 +7 495 6429451 **E:** info@domashniy.ru **W:** www.domashniy.ru **LP:** DG: Marina Khripunova – **MUZ-TV (Comm)** 105066 Moskva, ul. Olkhovskaya 4 +7 495 2131888 +7 495 2131867 **E:** info@muz-tv.ru **W:** muz-tv.ru **LP:** DG: Arman Davletyarov – **NTV (Comm)** 127000 Moskva, ul. Ak. Korolyova 12 +7 495 2177895 +7 495 2175103 **E:** ntv@ntv.ru **W:** ntv.ru **LP:** DG: Aleksey Zemskiy. – **PYATNITSA (Comm)** 129090 Moskva, Olimpiyskiy pr. 14 +7 495 7832306 **E:** info@friday.ru **W:** friday.ru **LP:** DG: Nikolay Kartoziya – **REN-TV (Comm)** 119847 Moskva, Zubovskiy bul. 17-1 +7 495 2465933 +7 495 2460655. **E:** press@ren-tv.com **W:** ren.tv **LP:** DG: Vladimir Tyulin – **STS (Comm)** 125254 Moskva, Leningradskiy pr. 31 +7 495 7856347 +7 495 7974101 **E:** ctc@ctc.ru **W:** ctc.ru **LP:** DG: Vyacheslav Murugov – **TNT (Comm)** 129272 Moskva, ul. Trifonovskaya 57-3 +7 495 2178188 +7 495 7481490 **E:** info@tnt-tv.ru **W:** tnt-online.ru **LP:** DG: Artur Dzhanibekyan – **TV-3 (Comm)** 117105 Moskva, Varshavskoye shosse 9 +7 495 9374039 **E:** info@tv3.ru **W:** tv3.ru **LP:** DG: Valeriy Fedorovich – **SPAS (Rlg)** 129515 Moskva, ul. Ak. Korolyova 13 +7 495 6510829 + 7 495 6510790 **E:** office@spas-tv.ru **W:** www.spastv.ru **LP:** DG: Boris Korchevnikov.

**Other Regional & Local Stations** not shown.

**DTT Tx Networks**
**Tx Operator:** RTRS 129515 Moskva, ul. Ak. Korolyova 13 +7 495 6480111 +7 495 6480111 **E:** rtrn@rtrn.ru **W:** www.rtrs.ru **M1:** Rossiya 1, Rossiya 24, Rossiya K, Karusel, Match TV, Pervyy kanal, NTV, OTR, 5-kanal, TV Tsentr, VGTRK Regional TV stns R. Rossii, Mayak, Vesti FM. **M2:** Domashniy, TV Zvezda, Mir TV, Muz-TV, Pyatnitsa, REN TV, Spas, STS, TNT, TV-3

| Re | Location | M1 | M2 | kW | Re | Location | M1 | M2 | kW |
|---|---|---|---|---|---|---|---|---|---|
| AD | Maykop | 45 | 22 | 5 | KY | Khanty-Mansiysk | 38 | 44 | 2 |
| AK | Barnaul | 27 | 58 | 5 | LI | Lipetsk | 30 | 40 | 1 |
| AM | Blagoveshchensk | 34 | 36 | 0.5 | MA | Magadan | 27 | 29 | 5 |
| AR | Arkhangelsk | 33 | 44 | 5 | MD | Saransk | 43 | 46 | 2 |
| BA | Ufa | 25 | 43 | 2 | ME | Yoshkar-Ola | 38 | 56 | 2 |
| BE | Belgorod | 43 | 46 | 5 | MO | Moskva | 30 | 24 | 10 |
| BR | Bryansk | 39 | 23 | 2 | MU | Murmansk | 44 | 55 | 1 |
| BU | Ulan-Ude | 30 | 32 | 2 | NE | Naryan-Mar | 26 | 30 | 0.25 |
| CB | Chelyabinsk | 24 | 40 | 2 | NN | N.Novgorod | 28 | 53 | 5 |
| CC | Groznyy | 32 | 59 | 2 | NO | V.Novgorod | 30 | 58 | 2 |
| CK | Anadyr | 21 | 26 | 0.25 | OB | Orenburg | 22 | 28 | 5 |
| CV | Cheboksary | 46 | 57 | 0.25 | OL | Oryol | 26 | 41 | 5 |
| DA | Makhachkala | 22 | 52 | 2 | OM | Omsk | 31 | 49 | 2 |
| IN | Nazran | 38 | 36 | 2 | PM | Vladivostok | 37 | 56 | 5 |
| IR | Irkutsk | 38 | 57 | 5 | PR | Perm | 23 | 49 | 10 |
| IV | Ivanovo | 59 | 57 | 1 | PS | Pskov | 49 | 56 | 2 |
| KA | Kaliningrad | 47 | 30 | 1 | PZ | Penza | 57 | 44 | 5 |
| KB | Nalchik | 34 | 21 | 5 | RA | Gorno-Altaysk | 24 | 32 | 1 |
| KC | Cherkessk | 58 | 59 | 1 | RK | Abakan | 24 | 32 | 1 |
| KD | Krasnodar | 39 | 60 | 5 | RO | Rostov-na-Donu | 37 | 38 | 5 |
| KE | Kemerovo | 23 | 43 | 2 | RS | Yakutsk | 33 | 46 | 5 |
| KH | Khabarovsk | 38 | 30 | 5 | RT | Kyzyl | 33 | 37 | 1 |
| KL | Kaluga | 46 | 44 | 5 | RY | Ryazan | 43 | 27 | 1 |
| KM | Petropavlovsk-K. | 22 | 26 | 2 | SA | Samara | 27 | 57 | 5 |
| KN | Krasnoyarsk | 25 | 45 | 5 | SL | Yu-Sakhalinsk | 21 | 51 | 1 |
| KO | Syktyvkar | 26 | 34 | 2 | SM | Smolensk | 39 | 46 | 1 |
| KS | Kostroma | 46 | 43 | 2 | SO | Vladikavkaz | 35 | 50 | 5 |
| KT | Petrozavodsk | 25 | 39 | 2 | SP | Sankt-Peterburg | 35 | 45 | 5 |
| KU | Kursk | 24 | 53 | 5 | SR | Saratov | 36 | 40 | 2 |
| KV | Kirov | 32 | 36 | 5 | ST | Stavropol | 57 | 32 | 1 |
| KX | Elista | 46 | 39 | 2 | SV | Yekaterinburg | 60 | 46 | 5 |

| Re | Location | M1 | M2 | kW | Re | Location | M1 | M2 | kW |
|---|---|---|---|---|---|---|---|---|---|
| TA | Tambov | 46 | 56 | 10 | VG | Volgograd | 37 | 39 | 5 |
| TL | Tula | 34 | 60 | 5 | VL | Vladimir | 36 | 50 | 5 |
| TO | Tomsk | 21 | 44 | 5 | VN | Voronezh | 52 | 43 | 5 |
| TS | Kazan | 36 | 53 | 5 | VO | Vologda | 34 | 35 | 5 |
| TV | Tver | 37 | 58 | 2 | YA | Yaroslavl | 39 | 36 | 5 |
| TY | Tyumen | 35 | 44 | 5 | YN | Nakhodka | 35 | 59 | 5 |
| UD | Izhevsk | 36 | 57 | 5 | YV | Birobidzhan | 34 | 37 | 2 |
| UL | Ulyanovsk | 56 | 59 | 5 | ZB | Chita | 24 | 34 | 5 |

**NB:** Only txs in top-level administrative capitals shown.
**Regional/Local licensees** not shown.

## CRIMEA
**NB:** The station listing can be found at the end of the Ukraine entry.

## RWANDA

**System:** DVB-T2 (MPEG4) [E]

**RWANDA BROADCASTING AGENCY (RBA) (Gov)** P.O.Box 83, Kigali +250 252576540 **E:** info@rba.co.rw **W:** www.rba.co.rw – **TV10 (Comm)** Plot 1187, Kigali Road, Kigali +250 25269150 **E:** info@tele10.co.rw **W:** www.tele10.co.rw **LP:** CEO: Eugene Nyagahene.

**DTT Tx Networks**
**Licensee:** Startimes **M(partly○):** RTV, TV10, CNN, TV5 Monde, France 24 Français, France 24 English, Al Jazeera, True Movies **Txs:** MFN – **Licensee:** TV10 **M○:** multiprgr **Txs:** MFN

## SABA (Netherlands)

**Systems:** # NTSC-M [A]; DVB-T (MPEG2) planned

**ATV RELAY (Aruba Broadcasting Co., Aruba):** ch11

## SAMOA

**System:** DVB-T2 (MPEG4) [E]

**TV1 (Comm)** P.O.Box 3691, Apia +685 24790 **W:** www.tv1samoa.tv **LP:** GM: Galumalemana Faiesea Matafeo – **TV3 (Comm)** Taufusi, Apia +685 33330 **E:** tvsamoa3@ipasifika.net **W:** www.facebook.com/tv3samoa **LP:** CEO: Atanoa Herbert Crichton – **EKFS TV (Rlg)** P.O.Box 96, Apia +685 27882 **LP:** CEO: Tofilau Elijah Ryan – **KTV (Rlg)** Sogi, Apia +685 21447 **E:** worshipcentre@samoa.ws **LP:** GM: Rev. Afereti Lui – **UPUMANA TV (Rlg)** Apia **LP:** Dir: Spa Silva.

**DTT Tx Network**
**Tx Operator:** Samoa Digital Company Ltd **M:** multiprgr **Txs:** MFN

## SAMOA (AMERICAN) (USA)

**System:** ATSC [A]

**Local Station** (Full power license; LP licenses not listed)
**KVZK-TV (Gov)** 100 KVZK St, Pago Pago AS 96799 +1 684 6334191 **E:** info@opi.gov.as **W:** www.facebook.com/pg/KVZKTV **LP:** Dir: Tuimavave T. Laupola **Tx:** Pago Pago ch5. **M:** KVZK-TV, KGMB/CBS, PBS, BBC World News.

## SAN MARINO

**System:** DVB-T (MPEG2) [E]

**SAN MARINO RTV (Pub)** Viale J.F.Kennedy 13, SM-47890 San Marino +378 0549 882000 **E:** amministrazione@sanmarinortv.sm **W:** www.smtvsanmarino.sm **LP:** Pres: Davide Gasperoni **M:** San Marino RTV, San Marino RTV HD, San Marino RTV2-4, San Marino RTV Sport R. San Marino Classic **Tx:** San Marino ch51 (10kW).

## SÃO TOMÉ & PRÍNCIPE

**System:** DVB-T2 (MPEG4) [E]

**TELEVISÃO SANTOMENSE (TVS) (Pub)** CP 420, Bairro da Quinta do Santo António, 420 São Tomé +239 2221041 +239 2221942 **E:**

tvs@cstome.net **W:** www.tvs.st.

**DTT Tx Network**
**Tx Operator:** Startimes **M:** TVS, RTP África **Txs:** MFN

## SAUDI ARABIA

**Systems:** DVB-T, DVB-T2 (MPEG4) [E]

**SAUDI BROADCASTING AUTHORITY (Gov)** ✉ P.O.Box 570, Riyadh 11421 ☎ +966 1 4014440 🖷 +966 1 4044192 **W:** www. sba.sa **Chs (Terr.):** Saudia TV, Saudi 2TV, Al-Riyadih, Al-Ekhbariya, Al-Eqtisadiyah, Al-Sunna, Al-Quran.

**DTT Tx Networks** (DVB-T2 exc. *=DVB-T)
**Tx Operator:** Ministry of Culture and Information **M1:** TV1, TV2, Al-Riyadih, Al-Ekhbariya, Al-Eqtisadiyah, Al-Sunna, A-Quran ⌘ General prgr, Second prgr, R.Quran, European prgr **M2:** Sindo TV, B Channel **M3:** O Channel, Kompas TV), **M4:** MBC1, MBC4, MBC Action **M5:** Fox **M6:** LBC Sat **M7:** n/a **M8:** ITV1, ITV2 **M9:** OSN First, OSN News, Al Yawm, Series Channel **M10:** ABP News, ABP Majha, ABP Ananda. (NB: Local variations may apply)

| Location | M1 | M2 | M3 | M4 | M5 | M6 | M7 | M8 | M9 | M10 |
|----------|----|----|----|----|----|----|----|----|----|-----|
| Jeddah | 30 | 21* | 23* | 25 | 29 | 31 | 35 | 41 | 43 | 45* |

+ nationwide network.

## SENEGAL

**System:** DVB-T2 (MPEG4) [E]

**RADIODIFFUSION TÉLÉVISION SÉNÉGALAISE (Pub)** ✉ BP 1765, Dakar ☎ +221 338217801 🖷 +221 338223490 **E:** rts@rts.sn **W:** www.rts.sn **L.P:** DG: Racine Talla **Chs:** RTS1, SN2. – **TÉLÉ FUTURS MÉDIAS (TFM) (Comm)** ✉ BP 17795, Dakar ☎ +221 338491644 **W:** www.igfm.sn **L.P:** DG: Mamoudou Ibra Kane.

**DTT Tx Network**
**Tx Operator:** Excaf Telecom Group **M:** RTS1, SN2, multiprgr **Txs:** nationwide MFN network.

## SERBIA

**System:** DVB-T2 (MPEG4) [E]

**National Stations**
**RADIO-TELEVIZIJA SRBIJE (RTS) (Pub)** ✉ Takovska 10, 11000 Beograd ☎ +381 11 3212000 **E:** rtstv@rts.rs **W:** www.rts.rs **L.P:** DG: Dragan Bujoševic **Chs (terr.):** RTS1, RTS2, RTS3 = **NACIONALNA TELEVIZIJA HAPPY (Comm)** ✉ Aleksandra Dubceka 14, 11080 Zemun ☎ +381 11 3778373 **E:** office@happytv.rs **W:** www.happytv. rs **L.P:** DG: Aleksandra Krstic – **O2.TV (Comm)** ✉ Autoput 22, 11080 Zemun ☎ +381 11 3012000 **W:** o2tv.rs **L.P:** CEO: Manja Grcic – **PRVA SRPSKA TELEVIZIJA (Comm)** ✉ Autoput 22, 11080 Zemun ☎ +381 11 2091000 **E:** produkcija@prva.rs **W:** www.prva.rs **L.P:** GM: Dragan Nenadovic – **TV PINK (Comm)** ✉ Neznanog junaka 1, 11000 Beograd ☎ +381 11 3063400 **E:** marketing@rtvpink.com **W:** www. rtvpink.com **L.P:** DG (Pink Int.): Željko Mitrovic.

**Local Stations** (via Mux 2 - DTT regions a-i*)
**K::CN K:** Dimitrija Tucovica 17, 11550 Lazarevac (a,h). **K::CN 1:** Cara Dušana 45, 18000 Niš (e). **K::CN Raška:** Dušanova 6, 36350 Raška (f). **KA TV:** Ibarska 10, 36000 Kraljevo (e,g). **Mostnet:** Jug Bogdanova 94, 18400 Prokuplje (e). **NTV:** Vojvode Mišica 50/I, 18000 Niš (e). **RTV Branicevo:** Bate Bulica bb, 12300 Petrovac na Mlavi (d). **RTV Novi Pazar:** Stane Bacanin 29, 36300 Novi Pazar (f,g). **Sandžak TV:** Dimitrija Tucovica bb, 36300 Novi Pazar (f). **Sandžacka TV Mreža:** Bogoljuba Cukica 9, 36320 Tutin (f). **Sat TV:** Bose Dimitrijevica 130a, 12000 Požarevac (d,h,l). **Sportska TV:** Micuna Pavlovica 1, 37000 Kruševac (e). **Studio B:** Masarikova 5, 11000 Beograd (a). **T1:** Zmaj Jovina 3, 19250 Majdanpek (d,i). **Televizija Plus:** Balaknska 71, 37000 Kruševac (e). **Televizija 5 plus:** Mihajla Pupina 1, 31000 Užice (g). **TV 4S:** Stojana Ljubica bb, 16205 Bojnik (f). **TMS Televizija Telemark:** Sindjeliceva bb, 32000 Cacak (g). **TV Aldi:** Maršala Tita 19, 17523 Preševo (b). **TV AS:** Kralja Milana 9, 15500 Šabac (c). **TV Belle Amie:** Trg Kralja Milana 6-8, 18000 Niš (b,e,i). **TV Bor:** Moše Pijade 19, 19210 Bor (d). **TV Bujanovac:** Karadjordjev trg bb, 17520 Bujanovac (b). **TV Caribrod:** Trg dr Zorana Djincica 2, 18320 Dimitrovgrad (i). **TV Diskos:** Rackovacka 22, 37230 Aleksandrovac (f). **TV F Kanal:** Trg oslobodjenja bb, 19000 Zajecar (d,i). **TV Galaksija 32:** PTC Vavilon, Železnicka bb, 32000 Cacak (g). **TV Gem:** Dimitrija Tucovica 1, 11550 Lazarevac (a). **TV Golija:** Milinka Kušica 23, 32250 Ivanjica (g). **TV**

**Istok:** Jasikovacka petlja bb, 19224 Salaš (d,i). **TV Jasenica:** Francuska 9/9, 11420 Smederevska Palanka (h). **TV Jedinstvo:** AVNOJ-a d, sprat 2, stan 7, 11090 Novi Pazar (f). **TV Jefimija:** Bircaninova 10, 37000 Kruševac (f). **TV K-1:** Radanska 66, 16000 Leskovac (e). **TV Kanal M:** Nemanjina bb, Paracin (h). **TV Kladovo:** Vinogradarska 15, 19320 Kladovo (d). **TV Kraljevo:** Konarevo bb, 36000 Kraljevo (e). **TV Kragujevac:** Branka Radicevica 9, 34000 Kragujevac (h). **TV Kruševac:** Trg kosovskih junaka 6, 37000 Kruševac (e). **TV Kuršumlija:** Palih boraca 79, 18430 Kuršumlija (f). **TV Laser:** Momcila Miloševica bb, 18360 Svrljig (e). **TV Lav Plus:** Skadarska 7, 32000 Cacak (g). **TV Leskovac:** Bulevar oslobodjenja 9, 16000 Leskovac (e). **TV Lotel Plus:** Maksima Gorkog 2, 15300 Loznica (c). **TV Melos:** Hajduk Veljkova 2, 36000 Kraljevo (e,g). **TV Mlava:** Bate Bulica bb, 12300 Petrovac na Mlavi (d). **TV Palma Plus:** Zeleznicka bb, 35000 Jagodina (h). **TV Pi Kanal:** Mite Gage 10, 18300 Pirot (i). **TV Podrinje:** Kneza Miloša 3, 15300 Loznica (c). **TV Požega:** Vojvode Mišica bb, 31210 Požega (g). **TV Pirot:** Branka Radicevica bb, 18300 Pirot (i). **TV Preševo:** Petnaestog novembra 90, 17523 Preševo (b). **TV Priboj:** Trg FAPA-a bb, 31330 Priboj (g). **TV Prima:** Vuka Karadžica bb, 31250 Bajina Bašta (g). **TV Ritam:** Gramace 12a, 17542 Vranjska Banja (b). **TV Sezam:** Moše Pijade 23, 19210 Bor (d). **TV Sunce:** Ilije Garašanina 36, Arandjelovac (h). **TV Šabac:** Kneza Lazara 1, 15000 Šabac (c). **TV Trans:** Badnjevska bb, 19300 Negotin (d). **TV Trstenik:** Knjeginje Milice bb, 37240 Trstenik (e). **TV Vranje:** Partizanska 17a, 17500 Vranje (b). **TV Vrnjacka Banja:** Vrnjacka 1, Vrnjacka Banja (f). **TV Vujic:** Užicka 25, 14104 Valjevo (c). **TV Zona plus:** Branka Radicevica 30, 18000 Niš (e). **VA Plus:** Norveških Interniraca 23, 14000 Valjevo (c). **Vranjska plus:** Oca Justina Popovica 3/3, 17500 Vranje (b).

*) local stns transmitted exclusively in lp DTT regions not listed

**DTT Tx Networks**
**Tx Operator:** JP Emisiona Technika i Veze (ETV) **W:** etv.rs **M1:** RTS1, RTS2, RTS3, Happy TV, Info, O2.TV, Prva, TV Pink ⌘ R. Beograd 1, R. Beograd 2, R. Beograd 202 **M2:** Local stations **M3**✪**:** Arena Sport 1-5, Minimx, Nickelodeon, Film Klub, Agro TV, Zenska TV, Kitchen TV, Hram TV, Info na dlanu, Sve na dlanu, Pink 2, Pink 3 Info, Pink Kids, Pink Serije, Pink Premium, Pink Movies, Pink Action, Pink Comedy, Pink Pedia

| Location | M1 | M2* | M3 | kW |
|----------|----|-----|----|----|
| Avala | 22 | 28a | 45 | 100 |
| Besna Kobila | 35 | 39b | 43 | 50 |
| Deli Jovan | 23 | 43d | 41 | 10 |
| Jastrebac | 27 | 38e | 42 | 50 |
| Kopaonik | 24 | 32f | 34 | 50 |
| Maljen | 32 | 34c | 37 | 10 |
| Ovcar | 23 | 36g | 39 | 80 |
| Rudnik | 26 | 29h | 35 | 32 |
| Tupižnica | 22 | 25i | 28 | 50 |

+ sites with txs below 10kW *) Local stns a-i, see above

**Vojvodina**

**RADIO-TELEVIZIJA VOJVODINE (RTV) (Pub)** ✉ Ignjata Pavlasa 3, 21101 Novi Sad ☎ +381 21 2101420 **E:** office@rtv.rs **W:** www.rtv. rs **L.P:** DG: Miodrag Koprivica **Chs:** RTV1, RTV2

**Local Stations** (via Mux 2 - DTT regions j-m)
**KTV Televizija:** Heroja Pinkija 75, 21000 Novi Sad (m). **Novosadska TV:** Trg Slobode 3, 21000 Novi Sad (k). **OK TV:** Jonošikova 127, 26210 Kovacica (l). **RTV Panonija:** Hajduk Veljkova 11, 21000 Novi Sad (j). **Sremska TV:** Zlatka Šnajdera 2, 22240 Šid (k). **Televizija SD:** Goranska 12, 11300 Smederevo (l). **TV Banat:** Omladinski trg 17, 26300 Vršac (l). **TV Delta:** Milana Simina 16, 21000 Novi Sad (k). **TV K9:** Dimitrija Bugarskog, 21000 Novi Sad (j). **TV Kanal 25:** Vidovdanska 12a, 25250 Odžaci (k), **TV Lav:** Stepe Stepanovica 6, 26300 Vršac (l). **TV Most:** Arse Teodorovica 5, 21000 Novi Sad (j,k). **TV Pancevo:** Nikole Djurkovica 1, 26101 Pancevo (l). **TV Petrovec:** Industrijska zona bb, 21470 Bácsky Petrovec (k). **TV Rubin:** Svetosavska 43, 23300 Kikinda (m). **TV Santos:** Koce Kolarova 29, 23000 Zrenjanin (m). **TV Viminacium:** Koste Abraševica 30, 12000 Požarevac (l). **TV YuEco:** Magnetna polja bb, 24000 Subotica (j).

**DTT Tx Networks**
**Tx Operator:** JP Emisiona Technika i Veze (ETV) **M1:** RTS1, RTS2, RTS3, RTV1, RTV2, Happy TV, Info, O2.TV, Prva, TV Pink ⌘ R. Beograd 1, R. Beograd 2, R. Beograd 202 **M2:** Local stations **M3**✪**:** Arena Sport 1-5, Minimax, Nickelodeon, Film Klub, Agro TV, Ženska TV, Kitchen TV, Hram TV, Info na dlanu, Sve na dlanu, Pink 2, Pink 3 Info, Pink Kids, Pink Serije, Pink Premium, Pink Movies, Pink Action, Pink Comedy, Pink Pedia, Pink Reality, Pink Western.

| Location | M1 | M2* | M3 | kW |
|----------|----|-----|----|----|
| Crveni Cot | 24 | 30k | 41 | 100 |
| Kikinda | 32 | 55m | 29 | 10 |

| Location | M1 | M2* | M3 | kW |
|---|---|---|---|---|
| Sombor | 40 | 43j | 34 | 10 |
| Subotica | 40 | 43j | 29 | 50 |
| Vršac | 25 | 31l | 37 | 50 |

*) Local stns j-l, see above

## SEYCHELLES

**System:** DVB-T2 (MPEG4) [E]

**SEYCHELLES BROADCASTING CORP. (SBC-TV) (Pub)** ▱
P.O.Box 321, Victoria, Mahé ☎ +248 4289611 **E:** tv@sbc.sc **W:** www.
sbc.sc **L.P:** CEO: Antoine Onezime

**DTT Tx Network**
**Tx Operator:** Startimes **M(partly⟳):** multiprgr **Txs:** MFN

## SIERRA LEONE

**System:** DVB-T2 (MPEG4) [E]

**SIERRA LEONE BROADCASTING CORP. (SLBC-TV) (Pub)** ▱
New England Ville, Freetown ☎ +232 22 240123 ▤ +232 22
240922 **W:** www.facebook.com/slbcnews.sl **L.P:** DG: Elvis Gbanabom
Hallowell.

**DTT Tx Network**
**Tx Operator:** Startimes **M(partly⟳):** multiprgr **Txs:** MFN

## SINGAPORE

**Systems:** DVB-T2 (MPEG4) [E]

**MEDIACORP PTE. LTD (Comm)** ▱ Caldecott Broadcast Centre,
Andrew Rd. Singapore, 299939 ☎ +65 63333888 ▤ +65 62538119 **W:**
www.mediacorp.sg **L.P:** CEO: Tham Loke Kheng.

**DTT Tx Networks**
**Tx Operator:** Mediacorp **M1:** Channel 5 HD, Suria HD **M2:** Channel 8
HD, Vasantham HD **M3:** Channel U, Okto, NewsAsia HD.

| Location | M2 | M3 | M4 |
|---|---|---|---|
| SFN | 29 | 31 | 33 |

## SLOVAKIA

**Systems:** DVB-T2 (MPEG4) [E]; § DVB-T (MPEG2, MPEG4)

**National Stations**
**ROZHLAS A TELEVÍZIA SLOVENSKÁ (RTVS) (Pub)** ▱ Mlynská
Dolina 28, 84545 Bratislava ☎ +421 2 60611111 **E:** press@rtvs.sk **W:**
www.rtvs.sk; www.rtvs.org **L.P:** DG: Jaroslav Rezník. **Chs:** STV1, STV2,
reg prgrs. – **TA3 (Comm)** ▱ Gagarinova 12, 82015 Bratislava 215 ☎
421 2 48203511 **E:** ta3@ta3.com **W:** www.ta3.com. **L.P:** DG: Martina
Kyselová – **TV JOJ (Comm)** ▱ P.O.Box 33, 83007 Bratislava 37 ☎
+421 2 59888111 **E:** joj@joj.sk **W:** www.joj.sk **L.P:** CEO: Marcel Grega.
**Chs:** TV JOJ, Plus. – **TV MARKÍZA (Comm)** ▱ Bratislavská 1/a, 84356
Bratislava 48 ☎ +421 2 68274111 **E:** sekretariatgr@markiza.sk **W:** www.
markiza.sk **L.P:** DG: Matthias Settele **Chs:** TV Markíza, Dajto, Doma.

**Local Stations** not shown.

**DTT Tx Networks** (DVB-T exc. where stated)
**Tx Operator:** Towercom, a.s. **W:** www.towercom.sk **M1:** CT1, CT2,
JOJ Cinema, TV Lux, TV8, Sport 1 **M2:** TV JOJ, Plus, WAU, TA3 **M3:**
STV1, STV1 HD, STV2, SVT2 HD **M4⟳(DVB-T2):** TV Markíza, Dajto,
Doma, Prisma Plus, Sport 2, Eurosport 1+2, Nickelodeon, VH1, Viasat
Explore, Viasat History, Viasat Nature, RIK.

| Location | M1 | M2 | M3 | M4 | kW |
|---|---|---|---|---|---|
| Banská Bystrica (Laskomer) | 49 | 51 | 33 | 40 | 50/20/2x25 |
| Banská Štiavnica (Sitno) | 50 | 21 | 48 | 31 | 2/50/35/13 |
| Bardejov (Magura) | 49 | 40 | 54 | 46 | 32/2x16/10 |
| Borský Mikuláš (Dubník) | - | 56 | 27 | - | 20/22 |
| Bratislava (Kamzík) | 44 | 56 | 27 | 39 | 50 |
| Hranovnica | - | 55 | - | - | 20 |
| Košice (Dubník) | 57 | - | 25 | 22 | 13/31/10 |
| Košice (Heringeš) | 50 | 59 | 25 | 21 | 20/17/20 |
| Košice (Makovica) | - | 59 | - | - | 16 |
| Královský Chlmec | - | 59 | - | - | 10 |
| Lucenec (Blatný vrch) | 49 | 60 | 33 | 32 | 32/16/20/10 |
| Námestovo (Magurka) | - | 59 | 26 | - | 20/10 |

| Location | M1 | M2 | M3 | M4 | kW |
|---|---|---|---|---|---|
| Nitra (Zobor) | 50 | 21 | - | 31 | 2/44/16 |
| Nové Mesto n.V. (V.Javorina) | 55 | 56 | 57 | 23 | 3x50/25 |
| Poprad (Hranovnica) | 41 | 56 | 24 | 39 | 2x50/2x20 |
| Roznava | - | 27 | 54 | - | 10/14 |
| Ruzomberok (Úložisko) | 44 | 59 | 26 | 46 | 50/3x20 |
| Snina (Magurica) | - | 59 | 25 | - | 21/20 |
| Stará L'ubovna (Kolník) | - | 55 | - | - | 25 |
| Trencin | - | 52 | 57 | - | 40/50 |
| Zilina (Krížava) | 35 | 52 | 32 | - | 2/18/5 |

+ sites with txs below 10kW. Pol=V.
**Local licensees** not shown.

## SLOVENIA

**System:** DVB-T (MPEG4) [E]

**National Stations**
**RADIOTELEVIZIJA SLOVENIJA (RTVSLO) (Pub)** ▱ Kolodvorska
2-4, 1000 Ljubljana ☎ +386 1 4752121 **E:** info@rtvslo.si **W:** www.
rtvslo.si **L.P:** DG: Igor Kadunc **Chs:** RTVSLO1, RTVSLO2, RTVSLO3, TV
Koper/Capodistria, Tele M. – **NOVA24TV (Comm)** ▱ Linhartova 13,
1000 Ljubljana ☎ +386 1 2355293 **E:** info@nova24tv.si **W:** nova24tv.
si – **TV3 MEDIAS (Comm)** ▱ Šmartinska cesta 152, 1000 Ljubljana
☎ +386 8 3874404 ▤ +386 8 3874402 **E:** info@tv3-medias.si **W:**
www.tv3m.si.

**Local Stations** not shown.

**DTT Tx Networks**
**Licensee:** RTVSLO **M1:** RTVSLO1, RTVSLO1 HD, RTVLO2, RTVSLO2
HD, RTVSLO3, ¹TV Koper/Capodistria, ²Tele M, local stns **M3:** TV3
Medias, NOVA24TV. **NB:** M2 not currently assigned.

| Location | M1* | M3 | kW | Location | M1* | M3 | kW |
|---|---|---|---|---|---|---|---|
| Beli Kriz | 27¹ | 33 | 5 | Boc | 27² | 37 | 5 |
| Golo Brdo | 27¹ | - | 5 | Plešivec | 27² | 37 | 25 |
| Krim | 32³ | 38 | 5 | Pohorje | 27² | 37 | 100 |
| Krvavec | 32³ | 38 | 100 | Skalnica | 27¹ | 33 | 5 |
| Kuk | 27¹ | 22 | 5 | Slavnik | 27¹ | 22 | 5 |
| Kum | 32³ | 38 | 5 | Tinjan | 27¹ | 33 | 5 |
| Nanos | 27¹ | 22 | 200 | Trdinov vrh | 32³ | 38 | 20 |
| Pecarovci | 27² | 37 | 5 | Trstelj | 27¹ | 33 | 25 |

+ sites with txs below 5kW *) Incl. reg. channels: ¹ ² see above
**Local licensees** not shown.

## SOLOMON ISLANDS

**NB:** No terrestrial TV station.

## SOMALIA

**System:** PAL-B/G [E]

**National Station**
**SOMALI NATIONAL TELEVISION (SNTV) (Pub)** ▱ Mogadishu **E:**
info@sntv.so **W:** sntv.so **Txs:** (-).

**Regional/Local Stations** not shown.

## SOUTH AFRICA

**Systems:** DVB-T2 (MPEG4) [SA]; § PAL-I [VHF=SA, UHF=E] ⬇2019

**SOUTH AFRICAN BROADCASTING CORP. (SABC) (Pub)** ▱
Private Bag XI, Auckland Park 2006 ☎ +27 11 7149111 ▤ +27 11
7143106 **E:** info@sabc.co.za **W:** www.sabc.co.za **L.P:** CEO (acting):
James Aguma. **Chs:** SABC1, SABC2, SABC3. – **E.TV (Comm)** ▱
Private Bag x9944, Sandton 2146 ☎ +27 21 4814500 ▤ +27 21
4814510 **E:** info@etv.co.za **W:** www.etv.co.za. – **M-NET (Comm)** ▱
P.O.Box 4950, Randburg 2125 ☎ +27 11 2893000 ▤ +27 11 7875763
**E:** inquiries@mnet.dstv.com **W:** m-net.dstv.com **L.P:** CEO: Yolisa Phahle.

**DTT Tx Networks**
**Licensee:** Sentech **W:** www.sentech.co.za **M:** SABC1, SABC2,
SABC3, e.tv **Txs:** MFN – **Licensee:** Multichoice **W:** www.multi-
choice.co.za **M⟳:** multiprgr. **Txs:** MFN

## SOUTH SUDAN

**Systems:** DVB-T2 (MPEG4); § PAL-B/G [E] ⬇2020

**National Station**
**SOUTH SUDAN BROADCASTING CORP. (SSBC) (Pub)** ⌨ Juba ☎ +211 912 452275 **L.P:** Dir: James Magok Chilim

**Local Stations** not shown.

**DTT Tx Network**
**Tx Operator:** SSBC **Mux:** mulriprgr **Txs:** MFN

**System:** DVB-T (MPEG2, MPEG4) [E]

**National Stations**
**TELEVISION ESPAÑOLA (TVE) (Pub)** ⌨ Avenida de Radiotelevision, 4 , Prado del Rey, 28223 Pozuelo de Alarcon (Madrid) ☎ +34 91 5817000 **E:** direccion.comunicacion@rtve.es **W:** www.rtve.es **L.P:** Pres (RTVE): José Antonio Sanchez. **Chs:** La 1, La 2, 24h, Clan, TDP – **ANTENA 3 (Comm)** ⌨ Carretera San Sebastian de los Reyes, 28700 Madrid ☎ +34 1 6320500 **W:** www.antena3.com – **CUATRO (Comm)** ⌨ Avenida de los Artesanos 6, 28760 Madrid ☎ +34 91 7367000 **E:** internet@cuatro.com **W:** www.cuatro.com – **LA SEXTA (Comm)** ⌨ C/ Virgilio, 2 Edificio 4, 28223 Pozuelo de Alarcón ☎ +34 91 8382966 **E:** rr.hh@lasexta.com **W:** www.lasexta.com – **TELECINCO (Comm)** ⌨ Ctra de Irún, Km 11,700, 28049 Madrid ☎ +34 902 155555 **E:** inversores@telecinco.es **W:** www.telecinco.es.

**Regional Stations (Pub)** (On Regional Muxes)
**AN)** Radio y Televisión de Andalucía (RTVA): Edificio Cana Sur, Avda. Josó Gálvez 1, 41092 Isla de la Cartuja (Sevilla) **W:** www.canalsur. es. Chs: Canal Sur, Canal Sur 2, Andalusía TV. **AR)** Corporación Aragonesa de Radio y Televisión (CARTV): Avda. Maria Zambrano 2, 50018 Zaragoza. **W:** www.cartv.es. Chs: Aragón TV. **AS)** Radioelevisión del Principado de Asturias (RTPA): Edificio RTPA, Parque Cientifico y Tecnológico de Gijon, c/ Luis Blanco 82, 33203 Gijon. **W:** www.rtpa. es. Chs: TPA7, TPA8. **BA)** Ente Público de Radiotelevisión de las Islas Baleares (EPRTVIB): c/ Madalena, 21 Polígon Son Bugadelles, 07180 Santa Ponça **W:** ib3tv.com. Ch: IB3 TV. **CA)** Corporació Catalana de Mitians Audivisuals (CCMA): HQ: Via Augusta 252, 4a planta, 08817 Barcelona; Televisió de Catalunya: Carrer de la TV3, s/n, 08970 Sant Joan Despi (Barcelona) **W:** www.ccma.cat. Chs: TV3, TV3 HD, 33, Canal Super3, 324, Canal 3XL, Esport 3. **CL)** Radio Televisión de Castilla y León: c/Monasterio San Millán de la Cogolla 30, 47015 Valladold **W:** www. rtvcyl.es Chs: CyLTV, La 8. **CM)** Castilla-La Mancha Media (CMM): C/ Río Alberche, s/n Polígono Santa Mª de Benquerencia, 45007 Toledo **W:** www.cmmedia.es. Chs: CMT, CMT 2. **EU)** Euskal Irrati Telebista (EITB): Capuchinos de Basurto 2, 48013 Bilbao **W:** www.eitb.eus Chs: ETB1, ETB2, ETB3. **GA)** Compañía de Radio-Televisión de Galicia (CRTVG): Bando - San Marcos s/n, 15820 Santiago de Compostela **W:** www. crtvg.es. Chs: TVG, tvG2. **MA)** Ente Público Radio Televisión Madrid (EPRTVM): Paseo del Príncipe 3, 28223 Pozuelo de Alarcón (Madrid). **W:** www.telemadrid.es. Chs: Telemadrid, Telemadrid HD, LaOtra. **MU)** Radiotelevisión de la Región de Murcia (RTRM): Plaza de San Agustín 4, 30005 Murcia. **W:** www.rtrm.es Chs: 7RM, 7RM HD. **VA)** Ràdiotelevisió Valenciana (RTVV): Polígon Accés Además s/n; 46100 Burjassot, València. **W:** www.rtvv.es. Chs: Canal Nou, Canal Nou Dos, Canal Nou 24. **NB.** Keys to region codes see National Radio section.

**Local Stations** not shown.

**DTT Tx Networks**
**Operator:** n/a **M1:** La 1, La 1 HD, La 2, 24h, Clan ✣ RNE R. Nacional, RNE R.5 **M2:** TDP, TDP HD, Clan HD, DKISS, TEN ✣ RNE R. Clásica HQ, RNE R.3 HQ, RNE R. Exterior, SER, Los40, Dial, Kiss FM, Hit FM **M3:** GOL, DMAX, Disney Channel, Paramount Channel ✣ Cadena 100, R. Maria, R. Marca, Vaughn R., esRadio **M4:** Antena 3, Antena 3 HD, laSexta, laSexta HD, Neox, Nova **M5:** Telecinco, Telecinco HD, Cuatro, Cuatro HD, FDF, Divinity **M6:** Boing, Energy, Mega, TRECE ✣ Onda Cero, Europa FM, Melodia FM, Cope **M7:** Atreseries HD, BeMad TV HD, RealMadrid TV HD **R:** Regional Muxes (see Regional Stations)

| Location | M1 | M2 | M3 | M4 | M5 | M6 | M7 | R |
|----------|----|----|----|----|----|----|----|---|
| Madrid | 58 | 41 | 33 | 59 | 49 | 26 | 22 | 55 |

+ nationwide MFN
**Local muxes** not shown.

**Systems:** ISDB-TB [E]; # PAL-B/G [E] ⬇2020

**National Stations** (ª=analogue)
**SRI LANKA RUPAVAHINI CORP. (SLRC) (Pub)** ⌨ P.O. Box 2204, Colombo 7 ☎ +94 11 2697491 ▤ +94 11 2695488 **L.P:** CEO: Gamini Somachandra Rasaputhra **E:** dg@rupavahini.lk **W:** www.rupavahini.lk **Chs:** Rupavahini, Channel Eye/Nethra TV. **Txs: Rupavahini:** Pidurutalagala ªch5 (20kW), Kokavil ªch8 (20 kW) & relay txs; **Channel Eye/Nethra TV:** Pidurutalagala ªch7 (20kW) & network – **INDEPENDENT TELEVISION NETWORK (ITN) (Comm)** ⌨ Wickramasinghepura, Battaramulla ☎ +94 11 2774424 ▤ +94 11 2774591 **E:** itnadm@slt.lk **W:** itn.lk **L.P:** Chmn: Rosmund Senaratne **Chs:** ITN, Vasantham TV **Txs Vasantham TV:** Deniyaya ªch9 (20kW), Colombo ªch12 (100kW), Yatiyantota ªch12 (100kW), Nayabedde ªch12 (3kW). – **MTV CHANNEL (PVT) LTD. (Comm)** ⌨ 7, Braybrook Pl., Colombo 2 ☎ +94 11 4792600 ▤ +94 11 2447308 **E:** info@media.maharaja.lk **L.P:** CEO: Gayirika Perusignhe. **Chs:** TV1 (English), Shakthi TV (Tamil), Sirasa TV (Singalese). **Txs: TV1/Shakthi:** Colombo ªch25 (5kW) & network; **Sirasa:** Colombo ªch23 (5kW) & network – **SWARNAVAHINI (EAP BROADCASTING CO. LTD.) (Comm)** ⌨ 676 Galle Rd, Colombo 3 ☎ +94 11 2599642 ▤ +94 11 2503788 **E:** admin@swarnavahini.lk **W:** www.swarnavahini.lk **L.P:** Chmn: Dayanath Jayasuriya. **Txs:** Colombo ªch34 (5kW) & network – **TELSHAN NETWORK (PVT) LTD. (TNL) (Comm)** ⌨ Innagale Estate Dampe-Piliyandala ☎ +94 11 2501681 ▤ +94 11 2575436 **E:** info@ tnltv.lk **W:** tnltv.lk **L.P:** Chmn/MD: Shantilal Nilkant Wickremesinghe **Txs:** Piliyandala ªch3 (20kW), Polgahawela ªch3 (1kW), Nuweraeliya ªch4 (40kW), Colombo ªch21 (22kW), Hantana (Kandy) ªch21 (22kW), Piliyandala ªch26 (22kW), Ratnapura ªch26 (1kW).

**Local Stations** not shown.

**System:** DVB-T (MPEG4) [E]

**CARRIB'IN TV (INTV) (Comm)** ⌨ BP 658 Gustavia CEDEX, F-97099 Saint-Barthélemy ☎ +590 590874362 ▤ +590 590510787 **E:** contact@caribintv.com **W:** www.caribintv.com

**DTT Tx Networks**
**Tx Operator:** TDF **Mux:** Guadeloupe La 1ère, France 2-5, France Ô, France 24, Arte, INTV **Txs:** ch41 (SFN).

**NB:** No terrestrial TV station.

**System:** DVB-T2 (MPEG4) [E]

**DTT Tx Network**
**Tx Operator:** Sure South Atlantic Ltd. ⌨ P.O.Box 2, Bishop's Rooms, Jamestown, St. Helena Island, South Atlantic Ocean STHL 1ZZ **E:** service@sure.co.sh **W:** www.sure.co.sh **Mux✪:** multiprgr (incl. Local TV1, Local TV2) ✣ Two radio prgrs **Txs:** (-).

**NB:** No terrestrial TV station.

**System:** NTSC-M [A]

**HELEN TELEVISION (HTS) (Comm)** ⌨ P.O. Box 621, The Morne, Castries ☎ +1 758 4524982 ▤ +1 758 4531737 **E:** news@htsstlucia. org **W:** www.htsstlucia.org **L.P:** MD: Linford Fevrier. **Txs:** Castries ch4 (20kW H) & ch5 (20kW H).

**System:** DVB-T (MPEG2) [E]

**LEEWARD BROADCASTING CORP. (LBC)** ⌨ P.O.Box 375, Philipsburg. **Tx:**(-).

**System:** DVB-T (MPEG4) [E]

**IOTV (Comm)** ✉ 7, route de Friar's Bay, F-97150 Saint-Martin ☎ +690 690343464 **W:** www.iotv.fr.

**DTT Tx Network**
**Tx Operator:** TDF **Mux:** Guadeloupe la 1ère, France 2-5, France Ô, France 24, Arte, IOTV **Txs:** ch41 (Terre Basse), ch43 (Pic Paradis).

## ST PIERRE & MIQUELON (France)

**System:** DVB-T (MPEG4) [E]

**SAINT-PIERRE ET MIQUELON LA 1ÈRE (Pub)** ✉ BP 4227, F-97500 Saint-Pierre et Miquelon ☎ +508 508411111 **W:** saintpierre-miquelon.la1ere.fr **L.P:** Dir: Gilles Marsauche.

**DTT Tx Network**
**Tx Operator:** TDF **Mux:** Saint-Pierre et Miquelon la 1ère, France 2-,5, France Ô, France 24, Arte **Txs:** ch35 (Phare de Galantry), ch37 (Cap à l'Aigle), ch41 (Pointe au Cheval).

## ST VINCENT & THE GRENADINES

**System:** NTSC-M [A]

**SVGTV (Gov)**✉ P.O.Box 705, Kingstown, St. Vincent ☎ +1 784 4561078 **E:** svgbc@vincysurf.com **W:** www.svg-tv.com **L.P:** MD: R. Paul MacLeish. **Txs:** (pol.H) Dorsetshirehill ch9 (0.4kW), Layouhill ch7 (0.04kW), Maroonhill ch7 (0.04kW), Belleislehill ch11 (0.06kW), Mustique ch11 (0.06kW), Bequia ch13 (0.06kW).

**Foreign TV Relay**
**TBN (USA):** Kingstown ch4.

## SUDAN

**System:** DVB-T2 (MPEG4)

**SUDAN TELEVISION (Gov)** ✉ P.O.Box 1094, Omdurman ☎ +249 183557398 🖷 +249 183553538 **E:** sudantvlive@sudanmail.net

**DTT Tx Network**
**Licensee:** Multichoice Sudan **M(partly☉):** multiprgr **Txs:** MFN

## SURINAME

**Systems:** DVB-T2 (MPEG4); § NTSC-M [A]

**National Stations** (ᵃ=analogue)
**SURINAAMSE TELEVISIE STICHTING (STVS) (Gov)** ✉ Stadiumlaan, Paramaribo ☎ +597 473032 🖷 +597 477216 **E:** info@stvs.sr **W:** stvs.sr **Txs:** Wageningen ᵃch7 (0.10kW), Paramaribo ᵃch8 (1kW), Moango ᵃch9 (0.01kW), Caranis ᵃch10 (0.10kW), Nickerie ᵃch11 (1kW). – **ALGEMENE TELEVISIE VERZORGING (ATV) (Comm)** ✉ Van het Hogerhuysstraat 58-60, Paramaribo ☎ +597 404611 🖷 +597 402660 **E:** info@atv.sr **W:** www.atv.sr **Txs:** Borokopondo ᵃch2 (1kW), Wageningen ᵃch6 (0.25kW), Moengo ᵃch7, Paramaribo ᵃch12 (0.4kW), Nickerie ᵃch13 (0.5kW).

**Local Stations** (all Comm) (ᵃ=analogue)
**Ampies Broadcasting Corp:** P.O.Box 885, Paramaribo; ᵃch4 (1kW). **Garuda TV:** Goudstraat 20, Paramaribo; ᵃch23. **Radika TV:** P.O.Box 1083, Paramaribo; ch14 (1kW). **Rapar Broadcasting Network (RBN):** P.O.Box 975, Paramaribo; ᵃch5 (2kW). **Rasonic:** Bataviastraat 2, Nickerie; ᵃch7 (1kW). **TV Apinti:** P.O.Box 595, Paramaribo; ch10 (1kW). **TV Sookha:** Batavaiastraat 25, Nickerie; tx:(-).

**DTT Tx Network**
**Licensee:** Wise NV **M:** multiprgr **Txs:** MFN.

## SWEDEN

**Systems:** DVB-T (MPEG2), DVB-T2 (MPEG4) [E]

**National Stations**
**SVERIGES TELEVISION AB (SVT) (Pub)** ✉ Oxenstiernsgatan 26-34, 105 10 Stockholm ☎ +46 8 7840000 **E:** info@svt.se **W:** www.svt.se **L.P:** MD: Hanna Stjärne. **Chs:** SVT1, SVT2, Kunskapskanalen, SVTB/SVT24, regional prgrs – **CANAL DIGITAL (Comm)** ✉ Tegeluddsvägen 7, 115 80 Stockholm ☎ +46 8 7722700 **E:** kundser-

vice@canaldigital.se **W:** www.canaldigital.se – **TV4 AB (Comm)** ✉ Tegeluddsvägen 3-5, 115 79 Stockholm ☎ +46 8 4594000 **E:** info@tv4.se **W:** www.tv4.se **L.P:** CEO (TV4 Group): Casten Almqvist – **VIASAT AB (Comm)** ✉ P.O.Box 17104, 104 62 Stockholm ☎ +46 8 56241060 **E:** info@viasat.se **W:** www.viasat.se **L.P:** CEO (MTG): Jørgen Madsen Lindemann.

**Local Stations** not shown.

**DTT Tx Networks** (DVB-T2 except where stated)
**Licensee:** Boxer TV Access AB **W:** www.boxer.se **M1 (DVB-T):** SVT1 (incl. reg. prgrs), SVT2 (incl. reg. prgrs), SVT Kunskapskanalen, SVTB/SVT24, Eurosport 1 **M2☉(exc.*) (DVB-T):** TV3, TV4*, TV4 Fakta, Sjuan, TV6*, Kanal 5, Kanal 9, Kanal 11 **M3☉(DVB-T):** TV8, Disney Channel/VH1, Nickelodeon/Comedy Central, TV10, Discovery Channel, MTV, TLC, TV12 **M5☉:** Axess TV, BBC World News, C More Series, Disney XD/BBC Earth, TNT, Cartoon Network, Boomerang, Local stations (Stockholm region only: Yle TV Finland), Fox, CNN, TV4 Film, Horse & Country TV, C More First, Eurosport 2, History, SF-kanalen/C More Sport, Investigation Discovery **M6☉(exc.*):** SVT1 HD (incl. reg. prgrs)*, SVT2 HD (incl. reg. prgrs)*, TV3 HD, TV4 HD, Kanal 5 HD, Animal Planet HD **M7☉:** C More Live HD/C More Hits HD, TV4 Sport HD, National Geographic HD, C More Football/Hockey/Stars, BBC Brit, Nick Jr., Travel Channel, Aljazeera

| Location | M1 | M2 | M3 | M5 | M6 | M7[1] | kW[1] |
|---|---|---|---|---|---|---|---|
| Arvidsjaur (Julträsk) | 34 | 24 | 30 | 42 | 25 | 37 | 50 |
| Bollnäs | 29 | 23 | 34 | 21 | 29 | 6 | 50 |
| Borlänge (Idkerberget) | 47 | 32 | 43 | 41 | 45 | 28 | 50 |
| Borås (Dalsjöfors) | 44 | 29 | 46 | 42 | 36 | 41 | 50 |
| Bäckefors | 35 | 22 | 31 | 26 | 25 | 5 | 50 |
| Emmaboda (Bälshult) | 21 | 28 | 46 | 45 | 47 | 8 | 50 |
| Filipstad (Klockarhöjden) | 42 | 30 | 33 | 23 | 46 | 40 | 50 |
| Finnveden (Bredaryd) | 26 | 48 | 31 | 35 | 38 | 7 | 50 |
| Gällivare | 33 | 28 | 40 | 46 | 43 | 22 | 50 |
| Gävle (Skogmur) | 27 | 24 | 26 | 30 | 46 | 9 | 50 |
| Göteborg (Brudaremossen) | 30 | 27 | 46 | 43 | 40 | 9 | 50 |
| Halmstad (Oskarström) | 21 | 28 | 45 | 47 | 32 | 7 | 10 |
| Helsingborg (Olympia) | 27 | 43 | 25 | 41 | 22 | 30 | 10 |
| Hudiksvall (Forsa) | 29 | 23 | 34 | 31 | 39 | 44 | 50 |
| Hörby (Sallerup) | 33 | 43 | 21 | 41 | 22 | 10 | 50 |
| Jönköping (Bondberget) | 28 | 23 | 33 | 35 | 40 | 6 | 50 |
| Kalix | 29 | 27 | 21 | 35 | 48 | 45 | 50 |
| Karlshamn | 27 | 24 | 42 | 41 | 30 | 8 | 50 |
| Karlskrona (Vämö) | 27 | 24 | 42 | 41 | 30 | 8 | 50 |
| Karlstad (Sörmon) | 42 | 30 | 44 | 28 | 46 | 40 | 50 |
| Kiruna (Kirunavaara) | 39 | 35 | 44 | 42 | 29 | 32 | 50 |
| Kisa | 29 | 38 | 30 | 43 | 42 | 6 | 50 |
| Lycksele (Knaften) | 45 | 28 | 22 | 38 | 48 | 35 | 50 |
| Malmö (Jägersro) | 33 | 43 | 25 | 41 | 22 | 10 | 50 |
| Mora (Eldris) | 22 | 25 | 35 | 44 | 42 | 38 | 50 |
| Motala (Ervasteby) | 27 | 45 | 41 | 43 | 39 | 21 | 50 |
| Norrköping (Krokek) | 36 | 46 | 47 | 32 | 28 | 5 | 50 |
| Nässjö | 22 | 23 | 33 | 35 | 25 | 6 | 50 |
| Pajala | 34 | 23 | 31 | 37 | 47 | 32 | 50 |
| Skellefteå | 23 | 26 | 46 | 43 | 31 | 6 | 50 |
| Skövde | 37 | 24 | 32 | 34 | 47 | 21 | 50 |
| Sollefteå (Multrå) | 46 | 44 | 31 | 24 | 21 | 26 | 50 |
| Stockholm (Nacka) | 23 | 42 | 39 | 32 | 45 | 21 | 50 |
| Storuman | 33 | 43 | 36 | 46 | 26 | 35 | 50 |
| Sundsvall (S Stadsberget) | 47 | 27 | 30 | 24 | 43 | 26 | 50 |
| Sunne (Blåbärskullen) | 36 | 39 | 47 | 26 | 34 | 7 | 50 |
| Sveg (Brickan) | 21 | 24 | 46 | 36 | 41 | 32 | 50 |
| Trollhättan | 23 | 22 | 31 | 28 | 25 | 9 | 50 |
| Tåsjö (Hoting) | 32 | 40 | 30 | 25 | 41 | 37 | 50 |
| Uddevalla (Herrestad) | 23 | 22 | 31 | 28 | 25 | 9 | 50 |
| Uppsala (Vedyxa) | 40 | 29 | 33 | 30 | 43 | 21 | 50 |
| Varberg (Grimeton) | 21 | 28 | 45 | 47 | 32 | 7 | 10 |
| Visby (Follingbo) | 31 | 44 | 48 | 48 | 37 | 22 | 50 |
| Vislanda (Nydala) | 40 | 44 | 37 | 39 | 34 | 8 | 50 |
| Vännäs (Granlundsberget) | 47 | 36 | 29 | 43 | 27 | 39 | 50 |
| Västervik (Fårhult) | 26 | 34 | 30 | 43 | 40 | 24 | 50 |
| Västerås (Lillhärad) | 44 | 22 | 34 | 38 | 31 | 35 | 50 |
| Ånge (Snöberg) | 42 | 37 | 40 | 45 | 28 | 38 | 50 |
| Älvsbyn | 36 | 39 | 47 | 38 | 32 | 45 | 50 |
| Örebro (Lockhyttan) | 29 | 25 | 33 | 38 | 48 | 35 | 50 |
| Örnsköldsvik (Ås) | 23 | 34 | 31 | 24 | 21 | 39 | 50 |
| Östersund (Brattåsen) | 27 | 45 | 48 | 36 | 22 | 38 | 50 |
| Össhammar (Valö) | 40 | 48 | 26 | 30 | 43 | 6 | 50 |
| Överkalix | 26 | 27 | 21 | 35 | 48 | 45 | 50 |

+ sites with txs below 10kW. ¹) Power refers to UHF chs

## SWITZERLAND

**System:** DVB-T (MPEG2) [E]

**SRG SSR (Pub)** ✉ Giacomettistrasse 1, 3000 Bern 31 ☎ +41 31

3509111 **E:** info@srgssr.ch **W:** www.srgssr.ch **L.P:** Pres: Jean-Michel Cina; DG: Gilles Marchand
**NB:** all txs of the three existing SRG SSR multiplexes will be gradually switched off until the end of 2019.

**Local/regional Licensees** not shown.

## SYRIA

**Systems:** # PAL-B/G [E]; DVB-T2 (MPEG4) planned

**National Stations**
**ORGANIZATION OF SYRIAN ARAB RADIO & TELEVISION (ORTAS) (Gov)** ✉ Ommayad Square, Damascus ☎ +963 11 2720700 🖷 +963 11 2234930 **E:** srtv@rtv.gov.sy **W:** www.ortas.gov.sy **Txs:** (pol.H) **Prgr 1:** Damascus ch4 (100kW) & netw. – **ADDOUNIA TV (Comm)** ✉ Damascus **W:** www.addounia.tv **Txs:** Damascus ch32 & netw.

**Local Station**
**Ugarit TV (Gov),** Latakia; tx:(-).

## TAIWAN (Rep. of China)

**System:** DVB-T (MPEG2, MPEG4) [A]

**TAIWAN BROADCASTING SYSTEM (TBS) (Pub)** ✉ 50, Lane 75, Kang-Ning Rd., Section 3, Taipei 114 ☎ +886 2 26332000 🖷 +886 2 26338124 **W:** www.tbs.org.tw **L.P:** Chair: Yaly Chao **NB:** TBS is the holding for the public service broadcasters CTS and PTS. **Chinese Television System (CTS)** ✉ 100, Kuang Fu South Rd, Taipei 106 ☎ +886 2 27510321 🖷 +886 2 27775414 **E:** wwwpub@mail.cts.com.tw **W:** www.cts.com.tw **Chs:** CTS HD, CTS Education & Culture, CTS News Channel, CTS Variety. **Public Television Service (PTS)** ✉ as TBS ☎ +886 2 26339122 🖷 +886 2 26338124 **E:** pub@mail.pts.org.tw **W:** www.pts.org.tw **Chs:** PTS, PTS2, PTS3, Hakka TV – **CHINA TELEVISION CO., LTD (CTV) (Comm)** ✉ 120, Chung-Yang Rd, Taipei 115 ☎ +886 2 27838308 🖷 +886 2 27826007 **E:** pubr@mail.chinatv.com.tw **W:** www.ctv.com.tw **L.P:** Chmn: Chiu Chia-Yu. **Chs:** CTV HD, CTV News Channel, CTV Bravo, CTV Classic. – **FORMOSA TELEVISION, INC. (FTV) (Comm)** ✉ 24/F, 30, Pa Te Road, Section 3, Tapei 105 ☎ +886 2 25702570 🖷 +886 2 25796633 **E:** service@ftv.com.tw **W:** www.ftv.com.tw **Chs:** FTV HD, FTV News, Follow Me TV, Four Seasons TV. **L.P:** Chairman: Kuo Bei-hong – **TAIWAN TELEVISION ENTERPRISE CO., LTD (TTV) (Comm)** ✉ 10, Pa Te Rd, Section 3, Taipei 10560 ☎ +886 2 25781515 🖷 +886 2 25799625 **E:** ref@email.ttv.com.tw **W:** www.ttv.com.tw **Chs:** TTV HD, TTV Finance, TTV News Channel, TTV Variety.

**DTT Tx Networks** (MPEG2 exc. *=MPEG4)
**Licensee:** CTS **M:** CTS HD*, CTS Education & Culture, CTS News Channel, CTS Variety – **Licensee:** PTS **M1:** PTS, PTS2, PTS3, Hakka TV **M2*:** PTS HD. – **Licensee:** CTV **M:** CTV HD*, CTV News Channel, CTV Bravo, CTV Classic – **Licensee:** FTV **M:** FTV HD*, FTV News, Follow Me TV, Four Seasons TV ⌘ Formosa Network. – **Licensee:** TTV **M:** TTV HD*, TTV Finance, TTV News Channel, TTV Variety.

| Location | PTS M1 | PTS M2 | CTS | CTV | FTV | TTV |
|---|---|---|---|---|---|---|
| SFN | 26 | 30 | 34 | 24 | 28 | 32 |

## TAJIKISTAN

**Systems:** DVB-T2 (MPEG4); § SECAM-D/K [R], § PAL-D/K [R]

**National Station**
**KUMITAI TELEVIZION VA RADIOI (Gov)** ✉ TV studios: Bekhzod St. 7a, 734013 Dushanbe ☎ +992 37 2224357 🖷 +992 37 2213459 info@ktr.tj **W:** www.ktr.tj **L.P:** Chmn: Asadulloi Rahmon **Chs:** TV Tojikiston, TV Safina, Jahonnamo, Bahoriston, TV Sinamo, Varzish Sport, Futbol, Shahnavoz.

**Local Stations, Foreign TV Relays** not shown.

**DTT Tx Network**
**Tx Operator:** Teleradiokom **M:** TV Tojikiston HD, TV Safina HD, Jahonnamo, Bahoriston, TV Sinamo HD, Varzish Sport HD, Futbol HD, Shahnavoz, Regional Stns **Txs:** ch46 (Dushanbe 2.5kW), ch49 (Khujand) + nationwide MFN.

## TANZANIA

**System:** DVB-T2 (MPEG4) [E]

**National Stations**
**TANZANIA BROADCASTING CORP. (TBC) (Pub)** ✉ P.O.Box 31519, Dar es Salaam ☎ +255 22 2700062 🖷 +255 22 2121315 **E:** info@tbc.go.tz **W:** tbc.go.tz **L.P:** DG: Clement Mshana **Chs:** TBC1, TBC2 – **CHANNEL 10 TV (Comm)** ✉ P.O.Box 19045, Dar es Salaam ☎ +255 22 2116341 🖷 +255 22 2113112 **E:** info@channelten.co.tz **W:** channelten.co.tz – **INDEPENDENT TV (ITV) (Comm)** ✉ P.O.Box 4374, Dar es Salaam ☎ +255 22 2775914 🖷 +255 22 2775915 **E:** info@itv.co.tz **W:** www.itv.co.tz – **STAR TV (Comm)** ✉ P.O.Box 1732, Mwanza ☎ +255 28 2503262 🖷 +255 28 2500713 **E:** marketing@startvtz.com **W:** startvtz.com.

**Local Stations** not shown.

**DTT Tx Networks**
**Licensee:** Basic Transmissions Ltd **M:** multiprgr **Txs:** MFN – **Licensee:** Star Media Tanzania Ltd (Startimes) **M✪:** multiprgr **Txs:** MFN – **Licensee:** Agape Associates Limited **M✪:** multiprgr **Txs:** MFN.

## THAILAND

**Systems:** DVB-T2 (MPEG4) [E]; § PAL-B/G [E] ⬇2020

**MCOT PLC (MODERNINE TV) (Gov)** ✉ 63/1 Rama IX Road, Huay Khwang, Bangkok 10320 ☎ +66 2 22016000 🖷 +66 2 22451960 **W:** www.mcot.net **Txs:** Bangkok ᵃch9 (20kW) & network. – **NATIONAL BROADCASTING SERVICES OF THAILAND (NBT) (Gov)** ✉ 90-91 New Phetchaburi Road, Huay Khwang, Bangkok 10320 ☎ +66 2 3182110 🖷 +66 2 3182991 **Txs:** Bangkok ᵃch11 (200kW) & relays. – **ROYAL ARMY TELEVISION (TV5) (Mil)** ✉ 210 Phaholyothin Rd, Sanam Pao, Bangkok 10400 ☎ +66 2 22710060 🖷 +66 2 22712515 **E:** army@tv5.co.th **W:** www.tv5.co.th **Txs:** Bangkok ᵃch5 (20kW) & network. – **THAI PUBLIC BROADCASTING SERVICE (TPBS) (Pub)** ✉ 1010 Shinawatra Tower III, 13 Vibhavadi Rangsit Road, Chatchuchak, Bangkok 10900 ☎ +66 2 27911000 🖷 +66 2 27911010 **E:** webmaster@thaipbs.or.th **W:** www.thaipbs.or.th **Txs:** Bangkok ᵃch29 (1000kW) & network. – **BANGKOK BROADCASTING & TELEVISION (BBTV) (Comm)** ✉ P.O.Box 4-56, Bangkok 10900 ☎ +66 2 2720010 🖷 +66 2 27202106 **E:** marketing@ch7.com **W:** www.ch7.com. **Txs:** Bangkok ᵃch7 (20kW) & network. – **BANGKOK ENTERTAINMENT CO. LTD. (CHANNEL 3) (Comm)** ✉ Floors 7, 15, 16, The Emporium Tower, Sukhumvit Road, Khlong Tan, Khlong Toey, Bangkok 10110 ☎ +66 2 22623333 🖷 +66 2 22041384 **W:** www.thaitv3.com **Txs:** Bangkok ᵃch32 (650kW) & network. (ᵃ=analogue)

**DTT Tx Networks** (under construction)
**Licensee:** MCOT **Mux 1:** multiprgr **Txs:** ch56 (Bangkok SFN) & nationwide MFN **Mux 2:** multiprgr **Txs:** ch43 (Bangkok SFN) & nationwide MFN **Mux 3:** multiprgr **Txs:** ch40 (Bangkok SFN) & nationwide MFN

## TIMOR-LESTE

**System:** PAL-G [E]

**RADIO TELEVISAUN TIMOR-LESTE (RTTL) (Pub)** ✉ Estrada Mercado Municipal, Caicoli. Dili **E:** info@rttlep.tl **W:** rttlep.tl ☎+670 3321827 **L.P:** Pres: Milena Soares Abrantes **Txs:** Dili ch23 & netw.

## TOGO

**System:** DVB-T2 (MPEG4) [E]

**National Stations**
**TÉLÉVISION TOGOLAISE (Gov)** ✉ BP 3286, Lomé ☎ +228 22215357 🖷 +228 22215786 **E:** televisiontogolaise@yahoo.fr **W:** tvt.tg **L.P:** DG: Kuessan Yovodévi – **TV2 (Comm)** ✉ Lomé ☎ +228 22514993 **L.P:** DG: Eudoxie Théophane.

**Local Station**
**TV7:** BP 81104, Lomé.

**DTT Tx Network**
**Tx Operator:** Startimes **M(partly✪):** multiprgr **Txs:** MFN

## TOKELAU (New Zealand)

**NB:** No terrestrial TV station.

## TONGA

**System:** DVB-T (MPEG4) [E]

**TONGA BROADCASTING COMMISSION (Gov)** ✉ P.O.Box 36, Nuku'alofa ☎ +676 23555 🖷 +676 24417 **E:** news@tonga-broadcasting.net **W:** www.tonga-broadcasting.net **LP:** GM: Timote Katoanga **Chs:** TV Tonga, TV Tonga 2 (incl. relay CCTV-9), TV Vava'u. – **DOULOS BROADCASTING NETWORK (Rlg)** ✉ P.O.Box 91, Nuku'alofa ☎ +676 23314 🖷 +676 23658 **W:** www.facebook.com/DoulosTVTonga **LP:** Dir: Gerhard Taukolo Taukolo.

**DTT Tx Networks**
**Tx Operator:** DigiTV (Tonga) Ltd. ✉ P.O.Box 875, Nuku'alofa **E:** customercare.tonga@digicelgroup.com **Mux✪:** multiprgr **Tx:** ch45V (Nuku'alofa 1kW).

## TRINIDAD & TOBAGO

**Systems:** DVB-T (MPEG4) [A]; # NTSC-M [A]

**TV4 (Gov)** ✉ P.O. Box 665, Port-of-Spain, Trinidad ☎ +1 868 62241414 🖷 +1 868 6220344 **E:** marketing@gisltd.tt **W:** www.facebook.com/ourtv4 **Txs:** ᵃch4, ᵃch16. – **ADVANCED COMMUNITY TV STATION (ACTS) (Pub)** ✉ 53B, Circular Road, San Fernando, Trinidad ☎ +1 868 6524855 **L.P:** CEO/Pres: Nelson Sammy-Guilarte **Tx:** ᵃch25. – **CCN-TV6 (Comm)** ✉ 35 Independence Sq, Port-of-Spain, Trinidad ☎ +1 868 6278806 🖷 +1 868 6271451 **W:** www.tv6tnt.com **L.P:** CEO: Dawn Thomas **Txs:** ᵃch6 (25kW) & ᵃch18 (1kW) (Trinidad), ᵃch19 (Tobago). – **C TELEVISION (CNMG) (Comm)** ✉ 11A Maraval Road, Port-of-Spain, Trinidad **W:** ctvtt.com **L.P:** CEO (acting): Julian Rogers **Txs:** ᵃch9, ᵃch13. – **GAYELLE TV (Comm)** ✉ 13 Southern Main Road, Curepe, Trinidad and Tobago, Curepe Village, Saint George, Trinidad ☎ +1 868 2906880 **E:** gayelletv@gmail.com **W:** www.facebook.com/GayelleTheCaribbean **Tx:** ᵃch23. (ᵃ=analogue)

**DTT Tx Networks**
**Licensee:** Green Dot Ltd ✉ 61 Mucurapo Road, St James, Trinidad ☎ +868 6284388 🖷 +868 6285197 **E:** info@gd.tt **W:** www.gd.tt **Mux 1-4:** multiprgr **Txs:** SFN.

## TRISTAN DA CUNHA (UK)

**NB:** No terrestrial TV station.

## TUNISIA

**System:** DVB-T (MPEG4) [E]

**TÉLÉVISION TUNISIENNE (Pub)** ✉ Avenue de la Ligue Arabe, 1002 Tunis ☎ +216 71800844 **E:** info@watania1.tn; info@.watania2.tn **W:** www.watania1.tn; www.watania2.tn **Chs:** Watanya 1; Watanya 2. – **ATTESSIA (Comm)** ✉ 12 Rue de l'Energie. 2035 Ariana **E:** digital@attessia.tv **W:** www.attessia.tv – **CHARTAGE+ (Comm)** ✉ Tunis **E:** communication@carthageplus.net – **EL HIWAR ETTOUNSI (Comm)** ✉ Avenue Habib Bourguiba, 1000 Tunis ☎ +216 71844855 **E:** contact@elhiwarettounsi.tv **W:** www.elhiwarettounsi.tv – **HANNIBAL TV (HTV) (Comm)** ✉ 885 Rue du 13 Août Choutrana II, 2036 Ariana ☎ +216 70944944 **E:** info@hannibaltv.com.tn **W:** www.hannibaltv.com.tn – **M TUNISIA (Comm)** ✉ Route de Bizerte, M'nihla, 2094 Ariana **W:** mtunisiatv.com – **TELVZA TV (Comm)** ✉ 42 Rue 8603, 2035 Ariana ☎ +216 56716123 **E:** commercial@telvza-tv.tn **W:** www.telvza-tv.tn – **TUNISNA TV (Comm)** ✉ ☎ +216 25226500 **E:** chaine.tunisna@gmail.com **W:** www.facebook.com/TunisnaTV.Officielle – **AL INSEN (Rlg)** ✉ Route de Sidi Mansour, 3000 Sfax **W:** www.facebook.com/Alinsen.tv.

**DTT Tx Networks**
**Tx Operator:** Office National de la Télédiffusion (ONT) **W:** www.telediffusion.net.tn **M:** Watanya 1, Watanya 2, Tunisna TV, Telvza TV, M Tunisia, Attesia, Al Insen, El Hiwar Ettounsi, Hannibal TV, Chartage+ ⌘ R. Nationale, R. Culturelle, R. Tunisie Chaîne Internationale.

| Location | ch | Location | ch |
|---|---|---|---|
| Trozza | 21 | Zarzis | 28 |
| Kchabta | 23 | Nefta | 28 |
| Ain Draham | 28 | Chaambi | 29 |
| Kef Errand | 30 | Souk Ejomaa | 44 |
| Zaghouan | 36 | Boukornine | 45 |

| Location | ch | Location | ch |
|---|---|---|---|
| Remada | 36 | Brourmet | 51 |
| Biadha | 37 | Goraa | 52 |
| Ksour Essaf | 38 | Tozeur | 55 |
| Ghraba | 41 | | |

## TURKEY

**Systems:** DVB-T2 (HEVC) [E]; § PAL-B/G [E]

**National Stations**
**TÜRKIYE RADYO TELEVIZYON KURUMU (TRT) (Pub)** ✉ TRT-TV Department, TRT Sitesi A Blok 427 Oran, 06109 Ankara ☎ +90 312 4901058 **E:** genel.sekreterlik@trt.net.tr **W:** www.trt.net.tr **Chs (terr.):** TRT1, TRT Haber, TRT3-Spor, TRT Çocuk, TRT Kurdî, TRT Avaz, TRT Türk, TRT Belgesel, TRT Müzik, TRT Diyanet, TRT Okul, Regional stns. – **ATV (Comm)** ✉ Barbaros Bulvari 125, Cam Han, Besiktas, Istanbul ☎ +90 216 4742020 **E:** editor@atv.com.tr **W:** www.atv.com.tr – **CNN TÜRK (Comm)** ✉ Hürriyet Media Towers, Evren Mah. Günesli, Bagcilar, 34204 Istanbul ☎ +90 212 4785856 🖷 +90 212 5500239 **E:** info@cnnturk.com **W:** www.cnnturk.com – **FLASH TV (Comm)** ✉ Catmamescit Mah., Tepebasi Cad., Elektrik Sok. 11, Istanbul ☎🖷 +90 212 2568282 **E:** flashtv-w@flashtv.com.tr **W:** www.flashtv.com.tr – **HABER TÜRK (Comm)** ✉ Tevfik Bey Mah. 20 Temmuz Cad 24, Sefaköy-Küçükçekmece, Istanbul ☎ +90 212 5805267 **W:** www.haberturk.com – **KANAL D (Comm)** ✉ Kanal D TV Center, 100. Yil Mahallesi, Bagcilar, 34204 Istanbul ☎ +90 212 4135111 **E:** bizeyazin@kanald.com.tr **W:** www.kanald.com.tr – **KANAL 7 (Comm)** ✉ Otakçilar Cad. 78, Eyüp, 34030 Istanbul ☎ +90 212 4378080 **E:** kanal7@kanal7com **W:** www.kanal7.com – **MELTEM TV (Comm)** ✉ Imönu Cad. 96, Besyol, Florya, 34295 Istanbul ☎ +90 212 6240999 **E:** bilgi@meltemtv.com.tr **W:** www.meltemtv.com.tr – **NTV (Comm)** ✉ Eskibüyükdere Cad. 61, Uso Center, Maslak, 80660 Istanbul ☎ +90 212 3350000 **W:** www.ntv.com.tr **Chs:** NTV, NTV Spor – **SHOW TV (Comm)** ✉ AKS Televizyon, Yapi Kredi Plaza, E Blok 1, Levent, 80620 Istanbul ☎ +90 212 3550101 **E:** info@showtvnet.com **W:** www.showtv.com.tr – **STAR TV (Comm)** ✉ Dogan TV Center, 100. Yil Mahallesi, 34204 Bagcilar, Istanbul ☎: +90 212 4135000 **E:** izleyicitemsilcisi@startv.com.tr **W:** www.star.com.tr – **TV8 (Comm)** ✉ Ihlamurdere Cad., Yesilçimen Sok. 5, OTIM, Besiktas, 80820 Istanbul ☎ +90 212 2885152 **E:** tv8@tv8.com.tr **W:** www.tv8.com.tr.

**Local Stations** not shown.

**DTT Tx Networks**
**Tx Operator:** Anten A.S. **W:** www.antenas.com.tr **Mux 1-6:** multiprgr.

| Location | M1 | M2 | M3 | M4 | M5 | M6 |
|---|---|---|---|---|---|---|
| Ankara (Çankaya) | 7 | 24 | 28 | 34 | 37 | 38 |

+ nationwide MFN under construction.

## TURKMENISTAN

**Systems:** DVB-T2 (MPEG4); § SECAM-D/K [R], § PAL-D/K [R]

**TELEWIDENIÝE, RADIOGEPLESIKLER WE KINEMATOGRAFIÝA BARADKY DÖWLET KOMITET (Gov)** ✉ Magtymguly köçesi 89, 744000 Asgabat ☎ +993 12 351515 🖷 +993 12 394470 **L.P:** Chmn: A. Kakaýewi **TV Studios:** ✉ 2003 St. 3, 744000 Asgabat **Chs:** Altyn Asyr Türkmenistan, Miras, Ýaslyk, TV4-Türkmenistan, Türkmen Owaz, Asgabat.

**DTT Tx Networks** (under construction)
**Tx Operator:** Ministry of Communications **Mux 1:** Altyn Asyr Türkmenistan, Miras, Ýaslyk, TV4-Türkmenistan, Türkmen Owaz, Asgabat (+ two HD simulcasts) **Mux 2-6:** multiprgr

| Location | M1 | M2 | M3 | M4 | M5 | M6 | kW |
|---|---|---|---|---|---|---|---|
| Asgabat | n/a | 43 | 48 | 58 | 60 | 62 | 1.3 |

+ nationwide MFN under construction.

## TURKS & CAICOS ISLANDS (UK)

**NB:** No terrestrial TV station.

## TUVALU

**System:** PAL-B [E]

**TUVALU MEDIA CORP. (TMC) (Pub)** ✉ Private Mail Bag, Funafuti

☎ +688 20139 📠 +688 20732 **E:** media@tuvalu.tv **Tx:** Funafuti ch n/a (0.02kW).

## UGANDA

**System:** DVB-T2 (MPEG4) [E]

**National Stations**
**UGANDA BROADCASTING CORP. (UBC) (Pub)** 📧 P.O.Box 2038, Kampala ☎ +256 41 4257034 📠 +256 41 4257252 **E:** customerservice@ubc.ug **W:** ubc.ug **LP:** Chmn: Simon Kaheru – **WBS TELEVISION (Comm)** 📧 P.O.Box 5914, Kampala ☎ +256 41 4344313 📠 +256 41 4345672 **E:** inquiry@wbs.ug **W:** www.wbs.ug.

**Local Stations** not shown.

**DTT Tx Networks**
**Licensee:** Multichoice Uganda 📧 Plot 1/13, Jinja Road, Shop No.2 ground Floor, Kampala **M:** KBC, NTV, QTV, KTN, Citizen, K24, Kiss TV **Txs:** MFN – **Licensee:** Zuku TV **M✪:** multiprgr **Txs:** MFN – **Licensee:** Startimes 📧 First Floor, Soliz House, Plot 23, Lumumba Avenue, P.O.Box 2300 Nakasero, Kampala, **M✪:** multiprgr **Txs:** MFN.

## UKRAINE

**Systems:** DVB-T (MPEG2, MPEG4) [E], DVB-T2 (MPEG4) [E]; § SECAM-D/K [R], § PAL-D/K [R]

**National Stations**
**NATSIONALNA SUSPILNA TELERADIOKOMPANIIA UKRAINY (NSTU) (Pub)** 📧 vul. Melnykova 42, 04119 Kyiv **W:** 1tv.com.ua **LP:** GD: Zurab Alasaniia. **Chs (terr.):** UA:Pershyi, UA:Kultura – **1+1 (Comm)** 📧 vul. Kyrylivska 23, 04080 Kyiv ☎ +380 44 4900101 **E:** feedback@1plus1.ua **W:** www.1plus1.ua **LP:** DG (1+1 Media): Oleksandr Tkachenko – **INTER (Comm)** 📧 vul. Dmytrivska 30, 01601 Kyiv ☎ +380 44 4906765 **E:** program@inter.ua **W:** inter.ua **LP:** CEO (U.A. Inter Media Group) Hanna Bezliudna – **5 KANAL (Comm)** 📧 vul. Elektrykiv 26, 04176 Kyiv ☎ +380 44 3517720 **E:** box@5.ua **W:** www.5.ua.

**Local Stations** not shown.

**DTT Tx Networks** (DVB-T2)
**Licensee Mux 1-3, 5:** Zeonbud **W:** www.zeonbud.com.ua **M1:** UA:Pershyi, Inter, 1+1, Ukraina, K1, NTN, ICTV, Enter-Film **M2:** Zoom, STB, TET, K2, Novyi kanal, M1, 5 kanal **M3:** Mega, Piksel TV, XSport, NLO, 2+2, Espreso **M5:** Priamyi HD, UA:Kultura, Eskulap TV/Local stns, Tsentralnyi kanal/112 Ukraina HD, Rada. **Local licensees** (DVB-T/MPEG2, MPEG4) not shown. **NB:** M4 currently not assigned.

| Location | M1 | M2 | M3 | M5 | kW |
|---|---|---|---|---|---|
| Andriivka | 50 | 40 | 43 | 42 | 3x4.9/4.9 |
| Bershad | 35 | 53 | 54 | 51 | 4.9 |
| Bilopillia | 55 | 42 | 51 | 33 | 5.5x |
| Buky | 62 | 61 | 29 | 37 | 1.26/2x0.4/1 |
| Cherkasy | 48 | 28 | 21 | 53 | 5.5 |
| Chernihiv | 22 | 34 | 35 | 61 | 5.7 |
| Dnipro | 26 | 35 | 25 | 40 | 5.5 |
| Ivano-Frankivsk | 42 | 41 | 31 | 58 | 0.9/2x2.8/ |
| Izium | 26 | 39 | 25 | 43 | 2.7 |
| Kamianets-Podilskyi | 22 | 29 | 51 | 44 | 2x1.1/2x2.3 |
| Kamianske | 22 | 40 | 55 | 28 | 0.5/2x1.1/1.1 |
| Kharkiv | 31 | 35 | 48 | 58 | 4.9 |
| Kherson | 34 | 58 | 39 | 44 | 3x2.6/1 |
| Khmelnytskyi | 22 | 29 | 51 | 50 | 5.2 |
| Kholmy | 22 | 49 | 54 | 61 | 2.4 |
| Khust | 39 | 53 | 56 | 61 | 2.7 |
| Kovel | 44 | 27 | 59 | 52 | 4.9/2.5/2x4.9 |
| Krasnohorivka | 26 | 37 | 41 | 51 | 3/2/2x1 |
| Krasnoperekopsk | 24 | 31 | 43 | 53 | 1.1 |
| Kropyvnytskyi | 49 | 53 | 22 | 47 | 5.4 |
| Kryvyi Rih | 41 | 51 | 54 | 38 | 5.5 |
| Kyiv | 26 | 31 | 49 | 29 | 12 |
| Lviv | 22 | 28 | 40 | 33 | 6.4 |
| Mariupol | 39 | 42 | 34 | 24 | 5 |
| Melitopol | 33 | 26 | 28 | 50 | 5.4/3x5.9 |
| Mykolaiv | 34 | 58 | 39 | 48 | 1.25/5.3/2x1 |
| Novodnistrovsk | 60 | 34 | 64 | 25 | 2.7/0.5/2x2.7 |
| Odesa | 43 | 32 | 39 | 23 | 4.5 |
| Olevsk | 51 | 52 | 53 | 43 | 2.8 |
| Petrovirivka | 35 | 41 | 47 | 33 | 3x5.4/5.4 |
| Podilsk | 62 | 43 | 54 | 40 | 5.4 |
| Pryluky | 52 | 27 | 56 | 32 | 5.1 |

| Location | M1 | M2 | M3 | M5 | kW |
|---|---|---|---|---|---|
| Rivne | 38 | 42 | 40 | 33 | 4.9 |
| Shostka | 24 | 59 | 58 | 60 | 5.2 |
| Starobilsk | 32 | 55 | 62 | 58 | 2.4 |
| Ternopil | 25 | 39 | 23 | 37 | 4.8 |
| Trostianets | 54 | 49 | 51 | 30 | 5.2 |
| Vasylivka | 29 | 41 | 57 | 36 | 4.7 |
| Vinnytsia | 39 | 32 | 31 | 49 | 3.6 |
| Zaporizhzhia | 43 | 31 | 49 | 57 | 3x3.1/2.9 |

+ sites with only txs below 1kW.

**NB:** Txs in **Donets Basin** not shown.

### CRIMEA
(under Russian administration)

**Systems:** DVB-T2 (MPEG4) [E]; § SECAM-D/K [R], § PAL-D/K [R]

**TRK "KRYM" (Gov)** 📧 295001 Simferopol, ul. Studencheskaya 14 ☎ +7 652 546406 **W:** 1tvcrimea.ru **Ch:** 1 Krym **Txs:** Simferopol ch12 (1kW) & netw. – **OBSHCHESTVENNAYA KRYMSKO-TATARSKAYA TRK (OKTT) (Pub)** 📧 295011 Simferopol, ul. Kozlova 45a **LP:** DG: Seyran Mambetov.

**Other Regional Stations/Local Stations** not shown.

**DTT Tx Networks**
**Tx Operator:** RTRS **M1:** Rossiya 1, Rossiya 24, Rossiya K, Karusel, Match TV, Pervyy kanal, NTV, OTR, 5-kanal, TV Tsentr ⌘ R. Rossii, Mayak, Vesti FM **M2:** Domashniy, TV Zvezda, Mir TV, Muz-TV, Pyatnitsa, REN TV, Spas, STS, TNT, TV-3 **M3:** 1 Krym, Krym 24, Millet, Mir 24, Che, Moskva 24, Local stns

| Location | M1 | M2 | M3 | kW |
|---|---|---|---|---|
| Simferopol | 36 | 37 | 58 | 0.2 |

+ MFN

## UNITED ARAB EMIRATES

**System:** DVB-T2 (MPEG4) [E]

**ABU DHABI MEDIA (Gov)** 📧 P.O.Box 637, Abu Dhabi ☎ +971 2 44451111 **E:** adtv@emi.co.ae **W:** www.adtv.ae **Chs:** Abu Dhabi TV, Emirate TV, AD Drama, AD Sports, YasTV – **AJMAN TV (Gov)** 📧 P.O.Box 422, Ajman ☎ +971 6 7465000 📠 +971 6 7465135 **E:** progajtv@ajmantv.com **W:** www.ajmantv.com – **DUBAI CHANNELS NETWORK (Gov)** 📧 P.O.Box 1695, Dubai ☎ +971 4 3077245 📠 +971 4 3374111 **W:** www.dcn.ae/dubaitv – **SHARJAH MEDIA CORP. (Gov)** 📧 P.O.Box 111, Sharjah ☎ +971 6 5661111 📠 +971 6 5669999 **W:** www.smc.ae.

**DTT Tx Networks**
**Tx Operator:** Abu Dhabi Media **M:** multiprgr **Txs:** (-) **Tx Operator:** Ajman TV **M:** multiprgr **Tx:** ch26 (Ajman) **Tx Operator:** Dubai Channels Network **M:** multiprgr **Txs:** (-) **Tx Operator:** Sharjah Media Corp. **M:** multiprgr **Txs:** (-)

## UNITED KINGDOM

**Systems:** DVB-T (MPEG2), DVB-T2 (MPEG4) [E]

**National Stations**
**BRITISH BROADCASTING CORP. (BBC) (Pub)** 📧 BBC Television Centre, 80 Wood Lane, London W12 4RJ ☎ +44 20 87438000 **W:** www.bbc.com/tv **LP:** DG: Tony Hall. **Chs (terr.):** BBC One (incl. regional prgrs), BBC Two, BBC Four, CBBC, CBeebies, BBC News, BBC Parliament, Alba **Reg: a) BBC Cambridgeshire:** Broadcasting House, Cambridge Business Park, Cowley Rd, Cambridge, CB4 0WZ; **b) BBC Isle of Man & Channel Islands:** 18-21 Parade Rd, St Helier JE2 3PL; **c) BBC East:** The Forum, Millennium Plain, Norwich NR2 1BH; **d) BBC East Midlands:** London Rd, Nottingham NG2 4UU; **e) BBC East Yorkshire & Lincolnshire:** Queen's Court, Hull HU1 3RH; **f) BBC London:** Marylebone High St., London W1A 6FL; **g) BBC North East & Cumbria:** Broadcasting Centre, Barrack Rd, Newcastle upon Tyne NE99 2NE; **h) BBC North West:** New Broadcasting House, Oxford Rd, Manchester M60 1SJ; **i) BBC Northern Ireland:** Ormeau Avenue, Belfast BT2 8HQ; **j) BBC Oxford:** 269 Banbury Rd, Summertown, Oxford, OX2 7DW; **k) BBC Scotland:** 40 Pacific Quay, Glasgow G51 1DA; **l) BBC South:** Broadcasting House, 10 Havelock Rd, Southampton SO14 7PU; **m) BBC South East:** The Great Hall, Mount Pleasant Rd, Tunbridge Wells TN1 1QQ; **n) BBC South West:** Broadcasting House, Seymour Rd, Plymouth PL3 5BD; **o) BBC Wales:** Llantrisant Rd, Cardiff CF5 2YQ; **p) BBC West:** Broadcasting House,

Whiteladies Rd, Bristol BS8 2LR; **q) BBC West Midlands:** Level 7, The Mailbox, Birmingham B1 1RF; **r) BBC Yorkshire:** 2 St Peter's Square, Leeds LS9 8AH – **CHANNEL FOUR TELEVISION CORP. (Pub)** ✉ 124 Horseferry Rd, London SW1P 2TX ☎ +44 20 73964444 **W:** www.channel4.com **L.P:** CEO: Alex Mahon – **S4C (WELSH FOURTH CHANNEL AUTHORITY) (Pub)** ✉ Park Ty Glas, Llanishen, Caerdydd/Cardiff CF14 5DU ☎ +44 2920 747444 **E:** s4c@s4c.co.uk **W:** www.s4c.co.uk **L.P:** CEO: Ian Jones – **INDEPENDENT TELEVISION NETWORK (ITV) (Comm)** ✉ London Television Centre, Upper Ground, London SE1 9LT ☎ +44 20 76201620 **W:** www.itv.com **L.P:** CEO: Carolyn McCall. **Chs:** ITV1 (incl. regional prgrs), ITV2, ITV3, ITV4. **Reg: a) ITV Anglia:** Anglia House, Norwich NR1 3JG; **b) ITV Border:** 1 Clifford Court, Cooper Way, Parkhouse, Carlisle CA3 0JG; **c) ITV Central:** Central Court, Gas Street, Birmingham B1 2JT; **d) ITV Channel Islands:** The Television Centre, St Helier, Jersey, Channel Islands JE1 3ZD; **e) ITV Cymru Wales:** T3 Assembly Square, Britannia Quay, Cardiff Bay CF10 4PL; **f) ITV Granada:** Quay St., Manchester M60 9EA; **g) ITV London:** 200 Gray's Inn Rd, London WC1X 8HF; **h) ITV Meridian:** New Cut Road, Vinters Park, Maidstone, Kent ME14 5NZ; **i) ITV Tyne Tees:** Television House, The Watermark, Gateshead, NE11 9SZ; **j) ITV West Country:** 470 Bath Rd, Bristol BS4 3HG; **k) ITV Yorkshire:** The Television Centre, 104 Kirkstall Rd, Leeds LS3 1JS  Emley Moor: ITV Calendar; **l) STV:** Pacific Quay, Glasgow G51 1PQ **W:** www.stv.tv; **m) UTV:** Havelock House, Ormeau Rd, Belfast BT7 1EB **W:** itv.com/utv. – **CHANNEL 5 BROADCASTING LTD (Comm)** ✉ 22 Long Acre, London WC2E 9LY ☎ +44 20 75505555 **W:** www.channel5.com – **SKY UK PLC (Comm)** ✉ Grant Way, Isleworth, London TW7 5QD ☎ +44 20 77053000 **W:** www.sky.com **L.P:** CEO: Jeremy Darroch.

**DTT Tx Networks** (DVB-T except where indicated otherwise) **Licensee Mux 1+3:** BBC **M1:** BBC One (incl. reg. prgrs a-r), BBC Two, CBBC, CBeebies, BBC Four, BBC Alba, BBC News, BBC Parliament, BBC RB1 ❊ BBC R.1, 1Xtra, R.2, R.3, R.4, R.4 Extra, R.5 Live, R.5 Live Sports Extra, R.6 Music, BBC Asian Network, BBCWS, BBC Local stations **M3 (DVB-T2):** BBC One HD, BBC Two HD, CBBC HD, ITV1 HD, Channel 4 HD, Channel 5 HD, Film 4 +1 – **Licensee Mux 2:** Digital 3&4 Ltd. **M2:** ITV (incl. reg. prgrs a-m), Channel 4, Channel 5, ITV 2, Channel 4 +1, More4, Film4, ITV4, ITV4 +1, E4, ITV +1, Sewing Quarter – **Licensee Mux 4:** SDN Ltd. **M4:** ITV3, Drama, 5 USA, ITV Be, ITV 2 +1, 5STAR, ITV3 +1, Quest, Channel 5 +1, My5, Paramount Network, ITV Be +1, ITV4 +1, True Entertainment, Blaze, CBS Action +1, CBS Reality, Horror Channel, Blaze +1, Quest +1, CITV, Ketchup TV, QVC, Hochanda, CCTV, Racing UK, CONNECT 4, SonLife, VisionTV, Planet Knowledge, Arise News, Loveworld, Television X❊, ADULT PARTY❊, Xpanded TV promo ❊ Capital, Absolute R., Heart – **Licensee Mux 5-8:** Arqiva **M5:** Pick, Dave, Really, E4 +1, Sony Movie Channel, Quest Red, Food Network, Challenge, Movies4Men, YourTV, Sky News, Sony Crime Network, Create and Craft, Gems TV, TJC, TBN UK, Kiss Me TV, Proud Dating, ADULT smileTV9 ❊talkSPORT **M6:** 4Music, Yesterday, Home, 5Spike, CBS Action, Travel Channel, 4seven, True Movies, CBS Drama, Dave ja vu, Talking Pictures TV, Ideal World, QVC Beauty, QVC Style, Pop, RT, ADULT smileTV2❊, ADULT Babestation❊, ❊ The Hits radio, KISS FRESH, Kiss, KISSTORY, Magic, heat, Kerrang!, Smooth R., Premier R,, Classic FM, LBC **M7 (DVB-T2):** 5USA +1, CBS Drama, Vintage TV, Quest Red +1, Keep it Country, BBC News HD, Al Jazeera Eng HD, Channel 4+1 HD, 4seven HD, RT HD, Seewing Quarter **M8 (DVB-T2):** 5STAR+1, More4 +1, Freesports, Forces TV, BT Showcase HD❊, CBeebies HD, Together, PBS America, QVC HD, QVC Beauty HD. **NB:** Some regional variations may apply. **Local/regional muxes** not shown.

| Location | 1° | 2° | 3 | 4 | 5 | 6 | 7 | 8 | kW |
|---|---|---|---|---|---|---|---|---|---|
| Angus | 60k | 53l | 57 | 54 | 58 | 49 | 31 | 37 | 3x20/3x10/2x4.5 |
| Beacon Hill | 60n | 53j | 57 | 42 | 45 | 51 | 33 | 34 | 3x20/3x10/4/1 |
| Belmont | 22e | 25k | 28 | 30 | 53 | 60 | 33 | 35 | (*) |
| Bilsdale | 26g | 29i | 23 | 43 | 46 | 40 | 31 | 37 | 3x100/3x50/18.5/5 |
| Black Hill | 46k | 43l | 40 | 41 | 44 | 47 | 32 | 35 | 6x100/43/12.5 |
| Blaenplwyf | 27o | 24e | 21 | 25 | 22 | 28 | - | - | 3x40/3x10 |
| Bluebell Hill | 46m | 43h | 40 | 45 | 39 | 54 | 32 | 34 | 6x20/4/1.5 |
| Brougher Mt. | 28i | 22m | 25 | 21 | 24 | 27 | - | 20 | |
| Caldbeck | 25g | 28b | 30 | 23 | 26 | 33 | 3x100/3x50/5/4 | | |
| Caldbeck | 27k | 24l | 22 | - | - | - | 2x50/100 | | |
| Caradon Hill | 28n | 25j | 22 | 21 | 24 | 27 | - | 3x100/3x50 | |
| Carmel | 60o | 53e | 57 | 54 | 58 | 49 | - | 3x20/3x10 | |
| Chatton | 45g | 42i | 49 | 41 | 44 | 47 | - | 3x20/3x10 | |
| Craigkelly | 27k | 24l | 21 | 42 | 45 | 39 | 33 | 34 | 3x20/3x10/11/3 |
| Crystal Palace | 23f | 26g | 30 | 25 | 22 | 28 | 33 | 35 | 6x200/43/13.5 |
| Darvel | 22k | 25l | 28 | 23 | 26 | 29 | 33 | 34 | 3x20/3x10/2x2.5 |
| Divis | 27i | 21m | 24 | 23 | 26 | 29 | - | 3x100/3x50/12.5/3.5 | |
| Dover | 50m | 51h | 53 | 55 | 59 | 48 | - | 3x80/3x40 | |
| Durris | 28k | 25l | 22 | 23 | 26 | 29 | 32 | 35 | 3x100/3x50/2x12.5 |
| Emley More | 47r | 44k | 41 | 51 | 52 | 48 | 32 | 34 | 5x174/87/55/17 |

| Location | 1° | 2° | 3 | 4 | 5 | 6 | 7 | 8 | kW |
|---|---|---|---|---|---|---|---|---|---|
| Hannington | 45l | 42h | 39 | 41 | 44 | 47 | 32 | 34 | 4x50/3x25/37/5.5 |
| Heathfield | 52m | 49h | 47 | 42 | 44 | 41 | - | 20 | |
| Huntshaw Cross | 50n | 59j | 55 | 48 | 52 | 56 | - | 3x20/3x10 | |
| Keelylang Hill | 46k | 43l | 50 | 42 | 45 | 49 | - | 3x20/3x10 | |
| Knockmore | 26k | 23l | 29 | 53 | 57 | 60 | - | 3x20/3x10 | |
| Limavady | 50i | 59m | 55 | 54 | 58 | 49 | - | 3x20/3x10 | |
| Llanddona | 57o | 60e | 53 | 43 | 46 | 50 | - | 3x20/3x10 | |
| Mendip | 49p | 54j | 58 | 48 | 56 | 52 | 33 | 35 | 6x100/72/17.5 |
| Midhurst | 55l | 56h | 58 | 54 | 59 | 50 | - | 3x20/3x10 | |
| Moel-y-Parc | 45o | 49e | 52 | 51 | 52 | 48 | 32 | 34 | 3x20/3x10 |
| Oxford | 53l | 60h | 57 | 50 | 59 | 55 | 31 | 37 | 3x100/3x50/16.5/6 |
| Pontop Pike | 58g | 54i | 49 | 50 | 59 | 55 | 33 | 34 | 3x100/3x50/34/9.5 |
| Preseli | 43o | 46e | 50 | 42 | 45 | 49 | - | 3x20/3x10 | |
| Redruth | 44n | 41j | 47 | 48 | 52 | 51 | - | 3x20/3x10 | |
| Ridge Hill | 28q | 25c | 22 | 21 | 24 | 27 | 32 | 34 | 3x20/3x10/10.5/4 |
| Ridge Hill | - | 29j | - | - | - | - | - | 20 | |
| Rosemarkie | 45k | 49l | 42 | 43 | 46 | 50 | - | 3x20/3x10 | |
| Rowridge | 24l | 27h | 21 | 25 | 22 | 28 | 31 | 37 | 3x200/3x50/24.5/25[1] |
| Rumster Forest | 27k | 24l | 21 | 30 | 59 | 55 | - | 3x20/3x10 | |
| Sandy Heath | 27a | 24a | 21 | 51 | 52 | 48 | 32 | 34 | 3x180/3x170/50/8.5 |
| Selkirk | 50k | 59l | 55 | 57 | 53 | 60 | - | 3x10/3x5 | |
| Stockland Hill | 26n | 23j | 29 | 25 | 22 | 28 | - | 3x50/3x25 | |
| Sudbury | 44c | 41a | 47 | 58 | 60 | 56 | - | 100 | |
| Sutton Coldfield | 43q | 46c | 40 | 42 | 45 | 39 | 33 | 35 | 6x200/89/8 |
| Talconeston | 55c | 59a | 50 | 42 | 45 | 50 | 31 | 37 | 6x100/27.5/10 |
| The Wrekin | 26q | 23c | 30 | 41 | 44 | 47 | - | 3x50/3x25/10/1.5 | |
| Waltham | 49d | 54c | 58 | 29 | 56 | 57 | 31 | 37 | 3x50/3x25/10/1.5 |
| Wenvoe | 41o | 44e | 47 | 42 | 45 | 49 | 31 | 37 | 3x100/3x50/47/12 |
| Winter Hill | 50h | 59f | 54 | 58 | 49 | 55 | 31 | 37 | 6x100/14/1 |

+ sites with txs below 10kW. Pol=H °) incl. reg. prgrs (NB: subregional prgrs not indicated) (*) 3x150/50/2x100/37/15kW

**NB:** In preparation for the re-assignment of the 700MHz band to mobile services, txs on chs 49-60 will gradually move to lower chs until 2020 (some channels will be changed more than once).

**Systems:** ATSC [A]; § NTSC-M [A] (some LPs only)

**Main National Networks**
(O&O = owned-and-operated) (*= Spanish-language networks)
**PUBLIC BROADCASTING SERVICE (PBS) (Pub)** ✉ 1320 Braddock Place, Alexandria, VA 22314-1698 ☎ +1 703 7395000 🖷 +1 703 7390775 **W:** www.pbs.org **L.P:** Pres/CEO: Paula A. Kerger. **Member Stations:** ca 350. – **ABC, INC (Comm)** (Subsidiary of Walt Disney Co.) ✉ 77 W. 66th St., New York, NY 10023-6298 ☎ +1 212 4567777 🖷 +1 212 4566850 **W:** abc.go.com **L.P:** Pres: John Hare. **O&O Stations:** KABC-TV Los Angeles CA ch7 (28.7kW); KFSN-TV Fresno CA ch30 (260kW); KGO-TV San Francisco CA ch7 (24kW); KTRK-TV Houston TX ch13 (32.4kW); WABC-TV New York, NY ch7 (34kW); WLS-TV Chicago IL ch44 (1000kW); WPVI-TV Philadelphia PA ch6 (30kW); WTVD Durham NC ch11 (45kW). **Full Power Affiliates:** ca 220. – **CBS BROADCASTING, INC (Comm)** (Subsidiary of CBS Corporation) ✉ 51 W. 52nd St, New York, NY 10019-6119 ☎ +1 212 9754321 🖷 +1 212 9754516 **W:** www.cbs.com **L.P:** Pres/CEO (CBS Corp.) (acting): Joe Iannielo. **O&O Stations:** KCBS-TV Los Angeles CA ch43 (1000kW); KCNC-TV Denver CO ch35 (1000kW); KDKA-TV Pittsburgh PA ch25 (1000kW); KOVR-TV Sacramento CA ch25 (760kW); KPIX-TV San Francisco CA ch29 (1000kW); KTVT-TV Dallas TX ch19 (1000kW); KYW-TV Philadelphia PA ch26 (790kW); WBBM-TV Chicago IL ch12 (8kW); WBZ-TV Boston MA ch30 (825kW); WCBS-TV New York NY ch33 (349kW); WCCO-TV Minneapolis MN ch32 (1000kW); WFOR-TV Miami FL ch22 (1000kW); WJZ-TV Baltimore MD ch13 (28.8kW); WWJ-TV Detroit MI ch44 (425kW). **Full Power Affiliates:** ca 210 – **ESTRELLA TV* (Comm)** ✉ Liberman Broadcasting, Inc.: 1845 Empire Avenue, Burbank, CA 91504 **W:** www.estrellatv.com **L.P:** Chmn (Liberman Broadcasting, Inc): Jose Liberman **O&O Stations:** KETD Denver CO ch46 (300kW); KMPX Dallas TX ch30 (1000kW); KPNZ Salt Lake City UT ch24 (450kW); KRCA Los Angeles CA ch35 (1000kW); KSDX-LD San Diego CA ch9 (0.275kW), KVPA-LD Phoenix AZ ch42 (15kW); KZJL Houston TX ch44 (1000kW); WASA-LD Port Jervis NY ch24 (15kW); WESV-LD Chicago IL ch40 (6kW) **Affiliates:** ca 53 – **FOX BROADCASTING CO. (Comm)** (Subsidiary of Twenty-First Century Fox, Inc.) ✉ 10201 W. Pico Blvd., Los Angeles, CA 90035 ☎ +1 310 3693716 🖷 +1 310 9693300 **W:** www.fox.com **L.P:** Chmn/CEO (Fox Networks Group): Peter Rice **O&O Stations:** KDFW Dallas TX ch35 (857kW); KMSP-TV Minneapolis MN ch9 (30kW); KRIV Houston TX ch26 (1000kW); KSAZ-TV Phoenix AZ ch10 (1000kW); KTBC Austin TX ch7 (98.6kW); KTTV Los Angeles CA ch11 (115kW); KTVU Oakland CA

ch44 (1000kW); WAGA Atlanta GA ch27 (1000kW); WFLD Chicago IL ch31 (1000kW); WFXT Boston MA ch31 (780kW); WHBQ-TV Memphis TN ch13 (95kW); WJBK Detroit MI ch7 (27kW); WJZY Charlotte NC ch47 (1000kW); WOFL Orlando FL ch22 (607kW); WOGX Ocala FL ch31 (500kW); WNYW New York NY ch44 (246kW); WTTG Washington DC ch36 (1000kW); WTVT Tampa Bay FL ch12 (72.3kW); WTXF-TV Philadelphia PA ch42 (1000kW). **Full Power Affiliates:** ca 220 – **ION TELEVISION (Comm)** (ION Media Networks, Inc.) ▣ 601 Clearwater Park Road, West Palm Beach, FL 33401 **W:** www.iontelevision.com **L.P:** Chmn/CEO (ION Media Networks): R. Brandon Burgess **O&O Stations:** 60 **Affiliates:** ca 48 – **LATV* (Comm)** (LATV Networks LLC) ▣ 2323 Corinth Avenue, Los Angeles, CA 90064 **W:** latv.com **L.P:** COO: Luca Bentivoglio **O&O Station:** KJLA Ventura CA ch49 (1000kW) **Affiliates:** ca 37 – **MYNETWORKTV, INC (Comm)** (Subsidiary of Twenty-First Century Fox, Inc.) ▣ 110201 W Pico Blvd Los Angeles, CA 90064-2606 **W:** www.mynetworktv.com **O&O Stations:** KCOP-TV Los Angeles CA ch13 (120kW); KDFI-TV Dallas TX ch36 (1000kW); KUTP Phoenix AZ ch26 (1000kW); KTXH Houston TX ch19 (421kW); WDCA Washington D.C ch35 (500kW); WFTC Minneapolis MI ch29 (1000kW); WMYT-TV Charlotte NC ch39 (225kW); WPWR-TV Gary IN ch51 (1000kW); WRBW Orlando FL:ch41 (763kW); WWOR-TV Secaucus NJ ch38 (170kW). **Full Power Affiliates:** ca 200. – **NBCUNIVERSAL, LLC (Comm)** (Division of Comcast Corp.) ▣ 30 Rockefeller Plaza, New York, NY 10112 ☎ +1 212 6644444 ▤ +1 212 6644085 **W:** www.nbc.com **L.P:** CEO: Stephen B. Burke. **O&O Stations:** KNBC Los Angeles CA ch36 (380kW); KNSD San Diego CA ch40 (370kW); KNTV San Francisco CA ch12 (103.1kW); KXAS-TV Dallas/Fort Worth, TX ch41 (891kW); WCAU Philadelphia PA ch34 (700kW); WMAQ-TV Chicago IL ch29 (350kW); WNBC New York, NY ch28 (200.2kW); WRC-TV Washington DC ch48 (813kW); WTVJ Miami FL ch31 (1000kW); WVIT Hartford CT ch35 (250kW). **Full Power Affiliates:** ca 220. – **THE CW NETWORK, LLC (Comm)** (Subsidiary of Warner Bros. Entertainment, Inc. and CBS Corporation) ▣ 4000 Warner Blvd., Burbank, CA 91522 ☎ +1 818 9775000 ▤ +1 818 9778310 **W:** www.cwtv.com **L.P:** Pres: Mark Pedowitz. **O&O Stations:** KBCW San Francisco CA ch45 (500kW); KMAX-TV Sacramento CA ch21 (1000kW); KSTW Seattle WA ch11 (100kW); WKBD-TV Detroit MI ch14 (185kW); WPCW Jeannette PA ch11 (30kW); WPSG Philadelphia PA ch32 (250kW); WTOG St. Petersburg FL ch44 (550kW); WUPA Atlanta GA ch43 (1000kW). **Full Power Affiliates:** ca 200. – **TELEMUNDO NETWORK GROUP, LLC (TELEMUNDO*) (Comm)** (Subsidiary of Telemundo Holdings, Inc.) ▣ 2290 West 8th Avenue, Hialeah, FL 33010 ☎ +1 305 8848200 ▤ +1 305 8897950 **W:** www.telemundo.com **L.P:** Pres/CEO (Telemundo Holdings, Inc): Luis Silberwasser. **O&O Stations:** KBLR Las Vegas NV ch40 (230kW); KDEN-TV Denver CO ch29 (540kW); KHRR Tucson AZ ch40 (396kW); KNSO Fresno CA ch11 (45kW); KSTS San Jose CA ch49 (257kW); KTAZ Phoenix AZ ch39 (550kW); KTMD Galveston TX ch48 (1000kW); KVEA Corona CA ch39 (1000kW); KVDA San Antonio TX ch38 (1000kW); KXTX-TV Dallas TX ch40 (1000kW); WNEU Merrimack NH ch34 (80kW); WNJU Linden NJ ch36 (650kW); WSNS-TV Chicago IL ch45 (665kW); WSCV Fort Lauderdale FL ch30 (1000kW). **Full Power Affiliates:** ca 45. – **UNIMAS* (Comm)** (Subsidiary of Univision Communications, Inc.) ▣ 9405 NW 41st Street, Miami, FL 33178-2301 ☎ +1 305 4713900 ▤ +1 305 4714065 **W:** www.unimas.com **L.P:** Pres/CEO (Univision Communications, Inc.): Vincent Sadusky. **O&O Stations:** KBTF-CD Bakersfield CA ch31 (15kW); KFPH-DT Phoenix AZ ch13 (240kW); KFTH-DT Alvin TX ch36 (1000kW); KFSF-DT Vallejo CA ch34 (150kW); KFTR-DT Los Angeles CA ch29 (400kW); KFTU-DT Douglas AZ ch36 (5kW); KNIC-DT Blanco TX ch18 (400kW); KSTR-DT Irving TX ch48 (225kW); KTFD-DT Boulder CO ch15 (200kW); KTFB-CA Bakersfield CA ch44 (0.25kW); KTFF-DT Porterville CA ch48 (197kW); KTFK-DT Stockton CA ch26 (850kW); KTFO-CD Austin, TX ch36 (15kW); KTFQ-DT Albuquerque NM ch22 (1000kW); WAMI-DT Hollywood FL ch47 (1000kW); WFPA-CA Philadelphia PA ch28 (15kW); WFTT-DT Tampa FL ch47 (650kW); WFUT-DT Newark NJ ch30 (200kW); WOTF-DT Melbourne FL ch43 (1000kW); WTNC-LD Raleigh NC ch40 (15kW); WUTF-DT Marlborough MA ch27 (100kW); WXFT-DT Aurora IL ch50 (172kW). **Full Power Affiliates:** ca 35. – **UNIVISION* (Comm)** (Subsidiary of Univision Communications, Inc.) ▣ 9405 NW 41 St., Miami, FL 33178-2301 ☎ +1 305 4713900 ▤ +1 305 4714065 **W:** www.univision.com **L.P:** Pres/CEO (Univision Communications, Inc.): Vincent Sadusky. **O&O Stations:** KABE-CD Bakersfield CA ch39 (15kW); KAKW-DT Killeen TX ch13 (45kW); KDTV-DT San Francisco CA ch51 (476.3kW); KFTV-DT Hanford CA ch20 (350kW); KMEX-DT Los Angeles CA ch34 (392kW); KTVW-DT Phoenix AZ ch33 (470kW); KUTH-DT Provo UT ch32 (194kW); KUVE-DT Green Valley AZ ch46 (70.8kW); KUVN-DT Garland TX ch23 (1000kW); KUVS-DT Modesto CA ch18 (500kW); KWEX-DT San Antonio TX ch41 (580kW); KXLN-DT Rosenberg TX ch45 (1000kW); WFDC-DT Arlington VA ch15 (325kW);

WGBO-DT Joliet IL ch38 (600kW); WQHS-DT Cleveland OH ch34 (525kW); WLTV-DT Miami FL ch23 (535kW); WXTV-DT Paterson NJ ch40 (300kW); WUVC-DT Fayetteville NC ch38 (500kW); WUVG-DT Athens GA ch48 (1000kW); WUVP-DT Vineland NJ ch29 (335kW). **Full Power Affiliates:** ca 45 – **TRINITY BROADCASTING NETWORK, INC (TBN) (Rlg)** ▣2442 Michelle Drive, Tustin, CA 92780 **W:** www.tbn.org **L.P:** Chmn: Matthew W. Crouch **O&O Stations:** KAAH-TV Honolulu HI ch27 (262kW); KDOR-TV Bartlesville OK ch17 (400kW); KDTX-TV Dallas TX ch45 (1000kW); KETH-TV Houston TX ch24 (900kW); KHCE-TV San Antonio TX ch16 (500kW); KITU-TV Beaumont TX ch33 (500kW); KLUJ-TV Harlingen TX ch34 (45kW); KNAT-TV Albuquerque NM ch24 (200kW); KNMT Portland OR ch45 (1000kW); KPAZ-TV Phoenix AZ ch20 (500kW); KPJR-TV Greeley CO ch38 (1000kW); KTAJ-TV St. Joseph MO ch21 (1000kW); KTBN-TV Santa Ana CA ch33 (1000kW); KTBO-TV Oklahoma City OK ch15 (500kW); KTBW-TV Tacoma WA ch14 (90kW); Holly Springs MS WBUY-TV ch41 (500kW); WCLJ-TV Bloomington IN ch42 (850kW); WDLI-TV Canton OH ch49 (200kW); WELF-TV Dalton GA ch16 (300kW); WGTW-TV Burlington NJ ch27 (160kW); WHFT-TV Miami FL ch46 (1000kW); WHLV-TV Cocoa FL ch32 (699kW); WHSG-TV Monroe GA ch44 (700kW); WJEB-TV Jacksonville FL ch44 (715kW); WKOI-TV Richmond, IN ch39 (500kW); WMCF-TV Montgomery AL ch46 (500kW); WMPV-TV Mobile AL ch20 (105kW); WMWC-TV Galesburg IL ch8 (23kW); WPGD-TV Hendersonville TN ch33 (1000kW); WRBJ-TV Magee MS ch34 (98kW); WSFJ-TV Newark OH ch24 (1000kW); WTBY-TV Poughkeepsie NY ch27 (800kW); WTCE-TV Fort Pierce FL ch38 (765kW); WTJP-TV Gadsden AL ch26 (150kW); WTPC-TV Virginia Beach VA ch7 (85kW); WWRS-TV Mayville WI ch43 (600kW); WWTO-TV La Salle IL ch10 (80kW). **Affiliates:** ca 11.

**Other Networks** (*= Spanish-language networks)
**CREATE (Pub)** ▣ American Public Television: 55 Summer St., 4th Floor, Boston, MA 02110 **W:** createtv.com – **MHZ WORLDVIEW (Pub)** ▣ 8101A Lee Highway, Falls Church, VA 22042 **W:** mhznetworks. org – **Vme* (Pub)** ▣ Vme Media, Inc.: 1001 Brickell Bay Drive Suite 1208 Miami, FL 33131 **W:** www.vmetv.com – **WORLD (Pub)** ▣ American Public Television: 55 Summer St., 4th Floor, Boston, MA 02110 **W:** worldchannel.org – **ACCUWEATHER CHANNEL (Comm)** ▣ AccuWeather Inc.: 385 Science Park Road, State College, PA 16803 **W:** www.accuweather.com – **ANTENNA TV (ATV) (Comm)** ▣ Tribune Broadcasting: 435 N. Michigan Ave., 6th Floor, Chicago, IL 60611 **W:** antennatv.tv – **AZTECA AMÉRICA* (Comm)** ▣ 601 Clearwater Park Road, West Palm Beach, FL 33401 **W:** www. aztecaamerica.com – **BOUNCE (Comm)** ▣ Bounce Media, LLC: P.O. Box 673252, Marietta, GA 30006 **W:** www.bouncetv.com – **COMET (Comm)** (Joint-venture of Metro-Goldwyn-Mayer and Sinclair Television Group, Inc.) ▣ Sinclair Television Group, Inc.: 10706 Beaver Dam Rd, Cockeysville, MD 21030 **W:** www.comettv.com – **COZI TV (Comm)** ▣ NBC Universal Media, LLC: 30 Rockefeller Plaza, New York, NY 10112 **W:** www.cozitv.com – **DECADES (Comm)** (Joint-venture of CBS Television Studios and Weigel Broadcasting Co.) ▣ Weigel Broadcasting Co.: 26 North Halsted, Chicago, IL 60661 **W:** www.decades.com – **ESCAPE (Comm)** ▣ Escape Media, LLC: 3500 Piedmont Road, Suite 400, Atlanta, GA 30305 **W:** www.escapetv. com – **GET TV (Comm)** ▣ CPE US Networks, Inc.: 10202 West Washington Boulevard, Culver City, CA 90232 **W:** www.get.tv – **GRIT (Comm)** ▣ GRIT Media, LLC: 1080 West Peachtree St, #309 Atlanta, GA 30309 **W:** www.grittv.com – **HEARTLAND (Comm)** ▣ Luken Communications[, LLC: 225 E 8th St, Chattanooga, TN 37402 **W:** www.watchheartlandtv.com – **HEROES AND ICONS (Comm)** ▣ H&I National Limited Partnership: 26 North Halsted, Chicago, IL 60661 **W:** www.handitv.com – **HSN (Comm)** ▣ HSN, Inc.: 2501 118th Ave N, St Petersburg, FL 33716 **W:** www.hsn.com – **ION LIFE (Comm)** ▣ ION Media Networks, Inc.: 601 Clearwater Park Road, West Palm Beach, FL 33401 **W:** ionlife.com – **JUSTICE NETWORK (Comm)** ▣ Justice Network, LLC: 318 E Bond Ave, West Memphis, AR 72301 **W:** www.justicenetworktv.com – **LAFF (Comm)** ▣ Laff Media, LLC: Suite 400, 3500 Piedmont Road NE, Atlanta, GA 30305 **W:** www.laff.com – **LIVE WELL NETWORK (Comm)** ▣ ABC, Inc (Subsidiary of Walt Disney Co.): 77 W. 66th St., New York, NY 10023-6298 **W:** livewellnetwork.com – **ME-TV NETWORK (Comm)** ▣ Weigel Broadcasting Co.: 26 North Halsted, Chicago, IL 60661 **W:** www.metv.com – **MOVIES! (Comm)** (Joint-venture of Weigel Broadcasting Co. and Twenty-First Century Fox, Inc.) ▣ Weigel Broadcasting Co.: 26 North Halsted, Chicago, IL 60661 **W:** moviestvnetwork.com – **QUBO (Comm)** ▣ Qubo Venture LLC: 601 Clearwater Park Road, West Palm Beach, FL 33401 **W:** qubo. com – **QVC (Comm)** ▣ QVC, Inc.: 1200 Wilson Drive, West Chester, PA 19380 **W:** www.qvc.com – **RETRO TV (Comm)** ▣ Retro Television, Inc.: P.O.Box 11409, Chattanooga, TN 37401 **W:** www.myretrotv. com – **START TV (Comm)** ▣ Start TV, LLC: 26 North Halsted,

Chicago, IL 60661 **W:** www.starttv.com – **TELEXCITOS\* (Comm)** ◫ Telemundo Network Group: 2290 West 8th Avenue, Hialeah, FL, 33010. **W:** www.telexitos.com – **THE FAMILY CHANNEL (Comm)** ◫ ValCom, Inc.: 429 Rockaway Valley Road, Boonton Township, NJ 07005 **W:** www.famchannel.com – **THIS TV (Comm)** ◫ This TV, LLC: 10250 Constellation Boulevard, Los Angeles, CA 90067-6241 **W:** thistv.com – **TUFF TV (Comm)** ◫ TUFF TV Network, LLC: 55 Marietta Street, N.W. Suite 1000, Atlanta, GA 30303 **W:** www.tufftv. com – **WEATHER NATION (Comm)** ◫ WeatherNation, Inc.: 8101 E. Prentice Ave #700, Greenwood Village, CO 80111 **W:** www.weather-nationtv.com – **YOUTOO AMERICA (Comm)** ◫ Center Post Networks, LLC: 808 E Abram St, Arlington, TX 76010-1209 **W:** youtooamerica. com – **ALMAVISION\* (Rlg)** ◫ Almavision TV, Inc.: 759 S. Central Ave. City, Los Angeles, CA 90021 **W:** almavision.com – **CORNERSTONE TV (Rlg)** ◫ Cornerstone Television, Inc.: 1 Signal Hill Dr, Wall, PA 15148 **W:** www.ctvn.org – **DAYSTAR TV (Rlg)** ◫ God Fellowship, Inc.: 3901 Hwy 121, Bedford, TX 76021 **W:** www.daystar.com – **ENLACE\* (Rlg)** ◫ Trinity Broadcasting Network, Inc.: 2823 West Irving Blvd., Irving, TX 75061 **W:** www.enlace.org – **HILLSONG CHANNEL (Rlg)** ◫ Trinity Broadcasting Network: 14171 Chambers Rd., Tustin, CA 92780 **W:** hillsong.com – **JUCE TV (Rlg)** ◫ Trinity Broadcasting Network, Inc.: 2442 Michelle Dr, Tustin, CA 92780 **W:** www.jucetv.com – **SMILE OF A CHILD TV (Rlg)** ◫ AMC Networks, Inc.: P.O.Box 10700, Santa Ana, CA 92711-0700 **W:** www.smileofachildtv.com – **THREE ANGELS BROADCASTING NETWORK (3ABN) (Rlg)** ◫ Three Angels Broadcasting, Inc.: 17466 Route 37,Johnston City, IL 62951 **W:** 3abn.org.

## Local Stations
There are about 9000 txs operated by local TV stations in the USA.

## TV STATIONS IN MAJOR TV MARKETS

### Atlanta, GA Area

| ch | kW | Sta | City of License | Callsign |
|---|---|---|---|---|
| 8 | 0.15 | GA | Toccoa | W08EG-D |
| 9 | 3 | GA | Atlanta | WEQT-LD |
| 10 | 80 | GA | Atlanta | WXIA-TV |
| 12 | 3 | GA | Atlanta | WDNV-LD |
| 13 | 0.14 | GA | Carrollton | W13DJ-D |
| 14 | 10 | GA | Atlanta | WAGC-LD |
| 15 | 15 | GA | Gainesville | WGGD-LD |
| 16 | 4 | GA | Atlanta | WYGA-CD |
| 19 | 1000 | GA | Atlanta | WGCL-TV |
| 20 | 1000 | GA | Atlanta | WPCH-TV |
| 21 | 55 | GA | Atlanta | WPBA |
| 22 | 15 | GA | Atlanta | WSKC-CD |
| 24 | 240 | GA | Toccoa | WGTA |
| 24 | 0.5 | GA | Suwanee | WVND-LD |
| 25 | 500 | GA | Atlanta | WATL |
| 26 | 2 | GA | Cumming | WLVO-LD |
| 26 | 3 | GA | Athens | W26EM-D |
| 27 | 1000 | GA | Atlanta | WAGA-TV |
| 28 | 12 | GA | Cleveland | WDWW-LD |
| 29 | 15 | GA | Athens | W29DN-D |
| 29 | 14 | GA | Atlanta | WANN-CD |
| 30 | 15 | GA | Atlanta | WTBS-LD |
| 31 | 1000 | GA | Rome | WPXA-TV |
| 35 | 15 | GA | Atlanta | WDTA-LD |
| 38 | 15 | GA | Atlanta | WIGL-LD |
| 40 | 15 | GA | Atlanta | WIRE-CD |
| 42 | 7 | GA | Atlanta | WTHC-LD |
| 39 | 1000 | GA | Atlanta | WSB-TV |
| 41 | 330 | GA | Atlanta | WATC-DT |
| 43 | 1000 | GA | Atlanta | WUPA |
| 44 | 1000 | GA | Monroe | WHSG-TV |
| 45 | 15 | GA | Atlanta | W45DX-D |
| 47 | 12.5 | GA | Norcross | WKTB-CD |
| 48 | 1000 | GA | Athens | WUVG-DT |
| 49 | 4 | GA | Macon | WUEO-LD |

### Boston, MA Area

| ch | kW | Sta | City of License | Callsign |
|---|---|---|---|---|
| 9 | 6.5 | NH | Manchester | WMUR-TV |
| 10 | 5 | MA | Norwell | WWDP |
| 11 | 30 | NH | Durham | WENH-TV |
| 19 | 700 | MA | Boston | WGBH-TV |
| 19 | 700 | MA | Boston | WFXZ-CD |
| 20 | 625 | MA | Boston | WCVB-TV |
| 27 | 400 | NH | Derry | WWJE-DT |
| 27 | 400 | MA | Marlborough | WUNI |
| 29 | 270 | MA | Worcester | WUTF-TV |
| 30 | 825 | MA | Boston | WBZ-TV |
| 31 | 780 | MA | Boston | WFXT |
| 32 | 300 | MA | Boston | WBPX-TV |

| ch | kW | Sta | City of License | Callsign |
|---|---|---|---|---|
| 32 | 300 | MA | Woburn | WDPX-TV |
| 33 | 100 | MA | Lowell | WYDN |
| 34 | 80 | NH | Merrimack | WNEU |
| 39 | 135 | MA | Boston | WSBK-TV |
| 40 | 3.5 | MA | Boston | W40BO-D |
| 42 | 1000 | MA | Cambridge | WLVI |
| 42 | 1000 | MA | Boston | WHDH |
| 43 | 500 | MA | Boston | WGBX-TV |
| 43 | 500 | NH | Nashua | WYCN-CD |
| 45 | 15 | MA | Boston | WCEA-LD |
| 46 | 11.2 | MA | Boston | WBTS-LD |

### Chicago, IL Area

| ch | kW | Sta | City of License | Callsign |
|---|---|---|---|---|
| 4 | 0.3 | IL | Chicago | WOCK-CD |
| 12 | 8 | IL | Chicago | WBBM-TV |
| 17 | 300 | IN | Gary | WYIN |
| 19 | 645 | IL | Chicago | WGN-TV |
| 20 | 15 | IL | Chicago | WPVN-CD |
| 24 | 15 | IL | Arlington Heights | WRJK-LP |
| 27 | 550 | IL | Chicago | WCIU-TV |
| 29 | 350 | IL | Chicago | WMAQ-TV |
| 29 | 350 | IL | Chicago | WSNS-TV |
| 30 | 15 | IL | Chicago | WDCI-LD |
| 31 | 1000 | IL | Chicago | WFLD |
| 31 | 1000 | IN | Gary | WPWR-TV |
| 32 | 15 | IL | Chicago | WMEU-CD |
| 32 | 11.1 | IL | La Salle | WSPU-LD |
| 34 | 4.3 | IL | Arlington Heights | WEDE-CD |
| 35 | 15 | IL | Naperville | WWTO-TV |
| 36 | 145 | IN | Hammond | WJYS |
| 38 | 600 | IL | Joliet | WGBO-DT |
| 39 | 15 | IL | Chicago | WWME-CD |
| 40 | 15 | IL | Sugar Grove | W40CN-D |
| 43 | 200 | IL | Chicago | WCPX-TV |
| 44 | 1000 | IL | Chicago | WLS-TV |
| 44 | 1000 | IL | Aurora | WXFT-DT |
| 47 | 300 | IL | Chicago | WTTW |
| 47 | 300 | IL | Chicago | WYCC |

### Dallas - Fort Worth, TX Area\

| ch | kW | Sta | City of License | Callsign |
|---|---|---|---|---|
| 5 | 3 | TX | Garland | KXDA-LD |
| 8 | 55 | TX | Dallas | WFAA |
| 9 | 13 | TX | Fort Worth | KFWD |
| 14 | 975 | TX | Dallas | KERA-TV |
| 18 | 15 | TX | Keene | KGSW-LD |
| 18 | 15 | TX | Dallas | KPFW-LD |
| 19 | 1000 | TX | Fort Worth | KTVT |
| 20 | 15 | TX | Dallas | KBOP-LD |
| 21 | 15 | TX | Mineral Wells | K21KJ-D |
| 21 | 2 | TX | Dallas | KWDA-LD |
| 23 | 1000 | TX | Garland | KUVN-DT |
| 24 | 925 | TX | Fort Worth | KXAS-TV |
| 25 | 15 | TX | Corsicana | K25FW-D |
| 26 | 4.45 | TX | Dallas | K26KC-D |
| 26 | 15 | TX | Mineral Wells | K47NT-D |
| 27 | 15 | TX | Britton | KODF-LD |
| 27 | 15 | TX | Stephenville | K27LU-D |
| 29 | 1000 | TX | Fort Worth | KTXA |
| 30 | 1000 | TX | Decatur | KMPX |
| 32 | 780 | TX | Dallas | KDAF |
| 34 | 15 | TX | Dallas | KJJM-LD |
| 35 | 1000 | TX | Dallas | KDFW |
| 36 | 1000 | TX | Dallas | KDFI |
| 39 | 1000 | TX | Lake Dallas | KAZD |
| 40 | 1000 | TX | Dallas | KXTX-TV |
| 42 | 1000 | TX | Arlington | KPXD-TV |
| 43 | 1000 | TX | Denton | KDTN |
| 44 | 15 | TX | Dallas | KLEG-CD |
| 45 | 15 | TX | Dallas | KDTX-TV |
| 46 | 600 | TX | Greenville | KTXD-TV |
| 47 | 0.19 | TX | Fort Worth | KUVN-DT |
| 48 | 1000 | TX | Irving | KSTR-DT |
| 51 | 15 | TX | Dallas | KHFD-LD |

### Denver, CO Area

| ch | kW | Sta | City of License | Callsign |
|---|---|---|---|---|
| 5 | 1.5 | CO | Cripple Creek | K05MD-D |
| 7 | 54 | CO | Denver | KMGH-TV |
| 9 | 45 | CO | Denver | KUSA |
| 11 | 16 | CO | Cheyenne | KQCK |
| 13 | 34 | CO | Broomfield | KBDI-TV |
| 15 | 1000 | CO | Boulder | KCEC |
| 16 | 15 | CO | Ft. Collins | KBRO-LD |
| 16 | 15 | CO | Denver | KHDT-LD |
| 17 | 15 | CO | Denver | KZCO-LD |
| 18 | 1000 | CO | Denver | KRMA-TV |

| ch | kW | Sta | City of License | Callsign |
|----|----|-----|-----------------|----------|
| 19 | 1000 | CO | Denver | KTVD |
| 20 | 10 | CO | Ft. Morgan | K20KE-D |
| 21 | 50 | CO | Ft. Collins | KFCT |
| 23 | 1000 | CO | Sterling | KCDO-TV |
| 24 | 0.25 | CO | Boulder | K24HQ-D |
| 24 | 7.5 | CO | Ft. Collins | KMLN-LD |
| 26 | 549 | CO | Boulder | KTFD-DT |
| 28 | 15 | CO | Denver | KLPD-LD |
| 29 | 800 | CO | Longmont | KDEN-TV |
| 31 | 15 | CO | Denver | KZDN-LD |
| 32 | 1000 | CO | Denver | KDVR |
| 33 | 15 | CO | Loveland | KAVC-LP |
| 34 | 1000 | CO | Denver | KWGN-TV |
| 35 | 1000 | CO | Denver | KCNC-TV |
| 38 | 1000 | CO | Greeley | KPJR-TV |
| 39 | 1 | CO | Denver | KQDK-CD |
| 40 | 75 | CO | Denver | KRMT |
| 41 | 15 | CO | Denver | KSBS-CD |
| 43 | 1000 | CO | Denver | KPXC-TV |
| 44 | 45 | CO | Ft. Collins | KDNF-LD |
| 45 | 100 | CO | Castle Rock | KETD |
| 46 | 15 | CO | Denver | KDEO-LD |
| 48 | 15 | CO | Boulder | K48MN-D |
| **Detroit, MI Area** | | | | |
| 7 | 27 | MI | Detroit | WJBK |
| 14 | 180 | MI | Detroit | WKBD-TV |
| 18 | 14 | MI | Detroit | WDWO-CD |
| 19 | 11.6 | MI | Detroit | WUDL-LD |
| 20 | 15 | MI | Detroit | WHNE-LD |
| 21 | 500 | MI | Detroit | WMYD |
| 23 | 15 | MI | Detroit | WUDT-LD |
| 33 | 4 | MI | Detroit | WHPS-CD |
| 39 | 1000 | MI | Mount Clemens | WADL |
| 40 | 2.3 | MI | Redford | WLPC-CD |
| 41 | 1000 | MI | Detroit | WXYZ-TV |
| 43 | 600 | MI | Detroit | WTVS |
| 44 | 425 | MI | Detroit | WWJ-TV |
| 45 | 872 | MI | Detroit | WDIV-TV |
| 50 | 345 | MI | Ann Arbor | WPXD-TV |
| **Houston, TX Area** | | | | |
| 7 | 0.3 | TX | Houston | KDHU-LD |
| 8 | 65 | TX | Houston | KUHT |
| 11 | 60 | TX | Houston | KHOU |
| 13 | 32 | TX | Houston | KTRK-TV |
| 15 | 15 | TX | Houston | KVVV-LD |
| 19 | 1000 | TX | Houston | KTXH |
| 21 | 10.5 | TX | Houston | KVQT-LD |
| 22 | 15 | TX | Lake Jackson | K22JW-D |
| 22 | 15 | TX | Missouri City | KUVM-LD |
| 23 | 350 | TX | Galveston | KLTJ |
| 24 | 1000 | TX | Houston | KETH-TV |
| 25 | 15 | TX | Livingston | KCTL-LD |
| 26 | 800 | TX | Houston | KRIV |
| 28 | 15 | TX | Houston | KUGB-CD |
| 30 | 15 | TX | Houston | KCVH-LD |
| 32 | 1000 | TX | Conroe | KPXB-TV |
| 34 | 15 | TX | Missouri City | KUVM-CD |
| 35 | 1000 | TX | Houston | KPRC-TV |
| 36 | 1000 | TX | Alvin | KFTH-DT |
| 38 | 1000 | TX | Houston | KIAH |
| 39 | 15 | TX | Houston | KZHO-LD |
| 41 | 1000 | TX | Baytown | KUBE-TV |
| 42 | 1000 | TX | Conroe | KTBU |
| 43 | 60 | TX | Houston | KHLM-LD |
| 44 | 1000 | TX | Houston | KZJL |
| 45 | 1000 | TX | Rosenberg | KXLN-DT |
| 46 | 15 | TX | Houston | KBPX-LD |
| 47 | 1000 | TX | Katy | KYAZ |
| 48 | 1000 | TX | Galveston | KTMD |
| 49 | 5 | TX | Houston | KEHO-LD |
| **Los Angeles, CA Area** | | | | |
| 2 | 3 | CA | Los Angeles | KHIZ-LD |
| 5 | 3 | CA | Banning | KRVD-LD |
| 7 | 29 | CA | Los Angeles | KABC-TV |
| 7 | 29 | CA | Riverside | KRCA |
| 8 | 3 | CA | Los Angeles | KFLA-LD |
| 8 | 0.1 | CA | Cherry Valley | KILA-LD |
| 9 | 25 | CA | Los Angeles | KCAL-TV |
| 10 | 3 | CA | Los Angeles | KIIO-LD |
| 10 | 3 | CA | Riverside | KZSW-LD |
| 11 | 115 | CA | Los Angeles | KTTV |

| ch | kW | Sta | City of License | Callsign |
|----|----|-----|-----------------|----------|
| 12 | 1 | CA | Los Angeles | KTBV-LD |
| 13 | 120 | CA | Los Angeles | KCOP-TV |
| 18 | 700 | CA | Long Beach | KSCI |
| 18 | 700 | CA | Huntington Beach | KOCE-TV |
| 22 | 15 | CA | Los Angeles | KMRZ-LD |
| 23 | 150 | CA | Twentynine Palms | KVMD |
| 23 | 1.5 | CA | Ventura | KIMG-LP |
| 23 | 15 | CA | Los Angeles | KSMV-LD |
| 26 | 475 | CA | San Bernardino | KVCR-DT |
| 27 | 8 | CA | Los Angeles | KHTV-CD |
| 27 | 8 | CA | Avalon | KAZA-TV |
| 28 | 220 | CA | Los Angeles | KCET |
| 28 | 155 | CA | Los Angeles | KLCS |
| 29 | 370 | CA | Ontario | KFTR-DT |
| 30 | 10 | CA | San Bernardino | KSGA-LP |
| 30 | 0.5 | CA | Ontario | KCIO-LD |
| 31 | 1000 | CA | Los Angeles | KTLA |
| 32 | 1000 | CA | Anaheim | KDOC-TV |
| 33 | 1000 | CA | Santa Ana | KTBN-TV |
| 34 | 500 | CA | Los Angeles | KMEX-DT |
| 36 | 665 | CA | Los Angeles | KNBC |
| 38 | 1000 | CA | San Bernardino | KPXN-TV |
| 38 | 1000 | CA | Inglewood | KILM |
| 39 | 1000 | CA | Corona | KVEA |
| 40 | 10 | CA | Los Angeles | KVHD-LD |
| 42 | 486 | CA | Los Angeles | KWHY-TV |
| 42 | 486 | CA | Garden Grove | KBEH |
| 43 | 540 | CA | Los Angeles | KCBS-TV |
| 44 | 1 | CA | Camarillo | KUHD-LD |
| 45 | 1 | CA | Van Nuys | KSKJ-CD |
| 46 | 15 | CA | Altadena | KTAV-LD |
| 50 | 15 | CA | Los Angeles | KNLA-CD |
| 50 | 15 | CA | Los Angeles | KNET-CD |
| 51 | 1000 | CA | Rancho Palos Verdes | KXLA |
| 51 | 1000 | CA | Ventura | KJLA |
| **Miami - Ft. Lauderdale, FL Area** | | | | |
| 7 | 158 | FL | Miami | WSVN |
| 10 | 128 | FL | Miami | WPLG |
| 11 | 3 | FL | Miami | WDFL-LD |
| 16 | 3 | FL | West Gate | W16CC-D |
| 17 | 15 | FL | Miami | W17DG-D |
| 18 | 1000 | FL | Miami | WPBT |
| 18 | 1000 | FL | Miami | WURH-CD |
| 18 | 1000 | FL | Boynton Beach | WXEL-TV |
| 19 | 1000 | FL | Miami | WSFL-TV |
| 20 | 870 | FL | Miami | WLRN-TV |
| 22 | 1000 | FL | Miami | WFOR-TV |
| 23 | 1000 | FL | Miami | WLTV-DT |
| 24 | 775 | FL | Hollywood | WAMI-DT |
| 25 | 415 | FL | Boca Raton | WBEC-TV |
| 30 | 1000 | FL | Fort Lauderdale | WSCV |
| 31 | 1000 | FL | Miami | WTVJ |
| 32 | 1000 | FL | Miami | WBFS-TV |
| 33 | 15 | FL | Miami | WJAN-CD |
| 34 | 15 | FL | Miami | WVFW-LD |
| 35 | 242 | FL | Miami | WPXM-TV |
| 38 | 5 | FL | Miami | WPMF-CD |
| 38 | 5 | FL | Miami | WFUN-LD |
| 43 | 15 | FL | Matecumbe | W43CB-D |
| 45 | 15 | FL | Miami | WGEN-LD |
| 46 | 1000 | FL | Miami | WHFT-TV |
| 50 | 15 | FL | Miami | WSBS-CD |
| 51 | 15 | FL | Miami | WLMF-LD |
| **Minneapolis - St. Paul, MI Area** | | | | |
| 9 | 30 | MN | Minneapolis | KMSP-TV |
| 11 | 45 | MN | Minneapolis | KARE |
| 14 | 15 | MN | St. Paul | K16HY-D |
| 16 | 470 | MN | St. Cloud | KPXM-TV |
| 17 | 15 | MN | Minneapolis | WUMN-LD |
| 19 | 0.43 | MN | Minneapolis | KKTW-LD |
| 19 | 6 | MN | River Falls | W47CO-D |
| 22 | 1000 | MN | Minneapolis | WUCW |
| 23 | 325 | MN | St. Paul | KTCI-TV |
| 24 | 1.5 | WI | Grantsburg | W24CL-D |
| 34 | 662 | MN | St. Paul | KTCA-TV |
| 25 | 15 | MN | Minneapolis | KJNK-LD |
| 27 | 291 | WI | Menomonie | WHWC-TV |
| 29 | 1000 | MN | Minneapolis | WFTC |
| 31 | 15 | MN | Minneapolis | WDMI-LD |
| 32 | 1000 | MN | Minneapolis | WCCO-TV |
| 33 | 15 | MN | Minneapolis | K33LN-D |

| ch | kW | Sta | City of License | Callsign |
|----|-----|-----|-----------------|----------|
| 35 | 755 | MN | St. Paul | KSTP-TV |
| 45 | 1000 | MN | Minneapolis | KSTC-TV |
| **New York, NY Area** | | | | |
| 2 | 0.3 | NY | New York | WKOB-LD |
| 3 | 7 | NJ | Middletown | WJLP |
| 4 | 0.3 | NJ | East Orange | WPXO-LD |
| 5 | 0.3 | NY | New York | WNYX-LD |
| 7 | 34 | NY | New York | WABC-TV |
| 8 | 41 | NJ | New Brunswick | WNJB |
| 8 | 41 | NJ | Montclair | WNJN |
| 9 | 3 | NY | Roslyn | W09CZ-D |
| 11 | 7.5 | NY | New York | WPIX |
| 12 | 0.3 | NY | Amityville | WPXU-LD |
| 13 | 4 | NJ | Newark | WNET |
| 13 | 4 | NY | New York | WMBQ-CD |
| 13 | 4 | NY | Manhattan | WNDT-CD |
| 17 | 1 | NJ | Morristown | WNMF-LD |
| 18 | 1000 | NJ | Newton | WMBC-TV |
| 20 | 15 | NY | Hempstead | W20CQ-D |
| 20 | 1.6 | NJ | Teaneck | W20EF-D |
| 21 | 90 | NY | Garden City | WLIW |
| 22 | 15 | NY | Newburgh | WEPT-CD |
| 23 | 7 | NJ | Edison | WDVB-CD |
| 23 | 7 | NJ | Jersey City | WTBY-TV |
| 23 | 655 | NY | Smithtown | WFTY-DT |
| 23 | 1.2 | NY | Poughkeepsie | W42AE |
| 24 | 151 | NY | New York | WNYE-TV |
| 25 | 58 | NJ | Secaucus | WWOR-TV |
| 25 | 58 | NY | New Rochelle | WRNN-TV |
| 25 | 2.4 | NY | Monticello | W25DY-D |
| 27 | 1000 | NY | Riverhead | WLNY-TV |
| 27 | 1.5 | NJ | Belvidere | W43CH-D |
| 28 | 1 | NY | New York | W28ES-D |
| 30 | 200 | NJ | Newark | WFUT-DT |
| 30 | 200 | NJ | Paterson | WXTV-DT |
| 31 | 100 | NY | New York | WPXN-TV |
| 32 | 7.5 | NY | New York | WXNY-LD |
| 32 | 1.9 | NY | Port Jervis | W32EI-D |
| 33 | 385 | NY | New York | WCBS-TV |
| 35 | 5 | NJ | Sussex | W35DK-D |
| 36 | 750 | NY | New York | WNBC |
| 36 | 340 | NJ | Linden | WNJU |
| 39 | 3 | NY | New York | WNYN-LD |
| 41 | 7.4 | NY | Paterson | WNJJ-LD |
| 44 | 426 | NY | New York | WNYW |
| 49 | 170 | CT | Bridgeport | WEDW |
| 49 | 170 | CT | Bridgeport | WZME |
| 49 | 1 | NJ | Hackettstown | W49BE-D |
| 50 | 1.7 | NY | New York | WBQM-LD |
| **Philadelphia, PA Area** | | | | |
| 2 | 9.4 | DE | Wilmington | KJWP |
| 4 | 10 | NJ | Atlantic City | WACP |
| 6 | 34 | PA | Philadelphia | WPVI-TV |
| 7 | 0.025 | PA | Allentown | W07DC-D |
| 9 | 81 | PA | Philadelphia | WPPT |
| 9 | 81 | PA | Bethlehem | WBPH-TV |
| 9 | 81 | PA | Allentown | WLVT-TV |
| 12 | 30 | NJ | Princton | WMCN-TV |
| 12 | 30 | DE | Wilmington | WHYY-TVP |
| 16 | 5 | NJ | Springville | WDUM-LD |
| 17 | 645 | PA | Philadelphia | WPHL-TV |
| 17 | 645 | NJ | Vineland | WUVP-DT |
| 22 | 145 | NJ | Camden | WNJS |
| 22 | 5.5 | NJ | Trenton | WPHY-CD |
| 22 | 197 | NJ | Trenton | WNJT |
| 24 | 15 | PA | Philadelphia | WPHA-CD |
| 24 | 0.007 | PA | Reading | W24CS-D |
| 26 | 790 | PA | Philadelphia | KYW-TV |
| 27 | 1.5 | NJ | Belvidere | W43CH-CD |
| 28 | 5.7 | PA | Philadelphia | WFPA-CD |
| 30 | 10 | PA | Philadelphia | WELL-LD |
| 31 | 200 | DE | Wilmington | WPPX-TV |
| 32 | 800 | PA | Philadelphia | WPSG |
| 33 | 3 | PA | Philadelphia | WZPA-LD |
| 34 | 700 | PA | Philadelphia | WCAU |
| 34 | 700 | PA | Mount Laurel | WWSI |
| 36 | 1.2 | PA | Darby | W36DO-D |
| 36 | 205 | NJ | Wildwood | WMGM-TV |
| 36 | 205 | NJ | Millville | WGTW-TV |
| 38 | 6 | NJ | Hammonton | WPSJ-CD |
| 42 | 620 | PA | Philadelphia | WTXF-TV |

| ch | kW | Sta | City of License | Callsign |
|----|-----|-----|-----------------|----------|
| 45 | 0.17 | PA | Allentown | WFMZ-TV |
| 45 | 15 | NJ | Atlantic City | W45CP-D |
| 48 | 15 | NJ | Atlantic City | W48DP-D |
| 50 | 15 | NJ | Glassboro | WQAV-CD |
| 50 | 5.5 | NJ | Willow Grove | WTVE |
| **Phoenix, AZ Area** | | | | |
| 8 | 40 | AZ | Phoenix | KAET |
| 10 | 48 | AZ | Phoenix | KSAZ-TV |
| 12 | 39 | AZ | Mesa | KPNX |
| 15 | 458 | AZ | Phoenix | KNXV-TV |
| 16 | 15 | AZ | Phoenix | KPHE-LD |
| 17 | 1000 | AZ | Phoenix | KPHO-TV |
| 18 | 3 | AZ | Phoenix | K18JL-D |
| 19 | 15 | AZ | Gila River Indian Co | KGRF-LD |
| 20 | 1000 | AZ | Phoenix | KPAZ-TV |
| 21 | 7 | AZ | Gila River Indian Co | KGRY-LD |
| 22 | 15 | AZ | Phoenix | KTVP-LD |
| 24 | 1000 | AZ | Phoenix | KTVK |
| 29 | 15 | AZ | Gila River Indian Co | KGRQ-LD |
| 26 | 1000 | AZ | Phoenix | KUTP |
| 31 | 645 | AZ | Tolleson | KPPX-TV |
| 33 | 470 | AZ | Phoenix | KTVW-DT |
| 36 | 15 | AZ | Phoenix | KAZT-CD |
| 38 | 15 | AZ | Phoenix | K38IZ-D |
| 39 | 550 | AZ | Phoenix | KTAZ |
| 40 | 14 | AZ | Phoenix | KEJR-LD |
| 41 | 5 | AZ | Phoenix | KPDF-CA |
| 42 | 15 | AZ | Phoenix | KVPA-LD |
| 46 | 15 | AZ | Phoenix | KDPH-LD |
| 49 | 531 | AZ | Phoenix | KASW |
| 50 | 15 | AZ | Globe | KFPB-LD |
| **San Francisco, CA Area** | | | | |
| 2 | 3 | CA | Middletown | KFTY-LD |
| 2 | 3 | CA | Morgan Hill | KQRO-LD |
| 3 | 2.5 | CA | San Francisco | KURK-LD |
| 4 | 3 | CA | San Rafael | KQSL-LD |
| 6 | 0.1 | CA | Petaluma | K06QM-D |
| 7 | 24 | CA | San Francisco | KGO-TV |
| 8 | 0.2 | CA | San Francisco | KDTS-LD |
| 11 | 0.039 | CA | San Francisco | K11WP-D |
| 11 | 1.8 | CA | Santa Cruz | KAAP-LD |
| 12 | 103 | CA | San Jose | KNTV |
| 13 | 0.004 | CA | Petaluma | KQTA-LD |
| 20 | 3.6 | CA | Greenfield | KSCZ-LD |
| 23 | 105 | CA | Cotati | KRCB |
| 26 | 6 | CA | Santa Rosa | KUKR-LD |
| 28 | 15 | CA | San Francisco | KCNZ-CD |
| 28 | 15 | CA | San Francisco | KMTP-TV |
| 28 | 15 | CA | San Francisco | KOFY-TV |
| 28 | 4 | CA | Santa Rosa | KDTV-CD |
| 28 | 15 | CA | Fremont | KEMO-TV |
| 29 | 1000 | CA | San Francisco | KPIX-TV |
| 30 | 1000 | CA | San Francisco | KQED |
| 30 | 310 | CA | San Jose | KQEH |
| 34 | 370 | CA | Vallejo | KFSF-DT |
| 36 | 550 | CA | San Jose | KICU-TV |
| 38 | 1000 | CA | San Francisco | KRON-TV |
| 39 | 1000 | CA | San Francisco | KCNS |
| 39 | 1000 | CA | Concord | KTNC-TV |
| 40 | 14 | CA | San Jose | KMMC-LD |
| 41 | 1000 | CA | San Jose | KKPX-TV |
| 42 | 15 | CA | San Francisco | KAXT-CD |
| 42 | 15 | CA | Palo Alto | KTLN-TV |
| 43 | 500 | CA | San Mateo | KPJK |
| 44 | 1000 | CA | Oakland | KTVU |
| 45 | 1000 | CA | San Francisco | KBCW |
| 49 | 257 | CA | San Jose | KSTS |
| 49 | 1 | CA | Santa Rosa | KZHD-LD |
| 51 | 476 | CA | San Francisco | KDTV-DT |
| 51 | 858 | CA | San Francisco | KTSF |
| **Seattle - Tacoma, WA Area** | | | | |
| 8 | 0.25 | WA | Seattle | K08OU-D |
| 9 | 22 | WA | Seattle | KCTS-TV |
| 11 | 100 | WA | Tacoma | KSTW |
| 13 | 30 | WA | Tacoma | KCPQ |
| 14 | 90 | WA | Tacoma | KTBW-TV |
| 17 | 0.5 | WA | Everett | K17IZ-D |
| 19 | 187 | WA | Centralia | KCKA |
| 19 | 165 | WA | Bellingham | KBCB |
| 22 | 15 | WA | Seattle | KCPQ |
| 24 | 4 | WA | Seattle | KRUM-LD |

| ch | kW | Sta | City of License | Callsign |
|---|---|---|---|---|
| 25 | 8 | WA | Aberdeen | K25CG-D |
| 25 | 1000 | WA | Seattle | KZJO |
| 25 | 6 | WA | North Bend | K25CH-D |
| 26 | 1 | WA | Bremerton | K26IC-D |
| 27 | 100 | WA | Tacoma | KBTC-TV |
| 28 | 0.5 | WA | Seattle | KIRO-TV |
| 29 | 2 | WA | Centralia | K29IA-D |
| 29 | 2 | WA | Everett | K29ED-D |
| 31 | 700 | WA | Everett | KONG |
| 33 | 400 | WA | Bellevue | KWPX-TV |
| 34 | 0.5 | WA | Seattle | KIRO-TV |
| 35 | 580 | WA | Bellingham | KVOS-TV |
| 38 | 1000 | WA | Seattle | KOMO-TV |
| 39 | 1000 | WA | Seattle | KIRO-TV |
| 42 | 6 | WA | Centralia | K42CM-D |
| 42 | 144 | WA | Tacoma | KWDK |
| 44 | 169 | WA | Seattle | KFFV |
| 46 | 0.5 | WA | Seattle | KUSE-LD |
| 47 | 1 | WA | Point Pulley | K47LG-D |
| 48 | 960 | WA | Seattle | KING-TV |
| 49 | 2 | WA | Puyallup | K49IX-D |
| 50 | 1000 | WA | Bellevue | KUNS-TV |
| 51 | 1 | WA | Seattle | KIRO-TV |

**Tampa - St. Petersburg, FL Area**

| ch | kW | Sta | City of License | Callsign |
|---|---|---|---|---|
| 7 | 32 | FL | St. Petersburg | WTTA |
| 7 | 32 | FL | Tampa | WFLA-TV |
| 10 | 69 | FL | St. Petersburg | WTSP |
| 12 | 72 | FL | Tampa | WTVT |
| 13 | 25 | FL | Tampa | WEDU |
| 13 | 25 | FL | Tampa | WEDQ |
| 14 | 3.5 | FL | Largo | WPDS-LD |
| 15 | 5 | FL | Orient City | W15CM-D |
| 16 | 15 | FL | Lealman | W16DQ-D |
| 18 | 5 | FL | Tampa | WSVT-LD |
| 19 | 1000 | FL | Lakeland | WMOR-TV |
| 20 | 15 | FL | Tampa | WARP-CD |
| 21 | 1000 | FL | Clearwater | WCLF |
| 23 | 5.5 | FL | Sebring | W23CN-D |
| 24 | 90 | FL | Sarasota | WWSB |
| 25 | 750 | FL | Venice | WFTT-DT |
| 26 | 5 | FL | Inverness | W26DP-D |
| 26 | 5.9 | FL | Clearwater | WXAX-CD |
| 26 | 14.9 | FL | Sarasota | WSNN-LD |
| 27 | 6 | FL | Port Charlotte | WBKH-LD |
| 28 | 15 | FL | Tampa | WTAM-LD |
| 29 | 1000 | FL | Tampa | WFTS-TV |
| 38 | 15 | FL | St. Petersburg | WSPF-CD |
| 40 | 3 | FL | St. Petersburg | W40CU-D |
| 42 | 257 | FL | Bradenton | WXPX-TV |
| 44 | 550 | FL | St. Petersburg | WTOG |
| 45 | 15 | FL | Tampa | WTBT-LD |
| 47 | 650 | FL | Tampa | WVEA-TV |
| 48 | 15 | FL | Oldsmar | WZRA-CD |
| 49 | 15 | FL | Tampa | WRMD-CD |

**Washington, DC Area**

| ch | kW | Sta | City of License | Callsign |
|---|---|---|---|---|
| 7 | 52 | DC | Washington | WJLA-TV |
| 9 | 52 | DC | Washington | WUSA |
| 9 | 52 | MD | Hagerstown | WJAL |
| 12 | 23 | WV | Martinsburg | WWPX-TV |
| 14 | 15 | DC | Washington | WWTD-LD |
| 15 | 1000 | DC | Washington | WDCW |
| 15 | 1000 | VA | Arlington | WFDC-DT |
| 20 | 7 | MD | Lake Shore | WQAW-LP |
| 23 | 10 | DC | Washington | WDDN-LD |
| 23 | 15 | VA | Dale City | WDWA-LP |
| 27 | 73 | DC | Washington | WETA-TV |
| 28 | 41 | VA | Frederick | WFPT |
| 32 | 15 | DC | Washington | WRZB-LD |
| 33 | 152 | DC | Washington | WHUT-TV |
| 34 | 1000 | VA | Manassas | WPXW-TV |
| 36 | 1000 | DC | Washington | WDCA |
| 36 | 1000 | DC | Washington | WTTG |
| 42 | 516 | MD | Annapolis | WMPT |
| 44 | 12 | DC | Washington | WIAV-LD |
| 44 | 12 | DC | Washington | WMDO-LD |
| 45 | 15 | DC | Washington | W45DN-D |
| 45 | 4.8 | VA | Woodstock | WDCO-LD |
| 48 | 813 | DC | Washington | WRC-TV |
| 48 | 813 | DC | Washington | WZDC-CD |

**NB:** A large number of stns is currently being relocated to new channels

(some are to close down alltogether), as part of a major freq reshuffle in connection with the assignment of the 700MHz band to mobile services.

## URUGUAY

**System:** ISDB-TB [A]

**National Station**
**TELEVISIÓN NACIONAL URUGUAY (TNU) (Gov)** ✉ Bvrd. Artigas 2552,11600 Montevideo ☎ +598 2 4871129 **E:** contacto@tnu.com.uy **W:** www.tnu.com.uy **Tx:** Montevideo ch30 & network.

**Key Local Stations**
**CANAL 10 (Comm)** ✉ Lorenzo Carnelli 1234, 11200 Montevideo ☎ +598 2 4002120 🖷 +598 2 4095812 **W:** www.canal10.com.uy **Tx:** Montevideo ch31 – **MONTE CARLO TELEVISIÓN (Comm)** ✉ Paraguay 2253, 11800 Montevideo ☎ +598 2 9247924 🖷 +598 2 9244444 **W:** www.montecarlotv.com.uy **Tx:** Montevideo ch29 – **TELEDOCE (Comm)** ✉ Enriqueta Compte y Rique 1276, 11800 Montevideo ☎ +598 2 2083363 🖷 +598 2 2083555 **E:** teledoce@teledoce.com **W:** www.teledoce.com **Tx:** Montevideo ch28.

**Other Local Stations** not shown.

## UZBEKISTAN

**System:** DVB-T2 (MPEG4) [E]; § DVB-T [E]

**National Stations**
**UZBEK TELEVISION (Gov)** ✉ Navoiy St. 69, 100011 Toshkent ☎+998 71 1141250 🖷 +998 71 1441332 **E:** info@mtrk.uz **W:** www.mtrk.uz **L.P:** Chmn: Alisher Xadjayev **Chs:** O'zbekiston, Yoshlar, Toshkent, Sport TV, Madaniyat va ma'rifat, Dunyo bo'ylab, Bolajon, regional stns.

**Local Stations** not shown.

**DTT Tx Networks (DVB-T2)**
**Licensee:** Uzdigital TV ✉ Amir Timur St. 109-A, 100084 Toshkent ☎ +998 71 1299000 🖷 +998 71 1505884 **E:** info@uzdtv.uz **W:** uzdtv.uz **M1:** O'zbekiston, Toshkent, Sport, Dunyo bo'ylab, Bolajon, Madaniyat va ma'rifat, Kino Teatr, Oilaviy, Mahalla, Yoshlar, Navo, Milliy TV, UzReport TV HD, Mening Yurtim, Z'or TV HD, Sevimli HD, Futbol TV HD, O'zbekiston 24 HD **M2✪:** Pervyy Kanal, Rossiya 1, NTV, Match TV, Zvezda Telekanal, TV Centr, TV 3, Rossiya 24, Karusel, Euronews, Ohkota i Rybalka, Discovery Channel, National Geographic, Eurosport 1, Kinohit, Kinopremiera **M3✪:** Disney Kanal, Kinosvidanye, Muz TV, RuTV, Telekafe, Match! Arena, Match! Futbol 1, Animmal Planet, Rossiya K, Dom Kino, Match! Futbol 2, Indinskoye Kino, TV 1000, TV 1000 Russkoye Kino, Viasat History, Viasat Explore **M4✪(exc.*):** UzReport TV*, Mening Yutim*, Sevimli TV*, Futbol TV*, Rossiya K, Dom Kino, Match! Futbol 2, Indinskoye Kino, TV 1000, TV 1000 Russkoye Kino, Viasat History, Viasat Explore **M5✪:** Discovery Science, Retro, Auto Plus, Nashe Novoe Kino, Rodnoe Kino, Detskiy Mir, Tehno 24, Fashion TV, Match! Igra, National Geographic HD, Nat Geo Wild HD, Travel Channel HD, Match! Futbol 1 HD

| Location | M1 | M2 | M3 | M4 | M5 | kW |
|---|---|---|---|---|---|---|
| Toshkent | 42 | 41 | 37 | 29 | (-) | 2 |

+ national MFN

## VANUATU

**Systems:** DVB-T2 (MPEG4) [E]

**National Station**
**TV BLONG VANUATU (Gov)** ✉ P.M.B. 049, Port Vila **W:** www.facebook.com/TelevisionBlongVanuatu **L.P:** Pres (VBTC): Johnety Jerette.

**Local Stations** not shown.

**DTT Tx Network**
**Tx Operator:** Telsat Pacific **W:** www.telsat.vu **M✪:** multiprgr **Txs:** (-) – **Tx Operator:** Vanuamadia Digital Media Ltd **W:** www.facebook.com/Vanuamadia-Digital-TV-Network-1662712960715323 **M(✪ exc.*):** VBTC* + multiprgr **Txs:** ch48 (SFN).

## VATICAN CITY STATE

**System:** DVB-T (MPEG4) [E]

**VATICAN MEDIA** ✉ Via del Pellegrino, I-00120 Vatican City ☎ +39

06 69885467 **E:** ctv@ctv.va **W:** www.vaticannews.va **Mux:** Vatican News HD ⌘ R. Vaticana 105 Live, R. Vaticana Europa/America, R. Vaticana Africa/Asia **Tx:** ch45 (Castel Gandolfo).

## VENEZUELA

**Systems:** ISDB-TB [A]; # NTSC-M [A] ⇩2020

**National Stations** (ᵃ=analogue)
**TVES (TELEVISORA VENEZOLANA SOCIAL) (Gov)** ▢ Caraças **W:** www.tves.gob.ve **Txs:** Caracas ᵃch2 & relay txs. – **VIVE (VISIÓN VENEZUELA) (Gov)** ▢ Final Av. Panteón, Foro Libertador, Edf. Biblioteca Nacional, AP-4, Altagracia, Caracas ☎+58 212 5051611 **E:** atencionciudadana@vive.gob.ve **W:** www.vive.gob.ve **Txs:** Caracas ᵃch25 & relay txs. – **VTV (VENEZOLANA DE TELEVISION) (Gov)** ▢ Ap. 2979, Caracas 1050. ☎ +58 212 2349581 **E:** atencionciudadano@ vtv.gob.ve **W:** www.vtv.gob.ve **Txs:** Caracas ᵃch8 (190kW) & relay txs. – **TELESUR (Pub)** ▢ Calle Vargas con Calle Santa Clara, edificio TeleSUR, Boleita Norte, Caracas ☎ +58 212 6000202 **E:** contactenos@ telesurtv.net **W:** www.telesurtv.net **Txs:** Caracas ᵃch49 & relay txs. – **GLOBOVISION (Comm)** ▢ Los Pinos, cruce con Calle Alameda, Qta. Globovisión, Urb. Alta Florida, Caracas ☎ +58 212 7301134 **E:** info@globovision.com **W:** globovision.com. **Txs:** Caracas ᵃch33 & relay txs. – **MERIDIANO TELEVISIÓN (Comm)** ▢ Final av. San Martin con Av. La Paz, Edificio Bloque De Armas, Caracas ☎ +58 212 4064516 🖷 +58 212 4515627 **E:** meridianotv@internet.ve **W:** www.meridiano.com. ve **Txs:** Caracas ᵃch39 & relay txs. – **TELEVEN (Comm)** ▢ Av. Romulo Gallegos con 4ta. transversal de horizonte, Edificio Televen, Caracas 1071 ☎ +58 212 2800151 **E:** webmaster@televen.com. **W:** www. televen.com. **Txs:** Caracas ᵃch10 & relay txs. – **VENEVISIÓN (Comm)** ▢ Av. La Salle, Edif, Venevision,Colinas de Los Caobos, Caracas 1050 ☎ +58 212 7089444 **W:** www.venevision.net. **Txs:** Caracas ᵃch4 (132kW) & relay txs. – **VALE TV (Rlg)** ▢ Final Av. La Salle, Quinta ValeTV, Colinas de Los Caobos, Caracas ☎+58 212 7939215 🖷 +58 212 7089743 **E:** webmaster@valetv.com **W:** www.valetv.com **Txs:** Caracas ᵃch5 (210kW) & relay txs.

**Local Stations** (Comm. exc. where stated)
**Amavision (Rlg):** Calle Selesiano, Colegio Pio XI, Puerto Ayacucho, Amazonas; Puerto Ayacucho ᵃch7 (6kW). **La Tele:** Calle Republica Dominicana, Boleita Sur, Caracas; ᵃch12. **Canal Metropolitano de Televisión:** Av. Circumvalacion El Sol, Centro Professional Santa Paula, Torre B, Piso 4, Santa Paula, Caracas; ᵃch51. **NCTV:** Urv. La Paz, Avenida 57 y Maracaibo, Maracaibo; ᵃch11 (108kW). **Omnivision:** Calle Milan, Edif. Omnivision, Los Ruices Sur, Caracas. Puma TV: Av. Sanatorio del Avila, Boleíta Norte, Caracas 1071; Maracaibo ᵃch53, Caracas ᵃch57. **Televisora Andina de Merida (Rlg):** Av. Bolivar, Calle 23 entre Av. 4-5, Merida 5101; Tachira ᵃch3 (33kW), Merida ᵃch6 (20kW). **Tele Bocono (Cult):** Calle 3, Qta. Caleuche, El Saman. Bocono; Trujillo ᵃch13 (4kW). **Telecaribe:** Centro Banaven (Cubo Negro), Torre C, Piso 1, of C-12, Chuao, Caracas; Anzoategui ᵃch9 (50kW), Nueva Esparta ᵃch12 (30kW). **Telecentro:** Avenide Pedro León Torres, esquina de la calle 47, Edificio Telecentro, Barquisimeto, (3001) Lara; ᵃch11 (100kW). **TV Guyana:** Puerto Ordaz, Bolivar; ch12 (125kW). **Telesol:** Calle Sucre no 15, Cumana, Sucre; ᵃch7 (12kW). **Televisora Regional del Tachira:** Av. Libertador, edif. Servicios Unidos, Piso 3, San Cristobal, Tachira; ᵃch6 (144kW). **Televisora de Oriente (TVO):** Puerto la Cruz, Anzoategui; ᵃch5 (50kW).

**DTT Tx Networks** (under construction)
**Licensee:** n/a **M1:** VTV, 123TV, Colombeia, Venevisión, Alba TV **M2:** ViVe, TeleSUR, Venevisión, Meridiano TV, Televen, TV ConCiencia **M3:** TVes, ANTV, SIBCI HD **M4:** CCTV, Ávila TV, PDVSA TV, RT en español.

| Location | M1 | M2 | M3 | M4 |
|---|---|---|---|---|
| Caracas | 22 | 23 | 24 | 25 |

+ nationwide MFN under construction.

## VIETNAM

**Systems:** DVB-T2 (MPEG2) [E]; § PAL-D/K [R] ⇩2020

**National Stations**
**VIETNAM TELEVISION (Gov)** ▢ 43 Nguyen Chi Thanh, Ba Dinh District, Hanoi ☎ +84 438355931 **E:** toasoan@vtv.vn **W:** www.vtv. vn **LP:** DG: Tran Binh Minh **Chs (terr.):** VTV1-16, VTV3 HD, VTV6 HD.

**Regional and Local Stations** not shown.

**DTT Tx Networks**
**Licensee:** Vietnam Multimedia Corporation ▢ 67B Ham Long Street, Hoan Kiem District, Hanoi ☎ +84 444550055 **E:** tvnet.gov.vn@gmail. com **W:** tvnet.gov.vn **M:** VTV1-16, VTV3 HD, VTV6 HD, Hanoi TV 1,

HTV1 **Txs:** ch26 (Hanoi 1.3kW) & nationwide netw.

## VIRGIN ISLANDS (American) (USA)

**System:** ATSC [A]

**Local Stations** (Full power licenses, LP licenses not listed)
**WCVI-TV (Rlg):** Christiansted. Tx: St. Croix ch23 (0.66kW). **WSVI (Comm):** Sunny Isle Shopping Center, Christiansted, VI 00820-4493. Tx: St. Croix ch20 (459kW). **WTJX-TV (Pub):** 58-158A Hay Place Hill S, St. Thomas, VI 20801. Tx: Charlotte Amalie ch44 (50kW). **WVXF (Comm):** 8000 Nisky Center, Suite 714, Saint Thomas, VI 00802. Tx: Charlotte Amalie ch17 (4.2kW). **WZVI (Comm):** satellite of WSVI. Tx: Charlotte Amalie ch43 (1.4kW).

## VIRGIN ISLANDS (British) (UK)

**System:** NTSC-M [A]

**CARRIBEAN BROADCAST NETWORK (BVI) LTD (Comm)** ▢ 2nd Floor, Chevelle Center Main Street, Road Town, Tortola VG 1110 ☎ +1 284 3463633 **E0:** carribeanbroadcasting@gmail.com **W:** www. cbnvirginislands.com **Tx:** ch51.

## WAKE ISLAND (USA)

**NB:** No terrestrial TV station.

## WALLIS & FUTUNA (France)

**System:** DVB-T (MPEG4) [E]

**WALLIS ET FUTUNA LA 1ÈRE (Pub)** ▢ BP 102, Pointe Matala, F-98600 Mata Utu ☎ +33 681722020 🖷 +33 681722346 **W:** wallisfu-tuna.la1ere.fr **L.P:** Dir: Etienne Morel.

**DTT Tx Network**
**Tx Operator:** TDF **M:** Wallis et Futuna la 1ère, France 2-5, France Ô, France 24, Arte **Txs:** ch34 (SFN).

## YEMEN

**System:** PAL-B [E]

**YEMEN GENERAL CORP. FOR RADIO & TV (Gov)** ▢ P.O.Box 1140, al-Guraf, Sana'a. **Txs:**(-).

## ZAMBIA

**System:** DVB-T2 (MPEG4) [E]

**National Stations**
**ZAMBIA NATIONAL BROADCASTING CORP. (Gov)** ▢ P.O.Box 50015, Lusaka 10101 ☎ +260 21 1254989 🖷 +260 21 1254317 **E:** znbctv@znbc.co.zm **W:** www.znbc.co.zm **LP:** DG: Richard Mwanza **Chs:** ZNBC TV1, ZNBC TV2 – **MUVI TV (Comm)** ▢ P.O.Box 33932, Lusaka 10101 ☎ +260 21 1253271 **E:** frontoffice@muvitv.com **W:** www.muvitv.com

**Local Stations** (all Comm)
**CBC:** 22nd Floor, Findeco House, Lusaka. **Copperbelt Broadcasting Services:** Ndola. **Mobi TV:** 25 Mwambula Rd, Lusaka. **Northrise TV:** Lusaka.

**DTT Tx Network**
**Licensee:** Multichoice Zambia ▢ P.O.Box 320011, Lusaka ☎ +260 21 1368300 **E:** mczambia@zambia.multichoice.co.za **M(partly⟳):** multiprgr **Txs:** MFN.

## ZIMBABWE

**Systems:** DVB-T2 (MPEG4) [E]; § PAL-B [E]

**ZIMBABWE TELEVISION (ZTV) (Gov)** ▢ P.O.Box HG 444, Highlands, Harare ☎ +263 4 498610 🖷 +263 4 498613 **E:** zbc@zbc. co.zw **W:** www.zbc.co.zw **Chs:** ZTV1, ZTV2.

**DTT Tx Network**
**Licensee:** Multichoice Zimbabwe **M(partly⟳):** multiprgr **Txs:** MFN.

# REFERENCE

## Section Contents

Main Country Index........656

Geographical Area Codes ...........................658

Abbreviations and Symbols ........................659

International Transmitter Sites................................660

Target Area Codes........662

Domestic SW Transmitter Sites................................663

DX Clubs.......................665

Standard Time & Frequency .....................668

International Organisations ................670

Selected Internet Resouces .....................671

Advertisers Index..........672

Features & Reviews

National Radio

International Radio

Frequency Lists

National Television

Reference

# MAIN COUNTRY INDEX

| | Nat | Int | CTB | TV | | Nat | Int | CTB | TV |
|---|---|---|---|---|---|---|---|---|---|
| Afghanistan | 66 | 456 | | 608 | Denmark | 186 | 468 | | 617 |
| Alaska | 67 | 456 | | 608 | Djibouti | 187 | 468 | | 618 |
| Albania | 67 | 456 | | 608 | Dominica | 188 | | | 618 |
| Algeria | 68 | 457 | | 608 | Dominican Republic | 188 | | | 618 |
| Andorra | 70 | | | 609 | Easter Island | 189 | | | 618 |
| Angola | 70 | 457 | | 609 | Ecuador | 189 | 468 | | 618 |
| Anguilla | 71 | 457 | | 609 | Egypt | 192 | 469 | | 618 |
| Antarctica | 71 | 457 | | 609 | El Salvador | 193 | | | 618 |
| Antigua & Barbuda | 71 | | | 609 | Equatorial Guinea | 194 | | | 619 |
| Argentina | 72 | 457 | | 609 | Eritrea | 194 | | 512 | 619 |
| Armenia | 79 | 458 | | 609 | Estonia | 194 | 469 | | 619 |
| Aruba | 80 | | | 609 | Eswatini | 195 | 469 | | 619 |
| Ascension Island | 80 | 458 | | 609 | Ethiopia | 195 | 469 | 513 | 619 |
| Australia | 80 | 458 | | 609 | Falkland Islands | 196 | | | 619 |
| Austria | 90 | 459 | | 610 | Faroe Islands | 196 | | | 619 |
| Azerbaijan | 91 | | | 610 | Fiji | 196 | | | 619 |
| Azores | 92 | | | 610 | Finland | 197 | 469 | | 620 |
| Bahamas | 93 | | | 610 | France | 198 | 470 | | 620 |
| Bahrain | 93 | 460 | | 610 | French Guiana | 207 | | | 621 |
| Bangladesh | 93 | 460 | | 610 | French Polynesia | 207 | | | 621 |
| Barbados | 94 | | | 611 | French So. & Antarctic Lands | 208 | | | 621 |
| Belarus | 95 | 461 | | 611 | Gabon | 208 | | | 621 |
| Belgium | 96 | 461 | | 611 | Galapagos Islands | 208 | | | 621 |
| Belize | 98 | | | 611 | Gambia | 208 | | | 621 |
| Benin | 98 | 461 | | 611 | Georgia | 208 | | | 622 |
| Bermuda | 99 | | | 612 | Germany | 210 | 470 | | 622 |
| Bhutan | 99 | | | 612 | Ghana | 223 | | | 623 |
| Bolivia | 99 | | | 612 | Gibraltar | 224 | | | 623 |
| Bonaire | 103 | 461 | | 612 | Greece | 224 | 473 | | 623 |
| Bosnia & Herzegovina | 104 | | | 612 | Greenland | 226 | | | 624 |
| Botswana | 105 | 461 | | 612 | Grenada | 226 | | | 624 |
| Brazil | 105 | | | 612 | Guadeloupe | 227 | | | 624 |
| British Indian Ocean Territory | 135 | | | 612 | Guam | 227 | 473 | | 624 |
| Brunei | 135 | | | 613 | Guatemala | 228 | | | 624 |
| Bulgaria | 135 | 461 | | 613 | Guinea | 229 | | | 624 |
| Burkina Faso | 136 | | | 613 | Guinea-Bissau | 229 | | | 624 |
| Burundi | 137 | | | 613 | Guyana | 230 | | | 624 |
| Cabo Verde | 137 | | | 613 | Haiti | 230 | | | 624 |
| Cambodia | 137 | | | 613 | Hawaii | 231 | | | 624 |
| Cameroon | 140 | 461 | | 613 | Honduras | 232 | | | 625 |
| Canada | 140 | 462 | | 613 | Hong Kong | 234 | | | 625 |
| Canary Islands | 148 | | | 614 | Hungary | 235 | | | 625 |
| Cayman Islands | 149 | | | 614 | Iceland | 236 | | | 625 |
| Central African Rep. | 149 | | | 614 | India | 237 | 473 | | 626 |
| Chad | 149 | | 511 | 614 | Indonesia | 242 | 476 | | 626 |
| Chile | 150 | | | 614 | Iran | 246 | 476 | 513 | 626 |
| China | 152 | 462 | 511 | 615 | Iraq | 248 | | | 626 |
| Christmas Island | 169 | | | 615 | Ireland | 249 | | | 626 |
| Cocos Islands | 170 | | | 615 | Israel | 251 | 477 | | 627 |
| Colombia | 170 | | | 615 | Italy | 252 | 478 | | 627 |
| Comoros | 175 | | | 615 | Jamaica | 254 | | | 627 |
| Congo (Dem. Rep.) | 175 | | | 615 | Japan | 255 | 478 | | 628 |
| Congo (Rep.) | 176 | | | 615 | Jordan | 259 | | | 628 |
| Cook Islands | 176 | | | 616 | Kazakstan | 259 | | | 628 |
| Costa Rica | 176 | | | 616 | Kenya | 260 | | | 628 |
| Côte d'Ivoire | 177 | | | 616 | Kiribati | 261 | | | 628 |
| Croatia | 177 | | | 616 | Korea (DPR) (North) | 261 | 479 | 514 | 628 |
| Cuba | 179 | 467 | 512 | 616 | Korea (Rep) (South) | 262 | 480 | 516 | 628 |
| Curaçao | 182 | | | 616 | Kosovo | 266 | | | 629 |
| Cyprus | 183 | 467 | | 616 | Kuwait | 266 | 481 | | 629 |
| Czechia | 184 | 468 | | 617 | Kyrgyzstan | 266 | 482 | | 629 |

| | Nat | Int | CTB | TV | | Nat | Int | CTB | TV |
|---|---|---|---|---|---|---|---|---|---|
| Laos | 268 | 482 | | 629 | Samoa (American) | 354 | | | 640 |
| Latvia | 268 | | | 629 | San Marino | 355 | | | 640 |
| Lebanon | 269 | | | 630 | São Tomé et Príncipe | 355 | 488 | | 640 |
| Lesotho | 270 | | | 630 | Saudi Arabia | 355 | 488 | | 641 |
| Liberia | 270 | | | 630 | Senegal | 356 | | | 641 |
| Libya | 270 | | | 630 | Serbia | 357 | | | 641 |
| Liechtenstein | 271 | | | 630 | Seychelles | 357 | | | 642 |
| Lithuania | 271 | 482 | | 630 | Sierra Leone | 357 | | | 642 |
| Lord Howe Island | 272 | | | 630 | Singapore | 358 | 488 | | 642 |
| Luxembourg | 272 | | | 630 | Slovakia | 358 | 489 | | 642 |
| Macau | 273 | | | 631 | Slovenia | 359 | | | 642 |
| Macedonia | 273 | 482 | | 631 | Solomon Islands | 361 | | | 642 |
| Madagascar | 273 | 482 | | 631 | Somalia | 361 | | 517 | 642 |
| Madeira | 273 | | | 631 | South Africa | 362 | 489 | | 642 |
| Malawi | 274 | | | 631 | South Sudan | 365 | | 517 | 642 |
| Malaysia | 274 | | | 631 | Spain | 365 | 491 | | 643 |
| Maldives | 277 | | | 631 | Sri Lanka | 375 | 492 | | 643 |
| Mali | 277 | 483 | | 632 | St Barthélemy | 376 | | | 643 |
| Malta | 278 | | | 632 | St Eustatius | 376 | | | 643 |
| Marshall Islands | 278 | | | 632 | St Helena | 376 | | | 643 |
| Martinique | 278 | | | 632 | St Kitts & Nevis | 376 | | | 643 |
| Mauritania | 279 | | | 632 | St Lucia | 376 | | | 643 |
| Mauritius | 279 | | | 632 | St Maarten | 376 | | | 643 |
| Mayotte | 279 | | | 632 | St Martin | 377 | | | 643 |
| Mexico | 279 | | | 632 | St Pierre & Miquelon | 377 | | | 644 |
| Micronesia | 286 | | | 632 | St Vincent | 377 | | | 644 |
| Moldova | 286 | 483 | | 633 | Sudan | 377 | 492 | 517 | 644 |
| Monaco | 288 | 483 | | 633 | Suriname | 378 | | | 644 |
| Mongolia | 288 | 483 | | 633 | Sweden | 378 | 492 | | 644 |
| Montenegro | 289 | | | 633 | Switzerland | 381 | 492 | | 644 |
| Montserrat | 289 | | | 633 | Syria | 382 | 492 | | 645 |
| Morocco | 289 | | | 633 | Taiwan (Rep. of China) | 383 | 493 | | 645 |
| Mozambique | 290 | | | 634 | Tajikistan | 385 | 493 | | 645 |
| Myanmar | 291 | | | 634 | Tanzania | 386 | 494 | | 645 |
| Namibia | 292 | | | 634 | Thailand | 387 | 494 | | 645 |
| Nauru | 292 | | | 634 | Timor-Leste | 389 | | | 645 |
| Nepal | 293 | | | 634 | Togo | 390 | | | 645 |
| Netherlands | 294 | 483 | | 634 | Tokelau | 390 | | | 645 |
| New Caledonia | 297 | | | 635 | Tonga | 390 | | | 646 |
| New Zealand | 298 | 483 | | 635 | Trinidad & Tobago | 391 | | | 646 |
| Nicaragua | 303 | | | 635 | Tristan da Cunha | 391 | | | 646 |
| Niger | 304 | | | 635 | Tunisia | 391 | | | 646 |
| Nigeria | 304 | 484 | 516 | 635 | Turkey | 392 | 495 | 517 | 646 |
| Niue | 305 | | | 636 | Turkmenistan | 394 | | | 646 |
| Norfolk Island | 305 | | | 636 | Turks & Caicos Is | 394 | | | 646 |
| Northern Mariana Is | 305 | 484 | | 636 | Tuvalu | 394 | | | 646 |
| Norway | 306 | 484 | | 636 | Uganda | 394 | | 517 | 647 |
| Oman | 307 | 484 | | 636 | Ukraine | 395 | 496 | | 647 |
| Pakistan | 307 | 485 | 516 | 636 | United Arab Emirates | 398 | | | 647 |
| Palau | 308 | 485 | | 636 | United Kingdom | 399 | 496 | | 647 |
| Panama | 308 | | | 636 | United States of America | 407 | 499 | | 648 |
| Papua New Guinea | 309 | | | 637 | Uruguay | 446 | | | 653 |
| Paraguay | 311 | | | 637 | Uzbekistan | 448 | 509 | | 653 |
| Peru | 312 | | | 637 | Vanuatu | 449 | | | 653 |
| Philippines | 322 | 485 | | 637 | Vatican City State | 449 | 509 | | 653 |
| Pitcairn Islands | 326 | | | 637 | Venezuela | 449 | | | 654 |
| Poland | 326 | 486 | | 637 | Vietnam | 451 | 510 | 518 | 654 |
| Portugal | 330 | | | 638 | Virgin Is (American) | 453 | | | 654 |
| Puerto Rico | 333 | | | 638 | Virgin Is (British) | 453 | | | 654 |
| Qatar | 334 | | | 639 | Wake Island | 453 | | | 654 |
| Réunion | 334 | | | 639 | Wallis & Futuna | 453 | | | 654 |
| Romania | 335 | 487 | | 639 | West Bank & Gaza (Palestine) | 252 | | | 627 |
| Russia | 337 | 487 | | 639 | Western Sahara | | | 518 | |
| Rwanda | 354 | | 516 | 640 | Yemen | 453 | | 518 | 654 |
| Saba | 354 | | | 640 | Zambia | 454 | 510 | | 654 |
| Samoa | 354 | | | 640 | Zimbabwe | 454 | | | 654 |

# GEOGRAPHICAL AREA CODES USED IN WRTH

Codes assigned by the International Telecommunications Union ITU (except * = WRTH code)

| Code | Country | Code | Country | Code | Country | Code | Country |
|------|---------|------|---------|------|---------|------|---------|
| ABW | Aruba | D | Germany | LBY | Libya | SDN | Sudan |
| AFG | Afghanistan | DGA | Diego Garcia | LCA | St. Lucia | SEN | Senegal |
| AFS | South Africa | DJI | Djibouti | LHW* | Lord Howe Island | SEY | Seychelles |
| AGL | Angola | DMA | Dominica | LIE | Liechtenstein | SHN | St. Helena |
| AIA | Anguilla | DNK | Denmark | LSO | Lesotho | SLM | Solomon Islands |
| ALB | Albania | DOM | Dominican Republic | LTU | Lithuania | SLV | El Salvador |
| ALG | Algeria | E | Spain | LUX | Luxembourg | SMA | American Samoa |
| ALS | Alaska | EGY | Egypt | LVA | Latvia | SMO | Samoa |
| AND | Andorra | EQA | Ecuador | MAC | Macao | SMR | San Marino |
| AOE | Western Sahara | ERI | Eritrea | MAF | St. Martin | SNG | Singapore |
| ARG | Argentina | EST | Estonia | MAU | Mauritius | SOM | Somalia |
| ARM | Armenia | ETH | Ethiopia | MCO | Monaco | SPM | St. Pierre & Miquelon |
| ARS | Saudi Arabia | F | France | MDA | Moldova | SRB | Serbia |
| ASC | Ascension Island | FIN | Finland | MDG | Madagascar | SRL | Sierra Leone |
| ATA | Antarctica | FJI | Fiji | MDR | Madeira | SSD | South Sudan |
| ATG | Antigua & Barbuda | FLK | Falkland Islands | MEX | Mexico | STP | São Tomé & Príncipe |
| AUS | Australia | FRO | Faroe Islands | MHL | Marshall Islands | SUI | Switzerland |
| AUT | Austria | FSA* | French So. & Ant. Lands | MKD | Macedonia | SUR | Suriname |
| AZE | Azerbaijan | FSM | Micronesia | MLA | Malaysia | SVK | Slovakia |
| AZR | Azores | G | United Kingdom | MLD | Maldives | SVN | Slovenia |
| B | Brazil | GAB | Gabon | MLI | Mali | SWZ | Eswatini |
| BAH | Bahamas | GAL* | Galapagos Islands | MLT | Malta | SXM | St Maarten |
| BDI | Burundi | GEO | Georgia | MNE | Montenegro | SYR | Syria |
| BEL | Belgium | GHA | Ghana | MNG | Mongolia | TCA | Turks & Caicos Islands |
| BEN | Benin | GIB | Gibraltar | MOZ | Mozambique | TCD | Chad |
| BER | Bermuda | GLP | Guadeloupe | MRA | Northern Mariana Is | TGO | Togo |
| BES | Bonaire / St Eustatius / | GMB | Gambia | MRC | Morocco | THA | Thailand |
|  | Saba | GNB | Guinea-Bissau | MRT | Martinique | TJK | Tajikistan |
| BFA | Burkina Faso | GNE | Equatorial Guinea | MSR | Montserrat | TKM | Turkmenistan |
| BGD | Bangladesh | GRC | Greece | MTN | Mauritania | TKL | Tokelau |
| BHR | Bahrain | GRD | Grenada | MWI | Malawi | TLS | Timor-Leste |
| BIH | Bosnia & Herzegovina | GRL | Greenland | MYT | Mayotte | TON | Tonga |
| BIO | British Indian Ocean | GTM | Guatemala | NCG | Nicaragua | TRC | Tristan da Cunha |
|  | Territory | GUF | French Guiana | NCL | New Caledonia | TRD | Trinidad & Tobago |
| BLM | St. Barthélemy | GUI | Guinea | NFK | Norfolk Island | TUN | Tunisia |
| BLR | Belarus | GUM | Guam | NGR | Niger | TUR | Turkey |
| BLZ | Belize | GUY | Guyana | NIG | Nigeria | TUV | Tuvalu |
| BOL | Bolivia | HKG | Hong Kong | NIU | Niue | TWN* | Taiwan |
| BOT | Botswana | HND | Honduras | NMB | Namibia | TZA | Tanzania |
| BRB | Barbados | HNG | Hungary | NOR | Norway | UAE | United Arab Emirates |
| BRM | Myanmar | HOL | Netherlands | NPL | Nepal | UGA | Uganda |
| BRU | Brunei | HRV | Croatia | NRU | Nauru | UKR | Ukraine |
| BTN | Bhutan | HTI | Haiti | NZL | New Zealand | URG | Uruguay |
| BUL | Bulgaria | HWA | Hawaii | OCE | French Polynesia | USA | United States of America |
| CAF | Central African Republic | I | Italy | OMA | Oman | UZB | Uzbekistan |
| CAN | Canada | ICO | Cocos (Keeling) Islands | PAK | Pakistan | VCT | St. Vincent & |
| CBG | Cambodia | IND | India | PAQ | Easter Island |  | the Grenadines |
| CHL | Chile | INS | Indonesia | PHL | Philippines | VEN | Venezuela |
| CHN | China (People's Rep. of) | IRL | Ireland | PLW | Palau | VIR | Virgin Islands |
| CHR | Christmas Island | IRN | Iran | PNG | Papua New Guinea | VRG | British Virgin Islands |
| CKH | Cook Islands | IRQ | Iraq | PNR | Panama | VTN | Vietnam |
| CLM | Colombia | ISL | Iceland | POL | Poland | VUT | Vanuatu |
| CLN | Sri Lanka | ISR | Israel | POR | Portugal | WAL | Wallis & Futuna |
| CME | Cameroon | J | Japan | PRG | Paraguay | WAK | Wake Island |
| CNR | Canary Islands | JMC | Jamaica | PRU | Peru | XGZ | Gaza Strip[1] |
| COD | Congo (Dem. Rep. of the) | JOR | Jordan | PSE* | Palestine[1] | XWB | West Bank[1] |
| COG | Congo (Rep. of the) | KAZ | Kazakhstan | PTC | Pitcairn Islands | YEM | Yemen |
| COM | Comoros | KEN | Kenya | PTR | Puerto Rico | ZMB | Zambia |
| CPV | Cabo Verde | KER | Iles Kerguelen | QAT | Qatar | ZWE | Zimbabwe |
| CTI | Côte d'Ivoire | KGZ | Kyrgyzstan | REU | Réunion |  |  |
| CTR | Costa Rica | KIR | Kiribati | RKS* | Kosovo | | |
| CUB | Cuba | KOR | Korea, South | ROD | Rodrigues | | |
| CUW | Curaçao | KRE | Korea, North | ROU | Romania | | |
| CVA | Vatican City State | KWT | Kuwait | RRW | Rwanda | | |
| CYM | Cayman Islands | LAO | Laos | RUS | Russia | | |
| CYP | Cyprus | LBN | Lebanon | S | Sweden | | |
| CZE | Czechia | LBR | Liberia | SCN | St. Kitts & Nevis | | |

[1]) The code "PSE" is used as target designation in the "COTB" section of International Radio; otherwise the codes "XGZ"/ "XWB" are used.

# ABBREVIATIONS & SYMBOLS USED IN WRTH

⌨ = Address
☎ = Telephone
🖷 = Fax
✪ = encrypted
⌘ = Radio via DTT
† = irregular
‡ = inactive
± = variable frequency

acc. = accepted
Admin. = Administration
alt. = alternate, alternative
AM = Amplitude Modulation
Ann. = Announcement
Ap. = Apartado
approx. = approximate(ly)
Assoc. = Association
Asst. = Assistant
Ave = Avenue, Avenida
B.P. = Boîte Postale
B'caster = Broadcaster
Bldg = Building
Bo = Barrio/Bairro
Broadc. = Broadcast(ing)
BS = Broadc. Stn/Sce
C = Chinese
C.P. = Case/Caixa Postal, Construction Permit
Ca = Calle
Cad. = Cadena
Cas. = Casilla
Cd. = Ciudad
Ce. = Central
CEO = Chief Exec. Officer
cf. = refer to
Ch. = Channel
Chmn. = Chairman/Chair
Cl. = Club(e)
Clan. = Clandestine
Co. = Company
Com. = Comunicações
comm. = commercial
Contr. = Controller
Corp. = Corporation
Cra. = Carrera
Cult. = Cultura, Cultural
D = Daily, On Demand audio
d = directional antenna
D.Prgr = Daily Programme(s)
DAB = Digital Audio Broadc.
DMB = Digital Multimedia Broadcasting
Dem. = Democratic
Dep. = Deputy
Dept. = Department
Depto. = Departamento
Desp. = Despacho
DG = Director General
Dif. = Difusora, Difusão
Diff. = Diffusion
Dir. = Director
Div. = Division
dom = domestic
DRM = Digital Radio Mondiale

DSB = Double Side Band
DST = Daylight Saving Time
DTT = Digital Terrestrial TV
DVB = Digital Video Broadc.
DX = Long Distance (Reception)
E = English
E: = Email
E.C = Electric Current
Ea. = East(ern)
Edif. = Edificio
Educ. = Education(al), Educación
e.g. = for example
Em. = Emis(s)ora
Eng. = Engineer(ing)
ERP = Effective Radiated Power
Esq. = Esquina
eQSL = electronic QSL
est. = estimated
Est. = Estado
exc. = except
excl. = excluding
exec. = executive
ext. = external
F = French
F.Pl. = Future Plan(s)
fed. = federal
FM = Frequency Modulation
Fr. = Father
Freq. = Frequency
Fri = Friday
FS = Foreign Service
Ft. = Fort
G = German
G.C = Geographical Coordinates
GD = General Director
gen. = general
GM = General Manager
Gov. = Government(al)
Gte. = Gerente
H = Horizontal Pol.
h(rs) = hour(s)
HD = High Definition
HQ = Headquarters
HS = Home Service
I = Italian
ID = (Station) Identification
i.e. = that is
Inc. = Incorporated
incl. = including
Inf. = Information
int. = international
IRC = Int. Reply Coupon
irr. = irregular
IS = Interval Signal
I./Is = Island/Islands
kHz = kiloHertz
L = Local, Live audio
L.P = Leading Personnel
L.T = Local Time
Langs. = Languages
Lp. = Low power (transmitter)

LSB = Lower Side Band
Ltd = Limited
LV = La Voz, La Voce
LW = Longwave
max. = maximum
M: = Multiplex
MD = Managing Director
MF = Mondays-Fridays
MFN = Multi Freq. Netw.
Mgr = Manager
MHz = MegaHertz
mil. = military
Min. = Ministry, Ministerio, Ministério
min(s) = minute(s)
Mon = Monday
Mpal. = Municipal
Mpo. = Município
Mt = Mount, Mountain
MW = Mediumwave
N. = News
NB = Note (Nota Bene)
n.f. = nominal frequency
n/a = not available, not applicable
nal. = nacional
nat. = national
nd = nondirectional antenna
NE = North East(ern)
Netw. = Network
No. = North(ern), Number
nom. = nominal
Nte = Norte
NW = North West(ern)
occ. = occasional(ly)
Op(s) = Operation(s)
Org. = Organisation
Ote. = Oeste
P = Portuguese, Podcast
P.O. = Post Office
P.R. = Public Relations, People's Republic
PD = Programme Director
pl. = planned
Pol. = Polarisation
Pop. = Population
Pr. = Praça
Pr.L = Principal Language(s)
Pres. = President
Priv. = Private
Prgr(s). = Programme(s)
Prod. = Production
Prov. = Province, Provincial
Pt. = Point
Pte. = Presidente
Pto. = Puerto
Pub = Public service
Pub(s) = Publication(s)
QSL = Reception Confirmation
R. = Radio, Rádio, Rádió Radyo, Radyo
r. = reported, repeater
Rdif. = Radiodifusion
R. Dif. = Radio Difusora
Rec. = Recording(s)

Reg. = Region(al)
Rel. = Relay(s), Relations
Rep. = Republic
Rev. = Reverend
rlg = religious
Rp. = Return Postage
Rpt. = (Reception) Report
S. = San(ta), Sán, Santo
s/off = sign off
s/on = sign on
SAE = Self Addressed Envelope
SAR = Special Administrative Region
Sat = Saturday, satellite
Sce. = Service
Sched. = Schedule
SE = South East(ern)
Secr. = Secretary
Sen. = Senior
SFN = Single Freq. Netw.
Sist. = Sistema
SM = Station Manager
So. = South(ern)
Soc. = Sociedad(e)
Sp. = Spanish
SS = Sat/Sun
SSB = Single Side Band
St = Saint, Street
Stn = Station
Str. = Street, Straße
Su. = Summer
Sun = Sunday
Superv. = Supervisor
SW = Shortwave South West(ern)
Syst. = System
tbd = to be defined
TD = Technical Director
techn. = technical
terr. = terrestrial
Thu = Thursday
tr(s) = transmission(s)
TRP = Transmitter Power
Tue = Tuesday
tx(s) = transmitter(s)
ul. = ulitsa, ulica
u.c. = under construction
Univ. = University
unk. = unknown
UHF = Ultra High Frequency
USB = Upper Side Band
UTC = Coordinated Universal Time
V = Vertical Pol.
V. = Verification
v. = varying/variable
VHF = Very High Frequency
VO = Voice of
W = Weekdays (Mon-Sat)
W: = Web
We. = West(ern)
Wed = Wednesday
Wi. = Winter
Wrp. = Weather Report

# TRANSMITTER SITES
## Location & Decode Tables

## INTERNATIONAL TRANSMITTER SITES

| Code | Site | Ctry | Lat | Long | SW | MW |
|------|------|------|-----|------|----|----|
| — | Unidentified Site | — | — | — | | |
| abh | Abu Hayan | BHR | 26N02 | 050E37 | ✓ | × |
| abs | Abis | EGY | 31N08 | 030E04 | ✓ | × |
| abz | Abu Zaabal | EGY | 30N16 | 031E22 | ✓ | × |
| ahw | Ahwaz, Bandar-e Mahshar | IRN | 30N37 | 049E12 | ✓ | ✓ |
| aia | The Valley | AIA | 18N13 | 063W01 | ✓ | ✓ |
| aja | Abuja, Lugbe | NIG | 08N58 | 007E22 | ✓ | × |
| alf | Omdurman, Al Fatihab | SDN | 15N35 | 032E27 | ✓ | × |
| alg | Aligarh | IND | 28N00 | 078E06 | ✓ | × |
| arm | Krasnodar, Tbilisskaya | RUS | 45N28 | 040E06 | ✓ | × |
| asc | English Bay | ASC | 07S54 | 014W23 | ✓ | × |
| asm | Asmara ‡ | ERI | 15N13 | 038E52 | ✓ | ✓ |
| avl | Vathy (Avlida municipality) | GRC | 38N23 | 023E36 | ✓ | × |
| bcq | Monticello, ME | USA | 46N20 | 067W49 | ✓ | × |
| bec | Béchar ‡ | ALG | 31N34 | 002W21 | ✓ | × |
| bei | Beijing, Doudian | CHN | 39N38 | 116E06 | ✓ | × |
| bej | La Habana, Bejucal ‡ | CUB | 22N52 | 082W20 | ✓ | × |
| bgl | Bengaluru, Doddaballapur | IND | 13N15 | 077E29 | ✓ | × |
| bib | Biblis | D | 49N41 | 008E29 | ✓ | × |
| bis | Bishkek, Krasnaya Rechka | KGZ | 42N53 | 074E59 | ✓ | ✓ |
| bji | Baoji, Qishan (Shaanxi prov.) | CHN | 34N42 | 106E56 | ✓ | × |
| bko | Bamako, Kati ‡ | MLI | 12N45 | 008W03 | ✓ | × |
| bnb | Bonab | IRN | 37N18 | 046E03 | × | ✓ |
| bnt | Bandar-e Torkaman | IRN | 36N54 | 054E03 | × | ✓ |
| boc | Bocaue (Bulacan prov.) | PHL | 14N48 | 120E55 | ✓ | × |
| bot | Selebi-Phikwe, Moepeng Hill | BOT | 21S57 | 027E38 | ✓ | ✓ |
| bph | Bangkok, Rasom | THA | 14N24 | 100E47 | × | ✓ |
| btr | Batrah | EGY | 31N10 | 031E26 | × | ✓ |
| bue | Buenos Aires, General Pacheco ‡ | ARG | 34S26 | 058W37 | ✓ | × |
| cah | Changchun (Jilin prov.) | CHN | 43N44 | 125E24 | × | ✓ |
| cer | Cërrik, Shtërmen | ALB | 41N00 | 020E00 | ✓ | × |
| cgr | Cape Gkreko | CYP | 34N58 | 034E05 | × | ✓ |
| chb | Choibalsan ‡ | MNG | 48N00 | 114E27 | × | ✓ |
| chc | Chuncheon (HLAN) | KOR | 37N56 | 127E43 | × | ✓ |
| chj | Chongjin | KRE | 41N46 | 129E42 | ✓ | ✓ |
| chr | Chabahar | IRN | 25N29 | 060E32 | × | ✓ |
| cni | Chennai | IND | 13N08 | 080E07 | ✓ | × |
| cph | Copenhagen ‡ | DNK | 55N40 | 012E34 | × | ✓ |
| dan | Dangjin (HLCA) | KOR | 36N58 | 126E37 | × | ✓ |
| dat | Datteln | D | 51N39 | 007E20 | ✓ | × |
| deh | Mingshi (Dehong pref., Yunnan prov.) | CHN | 24N27 | 098E36 | × | ✓ |
| del | Delhi | IND | 28N43 | 077E12 | ✓ | × |
| dha | Dhabbaya | UAE | 24N10 | 054E15 | ✓ | ✓ |
| diy | Diyarbakir, Toraman | TUR | 37N49 | 040E19 | × | ✓ |
| dji | Djibouti, Dorale | DJI | 11N34 | 043E04 | × | ✓ |
| dka | Dhaka, Kabirpur | BGD | 24N00 | 090E15 | ✓ | × |
| dof | Dongfang, (Hainan prov.) | CHN | 18N53 | 108E39 | × | ✓ |
| dol | Dole | TZA | 06S06 | 039E15 | ✓ | × |
| dro | Droitwich | G | 52N18 | 002W06 | × | ✓ |
| dsb | Dushanbe | TJK | 38N29 | 068E48 | ✓ | ✓ |
| ela | El Arish | EGY | 31N07 | 033E42 | × | ✓ |
| emr | Emirler | TUR | 39N24 | 032E51 | ✓ | × |
| erd | Bergen, Erdal | NOR | 60N27 | 005E13 | ✓ | × |
| erv | Gavar, Noratus | ARM | 40N25 | 045E11 | ✓ | × |
| ewn | Vandiver, AL | USA | 33N30 | 086W29 | ✓ | × |
| fan | Fangliao ‡ | TWN | 22N23 | 120E34 | ✓ | × |
| gal | Bacau, Galbeni | ROU | 46N45 | 026E51 | ✓ | × |
| gjw | Geja | ETH | 08N47 | 038E39 | ✓ | × |
| goh | Göhren | D | 53N32 | 011E37 | ✓ | × |
| goy | Seoul, Goyang. | KOR | 37N36 | 126E51 | ✓ | × |
| grg | Gorgan (Tentative location) | IRN | 36N51 | 056E26 | × | ✓ |
| grv | Greenville, NC | USA | 35N28 | 077W12 | ✓ | × |
| hab | La Habana, Bauta | CUB | 22N57 | 082W33 | ✓ | × |
| ham | Hamhung (Freedom FM) | KRE | 39N55 | 127E31 | × | × |
| hbn | Medorm (Babeldaob Island) | PLW | 07N27 | 134E29 | ✓ | × |
| hdn | Huadian (Jilin prov.) | CHN | 43N07 | 126E31 | × | ✓ |
| hdu | Guangzhou, Liantang (Huadu dist, Guangdong prov.) | CHN | 23N24 | 113E14 | × | × |
| hei | Shuangyashan (Heilongjiang prov.) | CHN | 46N43 | 131E13 | × | ✓ |
| hil | Hillerod | DNK | 55N56 | 012E19 | ✓ | × |
| hju | Haeju ‡ | KRE | 38N02 | 125E43 | ✓ | ✓ |
| hnl | Changzhou, Henglin (Jiangsu prov.) | CHN | 31N42 | 120E07 | × | ✓ |
| hqb | Haciqabul, Pirsaat ‡ | AZE | 40N03 | 049E03 | × | ✓ |
| hri | Furman, SC | USA | 32N41 | 081W08 | ✓ | × |
| huh | Hohhot, Bikeqi (Nei Menggu autonomous region) | CHN | 40N48 | 111E12 | ✓ | × |
| hwa | Hwaseong | KOR | 37N13 | 126E47 | ✓ | × |
| iba | Iba (Zambales prov.) | PHL | 15N22 | 119E57 | ✓ | × |

| Code | Site | Ctry | Lat | Long | SW | MW |
|---|---|---|---|---|---|---|
| inb | Red Lion, PA | USA | 39N54 | 076W35 | ✓ | ✗ |
| isl | Islamabad, Rawat ‡ | PAK | 33N28 | 073E12 | ✓ | ✗ |
| isr | Yavne ‡ | ISR | 31N54 | 034E45 | ✓ | ✗ |
| iss | Issoudun | F | 46N56 | 001E53 | ✓ | ✗ |
| jal | Jalandhar | IND | 31N09 | 075E47 | ✗ | ✓ |
| jan | Hwaseong, Jangan | KOR | 37N18 | 126E58 | ✓ | ✗ |
| jed | Jeddah, Al Khumra | ARS | 21N15 | 039E10 | ✓ | ✗ |
| jej | Jeju (HLAZ) | KOR | 33N29 | 126E23 | ✗ | ✓ |
| jhr | Milton, FL | USA | 30N39 | 087W05 | ✓ | ✗ |
| jin | Jinhua, Lanxi (Zhejiang prov.) | CHN | 29N07 | 119E19 | ✓ | ✗ |
| jnm | Hwaseong, Jeongnam | KOR | 37N09 | 127E00 | ✓ | ✗ |
| jol | Jolfa | IRN | 38N56 | 045E36 | ✗ | ✓ |
| kab | Kabul | AFG | 34N32 | 069E20 | ✓ | ✓ |
| kac | Karachi, Landhi ‡ | PAK | 24N51 | 067E13 | ✓ | ✗ |
| kan | Kangnam | KRE | 38N50 | 125E40 | ✗ | ✓ |
| kas | Kashgar (Kashi), Sayibage (Xinjiang Uighur auton. reg.) | CHN | 39N21 | 075E46 | ✓ | ✓ |
| kbd | Kuwait, Kabd | KWT | 29N09 | 047E46 | ✓ | ✗ |
| kch | Grigoriopol, Maiac | MDA | 47N17 | 029E25 | ✓ | ✓ |
| kho | Khost, Tani | AFG | 33N20 | 069N56 | ✗ | ✓ |
| kia | Bandar e-Kiashahr | IRN | 37N25 | 050E01 | ✗ | ✓ |
| kih | Kish Island | IRN | 26N34 | 053E56 | ✗ | ✓ |
| kim | Gimje | KOR | 35N49 | 126E52 | ✓ | ✗ |
| kkt | Chinsurah | IND | 23N02 | 088E21 | ✗ | ✓ |
| kll | Kall, Krekel | D | 50N29 | 006E31 | ✓ | ✗ |
| kmk | Kimchaek | KRE | 40N41 | 129E12 | ✗ | ✓ |
| kng | Kanggye | KRE | 41N01 | 126E39 | ✓ | ✗ |
| knx | Kununurra | AUS | 15S49 | 128E40 | ✓ | ✗ |
| kou | Kouhu | TWN | 23N32 | 120E10 | ✓ | ✗ |
| kuj | Kujang | KRE | 40N05 | 126E07 | ✓ | ✗ |
| kun | Kunming, Anning (Yunnan prov.) | CHN | 24N53 | 102E30 | ✓ | ✓ |
| kwt | Kuwait, Umm Al-Rimam | KWT | 29N31 | 047E40 | ✓ | ✓ |
| lam | Lampertheim | D | 49N36 | 008E32 | ✓ | ✗ |
| lha | Lhasa (Tibet auton. Region) | CHN | 29N39 | 091E15 | ✓ | ✗ |
| lra | Base Antártica Esperanza | ATA | 63S24 | 057W00 | ✓ | ✗ |
| luv | Lusaka, Makeni Ranch | ZMB | 15S32 | 028E00 | ✓ | ✗ |
| man | Manzini, Mpangela Ranch | SWZ | 26S20 | 031E36 | ✓ | ✗ |
| mdc | Talata Volonondry | MDG | 18S45 | 047E37 | ✓ | ✗ |
| mek | Mek'ele | ETH | 13N30 | 039E29 | ✗ | ✓ |
| mer | Mersin | TUR | 36N49 | 034E44 | ✗ | ✓ |
| mey | Meyerton, Bloemendal | AFS | 26S35 | 028E08 | ✓ | ✗ |
| min | Minhsiung | TWN | 23N34 | 120E26 | ✗ | ✓ |
| mlk | Bethel, PA ‡ | USA | 40N29 | 076W17 | ✓ | ✗ |
| mos | Moosbrunn | AUT | 48N00 | 016E28 | ✓ | ✗ |
| msk | Moskva | RUS | 55N45 | 037E37 | ✗ | ✓ |
| mth | Marathon Key, FL | USA | 24N42 | 081W05 | ✗ | ✓ |
| mul | Luanda, Mulenvos ‡ | AGL | 08S51 | 013E19 | ✗ | ✓ |
| mum | Mumbai | IND | 19N11 | 072E48 | ✗ | ✓ |
| mwv | Mahajanga II (Belobaka), Amparemahitsy | MDG | 15S43 | 046E26 | ✗ | ✓ |
| nau | Nauen | D | 52N39 | 012E55 | ✓ | ✗ |
| nls | Anchor Point, AK | ALS | 59N45 | 151W44 | ✓ | ✗ |

| Code | Site | Ctry | Lat | Long | SW | MW |
|---|---|---|---|---|---|---|
| nnn | Nanning (Guangxi Zhuang auton. region) | CHN | 22N48 | 108E11 | ✓ | ✗ |
| nob | Noblejas | E | 39N57 | 003W26 | ✓ | ✗ |
| nwn | Seoul, Taereung (Nowon district in Seoul) | KOR | 37N38 | 127E07 | ✓ | ✗ |
| omo | Can Tho, Thoi Hung | VTN | 10N07 | 105E34 | ✗ | ✓ |
| org | Ourgla ‡ | ALG | 31N55 | 005E04 | ✓ | ✗ |
| pad | Padova, Villa Estense (Challenger R.) ‡ | I | 45N09 | 011E42 | ✗ | ✓ |
| pan | Panaji | IND | 15N27 | 073E51 | ✓ | ✗ |
| pao | Paochung | TWN | 23N43 | 120E18 | ✓ | ✗ |
| par | Parakou | BEN | 09N21 | 002E37 | ✓ | ✗ |
| pga | Palangkaraya | INS | 02S13 | 113E55 | ✗ | ✓ |
| pht | Tinang | PHL | 15N22 | 120E37 | ✓ | ✗ |
| pin | Pinneberg | D | 53N40 | 009E48 | ✓ | ✗ |
| put | Puttalam | CLN | 07N58 | 079E48 | ✗ | ✓ |
| pyo | Pyongyang | KRE | 39N03 | 125E42 | ✓ | ✗ |
| qsh | Qasr-e Shirin | IRN | 34N27 | 045E37 | ✗ | ✓ |
| qui | Quito, Mount Pichincha | EQU | 00S10 | 078W32 | ✓ | ✗ |
| qvc | La Habana, Quivicán | CUB | 22N49 | 082W18 | ✓ | ✗ |
| raj | Rajkot | IND | 22N30 | 070E31 | ✗ | ✓ |
| ran | Rangitaiki | NZL | 38S51 | 176E26 | ✓ | ✗ |
| rbn | Rabouni | ALG | 27N33 | 008W06 | ✗ | ✓ |
| riy | Riyadh | ARS | 24N49 | 046E52 | ✓ | ✗ |
| rmi | Okeechobee, FL | USA | 27N27 | 080W56 | ✓ | ✗ |
| rnd | Randers | DNK | 56N27 | 010E02 | ✓ | ✗ |
| rno | New Orleans, LA | USA | 29N50 | 090W07 | ✓ | ✗ |
| rob | Rohrbach, Eja | D | 48N36 | 011E33 | ✓ | ✗ |
| rou | Roumoules | F | 43N48 | 006E10 | ✗ | ✓ |
| sag | Samgo ‡ | KRE | 38N02 | 126E32 | ✓ | ✗ |
| sai | Saipan, Agingan Point ‡ | MRA | 15N07 | 145E42 | ✓ | ✗ |
| sao | Pinheira | STP | 00N18 | 006E45 | ✓ | ✗ |
| sda | Agat, Facpi Point | GUM | 13N20 | 144E39 | ✓ | ✗ |
| seo | Seoul, Siheung (HLKX) | KOR | 37N25 | 126E45 | ✗ | ✓ |
| sha | Kunming, Shalang (Yunnan prov.) | CHN | 25N41 | 102E41 | ✓ | ✗ |
| she | She'ar Yashuv | ISR | 33N13 | 035E39 | ✗ | ✓ |
| sir | Sirjan | IRN | 29N36 | 055E47 | ✗ | ✓ |
| sko | Skopje, Sveti Nikole | MKD | 41N47 | 021E53 | ✗ | ✓ |
| sla | A'Seela | OMA | 21N55 | 059E37 | ✗ | ✓ |
| smg | Santa Maria di Galeria | CVA | 42N03 | 012E19 | ✓ | ✗ |
| sng | Singapore | SNG | 01N25 | 103E43 | ✓ | ✗ |
| snu | Sinuiju | KRE | 40N05 | 124E27 | ✗ | ✓ |
| sof | Sofia, Kostinbrod | BUL | 42N49 | 023E11 | ✓ | ✗ |
| swo | Sangwon | KRE | 38N53 | 126E06 | ✗ | ✓ |
| szg | Shijiazhuang, Nanpozhuan (Hebei prov.) | CHN | 38N13 | 114E06 | ✓ | ✗ |
| tac | Toshkent | UZB | 41N13 | 069E09 | ✓ | ✗ |
| thu | Thumrait | OMA | 17N38 | 053E56 | ✓ | ✗ |
| tig | Bucuresti | ROU | 44N45 | 026E06 | ✓ | ✗ |
| tin | Tinian ‡ | MRA | 15N03 | 145E36 | ✓ | ✗ |
| trm | Trincomalee, Perkara | CLN | 08N45 | 081E08 | ✓ | ✗ |
| tsh | Tanshui | TWN | 25N11 | 121E25 | ✓ | ✗ |

| Code | Site | Ctry | Lat | Long | SW | MW |
|------|------|------|-----|------|----|----|
| tts | Tartus | SYR | 34N57 | 035E53 | ✗ | ✓ |
| ttu | Tartu, Kavastu | EST | 58N25 | 027E06 | ✗ | ✓ |
| tut | Tuticorin | IND | 08N49 | 078E05 | ✗ | ✓ |
| twb | Bonaire, Belnem | BES | 12N06 | 068W17 | ✗ | ✓ |
| twr | Merizo | GUM | 13N17 | 144E40 | ✓ | ✗ |
| tww | Lebanon, TN | USA | 36N17 | 086W06 | ✓ | ✗ |
| tyb | Tayebad | IRN | 34N44 | 060E48 | ✓ | ✗ |
| uba | Ulaanbaatar, Khonkhor | MNG | 47N48 | 107E11 | ✓ | ✗ |
| udo | Udon Thani, Ban Dung | THA | 17N40 | 103E12 | ✓ | ✗ |
| uru | Ürümqi (Wurumqi), Hutubi (Xinjiang Uighur auton. reg) | CHN | 44N09 | 086E54 | ✓ | ✓ |
| ust | Taiwan (site unknown) | TWN | - | - | ✓ | ✓ |
| vie | Vientiane | LAO | 18N00 | 102E38 | ✓ | ✗ |
| vir | Virrat, Liedenpohja | FIN | 62N23 | 023E37 | ✓ | ✓ |
| vni | Son Tay | VTN | 21N12 | 105E22 | ✓ | ✗ |
| voh | Rancho Simi, CA | USA | 34N15 | 118W39 | ✓ | ✗ |
| vst | Anykš?iai, Viešintos | LTU | 55N42 | 024E59 | ✗ | ✓ |
| wav | Wavre | BEL | 50N45 | 004E35 | ✗ | ✓ |
| wcr | Nashville, TN | USA | 36N12 | 086W54 | ✓ | ✗ |
| wis | Winsen an der Aller | D | 52N40 | 009E52 | ✓ | ✗ |
| wnm | Weenermoor | D | 53N12 | 007E19 | ✓ | ✗ |
| wof | Woofferton | G | 52N19 | 002W43 | ✓ | ✗ |
| wrb | Morrison, TN | USA | 35N37 | 086W01 | ✓ | ✗ |
| xia | Xi'an, Xianyang (Shaanxi prov.) | CHN | 34N22 | 108E37 | ✓ | ✗ |
| xuw | Xuanwei (Yunnan prov.) | CHN | 26N08 | 104E01 | ✓ | ✓ |
| yam | Sakuragawa, Yamato (Ibaraki pref) | J | 36N10 | 139E49 | ✓ | ✗ |
| yan | Yangon (Mayangon) (Myanma R.) | BRM | 16N52 | 096E10 | ✓ | ✗ |
| zab | Zabol | IRN | 31N02 | 061E33 | ✗ | ✓ |
| zah | Zahedan | IRN | 29N28 | 060E52 | ✓ | ✗ |
| zak | Zakaki, Lady's Mile (Akrotiri Sovereign Base Area) | CYP | 34N37 | 033E00 | ✗ | ✓ |

**NB:** The columns marked '**SW**' and '**MW**' have by a '✓' or '✗' to indicate if the site has the capability to transmit on Mediumwave (and/or Longwave) or Shortwave as appropriate. Where the symbol ‡ is shown after a transmitter site name this indicates that the site is inactive or not being used for international broadcasting at the time of publication. Some inactive sites are in the process of being constructed, or repaired, while others are simply dormant and could possibly be used again.

If a site on the list is known to have been dismantled or decommissioned it will be removed.

© WRTH Publications Ltd. November 2018

# TARGET AREA CODES

| Code | Target Area | Code | Target Area | Code | Target Area | Code | Target Area |
|------|-------------|------|-------------|------|-------------|------|-------------|
| Af | Africa | CAs | Central Asia | IOc | Indian Ocean | Pac | Pacific Ocean |
| Am | Americas | Cau | Caucasia | LAm | Latin America | SAf | Southern Africa |
| As | Asia | CEu | Central Europe | ME | Middle East | SAm | South America |
| Atl | Atlantic Ocean | EAf | Eastern Africa | Med | Mediterranean | SAs | Southern Asia |
| BaS | Baltic Sea | EAs | Eastern Asia | NAf | Northern Africa | SEA | South East Asia |
| CAf | Central Africa | EEu | Eastern Europe | NAm | North America | WAf | Western Africa |
| CAm | Central America | Eu | Europe | NEu | Northern Europe | WAs | West Asia |
| Car | Caribbean | FE | Far East | NoS | North Sea | | |

# DOMESTIC SW TRANSMITTER SITES

Coordinate System: **WGS84** (rounded)

**NB:** For coordinates of sites that are jointly used for National and International/COTB services, see the International Transmitter Sites table

| Ctry | Site | Lat | Long | Ctry | Site | Lat | Long |
|------|------|-----|------|------|------|-----|------|
| AUS | Alice Springs | 23S42 | 133E53 | BRM | Naypyitaw | 19N45 | 096E11 |
| AUS | Bundaberg | 24S51 | 152E21 | BRM | Pyin U Lwin | 22N01 | 096E33 |
| AUS | Gunnedah | 30S58 | 150E15 | BRM | Yangon | 16N52 | 096E09 |
| AUS | Innisfail | 17S31 | 146E01 | BTN | Thimphu | 27N29 | 089E37 |
| AUS | Perth | 31S57 | 115E51 | CAF | Boali | 04N53 | 018E01 |
| AUS | Sydney | 33S52 | 151E12 | CAN | Calgary | 50N54 | 113W53 |
| AUS | Wee Waa | 30S12 | 149E26 | CAN | Toronto | 43N30 | 079W38 |
| AGL | Luanda | 08S51 | 013E19 | CHN | Fuzhou | 26N06 | 119E24 |
| AZE | Stepanakert | 39N49 | 046E44 | CHN | Hailar | 49N02 | 119E45 |
| B | Aparecida | 23S00 | 045W00 | CHN | Hezuo | 35N06 | 102E54 |
| B | Araguaína | 07S16 | 048W18 | CHN | Lingshi | 36N52 | 111E56 |
| B | Araraquara | 21S47 | 048W10 | CHN | Xichang | 27N49 | 102E14 |
| B | Belém | 01S27 | 048W29 | CHN | Xining | 36N38 | 101E36 |
| B | Boa Vista | 02N51 | 060W43 | CLM | Puerto Lleras | 03N16 | 073W22 |
| B | Brasilía | 15S36 | 048W08 | COD | Bukavu | 02S30 | 028E52 |
| B | Camboriú | 26S59 | 048W38 | COD | Bunia | 01N32 | 030E11 |
| B | Campo Grande | 20S24 | 054W35 | ERI | Asmara | 15N13 | 038E53 |
| B | Congonhas | 20S30 | 043W53 | ETH | Jijiga | 09N21 | 042E48 |
| B | Cruzeiro do Sul | 07S40 | 072W39 | GNE | Bata | 01N49 | 009E47 |
| B | Cuiabá | 15S36 | 056W06 | GNE | Malabo | 03N45 | 008E47 |
| B | Curitiba | 25S23 | 049W10 | GTM | Chiquimula | 14N48 | 089W32 |
| B | Foz do Iguaçu | 25S31 | 054W34 | GUI | Conakry | 09N41 | 013W32 |
| B | Goiânia | 16S43 | 049W18 | GUY | Georgetown | 06N46 | 058W14 |
| B | Ibitinga | 21S43 | 048W47 | IND | Aizawl | 23N43 | 092E43 |
| B | Limeira | 22S34 | 047W25 | IND | Bhopal | 23N15 | 077E29 |
| B | Londrina | 23S18 | 051W13 | IND | Gangtok | 27N20 | 088E40 |
| B | Manaus | 03S04 | 060W00 | IND | Hyderabad | 17N20 | 078E34 |
| B | Parintins | 02S38 | 056W44 | IND | Jaipur | 26N55 | 075E45 |
| B | Porto Alegre | 30S03 | 051W10 | IND | Jeypore | 18N55 | 082E34 |
| B | Porto Velho | 08S45 | 063W54 | IND | Kurseong | 26N55 | 088E19 |
| B | Rio Branco | 09S58 | 067W49 | IND | Leh | 34N07 | 077E35 |
| B | Santa Maria | 29S44 | 053W33 | IND | Port Blair | 11N37 | 092E45 |
| B | São Gonçalo | 22S49 | 043W04 | IND | Shillong | 25N34 | 091E56 |
| B | S. Gabriel da Cachoeira | 00S09 | 067W03 | IND | Srinagar | 34N02 | 074E54 |
| B | São Paulo | 23S33 | 046W39 | IND | Thiruvananthapuram | 08N27 | 076E56 |
| B | Tefé | 03S24 | 064W45 | INS | Fakfak | 02S55 | 132E18 |
| BGD | Shavar | 23N52 | 090E16 | INS | Nabire | 03S22 | 135E29 |
| BOL | Cochabamba | 17S23 | 066W11 | INS | Palangkaraya | 02S12 | 113E50 |
| BOL | La Paz | 16S30 | 068W08 | INS | Ternate | 00N48 | 127E23 |
| BOL | Reyes | 14S18 | 067W23 | INS | Wamena | 04S06 | 138E57 |
| BOL | Riberalta | 10S59 | 066W06 | J | Nagara | 35N28 | 140E12 |
| BOL | S. José de Chiquitos | 17S53 | 060W45 | J | Nemuro | 43N17 | 145E34 |
| BOL | S. Ana del Yacuma | 13S45 | 065W32 | KRE | Hamhung | 39N55 | 127E31 |
| BOL | Santa Cruz | 17S46 | 063W11 | LBR | Monrovia | 06N14 | 010W42 |
| BOL | Siglo Veinte | 18S23 | 066W38 | MDG | Ambohidrano | 18S47 | 047E29 |
| BOL | Yura | 20S02 | 066W10 | MEX | México | 19N26 | 099W08 |

| Ctry | Site | Lat | Long |
|------|------|-----|------|
| MNG | Altai | 46N19 | 096E15 |
| MNG | Mörön | 49N37 | 100E10 |
| NIG | Kaduna | 10N45 | 007E33 |
| NPL | Khumaltar | 27N39 | 085E20 |
| PNG | Alotau | 10S18 | 150E28 |
| PNG | Buka | 05S25 | 154E40 |
| PNG | Daru | 09S05 | 143E10 |
| PNG | Kavieng | 02S34 | 150E48 |
| PNG | Kerema | 07S59 | 145E46 |
| PNG | Kimbe | 05S36 | 150E10 |
| PNG | Kiunga | 06S07 | 141E17 |
| PNG | Kundiawa | 06S00 | 144E57 |
| PNG | Lae | 06S41 | 146E54 |
| PNG | Lorengau | 02S01 | 147E15 |
| PNG | Madang | 05S14 | 145E45 |
| PNG | Mendi | 06S13 | 143E39 |
| PNG | Popondetta | 08S45 | 148E15 |
| PNG | Port Moresby | 09S26 | 147E11 |
| PNG | Rabaul | 04S13 | 152E07 |
| PNG | Tabubil | 05S17 | 141E14 |
| PNG | Vanimo | 02S42 | 141E18 |
| PNG | Wabag | 05S28 | 143E40 |
| PNG | Wewak | 03S35 | 143E40 |
| PRU | Atalaya | 10S44 | 073W45 |
| PRU | Bolívar | 07S16 | 077W47 |
| PRU | Chachapoyas | 06S10 | 077W50 |
| PRU | Chazuta | 06S34 | 076W08 |
| PRU | Chilca | 12S31 | 076W44 |
| PRU | Cusco | 13S32 | 071W57 |
| PRU | Huancabamba | 05S14 | 079W24 |
| PRU | Huancavelica | 12S45 | 075W03 |
| PRU | Huanta | 12S54 | 074W13 |
| PRU | Huaraz | 09S33 | 077W31 |
| PRU | Iquitos | 03S51 | 073W13 |
| PRU | Jacobo Hunter | 16S27 | 071W33 |
| PRU | Líma | 12S06 | 077W03 |
| PRU | Puerto Maldonado | 12S37 | 069W11 |
| PRU | Quillabamba | 12S49 | 072W41 |
| PRU | Santiago de Chuco | 08S09 | 078W10 |
| PRU | Tarma | 11S28 | 075W41 |
| PRU | Urubamba | 13S18 | 072W07 |
| SLM | Honiara | 09S25 | 160E03 |
| SOM | Baydhabo | 03N07 | 043E39 |
| SOM | Garoowe | 08N24 | 048E29 |
| SOM | Hargaysa | 09N34 | 044E04 |
| TCD | N'Djamena | 12N07 | 015E04 |
| VTN | Buôn Mê Thuôt | 12N40 | 108E12 |
| VTN | Xuân Mai | 20N53 | 105E34 |
| VUT | Port-Vila | 17S45 | 168E22 |

# CLUBS FOR DXERS & INTERNATIONAL LISTENERS

This section lists non-commercial hobby clubs serving international radio enthusiasts. Most clubs are orientated to DXing, the reception of distant radio stations, some are devoted to programme listening. Many clubs produce bulletins on a regular basis. Sample copies of club periodicals are often available in pdf-format, or mailed upon request per post for return postage (contact the club for payment details). For officially multilingual countries, the language(s) used in club publications (and/or activities) is indicated when known; for non-English speaking countries also if a publication is partly or entirely in English (EE = English, FF = French, GG = German, II = Italian, JJ = Japanese, RR = Russian, SS = Spanish). This list does not include clubs run by commercial publications or by individual broadcasters.

## EUROPE

**European DX Council (EDXC)** (Umbrella organization of DX Clubs in Europe) c/o Kari Kivekäs, Parmaajanpolku 3 B 11, 00750 Helsinki Finland. General Secretary: Kari Kivekäs (**E:** ksk@sdxl.org), Assistant General Secretary: Jan-Mikael Nurmela, Finland (**E:** jmn@sdxl.org) **W:** edxcnews.wordpress.com

**AUSTRIA: Austrian DX Board (ADXB-OE)** (Club der Freunde elektronischer Medien - Rundfunk global), Postfach 1000, 1082 Wien. **E:** office@adxb-oe.org **W:** www.adxb-oe.org Pub: *Rundbrief* (quarterly, pdf). Annual DX camp. Member of AGDX (Germany); club members receive the monthly AGDX publication *Radio-Kurier - weltweit hören*.

**BELGIUM: DX-Antwerp**, Eugeen Fahylaan 40, 2100 Deurne. (Flemish) **E:** info@dx-antwerp.com **W:** www.dx-antwerp.com Pub: *DXA-Bulletin* (quarterly, pdf)

**CZECHIA/SLOVAKIA: Ceskoslovensky DX Club (CSDXC)**, Lorencova 5424, 76001 Zlín, Czechia. **E:** mail@dx.cz **W:** www.dx.cz Pub: *Radio* (pdf)

**DENMARK: Dansk DX Lytter Klub (DDXLK)**, P.O.Box 112, 8960 Randers SØ. **E:** ddxlk@ddxlk.dk **W:** www.ddxlk.dk Pub: *DX-AKTUELLT* (Swedish/Danish, joint publication with SDXF [Sweden]; bimonthly, printed & pdf)

**FINLAND: Finlands Svenska DX-Förbund rf (FSDXF)**, P.O.Box 9, 68601 Jakobstad (Umbrella organization of Swedish language DX clubs in Finland) – **Suomen DX-liitto ry (SDXL)**, Annankatu 31-33, C 49 c, 00100 Helsinki (Umbrella organization of Finnish language DX clubs) **E:** toimisto@sdxl.fi **W:** www.sdxl.fi Pub (Finnish/EE): *Radiomaailma* (8 times per year, pdf), *DXclusive* (pdf

**FRANCE: Radio Club des Écouteurs Lorrains**, 19 rue des Jeux, 54570 Foug. **E:** alinco54@orange.fr **W:** www.rcdel.fr – **Radio Club du Perche**, 82 bis, Coat Canton, 29140 Rosporden. **E:** g.lelouet@orange.fr **W:** radioclub.perche.free.fr – **Radio DX Club d'Auvergne et Francophonie**, c/o Frédéric Bolle, Centre Municipal P. M. Curie, 2 bis Rue du Clos Perret, 63100 Clermont-Ferrand. **E:** radiodxclub63@gmail.com **W:** www.radiodx63.fr – **Union des Écouteurs Français**, BP 31, 92242 Malakoff Cédéx. **E:** tsfinfo@u-e-f.net **W:** www.u-e-f.net

**GERMANY: Arbeitsgemeinschaft DX e.V. (AGDX)**, Postfach 1214, 61282 Bad Homburg (Umbrella organization for the German DX clubs adxb-DL, UKW/TV Arbeitskreis der AGDX, Worldwide DX Club, and for the Austrian DX-Board) **E:** mail@agdx.de **W:** www.agdx.de Pub: see ADDX. – **Assoziation Deutschsprachiger Kurzwellenhörer e.V. (ADDX)**, Scharsbergweg 14, 41189 Mönchengladbach. **E:** kurier@addx.de **W:** www.addx.de Pub (jointly for members of ADDX & AGDX, and ADXB-OE in Austria): *Radio-Kurier - weltweit hören* (monthly; printed & pdf) – **Assoziation**

**Junger DXer e.V. (adxb-DL)**, c/o Thomas Schubaur, Neufnachstr. 30, 86850 Fischach. **E:** dl1ts@t-online.de **W:** www.adxb-dl.de – **Hamburger Freunde des Rundfunkfernempfangs**, c/o Dieter Schäfer, Am Sportplatz 18, 24629 Kisdorf. **E:** dl1lad@darc.de – **Kurzwellenclub Schwalmtal e.V.**, c/o Helmut Reitzer Jr, Willy-Rösler-Str. 41, 41366 Schwalmtal. **E:** dk0kws@qsl.net **W:** www.qsl.net/dk0kws – **Kurzwellenfreunde Rhein/Ruhr e.V.**, c/o U. Schnelle, Kurfürstenstr. 37, 45883 Gelsenkirchen. **E:** kwfr-web@kwfr.de **W:** www.kwfr.de – **Kurzwellenfreunde Wuppertal (KWFW)**, c/o Werner Kortmann, Postfach 220342, 42373 Wuppertal – **Oldenburger Kurzwellenfreunde**, c/o Olaf C. Hänßler, Sandweg 98, 26135 Oldenburg **E:** olaf.haenssler@gmail.com – **Radiofreunde NRW**, c/o Christof Proft, Kurfürstenstr. 15, 52066 Aachen **E:** info@radiofreunde-nrw.de **W:** www.radiofreunde-nrw.de – **Rhein-Main-Radio-Club e.V. (RMRC)**, Postfach 700849, 60558 Frankfurt **E:** mail@rmrc.de **W:** www.rmrc.de. **UKW/TV Arbeitskreis der AGDX**, c/o H.-J. Kuhlo, Wilhelm-Leuschner-Str. 293B, 64347 Griesheim (FM/TV only) **E:** sekretariat@ukwtv.de **W:** www.ukwtv.de Pub: *Reflexion* (printed & pdf) – **Worldwide DX Club (WWDXC)**, Postfach 1214, 61282 Bad Homburg **E:** mail@wwdxc.de **W:** www.wwdxc.de. Pub: *DX Magazine* (EE; printed & pdf)

**HUNGARY: Hungarian DX Club**, c/o Tibor Szilagyi **E:** tiszi2035@yahoo.com.

**IRELAND: Irish DX Club**, c/o Edward Dunne, 17 Anville Drive, Kilmacud, Stillorgan, Co. Dublin **E:** irishdxclub@live.ie Pub: *MediaWatch* (by email)

**ITALY: Associazione Italiana Radioascolto (AIR)**, C.P. 1338, 10100 Torino (AD). **E:** redazione@air-radio.it **W:** www.air-radio.it Pub: *Radiorama* (monthly, pdf) – **BCL Sicilia Club**, c/o Roberto Scaglione, C.P. 119, Succursale 34, 90144 Palermo (PA). **E:** info@bcl-news.it **W:** www.bclnews.it – **Coordinamento del Radioascolto (Co.Rad)**, c/o Dario Monferini (Web-based umbrella organisation of various Italian DX clubs) **E:** info@corad.net **W:** www.corad.net – **FM-DX Italy**, c/o Fabrizio Carnevalini (Web-based, FM-TV DX only) **E:** fabrizio58it@yahoo.it **W:** www.fmdx.altervista.org – **Gruppo Ascolto Radio dello Stretto**, c/o Giovanni Sergi, Via Sibari 34, 98149 Messina (ME). (II) **E:** gsergi5050@hotmail.com **W:** polistenaweb.it/gars Pub: *Radio Notizie* (quarterly, printed & pdf) – **Gruppo d'Ascolto Radio Televisivo della Sicilia**, c/o Gioacchino Stallone, Via G.Falcone 11, Lotto 2, interno 3, 91025 Marsala (TP). (local activity) – **Gruppo Radio Ascolto Bologna**, c/o Elio Antonucci, Bologna (Web-based) **E:** radioascolto@elio.org **W:** www.elio.org/radioascolto – **Gruppo Radio Ascolto Utility World**, c/o Quirino Tirelli, Via T. Rossi 6, 82100 Benevento **E:** qtirell@hotmail.it – **Play-DX**, c/o Dario Monferini, Via Davanzati 8, 20158 Milano (MI). (II/EE/SS) (specialises in difficult DX) **E:** info@playdx.com **W:** www.playdx.com Pub: *PLAY-DX* (weekly)

**NETHERLANDS: Benelux DX Club (BDXC)**, Rietdekkerstraat 40, 1445 KG Purmerend. **E:** secretaris@bdxc.nl **W:** www.bdxc.nl Pub: *BDXC-Bulletin* (Dutch/EE, printed & pdf)

**RUSSIA: Club of DX-ers**, c/o Vadim Alexeew, Moscow **E:** rts-center@mtu-net.ru – **Russian DX League**, c/o Anatoly Klepov, Moscow **E:** rusdx@yandex.ru **W:** rusdx.narod.ru Pub: *RUS-DX* (separate RR/EE versions, by email) – **St. Petersburg DX Club**, c/o Alexander Beryozkin, P.O.Box 13, 192007 St. Petersburg **E:** dxspb@nrec.spb.ru Pub: *Broadcasting in Russian* (RR, biennial, printed)

**SPAIN: Asociación DX Barcelona (ADXB)**, P.O. Box 335, 08080 Barcelona. **E:** info@mundodx.net **W:** www.mundodx.net Pub: *MundoDX-Mundimedia* (SS/Catalan, DVD published 11 times per year with text, images & videos) – **Asociación Española**

**de Radioescucha (AER)**, Apartado 10014, 50080 Zaragoza. **E:** general@aer.org.es **W:** aer.org.es Pub: *El Dial (d), El Dial (e), El Dial (fm)* (pdf)

**SWEDEN: Arctic Radio Club (ARC)**, c/o Tore Larsson, Frejagatan 14A, 52 143 Falköping (MW/LW only) **E:** torelarsson.dx@gmail.com **W:** arcticradioclub.blogspot.com Pub: *MV-Eko* (Swedish/EE, pdf) – **Sveriges DX Förbund (SDXF)**, P.O.Box 1097, 40 523 Göteborg (Umbrella organization). **E:** registrator@sdxf.se **W:** www.sdxf.se Pub: *DX-aktuellt* (Swedish/Danish, joint publication with DDXLD, Denmark; bimonthly, printed & pdf). Local member clubs: **Northern Sweden: Radioklubben Marconi**, c/o Sven-Olof Forsgren, Box 84, 912 22 Vilhelmina ☎ +46 94 027048 – **Sundsvalls Radioamatörer (SK3BG)**, c/o Christer Byström, P.O.Box 173, 851 03 Sundsvall ☎ +46 60 561285 **W:** sk3bg.se **Central Sweden: Aros DX Club**, c/o Rolf Berglund Flisavägen 22, 723 53 Västerås. Contact: Magnus Jespersson ☎ +46 21 180505 **W:** 123minsida. se/cadsy/29301960 – **Delsbo Radioklubb (SK3PH)**, c/o Håkan Johansson, Tånggatan 25, 820 60 Delsbo. Contact: Dan Andersson ☎ +46 65 310320 **E:** drak_ph@hotmail.com **W:** sk3ph.se/wordpress – **Mälardalens Radiosällskap**, c/o Lars Skoglund, Radarvägen 22, 183 59 Täby ☎ +46 87 563292 **W:** hem.bredband.net/mrsdxing – **Norrköpings Distanslyssnare**, c/o Claes Olsson, Guldringen 68, 603 68 Norrköping ☎ +46 11 182223 **W:** ndl-dx.se **Southern Sweden: Malmö Kortvågsklubb**, c/o Dan Olsson, Högalidsvägen 77C, 244 36 Kävlinge ☎ +46 46 735445 **W:** www.mkvk.se – **Tibro DX-Klubb**, c/o Börje Sahlén, V. Långgatan 139A, 543 33 Tibro ☎ +46 50 413925 **W:** www.ugglenatt.cybersite.nu/Tibro-DX-klubb – **Västkustens DX-Klubb**, c/o Alf Persson, Malörtsvägen 3, 449 33 Nödinge ☎ +46 30 396464 **W:** wordpress.radiomuseet.se/vdxk

**UNITED KINGDOM: British DX Club (BDXC)**, 10 Hemdean Hill, Caversham, Reading RG4 7SB. **E:** bdxc@bdxc.org.uk **W:** www. bdxc.org.uk Pub: *Communication* (printed & pdf) – **International Shortwave League (ISWL)**, c/o Peter Lewis, 18 Bittaford Wood, Ivybridge, Devon, PL21 0ET. **E:** vfgnsu@yahoo.co.uk **W:** www.iswl. org.uk Pub: *Monitor* (pdf) – **Medium Wave Circle (MWC)**, c/o Herman Boel, Papeveld 3, 9320 Erembodegem-Aalst, Belgium (LW/MW only) **E:** herman@hermanboel.eu **W:** www.mwcircle.org Pub: *Medium Wave News* (pdf)

**CÔTE D'IVOIRE: DX-Ivoire**, c/o Jibirila Liasu, B.P. 197, Abidjan 20. (FF)

**KENYA: DX Listeners' Club**, c/o Oscar Machuki, PO Box 646, Kisii 4-0200. (EE/Swahili) (SW only) ☎ +254 721 534171 **E:** oscarmogire@yahoo.com

**NIGERIA: Africa DX Association**, c/o Mr. Friday I. Okoloise, NITEL, P.M.B. 23, Lafia, Plateau State. (EE) – **International DX Club**, Emmanuel Ezeani, P.O.Box 1633, Sokoto, Sokoto State. (EE) **E:** emmanuel_ezeani@yahoo.com

**RÉUNION: Club DX de La Réunion, E:** contest@rallye-dx.com **W:** www.rallye-dx.com (FF/EE, SW only)

**SÃO TOMÉ & PRÍNCIPE: Clube DX-STP**, c/o Petter Leal Bouças, Av. 12 de Julho, Vila Maria (C.P. 490), São Tomé. **E:** petterboudx@hotmail.com

**TANZANIA: Kemogemba DX Listeners Club**, c/o Ras Franz Manko Ngogo, P.O.Box 71, Tarime, Mara. (EE/Swahili) ☎ + 255 75 5814704 **E:** kemogemba@yahoo.com

**TOGO: Club Inter Amitié Radio**, CCF, B.P. 2090, Lomé. (FF) – **Groupe Endoc**, B.P. 2667, Lomé. (FF)

**TUNISIA: Club des Auditeurs et de l'Amitié**, c/o De Riadh Sakka, Route de Gremda Merkez Sahnoun, 3012 Sfax. (FF)

**UGANDA: International DX Club of East Africa**, c/o Samuel

Ouma, P.O. Box 565, Iganga. (EE) ☎ +256 772 444201 **E:** samuel. ouma@talk21.com **W:** www.facebook.com/idxeastafrica

**BANGLADESH: Aurora Listeners' Club**, c/o Miss Kakali Rani, Harida Khalsi-6403, Madhnagar-Natore-6400 – **Basupara DX Listeners Club**, c/o Asfaqul Alam, Basupara, Nandangachi, Rajshahi 6260. **E:** bdxls@uymail.com – **International Radio Listeners Club**, Konabari, P.O.Nilnagor, Gazipur, Dhaka. (EE/Bengali) – **Online DX Forum**, c/o MD Azizul Alam Al-Amin, Gourhanga, Ghoramara, Rajshahi 6100. **E:** mtech@rajbd.com. – **Wave Surfers' Association**, c/o Ashik Eqbal Tokon, Mohammadpur, Dhaka. **E:** rosedwlc@yahoo.com **W:** wsabd.webs.com; rosedwlc.webs.com. Pub: *DX-Net* (Bengali, quarterly)

**INDIA: Apollo DX International**, c/o Deepak Kumar Das, Dholi Sakra 843105, Dist. Muzaffarpur, Bihar – **Ardic DX Club**, c/o Jaisakthivel, T., Dept of Communication, Manonmaniam Sundranar University, Abishekapatti Post, Tirunelveli 627012, Tamil Nadu. ☎ +91 98413 66086 Pub: *DXers Guide* (EE quartely), *Sarvadesa Vanoli* (Tamil monthly). DX Prgr: Vaanoli Ulagam on AIR (Tamil). **E:** ardicdxclub@yahoo.co.in **W:** dxersguide.blogspot.com – **Asian DX League**, c/o Partha Sarathi Goswami, Kishalaya Book Stall, College Road, Siliguri 734001, West Bengal **E:** dxing@india.com – **Chaudhary Srota Sangh**, c/o Santosh Kumar (President), Kharauna Jairam, Kharauna Dih 843113, Dist. Muzaffarpur, Bihar – **Chaitak Listeners Club**, PO-BELDA, Naboday Pally, Dt-Paschim Medinipur 721424, WB **E:** sbchanu@gmail.com – **Chennai DX Club**, c/o K. Raja, 21 JP Koil St, Old Washermenpet, Chennai 600021, Tamil Nadu. **E:** chennaidxclub@gmail.com – **Foreign Radio Listeners' Club,** c/o Prasenjit Bhakat, 313/8 Ghoradhara, P.O Jhargram 721507, West Bengal. ☎ +91 3221 256084 **E:** frlclub@gmail.com – **Globe Radio DX Club (GRDXC)**, c/o Harjot Singh Brar, P.O.Box 158, Chandigarh 160017, Chandigarh. **E:** grdxc@yahoo.co.in – **Indian DX Club International**, GPO Box 646, Kolkata 700001, West Bengal. **E:** idxc.international@gmail.com **W:** www.idxci.in – **International DX Association**, c/o Bedanta Das, 1-No,Galiahati, Near Night School, Barpeta 781301, Assam. ☎ +91 3665 236267 **E:** das884@gmail.com Pub: *DX Times* (EE) – **Metali Listeners' Club**, c/o Mr Shivendu Paul, 49/36, Dr SG Dhar Lane, P.O. Khagra, Dist. Murshidabad 742103, West Bengal. metalilistenersclub@gmail.com ☎ +91 94348 58497 – **Minnakkal Kurinji DX Club**, c/o E. Selvaraj, Choolaimedu Street, Minnakkal Post, Dist. Namakkal 637505, Tamil Nadu. **E:** selvarajminnakkal@gmail. com – **Paribar Bandhu SWL Club**, c/o Mr Anand Mohan Bain, UCO Bank, 47/6, Nehru Nagar, P.O. Nehru Nagar, Bhilai, Dist. Durg 490020, Chattisgarh. **E:** anand_mohan10@yahoo.com ☎ +91 94255 21083, +91 78840 31648. – **Pollachi DX Club**, c/o Mr. N. Lakshmanan, Sri Mugha Bhavan, 44/77 Lac Colony, Dr Ansari Street, Pollachi 642001, Tamil Nadu. ☎ +91 98650 16402 **W:** pollachiradioclub.blogspot.com – **Span Radio Listeners' Club**, c/o A Ragu, Nandavankula Theru, Vedaraniam 614810, Tamil Nadu. ☎ +91 4369 318808 – **Utkarna Shrota Sangha**, c/o Mr. Rajib Bandopadhyay, Amrita Bhaban, P.O. Makardah 711409, Dist. Howrah, West Bengal ☎ +91 94334 28609, **E:** ussrajib@gmail.com – **World DX Club & Library**, c/o Baidyanath Upadhyaya, At Khairabarigaon, P.O. Khawrang, Udalguri 784509, Darrang, Assam. – **World DXing Club**, c/o Mr Madhab Ch. Sagour, 93/1, Mitrapara Road, P.O. Naihati 743 165, 24 Parganas (North), West Bengal. – **World Radio Club**, c/o Mr. Biswanath Mandal, Chak Harharia, P.O. Islampur 742304, Dist. Murshidabad, West Bengal ☎ +91 3481 236534 **E:** bmandalwrc@rediffmail.com – **Young Stars Radio Club**, c/o Mr Hari Madugula, 40 Hastinapura Colony, Raghavendra Residency-FF4, Sainikpuri, Hyderabad 500094, Andhra Pradesh. **W:** ysrc.webs.com – **Youth International Radio Listeners' Club**, c/o Mr. Pranab Kumar Roy, Shyamnagar, 741 155, Nadia, West Bengal. ☎ +91 3471 252163 **E:** etherbarta@gmail.com Pub: *Etherbarta* (Bengali), *Radio Monitors' Guide* (EE)

**INDONESIA: Borneo Listeners Club**, Jalan Penjajap Timur 3A, Pemangkat, Kalimantan Barat 79453. (Indonesian/EE). **E:** h.rudi@yahoo.co.id **W:** bielsiklub.blogspot.com Pub: *Mediator* – **Indonesian DX Club (IDXC)**, P.O.Box 50, Kutoarjo 54201. (EE/Indonesian).

**JAPAN: Asian Broadcasting Institute (ABI)**, P.O.Box 2334,

Ginza Branch, Japan Post, Tokyo 100-8698. **E:** info@abiweb.jp **W:** www.abiweb.jp – **Japan Short Wave Club (JSWC)**, P.O.Box 44, Kamakura 248-8691. (JJ/EE) ☎ 🖷 +81 467 432167 **W:** www5a. biglobe.ne.jp/~BCLSWL/jswc.html **E:** jswchq@live.jp Pub: *SW DX Guide* (JJ/EE) – **Nagoya DXers Circle (NDXC)**, c/o Shigenori Aoki, 2-51 Kasumori-cho, Nakamura-ku, Nagoya 453-0855. **W:** www. ndxc.16mb.com

**KOREA, SOUTH: Northeast Asian Broadcasting Institute (NEABI)**, c/o SeKyung Park, #103-302, Geumho Apt, 240-32 Yeomchang-dong, Gangseo-gu, Seoul 157-861. **E:** neabipress@ gmail.com **W:** www.neabi.org Pub: *Reports* (Korean, monthly)

**NEPAL: Friendship Radio Club**, c/o Mr Umesh Regmi, Tanki Sinuwari 5, District Morang, Biratnagar. **E:** friendshipradioclub@ yahoo.com – **Listeners' Club of Nepal** (Reg. No.144), P.O.Box 126, Biratnagar-4 – **Small Giant Radio Listener Club** (Reg. No.17), P.O.Box 21110, Kathmandu

**PAKISTAN: International Radio Listeners Club**, Karachi. **E:** irlclub@hotmail.com **W:** sites.google.com/site/irlclub – **National Society of Pakistani DXers**, c/o Liaqat Ali, E-161/1, Iqbal Park, opposite Adil Hospital, Defence Housing Society Rd, Lahore Cantt. – **Pakistani Shortwave Listeners' Association**, c/o Muhammad Imran Mehr, 38/2 Habib Colony, Bahawalpur 63108, Punjab. ☎ +92 334 6865847, +92 300 6801719. **E:** imran.mehr@gmail.com Pub: *Radio World* (bi-monthly by email) – **Shortwave Listeners Club**, c/o Israr Ahmad Chaudhary, Street #2, Madina Park, Sheikhupura 39350, Punjab. **E:** pals_swlc@yahoo.com – **Wonderful World of Shortwave (WWSW)**, c/o Baber Shehzad, 43 Habib Colony, Bahawalpur 63108, Punjab. **E:** baber73@yahoo.com. Pub: *News Letter of Pakistani DX-ers* (by email)

**SRI LANKA: Union of Asian DXers (UADX)**, c/o Victor Goonetilleke, "Shangri-La" 298 Kolamunne, Piliyandala. **E:** victor. goonetileke@gmail.com **W:** dxasia-uadx.blogspot.com (EE)

## PACIFIC

**AUSTRALIA: Australian Radio DX Club (ARDXC)**, c/o John Wright, 71 Hilton Avenue, Roselands NSW 2196. **E:** dxer1234@ gmail.com **W:** www.facebook.com/ARDXC.Inc Pub: *Australian DX News* (printed & pdf)

**NEW ZEALAND: New Zealand Radio DX League**, P.O. Box 178, Mangawhai 0540. **E:** secretary@radiodx.com **W:** www.radiodx.com Pub: *NZ DX Times* (monthly, pdf)

## NORTH AMERICA

**CANADA: Canadian International DX Club (CIDX)**, P.O.Box 67063-Lemoyne, St. Lambert, QC J4R 2T8. **E:** cidxclub@yahoo. com **W:** www.cidx.ca Pub: *The Messenger* (pdf, monthly) – **Club d'Ondes Courtes du Québec**, 5120, 35ème rue, Grand Mere, PO G9T 3N6. **E:** dduplessis@infoteck.qc.ca – **Ontario DX Association (ODXA)**, 3211 Centennial Drive, Apt. 23, Vernon, BC V1T 2T8. **E:** odxa@rogers.com **W:** www.facebook.com/groups/ontariodx – **Vancouver Shortwave Association**, P.O.Box 500, Vancouver, BC V5L 1C.

**MEXICO: Audio Pico DX Club**, c/o César Granillo, Ap. Postal 309, 94301 Orizaba, Veracruz – **Club DX Miguel Auza**, c/o Luis Antero Aguilar, Ap. Postal 38, 98330 Miguel Auza, Zacatecas – **Consultorio DX**, c/o Miguel Angel Rocha Gámez, Ap. Postal 31, 31820 Ascensión, Chihuahua – **Sociedad de Ingenieros Radioescuchas**, c/o Rafael Gustavo Grajeda Rosado, Ap. Postal 203, Admon. No.1, 91701 Veracruz, Veracruz. **E:** rggr681121@hotmail.com

**USA: Boston Area DXers,** c/o Paul Graveline, 9 Stirling St., Andover, MA 01810-1408 **W:** www.naswa.net/badx – **Central Indiana Shortwave Club**, c/o Steve Hammer, 2517 E. DePauw Road, Indianapolis, IN 46227-4404. – **DecalcoMania**, c/o Phil Bytheway, 9705 Mary NW, Seattle, WA 98117-2334. (Club for collectors of station promo, items and airchecks). **E:** phil_tekno@ yahoo.com **W:** www.anarc.org/decal Pub: *DecalcoMania* – **Hampton Roads DX Association**, c/o Dr. Marc Fink, P.O.Box 2681, Chesapeake, VA 23327-2681. ☎ +1 757 547 3668 **E:** familyfoot@ msn.com (LW, MW, SW, FM/TV) – **Indiana Recording Club**, c/o Bill Davies, 1729 E. 77th St., Indianapolis, IN 46240. (Club for airchecks and recordings of mediumwave stations). – **International Radio Club of America (IRCA)**, P.O.Box 60241, Lafayette, LA 70596. (MW only) **E:** ircamember@ircaonline.org **W:** www.ircaonline.org Pub: *DX Monitor* (printed & pdf) – **Longwave Club of America (LWCA)**, 9213 State Route 5 & 20, Bloomfield, NY 14469 **E:** hq.lwca@gmail. com **W:** www.lwca.org Pub: *The Lowdown* – **Miami Valley DX Club (MVDXC)**, P.O.Box 292132, Columbus, OH 43229. **W:** www.anarc. org/mvdxc Pub: *DX World.* – **Michigan Area Radio Enthusiasts Inc**, P.O.Box 200, Manchester, MI 48158. **E:** mare.radio@gmail.com – **Minnesota DX Club (MDXC)** c/o James Dale, 16330 Germane Ct W, Rosemount, MN 55068. **E:** mndxclub@charter.net Pub: *MDXC Newsletter* – **National Radio Club Inc (NRC)**, P.O.Box 473251, Aurora, CO 80047-3251. (MW only) **E:** sales@nrcdxas.org **W:** www. nrcdxas.org Pub: *DX News* (printed; bi-weekly in winter, monthly in summer), *E-DXN* (pdf) – **North American Shortwave Association (NASWA)**, P.O. Box 3292, Allentown, PA 18104 **E:** hq@naswa. net **W:** www.naswa.net Pub: *The Journal* (printed) and *Flashsheet* (pdf) – **Pacific Northwest/British Columbia DX Club**, c/o Bruce Portzer, 6546 19th Ave NE, Seattle WA 98115. **E:** phil_tekno@yahoo. com **W:** www.anarc.org/pnbcdxc Pub: *PNBCDXC newsletter* (every one or two months) – **Puna DX Club,** c/o Jerry Witham, P.O.Box 596, Keaau, HI 96749 **E:** punadxclub@mailcity.com – **Rocky Mountain Radio Listeners**, c/o Mike Curta, P.O.Box 470776, Aurora, CO 80047-0776. – **Southern California Area DXerS**, c/o Bill Fisher Sr., 6398 Pheasant Drive, Buena Park, CA 90620-1356. ☎ +1 714 522 6434 **E:** williamfishersr@gmail.com – **Worldwide TV-FM DX Association (WFTDA)**, P.O.Box 501, Somersville, CT 06072 (FM/ TV only). **E:** sales@wtfda.org **W:** www.wtfda.org Pub: *VUD* (pdf).

## SOUTH AMERICA

**ARGENTINA: Grupo DX Suquia (GDXS)**, c/o Oscar H. González, Int. Moscati 434, 5127 Río Primero, Cordoba. **E:** grupodxsuquia@yahoo. com.ar **W:** www.facebook.com/groups/GrupoDXSuquia & grupodx-suquia.wordpress.com Pub: *Circular DX* – **Grupo Radioescucha Argentino (GRA)**, c/o Marcelo A. Cornachioni, Alvarez Thomas 248, B1832DNF Lomas de Zamora, Buenos Aires. **E:** info@conexiongra. com.ar **W:** gruporadioescuchaargentino.wordpress.com

**BRAZIL: Associação DX do Brasil**, C.P. 4, 58300-970 Santa Rita, Paraiba. **E:** cartas@adxb.com.br **W:** www.adxb.com.br – **DX Clube do Brasil (DXCP)**, C.P. 1594, 09571-970 São Caetano do Sul (SP). **E:** dxcb@bol.com.br **W:** www.ondascurtas.com – **DX Clube Sem Fronteiras**, C.P. 77, CEP- 55002-970 Caruaru, Pernambuco. ☎ +55 81 997413846 **E:** antonioadx@yahoo.com.br, dxclubesemfronteiras@ hotmail.com **W:** www.dxclubesemfronteiras.com Pub: *Boletim "DX Sem Fronteiras"* (Quarterly, Portuguese, printed & pdf)

**CHILE: Club Diexista de Chile**, Calle 3 Ponienta 55, Talca. **E:** chiledxclub@mixmail.com **W:** www.galeon.com/chiledxclub Pub: *Radiograma* – **Federación de Clubes de Radioaficionados de Chile (FEDERACHI)**, c/o Héctor Frías Jofre, Dr. Eduardo Cruz Coke 389, Oficina C, Casilla 9570, Santiago 21. **E:** federachi@federachi.cl **W:** www.federachi.cl

**COLOMBIA: Grupo Internacional de Diexistas y Radioaficionados**, c/o Miguel Bayona. **E:** m-bayona@hotmail.com

**URUGUAY: DX Club Montevideo**, Calle Batovi 2068, 11800 Montevideo. **E:** diexman@adinet.com.uy, diexman@montevideo. com.uy

**VENEZUELA: Asociación Diexista de Venezuela**, Ap. Postal 65657, Caracas 1066-A. **E:** marl1@hotmail.com – **Asociación de la Amistad Internacional (CDXA)**, c/o San Gil Gonzáles Santiago, Ap. Postal 202, Barinas, Estado Barinas 5201-A. **E:** 40cdx-ainternacional@yahoo.com **W:** venezueladx.blogspot.com; www. facebook.com/groups/531629043622500 (Facebook group "Cadena DX")

# STANDARD TIME & FREQUENCY TRANSMISSIONS

## What are STFTs?

Standard Time and Frequency Transmissions (STFTs) are transmissions aimed at testing and calibrating radio receivers and synchronizing clocks. When broadcast on shortwave, STFTs usually consist of continuous AM and/or SSB transmissions of 'beeps' or 'pips' every second (often referred to as 'Time Signals'), with the time in UTC (or local time) announced at certain intervals. Some stations broadcast for 24 hours a day while other stations run for up to a few hours daily or on certain days of the week.

Also listed in this chapter is a selection of standard broadcast and VLF utility stations that broadcast regular timechecks in modes other than AM/SSB. The VLF transmitters of the maritime navigation networks Loran-C/Chayka on 100kHz and similar VLF txs primarily used for navigation purposes, except for txs of the "Beta" system of the Russian Navy and BPL in P.R. China, are not included.

## Using STFTs

STFTs are invaluable aids for the SW radio user. Not only do they allow listeners to synchronise clocks to UTC but they are also a handy tool for checking propagation and reception paths. Their most useful role for serious shortwave listeners, however, is for checking that equipment is performing as it should and to test for receiver frequency calibration errors.

## Checking Performance

It is possible to carry out tests on a variety of frequencies ranging from 2500 to 20000kHz. First select an appropriate set of STFTs, perhaps by saving them into a set of memory channels if your radio has the facility. A quick check can be made for the characteristic ticks and pulses to ensure that there is a good reception path and that the STFT is currently active, before moving on to the tests themselves. Don't forget that it is essential to allow the radio to warm up for at least one hour before starting these tests.

The object of the exercise is to mix the incoming STFT signal with an internally generated signal from the radio's Beat Frequency Oscillator (BFO) and then tune the radio until the resulting whistle, or heterodyne as it is known, drops down to zero. This process of tuning for 'zero beat' then ensures that the radio is on exactly the same frequency as the transmission – any error shown on the dial will be the receiver error and any drift in tone will be receiver drift.

For most radios it will suffice to select either upper or lower sideband mode with a wide filter setting and use a loudspeaker or pair of headphones with a good low frequency audio performance. Many SW receivers have internal speakers which are not good when it comes to reproducing low notes and are useless for this procedure.

As you carefully tune down and hear the note drop, you should find that the S-meter needle starts to fluctuate. This means that you are very close to 'zero beat'. The lower the rate of S-meter needle movement, the nearer you are to the end point. At this stage you will probably not be able to hear much in the headphones apart from a near silent carrier, and the meter will be your best guide as it will be indicating the 'phase error' between the STFT and your BFO. When your needle moves at its slowest rate, you have reached zero beat. Make a note of the dial reading as this will show the receiver error.

For those radios with particularly good filters, which may prevent a 'zero beat' approach, a similar technique can be used by switching to CW mode. This method requires the use of an audio digital frequency meter – ask around at your radio club and you will probably find one. First of all, refer to the manual and find the 'CW offset' frequency. This is the audio frequency which the receiver will produce when it is exactly tuned to the carrier of the STFT. Common values are 600Hz to 800Hz. Some radios allow the user to programme the CW offset, so make sure that it has not been changed before you start the tests.

The procedure is essentially the same as has just been described, except that you will be tuning the radio until the DFM reads 600Hz exactly, then the receiver dial will show you any error. By repeating this test on a number of frequencies, you can be confident that your radio is accurate, or at least be aware of any errors or developing problems, and of course these are handy techniques for testing a radio you are considering buying.

# STFT Stations, Schedules and Contact Information

## ARGENTINA

✉ Servicio de Hidrografía Naval, Observatorio Naval, Av. España 2099, 1107 Buenos Aires, Argentina ☎ +54 11 43611162 🖷 +54 11 43611162 E: onba@hidro.gov.ar W: www.hidro.gov.ar

| Location | Call | kHz | kW | Mode | Schedule |
|---|---|---|---|---|---|
| Buenos Aires | LOL | 10000 | 2 | AM | 1400-1500 (MF) |

## BELARUS

✉ 43-y uzel svyazi Voenno-morskogo Flota RF, Vileyka, Belarus.

| Location | Call | kHz | kW | Mode | Schedule |
|---|---|---|---|---|---|
| Vileyka | RJH69 | *25 | 300 | CW | 0706-0747 |

**Key:** *) :06-:25 on 25.0, :27-:30 on 25.1, :32-:35 on 25.5, :38-:41 on 23.0, :44-:47 on 20.5kHz.
**NB:** Site is operated by Russian Navy; see Russia for HQ.

## BRAZIL

✉ Divisão Serviço da Hora (DSHO), Observatório Nacional, R. Gal. José Cristino 77, São Cristóvão, Rio de Janeiro, CEP 20921-400, Brazil ☎ +55 21 35049100 🖷 +55 21 25806041 E: dsh@on.br W: www.horalegalbrasil.mct.on.br

| Location | Call | kHz | kW | Mode | Schedule |
|---|---|---|---|---|---|
| Rio de Janeiro | PPE | 10000 | 1 | AM/U | 24h |

## CANADA

✉ National Research Council Canada (NRC), 1200 Montreal Road, Bldg M-36, Ottawa, Ontario, K1A 0R6, Canada ☎ +1 613 9935698 🖷 +1 613 9521394 E: radio.chu@nrc-cnrc.gc.ca W: www.nrc-cnrc.gc.ca

| Location | Call | kHz | kW | Mode | Schedule |
|---|---|---|---|---|---|
| Ottawa | CHU | 3330 | 3 | AM/U | 24h |
| | CHU | 7850 | 5 | AM/U | 24h |
| | CHU | 14670 | 3 | AM/U | 24h |

## CHINA (P.R.)

✉ National Time Service Center (NTSC), Chinese Academy of Sciences, P.O.Box 18, Lintong 710600, Shaanxi, P.R.China ☎ +86 29 83890326 🖷 +86 29 83890196 E: kyc@ntsc.cas.cn W: www.ntsc.cas.cn

| Location | Call | kHz | kW | Mode | Schedule |
|---|---|---|---|---|---|
| Shangqiu | BPC | 68.5 | 90 | CW | 0000-2100 |
| Pucheng | BPL | 100 | 800 | - | 0530-1330 |
| Pucheng | BPM | 2500 | 10 | AM | 0730-0100 |
| | BPM | 5000 | 20 | AM | 24h |
| | BPM | 10000 | 20 | AM | 24h |

| Location | Call | kHz | kW | Mode | Schedule |
|---|---|---|---|---|---|
| | BPM | 15000 | 20 | AM | 0100-0900 |

## FRANCE

Laboratoire national de métrologie et d'essais - Système de Références Temps-Espace (LNE-SYRTE), 61 avenue de l'Observatoire, 75014 Paris, France ☎+33 140512070 ▤ +33 143255542 **E:** info.syrte@obspm.fr **W:** syrte.obspm.fr

| Location | Call | kHz | kW | Mode | Schedule |
|---|---|---|---|---|---|
| Allouis | (none) | 162 | 800 | PSK | 24h |

**NB:** Tx is leased from TDF

## GERMANY

Physikalisch-Technische Bundesanstalt (PTB), Bundesallee 100, 38116 Braunschweig, Germany ☎ +49 531 59230 **E:** time@ptb.de **W:** www.ptb.de

| Location | Call | kHz | kW | Mode | Schedule |
|---|---|---|---|---|---|
| Mainflingen | DCF77 | 77.5 | 50 | CW/PSK | 24h |

**NB:** Tx is leased from Media Broadcast.

## HAWAII (USA)

NIST radio station WWVH, P.O.Box 417, Kekaha, HI 96752, USA **E:** wwvh@boulder.nist.gov

| Location | Call | kHz | kW | Mode | Schedule |
|---|---|---|---|---|---|
| Kekaha, HI | WWVH | 2500 | 5 | AM | 24h |
| | WWVH | 5000 | 10 | AM | 24h |
| | WWVH | 10000 | 10 | AM | 24h |
| | WWVH | 15000 | 10 | AM | 24h |

**NB:** Time announced in female voice. NIST HQ: see USA.

## JAPAN

National Institute of Information and CommunicationsTechnology (NICT), Applied Electromagnetic Research Institute, Japan Standard Time Group, 4-2-1, Nukui-Kitamachi, Koganei, Tokyo 184-8795, Japan ☎ +81 42 3277567 ▤ +81 42 3276689 **E:** horonet@nict.go.jp **W:** jjy.nict.go.jp

| Location | Call | kHz | kW | Mode | Schedule |
|---|---|---|---|---|---|
| Mt. Ohtakadoya | JJY | 40 | 10 | CW | 24h |
| Mt. Hagane | JJY | 60 | 10 | CW | 24h |

## KOREA, SOUTH

Center for Time and Frequency, Korea Research Institute of Standards & Science (KRISS), 267 Gajeong-ro, Yuseong-gu, Daejeon 34113, Rep. of Korea ☎ +82 42 8685145 ▤ +82 42 8685287 **E:** dhyu@kriss.re.kr **W:** www.kriss.re.kr

| Location | Call | kHz | kW | Mode | Schedule |
|---|---|---|---|---|---|
| Daejeon | HLA | 5000 | 2 | AM | 24h |

**Key:** *) To start February 2019 (at KBS tx site)

## KYRGYZSTAN

Sukhoputnyy uzel svyazi Tikhookeanskogo flota VMF RF, Chaldybar, Kyrgyzstan.

| Location | Call | kHz | kW | Mode | Schedule |
|---|---|---|---|---|---|
| Chaldybar | RJH66 | *25 | 300 | CW | 0406-0447,1006-1047 |

**Key:** *) :06-:25 on 25.0, :27-:30 on 25.1, :32-:35 on 25.5, :38-:41 on 23.0, :44-:47 on 20.5kHz.

**NB:** Site is operated by Russian Navy; see Russia for HQ.

## RUSSIA

Generalniy Shtab Voenno-morskogo Flota RF (Russian Navy), St.Petersburg, Russia **W:** flot.com

| Location | Call | kHz | kW | Mode | Schedule |
|---|---|---|---|---|---|
| Arkhangelsk | RJH77 | *25 | 300 | CW | 0906-0947 |
| Khabarovsk | RAB99 | **25 | 300 | CW | 0206-0236, 0606-0636 |
| Krasnodar | RJH63 | **25 | 300 | CW+ | 1106-1140 |
| N.Novgorod | RJH90 | *25 | 300 | CW | 0806-0847 |

**Key:** *) :06-:25 on 25.0, :27-:30 on 25.1, :32-:35 on 25.5, :38-:41 on 23.0, :44-:47 on 20.5kHz; **) :06-:20 on 25.0, :21-:23 on 25.1, :24-:26 on 25.5, :27-:31 on 23.0, :32-:36(40) on 20.5kHz; +) also in FSK mode :36-:40 on 20.5kHz.

Main Metrological Center of the State Service for Time, Frequency and Earth rotation parameters determination (SSTFT), National Research Institute for Physicotechnical and Radio Engineering Measurements (FSUE "VNIIFTRI"), Moscow Region, 141570 Mendeleevo, Russia ☎+7 495 5350836 ▤ +7 495 5350871 **E:** office@vniiftri.ru **W:** www.vniiftri.ru

| Location | Call | kHz | kW | Mode | Schedule |
|---|---|---|---|---|---|
| Taldom | RBU | 66.6 | 50 | CW | 24h |
| Taldom | RWM | 4996 | 10 | CW | 24h |
| Taldom | RWM | 9996 | 10 | CW | 24h |
| Taldom | RWM | 14996 | 10 | CW | 24h |

**NB:** Txs are leased from RTRS.

East Siberian Branch of FSUE "VNIIFTR", 664056 Irkutsk, ul. Borodina 57, Russia ☎+7 3952 468303 ▤ +7 3952 463848 **E:** office@niiftri.irk.ru **W:** www.vniiftri-irk.ru

| Location | Call | kHz | kW | Mode | Schedule |
|---|---|---|---|---|---|
| Angarsk | RTZ | 50 | 10 | CW | 2000-1900 |

**NB:** Tx is leased from RTRS.

## SPAIN

Real Instituto y Observatorio de la Armada (ROA), Calle Cecilio Pujazón s/n, 11110 San Fernando, Spain ☎+34 956545590 ▤ +34 956599366 **W:** www.armada.mde.es

| Location | Call | kHz | kW | Mode | Schedule |
|---|---|---|---|---|---|
| San Fernando | EBC | 4998 | 1 | CW | 1030-1055 (MF) |
| | EBC | 15006 | 1 | CW | 1000-1025 (MF) |

## TAIWAN

National Time and Frequency Standard Laboratory, 12, Lane 551, Min-Tsu Road, Sec. 5, Yang-Mei, Taoyuan, 326, Rep. of China ☎+886 3 4244066 ▤ +886 3 4245474 **E:** linht@cht.com.tw **W:** www.stdtime.gov.tw

| Location | Call | kHz | kW | Mode | Schedule |
|---|---|---|---|---|---|
| Chung-Li | BSF | 77.5 | 1 | CW | 24h |

## UNITED KINGDOM

National Physical Laboratory, Hampton Road, Teddington, Middlesex, TW11 0LW, United Kingdom ☎ +44 20 89773222 **E:** time@npl.co.uk **W:** www.npl.co.uk

| Location | Call | kHz | kW | Mode | Schedule |
|---|---|---|---|---|---|
| Anthorn* | MSF | 60 | 15 | CW | 24h |
| Droitwich** | (none) | 198 | 500 | PSK | 24h |

**Key:** *) Tx is leased from Babcock; **) Tx is provided by Arqiva and carries BBC Radio 4/BBCWS prgrs.

## UNITED STATES OF AMERICA

National Institute of Standards and Technology (NIST), Physical Masurement Laboratory, Time & Frequency Division, 325 Broadway, M/S 847, Boulder, CO 80305-3328, USA ☎ +1 303 4973295 ▤ +1 303 4976461 **E:** inquiries@nist.gov **W:** www.nist.gov

NIST radio stations WWV/WWVB, 2000 East County Rd. 58, Ft. Collins, CO 80524 **E:** nist.radio@boulder.nist.gov **W:** wwv@nist.gov

| Location | Call | kHz | kW | Mode | Schedule |
|---|---|---|---|---|---|
| Ft. Collins, CO | WWVB | 60 | 50 | CW | 24h |
| | WWV | 2500 | 2.5 | AM | 24h |
| | WWV | 5000 | 10 | AM | 24h |
| | WWV | 10000 | 10 | AM | 24h |
| | WWV | 15000 | 10 | AM | 24h |
| | WWV | 20000 | 2.5 | AM | 24h |
| | WWV | 25000 | 2.5 | AM | 24h* |

**Key:** *) Experimental broadcast, trs may be interrupted or suspended without notice

**NB:** WWV: Time announced in male voice. See also under Hawaii.

# INTERNATIONAL BROADCASTING ORGANISATIONS & INSTITUTES

## ARAB STATES BROADCASTING UNION (ASBU)
⌨ CP 250, 1080 Tunis Cedex, Tunisia. Street address: Rue 8840, centre urban nord, Tunis, Tunisia
☎ +216 71849000 🖷 +216 71843054
**E:** asbu@asbu.net **W:** www.asbu.net
**LP:** DG: Abderrahim Souleymane

## ASIA-PACIFIC BROADCASTING UNION (ABU)
⌨ P.O.Box 12287, 50772 Kuala Lumpur, Malaysia
☎ +60 3 22823592 🖷 +60 3 22825292
**E:** info@abu.org.my **W:** www.abu.org.my
**LP:** Pres: Ryoichi Ueda; Secr. General: Javad Mottaghi

## ASIA-PACIFIC INSTITUTE FOR BROADCASTING DEVELOPMENT (AIBD)
⌨ P.O.Box 12066, 50766 Kuala Lumpur, Malaysia. Street address: Angkasapuri, Jalan Pantai Dalam, 50614 Kuala Lumpur, Malaysia
☎ +60 3 22824618 🖷 +60 3 22822761
**E:** info@aibd.org.my **W:** www.aibd.org.my
**LP:** Dir: Chang Jin

## ASIA-PACIFIC SATELLITE COMMUNICATIONS COUNCIL (APSCC)
⌨ Suite T-1602 Poonglim Iwantplus, 255-1 Seohyun-dong, Bundang-gu, Seongnam, Gyeonggi-do 463-862, Republic of Korea
☎ +82 31 7836244 🖷 +82 31 7836249
**E:** info@apscc.or.kr **W:** www.apscc.or.kr
**LP:** Pres: Gregg Daffner

## ASOCIACIÓN INTERNACIONAL DE RADIODIFUSIÓN (AIR)
⌨ Carlos Quijano 1264, 11100 Montevideo, Uruguay ☎ +598 2 9011319 🖷 +598 2 9080458
**E:** mail@airiab.com **W:** www.airiab.com
**LP:** Pres: José Louis Saca; DG: Juan Andres Lerena

## CARIBBEAN BROADCASTING UNION (CBU)
⌨ Caribbean Media Centre, Suite 1B, Building #6A, Harbour Industrial Estate, Harbour Road, St. Michael, 11145, Barbados
☎ +1 246 4301007 🖷 +1 246 2289524
**E:** info@caribroadcastunion.org **W:** caribroadcastunion.org
**LP:** CEO: Shida Bolai

## DIGITAL RADIO MONDIALE (DRM)
⌨ DRM Project Office, P.O.Box 360, CH-1218 Grand-Saconnex, Switzerland
**E:** projectoffice@drm.org **W:** www.drm.org
**LP:** Chair (DRM Consortium)/Pres (DRM Association): Ruxandra Obreja

## EUROPEAN BROADCASTING UNION (EBU)
⌨ L'Ancienne-Route 17A, CH-1218 Grand-Saconnex, Switzerland
☎ +41 22 7172111 🖷 +41 22 7474000
**E:** ebu@ebu.ch **W:** www.ebu.ch
**LP:** Pres: Jean-Paul Philippot; DG: Noel Curran

## HIGH FREQUENCY CO-ORDINATION CONFERENCE (HFCC)
**E:** info@hfcc.org **W:** www.hfcc.org
**LP:** Chmn: Jeff White

## INTERNATIONAL INSTITUTE OF COMMUNICATIONS (IIC)
⌨ Highlands House, 165 The Broadway, London, SW19 1NE, United Kingdom
☎ +44 20 85448076 🖷 +44 20 85448077
**E:** enquiries@iicom.org **W:** www.iicom.org
**LP:** Pres: Chris Chapman

## INTERNATIONAL TELECOMMUNICATIONS UNION (ITU)
⌨ Place des Nations, 1211 Genève 20, Switzerland
☎ +41 22 7305111 🖷 +41 22 7337256
**E:** itumail@itu.int **W:** www.itu.int
**LP:** Secr. General: Houlin Zhao; Deputy Secr. General: Malcolm Johnson

## NORTH AMERICAN BROADCASTERS ASSOCIATION (NABA)
⌨ P.O.Box 500, Station A, Toronto, Ontario, M5W 1E6, Canada
**E:** contact@nabanet.com **W:** nabanet.com
**LP:** Pres: Richard Friedel; DG: Michael McEwen

## PUBLIC MEDIA ALLIANCE
⌨ Arts 1.80, DEV, University of East Anglia, Norwich NR4 7TJ, United Kingdom
☎ +44 1603 592335
**E:** info@publicmediaalliance.org **W:** publicmediaalliance.org
**LP:** CEO: Sally-Ann Wilson

## SOUTHERN AFRICAN BROADCASTING ASSOCIATION (SABA)
⌨ c/o NBC, Pettenkoffer St., Windhoek North, Windhoek, Namibia
**E:** dantagonanuses@gmail.com **W:** www.facebook.com/Saba2017
**LP:** Pres: Stanley Similo; Secr. General: Ellen Nanuses

## UNION AFRICAINE DE RADIODIFFUSION (UAR)
⌨ BP 3237, Dakar, Senegal. Street address: Avenue Carde, Immeuble CSS, Dakar, Senegal
☎ +221 338211625 🖷 +221 338225113
**W:** www.facebook.com/African-Union-of-Broadcasting -1087484021294970
**LP:** CEO: Grégoire Ndjaka

## WORLD ASSOCIATION OF COMMUNITY RADIO BROADCASTERS (AMARC)
⌨ International Secretariat, 2 rue Sainte-Catherine Est, suite 102, Montréal, Quebec, H2X 1K4, Canada
☎ +1 514 9820351
**E:** secretariat@si.amarc.org **W:** www.amarc.org
**LP:** Pres: Emmanuel Boutterin; Secr. General: Francesco Diasio

## WORLD DAB
⌨ WorldDAB Project Office, 6th Floor, 55 New Oxford Street, London, WC1A 1BS, United Kingdom
☎ +44 20 70100742
**E:** info@worlddab.org **W:** www.worlddab.org
**LP:** Pres: Patrick Hannon

# SELECTED INTERNET RESOURCES FOR DXERS & RADIO LISTENERS

## GENERAL & LINK PAGES:
**BCL News:** bclnews.it
**BCL News** (Chinese): www.5bcl.com
**Bruce's AM Log:** bamlog.com
**DX Information Centre:** dxinfocentre.com
**DXing.com:** dxing.com
**DXing.info:** dxing.info
**DX Portal (Russian):** dxing.ru
**Canada's Original World Band Radio page:** dxer.ca
**European Radio Map:** radiomap.eu
**Hard-Core-DX:** hard-core-dx.com
**History of SW:** ontheshortwaves.com
**History of WRTH:** wrthhistory.com
**Radio Communication Archive:** dokufunk.org
**Radio Portal:** radio-portal.org
**Radio Heritage Foundation:** radioheritage.net
**World of Radio:** worldofradio.com
**World Radio Map:** worldradiomap.com

## DATABASES & SCHEDULES:
**ADDX Foreign Frequency List:**
  addx.de/Hfpdat/plaene.php
**AM Query:** fcc.gov/mb/audio/amq.html
**Asian Broadcasting Institute:** abiweb.jp
**Bi Newsletter:** geocities.jp/binewsjp
**Broadcasting in South & SE Asia:** asiawaves.net
**Canada & US AM Station Info:** topazdesigns.com/ambc
**Combined HF Skeds:** hfskeds.com/skeds
**DXAsia:** dxasia.info
**EiBi Shortwave Schedules:** eibi.de.vu
**Euro-African Medium Wave Guide:** emwg.info
**FM List:** fmlist.org
**MW List:** mwlist.org
**MW Masts:** mwmasts.com
**KOJE-KOH-KOMEX:** www.tapiokalmi.net/dx/koje
**Pacific Asian Log:** radioheritage.net/PAL_search.asp
**Prime Time Shortwave:** primetimeshortwave.com
**Short-wave Info:** short-wave.info
**SW Radio Resource Center:** shortwave.hfradio.org

## NEWS SOURCES AND BULLETINS:
**BC-DX Top News:** wwdxc.de/topnews.htm
**Diexman** (Spanish): www.galeon.com/diexman
**DX-Listening Digest:** worldofradio.com/dxldmid.html
**Shortwave Bulletin:** hard-core-dx.com/swb
**Ydun's Mediumwave Info:** mediumwave.info

## ONLINE RADIO:
mikesradioworld.com – live365.com – multilingualbooks.
com/online-radio.html – publicradiofan.com – radiobe-
ta.com – radiosure.com – radiotower.com – reciva.com
– shoutcast.com – tvradionetwork.com – web-radio.fm
– vtuner.com

**Web DX-listening:** globaltuners.com – onlinereceivers.
net – remotehams.com – sdrspace.com

## RECEIVERS, ANTENNAS:
**Dave's Radio Receiver page:** n9ewo.angelfire.com/
**RF Circuit Building Blocks Page:** qsl.net/wa1ion

## STATION IDENTIFICATION:
**Interval Signals Online:** intervalsignals.net
**National Anthems:** national-anthems.net –
  nationalanthems.info
**Interval Signal Database:** intervalsignals.org

## PROPAGATION:
**Solar Terrestrial Activity Report:** solen.info/solar
**Space Weather Prediction Center:** swpc.noaa.gov

## MAILING LISTS ETC:
**A-DX Mailingliste (G):** ratzer.at/A_DX_Info.php
**Hard-Core-DX mailing list:**
hard-core-dx.com/mailman/listinfo/hard-core-dx
**IRC at irc.starchat.net:** #mwdx & #swl
**Radio Globe DX** (French): rglobe.canalblog.com
**Lists at ml.free.fr:** Radio Globe DX (French): rglobe.canal-
blog.com & Euro Radio (Fr/Eng, eradio)
**Google groups:** groups.google.com/group/mwdx (E)
– groups.google.com/group/rusdx (E) – groups.google.
com/group/rusdxplus (Ru) – groups.google.com/group/
fr.rec.radio (F)
**Lists at Mailman.qth.net:** AMFMTVDX – SWL
**Lists at Yahoogroups.com:** ABDX – ASWLC – ausS-
WDXgroup – bangladx – bclnews (It.) – condiglist (S)
– BCDX2 – conexiondigital (S) – cumbre_dx – dexismo
(Port.) – DRM-shortwave-dx – drmna – dxld – dxingwith-
cumbre – dxplorer – dx_india – dx_rad (F) – dx_sasia
– fmdxitalia (It.) – harmonics – LatinMWDX – longwavera-
diostation-listening – media_dx (Ru.) – mwdx – mw-br
(Port.) – NORDX (Sw.) – NoticiasDX (S) – ondescourtes (F)
– open_dx (Ru.) – PakistanDXers – playdx2003 (It.) – ptdx
(Port.) – RadioBroadcasting – radioescutas (Port.) – RealDX
– recradioshortwave – SDRlist – sdr-users – shortwave
– ShortwaveBasics – shortwavedxing – shortwavelistening
– ShortWaveRadio – ShortwaveRadios – shortwave-radio
– shortwaves – shortwavesites – Shortwave-SWL-Antenna
– skywavesdx – skywavesmw – soft_radio – SWPirates
– SWR-Wordwide – thebasicsofshortwave – UDXF –
webreceivers
**Facebook.com:** Cumbre DX – I Love AM Radio – India
DXing Cooperation Forum – Indian DX Club International
– Mittelwellenfreunde (G) – No Mundo do Dexismo (Port.)
– Radio Listening Interest Group – Shortwave Radio
Station Listening – SWL for Shortwave Listeners – World
DX – World Shortwave Forum – WRTH – World Radio TV
Handbook.

# ADVERTISERS' INDEX

AOR ................................................................................... 4

Asociación DX Barcelona ..................................................... 39

Australian Radio DX Club ..................................................... 64

BBC World Service ............................................................... 2

British DX Club ................................................................... 64

Children's Radio Foundation ..................................... Inside back cover

CQ Amateur Radio ............................................................... 43

Encompass .......................................................................... 43

International Radio Club of America ...................................... 39

National Radio Club ................................................... 49 & 409

Nautel ................................................................... Back cover

New Zealand Radio DX League ............................................ 49

Radio Heritage Foundation ................................................. 64

Radio Listener's Guide ....................................................... 39

Radio User ......................................................................... 35

Studio DX ........................................................................ 253

The Spectrum Monitor ......................................................... 47

The SWLing Post ............................................................... 49

Universal Radio ................................................................. 23

WinRadio ..................................................... Inside front cover & 6

## ADVERTISING SALES

**Advertising sales manager:**

Advertising Sales Manager
PO Box 290
Oxford OX2 7FT
UK
Tel: +44 1865 339355
Fax: +44 1865 339301
Email: wrth@wrth.com